DIRECTORY
of
NURSING
HOMES
second edition

DIRECTORY of NURSING HOMES

second edition

**A state-by-state
listing of facilities and services**

Edited by Sam Mongeau

ORYX PRESS
1984

The rare Arabian Oryx is believed to have inspired the myth of the unicorn. This desert antelope became virtually extinct in the early 1960s. At that time several groups of international conservationists arranged to have 9 animals sent to the Phoenix Zoo to be the nucleus of a captive breeding herd. Today the Oryx population is over 400 and herds have been returned to reserves in Israel, Jordan, and Oman.

Library of Congress Cataloging in Publication Data
Main entry under title:

Directory of nursing homes.

  Includes index.
  1. Nursing homes—United States—Directories.
2. Long-term care facilities—United States—Directories.
I. Mongeau, Sam, 1951–
  RA997.A2D49   1984   362.1′6′02573   84-18994
ISBN 0-89774-145-5

TABLE OF CONTENTS

INTRODUCTION

The revised and expanded *Directory of Nursing Homes*, 2nd Edition lists 16,139 state licensed long-term care facilities throughout the United States and possessions. First published in 1982, this directory remains the only current guide to nursing care on several levels including facilities for those needing skilled care, those needing intermediate care, and care for the mentally retarded and/or developmentally disabled.

Arranged alphabetically by state, then city, each entry contains core information including address, telephone, number of beds, level of care provided, and Medicaid, Medicare, and/or Medi-Cal* certification. Additionally entries may include the name of the facility administrator, medical director/director of nursing, ownership type (profit, nonprofit, public), and languages spoken. New information for this edition includes numbers of full- and part-time staff members, admissions requirements with minimum age and/or gender restrictions, religious/fraternal/maternal organization affiliation, detailed listings of special activities and facilities, and a description, provided by the facility, which highlights outstanding social and/or rehabilitative programs, the facility's physical setting, or other information which describes the goals, philosophy, or atmosphere at a facility. Also included in this directory is a new index which lists facilities that are affiliated with a religious/fraternal/maternal organization. This index is arranged by state, then alphabetically by organization. Following this index is an alphabetical listing of facilities.

All information for this edition has been obtained either by questionnaire or from the most current state licensure publications. Entries having information obtained from sources other than questionnaire have an asterisk (*) to the right of the facility name. The Oryx Press strongly suggests that users of this directory contact facilities directly to verify standards, licensure, and available programs. Also, a listing in this directory is by no means an endorsement by The Oryx Press and no effort has been made on the part of the publisher to evaluate facilities or programs.

A directory of this size would be impossible to compile and publish without the participation and enthusiasm of a dedicated team. Those who have contributed greatly to this publication are Dorothy Goldstein, Sandy Bourelle, Linda Archer, Mike Fields, Anne Rhodes, Kelly Rhodes, Carol Borland, Peggy Klinger, Jean Pope, Don Graves, Linda Vespa, Laurie Pacult, Brian Flesher, Ann Gammons, Susan Slesinger, and Phyllis Steckler.

While every effort has been made to ensure that all information is both accurate and current within the confines of format and scope, the publisher does not assume and hereby disclaims any liability to any party for loss or damage caused by errors or omissions in the *Directory of Nursing Homes,* whether such errors or omissions result from negligence, accident, or any other cause. In the event of publication error or omission, the sole responsibility of the publisher will be the entry of corrected information in succeeding editions. Please direct all such information to: Editor, Directory of Nursing Homes, The Oryx Press, 2214 North Central at Encanto, Phoenix, Arizona 85004-1483.

*Medi-Cal is the name for the Medicaid program in the State of California.

LIST OF ABBREVIATIONS

Ave	Avenue	N	North
Blvd	Boulevard	NE	Northeast
Ct	Court	NW	Northwest
DO	Doctor of Osteopathy	Pkwy	Parkway
Dr	Doctor, Drive	PO	Post Office
E	East	pt	part-time
Ext	Extension	Rd	Road
Expwy	Expressway	Rev	Reverend
ft	full-time	RN	Registered Nurse
Fwy	Freeway	RR	Rural Route
Hwy	Highway	Rt	Route
ICF	Intermediate Care Facility	S	South

ICF — Intermediate Care Facility. A certified facility that meets federal standards and provides less extensive health related care and services. It has regular nursing service, but not around the clock. Most intermediate care facilities carry on rehabilitation programs, with an emphasis on personal care and social services. Mainly, these homes serve people who are not fully capable of living by themselves, yet are not necessarily ill enough to need 24-hour nursing care.

ICF/MR	Intermediate Care Facility for Mentally Retarded	SE	Southeast
		SNF	Skilled Nursing Facility

SNF — Skilled Nursing Facility. A facility that has been certified as meeting federal standards within the meaning of the Social Security Act. It provides the level of care that comes closest to hospital care with 24-hour nursing services. Regular medical supervision and rehabilitation therapy are also provided. Generally, a skilled nursing facility cares for convalescent patients and those with long-term illnesses.

Jr	Junior	Sr	Sister, Senior
Ln	Lane	St	Street
LPN	Licensed Practical Nurse	SW	Southwest
MD	Medical Doctor	W	West

DIRECTORY
of
NURSING HOMES

second edition

ALABAMA

ABBEVILLE

Henry County Hospital and Nursing Home*
Dothan Rd, Abbeville, AL, 36310 (205)
585-2241
Admin J Juanita Ham.
Licensure Skilled Care. *Beds* 60. *Certified* Medicaid; Medicare.
Ownership Public.

ALABASTER

Briarcliff Nursing Home Inc
850 NW 9th St, Alabaster, AL, 35007 (205)
663-3859
Admin Mary Alice Edmonds. *Medical Dir/Dir of Nursing* Harry Phillips MD.
Licensure Skilled Care; Intermediate Care.
Beds SNF 188; ICF 38. *Certified* Medicaid; Medicare.
Ownership Nonprofit.
Admissions Requirements Minimum age 18; Medical examination; Physician's request.
Staff RNs 4 (ft); LPNs 16 (ft), 9 (pt); Orderlies 3 (ft); Physical therapists; Speech therapists; Activities coordinators 2 (ft); Dietitians; Podiatrists.
Facilities Dining room; Activities room; Crafts room; Laundry room; Barber/Beauty shop; Library.
Activities Arts and Crafts; Cards; Games; Reading groups; Prayer groups; Movies; Shopping trips; Dances/Social or cultural gatherings.

ALBERTVILLE

Albertville Nursing Home Inc*
Rt 6, Albertville, AL, 35950 (205) 878-1398
Admin Audrey Cole.
Licensure Skilled Care; Intermediate Care.
Beds SNF 55; ICF 78. *Certified* Medicaid; Medicare.
Ownership Proprietary.

ALEXANDER CITY

Adams Nursing Home*
1423 Hillabee St, Alexander City, AL, 35010
(205) 329-9712
Admin Ellen Adams.

Licensure Intermediate Care. *Beds* 88. *Certified* Medicaid.
Ownership Proprietary.

Brown Nursing Home
Rt 1, Alexander City, AL, 35010 (205)
329-9061
Admin Mildred Jobe. *Medical Dir/Dir of Nursing* James Temple MD.
Licensure Skilled Care; Intermediate Care.
Beds 48. *Certified* Medicaid; Medicare.
Ownership Proprietary.
Admissions Requirements Minimum age 18; Medical examination; Physician's request.
Staff RNs 1 (ft), 2 (pt); LPNs 4 (ft), 1 (pt); Nurses aides 15 (ft); Activities coordinators 1 (ft); Dietitians 1 (ft).

Chapman Nursing Home Inc*
Rt 5, Box 283, Dadeville Hwy, Alexander City, AL, 35010 (205) 234-6366
Admin Margaret S Chapman.
Licensure Skilled Care. *Beds* 147. *Certified* Medicaid; Medicare.
Ownership Proprietary.

ALICEVILLE

Aliceville Manor Nursing Home*
17th St NW, Aliceville, AL, 35442 (205)
373-6307
Admin Mary Ellen Wheat.
Licensure Skilled Care; Intermediate Care.
Beds SNF 59; ICF 21. *Certified* Medicaid; Medicare.
Ownership Proprietary.

ALTOONA

Altoona Nursing Home Inc*
PO Box 68, Walnut Grove Rd, Altoona, AL, 35952 (205) 589-6395
Admin Celia Shell.
Licensure Skilled Care. *Beds* 50. *Certified* Medicaid; Medicare.
Ownership Proprietary.

ANDALUSIA

Columbia Nursing Home*
200 Hillcrest Dr, Andalusia, AL, 36420 (205)
222-4141

Admin Sybil C Barton Sox.
Licensure Skilled Care; Intermediate Care.
Beds SNF 40; ICF 8. *Certified* Medicaid; Medicare.
Ownership Nonprofit.

ANNISTON

Anniston Nursing Home*
PO Box 1825, 500 Leighton Ave, Anniston, AL, 36201 (205) 237-8053
Admin Carolyn H Beck.
Licensure Skilled Care. *Beds* 85. *Certified* Medicaid.
Ownership Proprietary.

Golden Springs Nursing Facility Inc
Coleman Rd, PO Box 1790, Anniston, AL, 36201 (205) 831-5730
Admin Becky Helton. *Medical Dir/Dir of Nursing* Dr Robert Lokey.
Licensure Skilled Care; Intermediate Care.
Beds 114. *Certified* Medicaid; Medicare.
Ownership Proprietary.
Admissions Requirements Medical examination; Physician's request.
Staff Physicians 1 (pt); RNs 3 (ft), 2 (pt); LPNs 7 (ft), 9 (pt); Orderlies 2 (ft), 2 (pt); Nurses aides 24 (ft), 15 (pt); Physical therapists 1 (ft); Activities coordinators 1 (ft); Dietitians 1 (ft).
Facilities Dining room; Physical therapy room; Activities room; Laundry room; Barber/Beauty shop; Library.
Activities Arts and Crafts; Cards; Games; Reading groups; Prayer groups; Movies; Shopping trips; Dances/Social or cultural gatherings.
Description The facility is modern and located in a quiet residential atmosphere with areas for the residents to be outside for activities and their personal enjoyment.

ARAB

Nursing Home of Arab Inc
209 2nd St SE, Arab, AL, 35016 (205) 586-3111
Admin Suzanne Shelton.
Licensure Skilled Care; Intermediate Care.
Beds SNF 40; ICF 27. *Certified* Medicaid; Medicare.
Ownership Proprietary.
Facilities Dining room; Activities room; Chapel; Laundry room; Barber/Beauty shop.

Activities Arts and Crafts; Cards; Games; Prayer groups; Movies; Dances/Social or cultural gatherings.

ASHLAND

Clay County Hospital and Nursing Home*
544 E 1st Ave, Ashland, AL, 36251 (205) 354-2131
Admin Jane M Williams.
Licensure Skilled Care; Intermediate Care.
Beds SNF 59; ICF 4. *Certified* Medicaid; Medicare.
Ownership Public.

ASHVILLE

Ashville-Whitney Nursing Home*
PO Box 130, Ashville, AL, 35953 (205) 594-5148
Admin Jimmy T Terrell.
Licensure Intermediate Care. *Beds* 43. *Certified* Medicaid.
Ownership Proprietary.

ATHENS

Athens Convalescent Center Inc*
611 W Market St, Athens, AL, 35611 (205) 232-1620
Admin John L Wallace.
Licensure Skilled Care; Intermediate Care.
Beds SNF 64; ICF 28. *Certified* Medicaid; Medicare.
Ownership Proprietary.

Limestone Health Facility Inc
1600 W Hobbs St, Athens, AL, 35611 (205) 232-3461
Admin Bill R Hunt. *Medical Dir/Dir of Nursing* Dr W K Shannon.
Licensure Skilled Care; Intermediate Care.
Beds SNF 86; ICF 50. *Certified* Medicaid; Medicare.
Ownership Proprietary.
Staff Physicians 1 (pt); RNs 2 (ft), 1 (pt); LPNs 6 (ft); Orderlies 1 (ft); Nurses aides 30 (ft), 10 (pt); Physical therapists 1 (pt); Reality therapists 2 (ft); Activities coordinators 2 (ft); Dietitians 1 (ft).

ATMORE

Atmore Nursing Care Center
715 E Laurel St, PO Box 589, Atmore, AL, 36504 (205) 368-9121
Admin Virginia Johns. *Medical Dir/Dir of Nursing* Harold Q Wilson MD.
Licensure Skilled Care; Intermediate Care.
Beds 100. *Certified* Medicaid; Medicare.
Ownership Proprietary.
Admissions Requirements Medical examination; Physician's request.
Staff Physicians 8 (pt); RNs 5 (ft), 2 (pt); LPNs 18 (ft), 10 (pt); Nurses aides 40 (ft), 20 (pt); Recreational therapists 1 (ft); Activities coordinators 1 (ft); Dietitians 2 (pt); Social workers 1 (ft).
Facilities Dining room; Activities room; Chapel; Crafts room; Laundry room; Barber/Beauty shop.
Activities Arts and Crafts; Reading groups; Prayer groups; Movies; Shopping trips; Dances/Social or cultural gatherings.

ATTALLA

Attalla Nursing Home Inc*
Rt 2, PO Box 239, 900 Stewart Ave, Attalla, AL, 35954 (205) 538-7852
Admin Ted H Cook.
Licensure Skilled Care; Intermediate Care.
Beds SNF 106; ICF 59. *Certified* Medicaid; Medicare.
Ownership Proprietary.

BESSEMER

Jones Valley Nursing Home*
PO Box 297, Bessemer, AL, 35020 (205) 425-4359
Admin Carrie Phillips.
Licensure Skilled Care; Intermediate Care.
Beds SNF 34; ICF 12. *Certified* Medicaid; Medicare.
Ownership Proprietary.

Livingston Nursing Home Inc*
4201 Bessemer Super Hwy, Bessemer, AL, 35020 (205) 428-3249
Admin Betty V Duncan.
Licensure Skilled Care; Intermediate Care.
Beds SNF 63; ICF 6. *Certified* Medicaid; Medicare.
Ownership Proprietary.

Meadowood Nursing Home*
820 Golf Course Rd, Bessemer, AL, 35020 (205) 425-5241
Admin Nella J Gossett.
Licensure Skilled Care; Intermediate Care.
Beds SNF 90; ICF 90. *Certified* Medicaid; Medicare.
Ownership Proprietary.

Norred Convalescent Home*
325 Selma Rd, Bessemer, AL, 35020 (205) 428-9383
Admin Ruth L Osborne.
Licensure Skilled Care; Intermediate Care.
Beds SNF 63; ICF 18. *Certified* Medicaid; Medicare.
Ownership Proprietary.

Ruby Hill Nursing Home Inc
507 Whitmore Dr, Bessemer, AL, 35020 (205) 428-3292
Admin Ruby L Hill. *Medical Dir/Dir of Nursing* Dr Clyde Varner.
Licensure Skilled Care; Intermediate Care.
Beds SNF 25; ICF 51. *Certified* Medicaid; Medicare.
Ownership Proprietary.
Facilities Dining room; Activities room; Crafts room; Laundry room.
Activities Arts and Crafts; Cards; Games; Reading groups; Prayer groups; Movies; Dances/Social or cultural gatherings.

BIRMINGHAM

A G Gaston Home for Senior Citizens
9225 Airport Rd, Birmingham, AL, 35217 (205) 849-2273
Admin Loretha Chappell. *Medical Dir/Dir of Nursing* Dr C R Hixon.
Licensure Skilled Care; Intermediate Care.
Beds SNF 39; ICF 12. *Certified* Medicare.
Ownership Proprietary.
Admissions Requirements Medical examination; Physician's request.
Staff Physicians 1 (ft); RNs 1 (ft), 3 (pt); LPNs 5 (ft), 3 (pt); Orderlies 4 (ft), 1 (pt); Nurses aides 9 (ft), 3 (pt); Activities coordinators 1 (ft); Dietitians 1 (pt); Dentists 1 (pt).
Facilities Dining room; Activities room; Laundry room.
Activities Arts and Crafts; Games; Prayer groups; Shopping trips; Dances/Social or cultural gatherings.

Avonwood Rest Home Inc*
4246 5th Ave S, Birmingham, AL, 35222 (205) 592-8101
Admin Eugene Lamberth.
Licensure Intermediate Care. *Beds* 56.
Ownership Proprietary.

Burgess Nursing Home*
1532 Bankhead Hwy W, Birmingham, AL, 35214 (205) 798-3871
Admin William H Burgess Jr.
Licensure Skilled Care. *Beds* 53. *Certified* Medicaid; Medicare.
Ownership Proprietary.

Civic Center Nursing Home*
1201 N 22nd St, Birmingham, AL, 35234 (205) 251-5271
Admin Annette Lee Malloy.
Licensure Skilled Care; Intermediate Care.
Beds SNF 85; ICF 10. *Certified* Medicaid; Medicare.
Ownership Nonprofit.

East Lake Health Care*
7110 1st Ave N, Birmingham, AL, 35206 (205) 836-5226
Admin John Mitchell Rutoskey.
Licensure Skilled Care; Intermediate Care.
Beds SNF 31; ICF 31. *Certified* Medicaid; Medicare.
Ownership Proprietary.

Estes Health Care Center—East*
733 Mary Vann Ln, Birmingham, AL, 35215 (205) 854-1361
Admin Michael Dray.
Licensure Skilled Care; Intermediate Care.
Beds SNF 102; ICF 18. *Certified* Medicaid; Medicare.
Ownership Proprietary.

Estes Health Care Center—Forestdale*
1000 Dugan Ave, Birmingham, AL, 35214 (205) 798-8780
Admin Mary Elizabeth Parker.
Licensure Skilled Care; Intermediate Care.
Beds SNF 60; ICF 60. *Certified* Medicaid; Medicare.
Ownership Proprietary.

Estes Health Care Center—Riverchase*
2500 Riverhaven Dr, Birmingham, AL, 35244
(205) 823-6760
Admin Dennis Lee.
Licensure Skilled Care; Intermediate Care.
Beds SNF 102; ICF 18. *Certified* Medicaid;
Medicare.
Ownership Proprietary.

Fairview Nursing and Convalescent Home*
1028 Bessemer Rd, Birmingham, AL, 35228
(205) 923-1777
Admin David B Johnston.
Licensure Skilled Care; Intermediate Care.
Beds SNF 154; ICF 11. *Certified* Medicaid;
Medicare.
Ownership Proprietary.

Hanover House*
39 Hanover Circle, Birmingham, AL, 35205
(205) 933-1828
Admin Ray R Wood.
Licensure Skilled Care. *Beds* 80.
Ownership Proprietary.

**Hillhaven Convalescent Center and Nursing
Home**
2728 10th Ave S, Birmingham, AL, 35205
(205) 933-7010
Admin Yolanda Brewer. *Medical Dir/Dir of
Nursing* Dr John Buckingham.
Licensure Skilled Care; Intermediate Care.
Beds 114. *Certified* Medicaid; Medicare.
Ownership Proprietary.
Admissions Requirements Medical examina-
tion; Physician's request.
Staff RNs 5 (ft); LPNs 8 (ft), 5 (pt); Orderlies 1
(ft), 1 (pt); Nurses aides 27 (ft), 13 (pt); Physical
therapists 1 (ft); Activities coordinators 1 (ft);
Dietitians 1 (ft).
Facilities Dining room; Physical therapy room;
Activities room; Barber/Beauty shop.
Activities Arts and Crafts; Cards; Games;
Reading groups; Prayer groups; Movies; Shop-
ping trips; Dances/Social or cultural gatherings.
Description Hillhaven is centrally located in
the Greater Birmingham area near many hospitals; provides nursing care under supervision of
attending physician and registered nurses;
activities, social service, physical therapy, and
specialized diets are available.

Jefferson County Home*
200 N Pine Hill Rd, Birmingham, AL, 35217
(205) 841-5533
Admin Lillian V Holmes.
Licensure Skilled Care; Intermediate Care.
Beds SNF 148; ICF 312. *Certified* Medicaid;
Medicare.
Ownership Public.

Kirkwood by the River*
3605 Ratliff Rd, Birmingham, AL, 36210 (205)
956-2184
Admin Duke Bradford.
Licensure Skilled Care. *Beds* 51.
Ownership Nonprofit.

Lakeview Nursing Home Inc*
8017 2nd Ave S, Birmingham, AL, 35206 (205)
836-4231
Admin Celia Shell.
Licensure Skilled Care; Intermediate Care.

Beds SNF 44; ICF 10. *Certified* Medicaid;
Medicare.
Ownership Proprietary.

Macdel Health Care Inc*
2211 18th St SW, Birmingham, AL, 35211
(205) 925-6484
Admin Rebecca J Etheridge.
Licensure Skilled Care; Intermediate Care.
Beds SNF 42; ICF 31. *Certified* Medicaid;
Medicare.
Ownership Proprietary.

Mary Lewis Convalescent Center Inc
2600 Highland Ave, Birmingham, AL, 35205
(205) 252-4397
Admin Clarence A Shelton III. *Medical Dir-
/Dir of Nursing* Joseph Lee MD.
Licensure Skilled Care; Intermediate Care.
Beds SNF 20; ICF 27. *Certified* Medicaid;
Medicare.
Ownership Proprietary.
Staff RNs 1 (ft), 1 (pt); LPNs 3 (ft), 3 (pt);
Nurses aides 10 (ft), 5 (pt); Activities coordina-
tors 1 (ft); Dietitians 1 (pt).
Facilities Dining room; Activities room; Crafts
room; Laundry room; Barber/Beauty shop.
Activities Arts and Crafts; Cards; Games;
Reading groups; Prayer groups; Movies; Shop-
ping trips; Dances/Social or cultural gatherings.

Methodist Home for the Aging*
1424 Montclair Rd, Birmingham, AL, 35201
(205) 956-4150
Admin A Wray Tomlin.
Licensure Skilled Care; Intermediate Care.
Beds SNF 105; ICF 16. *Certified* Medicaid;
Medicare.
Ownership Nonprofit.
Affiliation Methodist

Northway Convalescent Center*
1424 N 25 St, Birmingham, AL, 35234 (205)
328-5870
Admin Karen Waldrop.
Licensure Skilled Care; Intermediate Care.
Beds SNF 60; ICF 53. *Certified* Medicaid;
Medicare.
Ownership Proprietary.

Oak Knoll Manor Nursing Home*
824 6th Ave W, Birmingham, AL, 35204 (205)
787-2619
Admin Sue Mathews.
Licensure Skilled Care; Intermediate Care.
Beds SNF 72; ICF 28. *Certified* Medicaid;
Medicare.
Ownership Nonprofit.

Pine Hill Nursing Home
2350 Sweeny Hollow Rd, Birmingham, AL,
35215 (205) 853-2340
Admin Robert V Santini.
Licensure Skilled Care; Intermediate Care.
Beds SNF 47; ICF 9. *Certified* Medicaid;
Medicare.
Ownership Nonprofit.
Facilities Dining room; Physical therapy room;
Activities room; Chapel; Crafts room; Laundry
room; Barber/Beauty shop.
Activities Arts and Crafts; Games; Reading
groups; Prayer groups; Movies; Group walks.

Rose Manor Health Care
7755 4th Ave S, Birmingham, AL, 35206 (205)
833-0146
Admin Sarah J McKinney. *Medical Dir/Dir of
Nursing* Henry L Darnell Jr MD.
Licensure Skilled Care; Intermediate Care.
Beds SNF 100; ICF 12. *Certified* Medicaid;
Medicare.
Ownership Proprietary.
Admissions Requirements Medical examina-
tion; Physician's request.
Staff Physicians 1 (pt); RNs 2 (ft); LPNs 9 (ft),
3 (pt); Orderlies 3 (ft); Nurses aides 30 (ft);
Physical therapists 1 (pt); Reality therapists 1
(pt); Recreational therapists 1 (ft); Occupational
therapists 1 (pt); Speech therapists 1 (pt);
Activities coordinators 1 (ft); Dietitians 1 (ft);
Dentists 1 (pt); Ophthalmologists 1 (pt); Podia-
trists 1 (pt); Audiologists 1 (pt).
Facilities Dining room; Activities room; Chapel; Crafts room; Barber/Beauty shop.
Activities Arts and Crafts; Cards; Games;
Reading groups; Prayer groups; Movies; Shopping trips.
Description Rose Manor is located on 5 acres
of beautifully landscaped land. Picnics and outdoor activities are held when weather permits.

Saint Lukes Nursing Home*
1220 S 17th St, Birmingham, AL, 35205 (205)
933-2180
Admin Terry L Durham.
Licensure Skilled Care; Intermediate Care.
Beds SNF 42; ICF 41. *Certified* Medicaid;
Medicare.
Ownership Proprietary.

Saint Martins-in-the-Pines
4941 Montevallo Rd, Birmingham, AL, 35210
(205) 956-1831
Admin Jack K Holloway. *Medical Dir/Dir of
Nursing* Dr Charles Colvin.
Licensure Skilled Care. *Beds* 107.
Ownership Nonprofit.
Admissions Requirements Minimum age 65;
Medical examination.
Staff RNs 3 (ft), 2 (pt); LPNs 10 (ft), 2 (pt);
Orderlies 3 (ft), 1 (pt); Nurses aides 70 (ft);
Physical therapists 1 (pt); Activities coordina-
tors 3 (ft); Dietitians 1 (ft).
Affiliation Episcopal
Facilities Dining room; Physical therapy room;
Activities room; Chapel; Crafts room; Laundry
room; Barber/Beauty shop; Library.
Activities Arts and Crafts; Cards; Games;
Reading groups; Prayer groups; Movies; Shop-
ping trips; Dances/Social or cultural gatherings.
Description Complex also contains 106 apart-
ments for residential living.

South Haven Nursing Home
3141 Old Columbiana Rd, Birmingham, AL,
35226 (205) 822-1580
Admin Rheta S Skelton. *Medical Dir/Dir of
Nursing* Dr W C Browne.
Licensure Skilled Care; Intermediate Care.
Beds SNF 75; ICF 36. *Certified* Medicaid;
Medicare.
Ownership Proprietary.
Admissions Requirements Minimum age 65;
Medical examination; Physician's request.
Staff Physicians; RNs 5 (ft); LPNs 11 (ft);
Nurses aides 40 (ft), 10 (pt); Recreational thera-

pists; Speech therapists; Activities coordinators 1 (ft); Dietitians 1 (pt); Dentists 1 (pt); Podiatrists 1 (pt); Medical records person 1 (pt).
Facilities Dining room; Physical therapy room; Activities room; Chapel; Crafts room; Laundry room; Barber/Beauty shop; Library; TV rooms.
Activities Arts and Crafts; Cards; Games; Reading groups; Prayer groups; Movies; Shopping trips; Dances/Social or cultural gatherings; Ceramics.
Description South Haven is in its 20th year of service to the community and is continually striving to treat the whole person physically, mentally, emotionally, and spiritually while offering the very finest for your very dearest.

BOAZ

The Nursing Home of Boaz*
PO Box 368, Corley Ave, Boaz, AL, 35957 (205) 593-8380
Admin William E Hill.
Licensure Skilled Care; Intermediate Care.
Beds SNF 47; ICF 33. *Certified* Medicaid; Medicare.
Ownership Proprietary.

BREWTON

New Hope Manor*
Pineview St and 3rd Ave, Brewton, AL, 36426 (205) 867-6077
Admin Randolph M McDowell.
Licensure Skilled Care; Intermediate Care.
Beds SNF 82; ICF 22. *Certified* Medicaid; Medicare.
Ownership Proprietary.

BUTLER

Rush Nursing Center
PO Box 677, Butler, AL, 36904 (205) 459-2394
Admin Grace Morgan. *Medical Dir/Dir of Nursing* Dr Keith Aldridge.
Licensure Skilled Care; Intermediate Care.
Beds SNF 36; ICF 10. *Certified* Medicaid; Medicare.
Ownership Proprietary.
Admissions Requirements Physician's request.
Staff Physicians 4 (ft); RNs 2 (ft); LPNs 5 (ft); Orderlies 5 (ft); Nurses aides 11 (ft); Activities coordinators 1 (ft); Dietitians.

CAMDEN

Camden Nursing Facility
Ponderosa Rd, Camden, AL, 36726 (205) 682-4231
Admin Mildred Jobe. *Medical Dir/Dir of Nursing* Dr Sumpter Blackman.
Licensure Skilled Care. *Beds* 75. *Certified* Medicaid; Medicare.
Ownership Proprietary.
Admissions Requirements Medical examination; Physician's request.
Staff Physicians 3 (ft); RNs 2 (ft), 2 (pt); LPNs 6 (ft), 1 (pt); Nurses aides 25 (ft), 1 (pt); Activities coordinators 1 (ft); Dietitians 1 (ft); Dentists 1 (pt).
Facilities Dining room; Activities room; Crafts

room; Laundry room; Barber/Beauty shop; Library.
Activities Arts and Crafts; Cards; Games; Reading groups; Prayer groups; Movies; Shopping trips; Dances/Social or cultural gatherings.
Description A 75-dual-bed facility with modern equipment which strives to deliver quality nursing care to all residents. Complete activity program striving to include all residents in some type of activities. Full-time certified dietetic manager. Excellent year round climate.

CARBON HILL

Carbon Hill Health Care Inc*
516 E 4th Ave, Carbon Hill, AL, 35549 (205) 924-9940
Admin Jane Tidwell.
Licensure Intermediate Care. *Beds* 49.
Ownership Proprietary.

CENTRE

Cherokee County Nursing Home
Hospital Ave, Box 199, Centre, AL, 35960 (205) 927-5778
Admin Carol Peace. *Medical Dir/Dir of Nursing* C Clark Smeltzer Jr.
Licensure Skilled Care. *Beds* 53. *Certified* Medicare.
Ownership Public.
Admissions Requirements Medical examination.
Staff Physicians 5 (ft); RNs 1 (ft), 2 (pt); LPNs 6 (ft), 1 (pt); Orderlies 1 (pt); Nurses aides 17 (ft), 12 (pt); Activities coordinators 1 (ft); Dietitians 1 (pt); Dentists 1 (pt).
Facilities Dining room; Activities room; Chapel; Crafts room; Laundry room; Barber/Beauty shop.
Activities Arts and Crafts; Cards; Games; Reading groups; Prayer groups; Movies.
Description Patients have access to professional beauticians, organized volunteers, and bookmobile. Boy scouts, churches, and clubs have adopted nursing home patients.

CENTREVILLE

Bibb Medical Center Hospital and Nursing Home
164 Pierson Ave, Centreville, AL, 35042 (205) 926-7251
Admin Terry J Smith. *Medical Dir/Dir of Nursing* William O Owings MD.
Licensure Skilled Care; Intermediate Care.
Beds SNF 62; ICF 41. *Certified* Medicaid; Medicare.
Ownership Public.
Staff Physicians 4 (pt); RNs 2 (ft); LPNs 10 (ft), 2 (pt); Orderlies 7 (ft), 1 (pt); Nurses aides 25 (ft), 7 (pt); Physical therapists 1 (pt); Activities coordinators 1 (ft); Dietitians 1 (ft); Dentists 1 (pt); Ophthalmologists 1 (pt).
Facilities Dining room; Physical therapy room; Chapel; Barber/Beauty shop.
Activities Cards; Games; Reading groups; Prayer groups.
Description The facility is located in the heart of Alabama and is certified by the state health department and accredited by JCAH. It

includes an exercise track, a garden area, 2 large TV and visiting rooms, and 2 dining rooms. Also includes interdenominational religious activities and activities planned according to individual needs and requests.

CHATOM

Washington County Hospital and Nursing Home*
PO Box 400, Saint Stephens Ave, Chatom, AL, 36518 (205) 847-2223
Admin Hiller Dickerson.
Licensure Skilled Care. *Beds* 50. *Certified* Medicaid; Medicare.
Ownership Public.

CITRONELLE

Citronelle Convalescent Center
108 N 4th St, PO Drawer 38, Citronelle, AL, 36522 (205) 866-5509
Admin George L Keller. *Medical Dir/Dir of Nursing* John Prine MD.
Licensure Skilled Care; Intermediate Care.
Beds SNF 56; ICF 13. *Certified* Medicaid; Medicare.
Ownership Proprietary.
Admissions Requirements Minimum age 21; Medical examination; Physician's request.
Staff Physicians; RNs; LPNs; Nurses aides; Recreational therapists; Occupational therapists; Activities coordinators; Dietitians; Dentists; Ophthalmologists.
Facilities Dining room; Activities room; Crafts room; Laundry room; Barber/Beauty shop.
Activities Arts and Crafts; Cards; Games; Prayer groups; Shopping trips.

CLANTON

Clanton Health Care Center Inc
1705 Lay Dam Rd, Clanton, AL, 35045 (205) 755-4384
Admin Billy R Hatley. *Medical Dir/Dir of Nursing* Dr Kent Johns.
Licensure Skilled Care; Intermediate Care.
Beds SNF 40; ICF 10. *Certified* Medicaid; Medicare.
Ownership Proprietary.
Staff RNs 1 (ft), 3 (pt); LPNs 2 (ft), 3 (pt); Orderlies 2 (ft), 1 (pt); Nurses aides 10 (ft), 9 (pt); Activities coordinators 1 (ft); Dietitians 1 (ft).
Facilities Dining room; Activities room; Crafts room; Barber/Beauty shop.
Activities Arts and Crafts; Cards; Games; Reading groups; Prayer groups; Movies; Dances/Social or cultural gatherings.

Clanton Health Care—South
1005 Lay Dam Rd, Clanton, AL, 35045 (205) 255-4960
Admin Bill Hatley. *Medical Dir/Dir of Nursing* Dr Kent Johns.
Licensure Skilled Care; Intermediate Care.
Beds 119. *Certified* Medicaid; Medicare.
Ownership Proprietary.
Staff RNs 1 (ft), 3 (pt); LPNs 5 (ft), 5 (pt); Orderlies 2 (ft), 1 (pt); Nurses aides 12 (ft), 11 (pt); Activities coordinators 1 (ft).

Facilities Dining room; Activities room; Chapel; Crafts room; Barber/Beauty shop.
Activities Arts and Crafts; Cards; Games; Prayer groups; Movies; Dances/Social or cultural gatherings.
Description A new 119-bed skilled and intermediate facility has been constructed. Residents moved to the new facility in mid-summer 1984.

COLLINSVILLE

Collinsville Nursing Home Inc*
Drawer G, US Hwy 11, Collinsville, AL, 35961 (205) 524-2117
Admin Vera A Gressler.
Licensure Skilled Care; Intermediate Care.
Beds SNF 94; ICF 26. *Certified* Medicaid; Medicare.
Ownership Proprietary.

COOK SPRINGS

Baptist Home for Senior Citizens
PO Box 10, Cook Springs, AL, 35052 (205) 338-2221
Admin John M Pruitt. *Medical Dir/Dir of Nursing* Dr E H Edwards.
Licensure Skilled Care; Intermediate Care.
Beds SNF 93; ICF 33. *Certified* Medicaid; Medicare.
Ownership Nonprofit.
Admissions Requirements Minimum age 65; Medical examination; Physician's request.
Staff Physicians 1 (pt); RNs 4 (ft); LPNs 16 (ft); Nurses aides 41 (ft); Physical therapists 1 (pt); Speech therapists 1 (pt); Activities coordinators 1 (ft); Dietitians 1 (pt); Audiologists 1 (pt).
Affiliation Baptist
Facilities Dining room; Physical therapy room; Activities room; Chapel; Crafts room; Laundry room; Barber/Beauty shop.
Activities Arts and Crafts; Cards; Games; Reading groups; Prayer groups; Movies; Dances/Social or cultural gatherings.

CORDOVA

Cordova Nursing Home Inc
200 Highland St, Cordova, AL, 35550 (205) 483-9282
Admin Flora Robertson. *Medical Dir/Dir of Nursing* George H Weaver MD.
Licensure Skilled Care; Intermediate Care.
Beds SNF 94; ICF 10. *Certified* Medicaid; Medicare.
Ownership Proprietary.
Staff Physicians 1 (ft); RNs 4 (ft), 1 (pt); LPNs 14 (ft), 6 (pt); Nurses aides 29 (ft), 9 (pt); Activities coordinators 1 (ft); Dietitians 1 (ft).
Facilities Dining room; Activities room; Laundry room; Barber/Beauty shop.
Activities Arts and Crafts; Cards; Games.

CROSSVILLE

Crossville Nursing Home Inc
Hwy 227, PO Box 97, Crossville, AL, 35962 (205) 528-7844

Admin James F Holcomb. *Medical Dir/Dir of Nursing* Raymond C Ufford.
Licensure Skilled Care; Intermediate Care.
Beds SNF 25; ICF 43. *Certified* Medicaid; Medicare.
Ownership Proprietary.
Admissions Requirements Medical examination; Physician's request.
Staff Physicians 3 (pt); RNs 2 (ft); LPNs 7 (ft), 2 (pt); Nurses aides 32 (ft), 10 (pt); Activities coordinators 1 (ft); Dietitians 8 (ft), 5 (pt); Dentists 1 (pt); 11 (ft), 2 (pt).
Facilities Dining room; Physical therapy room; Activities room; Chapel; Crafts room; Laundry room; Barber/Beauty shop.
Activities Arts and Crafts; Cards; Games; Reading groups; Prayer groups; Movies; Shopping trips; Dances/Social or cultural gatherings.

CULLMAN

Cullman Health Care Center North*
1607 Main Ave NE, Cullman, AL, 35055 (205) 734-8745
Admin R Frank Brown Jr.
Licensure Skilled Care. *Beds* 165. *Certified* Medicaid; Medicare.
Ownership Proprietary.

DADEVILLE

Dadeville Convalescent Home*
237 Lafayette St, Dadeville, AL, 36853 (205) 825-9244
Admin Betty S Chapman.
Licensure Skilled Care; Intermediate Care.
Beds SNF 71; ICF 40. *Certified* Medicaid; Medicare.
Ownership Proprietary.

Easterwood Nursing Home
300 Columbus St, Dadeville, AL, 36853 (205) 825-7883
Admin Emma M Swindall. *Medical Dir/Dir of Nursing* Dr Jerry Swindall.
Licensure Skilled Care. *Beds* 29. *Certified* Medicaid; Medicare.
Ownership Proprietary.
Staff Physicians 1 (ft); RNs 1 (ft), 1 (pt); LPNs 2 (ft), 6 (pt); Nurses aides 6 (ft), 3 (pt); Recreational therapists 1 (pt); Activities coordinators 1 (pt).
Facilities Dining room; Activities room; Crafts room; Laundry room.
Activities Arts and Crafts; Cards; Games; Reading groups; Prayer groups; Shopping trips.
Description Once a month during the spring and summer months, weather permitting, patients are taken on a picnic and fishing trip.

Wilder Nursing Home*
PO Box 217, Lafayette St, Dadeville, AL, 36853 (205) 825-7881
Admin Frances Marie Melton.
Licensure Skilled Care; Intermediate Care.
Beds SNF 47; ICF 17. *Certified* Medicaid; Medicare.
Ownership Proprietary.

DAPHNE

Villa Mercy Inc*
PO Box 1096, 101 Villa Dr, Daphne, AL, 36526 (205) 626-2694
Admin Sr Mary Eileen Wilhelm.
Licensure Skilled Care. *Beds* 137. *Certified* Medicaid; Medicare.
Ownership Nonprofit.

DECATUR

Colonial Rest Home
Rt 1, Box 119, Decatur, AL, 35601 (205) 353-5567
Admin Maxine Tapscott. *Medical Dir/Dir of Nursing* Dr J B Wiley Jr.
Licensure Intermediate Care. *Beds* 43. *Certified* Medicaid.
Ownership Proprietary.
Admissions Requirements Medical examination; Physician's request.
Staff Physicians 1 (pt); RNs 1 (pt); LPNs 2 (ft), 2 (pt); Nurses aides 9 (ft), 10 (pt); Activities coordinators 1 (ft); Dietitians 1 (pt).
Facilities Dining room; Activities room; Laundry room.
Activities Arts and Crafts; Cards; Games; Shopping trips.
Description The facility is located in a quaint country setting.

Flint City Nursing Home Inc*
Rt 4, Box 500, Hwy 31 S, Decatur, AL, 35601 (205) 355-2418
Admin Berneal McKennie.
Licensure Skilled Care; Intermediate Care.
Beds SNF 46; ICF 30. *Certified* Medicaid; Medicare.
Ownership Proprietary.

Medical Park Convalescent Center Inc*
1306 14th Ave SE, Decatur, AL, 35601 (205) 355-6911
Admin James K Worthey.
Licensure Skilled Care; Intermediate Care.
Beds SNF 75; ICF 108. *Certified* Medicaid; Medicare.
Ownership Proprietary.

DEMOPOLIS

Woodhaven Manor Nursing Home*
105 W Windsor St, Demopolis, AL, 36732 (205) 289-2741
Admin Alice Hawkins.
Licensure Skilled Care; Intermediate Care.
Beds SNF 35; ICF 40. *Certified* Medicaid; Medicare.
Ownership Proprietary.

DOTHAN

Extendicare Health Center*
814 S Saint Andrews St, Dothan, AL, 36301 (205) 793-1177
Admin Helen Harrell.
Licensure Skilled Care; Intermediate Care.
Beds SNF 52; ICF 57. *Certified* Medicaid; Medicare.
Ownership Proprietary.

Wesley Manor Methodist Home for the Aging
210 Honeysuckle Rd, Dothan, AL, 36301 (205)
792-0921
Admin W J Mathis Jr. *Medical Dir/Dir of
Nursing* Donald Tysinger MD.
Licensure Skilled Care; Intermediate Care.
Beds SNF 62; ICF 54. *Certified* Medicaid;
Medicare.
Ownership Nonprofit.
Admissions Requirements Minimum age 62;
Medical examination.
Affiliation Methodist
Facilities Dining room; Physical therapy room;
Activities room; Chapel; Crafts room; Laundry
room; Barber/Beauty shop; Library.
Activities Arts and Crafts; Cards; Games;
Reading groups; Prayer groups; Movies; Shop-
ping trips; Dances/Social or cultural gatherings;
Ceramics.

DOUBLE SPRINGS

Estes Health Care Center—Double Springs*
PO Box 497, Hwy 33, Double Springs, AL,
35553 (205) 489-2136
Admin Willodean A Corbin.
Licensure Skilled Care; Intermediate Care.
Beds SNF 80; ICF 20. *Certified* Medicaid;
Medicare.
Ownership Proprietary.

EIGHT MILE

Estes Health Care Center—Oakridge*
4525 Saint Stephens Rd, Eight Mile, AL, 36613
(205) 452-0996
Admin Donald E Henle.
Licensure Skilled Care; Intermediate Care.
Beds SNF 86; ICF 86. *Certified* Medicaid;
Medicare.
Ownership Proprietary.

ELBA

Elba General Hospital and Nursing Home
987 Drayton St, Elba, AL, 36323 (205)
897-2257
Admin Steven A Nadeau. *Medical Dir/Dir of
Nursing* John Mason Kimmey MD.
Licensure Skilled Care. *Beds* SNF 71. *Certi-
fied* Medicaid; Medicare.
Ownership Public.
Admissions Requirements Medical examina-
tion; Physician's request.
Staff Physicians 3 (pt); RNs 3 (ft); LPNs 8 (ft);
Orderlies 5 (ft); Nurses aides 19 (ft); Physical
therapists 1 (pt); Activities coordinators 1 (ft);
Dietitians 1 (pt).
Facilities Dining room; Physical therapy room;
Activities room; Laundry room; Barber/Beauty
shop.
Activities Arts and Crafts; Games; Reading
groups; Prayer groups; Movies; Shopping trips;
Dances/Social or cultural gatherings; television.
Description A beautiful facility, adjoining Elba
General Hospital in a caring community. Many
social activities are offered enabling the patient
to remain a more active individual, maintaining independence as long as possible, as
well as providing enjoyment. Quality care is
goal.

ELMORE

Merry Wood Lodge Inc*
PO Box 7, Mount Hebron Rd, Elmore, AL,
36025 (205) 567-8484
Admin B Coleman Beale.
Licensure Skilled Care. *Beds* 124.
Ownership Proprietary.

ENTERPRISE

Enterprise Hospital and Nursing Home
Dothan Hwy 84 E, Enterprise, AL, 36330 (205)
347-9541
Admin Maurice Kilpatrick. *Medical Dir/Dir of
Nursing* David Rhyne MD.
Licensure Skilled Care; Intermediate Care.
Beds SNF 55; ICF 41. *Certified* Medicaid;
Medicare.
Ownership Public.
Admissions Requirements Medical examina-
tion; Physician's request.
Staff RNs 2 (ft); LPNs 13 (ft); Orderlies 6 (ft);
Nurses aides 48 (ft); Activities coordinators 4
(ft); Dietitians 1 (pt).
Facilities Dining room; Activities room; Crafts
room; Barber/Beauty shop.
Activities Arts and Crafts; Cards; Games;
Reading groups; Prayer groups; Movies; Shop-
ping trips; Dances/Social or cultural gatherings.
Description Hospital and nursing home are
located in same building. This close proximity
allows nursing home patients easy access to
hospital ancillary services; hospital has 6 intensive care beds.

EUFAULA

Eufaula Geriatric Center Inc*
430 Rivers St, Eufaula, AL, 36027 (205)
687-6627
Admin Betty Thornburg.
Licensure Skilled Care; Intermediate Care.
Beds SNF 120; ICF 60. *Certified* Medicaid;
Medicare.
Ownership Proprietary.

EUTAW

Greene County Hospital and Nursing Home
509 Wilson Ave, Eutaw, AL, 35462 (205)
372-3388
Admin John L Solomon. *Medical Dir/Dir of
Nursing* Dr Rucker Staggers.
Licensure Skilled Care; Intermediate Care.
Beds SNF 40; ICF 12. *Certified* Medicaid;
Medicare.
Ownership Public.
Admissions Requirements Physician's request.
Staff Physicians 5 (ft), 1 (pt); RNs 1 (ft), 1 (pt);
LPNs 6 (ft), 1 (pt); Orderlies 4 (ft); Nurses aides
14 (ft), 10 (pt); Physical therapists 1 (pt); Activi-
ties coordinators 1 (pt); Dietitians 1 (ft).
Facilities Dining room; Physical therapy room;
Laundry room; Barber/Beauty shop.
Activities Arts and Crafts; Cards; Games;
Reading groups; Dances/Social or cultural gath-
erings.

Description Local group performs on major
holidays; also school groups perform on a routine basis.

EVERGREEN

Evergreen Nursing Home Inc*
PO Box 391, Knoxville St, Evergreen, AL,
36401 (205) 578-3783
Admin James A Ansley.
Licensure Skilled Care; Intermediate Care.
Beds SNF 41; ICF 10. *Certified* Medicaid;
Medicare.
Ownership Proprietary.

FAIRFIELD

Fairfield Health Care Center
6825 Grasselli Rd, Fairfield, AL, 35064 (205)
780-3920
Admin Lee O'Dell. *Medical Dir/Dir of
Nursing* Jack C Whites MD.
Licensure Skilled Care; Intermediate Care.
Beds SNF 115; ICF 75. *Certified* Medicaid;
Medicare.
Ownership Proprietary.
Admissions Requirements Minimum age 21;
Medical examination; Physician's request.
Staff Physicians 1 (pt); RNs 3 (ft); LPNs 25
(ft), 10 (pt); Nurses aides 40 (ft), 20 (pt);
Physical therapists 1 (pt); Recreational thera-
pists 1 (pt); Occupational therapists 1 (pt); Spee-
ch therapists 1 (pt); Activities coordinators 2
(ft); Dietitians 1 (ft); Dentists 1 (pt); Podiatrists
1 (pt); Audiologists 1 (pt).
Facilities Dining room; Physical therapy room;
Activities room; Chapel; Crafts room; Laundry
room; Barber/Beauty shop; Treatment room.
Activities Arts and Crafts; Cards; Games;
Reading groups; Prayer groups; Movies; Shopping trips; Dances/Social or cultural gatherings.
Description Facility offers adopt-a-grandparent
program with elementary and special education
classes; clinical setting for nursing assistant
training program; member of AHCA and Alabama Nursing Home Association.

FAIRHOPE

Estes Health Care Center—Fairhope*
108 S Church St, Fairhope, AL, 36532 (205)
928-2153
Admin Donna Tucker.
Licensure Skilled Care; Intermediate Care.
Beds SNF 66; ICF 70. *Certified* Medicaid;
Medicare.
Ownership Proprietary.

Rosemont Nursing and Convalescent Center*
PO Drawer H, Highway 98, Fairhope, AL,
36532 (205) 928-2177
Admin John H Oldham.
Licensure Skilled Care; Intermediate Care.
Beds SNF 71; ICF 12. *Certified* Medicaid;
Medicare.
Ownership Proprietary.

FALKVILLE

Falkville Nursing Home Inc
3rd St, PO Box 409, Falkville, AL, 35622 (205)
784-5235
Admin Phillip Rollins. *Medical Dir/Dir of Nursing* Dinfsh Gandhi MD.
Licensure Skilled Care; Intermediate Care.
Beds SNF 75; ICF 30. *Certified* Medicaid; Medicare.
Ownership Proprietary.
Staff Physicians 5 (pt); RNs 2 (ft); LPNs 8 (ft), 1 (pt); Orderlies 5 (ft), 1 (pt); Nurses aides 35 (ft), 2 (pt); Physical therapists 1 (pt); Speech therapists 1 (pt); Activities coordinators 1 (ft), 1 (pt); Dietitians 1 (pt); Dentists 1 (pt); Audiologists 1 (pt).
Facilities Dining room; Physical therapy room; Activities room; Chapel; Laundry room; Barber/Beauty shop.
Activities Arts and Crafts; Cards; Games; Prayer groups; Shopping trips.

Summerford Nursing Home Inc
Hwy 31 North, PO Box 310, Falkville, AL, 35622 (205) 784-5275
Admin Robert D Summerford.
Licensure Skilled Care; Intermediate Care.
Beds SNF 163; ICF 33. *Certified* Medicaid; Medicare.
Ownership Proprietary.
Staff Physicians 3 (pt); RNs 4 (ft); LPNs 15 (ft), 1 (pt); Orderlies 7 (ft), 4 (pt); Nurses aides 56 (ft), 5 (pt); Physical therapists 1 (pt); Occupational therapists 1 (ft); Activities coordinators 6 (ft); Dietitians 1 (pt).
Facilities Dining room; Physical therapy room; Activities room; Chapel; Crafts room; Laundry room; Barber/Beauty shop.
Activities Arts and Crafts; Cards; Games; Reading groups; Prayer groups.

FAYETTE

Fayette County Hospital and Nursing Home
1653 Temple Ave N, Fayette, AL, 35555 (205) 932-5966
Admin Frank Wilbanks. *Medical Dir/Dir of Nursing* Henry Hodo Jr MD.
Licensure Skilled Care; Intermediate Care.
Beds SNF 85; ICF 16. *Certified* Medicaid; Medicare.
Ownership Public.
Staff RNs 2 (ft); LPNs 16 (ft); Orderlies 5 (ft); Nurses aides 21 (ft), 3 (pt); Physical therapists 1 (pt); Activities coordinators 1 (ft); Dietitians 1 (ft); Dentists 1 (pt).
Facilities Dining room; Physical therapy room; Activities room; Chapel; Crafts room; Laundry room; Barber/Beauty shop; Library.
Activities Arts and Crafts; Cards; Games; Reading groups; Prayer groups; Movies; Shopping trips; Dances/Social or cultural gatherings.
Description JCAH accredited.

FLORENCE

El Reposo Sanitarium*
Rt 5, Box 530, Florence, AL, 35630 (205) 757-2143
Admin Charles N Martin.
Licensure Intermediate Care. *Beds* 40. *Certified* Medicaid; Medicare.
Ownership Nonprofit.

**Eliza Memorial Hospital—
Mitchell-Hollingsworth Annex**
Flagg Circle, PO Box 818, Florence, AL, 35631 (205) 767-9401
Admin J T Whetstone. *Medical Dir/Dir of Nursing* Harry M Simpson MD.
Licensure Skilled Care; Intermediate Care.
Beds 202. *Certified* Medicaid; Medicare.
Admissions Requirements Medical examination; Physician's request.
Staff RNs 4 (ft), 2 (pt); LPNs 20 (ft), 4 (pt); Orderlies 10 (ft), 1 (pt); Nurses aides 56 (ft), 6 (pt); Physical therapists 1 (ft), 1 (pt); Recreational therapists 3 (pt); Activities coordinators 1 (ft); Dietitians 1 (ft); Dentists 1 (pt).
Facilities Dining room; Physical therapy room; Activities room; Crafts room; Laundry room; Barber/Beauty shop; Library.
Activities Arts and Crafts; Cards; Games; Dances/Social or cultural gatherings.
Description Facility offers respite care, geriatric day care, and exercise program for both men and women. New facility is under construction.

Glenwood Convalescent Center*
210 Ana Dr, Florence, AL, 35630 (205) 766-8963
Admin Timothy L Morrow.
Licensure Skilled Care. *Beds* 114. *Certified* Medicaid; Medicare.
Ownership Proprietary.

Rolling Acres Nursing Home*
PO Box 2386, 2107 Cloyd Blvd, Florence, AL, 35630 (205) 766-5771
Admin Bernice Oakley.
Licensure Skilled Care; Intermediate Care.
Beds SNF 118; ICF 16. *Certified* Medicaid; Medicare.
Ownership Proprietary.

FOLEY

Foley Nursing Home*
1700 N Alston St, Foley, AL, 36535 (205) 943-2781
Admin Paul W Philips Jr.
Licensure Skilled Care; Intermediate Care.
Beds SNF 74; ICF 80. *Certified* Medicaid; Medicare.
Ownership Proprietary.

FORT PAYNE

Mountain Manor Nursing Home Inc
403 13th St NW, Fort Payne, AL, 35967 (205) 845-5990
Admin Diane Talor. *Medical Dir/Dir of Nursing* Dr Timothy Decker.
Licensure Skilled Care; Intermediate Care.
Beds SNF 94; ICF 29. *Certified* Medicaid; Medicare.
Ownership Proprietary.
Staff Physicians 12 (ft); RNs 2 (ft); LPNs 11 (ft), 7 (pt); Orderlies 3 (ft); Nurses aides 30 (ft), 9 (pt); Activities coordinators 1 (ft); Dietitians 1 (ft); Dentists 1 (pt); Ophthalmologists 1 (pt).

Facilities Dining room; Activities room; Laundry room; Barber/Beauty shop; Two living rooms.
Activities Arts and Crafts; Cards; Games; Reading groups; Movies; Dances/Social or cultural gatherings.
Description A Beverly Enterprises facility featuring resident council, family council, family night, adopt-a-grandparent program, private and semi-private rooms.

GADSDEN

Gadsden Health Care Center Inc
1945 Davis Dr, Gadsden, AL, 35901 (205) 547-4938
Admin W R Lester. *Medical Dir/Dir of Nursing* Dr John B Keeling.
Licensure Skilled Care; Intermediate Care.
Beds 152. *Certified* Medicaid; Medicare.
Ownership Proprietary.
Facilities Dining room; Physical therapy room; Activities room; Chapel; Crafts room; Laundry room; Barber/Beauty shop.
Activities Arts and Crafts; Cards; Games; Reading groups; Prayer groups; Movies; Shopping trips; Dances/Social or cultural gatherings.

McGuffey Health Care Center Inc*
2301 Rainbow Dr, Gadsden, AL, 35901 (205) 543-3467
Admin Laurence A Baird.
Licensure Skilled Care; Intermediate Care.
Beds SNF 147; ICF 62. *Certified* Medicaid; Medicare.
Ownership Proprietary.

Mountain View Extended Care Center*
PO Box 1400, 3001 Scenic Hwy, Gadsden, AL, 35902 (205) 546-9266
Admin Tyler Barnes Jr.
Licensure Skilled Care. *Beds* 34. *Certified* Medicare.
Ownership Public.

Physicians Care Center*
700 Hutchins St, Gadsden, AL, 35901 (205) 543-7101
Admin Carroll Crane.
Licensure Skilled Care. *Beds* 71. *Certified* Medicaid; Medicare.
Ownership Proprietary.

GARDEN CITY

Garden City Health Care Center*
PO Box 258, Garden City, AL, 35070 (205) 352-6401
Admin Michael Andrew Cook.
Licensure Skilled Care; Intermediate Care.
Beds SNF 40; ICF 12. *Certified* Medicaid; Medicare.
Ownership Proprietary.

GARDENDALE

Gardendale Nursing Home
420 Dean Dr, Gardendale, AL, 35071 (205) 631-8700
Admin Faith M Hammock. *Medical Dir/Dir of Nursing* Luther Corley III.

Licensure Skilled Care; Intermediate Care.
Beds SNF 143; ICF 5. *Certified* Medicaid;
Medicare.
Ownership Proprietary.
Admissions Requirements Minimum age 18;
Medical examination; Physician's request.
Staff RNs 2 (ft), 2 (pt); LPNs 12 (ft), 3 (pt);
Nurses aides 100 (ft), 20 (pt); Recreational ther-
apists 2 (ft), 1 (pt); Dietitians 1 (pt).
Facilities Dining room; Physical therapy room;
Activities room; Chapel; Laundry room; Bar-
ber/Beauty shop.
Activities Arts and Crafts; Cards; Games; Pray-
er groups; Movies.
Description Facility is located in residential,
quiet area with spacious parking and a friendly
atmosphere.

GENEVA

Wiregrass Hospital and Nursing Home
1200 W Maple Ave, Geneva, AL, 36340 (205)
684-3655
Admin Roger Mayers. *Medical Dir/Dir of
Nursing* Dr H A Childs.
Licensure Skilled Care; Intermediate Care.
Beds 86. *Certified* Medicaid; Medicare.
Ownership Public.
Staff Physicians 1 (pt); RNs 5 (ft); LPNs 10
(ft); Nurses aides 28 (ft), 3 (pt); Activities coor-
dinators 1 (ft).
Facilities Dining room; Physical therapy room;
Crafts room; Laundry room; Barber/Beauty
shop.
Activities Arts and Crafts; Cards; Games;
Reading groups; Prayer groups; Movies; Shop-
ping trips; Dances/Social or cultural gatherings.

GEORGIANA

Homewood Manor Inc*
PO Drawer 189, Georgiana, AL, 36033 (205)
376-2267
Admin Alice Newton.
Licensure Skilled Care; Intermediate Care.
Beds SNF 56; ICF 5. *Certified* Medicaid;
Medicare.
Ownership Proprietary.

GLENCOE

Coosa Valley Convalescent Center*
426 Pineview Ave, Glencoe, AL, 35905 (205)
492-5350
Admin H M Andrew Cook.
Licensure Skilled Care; Intermediate Care.
Beds SNF 94; ICF 30. *Certified* Medicaid;
Medicare.
Ownership Proprietary.

GOODWATER

Goodwater Nursing Home*
Mountain St, Goodwater, AL, 35072 (205)
839-6711
Admin Marjorie K Robbins.
Licensure Skilled Care. *Beds* 42. *Cer-
tified* Medicaid; Medicare.
Ownership Proprietary.

GRAND BAY

Grand Bay Convalescent Home*
PO Box 328, Hwy 90 W, Grand Bay, AL,
36541 (205) 865-6443
Admin Marlene H Hart.
Licensure Intermediate Care. *Beds* 53. *Certi-
fied* Medicaid.
Ownership Proprietary.

GREENSBORO

Greensboro Nursing Home Inc*
PO Box 438, College St, Greensboro, AL,
36744 (205) 624-3054
Admin Daryl L Cargile.
Licensure Intermediate Care. *Beds* 102. *Certi-
fied* Medicaid.
Ownership Proprietary.

GREENVILLE

Greenville Nursing Home*
408 Country Club Dr, Greenville, AL, 36037
(205) 382-2693
Admin Jacob L Curfton Jr.
Licensure Skilled Care; Intermediate Care.
Beds SNF 66; ICF 52. *Certified* Medicaid;
Medicare.
Ownership Proprietary.

GUIN

Marion Sunset Manor*
1201 W 14th Ave, Guin, AL, 35563 (205)
468-3331
Admin Don E Bussey.
Licensure Skilled Care; Intermediate Care.
Beds SNF 33; ICF 18. *Certified* Medicaid;
Medicare.
Ownership Proprietary.

GUNTERSVILLE

Barfield Health Care Inc
Rt 6, Hwy 431 North, Guntersville, AL, 35976
(205) 582-3112
Admin Gerald Bell. *Medical Dir/Dir of
Nursing* Dr Dalton Diamond.
Licensure Skilled Care; Intermediate Care.
Beds SNF 38; ICF 65. *Certified* Medicaid;
Medicare.
Ownership Proprietary.
Admissions Requirements Medical examina-
tion; Physician's request.
Staff Physicians 2 (ft), 4 (pt); RNs 2 (ft), 2 (pt);
LPNs 4 (ft), 2 (pt); Orderlies 6 (ft), 2 (pt);
Nurses aides 32 (ft), 6 (pt); Physical therapists 1
(pt); Activities coordinators 1 (ft); Dietitians 1
(ft); Dentists 1 (ft).
Facilities Dining room; Activities room; Chap-
el; Crafts room; Laundry room; Barber/Beauty
shop; Library.
Activities Arts and Crafts; Cards; Games;
Reading groups; Prayer groups; Movies; Shop-
ping trips; Dances/Social or cultural gatherings;
Resident council.
Description Facility is located near Centersville

Lake and has 48 semi-private rooms with full
bath, 5 private rooms with full bath, and 2 private rooms with half bath.

HALEYVILLE

Crestview Manor
2201 11th Ave, Haleyville, AL, 35565 (205)
486-9478
Admin Alton Anderson.
Licensure Skilled Care; Intermediate Care.
Beds SNF 67; ICF 30. *Certified* Medicaid;
Medicare.
Ownership Proprietary.
Staff RNs 2 (ft), 2 (pt); LPNs 13 (ft), 2 (pt);
Orderlies 1 (ft); Nurses aides 50 (ft), 5 (pt);
Activities coordinators 1 (ft); Dietitians 1 (ft), 1
(pt).
Facilities Dining room; Activities room; Crafts
room; Laundry room; Barber/Beauty shop;
Library.
Activities Arts and Crafts; Cards; Games;
Reading groups; Prayer groups; Movies; Shop-
ping trips; Dances/Social or cultural gatherings.

HAMILTON

Marion County Nursing Home
1315 Military St South, Hamilton, AL, 35570
(205) 921-2183
Admin Brenda Ray. *Medical Dir/Dir of
Nursing* Charles Pyle MD.
Licensure Skilled Care; Intermediate Care.
Beds 69. *Certified* Medicaid; Medicare.
Ownership Proprietary.
Admissions Requirements Physician's request.
Staff RNs 2 (ft); LPNs 5 (ft), 5 (pt); Orderlies 7
(ft), 1 (pt); Nurses aides 13 (ft), 11 (pt); Physical
therapists 1 (pt); Recreational therapists 1 (ft);
Activities coordinators 1 (ft).

HANCEVILLE

Hanceville Nursing Home*
PO Box 409, US Highway 31 N, Hanceville,
AL, 35077 (205) 352-2251
Admin James D Moody.
Licensure Skilled Care; Intermediate Care.
Beds SNF 136; ICF 20. *Certified* Medicaid;
Medicare.
Ownership Proprietary.

HEFLIN

Cleburne County Hospital and Nursing Home
411 Ross St, Heflin, AL, 36264 (205) 463-2121
Admin Carolyn Parker. *Medical Dir/Dir of
Nursing* Dr David Justice.
Licensure Skilled Care. *Beds* 40. *Cer-
tified* Medicare.
Ownership Public.
Staff Physicians 3 (ft), 1 (pt); RNs 6 (ft), 4 (pt);
LPNs 12 (ft), 4 (pt); Orderlies 1 (ft), 2 (pt);
Nurses aides 13 (ft), 5 (pt); Activities coordina-
tors 1 (ft).
Facilities Dining room; Activities room; Chap-
el; Laundry room; Barber/Beauty shop;
Library.

HUEYTOWN

Hueytown Nursing Home Inc
190 Brooklane Dr, Hueytown, AL, 35020 (205) 491-2905
Admin Charlotte Hooton. *Medical Dir/Dir of Nursing* Dr David Barthold.
Licensure Intermediate Care. *Beds* 50. *Certified* Medicaid.
Ownership Proprietary.
Staff Physicians 1 (ft); RNs 1 (ft); LPNs 2 (ft), 4 (pt); Nurses aides 9 (ft), 6 (pt); Activities coordinators 1 (ft); Dietitians 4 (ft), 1 (pt).
Facilities Dining room; Activities room; Chapel; Laundry room; Barber/Beauty shop.
Activities Arts and Crafts; Cards; Games; Reading groups; Prayer groups; Movies; Shopping trips; Dances/Social or cultural gatherings.
Description One outstanding program is Flinthill Joy Ministry. Patients have at least one outing a month; each is made very special. Our patients look forward each month to see where they will be doing: going to a luau, to a park, or a fancy dinner.

Self Nursing Home Inc*
131 Crest Rd, Hueytown, AL, 35020 (205) 491-2411
Admin J A Self Jr.
Licensure Skilled Care; Intermediate Care.
Beds SNF 75; ICF 56. *Certified* Medicaid; Medicare.
Ownership Proprietary.

HUNTSVILLE

Big Spring Manor*
500 Saint Clair Ave SW, Huntsville, AL, 35801 (205) 539-5111
Admin Wendell R Stidger.
Licensure Skilled Care; Intermediate Care.
Beds SNF 102; ICF 30. *Certified* Medicaid; Medicare.
Ownership Proprietary.

Huntsville Nursing Home*
4320 Judith Ln SW, Huntsville, AL, 35805 (205) 837-1730
Admin Judy Hill Monroe.
Licensure Skilled Care; Intermediate Care.
Beds SNF 84; ICF 45. *Certified* Medicaid; Medicare.
Ownership Proprietary.

NHE—Huntsville*
105 Teakwood Dr, Huntsville, AL, 35801 (205) 881-5000
Admin Wendell Stidger.
Licensure Skilled Care; Intermediate Care.
Beds SNF 80; ICF 79. *Certified* Medicaid; Medicare.
Ownership Proprietary.

Parkview Village Ltd
2004 Max Luther Dr, Huntsville, AL, 35810 (205) 852-9290
Admin Rodney McBridge. *Medical Dir/Dir of Nursing* Tulio Figarola MD.
Licensure Skilled Care; Domiciliary Care.
Beds SNF 60; Domiciliary Care 35. *Certified* Medicare.
Ownership Proprietary.

Admissions Requirements Medical examination; Physician's request.
Staff Physicians 1 (ft); RNs 5 (ft), 3 (pt); LPNs 1 (ft), 5 (pt); Nurses aides 11 (ft), 11 (pt); Physical therapists 1 (ft); Speech therapists 1 (pt); Activities coordinators 1 (ft); Dietitians 1 (pt); Dentists 1 (pt).
Facilities Dining room; Physical therapy room; Activities room; Chapel; Crafts room; Laundry room; Barber/Beauty shop; Library; Pool; Shuffle boards; Horseshoe arena; Garden plots.
Activities Arts and Crafts; Cards; Games; Reading groups; Prayer groups; Movies; Shopping trips; Dances/Social or cultural gatherings.
Description Parkview Village is Huntsville's first retirement community and one of the finest in northern Alabama. Nursing home residents are offered a number of activities and treatments and receive the finest care available. Those in independent housing are offered many activities and receive nursing home care when needed.

JACKSON

Arrington Nursing Home*
2616 N College Ave, Jackson, AL, 36545 (205) 246-2476
Admin Wallace D Nelson.
Licensure Skilled Care; Intermediate Care.
Beds SNF 70; ICF 21. *Certified* Medicaid; Medicare.
Ownership Proprietary.

JACKSONVILLE

Jacksonville Nursing Home Inc*
410 W Wilson St, Jacksonville, AL, 36265 (205) 435-7704
Admin Vida Newell.
Licensure Skilled Care; Intermediate Care.
Beds SNF 121; ICF 46. *Certified* Medicaid; Medicare.
Ownership Proprietary.

JASPER

Ridgeview Health Care Center Inc*
907 11th St NE, Jasper, AL, 35501 (205) 384-3402
Admin Joe W Kelley Jr.
Licensure Skilled Care; Intermediate Care.
Beds SNF 48; ICF 56. *Certified* Medicaid; Medicare.
Ownership Proprietary.

Ridgewood Health Care Center Inc*
201 4th Ave N, Jasper, AL, 35501 (205) 221-4862
Admin J Frank Caldwell.
Licensure Skilled Care. *Beds* 98. *Certified* Medicaid; Medicare.
Ownership Proprietary.

Shadescrest Health Care Center*
PO Box 1012, 2600 Old Parrish Hwy, Jasper, AL, 35501 (205) 384-9086
Admin Paulette Key.
Licensure Skilled Care; Intermediate Care.

Beds SNF 77; ICF 30. *Certified* Medicaid; Medicare.
Ownership Proprietary.

KILLEN

Lauderdale Christian Nursing Home*
Rt 2, Killen, AL, 35645 (205) 757-2103
Admin Louis E Cottrell Jr.
Licensure Skilled Care; Intermediate Care.
Beds SNF 38; ICF 20. *Certified* Medicaid; Medicare.
Ownership Nonprofit.

LAFAYETTE

Lafayette Extended Care*
805 Hospital St SW, Lafayette, AL, 36862 (205) 864-8854
Admin Sarah M Williams.
Licensure Skilled Care. *Beds* 47. *Certified* Medicaid; Medicare.
Ownership Proprietary.

LaFayette Nursing Home Inc
1st St, Lafayette, AL, 36862 (205) 864-9371
Admin Glenda F Traylor. *Medical Dir/Dir of Nursing* Dr J M D Holmes.
Licensure Intermediate Care. *Beds* 45. *Certified* Medicaid.
Ownership Nonprofit.
Staff Physicians 1 (pt); RNs 1 (pt); LPNs 2 (ft), 3 (pt); Orderlies 3 (ft); Nurses aides 11 (ft); Activities coordinators 1 (ft); Dietitians 1 (ft).
Facilities Dining room; Laundry room; Barber/Beauty shop.
Activities Arts and Crafts; Prayer groups; Dances/Social or cultural gatherings.

LANETT

Lanett Geriatric Center Inc*
702 S 13th St, Lanett, AL, 36863 (205) 644-1111
Admin Janice Babb.
Licensure Skilled Care; Intermediate Care.
Beds SNF 44; ICF 21. *Certified* Medicaid; Medicare.
Ownership Proprietary.

LANGDALE

Lanier Memorial Hospital—Nursing Home
4800 48th St, Langdale, AL, 36864 (205) 756-3111
Admin Paul M Calmes. *Medical Dir/Dir of Nursing* R Bob Mullins MD.
Licensure Skilled Care; Intermediate Care.
Beds 75. *Certified* Medicaid; Medicare.
Ownership Nonprofit.
Admissions Requirements Medical examination; Physician's request.
Staff Physicians 30 (pt); RNs 3 (ft); LPNs 16 (ft); Orderlies 1 (ft); Nurses aides 27 (ft); Physical therapists 3 (ft); Recreational therapists 1 (ft); Speech therapists 1 (pt); Activities coordinators 1 (ft); Dietitians 2 (pt); Dentists 4 (pt); Podiatrists 1 (pt).
Facilities Dining room; Physical therapy room; Activities room; Chapel; Crafts room; Laundry

room; Barber/Beauty shop.
Activities Arts and Crafts; Cards; Games; Reading groups; Prayer groups; Movies; Dances/Social or cultural gatherings.

LINDEN

Marengo Nursing Home*
608 N Main St, Linden, AL, 36748 (205) 295-8631
Admin D P Philen.
Licensure Skilled Care; Intermediate Care.
Beds SNF 34; ICF 26. *Certified* Medicaid; Medicare.
Ownership Proprietary.

LINEVILLE

Lineville Geriatric Center Inc
Hwy 9, PO Box 545, Lineville, AL, 36266 (205) 396-2104
Admin Denise A Edwards. *Medical Dir/Dir of Nursing* George Smith MD.
Licensure Skilled Care; Intermediate Care.
Beds 81. *Certified* Medicaid; Medicare.
Ownership Proprietary.
Staff RNs 2 (ft), 1 (pt); LPNs 8 (ft); Orderlies 7 (ft), 1 (pt); Nurses aides 12 (ft), 4 (pt); Activities coordinators 1 (ft); Dietitians 1 (ft).

LUVERNE

Luverne Geriatric Center Inc
310 W 3rd St, Luverne, AL, 36049 (205) 335-5331
Admin Dale Sasser. *Medical Dir/Dir of Nursing* Dr James C Ray.
Licensure Skilled Care; Intermediate Care.
Beds SNF 94; ICF 43. *Certified* Medicaid; Medicare.
Ownership Proprietary.
Admissions Requirements Medical examination; Physician's request.
Staff Physicians 4 (pt); RNs 1 (ft), 1 (pt); LPNs 12 (ft), 5 (pt); Nurses aides 50 (ft), 15 (pt); Recreational therapists 1 (ft); Activities coordinators 1 (ft); Dietitians 1 (ft); Dentists 1 (pt).
Facilities Dining room; Activities room; Crafts room; Laundry room; Barber/Beauty shop.
Activities Arts and Crafts; Cards; Games; Reading groups; Prayer groups; Movies; Shopping trips; Dances/Social or cultural gatherings.

MADISON

Madison Manor Nursing Home*
PO Box 350, Wall Triana Hwy, Madison, AL, 35758 (205) 772-9243
Admin Carol Grubis.
Licensure Skilled Care; Intermediate Care.
Beds SNF 49; ICF 31. *Certified* Medicaid; Medicare.
Ownership Proprietary.

MARBURY

Holy Ghost Mission Nursing Home
PO Box 89, Marbury, AL, 36051 (205) 755-1139

Admin Mary Clarence. *Medical Dir/Dir of Nursing* W W Rennings MD.
Licensure Intermediate Care. *Beds* 20. *Certified* Medicaid.
Ownership Nonprofit.
Admissions Requirements Females only; Medical examination.
Staff RNs 2 (ft); LPNs 1 (ft); Orderlies 1 (ft); Nurses aides 5 (ft), 2 (pt); Activities coordinators 1 (pt); Dietitians 1 (ft), 1 (pt).
Affiliation Roman Catholic
Facilities Dining room; Activities room; Laundry room; Library.
Activities Games; Reading groups; Prayer groups; Movies.

MARION

Perry County Hospital and Nursing Home
Lafayette St, Marion, AL, 36756 (205) 683-6111
Admin Tommy R Harris.
Licensure Skilled Care; Intermediate Care.
Beds SNF 25; ICF 6. *Certified* Medicaid; Medicare.
Ownership Proprietary.
Admissions Requirements Medical examination; Physician's request.
Staff RNs 1 (ft), 1 (pt); LPNs 7 (ft), 2 (pt); Orderlies 3 (ft); Nurses aides 7 (ft), 2 (pt); Activities coordinators 1 (pt).
Facilities Dining room; Physical therapy room; Activities room; Chapel; Crafts room; Laundry room; Barber/Beauty shop.
Activities Arts and Crafts; Cards; Games; Reading groups; Prayer groups; Movies; Dances/Social or cultural gatherings.

Southland Nursing Home*
Fikes Ferry Rd, Marion, AL, 36756 (205) 683-6141
Admin Bill R Bolton.
Licensure Skilled Care; Intermediate Care.
Beds SNF 54; ICF 17. *Certified* Medicaid; Medicare.
Ownership Proprietary.

MCCALLA

Plantation Manor
PO Box 97, McCalla, AL, 35111 (205) 477-6161
Admin Cecil L Lee. *Medical Dir/Dir of Nursing* Cemal Goral MD.
Licensure Skilled Care; Intermediate Care.
Beds SNF 57; ICF 46. *Certified* Medicaid; Medicare.
Ownership Proprietary.
Admissions Requirements Medical examination; Physician's request.
Staff Physicians 1 (pt); RNs 1 (ft), 1 (pt); LPNs 9 (ft), 2 (pt); Orderlies 7 (ft), 2 (pt); Nurses aides 15 (ft), 5 (pt); Physical therapists 1 (pt); Recreational therapists 1 (ft); Activities coordinators 1 (ft); Dietitians 1 (pt); Dentists 1 (pt).

MOBILE

Allen Memorial Home*
735 S Washington Ave, Mobile, AL, 36690 (205) 433-2642

Admin Sr Scholastica.
Licensure Skilled Care; Intermediate Care.
Beds SNF 80; ICF 14. *Certified* Medicaid; Medicare.
Ownership Proprietary.

Cogburn Health Center Inc*
148 Tuscaloosa St, Mobile, AL, 36607 (205) 471-5431
Admin L Steven Roberts.
Licensure Skilled Care; Intermediate Care.
Beds SNF 142; ICF 8. *Certified* Medicaid; Medicare.
Ownership Proprietary.

Heritage Nursing and Convalescent Center
954 Navco Rd, Mobile, AL, 36690 (205) 473-8684
Admin John E Saad. *Medical Dir/Dir of Nursing* L D McLaughlin MD.
Licensure Skilled Care. *Beds* 174. *Certified* Medicaid; Medicare.
Ownership Proprietary.
Staff Physicians 1 (pt); RNs 9 (ft); LPNs 25 (ft); Nurses aides 45 (ft); Physical therapists 2 (pt); Recreational therapists 2 (ft); Speech therapists 1 (pt); Dietitians 1 (pt).
Facilities Dining room; Physical therapy room; Activities room; Chapel; Crafts room; Laundry room; Barber/Beauty shop.
Activities Arts and Crafts; Cards; Games; Reading groups; Prayer groups; Movies; Dances/Social or cultural gatherings.
Description The Heritage is staffed and equipped to provide skilled nursing care thoughout our facility. We also have a 72-bed "sub-acute" care unit providing highly sophisticated medical care to patients recently discharged from the hospital. VA approved.

Hillhaven Convalescent Center*
1758 Springhill Ave, Mobile, AL, 36607 (205) 479-0551
Admin Dee B Wilcher.
Licensure Skilled Care. *Beds* 174. *Certified* Medicaid; Medicare.
Ownership Proprietary.

Ideal Rest Home Inc*
1203 Government St, Mobile, AL, 36604 (205) 438-4566
Admin Mary G Turk.
Licensure Intermediate Care. *Beds* 49. *Certified* Medicaid.
Ownership Proprietary.

Lynwood Nursing Home*
4164 Halls Mill Rd, Mobile, AL, 36609 (205) 661-5404
Admin James T Lutes.
Licensure Skilled Care; Intermediate Care.
Beds SNF 77; ICF 50. *Certified* Medicaid; Medicare.
Ownership Proprietary.

Sacred Heart Residence*
1655 McGill Ave, Mobile, AL, 36604 (205) 476-6335
Admin Patricia Friel.
Licensure Skilled Care; Intermediate Care.
Beds SNF 50; ICF 75. *Certified* Medicaid; Medicare.
Ownership Nonprofit.

Southern Medical of Springhill Nursing Home
3717 Dauphin St, Mobile, AL, 36608 (205)
343-0909
Admin Jake Cureton. *Medical Dir/Dir of
Nursing* Dr Gerald Wallace.
Licensure Skilled Care; Intermediate Care.
Beds SNF 111; ICF 40. *Certified* Medicaid;
Medicare.
Ownership Proprietary.
Staff Physicians 3 (pt); RNs 2 (ft); LPNs 12
(ft), 1 (pt); Nurses aides 23 (ft); Physical thera-
pists 1 (ft); Recreational therapists 1 (ft); Speech
therapists 1 (ft); Activities coordinators 1 (ft);
Dietitians 1 (pt); Podiatrists 1 (pt); 1 (ft).
Facilities Dining room; Physical therapy room;
Activities room; Crafts room; Laundry room;
Barber/Beauty shop; Library.
Activities Arts and Crafts; Cards; Games;
Reading groups; Prayer groups; Movies; Shop-
ping trips; Dances/Social or cultural gatherings.
Description Facility is located in the Old
Mobile Springhill area adjacent to 204-bed
Springhill Memorial Hospital, next to 7-floor
medical building, and close to I-65 and I-10. A
health education class from a local high school
training in geriatrics works with our patients 8
hours a week.

Spring Hill Manor Nursing Home
3900 Old Shell Rd, PO Box 8395, Mobile, AL,
36608 (205) 342-5623
Admin Gerald B Hart.
Licensure Intermediate Care. *Beds* 34. *Certified* Medicaid.
Ownership Proprietary.
Facilities Dining room; Activities room; Crafts
room; Laundry room.
Activities Arts and Crafts; Cards; Games; Prayer groups; Movies; Shopping trips.

Twin Oaks Nursing Home Inc
857 Crawford Ln, Mobile, AL, 36617 (205)
476-3420
Admin Clarence M Ball Jr. *Medical Dir/Dir of
Nursing* Herbert Stone MD.
Licensure Skilled Care; Intermediate Care.
Beds SNF 30; ICF 80. *Certified* Medicaid;
Medicare.
Ownership Proprietary.
Admissions Requirements Physician's request.
Staff Physicians 2 (pt); RNs 2 (ft), 2 (pt); LPNs
9 (ft), 7 (pt); Nurses aides 26 (ft), 10 (pt);
Physical therapists 1 (ft); Recreational thera-
pists 1 (ft); Occupational therapists 1 (pt); Spee-
ch therapists 1 (pt); Activities coordinators 1
(ft); Dietitians 1 (ft); Podiatrists 1 (pt).
Facilities Dining room; Physical therapy room;
Activities room; Crafts room; Laundry room.
Activities Arts and Crafts; Cards; Games;
Reading groups; Prayer groups; Movies; Shop-
ping trips; Dances/Social or cultural gatherings.

MONROEVILLE

Monroe Manor
236 W Claiborne St, Monroeville, AL, 36460
(205) 575-2648
Admin Rebecca J Etheridge. *Medical Dir/Dir
of Nursing* Carl W Martens.
Licensure Intermediate Care. *Beds* 54. *Certified* Medicaid.
Ownership Proprietary.

Admissions Requirements Minimum age 21;
Medical examination; Physician's request.
Staff Physicians 3 (pt); LPNs 4 (ft), 2 (pt);
Nurses aides 10 (ft), 3 (pt); Activities coordina-
tors 1 (ft).
Facilities Dining room; Activities room; Chap-
el; Crafts room; Laundry room; Barber/Beauty
shop.
Activities Reading groups; Prayer groups.

Monroe Nursing Home Inc
Rt 2, Box 800, Monroeville, AL, 36460 (205)
575-3285
Admin Billy Jones. *Medical Dir/Dir of
Nursing* Jack Whetstone MD.
Licensure Skilled Care; Intermediate Care.
Beds SNF 51; ICF 24. *Certified* Medicaid;
Medicare.
Ownership Proprietary.
Admissions Requirements Medical examina-
tion; Physician's request.
Staff RNs 2 (ft); LPNs 7 (ft), 1 (pt); Nurses
aides 21 (ft), 3 (pt); Physical therapists 1 (pt);
Activities coordinators 1 (ft); Dietitians 1 (pt).
Facilities Dining room; Activities room; Bar-
ber/Beauty shop.

MONTGOMERY

**American Medical Nursing Center—
Montgomery***
1837 Upper Wetumpka Rd, Montgomery, AL,
36199 (205) 264-8416
Admin Carl S Burkhalter.
Licensure Skilled Care; Intermediate Care.
Beds SNF 121; ICF 64. *Certified* Medicaid;
Medicare.
Ownership Proprietary.

Cedar Crest
4490 Virginia Loop Rd, Montgomery, AL,
36116 (205) 281-6826
Admin Rebecca Hyier. *Medical Dir/Dir of
Nursing* Dr Michael Reeves.
Licensure Skilled Care; Intermediate Care.
Beds 110. *Certified* Medicaid; Medicare.
Ownership Proprietary.
Admissions Requirements Minimum age 16;
Medical examination; Physician's request.
Staff Physicians 4 (pt); RNs 1 (ft), 2 (pt); LPNs
9 (ft), 2 (pt); Nurses aides 30 (ft), 8 (pt);
Physical therapists 1 (ft); Recreational therapists
1 (ft); Occupational therapists 1 (pt); Speech
therapists 1 (pt); Activities coordinators 1 (ft);
Dietitians 1 (ft); Dentists 1 (pt); Podiatrists 1
(pt).
Facilities Dining room; Physical therapy room;
Activities room; Crafts room; Laundry room;
Barber/Beauty shop.
Activities Arts and Crafts; Cards; Games;
Reading groups; Prayer groups; Movies; Shopping trips; Dances/Social or cultural gatherings.
Description Facility features entire-day programs with various themes, monthly cocktail
parties, daily limousine rides, educational and
reflective programs, mental stimulation games,
discussion groups, luncheon and picnic outings,
excursion trips, crocheting club, seasonal activities and programed festivities for each holiday,
and in-house sponsored teas for various community organizations. Each wing has an
enclosed courtyard and garden.

**Father Purcell Memorial Exceptional
Children's Center***
2048 W Fairview Ave, Montgomery, AL, 36108
(205) 834-5590
Admin Thomas C Logan.
Licensure Skilled Care. *Beds* 52. *Cer-
tified* Medicare.
Ownership Nonprofit.

Father Walter Memorial Child Care Center
2815 Forbes Dr, Montgomery, AL, 36199 (205)
262-6421
Admin Audrey Wright.
Licensure Skilled Care. *Beds* 44. *Certified* Medicaid.
Ownership Nonprofit.
Admissions Requirements Medical examination; Physician's request.
Staff RNs 2 (ft), 1 (pt); LPNs 5 (ft); Orderlies 3
(ft); Nurses aides 20 (ft); Physical therapists 1
(pt); Recreational therapists 1 (pt); Dietitians 1
(pt); Dentists 1 (pt).
Affiliation Roman Catholic
Facilities Dining room; Activities room; Laundry room.
Activities Movies.
Description Center provides 24-hour skilled
nursing care for children up to 12 years old
with multiple physical and mental disabilities.

John Knox Manor Inc II
4401 Narrow Ln Rd, Montgomery, AL, 36199
(205) 281-6336
Admin Wanda Barnidge. *Medical Dir/Dir of
Nursing* Dr Donald Marshall.
Licensure Skilled Care; Intermediate Care.
Beds SNF 59; ICF 39. *Certified* Medicaid;
Medicare.
Ownership Nonprofit.
Admissions Requirements Minimum age 21;
Medical examination; Physician's request.
Staff RNs 3 (ft), 1 (pt); LPNs 10 (ft), 3 (pt);
Orderlies 3 (ft), 3 (pt); Nurses aides 30 (ft), 5
(pt); Physical therapists 1 (pt); Activities coor-
dinators 2 (ft); Dietitians 1 (pt).
Affiliation Presbyterian
Facilities Dining room; Physical therapy room;
Activities room; Chapel; Crafts room; Laundry
room; Barber/Beauty shop.
Activities Arts and Crafts; Cards; Games;
Reading groups; Prayer groups; Movies; Shop-
ping trips; Dances/Social or cultural gatherings.

Montgomery Health Care Center
520 S Hull St, Montgomery, AL, 36197 (205)
834-2920
Admin Lee Robbins. *Medical Dir/Dir of
Nursing* James Caple MD.
Licensure Skilled Care; Intermediate Care.
Beds SNF 284. *Certified* Medicaid; Medicare.
Ownership Proprietary.
Admissions Requirements Physician's request.
Staff Physicians 14 (ft); RNs 3 (ft); LPNs 27
(ft), 11 (pt); Orderlies 5 (ft); Nurses aides 65 (ft),
16 (pt); Physical therapists 2 (pt); Occupational
therapists 1 (pt); Speech therapists 3 (pt);
Activities coordinators 1 (ft); Dietitians 1 (ft);
Podiatrists 2 (pt).
Facilities Dining room; Physical therapy room;
Activities room; Laundry room; Barber/Beauty
shop.
Activities Arts and Crafts; Cards; Games;
Reading groups; Prayer groups; Movies; Shop-

ping trips; Dances/Social or cultural gatherings; Living history program; Camping; Current events; Quilting; Resident-Help-Resident program; Reminiscence resident council; Resident newsletter.
Description Facility has enclosed courtyard; Quality of Life Unit for Exceptional Young Adults; Quality of Life Unit for the Confused Resident. VA approved.

Oak Hill Health Care Inc
100 Perry Hill Rd, Montgomery, AL, 36193 (205) 272-0171
Admin Carolyn P Hopper. *Medical Dir/Dir of Nursing* Dr S J Selikoff.
Licensure Skilled Care; Intermediate Care.
Beds SNF 92; ICF 38. *Certified* Medicaid; Medicare.
Ownership Proprietary.
Admissions Requirements Medical examination; Physician's request.
Facilities Dining room; Physical therapy room; Activities room; Laundry room; Barber/Beauty shop; Library.
Activities Arts and Crafts; Cards; Games; Reading groups; Prayer groups; Movies; Shopping trips; Dances/Social or cultural gatherings.

South Haven Manor Nursing Home*
1300 E South Blvd, Montgomery, AL, 36116 (205) 288-0122
Admin Brunese O Seaborn.
Licensure Skilled Care. *Beds* 86. *Certified* Medicaid; Medicare.
Ownership Proprietary.

Tyson Manor Health Facility*
2020 N Country Club Dr, Montgomery, AL, 36106 (205) 263-1643
Admin Katie A Hester.
Licensure Skilled Care; Intermediate Care.
Beds SNF 101; ICF 24. *Certified* Medicaid; Medicare.
Ownership Proprietary.

Woodley Manor Nursing Home Inc
3312 Woodley Rd, Montgomery, AL, 36111 (205) 288-2780
Admin Juanita C Busby. *Medical Dir/Dir of Nursing* Dr Mont Highley.
Licensure Skilled Care; Intermediate Care.
Beds SNF 92; ICF 3. *Certified* Medicaid; Medicare.
Ownership Proprietary.
Admissions Requirements Minimum age 21; Medical examination; Physician's request.
Staff Physicians 1 (pt); RNs 4 (ft), 1 (pt); LPNs 6 (ft); Orderlies 2 (ft); Nurses aides 35 (ft), 3 (pt); Physical therapists 1 (pt); Activities coordinators 1 (ft); Dietitians 1 (ft); Podiatrists 1 (pt).
Facilities Dining room; Physical therapy room; Activities room; Crafts room; Laundry room; Barber/Beauty shop.
Activities Arts and Crafts; Cards; Games; Reading groups; Prayer groups; Shopping trips; Dances/Social or cultural gatherings.
Description This is a beautiful 95-bed nursing home located in a fine neighborhood. VA approved. Staffed by dedicated people with an average of 15 years experience.

MOULTON

Moulton Nursing Home Inc
300 Hospital St, PO Box 336, Moulton, AL, 35650 (205) 974-1146
Admin Michael A Gresik. *Medical Dir/Dir of Nursing* Robert Rhyne MD.
Licensure Skilled Care; Intermediate Care.
Beds SNF 71; ICF 65. *Certified* Medicaid; Medicare.
Ownership Proprietary.
Admissions Requirements Medical examination; Physician's request.
Staff RNs 5 (ft), 2 (pt); LPNs 9 (ft), 3 (pt); Nurses aides 65 (ft), 5 (pt); Physical therapists 1 (ft), 1 (pt); Speech therapists 1 (pt); Activities coordinators 1 (ft), 1 (pt); Dietitians 1 (ft), 1 (pt); Dentists 1 (pt); Podiatrists 1 (pt).
Facilities Dining room; Physical therapy room; Activities room; Chapel; Crafts room; Laundry room; Barber/Beauty shop; Speech therapy.
Activities Arts and Crafts; Cards; Games; Reading groups; Prayer groups; Shopping trips; Dances/Social or cultural gatherings; Activities for room bound patients.
Description The facility is located in a quiet rural area and hospital property adjoins the nursing home.

MOUNDVILLE

Moundville Nursing Home Inc
4th St, PO Box 607, Moundville, AL, 35474 (205) 371-2252
Admin Linda Massey. *Medical Dir/Dir of Nursing* Dr Larry Shelton.
Licensure Skilled Care; Intermediate Care.
Beds SNF 52; ICF 6. *Certified* Medicaid; Medicare.
Ownership Proprietary.
Staff RNs 1 (ft), 3 (pt); LPNs 4 (ft), 3 (pt); Orderlies 2 (ft), 1 (pt); Nurses aides 14 (ft), 4 (pt); Activities coordinators 1 (ft); Dietitians 1 (ft).
Facilities Dining room; Activities room; Chapel; Crafts room; Laundry room; Barber/Beauty shop.
Activities Arts and Crafts; Cards; Games; Reading groups; Prayer groups; Shopping trips.

MUSCLE SHOALS

Muscle Shoals Nursing Home*
200 Ala Ave, Muscle Shoals, AL, 35660 (205) 381-4330
Admin Myrtie M Ray.
Licensure Intermediate Care. *Beds* 52. *Certified* Medicaid.
Ownership Proprietary.

NORTHPORT

Estes Health Care Center—Glen Haven*
2201 32nd St, Northport, AL, 35476 (205) 339-5700
Admin Jim Turnipseed.
Licensure Skilled Care; Intermediate Care.
Beds SNF 99; ICF 66. *Certified* Medicaid; Medicare.
Ownership Proprietary.

Estes Health Care Center—North
600 34th St, Northport, AL, 35476 (205) 339-5900
Admin Jeana Trapp.
Licensure Skilled Care; Intermediate Care.
Beds SNF 40; ICF 28. *Certified* Medicaid; Medicare.
Ownership Proprietary.
Staff RNs 1 (ft), 1 (pt); LPNs 5 (ft), 4 (pt); Nurses aides 15 (ft), 7 (pt); Activities coordinators 1 (ft); Dietitians 1 (ft).
Facilities Dining room; Activities room; Chapel; Barber/Beauty shop.
Activities Arts and Crafts; Cards; Games; Reading groups; Prayer groups; Picnics.

Estes Health Care Center—Park Manor
82 Bypass, Northport, AL, 35476 (205) 339-5300
Admin Ron Smith.
Licensure Skilled Care; Intermediate Care.
Beds SNF 136; ICF 16. *Certified* Medicaid; Medicare.
Ownership Proprietary.

Forest Manor Inc*
2215 32nd St, Northport, AL, 35476 (205) 339-5400
Admin Donald W Peak.
Licensure Skilled Care; Intermediate Care.
Beds SNF 75; ICF 75. *Certified* Medicaid; Medicare.
Ownership Proprietary.

ONEONTA

Oneonta Manor Nursing Home*
210 Shirley St, Oneonta, AL, 35121 (205) 274-2365
Admin Laurel Massey.
Licensure Skilled Care; Intermediate Care.
Beds SNF 52; ICF 50. *Certified* Medicaid; Medicare.
Ownership Proprietary.

OPELIKA

Opelika Nursing Home*
1908½ Pepperell Pkwy, Opelika, AL, 36801 (205) 749-1471
Admin Mary Wallace Wilson.
Licensure Skilled Care; Intermediate Care.
Beds A 174; ICF 51. *Certified* Medicaid; Medicare.
Ownership Proprietary.

OPP

Covington Manor Inc
W Covington Ave, Opp, AL, 36467 (205) 493-3096
Admin Barbara K Ward. *Medical Dir/Dir of Nursing* Dr J G Dunn.
Licensure Skilled Care; Intermediate Care.
Beds SNF 73; ICF 16. *Certified* Medicaid; Medicare.
Ownership Proprietary.
Admissions Requirements Medical examination; Physician's request.
Staff RNs 1 (ft), 2 (pt); LPNs 8 (ft), 1 (pt); Orderlies 2 (ft), 2 (pt); Nurses aides 21 (ft), 6

(pt); Activities coordinators 1 (ft); Dietitians 1 (ft).
Facilities Dining room; Activities room; Laundry room; Barber/Beauty shop.
Activities Arts and Crafts; Cards; Games; Reading groups; Prayer groups.

Lakeview Manor Inc*
Paulk Ave, Opp, AL, 36467 (205) 493-4558
Admin Eula W McCord.
Licensure Skilled Care; Intermediate Care.
Beds SNF 45; ICF 45. *Certified* Medicaid; Medicare.
Ownership Proprietary.

OXFORD

Colonial Pines Health Care Center
1130 Hale St, Oxford, AL, 36203 (205) 831-0481
Admin Katie A Johnston. *Medical Dir/Dir of Nursing* Dr Paul Siehl.
Licensure Skilled Care; Intermediate Care.
Beds SNF 110; ICF 63. *Certified* Medicaid; Medicare.
Ownership Proprietary.
Facilities Dining room; Activities room; Chapel; Crafts room; Laundry room; Barber/Beauty shop.
Activities Arts and Crafts; Cards; Games; Reading groups; Prayer groups; Movies; Shopping trips; Dances/Social or cultural gatherings.

OZARK

Oak View Manor Inc*
Mixon Street Rd, Ozark, AL, 36360 (205) 774-2631
Admin Ann M Galloway.
Licensure Skilled Care; Intermediate Care.
Beds SNF 82; ICF 32. *Certified* Medicaid; Medicare.
Ownership Proprietary.

Ozark Nursing Home Inc*
Bryan Dr, Ozark, AL, 36360 (205) 774-2561
Admin E M Beverly.
Licensure Skilled Care. *Beds* 123. *Certified* Medicaid.
Ownership Proprietary.

PELL CITY

Ingram Manor Inc*
510 Wolf Creek Rd N, Pell City, AL, 35125 (205) 338-3329
Admin Katherine Ponder.
Licensure Skilled Care; Intermediate Care.
Beds SNF 32; ICF 42. *Certified* Medicaid; Medicare.
Ownership Proprietary.

Jack Cline Nursing Home*
Rt 3, Box 447, Pell City, AL, 35125 (205) 640-5212
Admin Billie Bischoff.
Licensure Intermediate Care. *Beds* 49. *Certified* Medicaid.
Ownership Proprietary.

PHENIX CITY

Parkwood Health Facility Inc*
3301 Stadium Dr, Phenix City, AL, 36867 (205) 297-0237
Admin Julia P Compton.
Licensure Skilled Care; Intermediate Care.
Beds SNF 39; ICF 35. *Certified* Medicaid; Medicare.
Ownership Proprietary.

Phenix City Nursing Home*
3900 Lakewood Dr, Phenix City, AL, 36867 (205) 298-8247
Admin Roland R Garney.
Licensure Skilled Care; Intermediate Care.
Beds SNF 66; ICF 10. *Certified* Medicaid; Medicare.
Ownership Proprietary.

PIEDMONT

Piedmont Hospital and Nursing Home
Calhoun St, PO Box 330, Piedmont, AL, 36272 (205) 447-6041
Admin Robert E Morrow. *Medical Dir/Dir of Nursing* Dr Russell Ulrich.
Licensure Skilled Care; Intermediate Care.
Beds 31. *Certified* Medicaid; Medicare.
Ownership Public.
Staff Physicians 1 (pt); RNs 1 (ft), 1 (pt); LPNs 5 (ft), 2 (pt); Orderlies 3 (ft), 2 (pt); Nurses aides 8 (ft), 3 (pt); Activities coordinators 1 (ft); Dietitians 1 (pt).

PLEASANT GROVE

Cottage Hill Nursing Home*
700 1st Ave, Pleasant Grove, AL, 35127 (205) 744-8330
Admin William G Allen Jr.
Licensure Skilled Care; Intermediate Care.
Beds SNF 44; ICF 20. *Certified* Medicaid; Medicare.
Ownership Proprietary.

Pleasant Grove Manor
PO Box 91, 30 7th St, Pleasant Grove, AL, 35127 (205) 744-8226
Admin Ruby Baker. *Medical Dir/Dir of Nursing* Dr David Barthold.
Licensure Skilled Care; Intermediate Care.
Beds SNF 89; ICF 109. *Certified* Medicaid; Medicare.
Ownership Proprietary.
Staff Physicians 1 (pt); RNs 3 (ft), 1 (pt); LPNs 19 (ft); Orderlies 6 (pt); Nurses aides 61 (ft), 12 (pt); Reality therapists 1 (pt); Recreational therapists 1 (pt); Occupational therapists 1 (pt); Speech therapists 1 (pt); Activities coordinators 1 (ft), 1 (pt); Dietitians 1 (ft); Dentists 1 (pt); Ophthalmologists 1 (pt); Podiatrists 1 (pt); Audiologists 1 (pt).

PRATTVILLE

Memorial Manor Multiple Care Center
750 Wetumpka St, Prattville, AL, 36067 (205) 365-2241
Admin Courtney A Marshall. *Medical Dir/Dir of Nursing* Dr William Sanders.

Licensure Skilled Care; Intermediate Care.
Beds SNF 58; ICF 14. *Certified* Medicaid; Medicare.
Ownership Proprietary.
Admissions Requirements Minimum age 30; Medical examination.
Staff RNs 2 (ft); LPNs 7 (ft); Orderlies 1 (ft); Nurses aides 21 (ft); Activities coordinators 1 (ft); Dietitians 1 (pt).
Facilities Dining room; Activities room; Barber/Beauty shop.
Activities Arts and Crafts; Cards; Games; Reading groups; Prayer groups; Movies; Shopping trips; Dances/Social or cultural gatherings.
Description Residents enjoy outstanding volunteer efforts by community groups, quality nursing care at a reasonable cost, and a friendly small-town rural atmosphere.

RED BAY

Red Bay Nursing Home
30305 10th Ave N, Red Bay, AL, 35582 (205) 356-4982
Admin Christine T Crutchfield. *Medical Dir/Dir of Nursing* Walker Dempsey MD.
Licensure Skilled Care; Intermediate Care.
Beds SNF 52; ICF 28. *Certified* Medicaid; Medicare.
Ownership Proprietary.
Admissions Requirements Physician's request.
Staff RNs 3 (ft); LPNs 8 (ft), 1 (pt); Nurses aides 23 (ft), 1 (pt); Activities coordinators 1 (ft); Dietitians 1 (pt).
Facilities Dining room; Activities room; Laundry room; Barber/Beauty shop.
Activities Games; Prayer groups; Dances/Social or cultural gatherings.

REFORM

Fountain Nursing Home*
PO Box 400, 2nd Ave NW, Reform, AL, 35481 (205) 375-6379
Admin Ellen W Meyer.
Licensure Skilled Care; Intermediate Care.
Beds SNF 58; ICF 27. *Certified* Medicaid; Medicare.
Ownership Proprietary.

ROANOKE

Rosser Nursing Home*
Seymore St, Roanoke, AL, 36274 (205) 863-4512
Admin Susie Rosser Minnifield.
Licensure Intermediate Care. *Beds* 50. *Certified* Medicaid.
Ownership Proprietary.

Traylor Nursing Home Inc
402 Yancy St, Roanoke, AL, 36274 (205) 863-6131
Admin Ronald L Traylor. *Medical Dir/Dir of Nursing* G W Everett MD.
Licensure Skilled Care; Intermediate Care.
Beds SNF 52; ICF 50. *Certified* Medicaid; Medicare.
Ownership Proprietary.
Admissions Requirements Medical examination; Physician's request.

Staff RNs 2 (ft), 3 (pt); LPNs 8 (ft), 1 (pt); Orderlies 2 (ft), 2 (pt); Nurses aides 23 (ft), 5 (pt); Activities coordinators 1 (ft); Dietitians 1 (pt).
Facilities Dining room; Activities room; Chapel; Crafts room; Laundry room; Barber/Beauty shop; Library.
Activities Arts and Crafts; Cards; Games; Reading groups; Shopping trips.

RUSSELLVILLE

Burns Nursing Home Inc*
701 Monroe St, Russellville, AL, 35653 (205) 332-4111
Admin Larry M DeArman.
Licensure Skilled Care. *Beds* 47. *Certified* Medicaid; Medicare.
Ownership Proprietary.

North Alabama Nursing Home
705 Gandy St, PO Box 608, Russellville, AL, 35653 (205) 332-3773
Admin Floree Thurman. *Medical Dir/Dir of Nursing* W P Hyatt.
Licensure Skilled Care; Intermediate Care.
Beds 50. *Certified* Medicaid; Medicare.
Ownership Proprietary.
Staff Physicians; RNs; LPNs; Orderlies; Nurses aides; Activities coordinators; Dietitians; Dentists.
Facilities Dining room; Activities room; Laundry room; Barber/Beauty shop.
Activities Games; Reading groups; Prayer groups; Movies.

Terrace Manor Nursing Home
Underwood Rd, Rt 1, PO Box 12, Russellville, AL, 35653 (205) 332-3826
Admin Roland Wade.
Licensure Skilled Care; Intermediate Care.
Beds 43. *Certified* Medicaid; Medicare.
Ownership Proprietary.

SCOTTSBORO

Jackson County Hospital and Nursing Home
Woods Cove Rd, PO Box 927, Scottsboro, AL, 35768 (205) 259-4444
Admin James K Mason.
Licensure Skilled Care; Intermediate Care.
Beds SNF 30; ICF 20. *Certified* Medicaid; Medicare.
Ownership Public.
Admissions Requirements Medical examination; Physician's request.
Staff RNs 1 (ft), 3 (pt); LPNs 5 (ft), 3 (pt); Orderlies 2 (ft), 1 (pt); Nurses aides 16 (ft), 4 (pt); Activities coordinators 1 (ft).
Facilities Dining room; Activities room; Chapel; Crafts room; Barber/Beauty shop.
Activities Arts and Crafts; Cards; Games; Reading groups; Prayer groups; Movies; Shopping trips; Dances/Social or cultural gatherings.
Description Facility adjoins the hospital which allows easy access to the laboratory, X-ray, and emergency room facilities.

Scottsboro Nursing Home
Cloverdale Rd, Scottsboro, AL, 35768 (205) 259-1505

Admin Jerry A Taylor. *Medical Dir/Dir of Nursing* Larry Bolton.
Licensure Skilled Care; Intermediate Care.
Beds SNF 75; ICF 20. *Certified* Medicaid; Medicare.
Ownership Proprietary.
Admissions Requirements Medical examination; Physician's request.
Staff Physicians 12 (ft); RNs 4 (ft); LPNs 6 (ft), 3 (pt); Nurses aides 25 (ft), 16 (pt); Activities coordinators 10 (ft), 1 (pt); Dietitians 1 (ft); Dentists 2 (pt); Social worker 1 (ft).
Facilities Dining room; Activities room; Chapel; Laundry room; Barber/Beauty shop; Library; Conference-exam room; Sunrooms; Spacious lobby; Sun patio.
Activities Arts and Crafts; Games; Reading groups; Prayer groups; Movies; Dances/Social or cultural gatherings; Summer outings; Birthday and Ice cream parties; Resident council.
Description Although conveniently located near hospital and doctors' offices, facility has country-living atmosphere.

SELMA

Dunn Rest Home
515 Mabry St, Selma, AL, 36701 (205) 872-3471
Admin Ellen B Dunn. *Medical Dir/Dir of Nursing* Dr William E Ehlert.
Licensure Skilled Care; Intermediate Care.
Beds SNF 87; ICF 6. *Certified* Medicaid; Medicare.
Ownership Proprietary.
Admissions Requirements Minimum age 21; Medical examination; Physician's request.
Staff Physicians 1 (ft), 10 (pt); RNs 3 (ft), 2 (pt); Orderlies 4 (ft), 4 (pt); Nurses aides 26 (ft), 6 (pt); Physical therapists 1 (pt); Activities coordinators 1 (ft); Dietitians 3 (pt); Dentists 1 (pt).
Facilities Dining room; Activities room; Laundry room; Barber/Beauty shop.
Activities Arts and Crafts; Cards; Games; Reading groups; Prayer groups; Movies; Shopping trips.
Description Dunn Rest Home is a 2-story cream brick structure of antebellum architecture, located in the "Old Town" section of Selma, and is on the National Register of Historic Places.

Lighthouse Convalescent Home
2911 Range Line Rd, Selma, AL, 36701 (205) 875-1868
Admin John Crear. *Medical Dir/Dir of Nursing* C L Lett MD.
Licensure Intermediate Care. *Beds* 48. *Certified* Medicaid.
Ownership Proprietary.
Staff RNs 1 (ft); LPNs 4 (ft), 1 (pt); Orderlies 3 (ft), 1 (pt); Nurses aides 3 (ft); Activities coordinators 1 (ft), 1 (pt); Dietitians 3 (ft), 2 (pt).
Facilities Dining room; Activities room; Laundry room.
Activities Arts and Crafts; Cards; Games; Prayer groups; Movies; Shopping trips.

Warren Manor Nursing Home
11 Bell Rd, Selma, AL, 36701 (205) 874-7425
Admin Kevin J Metz. *Medical Dir/Dir of*

Nursing Dr Freeman Singleton.
Licensure Skilled Care; Intermediate Care.
Beds SNF 112; ICF 16. *Certified* Medicaid; Medicare.
Ownership Proprietary.
Admissions Requirements Minimum age 21; Medical examination; Physician's request.
Staff Physicians 1 (pt); RNs 2 (ft), 1 (pt); LPNs 9 (ft), 7 (pt); Orderlies 6 (ft), 3 (pt); Nurses aides 26 (ft), 18 (pt); Physical therapists 1 (pt); Activities coordinators 1 (ft); Dietitians 1 (ft).
Facilities Dining room; Physical therapy room; Activities room; Crafts room; Laundry room; Barber/Beauty shop; Library.
Activities Arts and Crafts; Cards; Games; Reading groups; Prayer groups; Movies; Shopping trips; Dances/Social or cultural gatherings.
Description Warren Manor Nursing Home is prepared to meet the total nursing and social needs of geriatric and convalescent patients. Our home is pleasantly located, tastefully furnished, and staffed by qualified people who care. Warren Manor offers a way of life which preserves the dignity and personal worth of our guests.

SYLACAUGA

Marble City Nursing Home Inc*
PO Box 1123, Fayetteville Rd, Sylacauga, AL, 35150 (205) 245-7402
Admin Robert L Sprayberry.
Licensure Skilled Care; Intermediate Care.
Beds SNF 63; ICF 50. *Certified* Medicaid; Medicare.
Ownership Proprietary.

Sylacauga Hospital and Nursing Home
W Hickory St, Sylacauga, AL, 35150 (205) 249-4921
Admin Frank G Perryman. *Medical Dir/Dir of Nursing* Dr James G Wright.
Licensure Skilled Care; Intermediate Care.
Beds 52. *Certified* Medicaid; Medicare.
Ownership Public.
Staff RNs 1 (ft), 2 (pt); LPNs 6 (ft), 2 (pt); Nurses aides 17 (ft), 8 (pt); Physical therapists 1 (ft); Activities coordinators 1 (ft); Dietitians 1 (ft).
Facilities Dining room; Physical therapy room; Activities room; Chapel; Crafts room; Laundry room; Barber/Beauty shop; Library.
Activities Arts and Crafts; Games; Prayer groups; Dances/Social or cultural gatherings.

TALLADEGA

Talladega Nursing Home Inc
616 Chaffee St, Talladega, AL, 35160 (205) 362-4197
Admin W P Patterson. *Medical Dir/Dir of Nursing* Dr C Graves.
Licensure Skilled Care; Intermediate Care.
Beds SNF 73; ICF 128. *Certified* Medicaid; Medicare.
Ownership Public.
Admissions Requirements Medical examination.
Staff RNs 3 (ft); LPNs 13 (ft); Orderlies 2 (ft); Nurses aides 115 (ft); Occupational therapists 1 (ft); Activities coordinators 1 (ft); Dietitians 1

(ft).
Facilities Dining room; Activities room; Chapel; Crafts room; Laundry room; Barber/Beauty shop.
Activities Arts and Crafts; Cards; Games; Reading groups; Prayer groups; Movies; Shopping trips; Dances/Social or cultural gatherings.

TALLASSEE

The Nursing Home of Tallassee Inc*
Rt 2, PO Box 48A, Wetumpka Hwy, Tallassee, AL, 36078 (205) 283-3975
Admin Mellie Jones.
Licensure Skilled Care; Intermediate Care.
Beds SNF 59; ICF 22. *Certified* Medicaid; Medicare.
Ownership Proprietary.

THOMASVILLE

Thomasville Hospital and Nursing Home
1440 Hwy 43 N, Thomasville, AL, 36784 (205) 636-4431
Admin Rex Jackson. *Medical Dir/Dir of Nursing* Dr J L Dozier.
Licensure Skilled Care. *Beds* 50. *Certified* Medicare.
Ownership Public.
Staff RNs 2 (ft); LPNs 5 (ft), 2 (pt); Orderlies 2 (ft), 1 (pt); Nurses aides 14 (ft), 4 (pt); Activities coordinators 1 (ft).
Facilities Dining room; Chapel; Barber/Beauty shop; Library.
Activities Arts and Crafts; Games; Prayer groups; Movies; Shopping trips.

TROY

Pike Manor Inc*
PO Drawer 787, Elba Hwy, Troy, AL, 36081 (205) 566-0880
Admin Larry E Madison.
Licensure Skilled Care; Intermediate Care.
Beds SNF 112; ICF 52. *Certified* Medicaid; Medicare.
Ownership Proprietary.

TRUSSVILLE

Trussville Nursing Home Inc*
PO Box 65, Chalkville Rd, Trussville, AL, 35175 (205) 655-3227
Admin Joyce B McHugh.
Licensure Skilled Care; Intermediate Care.
Beds SNF 102; ICF 23. *Certified* Medicaid; Medicare.
Ownership Proprietary.

TUSCALOOSA

Heritage Health Care Center*
1101 Snows Mill Ave, Tuscaloosa, AL, 35406 (205) 759-5179
Admin George L Jackson.
Licensure Skilled Care; Intermediate Care.
Beds SNF 114; ICF 38. *Certified* Medicaid; Medicare.
Ownership Proprietary.

La Rocca Nursing Home*
403 34th Ave E, Tuscaloosa, AL, 35401 (205) 553-1341
Admin Lyman C Hardy Jr.
Licensure Skilled Care. *Beds* 75.
Ownership Proprietary.

TUSCUMBIA

Oak Crest Nursing Home Inc
813 Keller Ln, PO Box 647, Tuscumbia, AL, 35674 (205) 383-1535
Admin B F Grimmitt. *Medical Dir/Dir of Nursing* James Ashmore.
Licensure Skilled Care; Intermediate Care.
Beds SNF 90; ICF 19. *Certified* Medicaid; Medicare.
Ownership Proprietary.
Admissions Requirements Minimum age 21; Medical examination; Physician's request.
Staff Physicians 1 (ft), 1 (pt); RNs 2 (ft); LPNs 14 (ft); Orderlies 1 (ft); Nurses aides 35 (ft); Recreational therapists 1 (ft); Activities coordinators 1 (ft); Dietitians 1 (ft); Dentists 1 (pt).
Facilities Dining room; Physical therapy room; Activities room; Crafts room; Laundry room; Barber/Beauty shop; Library.
Activities Arts and Crafts; Cards; Games; Reading groups; Prayer groups; Dances/Social or cultural gatherings.

Shoals Nursing Home*
500 Hazleton St, Tuscumbia, AL, 35674 (205) 383-4541
Admin Clyde Ray Jr.
Licensure Skilled Care. *Beds* 103. *Certified* Medicaid; Medicare.
Ownership Proprietary.

TUSKEGEE

G and R Health Care Facility*
PO Box 659, Gautier St, Tuskegee, AL, 36083 (205) 727-1945
Admin William E Roberson.
Licensure Skilled Care; Intermediate Care.
Beds SNF 70; ICF 72. *Certified* Medicaid; Medicare.
Ownership Proprietary.

Magnolia Haven Nursing Home
650 Wright St, Tuskegee, AL, 36083 (205) 727-4960
Admin Clarence M Ball Jr. *Medical Dir/Dir of Nursing* Calvin Dowe.
Licensure Skilled Care; Intermediate Care.
Beds SNF 57; ICF 10. *Certified* Medicaid; Medicare.
Ownership Proprietary.
Admissions Requirements Medical examination; Physician's request.
Staff Physicians 1 (ft); RNs 1 (ft), 1 (pt); LPNs 5 (ft), 4 (pt); Orderlies 2 (ft), 4 (pt); Nurses aides 15 (ft), 13 (pt); Physical therapists 1 (ft), 1 (pt); Recreational therapists 1 (ft); Activities coordinators 1 (ft); Dietitians 1 (ft).
Facilities Dining room; Physical therapy room; Activities room; Crafts room; Laundry room; Barber/Beauty shop.
Activities Arts and Crafts; Cards; Games; Reading groups; Prayer groups; Movies; Shopping trips; Dances/Social or cultural gatherings.
Description Facility is beautifully and tastefully decorated for maximizing the patients comfort while receiving quality nursing care.

UNION SPRINGS

Bullock County Hospital and Nursing Home*
102 W Conecuh Ave, Union Springs, AL, 36089 (205) 738-3446
Admin Ray Hills.
Licensure Skilled Care. *Beds* 32. *Certified* Medicaid; Medicare.
Ownership Public.

VERNON

Lamar Convalescent Center Inc
Rt 1, Box 70, Vernon, AL, 35592 (205) 695-9313
Admin J W Spearman. *Medical Dir/Dir of Nursing* Dr William C Box.
Licensure Skilled Care; Intermediate Care.
Beds 83. *Certified* Medicaid; Medicare.
Ownership Proprietary.
Staff Physicians 3 (pt); RNs 1 (ft), 2 (pt); LPNs 8 (ft), 3 (pt); Orderlies 4 (ft), 2 (pt); Nurses aides 18 (ft), 4 (pt); Activities coordinators 1 (ft), 2 (pt); Dietitians 2 (ft).
Facilities Dining room; Activities room; Laundry room; Barber/Beauty shop.
Activities Arts and Crafts; Games; Reading groups; Prayer groups; Movies; Shopping trips; Dances/Social or cultural gatherings.
Description Lamar Convalescent Center is located in a quiet, wooded area 3 miles west of Vernon. The rural setting is ideal for rest and relaxation for the convalescent patient. Our wide array of activities and good southern foods make this center the choice for many area residents.

Lamar County Hospital and Nursing Home*
507 5th St SW, Vernon, AL, 35592 (205) 695-7111
Admin Robert E Morrow.
Licensure Skilled Care; Intermediate Care.
Beds SNF 61; ICF 10. *Certified* Medicaid; Medicare.
Ownership Public.

WETUMPKA

Valley Brook Park Inc
208 Marshall St, Wetumpka, AL, 36092 (205) 567-5131
Admin Glenda Bobo. *Medical Dir/Dir of Nursing* Dr Dunn Jr.
Licensure Skilled Care; Intermediate Care.
Beds SNF 57; ICF 23. *Certified* Medicaid; Medicare.
Ownership Proprietary.
Admissions Requirements Medical examination; Physician's request.
Staff Physicians 5 (pt); RNs 1 (ft), 2 (pt); LPNs 8 (ft), 2 (pt); Orderlies 6 (ft), 2 (pt); Nurses aides 20 (ft), 3 (pt); Recreational therapists 1 (ft); Activities coordinators 1 (ft); Dietitians 1 (ft).
Facilities Dining room; Activities room; Crafts

room; Laundry room; Barber/Beauty shop.
Activities Arts and Crafts; Games; Shopping
trips; Dances/Social or cultural gatherings.

WINFIELD

Winfield Nursing Home Inc*
Main St, Winfield, AL, 35594 (205) 487-4211
Admin Ross M Taylor Jr.
Licensure Skilled Care; Intermediate Care.
Beds SNF 70; ICF 53. *Certified* Medicaid;
Medicare.
Ownership Proprietary.

YORK

Sumter Nursing Home*
Rt 1, Box 415A, York, AL, 36925 (205)
392-5281
Admin B M Lanier.
Licensure Skilled Care; Intermediate Care.
Beds SNF 90; ICF 10. *Certified* Medicaid;
Medicare.
Ownership Public.

ALASKA

ANCHORAGE

Hope Park Cottage*
2805 Bering St, Anchorage, AK, 99503 (907)
274-1581
Admin Patrick J Londo.
Licensure Intermediate Care for Mentally
Retarded. *Beds* 10.
Ownership Public.

Our Lady of Compassion Care Center
4895 Cordova St, Anchorage, AK, 99503 (907)
562-2281
Admin John W Nugent. *Medical Dir/Dir of
Nursing* Dr Mark Agnew.
Licensure Skilled Care; Intermediate Care.
Beds 216. *Certified* Medicaid; Medicare.
Admissions Requirements Medical examina-
tion; Physician's request.
Staff Physical therapists 1 (ft); Reality thera-
pists 1 (ft); Recreational therapists 1 (ft);
Occupational therapists 1 (ft); Speech therapists
1 (ft); Activities coordinators 1 (ft); Dietitians 1
(ft).
Affiliation Roman Catholic
Facilities Dining room; Physical therapy room;
Activities room; Chapel; Crafts room; Laundry
room; Barber/Beauty shop.
Activities Arts and Crafts; Cards; Games;
Reading groups; Prayer groups; Movies.
Description Largest Alaskan facility with a
combination of rehabilitation and long-term
care.

CORDOVA

Cordova Community Hospital
PO Box 160, Cordova, AK, 99574 (907)
424-7552
Admin Edward Zeine. *Medical Dir/Dir of
Nursing* A D Tilgner MD.
Licensure Skilled Care; Intermediate Care.
Beds 8. *Certified* Medicaid; Medicare.
Staff Physicians 3 (pt); RNs 6 (ft); LPNs 3 (ft);
Nurses aides 5 (ft); Physical therapists 1 (pt);
Recreational therapists 1 (pt); Activities coordi-
nators 1 (pt); Dietitians 1 (pt); Dentists 1 (pt).
Facilities Dining room; Physical therapy room;
Activities room; Laundry room.
Activities Arts and Crafts; Cards; Games;
Reading groups; Prayer groups; Dances/Social
or cultural gatherings; Car rides around town.
Description Small rural nursing facility that
provides excellent one-on-one nursing care;

patient and employees receive attention like "family" due to long-term patient involvement with
long-term employees.

FAIRBANKS

Careage North Health Care Center*
PO Box 847, Fairbanks, AK, 99707 (907)
452-1921
Admin Sharon White.
Licensure Skilled Care; Intermediate Care.
Beds 101. *Certified* Medicaid; Medicare.

HOMER

South Peninsula Hospital*
PO Box 275, Homer, AK, 99603 (907)
235-8101
Admin Michael Herring.
Licensure Skilled Care; Intermediate Care.
Beds 4. *Certified* Medicaid; Medicare.

JUNEAU

Saint Ann's Nursing Home
415 6th St, Juneau, AK, 99801 (907) 586-3883
Admin Jack Buck. *Medical Dir/Dir of
Nursing* D White MD.
Licensure Skilled Care; Intermediate Care.
Beds 42. *Certified* Medicaid.
Admissions Requirements Medical examina-
tion; Physician's request.
Staff Physicians 1 (pt); RNs 4 (ft); LPNs 3 (ft);
Nurses aides 20 (ft); Physical therapists 1 (ft), 1
(pt); Recreational therapists 1 (ft); Occupational
therapists 1 (pt); Speech therapists 1 (pt);
Activities coordinators 1 (ft); Dietitians 1 (pt);
Dentists 1 (pt).
Facilities Dining room; Physical therapy room;
Activities room; Laundry room; Barber/Beauty
shop.
Activities Arts and Crafts; Cards; Games;
Reading groups; Movies.
Description Facility is located in a residential
area in the capital city of Alaska, within
walking distance of governmental offices and
shops, with a beautiful view of Gastineau
Channel and the mountains that completely
surrounds the facility.

KETCHIKAN

Island View Manor*
3100 Tongass Ave, Ketchikan, AK, 99901 (907)
225-5171
Admin Sr Barbara Haase.
Licensure Skilled Care; Intermediate Care.
Beds 44. *Certified* Medicaid; Medicare.

KODIAK

Kodiak Island Hospital
1915 E Rezanof, Kodiak, AK, 99615 (907)
486-3281
Admin Dan Van Weiringen.
Licensure Intermediate Care. *Beds* 19. *Certi-
fied* Medicaid.
Admissions Requirements Physician's request.
Staff Physicians 11 (ft); RNs 1 (ft); LPNs 3 (ft),
2 (pt); Nurses aides 6 (ft), 4 (pt); Physical thera-
pists 1 (ft); Activities coordinators 1 (ft); Dieti-
tians 1 (pt).
Affiliation Lutheran
Facilities Dining room; Physical therapy room;
Activities room; Crafts room; Laundry room;
Barber/Beauty shop; Library.
Activities Arts and Crafts; Cards; Games;
Reading groups; Prayer groups; Movies; Shop-
ping trips; Dances/Social or cultural gatherings;
Cooking events; Barbecues.
Description Patients rooms are individualized.
Patients are offered a hydromassage
(whirlpool), bath, or shower. A hair care room
is provided for hair styling. Activities include
dining out, picnics, and gardening.

NOME

Norton Sound Regional Hospital
PO Box 966, Nome, AK, 99762 (907) 443-5411
Admin Don Sloan. *Medical Dir/Dir of
Nursing* Dr Dennis Ohlragge.
Licensure Intermediate Care. *Beds* 6. *Certi-
fied* Medicaid.
Admissions Requirements Medical examina-
tion.
Staff Physicians 4 (ft); RNs 11 (ft); Nurses
aides 4 (ft); Activities coordinators 1 (ft); Dieti-
tians 1 (ft); Dentists 2 (ft); Audiologists 1 (ft);
Physical Therapy assistants 1 (ft); Optometrists
1 (ft).
Facilities Dining room; Physical therapy room;

Activities Arts and Crafts; Games; Shopping trips.

PALMER

Valley Hospital*
PO Box H, Palmer, AK, 99645 (907) 745-4813
Admin Eric Buckland.
Licensure Intermediate Care. *Beds* 2. *Certified* Medicaid.

PETERSBURG

Petersburg General Hospital
PO Box 589, Petersburg, AK, 99833 (907) 772-4291
Admin Craig S Slater. *Medical Dir/Dir of Nursing* D A Coon MD.
Licensure Skilled Care; Intermediate Care. *Beds* 12. *Certified* Medicaid; Medicare.
Admissions Requirements Minimum age 60; Medical examination; Physician's request.
Staff RNs 4 (ft), 3 (pt); Nurses aides 6 (ft), 1 (pt); Dietitians 1 (pt).
Description Facility is a small, home-town, 12-bed unit, "home away from home."

SEWARD

Wesleyan Nursing Home*
PO Box 456, Seward, AK, 99664 (907) 224-5241
Admin Mildred Pelch.
Licensure Skilled Care; Intermediate Care. *Beds* 64. *Certified* Medicaid; Medicare.

VALDEZ

Harborview Development Center
PO Box 487, Valdez, AK, 99686
Admin Patrick J Londo. *Medical Dir/Dir of Nursing* Dr Bernard Gerard.
Licensure Intermediate Care for Mentally Retarded. *Beds* 96. *Certified* Medicaid; Medicare.
Ownership Public.
Staff Physicians 5 (pt); RNs 9 (ft); LPNs 3 (ft); Nurses aides 66 (ft); Physical therapists 1 (ft); Recreational therapists 2 (ft); Occupational therapists 1 (ft); Dietitians 1 (pt); Dentists 1 (pt); Ophthalmologists 1 (pt); Audiologists 1 (pt); QMRPs 6 (ft).
Facilities Dining room; Physical therapy room; Activities room; Crafts room; Laundry room; Barber/Beauty shop; Library.
Activities Arts and Crafts; Games; Movies; Shopping trips; Dances/Social or cultural gatherings; Shopping trips.
Description Facility, located in a town of 4500 people, is entirely surrounded by tall mountains which meet tidewater. In-house training includes intensive programing in activities for daily living, as well as recreational activities and some vocational training. Hermon Hutchens Special School, a program of the local school district, accepts students over 21 and therefore can offer the residents of Harborview additional self-help training as well as preacademic and prevocational programs.

WRANGELL

Wrangell General Hospital and Long Term Care Facility*
PO Box 80, Wrangell, AK, 99929 (907) 874-3356
Admin Emma Ivy.
Licensure Skilled Care; Intermediate Care. *Beds* ICF 14. *Certified* Medicaid; Medicare.

ARIZONA

BISBEE

Copper Queen Community Hospital*
Cole Ave and Bisbee Rd, Bisbee, AZ, 85603
(602) 432-5383
Admin Leon E Haskell.
Licensure Intermediate Care. *Beds* 17.
Ownership Nonprofit.

CASA GRANDE

Hoemako Long Term Care*
1101 E Florence Blvd, Casa Grande, AZ, 85222
(602) 836-7401
Admin Robert Benjamin.
Licensure Skilled Care. *Beds* 29.
Ownership Nonprofit.

CHINLE

Chinle Nursing Home*
PO Box 910, Chinle, AZ, 86503 (602) 674-5216
Admin Verna Tsosie.
Licensure Skilled Care. *Beds* 79. *Certified* Medicare.
Ownership Nonprofit.

COTTONWOOD

Marcus J Lawrence Memorial Hospital Inc*
202 S Willard St, Cottonwood, AZ, 86326 (602)
634-2251
Admin Reid Wood.
Licensure Intermediate Care. *Beds* 20. *Certified* Medicare.
Ownership Nonprofit.

DOUGLAS

Southeast Arizona Medical Center
RR 1, Douglas, AZ, 85607 (602) 364-7931
Admin Steve Jackson. *Medical Dir/Dir of Nursing* George A Spikes.
Licensure Skilled Care. *Beds* 41. *Certified* Medicare.
Ownership Nonprofit.
Admissions Requirements Medical examination; Physician's request.
Staff Occupational therapists 1 (pt); Activities coordinators 1 (ft); Dietitians 1 (ft).
Facilities Dining room; Physical therapy room; Activities room; Chapel; Crafts room; Laundry

room; Barber/Beauty shop; Library.
Activities Arts and Crafts; Cards; Games; Reading groups; Prayer groups; Movies; Shopping trips; Dances/Social or cultural gatherings.

FLORENCE

Pinal County Nursing Home
1900 Central Ave, Florence, AZ, 85232 (602)
868-5854
Admin Charles Stevens. *Medical Dir/Dir of Nursing* O V Moreno MD.
Licensure Skilled Care. *Beds* 53.
Ownership Public.
Admissions Requirements Minimum age 16; Physician's request.
Staff Physicians 1 (ft); RNs 4 (ft); LPNs 15 (ft); Orderlies 8 (ft); Nurses aides 45 (ft); Physical therapists 1 (ft); Reality therapists 1 (ft); Speech therapists 1 (pt); Activities coordinators 1 (ft); Dietitians 1 (ft); Dentists 1 (ft); Ophthalmologists 1 (pt); Podiatrists 1 (pt); Audiologists 1 (pt).
Facilities Dining room; Physical therapy room; Activities room; Crafts room; Laundry room; Barber/Beauty shop; Library.
Activities Arts and Crafts; Cards; Games; Reading groups; Movies; Shopping trips; Dances/Social or cultural gatherings.
Description We are now engaged in an in-depth rehabilitation program. A physical therapist and medical doctor evaluate the residents and nursing service carries out the program. All departments are involved with the residents. A 12-passenger van and a 9-passenger station wagon are used to transport residents to various functions in this area plus Tucson and Phoenix.

Pinal General Hospital*
Adamsville Rd, Florence, AZ, 85232 (602)
868-5841
Admin Allan J Orler.
Licensure Intermediate Care. *Beds* 21. *Certified* Medicare.
Ownership Public.

GLENDALE

Glen Croft Care Center*
8641 N 67th Ave, Glendale, AZ, 85302 (602)
939-9475
Admin Levi Schlabach.

Licensure Skilled Care; Intermediate Care.
Beds SNF 24; ICF 40.
Ownership Nonprofit.

Glen Ridge Village
5910 W Northern Ave, Glendale, AZ, 85302
(602) 937-2779
Admin Ann Rollins. *Medical Dir/Dir of Nursing* Bienvenido Simwangco MD.
Licensure Skilled Care. *Beds* 135.
Ownership Nonprofit.
Admissions Requirements Medical examination.
Staff RNs 6 (ft), 1 (pt); LPNs 12 (ft), 3 (pt); Nurses aides 46 (ft); Physical therapists 1 (pt); Activities coordinators 1 (ft); Dietitians 1 (pt).
Facilities Dining room; Physical therapy room; Laundry room.
Activities Arts and Crafts; Games; Reading groups; Prayer groups; Movies; Shopping trips.

Glendale Care Center*
4704 W Diana, Glendale, AZ, 85302 (602)
247-3949
Admin Harvey L Hartzler.
Licensure Skilled Care; Intermediate Care; Personal Care. *Beds* SNF 98; ICF 63; Personal Care 31. *Certified* Medicare.
Ownership Proprietary.

Glendale Nursing Home
7022 N 48th Ave, Glendale, AZ, 85301 (602)
934-7265
Admin Marjorie G Hauser.
Licensure Skilled Care. *Beds* 61.
Ownership Proprietary.

GLOBE

Gila County General Hospital*
1100 Monroe St, Globe, AZ, 85501 (602)
425-5721
Admin John D Rollins.
Licensure Intermediate Care. *Beds* 69. *Certified* Medicare.
Ownership Public.

GREEN VALLEY

Santa Rita Health Care
150 N La Canada Dr, Green Valley, AZ, 85614
(602) 625-2500
Admin Laurie Pepper. *Medical Dir/Dir of*

Nursing Dr Alex McGlamery.
Licensure Skilled Care; Personal Care.
Beds SNF 81; Personal Care 19. *Certified* Medicare.
Ownership Proprietary.
Admissions Requirements Minimum age 16; Medical examination; Physician's request.
Facilities Dining room; Activities room; Chapel; Crafts room; Laundry room; Barber/Beauty shop; Library.
Activities Arts and Crafts; Cards; Games; Reading groups; Prayer groups; Movies; Shopping trips; Dances/Social or cultural gatherings.

KINGMAN

Kingman Health Care Center*
1081 Kathleen Ave, Kingman, AZ, 86401 (602) 793-2779
Admin Patsy A Hawtin.
Licensure Skilled Care; Personal Care.
Beds SNF 80; Personal Care 40.
Ownership Proprietary.

LAVEEN

American Indian Nursing Home
8201 W Baseline, PO Box 9, Laveen, AZ, 85339 (602) 237-3813
Admin Victor E Vallet.
Licensure Skilled Care; Personal Care.
Beds SNF 76.
Ownership Nonprofit.
Admissions Requirements Physician's request.
Staff RNs 5 (ft); LPNs 7 (ft); Orderlies 32 (ft); Physical therapists 2 (ft); Reality therapists 2 (ft); Recreational therapists 2 (ft); Activities coordinators 1 (ft); Dietitians 1 (ft).
Facilities Dining room; Physical therapy room; Activities room; Laundry room.
Activities Arts and Crafts; Cards; Games; Reading groups; Prayer groups; Movies; Shopping trips; Dances/Social or cultural gatherings.
Description American Indian Nursing Home was incorporated to provide care for Native Americans in a reservation setting with other Indians taking care of them, for utmost comfort.

MESA

Chula Vista Nursing Home*
60 S 58th St, Mesa, AZ, 85206 (602) 832-3903
Admin Jane Wagner.
Licensure Skilled Care; Intermediate Care.
Beds SNF 55; ICF 45.
Ownership Proprietary.

Cosada Villa Nursing Home*
420 W 10th Pl, Mesa, AZ, 85201 (602) 833-4226
Admin Robert L Sexton.
Licensure Skilled Care; Intermediate Care.
Beds SNF 82; ICF 92. *Certified* Medicare.
Ownership Proprietary.

East Mesa Care Center*
51 S 48th St, Mesa, AZ, 85206 (602) 832-8333
Admin Kenneth Trygg.
Licensure Skilled Care; Intermediate Care; Personal Care. *Beds* SNF 97; ICF 49; Personal Care 48.
Ownership Proprietary.

Golden Mesa Nursing Home
715 N Country Club, Mesa, AZ, 85201 (602) 969-1305
Admin William Constable.
Licensure Skilled Care. *Beds* 109.
Ownership Proprietary.
Admissions Requirements Minimum age 21; Medical examination; Physician's request.
Staff RNs 4 (ft); LPNs 4 (ft), 2 (pt); Nurses aides 29 (ft); Activities coordinators 2 (ft).
Facilities Dining room; Physical therapy room; Activities room; Laundry room; Barber/Beauty shop; Library.
Activities Arts and Crafts; Cards; Games; Reading groups; Prayer groups; Movies; Shopping trips; Dances/Social or cultural gatherings.
Description Golden Mesa is located in close proximity to 2 local hospitals. Barber and beautician are in the facility on a weekly basis to accomodate the needs of residents. Special projects are in progress involving the residents on an ongoing basis such as a garden, trips to the zoo, ice follies, and picnics.

Good Shephard Villa*
5848 E University Dr, Mesa, AZ, 85205 (602) 981-0098
Admin Knut H Mehl.
Licensure Skilled Care; Intermediate Care.
Beds SNF 50; ICF 30.
Ownership Nonprofit.

Las Flores Nursing Center
6458 E Broadway, Mesa, AZ, 85206 (602) 832-5160
Admin Peggy Wilson. *Medical Dir/Dir of Nursing* Joseph Chatham MD.
Licensure Skilled Care. *Beds* 100. *Certified* Medicare.
Ownership Proprietary.
Admissions Requirements Minimum age 16; Medical examination; Physician's request.
Staff Physicians 3 (pt); RNs 7 (ft), 6 (pt); LPNs 7 (ft), 1 (pt); Orderlies 1 (ft); Nurses aides 41 (ft), 3 (pt); Physical therapists 1 (ft); Occupational therapists 1 (pt); Speech therapists 1 (pt); Activities coordinators 1 (ft); Dietitians 1 (ft); Dentists 1 (pt); Podiatrists 1 (pt); Audiologists 1 (pt); Social workers 1 (ft), 1 (pt).
Facilities Dining room; Physical therapy room; Activities room; Crafts room; Laundry room; Barber/Beauty shop; Library.
Activities Arts and Crafts; Cards; Games; Reading groups; Prayer groups; Movies; Dances/Social or cultural gatherings.
Description Center offers dignified health care amid gracious surroundings; dining is a social experience rather than a necessity; tablecloths, stemware, and hostess service for all 3 meals, with attractive presentation with garnishes and delicious food; also specializes in rehabilitative services.

Mesa Christian Home
255 W Brown Rd, Mesa, AZ, 85201 (602) 833-3988
Admin Sherman M Rorvig.
Licensure Skilled Care; Intermediate Care; Personal Care. *Beds* SNF 112; ICF; Personal Care 45.
Ownership Nonprofit.
Staff RNs 14 (ft), 5 (pt); LPNs 10 (ft), 5 (pt); Orderlies 2 (ft), 2 (pt); Nurses aides 61 (ft), 20 (pt); Recreational therapists 1 (ft); Activities coordinators 3 (ft), 1 (pt).
Facilities Dining room; Physical therapy room; Activities room; Crafts room; Laundry room; Barber/Beauty shop; Library; Resident's kitchen.
Activities Arts and Crafts; Games; Reading groups; Movies; Shopping trips; Dances/Social or cultural gatherings; Swimming.
Description Mesa Christian Home offers a variety of daily activities including bingo, exercises, sing-a-longs, resident council, choir, and special rehabilitation groups to help the residents increase and maintain self-esteem. A special feature in the nursing home is Station Delta—behind electronically controlled "garden gates," the disoriented resident is able to roam through bright corridors leading to enclosed walkways that lead to outside gazebos and courtyards. Delta residents may enjoy van rides, music, picnics, and swimming.

Patterson Terrace Care Center
1825 W Emelita Ave, Mesa, AZ, 85202 (602) 964-0562
Admin Genevieve Stratton. *Medical Dir/Dir of Nursing* Dr Benton.
Licensure Skilled Care. *Beds* 64.
Ownership Proprietary.
Admissions Requirements Minimum age 16; Medical examination; Physician's request.
Staff RNs 1 (ft), 7 (pt); LPNs 1 (ft), 3 (pt); Nurses aides 17 (ft), 3 (pt); Activities coordinators 1 (ft); Rehabilitation Aides 1 (ft).
Facilities Dining room; Activities room; Chapel; Crafts room; Barber/Beauty shop; Library; Outdoor pool.
Activities Arts and Crafts; Cards; Games; Reading groups; Prayer groups; Movies; Shopping trips; Dances/Social or cultural gatherings; Exercise; Swimming; Resident council.

Royal Nursing Home
108 E 2nd Ave, Mesa, AZ, 85202 (602) 834-1490
Admin Bruce Grambley.
Licensure Skilled Care. *Beds* 46.
Ownership Proprietary.

NOGALES

Holy Cross Hospital and Health Center—Geriatric Center*
1230 Target Range Rd, Nogales, AZ, 85621 (602) 287-2771
Admin Walt Connolly.
Licensure Skilled Care. *Beds* 30.
Ownership Nonprofit.

PEORIA

Camelot Manor*
11311 N 99th Ave, Peoria, AZ, 85345 (602) 977-8373
Admin Sharon Kempton.

Licensure Personal Care. *Beds* Personal Care 48.
Ownership Proprietary.

Good Shepherd Retirement Center
10323 W Olive Ave, Peoria, AZ, 85345 (602) 974-2555
Admin Herbert Miller. *Medical Dir/Dir of Nursing* Harold Gries MD.
Licensure Skilled Care; Intermediate Care.
Beds SNF 116; ICF 97.
Ownership Nonprofit.
Admissions Requirements Medical examination; Physician's request.
Staff RNs 17 (ft); LPNs 17 (ft); Orderlies 5 (ft); Nurses aides 58 (ft); Physical therapists 2 (ft); Speech therapists 1 (pt); Activities coordinators 2 (ft), 1 (pt); Dietitians 1 (pt).
Affiliation Lutheran
Facilities Dining room; Physical therapy room; Activities room; Chapel; Crafts room; Laundry room; Barber/Beauty shop; Library.
Activities Arts and Crafts; Cards; Games; Reading groups; Prayer groups; Movies; Shopping trips; Dances/Social or cultural gatherings.
Description Good Shepherd program consists of a large nursing care facility and adjoining apartment complex with 72-independent-living, 1- and 2-bedroom apartments. Meals are optional in apartment complex, but emergency nursing services are available at all times. Length of stay in nursing facility may be permanent or short-term for a convalescent or respite stay. Restorative and rehabilitative programs are emphasized to expedite discharge to home, or lesser level of care. Registered physical therapists on duty 5 days a week enhance rehabilitative program, transportation services for residents of both nursing center and apartment complex, Sunday morning and Thursday morning worship services, Catholic Mass every Friday with Rosary every Wednesday evening. A very active auxiliary and volunteer service bring much love and light into the overall program.

PHOENIX

Acacia Convalescent Center*
1830 E Roosevelt, Phoenix, AZ, 85006 (602) 258-6569
Admin Barbara Brown.
Licensure Skilled Care. *Beds* 74. *Certified* Medicare.
Ownership Proprietary.

Arizona Eastern Star Home
4602 N 24th St, Phoenix, AZ, 85016 (602) 954-9178
Admin Hilda B Rubel.
Licensure Skilled Care. *Beds* 36.
Ownership Nonprofit.
Admissions Requirements Minimum age 18; Medical examination.
Staff RNs 4 (ft), 4 (pt); LPNs 1 (ft), 1 (pt); Nurses aides 18 (ft), 4 (pt); Activities coordinators; Dietitians.
Affiliation Order of Eastern Star
Facilities Dining room; Activities room; Chapel; Crafts room; Laundry room; Barber/Beauty shop; Library.
Activities Arts and Crafts; Cards; Games;

Reading groups; Prayer groups; Movies; Shopping trips; Dances/Social or cultural gatherings.
Description This home has supervisory care and skilled nursing care areas, both licensed by the state health department. The facility has available on call physicians, a physical therapist, dentist, and podiatrist.

Beatitudes Care Center*
1712 W Glendale Ave, Phoenix, AZ, 85021 (602) 995-2611
Admin Ken H Buckwald.
Licensure Skilled Care; Personal Care.
Beds SNF 156; Personal Care 120.
Ownership Nonprofit.

Bel Isle Nursing Home*
720 E Montebello, Phoenix, AZ, 85014 (602) 266-4122
Admin Daniel J Belisle.
Licensure Skilled Care. *Beds* 61.
Ownership Proprietary.

Bells Lodge
4202 N 20th Ave, Phoenix, AZ, 85015 (602) 264-3824
Admin Phyllis Scheetz.
Licensure Skilled Care. *Beds* 100.
Ownership Proprietary.
Admissions Requirements Medical examination; Physician's request.
Staff Physical therapists 1 (pt); Occupational therapists 1 (pt); Speech therapists 1 (pt); Activities coordinators 1 (ft); Dietitians 1 (pt).
Facilities Dining room; Laundry room; Barber/Beauty shop; Library; Lobby; Lounges; Enclosed patio.
Activities Arts and Crafts; Cards; Games; Reading groups; Prayer groups; Movies; Dances/Social or cultural gatherings.
Description Facility has just been totally refurbished including all new plumbing, air conditioning, newly carpeted; entire facility papered; all lounges and dining rooms refurnished.

Boyds Nursing Home
111 E Southern, Phoenix, AZ, 85040 (602) 276-4277
Admin Dorothy L Kennedy.
Licensure Skilled Care. *Beds* 47.
Ownership Proprietary.
Admissions Requirements Medical examination; Physician's request.
Staff RNs 3 (ft), 2 (pt); LPNs 1 (ft), 1 (pt); Orderlies 4 (ft); Activities coordinators 1 (ft).
Facilities Dining room; Laundry room.
Activities Arts and Crafts; Cards; Games; Reading groups; Prayer groups.
Description Facility receives all its patients through the long-term care of Maricopa Medical Center; therapists, medical director, and doctors are furnished by long-term care.

Capri Nursing Home*
1501 E Orangewood, Phoenix, AZ, 85020 (602) 944-1574
Admin William E Fay.
Licensure Skilled Care. *Beds* 59.
Ownership Proprietary.

Christian Care Nursing Home
11812 N 19th Ave, Phoenix, AZ, 85029 (602) 861-3241
Admin Dean Sloniger.
Licensure Skilled Care; Intermediate Care; Personal Care. *Beds* SNF 40; ICF 10; Personal Care 10.
Ownership Nonprofit.
Admissions Requirements Minimum age 18; Medical examination; Physician's request.
Staff RNs 2 (ft), 4 (pt); LPNs 3 (ft), 2 (pt); Orderlies 1 (ft); Nurses aides 13 (ft), 10 (pt); Activities coordinators 1 (pt); Dietitians 1 (ft).
Facilities Dining room; Activities room; Chapel; Crafts room; Laundry room; Barber/Beauty shop; Library.
Activities Arts and Crafts; Games; Prayer groups; Movies; Shopping trips.

Crestview Convalescent Lodge
2151 E Maryland, Phoenix, AZ, 85016 (602) 264-6427
Admin Michael L Fahey. *Medical Dir/Dir of Nursing* Dr Robert Armstrong.
Licensure Skilled Care. *Beds* 66.
Ownership Nonprofit.
Admissions Requirements Minimum age 62; Medical examination; Physician's request.
Staff RNs 4 (ft), 3 (pt); LPNs 4 (ft), 2 (pt); Nurses aides 19 (ft), 6 (pt); Activities coordinators 1 (ft).
Facilities Dining room; Activities room; Chapel; Laundry room; Barber/Beauty shop; Library.
Activities Arts and Crafts; Cards; Games; Reading groups; Prayer groups; Movies; Shopping trips; Dances/Social or cultural gatherings.
Description Our turnover ratio of patients and staff is very low compared to the rest of the industry, due to the fact that nursing care is of superior quality.

Desert Haven Nursing Center
2645 E Thomas Rd, Phoenix, AZ, 85016 (602) 956-8000
Admin Carolyn DeBiasi. *Medical Dir/Dir of Nursing* Dr Kienzle.
Licensure Skilled Care. *Beds* 115. *Certified* Medicare.
Ownership Proprietary.
Admissions Requirements Medical examination; Physician's request.
Facilities Dining room; Physical therapy room; Activities room; Laundry room; Barber/Beauty shop.
Activities Arts and Crafts; Cards; Games; Prayer groups; Movies; Shopping trips; Dances/Social or cultural gatherings.
Description Facility has an excellent restorative nursing program with emphasis on rehabilitation and an excellent activities program which specializes in reality therapy.

Desert Terrace
2509 N 24th St, Phoenix, AZ, 85008 (602) 273-1347
Admin Helen Cahill. *Medical Dir/Dir of Nursing* C Joseph Freund MD.
Licensure Skilled Care. *Beds* 108. *Certified* Medicare.
Ownership Proprietary.
Admissions Requirements Medical examination; Physician's request.

Staff RNs 7 (ft), 4 (pt); LPNs 6 (ft), 5 (pt); Orderlies 1 (ft); Nurses aides 40 (ft), 6 (pt); Physical therapists 1 (pt); Recreational therapists 1 (ft); Occupational therapists 1 (pt); Speech therapists 1 (pt); Activities coordinators 1 (ft); Dietitians 1 (ft); Dentists 1 (pt); Podiatrists 1 (pt); Audiologists 1 (pt).
Facilities Dining room; Physical therapy room; Activities room; Laundry room; Barber/Beauty shop.
Activities Arts and Crafts; Cards; Games; Reading groups; Prayer groups; Movies; Shopping trips; Dances/Social or cultural gatherings.

Highland Manor Nursing Home
4635 N 14th St, Phoenix, AZ, 85014 (602) 264-9039
Admin Elizabeth Holden. *Medical Dir/Dir of Nursing* Walter Neiri MD.
Licensure Skilled Care. *Beds* 107. *Certified* Medicare.
Ownership Proprietary.
Admissions Requirements Medical examination; Physician's request.
Staff Physicians 1 (pt); RNs 10 (ft), 1 (pt); LPNs 4 (ft), 1 (pt); Orderlies 1 (ft); Nurses aides 42 (ft), 1 (pt); Physical therapists 3 (pt); Occupational therapists 1 (pt); Speech therapists 1 (pt); Activities coordinators 2 (ft); Dietitians 1 (ft), 1 (pt); Dentists 1 (pt); Ophthalmologists 1 (pt); Podiatrists 1 (pt); Audiologists 1 (pt).
Languages Sign
Facilities Dining room; Physical therapy room; Laundry room; Barber/Beauty shop; Library.
Activities Arts and Crafts; Cards; Games; Reading groups; Prayer groups; Movies; Shopping trips; Dances/Social or cultural gatherings; Swimming.
Description Activities program has been greatly extended due to the addition of a new van with a wheelchair lift; imaginative activities director has initiated many new programs including swimming and sign language which are extremely beneficial to residents.

Hillhaven Health Care Center
531 W Thomas Rd, Phoenix, AZ, 85013 (602) 264-9651
Admin David K Niess. *Medical Dir/Dir of Nursing* William Semmens MD.
Licensure Skilled Care. *Beds* SNF 120; ICF 60; Medicare Certified 60. *Certified* Medicare.
Ownership Proprietary.
Admissions Requirements Minimum age 16; Physician's request.
Staff Physicians 1 (pt); RNs 15 (ft), 5 (pt); LPNs 35 (ft), 5 (pt); Nurses aides 60 (ft), 10 (pt); Physical therapists 2 (ft), 1 (pt); Recreational therapists 4 (ft); Occupational therapists 1 (ft); Speech therapists 1 (pt); Activities coordinators 1 (ft); Dietitians 1 (pt); Dentists 1 (pt); Podiatrists 1 (pt).
Facilities Dining room; Physical therapy room; Activities room; Crafts room; Laundry room; Barber/Beauty shop.
Activities Arts and Crafts; Cards; Games; Prayer groups; Movies; Shopping trips.
Description Facility features special staffing, training, and security for Alzheimer's disease and related disorder patients; primary care unit for sub-acute stays staffed soley with professional nurses.

Hilton Nursing Home
1031 N 34th St, Phoenix, AZ, 85008 (602) 273-1683
Admin Anthony Simonetti.
Licensure Skilled Care. *Beds* 58.
Ownership Proprietary.
Admissions Requirements Medical examination; Physician's request.
Staff Physicians 1 (pt); RNs 8 (ft); LPNs 5 (ft); Orderlies 8 (ft); Nurses aides 25 (ft); Physical therapists 1 (pt); Reality therapists 1 (pt); Recreational therapists 2 (ft); Occupational therapists 1 (pt); Speech therapists 1 (pt); Activities coordinators 1 (ft); Dietitians 1 (pt); Dentists 1 (pt); Ophthalmologists 1 (pt); Podiatrists 1 (pt); Audiologists 1 (pt).
Facilities Dining room; Activities room; Crafts room.
Activities Arts and Crafts; Cards; Games; Reading groups; Prayer groups; Movies; Shopping trips; Dances/Social or cultural gatherings; Trips to professional and college sports events.
Description Facility features young, enthusiatic administrative staff that offers many varied, exciting activities—a professional staff that cares. All staffing is well above state/federal guidelines.

Homestead Rest Home*
343 W Lynwood Ave, Phoenix, AZ, 85003 (602) 256-6772
Admin Lena Inman.
Licensure Personal Care. *Beds* 13.
Ownership Proprietary.

Kivel Geriatric Center
3020 N 36th St, Phoenix, AZ, 85018 (602) 956-3110
Admin Sonya O'Leary. *Medical Dir/Dir of Nursing* Jerome J Kastrul MD.
Licensure Skilled Care. *Beds* 82.
Ownership Nonprofit.
Admissions Requirements Minimum age 18; Medical examination; Physician's request.
Staff RNs 5 (ft), 4 (pt); LPNs 5 (ft), 5 (pt); Orderlies 2 (ft), 3 (pt); Nurses aides 26 (ft), 5 (pt); Physical therapists; Occupational therapists; Speech therapists; Activities coordinators 1 (ft); Dietitians 1 (ft); Podiatrists; Audiologists; Chaplain 1 (pt).
Affiliation Jewish
Facilities Dining room; Physical therapy room; Activities room; Crafts room; Laundry room; Barber/Beauty shop; Library; Kiln for ceramics.
Activities Arts and Crafts; Cards; Games; Reading groups; Prayer groups; Movies; Shopping trips; Dances/Social or cultural gatherings; Cooking classes; Ceramics.
Description The facility is part of the geriatric center. Emphasis is placed on restorative nursing and strong activities and social service programs which encourage maximum family and volunteer participation. Pastoral care services are also an integral part of the program.

Maryland Gardens
31 W Maryland, Phoenix, AZ, 85018 (602) 265-6834
Admin Cathy Williams. *Medical Dir/Dir of Nursing* Noreen Readel.
Beds 39.
Ownership Proprietary.
Admissions Requirements Medical examina-

tion.
Staff RNs 2 (ft); LPNs 4 (ft); Nurses aides 13 (ft), 6 (pt); Reality therapists 1 (ft); Recreational therapists 2 (ft); Activities coordinators 1 (ft); Dietitians 1 (ft).
Facilities Dining room; Activities room; Crafts room; Laundry room; Library.
Activities Arts and Crafts; Cards; Games; Reading groups; Prayer groups; Movies; Shopping trips; Dances/Social or cultural gatherings.
Description Maryland Gardens features apartment-style living, green lawns, citrus trees, enclosed facility, and home cooked meals served in a colonial-style dining room.

Mountain Aire Health Care Facility*
8825 S 7th St, Phoenix, AZ, 85040 (602) 243-6121
Admin Emmie Lester.
Licensure Skilled Care; Intermediate Care. *Beds* SNF 80; ICF 80.
Ownership Proprietary.

Orangewood Health Facility
7550 N 16th St, Phoenix, AZ, 85020 (602) 944-4455
Admin Lorimer R Olson. *Medical Dir/Dir of Nursing* John F Ganem MD.
Licensure Skilled Care; Personal Care. *Beds* SNF 40; Personal Care 24. *Certified* Medicare.
Ownership Nonprofit.
Admissions Requirements Minimum age 65.
Staff RNs 6 (ft), 2 (pt); LPNs 2 (ft), 1 (pt); Nurses aides 23 (ft), 1 (pt); Activities coordinators 1 (ft), 1 (pt).
Affiliation Baptist
Facilities Dining room; Physical therapy room; Activities room; Chapel; Crafts room; Laundry room; Barber/Beauty shop; Library; Shop.
Activities Arts and Crafts; Cards; Games; Reading groups; Prayer groups; Movies; Shopping trips.
Description Facility has continuing care program; member of American Association of Homes for the Aging.

Phoenix Mountain Nursing Center
13232 N Tatum Blvd, Phoenix, AZ, 85032 (602) 996-5200
Admin John White.
Licensure Skilled Care. *Beds* 127. *Certified* Medicare.
Ownership Proprietary.
Staff RNs 12 (ft), 2 (pt); LPNs 6 (ft), 2 (pt); Orderlies 2 (ft); Nurses aides 42 (ft), 6 (pt); Physical therapists 1 (ft); Reality therapists 1 (ft); Recreational therapists 1 (ft); Occupational therapists 1 (pt); Speech therapists 1 (pt); Activities coordinators 2 (ft); Dietitians 1 (ft); Dentists 1 (pt); Podiatrists 1 (pt); Audiologists 1 (pt).
Facilities Dining room; Physical therapy room; Activities room; Crafts room; Laundry room; Barber/Beauty shop; Library.
Activities Arts and Crafts; Cards; Games; Reading groups; Movies; Shopping trips; Dances/Social or cultural gatherings.

Phoenix Nursing and Convalescent Center— East
1342 E McDowell, Phoenix, AZ, 85006 (602) 254-6568

Admin Frances Neriz. *Medical Dir/Dir of Nursing* Sidney Axelrod MD.
Licensure Skilled Care. *Beds* 136.
Ownership Proprietary.
Admissions Requirements Minimum age Birth; Medical examination; Physician's request.
Staff RNs 3 (ft); LPNs 12 (ft); Orderlies 8 (ft); Nurses aides 32 (ft); Physical therapists 1 (ft); Recreational therapists 1 (ft); Respitory therapists 8 (ft).
Facilities Dining room; Physical therapy room; Activities room; Crafts room; Laundry room.
Activities Arts and Crafts; Cards; Games; Reading groups; Prayer groups; Movies; Shopping trips; Dances/Social or cultural gatherings; Resident council.
Description Facility has a respiratory unit with a director and full-time, 24-hour therapists; patients accepted on ventilators needing respiratory treatments for either long-term or short-term care. Also a pediatric unit for infants, toddlers, etc. requiring long-term or short-term care.

Phoenix Nursing and Convalescent Center— West*
1314 E McDowell, Phoenix, AZ, 85006 (602) 254-6568
Admin Robert Gundling.
Licensure Skilled Care. *Beds* 140. *Certified* Medicare.
Ownership Proprietary.

Sacred Heart Home for the Aged
1110 N 16th St, Phoenix, AZ, 85006 (602) 258-6677
Admin Sr Catherine Williamson.
Licensure Skilled Care; Intermediate Care; Personal Care. *Beds* SNF 35; ICF 30; Personal Care 63.
Ownership Nonprofit.
Admissions Requirements Minimum age 60; Medical examination.
Staff RNs 5 (ft), 4 (pt); LPNs 5 (ft), 3 (pt); Orderlies 1 (ft); Nurses aides 31 (ft), 10 (pt); Recreational therapists 3 (ft); Activities coordinators 1 (ft).
Affiliation Roman Catholic
Facilities Dining room; Physical therapy room; Activities room; Chapel; Crafts room; Laundry room; Barber/Beauty shop; Library.
Activities Arts and Crafts; Cards; Games; Reading groups; Prayer groups; Movies; Shopping trips; Dances/Social or cultural gatherings.
Description Sacred Heart Home cares for the poor aged as this is the apostolate of the Little Sisters of the Poor in all of their homes, which are located in 30 countries. Loving and personalized care is given in a religious atmosphere to those in their final years of life who are provided with physical and psychosocial care as well as the opportunity to draw closer to God. A day center program provides transportation, meals, and activities to 17 elderly of the surrounding community without charge.

San Juan Gardens
5602 N 7th St, Phoenix, AZ, 85014 (602) 248-9310
Admin Yolanda Burkholder. *Medical Dir/Dir of Nursing* Dr Robert Briggs.
Licensure Personal Care. *Beds* 16.
Ownership Proprietary.

Staff Physicians; RNs; LPNs; Orderlies; Nurses aides; Physical therapists; Reality therapists; Recreational therapists; Occupational therapists; Speech therapists; Activities coordinators; Dietitians; Dentists; Ophthalmologists; Podiatrists; Audiologists.
Facilities Dining room; Activities room; Crafts room; Laundry room; Barber/Beauty shop; Library.
Activities Arts and Crafts; Cards; Games; Reading groups; Prayer groups; Movies; Shopping trips; Dances/Social or cultural gatherings.

South Mountain Manor*
2211 E Southern Ave, Phoenix, AZ, 85040 (602) 276-7358
Admin Peggy Ann Constable.
Licensure Intermediate Care. *Beds* 115.
Ownership Proprietary.

Tanner Chapel Manor Nursing Home
2150 E Broadway, Phoenix, AZ, 85040 (602) 243-1735
Admin Grace Evans. *Medical Dir/Dir of Nursing* Dr Arthur Pelberg.
Licensure Skilled Care. *Beds* 50.
Ownership Nonprofit.
Admissions Requirements Minimum age 18; Medical examination; Physician's request.
Staff RNs 2 (ft), 4 (pt); LPNs 1 (ft); Orderlies 1 (ft); Nurses aides 21 (ft), 1 (pt); Activities coordinators 1 (ft).
Facilities Dining room; Physical therapy room; Activities room; Chapel; Crafts room; Laundry room; Barber/Beauty shop; Library.
Activities Arts and Crafts; Cards; Games; Reading groups; Prayer groups; Movies; Shopping trips; Dances/Social or cultural gatherings.

Vantage Convalescent Center
1856 E Thomas Rd, Phoenix, AZ, 85016 (602) 274-3508
Admin Arlie M Mason. *Medical Dir/Dir of Nursing* Dr Frances Sierakowski.
Licensure Skilled Care. *Beds* 84.
Ownership Proprietary.
Admissions Requirements Minimum age 18; Medical examination; Physician's request.
Staff RNs 5 (ft), 2 (pt); LPNs 5 (ft), 2 (pt); Orderlies 2 (ft); Nurses aides 29 (ft); Physical therapists; Occupational therapists 1 (pt); Speech therapists; Activities coordinators 1 (ft); Dietitians; Dentists; Ophthalmologists; Podiatrists; Audiologists.
Facilities Dining room; Physical therapy room; Laundry room; Barber/Beauty shop; Library.
Activities Arts and Crafts; Cards; Games; Reading groups; Prayer groups; Movies; Shopping trips; Dances/Social or cultural gatherings.
Description A caring staff, all nurses aides are put through the certified nursing assistant course and all personnel are trained to do rehabilitation.

Village Green
2932 N 14th St, Phoenix, AZ, 85014 (602) 264-5274
Admin Jeanne Y Caron. *Medical Dir/Dir of Nursing* Dr Noel Smith.
Beds 80.
Ownership Proprietary.
Admissions Requirements Medical examination.

Facilities Dining room; Activities room; Crafts room; Laundry room; Barber/Beauty shop; Library.
Activities Arts and Crafts; Cards; Games; Reading groups; Prayer groups; Movies; Shopping trips; Dances/Social or cultural gatherings.
Description Village Green is a top notch nursing home with top notch nursing care; exceptionally clean and very caring facility and staff; warm atmosphere similar to that of a home.

PRESCOTT

Hillside Care Center
621 Hillside Ave, Prescott, AZ, 86301 (602) 445-3446
Admin Virginia A Rohrer.
Licensure Skilled Care; Personal Care.
Beds SNF 57; Personal Care 45.
Ownership Proprietary.
Admissions Requirements Medical examination; Physician's request.
Facilities Dining room; Activities room; Crafts room; Laundry room; Barber/Beauty shop; Library.
Activities Arts and Crafts; Cards; Games; Reading groups; Prayer groups; Movies; Shopping trips; Dances/Social or cultural gatherings; Foster grandchildren program; Resident's garden.

Prescott Samaritan Village
1030 Scott Dr, Prescott, AZ, 86301 (602) 778-2450
Admin Dean Mertz.
Licensure Skilled Care; Personal Care.
Beds SNF 60; Personal Care 20.
Ownership Nonprofit.
Admissions Requirements Medical examination; Physician's request.
Staff Physicians 1 (pt); RNs 3 (ft), 4 (pt); LPNs 5 (ft), 3 (pt); Orderlies 2 (ft), 1 (pt); Nurses aides 18 (ft), 10 (pt); Physical therapists 1 (pt); Activities coordinators 1 (ft).
Affiliation Lutheran
Facilities Dining room; Physical therapy room; Activities room; Chapel; Crafts room; Laundry room; Barber/Beauty shop; Library; Solarium.
Activities Arts and Crafts; Cards; Games; Reading groups; Prayer groups; Movies; Shopping trips; Dances/Social or cultural gatherings; Foster grandparent program.
Description Prescott Samaritan Village is a multilevel facility located in the heart of Prescott. Motto is "In Christ's love, everyone is someone."

SAFFORD

Mountain View Nursing Center
1706 20th Ave, Safford, AZ, 85546 (602) 428-0630
Admin James A Shafer. *Medical Dir/Dir of Nursing* Fred W Knight MD.
Licensure Skilled Care. *Beds* 120.
Ownership Proprietary.
Admissions Requirements Minimum age 16; Medical examination; Physician's request.
Staff RNs 9 (ft), 1 (pt); LPNs 6 (ft); Nurses aides 39 (ft).

Facilities Dining room; Activities room; Crafts room; Laundry room; Barber/Beauty shop.
Activities Arts and Crafts; Cards; Games; Prayer groups; Movies; Shopping trips.

SCOTTSDALE

Casa Delmar
3333 N Civic Center, Scottsdale, AZ, 85251 (602) 947-7333
Admin Andrew J Kellogg. *Medical Dir/Dir of Nursing* Theodore Rudberg.
Licensure Skilled Care. *Beds* 130. *Certified* Medicare.
Ownership Proprietary.
Admissions Requirements Minimum age 16; Medical examination; Physician's request.
Staff Physicians 2 (pt); RNs 9 (ft), 3 (pt); LPNs 9 (ft), 2 (pt); Orderlies 10 (ft); Nurses aides 27 (ft), 3 (pt); Physical therapists 1 (ft); Reality therapists 1 (pt); Recreational therapists 1 (pt); Occupational therapists 1 (pt); Speech therapists 1 (pt); Activities coordinators 1 (ft); Dietitians 1 (ft); Podiatrists 1 (pt).
Facilities Dining room; Activities room; Crafts room; Laundry room; Barber/Beauty shop.
Activities Arts and Crafts; Cards; Games; Reading groups; Prayer groups; Movies; Shopping trips; Dances/Social or cultural gatherings.
Description Facility is located near doctors offices and Scottsdale Memorial Hospital and within walking distance of downtown Scottsdale. Spanish-style architecture is featured with plenty of outdoor patios, fountains, and activity areas.

Hayden Manor Nursing Home*
2501 N Hayden Rd, Scottsdale, AZ, 85257 (602) 949-1824
Admin Berde Groff.
Licensure Skilled Care. *Beds* 39.
Ownership Proprietary.

Monterey Nursing Center
7303 E Monterey, Scottsdale, AZ, 85251 (602) 947-7443
Admin Anne C DiPierro. *Medical Dir/Dir of Nursing* Dr Theodore Rudberg.
Licensure Skilled Care. *Beds* 90. *Certified* Medicare.
Ownership Proprietary.
Staff RNs 12 (ft), 4 (pt); LPNs 6 (ft), 1 (pt); Orderlies 1 (ft); Nurses aides 37 (ft), 3 (pt); Activities coordinators 2 (ft); Dietitians 1 (ft).
Facilities Dining room; Physical therapy room; Laundry room; Barber/Beauty shop.
Activities Arts and Crafts; Cards; Games; Reading groups; Prayer groups; Movies; Shopping trips; Dances/Social or cultural gatherings; Hydrotherapy.
Description Monterey is located in the cultural hub of beautiful Scottsdale, one block from Scottsdale Memorial Hospital. Elegant, charming surroundings provide a home-like atmosphere; chauffeured limousine is available for transportation and outings.

Scottsdale Christian Home
3339 N Civic Center, Scottsdale, AZ, 85251 (602) 949-5400
Admin Shirley Paulk. *Medical Dir/Dir of Nursing* Dr Gerald Wolfey.

Licensure Skilled Care. *Beds* 108.
Ownership Proprietary.
Admissions Requirements Minimum age 18; Medical examination; Physician's request.
Staff RNs 4 (ft), 3 (pt); LPNs 5 (ft), 4 (pt); Orderlies 5 (ft), 1 (pt); Nurses aides 22 (ft), 6 (pt); Physical therapists 1 (pt); Recreational therapists 1 (pt); Activities coordinators 1 (ft); Dietitians 1 (ft).
Facilities Dining room; Physical therapy room; Activities room; Crafts room; Laundry room; Barber/Beauty shop; Library.
Activities Arts and Crafts; Cards; Games; Reading groups; Prayer groups; Movies; Shopping trips; Dances/Social or cultural gatherings.
Description Facility offers gourmet dinners and 5-meal plans; includes 2 enclosed courtyard patios, and alarm systems on all doors.

Scottsdale Convalescent Plaza*
1475 N Granite Reef Rd, Scottsdale, AZ, 85257 (602) 990-1904
Admin Ross J Monaco.
Licensure Skilled Care. *Beds* 80. *Certified* Medicare.
Ownership Proprietary.

Scottsdale Village Square
2620 N 68th St, Scottsdale, AZ, 85257 (602) 946-6571
Admin Paul R Friedlan. *Medical Dir/Dir of Nursing* Ernest Bensch MD.
Licensure Skilled Care; Personal Care.
Beds 140.
Ownership Proprietary.
Staff RNs 2 (ft), 1 (pt); LPNs 6 (ft), 3 (pt); Nurses aides 12 (ft), 4 (pt); Physical therapists 1 (pt); Activities coordinators 1 (ft), 1 (pt); Dietitians 1 (pt).
Facilities Dining room; Physical therapy room; Activities room; Crafts room; Laundry room; Barber/Beauty shop; Library.
Activities Arts and Crafts; Cards; Games; Reading groups; Prayer groups; Movies; Shopping trips; Dances/Social or cultural gatherings; Bingo; Wine and cheese parties.
Description Facility offers all care from day care through skilled care in a well-landscaped and spacious area, convenient to shopping with free transportation included.

SIERRA VISTA

Sierra Vista Care Center*
660 Coronado Rd, Sierra Vista, AZ, 85635 (602) 459-4900
Admin Charles J Steck.
Licensure Skilled Care; Intermediate Care.
Beds SNF 56; ICF 44.
Ownership Proprietary.

SUN CITY

Beverly Manor Convalescent Center*
13101 N 103rd Ave, Sun City, AZ, 85351 (602) 972-1153
Admin Cynthia Lauzon.
Licensure Skilled Care; Intermediate Care.
Beds SNF 150; ICF 45. *Certified* Medicare.
Ownership Proprietary.

Sun Valley Lodge*
12415 N 103rd Ave, Sun City, AZ, 85351 (602) 933-0137
Admin Virginia Sylvis.
Licensure Skilled Care; Personal Care.
Beds SNF 64; Personal Care 50.
Ownership Nonprofit.

TEMPE

Friendship Village of Tempe Health Center
2645 E Southern, Tempe, AZ, 85282 (602) 831-0880
Admin Gayle Lagman. *Medical Dir/Dir of Nursing* Roger Boylan MD.
Licensure Skilled Care; Personal Care.
Beds SNF 60; Personal Care 30. *Certified* Medicare.
Ownership Nonprofit.
Admissions Requirements Minimum age 62; Physician's request.
Staff Physicians 1 (pt); RNs 15 (ft), 8 (pt); LPNs 6 (ft); Nurses aides 34 (ft), 24 (pt); Physical therapists 1 (ft); Recreational therapists 2 (ft); Occupational therapists 1 (pt); Speech therapists 1 (pt); Activities coordinators 1 (ft); Dietitians 1 (ft); Dentists 1 (pt); Podiatrists 1 (pt).
Facilities Dining room; Physical therapy room; Activities room; Chapel; Crafts room; Laundry room; Barber/Beauty shop; Library.
Activities Arts and Crafts; Cards; Games; Reading groups; Prayer groups; Movies; Shopping trips; Dances/Social or cultural gatherings; Lunch outings.
Description Facility offers a campus of care ranging from independent living, assisted living, outpatient therapy and services, skilled nursing, and home health care with adjunct psychological services when needed.

Westchester Care Center
6100 S Rural Rd, Tempe, AZ, 85283 (602) 831-8660
Admin Eliot C Higbee. *Medical Dir/Dir of Nursing* Richard O Flynn MD.
Licensure Skilled Care; Intermediate Care.
Beds SNF 49; ICF 51.
Ownership Nonprofit.
Admissions Requirements Medical examination; Physician's request.
Staff RNs 4 (ft), 9 (pt); LPNs 5 (ft), 10 (pt); Nurses aides 32 (ft), 17 (pt); Physical therapists 2 (pt); Occupational therapists 1 (pt); Speech therapists 1 (pt); Activities coordinators 1 (ft), 2 (pt); Dietitians 1 (ft); Dentists 1 (pt); Podiatrists 1 (pt).
Affiliation Volunteers of America
Facilities Dining room; Physical therapy room; Activities room; Chapel; Crafts room; Laundry room; Barber/Beauty shop; Day rooms; Resident lounge.
Activities Arts and Crafts; Cards; Games; Reading groups; Prayer groups; Movies; Shopping trips; Dances/Social or cultural gatherings.
Description Center provides a spacious, relaxed campus setting featuring independent living apartments, garden court apartments, and a skilled nursing facility. Emphasis is placed on restorative therapies. Short-term stays are available.

TUCSON

Arizona Elks Long Term Care Unit
1901 W Speedway, Tucson, AZ, 85745 (602) 623-5562
Admin Mildred V Boyd.
Licensure Intermediate Care. *Beds* 46.
Ownership Nonprofit.
Admissions Requirements Males only; Medical examination; Physician's request.
Facilities Dining room; Physical therapy room; Activities room.

Arizona William-Wesley
2611 N Warren Ave, Tucson, AZ, 85719 (602) 795-9574
Admin Mary Jane Lindsay. *Medical Dir/Dir of Nursing* William Farr MD.
Licensure Skilled Care. *Beds* 102.
Ownership Proprietary.
Admissions Requirements Medical examination; Physician's request.
Staff Physicians 1 (pt); RNs 4 (ft), 2 (pt); LPNs 3 (ft), 6 (pt); Orderlies 1 (ft); Nurses aides 33 (ft), 11 (pt); Physical therapists 1 (pt); Recreational therapists 1 (ft); Occupational therapists 1 (pt); Speech therapists 1 (pt); Activities coordinators 2 (ft); Dietitians 1 (ft); Dentists 1 (pt); Ophthalmologists 1 (pt); Podiatrists 1 (pt); Audiologists 1 (pt).
Facilities Dining room; Physical therapy room; Activities room; Chapel; Crafts room; Laundry room; Barber/Beauty shop; Library.
Activities Arts and Crafts; Cards; Games; Reading groups; Prayer groups; Movies; Shopping trips; Dances/Social or cultural gatherings; Employees' musical group.
Description The facility is centrally located in Tucson, a short distance from the university hospital, convenient to all major hospitals and medical complexes. It is situated on a quiet street which provides the restful atmosphere best suited to residents of a nursing facility. Life in this family-owned nursing home is enhanced by daily interesting activities.

Bonnie Brae's*
5838 E Pima St, Tucson, AZ, 85712 (602) 296-7151
Admin Annie M Markel.
Licensure Skilled Care. *Beds* 122.
Ownership Proprietary.

Desert Life Health Care
1919 W Orange Grove, Tucson, AZ, 85704 (602) 297-8311
Admin Thomas M Henry. *Medical Dir/Dir of Nursing* John Pifre MD.
Licensure Skilled Care; Intermediate Care; Personal Care. *Beds* SNF 120; ICF; Personal Care 53. *Certified* Medicare.
Ownership Proprietary.
Admissions Requirements Medical examination; Physician's request.
Staff RNs 7 (ft), 7 (pt); LPNs 20 (ft), 9 (pt); Nurses aides 64 (ft), 15 (pt); Physical therapists 2 (ft); Recreational therapists 1 (ft); Occupational therapists 1 (ft); Speech therapists 1 (ft); Activities coordinators 2 (ft), 2 (pt); Dietitians 1 (ft); Social workers 1 (ft); COTA 1 (pt); Physical therapy aides.
Facilities Dining room; Physical therapy room; Activities room; Chapel; Crafts room; Barber/Beauty shop; Library; TV lounge; Private patios; Jacuzzi; Occupational therapy room.
Activities Arts and Crafts; Cards; Games; Reading groups; Prayer groups; Movies; Shopping trips; Dances/Social or cultural gatherings; Special Olympics; Resident council; Music therapy; Reality orientation.

Devon Gables Health Care Center*
6150 E Grant Rd, Tucson, AZ, 85712 (602) 296-6181
Admin Donald P Connelly Sr.
Licensure Skilled Care; Personal Care.
Beds SNF 254; Personal Care 58.
Ownership Proprietary.

Flower Square Personal Care Center
2502 N Dodge Blvd, Tucson, AZ, 85716 (602) 323-3200
Admin Reid E Halpern.
Licensure Intermediate Care; Personal Care.
Beds ICF 120; Personal Care 120.
Ownership Proprietary.
Admissions Requirements Medical examination.
Facilities Dining room; Activities room; Chapel; Crafts room; Laundry room; Barber/Beauty shop; Library.
Activities Arts and Crafts; Cards; Games; Reading groups; Prayer groups; Movies; Shopping trips; Dances/Social or cultural gatherings.

Forrester's Old Pueblo Casita
2001 N Park Ave, Tucson, AZ, 85719 (602) 624-8877
Admin Elizabeth Stapleton.
Licensure Skilled Care. *Beds* 80.
Ownership Proprietary.
Admissions Requirements Medical examination; Physician's request.
Staff RNs 5 (ft); LPNs 6 (ft), 3 (pt); Orderlies 3 (ft); Nurses aides 30 (ft), 7 (pt); Activities coordinators 1 (ft), 1 (pt).
Facilities Dining room; Barber/Beauty shop; Library.
Activities Arts and Crafts; Cards; Games; Reading groups; Prayer groups; Movies; Shopping trips; Dances/Social or cultural gatherings.
Description Facility prides itself on a reputation of excellence in care, individuality, and rehabilitation.

Handmaker Jewish Geriatric Center
2221 N Rosemont, Tucson, AZ, 85712 (602) 881-2323
Admin Richard S Lamden. *Medical Dir/Dir of Nursing* Dr Robert Hirsch.
Licensure Skilled Care. *Beds* 120. *Certified* Medicare.
Ownership Nonprofit.
Admissions Requirements Medical examination.
Staff Physicians 3 (pt); Orderlies 2 (ft); Physical therapists 1 (ft), 2 (pt); Occupational therapists 1 (ft), 1 (pt); Speech therapists 1 (pt); Activities coordinators 1 (ft); Dietitians 1 (pt); Dentists 1 (pt); Podiatrists 1 (pt); Audiologists 1 (pt).
Affiliation Jewish
Facilities Dining room; Physical therapy room; Activities room; Chapel; Crafts room; Laundry room; Barber/Beauty shop; Library; Playground.

Activities Arts and Crafts; Cards; Games; Reading groups; Prayer groups; Movies; Shopping trips; Dances/Social or cultural gatherings.

La Hacienda Nursing Home*
2950 N Dodge Blvd, Tucson, AZ, 85716 (602) 795-6504
Admin Mary E Wood.
Licensure Skilled Care. *Beds* 64.
Ownership Proprietary.

Leewood Nursing Home*
1020 N Woodland Ave, Tucson, AZ, 85711 (602) 327-6261
Admin Donald M Dalton.
Licensure Skilled Care. *Beds* 86.
Ownership Proprietary.

Posada Del Sol Health Care Facility*
2250 N Craycroft, Tucson, AZ, 85712 (602) 886-5481
Admin Paul Wayne Eaton.
Licensure Skilled Care. *Beds* 256. *Certified* Medicare.
Ownership Public.

Santa Rosa Convalescent Center*
1650 N Santa Rosa Blvd, Tucson, AZ, 85712 (602) 795-1610
Admin William J Mitchell.
Licensure Skilled Care. *Beds* 144. *Certified* Medicare.
Ownership Proprietary.

Su Casa Personal Care
720 W 41st St, Tucson, AZ, 85713 (602) 624-0784
Admin Donna Jaime. *Medical Dir/Dir of Nursing* Dr Mario Valdez.
Licensure Personal Care. *Beds* 17.
Ownership Proprietary.
Admissions Requirements Medical examination; Physician's request.
Staff Physicians 1 (pt); RNs 3 (pt); LPNs 2 (ft), 1 (pt); Nurses aides 2 (ft), 2 (pt); Activities coordinators 1 (pt); Dietitians 1 (pt).
Facilities Dining room; Activities room; Laundry room; Barber/Beauty shop.
Activities Arts and Crafts; Cards; Games; Reading groups; Prayer groups; Movies; Shopping trips; Dances/Social or cultural gatherings.
Description Physical layout lends itself to gardening and other outdoor activities; several residents grow vegetables and flowers. Facility is set up campus-style, is small in size, and maintains a home-like atmosphere.

Valley House Health Care
5545 E Lee, Tucson, AZ, 85712 (602) 296-2306
Admin Jeffrey A Shepard. *Medical Dir/Dir of Nursing* Dr James Belitsos.
Licensure Skilled Care. *Beds* 147. *Certified* Medicare.
Ownership Proprietary.
Admissions Requirements Medical examination; Physician's request.
Staff Physicians 3 (pt); RNs 9 (ft), 15 (pt); LPNs 8 (ft), 9 (pt); Orderlies 1 (ft); Nurses aides 47 (ft), 17 (pt); Physical therapists 1 (pt); Occupational therapists 1 (pt); Speech therapists 1 (pt); Activities coordinators 2 (ft), 1 (pt); Dietitians 1 (ft); Dentists 1 (pt); Podiatrists 1 (pt); Audiologists 1 (pt).

Facilities Dining room; Physical therapy room; Activities room; Chapel; Crafts room; Laundry room; Barber/Beauty shop; Library.
Activities Arts and Crafts; Cards; Games; Reading groups; Prayer groups; Movies; Dances/Social or cultural gatherings; Exercises; Bell ringing.
Description Valley House Healthcare is the difference between providing care and "caring."

Villa Campana
6651 E Carondelet Dr, Tucson, AZ, 85710
Admin Mark Tornga. *Medical Dir/Dir of Nursing* James Belitson.
Licensure Skilled Care. *Beds* 120. *Certified* Medicare.
Ownership Proprietary.
Admissions Requirements Minimum age 55 (apartments only).
Staff Physicians 3 (pt); RNs 14 (ft); LPNs 23 (ft); Orderlies 5 (ft); Nurses aides 40 (ft); Physical therapists 5 (ft); Recreational therapists 1 (ft); Occupational therapists 2 (ft); Speech therapists 1 (ft); Activities coordinators 3 (ft); Dietitians 1 (pt); Dentists 1 (pt); Podiatrists 1 (pt); Audiologists 1 (pt).
Facilities Dining room; Physical therapy room; Activities room; Chapel; Crafts room; Laundry room; Barber/Beauty shop; Library.
Activities Arts and Crafts; Cards; Games; Reading groups; Prayer groups; Movies; Shopping trips; Dances/Social or cultural gatherings.
Description Facility is located on the former site of the Belin Mansion, which still enhances the living and social areas for the residents. Food is provided by some of Arizona's finest chefs.

Villa Maria Geriatric Center*
4310 E Grant Rd, Tucson, AZ, 85712 (602) 323-9351
Admin Sr Theresa Zynda.
Licensure Skilled Care. *Beds* 93.
Ownership Nonprofit.
Affiliation Roman Catholic

WILLCOX

Northern Cochise Nursing Home*
901 W Rex Allen Dr, Willcox, AZ, 85643 (602) 384-3541
Admin Joseph Abrutz Jr.
Licensure Skilled Care. *Beds* 24.
Ownership Nonprofit.

WINSLOW

Winslow Convalescent Center*
116 E Hillview, Winslow, AZ, 86407 (602) 289-4678
Admin Lois Miles.
Licensure Skilled Care. *Beds* 38.
Ownership Proprietary.

YUMA

Desert Manor Convalescent
2222 Ave A, Yuma, AZ, 85264 (602) 783-8831
Admin Elaine Chappell.
Licensure Skilled Care. *Beds* 143.
Ownership Proprietary.
Admissions Requirements Minimum age 18; Medical examination; Physician's request.
Staff RNs 15 (ft); LPNs 10 (ft); Nurses aides 40 (ft); Physical therapists 1 (pt); Reality therapists 1 (pt); Occupational therapists 1 (pt); Speech therapists 1 (pt); Activities coordinators 1 (ft); Dietitians 1 (pt); Podiatrists 1 (pt).
Facilities Dining room; Activities room; Chapel; Crafts room; Laundry room; Barber/Beauty shop; Library.
Activities Arts and Crafts; Cards; Games; Reading groups; Prayer groups; Movies; Shopping trips; Dances/Social or cultural gatherings.
Description We have a pet dog and a fish aquarium. Facility is beautifully decorated; has a great staff; features excellent food; and is very clean. We're very proud of our nursing facility. We give excellent care. Our people seem to like us.

ARKANSAS

ALEXANDER

Alexander Human Development Center
PO Box 320, Alexander, AR, 72002 (501) 847-3506
Admin Michael McCreight.
Licensure Intermediate Care for Mentally Retarded. *Beds* 153. *Certified* Medicaid.
Admissions Requirements Minimum age 21.
Staff Physicians 1 (pt); RNs 3 (ft); LPNs 9 (ft); Physical therapists 1 (pt); Recreational therapists 2 (ft); Occupational therapists 1 (pt); Speech therapists 3 (ft); Dietitians 1 (ft); Dentists 1 (pt); Audiologists 1 (ft); Mental retardation aides 126 (ft).
Facilities Dining room; Physical therapy room; Activities room; Library.
Activities Arts and Crafts; Games; Prayer groups; Movies; Shopping trips; Dances/Social or cultural gatherings.
Description Admission criteria: Must be at least 21 and diagnosed as mentally retarded/developmentally disabled prior to reaching the age of 18.

ARKADELPHIA

Arkadelphia Human Developmental Center*
PO Box 70, Arkadelphia, AR, 71923 (501) 246-8011
Admin Russ Burbank.
Licensure Intermediate Care for Mentally Retarded. *Beds* 167. *Certified* Medicaid.

Riverwood Convalescent Home*
PO Box 278, 108 Caddo St, Arkadelphia, AR, 71923 (501) 246-5566
Admin Jeanna Bearden.
Licensure Intermediate Care. *Beds* 120. *Certified* Medicaid.

Twin Rivers Medical Center*
Box 98, 1420 Pine St, Arkadelphia, AR, 71923 (501) 246-9801
Admin D W Gathright.
Licensure Intermediate Care. *Beds* 42. *Certified* Medicaid.

ASH FLAT

Ash Flat Convalescent Home*
Box 5A, Star Rt, Ash Flat, AR, 72535 (501) 994-2341

Admin Jo Ann Spurlock.
Licensure Skilled Care. *Beds* 105. *Certified* Medicaid.

ASHDOWN

Little River Nursing Home
5th and Locke, PO Box 67, Ashdown, AR, 71822 (501) 898-5101
Admin Daniel A Sawyer.
Licensure Intermediate Care. *Beds* 76. *Certified* Medicaid.
Admissions Requirements Physician's request.
Staff RNs 1 (ft), 1 (pt); LPNs 6 (ft); Orderlies 27 (ft); Physical therapists 1 (ft); Recreational therapists 1 (ft).
Facilities Dining room; Physical therapy room; Activities room.
Activities Arts and Crafts; Games; Reading groups; Prayer groups; Shopping trips.

Pleasant Manor Nursing Home
750 S Locust St, Ashdown, AR, 71822 (501) 898-5001, 5002
Admin Linda Faye O'Neal. *Medical Dir/Dir of Nursing* Dr Wayne Reid.
Licensure Intermediate Care. *Beds* 53. *Certified* Medicaid.
Admissions Requirements Medical examination; Physician's request.
Staff Physicians 1 (ft), 4 (pt); RNs 1 (ft); LPNs 6 (ft); Nurses aides 15 (ft); Recreational therapists 1 (ft); Activities coordinators 1 (ft); Dietitians 1 (ft).
Facilities Dining room; Physical therapy room; Activities room; Chapel; Crafts room; Laundry room; Barber/Beauty shop; Library.
Activities Arts and Crafts; Cards; Games; Reading groups; Prayer groups; Shopping trips; Dances/Social or cultural gatherings.

BATESVILLE

Intermed of Batesville*
PO Box 2698, Hwy 25 North, Batesville, AR, 72501 (501) 698-1853
Admin Richard L Case.
Licensure Skilled Care. *Beds* 140. *Certified* Medicaid.

Wood-Lawn Inc*
2901 Neeley St, Batesville, AR, 72501 (501) 793-7195

Admin Joyce Skinner.
Licensure Skilled Care. *Beds* 121. *Certified* Medicaid.

BELLA VISTA

Concordia Care Center
7 Professional Dr, Bella Vista, AR, 72712 (501) 855-3736
Admin Bermah L Vaughan. *Medical Dir/Dir of Nursing* Albert E Martin MD.
Licensure Skilled Care. *Beds* 82. *Certified* Medicaid; Medicare.
Staff RNs 1 (ft), 2 (pt); LPNs 7 (ft), 2 (pt); Orderlies 1 (ft), 1 (pt); Nurses aides 27 (ft), 4 (pt); Activities coordinators 1 (ft).
Facilities Dining room; Chapel; Crafts room; Laundry room; Barber/Beauty shop; Library.
Activities Arts and Crafts; Cards; Games; Reading groups; Prayer groups; Movies; Shopping trips; Dances/Social or cultural gatherings.

BENTON

Benton Retirement Inn
809 Kenwood Rd, Benton, AR, 72015 (501) 778-7417 and 778-7418
Admin Dianna Ballard. *Medical Dir/Dir of Nursing* Dr Marvin Kirk.
Licensure Skilled Care. *Beds* 140. *Certified* Medicaid.
Admissions Requirements Medical examination; Physician's request.
Staff RNs 2 (ft); LPNs 9 (ft), 10 (pt); Orderlies 3 (ft), 1 (pt); Nurses aides 30 (ft), 5 (pt); Activities coordinators 1 (ft); Dietitians 1 (pt); Dentists 1 (pt); Podiatrists 1 (pt).
Facilities Dining room; Activities room; Crafts room; Laundry room; Barber/Beauty shop.
Activities Arts and Crafts; Cards; Games; Reading groups; Prayer groups; Movies; Shopping trips; Dances/Social or cultural gatherings.
Description There are bimonthly bus rides for residents and senior olympic events yearly. The home is nestled under beautiful pine trees with a large front porch for sitting in the sun.

Benton Services Center Nursing Home*
Services Center Branch, Benton, AR, 72015 (501) 778-1111
Admin Harley I Tollefson.
Licensure Intermediate Care. *Beds* 630. *Certified* Medicaid.

Colonial Nursing Home*
PO Box 208, Benton, AR, 72015 (501)
623-6811
Admin Martha Allene Bean.
Licensure Skilled Care; Intermediate Care.
Beds SNF 71; ICF 142. *Certified* Medicaid.

Rose Care Center of Benton*
3300 Military Rd, Benton, AR, 72015 (501)
778-8282
Admin Kaye Keeler.
Licensure Intermediate Care. *Beds* 103. *Certified* Medicaid.

BENTONVILLE

Bentonville Manor Nursing Home
224 S Main, Bentonville, AR, 72712 (501)
273-3373
Admin Gwenda K Lawrence.
Licensure Skilled Care. *Beds* 67. *Certified* Medicaid.
Admissions Requirements Minimum age 18;
Medical examination; Physician's request.
Staff Physicians 10 (pt); RNs 1 (ft), 1 (pt);
LPNs 3 (ft), 7 (pt); Nurses aides 20 (ft), 7 (pt);
Physical therapists 2 (pt); Reality therapists 1
(pt); Recreational therapists 1 (pt); Occupational therapists 1 (pt); Speech therapists 1 (pt);
Activities coordinators 1 (pt); Dietitians 1 (pt);
Dentists 1 (pt); Ophthalmologists 1 (pt);
Audiologists 1 (pt).
Facilities Dining room; Activities room; Crafts
room; Laundry room; Barber/Beauty shop;
Library.
Activities Arts and Crafts; Cards; Games;
Reading groups; Prayer groups; Movies; Shopping trips; Dances/Social or cultural gatherings.
Description Our facility has an enclosed courtyard which enables disoriented residents to go
outside more often, and we have taxicab service to transport residents to another medical
facility, paid by Medicaid, when an ambulance
isn't necessary.

BERRYVILLE

Leisure Lodge Inc*
Rt 3, Box 1, Simpson Ave, Berryville, AR,
72616 (501) 423-2656
Admin Sharon Englebricht.
Licensure Intermediate Care. *Beds* 52. *Certified* Medicaid.

BLYTHEVILLE

Geriatrics Nursing Centers Inc*
1400 N Division, Blytheville, AR, 72315 (501)
763-0240
Admin David Grady.
Licensure Skilled Care. *Beds* 105. *Certified* Medicaid.

Keith Acres Nursing Home*
PO Box 716, 112 Clinton, Blytheville, AR,
72315 (501) 763-9213
Admin Jean L Carmon.
Licensure Intermediate Care. *Beds* 44. *Certified* Medicaid.

Mississippi County Nursing Home*
PO Box 108, 1501 N 10th St, Blytheville, AR,
72315 (501) 762-3220
Admin Sandra Ray.
Licensure Intermediate Care. *Beds* 70. *Certified* Medicaid.

Parkview Manor Nursing Home*
PO Box 664, 710 N Ruddle Rd, Blytheville,
AR, 72315 (501) 763-3654
Admin Louise T Roberts.
Licensure Intermediate Care. *Beds* 46. *Certified* Medicaid.

BOONEVILLE

Booneville Human Development Center
Box 327, Booneville, AR, 72927 (501)
675-2121
Admin Louis Brown.
Licensure Intermediate Care for Mentally
Retarded. *Beds* 210. *Certified* Medicaid.
Admissions Requirements Minimum age 21;
Medical examination.
Staff Physicians 1 (ft); RNs 3 (ft); LPNs 9 (ft);
Nurses aides 112 (ft); Recreational therapists 5
(ft); Dentists 1 (pt).
Facilities Dining room; Activities room; Chapel; Crafts room; Laundry room; Barber/Beauty
shop.
Activities Arts and Crafts; Cards; Games;
Reading groups; Movies; Shopping trips; Dances/Social or cultural gatherings.
Description Facility is a ICF/MR serving
ambulatory adults who are developmentally
disabled.

Oak Manor Nursing Center*
Route 4, Box 170, Booneville, AR, 72927 (501)
675-3763
Admin Eileen P Macklin.
Licensure Skilled Care. *Beds* 101. *Certified* Medicaid.

BRINKLEY

Cla-Clif Home for the Aged*
PO Box 671, N Hwy 49, Brinkley, AR, 72021
(501) 734-3636
Admin C L Clay.
Licensure Intermediate Care. *Beds* 77. *Certified* Medicaid.

Saint Joseph's Home*
509 S New York, Brinkley, AR, 72021 (501)
734-1818
Admin Opal Cavaliere.
Licensure Intermediate Care. *Beds* 28. *Certified* Medicaid.

CABOT

Cabot Manor Nursing Home Inc
615 W Main St, Cabot, AR, 72023 (501)
843-6181
Admin Barbara Norris. *Medical Dir/Dir of
Nursing* Dr Jerry Chapman.
Licensure Intermediate Care. *Beds* 75. *Certified* Medicaid.
Admissions Requirements Physician's request.
Staff RNs 1 (ft); LPNs 4 (ft); Orderlies 1 (ft);

Nurses aides 23 (ft), 12 (pt); Physical therapists
1 (pt); Activities coordinators 1 (ft); Dietitians
1 (pt); Dentists 1 (pt); Ophthalmologists 1 (pt).
Facilities Dining room; Laundry room.
Activities Arts and Crafts; Cards; Games;
Reading groups; Prayer groups; Shopping trips;
Dances/Social or cultural gatherings.
Description Facility provides home away from
home with a loving staff in a community that
ministers not only spiritually, but also physically and socially.

Rollins Nursing Home
PO Box 27, 428 W Locust, Cabot, AR, 72023
(501) 843-6021
Admin Nancy K Rollins. *Medical Dir/Dir of
Nursing* Dr Jerry Chapman.
Licensure Intermediate Care. *Beds* 37. *Certified* Medicaid.
Staff RNs 1 (ft); LPNs 2 (ft), 1 (pt); Orderlies 1
(ft); Nurses aides 9 (ft); Activities coordinators
1 (ft); Dietitians 1 (pt).
Facilities Dining room; Laundry room.
Activities Arts and Crafts; Games; Reading
groups; Prayer groups; Shopping trips.
Description Facility has a 65-passenger bus that
is used to take the residents on fishing trips,
outings, to country-western concerts, and sightseeing trips.

CALICO ROCK

White River Convalescent Home Inc*
PO Box 408, Chessman Rd, Calico Rock, AR,
72519 (501) 297-3719
Admin Dean Hudson.
Licensure Skilled Care. *Beds* 91. *Certified* Medicaid.

CAMDEN

Leisure Lodge Inc*
515 Bruce St, Camden, AR, 71701 (501)
836-6831
Admin Jean B Carmean.
Licensure Intermediate Care. *Beds* 70. *Certified* Medicaid.

Leisure Lodge Inc*
900 Magnolia Rd, Camden, AR, 71701 (501)
836-6833
Admin Bettye Wallace.
Licensure Skilled Care. *Beds* 106. *Certified* Medicare.

Longmeadow Nursing Home*
Rt 1, Box 843, Camden, AR, 71701 (501)
836-9337
Admin Valeria Ketchum.
Licensure Intermediate Care. *Beds* 69. *Certified* Medicaid.

Ouachita Convalescent Center Inc
1411 Country Club Rd, Camden, AR, 71701
(501) 836-4111
Admin Annie Jo Young. *Medical Dir/Dir of
Nursing* James Guthrie.
Licensure Skilled Care. *Beds* 142.
Staff RNs 2 (ft); LPNs 8 (ft), 3 (pt); Nurses
aides 29 (ft), 4 (pt); Activities coordinators 1
(ft); Dietitians 1 (ft).

CARAWAY

Lane's Rest Home Inc*
PO Box 518, Caraway, AR, 72419 (501)
482-3711
Admin Flossie Lane.
Licensure Intermediate Care. *Beds* 40. *Certified* Medicaid.

CARLISLE

Chambers Nursing Home Inc*
Rt 1, Box 234, Hwy 81 South, Carlisle, AR,
72024 (501) 552-7811
Admin Hazel J Glover.
Licensure Intermediate Care. *Beds* 52. *Certified* Medicaid.

J W Comer Nursing Home
Rt 1, Box 231, Carlisle, AR, 72024 (501)
552-3350
Admin Helen Comer. *Medical Dir/Dir of Nursing* Dr B E Holmes.
Licensure Intermediate Care. *Beds* 22.
Admissions Requirements Males only; Medical examination; Physician's request.
Staff Physicians 1 (pt); RNs 1 (ft); LPNs 1 (pt); Nurses aides 5 (ft), 2 (pt); Dietitians 1 (pt).
Facilities Dining room; Laundry room.
Activities Arts and Crafts; Cards; Games; Reading groups; Prayer groups; Shopping trips.

Zimmerman Nursing Home
Rt 1, Box 14, Carlisle, AR, 72024 (501)
552-7449
Admin John Zimmerman. *Medical Dir/Dir of Nursing* Dr Fred C Inman.
Licensure Intermediate Care. *Beds* 41. *Certified* Medicaid.
Staff Physicians 3 (ft), 1 (pt); RNs 1 (ft); LPNs 2 (ft), 1 (pt); Orderlies 2 (ft); Nurses aides 10 (ft); Physical therapists 1 (pt); Activities coordinators 1 (ft); Dietitians 1 (ft).
Facilities Dining room; Laundry room; Barber/Beauty shop.
Activities Cards; Games; Reading groups; Prayer groups; Shopping trips.

CARTHAGE

Carthage Nursing Home
Hwy 48 W, PO Box 35, Carthage, AR, 71725
(501) 254-2222
Admin Morgan Treadwell. *Medical Dir/Dir of Nursing* John Delamore.
Licensure Intermediate Care. *Beds* 85. *Certified* Medicaid.
Staff Physicians 3 (pt); RNs 1 (ft); LPNs 3 (ft), 2 (pt); Nurses aides 42 (ft), 5 (pt); Recreational therapists 1 (ft); Activities coordinators 1 (ft); Dietitians 1 (ft); Dentists 1 (pt); Ophthalmologists 1 (pt).
Facilities Dining room; Activities room; Laundry room; Barber/Beauty shop.
Activities Cards; Games; Reading groups; Prayer groups; Shopping trips; Dances/Social or cultural gatherings.
Description Facility primarily cares for residents with mental problems.

CHARLESTON

Greenhurst Nursing Home*
Box 458, NW 2nd and Vine Sts, Charleston, AR, 72933 (501) 965-7373
Admin A R Schaffer III.
Licensure Skilled Care. *Beds* 73. *Certified* Medicaid.

CLARKSVILLE

Clarksville Convalescent Home Inc*
400 Oak St, Clarksville, AR, 72830 (501)
754-8611
Admin Ronnie F Johnson.
Licensure Intermediate Care. *Beds* 105. *Certified* Medicaid.

Mickel Nursing Home*
Box 250, Hwy 64 E, Clarksville, AR, 72830
(501) 754-2052
Admin Mary Ann Eichenberger.
Licensure Skilled Care; Intermediate Care for Mentally Retarded. *Beds* SNF 24; ICF/MR 53.
Certified Medicaid.

CLINTON

Van Buren County Memorial Nursing Home
Rt 1, Hwy 65 S, Box 206, Clinton, AR, 72031
(501) 745-4660
Admin Bobbie Archer. *Medical Dir/Dir of Nursing* John A Hall MD.
Licensure Skilled Care. *Beds* 70. *Certified* Medicare.
Staff Physicians 6 (ft); RNs 1 (ft), 2 (pt); LPNs 8 (ft); Nurses aides 23 (ft), 6 (pt); Physical therapists 1 (pt); Activities coordinators 1 (ft); Dietitians 1 (ft); Dentists 1 (pt); Podiatrists 1 (pt).
Facilities Dining room; Activities room; Laundry room; Barber/Beauty shop.
Activities Arts and Crafts; Cards; Games; Reading groups; Prayer groups; Movies; Dances/Social or cultural gatherings.
Description Our facility has an in-depth reality orientation program with training films and educational materials entitled "From Here to Reality." All staff members receive 6 hours training and families of all new residents are invited to participate.

COLLEGE STATION

Jean's Nursing Home*
PO Box 161, College Station, AR, 72053 (501)
490-1533
Admin Eunice Reed.
Licensure Skilled Care. *Beds* 105. *Certified* Medicaid.

CONWAY

Convalescent Center Inc
Salem Rd, PO Box 608, Conway, AR, 72032
(501) 327-4421
Admin Cecilia Norman. *Medical Dir/Dir of Nursing* Dr Bob Banister.
Licensure Intermediate Care. *Beds* 108. *Certified* Medicaid; Medicare.
Admissions Requirements Medical examina-
tion.
Staff Physicians 1 (pt); RNs 2 (ft), 2 (pt); LPNs 5 (ft), 1 (pt); Orderlies 1 (ft); Nurses aides 50 (ft), 5 (pt); Activities coordinators 1 (ft); Dietitians 1 (pt).
Facilities Dining room; Activities room; Chapel; Laundry room; Barber/Beauty shop.
Activities Arts and Crafts; Cards; Games; Reading groups; Prayer groups; Movies; Dances/Social or cultural gatherings.

Conway Human Development Center
Siebenmorgen Rd, Conway, AR, 72032 (501)
329-6851
Admin Bob Clark.
Licensure Intermediate Care for Mentally Retarded. *Beds* 656. *Certified* Medicaid.
Admissions Requirements Minimum age 6; Medical examination.
Staff Physicians 2 (ft), 2 (pt); RNs 17 (ft); LPNs 83 (ft); Nurses aides 628 (ft); Physical therapists 2 (ft), 2 (pt); Occupational therapists 6 (ft); Speech therapists 10 (ft); Activities coordinators 24 (ft); Dietitians 3 (ft); Dentists 1 (ft); Audiologists 1 (ft).
Facilities Dining room; Physical therapy room; Activities room; Chapel; Crafts room; Laundry room; Barber/Beauty shop; Library.
Activities Cards; Games; Reading groups; Movies; Shopping trips; Dances/Social or cultural gatherings.
Description The Conway Human Development Center is comprised of 5 developmental teams; each team consists of from 5 to 8 living units. Basically, teams are divided by functioning levels of the clients. All teams provide a battery of common services with special services available as dictated by the specific needs of individual clients.

Heritage Center
619 Center St, Conway, AR, 72032 (501)
327-7642
Admin Kaye Adams. *Medical Dir/Dir of Nursing* Dr Tom Beasley.
Licensure Intermediate Care. *Beds* 55. *Certified* Medicaid; Medicare.
Admissions Requirements Medical examination; Physician's request.
Staff Physicians 1 (pt); RNs 1 (ft); LPNs 3 (ft), 2 (pt); Nurses aides 14 (ft), 5 (pt); Recreational therapists 1 (ft); Dietitians 1 (ft).
Facilities Dining room; Activities room; Barber/Beauty shop.
Activities Arts and Crafts; Cards; Games; Prayer groups; Shopping trips; Dances/Social or cultural gatherings.
Description Heritage Center is an attractive concrete block structure nestled in beautiful azaleas and located in the heart of Conway. The interior of white, accented with blue and brown, provides a comfortable home where residents are cared for by an excellent staff and kept busy with activities and family visitation.

Johnson's Meadowlake Home Inc
PO Box 1203, Meadowlake Rd, Conway, AR,
72032 (501) 329-9879
Admin James Johnson.
Licensure Intermediate Care. *Beds* 70. *Certified* Medicaid.
Admissions Requirements Medical examination; Physician's request.

Staff RNs 1 (ft); LPNs 4 (ft), 2 (pt); Orderlies 1 (ft); Nurses aides 19 (ft), 1 (pt); Activities coordinators 1 (ft).
Facilities Dining room; Activities room; Laundry room; Barber/Beauty shop.
Activities Arts and Crafts; Cards; Games; Reading groups; Prayer groups; Shopping trips; Dances/Social or cultural gatherings; Outings.
Description Facility is located on a 6-acre site in the city of Conway, approximately 500 feet from main street in a safe, quiet setting.

CORNING

Corning Nursing Home
100 W 5th and Walnut, Corning, AR, 72422 (501) 857-3100
Admin Carolyn Veach.
Licensure Intermediate Care. *Beds* 117. *Certified* Medicaid; Medicare.

CROSSETT

Leisure Lodge Inc
Waterwell Rd, Rt 1, PO Box 400, Crossett, AR, 71635 (501) 364-5721
Admin Elaine Colvin. *Medical Dir/Dir of Nursing* Dr D L Toon.
Licensure Intermediate Care. *Beds* 79. *Certified* Medicaid; Medicare.
Admissions Requirements Physician's request.
Staff RNs 2 (ft); LPNs 6 (ft); Nurses aides 28 (ft); Activities coordinators 1 (ft); Dietitians 1 (ft).
Facilities Dining room; Activities room; Laundry room; Barber/Beauty shop.
Activities Arts and Crafts; Cards; Games; Reading groups; Prayer groups; Movies; Shopping trips; Dances/Social or cultural gatherings.
Description In the spring and early summer we go on weekly trips to the park and zoo. Once a month we have a pie or cookie baking day. On the second Tuesday in each month residents are invited to a luncheon at one of the local churches.

DANVILLE

Mitchell's Nursing Home Inc
W 10th St, Box 10, Danville, AR, 72833 (501) 495-2914
Admin Maurine Mitchell. *Medical Dir/Dir of Nursing* Dr Walter P Harris.
Licensure Intermediate Care. *Beds* 92. *Certified* Medicaid.
Admissions Requirements Minimum age 18.
Staff Physicians 7 (ft); RNs 2 (ft); LPNs 7 (ft); Orderlies 1 (ft); Nurses aides 30 (ft); Physical therapists 1 (pt); Reality therapists 1 (pt); Recreational therapists 1 (pt); Occupational therapists 1 (pt); Activities coordinators 1 (pt); Dietitians 1 (pt).
Facilities Dining room; Activities room; Crafts room; Laundry room; Barber/Beauty shop.
Activities Arts and Crafts; Cards; Games; Reading groups; Prayer groups; Movies; Shopping trips.
Description The home is located in the Ozark Mountains in the valley between Danville Mountain and Mount Magazine, a good location with good climate. There are apartments

for the adult group and a community center close by which furnishes the noon meal and is open 5 days each week.

DARDANELLE

Dardanelle Nursing Center Inc
510 W Green, Dardanelle, AR, 72834 (501) 229-4884
Admin Johanna J Rivers. *Medical Dir/Dir of Nursing* Dr Gene D Ring.
Licensure Skilled Care. *Beds* 90. *Certified* Medicare.
Staff RNs 1 (ft), 1 (pt); LPNs 8 (ft), 1 (pt); Orderlies 2 (ft); Nurses aides 22 (ft), 1 (pt); Activities coordinators 1 (ft).
Facilities Dining room; Laundry room; Barber/Beauty shop.
Activities Arts and Crafts; Cards; Games; Movies; Shopping trips; Dances/Social or cultural gatherings.

DEQUEEN

DeQueen Nursing Home*
PO Box 1040, 216 S 3rd St, DeQueen, AR, 71832 (501) 642-2531
Admin Nancy C Dossey.
Licensure Intermediate Care. *Beds* 35. *Certified* Medicaid.

Dickinson Nursing Home*
PO Box 1040, 302 N Fourth St, DeQueen, AR, 71832 (501) 642-3317
Admin Nancy Dossey.
Licensure Intermediate Care. *Beds* 70. *Certified* Medicaid.

Ridgeview Lodge Nursing Home*
PO Box 71, Hwy 70 W, DeQueen, AR, 71832 (501) 642-3562, 3564
Admin Lawanda Rich.
Licensure Intermediate Care. *Beds* 105. *Certified* Medicaid.

DES ARC

Des Arc Convalescent Center*
Box 143-B, Rt 2, Des Arc, AR, 72040 (501) 256-4194
Admin Sue Margrave.
Licensure Skilled Care. *Beds* 80. *Certified* Medicaid.

DEWITT

DeWitt City Nursing Home*
Box 428, DeWitt, AR, 72042 (501) 946-3574
Admin Vivian Meins.
Licensure Intermediate Care. *Beds* 54. *Certified* Medicaid.

Leisure Lodge Inc*
PO Box 589, Hwy 152A, DeWitt, AR, 72042 (501) 946-3569
Admin Jim Auld.
Licensure Intermediate Care. *Beds* 140. *Certified* Medicaid.

DUMAS

Dumas Nursing Center*
960 E Bowles, Dumas, AR, 71639 (501) 382-6100
Admin Betty Fisher.
Licensure Skilled Care. *Beds* 80. *Certified* Medicaid.

EL DORADO

East Manor Nusing Center
100 Hargett Dr, El Dorado, AR, 71730 (501) 862-6681 and 862-6682
Admin Pat McMahen. *Medical Dir/Dir of Nursing* Luis Merced.
Licensure Intermediate Care. *Beds* 84. *Certified* Medicaid.
Staff Physicians 1 (ft), 2 (pt); RNs 1 (ft), 1 (pt); LPNs 5 (ft), 1 (pt); Nurses aides 17 (ft), 3 (pt); Physical therapists 1 (pt); Activities coordinators 1 (ft); Dietitians 1 (ft), 1 (pt); Dentists 1 (ft); Ophthalmologists 1 (ft); Social worker 1 (ft).
Facilities Dining room; Activities room; Crafts room; Laundry room; Barber/Beauty shop.
Activities Arts and Crafts; Cards; Games; Reading groups; Prayer groups; Shopping trips; Dances/Social or cultural gatherings.
Description Our facility has mostly mentally retarded residents who require much patience and love. Our staff is really great with these residents, who are happy and feel as if this is a home rather than a nursing center.

Hillsboro Manor Nursing Home*
PO Box 728, 1700 Short E Hillsboro, El Dorado, AR, 71730 (501) 862-5124
Admin John Reynolds.
Licensure Skilled Care. *Beds* 72. *Certified* Medicaid.

Hudson Memorial Nursing Home
700 N College, PO Box 750, El Dorado, AR, 71730 (501) 863-8131
Admin Rev Melvin Nussbaum. *Medical Dir/Dir of Nursing* Dr George W Warren.
Licensure Skilled Care. *Beds* 108.
Admissions Requirements Medical examination; Physician's request.
Staff RNs 3 (ft); LPNs 8 (ft), 3 (pt); Orderlies 2 (ft); Nurses aides 37 (ft), 8 (pt); Activities coordinators 1 (ft).
Facilities Dining room; Physical therapy room; Activities room; Crafts room; Laundry room; Barber/Beauty shop.
Activities Arts and Crafts; Games; Reading groups; Movies.

Oak Ridge Nursing Home*
Griffin and Leon, El Dorado, AR, 71730 (501) 862-5511
Admin Kleve R Bassford.
Licensure Skilled Care. *Beds* 180. *Certified* Medicaid.

ENGLAND

Delta Nursing Home Inc
416 Rest Ave, England, AR, 72046 (501) 842-3101

Admin Evelyn Fadick. *Medical Dir/Dir of Nursing* Tommy Braswell MD.
Licensure Intermediate Care. *Beds* 76. *Certified* Medicaid.
Admissions Requirements Medical examination.
Staff Physicians 2 (pt); RNs 2 (ft); LPNs 3 (ft); Orderlies 3 (ft); Nurses aides 41 (ft); Physical therapists 1 (pt); Reality therapists 1 (pt); Recreational therapists 1 (ft); Occupational therapists 1 (pt); Activities coordinators 1 (pt); Dietitians 1 (pt); Dentists 1 (pt); Ophthalmologists 1 (pt).
Facilities Dining room; Physical therapy room; Activities room; Chapel; Laundry room; Barber/Beauty shop; Library.
Activities Arts and Crafts; Cards; Games; Reading groups; Prayer groups; Movies; Shopping trips; Dances/Social or cultural gatherings.
Description Facility is designed to take care of people, and staff does a good job of it.

England Manor Nursing Home Inc
516 NE 4th St, PO Box 302, England, AR, 72046 (501) 842-2771
Admin Pattie Sue Cox. *Medical Dir/Dir of Nursing* Dr Thomas Braswell.
Licensure Intermediate Care. *Beds* 63. *Certified* Medicaid.
Admissions Requirements Minimum age 18; Medical examination; Physician's request.
Staff Physicians 3 (pt); RNs 1 (ft); LPNs 2 (ft), 1 (pt); Nurses aides 22 (ft); Activities coordinators 1 (ft); Dietitians 1 (ft), 2 (pt); Dentists 1 (pt); Ophthalmologists 1 (pt); Podiatrists 1 (pt); Audiologists 1 (pt).
Facilities Dining room; Activities room; Crafts room; Barber/Beauty shop.
Activities Arts and Crafts; Cards; Games; Reading groups; Prayer groups; Movies; Shopping trips.

EUREKA SPRINGS

Eureka Springs Convalescent Center
Rt 1, PO Box 23, Eureka Springs, AR, 72632 (501) 253-7038
Admin Carolyn Krecker. *Medical Dir/Dir of Nursing* Dr Jess D Green.
Licensure Skilled Care. *Beds* 100. *Certified* Medicaid.
Admissions Requirements Medical examination; Physician's request.
Staff Physicians 8 (pt); RNs 1 (ft), 1 (pt); LPNs 9 (ft), 1 (pt); Nurses aides 18 (ft), 4 (pt); Physical therapists 2 (pt); Recreational therapists 1 (ft); Occupational therapists 1 (pt); Speech therapists 1 (pt); Activities coordinators 1 (ft); Dietitians 1 (ft); Dentists 1 (pt); Ophthalmologists 1 (pt); Audiologists 1 (pt).
Facilities Dining room; Activities room; Chapel; Laundry room; Barber/Beauty shop.
Activities Arts and Crafts; Cards; Games; Reading groups; Prayer groups; Movies; Shopping trips; Dances/Social or cultural gatherings.
Description Facility is beautifully located on a hilltop in the heart of the resort Ozarks; active community involvement, including foster grandparent program.

FAYETTEVILLE

Apple Tree Inn
3100 Old Missouri Rd, Fayetteville, AR, 72701 (501) 521-4353
Admin Ginger Bridges. *Medical Dir/Dir of Nursing* James Patrick.
Licensure Intermediate Care. *Beds* 140. *Certified* Medicaid.
Admissions Requirements Medical examination; Physician's request.
Staff RNs 4 (ft); LPNs 15 (ft); Orderlies 4 (ft); Nurses aides 45 (ft); Physical therapists; Speech therapists; Activities coordinators; Dentists; Podiatrists.
Facilities Dining room; Activities room; Laundry room; Barber/Beauty shop.
Activities Arts and Crafts; Cards; Games; Reading groups; Prayer groups; Shopping trips; Dances/Social or cultural gatherings.

Fayetteville City Hospital—Geriatrics*
221 S School Ave, Fayetteville, AR, 72701 (501) 442-5100
Admin Alan Prather.
Licensure Skilled Care. *Beds* 104. *Certified* Medicaid.

Sunrise Manor Care Center*
1001 Rochier St, Fayetteville, AR, 72701 (501) 443-5211
Admin Perry A Wilson.
Licensure Skilled Care. *Beds* 147. *Certified* Medicaid.

FORDYCE

Dallas County Nursing Home Inc*
201 Clifton, Fordyce, AR, 71742 (501) 352-3155
Admin Thomas B Little.
Licensure Skilled Care. *Beds* 34. *Certified* Medicaid.

Southern Nursing Home
Smith and Baxter, PO Box 472, Fordyce, AR, 71742 (501) 352-2104
Admin Janice Roark. *Medical Dir/Dir of Nursing* Don G Howard MD.
Licensure Skilled Care. *Beds* 75. *Certified* Medicaid; Medicare.
Staff Physicians 3 (pt); RNs 1 (ft), 1 (pt); LPNs 6 (ft), 5 (pt); Nurses aides 20 (ft), 4 (pt); Activities coordinators 1 (ft); Dietitians 5 (ft), 5 (pt).
Facilities Dining room; Laundry room; Barber/Beauty shop.
Activities Arts and Crafts; Games; Reading groups; Prayer groups; Shopping trips; Dances/Social or cultural gatherings.

FORREST CITY

Borden Nursing Home
215 Mississippi Ave, PO Box 545, Forrest City, AR, 72335 (501) 633-5163
Admin Helen B Jones.
Licensure Intermediate Care. *Beds* 33. *Certified* Medicaid.
Staff Physicians 1 (pt); RNs 1 (ft); LPNs 3 (ft); Nurses aides 9 (ft), 9 (pt); Activities coordinators 1 (ft); Dietitians 1 (ft); Dentists 1 (pt);

Cooks 4 (ft).
Facilities Dining room; Activities room; Laundry room.
Activities Arts and Crafts; Games; Reading groups; Prayer groups; Shopping trips.

Crestpark Retirement Inn
603 Kittel Rd, PO Box 1033, Forrest City, AR, 72335 (501) 633-7630
Admin Janice Heath. *Medical Dir/Dir of Nursing* H N Cogburn MD.
Licensure Skilled Care. *Beds* 88. *Certified* Medicaid.
Admissions Requirements Medical examination; Physician's request.
Staff Physicians 10 (pt); RNs 1 (ft), 1 (pt); LPNs 4 (ft), 2 (pt); Nurses aides 22 (ft), 1 (pt); Activities coordinators 1 (ft); Dietitians 1 (ft), 1 (pt); Dentists 4 (pt); Ophthalmologists 1 (pt).
Facilities Dining room; Activities room; Crafts room; Laundry room; Barber/Beauty shop.
Activities Arts and Crafts; Cards; Games; Reading groups; Prayer groups; Movies; Shopping trips.

Geriatrics Nursing Centers Inc*
PO Box 1801, Forrest City, AR, 72335 (501) 633-7500
Admin Gerald Kimbrough.
Licensure Skilled Care. *Beds* 70. *Certified* Medicaid.

FORT SMITH

Armour Heights Nursing Home Inc*
3900 Armour Ave, Fort Smith, AR, 72904 (501) 782-8956
Admin Pam Hendershot.
Licensure Skilled Care. *Beds* 75. *Certified* Medicaid.

Medi-Homes Inc
4623 Rogers Ave, Fort Smith, AR, 72901 (501) 452-1541
Admin Nancy Stein. *Medical Dir/Dir of Nursing* Dr Mort Wilson.
Licensure Skilled Care. *Beds* 157. *Certified* Medicaid.
Admissions Requirements Medical examination; Physician's request.
Staff RNs 3 (ft), 2 (pt); LPNs 12 (ft), 2 (pt); Orderlies 1 (ft); Nurses aides 43 (ft), 7 (pt); Activities coordinators 1 (ft), 1 (pt); Dietitians 1 (pt).
Facilities Dining room; Activities room; Chapel; Crafts room; Laundry room.
Activities Arts and Crafts; Cards; Games.
Description Facility is a small nursing home specializing in individualized home-type care in a home-type country setting.

Methodist Nursing Home Inc*
1915 S 74th St, Fort Smith, AR, 72903 (501) 452-1611
Admin Eston L Smith.
Licensure Skilled Care. *Beds* 88. *Certified* Medicaid.
Affiliation Methodist

Oaks Lodge Rest Home Inc*
3310 Waldron Rd, Fort Smith, AR, 72904 (501) 783-3101, 3102

Admin Becky Birch.
Licensure Intermediate Care. *Beds* 105. *Certified* Medicaid.

Parkview Nursing Home*
425 N 51st St, Fort Smith, AR, 72903 (501) 452-0530
Admin Marcia Webb.
Licensure Intermediate Care. *Beds* 41. *Certified* Medicaid.

Rose Care Center of Fort Smith*
5301 Wheeler Ave, Fort Smith, AR, 72901 (501) 646-3454
Admin Jim Milford.
Licensure Skilled Care. *Beds* 187. *Certified* Medicaid.

Sparks Manor*
2121 Towson, Fort Smith, AR, 72901 (501) 441-5050
Admin Rosemary Lovette.
Licensure Skilled Care. *Beds* 45.

GENEVIA

Jean's Nursing Home
PO Box 161, Genevia, AR, 72053 (501) 490-1533
Admin Eunice Reed. *Medical Dir/Dir of Nursing* M A Jackson MD.
Licensure Skilled Care. *Beds* 105. *Certified* Medicaid.
Admissions Requirements Minimum age 18; Medical examination; Physician's request.
Staff Physicians 3 (pt); RNs 2 (ft), 1 (pt); LPNs 5 (ft), 2 (pt); Orderlies 3 (pt); Nurses aides 21 (ft), 4 (pt); Physical therapists 1 (pt); Recreational therapists 1 (ft); Occupational therapists 1 (pt); Speech therapists 1 (pt); Activities coordinators 1 (ft); Dietitians 1 (pt); Dentists 1 (pt); Ophthalmologists 1 (pt); Audiologists 17 (ft), 8 (pt).
Facilities Dining room; Physical therapy room; Activities room; Chapel; Crafts room; Laundry room; Barber/Beauty shop.
Activities Arts and Crafts; Cards; Games; Reading groups; Prayer groups; Movies; Dances/Social or cultural gatherings.
Description Our facility offers a "home away from home" atmosphere; serves 3 hot home-cooked meals per day and evening and night snacks. A birthday party is held on the last Friday of each month honoring the residents born in that month. Residents go on outings to the zoo, on picnics to Burns Park, visit the airport and tour the airplanes. Outdoor activities are held within the nursing home. Television is available and the newspaper is read to those who cannot read.

GLENWOOD

Glenwood Nursing Home*
Box 1390, Glenwood, AR, 71943 (501) 356-3953
Admin Roger Tidwell.
Licensure Intermediate Care. *Beds* 70. *Certified* Medicaid.

GRAVETTE

Gravette Manor
409 Dallas St, PO Box Drawer F, Gravette, AR, 72736 (501) 787-5381
Admin Bobbi Wilks. *Medical Dir/Dir of Nursing* Dr Billy V Hall.
Licensure Intermediate Care. *Beds* 83. *Certified* Medicaid; Medicare.
Admissions Requirements Physician's request.
Staff LPNs 3 (ft), 2 (pt); Nurses aides 22 (ft), 5 (pt); Activities coordinators 2 (ft); Dietitians 1 (pt).
Facilities Dining room; Activities room; Crafts room; Laundry room; Barber/Beauty shop.
Activities Arts and Crafts; Cards; Games; Reading groups; Prayer groups; Shopping trips; Dances/Social or cultural gatherings.
Description Facility has a fenced outdoor area with patio.

GREENWOOD

Pink Bud Home for the Golden Years Inc
Hwy 71, PO Box 592, Greenwood, AR, 72936 (501) 996-4125
Admin Evelyn E Corbin. *Medical Dir/Dir of Nursing* Vincy Hannaman.
Licensure Intermediate Care. *Beds* 38. *Certified* Medicaid.
Admissions Requirements Medical examination.
Staff Physicians 4 (pt); RNs 1 (ft); LPNs 3 (ft), 1 (pt); Nurses aides 12 (ft), 2 (pt); Physical therapists 1 (pt); Activities coordinators 1 (ft); Dietitians 1 (pt).
Facilities Dining room; Physical therapy room; Activities room; Crafts room; Laundry room; Barber/Beauty shop; Lobby.
Activities Arts and Crafts; Games; Reading groups; Prayer groups; Dances/Social or cultural gatherings.
Description This 38-bed facility is in the process of adding 37 beds to have total occupancy of 60 with room for 75; enjoyable programs and a dedicated staff.

GURDON

Pineview Nursing Home*
904 Seahorn St, Gurdon, AR, 71743 (501) 353-2566
Admin Jesse Crow.
Licensure Intermediate Care. *Beds* 50. *Certified* Medicaid.

HAMBURG

Leisure Lodge Inc*
Rt 3, PO Box 300, Hamburg, AR, 71646 (501) 853-8204
Admin Myrtle Cason.
Licensure Skilled Care. *Beds* 105. *Certified* Medicaid.

HAMPTON

Hampton Nursing Home
Hwy 167 S, PO Box 538, Hampton, AR, 71744 (510) 798-4272

Admin Linda Stringfellow. *Medical Dir/Dir of Nursing* Tom L Dunn MD.
Licensure Skilled Care. *Beds* 74. *Certified* Medicaid; Medicare.
Staff Physicians 1 (pt); RNs 1 (ft), 1 (pt); LPNs 9 (ft); Nurses aides 17 (ft), 9 (pt); Physical therapists 1 (pt); Activities coordinators 1 (ft); Dietitians 2 (ft); Dentists 1 (pt); Optometrists 1 (ft); Social workers 1 (ft), 1 (pt).
Facilities Dining room; Activities room; Crafts room; Laundry room; Barber/Beauty shop; Day room.
Activities Arts and Crafts; Games; Reading groups; Prayer groups; Movies; Shopping trips; Dances/Social or cultural gatherings; Fishing trips; Picnics; Special outing each summer; Fund raisers.
Description Hampton Nursing Home has excellent physician and nursing participation far beyond the call of duty. Administrative staff is efficient and available for consultation with family/staff. Dietary serves pleasurable meals. Maintenance keeps home clean and odor-free. Social/activity department is outstanding.

HARRISON

Harrison Nursing Home
Orendorff Ave, Harrison, AR, 72601 (501) 741-3438
Admin David Lipford. *Medical Dir/Dir of Nursing* Dr R H (Bob) Langston.
Licensure Skilled Care. *Beds* 102. *Certified* Medicaid; Medicare.
Admissions Requirements Physician's request.
Staff Physicians 8 (pt); RNs 1 (ft), 1 (pt); LPNs 8 (ft), 2 (pt); Orderlies 4 (ft); Nurses aides 25 (ft), 2 (pt); Physical therapists 1 (pt); Activities coordinators 1 (ft); Dietitians 1 (ft); Dentists 1 (pt).
Facilities Dining room; Activities room; Chapel; Crafts room; Laundry room; Barber/Beauty shop.
Activities Arts and Crafts; Cards; Games; Reading groups; Prayer groups; Shopping trips; Dances/Social or cultural gatherings.
Description Facility is placed on a hill overlooking Harrison, which is in the heart of the Ozark Mountains; provides 4 different activities a day, with a bus ride every Friday. This is a skilled nursing facility and able to take care of most any patient in almost any condition.

Hillcrest Home
315 E Sherman, Harrison, AR, 72601 (501) 741-5001
Admin Frederick G Helmuth.
Licensure Intermediate Care. *Beds* 67. *Certified* Medicaid; Medicare.
Admissions Requirements Minimum age 18.
Staff RNs 3 (ft); LPNs 4 (ft), 1 (pt); Orderlies 5 (ft); Nurses aides 9 (ft); Activities coordinators 1 (ft).
Affiliation Mennonite
Facilities Dining room; Activities room; Chapel; Crafts room; Laundry room; Library.
Activities Arts and Crafts; Games; Reading groups; Movies; Shopping trips.

Hilltop Nursing Center*
202 Tims Ave, Harrison, AR, 72601 (501) 741-7667

Admin Florence Richards.
Licensure Intermediate Care. *Beds* 140. *Certified* Medicaid.

HEBER SPRINGS

Geriatrics Nursing Center Inc*
1040 Weddingford Rd, Heber Springs, AR, 72543 (501) 362-8137
Admin Nancy Sue Thompson.
Licensure Skilled Care. *Beds* 140. *Certified* Medicaid.

Lakeland Lodge Nursing Home
600 S 11th St, Heber Springs, AR, 72543 (501) 362-3185
Admin Claudia Hansbro. *Medical Dir/Dir of Nursing* Nathan Poff MD.
Licensure Skilled Care. *Beds* 102. *Certified* Medicaid.
Admissions Requirements Medical examination; Physician's request.
Staff RNs; LPNs; Nurses aides; Physical therapists; Occupational therapists; Speech therapists; Activities coordinators; Dietitians; Dentists; Podiatrists.
Facilities Dining room; Activities room; Crafts room; Laundry room; Barber/Beauty shop.
Activities Arts and Crafts; Cards; Games; Reading groups; Prayer groups; Movies; Shopping trips; Dances/Social or cultural gatherings.

HELENA

Crestpark of Helena*
PO Box 768, 116 November Dr, Helena, AR, 72342 (501) 338-9886
Admin Alan Curtis.
Licensure Skilled Care. *Beds* 111. *Certified* Medicaid.

Crestpark of Helena—Intermediate*
PO Box 310, Hospital Dr, Helena, AR, 72342 (501) 338-3405
Admin Robert Doherty.
Licensure Intermediate Care. *Beds* 75. *Certified* Medicaid.

HOPE

Heather Manor
706 E Greenwood, Hope, AR, 71801 (501) 777-4673
Admin Nora McRoy. *Medical Dir/Dir of Nursing* Dr J C Little.
Licensure Skilled Care. *Beds* 105. *Certified* Medicaid.
Admissions Requirements Medical examination; Physician's request.
Staff Physicians 7 (pt); RNs 2 (ft); LPNs 9 (pt); Nurses aides 40 (ft); Physical therapists 1 (pt); Reality therapists 1 (pt); Recreational therapists 1 (pt); Speech therapists 1 (pt); Activities coordinators 1 (pt); Dietitians 1 (ft); Dentists 1 (pt).
Facilities Dining room; Physical therapy room; Activities room; Chapel; Crafts room; Laundry room; Barber/Beauty shop.
Activities Arts and Crafts; Cards; Games; Reading groups; Prayer groups; Movies; Shopping trips.
Description We have built a new addition and

also have a large, bright day room area and a beautiful sun porch. We have an adopt-a-grandparent program, parties, church services, and cable television.

Parkview Skilled of Hope
426 S Main, Hope, AR, 71801 (501) 777-4638
Admin Calvin Remy.
Licensure Skilled Care. *Beds* 55. *Certified* Medicaid; Medicare.

Pinehope Nursing Home*
1900 S Walker, Hope, AR, 71801 (501) 777-8855
Admin Ray Woodard.
Licensure Intermediate Care. *Beds* 105. *Certified* Medicaid.

HOT SPRINGS

Arkansas Health Care Center Inc*
909 Golf Links Rd, Hot Springs, AR, 71901 (501) 624-7149
Admin Carolyn Jones.
Licensure Skilled Care. *Beds* 152. *Certified* Medicaid.

Garland Convalescent Center*
600 Carpenter Dam Rd, Hot Springs, AR, 71901 (501) 262-2571
Admin Deannie Marie Freeman.
Licensure Skilled Care. *Beds* 105. *Certified* Medicaid.

Hot Springs Nursing Home*
1401 Park Ave, Hot Springs, AR, 71901 (501) 623-3781, 624-0616
Admin John D Stanfill.
Licensure Intermediate Care. *Beds* 140. *Certified* Medicaid.

Lakewood Convalescent Home
Rt 17, PO Box 661, Hot Springs, AR, 71901 (501) 262-1920
Admin Dorothy Smith. *Medical Dir/Dir of Nursing* Dr Kenneth Seifert.
Licensure Intermediate Care. *Beds* 50. *Certified* Medicaid; Medicare.
Admissions Requirements Minimum age 65; Medical examination; Physician's request.
Staff Physicians 4 (pt); RNs 1 (ft), 1 (pt); LPNs 5 (ft), 1 (pt); Nurses aides 25 (ft); Physical therapists 1 (pt); Occupational therapists 1 (pt); Speech therapists 1 (pt); Activities coordinators 1 (ft); Dietitians 1 (pt); Dentists 1 (pt); Audiologists 1 (pt).
Facilities Dining room; Crafts room; Laundry room; Barber/Beauty shop.
Activities Arts and Crafts; Games; Reading groups; Prayer groups; Movies; Shopping trips; Dances/Social or cultural gatherings.
Description Stately fieldstone home is situated in the peaceful verdant countryside outside Hot Springs. Mammoth pine and oak trees frame the green gabled roofline and huge crepe myrtle line the graceful driveway up to Lakewood Home.

Nucare Convalescent Center*
1316 Park Ave, Hot Springs, AR, 71901 (501) 624-2516

Admin Shirley Blocker.
Licensure Skilled Care. *Beds* 100. *Certified* Medicaid.

Quality Care Nursing Center*
351 Woodfin St, Hot Springs, AR, 71901 (501) 624-7149
Admin Ronald Nield.
Licensure Skilled Care. *Beds* 113. *Certified* Medicaid.

HUNTSVILLE

Meadowview Lodge*
PO Box 248, Huntsville, AR, 72740 (501) 738-2021
Admin George W Johnson.
Licensure Skilled Care. *Beds* 70. *Certified* Medicaid.

JACKSONVILLE

Jacksonville Convalescent Manor*
1320 W Braden, Jacksonville, AR, 72076 (501) 982-0521
Admin Julius Budelis Jr.
Licensure Skilled Care; Intermediate Care. *Beds* SNF 105; ICF 140. *Certified* Medicaid.

Jacksonville Nursing Home*
1701 S Hwy 161, Jacksonville, AR, 72076 (501) 982-5141
Admin Doris A Beard.
Licensure Intermediate Care. *Beds* 58. *Certified* Medicaid.

JASPER

Newton County Nursing Home*
PO Box 442, Jasper, AR, 72641 (501) 446-2333
Admin Mickey Yancy.
Licensure Intermediate Care. *Beds* 42. *Certified* Medicaid.

JONESBORO

Craighead County Nursing Home
Rt 9, Hwy 1 S, Box 32, Jonesboro, AR, 72401 (501) 932-7677
Admin Nevin Beachy. *Medical Dir/Dir of Nursing* J F Thomas MD.
Licensure Intermediate Care. *Beds* 57. *Certified* Medicaid.
Admissions Requirements Minimum age 40; Medical examination; Physician's request.
Staff Physicians 1 (pt); RNs 1 (ft); LPNs 4 (ft), 1 (pt); Nurses aides 13 (ft); Activities coordinators 1 (ft).
Facilities Dining room; Physical therapy room; Activities room; Barber/Beauty shop.
Activities Arts and Crafts; Cards; Games; Reading groups; Prayer groups; Shopping trips.
Description The program is geared to the needs of the residents with emphasis on caring, and respecting the individual.

Geriatrics Nursing Centers Inc*
800 Southwest Dr, Jonesboro, AR, 72401 (501) 935-7550

Admin Darius Mitchell.
Licensure Skilled Care. *Beds* 103. *Certified* Medicaid.

Jonesboro Human Development Center
4701 Colony Dr, Jonesboro, AR, 72401 (501) 932-4043
Admin John Robinett. *Medical Dir/Dir of Nursing* Dr Robert Lawrence.
Licensure Intermediate Care for Mentally Retarded. *Beds* 128. *Certified* Medicaid.
Admissions Requirements Minimum age 6; Medical examination.
Facilities Dining room; Physical therapy room; Activities room; Chapel; Crafts room; Laundry room; Library.
Activities Arts and Crafts; Movies; Shopping trips; Dances/Social or cultural gatherings.
Description Center provides individualized habilitative programs primarily for the severe-/profound range of individuals with a primary handicap of mental retardation; serves the ambulatory and nonambulatory.

Rose Care Center of Jonesboro
Rt 2, PO Box 182, Jonesboro, AR, 72401 (501) 932-3271
Admin Janet A Walden. *Medical Dir/Dir of Nursing* Dr Forrest Wisdom.
Licensure Skilled Care. *Beds* 108. *Certified* Medicaid.
Admissions Requirements Medical examination; Physician's request.
Staff Physicians 1 (pt); RNs 2 (ft); LPNs 12 (ft); Nurses aides 24 (ft), 5 (pt); Physical therapists 1 (pt); Reality therapists 1 (pt); Speech therapists 1 (pt); Activities coordinators 1 (ft); Dietitians 1 (ft); Dentists 1 (pt); Ophthalmologists 1 (pt).
Facilities Dining room; Activities room; Crafts room; Laundry room; Barber/Beauty shop.
Activities Arts and Crafts; Cards; Games; Reading groups; Prayer groups; Movies; Shopping trips; Dances/Social or cultural gatherings.
Description Located on a wooded 5-acre lot, Rose Care provides skilled nursing care in a home-like atmosphere; emphasis is placed on a holistic approach to health care including a number of programs designed to improve the social/psychological well-being of the residents as well as the physical well-being.

Rose Skillcare Nursing Center
2911 Brown's Ln, Jonesboro, AR, 72401 (501) 935-8330
Admin Forrest Wisdom. *Medical Dir/Dir of Nursing* G D Wisdom MD.
Licensure Skilled Care. *Beds* 152. *Certified* Medicaid; Medicare.
Admissions Requirements Minimum age 21; Medical examination; Physician's request.
Staff Physicians 2 (pt); RNs 1 (ft), 2 (pt); LPNs 14 (ft); Nurses aides 38 (ft), 1 (pt); Speech therapists 1 (pt); Activities coordinators 1 (ft); Dietitians 1 (pt); Dentists 1 (pt).
Facilities Dining room; Physical therapy room; Laundry room; Barber/Beauty shop.
Activities Arts and Crafts; Cards; Games; Prayer groups; Shopping trips; Dances/Social or cultural gatherings.
Description Social worker and activity director compose a monthy newsletter highlighting special events and chit-chat about residents or employees. Our physical therapy aide works under direction of a licensed physical therapist and works exclusively in giving whirlpool baths and other rehabilitative therapy.

JUDSONIA

Oakdale Nursing Home*
PO Box Q, Hwy 67-367, Judsonia, AR, 72081 (501) 729-3823, 268-2288
Admin Mason Ann Wiggins.
Licensure Skilled Care. *Beds* 100. *Certified* Medicaid.

JUNCTION CITY

Junction City Nursing Home*
Rt 1, Box 2, 220 Maple St, Junction City, AR, 71749 (501) 924-4522
Admin Thalaia Dison.
Licensure Intermediate Care. *Beds* 84. *Certified* Medicaid.

LAKE VILLAGE

Leisure Lodge
Hwy 65 and 82 S, PO Box 672, Lake Village, AR, 71653 (501) 265-5337
Admin Dennis L Hudgens. *Medical Dir/Dir of Nursing* Danny Berry.
Licensure Intermediate Care. *Beds* 85. *Certified* Medicaid.
Staff Physicians 1 (ft); RNs 1 (ft); LPNs 8 (ft); Nurses aides 28 (ft); Activities coordinators 1 (ft); Dietitians 1 (ft); Dentists 1 (pt).
Facilities Dining room; Activities room; Laundry room; Barber/Beauty shop.
Activities Arts and Crafts; Games; Prayer groups; Movies; Shopping trips; Dances/Social or cultural gatherings.

LEXA

Tri-State Nursing Home
Rt 1, Box 139 C, Lexa, AR, 72355 (501) 295-5717
Admin Annie M Surgeon. *Medical Dir/Dir of Nursing* Duong Ly MD.
Licensure Intermediate Care. *Beds* 51. *Certified* Medicaid.
Staff Physicians; RNs; LPNs 2 (ft), 2 (pt); Orderlies 2 (ft); Nurses aides 8 (ft); Recreational therapists 1 (ft); Activities coordinators 1 (ft); Dietitians 1 (ft); Dentists 1 (pt); Ophthalmologists 1 (pt).
Facilities Dining room; Activities room; Chapel; Crafts room; Laundry room; Barber/Beauty shop.
Activities Arts and Crafts; Cards; Games; Reading groups; Prayer groups.

LITTLE ROCK

Arkansas Easter Seals Research Center
2801 Lee Ave, Little Rock, AR, 72205 (501) 663-8331
Admin Larry Stang.
Licensure Intermediate Care for Mentally Retarded. *Beds* 25. *Certified* Medicaid.

Admissions Requirements Minimum age 3.
Staff Physicians 2 (pt); RNs 1 (ft), 1 (pt); LPNs 2 (ft), 2 (pt); Nurses aides 8 (ft), 8 (pt); Physical therapists 3 (ft); Recreational therapists 1 (ft), 1 (pt); Occupational therapists 3 (ft); Speech therapists 3 (ft), 1 (pt); Dietitians 1 (pt).
Facilities Dining room; Physical therapy room; Activities room; Crafts room; Laundry room.
Activities Arts and Crafts; Games; Reading groups; Prayer groups; Movies; Shopping trips.
Description This comprehensive health care facility provides alternative communication, evaluation, and training for nonverbal children.

Arkansas Nursing Home Inc*
PO Box 4042, 4115 W 16th St, Little Rock, AR, 72204 (501) 664-3926
Admin Jude Brummett.
Licensure Skilled Care. *Beds* 194. *Certified* Medicaid.

Fountainbleau Nursing Home
10905 W Markham St, Little Rock, AR, 72205 (501) 225-6501
Admin Deborah McMenis. *Medical Dir/Dir of Nursing* Jerry D Malott MD.
Licensure Intermediate Care. *Beds* 70. *Certified* Medicaid.
Admissions Requirements Medical examination; Physician's request.
Staff RNs 1 (ft); LPNs 3 (ft), 3 (pt); Nurses aides 20 (ft), 5 (pt); Activities coordinators 1 (ft).
Facilities Dining room; Activities room; Laundry room; Barber/Beauty shop.
Activities Arts and Crafts; Games; Reading groups; Prayer groups.
Description Residents are consulted daily in order to learn their likes and dislikes in order to more fully serve them.

Hillhaven of Little Rock*
5720 W Markham, Little Rock, AR, 72205 (501) 664-6200
Admin Ina Ward.
Licensure Skilled Care. *Beds* 174. *Certified* Medicaid; Medicare.

Leisure Lodge
800 Brookside Dr, Little Rock, AR, 72205 (501) 224-3940, 3941
Admin Bryn Pevahouse. *Medical Dir/Dir of Nursing* Dr Michael Hendren.
Licensure Intermediate Care. *Beds* 143. *Certified* Medicaid.
Staff Physicians 1 (ft); RNs 2 (ft), 2 (pt); LPNs 20 (ft), 2 (pt); Nurses aides 55 (ft), 5 (pt); Physical therapists 1 (pt); Occupational therapists 1 (pt); Activities coordinators 1 (ft); Dietitians 1 (pt); Dentists 1 (pt); Ophthalmologists 1 (pt); Podiatrists 1 (pt); Audiologists 1 (pt); Social workers 1 (ft).
Facilities Dining room; Activities room; Crafts room; Laundry room; Barber/Beauty shop; Library; Courtyard.
Activities Arts and Crafts; Cards; Games; Reading groups; Prayer groups; Shopping trips; Dances/Social or cultural gatherings; Exercise classes; Outings.

Little Rock Nursing Center
1516 Cumberland St, Little Rock, AR, 72202 (501) 374-7565

Admin Larry Buffington. *Medical Dir/Dir of Nursing* Carla Anderson-Brakhop.
Licensure Skilled Care. *Beds* 204. *Certified* Medicare.
Staff Physicians 1 (ft); RNs 3 (ft), 1 (pt); LPNs 18 (ft), 3 (pt); Orderlies 1 (ft); Nurses aides 60 (ft); Physical therapists 1 (pt); Reality therapists 1 (ft); Recreational therapists 1 (ft); Occupational therapists 1 (pt); Speech therapists 1 (pt); Activities coordinators 1 (ft); Dietitians 1 (pt).
Facilities Dining room; Physical therapy room; Activities room; Laundry room; Barber/Beauty shop; Library.
Activities Arts and Crafts; Games; Reading groups; Prayer groups; Movies; Shopping trips; Dances/Social or cultural gatherings.
Description This is one of 5 teaching nursing facilities in the United States. The following disciplines now have rotations: medical, pharmacy, physical therapy, occupational therapy, dental hygiene, and graduate nursing.

Mize Road Nursing Home*
8500 Mize Rd, Little Rock, AR, 72209 (501) 562-2964
Admin Greg Robertson.
Licensure Skilled Care. *Beds* 150. *Certified* Medicaid.

Presbyterian Village
500 N Brookside Dr, Little Rock, AR, 72205 (501) 225-0114
Admin Nelson Reinhardt. *Medical Dir/Dir of Nursing* James Flack MD.
Licensure Skilled Care; Intermediate Care. *Beds* 78.
Admissions Requirements Medical examination; Physician's request.
Staff Physicians 1 (pt); RNs 5 (ft); LPNs 13 (ft); Orderlies 2 (ft); Nurses aides 45 (ft); Physical therapists 1 (ft); Reality therapists 1 (pt); Occupational therapists 1 (pt); Speech therapists 1 (pt); Dietitians 1 (ft); Dentists 1 (pt); Podiatrists 1 (pt).
Affiliation Presbyterian
Facilities Dining room; Physical therapy room; Activities room; Chapel; Crafts room; Laundry room; Barber/Beauty shop; Library.
Activities Arts and Crafts; Cards; Games; Reading groups; Prayer groups; Movies; Shopping trips; Dances/Social or cultural gatherings.

Riley's Oak Hill Manor South
8701 Riley Dr, Little Rock, AR, 72205 (501) 224-2700
Admin Grace Bond. *Medical Dir/Dir of Nursing* Dr Harold Hedges.
Licensure Skilled Care. *Beds* 224.
Admissions Requirements Medical examination; Physician's request.
Staff RNs 5 (ft); LPNs 13 (ft), 2 (pt); Nurses aides 42 (ft), 6 (pt); Physical therapists 1 (pt); Recreational therapists 2 (ft); Dietitians 2 (ft); Dentists 1 (pt); Podiatrists 1 (pt); 1 (pt).
Facilities Dining room; Physical therapy room; Activities room; Chapel; Crafts room; Laundry room; Barber/Beauty shop; Library.
Activities Arts and Crafts; Cards; Games; Reading groups; Movies; Shopping trips; Dances/Social or cultural gatherings.

Southwest Homes*
3915 Dixon Rd, Little Rock, AR, 72206 (501) 888-4257, 4258
Admin Gerald O Geddes.
Licensure Intermediate Care. *Beds* 125. *Certified* Medicaid.

Trinity Court Inc*
2000 Main St, Little Rock, AR, 72206 (501) 375-9062
Admin Dorothy C Setliffe.
Licensure Skilled Care. *Beds* 160. *Certified* Medicaid.

Williamsburg Retirement Inn*
6301 Lee Ave, Little Rock, AR, 72205 (501) 663-9461
Admin Mima Cazort.
Licensure Intermediate Care. *Beds* 101. *Certified* Medicaid.

LONOKE

Golden Years Manor*
PO Box 244, 1010 Barnes, Lonoke, AR, 72086 (501) 676-3103
Admin Margaret S Bolls.
Licensure Skilled Care. *Beds* 101. *Certified* Medicaid.

Lonoke Nursing Home Inc*
PO Box 276, E Academy St, Lonoke, AR, 72086 (501) 676-2785
Admin Pam Plafcan.
Licensure Intermediate Care. *Beds* 53. *Certified* Medicaid.

MAGNOLIA

Magnolia Manor
301 S Boundry St, Magnolia, AR, 71753 (501) 234-1361
Admin Dorthay Gay. *Medical Dir/Dir of Nursing* Rodney Griffin.
Licensure Skilled Care. *Beds* 113. *Certified* Medicaid; Medicare.
Staff RNs 2 (ft), 2 (pt); LPNs 8 (ft).
Facilities Dining room; Activities room; Chapel; Crafts room; Laundry room; Barber/Beauty shop; Library.
Activities Arts and Crafts; Cards; Games; Reading groups; Shopping trips; Dances/Social or cultural gatherings.

Meadowbrook Nursing Home*
600 Lelia St, Magnolia, AR, 71753 (501) 234-7000
Admin Sandy McCullough.
Licensure Intermediate Care. *Beds* 140. *Certified* Medicaid.

MALVERN

Longmeadow Nursing Home of Malvern
910 Section Line Rd, PO Box 567, Malvern, AR, 72104 (501) 332-6934
Admin Ruth Ross. *Medical Dir/Dir of Nursing* Dr N B Kersh.
Licensure Intermediate Care. *Beds* 69. *Certified* Medicaid.
Staff RNs 1 (ft); LPNs 2 (ft), 3 (pt); Nurses

aides 20 (ft), 2 (pt); Speech therapists 1 (pt); Activities coordinators 1 (ft); Dietitians 1 (pt).
Affiliation Baptist
Facilities Dining room; Activities room; Laundry room; Barber/Beauty shop.
Activities Arts and Crafts; Cards; Games; Reading groups; Prayer groups; Movies; Shopping trips; Dances/Social or cultural gatherings.
Description Staff works very closely with the Ouachita Regional Mental Health Center. Their psychiatrist and psychologist see some of the residents; others attend day treatment classes and are seen by the speech therapist.

Malvern Nursing Home
Rt 8, Box 176, Malvern, AR, 72104 (501) 337-9581
Admin Jayne Howard. *Medical Dir/Dir of Nursing* C F Peters MD.
Licensure Skilled Care. *Beds* 95. *Certified* Medicaid.
Staff Activities coordinators 1 (ft).
Facilities Dining room; Laundry room; Barber/Beauty shop.
Activities Arts and Crafts; Movies; Shopping trips.

Stillmeadow Care Center
Rt 2, Box 11, Hwy 67 South, Malvern, AR, 72104 (501) 332-5251
Admin David Lipford. *Medical Dir/Dir of Nursing* Dr C F Peters.
Licensure Skilled Care. *Beds* 104. *Certified* Medicaid; Medicare.
Admissions Requirements Physician's request.
Staff Physicians 10 (pt); RNs 2 (ft), 2 (pt); LPNs 5 (ft), 5 (pt); Nurses aides 41 (ft), 10 (pt); Physical therapists 1 (pt); Activities coordinators 1 (ft); Dietitians 1 (pt); Dentists 1 (pt).
Facilities Dining room; Physical therapy room; Activities room; Chapel; Crafts room; Laundry room; Barber/Beauty shop.
Activities Arts and Crafts; Games; Reading groups; Prayer groups; Movies; Shopping trips; Dances/Social or cultural gatherings.
Description Stillmeadow Care Center has the only organized volunteer auxiliary in Arkansas. The auxiliary is very active and provides activities for residents. VA approved.

MANILA

Manila Nursing Home
PO Box 429, Manila, AR, 72442 (501) 561-4492 and 561-4733
Admin Bernard Wellman. *Medical Dir/Dir of Nursing* Eugene Shaneyfelt.
Licensure Intermediate Care. *Beds* 53. *Certified* Medicaid.
Staff RNs 1 (ft), 1 (pt); LPNs 2 (ft), 3 (pt); Nurses aides 12 (ft); Activities coordinators 1 (ft); Dietitians 1 (ft), 1 (pt).
Facilities Dining room; Activities room; Laundry room.
Activities Arts and Crafts; Games; Prayer groups; Shopping trips.
Description Facility is located on Main Street in a small town. Patients can walk to town to the coffee shop or to the dollar store. Church buses transport patients to any of the churches in town.

MARIANNA

Crestpark of Marianna*
PO Box 386, Hwy 79 W, Marianna, AR, 72360
(501) 295-3466
Admin Barbara Brady.
Licensure Intermediate Care. *Beds* 90. *Certified* Medicaid.

MARKED TREE

Three Rivers Nursing Center*
PO Box 519, Hines Circle, Marked Tree, AR,
72365 (501) 358-2432
Admin Dorothy Abbott Castro.
Licensure Intermediate Care. *Beds* 112. *Certified* Medicaid.

MARSHALL

Marshall Nursing Center
Main St, PO Box 356, Marshall, AR, 72650
(501) 448-3151
Admin Burt Glenn.
Licensure Intermediate Care. *Beds* 77. *Certified* Medicaid.
Admissions Requirements Medical examination; Physician's request.
Staff Physicians 3 (ft); RNs 1 (ft); LPNs 5 (ft),
1 (pt); Orderlies 2 (ft), 1 (pt); Nurses aides 23
(ft), 3 (pt); Physical therapists 1 (pt); Reality
therapists 1 (ft); Recreational therapists 1 (ft);
Activities coordinators 1 (ft); Dietitians 1 (pt);
Dentists 2 (pt); Ophthalmologists 1 (pt).
Facilities Dining room; Activities room; Laundry room.
Activities Arts and Crafts; Games; Prayer
groups; Movies.

MARVELL

Cedar Lodge Nursing Home Inc
PO Box 928, McKinley and Willis Sts, Marvell,
AR, 72366 (501) 829-2361
Admin Viola Forrest. *Medical Dir/Dir of
Nursing* Robert Miller MD.
Licensure Intermediate Care. *Beds* 132. *Certified* Medicaid.
Admissions Requirements Medical examination.
Staff Physicians 1 (pt); RNs 1 (ft), 1 (pt); LPNs
6 (ft), 1 (pt); Orderlies 2 (ft), 1 (pt); Nurses aides
53 (ft), 5 (pt); Activities coordinators 1 (ft); Dietitians 1 (ft).
Facilities Dining room; Laundry room; Barber/Beauty shop.
Activities Cards; Games; Prayer groups;
Shopping trips; Dances/Social or cultural gatherings.

MCCRORY

Woodruff County Nursing Home
Hwy 64, PO Box 407, McCrory, AR, 72101
(501) 731-2543
Admin C L Cross. *Medical Dir/Dir of
Nursing* Fred Wilson MD.
Licensure Skilled Care. *Beds* 68. *Certified* Medicare.
Admissions Requirements Medical examina-
tion.
Staff RNs 2 (ft), 1 (pt); LPNs 3 (ft), 5 (pt);
Nurses aides 19 (ft), 3 (pt); Physical therapists 3
(ft); Speech therapists 1 (pt); Activities coordi-
nators 1 (ft); Dietitians 1 (ft); Dentists 2 (ft).
Facilities Dining room; Physical therapy room;
Activities room; Chapel; Crafts room; Laundry
room; Barber/Beauty shop.
Activities Arts and Crafts; Games; Prayer
groups; Movies; Dances/Social or cultural gatherings.

MCGEHEE

Leisure Lodge Inc*
PO Box 610, 700 Westwood Dr, McGehee, AR,
71654 (501) 222-5450
Admin Jean Myers.
Licensure Skilled Care. *Beds* 140. *Certified* Medicaid.

MELBOURNE

Pioneer Nursing Home*
PO Box 395, N Dixon, Melbourne, AR, 72556
(501) 368-4377
Admin Opal Irene Cook.
Licensure Intermediate Care. *Beds* 64. *Certified* Medicaid.

MENA

Leisure Lodge Inc
100 9th St, Mena, AR, 71953 (501) 394-2617
Admin David Barnard. *Medical Dir/Dir of
Nursing* Dr Lon Sessler.
Licensure Intermediate Care. *Beds* 69. *Certified* Medicaid.
Admissions Requirements Medical examina-
tion; Physician's request.
Staff RNs 1 (ft); Nurses aides 48 (ft); Physical
therapists 1 (ft); Activities coordinators 1 (ft);
Dietitians 1 (ft).
Facilities Dining room; Activities room; Laun-
dry room.
Activities Arts and Crafts; Cards; Games; Pray-
er groups; Dances/Social or cultural gatherings.
Description Facility is a small, well-run,
friendly home amid the Ouachita Mountains.

Rich Mountain Manor
504 Hornbeck, Mena, AR, 71953 (501)
394-3511
Admin Vesta Smith.
Licensure Skilled Care. *Beds* 105. *Certified* Medicare.
Admissions Requirements Medical examina-
tion; Physician's request.
Staff Physicians 1 (pt); RNs 1 (ft), 1 (pt); LPNs
8 (ft); Nurses aides 27 (ft); Activities coordinators 1 (ft); Dietitians 1 (pt); Dentists 1 (pt).
Facilities Dining room; Physical therapy room;
Chapel; Laundry room; Barber/Beauty shop.
Activities Arts and Crafts; Cards; Games; Prayer groups; Movies; Dances/Social or cultural
gatherings.

MONETTE

Lane's Nursing Home*
PO Box 469, Monette, AR, 72447 (501)
486-5419
Admin James Cliff Lane.
Licensure Skilled Care. *Beds* 86. *Certified* Medicaid.

MONTICELLO

Leisure Lodge Inc
N Chester, PO Box 576, Monticello, AR, 71655
(501) 367-6852 or 367-6853
Admin Kent McRae. *Medical Dir/Dir of
Nursing* Dr A T Llana.
Licensure Skilled Care. *Beds* 124. *Certified* Medicaid; Medicare.
Admissions Requirements Medical examina-
tion.
Staff Physicians 6 (pt); RNs 2 (ft), 3 (pt); LPNs
8 (ft), 6 (pt); Orderlies 2 (pt); Nurses aides 28
(ft), 3 (pt); Physical therapists 1 (pt); Speech
therapists 1 (pt); Activities coordinators 1 (ft);
Dietitians 1 (ft); Dentists 1 (pt); Social director
1 (ft).
Facilities Dining room; Physical therapy room;
Activities room; Crafts room; Laundry room;
Barber/Beauty shop; Library.
Activities Arts and Crafts; Games; Reading
groups; Prayer groups; Shopping trips; Dances-
/Social or cultural gatherings.
Description A newly formed auxiliary provides
more activities, one-on-one visitation, and bet-
ter community involvement.

MORRILTON

Morrilton Manor
1212 W Childress, PO Box 635, Morrilton, AR,
72110 (501) 354-4585
Admin Judy Havlik. *Medical Dir/Dir of
Nursing* T H Hickey.
Licensure Skilled Care. *Beds* 122. *Certified* Medicaid.
Admissions Requirements Medical examina-
tion.
Staff Physicians 8 (pt); RNs 2 (ft), 3 (pt); LPNs
10 (ft), 1 (pt); Nurses aides 45 (ft); Physical
therapists 1 (pt); Activities coordinators 2 (ft);
Dietitians 1 (ft).
Facilities Dining room; Barber/Beauty shop.
Activities Arts and Crafts; Games; Prayer
groups; Movies; Shopping trips.

Riverview Manor*
Rt 3, Bridge St, Morrilton, AR, 72110 (501)
354-4647
Admin Vickie Cannon.
Licensure Intermediate Care. *Beds* 53. *Certified* Medicaid.

MOUNT IDA

Montgomery Country Nursing Home
Ray St, PO Box 885, Mount Ida, AR, 71957
(501) 867-2156
Admin Audean Kennedy. *Medical Dir/Dir of
Nursing* James Davis MD.
Licensure Intermediate Care. *Beds* 56. *Certified* Medicaid.

Admissions Requirements Medical examination.
Staff Physicians 1 (ft); RNs 2 (ft); LPNs 6 (ft), 1 (pt); Nurses aides 26 (ft); Activities coordinators 1 (pt); Dietitians 1 (pt); Dentists 1 (pt).
Facilities Dining room; Activities room; Chapel; Crafts room; Laundry room; Barber/Beauty shop; Library.
Activities Arts and Crafts; Cards; Games; Reading groups; Prayer groups; Movies; Shopping trips; Dances/Social or cultural gatherings; Community gospel singing.
Description Our home is unique due to the fact it is in a small rural community. Our employees are related to many of the residents and the atmosphere is open, much like a large family.

MOUNTAIN HOME

Baxter Manor Nursing Home*
Hospital Dr, Hwy 5 North, Mountain Home, AR, 72653 (501) 425-6203
Admin William P Flippo.
Licensure Intermediate Care. *Beds* 72. *Certified* Medicaid.

Chastain's of Mountain Home
1100 Pine Tree Ln, Mountain Home, AR, 72653 (501) 425-6316
Admin Louis Helvenston. *Medical Dir/Dir of Nursing* Dr Cheney.
Licensure Skilled Care. *Beds* 105. *Certified* Medicaid; Medicare.
Staff Physicians 9 (pt); RNs 3 (ft); LPNs 7 (ft); Nurses aides 27 (ft); Ophthalmologists 1 (pt); Podiatrists 1 (pt); Audiologists 1 (pt).
Facilities Dining room; Physical therapy room; Activities room; Chapel; Crafts room; Laundry room; Barber/Beauty shop; Library.
Activities Arts and Crafts; Cards; Games; Reading groups; Prayer groups; Movies; Shopping trips; Dances/Social or cultural gatherings; Fishing; Picnics.
Description VA approved.

Good Samaritan Nursing Home
3031 Turnage Dr, Mountain Home, AR, 72653 (501) 425-2494
Admin Arthur Rosenkotter.
Licensure Intermediate Care. *Beds* 70. *Certified* Medicaid; Medicare.

Leisure Lodge of Mountain Home*
PO Box 325, Mountain Home, AR, 72653 (501) 425-6931
Admin Gaylon Gammill.
Licensure Intermediate Care. *Beds* 86. *Certified* Medicaid.

MOUNTAIN VIEW

Compton's Oak Grove Lodge*
PO Box 526, Mountain View, AR, 72560 (501) 269-3239
Admin Wayne Moore.
Licensure Skilled Care. *Beds* 86. *Certified* Medicaid.

MURFREESBORO

Idlehour Nursing Center*
PO Box 666, 110 W 13th St, Murfreesboro, AR, 71958 (501) 285-2186
Admin Jean Reeder.
Licensure Intermediate Care. *Beds* 75. *Certified* Medicaid.

NASHVILLE

Benson's Nursing Home
1315 Hutchinson St, Nashville, AR, 71852 (501) 845-4933
Admin Willie Benson Jr. *Medical Dir/Dir of Nursing* Dr M H Wilmoth.
Licensure Intermediate Care. *Beds* 117. *Certified* Medicaid; Medicare.
Admissions Requirements Physician's request.
Staff Physicians 1 (ft), 6 (pt); RNs 1 (ft), 1 (pt); LPNs 2 (ft), 2 (pt); Nurses aides 15 (ft), 9 (pt); Physical therapists 1 (pt); Activities coordinators 1 (ft), 1 (pt); Dietitians 2 (ft); Dentists 3 (pt); Podiatrists 1 (pt).
Facilities Dining room; Activities room; Crafts room; Laundry room; Barber/Beauty shop; Church annex.
Activities Arts and Crafts; Cards; Games; Reading groups; Prayer groups; Movies; Shopping trips; Dances/Social or cultural gatherings.
Description Facility provides a live-at-home environment with courteous staff members for its residents, organized to effectively and efficiently meet the varying needs of its residents for health care and maintenance services, personnel care, and other services.

Colonial Nursing Home
311 W Henderson, Nashville, AR, 71852 (501) 845-4128
Admin Vickey Keeney. *Medical Dir/Dir of Nursing* Mary Ann Power RN.
Licensure Intermediate Care. *Beds* 50. *Certified* Medicaid; Medicare.
Staff RNs 1 (ft); LPNs 3 (ft); Nurses aides 10 (ft); Recreational therapists 1 (ft); Activities coordinators 1 (ft); Dietitians 2 (ft), 3 (pt).
Facilities Dining room; Laundry room; Barber/Beauty shop.
Activities Arts and Crafts; Cards; Games; Reading groups; Prayer groups; Movies; Shopping trips.
Description Facility features mostly private rooms, good, home cooking, and an experienced staff.

Guest House of Nashville*
PO Box 1680, Nashville, AR, 71852 (501) 845-3881
Admin Willa Jean Owens.
Licensure Skilled Care. *Beds* 70. *Certified* Medicaid.

Leisure Lodge Inc
PO Box 812, Nashville, AR, 71852 (501) 845-2021
Admin Beverly Starr. *Medical Dir/Dir of Nursing* Dr Joe King.
Licensure Intermediate Care. *Beds* 78. *Certified* Medicaid; Medicare.
Staff Physicians 6 (pt); RNs 3 (pt); LPNs 8 (pt); Nurses aides 28 (ft); Activities coordinators 1 (ft); Dietitians 1 (ft).
Facilities Dining room; Activities room; Chapel; Laundry room; Barber/Beauty shop.
Activities Arts and Crafts; Cards; Games; Reading groups; Prayer groups; Movies; Shopping trips; Dances/Social or cultural gatherings.

Nashville Nursing Home
810 N 8th, Nashville, AR, 71852 (501) 845-1616
Admin Frances Joan McCrary.
Licensure Intermediate Care. *Beds* 50. *Certified* Medicaid; Medicare.
Staff RNs 1 (ft); LPNs 4 (ft), 1 (pt); Nurses aides 12 (ft), 4 (pt); Activities coordinators 1 (ft); Dietitians 1 (pt).
Facilities Dining room; Activities room; Laundry room; Barber/Beauty shop.
Activities Arts and Crafts; Games; Reading groups; Movies; Shopping trips.
Description Our nursing home is a privately owned, modern health care facility providing a home for the sick and elderly with emphasis on serving their physical, emotional, and spiritual needs.

NEWPORT

Newport Healthcare Center Inc*
PO Drawer J, Newport, AR, 72112 (501) 523-6539
Admin Roger Snow.
Licensure Intermediate Care. *Beds* 105. *Certified* Medicaid.

Pinedale Nursing Home
1311 N Pecan St, Newport, AR, 72112 (501) 523-5881
Admin Marion Huckebey. *Medical Dir/Dir of Nursing* Guilford Dudley.
Licensure Skilled Care. *Beds* 103. *Certified* Medicaid; Medicare.
Admissions Requirements Medical examination; Physician's request.
Staff Physicians 1 (pt); RNs 1 (ft), 2 (pt); LPNs 9 (ft), 1 (pt); Orderlies 11 (ft), 4 (pt); Nurses aides 30 (ft), 8 (pt); Physical therapists 1 (pt); Recreational therapists 2 (ft); Activities coordinators 2 (ft); Dietitians 1 (pt); Dentists 1 (pt).
Facilities Dining room; Physical therapy room; Activities room; Laundry room; Barber/Beauty shop; Library.
Activities Arts and Crafts; Cards; Games; Reading groups; Prayer groups; Movies; Shopping trips; Dances/Social or cultural gatherings.

NORTH LITTLE ROCK

Mercy Nursing Home Inc
6401 E 47th St, North Little Rock, AR, 72117 (501) 945-2356
Admin Geraldine Robinson. *Medical Dir/Dir of Nursing* Dr W J Elders.
Licensure Intermediate Care. *Beds* 85. *Certified* Medicaid.
Staff Physicians 2 (pt); RNs 1 (ft); LPNs 4 (ft); Orderlies 5 (ft); Nurses aides 30 (ft); Physical therapists 1 (pt); Occupational therapists 1 (pt); Activities coordinators 1 (pt); Dietitians 1 (pt); Dentists 1 (pt).
Facilities Dining room; Physical therapy room;

Activities room; Chapel; Laundry room; Barber/Beauty shop.
Activities Games; Prayer groups.

Riley's Oak Hill Manor Inc*
2501 John Ashley Dr, North Little Rock, AR, 72114 (501) 758-3800
Admin James C Huskins.
Licensure Skilled Care. *Beds* 224. *Certified* Medicaid.

OLA

Yell County Nursing Home Inc*
PO Box 38, Hwy 10, Ola, AR, 72853 (501) 489-5237
Admin Barbara McCoy.
Licensure Intermediate Care. *Beds* 74. *Certified* Medicaid.

OSCEOLA

Osceola Nursing Home*
PO Box 545, Osceola, AR, 72370 (501) 563-3201
Admin Debra Thomas.
Licensure Skilled Care. *Beds* 96. *Certified* Medicaid.

OZARK

Ozark Nursing Home*
600 N 12th St, Ozark, AR, 72949 (501) 667-4791
Admin Gus J Schaffer.
Licensure Intermediate Care. *Beds* 118. *Certified* Medicaid.

PARAGOULD

Greene Acres Nursing Home
Rt 3, PO Box 805, Paragould, AR, 72450 (501) 236-3633
Admin Larry McFadden. *Medical Dir/Dir of Nursing* Asa Crow MD.
Licensure Intermediate Care. *Beds* 70. *Certified* Medicaid.
Ownership Nonprofit.
Admissions Requirements Physician's request.
Staff Physicians 14 (pt); RNs 1 (ft); LPNs 7 (ft), 5 (pt); Nurses aides 17 (ft), 6 (pt); Activities coordinators 1 (ft); Dietitians 1 (pt).
Facilities Dining room; Laundry room; Barber/Beauty shop.
Activities Arts and Crafts; Games; Reading groups; Dances/Social or cultural gatherings.
Description Facility is a nonprofit institution operated by an association of 15 civic and service organizations.

Home for the Golden Years Inc
Hwy 49 S, PO Box 218, Paragould, AR, 72450 (501) 236-7104
Admin Diana Goodman. *Medical Dir/Dir of Nursing* Dr Bennie Mitchell.
Licensure Skilled Care. *Beds* 180. *Certified* Medicaid; Medicare.
Admissions Requirements Medical examination.
Staff Physicians; RNs 2 (ft), 1 (pt); LPNs 14

(ft), 8 (pt); Nurses aides 39 (ft), 3 (pt); Activities coordinators 2 (ft); Dietitians 13 (ft), 1 (pt); Dentists.

PARIS

Logan County Nursing Home*
PO Box 431, Paris, AR, 72855 (501) 963-3186
Admin Ann Yarborough.
Licensure Intermediate Care. *Beds* 31. *Certified* Medicaid.

Paris Retirement Inn*
513 N Roseville, Paris, AR, 72855 (501) 963-3096
Admin Shirley Sorey.
Licensure Intermediate Care. *Beds* 72. *Certified* Medicaid.

PERRYVILLE

Perry County Nursing Center
PO Box 270, Perryville, AR, 72126 (501) 889-2499
Admin Michael Morton. *Medical Dir/Dir of Nursing* Dr Ben Hyatt.
Licensure Intermediate Care. *Beds* 65. *Certified* Medicaid.
Staff Physicians 1 (ft), 2 (pt); RNs 1 (ft), 2 (pt); LPNs 4 (ft), 3 (pt); Nurses aides 30 (ft), 8 (pt); Activities coordinators 1 (ft); Dietitians 1 (ft); Dentists 1 (ft).
Facilities Dining room; Physical therapy room; Laundry room; Barber/Beauty shop.
Activities Arts and Crafts; Cards; Games; Reading groups; Prayer groups; Movies; Shopping trips; Dances/Social or cultural gatherings.

PIGGOTT

Home for the Golden Years
450 S 9th St, PO Box 388, Piggott, AR, 72454 (501) 598-2291
Admin Gaye Wiley. *Medical Dir/Dir of Nursing* Jerry L Muse MD.
Licensure Skilled Care. *Beds* 105. *Certified* Medicaid.
Admissions Requirements Medical examination; Physician's request.
Staff Physicians 1 (pt); RNs 1 (ft), 3 (pt); LPNs 7 (ft), 2 (pt); Nurses aides 22 (ft), 2 (pt); Physical therapists 1 (pt); Activities coordinators 1 (ft); Dietitians 1 (pt).
Facilities Dining room; Physical therapy room; Activities room; Crafts room; Laundry room; Barber/Beauty shop.
Activities Arts and Crafts; Cards; Games; Reading groups; Prayer groups; Movies; Shopping trips; Dances/Social or cultural gatherings.
Description Facility features a beautiful, friendly small-town atmosphere (3800 population) and is located in northeast Arkansas on Crowley's Ridge. Residents enjoy 4 seasons, mild winters. Local hospital, 3 physicans service residents; outstanding activity programs.

PINE BLUFF

Davis Skilled Nursing Facility*
1111 W 12th St, Pine Bluff, AR, 71601 (501) 535-6800
Admin Robert L Dolan.
Licensure Skilled Care. *Beds* 100. *Certified* Medicaid.

Jefferson Convalescent Home Inc
3400 W 7th, PO Box 7223, Pine Bluff, AR, 71601 (501) 534-5681
Admin Margaret Moran.
Licensure Intermediate Care. *Beds* 50. *Certified* Medicaid.
Admissions Requirements Medical examination; Physician's request.
Staff RNs 1 (ft); LPNs 5 (ft), 1 (pt); Nurses aides 14 (ft), 2 (pt); Activities coordinators 1 (ft); Dietitians 1 (ft), 1 (pt).
Facilities Dining room; Activities room; Laundry room.
Activities Arts and Crafts; Games; Reading groups; Prayer groups; Movies.
Description Facility features monthly birthday parties, one of the best activities programs, and the best in nursing service. A very loving home for both staff and patients.

Loma Linda Rest Home Inc*
PO Box 1329, 1501 Bay St, Pine Bluff, AR, 71601 (501) 535-8878
Admin Carolyn Compton.
Licensure Intermediate Care. *Beds* 205. *Certified* Medicaid.

Oak Park Nursing Home
PO Box 8270, 2610 W 36th, Pine Bluff, AR, 71601 (501) 536-2972
Admin Jimmie Henson. *Medical Dir/Dir of Nursing* Shafgat Hussain.
Licensure Intermediate Care. *Beds* 67. *Certified* Medicaid.
Admissions Requirements Physician's request.
Staff RNs 1 (ft); LPNs 4 (ft); Nurses aides 12 (ft), 2 (pt); Activities coordinators 1 (ft).
Facilities Dining room; Activities room; Laundry room; Barber/Beauty shop.
Activities Arts and Crafts; Cards; Games; Reading groups; Prayer groups; Movies; Shopping trips; Dances/Social or cultural gatherings.

Pine Bluff Nursing Home
3701 S Main, PO Box 1310, Pine Bluff, AR, 71601 (501) 534-6614
Admin Stanley A Townsend. *Medical Dir/Dir of Nursing* Dr Ross Maynard.
Licensure Skilled Care. *Beds* 245. *Certified* Medicaid.
Staff Physicians 1 (pt); RNs 7 (ft); LPNs 25 (ft); Nurses aides 45 (ft); Physical therapists 1 (pt); Speech therapists 1 (pt); Activities coordinators 1 (ft); Dietitians 1 (pt); Dentists 1 (pt).
Facilities Dining room; Activities room; Laundry room; Barber/Beauty shop.
Activities Arts and Crafts; Games; Prayer groups; Movies; Shopping trips.

POCAHONTAS

Randolph County Nursing Home*
PO Box 331, 1405 Hospital Dr, Pocahontas, AR, 72455 (501) 892-5214
Admin Dickie C Smith.
Licensure Skilled Care. *Beds* 80. *Certified* Medicaid.

PRESCOTT

Hillcrest Nursing Home
1421 W 2nd St North, Prescott, AR, 71857 (501) 887-3811
Admin Margie Pickett.
Licensure Intermediate Care. *Beds* 70. *Certified* Medicaid.
Staff Physicians 1 (ft), 3 (pt); RNs 1 (ft); LPNs 8 (pt); Nurses aides 30 (pt); Activities coordinators 1 (ft).
Facilities Dining room; Activities room; Crafts room; Laundry room; Barber/Beauty shop.
Activities Arts and Crafts; Cards; Games; Reading groups; Prayer groups; Movies; Shopping trips; Dances/Social or cultural gatherings.

Prescott Nursing Center*
Rt 6, Box 227, Prescott, AR, 71857 (501) 887-3731
Admin Vealetta Kellebrew.
Licensure Skilled Care. *Beds* 111. *Certified* Medicaid.

RISON

Cleveland County Nursing Home*
PO Box 365, 501 E Magnolia, Rison, AR, 71665 (501) 325-6202, 6255
Admin Kay Osbourne.
Licensure Skilled Care. *Beds* 67. *Certified* Medicaid.

ROGERS

Heritage Park Nursing Home
1513 S Dixieland Rd, Rogers, AR, 72756 (501) 636-5841
Admin Alberta J Rogers. *Medical Dir/Dir of Nursing* Dr Jennings.
Licensure Skilled Care. *Beds* 140. *Certified* Medicaid.
Staff RNs 4 (ft), 2 (pt); LPNs 8 (ft), 1 (pt); Nurses aides 26 (ft), 3 (pt); Physical therapists 1 (pt); Recreational therapists 1 (ft); Speech therapists 1 (ft); Activities coordinators 1 (ft); Dietitians 1 (ft); Dentists 1 (pt).
Facilities Dining room; Activities room; Crafts room; Laundry room; Barber/Beauty shop; Library.
Activities Arts and Crafts; Cards; Games; Reading groups; Prayer groups; Movies; Shopping trips; Dances/Social or cultural gatherings.
Description The facility features a residents' rhythm band, monthly birthday parties, a wide variety of activities geared to patients in bed as well as ambulatory residents, and a whirlpool bath.

Medi-Home of Rogers
1603 W Walnut, Rogers, AR, 72756 (501) 636-9334

Admin Linda Neely. *Medical Dir/Dir of Nursing* Dr Robert Hall.
Licensure Intermediate Care. *Beds* 70. *Certified* Medicaid.
Admissions Requirements Medical examination; Physician's request.
Staff RNs 1 (ft); LPNs 3 (ft); Orderlies 3 (ft); Nurses aides 18 (ft); Activities coordinators 1 (ft); Dietitians 1 (ft).
Facilities Dining room; Activities room; Laundry room; Barber/Beauty shop.
Activities Arts and Crafts; Cards; Games; Prayer groups; Movies; Shopping trips; Dances/Social or cultural gatherings.

Rogers Nursing Center*
1151 W New Hope Rd, Rogers, AR, 72756 (501) 636-6290
Admin Alan Kilgore.
Licensure Skilled Care. *Beds* 140. *Certified* Medicaid.

RUSSELLVILLE

Legacy Lodge Nursing Home
900 W 12th St, Russellville, AR, 72801 (501) 968-5858
Admin Erby E Rowell. *Medical Dir/Dir of Nursing* Howard Kimball MD.
Licensure Skilled Care. *Beds* 122. *Certified* Medicaid.
Admissions Requirements Physician's request.
Staff Physicians 1 (pt); RNs 2 (ft); LPNs 14 (ft), 1 (pt); Orderlies 1 (ft); Nurses aides 24 (ft), 4 (pt); Physical therapists 3 (pt); Activities coordinators 1 (ft); Dietitians 1 (ft); Dentists 1 (pt); Ophthalmologists 1 (pt); Podiatrists 1 (pt).
Facilities Dining room; Activities room; Crafts room; Laundry room; Barber/Beauty shop.
Activities Arts and Crafts; Games; Prayer groups; Movies; Shopping trips; Dances/Social or cultural gatherings.

Russellville Nursing Home
1700 W "C" St, Russellville, AR, 72801 (501) 968-5256
Admin Linda Eoff. *Medical Dir/Dir of Nursing* W H Lane Jr.
Licensure Skilled Care. *Beds* 92. *Certified* Medicare.
Admissions Requirements Medical examination; Physician's request.
Staff RNs 1 (ft), 1 (pt); LPNs 5 (ft), 5 (pt); Nurses aides 23 (ft), 12 (pt); Activities coordinators 1 (ft); Dietitians 1 (pt); 10 (ft), 10 (pt).
Facilities Dining room; Laundry room; Barber/Beauty shop.
Activities Arts and Crafts; Games; Reading groups; Prayer groups; Movies; Dances/Social or cultural gatherings.

Stella Manor Nursing Home*
400 N Vancouver, Russellville, AR, 72801 (501) 968-4141
Admin Iris L Williams.
Licensure Skilled Care. *Beds* 144. *Certified* Medicaid.

SALEM

Oak Hills Manor Inc*
PO Box 397, Salem, AR, 72576 (501) 895-3817
Admin Claude Sutterfield.
Licensure Skilled Care. *Beds* 125. *Certified* Medicaid.

SEARCY

Byrd Haven Nursing Home*
PO Box 180, 105 S College, Searcy, AR, 72143 (501) 268-2324
Admin Ralph Byrd Jr.
Licensure Intermediate Care. *Beds* 47. *Certified* Medicaid.

Leisure Lodge Inc*
211 Aztec, Searcy, AR, 72143 (501) 268-6188
Admin Tommie Pemberton.
Licensure Skilled Care. *Beds* 245.
Certified Medicaid.

SHERIDAN

Grant County Nursing Home
Rt 2, PO Box 100 BB, Sheridan, AR, 72150 (501) 942-2183
Admin Brenda Mercer. *Medical Dir/Dir of Nursing* Dr Clyde Paulk.
Licensure Skilled Care. *Beds* 110. *Certified* Medicaid.
Staff Physicians 3 (ft); RNs 2 (ft), 1 (pt); LPNs 7 (ft), 3 (pt); Nurses aides 30 (ft), 2 (pt); Activities coordinators 1 (ft); Dietitians 1 (ft); Dentists 2 (ft).
Facilities Dining room; Activities room; Laundry room; Barber/Beauty shop.
Activities Arts and Crafts; Games; Reading groups; Prayer groups; Movies; Dances/Social or cultural gatherings.

SIDNEY

Sharp Nursing Home Inc
Sidney, AR, 72577 (501) 283-5335
Admin James Hollandsworth. *Medical Dir/Dir of Nursing* J R Baker.
Licensure Intermediate Care. *Beds* 67. *Certified* Medicaid.
Admissions Requirements Medical examination.
Staff Physicians 1 (pt); RNs 1 (ft), 1 (pt); LPNs 5 (ft), 4 (pt); Nurses aides 10 (ft), 13 (pt); Activities coordinators 2 (pt); Dietitians 1 (pt).
Facilities Dining room; Laundry room; Barber/Beauty shop.
Activities Arts and Crafts; Cards; Games; Prayer groups; Movies; Dances/Social or cultural gatherings.

SILOAM SPRINGS

Woodland Manor Inc
811 W Elgin, Siloam Springs, AR, 72761 (501) 524-3128
Admin Montie Vest.
Licensure Skilled Care. *Beds* 120. *Certified* Medicaid; Medicare.

SMACKOVER

Smackover Nursing Home
210 E 5th St, PO Drawer J, Smackover, AR, 71762 (501) 725-3871
Admin Earnest Allen. *Medical Dir/Dir of Nursing* Dr George W Warren.
Licensure Skilled Care. *Beds* 80.
Admissions Requirements Medical examination.
Staff RNs 2 (ft); LPNs 5 (ft), 1 (pt); Orderlies 1 (ft); Activities coordinators 1 (ft).
Affiliation Methodist
Facilities Dining room; Activities room; Laundry room; Barber/Beauty shop; Library.
Activities Arts and Crafts; Cards; Games; Reading groups; Prayer groups; Movies; Shopping trips; Dances/Social or cultural gatherings; Picnics; Bus rides.
Description Smackover Nursing Home provides 24-hour nursing care, social activities, and any other services required to meet the needs of the residents.

SPRINGDALE

Holland Nursing Center—North*
PO Box Drawer 685, 2501 Lowell Rd, Springdale, AR, 72764 (501) 756-9000
Admin Deanna Shackelford.
Licensure Intermediate Care. *Beds* 56. Certified Medicaid.

Holland Nursing Center—West
802 SW End St, PO Box Drawer 685, Springdale, AR, 72764 (501) 756-1600
Admin Tommy Holland.
Licensure Intermediate Care. *Beds* 30. Certified Medicaid.

Pleasant Valley Nursing Center*
102 N Gutensohn, Springdale, AR, 72764 (501) 756-0330
Admin Sherman Honea.
Licensure Skilled Care. *Beds* 140. Certified Medicaid.

STAMPS

Homestead Manor Inc*
405 North St, Stamps, AR, 71860 (501) 533-4444
Admin Mary Jane Allen.
Licensure Skilled Care. *Beds* 105. Certified Medicaid.

STAR CITY

Gardner Nursing Home*
N Drew St, Star City, AR, 71667 (501) 628-4144
Admin Anna Belle Smith.
Licensure Intermediate Care. *Beds* 72. Certified Medicaid.

Star City Nursing Center*
Victory and Ford Sts, Star City, AR, 71667 (501) 628-4295
Admin Billie Weast.
Licensure Skilled Care. *Beds* 87. Certified Medicaid.

STUTTGART

Crestpark of Stuttgart Inc*
PO Box 790, Stuttgart, AR, 72160 (501) 673-1657
Admin Brenda J Dunbar.
Licensure Intermediate Care. *Beds* 74. Certified Medicaid.

Rose Care Center of Stuttgart*
PO Box 426, 2211 E 22nd St, Stuttgart, AR, 72160 (501) 673-6981
Admin Lucille Harper.
Licensure Skilled Care. *Beds* 90. Certified Medicaid.

TAYLOR

Taylor Nursing Home Inc
PO Box 280, Rt 2, Robinson St, Taylor, AR, 71861 (501) 694-3781
Admin Ruby Pyle.
Licensure Intermediate Care. *Beds* 41. Certified Medicaid; Medicare.
Admissions Requirements Medical examination; Physician's request.
Staff Physicians 3 (pt); RNs 1 (ft); LPNs 1 (ft), 6 (pt); Nurses aides 11 (ft); Activities coordinators 1 (ft); Dentists 1 (pt).
Facilities Dining room; Activities room; Crafts room; Laundry room; Barber/Beauty shop.
Activities Arts and Crafts; Cards; Games.

TEXARKANA

Evergreen Place*
PO Box 1401, 1101 E 36th, Texarkana, AR, 75502 (501) 773-7515
Admin Virginia Rush.
Licensure Intermediate Care. *Beds* 69. Certified Medicaid.
Ownership Proprietary.

Medicalodge of Texarkana*
1621 E 42nd St, Texarkana, AR, 75502 (501) 774-3581
Admin Ronald Jordison.
Licensure Skilled Care. *Beds* 105. Certified Medicaid; Medicare.
Ownership Proprietary.

Oakwood Place*
PO Box 1401, 307 Pinehurst, Texarkana, AR, 75501 (501) 773-2341
Admin Darlene Majors.
Licensure Intermediate Care. *Beds* 42. Certified Medicaid; Medicare.
Ownership Proprietary.

Parkview of Texarkana*
2415 Marietta St, Texarkana, AR, 75502 (501) 774-4662
Admin James Schimke.
Licensure Intermediate Care. *Beds* 52. Certified Medicaid.

TRUMANN

Melody Nursing Center*
333 Melody Dr, Trumann, AR, 72472 (501) 483-7623

Admin Kenneth K Yarbrough.
Licensure Skilled Care. *Beds* 77. Certified Medicaid.

VAN BUREN

Brownwood Manor*
1404 N 28th St, Van Buren, AR, 72956 (501) 474-8021
Admin Juanita Broadrick.
Licensure Skilled Care. *Beds* 99. Certified Medicaid.

New Haven O'Rest Nursing Home*
2010 Alma Hwy, Van Buren, AR, 72956 (501) 474-6885
Admin Gelene Hendershot.
Licensure Skilled Care. *Beds* 152. Certified Medicaid.

Van Buren Nursing Center*
2228 Pointer Trail West, Van Buren, AR, 72956 (501) 474-8021
Admin Mary Jane Bennett.
Licensure Intermediate Care. *Beds* 105. Certified Medicaid.

WALDRON

Pinewood Convalescent Home
PO Box Q, Waldron, AR, 72958 (501) 637-3171
Admin Sr Donald Mary Lynch. *Medical Dir/Dir of Nursing* Jose Rodriguez MD.
Licensure Skilled Care. *Beds* 85.
Admissions Requirements Medical examination; Physician's request.
Staff Physicians 4 (ft); RNs 2 (ft), 1 (pt); LPNs 2 (ft), 5 (pt); Nurses aides 17 (ft), 10 (pt); Activities coordinators 1 (ft); Dentists 1 (pt).
Affiliation Roman Catholic
Facilities Dining room; Activities room; Laundry room; Barber/Beauty shop; Library.
Activities Arts and Crafts; Cards; Games; Reading groups; Prayer groups; Movies; Dances/Social or cultural gatherings.
Description Pinewood Nursing Home is nestled in the Ouachita National Forest serving the people of Scott County, many of whom are long-time residents of the county. Programs are varied and meet the needs of the present resident group. Resident council assists in planning and programs; very active volunteer group assist with the many activities.

WALNUT RIDGE

Lawrence Hall Nursing Home
1309 Hwy 25 W, Walnut Ridge, AR, 72476 (501) 886-1295
Admin John Johnson. *Medical Dir/Dir of Nursing* Dr J B Elders.
Licensure Skilled Care. *Beds* 104. Certified Medicaid.
Staff RNs 2 (ft), 1 (pt); LPNs 10 (ft); Nurses aides 26 (ft), 1 (pt); Activities coordinators 1 (pt).
Facilities Dining room; Physical therapy room; Activities room; Crafts room; Laundry room; Barber/Beauty shop.
Activities Arts and Crafts; Cards; Games;

Reading groups; Prayer groups; Movies; Shopping trips; Dances/Social or cultural gatherings; Church.
Description JCAH accredited.

Sheltering Arms Nursing Home Inc
311 NW 2nd St, Walnut Ridge, AR, 72476 (501) 886-3770
Admin Debbie Lacy. *Medical Dir/Dir of Nursing* Robert Quevillon MD.
Licensure Intermediate Care. *Beds* 36. *Certified* Medicaid; Medicare.
Admissions Requirements Medical examination; Physician's request.
Staff Physicians 1 (pt); RNs 1 (ft); LPNs 3 (ft), 1 (pt); Nurses aides 7 (ft), 3 (pt); Physical therapists 1 (pt); Activities coordinators 1 (ft); Dietitians 1 (pt); Dentists 1 (pt).
Facilities Dining room; Activities room; Laundry room; Library.
Activities Arts and Crafts; Cards; Games; Reading groups; Prayer groups; Movies; Shopping trips; Dances/Social or cultural gatherings.
Description The home is small with 36-beds, and though staffed 24 hours by licensed personnel, retains a home-like quality found in few long-term care settings. All residents are treated with the utmost respect and all are loved and allowed to show love. Family, friends, and ministers are encouraged to come and truly make the residents feel at home.

Walnut Ridge Convalescent Center
Hwy 25 W, Walnut Ridge, AR, 72476 (501) 886-9022
Admin Robert Davis. *Medical Dir/Dir of Nursing* Ralph Joseph MD.
Licensure Skilled Care. *Beds* 105. *Certified* Medicaid.
Admissions Requirements Medical examination; Physician's request.
Staff Physicians 2 (pt); RNs 1 (ft), 1 (pt); LPNs 8 (ft), 1 (pt); Nurses aides 33 (ft); Physical therapists 1 (pt); Activities coordinators 1 (ft); Dietitians 1 (pt); Dentists 1 (pt); Ophthalmologists 1 (pt).
Facilities Dining room; Chapel; Laundry room; Barber/Beauty shop.
Activities Arts and Crafts; Cards; Games; Reading groups; Prayer groups; Movies; Dances/Social or cultural gatherings.

WARREN

Autumn Hills Nursing Center Inc
Hwy 4 E, Rt 3, PO Box 145C, Warren, AR, 71671 (501) 226-6766
Admin Ila Blevins.
Licensure Intermediate Care. *Beds* 105. *Certified* Medicaid; Medicare.
Admissions Requirements Medical examination; Physician's request.
Staff Physicians 1 (pt); RNs 2 (ft); LPNs 7 (ft), 3 (pt); Nurses aides 25 (ft), 20 (pt); Physical therapists 1 (pt); Speech therapists 1 (pt); Activities coordinators 1 (ft); Dietitians 1 (pt).
Facilities Dining room; Chapel; Laundry room; Barber/Beauty shop.
Activities Arts and Crafts; Games; Prayer groups; Shopping trips.

Pine Lodge of Warren*
730 E Church St, Warren, AR, 71671 (501) 226-5843
Admin Dorothy Sue Wagnon.
Licensure Skilled Care. *Beds* 99. *Certified* Medicaid.

South East Arkansas Human Development Center
Rt 3, 1 Center Circle, Warren, AR, 71671 (501) 226-6774
Admin Thomas M Lewins. *Medical Dir/Dir of Nursing* Dr Kerry Pennington.
Licensure Intermediate Care for Mentally Retarded. *Beds* 76. *Certified* Medicaid.
Admissions Requirements Minimum age 6; Medical examination.
Staff Physicians 2 (pt); RNs 2 (ft); LPNs 4 (ft); Physical therapists 1 (pt); Occupational therapists 1 (pt); Speech therapists 1 (ft); Activities coordinators 2 (ft); Dietitians 1 (pt); Dentists 1 (pt); Mental retardation aides 52 (ft).
Facilities Dining room; Physical therapy room; Activities room; Crafts room; Laundry room; Barber/Beauty shop; Library.
Activities Arts and Crafts; Cards; Games; Prayer groups; Movies; Shopping trips; Dances/Social or cultural gatherings.
Description Southeast Arkansas Human Development Center is a 76-bed ICF/MR facility which serves mentally retarded/developmentally disabled individuals of all levels of retardation. Facility includes both a residential and a day service component. The facility also includes 2 transitional living group homes, which are the only homes operated by Developmental Disabilities Services operating under the 15-bed-or-less ICF/MR regulations.

WEST MEMPHIS

Geriatrics Nursing Centers Inc*
610 S Avalon St, West Memphis, AR, 72301 (501) 735-4543
Admin Dorothy Person.
Licensure Skilled Care. *Beds* 155. *Certified* Medicaid.

Leisure Lodge Inc*
111 E Jackson Ave, West Memphis, AR, 72301 (501) 735-5174
Admin Robin Gray.
Licensure Intermediate Care. *Beds* 84. *Certified* Medicaid.

WILMOT

Ashley Manor*
PO Box 96, Lake St, Wilmot, AR, 71676 (501) 473-2291
Admin Tony Cooper.
Licensure Intermediate Care. *Beds* 68. *Certified* Medicaid.

Wilmot Nursing Home*
PO Box 188, Wilmot, AR, 71676 (501) 473-5505
Admin Rick Eddings.
Licensure Intermediate Care. *Beds* 32. *Certified* Medicaid.

WYNNE

Crestpark of Wynne—Intermediate
901 Cleveland, PO Box 1127, Wynne, AR, 72396 (501) 238-3263
Admin Charlotte Baskins.
Licensure Intermediate Care. *Beds* 40. *Certified* Medicaid.
Admissions Requirements Medical examination; Physician's request.
Staff RNs 1 (ft); LPNs 1 (ft), 2 (pt); Nurses aides 8 (ft), 2 (pt); Activities coordinators 1 (ft); Dietitians 1 (ft).
Facilities Dining room; Laundry room.
Activities Cards; Games; Reading groups; Prayer groups; Shopping trips.
Description Facility is surrounded by large lawn areas with many trees for residents' enjoyment when weather permits. A great recreation program is provided with exercise program daily, nature walks, holiday parties, monthly birthday parties, spelling bees, picnics, Bible studies, singing groups, church activities, and shopping trips.

Crestpark of Wynne—Skilled*
PO Box 1127, Arkansas and Rowena Sts, Wynne, AR, 72396 (501) 238-7941
Admin Ollie Lou Suggs.
Licensure Skilled Care. *Beds* 112. *Certified* Medicaid.

Village Creek Manor*
PO Box 276, Wynne, AR, 72396 (501) 238-2378, 2379
Admin Barbara J Cody.
Licensure Intermediate Care. *Beds* 100. *Certified* Medicaid.

YELLVILLE

Marion County Nursing Home*
PO Drawer 309, Yellville, AR, 72687 (501) 449-4201
Admin W Gale Dobbs.
Licensure Intermediate Care. *Beds* 61. *Certified* Medicaid.

CALIFORNIA

ALAMEDA

Marina Convalescent Center Inc*
3201 Fernside Blvd, Alameda, CA, 94501 (415)
523-2363
Admin Martin Neeham.
Licensure Skilled Care. *Beds* 33. *Certified* Medicare.
Ownership Proprietary.

Prather Methodist Memorial Home*
508 Westline Dr, Alameda, CA, 94501 (415)
521-5765
Admin Gail A Miller.
Licensure Skilled Care. *Beds* 151. *Certified* Medicare; Medi-Cal.
Ownership Nonprofit.

Shoreline North Convalescent Hospital
516 Willow Ave, Alameda, CA, 94501 (415)
521-5600
Admin James Eimers. *Medical Dir/Dir of Nursing* H A Lints MD.
Licensure Skilled Care. *Beds* 182. *Certified* Medicare; Medi-Cal.
Ownership Proprietary.
Admissions Requirements Medical examination.
Staff RNs 9 (ft); LPNs 21 (ft); Nurses aides 80 (ft), 12 (pt); Physical therapists 1 (ft), 2 (pt); Recreational therapists 1 (ft); Occupational therapists 2 (pt); Speech therapists 1 (pt); Activities coordinators 1 (ft), 2 (pt); Dietitians 1 (ft); Dentists 1 (pt); Podiatrists 1 (pt).
Facilities Dining room; Physical therapy room; Activities room; Crafts room; Laundry room; Barber/Beauty shop.
Activities Arts and Crafts; Cards; Games; Reading groups; Prayer groups; Movies; Shopping trips; Dances/Social or cultural gatherings.
Description The facility has central bay area location 1 ½ blocks from the beach with nearby medical centers. Specialties are sub-acute, terminal with hospice philosophy, Alzheimer's and other related brain disorders, physical, occupational, and speech therapies, and family support meetings.

Shoreline South Intermediate Care Facility*
430 Willow St, Alameda, CA, 94501 (415)
523-8857
Admin Georgina Jones.

Licensure Intermediate Care. *Beds* 166. *Certified* Medi-Cal.
Ownership Proprietary.

South Shore Convalescent Hospital
625 Willow St, Alameda, CA, 94501 (415)
523-3772
Admin Barbara Lee Olson. *Medical Dir/Dir of Nursing* Lester Johnson MD.
Licensure Skilled Care. *Beds* 26. *Certified* Medicare.
Ownership Proprietary.
Admissions Requirements Physician's request.
Staff RNs 1 (ft), 1 (pt); LPNs 4 (ft), 3 (pt); Orderlies 1 (ft), 1 (pt); Nurses aides 14 (ft), 6 (pt); Recreational therapists 1 (ft); Activities coordinators 1 (ft); Dietitians 1 (ft).
Facilities Dining room; Activities room; Crafts room; Laundry room.
Activities Arts and Crafts; Cards; Games; Reading groups; Prayer groups; Movies.

The Waters Edge
2401 Blanding Ave, Alameda, CA, 94501 (415)
522-1084
Admin Christian Zimmerman.
Licensure Skilled Care. *Beds* 120.
Certified Medi-Cal.
Ownership Proprietary.

ALHAMBRA

Alhambra Convalescent Home
415 S Garfield, Alhambra, CA, 91801 (213)
282-3151
Admin Rose Bower. *Medical Dir/Dir of Nursing* Dr Julitta Phillips.
Licensure Skilled Care. *Beds* 57. *Certified* Medicare; Medi-Cal.
Ownership Proprietary.
Staff RNs 2 (ft), 3 (pt); LPNs 2 (ft), 6 (pt); Orderlies 3 (ft), 4 (pt); Nurses aides 19 (ft), 5 (pt); Physical therapists 1 (ft); Reality therapists 1 (pt); Recreational therapists 1 (pt); Occupational therapists 1 (pt); Speech therapists 1 (pt); Activities coordinators 1 (ft), 1 (pt); Dietitians 1 (pt); Dentists 1 (pt); Ophthalmologists 1 (pt); Podiatrists 1 (pt); Audiologists 1 (pt).
Facilities Dining room; Activities room.
Activities Arts and Crafts; Cards; Games; Reading groups; Prayer groups; Movies; Shopping trips; Dances/Social or cultural gatherings.
Description Facility has patio, fountain, and beautiful trees. Varied and full activities pro-

gram including concerts by volunteers (piano, voice, violin, harpsichord), special performances, international dances, barbecues, pet day, baby day, movies, travels, monthly and "100-year old" birthday parties.

Brykirk Extended Care Hospital*
2339 W Valley Blvd, Alhambra, CA, 91803
(213) 289-7809
Admin Sheryl L Brykman.
Licensure Skilled Care. *Beds* 43. *Certified* Medicare; Medi-Cal.
Ownership Proprietary.

California PEO Home*
700 N Stoneman Ave, Alhambra, CA, 91801
(213) 289-5284
Admin Marjorie Jackson.
Licensure Skilled Care. *Beds* 44. *Certified* Medicare; Medi-Cal.
Ownership Nonprofit.

Home for the Aged of Protestant Episcopal Church
1428 S Marengo Ave, Alhambra, CA, 91803
(213) 576-1032
Admin G W Cummings.
Licensure Skilled Care; Intermediate Care.
Beds SNF 99; ICF 99. *Certified* Medicare; Medi-Cal.
Ownership Nonprofit.
Admissions Requirements Minimum age 62.
Staff Physicians 2 (ft); RNs 18 (ft); LPNs 6 (ft); Orderlies 7 (ft); Nurses aides 64 (ft); Physical therapists 3 (ft).
Affiliation Episcopal
Facilities Dining room; Physical therapy room; Activities room; Chapel; Crafts room; Laundry room; Barber/Beauty shop; Library.
Activities Arts and Crafts; Cards; Games; Reading groups; Prayer groups; Movies; Shopping trips; Dances/Social or cultural gatherings.

Lutheran Health Facility
2400 S Fremont, Alhambra, CA, 91803 (213)
289-6211
Admin Jerry McConnell.
Licensure Skilled Care. *Beds* 50. *Certified* Medicare; Medi-Cal.
Ownership Nonprofit.
Affiliation Lutheran

West Convalescent Hospital of Atherton Baptist Homes
715 W Commonwealth, Alhambra, CA, 91801 (213) 289-4178
Admin Arthur S Hyde. *Medical Dir/Dir of Nursing* Dr Gayle Thompson.
Licensure Skilled Care. *Beds* 57. *Certified* Medicare; Medi-Cal.
Ownership Nonprofit.
Admissions Requirements Minimum age 65; Medical examination; Physician's request.
Staff RNs 4 (ft); LPNs 3 (ft), 4 (pt); Nurses aides 28 (ft), 2 (pt); Activities coordinators 1 (ft), 1 (pt); Dietitians 1 (pt).
Affiliation Baptist
Facilities Dining room; Physical therapy room; Activities room; Chapel; Crafts room; Laundry room; Barber/Beauty shop; Library.
Activities Arts and Crafts; Games; Reading groups; Prayer groups; Movies; Shopping trips; Dances/Social or cultural gatherings; Sing-a-longs.
Description Atherton Baptist Homes is a Christian retirement community dedicated to providing professional Christian workers and lay retirees adequate, affordable housing in a quality living environment. Atherton provides individuals with a variety of living plans and personal and skilled nursing services in response to changing needs. Atherton provides residents a lifestyle encompassing dignity, independence, security, and comfort. Atherton enjoys historic ties with the American Baptist Churches of the Pacific Southwest, and individual churches provide consistent financial support. Atherton's ownership, however, is vested in its trustees. (The American Baptist Churches has no real or implied responsibility for its operation.) Atherton is a nonprofit corporation dependent upon the gifts of friends who make it possible for the homes to assist those with special needs.

ALPINE

Alpine Convalescent Center*
PO Box 458, 2120 Alpine Blvd, Alpine, CA, 92001 (714) 445-2644
Admin R Patrick Doyle.
Licensure Skilled Care; Intermediate Care for Mentally Retarded. *Beds* 99. *Certified* Medi-Cal.
Ownership Proprietary.

ALTA LOMA

Alta Loma Convalescent Hospital
9333 La Mesa Dr, Alta Loma, CA, 91701 (714) 987-2501
Admin Emil W Lenkey.
Licensure Skilled Care. *Beds* 59. *Certified* Medicare; Medi-Cal.
Ownership Proprietary.

ALTADENA

Scripps Home
2212 N El Molino, Altadena, CA, 91001 (818) 798-0934
Admin James W Graunke. *Medical Dir/Dir of Nursing* Dr Carol Thrun.
Licensure Skilled Care; Intermediate Care.
Beds 49.
Ownership Nonprofit.
Admissions Requirements Minimum age 70; Medical examination.
Staff Physicians 1 (pt); RNs 5 (ft), 5 (pt); Nurses aides 14 (ft), 14 (pt); Physical therapists 2 (pt); Activities coordinators 1 (ft); Podiatrists 2 (pt).
Facilities Dining room; Physical therapy room; Activities room; Laundry room; Barber/Beauty shop; Library.
Activities Arts and Crafts; Games; Prayer groups; Movies; Shopping trips; Dances/Social or cultural gatherings; Current events, poetry, drama groups.
Description The Scripps Home is a life care facility for the low-moderate income elderly of the Pasadena area.

ALTURAS

Warnerview Convalescent Hospital*
225 McDowell Ave, Alturas, CA, 96101 (916) 233-3416
Admin Lawrence Eckman.
Licensure Skilled Care. *Beds* 59. *Certified* Medicare; Medi-Cal.
Ownership Nonprofit.

ANAHEIM

Anaheim Terrace Convalescent Hospital
141 S Knott Ave, Anaheim, CA, 92804 (714) 821-7310
Admin Frances Hoogstad. *Medical Dir/Dir of Nursing* Stanley Friedman MD.
Licensure Skilled Care. *Beds* 99. *Certified* Medicare; Medi-Cal.
Ownership Proprietary.
Admissions Requirements Medical examination; Physician's request.
Facilities Dining room; Physical therapy room; Activities room; Crafts room; Laundry room; Barber/Beauty shop.
Activities Arts and Crafts; Cards; Games; Reading groups; Prayer groups; Movies; Shopping trips.
Description Facility features a friendly, warm, home-like environment with individualized programs for each patient; bedside dental, visual, and podiatry care are given.

Beverly Manor Convalescent Hospital
3067 Orange Ave, Anaheim, CA, 92804 (714) 827-2440
Admin Carolyn Carlsen-Rouzier. *Medical Dir/Dir of Nursing* Franklin Hanauer MD.
Licensure Skilled Care. *Beds* 83. *Certified* Medicare; Medi-Cal.
Ownership Proprietary.
Staff RNs 2 (ft); LPNs 6 (ft), 4 (pt); Nurses aides 20 (ft), 20 (pt); Activities coordinators 1 (ft).
Facilities Dining room; Physical therapy room; Activities room; Crafts room; Laundry room; Barber/Beauty shop.
Activities Arts and Crafts; Cards; Games; Reading groups; Prayer groups; Movies; Dances/Social or cultural gatherings.
Description Facility features an adopt-

a-grandparent program where children of all ages spend time with their adopted grandparents. A newly redecorated facility truly pleasant inside and outside; conveniently located next door to an acute hospital.

Buena Vista Convalescent Hospital*
1440 S Euclid St, Anaheim, CA, 92802 (714) 535-7264
Admin Jane Beaver.
Licensure Skilled Care. *Beds* 99. *Certified* Medicare; Medi-Cal.
Ownership Proprietary.

Casa Grande Intermediate Care Facility
3615 W Ball Rd, Anaheim, CA, 92804 (714) 826-4400
Admin Candy Bennett. *Medical Dir/Dir of Nursing* Robert Roany.
Licensure Intermediate Care. *Beds* 91. *Certified* Medi-Cal.
Ownership Proprietary.
Admissions Requirements Minimum age 15.
Facilities Dining room; Physical therapy room; Activities room; Crafts room.
Activities Arts and Crafts; Cards; Games; Reading groups; Movies; Shopping trips; Dances/Social or cultural gatherings.
Description We participate in special treatment programing for the developmentally disabled. In addition to the many activity rooms, we have a huge side yard which affords opportunities for many recreational activities.

Casa Pacifica
861 S Harbor Blvd, Anaheim, CA, 92805 (714) 635-8131
Admin Caroline Downey. *Medical Dir/Dir of Nursing* John D Cowles MD.
Licensure Skilled Care. *Beds* 99. *Certified* Medicare; Medi-Cal.
Ownership Proprietary.
Admissions Requirements Minimum age 55.
Staff RNs 2 (ft), 1 (pt); LPNs 9 (ft), 2 (pt); Nurses aides 50 (ft), 5 (pt); Physical therapists 1 (pt); Speech therapists 1 (pt); Activities coordinators 1 (ft), 1 (pt); Dietitians 1 (pt); Podiatrists 1 (pt).
Facilities Dining room; Activities room; Crafts room; Laundry room; Barber/Beauty shop.
Activities Arts and Crafts; Games; Prayer groups; Movies; Dances/Social or cultural gatherings.

Extended Care Hospital of Anaheim*
501 S Beach Blvd, Anaheim, CA, 92804 (714) 828-7730
Admin Marc Landry.
Licensure Skilled Care. *Beds* 250. *Certified* Medicare; Medi-Cal.
Ownership Proprietary.

Fountainbleau Nursing Centre*
3415 W Ball Rd, Anaheim, CA, 92804 (714) 826-8950
Admin Jaime Deutsch.
Licensure Skilled Care. *Beds* 152. *Certified* Medicare; Medi-Cal.
Ownership Proprietary.

Grand Care Convalescent Hospital*
2040 S Euclid St, Anaheim, CA, 92802 (714) 636-2800

Admin Ronald G Stinebiser.
Licensure Skilled Care. *Beds* 94. *Certified* Medicare; Medi-Cal.
Ownership Proprietary.

Guidance Center Sanitarium
1135 Leisure Ct, Anaheim, CA, 92801 (714) 772-1353
Admin George C Scholl. *Medical Dir/Dir of Nursing* Roland L Atiga MD.
Licensure Skilled Care. *Beds* 115.
Certified Medi-Cal.
Ownership Proprietary.
Admissions Requirements Minimum age 21.
Staff Physicians 5 (pt); RNs 6 (ft), 1 (pt); LPNs 10 (ft), 1 (pt); Orderlies 7 (ft); Nurses aides 20 (ft); Physical therapists 1 (pt); Reality therapists 1 (pt); Recreational therapists 2 (ft); Occupational therapists 1 (pt); Speech therapists 1 (pt); Activities coordinators 1 (ft); Dietitians 1 (pt); Dentists 1 (pt); Ophthalmologists 1 (pt); Podiatrists 1 (pt); Audiologists 1 (pt).
Facilities Dining room; Physical therapy room; Activities room; Crafts room; Laundry room; Barber/Beauty shop.
Activities Arts and Crafts; Cards; Games; Reading groups; Prayer groups; Movies; Shopping trips; Dances/Social or cultural gatherings.
Description A closed protective environment with planned activities to include reality orientation and behavorial modification for the mentally ill.

Hillhaven Convalescent Hospital
1130 W La Palma Ave, Anaheim, CA, 92801 (714) 772-7480
Admin Thomas Hines. *Medical Dir/Dir of Nursing* Seawright Anderson MD.
Licensure Skilled Care. *Beds* 72. *Certified* Medicare; Medi-Cal.
Ownership Proprietary.
Admissions Requirements Medical examination; Physician's request.
Staff RNs 3 (pt); Nurses aides 5 (ft), 20 (pt); Activities coordinators 1 (ft); Dietitians 1 (pt).
Facilities Dining room; Physical therapy room; Activities room; Laundry room; Barber/Beauty shop; Library.
Activities Arts and Crafts; Cards; Games; Movies; Shopping trips; Dances/Social or cultural gatherings.
Description Facility is beautifully kept; provides all therapies required; activities department provides an excellent program designed to meet all levels of care.

Lutheran Health Facility of Anaheim
891 S Walnut St, Anaheim, CA, 92802 (714) 776-7150
Admin Marion L Hopkins. *Medical Dir/Dir of Nursing* Dr Stanley Kerkhoff.
Licensure Skilled Care. *Beds* 33.
Certified Medi-Cal.
Ownership Nonprofit.
Admissions Requirements Minimum age 65; Medical examination; Physician's request.
Staff Physicians 1 (pt); RNs 1 (ft), 2 (pt); LPNs 3 (ft), 3 (pt); Orderlies 1 (ft); Nurses aides 13 (ft); Activities coordinators 1 (ft); Dietitians 1 (pt); Podiatrists 1 (pt).
Affiliation Lutheran
Facilities Dining room.
Activities Arts and Crafts; Games; Reading

groups; Prayer groups; Movies.
Description Facility is part of an 11-acre retirement community located ½ mile north of Disneyland; able to serve only the campus residents due to a limited number of beds.

Orangeview Convalescent Hospital*
1720 W Orange, Anaheim, CA, 92804 (714) 776-1720
Admin Clyde D Vineyard.
Licensure Skilled Care. *Beds* 36. *Certified* Medicare; Medi-Cal.
Ownership Proprietary.

Parkview Convalescent Hospital*
1514 E Lincoln Ave, Anaheim, CA, 92805 (714) 774-2222
Admin Elwin E Goings.
Licensure Skilled Care. *Beds* 41. *Certified* Medicare; Medi-Cal.
Ownership Proprietary.

Saint Elizabeth Convalescent Hospital*
3435 W Ball Rd, Anaheim, CA, 92804 (714) 827-5880
Admin William Cloonan.
Licensure Skilled Care. *Beds* 97. *Certified* Medicare; Medi-Cal.
Ownership Proprietary.

ANDERSON

Hospitality House Nursing Home*
1450 Happy Valley Rd, Anderson, CA, 96007 (916) 241-2804
Admin Robert W Roy.
Licensure Skilled Care. *Beds* 34. *Certified* Medicare; Medi-Cal.
Ownership Proprietary.

ANGWIN

Pine Breeze Convalescent Hospital*
295 Pine Breeze Dr, Angwin, CA, 94508 (707) 965-2461
Admin Merle Prusia.
Licensure Skilled Care. *Beds* 59.
Ownership Proprietary.

ANTIOCH

Antioch Convalescent Hospital*
1210 A St, Antioch, CA, 94509 (415) 757-8787
Admin Clara Thompson.
Licensure Skilled Care. *Beds* 99. *Certified* Medicare; Medi-Cal.
Ownership Proprietary.

Cavallo Convalescent Hospital
1907 Cavallo Rd, Antioch, CA, 94509 (415) 757-5442
Admin Rilda M Scarfo. *Medical Dir/Dir of Nursing* Mark Dechter MD and Barbara Franzen MD.
Licensure Skilled Care. *Beds* 38. *Certified* Medicare; Medi-Cal.
Ownership Proprietary.
Admissions Requirements Minimum age 18; Medical examination.
Staff Physicians 2 (ft); RNs 1 (ft), 1 (pt); LPNs

3 (ft), 2 (pt); Orderlies 1 (pt); Nurses aides 10 (ft), 4 (pt); Recreational therapists 1 (ft); Activities coordinators 1 (ft).
Facilities Dining room; Activities room; Crafts room; Laundry room; Barber/Beauty shop.
Activities Arts and Crafts; Cards; Games; Reading groups; Prayer groups; Movies; Shopping trips; Dances/Social or cultural gatherings; Barbecues; Resident council; Exercise class; Mass once a month; Bible study; Adult education class..
Description Small facility that has a special activity each month ranging from carnivals, bazzaars, and wine testing to home-made ice cream. All events include the family and are free of charge. Large participation by staff and family.

Lone Tree Convalescent Hospital
4001 Lone Tree Way, Antioch, CA, 94509 (415) 754-0470
Admin John Bird. *Medical Dir/Dir of Nursing* Abe Kaplan MD.
Licensure Skilled Care. *Beds* 99. *Certified* Medicare; Medi-Cal.
Ownership Proprietary.
Staff Physicians 1 (pt); RNs 3 (ft), 1 (pt); LPNs 3 (ft), 6 (pt); Orderlies 2 (pt); Nurses aides 24 (ft), 16 (pt); Physical therapists 1 (pt); Occupational therapists 1 (pt); Speech therapists 1 (pt); Activities coordinators 2 (pt); Dietitians 1 (pt); Dentists 1 (pt); Podiatrists 1 (pt).
Facilities Dining room; Physical therapy room; Activities room; Laundry room; Barber/Beauty shop.
Activities Arts and Crafts; Cards; Games; Prayer groups; Movies; Shopping trips.
Description Facility is situated in a rural area with a nice view. Special family-style dining is offered for appropriate patients.

ARCADIA

Arcadia Convalescent Hospital Inc*
1601 S Baldwin Ave, Arcadia, CA, 91006 (213) 445-2170
Admin Clarizio Orlando.
Licensure Skilled Care. *Beds* 74. *Certified* Medicare; Medi-Cal.
Ownership Proprietary.

Huntington Drive Convalescent Hospital
400 W Huntington Dr, Arcadia, CA, 91106 (818) 445-2421
Admin Ann E Koeckeitz. *Medical Dir/Dir of Nursing* F Kunze MD.
Licensure Skilled Care. *Beds* 99. *Certified* Medicare; Medi-Cal.
Ownership Proprietary.
Admissions Requirements Physician's request.
Staff RNs 4 (ft), 3 (pt); LPNs 9 (ft), 4 (pt); Nurses aides 34 (ft), 1 (pt); Activities coordinators 1 (ft).
Facilities Dining room; Physical therapy room; Activities room; Crafts room; Laundry room; Barber/Beauty shop.
Activities Arts and Crafts; Games; Reading groups; Prayer groups; Movies; Dances/Social or cultural gatherings.

ARLINGTON

Alta Vista Healthcare*
9020 Garfield Ave, Arlington, CA, 92503 (714) 688-8200
Admin Gary Dickerson.
Licensure Skilled Care. *Beds* 107. *Certified* Medicare; Medi-Cal.
Ownership Proprietary.

ARROYO GRANDE

South County Convalescent Center*
1212 Farroll Ave, Arroyo Grande, CA, 93420 (805) 489-8137
Admin George Sigler.
Licensure Skilled Care; Intermediate Care. *Beds* SNF 83; ICF 16. *Certified* Medicare; Medi-Cal.
Ownership Proprietary.

ARTESIA

Pilgrims Convalescent Hospital
11614 E 183rd St, Artesia, CA, 90701 (213) 865-5218
Admin Edith Wray. *Medical Dir/Dir of Nursing* Dr J Hoekzema.
Licensure Skilled Care. *Beds* 59. *Certified* Medicare; Medi-Cal.
Ownership Nonprofit.
Admissions Requirements Minimum age 65; Medical examination.
Staff RNs 1 (ft), 4 (pt); LPNs 8 (ft), 2 (pt); Nurses aides 19 (ft), 5 (pt); Physical therapists 1 (pt); Activities coordinators 1 (ft); Dietitians 1 (pt).
Affiliation Christian Reformed
Facilities Dining room; Laundry room; Barber-/Beauty shop; Library.
Activities Arts and Crafts; Games; Movies; Church program and outings to church luncheons; Bible classes.
Description We are a 3 phase facility: individual living, residential, and skilled nursing—dedicated to physical as well as spiritual needs of the elderly.

Twin Palms Sanitarium*
11900 E Artesia Blvd, Artesia, CA, 90701 (213) 865-0271
Admin Catherine M Eichberg.
Licensure Skilled Care. *Beds* 222.
Certified Medi-Cal.
Ownership Proprietary.

ATASCADERO

Country Care Convalescent Hospital*
14900 El Camino Real, Atascadero, CA, 93422 (805) 466-0282
Admin John M Arrambide.
Licensure Skilled Care. *Beds* 40. *Certified* Medicare; Medi-Cal.
Ownership Nonprofit.

Danish Convalescent Home*
10805 El Camino Real, Atascadero, CA, 93422 (805) 466-9254
Admin Roy B Jensen.

Licensure Skilled Care. *Beds* 64. *Certified* Medicare; Medi-Cal.
Ownership Proprietary.

AUBERRY

Wish-I-Ah Lodge*
35680 N Wish-I-Ah Rd, Auberry, CA, 93602 (209) 855-2211
Admin Theodore Harwick.
Licensure Skilled Care. *Beds* 135.
Certified Medi-Cal.
Ownership Proprietary.

AUBURN

Auburn Convalescent Hospital*
260 Racetrack St, Auburn, CA, 95603 (916) 885-7051
Admin Martin C Klein.
Licensure Skilled Care. *Beds* 84. *Certified* Medicare; Medi-Cal.
Ownership Proprietary.

Auburn Ravine Terrace*
750 Auburn Ravine Terrace, Auburn, CA, 95603 (916) 823-6131
Admin David L Ferguson.
Licensure Skilled Care. *Beds* 56.
Certified Medi-Cal.
Ownership Nonprofit.

Hilltop Manor Convalescent Hospital 2*
12225 Shale Ridge Ln, Auburn, CA, 95603 (916) 885-7511
Admin Bradley J Wilcox.
Licensure Skilled Care. *Beds* 230. *Certified* Medicare; Medi-Cal.
Ownership Proprietary.

BAKERSFIELD

Bakersfield Convalescent Hospital*
730 34th St, Bakersfield, CA, 93301 (805) 327-7687
Admin Olive Marean.
Licensure Skilled Care. *Beds* 150. *Certified* Medicare; Medi-Cal.
Ownership Proprietary.

Beverly Manor Convalescent Hospital*
3601 San Dimas, Bakersfield, CA, 93301 (805) 323-2894
Admin Jerome Sturz.
Licensure Skilled Care. *Beds* 99. *Certified* Medicare; Medi-Cal.
Ownership Proprietary.

Colonial Convalescent Hospital*
1611 Height St, Bakersfield, CA, 93305 (805) 872-0705
Admin James Williams.
Licensure Skilled Care. *Beds* 120. *Certified* Medicare; Medi-Cal.
Ownership Proprietary.

Crestwood Manor
6600 Eucalyptus Dr, Bakersfield, CA, 93306 (805) 366-5757
Admin Cornel Artho. *Medical Dir/Dir of*

Nursing Arthur Unger MD.
Licensure Skilled Care. *Beds* 109. *Certified* Medicare.
Ownership Proprietary.
Admissions Requirements Minimum age 18.
Facilities Dining room; Activities room; Crafts room; Laundry room; Barber/Beauty shop; Library.
Activities Arts and Crafts; Cards; Games; Reading groups; Prayer groups; Movies; Shopping trips; Dances/Social or cultural gatherings.
Description The major thrust of this facility is to provide a special rehabilitation program for chronically mentally ill patients in the southern San Joaquin Valley.

Hilltop Convalescent Hospital*
1601 Height St, Bakersfield, CA, 93305 (805) 872-2324
Admin James H Williams.
Licensure Skilled Care. *Beds* 117. *Certified* Medicare; Medi-Cal.
Ownership Proprietary.

Manor Lodge Convalescent Hospital
2607 Mount Vernon Ave, Bakersfield, CA, 93306 (805) 871-8733
Admin Roberta Mills. *Medical Dir/Dir of Nursing* Patrick Daley.
Licensure Skilled Care. *Beds* 37. *Certified* Medicare; Medi-Cal.
Ownership Proprietary.
Admissions Requirements Medical examination; Physician's request.
Staff RNs 1 (ft), 2 (pt); LPNs 3 (ft), 4 (pt); Nurses aides 10 (ft), 5 (pt); Activities coordinators 1 (ft).

Parkview Julian Convalescent Hospital
1801 Julian Ave, Bakersfield, CA, 93304 (805) 831-9150
Admin Frank Denham. *Medical Dir/Dir of Nursing* Samuel Schreiber MD.
Licensure Skilled Care. *Beds* 99. *Certified* Medicare; Medi-Cal.
Ownership Proprietary.
Admissions Requirements Physician's request.
Staff RNs 2 (ft); LPNs 10 (ft); Nurses aides 25 (ft).
Facilities Dining room; Physical therapy room; Activities room; Barber/Beauty shop.
Activities Arts and Crafts; Cards; Games; Reading groups; Movies; Dances/Social or cultural gatherings; Outside entertainment.
Description Facility is located in residential setting.

Parkview Real Convalescent Hospital*
329 N Real Rd, Bakersfield, CA, 93309 (805) 327-7107
Admin Frank Denham.
Licensure Skilled Care. *Beds* 164. *Certified* Medicare; Medi-Cal.
Ownership Proprietary.

Riverside Cottage Rest Home*
1131 S "H" St, Bakersfield, CA, 93304 (805) 831-9126
Admin Roberta Mills.
Licensure Intermediate Care. *Beds* 15. *Certified* Medi-Cal.
Ownership Proprietary.

Rosewood Health Facility
1301 New Stine Rd, Bakersfield, CA, 93309
(805) 834-5757
Admin Jo Ann Matters. *Medical Dir/Dir of Nursing* M C Barnard II MD.
Licensure Skilled Care. *Beds* 76. *Certified* Medicare; Medi-Cal.
Ownership Nonprofit.
Admissions Requirements Medical examination; Physician's request.
Affiliation Baptist
Facilities Dining room; Physical therapy room; Activities room; Chapel; Crafts room; Laundry room; Barber/Beauty shop; Library.
Activities Arts and Crafts; Cards; Games; Reading groups; Prayer groups; Movies; Shopping trips; Dances/Social or cultural gatherings.

Shady Manor Convalescent Hospital
2901 S "H" St, Bakersfield, CA, 93304 (805) 831-0765
Admin Astrik A Lott.
Licensure Skilled Care. *Beds* 37. *Certified* Medicare.
Ownership Proprietary.
Admissions Requirements Medical examination; Physician's request.
Staff RNs 1 (ft), 1 (pt); LPNs 3 (ft), 2 (pt); Nurses aides 9 (ft), 5 (pt); Activities coordinators 1 (pt).
Facilities Dining room; Activities room; Laundry room.
Activities Arts and Crafts; Cards; Games; Prayer groups; Movies; Shopping trips; Dances/Social or cultural gatherings.
Description Facility is located in southwest Bakersfield near bus lines and shopping center. Small and homey facility specializing in individualized care and great cooking.

Town and Country Intermediate Care Facility*
40½ Sterling Rd, Bakersfield, CA, 93307 (805) 366-7990
Admin Roberta Mills.
Licensure Intermediate Care. *Beds* 18. *Certified* Medi-Cal.
Ownership Proprietary.

Valley Convalescent Hospital
1205 8th St, Bakersfield, CA, 93304 (805) 324-9468
Admin Carlos R Lewis. *Medical Dir/Dir of Nursing* Samuel Schrieber.
Licensure Skilled Care. *Beds* 87. *Certified* Medicare; Medi-Cal.
Ownership Proprietary.
Staff Physicians 6 (ft); RNs 1 (ft), 2 (pt); Orderlies 1 (ft); Nurses aides 27 (ft), 8 (pt); Physical therapists 1 (pt); Recreational therapists 1 (pt); Occupational therapists 1 (pt); Speech therapists 1 (pt); Activities coordinators 1 (ft); Dietitians 1 (ft); Dentists 1 (pt); Ophthalmologists 1 (pt); Podiatrists 1 (pt); Audiologists 1 (pt).
Facilities Dining room; Physical therapy room; Activities room; Crafts room; Laundry room; Barber/Beauty shop; Library.
Activities Arts and Crafts; Cards; Games; Reading groups; Prayer groups; Movies; Shopping trips; Dances/Social or cultural gatherings.
Description Our facility has a locked section with an open garden setting. Our facility also has an unlocked section for patients who do not wander.

Villa Terrace Intermediate Care Facility*
721 8th St, Bakersfield, CA, 93304 (805) 324-1400
Admin Larry T Pontious.
Licensure Intermediate Care. *Beds* 20. *Certified* Medi-Cal.
Ownership Proprietary.

BALDWIN PARK

Baldwin Park Convalescent Hospital*
14518 E Los Angeles St, Baldwin Park, CA, 91706 (213) 337-7229
Admin Ann M Whitefoot.
Licensure Skilled Care. *Beds* 49.
Certified Medi-Cal.
Ownership Proprietary.

Baldwin Park Health Care Center
14318 Ohio St, Baldwin Park, CA, 91706 (213) 960-1971
Admin A Rzepnick. *Medical Dir/Dir of Nursing* Ron Atturi.
Licensure Skilled Care. *Beds* 98. *Certified* Medicare; Medi-Cal.
Ownership Proprietary.
Admissions Requirements Physician's request.
Staff Physicians 4 (pt); RNs 1 (ft); LPNs 7 (ft); Orderlies 3 (ft); Nurses aides 23 (ft); Physical therapists 1 (pt); Occupational therapists 1 (pt); Speech therapists 1 (pt); Activities coordinators 1 (ft); Dietitians 1 (ft); Dentists 1 (pt); Ophthalmologists 1 (pt); Podiatrists 1 (pt); Audiologists 1 (pt).
Facilities Dining room; Physical therapy room; Activities room; Chapel; Crafts room; Laundry room; Barber/Beauty shop; Library.
Activities Arts and Crafts; Cards; Games; Reading groups; Prayer groups; Movies; Shopping trips; Adult Education.

Golden State Habilitation Convalescent Center
1758 Big Dalton Ave, Baldwin Park, CA, 91706 (818) 962-3274
Admin Michael C O'Neil.
Licensure Skilled Care; Intermediate Care for Mentally Retarded. *Beds* 155. *Certified* Medi-Cal.
Ownership Proprietary.
Staff Physicians 1 (pt); RNs 8 (ft); LPNs 12 (ft); Orderlies 34 (ft); Nurses aides 40 (ft); Physical therapists 1 (pt); Occupational therapists 1 (pt); Speech therapists 1 (pt); Activities coordinators 1 (ft); Dietitians 1 (pt); Dentists 1 (pt); Ophthalmologists 1 (pt); Podiatrists 1 (pt); Audiologists 1 (pt).
Facilities Dining room; Physical therapy room; Activities room; Laundry room; Barber/Beauty shop.
Activities Arts and Crafts; Cards; Games; Movies; Shopping trips; Dances/Social or cultural gatherings.
Description Facility has 6 full-time adult education classes offered on premises 6 days a week.

Mooney Convalescent Hospital
3541 Puente Ave, Baldwin Park, CA, 91706 (818) 962-1043
Admin Ruby Conway. *Medical Dir/Dir of Nursing* Jesus Arenas MD.
Licensure Skilled Care. *Beds* 49. *Certified* Medicare; Medi-Cal.

Ownership Proprietary.
Staff RNs 1 (ft), 1 (pt); LPNs 4 (ft), 1 (pt); Orderlies 1 (ft); Nurses aides 11 (ft), 1 (pt); Activities coordinators 1 (ft).
Facilities Dining room; Activities room; Laundry room; Barber/Beauty shop.
Activities Arts and Crafts; Cards; Games; Prayer groups; Shopping trips; Entertainment.

Tri-City Golden Age Convalescent Hospital and Home*
14475 Ituni St, Baldwin Park, CA, 91706 (213) 962-7095
Admin Josephine Spaun.
Licensure Skilled Care. *Beds* 97. *Certified* Medicare; Medi-Cal.
Ownership Nonprofit.

BANNING

Banning Convalescent Hospital
3476 Wilson, Banning, CA, 92220 (714) 849-4723
Admin Daniel Shoopman. *Medical Dir/Dir of Nursing* Ronald Rothe MD.
Licensure Skilled Care. *Beds* 64. *Certified* Medicare; Medi-Cal.
Ownership Proprietary.
Staff RNs 1 (ft), 2 (pt); LPNs 4 (ft), 4 (pt); Nurses aides 14 (ft), 12 (pt); Activities coordinators 1 (ft); Dietitians 1 (pt).
Facilities Dining room; Physical therapy room; Activities room; Laundry room; Barber/Beauty shop.
Activities Arts and Crafts; Cards; Games; Reading groups; Prayer groups; Movies.

BEAUMONT

Beaumont Convalescent Hospital
1441 N Michigan Ave, Beaumont, CA, 92223 (714) 845-1166
Admin John Parfih. *Medical Dir/Dir of Nursing* Robert Payton MD.
Licensure Skilled Care. *Beds* 87. *Certified* Medicare; Medi-Cal.
Ownership Proprietary.
Admissions Requirements Medical examination; Physician's request.
Staff RNs 2 (ft), 1 (pt); LPNs 9 (ft), 2 (pt); Orderlies 1 (ft); Nurses aides 36 (ft), 3 (pt); Physical therapists 1 (ft); Occupational therapists 1 (pt); Speech therapists 1 (pt); Activities coordinators 1 (ft); Dietitians 1 (pt); Dentists 1 (pt).
Facilities Dining room; Physical therapy room; Activities room; Laundry room; Barber/Beauty shop.
Activities Arts and Crafts; Cards; Games; Prayer groups; Movies; Shopping trips.

Valley View Home
40901 E 8th, Beaumont, CA, 92223 (714) 845-3125
Admin Peter D Bennett. *Medical Dir/Dir of Nursing* Charles Hyman MD.
Licensure Intermediate Care. *Beds* 57. *Certified* Medi-Cal.
Ownership Proprietary.
Admissions Requirements Minimum age 3; Physician's request.

Facilities Dining room; Activities room; Crafts room; Laundry room.
Activities Arts and Crafts; Cards; Games; Prayer groups; Movies; Shopping trips; Dances/Social or cultural gatherings.
Description Valley View Home is dedicated to providing individualized habilitative training to clients with developmental disabilities through an interdisciplinary approach. Staff's time, effort, energy, and resources are put into preparing clients to become healthy happy citizens with as many independent skills as their potential warrants.

BELL GARDENS

Bell Gardens Convalescent Center*
5648 Gotham St, Bell Gardens, CA, 90201 (213) 927-2641
Admin Rachel Slomovic.
Licensure Skilled Care. *Beds* 125. *Certified* Medicare; Medi-Cal.
Ownership Proprietary.

Del Rio Convalescent Center
7002 E Gage Ave, Bell Gardens, CA, 90201 (213) 773-7881
Admin Glenn Thune. *Medical Dir/Dir of Nursing* Dr Michael Platt.
Licensure Skilled Care. *Beds* 99.
Certified Medi-Cal.
Ownership Proprietary.
Facilities Dining room; Physical therapy room; Activities room; Crafts room; Laundry room; Barber/Beauty shop; Library.
Activities Arts and Crafts; Cards; Games; Reading groups; Prayer groups; Movies; Shopping trips; Dances/Social or cultural gatherings.
Description Facility is located on 4 ½ acres of beautifully landscaped grounds where patients can walk around. Also, facility has perimeter fence and locked gates and is able to accomodate patients who are confused and wanderers.

Del Rio Sanitarium
7004 E Gage Ave, Bell Gardens, CA, 90201 (213) 773-7881
Admin Glenn Thune.
Licensure Skilled Care. *Beds* 84.
Certified Medi-Cal.
Ownership Proprietary.
Facilities Dining room; Physical therapy room; Activities room; Crafts room; Laundry room; Barber/Beauty shop; Library.
Activities Arts and Crafts; Cards; Games; Reading groups; Prayer groups; Movies; Shopping trips; Dances/Social or cultural gatherings.
Description Facility is a locked geriatric facility and has perimeter fence around it. The 4 ½ acres of grounds are beautifully landscaped.

BELLFLOWER

Bellflower Convalescent Hospital*
9710 E Artesia Ave, Bellflower, CA, 90706 (213) 925-2274
Admin Pompeyo Rosales.
Licensure Skilled Care. *Beds* 49. *Certified* Medicare; Medi-Cal.
Ownership Proprietary.

Bellflower Golden Age Convalescent Home*
9028 Rose St, Bellflower, CA, 90706 (213) 867-8973
Admin Rose Marie Vigil.
Licensure Skilled Care. *Beds* 53. *Certified* Medicare; Medi-Cal.
Ownership Nonprofit.

Bird Haven Christian Convalescent Hospital*
16910 Woodruff Ave, Bellflower, CA, 90706 (213) 867-1761
Admin Helen Ford.
Licensure Skilled Care. *Beds* 99. *Certified* Medicare; Medi-Cal.
Ownership Proprietary.

Woodruff Convalescent Center
17836 S Woodruff Ave, Bellflower, CA, 90706 (213) 925-8457
Admin Martin Simon. *Medical Dir/Dir of Nursing* Lawrence Wallington MD.
Licensure Skilled Care. *Beds* 140. *Certified* Medicare; Medi-Cal.
Ownership Proprietary.
Admissions Requirements Minimum age 16; Medical examination; Physician's request.
Staff RNs 4 (ft), 5 (pt); LPNs 6 (ft), 1 (pt); Orderlies 1 (ft); Nurses aides 52 (ft); Activities coordinators 2 (ft); Dietitians 1 (ft).
Facilities Dining room; Physical therapy room; Activities room; Crafts room; Barber/Beauty shop.
Activities Arts and Crafts; Games; Prayer groups; Movies.

BELMONT

Belmont Convalescent Hospital
1041 Hill St, Belmont, CA, 94002 (415) 591-7181
Admin Mary Lou South. *Medical Dir/Dir of Nursing* Jonathan F Feinberg.
Licensure Skilled Care. *Beds* 33.
Ownership Proprietary.
Admissions Requirements Medical examination.
Staff RNs 2 (ft), 2 (pt); LPNs 1 (ft), 1 (pt); Nurses aides 8 (ft), 1 (pt); Physical therapists 1 (pt); Activities coordinators 1 (pt).
Facilities Dining room; Activities room; Laundry room; Barber/Beauty shop.
Activities Arts and Crafts; Cards; Games; Reading groups; Prayer groups; Movies; Van rides.

Carlmont Convalescent Hospital*
2140 Carlmont Dr, Belmont, CA, 94002 (415) 591-9601
Admin Anne B Dattola.
Licensure Skilled Care. *Beds* 59.
Certified Medi-Cal.
Ownership Proprietary.

BERKELEY

Ashby Geriatric Hospital Inc*
2270 Ashby Ave, Berkeley, CA, 94705 (415) 841-9494
Admin Bradley M Besaw.

Licensure Skilled Care. *Beds* 31. *Certified* Medicare; Medi-Cal.
Ownership Proprietary.

Berkeley Hills Convalescent Hospital*
2223 Ashby Ave, Berkeley, CA, 94705 (415) 843-7007
Admin Suellen Rideout.
Licensure Skilled Care. *Beds* 36. *Certified* Medicare; Medi-Cal.
Ownership Proprietary.

Chaparrel House
1309 Allston Way, Berkeley, CA, 94702 (415) 848-8774
Admin Evelyn B Huden. *Medical Dir/Dir of Nursing* L Craig MD.
Licensure Intermediate Care. *Beds* 49. *Certified* Medi-Cal.
Ownership Nonprofit.
Staff RNs 1 (pt); LPNs 7 (ft); Nurses aides 10 (ft), 4 (pt); Activities coordinators 1 (ft).
Facilities Dining room; Activities room; Crafts room; Laundry room; Barber/Beauty shop.
Activities Arts and Crafts; Cards; Games; Reading groups; Prayer groups; Movies; Shopping trips.
Description Residents have choice of 2 entrees at lunch and dinner. Residents are encouraged to be independent and individuals in every way.

Claremont Convalescent Hospital*
2500 Ashby Ave, Berkeley, CA, 94705 (415) 841-5260
Admin Jon T Colucci.
Licensure Skilled Care. *Beds* 36. *Certified* Medicare; Medi-Cal.
Ownership Nonprofit.

Elmwood Convalescent Hospital
2829 Shattuck Ave, Berkeley, CA, 94705 (415) 848-3760
Admin Dick A Isaacs. *Medical Dir/Dir of Nursing* Dr Gillis Esslinger.
Licensure Skilled Care. *Beds* 81. *Certified* Medicare; Medi-Cal.
Ownership Proprietary.
Admissions Requirements Physician's request.
Staff Physicians 3 (pt); RNs 4 (ft); LPNs 8 (ft); Nurses aides 34 (ft), 5 (pt); Physical therapists 1 (pt); Occupational therapists 1 (pt); Activities coordinators 1 (ft); Dietitians 1 (pt); Dentists 1 (pt); Podiatrists 1 (pt).
Facilities Dining room; Activities room; Crafts room; Barber/Beauty shop.
Activities Arts and Crafts; Cards; Games; Reading groups; Prayer groups; Movies; Trips to restaurants and parks.
Description A lovely clean facility built around a landscaped, carpeted, patio; an intensive physical therapy program; extensive activity calendar, and a consistently humanistic approach to service to residents.

Kyakameena Sanitorium 2
2131 Carleton St, Berkeley, CA, 94704 (415) 843-2131
Admin Portia H Strause. *Medical Dir/Dir of Nursing* Roxanne Fiscella.
Licensure Skilled Care. *Beds* 59. *Certified* Medicare; Medi-Cal.
Ownership Proprietary.

Admissions Requirements Medical examination; Physician's request.
Staff RNs 1 (ft), 1 (pt); LPNs 6 (ft), 2 (pt); Nurses aides 21 (ft), 5 (pt); Physical therapists 1 (pt); Occupational therapists 1 (pt); Activities coordinators 1 (ft); Dietitians 1 (pt).
Facilities Dining room; Laundry room; Barber/Beauty shop.
Activities Arts and Crafts; Cards; Games; Reading groups; Prayer groups; Movies; Shopping trips; Dances/Social or cultural gatherings.

BIG PINE

Inyo County Sanitorium*
County Rd, Box 88, Big Pine, CA, 93513 (714) 938-2411
Admin Michael Cosenza.
Licensure Skilled Care. *Beds* 45. *Certified* Medicare; Medi-Cal.
Ownership Public.

BLOOMINGTON

Intercommunity Center of Bloomington*
18612 Santa Ana, Bloomington, CA, 92316 (714) 877-1201
Admin Ben Bollinger.
Licensure Intermediate Care; Intermediate Care for Mentally Retarded. *Beds* 96.
Certified Medi-Cal.
Ownership Nonprofit.

BLYTHE

Blythe Convalescent Hospital
285 W Chanslor Way, Blythe, CA, 92225 (619) 922-8176
Admin John Ryan. *Medical Dir/Dir of Nursing* William Wiley MD.
Licensure Skilled Care. *Beds* 50.
Certified Medi-Cal.
Ownership Proprietary.
Admissions Requirements Medical examination; Physician's request.
Staff Physicians 1 (pt); RNs 2 (ft); LPNs 3 (ft), 1 (pt); Orderlies 1 (ft); Nurses aides 13 (ft), 5 (pt); Physical therapists 1 (pt); Reality therapists 1 (pt); Recreational therapists 1 (ft); Occupational therapists 1 (pt); Activities coordinators 1 (ft); Dietitians 1 (ft); Dentists 1 (pt); Ophthalmologists 1 (pt); Podiatrists 1 (pt); Audiologists 1 (pt).
Facilities Dining room; Activities room; Crafts room; Laundry room; Barber/Beauty shop.
Activities Arts and Crafts; Cards; Games; Reading groups; Prayer groups; Shopping trips; Dances/Social or cultural gatherings.

BRAWLEY

Royal Convalescent Hospital Inc*
320 W Cattle Call Dr, Brawley, CA, 92227 (714) 344-5431
Admin Tobias Friedman.
Licensure Skilled Care. *Beds* 99. *Certified* Medicare; Medi-Cal.
Ownership Proprietary.

BUENA PARK

Farmdale Convalescent Hospital*
8520 Western Ave, Buena Park, CA, 90620 (714) 828-8222
Admin Theresa J McAlpine.
Licensure Skilled Care. *Beds* 143. *Certified* Medicare; Medi-Cal.
Ownership Proprietary.

Orange West Convalescent Hospital
9021 Knott Ave, Buena Park, CA, 90620 (714) 826-2330
Admin Will Vernon.
Licensure Skilled Care. *Beds* 99. *Certified* Medicare; Medi-Cal.
Ownership Proprietary.

BURBANK

Beverly Manor*
925 W Alameda Ave, Burbank, CA, 91506 (213) 849-6766
Admin Cleo Phillips.
Licensure Skilled Care. *Beds* 89. *Certified* Medicare; Medi-Cal.
Ownership Proprietary.

Beverly Manor Convalescent Hospital
1041 S Main St, Burbank, CA, 91506 (818) 843-2330
Admin Berna-Dean Darms. *Medical Dir/Dir of Nursing* Dr Valentine Birds.
Licensure Skilled Care. *Beds* 188. *Certified* Medicare; Medi-Cal.
Ownership Proprietary.
Admissions Requirements Medical examination.
Staff Physicians 32 (pt); RNs 8 (ft), 6 (pt); LPNs 11 (ft), 6 (pt); Nurses aides 67 (ft), 1 (pt); Physical therapists 2 (pt); Occupational therapists 1 (pt); Speech therapists 3 (pt); Activities coordinators 2 (ft); Dietitians 1 (pt); Dentists 1 (pt); Ophthalmologists 2 (pt); Podiatrists 3 (pt); Audiologists 1 (pt).
Facilities Dining room; Physical therapy room; Activities room; Crafts room; Laundry room; Barber/Beauty shop.
Activities Arts and Crafts; Cards; Games; Reading groups; Prayer groups; Movies; Shopping trips; Dances/Social or cultural gatherings; Grooming class; Reality class; Restorative exercise; Cooking classes; Patient council; Birthday parties; Adult education; Outings.
Description The hospital has 73 spacious semi-private rooms, many with access to patio; 2 private rooms; clean and bright environment; and large, spacious activity areas. Special monthly activities include candlelight dinner and country-style breakfast.

Burbank Convalescent Hospital*
2710 W Olive Ave, Burbank, CA, 91505 (213) 849-1521
Admin Clarizo Orlando.
Licensure Skilled Care. *Beds* 54. *Certified* Medicare; Medi-Cal.
Ownership Proprietary.

Cypress Convalescent Center*
700 N 1st St, Burbank, CA, 91502 (213) 842-8169

Admin Michael O'Neil.
Licensure Skilled Care. *Beds* 70. *Certified* Medicare; Medi-Cal.
Ownership Proprietary.

Magnolia Health Center
620 N 1st St, Burbank, CA, 91502 (213) 843-4433
Admin Susan Sims. *Medical Dir/Dir of Nursing* Dr Mark Schenkel.
Licensure Skilled Care. *Beds* 99.
Certified Medi-Cal.
Ownership Proprietary.
Admissions Requirements Minimum age 30.
Staff RNs 1 (ft), 1 (pt); LPNs 7 (ft), 5 (pt); Nurses aides 30 (ft); Physical therapists; Recreational therapists; Occupational therapists; Speech therapists; Activities coordinators; Dietitians; Dentists; Ophthalmologists; Podiatrists; Audiologists.

Saint Joseph's Medical Center—Esther Pariseau Pavilion
2727 W Alameda Ave, Burbank, CA, 91505 (213) 843-3444
Admin Scott T Seamons.
Licensure Skilled Care. *Beds* 149. *Certified* Medicare; Medi-Cal.
Ownership Nonprofit.
Affiliation Roman Catholic
Description Facility offers occupational, physical and speech pathology/audio therapy, and social services.

Wesley Nursing Home*
227 E Grinnell Dr, Burbank, CA, 91502 (213) 845-7484
Admin Charlotte Doncaster.
Licensure Skilled Care. *Beds* 44. *Certified* Medicare; Medi-Cal.
Ownership Nonprofit.

BURLINGAME

Bayview Convalescent Hospital
1100 Trousdale Dr, Burlingame, CA, 94010 (415) 692-3758
Admin Samuel G Bergstrom. *Medical Dir/Dir of Nursing* Robert Minkowsky.
Licensure Skilled Care. *Beds* 281. *Certified* Medicare; Medi-Cal.
Ownership Proprietary.
Admissions Requirements Minimum age 60; Physician's request.
Staff RNs 10 (ft), 10 (pt); LPNs 10 (ft), 13 (pt); Nurses aides 68 (ft), 29 (pt); Physical therapists 2 (pt); Occupational therapists 1 (pt); Speech therapists 1 (pt); Activities coordinators 2 (ft); Dietitians 1 (ft); Dentists 1 (pt); Podiatrists 1 (pt).
Facilities Dining room; Physical therapy room; Laundry room; Barber/Beauty shop.
Activities Arts and Crafts; Cards; Games; Reading groups; Prayer groups; Movies; Shopping trips; Dances/Social or cultural gatherings.
Description The music department, in conjunction with the activities department, provides stimulation and variety of programs.

Hillhaven Convalescent Hospital*
1609 Trousdale Dr, Burlingame, CA, 94010 (415) 697-1865

Admin Sally Brown.
Licensure Skilled Care. *Beds* 85. *Certified* Medicare; Medi-Cal.
Ownership Proprietary.

CALISTOGA

Calistoga Convalescent Hospital
1715 Washington St, Calistoga, CA, 94515
(707) 942-6253
Admin Mary E Robinson. *Medical Dir/Dir of Nursing* Dr D O'Neil.
Licensure Skilled Care. *Beds* 72. *Certified* Medicare; Medi-Cal.
Ownership Proprietary.
Admissions Requirements Physician's request.
Facilities Dining room; Physical therapy room; Activities room; Crafts room; Laundry room; Barber/Beauty shop; Library.
Activities Arts and Crafts; Games; Reading groups; Prayer groups; Movies; Dances/Social or cultural gatherings.

CAMARILLO

Camarillo Convalescent Hospital
205 Granada St, Camarillo, CA, 93010 (805) 482-9805
Admin Margaret Devoir. *Medical Dir/Dir of Nursing* Leonard Ackland MD.
Licensure Skilled Care. *Beds* 114. *Certified* Medicare; Medi-Cal.
Ownership Proprietary.
Admissions Requirements Physician's request.
Facilities Dining room; Activities room; Crafts room; Laundry room; Barber/Beauty shop.
Activities Arts and Crafts; Games; Reading groups; Movies; Shopping trips.

CAMPBELL

Arndt Convalescent Hospital*
3333 S Bascom Ave, Campbell, CA, 95008
(408) 377-1183
Admin Opal A Schlesinger.
Licensure Skilled Care. *Beds* 57.
Certified Medi-Cal.
Ownership Proprietary.

Camden Convalescent Hospital*
1331 Camden Ave, Campbell, CA, 95008 (408) 377-4030
Admin Margaret Jo Randall.
Licensure Skilled Care. *Beds* 59.
Certified Medi-Cal.
Ownership Proprietary.

Eldercare Convalescent Hospital
238 Virginia Ave, Campbell, CA, 95008 (408) 379-8114
Admin Terry Smith-Campbell. *Medical Dir/Dir of Nursing* Norman Woods MD.
Licensure Skilled Care. *Beds* 25. *Certified* Medicare; Medi-Cal.
Ownership Proprietary.
Admissions Requirements Medical examination; Physician's request.
Staff RNs 2 (ft), 3 (pt); LPNs 3 (ft), 2 (pt); Nurses aides 8 (ft), 4 (pt); Physical therapists; Recreational therapists; Occupational thera-

pists; Speech therapists; Activities coordinators 1 (ft); Dietitians; Dentists; Ophthalmologists; Podiatrists.
Facilities Dining room; Activities room; Crafts room.
Activities Arts and Crafts; Cards; Games; Reading groups; Prayer groups; Movies; Shopping trips; Dances/Social or cultural gatherings.

CANOGA PARK

Beverly Manor Convalescent Hospital
7940 Topanga Canyon Blvd, Canoga Park, CA, 91304 (213) 347-3800
Admin Barbara A Emert. *Medical Dir/Dir of Nursing* Robert Watson MD.
Licensure Skilled Care. *Beds* 149. *Certified* Medicare; Medi-Cal.
Ownership Proprietary.
Admissions Requirements Medical examination; Physician's request.
Staff RNs 12 (ft); LPNs 13 (ft); Nurses aides 52 (ft); Physical therapists 2 (ft); Reality therapists 1 (ft); Recreational therapists 2 (ft); Occupational therapists 1 (ft), 1 (pt); Speech therapists 1 (pt); Activities coordinators 2 (ft); Dietitians 1 (pt).
Facilities Dining room; Physical therapy room; Activities room; Chapel; Laundry room; Barber/Beauty shop; Library; Music room.
Activities Arts and Crafts; Cards; Games; Reading groups; Movies; Shopping trips; Dances/Social or cultural gatherings; Dining out.
Description Facility has a complete rehabilitation program, physical therapy, occupational therapy, and speech programs, and a well organized and very active stroke club. Once-a-month has a candlelight dinner with entertainment and once-a-month residents dine out for lunch.

Canoga Terrace Convalescent Hospital*
22029 Saticoy St, Canoga Park, CA, 91304
(213) 887-7050
Admin Marilyn Morris.
Licensure Skilled Care. *Beds* 200. *Certified* Medicare; Medi-Cal.
Ownership Proprietary.

Golden State West Valley Convalescent Hospital*
7057 Shoup Ave, Canoga Park, CA, 91304
(213) 348-8422
Admin Marie S Mills.
Licensure Skilled Care. *Beds* 99. *Certified* Medicare; Medi-Cal.
Ownership Proprietary.

Holiday Manor Nursitarium
20554 Roscoe Blvd, Canoga Park, CA, 91306
(213) 465-3328
Admin Marsha D Todd.
Licensure Skilled Care. *Beds* 92. *Certified* Medicaid; Medicare; Medi-Cal.
Ownership Proprietary.

Topanga Terrace Convalescent Center
22125 Roscoe Blvd, Canoga Park, CA, 91304
(213) 883-7292
Admin Nicholas Deutsch. *Medical Dir/Dir of Nursing* Edwin Marcus MD.
Licensure Skilled Care. *Beds* 112. *Cer-*

tified Medicare; Medi-Cal.
Ownership Proprietary.
Admissions Requirements Minimum age 18; Physician's request.
Staff RNs 6 (ft), 1 (pt); LPNs 6 (ft), 2 (pt); Orderlies 7 (ft); Nurses aides 29 (ft), 4 (pt); Activities coordinators 1 (ft), 1 (pt); Dietitians 1 (pt).
Facilities Dining room; Physical therapy room; Activities room; Chapel; Laundry room; Barber/Beauty shop.
Activities Arts and Crafts; Cards; Games; Prayer groups; Movies; Dances/Social or cultural gatherings.

CAPISTRANO BEACH

Beverly Manor Convalescent Hospital
35410 Del Rey, Capistrano Beach, CA, 92624
(714) 496-5786
Admin Carolyn Carlsen-Rouzier. *Medical Dir/Dir of Nursing* Dr B Bundy.
Licensure Skilled Care. *Beds* 127. *Certified* Medicare; Medi-Cal.
Ownership Proprietary.
Admissions Requirements Minimum age 21.
Staff RNs 20 (ft); LPNs 20 (ft); Nurses aides 90 (ft); Activities coordinators 1 (ft); Dietitians 1 (ft).
Facilities Dining room; Physical therapy room; Activities room; Crafts room; Laundry room; Barber/Beauty shop.
Activities Arts and Crafts; Cards; Games; Reading groups; Prayer groups; Movies; Shopping trips.

CAPITOLA

Eldercare Convalescent Hospital*
1935 Wharf Rd, Capitola, CA, 95010 (408) 476-0770
Admin Ralph N Tisdial.
Licensure Skilled Care. *Beds* 25. *Certified* Medicare; Medi-Cal.
Ownership Proprietary.

Golden Age Convalescent Hospital
523 Burlingame, Capitola, CA, 95010 (408) 475-0722
Admin John Smith. *Medical Dir/Dir of Nursing* Paul Weiss MD.
Licensure Skilled Care. *Beds* 40. *Certified* Medicare.
Ownership Proprietary.
Admissions Requirements Minimum age 56; Physician's request.
Staff Physicians 2 (pt); RNs 1 (ft), 3 (pt); LPNs 4 (ft), 3 (pt); Orderlies 2 (pt); Nurses aides 4 (ft), 9 (pt).
Facilities Dining room; Activities room; Laundry room; Barber/Beauty shop.
Activities Arts and Crafts; Cards; Games; Reading groups; Prayer groups; Movies; Shopping trips; Dances/Social or cultural gatherings.
Description Facility features a home-like setting and personnel taking care of patients as if they were their own relatives or parents.

CARLSBAD

Lutheran Health Facility of Carlsbad
201 Grand Ave, Carlsbad, CA, 92008 (714)
729-4983
Admin Thomas K Pembleton Jr. *Medical Dir-/Dir of Nursing* Dr Albert Freiberger.
Licensure Skilled Care. *Beds* 59. *Certified* Medicare; Medi-Cal.
Ownership Nonprofit.
Admissions Requirements Physician's request.
Staff Physicians 1 (pt); RNs 4 (ft), 3 (pt); LPNs
1 (pt); Nurses aides 20 (ft), 15 (pt); Physical
therapists 1 (pt); Occupational therapists 1 (pt);
Speech therapists 1 (pt); Activities coordinators
1 (pt); Dietitians 1 (pt).
Affiliation Lutheran
Facilities Dining room; Physical therapy room;
Activities room; Barber/Beauty shop.
Activities Arts and Crafts; Cards; Games;
Reading groups; Prayer groups; Movies; Dances/Social or cultural gatherings.
Description Lutheran Health Facility of Carlsbad offers skilled nursing care and is situated
across the street from Carlsbad by the Sea
Retirement Home, sharing its waters-edge location by the Pacific Ocean.

CARMEL

Carmel Convalescent Hospital*
Hwy 1 at Valley Way, Carmel, CA, 93921 (408)
624-8296
Admin Tanis Clark Jr.
Licensure Skilled Care. *Beds* 65. *Certified* Medicare; Medi-Cal.
Ownership Proprietary.

Carmel Valley Manor
8545 Carmel Valley Rd, Carmel, CA, 93921
(408) 624-1281
Admin John P Doolittle. *Medical Dir/Dir of
Nursing* David Thorngate MD.
Licensure Skilled Care. *Beds* 28. *Certified* Medicare; Medi-Cal.
Ownership Nonprofit.
Admissions Requirements Minimum age 65;
Medical examination; Physician's request.
Staff Physicians 2 (pt); RNs 3 (ft), 7 (pt); LPNs
1 (ft); Orderlies 2 (ft), 1 (pt); Nurses aides 14
(ft), 4 (pt); Physical therapists 1 (pt); Recreational therapists 1 (pt); Occupational therapists
1 (pt); Activities coordinators 1 (pt); Dietitians
1 (pt); Dentists 1 (pt); Podiatrists 1 (pt).
Affiliation Congregational
Facilities Dining room; Physical therapy room;
Activities room; Chapel; Crafts room; Laundry
room; Barber/Beauty shop; Library.
Activities Arts and Crafts; Games; Reading
groups; Prayer groups; Movies; Shopping trips;
Dances/Social or cultural gatherings; Picnics;
Barbecues; Scenic rides.

CARMICHAEL

Carmichael Convalescent Hospital
8336 Fair Oaks Blvd, Carmichael, CA, 95608
(916) 944-3100
Admin Carole Henry. *Medical Dir/Dir of
Nursing* Lloyd D Bowles MD.
Licensure Skilled Care. *Beds* 126. *Cer-

tified* Medicare; Medi-Cal.
Ownership Proprietary.
Facilities Dining room; Physical therapy room;
Activities room; Crafts room; Laundry room;
Barber/Beauty shop; Library.
Activities Arts and Crafts; Cards; Games;
Reading groups; Prayer groups; Movies; Dances/Social or cultural gatherings.

Crestwood Manor—Carmichael
4741 Engle Rd, Carmichael, CA, 95608 (916)
483-8424
Admin Rufus L McDonald. *Medical Dir/Dir
of Nursing* Dr Donald N ReVille.
Beds 80. *Certified* Medi-Cal.
Ownership Proprietary.
Admissions Requirements Minimum age 18;
Medical examination; Physician's request.
Staff Physicians 6 (pt); RNs 2 (ft), 2 (pt); LPNs
8 (ft), 5 (pt); Orderlies 10 (ft), 2 (pt); Nurses
aides 7 (ft), 3 (pt); Recreational therapists 1 (ft);
Activities coordinators 1 (ft); Dietitians 1 (pt).
Facilities Dining room; Activities room; Crafts
room; Library.
Activities Arts and Crafts; Cards; Games;
Reading groups; Prayer groups; Movies; Shopping trips; Dances/Social or cultural gatherings;
Bus mobility; Vocational training.

El Camino Convalescent Hospital*
2540 Carmichael Way, Carmichael, CA, 95608
(916) 482-0465
Admin Jame Cook.
Licensure Skilled Care. *Beds* 170. *Certified* Medicare; Medi-Cal.
Ownership Proprietary.

Eskaton Manzanita Manor
5318 Manzanita Ave, Carmichael, CA, 95608
(916) 331-8513
Admin Louis H Koff. *Medical Dir/Dir of
Nursing* Dr D ReVille.
Licensure Skilled Care. *Beds* 99. *Certified* Medicare; Medi-Cal.
Ownership Nonprofit.
Staff RNs 5 (ft), 1 (pt); LPNs 12 (ft), 2 (pt);
Nurses aides 35 (ft), 15 (pt); Physical therapists
1 (ft); Recreational therapists 1 (ft); Occupational therapists 1 (ft); Speech therapists 1 (ft);
Dietitians 1 (pt); Dentists 1 (pt); Podiatrists 1
(pt).
Facilities Dining room; Physical therapy room;
Activities room; Crafts room; Laundry room;
Barber/Beauty shop; Library.
Activities Arts and Crafts; Cards; Games;
Reading groups; Prayer groups; Movies; Shopping trips; Dances/Social or cultural gatherings.
Description The facility specializes in short-term sub-acute rehabilitation care and is recognized in northern California as a primary treatment site for post-acute rehabilitation
admissions.

Mission Oaks Convalescent Hospital*
3630 Mission Ave, Carmichael, CA, 95608
(916) 488-1580
Admin Donald J Hunter.
Licensure Skilled Care. *Beds* 138. *Certified* Medicare; Medi-Cal.
Ownership Proprietary.

Mountain Manor
6101 Fair Oaks Blvd, Carmichael, CA, 95608
(916) 488-7211
Admin Stuart Drake.
Licensure Intermediate Care. *Beds* 47. *Certified* Medi-Cal.
Ownership Proprietary.
Admissions Requirements Minimum age 62;
Physician's request.
Staff RNs 1 (ft), 2 (pt); LPNs 3 (ft), 2 (pt);
Orderlies 1 (ft); Nurses aides 10 (ft); Activities
coordinators 1 (ft).
Facilities Dining room; Physical therapy room;
Activities room; Crafts room; Laundry room;
Barber/Beauty shop.
Activities Arts and Crafts; Cards; Games;
Reading groups; Prayer groups; Movies; Shopping trips; Dances/Social or cultural gatherings;
Bingo; Exercise; Ceramics.

Walnut Whitney Convalescent Hospital
3529 Walnut Ave, Carmichael, CA, 95608
(916) 488-8601
Admin Richard L Thorpe. *Medical Dir/Dir of
Nursing* William E Hedges MD.
Licensure Skilled Care. *Beds* 126. *Certified* Medicare; Medi-Cal.
Ownership Proprietary.
Admissions Requirements Medical examination; Physician's request.
Staff Physicians 35 (pt); RNs 6 (ft), 6 (pt);
LPNs 10 (ft), 5 (pt); Nurses aides 40 (ft), 10
(pt); Physical therapists 1 (pt); Reality therapists
1 (pt); Recreational therapists 1 (pt); Occupational therapists 1 (pt); Speech therapists 1 (pt);
Activities coordinators 2 (ft); Dietitians 1 (pt);
Dentists 1 (pt); Ophthalmologists 1 (pt); Podiatrists 1 (pt); Audiologists 1 (pt).

CASTRO VALLEY

Chabot Convalescent Hospital*
20259 Lake Chabot Rd, Castro Valley, CA,
94546 (415) 351-3700
Admin Mark T Tollefson.
Licensure Skilled Care. *Beds* 95. *Certified* Medicare; Medi-Cal.
Ownership Proprietary.

Redwood Convalescent Hospital
22103 Redwood Rd, Castro Valley, CA, 94546
(415) 537-8848
Admin Robert J Myers.
Licensure Skilled Care. *Beds* 70. *Certified* Medicare; Medi-Cal.
Ownership Proprietary.
Admissions Requirements Medical examination; Physician's request.
Staff Physicians 1 (pt); RNs 3 (ft), 2 (pt); LPNs
7 (ft), 3 (pt); Orderlies 1 (ft); Nurses aides 27
(ft), 2 (pt); Physical therapists 1 (pt); Activities
coordinators 1 (ft), 1 (pt); Dietitians 1 (pt).
Facilities Dining room; Physical therapy room;
Activities room; Chapel; Crafts room; Laundry
room; Barber/Beauty shop.
Activities Arts and Crafts; Cards; Games;
Reading groups; Prayer groups; Movies; Shopping trips; Dances/Social or cultural gatherings.
Description Original 48-bed facility built in
1965 with an addition of 22 added in 1970. All
patient rooms semi-private (2 beds). Excellent
location to acute hospitals and bus lines.

Saint Annes Convalescent Hospital
22424 Charlene Way, Castro Valley, CA, 94546
(415) 537-5944
Admin Marguerite Balaz. *Medical Dir/Dir of Nursing* Andrew May MD.
Licensure Skilled Care. *Beds* 48. *Certified* Medicare; Medi-Cal.
Ownership Proprietary.
Admissions Requirements Medical examination; Physician's request.
Facilities Dining room; Activities room; Crafts room; Laundry room; Barber/Beauty shop.
Activities Arts and Crafts; Cards; Games; Prayer groups; Movies; Dances/Social or cultural gatherings.

Saint John of Kronstadt Nursing Home
4432 James Ave, PO Box 2794, Castro Valley, CA, 94546 (415) 889-7000
Admin Fred Sanciangco. *Medical Dir/Dir of Nursing* Andrew May MD.
Licensure Skilled Care. *Beds* 49. *Certified* Medicare; Medi-Cal.
Ownership Nonprofit.
Staff Physicians 6 (pt); RNs 1 (ft), 4 (pt); LPNs 3 (ft), 6 (pt); Nurses aides 12 (ft), 5 (pt); Physical therapists 1 (pt); Occupational therapists 1 (pt); Speech therapists 1 (pt); Activities coordinators 1 (ft), 1 (pt); Dietitians 1 (pt); Dentists 1 (pt); Podiatrists 1 (pt).
Affiliation Russian Orthodox
Facilities Dining room; Activities room; Chapel; Laundry room; TV Room.
Activities Arts and Crafts; Cards; Games; Reading groups; Prayer groups; Movies.
Description Facility is located in the hills of Castro Valley providing outstanding care to Medicare and Medi-Cal eligible patients and desires long-term patients who are of Russian-American descent. A Russian Orthodox chapel is available for those who desire to pursue their religious convictions.

St Joseph Convalescent Hospital Inc
18949 Redwood Rd, Castro Valley, CA, 94546 (415) 886-1101
Admin Marianne Quenneville. *Medical Dir/Dir of Nursing* Andrew May Jr MD.
Licensure Skilled Care. *Beds* 82. *Certified* Medicare; Medi-Cal.
Ownership Proprietary.
Staff RNs 3 (pt); LPNs 1 (ft), 5 (pt); Nurses aides 6 (ft), 4 (pt); Activities coordinators 1 (ft); Dietitians 1 (pt); Dentists 1 (pt); Podiatrists 1 (pt).
Facilities Dining room; Activities room; Crafts room; Laundry room; Barber/Beauty shop.
Activities Arts and Crafts; Cards; Games; Reading groups; Prayer groups; Movies; Shopping trips; Dances/Social or cultural gatherings.
Description Although this facility maintains a state license as skilled nursing, it accepts only those residents classified as "Intermediate Care." Facility provides nursing care on a 24-hour basis to the ambulatory elderly.

Stanton Hill Convalescent Hospital Inc*
20090 Stanton Ave, Castro Valley, CA, 94546 (415) 538-8464
Admin Joy M Susko.
Licensure Skilled Care. *Beds* 50. *Certified* Medicare; Medi-Cal.
Ownership Proprietary.

CERES

Hale Aloha Convalescent Hospital
1711 Richland Ave, Ceres, CA, 95307 (209) 537-4581
Admin John S Poat. *Medical Dir/Dir of Nursing* Amos Henry MD.
Licensure Skilled Care. *Beds* 46. *Certified* Medicare; Medi-Cal.
Ownership Proprietary.
Admissions Requirements Physician's request.
Staff RNs 1 (ft), 1 (pt); LPNs 2 (ft), 2 (pt); Orderlies 2 (ft); Nurses aides 10 (ft), 3 (pt); Activities coordinators 1 (ft).
Facilities Dining room; Laundry room.
Activities Arts and Crafts; Games; Dances/Social or cultural gatherings.

CHATSWORTH

Chatsworth Health and Rehabilitation Center
21820 Craggy View St, Chatsworth, CA, 91311 (213) 882-8233
Admin Myra S Burman. *Medical Dir/Dir of Nursing* Carl M Friedman MD.
Licensure Skilled Care. *Beds* 132. *Certified* Medicare.
Ownership Proprietary.
Admissions Requirements Minimum age 18; Physician's request.
Staff Physical therapists; Recreational therapists 15 (ft); Occupational therapists; Speech therapists; Activities coordinators 2 (ft); Dietitians.
Facilities Dining room; Activities room; Crafts room; Barber/Beauty shop; Library.
Activities Arts and Crafts; Cards; Games; Reading groups; Movies; Shopping trips; Dances/Social or cultural gatherings.
Description Center has special treatment program funded by state of California for mentally disabled. Psychiatrist available in facility 4 days per week.

Chatsworth Park Convalescent Hospital
10610 Owensmouth Ave, Chatsworth, CA, 91311 (213) 882-3200
Admin Marcia Fischbach. *Medical Dir/Dir of Nursing* Dr John Diehl.
Licensure Skilled Care. *Beds* SNF 75; ICF 53. *Certified* Medicare; Medi-Cal.
Ownership Proprietary.
Admissions Requirements Minimum age 50; Physician's request.
Staff Physicians 12 (pt); RNs 4 (ft), 2 (pt); LPNs 4 (ft), 3 (pt); Nurses aides 30 (ft), 4 (pt); Physical therapists 1 (pt); Recreational therapists 1 (ft); Speech therapists 1 (pt); Activities coordinators 1 (ft); Dietitians 1 (pt); Dentists 1 (pt); Ophthalmologists 1 (pt); Podiatrists 1 (pt); Audiologists 1 (pt).
Facilities Dining room; Physical therapy room; Activities room; Crafts room; Laundry room; Barber/Beauty shop; Library.
Activities Arts and Crafts; Cards; Games; Reading groups; Prayer groups; Movies; Dances/Social or cultural gatherings.

CHERRY VALLEY

Sunset Haven Convalescent Hospital*
9246 Avenida Mira Villa, Cherry Valley, CA, 92223 (714) 845-3194
Admin Doug Padgett.
Licensure Skilled Care. *Beds* 59.
Certified Medi-Cal.
Ownership Nonprofit.

CHICO

Beverly Manor Convalescent Hospital*
188 Cohasset Ln, Chico, CA, 95926 (916) 343-6084
Admin Mary E Granneman.
Licensure Skilled Care. *Beds* 76. *Certified* Medicare; Medi-Cal.
Ownership Proprietary.

Chico Convalescent Hospital*
1645 The Esplanade, Chico, CA, 95926 (916) 343-6045
Admin Janet M Walston.
Licensure Skilled Care. *Beds* 59. *Certified* Medicare; Medi-Cal.
Ownership Proprietary.

Crestwood Convalescent Hospital
587 Rio Lindo Ave, Chico, CA, 95926 (916) 345-1306
Admin Larry E Bradley. *Medical Dir/Dir of Nursing* Philip Morgans MD.
Licensure Skilled Care. *Beds* 184. *Certified* Medicare; Medi-Cal.
Ownership Proprietary.
Admissions Requirements Medical examination; Physician's request.
Staff RNs 6 (ft), 4 (pt); LPNs 14 (ft), 3 (pt); Orderlies 4 (ft); Nurses aides 59 (ft), 7 (pt); Physical therapists 3 (pt); Recreational therapists 1 (ft); Activities coordinators 1 (ft); Dietitians 1 (ft).
Facilities Dining room; Physical therapy room; Activities room; Laundry room; Barber/Beauty shop.
Activities Arts and Crafts; Cards; Games; Reading groups; Prayer groups; Movies; Shopping trips; Dances/Social or cultural gatherings.
Description Crestwood—Chico, with 184 beds, is the largest SNF in the northern valley area. Although large enough to have a full-time registered dietician directing the dietary department, the facility provides a warm atmosphere that emphasizes an individual's sense of security and well being. We have a full-time physical therapy department and also offer occupational therapy and speech therapy. Social and educational programs are available to suit various levels of participation, as are volunteer support groups to ensure that individuals' needs are addressed.

Riverside Convalescent Hospital
375 Cohasset Rd, Chico, CA, 95926 (916) 343-5595
Admin Brian Jennings.
Licensure Skilled Care. *Beds* 70. *Certified* Medicare; Medi-Cal.
Ownership Proprietary.
Facilities Dining room; Physical therapy room; Activities room; Crafts room; Laundry room;

Barber/Beauty shop; Library.
Activities Arts and Crafts; Cards; Games; Reading groups; Prayer groups; Movies; Shopping trips; Dances/Social or cultural gatherings.
Description Facility offers quality care.

CHOWCHILLA

Chowchilla Convalescent Hospital
1000 Ventura St, Chowchilla, CA, 93610 (209) 665-4826
Admin Beverly P Brown. *Medical Dir/Dir of Nursing* Thomas F Way MD.
Licensure Skilled Care. *Beds* 65. *Certified* Medicare; Medi-Cal.
Ownership Proprietary.
Admissions Requirements Minimum age 18; Medical examination; Physician's request.
Staff Physicians 4 (pt); RNs 1 (ft), 2 (pt); LPNs 6 (ft), 2 (pt); Nurses aides 27 (ft); Physical therapists 1 (pt); Occupational therapists 1 (pt); Speech therapists 1 (pt); Activities coordinators 1 (ft); Dietitians 1 (pt); Dentists 1 (pt); Ophthalmologists 1 (pt); Podiatrists 1 (pt); Audiologists 1 (pt).
Facilities Dining room; Activities room; Crafts room; Laundry room; Barber/Beauty shop.
Activities Arts and Crafts; Cards; Games; Reading groups; Prayer groups; Movies; Shopping trips; Dances/Social or cultural gatherings.
Description Our activities program is outstanding. We have a covered patio and shade trees throughout the grounds, which are excellent for outside activities.

CHULA VISTA

Collingwood Manor*
553 F St, Chula Vista, CA, 92010 (714) 426-8611
Admin Mary C Norwood.
Licensure Intermediate Care. *Beds* 88. *Certified* Medi-Cal.
Ownership Nonprofit.

Fredericka Convalescent Hospital*
111 3rd Ave, Chula Vista, CA, 92010 (714) 427-2777
Admin James F Emerson.
Licensure Skilled Care. *Beds* 163. *Certified* Medicare; Medi-Cal.
Ownership Nonprofit.

CITY OF INDUSTRY

El-Encanto Convalescent Hospital
555 El Encanto Dr, City of Industry, CA, 91744 (818) 336-1274
Admin Buck L Perkins. *Medical Dir/Dir of Nursing* Dr Sergio Andrate.
Licensure Skilled Care; Intermediate Care for Mentally Retarded. *Beds* SNF 159; ICF/MR 89. *Certified* Medicare; Medi-Cal.
Ownership Nonprofit.
Admissions Requirements Minimum age 18.
Staff Physicians 5 (pt); RNs 4 (ft), 6 (pt); LPNs 24 (ft), 2 (pt); Nurses aides 99 (ft); Physical therapists 1 (ft); Occupational therapists 1 (pt); Activities coordinators 1 (ft); Dietitians 1 (ft); Dentists 1 (pt); Podiatrists 1 (pt).

Facilities Dining room; Physical therapy room; Activities room; Crafts room; Laundry room; Barber/Beauty shop.
Activities Arts and Crafts; Cards; Games; Reading groups; Movies; Shopping trips; Dances/Social or cultural gatherings.
Description The facility is one of the few in which each room is temperature controlled. Dietary department is staffed with a regular dietician and a consultant chef. Facility has a van for transportation. The hospital is located on a quiet, private street with security. Level of staffing is high with 3.6 hours of nursing care per patient.

CLAREMONT

Claremont Convalescent Hospital
650 W Harrison Ave, Claremont, CA, 91711 (714) 626-1227
Admin Floy Biggs. *Medical Dir/Dir of Nursing* Rinard Hart.
Licensure Skilled Care. *Beds* 58. *Certified* Medicare; Medi-Cal.
Ownership Nonprofit.
Staff RNs 4 (ft); LPNs 6 (ft); Orderlies 1 (ft); Nurses aides 19 (ft); Activities coordinators 1 (ft).
Facilities Dining room; Activities room; Crafts room; Laundry room; Barber/Beauty shop; Library; Pool room; Sewing room; Meeting hall.
Activities Arts and Crafts; Cards; Games; Reading groups; Prayer groups; Movies.
Description The nursing home is on the grounds of a 15-acre retirement complex. The grounds include a home health agency and PSU units. Beautiful grounds and tender loving care make facility very lovely.

Hillhaven Convalescent Hospital
590 Indian Hill, Claremont, CA, 91711 (714) 624-4511
Admin Mary Ann Ferguson. *Medical Dir/Dir of Nursing* Richard Hart MD.
Licensure Skilled Care. *Beds* 99. *Certified* Medicare; Medi-Cal.
Ownership Proprietary.
Staff Physicians 1 (ft); RNs 3 (ft), 3 (pt); LPNs 11 (ft), 4 (pt); Physical therapists 1 (pt); Reality therapists 1 (pt); Occupational therapists 1 (pt); Speech therapists 1 (pt); Activities coordinators 1 (ft); Dietitians 1 (pt); Dentists 1 (pt); Ophthalmologists 1 (pt); Podiatrists 1 (pt); Audiologists 1 (pt).
Facilities Dining room; Physical therapy room; Activities room; Crafts room; Laundry room; Barber/Beauty shop; Visitors parlor.
Activities Arts and Crafts; Cards; Games; Reading groups; Prayer groups; Movies; Shopping trips; Dances/Social or cultural gatherings.

Pilgrim Place Health Services Center*
277 Harrison Ave, Claremont, CA, 91711 (714) 624-2084
Admin George Worth.
Licensure Skilled Care. *Beds* 49. *Certified* Medicare; Medi-Cal.
Ownership Nonprofit.

CLOVERDALE

Manzanita Manor Convalescent Hospital*
300 Cherry Creek Rd, Cloverdale, CA, 95425 (707) 894-5201
Admin Dieter Miesler.
Licensure Skilled Care. *Beds* 72. *Certified* Medicare; Medi-Cal.
Ownership Proprietary.

CLOVIS

Clovis Convalescent Hospital*
111 Barstow Ave, Clovis, CA, 93612 (209) 299-2591
Admin Brenda Caprioglio.
Licensure Skilled Care. *Beds* 57. *Certified* Medicare; Medi-Cal.
Ownership Proprietary.

Clovis Nursing Home*
2604 Clovis Ave, Clovis, CA, 93612 (209) 291-2173
Admin Carl Lamoreaux.
Licensure Skilled Care. *Beds* 81. *Certified* Medicare.
Ownership Proprietary.

COLTON

Grand Terrace Convalescent Hospital
12000 Mount Vernon, Colton, CA, 92324 (714) 825-5221
Admin Diane Herschberg. *Medical Dir/Dir of Nursing* Richard Neil.
Licensure Skilled Care. *Beds* 59. *Certified* Medicare; Medi-Cal.
Ownership Proprietary.
Staff Physicians 7 (pt); RNs 1 (ft), 4 (pt); LPNs 3 (ft), 4 (pt); Orderlies 4 (ft); Nurses aides 15 (ft), 10 (pt); Physical therapists 1 (ft); Occupational therapists 1 (pt); Speech therapists 1 (pt); Activities coordinators 1 (ft); Dietitians 1 (pt); Dentists 1 (pt); Ophthalmologists 1 (pt); Podiatrists 1 (pt).
Facilities Dining room; Physical therapy room; Activities room; Laundry room; Barber/Beauty shop; Library.
Activities Arts and Crafts; Cards; Games; Reading groups; Prayer groups; Movies; Dances/Social or cultural gatherings.

Olivewood Convalescent Hospital
23185 Washington Ave, Colton, CA, 92324 (714) 824-1530
Admin J William Westphal. *Medical Dir/Dir of Nursing* Bernard Tilton MD.
Licensure Skilled Care. *Beds* 99. *Certified* Medicare; Medi-Cal.
Ownership Nonprofit.
Admissions Requirements Medical examination; Physician's request.
Facilities Dining room; Physical therapy room; Activities room; Barber/Beauty shop.
Activities Arts and Crafts; Games; Reading groups; Prayer groups; Movies.

COMPTON

Compton Convalescent Hospital
2309 N Santa Fe Ave, Compton, CA, 90222
(213) 639-8111
Admin Robert Lee Pruett. *Medical Dir/Dir of Nursing* Sidney Wasserman MD.
Licensure Skilled Care. *Beds* 99. *Certified* Medicare; Medi-Cal.
Ownership Proprietary.
Admissions Requirements Minimum age 30; Physician's request.
Staff RNs 2 (ft); LPNs 10 (ft); Orderlies 6 (ft); Nurses aides 50 (ft); Physical therapists; Recreational therapists; Occupational therapists; Speech therapists; Activities coordinators; Dietitians; Dentists; Ophthalmologists; Podiatrists; Audiologists.
Facilities Dining room; Physical therapy room; Activities room; Laundry room; Barber/Beauty shop.
Activities Arts and Crafts; Cards; Games; Reading groups; Prayer groups; Movies; Shopping trips; Dances/Social or cultural gatherings.
Description We make a float for the Christmas parade in Compton every year. All kinds of community functions are enjoyed by the residents.

CONCORD

Bayberry Convalescent Hospital*
2151 Central St, Concord, CA, 94520 (415) 825-1300
Admin Beulah Mullin.
Licensure Skilled Care. *Beds* 99. *Certified* Medicare; Medi-Cal.
Ownership Nonprofit.

Casa San Miguel
1050 San Miguel Rd, Concord, CA, 94518 (415) 825-4280
Admin Lenore Shenker.
Licensure Skilled Care; Intermediate Care. *Beds* SNF 150; ICF 50. *Certified* Medicare; Medi-Cal.
Ownership Proprietary.

Hacienda Convalescent Hospital
3318 Willow Pass, Concord, CA, 94520 (415) 689-9222
Admin Shirley M Begovich. *Medical Dir/Dir of Nursing* D K Fisher MD.
Licensure Skilled Care. *Beds* 83. *Certified* Medicare; Medi-Cal.
Ownership Proprietary.
Admissions Requirements Minimum age 65; Medical examination; Physician's request.
Staff RNs 3 (ft), 6 (pt); LPNs 5 (ft), 2 (pt); Nurses aides 30 (ft), 6 (pt); Physical therapists 1 (pt); Occupational therapists 1 (pt); Speech therapists 1 (pt); Activities coordinators 1 (ft); Podiatrists 1 (pt).
Facilities Dining room; Physical therapy room; Activities room; Laundry room; Barber/Beauty shop.
Activities Arts and Crafts; Cards; Games; Reading groups; Prayer groups.
Description Facility offers an extensive physical therapy and rehabilitative therapy program. Also offers select menu for those who are alert.

Park-Lane Convalescent Hospital*
1034 Oak Grove Rd, Concord, CA, 94518 (415) 689-0567
Admin Byron L Ross.
Licensure Skilled Care. *Beds* 49. *Certified* Medicare; Medi-Cal.
Ownership Proprietary.

Valley Manor Convalescent Hospital
3806 Clayton Rd, Concord, CA, 94521 (415) 689-2266
Admin Bob R Lauderdale. *Medical Dir/Dir of Nursing* Eugene B Whitney.
Licensure Skilled Care; Intermediate Care. *Beds* 223. *Certified* Medicare; Medi-Cal.
Ownership Proprietary.
Admissions Requirements Medical examination.
Staff RNs 9 (ft), 4 (pt); LPNs 15 (ft), 8 (pt); Nurses aides 72 (ft), 10 (pt); Physical therapists 1 (ft); Speech therapists 1 (pt); Activities coordinators 3 (ft); Dietitians 1 (ft); Dentists 1 (pt); Ophthalmologists 1 (pt); Podiatrists 1 (pt); Audiologists 1 (pt).
Facilities Dining room; Physical therapy room; Activities room; Crafts room; Laundry room; Barber/Beauty shop; Library.
Activities Arts and Crafts; Cards; Games; Reading groups; Prayer groups; Movies; Shopping trips; Dances/Social or cultural gatherings.
Description A 3-building facility located in a quiet outlying district of a city of over 100,000; attractive setting with view of mountains. Family-style dining for those able to participate. Special dinners and barbecues throughout the year.

CORONA

Corona Gables Retirement Home and Convalescent Hospital*
1400 Circle City Dr, Corona, CA, 91720 (714) 735-0252
Admin Mona L Fisk.
Licensure Skilled Care. *Beds* 80. *Certified* Medicare; Medi-Cal.
Ownership Proprietary.

COSTA MESA

Bay View Convalescent Hospital*
2055 Thurin St, Costa Mesa, CA, 92627 (714) 642-3505
Admin Donald J Beld.
Licensure Skilled Care. *Beds* 59. *Certified* Medicare; Medi-Cal.
Ownership Proprietary.

Beverly Manor Convalescent Hospital
340 Victoria Ave, Costa Mesa, CA, 92627 (714) 642-0387
Admin Jeanne Beach. *Medical Dir/Dir of Nursing* Alan Greenberg MD.
Licensure Skilled Care. *Beds* 79. *Certified* Medicare; Medi-Cal.
Ownership Proprietary.
Staff RNs 6 (ft); LPNs 8 (ft); Orderlies 6 (ft), 2 (pt); Nurses aides 26 (ft), 2 (pt); Recreational therapists 1 (ft).
Facilities Dining room; Physical therapy room; Activities room; Crafts room; Laundry room; Barber/Beauty shop.
Activities Arts and Crafts; Games; Reading groups; Prayer groups; Movies; Field trips; Museums; Dining out.

Mesa Verde Convalescent Hospital*
661 Center St, Costa Mesa, CA, 92647 (714) 548-5585
Admin Barbara Wunsch.
Licensure Skilled Care. *Beds* 80.
Ownership Proprietary.

Port Mesa Convalescent Hospital
2570 Newport Blvd, Costa Mesa, CA, 92627 (714) 642-0400
Admin Ronald A Reynolds. *Medical Dir/Dir of Nursing* Young Kim MD.
Licensure Skilled Care. *Beds* 133. *Certified* Medicare; Medi-Cal.
Ownership Proprietary.
Admissions Requirements Physician's request.
Facilities Dining room; Activities room; Crafts room; Laundry room; Barber/Beauty shop.
Activities Arts and Crafts; Cards; Games; Reading groups; Movies; Shopping trips; Dances/Social or cultural gatherings.

COVINA

Badillo Convalescent Hospital*
519 W Badillo St, Covina, CA, 91722 (213) 332-6406
Admin Natan Gierowitz.
Licensure Skilled Care. *Beds* 52. *Certified* Medicare; Medi-Cal.
Ownership Proprietary.

Covina Convalescent Center*
261 W Badillo St, Covina, CA, 91722 (213) 339-1281
Admin Gary Vernon.
Licensure Skilled Care. *Beds* 99. *Certified* Medicare; Medi-Cal.
Ownership Proprietary.

Rowland
330 W Rowland Ave, Covina, CA, 91723 (213) 967-2741
Admin Anthony Kalomas. *Medical Dir/Dir of Nursing* E Mason MD.
Licensure Skilled Care. *Beds* 126. *Certified* Medicare; Medi-Cal.
Ownership Proprietary.
Admissions Requirements Minimum age 65.
Staff RNs 4 (ft), 2 (pt); LPNs 7 (ft), 2 (pt); Orderlies 3 (ft); Nurses aides 47 (ft), 6 (pt); Physical therapists 1 (ft); Recreational therapists 1 (pt); Speech therapists 1 (pt); Activities coordinators 1 (ft), 1 (pt); Dietitians 1 (pt); Dentists 1 (pt); Podiatrists 1 (pt).
Facilities Dining room; Physical therapy room; Activities room; Chapel; Crafts room; Laundry room; Barber/Beauty shop; Library.
Activities Arts and Crafts; Cards; Games; Reading groups; Prayer groups; Movies; Shopping trips; Dances/Social or cultural gatherings.
Description The facility, which was built in 1970, has 48 rooms with 2 beds in each and 10 rooms with 3 beds in each. Rooms are large and well-lighted with piped-in oxygen in each.

CRESCENT CITY

Crescent City Convalescent Hospital*
1280 Marshall St, Crescent City, CA, 95531
(707) 464-6151
Admin Randall Brigham.
Licensure Skilled Care. *Beds* 99. *Certified* Medicare; Medi-Cal.
Ownership Proprietary.

CULVER CITY

Marina Convalescent Hospital
5240 Sepulveda Ave, Culver City, CA, 90230
(213) 391-7266
Admin Robert Lee. *Medical Dir/Dir of Nursing* Dr Keating.
Licensure Skilled Care. *Beds* 116. *Certified* Medicare; Medi-Cal.
Ownership Proprietary.
Staff RNs 3 (ft), 4 (pt); LPNs 9 (ft), 2 (pt); Orderlies 5 (ft); Nurses aides 28 (ft), 5 (pt); Physical therapists 1 (pt); Recreational therapists 1 (ft); Occupational therapists 1 (pt); Speech therapists 1 (pt); Activities coordinators 1 (ft); Dietitians 1 (ft); Dentists 1 (pt); Ophthalmologists 1 (pt); Podiatrists 1 (pt); Audiologists 1 (pt).
Facilities Dining room; Physical therapy room; Activities room; Crafts room; Laundry room; Barber/Beauty shop; Staff developer.
Activities Arts and Crafts; Cards; Games; Reading groups; Prayer groups; Movies.
Description Marina has recently started a rehabilitation program. Programs scheduled are distinct part, respiratory program and IV therapy. Marina is currently undergoing a complete interior redecoration.

Marycrest Manor
10664 Saint James Dr, Culver City, CA, 90230
(213) 838-2778
Admin Sr Margaret Mary. *Medical Dir/Dir of Nursing* Richard J Doherty MD.
Licensure Skilled Care. *Beds* 59. *Certified* Medicare; Medi-Cal.
Ownership Nonprofit.
Admissions Requirements Minimum age 70; Females only; Medical examination; Physician's request.
Staff Physicians 30 (pt); RNs 5 (ft), 6 (pt); LPNs 3 (ft), 2 (pt); Nurses aides 26 (ft), 12 (pt); Physical therapists 1 (pt); Activities coordinators 1 (ft), 4 (pt); Dietitians 1 (pt); Dentists 1 (pt); Podiatrists 1 (pt).
Affiliation Roman Catholic
Facilities Dining room; Physical therapy room; Activities room; Chapel; Library.
Activities Cards; Games; Prayer groups; Movies; Shopping trips; Visiting entertainers.
Description Marycrest provides a serene and happy atmosphere, a gracious environment, and quality nursing care for frail elderly ladies who are unable to live alone, and/or who are in need of skilled nursing care on a 24-hour basis. Private and semi-private rooms are available. Each room has a private bathroom, and an outdoor patio. Admission is from a waiting list. Services provided: 24-hour nursing care, special diets, pastoral care, religious services, physical therapy, recreational activities, entertainment, beauty salon, outdoor walks.

CUPERTINO

Pleasant View Convalescent Hospital
22590 Voss Ave, Cupertino, CA, 95014 (408) 253-9034
Admin Kenneth V Dunton. *Medical Dir/Dir of Nursing* Fred W Schwertley MD.
Licensure Skilled Care. *Beds* 170. *Certified* Medicare; Medi-Cal.
Ownership Proprietary.
Admissions Requirements Minimum age 16; Medical examination.
Staff Physicians 1 (pt); RNs 12 (ft); LPNs 11 (ft); Orderlies 10 (ft), 2 (pt); Nurses aides 57 (ft), 11 (pt); Physical therapists 1 (ft); Activities coordinators 1 (ft); Dietitians 1 (ft); Pharmacist; Physical therapy aides 3 (ft).
Facilities Dining room; Physical therapy room; Activities room; Barber/Beauty shop.
Activities Arts and Crafts; Cards; Games; Reading groups; Movies; Shopping trips; Dances/Social or cultural gatherings.

Sunny View Manor
22445 Cupertino Rd, Cupertino, CA, 95014
(408) 253-4300
Admin Ron Zielske. *Medical Dir/Dir of Nursing* F W Schwertley MD.
Licensure Skilled Care. *Beds* 45.
Certified Medi-Cal.
Ownership Nonprofit.
Admissions Requirements Minimum age 62; Medical examination.
Affiliation Lutheran
Facilities Dining room; Physical therapy room; Activities room; Chapel; Crafts room; Laundry room; Barber/Beauty shop; Library.
Activities Arts and Crafts; Games; Movies; Shopping trips.

DALY CITY

Saint Francis Convalescent Pavilion Inc*
99 Escuela Dr, Daly City, CA, 94015 (415) 994-3200
Admin Joseph D Echelberry.
Licensure Skilled Care. *Beds* 239. *Certified* Medicare; Medi-Cal.
Ownership Proprietary.

Saint Francis Heights Convalescent Hospital*
35 Escuela Dr, Daly City, CA, 94015 (415) 755-9515
Admin Susan S Edwards.
Licensure Skilled Care. *Beds* 102. *Certified* Medicare; Medi-Cal.
Ownership Proprietary.

DANVILLE

Diablo Convalescent Hospital*
336 Diablo Rd, Danville, CA, 94526 (415) 837-5536
Admin Ann Aldenhuysen.
Licensure Skilled Care. *Beds* 52.
Certified Medi-Cal.
Ownership Proprietary.

DAVIS

Driftwood Convalescent Hospital
1850 E 8th St, Davis, CA, 95616 (916) 756-1800
Admin J Craig Coogan. *Medical Dir/Dir of Nursing* S Schaffer MD.
Licensure Skilled Care. *Beds* 124. *Certified* Medicare; Medi-Cal.
Ownership Proprietary.
Staff Physicians 3 (pt); RNs 9 (ft), 4 (pt); LPNs 4 (ft), 1 (pt); Orderlies 6 (ft), 2 (pt); Nurses aides 34 (ft), 18 (pt); Physical therapists 1 (pt); Recreational therapists 1 (pt); Speech therapists 1 (pt); Activities coordinators 1 (ft), 1 (pt); Dietitians 1 (pt); Dentists 1 (pt); Podiatrists 1 (pt); Audiologists 1 (pt).
Facilities Dining room; Physical therapy room; Activities room; Laundry room; Barber/Beauty shop.
Activities Arts and Crafts; Cards; Games; Reading groups; Prayer groups; Movies; Shopping trips; Dances/Social or cultural gatherings.

Sierra Health Care Convalescent Hospital*
715 Pole Line Rd, Davis, CA, 95616 (916) 756-4900
Admin Thomas E Clements.
Licensure Skilled Care. *Beds* 132. *Certified* Medicare; Medi-Cal.
Ownership Proprietary.

DELANO

Browning Manor Convalescent Hospital
729 Browning, Delano, CA, 93215 (805) 725-2501
Admin Carolyn Johnson. *Medical Dir/Dir of Nursing* Erwood Edgar MD.
Licensure Skilled Care. *Beds* 53. *Certified* Medicare; Medi-Cal.
Ownership Proprietary.
Staff RNs; LPNs; Orderlies; Nurses aides; Physical therapists; Activities coordinators; Dietitians.
Facilities Dining room; Activities room; Laundry room; Barber/Beauty shop.
Activities Arts and Crafts; Cards; Games; Reading groups; Prayer groups; Movies; Shopping trips; Dances/Social or cultural gatherings.

DESERT HOT SPRINGS

Angel View Childrens Habilitation Center
12-379 Miracle Hill Rd, Desert Hot Springs, CA, 92240 (714) 329-6471
Admin Henry Kotzen. *Medical Dir/Dir of Nursing* Carl Reller MD.
Licensure Intermediate Care. *Beds* 52. *Certified* Medi-Cal.
Ownership Nonprofit.
Admissions Requirements Minimum age 3; Medical examination.
Staff RNs 1 (ft), 3 (pt); LPNs 8 (ft), 2 (pt); Nurses aides 40 (ft); Physical therapists 1 (pt); Occupational therapists 1 (ft); Speech therapists 1 (pt); Activities coordinators 1 (ft); Dietitians 1 (pt); Dentists 1 (pt); Audiologists 1 (pt).
Facilities Dining room; Physical therapy room; Activities room; Crafts room; Barber/Beauty shop; Library; Swimming and therapy pool.

Activities Arts and Crafts; Games; Reading groups; Movies; Shopping trips; Dances/Social or cultural gatherings.
Description Facility is primarily a habilitation facility for school age individuals to enable them to enter a less restrictive environment.

DINUBA

Dinuba Convalescent Hospital*
1730 S College, Dinuba, CA, 93618 (209) 591-3300
Admin Jimmie Evans.
Licensure Skilled Care. *Beds* 99. *Certified* Medicare; Medi-Cal.
Ownership Proprietary.

DOWNEY

Downey Community Health Center*
8425 Iowa St, Downey, CA, 90241 (213) 862-4119
Admin John Hryze.
Licensure Skilled Care. *Beds* 115. *Certified* Medicare; Medi-Cal.
Ownership Proprietary.

Lakewood Park Health Center
12023 S Lakewood Blvd, Downey, CA, 90242 (213) 869-0978
Admin Charles E Steen.
Licensure Skilled Care; Intermediate Care.
Beds SNF 207; ICF 24. *Certified* Medicare; Medi-Cal.
Ownership Proprietary.
Facilities Dining room; Physical therapy room; Activities room; Crafts room; Barber/Beauty shop; Library.
Activities Arts and Crafts; Cards; Games; Reading groups; Prayer groups; Movies; Shopping trips; Dances/Social or cultural gatherings.

Pico Downey Golden Age Convalescent Home
9300 Telegraph Rd, Downey, CA, 90240 (213) 869-2567
Admin Marilyn Spaun. *Medical Dir/Dir of Nursing* Joel M Sandler MD.
Licensure Skilled Care. *Beds* 70. *Certified* Medicare; Medi-Cal.
Ownership Nonprofit.
Admissions Requirements Minimum age 18; Medical examination; Physician's request.
Staff RNs 1 (ft), 2 (pt); LPNs 8 (ft), 2 (pt); Nurses aides 2 (pt); Physical therapists 1 (pt); Recreational therapists 1 (pt); Occupational therapists 1 (pt); Speech therapists 1 (pt); Activities coordinators 1 (ft); Dietitians 1 (pt); Dentists 1 (pt); Ophthalmologists 1 (pt); Podiatrists 1 (pt).
Facilities Dining room; Barber/Beauty shop.

Westview Convalescent Hospital
13007 S Paramount Blvd, Downey, CA, 90242 (213) 923-9301
Admin Fred O'Hare. *Medical Dir/Dir of Nursing* Dr Johnson.
Licensure Skilled Care. *Beds* 99. *Certified* Medicare; Medi-Cal.
Ownership Proprietary.
Staff RNs 2 (ft); LPNs 9 (ft); Orderlies 3 (ft); Nurses aides 19 (ft); Physical therapists 1 (ft);

Recreational therapists 1 (ft).
Facilities Dining room; Physical therapy room; Activities room; Chapel; Crafts room; Laundry room; Barber/Beauty shop; Library.
Activities Arts and Crafts; Cards; Games; Reading groups; Prayer groups; Movies; Shopping trips; Dances/Social or cultural gatherings.

DUARTE

Buena Vista Manor
1300 Royal Oaks Dr, Duarte, CA, 91010 (213) 359-8141
Admin Bob Barton. *Medical Dir/Dir of Nursing* Ferdinand Kunze MD.
Licensure Skilled Care. *Beds* 59. *Certified* Medicare; Medi-Cal.
Ownership Nonprofit.
Admissions Requirements Minimum age 62.
Staff Physicians 3 (pt); RNs 1 (ft), 1 (pt); LPNs 7 (ft), 2 (pt); Orderlies 1 (pt); Nurses aides 22 (ft), 2 (pt); Recreational therapists 1 (ft); Occupational therapists 1 (pt); Activities coordinators 1 (pt); Dietitians 1 (ft).
Affiliation Presbyterian
Facilities Dining room; Activities room; Crafts room; Laundry room; Barber/Beauty shop; Library; Hospice room.
Activities Arts and Crafts; Cards; Games; Reading groups; Prayer groups; Movies; Shopping trips; Dances/Social or cultural gatherings; Teas; Exercise; Brunches.
Description Buena Vista Manor is surrounded by many health care facilities, City of Hope, and Santa Teresita hospital, and is very accessible to all cities in the San Gabriel valley. Patients participate annually in a foster grandparent program and the wheelchair olympics.

Community Care Center*
2335 S Mountain Ave, Duarte, CA, 91010 (213) 357-3207
Admin William J Cartwright.
Licensure Skilled Care. *Beds* 176.
Certified Medi-Cal.
Ownership Proprietary.

Highland Convalescent Hospital*
1340 Highland Ave, Duarte, CA, 91010 (213) 359-9171
Admin Frank Garcia Jr.
Licensure Skilled Care. *Beds* 58. *Certified* Medicare; Medi-Cal.
Ownership Proprietary.

Monrovia Convalescent Hospital*
1220 E Huntington, Duarte, CA, 91010 (213) 359-6618
Admin Sherman Davidson.
Licensure Skilled Care. *Beds* 72. *Certified* Medicare; Medi-Cal.
Ownership Proprietary.

Westminster Gardens Health Center*
2030 E Huntington Dr, Duarte, CA, 91010 (213) 359-2571
Admin Ingri Godley.
Licensure Skilled Care. *Beds* 64.
Ownership Nonprofit.

EAGLE ROCK

Ararat Convalescent Hospital
2373 Colorado Blvd, Eagle Rock, CA, 90041 (213) 257-8144
Admin Gordon Dagg. *Medical Dir/Dir of Nursing* J S Boyajian MD.
Licensure Skilled Care. *Beds* 42. *Certified* Medicare.
Ownership Nonprofit.
Staff Physicians 3 (ft); RNs 2 (ft); Nurses aides 13 (ft); Activities coordinators 1 (ft).
Languages Armenian; Arabic; Iranian; Turkish; French; Russian; Italian
Facilities Dining room; Activities room.
Activities Arts and Crafts; Cards; Games; Dances/Social or cultural gatherings.
Description Facility established for elderly Armenians. Nursing staff is bilingual.

Solheim Lutheran Home for the Aged
2236 Merton Ave, Eagle Rock, CA, 90041 (213) 257-7518
Admin Elizabeth C Batchelder. *Medical Dir/Dir of Nursing* Dr Ralph Boyd.
Licensure Skilled Care. *Beds* 19.
Certified Medi-Cal.
Ownership Nonprofit.
Admissions Requirements Minimum age 62; Medical examination; Physician's request.
Staff RNs 1 (ft), 1 (pt); LPNs 2 (ft), 3 (pt); Nurses aides 12 (ft); Activities coordinators 1 (pt).
Affiliation Lutheran
Facilities Dining room; Activities room; Chapel; Laundry room; Barber/Beauty shop; Library.
Activities Arts and Crafts; Games; Reading groups; Prayer groups; Movies; Shopping trips.

EL CAJON

Anza Convalescent Hospital*
622 S Anza St, El Cajon, CA, 92020 (714) 442-3391
Admin Richard Mendlen.
Licensure Skilled Care. *Beds* 160. *Certified* Medicare; Medi-Cal.
Ownership Proprietary.

Carroll's Convalescent Hospital*
109 E Chase Ave, El Cajon, CA, 92020 (714) 442-9833
Admin Roger L Caddell.
Licensure Skilled Care. *Beds* 57. *Certified* Medicare; Medi-Cal.
Ownership Proprietary.

Carroll's Intermediate Care
151 Claydelle Ave, El Cajon, CA, 92020 (714) 442-0245
Admin Joann Prather. *Medical Dir/Dir of Nursing* Dr Palmer.
Licensure Intermediate Care. *Beds* 65. *Certified* Medi-Cal.
Ownership Proprietary.
Admissions Requirements Physician's request.
Staff LPNs 3 (ft); Nurses aides 7 (ft); Activities coordinators 1 (ft); Dietitians 1 (pt).
Facilities Dining room; Activities room; Crafts

room; Laundry room; Barber/Beauty shop.
Activities Arts and Crafts; Games; Reading
groups; Prayer groups; Movies.

Carroll's Intermediate Care—Anza*
654 S Anza, El Cajon, CA, 92020 (714)
440-5005
Admin Roger L Caddell.
Licensure Intermediate Care. *Beds* 120. *Certified* Medi-Cal.
Ownership Proprietary.

Carroll's Skilled Nursing Facility—Lexington*
444 W Lexington, El Cajon, CA, 92020 (714)
442-7114
Admin Roger L Caddell.
Licensure Skilled Care. *Beds* 50.
Certified Medi-Cal.
Ownership Proprietary.

El Cajon Valley Convalescent Center
510 E Washington Ave, El Cajon, CA, 92020
(714) 440-1211
Admin H A Bunn and D Bunn.
Licensure Skilled Care. *Beds* 256. *Certified* Medicare; Medi-Cal.
Ownership Proprietary.
Facilities Dining room; Physical therapy room;
Activities room; Crafts room; Laundry room;
Barber/Beauty shop; Library.
Activities Arts and Crafts; Games.

Helix View Nursing Home Inc*
1201 S Orange Ave, El Cajon, CA, 92020 (714)
442-0255
Admin Daniel Bunn.
Licensure Skilled Care. *Beds* 66. *Certified* Medicare; Medi-Cal.
Ownership Proprietary.

Lo-Har Lodge Incorporated*
794 Dorothy St, El Cajon, CA, 92020 (714)
444-8270
Admin Berry T Crow.
Licensure Skilled Care. *Beds* 32.
Ownership Proprietary.

Madison Convalescent Center
1391 E Madison Ave, El Cajon, CA, 92021
(714) 444-1107
Admin Aleene Brown. *Medical Dir/Dir of
Nursing* Frank Flint.
Licensure Skilled Care. *Beds* 96. *Certified* Medicare; Medi-Cal.
Ownership Proprietary.
Admissions Requirements Physician's request.
Staff RNs 4 (ft); LPNs 8 (ft), 2 (pt); Orderlies 3
(ft); Nurses aides 22 (ft), 7 (pt); Physical therapists 1 (pt); Occupational therapists; Speech
therapists; Activities coordinators 1 (ft); Dietitians 1 (pt).
Facilities Dining room; Physical therapy room;
Activities room; Crafts room; Laundry room;
Barber/Beauty shop; Library.
Activities Arts and Crafts; Games; Prayer
groups; Movies; Shopping trips; Bingo; Music
therapy.

Magnolia Center*
635 Magnolia, El Cajon, CA, 92020 (714)
442-8826
Admin Jean M Robbins.

Licensure Skilled Care. *Beds* 99. *Certified* Medicare; Medi-Cal.
Ownership Proprietary.

Royal Home
12436 Royal Rd, El Cajon, CA, 92021 (619)
443-3886
Admin James E Carter I. *Medical Dir/Dir of
Nursing* Frank Fint MD.
Licensure Skilled Care. *Beds* 19. *Certified* Medicare.
Ownership Proprietary.
Staff RNs 1 (ft), 2 (pt); LPNs 1 (ft), 3 (pt);
Nurses aides 2 (ft), 4 (pt); Activities coordinators 1 (ft).
Facilities Dining room; Laundry room; Patio.
Activities Arts and Crafts; Cards; Games;
Reading groups; Prayer groups; Shopping trips.
Description Facility features a home-like
atmosphere and personalized care.

TLC Convalescent Hospital*
1340 E Madison Ave, El Cajon, CA, 92021
(714) 442-8855
Admin Donald L Linfesty.
Licensure Skilled Care; Intermediate Care.
Beds SNF 87; ICF 12. *Certified* Medicare;
Medi-Cal.
Ownership Proprietary.

Vista Del Cerro Convalescent Center
675 E Bradley Ave, El Cajon, CA, 92021 (714)
448-6633
Admin Clyde Prince. *Medical Dir/Dir of
Nursing* Charles Miller MD.
Licensure Skilled Care. *Beds* 56. *Certified* Medicare; Medi-Cal.
Ownership Proprietary.
Admissions Requirements Physician's request.
Staff RNs 4 (ft); LPNs 9 (ft); Nurses aides 30
(ft); Physical therapists 1 (pt); Recreational therapists 1 (pt); Activities coordinators 1 (ft); Podiatrists 1 (pt).
Facilities Dining room; Laundry room.
Activities Arts and Crafts; Cards; Games;
Reading groups; Prayer groups; Shopping trips.
Description There is a large area around one
building for the wandering patient to walk; they
are free to go in and out of the building as they
desire. The facility is very close to a shopping
center.

EL CENTRO

Valley Convalescent Hospital*
1700 S Imperial Ave, El Centro, CA, 92243
(714) 352-8471
Admin Mary Werner.
Licensure Skilled Care. *Beds* 123.
Certified Medi-Cal.
Ownership Proprietary.

EL CERRITO

Carlson Convalescent Hospital Inc
3230 Carlson Blvd, El Cerrito, CA, 94530 (415)
525-3212
Admin Ruby Shields. *Medical Dir/Dir of
Nursing* James E DeWitt MD.
Licensure Skilled Care. *Beds* 45. *Certified* Medicare; Medi-Cal.

Ownership Proprietary.
Admissions Requirements Medical examination; Physician's request.
Staff RNs 1 (ft), 1 (pt); LPNs 3 (ft), 2 (pt);
Nurses aides 11 (ft), 10 (pt); Physical therapists
1 (pt); Occupational therapists 1 (pt); Activities
coordinators 1 (ft); Dietitians 1 (ft), 1 (pt); Dentists 1 (pt); Podiatrists 1 (pt).
Facilities Dining room; Activities room; Laundry room.
Activities Arts and Crafts; Games; Prayer
groups; Movies; Dances/Social or cultural gatherings.

EL MONTE

Chandler Care Center—El Monte*
3825 N Durfee Ave, El Monte, CA, 91732 (213)
444-2535
Admin Charlotte R Ulrich.
Licensure Skilled Care. *Beds* 139. *Certified* Medicare; Medi-Cal.
Ownership Proprietary.

Chandler Care Center—Romona*
12036 Ramona Blvd, El Monte, CA, 91732
(213) 448-9851
Admin Danny J Amador.
Licensure Skilled Care. *Beds* 99. *Certified* Medicare; Medi-Cal.
Ownership Proprietary.

Cherrylee Lodge Sanitarium*
5053 N Peck Rd, El Monte, CA, 91732 (213)
448-4248
Admin Veronica A Beckos.
Licensure Skilled Care. *Beds* 46. *Certified* Medicare; Medi-Cal.
Ownership Proprietary.

El Monte Convalescent Hospital
4096 Easy St, El Monte, CA, 91731 (213)
442-1500
Admin Lilly P Telles. *Medical Dir/Dir of
Nursing* Donald E Medanis.
Licensure Skilled Care. *Beds* 99. *Certified* Medicare; Medi-Cal.
Ownership Proprietary.
Staff Physicians 12 (pt); RNs 3 (ft), 2 (pt);
LPNs 5 (ft), 4 (pt); Orderlies 4 (ft), 2 (pt);
Nurses aides 35 (ft), 9 (pt); Physical therapists 1
(pt); Occupational therapists 1 (pt); Speech therapists 1 (pt); Activities coordinators 2 (ft); Dietitians 1 (pt); Dentists 1 (pt); Podiatrists 1 (pt);
Audiologists 1 (pt).
Facilities Dining room; Physical therapy room;
Activities room; Crafts room; Laundry room;
Barber/Beauty shop; Library.
Activities Arts and Crafts; Cards; Games;
Reading groups; Prayer groups; Movies; Bingo;
Lunch outings.
Description Facility features very good food
and an excellent activity program.

El Monte Golden Age Convalescent Home*
11900 Ramona Blvd, El Monte, CA, 91732
(213) 442-5721
Admin Ray Fischella.
Licensure Skilled Care. *Beds* 148. *Certified* Medicare.
Ownership Nonprofit.

Elmcrest Convalescent Hospital*
3111 Santa Anita Ave, El Monte, CA, 91733
(213) 443-0218
Admin Alfred H Jones.
Licensure Skilled Care. *Beds* 96. *Certified* Medicare; Medi-Cal.
Ownership Proprietary.

Idle Acre Sanitarium and Convalescent Hospital*
5044 Buffington Rd, El Monte, CA, 91732
(213) 443-1351
Admin Kenneth Thompson.
Licensure Skilled Care. *Beds* 53.
Certified Medi-Cal.
Ownership Proprietary.

Sunset Manor Convalescent Hospital
2720 Nevada Ave, El Monte, CA, 91733 (213)
443-9425
Admin F D Adams. *Medical Dir/Dir of Nursing* Richard Hart MD.
Licensure Skilled Care. *Beds* 81. *Certified* Medicare; Medi-Cal.
Ownership Proprietary.
Admissions Requirements Minimum age 18; Physician's request.
Staff Physicians 10 (pt); RNs 1 (ft), 2 (pt); LPNs 6 (ft), 4 (pt); Orderlies 4 (ft), 2 (pt); Nurses aides 26 (ft), 9 (pt); Physical therapists 2 (pt); Occupational therapists 1 (pt); Speech therapists 1 (pt); Activities coordinators 1 (ft); Dietitians 1 (ft); Dentists 1 (pt); Ophthalmologists 1 (pt); Podiatrists 1 (pt).
Languages Sign
Facilities Dining room; Activities room; Crafts room; Barber/Beauty shop.
Activities Arts and Crafts; Cards; Games; Reading groups; Prayer groups; Movies.
Description Facility has a large deaf population; staff knows sign language; offers full activity program.

Wellesley Manor Convalescent Hospital
11210 Lower Azusa Rd, El Monte, CA, 91731
(213) 442-6863
Admin Gita D Wheelis. *Medical Dir/Dir of Nursing* R Atiga MD.
Licensure Skilled Care. *Beds* 90. *Certified* Medicare; Medi-Cal.
Ownership Proprietary.
Staff RNs 2 (ft); LPNs 8 (ft); Activities coordinators 15 (ft).
Facilities Dining room; Physical therapy room; Activities room; Laundry room; Barber/Beauty shop.
Activities Arts and Crafts; Cards; Games; Reading groups; Prayer groups; Movies; Dances/Social or cultural gatherings.

ELK GROVE

Elk Grove Convalescent Hospital*
9461 Batey Ave, Elk Grove, CA, 95624 (916)
685-9525
Admin Betty M Dever.
Licensure Skilled Care. *Beds* 130. *Certified* Medicare; Medi-Cal.
Ownership Proprietary.

ENCINITAS

Ocean View Convalescent Hospital
900 Santa Fe Dr, Encinitas, CA, 92024 (714)
753-6423
Admin Gary W Novack. *Medical Dir/Dir of Nursing* Dr Arthur Edwards.
Licensure Skilled Care. *Beds* 99. *Certified* Medicare; Medi-Cal.
Ownership Proprietary.
Admissions Requirements Medical examination.
Staff RNs 5 (ft), 4 (pt); LPNs 5 (ft), 4 (pt); Orderlies 3 (pt); Nurses aides 30 (ft), 7 (pt); Physical therapists 1 (pt); Recreational therapists 1 (pt); Occupational therapists 1 (pt); Speech therapists 1 (pt); Activities coordinators 1 (ft); Dietitians 1 (pt); Dentists 1 (pt); Ophthalmologists 1 (pt); Podiatrists 2 (pt); Audiologists 1 (pt).
Facilities Dining room; Physical therapy room; Activities room; Chapel; Crafts room; Laundry room; Barber/Beauty shop; Library.
Activities Arts and Crafts; Games; Reading groups; Prayer groups; Movies; Shopping trips; Dances/Social or cultural gatherings.

ENCINO

Encino Terrace Convalescent Hospital*
16530 Ventura Blvd, Encino, CA, 91436 (213)
788-0300
Admin Arnold Freed.
Licensure Skilled Care. *Beds* 68.
Ownership Proprietary.

ESCONDIDO

Beverly Manor Convalescent Hospital
421 E Mission Ave, Escondido, CA, 92025
(714) 747-0430
Admin Vic Tose. *Medical Dir/Dir of Nursing* Raymond Dann MD.
Licensure Skilled Care. *Beds* 180. *Certified* Medicare; Medi-Cal.
Ownership Proprietary.
Admissions Requirements Medical examination; Physician's request.
Facilities Dining room; Physical therapy room; Activities room; Crafts room; Laundry room; Barber/Beauty shop; Library; TV/Living room.
Activities Arts and Crafts; Cards; Games; Reading groups; Prayer groups; Movies; Shopping trips; Dances/Social or cultural gatherings.
Description We are a progressive and rehabilitative oriented facility specializing in stroke and fracture therapies.

Escondido Convalescent Center
201 N Fig St, Escondido, CA, 92025 (619)
746-0303
Admin Sarah Lindsay. *Medical Dir/Dir of Nursing* Dr Thomas E Rastle.
Licensure Skilled Care. *Beds* 74. *Certified* Medicare; Medi-Cal.
Ownership Proprietary.
Staff RNs 5 (ft), 3 (pt); LPNs 2 (ft), 4 (pt); Nurses aides 29 (ft), 10 (pt); Physical therapists 1 (ft); Occupational therapists 1 (pt); Speech therapists 1 (pt); Activities coordinators 1 (ft).
Facilities Dining room; Physical therapy room;

Activities room; Laundry room; Barber/Beauty shop.
Activities Arts and Crafts; Cards; Games; Reading groups; Prayer groups; Shopping trips.
Description Facility is located one block from an acute hospital. Has recently expanded rehabilitation department and has an affiliation with a home health agency.

Hilltop Convalescent Center
1260 E Ohio St, Escondido, CA, 92025 (714)
746-1100
Admin Marie Kessler. *Medical Dir/Dir of Nursing* Craig Banta MD.
Licensure Skilled Care. *Beds* 98. *Certified* Medicare; Medi-Cal.
Ownership Proprietary.
Staff Physical therapists 1 (ft); Occupational therapists 1 (ft); Speech therapists 1 (ft); Activities coordinators 1 (ft).
Facilities Dining room; Physical therapy room; Activities room; Crafts room; Laundry room; Barber/Beauty shop.
Activities Arts and Crafts; Cards; Games; Reading groups; Prayer groups; Movies; Shopping trips; Dances/Social or cultural gatherings.

Redwood Terrace Lutheran Home
710 W 13th Ave, Escondido, CA, 92025 (714)
747-4306
Admin Daniel H Johnson. *Medical Dir/Dir of Nursing* Stephen D Smith MD.
Licensure Skilled Care; Intermediate Care.
Beds SNF 30; ICF 29.
Ownership Nonprofit.
Admissions Requirements Minimum age 62; Medical examination; Physician's request.
Staff RNs 5 (ft), 7 (pt); LPNs 2 (pt); Nurses aides 17 (ft), 12 (pt); Activities coordinators 1 (ft).
Affiliation Lutheran
Facilities Dining room; Physical therapy room; Activities room; Chapel; Crafts room; Laundry room; Barber/Beauty shop; Library.
Activities Arts and Crafts; Cards; Games; Reading groups; Prayer groups; Movies; Shopping trips; Dances/Social or cultural gatherings.

Valle Vista Convalescent Hospital Inc*
1025 W 2nd St, Escondido, CA, 92025 (714)
745-1288
Admin C R Cook.
Licensure Skilled Care. *Beds* 53. *Certified* Medicare; Medi-Cal.
Ownership Proprietary.

EUREKA

Crestwood Manor*
2370 Buhne, Eureka, CA, 95501 (707)
442-5721
Admin Clete Weller.
Licensure Skilled Care. *Beds* 82.
Certified Medi-Cal.
Ownership Proprietary.

Granada Convalescent Hospital
2885 Harris St, Eureka, CA, 95501 (707)
443-1627
Admin Tom Sutton. *Medical Dir/Dir of Nursing* Ken Stiver MD.
Licensure Skilled Care. *Beds* 87. *Cer-*

tified Medicare; Medi-Cal.
Ownership Proprietary.
Admissions Requirements Minimum age 5.
Staff RNs 4 (ft), 2 (pt); LPNs 4 (ft), 2 (pt);
Orderlies 3 (ft), 6 (pt); Nurses aides 25 (ft), 13
(pt); Physical therapists 1 (ft); Speech therapists
1 (ft); Activities coordinators 1 (ft).
Facilities Dining room; Physical therapy room;
Activities room; Crafts room; Laundry room;
Barber/Beauty shop.
Activities Arts and Crafts; Cards; Games;
Reading groups; Prayer groups; Movies; Shop-
ping trips; Dances/Social or cultural gatherings.
Description Residents participate in local
parades, going to the zoo, annual dinner/dance,
selling raffle rickets for annual quilt show, and
participation in the annual bazaar for the sale of
crafts made during the year.

Pacific Convalescent Hospital
2211 Harrison Ave, Eureka, CA, 95501 (707)
443-9767
Admin Robert O'Keefe. *Medical Dir/Dir of
Nursing* Ken Stiver MD.
Licensure Skilled Care. *Beds* 66. *Cer-
tified* Medicare; Medi-Cal.
Ownership Proprietary.
Staff RNs 2 (ft), 2 (pt); LPNs 4 (ft), 3 (pt);
Orderlies 4 (ft), 2 (pt); Nurses aides 20 (ft), 7
(pt); Physical therapists 1 (ft); Speech therapists
1 (ft); Activities coordinators 1 (ft).
Facilities Dining room; Physical therapy room;
Activities room; Crafts room; Laundry room;
Barber/Beauty shop.
Activities Arts and Crafts; Cards; Games;
Reading groups; Prayer groups; Movies; Shop-
ping trips; Dances/Social or cultural gatherings.
Description Patients participate in local
parades, going to the zoo, annual dinner/dance,
selling raffle tickets for annual quilt, and participation in annual bazaar for the sale of crafts
made during the year.

Sea View Convalescent Hospital
8400 Purdue Dr, Eureka, CA, 95501 (707)
443-5668
Admin Kary Karges. *Medical Dir/Dir of
Nursing* Ken Stiver MD.
Licensure Skilled Care. *Beds* 99. *Cer-
tified* Medicare; Medi-Cal.
Ownership Proprietary.
Staff Physicians; RNs; LPNs; Orderlies;
Nurses aides; Physical therapists; Reality thera-
pists; Occupational therapists; Speech thera-
pists; Activities coordinators; Dietitians;
Dentists; Ophthalmologists; Podiatrists.
Facilities Dining room; Physical therapy room;
Activities room; Crafts room; Laundry room;
Barber/Beauty shop.
Activities Arts and Crafts; Cards; Games;
Movies; Dances/Social or cultural gatherings;
Trips to parks; Picnics; Float making.

Sunset Convalescent Hospital
2353 23rd St, Eureka, CA, 95501 (707)
443-1627
Admin Robert Bates. *Medical Dir/Dir of
Nursing* Dr Ken Stiver.
Licensure Skilled Care. *Beds* 99. *Cer-
tified* Medicare; Medi-Cal.
Ownership Proprietary.
Admissions Requirements Medical examina-
tion; Physician's request.

Facilities Dining room; Physical therapy room;
Activities room; Crafts room; Laundry room;
Barber/Beauty shop; Library; Speech Therapy
Room.
Activities Arts and Crafts; Cards; Games;
Reading groups; Prayer groups; Movies; Shopping trips; Dances/Social or cultural gatherings.
Description A progressive rehabilitation oriented facility that is connected to an acute care
facility for easy access. Have full-time physical
therapist and speech therapist on staff with
facility's own transportation for resident's visits.

FAIRFIELD

La Mariposa Convalescent Hospital Inc*
1244 Travis Blvd, Fairfield, CA, 94533 (707)
422-7750
Admin Robert T Farrell.
Licensure Skilled Care. *Beds* 99. *Certified* Medicare; Medi-Cal.
Ownership Proprietary.

Suisun Valley Manor*
1255 Travis Blvd, Fairfield, CA, 94533 (707)
425-0623
Admin Linda Stratton.
Licensure Skilled Care. *Beds* 99. *Certified* Medicare; Medi-Cal.
Ownership Proprietary.

Sunny Acres Convalescent Hospital
1260 Travis Blvd, Fairfield, CA, 94533 (707)
425-0669
Admin Annette S Eugenis. *Medical Dir/Dir of
Nursing* Dr Edward Lopez.
Licensure Skilled Care. *Beds* 90. *Cer-
tified* Medicare; Medi-Cal.
Ownership Proprietary.
Admissions Requirements Medical examina-
tion.
Staff RNs 2 (ft), 4 (pt); LPNs 5 (ft), 5 (pt);
Nurses aides 29 (ft), 11 (pt); Activities coordi-
nators 1 (ft).
Facilities Dining room; Activities room; Crafts
room; Laundry room; Barber/Beauty shop.
Activities Arts and Crafts; Cards; Games;
Reading groups; Prayer groups; Movies; Shop-
ping trips; Dances/Social or cultural gatherings;
Outside facility activities; Wine & cheese
tasting; Nature walks; Picnics; Exercise; Resi-
dential council.

FALLBROOK

Fallbrook Convalescent Hospital*
325 Potter St, Fallbrook, CA, 92028 (714)
728-2330
Admin Robert Durbin.
Licensure Skilled Care. *Beds* 54. *Certified* Medicare; Medi-Cal.
Ownership Proprietary.

FILLMORE

Fillmore Convalescent Center
118 B St, Fillmore, CA, 93015 (805) 524-0083
Admin Brad Davis. *Medical Dir/Dir of
Nursing* Dinko Rosic MD.

Licensure Skilled Care; Intermediate Care.
Beds SNF 89; ICF 3. *Certified* Medicare;
Medi-Cal.
Ownership Proprietary.
Admissions Requirements Medical examina-
tion; Physician's request.
Staff Physicians 13 (pt); RNs 1 (ft), 5 (pt);
LPNs 6 (ft); Physical therapists 1 (pt); Occupa-
tional therapists 1 (pt); Speech therapists 1 (pt);
Activities coordinators 1 (ft); Dietitians 1 (pt);
Dentists 1 (pt); Podiatrists 1 (pt).
Facilities Dining room; Physical therapy room;
Activities room; Crafts room; Laundry room;
Barber/Beauty shop.
Activities Arts and Crafts; Games; Reading
groups; Prayer groups; Movies; Shopping trips;
Dances/Social or cultural gatherings; Resident
council; Cooking; Sewing.
Description Facility is situated among orange
groves, a medical group is within walking dis-
tance; friendly atmosphere is maintained.

FOLSOM

Folsom Convalescent Hospital
510 Mill St, Folsom, CA, 95630 (916) 985-3641
Admin D V Callaway. *Medical Dir/Dir of
Nursing* Dr Paul Rhoads.
Licensure Skilled Care. *Beds* 99. *Cer-
tified* Medicare; Medi-Cal.
Ownership Proprietary.
Staff RNs 6 (ft), 2 (pt); LPNs 6 (ft), 3 (pt);
Orderlies 4 (ft), 2 (pt); Nurses aides 60 (ft), 20
(pt); Physical therapists 1 (pt); Reality therapists
1 (pt); Recreational therapists 1 (ft); Occupa-
tional therapists 1 (pt); Speech therapists 1 (pt);
Activities coordinators 1 (ft); Dietitians 1 (pt);
Dentists 1 (pt); Ophthalmologists 1 (pt); Podia-
trists 1 (pt); Audiologists 1 (pt).
Facilities Dining room; Physical therapy room;
Activities room; Crafts room; Laundry room;
Barber/Beauty shop.
Activities Arts and Crafts; Cards; Games;
Reading groups; Prayer groups; Movies; Shop-
ping trips; Dances/Social or cultural gatherings.
Description Facility is located in the suburbs of
Sacramento, in a small community of 8000,
who support the facility with loving volunteers
providing plenty of activities and tender loving
care.

FONTANA

Casa Maria Convalescent Hospital
17933 San Bernardino Ave, Fontana, CA,
92335 (714) 877-1555
Admin Lois Easterday. *Medical Dir/Dir of
Nursing* Robert Bom MD.
Licensure Skilled Care. *Beds* 57. *Cer-
tified* Medicare; Medi-Cal.
Ownership Proprietary.
Admissions Requirements Physician's request.
Staff Physicians 5 (pt); RNs 3 (ft); LPNs 2 (ft),
5 (pt); Orderlies 3 (ft); Nurses aides 14 (ft), 6
(pt); Physical therapists 1 (pt); Reality therapists
1 (pt); Recreational therapists 1 (pt); Speech
therapists 1 (pt); Activities coordinators 1 (ft);
Dietitians 1 (pt); Dentists 1 (pt); Podiatrists 1
(pt); Audiologists 1 (pt).
Facilities Dining room; Physical therapy room;
Activities room; Chapel; Crafts room; Laundry

room; Barber/Beauty shop.
Activities Arts and Crafts; Cards; Games;
Reading groups; Prayer groups; Movies; Shopping trips; Dances/Social or cultural gatherings.

Citrus Care Convalescent Hospital
9440 Citrus Ave, Fontana, CA, 92335 (714)
823-3481
Admin Dorothy Ransom. *Medical Dir/Dir of Nursing* Robert Bom MD.
Licensure Skilled Care. *Beds* 99. *Certified* Medicare; Medi-Cal.
Ownership Proprietary.
Admissions Requirements Minimum age 21;
Physician's request.
Staff RNs 2 (ft), 2 (pt); LPNs 11 (ft), 2 (pt);
Nurses aides 72 (ft), 6 (pt); Physical therapists 1
(ft); Occupational therapists 1 (ft); Speech therapists 1 (ft).
Facilities Dining room; Physical therapy room;
Activities room; Crafts room; Laundry room;
Barber/Beauty shop.
Activities Arts and Crafts; Cards; Games;
Reading groups; Movies; Shopping trips; Dances/Social or cultural gatherings.
Description Facility is a rehabilitation center
and specializes in hip fractures and CVAs.
Physical, speech, and occupational therapy 5
days a week; licensed nurses 24-hours a day.

Laurel Avenue Convalescent Hospital*
7509 N Laurel Ave, Fontana, CA, 92335 (714)
822-8066
Admin David G Beld.
Licensure Skilled Care. *Beds* 99. *Certified* Medicare; Medi-Cal.
Ownership Proprietary.

FORTUNA

Saint Luke Manor*
2321 Newberg Rd, Fortuna, CA, 95540 (707)
725-4467
Admin George Demant.
Licensure Skilled Care. *Beds* 57. *Certified* Medicare; Medi-Cal.
Ownership Nonprofit.

FOWLER

Fowler Convalescent Hospital
306 E Tulare St, Fowler, CA, 93625 (209)
834-2542
Admin Karen Loesch. *Medical Dir/Dir of Nursing* Bob Landford MD.
Licensure Skilled Care. *Beds* 49. *Certified* Medicare; Medi-Cal.
Ownership Proprietary.
Admissions Requirements Minimum age 18.
Staff Physicians; RNs; LPNs; Orderlies;
Nurses aides; Physical therapists; Reality therapists; Recreational therapists; Occupational
therapists; Speech therapists; Activities coordinators; Dietitians; Dentists; Ophthalmologists;
Podiatrists; Audiologists.
Facilities Dining room; Activities room; Crafts
room; Laundry room; Barber/Beauty shop.
Activities Arts and Crafts; Cards; Games;
Reading groups; Prayer groups; Movies; Shopping trips; Dances/Social or cultural gatherings.

Kings Vista Convalescent Hospital*
8448 E Adams Ave, Fowler, CA, 93625 (209)
834-2519
Admin Carrie Stauber.
Licensure Skilled Care. *Beds* 49.
Certified Medi-Cal.
Ownership Proprietary.

FREMONT

Crestwood Rehabilitation and Convalescent Hospital
2500 Country Dr, Fremont, CA, 94536 (415)
792-4242
Admin Tom Curry. *Medical Dir/Dir of Nursing* Dr P Loeb.
Licensure Skilled Care. *Beds* 126. *Certified* Medicare.
Ownership Proprietary.
Staff RNs 4 (ft), 2 (pt); LPNs 7 (ft), 5 (pt);
Orderlies 5 (ft); Nurses aides 55 (ft), 5 (pt);
Physical therapists 1 (ft); Reality therapists 1
(pt); Recreational therapists 1 (pt); Occupational therapists 1 (pt); Speech therapists 1 (pt);
Activities coordinators 2 (ft); Dietitians 1 (ft);
Dentists 1 (pt); Podiatrists 2 (pt).
Facilities Dining room; Physical therapy room;
Activities room; Laundry room; Barber/Beauty
shop.
Activities Arts and Crafts; Cards; Games;
Reading groups; Prayer groups; Movies; Shopping trips; Dances/Social or cultural gatherings.
Description Facility offers a weekly formal, fine
dining program. Residents are waited on as if in
a restaurant and are able to request seconds and
choose from a dessert cart.

Driftwood Convalescent Hospital
39022 Presidio Way, Fremont, CA, 94538 (415)
792-3743
Admin Joan Collins. *Medical Dir/Dir of Nursing* Phillip M Loeb MD.
Licensure Skilled Care. *Beds* 122. *Certified* Medicare.
Ownership Proprietary.
Admissions Requirements Physician's request.
Facilities Dining room; Physical therapy room;
Activities room; Laundry room; Barber/Beauty
shop.
Activities Arts and Crafts; Cards; Games;
Reading groups; Shopping trips; Dances/Social
or cultural gatherings.

Fremont Convalescent Hospital*
2171 Mowry Ave, Fremont, CA, 94536 (415)
793-8383
Admin Imogene Ellwanger.
Licensure Skilled Care. *Beds* 88. *Certified* Medicare; Medi-Cal.
Ownership Proprietary.

Park Central Convalescent Hospital
2100 Parkside Dr, Fremont, CA, 94536 (415)
797-5300
Admin Carol Carrell. *Medical Dir/Dir of Nursing* Phillip M Loeb MD.
Licensure Skilled Care. *Beds* 99. *Certified* Medicare; Medi-Cal.
Ownership Proprietary.
Staff RNs 3 (ft), 4 (pt); LPNs 4 (ft), 6 (pt);
Nurses aides 25 (ft), 4 (pt); Physical therapists 1

(ft); Speech therapists 1 (pt); Activities coordinators 1 (ft); Dietitians 1 (ft); Dentists 1 (pt);
Podiatrists 1 (pt); Audiologists 1 (pt).

Parkmont Convalescent Hospital*
2400 Parkside Dr, Fremont, CA, 94536 (415)
793-7222
Admin Imogene Ellwanger.
Licensure Skilled Care. *Beds* 85. *Certified* Medicare; Medi-Cal.
Ownership Proprietary.

Westwood*
4303 Stevenson Blvd, Fremont, CA, 94538
(415) 657-6000
Admin Richard A Knowles.
Licensure Skilled Care. *Beds* 118.
Certified Medi-Cal.
Ownership Proprietary.

FRESNO

Beverly Manor Convalescent Hospital
2715 Fresno St, Fresno, CA, 93721 (209)
486-4433
Admin Laverle A Emmerson. *Medical Dir/Dir of Nursing* Dr Jing and Dr Woo.
Licensure Skilled Care. *Beds* 216. *Certified* Medicare; Medi-Cal.
Ownership Proprietary.

California Home for the Aged Inc*
6720 E Kings Canyon Rd, Fresno, CA, 93727
(209) 251-8414
Admin Louise Emerzian.
Licensure Skilled Care. *Beds* 66. *Certified* Medicare; Medi-Cal.
Ownership Nonprofit.

Country View Convalescent Hospital
925 N Cornelia Ave, Fresno, CA, 93706 (209)
275-4786
Admin Cheryl Mitchum. *Medical Dir/Dir of Nursing* Dr Alvin Chaffin.
Licensure Skilled Care. *Beds* 59. *Certified* Medicare; Medi-Cal.
Ownership Proprietary.
Admissions Requirements Physician's request.
Staff Physicians 1 (pt); RNs 1 (ft), 2 (pt); LPNs
3 (ft), 3 (pt); Orderlies 2 (ft), 2 (pt); Nurses aides
11 (ft), 4 (pt); Physical therapists 1 (pt); Reality
therapists 1 (ft); Recreational therapists 1 (ft);
Occupational therapists 1 (pt); Speech therapists 1 (pt); Activities coordinators 1 (ft); Dietitians 1 (pt); Dentists 1 (pt); Ophthalmologists 1
(pt); Podiatrists 1 (pt); Audiologists 1 (pt).

Fresno Care and Guidance Center*
1715 S Cedar Ave, Fresno, CA, 93702 (209)
237-8377
Admin Hilma Mitchell.
Licensure Skilled Care. *Beds* 99.
Certified Medi-Cal.
Ownership Proprietary.

Fresno Convalescent Hospital
3003 N Mariposa St, Fresno, CA, 93703 (209)
222-7416
Admin Jean Dresslar. *Medical Dir/Dir of Nursing* Graham Ruff MD.
Licensure Skilled Care. *Beds* 116. *Certified* Medicare; Medi-Cal.

Ownership Nonprofit.
Admissions Requirements Medical examination; Physician's request.
Staff RNs 4 (ft), 4 (pt); LPNs 3 (ft), 5 (pt); Orderlies 2 (ft), 1 (pt); Nurses aides 40 (ft), 11 (pt); Activities coordinators 2 (pt); Dietitians 1 (pt); Podiatrists 1 (pt).
Facilities Dining room; Physical therapy room; Activities room; Crafts room; Laundry room; Barber/Beauty shop.
Activities Arts and Crafts; Games; Movies; Musical programs; Exercise programs; Excursions in facility van.

Fresno Westview Convalescent Hospital
2772 S Fig Ave, Fresno, CA, 93706 (209) 485-3750
Admin Juanita R Basye. *Medical Dir/Dir of Nursing* E H Holvey MD.
Licensure Skilled Care; Intermediate Care. *Beds* SNF 120; ICF 79. *Certified* Medi-Cal.
Ownership Proprietary.
Admissions Requirements Minimum age 5.
Staff Physicians 3 (pt); RNs 4 (ft), 5 (pt); LPNs 13 (ft), 5 (pt); Orderlies 17 (ft), 8 (pt); Nurses aides 54 (ft), 14 (pt); Physical therapists 1 (pt); Reality therapists 2 (ft); Recreational therapists 1 (ft); Occupational therapists 1 (ft); Speech therapists 1 (pt); Activities coordinators 4 (ft), 2 (pt); Dietitians 3 (pt); Dentists 1 (pt); Ophthalmologists 4 (pt); Podiatrists 1 (pt); Audiologists 1 (pt).
Facilities Dining room; Physical therapy room; Activities room; Crafts room; Laundry room; Barber/Beauty shop.
Activities Arts and Crafts; Cards; Games; Reading groups; Prayer groups; Movies; Shopping trips; Dances/Social or cultural gatherings; Camping; fishing; county fair.

Hillcrest Convalescent Hospital
3672 N 1st St, Fresno, CA, 93726 (209) 227-5383
Admin Daniel A Kotyk. *Medical Dir/Dir of Nursing* W A Rohlfing MD.
Licensure Skilled Care. *Beds* 65. *Certified* Medicare; Medi-Cal.
Ownership Proprietary.
Facilities Dining room; Physical therapy room; Activities room; Crafts room; Laundry room; Barber/Beauty shop; Library.
Activities Arts and Crafts; Cards; Games; Reading groups; Prayer groups; Movies; Shopping trips; Dances/Social or cultural gatherings.
Description Facility features pet therapy, youth, and elderly programs.

Hope Manor
1665 M St, Fresno, CA, 93721 (209) 268-5361
Admin John F Einhart. *Medical Dir/Dir of Nursing* J Malcolm Masten MD.
Licensure Skilled Care; Intermediate Care. *Beds* SNF 85; ICF 70. *Certified* Medicare; Medi-Cal.
Ownership Proprietary.
Admissions Requirements Medical examination; Physician's request.
Staff Physicians 1 (pt); RNs 2 (ft), 1 (pt); LPNs 14 (ft), 2 (pt); Orderlies 10 (ft); Nurses aides 50 (ft); Physical therapists 1 (ft), 1 (pt); Speech therapists 1 (pt); Activities coordinators 2 (ft), 2 (pt); Dietitians 1 (pt); Dentists 1 (pt); Podiatrists 1 (pt).

Facilities Dining room; Physical therapy room; Activities room; Chapel; Crafts room; Laundry room; Barber/Beauty shop; Library; Dentist office.
Activities Arts and Crafts; Cards; Games; Reading groups; Prayer groups; Movies; Dances/Social or cultural gatherings; Video games.
Description Facility is serving yesterday's youth in 5-story high rise with a home-like atmosphere. Providing 3 levels of care—at the least possible cost.

Hy Lond Convalescent Hospital
3408 E Shields Ave, Fresno, CA, 93726 (209) 227-4063
Admin Laverle A Emmerson.
Licensure Skilled Care. *Beds* 121. *Certified* Medicare; Medi-Cal.
Ownership Proprietary.

Hy-Pana House Convalescent Hospital*
3510 E Shields Ave, Fresno, CA, 93726 (209) 222-4807
Admin Patrick Uribe.
Licensure Skilled Care. *Beds* 112. *Certified* Medicare; Medi-Cal.
Ownership Proprietary.

Manning Gardens Convalescent Hospital
2113 E Manning Ave, Fresno, CA, 93725 (209) 834-2586
Admin Cary J Hanson.
Licensure Skilled Care. *Beds* 59. *Certified* Medicare; Medi-Cal.
Ownership Proprietary.
Staff Physicians 5 (pt); RNs 1 (ft), 1 (pt); LPNs 5 (ft), 2 (pt); Nurses aides 25 (ft), 5 (pt); Physical therapists 1 (pt); Speech therapists 1 (pt); Activities coordinators 1 (ft), 1 (pt); Dietitians 1 (pt); Dentists 1 (pt); Podiatrists 1 (pt).

Manning Gardens Town House
1233 A St, Fresno, CA, 93706 (209) 268-6317
Admin Jonathon C Freer. *Medical Dir/Dir of Nursing* Dr Rohlfim.
Licensure Skilled Care. *Beds* 80. *Certified* Medicare; Medi-Cal.
Ownership Proprietary.
Staff Orderlies 2 (ft); Nurses aides; Nurses aides 35 (ft), 10 (pt); Activities coordinators 1 (ft), 1 (pt); Dietitians 1 (ft).
Facilities Dining room; Physical therapy room; Activities room; Crafts room; Barber/Beauty shop.
Activities Arts and Crafts; Cards; Games; Reading groups; Prayer groups; Movies; Shopping trips; Dances/Social or cultural gatherings.

Nazareth House*
2121 N 1st St, Fresno, CA, 93703 (209) 237-2257
Admin Sr Teresa O'Conn.
Licensure Skilled Care. *Beds* 12.
Ownership Nonprofit.

Pacific Gardens Convalescent Center Inc*
577 S Peach Ave, Fresno, CA, 93727 (209) 251-8463
Admin Norman Kizirian.
Licensure Skilled Care. *Beds* 180. *Certified* Medicare; Medi-Cal.
Ownership Proprietary.

Raintree Convalescent Hospital
5265 E Huntington Ave, Fresno, CA, 93727 (209) 251-8244
Admin Margaret A Tynan. *Medical Dir/Dir of Nursing* Joan E Rubinstein MD.
Licensure Skilled Care. *Beds* 49. *Certified* Medicare.
Ownership Proprietary.
Admissions Requirements Physician's request.
Staff RNs 1 (ft); LPNs 2 (ft); Nurses aides 11 (ft); Physical therapists 1 (pt); Speech therapists 1 (pt); Activities coordinators 1 (ft); Dietitians 1 (pt); Dentists 1 (pt); Podiatrists 1 (pt); Audiologists 1 (pt).
Facilities Dining room; Activities room; Laundry room.
Activities Arts and Crafts; Cards; Games; Reading groups; Prayer groups; Movies; Dances/Social or cultural gatherings.

Riley Nursing Home*
541 N Fulton, Fresno, CA, 93727 (209) 237-0261
Admin Angela Shoberg.
Licensure Skilled Care. *Beds* 25. *Certified* Medicare; Medi-Cal.
Ownership Proprietary.

San Joaquin Gardens Health Facility
5555-59 N Fresno St, Fresno, CA, 93710 (209) 439-4770
Admin Jerry E Warren. *Medical Dir/Dir of Nursing* Edwin G Wiens MD.
Licensure Skilled Care; Intermediate Care. *Beds* SNF 56; ICF 32. *Certified* Medicare; Medi-Cal.
Ownership Nonprofit.
Staff RNs 4 (ft), 3 (pt); LPNs 3 (ft), 5 (pt); Nurses aides 15 (ft), 23 (pt); Reality therapists 1 (pt); Recreational therapists 2 (ft).
Facilities Dining room; Activities room; Chapel; Crafts room; Laundry room; Barber/Beauty shop; Library.
Activities Arts and Crafts; Games; Reading groups; Movies; Shopping trips; Dances/Social or cultural gatherings.
Description The health facility is an integral part of a continuing care retirement community and primarily serves the needs of those residents. From time to time residents are admitted directly to the heatlh center from the community.

Sierra View Convalescent Hospital*
668 E Bullard Ave, Fresno, CA, 93710 (209) 439-4461
Admin Charles Roy Wagner.
Licensure Skilled Care; Intermediate Care. *Beds* SNF 26; ICF 59. *Certified* Medi-Cal.
Ownership Nonprofit.

Sunnyside Convalescent Hospital*
2939 S Peach Ave, Fresno, CA, 93725 (209) 233-6248
Admin Michael L Fellen.
Licensure Skilled Care; Intermediate Care. *Beds* SNF 100; ICF 16. *Certified* Medi-Cal.
Ownership Proprietary.

Terrace Care Convalescent Hospital
2020 N Weber Ave, Fresno, CA, 93705 (209) 237-0883
Admin Charles E Eggleston. *Medical Dir/Dir of*

Nursing Dr Walter Rohlfing.
Licensure Skilled Care. *Beds* 233. *Certified* Medicare; Medi-Cal.
Ownership Proprietary.
Admissions Requirements Medical examination; Physician's request.
Staff RNs 10 (ft), 5 (pt); LPNs 13 (ft), 6 (pt); Nurses aides 62 (ft), 28 (pt); Physical therapists 1 (ft); Occupational therapists 1 (ft); Activities coordinators 3 (ft).
Facilities Dining room; Physical therapy room; Activities room; Chapel; Crafts room; Laundry room; Barber/Beauty shop.
Activities Arts and Crafts; Cards; Games; Prayer groups; Movies; Dances/Social or cultural gatherings.
Description Terrace Care residents enjoy 4 garden patio areas, many with direct resident access. Activities are tailored to each resident's abilities, and include a pet therapy program. Rehabilitative services include speech, occupational therapy and in- and outpatient physical therapy. The facility has developed 4 innovative dining programs including family-style dining.

Twilight Haven
1717 S Winery Ave, Fresno, CA, 93727 (209) 251-8417
Admin Leonard P Kelly. *Medical Dir/Dir of Nursing* Mrs Dadian.
Licensure Skilled Care. *Beds* 43. *Certified* Medicare; Medi-Cal.
Ownership Nonprofit.
Admissions Requirements Minimum age 62.
Staff Physicians; RNs; LPNs; Orderlies; Nurses aides; Activities coordinators; Dietitians.
Facilities Dining room; Activities room; Chapel; Laundry room; Barber/Beauty shop.
Activities Arts and Crafts; Games; Prayer groups; Movies; Shopping trips; Dances/Social or cultural gatherings.

Valley Care and Guidance Center*
9919 S Elm Ave, Fresno, CA, 93706 (209) 834-5351
Admin Michael Riley.
Licensure Skilled Care. *Beds* 79.
Certified Medi-Cal.
Ownership Proprietary.

Valley Convalescent Hospital
4840 E Tulare Ave, Fresno, CA, 93727 (209) 251-7161
Admin Patricia Churchill. *Medical Dir/Dir of Nursing* W A Rohlfing MD.
Licensure Skilled Care. *Beds* 99. *Certified* Medicare; Medi-Cal.
Ownership Proprietary.
Admissions Requirements Physician's request.
Staff Physicians 1 (pt); RNs 4 (ft), 5 (pt); LPNs 5 (ft), 2 (pt); Nurses aides 40 (ft), 3 (pt); Physical therapists 1 (pt); Recreational therapists 1 (ft); Speech therapists 1 (pt); Dietitians 1 (pt).
Facilities Dining room; Physical therapy room; Activities room; Laundry room; Barber/Beauty shop; Library.
Activities Arts and Crafts; Cards; Games; Prayer groups; Movies; Dances/Social or cultural gatherings.
Description A strong emphasis is placed on

rehabilitation with physical, speech, and recreational therapy as well as the use of Clinitron beds in the treatment of decubitus ulcers.

FULLERTON

Fairway Convalescent Center
2800 N Harbor Blvd, Fullerton, CA, 92635 (714) 871-9202
Admin William K Schifferli. *Medical Dir/Dir of Nursing* Dr Bruce Mutter.
Licensure Skilled Care. *Beds* 79. *Certified* Medicare; Medi-Cal.
Ownership Proprietary.
Staff RNs 1 (ft), 2 (pt); LPNs 5 (ft), 6 (pt); Orderlies 2 (ft); Nurses aides 26 (ft), 6 (pt); Physical therapists 1 (pt); Recreational therapists 1 (pt); Occupational therapists 1 (pt); Speech therapists 1 (pt); Activities coordinators 1 (ft), 1 (pt); Dietitians 1 (pt); Dentists 1 (pt); Ophthalmologists 1 (pt); Podiatrists 1 (pt); Audiologists 1 (pt).
Facilities Dining room; Physical therapy room; Activities room; Crafts room; Laundry room; Barber/Beauty shop; Speech therapy room; Whirlpool room.
Activities Arts and Crafts; Cards; Games; Reading groups; Prayer groups; Movies; Shopping trips; Dances/Social or cultural gatherings; Adult education for cooking classes, music..
Description Facility is moving further into the area of rehabilitative medicine; has an RPT who works with a physical therapy aide 5 days a week doing QID and BID treatments. Clinitron beds used in the treatment of decubitus ulcers. Facility has a very forward-thinking staff that is highly concerned with the residents quality of life.

Fullerton Care Convalescent Hospital
2222 N Harbor, Fullerton, CA, 92635 (714) 992-5701
Admin John R Torrez. *Medical Dir/Dir of Nursing* Bruce Mutter.
Licensure Skilled Care. *Beds* 300. *Certified* Medicare; Medi-Cal.
Ownership Proprietary.
Admissions Requirements Physician's request.
Facilities Dining room; Physical therapy room; Activities room; Chapel; Crafts room; Laundry room; Barber/Beauty shop.
Activities Arts and Crafts; Cards; Games; Reading groups; Prayer groups; Movies; Shopping trips; Dances/Social or cultural gatherings.
Description Facility has an excellent reputation for therapy in community.

Gordon Lane Convalescent Hospital
1821 E Chapman Ave, Fullerton, CA, 92631 (714) 879-7301
Admin Carolyn L Innis. *Medical Dir/Dir of Nursing* Frank Amato MD.
Licensure Skilled Care. *Beds* 99.
Ownership Proprietary.
Admissions Requirements Medical examination; Physician's request.
Facilities Dining room; Physical therapy room; Activities room; Crafts room; Laundry room; Barber/Beauty shop; Library.
Activities Arts and Crafts; Cards; Games; Reading groups; Prayer groups; Movies; Shopping trips; Dances/Social or cultural gatherings;

Parties, special entertainment.
Description An all private facility which offers a wonderful activity program full of fun and challenging activities and events, with a special program for the disoriented as well as visually and hearing impaired patients. Facility's meals are outstanding.

Sunhaven Convalescent and Rehabilitation Hospital
201 E Bastanchury Rd, Fullerton, CA, 92635 (714) 870-0060
Admin Sally Kuster. *Medical Dir/Dir of Nursing* J Soffice MD.
Licensure Skilled Care. *Beds* 59. *Certified* Medicare; Medi-Cal.
Ownership Proprietary.
Admissions Requirements Medical examination; Physician's request.
Staff RNs 2 (ft); LPNs 6 (ft), 3 (pt); Orderlies 20 (ft); Nurses aides 10 (ft); Activities coordinators 1 (ft).
Facilities Dining room; Activities room; Crafts room; Barber/Beauty shop.
Activities Arts and Crafts; Cards; Games; Reading groups; Prayer groups; Dances/Social or cultural gatherings.
Description Smaller facility lends itself to a homier atmosphere; top-level skilled nursing care with a wide range of activities to meet the needs and interests of all.

Sunny Hills Convalescent Hospital*
330 W Bastanchury Rd, Fullerton, CA, 92635 (714) 879-4511
Admin Kathleen Lester.
Licensure Skilled Care. *Beds* 99. *Certified* Medicare; Medi-Cal.
Ownership Proprietary.

Wilshire Convalescent Hospital
245 E Wilshire, Fullerton, CA, 92632 (871) 871-6020
Admin Beverly Markle. *Medical Dir/Dir of Nursing* Dr John Cowles.
Licensure Skilled Care. *Beds* 99. *Certified* Medicare; Medi-Cal.
Ownership Proprietary.
Admissions Requirements Medical examination; Physician's request.
Staff RNs 3 (ft); LPNs 6 (ft); Nurses aides 24 (ft); Activities coordinators 1 (ft); Dietitians 1 (ft).
Facilities Dining room; Activities room; Crafts room; Laundry room; Barber/Beauty shop; Patio.
Activities Arts and Crafts; Cards; Games; Reading groups; Prayer groups; Movies; Shopping trips; Dances/Social or cultural gatherings; Monthly buffets; Field trips.
Description The facility offers a home-like atmosphere with personalized care, pleasant surroundings, and excellent food.

GALT

Royal Oaks Convalescent Hospital*
144 F St, Galt, CA, 95632 (209) 745-1537
Admin Margherita Fagan.
Licensure Skilled Care. *Beds* 99. *Certified* Medicare; Medi-Cal.
Ownership Proprietary.

GARDEN GROVE

Chapman Harbor Convalescent Hospital*
12232 Chapman Ave, Garden Grove, CA,
92640 (714) 971-5517
Admin Keith T Goodell.
Licensure Skilled Care. *Beds* 78. *Certified* Medicare; Medi-Cal.
Ownership Proprietary.

Garden Grove Convalescent Hospital*
12882 Shackleford Ln, Garden Grove, CA,
92641 (714) 638-9470
Admin Emanuel Newman.
Licensure Skilled Care. *Beds* 99. *Certified* Medicare; Medi-Cal.
Ownership Proprietary.

Haster Convalescent Hospital
12681 Haster St, Garden Grove, CA, 92640
(714) 971-2153
Admin Esther Abney. *Medical Dir/Dir of
Nursing* John Cowles MD.
Licensure Skilled Care. *Beds* 132. *Certified* Medicare; Medi-Cal.
Ownership Proprietary.
Admissions Requirements Physician's request.
Staff RNs 4 (ft); LPNs 8 (ft); Activities coordinators 2 (ft).
Facilities Dining room; Physical therapy room;
Activities room; Chapel; Crafts room; Laundry
room; Barber/Beauty shop; Library.
Activities Arts and Crafts; Cards; Games;
Reading groups; Prayer groups; Movies; Shopping trips; Dances/Social or cultural gatherings.
Description We have a distinct Medicare wing
(20 beds). We focus on the individual with
24-hour licensed nursing care. Physical therapy
rehabilitates patient to his/her highest potential
to return home.

Hy-Lond Home*
9861 W 11 St, Garden Grove, CA, 92644 (714)
531-8741
Admin Lila Russavage.
Licensure Skilled Care; Intermediate Care for
Mentally Retarded. *Beds* 159. *Certified* Medi-Cal.
Ownership Proprietary.

Meadow View Park
13392 Taft Ave, Garden Grove, CA, 92643
(714) 638-5450
Admin Beata E Chapman. *Medical Dir/Dir of
Nursing* Dr S Osburn.
Licensure Skilled Care; Intermediate Care.
Beds 59. *Certified* Medicare; Medi-Cal.
Ownership Proprietary.
Staff Physicians 3 (pt); RNs 1 (ft), 1 (pt); LPNs
5 (ft), 4 (pt); Physical therapists 1 (pt); Occupational therapists 1 (pt); Speech therapists 1 (pt);
Activities coordinators 1 (pt); Dietitians 1 (pt);
Dentists 1 (pt); Podiatrists 1 (pt); Audiologists 1
(pt); Program director 1 (ft).
Facilities Dining room; Physical therapy room;
Activities room; Crafts room; Laundry room.
Activities Arts and Crafts; Reading groups;
Prayer groups; Movies; Shopping trips; Dances-
/Social or cultural gatherings; Outings to restaurants.
Description The facility offers 56 hours of

structured activities per week centered around
the individual client's assessed needs; reassessment of each client is made every 6 months.

Orangegrove Rehabilitation Hospital
12332 Garden Grove, Garden Grove, CA,
92643 (714) 534-1041
Admin James D Baker III. *Medical Dir/Dir of
Nursing* Gordon Glasgow MD.
Licensure Skilled Care. *Beds* 99. *Certified* Medicare; Medi-Cal.
Ownership Proprietary.
Admissions Requirements Minimum age 12;
Medical examination; Physician's request.
Staff Physicians 6 (ft); RNs 8 (ft), 2 (pt); LPNs
10 (ft), 2 (pt); Orderlies 5 (ft); Nurses aides 35
(ft), 2 (pt); Physical therapists 6 (ft); Reality
therapists 1 (pt); Recreational therapists 1 (pt);
Occupational therapists 3 (ft); Speech therapists
1 (ft), 1 (pt); Activities coordinators 1 (ft), 1
(pt); Dietitians 1 (ft); Dentists 1 (pt); Ophthalmologists 1 (pt); Podiatrists 1 (ft); Audiologists
1 (pt).
Facilities Dining room; Physical therapy room;
Activities room; Chapel; Crafts room; Laundry
room; Barber/Beauty shop; Library.
Activities Arts and Crafts; Cards; Games;
Reading groups; Prayer groups; Movies; Shopping trips; Dances/Social or cultural gatherings.
Description Facility has an acute and restorative rehabilitation program which includes
physical therapy, occupational therapy, and
speech therapy 6 days a week. Excellent activity
program includes outings, shopping trips,
luncheons, movies. Very caring and professional staff in a home-like atmosphere. JCAH
accredited.

Pacific Haven Convalescent Home
12072 Trask Ave, Garden Grove, CA, 92643
(714) 534-1942
Admin Norman W Gunsolley. *Medical Dir-
/Dir of Nursing* J D Cowles MD.
Licensure Skilled Care. *Beds* 99. *Certified* Medicare; Medi-Cal.
Ownership Nonprofit.
Admissions Requirements Medical
examination; Physician's request.
Staff Physicians 17 (pt); RNs 2 (ft), 2 (pt);
LPNs 11 (ft); Nurses aides 38 (ft); Physical therapists 1 (pt); Occupational therapists 1 (pt);
Speech therapists 1 (pt); Activities coordinators
1 (ft); Dietitians 1 (pt); Dentists 1 (pt); Ophthalmologists 1 (pt); Podiatrists 1 (pt); Audiologists
1 (pt).
Affiliation Church of Latter-Day Saints (Mormon)
Facilities Dining room; Physical therapy room;
Activities room; Chapel; Crafts room; Laundry
room; Barber/Beauty shop; Library.
Activities Arts and Crafts; Cards; Games;
Reading groups; Prayer groups; Movies; Shopping trips; Dances/Social or cultural gatherings;
Cooking classes.
Description Facility has an excellent housekeeping department; attempts to provide interesting as well as nutritious meals; features an
active resident and family council. Facility has
an 18-bed section for higher level care patients.

Palm Grove Convalescent Center*
13075 Blackbird St, Garden Grove, CA, 92640
(714) 530-6322

Admin Michael Dufresne.
Licensure Skilled Care. *Beds* 126. *Certified* Medicare; Medi-Cal.
Ownership Proprietary.

GARDENA

Alondra Nursing Home*
1140 W Rosecrans Ave, Gardena, CA, 90247
(213) 323-3194
Admin George Curtis.
Licensure Skilled Care. *Beds* 99. *Certified* Medicare; Medi-Cal.
Ownership Proprietary.

Ayer Lar Sanitarium
16530 S Broadway, Gardena, CA, 90248 (213)
329-7581
Admin Lee M Ayers. *Medical Dir/Dir of
Nursing* George Lee MD.
Licensure Skilled Care. *Beds* 50. *Certified* Medicare; Medi-Cal.
Ownership Proprietary.
Staff Physicians 1 (pt); RNs 1 (ft), 2 (pt); LPNs
3 (ft), 1 (pt); Nurses aides 14 (ft), 6 (pt);
Physical therapists 1 (pt); Reality therapists 1
(pt); Speech therapists 1 (pt); Activities coordinators 1 (pt); Dietitians 1 (pt); Dentists 1 (pt);
Ophthalmologists 1 (pt); Podiatrists 1 (pt);
Audiologists 1 (pt).
Facilities Activities room; Crafts room; Laundry room; Barber/Beauty shop.
Activities Arts and Crafts; Cards; Games;
Reading groups; Prayer groups; Movies; Dances/Social or cultural gatherings.
Description This is a small facility with an
excellent staff-to-resident ratio, offering a home-like atmosphere for residents.

Clear View Convalescent Center
15823 S Western Ave, Gardena, CA, 90247
(213) 770-3131
Admin W Lee Towns. *Medical Dir/Dir of
Nursing* W Al Fadly MD.
Beds 99. *Certified* Medi-Cal.
Ownership Proprietary.
Admissions Requirements Minimum age 18;
Physician's request.
Staff Physicians 2 (pt); RNs 2 (ft); LPNs 7 (ft);
Orderlies 2 (ft); Nurses aides 60 (ft); Physical
therapists 1 (pt); Reality therapists 1 (pt); Recreational therapists 1 (pt); Occupational therapists
1 (pt); Speech therapists 1 (pt); Activities coordinators 1 (pt); Dietitians 1 (pt); Dentists 1 (pt);
Ophthalmologists 1 (pt); Podiatrists 1 (pt);
Audiologists 1 (pt).
Facilities Dining room; Physical therapy room;
Activities room; Crafts room; Laundry room;
Barber/Beauty shop.
Activities Arts and Crafts; Cards; Games;
Reading groups; Prayer groups; Movies; Shopping trips; Dances/Social or cultural gatherings.
Description Long-term care facility catering to
confused, disoriented patients including Alzheimer's. Modern constructed building. This,
and sister facility, Clear View Sanitarium, (on
same site) are considered "locked" facilities to
contain those who wander.

Clear View Sanitarium
15823 S Western Ave, Gardena, CA, 90247
(213) 538-2323

Admin Arnold Niederman. *Medical Dir/Dir of Nursing* W Al Fadly MD.
Beds 73. *Certified* Medi-Cal.
Ownership Proprietary.
Admissions Requirements Minimum age 18; Physician's request.
Staff Physicians 1 (pt); RNs 2 (ft); LPNs 7 (ft); Orderlies 2 (ft); Nurses aides 45 (ft); Physical therapists 1 (pt); Reality therapists 1 (pt); Recreational therapists 1 (pt); Occupational therapists 1 (pt); Speech therapists 1 (pt); Activities coordinators 1 (ft); Dietitians 1 (pt); Dentists 1 (pt); Ophthalmologists 1 (pt); Podiatrists 1 (pt); Audiologists 1 (pt).
Facilities Dining room; Physical therapy room; Activities room; Crafts room; Laundry room; Barber/Beauty shop; Large, spacious grounds.
Activities Arts and Crafts; Cards; Games; Reading groups; Prayer groups; Movies; Shopping trips; Dances/Social or cultural gatherings.
Description Locked, long-term care facility operating with the same ownership since 1937. Modern, seismically constructed facility.

Gardena Convalescent Center*
14819 S Vermont, Gardena, CA, 90247 (213) 321-6571
Admin Dorothy Bryson.
Licensure Skilled Care. *Beds* 74. *Certified* Medicare; Medi-Cal.
Ownership Proprietary.

Las Flores Convalescent Hospital
14165 Purche Ave, Gardena, CA, 90249 (213) 323-4570
Admin Diana Fortune. *Medical Dir/Dir of Nursing* Burton H Goldman MD.
Licensure Skilled Care. *Beds* 99. *Certified* Medicare; Medi-Cal.
Ownership Proprietary.
Admissions Requirements Minimum age 21; Medical examination; Physician's request.
Staff RNs 1 (ft), 1 (pt); LPNs 9 (ft), 2 (pt); Nurses aides 47 (ft), 1 (pt); Physical therapists 1 (pt); Recreational therapists 1 (ft); Occupational therapists 1 (pt); Speech therapists 1 (pt); Dietitians 1 (ft), 1 (pt); Dentists 1 (pt); Ophthalmologists 1 (pt); Podiatrists 1 (pt); Audiologists 1 (pt).
Facilities Dining room; Physical therapy room; Activities room; Crafts room; Laundry room; Barber/Beauty shop.
Activities Arts and Crafts; Cards; Games; Reading groups; Prayer groups; Movies; Shopping trips; Dances/Social or cultural gatherings.

South Bay Keiro Nursing Home*
15115 S Vermont, Gardena, CA, 90247 (213) 532-0700
Admin Edwin Hiroto.
Licensure Skilled Care. *Beds* 98. *Certified* Medicare.
Ownership Nonprofit.

GILROY

Driftwood Convalescent Hospital*
8170 Murray Ave, Gilroy, CA, 95020 (408) 842-9311
Admin Gerald E Hunter.
Licensure Skilled Care. *Beds* 132. *Certified* Medicare; Medi-Cal.

Ownership Proprietary.

GLENDALE

Allenvale Convalescent Hospital*
201 Allen Ave, Glendale, CA, 91201 (213) 849-1969
Admin Bruce Wolfe.
Licensure Skilled Care. *Beds* 94. *Certified* Medicare; Medi-Cal.
Ownership Proprietary.

Autumn Hills
430 N Glendale Ave, Glendale, CA, 91206 (213) 246-5677
Admin Kenneth B Thompson. *Medical Dir/Dir of Nursing* Dr Donald Doty.
Licensure Skilled Care. *Beds* 99. *Certified* Medicare; Medi-Cal.
Ownership Proprietary.
Admissions Requirements Physician's request.
Staff Physicians 20 (pt); RNs 2 (ft), 1 (pt); Nurses aides 30 (ft); Physical therapists 1 (pt); Reality therapists 1 (pt); Recreational therapists 1 (pt); Occupational therapists 1 (pt); Speech therapists 1 (pt); Activities coordinators 1 (ft); Dietitians 1 (pt); Dentists 1 (pt); Ophthalmologists 1 (pt); Podiatrists 1 (pt); Audiologists 1 (pt).
Facilities Dining room; Physical therapy room; Activities room; Crafts room; Laundry room; Barber/Beauty shop.
Activities Arts and Crafts; Cards; Games; Reading groups; Prayer groups; Movies; Shopping trips; Dances/Social or cultural gatherings; Variety.

Beverly Manor Convalescent Hospital
630 W Broadway, Glendale, CA, 91204 (818) 247-3345
Admin William Mathies. *Medical Dir/Dir of Nursing* Albert P Killian MD.
Licensure Skilled Care; Intermediate Care.
Beds 140. *Certified* Medicare; Medi-Cal.
Ownership Proprietary.
Facilities Dining room; Physical therapy room; Activities room; Laundry room; Barber/Beauty shop; Library.
Activities Arts and Crafts; Cards; Games; Reading groups; Prayer groups; Movies; Shopping trips; Dances/Social or cultural gatherings; Wheelchair walks; Adopt-a-grandparent; Adopt-a-friend.
Description RN supervisor in facility 24-hours; active 7 day per week, restorative nursing program; comprehensive activities program; full range of therapy services (occupational, physical, and speech); all rooms are 3-bed, 2-bed, or private; comprehensive activities program.

Broadway Manor Convalescent Hospital
605 W Broadway, Glendale, CA, 91204 (213) 246-7174
Admin Ralph M Guarino. *Medical Dir/Dir of Nursing* Albert Killian MD.
Licensure Skilled Care. *Beds* 78. *Certified* Medicare; Medi-Cal.
Ownership Proprietary.
Staff Physicians 16 (pt); RNs 2 (ft), 2 (pt); LPNs 6 (ft), 6 (pt); Orderlies 8 (ft), 2 (pt); Nurses aides 14 (ft), 6 (pt); Physical therapists 2

(ft), 3 (pt); Occupational therapists 1 (pt); Speech therapists 1 (pt); Activities coordinators 1 (ft); Dietitians 1 (ft); Dentists 1 (pt); Ophthalmologists 1 (pt); Podiatrists 1 (pt); Audiologists 1 (pt).
Facilities Dining room; Physical therapy room; Activities room; Crafts room; Laundry room; Barber/Beauty shop.
Activities Arts and Crafts; Games; Prayer groups; Movies; Dances/Social or cultural gatherings.
Description Each room has a sliding glass door opening onto a patio. Candelight dinners are featured where there is special food, music, and entertainment that patients can invite their families to attend.

Cal Haven Convalescent Hospital
445 W Broadway, Glendale, CA, 91204 (818) 241-2157
Admin Edward V Hamilton. *Medical Dir/Dir of Nursing* Dr A P Killian.
Licensure Skilled Care. *Beds* 35. *Certified* Medicare; Medi-Cal.
Ownership Proprietary.
Admissions Requirements Minimum age 40; Medical examination.
Staff Physicians 1 (pt); RNs 2 (ft), 2 (pt); LPNs 3 (ft), 4 (pt); Orderlies 2 (ft), 1 (pt); Nurses aides 9 (ft), 7 (pt); Physical therapists 1 (pt); Reality therapists 1 (pt); Recreational therapists 1 (pt); Occupational therapists 1 (pt); Speech therapists 1 (pt); Activities coordinators 1 (ft), 1 (pt); Dietitians 1 (pt); Dentists 1 (pt); Ophthalmologists 1 (pt); Podiatrists 1 (pt); Audiologists 1 (pt).
Facilities Dining room; Physical therapy room; Activities room; Crafts room; Laundry room; Barber/Beauty shop; Library; Patios.
Activities Arts and Crafts; Cards; Games; Reading groups; Prayer groups; Movies; Shopping trips; Dances/Social or cultural gatherings; Walks in area.
Description We feel we can take care of the long-term patient better because we are a small facility and therefore give more personal care and attention to the resident and their families.

Casa Verdugo Convalescent Lodge*
1208 S Central Ave, Glendale, CA, 91204 (213) 246-5516
Admin Paul M Swanson.
Licensure Skilled Care. *Beds* 48. *Certified* Medicare.
Ownership Nonprofit.

Chandler Convalescent Hospital*
525 S Central Ave, Glendale, CA, 91204 (213) 240-1610
Admin Henry Levine.
Licensure Skilled Care. *Beds* 106. *Certified* Medicare; Medi-Cal.
Ownership Proprietary.

Dreiers Sanitarium
1400 W Glenoaks Blvd, Glendale, CA, 91201 (213) 242-1183
Admin Dolores D Haedrich. *Medical Dir/Dir of Nursing* George Papkin MD.
Licensure Skilled Care. *Beds* 59. *Certified* Medicare; Medi-Cal.
Ownership Proprietary.
Staff Physicians 1 (pt); RNs 1 (ft), 3 (pt); LPNs

2 (ft), 4 (pt); Orderlies 1 (ft), 1 (pt); Nurses aides 18 (ft), 3 (pt); Activities coordinators 1 (ft).
Facilities Dining room; Activities room; Crafts room; Laundry room; Barber/Beauty shop.
Activities Arts and Crafts; Cards; Games; Reading groups; Prayer groups; Movies; Dances/Social or cultural gatherings.
Description Facility features an adopt-a-grandparent program with local school children every other week, professional entertainment at least once or twice a month, and full-length movies at least once a month.

Elms Convalescent Hospital
212 W Chevy Chase Dr, Glendale, CA, 91205 (213) 240-6720
Admin Ruth R Ryder. *Medical Dir/Dir of Nursing* Albert Killian MD.
Licensure Skilled Care. *Beds* 52. *Certified* Medicare; Medi-Cal.
Ownership Proprietary.
Staff RNs 1 (ft), 1 (pt); LPNs 4 (ft), 5 (pt); Orderlies 2 (ft); Nurses aides 12 (ft), 6 (pt); Physical therapists 1 (pt); Activities coordinators 1 (ft), 1 (pt).
Facilities Dining room; Laundry room; Barber/Beauty shop.
Activities Arts and Crafts; Cards; Games; Reading groups; Prayer groups; Movies; Shopping trips.

Glenoaks Convalescent Hospital
409 W Glenoaks Blvd, Glendale, CA, 91202 (818) 240-4300
Admin Pamela Hamilton. *Medical Dir/Dir of Nursing* O W Janes MD.
Licensure Skilled Care. *Beds* 94. *Certified* Medicare; Medi-Cal.
Ownership Proprietary.
Admissions Requirements Medical examination; Physician's request.
Staff RNs 3 (ft), 2 (pt); LPNs 7 (ft), 3 (pt); Nurses aides 40 (ft), 2 (pt); Reality therapists 1 (ft); Recreational therapists 1 (ft); Activities coordinators 1 (ft); Dietitians 1 (ft).
Facilities Dining room; Physical therapy room; Activities room; Crafts room; Laundry room; Barber/Beauty shop; Library.
Activities Arts and Crafts; Cards; Games; Reading groups; Prayer groups; Movies; Shopping trips; Dances/Social or cultural gatherings.
Description Facility features a courtyard patio accessible from interior rooms and individualized activity and social services programs.

Glenridge Center
611 S Central, Glendale, CA, 91203 (213) 246-6591
Admin Rodney Meacham. *Medical Dir/Dir of Nursing* R Cabnenn MD.
Licensure Skilled Care. *Beds* ICF 116. *Certified* Medicare.
Ownership Proprietary.
Admissions Requirements Minimum age 3.
Staff Physicians 2 (pt); RNs 10 (ft), 5 (pt); LPNs 10 (ft), 5 (pt); Orderlies 25 (ft); Nurses aides 35 (ft); Physical therapists 1 (ft); Recreational therapists 1 (ft); Occupational therapists 1 (pt); Speech therapists 1 (pt); Activities coordinators 1 (ft); Dietitians 1 (ft); Dentists 1 (pt); Ophthalmologists 1 (pt); Podiatrists 1 (pt); Audiologists 1 (pt).
Facilities Dining room; Physical therapy room;

Activities room; Crafts room; Laundry room; Barber/Beauty shop.
Activities Arts and Crafts; Games; Movies; Shopping trips; Dances/Social or cultural gatherings.

Long Term Care Inc
1505 Colby Dr, Glendale, CA, 91205 (213) 247-4476
Admin Carroll Gillespie.
Licensure Skilled Care. *Beds* 94. *Certified* Medicare; Medi-Cal.
Ownership Proprietary.
Staff RNs 1 (ft), 4 (pt); LPNs 13 (ft), 4 (pt); Orderlies 6 (ft), 1 (pt); Nurses aides 38 (ft), 6 (pt); Physical therapists 1 (pt); Recreational therapists 2 (ft); Occupational therapists 1 (pt); Speech therapists 1 (pt); Dietitians 1 (pt).
Facilities Dining room; Activities room; Crafts room; Barber/Beauty shop.
Activities Arts and Crafts; Cards; Games; Prayer groups; Movies.

Royale Oaks Convalescent Hospital*
250 N Verdugo Rd, Glendale, CA, 91206 (213) 244-1133
Admin Charolette Dufresne.
Licensure Skilled Care. *Beds* 136. *Certified* Medicare; Medi-Cal.
Ownership Proprietary.

Tropico Convalescent Hospital*
130 W Los Feliz Rd, Glendale, CA, 91204 (213) 245-3978
Admin Roberta Gayor.
Licensure Skilled Care. *Beds* 56. *Certified* Medicare; Medi-Cal.
Ownership Proprietary.

Windsor Manor*
1230 E Windsor Rd, Glendale, CA, 91205 (213) 245-1623
Admin John K Hughes.
Licensure Skilled Care. *Beds* 28.
Certified Medi-Cal.
Ownership Nonprofit.

GLENDORA

Adventist Convalescent Hospital
435 E Gladstone, Glendora, CA, 91740 (213) 963-5955
Admin Warren Runyan. *Medical Dir/Dir of Nursing* Onn T Chan MD.
Licensure Skilled Care. *Beds* 118. *Certified* Medicare; Medi-Cal.
Ownership Nonprofit.
Admissions Requirements Medical examination; Physician's request.
Staff RNs 6 (ft), 4 (pt); LPNs 8 (ft), 1 (pt); Orderlies 2 (ft); Nurses aides 40 (ft), 4 (pt); Activities coordinators 1 (ft).
Affiliation Seventh-Day Adventist
Facilities Dining room; Physical therapy room; Activities room; Chapel; Crafts room; Laundry room; Barber/Beauty shop; Library.
Activities Arts and Crafts; Games; Reading groups; Prayer groups; Movies; Shopping trips; Dances/Social or cultural gatherings.

Community Convalescent Hospital of Glendora
638 E Colorado Ave, Glendora, CA, 91740 (213) 963-6091
Admin G Slapper. *Medical Dir/Dir of Nursing* Onn T Chan MD.
Licensure Skilled Care. *Beds* 96. *Certified* Medicare; Medi-Cal.
Ownership Proprietary.
Admissions Requirements Physician's request.
Staff Physicians 1 (pt); RNs 1 (ft), 3 (pt); LPNs 6 (ft), 7 (pt); Orderlies 3 (ft); Nurses aides 27 (ft), 7 (pt); Physical therapists 1 (pt); Speech therapists 1 (pt); Activities coordinators 1 (ft); Dietitians 1 (pt); Dentists 1 (pt); Ophthalmologists 1 (pt); Podiatrists 1 (pt).
Facilities Dining room; Physical therapy room; Activities room; Barber/Beauty shop.
Activities Arts and Crafts; Cards; Games; Prayer groups; Movies; Shopping trips.

Oakview Convalescent Hospital
805 W Arrow Hwy, Glendora, CA, 91740 (818) 331-0781
Admin Gregory S Davis. *Medical Dir/Dir of Nursing* George Magallon MD.
Licensure Skilled Care. *Beds* 282. *Certified* Medicare; Medi-Cal.
Ownership Proprietary.
Staff RNs 6 (ft); LPNs 30 (ft); Orderlies 10 (ft); Nurses aides 110 (ft); Physical therapists 2 (ft); Occupational therapists 1 (pt); Speech therapists 1 (pt); Activities coordinators 5 (ft); Dietitians 1 (ft); Dentists 1 (pt).
Facilities Dining room; Physical therapy room; Activities room; Crafts room; Laundry room; Barber/Beauty shop.
Activities Arts and Crafts; Games; Reading groups; Movies; Shopping trips; Dances/Social or cultural gatherings.

San Dimas Golden Age Convalescent Home*
1033 E Arrow Hwy, Glendora, CA, 91740 (213) 963-7531
Admin Herbert G Thompson.
Licensure Skilled Care. *Beds* 98. *Certified* Medicare; Medi-Cal.
Ownership Nonprofit.

GRANADA HILLS

Columbia Convalescent Center*
10626 Balboa Blvd, Granada Hills, CA, 91344 (213) 368-2802
Admin Evelyn Dold.
Licensure Skilled Care. *Beds* 99. *Certified* Medicare; Medi-Cal.
Ownership Proprietary.

Granada Hills Convalescent Hospital*
16123 Chatsworth, Granada Hills, CA, 91344 (213) 365-5645
Admin Abraham Birnbaum.
Licensure Skilled Care. *Beds* 48. *Certified* Medicare; Medi-Cal.
Ownership Proprietary.

Magnolia Gardens Convalescent Hospital
17922 San Fernando Mission Blvd, Granada Hills, CA, 91344 (818) 360-1864
Admin W Bob Turner. *Medical Dir/Dir of Nursing* Israel Feingold MD.
Licensure Skilled Care. *Beds* 99. *Cer-*

tified Medicare; Medi-Cal.
Ownership Proprietary.
Admissions Requirements Physician's request.
Staff RNs 7 (ft), 2 (pt); LPNs 8 (ft), 3 (pt); Orderlies 2 (ft), 3 (pt); Nurses aides 20 (ft), 2 (pt); Activities coordinators 1 (ft), 1 (pt).
Facilities Dining room; Physical therapy room; Activities room; Chapel; Crafts room; Laundry room; Barber/Beauty shop; Library; TV room.
Activities Arts and Crafts; Cards; Games; Reading groups; Prayer groups; Movies; Dances/Social or cultural gatherings.
Description Facility seeks to maintain the highest level of dignity and care possible for the patients, to help patients do "as much, as well, and for as long" as they can.

Rinaldi Convalescent Hospital*
16553 Rinaldi St, Granada Hills, CA, 91344 (213) 360-1003
Admin David L Hibarger.
Licensure Skilled Care. *Beds* 99. *Certified* Medicare; Medi-Cal.
Ownership Proprietary.

GRASS VALLEY

Golden Empire Convalescent Hospital*
121 Dorsey Dr, Grass Valley, CA, 95945 (916) 273-1316
Admin Cleolue White.
Licensure Skilled Care. *Beds* 150. *Certified* Medicare; Medi-Cal.
Ownership Proprietary.

Grass Valley Convalescent Hospital
107 Catherine Ln, Grass Valley, CA, 95945 (916) 273-4447
Admin Betty Rhodes. *Medical Dir/Dir of Nursing* Jerome Frey MD.
Licensure Skilled Care. *Beds* 59. *Certified* Medicare; Medi-Cal.
Ownership Proprietary.
Admissions Requirements Physician's request.
Staff RNs 3 (ft); LPNs 3 (ft), 4 (pt); Orderlies 1 (ft); Nurses aides 18 (ft), 7 (pt); Activities coordinators 1 (ft); Dietitians 1 (ft).
Facilities Dining room; Activities room; Crafts room; Laundry room; Barber/Beauty shop; Library; TV room.
Activities Arts and Crafts; Games; Reading groups; Prayer groups; Movies; Shopping trips; Dances/Social or cultural gatherings.
Description Facility is located in the Sierra foothills conveniently located near many physicians' offices and acute care hospital; quality care given in a family atmosphere.

Oak Park Nursing Center Inc*
10716 Cedar Ave, Grass Valley, CA, 95945 (916) 273-2470
Admin Iva Jean Harmon.
Licensure Skilled Care. *Beds* 27.
Certified Medi-Cal.
Ownership Proprietary.

Spring Hill Manor Convalescent Hospital
10355 Joerschke Dr, Grass Valley, CA, 95945 (916) 273-7247
Admin Anne Peterson. *Medical Dir/Dir of Nursing* Jerome F Frey MD.
Licensure Skilled Care. *Beds* 49. *Cer-*

tified Medicare; Medi-Cal.
Ownership Proprietary.
Admissions Requirements Physician's request.
Staff RNs 1 (ft), 2 (pt); LPNs 4 (ft); Nurses aides 36 (ft), 4 (pt).
Facilities Dining room.
Activities Arts and Crafts; Prayer groups.
Description Small, clean, well-maintained nursing facility, free of offensive odors.

GREENBRAE

Greenbrae Convalescent Hospital Inc*
1220 S Eliseo Dr, Greenbrae, CA, 94904 (415) 461-9700
Admin E Pat Kelly.
Licensure Skilled Care. *Beds* 72. *Certified* Medicare; Medi-Cal.
Ownership Nonprofit.

HACIENDA HEIGHTS

Helen Evans Home for Retarded Children
15125 Gale Ave, Hacienda Heights, CA, 91745 (213) 330-4048
Admin Thomas Evans. *Medical Dir/Dir of Nursing* Rolando Atiga MD.
Licensure Intermediate Care for Mentally Retarded. *Beds* 59. *Certified* Medi-Cal.
Ownership Proprietary.
Staff RNs 3 (ft), 7 (pt); Nurses aides 27 (ft), 13 (pt); Activities coordinators 1 (ft).
Facilities Dining room; Activities room.
Activities Arts and Crafts; Outings.
Description The Helen Evans Home provides a stimulating and caring environment for the young developmentally disabled child. Therapy, consultation, and 24-hour nursing care maximize the potential of each child. The facility enjoys excellent rapport with parents, schools, licensing, and regional center agencies.

HANFORD

Hacienda Convalescent Hospitals Inc
361 E Grangeville Blvd, Hanford, CA, 93230 (209) 582-9221
Admin Robert Barker. *Medical Dir/Dir of Nursing* George Guerwsey MD.
Licensure Skilled Care. *Beds* 133. *Certified* Medicare; Medi-Cal.
Ownership Proprietary.
Admissions Requirements Physician's request.
Facilities Dining room; Physical therapy room; Activities room; Laundry room; Barber/Beauty shop.
Activities Arts and Crafts; Cards; Games; Reading groups; Prayer groups; Movies; Shopping trips; Dances/Social or cultural gatherings.

Hillhaven Convalescent Hospital*
1007 W Lacey Blvd, Hanford, CA, 93230 (209) 582-2871
Admin Floyd E Hull.
Licensure Skilled Care. *Beds* 124. *Certified* Medicare; Medi-Cal.
Ownership Proprietary.

Kings Convalescent Hospital
851 Leslie Ln, Hanford, CA, 93230 (209) 582-4414
Admin Sheila Ockey. *Medical Dir/Dir of Nursing* Dr George Guernsey.
Licensure Skilled Care. *Beds* 59.
Certified Medi-Cal.
Ownership Proprietary.
Admissions Requirements Physician's request.
Staff Physicians 22 (pt); RNs 1 (ft), 4 (pt); LPNs 4 (ft), 7 (pt); Nurses aides 22 (ft), 11 (pt); Physical therapists 1 (pt); Occupational therapists 1 (pt); Speech therapists 1 (pt); Activities coordinators 1 (ft); Dietitians 1 (pt); Dentists 1 (pt); Podiatrists 1 (pt).
Facilities Dining room; Activities room; Crafts room; Laundry room; Barber/Beauty shop.
Activities Arts and Crafts; Cards; Games; Reading groups; Prayer groups; Movies; Shopping trips; Dances/Social or cultural gatherings.
Description Hospital is very attractive both inside and out, with a homey atmosphere. The patients are encouraged to make their rooms as personal as possible. Patients participate in parties for all the special holidays; the older patients honored on Mother's and Father's Day (age 99+). The employees and patients dress up for Halloween and have a king and queen.

HAWTHORNE

Golden West Convalescent Hospital
11834 Inglewood Ave, Hawthorne, CA, 90250 (213) 679-1461
Admin Lydia P Milligan. *Medical Dir/Dir of Nursing* Marvin H Stein MD.
Licensure Skilled Care. *Beds* 105. *Certified* Medicare; Medi-Cal.
Ownership Proprietary.
Admissions Requirements Minimum age 35.
Staff RNs 4 (ft), 4 (pt); LPNs 6 (ft), 5 (pt); Orderlies 4 (ft); Nurses aides 32 (ft); Activities coordinators 1 (ft).
Facilities Dining room; Physical therapy room; Activities room; Crafts room; Laundry room; Barber/Beauty shop; Library.
Activities Arts and Crafts; Cards; Games; Reading groups; Prayer groups; Movies; Shopping trips; Dances/Social or cultural gatherings.
Description Facility has a live-in dog named Dutchess that was nationally publicized in the National Enquirer and the Los Angeles Times. Local made short documentaries on Dutchess. Dutchess is loved by every patient, and sometimes serves as a therapist. Dutchess came from the Los Angeles pound and was adopted by the patients of Golden West Convalescent Hospital.

Hawthorne Convalescent Center
11630 S Grevillea Ave, Hawthorne, CA, 90250 (213) 679-9732
Admin Esther Williams. *Medical Dir/Dir of Nursing* Daryl Hutchinson.
Licensure Skilled Care. *Beds* 88. *Certified* Medicare; Medi-Cal.
Ownership Proprietary.

South Bay Child Care Center*
13812 Cordary Ave, Hawthorne, CA, 90250 (213) 679-9223
Admin Ethel Holtzclaw.
Licensure Skilled Care; Intermediate Care for

Mentally Retarded. *Beds* 90. *Certified* Medicare; Medi-Cal.
Ownership Proprietary.

Southwest Convalescent Center
13922 Cerise Ave, Hawthorne, CA, 90250 (213) 675-3304
Admin Margaret Westerfield. *Medical Dir/Dir of Nursing* Michael Platt MD.
Licensure Skilled Care. *Beds* 99. *Certified* Medicare; Medi-Cal.
Ownership Proprietary.
Staff RNs 2 (ft), 2 (pt); LPNs 6 (ft), 3 (pt); Orderlies 2 (ft), 1 (pt); Nurses aides 30 (ft), 15 (pt); Recreational therapists 1 (ft), 1 (pt); Dietitians 1 (pt).
Facilities Dining room; Physical therapy room; Activities room; Crafts room; Laundry room; Barber/Beauty shop; Classroom.
Activities Arts and Crafts; Cards; Games; Reading groups; Prayer groups; Movies; Shopping trips.
Description Facility provides structured setting for the disturbed elderly patient in a loving atmosphere.

HAYWARD

Barrett Convalescent Hospital Inc
1625 Denton Ave, Hayward, CA, 94545 (415) 352-0210
Admin Margie R Melone. *Medical Dir/Dir of Nursing* Dr Andrew May Jr.
Licensure Skilled Care. *Beds* 74. *Certified* Medicare; Medi-Cal.
Ownership Proprietary.
Staff Physicians 7 (pt); RNs 3 (ft); LPNs 7 (ft); Orderlies 1 (pt); Nurses aides 44 (ft); Physical therapists 1 (pt); Recreational therapists 1 (ft); Speech therapists 1 (pt); Activities coordinators 1 (ft); Dietitians 1 (ft); Dentists 1 (pt); Podiatrists 1 (pt).
Facilities Dining room; Physical therapy room; Activities room; Chapel; Crafts room; Laundry room.
Activities Arts and Crafts; Games; Reading groups; Prayer groups; Dances/Social or cultural gatherings.

Bartlett Convalescent Hospital*
718 Bartlett Ave, Hayward, CA, 94541 (415) 785-3630
Admin Marvin D Carrigan.
Licensure Skilled Care. *Beds* 48. *Certified* Medicare; Medi-Cal.
Ownership Proprietary.

Bassard Rehabilitation Hospital
3269 D St, Hayward, CA, 94541 (415) 537-6700
Admin Yvonne Bassard. *Medical Dir/Dir of Nursing* Dr Leslie Harper.
Licensure Skilled Care. *Beds* 71. *Certified* Medicare; Medi-Cal.
Ownership Proprietary.
Staff Physicians 3 (pt); RNs 1 (ft), 2 (pt); LPNs 3 (ft), 4 (pt); Orderlies 1 (ft); Physical therapists 1 (pt); Occupational therapists 1 (pt); Speech therapists 1 (pt); Activities coordinators 1 (pt); Dietitians 1 (pt); Dentists 1 (pt); Ophthalmologists 1 (pt); Podiatrists 1 (pt).
Facilities Dining room; Activities room; Chap-

el; Crafts room; Laundry room; Barber/Beauty shop.
Activities Arts and Crafts; Cards; Games; Reading groups; Prayer groups; Movies.

Bethesda Home
22427 Montgomery St, Hayward, CA, 94541 (415) 538-8300
Admin Donald G Williams. *Medical Dir/Dir of Nursing* William Arthur MD.
Licensure Skilled Care. *Beds* 40. *Certified* Medicare; Medi-Cal.
Ownership Nonprofit.
Staff RNs 1 (ft), 3 (pt); Nurses aides 16 (ft); Physical therapists 1 (pt); Activities coordinators 1 (ft); Dietitians 1 (pt); Dentists 1 (pt); Podiatrists 1 (pt).
Facilities Dining room; Activities room; Chapel; Crafts room; Laundry room; Barber/Beauty shop.
Activities Prayer groups; Movies; Shopping trips.

Blossom Convalescent Hospital
494 Blossom Way, Hayward, CA, 94541 (415) 538-2060
Medical Dir/Dir of Nursing Thomas E Richmond MD.
Licensure Skilled Care. *Beds* 99. *Certified* Medicare; Medi-Cal.
Ownership Proprietary.
Facilities Dining room; Physical therapy room; Activities room; Chapel; Crafts room; Laundry room; Barber/Beauty shop; Library.
Activities Arts and Crafts; Cards; Games; Reading groups; Prayer groups; Movies; Shopping trips; Dances/Social or cultural gatherings.
Description A vital and stimulating facility, set in a lovely tree-lined residential neighborhood. Staff goal is to give the best care possible to residents. Offers an active and creative activity program where residents can learn or develop new skills.

Creekside Terrace Intermediate Care Facility Inc*
629 Hampton Rd, Hayward, CA, 94541 (415) 276-5403
Admin Bradley M Besaw.
Licensure Intermediate Care. *Beds* 25. *Certified* Medi-Cal.
Ownership Proprietary.

Driftwood Manor*
19700 Hesperian Blvd, Hayward, CA, 94541 (415) 785-2880
Admin Candis Lompe.
Licensure Skilled Care. *Beds* 85. *Certified* Medicare; Medi-Cal.
Ownership Proprietary.

Eden West Rehabilitation Hospital
1805 West St, Hayward, CA, 94545 (415) 783-4811
Admin Michael Kochowiec. *Medical Dir/Dir of Nursing* Dr Sharp.
Licensure Skilled Care. *Beds* 99. *Certified* Medicare; Medi-Cal.
Ownership Proprietary.
Admissions Requirements Minimum age 18.
Staff RNs 2 (ft), 2 (pt); LPNs 12 (ft), 4 (pt); Orderlies 3 (ft); Nurses aides 30 (ft), 6 (pt); Physical therapists 1 (ft); Recreational therapists

1 (ft); Occupational therapists 1 (pt); Speech therapists 1 (pt); Activities coordinators 1 (ft); Dietitians 1 (pt); Dentists 1 (pt); Podiatrists 1 (pt).
Facilities Dining room; Physical therapy room; Activities room; Laundry room; Barber/Beauty shop; Library.
Activities Arts and Crafts; Cards; Games; Reading groups; Prayer groups; Movies; Shopping trips; Dances/Social or cultural gatherings.
Description The facility serves many young people and offers large outside area, many activities, strong social life, and excellent staff.

Gateway Care Convalescent Hospital*
26660 Patrick Ave, Hayward, CA, 94544 (415) 782-1845
Admin Arthur K Gross.
Licensure Skilled Care. *Beds* 99. *Certified* Medicare; Medi-Cal.
Ownership Proprietary.

Glen Ellen Convalescent Hospital*
21568 Banyan St, Hayward, CA, 94541 (415) 538-2348
Admin Oleta Dillard.
Licensure Intermediate Care. *Beds* 26. *Certified* Medi-Cal.
Ownership Proprietary.

Hayward Convalescent Hospital
1832 B St, Hayward, CA, 94541 (415) 538-3866
Admin James C Brown. *Medical Dir/Dir of Nursing* Dr B F Royce.
Licensure Skilled Care. *Beds* 99. *Certified* Medicare; Medi-Cal.
Ownership Proprietary.
Admissions Requirements Medical examination.
Staff RNs 1 (ft), 1 (pt); LPNs 10 (ft), 1 (pt); Orderlies 1 (ft); Nurses aides 45 (ft), 3 (pt); Activities coordinators 1 (ft), 1 (pt).
Facilities Dining room; Physical therapy room; Activities room; Crafts room; Laundry room; Barber/Beauty shop.
Activities Arts and Crafts; Cards; Games; Reading groups; Prayer groups; Movies; Shopping trips; A's baseball games; Picnics; Barbeques.

Hayward Rehabilitation Hospital
1768 B St, Hayward, CA, 94541 (415) 538-4424
Admin William R Collins.
Licensure Skilled Care. *Beds* 72.
Certified Medicare.
Ownership Proprietary.
Admissions Requirements Medical examination; Physician's request.
Staff Physicians 4 (ft), 4 (pt); RNs 3 (ft), 3 (pt); LPNs 5 (ft), 6 (pt); Orderlies 2 (ft); Nurses aides 28 (ft), 3 (pt); Physical therapists 1 (ft); Recreational therapists 1 (ft); Occupational therapists 1 (pt); Speech therapists 1 (pt); Activities coordinators 1 (pt); Dietitians 1 (ft); Dentists 1 (pt); Ophthalmologists 1 (pt); Podiatrists 1 (pt); Audiologists 1 (pt).
Facilities Dining room; Physical therapy room; Crafts room; Laundry room.
Activities Arts and Crafts; Cards; Games; Reading groups; Prayer groups; Movies; Shopping trips; Dances/Social or cultural gatherings.

Description Our staff developer put on a BRN 6-credit class seminar on Alzheimer's Disease which was standing room only.

Holly Tree Convalescent Hospital
553 Smalley Ave, Hayward, CA, 94541 (415) 537-2755
Admin Shirley A Ernest. *Medical Dir/Dir of Nursing* J J Robbins MD.
Licensure Skilled Care. *Beds* 30. *Certified* Medicare; Medi-Cal.
Ownership Proprietary.
Staff RNs 1 (ft), 2 (pt); LPNs 2 (ft), 1 (pt); Orderlies 2 (ft); Nurses aides 4 (ft), 4 (pt); Activities coordinators 1 (ft).
Facilities Dining room; Activities room; Crafts room; Laundry room.
Activities Arts and Crafts; Cards; Games; Reading groups; Movies; Shopping trips; Dances/Social or cultural gatherings.
Description Facility is in a residential neighborhood and has a wheelchair ramp, also has an equipped van so community participation can occur. Residents enjoy the East Bay regional parks and going to the major league baseball games.

Majestic Pines Convalescent Hospital
1628 B St, Hayward, CA, 94541 (415) 582-4639
Admin Valerie Capone. *Medical Dir/Dir of Nursing* William Arthur.
Licensure Skilled Care. *Beds* 75. *Certified* Medicare; Medi-Cal.
Ownership Proprietary.
Admissions Requirements Medical examination; Physician's request.
Staff RNs 3 (ft), 3 (pt); LPNs 7 (ft), 1 (pt); Orderlies 2 (ft); Nurses aides 23 (ft), 6 (pt); Recreational therapists 1 (ft); Activities coordinators 1 (ft).
Facilities Dining room; Physical therapy room; Activities room; Crafts room; Laundry room; Barber/Beauty shop.
Activities Arts and Crafts; Cards; Games; Reading groups; Prayer groups; Movies; Shopping trips; Dances/Social or cultural gatherings.

Parkview Convalescent Hospital*
27350 Tampa Ave, Hayward, CA, 94544 (415) 783-8150
Admin Robert O Ewing.
Licensure Skilled Care. *Beds* 121. *Certified* Medicare; Medi-Cal.
Ownership Proprietary.

Saint Christopher Convalescent Hospital
22822 Myrtle St, Hayward, CA, 94541 (415) 537-4844
Admin Linda Reichwein. *Medical Dir/Dir of Nursing* Andrew May MD.
Licensure Skilled Care. *Beds* 36.
Certified Medi-Cal.
Ownership Proprietary.

Saint Michael Convalescent Hospital*
25919 Gading Rd, Hayward, CA, 94544 (415) 782-8424
Admin Elizabeth Christian.
Licensure Skilled Care. *Beds* 99. *Certified* Medicare; Medi-Cal.
Ownership Proprietary.

Saint Therese Convalescent Hospital Inc
21863 Vallejo St, Hayward, CA, 94541 (415) 538-3811
Admin Linda Reichwein. *Medical Dir/Dir of Nursing* Andrew May MD.
Licensure Skilled Care. *Beds* 36.
Certified Medi-Cal.
Ownership Proprietary.

Stonehaven Convalescent Hospital Inc
1782 B St, Hayward, CA, 94541 (415) 581-3766
Admin Bradley Besaw. *Medical Dir/Dir of Nursing* Andrew May MD.
Licensure Skilled Care. *Beds* 25.
Certified Medi-Cal.
Ownership Proprietary.
Admissions Requirements Physician's request.
Facilities Dining room; Activities room; Crafts room; Laundry room.
Activities Arts and Crafts; Cards; Games; Reading groups; Prayer groups; Movies; Dances/Social or cultural gatherings.
Description Facility is small enough to provide personal attention and individualized programs.

Sunset Boulevard Convalescent Hospital*
442 Sunset Blvd, Hayward, CA, 94541 (415) 582-8311
Admin Charles W Drake.
Licensure Skilled Care. *Beds* 99. *Certified* Medicare; Medi-Cal.
Ownership Proprietary.

Sunset Boulevard Convalescent Hospital 1*
458 Sunset Blvd, Hayward, CA, 94541 (415) 582-8311
Admin Charles W Drake.
Licensure Intermediate Care. *Beds* 26. *Certified* Medi-Cal.
Ownership Proprietary.

HEALDSBURG

Healdsburg Convalescent Center
14745 Grove St, Healdsburg, CA, 95448 (707) 433-4813
Admin Arlene Garietz. *Medical Dir/Dir of Nursing* Richard Ganz MD.
Licensure Skilled Care. *Beds* 46. *Certified* Medicare; Medi-Cal.
Ownership Proprietary.
Facilities Dining room; Activities room; Laundry room.
Activities Arts and Crafts; Cards; Games; Religious services weekly; Beauty services.

HEMET

Hemet Convalescent Hospital*
40300 E Devonshire Ave, Hemet, CA, 92343 (714) 925-2571
Admin Betty J Markham.
Licensure Skilled Care. *Beds* 99. *Certified* Medicare; Medi-Cal.
Ownership Proprietary.

Hillhaven Convalescent Center*
275 N San Jacinto St, Hemet, CA, 92343 (714) 658-9441
Admin Linda F Williams.

Licensure Skilled Care. *Beds* 99. *Certified* Medicare; Medi-Cal.
Ownership Proprietary.
Description Facility offers outpatient service and physical therapy.

Meadowbrook Convalescent Hospital Inc
461 E Johnston, Hemet, CA, 92343 (714) 658-2293
Admin Arthur L Brook. *Medical Dir/Dir of Nursing* Dr D Michael Crile.
Licensure Skilled Care. *Beds* 64. *Certified* Medicare; Medi-Cal.
Ownership Proprietary.
Staff RNs 1 (ft), 2 (pt); LPNs 3 (ft), 3 (pt); Orderlies 1 (ft), 2 (pt); Nurses aides 20 (ft), 15 (pt); Activities coordinators 1 (ft), 1 (pt).
Facilities Dining room; Activities room; Laundry room; Barber/Beauty shop.
Activities Arts and Crafts; Games; Prayer groups; Movies; Shopping trips; Dances/Social or cultural gatherings; Music entertainment.
Description Facility features beautiful yards and a country setting, fire alarms connected directly with local fire station, and burglar alarm connected with police department.

Ramona Manor Convalescent Hospital
485 W Johnston Ave, Hemet, CA, 92343 (714) 925-2645
Admin Arthur E Brandt. *Medical Dir/Dir of Nursing* Michael Crile MD.
Licensure Skilled Care. *Beds* 99. *Certified* Medicare; Medi-Cal.
Ownership Proprietary.
Admissions Requirements Medical examination; Physician's request.
Staff RNs 6 (ft), 3 (pt); LPNs 5 (ft), 4 (pt); Orderlies 1 (ft), 1 (pt); Nurses aides 30 (ft), 6 (pt); Physical therapists 1 (ft); Occupational therapists 1 (pt); Speech therapists 1 (pt); Activities coordinators 1 (ft); Dietitians 1 (pt); Dentists 1 (pt); Podiatrists 1 (pt); Audiologists 1 (pt).
Facilities Dining room; Physical therapy room; Activities room; Crafts room; Laundry room; Barber/Beauty shop; Library; Speech therapy room.
Activities Arts and Crafts; Cards; Games; Prayer groups; Movies; Shopping trips; Dances/Social or cultural gatherings; Various parties and entertainment by community groups.
Description As of January, 1984, this facility has been completely redecorated and upgraded. It offers spacious grounds surrounding the facility in a semi-rural location. There is much community involvement and an outstanding activities program.

HERMOSA BEACH

Bay Shore Sanitarium*
160 Manhattan Ave, Hermosa Beach, CA, 90254 (213) 372-2090
Admin Bernard G Wayne.
Licensure Skilled Care. *Beds* 49. *Certified* Medicare; Medi-Cal.
Ownership Proprietary.

HIGHLAND

Hillhaven Highland House
7534 Palm Ave, Highland, CA, 92346 (714)
862-0611
Admin Cody D Gates. *Medical Dir/Dir of
Nursing* Dr Raymond West.
Licensure Skilled Care. *Beds* 99. *Certified* Medicare; Medi-Cal.
Ownership Proprietary.
Admissions Requirements Physician's request.
Facilities Dining room; Physical therapy room;
Activities room; Crafts room; Laundry room;
Barber/Beauty shop; Library.
Activities Arts and Crafts; Cards; Games;
Reading groups; Movies; Shopping trips; Dances/Social or cultural gatherings.

Sierra Vista*
3455 E Highland Ave, Highland, CA, 92346
(714) 862-6454
Admin Douglas Lehnhoff.
Licensure Skilled Care. *Beds* 120.
Certified Medi-Cal.
Ownership Proprietary.

HOLLISTER

Hazel Hawkins Memorial Hospital
3110 Southside Rd, Hollister, CA, 95023 (408)
637-5353
Admin Thomas J Harn. *Medical Dir/Dir of
Nursing* L Andres MD.
Licensure Skilled Care. *Beds* 52. *Certified* Medicare; Medi-Cal.
Ownership Public.
Admissions Requirements Physician's request.
Staff Physicians 12 (pt); RNs 3 (ft); LPNs 3
(pt); Nurses aides 12 (ft), 3 (pt); Physical therapists 1 (pt); Occupational therapists 1 (pt); Speech therapists 1 (pt); Activities coordinators 1
(ft); Dietitians 1 (ft); Dentists 1 (pt).
Facilities Dining room; Physical therapy room;
Activities room; Barber/Beauty shop.
Activities Arts and Crafts; Cards; Games;
Reading groups; Prayer groups; Movies; Shopping trips; Dances/Social or cultural gatherings.
Description The hospital is located in a rural
setting and is beautifully landscaped. The
atmosphere is made cheerful by picture windows surrounding 2 inner atriums. Patient care
is enhanced by involving entire staff and their
families in many special patient activities.

Hollister Convalescent Hospital
900 Sunset Dr, Hollister, CA, 95023 (408)
637-5772
Medical Dir/Dir of Nursing Robert D Quinn
MD.
Licensure Skilled Care. *Beds* 70. *Certified* Medicare; Medi-Cal.
Ownership Proprietary.
Staff RNs 3 (ft); LPNs 2 (pt); Orderlies 2 (ft);
Nurses aides 25 (ft); Physical therapists 1 (ft);
Occupational therapists 1 (ft); Speech therapists
1 (ft); Activities coordinators 1 (ft); Dietitians 1
(ft).
Facilities Dining room; Physical therapy room;
Activities room; Chapel; Laundry room; Barber/Beauty shop; Library.
Activities Arts and Crafts; Cards; Games;
Reading groups; Prayer groups; Movies; Shop-

ping trips; Dances/Social or cultural gatherings;
Group discussions with staff.
Description Hollister Convalescent Hospital is
a 70-bed facility with 2 large patio areas and
greenhouse for residents use. Also featured are
daily activities for residents, in room programs
bookmobile services and weekly church services.

HOLLYWOOD

Orchard Gables*
1277 N Wilcox Ave, Hollywood, CA, 90038
(213) 469-7231
Admin Rita Rohkar.
Licensure Skilled Care. *Beds* 59. *Certified* Medicare; Medi-Cal.
Ownership Proprietary.

HUNTINGTON BEACH

Garfield Care Convalescent Hospital*
7781 Garfield Ave, Huntington Beach, CA,
92648 (714) 847-9671
Admin Bill Mohr.
Licensure Skilled Care. *Beds* 59. *Certified* Medicare; Medi-Cal.
Ownership Proprietary.

Huntington Beach Convalescent Hospital
18811 Florida St, Huntington Beach, CA,
92648 (714) 847-3515
Admin Wayne D Kyckelhahn. *Medical Dir/Dir of Nursing* Victor Siew MD.
Licensure Skilled Care; Intermediate Care.
Beds SNF 123; ICF 59. *Certified* Medicare;
Medi-Cal.
Ownership Proprietary.
Admissions Requirements Minimum age 60.
Staff RNs 15 (ft), 6 (pt); LPNs 15 (ft), 8 (pt);
Nurses aides 35 (ft), 14 (pt); Physical therapists
1 (pt); Reality therapists 3 (ft); Recreational
therapists 1 (pt); Occupational therapists 1 (pt);
Speech therapists 1 (pt); Activities coordinators
1 (ft); Dietitians 1 (ft); Dentists 1 (pt); Ophthalmologists 1 (pt); Podiatrists 1 (pt); Audiologists
1 (pt).
Facilities Dining room; Physical therapy room;
Activities room; Chapel; Crafts room; Laundry
room; Barber/Beauty shop; Library.
Activities Arts and Crafts; Cards; Games;
Reading groups; Prayer groups; Movies; Shopping trips; Dances/Social or cultural gatherings.
Description Located in a 14-acre medical campus, the Huntington Beach Convalescent
Hospital is connected to Pacifica Community
Hospital and is within easy walking distance of
a retirement residence, board and care home,
pharmacy, several professional buildings, and 2
shopping centers. Patients are able to enjoy a
private 2-acre park.

Huntington Valley Convalescent Hospital
8382 Newman Ave, Huntington Beach, CA,
92647 (714) 842-5551
Admin Sheila Zoldan. *Medical Dir/Dir of
Nursing* Victor Siew MD.
Licensure Skilled Care. *Beds* 144. *Certified* Medicare; Medi-Cal.
Ownership Proprietary.
Admissions Requirements Physician's request.

Staff Physicians 1 (pt); RNs 4 (ft), 3 (pt);
Nurses aides 30 (ft), 10 (pt); Physical therapists
1 (ft); Recreational therapists 1 (ft); Occupational therapists 1 (ft); Speech therapists 1 (ft);
Activities coordinators 1 (ft); Dietitians 1 (pt);
Dentists 1 (pt); Ophthalmologists 1 (pt); Podiatrists 1 (pt); Audiologists 1 (pt).

HUNTINGTON PARK

Huntington Park Convalescent Center
6419-29 Miles Ave, Huntington Park, CA,
90255 (213) 589-5941
Admin Ted Stulz. *Medical Dir/Dir of Nursing* Edward Panzer MD.
Licensure Skilled Care. *Beds* 99. *Certified* Medicare; Medi-Cal.
Ownership Proprietary.
Admissions Requirements Physician's request.
Facilities Dining room; Physical therapy room;
Activities room; Chapel; Crafts room; Laundry
room; Barber/Beauty shop; Library.
Activities Arts and Crafts; Cards; Games;
Reading groups; Prayer groups; Movies; Shopping trips.

IMPERIAL

Imperial Manor Inc
100 E 2nd, Imperial, CA, 92251 (714) 355-2858
Admin Mary Ellen Werner. *Medical Dir/Dir of
Nursing* Dr Keith MacGaffey.
Licensure Skilled Care. *Beds* 25.
Certified Medi-Cal.
Ownership Proprietary.
Admissions Requirements Minimum age 16;
Medical examination; Physician's request.
Staff RNs 1 (ft), 1 (pt); LPNs 3 (ft); Nurses
aides 6 (ft); Activities coordinators 1 (pt).
Affiliation Volunteers of America
Facilities Dining room; Activities room; Laundry room.
Activities Arts and Crafts; Cards; Games; Prayer groups; Movies; Shopping trips.

INDIO

Desert Palms Convalescent Hospital*
82-262 Valencia St, Indio, CA, 92201 (714)
347-7779
Admin John W Ryan.
Licensure Skilled Care. *Beds* 68. *Certified* Medicare; Medi-Cal.
Ownership Proprietary.

Mul-Care Desert Convalescent Hospital*
45-500 Aladdin St, Indio, CA, 92201 (714)
347-0876
Admin G Mulcahy and E S Mulcahy.
Licensure Skilled Care. *Beds* 64. *Certified* Medicare; Medi-Cal.
Ownership Proprietary.

INGLEWOOD

Angelus Convalescent Center—East
1001 S Osage Ave, Inglewood, CA, 90308 (213)
674-3216
Admin Jerry Eisinger. *Medical Dir/Dir of
Nursing* Dr Richard Liu.

Licensure Skilled Care. *Beds* 55. *Certified* Medicare; Medi-Cal.
Ownership Proprietary.
Admissions Requirements Minimum age 21; Medical examination; Physician's request.
Staff Physicians 24 (pt); RNs 4 (pt); LPNs 4 (ft), 3 (pt); Orderlies 1 (ft); Nurses aides 20 (ft), 4 (pt) 13F 1 (pt); Occupational therapists 1 (pt); Speech therapists 1 (pt); Activities coordinators 1 (ft); Dietitians 1 (pt); Dentists 1 (pt); Ophthalmologists 1 (pt); Podiatrists 1 (pt); Audiologists 1 (pt).
Facilities Dining room; Physical therapy room; Activities room; Laundry room.
Activities Arts and Crafts; Cards; Games; Reading groups; Prayer groups; Movies; Shopping trips; Dances/Social or cultural gatherings.
Description Facility is part of CAHF training program to upgrade CNAIS to LVNIS and also sponsors a community wide CNA program.

Angelus Convalescent Center—West
950 S Flower Ave, Inglewood, CA, 90508 (213) 674-3216
Admin Jerry Eisinger.
Licensure Skilled Care. *Beds* 59. *Certified* Medicare; Medi-Cal.
Ownership Proprietary.

Centinela Park Convalescent Hospital
515 Centinela Blvd, Inglewood, CA, 90302 (213) 674-4500
Admin Thomas Erdosi. *Medical Dir/Dir of Nursing* Richard Heath MD.
Licensure Skilled Care. *Beds* 69. *Certified* Medicare; Medi-Cal.
Ownership Proprietary.
Staff RNs 1 (ft), 3 (pt); LPNs 6 (ft), 3 (pt); Nurses aides 20 (ft), 14 (pt).
Facilities Dining room; Activities room; Laundry room; Barber/Beauty shop.
Activities Arts and Crafts; Cards; Games; Reading groups; Prayer groups; Movies.
Description Facility offers excellent care.

Inglewood Convalarium*
100 S Hillcrest Blvd, Inglewood, CA, 90301 (213) 677-9114
Admin Pearl E Williams.
Licensure Skilled Care. *Beds* 99. *Certified* Medicare; Medi-Cal.
Ownership Proprietary.

Palomar Convalescent Hospital*
301 N Centinela, Inglewood, CA, 90302 (213) 674-2660
Admin Nelson T Roberts.
Licensure Intermediate Care. *Beds* 99. *Certified* Medicare.
Ownership Proprietary.

Saint Erne Sanitarium
527 W Regent St, Inglewood, CA, 90301 (213) 674-7851
Admin Maurice P Playford. *Medical Dir/Dir of Nursing* Frederick Krieger MD.
Licensure Skilled Care. *Beds* 276. *Certified* Medicare; Medi-Cal.
Ownership Proprietary.
Admissions Requirements Minimum age 21; Medical examination; Physician's request.
Staff RNs; LPNs; Orderlies; Nurses aides; Physical therapists; Reality therapists; Recrea-

tional therapists; Occupational therapists; Speech therapists; Activities coordinators; Dietitians; Dentists; Ophthalmologists; Podiatrists; Audiologists.
Facilities Dining room; Activities room; Laundry room; Barber/Beauty shop.
Activities Arts and Crafts; Cards; Games; Reading groups; Prayer groups; Movies; Shopping trips; Dances/Social or cultural gatherings.
Description Saint Erne Sanitarium is a skilled nursing facility geared to the care of the geriatric patient with mental disorders.

JACKSON

Kit Carson Convalescent Hospital[A]
811 Court St, Jackson, CA, 95642 (209) 223-2231
Admin Meredith J Miller.
Licensure Skilled Care. *Beds* 84. *Certified* Medicare; Medi-Cal.
Ownership Proprietary.

KENTFIELD

Bayside Convalescent Hospital
1251 S Eliseo Dr, Kentfield, CA, 94904 (415) 461-1900
Admin Susan S Edwards. *Medical Dir/Dir of Nursing* Martin Albion MD.
Licensure Skilled Care. *Beds* 99. *Certified* Medicare; Medi-Cal.
Ownership Proprietary.
Staff RNs 10 (ft), 2 (pt); LPNs 6 (ft), 4 (pt); Orderlies 30 (ft), 10 (pt); Physical therapists 2 (ft), 2 (pt); Occupational therapists 1 (pt); Speech therapists 1 (pt); Activities coordinators 1 (ft); Dietitians 1 (pt); Ophthalmologists; Podiatrists; Audiologists.

LA CRESCENTA

Verdugo Vista Convalescent Hospital*
3050 Montrose Ave, La Crescenta, CA, 91214 (213) 248-0322
Admin Elaine Silverman.
Licensure Skilled Care. *Beds* 92. *Certified* Medicare; Medi-Cal.
Ownership Proprietary.

LA HABRA

La Habra Convalescent Hospital
1233 W La Habra Blvd, La Habra, CA, 90631 (213) 691-0781
Admin Gail A Pearu. *Medical Dir/Dir of Nursing* Jorge Soffici.
Licensure Skilled Care. *Beds* 49. *Certified* Medicare; Medi-Cal.
Ownership Nonprofit.
Admissions Requirements Medical examination; Physician's request.
Staff RNs 3 (ft), 3 (pt); LPNs 1 (ft), 3 (pt); Orderlies 4 (ft); Nurses aides 12 (ft), 6 (pt); Activities coordinators 1 (ft).

LA JOLLA

Cloisters of La Jolla Convalescent Hospital
7160 Fay Ave, La Jolla, CA, 92037 (714) 459-4361
Admin Paul N Ellingsen. *Medical Dir/Dir of Nursing* Arthur Edwards MD.
Licensure Skilled Care. *Beds* 59.
Ownership Proprietary.
Staff RNs 4 (ft), 5 (pt); LPNs 3 (ft), 2 (pt); Nurses aides 16 (ft), 6 (pt); Activities coordinators 1 (ft).
Facilities Dining room; Barber/Beauty shop.
Activities Arts and Crafts; Cards; Games; Reading groups; Prayer groups; Movies; Shopping trips; Dances/Social or cultural gatherings.

La Jolla Convalescent Hospital*
6211 La Jolla Hermosa Ave, La Jolla, CA, 92037 (714) 454-0739
Admin Donald M Perry.
Licensure Skilled Care. *Beds* 41.
Ownership Nonprofit.

Torrey Pines Convalescent Hospital*
2552 Torrey Pines Rd, La Jolla, CA, 92037 (714) 453-5810
Admin Donald Veverka.
Licensure Skilled Care. *Beds* 161. *Certified* Medicare; Medi-Cal.
Ownership Proprietary.

White Sands of La Jolla
7450 Olivetas Ave, La Jolla, CA, 92037 (714) 454-4201
Admin David C Goodin. *Medical Dir/Dir of Nursing* L J Schwartz MD.
Licensure Skilled Care. *Beds* 50.
Ownership Nonprofit.
Admissions Requirements Minimum age 62; Medical examination; Physician's request.
Staff Physicians 4 (pt); RNs 2 (ft), 3 (pt); LPNs 2 (ft), 5 (pt); Nurses aides 20 (ft), 4 (pt); Physical therapists 1 (pt); Occupational therapists 1 (pt); Speech therapists 1 (pt); Activities coordinators 1 (ft); Dietitians 1 (pt); Dentists 1 (pt); Podiatrists 1 (pt); Audiologists 1 (pt).
Affiliation Presbyterian
Facilities Dining room; Physical therapy room; Activities room; Chapel; Crafts room; Laundry room; Barber/Beauty shop; Library.
Activities Arts and Crafts; Cards; Games; Reading groups; Prayer groups; Movies; Shopping trips; Dances/Social or cultural gatherings.
Description White Sands is located on the Pacific Ocean shore; the solarium, activities room, and more than half the patients' rooms have ocean views and patios. Our activities program includes a pet cat, who is much loved by patients and staff. The cat is helpful especially with depressed and gavely ill patients and for reality orientation.

LA MESA

Beverly Manor Convalescent Hospital
5696 Lake Murray Blvd, La Mesa, CA, 92041 (714) 460-7871
Admin Marilyn Ryan. *Medical Dir/Dir of Nursing* Arvin J Klein MD.
Licensure Skilled Care. *Beds* 99. *Certified* Medicare; Medi-Cal.

Ownership Proprietary.
Admissions Requirements Medical examination; Physician's request.
Staff RNs 3 (ft), 1 (pt); LPNs 10 (ft), 3 (pt); Orderlies 2 (ft); Nurses aides 40 (ft), 5 (pt); Physical therapists 1 (pt); Recreational therapists 1 (ft); Occupational therapists 1 (pt); Speech therapists 1 (pt); Dietitians 1 (pt); Dentists 1 (pt); Ophthalmologists 1 (pt); Podiatrists 1 (pt); Audiologists 1 (pt).
Facilities Dining room; Physical therapy room; Activities room; Crafts room; Laundry room; Barber/Beauty shop.
Activities Arts and Crafts; Cards; Games; Reading groups; Prayer groups; Movies; Shopping trips; Dances/Social or cultural gatherings.
Description Facility sets high standards, is rehabilitation-oriented, and provides services for total patient care.

California Convalescent Hospital of La Mesa
8787 Center Dr, La Mesa, CA, 92041 (714) 460-4444
Admin Judith Cox. *Medical Dir/Dir of Nursing* Robert Pullman MD.
Licensure Skilled Care. *Beds* 90. *Certified* Medicare; Medi-Cal.
Ownership Proprietary.
Staff Physicians 1 (pt); RNs 3 (ft); LPNs 20 (ft); Nurses aides 35 (ft); Physical therapists 1 (ft), 1 (pt); Recreational therapists 1 (ft); Occupational therapists 1 (pt); Speech therapists 1 (pt); Activities coordinators 1 (pt); Dietitians 1 (pt); Dentists 1 (pt); Podiatrists 1 (pt); Psychologists 1 (ft).

Community Convalescent Hospital of La Mesa
8665 La Mesa Blvd, La Mesa, CA, 92041 (714) 465-0702
Admin Kenneth M Steele.
Licensure Skilled Care. *Beds* 122. *Certified* Medicare; Medi-Cal.
Ownership Proprietary.

Hacienda de la Mesa Convalescent Hospital*
7760 Parkway Dr, La Mesa, CA, 92041 (714) 469-0124
Admin Siegmund Diener.
Licensure Skilled Care. *Beds* 51. *Certified* Medicare; Medi-Cal.
Ownership Proprietary.

Hilldale Convalescent Center*
7979 La Mesa Blvd, La Mesa, CA, 92041 (714) 465-8010
Admin Kathryn Mumford.
Licensure Skilled Care; Intermediate Care for Mentally Retarded. *Beds* 57. *Certified* Medicare; Medi-Cal.
Ownership Proprietary.

La Mesa Convalescent Hospital*
7800 Parkway Dr, La Mesa, CA, 92041 (714) 460-2330
Admin Arthur E Brandt.
Licensure Skilled Care. *Beds* 110. *Certified* Medicare; Medi-Cal.
Ownership Proprietary.

San Diego Convalescent Hospital*
3780 Massachusetts Ave, La Mesa, CA, 92041 (714) 465-1313
Admin Leonard G Willett.

Licensure Skilled Care. *Beds* 94. *Certified* Medicare; Medi-Cal.
Ownership Proprietary.

LA MIRADA

Imperial Convalescent Center
11926 La Mirada Blvd, La Mirada, CA, 90638 (213) 943-7156
Admin Gail A Pearce. *Medical Dir/Dir of Nursing* Clodimiro Rodriquez MD.
Licensure Skilled Care. *Beds* 99. *Certified* Medicare; Medi-Cal.
Ownership Nonprofit.
Admissions Requirements Medical examination; Physician's request.
Staff RNs 3 (ft), 3 (pt); Nurses aides 31 (ft), 1 (pt); Activities coordinators 1 (ft), 1 (pt); Social workers 1 (ft); Restorative CNA 1 (ft).
Facilities Dining room; Activities room; Barber/Beauty shop.
Activities Arts and Crafts; Cards; Games; Reading groups; Prayer groups; Movies; Garden clubs; Park outings; Adult education; Cooking class; Holiday festivities.
Description Facility offers progressive restorative feeding program, specialized exercise program, and social services.

Mirada Hills Rehabilitation and Convalescent Hospital
12200 S La Mirada Blvd, La Mirada, CA, 90638 (213) 947-8691
Admin Donna Aten. *Medical Dir/Dir of Nursing* William Welsh DO.
Licensure Skilled Care. *Beds* 158. *Certified* Medicare; Medi-Cal.
Ownership Nonprofit.
Admissions Requirements Medical examination; Physician's request.
Staff Physicians 2 (pt); RNs 6 (ft), 4 (pt); LPNs 13 (ft), 8 (pt); Orderlies 4 (ft), 1 (pt); Nurses aides 60 (ft), 15 (pt); Activities coordinators 3 (ft).
Facilities Dining room; Physical therapy room; Activities room; Crafts room; Laundry room; Barber/Beauty shop; Library; Occupational therapy room; Speech therapy room.
Activities Arts and Crafts; Cards; Games; Reading groups; Prayer groups; Movies; Shopping trips; Dances/Social or cultural gatherings.
Description Facility specializes in geriatric rehabilitation and sub-acute care.

LA VERNE

Woods Memorial Convalescent Hospital
2600 A St, La Verne, CA, 91750 (714) 593-4917
Admin Jack Hansen. *Medical Dir/Dir of Nursing* Eugene St Clair MD.
Licensure Skilled Care. *Beds* 75. *Certified* Medicare; Medi-Cal.
Ownership Nonprofit.
Admissions Requirements Minimum age 65.
Facilities Dining room; Activities room; Chapel; Crafts room; Laundry room; Barber/Beauty shop; Library.
Activities Arts and Crafts; Cards; Games; Reading groups; Prayer groups; Movies; Shopping trips; Dances/Social or cultural gatherings.

LAFAYETTE

Francis Convalescent Home
3721 Mt Diablo Blvd, Lafayette, CA, 94549 (415) 284-5544
Admin F J Whalley. *Medical Dir/Dir of Nursing* Dennis Stone MD.
Licensure Skilled Care. *Beds* 30. *Certified* Medicare; Medi-Cal.
Ownership Proprietary.
Facilities Dining room; Activities room; Laundry room.
Activities Arts and Crafts; Cards; Games; Reading groups; Prayer groups; Movies.
Description Long-term convalescent facility featuring skilled nursing care of distinction.

Lafayette Convalescent Hospital*
1010 1st St, Lafayette, CA, 94549 (415) 284-1420
Admin Ruby D Brown.
Licensure Skilled Care. *Beds* 52. *Certified* Medicare; Medi-Cal.
Ownership Proprietary.

LAGUNA BEACH

The Gardens—Laguna Convalescent Center*
450 Glenneyre, Laguna Beach, CA, 92651 (714) 494-8075
Admin Robert Kipper.
Licensure Skilled Care. *Beds* 47. *Certified* Medicare.
Ownership Proprietary.

LAGUNA HILLS

Beverly Manor Convalescent Hospital*
24452 Via Estrada, Laguna Hills, CA, 92653 (714) 837-8000
Admin Stanley F Main.
Licensure Skilled Care. *Beds* 218. *Certified* Medicare; Medi-Cal.
Ownership Proprietary.
Description Facility offers outpatient service and physical therapy. JCAH approved.

LAKEPORT

Lakeport Skilled Nursing Center Inc
625 16th St, Lakeport, CA, 95453 (707) 263-6101
Admin Patricia A Treppa. *Medical Dir/Dir of Nursing* Donald L Browning MD.
Licensure Skilled Care. *Beds* 90. *Certified* Medicare; Medi-Cal.
Ownership Proprietary.
Admissions Requirements Medical examination; Physician's request.
Staff Physicians 10 (pt); RNs 5 (ft); LPNs 8 (ft); Physical therapists 2 (pt); Occupational therapists 1 (pt); Speech therapists 1 (pt); Activities coordinators 1 (ft); Dietitians 1 (ft); Dentists 1 (pt); Ophthalmologists 1 (pt); Podiatrists 1 (pt).
Facilities Dining room; Physical therapy room; Activities room; Crafts room; Laundry room; Barber/Beauty shop.
Activities Arts and Crafts; Cards; Games; Reading groups; Prayer groups; Movies; Shop-

ping trips; Dances/Social or cultural gatherings.
Description The facility is located 2 blocks from beautiful Cleer Lake, largest natural lake in California, in a resort setting 2 1/2 hours from San Francisco, Sacramento, and Eureka and 1 1/2 hours from the ocean.

LAKESIDE

Woodside Manor Sanitarium*
11962 Woodside Ave, Lakeside, CA, 92040 (714) 561-1222
Admin Michelle McAfee.
Licensure Skilled Care. *Beds* 94.
Certified Medi-Cal.
Ownership Proprietary.

LAKEVIEW TERRACE

Canyon Convalescent Hospital
11505 Kagel Canyon, Lakeview Terrace, CA, 91342 (213) 896-5391
Admin John Teige. *Medical Dir/Dir of Nursing* Dr H M Cohen.
Licensure Skilled Care. *Beds* 126. *Certified* Medicare; Medi-Cal.
Ownership Proprietary.
Facilities Dining room; Physical therapy room; Activities room; Crafts room; Barber/Beauty shop; Library.
Activities Arts and Crafts; Cards; Games; Reading groups; Prayer groups; Movies; Shopping trips; Dances/Social or cultural gatherings.

LANCASTER

Antelope Valley Convalescent Hospital and Nursing Home*
44445 N 15th St W, Lancaster, CA, 93534 (805) 948-7501
Admin Maurice H Potkin.
Licensure Skilled Care. *Beds* 193.
Ownership Proprietary.

Lancaster Convalescent Hospital*
1642 W Ave J, Lancaster, CA, 93534 (805) 942-8463
Admin Genevieve Skidmore.
Licensure Skilled Care. *Beds* 99. *Certified* Medicare; Medi-Cal.
Ownership Proprietary.

Mayflower Gardens Convalescent Hospital
6705 W Ave "M", Lancaster, CA, 93534 (805) 943-3212
Admin P Dumin. *Medical Dir/Dir of Nursing* C Pathmarajah MD.
Licensure Skilled Care. *Beds* 48. *Certified* Medicare; Medi-Cal.
Ownership Nonprofit.
Staff Physicians 1 (ft), 3 (pt); RNs 2 (ft), 1 (pt); LPNs 5 (ft); Nurses aides 14 (ft), 3 (pt); Physical therapists 1 (pt); Reality therapists 1 (ft); Recreational therapists 1 (ft); Speech therapists 1 (pt); Activities coordinators 1 (ft); Dietitians 1 (pt); Podiatrists 1 (pt); Geriatric nurse practitioners 1 (ft).
Facilities Dining room; Physical therapy room; Activities room; Chapel; Crafts room; Barber/Beauty shop; Library.

Activities Arts and Crafts; Games; Reading groups; Prayer groups; Movies; Shopping trips; Dances/Social or cultural gatherings.
Description This small facility is located on a quiet hillside in the upper desert surrounded by blooming almond trees and wildflowers in the spring. The rest of the year the weather is mild. We offer varied activities, bus rides, and a full-time geriatric nurse practitioner on staff.

LARKSPUR

Tamalpais*
501 Via Casitas, Larkspur, CA, 94904 (415) 461-2300
Admin Robert E Vidaurri.
Licensure Skilled Care; Intermediate Care.
Beds SNF 25; ICF 27.
Ownership Nonprofit.

LAWNDALE

Park Imperial Lodge
15100 S Prairie Blvd, Lawndale, CA, 90250 (213) 679-3344
Admin Katy Link. *Medical Dir/Dir of Nursing* Darryl Hutchison.
Licensure Skilled Care. *Beds* 59. *Certified* Medicare; Medi-Cal.
Ownership Proprietary.
Admissions Requirements Physician's request.
Staff Physicians 11 (pt); RNs 1 (ft), 2 (pt); LPNs 5 (ft), 2 (pt); Nurses aides 18 (ft), 4 (pt); Physical therapists 1 (pt); Recreational therapists 1 (pt); Speech therapists 1 (pt); Activities coordinators 1 (ft); Dietitians 1 (pt); Dentists 1 (pt); Ophthalmologists 1 (pt); Podiatrists 1 (pt).
Facilities Dining room; Activities room; Laundry room; Barber/Beauty shop.
Activities Arts and Crafts; Cards; Games; Reading groups; Prayer groups; Shopping trips; Dances/Social or cultural gatherings.
Description This small, 59-bed facility with a very home-like environment which gives very personalized care due to its size. We offer a strong activities program.

LEMON GROVE

Cresta Loma Convalescent and Guest Home
7922 Palm St, Lemon Grove, CA, 92045 (714) 464-3488
Admin Phillip O Jordan. *Medical Dir/Dir of Nursing* Simon Brumbaugh.
Licensure Skilled Care. *Beds* 99. *Certified* Medicare; Medi-Cal.
Ownership Proprietary.
Admissions Requirements Medical examination; Physician's request.
Staff RNs 3 (ft), 1 (pt); LPNs 7 (ft), 4 (pt); Orderlies 3 (ft); Nurses aides 30 (ft), 4 (pt); Physical therapists 2 (pt); Activities coordinators 2 (pt); Dietitians 1 (pt).
Facilities Dining room; Physical therapy room; Activities room; Chapel; Crafts room; Laundry room; Barber/Beauty shop; Patios.
Activities Arts and Crafts; Cards; Games; Reading groups; Prayer groups; Movies; Shopping trips; Dances/Social or cultural gatherings; Music concerts.
Description Facility stresses rehabilitation and

offers excellent accomodations for reduced need in level of care. But if there is a decline in health, increased level of care can be accomplished without a complete move from the facility.

Lemon Grove Convalescent Center*
8351 Broadway, Lemon Grove, CA, 92045 (714) 463-0294
Admin Alma E Howe.
Licensure Skilled Care. *Beds* 165. *Certified* Medicare; Medi-Cal.
Ownership Proprietary.

Monte Vista Lodge
2211 Massachusetts Ave, Lemon Grove, CA, 92045 (619) 465-1331
Admin Violet M Hertzberg. *Medical Dir/Dir of Nursing* David Trott MD.
Licensure Skilled Care. *Beds* 21.
Ownership Proprietary.
Facilities Dining room; Activities room; Chapel; Crafts room; Laundry room; Barber/Beauty shop; Library.
Activities Arts and Crafts; Cards; Games; Prayer groups; Shopping trips; Dances/Social or cultural gatherings.
Description Facility features ground-level apartments with a variety of types availabe. Residents can rent them furnished, unfurnished, or partly furnished, depending upon how many of their own things they want to bring. Each apartment is tastefully decorated with draperies and carpeting. Each has a private tile bath with both tub and shower, a handy kitchenette for preparing snacks, and a large dressing room with ample wardrobe space.

LIVERMORE

Hacienda Convalescent Hospitals Inc
76 Fenton St, Livermore, CA, 94550 (415) 443-1800
Admin Marjorie Stout. *Medical Dir/Dir of Nursing* Lionel Pfefer MD.
Licensure Skilled Care. *Beds* 83. *Certified* Medicare; Medi-Cal.
Ownership Proprietary.
Admissions Requirements Physician's request.
Staff Physicians 1 (pt); RNs 4 (ft), 1 (pt); LPNs 4 (ft), 4 (pt); Physical therapists 1 (pt); Speech therapists 1 (pt); Activities coordinators 2 (pt); Dietitians 1 (ft), 1 (pt); Dentists 1 (pt); Podiatrists 1 (pt).
Facilities Dining room; Physical therapy room; Activities room; Barber/Beauty shop; Library.
Activities Arts and Crafts; Cards; Games; Prayer groups; Shopping trips; Dances/Social or cultural gatherings.
Description Facility offers a select food menu where a patient can choose own meals 3 times a day; lovely protected outdoor patio; next to Valley Memorial Hospital.

Livermore Manor Convalescent Hospital
788 Holmes St, Livermore, CA, 94550 (415) 447-2280
Admin Garland B Hutchins. *Medical Dir/Dir of Nursing* Robert Berson MD.
Licensure Skilled Care. *Beds* 37. *Certified* Medicare; Medi-Cal.
Ownership Proprietary.

Staff RNs 1 (ft), 2 (pt); LPNs 3 (ft), 2 (pt); Orderlies 1 (ft); Physical therapists 1 (pt); Activities coordinators 1 (ft); Dietitians 1 (pt); Dentists 1 (pt); Podiatrists 1 (pt).
Facilities Dining room; Laundry room.
Activities Arts and Crafts; Games; Prayer groups; Movies; Dances/Social or cultural gatherings.

LIVINGSTON

Grace Nursing Home Inc
13435 W Peach Ave, Livingston, CA, 95334 (209) 394-2440
Admin Wilmont Koehn. *Medical Dir/Dir of Nursing* Donald F Harrington.
Licensure Skilled Care. *Beds* 26.
Certified Medi-Cal.
Ownership Nonprofit.
Admissions Requirements Medical examination; Physician's request.
Affiliation Church of God
Facilities Dining room; Physical therapy room; Activities room; Chapel; Laundry room.
Activities Arts and Crafts; Games; Reading groups.
Description We try to provide good nursing care in a Christian environment.

LODI

Bechthold Convalescent Hospital
610 S Fairmout Ave, Lodi, CA, 95240 (209) 368-1374
Admin Greg Christensen.
Licensure Skilled Care; Intermediate Care.
Beds SNF 25; ICF 3. *Certified* Medicare; Medi-Cal.
Ownership Proprietary.
Staff RNs 1 (ft), 1 (pt); LPNs 20 (ft), 4 (pt); Nurses aides 12 (ft), 6 (pt); Activities coordinators 1 (pt).
Facilities Dining room; Physical therapy room; Activities room; Laundry room.
Activities Arts and Crafts; Games; Reading groups; Prayer groups; Movies.

Delta Convalescent
1334 S Ham Ln, Lodi, CA, 95240 (209) 334-3825
Admin Albert C Cross. *Medical Dir/Dir of Nursing* Paul M Inae MD.
Licensure Skilled Care; Intermediate Care.
Beds SNF 68; ICF 6. *Certified* Medicare; Medi-Cal.
Ownership Proprietary.
Staff RNs 2 (ft), 3 (pt); LPNs 4 (ft), 4 (pt); Nurses aides 15 (ft), 17 (pt); Activities coordinators 1 (ft).
Facilities Dining room; Physical therapy room; Activities room; Crafts room; Laundry room; Barber/Beauty shop.
Activities Arts and Crafts; Games; Reading groups; Prayer groups; Movies; Dances/Social or cultural gatherings.

Fairmont Rehabilitation Hospital
950 S Fairmont Ave, Lodi, CA, 95240 (209) 368-0693
Admin L Samuelson. *Medical Dir/Dir of Nursing* Dr Williams.

Licensure Skilled Care. *Beds* 59. *Certified* Medicare; Medi-Cal.
Ownership Proprietary.

Gross Convalescent Hospital
321 W Turner Rd, Lodi, CA, 95240 (209) 334-3760
Admin Oscar Gross. *Medical Dir/Dir of Nursing* Dr Warren A Plowman.
Licensure Skilled Care. *Beds* 87. *Certified* Medicare; Medi-Cal.
Ownership Proprietary.
Admissions Requirements Minimum age 40; Medical examination; Physician's request.
Staff RNs 3 (ft), 2 (pt); LPNs 4 (ft), 3 (pt); Nurses aides 40 (ft), 5 (pt).
Facilities Dining room; Physical therapy room; Activities room; Chapel; Crafts room; Laundry room; Barber/Beauty shop; Library.
Activities Arts and Crafts; Cards; Games; Reading groups; Prayer groups; Movies; Shopping trips; Dances/Social or cultural gatherings.
Description One of Lodi's first nursing homes, this one-story complex of California-Hawaiian design has many outdoor gardens combining spacious beauty with a restful atmosphere and gracious living.

Vienna Golden State Convalescent Hospital*
800 S Ham Ln, Lodi, CA, 95240 (209) 368-7141
Admin Kenneth D Heffel.
Licensure Skilled Care. *Beds* 134. *Certified* Medicare; Medi-Cal.
Ownership Proprietary.

Vista Ray Convalescent Hospital*
1120 Sylvia Dr, Lodi, CA, 95240 (209) 368-6641
Admin Alfred Johnson.
Licensure Skilled Care. *Beds* 72. *Certified* Medicare; Medi-Cal.
Ownership Proprietary.

Vista Ray Convalescent Hospital 2*
1108 Sylvia Dr, Lodi, CA, 95240 (209) 368-0677
Admin Alfred Johnson.
Licensure Skilled Care. *Beds* 42. *Certified* Medicare; Medi-Cal.
Ownership Proprietary.

LOMA LINDA

Heritage Gardens
25271 Barton Rd, Loma Linda, CA, 92354 (714) 796-0216
Admin J William Westphal. *Medical Dir/Dir of Nursing* Raymond West MD.
Licensure Skilled Care. *Beds* 103. *Certified* Medicare; Medi-Cal.
Ownership Proprietary.
Facilities Dining room; Physical therapy room; Activities room; Crafts room; Laundry room; Barber/Beauty shop; Library.
Activities Arts and Crafts; Games; Prayer groups; Shopping trips.

Linda Valley Convalescent Hospital*
25383 Cole St, Loma Linda, CA, 92354 (714) 796-0235
Admin Dinning R Clifford.

Licensure Skilled Care. *Beds* 83. *Certified* Medicare; Medi-Cal.
Ownership Proprietary.

Mount View Child Care Center Inc
10132 Mount View Ave, Loma Linda, CA, 92354 (714) 796-0030
Admin Gail Horrigan. *Medical Dir/Dir of Nursing* Dr Robert McCormick.
Licensure Intermediate Care for Mentally Retarded. *Beds* 59. *Certified* Medi-Cal.
Ownership Proprietary.
Admissions Requirements Minimum age Birth.
Staff Physicians; RNs; Orderlies; Nurses aides; Physical therapists; Recreational therapists; Occupational therapists; Speech therapists; Activities coordinators; Dietitians; Dentists; Ophthalmologists; Audiologists.
Facilities Dining room; Activities room; Laundry room.
Activities Arts and Crafts; Games; Movies; Shopping trips.

LOMITA

Lomita Golden Age Convalescent Home
1955 W Lomita Blvd, Lomita, CA, 90717 (213) 325-1970
Admin Iris Doiron. *Medical Dir/Dir of Nursing* Stephen Russell MD.
Licensure Skilled Care. *Beds* 71. *Certified* Medicare; Medi-Cal.
Ownership Proprietary.

Peninsula Rehabilitation Center*
26303 S Western Ave, Lomita, CA, 90717 (213) 325-3202
Admin Jerry Sass.
Licensure Skilled Care. *Beds* 48. *Certified* Medicare; Medi-Cal.
Ownership Proprietary.
Description Facility offers occupation and physical therapy, speech pathology/audiology.

LOMPOC

Lompoc Hospital District Convalescent Care Center*
3rd and Walnut Sts, Lompoc, CA, 93436 (805) 736-3466
Admin William E Diebner.
Licensure Skilled Care; Intermediate Care.
Beds SNF 50; ICF 24. *Certified* Medicare; Medi-Cal.
Ownership Public.

LONE PINE

Southern Inyo County Sanatorium*
103 Pangborn, Lone Pine, CA, 93545 (714) 876-5537
Admin Michael Cosenza.
Licensure Skilled Care. *Beds* 51. *Certified* Medicare; Medi-Cal.
Ownership Public.

LONG BEACH

Akin's Convalescent Hospital*
2750 Atlantic Ave, Long Beach, CA, 90806

(213) 424-8101
Admin Ronald M Akin.
Licensure Skilled Care. *Beds* 109. *Certified* Medicare; Medi-Cal.
Ownership Proprietary.

Alamitos Belmont Rehabilitation Hospital
3901 E 4th St, Long Beach, CA, 90814 (213) 434-8421
Admin Alan H Anderson. *Medical Dir/Dir of Nursing* Robert Pinder MD.
Licensure Skilled Care. *Beds* 97. *Certified* Medicare; Medi-Cal.
Ownership Proprietary.
Admissions Requirements Physician's request.
Staff Physicians 6 (pt); RNs 10 (ft), 8 (pt); LPNs 10 (ft), 6 (pt); Nurses aides 36 (ft), 28 (pt); Physical therapists 8 (ft); Recreational therapists 1 (ft), 2 (pt); Occupational therapists 4 (ft), 1 (pt); Speech therapists 1 (ft), 2 (pt); Dietitians 1 (ft); Dentists 1 (pt); Podiatrists 1 (pt); Audiologists 1 (pt).
Facilities Dining room; Physical therapy room; Activities room; Crafts room; Laundry room; Barber/Beauty shop; Occupational therapy; Conference rooms.
Activities Arts and Crafts; Cards; Games; Reading groups; Prayer groups; Movies; Shopping trips; Dances/Social or cultural gatherings; Special dinners and luncheons.
Description Skilled nursing facility with 80% of the beds for rehabilitating patients. Average length of stay is 32 days. Ninety-five percent of our patients return to former living conditions; 5% are transferred to long-term facilities.

Bay Convalescent Hospital
5901 Downey Ave, Long Beach, CA, 90805 (213) 636-1961
Admin Eli Berkovitz. *Medical Dir/Dir of Nursing* F A James MD.
Licensure Skilled Care. *Beds* 70. *Certified* Medicare; Medi-Cal.
Ownership Proprietary.
Admissions Requirements Minimum age 18; Medical examination; Physician's request.
Staff RNs 1 (ft), 1 (pt); LPNs 4 (ft), 1 (pt); Nurses aides 20 (ft), 1 (pt); Activities coordinators 1 (ft).
Facilities Dining room; Physical therapy room; Activities room; Laundry room; Barber/Beauty shop.
Activities Arts and Crafts; Cards; Games; Movies.
Description Facility is exceptionally clean, odor free, with a warm staff and warm atmosphere featuring friendly service.

Bel Vista Convalescent Hospital Inc
5001 E Anaheim St, Long Beach, CA, 90804 (213) 494-5001
Admin Hilary Pomatto and Irene Pomatto.
Licensure Skilled Care. *Beds* 46. *Certified* Medicare; Medi-Cal.
Ownership Proprietary.
Admissions Requirements Medical examination; Physician's request.
Staff RNs 3 (ft); LPNs 4 (ft); Nurses aides 24 (ft); Physical therapists 1 (pt); Reality therapists 1 (pt); Recreational therapists 1 (pt); Activities coordinators 1 (ft).
Activities Arts and Crafts; Games; Prayer groups.

Bixby Knolls Towers Nursing Home*
3747 Atlantic Ave, Long Beach, CA, 90807 (213) 426-6123
Admin Verna Harshfield.
Licensure Skilled Care. *Beds* 124. *Certified* Medicare; Medi-Cal.
Ownership Nonprofit.

California Convalescent Hospital
3850 E Esther St, Long Beach, CA, 90804 (213) 498-3368
Admin Sharon Kurtz. *Medical Dir/Dir of Nursing* Thomas Hendon MD.
Licensure Skilled Care. *Beds* 99. *Certified* Medicare; Medi-Cal.
Ownership Proprietary.
Facilities Dining room; Barber/Beauty shop.
Activities Arts and Crafts; Cards; Games; Reading groups; Prayer groups; Movies; Dances/Social or cultural gatherings.

Casa de Belita Convalescent Center Inc*
723 E 9th St, Long Beach, CA, 90813 (213) 437-2797
Admin Matt Weinstock.
Licensure Skilled Care. *Beds* 52. *Certified* Medicare.
Ownership Proprietary.

Catered Manor*
4010 Virginia Rd, Long Beach, CA, 90807 (213) 427-8113
Admin Marilyn Beard.
Licensure Skilled Care. *Beds* 83. *Certified* Medicare; Medi-Cal.
Ownership Proprietary.

Centralia Convalescent Center Inc
5401 E Centralia St, Long Beach, CA, 90808 (213) 421-4717
Admin Leonard Einhorn. *Medical Dir/Dir of Nursing* Francis James MD.
Licensure Skilled Care. *Beds* 109. *Certified* Medicare; Medi-Cal.
Ownership Proprietary.
Staff RNs; LPNs; Orderlies; Nurses aides; Physical therapists; Recreational therapists; Speech therapists; Activities coordinators; Dietitians; Dentists; Ophthalmologists; Podiatrists; Audiologists.
Facilities Dining room; Physical therapy room; Activities room; Crafts room; Laundry room; Barber/Beauty shop; Library.
Activities Arts and Crafts; Cards; Games; Reading groups; Prayer groups; Movies; Shopping trips.

Coastview Convalescent Hospital*
455 Columbia St, Long Beach, CA, 90806 (213) 426-0537
Admin Charles Bird.
Licensure Skilled Care. *Beds* 150. *Certified* Medicare; Medi-Cal.
Ownership Proprietary.

Colonial Manor Convalescent Hospital—Extended Care Facility*
1913 E 5th St, Long Beach, CA, 90812 (213) 432-5751
Admin John B Hornung.
Licensure Skilled Care. *Beds* 181. *Certified* Medicare; Medi-Cal.
Ownership Proprietary.

Columbia Convalescent Home
521 E Columbia St, Long Beach, CA, 90806 (213) 426-2557
Admin Zoltan Schwartz. *Medical Dir/Dir of Nursing* Ferdinand Kunze.
Licensure Skilled Care. *Beds* 48. *Certified* Medicare; Medi-Cal.
Ownership Proprietary.
Admissions Requirements Minimum age 35; Physician's request.
Staff RNs 1 (ft), 1 (pt); LPNs 3 (ft), 4 (pt); Orderlies 1 (ft); Nurses aides 11 (ft), 5 (pt); Recreational therapists 1 (pt); Activities coordinators 1 (ft); Dietitians 1 (pt).
Facilities Dining room; Activities room; Laundry room; Barber/Beauty shop.
Activities Arts and Crafts; Games; Reading groups; Prayer groups; Movies; Dances/Social or cultural gatherings; Daily exercises; Reality orientation.
Description Facility specializes in a less institutional atmosphere and a more home-like environment. Patients viewed as individuals not numbers.

Crest Knoll Convalescent Hospital
260 E Market St, Long Beach, CA, 90805 (213) 774-2872
Admin Karlin Reich Schultz. *Medical Dir/Dir of Nursing* Dr Platt.
Licensure Skilled Care. *Beds* 112. *Certified* Medicare; Medi-Cal.
Ownership Proprietary.
Admissions Requirements Medical examination; Physician's request.
Staff RNs 5 (ft), 5 (pt); LPNs 8 (ft), 10 (pt); Orderlies 5 (ft), 2 (pt); Nurses aides 35 (ft), 3 (pt); Activities coordinators 1 (ft).

Eastwood Convalescent Hospital
4029 E Anaheim St, Long Beach, CA, 90804 (213) 434-4421
Admin Ronald M Akin. *Medical Dir/Dir of Nursing* David E Jewell MD.
Licensure Skilled Care. *Beds* 75. *Certified* Medicare; Medi-Cal.
Ownership Proprietary.
Admissions Requirements Minimum age 18; Medical examination; Physician's request.
Staff RNs 2 (ft), 1 (pt); LPNs 6 (ft), 1 (pt); Orderlies 1 (ft); Nurses aides 27 (ft), 3 (pt); Activities coordinators; Dietitians.
Facilities Dining room; Activities room; Laundry room; Barber/Beauty shop.
Activities Arts and Crafts; Cards; Games; Reading groups; Prayer groups; Movies; Shopping trips; Dances/Social or cultural gatherings.

Edgewater Convalescent Hospital
2625 E 4th St, Long Beach, CA, 90814 (213) 434-0974
Admin Debbie Ketland Krevel. *Medical Dir/Dir of Nursing* Dr Paul Lorhan.
Licensure Skilled Care. *Beds* 81. *Certified* Medicare; Medi-Cal.
Ownership Proprietary.
Admissions Requirements Minimum age 21; Physician's request.
Facilities Dining room; Physical therapy room; Activities room; Crafts room; Laundry room; Barber/Beauty shop; Library.
Activities Arts and Crafts; Cards; Games; Reading groups; Prayer groups; Movies; Shop-

ping trips; Dances/Social or cultural gatherings.
Description Facility features good food and an excellent nursing staff.

Empress Convalescent Center
1020 Termino Ave, Long Beach, CA, 90804
(213) 433-6791
Admin James A Pine.
Licensure Skilled Care. *Beds* 133. *Certified* Medicare; Medi-Cal.
Ownership Proprietary.
Admissions Requirements Physician's request.

Ennoble Center of Long Beach*
2666 Grand Ave, Long Beach, CA, 90815 (213) 426-8187
Admin Tom Williams.
Licensure Intermediate Care; Intermediate Care for Mentally Retarded. *Beds* 99.
Ownership Nonprofit.

Extended Care Hospital of Long Beach
3232 E Artesia Blvd, Long Beach, CA, 90805
(213) 423-6401
Admin Norman Miller. *Medical Dir/Dir of Nursing* Dr Platt.
Licensure Skilled Care. *Beds* 240. *Certified* Medicare; Medi-Cal.
Ownership Proprietary.
Admissions Requirements Minimum age 18.
Staff RNs 5 (ft), 4 (pt); LPNs 14 (ft), 7 (pt); Orderlies 8 (ft), 2 (pt); Nurses aides 33 (ft), 14 (pt); Activities coordinators 1 (ft); Dietitians 1 (ft).
Facilities Dining room; Physical therapy room; Activities room; Laundry room; Barber/Beauty shop.
Activities Arts and Crafts; Cards; Games; Reading groups; Prayer groups; Movies.

Grand Avenue Convalescent Hospital*
1730 Grand Ave, Long Beach, CA, 90804 (213) 597-8817
Admin Ben C Jakobovits.
Licensure Skilled Care. *Beds* 117. *Certified* Medicare; Medi-Cal.
Ownership Proprietary.

Hacienda Convalescent Hospital
2725 E Broadway, Long Beach, CA, 90803
(213) 434-4494
Admin K M Treu. *Medical Dir/Dir of Nursing* Edward R Woerz MD.
Licensure Skilled Care. *Beds* 98. *Certified* Medicare; Medi-Cal.
Ownership Proprietary.
Admissions Requirements Minimum age 50; Physician's request.
Staff Physicians 3 (pt); RNs 3 (ft); LPNs 9 (ft), 3 (pt); Orderlies 6 (ft); Nurses aides 30 (ft); Physical therapists 3 (pt); Reality therapists 1 (pt); Recreational therapists 1 (pt); Occupational therapists 2 (pt); Speech therapists 1 (pt); Activities coordinators 1 (ft); Dietitians 1 (pt); Dentists 1 (pt); Podiatrists 1 (pt); Audiologists 1 (pt).
Facilities Dining room; Physical therapy room; Activities room; Chapel; Crafts room; Barber/Beauty shop; Library.
Activities Arts and Crafts; Cards; Games; Reading groups; Prayer groups; Movies; Shopping trips.

Hillcrest Convalescent Hospital Inc
3401 Cedar Ave, Long Beach, CA, 90807 (213) 426-4461
Admin Angel Ramos. *Medical Dir/Dir of Nursing* Paul Lorhan MD.
Licensure Skilled Care. *Beds* 154. *Certified* Medicare; Medi-Cal.
Ownership Proprietary.
Admissions Requirements Minimum age 18.
Staff RNs 5 (ft); LPNs 12 (ft), 4 (pt); Orderlies 6 (ft); Nurses aides 60 (ft), 10 (pt); Activities coordinators 2 (ft).
Facilities Dining room; Physical therapy room; Activities room; Crafts room; Laundry room; Barber/Beauty shop; Educational room.
Activities Arts and Crafts; Cards; Games; Reading groups; Prayer groups; Movies; Shopping trips; Dances/Social or cultural gatherings; Reality orientation; Group sessions; Current events; Entertainment by special groups; Music; Rhythm band; Cartoon shows.
Description Social service designer meets with the MS patients on a weekly basis to discuss concerns and issues that interest them. Since most of these patients are alert, these sessions help in expressing their feelings and frustrations. Facility has a special activity program for the confused and disoriented.

Intercommunity Sanitarium*
2626 Grand Ave, Long Beach, CA, 90815 (213) 427-8915
Admin Robert L Pruitt.
Licensure Skilled Care. *Beds* 147.
Certified Medi-Cal.
Ownership Nonprofit.

Marlora Manor Convalescent Hospital
3801 E Anaheim St, Long Beach, CA, 90804
(213) 494-3311
Admin Marilyn Hauser.
Licensure Skilled Care. *Beds* 99. *Certified* Medicare; Medi-Cal.
Ownership Proprietary.

Palmcrest Medallion Convalescent Hospital
3355 Pacific Pl, Long Beach, CA, 90806 (213) 595-4336
Admin Shirley H Feingold. *Medical Dir/Dir of Nursing* George Bryant MD.
Licensure Skilled Care. *Beds* 99. *Certified* Medicare; Medi-Cal.
Ownership Proprietary.
Admissions Requirements Minimum age 55; Medical examination; Physician's request.
Staff Physicians 1 (pt); RNs 2 (ft), 1 (pt); LPNs 7 (ft), 1 (pt); Nurses aides 35 (ft), 6 (pt); Physical therapists 1 (ft), 1 (pt); Reality therapists 1 (pt); Recreational therapists 1 (ft); Occupational therapists 1 (pt); Speech therapists 1 (pt); Dietitians 1 (pt); Dentists 1 (pt); Podiatrists 1 (pt).
Facilities Dining room; Physical therapy room; Activities room; Chapel; Laundry room; Barber/Beauty shop.
Activities Arts and Crafts; Games; Reading groups; Prayer groups; Movies; Dances/Social or cultural gatherings.
Description Annual "Fantasy Cruise" where facility is transformed into a "Love Boat" and docks at a different port every year. Authentic

costumes are worn by staff members and patients, authentic cuisine is served throughout the day, and authentic entertainment is given.

Palmcrest North Convalescent Hospital
3501 Cedar Ave, Long Beach, CA, 90807 (213) 595-1731
Admin Richard Feingold. *Medical Dir/Dir of Nursing* David B Bockoff MD.
Licensure Skilled Care. *Beds* 99. *Certified* Medicare; Medi-Cal.
Ownership Proprietary.
Admissions Requirements Minimum age 40; Medical examination; Physician's request.
Staff RNs 2 (ft), 1 (pt); LPNs 8 (ft), 1 (pt); Orderlies 5 (ft); Nurses aides 55 (ft); Recreational therapists 1 (ft); Activities coordinators 1 (ft); Dietitians 1 (ft); Podiatrists 1 (pt).
Facilities Dining room; Physical therapy room; Activities room; Crafts room; Laundry room; Barber/Beauty shop; Library; Theater; Art Gallery; Greenhouse.
Activities Arts and Crafts; Cards; Games; Reading groups; Prayer groups; Movies; Shopping trips; Dances/Social or cultural gatherings; Art show openings; Special entertainment.
Description Facility features simulated 3-day cruises to exotic lands; special meals and costumes for all holidays; weekly church services; art instruction with kiln on premises for ceramics.

Royal Care Skilled Nursing Facility*
2725 Pacific Ave, Long Beach, CA, 90806 (213) 427-7493
Admin Gerald Price.
Licensure Skilled Care. *Beds* 98. *Certified* Medicare; Medi-Cal.
Ownership Proprietary.

Santa Fe Convalescent Hospital*
3294 Santa Fe Ave, Long Beach, CA, 90810 (213) 424-0757
Admin Michael Kremer.
Licensure Skilled Care. *Beds* 87. *Certified* Medicare; Medi-Cal.
Ownership Proprietary.

Seaside Care Center*
490 W 14th St, Long Beach, CA, 90813 (213) 591-8701
Admin Thomas Higgins.
Licensure Skilled Care; Intermediate Care for Mentally Retarded. *Beds* 99. *Certified* Medicare.
Ownership Proprietary.

Walnut Convalescent Hospital
1201 Walnut Ave, Long Beach, CA, 90813
(213) 591-7621
Admin Dena Francis. *Medical Dir/Dir of Nursing* Alan Greenburg MD.
Licensure Skilled Care. *Beds* 78. *Certified* Medicare; Medi-Cal.
Ownership Proprietary.
Admissions Requirements Physician's request.
Staff RNs 2 (ft); LPNs 5 (ft); Orderlies 5 (ft); Nurses aides 14 (ft); Activities coordinators 1 (ft); Dietitians 1 (ft).
Facilities Dining room; Physical therapy room; Activities room; Crafts room; Laundry room; Barber/Beauty shop.

Activities Arts and Crafts; Cards; Games; Reading groups; Prayer groups; Movies; Shopping trips; Dances/Social or cultural gatherings.

Willow Lake Convalescent Hospital*
2615 Grand Ave, Long Beach, CA, 90815 (213) 426-6141
Admin Margaret F Emery.
Licensure Skilled Care. *Beds* 160. *Certified* Medicare; Medi-Cal.
Ownership Nonprofit.

LOS ALAMITOS

Alamitos West Convalescent Hospital
3902 Katella Ave, Los Alamitos, CA, 90720 (213) 596-5561
Admin Nita I Lindsey. *Medical Dir/Dir of Nursing* John D Cowles.
Licensure Skilled Care. *Beds* 199. *Certified* Medicare; Medi-Cal.
Ownership Proprietary.
Admissions Requirements Minimum age 50; Medical examination; Physician's request.
Staff RNs 5 (ft), 5 (pt); LPNs 15 (ft), 10 (pt); Orderlies 4 (ft); Nurses aides 45 (ft), 5 (pt); Physical therapists 1 (ft), 1 (pt); Recreational therapists 1 (pt); Occupational therapists 1 (pt); Speech therapists 1 (pt); Activities coordinators 2 (ft); Dietitians 1 (pt).
Facilities Dining room; Physical therapy room; Activities room; Crafts room; Laundry room; Barber/Beauty shop.
Activities Arts and Crafts; Games; Reading groups; Prayer groups; Movies; Shopping trips; Dances/Social or cultural gatherings.
Description Facility is very centrally located (there is a large acute hospital on same block and a demodialysis center on the next block). The facility itself is spacious, bright, and cheerfully decorated.

LOS ALTOS

Beverly Manor Convalescent Hospital*
809 Fremont Ave, Los Altos, CA, 94022 (415) 941-5255
Admin Karen Faria.
Licensure Skilled Care. *Beds* 152. *Certified* Medicare; Medi-Cal.
Ownership Proprietary.
Description JCAH approved.

Pilgrim Haven Health Facility
373 Pine Ln, Los Altos, CA, 94022 (408) 948-8291
Admin William G Maxwell. *Medical Dir/Dir of Nursing* Harold Cramer MD.
Licensure Skilled Care. *Beds* 66. *Certified* Medicare; Medi-Cal.
Ownership Nonprofit.
Admissions Requirements Minimum age 62; Medical examination.
Staff Physicians 1 (pt); RNs 11 (pt); LPNs 2 (pt); Nurses aides 18 (ft), 8 (pt); Activities coordinators 1 (ft), 1 (pt); Dietitians 1 (ft).
Affiliation Baptist
Facilities Dining room; Activities room; Chapel; Crafts room; Laundry room; Barber/Beauty shop; Library.
Activities Arts and Crafts; Cards; Games;

Movies; Shopping trips; Dances/Social or cultural gatherings.
Description The facility is located in a quiet residential neighborhood is campus-style and is moderately priced.

LOS ANGELES

Alcott Rehabilitation Hospital
3551 W Olympic Blvd, Los Angeles, CA, 90019 (213) 737-2000
Admin Belle Yarmish.
Licensure Skilled Care. *Beds* 121. *Certified* Medicare; Medi-Cal.
Ownership Proprietary.
Admissions Requirements Medical examination; Physician's request.
Staff Physicians 1 (pt); RNs 8 (ft); LPNs 10 (ft); Orderlies 10 (ft); Nurses aides 50 (ft); Physical therapists 5 (ft).
Facilities Dining room; Physical therapy room; Activities room; Chapel; Crafts room; Laundry room; Barber/Beauty shop; Library.
Activities Arts and Crafts; Cards; Games; Reading groups; Prayer groups; Movies; Shopping trips; Dances/Social or cultural gatherings.
Description A complete rehabilitation hospital with a high nursing ratio for high acuity care.

Alden Terrace Convalescent Hospital
1241 S Lake St, Los Angeles, CA, 90006 (213) 382-8461
Admin Vivian Chianello. *Medical Dir/Dir of Nursing* Dr F Evans Powell.
Licensure Skilled Care. *Beds* 121. *Certified* Medicare; Medi-Cal.
Ownership Proprietary.
Admissions Requirements Physician's request.
Facilities Dining room; Physical therapy room; Activities room; Crafts room; Laundry room; Barber/Beauty shop.
Activities Arts and Crafts; Cards; Games; Reading groups; Prayer groups; Movies.

Alexandria Convalescent Hospital*
1515 N Alexandria, Los Angeles, CA, 90027 (213) 660-1800
Admin Salamon Mandel.
Licensure Skilled Care. *Beds* 150. *Certified* Medicare; Medi-Cal.
Ownership Proprietary.

Alpha-Wilshire Convalescent Hospital*
915 S Crenshaw Blvd, Los Angeles, CA, 90019 (213) 937-5466
Admin David Elliott.
Licensure Skilled Care. *Beds* 98. *Certified* Medicare; Medi-Cal.
Ownership Proprietary.

Amberwood Convalescent Hospital
6071 York Blvd, Los Angeles, CA, 90042 (213) 254-3407
Admin Jacqueline R O'Connor. *Medical Dir/Dir of Nursing* Julita Phillips MD.
Licensure Skilled Care. *Beds* 107. *Certified* Medicare; Medi-Cal.
Ownership Proprietary.
Admissions Requirements Minimum age 18.
Facilities Dining room; Physical therapy room; Activities room; Laundry room; Barber/Beauty shop.

Activities Arts and Crafts; Cards; Games; Reading groups; Prayer groups; Movies; Dances/Social or cultural gatherings.

Angels Nursing Center Inc
415 S Union Ave, Los Angeles, CA, 90017 (213) 484-0784
Admin Michele Nichols. *Medical Dir/Dir of Nursing* M Salant MD.
Licensure Skilled Care. *Beds* 49. *Certified* Medicare; Medi-Cal.
Ownership Proprietary.
Admissions Requirements Physician's request.
Staff Physicians 6 (pt); RNs 1 (ft), 3 (pt); LPNs 3 (ft), 4 (pt); Orderlies 2 (ft), 6 (pt); Nurses aides 7 (ft), 8 (pt); Physical therapists 1 (pt); Recreational therapists 1 (pt); Occupational therapists 1 (pt); Speech therapists 1 (pt), Activities coordinators 1 (ft), 1 (pt); Dietitians 1 (pt); Dentists 1 (pt).
Facilities Dining room; Activities room; Crafts room; Laundry room.
Activities Arts and Crafts; Cards; Games; Reading groups; Prayer groups; Shopping trips; Dances/Social or cultural gatherings.
Description Facility features excellent skilled nursing care in a home-like atmosphere.

Beverly Palms Rehabilitation Hospital*
8000 Beverly Blvd, Los Angeles, CA, 90048 (213) 651-3200
Admin Hyman Jampol.
Licensure Skilled Care. *Beds* 41. *Certified* Medicare; Medi-Cal.
Ownership Proprietary.
Description Facility offers occupational and physical therapy as well as speech pathology/audiology. JCAH approved.

Beverly West Convalescent Hospital
1516 Sawtelle Blvd, Los Angeles, CA, 90025 (213) 477-5501
Admin David A Bianchi. *Medical Dir/Dir of Nursing* Michael Clements.
Licensure Skilled Care. *Beds* 113. *Certified* Medicare; Medi-Cal.
Ownership Proprietary.
Facilities Dining room; Physical therapy room; Activities room; Crafts room; Laundry room; Barber/Beauty shop.
Activities Arts and Crafts; Cards; Games; Reading groups; Prayer groups; Movies; Dances/Social or cultural gatherings.

Bonnie Brae Manor Convalescent Hospital*
420 S Bonnie Brae, Los Angeles, CA, 90057 (213) 483-8144
Admin Leslie Grant.
Licensure Skilled Care. *Beds* 59. *Certified* Medicare; Medi-Cal.
Ownership Proprietary.

Brier Oak Terrace Convalescent Center
5154 Sunset Blvd, Los Angeles, CA, 90027 (213) 663-3951
Admin Frank J Garcia Jr. *Medical Dir/Dir of Nursing* Steven Jacobs MD.
Licensure Skilled Care. *Beds* 159. *Certified* Medicare; Medi-Cal.
Ownership Proprietary.
Staff Physicians 22 (pt); RNs 5 (ft); LPNs 10 (ft); Orderlies 9 (ft); Nurses aides 22 (ft); Physical therapists 2 (pt); Reality therapists 1

(pt); Occupational therapists 1 (pt); Speech therapists 1 (pt); Activities coordinators 1 (ft); Dietitians 1 (pt); Dentists 1 (pt); Ophthalmologists 1 (pt); Podiatrists 1 (pt); Audiologists 1 (pt).
Facilities Dining room; Physical therapy room; Activities room; Crafts room; Laundry room; Barber/Beauty shop.
Activities Arts and Crafts; Cards; Games; Reading groups; Prayer groups; Movies; Shopping trips; Dances/Social or cultural gatherings.
Description Facility presently provides subacute care for IV, respirator, tracheotomy, NG tube, dialysis, enteral feeding, etc.

Buena Ventura Convalescent Hospital
1016 S Record St, Los Angeles, CA, 90023
(213) 268-0106
Admin Wayne H Beck. *Medical Dir/Dir of Nursing* Louis T Bascoy MD.
Licensure Skilled Care. *Beds* 99. *Certified* Medicare; Medi-Cal.
Ownership Proprietary.
Staff RNs 2 (ft), 1 (pt); LPNs 6 (ft), 6 (pt); Orderlies 3 (ft), 1 (pt); Nurses aides 25 (ft), 8 (pt); Physical therapists 1 (pt); Occupational therapists 1 (pt); Speech therapists 1 (pt); Activities coordinators 1 (ft); Dietitians 1 (ft); Dentists 1 (pt); Ophthalmologists 1 (pt); Podiatrists 1 (pt); Audiologists 1 (pt).
Facilities Dining room; Physical therapy room; Activities room; Crafts room; Laundry room; Barber/Beauty shop.
Activities Arts and Crafts; Cards; Games; Prayer groups; Movies; Dances/Social or cultural gatherings.

Burlington Convalescent Hospital*
845 S Burlington, Los Angeles, CA, 90048 (213) 381-5585
Admin Robert Jones.
Licensure Skilled Care. *Beds* 124. *Certified* Medicare; Medi-Cal.
Ownership Proprietary.

California Convalescent Center 1*
909 S Lake St, Los Angeles, CA, 90006 (213) 385-7301
Admin James W Whitney.
Licensure Skilled Care. *Beds* 66. *Certified* Medicare; Medi-Cal.
Ownership Proprietary.

California Convalescent Center 2*
1154 S Alvarado St, Los Angeles, CA, 90006
(213) 385-1715
Admin Robert A Seril.
Licensure Skilled Care. *Beds* 72. *Certified* Medicare; Medi-Cal.
Ownership Proprietary.

Chandler Care Center—Fairfax*
1020 S Fairfax Ave, Los Angeles, CA, 90019
(213) 938-2451
Admin Charlotte Ulrich.
Licensure Skilled Care. *Beds* 120. *Certified* Medicare; Medi-Cal.
Ownership Proprietary.

Cheviot Garden Convalescent Hospital*
3533 Motor Ave, Los Angeles, CA, 90034 (213) 836-8900
Admin Rita Rohkar.

Licensure Skilled Care. *Beds* 99. *Certified* Medicare; Medi-Cal.
Ownership Proprietary.

College Vista Convalescent Hospital
4681 Eaglerock Blvd, Los Angeles, CA, 90041
(213) 257-8151
Admin Lowell E Craddock. *Medical Dir/Dir of Nursing* Albert Killian MD.
Licensure Skilled Care. *Beds* 49. *Certified* Medicare; Medi-Cal.
Ownership Proprietary.
Admissions Requirements Minimum age 21.
Staff Physicians 1 (pt); RNs 1 (ft), 1 (pt); LPNs 3 (ft), 3 (pt); Nurses aides 15 (ft), 5 (pt); Physical therapists 1 (pt); Occupational therapists 1 (pt); Speech therapists 1 (pt); Activities coordinators 1 (ft); Dietitians 1 (pt); Dentists 1 (pt); Podiatrists 1 (pt).
Facilities Dining room; Physical therapy room; Activities room; Laundry room; Barber/Beauty shop.
Activities Arts and Crafts; Games; Reading groups; Shopping trips.

Convalescent Care Center
230 E Adams Blvd, Los Angeles, CA, 90011
(213) 748-0491
Admin Charles V Adams. *Medical Dir/Dir of Nursing* William Cottles MD.
Licensure Skilled Care. *Beds* 88. *Certified* Medicare; Medi-Cal.
Ownership Proprietary.
Admissions Requirements Minimum age 18; Physician's request.
Staff RNs 1 (ft), 4 (pt); LPNs 7 (ft), 6 (pt); Orderlies 1 (pt); Nurses aides 21 (ft), 4 (pt); Physical therapists 1 (pt); Activities coordinators 1 (ft); Dietitians 1 (ft).

Convalescent Hospital Casa Descanso
4515 Huntington Dr, Los Angeles, CA, 90032
(213) 225-5991
Admin Georgianna Tucci. *Medical Dir/Dir of Nursing* Dr Marvin Salant.
Licensure Skilled Care. *Beds* 99. *Certified* Medicare; Medi-Cal.
Ownership Proprietary.
Admissions Requirements Minimum age 45; Medical examination; Physician's request.
Staff Physicians 5 (pt); RNs 1 (ft), 1 (pt); LPNs 7 (ft), 2 (pt); Orderlies 7 (ft); Nurses aides 29 (ft), 2 (pt); Physical therapists 1 (pt); Reality therapists 1 (ft); Recreational therapists 1 (pt); Occupational therapists 1 (pt); Speech therapists 1 (pt); Activities coordinators 1 (ft), 1 (pt); Dietitians 1 (ft); Dentists 1 (pt); Ophthalmologists 1 (pt); Podiatrists 1 (pt); Audiologists 1 (pt).
Facilities Dining room; Activities room; Crafts room; Laundry room; Barber/Beauty shop.
Activities Arts and Crafts; Cards; Games; Reading groups; Prayer groups; Movies; Shopping trips; Dances/Social or cultural gatherings.

Coronado Sanitarium
2534 Beverly Blvd, Los Angeles, CA, 90057
(213) 380-3186
Admin Lilly Binnbaum. *Medical Dir/Dir of Nursing* Dr Ferdinand Kunze.
Licensure Skilled Care. *Beds* 22. *Certified* Medicare.
Ownership Proprietary.

Admissions Requirements Physician's request.
Facilities Dining room; Activities room; Crafts room; Laundry room.
Activities Arts and Crafts; Cards; Games; Reading groups; Prayer groups.

Country Villa South Convalescent Center*
3515 Overland Ave, Los Angeles, CA, 90034
(213) 839-5201
Admin Stephen Reissman.
Licensure Skilled Care. *Beds* 87. *Certified* Medicare; Medi-Cal.
Ownership Proprietary.

Country Villa Westwood Convalescent Center
12121 Santa Monica, Los Angeles, CA, 90025
(213) 826-0821
Admin Sharon Kimbrough. *Medical Dir/Dir of Nursing* Paul Meyer MD.
Licensure Skilled Care. *Beds* 93. *Certified* Medicare; Medi-Cal.
Ownership Proprietary.
Staff Physicians 13 (ft); RNs 2 (ft); LPNs 7 (ft), 7 (pt); Orderlies 8 (ft); Nurses aides 31 (ft); Physical therapists 1 (ft); Recreational therapists 1 (pt); Occupational therapists 1 (ft); Speech therapists 1 (ft); Activities coordinators 1 (ft), 1 (pt); Dietitians 1 (ft), 1 (pt); Dentists 1 (pt); Ophthalmologists 1 (pt); Podiatrists 1 (pt); Audiologists 1 (pt).
Facilities Dining room; Physical therapy room; Activities room; Laundry room; Barber/Beauty shop.
Activities Arts and Crafts; Cards; Games; Reading groups; Prayer groups; Movies; Shopping trips; Dances/Social or cultural gatherings; Beach trips.
Description The most outstanding feature of Country Villa Westwood is the loving, concerned staff, many of whom have been working here 10 years or longer. Many of the rooms have direct access to the very large patio with beautiful flowers.

Country Villa Wilshire*
855 N Fairfax Ave, Los Angeles, CA, 90046
(213) 870-8781
Admin T M Henry.
Licensure Skilled Care. *Beds* 81. *Certified* Medicare; Medi-Cal.
Ownership Proprietary.

Crenshaw Nursing Home
1900 S Longwood Ave, Los Angeles, CA, 90016
(213) 935-1158
Admin Brian Gaffney. *Medical Dir/Dir of Nursing* Dr Powell.
Licensure Skilled Care. *Beds* 55. *Certified* Medicare; Medi-Cal.
Ownership Proprietary.
Admissions Requirements Minimum age 18.
Staff Physicians 9 (pt); RNs 3 (pt); LPNs 6 (ft); Orderlies 7 (ft); Nurses aides 45 (ft), 6 (pt); Physical therapists 1 (pt); Reality therapists 1 (pt); Recreational therapists 1 (ft); Occupational therapists 1 (pt); Speech therapists 1 (pt); Activities coordinators 1 (ft); Dietitians 1 (pt); Dentists 1 (pt); Ophthalmologists 1 (pt); Podiatrists 1 (pt); Audiologists 1 (pt).
Facilities Dining room; Physical therapy room; Activities room; Crafts room; Laundry room; Barber/Beauty shop.
Activities Arts and Crafts; Cards; Games;

Reading groups; Prayer groups; Movies; Dances/Social or cultural gatherings; Monthly outings to points of interest.
Description The facility tends to have a higher male patient census which is unusual, probably because we are a veteran's administration contract nursing home.

Culver West Convalescent Hospital
4035 Grandview Blvd, Los Angeles, CA, 90066 (213) 870-9071
Admin Florence Patton.
Licensure Skilled Care. *Beds* 91. *Certified* Medicare; Medi-Cal.
Ownership Proprietary.
Admissions Requirements Physician's request.
Staff Physical therapists 1 (pt); Recreational therapists 1 (pt); Activities coordinators 1 (ft), 1 (pt).
Facilities Dining room; Physical therapy room; Activities room; Barber/Beauty shop; Library; TV room.
Activities Arts and Crafts; Games; Prayer groups; Movies; Dances/Social or cultural gatherings; Adopt-a-grandparent.
Description Facility has an agreement with Los Angeles city school (McBride School for Handicapped) to have young adults (16-22) work with patients learning to do activities. It works out well as both groups move slowly and all are compatible.

Dunlap Sanitarium*
6011 West Blvd, Los Angeles, CA, 90043 (213) 292-0748
Admin Richard E Foster.
Licensure Skilled Care. *Beds* 40. *Certified* Medicare; Medi-Cal.
Ownership Proprietary.

East Los Angeles Convalescent Hospital
101 S Fickett St, Los Angeles, CA, 90033 (213) 261-8108
Admin Luzvininda Mondonedo. *Medical Dir-/Dir of Nursing* Louis T Bascoy.
Licensure Skilled Care. *Beds* 99. *Certified* Medicare; Medi-Cal.
Ownership Proprietary.
Admissions Requirements Medical examination; Physician's request.
Staff Physicians 8 (pt); RNs 2 (ft), 1 (pt); Orderlies 30 (ft), 4 (pt).
Facilities Dining room; Activities room; Crafts room; Laundry room.
Activities Arts and Crafts; Cards; Games; Reading groups; Prayer groups; Movies; Shopping trips; Dances/Social or cultural gatherings; Visits by prominent singing, television and radio groups.

Eastern Star Home*
11725 Sunset Blvd, Los Angeles, CA, 90049 (213) 472-1251
Admin Mary Lou McElroy.
Licensure Skilled Care. *Beds* 38.
Ownership Nonprofit.
Affiliation Order of Eastern Star

Eaton Care Nursing Center*
3737 Don Felipe Dr, Los Angeles, CA, 90008 (213) 295-7737
Admin Larry J Will.

Licensure Skilled Care. *Beds* 99. *Certified* Medicare; Medi-Cal.
Ownership Proprietary.

Echo Park Skilled Nursing Facility Hospital Inc*
1633 E Echo Park Ave, Los Angeles, CA, 90026 (213) 628-4115
Admin Eunice R Kundis.
Licensure Skilled Care. *Beds* 62. *Certified* Medicare; Medi-Cal.
Ownership Proprietary.

Elizabeth Manor*
2201 Miramar St, Los Angeles, CA, 90057 (213) 383-0644
Admin Varina Newcomb.
Licensure Skilled Care. *Beds* 99. *Certified* Medi-Cal.
Ownership Nonprofit.

Extended Care Hospital of Los Angeles*
340 S Alvarado St, Los Angeles, CA, 90057 (213) 483-6520
Admin Raymond Marks.
Licensure Skilled Care. *Beds* 180. *Certified* Medicare; Medi-Cal.
Ownership Proprietary.

Flora Terrace Convalescent Hospital Inc*
5916 W Pico Blvd, Los Angeles, CA, 90035 (213) 939-3184
Admin Flora Rosman.
Licensure Skilled Care. *Beds* 66. *Certified* Medicare; Medi-Cal.
Ownership Proprietary.

Flora Terrace West Convalescent and Rehabilitation Hospital*
6070 W Pico Blvd, Los Angeles, CA, 90035 (213) 653-3980
Admin Romy Rosman.
Licensure Skilled Care. *Beds* 49. *Certified* Medicare; Medi-Cal.
Ownership Proprietary.

Fountain Gardens Convalescent Hospital*
2222 Santa Ana Blvd, Los Angeles, CA, 90059 (213) 564-4461
Admin Celia Markovitz.
Licensure Skilled Care. *Beds* 99. *Certified* Medicare; Medi-Cal.
Ownership Proprietary.

Fountain View Convalescent Hospital*
5310 Fountain, Los Angeles, CA, 90029 (213) 461-9961
Admin Alex Snukal.
Licensure Skilled Care. *Beds* 99. *Certified* Medicare; Medi-Cal.
Ownership Proprietary.

Garden Crest Convalescent Hospital Inc*
909 N Lucile Ave, Los Angeles, CA, 90026 (213) 663-8281
Admin Lester Barron.
Licensure Skilled Care. *Beds* 72. *Certified* Medicare; Medi-Cal.
Ownership Proprietary.

Garden Plaza Convalescent Hospital*
12029 S Avalon Blvd, Los Angeles, CA, 90061 (213) 756-8191

Admin William H Johnson.
Licensure Skilled Care. *Beds* 99. *Certified* Medicare; Medi-Cal.
Ownership Proprietary.

Good Hope Convalescent Hospital*
2000 W Washington Blvd, Los Angeles, CA, 90018 (213) 735-5146
Admin Robert Smith.
Licensure Skilled Care. *Beds* 93. *Certified* Medicare; Medi-Cal.
Ownership Proprietary.

Good Shepherd Nursing Home Inc*
9705 Holmes Ave, Los Angeles, CA, 90002 (213) 564-7851
Admin Romalis Lane.
Licensure Skilled Care. *Beds* 32. *Certified* Medicare; Medi-Cal.
Ownership Proprietary.

Grand Park Convalescent Hospital*
2312 W 8th St, Los Angeles, CA, 90057 (213) 382-7315
Admin Jeanne Willard.
Licensure Skilled Care. *Beds* 151. *Certified* Medicare; Medi-Cal.
Ownership Proprietary.

Guardian Convalescent Hospital*
533 S Fairfax Ave, Los Angeles, CA, 90036 (213) 931-1061
Admin Sigmund Gest.
Licensure Skilled Care. *Beds* 93. *Certified* Medicare; Medi-Cal.
Ownership Proprietary.

Hancock Park Convalescent Hospital
505 N La Brea Ave, Los Angeles, CA, 90036 (213) 937-4860
Licensure Skilled Care. *Beds* 141. *Certified* Medicare; Medi-Cal.
Ownership Proprietary.
Admissions Requirements Minimum age 20; Medical examination; Physician's request.
Staff RNs 10 (ft); LPNs 17 (ft); Nurses aides 54 (ft); Physical therapists 4 (ft); Recreational therapists 1 (ft); Occupational therapists 1 (ft); Speech therapists 1 (ft); Activities coordinators 1 (ft); Dietitians 1 (pt); Dentists 1 (pt); Ophthalmologists 1 (pt); Podiatrists 1 (pt); Audiologists 1 (pt).

Hollenbeck Home for Aged Convalescent Unit
573 S Boyle Ave, Los Angeles, CA, 90033 (213) 263-6195
Admin William G Heideman. *Medical Dir/Dir of Nursing* John Walters MD.
Licensure Skilled Care; Intermediate Care for Mentally Retarded. *Beds* SNF 84; ICF/MR 28.
Certified Medicare; Medi-Cal.
Ownership Nonprofit.
Admissions Requirements Minimum age 65; Medical examination.
Staff Physicians 1 (pt); RNs 2 (ft), 1 (pt); LPNs 7 (ft), 2 (pt); Orderlies 1 (ft); Nurses aides 39 (ft), 2 (pt); Physical therapists 1 (pt); Recreational therapists 1 (ft), 1 (pt); Occupational therapists 1 (pt); Speech therapists 1 (pt); Activities coordinators 1 (ft); Dietitians 1 (pt); Dentists 1 (pt); Podiatrists 1 (pt).
Facilities Dining room; Physical therapy room; Activities room; Chapel; Crafts room; Laundry

room; Barber/Beauty shop; Library; Ice cream parlor.
Activities Arts and Crafts; Games; Reading groups; Prayer groups; Shopping trips.

Hyde Park Convalescent Hospital
6520 W Blvd, Los Angeles, CA, 90043 (213) 753-1354
Admin Elaine M Wiesel.
Licensure Skilled Care. *Beds* 72. *Certified* Medicare; Medi-Cal.
Ownership Proprietary.
Admissions Requirements Minimum age 21.
Staff Physicians; RNs; LPNs; Orderlies; Nurses aides; Physical therapists; Reality therapists; Recreational therapists; Occupational therapists; Speech therapists; Activities coordinators; Dietitians; Dentists; Ophthalmologists; Podiatrists; Audiologists.
Facilities Dining room; Activities room; Crafts room; Laundry room; Barber/Beauty shop.
Activities Arts and Crafts; Cards; Games; Reading groups; Prayer groups; Movies.
Description VA approved.

Hy-Lond Convalescent Hospital*
3002 Rowena Ave, Los Angeles, CA, 90039 (213) 666-1544
Admin Kathy Tekle-Mariam.
Licensure Skilled Care. *Beds* 131. *Certified* Medicare; Medi-Cal.
Ownership Proprietary.

Japanese Retirement Home
325 S Boyle St, Los Angeles, CA, 90033 (213) 263-9651
Admin Edwin C Hiroto. *Medical Dir/Dir of Nursing* Dr Sakaye Shigekawa.
Licensure Intermediate Care; Board care. *Beds* 96. *Certified* Medicare; Medi-Cal.
Ownership Nonprofit.
Staff RNs 1 (ft); LPNs 2 (ft), 4 (pt); Nurses aides 17 (ft), 10 (pt); Activities coordinators 1 (ft), 1 (pt); Dietitians 1 (pt).
Languages Japanese
Facilities Dining room; Activities room; Crafts room; Laundry room; Barber/Beauty shop; Library; Auditorium.
Activities Arts and Crafts; Games; Reading groups; Prayer groups; Movies; Shopping trips; Dances/Social or cultural gatherings; Music group.
Description Facility programed to needs of Japanese-Americans (e.g., diet, programs, staff, etc.).

Keiro Nursing Home*
2221 Lincoln Park Ave, Los Angeles, CA, 90031 (213) 225-1393
Admin Margaret Hiroto.
Licensure Skilled Care. *Beds* 87. *Certified* Medicare; Medi-Cal.
Ownership Nonprofit.
Languages Japanese

Kennedy Convalescent Hospital*
619 N Fairfax Ave, Los Angeles, CA, 90036 (213) 651-5331
Admin Solomon Gruer.
Licensure Skilled Care. *Beds* 97. *Certified* Medicare; Medi-Cal.
Ownership Proprietary.

Kingsley Manor Convalescent Hospital
1055 N Kingsley Dr, Los Angeles, CA, 90029 (213) 661-1128
Admin John Farnsworth. *Medical Dir/Dir of Nursing* A F Killian MD.
Licensure Skilled Care. *Beds* 51. *Certified* Medicare; Medi-Cal.
Ownership Nonprofit.
Admissions Requirements Medical examination; Physician's request.
Staff RNs 1 (ft), 8 (pt); LPNs 7 (ft), 4 (pt); Nurses aides 22 (ft), 2 (pt); Physical therapists 1 (pt); Occupational therapists 1 (pt); Speech therapists 1 (pt); Activities coordinators 1 (ft); Dietitians 1 (pt); Dentists 1 (pt); Ophthalmologists 1 (pt); Podiatrists 1 (pt).
Facilities Dining room; Activities room; Chapel; Crafts room; Barber/Beauty shop; Library.
Activities Arts and Crafts; Cards; Games; Prayer groups; Movies; Shopping trips; Dances-/Social or cultural gatherings; Pen Pals; Excursions.
Description Kingsley Manor Convalescent Hospital is the skilled nursing unit for Kingsley Manor, a retirement facility which is a Hollywood landmark. It is one level of 3 levels of care: residential care, personal service care, and skilled nursing care.

Lakewood Manor North
831 S Lake St, Los Angeles, CA, 90057 (213) 380-9175
Admin Arthur F Elliott. *Medical Dir/Dir of Nursing* Dr Marvin Salant.
Licensure Skilled Care. *Beds* 99. *Certified* Medicare; Medi-Cal.
Ownership Proprietary.
Admissions Requirements Physician's request.
Staff Physicians 8 (pt); RNs 1 (ft), 3 (pt); LPNs 22 (ft), 6 (pt); Orderlies 16 (ft), 5 (pt); Nurses aides 30 (ft), 15 (pt); Physical therapists 4 (pt); Reality therapists 1 (pt); Recreational therapists 1 (pt); Occupational therapists 2 (pt); Speech therapists 2 (pt); Activities coordinators 2 (pt); Dietitians 3 (pt); Dentists 2 (pt); Ophthalmologists 1 (pt); Podiatrists 1 (pt); Audiologists 1 (pt).
Facilities Dining room; Physical therapy room; Activities room; Barber/Beauty shop.
Activities Arts and Crafts; Cards; Games; Reading groups; Prayer groups; Movies; Dances/Social or cultural gatherings.
Description Facility is a 12-year family operation with an excellent activities program and educational facility.

Longwood Manor Sanitarium*
4853 W Washington, Los Angeles, CA, 90016 (213) 935-1157
Admin Jon Fletcher.
Licensure Skilled Care. *Beds* 123. *Certified* Medicare; Medi-Cal.
Ownership Proprietary.

Manchester Manor Convalescent Hospital*
837 W Manchester, Los Angeles, CA, 90044 (213) 753-1789
Admin Mable Crockett.
Licensure Skilled Care. *Beds* 49.
Certified Medi-Cal.
Ownership Proprietary.

Maple Convalescent Hospital
2625 S Maple Ave, Los Angeles, CA, 90011 (213) 747-6371
Admin Andre Pollak. *Medical Dir/Dir of Nursing* Dr Edward J Panzer.
Licensure Skilled Care. *Beds* 56. *Certified* Medicare; Medi-Cal.
Ownership Proprietary.
Facilities Dining room; Activities room; Laundry room.
Activities Arts and Crafts; Cards; Games; Prayer groups; Movies.

Mar Vista Sanitarium
3966 Marcasel Ave, Los Angeles, CA, 90066 (213) 870-3716
Admin Ruth Von Buskirk. *Medical Dir/Dir of Nursing* Dr Daniel Weston.
Licensure Skilled Care. *Beds* 68.
Ownership Proprietary.
Admissions Requirements Minimum age 50; Females only
Staff RNs 2 (ft), 1 (pt); LPNs 3 (ft), 3 (pt); Nurses aides 30 (ft), 15 (pt); Activities coordinators 1 (ft), 1 (pt); Dietitians 1 (ft).
Facilities Dining room; Activities room; Laundry room; Barber/Beauty shop.
Activities Arts and Crafts; Cards; Games; Reading groups; Movies.
Description A stately old home with a fenced outdoor area for patients who wander. This a locked facility for patients who wander.

Meadowbrook Manor Sanitarium
3951 East Blvd, Los Angeles, CA, 90066 (213) 870-0380
Admin J Krider. *Medical Dir/Dir of Nursing* Paul Berns MD.
Licensure Skilled Care. *Beds* 77. *Certified* Medicare.
Ownership Proprietary.
Admissions Requirements Minimum age 18; Medical examination; Physician's request.
Facilities Dining room; Activities room; Laundry room.
Activities Arts and Crafts; Games; Reading groups; Prayer groups; Movies; Shopping trips; Dances/Social or cultural gatherings.
Description Meadowbrook Manor is a fully licensed 77-bed skilled nursing facility specializing in the rehabilitation of the chronic psychiatric patient who is in need of a highly structured environment. For this reason, our exterior doors are locked and the exterior patios are fenced. This also ensures the family that the patient will be supervised without fear of outside distraction. Patients are admitted from acute psychiatric units, board and care placements, and recommendations from the Office of Mental Health. Individual treatment plans are developed through a multidisciplinary team meeting.

Midwilshire Convalescent Hospital
676 S Bonnie Brae, Los Angeles, CA, 90057 (213) 483-9921
Admin Al Ganzenhuber. *Medical Dir/Dir of Nursing* Dean Moore MD.
Licensure Skilled Care. *Beds* 80. *Certified* Medicare; Medi-Cal.
Ownership Proprietary.
Staff Physicians 3 (ft), 6 (pt); RNs 1 (ft), 1 (pt); LPNs 5 (ft), 3 (pt); Nurses aides 25 (ft);

Physical therapists; Occupational therapists; Speech therapists; Activities coordinators; Dietitians; Dentists; Podiatrists.
Facilities Dining room; Physical therapy room; Activities room; Laundry room; Barber/Beauty shop.
Activities Arts and Crafts; Cards; Games; Reading groups; Movies; Shopping trips.

Minami Keiro Nursing Home*
3619 N Mission Rd, Los Angeles, CA, 90031 (213) 225-1393
Admin Margaret Hiroto.
Licensure Skilled Care. *Beds* 97. *Certified* Medicare; Medi-Cal.
Ownership Nonprofit.
Languages Japanese

Nazareth House
3333 Manning Ave, Los Angeles, CA, 90064 (213) 839-2361
Admin Sr Malachy McSweeney.
Licensure Skilled Care. *Beds* 12. *Certified* Medicare.
Ownership Nonprofit.
Admissions Requirements Minimum age 65; Medical examination; Physician's request.
Affiliation Roman Catholic
Facilities Dining room; Activities room; Chapel; Crafts room; Laundry room; Barber/Beauty shop; Library.

Olympia Convalescent Hospital
1100 S Alvarado St, Los Angeles, CA, 90006 (213) 487-3000
Admin Otto Schwartz. *Medical Dir/Dir of Nursing* Dr Marvin Salant.
Licensure Skilled Care. *Beds* 135. *Certified* Medicare; Medi-Cal.
Ownership Proprietary.
Facilities Dining room; Physical therapy room; Activities room; Laundry room; Barber/Beauty shop; Library.
Activities Arts and Crafts; Cards; Games; Reading groups; Prayer groups; Movies; Dances/Social or cultural gatherings.

Paradise Convalescent Hospital*
2415 S Western Ave, Los Angeles, CA, 90018 (213) 734-1101
Admin J Sinay.
Licensure Skilled Care. *Beds* 99. *Certified* Medicare; Medi-Cal.
Ownership Proprietary.

Park Vista Convalescent Hospital*
5125 Monte Vista St, Los Angeles, CA, 90042 (213) 254-6125
Admin Gordon Dagg.
Licensure Skilled Care. *Beds* 59. *Certified* Medicare; Medi-Cal.
Ownership Proprietary.

RGR Sanitarium
12001 Santa Monica Blvd, Los Angeles, CA, 90025 (213) 478-0273
Admin Ida H Rios. *Medical Dir/Dir of Nursing* Harry J Silver MD.
Licensure Skilled Care. *Beds* 59. *Certified* Medicare; Medi-Cal.
Ownership Proprietary.
Facilities Dining room; Physical therapy room; Activities room; Crafts room; Laundry room;

Barber/Beauty shop.
Activities Arts and Crafts; Cards; Games; Movies; Shopping trips.

Rubins Brierwood Terrace
1480 S La Cienega Blvd, Los Angeles, CA, 90035 (213) 655-8390
Admin Morr S Zyskind. *Medical Dir/Dir of Nursing* Dr Morris Miller.
Licensure Skilled Care. *Beds* 41. *Certified* Medicare; Medi-Cal.
Ownership Proprietary.
Admissions Requirements Minimum age 55; Medical examination; Physician's request.
Staff RNs 1 (ft), 1 (pt); LPNs 3 (ft), 3 (pt); Orderlies 2 (ft); Nurses aides 25 (ft); Physical therapists 1 (pt); Recreational therapists 1 (ft); Occupational therapists 1 (pt); Speech therapists 1 (pt); Activities coordinators 1 (pt); Dietitians 1 (pt); Dentists 1 (pt); Ophthalmologists 1 (pt); Podiatrists 1 (pt); Audiologists 1 (pt).
Facilities Dining room; Activities room; Crafts room; Laundry room.
Activities Arts and Crafts; Cards; Games; Reading groups; Prayer groups; Dances/Social or cultural gatherings.
Description Facility is a 41-bed facility in a garden setting with private and semiprivate rooms.

Saint John of God Nursing Hospital*
2035 W Adams Blvd, Los Angeles, CA, 90018 (213) 731-0641
Admin Timothy W Dettman.
Licensure Skilled Care; Intermediate Care.
Beds SNF 68; ICF 22. *Certified* Medicare; Medi-Cal.
Ownership Nonprofit.

Serrano Convalescent Hospital—North
5401 Fountain Ave, Los Angeles, CA, 90029 (213) 465-2106
Admin Lydia F Cruz. *Medical Dir/Dir of Nursing* Dr Maffuz Michael.
Licensure Skilled Care. *Beds* 99. *Certified* Medicare; Medi-Cal.
Ownership Proprietary.
Admissions Requirements Minimum age 65.
Staff Physicians 1 (pt); RNs 2 (ft); LPNs 5 (ft), 5 (pt); Orderlies 5 (ft), 1 (pt); Nurses aides 24 (ft); Occupational therapists 1 (pt); Speech therapists 1 (pt); Activities coordinators 1 (pt); Dietitians 1 (ft); Dentists 1 (pt); Ophthalmologists 1 (pt); Podiatrists 1 (pt); Audiologists 1 (pt).
Facilities Dining room; Physical therapy room; Activities room; Crafts room; Laundry room; Barber/Beauty shop.
Activities Arts and Crafts; Cards; Games; Reading groups; Movies; Dances/Social or cultural gatherings.
Description We provide fine skilled nursing home care. We are certified in the Medicare and Medi-Cal program.

Serrano Convalescent Hospital—South*
5400 Fountain Ave, Los Angeles, CA, 90029 (213) 461-4301
Admin Trudi Weimer.
Licensure Skilled Care. *Beds* 99. *Certified* Medicare; Medi-Cal.
Ownership Proprietary.

Sharon Convalescent Hospital
8167 W 3rd St, Los Angeles, CA, 90048 (213) 655-2023
Admin Jean B Salkind.
Licensure Skilled Care. *Beds* 86. *Certified* Medicare; Medi-Cal.
Ownership Proprietary.
Admissions Requirements Minimum age 65; Physician's request.
Staff RNs; LPNs; Orderlies; Nurses aides; Physical therapists; Recreational therapists.
Facilities Dining room; Physical therapy room; Activities room; Laundry room; Barber/Beauty shop.
Activities Arts and Crafts; Cards; Games; Reading groups; Prayer groups; Movies.

Skyline Convalescent Hospital*
3032 Rowena Ave, Los Angeles, CA, 90039 (213) 665-1185
Admin Kathleen Reinke.
Licensure Skilled Care. *Beds* 99. *Certified* Medicare; Medi-Cal.
Ownership Proprietary.

Sparr Convalescent Hospital
2367 W Pico Blvd, Los Angeles, CA, 90006 (213) 388-1481
Admin Mildred Garcia. *Medical Dir/Dir of Nursing* Dr Harry Silver.
Licensure Skilled Care. *Beds* 65. *Certified* Medicare.
Ownership Proprietary.
Admissions Requirements Minimum age 18; Medical examination; Physician's request.
Staff Physicians 10 (pt); RNs 2 (pt); LPNs 3 (pt); Nurses aides 3 (pt); Activities coordinators 1 (ft).
Facilities Dining room; Physical therapy room; Activities room; Chapel; Crafts room; Laundry room; Barber/Beauty shop; Library; 2 Patios.
Activities Arts and Crafts; Cards; Games; Reading groups; Prayer groups; Movies; Shopping trips; Dances/Social or cultural gatherings; Resident council.
Description Sparr is outstanding for its staff teamwork and home-like atmosphere. With good, trained personnel, we provide excellent patient care and necessary special services. With the hospital's cleanliness, nutritional home-style cooking, and pets for the residents to enjoy, the residents feel this is the closest place to home.

Sunray East Convalescent Hospital*
3210 W Pico Blvd, Los Angeles, CA, 90019 (213) 734-2173
Admin Mildred Garcia.
Licensure Skilled Care. *Beds* 99. *Certified* Medicare; Medi-Cal.
Ownership Proprietary.

Sunray North Convalescent Hospital*
3233 W Pico Blvd, Los Angeles, CA, 90019 (213) 734-9122
Admin Jordan Fishman.
Licensure Skilled Care. *Beds* 95. *Certified* Medicare; Medi-Cal.
Ownership Proprietary.

Sunshine Terrace Convalescent Hospital Inc*
7951 Beverly Blvd, Los Angeles, CA, 90048 (213) 655-1500

Admin A Goldstein.
Licensure Skilled Care. *Beds* 50.
Ownership Proprietary.

Sycamore Park Convalescent Hospital
4585 N Figueroa, Los Angeles, CA, 90065 (213) 223-3441
Admin Robert M Snukal. *Medical Dir/Dir of Nursing* Dr Kunze.
Licensure Skilled Care. *Beds* 90. *Certified* Medicare; Medi-Cal.
Ownership Proprietary.
Staff RNs 2 (ft); LPNs 11 (ft), 2 (pt); Orderlies 4 (ft); Nurses aides 25 (ft); Physical therapists 1 (pt); Speech therapists 1 (pt); Activities coordinators 1 (ft); Dietitians 1 (pt); Dentists 1 (pt); Ophthalmologists 1 (pt); Podiatrists 1 (pt); Audiologists 1 (pt).
Facilities Dining room; Physical therapy room; Activities room; Chapel; Crafts room; Laundry room; Barber/Beauty shop; TV room.
Activities Arts and Crafts; Cards; Games; Reading groups; Prayer groups; Shopping trips.

Temple Park Convalescent Hospital*
2411 W Temple St, Los Angeles, CA, 90026 (213) 380-3210
Admin Helene Kohn.
Licensure Skilled Care. *Beds* 99. *Certified* Medicare; Medi-Cal.
Ownership Proprietary.

United Cerebral Palsy/Spastic Childrens Foundation
1307 W 105th St, Los Angeles, CA, 90044 (213) 757-9361
Admin Jack Moe. *Medical Dir/Dir of Nursing* Richard Koch MD.
Licensure Intermediate Care. *Beds* 54. *Certified* Medi-Cal.
Ownership Nonprofit.
Admissions Requirements Minimum age 18.
Staff RNs 1 (ft), 1 (pt); LPNs 5 (ft); Nurses aides 26 (ft); Physical therapists 1 (ft); Recreational therapists 1 (pt); Occupational therapists 1 (pt); Speech therapists 1 (pt); Activities coordinators 1 (ft); Dietitians 1 (pt); Dentists 1 (pt); Ophthalmologists 1 (pt); Podiatrists 1 (pt); Audiologists 1 (pt).
Facilities Dining room; Physical therapy room; Activities room; Crafts room; Laundry room; Barber/Beauty shop; Communications lab; Pool.
Activities Arts and Crafts; Cards; Games; Reading groups; Prayer groups; Movies; Shopping trips; Dances/Social or cultural gatherings; Several Clubs.

Vermont Knolls Convalescent Hospital*
11234 S Vermont Ave, Los Angeles, CA, 90044 (213) 754-3173
Admin Victor Rodgers.
Licensure Skilled Care. *Beds* 99. *Certified* Medicare; Medi-Cal.
Ownership Proprietary.

Vernon Convalescent Hospital*
1037 W Vernon, Los Angeles, CA, 90037 (213) 232-4895
Admin Edward Markovitz.
Licensure Skilled Care. *Beds* 99. *Certified* Medicare; Medi-Cal.
Ownership Proprietary.

View Heights Convalescent Hospital*
12619 S Avalon Blvd, Los Angeles, CA, 90061 (213) 757-1881
Admin Monica A Fenton.
Licensure Skilled Care. *Beds* 163. *Certified* Medicare; Medi-Cal.
Ownership Proprietary.

Virgil Sanitarium and Convalescent Hospital*
975 N Virgil Ave, Los Angeles, CA, 90029 (213) 665-5793
Admin Nancy S Chow.
Licensure Skilled Care. *Beds* 99. *Certified* Medicare; Medi-Cal.
Ownership Proprietary.

Vista Del Mar Care Center*
11620 Washington Blvd, Los Angeles, CA, 90066 (213) 391-6476
Admin Terry M Henry.
Licensure Skilled Care. *Beds* 50. *Certified* Medicare; Medi-Cal.
Ownership Proprietary.

Washington Nursing and Convalescent
2300 W Washington, Los Angeles, CA, 90018 (213) 731-0861
Admin Henry Pagkalinawan. *Medical Dir/Dir of Nursing* Leroy Ewell MD.
Licensure Skilled Care. *Beds* 59. *Certified* Medicare.
Ownership Proprietary.
Admissions Requirements Medical examination; Physician's request.
Staff Physicians 8 (pt); RNs 1 (ft), 2 (pt); LPNs 3 (ft), 3 (pt); Orderlies 2 (ft); Nurses aides 16 (ft), 8 (pt); Physical therapists 1 (pt); Occupational therapists 1 (pt); Speech therapists 1 (pt); Activities coordinators 1 (ft); Dietitians 1 (pt); Dentists 1 (pt); Ophthalmologists 1 (pt); Podiatrists 1 (pt).
Facilities Dining room; Activities room; Crafts room; Laundry room; Barber/Beauty shop.
Activities Arts and Crafts; Cards; Games; Reading groups; Prayer groups; Dances/Social or cultural gatherings.

WCTU Home for Women
2235 Norwalk Ave, Los Angeles, CA, 90041 (213) 255-7108
Admin M E Hammarstrom.
Licensure Skilled Care. *Beds* 25. *Certified* Medicare.
Ownership Nonprofit.

Western Convalescent Hospital*
2190 W Adams Blvd, Los Angeles, CA, 90018 (213) 737-7778
Admin Frank Garcia.
Licensure Skilled Care. *Beds* 129. *Certified* Medicare; Medi-Cal.
Ownership Proprietary.

Westlake Convalescent Hospital
316 S Westlake Ave, Los Angeles, CA, 90057 (213) 484-0510
Admin Neng F Chen. *Medical Dir/Dir of Nursing* Dr Marvin Salante.
Licensure Skilled Care. *Beds* SNF 99; ICF 15.
Certified Medicare; Medi-Cal.
Ownership Proprietary.
Admissions Requirements Physician's request.
Facilities Dining room; Activities room; Crafts room; Laundry room; Barber/Beauty shop; Library.
Activities Arts and Crafts; Cards; Games; Reading groups; Prayer groups; Movies; Dances/Social or cultural gatherings.
Description Westlake Convalescent Hospital is only a few minutes away from downtown Los Angeles. RNs and LVNs are on duty 24 hours along with CNAs, therapists, activities director, and social workers to ensure patient's well being.

LOS BANOS

Los Banos Convalescent Hospital
931 Idaho Ave, Los Banos, CA, 93635 (209) 826-0790
Admin Albert J Wahlbaker. *Medical Dir/Dir of Nursing* Carol Sakurkin MD.
Licensure Skilled Care. *Beds* 51. *Certified* Medicare; Medi-Cal.
Ownership Proprietary.
Admissions Requirements Medical examination; Physician's request.
Staff Physicians 1 (pt); RNs 1 (ft), 1 (pt); LPNs 3 (ft), 2 (pt); Nurses aides 10 (ft), 1 (pt); Physical therapists 1 (pt); Activities coordinators 1 (ft); Dietitians 1 (pt); Podiatrists 1 (pt).
Facilities Dining room; Activities room; Crafts room; Laundry room; Barber/Beauty shop.
Activities Arts and Crafts; Games; Movies; Dances/Social or cultural gatherings.
Description The facility hopes to start construction of a new wing in late February or early March, 1984. The wing will add 8 beds to the current figure of 51. It will also add a separate activity/crafts room with an area for a beauty shop. Basically, 3,365 sq ft will be added to the existing 10,554 sq ft.

LOS GATOS

Bethesda Manor and Convalescent Center
371 Los Gatos Blvd, Los Gatos, CA, 95030 (408) 356-3116
Admin Roberta S Ross. *Medical Dir/Dir of Nursing* David Morgan MD.
Licensure Skilled Care. *Beds* 124. *Certified* Medicare; Medi-Cal.
Ownership Nonprofit.
Staff Physicians 1 (pt); RNs 6 (ft), 2 (pt); Orderlies 5 (ft), 2 (pt); Nurses aides 40 (ft), 20 (pt); Physical therapists 2 (pt); Reality therapists 1 (pt); Recreational therapists 1 (pt); Occupational therapists 1 (pt); Speech therapists 1 (pt); Activities coordinators 2 (ft); Dietitians 1 (ft); Dentists 1 (pt); Ophthalmologists 1 (pt); Podiatrists 1 (pt); Audiologists 1 (pt).
Affiliation Disciples of Christ
Facilities Dining room; Physical therapy room; Activities room; Crafts room; Laundry room; Barber/Beauty shop; Library.
Activities Arts and Crafts; Cards; Games; Reading groups; Prayer groups; Movies; Shopping trips; Dances/Social or cultural gatherings.
Description Bethesda Convalescent Center emphasizes the treatment of the total patient, physically and spiritually, by using an agressive activity program approach which keeps residents busy and striving towards self-sufficiency.

Beverly Manor Convalescent Hospital
14966 Terreno De Flores Ln, Los Gatos, CA, 95030 (408) 356-8136
Admin Laney Hendrickson. *Medical Dir/Dir of Nursing* Dr William Garcia.
Licensure Skilled Care. *Beds* 65. *Certified* Medicare; Medi-Cal.
Ownership Proprietary.
Staff RNs 2 (ft); LPNs 5 (ft); Nurses aides 15 (ft), 1 (pt); Physical therapists; Occupational therapists; Speech therapists; Activities coordinators 1 (ft); Dietitians; Dentists; Podiatrists.
Facilities Dining room; Activities room; Crafts room; Laundry room; Barber/Beauty shop.
Activities Arts and Crafts; Cards; Games; Reading groups; Prayer groups; Movies; Shopping trips; Dances/Social or cultural gatherings.

Beverly Manor Convalescent Hospital*
350 De Soto Dr, Los Gatos, CA, 95030 (408) 356-9151
Admin Susan E Bazsuly.
Licensure Skilled Care. *Beds* 73. *Certified* Medicare; Medi-Cal.
Ownership Proprietary.

Gem Convalescent Hospital*
15245 National Ave, Los Gatos, CA, 95030 (408) 356-2151
Admin Beatrice M Straub.
Licensure Skilled Care. *Beds* 65.
Certified Medi-Cal.
Ownership Proprietary.

Lark Manor Convalescent Hospital*
16605 Lark Ave, Los Gatos, CA, 95030 (408) 356-9146
Admin Sandra L Karr.
Licensure Skilled Care. *Beds* 30.
Certified Medi-Cal.
Ownership Proprietary.

Los Gatos Convalescent Hospital*
16412 Los Gatos Blvd, Los Gatos, CA, 95030 (408) 356-2191
Admin Melba Arbuckle.
Licensure Skilled Care. *Beds* 48. *Certified* Medicare; Medi-Cal.
Ownership Proprietary.

Los Gatos Meadows Geriatric Hospital
110 Wood Rd, Los Gatos, CA, 95030 (408) 354-6611
Admin Erling G Anderson. *Medical Dir/Dir of Nursing* Donald Conlon MD.
Licensure Skilled Care. *Beds* 39. *Certified* Medicare.
Ownership Nonprofit.
Admissions Requirements Minimum age 65; Medical examination; Physician's request.
Affiliation Episcopal
Facilities Dining room; Physical therapy room; Activities room; Chapel; Crafts room; Laundry room; Barber/Beauty shop; Library.
Activities Arts and Crafts; Cards; Games; Reading groups; Prayer groups; Movies; Shopping trips; Dances/Social or cultural gatherings.
Description Once part of California's historic Rancho Rinconada de Los Gatos, Los Gatos Meadows was selected for its combination of natural scenic beauty and convenient proximity to the San Francisco Bay area.

LYNWOOD

Community Convalescent Hospital*
3611 Imperial Hwy, Lynwood, CA, 90262 (213) 537-2500
Admin Ron Dodgen.
Licensure Skilled Care. *Beds* 99. *Certified* Medicare; Medi-Cal.
Ownership Proprietary.

Lynwood Care Center
3598 E Century Blvd, Lynwood, CA, 90262 (213) 639-5220
Admin Ronald Morgan. *Medical Dir/Dir of Nursing* Ramon Cabrera MD.
Licensure Skilled Care. *Beds* 128. *Certified* Medicare; Medi-Cal.
Ownership Proprietary.
Admissions Requirements Minimum age 3; Medical examination; Physician's request.
Staff Physicians 1 (pt); RNs 4 (ft), 2 (pt); LPNs 6 (ft), 2 (pt); Orderlies 8 (ft), 1 (pt); Nurses aides 35 (ft), 6 (pt); Physical therapists 1 (pt); Occupational therapists 1 (pt); Speech therapists 1 (pt); Activities coordinators 1 (ft); Dietitians 1 (pt); Dentists 1 (pt); Ophthalmologists 1 (pt); Podiatrists 1 (pt); Audiologists 1 (pt).
Facilities Dining room; Physical therapy room; Activities room; Crafts room; Laundry room; Barber/Beauty shop.
Activities Arts and Crafts; Cards; Games; Movies; Shopping trips.
Description ICF/DD program for mentally retarded.

Majestic Convalescent Center*
3565 E Imperial Hwy, Lynwood, CA, 90206 (213) 638-9377
Admin Stephen Hooker.
Licensure Skilled Care. *Beds* 98. *Certified* Medicare; Medi-Cal.
Ownership Proprietary.

Marlinda Nursing Home
3615 Imperial Hwy, Lynwood, CA, 90262 (213) 639-4623
Admin Linda Richards. *Medical Dir/Dir of Nursing* Dr Robert Tsai.
Licensure Skilled Care. *Beds* 130. *Certified* Medicare; Medi-Cal.
Ownership Proprietary.
Staff RNs 6 (ft); LPNs 10 (ft); Orderlies 4 (ft); Nurses aides 50 (ft); Physical therapists 1 (ft); Recreational therapists 1 (ft); Occupational therapists 1 (ft); Activities coordinators 1 (pt); Dietitians 1 (pt).
Facilities Dining room; Physical therapy room; Activities room; Crafts room; Laundry room; Barber/Beauty shop.
Activities Arts and Crafts; Cards; Games; Reading groups; Prayer groups; Movies; Shopping trips; Dances/Social or cultural gatherings.

Marlinda West Nursing Home*
3333 E Imperial Hwy, Lynwood, CA, 90262 (213) 631-6122
Admin H H Lang.
Licensure Skilled Care. *Beds* 90.
Certified Medi-Cal.
Ownership Proprietary.

MADERA

Madera Convalescent Hospital
517 S "A" St, Madera, CA, 93637 (209) 673-9228
Admin Elvera Gamboa. *Medical Dir/Dir of Nursing* Dr Robert Rowe.
Licensure Skilled Care. *Beds* 124. *Certified* Medicare; Medi-Cal.
Ownership Proprietary.
Staff RNs 4 (ft), 2 (pt); LPNs 9 (ft), 3 (pt); Orderlies 2 (ft); Nurses aides 20 (ft), 3 (pt); Physical therapists 1 (pt); Occupational therapists 1 (pt); Speech therapists 1 (pt); Activities coordinators 1 (ft); Dietitians 1 (pt); Dentists 1 (pt); Podiatrists 1 (pt).
Facilities Dining room; Physical therapy room; Activities room; Chapel; Laundry room.
Activities Arts and Crafts; Cards; Games; Reading groups; Prayer groups; Movies; Shopping trips.

Westgate Manor Convalescent Hospital*
1700 Howard Rd, Madera, CA, 93637 (209) 673-9278
Admin Anna Marie Perry.
Licensure Skilled Care. *Beds* 64. *Certified* Medicare; Medi-Cal.
Ownership Proprietary.

MANTECA

Manteca Convalescent Hospital
410 Eastwood Ave, Manteca, CA, 95336 (209) 239-1222
Admin Maxine Niel. *Medical Dir/Dir of Nursing* Dr Russell Carter.
Licensure Skilled Care. *Beds* 99. *Certified* Medicare; Medi-Cal.
Ownership Nonprofit.
Admissions Requirements Minimum age 16; Medical examination; Physician's request.
Staff RNs 5 (ft), 5 (pt); LPNs 4 (ft), 3 (pt); Orderlies 1 (ft); Nurses aides 41 (ft), 17 (pt); Physical therapists 1 (ft); Activities coordinators 1 (ft).
Facilities Dining room; Physical therapy room; Activities room; Laundry room; Barber/Beauty shop.
Activities Arts and Crafts; Cards; Games; Reading groups; Prayer groups; Movies; Shopping trips.
Description Facility features rehabilitation services, physical therapy, speech and occupational therapy, as well as in- and out-patient services.

Palm Haven Convalescent Hospital*
469 E North St, Manteca, CA, 95336 (209) 823-1788
Admin Joseph Zorichak.
Licensure Skilled Care. *Beds* 99.
Ownership Proprietary.

MARIPOSA

Mariposa Manor*
5201 Crystal Aire Dr, Mariposa, CA, 95338 (209) 966-2244
Admin Frank J Williams.
Licensure Skilled Care. *Beds* 23.

Certified Medi-Cal.
Ownership Proprietary.

MARTINEZ

Alhambra Convalescent Hospital*
331 Ilene St, Martinez, CA, 94553 (415)
228-2020
Admin Lowell Callaway.
Licensure Skilled Care. *Beds* 42. *Certified* Medicare; Medi-Cal.
Ownership Proprietary.

Martinez Convalescent Hospital*
4110 Alhambra Way, Martinez, CA, 94553
(415) 228-4260
Admin Michael W Hart.
Licensure Skilled Care. *Beds* 36.
Certified Medi-Cal.
Ownership Proprietary.

Mount Diablo Nursing Center
1790 Muir Rd, Martinez, CA, 94553 (415)
228-8383
Admin Melinda L Hutchings. *Medical Dir/Dir of Nursing* Dr Carlos Anderson.
Licensure Skilled Care. *Beds* 99. *Certified* Medicare; Medi-Cal.
Ownership Proprietary.
Staff Physicians 1 (pt); RNs 2 (ft), 2 (pt);
Nurses aides 18 (ft), 6 (pt); Physical therapists 1
(pt); Recreational therapists 1 (pt); Occupational therapists 1 (pt); Speech therapists 1 (pt);
Activities coordinators 1 (ft), 1 (pt); Dietitians
1 (pt); Dentists 1 (pt); Ophthalmologists 1 (pt);
Podiatrists 1 (pt); Audiologists 1 (pt); LVNs 5
(ft), 3 (pt).
Facilities Dining room; Physical therapy room;
Activities room; Laundry room; Barber/Beauty
shop; Living room; Lounge.
Activities Arts and Crafts; Cards; Games;
Reading groups; Prayer groups; Movies; Shopping trips; Dances/Social or cultural gatherings;
Sightseeing tours; Visits to senior center; Adult
education classes.

MARYSVILLE

Marysville Convalescent Hospital
1617 Ramirez St, Marysville, CA, 95901 (916)
742-7311
Admin Henry Delamere. *Medical Dir/Dir of Nursing* Charles Cotham.
Licensure Skilled Care; Intermediate Care.
Beds SNF 82; ICF 4. *Certified* Medicare;
Medi-Cal.
Ownership Proprietary.
Admissions Requirements Physician's request.
Staff Physicians 1 (ft), 3 (pt); RNs 1 (ft), 3 (pt);
LPNs 8 (ft), 10 (pt); Nurses aides 8 (ft), 16 (pt);
Physical therapists 1 (ft), 2 (pt); Speech therapists 1 (pt); Activities coordinators 1 (ft); Dietitians 1 (ft), 1 (pt); Dentists 3 (pt); Podiatrists 2
(pt).
Facilities Dining room; Physical therapy room;
Activities room; Crafts room; Laundry room;
Barber/Beauty shop; Large day room for all
outside activities; Church and entertainment.
Activities Arts and Crafts; Games; Prayer
groups; Movies; Shopping trips; Dances/Social
or cultural gatherings.

Description Quiet residential area easily accessible to town. Two patients to each room;
adjoining private patio. Extra large patio to
accomodate visiting family and friends which
is also used for patient excercise area as well as
barbecues and other social needs. Patient care
is first and foremost with all the staff, regardless
of duties. We provide a pleasant and home-style
atmosphere.

MAYWOOD

Pine Crest Convalescent Hospital
6025 Pine Ave, Maywood, CA, 90270 (213)
560-0720
Admin Kathy Keil. *Medical Dir/Dir of Nursing* Edward Panzer MD.
Licensure Skilled Care. *Beds* 133. *Certified* Medicare; Medi-Cal.
Ownership Proprietary.
Staff RNs; LPNs; Orderlies; Nurses aides;
Physical therapists; Reality therapists; Recreational therapists; Occupational therapists; Speech therapists; Activities coordinators;
Dietitians; Dentists; Ophthalmologists; Podiatrists; Audiologists.
Facilities Dining room; Physical therapy room;
Activities room; Laundry room; Barber/Beauty
shop.
Activities Arts and Crafts; Cards; Games;
Reading groups; Prayer groups; Movies; Shopping trips; Dances/Social or cultural gatherings.
Description Hospital has a well-established
rehabilitation program and a Medicare distinct
part consisting of 33 beds.

MENLO PARK

College Park Convalescent Hospital*
1275 Crane St, Menlo Park, CA, 94025 (415)
322-7261
Admin William Collins.
Licensure Skilled Care. *Beds* 160. *Certified* Medicare; Medi-Cal.
Ownership Proprietary.

Convalescent Hospital University Branch*
2122 Santa Cruz Ave, Menlo Park, CA, 94025
(415) 854-4020
Admin Basil A Hogan.
Licensure Skilled Care. *Beds* 80. *Certified* Medicare; Medi-Cal.
Ownership Proprietary.

Hillhaven Convalescent Hospital*
16 Coleman Pl, Menlo Park, CA, 94025 (415)
326-0802
Admin Mary J Hommowun.
Licensure Skilled Care. *Beds* 53. *Certified* Medicare; Medi-Cal.
Ownership Proprietary.

Le Havre Convalescent Hospital*
800 Roble Ave, Menlo Park, CA, 94025 (415)
623-6189
Admin Suzanne Heisler.
Licensure Skilled Care. *Beds* 54. *Certified* Medicare; Medi-Cal.
Ownership Proprietary.

Sharon Heights Convalescent Hospital
1185 Monte Rosa Dr, Menlo Park, CA, 94025
(415) 854-4230
Admin Leslee J Kullijian. *Medical Dir/Dir of Nursing* Morris Gutterman MD.
Licensure Skilled Care. *Beds* 96. *Certified* Medicare.
Ownership Proprietary.
Admissions Requirements Physician's request.
Staff RNs 5 (ft), 7 (pt); Orderlies 6 (ft); Nurses
aides 30 (ft), 5 (pt); Physical therapists 1 (ft);
Occupational therapists 1 (pt); Speech therapists 1 (pt); Activities coordinators 2 (ft); Dietitians 1 (pt); Dentists 1 (pt); Podiatrists 1 (pt);
Social workers; LVNs 5 (ft), 4 (pt).
Facilities Dining room; Physical therapy room;
Activities room; Chapel; Laundry room; Barber/Beauty shop; Library.
Activities Arts and Crafts; Cards; Games;
Reading groups; Movies; Dances/Social or cultural gatherings; Happy hour; Church services;
Adult education.
Description The facility is nestled in the hills of
Sharon Heights. Patios and courtyards are
available for residents and their families. The
hospital offers individualized nursing care and
a wide range of social activities. A caring staff
not only treats the patients' physical ailments
but also emphasizes the emotional, psychological, and spiritual needs of each patient.

MENTONE

Braswell's Ivy Retreat
2278 Nice St, Mentone, CA, 92359 (714)
794-1189
Admin James W Braswell. *Medical Dir/Dir of Nursing* H Jay Cozzolino.
Licensure Skilled Care. *Beds* 50. *Certified* Medicare; Medi-Cal.
Ownership Proprietary.
Staff RNs 1 (ft), 3 (pt); LPNs 3 (ft), 2 (pt);
Orderlies 2 (ft); Nurses aides 20 (ft), 1 (pt);
Activities coordinators 1 (ft); Dietitians 1 (ft).
Facilities Dining room; Activities room; Laundry room; Barber/Beauty shop.
Activities Arts and Crafts; Games; Reading
groups; Prayer groups; Movies; Dances/Social
or cultural gatherings.

MERCED

Franciscan Convalescent Hospital*
3169 M St, Merced, CA, 95340 (209) 722-6231
Admin John Sears.
Licensure Skilled Care. *Beds* 71. *Certified* Medicare; Medi-Cal.
Ownership Proprietary.
Affiliation Roman Catholic

Hy-Lond Convalescent Hospital
3170 M St, Merced, CA, 95340 (209) 723-1056
Admin Lawrence L Thompson.
Licensure Skilled Care. *Beds* 121. *Certified* Medicare; Medi-Cal.
Ownership Proprietary.

La Sierra Convalescent Hospital
2424 M St, Merced, CA, 95340 (209) 723-4224
Admin Charles Roy Wagner. *Medical Dir/Dir of Nursing* Dr Arthur Dahlem.

Licensure Skilled Care. *Beds* 68. *Certified* Medicare; Medi-Cal.
Ownership Proprietary.
Admissions Requirements Medical examination; Physician's request.
Staff Physicians 1 (pt); RNs 1 (ft), 1 (pt); LPNs 5 (ft), 1 (pt); Orderlies 2 (ft), 1 (pt); Nurses aides 38 (ft), 6 (pt); Physical therapists 1 (pt); Occupational therapists 1 (pt); Speech therapists 1 (pt); Activities coordinators 1 (ft); Dietitians 1 (pt); Dentists 1 (pt); Podiatrists 1 (pt); Audiologists 1 (pt).

Merced Convalescent Hospital
510 W 26th St, Merced, CA, 95340 (209) 723-2911
Admin Charles Roy Wagner. *Medical Dir/Dir of Nursing* Dr Arthur Dahlem.
Licensure Skilled Care. *Beds* 79. *Certified* Medicare; Medi-Cal.
Ownership Proprietary.
Admissions Requirements Medical examination; Physician's request.
Staff Physicians 1 (pt); RNs 1 (ft), 1 (pt); LPNs 5 (ft), 2 (pt); Orderlies 3 (ft); Nurses aides 28 (ft), 12 (pt); Physical therapists 1 (pt); Occupational therapists 1 (pt); Speech therapists 1 (pt); Activities coordinators 1 (ft); Dietitians 1 (pt); Dentists 1 (pt); Podiatrists 1 (pt); Audiologists 1 (pt).

Merced Manor
1255 B St, Merced, CA, 95340 (209) 723-8814
Admin Linda S Wahlbaker. *Medical Dir/Dir of Nursing* Arthur Harris MD.
Licensure Skilled Care. *Beds* 92. *Certified* Medicare.
Ownership Proprietary.
Admissions Requirements Minimum age 18; Medical examination; Physician's request.
Staff Physicians 2 (pt); RNs 1 (ft), 2 (pt); LPNs 6 (ft), 8 (pt); Orderlies 11 (ft), 4 (pt); Nurses aides 8 (ft), 6 (pt); Recreational therapists 2 (ft).
Facilities Dining room; Activities room; Crafts room; Laundry room; Barber/Beauty shop.
Activities Arts and Crafts; Cards; Games; Reading groups; Prayer groups; Movies; Shopping trips; Dances/Social or cultural gatherings.

MILL VALLEY

Hillhaven Convalescent Hospital*
505 Miller Ave, Mill Valley, CA, 94941 (415) 388-8244
Admin Jay Roberts.
Licensure Skilled Care. *Beds* 120. *Certified* Medicare; Medi-Cal.
Ownership Proprietary.

The Redwoods*
40 Camino Alto, Mill Valley, CA, 94941 (415) 383-3141
Admin Jean Naquin.
Licensure Skilled Care. *Beds* 58. *Certified* Medicare; Medi-Cal.
Ownership Nonprofit.

MILLBRAE

Millbrae Serra Convalescent Hospital*
150 Hemlock Ave, Millbrae, CA, 94030 (415)

697-8386
Admin Michael Vano.
Licensure Skilled Care. *Beds* 131.
Certified Medi-Cal.
Ownership Proprietary.

Sheltering Pine Convalescent Hospital
33 Mateo Ave, Millbrae, CA, 94030 (415) 583-8937
Admin G S Karki. *Medical Dir/Dir of Nursing* Irving Stern MD.
Licensure Skilled Care. *Beds* 120. *Certified* Medicare; Medi-Cal.
Ownership Proprietary.
Facilities Dining room; Physical therapy room; Activities room; Chapel; Crafts room; Laundry room; Barber/Beauty shop; Library.
Activities Arts and Crafts; Cards; Games; Reading groups; Prayer groups; Movies; Shopping trips; Dances/Social or cultural gatherings.
Description Both the convalescent hospital and the retirement center are co-located in a residential area each having an excellent environment.

MILPITAS

Eldercare Convalescent Hospital
120 Corning Ave, Milpitas, CA, 95035 (408) 262-0217
Admin Terry Smith-Campbell. *Medical Dir-/Dir of Nursing* Dr Norman Woods.
Licensure Skilled Care. *Beds* 25.
Certified Medicare; Medi-Cal.
Ownership Proprietary.
Staff Physicians 1 (ft), 1 (pt); RNs 2 (ft), 2 (pt); LPNs 2 (ft), 4 (pt); Nurses aides 7 (ft), 4 (pt); Physical therapists 1 (pt); Reality therapists 1 (pt); Recreational therapists 1 (pt); Occupational therapists 1 (pt); Speech therapists 1 (pt); Activities coordinators 1 (ft); Dietitians 1 (ft), 3 (pt); Dentists 1 (ft); Podiatrists 1 (ft).
Facilities Dining room; Activities room; Crafts room; Laundry room.
Activities Arts and Crafts; Cards; Games; Reading groups; Prayer groups; Movies; Shopping trips; Dances/Social or cultural gatherings; Patient council.
Description Very small, family-type facility that is quieter than most. Good activity program with outings to movies, restaurants, parks, and shopping. Many volunteers present donations to patients.

MODESTO

Casa De Modesto
1745 Eldena Way, Modesto, CA, 95350 (209) 529-4950
Admin Felton Daniels.
Licensure Skilled Care. *Beds* 59.
Certified Medi-Cal.
Ownership Nonprofit.

Crestwood Manor*
1400 Celeste Dr, Modesto, CA, 95355 (209) 526-8050
Admin George Lytal.
Licensure Skilled Care. *Beds* 192.
Certified Medi-Cal.
Ownership Proprietary.

Driftwood Convalescent Hospital*
1611 Scenic Dr, Modesto, CA, 95350 (209) 523-5667
Admin Catherine Haley.
Licensure Skilled Care. *Beds* 99. *Certified* Medicare; Medi-Cal.
Ownership Proprietary.

Edson Convalescent Hospital*
3456 McHenry Ave, Modesto, CA, 95350 (209) 577-3200
Admin David G Howell.
Licensure Skilled Care. *Beds* 25. *Certified* Medicare; Medi-Cal.
Ownership Proprietary.

Evergreen Convalescent Hospital Inc*
2030 Evergreen Ave, Modesto, CA, 95350 (209) 577-1055
Admin B V Cipponeri.
Licensure Skilled Care. *Beds* 70. *Certified* Medicare; Medi-Cal.
Ownership Proprietary.

Hillhaven Convalescent Hospital
1310 W Granger Ave, Modesto, CA, 95350 (209) 524-4817
Admin Terry L Mundy. *Medical Dir/Dir of Nursing* Marvin Montgomery MD.
Licensure Skilled Care. *Beds* 104. *Certified* Medicare; Medi-Cal.
Ownership Proprietary.
Staff RNs 7 (ft); LPNs 11 (ft); Orderlies 4 (ft); Nurses aides 42 (ft); Physical therapists 1 (pt); Occupational therapists 1 (pt); Speech therapists 1 (pt); Activities coordinators 1 (ft), 1 (pt); Dietitians 1 (pt); Podiatrists 1 (pt).
Facilities Dining room; Physical therapy room; Activities room; Crafts room; Laundry room; Barber/Beauty shop.
Activities Arts and Crafts; Cards; Games; Reading groups; Prayer groups; Movies; Shopping trips; Dances/Social or cultural gatherings.

Hy-Lond Convalescent Hospital
1900 Coffee Rd, Modesto, CA, 95350 (209) 526-1775
Admin Fernando Rodriquez. *Medical Dir/Dir of Nursing* Mattice Harris MD.
Licensure Skilled Care. *Beds* 120. *Certified* Medicare; Medi-Cal.
Ownership Proprietary.
Admissions Requirements Medical examination.
Staff RNs 4 (ft), 2 (pt); LPNs 12 (ft), 3 (pt); Physical therapists 1 (ft); Reality therapists 1 (pt); Recreational therapists 1 (pt); Speech therapists 1 (pt); Activities coordinators 1 (ft), 1 (pt); Dietitians 1 (ft), 1 (pt); Dentists 1 (pt); Ophthalmologists 1 (pt); Podiatrists 1 (pt); Audiologists 1 (pt).
Facilities Dining room; Physical therapy room; Activities room; Crafts room; Laundry room; Barber/Beauty shop; Library.
Activities Arts and Crafts; Cards; Games; Reading groups; Prayer groups; Movies; Shopping trips; Dances/Social or cultural gatherings.
Description A company with a high standard of nursing care above all else. Excellent restorative program with out-patient program being developed.

Modesto Convalescent Hospital*
515 E Orangeburg Ave, Modesto, CA, 95350
(209) 529-0516
Admin Loretta Smith.
Licensure Skilled Care. *Beds* 70. *Certified* Medicare; Medi-Cal.
Ownership Proprietary.

Orangeburg Convalescent Hospital*
823 E Orangeburg Ave, Modesto, CA, 95350
(209) 524-4641
Admin Rebecca Jane Collins.
Licensure Skilled Care. *Beds* 40. *Certified* Medicare; Medi-Cal.
Ownership Proprietary.

Reno Avenue Convalescent Hospital*
1028 Reno Ave, Modesto, CA, 95351 (209)
524-1146
Admin Rebecca Jane Collins.
Licensure Skilled Care. *Beds* 25. *Certified* Medicare; Medi-Cal.
Ownership Proprietary.

Yosemite Convalescent Hospital Inc
159 E Orangeburg Ave, Modesto, CA, 95350
(209) 526-2811
Admin Juanita Boyson. *Medical Dir/Dir of Nursing* Dr Grant Bare.
Licensure Skilled Care. *Beds* 99. *Certified* Medicare; Medi-Cal.
Ownership Proprietary.
Admissions Requirements Physician's request.
Staff Physicians 1 (pt); RNs 1 (ft), 1 (pt); LPNs 9 (ft); Orderlies 3 (ft); Nurses aides 33 (ft), 9 (pt); Physical therapists 1 (pt); Occupational therapists 1 (pt); Speech therapists 1 (pt); Activities coordinators 1 (ft); Dietitians 1 (pt); Dentists 1 (pt); Podiatrists 1 (pt).
Facilities Dining room; Physical therapy room; Activities room; Laundry room; Barber/Beauty shop.
Activities Arts and Crafts; Cards; Games; Reading groups; Movies; Shopping trips; Dances/Social or cultural gatherings.
Description A good "home away from home" with 24-hour nursing care and an excellent activity program.

MONROVIA

Beverly Manor Convalescent Hospital*
615 W Duarte Rd, Monrovia, CA, 91016 (213)
358-4547
Admin Floy Wulk.
Licensure Skilled Care. *Beds* 99. *Certified* Medicare; Medi-Cal.
Ownership Proprietary.
Description JCAH approved.

MONTCLAIR

Montclair Manor Convalescent Hospital
5119 Bandera St, Montclair, CA, 91763 (714)
626-1294
Admin Rosalie Mitchell. *Medical Dir/Dir of Nursing* Robert Bom MD.
Licensure Skilled Care. *Beds* 59. *Certified* Medicare; Medi-Cal.
Ownership Proprietary.
Admissions Requirements Minimum age 16;

Physician's request.
Staff RNs 1 (ft), 2 (pt); LPNs 3 (ft), 2 (pt); Orderlies 3 (ft), 1 (pt); Nurses aides 15 (ft), 6 (pt); Physical therapists 2 (pt); Recreational therapists 1 (ft); Occupational therapists 1 (pt); Speech therapists 1 (pt); Dietitians 1 (pt); Dentists 1 (pt); Ophthalmologists 1 (pt); Podiatrists 1 (pt).
Facilities Dining room; Activities room; Crafts room; Laundry room; Barber/Beauty shop; Library.
Activities Arts and Crafts; Cards; Games; Prayer groups; Shopping trips; Dances/Social or cultural gatherings; Outdoor outings and picnics.
Description A recently refurbished facility with a full census and steady, dependable, and kind staff.

Monte Vista Child Care Center
9140 Monte Vista, Montclair, CA, 91763 (714)
624-2774
Admin Barbara Risinger.
Licensure Intermediate Care for Mentally Retarded. *Beds* 58. *Certified* Medi-Cal.
Ownership Proprietary.
Admissions Requirements Minimum age 8; Medical examination; Physician's request.
Staff RNs; LPNs; Orderlies; Nurses aides; Activities coordinators.
Facilities Dining room; Crafts room; Laundry room; Program rooms.
Activities Arts and Crafts; Movies; Shopping trips.
Description Monte Vista is a facility with a real touch of home atmosphere. Many activities for the residents and lots of love is shared with them from staff. Extensive developmentally based recreational activities.

Suntown at Montclair Convalescent Hospital
9620 Fremont Ave, Montclair, CA, 91763 (714)
621-4751
Admin Benjamin F Davis. *Medical Dir/Dir of Nursing* Herman Mirkin MD.
Licensure Skilled Care. *Beds* 140. *Certified* Medicare; Medi-Cal.
Ownership Proprietary.
Staff RNs 5 (ft), 4 (pt); LPNs 9 (ft), 8 (pt); Orderlies 1 (ft), 1 (pt); Nurses aides 52 (ft), 10 (pt); Physical therapists 1 (pt); Reality therapists 1 (pt); Recreational therapists 1 (pt); Occupational therapists 1 (pt); Speech therapists 1 (pt); Activities coordinators 2 (ft); Dietitians 1 (pt); Dentists 1 (pt); Ophthalmologists 1 (pt); Podiatrists 1 (pt).
Facilities Dining room; Physical therapy room; Activities room; Crafts room; Laundry room; Barber/Beauty shop; Library; Coffee room.
Activities Arts and Crafts; Cards; Games; Reading groups; Prayer groups; Movies; Dances/Social or cultural gatherings; Parties.
Description Restorative program provides a therapeutic environment whose objective is to help patients increase their functional level, adjust to their disability, and achieve maximum independence. A full range of services is available for those with physical and neurological disabilities including fractures, amputations, stroke, head injury, and arthritis.

MONTEBELLO

Montebello Convalescent Hospital*
1035 W Beverly Blvd, Montebello, CA, 90640
(213) 724-1315
Admin Mary B Ringen.
Licensure Skilled Care. *Beds* 99. *Certified* Medicare; Medi-Cal.
Ownership Proprietary.

Rio Hondo Convalescent Hospital
273 E Beverly Blvd, Montebello, CA, 90640
(213) 724-5100
Admin Ann S Walshe. *Medical Dir/Dir of Nursing* Dr L Pollock.
Licensure Skilled Care; Intermediate Care. *Beds* 200. *Certified* Medicare; Medi-Cal.
Ownership Proprietary.
Admissions Requirements Minimum age 18; Medical examination; Physician's request.
Staff Physicians 20 (ft); RNs 15 (ft); LPNs 20 (ft); Orderlies 10 (ft); Nurses aides 80 (ft); Physical therapists 1 (ft); Occupational therapists; Speech therapists; Activities coordinators 3 (ft); Dietitians 1 (ft); Dentists; Ophthalmologists; Podiatrists; Audiologists.
Facilities Dining room; Physical therapy room; Activities room; Crafts room; Laundry room; Barber/Beauty shop.
Activities Arts and Crafts; Cards; Games; Reading groups; Prayer groups; Movies; Shopping trips.
Description VA approved.

MONTECITO

Casa Dorinda
300 Hot Springs Rd, Montecito, CA, 93108
(805) 969-8026
Admin William Ducharme. *Medical Dir/Dir of Nursing* Dr Robert Hartzman.
Licensure Skilled Care. *Beds* 47. *Certified* Medicare; Medi-Cal.
Ownership Proprietary.
Admissions Requirements Medical examination.
Staff Physicians 1 (pt); RNs 8 (ft), 3 (pt); LPNs 4 (ft), 1 (pt); Nurses aides 13 (ft); Physical therapists 2 (ft); Occupational therapists 1 (pt); Speech therapists 1 (pt); Activities coordinators 1 (ft), 1 (pt); Dietitians 1 (pt); Dentists 1 (pt); Podiatrists 1 (pt).
Facilities Dining room; Physical therapy room; Activities room; Crafts room; Laundry room; Barber/Beauty shop; Library.
Activities Arts and Crafts; Cards; Games; Reading groups; Prayer groups; Movies; Shopping trips; Dances/Social or cultural gatherings; Picnics; Rides; Barbecues.

MONTEREY

Ave Maria Convalescent Hospital*
1249 Josselyn, Monterey, CA, 93940 (408)
373-1216
Admin M Constance.
Licensure Skilled Care. *Beds* 30.
Certified Medi-Cal.
Ownership Nonprofit.
Affiliation Roman Catholic

Beverly Manor Convalescent Hospital
23795 W R Holman Hwy, Monterey, CA,
93940 (408) 624-1875
Admin Susan E Bazsuly. *Medical Dir/Dir of
Nursing* Donald M Dubrasich MD.
Licensure Skilled Care. *Beds* 99. *Certified* Medicare; Medi-Cal.
Ownership Proprietary.
Admissions Requirements Physician's request.
Facilities Dining room; Physical therapy room;
Activities room; Crafts room; Laundry room;
Barber/Beauty shop; Library.
Activities Arts and Crafts; Cards; Games;
Reading groups; Prayer groups; Movies; Shopping trips; Dances/Social or cultural gatherings.

Driftwood Convalescent Hospital
1575 Skyline Dr, Monterey, CA, 93940 (408)
373-2731
Admin Dorothy Filson.
Licensure Skilled Care. *Beds* 77.
Ownership Proprietary.

Monterey Convalescent Hospital*
735 Pacific St, Monterey, CA, 93940 (408)
373-1323
Admin Charlene Henion.
Licensure Skilled Care. *Beds* 52. *Certified* Medicare; Medi-Cal.
Ownership Proprietary.

Monterey Pines Skilled Nursing Facility
1501 Skyline Dr, Monterey, CA, 93940 (408)
373-3716
Admin Thomas Upton. *Medical Dir/Dir of
Nursing* Nello Torri MD.
Licensure Skilled Care. *Beds* 99. *Certified* Medicare; Medi-Cal.
Ownership Proprietary.
Staff Physicians 1 (pt); RNs 3 (ft); LPNs 6 (ft);
Orderlies 3 (ft); Nurses aides 20 (ft); Physical
therapists 1 (pt); Occupational therapists 1 (pt);
Speech therapists 1 (pt); Activities coordinators
1 (ft); Dietitians 1 (pt); Dentists 1 (pt); Podiatrists 1 (pt).
Facilities Dining room; Physical therapy room;
Activities room.
Activities Arts and Crafts; Cards; Games;
Reading groups; Prayer groups; Movies; Shopping trips; Dances/Social or cultural gatherings.
Description Facility is located high on a
forested hillside overlooking Monterey Bay.
Monterey Pines skilled nursing facility offers
short-term and long-term care with excellent
therapy and activity programs.

MONTEREY PARK

Hillhaven Health Care
610 N Garfield Ave, Monterey Park, CA, 91754
(213) 573-3141
Admin Ferri Fathi. *Medical Dir/Dir of
Nursing* Sander Peck.
Licensure Skilled Care. *Beds* 99. *Certified* Medicare; Medi-Cal.
Ownership Proprietary.
Staff RNs 3 (ft); LPNs 8 (ft); Orderlies 4 (ft);
Nurses aides 42 (ft); Physical therapists 1 (pt);
Reality therapists 1 (pt); Recreational therapists
1 (pt); Occupational therapists 1 (pt); Speech
therapists 1 (pt); Activities coordinators 1 (ft);
Dietitians 1 (pt); Dentists 1 (pt); Ophthalmolo-

gists 1 (pt); Podiatrists 1 (pt); Audiologists 1
(pt).
Facilities Dining room; Physical therapy room;
Activities room; Crafts room; Laundry room;
Barber/Beauty shop.
Activities Arts and Crafts; Cards; Games;
Reading groups; Prayer groups; Movies; Shopping trips; Dances/Social or cultural gatherings.
Description Facility features an extensive
rehabilitation program, a sunny and cheerful
physical plant; and is one-half block away from
an interstate freeway.

Monterey Park Convalescent Hospital*
416 N Garfield Ave, Monterey Park, CA, 91754
(213) 280-0280
Admin Alan John.
Licensure Skilled Care. *Beds* 89. *Certified* Medicare; Medi-Cal.
Ownership Proprietary.

MONTROSE

Montrose Convalescent Hospital
2123 Verdugo Blvd, Montrose, CA, 91020
(213) 249-3925
Admin Marcia S Weldon. *Medical Dir/Dir of
Nursing* Dr Albert Killian.
Licensure Skilled Care. *Beds* 59. *Certified* Medicare; Medi-Cal.
Ownership Proprietary.
Admissions Requirements Medical examination; Physician's request.
Facilities Dining room; Activities room; Crafts
room; Laundry room; Barber/Beauty shop.
Activities Arts and Crafts; Cards; Games;
Reading groups; Prayer groups; Movies; Shopping trips; Dances/Social or cultural gatherings.
Description This small facility, nestled in the
hills above Glendale, provides professional care
and services in a home atmosphere.

Verdugo Valley Convalescent Hospital*
2635 Honolulu Ave, Montrose, CA, 91020
(213) 248-6856
Admin Khatchadurian.
Licensure Skilled Care. *Beds* 138. *Certified* Medicare; Medi-Cal.
Ownership Proprietary.

MORGAN HILL

Eldercare Convalescent Hospital*
16095 Church St, Morgan Hill, CA, 95037
(408) 779-7346
Admin L Armstrong.
Licensure Skilled Care. *Beds* 25. *Certified* Medicare; Medi-Cal.
Ownership Proprietary.

Hillview Convalescent Hospital*
530 W Dunne Ave and Laselva, Morgan Hill,
CA, 95037 (408) 779-3633
Admin James C Ross.
Licensure Skilled Care. *Beds* 52.
Certified Medi-Cal.
Ownership Proprietary.

Pleasant Acres Convalescent Hospital*
17090 Peak Ave, Morgan Hill, CA, 95037 (408)
779-2252

Admin Ralph N Tisdial.
Licensure Skilled Care. *Beds* 29. *Certified* Medicare; Medi-Cal.
Ownership Proprietary.

MORRO BAY

Morro Bay Convalescent Center*
Hwy 1 at S Bay Blvd, Morro Bay, CA, 93442
(805) 772-2237
Admin Pauline I Elders.
Licensure Skilled Care. *Beds* 74. *Certified* Medicare; Medi-Cal.
Ownership Proprietary.

MOUNTAIN VIEW

Grant Cuesta Convalescent Hospital Inc
1949 Grant Rd, Mountain View, CA, 94040
(415) 986-2990
Admin Dorothy Kardashian. *Medical Dir/Dir
of Nursing* Harry Wong MD.
Licensure Skilled Care. *Beds* 99. *Certified* Medicare; Medi-Cal.
Ownership Proprietary.
Staff Physicians 1 (pt); RNs 6 (ft); LPNs 5 (ft);
Orderlies 2 (ft); Nurses aides 34 (ft); Physical
therapists 1 (pt); Reality therapists 1 (pt); Recreational therapists 1 (pt); Occupational therapists
1 (pt); Speech therapists 1 (pt); Activities coordinators 1 (pt); Dietitians 1 (pt); Dentists 1 (pt);
Podiatrists 1 (pt).
Facilities Dining room; Physical therapy room;
Activities room; Crafts room; Laundry room;
Barber/Beauty shop.
Activities Arts and Crafts; Cards; Games;
Reading groups; Movies; Dances/Social or cultural gatherings.
Description Family information series started
in May 1984.

Julia Convalescent Hospital
276 Sierra Vista Ave, Mountain View, CA,
94042 (415) 967-5714
Admin Marjorie Thomas. *Medical Dir/Dir of
Nursing* Dr Steven Tillis.
Licensure Skilled Care. *Beds* 99. *Certified* Medicare; Medi-Cal.
Ownership Proprietary.
Staff Physicians; RNs; LPNs; Orderlies;
Nurses aides; Physical therapists; Reality therapists; Recreational therapists; Occupational
therapists; Speech therapists; Activities coordinators; Dietitians; Dentists; Ophthalmologists;
Podiatrists.
Facilities Dining room; Physical therapy room;
Activities room; Crafts room; Barber/Beauty
shop; TV rooms.
Activities Arts and Crafts; Cards; Games; Prayer groups; Movies; Dances/Social or cultural
gatherings; Adult education classes.
Description Intensive convalescent care center
takes sub-acute type patients (IV, respirator,
TPN, tracheotomy, etc.); medical director in-house 8 hours per week.

Mountain View Convalescent Hospital
2530 Solace Ct, Mountain View, CA, 94040
(408) 961-6161
Admin Elayne Groton. *Medical Dir/Dir of
Nursing* Harry Wong.

Licensure Skilled Care. *Beds* 138. *Certified* Medicare; Medi-Cal.
Ownership Proprietary.
Admissions Requirements Physician's request.
Staff RNs 9 (ft), 4 (pt); LPNs 7 (ft), 6 (pt); Orderlies 7 (ft), 1 (pt); Nurses aides 54 (ft), 10 (pt); Activities coordinators 2 (ft), 1 (pt).
Facilities Dining room; Physical therapy room; Activities room; Crafts room; Laundry room; Barber/Beauty shop; Library.
Activities Arts and Crafts; Cards; Games; Reading groups; Movies; Dances/Social or cultural gatherings.
Description We are located across the street from El Camino Hospital, which enables physicians to visit easily. We offer IV therapy as ordered. Our most outstanding new program is a family adjustment group.

Villa Siena*
1855 Miramonte Ave, Mountain View, CA, 94040 (415) 961-6484
Admin Sr Mary De Crus.
Licensure Intermediate Care. *Beds* 20. *Certified* Medi-Cal.
Ownership Nonprofit.

NAPA

Hy-Lond Convalescent Hospital*
705 Trancas St, Napa, CA, 94558 (707) 255-6060
Admin Robert W Bates.
Licensure Skilled Care. *Beds* 120. *Certified* Medicare; Medi-Cal.
Ownership Proprietary.

Piners Convalescent Hospital Inc*
1800 Pueblo Ave, Napa, CA, 94558 (707) 224-7925
Admin Fern Piner Tinker.
Licensure Skilled Care. *Beds* 49. *Certified* Medi-Cal.
Ownership Proprietary.

Redwood Christian Convalescent Hospital*
2465 Redwood Rd, Napa, CA, 94558 (707) 255-3012
Admin Clement J Doran Jr.
Licensure Skilled Care. *Beds* 59. *Certified* Medicare; Medi-Cal.
Ownership Proprietary.

Roberts Nursing Home*
3415 Browns Valley Rd, Napa, CA, 94558 (707) 224-2580
Admin Edythe Cambra.
Licensure Skilled Care. *Beds* 35. *Certified* Medi-Cal.
Ownership Proprietary.

Silverado Convalescent Hospital*
2300 Brown St, Napa, CA, 94558 (707) 226-1821
Admin Vikki M Forbes.
Licensure Skilled Care. *Beds* 84. *Certified* Medicare; Medi-Cal.
Ownership Proprietary.

NATIONAL CITY

Continana Convalescent Hospital*
220 E 24th St, National City, CA, 92050 (714) 474-6741
Admin Walter N Ross.
Licensure Skilled Care. *Beds* 99. *Certified* Medicare; Medi-Cal.
Ownership Proprietary.

Friendship Homes Inc*
2328 E 6th St, National City, CA, 92050 (714) 474-6611
Admin Charles I Cheneweth.
Licensure Skilled Care; Intermediate Care for Mentally Retarded. *Beds* SNF 27; ICF/MR 59.
Certified Medicare.
Ownership Proprietary.

Friendship Manor Convalescent Center
902 Euclid Ave, National City, CA, 92050 (619) 267-9220
Admin J Edwin Cheneweth. *Medical Dir/Dir of Nursing* C G Maloney MD.
Licensure Skilled Care. *Beds* 104. *Certified* Medicare; Medi-Cal.
Ownership Proprietary.
Admissions Requirements Medical examination; Physician's request.
Staff RNs 7 (ft), 2 (pt); LPNs 5 (ft), 2 (pt); Nurses aides 40 (ft), 7 (pt); Physical therapists 1 (ft); Recreational therapists 1 (ft); Activities coordinators 1 (ft).
Facilities Dining room; Physical therapy room; Activities room; Laundry room; Barber/Beauty shop; Conference room; TV lounge.
Activities Arts and Crafts; Cards; Games; Prayer groups; Movies; Shopping trips; Dances/Social or cultural gatherings; Picnics, Outings.
Description This facility has a patio access in every room. Our physical therapy department is outstanding, and our record for discharging rehabilitated patients is the finest in the area.

Hillcrest Manor Sanitarium
1889 National City Blvd, National City, CA, 92050 (619) 477-1176
Admin Gary R Byrnes. *Medical Dir/Dir of Nursing* M Brent Campbell MD.
Licensure Skilled Care. *Beds* 85. *Certified* Medicare; Medi-Cal.
Ownership Proprietary.
Admissions Requirements Minimum age 35; Medical examination; Physician's request.
Staff RNs 4 (ft), 2 (pt); LPNs 5 (ft); Nurses aides 38 (ft), 2 (pt); Activities coordinators 2 (ft).
Facilities Dining room; Physical therapy room; Activities room; Enclosed patio.
Activities Arts and Crafts; Cards; Games; Reading groups; Prayer groups; Movies; Shopping trips; Dances/Social or cultural gatherings.
Description Hillcrest Manor Sanitarium is primarily for adult long-term mental patients who need a protective environment and are primarily in need of skilled nursing care. Patients with mental diseases are accepted whose mental symptoms have stabilized or abated to the point that they do not constitute a psychiatric problem.

Paradise Valley Manor*
2575 E 8th St, National City, CA, 92050 (714) 474-8301
Admin Parker G Winslow.
Licensure Skilled Care. *Beds* 83. *Certified* Medicare; Medi-Cal.
Ownership Nonprofit.

NEWBURY PARK

Mary Health of Sick Convalescent and Nursing Hospital
2929 Theresa Dr, Newbury Park, CA, 91320 (805) 498-3644
Admin Charles F Comley.
Licensure Skilled Care. *Beds* 61. *Certified* Medicare; Medi-Cal.
Ownership Nonprofit.

Ventura Estates
915 Estates Dr, Newbury Park, CA, 91320 (805) 498-3691
Admin Elwood Sherrard. *Medical Dir/Dir of Nursing* Arthur C Fingerle MD.
Licensure Intermediate Care. *Beds* 18. *Certified* Medi-Cal.
Ownership Nonprofit.
Staff RNs 1 (ft), 3 (pt); LPNs 2 (pt); Nurses aides 1 (ft), 2 (pt); Activities coordinators 1 (ft); Podiatrists 1 (pt).
Affiliation Seventh-Day Adventist
Facilities Dining room; Activities room; Chapel; Crafts room; Laundry room; Barber/Beauty shop; Library.
Activities Arts and Crafts; Games; Reading groups; Prayer groups; Movies; Shopping trips; Exercises.

Ventura Estates Health Manor
915 Estates Dr, Newbury Park, CA, 91320 (805) 498-3691
Admin Elwood Sherrard. *Medical Dir/Dir of Nursing* Arthur C Fingerle MD.
Licensure Skilled Care. *Beds* 48. *Certified* Medicare; Medi-Cal.
Ownership Nonprofit.
Staff RNs 1 (pt); LPNs 2 (ft), 1 (pt); Nurses aides 19 (ft), 5 (pt); Physical therapists 1 (pt); Activities coordinators 1 (ft); Podiatrists 1 (pt).
Affiliation Seventh-Day Adventist
Facilities Dining room; Activities room; Chapel; Crafts room; Laundry room; Barber/Beauty shop; Library.
Activities Arts and Crafts; Games; Reading groups; Prayer groups; Movies; Shopping trips; Exercises; Individual activities.

NEWHALL

Newhall Nursing Home*
23801 San Fernando Rd, Newhall, CA, 91321 (805) 259-3660
Admin Mike Konrad.
Licensure Skilled Care. *Beds* 99. *Certified* Medicare; Medi-Cal.
Ownership Proprietary.

NEWMAN

San Luis Convalescent Hospital
709 N St, Newman, CA, 95360 (209) 862-2862
Admin Avenal Miller. *Medical Dir/Dir of Nursing* Dr La Torre.
Licensure Skilled Care. *Beds* 71. *Certified* Medicare; Medi-Cal.
Ownership Proprietary.
Staff Nurses aides 19 (ft).
Facilities Dining room; Activities room; Laundry room; Barber/Beauty shop.
Activities Arts and Crafts; Cards; Games; Reading groups; Prayer groups; Movies.

NEWPORT BEACH

Flagship Convalescent Center*
466 Flagship Rd, Newport Beach, CA, 92663 (714) 642-8044
Admin Allen J June.
Licensure Skilled Care. *Beds* 99. *Certified* Medicare; Medi-Cal.
Ownership Proprietary.

Newport Convalescent Center*
1555 Superior Ave, Newport Beach, CA, 92660 (714) 646-7764
Admin Ruthe Hamilton.
Licensure Skilled Care. *Beds* 74. *Certified* Medicare; Medi-Cal.
Ownership Proprietary.

Park Superior Healthcare*
1445 Superior Ave, Newport Beach, CA, 92660 (714) 642-2410
Admin Alice Riddell.
Licensure Skilled Care. *Beds* 96. *Certified* Medicare; Medi-Cal.
Ownership Proprietary.

NORTH HOLLYWOOD

All Saints Convalescent Center*
11810 Saticoy St, North Hollywood, CA, 91605 (213) 982-4600
Admin Hale J Scott.
Licensure Skilled Care. *Beds* 128. *Certified* Medicare.
Ownership Proprietary.

Chandler Convalescent Hospital Inc
12140 Chandler Blvd, North Hollywood, CA, 91607 (213) 985-1814
Admin Arthur E Goldfarb. *Medical Dir/Dir of Nursing* Dr Sandor Zuckerman.
Licensure Skilled Care. *Beds* 201. *Certified* Medicare; Medi-Cal.
Ownership Proprietary.
Staff RNs 4 (ft); LPNs 12 (ft); Nurses aides 48 (ft); Physical therapists 2 (pt); Recreational therapists 2 (pt); Occupational therapists 1 (pt); Speech therapists 1 (pt); Activities coordinators 1 (pt); Dietitians 1 (ft), 1 (pt); Dentists 1 (pt); Ophthalmologists 1 (pt); Podiatrists 2 (pt); Audiologists 1 (pt).
Facilities Dining room; Activities room; Crafts room; Laundry room; Barber/Beauty shop.
Activities Arts and Crafts; Cards; Games; Movies.
Description Facility is clean, large, friendly,

odorless, centrally located in North Hollywood featuring excellent care and dedication to patients.

Golden State Colonial Convalescent Hospital Inc*
10830 Oxnard St, North Hollywood, CA, 91606 (213) 877-0917
Admin Betty Zimmer.
Licensure Skilled Care. *Beds* 49. *Certified* Medicare.
Ownership Proprietary.

Laurelwood Convalescent Center*
13000 Victory Blvd, North Hollywood, CA, 91606 (213) 985-5990
Admin Lynn Lewarton.
Licensure Skilled Care. *Beds* 99. *Certified* Medicare; Medi-Cal.
Ownership Proprietary.

North Hollywood Extended Care
6120 Vineland, North Hollywood, CA, 91606 (213) 763-6275
Admin Deborah Collins.
Licensure Skilled Care. *Beds* 72. *Certified* Medicare; Medi-Cal.
Ownership Proprietary.
Admissions Requirements Physician's request.
Staff RNs 1 (ft), 1 (pt); LPNs 6 (ft); Nurses aides 25 (ft); Physical therapists 1 (ft); Reality therapists 1 (ft); Recreational therapists 1 (ft); Speech therapists 1 (pt); Activities coordinators 1 (ft); Dietitians 1 (pt); Dentists 1 (pt); Ophthalmologists 1 (pt); Podiatrists 1 (pt); Audiologists 1 (pt).
Facilities Dining room; Physical therapy room; Activities room; Laundry room; Barber/Beauty shop.
Activities Arts and Crafts; Games; Reading groups; Prayer groups; Shopping trips.
Description North Hollywood Extended Care is warm, bright, and cheerful facility that offers a pleasing, comfortable environment for all residents. All departments in the facility work toward the best care possible to enhance the patients quality of life.

Riverside Convalescent Hospital
12750 Riverside Dr, North Hollywood, CA, 91607 (213) 766-6105
Admin Deline Davis.
Licensure Skilled Care. *Beds* 108. *Certified* Medicare; Medi-Cal.
Ownership Proprietary.
Admissions Requirements Minimum age 50; Medical examination; Physician's request.
Staff RNs; LPNs; Orderlies; Nurses aides; Physical therapists; Reality therapists; Recreational therapists; Occupational therapists; Speech therapists; Activities coordinators; Dietitians; Dentists; Ophthalmologists; Podiatrists; Audiologists.
Facilities Dining room; Physical therapy room; Activities room; Crafts room; Laundry room; Barber/Beauty shop.
Activities Arts and Crafts; Cards; Games; Reading groups; Prayer groups; Movies; Shopping trips; Dances/Social or cultural gatherings.
Description Resident and family candlelight dinners are held monthly and hosted by the resident council.

Saint Elizabeth Toluca Convalescent Hospital*
10425 Magnolia Blvd, North Hollywood, CA, 91601 (213) 984-2918
Admin Robert T Moore.
Licensure Skilled Care. *Beds* 52. *Certified* Medicare; Medi-Cal.
Ownership Nonprofit.

Valley Palms Convalescent Hospital*
13400 Sherman Way, North Hollywood, CA, 91605 (213) 983-0103
Admin Arthur E Goldfarb.
Licensure Skilled Care. *Beds* 99. *Certified* Medicare; Medi-Cal.
Ownership Proprietary.

NORWALK

Bird Haven Christian Convalescent Hospital*
12350 Rosecrans, Norwalk, CA, 90650 (213) 921-6624
Admin Andrea Fostvedt.
Licensure Skilled Care. *Beds* 59. *Certified* Medicare; Medi-Cal.
Ownership Proprietary.

Glen Terrace Convalescent Center*
11510 Imperial Hwy, Norwalk, CA, 90650 (213) 868-6791
Admin Donnell Piraro.
Licensure Skilled Care. *Beds* 99. *Certified* Medicare; Medi-Cal.
Ownership Proprietary.

Intercommunity Convalescent Hospital*
12627 Studebaker Rd, Norwalk, CA, 90650 (213) 868-4767
Admin Michael Spence.
Licensure Skilled Care. *Beds* 86. *Certified* Medicare; Medi-Cal.
Ownership Proprietary.

Rancho Los Padres Convalescent Hospital
10625 Leffingwell Rd, Norwalk, CA, 90650 (213) 864-2541
Admin Sandra Puskarich. *Medical Dir/Dir of Nursing* Clarence Spense.
Licensure Skilled Care. *Beds* 99. *Certified* Medicare; Medi-Cal.
Ownership Proprietary.
Facilities Dining room; Activities room; Crafts room; Laundry room; Barber/Beauty shop.
Activities Arts and Crafts; Cards; Games; Reading groups; Prayer groups; Movies; Shopping trips; Dances/Social or cultural gatherings.

Southland Geriatric Center
11701 Studebaker Rd, Norwalk, CA, 90650 (213) 868-9761
Admin Gilbert C Moore. *Medical Dir/Dir of Nursing* James H Holman MD.
Licensure Skilled Care; Intermediate Care.
Beds SNF 80; ICF 40. *Certified* Medicare; Medi-Cal.
Ownership Nonprofit.
Admissions Requirements Minimum age 55.
Staff RNs 3 (ft), 5 (pt); LPNs 8 (ft), 6 (pt); Orderlies 4 (ft); Nurses aides 49 (ft), 14 (pt); Physical therapists 1 (pt); Occupational therapists 1 (pt); Speech therapists 2 (pt); Activities coordinators 1 (ft), 2 (pt); Dietitians 1 (pt); Dentists 1 (pt); Ophthalmologists 1 (pt); Podia-

trists 1 (pt).
Affiliation Lutheran
Facilities Dining room; Physical therapy room; Activities room; Chapel; Crafts room; Laundry room; Barber/Beauty shop; Library.
Activities Arts and Crafts; Cards; Games; Reading groups; Prayer groups; Movies; Shopping trips; Dances/Social or cultural gatherings.
Description Southland specializes in geriatric care and rehabilitation.

Villa Elena Convalescent Hospital*
13226 Studebaker, Norwalk, CA, 90650 (213) 868-0591
Admin Alice Griswold.
Licensure Skilled Care. *Beds* 98. *Certified* Medicare; Medi-Cal.
Ownership Proprietary.

NOVATO

Canyon Manor
655 Canyon Rd, Novato, CA, 94947 (415) 892-1628
Admin Richard Evatz. *Medical Dir/Dir of Nursing* Jeffrey Berlant MD.
Licensure Skilled Care. *Beds* 89. *Certified* Medicare; Medi-Cal.
Ownership Proprietary.
Admissions Requirements Minimum age 18.
Facilities Dining room; Activities room; Crafts room; Library.
Activities Arts and Crafts; Cards; Games; Reading groups; Shopping trips; Dances/Social or cultural gatherings.
Description A residential treatment center for the adult mentally ill.

Hill Road Convalescent Hospital*
1565 Hill Rd, Novato, CA, 94947 (415) 897-6161
Admin Carolyn Hankinson.
Licensure Skilled Care. *Beds* 187. *Certified* Medicare; Medi-Cal.
Ownership Proprietary.

OAKDALE

Oakdale Convalescent Hospital*
275 S Oak St, Oakdale, CA, 95361 (209) 847-0367
Admin Buren Boone.
Licensure Skilled Care. *Beds* 78. *Certified* Medicare; Medi-Cal.
Ownership Proprietary.

OAKHURST

Sierra Meadows Convalescent Hospital
40131 Hwy 49, Oakhurst, CA, 93644 (209) 683-2992
Admin Darlene Hayes. *Medical Dir/Dir of Nursing* C Mitchell MD.
Licensure Skilled Care. *Beds* 59. *Certified* Medicare; Medi-Cal.
Ownership Nonprofit.
Admissions Requirements Physician's request.
Staff RNs 1 (ft), 4 (pt); LPNs 2 (ft), 5 (pt); Orderlies 1 (ft); Nurses aides 12 (ft), 16 (pt); Speech therapists 1 (pt); Activities coordinators

1 (ft).
Facilities Dining room; Laundry room; Barber/Beauty shop; Library; Adjacent emergicenter, lab and x-ray.
Activities Arts and Crafts; Cards; Games; Reading groups; Prayer groups; Movies; Shopping trips; Dances/Social or cultural gatherings.
Description Facility serves 25-30 meals a day to meals-on-wheels program; has geriatric nurse practitioner; rural mountain setting in a small community.

OAKLAND

Alpha Convalescent Hospital
3550 Foothill Blvd, Oakland, CA, 94601 (415) 534-5026
Admin Clarence Schlenker. *Medical Dir/Dir of Nursing* Dr Karl Konstantin.
Licensure Skilled Care. *Beds* 30. *Certified* Medicare; Medi-Cal.
Ownership Proprietary.
Admissions Requirements Minimum age 45; Medical examination; Physician's request.
Staff Physicians 4 (pt); RNs 1 (ft), 1 (pt); LPNs 2 (ft), 2 (pt); Orderlies 1 (ft); Nurses aides 10 (ft); Recreational therapists 1 (pt); Activities coordinators 1 (pt); Dietitians 1 (pt); Dentists 1 (pt); Ophthalmologists 1 (pt); Podiatrists 1 (pt).
Facilities Dining room; Activities room; Laundry room.
Activities Arts and Crafts; Cards; Games; Reading groups; Prayer groups; Movies; Shopping trips.

Altenheim Inc
1720 MacArthur Blvd, Oakland, CA, 94602 (415) 530-4013
Admin Helen P Cathey. *Medical Dir/Dir of Nursing* Jean Sharp MD.
Licensure Skilled Care. *Beds* 16.
Certified Medi-Cal.
Ownership Nonprofit.
Admissions Requirements Minimum age 60; Medical examination; Physician's request.
Staff Physicians 1 (pt); RNs 1 (ft), 2 (pt); LPNs 2 (ft), 1 (pt); Orderlies 1 (ft); Nurses aides 7 (ft), 3 (pt); Activities coordinators 1 (ft); Dietitians 1 (pt).
Affiliation Altenheim Society
Facilities Dining room; Activities room; Laundry room; Barber/Beauty shop; Library.
Activities Arts and Crafts; Games; Reading groups; Prayer groups; Movies; Shopping trips.
Description Facility has a full-time gerontologist on staff who provides individual counseling, group counseling, and continuing education classes. She also runs a reminiscence class for patients.

Beulah Home Inc*
4690 Tompkins Ave, Oakland, CA, 94619 (415) 531-4830
Admin James P Roth.
Licensure Skilled Care. *Beds* 17.
Certified Medi-Cal.
Ownership Nonprofit.

Clinton Village Convalescent Hospital
1833 10th Ave, Oakland, CA, 94606 (415) 536-6512
Admin Tom C Duarte. *Medical Dir/Dir of*

Nursing John Chokatos MD.
Licensure Skilled Care. *Beds* 99. *Certified* Medicare; Medi-Cal.
Ownership Proprietary.
Admissions Requirements Minimum age 65; Medical examination; Physician's request.
Facilities Dining room; Physical therapy room; Activities room; Chapel; Crafts room; Laundry room; Barber/Beauty shop; Library.
Activities Arts and Crafts; Cards; Games; Reading groups; Prayer groups; Movies; Shopping trips; Dances/Social or cultural gatherings; Social work.
Description This facility is unique in that we provide the optimum in social work services due to our social worker administrative staff including the owner.

Coberly Green Intermediate Care Facility
2420 Fruitvale Ave, Oakland, CA, 94601 (415) 532-5090
Admin Jeannie Griffin. *Medical Dir/Dir of Nursing* W H Arthur.
Licensure Intermediate Care. *Beds* 21. *Certified* Medi-Cal.
Ownership Proprietary.
Staff RNs 1 (ft); LPNs 1 (pt); Nurses aides 3 (ft); Activities coordinators 1 (pt).
Facilities Dining room; Activities room; Crafts room; Laundry room.
Activities Arts and Crafts; Cards; Games; Reading groups; Prayer groups; Movies; Shopping trips; Dances/Social or cultural gatherings.

Dowling Convalescent Hospital*
451 28th St, Oakland, CA, 94609 (415) 893-4066
Admin Ponselle R Lane.
Licensure Skilled Care. *Beds* 30.
Certified Medi-Cal.
Ownership Proprietary.

Garfield Nursing Home Inc
1441 28th Ave, Oakland, CA, 94601 (415) 536-8111
Admin Jeffrey P Lambkin. *Medical Dir/Dir of Nursing* Martin Held MD.
Licensure Skilled Care. *Beds* 96.
Certified Medi-Cal.
Ownership Proprietary.
Admissions Requirements Minimum age 57.
Staff RNs 7 (ft), 1 (pt); LPNs 13 (ft); Nurses aides 33 (ft), 16 (pt); Recreational therapists 3 (ft); Occupational therapists 1 (ft); Activities coordinators 2 (ft), 4 (pt).
Facilities Dining room; Physical therapy room; Activities room; Crafts room; Laundry room; Barber/Beauty shop.
Activities Arts and Crafts; Cards; Games; Reading groups; Prayer groups; Movies; Shopping trips; Dances/Social or cultural gatherings.
Description Founded in 1980, the Garfield Geropsychiatric Hospital provides diagnosis, evaluation, and treatment for severely impaired elderly patients. Upon admission to the facility, each patient is assigned to a treatment team that consists of a psychiatrist, a registered nurse, a primary therapist, an internist, a rehabilitation specialist, and a dietician. Treatment programs, which are tailored to the individual patient's needs, could combine behavior therapy, psychotherapy, group activities, and medication therapy. Throughout treatment,

staff emphasize rehabilitation and work to reestablish the patient's links to the community through family, friends, and community groups.

High Street Convalescent Hospital
3145 High St, Oakland, CA, 94619 (415) 533-9970
Admin Joe Vance. *Medical Dir/Dir of Nursing* Dr Richmond.
Licensure Skilled Care. *Beds* 44. *Certified* Medicare; Medi-Cal.
Ownership Proprietary.
Admissions Requirements Medical examination; Physician's request.
Staff RNs 2 (ft), 4 (pt); LPNs 2 (ft), 6 (pt); Nurses aides 15 (ft), 11 (pt); Physical therapists 1 (pt); Occupational therapists 1 (pt); Speech therapists 1 (pt); Activities coordinators 1 (ft); Dentists 1 (pt); Podiatrists 1 (pt).
Facilities Dining room; Activities room; Barber/Beauty shop.
Activities Arts and Crafts; Cards; Games; Reading groups; Prayer groups; Movies; Shopping trips; Dances/Social or cultural gatherings; Animals visits.

Highview Convalescent Hospital
1301 E 31st St, Oakland, CA, 94602 (415) 534-2295
Admin Marguerite O Balaz. *Medical Dir/Dir of Nursing* Felix Bongiorno.
Licensure Skilled Care. *Beds* 81. *Certified* Medicare; Medi-Cal.
Ownership Proprietary.
Admissions Requirements Minimum age 55; Medical examination; Physician's request.
Staff RNs 1 (ft), 3 (pt); LPNs 6 (ft), 3 (pt); Nurses aides 21 (ft), 6 (pt); Physical therapists 1 (ft); Recreational therapists 1 (ft); Occupational therapists 1 (ft); Speech therapists 1 (pt); Activities coordinators 1 (pt); Dietitians 1 (ft), 1 (pt); Dentists 1 (pt); Ophthalmologists 1 (pt); Podiatrists 1 (pt).
Facilities Dining room; Activities room; Crafts room; Laundry room; Barber/Beauty shop.
Activities Arts and Crafts; Cards; Games; Reading groups; Prayer groups; Movies; Dances/Social or cultural gatherings.
Description For all holidays and during the spring and summer months, dinner parties are given on the patio for patients, families, and friends.

Hillhaven Convalescent Hospital*
3030 Webster St, Oakland, CA, 94609 (415) 451-3856
Admin Margaret M Boyd.
Licensure Skilled Care. *Beds* 98. *Certified* Medicare; Medi-Cal.
Ownership Proprietary.

Home for Jewish Parents
2780 26th Ave, Oakland, CA, 94601 (415) 536-4604
Admin Ben Laub. *Medical Dir/Dir of Nursing* Dr P Loeb.
Licensure Skilled Care. *Beds* 57. *Certified* Medicare; Medi-Cal.
Ownership Nonprofit.
Staff RNs 6 (ft); LPNs 6 (ft); Orderlies 1 (ft); Nurses aides 24 (ft); Physical therapists 3 (pt); Reality therapists 1 (pt); Occupational thera-

pists 1 (pt); Speech therapists 1 (pt); Activities coordinators 1 (ft); Dietitians 1 (ft); Dentists 1 (pt); Ophthalmologists 1 (pt); Podiatrists 1 (pt).
Affiliation Jewish
Facilities Dining room; Physical therapy room; Activities room; Chapel; Crafts room; Laundry room; Barber/Beauty shop; Library.
Activities Arts and Crafts; Cards; Games; Reading groups; Prayer groups; Movies; Shopping trips; Dances/Social or cultural gatherings.

Horizon Convalescent Hospital*
475 29th St, Oakland, CA, 94609 (415) 832-3222
Admin Robert D Sands.
Licensure Skilled Care. *Beds* 137. *Certified* Medicare; Medi-Cal.
Ownership Proprietary.

Lake Park Retirement Residence
1850 Alice St, Oakland, CA, 94612 (415) 835 5511
Admin James P Hempler.
Licensure Skilled Care. *Beds* 26. *Certified* Medicare.
Ownership Nonprofit.
Admissions Requirements Minimum age 65; Medical examination.
Affiliation Methodist
Facilities Dining room; Physical therapy room; Activities room; Chapel; Crafts room; Laundry room; Barber/Beauty shop; Library.
Activities Arts and Crafts; Cards; Games; Reading groups; Prayer groups; Movies; Shopping trips; Dances/Social or cultural gatherings.

Lakeshore Convalescent Hospital
1901 3rd Ave, Oakland, CA, 94606 (415) 834-9880
Admin R E Haworth. *Medical Dir/Dir of Nursing* Robert Tufft MD.
Licensure Skilled Care. *Beds* 38. *Certified* Medicare; Medi-Cal.
Ownership Proprietary.
Admissions Requirements Medical examination.
Staff RNs 1 (ft), 1 (pt); LPNs 4 (ft); Orderlies 1 (ft); Nurses aides 10 (ft), 3 (pt); Physical therapists 1 (pt); Recreational therapists 1 (ft); Activities coordinators 1 (ft); Dietitians 3 (ft), 1 (pt).
Facilities Dining room; Physical therapy room; Activities room; Chapel; Crafts room; Laundry room.
Activities Arts and Crafts; Cards; Games; Reading groups; Prayer groups; Movies; Shopping trips; Dances/Social or cultural gatherings.
Description Facility offers physical therapy daily on physicians orders. Facility is close to shopping and restaurants and is located 2 blocks from Lake Merritt.

MacArthur Convalescent Hospital*
309 MacArthur Blvd, Oakland, CA, 94610 (415) 836-3777
Admin Richard Traylor.
Licensure Skilled Care. *Beds* 53. *Certified* Medicare; Medi-Cal.
Ownership Proprietary.

McClure Convalescent Hospital
2910 McClure St, Oakland, CA, 94609 (415) 836-3677

Admin Daniel W Alger. *Medical Dir/Dir of Nursing* Dr F Bongiorno.
Licensure Skilled Care. *Beds* 59. *Certified* Medicare; Medi-Cal.
Ownership Proprietary.
Staff RNs 1 (ft), 3 (pt); LPNs 5 (ft), 4 (pt); Nurses aides 17 (ft), 10 (pt); Physical therapists 1 (pt); Recreational therapists 1 (pt); Occupational therapists 1 (pt); Speech therapists 1 (pt); Activities coordinators 1 (pt); Dietitians 1 (pt); Dentists 1 (pt); Podiatrists 1 (pt).
Facilities Dining room; Activities room; Chapel; Crafts room; Laundry room; Barber/Beauty shop.
Activities Arts and Crafts; Cards; Games; Movies; Shopping trips; Dances/Social or cultural gatherings; Monthly outings.
Description Facility has an aggressive rehabilitation program enabling a large number of patients to be discharged home or to a lower level of care after a short stay.

Midtown Convalescent Hospital*
3020 E 15th St, Oakland, CA, 94601 (415) 261-5613
Admin Helen D Anderson.
Licensure Skilled Care. *Beds* 140. *Certified* Medicare; Medi-Cal.
Ownership Proprietary.

Oak Manor Convalescent Center*
3121 Fruitvale Ave, Oakland, CA, 94602 (415) 534-5169
Admin Kathleen A Roth.
Licensure Skilled Care. *Beds* 122. *Certified* Medicare; Medi-Cal.
Ownership Proprietary.

Oak Tree Convalescent Hospital*
2777 Foothill Blvd, Oakland, CA, 94601 (415) 261-3172
Admin Bernadine Walker.
Licensure Skilled Care. *Beds* 49. *Certified* Medicare; Medi-Cal.
Ownership Proprietary.

Oakridge Convalescent Hospital*
2919 Fruitvale Ave, Oakland, CA, 94602 (415) 261-8564
Admin Carole Tomey.
Licensure Skilled Care. *Beds* 99. *Certified* Medicare; Medi-Cal.
Ownership Proprietary.

Pacific Care Convalescent Hospital*
3025 High St, Oakland, CA, 94619 (415) 261-5200
Admin Frankie Ingram.
Licensure Skilled Care. *Beds* 99. *Certified* Medicare; Medi-Cal.
Ownership Proprietary.

Park Merritt Intermediate Care
525 E 18th St, Oakland, CA, 94606 (415) 834-8491
Admin Helen L Arbogast.
Licensure Intermediate Care. *Beds* 24. *Certified* Medi-Cal.
Ownership Proprietary.
Facilities Dining room; Activities room; Laundry room.
Activities Arts and Crafts; Cards; Games; Reading groups; Prayer groups; Movies; Shop-

ping trips; Dances/Social or cultural gatherings.
Description Facility is located 5 blocks from
Lake Merritt. Small, family-owned intermediate care facility providing personal attention,
excellent food, and a friendly atmosphere.

Piedmont Gardens Health Facility
110 41st St, Oakland, CA, 94611 (415)
654-7172
Admin Linda L Garland. *Medical Dir/Dir of
Nursing* Dr William Weeder.
Licensure Skilled Care; Intermediate Care.
Beds SNF 47; ICF 47. *Certified* Medicare;
Medi-Cal.
Ownership Nonprofit.
Admissions Requirements Medical examina-
tion; Physician's request.
Staff RNs 3 (ft), 7 (pt); LPNs 6 (ft), 4 (pt);
Nurses aides 21 (ft), 7 (pt); Physical therapists 1
(pt); Activities coordinators 1 (ft); Dietitians 1
(pt).
Affiliation Baptist
Facilities Dining room; Physical therapy room;
Activities room; Chapel; Crafts room; Laundry
room; Barber/Beauty shop; Library.
Activities Arts and Crafts; Games; Prayer
groups; Movies; Shopping trips; Dances/Social
or cultural gatherings.

Salem Lutheran Home Skilled Nursing Facility
3003 Fruitvale Ave, Oakland, CA, 94602 (415)
534-3219
Admin Paul Basting. *Medical Dir/Dir of
Nursing* Robert W Tufft MD.
Licensure Skilled Care. *Beds* 35. *Cer-
tified* Medicare; Medi-Cal.
Ownership Nonprofit.
Admissions Requirements Minimum age 62;
Medical examination; Physician's request.
Staff RNs 5 (pt); LPNs 3 (pt); Nurses aides 15
(pt); Activities coordinators 1 (ft); Dietitians 1
(ft).
Affiliation Lutheran
Facilities Dining room; Activities room; Laun-
dry room; Barber/Beauty shop.
Activities Cards; Games; Prayer groups;
Movies; Shopping trips; Dances/Social or cul-
tural gatherings.
Description We at Salem Lutheran Nursing
Unit take pride in having a family night every
3 months. Family members, residents, and staff
meet in the evening to enjoy dinner or light
repast, musical program, and/or a speaker.

Terrace Convalescent Hospital*
1935 Seminary Ave, Oakland, CA, 94621 (415)
635-6858
Admin William Nicholson Jr.
Licensure Skilled Care. *Beds* 99.
Ownership Proprietary.

**Wayne Rounseville Memorial Convalescent
Hospital**
210 40th Street Way, Oakland, CA, 94611 (415)
658-2041
Admin J Ralph Holder. *Medical Dir/Dir of
Nursing* Thomas Richmond MD.
Licensure Skilled Care. *Beds* 70. *Cer-
tified* Medicare; Medi-Cal.
Ownership Proprietary.
Staff RNs 6 (ft); LPNs 10 (ft); Nurses aides 32
(ft); Physical therapists 1 (pt); Reality therapists
1 (pt); Recreational therapists 1 (pt); Occupa-

tional therapists 1 (pt); Speech therapists 1 (pt);
Activities coordinators 1 (ft), 1 (pt); Dietitians
1 (pt).
Facilities Dining room; Physical therapy room;
Activities room; Crafts room; Laundry room;
Barber/Beauty shop; Library.
Activities Arts and Crafts; Cards; Games;
Reading groups; Prayer groups; Movies; Shop-
ping trips; Dances/Social or cultural gatherings.
Description Facility features a family meeting
night each month along with patient-relative
council.

Willow Tree Convalescent Hospital Ltd
2124 57th Ave, Oakland, CA, 94621 (415)
261-2628
Admin Luealisyrine Cannon. *Medical Dir/Dir
of Nursing* Dr Karl Konstantin.
Licensure Skilled Care. *Beds* 82. *Certified* Medicare; Medi-Cal.
Ownership Proprietary.
Staff Physicians 7 (ft); RNs 1 (ft), 3 (pt); LPNs
7 (ft); Orderlies 3 (ft); Nurses aides 20 (ft);
Physical therapists 1 (ft); Reality therapists 1
(ft); Occupational therapists 1 (pt); Speech therapists 1 (pt); Activities coordinators 1 (ft); Dietitians 1 (pt); Dentists 1 (pt); Ophthalmologists 1
(pt); Podiatrists 1 (pt).
Facilities Dining room; Physical therapy room;
Activities room; Crafts room; Laundry room;
Barber/Beauty shop; Library.
Activities Arts and Crafts; Cards; Games;
Reading groups; Prayer groups; Dances/Social
or cultural gatherings; Project Outreach.

OCEANSIDE

Tri-City Convalescent Center
3232 Thunder Dr, Oceanside, CA, 92054 (714)
433-1544
Admin Jan B Noonan. *Medical Dir/Dir of
Nursing* Dr Harry Brookler.
Licensure Skilled Care. *Beds* 93. *Cer-
tified* Medicare; Medi-Cal.
Ownership Proprietary.
Staff RNs 6 (ft), 4 (pt); LPNs 3 (ft), 5 (pt);
Orderlies 1 (ft); Nurses aides 48 (ft), 16 (pt);
Physical therapists 1 (ft); Occupational thera-
pists 1 (ft); Speech therapists 1 (pt); Activities
coordinators 1 (ft).
Facilities Dining room; Physical therapy room;
Activities room; Laundry room; Barber/Beauty
shop.
Activities Arts and Crafts; Cards; Games;
Reading groups; Prayer groups; Movies; Shop-
ping trips; Dances/Social or cultural gatherings.

OJAI

Acacias NRTA and AARP Nursing Home
601 N Montgomery Ave, Ojai, CA, 93023 (805)
646-8124
Admin Dolores Diehl. *Medical Dir/Dir of
Nursing* Dr King.
Licensure Skilled Care. *Beds* 50. *Cer-
tified* Medicare; Medi-Cal.
Ownership Nonprofit.
Admissions Requirements Minimum age 62.
Facilities Dining room; Activities room; Laun-
dry room; Barber/Beauty shop; Library.

Activities Arts and Crafts; Games; Reading
groups; Prayer groups; Movies; Shopping trips;
Dances/Social or cultural gatherings.

**Ojai Valley Community Hospital—Skilled
Nursing Department**
1306 Maricopa Hwy, Ojai, CA, 93023 (805)
646-5586
Admin Larry Meyer. *Medical Dir/Dir of
Nursing* Fred Fauvre MD.
Licensure Skilled Care. *Beds* 67. *Cer-
tified* Medicare; Medi-Cal.
Ownership Proprietary.
Admissions Requirements Medical examina-
tion; Physician's request.
Facilities Dining room; Activities room;
Laundry room; Barber/Beauty shop.
Activities Arts and Crafts; Cards; Games;
Reading groups; Prayer groups; Movies; Shop-
ping trips; Dances/Social or cultural gatherings.

Saint Josephs Convalescent Hospital
2464 E Ojai Ave, PO Box 760, Ojai, CA, 93023
(805) 646-1466
Admin Brother Scully. *Medical Dir/Dir of
Nursing* Dr J Rupp.
Licensure Skilled Care. *Beds* 28. *Cer-
tified* Medicare; Medi-Cal.
Ownership Nonprofit.
Admissions Requirements Minimum age 16;
Medical examination; Physician's request.
Staff Physicians 17 (pt); RNs 2 (ft), 4 (pt);
LPNs 7 (pt); Nurses aides 7 (ft), 13 (pt);
Physical therapists 1 (pt); Occupational thera-
pists 1 (pt); Speech therapists 1 (pt); Activities
coordinators 1 (ft); Dietitians 1 (pt); Dentists 1
(pt); Ophthalmologists 1 (pt); Podiatrists 2 (pt);
Audiologists 1 (pt).
Affiliation Roman Catholic
Facilities Dining room; Physical therapy room;
Activities room; Chapel; Crafts room; Barber-
/Beauty shop; Library.
Activities Arts and Crafts; Cards; Games;
Reading groups; Prayer groups; Movies; Dan-
ces/Social or cultural gatherings.

ONTARIO

Bella Vista Convalescent Hospital Inc
933 E Deodar St, Ontario, CA, 91764 (714)
985-2731
Admin Elizabeth McClure. *Medical Dir/Dir of
Nursing* R L McBurney MD.
Licensure Skilled Care. *Beds* 59. *Cer-
tified* Medicare; Medi-Cal.
Ownership Proprietary.
Admissions Requirements Minimum age 21;
Medical examination; Physician's request.
Staff RNs 1 (ft), 1 (pt); LPNs 4 (ft), 3 (pt);
Orderlies 1 (ft); Nurses aides 19 (ft), 6 (pt);
Activities coordinators 1 (ft).
Facilities Dining room; Activities room; Crafts
room; Laundry room; Barber/Beauty shop;
Library.
Activities Arts and Crafts; Cards; Games;
Reading groups; Prayer groups; Movies; Shop-
ping trips.

Home of Angels
540 W Maple St, Ontario, CA, 91761 (714)
986-5668
Admin Mavis Moretta. *Medical Dir/Dir of

Nursing H Daniel Baernstein MD.
Licensure Skilled Care. *Beds* 59.
Certified Medi-Cal.
Ownership Proprietary.
Admissions Requirements Medical examination.
Staff Physicians 2 (ft); RNs 2 (ft); Nurses aides 16 (ft), 4 (pt); Physical therapists 1 (pt); Occupational therapists 1 (pt); Activities coordinators 1 (ft), 1 (pt); Dietitians 1 (pt); Dentists 1 (pt).
Activities Arts and Crafts; Movies.
Description Home of Angels takes care of critical and terminally ill babies and small children. They are housed in brightly painted and decorated wards with a certified nursing assistant present on all 3 shifts. Lincoln School for the Developmentally Disabled is available and transport is by school bus (wheelchair). Activities are limited because of age and physical condition of the children; physical therapy is conducted daily.

Inland Christian Home Inc
1950 S Mountain Ave, Ontario, CA, 91761 (714) 983-0084
Admin Peter Edwin Hoekstra. *Medical Dir/Dir of Nursing* Dr Ron Davis.
Licensure Skilled Care. *Beds* 29. *Certified* Medicare; Medi-Cal.
Ownership Nonprofit.
Admissions Requirements Medical examination; Physician's request.
Staff RNs 1 (ft), 5 (pt); LPNs 3 (ft), 5 (pt); Nurses aides 8 (ft); Activities coordinators 1 (ft); Dietitians 1 (ft); Podiatrists 1 (pt).
Affiliation Christian Reformed
Facilities Dining room; Physical therapy room; Activities room; Crafts room; Laundry room; Barber/Beauty shop; Library; Recreational hall.
Activities Arts and Crafts; Cards; Games; Reading groups; Prayer groups; Movies; Shopping trips; Dances/Social or cultural gatherings; Bus trips.

Ontario Nursing Home Inc
1661 S Euclid Ave, Ontario, CA, 91761 (714) 984-6713
Admin Elizabeth McClure. *Medical Dir/Dir of Nursing* Dr R L McBurney.
Licensure Skilled Care. *Beds* 59. *Certified* Medicare; Medi-Cal.
Ownership Proprietary.
Admissions Requirements Minimum age 18; Medical examination; Physician's request.
Facilities Dining room; Physical therapy room; Activities room; Crafts room; Laundry room; Barber/Beauty shop; Library; Patio.
Activities Arts and Crafts; Cards; Games; Reading groups; Prayer groups; Movies; Shopping trips; Dances/Social or cultural gatherings.
Description Facility cannot take patients who wander. Superb activity program includes evening and weekend programs. Restorative nursing assistant on hand 7 days a week.

Plott Nursing Home
800 E 5th St, Ontario, CA, 91764 (714) 984-8629
Admin Thomas Plott. *Medical Dir/Dir of Nursing* Robert Bom MD.
Licensure Skilled Care. *Beds* 57. *Certified* Medicare; Medi-Cal.

Ownership Proprietary.
Admissions Requirements Physician's request.
Staff RNs 1 (ft), 1 (pt); LPNs 3 (ft), 3 (pt); Nurses aides 15 (ft), 5 (pt); Activities coordinators 1 (ft); Dietitians 1 (ft); Dentists 1 (pt); Podiatrists 1 (pt).
Facilities Dining room; Activities room; Laundry room; Barber/Beauty shop.
Activities Arts and Crafts; Cards; Games; Reading groups; Prayer groups; Movies; Shopping trips; Dances/Social or cultural gatherings.
Description Facility features ambulation program where all patients who can bear weight or walk are ambulated daily.

ORANGE

Fountain Convalescent Hospital Inc
1835 W La Veta Ave, Orange, CA, 92668 (714) 532-6848
Admin Craig Fukushima. *Medical Dir/Dir of Nursing* Bruce Muttey MD.
Licensure Skilled Care. *Beds* 231. *Certified* Medicare; Medi-Cal.
Ownership Proprietary.
Admissions Requirements Physician's request.
Staff Physicians 30 (ft); RNs 10 (ft), 2 (pt); LPNs 24 (ft), 4 (pt); Orderlies 10 (ft); Nurses aides 57 (ft), 2 (pt); Physical therapists 1 (ft); Occupational therapists 1 (ft); Speech therapists 1 (ft); Activities coordinators 1 (ft); Dietitians 1 (pt); Dentists 1 (pt); Ophthalmologists 1 (pt); Podiatrists 1 (pt); Audiologists 1 (pt).
Facilities Dining room; Physical therapy room; Activities room; Crafts room; Laundry room; Barber/Beauty shop; Library.
Activities Arts and Crafts; Cards; Games; Reading groups; Prayer groups; Movies; Shopping trips; Dances/Social or cultural gatherings; Ball games.
Description The subacute section featuring 10 Clinitron beds accepts IV's, hyperalimentation, Dickman catheters, and tracheotomies.

HIllhaven Convalescent Hospital*
920 W La Veta St, Orange, CA, 92668 (714) 633-3568
Admin Robert E Karnatz.
Licensure Skilled Care. *Beds* 110. *Certified* Medicare; Medi-Cal.
Ownership Proprietary.

Royal Grove Convalescent Hospital*
238 S Flower St, Orange, CA, 92668 (714) 978-6261
Admin Mary Corrine Bart.
Licensure Skilled Care. *Beds* 43. *Certified* Medicare; Medi-Cal.
Ownership Proprietary.

ORANGEVALE

Orangevale Convalescent Hospital*
9260 Loma Ln, Orangevale, CA, 95662 (916) 988-1935
Admin J E Carper.
Licensure Skilled Care. *Beds* 25. *Certified* Medicare; Medi-Cal.
Ownership Proprietary.

ORINDA

Orinda Rehabilitation and Convalescent Hospital
11 Altarinda Rd, Orinda, CA, 94563 (415) 254-6500
Admin Selma R Cronin. *Medical Dir/Dir of Nursing* Richard Homrighausen MD.
Licensure Skilled Care. *Beds* 49. *Certified* Medicare.
Ownership Proprietary.
Admissions Requirements Medical examination; Physician's request.
Staff RNs 3 (ft), 6 (pt); LPNs 1 (ft); Orderlies 4 (ft); Nurses aides 20 (ft), 7 (pt); Activities coordinators 1 (ft); Dietitians 1 (pt).
Facilities Dining room; Physical therapy room; Activities room; Laundry room; Barber/Beauty shop; Sundeck.
Activities Arts and Crafts; Cards; Games; Reading groups; Prayer groups; Movies.
Description Orinda Convalescent Hospital is best known for its reputation in quality nursing and restorative services. Our nursing staff ratio is one CNA to every 5 patients on the day shift. Physical therapy is conducted 2-3 times daily, 6 days a week.

OROVILLE

Gilmore Lane Convalescent Hospital
1 Gilmore Ln, Oroville, CA, 95965 (916) 534-1353
Admin Harold L Cook. *Medical Dir/Dir of Nursing* Dr Olson.
Licensure Skilled Care. *Beds* 50. *Certified* Medicare; Medi-Cal.
Ownership Proprietary.
Admissions Requirements Physician's request.
Staff Physicians 12 (ft); RNs 2 (ft), 2 (pt); LPNs 4 (ft), 2 (pt); Orderlies 1 (ft); Nurses aides 16 (ft), 3 (pt); Physical therapists 1 (ft); Reality therapists 1 (pt); Recreational therapists 1 (ft); Occupational therapists 1 (pt); Speech therapists 1 (pt); Activities coordinators 1 (ft); Dietitians 1 (pt); Dentists 1 (pt); Ophthalmologists 1 (pt); Podiatrists 2 (pt).
Facilities Dining room; Physical therapy room; Activities room; Crafts room; Laundry room; Barber/Beauty shop.
Activities Arts and Crafts; Cards; Games; Reading groups; Prayer groups; Movies; Dances/Social or cultural gatherings.
Description Facility provides for friendly home-like setting for short-term recuperation or longer stays. Adjacent to an acute hospital and close to all services.

Lakeview Nursing Home Inc
1912 20th St, Oroville, CA, 95965 (916) 533-1874
Admin Nellie K Walker. *Medical Dir/Dir of Nursing* W R Olson MD.
Licensure Skilled Care. *Beds* 28. *Certified* Medicare.
Ownership Proprietary.
Admissions Requirements Physician's request.
Staff RNs 1 (ft); LPNs 3 (ft), 1 (pt); Nurses aides 11 (ft); Physical therapists 1 (pt); Reality therapists 1 (pt); Recreational therapists 1 (ft); Occupational therapists 1 (pt); Speech therapists 1 (pt); Activities coordinators 1 (ft); Dieti-

tians 1 (pt); Dentists 1 (pt); Podiatrists 1 (pt).
Facilities Dining room; Activities room; Laundry room.
Activities Arts and Crafts; Cards; Games; Reading groups; Prayer groups; Movies; Dances/Social or cultural gatherings.
Description Facility is located in a wonderful country setting.

Oroville Community Convalescent Hospital*
1511 Robinson St, Oroville, CA, 95965 (916) 534-5701
Admin A Perreras and P Beltran.
Licensure Skilled Care. *Beds* 41.
Ownership Proprietary.

OXNARD

Glenwood Convalescent Hospital
1300 N "C" St, Oxnard, CA, 93030 (805) 983-0305
Admin Jerry Wells. *Medical Dir/Dir of Nursing* E Falcon MD.
Licensure Skilled Care. *Beds* 99.
Ownership Proprietary.
Admissions Requirements Minimum age 18.
Staff RNs 5 (ft); LPNs 10 (ft); Nurses aides 40 (ft); Physical therapists 1 (pt); Reality therapists 1 (pt); Recreational therapists 1 (pt); Occupational therapists 1 (pt); Speech therapists 1 (pt); Activities coordinators 1 (ft); Dietitians 1 (pt); Dentists 1 (pt); Ophthalmologists 1 (pt); Podiatrists 1 (pt); Audiologists 1 (pt).
Facilities Dining room; Physical therapy room; Activities room; Crafts room; Laundry room; Barber/Beauty shop; Library.
Activities Arts and Crafts; Cards; Games; Reading groups; Prayer groups; Movies; Shopping trips.
Description A 99-bed modern skilled nursing facility with all of the latest in equipment to care for the short-term rehabilitation patient and the long-term chronic patient.

Maywood Acres Healthcare*
2641 S "C" St, Oxnard, CA, 93030 (805) 487-7840
Admin Nancy J Moore.
Licensure Skilled Care. *Beds* 98. *Certified* Medicare; Medi-Cal.
Ownership Proprietary.

Oxnard Manor Convalescent Hospital
1400 W Gonzlaes Rd, Oxnard, CA, 93030 (805) 983-0324
Admin Frank Donovan. *Medical Dir/Dir of Nursing* Dr Loder.
Licensure Skilled Care. *Beds* 82. *Certified* Medicare; Medi-Cal.
Ownership Proprietary.
Admissions Requirements Medical examination; Physician's request.
Facilities Dining room; Laundry room.
Activities Arts and Crafts; Cards; Games; Reading groups; Shopping trips; Dances/Social or cultural gatherings.
Description Oxnard Manor Convalescent Hospital tries to convey a home-like atmosphere for our patients. Also the staff cares for the patients like they are their own mothers and fathers.

Pleasant Valley Intermediate Care Facility
5235 S "J" St, Oxnard, CA, 93030 (805) 488-3696
Admin John P Devine.
Licensure Intermediate Care. *Beds* 73. *Certified* Medi-Cal.
Ownership Proprietary.

Pleasant Valley Rehabilitation and Convalescent Hospital
5225 S "J" St, Oxnard, CA, 93030 (805) 488-3696
Admin John P Devine. *Medical Dir/Dir of Nursing* Joseph McGuire MD.
Licensure Skilled Care. *Beds* 193. *Certified* Medicare; Medi-Cal.
Ownership Proprietary.
Admissions Requirements Medical examination; Physician's request.
Staff RNs 8 (ft), 6 (pt); LPNs 13 (ft), 3 (pt); Nurses aides 58 (ft), 16 (pt); Recreational therapists 1 (ft); Activities coordinators 2 (ft).
Facilities Dining room; Activities room; Laundry room; Barber/Beauty shop.
Activities Arts and Crafts; Cards; Games; Reading groups; Prayer groups; Movies; Shopping trips; Dances/Social or cultural gatherings.

PACIFIC GROVE

Canterbury Woods
651 Sinex Ave, Pacific Grove, CA, 93950 (408) 373-3111
Admin Robert B Butterfield. *Medical Dir/Dir of Nursing* Dr E Kolb.
Licensure Skilled Care. *Beds* 18. *Certified* Medicare.
Ownership Nonprofit.
Admissions Requirements Minimum age 62; Medical examination.
Staff Physicians 1 (pt); RNs 4 (ft), 3 (pt); Nurses aides 6 (ft), 6 (pt); Physical therapists 1 (pt); Occupational therapists 1 (pt); Speech therapists 1 (pt); Activities coordinators 1 (pt); Dietitians 1 (pt); Dentists 1 (pt); Podiatrists 1 (pt).
Affiliation Episcopal
Facilities Dining room; Physical therapy room; Activities room; Chapel; Crafts room; Laundry room; Barber/Beauty shop; Library.
Activities Arts and Crafts; Cards; Games; Reading groups; Prayer groups; Movies; Shopping trips; Dances/Social or cultural gatherings.
Description The facility provides life care in a beautiful retirement setting with no increase in cost for skilled care.

Pacific Grove Convalescent Hospital
200 Lighthouse Ave, Pacific Grove, CA, 93950 (408) 375-2695
Admin Tranis Clark Jr. *Medical Dir/Dir of Nursing* Blaney B Blodgett MD.
Licensure Skilled Care. *Beds* 51. *Certified* Medicare; Medi-Cal.
Ownership Nonprofit.
Admissions Requirements Minimum age 65; Medical examination; Physician's request.
Staff RNs 3 (ft), 4 (pt); LPNs 1 (ft), 1 (pt); Activities coordinators 1 (ft).
Affiliation Methodist
Facilities Dining room; Activities room; Crafts room; Laundry room; Barber/Beauty shop.
Activities Arts and Crafts; Cards; Games;

Reading groups; Prayer groups; Movies; Shopping trips; Dances/Social or cultural gatherings; Special outings.
Description Facility offers one private room, one 4-bed, all others 2- and 3-bed. Located near ocean front with ocean view from 2 sides of building.

PACIFICA

Linda Mar Convalescent Hospital
751 San Pedro Rd, Pacifica, CA, 94044 (415) 359-4800
Admin Cheryl Weiss. *Medical Dir/Dir of Nursing* Erich Neiderruther.
Licensure Skilled Care. *Beds* 65. *Certified* Medicare; Medi-Cal.
Ownership Proprietary.
Admissions Requirements Minimum age 18; Physician's request.
Staff RNs 3 (ft); LPNs 4 (ft); Nurses aides 20 (ft), 5 (pt); Activities coordinators 1 (ft).
Facilities Dining room; Activities room; Barber/Beauty shop.
Activities Arts and Crafts; Cards; Games; Reading groups; Prayer groups; Movies; Dances/Social or cultural gatherings; Outings.
Description Linda Mar Convalescent Hospital is located on a little country road only a few blocks from the sea. We have an extremely caring and loving staff who all contribute to a home-like atmosphere. Almost all of our residents are out of bed and dressed every day.

Pacifica Convalescent Hospital
385 Esplanade Ave, Pacifica, CA, 94044 (415) 993-5576
Admin Betty J Ellis. *Medical Dir/Dir of Nursing* C Allen Wall MD.
Licensure Skilled Care. *Beds* 68. *Certified* Medicare; Medi-Cal.
Ownership Proprietary.
Admissions Requirements Medical examination; Physician's request.
Staff Physicians 2 (ft); RNs 3 (ft), 5 (pt); LPNs 2 (ft), 4 (pt); Orderlies 1 (pt); Nurses aides 9 (ft), 14 (pt); Physical therapists 2 (ft), 1 (pt); Recreational therapists 1 (ft), 2 (pt); Occupational therapists 1 (pt); Speech therapists 1 (pt); Activities coordinators 1 (pt); Dietitians 1 (pt); Dentists 1 (pt); Ophthalmologists 1 (pt); Podiatrists 1 (pt); Audiologists 1 (pt).
Facilities Dining room; Physical therapy room; Laundry room; Barber/Beauty shop.
Activities Arts and Crafts; Cards; Games; Reading groups; Prayer groups; Movies; Shopping trips; Dances/Social or cultural gatherings.
Description Facility is a primarily short-term skilled nursing and rehabilitation hospital.

PALM SPRINGS

California Nursing and Rehabilitation Center of Palm Springs
2299 N Indian Ave, Palm Springs, CA, 92262 (619) 325-2937
Admin Carol Van Horst. *Medical Dir/Dir of Nursing* Charles Supply MD.
Licensure Skilled Care. *Beds* 80. *Certified* Medicare; Medi-Cal.
Ownership Proprietary.

Admissions Requirements Medical examination; Physician's request.
Staff Physicians 1 (pt); RNs 4 (ft), 2 (pt); LPNs 4 (ft), 5 (pt); Orderlies 2 (ft); Nurses aides 20 (ft), 3 (pt); Physical therapists 1 (pt); Occupational therapists 1 (pt); Speech therapists 1 (pt); Activities coordinators 1 (ft); Dietitians 1 (pt); Dentists 1 (pt); Ophthalmologists 1 (pt); Podiatrists 1 (pt); Audiologists 1 (pt).
Facilities Dining room; Physical therapy room; Activities room; Crafts room; Laundry room; Barber/Beauty shop.
Activities Arts and Crafts; Cards; Games; Reading groups; Prayer groups; Movies; Shopping trips; Dances/Social or cultural gatherings.
Description California Nursing offers a family-like atmosphere and a caring staff. All rooms have patios and many have fireplaces. Selective menu is available, and activities to meet everyone's needs. Jacuzzi pool is in a garden setting with lovely grounds.

Coachella House Inc*
2990 E Ramon Rd, Palm Springs, CA, 92262 (714) 323-2638
Admin Marilyn D Dodd.
Licensure Skilled Care. *Beds* 99. *Certified* Medicare; Medi-Cal.
Ownership Proprietary.

Palm Springs Healthcare
277 S Sunrise Way, Palm Springs, CA, 92262 (714) 327-8541
Admin Jacqueline Arcara. *Medical Dir/Dir of Nursing* William Thompson.
Licensure Skilled Care. *Beds* 99. *Certified* Medicare; Medi-Cal.
Ownership Proprietary.
Staff RNs 3 (ft), 2 (pt); LPNs 8 (ft), 2 (pt); Orderlies 3 (ft); Nurses aides 48 (ft); Reality therapists 1 (pt); Occupational therapists 1 (pt); Speech therapists 1 (pt); Activities coordinators 1 (ft); Dietitians 1 (pt); Dentists 1 (pt); Ophthalmologists 1 (pt); Podiatrists 1 (pt); Audiologists 1 (pt).
Facilities Dining room; Physical therapy room; Activities room; Crafts room; Laundry room; Barber/Beauty shop.
Activities Arts and Crafts; Cards; Games; Reading groups; Prayer groups; Movies; Shopping trips.
Description Facility features a new position, a full-time patient advocate, to deal with daily and ongoing problems. It adds that finishing touch so long needed in convalescent homes. Videoscope 3x5' TV screen and VCR equipment is available to show any movies available.

PALO ALTO

Casa Olga Intermediate Health Care Facility*
180 Hamilton Ave, Palo Alto, CA, 94306 (415) 325-7821
Admin Robert Waldsmith.
Licensure Intermediate Care. *Beds* 144. *Certified* Medi-Cal.
Ownership Proprietary.

Channing House
850 Webster St, Palo Alto, CA, 94301 (415) 327-0950
Admin James N Mann. *Medical Dir/Dir of*

Nursing Walter Bortz MD.
Licensure Skilled Care; Personal Care.
Beds SNF 14; Personal Care 32.
Ownership Nonprofit.
Admissions Requirements Minimum age 65; Medical examination.
Staff RNs 4 (ft), 4 (pt); Nurses aides 11 (ft), 3 (pt); Activities coordinators 1 (pt).
Facilities Dining room; Physical therapy room; Activities room; Laundry room; Barber/Beauty shop; Library.
Activities Arts and Crafts; Cards; Games; Reading groups; Movies.
Description Channing House is a nonprofit, charitable, community care facility for the elderly which incorporates a 14-bed SNF and 32-bed personal care unit—serving the 260 residents enjoying life care apartment living.

Hillhaven Convalescent Hospital*
911 Bryant St, Palo Alto, CA, 94301 (415) 327-0511
Admin Irmke Schoebel.
Licensure Skilled Care. *Beds* 66. *Certified* Medicare; Medi-Cal.
Ownership Proprietary.

Pine Creek Center*
4277 Miranda Ave, Palo Alto, CA, 94306 (415) 941-9910
Admin Harry S Lewis.
Licensure Skilled Care. *Beds* 50.
Certified Medi-Cal.
Ownership Proprietary.

PANORAMA CITY

Panorama Terrace West Convalescent Hospital*
9541 Van Nuys Blvd, Panorama City, CA, 91402 (213) 893-6385
Admin Kathy Tekle-Mariam.
Licensure Skilled Care. *Beds* 151. *Certified* Medicare; Medi-Cal.
Ownership Proprietary.

Sun Air Convalescent Hospital*
14857 Roscoe Blvd, Panorama City, CA, 91402 (213) 894-5707
Admin Rosalind Kogler.
Licensure Skilled Care. *Beds* 98. *Certified* Medicare; Medi-Cal.
Ownership Proprietary.

PARADISE

Cypress Acres
6900 Clark Rd, Paradise, CA, 95969 (916) 877-9316
Admin Jean K Filer. *Medical Dir/Dir of Nursing* M W Farr MD.
Licensure Intermediate Care. *Beds* 29. *Certified* Medi-Cal.
Ownership Proprietary.
Admissions Requirements Medical examination; Physician's request.
Staff RNs 2 (pt); LPNs 1 (ft), 2 (pt); Nurses aides 7 (ft), 1 (pt); Occupational therapists 1 (pt); Speech therapists 1 (pt); Activities coordinators 1 (pt); Dietitians 1 (pt); Dentists 1 (pt); Podiatrists 1 (pt).
Facilities Dining room; Physical therapy room;

Activities room; Crafts room; Laundry room; Library.
Activities Arts and Crafts; Cards; Games; Reading groups; Movies; Shopping trips; Dances/Social or cultural gatherings.
Description Small, lovely facility nestled among the oaks and pine trees. Lovely antiques, collected by Jean Filer, enhance the entry way and lobby of the facility providing a beautiful home-like atmosphere for residents to enjoy.

Cypress Acres Convalescent Hospital
1633 Cypress Ln, Paradise, CA, 95969 (916) 877-9316
Admin Jean Filer. *Medical Dir/Dir of Nursing* M Wesley Farr MD.
Licensure Skilled Care. *Beds* 108. *Certified* Medicare; Medi-Cal.
Ownership Proprietary.
Admissions Requirements Medical examination; Physician's request.
Staff RNs 8 (ft), 3 (pt); LPNs 6 (ft), 1 (pt); Orderlies 2 (ft); Nurses aides 26 (ft), 21 (pt); Physical therapists 2 (ft); Occupational therapists 1 (pt); Speech therapists 1 (pt); Activities coordinators 1 (pt); Dietitians 1 (pt); Dentists 1 (pt); Podiatrists 1 (pt).
Facilities Dining room; Physical therapy room; Activities room; Crafts room; Laundry room; Barber/Beauty shop; Library.
Activities Arts and Crafts; Cards; Games; Reading groups; Prayer groups; Movies; Shopping trips; Dances/Social or cultural gatherings.
Description Cypress Acres Convalescent Hospital is situated among the tall pines in Paradise, California. Beautiful feathery pines dazzle the eye against the azure blue sky. The spirit soars to the sky and is touched by the Creator's hand.

Edgewood Care Home
5374 Edgewood Ln, Paradise, CA, 95969 (916) 877-4357
Admin Lee Exum.
Licensure Intermediate Care. *Beds* 14. *Certified* Medicare.
Ownership Proprietary.
Admissions Requirements Minimum age 18; Medical examination.
Staff RNs 1 (pt); LPNs 3 (ft); Orderlies 3 (ft); Nurses aides 3 (ft); Activities coordinators 1 (ft); Dietitians 1 (pt).
Facilities Dining room; Physical therapy room; Activities room; Laundry room.
Activities Arts and Crafts; Cards; Games; Reading groups; Prayer groups; Movies; Shopping trips.

Paradise Convalescent Hospital*
7419 Skyway, Paradise, CA, 95969 (916) 877-7676
Admin Dixie Pena.
Licensure Skilled Care. *Beds* 44.
Certified Medi-Cal.
Ownership Proprietary.

PARAMOUNT

Bird Haven Christian Convalescent Hospital*
7039 Alondra Blvd, Paramount, CA, 90723 (213) 531-0990
Admin Mary L Muir.

Licensure Skilled Care. *Beds* 99. *Certified* Medicare; Medi-Cal.
Ownership Proprietary.

Paramount Convalescent Hospital*
8558 E Rosecrans Ave, Paramount, CA, 90723
(213) 634-6877
Admin June McKee.
Licensure Skilled Care. *Beds* 59. *Certified* Medicare.
Ownership Proprietary.

Terrace Gardens Convalescent Center*
8835 Vans Ave, Paramount, CA, 90723 (213)
634-8221
Admin Simon Yazbeck.
Licensure Skilled Care. *Beds* 173. *Certified* Medicare; Medi-Cal.
Ownership Proprietary.

PASADENA

The Californian—Pasadena Convalescent Hospital*
120 Bellefontaine, Pasadena, CA, 91105 (213)
793-5114
Admin A R Bower.
Licensure Skilled Care. *Beds* 82. *Certified* Medicare; Medi-Cal.
Ownership Proprietary.

Congress Convalescent Hospital*
716 S Fair Oaks Ave, Pasadena, CA, 91105
(213) 793-6127
Admin Ann Walshe.
Licensure Skilled Care. *Beds* 75. *Certified* Medicare; Medi-Cal.
Ownership Proprietary.

Eisenhower Nursing and Convalescent Hospital
1470 N Fair Oaks, Pasadena, CA, 91103 (213)
798-9133
Admin Marcella Brown. *Medical Dir/Dir of Nursing* Ferdinand Kunze MD.
Licensure Skilled Care. *Beds* 71. *Certified* Medicare; Medi-Cal.
Ownership Proprietary.
Staff RNs 1 (ft); LPNs 5 (ft); Nurses aides 20 (ft); Activities coordinators 1 (ft); Dietitians 1 (ft).

Fairwood Convalescent Hospital*
1810 N Fair Oaks, Pasadena, CA, 91103 (213)
935-1262
Admin Ethel Holtzclaw.
Licensure Skilled Care. *Beds* 78. *Certified* Medicare; Medi-Cal.
Ownership Proprietary.

Golden Age Convalescent Home
1450 N Fair Oaks Ave, Pasadena, CA, 91103
(213) 791-1948
Admin Dennis L Toy. *Medical Dir/Dir of Nursing* Dr Haig Manjikian.
Licensure Skilled Care. *Beds* 96. *Certified* Medicare; Medi-Cal.
Ownership Nonprofit.
Admissions Requirements Minimum age 18.
Staff RNs 1 (ft), 2 (pt); LPNs 8 (ft), 1 (pt); Orderlies 6 (ft); Nurses aides 39 (ft), 2 (pt); Physical therapists 1 (ft), 1 (pt); Recreational therapists 1 (ft); Speech therapists 1 (pt); Activi-

ties coordinators 1 (ft); Dietitians 1 (pt); Dentists 1 (pt); Ophthalmologists 1 (pt); Podiatrists 1 (pt); Audiologists 1 (pt).
Facilities Dining room; Physical therapy room; Activities room; Chapel; Laundry room; Barber/Beauty shop; Library.
Activities Arts and Crafts; Movies; Dances/Social or cultural gatherings.
Description Pasadena Golden Age has a contract with the Los Angeles County Regional Occupational Program (ROP). The ROP allows senior high school students and interested adults to participate in the clinical, hands-on aspect of their training as nurses aides culminuating in their becoming certified nurses aides.

Hacienda Convalescent Hospital—North
1920 N Fair Oaks Ave, Pasadena, CA, 91103
(818) 798-6777
Admin Helen Cox. *Medical Dir/Dir of Nursing* Paul Oliek MD.
Licensure Skilled Care. *Beds* 80. *Certified* Medicare; Medi-Cal.
Ownership Proprietary.
Admissions Requirements Medical examination; Physician's request.
Facilities Dining room; Physical therapy room; Activities room; Crafts room; Laundry room; Barber/Beauty shop.
Activities Arts and Crafts; Cards; Games; Reading groups; Prayer groups; Movies; Shopping trips; Dances/Social or cultural gatherings.
Description Facility features family counseling support group weekly; training center for residents (MDs) from Glendale Adventist Hospital.

Hacienda Convalescent Hospital—South*
1899 N Raymond Ave, Pasadena, CA, 91103
(213) 798-6777
Admin Sheryl Hancock.
Licensure Skilled Care. *Beds* 99. *Certified* Medicare; Medi-Cal.
Ownership Proprietary.

Kent Convalescent Hospital*
1640 N Fair Oaks Ave, Pasadena, CA, 91103
(213) 798-1175
Admin Dorothy J Phillips.
Licensure Skilled Care. *Beds* 99.
Certified Medi-Cal.
Ownership Proprietary.

Marlinda Convalescent Hospital at Pasadena*
2637 E Washington, Pasadena, CA, 91107 (213)
798-8991
Admin Martha E Lang.
Licensure Skilled Care. *Beds* 50. *Certified* Medicare; Medi-Cal.
Ownership Proprietary.

Marlinda-Imperial Convalescent Hospital
150 Bellefontaine, Pasadena, CA, 91101 (213)
796-1103
Admin Martha E Lang. *Medical Dir/Dir of Nursing* Ray George MD.
Licensure Skilled Care. *Beds* 130. *Certified* Medicare; Medi-Cal.
Ownership Proprietary.
Staff Physicians 30 (ft); RNs 6 (ft), 1 (pt); LPNs 8 (ft), 2 (pt); Orderlies 4 (ft); Nurses aides 35 (ft); Physical therapists 1 (ft); Occupational

therapists 1 (ft); Speech therapists 1 (ft); Activities coordinators 1 (ft); Dietitians 1 (ft); Dentists 1 (pt); Ophthalmologists 1 (pt); Podiatrists 1 (pt).

Monte Vista Grove Homes*
2889 San Pasqual, Pasadena, CA, 91107 (213)
792-2712
Admin Adrian K Roberts.
Licensure Skilled Care. *Beds* 40.
Ownership Nonprofit.

Park Marino Convalescent Center*
2585 E Washington, Pasadena, CA, 91107 (213)
798-6753
Admin Kitty Batho.
Licensure Skilled Care. *Beds* 99.
Ownership Proprietary.

Pasadena Care Convalescent Hospital*
1836 N Fair Oaks Ave, Pasadena, CA, 91103
(213) 798-9125
Admin Corinne Bart.
Licensure Skilled Care. *Beds* 99. *Certified* Medicare; Medi-Cal.
Ownership Proprietary.

Robinson Home
275 Robincroft Dr, Pasadena, CA, 91104 (213)
794-7144
Admin Herbert G Thompson. *Medical Dir/Dir of Nursing* Peter Dunn MD.
Licensure Skilled Care. *Beds* 30. *Certified* Medicare; Medi-Cal.
Ownership Proprietary.
Admissions Requirements Minimum age 18.
Staff RNs 1 (ft); LPNs 4 (ft), 2 (pt); Orderlies 3 (ft); Nurses aides 4 (ft); Physical therapists 1 (pt); Reality therapists 1 (pt); Recreational therapists 1 (ft); Occupational therapists 1 (pt); Speech therapists 1 (pt); Activities coordinators 1 (ft); Dietitians 1 (pt); Dentists 1 (pt); Ophthalmologists 1 (pt); Podiatrists 1 (pt); Audiologists 1 (pt).
Facilities Dining room; Physical therapy room; Activities room; Chapel; Crafts room; Laundry room; Barber/Beauty shop; Library.
Activities Arts and Crafts; Cards; Games; Reading groups; Prayer groups; Movies; Shopping trips; Dances/Social or cultural gatherings.
Description Facility is located on 4 ½ acres of beautifully landscaped grounds on a hill overlooking Pasadena with mountain vistas to the north and south.

Sophia Lyn Convalescent Hospital*
1570 N Fair Oaks Ave, Pasadena, CA, 91103
(213) 798-0558
Admin Robert N Taylor.
Licensure Skilled Care. *Beds* 54. *Certified* Medicare; Medi-Cal.
Ownership Proprietary.

Villa Gardens Health Care Unit
842 E Villa St, Pasadena, CA, 91101 (213)
681-8704
Admin Jean Brophy. *Medical Dir/Dir of Nursing* Dr Stanley Cuba.
Licensure Skilled Care. *Beds* 31. *Certified* Medicare; Medi-Cal.
Ownership Nonprofit.
Admissions Requirements Minimum age 62; Medical examination.

Staff RNs 1 (ft); LPNs 2 (ft), 3 (pt); Nurses aides 12 (ft), 5 (pt); Physical therapists; Occupational therapists; Speech therapists; Activities coordinators 1 (ft); Dietitians; Dentists; Podiatrists.
Facilities Dining room; Chapel; Laundry room; Barber/Beauty shop; Library.
Activities Arts and Crafts; Reading groups; Prayer groups; Movies; Shopping trips; Dances-/Social or cultural gatherings.
Description Villa Gardens has a 50-year reputation of quality care and excellence. It is a small community located amid beautiful gardens and is a multilevel care facility providing apartments and personal services as well as skilled nursing. Located near major shopping areas, churches, and restaurants, Villa Gardens is a very convenient as well as an enjoyable home.

Villa Oaks Convalescent Hospital*
1515 N Fair Oaks Ave, Pasadena, CA, 91103 (213) 798-1111
Admin Robert Taylor.
Licensure Skilled Care. *Beds* 49. *Certified* Medicare; Medi-Cal.
Ownership Proprietary.

PASO ROBLES

Paso Robles Convalescent Hospital
321 12th St, Paso Robles, CA, 93446 (805) 238-4637
Admin George G Brudney. *Medical Dir/Dir of Nursing* Dr O Atkinson.
Licensure Skilled Care. *Beds* 50. *Certified* Medicare; Medi-Cal.
Ownership Proprietary.
Staff Physicians 1 (pt); RNs 2 (ft), 1 (pt); LPNs 3 (ft), 2 (pt); Nurses aides 13 (ft), 3 (pt); Physical therapists 1 (pt); Recreational therapists 1 (pt); Occupational therapists 1 (pt); Speech therapists 1 (pt); Activities coordinators 1 (ft); Dietitians 1 (pt); Dentists 1 (pt); Podiatrists 1 (pt); Audiologists 1 (pt).
Facilities Dining room; Activities room; Crafts room; Laundry room; Barber/Beauty shop.
Activities Arts and Crafts; Cards; Games; Reading groups; Prayer groups; Movies; Shopping trips; Dances/Social or cultural gatherings.
Description Facility features trips into community senior citizens activities center.

PERRIS

Medical Arts Convalescent Hospital
2225 N Perris Blvd, Perris, CA, 92370 (714) 657-2135
Admin Lilly M Swegles. *Medical Dir/Dir of Nursing* Harry Fandrich MD.
Licensure Skilled Care. *Beds* 99. *Certified* Medicare; Medi-Cal.
Ownership Proprietary.
Staff RNs 2 (ft), 2 (pt); Orderlies 2 (ft); Nurses aides 27 (ft), 14 (pt); Activities coordinators 1 (ft).
Facilities Dining room; Physical therapy room; Laundry room; Barber/Beauty shop; Library.
Activities Arts and Crafts; Cards; Games; Reading groups; Prayer groups; Movies; Shopping trips; Dances/Social or cultural gatherings.

Description Facility features a distinct part 30-bed sub acute section for in- and outpatients.

PETALUMA

Beverly Manor of Petaluma
101 Monroe St, Petaluma, CA, 94952 (707) 763-4109
Admin Tom Owens. *Medical Dir/Dir of Nursing* Dr Besses.
Licensure Skilled Care. *Beds* 99. *Certified* Medicare; Medi-Cal.
Ownership Proprietary.
Staff RNs 4 (ft); LPNs 5 (ft); Nurses aides 38 (ft); Physical therapists; Reality therapists; Recreational therapists; Occupational therapists; Speech therapists; Activities coordinators; Dietitians; Dentists; Ophthalmologists; Podiatrists; Audiologists.
Facilities Dining room; Physical therapy room; Activities room; Chapel; Crafts room; Laundry room; Barber/Beauty shop; Library.
Activities Arts and Crafts; Cards; Games; Prayer groups; Movies; Shopping trips; Dances/Social or cultural gatherings.

Crestview Convalescent Hospital
523 Hayes Ave, Petaluma, CA, 94952 (707) 763-2457
Admin Donald Bais. *Medical Dir/Dir of Nursing* Dean O'Neil MD.
Licensure Skilled Care. *Beds* 90. *Certified* Medicare; Medi-Cal.
Ownership Proprietary.
Admissions Requirements Minimum age 60; Medical examination; Physician's request.
Staff RNs 4 (ft); LPNs 6 (ft); Orderlies 4 (ft); Nurses aides 30 (ft); Physical therapists 1 (pt); Occupational therapists 1 (pt); Speech therapists 1 (pt); Activities coordinators 1 (ft); Dietitians 1 (pt); Dentists 1 (pt); Ophthalmologists 1 (pt); Podiatrists 1 (pt); Audiologists 1 (pt).
Facilities Dining room; Physical therapy room; Activities room; Barber/Beauty shop.
Activities Arts and Crafts; Cards; Games; Movies.
Description Facility is a 90-bed SNF in a scenic location with view of city of Petaluma. We have good physical, occupational, and speech therapy programs.

Hacienda Convalescent Hospital
300 Douglas St, Petaluma, CA, 94952 (707) 763-6887
Admin Vito J Genna. *Medical Dir/Dir of Nursing* James Simon MD.
Licensure Skilled Care. *Beds* 98. *Certified* Medicare; Medi-Cal.
Ownership Proprietary.
Facilities Dining room; Physical therapy room; Activities room; Crafts room; Laundry room; Barber/Beauty shop; Library.
Activities Arts and Crafts; Cards; Games; Reading groups; Prayer groups; Movies; Shopping trips; Dances/Social or cultural gatherings.
Description VA contracts are available and the facility features an excellent rehabilitation program.

The Oaks
450 Hayes Ln, Petaluma, CA, 94952 (707) 778-8686
Admin Betty L Green. *Medical Dir/Dir of Nursing* John Rodnick MD.
Licensure Skilled Care. *Beds* 59. *Certified* Medicare; Medi-Cal.
Ownership Proprietary.
Staff Physicians 4 (pt); RNs 4 (ft), 3 (pt); LPNs 3 (ft), 4 (pt); Orderlies 3 (ft); Nurses aides 34 (ft); Physical therapists 2 (pt); Recreational therapists 1 (pt); Occupational therapists 1 (pt); Speech therapists 1 (pt); Activities coordinators 1 (ft); Dietitians 1 (pt); Dentists 1 (pt); Ophthalmologists 1 (pt); Podiatrists 1 (pt); Audiologists 1 (pt).
Facilities Dining room; Physical therapy room; Activities room; Chapel; Crafts room; Laundry room; Barber/Beauty shop; Library.
Activities Arts and Crafts; Cards; Games; Reading groups; Prayer groups; Movies; Shopping trips; Dances/Social or cultural gatherings; Outside entertainment.
Description Beautiful view of Petaluma, homelike care given to residents, and maintenance exercise are given to all residents as required.

Petaluma Convalescent Hospital
1115 B St, Petaluma, CA, 94952 (707) 763-6871
Admin Barbara Spiro-Garner. *Medical Dir/Dir of Nursing* Dean O'Neil MD.
Licensure Skilled Care. *Beds* 90. *Certified* Medicare; Medi-Cal.
Ownership Proprietary.
Staff Physicians; RNs; LPNs; Orderlies; Nurses aides; Physical therapists; Recreational therapists; Occupational therapists; Speech therapists; Activities coordinators; Dietitians; Dentists; Ophthalmologists; Podiatrists; Audiologists.
Facilities Dining room; Physical therapy room; Activities room; Crafts room; Laundry room; Barber/Beauty shop.
Activities Arts and Crafts; Cards; Games; Reading groups; Prayer groups; Movies; Dances/Social or cultural gatherings.

PICO RIVERA

Colonial Gardens Nursing Home*
7246 S Rosemead Blvd, Pico Rivera, CA, 90660 (213) 949-2591
Admin David H Lewis.
Licensure Skilled Care. *Beds* 97. *Certified* Medi-Cal.
Ownership Proprietary.

El Rancho Vista Convalescent Center*
8925 Mines Ave, Pico Rivera, CA, 90660 (213) 692-0319
Admin Dave Freilino.
Licensure Skilled Care. *Beds* 86. *Certified* Medicare; Medi-Cal.
Ownership Proprietary.

Riviera Nursing and Convalescent Home Inc
8203 Telegraph Rd, Pico Rivera, CA, 90660 (213) 923-0994
Admin Mark Wilson. *Medical Dir/Dir of Nursing* Lawrence Pollock MD.
Licensure Skilled Care. *Beds* 154. *Cer-*

tified Medicare; Medi-Cal.
Ownership Proprietary.
Staff Physicians 1 (pt); RNs 4 (ft), 2 (pt); LPNs 9 (ft), 4 (pt); Orderlies 6 (ft); Nurses aides 40 (ft), 5 (pt); Physical therapists 1 (ft); Speech therapists 1 (pt); Activities coordinators 1 (ft); Dietitians 1 (pt); Dentists 1 (pt); Ophthalmologists 1 (pt); Podiatrists 1 (pt); Audiologists 1 (pt).
Facilities Dining room; Physical therapy room; Activities room; Laundry room; Barber/Beauty shop; Living room.
Activities Arts and Crafts; Cards; Games; Prayer groups; Dances/Social or cultural gatherings.
Description Facility specializes in post stroke and post hip surgery rehabilitation.

Saint Theresa Convalescent Hospital
9140 Verner St, Pico Rivera, CA, 90660 (213) 948-1961
Admin Charles V Williams. *Medical Dir/Dir of Nursing* J E Altamirano MD.
Licensure Skilled Care. *Beds* 99. *Certified* Medicare; Medi-Cal.
Ownership Proprietary.
Admissions Requirements Physician's request.
Staff RNs 3 (ft), 2 (pt); LPNs 6 (ft), 3 (pt); Nurses aides 20 (ft), 4 (pt); Physical therapists 1 (pt); Reality therapists 1 (pt); Recreational therapists 1 (pt); Occupational therapists 1 (pt); Speech therapists 1 (pt); Activities coordinators 1 (ft); Dietitians 1 (pt); Dentists 1 (pt); Ophthalmologists 1 (pt); Podiatrists 1 (pt); Audiologists 1 (pt).
Facilities Dining room; Physical therapy room; Activities room; Crafts room; Laundry room; Barber/Beauty shop; Large outdoor patio and side yard.
Activities Arts and Crafts; Cards; Games; Reading groups; Prayer groups; Movies; Gardening club; Kite flying.
Description Facility is extremely warm with a newly decorated interior (all patient rooms repainted, new drapes and cubicles); outstanding activity program. Outdoor activities are available without leaving facility.

PITTSBURG

Pittsburg Manor Convalescent Hospital
535 School St, Pittsburg, CA, 94565 (415) 432-3831
Admin Sandra Long. *Medical Dir/Dir of Nursing* Edwin Boysen.
Licensure Skilled Care. *Beds* 49. *Certified* Medicare; Medi-Cal.
Ownership Proprietary.
Admissions Requirements Physician's request.
Staff Physicians 6 (pt); RNs 3 (pt); LPNs 3 (ft), 3 (pt); Nurses aides 10 (ft), 7 (pt); Physical therapists 1 (pt); Occupational therapists 1 (pt); Speech therapists 1 (pt); Activities coordinators 1 (pt); Dietitians 1 (pt); Dentists 1 (pt); Podiatrists 1 (pt).
Facilities Dining room; Physical therapy room; Activities room; Crafts room; Laundry room.
Activities Arts and Crafts; Cards; Games; Reading groups; Movies.
Description Every spring and fall the more alert patients are taken on field trips to Napa Valley wineries. The patients often go out to lunch and other afternoon trips.

PLACERVILLE

El Dorado Convalescent Hospital
3280 Washington St, Placerville, CA, 95667 (916) 622-6842
Admin Louis J Yost. *Medical Dir/Dir of Nursing* Ted Christy MD.
Licensure Skilled Care. *Beds* 99. *Certified* Medicare; Medi-Cal.
Ownership Proprietary.
Admissions Requirements Medical examination; Physician's request.
Staff RNs 3 (ft), 5 (pt); LPNs 2 (ft), 2 (pt); Nurses aides 25 (ft), 5 (pt).
Facilities Dining room; Physical therapy room; Activities room; Crafts room; Laundry room; Barber/Beauty shop; Library.
Activities Arts and Crafts; Cards; Games; Reading groups; Prayer groups; Movies; Shopping trips; Dances/Social or cultural gatherings.

Placerville Pines Convalescent Hospital
1040 Marshall Way, Placerville, CA, 95667 (916) 622-3400
Admin Louis J Yost.
Licensure Skilled Care. *Beds* 99. *Certified* Medicare; Medi-Cal.
Ownership Proprietary.
Facilities Dining room; Physical therapy room; Activities room; Chapel; Crafts room; Laundry room; Barber/Beauty shop; Library.
Activities Arts and Crafts; Cards; Games; Reading groups; Prayer groups; Movies; Shopping trips.

PLAYA DEL REY

Playa Del Rey Care Convalescent Hospital*
7716 Manchester Ave, Playa Del Rey, CA, 92343 (213) 923-4694
Admin Tom Hix.
Licensure Skilled Care. *Beds* 99. *Certified* Medicare; Medi-Cal.
Ownership Proprietary.

PLEASANT HILL

Baywood Convalescent Hospital*
550 Patterson Blvd, Pleasant Hill, CA, 94523 (415) 939-5400
Admin Charlene May.
Licensure Skilled Care. *Beds* 166. *Certified* Medicare; Medi-Cal.
Ownership Proprietary.

Cypress Convalescent Hospital*
540 Patterson Blvd, Pleasant Hill, CA, 94523 (415) 932-3850
Admin Alice Ewing.
Licensure Skilled Care. *Beds* 105. *Certified* Medicare.
Ownership Proprietary.

Oak Park Convalescent Hospital*
1625 Oak Park Blvd, Pleasant Hill, CA, 94523 (415) 935-5222
Admin John Milford.
Licensure Skilled Care. *Beds* 51. *Certified* Medicare; Medi-Cal.
Ownership Proprietary.

Rosewood Convalescent Hospital
1911 Oak Park Blvd, Pleasant Hill, CA, 94523 (415) 935-6630
Admin John R Maguire. *Medical Dir/Dir of Nursing* Dr D K Fisher.
Licensure Skilled Care. *Beds* 117. *Certified* Medicare; Medi-Cal.
Ownership Proprietary.
Staff RNs 9 (ft); LPNs 11 (ft); Nurses aides 38 (ft); Physical therapists 1 (pt); Speech therapists 1 (ft); Activities coordinators 1 (ft); Dietitians 1 (pt); Dentists 1 (pt); Ophthalmologists 1 (pt); Podiatrists 1 (pt).
Facilities Dining room; Physical therapy room; Activities room; Laundry room; Barber/Beauty shop; Library.
Activities Arts and Crafts; Cards; Games; Reading groups; Prayer groups; Movies; Shopping trips; Dances/Social or cultural gatherings.

POMONA

Country House*
1041 S White Ave, Pomona, CA, 91766 (213) 623-0581
Admin Dorothy Broadway.
Licensure Skilled Care; Intermediate Care for Mentally Retarded. *Beds* 91. *Certified* Medi-Cal.
Ownership Proprietary.

Foothill Convalescent Hospital*
219 E Foothill Blvd, Pomona, CA, 91767 (714) 593-1391
Admin George Curtis.
Licensure Skilled Care. *Beds* 99. *Certified* Medicare.
Ownership Proprietary.

Landmark Medical Center
2030 N Garey Ave, Pomona, CA, 91767 (714) 593-2585
Admin Cunnison Roberts. *Medical Dir/Dir of Nursing* William E Sigurdson MD.
Licensure Skilled Care. *Beds* 95. *Certified* Medi-Cal.
Ownership Proprietary.
Staff Physicians 3 (pt); RNs 4 (ft), 2 (pt); LPNs 4 (ft), 9 (pt); Nurses aides 20 (ft), 3 (pt); Activities coordinators 1 (pt); Dietitians 1 (ft).
Languages Spanish
Facilities Dining room; Activities room; Crafts room; Laundry room; Barber/Beauty shop; Library.
Activities Arts and Crafts; Games; Movies; Shopping trips; Dances/Social or cultural gatherings; Birthday and holiday parties.
Description Certified for "Special Treatment Program" (paid by Medi-Cal if patient is approved); provides 27 hours a week of various therapy training; school activities, recreation therapy, remotivation and socialization, etc. Easy access to shopping, parks, and transportation.

Lanterman State Hospital and Development Center
3530 Pomona Blvd, Pomona, CA, 91766 (714) 595-1221
Admin Harry A Lewis. *Medical Dir/Dir of Nursing* G Kenneth Wood MD.
Licensure Skilled Care; Intermediate Care for

Developmentally Disabled. *Beds* SNF 311;
Intermediate Care for Developmentally Disabled 908. *Certified* Medicare; Medi-Cal.
Ownership Public.
Staff Physicians 24 (ft).
Facilities Dining room; Physical therapy room;
Activities room; Chapel; Crafts room; Laundry
room; Barber/Beauty shop; Library; Recreational facilities outdoors; Rustic camp; Swimming pool.
Activities Arts and Crafts; Cards; Games;
Reading groups; Prayer groups; Movies; Shopping trips; Dances/Social or cultural gatherings.
Description This is a state facility for the
developmentally disabled. Acute, skilled
nursing, and intermediate care are provided to
approximately 1200 individuals who are mentally retarded.

Laurel Park—A Center for Effective Living*
1425 Laurel Ave, Pomona, CA, 91768 (714)
622-1069
Admin Ruth C Braswell.
Licensure Skilled Care. *Beds* 43.
Certified Medi-Cal.
Ownership Proprietary.

**Mount San Antonio Gardens Congregational
Homes***
900 E Harrison Ave, Pomona, CA, 91767 (714)
624-5061
Admin Theodore Radamaker.
Licensure Skilled Care. *Beds* 55. *Certified* Medicare; Medi-Cal.
Ownership Nonprofit.

Olive Vista—A Center for Problems of Living*
2350 Culver Ct, Pomona, CA, 91766 (213)
628-6024
Admin C Allen Brashwell.
Licensure Skilled Care. *Beds* 120.
Certified Medi-Cal.
Ownership Proprietary.

Palomares Center
250 W Artesia, Pomona, CA, 91768 (213)
623-3564
Admin Robert Foster. *Medical Dir/Dir of
Nursing* Valentine G Birds MD.
Licensure Skilled Care. *Beds* 175. *Certified* Medicare; Medi-Cal.
Ownership Proprietary.
Admissions Requirements Minimum age 20;
Physician's request.
Staff Physicians 1 (pt); RNs 5 (ft), 4 (pt); LPNs
13 (ft), 5 (pt); Orderlies 7 (ft), 3 (pt); Nurses
aides 49 (ft), 19 (pt); Physical therapists 2 (ft);
Occupational therapists 1 (pt); Speech therapists 1 (pt); Activities coordinators 1 (ft), 2 (pt);
Dietitians 1 (pt); Dentists 1 (pt); Ophthalmologists 1 (pt); Podiatrists 1 (pt); Audiologists 1
(pt).
Facilities Dining room; Physical therapy room;
Activities room; Chapel; Crafts room; Laundry
room; Barber/Beauty shop; Library.
Activities Arts and Crafts; Cards; Games;
Reading groups; Prayer groups; Movies; Shopping trips; Dances/Social or cultural gatherings.

Park Place Convalescent Hospital*
1550 N Park Ave, Pomona, CA, 91768 (213)
623-0791
Admin Harold Moser.

Licensure Skilled Care. *Beds* 231.
Certified Medi-Cal.
Ownership Proprietary.

**Pomona Golden Age Convalescent Hospital and
Nursing Home**
215 W Pearl St, Pomona, CA, 91768 (714)
622-1067
Admin Ron Millett. *Medical Dir/Dir of
Nursing* Felimon Soria.
Licensure Skilled Care. *Beds* 81. *Certified* Medicare; Medi-Cal.
Ownership Nonprofit.
Staff RNs 1 (ft), 1 (pt); LPNs 8 (ft), 4 (pt);
Orderlies 8 (ft), 3 (pt); Nurses aides 30 (ft), 6
(pt); Physical therapists 1 (pt); Reality therapists
1 (pt); Recreational therapists 1 (ft), 2 (pt);
Occupational therapists 1 (pt); Speech therapists 1 (pt); Activities coordinators 1 (pt); Dietitians 1 (ft), 1 (pt); Dentists 1 (pt);
Ophthalmologists 1 (pt); Podiatrists 1 (pt);
Audiologists 1 (pt).
Facilities Dining room; Activities room; Laundry room; Barber/Beauty shop.
Activities Arts and Crafts; Cards; Games;
Reading groups; Prayer groups; Movies; Shopping trips; Dances/Social or cultural gatherings.

Pomona Vista Convalescent Hospital
651 N Main St, Pomona, CA, 91767 (714)
623-2481
Admin LaWanda Olson. *Medical Dir/Dir of
Nursing* Dr Valentine Birds.
Licensure Skilled Care. *Beds* 66. *Certified* Medicare; Medi-Cal.
Ownership Proprietary.
Admissions Requirements Physician's request.
Staff RNs 1 (ft), 2 (pt); LPNs 4 (ft), 4 (pt);
Nurses aides 42 (ft); Activities coordinators 1
(ft); Dietitians 1 (pt).
Facilities Dining room; Activities room; Barber/Beauty shop.
Activities Arts and Crafts; Games; Reading
groups; Prayer groups; Movies; Shopping trips.
Description Facility is small, with home-type
decorations and atmosphere.

Towne Avenue Convalescent Hospital*
2351 S Towne Ave, Pomona, CA, 91766 (714)
628-1245
Admin Glen A Crume.
Licensure Skilled Care. *Beds* 84. *Certified* Medicare; Medi-Cal.
Ownership Proprietary.

PORTERVILLE

Hacienda Convalescent Hospital*
301 W Putnam, Porterville, CA, 93257 (209)
784-7375
Admin James D Loyd.
Licensure Skilled Care. *Beds* 139. *Certified* Medicare; Medi-Cal.
Ownership Proprietary.

Valley Care Center
661 W Poplar Ave, Porterville, CA, 93257
(209) 784-8371
Admin Donald Smith. *Medical Dir/Dir of
Nursing* Robert Dexter MD.
Licensure Skilled Care. *Beds* 55. *Certified* Medicare; Medi-Cal.

Ownership Proprietary.
Staff Physicians 1 (pt); RNs 1 (ft), 1 (pt); LPNs
6 (ft); Orderlies 1 (ft); Nurses aides 14 (ft), 2
(pt); Activities coordinators 1 (ft); Dietitians 1
(pt); Dentists 1 (pt); Podiatrists 1 (pt).
Facilities Dining room; Activities room; Crafts
room; Laundry room; Barber/Beauty shop.
Activities Arts and Crafts; Cards; Games; Prayer groups; Movies; Dances/Social or cultural
gatherings; Green house gardening.

Villa Manor Care Center Inc
350 N Villa, Porterville, CA, 93257 (209)
784-6644
Admin R Wesley Jordan. *Medical Dir/Dir of
Nursing* Robert Dexter MD.
Licensure Skilled Care. *Beds* 89. *Certified* Medicare; Medi-Cal.
Ownership Proprietary.
Staff Physicians 1 (pt); RNs 2 (ft), 2 (pt); LPNs
10 (ft), 3 (pt); Nurses aides 35 (ft), 10 (pt);
Physical therapists 1 (pt); Recreational therapists 1 (pt); Occupational therapists 1 (pt); Speech therapists 1 (pt); Activities coordinators 1
(ft); Dietitians 1 (pt); Dentists 1 (pt); Podiatrists
1 (pt).
Facilities Dining room; Activities room; Laundry room; Barber/Beauty shop.
Activities Arts and Crafts; Cards; Games;
Reading groups; Prayer groups; Movies; Shopping trips; Dances/Social or cultural gatherings.
Description Facility features Early American
decor, set off by fine paintings and tapestries,
and 2 beautiful parlors for entertaining family
and friends. Atmosphere is as close as possible
to that of a home.

PORTOLA VALLEY

The Sequoias*
501 Portola Rd, Portola Valley, CA, 94025
(415) 851-1501
Admin John E Dillon.
Licensure Skilled Care. *Beds* 48.
Ownership Nonprofit.

QUINCY

Quincy Convalescent Hospital
PO Box L, Quincy, CA, 95971 (916) 283-2110
Admin Merry Nickerson. *Medical Dir/Dir of
Nursing* Dr Price.
Licensure Skilled Care. *Beds* 57. *Certified* Medicare; Medi-Cal.
Ownership Proprietary.
Staff Physicians; RNs; LPNs; Orderlies;
Nurses aides; Physical therapists; Recreational
therapists; Speech therapists; Activities coordinators; Dietitians; Dentists; Podiatrists;
Audiologists.
Facilities Dining room; Physical therapy room;
Activities room; Laundry room; Barber/Beauty
shop; Library.
Activities Arts and Crafts; Cards; Games;
Reading groups; Prayer groups; Movies; Dances/Social or cultural gatherings; Exercise program at local college.

RANCHO CORDOVA

Casa Coloma Health Care Center*
10410 Coloma Rd, Rancho Cordova, CA,
95670 (916) 363-4843
Admin Arden Millermon.
Licensure Skilled Care. *Beds* 99. *Certified* Medicare; Medi-Cal.
Ownership Proprietary.

RED BLUFF

Brentwood Convalescent Hospital*
1795 Walnut St, Red Bluff, CA, 96080 (916)
527-2046
Admin Joseph Fernandez.
Licensure Skilled Care. *Beds* 55. *Certified* Medicare; Medi-Cal.
Ownership Proprietary.

Cedars Convalescent Hospital*
555 Luther Rd, Red Bluff, CA, 96080 (916)
527-6232
Admin Maxine Niel.
Licensure Skilled Care. *Beds* 56. *Certified* Medicare; Medi-Cal.
Ownership Proprietary.

Tehema County Health Center
1850 Walnut St, Red Bluff, CA, 96080 (916)
527-0350
Admin Nora M Roberson. *Medical Dir/Dir of
Nursing* Eva Jalkotzy.
Licensure Skilled Care. *Beds* 40. *Certified* Medicare; Medi-Cal.
Ownership Public.
Staff Physicians; RNs; LPNs; Orderlies;
Nurses aides; Physical therapists; Reality therapists; Recreational therapists; Occupational
therapists; Speech therapists; Activities coordinators; Dietitians; Dentists; Ophthalmologists;
Podiatrists; Audiologists.
Facilities Dining room; Physical therapy room;
Activities room; Crafts room; Laundry room.
Activities Arts and Crafts; Cards; Games;
Reading groups; Prayer groups; Movies.

REDDING

Beverly Manor Convalescent Hospital*
1836 Gold St, Redding, CA, 96001 (916)
241-6756
Admin James Majerus.
Licensure Skilled Care. *Beds* 89. *Certified* Medicare; Medi-Cal.
Ownership Proprietary.

Crestwood Convalescent Hospital*
2490 Court St, Redding, CA, 96001 (916)
246-0600
Admin Linda Rink.
Licensure Skilled Care. *Beds* 113. *Certified* Medicare; Medi-Cal.
Ownership Proprietary.

Shasta Convalescent Hospital
3550 Churn Creek Rd, Redding, CA, 96002
(916) 222-3630
Admin Harold Becker.
Licensure Skilled Care. *Beds* 165. *Certified* Medicare; Medi-Cal.

Ownership Proprietary.

REDLANDS

Beverly Manor Convalescent Hospital*
700 E Highland Ave, Redlands, CA, 92373
(714) 793-2678
Admin Barbara Ann Gorman.
Licensure Skilled Care. *Beds* 82. *Certified* Medicare; Medi-Cal.
Ownership Proprietary.
Description JCAH approved.

Brookside Care Convalescent Hospital
105 Terracina Blvd, Redlands, CA, 92373 (714)
793-2271
Admin Ann E Gaal. *Medical Dir/Dir of
Nursing* William Thompson MD.
Licensure Skilled Care. *Beds* 97. *Certified* Medicare; Medi-Cal.
Ownership Proprietary.
Staff Physicians; RNs; LPNs; Orderlies;
Nurses aides; Physical therapists; Occupational
therapists; Speech therapists; Activities coordinators; Dietitians; Dentists; Ophthalmologists;
Podiatrists; Audiologists.
Facilities Dining room; Physical therapy room;
Activities room; Barber/Beauty shop.
Activities Arts and Crafts; Cards; Games;
Reading groups; Prayer groups; Movies; Shopping trips; Dances/Social or cultural gatherings.

**Plymouth Village Redlands Convalescent
Hospital**
819 Salem Dr, Redlands, CA, 92373 (714)
793-3371
Admin Robert L Balsley. *Medical Dir/Dir of
Nursing* Dr James Gillespie.
Licensure Skilled Care. *Beds* 48. *Certified* Medicare; Medi-Cal.
Ownership Nonprofit.
Admissions Requirements Medical examination; Physician's request.
Staff RNs 2 (ft), 6 (pt); LPNs 3 (ft), 4 (pt);
Orderlies 2 (pt); Nurses aides 17 (ft), 5 (pt);
Recreational therapists 1 (ft); Activities coordinators 1 (ft); Dietitians 1 (pt).
Affiliation Baptist
Facilities Dining room; Physical therapy room;
Activities room; Chapel; Crafts room; Laundry
room; Barber/Beauty shop.
Activities Arts and Crafts; Games; Prayer
groups; Movies; Shopping trips; Dances/Social
or cultural gatherings.

Terracina Convalescent Hospital
1620 Fern Ave, Redlands, CA, 92373 (714)
793-2609
Admin Ritchie Wetherwax. *Medical Dir/Dir of
Nursing* Bernard E Telton MD.
Licensure Skilled Care. *Beds* 78. *Certified* Medicare; Medi-Cal.
Ownership Proprietary.
Admissions Requirements Minimum age 18.
Staff Physicians 1 (pt); RNs 1 (ft), 2 (pt); LPNs
6 (ft), 5 (pt); Orderlies 2 (ft), 3 (pt); Nurses aides
24 (ft), 11 (pt); Physical therapists 1 (pt); Occupational therapists 1 (pt); Speech therapists 1
(pt); Activities coordinators 1 (ft); Dietitians 1
(pt); Dentists 1 (pt); Ophthalmologists 1 (pt);
Podiatrists 1 (pt); Audiologists 1 (pt).
Facilities Dining room; Physical therapy room;

Activities room; Laundry room; Barber/Beauty
shop.
Activities Arts and Crafts; Games; Reading
groups; Prayer groups; Movies; Shopping trips;
Dances/Social or cultural gatherings.
Description A home health agency is now associated with the facility.

REDWOOD CITY

Cordelleras Center*
200 Edmonds Rd, Redwood City, CA, 94062
(415) 397-1890
Admin Henry Lewis.
Licensure Skilled Care. *Beds* 120.
Certified Medi-Cal.
Ownership Proprietary.

Devonshire Oaks
3635 Jefferson Ave, Redwood City, CA, 94062
(415) 366-9503
Admin Pearl Farkas. *Medical Dir/Dir of
Nursing* Dr Henry Mayer.
Licensure Skilled Care. *Beds* 39.
Ownership Proprietary.
Staff Physicians 1 (pt); RNs 2 (ft), 3 (pt); LPNs
2 (ft), 1 (pt); Nurses aides 15 (ft), 4 (pt); Activities coordinators 1 (ft); Dietitians 1 (pt).
Facilities Dining room; Activities room; Laundry room; Barber/Beauty shop; Library.
Activities Arts and Crafts; Cards; Games;
Prayer groups; Movies.

Laurel Glen Convalescent Hospital*
885 Woodside Rd, Redwood City, CA, 94061
(415) 368-4174
Admin Daniel Sheehan.
Licensure Skilled Care. *Beds* 45. *Certified* Medicare; Medi-Cal.
Ownership Proprietary.

REEDLEY

Pleasant View Manor
856 S Reed, Reedley, CA, 93654 (209)
638-3615
Admin Edwin Schmidt. *Medical Dir/Dir of
Nursing* Menno S Gaede MD.
Licensure Skilled Care. *Beds* 99.
Certified Medi-Cal.
Ownership Nonprofit.
Admissions Requirements Medical examination; Physician's request.
Staff RNs 5 (ft), 5 (pt); LPNs 6 (ft), 3 (pt);
Orderlies 1 (ft); Nurses aides 39 (ft), 11 (pt);
Activities coordinators 2 (ft); Dietitians 10 (ft),
5 (pt).
Affiliation Mennonite
Facilities Dining room; Activities room; Crafts
room; Laundry room; Barber/Beauty shop;
Library.
Activities Arts and Crafts; Games; Prayer
groups; Movies; Dances/Social or cultural gatherings.
Description Volunteer program is excellent.
Daily they assist with passing juices, helping
with crafts, beauty shop, and Bible studies. Also
their fund raisers provide extra items for
patient comfort. Nurses aide trainees perform

clinical training on-site. Facility has a nice location, pleasant atmosphere, and no offensive odors.

Reedley Convalescent Hospital*
1090 E Dinuba Ave, Reedley, CA, 93654 (209) 638-3577
Admin Marjory Norris.
Licensure Skilled Care. *Beds* 56. *Certified* Medicare; Medi-Cal.
Ownership Proprietary.

Sierra View Homes Inc
1155 E Springfield, Reedley, CA, 93654 (209) 638-9226
Admin Wendell Rempel. *Medical Dir/Dir of Nursing* Marden C Habegger MD.
Licensure Skilled Care. *Beds* 59. *Certified* Medicare; Medi-Cal.
Ownership Nonprofit.
Admissions Requirements Medical examination; Physician's request.
Staff RNs 6 (ft); LPNs 1 (ft), 1 (pt); Nurses aides 24 (ft), 3 (pt); Activities coordinators 1 (ft).
Affiliation Mennonite
Facilities Dining room; Activities room; Crafts room; Laundry room; Barber/Beauty shop; Library.
Activities Arts and Crafts; Games; Movies; Dances/Social or cultural gatherings.

RESEDA

Convalescent Center of Reseda*
6740 Wilbur Ave, Reseda, CA, 91335 (213) 881-2302
Admin Ronald D O'Haver.
Licensure Skilled Care. *Beds* 99. *Certified* Medicare; Medi-Cal.
Ownership Proprietary.

Corbin Convalescent Hospital*
7120 Corbin Ave, Reseda, CA, 91335 (213) 881-4540
Admin Gita Wheelis.
Licensure Skilled Care. *Beds* 157. *Certified* Medicare; Medi-Cal.
Ownership Proprietary.

Menorah Village*
7150 Tampa Ave, Reseda, CA, 91335 (213) 345-1746
Admin Ray Shapero.
Licensure Skilled Care; Intermediate Care.
Beds SNF 66; ICF 33. *Certified* Medi-Cal.
Ownership Nonprofit.

Reseda Arms Convalescent Hospital*
7836 Reseda Blvd, Reseda, CA, 91335 (213) 881-7414
Admin Robert Garrick.
Licensure Skilled Care. *Beds* 97. *Certified* Medicare; Medi-Cal.
Ownership Proprietary.

RHEEM

Rheem Valley Convalescent Hospital
332 Park St, Rheem, CA, 94570 (415) 376-5995
Admin Elizabeth Schmidt. *Medical Dir/Dir of Nursing* Gary Miller DO.
Licensure Skilled Care. *Beds* 49. *Certified* Medicare; Medi-Cal.
Ownership Proprietary.
Admissions Requirements Minimum age 55; Medical examination; Physician's request.
Staff Physicians 4 (pt); RNs 3 (ft), 5 (pt); LPNs 2 (ft); Nurses aides 10 (ft), 25 (pt); Physical therapists 1 (pt); Speech therapists 1 (pt); Activities coordinators 1 (pt); Dietitians 1 (pt); Dentists 1 (pt); Podiatrists 1 (pt).
Facilities Dining room; Physical therapy room; Activities room; Crafts room; Barber/Beauty shop; Sitting rooms.
Activities Arts and Crafts; Games; Reading groups; Prayer groups; Movies; Dances/Social or cultural gatherings; Volunteers groups and/or individual.
Description Rheem Valley Convalescent Hospital is a one-level building nestled in the hills of a suburban area, surrounded by beautiful landscaping which is available for patients leisure activities. A family night presented one night every month brings patients, staff, family, and friends together for an informative and social evening.

RIALTO

Crestview Convalescent Hospital
1471 S Riverside, Rialto, CA, 92376 (714) 877-1361
Admin Alice T Farley. *Medical Dir/Dir of Nursing* Roy V Berglund MD.
Licensure Skilled Care. *Beds* 201. *Certified* Medicare.
Ownership Proprietary.
Staff Physicians 1 (pt); RNs 4 (ft), 3 (pt); LPNs 20 (ft), 8 (pt); Orderlies 9 (ft), 3 (pt); Nurses aides 69 (ft), 25 (pt); Physical therapists 2 (pt); Occupational therapists 1 (pt); Speech therapists; Activities coordinators 2 (ft); Dietitians 1 (ft); Dentists 1 (pt); Podiatrists 1 (pt); Audiologists 1 (pt).
Facilities Dining room; Physical therapy room; Activities room; Laundry room; Barber/Beauty shop.
Activities Arts and Crafts; Cards; Games; Prayer groups; Movies; Shopping trips; Dances/Social or cultural gatherings.
Description Residents enjoy daily exercise program. Twenty beds are reserved for Medicare distinct part. Two LVNs are assigned to care for these 20 patients with 4 aides to help them. Specialized rehabilitation program.

RICHMOND

Ellen S Memorial Convalescent Hospital*
2716 Ohio Ave, Richmond, CA, 94804 (415) 233-6720
Admin E B Griffin Jr.
Licensure Skilled Care. *Beds* 43.
Ownership Proprietary.

Greenridge Heights Convalescent Hospital*
2150 Pyramid Dr, Richmond, CA, 94803 (415) 222-1242
Admin Ronald K Martin.

Licensure Skilled Care. *Beds* 59. *Certified* Medicare; Medi-Cal.
Ownership Proprietary.

Shields and Terrell Convalescent Hospital*
1919 Cutting Blvd, Richmond, CA, 94804 (415) 233-8513
Admin William M Shields.
Licensure Skilled Care. *Beds* 84. *Certified* Medicare; Medi-Cal.
Ownership Proprietary.

Walker Convalescent Hospital Inc*
955 23rd St, Richmond, CA, 94804 (415) 235-6550
Admin Johnnie M Walker.
Licensure Intermediate Care. *Beds* 25. *Certified* Medicare.
Ownership Proprietary.

RIPON

Bethany Home Society San Joaquin County
930 W Main St, Ripon, CA, 95366 (209) 599-4221
Admin Kenneth M Hekman.
Licensure Skilled Care. *Beds* 74. *Certified* Medicare; Medi-Cal.
Ownership Nonprofit.
Admissions Requirements Minimum age 21; Medical examination; Physician's request.
Staff RNs 2 (ft), 4 (pt); LPNs 4 (ft), 6 (pt); Nurses aides 20 (ft), 10 (pt); Physical therapists 2 (pt); Activities coordinators 1 (ft); Dietitians 1 (pt); Podiatrists 1 (pt).
Facilities Dining room; Physical therapy room; Activities room; Crafts room; Laundry room; Barber/Beauty shop; Library.
Activities Arts and Crafts; Games; Prayer groups; Movies; Shopping trips.
Description Facility is noted for quality of care as indicated by a zero-deficiency survey by the California Department of Health in 1983.

RIVERBANK

Riverbluff Convalescent Hospital*
2649 W Topeka, Riverbank, CA, 95367 (209) 869-2569
Admin Mary E Baker.
Licensure Skilled Care. *Beds* 99. *Certified* Medicare; Medi-Cal.
Ownership Proprietary.

RIVERSIDE

Arlington Gardens Convalescent Hospital
3766 Nye Ave, Riverside, CA, 92505 (714) 689-2340
Admin Eileen McPherson. *Medical Dir/Dir of Nursing* Stanley Chartier MD.
Licensure Skilled Care. *Beds* 27. *Certified* Medicare; Medi-Cal.
Ownership Proprietary.
Staff RNs 1 (ft), 1 (pt); LPNs 2 (ft), 2 (pt); Nurses aides 6 (ft), 4 (pt); Physical therapists 1 (pt); Reality therapists 1 (pt); Recreational therapists 1 (pt); Occupational therapists 1 (pt); Speech therapists 1 (pt); Activities coordinators 1 (ft); Dietitians 1 (pt); Dentists 1 (pt); Ophthal-

mologists 1 (pt); Podiatrists 1 (pt); Audiologists 1 (pt).
Facilities Dining room; Activities room; Crafts room; Laundry room; Barber/Beauty shop.
Activities Arts and Crafts; Cards; Games; Reading groups; Prayer groups; Shopping trips; Dances/Social or cultural gatherings.

Beverly Manor Convalescent Hospital
4768 Palm Ave, Riverside, CA, 92501 (714) 686-9000
Admin Fred W Mikesell. *Medical Dir/Dir of Nursing* Rodney Soholt MD.
Licensure Skilled Care. *Beds* 49. *Certified* Medicare; Medi-Cal.
Ownership Proprietary.
Admissions Requirements Minimum age 18.
Staff RNs 2 (ft); LPNs 3 (ft); Orderlies 3 (ft); Nurses aides 11 (ft); Physical therapists 1 (pt); Recreational therapists 1 (pt); Occupational therapists 1 (pt); Speech therapists 1 (pt); Activities coordinators 1 (ft); Dietitians 1 (pt); Dentists 1 (pt); Ophthalmologists 1 (pt); Podiatrists 1 (pt); Audiologists 1 (pt).
Facilities Dining room; Physical therapy room; Activities room; Laundry room; Barber/Beauty shop; Library.
Activities Arts and Crafts; Cards; Games; Reading groups; Movies; Shopping trips; Dances/Social or cultural gatherings.
Description Facility features adult education programs and a facility band.

Beverly Manor Sanitarium
4580 Palm Ave, Riverside, CA, 92501 (714) 684-7701
Admin Charles Eggleston. *Medical Dir/Dir of Nursing* Dr L Murad.
Licensure Skilled Care. *Beds* 120.
Certified Medi-Cal.
Ownership Proprietary.
Admissions Requirements Minimum age 18; Medical examination; Physician's request.
Staff Physicians; RNs; LPNs; Orderlies; Nurses aides; Occupational therapists; Speech therapists; Activities coordinators; Dietitians; Dentists; Ophthalmologists; Podiatrists; Audiologists.

Chapman Convalescent Hospital*
4301 Caroline Ct, Riverside, CA, 92506 (714) 683-7111
Admin Betty Lou Beeman.
Licensure Skilled Care. *Beds* 33.
Certified Medi-Cal.
Ownership Proprietary.

Community Convalescent Center
4070 Jurupa Ave, Riverside, CA, 92506 (714) 682-2522
Admin Bruce W Bennett. *Medical Dir/Dir of Nursing* H H Stone MD.
Licensure Skilled Care. *Beds* 158. *Certified* Medicare; Medi-Cal.
Ownership Proprietary.
Staff Physicians 1 (pt); RNs 7 (ft), 7 (pt); LPNs 10 (ft), 7 (pt); Orderlies 5 (ft), 2 (pt); Nurses aides 66 (ft), 28 (pt); Physical therapists 3 (ft); Reality therapists 1 (ft); Occupational therapists 1 (pt); Speech therapists 1 (pt); Activities coordinators 3 (ft), 1 (pt); Dietitians 1 (pt); Dentists 1 (pt); Podiatrists 1 (pt).
Facilities Dining room; Physical therapy room;

Activities room; Crafts room; Barber/Beauty shop; Library.
Activities Arts and Crafts; Cards; Games; Reading groups; Prayer groups; Movies; Shopping trips; Dances/Social or cultural gatherings.

Cypress Gardens Convalescent Hospital
9025 Colorado Ave, Riverside, CA, 92503 (714) 688-3643
Admin Gretchen Reynolds. *Medical Dir/Dir of Nursing* Rodney Soholt.
Licensure Skilled Care. *Beds* 120. *Certified* Medicare; Medi-Cal.
Ownership Proprietary.
Admissions Requirements Minimum age 18.
Staff RNs 6 (ft), 4 (pt); LPNs 7 (ft), 2 (pt); Orderlies 3 (ft); Nurses aides 45 (ft); Physical therapists 1 (pt); Occupational therapists 1 (pt); Speech therapists 1 (pt); Activities coordinators 2 (ft); Dietitians 1 (ft); Dentists 1 (pt); Ophthalmologists 1 (pt); Podiatrists 1 (pt); Audiologists 1 (pt).
Facilities Dining room; Physical therapy room; Activities room; Crafts room; Laundry room; Barber/Beauty shop.
Activities Arts and Crafts; Cards; Games; Reading groups; Prayer groups; Movies; Shopping trips; Dances/Social or cultural gatherings.

Extended Care Hospital of Riverside*
8171 Magnolia Ave, Riverside, CA, 92504 (714) 687-3842
Admin Shirley Y Leedy.
Licensure Skilled Care. *Beds* 99. *Certified* Medicare; Medi-Cal.
Ownership Proprietary.

La Sierra Convalescent Hospital*
11162 Palm Terrace Ln, Riverside, CA, 92505 (714) 687-7330
Admin Onie L Denson.
Licensure Skilled Care. *Beds* 75. *Certified* Medicare; Medi-Cal.
Ownership Proprietary.

Lakeview Developmental Disability Center*
8781 Lakeview Ave, Riverside, CA, 92509 (714) 685-1531
Admin Violet Livingston.
Licensure Skilled Care; Intermediate Care for Mentally Retarded. *Beds* 188. *Certified* Medicare; Medi-Cal.
Ownership Proprietary.

Magnolia Convalescent Hospital*
8133 Magnolia Ave, Riverside, CA, 92504 (714) 688-4321
Admin Raymond N Beeman.
Licensure Skilled Care. *Beds* 94. *Certified* Medicare; Medi-Cal.
Ownership Proprietary.

Miller's Progressive Care
8951 Granite Hill Dr, Riverside, CA, 92509 (714) 685-7474
Admin W W Miller. *Medical Dir/Dir of Nursing* Raymond West MD.
Licensure Skilled Care. *Beds* 70.
Ownership Proprietary.
Facilities Dining room; Activities room; Crafts room; Laundry room; Barber/Beauty shop.
Activities Arts and Crafts; Cards; Games;

Reading groups; Prayer groups; Movies; Shopping trips; Dances/Social or cultural gatherings; Adult education from local school district.

Mission Convalescent Hospital*
8487 Magnolia Ave, Riverside, CA, 92504 (714) 688-2222
Admin Jack E Easterday.
Licensure Skilled Care. *Beds* 40. *Certified* Medicare; Medi-Cal.
Ownership Proprietary.

Orangetree Convalescent Hospital*
4000 Harrison St, Riverside, CA, 92503 (714) 785-6060
Admin A M Richards.
Licensure Skilled Care. *Beds* 140. *Certified* Medicare; Medi-Cal.
Ownership Proprietary.

Plymouth Tower
3401 Lemon St, Riverside, CA, 92501 (714) 686-8202
Admin Naomi R Keener. *Medical Dir/Dir of Nursing* Dr Herman Stone.
Licensure Skilled Care. *Beds* 36.
Certified Medi-Cal.
Ownership Nonprofit.
Admissions Requirements Medical examination; Physician's request.
Affiliation Church of Christ
Facilities Dining room; Activities room; Laundry room; Library; Multi-purpose room.
Activities Arts and Crafts; Cards; Games; Reading groups; Prayer groups; Movies; Shopping trips; Dances/Social or cultural gatherings.
Description Facility is close to downtown area, library, post office, and churches.

Villa Convalescent Hospital
8965 Magnolia Ave, Riverside, CA, 92503 (714) 689-5788
Admin Larry J Mays. *Medical Dir/Dir of Nursing* Robert H Bom MD.
Licensure Skilled Care. *Beds* 49.
Certified Medi-Cal.
Ownership Proprietary.
Staff RNs 1 (ft), 1 (pt); Nurses aides 10 (ft), 5 (pt); Activities coordinators 1 (ft); Dietitians 1 (pt).
Facilities Dining room; Activities room; Crafts room; Laundry room; Barber/Beauty shop.
Activities Arts and Crafts; Cards; Games; Reading groups; Prayer groups; Movies; Shopping trips; Dances/Social or cultural gatherings.

ROSEMEAD

California Christian Home*
8417 E Mission Dr, Rosemead, CA, 91770 (213) 287-0438
Admin James R Bennett.
Licensure Skilled Care. *Beds* 59.
Certified Medi-Cal.
Ownership Nonprofit.

Del Mar Convalescent Hospital*
3136 N Del Mar Ave, Rosemead, CA, 91770 (213) 288-8353
Admin Charles P Leggett.

Licensure Skilled Care. *Beds* 59. *Certified* Medicare; Medi-Cal.
Ownership Proprietary.

Green Acres Lodge*
8101 E Hill Dr, Rosemead, CA, 91770 (213) 280-5682
Admin Baird D Wayne.
Licensure Skilled Care. *Beds* 85. *Certified* Medicare; Medi-Cal.
Ownership Proprietary.

Monterey Sanitarium*
1267 San Gabriel Blvd, Rosemead, CA, 91770 (213) 280-3220
Admin Harold J Moser.
Licensure Skilled Care. *Beds* 132.
Certified Medi-Cal.
Ownership Proprietary.

San Gabriel Convalescent Center
8035 E Hill Dr, Rosemead, CA, 91770 (213) 280-4820
Admin Jan Stine. *Medical Dir/Dir of Nursing* Richard Dwyer MD.
Licensure Skilled Care; Intermediate Care for Mentally Retarded. *Beds* SNF 96; ICF/MR 55.
Certified Medicare; Medi-Cal.
Ownership Proprietary.
Admissions Requirements Medical examination; Physician's request.
Staff RNs 3 (ft), 3 (pt); LPNs 6 (ft), 4 (pt); Nurses aides; Physical therapists; Reality therapists; Recreational therapists; Occupational therapists; Speech therapists; Activities coordinators 1 (ft); Dietitians; Dentists; Ophthalmologists; Podiatrists; Audiologists.
Facilities Dining room; Physical therapy room; Activities room; Crafts room; Barber/Beauty shop.
Activities Arts and Crafts; Cards; Games; Reading groups; Prayer groups; Movies; Shopping trips; Dances/Social or cultural gatherings.
Description Developmentally disabled patients admitted age 8 and above; geriatric patients, 50 and older.

ROSEVILLE

Hacienda Convalescent Hospital*
600 Sunrise Ave, Roseville, CA, 95678 (916) 782-3131
Admin Donald D Williams.
Licensure Skilled Care. *Beds* 98. *Certified* Medicare; Medi-Cal.
Ownership Proprietary.

Roseville Convalescent Hospital
1161 Cirby St, Roseville, CA, 95678 (916) 782-1238
Admin Bernice Schrabeck. *Medical Dir/Dir of Nursing* Richard Chun MD.
Licensure Skilled Care. *Beds* 210. *Certified* Medicare; Medi-Cal.
Ownership Proprietary.
Admissions Requirements Medical examination; Physician's request.
Staff RNs 7 (ft), 4 (pt); LPNs 12 (ft), 5 (pt); Orderlies 2 (ft); Nurses aides 56 (ft), 24 (pt); Physical therapists 1 (pt); Occupational therapists 1 (pt); Speech therapists 1 (pt); Activities coordinators 2 (ft); Dietitians 1 (ft); Dentists 1

(pt); Ophthalmologists 1 (pt); Podiatrists 1 (pt); Audiologists 1 (pt).
Facilities Dining room; Physical therapy room; Activities room; Chapel; Crafts room; Laundry room; Barber/Beauty shop; Library.
Activities Arts and Crafts; Cards; Games; Reading groups; Prayer groups; Movies; Shopping trips; Dances/Social or cultural gatherings.
Description Roseville Convalescent Hospital is located in the Sierra Nevada foothills with easy access to metropolitan shopping to the west or mountain solitude and gold panning to the east.

Sierra Convalescent Hospital
310 Oak Ridge Dr, Roseville, CA, 95678 (916) 782-3188
Admin Robert J Garber. *Medical Dir/Dir of Nursing* Donald Reville MD.
Licensure Skilled Care. *Beds* 67. *Certified* Medicare; Medi-Cal.
Ownership Proprietary.
Admissions Requirements Medical examination; Physician's request.
Staff RNs 6 (ft), 3 (pt); Nurses aides 50 (ft), 15 (pt); Physical therapists 1 (pt); Recreational therapists 1 (ft); Occupational therapists 1 (pt); Speech therapists 1 (pt); Activities coordinators 1 (ft); Dietitians 1 (ft); Dentists 1 (pt); Podiatrists 1 (pt); Audiologists 1 (pt).
Facilities Dining room; Physical therapy room; Activities room; Crafts room; Laundry room; Barber/Beauty shop; Library.
Activities Arts and Crafts; Cards; Games; Reading groups; Prayer groups; Movies; Shopping trips; Dances/Social or cultural gatherings.

RUBIDOUX

Mount Rubidoux Convalescent Hospital
6401 33rd St, Rubidoux, CA, 92509 (714) 681-2200
Admin Bertha Campos. *Medical Dir/Dir of Nursing* Dr Robert Bom.
Licensure Skilled Care; Intermediate Care. *Beds* 99. *Certified* Medicare; Medi-Cal.
Ownership Proprietary.
Admissions Requirements Physician's request.
Staff RNs 2 (ft), 2 (pt); LPNs 7 (ft), 3 (pt); Orderlies 4 (ft); Nurses aides 26 (ft), 5 (pt); Physical therapists 1 (pt); Activities coordinators 4 (ft).
Facilities Dining room; Activities room; Laundry room; Barber/Beauty shop; TV room; Enclosed outdoor patios.
Activities Arts and Crafts; Cards; Games; Reading groups; Prayer groups; Movies; Shopping trips; Dances/Social or cultural gatherings; Cooking classes.
Description Facility has classes to certify nurse assistants. Located at the end of a cul-de-sac with 17 acres of land; every room is individualized with different wallpaper and color coordinated bedspreads.

SACRAMENTO

Arden Memorial Convalescent Hospital
3400 Alta Arden Expwy, Sacramento, CA, 95825 (916) 481-5500
Admin Harold D Mays. *Medical Dir/Dir of Nursing* B G Wagner MD.

Licensure Skilled Care. *Beds* 190. *Certified* Medicare; Medi-Cal.
Ownership Proprietary.
Staff RNs 6 (ft), 6 (pt); LPNs 11 (ft), 5 (pt); Nurses aides 63 (ft), 13 (pt); Activities coordinators 1 (ft).
Facilities Dining room; Physical therapy room; Activities room; Crafts room; Laundry room; Barber/Beauty shop.
Activities Arts and Crafts; Cards; Games; Reading groups; Prayer groups; Movies; Dances/Social or cultural gatherings.

Ashland Manor*
500 Jessie Ave, Sacramento, CA, 95838 (916) 922-7177
Admin Dorris Ash.
Licensure Skilled Care. *Beds* 162. *Certified* Medicare; Medi-Cal.
Ownership Proprietary.

Center Skilled Nursing Facility
2257 Fair Oaks Blvd, Sacramento, CA, 95825 (916) 922-8351
Admin Darrell Zimmerman. *Medical Dir/Dir of Nursing* William T Kelley MD.
Licensure Skilled Care. *Beds* 139. *Certified* Medicare; Medi-Cal.
Ownership Proprietary.
Admissions Requirements Physician's request.
Staff RNs 8 (ft), 2 (pt); LPNs 9 (ft), 2 (pt); Orderlies 3 (ft); Nurses aides 45 (ft), 8 (pt); Activities coordinators 1 (ft); Dietitians 1 (ft).
Facilities Dining room; Physical therapy room; Activities room; Crafts room; Laundry room; Barber/Beauty shop.
Activities Arts and Crafts; Cards; Games; Reading groups; Prayer groups; Movies; Shopping trips; Dances/Social or cultural gatherings; Outside expeditions to railroad museum, zoo, etc.

Crestwood Manor
2600 Stockton Blvd, Sacramento, CA, 95817 (916) 452-1431
Admin Doris Ross. *Medical Dir/Dir of Nursing* Donald Slaughter MD.
Licensure Skilled Care. *Beds* 130. *Certified* Medicare; Medi-Cal.
Ownership Proprietary.
Admissions Requirements Minimum age 18; Medical examination; Physician's request.
Staff Physicians 1 (pt); RNs 5 (ft); LPNs 10 (ft), 4 (pt); Orderlies 15 (ft); Nurses aides 60 (ft); Recreational therapists 1 (ft); Occupational therapists 1 (ft); Activities coordinators 2 (ft); Dietitians 1 (ft).
Facilities Dining room; Activities room; Crafts room; Laundry room; Barber/Beauty shop; Library.
Activities Arts and Crafts; Cards; Games; Reading groups; Prayer groups; Movies; Shopping trips; Dances/Social or cultural gatherings.
Description Crestwood-Sacramento is a locked psychiatric treatment center that specializes in the use of behavior modification techniques to help those people with chronic mental problems and low frustration tolerance.

Elizabeth Manor Convalescent Hospital*
5000 Folsom Blvd, Sacramento, CA, 95819 (916) 452-4191

Admin Janice A McDonald.
Licensure Skilled Care. *Beds* 121.
Ownership Proprietary.

Eskaton Glenwood Manor
501 Jessie Ave, Sacramento, CA, 95838 (916)
922-8855
Admin Fred Stacey. *Medical Dir/Dir of
Nursing* Justin English MD.
Licensure Intermediate Care. *Beds* 128. *Certi-
fied* Medi-Cal.
Ownership Nonprofit.
Admissions Requirements Minimum age 65;
Medical examination; Physician's request.
Staff RNs 4 (ft); LPNs 4 (ft); Nurses aides 17
(ft); Activities coordinators 2 (ft).
Facilities Dining room; Physical therapy room;
Activities room; Crafts room; Laundry room;
Barber/Beauty shop; Library.
Activities Arts and Crafts; Cards; Games;
Reading groups; Prayer groups; Movies; Shop-
ping trips; Dances/Social or cultural gatherings.
Description Eskaton Glenwood Manor is
located in a semi-rural setting with large, beau-
tiful landscaped yards and patios all secured for
resident safety.

Florin Convalescent Hospital*
7400 24th St, Sacramento, CA, 95822 (916)
422-4825
Admin Don Zimmerman.
Licensure Skilled Care. *Beds* 118. *Certified* Medicare; Medi-Cal.
Ownership Proprietary.

Garden Court Convalescent Hospital
2291 Fair Oaks Blvd, Sacramento, CA, 95825
(916) 927-2741
Admin Michael A Hideiros. *Medical Dir/Dir
of Nursing* W Dugdale MD.
Licensure Skilled Care. *Beds* 63. *Certified* Medicare; Medi-Cal.
Ownership Proprietary.
Admissions Requirements Minimum age 40;
Medical examination; Physician's request.
Staff Physicians 1 (pt); RNs 1 (ft), 1 (pt); LPNs
7 (ft), 2 (pt); Orderlies 4 (ft), 1 (pt); Nurses aides
28 (ft), 8 (pt); Physical therapists 1 (pt); Occu-
pational therapists 1 (pt); Speech therapists 1
(pt); Activities coordinators 1 (ft); Dietitians 1
(pt); Dentists 1 (pt); Ophthalmologists 1 (pt);
Podiatrists 1 (pt); Audiologists 1 (pt).
Facilities Dining room; Physical therapy room;
Activities room; Laundry room; Barber/Beauty
shop.
Activities Arts and Crafts; Cards; Games;
Reading groups; Prayer groups; Shopping trips;
Dances/Social or cultural gatherings.
Description Facility is located in beautiful east
Sacramento, close to 3 acute hospitals, doctors
offices, and new shopping center. Facility offers
active recreation program including adult edu-
cation.

Gardens Skilled Nursing Facility
2221 Fair Oaks Blvd, Sacramento, CA, 95825
(916) 927-1802
Admin Darrell Zimmerman. *Medical Dir/Dir
of Nursing* Kenneth Hodge MD.
Licensure Intermediate Care for Mentally
Retarded. *Beds* 56. *Certified* Medi-Cal.
Ownership Proprietary.
Admissions Requirements Minimum age 16.

Staff RNs 5 (ft); LPNs 2 (ft); Orderlies 27 (ft);
Activities coordinators 1 (ft).
Facilities Dining room; Physical therapy room;
Activities room; Laundry room.
Activities Arts and Crafts; Cards; Games;
Reading groups; Movies; Shopping trips; Dan-
ces/Social or cultural gatherings.
Description This 56-bed facility serves
developmentally disabled (physically handicapped) young adults with the primary goal
being to afford clients opportunities/programs
designed to develop their capabilities to their
maximum potential.

Greenhaven Country Place
455 Florin Rd, Sacramento, CA, 95831 (916)
393-2550
Admin Douglas R Goertzen.
Licensure Skilled Care; Intermediate Care.
Beds SNF 140; ICF 8. *Certified* Medicare;
Medi-Cal.
Ownership Proprietary.
Facilities Dining room; Physical therapy room;
Activities room; Laundry room; Barber/Beauty
shop; Library.
Activities Arts and Crafts; Cards; Games;
Reading groups; Prayer groups; Movies; Dan-
ces/Social or cultural gatherings.
Description Adult day care facility activities are
integrated with those of the residents, providing
reality orientation, stimulation projects, sports,
etc. There is a full spectrum of volunteers from
senior companions to students, as well as elementary school pen pals. The residents enjoy a
country setting overlooking a lake.

Heritage Convalescent Hospital
5255 Hemlock St, Sacramento, CA, 95841
(916) 331-4590
Admin Sheila Waddell. *Medical Dir/Dir of
Nursing* William Hedges MD.
Licensure Skilled Care. *Beds* 99. *Certified* Medicare; Medi-Cal.
Ownership Proprietary.
Staff Physicians 1 (pt); RNs 3 (ft), 1 (pt); LPNs
12 (ft), 2 (pt); Orderlies 2 (ft), 1 (pt); Nurses
aides 45 (ft), 6 (pt); Physical therapists 2 (pt);
Reality therapists 1 (pt); Recreational therapists
2 (pt); Occupational therapists 1 (pt); Speech
therapists 1 (pt); Activities coordinators 2 (ft);
Dietitians 1 (pt); Dentists 1 (pt); Ophthalmolo-
gists 1 (pt); Podiatrists 1 (pt); Audiologists 1
(pt).
Facilities Dining room; Physical therapy room;
Activities room; Crafts room; Laundry room;
Barber/Beauty shop.
Activities Arts and Crafts; Cards; Games;
Reading groups; Prayer groups; Movies; Shop-
ping trips; Dances/Social or cultural gatherings.

Hillhaven Convalescent Hospital*
862 39th St, Sacramento, CA, 95816 (916)
455-3014
Admin Patricia Linn.
Licensure Skilled Care. *Beds* 89. *Certified* Medicare; Medi-Cal.
Ownership Proprietary.

Hillhaven—Sherwood Convalescent Hospital*
4700 Elvas Ave, Sacramento, CA, 95819 (916)
452-5752
Admin Mary Tommolilo.

Licensure Skilled Care. *Beds* 62. *Certified* Medicare; Medi-Cal.
Ownership Proprietary.

Hy-Lond Convalescent Hospital*
4635 College Oak Dr, Sacramento, CA, 95841
(916) 481-7434
Admin Sylvia A Hatfield.
Licensure Skilled Care. *Beds* 120. *Certified* Medicare; Medi-Cal.
Ownership Proprietary.

**Mount Olivette Meadows Convalescent
Hospital***
2240 Northrop Ave, Sacramento, CA, 95825
(916) 927-1337
Admin Ronald T Vanderbeek.
Licensure Skilled Care; Intermediate Care for
Mentally Retarded. *Beds* 58. *Certified* Medi-
Cal.
Ownership Proprietary.

Park Sutter Convalescent Hospital
2600 L St, Sacramento, CA, 95816 (916)
444-7290
Admin Winnie-Ruth Stevenson. *Medical Dir-
/Dir of Nursing* Justin English MD.
Licensure Skilled Care. *Beds* 132. *Cer-
tified* Medicare; Medi-Cal.
Ownership Proprietary.
Facilities Dining room; Physical therapy room;
Activities room; Barber/Beauty shop; Library.
Activities Arts and Crafts; Cards; Games;
Reading groups; Prayer groups; Movies; Dan-
ces/Social or cultural gatherings.
Description Our facility is the largest in the
heart of Sacramento. It is located just off the
expressway and bus lines. We have an ongoing
activity program. Our speciality is giving love
along with care.

Pioneer House*
415 P St, Sacramento, CA, 95814 (916)
442-4906
Admin Philip S Richardson.
Licensure Skilled Care. *Beds* 50.
Certified Medi-Cal.
Ownership Nonprofit.

Quinlan Manor*
919 8th Ave, Sacramento, CA, 95818 (916)
922-7177
Admin Ann Pelzman.
Licensure Intermediate Care. *Beds* 22. *Certified* Medi-Cal.
Ownership Proprietary.

Riverside Convalescent Hospital
1090 Rio Ln, Sacramento, CA, 95822 (916)
446-2506
Admin Helen B Edington. *Medical Dir/Dir of
Nursing* G W O'Brien MD.
Licensure Skilled Care. *Beds* 51. *Cer-
tified* Medicare; Medi-Cal.
Ownership Proprietary.
Admissions Requirements Medical examina-
tion; Physician's request.
Staff RNs 2 (ft); LPNs 3 (ft), 3 (pt); Nurses
aides 31 (ft), 5 (pt); Physical therapists 2 (pt);
Recreational therapists 1 (ft); Occupational
therapists 1 (pt); Speech therapists 1 (pt);
Activities coordinators 1 (ft); Dietitians 1 (pt);
Dentists 1 (pt); Ophthalmologists 1 (pt); Podia-

trists 1 (pt).
Facilities Dining room; Physical therapy room; Activities room; Crafts room; Laundry room; Barber/Beauty shop; Library.
Activities Arts and Crafts; Cards; Games; Reading groups; Prayer groups; Movies; Dances/Social or cultural gatherings.

Royal Manor Convalescent Hospital Inc*
5901 Lemon Hill Ave, Sacramento, CA, 95824
(916) 383-2741
Admin Arden Millerman.
Licensure Skilled Care. *Beds* 49. *Certified* Medicare; Medi-Cal.
Ownership Proprietary.

Sacramento Convalescent Hospital*
3700 H St, Sacramento, CA, 95816 (916) 452-3592
Admin Chris J Bryant.
Licensure Skilled Care. *Beds* 86. *Certified* Medicare; Medi-Cal.
Ownership Proprietary.

Saylor Lane Convalescent Hospital
3500 Folsom Blvd, Sacramento, CA, 95816
(916) 457-6521
Admin Louise U Muller. *Medical Dir/Dir of Nursing* Dr James Coyle.
Licensure Skilled Care. *Beds* 42. *Certified* Medicare; Medi-Cal.
Ownership Proprietary.
Admissions Requirements Medical examination; Physician's request.
Facilities Dining room; Physical therapy room; Activities room; Crafts room; Laundry room; Barber/Beauty shop.
Activities Arts and Crafts; Cards; Games; Prayer groups; Movies; Dances/Social or cultural gatherings; Outings; Picnics; Musicals.
Description Facility is a small, personal-type facility featuring daily activities and special affairs for holiday and birthdays; newly refurnished and updated; very light and cheerful atmosphere.

Trinity House
2701 Capitol Ave, Sacramento, CA, 95816
(916) 446-4806
Admin Philip S Richardson. *Medical Dir/Dir of Nursing* Dr Justin English.
Licensure Skilled Care. *Beds* 29.
Certified Medi-Cal.
Ownership Nonprofit.
Admissions Requirements Minimum age 62; Medical examination.
Staff Physicians 1 (pt); RNs 1 (ft), 1 (pt); LPNs 4 (ft); Orderlies 1 (ft), 1 (pt); Nurses aides 8 (ft), 2 (pt); Physical therapists 1 (pt); Speech therapists 1 (pt); Activities coordinators 1 (ft); Dietitians 1 (pt); Dentists 1 (pt); Ophthalmologists 1 (pt); Podiatrists 1 (pt); Audiologists 1 (pt).
Facilities Dining room; Activities room; Laundry room; Barber/Beauty shop; Library.
Activities Arts and Crafts; Cards; Games; Reading groups; Prayer groups; Movies; Shopping trips; Dances/Social or cultural gatherings.
Description Trinity House is unique in that it provides independent living, personal care, and skilled nursing in one facility. A resident's physically and emotionally changing needs can be accomodated without the trauma of transfer.

Valley Skilled Nursing Facility*
2120 Stockton Blvd, Sacramento, CA, 95817
(916) 452-6631
Admin Gwen Wilson.
Licensure Skilled Care. *Beds* 59. *Certified* Medicare; Medi-Cal.
Ownership Proprietary.

SAINT HELENA

Vintage Convalescent Hospital*
830 Pratt Ave, Saint Helena, CA, 94574 (707) 963-2791
Admin Michael Giardullo.
Licensure Skilled Care. *Beds* 70. *Certified* Medicare; Medi-Cal.
Ownership Proprietary.

SALINAS

Casa Serena de Salinas
720 E Romie Ln, Salinas, CA, 93901 (408) 424-8072
Admin Ronald L Walton. *Medical Dir/Dir of Nursing* Dr Engerhorn.
Licensure Skilled Care. *Beds* 96. *Certified* Medicare; Medi-Cal.
Ownership Proprietary.
Staff RNs 5 (ft); LPNs 6 (ft), 4 (pt); Orderlies 4 (ft); Nurses aides 40 (ft), 5 (pt); Physical therapists 1 (pt); Occupational therapists 1 (pt); Speech therapists 1 (pt); Activities coordinators 2 (ft); Dietitians 1 (pt).
Facilities Dining room; Physical therapy room; Activities room; Crafts room; Laundry room; Barber/Beauty shop; Living room; Speech therapy room; Occupational therapy room.
Activities Arts and Crafts; Games; Reading groups; Prayer groups; Movies; Shopping trips; Dances/Social or cultural gatherings; Candlelight dinners; Barbecues.
Description This is a new, modern, Spanish-style convalescent hospital. Each patient room opens onto a private or inner courtyard and the bird atrium and fish aquarium can be viewed from patients lobby, living room, and dining area. Hospital provides excellent patient care with complete outpatient therapy department. Beautiful facility, excellent care, higher staffing, and quality meals earned the facility the reputation as the best in the area.

Driftwood Convalescent Hospital
350 Iris Dr, Salinas, CA, 93906 (408) 449-1515
Admin Rebecca Garrigan. *Medical Dir/Dir of Nursing* Raymond L Hack MD.
Licensure Skilled Care. *Beds* 99. *Certified* Medicare; Medi-Cal.
Ownership Proprietary.

Katherine Convalescent Hospital*
315 Alameda St, Salinas, CA, 93901 (408) 424-1878
Admin Mary Klugherz.
Licensure Skilled Care. *Beds* 51. *Certified* Medicare; Medi-Cal.
Ownership Proprietary.

Romie Lane Convalescent Hospital
637 E Romie Lane, Salinas, CA, 93901 (408) 424-0687

Admin Frank J Balestrieri. *Medical Dir/Dir of Nursing* Dr A L Wessels.
Licensure Skilled Care. *Beds* 99. *Certified* Medicare; Medi-Cal.
Ownership Proprietary.
Admissions Requirements Medical examination; Physician's request.
Staff Physicians; RNs; LPNs; Orderlies; Nurses aides; Physical therapists; Reality therapists; Recreational therapists; Occupational therapists; Speech therapists; Activities coordinators; Dietitians; Dentists; Podiatrists.
Facilities Dining room; Physical therapy room; Activities room; Laundry room; Barber/Beauty shop; TV room with pool table.
Activities Arts and Crafts; Cards; Games; Reading groups; Prayer groups; Movies; Shopping trips; Dances/Social or cultural gatherings; Field trips.
Description The facility is located on a street populated primarily by medical buildings with acute care one-block away. Dentists, doctors, and pharmacies are very near. Our facility offers a social dining program which is excellent.

Skyline Convalescent Hospital
348 Iris Dr, Salinas, CA, 93901 (408) 449-5401
Admin David A Holtz. *Medical Dir/Dir of Nursing* Raymond Hack MD.
Licensure Skilled Care. *Beds* 80. *Certified* Medicare; Medi-Cal.
Ownership Proprietary.
Staff RNs 2 (ft), 3 (pt); LPNs 8 (ft), 2 (pt); Nurses aides 31 (ft), 4 (pt); Physical therapists 3 (pt); Recreational therapists 1 (pt); Occupational therapists 1 (pt); Speech therapists 1 (pt); Activities coordinators 1 (ft); Dietitians 1 (ft), 1 (pt); Dentists 1 (pt); Ophthalmologists 1 (pt); Podiatrists 1 (pt); Audiologists 1 (pt).
Facilities Dining room; Physical therapy room; Activities room; Laundry room; Barber/Beauty shop.
Activities Arts and Crafts; Cards; Games; Reading groups; Prayer groups; Movies; Dances/Social or cultural gatherings.
Description Facility is located in the beautiful, clean surroundings of a quiet residential area minutes from the Monterey Peninsula and the heart of the Salinas Valley. Skyline Convalescent Hospital offers quality professional nursing care and a warm, loving environment to its patients.

SAN ANDREAS

Mark Twain Convalescent Hospital*
900 Mountain Ranch Rd, San Andreas, CA, 95249 (209) 754-3823
Admin Elaine Hoff.
Licensure Skilled Care. *Beds* 99. *Certified* Medicare; Medi-Cal.
Ownership Proprietary.

San Andreas Convalescent Hospital*
556 Toyon Rd, San Andreas, CA, 95249 (209) 754-4213
Admin Elaine Hoff.
Licensure Skilled Care. *Beds* 30. *Certified* Medicare; Medi-Cal.
Ownership Proprietary.

SAN BERNARDINO

Arrowhead Home*
4343 Sierra Way, San Bernardino, CA, 92404
(714) 886-4731
Admin Donald N Popovich.
Licensure Intermediate Care. *Beds* 58. *Certified* Medi-Cal.
Ownership Proprietary.

Del Rosa Convalescent Hospital
1311 Date St, San Bernardino, CA, 92404 (714) 882-3316
Admin Dan L Murray. *Medical Dir/Dir of Nursing* Dr Leslie Musad.
Licensure Skilled Care. *Beds* 99. *Certified* Medicare; Medi-Cal.
Ownership Proprietary.
Admissions Requirements Minimum age 16; Medical examination; Physician's request.
Staff Physicians 46 (pt); RNs 4 (ft), 4 (pt); LPNs 7 (ft), 4 (pt); Nurses aides 33 (ft), 9 (pt); Physical therapists 1 (ft), 1 (pt); Occupational therapists 1 (pt); Speech therapists 1 (pt); Activities coordinators 1 (ft); Dietitians 1 (pt); Dentists 1 (pt); Podiatrists 1 (pt); Audiologists 1 (pt).
Facilities Dining room; Physical therapy room; Activities room; Barber/Beauty shop; Library.
Activities Arts and Crafts; Cards; Games; Reading groups; Prayer groups; Movies; Shopping trips; Dances/Social or cultural gatherings.

Hillcrest Nursing Home*
4280 Cypress Dr, San Bernardino, CA, 92407
(714) 882-2965
Admin C David Benfield.
Licensure Skilled Care. *Beds* 59.
Certified Medi-Cal.
Ownership Proprietary.

Medical Center Convalescent Hospital*
467 E Gilbert St, San Bernardino, CA, 92404
(714) 884-4781
Admin Ann Ethridge.
Licensure Skilled Care. *Beds* 99. *Certified* Medicare; Medi-Cal.
Ownership Proprietary.

Parkside Convalescent Hospital
1676 N Muscott St, San Bernardino, CA, 92405 (714) 887-6481
Admin Anita I Page. *Medical Dir/Dir of Nursing* Dr David Phillips.
Licensure Skilled Care. *Beds* 99. *Certified* Medicare; Medi-Cal.
Ownership Proprietary.
Admissions Requirements Medical examination; Physician's request.
Facilities Dining room; Physical therapy room; Activities room; Chapel; Crafts room; Laundry room; Barber/Beauty shop.
Activities Arts and Crafts; Games; Reading groups; Prayer groups; Movies.

Shandin Hills Convalescent Hospital*
4160 4th Ave, San Bernardino, CA, 92407
(714) 886-6786
Admin Patrick Clisham.
Licensure Skilled Care. *Beds* 29.
Certified Medi-Cal.
Ownership Proprietary.

Shandin Hills Sanitarium
4164 N 4th Ave, San Bernardino, CA, 92407
(714) 886-6786
Admin Janet L Shelburn.
Licensure Skilled Care. *Beds* 49.
Certified Medi-Cal.
Ownership Proprietary.

Shea Convalescent Hospital*
1335 N Waterman Ave, San Bernardino, CA, 92404 (714) 885-0268
Admin Robert J Peacock.
Licensure Skilled Care. *Beds* 120. *Certified* Medicare; Medi-Cal.
Ownership Proprietary.

Valley Convalescent Hospital
1680 N Waterman Ave, San Bernardino, CA, 92404 (714) 886-5291
Admin Stanley R Smith. *Medical Dir/Dir of Nursing* Allan F Sterling MD.
Licensure Skilled Care. *Beds* 122. *Certified* Medicare; Medi-Cal.
Ownership Proprietary.
Admissions Requirements Minimum age 1 yr; Physician's request.
Staff Physicians; RNs; LPNs; Orderlies; Nurses aides; Physical therapists; Reality therapists; Recreational therapists; Occupational therapists; Speech therapists; Activities coordinators; Dietitians; Dentists; Ophthalmologists; Podiatrists; Audiologists.
Facilities Dining room; Physical therapy room; Activities room; Chapel; Crafts room; Laundry room; Barber/Beauty shop; Library.
Activities Arts and Crafts; Games; Prayer groups; Movies; Shopping trips.
Description Valley is 50% private, 25% Medicare and has 1, 2, and 3 bedrooms available, each with its own bathroom. The facility does use IV therapy when ordered by the physician. Approximately 40 different physicians attend patients at Valley. The facility is located next door to the San Bernadino Medical Group's Clinic and 2 blocks from Saint Bernardine's Hospital.

Waterman Convalescent Hospital*
1850 N Waterman Ave, San Bernardino, CA, 92404 (714) 882-1215
Admin Elizabeth Plott.
Licensure Skilled Care. *Beds* 166. *Certified* Medicare; Medi-Cal.
Ownership Proprietary.

SAN BRUNO

San Bruno Convalescent Hospital*
890 El Camino Real, San Bruno, CA, 94066
(415) 583-7768
Admin Kenneth J Hargraves.
Licensure Skilled Care. *Beds* 45.
Certified Medi-Cal.
Ownership Public.

SAN DIEGO

Alvarado Convalescent and Rehabilitation Hospital*
6599 Alvarado Rd, San Diego, CA, 92120 (714) 286-7421
Admin William E Stover.
Licensure Skilled Care. *Beds* 299.
Ownership Proprietary.
Description Facility offers occupational and physical therapy, outpatient service, speech pathology/audiology.

Arroyo Vista Convalescent Center
3022 45th St, San Diego, CA, 92105 (714) 283-5855
Admin Gilbert Fimbres. *Medical Dir/Dir of Nursing* Dr A K Williams.
Licensure Skilled Care. *Beds* 53. *Certified* Medicare; Medi-Cal.
Ownership Proprietary.
Staff RNs 4 (ft), 1 (pt); LPNs 3 (ft), 1 (pt); Orderlies 3 (ft); Nurses aides 15 (ft), 5 (pt); Physical therapists 1 (ft); Recreational therapists 1 (ft); Occupational therapists 1 (pt); Speech therapists 1 (pt); Activities coordinators 1 (ft); Dietitians 1 (ft); Dentists 1 (pt).
Facilities Dining room; Physical therapy room; Activities room; Laundry room; Barber/Beauty shop; Library.
Activities Arts and Crafts; Cards; Games; Reading groups; Movies; Dances/Social or cultural gatherings.
Description Facility features Spanish-style architecture with an inner patio which provides a home-like atmosphere.

Childrens Convalescent Hospital
8022 Birmingham Dr, San Diego, CA, 92123
(714) 292-3455
Admin Joyce M Turner. *Medical Dir/Dir of Nursing* Marilyn Jones MD.
Licensure Skilled Care; Intermediate Care for Mentally Retarded. *Beds* SNF 6; ICF/MR 49.
Certified Medi-Cal.
Ownership Nonprofit.
Admissions Requirements Medical examination.
Staff Physicians 6 (pt); RNs 4 (ft), 3 (pt); LPNs 2 (ft); Nurses aides 20 (ft), 35 (pt); Physical therapists 2 (pt); Recreational therapists 1 (ft); Occupational therapists 2 (pt); Activities coordinators 1 (ft); Dietitians 1 (pt); Dentists 2 (pt); Ophthalmologists 2 (pt).
Facilities Dining room; Physical therapy room; Activities room; Crafts room; Laundry room; Activity rooms.
Activities Arts and Crafts; Games; Prayer groups; Movies; Shopping trips; Dances/Social or cultural gatherings; Sensori motor program; ELAP–Electrical Leisure Activities Program.
Description Facility provides developmental programs in recreation, physical therapy, sensori motor, oral facilitation, mealtime skills, toilet and habit training, activities of daily living, and socialization as written in behavioral objectives by a multidisciplinary team and carried out daily by the nursing assistants.

Cloisters of Mission Hills Convalescent Hospital*
3680 Reynard Way, San Diego, CA, 92103
(714) 297-4484
Admin L M Gray.
Licensure Skilled Care. *Beds* 70. *Certified* Medicare; Medi-Cal.
Ownership Nonprofit.

Del Capri Terrace Convalescent Hospital*
5602 University Ave, San Diego, CA, 92105
(714) 583-1993
Admin Ellena R Church.
Licensure Skilled Care. *Beds* 87. *Certified* Medicare; Medi-Cal.
Ownership Proprietary.

Euclid Convalescent Center*
1350 N Euclid Ave, San Diego, CA, 92105
(714) 263-2166
Admin Berry T Crow.
Licensure Skilled Care. *Beds* 99. *Certified* Medicare; Medi-Cal.
Ownership Proprietary.

Fraser Intermediate Care Facility
726 Torrance St, San Diego, CA, 92103 (714)
296-2175
Admin Barbara C Carter. *Medical Dir/Dir of Nursing* Dr Sam C Hsich.
Licensure Intermediate Care. *Beds* 36. *Certified* Medi-Cal.
Ownership Proprietary.
Admissions Requirements Medical examination; Physician's request.
Staff LPNs 4 (ft), 3 (pt); Nurses aides 5 (ft), 3 (pt); Activities coordinators 1 (pt).

Frost Street Convalescent Hospital
8060 Frost St, San Diego, CA, 92123 (714)
278-4750
Admin Gary D Devoir. *Medical Dir/Dir of Nursing* Arthur G Edwards.
Licensure Skilled Care. *Beds* 99. *Certified* Medicare; Medi-Cal.
Ownership Proprietary.
Facilities Dining room; Physical therapy room; Barber/Beauty shop.
Activities Arts and Crafts; Cards; Games; Reading groups; Prayer groups.

Genesee East Health Center
2828 Meadowlark Dr, San Diego, CA, 92123
(714) 277-6460
Admin Rick Mendlen. *Medical Dir/Dir of Nursing* Henry Brookler MD.
Licensure Skilled Care. *Beds* 305. *Certified* Medicare; Medi-Cal.
Ownership Proprietary.
Admissions Requirements Physician's request.
Facilities Dining room; Physical therapy room; Activities room; Laundry room; Barber/Beauty shop.
Activities Arts and Crafts; Cards; Games; Reading groups; Prayer groups; Movies; Shopping trips; Dances/Social or cultural gatherings.
Description Facility features complete rehabilitation services for the elderly.

Golden Hill Convalescent Hospital
1201 34th St, San Diego, CA, 92102 (714)
232-2946
Admin Melody A Wohfeil. *Medical Dir/Dir of Nursing* A K Williams.
Licensure Skilled Care. *Beds* 99. *Certified* Medicare; Medi-Cal.
Ownership Proprietary.
Admissions Requirements Minimum age 40; Medical examination; Physician's request.
Staff Physicians; RNs; LPNs; Orderlies; Nurses aides; Physical therapists; Reality therapists; Recreational therapists; Occupational

therapists; Speech therapists; Activities coordinators; Dietitians; Dentists; Ophthalmologists; Podiatrists; Audiologists.
Facilities Dining room; Physical therapy room; Activities room; Crafts room; Laundry room; Barber/Beauty shop; Library.
Activities Arts and Crafts; Cards; Games; Reading groups; Prayer groups; Movies; Shopping trips; Dances/Social or cultural gatherings.
Description Facility features quality individualized medical, nursing, and rehabilitative service; gourmet foods, selective diets, and therapeutic diets; private and semi-private accomadations.

Hillcrest Rehabilitation and Convalescent Center
3520 4th Ave, San Diego, CA, 92103 (714)
291-5270
Admin Trudy Murray. *Medical Dir/Dir of Nursing* Dr Brookler.
Licensure Skilled Care. *Beds* 194. *Certified* Medicare; Medi-Cal.
Ownership Proprietary.
Admissions Requirements Physician's request.
Facilities Dining room; Physical therapy room; Activities room; Crafts room; Barber/Beauty shop; Library.
Activities Arts and Crafts; Cards; Games; Reading groups; Prayer groups; Movies; Shopping trips; Dances/Social or cultural gatherings.
Description Facility features excellent rehabilitation services.

Kearny Mesa Convalescent and Nursing Home*
7675 Family Circle Dr, San Diego, CA, 92111
(714) 278-8121
Admin Richard J Hebbel.
Licensure Skilled Care. *Beds* 98. *Certified* Medicare; Medi-Cal.
Ownership Proprietary.

Knollwood West Convalescent Hospital*
7944 Birmingham Dr, San Diego, CA, 92123
(714) 278-8810
Admin Ralph Roth and Allan Roth.
Licensure Skilled Care. *Beds* 166. *Certified* Medicare; Medi-Cal.
Ownership Proprietary.
Description Facility offers outpatient service, physical therapy, speech pathology/audiology.

Meadowlark Convalescent Hospital
8001 Birmingham Dr, San Diego, CA, 92123
(619) 279-7701
Admin Mary M Doherty. *Medical Dir/Dir of Nursing* Renato Masilungan MD.
Licensure Skilled Care. *Beds* 92. *Certified* Medicare; Medi-Cal.
Ownership Proprietary.
Admissions Requirements Minimum age 18.
Staff RNs 4 (ft), 2 (pt); LPNs 6 (ft), 3 (pt); Physical therapists 1 (ft), 2 (pt); Activities coordinators 1 (ft).
Facilities Dining room; Physical therapy room; Activities room; Laundry room.
Activities Arts and Crafts; Cards; Games; Reading groups; Prayer groups; Movies; Family dinners.

Mission Convalescent Hospital*
4033 6th Ave Extension, San Diego, CA, 92103
(714) 297-4086
Admin Gary Novack.
Licensure Skilled Care. *Beds* 97. *Certified* Medicare; Medi-Cal.
Ownership Proprietary.

Nazareth House
6333 Rancho Mission Rd, San Diego, CA,
92108 (714) 563-0480
Admin Gertrud Clare. *Medical Dir/Dir of Nursing* Michael G Kielty.
Licensure Skilled Care; Intermediate Care.
Beds SNF 30; ICF 8. *Certified* Medi-Cal.
Ownership Nonprofit.
Admissions Requirements Medical examination; Physician's request.
Staff RNs 2 (ft); LPNs 1 (ft); Nurses aides 10 (ft), 2 (pt); Activities coordinators 1 (ft).
Affiliation Roman Catholic
Facilities Dining room; Activities room; Chapel; Crafts room; Laundry room; Barber/Beauty shop.
Activities Arts and Crafts; Cards; Games; Reading groups; Prayer groups; Movies; Shopping trips; Dances/Social or cultural gatherings.
Description Residential facility has 88 beds and most patients come from residential. Facility has a long waiting list. Residents are happy to know they will be cared for in ICF or SNF in case they need it. Patients given lots of tender loving care.

Paradise Hills Convalescent Center
6061 Banbury St, San Diego, CA, 92139 (714)
475-2211
Admin Roger L Caddell. *Medical Dir/Dir of Nursing* May Nelson MD.
Licensure Skilled Care. *Beds* 160. *Certified* Medicare; Medi-Cal.
Ownership Proprietary.
Staff RNs 12 (ft), 2 (pt); LPNs 9 (ft), 1 (pt); Orderlies 3 (ft), 1 (pt); Nurses aides 52 (ft), 7 (pt); Activities coordinators 2 (ft), 1 (pt).
Facilities Dining room; Physical therapy room; Activities room; Crafts room; Laundry room; Barber/Beauty shop; Library.
Activities Arts and Crafts; Cards; Games; Reading groups; Prayer groups; Movies; Dances/Social or cultural gatherings.

Point Loma Convalescent Hospital
3202 Duke St, San Diego, CA, 92110 (714)
224-4141
Admin Vivian E Herrmann. *Medical Dir/Dir of Nursing* Kenneth Taylor MD.
Licensure Skilled Care. *Beds* 120. *Certified* Medicare; Medi-Cal.
Ownership Proprietary.
Admissions Requirements Minimum age 18; Medical examination; Physician's request.
Staff RNs 5 (ft), 3 (pt); LPNs 4 (ft), 3 (pt); Nurses aides 29 (ft), 15 (pt); Physical therapists; Activities coordinators; Dietitians.
Facilities Dining room; Physical therapy room; Laundry room; Barber/Beauty shop; Living room.
Activities Arts and Crafts; Cards; Games; Reading groups; Prayer groups; Movies; Shopping trips; Outside activities.

San Diego Hebrew Home for the Aged*
4075 54th St, San Diego, CA, 92105 (714)
582-5168
Admin Michael J Ellentuck.
Licensure Skilled Care. *Beds* 71. *Certified* Medicare; Medi-Cal.
Ownership Nonprofit.
Affiliation Jewish

San Diego Intermediate Care Center
1119 28th St, San Diego, CA, 92102 (714)
233-0505
Admin Marietta Vaughn. *Medical Dir/Dir of Nursing* Dr J P De Luca.
Licensure Intermediate Care. *Beds* 37. *Certified* Medi-Cal.
Ownership Proprietary.
Admissions Requirements Minimum age 18;
Medical examination.
Staff Physicians 1 (ft), 1 (pt); RNs 1 (pt); LPNs 3 (ft), 4 (pt); Nurses aides 5 (ft), 3 (pt); Recreational therapists 1 (ft), 1 (pt).
Facilities Dining room; Activities room; Laundry room; Library.
Activities Arts and Crafts; Games; Reading groups; Prayer groups; Movies; Dances/Social or cultural gatherings; Outdoor activities/picnics.

SAN DIMAS

Casa Bonita Convalescent Hospital
535 E Bonita Ave, San Dimas, CA, 91773 (714)
599-1248
Admin Donald J Archibald. *Medical Dir/Dir of Nursing* Dr George McGallon.
Licensure Skilled Care. *Beds* 106. *Certified* Medicare; Medi-Cal.
Ownership Proprietary.
Admissions Requirements Physician's request.
Facilities Dining room; Physical therapy room; Activities room; Crafts room; Laundry room; Barber/Beauty shop.
Activities Arts and Crafts; Cards; Games; Reading groups; Prayer groups; Movies; Shopping trips.

SAN FERNANDO

Country Manor Convalescent Hospital*
11723 Fenton Ave, San Fernando, CA, 91342
(213) 899-0251
Admin Vernon B Monson.
Licensure Skilled Care. *Beds* 99.
Ownership Proprietary.

Forester Haven*
12249 N Lopez Canyon Rd, San Fernando,
CA, 91342 (213) 899-7422
Admin Mary Wiggins.
Licensure Skilled Care. *Beds* 49.
Certified Medi-Cal.
Ownership Nonprofit.

SAN FRANCISCO

Beverly Manor Convalescent Hospital*
1477 Grove St, San Francisco, CA, 94117 (415)
563-0565
Admin Frank Garrison.

Licensure Skilled Care. *Beds* 168. *Certified* Medicare; Medi-Cal.
Ownership Proprietary.

Bowman-Harrison Convalescent Hospital*
1020 Haight St, San Francisco, CA, 94117 (415)
552-3198
Admin Paul M Levesque.
Licensure Skilled Care. *Beds* 21.
Ownership Proprietary.

Broderick Convalescent Hospital
1421 Broderick St, San Francisco, CA, 94115
(415) 922-3244
Admin Barbara Rentz-Champagne. *Medical Dir/Dir of Nursing* Dr Joseph Muscat.
Licensure Skilled Care. *Beds* 48. *Certified* Medicare; Medi-Cal.
Ownership Proprietary.
Admissions Requirements Physician's request.
Staff RNs 2 (ft); LPNs 7 (ft); Nurses aides 13 (ft), 9 (pt); Activities coordinators 1 (ft); Dentists; Ophthalmologists; Podiatrists; Audiologists.
Facilities Dining room; Physical therapy room; Activities room; Chapel; Crafts room; Laundry room; Barber/Beauty shop; Library.
Activities Arts and Crafts; Cards; Games; Reading groups; Prayer groups; Dances/Social or cultural gatherings.
Description The facility provides quality care, both medical and rehabilitative services. The hospital has a bilingual staff; menus are planned according to the cultural background and personal preference of the patients. Volunteers from social service organizations and church-sponsored outreach programs are helpful.

California Convalescent Hospital*
2704 California St, San Francisco, CA, 94115
(415) 931-7846
Admin Mary Ellen Forrest.
Licensure Skilled Care. *Beds* 29.
Ownership Proprietary.

Central Gardens
1355 Ellis St, San Francisco, CA, 94115 (415)
567-2967
Admin Richard Lieberman. *Medical Dir/Dir of Nursing* Arthur Z Cerf MD.
Licensure Skilled Care. *Beds* 88. *Certified* Medicare; Medi-Cal.
Ownership Proprietary.
Staff RNs 3 (ft), 5 (pt); LPNs 7 (ft), 3 (pt); Nurses aides 26 (ft), 13 (pt); Activities coordinators 1 (ft).
Facilities Dining room; Physical therapy room; Laundry room.
Activities Arts and Crafts; Cards; Reading groups; Prayer groups; Movies; Shopping trips.
Description Facility has 24-hour licensed nursing care with private or semi-private rooms. Lounges are airy and light. Two central gardens are available for patient use. No stairs—all patient facilities are on one level. Individualized rehabilitative services.

Convalescent Center Mission Street Inc*
5767 Mission St, San Francisco, CA, 94112
(415) 584-3294
Admin Cheryl Weiss.

Licensure Skilled Care. *Beds* 53. *Certified* Medicare; Medi-Cal.
Ownership Proprietary.

Hayes Convalescent Hospital*
1250 Hayes St, San Francisco, CA, 94117 (415)
931-8806
Admin Eli Chalich.
Licensure Skilled Care. *Beds* 34. *Certified* Medicare; Medi-Cal.
Ownership Proprietary.

Hebrew Home for Aged Disabled
302 Silver Ave, San Francisco, CA, 94112 (415)
334-2500
Admin Jerry Levine. *Medical Dir/Dir of Nursing* Dr Bernard Blumberg.
Licensure Skilled Care. *Beds* 345. *Certified* Medicare; Medi-Cal.
Ownership Nonprofit.
Admissions Requirements Minimum age 65;
Medical examination; Physician's request.
Staff Physicians 4 (pt); RNs 29 (ft), 4 (pt); LPNs 5 (ft), 1 (pt); Orderlies 12 (ft); Nurses aides 97 (ft), 13 (pt); Physical therapists 1 (ft); Recreational therapists 1 (ft); Occupational therapists 1 (pt); Speech therapists 1 (pt); Activities coordinators 1 (ft); Dietitians 1 (ft), 1 (pt); Dentists 2 (pt); Ophthalmologists 1 (pt); Podiatrists 3 (pt).
Affiliation Jewish
Facilities Dining room; Physical therapy room; Activities room; Chapel; Crafts room; Laundry room; Barber/Beauty shop; Library.
Activities Arts and Crafts; Cards; Games; Reading groups; Prayer groups; Movies; Shopping trips; Dances/Social or cultural gatherings.
Description Staff provides comprehensive geriatric services to those who are ambulatory, chronically ill or physically, mentally, or psychologically impaired in a way that is personal and sensitive to individual needs.

The Heritage
3400 Laguna St, San Francisco, CA, 94123
(415) 567-6900
Admin Edward J Bednedict. *Medical Dir/Dir of Nursing* Dr John Henderson.
Licensure Skilled Care. *Beds* 32.
Ownership Nonprofit.
Admissions Requirements Minimum age 65.
Staff Physicians 1 (pt); RNs 4 (pt); LPNs 3 (pt); Nurses aides 11 (ft), 3 (pt); Activities coordinators 1 (ft); Dietitians 1 (pt); Ophthalmologists 1 (pt).
Facilities Dining room; Activities room; Chapel; Barber/Beauty shop; Library.
Activities Games; Reading groups; Movies; SPCA pet visitation; Singing.

Hillhaven Convalescent Center*
2043 19th Ave, San Francisco, CA, 94116 (415)
661-8787
Admin Nancy L Hopp.
Licensure Skilled Care. *Beds* 140. *Certified* Medicare; Medi-Cal.
Ownership Proprietary.

Laurel Heights Convalescent Hospital*
2740 California St, San Francisco, CA, 94115
(415) 567-3133

Admin Jill Lee.
Licensure Intermediate Care. *Beds* 32.
Ownership Proprietary.

Mission Villa Convalescent Hospital
1420 Hampshire St, San Francisco, CA, 94110
(415) 285-7660
Admin Richard Traylor. *Medical Dir/Dir of Nursing* Richard Munter MD.
Licensure Skilled Care. *Beds* 51. *Certified* Medicare; Medi-Cal.
Ownership Proprietary.
Admissions Requirements Medical examination.
Staff Physicians; RNs; LPNs; Orderlies; Nurses aides; Physical therapists; Reality therapists; Recreational therapists; Occupational therapists; Speech therapists; Activities coordinators; Dietitians; Dentists; Ophthalmologists; Podiatrists; Audiologists.
Facilities Dining room; Physical therapy room; Activities room; Laundry room; Barber/Beauty shop.
Activities Arts and Crafts; Games; Reading groups; Prayer groups; Movies; Dances/Social or cultural gatherings; Outings; Field trips.
Description The facility has a sunny bright atmosphere with center patio and fountain.

Pine Towers Convalescent Hospital Inc
2707 Pine St, San Francisco, CA, 94115 (415) 563-7600
Admin Janis M Jones. *Medical Dir/Dir of Nursing* Robert V Brody.
Licensure Skilled Care. *Beds* 120. *Certified* Medicare; Medi-Cal.
Ownership Proprietary.
Admissions Requirements Physician's request.
Staff RNs 7 (ft), 2 (pt); LPNs 12 (ft), 3 (pt); Orderlies 4 (ft), 2 (pt); Nurses aides 33 (ft), 12 (pt); Physical therapists 1 (pt); Recreational therapists 1 (ft); Occupational therapists 1 (pt); Speech therapists 1 (pt); Activities coordinators 1 (ft); Dietitians 1 (pt); Dentists 1 (pt).
Facilities Dining room; Physical therapy room; Activities room; Laundry room; Barber/Beauty shop; 5 Day rooms.
Activities Arts and Crafts; Cards; Games; Reading groups; Prayer groups; Movies; Shopping trips; Dances/Social or cultural gatherings; Social outings; Singing group trips.
Description The facility is a 5-story building with programs and special care unit for Alzheimer's patients. We have a van with a wheelchair lift for outings; activities are planned for 12 hours per day, 7 days per week.

Potrero Hill Convalescent Hospital*
331 Pennsylvania Ave, San Francisco, CA, 94107 (415) 647-3587
Admin Nester H Yallico.
Licensure Skilled Care. *Beds* 50. *Certified* Medicare; Medi-Cal.
Ownership Proprietary.

Saint Annes Home
300 Lake St, San Francisco, CA, 94118 (415) 751-6510
Admin Sr Mauree Courtney. *Medical Dir/Dir of Nursing* Dr Henry Cuniberti.
Licensure Skilled Care; Intermediate Care.
Beds SNF 48; ICF 48. *Certified* Medi-Cal.

Ownership Nonprofit.
Admissions Requirements Minimum age 60; Medical examination.
Staff Physicians 3 (ft), 9 (pt); RNs 4 (ft); LPNs 6 (ft); Orderlies 1 (ft); Nurses aides 20 (ft), 8 (pt); Physical therapists 1 (pt); Recreational therapists 2 (ft); Activities coordinators 1 (ft); Dietitians 6 (ft), 2 (pt); Dentists 2 (pt); Podiatrists 2 (pt).
Affiliation Roman Catholic
Facilities Dining room; Physical therapy room; Activities room; Chapel; Crafts room; Laundry room; Barber/Beauty shop; Library; Ice cream shop; Country store.
Activities Arts and Crafts; Cards; Games; Reading groups; Prayer groups; Movies; Shopping trips; Dances/Social or cultural gatherings; Resident council.
Description The Little Sisters of the Poor, together with their staff, endeavor to give quality care at all times. A resident receives total care from the moment of admission until the time of death. No resident is sent away at the time of death—a person stays with him/her around the clock.

San Francisco Community Convalescent Hospital
2655 Bush St, San Francisco, CA, 94115 (415) 922-4141
Admin Jocelyn S Carter. *Medical Dir/Dir of Nursing* Ricahrd Lanzerotti MD.
Licensure Skilled Care. *Beds* 116. *Certified* Medicare; Medi-Cal.
Ownership Proprietary.
Staff Physicians 3 (pt); RNs 13 (ft), 3 (pt); LPNs 10 (ft), 6 (pt); Nurses aides 40 (ft), 20 (pt); Physical therapists 2 (ft); Recreational therapists 3 (ft); Occupational therapists 1 (pt); Speech therapists 1 (pt); Activities coordinators 1 (ft); Dietitians 1 (ft); Dentists 1 (pt); Podiatrists 1 (pt).
Facilities Dining room; Physical therapy room; Activities room; Crafts room; Laundry room; Barber/Beauty shop.
Activities Arts and Crafts; Cards; Games; Reading groups; Prayer groups; Movies; Dances/Social or cultural gatherings.
Description Rehabilitation oriented facility providing individualized physical therapy, occupation therapy, and speech therapy maintenance programs. Facility is able to provide home health care after discharge.

San Francisco Convalescent Center
1359 Pine St, San Francisco, CA, 94109 (415) 673-8405
Admin Gary Collins. *Medical Dir/Dir of Nursing* Dr Richard Lanzerlti.
Licensure Skilled Care. *Beds* 172. *Certified* Medicare; Medi-Cal.
Ownership Proprietary.
Admissions Requirements Medical examination.
Staff RNs 7 (ft), 4 (pt); LPNs 20 (ft), 15 (pt); Nurses aides 50 (ft), 20 (pt); Physical therapists 2 (ft), 1 (pt); Recreational therapists 1 (ft); Occupational therapists 1 (ft); Speech therapists 1 (ft); Activities coordinators 2 (ft); Dietitians 1 (pt); Dentists 1 (pt); Podiatrists 1 (pt).
Facilities Dining room; Physical therapy room; Activities room; Chapel; Crafts room; Laundry room; Barber/Beauty shop; Library; Parking

garage.
Activities Arts and Crafts; Cards; Games; Reading groups; Prayer groups; Movies; Shopping trips; Dances/Social or cultural gatherings; Field trips.
Description Facility has rehabilitation team and social worker on staff; lunch and dining facility with hostess to serve residents restaurant-style; outside patio with view of city; parking available in garage.

Sequoias San Francisco Convalescent Hospital*
Box 7, 1501 Post St, San Francisco, CA, 94109
(415) 922-9700
Admin Robert A Mize.
Licensure Skilled Care. *Beds* 49. *Certified* Medicare; Medi-Cal.
Ownership Nonprofit.

Sheffield Convalescent Hospital*
1133 S Van Ness Ave, San Francisco, CA, 94110 (415) 647-3117
Admin Mary Ellen Forrest.
Licensure Skilled Care. *Beds* 34.
Ownership Proprietary.

Sunnyside Van Ness Convalescent Hospital
1218 S Van Ness Ave, San Francisco, CA, 94110 (415) 647-6365
Admin Gladys Straus. *Medical Dir/Dir of Nursing* Dr Robert Durand.
Licensure Skilled Care. *Beds* 36. *Certified* Medicare; Medi-Cal.
Ownership Proprietary.
Admissions Requirements Medical examination; Physician's request.
Staff RNs 3 (ft), 4 (pt); LPNs 3 (ft), 1 (pt); Orderlies 1 (ft); Physical therapists 1 (ft), 1 (pt); Occupational therapists 1 (pt); Speech therapists 1 (pt); Activities coordinators 1 (ft), 1 (pt); Dietitians 3 (ft); Dentists 1 (pt); Ophthalmologists 1 (pt); Podiatrists 1 (pt); Audiologists 1 (pt).
Facilities Dining room; Physical therapy room; Activities room; Laundry room; Library.
Activities Arts and Crafts; Cards; Games; Reading groups; Prayer groups; Movies; Shopping trips; Dances/Social or cultural gatherings; Wheel of Fortune.
Description Facility features Chinese New Year celebration, takes patients to Ice Follies, celebrates either a state or country each month while giving a short biography and serving appropriate food indigenious to the area described.

Victorian Convalescent Hospital Inc
2121 Pine St, San Francisco, CA, 94115 (415) 922-5085
Medical Dir/Dir of Nursing Robert Minkowsky.
Licensure Skilled Care. *Beds* 90. *Certified* Medicare; Medi-Cal.
Ownership Proprietary.
Staff Physicians 1 (pt); RNs 4 (ft); Physical therapists 1 (pt); Reality therapists 1 (pt); Occupational therapists 1 (pt); Speech therapists 1 (pt); Activities coordinators 1 (ft), 1 (pt); Dentists 1 (pt).
Facilities Dining room; Physical therapy room; Activities room; Laundry room; Barber/Beauty shop.
Activities Arts and Crafts; Cards; Games;

Reading groups; Prayer groups; Movies; Shopping trips; Dances/Social or cultural gatherings.

SAN GABRIEL

Alderwood Manor Convalescent Hospital*
115 Bridge St, San Gabriel, CA, 91775 (213) 289-4439
Admin Carolyn L Zera.
Licensure Skilled Care. *Beds* 98. *Certified* Medicare.
Ownership Proprietary.

Broadway Convalescent Hospital
112 E Broadway, San Gabriel, CA, 91776 (818) 285-2165
Admin Dale Mueller. *Medical Dir/Dir of Nursing* F Kunze MD.
Licensure Skilled Care. *Beds* 59. *Certified* Medicare; Medi-Cal.
Ownership Proprietary.
Staff RNs 2 (ft); LPNs 6 (ft); Physical therapists 1 (pt); Occupational therapists 1 (pt); Speech therapists 1 (pt); Activities coordinators 1 (ft); Dietitians 1 (pt); Dentists 1 (pt); Ophthalmologists 1 (pt); Podiatrists 1 (pt).
Facilities Dining room; Physical therapy room; Activities room; Crafts room; Laundry room; Barber/Beauty shop; Library.
Activities Arts and Crafts; Cards; Games; Reading groups; Prayer groups; Movies; Shopping trips; Dances/Social or cultural gatherings; Adopt-a-grandparent program.
Description Small family-oriented facility.

Community Convalescent Hospital of San Gabriel
537 W Live Oak, San Gabriel, CA, 91776 (213) 289-3763
Admin Anthony Riggio. *Medical Dir/Dir of Nursing* James Femino MD.
Licensure Skilled Care. *Beds* 99. *Certified* Medicare; Medi-Cal.
Ownership Nonprofit.
Admissions Requirements Physician's request.
Staff RNs 4 (ft), 1 (pt); LPNs 10 (ft), 2 (pt); Orderlies 1 (ft); Nurses aides 35 (ft).
Facilities Dining room; Physical therapy room; Activities room; Laundry room; Barber/Beauty shop.
Activities Arts and Crafts; Cards; Games; Reading groups; Prayer groups; Movies.

Fernview Convalescent Hospital*
126 N San Gabriel Blvd, San Gabriel, CA, 91775 (213) 285-3131
Admin Homer Sommerville.
Licensure Skilled Care. *Beds* 75. *Certified* Medicare; Medi-Cal.
Ownership Proprietary.
Description JCAH approved.

Mission Convalescent Hospital*
909 W Santa Anita, San Gabriel, CA, 91775 (213) 289-5365
Admin Karin Barrett.
Licensure Skilled Care. *Beds* 99. *Certified* Medicare; Medi-Cal.
Ownership Proprietary.

Mission Lodge Sanitarium
824 S Gladys Ave, San Gabriel, CA, 91776 (818) 287-0753
Admin Norman E Gagliardi. *Medical Dir/Dir of Nursing* Douglas Copley MD.
Licensure Skilled Care. *Beds* 133.
Certified Medi-Cal.
Ownership Proprietary.
Staff RNs 4 (ft), 3 (pt); LPNs 6 (ft), 4 (pt); Nurses aides 53 (ft), 12 (pt); Activities coordinators 2 (ft).
Facilities Dining room; Activities room; Crafts room; Laundry room; Barber/Beauty shop.
Activities Arts and Crafts; Cards; Games; Reading groups; Prayer groups; Movies; Shopping trips; Adult education; Special sports programs; Mini-socials.
Description Facility specializes in the care of those afflicted with Alzheimer's disease. Provides a safe, secure environment with pleasant surroundings.

San Marino Manor
6812 N Oak St, San Gabriel, CA, 91775 (213) 446-5263
Admin James W Whitney. *Medical Dir/Dir of Nursing* Gary Schlecter MD.
Licensure Skilled Care. *Beds* 76. *Certified* Medicare; Medi-Cal.
Ownership Proprietary.
Admissions Requirements Minimum age 45; Medical examination; Physician's request.
Facilities Dining room; Activities room; Crafts room; Laundry room; Barber/Beauty shop.
Activities Arts and Crafts; Games; Prayer groups; Movies.

SAN JACINTO

Colonial Convalescent Hospital Inc*
39241 W 7th St, San Jacinto, CA, 92383 (714) 654-9347
Admin Jean E Reed.
Licensure Skilled Care. *Beds* 44. *Certified* Medicare; Medi-Cal.
Ownership Proprietary.

SAN JOSE

Bellerose Convalescent Hospital
160 Bellerose Dr, San Jose, CA, 95128 (408) 286-4161
Admin Francisco Cerezo. *Medical Dir/Dir of Nursing* Dr Jackson Mathieu.
Licensure Skilled Care. *Beds* 39.
Ownership Proprietary.
Staff RNs 1 (ft), 2 (pt); LPNs 3 (ft), 2 (pt); Orderlies 1 (ft); Nurses aides 9 (ft), 3 (pt); Activities coordinators 1 (ft); Dietitians 1 (pt); Podiatrists 1 (pt).
Facilities Dining room; Activities room; Laundry room; Barber/Beauty shop.
Activities Arts and Crafts; Cards; Games; Reading groups; Prayer groups; Movies; Dances/Social or cultural gatherings; Outings.

Bethany Convalescent Hospital
180 N Jackson Ave, San Jose, CA, 95116 (408) 259-8700
Admin Elizabeth Callahan. *Medical Dir/Dir of Nursing* Richard Handy MD.

Licensure Skilled Care. *Beds* 199. *Certified* Medicare; Medi-Cal.
Ownership Nonprofit.
Admissions Requirements Minimum age 18.
Staff RNs 8 (ft); LPNs 15 (ft); Nurses aides 58 (ft); Physical therapists 1 (pt); Recreational therapists 3 (ft); Occupational therapists 1 (pt); Speech therapists 1 (pt); Activities coordinators 1 (pt); Dietitians 1 (pt).
Affiliation Disciples of Christ
Facilities Dining room; Physical therapy room; Activities room; Chapel; Crafts room; Laundry room; Barber/Beauty shop; Library.
Activities Arts and Crafts; Cards; Games; Reading groups; Prayer groups; Movies; Shopping trips.

California PEO Home—San Jose Unit
5203 Alum Rock Ave, San Jose, CA, 95127 (408) 251-9030
Admin Evelyn Niederbrach.
Licensure Skilled Care. *Beds* 22. *Certified* Medicare.
Ownership Nonprofit.

Casa Serena
1990 Fruitdale Ave, San Jose, CA, 95128 (408) 998-8447
Admin George Vickerman. *Medical Dir/Dir of Nursing* Dr William Weller.
Licensure Skilled Care. *Beds* 129. *Certified* Medicare; Medi-Cal.
Ownership Proprietary.
Admissions Requirements Medical examination; Physician's request.
Staff Physicians 1 (pt); RNs 10 (ft), 2 (pt); LPNs 13 (ft), 2 (pt); Nurses aides 57 (ft), 6 (pt); Physical therapists 1 (ft); Activities coordinators 2 (ft); Dietitians 1 (ft).
Facilities Dining room; Physical therapy room; Activities room; Chapel; Crafts room; Laundry room; Barber/Beauty shop; Library.
Activities Arts and Crafts; Cards; Games; Reading groups; Prayer groups; Movies; Shopping trips; Dances/Social or cultural gatherings.
Description Facility features a beautiful, enclosed aviary. Every room has access (opening) to a patio. Inpatient hospice service provided. Inpatient Alzheimer service. Closed circuit TV service for video cassette programing (i.e., movies, facility functions, etc.).

Crestwood Manor*
1425 Fruitdale Ave, San Jose, CA, 95128 (408) 275-1010
Admin John Suggs.
Licensure Skilled Care. *Beds* 174. *Certified* Medicare; Medi-Cal.
Ownership Proprietary.

Driftwood Convalescent Hospital
2065 Los Gatos-Almaden Rd, San Jose, CA, 95124 (408) 377-9275
Admin Sandra Lawson. *Medical Dir/Dir of Nursing* Dr Robert Reid.
Licensure Skilled Care. *Beds* 77. *Certified* Medicare; Medi-Cal.
Ownership Proprietary.
Staff RNs 4 (ft), 2 (pt); LPNs 5 (ft), 4 (pt); Orderlies 1 (ft); Nurses aides 20 (ft), 10 (pt); Activities coordinators 1 (ft); Dietitians 1 (ft).
Facilities Dining room; Physical therapy room; Activities room; Laundry room; Barber/Beauty

shop.
Activities Arts and Crafts; Cards; Games; Prayer groups; Movies; Dances/Social or cultural gatherings.

El Dorado Guidance Center*
101 Jose Figueres Ave, San Jose, CA, 95116
(408) 251-0110
Admin Adele Vernon.
Licensure Skilled Care. *Beds* 99.
Certified Medi-Cal.
Ownership Proprietary.

Empress Convalescent Hospital*
1299 S Bascom Ave, San Jose, CA, 95128 (408) 287-0616
Admin George G Ramirez.
Licensure Skilled Care. *Beds* 67. *Certified* Medicare; Medi-Cal.
Ownership Proprietary.

The Herman Sanitarium*
2295 Plummer Ave, San Jose, CA, 95125 (408) 269-0701
Admin Robert Sollis.
Licensure Skilled Care. *Beds* 99.
Certified Medi-Cal.
Ownership Proprietary.

Homewood Convalescent Hospital Inc
75 N 13th St, San Jose, CA, 95112 (408) 295-2665
Admin Anne Morgan. *Medical Dir/Dir of Nursing* Dr William Ness.
Licensure Skilled Care. *Beds* 58. *Certified* Medicare; Medi-Cal.
Ownership Nonprofit.
Admissions Requirements Medical examination; Physician's request.
Facilities Dining room; Activities room; Laundry room; Barber/Beauty shop.
Activities Arts and Crafts; Cards; Games; Movies.

Lincoln Glen Intermediate Care*
2671 Plummer Ave, San Jose, CA, 95125 (408) 265-3222
Admin Dan Wiebe.
Licensure Intermediate Care. *Beds* 59. *Certified* Medi-Cal.
Ownership Nonprofit.

Marcus Manor Convalescent Hospital
264 N Morrison Ave, San Jose, CA, 95126 (408) 297-4420
Admin Steve R Marcus. *Medical Dir/Dir of Nursing* Karin Goodman MD.
Licensure Skilled Care; Nursing Care. *Beds* 32.
Certified Medi-Cal.
Ownership Proprietary.
Admissions Requirements Minimum age 18; Medical examination; Physician's request.
Staff RNs 1 (ft), 3 (pt); LPNs 2 (ft), 3 (pt); Nurses aides 9 (ft), 4 (pt); Activities coordinators 1 (ft).
Facilities Dining room; Activities room; Laundry room.
Activities Arts and Crafts; Cards; Games; Prayer groups; Movies.
Description Facility is small and home-like; owned and operated by a Christian family with a caring staff dedicated to the residents needs; located in a convenient central location.

Mount Pleasant Convalescent Hospital Inc
1355 Clayton Rd, San Jose, CA, 95127 (408) 251-3070
Admin Irene Lello. *Medical Dir/Dir of Nursing* Dr Albert Currlin.
Licensure Skilled Care. *Beds* 56.
Certified Medi-Cal.
Ownership Proprietary.
Staff RNs 3 (ft), 2 (pt); LPNs 2 (ft), 1 (pt); Orderlies 1 (ft); Nurses aides 18 (ft), 3 (pt); Activities coordinators 1 (ft).
Facilities Dining room; Activities room; Chapel; Laundry room; Barber/Beauty shop.
Activities Arts and Crafts; Cards; Games; Prayer groups; Movies.
Description Our facility (56-bed capacity) is located in the east foothills of San Jose. We have beautiful grounds for the patients to enjoy outdoors. We take pride in providing quality care for our patients over the past 21 years. Family owned and operated.

Northlake Convalescent Hospital*
340 Northlake Dr, San Jose, CA, 95117 (408) 296-5460
Admin William A Ruff Jr.
Licensure Skilled Care. *Beds* 83. *Certified* Medicare; Medi-Cal.
Ownership Proprietary.

Park View Nursing Center*
120 Jose Figueres Ave, San Jose, CA, 95116 (408) 272-1400
Admin Larry Mobley.
Licensure Skilled Care. *Beds* 99. *Certified* Medicare; Medi-Cal.
Ownership Proprietary.

Plum Tree Convalescent Hospital
2580 Samaritan Dr, San Jose, CA, 95124 (408) 356-8181
Admin Margorie A Hauer. *Medical Dir/Dir of Nursing* David Morgan MD.
Licensure Skilled Care. *Beds* 76. *Certified* Medicare; Medi-Cal.
Ownership Nonprofit.
Staff RNs 3 (ft), 7 (pt); LPNs 3 (ft); Nurses aides 27 (ft), 3 (pt); Physical therapists; Reality therapists; Recreational therapists; Occupational therapists; Activities coordinators 1 (ft), 1 (pt); Dietitians; Dentists; Ophthalmologists; Podiatrists; Audiologists.
Facilities Dining room; Physical therapy room; Activities room; Crafts room; Laundry room; Barber/Beauty shop.
Activities Arts and Crafts; Cards; Games; Reading groups; Prayer groups; Movies; Shopping trips; Dances/Social or cultural gatherings.
Description Hospital strives to provide attractive, comfortable, and properly maintained facilities in the interest of the patients' welfare, and to always be considered as useful participants in community's well being.

San Jose Care and Guidance Center
401 Ridge Vista Ave, San Jose, CA, 95127 (408) 923-7232
Admin Yvonne Molanan. *Medical Dir/Dir of Nursing* Dr Mayerle.
Licensure Skilled Care; Special Treatment Program. *Beds* 116. *Certified* Medi-Cal.
Ownership Proprietary.
Admissions Requirements Minimum age 21.

Staff Physicians 2 (ft); RNs 6 (ft), 2 (pt); LPNs 8 (ft), 4 (pt).
Facilities Dining room; Activities room; Crafts room.
Activities Arts and Crafts; Cards; Games; Prayer groups; Movies; Shopping trips; Dances/Social or cultural gatherings.

San Tomas Convalescent Hospital*
3580 Payne Ave, San Jose, CA, 95117 (408) 248-7100
Admin Alice K Mau.
Licensure Skilled Care. *Beds* 70. *Certified* Medicare; Medi-Cal.
Ownership Proprietary.

Skyline Convalescent Hospital*
2065 Forest Ave, San Jose, CA, 95128 (408) 298-3950
Admin Mary MacPherson.
Licensure Skilled Care. *Beds* 277. *Certified* Medicare; Medi-Cal.
Ownership Proprietary.

West Park Convalescent Hospital
1250 S Winchester Blvd, San Jose, CA, 95128 (408) 241-8666
Admin Martha Perry. *Medical Dir/Dir of Nursing* Harry Wong MD.
Licensure Skilled Care. *Beds* 169. *Certified* Medicare; Medi-Cal.
Ownership Proprietary.
Staff Physicians 1 (pt); RNs 4 (ft), 6 (pt); LPNs 12 (ft); Nurses aides 61 (ft); Physical therapists 1 (ft); Occupational therapists 1 (ft), 1 (pt); Speech therapists 1 (ft), 1 (pt); Activities coordinators 1 (ft); Dietitians 1 (pt); Dentists 1 (pt); Podiatrists 1 (pt).
Facilities Dining room; Physical therapy room; Activities room; Laundry room; Barber/Beauty shop; Library; Protected patios.
Activities Arts and Crafts; Cards; Games; Reading groups; Prayer groups; Movies; Shopping trips; Dances/Social or cultural gatherings; Live Oak community and core groups; In-room activities; Religious meetings-various denominations; Ministerial in-room visits; Barbecues.
Description Facility features restorative graded dining in 4 classifications: feeders, feeder retraining, social, and family-style dining; monthly newsletter, resident council, and resident board. Developing community within the home to promote relationships between families and staff. To raise level of care and quality of life of individuals to fullest potential, there are monthly employee recognition and achievement awards with potluck for staff and residents together; special services; speech, social services, dentist, consultants, (all departments); early riser breakfast in dining room cooked to residents order (within diet order); very active and supportive auxiliary group.

Westgate Convalescent Center
1601 Petersen Ave, San Jose, CA, 95129-4898 (408) 253-7502
Admin Joann Fractman. *Medical Dir/Dir of Nursing* Norman P Woods MD.
Licensure Skilled Care. *Beds* 268. *Certified* Medicare; Medi-Cal.
Ownership Proprietary.
Admissions Requirements Medical examina-

tion; Physician's request.
Staff RNs 21 (ft), 3 (pt); Nurses aides 76 (ft), 15 (pt); Physical therapists; Recreational therapists 1 (ft); Occupational therapists; Speech therapists; Activities coordinators 1 (ft); Dietitians; Dentists; Ophthalmologists; Podiatrists; Audiologists; LVNs 14 (ft), 5 (pt); Social Workers 1 (ft).
Facilities Dining room; Physical therapy room; Activities room; Laundry room; Barber/Beauty shop; Library; 5 Lounges.
Activities Arts and Crafts; Games; Movies; Dances/Social or cultural gatherings; Exercise class.

Willow Glen Convalescent Hospital Rest Care Center*
1267 Meridian Ave, San Jose, CA, 95125 (408) 265-4211
Admin Helen K Kim.
Licensure Skilled Care. *Beds* 152. *Certified* Medicare; Medi-Cal.
Ownership Proprietary.
Description JCAH approved.

SAN LEANDRO

Bancroft Convalescent Hospital*
1475 Bancroft Ave, San Leandro, CA, 94577 (415) 483-1680
Admin Edith E Parrott.
Licensure Skilled Care. *Beds* 39. *Certified* Medicare; Medi-Cal.
Ownership Proprietary.

Jones Convalescent Hospital
524 Callan Ave, San Leandro, CA, 94577 (415) 483-6200
Admin C C Monedero. *Medical Dir/Dir of Nursing* Steven Rosenthal MD.
Licensure Skilled Care. *Beds* 25.
Ownership Proprietary.
Admissions Requirements Medical examination; Physician's request.
Staff RNs 1 (ft), 4 (pt); LPNs 2 (ft), 3 (pt); Nurses aides 7 (ft), 2 (pt) #13I 1 (pt); Activities coordinators 1 (ft); Dietitians 1 (pt).
Facilities Dining room; Activities room; Crafts room; Laundry room; Barber/Beauty shop.
Activities Arts and Crafts; Cards; Games; Prayer groups; Movies; Dances/Social or cultural gatherings.
Description Facility takes private patients only.

Parkland Convalescent Hospital Inc*
1440 168th Ave, San Leandro, CA, 94578 (415) 278-4323
Admin Nancy Zant.
Licensure Skilled Care. *Beds* 176. *Certified* Medicare; Medi-Cal.
Ownership Proprietary.

Saint Luke's Extended Care Hospital & Nursing Centre
1652 Mono Ave, San Leandro, CA, 94578 (415) 357-5351
Admin Guy R Seaton. *Medical Dir/Dir of Nursing* Andrew May MD.
Licensure Skilled Care. *Beds* 70. *Certified* Medicare; Medi-Cal.
Ownership Proprietary.
Admissions Requirements Medical examina-

tion; Physician's request.
Staff RNs 3 (ft); LPNs 5 (ft), 1 (pt); Nurses aides 22 (ft); Physical therapists 1 (pt); Reality therapists 1 (ft); Recreational therapists 1 (pt); Occupational therapists 1 (pt); Speech therapists 1 (pt); Activities coordinators 1 (ft); Dietitians 1 (pt); Dentists 1 (pt); Ophthalmologists 1 (pt); Podiatrists 1 (pt); Audiologists 1 (pt).
Facilities Dining room; Physical therapy room; Activities room; Crafts room; Barber/Beauty shop; Library.
Activities Arts and Crafts; Cards; Games; Reading groups; Prayer groups; Movies; Shopping trips; Dances/Social or cultural gatherings.
Description Accredited by Joint Commission on Accreditation of Hospitals with a distinct part for Medicare patients that provides subacute care. The nursing centre is equipped to provide care for the short stay, convalescent, and long-term care patient. A complete social service department is maintained.

San Leandro Convalescent Hospital*
368 Juana Ave, San Leandro, CA, 94577 (415) 357-4015
Admin Emery E Reuss.
Licensure Skilled Care. *Beds* 59. *Certified* Medicare; Medi-Cal.
Ownership Proprietary.

Washington Convalescent Hospital*
2274 Washington Ave, San Leandro, CA, 94577 (415) 483-7671
Admin Juanita V Norman.
Licensure Skilled Care. *Beds* 25. *Certified* Medicare.
Ownership Proprietary.

Washington Manor Convalescent Hospital*
14766 Washington, San Leandro, CA, 94578 (415) 352-2211
Admin Hugh B Herring.
Licensure Skilled Care. *Beds* 99. *Certified* Medicare; Medi-Cal.
Ownership Proprietary.

SAN LUIS OBISPO

Cabrillo Extended Care Hospital*
3033 Augusta St, San Luis Obispo, CA, 93401 (805) 544-5100
Admin Wayne A Evans.
Licensure Intermediate Care. *Beds* 162. *Certified* Medicare; Medi-Cal.
Ownership Proprietary.

Casa De Vida*
879 Meinecke St, San Luis Obispo, CA, 93401 (805) 544-5332
Admin George Brudney.
Licensure Skilled Care; Intermediate Care for Mentally Retarded. *Beds* 99.
Ownership Proprietary.

Hacienda Convalescent Hospital*
1425 Woodside Dr, San Luis Obispo, CA, 93401 (805) 543-0210
Admin Bryan Roldan.
Licensure Skilled Care. *Beds* 163. *Certified* Medicare; Medi-Cal.
Ownership Proprietary.

SAN MATEO

Brookside Convalescent Hospital*
2620 Flores St, San Mateo, CA, 94403 (415) 349-2161
Admin Irene Pope.
Licensure Skilled Care. *Beds* 100. *Certified* Medicare; Medi-Cal.
Ownership Nonprofit.

Hillsdale Manor Convalescent Hospital
2883 S Norfolk St, San Mateo, CA, 94403 (415) 341-8781
Admin Leona Kuhl. *Medical Dir/Dir of Nursing* Dr Donald Jaffe.
Licensure Skilled Care. *Beds* 59. *Certified* Medicare; Medi-Cal.
Ownership Proprietary.
Admissions Requirements Medical examination; Physician's request.
Staff Physicians 1 (pt); RNs 4 (ft), 1 (pt); LPNs 2 (ft), 3 (pt); Nurses aides 17 (ft), 6 (pt); Physical therapists 1 (pt); Activities coordinators 1 (ft); Dietitians 1 (pt); Dentists 1 (pt); Podiatrists 1 (pt).
Facilities Dining room; Physical therapy room; Activities room; Crafts room; Laundry room; Barber/Beauty shop; Library; Enclosed patio.
Activities Arts and Crafts; Cards; Games; Reading groups; Prayer groups; Movies; Shopping trips; Dances/Social or cultural gatherings.
Description This center has a relatively small, home-like setting; enclosed patio; caring, long-term staff; aggressive activity program; total staff involvement in patient care; and established facility. The hospital will soon be adding on a residential care facility.

San Mateo Convalescent Hospital
453 N San Mateo Dr, San Mateo, CA, 94401 (415) 342-6255
Admin Betty J Frint. *Medical Dir/Dir of Nursing* Robert George Spencer.
Licensure Skilled Care. *Beds* 34. *Certified* Medicare; Medi-Cal.
Ownership Proprietary.
Staff RNs 3 (ft), 2 (pt); LPNs 2 (ft); Nurses aides 14 (ft), 2 (pt); Activities coordinators 1 (ft), 1 (pt).
Facilities Multipurpose room.
Activities Arts and Crafts; Cards; Games; Reading groups; Prayer groups; Movies; Dances/Social or cultural gatherings.

SAN PABLO

Brookvue Convalescent Hospital
13328 San Pablo Ave, San Pablo, CA, 94806 (415) 235-3720
Admin William Kruse. *Medical Dir/Dir of Nursing* Dr Richard Williams.
Licensure Skilled Care. *Beds* 99. *Certified* Medicare; Medi-Cal.
Ownership Proprietary.
Staff Physicians 1 (pt); RNs 3 (ft), 3 (pt); LPNs 8 (ft), 5 (pt); Orderlies 2 (pt); Nurses aides 24 (ft), 20 (pt); Physical therapists 1 (pt); Reality therapists 1 (pt); Recreational therapists 1 (pt); Occupational therapists 1 (pt); Speech therapists 1 (pt); Activities coordinators 1 (ft); Dietitians 1 (pt); Dentists 1 (pt); Ophthalmologists 1 (pt); Podiatrists 1 (pt); Audiologists 1 (pt).

Facilities Dining room; Physical therapy room; Activities room; Crafts room; Laundry room; Barber/Beauty shop.
Activities Arts and Crafts; Cards; Games; Reading groups; Prayer groups; Movies; Shopping trips; Dances/Social or cultural gatherings.

Church Lane Convalescent Hospital*
1900 Church Ln, San Pablo, CA, 94806 (415) 235-5514
Admin Francis Davis.
Licensure Skilled Care. *Beds* 80. *Certified* Medicare; Medi-Cal.
Ownership Proprietary.

Greenvale Convalescent Hospital*
2140 Vale Rd, San Pablo, CA, 94806 (415) 235-1052
Admin Eric Mawson.
Licensure Skilled Care. *Beds* 57. *Certified* Medicare; Medi-Cal.
Ownership Proprietary.

Monterey Care Center*
13484 San Pablo Ave, San Pablo, CA, 94806 (415) 237-5711
Admin Paul D Tunnell.
Licensure Skilled Care. *Beds* 202.
Ownership Proprietary.

SAN PEDRO

Harbor Crest Pavilion (D P of San Pedro Peninsula Hospital)
1322 W 6th St, San Pedro, CA, 90732 (213) 547-0851
Admin L R Smith. *Medical Dir/Dir of Nursing* Dr Bernard Korn.
Licensure Skilled Care. *Beds* 90. *Certified* Medicare; Medi-Cal.
Ownership Proprietary.
Staff RNs 2 (ft), 1 (pt); LPNs 9 (ft); Nurses aides 36 (ft); Activities coordinators 1 (ft); Dietitians 1 (pt).
Facilities Dining room; Activities room; Laundry room; Barber/Beauty shop; Library.
Activities Arts and Crafts; Cards; Games; Reading groups; Prayer groups; Movies; Dances/Social or cultural gatherings.
Description Facility has the designation of SNF-ICU for the section for short-term, higher accuity Medicare patients.

Harbor View House*
921 S Beacon St, San Pedro, CA, 90731 (213) 547-2402
Admin James Crumpler.
Licensure Intermediate Care. *Beds* 83. *Certified* Medi-Cal.
Ownership Nonprofit.

Little Sisters of the Poor
2100 S Western Ave, San Pedro, CA, 90732 (213) 548-0625
Admin Sr Kathleen Bartz. *Medical Dir/Dir of Nursing* Matthew Mickiewicz MD.
Licensure Skilled Care; Intermediate Care.
Beds SNF 48; ICF 48. *Certified* Medi-Cal.
Ownership Nonprofit.
Admissions Requirements Minimum age 60; Medical examination.
Affiliation Roman Catholic

Facilities Dining room; Physical therapy room; Activities room; Chapel; Crafts room; Laundry room; Barber/Beauty shop; Library; Medical offices; Country store; Ice cream parlor.
Activities Arts and Crafts; Cards; Games; Reading groups; Prayer groups; Movies; Shopping trips; Dances/Social or cultural gatherings.
Description The Little Sisters of the Poor have been serving the elderly poor of the Los Angeles area for almost 80 years. Our facility overlooks the Los Angeles Harbor and Pacific Ocean and offers residents a family-type atmosphere where they are cared for until death.

Los Palos Convalescent Hospital
1430 W 6th St, San Pedro, CA, 90732 (213) 832-6431
Admin C D Valdomar. *Medical Dir/Dir of Nursing* Dr M S Mickiewicz.
Licensure Skilled Care. *Beds* 99. *Certified* Medicare; Medi-Cal.
Ownership Proprietary.
Staff RNs 3 (ft), 2 (pt); LPNs 5 (ft), 1 (pt); Orderlies 40 (ft), 2 (pt); Physical therapists 1 (pt); Reality therapists 1 (pt); Recreational therapists 1 (ft); Occupational therapists 1 (pt); Speech therapists 1 (pt); Activities coordinators 1 (ft), 1 (pt); Dietitians 7 (ft), 1 (pt).
Facilities Dining room; Physical therapy room; Activities room; Crafts room; Laundry room; Barber/Beauty shop; Inside patio.
Activities Arts and Crafts; Cards; Games; Reading groups; Prayer groups; Movies; Shopping trips; Dances/Social or cultural gatherings; Adult Education; Patient Council.
Description Besides excellent patient care, facility has an adoption program with 2 different schools which is ongoing with every patient adopting a grandchild; also has church and individual adoption program.

Seacrest Convalescent Hospital*
1416 W 6th St, San Pedro, CA, 90732 (213) 833-3526
Admin Celia D Valdomar.
Licensure Skilled Care. *Beds* 80. *Certified* Medicare; Medi-Cal.
Ownership Proprietary.

SAN RAFAEL

Aldersly Inc—Danish Home Senior Citizens
326 Mission Ave, San Rafael, CA, 94901 (415) 453-7425
Admin Stephanie Sutton. *Medical Dir/Dir of Nursing* Dallas Wagner MD.
Licensure Skilled Care. *Beds* 13.
Ownership Nonprofit.
Admissions Requirements Minimum age 62; Medical examination; Physician's request.
Staff Physicians 1 (pt); RNs 1 (ft), 3 (pt); LPNs 2 (ft), 2 (pt); Nurses aides 5 (ft), 2 (pt); Activities coordinators 2 (pt).
Languages Danish
Facilities Dining room; Activities room; Chapel; Crafts room; Laundry room; Barber/Beauty shop; Library; Lounges; Kitchen; Clinic.
Activities Cards; Games; Reading groups; Movies; Shopping trips; Dances/Social or cultural gatherings; Educational programs; Health lectures.
Description Facility is spread out on 3 acres

with beautiful gardens; a 2-story red-brick complex established in 1921 as a Danish home. Open to non-Danes, but do have a very strong Danish atmosphere.

Fifth Avenue Convalescent Hospital Inc
1601 5th Ave, San Rafael, CA, 94901 (415) 456-7170
Admin Melanie Farkas. *Medical Dir/Dir of Nursing* Dr Janice Barry.
Licensure Skilled Care. *Beds* 57. *Certified* Medicare; Medi-Cal.
Ownership Proprietary.
Admissions Requirements Physician's request.
Staff RNs 4 (ft); LPNs 2 (ft), 2 (pt); Nurses aides 16 (ft), 5 (pt); Physical therapists 1 (ft); Activities coordinators 1 (ft).
Facilities Dining room; Laundry room; Barber/Beauty shop.
Activities Arts and Crafts; Cards; Games; Reading groups; Prayer groups; Movies.
Description Fifth Avenue is a small, rehabilitation oriented, 57-bed skilled nursing facility. We have a physical therapist on staff and occupational therapy and speech therapy are available upon request. Each patient, whether short- or long-term placements, is encouraged to reach their optimum level of independence and individuality.

Hillhaven Convalescent Hospital*
233 West End Blvd, San Rafael, CA, 94901 (415) 456-5054
Admin Julie Butler.
Licensure Skilled Care. *Beds* 55. *Certified* Medicare; Medi-Cal.
Ownership Proprietary.

Hillside Manor Convalescent Hospital*
81 Professional Center Pkwy, San Rafael, CA, 94903 (415) 479-5161
Admin Paul Levesque.
Licensure Skilled Care. *Beds* 99.
Ownership Proprietary.

Linda Terra Convalescent Hospital*
45 Professional Center Pkwy, San Rafael, CA, 94903 (415) 479-3610
Admin James McAndrew.
Licensure Skilled Care. *Beds* 99. *Certified* Medicare; Medi-Cal.
Ownership Proprietary.

Nazareth House*
245 Nova Albion Way, San Rafael, CA, 94903 (415) 479-8282
Admin Sr Teresa Grant.
Licensure Skilled Care. *Beds* 21.
Certified Medi-Cal.
Ownership Nonprofit.

Northgate Convalescent Hospital*
40 Professional Pkwy, San Rafael, CA, 94903 (415) 479-1230
Admin Rene Sommer.
Licensure Skilled Care. *Beds* 49. *Certified* Medicare.
Ownership Proprietary.

Rafael Convalescent Hospital*
234 N San Pedro Rd, San Rafael, CA, 94903 (415) 479-3450
Admin Timothy Egan.

Licensure Skilled Care. *Beds* 168. *Certified* Medicare; Medi-Cal.
Ownership Proprietary.

SANGER

Maple Grove Intermediate Care Home*
1808 5th St, Sanger, CA, 93657 (209) 875-6110
Admin Donald J Botts Jr.
Licensure Intermediate Care. *Beds* 18. *Certified* Medi-Cal.
Ownership Proprietary.

Sanger Convalescent Hospital*
2550 9th St, Sanger, CA, 93657 (209) 875-6501
Admin Ron Preston.
Licensure Skilled Care. *Beds* 99.
Certified Medicare; Medi-Cal.
Ownership Proprietary.

SANTA ANA

Carehouse Convalescent Hospital
1800 Old Tustin Rd, Santa Ana, CA, 92701
(714) 835-4900
Admin Matthew R Weinstock. *Medical Dir-/Dir of Nursing* Gordon Glasgow MD.
Licensure Skilled Care. *Beds* 150. *Certified* Medicare; Medi-Cal.
Ownership Proprietary.
Admissions Requirements Medical examination.
Staff RNs 8 (ft), 3 (pt); LPNs 8 (ft), 1 (pt); Orderlies 4 (ft); Nurses aides 57 (ft), 4 (pt); Physical therapists 1 (pt); Activities coordinators 2 (ft); Dietitians 1 (ft).
Facilities Dining room; Physical therapy room; Activities room; Crafts room; Laundry room; Barber/Beauty shop; Library; Transportation van.
Activities Arts and Crafts; Cards; Games; Prayer groups; Movies; Shopping trips; Dances/Social or cultural gatherings; Swimming; Bowling; Tennis; Picnics; Outings; Adopt-a-grandparent.
Description Facility provides quality care with the most advanced equipment available, including Clinitron beds, enteral feeding, laboratory, X-ray, and oxygen. Social director plans a wide range of activities, both at the facility and out in the community (i.e., tennis, swimming, senior olympics). The library, day room, and garden patio are designed for relaxation and pleasant visits with family and friends.

Chandler Care Center—Bristol*
1209 W Hemlock Way, Santa Ana, CA, 92707
(714) 546-1966
Admin Geertruida Strano.
Licensure Skilled Care. *Beds* 146. *Certified* Medicare; Medi-Cal.
Ownership Proprietary.

Country Club Convalescent Hospital Inc*
20362 SW Santa Ana Ave, Santa Ana, CA,
92707 (714) 549-3061
Admin Isabel C Hernandez.
Licensure Skilled Care. *Beds* 41.
Ownership Proprietary.

Hillhaven Convalescent Hospital
2210 E 1st St, Santa Ana, CA, 92705 (714)
547-7091
Admin Jacqueline Lanter. *Medical Dir/Dir of Nursing* Edgar Stewart MD.
Licensure Skilled Care. *Beds* 99. *Certified* Medicare; Medi-Cal.
Ownership Proprietary.
Admissions Requirements Physician's request.
Staff RNs 3 (ft), 4 (pt); LPNs 6 (ft), 4 (pt); Orderlies 3 (ft); Nurses aides 28 (ft), 3 (pt); Occupational therapists 1 (ft); Speech therapists 1 (ft); Activities coordinators 1 (ft); Dietitians 1 (ft).
Facilities Dining room; Physical therapy room; Activities room; Laundry room; Barber/Beauty shop; Library.
Activities Arts and Crafts; Cards; Games; Prayer groups; Movies; Shopping trips; Dances/Social or cultural gatherings.

Royale Convalescent Hospital
1030 W Warner Ave, Santa Ana, CA, 92707
(714) 546-6450
Admin Marshall N Horsman. *Medical Dir/Dir of Nursing* H M Sung MD.
Licensure Skilled Care. *Beds* 261. *Certified* Medicare; Medi-Cal.
Ownership Proprietary.
Admissions Requirements Minimum age 21; Medical examination; Physician's request.
Staff RNs 10 (ft); LPNs 20 (ft); Orderlies 20 (ft); Nurses aides 60 (ft); Physical therapists 1 (pt); Recreational therapists 2 (ft); Occupational therapists 1 (pt); Speech therapists 1 (pt); Activities coordinators 1 (ft); Dietitians 1 (pt); Dentists 1 (pt); Ophthalmologists 1 (pt); Podiatrists 1 (pt); Audiologists 1 (pt).
Facilities Dining room; Physical therapy room; Activities room; Crafts room; Laundry room; Barber/Beauty shop; Library.
Activities Arts and Crafts; Cards; Games; Reading groups; Prayer groups; Movies; Shopping trips; Dances/Social or cultural gatherings; Music therapy; World affairs; Current events; Resident and family councils.

Saint Edna Convalescent Center*
1929 N Fairview St, Santa Ana, CA, 92706
(714) 839-7800
Admin Rita A Byrne.
Licensure Skilled Care. *Beds* 136. *Certified* Medicare; Medi-Cal.
Ownership Proprietary.

Town and Country Manor Health Care Center
555 E Memory Ln, Santa Ana, CA, 92706
(714) 547-7581
Admin Gail A Conser. *Medical Dir/Dir of Nursing* S A Kerkhoff MD.
Licensure Skilled Care; Intermediate Care. *Beds* 122. *Certified* Medicare; Medi-Cal.
Ownership Nonprofit.
Admissions Requirements Physician's request.
Staff Physicians 1 (pt); RNs 3 (ft), 5 (pt); LPNs 5 (ft), 3 (pt); Nurses aides 22 (ft), 6 (pt); Activities coordinators 2 (ft); Dietitians 1 (ft).
Facilities Dining room; Physical therapy room; Activities room; Chapel; Crafts room; Laundry room; Barber/Beauty shop; Library.
Activities Arts and Crafts; Games; Reading groups; Prayer groups; Movies; Shopping trips.

SANTA BARBARA

Beverly Manor Convalescent Hospital*
2225 de la Vina St, Santa Barbara, CA, 93105
(805) 963-1861
Admin Jon M McDermott.
Licensure Skilled Care. *Beds* 68. *Certified* Medicare; Medi-Cal.
Ownership Proprietary.
Description JCAH approved.

Extended Care Hospital of Santa Barbara
160 S Patterson Ave, Santa Barbara, CA, 93111
(805) 964-4871
Admin W Howard Wortman. *Medical Dir/Dir of Nursing* Paul Aijian MD.
Licensure Skilled Care. *Beds* 150. *Certified* Medicare; Medi-Cal.
Ownership Proprietary.
Admissions Requirements Medical examination; Physician's request.
Staff RNs 10 (ft), 1 (pt); LPNs 12 (ft); Orderlies 10 (ft); Nurses aides 42 (ft); Physical therapists 1 (ft); Recreational therapists 2 (ft); Occupational therapists 1 (pt); Speech therapists 1 (pt); Activities coordinators 1 (ft); Dietitians 1 (pt); Dentists 1 (pt); Ophthalmologists 1 (pt); Podiatrists 1 (pt); Audiologists 1 (pt).
Facilities Dining room; Physical therapy room; Activities room; Crafts room; Laundry room; Barber/Beauty shop.
Activities Arts and Crafts; Cards; Games; Reading groups; Prayer groups; Movies; Shopping trips; Dances/Social or cultural gatherings.

Hillside House Inc*
1235 Veronica Springs Rd, Santa Barbara, CA,
93105 (805) 687-0788
Admin Cecil C Cooprider.
Licensure Skilled Care. *Beds* 59.
Certified Medi-Cal.
Ownership Nonprofit.

Hy-Lond Convalescent Hospital*
3880 Via Lucero, Santa Barbara, CA, 93110
(805) 687-6651
Admin Kenton H Brenegan.
Licensure Skilled Care. *Beds* 189.
Ownership Proprietary.

Oak Park Convalescent Hospital*
623 W Junipero St, Santa Barbara, CA, 93105
(805) 682-7443
Admin Jeannette M McClain.
Licensure Skilled Care. *Beds* 138. *Certified* Medicare; Medi-Cal.
Ownership Proprietary.

Samarkand Convalescent Hospital
2566 Treasure Dr, Santa Barbara, CA, 93105
(805) 687-0701
Admin Carol Curlette. *Medical Dir/Dir of Nursing* Dr Robert Hartzman.
Licensure Skilled Care. *Beds* 59. *Certified* Medicare; Medi-Cal.
Ownership Nonprofit.
Admissions Requirements Minimum age 62; Medical examination; Physician's request.
Staff Physicians 1 (pt); RNs 10 (ft), 2 (pt); Nurses aides 25 (ft); Activities coordinators 1 (ft); Dietitians 1 (ft).
Affiliation Evangelical Covenant Church
Facilities Dining room; Physical therapy room;

Activities room; Laundry room; Barber/Beauty shop; Library.
Activities Arts and Crafts; Games; Reading groups; Prayer groups; Movies; Shopping trips; Dances/Social or cultural gatherings.
Description Situated between mountains and sea, Samarkand spans 16 acres of gently rolling land dotted with Spanish-style buildings highlighted by colorful, well-manicured flower gardens. The health center functions primarily for care of people who entered Samarkand as residents of its community care facility.

Santa Barbara Convalescent Hospital*
540 W Pueblo St, Santa Barbara, CA, 93105
(805) 682-7174
Admin Kehar S Johl.
Licensure Skilled Care. *Beds* 62. *Certified* Medicare; Medi-Cal.
Ownership Proprietary.

Valle Verde Health Facility
900 Calle De Los Amigos, Santa Barbara, CA, 93105 (805) 687-1571
Admin William R Webster. *Medical Dir/Dir of Nursing* Henry L Holderman MD.
Licensure Skilled Care. *Beds* 54. *Certified* Medicare; Medi-Cal.
Ownership Nonprofit.
Staff Physicians 4 (pt); RNs 6 (ft), 6 (pt); LPNs 1 (ft), 1 (pt); Nurses aides 15 (ft), 8 (pt); Physical therapists 1 (pt); Activities coordinators 1 (ft), 1 (pt); Dietitians 1 (pt); Podiatrists 1 (pt).
Affiliation Baptist
Facilities Dining room; Physical therapy room; Activities room; Chapel; Crafts room; Laundry room; Barber/Beauty shop; Library; Dental clinic, Grocery and variety store.
Activities Arts and Crafts; Cards; Games; Reading groups; Prayer groups; Movies; Shopping trips; Dances/Social or cultural gatherings; Resident string quartet; Trips; Putting green.
Description Valle Verde's 226 garden apartments and 54 SNF beds are located on 56 beautiful acres, one mile off the Pacific Ocean and within view of the Santa Ynez Mountains. Public transportation connects campus to many shopping centers and parks in beautiful Santa Barbara.

Vista Del Monte
3775 Modoc Rd, Santa Barbara, CA, 93105
(805) 687-0793
Admin Timothy F Wetzel. *Medical Dir/Dir of Nursing* Dr James N Fisher.
Licensure Skilled Care. *Beds* 16. *Certified* Medicare; Medi-Cal.
Ownership Nonprofit.
Admissions Requirements Minimum age 62; Medical examination.
Staff RNs 2 (ft), 8 (pt); LPNs 1 (ft), 3 (pt); Orderlies 6 (ft), 8 (pt); Nurses aides 1 (ft), 6 (pt); Activities coordinators 1 (ft), 1 (pt); Dietitians 1 (pt).
Facilities Dining room; Laundry room; Barber/Beauty shop; Library; Lounges for personal "get-togethers"; Large meeting room and main lounge adjacent to dining room.
Activities Arts and Crafts; Cards; Games; Reading groups; Movies; Shopping trips.

SANTA CLARA

Hy-Lond Convalescent Hospital
991 Clyde Ave, Santa Clara, CA, 95050 (408) 988-7666
Admin Bruce Strayer. *Medical Dir/Dir of Nursing* Harry Wong MD.
Licensure Skilled Care. *Beds* 200. *Certified* Medicare; Medi-Cal.
Ownership Proprietary.
Admissions Requirements Minimum age 18; Medical examination; Physician's request.
Staff RNs 9 (ft), 2 (pt); LPNs 14 (ft), 6 (pt); Orderlies 21 (ft), 3 (pt); Nurses aides 67 (ft), 8 (pt); Activities coordinators 2 (ft); Dietitians 1 (ft).
Facilities Dining room; Physical therapy room; Activities room; Crafts room; Barber/Beauty shop.
Activities Arts and Crafts; Cards; Games; Reading groups; Prayer groups; Movies; Shopping trips; Dances/Social or cultural gatherings.

Mission Skilled Nursing Facility*
410 N Winchester Blvd, Santa Clara, CA, 95050 (408) 248-3736
Admin Larry Blitz.
Licensure Skilled Care. *Beds* 111. *Certified* Medicare; Medi-Cal.
Ownership Proprietary.

SANTA CRUZ

Batterson Nursing Home and Convalescent Center
2555 Mattison Ln, Santa Cruz, CA, 95060 (408) 475-4065
Admin Ruth B Findlay. *Medical Dir/Dir of Nursing* Francis M Jacks MD.
Licensure Skilled Care. *Beds* 40. *Certified* Medicare.
Ownership Proprietary.
Admissions Requirements Minimum age 18; Medical examination; Physician's request.
Staff RNs 2 (ft), 4 (pt); LPNs 2 (pt); Orderlies 2 (ft), 1 (pt); Nurses aides 13 (ft), 7 (pt); Physical therapists; Occupational therapists; Speech therapists; Activities coordinators 1 (ft); Dietitians; Dentists.
Facilities Dining room; Activities room.
Activities Arts and Crafts; Cards; Games; Reading groups; Movies.
Description This is a small facility catering to patients wishes with beautiful flower gardens for wheelchair rides, and outdoor porch overlooking grounds. Each room has window which oversee gardens, and a large solarium with all windows facing street and gardens. Private ambulatory rooms with private bathrooms for those who stay on as private patients after recovering from illness; Christmas and Easter Mass for all who wish to attend.

Beverly Manor of Santa Cruz
1098 38th Ave, Santa Cruz, CA, 95060 (408) 475-6900
Admin Donna Hayes. *Medical Dir/Dir of Nursing* Dr R Scott.
Licensure Skilled Care. *Beds* 99. *Certified* Medicare.
Ownership Proprietary.
Staff RNs 3 (ft), 3 (pt); LPNs 6 (ft), 4 (pt);

Orderlies 4 (ft); Nurses aides 35 (ft), 15 (pt); Recreational therapists 1 (ft), 1 (pt); Activities coordinators.
Facilities Dining room; Physical therapy room; Activities room; Crafts room; Laundry room; Barber/Beauty shop.
Activities Arts and Crafts; Cards; Games; Reading groups; Prayer groups; Movies; Shopping trips.

Brommer Manor
2000 Brommer St, Santa Cruz, CA, 95060
(408) 476-5500
Admin Norma K Colby.
Licensure Skilled Care. *Beds* 38. *Certified* Medicare; Medi-Cal.
Ownership Proprietary.
Activities Arts and Crafts; Cards; Games; Reading groups; Movies; Shopping trips; Dances/Social or cultural gatherings.

Cresthaven Inc
740 17th Ave, Santa Cruz, CA, 95062 (408) 475-3812
Admin Romeo Hernandez. *Medical Dir/Dir of Nursing* Dr John Catlin.
Licensure Skilled Care. *Beds* 20.
Certified Medi-Cal.
Ownership Proprietary.
Admissions Requirements Minimum age 50; Medical examination.
Staff Physicians 1 (pt); RNs 1 (ft), 2 (pt); LPNs 2 (ft), 1 (pt); Nurses aides 3 (ft), 2 (pt); Recreational therapists 1 (pt); Activities coordinators 1 (pt); Dietitians 1 (ft), 1 (pt); Dentists 1 (pt); Ophthalmologists 1 (pt); Podiatrists 1 (pt).
Facilities Dining room; Activities room; Chapel; Crafts room; Laundry room; Barber/Beauty shop.
Activities Arts and Crafts; Cards; Games; Reading groups; Prayer groups; Movies; Shopping trips; Dances/Social or cultural gatherings.

Driftwood Convalescent Hospital
675 24th Ave, Santa Cruz, CA, 95060 (408) 475-6323
Admin Elizabeth P Byrne. *Medical Dir/Dir of Nursing* Dr Allan Martin.
Licensure Skilled Care. *Beds* 92. *Certified* Medicare; Medi-Cal.
Ownership Proprietary.
Admissions Requirements Minimum age 18.
Staff RNs 5 (ft); LPNs 4 (ft); Orderlies 4 (ft); Nurses aides 35 (ft); Occupational therapists 1 (pt); Speech therapists 1 (pt); Activities coordinators 1 (ft); Dietitians 1 (ft); Dentists 1 (pt); Ophthalmologists 1 (pt); Podiatrists 1 (pt); Audiologists 1 (pt).
Facilities Dining room; Physical therapy room; Activities room; Crafts room; Laundry room; Barber/Beauty shop.
Activities Arts and Crafts; Cards; Games; Reading groups; Prayer groups; Movies.

Garden Nursing Home and Convalescent Hospital*
1410 Ocean St, Santa Cruz, CA, 95062 (408) 423-6045
Admin Cheryl A Mitchum.
Licensure Skilled Care. *Beds* 55. *Certified* Medicare; Medi-Cal.
Ownership Proprietary.

Harbor Hills
1171 7th Ave, Santa Cruz, CA, 95062 (408) 476-1700
Admin Joyce Bahnsen. *Medical Dir/Dir of Nursing* Ron Krasner MD.
Licensure Skilled Care. *Beds* 99.
Certified Medi-Cal.
Ownership Proprietary.
Admissions Requirements Minimum age 18; Physician's request.
Staff Physicians 5 (pt); RNs 3 (ft), 1 (pt); LPNs 5 (ft), 5 (pt); Nurses aides 32 (ft), 12 (pt); Activities coordinators 1 (ft); Dietitians 1 (ft); Dentists 1 (pt).
Facilities Dining room; Activities room; Crafts room; Laundry room; Barber/Beauty shop; Library; TV room.
Activities Arts and Crafts; Cards; Games; Movies; Shopping trips; Dances/Social or cultural gatherings.
Description Harbor Hills is a locked psychiatric facility admitting patients with a primary diagnosis of mental illness. The special treatment program and professional interdisciplinary team augments nursing staff.

Hillhaven Extended Care Hospital
1115 Capitola Rd, Santa Cruz, CA, 95060 (408) 475-4055
Admin Marise Huhne. *Medical Dir/Dir of Nursing* Dr Anthony Tyler.
Licensure Skilled Care. *Beds* 149. *Certified* Medicare; Medi-Cal.
Ownership Proprietary.
Admissions Requirements Medical examination; Physician's request.
Staff RNs 3 (ft); LPNs 6 (ft); Nurses aides 32 (ft); Physical therapists 1 (ft); Occupational therapists 1 (ft); Speech therapists 1 (ft); Activities coordinators 2 (ft); Dietitians 2 (ft); Dentists 1 (ft); Ophthalmologists 1 (ft); Podiatrists 1 (ft); Audiologists 1 (ft).
Facilities Dining room; Physical therapy room; Activities room; Crafts room; Laundry room; Barber/Beauty shop; Library.
Activities Arts and Crafts; Cards; Games; Reading groups; Prayer groups; Movies; Dances/Social or cultural gatherings.
Description Facility has an extensive activity program including "happy feet ambulation," special restorative feeding program, validation therapy, art therapy, music therapy, movement therapy, and a wide variety of entertainment programs and social functions.

Live Oak Skilled Nursing and Manor
2990 Soquel Ave, Santa Cruz, CA, 95060 (408) 475-8832
Admin Joseph Nadler. *Medical Dir/Dir of Nursing* Allen Martin MD.
Licensure Skilled Care; Intermediate Care.
Beds 109; ICF 105. *Certified* Medicare.
Ownership Proprietary.
Staff Physicians 35 (pt); RNs 6 (ft), 4 (pt); LPNs 13 (ft), 6 (pt); Orderlies 11 (ft), 4 (pt); Nurses aides 28 (ft), 14 (pt); Physical therapists 2 (pt); Reality therapists 1 (ft); Recreational therapists 5 (ft), 2 (pt); Occupational therapists 1 (pt); Speech therapists 1 (pt); Activities coordinators 1 (ft); Dietitians 1 (pt); Dentists 1 (pt); Ophthalmologists 1 (pt); Podiatrists 1 (pt); Audiologists 1 (pt).
Facilities Dining room; Physical therapy room;

Activities room; Chapel; Crafts room; Laundry room; Barber/Beauty shop; Library.
Activities Arts and Crafts; Cards; Games; Reading groups; Movies; Dances/Social or cultural gatherings.
Description We have both skilled nursing facility and intermediate care facility units. We employ 5 full-time activity directors who are on duty from 8:00 am to 8:00 pm.

Rose Crest Nursing Home
941 El Dorado Ave, Santa Cruz, CA, 95060 (408) 475-7544
Admin Beverly Lowland. *Medical Dir/Dir of Nursing* Dr Allen Martin.
Beds 28. *Certified* Medi-Cal.
Ownership Proprietary.
Admissions Requirements Minimum age 50.
Staff RNs 1 (ft), 3 (pt); LPNs 2 (ft), 5 (pt); Nurses aides 5 (ft), 10 (pt); Activities coordinators 1 (pt); Dietitians 1 (ft), 3 (pt).
Facilities Dining room; Activities room; Laundry room.
Activities Arts and Crafts; Cards; Games; Reading groups; Movies; Shopping trips; Dances/Social or cultural gatherings.
Description Facility specializes in care for the geri-psychiatric patient, wanderers, confused, and disoriented; must be ambulatory.

SANTA MARIA

Continana Convalescent Hospital
830 E Chapel, Santa Maria, CA, 93454 (805) 922-6657
Admin James G Golden. *Medical Dir/Dir of Nursing* Paul Cook MD.
Licensure Skilled Care. *Beds* 59. *Certified* Medicare; Medi-Cal.
Ownership Proprietary.
Admissions Requirements Minimum age 16; Medical examination; Physician's request.
Staff Physicians 1 (pt); RNs 5 (ft), 4 (pt); Orderlies 3 (ft); Nurses aides 20 (ft), 3 (pt); Physical therapists 1 (pt); Reality therapists 1 (pt); Recreational therapists 1 (pt); Occupational therapists 1 (pt); Speech therapists 1 (pt); Activities coordinators 1 (ft); Dietitians 1 (pt); Dentists 1 (pt); Ophthalmologists 1 (pt); Podiatrists 1 (pt); Audiologists 1 (pt); LVNs 3 (ft), 3 (pt).
Facilities Dining room; Physical therapy room; Activities room; Crafts room; Laundry room; Barber/Beauty shop.
Activities Arts and Crafts; Cards; Games; Reading groups; Prayer groups; Movies; Shopping trips; Dances/Social or cultural gatherings.
Description The owner of this facility also owns a 48-bed rest home in the same city; patients who recuperate at a lower level of care can be transferred to this facility if they request it.

Kimberly Convalescent Hospital
820 W Cook St, Santa Maria, CA, 93454 (805) 925-8877
Admin Carroll Silvera.
Licensure Skilled Care. *Beds* 55. *Certified* Medicare; Medi-Cal.
Ownership Proprietary.

Villa Maria Convalescent Hospital
425 E Barcellus, Santa Maria, CA, 93454 (805) 922-3558
Admin Laurie Osborn-Smith. *Medical Dir/Dir of Nursing* Joseph Cohan MD.
Licensure Skilled Care. *Beds* 88. *Certified* Medicare; Medi-Cal.
Ownership Proprietary.
Staff Physicians 1 (ft); RNs 7 (ft), 2 (pt); Orderlies 6 (ft); Nurses aides 37 (ft); Physical therapists 1 (pt); Reality therapists 1 (pt); Recreational therapists 1 (pt); Occupational therapists 1 (pt); Speech therapists 1 (pt); Activities coordinators 1 (ft); Dietitians 1 (pt); Dentists 1 (pt); Ophthalmologists 1 (pt); Podiatrists 1 (pt); Audiologists 1 (pt); LVNs 6 (ft), 3 (pt).
Facilities Dining room; Physical therapy room; Activities room; Crafts room; Laundry room; Barber/Beauty shop; Library.
Activities Arts and Crafts; Cards; Games; Reading groups; Prayer groups; Movies; Shopping trips; Dances/Social or cultural gatherings; Monthly luncheons; Holiday programs.
Description The facility is centrally located in Santa Maria, adjacent to an acute hospital and medical plazas. The hospital provides rehabilitation programs and quality nursing services. Cable TV and HBO are provided with large-screen TV.

SANTA MONICA

Arizona Convalescent Hospital*
1330 17th St, Santa Monica, CA, 90404 (213) 829-5411
Admin Peter J Steenblock.
Licensure Skilled Care. *Beds* 72. *Certified* Medicare; Medi-Cal.
Ownership Proprietary.

Bay Vista Convalescent Hospital*
1338 20th St, Santa Monica, CA, 90404 (213) 870-9761
Admin Piraro Donnell.
Licensure Skilled Care. *Beds* 154. *Certified* Medicare; Medi-Cal.
Ownership Proprietary.

Berkley Convalescent Hospital*
Arizona at 17th St, Santa Monica, CA, 90404 (213) 393-2705
Admin Scott R Jensen.
Licensure Skilled Care. *Beds* 54.
Ownership Proprietary.

Berkley East Convalescent Hospital*
2021 Arizona Ave, Santa Monica, CA, 90404 (213) 451-4748
Admin Paul Bartolucci.
Licensure Skilled Care. *Beds* 235.
Ownership Proprietary.
Description Facility offers occupational and physical therapy, speech pathology/audiology.

Berkshire, A Skilled Nursing Facility
2602 Broadway, Santa Monica, CA, 90404 (213) 453-8816
Admin William K Kolodin. *Medical Dir/Dir of Nursing* James H Shumaker MD.
Licensure Skilled Care. *Beds* 33.
Ownership Proprietary.
Admissions Requirements Minimum age 62.

Staff RNs 1 (ft), 2 (pt); LPNs 2 (ft), 2 (pt); Nurses aides 12 (ft), 3 (pt); Physical therapists 1 (pt); Recreational therapists 1 (pt); Occupational therapists 1 (pt); Speech therapists 1 (pt); Activities coordinators 1 (ft), 1 (pt); Dietitians 1 (pt); Dentists 1 (pt); Ophthalmologists 1 (pt); Podiatrists 1 (pt); Audiologists 1 (pt).
Facilities Dining room; Activities room; Laundry room; Barber/Beauty shop.
Activities Arts and Crafts; Cards; Games; Prayer groups; Movies; Dances/Social or cultural gatherings; Barbecues; Emeritus college classes.
Description Lovely, small facility surrounded by large garden area with many patios. Staff offers kind, gentle attention. Also a residential care home is located on same grounds for 22 residents.

Beverly Manor Convalescent Hospital*
1340 15th St, Santa Monica, CA, 90404 (213) 451-9706
Admin James Scadlock.
Licensure Skilled Care. *Beds* 227. *Certified* Medicare; Medi-Cal.
Ownership Proprietary.
Description JCAH approved.

Cosgrove Convalescent Hospital*
1323 17th St, Santa Monica, CA, 90404 (213) 829-4328
Admin Paul W Cosgrove.
Licensure Skilled Care. *Beds* 49. *Certified* Medicare; Medi-Cal.
Ownership Proprietary.

Crescent Bay Convalescent Hospital*
1437 14th St, Santa Monica, CA, 90404 (213) 394-3726
Admin Sherman Miller.
Licensure Skilled Care. *Beds* 69. *Certified* Medicare; Medi-Cal.
Ownership Proprietary.

Fireside Convalescent Hospital*
947 3rd St, Santa Monica, CA, 90403 (213) 393-0475
Admin N R Chivi.
Licensure Skilled Care. *Beds* 66. *Certified* Medicare; Medi-Cal.
Ownership Proprietary.

Good Shepherd Convalescent Hospital*
1131 Arizona Ave, Santa Monica, CA, 90404 (213) 451-4809
Admin Paul W Cosgrove.
Licensure Skilled Care. *Beds* 48. *Certified* Medicare; Medi-Cal.
Ownership Proprietary.

Santa Monica Care Convalescent Hospital
1321 Franklin, Santa Monica, CA, 90404 (213) 828-5597
Admin Stephen Fitch. *Medical Dir/Dir of Nursing* Victor Wylie MD.
Licensure Skilled Care. *Beds* 59. *Certified* Medicare; Medi-Cal.
Ownership Proprietary.
Staff RNs 1 (ft), 4 (pt); Orderlies 2 (ft), 1 (pt); Nurses aides 9 (ft), 4 (pt); Physical therapists 1 (ft); Occupational therapists 1 (pt); Speech therapists 1 (pt); Activities coordinators 1 (ft); Dentists 1 (pt); Podiatrists 1 (pt); Audiologists 1 (pt).

Facilities Dining room; Physical therapy room; Activities room; Barber/Beauty shop.
Activities Arts and Crafts; Cards; Games; Prayer groups; Movies.

Santa Monica Convalarium
1320 20th St, Santa Monica, CA, 90404 (213) 829-4301
Admin Carol Wagner. *Medical Dir/Dir of Nursing* Phillip Rossman MD.
Licensure Skilled Care. *Beds* 59. *Certified* Medicare.
Ownership Proprietary.
Staff RNs 3 (ft), 3 (pt); LPNs 3 (ft), 2 (pt); Orderlies 1 (ft), 1 (pt); Physical therapists 1 (pt); Reality therapists 1 (pt); Recreational therapists 1 (ft); Occupational therapists 1 (pt); Speech therapists 1 (pt); Activities coordinators 1 (ft); Dietitians 1 (pt); Dentists 1 (pt); Ophthalmologists 1 (pt); Podiatrists 1 (pt); Audiologists 1 (pt).
Facilities Dining room; Activities room; Crafts room; Barber/Beauty shop; Library; Patio area.
Activities Arts and Crafts; Cards; Games; Movies; Shopping trips; Dances/Social or cultural gatherings; Non-denomination meetings; Adult education.
Description Facility is a small, low-key place to live; encourages a home-like atmosphere. The facility is unusually clean and well kept. Accepts many types of patients from the very alert rehabilitation candidate to the terminally ill individual.

Santa Monica Lodge
2250 29th St, Santa Monica, CA, 90405 (213) 450-7694 and 450-7695
Admin Ruth Gelford. *Medical Dir/Dir of Nursing* Paul A Berns MD.
Licensure Skilled Care. *Beds* 44. *Certified* Medicare.
Ownership Proprietary.
Admissions Requirements Physician's request.
Staff Physicians 17 (ft); RNs 1 (ft), 3 (pt); LPNs 3 (ft), 5 (pt); Orderlies 1 (ft), 2 (pt); Nurses aides 12 (ft), 1 (pt); Physical therapists 1 (pt); Recreational therapists 1 (pt); Speech therapists 1 (pt); Activities coordinators 1 (pt); Dietitians 1 (pt); Dentists 1 (pt); Ophthalmologists 1 (pt); Podiatrists 1 (pt).
Facilities Dining room; Laundry room; Barber/Beauty shop.
Activities Arts and Crafts; Cards; Games; Reading groups; Prayer groups; Movies; Shopping trips; Dances/Social or cultural gatherings.
Description A home-like environment is provided by the staff, who focus on the individual needs of each patient, thus giving the feeling of care and comfort.

Santa Monica Lodge—Unit 2*
2828 W Pico Blvd, Santa Monica, CA, 90405 (213) 392-3094
Admin Denise Sutton.
Licensure Skilled Care. *Beds* 42.
Certified Medi-Cal.
Ownership Proprietary.

SANTA PAULA

Santa Paula Healthcare*
220 W Main St, Santa Paula, CA, 93060 (805)

525-6621
Admin Eloise Hibbard.
Licensure Skilled Care. *Beds* 49. *Certified* Medicare; Medi-Cal.
Ownership Proprietary.

Twin Pines Healthcare
250 March St, Santa Paula, CA, 93060 (805) 525-7134
Admin Eloise K Hibbard. *Medical Dir/Dir of Nursing* Samuel R Edwards MD.
Licensure Skilled Care. *Beds* 99. *Certified* Medicare; Medi-Cal.
Ownership Proprietary.
Admissions Requirements Physician's request.
Facilities Dining room; Activities room; Barber/Beauty shop.
Activities Arts and Crafts; Dances/Social or cultural gatherings.

SANTA ROSA

Driftwood Convalescent Hospital*
850 Sonoma Ave, Santa Rosa, CA, 95404 (707) 544-7750
Admin Elizabeth Lee.
Licensure Skilled Care. *Beds* 181. *Certified* Medicare; Medi-Cal.
Ownership Proprietary.

London House Convalescent Hospital
4650 Hoen Ave, Santa Rosa, CA, 95405 (707) 546-0471
Admin Jay Underwood. *Medical Dir/Dir of Nursing* Gertrude Van Steyn MD.
Licensure Skilled Care. *Beds* 99. *Certified* Medicare; Medi-Cal.
Ownership Proprietary.
Admissions Requirements Medical examination; Physician's request.
Staff RNs 9 (ft); LPNs 6 (ft); Nurses aides 65 (ft); Physical therapists 1 (ft); Recreational therapists 1 (ft); Occupational therapists 1 (pt); Speech therapists 1 (pt); Activities coordinators 1 (ft); Dietitians 1 (ft); Dentists 1 (pt); Ophthalmologists 1 (pt); Podiatrists 1 (pt); Audiologists 1 (pt).
Facilities Dining room; Physical therapy room; Activities room; Chapel; Crafts room; Laundry room; Barber/Beauty shop; Library; TV lounge.
Activities Arts and Crafts; Cards; Games; Reading groups; Prayer groups; Movies; Shopping trips; Dances/Social or cultural gatherings.
Description Facility features a director of nursing who is an 8-year employee, homemade meals, and a physical therapy program.

Maralie Convalescent Hospital
2080 Guerneville Rd, Santa Rosa, CA, 95401 (707) 542-1510
Admin Steven M Tanoy. *Medical Dir/Dir of Nursing* William Hopper MD.
Licensure Skilled Care. *Beds* 52. *Certified* Medicare; Medi-Cal.
Ownership Proprietary.
Admissions Requirements Minimum age 18; Medical examination; Physician's request.
Staff RNs 2 (ft), 3 (pt); LPNs 4 (ft), 2 (pt); Orderlies 17 (ft), 5 (pt); Physical therapists 2 (pt); Activities coordinators 1 (ft), 1 (pt).
Facilities Dining room; Physical therapy room; Activities room; Crafts room; Laundry room;

Barber/Beauty shop.
Activities Arts and Crafts; Games; Reading groups; Prayer groups; Movies; Shopping trips; Dances/Social or cultural gatherings.

Montgomery Manor*
3751 Montgomery Dr, Santa Rosa, CA, 95405
(707) 525-1250
Admin Dorothy J Bennett.
Licensure Skilled Care. *Beds* 122. *Certified* Medicare; Medi-Cal.
Ownership Proprietary.

Santa Rosa Convalescent Hospital
446 Arrowood Dr, Santa Rosa, CA, 95407
(707) 528-2100
Admin Henry Weiland. *Medical Dir/Dir of Nursing* Kenneth Wong MD.
Licensure Skilled Care. *Beds* 59. *Certified* Medicare; Medi-Cal.
Ownership Proprietary.

Summerfield Convalescent Hospital
1280 Summerfield Rd, Santa Rosa, CA, 95405
(707) 539-1515
Admin Arlene Garietz. *Medical Dir/Dir of Nursing* Michael MacLean MD.
Licensure Skilled Care. *Beds* 70. *Certified* Medicare; Medi-Cal.
Ownership Proprietary.
Facilities Dining room; Activities room; Crafts room; Laundry room.
Activities Arts and Crafts; Cards; Games; Reading groups; Prayer groups; Movies; Dances/Social or cultural gatherings.

SANTEE

Edgemoor Geriatric Hospital
9065 Edgemoor Dr, Santee, CA, 92071 (714) 448-2411
Admin Francoise R Euliss. *Medical Dir/Dir of Nursing* William Bailey MD.
Licensure Skilled Care. *Beds* 342. *Certified* Medicare; Medi-Cal.
Ownership Public.
Admissions Requirements Minimum age 18; Medical examination.
Staff Physicians 2 (ft), 2 (pt); RNs 21 (ft), 10 (pt); LPNs 8 (ft); Nurses aides 90 (ft), 15 (pt); Physical therapists 3 (ft); Reality therapists 2 (ft); Recreational therapists 2 (ft); Occupational therapists 1 (ft), 1 (pt); Speech therapists 1 (pt); Activities coordinators 1 (ft); Dietitians 2 (ft); Dentists 1 (pt); Ophthalmologists 1 (pt); Podiatrists 1 (pt).
Facilities Dining room; Physical therapy room; Activities room; Chapel; Crafts room; Laundry room; Barber/Beauty shop; Library.
Activities Arts and Crafts; Games; Reading groups; Prayer groups; Movies; Shopping trips; Field trips.

SARATOGA

Odd Fellows Home of California Infirmary
14500 Fruitvale Ave, Saratoga, CA, 95070 (408) 867-3891
Admin Jack D Knighton.
Licensure Skilled Care; Intermediate Care. *Beds* SNF 62; ICF 6. *Certified* Medicare;

Medi-Cal.
Ownership Nonprofit.
Admissions Requirements Minimum age 65; Medical examination.
Affiliation Independent Order of Odd Fellows

Our Lady of Fatima Villa*
20400 Saratoga-Los Gatos Rd, Saratoga, CA, 95070 (408) 867-3100
Admin Sr Margaret Newe.
Licensure Skilled Care. *Beds* 85. *Certified* Medicare; Medi-Cal.
Ownership Nonprofit.
Affiliation Roman Catholic

Saratoga Place Skilled Nursing Facility*
18611 Sousa Ln, Saratoga, CA, 95070 (408) 378-8875
Admin Opal Schlesinger.
Licensure Skilled Care. *Beds* 38.
Certified Medi-Cal.
Ownership Proprietary.

SEAL BEACH

Beverly Manor Convalescent Hospital
3000 Beverly Manor Rd, Seal Beach, CA, 90740 (213) 598-2477
Admin Walter Hekimian. *Medical Dir/Dir of Nursing* Dr Alan Greenberg.
Licensure Skilled Care. *Beds* 198. *Certified* Medicare; Medi-Cal.
Ownership Proprietary.
Admissions Requirements Medical examination; Physician's request.
Staff RNs 10 (ft), 4 (pt); LPNs 10 (ft), 7 (pt); Nurses aides 60 (ft), 15 (pt); Physical therapists 1 (ft); Reality therapists 1 (pt); Recreational therapists 1 (pt); Occupational therapists 1 (pt); Speech therapists 1 (pt); Activities coordinators 2 (ft); Dietitians 1 (ft).
Facilities Dining room; Physical therapy room; Activities room; Crafts room; Laundry room; Barber/Beauty shop; Fireside room.
Activities Arts and Crafts; Cards; Games; Reading groups; Prayer groups; Movies; Shopping trips; Dances/Social or cultural gatherings; Bowling.
Description The facility has predominately large 2-bed rooms located next to Leisure World retirement community, a full-staff physical therapy program, 7-day-a-week activity program, and comfortable weather all year.

SEBASTOPOL

Fircrest Convalescent Hospital
7025 Corline Ct, Sebastopol, CA, 95472 (707) 823-7444
Admin Eric Mawson.
Licensure Skilled Care. *Beds* 49. *Certified* Medicare; Medi-Cal.
Ownership Proprietary.

Gravenstein Convalescent Hospital
1035 Gravenstein Ave, Sebastopol, CA, 95472
(707) 823-7675
Admin Richard A Clark.

Licensure Skilled Care. *Beds* 95. *Certified* Medicare; Medi-Cal.
Ownership Proprietary.

Sebastopol Convalescent Hospital*
477 Petaluma Ave, Sebastopol, CA, 95472
(707) 823-7855
Admin Fred Lenschmidt.
Licensure Skilled Care. *Beds* 35. *Certified* Medicare; Medi-Cal.
Ownership Proprietary.

SELMA

Bethel Lutheran Home Inc*
2280 Dockery Ave, Selma, CA, 93662 (209) 896-4900
Admin Ken Truckenbrod.
Licensure Skilled Care. *Beds* 30.
Certified Medi-Cal.
Ownership Nonprofit.

Selma Convalescent Hospital*
2108 Stillman St, Selma, CA, 93662 (209) 896-4990
Admin Ida Lee.
Licensure Skilled Care. *Beds* 34.
Certified Medi-Cal.
Ownership Proprietary.

SEPULVEDA

Sheraton Convalescent Hospital*
9655 Sepulveda Blvd, Sepulveda, CA, 91343
(213) 892-8665
Admin Judith L Starr. *Medical Dir/Dir of Nursing* Melvin Kirschner MD.
Licensure Skilled Care. *Beds* 99. *Certified* Medicare; Medi-Cal.
Ownership Proprietary.
Admissions Requirements Physician's request.
Staff RNs; LPNs; Orderlies; Nurses aides; Physical therapists; Reality therapists; Recreational therapists; Occupational therapists; Speech therapists; Activities coordinators; Dietitians; Dentists.
Facilities Dining room; Physical therapy room; Activities room; Crafts room; Laundry room; Barber/Beauty shop; Library.
Activities Arts and Crafts; Cards; Games; Reading groups; Prayer groups; Movies; Shopping trips; Dances/Social or cultural gatherings.
Description A great deal of tender loving care is given to all including families.

SHAFTER

Shafter Convalescent Hospital*
140 E Tulare Ave, Shafter, CA, 93263 (805) 746-3912
Admin T Wayne Smith.
Licensure Skilled Care. *Beds* 99. *Certified* Medicare; Medi-Cal.
Ownership Proprietary.

SHERMAN OAKS

Sherman Oaks Convalescent Hospital*
14401 Huston St, Sherman Oaks, CA, 91423
(213) 986-7242

Admin Edith Schuler.
Licensure Skilled Care. *Beds* 120. *Certified* Medicare; Medi-Cal.
Ownership Proprietary.

SIGNAL HILL

Saint Christopher Convalescent Hospital and Sanitarium*
1880 Dawson St, Signal Hill, CA, 90806 (213) 433-0408
Admin Dorothy K Oleson.
Licensure Skilled Care. *Beds* 59. *Certified* Medicare; Medi-Cal.
Ownership Proprietary.

SOLVANG

Santa Ynez Valley Recovery Residence*
636 Atterdag Rd, Solvang, CA, 93463 (805) 688-3263
Admin F Massingill.
Licensure Skilled Care; Intermediate Care.
Beds SNF 40; ICF 10. *Certified* Medicare; Medi-Cal.
Ownership Nonprofit.

SONOMA

London House Convalescent Hospital
678 2nd St W, Sonoma, CA, 95476 (707) 938-1096
Admin Donald H Bais. *Medical Dir/Dir of Nursing* Richard F H Kirk MD.
Licensure Skilled Care. *Beds* 83. *Certified* Medicare; Medi-Cal.
Ownership Proprietary.
Admissions Requirements Minimum age 20; Medical examination; Physician's request.
Staff Physicians 1 (pt); RNs 4 (ft); LPNs 5 (ft); Orderlies 3 (ft); Nurses aides 60 (ft); Physical therapists 1 (pt); Reality therapists 1 (pt); Occupational therapists 1 (pt); Speech therapists 1 (pt); Activities coordinators 1 (ft); Dietitians 1 (ft); Dentists 1 (pt); Ophthalmologists 1 (pt); Podiatrists 1 (pt); Audiologists 1 (pt).
Facilities Dining room; Physical therapy room; Activities room; Crafts room; Laundry room; Barber/Beauty shop.
Activities Arts and Crafts; Cards; Games; Reading groups; Prayer groups; Movies; Shopping trips.

Mission Convalescent Hospital*
1250 Broadway, Sonoma, CA, 95476 (707) 938-8406
Admin James S O'Hare.
Licensure Skilled Care. *Beds* 144. *Certified* Medicare; Medi-Cal.
Ownership Proprietary.

Sonoma Acres*
765 Donald Ave, Sonoma, CA, 95476 (707) 996-2161
Admin Clyde Bailey.
Licensure Skilled Care. *Beds* 32.
Ownership Proprietary.

SONORA

Sonora Convalescent Hospital Inc*
538 Ponderosa Dr, Sonora, CA, 95370 (209) 532-3668
Admin E G Wilson.
Licensure Skilled Care. *Beds* 36. *Certified* Medicare; Medi-Cal.
Ownership Proprietary.

SOUTH GATE

State Convalescent Hospital*
8455 State St, South Gate, CA, 90280 (213) 564-7761
Admin Carolyn Madison.
Licensure Skilled Care. *Beds* 99. *Certified* Medicare; Medi-Cal.
Ownership Proprietary.

SOUTH PASADENA

Braewood Convalescent Center*
1625 Meridian Ave, South Pasadena, CA, 91030 (213) 255-1585
Admin Donald G Laws.
Licensure Skilled Care. *Beds* 90.
Ownership Proprietary.

The South Pasadena Convalescent Hospital and Sanitarium*
904 Mission St, South Pasadena, CA, 91030 (213) 799-9571
Admin H Kohn and M Harrison.
Licensure Skilled Care. *Beds* 136. *Certified* Medicare; Medi-Cal.
Ownership Proprietary.

SPRING VALLEY

Mount Miguel Covenant Village
325 Kempton St, Spring Valley, CA, 92077 (619) 479-4790
Admin Dwayne Gabrielson. *Medical Dir/Dir of Nursing* Andrew Alongi.
Licensure Skilled Care; Intermediate Care.
Beds SNF 83; ICF 16. *Certified* Medicare; Medi-Cal.
Ownership Nonprofit.
Admissions Requirements Minimum age 55; Medical examination.
Staff RNs 3 (ft), 4 (pt); LPNs 7 (ft), 6 (pt); Nurses aides 25 (ft), 25 (pt); Activities coordinators 1 (ft), 3 (pt).
Affiliation Evangelical Congregational Church
Facilities Dining room; Physical therapy room; Activities room; Chapel; Laundry room; Barber/Beauty shop; Library.
Activities Arts and Crafts; Games; Reading groups; Prayer groups; Movies; Dances/Social or cultural gatherings.
Description Facility is located just outside San Diego, surrounded by mountain and reservoir views. Facility is part of a life-care community that is able to serve its residents, lacking only an acute care hospital.

Spring Valley Convalescent Hospital
9009 Campo Rd, Spring Valley, CA, 92077 (714) 460-2711

Admin Violet K Mathews. *Medical Dir/Dir of Nursing* Dr Charles Miller.
Licensure Skilled Care. *Beds* 75. *Certified* Medicare; Medi-Cal.
Ownership Proprietary.
Admissions Requirements Medical examination; Physician's request.
Staff RNs 8 (ft); LPNs 11 (ft); Orderlies 2 (ft); Nurses aides 29 (ft); Recreational therapists 1 (pt).
Facilities Dining room; Physical therapy room; Activities room; Laundry room; Barber/Beauty shop; Library.
Activities Arts and Crafts; Games; Reading groups; Prayer groups; Movies; Shopping trips; Dances/Social or cultural gatherings; Dining out.
Description Highly qualified staff provides exceptional quality health care for all residents. Facility is pleased to have dedicated and enthusiastic department heads and staff who work toward the goal of providing the best health care possible to the community.

Wilson Manor Convalescent Hospital Inc
8625 La Mar St, Spring Valley, CA, 92077 (714) 461-3222
Admin Marilyn Granger. *Medical Dir/Dir of Nursing* Dr R C Bock.
Licensure Skilled Care. *Beds* 50. *Certified* Medicare; Medi-Cal.
Ownership Proprietary.
Staff RNs 1 (ft), 1 (pt); LPNs 7 (ft), 1 (pt); Orderlies 1 (ft); Nurses aides 18 (ft), 2 (pt); Recreational therapists 1 (ft); 15 (ft).
Facilities Dining room; Physical therapy room; Activities room; Chapel; Crafts room; Laundry room; Barber/Beauty shop.
Activities Arts and Crafts; Cards; Games; Reading groups; Prayer groups; Movies.

STANTON

Quaker Gardens*
12151 Dale St, Stanton, CA, 90680 (714) 530-9100
Admin Hal B Dallke.
Licensure Skilled Care. *Beds* 38.
Ownership Nonprofit.

STOCKTON

Chateau Convalescent Hospital*
1221 Rose Marie Ln, Stockton, CA, 95207 (209) 477-2664
Admin Beverly Cortner.
Licensure Intermediate Care. *Beds* 99.
Ownership Nonprofit.

Crestwood Convalescent Hospital*
442 Hampton St, Stockton, CA, 95204 (209) 466-0456
Admin Janet Eisenbeis.
Licensure Skilled Care. *Beds* 100.
Ownership Proprietary.

Crestwood Manor
1130 Monaco Ct, Stockton, CA, 95207 (209) 478-2060
Admin John L Blaufus. *Medical Dir/Dir of Nursing* John Larson MD.

Licensure Skilled Care. *Beds* 184. *Certified* Medicare; Medi-Cal.
Ownership Proprietary.
Staff Physicians 1 (ft), 8 (pt); RNs 5 (ft), 7 (pt); LPNs 13 (ft), 12 (pt); Nurses aides 61 (ft), 14 (pt); Recreational therapists 1 (ft); Activities coordinators 3 (ft), 1 (pt); Dietitians 1 (ft); Dentists 1 (pt); Podiatrists 1 (pt).
Facilities Dining room; Activities room; Crafts room; Barber/Beauty shop.
Activities Arts and Crafts; Cards; Games; Reading groups; Prayer groups; Movies; Shopping trips; Dances/Social or cultural gatherings.
Description Facility serves a mentally disordered population ranging in age from the 20s through the geriatric years. The facility is divided into 3 primary components, the largest of which is the 127-capacity Special Treatment Program. This is composed of 2 segments, the STP and the STP Maintenance. This state-funded program is designed to help residents improve basic living skills and adjust to their illnesses so they can return to the community. The maintenance segment is designed to meet the individual needs of the residents to avoid regression to a higher level of care. A smaller unit of the facility houses residents with both mental and physical ailments who require long-term custodial care. The newest unit in the facility is the Gero-Psychiatric Unit. This county-funded program is solely for San Joaquin County residents who are admitted on an involuntary basis. This is a short-term extensive treatment program with an average stay of just over 30 days.

Elmhaven Convalescent Hospital Inc*
6940 Pacific Ave, Stockton, CA, 95207 (209) 477-4817
Admin Bernice Wahler.
Licensure Skilled Care. *Beds* 128. *Certified* Medicare; Medi-Cal.
Ownership Proprietary.

Glen Convalescent Hospital*
5964 Glen St, Stockton, CA, 95207 (209) 477-1816
Admin Joseph Castagna Jr.
Licensure Skilled Care. *Beds* 18. *Certified* Medicare; Medi-Cal.
Ownership Proprietary.

Hillhaven Rehabilitation and Convalescent Hospital*
1630 N Edison St, Stockton, CA, 95204 (209) 948-8762
Admin Richard Hart.
Licensure Skilled Care. *Beds* 98. *Certified* Medicare; Medi-Cal.
Ownership Proprietary.

Hy-Pana House Convalescent Hospital*
4520 N El Dorado, Stockton, CA, 95207 (209) 477-0271
Admin Phil Sullivan.
Licensure Skilled Care. *Beds* 117. *Certified* Medicare; Medi-Cal.
Ownership Proprietary.

La Salette Rehabilitation and Convalescent Hospital*
537 E Fulton St, Stockton, CA, 95204 (209) 466-2066

Licensure Skilled Care. *Beds* 122. *Certified* Medicare; Medi-Cal.
Ownership Proprietary.

Magnolia Convalescent Hospital
1032 N Lincoln St, Stockton, CA, 95203 (209) 466-5341
Admin Philip Sullivan. *Medical Dir/Dir of Nursing* Dr Robert Leggett.
Licensure Skilled Care. *Beds* 68. *Certified* Medicare; Medi-Cal.
Ownership Proprietary.

Plymouth Square
1319 N Madison, Stockton, CA, 95202 (209) 466-4341
Licensure Skilled Care. *Beds* 38.
Certified Medi-Cal.
Ownership Nonprofit.

Stockton Convalescent Hospital
2740 N California St, Stockton, CA, 95204 (209) 466-3522
Admin Margherita Fagan. *Medical Dir/Dir of Nursing* George Shilling.
Licensure Skilled Care. *Beds* 99. *Certified* Medicare; Medi-Cal.
Ownership Proprietary.
Admissions Requirements Physician's request.
Staff RNs 10 (ft); LPNs 10 (ft); Orderlies 5 (ft); Nurses aides 50 (ft); Recreational therapists 1 (ft); Activities coordinators 1 (ft); Dietitians 1 (ft).
Facilities Dining room; Physical therapy room; Activities room; Crafts room; Laundry room; Barber/Beauty shop; Library.
Activities Arts and Crafts; Cards; Games; Reading groups; Prayer groups; Movies; Shopping trips; Dances/Social or cultural gatherings.
Description Facility has been recently redecorated and has lovely grounds. Also features a very full activity program.

STUDIO CITY

Imperial Convalescent Hospital*
11441 Ventura Blvd, Studio City, CA, 91604 (213) 980-8200
Admin Catherine Mason.
Licensure Skilled Care. *Beds* 130.
Certified Medi-Cal.
Ownership Proprietary.

Studio City Convalescent Hospital
11429 Ventura Blvd, Studio City, CA, 91604 (213) 766-9551
Admin Eunice Fletcher. *Medical Dir/Dir of Nursing* Dr D W Donahue.
Licensure Skilled Care. *Beds* 99. *Certified* Medicare; Medi-Cal.
Ownership Proprietary.
Admissions Requirements Minimum age 75; Medical examination; Physician's request.
Staff Physicians 12 (pt); RNs 3 (ft), 2 (pt); LPNs 5 (ft); Orderlies 3 (ft); Nurses aides 37 (ft); Physical therapists 1 (pt); Recreational therapists 1 (ft); Occupational therapists 1 (pt); Speech therapists 1 (pt); Activities coordinators 1 (ft); Dietitians 1 (ft); Dentists 1 (pt); Ophthalmologists 1 (pt); Podiatrists 1 (pt); Audiologists 1 (pt).
Facilities Dining room; Activities room; Crafts

room; Laundry room; Barber/Beauty shop; Library; Patios.
Activities Arts and Crafts; Cards; Games; Reading groups; Movies; Dances/Social or cultural gatherings; Religious services.
Description Facility employs only certified aids; patient care is top priority; well organized and individual planned activities; geriatric specialist physicians on staff.

SUN CITY

Sun City Convalescent Center
27600 Encanto Dr, Sun City, CA, 92381 (714) 679-6858
Admin Roy Nee. *Medical Dir/Dir of Nursing* Dr Rex LaGrange.
Licensure Skilled Care. *Beds* 99. *Certified* Medicare; Medi-Cal.
Ownership Proprietary.
Admissions Requirements Minimum age 50; Physician's request.
Staff RNs 1 (ft), 2 (pt); LPNs 7 (ft), 5 (pt); Nurses aides 29 (ft), 7 (pt); Physical therapists 1 (pt); Activities coordinators 1 (ft).
Facilities Dining room; Physical therapy room; Activities room; Crafts room; Laundry room; Barber/Beauty shop.
Activities Arts and Crafts; Reading groups; Prayer groups; Movies; Dances/Social or cultural gatherings.
Description A recent addition to staff is Doc, a beautiful cocker spaniel who has yet to meet anyone he doesn't like or who doesn't adore him.

SUNLAND

Diana Lynn Lodge*
8647 Fenwick St, Sunland, CA, 91040 (213) 352-1421
Admin Marc R Toro.
Licensure Skilled Care. *Beds* 59. *Certified* Medicare; Medi-Cal.
Ownership Proprietary.

High Valley Lodge
7912 Topley Ln, Sunland, CA, 91040 (213) 352-3158
Admin William Kite. *Medical Dir/Dir of Nursing* Dr F Morada.
Licensure Skilled Care. *Beds* 50. *Certified* Medicare; Medi-Cal.
Ownership Proprietary.
Admissions Requirements Minimum age 18.
Staff RNs 1 (ft), 2 (pt); LPNs 3 (ft), 1 (pt); Orderlies 3 (ft); Nurses aides 12 (ft), 3 (pt); Physical therapists 1 (pt); Occupational therapists 1 (pt); Speech therapists 1 (pt); Activities coordinators 1 (ft); Dietitians 1 (pt); Dentists 1 (pt); Podiatrists 1 (pt).
Facilities Dining room; Physical therapy room; Activities room; Crafts room; Laundry room; Barber/Beauty shop; Library.
Activities Arts and Crafts; Cards; Games; Reading groups; Prayer groups; Movies; Shopping trips; Dances/Social or cultural gatherings.
Description High Valley Lodge is a very homey little hospital that is Medicare, and Medi-cal approved. It is on a dead-end street which makes it very peaceful and quiet. The facility

has a home-like atmosphere. The staff gives tender loving care. There is a large patio where social events take place.

Lakeview Terrace Sanitarium
PO Box 399, Sunland, CA, 91040 (213) 896-7452
Admin Beatryce Moyle. *Medical Dir/Dir of Nursing* James C Johnson.
Licensure Skilled Care. *Beds* 87. *Certified* Medicare.
Ownership Proprietary.
Staff Physicians 1 (pt); RNs 1 (ft), 1 (pt); LPNs 6 (ft), 4 (pt); Orderlies 8 (ft); Nurses aides 19 (ft); Physical therapists 1 (pt); Recreational therapists 1 (pt); Occupational therapists 1 (pt); Speech therapists 1 (pt); Activities coordinators 1 (ft); Dietitians 1 (pt); Dentists 1 (pt); Ophthalmologists 1 (pt); Podiatrists 1 (pt); Audiologists 1 (pt).
Facilities Dining room; Activities room; Crafts room; Laundry room; Barber/Beauty shop; Library.
Activities Arts and Crafts; Cards; Games; Reading groups; Prayer groups; Movies; Shopping trips; Dances/Social or cultural gatherings.
Description Safe, comfortable environment with expanded activity program (including off-site programs and trips) to meet the needs of the difficult patient.

Shadow Hill Convalescent Hospital
10158 Sunland Blvd, Sunland, CA, 91040 (213) 353-7800
Admin Orlando Clarizio. *Medical Dir/Dir of Nursing* Dr James Johnson.
Licensure Skilled Care. *Beds* 67. *Certified* Medicare; Medi-Cal.
Ownership Proprietary.
Staff Physicians 12 (pt); RNs 1 (ft), 1 (pt); LPNs 6 (ft); Orderlies 2 (ft); Nurses aides 22 (ft); Physical therapists 1 (pt); Recreational therapists 1 (ft); Occupational therapists 1 (ft); Speech therapists 1 (pt); Activities coordinators 1 (ft); Dietitians 1 (ft), 1 (pt); Dentists 1 (pt); Ophthalmologists 1 (pt); Podiatrists 1 (pt); Audiologists 1 (pt).
Facilities Dining room; Physical therapy room; Activities room; Crafts room; Laundry room; Barber/Beauty shop.
Activities Arts and Crafts; Cards; Games; Reading groups; Prayer groups; Movies; Shopping trips; Dances/Social or cultural gatherings.
Description Our facility is located in the hills of Sunland, California featuring a natural atmosphere. We accommodate private, Medi-Cal, medical pending, and Medicare patients. Activity and social services offered 7 days a week. Accommodate most religions and several languages.

SUNNYVALE

Hy-Lond Convalescent Hospital*
797 E Fremont Ave, Sunnyvale, CA, 94087 (408) 738-4880
Admin Sharon Gately.
Licensure Skilled Care. *Beds* 99. *Certified* Medicare; Medi-Cal.
Ownership Proprietary.

Idylwood Acres Convalescent Hospital*
1002 Fremont Ave, Sunnyvale, CA, 94087 (408) 739-2383
Admin Richard B Hart.
Licensure Skilled Care. *Beds* 185. *Certified* Medicare; Medi-Cal.
Ownership Proprietary.

Sunnyvale Convalescent Hospital*
1291 S Bernardo Ave, Sunnyvale, CA, 94087 (408) 245-8070
Admin William J Kennedy.
Licensure Skilled Care. *Beds* 99. *Certified* Medicare; Medi-Cal.
Ownership Proprietary.

SUSANVILLE

Susanville Convalescent Hospital
2005 River St, Susanville, CA, 96130 (916) 257-5341
Admin George Eslinger. *Medical Dir/Dir of Nursing* Dr Kenneth Korver.
Licensure Skilled Care. *Beds* 96. *Certified* Medicare; Medi-Cal.
Ownership Proprietary.
Admissions Requirements Physician's request.
Staff RNs 4 (ft), 1 (pt); LPNs 10 (ft), 1 (pt); Orderlies 3 (ft); Nurses aides 46 (ft); Physical therapists 1 (pt); Speech therapists 1 (pt); Activities coordinators 1 (ft); Dietitians 1 (pt); Dentists 1 (pt); Podiatrists 1 (pt); Audiologists 1 (pt).
Facilities Dining room; Physical therapy room; Activities room; Laundry room; Barber/Beauty shop; Library.
Activities Arts and Crafts; Cards; Games; Movies; Shopping trips.
Description Excellent nursing care in small rural town located in Sierra Nevada mountains.

SYLMAR

Astoria Convalescent Hospital
14040 Astoria, Sylmar, CA, 91342 (213) 367-5881
Admin John Franklin. *Medical Dir/Dir of Nursing* Harold Cohen.
Licensure Skilled Care; Intermediate Care.
Beds SNF 99; ICF 100. *Certified* Medicare; Medi-Cal.
Ownership Proprietary.
Admissions Requirements Minimum age 65; Medical examination; Physician's request.
Staff Physicians 30 (pt); RNs 3 (ft), 3 (pt); LPNs 10 (ft), 6 (pt); Nurses aides 60 (ft), 5 (pt); Physical therapists 2 (pt); Recreational therapists 2 (ft); Occupational therapists 2 (pt); Speech therapists 2 (pt); Activities coordinators 2 (ft); Dietitians 1 (pt); Dentists 2 (pt); Ophthalmologists 2 (pt); Podiatrists 3 (pt); Audiologists 2 (pt); Social workers 2 (ft).
Facilities Dining room; Physical therapy room; Activities room; Chapel; Crafts room; Laundry room; Barber/Beauty shop; Library.
Activities Arts and Crafts; Cards; Games; Reading groups; Prayer groups; Movies; Shopping trips; Dances/Social or cultural gatherings.
Description Facility features modern showers in each room, carpeting, all wood furniture,

rural setting, large nursing staff, classroom, adopt-a-grandparent program, and full acre of outdoor space.

Country Hills Convalescent Hospital
14122 Hubbard St, Sylmar, CA, 91342 (213) 361-0191
Admin Kent Berkey. *Medical Dir/Dir of Nursing* Valentine Birds MD.
Licensure Skilled Care. *Beds* 75. *Certified* Medicare; Medi-Cal.
Ownership Proprietary.
Staff RNs 3 (ft); LPNs 8 (ft), 4 (pt); Orderlies 5 (ft); Nurses aides 16 (ft), 1 (pt); Activities coordinators 1 (ft); Dietitians 1 (pt).
Facilities Dining room; Physical therapy room; Activities room; Laundry room; Barber/Beauty shop; Library.
Activities Arts and Crafts; Cards; Games; Movies; Shopping trips; Dances/Social or cultural gatherings.
Description Set back 100 yards from the street, Country Hills offers a quiet, relaxed setting for skilled nursing care. The facility is characterized by a quality-oriented, stable staff with a strong rehabilitative orientation.

Foothill Health and Rehabilitation Center
12260 Foothill Blvd, Sylmar, CA, 91342 (213) 899-9545
Admin C W Hunter. *Medical Dir/Dir of Nursing* J Clarfield MD.
Licensure Skilled Care. *Beds* 150. *Certified* Medicare; Medi-Cal.
Ownership Proprietary.
Facilities Dining room; Activities room; Crafts room; Laundry room; Barber/Beauty shop; Library.
Activities Arts and Crafts; Cards; Games; Reading groups; Prayer groups; Movies; Shopping trips; Dances/Social or cultural gatherings.
Description Facility features special treatment program for emotionally ill MDS patients.

Mountain View Sanitarium
13333 Fenton Ave, Sylmar, CA, 91342 (818) 367-1633
Admin Norman A Zecca. *Medical Dir/Dir of Nursing* David Parker MD.
Licensure Skilled Care. *Beds* 114. *Certified* Medicare; Medi-Cal.
Ownership Proprietary.
Admissions Requirements Minimum age 35; Medical examination; Physician's request.
Staff RNs 4 (ft), 3 (pt); LPNs 6 (ft), 2 (pt); Nurses aides 32 (ft), 10 (pt); Physical therapists 1 (pt); Occupational therapists 1 (pt); Speech therapists 1 (pt); Activities coordinators 1 (ft); Dietitians 1 (pt); Dentists 1 (pt); Ophthalmologists 1 (pt); Podiatrists 1 (pt); Audiologists 1 (pt).
Facilities Dining room; Physical therapy room; Activities room; Barber/Beauty shop.
Activities Arts and Crafts; Cards; Games; Reading groups; Prayer groups; Movies; Dances/Social or cultural gatherings; Outings; Luncheons; Picnics.

United Cerebral Palsy/Spastic Children's Foundation
12831 Maclay St, Sylmar, CA, 91342 (818) 365-8081
Admin A Mae Stephenson. *Medical Dir/Dir of*

Nursing Richard Koch.
Licensure Skilled Care; Intermediate Care.
Beds 141. *Certified* Medicare; Medi-Cal.
Ownership Nonprofit.
Admissions Requirements Minimum age 16.
Staff Physicians 4 (pt); RNs 7 (ft); LPNs 7 (ft);
Nurses aides 70 (ft); Physical therapists 1 (pt);
Recreational therapists 1 (pt); Occupational
therapists 1 (pt); Speech therapists 1 (pt);
Activities coordinators 1 (ft); Dietitians 1 (pt);
Dentists 2 (pt); Ophthalmologists 2 (pt); Podia-
trists 1 (pt); Audiologists 1 (pt).
Facilities Dining room; Physical therapy room;
Activities room; Crafts room; Laundry room;
Barber/Beauty shop; Library; Educational class-
rooms.
Activities Arts and Crafts; Cards; Games;
Reading groups; Prayer groups; Movies; Shop-
ping trips; Non-verbal communication training.
Description Facility incorporates medi-
cal/nursing needs with a developmental
program aimed at maximizing each client's
highest potential regardless of physical disabilities.

TAFT

West Side Nursing Home
111 W Ash St, Taft, CA, 93268 (805) 763-3333
Admin Larry E Clements. *Medical Dir/Dir of
Nursing* James Jenke MD.
Licensure Skilled Care. *Beds* 34. *Cer-
tified* Medicare; Medi-Cal.
Ownership Public.
Staff RNs 3 (ft), 1 (pt); LPNs 2 (ft), 4 (pt);
Nurses aides 10 (ft), 10 (pt); Activities coordi-
nators 1 (ft).
Facilities Dining room; Laundry room; Barber-
/Beauty shop.
Activities Arts and Crafts; Cards; Games;
Reading groups; Prayer groups; Shopping trips;
Dances/Social or cultural gatherings.

TARZANA

Extended Care Hospital of Tarzana
5650 Reseda Blvd, Tarzana, CA, 91356 (213)
881-4261
Admin Jeanne Russell. *Medical Dir/Dir of
Nursing* Dr Barnett.
Licensure Skilled Care. *Beds* 192. *Cer-
tified* Medicare; Medi-Cal.
Ownership Proprietary.
Facilities Dining room; Physical therapy room;
Activities room; Laundry room; Barber/Beauty
shop; Library.
Activities Arts and Crafts; Games; Prayer
groups; Movies; Dances/Social or cultural gath-
erings.

TEMPLE CITY

Evergreen Convalescent Center Inc
10786 Live Oak Ave, Temple City, CA, 91780
(213) 447-5404
Admin Christine Rosensteel. *Medical Dir/Dir
of Nursing* Jack Baker MD.
Licensure Skilled Care. *Beds* 59. *Certified* Medicare; Medi-Cal.
Ownership Proprietary.
Staff Physicians 1 (pt); RNs 1 (ft), 1 (pt); LPNs

4 (ft), 4 (pt); Orderlies 5 (ft), 1 (pt); Nurses aides
10 (ft), 1 (pt); Physical therapists 1 (pt); Occupational therapists 1 (pt); Speech therapists 1
(pt); Activities coordinators 1 (ft); Dietitians 1
(pt); Dentists 1 (pt); Ophthalmologists 1 (pt);
Podiatrists 1 (pt); Audiologists 1 (pt).
Facilities Dining room; Physical therapy room;
Activities room; Laundry room; Barber/Beauty
shop; Patio.
Activities Arts and Crafts; Games; Reading
groups; Movies; Shopping trips; Dances/Social
or cultural gatherings.
Description Evergreen is a small facility and is
able to provide more individual attention to
each patient. Everyone knows everyone, as in a
small town. Our goal is to try to maintain a
home-like atmosphere for our patients.

Santa Anita Convalescent Hospital
5522 Gracewood Ave, Temple City, CA, 91780
(213) 579-0310
Admin Frank Schrader. *Medical Dir/Dir of
Nursing* Dr Scarbough.
Licensure Skilled Care. *Beds* 367. *Cer-
tified* Medicare; Medi-Cal.
Ownership Proprietary.
Staff Physicians 1 (ft); RNs 8 (ft); LPNs 15 (ft);
Orderlies 8 (ft); Nurses aides 89 (ft); Physical
therapists 2 (ft); Reality therapists 1 (pt); Recre-
ational therapists 1 (ft), 1 (pt); Occupational
therapists 1 (pt); Speech therapists 2 (pt);
Activities coordinators 1 (ft); Dietitians 1 (ft);
Dentists 2 (pt); Audiologists 1 (pt).
Facilities Dining room; Physical therapy room;
Activities room; Chapel; Laundry room; Bar-
ber/Beauty shop.
Activities Arts and Crafts; Cards; Games;
Reading groups; Prayer groups; Movies; Shop-
ping trips.

Temple City Convalescent Hospital*
5101 Tyler Ave, Temple City, CA, 91780 (213)
443-3028
Admin Brian Elliot.
Licensure Skilled Care. *Beds* 59. *Cer-
tified* Medicare; Medi-Cal.
Ownership Proprietary.
Description JCAH approved.

THOUSAND OAKS

Thousand Oaks Convalarium*
93 W Avenida de los Arboles, Thousand Oaks,
CA, 91360 (805) 492-2444
Admin Jolana K Borlaug.
Licensure Skilled Care. *Beds* 124. *Cer-
tified* Medicare; Medi-Cal.
Ownership Proprietary.

TIBURON

**Marin Convalescent and Rehabilitation
Hospital**
30 Hacienda Dr, Tiburon, CA, 94920 (415)
435-4554
Admin Mary Kelly.
Licensure Skilled Care. *Beds* 56. *Cer-
tified* Medicare; Medi-Cal.
Ownership Proprietary.
Staff RNs 3 (ft), 6 (pt); Orderlies 2 (ft), 2 (pt);
Physical therapists 1 (pt); Activities coordina-

tors 1 (ft); Dietitians 1 (pt).
Facilities Dining room; Physical therapy room;
Laundry room.
Activities Arts and Crafts; Games; Reading
groups; Prayer groups; Movies; Shopping trips.
Description The hospital has a beautiful central
patio and enclosed garden room with fish pond,
waterfall, lava rock walls, and tropical plants,
which is used for visiting, parties, and dinners
during the summer months.

TORRANCE

Bay Crest Convalescent Hospital
3750 Garnet Ave, Torrance, CA, 90503 (213)
371-2431
Admin Steven P Hass. *Medical Dir/Dir of
Nursing* Dr Harold C Dorin.
Licensure Skilled Care. *Beds* 79. *Cer-
tified* Medicare; Medi-Cal.
Ownership Proprietary.
Admissions Requirements Minimum age 40;
Physician's request.
Staff RNs 1 (ft), 2 (pt); LPNs 7 (ft), 1 (pt);
Orderlies 2 (ft); Nurses aides 27 (ft), 3 (pt);
Activities coordinators 1 (ft).
Facilities Dining room; Activities room; Laun-
dry room; Barber/Beauty shop.
Activities Arts and Crafts; Cards; Games; Pray-
er groups; Movies; Shopping trips;
Dances/Social or cultural gatherings; Adult
education.

Bay Harbor Rehabilitation Center
3620 Lomita Blvd, Torrance, CA, 90505 (213)
378-8587
Admin Donald I Brunn. *Medical Dir/Dir of
Nursing* Stephen Russell MN.
Licensure Skilled Care. *Beds* 212. *Cer-
tified* Medicare.
Ownership Nonprofit.
Staff Physicians 1 (pt); RNs 14 (ft), 4 (pt);
LPNs 28 (ft), 6 (pt); Orderlies 4 (ft); Nurses
aides 62 (ft), 5 (pt); Physical therapists 4 (ft), 1
(pt); Recreational therapists 3 (ft); Occupational
therapists 3 (ft); Speech therapists 1 (ft); Dietitians 1 (pt).
Facilities Dining room; Physical therapy room;
Activities room; Crafts room; Barber/Beauty
shop.
Activities Arts and Crafts; Cards; Games;
Reading groups; Prayer groups; Movies; Shopping trips; Dances/Social or cultural gatherings.
Description The center is accredited by JCAH
and specializes in intensive rehabilitation programs for adults and also provides a limited
number of long-term care or nursing home
beds.

Best Care Convalescent Hospital Corp*
22035 S Vermont Ave, Torrance, CA, 90502
(213) 775-6427
Admin Rody Tamparong.
Licensure Skilled Care. *Beds* 200. *Certified* Medicare; Medi-Cal.
Ownership Proprietary.

**Del Amo Gardens Sanitarium and Convalescent
Hospital***
22419 Kent Ave, Torrance, CA, 90505 (213)
378-4233
Admin Jack Saylin.

Licensure Skilled Care. *Beds* 94. *Certified* Medicare.
Ownership Proprietary.

Driftwood Convalescent Center
4109 Emerald Ave, Torrance, CA, 90503 (213) 371-4628
Admin Barbara Usher. *Medical Dir/Dir of Nursing* Brice T Martin MD.
Licensure Skilled Care. *Beds* 99. *Certified* Medicare; Medi-Cal.
Ownership Proprietary.
Admissions Requirements Minimum age 18; Medical examination; Physician's request.
Staff RNs 1 (ft), 1 (pt); LPNs 8 (ft), 2 (pt); Nurses aides 32 (ft); Recreational therapists 1 (pt); Activities coordinators 1 (ft); Dietitians 1 (pt).
Facilities Dining room; Physical therapy room; Activities room; Crafts room; Laundry room; Barber/Beauty shop; Living room.
Activities Arts and Crafts; Cards; Games; Reading groups; Prayer groups; Movies; Shopping trips; Dances/Social or cultural gatherings; Picnics; Olympiatrics; Barbecues; Music and singing; Zoo animals.
Description The facility has recently been beautifully redecorated in Country French and features family dining.

Earlwood Convalescent Hospital
20820 Early St, Torrance, CA, 90503 (213) 371-1228
Admin Claire D Crocker. *Medical Dir/Dir of Nursing* Dale Vanderbrink MD.
Licensure Skilled Care. *Beds* 87. *Certified* Medicare; Medi-Cal.
Ownership Proprietary.
Admissions Requirements Medical examination; Physician's request.
Staff RNs 1 (ft), 1 (pt); LPNs 9 (ft), 2 (pt); Physical therapists 2 (pt); Speech therapists 1 (pt); Activities coordinators 1 (ft); Dietitians 1 (pt); Podiatrists 1 (pt).
Facilities Dining room; Activities room; Laundry room; Barber/Beauty shop; Library.
Activities Arts and Crafts; Cards; Games; Reading groups; Prayer groups; Movies; Shopping trips.
Description Facility provides good physical and speech therapy, very pleasant surroundings, patio rooms, rooms primarily semi-private, and excellent nursing care.

Harbor Convalescent Hospital*
21521 S Vermont Ave, Torrance, CA, 90502 (213) 320-0961
Admin Ofelia T David.
Licensure Skilled Care. *Beds* 118. *Certified* Medicare; Medi-Cal.
Ownership Proprietary.

Heritage Convalescent Center of Torrance*
21414 S Vermont Ave, Torrance, CA, 90502 (213) 320-8714
Admin Norma C Kendell.
Licensure Skilled Care. *Beds* 166. *Certified* Medicare; Medi-Cal.
Ownership Proprietary.

Mira Costa Convalescent Hospital*
4320 Miracopa St, Torrance, CA, 90503 (213) 542-5555

Admin Warren R Bratland.
Licensure Skilled Care. *Beds* 124.
Certified Medi-Cal.
Ownership Proprietary.

Royalwood Convalescent Hospital
22520 Maple Ave, Torrance, CA, 90505 (213) 326-9131
Admin Dawn Didion. *Medical Dir/Dir of Nursing* Dr Harry Silver.
Licensure Skilled Care. *Beds* 110. *Certified* Medicare; Medi-Cal.
Ownership Proprietary.
Staff Physicians 1 (pt); RNs 13 (ft); LPNs 21 (ft); Orderlies 43 (ft); Physical therapists 1 (pt); Reality therapists 1 (pt); Recreational therapists 1 (ft); Occupational therapists 1 (pt); Speech therapists 1 (pt); Activities coordinators 1 (ft); Dietitians 1 (ft); Dentists 1 (pt); Ophthalmologists 1 (pt); Podiatrists 1 (pt); Audiologists 1 (pt).
Facilities Dining room; Physical therapy room; Activities room; Crafts room; Laundry room; Barber/Beauty shop.
Activities Arts and Crafts; Cards; Games; Reading groups; Prayer groups; Movies.

Sunnyside Nursing Center
22617 S Vermont Ave, Torrance, CA, 90502 (213) 320-4130
Admin Mark Deutsch. *Medical Dir/Dir of Nursing* Dr Allan Greenberg.
Licensure Skilled Care. *Beds* 263. *Certified* Medicare; Medi-Cal.
Ownership Proprietary.
Staff Physicians 15 (pt); RNs 7 (ft), 4 (pt); LPNs 18 (ft), 5 (pt); Nurses aides 100 (ft), 25 (pt); Physical therapists 1 (ft), 3 (pt); Recreational therapists 6 (ft); Occupational therapists 1 (pt); Speech therapists 1 (pt); Dietitians 1 (pt); Dentists 1 (pt); Ophthalmologists 1 (pt); Podiatrists 1 (pt).
Facilities Dining room; Physical therapy room; Activities room; Crafts room; Laundry room; Barber/Beauty shop; Library.
Activities Arts and Crafts; Cards; Games; Reading groups; Prayer groups; Movies; Dances/Social or cultural gatherings; Outings.
Description A 125-bed section in the facility provies a secured environment for those confused patients who may wander.

Torrance Convalescent Hospital
4315 Torrance Blvd, Torrance, CA, 90503 (213) 772-5782
Admin Martin Kahan. *Medical Dir/Dir of Nursing* Dr George Csengeri.
Licensure Skilled Care. *Beds* 99. *Certified* Medicare; Medi-Cal.
Ownership Proprietary.
Admissions Requirements Minimum age 18; Physician's request.
Staff Physicians 1 (pt); RNs 3 (ft), 3 (pt); LPNs 7 (ft); Nurses aides 25 (ft), 10 (pt); Physical therapists 2 (pt); Occupational therapists 1 (pt); Speech therapists 1 (pt); Activities coordinators 1 (ft); Dietitians 1 (pt); Dentists 2 (pt); Ophthalmologists 1 (pt); Podiatrists 1 (pt); Audiologists 1 (pt).
Facilities Dining room; Physical therapy room; Activities room; Chapel; Crafts room; Laundry room; Barber/Beauty shop; Library.
Activities Arts and Crafts; Cards; Games;

Reading groups; Prayer groups; Movies.
Description Facility is clean, bright, and cheerful.

West Torrance Convalescent Hospital*
4333 Torrance Blvd, Torrance, CA, 90503 (213) 772-4021
Admin Frank Oehlbaum.
Licensure Skilled Care. *Beds* 96. *Certified* Medicare; Medi-Cal.
Ownership Proprietary.

TRACY

Tracy Convalescent Hospital
545 W Beverly Pl, Tracy, CA, 95376 (209) 835-6034
Admin Ruby Rakow. *Medical Dir/Dir of Nursing* H L McClelland MD.
Licensure Skilled Care. *Beds* 49. *Certified* Medicare; Medi-Cal.
Ownership Proprietary.
Staff Physicians; RNs 1 (ft), 2 (pt); LPNs 4 (ft), 1 (pt); Nurses aides 19 (ft), 10 (pt); Physical therapists; Speech therapists; Activities coordinators 1 (ft); Dietitians; Dentists; Ophthalmologists; Podiatrists; Audiologists.
Facilities Dining room; Physical therapy room; Activities room; Crafts room; Laundry room; Barber/Beauty shop; Library.
Activities Arts and Crafts; Cards; Games; Reading groups; Prayer groups; Movies.

TUJUNGA

Community Convalescent Center of Sunland Tujunga*
7660 Wyngate St, Tujunga, CA, 91042 (213) 352-1454
Admin C T McDonald.
Licensure Skilled Care. *Beds* 92. *Certified* Medicare; Medi-Cal.
Ownership Proprietary.
Description JCAH approved.

Oakview Convalescent Hospital*
9166 Tujunga Canyon, Tujunga, CA, 91042 (213) 352-4426
Admin Homer Summerville.
Licensure Skilled Care. *Beds* 49. *Certified* Medicare; Medi-Cal.
Ownership Proprietary.
Description JCAH approved.

Sunair Home for Asthmatic Children
7754 McGroarty Ave, Tujunga, CA, 91042 (818) 352-1461
Admin Damon DeCrow.
Licensure Intermediate Care. *Beds* 39. *Certified* Medi-Cal.
Ownership Nonprofit.
Admissions Requirements Minimum age 5; Medical examination.
Staff Physicians 1 (pt); RNs 4 (ft), 1 (pt); LPNs 2 (ft), 1 (pt); Recreational therapists 1 (pt); Speech therapists 1 (pt); Activities coordinators 1 (pt); Dietitians 1 (pt).
Facilities Dining room; Activities room; Crafts room; Laundry room; Library.
Activities Arts and Crafts; Games; Reading groups; Movies; Shopping trips; Dances/Social

or cultural gatherings.
Description Facility has served children with asthma and other medical conditions for 46 years.

TULARE

Merritt Manor Convalescent Hospital
604 E Merritt Ave, Tulare, CA, 93274 (209) 686-1601
Admin Shirley Jensen. *Medical Dir/Dir of Nursing* Erwood G Edgar MD.
Licensure Skilled Care. *Beds* 98. *Certified* Medicare; Medi-Cal.
Ownership Proprietary.
Admissions Requirements Medical examination; Physician's request.
Staff RNs 1 (ft), 1 (pt); LPNs 8 (ft), 2 (pt); Nurses aides 33 (ft), 7 (pt); Activities coordinators 1 (ft); Dietitians 1 (ft).
Facilities Dining room; Activities room; Crafts room; Laundry room; Barber/Beauty shop.
Activities Arts and Crafts; Cards; Games; Reading groups; Prayer groups; Movies; Shopping trips; Dances/Social or cultural gatherings.
Description Facility staff gives high quality care; pride taken in the activities provided by a long-employed activities coordinator.

Terrace Park Convalescent Hospital
680 E Merritt St, Tulare, CA, 93274 (209) 686-8581
Admin Marlene Luiz. *Medical Dir/Dir of Nursing* Erwood G Edgor MD.
Licensure Skilled Care. *Beds* 97. *Certified* Medicare; Medi-Cal.
Ownership Proprietary.
Admissions Requirements Physician's request.
Staff RNs 1 (ft), 2 (pt); LPNs 10 (ft), 6 (pt); Orderlies 1 (pt); Nurses aides 36 (ft), 12 (pt); Activities coordinators 1 (ft), 1 (pt); Dietitians 1 (ft); Podiatrists 1 (pt); Audiologists 1 (pt).
Facilities Dining room; Physical therapy room; Activities room; Crafts room; Laundry room; Barber/Beauty shop.
Activities Arts and Crafts; Cards; Games; Reading groups; Prayer groups; Movies; Shopping trips; Dances/Social or cultural gatherings.
Description A program started where pets are now part of the facility. Facility has a nice patio area so the patients may eat outside when the weather permits.

TURLOCK

Bel-Air Lodge Convalescent Hospital*
180 Starr Ave, Turlock, CA, 95380 (209) 632-1075
Admin Mary E Baker.
Licensure Skilled Care. *Beds* 31.
Certified Medi-Cal.
Ownership Proprietary.

Brandel Manor
1801 N Olive Ave, Turlock, CA, 95380 (209) 632-3141
Admin Jeanne Daniel. *Medical Dir/Dir of Nursing* Robert Clark MD.
Licensure Skilled Care. *Beds* 145. *Certified* Medicare; Medi-Cal.
Ownership Nonprofit.

Admissions Requirements Medical examination; Physician's request.
Staff RNs 6 (ft), 6 (pt); LPNs 8 (ft), 4 (pt); Orderlies 2 (ft), 1 (pt); Nurses aides 31 (ft), 30 (pt).
Affiliation Evangelical Covenant Church
Facilities Dining room; Physical therapy room; Activities room; Chapel; Crafts room; Barber-/Beauty shop; Smoking room.
Activities Arts and Crafts; Games; Reading groups; Prayer groups; Movies; Shopping trips; Dances/Social or cultural gatherings.
Description Brandel Manor is a distinct part of Emanuel Hospital, and is situated within the Convenant Village complex. This complex includes a retirement community and a board and care facility.

Elness Convalescent Hospital*
812 W Main St, Turlock, CA, 95380 (209) 632-3973
Admin Mary E Baker.
Licensure Skilled Care. *Beds* 99. *Certified* Medicare; Medi-Cal.
Ownership Proprietary.

TUSTIN

Tustin Convalescent Hospital*
165 N Myrtle St, Tustin, CA, 92680 (714) 832-9200
Admin Loretta Myers.
Licensure Skilled Care. *Beds* 59. *Certified* Medicare; Medi-Cal.
Ownership Proprietary.

Tustin Manor*
1051 Bryan St, Tustin, CA, 92680 (714) 832-6780
Admin Donald J Beld.
Licensure Intermediate Care. *Beds* 99. *Certified* Medi-Cal.
Ownership Proprietary.

UKIAH

Driftwood Convalescent Hospital*
1162 S Dora St, Ukiah, CA, 95482 (707) 462-1436
Admin Dana June Harris.
Licensure Skilled Care. *Beds* 68. *Certified* Medicare; Medi-Cal.
Ownership Proprietary.

Hacienda Convalescent Hospital*
131 Whitmore Ln, Ukiah, CA, 95482 (707) 462-6636
Admin Charles T Byerly.
Licensure Skilled Care; Intermediate Care for Mentally Retarded. *Beds* 113. *Certified* Medicare; Medi-Cal.
Ownership Proprietary.

Ukiah Convalescent Hospital*
1349 S Dora St, Ukiah, CA, 95482 (707) 462-8864
Admin J S Pritchard.
Licensure Skilled Care. *Beds* 58. *Certified* Medicare; Medi-Cal.
Ownership Proprietary.

UPLAND

Shea Convalescent Hospital*
867 E 11th St, Upland, CA, 91786 (714) 985-1981
Admin Barbara A Emert.
Licensure Skilled Care. *Beds* 99. *Certified* Medicare; Medi-Cal.
Ownership Proprietary.

Upland Convalescent Hospital*
1221 E Arrow Hwy, Upland, CA, 91786 (714) 985-1903
Admin William C Milton. *Medical Dir/Dir of Nursing* C Sanborn Jr MD.
Licensure Skilled Care. *Beds* 208. *Certified* Medicare; Medi-Cal.
Ownership Proprietary.
Admissions Requirements Minimum age 18.
Staff Physicians; RNs; LPNs; Nurses aides; Physical therapists; Recreational therapists; Occupational therapists; Speech therapists; Dietitians; Dentists; Ophthalmologists; Podiatrists; Audiologists; Gerontological nurse practitioner.
Facilities Dining room; Physical therapy room; Activities room; Laundry room; Barber/Beauty shop.
Activities Arts and Crafts; Cards; Games; Reading groups; Prayer groups; Movies.

VACAVILLE

Windsor House Convalescent Hospital*
101 S Orchard St, Vacaville, CA, 95688 (707) 448-6458
Admin Richard Schacten.
Licensure Skilled Care. *Beds* 86. *Certified* Medicare; Medi-Cal.
Ownership Proprietary.

VALLEJO

Crestwood Manor
2201 Tuolumne, Vallejo, CA, 94590 (707) 552-0215
Admin June Gaylord. *Medical Dir/Dir of Nursing* Matthew Gibbons MD.
Licensure Skilled Care. *Beds* 102. *Certified* Medicare.
Ownership Proprietary.
Admissions Requirements Minimum age 18; Medical examination; Physician's request.
Staff Physicians 2 (pt); RNs 6 (ft), 2 (pt); LPNs 2 (ft); Nurses aides 20 (ft); Occupational therapists 1 (ft); Activities coordinators 1 (ft); Dietitians 1 (pt); Dentists 1 (pt); Ophthalmologists 1 (pt); Podiatrists 1 (pt).
Facilities Dining room; Activities room; Crafts room; Laundry room; Barber/Beauty shop.
Activities Arts and Crafts; Cards; Games; Reading groups; Prayer groups; Movies; Shopping trips; Dances/Social or cultural gatherings.
Description The residents of Crestwood Manor, Vallejo, participate in a variety of therapeutic activities, including a Medi-Cal funded treatment program as well as a specially funded county rehabilitation program. These highly respected programs offer various forms of therapy and education including individual and group therapy, therapeutic recreation, training in communication, grooming, money manage-

ment, impulse control, and independent living. Our staff includes rehabilitation specialists; licensed nurses, skilled in psychiatric care; and an activities director.

Heartwood Avenue Living Center
1044 Heartwood Ave, Vallejo, CA, 94590 (707) 643-2793
Admin Elliott Silver. *Medical Dir/Dir of Nursing* Alan Plutchok MD.
Licensure Skilled Care. *Beds* 57.
Certified Medi-Cal.
Ownership Proprietary.
Admissions Requirements Minimum age 18; Medical examination; Physician's request.
Staff Physicians 1 (pt); RNs 2 (ft), 3 (pt); LPNs 3 (ft), 3 (pt); Nurses aides 19 (ft), 5 (pt); Occupational therapists 1 (pt); Activities coordinators 1 (ft); Dietitians 1 (pt); Dentists 1 (pt); Podiatrists 1 (pt).
Facilities Dining room; Activities room; Crafts room; Barber/Beauty shop; Library.
Activities Arts and Crafts; Cards; Games; Reading groups; Prayer groups; Movies; Shopping trips; Dances/Social or cultural gatherings.
Description Holistic care program featuring life-long care; many young residents; house pets, including dog; basic foods program; active activity program.

Louisiana Living Center
1101 Louisiana St, Vallejo, CA, 94590 (707) 643-2793
Admin Elliott Silver. *Medical Dir/Dir of Nursing* Alan Plutchok MD.
Licensure Skilled Care. *Beds* 37. *Certified* Medicare; Medi-Cal.
Ownership Proprietary.
Admissions Requirements Minimum age 18; Medical examination; Physician's request.
Staff Physicians 1 (pt); RNs 3 (ft), 3 (pt); LPNs 1 (ft), 2 (pt); Nurses aides 10 (ft), 4 (pt); Occupational therapists 1 (pt); Activities coordinators 1 (ft); Dietitians 1 (pt); Dentists 1 (pt); Podiatrists 1 (pt).
Facilities Dining room; Activities room; Crafts room; Barber/Beauty shop; Library.
Activities Arts and Crafts; Cards; Games; Reading groups; Prayer groups; Movies; Shopping trips; Dances/Social or cultural gatherings.
Description Holistic care program for permanently disabled people needing life-long care. Small facility with a staff very close to residents. Facility pets include a dog. Basic foods program offered.

Maxicare Convalescent Hospital*
2200 Tuolumne, Vallejo, CA, 94590 (707) 644-7401
Admin Frank L Smith.
Licensure Skilled Care. *Beds* 166. *Certified* Medicare; Medi-Cal.
Ownership Proprietary.

Springs Road Living Center
1527 Springs Rd, Vallejo, CA, 94590 (707) 643-2793
Admin Elliott Silver. *Medical Dir/Dir of Nursing* Alan Plutchok MD.
Licensure Skilled Care. *Beds* 62. *Certified* Medicare; Medi-Cal.
Ownership Proprietary.
Admissions Requirements Minimum age 18;

Medical examination; Physician's request.
Staff RNs 1 (ft), 5 (pt); LPNs 4 (ft), 1 (pt); Nurses aides 20 (ft), 8 (pt); Occupational therapists 1 (pt); Activities coordinators 1 (ft); Dietitians 1 (pt); Dentists 1 (pt); Podiatrists 1 (pt).
Facilities Dining room; Activities room; Crafts room; Barber/Beauty shop; Library.
Activities Arts and Crafts; Cards; Games; Reading groups; Prayer groups; Movies; Shopping trips; Dances/Social or cultural gatherings.
Description Holistic care program for life-long chronically ill people; basic foods program; facility program is 10 years old; age mix from 20-100.

Vallejo Convalescent Hospital*
900 Sereno Dr, Vallejo, CA, 94590 (707) 643-8453
Admin Max B O'Melia.
Licensure Skilled Care. *Beds* 99. *Certified* Medicare; Medi-Cal.
Ownership Proprietary.

VAN NUYS

Balowen Convalescent Hospital*
16955 Van Owens St, Van Nuys, CA, 91406 (213) 987-3606
Admin Delva W Larson.
Licensure Skilled Care. *Beds* 50. *Certified* Medicare; Medi-Cal.
Ownership Proprietary.

Beverly Manor Convalescent Hospital*
6700 Sepulveda Blvd, Van Nuys, CA, 91401 (213) 988-2501
Admin David Lefitz.
Licensure Skilled Care. *Beds* 201. *Certified* Medicare; Medi-Cal.
Ownership Proprietary.

Hacienda Convalescent Hospital*
6600 Sepulveda Blvd, Van Nuys, CA, 91401 (213) 786-0020
Admin Sheryl Hancock.
Licensure Skilled Care. *Beds* 125. *Certified* Medicare; Medi-Cal.
Ownership Proprietary.

Sepulveda Convalescent Hospital Inc*
5510 Sepulveda Blvd, Van Nuys, CA, 91401 (213) 782-6800
Admin Lawrence Gross.
Licensure Skilled Care. *Beds* 115. *Certified* Medicare; Medi-Cal.
Ownership Proprietary.

Sherwood Convalescent Hospital*
13524 Sherman Way, Van Nuys, CA, 91405 (213) 786-3470
Admin Patricia Ives.
Licensure Skilled Care. *Beds* 99. *Certified* Medicare; Medi-Cal.
Ownership Proprietary.

VENTURA

The California-Ventura Convalescent Hospital*
4020 Loma Vista Rd, Ventura, CA, 93003 (805) 642-4196
Admin Norman R Hanson.

Licensure Skilled Care. *Beds* 67. *Certified* Medicare; Medi-Cal.
Ownership Proprietary.

The Venturan Convalescent Center*
4904 Telegraph Rd, Ventura, CA, 93003 (805) 642-4101
Admin Charles A McClain.
Licensure Skilled Care. *Beds* 89. *Certified* Medicare; Medi-Cal.
Ownership Proprietary.

VERDUGO CITY

Rockhaven Sanitarium*
2713 Honolulu Ave, Verdugo City, CA, 91046 (213) 249-2838
Admin Patricia Traviss.
Licensure Skilled Care. *Beds* 80.
Ownership Proprietary.

VICTORVILLE

Desert Knolls Convalescent Hospital*
14973 Hesperia Rd, Victorville, CA, 92392 (714) 245-1558
Admin Gary L Bechtold.
Licensure Skilled Care. *Beds* 126. *Certified* Medicare; Medi-Cal.
Ownership Proprietary.

VISALIA

Delta Convalescent Hospital*
514 N Bridge St, Visalia, CA, 93277 (209) 732-8614
Admin Harold Miller.
Licensure Skilled Care. *Beds* 39.
Certified Medi-Cal.
Ownership Proprietary.

Kaweah Manor Convalescent Hosptial*
3710 W Tulare, Visalia, CA, 93277 (209) 732-2244
Admin Amelia Drew.
Licensure Skilled Care. *Beds* 99. *Certified* Medicare; Medi-Cal.
Ownership Proprietary.

Linwood Gardens Convalescent Center
4444 W Meadow Ln, Visalia, CA, 93277 (209) 627-1241
Admin Martha E Lo Presti. *Medical Dir/Dir of Nursing* E P Brauner MD.
Licensure Skilled Care. *Beds* 98. *Certified* Medicare; Medi-Cal.
Ownership Proprietary.
Admissions Requirements Medical examination; Physician's request.
Staff RNs 1 (ft), 3 (pt); LPNs 8 (ft); Orderlies 4 (ft); Nurses aides 45 (ft), 10 (pt); Physical therapists 1 (ft); Speech therapists 1 (pt); Activities coordinators 1 (ft); Dietitians 1 (ft), 1 (pt).
Facilities Dining room; Physical therapy room; Activities room; Crafts room; Laundry room; Barber/Beauty shop.
Activities Arts and Crafts; Cards; Games; Reading groups; Prayer groups; Movies; Shopping trips; Dances/Social or cultural gatherings.
Description This facility, built in 1980, is

designed as a wheel with a single circular nursing station connecting 5 wings. Administration and dietary department are in different areas.

Visalia Convalescent Hospital
1925 E Houston St, Visalia, CA, 93277 (209) 732-6661
Admin Delores L Helberg. *Medical Dir/Dir of Nursing* L D Farrelly MD.
Licensure Skilled Care; Intermediate Care. *Beds* SNF 149; ICF 23. *Certified* Medicare; Medi-Cal.
Ownership Proprietary.
Admissions Requirements Minimum age 18; Medical examination; Physician's request.
Facilities Dining room; Physical therapy room; Activities room; Crafts room; Laundry room; Barber/Beauty shop.
Activities Arts and Crafts; Cards; Games; Reading groups; Prayer groups; Movies; Shopping trips; Dances/Social or cultural gatherings.

VISTA

Vista Golden Age Convalescent Home*
304 N Melrose Dr, Vista, CA, 92083 (714) 724-8222
Admin Jack Hermes.
Licensure Skilled Care. *Beds* 35.
Certified Medi-Cal.
Ownership Nonprofit.

WALNUT CREEK

Arroyo-Creekside Convalescent Hospital
1310 Creekside Dr, Walnut Creek, CA, 94596 (415) 939-1090
Admin Shirley B Begovich. *Medical Dir/Dir of Nursing* Dr Carlos Anderson.
Licensure Skilled Care. *Beds* 42. *Certified* Medicare; Medi-Cal.
Ownership Proprietary.
Admissions Requirements Physician's request.
Staff RNs 1 (ft), 2 (pt); LPNs 3 (ft), 5 (pt); Nurses aides 12 (ft), 4 (pt).
Facilities Dining room; Physical therapy room; Activities room; Laundry room; Barber/Beauty shop.
Activities Arts and Crafts; Cards; Games; Reading groups; Prayer groups; Movies; Dances/Social or cultural gatherings.
Description Forty-two-bed facility set in Tree Creek area which gives a more home-like setting for our residents. Easy freeway access, south of Walnut Creek about one mile from Broadway Plaza.

Rossmoor Manor
1224 Rossmoor Pkwy, Walnut Creek, CA, 94595 (415) 937-7450
Admin Eva Hecker. *Medical Dir/Dir of Nursing* Roland Schoen MD.
Licensure Skilled Care. *Beds* 180. *Certified* Medicare; Medi-Cal.
Ownership Nonprofit.
Staff RNs 13 (ft), 3 (pt); Orderlies 6 (ft); Nurses aides 75 (ft); Physical therapists 1 (ft); Activities coordinators 1 (ft); LVNs 11 (ft).
Facilities Dining room; Physical therapy room; Activities room; Laundry room; Barber/Beauty

shop.
Activities Arts and Crafts; Cards; Games; Reading groups; Prayer groups; Movies; Dances/Social or cultural gatherings.
Description We specialize in rehabilitation nursing and are very active in the Medicare program. Our lovely garden-like setting enhances the healing process and lifts the spirits of patients.

San Marco Convalescent Hospital*
130 Tampico St, Walnut Creek, CA, 94598 (415) 933-7970
Admin Lee S Murillo.
Licensure Skilled Care. *Beds* 128. *Certified* Medicare; Medi-Cal.
Ownership Proprietary.
Description Facility offers outpatient services and physical therapy. JCAH approved.

Walnut Creek Convalescent Hospital Inc*
2015 Mount Diablo Blvd, Walnut Creek, CA, 94596 (415) 935-2222
Admin Rae Hathcock.
Licensure Skilled Care. *Beds* 93. *Certified* Medicare; Medi-Cal.
Ownership Proprietary.

Ygnacio Convalescent Hospital*
1449 Ygnacio Valley Rd, Walnut Creek, CA, 94598 (415) 939-5820
Admin Zona Kalustian.
Licensure Skilled Care. *Beds* 99. *Certified* Medicare; Medi-Cal.
Ownership Nonprofit.

WATSONVILLE

Pajaro Convalescent Hospital*
421 Arthur Rd, Watsonville, CA, 95076 (408) 724-7505
Admin Bonnie Reese.
Licensure Skilled Care. *Beds* 87. *Certified* Medicare; Medi-Cal.
Ownership Proprietary.

Pajaro West Convalescent Hospital*
425 Arthur Rd, Watsonville, CA, 95076 (408) 724-7505
Admin Bonnie Reese.
Licensure Skilled Care. *Beds* 95. *Certified* Medicare; Medi-Cal.
Ownership Proprietary.

Valley Convalescent Hospital*
919 Freedom Blvd, Watsonville, CA, 95076 (408) 722-3581
Admin Richard Murphy.
Licensure Skilled Care. *Beds* 59. *Certified* Medicare; Medi-Cal.
Ownership Proprietary.

WEED

Weed Convalescent Hospital*
445 Park St, Weed, CA, 96094 (916) 938-4429
Admin Gary Ralston.
Licensure Skilled Care. *Beds* 53. *Certified* Medicare; Medi-Cal.
Ownership Proprietary.

WEST COVINA

Ambassador Convalescent Hospital
1495 Cameron Ave, West Covina, CA, 91790 (213) 962-4461
Admin Alan M Hull. *Medical Dir/Dir of Nursing* P H Lagrosa MD.
Licensure Skilled Care. *Beds* 99. *Certified* Medicare; Medi-Cal.
Ownership Proprietary.
Admissions Requirements Minimum age 45; Medical examination; Physician's request.
Staff RNs 3 (ft), 2 (pt); LPNs 5 (ft), 4 (pt); Orderlies 4 (ft); Nurses aides 30 (ft), 5 (pt); Physical therapists 1 (pt); Reality therapists 1 (pt); Recreational therapists 1 (pt); Occupational therapists 1 (pt); Speech therapists 1 (pt); Activities coordinators 1 (ft); Dietitians 1 (ft); Dentists 1 (pt); Ophthalmologists 1 (pt); Podiatrists 1 (pt); Audiologists 1 (pt).
Facilities Dining room; Physical therapy room; Activities room; Chapel; Crafts room; Laundry room; Barber/Beauty shop; Library.
Activities Arts and Crafts; Cards; Games; Reading groups; Prayer groups; Movies; Shopping trips; Dances/Social or cultural gatherings.
Description Facility has a 7-day-a-week restorative and rehabilitative programs, with 2 full-time restorative aides, twice a day physical therapy treatments, speech therapy, occupational therapy, and hydrotherapy; specializes in rehabilitation of recent stroke or hip fracture patients.

Beverly Manor Convalescent Hospital
850 S Sunkist Ave, West Covina, CA, 91790 (818) 962-3368
Admin Dorothy Pratt. *Medical Dir/Dir of Nursing* Dr Forrest Tennant.
Licensure Skilled Care. *Beds* 54. *Certified* Medicare; Medi-Cal.
Ownership Proprietary.

Clara Baldwin Stocker Home for Women*
527 S Valinda Ave, West Covina, CA, 91790 (213) 962-7151
Admin Robert P Mullender.
Licensure Skilled Care. *Beds* 48. *Certified* Medicare; Medi-Cal.
Ownership Nonprofit.
Admissions Requirements Females only

Colonial Manor Convalescent Hospital*
919 N Sunset, West Covina, CA, 91790 (213) 962-4489
Admin David T Perry.
Licensure Skilled Care. *Beds* 54. *Certified* Medicare; Medi-Cal.
Ownership Proprietary.

Lark Ellen Towers Convalescent Hospital
1350 San Bernardino Rd, West Covina, CA, 91790 (213) 966-7558
Admin Samuel Mintz. *Medical Dir/Dir of Nursing* S Dhand MD.
Licensure Skilled Care. *Beds* 40. *Certified* Medicare.
Ownership Proprietary.
Admissions Requirements Minimum age 45; Medical examination; Physician's request.
Staff Physicians 1 (ft), 3 (pt); RNs 1 (ft), 2 (pt); LPNs 3 (ft), 3 (pt); Nurses aides 11 (ft), 3 (pt); Activities coordinators 1 (ft); Dietitians 1 (ft).

Facilities Dining room; Activities room; Crafts room; Laundry room; Barber/Beauty shop; Library; Independence Hall for movies, parties..
Activities Arts and Crafts; Cards; Games; Movies; Shopping trips; Dances/Social or cultural gatherings.
Description Lake Ellen features monthly rates; spacious single and double suites, with refrigerator and kitchen units, wall-to-wall carpeting, drapes, and air conditioning; scheduled transportion to shopping centers and doctor's offices within driving radius; 24-hour staffing; 3 well-balanced meals every day, plus snacks and nourishment; holiday buffets; entertainment with social hours and films; safety-depth swimming pool, exercise classes, and indoor hot water whirlpool; weekly housekeeping; exciting junkets planned by coordinator.

WEST RIVERSIDE

Vista Pacifica Convalescent Home
3662 W Pacific Ave, West Riverside, CA, 92509 (714) 686-4362
Admin Allen C Braswell. *Medical Dir/Dir of Nursing* Paul DeSilva MD.
Licensure Skilled Care. *Beds* 49. *Certified* Medicare; Medi-Cal.
Ownership Proprietary.
Admissions Requirements Medical examination; Physician's request.
Staff Physicians 4 (ft); RNs 1 (ft); LPNs 3 (ft); Nurses aides 15 (ft), 4 (pt); Speech therapists 1 (pt); Activities coordinators 1 (ft); Dietitians 1 (pt); Dentists 1 (pt); Podiatrists 1 (ft).
Facilities Dining room; Activities room.
Activities Arts and Crafts; Cards; Games; Reading groups; Prayer groups; Movies; Shopping trips; Dances/Social or cultural gatherings.
Description Activity program is a very busy one with a large volunteer society. Facility has 3 spacious rooms for daily programs and has weekly outings and evening activities. Well kept grounds accentuate a park-like setting with easy access to outdoors for wheelchairs.

Vista Pacificia—A Center for Rehabilitation and Growth*
3674 Pacific Ave, West Riverside, CA, 92509 (714) 682-4833
Admin C Allen Braswell.
Licensure Skilled Care. *Beds* 110.
Certified Medi-Cal.
Ownership Proprietary.

WEST SACRAMENTO

Somerset Golden State Convalescent Hospital*
2215 Oakmont St, West Sacramento, CA, 95691 (916) 371-1890
Admin Donald J Hunter.
Licensure Skilled Care. *Beds* 99. *Certified* Medicare; Medi-Cal.
Ownership Proprietary.

WESTMINSTER

Hy-Lond Convalescent Hospital
240 Hospital Circle, Westminster, CA, 92683

(714) 892-6686
Admin Ruth Johnson. *Medical Dir/Dir of Nursing* Dr John Cowles.
Licensure Skilled Care. *Beds* 99. *Certified* Medicare; Medi-Cal.
Ownership Proprietary.
Admissions Requirements Physician's request.
Staff RNs 5 (ft), 4 (pt); LPNs 7 (ft), 3 (pt); Orderlies 2 (ft); Nurses aides 23 (ft), 19 (pt); Activities coordinators 1 (ft).
Facilities Dining room; Physical therapy room; Activities room; Crafts room; Laundry room; Barber/Beauty shop.
Activities Arts and Crafts; Games; Reading groups; Movies; Shopping trips; Dances/Social or cultural gatherings.
Description Facility features candlelight dinner, pet appreciation show, graduation ceremony, kitchen band, exercise program, and style show.

Stanley Convalescent Hospital
14102 Springdale St, Westminster, CA, 92683 (714) 893-0026
Admin Robert Moses. *Medical Dir/Dir of Nursing* John D Cowles MD.
Licensure Skilled Care. *Beds* 30. *Certified* Medicare; Medi-Cal.
Ownership Proprietary.
Admissions Requirements Minimum age 65.
Staff RNs 6 (pt); LPNs 1 (ft), 1 (pt); Nurses aides 6 (ft), 3 (pt); Activities coordinators 1 (ft); Dietitians 2 (ft), 2 (pt).
Facilities Dining room; Activities room; Crafts room; Laundry room; Barber/Beauty shop.
Activities Arts and Crafts; Games; Movies; Shopping trips.

WHITTIER

Beemans Sanitarium
14015 E Telegraph Rd, Whittier, CA, 90604 (213) 944-3292 and 941-0116
Admin Ann Whitefoot. *Medical Dir/Dir of Nursing* Donn D Beeman MD.
Licensure Skilled Care. *Beds* 74. *Certified* Medicare; Medi-Cal.
Ownership Proprietary.
Admissions Requirements Minimum age 45.
Staff Physicians 1 (ft); RNs 1 (ft), 1 (pt); LPNs 8 (ft); Nurses aides 30 (ft); Activities coordinators 1 (ft); Dietitians 1 (ft).
Facilities Dining room; Activities room; Chapel; Crafts room; Laundry room; Barber/Beauty shop.
Activities Arts and Crafts; Cards; Games; Movies; Church services; Exercise program; Yoga; Birthday parties once monthly; Ice cream social once monthly; Money management for country store.
Description Facility has especially lovely grounds that the patients can go out and enjoy any time the weather permits. Locked facility; the doors to the patios are not locked, but the patient cannot get to the outside streets.

Beverly Manor Convalescent Hospital—East*
10426 Bogardus, Whittier, CA, 90603 (213) 691-2291
Admin Dale Mueller.
Licensure Skilled Care. *Beds* 160. *Certified* Medicare; Medi-Cal.
Ownership Proprietary.

Beverly Manor Convalescent Hospital—West*
12385 E Washington, Whittier, CA, 90606 (213) 693-7701
Admin Darlene Curley.
Licensure Skilled Care. *Beds* 162. *Certified* Medicare; Medi-Cal.
Ownership Proprietary.

Doctors Convalescent Hospital
7926 S Painter Ave, Whittier, CA, 90602 (213) 693-5618
Admin H L Boulenaz and K M Boulenaz.
Medical Dir/Dir of Nursing Lawrence Pollock.
Licensure Skilled Care. *Beds* 36.
Certified Medi-Cal.
Ownership Proprietary.
Admissions Requirements Minimum age 21; Medical examination; Physician's request.
Staff Physicians 1 (pt); RNs 1 (ft), 2 (pt); LPNs 2 (ft), 3 (pt); Nurses aides 13 (ft), 1 (pt); Physical therapists 1 (pt); Recreational therapists 1 (pt); Occupational therapists 1 (pt); Speech therapists 1 (pt); Activities coordinators 1 (ft); Dietitians 1 (pt); Dentists 1 (pt); Ophthalmologists 1 (pt); Podiatrists 2 (pt); Audiologists 1 (pt).

Shea Convalescent Hospital*
7716 S Pickering Ave, Whittier, CA, 90602 (213) 693-9229
Admin Helen W Saunderson.
Licensure Skilled Care. *Beds* 54. *Certified* Medicare; Medi-Cal.
Ownership Proprietary.

Sorenson Convalescent Hospital*
7931 Sorenson Ave, Whittier, CA, 90606 (213) 698-0451
Admin Doris M Ruff.
Licensure Skilled Care. *Beds* 59. *Certified* Medicare; Medi-Cal.
Ownership Proprietary.

WILLIAMS

Valley West Convalescent Hospital
1224 E St, Williams, CA, 95987 (916) 473-5321
Admin Duane S Reed. *Medical Dir/Dir of Nursing* Charles McCarl MD.
Licensure Skilled Care. *Beds* 59.
Certified Medi-Cal.
Ownership Proprietary.
Admissions Requirements Medical examination; Physician's request.
Staff Physicians 8 (ft); RNs 8 (ft); LPNs 7 (ft); Nurses aides 20 (ft); Physical therapists 1 (ft); Speech therapists 1 (pt); Activities coordinators 1 (ft); Dietitians 1 (pt); Dentists 1 (pt); Podiatrists 1 (pt).
Facilities Dining room; Activities room; Crafts room; Laundry room; Barber/Beauty shop.
Activities Arts and Crafts; Cards; Games; Reading groups; Prayer groups; Movies; Dances/Social or cultural gatherings.

WILLITS

Northbrook Manor Convalescent Hospital
64 Northbrook Way, Willits, CA, 95490 (707) 459-5592
Admin R Wayne Grigsby. *Medical Dir/Dir of*

Nursing John Glyer MD.
Licensure Skilled Care. *Beds* 70. *Certified* Medicare; Medi-Cal.
Ownership Proprietary.
Admissions Requirements Medical examination; Physician's request.
Staff RNs 2 (ft); LPNs 9 (ft), 2 (pt); Orderlies 1 (ft); Nurses aides 34 (ft), 6 (pt); Physical therapists 1 (pt); Occupational therapists 1 (pt); Speech therapists 3 (pt); Activities coordinators 1 (ft); Dietitians 1 (pt).
Facilities Dining room; Physical therapy room; Activities room; Barber/Beauty shop; Visiting room.
Activities Arts and Crafts; Cards; Games; Reading groups; Movies; Shopping trips; Dances/Social or cultural gatherings.
Description Facility is located in beautiful redwood and wine country. We are a small community featuring a wholesome atmosphere.

WILLOW

Willow View Manor
320 N Crawford, Willow, CA, 95988 (916) 934-2834
Admin Ruthe Hamilton. *Medical Dir/Dir of Nursing* Joseph Duba MD.
Licensure Skilled Care. *Beds* 79. *Certified* Medicare.
Ownership Proprietary.
Staff Physicians 5 (pt); RNs 2 (ft), 2 (pt); LPNs 6 (ft), 6 (pt); Orderlies 3 (ft); Nurses aides 28 (ft), 2 (pt); Physical therapists 1 (pt); Recreational therapists 1 (ft); Occupational therapists 1 (pt); Speech therapists 1 (pt); Activities coordinators 1 (ft); Dietitians 1 (pt); Dentists 2 (pt); Ophthalmologists 1 (pt); Podiatrists 1 (pt); Audiologists 1 (pt).
Facilities Dining room; Physical therapy room; Activities room; Laundry room; Barber/Beauty shop.
Activities Arts and Crafts; Cards; Games; Reading groups; Prayer groups; Movies; Shopping trips; Dances/Social or cultural gatherings.

WOODLAND

Alderson Convalescent Hospital*
124 Walnut St, Woodland, CA, 95695 (916) 662-9161
Admin Thomas E Mullen.
Licensure Skilled Care; Intermediate Care.
Beds SNF 98; ICF 57. *Certified* Medicare; Medi-Cal.
Ownership Proprietary.

Countryside Intermediate Care Facility*
435 Aspen St, Woodland, CA, 95695 (916) 662-3128
Admin Santi Miguel.
Licensure Intermediate Care. *Beds* 30. *Certified* Medi-Cal.
Ownership Proprietary.

Hacienda Convalescent Hospital*
625 Cottonwood St, Woodland, CA, 95695 (916) 662-9193
Admin Greg Bordenkircher.

Licensure Skilled Care. *Beds* 98. *Certified* Medicare; Medi-Cal.
Ownership Proprietary.

Stollwood Convalescent Hospital*
135 Woodland Ave, Woodland, CA, 95695 (916) 662-1290
Admin Sheila A Hess.
Licensure Skilled Care. *Beds* 48. *Certified* Medicare; Medi-Cal.
Ownership Nonprofit.

Woodland Skilled Nursing Facility*
678 3rd Ave, Woodland, CA, 95695 (916) 662-9643
Admin David J Tarpin.
Licensure Skilled Care; Intermediate Care.
Beds SNF 55; ICF 41. *Certified* Medicare; Medi-Cal.
Ownership Proprietary.

YREKA

Beverly Manor Convalescent Hospital*
1515 Oregon St, Yreka, CA, 96097 (916) 842-4361
Admin Jerry Pearl.
Licensure Skilled Care. *Beds* 99. *Certified* Medicare; Medi-Cal.
Ownership Proprietary.

YUBA CITY

Driftwood Convalescent Hospital
1220 Plumas St, Yuba City, CA, 95991 (916) 671-0550
Admin Grace Sawyer. *Medical Dir/Dir of Nursing* Charles Cotham.
Licensure Skilled Care. *Beds* 59. *Certified* Medicare; Medi-Cal.
Ownership Proprietary.
Admissions Requirements Physician's request.
Staff Physicians 1 (ft), 2 (pt); RNs 1 (ft), 2 (pt); LPNs 4 (ft), 8 (pt); Nurses aides 6 (ft); Physical therapists 1 (ft), 2 (pt); Speech therapists 1 (pt); Activities coordinators 1 (ft); Dietitians 1 (ft), 1 (pt); Dentists 2 (pt); Podiatrists 2 (pt).
Facilities Dining room; Physical therapy room; Activities room; Laundry room; Barber/Beauty shop; Day room.
Activities Arts and Crafts; Games; Prayer groups; Movies; Shopping trips; Dances/Social or cultural gatherings.
Description We have a quiet country setting. Large trees provide a lovely shaded area for patients and their visitors. The rooms, shared by 2 patients, have a private patio complete with plants and flowers surrounding them. Facility is easily accessable to acute hospitals and town. Our pride is in the care and comfort of our patients.

Hillhaven Convalescent Hospital
521 Lorel Way, Yuba City, CA, 95991 (916) 674-9140
Admin Clarence Shackelford. *Medical Dir/Dir of Nursing* Charles Cotham MD.
Licensure Skilled Care. *Beds* 151. *Certified* Medicare; Medi-Cal.
Ownership Proprietary.
Facilities Dining room; Physical therapy room;

Activities room; Crafts room; Laundry room; Barber/Beauty shop.
Activities Arts and Crafts; Cards; Games; Reading groups; Movies; Shopping trips; Dances/Social or cultural gatherings.
Description Facility is operated according to the Hillhaven standard of excellence featuring a campus-type complex consisting of nonlicensed apartments, 2 residential care facilities, and a separate convalescent hospital.

YUCAIPA

Braswell's Yucaipa Valley Convalescent Hospital
35253 Ave H, Yucaipa, CA, 92399 (714) 795-2476
Admin Betty J Dennett. *Medical Dir/Dir of Nursing* H J Cozzolino MD.
Licensure Skilled Care. *Beds* 59. *Certified* Medicare; Medi-Cal.
Ownership Proprietary.
Staff RNs 2 (ft), 1 (pt); LPNs 3 (ft), 2 (pt); Orderlies 1 (pt); Physical therapists 1 (pt); Speech therapists 1 (pt); Activities coordinators 1 (ft).
Facilities Dining room; Physical therapy room; Activities room; Crafts room; Laundry room; Barber/Beauty shop.
Activities Arts and Crafts; Games; Reading groups; Prayer groups; Movies; Dances/Social or cultural gatherings.
Description Facility is located in a quiet residential setting near Oak Glen, specializing in excellent nursing care with lots of tender loving care; making the patients as happy and well as possible; and making them feel at home.

Community Convalescent Center of Yucaipa/Calimesa*
13542 2nd St, Yucaipa, CA, 92399 (714) 795-2421
Admin William C Fehr.
Licensure Skilled Care. *Beds* 82. *Certified* Medicare; Medi-Cal.
Ownership Proprietary.

YUCCA VALLEY

Hi-Desert Convalescent Hospital*
55475 Santa Fe Trail, Yucca Valley, CA, 92284 (714) 365-7635
Admin Kensett J Moyle III.
Licensure Skilled Care. *Beds* 99. *Certified* Medicare; Medi-Cal.
Ownership Proprietary.

COLORADO

AGUILAR

Simpsons Foster Care*
212 W Main, Aguilar, CO, 81082 (303)
941-4169
Admin Dorothy Simpson.
Licensure Developmentally Disabled. *Beds* 4.
Ownership Proprietary.

AKRON

**Washington County Public Hospital and
Nursing Home Unit***
465 Main St, Akron, CO, 80720 (303) 345-2211
Admin Charles K Gulley.
Licensure Skilled Care. *Beds* 24. *Certified* Medicaid; Medicare.
Ownership Nonprofit.

ALAMOSA

Evergreen Nursing Home*
PO Box 1149, 1991 Carroll St, Alamosa, CO,
81101 (303) 589-4951
Admin Ronald W Haught.
Licensure Skilled Care. *Beds* 60. *Certified* Medicaid.
Ownership Proprietary.

La Posada
522 Alamosa, Alamosa, CO, 81101 (303)
589-3673
Admin Luis B Medina.
Licensure Intermediate Care. *Beds* 5.
Ownership Nonprofit.

Stephens House*
309 San Juan, Alamosa, CO, 81101 (303)
589-5135
Admin Elaine C Marrangoni.
Licensure Developmentally Disabled. *Beds* 7.
Ownership Nonprofit.

ARVADA

Ames Way House*
8130 Ames Way, Arvada, CO, 80005 (303)
424-2713
Admin Richard Mason.
Licensure Intermediate Care for Mentally
Retarded. *Beds* 8.
Ownership Nonprofit.

Arvada Health Care Center Inc*
6121 W 60 Ave, Arvada, CO, 80002 (303)
420-4550
Admin Sonia Gale Morgan.
Licensure Skilled Care; Intermediate Care.
Beds SNF 23; ICF 31. *Certified* Medicaid.
Ownership Proprietary.

Cochran Family Care Home
7552 Pierce, Arvada, CO, 80003 (303)
420-0967
Admin Elwood Cochran.
Licensure Intermediate Care. *Beds* SNF.
Ownership Proprietary.

Colorado Lutheran Health Care Center*
7991 W 71 Ave, Arvada, CO, 80005 (303)
422-5088
Admin Donald C Colander.
Licensure Skilled Care. *Beds* 120. *Certified* Medicaid.
Ownership Nonprofit.

58th Avenue*
19825 W 58th Ave, Arvada, CO, 80005 (303)
424-6824
Admin Richard Mason.
Licensure Residential MR Care. *Beds* 8. *Certified* Medicaid.
Ownership Nonprofit.

King Family Care Home
8640 Calvin Dr, Arvada, CO, 80002 (303)
425-6141
Admin Jeanette King.
Licensure Intermediate Care. *Beds* 2.
Ownership Proprietary.

Lake View*
11059 W 82nd Pl, Arvada, CO, 80003 (303)
425-1327
Admin Ruth Stallings.
Licensure Intermediate Care for Mentally
Retarded. *Beds* 8.
Ownership Proprietary.

Lee Street*
6039 Lee St, Arvada, CO, 80004 (303)
423-7158
Admin Richard Mason.
Licensure Intermediate Care for Mentally
Retarded. *Beds* 7.
Ownership Nonprofit.

Spring Valley*
5900 Nelson Court, Arvada, CO, 80005 (303)
423-7158
Admin Richard Mason.
Licensure Residential MR Care. *Beds* 8. *Certified* Medicaid.
Ownership Nonprofit.

AURORA

Beeler Street East
1455 Beeler St, Aurora, CO, 80010 (303)
364-7249
Admin Betty Morton. *Medical Dir/Dir of
Nursing* Mr Stephen Gilson.
Licensure Intermediate Care for Mentally
Retarded. *Beds* 15.
Ownership Nonprofit.
Admissions Requirements Minimum age 18;
Medical examination; Physician's request.
Staff Physicians 2 (pt); RNs 1 (ft), 1 (pt); Recreational therapists 1 (pt); Dietitians 1 (pt).

Camellia Care Center Inc
500 Geneva St, Aurora, CO, 80010 (303)
364-9311
Admin Kay Hunter. *Medical Dir/Dir of
Nursing* Francis D Burdick MD.
Licensure Skilled Care; Intermediate Care.
Beds SNF 113; ICF 59. *Certified* Medicaid;
Medicare.
Ownership Proprietary.
Admissions Requirements Minimum age 45;
Medical examination; Physician's request.
Staff RNs 12 (ft); LPNs 21 (ft); Orderlies 8 (ft);
Nurses aides 43 (ft); Activities coordinators 2
(ft); Dietitians 2 (ft).
Facilities Dining room; Physical therapy room;
Activities room; Crafts room; Laundry room;
Barber/Beauty shop; 5 Solariums.
Activities Arts and Crafts; Cards; Games;
Reading groups; Prayer groups; Shopping trips;
Dances/Social or cultural gatherings.
Description Facility features a family support
group the second Tuesday every month; a shopper provides purchases for residents who cannot go out every Wednesday. One story
building, no stairs, steps, or elevators. Canopy
driveway front entry. Day care program with a
limit of 6 day care clients per day.

Cherry Creek Nursing Center Inc
14699 E Hampden Ave, Aurora, CO, 80014
(303) 693-0111

Admin Peter J Lapcheske. *Medical Dir/Dir of Nursing* Thomas McCloskey.
Licensure Skilled Care. *Beds* 255.
Ownership Proprietary.
Admissions Requirements Physician's request.
Staff RNs 18 (ft); LPNs 2 (ft); Orderlies 4 (ft); Nurses aides 34 (ft); Reality therapists 1 (ft); Recreational therapists 1 (ft); Activities coordinators 1 (ft).
Facilities Dining room; Physical therapy room; Activities room; Chapel; Crafts room; Laundry room; Barber/Beauty shop; Library.
Activities Arts and Crafts; Cards; Games; Reading groups; Prayer groups; Movies; Shopping trips; Dances/Social or cultural gatherings; Dog races; Horse races; Tours; Mountain trips.
Description Facility was built to serve private pay clients only; features large rooms, 20 suites and other deluxe rooms and above average staffing.

Delmar*
10801 Delmar Pkwy, Aurora, CO, 80010 (303) 696-7002
Admin Dennis Kirkman.
Licensure Residential MR Care. *Beds* 8. *Certified* Medicaid.
Ownership Nonprofit.

Golden Age Manor—Aurora*
10201 E 3rd Ave, Aurora, CO, 80010 (303) 364-3364
Admin Larry Book.
Licensure Skilled Care. *Beds* 120. *Certified* Medicaid; Medicare.
Ownership Proprietary.

Mountain View House*
1125 Dayton St, Aurora, CO, 80010 (303) 341-2086
Admin John Meeker.
Licensure Intermediate Care for Mentally Retarded. *Beds* 8.
Ownership Nonprofit.

Ponderosa*
11204 E Ironton, Aurora, CO, 80012 (303) 752-1920
Admin Dennis Kirkman.
Licensure Residential MR Care. *Beds* 8. *Certified* Medicaid.
Ownership Nonprofit.

Sable Care Center Inc
656 Dillon Way, Aurora, CO, 80011 (303) 344-0636
Admin Paul A Sullivan. *Medical Dir/Dir of Nursing* Frances Burdrik.
Licensure Skilled Care. *Beds* 1210. *Certified* Medicaid; Medicare.
Ownership Proprietary.
Facilities Dining room; Physical therapy room; Activities room; Barber/Beauty shop; Library.
Activities Arts and Crafts; Games; Reading groups; Prayer groups; Movies; Shopping trips; Dances/Social or cultural gatherings.

Village East*
1505 S Ironton, Aurora, CO, 80012 (303) 696-7002
Admin Dennis Kirkman.
Licensure Residential MR Care. *Beds* 8. *Certified* Medicaid.

Ownership Nonprofit.

BAYFIELD

Valley View Residential Care Home
RT 1, Bayfield, CO, 81122 (303) 884-2200
Admin Arline M Beaver.
Licensure Intermediate Care. *Beds* 8.
Ownership Proprietary.

BERTHOUD

Grandview Manor
855 Franklin St, PO Box 70, Berthoud, CO, 80513 (303) 532-2683
Admin Martin F Kuhn. *Medical Dir/Dir of Nursing* Dr David McCarty.
Licensure Skilled Care. *Beds* 54. *Certified* Medicare.
Ownership Proprietary.
Admissions Requirements Medical examination; Physician's request.
Staff RNs 4 (ft), 4 (pt); LPNs 1 (ft); Nurses aides 13 (ft), 6 (pt).
Facilities Dining room; Activities room; Laundry room.
Activities Arts and Crafts; Cards; Games; Reading groups; Prayer groups; Movies; Shopping trips; Dances/Social or cultural gatherings.

BOONE

Boone Guest Home*
526 Main St, Boone, CO, 81025 (303) 947-3045
Admin Ed Jordan and Louise Jordan.
Licensure Developmentally Disabled.
Beds 17.
Ownership Proprietary.

BOULDER

Beverly Manor
2121 Mesa Dr, Boulder, CO, 80302 (303) 442-4037
Admin Susan Conversano. *Medical Dir/Dir of Nursing* Frank Bolles MD.
Licensure Skilled Care; Intermediate Care.
Beds SNF 152; ICF 24. *Certified* Medicaid; Medicare.
Ownership Proprietary.
Staff RNs 12 (ft), 2 (pt); LPNs 20 (ft), 2 (pt); Orderlies 12 (ft), 5 (pt); Nurses aides 30 (ft), 5 (pt); Physical therapists 1 (ft); Occupational therapists 1 (pt); Speech therapists 1 (pt); Activities coordinators 2 (ft); Dietitians 1 (pt); Dentists 1 (pt); Ophthalmologists 1 (pt); Podiatrists 1 (pt); Audiologists 1 (pt).
Facilities Dining room; Physical therapy room; Activities room; Laundry room; Barber/Beauty shop; Patio; Garden spaces.
Activities Arts and Crafts; Cards; Games; Reading groups; Prayer groups; Movies; Shopping trips; Dances/Social or cultural gatherings.
Description Recently remodeled facility sits on a hill with spectacular view; located in a quiet location with outdoor areas, balconies, or patio accessible from all 4 floors. Home Health Agency provides continuum of care.

Boulder Good Samaritan Health Care Center
2525 Taft Dr, Boulder, CO, 80302 (303) 449-6157
Admin Dwight J Boe. *Medical Dir/Dir of Nursing* Darvin Smith MD.
Licensure Skilled Care. *Beds* 60. *Certified* Medicaid.
Ownership Nonprofit.
Admissions Requirements Minimum age 55; Medical examination; Physician's request.
Staff RNs 3 (ft), 8 (pt); LPNs 1 (pt); Nurses aides 14 (ft), 7 (pt); Physical therapists 1 (pt); Recreational therapists 1 (ft), 1 (pt); Dietitians 1 (pt).
Affiliation Lutheran
Facilities Dining room; Physical therapy room; Activities room; Chapel; Crafts room; Laundry room; Barber/Beauty shop; Library; Indoor, heated swimming pool.
Activities Arts and Crafts; Cards; Games; Reading groups; Prayer groups; Movies; Shopping trips; Dances/Social or cultural gatherings.
Description Quality, loving care in a Christian atmosphere can be found at Boulder Good Samaritan Health Care Center located next to the University of Colorado in culturally diverse Boulder, Colorado. Innovative, interesting activities are planned with the needs of each resident in mind.

Boulder Manor*
4685 Baseline Rd, Boulder, CO, 80302 (303) 494-0535
Admin Vernon Tott.
Licensure Skilled Care; Intermediate Care.
Beds SNF 120; ICF 60. *Certified* Medicaid.
Ownership Proprietary.

Carmel Ltd
1005 12th St, Boulder, CO, 80302 (303) 444-0573
Admin James Graves. *Medical Dir/Dir of Nursing* Marvin Dunaway MD.
Licensure Intermediate Care for Mentally Retarded. *Beds* 75. *Certified* Medicaid; Medicare.
Ownership Proprietary.
Admissions Requirements Minimum age 18; Medical examination.
Staff Physicians 5 (pt); RNs 1 (pt); LPNs 5 (ft)O; Orderlies 9 (pt); Nurses aides 8 (ft); Physical therapists 1 (pt); Recreational therapists 1 (pt); Activities coordinators 1 (pt); Dietitians 1 (pt); Podiatrists 1 (pt).
Facilities Dining room; Activities room; Crafts room; Laundry room; Library.
Activities Arts and Crafts; Games; Movies; Shopping trips; Dances/Social or cultural gatherings.

Frasier Meadows Manor
350 Ponca Pl, Boulder, CO, 80303 (303) 499-8412
Admin David M Reyes. *Medical Dir/Dir of Nursing* James T Murphy MD.
Licensure Skilled Care. *Beds* 60. *Certified* Medicaid.
Ownership Nonprofit.
Admissions Requirements Minimum age 65; Medical examination; Physician's request.
Staff Physicians 1 (pt); RNs 8 (ft); LPNs 16 (ft); Nurses aides 40 (ft); Physical therapists 1 (pt); Recreational therapists 1 (ft); Activities

coordinators 2 (ft); Dietitians 1 (ft).
Affiliation Methodist
Facilities Dining room; Physical therapy room; Activities room; Chapel; Crafts room; Laundry room; Barber/Beauty shop; Library.
Activities Arts and Crafts; Cards; Games; Reading groups; Prayer groups; Movies; Shopping trips; Dances/Social or cultural gatherings.
Description Located at the base of the Rocky Mountain foothills, this facility provides a very high quality of continuing care retirement living.

Johnson House*
1478 Meadowlark Dr, Boulder, CO, 80303 (303) 494-6249
Admin Kevin Boyle.
Licensure Residential MR Care. *Beds* 8. *Certified* Medicaid.
Ownership Nonprofit.

Kelwood*
1080 13th St, Boulder, CO, 80302 (303) 444-4596
Admin Brenda Denzel.
Licensure Intermediate Care for Mentally Retarded. *Beds* 10. *Certified* Medicaid.
Ownership Nonprofit.

Manhattan Apartments*
435 Manhattan Dr, Boulder, CO, 80303 (303) 441-1090
Admin Brenda Raines Denzel.
Licensure Residential MR Care. *Beds* 8.
Ownership Nonprofit.

BRIGHTON

Bethesda Care Center*
2025 Egbert St, Brighton, CO, 80601 (303) 659-4580
Admin Gerald S Smith.
Licensure Skilled Care. *Beds* 120. *Certified* Medicaid.
Ownership Proprietary.

Beverly Manor of Brighton
2311 E Bridge St, Brighton, CO, 80601 (303) 659-2253
Admin Marcia House.
Licensure Intermediate Care. *Beds* 112. *Certified* Medicaid.
Ownership Proprietary.
Description Facility has consulting psychologist and security unit for confused and wanderers.

Family Care Services*
2620 E 165th Ave, Brighton, CO, 80601 (303) 451-9105
Admin Eileen Wilson.
Licensure Developmentally Disabled. *Beds* 5.
Ownership Proprietary.

7th Street*
441 S 7th St, Brighton, CO, 80609 (303) 429-9714
Admin Jo Vincelli.
Licensure Intermediate Care for Mentally Retarded. *Beds* 9. *Certified* Medicaid.
Ownership Nonprofit.

BRUSH

Eben Ezer Lutheran Care Center
PO Box 344, Brush, CO, 80723 (303) 842-2861
Admin Robert A Herrboldt. *Medical Dir/Dir of Nursing* Dr Robert Kulp.
Licensure Skilled Care; Intermediate Care.
Beds SNF 88; ICF 42. *Certified* Medicaid; Medicare.
Ownership Nonprofit.
Admissions Requirements Medical examination; Physician's request.
Staff Physicians 9 (pt); RNs 6 (ft), 5 (pt); LPNs 9 (ft), 3 (pt); Orderlies 1 (pt); Nurses aides 33 (ft), 30 (pt); Physical therapists 1 (pt); Recreational therapists 1 (ft); Occupational therapists 1 (pt); Speech therapists 1 (pt); Activities coordinators 2 (ft), 2 (pt); Dietitians 1 (ft), 1 (pt); Dentists 1 (pt); Ophthalmologists 1 (pt); Podiatrists 1 (pt); Audiologists 1 (pt).
Affiliation Lutheran
Facilities Dining room; Activities room; Chapel; Crafts room; Laundry room; Barber/Beauty shop; Library; Hubbard tub.
Activities Arts and Crafts; Cards; Games; Reading groups; Prayer groups; Movies; Shopping trips; Dances/Social or cultural gatherings.
Description The center is located on a beautiful 12-acre campus with hundreds of pine trees and a lovely church which has been set aside as a historical place by the Department of Interior; excellent activity program; full-time chaplain; nurse practioner; home health care with life-line; day care; board and care rooms.

Sunset Manor*
2200 Edison St, Brush, CO, 80723 (303) 842-2825
Admin Donald G Llewellyn.
Licensure Skilled Care; Intermediate Care.
Beds SNF 48; ICF 36. *Certified* Medicaid; Medicare.
Ownership Proprietary.

BURLINGTON

Grace Manor*
Rt 1, PO Box 29A, 465 5th St, Burlington, CO, 80807 (303) 346-7512
Admin Anne Harwood.
Licensure Intermediate Care. *Beds* 50. *Certified* Medicaid.
Ownership Proprietary.

Martin House Burlington Residential Care Facility
1776 Martin, Burlington, CO, 80807 (303) 346-8550
Admin ZuAnn Hogan.
Licensure Intermediate Care for Mentally Retarded. *Beds* 8.
Ownership Nonprofit.
Admissions Requirements Minimum age 16; Females only; Medical examination.
Facilities Dining room; Activities room; Crafts room; Laundry room.
Activities Arts and Crafts; Cards; Games; Reading groups; Movies; Shopping trips; Dances/Social or cultural gatherings.
Description Facility provides vocational and life enrichment classes at a sheltered workshop; clients and their needs are the number one con-

cern; moderate care given under the sponsorship of the East Central Colorado Regional Board for Developmental Disabilities.

CANON

Barr House*
1115 Barr, Canon, CO, 81212 (303) 275-0017
Admin Roger Jensen.
Licensure Intermediate Care for Mentally Retarded. *Beds* 8. *Certified* Medicaid.
Ownership Nonprofit.

CANON CITY

Bethesda Care Center
515 Fairview St, Canon City, CO, 81212 (303) 275-0665
Admin Joseph E Stock. *Medical Dir/Dir of Nursing* Dr Jack Vincent.
Licensure Skilled Care. *Beds* 120. *Certified* Medicaid.
Ownership Nonprofit.
Admissions Requirements Physician's request.
Staff Physicians 1 (pt); RNs 4 (ft), 5 (pt); LPNs 4 (ft), 5 (pt); Orderlies 1 (ft); Nurses aides 39 (ft), 20 (pt); Activities coordinators 1 (ft), 2 (pt); Dietitians 1 (pt).
Facilities Dining room; Activities room; Crafts room; Laundry room; Barber/Beauty shop.
Activities Arts and Crafts; Cards; Games; Reading groups; Prayer groups; Movies; Shopping trips; Dances/Social or cultural gatherings.
Description VA approved.

Canon Lodge
905 Harding Ave, PO Box 1380, Canon City, CO, 81212 (303) 275-4106
Admin Judith P Cloyd. *Medical Dir/Dir of Nursing* Dr Kon Wyatt.
Licensure Skilled Care. *Beds* 60. *Certified* Medicaid.
Ownership Proprietary.
Admissions Requirements Medical examination; Physician's request.
Staff RNs 3 (ft); Orderlies 1 (ft), 2 (pt); Nurses aides 14 (ft), 3 (pt); Activities coordinators 1 (ft); Dietitians 1 (pt).
Facilities Dining room; Activities room; Chapel; Crafts room; Barber/Beauty shop; Library.
Activities Arts and Crafts; Cards; Games; Reading groups; Prayer groups; Movies; Shopping trips; Dances/Social or cultural gatherings.
Description Facility is presently undergoing extensive remodeling inside; known interstate for good patient care; home-like atmosphere provided to patients and their families and friends.

Field House*
PO Box 1249, Canon City, CO, 81212 (303) 275-0031
Admin Roger Jensen.
Licensure Intermediate Care for Mentally Retarded. *Beds* 8. *Certified* Medicaid.
Ownership Nonprofit.

Hildebrand Care Center
1401 Phay St, Canon City, CO, 81212 (303) 275-8656
Admin Joyce L Stapleton. *Medical Dir/Dir of*

Nursing Dr Jack Vincent.
Licensure Skilled Care. *Beds* 120. *Certified* Medicaid; Medicare.
Ownership Proprietary.
Admissions Requirements Medical examination.
Staff RNs 9 (ft), 2 (pt); LPNs 10 (ft); Orderlies 6 (ft); Nurses aides 35 (ft), 5 (pt); Reality therapists 1 (pt); Activities coordinators 1 (ft), 1 (pt); Dietitians 1 (pt).
Affiliation Independent Order of Odd Fellows
Facilities Dining room; Physical therapy room; Activities room; Chapel; Crafts room; Laundry room; Barber/Beauty shop; Library; Picnics; Fishing trips.
Activities Arts and Crafts; Cards; Games; Reading groups; Prayer groups; Movies; Shopping trips; Dances/Social or cultural gatherings.
Description Facility is now licensed for 5 Medicare beds; provides an adult day care program called "Eldercare"; also a respite program.

Saint Thomas More Hospital and Progressive Care Center*
1019 Sheridan, Canon City, CO, 81212 (303) 275-3381
Admin Sr M Judith Kuhn.
Licensure Skilled Care. *Beds* 105. *Certified* Medicaid.
Ownership Nonprofit.

Valley View Health Care Center*
2120 N 10 St, Canon City, CO, 81212 (303) 275-7569
Admin Barry W Singleton.
Licensure Skilled Care. *Beds* 60. *Certified* Medicaid.
Ownership Proprietary.

Westridge Apartments*
329 Rudd, Canon City, CO, 80212 (303) 275-1616
Admin Roger G Jensen.
Licensure Intermediate Care for Mentally Retarded. *Beds* 8. *Certified* Medicaid.
Ownership Nonprofit.

CASTLE ROCK

Silver State Nursing Home*
4001 Home St, Castle Rock, CO, 80104 (303) 688-3174
Admin Al Weidman.
Licensure Skilled Care; Intermediate Care. *Beds* SNF 59; ICF 21. *Certified* Medicaid.
Ownership Nonprofit.

CHEYENNE

Cheyenne Manor
561 W 1st North, Cheyenne, CO, 80810 (303) 767-5602
Admin Gary L Bauermeister. *Medical Dir/Dir of Nursing* Jean Bauermeister.
Licensure Intermediate Care. *Beds* 45. *Certified* Medicaid; Medicare.
Ownership Proprietary.
Admissions Requirements Medical examination; Physician's request.
Staff Physicians 2 (pt); RNs 1 (pt); LPNs 4 (ft), 1 (pt); Orderlies 1 (pt); Nurses aides 9 (ft), 4

(pt); Physical therapists 1 (pt); Activities coordinators 1 (ft); Dietitians 1 (pt); Dentists 1 (pt).
Facilities Dining room; Activities room; Chapel; Laundry room; Barber/Beauty shop.
Activities Arts and Crafts; Cards; Games; Movies; Shopping trips.

CLIFTON

Laurel Lane*
3301 Laural Ln, Clifton, CO, 81520 (303) 243-3702
Admin Laura Schumacher.
Licensure Residential MR Care. *Beds* 8. *Certified* Medicaid.
Ownership Nonprofit.

COLLBRAN

Plateau Valley Hospital District Nursing Home
PO Box 88, Collbran, CO, 81624 (303) 245-3981
Admin Sharon Hill. *Medical Dir/Dir of Nursing* Charles F King MD.
Licensure Intermediate Care. *Beds* 26. *Certified* Medicaid.
Ownership Nonprofit.
Admissions Requirements Medical examination; Physician's request.
Staff Physicians 1 (ft); RNs 1 (ft), 5 (pt); LPNs 1 (ft); Orderlies 1 (ft); Nurses aides 6 (ft), 7 (pt); Physical therapists 1 (pt); Activities coordinators 1 (ft); Dietitians 1 (pt); Dentists 1 (pt).
Facilities Dining room; Activities room; Crafts room.
Activities Arts and Crafts; Cards; Games; Reading groups; Prayer groups; Movies; Shopping trips; Dances/Social or cultural gatherings.
Description Small, rural facility with home-like atmosphere; residents receive close attention from staff and personnel.

COLORADO SPRINGS

Beverly Hills Recovery Center*
1795 Monterey Rd, Colorado Springs, CO, 80930 (303) 471-7850
Admin Joyce Hamm.
Licensure Skilled Care; Intermediate Care. *Beds* SNF 60; ICF 60. *Certified* Medicaid; Medicare.
Ownership Proprietary.

Cedarwood Health Care Center Inc*
924 W Kiowa St, Colorado Springs, CO, 80905 (303) 636-5221
Admin Berna Mae Smith.
Licensure Skilled Care; Intermediate Care. *Beds* SNF 60; ICF 40. *Certified* Medicaid; Medicare.
Ownership Proprietary.

Cheyenne Mountain Nursing Center*
835 Tenderfoot Hill Rd, Colorado Springs, CO, 80906 (303) 576-8380
Admin Ann Bates.
Licensure Skilled Care. *Beds* 120. *Certified* Medicare.
Ownership Proprietary.

Colonial Columns Nursing Center Inc*
1340 E Fillmore St, Colorado Springs, CO, 80907 (303) 473-1105
Admin Karl Schmidt.
Licensure Skilled Care; Intermediate Care. *Beds* SNF 50; ICF 43. *Certified* Medicaid.
Ownership Proprietary.

Fairview Care Center*
PO Box 7690, 825 S Hancock Ave, Colorado Springs, CO, 80933 (303) 635-2532
Admin Linda F Kruse.
Licensure Skilled Care. *Beds* 60. *Certified* Medicaid.
Ownership Proprietary.

Garden of the Gods Care Center*
PO Box 6129, 104 Lois Ln, Colorado Springs, CO, 80934 (303) 635-2569
Admin Marilyn J Campell Myers.
Licensure Skilled Care. *Beds* 52. *Certified* Medicaid; Medicare.
Ownership Proprietary.

Laurel Manor Care Center*
920 S Chelton Rd, Colorado Springs, CO, 80910 (303) 473-7780
Admin Grady Haught.
Licensure Skilled Care; Intermediate Care. *Beds* SNF 100; ICF 8. *Certified* Medicaid.
Ownership Nonprofit.

Martin Luther Home*
Hampton Dr, Colorado Springs, CO, 80909
Admin Sandra S Volker.
Licensure Residential DD Care. *Beds* 8.
Ownership Nonprofit.
Affiliation Lutheran

Medalion Health-Center
1719 E Bijou, Colorado Springs, CO, 80909 (303) 471-4800
Admin Marshall C Hjelte. *Medical Dir/Dir of Nursing* Lyle Graham DO.
Licensure Skilled Care. *Beds* 32. *Certified* Medicare.
Ownership Nonprofit.
Admissions Requirements Minimum age 14; Physician's request.
Staff RNs 6 (ft), 1 (pt); Nurses aides 15 (ft), 2 (pt); Physical therapists 1 (pt); Activities coordinators 1 (ft); Dietitians 1 (pt); Dentists 1 (pt); Podiatrists 1 (pt).
Facilities Dining room; Chapel; Laundry room; Barber/Beauty shop; Library; Swimming pool and deck.
Activities Arts and Crafts; Games; Reading groups; Prayer groups; Movies; Shopping trips; Dances/Social or cultural gatherings.
Description Facility is located in beautiful Colorado Springs, at the foot of Pikes Peak.

Norton Nursing Home Inc*
2612 W Cucharras St, Colorado Springs, CO, 80904 (303) 632-7474
Admin Olga M Pratt.
Licensure Skilled Care; Intermediate Care; Residential Care. *Beds* SNF 60; ICF 31; Residential Care 10. *Certified* Medicaid; Medicare.
Ownership Proprietary.

Pikes Peak Manor Inc
2719 N Union Blvd, Colorado Springs, CO,
80909 (303) 636-1676
Admin James Sanner. *Medical Dir/Dir of
Nursing* John McWilliams MD.
Licensure Skilled Care; Intermediate Care.
Beds SNF 146; ICF 94. *Certified* Medicaid;
Medicare.
Ownership Proprietary.
Staff RNs 11 (ft), 5 (pt); LPNs 9 (ft), 10 (pt);
Orderlies 1 (ft), 1 (pt); Nurses aides 44 (ft), 16
(pt); Physical therapists 3 (pt); Recreational
therapists 1 (ft), 2 (pt); Occupational therapists
1 (pt); Speech therapists 1 (pt); Activities coor-
dinators 2 (pt); Dietitians 1 (ft).
Facilities Dining room; Activities room; Crafts
room; Laundry room; Barber/Beauty shop.
Activities Arts and Crafts; Cards; Games;
Reading groups; Prayer groups; Movies; Shopping trips; Dances/Social or cultural gatherings.
Description Pikes Peak Manor has a beautiful
view of the mountains, especially Pikes Peak,
from rooms and grounds.

Prospect Lake Nursing Center
1420 E Fountain Blvd, Colorado Springs, CO,
80910 (303) 632-7604
Admin Barbara G Strombeck. *Medical Dir/Dir
of Nursing* Dr Lester Williams.
Licensure Skilled Care. *Beds* 49. *Cer-
tified* Medicaid; Medicare.
Ownership Proprietary.
Admissions Requirements Medical examina-
tion; Physician's request.
Staff RNs 3 (ft), 6 (pt); Orderlies 2 (pt); Nurses
aides 8 (ft), 7 (pt); Recreational therapists 1 (ft).
Facilities Dining room.
Activities Arts and Crafts; Cards; Games;
Reading groups; Prayer groups; Movies; Shop-
ping trips; Dances/Social or cultural gatherings;
Swimming and bowling outside facility;
Involvement in other community activities.
Description Facility features an 8-passenger
van with wheelchair lift, several clients partici-
pate in special olympics; special interest volun-
teer groups, and special duty aides.

Saint Clare Health Care Facility
1440 E Fountain Blvd, Colorado Springs, CO,
80910 (303) 632-3752
Admin M Carmelia Lohaus.
Licensure Skilled Care. *Beds* 40.
Ownership Nonprofit.

Springs Village Recovery Center*
PO Box 7690, 110 W Van Buren, Colorado
Springs, CO, 80909 (303) 475-8686
Admin Linda Kruse.
Licensure Skilled Care; Intermediate Care;
Residential Care. *Beds* SNF 60; ICF 60; Resi-
dential Care 17. *Certified* Medicaid; Medicare.
Ownership Proprietary.

Stroh Residential Home*
2129 N Nevada, Colorado Springs, CO, 80907
(303) 473-7374
Admin Wayne D Stroh and Marjorie M Stroh.
Licensure Developmentally Disabled.
Beds 10.
Ownership Proprietary.

Sunnyrest Sanatorium
2400 E Cache La Poudre St, Colorado Springs,
CO, 80909 (303) 471-8700
Admin Cynthia J Cordle. *Medical Dir/Dir of
Nursing* Dr H H Rodman.
Licensure Skilled Care. *Beds* 107. *Cer-
tified* Medicaid.
Ownership Nonprofit.
Admissions Requirements Medical examina-
tion; Physician's request.
Staff RNs 6 (ft), 6 (pt); LPNs 2 (ft), 6 (pt);
Nurses aides 56 (ft), 4 (pt); Activities coordina-
tors 1 (ft), 1 (pt).
Facilities Dining room; Physical therapy room;
Activities room; Laundry room; Barber/Beauty
shop.
Activities Arts and Crafts; Cards; Games;
Reading groups; Prayer groups; Movies; Shop-
ping trips; Dances/Social or cultural gatherings.
Description Facilty features family conferences,
patient meal planning, and special birthday
meal.

Terrace Gardens Health Care Center*
2438 Fountain Blvd, Colorado Springs, CO,
80909 (303) 473-8000
Admin Delores L Heindenreich.
Licensure Skilled Care; Intermediate Care.
Beds SNF 60; ICF 60. *Certified* Medicaid;
Medicare.
Ownership Proprietary.

Union Printers Home*
PO Box 817, Pikes Peak and Union Blvd, Col-
orado Springs, CO, 80901 (303) 634-3711
Admin Donald M Fifield.
Licensure Skilled Care; Intermediate Care.
Beds SNF 65; ICF 32.
Ownership Nonprofit.

Whoolery's Residential Care Facility
607 Lansing Dr, Colorado Springs, CO, 80909
(303) 596-2621
Admin Angeline Whoolery.
Licensure Intermediate Care for Mentally
Retarded. *Beds* 4.
Ownership Proprietary.
Admissions Requirements Minimum age 18;
Females only; Medical examination.
Facilities Dining room; Laundry room.
Activities Arts and Crafts; Cards; Games;
Reading groups; Prayer groups; Movies; Shop-
ping trips; Dances/Social or cultural gatherings.
Description Facility is not considered a nursing
home with only 4 moderately MR's that are in
sheltered workshop; no staff for there is not a
need; therapies and illnesses are taken care of
by private professionals.

COMMERCE

The Ruth Owen Family Care Home*
6801 E 64th Ave, Commerce, CO, 80022 (303)
287-7984
Admin Ruth Owen.
Licensure Intermediate Care. *Beds* 2.
Ownership Proprietary.

COMMERCE CITY

Adams Manor Nursing Home*
7150 Poplar St, Commerce City, CO, 80022
(303) 287-0269
Admin B A "Suzie" Foley.
Licensure Skilled Care; Intermediate Care.
Beds SNF 84; ICF 32. *Certified* Medicaid;
Medicare.
Ownership Proprietary.

Country Manor Nursing Home*
5230 E 66th Way, Commerce City, CO, 80022
(303) 287-8016
Admin Marcia House.
Licensure Skilled Care; Intermediate Care.
Beds SNF 79; ICF 42. *Certified* Medicaid;
Medicare.
Ownership Proprietary.

Crocker Family Care Home
6050 Ivanhoe, Commerce City, CO, 80022
(303) 287-7604
Admin Shirley Crocker.
Licensure Intermediate Care. *Beds* 4.
Ownership Proprietary.

Giles Family Care Home*
6391 Quebec St, Commerce City, CO, 80222
(303) 287-0673
Admin Mildred Giles.
Licensure Intermediate Care. *Beds* 4.
Ownership Proprietary.

CORTEZ

Vista Grande Nursing
1221 N Mildred Rd, Cortez, CO, 81321 (303)
565-3451
Admin Tom Kish. *Medical Dir/Dir of
Nursing* Edward Merritt MD.
Licensure Skilled Care. *Beds* 76. *Cer-
tified* Medicaid; Medicare.
Ownership Proprietary.
Admissions Requirements Medical examina-
tion; Physician's request.
Staff Physicians 10 (ft); RNs 3 (ft), 2 (pt);
LPNs 7 (ft), 2 (pt); Nurses aides 26 (ft), 4 (pt);
Physical therapists 2 (ft); Reality therapists 1
(ft); Recreational therapists 1 (ft); Activities
coordinators 1 (ft); Dietitians 1 (ft); Dentists 10
(pt).
Facilities Dining room; Physical therapy room;
Activities room; Chapel; Laundry room; Bar-
ber/Beauty shop.
Activities Arts and Crafts; Cards; Games;
Reading groups; Prayer groups; Movies; Shop-
ping trips; Dances/Social or cultural gatherings;
Short scenic trips; Picnics.
Description Facility features large rooms with a
beautiful view from each window; attached to
Southwest Memorial Hospital; enjoys commu-
nity support.

CORY

Horizons Nursing Home Inc
Cory, CO, 81414-0160 (303) 835-3113
Admin June M Schwantes. *Medical Dir/Dir of
Nursing* Charles T Frey MD.
Licensure Skilled Care. *Beds* 60. *Cer-

tified Medicaid; Medicare.
Ownership Proprietary.
Admissions Requirements Minimum age 16;
Physician's request.
Staff RNs 4 (ft), 4 (pt); LPNs 3 (ft), 3 (pt);
Orderlies 2 (ft), 1 (pt); Nurses aides 19 (ft), 7
(pt); Reality therapists 1 (ft); Recreational thera-
pists 1 (ft); Activities coordinators 1 (ft).
Facilities Dining room; Physical therapy room;
Activities room; Chapel; Crafts room; Laundry
room; Barber/Beauty shop; Library.
Activities Arts and Crafts; Cards; Games;
Reading groups; Prayer groups; Movies; Shop-
ping trips; Dances/Social or cultural gatherings;
Church groups come in on Sunday.
Description The atmosphere is very friendly
and home-like; residents are encouraged to be
themselves. Home cooking and baking is provided.

CRAIG

Valley View Manor*
943 W 8th Dr, Craig, CO, 81625 (303)
824-4432
Admin John Filkoski.
Licensure Skilled Care; Intermediate Care.
Beds SNF 54; ICF 6. *Certified* Medicaid.
Ownership Proprietary.

Victory Way House*
1243 E Victoria Way, Craig, CO, 80477 (303)
879-4466
Admin Christine K Collins.
Licensure Residential MR Care. *Beds* 8.
Ownership Nonprofit.

CRIPPLE CREEK

Hill Top Nursing Home and Community Clinc
"A" St and Hettig Ave, Cripple Creek, CO,
80813 (303) 689-2931
Admin Max Dietze.
Licensure Intermediate Care. *Beds* 60. *Certi-
fied* Medicaid.
Ownership Proprietary.
Staff Physicians 2 (pt); RNs 2 (ft); LPNs 6 (ft);
Orderlies 3 (ft); Nurses aides 12 (ft); Physical
therapists 1 (pt); Activities coordinators 1 (ft), 1
(pt); Dietitians 1 (ft); Dentists 1 (pt); Podiatrists
1 (pt).
Affiliation Lutheran
Facilities Dining room; Activities room; Laun-
dry room; Barber/Beauty shop; Library.
Activities Arts and Crafts; Cards; Games; Pray-
er groups; Movies; Shopping trips;
Dances/Social or cultural gatherings.

DEL NORTE

**Saint Joseph's Hospital and Nursing Home of
Del Norte Inc**
1280 Grande, Del Norte, CO, 81132 (303)
657-3311
Admin Robert Otts. *Medical Dir/Dir of
Nursing* Norman Haug MD.
Licensure Skilled Care. *Beds* 30. *Cer-
tified* Medicaid.
Ownership Nonprofit.
Admissions Requirements Medical examina-

tion.
Staff RNs 1 (ft), 2 (pt); LPNs 2 (ft), 3 (pt);
Physical therapists 1 (pt); Occupational thera-
pists 1 (ft); Activities coordinators 1 (ft);
Dietitians 1 (pt).
Affiliation Roman Catholic
Facilities Dining room; Physical therapy room;
Activities room; Chapel; Crafts room; Laundry
room; Barber/Beauty shop; Library.
Activities Arts and Crafts; Cards; Games;
Reading groups; Prayer groups; Movies; Shop-
ping trips; Dances/Social or cultural gatherings.

DELTA

Bethesda Care Center*
2050 S Main St, Delta, CO, 81416 (303)
874-9773
Admin LaRoyce C Shepard.
Licensure Skilled Care. *Beds* 110. *Certified* Medicaid; Medicare.
Ownership Nonprofit.

Delta Care Center
1102 Grand Ave, Delta, CO, 81416 (303)
874-5773
Admin LaVerne Sharpe.
Licensure Intermediate Care. *Beds* 40. *Certi-
fied* Medicaid.
Ownership Proprietary.
Admissions Requirements Physician's request.
Staff RNs 1 (ft); LPNs 4 (ft), 2 (pt); Nurses
aides 6 (ft), 4 (pt); Physical therapists 1 (pt);
Recreational therapists 1 (ft); Activities coordinators 1 (ft); Dietitians 1 (pt); Dentists 1 (pt);
Podiatrists 1 (pt).
Facilities Dining room; Activities room; Crafts
room; Laundry room.
Activities Arts and Crafts; Cards; Games;
Reading groups; Prayer groups; Movies; Shopping trips; Dances/Social or cultural gatherings.
Description Pride taken in interrelationship
between residents and staff, and nice homey
atmosphere with quality professional backing;
aquatic and swimming activities are outstanding. Facility is located within walking distance of downtown shopping but in a quiet and
peaceful neighborhood.

DENVER

Arkansas Manor Nursing Home Inc
3185 W Arkansas, Denver, CO, 80219 (303)
922-1169
Admin Betty McDonald. *Medical Dir/Dir of
Nursing* Frank I Dubin MD.
Licensure Skilled Care; Intermediate Care.
Beds SNF 110; ICF 10. *Certified* Medicaid.
Ownership Proprietary.
Admissions Requirements Minimum age 65.
Facilities Dining room; Laundry room; Barber-
/Beauty shop; Library.
Activities Arts and Crafts; Games; Reading
groups; Prayer groups; Movies; Shopping trips;
Dances/Social or cultural gatherings.

Asbury Circle Nursing Home Inc*
4660 E Asbury Circle, Denver, CO, 80222 (303)
756-1546
Admin Lavern O Huenergardt.

Licensure Skilled Care; Intermediate Care.
Beds SNF 60; ICF 22. *Certified* Medicaid.
Ownership Proprietary.

Aspen Siesta*
5353 E Yale Ave, Denver, CO, 80222 (303)
757-1209
Admin Ruth D Horsley.
Licensure Skilled Care. *Beds* 70.
Ownership Proprietary.

Bella Vita Towers Inc
4450 E Jewell Ave, Denver, CO, 80222 (303)
757-7438
Admin Carl T Zarlengo. *Medical Dir/Dir of
Nursing* Francis Burdick MD.
Licensure Skilled Care. *Beds* 136. *Cer-
tified* Medicaid.
Ownership Proprietary.
Admissions Requirements Minimum age 50.
Staff RNs 9 (ft), 2 (pt); LPNs 6 (ft), 4 (pt);
Orderlies 2 (ft), 1 (pt); Nurses aides 45 (ft), 4
(pt); Activities coordinators 1 (ft); Dietitians 1
(pt).
Facilities Dining room; Physical therapy room;
Activities room; Chapel; Crafts room; Laundry
room; Barber/Beauty shop.
Activities Arts and Crafts; Cards; Games;
Reading groups; Prayer groups; Movies; Shop-
ping trips.

Berkley Manor Care Center
735 S Locust, Denver, CO, 80224 (303)
320-4377
Admin Ann Melurdy. *Medical Dir/Dir of
Nursing* Francis Burdick MD.
Licensure Skilled Care; Intermediate Care.
Beds 60. *Certified* Medicaid.
Ownership Proprietary.
Admissions Requirements Minimum age 50;
Medical examination; Physician's request.
Facilities Dining room; Activities room; Laun-
dry room; Barber/Beauty shop.
Activities Arts and Crafts; Cards; Games;
Reading groups; Prayer groups; Movies; Shop-
ping trips; Dances/Social or cultural gatherings.
Description Expansion of facility is planned
this year to 60 skilled (10 intensive care beds),
40 intermediate, and 20 residential beds.

Beth Israel Hospital and Geriatric Center
1601 Lowell Blvd, Denver, CO, 80204 (303)
825-2190
Admin Harry Yaffe. *Medical Dir/Dir of
Nursing* Dr Sydney Foster.
Licensure Skilled Care; Intermediate Care.
Beds SNF 82; ICF 65. *Certified* Medicaid;
Medicare.
Ownership Nonprofit.
Admissions Requirements Minimum age 15;
Physician's request.
Staff Physicians 1 (ft); RNs 5 (ft), 3 (pt); LPNs
18 (ft); Orderlies 2 (ft); Nurses aides 32 (ft), 2
(pt); Physical therapists 1 (pt); Occupational
therapists 1 (pt); Speech therapists 1 (pt);
Activities coordinators 3 (ft); Dietitians 1 (pt);
Dentists 1 (pt); Podiatrists 1 (pt); Audiologists 1
(pt).
Affiliation Jewish
Facilities Dining room; Activities room; Chap-
el; Crafts room; Laundry room; Barber/Beauty
shop; Library.
Activities Arts and Crafts; Cards; Games;

Reading groups; Movies; Shopping trips; Dances/Social or cultural gatherings.
Description Facility has an Alzheimer's secured unit.

Beverly Manor Nursing Home*
3131 S Federal Blvd, Denver, CO, 80209 (303) 761-0260
Admin Gary R House.
Licensure Skilled Care; Intermediate Care.
Beds SNF 88; ICF 89. *Certified* Medicaid; Medicare.
Ownership Proprietary.

Bragg Residential Care Home Inc*
1461 Cook St, Denver, CO, 80206 (303) 355-0035
Admin Ellen M Bragg.
Licensure Developmentally Disabled. *Beds* 6.
Ownership Proprietary.

Burton Family Care Home
3553 Hudson, Denver, CO, 80207 (303) 321-3693
Admin Oleria P Burton.
Licensure Intermediate Care for Mentally Retarded. *Beds* 4.
Ownership Proprietary.

Charm Cove Nursing Home Inc*
1825 S Federal Blvd, Denver, CO, 80219 (303) 935-4609
Admin S Adelia Fitzsimmons.
Licensure Skilled Care; Intermediate Care.
Beds SNF 75; ICF 8. *Certified* Medicaid.
Ownership Proprietary.

Civitan House*
2790 E 2nd Ave, Denver, CO, 81301 (303) 259-2464
Admin Richard F Sheridan.
Beds 8.
Ownership Nonprofit.

Costigan Family Care Home*
600 S Quitman, Denver, CO, 80219 (303) 934-4906
Admin Arabella M Costigan.
Licensure Intermediate Care. *Beds* 4.
Ownership Proprietary.

David Gottesfield House*
8160 Linsvale Ave, Denver, CO, 80211 (303) 458-8242
Admin Timothy O'Neil.
Licensure Residential MR Care. *Beds* 8.
Ownership Nonprofit.

Davis Nursing Home Inc
1440 Vine St, Denver, CO, 80206 (303) 399-0350
Admin H Virgil Davis. *Medical Dir/Dir of Nursing* Robert McKenna MD.
Licensure Skilled Care; Intermediate Care.
Beds SNF 120; ICF 117.
Ownership Proprietary.
Staff RNs 10 (ft); LPNs 9 (ft); Orderlies 1 (ft); Nurses aides 45 (ft); Physical therapists 1 (ft).
Facilities Dining room; Physical therapy room; Activities room; Chapel; Crafts room; Laundry room; Barber/Beauty shop; Library.

Activities Arts and Crafts; Cards; Games; Reading groups; Prayer groups; Movies; Shopping trips.

Frickell Family Care Home*
4988 Stuart St, Denver, CO, 80212 (303) 455-9398
Admin Mary Frickell.
Licensure Intermediate Care. *Beds* 4.
Ownership Proprietary.

Highlands Center Inc*
1920 High St, Denver, CO, 80218 (303) 320-5871
Admin Tom Beisler.
Licensure Intermediate Care. *Beds* 52. *Certified* Medicaid.
Ownership Proprietary.

Holly Heights Nursing Home Inc*
6000 E Iliff, Denver, CO, 80222 (303) 757-5441
Admin Janet L Snipes.
Licensure Skilled Care; Intermediate Care.
Beds SNF 60; ICF 91. *Certified* Medicaid; Medicare.
Ownership Proprietary.

Iliff Nursing Care Center*
6060 E Iliff, Denver, CO, 80222 (303) 759-4221
Admin Dorothy Boggio.
Licensure Skilled Care; Intermediate Care.
Beds SNF 120; ICF 60. *Certified* Medicaid.
Ownership Proprietary.

Ivy Manor Nursing Home*
2205 W 29th Ave, Denver, CO, 80211 (303) 458-1112
Admin Marjorie Eller.
Licensure Skilled Care; Intermediate Care.
Beds SNF 120; ICF 60. *Certified* Medicaid; Medicare.
Ownership Proprietary.

Ladies Relief Society of Denver
4115 W 38th Ave, Denver, CO, 80212 (303) 455-9513
Admin Ann R Brown.
Licensure Intermediate Care. *Beds* 26.
Ownership Nonprofit.
Admissions Requirements Minimum age 65; Females only; Medical examination; Physician's request.
Staff RNs 1 (pt); LPNs 6 (ft); Nurses aides 6 (ft), 2 (pt); Activities coordinators 1 (ft); Dietitians 1 (pt).
Facilities Dining room; Laundry room; Barber/Beauty shop; Library.
Activities Cards; Prayer groups; Movies; Shopping trips; General entertainment.
Description A unique facility for women only. Average age of residents is 90. Three meals per day, personal laundry, housekeeping, and nurse 24 hours per day are furnished. Facility open since 1898, similar to a sorority house, and furnished with antiques.

Laradon Hall—Society for Exceptional Children*
E 51st Ave and Lincoln St, Denver, CO, 80216 (303) 295-6379
Admin Helen Murphy.

Licensure Intermediate Care for Mentally Retarded. *Beds* 83.
Ownership Nonprofit.

Lena Crews Family Care Home*
838 S Vallejo, Denver, CO, 80223 (303) 936-1414
Admin Lena Crews.
Licensure Intermediate Care. *Beds* 2.
Ownership Proprietary.

Leslie Family Care Home
5231 Lowell Blvd, Denver, CO, 80221 (303) 455-2289
Admin C M Leslie.
Licensure Intermediate Care. *Beds* 4.
Ownership Proprietary.

Martin Family Care Home*
1996 S Newton, Denver, CO, 80219 (303) 935-7528
Admin Mary E Martin.
Licensure Intermediate Care. *Beds* 3.
Ownership Proprietary.

Mazotti Family Care Home*
2767 W 38th Ave, Denver, CO, 80211 (303) 433-5933
Admin Jeannie Mazotti.
Licensure Intermediate Care. *Beds* 4.
Ownership Proprietary.

McCallum Family Care Center*
2536 Downing, Denver, CO, 80205 (303) 355-6524
Admin Willie H McCallum.
Licensure Intermediate Care. *Beds* 4.
Ownership Proprietary.

McCovy Goldon Age Home Inc*
2858 California St, Denver, CO, 80205 (303) 623-3428
Admin Gertrude McCovy.
Licensure Developmentally Disabled. *Beds* 8.
Ownership Nonprofit.

Montclaire Manor Nursing Home*
5775 E 8th Ave, Denver, CO, 80220 (303) 320-4600
Admin Robert E Moore Jr.
Licensure Skilled Care; Intermediate Care.
Beds SNF 180; ICF 75. *Certified* Medicaid; Medicare.
Ownership Nonprofit.

Mount Sinai Nursing Home Inc*
2741 Federal Blvd, Denver, CO, 80211 (303) 455-3693
Admin Paul Sullivan.
Licensure Skilled Care; Intermediate Care.
Beds SNF 32; ICF 32. *Certified* Medicaid.
Ownership Proprietary.

Mullen Home for the Elderly
3629 29th Ave, Denver, CO, 80211 (303) 433-7221
Admin Sr Cecilia Honigfort.
Licensure Skilled Care; Intermediate Care.
Beds SNF 42; ICF 76. *Certified* Medicaid; Medicare.
Ownership Nonprofit.

Nikkel Family Care Home*
5030 W Park Pl, Denver, CO, 80219 (303)
936-6430
Admin Mildred I Nikkel.
Licensure Intermediate Care. *Beds* 6.
Ownership Proprietary.

Park Avenue Baptist Home
1535 Park Ave, Denver, CO, 80218 (303)
832-9323
Admin Bernard C Heese. *Medical Dir/Dir of
Nursing* J Franklin Moore.
Licensure Skilled Care; Intermediate Care;
Residential Care. *Beds* SNF 57; ICF 57; Residential Care 10. *Certified* Medicaid.
Ownership Nonprofit.
Admissions Requirements Minimum age 50.
Staff RNs 7 (ft); LPNs 10 (ft); Orderlies 10 (ft);
Nurses aides 25 (ft); Recreational therapists 2
(ft); Dietitians 1 (pt); Dentists 1 (pt).
Affiliation Baptist
Facilities Dining room; Physical therapy room;
Activities room; Chapel; Crafts room; Barber-
/Beauty shop; Library.
Activities Arts and Crafts; Cards; Games;
Reading groups; Prayer groups; Movies; Shopping trips; Dances/Social or cultural gatherings.

Parkview Manor Nursing Home Inc*
3105 W Arkansas Ave, Denver, CO, 80219
(303) 936-3497
Admin Ruth E Thomann.
Licensure Skilled Care; Intermediate Care.
Beds SNF 88; ICF 2. *Certified* Medicaid.
Ownership Proprietary.

Presbyterian Medical Center*
1719 E 19th Ave, Denver, CO, 80218 (303)
839-6000
Admin Errol Biggs.
Licensure Intermediate Care. *Beds* 24.
Ownership Nonprofit.

Regency Rehabilitation Enterprises*
1500 Hooker, Denver, CO, 80204 (303)
534-5968
Admin Vera J Kloepfer.
Licensure Skilled Care; Rehabilitation.
Beds SNF 56; Rehabilitaiton 96. *Certified* Medicaid; Medicare.
Ownership Proprietary.

Rocky Mountain Health Care Center
2201 Downing St, Denver, CO, 80205 (303)
861-4825
Admin Vernon Tott. *Medical Dir/Dir of
Nursing* Werner Prenzlau MD.
Licensure Skilled Care; Intermediate Care.
Beds SNF 60; ICF 60.
Ownership Proprietary.
Admissions Requirements Minimum age 18.
Staff RNs 9 (ft), 3 (pt); LPNs 4 (ft), 2 (pt);
Orderlies 7 (ft); Nurses aides 17 (ft); Physical
therapists 1 (pt); Recreational therapists 1 (ft), 2
(pt); Occupational therapists 1 (pt); Activities
coordinators 1 (ft), 2 (pt); Dietitians 1 (ft); Dentists 1 (pt); Podiatrists 1 (ft).
Facilities Dining room; Activities room; Crafts
room; Laundry room.
Activities Arts and Crafts; Cards; Games;
Reading groups; Prayer groups; Movies; Shopping trips; Dances/Social or cultural gatherings.

Rose Mary's Home
7939 Pecos St, Denver, CO, 80221 (303)
429-1857
Admin Rose Mary Hoff.
Licensure Intermediate Care. *Beds* 4.
Ownership Proprietary.

Saint Paul Health Center*
1667 Saint Paul St, Denver, CO, 80206 (303)
399-2040
Admin Richard J Whelan.
Licensure Skilled Care; Intermediate Care.
Beds SNF 104; ICF 156. *Certified* Medicaid;
Medicare.
Ownership Proprietary.

South Monaco Care Center
895 S Monaco, Denver, CO, 80222 (303)
321-3110
Admin Palma Chambers.
Licensure Skilled Care. *Beds* 60.
Ownership Proprietary.
Admissions Requirements Minimum age 65;
Medical examination.
Staff RNs 6 (ft); LPNs 2 (ft); Orderlies 2 (ft);
Nurses aides 14 (ft); Recreational therapists 1
(ft).
Facilities Dining room; Physical therapy room;
Activities room; Laundry room; Barber/Beauty
shop.
Activities Arts and Crafts; Cards; Games;
Reading groups.

Stovall Care Center
3345 Forest St, Denver, CO, 80207 (303)
355-1666
Admin Viola B Garlington. *Medical Dir/Dir of
Nursing* Jitze DeJong MD.
Licensure Skilled Care. *Beds* 60. *Certified* Medicaid; Medicare.
Ownership Nonprofit.
Admissions Requirements Minimum age 27;
Medical examination; Physician's request.
Staff RNs 4 (ft), 3 (pt); LPNs 2 (ft), 2 (pt);
Orderlies 3 (ft), 1 (pt); Nurses aides 14 (ft), 1
(pt); Activities coordinators 1 (ft); Social workers 1 (ft).
Affiliation Baptist
Facilities Activities room; Crafts room; Laundry room; Barber/Beauty shop; Library.
Activities Arts and Crafts; Cards; Games;
Prayer groups; Movies; Dances/Social or cultural gatherings.
Description Stovall Care Center is part of a
complex that includes a 105-unit apartment
building for independent living and a senior
center which has daily activities for the elderly
including a food site.

Sunny Acres Villa Inc
2501 E 104th Ave, Denver, CO, 80233 (303)
452-4181
Admin Leon F Adkins. *Medical Dir/Dir of
Nursing* Dr Robert Jardine.
Licensure Skilled Care; Intermediate Care.
Beds SNF 110; ICF 8. *Certified* Medicare.
Ownership Nonprofit.
Admissions Requirements Minimum age 62;
Medical examination.
Staff RNs 7 (ft), 8 (pt); LPNs 8 (ft), 5 (pt);
Nurses aides 28 (ft), 13 (pt); Physical therapists
1 (ft); Activities coordinators 2 (ft); Dietitians 2
(ft).

Facilities Dining room; Physical therapy room;
Activities room; Chapel; Crafts room; Laundry
room; Barber/Beauty shop; Library.
Activities Arts and Crafts; Cards; Games; Prayer groups; Movies; Shopping trips; Dances/Social or cultural gatherings.
Description Sunny Acres is part of a nonprofit
corporation, Colorado's largest and finest life
care community. In addition to life care residents, Sunny Acres health care facility is now
accepting Medicare and private pay patients.

Sunny Hill*
3400 E 34th Ave, Denver, CO, 80205 (303)
333-3439
Admin Lillian Duran.
Licensure Intermediate Care for Mentally
Retarded. *Beds* 10.
Ownership Proprietary.

Tiger Residential Programs (Fairview House)
6000 E Evans, Bldg 3, Suite 205, Denver, CO,
80222
Admin Gary Davidson.
Licensure Intermediate Care for Mentally
Retarded. *Beds* 14. *Certified* Medicaid; Medicare.
Ownership Nonprofit.
Admissions Requirements Minimum age 18.
Staff RNs 1 (ft); Recreational therapists 1 (pt);
Dietitians 1 (pt); Counselors 14 (ft).
Facilities Dining room; Activities room; Laundry room.
Activities Arts and Crafts; Games; Movies;
Shopping trips; Dances/Social or cultural gatherings; Camping.
Description The 2 group homes provide a
home-like environment for severely to moderately retarded adults, all ambulatory, with
some other physical handicaps; programs have
been very successful in improving functioning
levels.

University Hills Christian Nursing Home
2480 S Clermont, Denver, CO, 80222 (303)
758-4528
Admin Elmer Houtsma. *Medical Dir/Dir of
Nursing* William Hines MD.
Licensure Skilled Care; Intermediate Care.
Beds SNF 31; ICF 31. *Certified* Medicaid.
Ownership Nonprofit.
Admissions Requirements Minimum age 60;
Medical examination; Physician's request.
Staff Activities coordinators 2 (ft); Dietitians 1
(pt).
Facilities Dining room; Physical therapy room;
Activities room; Chapel; Crafts room; Laundry
room; Barber/Beauty shop; Library; Overnight
guest room.
Activities Arts and Crafts; Cards; Games;
Reading groups; Prayer groups; Movies; Shopping trips; Bowling.

Valley Hi Nursing Home Inc
4686 E Asbury Circle, Denver, CO, 80222 (303)
756-1566
Admin Caroline J Stewart. *Medical Dir/Dir of
Nursing* Francis Burdick MD.
Licensure Skilled Care. *Beds* 100. *Certified* Medicaid; Medicare.
Ownership Proprietary.
Admissions Requirements Minimum age 50.
Staff RNs 9 (ft), 4 (pt); LPNs 2 (ft), 2 (pt);

Reality therapists 2 (ft); Recreational therapists 2 (ft); Occupational therapists 2 (ft); Activities coordinators 1 (ft); Dietitians 1 (ft); Dentists 1 (pt); Ophthalmologists 1 (pt); Podiatrists 1 (pt); Audiologists 1 (pt).
Facilities Dining room; Activities room; Crafts room; Laundry room; Barber/Beauty shop.
Activities Arts and Crafts; Cards; Games; Reading groups; Movies; Shopping trips; Dances/Social or cultural gatherings.

Valley Manor Nursing Home
4601 E Asbury Circle, Denver, CO, 80222 (303) 757-1228
Admin Caroline Williams. *Medical Dir/Dir of Nursing* Francis Burdick MD.
Licensure Skilled Care; Intermediate Care.
Beds SNF 45; ICF 39. *Certified* Medicaid; Medicare.
Ownership Proprietary.
Admissions Requirements Minimum age 55; Physician's request.
Staff Physicians 32 (pt); RNs 5 (ft), 5 (pt); LPNs 2 (ft), 2 (pt); Orderlies 3 (ft); Nurses aides 18 (ft), 3 (pt); Physical therapists 1 (pt); Recreational therapists 1 (ft); Occupational therapists; Speech therapists; Activities coordinators 1 (ft); Dietitians; Dentists; Ophthalmologists; Podiatrists; Audiologists.
Facilities Dining room; Activities room; Crafts room; Laundry room; Barber/Beauty shop; Library.
Activities Arts and Crafts; Cards; Games; Reading groups; Prayer groups; Movies; Shopping trips; Dances/Social or cultural gatherings; Bus trips; Picnics; Fishing trips; Circus outings; Chamber music concerts.
Description Valley is a one-floor facility surrounded by well-kept grounds and patio space. Small size enables the provision of personalized care in a home-like atmosphere. Staff knowledge and training promotes optimal geriatric medical services as well.

Williams Family Care Home
3245 W 23rd Ave, Denver, CO, 80211 (303) 477-6939
Admin Dorothy Williams.
Licensure Intermediate Care. *Beds* 4.
Ownership Proprietary.

Yellow House*
3445 W Mansfield, Denver, CO, 80236 (303) 789-2463
Admin Sally Neuville.
Licensure Developmentally Disabled.
Beds 17.
Ownership Proprietary.

DURANGO

Browning House*
205 W Park Ave, Durango, CO, 81301 (303) 259-2887
Admin Richard F Sheridan.
Licensure Intermediate Care for Mentally Retarded. *Beds* 8.
Ownership Nonprofit.

Four Corners Health Care Center*
2911 Junction St, Durango, CO, 81301 (303) 247-2215

Admin Lillian Marlau.
Licensure Skilled Care; Intermediate Care.
Beds SNF 60; ICF 58. *Certified* Medicaid.
Ownership Proprietary.

EADS

Weisbrod Memorial County Hospital and Nursing Home
1208 Luther St, Eads, CO, 81036 (303) 438-5401
Admin Andrew Wills. *Medical Dir/Dir of Nursing* Michael Fuhrman DO.
Licensure Intermediate Care. *Beds* 24. *Certified* Medicaid; Medicare.
Ownership Public.
Staff Physicians 2 (pt); RNs 6 (ft), 2 (pt); LPNs 3 (ft), 2 (pt); Nurses aides 6 (ft), 7 (pt); Activities coordinators 1 (ft); Dentists 1 (pt).
Facilities Dining room; Activities room; Crafts room.
Activities Arts and Crafts; Cards; Games; Prayer groups; Movies; Shopping trips; Dances/Social or cultural gatherings.
Description Activities include picnics, barbecues, Adopt-a-grandparent program, entertainments and mingling of senior citizens and 4-H clubs, dinners and meeting with family support group, and very special formal parties for Thanksgiving and Christmas.

EDGEWATER

JTN Nursing Care Facility
5361 W 26th Ave, Edgewater, CO, 80214 (303) 233-6533
Admin Gerald Smith.
Licensure Skilled Care. *Beds* 42. *Certified* Medicaid; Medicare.
Ownership Proprietary.

ELDORADO SPRINGS

Chester House*
3786 Eldorado Springs Drive, Eldorado Springs, CO, 80025 (303) 444-0573
Admin John Kelley.
Licensure Residential MR Care. *Beds* 8. *Certified* Medicaid.
Ownership Proprietary.

ENGLEWOOD

Cherry Hills Nursing Home
3575 S Washington St, Englewood, CO, 80110 (303) 789-2265
Admin Forrest L Douthit. *Medical Dir/Dir of Nursing* Dr Angela Heaton.
Licensure Skilled Care; Intermediate Care.
Beds SNF 89; ICF 6. *Certified* Medicaid; Medicare.
Ownership Proprietary.
Admissions Requirements Medical examination; Physician's request.
Staff RNs 5 (ft), 4 (pt); LPNs 3 (ft), 4 (pt); Orderlies 2 (ft); Nurses aides 38 (ft), 10 (pt); Physical therapists 1 (pt); Recreational therapists 1 (pt); Occupational therapists 1 (pt); Speech therapists 1 (pt); Activities coordinators 1 (ft); Dietitians 1 (ft); Dentists 1 (pt); Podiatrists

1 (pt).
Facilities Dining room; Physical therapy room; Activities room; Laundry room; Barber/Beauty shop; Library.
Activities Arts and Crafts; Cards; Games; Reading groups; Prayer groups; Movies; Shopping trips; Dances/Social or cultural gatherings.

Cherry Park Health Care Facility*
3636 S Pearl St, Englewood, CO, 80110 (303) 761-1640
Admin Joanne Freemen.
Licensure Skilled Care; Intermediate Care.
Beds SNF 52; ICF 44. *Certified* Medicaid.
Ownership Proprietary.

Englewood House*
3198 S Delaware, Englewood, CO, 80110 (303) 696-7002
Admin John Meeker.
Licensure Developmentally Disabled. *Beds* 8.
Ownership Nonprofit.

Julia Temple Center*
3401 S Lafayette St, Englewood, CO, 80110 (303) 761-0075
Admin Marcia Pilgrim.
Licensure Skilled Care; Intermediate Care.
Beds SNF 59; ICF 77. *Certified* Medicaid.
Ownership Proprietary.

ERIE

Bland Residential Care Home
RR 1 Box 5050, Erie, CO, 80516 (303) 447-9196
Admin Marie Bland.
Licensure Intermediate Care. *Beds* 6.
Ownership Proprietary.

ESTES PARK

Bide-A-Wee
411 Stanley Ave, Estes Park, CO, 80571 (303) 586-4650
Admin Patricia Swainston.
Licensure Intermediate Care. *Beds* 8.
Ownership Proprietary.

FAIRPLAY

McNamara Mercy Hospital and Nursing Home*
525 Costello, Fairplay, CO, 80440 (303) 836-2701
Admin William D Phipps.
Licensure Skilled Care. *Beds* 14. *Certified* Medicaid; Medicare.
Ownership Public.

FLORENCE

Colorado State Veterans Nursing Home
Moore Dr, Florence, CO, 81226 (303) 784-6331
Admin Marie R Baughman. *Medical Dir/Dir of Nursing* Dr John Buglewicz.
Licensure Skilled Care. *Beds* 120. *Certified* Medicaid.
Ownership Public.
Admissions Requirements Medical examina-

tion; Physician's request.
Staff RNs 10 (ft); LPNs 8 (ft); Orderlies 4 (ft); Nurses aides 29 (ft); Activities coordinators 1 (ft).
Facilities Dining room; Physical therapy room; Activities room; Chapel; Crafts room; Laundry room; Barber/Beauty shop.
Activities Arts and Crafts; Cards; Games; Reading groups; Prayer groups; Movies; Shopping trips; Dances/Social or cultural gatherings; Pet therapy; Music therapy.
Description Facility has special half doors, fenced yard, and music therapy for Alzheimer's patients.

Saint Joseph Manor
3rd and Washington Ave, Florence, CO, 81226 (303) 784-6361
Admin John H Vowell Jr. *Medical Dir/Dir of Nursing* Peter J Gamache MD.
Licensure Skilled Care. *Beds* 39. *Certified* Medicaid.
Ownership Nonprofit.
Admissions Requirements Minimum age 50; Medical examination; Physician's request.
Staff Physicians 3 (pt); RNs 1 (ft), 2 (pt); LPNs 3 (ft), 5 (pt); Nurses aides 7 (ft), 11 (pt); Physical therapists 1 (pt); Reality therapists 1 (pt); Recreational therapists 1 (pt); Occupational therapists 1 (pt); Activities coordinators 1 (ft); Dietitians 1 (pt); Dentists 1 (pt); Ophthalmologists 1 (pt).
Affiliation Roman Catholic
Facilities Dining room; Activities room; Chapel; Crafts room; Laundry room; Barber/Beauty shop.
Activities Arts and Crafts; Cards; Games; Reading groups; Prayer groups; Movies; Shopping trips; Dances/Social or cultural gatherings.

FORT COLLINS

Columbine Care Center*
421 Parker St, Fort Collins, CO, 80525 (303) 482-1584
Admin Jean Niedringhaus.
Licensure Skilled Care; Intermediate Care; Residential Care. *Beds* SNF 65; ICF 55; Residential Care 5. *Certified* Medicaid; Medicare.
Ownership Proprietary.

Evans House*
730 Matthew, Fort Collins, CO, 80521 (303) 482-5035
Admin Pat Norton and Mae Wise.
Licensure Residential MR Care. *Beds* 8. *Certified* Medicaid.
Ownership Proprietary.

Eventide—South
1000 Stuart St, Fort Collins, CO, 80521 (303) 482-5712
Admin Dennis Karnowski. *Medical Dir/Dir of Nursing* David K Allen MD.
Licensure Skilled Care; Intermediate Care; Residential Care. *Beds* SNF 120; ICF 60; Residential Care 50. *Certified* Medicaid; Medicare.
Ownership Proprietary.
Admissions Requirements Minimum age 6 months; Medical examination; Physician's request.
Staff Physicians 30 (pt); RNs 8 (ft), 6 (pt);

LPNs 15 (ft), 5 (pt); Orderlies 2 (ft); Nurses aides 40 (ft), 10 (pt); Physical therapists 1 (pt); Reality therapists 1 (ft); Recreational therapists 1 (ft); Occupational therapists 1 (pt); Speech therapists 1 (pt); Activities coordinators 1 (ft); Dietitians 1 (pt); Dentists 1 (pt); Ophthalmologists 1 (pt); Podiatrists 1 (pt); Audiologists 1 (pt).
Facilities Dining room; Physical therapy room; Activities room; Crafts room; Laundry room; Barber/Beauty shop; Library.
Activities Arts and Crafts; Cards; Games; Reading groups; Prayer groups; Movies; Shopping trips; Dances/Social or cultural gatherings.
Description Facility has expansive landscaping and patio areas; geriatric nurse practitioner on staff.

Fort Collins Good Samaritan Retirement Village
508 County Rd 34, Fort Collins, CO, 80525 (303) 226-4909
Admin Eugene N Fox. *Medical Dir/Dir of Nursing* Dr Joseph Lopez.
Licensure Skilled Care. *Beds* 55. *Certified* Medicaid; Medicare.
Ownership Nonprofit.
Admissions Requirements Minimum age 55; Medical examination.
Affiliation Lutheran
Facilities Dining room; Physical therapy room; Activities room; Chapel; Crafts room; Barber/Beauty shop; Library.
Activities Arts and Crafts; Cards; Games; Reading groups; Movies; Shopping trips; Dances/Social or cultural gatherings; Daily devotions; Weekly Bible study.
Description Fort Collins Good Samaritan is ideally situated in the country with a beautiful view of the mountains from several rooms in the facility and provides a full range of activities, emergency services, and free transportation service into Fort Collins for both apartment and nursing residents.

Fort Collins Health Care Center
1000 Lemay Ave, Fort Collins, CO, 80524 (303) 482-7925
Admin Stephen Miles. *Medical Dir/Dir of Nursing* Dr Harold Dupper.
Licensure Skilled Care; Intermediate Care. *Beds* SNF 50; ICF 50. *Certified* Medicaid; Medicare.
Ownership Proprietary.
Admissions Requirements Physician's request.
Staff RNs 2 (ft), 5 (pt); LPNs 2 (ft), 5 (pt); Orderlies 1 (ft), 2 (pt); Nurses aides 8 (ft), 27 (pt); Activities coordinators 1 (pt).
Facilities Dining room; Physical therapy room; Activities room; Crafts room; Laundry room; Barber/Beauty shop.
Activities Arts and Crafts; Games; Movies; Shopping trips; Dances/Social or cultural gatherings.
Description Recently remodeled facility has a warm atmosphere; located close to hospital.

Golden West Nursing Home Inc
1005 E Elizabeth St, Fort Collins, CO, 80521 (303) 482-2525
Admin Scott Nelson. *Medical Dir/Dir of Nursing* Dr William Abbey.
Licensure Intermediate Care; Residential Care.

Beds ICF 50; Residential Care 10.
Ownership Proprietary.
Admissions Requirements Physician's request.
Staff RNs 3 (pt); LPNs 2 (ft), 4 (pt); Nurses aides 5 (ft), 11 (pt); Activities coordinators 1 (ft); Dietitians 1 (pt).
Facilities Dining room; Activities room; Laundry room; Barber/Beauty shop; Library.
Activities Arts and Crafts; Cards; Games; Reading groups; Prayer groups; Movies; Shopping trips.
Description Facility is located 2 blocks away from hospital; all private pay; professional nurses staffed 24 hours around the clock; offer free blood pressure tests for senior citizens every Friday.

Mountain Duplex*
822 W Mountain, Fort Collins, CO, 80524 (303) 484-1609
Admin Mae Wise.
Licensure Residential MR Care. *Beds* 8.
Ownership Proprietary.

Pioneer Home*
811 E Myrtle St, Fort Collins, CO, 80521 (303) 482-5035
Admin J Klein.
Licensure Intermediate Care for Mentally Retarded. *Beds* 34. *Certified* Medicaid.
Ownership Proprietary.

Remington Street House*
418 Remington, Fort Collins, CO, 80524 (303) 493-5374
Admin Patricia Norton.
Licensure Residential MR Care. *Beds* 8.
Ownership Proprietary.

Riverside/Four Seasons Health Care Center
1020 Patton St, Fort Collins, CO, 80521 (303) 484-6133
Admin Philip J Grimm. *Medical Dir/Dir of Nursing* Steven Tippen MD.
Licensure Skilled Care. *Beds* 106. *Certified* Medicaid.
Ownership Proprietary.
Staff RNs 6 (ft), 1 (pt); LPNs 7 (ft), 2 (pt); Nurses aides 24 (ft), 2 (pt); Activities coordinators 1 (ft); Dietitians 1 (ft).
Facilities Dining room; Activities room; Crafts room; Laundry room; Barber/Beauty shop; Library; Private courtyard; Solar greenhouse.
Activities Arts and Crafts; Cards; Games; Reading groups; Prayer groups; Movies; Shopping trips; Dances/Social or cultural gatherings; Men's group; Exercise group; Reality orientation group.
Description Facility is located just 2 blocks from local physicians' offices and the Fort Collins Community Hospital in a quiet residential setting; Four Season's moss rock exterior, large entrance patio, and private courtyard enhances clients surroundings and comfort. Four Seasons is a new member of ARA Living Centers and joins 3 other ARA living centers in the Larimer County, Colorado, community.

Smith House*
722 Smith, Fort Collins, CO, 80521 (303) 484-6133
Admin Patricia Norton.
Licensure Residential MR Care. *Beds* 8. *Certi-

fied Medicaid.

FORT MORGAN

Gayle Street Residential Center*
425 Gayle St, Fort Morgan, CO, 80701 (303) 867-5365
Admin William E Duffield.
Licensure Developmentally Disabled. *Beds* 9.
Ownership Nonprofit.

Valley View Villa Nursing Home*
815 Fremont, Fort Morgan, CO, 80701 (303) 867-8261
Admin Fred Nuss.
Licensure Skilled Care. *Beds* 120. *Certified* Medicaid.
Ownership Proprietary.

FOWLER

Fowler Health Care Center*
2nd and Florence St, Fowler, CO, 81039 (303) 263-4234
Admin Fred Stapleton.
Licensure Intermediate Care. *Beds* 47. *Certified* Medicaid.
Ownership Proprietary.

FRUITA

Lower Valley Hospital and Nursing Home
228 N Cherry St, Fruita, CO, 81521 (303) 858-9871
Admin Carroll Rushold. *Medical Dir/Dir of Nursing* E R Orr MD.
Licensure Skilled Care; Intermediate Care.
Beds SNF 45; ICF 45. *Certified* Medicaid; Medicare.
Ownership Nonprofit.
Admissions Requirements Physician's request.
Staff Physicians 8 (ft); RNs 12 (ft); LPNs 10 (ft); Orderlies 4 (ft); Nurses aides 50 (ft); Physical therapists 1 (ft); Reality therapists 1 (ft); Recreational therapists 1 (ft); Occupational therapists 1 (ft); Speech therapists 1 (pt); Activities coordinators 1 (ft); Dietitians 2 (ft); Dentists 1 (ft); Ophthalmologists 1 (ft); Podiatrists 1 (ft); Audiologists 1 (ft).
Facilities Dining room; Physical therapy room; Activities room; Crafts room; Laundry room; Barber/Beauty shop.
Activities Arts and Crafts; Cards; Games; Reading groups; Prayer groups; Movies; Shopping trips; Dances/Social or cultural gatherings.
Description Nursing home is connected to a general medical surgical hospital offering a complete range of hospital services. Also available are 75 units of low-income housing for the elderly and handicapped which are owned by the Lower Valley Hospital Association.

GLENWOOD SPRINGS

Glen Valley Nursing Home*
PO Box 1179, 2305 Blake Ave, Glenwood Springs, CO, 81601 (303) 945-5476
Admin Alice Applegate Letang.
Licensure Intermediate Care. *Beds* 60.

Certified Medicaid.
Ownership Proprietary.

GRAND JUNCTION

Bethesda Care Center*
2825 Patterson Rd, Grand Junction, CO, 81501 (303) 242-7356
Admin Paul M Whisler.
Licensure Intermediate Care. *Beds* 60. *Certified* Medicaid.
Ownership Nonprofit.

Beverly Manor of Grand Junction
2425 Teller Ave, Grand Junction, CO, 81501 (303) 243-3381
Admin Keith L Hieb. *Medical Dir/Dir of Nursing* James Ross MD.
Licensure Skilled Care. *Beds* 120. *Certified* Medicaid; Medicare.
Ownership Proprietary.
Staff Physicians 20 (pt); RNs 10 (ft), 5 (pt); LPNs 5 (ft), 4 (pt); Orderlies 4 (ft); Nurses aides 40 (ft), 5 (pt); Physical therapists 1 (pt); Reality therapists 1 (pt); Recreational therapists 1 (pt); Occupational therapists 1 (pt); Speech therapists 1 (pt); Activities coordinators 1 (ft); Dietitians 1 (pt); Dentists 1 (pt); Podiatrists 1 (pt).
Facilities Dining room; Physical therapy room; Activities room; Laundry room; Barber/Beauty shop.
Activities Arts and Crafts; Cards; Games; Reading groups; Prayer groups; Movies; Shopping trips; Dances/Social or cultural gatherings.
Description Newly renovated facility committed to quality of care.

Casa Primera
1051 Rood Ave, State Home and Training School Box 2568, Grand Junction, CO, 81501 (303) 243-2304
Admin Fred Burmeister.
Licensure Intermediate Care for Mentally Retarded. *Beds* 9.
Ownership Public.

Grand Junction Regional Center*
2800 D Rd, Grand Junction, CO, 81501 (303) 245-2100
Admin William H Jackson.
Licensure Intermediate Care for Mentally Retarded. *Beds* 370. *Certified* Medicaid.
Ownership Public.

Hilltop Rehabilitation Center*
1100 Patterson Rd, Grand Junction, CO, 81501 (303) 242-8980
Admin Ronald W Cronk.
Licensure Skilled Care. *Beds* 58. *Certified* Medicare.
Ownership Nonprofit.

Lavilla Grande Care Center
2501 Little Bookcliffe Dr, Grand Junction, CO, 81501 (303) 245-1211
Admin Terry and Betty Stephenson. *Medical Dir/Dir of Nursing* Dr Douglas C Shenk.
Licensure Skilled Care. *Beds* 119. *Certified* Medicaid.
Ownership Nonprofit.
Admissions Requirements Medical examination.

Staff RNs 6 (ft), 3 (pt); LPNs 5 (ft), 2 (pt); Nurses aides 26 (ft), 12 (pt); Physical therapists 1 (ft); Activities coordinators 1 (ft).
Facilities Dining room; Physical therapy room; Activities room; Chapel; Crafts room; Barber/Beauty shop; Kitchen.
Activities Arts and Crafts; Cards; Games; Reading groups; Prayer groups; Movies; Shopping trips; Dances/Social or cultural gatherings; Pet therapy.

Mesa Manor Nursing Center*
2901 N 12th St, Grand Junction, CO, 81501 (303) 243-7211
Admin Eugene H Knight.
Licensure Skilled Care. *Beds* 108. *Certified* Medicaid; Medicare.
Ownership Proprietary.

GREELEY

Bonell Good Samaritan Center*
708 22nd St, Greeley, CO, 80631 (303) 352-6082
Admin Mark Turk.
Licensure Skilled Care; Intermediate Care.
Beds SNF 173; ICF 106. *Certified* Medicaid; Medicare.
Ownership Nonprofit.

Centennial Health Care Center*
1637 29th Ave Pl, Greeley, CO, 80631 (303) 356-8181
Admin Russell Lancaster.
Licensure Skilled Care; Intermediate Care.
Beds SNF 60; ICF 60. *Certified* Medicaid.
Ownership Proprietary.

Fairacres Manor Inc*
1700 18th Ave, Greeley, CO, 80631 (303) 353-3370
Admin Lavern Weber.
Licensure Skilled Care. *Beds* 116. *Certified* Medicaid.
Ownership Proprietary.

Kenton Manor*
850 27th Ave, Greeley, CO, 80631 (303) 353-1018
Admin Gary Robertson.
Licensure Skilled Care; Intermediate Care.
Beds SNF 60; ICF 60. *Certified* Medicaid.
Ownership Proprietary.

New Life Center
1819 Birch Ave, Greeley, CO, 80631 (303) 353-0535
Admin Pauline Bonner.
Licensure Intermediate Care for Mentally Retarded. *Beds* 56. *Certified* Medicaid; Medicare.
Ownership Proprietary.
Staff Physicians 5 (ft); RNs 3 (ft); LPNs 4 (pt); Nurses aides 16 (ft); Recreational therapists 4 (ft); Occupational therapists 1 (ft); Activities coordinators 1 (ft); Dietitians 1 (ft); Dentists 3 (ft); Ophthalmologists 1 (pt); Podiatrists 1 (ft); Audiologists 2 (pt).
Facilities Dining room; Activities room; Laundry room; 2 Vans.
Activities Arts and Crafts; Cards; Games; Reading groups; Prayer groups; Movies; Shop-

ping trips; Dances/Social or cultural gatherings; Olympics; Ball games; College for Living.
Description Monday through Friday, the residents are involved in day programing outside the facility. At New Life Center, residents are on programs to enhance their self-help, social skills, and domestic skills. Various in and out-of-house activities are provided. New Life Center has 2 vans to provide transportation.

Wareheime Residential Care*
1429 12th Ave, Greeley, CO, 80631 (303) 352-2949
Admin Zella Mae Wareheime.
Licensure Intermediate Care for Mentally Retarded. *Beds* 8.
Ownership Proprietary.

Weld County Community Center Group Home*
1618 11th Ave, Greeley, CO, 80631 (303) 339-5360
Admin John H Wooster.
Licensure Intermediate Care for Mentally Retarded. *Beds* 6.
Ownership Nonprofit.

GUNNISON

Gunnison Nursing Home
1500 W Tomichi Ave, Gunnison, CO, 81230 (303) 641-0704
Admin Clair Krehbiel. *Medical Dir/Dir of Nursing* Dr Ron Meyer.
Licensure Skilled Care; Intermediate Care.
Beds SNF 8; ICF 40. *Certified* Medicaid; Medicare.
Ownership Nonprofit.
Admissions Requirements Medical examination; Physician's request.
Staff RNs 4 (ft), 3 (pt); LPNs 1 (ft), 2 (pt); Nurses aides 6 (ft), 18 (pt); Recreational therapists 1 (ft); Activities coordinators 1 (ft).
Facilities Dining room; Physical therapy room; Activities room; Crafts room; Barber/Beauty shop.
Activities Arts and Crafts; Cards; Games; Reading groups; Prayer groups; Movies; Shopping trips; Dances/Social or cultural gatherings.
Description We spotlight home-cooked meals (all prepared from scratch), ala-carte breakfast, a wholesome living environment, and loving personal care by all staff.

HAXTUN

Haxtun Hospital District
253 W Fletcher St, PO Box 308, Haxtun, CO, 80731 (303) 774-6123
Admin Doug McMillan. *Medical Dir/Dir of Nursing* Dr James Ley.
Licensure Intermediate Care. *Beds* 16. *Certified* Medicaid; Medicare.
Ownership Proprietary.
Facilities Dining room; Chapel; Laundry room.
Activities Arts and Crafts; Cards; Games; Reading groups; Prayer groups; Shopping trips.

HOLLY

Holly Nursing Care Center
320 N 8th, Holly, CO, 81407 (303) 537-6555
Admin Mary C Arthur. *Medical Dir/Dir of Nursing* R G Ward DO.
Licensure Intermediate Care. *Beds* 60. *Certified* Medicaid.
Ownership Proprietary.

HOLYOKE

Prairie Vista Care Center
816 S Interocean Ave, Holyoke, CO, 80734 (303) 854-2251
Medical Dir/Dir of Nursing Dr Myrlen Chesnut.
Licensure Intermediate Care. *Beds* 55. *Certified* Medicaid; Medicare.
Ownership Proprietary.
Admissions Requirements Minimum age 55; Medical examination; Physician's request.
Staff RNs 1 (pt); LPNs 5 (ft), 1 (pt); Nurses aides 18 (ft), 3 (pt); Physical therapists 1 (pt); Occupational therapists; Speech therapists; Activities coordinators 1 (ft), 1 (pt); Dietitians; Dentists.
Facilities Dining room; Physical therapy room; Activities room; Crafts room; Laundry room; Barber/Beauty shop.
Activities Arts and Crafts; Games; Reading groups; Prayer groups; Movies; Shopping trips; Dances/Social or cultural gatherings.
Description Facility is in a rural area offering daily activities with at least 20 volunteers that bring community awareness and excitement to residents. Environment is home-like; staff specializes in "spoiling" residents.

HOMELAKE

Colorado State Veterans Center*
Box 20, 3749 Sherman Ave, Homelake, CO, 81135 (303) 852-3591
Admin Ambrose Rodriguez.
Licensure Intermediate Care. *Beds* 33. *Certified* Medicaid.
Ownership Public.

HUGO

Lincoln Community Hospital and Nursing Home
PO Box 248, Hugo, CO, 80821 (303) 743-2421
Admin Delores Nance. *Medical Dir/Dir of Nursing* Thomas Jeffers.
Licensure Skilled Care. *Beds* 35. *Certified* Medicaid; Medicare.
Ownership Public.
Admissions Requirements Medical examination; Physician's request.
Staff Physicians 3 (ft); RNs 5 (ft), 5 (pt); LPNs 5 (ft); Orderlies 1 (ft); Nurses aides 16 (ft), 4 (pt); Activities coordinators 1 (ft).
Facilities Activities room; Laundry room.
Activities Arts and Crafts; Cards; Games; Reading groups; Prayer groups; Movies; Shopping trips; Dances/Social or cultural gatherings.

JULESBURG

Al Mar Residence*
823 W 9th St, Julesburg, CO, 80737 (303) 522-7121
Admin William Duffield.
Beds 8. *Certified* Medicare.
Ownership Nonprofit.

Sedgwick County Hospital and Nursing Home
900 Cedar St, Julesburg, CO, 80737 (303) 474-3323
Admin Merlin Aalborg. *Medical Dir/Dir of Nursing* Kevin Shafer OD.
Licensure Intermediate Care. *Beds* 32. *Certified* Medicaid.
Ownership Public.
Admissions Requirements Medical examination; Physician's request.
Staff RNs 1 (ft); LPNs 6 (ft); Orderlies 1 (ft); Nurses aides 3 (ft), 11 (pt); Physical therapists 1 (pt); Recreational therapists 1 (pt); Activities coordinators 1 (pt); Dietitians 1 (pt); Podiatrists 1 (pt).
Facilities Dining room; Physical therapy room; Chapel; Crafts room; Laundry room; Barber/Beauty shop; Library.
Activities Arts and Crafts; Cards; Games; Shopping trips.

LA JUNTA

Adult Care Services
514 W 10th, La Junta, CO, 81050 (303) 384-5412
Admin Dana Froelich. *Medical Dir/Dir of Nursing* Dr C C Weber.
Licensure Skilled Care; Intermediate Care.
Beds 150.
Ownership Nonprofit.
Admissions Requirements Minimum age 15; Physician's request.
Staff Physicians 1 (pt); RNs 6 (ft); LPNs 12 (ft), 1 (pt); Orderlies 1 (pt); Nurses aides 34 (ft); Activities coordinators 3 (ft); Dietitians 1 (ft).
Affiliation Mennonite
Facilities Dining room; Physical therapy room; Activities room; Chapel; Crafts room; Laundry room; Barber/Beauty shop.
Activities Arts and Crafts; Cards; Games; Reading groups; Prayer groups; Movies; Dances/Social or cultural gatherings.

Lovato Residential Care Facility*
302 Carson, La Junta, CO, 81050 (303) 384-7687
Admin Josie Lovato.
Licensure Intermediate Care. *Beds* 10.
Ownership Proprietary.

Matthews Care Home*
821 San Juan, La Junta, CO, 81050 (303) 384-2246
Admin Orley W Matthews.
Licensure Intermediate Care. *Beds* 10.
Ownership Proprietary.

Southeastern Colorado Family Guidance and Mental Health Center Inc
1200 Carson PO Box 678, La Junta, CO, 81050 (303) 384-5446
Admin Billy C Chastain.

Licensure Intermediate Care. *Beds* 11.
Ownership Nonprofit.

LAKEWOOD

Allison Nursing Care Center*
1660 Allison St, Lakewood, CO, 80215 (303) 232-7177
Admin Juanita Stevens.
Licensure Skilled Care; Intermediate Care.
Beds SNF 60; ICF 60. *Certified* Medicaid.
Ownership Proprietary.

Applewood Hills Care Centre Inc
1625 Simms St, Lakewood, CO, 80215 (303) 238-8161
Admin Geraldine J Loomis. *Medical Dir/Dir of Nursing* Jitze DeJong MD.
Licensure Skilled Care. *Beds* 60. *Certified* Medicaid; Medicare.
Ownership Proprietary.
Staff RNs 5 (ft), 2 (pt); LPNs 2 (ft), 2 (pt); Orderlies 2 (ft), 1 (pt); Nurses aides 12 (ft), 5 (pt); Recreational therapists 1 (ft); Occupational therapists 1 (ft).
Facilities Dining room; Activities room; Laundry room; Barber/Beauty shop.
Activities Arts and Crafts; Cards; Games; Reading groups; Prayer groups; Movies; Shopping trips; Dances/Social or cultural gatherings; Exercises.
Description Facility specializes in Alzheimer's and confused residents.

Bethany Care Center*
5301 W 1st Ave, Lakewood, CO, 80226 (303) 238-8333
Admin Dale R Turner.
Licensure Skilled Care; Intermediate Care.
Beds SNF 120; ICF 100. *Certified* Medicaid.
Ownership Nonprofit.

Briarwood Way
11503 S Briarway Dr, Lakewood, CO, 80226 (303) 988-7776
Admin Christine McHugh.
Licensure Intermediate Care for Mentally Retarded. *Beds* 6.
Ownership Proprietary.
Admissions Requirements Minimum age 21; Females only; Medical examination; Physician's request.
Facilities Dining room; Activities room; Crafts room; Laundry room.
Activities Cards; Games; Reading groups; Shopping trips; Dances/Social or cultural gatherings.

Cedars Health Center
1599 Ingalls, Lakewood, CO, 80216 (303) 232-3551
Admin Elaine Mack. *Medical Dir/Dir of Nursing* Francis Burdick MD.
Licensure Skilled Care; Intermediate Care.
Beds SNF 120; ICF 60. *Certified* Medicaid; Medicare.
Ownership Proprietary.
Admissions Requirements Minimum age 55; Medical examination; Physician's request.
Facilities Dining room; Physical therapy room; Activities room; Chapel; Crafts room; Laundry room; Barber/Beauty shop; Library.

Activities Arts and Crafts; Cards; Games; Reading groups; Prayer groups; Movies; Shopping trips; Dances/Social or cultural gatherings; Bus trips; Camping.
Description Facility has private and semi-private rooms; in-house therapy team; pet therapy available; facility caters to the geriatric patient both for long term placement and short term restorative placement.

Charm Acres Health Care Center Inc*
1650 Allison St, Lakewood, CO, 80215 (303) 238-1275
Admin Sally Jones.
Licensure Skilled Care; Intermediate Care.
Beds SNF 143; ICF 37. *Certified* Medicaid.
Ownership Proprietary.

Desserich House*
9150 Morrison Rd, Lakewood, CO, 80227 (303) 985-7310
Admin Richard Mason.
Licensure Developmentally Disabled. *Beds* 7.
Ownership Nonprofit.

Everett Court Community
1325 Everett Ct, Lakewood, CO, 80215 (303) 238-0501
Admin Melanie Tem.
Licensure Intermediate Care. *Beds* 74. *Certified* Medicaid.
Ownership Proprietary.

Garden Manor Nursing Home Inc
115 Ingalls St, Lakewood, CO, 80226 (303) 237-1325
Admin Jennifer Golden. *Medical Dir/Dir of Nursing* Dr David Zimmerman.
Licensure Skilled Care; Intermediate Care.
Beds SNF 60; ICF 60. *Certified* Medicaid; Medicare.
Ownership Proprietary.
Admissions Requirements Minimum age 65; Medical examination; Physician's request.
Staff RNs 5 (ft); LPNs 3 (ft); Orderlies 4 (ft); Nurses aides 15 (ft), 8 (pt); Physical therapists 1 (pt); Reality therapists 2 (pt); Occupational therapists 1 (pt); Dietitians 1 (pt); Dentists 1 (pt); Podiatrists 1 (pt).
Facilities Dining room; Physical therapy room; Activities room; Chapel; Crafts room; Barber/Beauty shop.
Activities Arts and Crafts; Cards; Games; Reading groups; Prayer groups; Movies; Shopping trips; Dances/Social or cultural gatherings; Current events; Resident council; Remotivation cart; Reality orientation.
Description Dynamic staff geared to helping resident obtain his/her optimum level of functioning even after discharging to residential setting when condition improves. VA approved.

Glen Ayr Health Center*
1655 Eaton St, Lakewood, CO, 80214 (303) 238-5363
Admin David C Quinlivan.
Licensure Skilled Care; Intermediate Care.
Beds SNF 59; ICF 60. *Certified* Medicaid; Medicare.
Ownership Proprietary.

Grand Place*
10365 W Grand Pl, Lakewood, CO, 80123 (303) 978-0951
Admin Richard Mason.
Licensure Residential MR Care. *Beds* 7. *Certified* Medicaid.
Ownership Nonprofit.

Jewell House*
8640 W Jewell Ave, Lakewood, CO, 80226 (303) 424-2713
Admin Richard Mason.
Licensure Residential MR Care. *Beds* 8. *Certified* Medicaid.
Ownership Nonprofit.

Lakewood Nursing Home
1432 Depew St, Lakewood, CO, 80215 (303) 238-1376
Admin Riva Weissbrot. *Medical Dir/Dir of Nursing* Dr Leonard Levisohn.
Licensure Skilled Care; Intermediate Care.
Beds 153. *Certified* Medicaid.
Ownership Proprietary.
Staff RNs 11 (ft); LPNs 7 (ft), 1 (pt); Nurses aides 45 (ft); Physical therapists 1 (pt); Speech therapists 1 (pt); Activities coordinators 1 (ft), 1 (pt); Dietitians 1 (pt); Dentists 1 (pt); Podiatrists 1 (pt).
Facilities Dining room; Physical therapy room; Activities room; Laundry room; Barber/Beauty shop.
Activities Arts and Crafts; Cards; Games; Reading groups; Prayer groups; Movies; Shopping trips; Dances/Social or cultural gatherings.

Leisure Chateau
1685 Eaton St, Lakewood, CO, 80215 (303) 232-4405
Admin Anne E Chapman. *Medical Dir/Dir of Nursing* Werner Prenzlau MD.
Licensure Skilled Care; Intermediate Care.
Beds SNF 60; ICF 85. *Certified* Medicaid; Medicare.
Ownership Proprietary.
Admissions Requirements Minimum age 21.
Staff RNs; LPNs; Orderlies; Nurses aides; Physical therapists; Recreational therapists; Speech therapists; Activities coordinators; Dietitians; Dentists; Podiatrists.
Facilities Dining room; Physical therapy room; Activities room; Crafts room; Laundry room; Barber/Beauty shop; Library.
Activities Arts and Crafts; Cards; Games; Reading groups; Prayer groups; Movies; Shopping trips; Dances/Social or cultural gatherings.
Description This facility offers clean environment, well-decorated spacious rooms, delicious meals (kosher upon request), and a professional staff.

Nina Van Sant Residential Care Facility*
639 Elm, Lakewood, CO, 81054 (303) 456-0527
Admin Nina Van Sant.
Licensure Intermediate Care. *Beds* 6.
Ownership Proprietary.

Parkside House*
8355 W 19th Ave, Lakewood, CO, 80215 (303) 238-5447
Admin Richard Mason.

Licensure Intermediate Care for Mentally Retarded. *Beds* 7.
Ownership Nonprofit.

Villa Manor Nursing Home*
7950 W Mississippi Ave, Lakewood, CO, 80226 (303) 986-4511
Admin Jerry Weeter.
Licensure Skilled Care; Intermediate Care.
Beds SNF 120; ICF 120. *Certified* Medicaid; Medicare.
Ownership Proprietary.

Western Hills Nursing Home*
1625 Carr St, Lakewood, CO, 80215 (303) 238-6881
Admin Susan Harrington.
Licensure Skilled Care; Intermediate Care.
Beds SNF 118; ICF 60. *Certified* Medicaid; Medicare.
Ownership Proprietary.

Westland Manor Nursing Center
1150 Oak St, Lakewood, CO, 80215 (303) 238-7505
Admin Mavis C Heary. *Medical Dir/Dir of Nursing* Robert Starr.
Licensure Skilled Care; Intermediate Care.
Beds SNF 53; ICF 95. *Certified* Medicaid; Medicare.
Ownership Proprietary.
Facilities Dining room; Activities room; Laundry room; Barber/Beauty shop.
Activities Arts and Crafts; Cards; Games; Prayer groups; Movies; Shopping trips; Dances/Social or cultural gatherings.

LAMAR

Sandhaven Nursing Home
PO Box 191, Lamar, CO, 81052 (303) 336-3434
Admin David J Stang. *Medical Dir/Dir of Nursing* Eldonna Mosier.
Licensure Intermediate Care. *Beds* 60. *Certified* Medicaid.
Ownership Proprietary.
Admissions Requirements Physician's request.
Staff RNs 2 (ft); LPNs 3 (ft), 1 (pt); Nurses aides 20 (ft), 3 (pt); Activities coordinators 2 (ft); Dietitians 1 (ft).
Facilities Dining room; Activities room; Crafts room; Laundry room; Barber/Beauty shop.
Activities Arts and Crafts; Cards; Games; Reading groups; Prayer groups; Movies; Shopping trips; Dances/Social or cultural gatherings.
Description Sandhaven has a beautiful yard with lots of flowers; street traffic is very minimal. The caring staff is well trained in geriatric care, validation therapy, and the importance of Sandhaven being a home, not an institution. Pets enjoyed by residents.

LAS ANIMAS

Bent County Memorial Hospital and Nursing Home
810 3rd St, Las Animas, CO, 81054 (303) 456-1340
Admin Joseph Grabowski. *Medical Dir/Dir of Nursing* L S Sampson.

Licensure Skilled Care. *Beds* 49. *Certified* Medicare.
Ownership Public.
Staff Physicians 3 (ft); RNs 5 (ft); LPNs 3 (ft); Activities coordinators 1 (ft), 1 (pt); Dietitians 1 (pt); Dentists 1 (pt).
Facilities Dining room; Activities room; Barber/Beauty shop.
Activities Arts and Crafts; Cards; Games; Reading groups; Prayer groups; Movies; Shopping trips; Dances/Social or cultural gatherings.

Bueno's Group Home*
PO Box 385, 903 Vine, Las Animas, CO, 81054 (303) 456-1125
Admin Elizabeth Bueno.
Licensure Developmentally Disabled. *Beds* 9.
Ownership Proprietary.

Ivah Hansen Residential Care Facility*
924 6th St, Las Animas, CO, 81054 (303) 456-0919
Admin Ivah Hansen.
Licensure Intermediate Care. *Beds* 6.
Ownership Proprietary.

Jordan and Cole Residential Care Facility*
1108 4th St, Las Animas, CO, 81054 (303) 456-1764
Admin Mary E Cole.
Licensure Skilled Care. *Beds* 10.
Ownership Proprietary.

Lela Wilson's Residential Care Facility
403 Vigil, Las Animas, CO, 81054 (303) 456-1764
Admin Lela Wilson.
Licensure Intermediate Care. *Beds* 6.
Ownership Proprietary.

Lucero Residential Care Facility*
920 Vine, Las Animas, CO, 81054 (303) 456-0643
Admin Maria Lucero.
Licensure Intermediate Care. *Beds* 10.
Ownership Proprietary.

Seal Residential Care Home*
401 Elm, Las Animas, CO, 81054 (303) 456-1181
Admin Margaret Seal.
Licensure Intermediate Care. *Beds* 2.
Ownership Proprietary.

LIMON

Prairie View Nursing Home*
1720-1750 Circle Ln, Limon, CO, 80828 (303) 775-9583
Admin Joe A McKinley Jr.
Licensure Intermediate Care. *Beds* 60. *Certified* Medicaid.
Ownership Proprietary.

LITTLETON

Cherrelyn Manor Nursing Home
5555 S Elati St, Littleton, CO, 80120 (303) 798-8686
Admin Jo Ann Becker. *Medical Dir/Dir of Nursing* Dr John Van Buskirk.

Licensure Skilled Care; Intermediate Care.
Beds SNF 186; ICF 83. *Certified* Medicaid; Medicare.
Ownership Proprietary.
Facilities Dining room; Activities room; Chapel; Crafts room; Laundry room; Barber/Beauty shop.
Activities Arts and Crafts; Cards; Games; Reading groups; Prayer groups; Movies; Shopping trips; Dances/Social or cultural gatherings.

Good Shepard Lutheran Home of the West*
445 West Berry Ave, Littleton, CO, 80120 (303) 795-2061
Admin Ronald Drews.
Licensure Intermediate Care for Mentally Retarded. *Beds* 40. *Certified* Medicaid.
Ownership Nonprofit.
Affiliation Lutheran

Littleton House
1869 Littleton Blvd, Littleton, CO, 80120 (303) 794-0641
Admin Bruce Anderson.
Licensure Intermediate Care for Mentally Retarded. *Beds* 7.
Ownership Nonprofit.

Littleton Manor Nursing Home
5822 S Lowell Way, Littleton, CO, 80123 (303) 798-2497
Admin M Margaret Norton. *Medical Dir/Dir of Nursing* Dr Thomas Pulk.
Licensure Skilled Care. *Beds* 45. *Certified* Medicare.
Ownership Proprietary.
Admissions Requirements Medical examination; Physician's request.
Staff Physicians 1 (pt); RNs 2 (ft), 7 (pt); LPNs 1 (ft), 1 (pt); Nurses aides 12 (ft), 6 (pt); Physical therapists 1 (pt); Reality therapists 1 (pt); Recreational therapists 1 (ft); Occupational therapists 1 (pt); Speech therapists 1 (pt); Activities coordinators 1 (ft); Dietitians 1 (pt); Dentists 1 (pt); Podiatrists 1 (pt); Social workers 1 (pt).
Facilities Dining room; Physical therapy room; Activities room; Crafts room; Barber/Beauty shop.
Activities Arts and Crafts; Cards; Games; Reading groups; Prayer groups; Movies; Shopping trips; Dances/Social or cultural gatherings.
Description Some of the most successful programs here include pet therapy, children's hour with children from newborn to toddler age, family nights, monthly family support groups, clown therapy, storyhour groups, preschool visitors, current events program, and Friday socials with entertainment from belly dancers to harpist.

LONGMONT

Applewood Living Center
1800 Stroh Pl, Longmont, CO, 80501 (303) 776-6081
Admin Donna Harding. *Medical Dir/Dir of Nursing* David McCarty Sr MD.
Licensure Skilled Care; Intermediate Care.
Beds SNF 60; ICF 60. *Certified* Medicaid.
Ownership Proprietary.
Admissions Requirements Medical examina-

tion; Physician's request.
Staff RNs 10 (ft); LPNs 4 (pt); Nurses aides 40 (ft); Recreational therapists 1 (ft); Activities coordinators 1 (ft); Dietitians 1 (ft).
Facilities Dining room; Physical therapy room; Activities room; Chapel; Crafts room; Laundry room; Barber/Beauty shop.
Activities Arts and Crafts; Cards; Games; Reading groups; Prayer groups; Movies; Dances/Social or cultural gatherings.

Country View Care Center*
Rt 1, PO Box 271, Longmont, CO, 80501 (303) 535-4491
Admin Thomas Paul Malik.
Licensure Intermediate Care for Mentally Retarded. *Beds* 87.
Ownership Proprietary.

Foothills Care Center Inc*
1440 Coffman St, Longmont, CO, 80501 (303) 776-2814
Admin Douglas E Spies.
Licensure Skilled Care; Intermediate Care.
Beds SNF 120; ICF 60. *Certified* Medicaid; Medicare.
Ownership Proprietary.

LOVELAND

Eden Valley Nursing Home
6263 N County Rd Number 29, Loveland, CO, 80537 (303) 667-6911
Admin Paul Anderson.
Licensure Skilled Care; Intermediate Care.
Beds SNF 14; ICF 13. *Certified* Medicaid; Medicare.
Ownership Nonprofit.
Staff Physicians 1 (pt); RNs 4 (ft), 1 (pt); Orderlies 3 (ft); Nurses aides 4 (ft), 1 (pt); Physical therapists 1 (pt); Recreational therapists 1 (pt); Activities coordinators 1 (pt).
Affiliation Seventh-Day Adventist
Facilities Dining room; Activities room; Chapel; Barber/Beauty shop; Library.
Activities Arts and Crafts; Reading groups; Prayer groups; Movies; Shopping trips; Dances/Social or cultural gatherings.
Description Eden Valley is located in a quiet country setting surrounded by the foothills of the Rocky Mountains. Provides nutritious vegetarian meals; natural treatment is choice for patients. Pure air, sunshine, opportunities for hiking, and water therapy benefit patients. A missionary training school on the premises offers a youthful atmosphere.

Loveland Good Samaritan Village
2101 S Garfield, Loveland, CO, 80537 (303) 669-3100
Admin Leland Johnson.
Licensure Skilled Care. *Beds* 60. *Certified* Medicaid; Medicare.
Ownership Nonprofit.
Admissions Requirements Medical examination; Physician's request.
Staff RNs; LPNs; Orderlies; Nurses aides; Occupational therapists; Activities coordinators.
Affiliation Lutheran
Facilities Dining room; Activities room; Chapel; Crafts room; Laundry room; Barber-

/Beauty shop; Library.
Activities Arts and Crafts; Games; Reading groups; Shopping trips; Dances/Social or cultural gatherings.
Description Facility also has 128 apartment and duplex units for retirement living in a comfortable and secure setting.

North Shore Manor Inc*
1365 W 29th St, Loveland, CO, 80537 (303) 667-6111
Admin Barry Fancher.
Licensure Skilled Care; Intermediate Care.
Beds SNF 120; ICF 32. *Certified* Medicaid; Medicare.
Ownership Proprietary.

Sierra Vista Nursing Home
821 Duffield Ct, Loveland, CO, 80537 (303) 669-0345
Admin Rad Hazen. *Medical Dir/Dir of Nursing* Dr Thomas Kasenberg.
Licensure Skilled Care; Intermediate Care.
Beds SNF 60; ICF 83. *Certified* Medicare.
Ownership Proprietary.
Admissions Requirements Medical examination; Physician's request.
Facilities Dining room; Physical therapy room; Activities room; Crafts room; Laundry room; Barber/Beauty shop; Library.
Activities Arts and Crafts; Cards; Games; Reading groups; Prayer groups; Movies; Shopping trips; Dances/Social or cultural gatherings.
Description Facility stresses quality nursing care in a beautifully designed, home-like setting.

Twin Pines Nursing Home
907 W Sixth St, Loveland, CO, 80537 (303) 667-0394
Admin Eva Trower.
Licensure Skilled Care. *Beds* 60. *Certified* Medicaid; Medicare.
Ownership Proprietary.

MANITOU SPRINGS

Cheyenne Village
183 Crystal Park Rd, Manitou Springs, CO, 80829 (303) 685-5666
Admin Linda Bloom Brannen. *Medical Dir/Dir of Nursing* W Ryder MD.
Licensure Intermediate Care for Mentally Retarded. *Beds* 40.
Ownership Proprietary.
Admissions Requirements Minimum age 18.

MANZANOLA

Horne Home*
521 N Canal, Manzanola, CO, 81085 (303) 465-5795
Admin Rozanna R Horn.
Licensure Intermediate Care. *Beds* 10.
Ownership Proprietary.

MEEKER

Walbridge Memorial Convalescent Wing*
345 Cleveland, Meeker, CO, 81641 (303)

878-5047
Admin John Osse.
Licensure Skilled Care. *Beds* 25. *Certified* Medicaid.
Ownership Public.

MONTE VISTA

Willowcrest Retirement Manor
2277 East Dr, Monte Vista, CO, 81144 (303) 852-5138
Admin Etha Martinson. *Medical Dir/Dir of Nursing* Dr Jack Jordan.
Licensure Intermediate Care. *Beds* 60. *Certified* Medicaid.
Ownership Proprietary.
Admissions Requirements Medical examination; Physician's request.
Staff RNs 1 (ft); LPNs 4 (ft), 1 (pt); Orderlies 3 (ft); Nurses aides 13 (ft); Physical therapists 1 (pt); Activities coordinators 1 (ft), 1 (pt); Dietitians 1 (ft).
Facilities Dining room; Activities room; Chapel; Crafts room; Laundry room; Barber/Beauty shop; Library.
Activities Arts and Crafts; Cards; Games; Reading groups; Movies; Shopping trips; Dances/Social or cultural gatherings; Bible study; Sing-a-longs; Music programs.

MONTROSE

Developmental Disabilities Council*
447 S 4th St, Montrose, CO, 81401 (303) 249-2972
Admin Sharon White.
Licensure Intermediate Care for Mentally Retarded. *Beds* 8. *Certified* Medicaid.
Ownership Nonprofit.

Evergreen Care Centre
300 N Cascade Ave, Montrose, CO, 81401 (303) 249-7764
Admin Gale George.
Licensure Intermediate Care. *Beds* 60. *Certified* Medicaid.
Ownership Proprietary.
Staff RNs 2 (ft); LPNs 6 (ft); Nurses aides 17 (ft); Physical therapists 1 (ft); Activities coordinators 3 (ft).
Facilities Dining room; Physical therapy room; Activities room; Crafts room; Laundry room; Barber/Beauty shop.
Activities Arts and Crafts; Cards; Movies; Shopping trips; Dances/Social or cultural gatherings.
Description Pride taken on the outstanding care given. Residents are encouraged to take an active part in the society.

San Juan Living Center*
1043 Ridge, Montrose, CO, 81401 (303) 249-9683
Admin William F Morgan.
Licensure Skilled Care; Intermediate Care for Mentally Retarded. *Beds* SNF 60; ICF/MR 48.
Certified Medicaid.
Ownership Proprietary.

Spruce Lodge*
16357 Chipeta Dr, Montrose, CO, 81401 (303) 249-1133
Admin Sharon White.
Licensure Developmentally Disabled.
Beds 12.
Ownership Nonprofit.

Valley Manor Care Center
1401 S Cascade Ave, Montrose, CO, 81401 (303) 249-9634
Admin Harry Pelovsky. *Medical Dir/Dir of Nursing* Dr Robert Van Gemert.
Licensure Skilled Care; Intermediate Care.
Beds SNF 98; ICF 22. *Certified* Medicaid; Medicare.
Ownership Nonprofit.
Admissions Requirements Medical examination; Physician's request.
Staff RNs 6 (ft), 3 (pt); LPNs 4 (ft), 2 (pt); Nurses aides 31 (ft), 30 (pt); Physical therapists 2 (pt); Recreational therapists 2 (pt); Speech therapists 1 (pt); Activities coordinators 1 (ft); Dietitians 1 (pt); Dentists 1 (pt); Audiologists 1 (pt).
Facilities Dining room; Physical therapy room; Activities room; Chapel; Crafts room; Laundry room; Barber/Beauty shop.
Activities Arts and Crafts; Cards; Games; Reading groups; Prayer groups; Movies; Shopping trips; Dances/Social or cultural gatherings.
Description Facility has an outstanding nursing staff and offers the widest range of programs in western Colorado.

MORRISON

Bear Creek Nursing Center*
150 Spring Creek, Morrison, CO, 80465 (303) 697-8181
Admin Charles Marriott.
Licensure Skilled Care; Intermediate Care.
Beds SNF 120; ICF 60. *Certified* Medicaid; Medicare.
Ownership Proprietary.

NORTHGLENN

Castle Gardens Nursing Home
401 Malley Dr, Northglenn, CO, 80233 (303) 452-4700
Admin Sondra Eppard. *Medical Dir/Dir of Nursing* Dr Robert Jardine.
Licensure Skilled Care. *Beds* 180. *Certified* Medicaid; Medicare.
Ownership Proprietary.
Facilities Dining room; Physical therapy room; Activities room; Chapel; Crafts room; Laundry room; Barber/Beauty shop.
Activities Arts and Crafts; Cards; Games; Reading groups; Prayer groups; Movies; Shopping trips; Dances/Social or cultural gatherings.

OLATHE

Colorow Care Center
750 8th St, PO Box 710, Olathe, CO, 81425 (303) 323-5504
Admin Mary Pfalzgraff. *Medical Dir/Dir of Nursing* Dr Simon.

Licensure Intermediate Care. *Beds* 60. *Certified* Medicaid.
Ownership Proprietary.
Admissions Requirements Physician's request.
Staff RNs 2 (ft); LPNs 6 (ft), 2 (pt); Nurses aides 18 (ft), 3 (pt); Physical therapists 1 (pt); Activities coordinators 1 (ft), 1 (pt); Dietitians 1 (ft), 1 (pt).
Facilities Dining room; Physical therapy room; Activities room; Crafts room; Laundry room; Barber/Beauty shop; Library.
Activities Arts and Crafts; Cards; Games; Reading groups; Prayer groups; Movies; Shopping trips.
Description Facility is located in the beautiful Uncompahgre Valley, Olathe situated off U.S. 50 between the communities of Delta and Montrose, Colorado. The area is a mecca for retirement because of its ideal climate, short winters, beautiful springs, summers, and falls. The facility, carpeted throughout, overlooks the valley.

Harold Group Home*
418 Hersum, Olathe, CO, 81425 (303) 323-5831
Admin John Harold.
Licensure Residential MR Care. *Beds* 18.
Ownership Proprietary.

ORDWAY

Crowley County Nursing Center
401 Idaho PO Box 488, Ordway, CO, 81063 (303) 267-3561
Admin A Habib Khaliqi.
Licensure Intermediate Care. *Beds* 59. *Certified* Medicaid; Medicare.
Ownership Nonprofit.
Staff RNs 2 (ft); LPNs 4 (ft); Orderlies 1 (ft); Nurses aides 15 (ft), 5 (pt); Physical therapists 1 (pt); Dietitians 1 (pt).
Facilities Dining room; Activities room; Chapel; Laundry room; Barber/Beauty shop.
Activities Cards; Games; Prayer groups; Movies; Shopping trips; Dances/Social or cultural gatherings.

PALISADE

Palisade Nursing Home*
151 E 3rd St, Palisade, CO, 81526 (303) 464-7500
Admin Ardath Hunt.
Licensure Skilled Care; Intermediate Care.
Beds 96. *Certified* Medicaid.
Ownership Proprietary.

PAONIA

Bethesda Care Center of Paonia*
Box 1048, Meadowbrook and Paonia Ave, Paonia, CO, 81428 (303) 527-4837
Admin Shirley Steen.
Licensure Skilled Care. *Beds* 60. *Certified* Medicaid.
Ownership Nonprofit.

PUEBLO

Belmont Lodge Inc*
1601 Constitution Rd, Pueblo, CO, 81001 (303) 584-2400
Admin James Stephens.
Licensure Skilled Care. *Beds* 95. *Certified* Medicaid; Medicare.
Ownership Proprietary.

Citadel Health Care*
431 Quincy, Pueblo, CO, 81005 (303) 545-0112
Admin William Arnol Nance.
Licensure Intermediate Care; Residential Care.
Beds ICF 34; Residential Care 4. *Certified* Medicaid.
Ownership Proprietary.

Cordova Residential Care*
2108 E 12th, Pueblo, CO, 81001 (303) 546-1475
Admin Donna Cordova.
Licensure Intermediate Care. *Beds* 8.
Ownership Proprietary.

J and C Residential Care Facility*
328 Colorado, Pueblo, CO, 81004 (303) 546-1875
Admin Lydia Jordan.
Licensure Intermediate Care. *Beds* 10.
Ownership Proprietary.

Pueblo County Board for Developmental Disabilities*
2202 and 2208 E 6th St, Pueblo, CO, 81001 (303) 544-3258, 545-8924
Admin Lawrence A Valasco.
Licensure Intermediate Care for Mentally Retarded. *Beds* 16.
Ownership Nonprofit.

Sharmar Nursing Center
1201 W Abriendo Ave, Pueblo, CO, 81005 (303) 544-1173
Admin Donald J Prose. *Medical Dir/Dir of Nursing* Harvey W Phelp.
Licensure Intermediate Care; Intermediate Care for Mentally Retarded. *Beds* ICF 42; ICF/MR 15. *Certified* Medicaid.
Ownership Proprietary.
Admissions Requirements Physician's request.
Staff RNs 2 (ft); LPNs 3 (ft); Orderlies 5 (ft); Nurses aides 10 (ft); Physical therapists 1 (pt); Recreational therapists 2 (ft); Occupational therapists 1 (pt); Speech therapists 1 (pt); Activities coordinators 1 (pt); Dietitians 1 (pt); Dentists 1 (pt); Ophthalmologists 1 (pt); Podiatrists 1 (pt); Audiologists 1 (pt).
Facilities Dining room; Physical therapy room; Activities room; Chapel; Crafts room; Laundry room; Barber/Beauty shop; Library.
Activities Arts and Crafts; Cards; Games; Reading groups; Prayer groups; Movies; Shopping trips; Dances/Social or cultural gatherings.
Description We specialize in Alzheimer's disease, wandering, and chronic mental disorders.

Spanish Peaks Mental Health Center*
2117 N Grand Ave, Pueblo, CO, 81001 (303) 544-6373
Admin Gilbert A Sanchez.
Licensure Intermediate Care. *Beds* 10.
Ownership Nonprofit.

State Home and Training School—Eleventh St
2206 E 11th St, Pueblo, CO, 81001 (303) 534-1170
Admin Larry I Dalton.
Licensure Intermediate Care for Mentally Retarded. *Beds* 10.
Ownership Public.

State Home and Training School—Tenth St*
2201 E 10th St, Pueblo, CO, 81003 (303) 534-1170
Admin Lawrence Valasco.
Licensure Intermediate Care for Mentally Retarded. *Beds* 10.
Ownership Public.

Villa Pueblo Towers
1111 Bonforte Blvd, Pueblo, CO, 81001 (303) 545-5911
Admin W D McMullen. *Medical Dir/Dir of Nursing* D Manolis MD.
Licensure Skilled Care. *Beds* 32. *Certified* Medicare.
Ownership Nonprofit.
Admissions Requirements Minimum age 62; Medical examination.
Facilities Dining room; Activities room; Chapel; Laundry room; Library.
Activities Cards; Games; Prayer groups; Movies; Shopping trips; Dances/Social or cultural gatherings.
Description Villa Pueblo Towers is a life care retirement community. Program guarantees lifetime nursing care in addition to a wide range of residential services.

RIFLE

E Dene Moore Memorial Home
707 E 5th, Rifle, CO, 81650 (303) 625-1510
Admin Ed Gast.
Licensure Skilled Care. *Beds* 57. *Certified* Medicaid; Medicare.
Ownership Proprietary.
Admissions Requirements Medical examination.
Staff RNs 4 (ft); LPNs 3 (ft); Orderlies 4 (ft); Nurses aides 20 (ft); Physical therapists 1 (pt); Occupational therapists 1 (pt); Speech therapists 1 (pt); Activities coordinators 1 (ft); Dietitians 1 (ft); Dentists 1 (pt); Podiatrists 1 (pt).
Facilities Dining room; Physical therapy room; Crafts room; Laundry room; Barber/Beauty shop; Library.
Activities Arts and Crafts; Cards; Games; Prayer groups; Movies; Shopping trips; Dances/Social or cultural gatherings.

ROCKY FORD

Bauer-Home Residential Care
803 Maple Ave, Rocky Ford, CO, 81067 (303) 254-7638
Admin CLara M Bauer.
Licensure Intermediate Care. *Beds* 10.
Ownership Proprietary.

Malouff Manor*
28111 Rd 20, Rocky Ford, CO, 81067 (303) 384-8741
Admin Sam Maxwell.

Licensure Intermediate Care for Mentally Retarded. *Beds* 8.
Ownership Nonprofit.

Pioneers Memorial Hospital and Nursing Home
12th St and Washington Ave, Rocky Ford, CO, 81067 (303) 254-3314
Admin Donald Klassen.
Licensure Intermediate Care. *Beds* 65. *Certified* Medicaid; Medicare.
Ownership Nonprofit.
Staff RNs 1 (ft), 1 (pt); LPNs 7 (ft), 1 (pt); Nurses aides 20 (ft), 1 (pt).
Affiliation Mennonite
Facilities Dining room; Physical therapy room; Activities room; Chapel; Crafts room; Laundry room; Barber/Beauty shop; Library.
Activities Arts and Crafts; Cards; Games; Reading groups; Prayer groups; Movies.

SALIDA

Columbine Manor*
530 W 16th St, Salida, CO, 81201 (303) 539-6112
Admin Farice Filbert.
Licensure Skilled Care; Intermediate Care.
Beds SNF 50; ICF 10. *Certified* Medicaid.
Ownership Proprietary.

I Street House
1110 I St, Salida, CO, 81201 (303) 539-3423
Admin Pam Thompson Arbogast.
Licensure Intermediate Care for Mentally Retarded. *Beds* 8.
Ownership Proprietary.
Admissions Requirements Minimum age 18; Medical examination.
Staff RNs 1 (pt); Physical therapists 1 (pt); Occupational therapists 1 (pt); Speech therapists 1 (pt); Activities coordinators 1 (ft).
Facilities Dining room; Activities room; Laundry room.
Activities Arts and Crafts; Cards; Games; Movies; Shopping trips; Dances/Social or cultural gatherings.
Description I Street House is a group home for MR adults in a small mountain community; house is located in a residential area and clients are integrated into community activities.

SIMLA

Good Samaritan Center*
PO Box 38, 320 Pueblo Ave, Simla, CO, 80835 (303) 541-2269
Admin Nick Susuras Sr.
Licensure Intermediate Care. *Beds* 32. *Certified* Medicaid.
Ownership Nonprofit.

SPRINGFIELD

Southeast Colorado Hospital and LTC*
373 E 10th Ave, Springfield, CO, 81073 (303) 523-4501
Admin Edna Chenoweth.
Licensure Skilled Care. *Beds* 65. *Certified* Medicaid; Medicare.

Ownership Public.

STEAMBOAT SPRINGS

Routt Memorial Hospital—Extended Care Facility
160 Park Ave, PO Box 9016, Steamboat Springs, CO, 80477 (303) 879-2300
Admin Thomas Flickinger. *Medical Dir/Dir of Nursing* Dr Mark McCaulley.
Licensure Skilled Care. *Beds* 52. *Certified* Medicaid; Medicare.
Ownership Nonprofit.
Staff RNs 9 (ft), 1 (pt); LPNs 3 (ft); Orderlies 1 (pt); Nurses aides 7 (ft); Activities coordinators 1 (ft); Dietitians 1 (pt).
Facilities Dining room; Activities room; Barber/Beauty shop.
Activities Arts and Crafts; Cards; Games; Reading groups; Prayer groups; Movies; Shopping trips; Dances/Social or cultural gatherings; Children's Day Care—Intergenerational Program.
Description Facility houses a day care center for children aged 6 weeks to 6 years. Both age groups participate in an intergenerational program, consisting of combined activities, exercise, art, special friend program, and social gatherings. Elderly residents are able to maintain their community contacts and morale is boosted highly with their daily exposure to the children.

STERLING

Clark Residential Care Facility
117 Clark St, Sterling, CO, 80751 (303) 522-2656
Admin William Duffield.
Licensure Developmentally Disabled.
Beds 12.
Ownership Nonprofit.

Devonshire Acres
1330 N Sidney Ave, PO Drawer 392, Sterling, CO, 80751 (303) 522-4888
Admin Gloria Kaiser. *Medical Dir/Dir of Nursing* Dr Robert Fillion.
Licensure Skilled Care; Intermediate Care.
Beds 90. *Certified* Medicaid; Medicare.
Ownership Proprietary.
Admissions Requirements Medical examination; Physician's request.
Staff RNs 4 (ft); LPNs 7 (ft), 8 (pt); Nurses aides 27 (ft), 6 (pt); Activities coordinators 1 (ft), 1 (pt); Dietitians 1 (pt).
Facilities Dining room; Physical therapy room; Activities room; Chapel; Laundry room; Barber/Beauty shop; Library.
Activities Arts and Crafts; Cards; Games; Reading groups; Prayer groups; Movies; Shopping trips; Dances/Social or cultural gatherings.
Description Good quality care and the semi-independent departments appear as very bright spots in the complex.

North Division Residential Center*
223 N Division, Sterling, CO, 80751 (303) 522-2430
Admin William E Duffield.

Licensure Intermediate Care for Mentally Retarded. *Beds* 6.
Ownership Nonprofit.

Rose Arbor Nursing Home
1420 S 3rd Ave, Sterling, CO, 80751 (303) 522-2933
Admin Linda McClatchey. *Medical Dir/Dir of Nursing* M J Ollhoff DO.
Licensure Skilled Care; Intermediate Care.
Beds SNF 60; ICF 60. *Certified* Medicaid; Medicare.
Ownership Proprietary.
Admissions Requirements Medical examination; Physician's request.
Facilities Dining room; Physical therapy room; Activities room; Laundry room; Barber/Beauty shop; Van.
Activities Arts and Crafts; Games; Reading groups; Prayer groups; Shopping trips; Dances-/Social or cultural gatherings.
Description Facility has monthly stroke, diabetic, and Alzheimer's groups; participates in community meet and eat program twice weekly.

THORNTON

Alpine Manor
501 Thornton Parkway, Thornton, CO, 80229 (303) 452-6101
Admin Terrylea Entsminger. *Medical Dir/Dir of Nursing* Robert Jardine MD.
Licensure Skilled Care; Intermediate Care.
Beds SNF 60; ICF 60. *Certified* Medicaid.
Ownership Proprietary.
Admissions Requirements Medical examination.
Staff RNs 9 (ft), 4 (pt); LPNs 6 (ft), 2 (pt); Orderlies 1 (ft); Nurses aides 33 (ft), 7 (pt); Activities coordinators 1 (ft).

TRINIDAD

Alta Vista Group Home*
301 E Second, Trinidad, CO, 81082 (303) 846-4409
Admin Rae Bulson.
Licensure Developmentally Disabled. *Beds* 8.
Ownership Nonprofit.

Trinidad State Nursing Home*
409 Benedicta Ave, Trinidad, CO, 81082 (303) 846-9291
Admin William T McFetridge.
Licensure Skilled Care; Intermediate Care.
Beds SNF 128; ICF 105. *Certified* Medicaid.
Ownership Public.

WALSENBURG

Walsenburg Care Center Inc
135 W 7th St, Walsenburg, CO, 81089 (303) 738-2750
Admin Robert Turner. *Medical Dir/Dir of Nursing* Arthur Vialpando MD.
Licensure Skilled Care; Intermediate Care.
Beds 50. *Certified* Medicaid.
Ownership Proprietary.
Admissions Requirements Physician's request.

Staff Physicians 1 (pt); RNs 3 (ft), 1 (pt); LPNs 2 (ft), 1 (pt); Orderlies 1 (ft); Nurses aides 15 (ft), 5 (pt); Physical therapists 1 (pt); Occupational therapists 1 (pt); Speech therapists 1 (pt); Activities coordinators 1 (ft); Dietitians 1 (pt); Dentists 1 (pt); Podiatrists 1 (pt).
Facilities Dining room; Activities room; Crafts room; Laundry room; Barber/Beauty shop; Library; Living room.
Activities Arts and Crafts; Cards; Games; Reading groups; Prayer groups; Movies; Shopping trips; Dances/Social or cultural gatherings.
Description Facility features private and semi-private rooms, wheelchair lift, and meals in dining room with snacks several times a day.

WELD COUNTY

Country View Care Center*
5425 Weld County Rd 32, Weld County, CO, 80501 (303) 444-0489, 535-4491
Admin Thomas Paul Malik.
Licensure Intermediate Care for Mentally Retarded. *Beds* 87. *Certified* Medicaid.
Ownership Proprietary.

WESTMINSTER

Adams Group Home*
7666 Stuart St, Westminster, CO, 80030 (303) 427-2779
Admin Jo Vincelli.
Licensure Intermediate Care for Mentally Retarded. *Beds* 8. *Certified* Medicaid.
Ownership Nonprofit.

Aspen Care Center—East
7481 Knox Pl, Westminster, CO, 80030 (303) 427-7101
Admin John R Bahl. *Medical Dir/Dir of Nursing* Dr Foster Cline.
Licensure Skilled Care; Intermediate Care.
Beds SNF 60; ICF 60. *Certified* Medicaid; Medicare.
Ownership Proprietary.
Staff RNs 7 (ft); LPNs 8 (ft); Orderlies 2 (ft); Nurses aides 40 (ft).
Facilities Dining room; Activities room; Crafts room; Barber/Beauty shop; Library.
Activities Arts and Crafts; Cards; Games; Reading groups; Prayer groups; Movies; Shopping trips; Dances/Social or cultural gatherings.

Aspen Care Center—West
7490 Lowell Blvd, Westminster, CO, 80030 (303) 428-7481
Admin Carolyn S Westin. *Medical Dir/Dir of Nursing* Dr Foster Cline.
Licensure Skilled Care; Intermediate Care.
Beds SNF 163; ICF 31. *Certified* Medicaid; Medicare.
Ownership Proprietary.
Admissions Requirements Medical examination.
Staff RNs 8 (ft), 3 (pt); LPNs 14 (ft), 3 (pt); Orderlies 1 (ft); Nurses aides 50 (ft), 7 (pt); Activities coordinators 1 (ft).
Facilities Dining room; Activities room; Laundry room; Barber/Beauty shop; Library.
Activities Arts and Crafts; Cards; Games; Reading groups; Prayer groups; Movies; Shop-

ping trips; Dances/Social or cultural gatherings.
Description Facility contains a secured, structured area for the confused, wandering elderly, and for some more difficult to handle residents.

Johnson Home
4354 Apex Ln, Westminster, CO, 80030 (303) 427-2779
Admin Marlene J Johnson.
Licensure Intermediate Care. *Beds* 7.
Ownership Proprietary.
Facilities Dining room; Activities room; Laundry room.
Description This is a home where all live as one family.

Plaza Care Center
7045 Stuart St, Westminster, CO, 80030 (303) 427-7045
Admin Hiefa A Phillips. *Medical Dir/Dir of Nursing* Jitze DeJong MD.
Licensure Intermediate Care. *Beds* 103. *Certified* Medicaid; Medicare.
Ownership Proprietary.
Admissions Requirements Minimum age 21.
Staff RNs 3 (ft), 1 (pt); LPNs 5 (ft), 2 (pt); Nurses aides 12 (ft), 3 (pt); Recreational therapists 1 (ft), 1 (pt); Activities coordinators 1 (ft), 1 (pt).

WHEAT RIDGE

Christopher House Nursing Home*
6270 W 38th Ave, Wheat Ridge, CO, 80033 (303) 421-2272
Admin Louis C Lilly.
Licensure Skilled Care. *Beds* 90.
Ownership Proprietary.

Independence House*
3900 Independence Court, Wheat Ridge, CO, 80030 (303) 433-2801
Admin Timothy O'Neil.
Licensure Intermediate Care for Mentally Retarded. *Beds* 8.
Ownership Nonprofit.

Johnstone Developmental Center*
5361 W 26th Ave, Wheat Ridge, CO, 80214 (303) 233-8518
Admin Richard Mason.
Licensure Intermediate Care for Mentally Retarded. *Beds* 40. *Certified* Medicaid.
Ownership Nonprofit.

Sheridan Manor Nursing Home Inc*
3315 Sheridan Blvd, Wheat Ridge, CO, 80212 (303) 237-9521
Admin Rhonda Buck.
Licensure Skilled Care. *Beds* 56. *Certified* Medicaid; Medicare.
Ownership Proprietary.

Wheat Ridge Regional Center
10285 Ridge Rd, Wheat Ridge, CO, 80033 (303) 424-7791
Admin Kayo Sunada. *Medical Dir/Dir of Nursing* Gabriel Bonnet MD.
Licensure Intermediate Care for Mentally Retarded; Skilled Care for Mentally Retarded.
Beds ICF/MR 492; Skilled Care for Mentally Retarded 76. *Certified* Medicaid.

Ownership Public.
Admissions Requirements Medical examination; Physician's request.
Staff Physicians 2 (ft), 2 (pt); RNs 36 (ft); Nurses aides 381 (ft); Physical therapists 5 (ft); Recreational therapists 8 (ft), 1 (pt); Occupational therapists 4 (ft); Speech therapists 1 (ft), 2 (pt); Activities coordinators 1 (ft); Dietitians 1 (ft).
Facilities Dining room; Physical therapy room; Activities room; Chapel; Crafts room; Barber/Beauty shop; Library.
Activities Arts and Crafts; Games; Movies; Shopping trips; Dances/Social or cultural gatherings.

Wide Horizon Inc*
8900 W 38th Ave, Wheat Ridge, CO, 80033 (303) 424-4445
Admin Marcus C Thrane.
Licensure Skilled Care. *Beds* 30.
Ownership Nonprofit.

WHEATRIDGE

Columbine Manor Inc
3835 Harlan St, Wheatridge, CO, 80033 (303) 422-2338
Admin Paul M Asselin. *Medical Dir/Dir of Nursing* Robert Starr MD.
Licensure Skilled Care; Intermediate Care. *Beds* SNF 44; ICF 107. *Certified* Medicaid; Medicare.
Ownership Proprietary.
Admissions Requirements Minimum age 65; Medical examination.
Staff Physicians 1 (pt); RNs 4 (ft), 9 (pt); LPNs 5 (ft), 8 (pt); Nurses aides 31 (ft), 16 (pt); Physical therapists 1 (pt); Occupational therapists 1 (pt); Speech therapists 1 (pt); Activities coordinators 2 (ft); Dietitians 1 (pt); Dentists 1 (pt); Podiatrists 1 (pt).
Facilities Dining room; Physical therapy room; Activities room; Crafts room; Laundry room; Barber/Beauty shop.
Activities Arts and Crafts; Cards; Games; Reading groups; Prayer groups; Movies; Shopping trips; Dances/Social or cultural gatherings; Swimming; Overnight camping; Culinary arts.
Description Nestled in the neighborly and small community of Wheatridge and at the threshold of the majestic Colorado Rocky Mountains, life at Columbine Manor creates a warm, gracious atmosphere for nursing home residents and their families.

Mountain Vista Nursing Home
4800 Tabor St, Wheatridge, CO, 80033 (303) 421-4161
Admin Joyce Petersen. *Medical Dir/Dir of Nursing* Charles Davis MD.
Licensure Skilled Care. *Beds* 90. *Certified* Medicaid; Medicare.
Ownership Nonprofit.
Staff RNs 5 (ft), 12 (pt); LPNs 2 (ft), 2 (pt); Orderlies 3 (pt); Nurses aides 18 (ft), 26 (pt); Physical therapists 2 (pt); Activities coordinators 1 (ft), 3 (pt); Dietitians 2 (pt); Dentists 1 (pt); Podiatrists 1 (pt).
Affiliation Baptist
Facilities Dining room; Physical therapy room; Activities room; Chapel; Crafts room; Laundry room; Barber/Beauty shop; Library.
Activities Arts and Crafts; Cards; Games; Reading groups; Movies.
Description Facility faces the Rocky Mountains for a spectacular view.

Wheatridge Manor Nursing Home Inc
2920 Fenton St, Wheatridge, CO, 80214 (303) 238-0481
Admin Sylvia Sara Ruda. *Medical Dir/Dir of Nursing* Dr Paul Fishman.
Licensure Skilled Care. *Beds* 84. *Certified* Medicaid; Medicare.
Ownership Proprietary.
Admissions Requirements Medical examination.
Facilities Dining room; Physical therapy room; Activities room; Crafts room; Laundry room; Barber/Beauty shop; Library.
Activities Arts and Crafts; Cards; Games; Reading groups; Prayer groups; Movies; Shopping trips; Dances/Social or cultural gatherings; Church services.
Description Facility offers private and semi-private rooms all on ground floor, husband and wife units, century tubs (whirlpools), lab and X-ray service, special diets, air conditioning, sprinkler system and fire control.

WINDSOR

Windsor Health Care
710 3rd St, PO Box 999, Windsor, CO, 80550 (303) 686-7474
Admin Diana Nusbaum. *Medical Dir/Dir of Nursing* E D Kadlub MD.
Licensure Skilled Care; Intermediate Care. *Beds* SNF 114; ICF 6. *Certified* Medicaid.
Ownership Proprietary.
Staff RNs 6 (ft), 4 (pt); LPNs 9 (ft), 3 (pt); Nurses aides 27 (ft), 14 (pt); Recreational therapists 1 (ft); Dietitians 1 (ft).
Facilities Dining room; Activities room; Crafts room; Laundry room; Barber/Beauty shop.
Activities Arts and Crafts; Cards; Games; Reading groups; Movies; Shopping trips; Dances/Social or cultural gatherings.
Description Facility is located in small town with a rural setting; specializes in geriatric mental health, OBS, and Alzheimer's disease.

WRAY

Cedardale Health Care Facility
324 W 7th St, Wray, CO, 80758 (303) 332-5375
Admin Lloyd J Oleson.
Licensure Intermediate Care. *Beds* 33. *Certified* Medicaid; Medicare.
Ownership Proprietary.
Admissions Requirements Medical examination.
Staff RNs 2 (ft); LPNs 2 (ft), 1 (pt); Nurses aides 12 (ft); Activities coordinators 1 (ft).
Facilities Dining room; Physical therapy room; Activities room; Crafts room; Laundry room; Barber/Beauty shop.
Activities Arts and Crafts; Cards; Games; Reading groups; Prayer groups; Movies; Shopping trips; Dances/Social or cultural gatherings.

Description Facility stresses a home-like atmosphere, individual and personal care, and good food.

Renotta Nursing Home
815 Franklin St, Wray, CO, 80758 (303) 332-4856
Admin Stanley C Fisher.
Licensure Intermediate Care. *Beds* 38. *Certified* Medicaid.
Ownership Proprietary.
Staff Physicians 2 (pt); RNs 2 (ft); LPNs 1 (ft), 6 (pt); Orderlies 1 (ft); Nurses aides 6 (ft), 15 (pt); Activities coordinators 1 (pt); Dietitians 1 (ft).
Facilities Dining room; Activities room; Crafts room; Laundry room; Barber/Beauty shop.
Activities Arts and Crafts; Cards; Games; Movies; Shopping trips.

YUMA

Life Care Center—Yuma*
323 W 9th Ave, Yuma, CO, 80759 (303) 848-2403
Admin Wayne Lee Butte.
Licensure Skilled Care. *Beds* 60. *Certified* Medicaid.
Ownership Proprietary.

CONNECTICUT

ASHFORD

Evangelical Baptist Home*
RFD 1, Box 131, Ashford, CT, 06278 (203) 429-2743
Licensure Intermediate Care. *Beds* 30.
Ownership Nonprofit.
Languages French, German, Russian, Polish
Affiliation Baptist

AVON

Avon Convalescent Home Inc*
652 W Avon Rd, Avon, CT, 06001 (203) 673-2521
Beds 120. *Certified* Medicaid; Medicare.
Ownership Proprietary.

Brightview Nursing and Retirement Center Ltd*
220 Scoville Rd, Avon, CT, 06001 (203) 673-3265
Beds 56.
Ownership Proprietary.
Languages Italian, Polish

BLOOMFIELD

Canterbury Villa of Bloomfield*
160 Coventry St, Bloomfield, CT, 06002 (203) 243-2995
Licensure Intermediate Care. *Beds* 113. *Certified* Medicaid.
Ownership Proprietary.
Staff RNs 3 (ft); LPNs 3 (ft); Nurses aides 4 (ft); Dietitians.
Languages Spanish, Tamil, Parsi, Malayalam, Telugu
Activities Arts and Crafts; Shopping trips; Dances/Social or cultural gatherings; Exercise groups.

Oak Ridge Convalescent Center Inc
55 Tunxis Ave, Bloomfield, CT, 06002 (203) 242-0703
Medical Dir/Dir of Nursing Dr Daniel Marshall.
Licensure Skilled Care. *Beds* 120. *Certified* Medicaid; Medicare.
Ownership Proprietary.
Admissions Requirements Minimum age 14; Medical examination; Physician's request.
Staff RNs 6 (ft), 2 (pt); LPNs 4 (ft); Nurses

aides 38 (ft), 1 (pt); Physical therapists 1 (pt); Recreational therapists 2 (ft); Dietitians 1 (pt); Dentists 1 (pt); Ophthalmologists 1 (pt); Podiatrists 1 (pt); Audiologists 1 (pt).
Facilities Dining room; Physical therapy room; Activities room; Crafts room; Laundry room; Barber/Beauty shop.
Activities Arts and Crafts; Cards; Games; Reading groups; Prayer groups; Movies; Shopping trips; Dances/Social or cultural gatherings.
Description We are a skilled nursing facility in a rural setting, offering a complete program of services and recreational therapy to assist our residents to reach the maximum of their abilities and to live a full life style.

Wintonbury Manor Inc
140 Park Ave, Bloomfield, CT, 06002 (203) 243-9591
Medical Dir/Dir of Nursing Dr S K Basu.
Licensure Skilled Care; Intermediate Care; Rest Home. *Beds* SNF 120; Rest Home 30.
Certified Medicaid; Medicare.
Ownership Proprietary.
Admissions Requirements Minimum age 16; Medical examination; Physician's request.
Staff RNs 11 (ft), 13 (pt); LPNs 8 (ft), 4 (pt); Orderlies 1 (ft); Nurses aides 42 (ft), 16 (pt); Physical therapists 1 (ft), 3 (pt); Recreational therapists 2 (ft), 1 (pt); Speech therapists 1 (pt); Activities coordinators 1 (ft); Dietitians 1 (pt).
Languages Polish, Korean, Spanish
Facilities Dining room; Physical therapy room; Activities room; Crafts room; Barber/Beauty shop; Library.
Activities Arts and Crafts; Cards; Games; Reading groups; Prayer groups; Movies; Shopping trips; Dances/Social or cultural gatherings.
Description Facility is committed to physical therapy and to quality of life; a pet dog provides residents with much enjoyment.

BRANFORD

Branford Hills Health Care Center*
Alps Rd, Branford, CT, 06405 (203) 481-6221
Licensure Skilled Care. *Beds* 120. *Certified* Medicaid; Medicare.
Ownership Proprietary.
Staff LPNs 28 (ft); Nurses aides 72 (ft); Physical therapists 2 (ft); Activities coordinators 5 (ft); Dietitians; Social workers 2 (ft).
Languages Polish, Italian

Activities Arts and Crafts; Games; Dances/Social or cultural gatherings; Cooking; Gardening; Resident newspaper and council; Exercises.

BRIDGEPORT

Burroughs Home Inc*
2470 Fairfield Ave, Bridgeport, CT, 06605 (203) 334-0293
Licensure Intermediate Care. *Beds* 25.
Ownership Nonprofit.

Dinan Memorial Center*
500 Bond St, Bridgeport, CT, 06610 (203) 384-6400
Licensure Skilled Care; Intermediate Care.
Beds 480. *Certified* Medicaid; Medicare.
Ownership Public.
Staff RNs 32 (ft), 1 (pt); LPNs 52 (ft), 1 (pt); Nurses aides 230 (ft), 1 (pt); Physical therapists 15 (ft), 1 (pt); Activities coordinators 13 (ft), 1 (pt); Social workers 2 (ft).

Golden Heights Manor Inc*
62 Coleman St, Bridgeport, CT, 06604 (203) 367-8444
Licensure Skilled Care; Intermediate Care.
Beds 140. *Certified* Medicaid; Medicare.
Ownership Proprietary.
Staff RNs 11 (ft); LPNs 14 (ft); Nurses aides 42 (ft); Activities coordinators 1 (ft).
Languages Italian, Portuguese, Spanish, Polish
Activities Arts and Crafts; Prayer groups; Movies; Shopping trips; Resident council.

Laurel Avenue Rest Home Inc*
217 Laurel Ave, Bridgeport, CT, 06605 (203) 367-0945
Licensure Intermediate Care. *Beds* 12.
Ownership Proprietary.

Park Avenue Restorative Health Care Center*
725 Park Ave, Bridgeport, CT, 06604 (203) 366-3653
Licensure Skilled Care; Intermediate Care.
Beds 132. *Certified* Medicaid; Medicare.
Ownership Proprietary.
Staff RNs 25 (ft); LPNs 18 (ft); Activities coordinators 2 (ft); Social workers 1 (pt).
Languages Spanish, French, Italian, German, Russian, Lithuanian
Activities Arts and Crafts; Games; Reading groups; Prayer groups; Reality orientation.

Roncalli Health Center Inc*
425 Grant St, Bridgeport, CT, 06610 (203) 366-5255
Licensure Skilled Care; Intermediate Care.
Beds 150. *Certified* Medicaid; Medicare.
Ownership Nonprofit.
Staff RNs 9 (ft); LPNs 14 (ft); Nurses aides 58 (ft); Physical therapists 1 (ft); Activities coordinators 2 (ft).
Languages Russian, Italian, Spanish, Polish, French, German

Sterling Home of Bridgeport
354 Prospect St, Bridgeport, CT, 06604
Admin Marie C Franck.
Licensure Residential Care. *Beds* 25.
Ownership Nonprofit.
Admissions Requirements Minimum age 65; Females only; Medical examination; Physician's request.
Staff Dietitians; Podiatrists.
Facilities Dining room; Physical therapy room; Activities room; Chapel; Laundry room; Barber/Beauty shop; Library; Plant room.
Activities Arts and Crafts; Cards; Games; Prayer groups; Shopping trips; Dances/Social or cultural gatherings.
Description Each resident has her own sitting room and separate bedroom which she may furnish with her own furniture; 2 hot meals are served daily and residents are given supper items to eat in their rooms; religious services are held periodically and entertainment provided frequently. Facility has a large sitting room with air conditioning, a small card room, and 2 spacious screened porches.

Sylvan Manor Inc*
1037 Sylvan Ave, Bridgeport, CT, 06606 (203) 372-3508
Licensure Skilled Care. *Beds* 40. *Certified* Medicaid; Medicare.
Ownership Proprietary.
Staff LPNs 5 (ft), 1 (pt); Nurses aides 12 (ft), 1 (pt); Physical therapists 1 (ft); Activities coordinators 1 (ft).
Languages Slavic, Italian

BRISTOL

Bristol Convalescent Home Inc
456 King St, Bristol, CT, 06010 (203) 583-1827
Medical Dir/Dir of Nursing Dr Steven Isaacs.
Licensure Skilled Care. *Beds* 160. *Certified* Medicaid; Medicare.
Ownership Proprietary.
Admissions Requirements Minimum age 14; Medical examination; Physician's request.
Staff Physicians 10 (pt); RNs 6 (ft), 4 (pt); LPNs 14 (ft), 9 (pt); Orderlies 8 (ft), 2 (pt); Nurses aides 37 (ft), 26 (pt); Physical therapists 1 (ft); Recreational therapists 3 (ft); Occupational therapists 1 (pt); Speech therapists 1 (pt); Dietitians 1 (pt); Dentists 1 (pt); Ophthalmologists 1 (pt); Podiatrists 1 (pt).
Languages Italian, French, Polish
Facilities Dining room; Physical therapy room; Activities room; Crafts room; Barber/Beauty shop.
Activities Arts and Crafts; Cards; Games; Reading groups; Prayer groups; Movies; Shopping trips; Dances/Social or cultural gatherings.

Countryside Manor Inc*
1660 Stafford Ave, Bristol, CT, 06010 (203) 583-8483
Admin Dorothy Hultman.
Licensure Intermediate Care. *Beds* 59. *Certified* Medicaid.
Ownership Proprietary.
Staff RNs 5 (ft); LPNs 4 (ft); Physical therapists 1 (ft); Recreational therapists 1 (ft); Dietitians 1 (ft); Social workers 1 (ft).
Languages Polish, Italian, German, Swedish
Activities Prayer groups; Arts and Crafts; Shopping trips; Bus trips; Special education.

Nursing Care Center of Bristol*
61 Bellevue Ave, Bristol, CT, 06010 (203) 589-1682
Licensure Skilled Care. *Beds* 132. *Certified* Medicaid; Medicare.
Ownership Proprietary.
Staff RNs 22 (ft); LPNs 20 (ft); Nurses aides 68 (ft); Recreational therapists; Social workers.
Languages French, Polish, Japanese

BROOKLYN

Brooklyn Rest Home*
Wolf Den Rd, Brooklyn, CT, 06234 (203) 774-2260
Licensure Intermediate Care. *Beds* 30. *Certified* Medicaid.
Ownership Proprietary.
Staff RNs 4 (ft); LPNs 3 (ft); Nurses aides 15 (ft); Activities coordinators 1 (ft).
Languages French, Polish
Activities Theraputic recreation.

Norcliffe Rest Home Inc*
Canterbury Rd, Brooklyn, CT, 06234 (203) 774-3296
Licensure Intermediate Care. *Beds* 60. *Certified* Medicaid.
Ownership Proprietary.
Staff RNs 7 (ft); Nurses aides 8 (ft); Activities coordinators 1 (ft); Dietitians 1 (ft).
Languages French, Polish, Italian

Pierce Memorial Baptist Home Inc
Rt 169, Brooklyn, CT, 06234 (203) 774-9050
Medical Dir/Dir of Nursing Lavius Robinson.
Licensure Skilled Care; Intermediate Care.
Beds SNF 30; ICF 15. *Certified* Medicaid; Medicare.
Ownership Nonprofit.
Staff Physicians 6 (pt); RNs 3 (ft), 8 (pt); LPNs 1 (ft), 7 (pt); Nurses aides 19 (ft), 6 (pt); Physical therapists 1 (pt); Recreational therapists 1 (ft), 1 (pt); Speech therapists 1 (pt); Dietitians 1 (pt); Dentists 1 (pt); Ophthalmologists 2 (pt); Podiatrists 1 (pt).
Languages German, Greek, Spanish, Finnish, French
Affiliation Baptist
Facilities Dining room; Physical therapy room; Activities room; Chapel; Crafts room; Laundry room; Library.
Activities Arts and Crafts; Games; Reading groups; Prayer groups; Movies; Shopping trips; Dances/Social or cultural gatherings; Swimming; Dining out.

CANAAN

Geer Memorial Health Center
S Canaan Rd, PO Box 817, Canaan, CT, 06018 (203) 824-5137
Admin Daniel J Swinyar. *Medical Dir/Dir of Nursing* Malcolm M Brown MD.
Licensure Skilled Care. *Beds* 120. *Certified* Medicaid; Medicare.
Ownership Nonprofit.
Admissions Requirements Minimum age 16; Medical examination; Physician's request.
Staff Physicians 23 (pt); RNs 10 (ft), 7 (pt); LPNs 4 (ft), 2 (pt); Orderlies 4 (ft); Nurses aides 35 (ft), 31 (pt); Physical therapists 1 (pt); Recreational therapists 1 (pt); Occupational therapists 1 (pt); Speech therapists 1 (pt); Activities coordinators 1 (ft), 1 (pt); Dietitians 1 (pt); Podiatrists 1 (pt); Audiologists 1 (pt).
Affiliation Seventh-Day Adventist
Facilities Dining room; Physical therapy room; Activities room; Chapel; Crafts room; Laundry room; Barber/Beauty shop; Library.
Activities Arts and Crafts; Cards; Games; Reading groups; Prayer groups; Movies; Shopping trips; Dances/Social or cultural gatherings.

CHESHIRE

Cheshire Rehabilitation and Convalescent Center
745 Milldale Rd, Cheshire, CT, 06410 (203) 272-7285
Admin Mary J Fihr. *Medical Dir/Dir of Nursing* Edward Oxnard MD.
Licensure Skilled Care; Intermediate Care.
Beds SNF 80; ICF 40. *Certified* Medicaid; Medicare.
Ownership Proprietary.
Staff Physicians 4 (pt); RNs 14 (ft), 6 (pt); LPNs 7 (ft), 1 (pt); Nurses aides 31 (ft), 12 (pt); Physical therapists 2 (ft); Recreational therapists 2 (ft), 1 (pt); Occupational therapists 1 (pt); Speech therapists 1 (pt); Dietitians 1 (pt); Dentists 1 (pt); Ophthalmologists 1 (pt); Podiatrists 1 (pt); Audiologists 1 (pt).
Languages Spanish, French
Facilities Dining room; Physical therapy room; Activities room; Chapel; Crafts room; Laundry room; Barber/Beauty shop.
Activities Arts and Crafts; Cards; Games; Reading groups; Prayer groups; Movies; Shopping trips; Dances/Social or cultural gatherings.
Description Cheshire Convalescent Center offers annual art show and sale, Independence Day picnic, Oktoberfest, and bowling banquet for residents and their families.

Elim Park Baptist Home Inc
140 Cook Hill Rd, Cheshire, CT, 06410 (203) 272-3547
Medical Dir/Dir of Nursing Gerhard T Mack MD.
Licensure Skilled Care; Intermediate Care; Home for the Aged. *Beds* SNF 60; ICF 30; Home For The Aged 52. *Certified* Medicaid; Medicare.
Ownership Nonprofit.
Admissions Requirements Minimum age 60; Medical examination.
Staff RNs 6 (ft), 13 (pt); LPNs 1 (ft), 4 (pt); Nurses aides 17 (ft), 29 (pt); Activities coordi-

nators 2 (ft).
Affiliation Baptist
Facilities Dining room; Physical therapy room; Activities room; Chapel; Crafts room; Laundry room; Barber/Beauty shop; Library.
Activities Arts and Crafts; Games; Reading groups; Prayer groups; Movies; Shopping trips; Dances/Social or cultural gatherings.
Description Facility consists of 64,000 square feet of space located in the rural section of town on 21 acres of land.

New Lakeview Convalescent Home*
50 Hazel Dr, Cheshire, CT, 06410 (203) 272-7204
Licensure Skilled Care; Intermediate Care. *Beds* 210. *Certified* Medicaid; Medicare.
Ownership Proprietary.
Staff RNs 14 (ft); LPNs 20 (ft); Nurses aides 61 (ft); Activities coordinators 3 (ft), 1 (pt); Social workers 2 (ft).
Languages Italian, Spanish, Japanese, Korean, German, Portuguese

CHESTER

Aaron Manor Health Care Facility*
Rt 148, Chester, CT, 06412 (203) 526-5316
Licensure Intermediate Care. *Beds* 60. *Certified* Medicaid.
Ownership Proprietary.
Staff LPNs 4 (ft), 1 (pt); Nurses aides 8 (ft), 1 (pt); Activities coordinators 1 (ft).
Activities Arts and Crafts; Games; Movies; Dances/Social or cultural gatherings.

Chesterfields Chronic and Convalescent Hospital*
132 Main St, Chester, CT, 06412 (203) 526-5363
Licensure Skilled Care. *Beds* 60. *Certified* Medicaid; Medicare.
Ownership Proprietary.
Staff RNs 5 (ft), 1 (pt); LPNs 5 (ft), 1 (pt); Nurses aides 25 (ft), 1 (pt).
Languages Greek, Italian
Activities Arts and Crafts; Games; Movies; Bus trips; Music.

CLINTON

Clinton Health Care Center
5 Harbor Pkwy, Clinton, CT, 06413 (203) 669-5717
Medical Dir/Dir of Nursing Arnold C Winokur MD.
Licensure Intermediate Care. *Beds* 40. *Certified* Medicaid.
Ownership Proprietary.
Admissions Requirements Minimum age 16; Medical examination; Physician's request.
Staff Physicians 6 (pt); RNs 3 (ft), 2 (pt); LPNs 1 (ft), 2 (pt); Orderlies 1 (ft); Nurses aides 6 (ft), 10 (pt); Physical therapists 1 (pt); Reality therapists 1 (ft); Recreational therapists 1 (ft); Occupational therapists 1 (pt); Speech therapists 2 (pt); Activities coordinators 1 (pt); Dietitians 1 (pt); Dentists 1 (pt); Ophthalmologists 1 (pt); Podiatrists 1 (pt); Audiologists 1 (pt).
Languages Spanish, German

COLCHESTER

Colchester Convalescent Home
Harrington Ct, Colchester, CT, 06415 (203) 537-2339
Medical Dir/Dir of Nursing Dr Carl Conrad.
Licensure Skilled Care. *Beds* 120. *Certified* Medicaid; Medicare.
Ownership Proprietary.
Admissions Requirements Medical examination; Physician's request.
Staff Physicians; Dietitians; Nurses aides.
Languages Polish, French, Japanese, Spanish, Russian
Facilities Dining room; Physical therapy room; Activities room; Chapel; Laundry room.
Activities Arts and Crafts; Cards; Games; Reading groups; Prayer groups; Movies; Shopping trips; Dances/Social or cultural gatherings.

Liberty Hall Convalescent Home*
9 Harrington Ct, Colchester, CT, 06415 (203) 537-5053
Licensure Skilled Care. *Beds* 60. *Certified* Medicaid; Medicare.
Ownership Proprietary.
Staff RNs 6 (ft); LPNs 3 (ft).
Languages Polish, French
Activities Arts and Crafts; Games; Reading groups; Prayer groups; Dances/Social or cultural gatherings; Cooking; Sing-a-longs.

CROMWELL

Cromwell Crest Convalescent Home Inc*
385 Main St, Cromwell, CT, 06416 (203) 635-5613
Licensure Skilled Care; Intermediate Care. *Beds* 90. *Certified* Medicaid; Medicare.
Ownership Proprietary.
Staff RNs 8 (ft), 1 (pt); LPNs 4 (ft); Nurses aides 23 (ft); Physical therapists 1 (ft).
Languages Spanish, Italian
Activities Arts and Crafts; Cards; Games; Reading groups; Prayer groups; Movies; Shopping trips; Dances/Social or cultural gatherings; Exercises; Current events.

Pilgrim Manor
52 Missionary Rd, Cromwell, CT, 06416 (203) 635-5511
Admin Glenn A West and Mark N Carlson.
Medical Dir/Dir of Nursing Dr Thomas Lambe.
Licensure Skilled Care; Intermediate Care; Home for the Aged. *Beds* SNF 30; ICF 30; Home For The Aged 52. *Certified* Medicaid.
Ownership Nonprofit.
Admissions Requirements Minimum age 60; Medical examination.
Staff Physicians; Dietitians; Nurses aides.
Languages Swedish, German
Affiliation Evangelical Covenant Church
Facilities Dining room; Physical therapy room; Activities room; Crafts room; Laundry room; Barber/Beauty shop; Library.
Activities Arts and Crafts; Games; Reading groups; Prayer groups; Movies; Shopping trips; Dances/Social or cultural gatherings.

Ridgeview Rest Home Inc
154 Berlin Rd, Cromwell, CT, 06416 (203) 828-6381
Medical Dir/Dir of Nursing Lawrence Koch MD.
Licensure Intermediate Care. *Beds* 60. *Certified* Medicaid.
Ownership Proprietary.
Admissions Requirements Minimum age 45.
Staff RNs 3 (ft); Nurses aides 7 (ft); Activities coordinators 1 (ft).
Languages Italian, French
Facilities Dining room; Activities room; Crafts room; Laundry room; Barber/Beauty shop.
Activities Arts and Crafts; Cards; Games; Reading groups; Prayer groups; Movies; Shopping trips.

DANBURY

Danbury Pavilion Healthcare
22 Hospital Ave, Danbury, CT, 06810 (203) 744-3700
Medical Dir/Dir of Nursing Dr Alan Shafto MD.
Licensure Skilled Care. *Beds* 150. *Certified* Medicaid; Medicare.
Ownership Proprietary.
Admissions Requirements Medical examination.
Staff Physicians 4 (ft); RNs 18 (ft); LPNs 7 (ft); Nurses aides 84 (ft); Physical therapists 2 (ft); Recreational therapists 2 (ft), 1 (pt); Speech therapists 1 (pt); Dietitians 1 (pt); Dentists 1 (pt); Ophthalmologists 1 (pt); Podiatrists 2 (pt); Audiologists 1 (pt).
Languages Spanish
Facilities Dining room; Physical therapy room; Activities room; Chapel; Crafts room; Laundry room; Barber/Beauty shop; Library; Outdoor patio.
Activities Arts and Crafts; Cards; Games; Reading groups; Prayer groups; Movies; Shopping trips; Dances/Social or cultural gatherings.

Filosa Convalescent Home Inc*
13 Hakim St, Danbury, CT, 06810 (203) 744-3366
Licensure Skilled Care. *Certified* Medicaid; Medicare.
Ownership Proprietary.
Staff RNs 16 (ft); LPNs 5 (ft); Nurses aides 23 (ft); Physical therapists 1 (ft); Activities coordinators 1 (ft), 1 (pt); Social workers 2 (ft).
Languages Spanish, Polish, Arabic, German, Swedish

Glen Hill Convalescent Center*
Glen Hill Rd, Danbury, CT, 06810 (203) 744-2840
Licensure Skilled Care; Intermediate Care. *Beds* 90. *Certified* Medicaid; Medicare.
Ownership Proprietary.
Staff RNs 14 (ft); LPNs 7 (ft); Nurses aides 35 (ft); Recreational therapists 2 (ft); Respiratory therapists 2 (ft).
Languages Spanish, French, Portugese

Mediplex of Danbury*
107 Osborne St, Danbury, CT, 06810 (203) 792-8102
Licensure Skilled Care; Intermediate Care.

Beds 120. *Certified* Medicaid; Medicare.
Ownership Proprietary.
Staff LPNs 28 (ft); Nurses aides 52 (ft);
Physical therapists 2 (ft); Activities coordinators 2 (ft), 1 (pt); Social workers 1 (ft).
Languages Spanish, Hungarian, German, French
Activities Arts and Crafts; Games; Dances/Social or cultural gatherings; Outings; Music.

DANIELSON

Canterbury Villa of Danielson Inc*
65 Westcott Rd, Danielson, CT, 06239 (203)
774-9540
Licensure Skilled Care; Intermediate Care.
Beds 180. *Certified* Medicaid; Medicare.
Ownership Proprietary.
Staff RNs 10 (ft), 1 (pt); LPNs 17 (ft), 1 (pt);
Nurses aides 50 (ft), 1 (pt); Physical therapists 1
(ft); Activities coordinators 3 (ft); Dietitians 1
(ft); Social workers 1 (ft).
Languages French, Finnish

DARIEN

Darien Convalescent Center*
599 Boston Post Rd, Darien, CT, 06820 (203)
655-7727
Licensure Skilled Care; Intermediate Care.
Beds 90. *Certified* Medicare.
Ownership Proprietary.
Staff RNs 11 (ft), 1 (pt); LPNs 4 (ft), 1 (pt);
Nurses aides 36 (ft), 1 (pt); Physical therapists 1
(ft), 1 (pt); Activities coordinators 5 (ft), 1 (pt);
Social workers 2 (ft), 1 (pt).
Languages Spanish, Portugese, French, Yiddish

DAYVILLE

Westview Convalescent Center Inc
Rt 1, Ware Rd, Dayville, CT, 06241 (203)
774-8574
Admin Eileen Panteleakes. *Medical Dir/Dir of Nursing* Dr R Philip Goyette.
Licensure Skilled Care. *Beds* 90. *Certified* Medicaid; Medicare.
Ownership Proprietary.
Admissions Requirements Minimum age 14;
Medical examination.
Staff Physicians 2 (pt); RNs 8 (ft); LPNs 15
(ft); Nurses aides 32 (ft); Physical therapists 1
(ft); Reality therapists 1 (pt); Recreational therapists 2 (ft); Speech therapists 1 (pt); Activities
coordinators 1 (ft); Dietitians 1 (ft); Dentists 1
(pt); Ophthalmologists 1 (pt); Podiatrists 1 (pt);
Audiologists 1 (pt).
Languages French, Polish, Swedish, Spanish,
Finnish
Facilities Dining room; Physical therapy room;
Activities room; Crafts room; Laundry room;
Barber/Beauty shop; Library.
Activities Arts and Crafts; Cards; Games;
Reading groups; Prayer groups; Movies; Shopping trips; Dances/Social or cultural gatherings.
Description The facility's priority goal is to provide an aggressive rehabilitation program to the
residents, which in many cases allows the residents to return to their homes. The staff makes
every effort to provide a friendly, home-type

environment, which together with an active
recreation program, provides constant social
stimulation.

DEEP RIVER

Deep River Convalescent Home Inc*
59 Elm St, Deep River, CT, 06417 (203)
526-5902
Licensure Skilled Care. *Beds* 30. *Certified* Medicaid.
Ownership Proprietary.
Staff RNs 3 (ft); Nurses aides 18 (ft); Activities
coordinators 1 (ft); Social workers 1 (ft).
Languages Greek, French, Russian
Activities Outings; Therapeutic recreation.

DERBY

Derby Nursing Center*
Chatfield St, Derby, CT, 06418 (203) 735-7401
Licensure Skilled Care; Intermediate Care.
Beds 120. *Certified* Medicaid; Medicare.
Ownership Proprietary.
Staff RNs 12 (ft); LPNs 6 (ft); Nurses aides 48
(ft); Activities coordinators; Dietitians.
Languages Italian, Polish
Activities Arts and Crafts; Games; Reading
groups; Movies.

Marshall Lane Manor*
101 Marshall Ln, Derby, CT, 06418 (203)
734-3393
Medical Dir/Dir of Nursing John J Narowski
MD.
Licensure Intermediate Care. *Beds* 120. *Certified* Medicaid.
Ownership Proprietary.
Admissions Requirements Medical examination.
Staff RNs 17 (ft); LPNs; Nurses aides 11 (ft);
Activities coordinators 2 (ft); Dietitians 1 (ft).
Languages Italian, Polish, Spanish
Facilities Dining room; Physical therapy room;
Activities room; Chapel; Crafts room; Laundry
room; Barber/Beauty shop; Library; TV room.
Activities Arts and Crafts; Cards; Games;
Reading groups; Prayer groups; Movies; Shopping trips; Dances/Social or cultural gatherings.
Description Facility is located in a rural setting,
yet is close to shopping centers and main
highway.

DURHAM

Dogwood Acres Intermediate Care Facility
Rt 1, Brick Lane, Box 301F, Durham, CT,
06422 (203) 349-8000
Admin Thomas Reese. *Medical Dir/Dir of
Nursing* Dr Karen Warner.
Licensure Intermediate Care. *Beds* 29. *Certified* Medicaid.
Ownership Proprietary.
Admissions Requirements Minimum age 14.
Staff Physicians 1 (pt); RNs 1 (ft), 8 (pt);
Orderlies 1 (ft), 1 (pt); Nurses aides 4 (ft), 11
(pt); Physical therapists 1 (pt); Recreational
therapists 1 (pt); Activities coordinators 1 (pt);
Dietitians 1 (pt); Dentists 1 (pt); Ophthalmologists 1 (pt); Podiatrists 1 (pt); Audiologists 1

(pt).
Facilities Dining room; Activities room; Laundry room.
Activities Arts and Crafts; Cards; Games;
Reading groups; Prayer groups; Movies; Shopping trips; Dances/Social or cultural gatherings.
Description This is an older, wood-frame
facility with a home-like atmosphere; originally
part of the facility and grounds were a farm and
farmhouse.

Twin Maples Home Inc*
New Haven Rd, Durham, CT, 06422 (203)
349-1041
Licensure Intermediate Care. *Beds* 44. *Certified* Medicaid.
Ownership Proprietary.
Staff RNs 5 (ft); Nurses aides 5 (ft); Activities
coordinators 1 (ft).
Languages Polish, Italian
Activities Therapeutic recreation; Sheltered
workshops.

EAST HAMPTON

Cobalt Lodge Convalescent Home*
Rt 151, PO Box 246, East Hampton, CT,
06414 (203) 267-9034
Licensure Skilled Care. *Beds* 60. *Certified* Medicaid; Medicare.
Ownership Proprietary.
Staff RNs 4 (ft); LPNs 5 (ft); Nurses aides 20
(ft); Activities coordinators; Dietitians.
Languages Polish, Italian
Activities Arts and Crafts; Games; Prayer
groups; Movies.

Lakeside Residential Care Facility*
9 W High St, East Hampton, CT, 06424 (203)
267-2038
Licensure Intermediate Care. *Beds* 41.
Ownership Proprietary.
Activities Arts and Crafts; Games; Mental
health programs.

EAST HARTFORD

Burnside Convalescent Home Inc*
870 Burnside Ave, East Hartford, CT, 06108
(203) 289-9571
Licensure Skilled Care; Intermediate Care.
Beds 90. *Certified* Medicare.
Ownership Proprietary.
Staff RNs 7 (ft), 1 (pt); LPNs 4 (ft), 1 (pt);
Nurses aides 25 (ft), 1 (pt); Activities coordinators 1 (ft), 1 (pt); Dietitians 1 (pt); Social workers 1 (pt).
Languages Polish, French
Activities Arts and Crafts; Games; Prayer
groups; Movies; Dances/Social or cultural gatherings.

Riverside Health Care Center*
745 Main St, East Hartford, CT, 06108 (203)
528-2167
Licensure Skilled Care; Intermediate Care.
Beds 360. *Certified* Medicaid; Medicare.
Ownership Proprietary.
Staff Physicians; RNs 219 (ft); Physical therapists; Activities coordinators 7 (ft); Dietitians;
Social workers.

Languages Lithuanian, Estonian, Hebrew, Spanish, Portugese, Italian
Activities Arts and Crafts; Games; Reading groups; Prayer groups; Movies; Shopping trips; Dances/Social or cultural gatherings; AA group; Cooking.

Saint Elizabeth Health Care Center
51 Applegate Ln, East Hartford, CT, 06118
(203) 568-7520
Admin Jonathan A Neagle. *Medical Dir/Dir of Nursing* Michael Jacuch MD.
Licensure Skilled Care. *Beds* 180. *Certified* Medicaid; Medicare.
Ownership Nonprofit.
Admissions Requirements Minimum age 14; Medical examination; Physician's request.
Staff Physicians 5 (pt); RNs 5 (ft), 19 (pt); LPNs 7 (ft), 12 (pt); Orderlies 2 (ft); Nurses aides 58 (ft), 14 (pt); Physical therapists 1 (pt); Recreational therapists 3 (ft).
Languages Spanish, Italian, French, German, Polish, Dutch
Affiliation Roman Catholic
Facilities Dining room; Physical therapy room; Activities room; Chapel; Crafts room; Laundry room; Barber/Beauty shop; Library; Lounges.
Activities Arts and Crafts; Cards; Games; Prayer groups; Movies; Shopping trips; Dances/Social or cultural gatherings.
Description Facility follows a holistic approach to health care.

EAST HAVEN

East Haven Rest Home*
83 Main St, East Haven, CT, 06512 (203) 467-5828
Licensure Intermediate Care. *Beds* 20.
Staff RNs 4 (ft), 1 (pt); LPNs 1 (ft), 1 (pt).
Languages Italian

Talmadge Park Health Care*
Talmadge Ave, East Haven, CT, 06512 (203) 469-2316
Licensure Skilled Care; Intermediate Care.
Beds 30. *Certified* Medicaid; Medicare.
Staff RNs 11 (ft); LPNs 4 (ft); Nurses aides 24 (ft); Activities coordinators 3 (ft); Social workers 1 (ft).
Languages Italian
Activities Arts and Crafts; Games; Movies; Dances/Social or cultural gatherings; Picnics; Current events; Cooking; Exercises; Sensory intergration.

Teresa Rest Home Inc
57 Main St, PO Box 313, East Haven, CT, 06512
Admin Josephine Santino. *Medical Dir/Dir of Nursing* Dr Edward Scherr.
Licensure Residential Home. *Beds* 21.
Ownership Proprietary.
Admissions Requirements Minimum age 50; Medical examination.
Staff Nurses aides 3 (ft), 3 (pt); Recreational therapists 1 (ft); Podiatrists.

EAST WINDSOR

Prospect Hill Rehabilitation Center*
96 Prospect Hill Rd, East Windsor, CT, 06088
(203) 623-4846
Licensure Skilled Care; Intermediate Care.
Beds 120. *Certified* Medicaid.
Ownership Proprietary.
Staff LPNs 39 (ft); Nurses aides 75 (ft); Physical therapists 1 (ft); Activities coordinators 2 (ft); Social workers 1 (ft).
Languages French, Italian, Polish
Activities Games; Movies; Dances/Social or cultural gatherings; Music; Discussion groups; Resident council.

ENFIELD

Enfield Nursing Center*
612 Hazard Ave, Enfield, CT, 06082 (203) 749-8388
Licensure Skilled Care; Intermediate Care.
Beds 130. *Certified* Medicaid; Medicare.
Ownership Proprietary.
Staff RNs 3 (ft); LPNs 3 (ft); Social workers 1 (ft).
Languages Italian
Activities Arts and Crafts; Shopping trips; Dances/Social or cultural gatherings; Church; Disscusions; Resident council.

Parkway Pavilion Healthcare
1157 Enfield St, Enfield, CT, 06082 (203) 745-1641
Medical Dir/Dir of Nursing Dr George Donahue.
Licensure Skilled Care. *Beds* 140.
Certified Medicaid; Medicare.
Ownership Proprietary.
Admissions Requirements Minimum age 14; Medical examination; Physician's request.
Staff Physicians 8 (pt); RNs 4 (ft), 18 (pt); LPNs 4 (ft), 12 (pt); Orderlies 3 (pt); Nurses aides 15 (ft), 36 (pt); Physical therapists 1 (pt); Reality therapists 1 (pt); Speech therapists 1 (pt); Activities coordinators 2 (ft), 1 (pt); Dietitians 1 (pt); Dentists 1 (pt); Ophthalmologists 1 (pt); Podiatrists 1 (pt); Audiologists 1 (pt).
Languages Polish, Italian
Facilities Dining room; Physical therapy room; Activities room; Chapel; Crafts room; Laundry room; Barber/Beauty shop; Library.
Activities Arts and Crafts; Cards; Games; Reading groups; Prayer groups; Movies; Shopping trips; Dances/Social or cultural gatherings.

Saint Joseph's Residence
1365 Enfield St, Enfield, CT, 06082 (203) 741-0791
Medical Dir/Dir of Nursing Brendan Maganran MD.
Licensure Skilled Care; Intermediate Care.
Beds 94. *Certified* Medicaid; Medicare.
Ownership Nonprofit.
Languages French, Spanish, Italian, Polish, German, Lithuanian
Affiliation Roman Catholic
Facilities Dining room; Physical therapy room; Activities room; Chapel; Crafts room; Laundry room; Barber/Beauty shop; Library.
Activities Arts and Crafts; Cards; Games; Prayer groups; Movies; Shopping trips; Dances/So-

cial or cultural gatherings.
Description Day center for elderly of the neighboring towns; 27 elderly enrolled in program.

ESSEX

Highland Hall Manor
16 Prospect St, Essex, CT, 06426
Medical Dir/Dir of Nursing Dr John Stanford.
Admissions Requirements Minimum age 21.
Staff Nurses aides 8 (ft), 4 (pt).
Facilities Dining room; Activities room; Laundry room.
Activities Cards; Games; Movies; Shopping trips.

Pettipaug Manor
57 S Main St, Essex, CT, 06426 (203) 767-8422
Medical Dir/Dir of Nursing John Stanford MD.
Licensure Intermediate Care. *Beds* 49. *Certified* Medicaid.
Ownership Proprietary.
Admissions Requirements Minimum age 21; Medical examination; Physician's request.
Staff RNs 4 (ft); LPNs 2 (pt); Nurses aides 7 (ft); Recreational therapists 1 (ft).
Facilities Dining room; Activities room.
Activities Arts and Crafts; Cards; Games; Reading groups; Prayer groups; Movies; Shopping trips; Dances/Social or cultural gatherings; Swimming.
Description Facility supports supervised, therapeutic recreational programs including swimming pool activities.

FAIRFIELD

Carolton Chronic and Convalescent Hospital Inc
400 Mill Plain Rd, Fairfield, CT, 06430 (203) 255-3573
Medical Dir/Dir of Nursing Dr Richard Van de Berghe.
Licensure Skilled Care. *Beds* 219. *Certified* Medicaid; Medicare.
Ownership Proprietary.
Staff RNs 29 (ft), 26 (pt); LPNs 8 (ft), 10 (pt); Nurses aides 96 (ft), 19 (pt); Physical therapists 4 (ft); Recreational therapists 4 (ft); Occupational therapists 3 (pt); Speech therapists 3 (pt); Dietitians 1 (ft).
Languages Spanish, Dutch, Italian, Russian, Yiddish
Facilities Dining room; Physical therapy room; Activities room; Laundry room; Barber/Beauty shop; Library; Physical therapy swimming pool.
Activities Arts and Crafts; Cards; Games; Reading groups; Prayer groups; Movies.
Description Modern up-to-date facility is located in rural setting with all rooms on ground floor. Patients receive best possible care available.

Jewish Home for the Elderly of Fairfield County*
175 Jefferson St, Fairfield, CT, 06432 (203) 374-9461
Licensure Skilled Care; Intermediate Care.

Beds 120. *Certified* Medicaid; Medicare.
Ownership Nonprofit.
Staff RNs 50 (ft); LPNs 12 (ft); Nurses aides
101 (ft); Activities coordinators 4 (ft); Social
workers 2 (ft).
Languages Hebrew, French, Spanish, Portuguese
Affiliation Jewish
Activities Arts and Crafts; Reading groups;
Movies; Shopping trips; Dances/Social or cultural gatherings; Music; Current events;
Picnics; Sheltered workshops.

North Fairfield Geriatric Center Inc*
118 Jefferson St, Fairfield, CT, 06432 (203)
372-4501
Licensure Skilled Care. *Beds* 112. *Certified* Medicaid; Medicare.
Ownership Proprietary.
Staff RNs 12 (ft); LPNs 7 (ft); Nurses aides 58
(ft); Activities coordinators 5 (ft); Social workers 1 (ft).
Languages French, Polish, German, Italian,
Hebrew, Spanish

FARMINGTON

Care Manor of Farmington
Scott Swamp Rd, Farmington, CT, 06032 (203)
677-7707
Admin Martin Meighan. *Medical Dir/Dir of
Nursing* N A C Mohanraj MD.
Licensure Skilled Care. *Beds* 120. *Certified* Medicaid; Medicare.
Ownership Proprietary.
Staff RNs 6 (ft), 8 (pt); LPNs 6 (ft), 8 (pt);
Nurses aides 25 (ft), 20 (pt); Physical therapists
1 (pt); Recreational therapists 2 (ft); Speech
therapists 1 (pt); Dietitians 1 (ft); Dentists 1
(pt); Ophthalmologists 1 (pt); Podiatrists 1 (pt);
Audiologists 1 (pt).
Languages Spanish, French, Polish
Facilities Dining room; Physical therapy room;
Activities room; Chapel; Crafts room; Laundry
room; Barber/Beauty shop.
Activities Arts and Crafts; Cards; Games;
Reading groups; Prayer groups; Movies; Shopping trips; Dances/Social or cultural gatherings.
Description We have an active recreation
department, highlighting outside trips weekly
from spring to fall. Trips includes bowling,
movies, and dining out. Our Family Council is
an active group of family members meeting
monthly for dinner, discussions, and orienting
new members to our facility.

Farmington Convalescent Home*
Rt 6, Colt Hwy, Farmington, CT, 06032 (203)
677-1671
Licensure Skilled Care; Intermediate Care.
Beds 70. *Certified* Medicaid; Medicare.
Ownership Proprietary.
Staff RNs 6 (ft), 1 (pt); LPNs 5 (ft), 1 (pt);
Nurses aides 25 (ft), 1 (pt); Dietitians; Activities coordinators 1 (ft), 1 (pt).
Languages French, Polish
Activities Arts and Crafts; Games; Movies;
Dances/Social or cultural gatherings; Reality
orientation; Holiday celebrations.

FORESTVILLE

Forestville Nursing Center
23 Fair St, Forestville, CT, 06010 (203)
589-2923
Medical Dir/Dir of Nursing Dr Moschello.
Licensure Skilled Care. *Beds* 120. *Certified* Medicaid; Medicare.
Ownership Proprietary.
Admissions Requirements Minimum age 14;
Medical examination.
Staff Physicians 6 (pt); RNs 14 (ft), 3 (pt);
LPNs 7 (ft), 5 (pt); Orderlies 2 (ft), 2 (pt);
Nurses aides 50 (ft), 22 (pt); Physical therapists
1 (ft), 2 (pt); Recreational therapists 4 (ft), 1 (pt);
Occupational therapists 1 (ft); Speech therapists
2 (ft); Activities coordinators 1 (ft); Dietitians 1
(pt).
Languages Greek, Polish, Italian, French,
Spanish
Facilities Dining room; Physical therapy room;
Activities room; Crafts room; Laundry room;
Barber/Beauty shop.
Activities Arts and Crafts; Cards; Games;
Reading groups; Prayer groups; Movies; Shopping trips; Dances/Social or cultural gatherings.
Description In addition to our Geriatric program, we provide rehabilitation programs
geared to the long-term rehabilitation of traumatically brain injured adults. Services offered:
physical therapy, occupational therapy, speech
therapy, psychology, learning center, and therapeutic recreation.

GLASTONBURY

Salmon Brook Convalescent Home*
72 Salmon Brook Dr, Glastonbury, CT, 06033
(203) 633-5244
Licensure Skilled Care; Intermediate Care.
Beds 120. *Certified* Medicaid; Medicare.
Ownership Proprietary.
Staff RNs 14 (ft), 1 (pt); LPNs 44 (ft), 1 (pt);
Nurses aides 2 (ft); Activities coordinators 2
(ft); Dietitians 13 (pt).
Languages Italian, Spanish
Activities Arts and Crafts; Prayer groups;
Movies; Shopping trips; Musicals.

GREENWICH

**Greenwich Laurelton Nursing and Convalescent
Home***
1188 King St, Greenwich, CT, 06830 (203)
531-8300
Licensure Skilled Care. *Beds* 75. *Certified* Medicaid; Medicare.
Ownership Proprietary.
Staff RNs 7 (ft); LPNs 4 (ft); Nurses aides 27
(ft); Physical therapists 1 (ft); Recreational therapists 1 (ft); Dietitians 1 (ft).
Languages Italian, Polish, Spanish

Nathaniel Witherell
70 Parsonage Rd, Greenwich, CT, 06830 (203)
869-4130
Medical Dir/Dir of Nursing Diane Mickley.
Licensure Skilled Care. *Beds* 200. *Certified* Medicaid; Medicare.
Ownership Public.
Admissions Requirements Minimum age 18;

Physician's request.
Staff Physicians 1 (pt); RNs 28 (ft), 4 (pt);
LPNs 7 (ft), 3 (pt); Nurses aides 57 (ft), 23 (pt);
Physical therapists 2 (ft); Recreational therapists
2 (ft), 1 (pt); Occupational therapists 1 (ft);
Speech therapists 1 (pt); Activities coordinators
1 (ft); Dietitians 1 (ft); Dentists 2 (pt); Podiatrists 3 (pt); Audiologists 1 (pt).
Languages Spanish, German, Italian, French
Facilities Dining room; Physical therapy room;
Activities room; Chapel; Crafts room; Laundry
room; Barber/Beauty shop; Library; Auditorium.
Activities Arts and Crafts; Cards; Games;
Reading groups; Prayer groups; Movies; Dances/Social or cultural gatherings; Bell choir;
Cooking/Baking clubs.
Description Facility is set on 8 acres in beautiful
residential area of northern Greenwich.

Putnam-Weaver Nursing Home*
Weaver St, Greenwich, CT, 06830 (203)
869-3553
Licensure Skilled Care. *Beds* 60.
Ownership Proprietary.
Staff RNs 7 (ft); Nurses aides 31 (ft); Dietitians
1 (ft).
Languages Spanish, Italian

GROTON

Fairview
Starr Hill Rd, Groton, CT, 06340 (203)
445-7478
Medical Dir/Dir of Nursing Richard Brent.
Licensure Skilled Care; Intermediate Care.
Beds 60. *Certified* Medicaid; Medicare.
Ownership Nonprofit.
Admissions Requirements Minimum age 14;
Medical examination; Physician's request.
Staff Physicians 2 (pt); RNs 10 (ft), 7 (pt);
LPNs 5 (pt); Orderlies 1 (pt); Nurses aides 12
(ft), 24 (pt); Physical therapists 1 (ft); Recreational therapists 2 (ft); Speech therapists 1 (pt);
Activities coordinators 1 (ft); Dietitians 1 (pt);
Dentists 1 (pt).
Languages Tagalog
Affiliation Independent Order of Odd Fellows
Facilities Dining room; Physical therapy room;
Activities room; Chapel; Crafts room; Laundry
room; Barber/Beauty shop; Auditorium.
Activities Arts and Crafts; Cards; Games;
Reading groups; Prayer groups; Movies; Shopping trips; Dances/Social or cultural gatherings;
Outside scenic trips; Dine out club.
Description Facility is comprised of modern
facilities on 41 acres of land with a spectacular
view overlooking the Thames River across
from the U.S. Coast Guard Academy.

**Groton Regency Retirement and Nursing
Center**
1145 Poquonnock Rd, Groton, CT, 06340
(203) 446-9960
Medical Dir/Dir of Nursing Dr Richard Benton.
Licensure Skilled Care; Intermediate Care.
Beds 270. *Certified* Medicaid; Medicare.
Ownership Proprietary.
Staff Physicians 2 (pt); RNs 14 (ft), 2 (pt);
LPNs 12 (ft), 3 (pt); Nurses aides 55 (ft), 15
(pt); Physical therapists 1 (pt); Recreational

therapists 5 (ft); Speech therapists 1 (pt); Dietitians 1 (ft); Podiatrists 1 (pt).
Languages French, Greek, Italian
Facilities Dining room; Physical therapy room; Activities room; Chapel; Crafts room; Laundry room; Barber/Beauty shop; Library.
Activities Arts and Crafts; Cards; Games; Reading groups; Prayer groups; Movies; Shopping trips; Dances/Social or cultural gatherings.

GUILFORD

Fowler Convalescent Care Center Inc
10 Boston Post Rd, Guilford, CT, 06437 (203) 453-3725
Medical Dir/Dir of Nursing Martin E Fink.
Licensure Skilled Care. *Beds* 90. *Certified* Medicaid; Medicare.
Ownership Proprietary.
Admissions Requirements Minimum age 14; Medical examination; Physician's request.
Staff Physicians 1 (pt); RNs 8 (ft), 12 (pt); LPNs 3 (ft), 1 (pt); Orderlies 1 (ft); Nurses aides 20 (ft), 22 (pt); Physical therapists 1 (pt); Recreational therapists 1 (ft), 1 (pt); Speech therapists 1 (pt); Dietitians 4 (ft), 1 (pt).
Facilities Dining room; Physical therapy room; Activities room; Crafts room; Laundry room; Barber/Beauty shop.
Activities Arts and Crafts; Cards; Games; Reading groups; Prayer groups; Movies; Shopping trips; Dances/Social or cultural gatherings.
Description Center is located on the shoreline with brightly colored flower gardens. A large shaded patio is often used in warm weather for activities. Patient rooms are fashioned in colonial setting. An active recreational program features a kiln used for patient ceramics that are sold to the public.

West Lake Lodge Convalescent Hospital
109 West Lake Ave, Guilford, CT, 06437 (203) 488-9142
Admin Mary D Carpenella. *Medical Dir/Dir of Nursing* John Schiavone MD.
Licensure Skilled Care. *Beds* 60. *Certified* Medicaid; Medicare.
Ownership Proprietary.
Admissions Requirements Medical examination.
Staff RNs 7 (ft), 6 (pt); LPNs 1 (ft), 2 (pt); Orderlies 6 (ft); Nurses aides 27 (ft), 6 (pt); Physical therapists 1 (pt); Recreational therapists 1 (ft); Speech therapists 1 (pt); Dietitians 1 (pt).
Languages Italian, French, Polish
Facilities Dining room; Physical therapy room; Activities room; Crafts room; Laundry room; Barber/Beauty shop.
Activities Arts and Crafts; Cards; Games; Reading groups; Prayer groups; Movies.
Description Lodge is located in the picturesque town of Guilford on spacious grounds; homelike atmosphere makes the transition from private home to health facility much smoother.

HAMDEN

Arden House*
850 Mix Ave, Hamden, CT, 06514 (203) 281-3500
Licensure Skilled Care; Intermediate Care.
Beds 360. *Certified* Medicaid; Medicare.
Ownership Proprietary.
Staff RNs 32 (ft); LPNs 14 (ft); Nurses aides 98 (ft); Activities coordinators 7 (ft).
Languages Italian
Activities Arts and Crafts; Games; Reading groups; Movies; Shopping trips; Dances/Social or cultural gatherings; Resident volunteers; Discussion groups; Sheltered workshops; Resident council; Cooking; Newspaper.

Hamden Health Care Facility*
1270 Sherman Ln, Hamden, CT, 06514 (203) 281-7555
Licensure Skilled Care; Intermediate Care.
Beds 90. *Certified* Medicaid; Medicare.
Ownership Proprietary.
Staff RNs 14 (ft); LPNs 8 (ft), 1 (pt); Physical therapists 2 (ft); Social workers 1 (ft); Others 119 (ft), 9 (pt).
Languages Spanish, Italian

Hyde Park Convalescent Home Inc*
1840 State St, Hamden, CT, 06511 (203) 624-1558
Licensure Skilled Care. *Beds* 26. *Certified* Medicaid; Medicare.
Ownership Proprietary.
Staff RNs 3 (ft); Nurses aides 4 (ft).
Languages Italian
Activities Arts and Crafts; Games; Reading groups; Prayer groups; Movies; Dances/Social or cultural gatherings; Current events; Discussion groups.

Whitney Center Medical Unit
200 Leeder Hill Dr, Hamden, CT, 06517 (203) 281-6745
Medical Dir/Dir of Nursing A Dolinsky MD.
Licensure Skilled Care. *Beds* 59. *Certified* Medicaid; Medicare.
Ownership Nonprofit.
Admissions Requirements Medical examination; Physician's request.
Staff RNs 6 (ft); LPNs 3 (ft); Nurses aides 23 (ft); Physical therapists 1 (ft), 1 (pt); Recreational therapists 2 (ft); Speech therapists 1 (pt); Dietitians 1 (pt); Dentists 1 (pt); Podiatrists 1 (pt).
Languages Italian, German
Facilities Dining room; Physical therapy room; Activities room; Barber/Beauty shop.
Activities Arts and Crafts; Cards; Games; Reading groups; Prayer groups; Movies; Shopping trips; Dances/Social or cultural gatherings.

Whitney Manor Convalescent Center Inc
2800 Whitney Ave, Hamden, CT, 06518 (203) 288-6230
Admin Lawrence Amkraut. *Medical Dir/Dir of Nursing* Ronald E Coe MD.
Licensure Skilled Care. *Beds* 150. *Certified* Medicaid; Medicare.
Ownership Proprietary.
Admissions Requirements Minimum age 14; Medical examination; Physician's request.
Staff Physicians 15 (pt); RNs 15 (ft), 5 (pt); LPNs 7 (ft), 4 (pt); Orderlies 5 (ft); Nurses aides 60 (ft), 20 (pt); Physical therapists 1 (pt); Recreational therapists 3 (ft), 1 (pt); Occupational therapists 1 (pt); Speech therapists 1 (pt); Activities coordinators 1 (ft); Dietitians 1 (pt); Dentists 2 (pt); Ophthalmologists 1 (pt); Podiatrists 1 (pt); Audiologists 1 (pt).
Languages Italian, Spanish, French
Facilities Dining room; Physical therapy room; Activities room; Chapel; Crafts room; Laundry room; Barber/Beauty shop.
Activities Arts and Crafts; Cards; Games; Reading groups; Prayer groups; Movies; Shopping trips; Dances/Social or cultural gatherings.
Description This is a modern skilled nursing facility centrally located in a residential area on the bus line; under same ownership-management for 12 years.

HARTFORD

Avery Nursing Home
705 New Britain Ave, Hartford, CT, 06106 (203) 527-9126
Medical Dir/Dir of Nursing Dr John T Beebe.
Licensure Skilled Care. *Beds* 90. *Certified* Medicaid; Medicare.
Ownership Nonprofit.
Staff Physicians; Nurses aides.
Languages Spanish, Polish, Russian, French
Activities Prayer groups.

Buckley Convalescent Home
210 George St, Hartford, CT, 06114 (203) 249-9166
Medical Dir/Dir of Nursing John Wells.
Licensure Skilled Care. *Beds* 120. *Certified* Medicaid; Medicare.
Ownership Proprietary.
Admissions Requirements Minimum age 18; Medical examination; Physician's request.
Staff Physicians 10 (pt); RNs 5 (ft), 4 (pt); LPNs 6 (ft), 8 (pt); Orderlies 5 (ft); Nurses aides 40 (ft); Physical therapists 1 (ft); Recreational therapists 2 (ft); Speech therapists 1 (pt); Dietitians 1 (ft), 1 (pt); Dentists 1 (pt); Ophthalmologists 1 (pt); Podiatrists 1 (pt); Audiologists 1 (pt).
Languages Polish, French, Italian, Spanish, Japanese
Facilities Dining room; Physical therapy room; Activities room; Laundry room; Barber/Beauty shop.
Activities Arts and Crafts; Cards; Games; Reading groups; Prayer groups; Movies; Shopping trips; Dances/Social or cultural gatherings.
Description Facility is located in the south end of Hartford convenient to bus lines and near interstate highways.

The Gables Convalescent Home Inc*
276 Washington St, Hartford, CT, 06106 (203) 522-8209
Licensure Skilled Care. *Beds* 73. *Certified* Medicaid; Medicare.
Ownership Proprietary.
Staff RNs 4 (ft), 1 (pt); LPNs 7 (ft); Nurses aides 25 (ft), 1 (pt); Activities coordinators 2 (ft), 1 (pt); Dietitians 1 (ft); Social workers 1 (ft).
Languages Spanish, Polish
Activities Arts and Crafts; Games; Prayer groups; Music; Psychogeriatric group; Reality orientation; Remotivation.

Greenwood Health Center
5 Greenwood St, Hartford, CT, 06106 (203) 236-2901
Medical Dir/Dir of Nursing Dr Giarnella.
Licensure Skilled Care. *Beds* 240. *Certified* Medicaid; Medicare.
Ownership Proprietary.
Admissions Requirements Medical examination.
Staff Physicians 2 (pt); RNs 17 (ft), 9 (pt); LPNs 17 (ft), 19 (pt); Nurses aides 56 (ft), 37 (pt); Physical therapists 1 (ft); Recreational therapists 3 (ft), 1 (pt); Speech therapists 1 (pt); Dietitians 1 (ft); Dentists 1 (pt); Ophthalmologists 1 (pt); Podiatrists 1 (pt); Audiologists 1 (pt).
Languages Spanish, Polish
Facilities Dining room; Physical therapy room; Laundry room; TV room.
Activities Arts and Crafts; Cards; Games; Reading groups; Prayer groups; Movies; Shopping trips; Dances/Social or cultural gatherings; Discussion groups; Dinner club; Cooking groups; Exercise; Resident council; Sensory groups; Pet therapy; Newspapers.
Description Greenwood has an exceptional volunteer program with over 150 people. Facility is very conveniently located to all major highways in the Hartford area and to local hospitals and doctors offices. VA approved.

Hebrew Home and Hospital
615 Tower Ave, Hartford, CT, 06112 (203) 242-6207
Licensure Skilled Care. *Beds* SNF 262; ICF 8.
Certified Medicaid; Medicare.
Ownership Nonprofit.
Staff Physicians; Dietitians; Nurses aides.
Languages Yiddish, Hebrew
Affiliation Jewish
Activities Prayer groups; Arts and Crafts; Shopping trips.

Hillside Manor Nursing Home*
151 Hillside Ave, Hartford, CT, 06106 (203) 278-1060
Licensure Skilled Care. *Beds* 180. *Certified* Medicaid; Medicare.
Ownership Proprietary.
Staff RNs 10 (ft); LPNs 10 (ft); Nurses aides 70 (ft); Physical therapists 2 (ft); Occupational therapists 1 (ft); Activities coordinators 3 (ft); COTA 2 (ft); Social workers 2 (ft).
Languages Spanish, Portuguese, French, Polish, Yiddish
Activities Theraputic recreation.

Lorraine Manor*
25 Lorraine St, Hartford, CT, 06105 (203) 233-8241
Licensure Skilled Care; Intermediate Care.
Beds 270. *Certified* Medicaid.
Ownership Proprietary.
Staff Physicians; RNs 1 (ft), 10 (pt); LPNs 14 (ft); Nurses aides 95 (ft); Physical therapists 3 (ft); Occupational therapists 1 (ft); Activities coordinators 6 (ft); Social workers 2 (ft); Special educator 1 (ft).
Languages Polish, Spanish, French
Activities Arts and Crafts; Shopping trips; Dances/Social or cultural gatherings; Pet therapy; Music therapy.

Noble Building Intermediate Care Facility*
705 New Britain Ave, Hartford, CT, 06106 (203) 527-9126
Licensure Intermediate Care. *Beds* 57. *Certified* Medicaid.
Ownership Nonprofit.
Staff LPNs 9 (ft), 1 (pt); Activities coordinators 1 (ft), 1 (pt); Social workers 1 (pt).
Languages Spanish, Polish, Russian, French
Affiliation Congregational

JEWETT CITY

Summit Convalescent Home
15 Preston Rd, Jewett City, CT, 06351 (203) 376-4438
Licensure Skilled Care. *Beds* 90. *Certified* Medicaid; Medicare.
Ownership Proprietary.
Staff Physicians; Dietitians; Nurses aides.
Languages French, Polish, Italian, Greek, Finnish
Activities Prayer groups; Dances/Social or cultural gatherings.

KENSINGTON

Ledgecrest Convalescent Home*
154 Kensington Rd, Kensington, CT, 06037 (203) 828-4946
Licensure Skilled Care. *Beds* 60. *Certified* Medicaid; Medicare.
Ownership Proprietary.
Staff Physicians; RNs 14 (ft), 1 (pt); LPNs 6 (ft), 1 (pt); Nurses aides 44 (ft), 1 (pt); Activities coordinators; Dietitians; Social workers 1 (ft).
Languages Polish, Italian, Spanish
Activities Arts and Crafts; Games; Movies; Dances/Social or cultural gatherings; Church services.

LITCHFIELD

Rose-Haven*
North St, Litchfield, CT, 06759 (203) 567-9475
Licensure Skilled Care. *Beds* 25.
Ownership Proprietary.
Staff RNs 3 (ft), 1 (pt); LPNs 2 (ft), 1 (pt); Nurses aides 8 (ft), 1 (pt); Activities coordinators 1 (pt); Dietitians 1 (pt).
Languages Italian, French

MADISON

Watrous Nursing Home Inc
9 Neck Rd, Madison, CT, 06443 (203) 245-9483
Medical Dir/Dir of Nursing Arnold Winokur MD.
Licensure Skilled Care. *Beds* 45. *Certified* Medicaid; Medicare.
Ownership Proprietary.
Staff Physicians; Dietitians; Nurses aides.
Facilities Dining room; Physical therapy room; Activities room; Barber/Beauty shop.
Activities Arts and Crafts; Cards; Games; Reading groups; Prayer groups; Movies; Shopping trips; Dances/Social or cultural gatherings.
Description Home is located in a quiet residential setting close to the Long Island Sound;

offers a very home-like environment for those requiring long-term care.

MANCHESTER

Crestfield Convalescent Home
565 Vernon St, Manchester, CT, 06040 (203) 643-5151
Licensure Skilled Care. *Beds* 95. *Certified* Medicaid; Medicare.
Ownership Proprietary.
Staff Physicians; Dietitians; Nurses aides.
Languages Italian, Polish, French, Spanish
Facilities Dining room; Physical therapy room; Activities room; Barber/Beauty shop.
Activities Arts and Crafts; Cards; Games; Reading groups; Prayer groups; Movies; Shopping trips; Dances/Social or cultural gatherings.
Description Facility has a beautiful country setting.

Fenwood Manor Inc
565 Vernon Rd, Manchester, CT, 06040 (203) 643-5151
Licensure Intermediate Care. *Beds* 60.
Ownership Proprietary.
Staff Physicians; Dietitians; Nurses aides.
Languages Polish, Italian, French, Spanish
Facilities Dining room; Physical therapy room; Activities room; Barber/Beauty shop.
Activities Arts and Crafts; Cards; Games; Reading groups; Prayer groups; Movies; Shopping trips; Dances/Social or cultural gatherings.
Description Facility is situated in a beautiful country setting.

Holiday House*
29 Cottage St, Manchester, CT, 06040 (203) 649-2358
Admin Katherine M Giblin.
Licensure Intermediate Care. *Beds* 27. *Certified* Medicaid; Medicare.
Ownership Proprietary.
Staff RNs 2 (ft); LPNs 1 (ft), 1 (pt); Nurses aides 4 (ft); Social workers.
Languages French, German, Polish, Italian
Activities Arts and Crafts; Movies; Sing-a-long; Picnics.

Laurel Living Center*
91 Chestnut St, Manchester, CT, 06040 (203) 649-4519
Licensure Home for the aged. *Beds* 43.
Ownership Proprietary.
Languages Italian, Spanish, French
Activities Arts and Crafts; Games; Movies; Dances/Social or cultural gatherings; Field trips.

Manchester Manor Nursing Home*
385 W Center St, Manchester, CT, 06040 (203) 646-0129
Licensure Skilled Care; Intermediate Care.
Beds 45.
Ownership Proprietary.
Staff RNs 8 (ft); Nurses aides 20 (ft), 1 (pt); Activities coordinators 1 (ft); Dietitians 1 (ft); Social workers 1 (ft).
Languages French, Italian, German
Activities Arts and Crafts; Cards; Games; Reading groups; Movies.

Manchester Manor Rest Home*
385 W Center St, Manchester, CT, 06040 (203) 646-0129
Licensure Intermediate Care. *Beds* 71. *Certified* Medicaid.
Ownership Proprietary.
Staff RNs 5 (ft); LPNs 2 (ft); Nurses aides 12 (ft); Activities coordinators 1 (ft); Dietitians 1 (ft); Social workers 1 (ft).
Languages French, Italian, German
Activities Arts and Crafts; Games; Movies.

Meadows Manor Inc
333 Bidwell St, Manchester, CT, 06040 (203) 647-9191
Admin Philip S Viner. *Medical Dir/Dir of Nursing* Robert K Butterfield MD.
Licensure Skilled Care; Intermediate Care. *Beds* 518. *Certified* Medicaid; Medicare.
Ownership Proprietary.
Admissions Requirements Minimum age 14; Medical examination.
Staff Physicians 5 (pt); RNs 38 (ft); LPNs 32 (ft); Nurses aides 132 (ft); Physical therapists 1 (ft), 2 (pt); Speech therapists 1 (pt); Activities coordinators 9 (ft); Dietitians 1 (ft); Dentists 1 (pt); Ophthalmologists 1 (pt); Podiatrists 2 (pt); Audiologists 1 (pt).
Languages French, Italian, Spanish
Facilities Dining room; Physical therapy room; Activities room; Chapel; Crafts room; Laundry room; Barber/Beauty shop; Library.
Activities Arts and Crafts; Cards; Games; Reading groups; Prayer groups; Movies; Shopping trips; Dances/Social or cultural gatherings.
Description Meadows Manor is located in Manchester, "The City of Village Charm," a rural setting within minutes of downtown.

MARLBOROUGH

Lord Marlborough Manor
85 Stage Harbor Rd, Marlborough, CT, 06447 (203) 295-9531
Medical Dir/Dir of Nursing Dr Donald Timmerman.
Licensure Intermediate Care. *Beds* 120. *Certified* Medicaid.
Ownership Proprietary.
Admissions Requirements Minimum age 16; Medical examination.
Staff RNs 7 (ft); LPNs 2 (ft); Nurses aides 13 (ft); Recreational therapists 2 (ft).
Languages Polish, Italian, Dutch, German, French
Facilities Dining room; Activities room; Chapel; Laundry room; Barber/Beauty shop; Library.
Activities Arts and Crafts; Cards; Games; Reading groups; Prayer groups; Movies; Shopping trips; Dances/Social or cultural gatherings.

MERIDEN

The Bradley Home Infirmary*
PO Box 886, 320 Colony St, Meriden, CT, 06450 (203) 235-5716
Licensure Skilled Care. *Beds* 30.
Ownership Nonprofit.
Staff RNs 7 (ft); Nurses aides 14 (ft).
Languages Spanish, German, Polish, French

Activities Arts and Crafts; Games; Movies; Shopping trips; Dances/Social or cultural gatherings; Cooking; Exercises; Picnics; Discussion groups; Resident council.

Corner House Nursing Inc*
1 Griswold St, Meriden, CT, 06450 (203) 237-2257
Licensure Intermediate Care. *Beds* 30. *Certified* Medicaid.
Ownership Proprietary.
Staff RNs 8 (ft); LPNs 2 (ft); Nurses aides 7 (ft); Activities coordinators 1 (ft); Dietitians 2 (ft).
Languages French, Polish
Activities Arts and Crafts; Games; Dances/Social or cultural gatherings.

The Curtis Home Infimary*
380 Crown St, Meriden, CT, 06450 (203) 235-4338
Licensure Skilled Care. *Beds* 29. *Certified* Medicaid.
Ownership Nonprofit.
Staff Nurses aides 8 (ft).
Languages Polish, Italian, Spanish, German, French
Activities Arts and Crafts; Games; Movies; Dances/Social or cultural gatherings; Sing-a-longs; Excursions.

Meriden Nursing Home*
845 Paddock Ave, Meriden, CT, 06450 (203) 238-2645
Licensure Skilled Care. *Beds* 120. *Certified* Medicaid; Medicare.
Ownership Proprietary.
Staff RNs 7 (ft); LPNs 5 (ft), 1 (pt); Nurses aides 40 (ft); Activities coordinators 2 (ft); Social workers 1 (ft).
Languages Spanish, German, Italian, Hungarian, Polish

Miller Memorial—Community
360 Broad St, Meriden, CT, 06450 (203) 237-8815
Medical Dir/Dir of Nursing Dr John Flynn.
Licensure Skilled Care; Intermediate Care. *Beds* SNF 3; ICF 60. *Certified* Medicaid; Medicare.
Ownership Nonprofit.
Admissions Requirements Minimum age 62; Medical examination.
Staff RNs 3 (ft), 17 (pt); LPNs 1 (ft), 6 (pt); Nurses aides 16 (ft), 7 (pt); Physical therapists 1 (pt); Recreational therapists 2 (ft); Dietitians 1 (pt).
Languages Polish, French, Spanish
Facilities Dining room; Physical therapy room; Activities room; Chapel; Crafts room; Laundry room; Barber/Beauty shop; Library; Lounges; Snack nooks.
Activities Arts and Crafts; Cards; Games; Reading groups; Prayer groups; Movies; Shopping trips; Dances/Social or cultural gatherings.
Description "Life is precious and significant." Miller Memorial Community offers gracious living in a dignified and caring atmosphere providing total care in a village setting with intercom system, central air conditioning, private dining room, and scenic patios; independent

cottages and efficiencies, rest home with nursing supervision, skilled nursing home, personal physician, complete professional staff.

Mills Manor Convalescent Home*
292 Thorpe Ave, Meriden, CT, 06450 (203) 237-1206
Licensure Skilled Care. *Beds* 30. *Certified* Medicaid; Medicare.
Ownership Proprietary.
Staff RNs 3 (ft), 1 (pt); LPNs 1 (ft); Nurses aides 9 (ft), 1 (pt); Activities coordinators 1 (pt).
Activities Arts and Crafts; Games; Movies; Shopping trips; Dances/Social or cultural gatherings; Music.

Royal Crest Convalescent and Rest Home*
33 Roy St, Meriden, CT, 06450 (203) 237-8457
Licensure Skilled Care; Intermediate Care. *Beds* SNF 120; ICF 59. *Certified* Medicaid; Medicare.
Ownership Proprietary.
Staff RNs 3 (ft); LPNs 15 (ft).
Languages Spanish, Polish
Activities Arts and Crafts; Shopping trips; Dances/Social or cultural gatherings; Workshops; Music; Current events.

Thomas A Cocomo Memorial*
33 Cone Ave, Meriden, CT, 06450 (203) 238-1606
Admin Carmen C Cocomo.
Licensure Intermediate Care. *Beds* 90. *Certified* Medicaid.
Languages German, Polish, Italian

Westfield Manor Health Care Center*
65 Westfield Rd, Meriden, CT, 06450 (203) 238-1291
Licensure Skilled Care; Intermediate Care. *Beds* 120. *Certified* Medicaid; Medicare.
Ownership Proprietary.
Staff RNs 15 (ft); LPNs 10 (ft); Nurses aides 45 (ft).
Languages Italian, Polish, French, Spanish
Activities Arts and Crafts; Games.

MIDDLEBURY

Middlebury Convalescent Home Inc*
778 Middlebury Rd, Middlebury, CT, 06762 (203) 758-2471
Licensure Skilled Care. *Beds* 58. *Certified* Medicaid; Medicare.
Ownership Proprietary.
Staff RNs 9 (ft); LPNs 1 (ft), 1 (pt); Nurses aides 17 (ft).
Languages Italian, Polish, Lithuanian
Activities Recreation and art therapy; Music.

MIDDLETOWN

Lutheran Home of Middletown Inc
Ridgewood Rd, Middletown, CT, 06457 (203) 347-7479
Admin Arnold R Eggert. *Medical Dir/Dir of Nursing* Dr Matthew Raider.
Licensure Skilled Care. *Beds* 28. *Certified* Medicaid.
Ownership Nonprofit.
Admissions Requirements Minimum age 65;

Medical examination.
Staff Physicians 5 (pt); RNs 3 (ft), 4 (pt);
Nurses aides 6 (ft), 9 (pt); Physical therapists 1
(pt); Activities coordinators 1 (ft), 1 (pt); Dietitians 1 (pt); Dentists 1 (pt); Podiatrists 1 (pt).
Languages Spanish, German, Polish, Swedish,
Italian
Affiliation Lutheran
Facilities Dining room; Physical therapy room;
Activities room; Crafts room; Laundry room;
Barber/Beauty shop; Library; Solariums.
Activities Arts and Crafts; Cards; Games;
Reading groups; Prayer groups; Movies; Shopping trips; Dances/Social or cultural gatherings;
Bingo; Out trips.
Description Facility features fund raiser for
Arthritis Foundation; one-day fair, proceeds
used for patient activities; film strip presentations for public relations to outside groups.

Middlesex Convalescent Center Inc
100 Randolph Rd, Middletown, CT, 06457
(203) 344-0353
Medical Dir/Dir of Nursing A Wazed Mahmud
MD.
Licensure Skilled Care; Intermediate Care.
Beds 150. *Certified* Medicaid; Medicare.
Ownership Proprietary.
Admissions Requirements Minimum age 14;
Medical examination; Physician's request.
Staff RNs 8 (ft), 8 (pt); LPNs 9 (ft), 9 (pt);
Nurses aides 34 (ft), 33 (pt); Physical therapists
1 (ft); Recreational therapists 1 (ft), 1 (pt); Occupational therapists 1 (pt); Speech therapists 1
(pt); Activities coordinators 1 (ft); Dietitians 1
(pt).
Languages Spanish, Italian, Polish
Facilities Dining room; Physical therapy room;
Activities room; Chapel; Crafts room; Laundry
room; Barber/Beauty shop.
Activities Arts and Crafts; Cards; Games;
Reading groups; Prayer groups; Movies; Shopping trips; Dances/Social or cultural gatherings.

Middletown Healthcare Center Inc*
111 Church St, Middletown, CT, 06457 (203)
347-7286
Licensure Intermediate Care. *Beds* 180.
Ownership Proprietary.
Staff RNs 12 (ft), 1 (pt); LPNs 15 (ft), 1 (pt);
Nurses aides 32 (ft); Activities coordinators 5
(ft), 1 (pt); Social workers 4 (ft).
Languages Italian, Polish, Spanish

Queen's Convalescent Inc
600 Highland Ave, PO Box 1056, Middletown,
CT, 06457 (203) 347-3315
Medical Dir/Dir of Nursing Felix G Sheehan
MD.
Licensure Skilled Care. *Beds* 90. *Certified* Medicaid; Medicare.
Ownership Proprietary.
Admissions Requirements Minimum age 21;
Medical examination.
Staff Physicians 4 (pt); RNs 6 (ft), 4 (pt); LPNs
3 (ft), 4 (pt); Orderlies 3 (ft), 2 (pt); Nurses aides
28 (ft), 13 (pt); Physical therapists 1 (pt); Recreational therapists 1 (ft), 1 (pt).
Languages Italian, German
Facilities Dining room; Physical therapy room;
Activities room; Chapel; Crafts room; Laundry
room; Barber/Beauty shop; Library.
Activities Arts and Crafts; Cards; Games;

Reading groups; Prayer groups; Movies; Shopping trips; Entertainment.
Description Facility is well-situated, light, and
airy.

Ridgewood Central Inc—Health Care Facility*
955 Washington St Ext, Middletown, CT,
06457 (203) 347-5604
Licensure Skilled Care. *Beds* 90. *Certified* Medicaid; Medicare.
Ownership Proprietary.
Staff RNs 59 (ft).
Languages Italian, Greek, German, Hebrew,
French
Activities Arts and Crafts; Games; Movies;
Music; Exercises; Sing-a-longs.

Sanibel Convalescent Home
S Main St, Middletown, CT, 06457 (203)
347-1696
Licensure Skilled Care. *Beds* 60. *Certified* Medicaid.
Ownership Proprietary.
Staff Physicians; Dietitians; Nurses aides.
Languages Polish, Italian, German
Activities Prayer groups; Arts and Crafts; Shopping trips.

MILFORD

Golden Hill Nursing Home
2028 Bridgeport Ave, Milford, CT, 06460 (203)
877-0371
Medical Dir/Dir of Nursing Dr Thelma Batiancila.
Licensure Skilled Care. *Beds* 120.
Certified Medicaid; Medicare.
Ownership Proprietary.
Admissions Requirements Minimum age 14;
Medical examination.
Staff RNs 11 (ft), 8 (pt); LPNs 4 (ft), 8 (pt);
Nurses aides 38 (ft), 22 (pt); Physical therapists
1 (ft), 1 (pt); Recreational therapists 2 (ft), 3 (pt);
Occupational therapists 1 (ft); Speech therapists
1 (ft); Activities coordinators 1 (ft), 3 (pt); Dietitians 1 (ft); Dentists 1 (ft); Podiatrists 1 (ft);
Audiologists 1 (ft).
Languages Italian, Hungarian, Spanish, Swedish, Philipino
Facilities Dining room; Physical therapy room;
Activities room; Chapel; Crafts room; Barber-
/Beauty shop.
Activities Arts and Crafts; Cards; Games;
Reading groups; Prayer groups; Movies; Shopping trips; Dances/Social or cultural gatherings.
Description Golden Hill has a friendly, warm
atmosphere and is just minutes from downtown Milford. Patients enjoy restaurant atmosphere with waitress service and selective menus
in main dining room. Along with comprehensive geriatric services, Golden Hill offers
2 special programs: traumatic brain injury, and
nutrition.

Milford Heights Nursing Home*
195 Platt St, Milford, CT, 06460 (203)
878-5958
Licensure Skilled Care. *Beds* 120. *Certified* Medicaid; Medicare.
Ownership Proprietary.
Staff LPNs 12 (ft); Nurses aides 35 (ft); Activities coordinators 2 (ft); Social workers 1 (ft).

Languages Polish, Spanish, Italian, Ukranian
Activities Arts and Crafts; Games;
Dances/Social or cultural gatherings; Outside
entertainment.

Pond Point Skilled Nursing Facility*
60 Platt St, Milford, CT, 06460 (203) 878-5786
Licensure Skilled Care; Intermediate Care.
Beds 142. *Certified* Medicaid; Medicare.
Ownership Proprietary.
Staff RNs 24 (ft); LPNs 9 (ft); Nurses aides 41
(ft); Activities coordinators 3 (ft); Dietitians 1
(ft).
Languages Polish, Italian, Spanish

MOODUS

Chestelm Convalescent Home
Town St, Moodus, CT, 06469 (203) 873-1455
Medical Dir/Dir of Nursing Dr Phillip Berwick.
Licensure Skilled Care; Intermediate Care.
Beds SNF 50; ICF 13. *Certified* Medicaid.
Ownership Proprietary.
Staff Physicians 5 (pt); RNs 7 (ft), 4 (pt); LPNs
3 (ft), 5 (pt); Nurses aides 18 (ft), 9 (pt);
Physical therapists 1 (pt); Recreational therapists 2 (ft); Occupational therapists 1 (pt); Speech therapists 1 (pt); Activities coordinators 1
(pt); Dietitians 1 (pt); Dentists 1 (pt); Podiatrists 1 (pt); Audiologists 1 (pt).
Languages Czech, French, Italian, Polish
Facilities Dining room; Physical therapy room;
Activities room; Crafts room; Laundry room;
Library.
Activities Arts and Crafts; Cards; Games;
Reading groups; Movies; Shopping trips; Dances/Social or cultural gatherings.
Description Chestelm is a converted estate kept
in a home-like atmosphere with sitting rooms,
dining rooms, recreation area, and a newly built
annex. Our dietary department, under the
direct supervision of a dietary consultant, specializes in home-style cooking. Chestelm is devoted to the comfort care and well-being of every
resident.

MYSTIC

Mary Elizabeth Convalescent Home*
28 Broadway, Mystic, CT, 06355 (203)
536-9655
Licensure Skilled Care. *Beds* 50. *Certified* Medicaid; Medicare.
Ownership Proprietary.
Staff RNs 8 (ft), 1 (pt); LPNs 3 (ft), 1 (pt);
Nurses aides 27 (ft), 1 (pt).

Mystic Manor Inc
475 High St, Mystic, CT, 06355 (203) 536-2167
and 536-6070
Admin Samuel Whipple. *Medical Dir/Dir of
Nursing* L Edwin Sproul MD.
Licensure Skilled Care. *Beds* 60. *Certified* Medicaid; Medicare.
Ownership Proprietary.
Admissions Requirements Minimum age 14;
Medical examination.
Staff Physicians 5 (pt); RNs 2 (ft), 16 (pt);
LPNs 3 (ft), 1 (pt); Nurses aides 16 (ft), 21 (pt);
Physical therapists 1 (pt); Recreational thera-

pists 2 (pt); Speech therapists 1 (pt); Dietitians 1 (ft); Dentists 1 (pt); Podiatrists 1 (pt); Audiologists 1 (pt).
Languages Korean
Facilities Dining room; Physical therapy room; Activities room; Chapel; Laundry room; Library; Dental care unit; Medical examination and treatment room.
Activities Arts and Crafts; Cards; Games; Reading groups; Prayer groups; Movies; Dances/Social or cultural gatherings; Outing trips.
Description Mystic Manor is located in the beautiful, historic, seafaring New England village of Mystic. Facility is located high on a hill overlooking the Mystic River Valley with 8 acres of park-like grounds; specializes in rehabilitative and long-term care.

Rita's Rest Home
14 Godfrey St, Mystic, CT, 06355
Medical Dir/Dir of Nursing Dr Weiss.
Admissions Requirements Minimum age 21.
Staff Nurses aides 8 (ft), 4 (pt).
Facilities Dining room; Activities room; Laundry room.
Activities Cards; Reading groups; Shopping trips.

NAUGATUCK

Glendale Health Care Center Inc*
4 Hazel Ave, Naugatuck, CT, 06770 (203) 723-1456
Licensure Skilled Care; Intermediate Care.
Beds 120. *Certified* Medicaid; Medicare.
Ownership Proprietary.
Staff RNs 16 (ft); LPNs 5 (ft); Nurses aides 66 (ft); Physical therapists 1 (ft); Activities coordinators 2 (ft); Social workers 1 (ft).
Languages German, Italian, French, Swedish, Polish

Jones Nursing Home Inc
41 Millville Ave, Naugatuck, CT, 06770 (203) 729-4529
Licensure Skilled Care. *Beds* 57. *Certified* Medicaid.
Ownership Proprietary.
Staff Physicians; Dietitians.
Languages Portugese, Russian, Italian, French
Activities Prayer groups; Arts and Crafts; Shopping trips.

NEW BRITAIN

Andrew House Healthcare
66 Clinic Dr, New Britain, CT, 06051 (203) 225-8608
Medical Dir/Dir of Nursing Dr Edward Martin.
Licensure Skilled Care. *Beds* 90.
Certified Medicaid; Medicare.
Ownership Proprietary.
Admissions Requirements Physician's request.
Staff RNs; LPNs; Nurses aides; Physical therapists 1 (pt); Reality therapists 1 (ft), 1 (pt); Recreational therapists 1 (ft), 1 (pt); Activities coordinators.
Languages Polish, Spanish, French
Facilities Dining room; Physical therapy room; Laundry room; Barber/Beauty shop.

Activities Arts and Crafts; Cards; Games; Reading groups; Prayer groups; Movies; Shopping trips; Dances/Social or cultural gatherings.
Description Located within 2 miles of New Britain General Hospital and across the street from a clinic where a group of 39 physicians have their practices, facility offers both semi-private and private room accomodations.

Brittany Farms Health Center
400 Brittany Farms Rd, New Britain, CT, 06053 (203) 224-3111
Admin Thomas V Tolisano. *Medical Dir/Dir of Nursing* Dr D Balaz and Dr P Sereny.
Licensure Skilled Care; Intermediate Care.
Beds 120. *Certified* Medicaid; Medicare.
Ownership Proprietary.
Admissions Requirements Minimum age 18; Medical examination; Physician's request.
Staff Physicians 5 (pt); RNs 40 (ft), 2 (pt); LPNs 3 (ft), 1 (pt); Orderlies 2 (ft); Nurses aides 84 (ft); Physical therapists 3 (ft); Reality therapists 2 (pt); Recreational therapists 5 (ft), 1 (pt); Speech therapists 1 (pt); Activities coordinators 5 (ft), 1 (pt); Dietitians 1 (ft); Dentists 1 (pt); Ophthalmologists 1 (pt); Podiatrists 1 (pt); Audiologists 1 (pt).
Languages Polish, Spanish, Italian
Facilities Dining room; Physical therapy room; Activities room; Crafts room; Laundry room; Barber/Beauty shop; Library.
Activities Arts and Crafts; Cards; Games; Reading groups; Prayer groups; Movies; Shopping trips; Dances/Social or cultural gatherings.
Description Facility located in country setting, on bus line, close to major shopping and highways; excellent rehabilitation program; several self-help groups, mental health, AA, well organized patient care planning to include rehabilitation discharge planning, long and short-term goals. VA approved.

Jerome Home*
975 Corbin Ave, New Britain, CT, 06052 (203) 299-3707
Licensure Intermediate Care. *Beds* 60. *Certified* Medicaid.
Ownership Nonprofit.
Staff RNs 4 (ft); LPNs 5 (ft); Nurses aides 12 (ft); Recreational therapists; Activities coordinators 1 (ft); Dietitians 3 (ft).
Languages French, Polish
Activities Arts and Crafts; Games; Dances/Social or cultural gatherings; Exercises; Musicals; Outings; Outside entertainment.

Lexington Convalescent Home Inc
32 Lexington St, New Britain, CT, 06052 (203) 225-6397
Medical Dir/Dir of Nursing Abraham Bernstein.
Licensure Skilled Care. *Beds* 65. *Certified* Medicaid; Medicare.
Ownership Proprietary.
Admissions Requirements Minimum age 18; Medical examination; Physician's request.
Staff RNs 4 (ft), 1 (pt); LPNs 5 (ft); Orderlies 1 (ft), 1 (pt); Nurses aides 18 (ft), 9 (pt); Physical therapists 1 (pt); Reality therapists 1 (ft), 1 (pt); Recreational therapists 1 (ft), 1 (pt).
Languages French, Italian, Polish, Spanish
Facilities Dining room; Physical therapy room; Activities room; Crafts room; Laundry room.

Activities Arts and Crafts; Cards; Games; Reading groups; Prayer groups; Movies; Shopping trips; Entertainment; Pet therapy.
Description Although an older facility, good nursing care is provided; on a local bus line and within walking distance of downtown area; surrounded by the beauty and accessibility of Walnut Hill Park.

Monsignor Bojnowski Manor Inc
50 Pulaski St, New Britain, CT, 06053 (203) 229-0336
Medical Dir/Dir of Nursing L B Slysz MD.
Licensure Skilled Care. *Beds* 60. *Certified* Medicaid; Medicare.
Ownership Nonprofit.
Admissions Requirements Minimum age 14; Medical examination.
Staff RNs 6 (ft), 4 (pt); LPNs 4 (ft), 3 (pt); Nurses aides 22 (ft), 6 (pt); Physical therapists 1 (pt); Recreational therapists 1 (ft); Occupational therapists 1 (pt); Speech therapists 1 (pt); Activities coordinators 1 (pt); Dietitians 1 (pt); Dentists 1 (pt); Podiatrists 1 (pt); Audiologists 1 (pt).
Languages Polish, Spanish, German, French
Affiliation Roman Catholic
Facilities Dining room; Physical therapy room; Activities room; Chapel; Crafts room; Laundry room; Barber/Beauty shop; Library.
Activities Arts and Crafts; Cards; Games; Reading groups; Prayer groups; Movies; Shopping trips.
Description Facility features family gatherings for anniversary, birthday parties, and outdoor picnics during the summer; Christmas Festival of Lights outing.

Walnut Hill Convalescent Home
55 Grand St, New Britain, CT, 06052 (203) 223-3617
Medical Dir/Dir of Nursing Stephen Greenberg MD.
Licensure Skilled Care. *Beds* 180. *Certified* Medicaid; Medicare.
Ownership Proprietary.
Admissions Requirements Minimum age 14; Physician's request.
Staff RNs 11 (ft), 4 (pt); LPNs 8 (ft), 14 (pt); Orderlies 7 (ft); Nurses aides 55 (ft), 6 (pt); Physical therapists 1 (ft); Recreational therapists 2 (ft); Activities coordinators 1 (ft); Dietitians 1 (ft), 1 (pt).
Languages Polish, Spanish, Italian
Facilities Dining room; Physical therapy room; Activities room; Chapel; Crafts room; Barber/Beauty shop.
Activities Arts and Crafts; Cards; Games; Reading groups; Prayer groups; Movies.
Description Rehabilitation program includes a nurse and aide who teach all ADL skills to all new admissions. Alzheimer's support group meeting conducted monthly for the community.

NEW CANAAN

Waveny Care Center*
3 Farm Rd, New Canaan, CT, 06840 (203) 966-8725
Licensure Skilled Care. *Beds* 60. *Certified* Medicaid; Medicare.

Ownership Nonprofit.
Staff RNs 13 (ft), 1 (pt); LPNs 8 (ft), 1 (pt); Nurses aides 24 (ft), 1 (pt); Physical therapists 2 (ft), 1 (pt); Activities coordinators 3 (ft), 1 (pt); Social workers 1 (ft), 1 (pt).
Languages Spanish, French, German, Italian, Danish, Swedish, Hungarian

NEW HAVEN

Carewell Rest Home*
260 Dwight St, New Haven, CT, 06511 (203) 562-8596
Licensure Intermediate Care. *Beds* 45. *Certified* Medicaid.
Ownership Proprietary.
Staff RNs 4 (ft); LPNs 5 (ft); Nurses aides 12 (ft); Activities coordinators 1 (ft).
Languages Italian, Spanish, French
Activities Therapeutic recreation.

Cove Manor Convalescent Center Inc
36 Morris Cove Rd, New Haven, CT, 06512 (203) 467-6357
Medical Dir/Dir of Nursing Charles H Hodgkins Jr MD.
Licensure Skilled Care. *Beds* 70. *Certified* Medicaid; Medicare.
Ownership Proprietary.
Admissions Requirements Minimum age 21.
Staff RNs 5 (ft), 5 (pt); LPNs 8 (ft), 3 (pt); Nurses aides 21 (ft), 5 (pt); Recreational therapists 1 (ft), 1 (pt); Speech therapists 1 (pt); Dietitians 1 (pt); Dentists 1 (pt); Ophthalmologists 1 (pt); Podiatrists 1 (pt); Audiologists 1 (pt).
Languages Italian, Polish, Russian, Spanish
Facilities Dining room; Physical therapy room; Activities room; Crafts room; Laundry room; Barber/Beauty shop.
Activities Arts and Crafts; Cards; Games; Reading groups; Prayer groups; Movies; Shopping trips; Dances/Social or cultural gatherings.
Description Facility is located amid spacious grounds with a thermopane enclosed solarium and dining room overlooking the sea, one of New England's newest and most modern rehabilitation centers for convalescent, post-operative, orthopedic patients, and retired guests; private and semi-private accommodations; registered nurses in attendance; physical therapy treatments.

Jewish Home for the Aged
169 Davenport Ave, New Haven, CT, 06519 (203) 789-1650
Medical Dir/Dir of Nursing Dr Jacqueline Hutcher-Henchel.
Licensure Skilled Care. *Beds* 150. *Certified* Medicaid; Medicare.
Ownership Nonprofit.
Admissions Requirements Minimum age 65; Medical examination.
Staff Physicians 1 (ft), 1 (pt); RNs 17 (ft); LPNs 16 (ft); Nurses aides 60 (ft); Physical therapists 2 (ft); Reality therapists 1 (ft); Recreational therapists 3 (ft); Dietitians 2 (ft); Dentists 1 (pt); Podiatrists 1 (pt).
Languages Hebrew, Yiddish, Russian, Polish, Italian, Spanish
Affiliation Jewish
Facilities Dining room; Physical therapy room;

Activities room; Chapel; Crafts room; Barber-/Beauty shop; Library.
Activities Arts and Crafts; Cards; Games; Reading groups; Prayer groups; Movies; Shopping trips; Dances/Social or cultural gatherings; Discussion groups; Music groups; Art groups.
Description The psychosocial and psychiatric supports are in place through a unit team concept. The team meets weekly as routine, more often if needed, and on rotation basis with consultant psychiatrist. Facility has not experienced a discharge to a psychiatric institution in over 3 years, though dealing with the frail, elderly, and severely organic population.

New Fairview Hall Convalescent Home
181 Clifton St, New Haven, CT, 06513 (203) 467-1666
Medical Dir/Dir of Nursing A Dolinsky MD and A Mancini MD.
Licensure Skilled Care. *Beds* 195. *Certified* Medicaid; Medicare.
Ownership Proprietary.
Admissions Requirements Medical examination; Physician's request.
Staff Physicians; RNs; LPNs; Nurses aides; Physical therapists; Recreational therapists; Speech therapists; Activities coordinators; Dietitians; Dentists; Ophthalmologists; Podiatrists; Audiologists.
Languages Italian, German, Polish, Greek, French
Facilities Dining room; Physical therapy room; Activities room; Crafts room; Laundry room.
Activities Arts and Crafts; Cards; Games; Reading groups; Prayer groups; Movies; Shopping trips; Dances/Social or cultural gatherings.
Description Facility is located in an attractive suburban residential area with two hospitals within a 10-minute drive; designed with a home-like atmosphere and modern medical facilities; built with one objective in mind—to provide guests with every modern comfort and convenience for post-operative and long-term care; each resident's requirements are carefully attended to by a professional staff.

New Haven Convalescent Center
50 Mead St, New Haven, CT, 06511 (203) 777-3491
Medical Dir/Dir of Nursing Dr Michael Devbaty.
Licensure Skilled Care. *Beds* 89. *Certified* Medicaid; Medicare.
Ownership Proprietary.
Staff RNs 11 (ft), 9 (pt); LPNs 3 (ft), 5 (pt); Nurses aides 30 (ft), 17 (pt); Dietitians 1 (pt).
Languages Italian, Slavic
Facilities Dining room; Activities room; Crafts room; Barber/Beauty shop.
Activities Arts and Crafts; Cards; Games; Reading groups; Prayer groups; Movies; Dances/Social or cultural gatherings.

Parkview Medical Recovery Center
915 Boulevard, New Haven, CT, 06511 (203) 865-5155
Medical Dir/Dir of Nursing Quiyam Merjtaba MD.
Licensure Skilled Care. *Beds* 120. *Certified* Medicaid; Medicare.
Ownership Proprietary.
Admissions Requirements Minimum age 16;

Medical examination; Physician's request.
Staff Physicians 4 (pt); RNs 7 (ft); LPNs 10 (ft); Nurses aides 47 (ft); Physical therapists 1 (pt); Recreational therapists 2 (ft); Speech therapists 1 (pt); Dietitians 1 (pt); Dentists 1 (pt); Ophthalmologists 1 (pt); Podiatrists 1 (pt); Audiologists 1 (pt).
Languages Polish, Spanish, Italian
Facilities Dining room; Physical therapy room; Activities room; Chapel; Crafts room; Laundry room; Barber/Beauty shop; Library.
Activities Arts and Crafts; Cards; Games; Reading groups; Prayer groups; Movies; Shopping trips; Dances/Social or cultural gatherings.

Regis Multi-Health Center*
1354 Chapel St, New Haven, CT, 06511 (203) 865-0505
Licensure Skilled Care; Intermediate Care. *Beds* 125. *Certified* Medicaid; Medicare.
Ownership Proprietary.
Staff LPNs 18 (ft); Nurses aides 46 (ft); Physical therapists 1 (pt); Activities coordinators 2 (ft), 1 (pt); Social workers 1 (ft).
Languages Ukrainain, Polish, Spanish, Italian

Riverview Rest Home Inc
92-94 Lexington Ave, New Haven, CT, 06513
Admin Natalie Iovieno.
Licensure Residential Care. *Certified* Medicaid; Medicare.
Ownership Proprietary.
Staff Dietitians.
Facilities Dining room; Laundry room; Smoking room.
Activities Games; Prayer groups; Movies.

Saint Johns Health Center*
54 E Ramsdell St, New Haven, CT, 06515 (203) 389-9558
Licensure Skilled Care; Intermediate Care. *Beds* 90. *Certified* Medicaid; Medicare.
Ownership Nonprofit.
Staff RNs 9 (ft); LPNs 6 (ft); Nurses aides 38 (ft); Activities coordinators 1 (ft), 1 (pt); Social workers 1 (pt).
Languages Spanish

Winthrop Continuing Care Center
240 Winthrop Ave, New Haven, CT, 06511 (203) 789-0500
Medical Dir/Dir of Nursing Bret Gerstenhaber MD.
Licensure Skilled Care; Intermediate Care. *Beds* 240. *Certified* Medicaid; Medicare.
Ownership Proprietary.
Admissions Requirements Medical examination; Physician's request.
Staff Physicians 6 (pt); RNs 9 (ft); LPNs 30 (ft); Orderlies 6 (ft); Nurses aides 63 (ft); Physical therapists 1 (ft); Occupational therapists 1 (pt); Speech therapists 1 (pt); Activities coordinators 4 (ft); Dietitians 1 (ft); Dentists 1 (pt); Ophthalmologists 1 (pt); Podiatrists 1 (pt); Audiologists 1 (pt).
Languages Spanish, Italian
Facilities Dining room; Physical therapy room; Activities room; Laundry room; Barber/Beauty shop.
Activities Arts and Crafts; Cards; Games; Reading groups; Prayer groups; Movies; Shopping trips; Dances/Social or cultural gatherings.
Description Facility has a skilled pulmonary

unit consisting of 30 beds capable of maintaining 8 patients on respirators (ventilators). The unit has piped in oxygen and is self-sustaining.

NEW LONDON

Beechwood Manor
31 Vauxhall St, New London, CT, 06320 (203) 442-4363
Medical Dir/Dir of Nursing Clemens E Prokesch MD.
Licensure Skilled Care. *Beds* 45. *Certified* Medicaid; Medicare.
Ownership Proprietary.
Staff RNs 6 (ft), 2 (pt); LPNs 2 (ft), 1 (pt); Orderlies 1 (ft); Nurses aides 12 (ft), 7 (pt); Physical therapists 1 (pt); Recreational therapists 1 (ft); Dietitians 1 (pt); Dentists 1 (pt); Podiatrists 1 (pt).
Facilities Dining room; Physical therapy room; Activities room; Laundry room; Barber/Beauty shop.
Activities Arts and Crafts; Games; Reading groups; Prayer groups; Movies; Shopping trips.
Description Facility is a gracious mansion built at the turn of the century; it retains all its charm while still providing a high level of skilled services.

Briarcliff Manor
179 Colman St, New London, CT, 06320 (203) 443-5376
Medical Dir/Dir of Nursing Dr Morris Sulman.
Licensure Home for the aged. *Beds* 25. *Certified* Medicaid; Medicare.
Ownership Proprietary.
Admissions Requirements Minimum age 21.
Staff Nurses aides 6 (ft), 4 (pt).
Languages Italian, Spanish
Facilities Dining room; Laundry room.
Activities Cards; Games; Prayer groups.

Camelot
89 Viets St, New London, CT, 06320 (203) 447-1471
Medical Dir/Dir of Nursing Melvin A Yoselevsky MD.
Licensure Skilled Care. *Beds* 60. *Certified* Medicaid; Medicare.
Ownership Proprietary.
Staff Physicians 18 (pt); RNs 2 (ft), 8 (pt); LPNs 3 (pt); Nurses aides 9 (ft), 19 (pt); Physical therapists 1 (pt); Reality therapists 1 (ft); Recreational therapists 1 (ft); Speech therapists 1 (pt); Dietitians 1 (pt); Dentists 1 (pt); Podiatrists 1 (pt); Audiologists 1 (pt).
Languages Spanish, Italian, German
Facilities Dining room; Physical therapy room; Activities room; Crafts room; Laundry room; Barber/Beauty shop.
Activities Arts and Crafts; Games; Reading groups; Prayer groups; Movies; Shopping trips.

Nutmeg Pavilion Healthcare*
78 Viets St, New London, CT, 06320 (203) 447-1416
Licensure Skilled Care; Intermediate Care. *Beds* 140. *Certified* Medicaid; Medicare.
Ownership Proprietary.
Staff RNs 18 (ft); Nurses aides 25 (ft); Physical

therapists 2 (ft); Social workers 1 (ft).
Languages Spanish, Italian
Activities Arts and Crafts; Games; Reading groups; Dances/Social or cultural gatherings; Reality orientation; Music.

NEW MILFORD

Candlewood Valley Care Center
30 Park Ln E, New Milford, CT, 06776 (203) 355-0971
Medical Dir/Dir of Nursing Robert L McDonald MD.
Licensure Skilled Care; Intermediate Care; Residential Care. *Beds* SNF 60; ICF 44; Residential Care 44. *Certified* Medicaid; Medicare.
Ownership Proprietary.
Admissions Requirements Minimum age 14.
Staff Physicians 8 (pt); RNs 12 (ft), 6 (pt); LPNs 8 (ft), 4 (pt); Nurses aides 32 (ft), 22 (pt); Physical therapists 1 (ft); Reality therapists 1 (pt); Recreational therapists 4 (ft); Occupational therapists 1 (ft); Speech therapists 1 (pt); Dietitians 1 (ft); Dentists 2 (pt); Ophthalmologists 2 (pt); Podiatrists 2 (pt); Audiologists 1 (pt).
Languages French, Italian, Spanish, German, Polish
Facilities Dining room; Physical therapy room; Activities room; Crafts room; Laundry room; Barber/Beauty shop; Library.
Activities Arts and Crafts; Cards; Games; Reading groups; Prayer groups; Movies; Shopping trips; Dances/Social or cultural gatherings; Community projects.
Description A familiy owned long-term care facility providing multiple levels of care permitting movement of clients as care needs indicate. Facility has been in operation for 37 years, moving to modern, one-floor building 10 years ago.

New Milford Nursing Home*
19 Poplar St, New Milford, CT, 06776 (203) 354-9365
Licensure Skilled Care; Intermediate Care. *Beds* 99. *Certified* Medicaid; Medicare.
Ownership Proprietary.
Staff RNs 15 (ft); LPNs 14 (ft); Nurses aides 53 (ft); Physical therapists 1 (ft); Activities coordinators 1 (ft); Social workers 1 (ft).
Languages Polish, German, Hebrew, Italian

NEWINGTON

Bel-Air Manor*
256 New Britain Ave, Newington, CT, 06111 (203) 666-5689
Licensure Intermediate Care. *Beds* 71. *Certified* Medicaid.
Ownership Proprietary.
Staff RNs 6 (ft); LPNs 2 (ft); Nurses aides 11 (ft); Activities coordinators 1 (ft), 1 (pt).
Languages Polish, French, Italian
Activities Arts and Crafts; Games; Prayer groups; Shopping trips; Dances/Social or cultural gatherings; Exercises; Baking; Lunches out.

Jefferson House
1 John H Stewart Dr, Newington, CT, 06111 (203) 667-4453

Medical Dir/Dir of Nursing Dr Arthur Wolf.
Licensure Intermediate Care. *Beds* SNF 60; ICF 30. *Certified* Medicaid; Medicare.
Ownership Nonprofit.
Staff RNs 13 (ft); LPNs 10 (ft); Nurses aides 40 (ft); Physical therapists 5 (ft), 1 (pt); Recreational therapists 3 (ft), 1 (pt); Dietitians 2 (ft).
Languages Spanish, Polish, French
Facilities Dining room; Physical therapy room; Activities room; Crafts room; Laundry room; Barber/Beauty shop; Library.
Activities Arts and Crafts; Cards; Games; Reading groups; Prayer groups; Movies; Shopping trips; Dances/Social or cultural gatherings.
Description Hot lunch program available from 1-3 p.m. daily for community frail elderly; nutritional meal and recreation program daily; transportation provided; offer adult day care services in Town of Manchester, Monday-Friday, 8:00 a.m.-5:00 p.m.

Mediplex of Newington*
240 Church St, Newington, CT, 06111 (203) 667-2256
Licensure Skilled Care; Intermediate Care. *Beds* 120. *Certified* Medicaid; Medicare.
Ownership Proprietary.
Staff Physicians; RNs 8 (ft); LPNs 4 (ft); Nurses aides 27 (ft); Physical therapists 2 (ft); Activities coordinators 2 (ft); Social workers 1 (ft).
Languages Portuguese, Spanish, Polish, French
Activities Arts and Crafts; Reading groups; Shopping trips; Dances/Social or cultural gatherings; Music; Current events.

NEWTOWN

Ashlar of Newtown*
Toddy Hill Rd, Newtown, CT, 06470 (203) 426-5847
Licensure Skilled Care; Intermediate Care. *Beds* 156. *Certified* Medicaid; Medicare.
Ownership Proprietary.
Staff RNs 22 (ft), 1 (pt); LPNs 10 (ft), 1 (pt); Nurses aides 64 (ft), 1 (pt); Physical therapists 1 (ft), 1 (pt); Activities coordinators 3 (ft), 1 (pt); Social workers 1 (ft), 1 (pt).
Languages Spanish, German, Italian, French
Affiliation Masons

NORTH HAVEN

Montowese Convalescent Home*
163 Quinnipiac Ave, North Haven, CT, 06473 (202) 777-2284
Licensure Skilled Care. *Beds* 60. *Certified* Medicaid; Medicare.
Ownership Proprietary.
Staff RNs 12 (ft); LPNs 6 (ft); Nurses aides 27 (ft); Activities coordinators 2 (ft); Social workers 2 (ft).
Languages Portuguese, Italian, French, Spanish, Slavic, Oriental, Urdo

NORWALK

Fairfield Manor Health Care Center
23 Prospect Ave, Norwalk, CT, 06850 (203)

853-0010
Medical Dir/Dir of Nursing Robert Yazmer
MD.
Licensure Skilled Care; Intermediate Care.
Beds 210. *Certified* Medicaid; Medicare.
Ownership Proprietary.
Admissions Requirements Minimum age 17.
Staff RNs 11 (ft), 11 (pt); LPNs 10 (ft), 10 (pt);
Orderlies 3 (ft); Nurses aides 65 (ft), 25 (pt);
Physical therapists 1 (ft), 1 (pt); Recreational
therapists 1 (ft); Occupational therapists 1 (ft), 1
(pt); Speech therapists 1 (ft); Activities coordi-
nators 2 (ft); Dietitians 1 (ft), 1 (pt).
Languages Haitian, French, Spanish, Italian,
Polish
Facilities Dining room; Physical therapy room;
Activities room; Chapel; Crafts room; Laundry
room; Barber/Beauty shop; Library.
Activities Arts and Crafts; Cards; Games;
Reading groups; Prayer groups; Movies; Shopping trips; Dances/Social or cultural gatherings.
Description At Fairfield Manor caring is trans-
lated into action with professional rehabilitative
and therapeutic programs—striving to rebuild
the quality of life for the elderly and disabled.
We offer physical therapy, lanuage and
auditory therapies, therapeutic recreation, occupational therapy, and a newly developed geropsychiatric care program—in addition to quality
long-term nursing and medical care.

Lea Manor Convalescent Home Inc
17 Nelson Ave, Norwalk, CT, 06851 (203)
847-9389
Medical Dir/Dir of Nursing Dr Stephan Ham-
merman.
Licensure Skilled Care. *Beds* 36. *Cer-
tified* Medicaid.
Ownership Proprietary.
Staff Physicians; Dietitians; Nurses aides.
Languages Italian, Polish, Spanish, Czech
Facilities Dining room; Physical therapy room;
Activities room; Chapel; Crafts room; Laundry
room.
Description Facility features home-like atmos-
phere with personal attention.

Notre Dame Convalescent Home Inc
76 W Rocks Rd, Norwalk, CT, 06851 (203)
847-5893
Medical Dir/Dir of Nursing Dr James Griffith.
Licensure Skilled Care. *Beds* 60. *Cer-
tified* Medicaid.
Ownership Nonprofit.
Admissions Requirements Minimum age 14;
Medical examination; Physician's request.
Staff Physicians 12 (pt); RNs 4 (ft), 12 (pt);
LPNs 3 (ft); Nurses aides 26 (ft), 6 (pt);
Physical therapists 1 (pt); Recreational thera-
pists 1 (ft); Speech therapists 1 (pt); Activities
coordinators 1 (ft); Dietitians 1 (pt); Dentists 1
(pt); Podiatrists 1 (pt); Audiologists 1 (pt);
Optometrists 1 (pt).
Languages French
Affiliation Roman Catholic
Facilities Dining room; Physical therapy room;
Activities room; Chapel; Laundry room; Bar-
ber/Beauty shop; Library; Lounge.
Activities Arts and Crafts; Cards; Games;
Reading groups; Prayer groups; Movies; Shop-
ping trips.
Description Home offers urban seclusion on a
5-acre estate, operated by and with the direct

involvement of the Paris-based order of the Sisters of St Thomas of Villanova; resident priest
and multidenominational chapel; skilled
nursing with a wide range of personalized services offered.

NORWICH

Convalescent Center of Norwich Inc
60 Crouch Ave, Norwich, CT, 06360 (203)
889-2631
Admin Peter J Eatandelle. *Medical Dir/Dir of
Nursing* Dr Torres.
Licensure Skilled Care. *Beds* 119. *Cer-
tified* Medicaid; Medicare.
Ownership Proprietary.
Admissions Requirements Minimum age 14;
Medical examination; Physician's request.
Staff Physicians 6 (pt); RNs 8 (ft), 14 (pt);
LPNs 6 (ft), 10 (pt); Orderlies 3 (pt); Nurses
aides 27 (ft), 41 (pt); Physical therapists 2 (pt);
Reality therapists 1 (pt); Recreational therapists
2 (ft); Speech therapists 1 (pt); Activities coordi-
nators 2 (pt); Dietitians 2 (pt); Dentists 1 (pt);
Ophthalmologists 1 (pt); Podiatrists 1 (pt);
Audiologists 1 (pt).
Languages Polish, French
Facilities Dining room; Physical therapy room;
Activities room; Chapel; Laundry room; Bar-
ber/Beauty shop.
Activities Arts and Crafts; Cards; Games;
Reading groups; Prayer groups; Movies; Shop-
ping trips; Dances/Social or cultural gatherings.
Description Facility is off the highway on a
dead-end street; different animals and their
trainers come in once a week.

Elmachri Convalescent Home*
251 Washington St, Norwich, CT, 06360 (203)
889-1721
Medical Dir/Dir of Nursing David G Rousseau
MD.
Licensure Skilled Care. *Beds* SNF 20; ICF 10.
Certified Medicaid; Medicare.
Ownership Proprietary.
Staff RNs 1 (ft), 9 (pt); LPNs 3 (pt); Nurses
aides 8 (ft), 12 (pt); Recreational therapists 1
(ft), 2 (pt); Dietitians 2 (ft), 2 (pt).
Languages Spanish, French, Italian, Polish
Facilities Activities room.
Activities Arts and Crafts; Cards; Games;
Movies; Shopping trips; Dances/Social or cul-
tural gatherings.

Fairlawn Convalescent Home*
5 Rockwell Terrace, Norwich, CT, 06360 (203)
887-7690
Licensure Skilled Care. *Beds* 45. *Cer-
tified* Medicaid.
Ownership Proprietary.
Staff RNs 9 (ft); LPNs 3 (ft); Nurses aides 17
(ft); Activities coordinators 1 (ft).
Languages Polish, French, Russian
Activities Therapeutic recreation.

Hamilton Pavilion Healthcare*
50 Palmer St, Norwich, CT, 06360 (203)
889-8358
Licensure Skilled Care; Intermediate Care.
Beds 160. *Certified* Medicaid; Medicare.
Ownership Proprietary.
Staff RNs 21 (ft); LPNs 11 (ft); Nurses aides 38

(ft); Activities coordinators 4 (ft); Social workers 1 (ft).
Languages French, Polish, Italian

Norwichtown Convalescent Home*
93 W Town St, Norwich, CT, 06360 (203)
889-2614
Admin Herbert Kallen.
Licensure Skilled Care. *Beds* 120. *Certified* Medicaid; Medicare.
Ownership Proprietary.
Staff RNs 8 (ft); LPNs 12 (ft); Nurses aides 35
(ft); Activities coordinators 2 (ft); Social workers 1 (ft).
Activities Bus trips; Cocktail lounge; Dinner
and theater; State park outings; Restaurant outings.

OLD SAYBROOK

Ferry Point Skilled Nursing Care Facility*
175 Ferry Rd, Old Saybrook, CT, 06475 (203)
388-4677
Licensure Skilled Care. *Beds* 120. *Certified* Medicaid; Medicare.
Ownership Proprietary.
Staff RNs 9 (ft); LPNs 10 (ft); Physical therapists 1 (ft); Activities coordinators 1 (ft); Social
workers 1 (ft).
Languages Italian, French

Saybrook Convalescent Hospital*
1775 Boston Post Rd, Old Saybrook, CT,
06457 (203) 399-6216
Licensure Skilled Care. *Beds* 120. *Certified* Medicaid; Medicare.
Ownership Proprietary.
Staff RNs 22 (ft); LPNs 7 (ft); Nurses aides 50
(ft); Physical therapists 2 (ft); Activities coordinators 2 (ft).
Languages French, Italian

ORANGE

The Lydiana Corp
PO Box 945, Orange, CT, 06477 (203)
878-0613
Admin Jean M Mario. *Medical Dir/Dir of
Nursing* Aleflor Ragaza.
Licensure Intermediate Care. *Beds* 27. *Certi-
fied* Medicaid.
Ownership Proprietary.
Admissions Requirements Minimum age 15.
Staff Physicians 1 (ft), 2 (pt); RNs 2 (ft), 8 (pt);
Nurses aides 4 (ft), 4 (pt); Physical therapists 1
(pt); Recreational therapists 1 (ft); Occupational
therapists 1 (pt); Activities coordinators 1 (ft);
Dietitians 1 (ft); Dentists 1 (pt); Ophthalmolo-
gists 1 (pt); Podiatrists 1 (pt); Audiologists 1
(pt).
Facilities Dining room; Laundry room.
Activities Arts and Crafts; Cards; Games;
Reading groups; Prayer groups; Movies; Shopping trips; Dances/Social or cultural gatherings.
Description The Lydian is situated on 4 acres
of land in a small town; a family-owned and
operated business for 26 years; provides individualized care in a home-like atmosphere.

Orange Health Care Center
225 Boston Post Rd, Orange, CT, 06477 (203)
799-2500
Medical Dir/Dir of Nursing Evan M Ginsberg
MD.
Licensure Skilled Care. *Beds* SNF 43; ICF 7.
Certified Medicaid; Medicare.
Ownership Proprietary.
Admissions Requirements Minimum age 14.
Staff Physicians 3 (pt); RNs 7 (ft), 5 (pt); LPNs
5 (pt); Nurses aides 6 (ft), 15 (pt); Recreational
therapists 1 (ft); Speech therapists 1 (pt); Dieti-
tians 1 (pt); Dentists 1 (pt); Ophthalmologists 1
(pt); Podiatrists 3 (pt); Audiologists 1 (pt).
Languages Italian, German, Spanish
Facilities Dining room; Physical therapy room;
Activities room; Crafts room; Laundry room;
Barber/Beauty shop.
Activities Arts and Crafts; Cards; Games;
Reading groups; Prayer groups; Movies; Shopping trips; Dances/Social or cultural gatherings.
Description Orange Health Care Center,
opened to the public in 1948, is a 50-bed
facility with private and semi-private rooms,
complete nursing and personal services,
physical therapy, dental services, podiatry services, dental services, optometry services, recreational program, social services, and staff food
supervisor with bi-monthly dietitian. Presently,
we are constructing an addition and remodeling
to accomodate a 60 bed facility.

PLAINFIELD

Crest Haven Rest Home*
34 Pleasant St, Plainfield, CT, 06374 (203)
564-8414
Licensure Intermediate Care. *Beds* 30. *Certified* Medicaid.
Ownership Proprietary.
Staff RNs 1 (ft), 1 (pt); LPNs 3 (ft); Nurses
aides 4 (ft); Activities coordinators 1 (pt); Dietitians 1 (pt).
Activities Arts and Crafts; Games; Prayer
groups; Shopping trips; Dances/Social or cultural gatherings; Picnics; Sing-a-longs.

Villa Maria Convalescent Home Inc
20 Babcock Ave, Plainfield, CT, 06374 (203)
564-8889
Admin Daniel E Disco and Natalie D Disco.
Medical Dir/Dir of Nursing Philip Goyette.
Licensure Skilled Care. *Beds* 52. *Cer-
tified* Medicaid; Medicare.
Ownership Proprietary.
Admissions Requirements Medical examina-
tion; Physician's request.
Staff Physicians 1 (pt); RNs 5 (ft), 5 (pt); LPNs
3 (ft), 3 (pt); Nurses aides 17 (ft), 7 (pt);
Physical therapists 1 (pt); Recreational thera-
pists 1 (ft); Activities coordinators 1 (ft); Dieti-
tians 1 (pt); Dentists 1 (pt); Ophthalmologists 1
(pt); Podiatrists 1 (pt); Audiologists 1 (pt).
Languages French
Facilities Dining room; Physical therapy room;
Activities room; Chapel; Crafts room; Laundry
room; Barber/Beauty shop; Library.
Activities Arts and Crafts; Cards; Games;
Reading groups; Prayer groups; Movies; Shopping trips; Dances/Social or cultural gatherings.
Description Family council program meets
monthly in the evening with staff participation

and concerned families.

PLAINVILLE

Plainville Convalescent Home Inc*
269 Farmington Ave, Plainville, CT, 06062
(203) 747-5579
Licensure Skilled Care; Intermediate Care.
Beds 120. *Certified* Medicaid; Medicare.
Ownership Nonprofit.
Staff RNs 21 (ft); LPNs 7 (ft); Nurses aides 48
(ft); Activities coordinators 2 (ft); Dietitians 1
(ft).
Languages French, Italian, Polish, Chinese,
Vietnamese

PLYMOUTH

Cook-Willow Convalescent Hospital Inc*
41 Hillside Ave, Plymouth, CT, 06782 (203)
283-4424
Admin Susan C Armstrong.
Licensure Skilled Care. *Beds* 30. *Cer-
tified* Medicaid.
Ownership Proprietary.
Staff RNs 5 (ft); LPNs 1 (ft); Activities coordi-
nators 1 (ft).
Activities Therapeutic recreation.

PORTLAND

Portland Convalescent Center Inc*
333 Main St, Portland, CT, 06480 (203)
342-0370
Licensure Skilled Care. *Beds* 89. *Certified* Medicaid; Medicare.
Ownership Proprietary.
Staff LPNs 13 (ft), 1 (pt); Nurses aides 37 (ft), 1
(pt); Physical therapists 1 (pt); Activities coordinators 1 (ft), 1 (pt).
Languages Polish, German, Italian, French
Activities Arts and Crafts; Games; Movies;
Dances/Social or cultural gatherings; Newspaper.

PROSPECT

Eastview Manor Inc*
PO Box 7037, 170 Scott Rd, Prospect, CT,
06712 (203) 758-5491
Licensure Skilled Care. *Beds* 30. *Cer-
tified* Medicaid.
Ownership Proprietary.
Staff RNs 5 (ft); LPNs 4 (ft); Nurses aides 11
(ft); Activities coordinators 1 (ft).
Languages Italian, French, Portuguese, Lithu-
anian, German, Spanish
Activities Arts and Crafts; Games; Movies;
Dances/Social or cultural gatherings; Outdoor
activities; Music.

Woodside Care Center*
Summit Rd, Prospect, CT, 06712 (203)
758-4431
Licensure Skilled Care; Intermediate Care.
Beds 150. *Certified* Medicaid; Medicare.
Ownership Proprietary.
Staff LPNs 27 (ft); Nurses aides 55 (ft); Activi-
ties coordinators 2 (ft), 1 (pt).
Languages Italian, German

Activities Games; Prayer groups; Singing
group.

PUTNAM

Matulaitis Nursing Home Inc
Thurber Rd, Putnam, CT, 06260 (203)
928-7976
Licensure Skilled Care; Intermediate Care.
Beds SNF 60; ICF 59. *Certified* Medicaid.
Ownership Nonprofit.
Admissions Requirements Medical examina-
tion.
Staff Physicians 7 (pt); RNs 12 (ft), 2 (pt);
LPNs 1 (ft), 2 (pt); Nurses aides 36 (ft), 6 (pt);
Physical therapists 1 (pt); Recreational thera-
pists 2 (ft); Speech therapists 1 (pt); Dietitians 1
(ft); Dentists 1 (pt); Ophthalmologists 1 (pt);
Podiatrists 1 (pt); Audiologists 1 (pt).
Languages Lithuanian, French, Polish, Span-
ish, Swedish, German, Italian
Affiliation Roman Catholic
Facilities Dining room; Physical therapy room;
Activities room; Chapel; Crafts room; Laundry
room; Barber/Beauty shop; Library.
Activities Arts and Crafts; Cards; Games;
Reading groups; Prayer groups; Movies; Shop-
ping trips; Dances/Social or cultural gatherings.

RIDGEFIELD

Altnacraig Convalescent Home Inc*
55 High Ridge Ave, Ridgefield, CT, 06877
(203) 438-6890

ROCKVILLE

Rockville Memorial Nursing Home*
22 South St, Rockville, CT, 06066 (203)
875-0771
Licensure Skilled Care; Intermediate Care.
Beds 150. *Certified* Medicaid; Medicare.
Ownership Proprietary.
Staff RNs 22 (ft), 1 (pt); LPNs 44 (ft), 1 (pt);
Nurses aides 13 (ft), 1 (pt); Activities coordina-
tors; Dietitians 2 (ft), 1 (pt).
Languages French, Polish, Italian, Russian,
Spanish, Lithuanian, Hawaiian

ROCKY HILL

Elm Hill Convalescent and Rest Home
45 Elm St, Rocky Hill, CT, 06067 (203)
529-8661
Medical Dir/Dir of Nursing A Golden.
Licensure Skilled Care; Intermediate Care.
Beds 150. *Certified* Medicaid; Medicare.
Admissions Requirements Physician's request.
Staff RNs 10 (ft), 11 (pt); LPNs 11 (ft), 9 (pt);
Nurses aides 37 (ft), 18 (pt); Physical therapists
1 (pt); Recreational therapists 3 (ft), 1 (pt).
Languages Polish, Italian
Facilities Dining room; Physical therapy room;
Activities room; Chapel; Crafts room; Laundry
room; Barber/Beauty shop; Library.
Activities Arts and Crafts; Cards; Games;
Reading groups; Prayer groups; Movies; Shop-
ping trips; Dances/Social or cultural gatherings;
Poetry and music appreciation; Exercises;
Reality orientation.

Description Facility sponsors out-trips to historical places such as Dinosaur Park, Rocky Hill Ferry, and old Wethersfield.

Maple View Manor Inc*
856 Maple St, Rocky Hill, CT, 06067 (203) 563-2861
Licensure Skilled Care. *Beds* 120. *Certified* Medicaid; Medicare.
Ownership Nonprofit.
Staff RNs 8 (ft); LPNs 7 (ft); Nurses aides 22 (ft); Activities coordinators 1 (ft); Dietitians 1 (ft).
Languages Spanish, French

West Hill Convalescent Home*
60 West St, Rocky Hill, CT, 06067 (203) 529-2521
Admin Malcolm Glazer.
Licensure Skilled Care. *Beds* 120. *Certified* Medicaid; Medicare.
Ownership Proprietary.
Staff RNs 11 (ft), 1 (pt); LPNs 7 (ft), 1 (pt); Nurses aides 43 (ft), 1 (pt); Physical therapists 1 (ft), 1 (pt); Activities coordinators 2 (ft), 1 (pt); Dietitians 1 (ft), 1 (pt).
Languages French, Polish, German, Italian
Activities Arts and Crafts; Games; Shopping trips.

SALISBURY

Whitridge Nursing Wing*
Lower Cobble Rd, Salisbury, CT, 06068 (203) 435-9851
Licensure Skilled Care. *Beds* 30. *Certified* Medicaid; Medicare.
Ownership Proprietary.
Staff RNs 7 (ft), 1 (pt); Nurses aides 12 (ft); Dietitians 1 (ft).
Languages Spanish, Italian, Chinese, German, French
Activities Arts and Crafts; Movies; Dances/Social or cultural gatherings; Musical programs; Greenhouse.

SHELTON

Flora and Mary Hewitt Memorial Hospital Inc
230 Coram Ave, Shelton, CT, 06484 (203) 735-4671 and 735-4672
Medical Dir/Dir of Nursing Murugesapillai Koneswaran MD SNF and Donald P Roach MD ICF.
Licensure Skilled Care; Intermediate Care. *Beds* 210. *Certified* Medicaid; Medicare.
Ownership Nonprofit.
Admissions Requirements Minimum age 16; Medical examination; Physician's request.
Staff RNs 8 (ft), 16 (pt); LPNs 11 (ft), 6 (pt); Nurses aides 34 (ft), 62 (pt); Physical therapists 1 (ft), 2 (pt); Recreational therapists 3 (ft), 1 (pt); Speech therapists 1 (pt); Dietitians 1 (ft), 1 (pt); Dentists 1 (pt); Podiatrists 4 (pt).
Languages Italian, Polish, Spanish
Facilities Dining room; Physical therapy room; Activities room; Chapel; Crafts room; Laundry room; Barber/Beauty shop; Library.
Activities Arts and Crafts; Cards; Games; Reading groups; Prayer groups; Movies; Shopping trips; Dances/Social or cultural gatherings.

Description Through a grant received from the New Haven Foundation, Hewitt is in the process of developing programs which would enable it to become a teaching center for all aspects of long-term care. Clinic training is already in place through agreements with Quinnipiac College, Southern Connecticut State University baccalaureate nursing program, Yale University School of Public Health, Shelton High School nurse assistant program, and Ansonia High School nurse assistant program.

Gardner Heights Convalescent Center Inc*
172 Rocky Rest Rd, Shelton, CT, 06484 (203) 929-1481
Licensure Skilled Care; Intermediate Care. *Beds* 89. *Certified* Medicaid.
Ownership Nonprofit.
Staff RNs 9 (ft), 1 (pt); LPNs 7 (ft), 1 (pt); Nurses aides 30 (ft), 1 (pt); Activities coordinators 1 (ft), 1 (pt); Social workers 1 (pt).
Languages Polish, Italian
Activities Arts and Crafts; Prayer groups; Cooking; Happy hour; Reality orientation.

Shelton Lakes Residence and Health Care*
5 Lake Rd, Shelton, CT, 06484 (203) 736-2635
Beds 59.
Ownership Nonprofit.
Languages Spanish, Polish Italian, German, Portuguese

United Methodist Convalescent Homes of Connecticut Inc
584 Long Hill Ave, Shelton, CT, 06484 (203) 929-5321
Medical Dir/Dir of Nursing M Koneswaraw MD.
Licensure Skilled Care. *Beds* 120. *Certified* Medicaid; Medicare.
Ownership Nonprofit.
Admissions Requirements Minimum age 16; Medical examination; Physician's request.
Staff Physicians 22 (pt); RNs 10 (ft), 12 (pt); LPNs 4 (ft), 2 (pt); Nurses aides 61 (ft), 20 (pt); Physical therapists 2 (pt); Recreational therapists 2 (ft); Dietitians 1 (pt); Dentists 1 (pt); Ophthalmologists 3 (pt); Podiatrists 3 (pt); Audiologists 2 (pt).
Affiliation Methodist
Facilities Dining room; Physical therapy room; Activities room; Chapel; Crafts room; Laundry room; Barber/Beauty shop; Library.
Activities Arts and Crafts; Cards; Games; Reading groups; Prayer groups; Movies; Shopping trips.

SIMSBURY

Holly Hill Convalescent Home
40 Firetown Rd, Simsbury, CT, 06070 (203) 658-4407
Medical Dir/Dir of Nursing Dr Ronald Josephson.
Licensure Skilled Care. *Beds* 60. *Certified* Medicaid.
Ownership Proprietary.
Admissions Requirements Minimum age 14.
Staff RNs 4 (ft), 8 (pt); LPNs 6 (pt); Nurses aides 20 (ft), 8 (pt); Physical therapists 1 (ft); Recreational therapists 2 (pt).
Languages French, German

Facilities Dining room; Physical therapy room; Activities room; Laundry room.
Activities Arts and Crafts; Games; Reading groups; Prayer groups; Movies; Shopping trips; Dances/Social or cultural gatherings.

McLean Home*
75 Great Pond Rd, Simsbury, CT, 06070 (203) 658-2254
Licensure Skilled Care; Intermediate Care. *Beds* 58. *Certified* Medicaid; Medicare.
Ownership Nonprofit.
Staff Physicians 1 (pt); LPNs 36 (ft), 1 (pt); Physical therapists 1 (pt); Dietitians 1 (pt); Dentists 1 (pt); Social workers 1 (ft), 1 (pt).
Languages French, German, Polish, Ukrainian, Laotion

SOUTH WILLINGTON

Willington Convalescent Home Inc*
Rt 32, South Willington, CT, 06265 (203) 429-9331
Licensure Skilled Care. *Beds* 42. *Certified* Medicaid; Medicare.
Ownership Proprietary.
Staff RNs 5 (ft); LPNs 3 (ft); Physical therapists 1 (ft); Dietitians 1 (ft); Social workers 1 (ft).
Languages German, French, Polish, Spanish, Portuguese
Activities Arts and Crafts; Games; Movies; Shopping trips; Volunteer group.

SOUTH WINDSOR

South Windsor Convalescent Home Inc*
1060 Main St, South Windsor, CT, 06074 (203) 289-7771
Licensure Skilled Care. *Beds* 120. *Certified* Medicaid; Medicare.
Ownership Proprietary.
Staff RNs 12 (ft), 1 (pt); LPNs 4 (ft), 1 (pt); Nurses aides 33 (ft); Physical therapists 1 (ft); Activities coordinators 2 (ft); Social workers 1 (ft).
Languages French, Polish
Activities Arts and Crafts; Games; Movies; Shopping trips; Dances/Social or cultural gatherings.

SOUTHBURY

Lutheran Home of Southbury Inc
990 Main St N, Southbury, CT, 06488 (203) 264-9135
Admin David D Boyd. *Medical Dir/Dir of Nursing* George L Cushman MD.
Licensure Skilled Care; Intermediate Care; Home for the Aged. *Beds* SNF 60; ICF 60; Home For The Aged 31. *Certified* Medicaid.
Ownership Nonprofit.
Admissions Requirements Minimum age 65; Medical examination; Physician's request.
Staff Physicians 7 (pt); RNs 3 (ft), 9 (pt); LPNs 4 (pt); Nurses aides 11 (ft), 14 (pt); Physical therapists 1 (pt); Occupational therapists 1 (pt); Speech therapists 1 (pt); Activities coordinators 1 (ft); Dietitians 1 (pt); Dentists 1 (pt); Ophthalmologists 1 (pt); Podiatrists 1 (pt); Audiologists

1 (pt).
Affiliation Lutheran
Facilities Dining room; Physical therapy room; Activities room; Chapel; Crafts room; Laundry room; Barber/Beauty shop; Library.
Activities Arts and Crafts; Cards; Games; Reading groups; Prayer groups; Movies; Shopping trips; Dances/Social or cultural gatherings.

River Glen Continuing Care Center*
S Britain Rd, Southbury, CT, 06488 (203) 264-9600
Licensure Skilled Care; Intermediate Care.
Beds 60. *Certified* Medicaid; Medicare.
Ownership Proprietary.
Staff LPNs 18 (ft); Nurses aides 33 (ft); Physical therapists 1 (ft); Occupational therapists 1 (ft); Activities coordinators 1 (ft); Social workers 1 (ft).
Languages Italian, Spanish, Lithuanian
Activities Therapeutic recreation.

SOUTHINGTON

Ridgewood Health Care Facility Inc*
582 Meriden Ave, Southington, CT, 06489 (203) 628-0388
Licensure Skilled Care. *Beds* 38. *Certified* Medicaid.
Ownership Proprietary.
Staff RNs 9 (ft); Nurses aides 10 (ft), 1 (pt); Activities coordinators 1 (ft).
Languages Polish, Italian, French, German
Activities Therapeutic recreation.

Woodmere Health Care Center*
261 Summit St, Southington, CT, 06489 (203) 628-0364
Licensure Skilled Care; Intermediate Care.
Beds 120. *Certified* Medicare.
Ownership Proprietary.
Staff RNs 11 (ft); LPNs 11 (ft); Physical therapists 1 (ft); Activities coordinators 4 (ft).
Languages French, Italian, Spanish
Activities Arts and Crafts; Games; Prayer groups; Shopping trips; Dances/Social or cultural gatherings; Discussion groups; Baking; Music; Newsletter.

SOUTHPORT

Southport Manor Convalescent Center
930 Mill Hill Terrace, Southport, CT, 06490 (203) 259-7894
Medical Dir/Dir of Nursing Dr Kenneth Higgins.
Licensure Skilled Care. *Beds* 140. *Certified* Medicaid; Medicare.
Ownership Proprietary.
Admissions Requirements Minimum age 18; Medical examination; Physician's request.
Staff Physicians 2 (pt); RNs 13 (ft), 22 (pt); LPNs 2 (ft), 7 (pt); Nurses aides 61 (ft), 6 (pt); Physical therapists 1 (ft); Recreational therapists 3 (ft); Occupational therapists 1 (pt); Speech therapists 1 (pt); Dietitians 1 (pt); Dentists 1 (pt); Ophthalmologists 1 (pt); Podiatrists 1 (pt).
Languages Spanish
Facilities Dining room; Physical therapy room; Activities room; Laundry room; Barber/Beauty shop.

Activities Arts and Crafts; Cards; Games; Reading groups; Prayer groups; Movies.
Description Southport Manor is located on 10 acres of carefully landscaped woodlands in the Oak Park section of Southport, Connecticut. The first impression is one of a resort setting, a magnificent estate-like atmosphere—perfect setting for a healing environment.

STAMFORD

Courtland Gardens*
59 Courtland Ave, Stamford, CT, 06902 (203) 359-2000
Licensure Skilled Care; Intermediate Care.
Beds 180. *Certified* Medicare.
Ownership Proprietary.
Staff RNs 24 (ft); LPNs 22 (ft); Nurses aides 110 (ft); Activities coordinators; Dietitians.
Languages French, Spanish, Polish

Homestead Convalescent Home*
160 Glenbrook Rd, Stamford, CT, 06902 (203) 359-2000
Licensure Skilled Care. *Beds* 87. *Certified* Medicaid; Medicare.
Ownership Proprietary.
Staff RNs 15 (ft); LPNs 9 (ft); Nurses aides 49 (ft); Activities coordinators 2 (ft).
Languages French, Spanish, Polish

Smith House Skilled Nursing Facility*
88 Rockrimmon Rd, Stamford, CT, 06903 (203) 322-3428
Licensure Skilled Care; Intermediate Care.
Beds 128. *Certified* Medicaid; Medicare.
Ownership Public.
Staff RNs 19 (ft); LPNs 18 (ft); Nurses aides 61 (ft); Physical therapists 2 (ft) Activities coordinators 2 (ft); Social works 2 (ft).
Languages Spanish, Italian, French, German, Hebrew, Yiddish, Polish

STRATFORD

Lord Chamberlain—Skilled Nursing Facility
7003 Main St, Stratford, CT, 06497 (203) 375-5894
Medical Dir/Dir of Nursing Dr Saul Feldman.
Licensure Skilled Care; Intermediate Care.
Beds SNF 180; ICF 60. *Certified* Medicaid; Medicare.
Ownership Proprietary.
Admissions Requirements Physician's request.
Staff Physicians; RNs; LPNs; Orderlies; Nurses aides; Physical therapists; Reality therapists; Recreational therapists; Occupational therapists; Speech therapists; Activities coordinators; Dietitians; Dentists; Ophthalmologists; Podiatrists; Audiologists.
Languages Spanish, Polish, Hebrew, French, Italian, Greek, German
Facilities Dining room; Physical therapy room; Activities room; Chapel; Crafts room; Laundry room; Barber/Beauty shop; Library; Greenhouse.
Activities Arts and Crafts; Cards; Games; Reading groups; Prayer groups; Movies; Shopping trips; Dances/Social or cultural gatherings; Picnics; Horticulture in greenhouse.
Description Facility features physical therapy,

dental hygienist, infection control department, greenhouse, kosher style diet if desired, beauty shop/tonsorial services, computer EKG, admission clothing marker machine, and air conditioning.

TORRINGTON

Adams House Healthcare
80 Fern Dr, Torrington, CT, 06790 (203) 482-7668
Medical Dir/Dir of Nursing Dr Frank Vanoni.
Licensure Skilled Care. *Beds* 90. *Certified* Medicaid; Medicare.
Ownership Proprietary.
Staff RNs 8 (ft), 5 (pt); LPNs 3 (ft), 4 (pt); Nurses aides 14 (ft), 29 (pt); Physical therapists 1 (pt); Recreational therapists 1 (ft), 1 (pt).
Languages Polish, Italian, Lebanese, French, German, Hungarian
Facilities Dining room; Physical therapy room; Laundry room; Barber/Beauty shop.
Activities Arts and Crafts; Cards; Games; Reading groups; Prayer groups; Movies; Shopping trips; Dances/Social or cultural gatherings.

Torrington Extend-A-Care Center
225 Wyoming Ave, Torrington, CT, 06790 (203) 482-8563
Admin Christopher S Smith. *Medical Dir/Dir of Nursing* Dr Herbert.
Licensure Skilled Care. *Beds* 120. *Certified* Medicaid; Medicare.
Ownership Proprietary.
Admissions Requirements Medical examination; Physician's request.
Staff Physicians 1 (pt); RNs 9 (ft), 6 (pt); LPNs 8 (ft), 8 (pt); Nurses aides 29 (ft), 18 (pt); Physical therapists 1 (pt); Recreational therapists 1 (ft), 1 (pt); Activities coordinators 1 (ft); Dietitians 1 (pt).
Languages Italian, Korean, Spanish
Facilities Dining room; Physical therapy room; Activities room; Chapel; Crafts room; Laundry room; Barber/Beauty shop; TV lounge.
Activities Arts and Crafts; Cards; Games; Reading groups; Prayer groups; Movies; Dances/Social or cultural gatherings.

Wolcott Hall
215 Forest St, Torrington, CT, 06790 (203) 482-8554
Admin K G Fabelausky. *Medical Dir/Dir of Nursing* Dr Alfred Finn.
Licensure Skilled Care. *Beds* 89. *Certified* Medicaid; Medicare.
Ownership Proprietary.
Admissions Requirements Minimum age 14.
Staff Physicians 20 (pt); RNs 11 (ft), 3 (pt); LPNs 3 (ft), 2 (pt); Nurses aides 24 (ft), 9 (pt); Physical therapists 1 (pt); Reality therapists 1 (pt); Recreational therapists 1 (ft), 1 (pt); Speech therapists 1 (pt); Dentists 1 (pt); Ophthalmologists 1 (pt); Podiatrists 1 (pt); Audiologists 1 (pt).
Languages Polish, Italian, German, Slavic, French
Facilities Dining room; Physical therapy room; Activities room; Crafts room; Laundry room; Barber/Beauty shop; Library; Patient lounges.
Activities Arts and Crafts; Cards; Games; Reading groups; Prayer groups; Movies; Shop-

ping trips; Dances/Social or cultural gatherings; Formal dinners; Exercise groups; Pet therapy; Resident council; Cocktail parties.
Description Facility buildings were once part of an estate and the Victorian architecture lends a unique quality; grounds are magnificent, surrounding the building with marble fountains, flowering bushes, and lush greenery.

TRUMBULL

Saint Joseph's Manor
6448 Main St, Trumbull, CT, 06611 (203) 268-6204
Medical Dir/Dir of Nursing Everitt P Dolan MD.
Licensure Skilled Care; Intermediate Care; Residential Care. *Beds* 288. *Certified* Medicaid; Medicare.
Ownership Nonprofit.
Admissions Requirements Minimum age 60; Medical examination; Physician's request.
Staff Physicians 5 (pt); RNs 15 (ft), 43 (pt); LPNs 8 (ft), 7 (pt); Orderlies 2 (pt); Nurses aides 91 (ft), 35 (pt); Physical therapists 1 (ft); Recreational therapists 3 (ft); Occupational therapists 1 (pt); Speech therapists 1 (pt); Activities coordinators 1 (ft), 1 (pt); Dietitians 1 (ft); Dentists 2 (pt); Ophthalmologists 3 (pt); Podiatrists 2 (pt); Audiologists 1 (pt).
Affiliation Roman Catholic
Facilities Dining room; Physical therapy room; Activities room; Chapel; Crafts room; Laundry room; Barber/Beauty shop; Library; Store.
Activities Arts and Crafts; Games; Prayer groups; Movies; Shopping trips; Dances/Social or cultural gatherings; Music sessions.
Description Facility is a multi-care level nursing home with adjacent independent living apartment house (50 units) and individual homes (36 units); suburban setting; bus service; resident Roman Catholic chaplain, daily mass, etc.; Staff-resident ratio better that 1:1; support services available as needed; outpatient clinic; pharmacy; full recreational program.

Trumbull Saint Mary's Convalescent Home and Rest Home
401 Unity Rd, Trumbull, CT, 06611 (203) 372-6879
Medical Dir/Dir of Nursing Dr James D Garrity.
Licensure Skilled Care 10B. *Beds* SNF 23; ICF 6. *Certified* Medicaid.
Ownership Proprietary.
Admissions Requirements Minimum age 15; Medical examination; Physician's request.
Staff Physicians 1 (pt); RNs 8 (ft); LPNs 1 (pt); Nurses aides 10 (ft); Recreational therapists 1 (ft); Dietitians 1 (pt); Dentists 1 (pt); Podiatrists 1 (pt).
Languages Italian, French, German, Yiddish
Activities Prayer groups; Arts and Crafts; Shopping trips.

VERNON

Vernon Manor Health Care Facility
180 Regan Rd, Vernon, CT, 06066 (203) 871-0385
Medical Dir/Dir of Nursing Neil H Brooks MD.
Licensure Skilled Care. *Beds* 120. *Certified* Medicaid; Medicare.
Ownership Proprietary.
Staff Physicians 15 (pt); RNs 12 (ft), 10 (pt); LPNs 4 (ft), 6 (pt); Nurses aides 45 (ft), 50 (pt); Physical therapists 1 (pt); Reality therapists 2 (pt); Recreational therapists 2 (ft); Speech therapists 1 (pt); Activities coordinators 1 (ft); Dietitians 1 (pt); Dentists 1 (pt); Ophthalmologists 1 (pt); Podiatrists 1 (pt); Audiologists 1 (pt).
Languages Italian, Polish, French
Facilities Dining room; Physical therapy room; Activities room; Chapel; Crafts room; Laundry room; Barber/Beauty shop; Library; Dental and examination room; Greenhouse; Garden.
Activities Arts and Crafts; Cards; Games; Reading groups; Prayer groups; Movies; Shopping trips; Dances/Social or cultural gatherings; Ceramics.
Description Vernon Manor has a beautifully decorated, air-conditioned, home-like environment, staffed with dedicated individuals to meet preferences and needs. Full complement of therapies and activities; complete housekeeping and laundry services; resident council and roombound programs available; choice menu and diets offered; beautician available. Inquires are welcomed.

WALLINGFORD

Masonic Home and Hospital*
PO Box 70, Wallingford, CT, 06492 (203) 265-0931
Licensure Skilled Care; Intermediate Care. *Beds* 237. *Certified* Medicaid; Medicare.
Ownership Nonprofit.
Staff RNs 146 (ft); Nurses aides 25 (ft).
Languages German, French, Spanish, Polish, Italian, Hungarian, Portuguese
Affiliation Masons

New Brook Hollow Health Care Center Inc*
55 Kondracki Ln, Wallingford, CT, 06492 (203) 265-6771
Licensure Skilled Care; Intermediate Care. *Beds* 180. *Certified* Medicare.
Ownership Proprietary.
Staff RNs 20 (ft), 1 (pt); LPNs 11 (ft), 13 (pt); Physical therapists 1 (pt); Activities coordinators 4 (ft); Dietitians 1 (ft); Social workers 2 (ft).
Languages Italian, French, Polish
Activities Arts and Crafts; Games; Prayer groups; Movies; Shopping trips; Dances/Social or cultural gatherings; Music; Cooking; Resident council.

Skyview Convalescent Hospital Inc*
Marc Dr, Wallingford, CT, 06492 (202) 265-0981
Licensure Skilled Care; Intermediate Care. *Beds* 60. *Certified* Medicaid; Medicare.
Ownership Proprietary.
Staff LPNs 8 (ft), 1 (pt); Nurses aides 24 (ft), 1 (pt); Activities coordinators 1 (ft); Social workers 1 (ft).
Languages Italian, Polish

Wallingford Convalescent Home Inc*
181 E Main St, Wallingford, CT, 06492 (203) 265-1661
Licensure Skilled Care; Intermediate Care. *Beds* 130. *Certified* Medicaid; Medicare.
Ownership Proprietary.
Staff RNs 14 (ft); LPNs 17 (ft); Nurses aides 63 (ft); Activities coordinators 3 (ft); Social workers 1 (ft).
Languages Spanish, Italian, Polish

WAREHOUSE POINT

D'Amore Rest Haven Inc*
171 Main St, Warehouse Point, CT, 06088 (203) 623-3174
Licensure Intermediate Care. *Beds* 90. *Certified* Medicaid.
Ownership Proprietary.
Staff RNs 3 (ft).
Languages Polish, French, Spanish, Italian

WATERBURY

Birchwood Rest Home Inc*
140 Willow St, Waterbury, CT, 06710 (203) 754-6536
Licensure Intermediate Care. *Beds* 23. *Certified* Medicaid.
Ownership Proprietary.
Staff RNs 4 (ft); LPNs 6 (ft); Nurses aides 6 (ft); Activities coordinators 1 (ft); Dietitians 1 (ft).
Languages Lithuanian, Russian, Italian

Cedar Lane Rehabilitational Health Care Center
128 Cedar Ave, Waterbury, CT, 06705 (203) 757-9271
Medical Dir/Dir of Nursing Louis Olore MD.
Licensure Skilled Care. *Beds* 180. *Certified* Medicaid; Medicare.
Ownership Proprietary.
Admissions Requirements Minimum age 14; Medical examination; Physician's request.
Staff RNs 15 (ft), 20 (pt); LPNs 20 (ft), 12 (pt); Nurses aides 60 (ft), 20 (pt); Physical therapists 2 (ft), 2 (pt); Recreational therapists 3 (ft), 1 (pt); Occupational therapists 2 (ft); Dietitians 1 (pt).
Languages Italian, French, Spanish
Facilities Dining room; Physical therapy room; Activities room; Chapel; Crafts room; Laundry room; Barber/Beauty shop; Library.
Activities Arts and Crafts; Cards; Games; Reading groups; Prayer groups; Movies; Shopping trips; Dances/Social or cultural gatherings.
Description Rehabilitation services are specially designed, equipped, and staffed to provide complete traumatic brain injury and pulmonary care.

Cliff Health Care Facility Inc*
21 Cliff St, Waterbury, CT, 06710 (203) 753-0344
Licensure Skilled Care. *Beds* 52. *Certified* Medicaid.
Ownership Proprietary.
Staff RNs 5 (ft); LPNs 4 (ft); Social workers 1 (ft).
Languages Polish, Spanish, German, French, Italian

East End Convalescent Home Inc
3396 E Main St, Waterbury, CT, 06710 (203)
754-2161
Medical Dir/Dir of Nursing Louis Olore MD.
Licensure Skilled Care. *Beds* 60. *Certified* Medicaid; Medicare.
Ownership Proprietary.
Admissions Requirements Minimum age 14;
Physician's request.
Staff Physicians 4 (pt); RNs 5 (ft), 10 (pt);
LPNs 2 (ft), 2 (pt); Nurses aides 15 (ft), 10 (pt);
Physical therapists 1 (pt); Speech therapists 1
(pt); Activities coordinators 1 (pt); Dietitians 1
(pt); Dentists 1 (pt); Ophthalmologists 1 (pt);
Podiatrists 1 (pt); Audiologists 1 (pt).
Languages Italian, Spanish, French
Facilities Dining room; Physical therapy room;
Activities room; Chapel; Crafts room; Laundry
room; Barber/Beauty shop.
Activities Arts and Crafts; Cards; Games;
Reading groups; Prayer groups; Movies; Shopping trips; Dances/Social or cultural gatherings.
Description This is a small nursing facility in a
country setting.

Fleetcrest Manor Inc
62 Fleet St, PO Box 4147, Waterbury, CT,
06704 (203) 755-3383
Licensure Intermediate Care. *Beds* 18. *Certified* Medicaid.
Ownership Proprietary.
Staff Physicians 1 (pt); RNs 3 (ft); Nurses aides
5 (ft); Recreational therapists 1 (pt).
Languages Italian
Facilities Dining room.
Activities Arts and Crafts; Cards; Games; Prayer groups; Movies; Shopping trips; Dances/Social or cultural gatherings.

Grove Manor Nursing Home Inc*
145 Grove St, Waterbury, CT, 06710 (203)
753-7205
Licensure Skilled Care. *Beds* 60. *Certified* Medicaid; Medicare.
Ownership Proprietary.
Staff RNs 5 (ft), 1 (pt); LPNs 4 (ft), 1 (pt);
Nurses aides 17 (ft), 1 (pt); Activities coordinators 1 (ft); Dietitians 1 (ft); Social workers 1
(pt).
Languages Italian, French, Spanish, Filipino

Hillside Manor Retirement Home
157 Hillside Ave, Waterbury, CT, 06710 (203)
755-2216
Admin Adoree L Meenan. *Medical Dir/Dir of
Nursing* H Crane Huber MD.
Licensure Intermediate Care. *Beds* 23.
Ownership Proprietary.
Admissions Requirements Minimum age 50.
Staff RNs 3 (pt); LPNs 2 (ft); Nurses aides 1
(ft), 6 (pt); Activities coordinators 1 (pt); Dietitians 1 (pt).
Languages French, Polish, Italian, German
Facilities Dining room; Activities room;
Library.
Activities Arts and Crafts; Cards; Games;
Reading groups; Prayer groups; Movies; Shopping trips; Dances/Social or cultural gatherings.
Description Facility features quality living for
special private residents who prefer selectivity
to large groups.

Hope Hall Convalescent Home Inc*
355 Piedmont St, Waterbury, CT, 06706 (203)
756-3617
Licensure Skilled Care. *Beds* 34.
Ownership Proprietary.
Staff RNs 2 (ft); LPNs 1 (ft); Nurses aides 5
(ft); Activities coordinators 1 (ft); Social workers 1 (ft).
Languages French, Polish, Lithuanian
Activities Arts and Crafts; Prayer groups; Exercises; Music.

Mattatuck Health Care Facility Inc
9 Cliff St, Waterbury, CT, 06710 (203)
573-9924
Medical Dir/Dir of Nursing Joseph A Vincitonio MD.
Licensure Intermediate Care. *Beds* 43.
Certified Medicaid; Medicare.
Ownership Proprietary.
Admissions Requirements Minimum age 14;
Medical examination; Physician's request.
Staff Physicians 1 (pt); RNs 3 (ft), 2 (pt); LPNs
1 (pt); Nurses aides 4 (ft), 3 (pt); Recreational
therapists 1 (ft); Dietitians 1 (pt); Dentists 1
(pt); Podiatrists 1 (pt).
Languages Italian
Activities Prayer groups; Arts and Crafts; Shopping trips.

Medicare Pavilion Corp*
1132 Meriden Rd, Waterbury, CT, 06705 (203)
757-1228
Licensure Skilled Care; Intermediate Care.
Beds 94. *Certified* Medicaid; Medicare.
Ownership Proprietary.
Staff RNs 6 (ft); LPNs 10 (ft); Nurses aides 36
(ft); Physical therapists 1 (ft); Activities coordinators 2 (ft); Social workers 1 (ft).
Languages Italian, Lithuanian, Spanish,
French, German
Activities Arts and Crafts; Games; Dances/Social or cultural gatherings; Exercises; Current
events; Sing-a-longs.

Oakcliff Convalescent Home Inc
71 Plaza Ave, Waterbury, CT, 06710 (203)
754-6015
Medical Dir/Dir of Nursing Arthur Sullivan
MD.
Licensure Skilled Care. *Beds* 75. *Certified* Medicaid; Medicare.
Ownership Proprietary.
Admissions Requirements Minimum age 18;
Medical examination.
Staff RNs 8 (ft), 1 (pt); LPNs 3 (ft), 3 (pt);
Nurses aides 21 (ft), 5 (pt); Physical therapists 1
(pt); Recreational therapists 1 (ft), 1 (pt); Speech
therapists 1 (pt); Activities coordinators 1 (ft);
Dietitians 1 (pt); Dentists 1 (pt); Ophthalmologists 1 (pt); Podiatrists 1 (pt).
Languages French, Lithuanian, Spanish
Facilities Dining room; Physical therapy room;
Activities room; Crafts room; Laundry room.
Activities Arts and Crafts; Cards; Games;
Reading groups; Prayer groups; Movies; Shopping trips; Dances/Social or cultural gatherings.
Description Facility is a brick, fire-resistant
building which also supports an adult day care
facility (with about 30 guests) operating from 8
am to 3 pm.

Park Manor Convalescent Home
1312 W Main St, Waterbury, CT, 06708 (203)
757-9464
Medical Dir/Dir of Nursing Arthur Sullivan
MD.
Licensure Skilled Care. *Beds* 148. *Certified* Medicaid; Medicare.
Ownership Proprietary.
Staff RNs 3 (ft), 13 (pt); LPNs 6 (ft), 18 (pt);
Nurses aides 20 (ft), 42 (pt); Recreational therapists 2 (ft), 1 (pt); Dietitians 1 (ft).
Languages Spanish, Turkish, French, Italian,
Lithuanian, Polish
Facilities Dining room; Physical therapy room;
Activities room; Crafts room; Laundry room;
Barber/Beauty shop; TV lounges.
Activities Arts and Crafts; Cards; Games;
Reading groups; Prayer groups; Movies; Shopping trips; Dances/Social or cultural gatherings.

Pine Manor Rest Home
53 Pine St, Waterbury, CT, 06710 (203)
756-5187
Medical Dir/Dir of Nursing Dr Joseph Sklauer.
Licensure Intermediate Care. *Beds* 18. *Certified* Medicaid.
Ownership Proprietary.
Admissions Requirements Minimum age 50;
Physician's request.
Staff RNs 1 (ft), 3 (pt); LPNs 1 (pt); Nurses
aides 3 (ft), 2 (pt); Recreational therapists 1 (ft);
Dietitians 1 (pt); Dentists 1 (pt); Ophthalmologists 1 (pt); Podiatrists 1 (pt); Audiologists 1
(pt).
Languages Spanish, Italian, French, Polish
Facilities Dining room; Activities room; Chapel; Laundry room.
Activities Arts and Crafts; Cards; Games;
Reading groups; Prayer groups; Movies; Shopping trips; Dances/Social or cultural gatherings;
Outside activities.
Description Small facility operates in a home-like atmosphere as one big family; goal is to
keep residents well, happy, and content and to
function at maximum capacity without institutional type living.

Rose Manor*
107 S View St, Waterbury, CT, 06706 (203)
754-0786
Licensure Intermediate Care. *Beds* 22. *Certified* Medicaid.
Ownership Proprietary.
Staff RNs 5 (ft), 1 (pt); Nurses aides 7 (ft), 1
(pt).
Languages Italian, Greek, Spanish
Affiliation Roman Catholic
Activities Arts and Crafts; Games; Shopping
trips; Dances/Social or cultural gatherings;
Picnics.

Waterbury Convalescent Center Inc*
2817 N Main St, Waterbury, CT, 06704 (203)
757-0731
Licensure Skilled Care; Intermediate Care.
Beds 120. *Certified* Medicaid; Medicare.
Ownership Proprietary.
Staff RNs 7 (ft), 1 (pt); LPNs 12 (ft); Nurses
aides 35 (ft); Activities coordinators 2 (ft);
Social workers 1 (ft).
Languages Spanish, Italian, Polish

Activities Arts and Crafts; Cards; Games; Reading groups; Prayer groups; Movies; Shopping trips; Dances/Social or cultural gatherings.

Waterbury Nursing Center*
1243 W Main St, Waterbury, CT, 06708 (203) 757-0561
Licensure Skilled Care; Intermediate Care. *Beds* 129. *Certified* Medicaid; Medicare.
Ownership Proprietary.
Staff RNs 19 (ft); LPNs 6 (ft); Nurses aides 48 (ft); Activities coordinators 3 (ft).
Languages German, Lithuanian, Polish, Italian, Spanish

Whitewood Manor Nursing Home*
177 Whitewood Rd, Waterbury, CT, 06708 (203) 757-9491
Licensure Skilled Care; Intermediate Care. *Beds* 180. *Certified* Medicare.
Ownership Proprietary.
Staff RNs 32 (ft); LPNs 15 (ft); Nurses aides 68 (ft); Activities coordinators; Dietitians; Social workers.
Languages Portuguese, Yiddish, Italian, French, German

Willow Rest Home*
94 Willow St, Waterbury, CT, 06710 (203) 753-5442
Licensure Intermediate Care. *Beds* 17. *Certified* Medicaid.
Ownership Proprietary.
Staff RNs 4 (ft); Nurses aides 3 (ft); Activities coordinators 1 (ft).
Languages French
Activities Arts and Crafts; Movies; Shopping trips; Therapeutic recreation; Dining out.

Woodland Rest Home Inc*
3584 E Main St, Waterbury, CT, 06705 (203) 754-4181
Licensure Intermediate Care. *Beds* 90. *Certified* Medicaid.
Ownership Proprietary.
Staff RNs 7 (ft); LPNs 3 (ft); Nurses aides 14 (ft).
Languages Portuguese, Italian
Activities Arts and Crafts; Games; Adult education.

WATERFORD

Canterbury Villa of Waterford Inc
171 Rope Ferry Rd, Waterford, CT, 06385 (203) 443-8357
Medical Dir/Dir of Nursing Dr R Brent.
Licensure Skilled Care. *Beds* 150. *Certified* Medicaid; Medicare.
Ownership Proprietary.
Admissions Requirements Minimum age 15.
Staff Physicians 1 (ft); RNs 12 (ft), 9 (pt); LPNs 13 (ft), 7 (pt); Nurses aides 33 (ft), 45 (pt); Physical therapists 1 (ft); Activities coordinators 1 (ft), 2 (pt).
Languages Spanish, German, Italian, French
Facilities Dining room; Physical therapy room; Activities room; Crafts room; Laundry room; Barber/Beauty shop.
Activities Arts and Crafts; Games; Reading groups; Prayer groups; Movies; Shopping trips; Dances/Social or cultural gatherings.

Greentree Manor Convalescent Home*
4 Greentree Dr, Waterford, CT, 06385 (203) 442-0647
Licensure Skilled Care. *Beds* 90. *Certified* Medicaid; Medicare.
Ownership Proprietary.
Staff RNs 14 (ft); LPNs 7 (ft); Nurses aides 36 (ft); Activities coordinators 2 (ft); Social workers 1 (ft).
Languages Greek, Korean, Tagalog, Spanish, German, Polish, Italian
Activities Arts and Crafts; Games; Reading groups; Dances/Social or cultural gatherings; Music.

New London Convalescent Home*
88 Clark Ln, Waterford, CT, 06385 (203) 442-0471
Licensure Skilled Care. *Beds* 120. *Certified* Medicaid; Medicare.
Ownership Proprietary.
Staff RNs 14 (ft); LPNs 12 (ft); Nurses aides 46 (ft); Physical therapists.
Languages French
Activities Arts and Crafts; Games; Prayer groups; Movies; Dances/Social or cultural gatherings.

WATERTOWN

Waterbury Extended Care Facility Inc
35 Bunker Hill Rd, Watertown, CT, 06795 (203) 274-5428
Licensure Skilled Care. *Beds* 60. *Certified* Medicaid; Medicare.
Ownership Proprietary.
Staff Physicians; Dietitians.
Languages Italian, French
Activities Prayer groups; Arts and Crafts; Shopping trips.

Watertown Convalarium
560 Woodbury Rd, Watertown, CT, 06795 (203) 274-6748
Licensure Skilled Care. *Beds* 36. *Certified* Medicaid.
Ownership Nonprofit.
Staff Physicians; Dietitians; Nurses aides.
Languages Italian, French
Activities Prayer groups; Arts and Crafts; Shopping trips.

WEST HARTFORD

Brookview Convalescent Home
130 Loomis Dr, West Hartford, CT, 06107 (203) 521-8700
Admin Patricia Fried. *Medical Dir/Dir of Nursing* Robert Safer MD.
Licensure Skilled Care; Intermediate Care. *Beds* SNF 88; ICF 90. *Certified* Medicaid; Medicare.
Ownership Proprietary.
Admissions Requirements Medical examination; Physician's request.
Staff RNs 10 (ft), 34 (pt); LPNs 2 (ft), 9 (pt); Nurses aides 14 (ft), 74 (pt); Physical therapists 1 (pt); Recreational therapists 2 (ft), 1 (pt); Activities coordinators 1 (ft).
Facilities Dining room; Physical therapy room; Activities room; Crafts room; Laundry room;

Barber/Beauty shop.
Activities Arts and Crafts; Cards; Games; Reading groups; Prayer groups; Movies; Shopping trips; Dances/Social or cultural gatherings; Garden club; Jewish community group; Overnight trips; Family dinners.
Description Brookview offers an individualized program of health care in a lovely residential area of West Hartford, within walking distance of West Hartford Center. Scenic trout brook runs adjacent to the property on which the facility stands.

Hughes Convalescent Inc
29 Highland St, West Hartford, CT, 06119 (203) 236-5623
Medical Dir/Dir of Nursing Joseph J Lucas MD.
Licensure Skilled Care. *Beds* 180. *Certified* Medicaid; Medicare.
Ownership Proprietary.
Admissions Requirements Minimum age 14; Medical examination; Physician's request.
Staff Physicians 5 (pt); RNs 23 (ft), 12 (pt); LPNs 8 (ft), 4 (pt); Orderlies 2 (ft); Nurses aides 78 (ft); Physical therapists 3 (pt); Recreational therapists 3 (ft), 1 (pt); Speech therapists 1 (pt); Dietitians 1 (pt); Dentists 1 (pt); Podiatrists 2 (pt).
Languages Spanish, Italian, Polish, German, French, Portuguese
Facilities Dining room; Physical therapy room; Activities room; Chapel; Crafts room; Laundry room; Barber/Beauty shop; Library.
Activities Arts and Crafts; Cards; Games; Reading groups; Prayer groups; Movies; Shopping trips; Dances/Social or cultural gatherings.

Mercyknoll
243 Steele Rd, West Hartford, CT, 06117 (203) 236-3503
Licensure Skilled Care. *Beds* 22.
Ownership Nonprofit.
Staff Physicians; Dietitians.
Languages Polish
Activities Prayer groups; Arts and Crafts; Shopping trips.

Saint Mary Home*
291 Steele Rd, West Hartford, CT, 06117 (203) 236-1924
Licensure Intermediate Care; Home for the aged. *Beds* 167. *Certified* Medicaid.
Ownership Nonprofit.
Staff Physicians 1 (pt); RNs 2 (ft), 1 (pt); LPNs 1 (pt); Nurses aides 5 (ft), 1 (pt); Physical therapists; Occupational therapists; Speech therapists; Dietitians; Social workers 1 (ft).
Languages Spanish, French, German
Affiliation Roman Catholic
Activities Arts and Crafts; Games; Prayer groups; Dances/Social or cultural gatherings; Outings.

West Hartford Manor*
2432 Albany Ave, West Hartford, CT, 06117 (203) 236-3557
Licensure Skilled Care. *Beds* 120. *Certified* Medicaid; Medicare.
Ownership Proprietary.
Staff RNs 12 (ft); LPNs 3 (ft); Nurses aides 43 (ft); Physical therapists 1 (ft); Activities coordinators 2 (ft); Social workers 1 (ft).

Languages Spanish
Activities Reading groups; Prayer groups; Dances/Social or cultural gatherings; Current events.

WEST HAVEN

Arterburn Convalescent Home
267 Union Ave, West Haven, CT, 06516 (203) 934-5256
Medical Dir/Dir of Nursing Dominic B Schioppo MD.
Licensure Intermediate Care. *Beds* 40. *Certified* Medicaid.
Ownership Proprietary.
Admissions Requirements Minimum age 18; Medical examination; Physician's request.
Staff RNs 3 (ft), 3 (pt); LPNs 3 (ft); Nurses aides 10 (ft), 4 (pt); Recreational therapists 1 (ft).
Languages Italian, Spanish, Polish
Facilities Dining room; Activities room; Crafts room; Laundry room; Barber/Beauty shop.
Activities Arts and Crafts; Cards; Games; Prayer groups; Movies; Shopping trips.
Description Facility has been in operation for the past 40 years; as of May 1982, changed from a skilled care to intermediate care facility; referrals come from local agencies, physicians, Visiting Nurse Association, senior citizen center, 2 general hospitals, and people who have either had a family member or friend previously placed in facility.

Bentley Gardens Nursing Home
310 Terrace Ave, West Haven, CT, 06516 (203) 932-2247
Medical Dir/Dir of Nursing Dr John Milici.
Licensure Skilled Care. *Beds* 97. *Certified* Medicare.
Ownership Proprietary.
Admissions Requirements Minimum age 21; Medical examination.
Staff RNs 13 (ft), 9 (pt); LPNs 5 (ft), 4 (pt); Nurses aides 19 (ft), 3 (pt); Physical therapists 1 (ft); Recreational therapists 2 (ft), 2 (pt); Activities coordinators 1 (ft).
Languages Italian, Spanish
Facilities Dining room; Physical therapy room; Activities room; Chapel; Crafts room; Laundry room; Barber/Beauty shop; Library; Garden and patio.
Activities Arts and Crafts; Cards; Games; Reading groups; Prayer groups; Movies; Shopping trips; Dances/Social or cultural gatherings.
Description Bentley Gardens is a modern, fully-equipped skilled nursing facility, recognized for its high standards of personal care, skilled nursing care, and rehabilitative services. Staff is dedicated to the concept of preserving human dignity as well as maintaining optimal physical health.

Breakers Convalescent Home
307 Beech St, West Haven, CT, 06516 (203) 934-7943
Licensure Skilled Care. *Beds* 39. *Certified* Medicaid; Medicare.
Ownership Proprietary.
Staff Physicians; Dietitians; Nurses aides.

Languages Italian
Activities Prayer groups; Arts and Crafts; Shopping trips.

Harbor View Manor*
308 Savin Ave, West Haven, CT, 06516 (203) 932-6411
Licensure Intermediate Care. *Beds* 120. *Certified* Medicaid.
Ownership Proprietary.
Staff RNs 4 (ft), 1 (pt); LPNs 7 (ft); Nurses aides 14 (ft); Activities coordinators 2 (ft), 1 (pt); Social workers 1 (ft).
Languages Spanish, French
Activities Arts and Crafts; Movies; Shopping trips; Dances/Social or cultural gatherings; Picnics; Discussion groups.

Hawkins Rest Home
588 Ocean Ave, West Haven, CT, 06516 (203) 934-2676
Medical Dir/Dir of Nursing Dr John Milici.
Licensure Intermediate Care. *Beds* 39. *Certified* Medicaid.
Ownership Proprietary.
Admissions Requirements Minimum age 21; Medical examination; Physician's request.
Staff Physicians 2 (pt); RNs 3 (ft), 4 (pt); LPNs 1 (ft); Nurses aides 6 (ft), 4 (pt); Physical therapists 1 (pt); Activities coordinators 1 (ft); Dietitians 1 (pt); Dentists 1 (pt); Podiatrists 1 (pt); Audiologists 1 (pt).
Languages German, Spanish
Facilities Dining room; Activities room; Crafts room; Laundry room.
Activities Arts and Crafts; Cards; Games; Reading groups; Prayer groups; Movies; Shopping trips; Dances/Social or cultural gatherings.
Description Home is located on Long Island Sound offering home-like atmosphere, home cooking, outings, picnics, and outstanding nursing care.

Sound View Specialized Care Center
Care Ln, West Haven, CT, 06516 (203) 934-7955
Licensure Skilled Care. *Beds* 100. *Certified* Medicaid; Medicare.
Ownership Proprietary.
Staff Physicians; Dietitians; Nurses aides.
Languages Italian, Slavic
Activities Prayer groups; Arts and Crafts; Shopping trips.

West Haven Nursing Center
555 Saw Mill Rd, West Haven, CT, 06516 (203) 934-8326 and 934-8327
Medical Dir/Dir of Nursing Dominic B Schioppo MD.
Licensure Skilled Care. *Beds* 120. *Certified* Medicaid; Medicare.
Ownership Proprietary.
Staff Physicians 1 (pt); RNs 10 (ft); LPNs 8 (ft); Nurses aides 42 (ft); Physical therapists 1 (pt); Recreational therapists 2 (ft); Speech therapists 1 (pt); Dietitians 1 (pt); Dentists 1 (pt); Ophthalmologists 1 (pt); Podiatrists 1 (pt); Audiologists 1 (pt).
Facilities Dining room; Physical therapy room; Activities room; Laundry room; Barber/Beauty shop.
Activities Arts and Crafts; Cards; Games; Reading groups; Movies; Dances/Social or cul-

tural gatherings.

WESTPORT

The Regency of Westport*
1 Burr Rd, Westport, CT, 06880 (203) 226-4201
Licensure Skilled Care; Intermediate Care. *Beds* SNF 30; ICF 90. *Certified* Medicaid; Medicare.
Ownership Proprietary.
Staff RNs 25 (ft); LPNs 4 (ft); Nurses aides 42 (ft); Physical therapists 4 (ft); Activities coordinators 3 (ft); Social workers 1 (ft), 1 (pt).
Languages Spanish, French, Italian, Polish, Hungarian, Norwegian
Activities Arts and Crafts; Movies; Shopping trips; Dances/Social or cultural gatherings; Gardening.

WETHERSFIELD

Wethersfield Manor*
341 Jordan Ln, Wethersfield, CT, 06109 (203) 563-0101
Licensure Intermediate Care. *Beds* 60. *Certified* Medicaid; Medicare.
Ownership Proprietary.
Staff Nurses aides 5 (ft); Physical therapists 1 (ft), 10 (pt); Activities coordinators 1 (ft); Dietitians.
Languages Italian, Portuguese, Polish, French, German, Spanish, Hebrew
Activities Arts and Crafts; Games; Shopping trips; Dances/Social or cultural gatherings.

WILLIMANTIC

Canterbury Villa of Willimantic*
595 Valley St, Willimantic, CT, 06226 (203) 423-2597
Admin Peter C Kern.
Licensure Skilled Care; Intermediate Care. *Beds* 120. *Certified* Medicaid; Medicare.
Ownership Proprietary.
Staff RNs 6 (ft); LPNs 7 (ft); Orderlies 30 (ft); Physical therapists 1 (ft); Activities coordinators 1 (ft).
Languages French, Polish, Italian
Activities Arts and Crafts; Games; Dances/Social or cultural gatherings; Exercises; Current events.

Natchaug Hospital Inc
189 Storrs Rd, Willimantic, CT, 06226 (203) 423-2514
Licensure Skilled Care. *Beds* 8. *Certified* Medicaid; Medicare.
Ownership Nonprofit.
Staff Physicians; Dietitians; Nurses aides.
Languages Russian, French, Spanish, German, Hebrew
Activities Prayer groups; Arts and Crafts; Shopping trips.

WINDHAM

Abbey Manor
Rt 14, Windham, CT, 06280 (203) 423-4636
Medical Dir/Dir of Nursing Dr William Ellzey.

Licensure Skilled Care. *Beds* 60. *Certified* Medicaid; Medicare.
Ownership Proprietary.
Admissions Requirements Minimum age 14.
Staff Physicians 10 (ft); RNs 9 (ft); LPNs 7 (ft); Nurses aides 33 (ft); Physical therapists 1 (ft); Recreational therapists 1 (ft); Speech therapists 1 (ft); Activities coordinators 1 (ft); Dietitians 1 (ft); Dentists 1 (ft); Ophthalmologists 1 (ft); Podiatrists 1 (ft); Audiologists 1 (ft).
Languages French, Polish, Russian
Facilities Dining room; Physical therapy room; Activities room; Chapel; Laundry room; Barber/Beauty shop; Library.
Activities Arts and Crafts; Cards; Games; Reading groups; Prayer groups; Movies; Shopping trips; Dances/Social or cultural gatherings.

WINDSOR

Kimberly Hall Nursing Home—North
1 Kimberly Dr, Windsor, CT, 06095 (203) 688-6443
Admin Barry W Coccimo. *Medical Dir/Dir of Nursing* Jabbour Nakhoul MD.
Licensure Skilled Care. *Beds* 150. *Certified* Medicaid; Medicare.
Ownership Proprietary.
Staff Physicians 1 (pt).
Facilities Dining room; Physical therapy room; Activities room; Chapel; Crafts room; Laundry room; Barber/Beauty shop; Library; TV lounges; Inner courtyards.
Activities Arts and Crafts; Cards; Games; Reading groups; Prayer groups; Movies.
Description Kimberly Hall is fully equipped and staffed to provide every guest with the maximum in comfort and personal attention and the ultimate in professional care. Licensed nurses are on duty 24-hours a day. Doctors and consulting specialists are always on call. A reassuring variety of services, diagnostic and therapeutic, are available.

Kimberly Hall Nursing Home—South*
1 Kimberly Dr, Windsor, CT, 06095 (203) 688-6443
Licensure Intermediate Care. *Beds* 180. *Certified* Medicaid; Medicare.
Ownership Proprietary.
Staff RNs 16 (ft); LPNs 7 (ft); Nurses aides 78 (ft); Activities coordinators 3 (ft).
Languages Spanish, Italian, Portuguese, Laotian

Mountain View Healthcare
581 Poquonock Ave, Windsor, CT, 06095 (203) 688-7211
Medical Dir/Dir of Nursing Joseph Misiak MD.
Licensure Skilled Care. *Beds* 120. *Certified* Medicaid; Medicare.
Ownership Proprietary.
Admissions Requirements Medical examination; Physician's request.
Staff Physicians; RNs; LPNs; Nurses aides; Physical therapists 1 (ft), 1 (pt); Recreational therapists 2 (ft); Speech therapists; Dietitians; Dentists; Podiatrists.
Languages Italian, Polish
Facilities Dining room; Physical therapy room; Laundry room; Library.

Activities Arts and Crafts; Cards; Games; Reading groups; Reading groups; Prayer groups; Movies; Dances/Social or cultural gatherings.
Description Mountain View has a residential chorus which gives 3 concerts a year. This chorus travels to area nursing homes to entertain. We offer 4 special events a year including Special Olympics. We have a large volunteer group as well as a library program.

Windsor Hall Nursing and Rest Home
519 Palisado Ave, Windsor, CT, 06095 (203) 688-4918
Medical Dir/Dir of Nursing Dr George Donahue.
Licensure Skilled Care; Intermediate Care. *Beds* 60. *Certified* Medicaid.
Ownership Proprietary.
Admissions Requirements Minimum age 14; Medical examination; Physician's request.
Staff Physicians 11 (pt); RNs 13 (ft), 3 (pt); LPNs 5 (ft), 2 (pt); Orderlies 3 (ft), 3 (pt); Nurses aides 19 (ft), 13 (pt); Physical therapists 1 (pt); Recreational therapists 3 (ft); Speech therapists 1 (pt); Dietitians 1 (ft), 1 (pt); Dentists 1 (pt); Podiatrists 1 (pt).
Languages Polish, French, German, Sign Language
Facilities Dining room; Physical therapy room; Activities room; Crafts room; Laundry room; Barber/Beauty shop.
Activities Arts and Crafts; Cards; Games; Reading groups; Prayer groups; Movies; Shopping trips.

WINDSOR LOCKS

Bickford Convalescent Home
14 Main St, Windsor Locks, CT, 06096 (203) 623-4351
Medical Dir/Dir of Nursing John J Kennedy Jr MD.
Licensure Skilled Care; Rest Home. *Beds* 48; Rest Home 11. *Certified* Medicaid.
Ownership Proprietary.
Admissions Requirements Physician's request.
Staff RNs 4 (ft), 5 (pt); LPNs 9 (pt); Nurses aides 17 (ft), 22 (pt); Physical therapists 1 (pt); Recreational therapists 1 (ft), 1 (pt).
Languages Polish, Italian, French
Facilities Physical therapy room; Activities room; Laundry room; Barber/Beauty shop.
Activities Arts and Crafts; Games; Reading groups; Prayer groups; Movies; Shopping trips; Dances/Social or cultural gatherings.

WINSTED

Highland Acres Extend-A-Care Center
108 E Lake St, Winsted, CT, 06098 (203) 379-8591
Medical Dir/Dir of Nursing Dr David Hebert.
Licensure Skilled Care; Intermediate Care. *Beds* 75. *Certified* Medicaid; Medicare.
Ownership Nonprofit.
Admissions Requirements Minimum age 14.
Staff RNs 5 (ft), 10 (pt); LPNs 1 (ft), 1 (pt); Nurses aides 9 (ft), 15 (pt); Physical therapists 1 (pt); Recreational therapists 1 (ft), 1 (pt); Dietitians 1 (pt).

Languages French, Italian, German
Facilities Dining room; Physical therapy room; Activities room; Chapel; Laundry room; Barber/Beauty shop; Library.
Activities Arts and Crafts; Cards; Games; Reading groups; Prayer groups; Movies; Shopping trips; Dances/Social or cultural gatherings.

WOLCOTT

Wolcott Rest Home*
55 Beach Rd, Wolcott, CT, 06716 (203) 879-0600
Licensure Intermediate Care. *Beds* 20.
Ownership Proprietary.
Languages French, Italian

Wolcott View Manor*
50 Beach Rd, Wolcott, CT, 06716 (203) 879-1479
Licensure Intermediate Care. *Beds* 59. *Certified* Medicaid.
Ownership Proprietary.
Staff RNs 3 (ft); Nurses aides 4 (ft); Activities coordinators 3 (ft); Dietitians 1 (ft); Social workers 1 (ft).
Languages French, Italian

DELAWARE

BRIDGEVILLE

Reynold's Boarding Home*
Rt 1, Box 290, Bridgeville, DE, 19933 (302) 337-7716
Admin Catherine Reynolds.
Licensure Residental Care. *Beds* 6.

CLAYMONT

Riverview House*
7811 Governor Printz Blvd, Claymont, DE, 19703 (302) 798-6681
Admin Lacinda Rowles.
Licensure Intermediate Care. *Beds* 70. *Certified* Medicaid.

Rosewood Rest Home*
3 Wistar St, Claymont, DE, 19703 (302) 798-9620
Admin Nancy Olsen.
Licensure Intermediate Care. *Beds* 13. *Certified* Medicaid.

DELAWARE CITY

Governor Bacon Health Center—Tilton Building*
Delaware City, DE, 19706 (302) 834-9201
Admin C Ronald McGinnis.
Licensure Intermediate Care. *Beds* 122. *Certified* Medicaid.

DELMAR

Shangri-La Nursing Home*
Delaware Ave, Delmar, DE, 19940 (302) 846-3031
Admin Margaret Barnes.
Licensure Skilled Care; Intermediate Care. *Beds* 120. *Certified* Medicaid; Medicare.

DOVER

Courtland Manor Nursing and Convalescent Home*
1175 McKee Rd, Dover, DE, 19901 (302) 674-0566
Admin Irma M Schurman.
Licensure Skilled Care; Intermediate Care. *Beds* 100. *Certified* Medicaid; Medicare.

Crescent Farm Convalescing and Nursing Home*
Rt 6, Box 131, Artis Dr, Dover, DE, 19901 (302) 734-5953
Admin Louzena Melvin.
Licensure Intermediate Care. *Beds* 80. *Certified* Medicaid.

Palmer Home Inc*
115 American Ave, Dover, DE, 19901 (302) 734-5591
Admin Iva Arnold.
Licensure Residential Care. *Beds* 4.

FELTON

Felton Convalescent Home
Church and High Sts, Felton, DE, 19943 (302) 284-4667
Admin Beverly Veihman.
Licensure Intermediate Care. *Beds* 11. *Certified* Medicaid.
Staff RNs 1 (pt); LPNs 1 (ft), 2 (pt); Nurses aides 7 (ft), 2 (pt); Podiatrists 1 (pt).
Facilities Dining room; Activities room; Laundry room.
Activities Prayer groups.
Description Facility is a small family-type home featuring good home cooking and a lot of tender loving care. Each resident is a person in their own right and treated as such.

Golden Years Manor*
Church and Sewell, Felton, DE, 19943 (302) 284-4510
Admin Sandra Schurman.
Licensure Intermediate Care. *Beds* 12. *Certified* Medicaid.

GREENWOOD

Country Rest Home
Greenwood, DE, 19950 (302) 349-4114
Admin Mark Yoder.
Licensure Intermediate Care. *Beds* 32. *Certified* Medicaid.
Admissions Requirements Medical examination; Physician's request.
Staff Physicians 1 (pt); RNs 1 (pt); LPNs 2 (ft), 3 (pt); Orderlies 1 (pt); Nurses aides 25 (pt); Activities coordinators 1 (ft).
Affiliation Mennonite
Facilities Dining room; Lobby.

Activities Arts and Crafts; Cards; Games; Reading groups; Movies; Shopping trips; Trips.
Description Usually the day before mothers day, there is a picnic for guests and their families. Activities director often takes our guests for rides in the country.

Mast Boarding Home*
Rt 1, Box 201, Greenwood, DE, 19950 (302) 349-4179
Admin Sally Mast.
Licensure Residential Care. *Beds* 4.

HARRINGTON

Haven Hill Residential Home*
Rt 2, Box 215, Harrington, DE, 19952 (302) 398-8854
Admin Ms Norman Rust.
Licensure Residential Care. *Beds* 6.

HOCKESSIN

Cokesbury Village
Lancaster Pike and Loveville Rd, Hockessin, DE, 19707 (302) 239-2371
Admin William L Scott. *Medical Dir/Dir of Nursing* William L Jaffee MD.
Licensure Skilled Care. *Beds* 55. *Certified* Medicare.
Admissions Requirements Minimum age 60; Medical examination.
Staff Physicians 3 (pt); RNs 3 (ft), 15 (pt); LPNs 2 (ft), 1 (pt); Nurses aides 12 (ft), 12 (pt); Physical therapists 1 (pt); Activities coordinators 1 (pt).
Affiliation Methodist
Facilities Dining room; Physical therapy room; Activities room; Chapel; Crafts room; Laundry room; Barber/Beauty shop; Library; Store; Woodshop.
Activities Arts and Crafts; Cards; Games; Reading groups; Prayer groups; Movies; Shopping trips; Dances/Social or cultural gatherings.

Episcopal Church Home
Rt 3 Box 233, Hockessin, DE, 19707 (302) 998-0181
Admin Davie Anna Alleman. *Medical Dir/Dir of Nursing* Tae Sup Song.
Licensure Skilled Care; Intermediate Care. *Beds* 122. *Certified* Medicaid; Medicare.
Admissions Requirements Minimum age 14;

Medical examination; Physician's request.
Staff RNs 8 (ft), 7 (pt); LPNs 8 (ft), 8 (pt); Nurses aides 35 (ft), 45 (pt); Physical therapists 1 (pt); Activities coordinators 1 (ft); Dietitians 1 (pt).
Affiliation Episcopal
Facilities Dining room; Physical therapy room; Activities room; Chapel; Crafts room; Laundry room; Barber/Beauty shop; Library.
Activities Arts and Crafts; Cards; Games; Reading groups; Prayer groups; Movies; Shopping trips.

LEWES

Lewes Convalescent Center*
440 Market St, Lewes, DE, 19958 (302) 645-6606
Admin Christine Evans.
Licensure Skilled Care; Intermediate Care.
Beds SNF 50; ICF 40. *Certified* Medicaid; Medicare.

MILFORD

Ingram's Rest Home*
Rt 1, Rehoboth Hwy, Milford, DE, 19963 (302) 422-4351
Admin Virginia Ingram.
Licensure Intermediate Care. *Beds* 14. *Certified* Medicare.

Milford Manor
700 Marvel Rd, Milford, DE, 19963 (302) 422-3303
Admin Madelyn LaGuardia. *Medical Dir/Dir of Nursing* Harvey Mast MD.
Licensure Skilled Care; Intermediate Care; Residential Care. *Beds* SNF 24; ICF 88; Residential Care 14. *Certified* Medicaid; Medicare.
Admissions Requirements Minimum age 50; Medical examination.
Staff RNs 2 (ft), 4 (pt); LPNs 8 (ft), 4 (pt); Nurses aides 24 (ft), 28 (pt); Physical therapists 1 (pt); Activities coordinators 1 (ft), 1 (pt); Dietitians 1 (pt).
Facilities Dining room; Physical therapy room; Activities room; Crafts room; Laundry room; Barber/Beauty shop.
Activities Arts and Crafts; Cards; Games; Reading groups; Prayer groups; Movies; Shopping trips; Dances/Social or cultural gatherings.

MILLSBORO

Maple Grove Convalescent Center
Box 302, Millsboro, DE, 19966 (302) 934-9281
Admin William T Willin Jr. *Medical Dir/Dir of Nursing* Dr Ascaro.
Licensure Intermediate Care. *Beds* 43. *Certified* Medicaid.
Staff Physicians 4 (pt); RNs 1 (ft); LPNs 3 (ft); Nurses aides 15 (ft), 15 (pt); Physical therapists 1 (pt); Activities coordinators 1 (pt); Dietitians 1 (pt); Dentists 1 (pt); Podiatrists 1 (pt).
Facilities Dining room; Activities room; Laundry room; Barber/Beauty shop.
Activities Arts and Crafts; Cards; Games; Prayer groups; Movies.
Description Facility is small and informal

enough to provide individualized care to each resident; residents are encouraged to bring a favorite chair; free TV service with hookups provided in each room.

NEWARK

Churchman Village
4949 Ogletown-Stanton Rd, Newark, DE, 19713 (302) 998-6900
Admin Terrence McBride. *Medical Dir/Dir of Nursing* Dr E C Hewlett.
Licensure Skilled Care; Intermediate Care.
Beds 100. *Certified* Medicaid; Medicare.
Staff Physicians; RNs; LPNs; Nurses aides; Physical therapists; Activities coordinators; Dietitians.
Facilities Dining room; Physical therapy room; Activities room; Chapel; Crafts room; Laundry room; Barber/Beauty shop.
Activities Arts and Crafts; Cards; Games; Reading groups; Prayer groups; Movies; Shopping trips; Dances/Social or cultural gatherings.
Description New facility opened January 1984; staff presently being organized; retirement apartments also available.

Jeanne Jugan Residence
185 Salem Church Rd, Newark, DE, 19713 (302) 368-5886
Admin Sr Gerard Mary Bradley. *Medical Dir/Dir of Nursing* S W Bartoshesky MD.
Licensure Skilled Care; Intermediate Care; Residential Care. *Beds* SNF 22; ICF 60; Residential Care 36. *Certified* Medicaid.
Admissions Requirements Minimum age 60; Medical examination.
Staff Physicians 3 (pt); RNs 5 (ft), 2 (pt); LPNs 4 (ft), 6 (pt); Nurses aides 24 (ft), 12 (pt); Physical therapists 1 (pt); Reality therapists 1 (pt); Recreational therapists 1 (pt); Occupational therapists 1 (pt); Speech therapists 1 (pt); Activities coordinators 1 (ft); Dietitians 1 (pt); Dentists 1 (pt); Podiatrists 1 (pt); Audiologists 1 (pt).
Affiliation Roman Catholic
Facilities Dining room; Physical therapy room; Activities room; Chapel; Crafts room; Laundry room; Barber/Beauty shop; Library.
Activities Arts and Crafts; Cards; Games; Reading groups; Prayer groups; Movies; Shopping trips; Dances/Social or cultural gatherings.
Description We admit the elderly who are poor or of limited assets.

Newark Manor Nursing Home Inc
254 W Main St, Newark, DE, 19711 (302) 731-5576
Admin Russell L Ellis. *Medical Dir/Dir of Nursing* David Messinger.
Licensure Intermediate Care. *Beds* 53.
Staff Physicians 1 (pt); RNs 8 (pt); LPNs 2 (pt); Nurses aides 11 (ft), 22 (pt); Reality therapists 1 (pt); Recreational therapists 1 (pt); Activities coordinators 1 (ft).
Facilities Dining room; Physical therapy room; Activities room; Crafts room; Laundry room; Barber/Beauty shop; Library.
Activities Arts and Crafts; Cards; Games; Reading groups; Movies; Shopping trips; Dances/Social or cultural gatherings; Remotivation therapy.

Description Facility features gracious living in a residential setting, in a small, private, intermediate care nursing home with the advantage of giving more personal care, with the amenities of a large facility. Both private and semi-private accomodations; owner-administrated facility with a dedicated staff.

SEAFORD

Fair Holme Convalescent Center*
117 Willey St, Seaford, DE, 19973 (302) 629-9440
Admin Dolores F McDaniel.
Licensure Intermediate Care. *Beds* 7. *Certified* Medicaid.

Methodist Manor House*
1001 Middleford Rd, Seaford, DE, 19973 (302) 629-4593
Admin Doris M Walls.
Licensure Skilled Care. *Beds* 50. *Certified* Medicaid; Medicare.
Affiliation Methodist

Seaford Health Care Center
1100 Norman Eskridge Hwy, Seaford, DE, 19973 (302) 629-3575
Admin Janet Giordano. *Medical Dir/Dir of Nursing* Dr Eduardo Jilaca.
Licensure Skilled Care; Intermediate Care.
Beds SNF 66; ICF 56. *Certified* Medicaid; Medicare.
Admissions Requirements Minimum age 15; Medical examination.
Staff Physicians 14 (pt); RNs 2 (ft), 4 (pt); LPNs 6 (ft), 11 (pt); Orderlies 1 (pt); Nurses aides 30 (ft), 25 (pt); Physical therapists 1 (pt); Speech therapists 1 (pt); Activities coordinators 1 (ft), 2 (pt); Dietitians 1 (pt); Dentists 1 (pt); Ophthalmologists 1 (pt); Podiatrists 1 (pt).
Facilities Dining room; Physical therapy room; Activities room; Chapel; Crafts room; Laundry room; Barber/Beauty shop; Library.
Activities Arts and Crafts; Cards; Games; Reading groups; Prayer groups; Movies; Shopping trips; Dances/Social or cultural gatherings.
Description Facility is certified for Maryland and Delaware Medicaid and Medicare, located on Norman Eskridge Highway approximately one mile from Nanticoke Memorial Hospital; has 5 retirement rooms; active resident council, monthly newsletter that is shared with the community, and many activities that include community involvement.

SMYRNA

Kent Convalescent Center
1455 S duPont Hwy, Smyrna, DE, 19977 (302) 653-5085
Admin Amy L Niland. *Medical Dir/Dir of Nursing* Concordia Maqsonac MD.
Licensure Skilled Care; Intermediate Care.
Beds SNF 36; ICF 58. *Certified* Medicaid; Medicare.
Admissions Requirements Medical examination.
Staff RNs 2 (ft), 8 (pt); LPNs 3 (ft), 9 (pt); Orderlies 2 (pt); Activities coordinators 1 (ft).
Facilities Dining room; Physical therapy room;

Activities room; Laundry room; Barber/Beauty shop; Library.
Activities Arts and Crafts; Games; Reading groups; Prayer groups; Movies; Shopping trips; Dances/Social or cultural gatherings.
Description Modern, spacious nursing facility located in a country setting only 10 minutes from local hospital; wide variety of social and activity programs offered, as well as ancillary services.

Scott Nursing Home
Main and Mount Vernon Sts, Smyrna, DE, 19977 (302) 653-8554
Admin Marjorie Capers. *Medical Dir/Dir of Nursing* Dr Ciriaco G Bongalos Jr.
Licensure Intermediate Care. *Beds* 33. *Certified* Medicaid.
Facilities Dining room; Activities room; Laundry room.
Activities Arts and Crafts; Cards; Games; Reading groups; Prayer groups; Movies; Music therapy; Horticulture.
Description Small nursing home located in a small town adjacent to stores with a homey atmosphere; family business started in 1944.

TOWNSEND

Mundey Manor
Rt 1, Box 65A, Townsend, DE, 19734 (302) 378-2860
Admin Katheryn E Mundey.
Licensure Residential Care. *Beds* 6.
Admissions Requirements Minimum age 60; Males only

WILMINGTON

Brandywine Convalescent Home
505 Greenbank Rd, Wilmington, DE, 19808 (302) 998-0101
Admin Mary Woodstock. *Medical Dir/Dir of Nursing* James Harkness DO.
Licensure Skilled Care; Intermediate Care.
Beds 106. *Certified* Medicaid; Medicare.
Staff Physicians 1 (ft); RNs 1 (ft), 11 (pt); LPNs 3 (ft), 3 (pt); Nurses aides 17 (ft), 22 (pt); Physical therapists 1 (ft); Speech therapists 1 (ft); Activities coordinators 1 (ft); Dietitians 1 (ft); Dentists 1 (ft); Podiatrists 1 (ft); Technicians 2 (ft), 4 (pt).
Facilities Dining room; Physical therapy room; Activities room; Crafts room; Laundry room; Barber/Beauty shop; Library.
Activities Arts and Crafts; Cards; Games; Reading groups; Prayer groups; Movies; Dances/Social or cultural gatherings.
Description Facility is located in spacious country surroundings where both patients and families can be outside; beginning each May cookouts are provided for residents.

Chariot Nursing and Convalescent Home*
2735 W 6th St, Wilmington, DE, 19807 (302) 654-7616
Admin Paul A Paradise Jr.
Licensure Intermediate Care. *Beds* 30. *Certified* Medicaid.

Daybreak Lodge*
2801 W 6th St, Wilmington, DE, 19805 (302) 654-4493
Admin Leonard Leeds.
Licensure Skilled Care; Intermediate Care.
Beds 150. *Certified* Medicaid; Medicare.

Foulk Manor*
407 Foulk Rd, Wilmington, DE, 19803 (302) 655-6249
Admin Jessie Tink.
Licensure Skilled Care; Intermediate Care; Residential Care. *Beds* SNF 25; ICF 31; Residential Care 51. *Certified* Medicaid; Medicare.

Foulk Manor Infirmary—North
1212 Foulk Rd, Wilmington, DE, 19803 (302) 478-4296
Admin Irene Owens. *Medical Dir/Dir of Nursing* D W MacKelcan MD.
Licensure Skilled Care; Intermediate Care.
Beds SNF 25; ICF 18.
Ownership Proprietary.
Admissions Requirements Minimum age 65; Medical examination; Physician's request.
Staff Physicians 1 (pt); RNs 6 (ft), 14 (pt); Nurses aides 9 (ft), 17 (pt); Physical therapists 1 (pt); Activities coordinators 1 (ft), 2 (pt); Dietitians 1 (ft); Podiatrists 1 (pt).
Facilities Dining room; Physical therapy room; Activities room; Crafts room; Laundry room; Barber/Beauty shop; Library.
Activities Arts and Crafts; Cards; Games; Reading groups; Prayer groups; Movies; Shopping trips; Dances/Social or cultural gatherings.
Description This is a profit making facility in suburban, north Wilmington, located close to many historical sites and convenient to concerts and other functions.

Gibbs Boarding Home*
177 Bunche Blvd, Wilmington, DE, 19801 (302) 658-4739
Admin Mary Gibbs.
Licensure Residential Care. *Beds* 5.

Hillside House
810 S Broom St, Wilmington, DE, 19805 (302) 652-1181
Admin K M Renshaw. *Medical Dir/Dir of Nursing* D W MacKelcan MD.
Licensure Skilled Care; Intermediate Care.
Beds SNF 68; ICF 36. *Certified* Medicaid; Medicare.
Admissions Requirements Medical examination.
Staff Physicians 1 (pt); RNs 4 (ft), 6 (pt); LPNs 6 (ft), 7 (pt); Nurses aides 30 (ft), 17 (pt); Physical therapists 1 (pt); Occupational therapists; Speech therapists; Activities coordinators 1 (ft), 1 (pt); Dietitians.
Facilities Dining room; Physical therapy room; Activities room; Barber/Beauty shop.
Activities Arts and Crafts; Games; Shopping trips; Dances/Social or cultural gatherings; Sightseeing trips.
Description This is a 4-story facility with intermediate nursing on one floor and skilled/intermediate on the other 2 patient care floors; located in a nice residential community with emphasis on quality nursing care.

Home for Aged Women—Minquadale Home Inc
1109 Gilpin Ave, Wilmington, DE, 19806 (302) 655-6411
Admin Mrs E C Reese. *Medical Dir/Dir of Nursing* Frederick A Bowdle MD.
Licensure Intermediate Care; Residential Care.
Beds 43; Residential Care 5. *Certified* Medicaid.
Admissions Requirements Minimum age 65; Medical examination.
Staff Physicians 1 (pt); RNs 2 (ft), 1 (pt); LPNs 3 (ft), 1 (pt); Nurses aides 10 (ft), 3 (pt); Physical therapists 1 (pt); Activities coordinators 1 (ft), 2 (pt); Dietitians 1 (pt).
Facilities Dining room; Physical therapy room; Activities room; Crafts room; Laundry room; Barber/Beauty shop; Library.
Activities Arts and Crafts; Cards; Games; Reading groups; Prayer groups; Movies; Shopping trips.
Description Residence for men and woman over the age of 65. When they become ill they are moved to the infirmary until they recover or die. Total lifetime care is given.

Kentmere, The Home of Merciful Rest Society Inc
1900 Lovering Ave, Wilmington, DE, 19806 (302) 652-3311
Admin Frieda E Enss. *Medical Dir/Dir of Nursing* Stephen Bartoshesky.
Licensure Skilled Care; Intermediate Care.
Beds SNF 49; ICF 37. *Certified* Medicaid; Medicare.
Admissions Requirements Minimum age 18; Medical examination.
Staff RNs 4 (ft), 5 (pt); LPNs 4 (ft); Nurses aides 20 (ft), 15 (pt); Physical therapists 1 (pt); Activities coordinators 1 (ft), 2 (pt); Dietitians 1 (pt); Ophthalmologists 1 (pt); Podiatrists 1 (pt).
Facilities Dining room; Physical therapy room; Activities room; Chapel; Crafts room; Laundry room; Barber/Beauty shop; Gift shop; Volunteer office.
Activities Arts and Crafts; Cards; Games; Reading groups; Prayer groups; Movies; Shopping trips; Dances/Social or cultural gatherings; Poetry group; Current events club; Garden club; Armchair travel club; Residents council.
Description A nonprofit skilled care and intermediate care facility that seeks to stimulate interest by the residents in creative activity and provide them with a sense of dignity. The tradition of a warm, home-like atmosphere and the well-being of the residents are assured by the personal involvement of Board members.

Mary Campbell Center
4641 Weldin Rd, Wilmington, DE, 19803 (302) 762-6025
Admin Catherine LaPenta. *Medical Dir/Dir of Nursing* Joseph B McManus MD.
Licensure Intermediate Care. *Beds* 56. *Certified* Medicaid.
Admissions Requirements Minimum age 16; Medical examination; Physician's request.
Facilities Dining room; Physical therapy room; Activities room; Crafts room; Laundry room; Barber/Beauty shop; Library.
Activities Arts and Crafts; Cards; Games; Reading groups; Prayer groups; Movies; Shop-

ping trips; Dances/Social or cultural gatherings; Swimming; Bowling.
Description A barrier-free facility for multihandicapped young adults dedicated to providing services in as de-institutionalized a setting as possible. The facility operates a respite service giving the handicapped and their families an opportunity to experience and enjoy time away from each other. In addition to professional staffing, over 150 volunteers donate time to build the confidence and raise the capabilities of the residents. The facility is growing, with plans for a hydrotherapy program and expanded learning center for computer room.

Masonic Home of Delaware Inc
4800 Lancaster Pike, Wilmington, DE, 19807
(302) 994-4434
Admin Claude A Husted. *Medical Dir/Dir of Nursing* Dr LeRoy Kimble.
Licensure Intermediate Care; Residential Care.
Beds ICF 8; Residential Care 32.
Admissions Requirements Medical examination.
Staff Physicians 2 (pt); RNs 3 (ft), 2 (pt); LPNs 2 (ft); Nurses aides 17 (ft); Dietitians 1 (pt).
Affiliation Masons
Facilities Dining room; Activities room; Chapel; Crafts room; Laundry room; Barber/Beauty shop; Library; Smoking lounge, TV room.
Activities Arts and Crafts; Movies; Shopping trips; Dances/Social or cultural gatherings.
Description Home has a pleasant rural setting and yet is convenient to shopping and cultural activities.

Methodist Country House*
4830 Kennett Pike, Wilmington, DE, 19807
(302) 654-5101
Admin W O Hackett.
Licensure Skilled Care; Intermediate Care.
Beds SNF 67; ICF 22. *Certified* Medicaid; Medicare.
Affiliation Methodist

Milton and Hattie Kutz Home Inc
704 River Rd, Wilmington, DE, 19809 (302) 764-7000
Admin Daniel G Thurman. *Medical Dir/Dir of Nursing* M Javed Gilani MD.
Licensure Intermediate Care. *Beds* 82. *Certified* Medicaid.
Staff Physicians 1 (pt); RNs 5 (ft), 5 (pt); LPNs 1 (ft), 2 (pt); Nurses aides 24 (ft), 4 (pt); Physical therapists 1 (pt); Recreational therapists 1 (ft); Speech therapists 1 (pt); Activities coordinators 1 (ft); Dietitians 1 (pt); Podiatrists 1 (pt).
Affiliation Jewish
Facilities Dining room; Physical therapy room; Activities room; Chapel; Crafts room; Laundry room; Barber/Beauty shop; Library.
Activities Arts and Crafts; Cards; Games; Reading groups; Movies; Shopping trips; Dances/Social or cultural gatherings.
Description Social components of care are emphasized in a warm atmosphere; active recreational program also includes music therapy. Psychiatric consultation and inservice training help staff to meet the needs of mentally impaired and emotionally disturbed residents.

Orsini Boarding Home*
703 Greenbank Rd, Wilmington, DE, 19808
(302) 999-0409
Admin Gloria Orsini.
Licensure Residential Care. *Beds* 6.

Tilton Terrace
801 N Broom St, Wilmington, DE, 19806 (302) 652-3861
Admin James F Moran. *Medical Dir/Dir of Nursing* Dr Marvin H Dorph.
Licensure Skilled Care; Intermediate Care.
Beds 92. *Certified* Medicaid; Medicare.
Staff RNs 6 (ft), 8 (pt); LPNs 6 (ft), 3 (pt); Nurses aides 28 (ft), 26 (pt); Physical therapists 1 (pt); Activities coordinators 2 (ft); Dietitians 1 (pt).
Facilities Dining room; Physical therapy room; Activities room; Chapel; Crafts room; Laundry room; Barber/Beauty shop.
Activities Arts and Crafts; Cards; Games; Reading groups; Prayer groups; Movies; Shopping trips; Dances/Social or cultural gatherings.

DISTRICT OF COLUMBIA

WASHINGTON

Army Distaff Hall*
6200 Oregon Ave NW, Washington, DC, 20015
(202) 966-3073
Admin Melvin Kuhn.
Licensure Intermediate Care; Residential Care.
Beds ICF 48; Residential Care 265.

Baptist Home of DC*
4700 Nebraska Ave NW, Washington, DC,
20016 (202) 363-9644
Admin David Lyon.
Licensure Skilled Care; Intermediate Care.
Beds 47. *Certified* Medicaid; Medicare.
Affiliation Baptist

Capitol Health Care Center Inc
900 3rd St NE, Washington, DC, 20005 (202)
546-4513
Admin Barbara Savory.
Licensure Intermediate Care. *Certified* Medicaid.

DC Village*
2 Village Ln SW, Washington, DC, 20032 (202)
629-8201
Admin Don Hall.
Licensure Skilled Care; Intermediate Care.
Beds SNF 51; ICF 488. *Certified* Medicaid;
Medicare.

Health Care Institute
1380 Southern Ave SE, Washington, DC, 20015
Admin Joseph G Mraz. *Medical Dir/Dir of
Nursing* Dr Joseph Robinson.
Licensure Skilled Care; Intermediate Care.
Beds 180. *Certified* Medicaid; Medicare.
Ownership Nonprofit.
Admissions Requirements Minimum age 55;
Medical examination.
Staff RNs 16 (ft), 4 (pt); LPNs 16 (ft), 4 (pt);
Nurses aides 60 (ft), 5 (pt); Physical therapists 1
(ft); Recreational therapists 1 (ft), 3 (pt); Activities coordinators 1 (ft); Dietitians 1 (pt).
Facilities Dining room; Physical therapy room;
Activities room; Crafts room; Laundry room;
Barber/Beauty shop.
Activities Arts and Crafts; Cards; Games;
Reading groups; Prayer groups; Movies; Shopping trips; Dances/Social or cultural gatherings.
Description Master's prepared nurses known as
clinical chiefs run each of the 3 units of 60 residents each.

J B Johnson Nursing Center*
901 1st St NW, Washington, DC, 20015 (202)
289-7715
Admin Gail L Walsh.
Licensure Intermediate Care. *Beds* 244. *Certified* Medicaid.

Jeanne Jugan Residence*
4200 Harewood Rd NE, Washington, DC,
20005 (202) 269-1831
Admin Sr Genevieve M Lanahan.
Licensure Skilled Care; Intermediate Care.
Beds SNF 25; ICF 75.

Lisner Home Inc
5425 Western Ave NW, Washington, DC,
20015 (202) 966-6667
Admin Ward Orem. *Medical Dir/Dir of
Nursing* James Brodsky MD.
Licensure Intermediate Care. *Beds* 25. *Certified* Medicaid.

MarSalle Centers Associates*
2131 O St NW, Washington, DC, 20037 (202)
785-2577
Admin P J Condray.
Licensure Skilled Care; Intermediate Care.
Beds SNF 41; ICF 160. *Certified* Medicare.

Masonic and Eastern Star Home*
6000 New Hampshire Ave NE, Washington,
DC, 20011 (202) 882-9300
Admin George Worth.
Licensure Skilled Care; Intermediate Care.
Beds SNF 57; ICF 50.
Affiliation Masons

Methodist Home of DC*
4901 Connecticut Ave NW, Washington, DC,
20008 (202) 966-7623
Admin Elsie D Lesko.
Licensure Intermediate Care. *Beds* 97. *Certified* Medicaid.
Affiliation Methodist

Presbyterian Home of DC*
3050 Military Rd NW, Washington, DC, 20015
(202) 363-8310
Admin Robert Bell.
Licensure Intermediate Care; Residential Care.
Beds SNF 32; Residential Care 132. *Certified* Medicaid.
Affiliation Presbyterian

Thomas House
1330 Massachusetts Ave NW, Washington,
DC, 20005 (202) 628-3844
Admin David Zwald. *Medical Dir/Dir of
Nursing* Dr Gregory Paulson.
Licensure Intermediate Care. *Beds* 50. *Certified* Medicaid.
Admissions Requirements Minimum age 62;
Medical examination.
Affiliation Baptist
Facilities Dining room; Physical therapy room;
Activities room; Chapel; Crafts room; Laundry
room; Barber/Beauty shop; Library.
Activities Arts and Crafts; Cards; Games;
Reading groups; Prayer groups; Movies; Shopping trips; Dances/Social or cultural gatherings.
Description Thomas House is a luxury retirement community that offers continuing care to
older citizens in the heart of downtown
Washington. Provides many services that
include a 50-bed intermediate care nursing
facility as well as a range of services for the
independent elderly person.

Washington Center for the Aging*
2601 18th St NE, Washington, DC, 20018 (202)
269-1530
Admin Roger Perry.

Washington Home for Incurables
3720 Upton St NW, Washington, DC, 20016
(202) 966-3720
Admin Louis Prebil. *Medical Dir/Dir of
Nursing* Valery Portnoi MD.
Licensure Skilled Care; Intermediate Care.
Beds 178. *Certified* Medicaid; Medicare.
Admissions Requirements Minimum age 16.
Staff Physicians 3 (pt); RNs 9 (ft); LPNs 17
(ft); Orderlies 9 (ft); Nurses aides 87 (ft);
Physical therapists 1 (ft); Reality therapists 1
(ft); Recreational therapists 2 (ft); Occupational
therapists 1 (ft); Speech therapists 1 (pt); Activities coordinators 1 (pt); Dietitians 1 (ft); Dentists 1 (pt); Podiatrists 1 (pt); Audiologists 1
(pt); Psychologists 1 (pt); Neurologists 1 (pt).
Facilities Dining room; Physical therapy room;
Activities room; Chapel; Crafts room; Laundry
room; Barber/Beauty shop; Library.
Activities Arts and Crafts; Cards; Games;
Reading groups; Prayer groups; Movies; Shopping trips; Dances/Social or cultural gatherings;
Special event luncheons.

Description Facility includes a 6-bed hospice unit, one of the first in the country; home is affiliated with George Washington University School of Medicine.

Wisconsin Avenue Nursing Home
3333 Wisconsin Ave NW, Washington, DC, 20015 (202) 362-5500
Admin Sybil Hunter. *Medical Dir/Dir of Nursing* Joel Mulhauser.
Licensure Skilled Care; Intermediate Care.
Beds 355. *Certified* Medicaid; Medicare.
Facilities Dining room; Physical therapy room; Activities room; Crafts room; Laundry room; Barber/Beauty shop; Library.
Activities Arts and Crafts; Cards; Games; Reading groups; Prayer groups; Movies; Shopping trips; Dances/Social or cultural gatherings.

FLORIDA

ALTAMONTE SPRINGS

Life Care Center of Altamonte Springs
989 Orienta Ave, Altamonte Springs, FL,
32701 (305) 831-3446
Medical Dir/Dir of Nursing Charles A Morgan
MD.
Licensure Skilled Care. *Beds* 240. *Certified* Medicaid; Medicare.
Ownership Proprietary.
Admissions Requirements Medical examination.
Staff Physicians 1 (pt); RNs 12 (ft); LPNs 23
(ft); Orderlies 4 (ft); Nurses aides 73 (ft);
Physical therapists 3 (ft); Speech therapists 1
(pt); Activities coordinators 1 (ft); Dietitians 1
(ft), 1 (pt).
Facilities Dining room; Physical therapy room;
Activities room; Laundry room; Barber/Beauty
shop.
Activities Arts and Crafts; Cards; Games; Prayer groups; Movies; Shopping trips.

ALTOONA

Lakeview Terrace Medical Care Facility
PO Drawer 100, Altoona, FL, 32702
Admin Linda Rowe. *Medical Dir/Dir of
Nursing* Glenn Miles MD.
Licensure Skilled Care. *Beds* 20.
Ownership Proprietary.
Admissions Requirements Minimum age 65;
Medical examination; Physician's request.
Staff Physicians 1 (pt); RNs 4 (ft), 4 (pt); LPNs
4 (ft), 5 (pt); Nurses aides 16 (ft), 11 (pt); Activities coordinators 1 (ft); Dietitians 1 (pt); Gerontologists 1 (ft); Physician assistants 1 (pt).
Facilities Dining room; Activities room; Crafts
room; Barber/Beauty shop; Library.
Activities Arts and Crafts; Cards; Games; Prayer groups; Movies; Shopping trips;
Dances/Social or cultural gatherings.
Description This is a life care retirement community offering a continuum of care through 4
Florida state licenses: life care, skilled nursing
facility, adult congregate living, and home
health. These licenses allow extended personal
and health services exclusively to residents.

Lakeview Terrace Medical Care Facility*
PO Drawer 100, Altoona, FL, 32702 (904)
669-3030
Licensure Intermediate Care. *Beds* 20.
Ownership Proprietary.

APALACHICOLA

Apalachicola Health Care Center
150 10th St, Apalachicola, FL, 32320 (904)
653-8844
Admin Lila L Ritch. *Medical Dir/Dir of
Nursing* Chai Seerebutra MD.
Licensure Skilled Care. *Beds* 60.
Ownership Proprietary.
Admissions Requirements Minimum age 16;
Medical examination; Physician's request.
Staff RNs 2 (ft), 1 (pt); LPNs 3 (ft), 4 (pt);
Nurses aides 13 (ft), 7 (pt); Recreational therapists 1 (ft), 1 (pt); Activities coordinators 1 (ft);
Dietitians 1 (ft), 1 (pt).
Facilities Dining room; Physical therapy room;
Activities room; Chapel; Crafts room; Laundry
room; Barber/Beauty shop.
Activities Arts and Crafts; Cards; Games;
Reading groups; Prayer groups; Movies; Shopping trips; Dances/Social or cultural gatherings.
Description Facility features outstanding
quality patient care. Also, volunteers are recognized and rewarded annually.

ARCADIA

Desoto Manor Nursing Home*
1002 N Brevard, Arcadia, FL, 33821 (813)
494-5766
Licensure Skilled Care. *Beds* 60. *Certified* Medicaid; Medicare.
Ownership Proprietary.
Languages Spanish, Italian

AUBURNDALE

Briar Hill Nursing Center
2901 Jersey Rd, Auburndale, FL, 33823 (813)
967-4125
Medical Dir/Dir of Nursing Arturo Perez MD.
Licensure Skilled Care. *Beds* 120.
Ownership Proprietary.
Admissions Requirements Minimum age 21;
Medical examination; Physician's request.
Staff Physicians 1 (ft), 4 (pt); RNs 4 (ft); LPNs
7 (ft), 6 (pt); Nurses aides 24 (ft), 18 (pt);
Physical therapists 1 (ft); Activities coordinators 2 (ft); Dietitians 2 (ft); Dentists 1 (pt);
Audiologists 1 (pt).
Facilities Dining room; Physical therapy room;
Activities room; Chapel; Crafts room; Laundry
room; Barber/Beauty shop; Library.

Activities Arts and Crafts; Cards; Games;
Reading groups; Prayer groups; Movies; Shopping trips; Dances/Social or cultural gatherings.
Description Spacious new facility, winner of
1984 interior design award; large landscaped
courtyard, solariums, resident kitchen, fishing
pond, 10 acres with huge oak trees; innovative
staff with geriatric nurse practitioner and physician's office in the facility.

AVON PARK

Hillcrest Nursing Home
80 Stratford Rd, Avon Park, FL, 33825 (813)
453-6675
Medical Dir/Dir of Nursing Donald B Geldart
MD.
Licensure Skilled Care. *Beds* 90. *Certified* Medicaid.
Ownership Proprietary.
Staff Physicians 8 (pt); RNs 3 (ft), 4 (pt); LPNs
7 (ft), 6 (pt); Nurses aides 22 (ft); Physical therapists 1 (pt); Speech therapists 1 (pt); Activities
coordinators 1 (pt); Dietitians 1 (pt); Dentists 1
(pt); Podiatrists 1 (pt).
Languages French, Spanish, German, Walon,
Kituba, Ishiluba
Facilities Dining room; Physical therapy room;
Activities room; Barber/Beauty shop; Library.
Activities Arts and Crafts; Cards; Games;
Reading groups; Prayer groups; Movies; Shopping trips; Dances/Social or cultural gatherings.

BARTOW

Bartow Convalescent Center
2055 E Georgia St, Bartow, FL, 33830 (813)
533-0578
Admin Richard J Kuhlmeyer. *Medical Dir/Dir
of Nursing* Harold K Mines MD.
Licensure Skilled Care. *Beds* 120. *Certified* Medicaid; Medicare.
Ownership Proprietary.
Admissions Requirements Medical examination; Physician's request.
Staff RNs 4 (ft), 1 (pt); LPNs 7 (ft); Nurses
aides 40 (ft); Physical therapists 1 (pt); Reality
therapists 1 (pt); Recreational therapists 1 (pt);
Occupational therapists 1 (pt); Speech therapists 1 (pt); Activities coordinators 1 (ft); Dietitians 1 (pt); Dentists 1 (pt); Ophthalmologists 1
(pt); Podiatrists 1 (pt); Audiologists 1 (pt).
Languages Spanish

Facilities Dining room; Physical therapy room; Activities room; Crafts room; Laundry room; Barber/Beauty shop; Library.
Activities Arts and Crafts; Cards; Games; Reading groups; Prayer groups; Movies; Shopping trips; Dances/Social or cultural gatherings.

Rohr Home
2010 E Georgia St, Bartow, FL, 33830 (813) 533-1111
Medical Dir/Dir of Nursing Robert Rieman MD.
Licensure Skilled Care. *Beds* 60. *Certified* Medicaid.
Ownership Public.
Admissions Requirements Minimum age 21; Medical examination; Physician's request.
Staff Physicians 5 (pt); RNs 4 (ft), 1 (pt); LPNs 5 (ft), 1 (pt); Orderlies 4 (ft); Nurses aides 25 (ft); Physical therapists 1 (pt); Activities coordinators 1 (ft); Dietitians 1 (ft).
Languages Spanish, German
Facilities Dining room; Laundry room; Barber/Beauty shop; Library; Screened porch and patio area.
Activities Arts and Crafts; Cards; Games; Prayer groups; Movies; Educational program; Library program.
Description Rohr Home and Polk General Hospital share the same board of trustees and hospital ancillary services are available for Rohr Home residents.

BELLE GLADE

Sunset Heights Nursing Home
200 SW 9th St, Belle Glade, FL, 33430 (305) 996-9176
Licensure Skilled Care. *Beds* 25. *Certified* Medicaid.
Ownership Nonprofit.
Staff Physicians; Dietitians; Nurses aides.
Languages Spanish, Italian
Activities Prayer groups; Arts and Crafts; Shopping trips.

BLOUNSTOWN

Apalachicola Valley Nursing Center*
1510 Crozier St, Blounstown, FL, 32424 (904) 674-5464
Licensure Skilled Care; Intermediate Care.
Beds 80. *Certified* Medicaid.
Ownership Proprietary.
Staff RNs 4 (ft); LPNs 9 (ft); Nurses aides 24 (ft).

BOCA RATON

Boca Raton Convalescent Center
755 Meadows Rd, Boca Raton, FL, 33432 (305) 391-5200
Medical Dir/Dir of Nursing Dr Dullaghan.
Licensure Skilled Care. *Beds* 120. *Certified* Medicaid; Medicare.
Ownership Proprietary.
Admissions Requirements Medical examination.
Staff RNs 7 (ft), 2 (pt); LPNs 8 (ft), 2 (pt); Nurses aides 35 (ft), 8 (pt); Physical therapists 1

(ft); Reality therapists 1 (ft); Recreational therapists 3 (pt); Occupational therapists 1 (ft); Speech therapists 1 (ft); Activities coordinators 1 (ft), 3 (pt); Dietitians 1 (ft); Dentists 1 (ft); Ophthalmologists 1 (ft); Podiatrists 3 (ft); Audiologists 1 (ft).
Languages Spanish
Facilities Dining room; Physical therapy room; Activities room; Crafts room; Laundry room; Barber/Beauty shop; Library; Outdoor screened patio.
Activities Arts and Crafts; Cards; Games; Reading groups; Prayer groups; Movies; Shopping trips; Dances/Social or cultural gatherings; Plays; Fashion shows; Happy hour.
Description Facility is adjacent to Boca Raton Community Hospital; JCAH accredited; dynamic activities program; day and evening attention 7 days a week; Medicare and private; very professional, caring staff.

Fountains Nursing Home*
3800 N Federal Hwy, Boca Raton, FL, 33437 (305) 395-7510
Licensure Skilled Care. *Beds* 51. *Certified* Medicaid; Medicare.
Ownership Proprietary.
Staff RNs 4 (ft); Nurses aides 17 (ft).

Saint Andrews Estates Medical Center*
6152 N Verde Trail, Boca Raton, FL, 33433 (305) 368-6906
Licensure Skilled Care; Intermediate Care.
Beds SNF 30; ICF 30. *Certified* Medicare.
Ownership Nonprofit.
Staff RNs 11 (ft); LPNs 3 (ft); Nurses aides 11 (ft); 11 (ft).
Languages Spanish

BONIFAY

Bonifay Nursing Home
108 Wagner Rd, Bonifay, FL, 32425 (904) 547-2418
Medical Dir/Dir of Nursing H E Brooks MD.
Licensure Skilled Care. *Beds* 60. *Certified* Medicaid.
Ownership Proprietary.
Admissions Requirements Minimum age 16; Medical examination.
Staff RNs 3 (ft), 2 (pt); LPNs 3 (ft), 3 (pt); Nurses aides 21 (ft), 3 (pt); Activities coordinators 1 (ft), 1 (pt).
Facilities Dining room; Physical therapy room; Activities room; Laundry room; Barber/Beauty shop; Library.
Activities Arts and Crafts; Cards; Games; Reading groups; Prayer groups; Movies; Dances/Social or cultural gatherings.

BOYNTON BEACH

Boulevard Manor Nursing Center
2839 S Seacrest Blvd, Boynton Beach, FL, 33435 (305) 732-2467
Medical Dir/Dir of Nursing Dr Nayer.
Licensure Skilled Care. *Beds* 110. *Certified* Medicaid; Medicare.
Ownership Proprietary.
Admissions Requirements Minimum age 16; Medical examination; Physician's request.

Staff Physicians 1 (ft); RNs 10 (ft); LPNs 7 (ft); Orderlies 2 (ft); Nurses aides 37 (ft); Physical therapists 2 (ft); Reality therapists 1 (ft); Recreational therapists 2 (ft); Occupational therapists 1 (ft), 1 (pt); Speech therapists 1 (pt); Activities coordinators 1 (ft); Dietitians 1 (pt); Dentists 1 (pt); Ophthalmologists 1 (pt); Podiatrists 1 (pt); Audiologists 1 (pt).
Languages French, Spanish, Norwegian, German, Taiwanese
Facilities Dining room; Physical therapy room; Activities room; Crafts room; Laundry room; Barber/Beauty shop; Library.
Activities Arts and Crafts; Cards; Games; Reading groups; Prayer groups; Movies; Shopping trips; Dances/Social or cultural gatherings.
Description Adjacent to Bethesda Hospital, facility includes luxury suites, private bath or shower in all rooms, color TV with remote control, home-like furnishings, and full-time chauffeur on staff.

BRADENTON

Asbury Towers
1533 4th Ave W, Bradenton, FL, 33505 (813) 747-1881
Medical Dir/Dir of Nursing W Wentzel MD.
Licensure Skilled Care. *Beds* 34.
Ownership Nonprofit.
Staff RNs 3 (ft), 3 (pt); LPNs 5 (ft), 6 (pt); Nurses aides 7 (ft), 6 (pt); Activities coordinators 1 (ft).
Affiliation Methodist
Facilities Dining room; Activities room; Chapel; Crafts room; Laundry room; Barber/Beauty shop; Library.
Activities Arts and Crafts; Cards; Games; Reading groups; Prayer groups; Movies; Shopping trips; Dances/Social or cultural gatherings.

Bradenton Convalescent Center*
105 15th St E, Bradenton, FL, 33505 (813) 748-4031
Licensure Skilled Care. *Beds* 110. *Certified* Medicaid.
Ownership Proprietary.

Bradenton Manor*
1700 21st Ave W, Bradenton, FL, 33505 (813) 748-4161
Licensure Skilled Care. *Beds* 59.
Ownership Nonprofit.
Admissions Requirements Medical examination; Physician's request.
Staff RNs 4 (ft), 3 (pt); LPNs 5 (ft), 5 (pt); Nurses aides 21 (ft), 4 (pt); Activities coordinators 1 (ft); Dietitians 1 (pt).
Affiliation Presbyterian

Carol Lou Mora Care Center*
2010 59th St W, Bradenton, FL, 33506 (813) 792-1515
Licensure Skilled Care. *Beds* 120. *Certified* Medicaid; Medicare.
Ownership Proprietary.
Staff RNs 5 (ft); LPNs 13 (ft); Nurses aides 29 (ft).

Greenbriar Nursing Center*
210 21st Ave W, Bradenton, FL, 33505 (813) 747-3786

Licensure Skilled Care. *Beds* 60. *Certified* Medicaid; Medicare.
Ownership Proprietary.
Staff RNs 5 (ft); LPNs 4 (ft); Nurses aides 18 (ft).

Manatee Convalescent Center Inc
302 Manatee Ave E, Bradenton, FL, 33508 (813) 746-6131
Admin Joanne Proffitt.
Licensure Skilled Care. *Beds* 147. *Certified* Medicaid; Medicare.
Ownership Proprietary.
Admissions Requirements Medical examination.
Staff RNs 6 (ft), 3 (pt); LPNs 11 (ft); Nurses aides 46 (ft), 10 (pt); Recreational therapists; Occupational therapists; Speech therapists; Activities coordinators 2 (ft); Dietitians; Dentists; Ophthalmologists; Podiatrists; Audiologists.
Languages Spanish
Facilities Dining room; Physical therapy room; Activities room; Chapel; Crafts room; Laundry room; Barber/Beauty shop.
Activities Arts and Crafts; Cards; Games; Reading groups; Prayer groups; Movies; Shopping trips; Dances/Social or cultural gatherings.

Shores Health Center
1700 3rd Ave W, Bradenton, FL, 33505 (813) 748-1700
Medical Dir/Dir of Nursing Michael Holsworth MD.
Licensure Skilled Care. *Beds* 21. *Certified* Medicare.
Ownership Proprietary.
Admissions Requirements Minimum age 64; Medical examination; Physician's request.
Staff RNs 2 (ft), 3 (pt); LPNs 4 (ft), 2 (pt); Nurses aides 6 (ft), 1 (pt); Activities coordinators 2 (ft).
Facilities Dining room; Activities room; Chapel; Crafts room; Laundry room; Barber/Beauty shop; Library.
Activities Arts and Crafts; Cards; Games; Reading groups; Prayer groups; Movies; Shopping trips; Dances/Social or cultural gatherings.

Suncoast Manor Nursing Home*
2010 Manatee Ave E, Bradenton, FL, 33505 (813) 747-3706
Licensure Skilled Care. *Beds* 208. *Certified* Medicaid; Medicare.
Ownership Proprietary.
Staff RNs 6 (ft); LPNs 8 (ft); Nurses aides 30 (ft).

BRISTOL

Liberty Intermediate Care—Bristol*
PO Box 66, Bristol, FL, 32321 (904) 643-2256
Licensure Intermediate Care for Mentally Retarded. *Beds* 80. *Certified* Medicaid; Medicare.
Ownership Proprietary.
Staff RNs 2 (ft); LPNs 3 (ft); Nurses aides 31 (ft); 16 (ft).

BROOKSVILLE

Brooksville Nursing Manor
1114 Chatman Blvd, Brooksville, FL, 33512 (904) 796-6701
Medical Dir/Dir of Nursing James M Marlowe MD.
Licensure Skilled Care. *Beds* 180. *Certified* Medicaid; Medicare.
Ownership Proprietary.
Admissions Requirements Minimum age 18.
Staff Nurses aides 34 (ft); Dietitians 15 (ft).
Activities Arts and Crafts; Cards; Games; Reading groups; Prayer groups; Movies; Dances/Social or cultural gatherings.

Eastbrooke Health Care Center*
10295 N Howell Ave, Brooksville, FL, 33512 (904) 799-1451
Beds 120.
Ownership Proprietary.

CAPE CORAL

Cape Coral Nursing Pavilion
2629 Del Prado Blvd, Cape Coral, FL, 33904 (813) 574-4434
Medical Dir/Dir of Nursing Lawrence D Hughes.
Licensure Skilled Care. *Beds* 120. *Certified* Medicaid; Medicare.
Ownership Proprietary.
Admissions Requirements Minimum age 16; Medical examination; Physician's request.
Staff RNs 11 (ft); LPNs 12 (ft); Orderlies 4 (ft); Nurses aides 40 (ft); Physical therapists 2 (ft); Occupational therapists 1 (ft); Speech therapists 1 (ft); Activities coordinators 1 (ft); Dietitians 1 (ft); Podiatrists 1 (pt).
Languages Spanish
Facilities Dining room; Physical therapy room; Activities room; Chapel; Crafts room; Laundry room; Barber/Beauty shop; Library.
Activities Arts and Crafts; Cards; Games; Reading groups; Prayer groups; Movies; Dances/Social or cultural gatherings; Birthday parties; Sing-a-longs; Wine and cheese parties.
Description We are located in a most appealing Florida Gulf Coast community, easily accessible by highway or air transportation. The Pavilion is near a hospital and medical complex. From the moment you drive onto our beautifully landscaped grounds, we think you will feel the atmosphere of love and caring we try to engender.

CHIPLEY

Washington County Convalescent Center*
805 Usery Rd, Chipley, FL, 32428 (904) 638-4654
Beds 120.
Ownership Proprietary.

CLEARWATER

Belleair East Health Center
1150 Ponce de Leon Blvd, Clearwater, FL, 33516
Admin T P Schluter. *Medical Dir/Dir of*

Nursing David Longacre MD.
Licensure Skilled Care. *Beds* 120. *Certified* Medicaid.
Ownership Proprietary.
Admissions Requirements Minimum age 18; Medical examination; Physician's request.
Staff Physicians 1 (pt); RNs 14 (ft), 11 (pt); LPNs 9 (ft), 8 (pt); Orderlies 4 (ft), 2 (pt); Nurses aides 48 (ft), 27 (pt); Physical therapists 2 (ft); Reality therapists 1 (pt); Recreational therapists 2 (ft); Occupational therapists 1 (pt); Speech therapists 1 (pt); Activities coordinators 1 (ft); Dietitians 1 (pt); Dentists 1 (pt); Podiatrists 1 (pt); Audiologists 1 (pt).
Facilities Dining room; Physical therapy room; Activities room; Chapel; Crafts room; Laundry room; Barber/Beauty shop; Library.
Activities Arts and Crafts; Cards; Games; Reading groups; Prayer groups; Movies; Shopping trips; Dances/Social or cultural gatherings.
Description Facility offers large semi-private and private rooms with individual private bathrooms, whirlpool therapeutic tubs, 24-hour professional nursing staff, beautiful park-like setting, and elegant, gracious living.

Bruce Manor Nursing Home
1100 Pine St, Clearwater, FL, 33516 (813) 422-7106
Medical Dir/Dir of Nursing Dr Joseph Baird.
Licensure Skilled Care. *Beds* 76.
Ownership Proprietary.
Admissions Requirements Minimum age 16; Medical examination; Physician's request.
Staff RNs 3 (ft), 3 (pt); LPNs 5 (ft), 2 (pt); Nurses aides 32 (ft), 5 (pt); Activities coordinators 1 (ft); 17 (ft), 5 (pt).
Languages Spanish
Facilities Dining room; Activities room; Crafts room; Barber/Beauty shop.
Activities Arts and Crafts; Cards; Games; Prayer groups; Movies; Dances/Social or cultural gatherings.

Clearwater Convalescent Center*
1270 Turner St, Clearwater, FL, 33516 (813) 443-7639
Licensure Skilled Care. *Beds* 120. *Certified* Medicaid; Medicare.
Ownership Proprietary.
Staff RNs 4 (ft); LPNs 7 (ft); Nurses aides 26 (ft); 16 (ft).

Druid Hills Nursing Home*
905 S Highland Ave, Clearwater, FL, 33516 (813) 442-9606
Licensure Skilled Care. *Beds* 94. *Certified* Medicaid.
Ownership Proprietary.
Staff RNs 15 (ft); LPNs 10 (ft); Nurses aides 30 (ft); 22 (ft).
Languages Spanish, French, German, Belgian

Highland Pines Nursing Manor
1111 S Highland Ave, Clearwater, FL, 33516 (813) 446-0581
Medical Dir/Dir of Nursing Mark S Franklin DO.
Licensure Skilled Care. *Beds* 120.
Ownership Proprietary.
Staff Nurses aides 14 (ft); Dietitians 15 (pt).
Facilities Dining room; Activities room; Crafts room; Laundry room; Barber/Beauty shop;

Library.
Activities Arts and Crafts; Cards; Games; Reading groups; Prayer groups; Movies; Shopping trips; Dances/Social or cultural gatherings.

Morton F Plant Rehabilitation and Nursing Center
1250 S Fort Harrison Ave, Clearwater, FL, 33516 (813) 442-2109
Medical Dir/Dir of Nursing R Chris Brown MD.
Licensure Skilled Care. *Beds* 126. *Certified* Medicaid; Medicare.
Ownership Nonprofit.
Admissions Requirements Minimum age 18; Medical examination.
Staff RNs 13 (ft), 2 (pt); LPNs 8 (ft), 3 (pt); Orderlies 3 (ft); Nurses aides 46 (ft), 3 (pt); Physical therapists 8 (ft), 2 (pt); Recreational therapists 2 (ft); Occupational therapists 1 (ft), 2 (pt); Speech therapists 1 (ft); Dietitians 1 (ft).
Facilities Dining room; Activities room; Laundry room; Barber/Beauty shop.
Activities Arts and Crafts; Cards; Games; Prayer groups; Movies; Shopping trips; Dances/Social or cultural gatherings; Restaurant outings; Baking.
Description Facility offers well-rounded activities program for all patients.

Oak Bluffs Nursing Center
420 Bay Ave, Clearwater, FL, 33516 (813) 461-4466
Medical Dir/Dir of Nursing Dr Charles Becker.
Licensure Skilled Care. *Beds* 60.
Ownership Nonprofit.
Staff RNs 4 (ft), 2 (pt); LPNs 4 (ft); Orderlies 1 (pt); Nurses aides 22 (ft), 4 (pt); Activities coordinators 1 (ft); Dietitians 1 (ft).
Facilities Dining room; Physical therapy room; Activities room; Chapel; Crafts room; Laundry room; Barber/Beauty shop; Library.
Activities Arts and Crafts; Cards; Games; Reading groups; Prayer groups; Shopping trips; Dances/Social or cultural gatherings.
Description Facility offers a breathtaking view of Gulf beaches.

Oak Cove Health Center
210 S Osceola Ave, Clearwater, FL, 33516 (813) 441-3763
Admin Willis J Gregson. *Medical Dir/Dir of Nursing* Dr Charles O Becker.
Licensure Skilled Care. *Beds* 56. *Certified* Medicare.
Ownership Nonprofit.
Admissions Requirements Minimum age 65.
Staff RNs 4 (ft); LPNs 6 (ft); Orderlies 1 (ft); Nurses aides 15 (ft); Activities coordinators 1 (ft).
Facilities Dining room; Activities room; Crafts room; Laundry room; Barber/Beauty shop; Library.
Activities Arts and Crafts; Cards; Games; Reading groups; Prayer groups; Movies; Shopping trips; Dances/Social or cultural gatherings.
Description Facility is located on the edge of Clearwater Bay and the Gulf of Mexico, close to community services, shopping, banking, churches, and cultural activities.

Osceola Inn
221 N Osceola, Clearwater, FL, 33515 (813) 461-3321
Medical Dir/Dir of Nursing Gaylord Church MD.
Licensure Skilled Care. *Beds* 13.
Ownership Nonprofit.
Admissions Requirements Minimum age 65; Medical examination.
Staff RNs 2 (ft), 3 (pt); LPNs 1 (ft), 3 (pt); Nurses aides 6 (ft), 3 (pt); Activities coordinators 1 (pt); Dietitians 1 (pt).
Languages French
Affiliation Presbyterian
Facilities Dining room; Activities room; Chapel; Laundry room; Barber/Beauty shop; Library.
Activities Arts and Crafts; Cards; Games; Reading groups; Prayer groups; Dances/Social or cultural gatherings.

Sunset Point Nursing Center
1980 Sunset Point Rd, Clearwater, FL, 33515 (813) 443-1588
Medical Dir/Dir of Nursing Dr Raymond Zimmerman.
Licensure Skilled Care; Intermediate Care. *Beds* SNF 72; ICF 48. *Certified* Medicaid; Medicare.
Ownership Proprietary.
Staff Physicians 1 (pt); RNs 4 (ft), 3 (pt); LPNs 8 (ft), 2 (pt); Physical therapists 1 (pt); Recreational therapists 1 (pt); Occupational therapists 1 (pt); Speech therapists 1 (pt); Activities coordinators 1 (ft); Dietitians 1 (pt); Dentists 1 (pt); Ophthalmologists 1 (pt); Podiatrists 1 (pt); Audiologists 1 (pt).
Facilities Dining room; Physical therapy room; Activities room; Crafts room; Barber/Beauty shop; Library.
Activities Arts and Crafts; Cards; Games; Reading groups; Prayer groups; Movies; Shopping trips; Dances/Social or cultural gatherings.
Description Our facility provides an outstanding activities program, and our director serves as president of the activities association.

CLERMONT

Lake Highlands Nursing Home
151 E Minnehaha Ave, Clermont, FL, 32711 (904) 394-2188
Licensure Skilled Care. *Beds* 142. *Certified* Medicaid; Medicare.
Ownership Proprietary.
Staff Nurses aides 45 (ft).
Languages Spanish, French, Swedish
Activities Prayer groups; Dances/Social or cultural gatherings.

CLEWISTON

Clewiston Health Care Center*
300 Gloria St, Clewiston, FL, 33440 (813) 983-5123
Licensure Skilled Care. *Beds* 120. *Certified* Medicaid.
Ownership Proprietary.
Staff Nurses aides 19 (ft); 20 (ft).

CORAL GABLES

New Riveria Health Resort
6901 Yumuri St, Coral Gables, FL, 33146 (305) 661-0078
Licensure Skilled Care. *Beds* 52. *Certified* Medicaid; Medicare.
Ownership Proprietary.
Staff RNs 3 (ft), 1 (pt); LPNs 3 (ft); Nurses aides 20 (ft); Physical therapists 1 (pt); Dietitians 1 (pt).
Languages Spanish
Facilities Dining room; Activities room; Laundry room; Barber/Beauty shop.
Activities Arts and Crafts; Games; Movies.

CRAWFORDVILLE

Wakulla Manor*
PO Box 549, Crawfordville, FL, 32433 (904) 926-7181
Licensure Skilled Care. *Beds* 120. *Certified* Medicaid; Medicare.
Ownership Proprietary.
Staff RNs 8 (ft); LPNs 8 (ft); Nurses aides 25 (ft); 18 (ft).
Languages Spanish

CRESCENT CITY

Lakeshore Nursing Home*
100 Lake St, Crescent City, FL, 32012 (904) 698-2222
Licensure Skilled Care. *Beds* 92. *Certified* Medicaid.
Ownership Public.
Staff RNs 9; LPNs 6 (ft); Nurses aides 29 (ft).

CRESTVIEW

Crestview Nursing and Convalescent Manor*
1849 E 1st St, Crestview, FL, 32536 (904) 682-5322
Licensure Skilled Care. *Beds* 60. *Certified* Medicaid; Medicare.
Ownership Proprietary.
Staff RNs 5 (ft); LPNs 7 (ft); Nurses aides 20 (ft).

CRYSTAL RIVER

Crystal River Geriatric Center
136 NE 12th Ave, Crystal River, FL, 32629 (904) 795-5044
Medical Dir/Dir of Nursing Dr Carlos Gonzalez.
Licensure Skilled Care; Intermediate Care. *Beds* 150. *Certified* Medicaid; Medicare.
Ownership Proprietary.
Admissions Requirements Minimum age 16.
Staff Physical therapists 1 (pt); Occupational therapists 1 (pt); Speech therapists 1 (pt); Activities coordinators 1 (ft); Dietitians 1 (pt); Dentists 1 (pt); Podiatrists 1 (pt).
Languages Spanish, German
Facilities Dining room; Physical therapy room; Activities room; Laundry room; Barber/Beauty shop.
Activities Arts and Crafts; Cards; Games; Reading groups; Prayer groups; Movies; Dan-

ces/Social or cultural gatherings.
Description VA approved.

DADE CITY

Dade City Geriatric Center
805 W Coleman Ave, Dade City, FL, 33525
(904) 567-8615
Medical Dir/Dir of Nursing Dr McBath.
Licensure Skilled Care. *Beds* 120. *Certified* Medicaid; Medicare.
Ownership Proprietary.
Admissions Requirements Minimum age 16;
Medical examination; Physician's request.
Staff Physicians 12 (pt); RNs 5 (pt); LPNs 14
(pt); Nurses aides 36 (pt); Physical therapists 1
(pt); Recreational therapists 1 (pt); Occupational therapists 1 (pt); Speech therapists 1 (pt);
Activities coordinators 1 (pt); Dietitians 1 (pt);
Dentists 1 (pt); Podiatrists 1 (pt); Audiologists 1
(pt).
Languages Spanish
Facilities Dining room; Physical therapy room;
Activities room; Laundry room; Barber/Beauty
shop.
Activities Arts and Crafts; Cards; Games;
Reading groups; Prayer groups; Movies; Shopping trips; Dances/Social or cultural gatherings.
Description VA approved.

Pasco Nursing and Rehabilitation Center
447 N 5th St, Dade City, FL, 33525 (904)
567-1978
Licensure Skilled Care. *Beds* 40. *Certified* Medicare.
Ownership Proprietary.
Admissions Requirements Minimum age 16;
Medical examination; Physician's request.
Staff RNs 2 (ft), 1 (pt); LPNs 2 (ft), 2 (pt);
Nurses aides 20 (ft); Occupational therapists 1
(pt); Activities coordinators 1 (ft); Dietitians 1
(pt).
Languages Spanish
Facilities Dining room.
Activities Arts and Crafts; Cards; Games;
Reading groups; Prayer groups; Movies; Shopping trips; Dances/Social or cultural gatherings.

Royal Oak Nursing Resort*
700 Royal Oak Ln, Dade City, FL, 33525 (813)
847-6068
Licensure Skilled Care. *Beds* 120.
Ownership Nonprofit.

DANIA

Dania Nursing Home*
440 Phippen Rd, Dania, FL, 33004 (305)
927-0508
Licensure Skilled Care. *Beds* 88. *Certified* Medicaid; Medicare.
Ownership Proprietary.
Staff RNs 3 (ft); LPNs 10 (ft); Nurses aides 30
(ft).
Languages French, Hebrew, Yiddish

DAVENPORT

William L Hargrave Health Center
206 W Orange St, Davenport, FL, 33827 (813)

422-4961
Medical Dir/Dir of Nursing Edward Jukes.
Licensure Skilled Care. *Beds* 60. *Certified* Medicaid.
Ownership Nonprofit.
Admissions Requirements Minimum age 70;
Medical examination.
Staff Physicians 2 (ft); RNs 3 (ft), 1 (pt); LPNs
7 (ft); Nurses aides 26 (ft), 1 (pt); Occupational
therapists 1 (pt); Speech therapists 1 (pt);
Activities coordinators 2 (ft), 1 (pt); Dietitians
1 (pt); Dentists 3 (pt); Ophthalmologists 1 (pt);
Podiatrists 1 (pt); Audiologists 1 (pt).
Affiliation Episcopal
Facilities Dining room; Activities room; Chapel; Crafts room; Laundry room; Barber/Beauty
shop; Library.
Activities Arts and Crafts; Cards; Games;
Reading groups; Prayer groups; Movies; Shopping trips; Dances/Social or cultural gatherings;
Church activities.
Description Facility is located in a quiet, small
town in the country with access for entertainment and cultural events; such as Polk Community College, 20 minutes; Cypress Gardens,
20 minutes; Disney World, 40 minutes; Sea
World, 40 minutes; Orlando, one hour; various
plays and exhibits are available through the
Winter Haven Community Center and the city
of Lakeland.

DAVIE

Broward Association for Retarded Citizens*
2750 SW 75th Ave, Davie, FL, 33314 (305)
474-5277
Licensure Intermediate Care for Mentally
Retarded. *Beds* 36. *Certified* Medicaid.
Ownership Nonprofit.

DAYTONA BEACH

Clyatt Memorial Center*
1001 S Beach St, Daytona Beach, FL, 32014
(904) 258-3334
Licensure Skilled Care. *Beds* 99. *Certified* Medicaid; Medicare.
Ownership Nonprofit.
Staff RNs 3 (ft); LPNs 7 (ft); Nurses aides 31
(ft); 20 (ft).

Daytona Beach Geriatric Center
1055 3rd St, Daytona Beach, FL, 32017 (904)
252-3686
Medical Dir/Dir of Nursing Dr Ronald Cabreza.
Licensure Skilled Care. *Beds* 180. *Certified* Medicaid; Medicare.
Ownership Proprietary.
Admissions Requirements Minimum age 18;
Medical examination; Physician's request.
Staff Orderlies 2 (ft); Physical therapists; Recreational therapists; Occupational therapists;
Speech therapists; Activities coordinators 1 (ft);
Dietitians 1 (ft).
Facilities Dining room; Physical therapy room;
Activities room; Laundry room; Barber/Beauty
shop; Conference room; Treatment room.
Activities Arts and Crafts; Cards; Games;
Reading groups; Prayer groups; Movies; Dances/Social or cultural gatherings.

Description Facility features beautifully landscaped grounds with inside garden area, several
large courtyards, excellent dancing and singing
programs during the week, and a dedicated,
professional staff.

**Daytona Beach Olds Hall Good Samaritan
Nursing Center**
325 S Segrave St, Daytona Beach, FL, 32014
(904) 253-6791
Medical Dir/Dir of Nursing Grant Brummett
MD.
Licensure Intermediate Care. *Beds* 120. *Certified* Medicaid.
Ownership Nonprofit.
Admissions Requirements Minimum age 16;
Medical examination.
Staff RNs 3 (ft), 4 (pt); LPNs 4 (ft), 11 (pt);
Orderlies 1 (ft), 1 (pt); Nurses aides 26 (ft), 13
(pt); Reality therapists 1 (ft); Activities coordinators 1 (ft); Dietitians 1 (pt); Dentists 1 (pt);
Podiatrists 1 (pt).
Affiliation Lutheran
Facilities Dining room; Activities room; Chapel; Crafts room; Laundry room; Barber/Beauty
shop; Library.
Activities Arts and Crafts; Cards; Games;
Reading groups; Prayer groups; Movies; Shopping trips; Dances/Social or cultural gatherings;
Adopt-a-grandparent program; Farmer's market; Picnics at state park.
Description Olds Hall Good Samaritan offers
private and semi-private rooms in an atmosphere conducive to each resident being able to
follow the spiritual program of his/her choice.

Golden Age Health Care
324 Wilder Blvd, Daytona Beach, FL, 32014
(904) 252-2600
Medical Dir/Dir of Nursing Dr James Carratt.
Licensure Skilled Care. *Beds* 192. *Certified* Medicaid; Medicare.
Ownership Proprietary.
Admissions Requirements Minimum age 16;
Medical examination.
Staff RNs 14 (ft); LPNs 14 (ft); Orderlies 4 (ft);
Nurses aides 54 (ft); Activities coordinators 1
(ft); Dietitians 1 (ft).
Facilities Dining room; Physical therapy room;
Laundry room; Barber/Beauty shop.
Activities Arts and Crafts; Games; Movies;
Dances/Social or cultural gatherings.

Holiday Care Center
1031 S Beach St, Daytona Beach, FL, 32014
(904) 255-2453
Medical Dir/Dir of Nursing C M Crouch MD.
Licensure Skilled Care. *Beds* 48. *Certified* Medicaid.
Ownership Proprietary.
Admissions Requirements Minimum age 18;
Medical examination; Physician's request.
Staff RNs 1 (ft), 2 (pt); LPNs 3 (ft), 1 (pt);
Nurses aides 11 (ft), 8 (pt); Activities coordinators 1 (ft).
Facilities Dining room; Activities room; Crafts
room; Laundry room; Barber/Beauty shop;
Library.
Activities Arts and Crafts; Cards; Games; Prayer groups; Movies; Dances/Social or cultural
gatherings.

DEBARY

DeBary Manor
60 N Hwy 17-92, DeBary, FL, 32713 (305) 668-4426
Admin Patrick Lane. *Medical Dir/Dir of Nursing* Louis Perez MD.
Licensure Skilled Care. *Beds* 93. *Certified* Medicaid.
Ownership Proprietary.
Staff Physicians; Dietitians; Nurses aides.
Languages Spanish, German, French
Facilities Dining room; Crafts room; Laundry room; Barber/Beauty shop; Library.
Activities Arts and Crafts; Cards; Games; Reading groups; Prayer groups; Movies; Shopping trips.

DEFUNIAK SPRINGS

Walton County Convalescent Center*
PO Box 745, Rt 6, DeFuniak Springs, FL, 32433 (904) 892-2176
Licensure Skilled Care. *Beds* 107. *Certified* Medicaid.
Ownership Proprietary.
Staff RNs 4 (ft); LPNs 5 (ft); Nurses aides 22 (ft); 22 (ft).

DELAND

Alliance Nursing Center*
151 Winnemissett W, Deland, FL, 32720 (904) 734-6401
Licensure Skilled Care. *Beds* 60. *Certified* Medicaid; Medicare.
Ownership Nonprofit.
Staff RNs 4 (ft); LPNs 8 (ft); Nurses aides 15 (ft); 11 (ft).
Languages Spanish
Affiliation Christian and Missionary Alliance Foundation

Deland Convalescent Center*
451 S Amelia Ave, Deland, FL, 32720 (904) 734-8614
Licensure Skilled Care. *Beds* 65. *Certified* Medicaid; Medicare.
Ownership Proprietary.
Staff RNs 1 (ft); LPNs 7 (ft); Nurses aides 19 (ft).
Languages Spanish, German

Ridgecrest Manor
1113 N Stone St, PO Box 880, Deland, FL, 32720 (904) 734-6200
Medical Dir/Dir of Nursing Curt N Rausch MD.
Licensure Skilled Care; Intermediate Care.
Beds 134. *Certified* Medicaid; Medicare.
Ownership Proprietary.
Admissions Requirements Medical examination; Physician's request.
Staff RNs 6 (ft), 5 (pt); LPNs 6 (ft), 2 (pt); Orderlies 6 (ft); Nurses aides 38 (ft); Physical therapists; Reality therapists; Recreational therapists; Occupational therapists; Speech therapists; Activities coordinators 1 (ft), 1 (pt); Dietitians 1 (ft), 1 (pt); Dentists; Ophthalmologists; Podiatrists 1 (pt); Audiologists.
Facilities Dining room; Physical therapy room; Activities room; Chapel; Crafts room; Laundry room; Barber/Beauty shop; Library.
Activities Arts and Crafts; Cards; Games; Reading groups; Prayer groups; Movies; Shopping trips; Dances/Social or cultural gatherings; Exercise programs; Concerts; Musical sing-a-longs; Protestant and Catholic weekly services.
Description Facility is only 3 minutes from West Vousia Memorial Hospital.

University Convalescent Center—East*
919 E New York Ave, Deland, FL, 32720 (904) 734-9083
Licensure Skilled Care. *Beds* 60. *Certified* Medicaid; Medicare.
Ownership Proprietary.
Staff RNs 6 (ft); LPNs 7 (ft); Nurses aides 18 (ft).
Languages Spanish

University Convalescent Center—West
545 W Euclid Ave, Deland, FL, 32720 (904) 734-9085
Licensure Skilled Care. *Beds* 60. *Certified* Medicaid; Medicare.
Ownership Proprietary.
Admissions Requirements Minimum age 18; Medical examination; Physician's request.
Staff RNs 2 (ft), 1 (pt); LPNs 6 (ft), 1 (pt); Orderlies 1 (ft); Nurses aides 19 (ft), 3 (pt); Physical therapists; Occupational therapists; Speech therapists; Activities coordinators 1 (ft); Dietitians; Audiologists.
Facilities Dining room; Activities room; Crafts room; Laundry room; Barber/Beauty shop; Library.
Activities Arts and Crafts; Cards; Games; Reading groups; Prayer groups; Movies; Dances/Social or cultural gatherings; Exercise; Church; Reality orientation.
Description Facility offers home-like atmosphere with great activity and social programs, and is located on a quiet street. Staff members have been long-time employees. Facility has earned superior rating.

Van Hook School
4481 Mells Rd, Deland, FL, 32724 (904) 985-4284
Medical Dir/Dir of Nursing JoAnn Brown.
Licensure Intermediate Care for Mentally Retarded. *Beds* 44.
Ownership Proprietary.
Admissions Requirements Minimum age 6; Medical examination.
Staff RNs 1 (ft); Nurses aides 9 (ft).
Facilities Dining room; Crafts room.
Description We are a residential home/school for the mentally retarded.

DELRAY BEACH

Health Care Center at Abbey Delray South*
1717 Care Retirement Communities Inc, Delray Beach, FL, 33445 (305) 278-3249
Beds 60.
Ownership Nonprofit.

Health Center at Abbey Delray
2000 Lowson Blvd, Delray Beach, FL, 33444 (305) 278-3249

Admin Teresa L Moore.
Licensure Skilled Care. *Beds* 100. *Certified* Medicaid; Medicare.
Ownership Nonprofit.
Admissions Requirements Medical examination; Physician's request.
Staff RNs 9 (ft), 6 (pt); LPNs 3 (ft), 1 (pt); Orderlies 1 (ft); Nurses aides 34 (ft), 3 (pt); Physical therapists 1 (pt); Recreational therapists 1 (ft); Speech therapists 1 (pt); Activities coordinators 1 (ft); Dietitians 1 (pt).
Facilities Dining room; Physical therapy room; Activities room; Chapel; Barber/Beauty shop; Library.
Activities Arts and Crafts; Cards; Games; Reading groups; Prayer groups; Movies; Dances/Social or cultural gatherings; Patients' council; Monthly field trips.
Description Facility offers family members the opportunity to participate in monthly family council meetings to discuss common concerns, have questions answered, meet staff members, and attend educational programs.

DOWLING PARK

J Ralph Smith Health Center
Rt 5, Box 88, Dowling Park, FL, 32060 (904) 776-1009
Medical Dir/Dir of Nursing Susan H Allen MD.
Licensure Skilled Care; Intermediate Care.
Beds SNF 91; ICF 16. *Certified* Medicaid; Medicare.
Ownership Nonprofit.
Admissions Requirements Minimum age 18; Medical examination.
Staff Physicians 1 (ft); RNs 7 (ft), 2 (pt); LPNs 12 (ft), 5 (pt); Orderlies 2 (ft), 1 (pt); Nurses aides 55 (ft), 14 (pt); Physical therapists; Occupational therapists 1 (ft); Speech therapists; Activities coordinators 2 (ft), 1 (pt); Dietitians 1 (ft); Dentists; Podiatrists.
Affiliation Advent Christian Church
Facilities Dining room; Physical therapy room; Activities room; Chapel; Crafts room; Laundry room; Barber/Beauty shop; Library.
Activities Arts and Crafts; Games; Reading groups; Prayer groups; Movies; Shopping trips; Dances/Social or cultural gatherings.
Description A unique village on the banks of the Suwannee River includes a nonprofit children's home, center for marriage and family counseling, comprehensive retirement center, rural health clinic, and intermediate and skilled nursing facilities licensed by the state of Florida.

DUNEDIN

Dunedin Care Center*
1351 San Christopher, Dunedin, FL, 33528 (813) 736-1421
Licensure Skilled Care. *Beds* 103. *Certified* Medicaid; Medicare.
Ownership Proprietary.
Staff RNs 5 (ft); LPNs 7 (ft); Nurses aides 30 (ft).
Languages German, French, Spanish

Spanish Gardens Nursing and Convalescent Center
1061 Virginia St, Dunedin, FL, 33528 (813) 733-2619
Medical Dir/Dir of Nursing Norman Urich DO.
Licensure Skilled Care. *Beds* 93. *Certified* Medicaid; Medicare.
Ownership Proprietary.
Admissions Requirements Minimum age 18; Medical examination; Physician's request.
Staff RNs 3 (ft); LPNs 12 (ft); Orderlies 2 (ft); Nurses aides 25 (ft); Physical therapists 2 (pt); Recreational therapists 1 (ft); Occupational therapists 2 (pt); Speech therapists 2 (pt); Activities coordinators 1 (ft); Dietitians 1 (ft); Podiatrists 1 (pt); Audiologists 2 (pt).
Languages Spanish
Facilities Dining room; Physical therapy room; Activities room; Chapel; Crafts room; Laundry room; Barber/Beauty shop; Library; Covered patio.
Activities Arts and Crafts; Cards; Games; Reading groups; Prayer groups; Movies; Shopping trips; Dances/Social or cultural gatherings; Picnics; Beach outings.
Description Center provides a family support group to assist families in adjusting to their decision for nursing home placement.

EUSTIS

Eustis Manor Inc
2810 Ruleme St, Eustis, FL, 32726
Admin Danny K Prince. *Medical Dir/Dir of Nursing* Dr B W Price.
Licensure Skilled Care. *Beds* 120. *Certified* Medicaid.
Ownership Proprietary.
Admissions Requirements Medical examination.
Staff Physicians 13 (pt); RNs 6 (ft), 1 (pt); LPNs 8 (ft), 2 (pt); Nurses aides 38 (ft); Physical therapists 3 (pt); Reality therapists 1 (pt); Speech therapists 2 (pt); Activities coordinators 1 (ft); Dietitians 1 (ft); Dentists; Ophthalmologists; Podiatrists; Audiologists.
Facilities Dining room; Laundry room; Barber/Beauty shop.
Activities Arts and Crafts; Cards; Games; Reading groups; Prayer groups; Movies; Shopping trips; Dances/Social or cultural gatherings.

Lake Eustis Care Center
411 W Woodward Ave, Eustis, FL, 32726 (904) 357-3565
Licensure Skilled Care. *Beds* 45. *Certified* Medicaid; Medicare.
Ownership Proprietary.
Staff RNs 3 (ft); LPNs 3 (ft), 3 (pt); Orderlies 2 (ft), 2 (pt); Nurses aides 9 (ft), 6 (pt); Activities coordinators 1 (ft); Dietitians 1 (ft).
Facilities Dining room; Activities room; Chapel; Laundry room; Barber/Beauty shop.
Activities Arts and Crafts; Cards; Games; Reading groups; Prayer groups.

Oakwood Convalescent Center*
301 S Bay St, Eustis, FL, 32726 (904) 357-8105
Licensure Skilled Care. *Beds* 120. *Certified* Medicaid; Medicare.
Ownership Proprietary.

Staff RNs 4 (ft); LPNs 10 (ft); Nurses aides 43 (ft).

FERNANDINA BEACH

Amelia Island Care Center
2700 Atlantic Ave, Fernandina Beach, FL, 32034 (904) 261-5518
Medical Dir/Dir of Nursing Kathy Morris RN.
Licensure Intermediate Care for Mentally Retarded. *Certified* Medicaid.
Ownership Proprietary.
Staff RNs 2 (ft); LPNs 10 (ft); Nurses aides 36 (ft).
Languages Spanish, Tagalog

FOREST CITY

Florida Living Nursing Center
PO Box 3186, Forest City, FL, 32751 (305) 862-6263
Medical Dir/Dir of Nursing Michael Gebauer MD.
Licensure Skilled Care. *Beds* 104. *Certified* Medicaid; Medicare.
Ownership Nonprofit.
Admissions Requirements Minimum age 16; Medical examination; Physician's request.
Staff Physicians 1 (pt); RNs 3 (ft), 3 (pt); LPNs 10 (ft), 7 (pt); Orderlies 5 (ft), 2 (pt); Nurses aides 33 (ft), 10 (pt); Physical therapists; Speech therapists; Activities coordinators 2 (ft), 1 (pt); Podiatrists.
Languages Spanish
Affiliation Seventh-Day Adventist
Facilities Dining room; Physical therapy room; Activities room; Chapel; Crafts room; Laundry room; Barber/Beauty shop; Library.
Activities Arts and Crafts; Games; Reading groups; Prayer groups; Movies; Shopping trips; Dances/Social or cultural gatherings.
Description Facility located in a beautiful rural setting close to shopping and only 30 miles from Walt Disney World. Specialty is physical therapy and rehabilitative nursing.

FORT LAUDERDALE

Alden House
1800 E Oakland Park Blvd, Fort Lauderdale, FL, 33307 (305) 565-7785
Licensure Skilled Care. *Beds* 84. *Certified* Medicaid; Medicare.
Ownership Proprietary.
Staff Physicians; Dietitians; Nurses aides.

Ann Stock Center*
1790 SW 43rd Way, Fort Lauderdale, FL, 3317 (305) 584-8000
Licensure Intermediate Care for Mentally Retarded. *Beds* 16. *Certified* Medicaid.
Ownership Proprietary.

Broward Convalescent Home*
1330 S Andrews Ave, Fort Lauderdale, FL, 33316 (305) 524-5587
Licensure Skilled Care. *Beds* 198. *Certified* Medicaid; Medicare.
Ownership Proprietary.

Staff RNs 13 (ft); LPNs 17 (ft); Nurses aides 45 (ft); 26 (ft).
Languages Spanish, French

Center for Living
2000 E Commercial Blvd, Fort Lauderdale, FL, 33308 (305) 771-2300
Medical Dir/Dir of Nursing Dr Alex Leeds.
Licensure Skilled Care; Intermediate Care.
Beds SNF 209; ICF 44. *Certified* Medicaid; Medicare.
Ownership Proprietary.
Admissions Requirements Minimum age 18.
Staff Physicians 1 (pt); RNs 15 (ft); LPNs 24 (ft); Orderlies 5 (ft); Nurses aides 90 (ft); Physical therapists 1 (ft); Recreational therapists 3 (ft); Speech therapists 1 (pt); Activities coordinators 1 (ft); Dietitians 1 (ft); Podiatrists 1 (pt).
Languages German, Spanish, Italian, Yiddish
Facilities Dining room; Physical therapy room; Activities room; Laundry room; Barber/Beauty shop; Library.
Activities Arts and Crafts; Cards; Games; Reading groups; Prayer groups; Movies; Dances/Social or cultural gatherings.

Daystar Inc*
3800 Flamingo Rd, Fort Lauderdale, FL, 33314 (305) 473-0212
Licensure Skilled Care; Intermediate Care.
Beds SNF 31; ICF 13. *Certified* Medicaid; Medicare.
Ownership Proprietary.
Languages Spanish, German, Japanese
Affiliation Christian Science

Harbor Beach Convalescent Home
1615 S Miami Rd, Fort Lauderdale, FL, 33316 (305) 523-5673
Medical Dir/Dir of Nursing Guillermo Rodriquez.
Licensure Skilled Care. *Beds* 59.
Ownership Proprietary.
Admissions Requirements Minimum age 16.
Staff Physicians 10 (ft); RNs 4 (ft); LPNs 4 (ft); Orderlies 2 (ft), 1 (pt); Nurses aides 18 (ft); Reality therapists 1 (ft); Recreational therapists 1 (ft); Activities coordinators 1 (ft); Dietitians 1 (ft); Podiatrists 2 (ft).
Facilities Dining room; Physical therapy room; Activities room; Crafts room; Laundry room; Barber/Beauty shop; Library; 3 Outdoor patios.
Activities Arts and Crafts; Cards; Games; Reading groups; Prayer groups; Movies; Shopping trips; Dances/Social or cultural gatherings; Culture months; Adopt-a-grandparent program.
Description HBCH is a small, private, skilled care facility. Staff takes pride in patient care. Building is on one level with 3 patios off the main hallway. Facility offers a wide range of activity programs including physical, speech, and occupational therapy. HBCH is a home away from home and a place where the convalescents reside in comfort and the aged dwell with dignity.

Manor Pines Convalescent Center*
1701 NE 26th St, Fort Lauderdale, FL, 33305 (305) 566-8353
Licensure Skilled Care. *Beds* 206. *Certified* Medicaid.

Ownership Proprietary.
Staff RNs 18 (ft); LPNs 15 (ft); Nurses aides 62 (ft); 33 (ft).

Monticello Manor
1701 N Federal Hwy, Fort Lauderdale, FL, 33308 (305) 564-3237
Licensure Skilled Care. *Beds* 34.
Ownership Proprietary.
Admissions Requirements Minimum age 16; Medical examination; Physician's request.
Staff RNs 4 (ft); LPNs 2 (ft); Nurses aides 8 (ft), 1 (pt); Physical therapists 1 (pt); Reality therapists 1 (pt); Recreational therapists 1 (pt); Occupational therapists 1 (pt); Speech therapists 1 (pt); Activities coordinators 1 (pt); Dietitians 1 (pt); Dentists 1 (pt); Podiatrists 1 (pt).
Facilities Dining room; Physical therapy room; Activities room; Crafts room; Laundry room; Barber/Beauty shop.
Activities Arts and Crafts; Cards; Games; Reading groups; Prayer groups; Movies.
Description Small facility with many happy residents; love surrounds them and dedication of staff is most important.

Mount Vernon Manor*
2331 NE 53rd St, Fort Lauderdale, FL, 33308 (305) 771-0739
Licensure Skilled Care. *Beds* 29.
Ownership Proprietary.
Staff RNs 3 (ft); LPNs 2 (ft); Nurses aides 11 (ft).
Languages Spanish, German

Sheffield Nursing and Rehabilitation Center
2675 N Andrews Ave, Fort Lauderdale, FL, 33311 (305) 563-5711
Medical Dir/Dir of Nursing Dr A Leeds.
Licensure Skilled Care. *Beds* 118. *Certified* Medicaid; Medicare.
Ownership Proprietary.
Admissions Requirements Medical examination; Physician's request.
Staff Physicians 1 (pt); RNs 5 (ft), 3 (pt); LPNs 8 (ft), 6 (pt); Orderlies 4 (ft); Nurses aides 33 (ft), 9 (pt); Physical therapists 1 (ft), 1 (pt); Speech therapists 1 (ft); Activities coordinators 2 (ft); Dietitians 1 (ft), 1 (pt); Dentists 1 (pt); Ophthalmologists 1 (pt); Podiatrists 1 (pt); Audiologists 1 (pt); 1 (ft).
Facilities Dining room; Physical therapy room; Activities room; Crafts room; Laundry room; Barber/Beauty shop; Library.
Activities Arts and Crafts; Cards; Games; Reading groups; Prayer groups; Movies; Shopping trips; Dances/Social or cultural gatherings.
Description Facility features a large courtyard; churches nearby; ongoing adult education programs, and a musical therapy program. Centrally located near public transportation.

FORT MEYERS

Calusa Retirement Center*
2525 E 1st St, Fort Meyers, FL, 33901 (813) 332-3333
Beds 60.
Ownership Nonprofit.
Affiliation Baptist

FORT MYERS

Beacon-Donegan Manor
8400 Beacon Blvd, Fort Myers, FL, 33911 (813) 936-1300
Admin Jeannine Tucker.
Licensure Skilled Care; Intermediate Care.
Beds SNF 98; ICF 52. *Certified* Medicaid; Medicare.
Ownership Proprietary.
Staff Physicians; Dietitians; Nurses aides.
Languages Spanish
Facilities Dining room; Physical therapy room; Activities room; Crafts room; Laundry room; Barber/Beauty shop.
Activities Arts and Crafts; Cards; Games; Reading groups; Prayer groups; Movies; Shopping trips; Dances/Social or cultural gatherings.

Fort Myers Care Center*
13755 Golf Club Pkwy, Fort Myers, FL, 33906 (813) 482-2848
Beds 102.
Ownership Proprietary.

Gulf Coast Center*
PO Box 2369, Fort Myers, FL, 33902 (813) 692-2151 *Certified* Medicaid.
Ownership Public.

Lee Convalescent Center*
2826 Cleveland Ave, Fort Myers, FL, 33901 (813) 334-1091
Licensure Skilled Care; Intermediate Care.
Beds SNF 120; ICF 26. *Certified* Medicaid; Medicare.
Ownership Proprietary.
Staff RNs 16 (ft); LPNs 10 (ft); Nurses aides 48 (ft).

Sandy Park Rehabilitation Center*
Buckingham Rd, Fort Myers, FL, 33902 (813) 694-5528
Licensure Intermediate Care for Mentally Retarded. *Beds* 48.
Ownership Proprietary.

Shady Rest Nursing Home*
2300 N Airport Rd, Fort Myers, FL, 33905 (813) 936-2357
Licensure Skilled Care. *Beds* 105. *Certified* Medicaid.
Ownership Public.
Staff RNs 13 (ft); LPNs 11 (ft); Nurses aides 34 (ft); 24 (ft).
Languages Spanish

Shell Point Village Nursing Pavilion
Shell Point Blvd, Rt 12, Fort Myers, FL, 33901 (813) 481-2141
Medical Dir/Dir of Nursing E Ernest Pierleoni MD.
Licensure Skilled Care; Intermediate Care.
Beds SNF 164; ICF 16. *Certified* Medicare.
Ownership Nonprofit.
Admissions Requirements Medical examination.
Staff Physicians 2 (ft), 1 (pt); RNs 10 (ft), 7 (pt); LPNs 10 (ft), 4 (pt); Orderlies 1 (ft); Nurses aides 54 (ft); Physical therapists 1 (ft); Occupational therapists 1 (pt); Speech therapists 1 (pt); Activities coordinators 1 (ft); Dentists 1 (pt); Physical therapy aide 1 (ft).

Languages Spanish, German, Italian, Tagalog
Affiliation Christian and Missionary Alliance Foundation
Facilities Dining room; Physical therapy room; Activities room; Chapel; Crafts room; Barber-/Beauty shop; Screened patio; Waterfront picnic area.
Activities Arts and Crafts; Cards; Games; Reading groups; Prayer groups; Movies; Shopping trips; Dances/Social or cultural gatherings; Music groups; Exercise club; Current events; Pet program; Birthday celebrations.
Description This is a life care facility with the capacity to admit from the community as well; 180-bed nursing pavilion is an integral part of a comprehensive retirement village set on 75 acres of riverfront property close to the Gulf of Mexico; includes a complete rehabilitation agency serving both in- and outpatients.

FORT PIERCE

Abbiejean Russell Care Center
700 S 29th St, Fort Pierce, FL, 33456 (305) 465-7560
Admin R C Schriever. *Medical Dir/Dir of Nursing* Richard F Kaine MD.
Licensure Skilled Care. *Beds* 79. *Certified* Medicaid.
Ownership Nonprofit.
Admissions Requirements Minimum age 21; Medical examination; Physician's request.
Staff Physicians 3 (pt); RNs 3 (ft), 2 (pt); LPNs 8 (ft), 3 (pt); Orderlies 2 (ft); Nurses aides 26 (ft), 1 (pt); Physical therapists 4 (pt); Occupational therapists 2 (pt); Speech therapists 2 (pt); Activities coordinators 2 (ft); Dietitians 1 (pt); Dentists 1 (pt); Podiatrists 1 (pt); Audiologists 1 (pt); Psychologist 1 (pt).
Languages Spanish, German, Polish
Facilities Dining room; Physical therapy room; Activities room; Laundry room; Barber/Beauty shop; Library; Large screened patio; Large fenced yeard; Shuffleboard court; Outdoor barbecue.
Activities Arts and Crafts; Cards; Games; Reading groups; Prayer groups; Movies; Shopping trips; Dances/Social or cultural gatherings; Morning fitness class; Weekly cooking class.
Description Facility features outdoor hydroponic gardens, nurses appreciation day each month, and the election of resident and employee of the month.

Easter Manor Nursing Home*
611 S 13th St, Fort Pierce, FL, 33454 (305) 465-5262
Licensure Skilled Care. *Beds* 171. *Certified* Medicaid; Medicare.
Ownership Proprietary.
Staff RNs 8 (ft); LPNs 16 (ft); Nurses aides 46 (ft).
Languages Spanish, French, Tagalog

Fort Pierce Care Center
703 S 29th St, Fort Pierce, FL, 33450 (305) 466-3322
Medical Dir/Dir of Nursing Carmen Ebalo MD.
Licensure Skilled Care. *Beds* 102.
Ownership Proprietary.
Admissions Requirements Minimum age 16;

Medical examination.
Staff RNs 5 (ft), 6 (pt); LPNs 4 (ft), 7 (pt);
Orderlies 1 (ft); Nurses aides 30 (ft), 7 (pt);
Activities coordinators 1 (ft); Dietitians 1 (ft).
Facilities Dining room; Physical therapy room;
Activities room; Laundry room; Barber/Beauty
shop.

FORT WALTON BEACH

Fort Walton Developmental Center*
113 Barks Dr, Fort Walton Beach, FL, 32548
(904) 434-5311
Licensure Intermediate Care for Mentally
Retarded. *Beds* 63.

Gulf Convalescent Center
114 3rd St SE, Fort Walton Beach, FL, 32548
(904) 243-6135
Medical Dir/Dir of Nursing Dr D'Amore.
Licensure Skilled Care. *Beds* 120. *Certified* Medicaid; Medicare.
Ownership Proprietary.
Admissions Requirements Medical examination; Physician's request.
Staff RNs 3 (ft), 3 (pt); LPNs 8 (ft), 4 (pt);
Nurses aides 44 (ft), 15 (pt); Physical therapists
1 (pt); Occupational therapists; Speech therapists; Activities coordinators 1 (pt); Dietitians 1
(pt); Dentists 1 (pt); Podiatrists 1 (pt).
Languages Spanish, French, Japanese
Facilities Dining room; Physical therapy room;
Activities room; Laundry room; Barber/Beauty
shop; Library.
Activities Arts and Crafts; Cards; Games;
Reading groups; Prayer groups; Shopping trips;
Dances/Social or cultural gatherings.

Westwood Retirement Center*
1001 Mar-Walt Dr, Fort Walton Beach, FL,
32548 (904) 863-5471
Beds 60. *Certified* Medicaid; Medicare.
Ownership Proprietary.

GAINESVILLE

Community Convalescent Center*
100 SW 16th Ave, Gainesville, FL, 32601 (904)
376-2461
Licensure Skilled Care. *Beds* 120. *Certified* Medicaid; Medicare.
Ownership Proprietary.
Staff RNs 8 (ft); LPNs 7 (ft); Nurses aides 26
(ft); 14 (ft).

Gainesville Nursing Center
4000 SW 20th Ave, Gainesville, FL, 32608
(904) 377-1981
Medical Dir/Dir of Nursing Dr Jernigan.
Licensure Skilled Care. *Beds* 93. *Certified* Medicaid.
Ownership Proprietary.
Admissions Requirements Minimum age 18;
Medical examination.
Staff Physicians 3 (pt); RNs 4 (ft), 1 (pt); LPNs
6 (ft), 2 (pt); Orderlies 2 (ft), 1 (pt); Nurses aides
40 (ft), 10 (pt); Physical therapists 1 (pt);
Reality therapists 1 (ft); Recreational therapists
1 (ft); Activities coordinators 1 (ft), 1 (pt); Dietitians 1 (pt); Podiatrists 1 (pt).
Facilities Dining room; Physical therapy room;

Activities room; Crafts room; Laundry room;
Barber/Beauty shop; Library.
Activities Arts and Crafts; Cards; Games;
Reading groups; Prayer groups; Movies.
Description Medical director from Faculty of
Family Practice, University of Florida at
Gainesville; students come to home for
medical training.

Regency Oaks*
3250 SW 41st Pl, Gainesville, FL, 32601 (904)
378-1558
Medical Dir/Dir of Nursing William Warrick
III MD.
Licensure Skilled Care. *Beds* 119. *Certified* Medicaid; Medicare.
Ownership Proprietary.
Admissions Requirements Minimum age 16;
Medical examination; Physician's request.
Staff Physicians 1 (ft), 1 (pt); RNs 8 (ft), 2 (pt);
LPNs 12 (ft), 4 (pt); Orderlies 4 (ft); Nurses
aides 31 (ft), 10 (pt); Physical therapists 1 (ft);
Reality therapists 1 (ft); Recreational therapists
1 (ft); Occupational therapists 1 (ft); Speech
therapists 1 (ft); Activities coordinators 1 (ft);
Dietitians 1 (ft); Dentists 1 (pt); Ophthalmologists 1 (pt); Podiatrists 1 (pt); Audiologists 1
(pt).
Facilities Dining room; Physical therapy room;
Activities room; Laundry room; Barber/Beauty
shop.
Activities Arts and Crafts; Cards; Games;
Reading groups; Prayer groups; Movies; Shopping trips; Dances/Social or cultural gatherings.
Description Regency Oaks is a skilled nursing
facility servicing Alaclua and surrounding communities. We are a Unicare Health Facility
whose philosophy is respect for dignity. We are
proud to serve the health care needs of America.

Sunland Center—Gainesville Facility I
PO Box 1150, Gainesville, FL, 32602 (904)
395-1455
Medical Dir/Dir of Nursing Dr Charles Williams.
Licensure Intermediate Care for Mentally
Retarded. *Beds* 120. *Certified* Medicaid;
Medicare.
Ownership Public.
Admissions Requirements Medical examination.
Staff Physicians 1 (ft); RNs 4 (ft), 2 (pt); LPNs
2 (ft); Orderlies 12 (ft), 8 (pt); Nurses aides 139
(ft); Physical therapists 1 (pt); Recreational therapists 8 (ft); Occupational therapists 3 (ft), 1
(pt); Speech therapists 1 (ft); Activities coordinators 8 (ft); Dietitians 1 (ft); Dentists 4 (ft);
Ophthalmologists 1 (pt); Podiatrists 1 (pt);
Audiologists 1 (ft).
Facilities Dining room; Physical therapy room;
Activities room; Chapel; Crafts room; Laundry
room; Barber/Beauty shop; Library; Gymnasium.
Activities Arts and Crafts; Games; Movies;
Shopping trips; Dances/Social or cultural gatherings.
Description This is a program for up to 120
severe/profound individuals of all ages; the
only requirement is that they must benefit from
the program. Facility also specializes in nonambulatory care.

Sunland Center—Gainesville Facility II*
PO Box 1150, Gainesville, FL, 32602 (904)
376-5381
Licensure Intermediate Care for Mentally
Retarded. *Beds* 120.
Ownership Public.

Sunland Center—Gainesville Facility III*
PO Box 1150, Gainesville, FL, 32602 (904)
376-5381
Licensure Intermediate Care for Mentally
Retarded. *Beds* 60.
Ownership Public.

GLENWOOD

Duvall Home for Retarded Children
3395 Grand Ave, Glenwood, FL, 32722 (904)
734-2874
Admin W Blake Davis.
Licensure Intermediate Care for Mentally
Retarded. *Beds* 250.
Ownership Nonprofit.
Staff RNs 1 (ft), 2 (pt); LPNs 5 (ft), 2 (pt);
Orderlies 8 (ft); Nurses aides 104 (ft), 9 (pt);
Physical therapists 1 (ft); Recreational therapists
4 (ft); Activities coordinators 1 (ft).
Languages Spanish
Facilities Dining room; Physical therapy room;
Activities room; Crafts room; Laundry room;
Barber/Beauty shop.
Activities Arts and Crafts; Games; Reading
groups; Movies; Shopping trips; Dances/Social
or cultural gatherings.
Description The Duvall Home in Glenwood,
Florida is nestled among orange, oak, and huge,
old camphor trees. There are 2 modern residence halls, a physical therapy complex,
olympic-sized swimming pool, and the
administration building.

GOULDS

Lincoln Memorial Nursing Home
11295 SW 216th St, Goulds, FL, 33170 (305)
235-7461
Medical Dir/Dir of Nursing Manuel E Abella
MD.
Licensure Skilled Care. *Beds* 32. *Certified* Medicaid; Medicare.
Ownership Nonprofit.
Admissions Requirements Minimum age 16;
Medical examination; Physician's request.
Staff Physicians 2 (pt); RNs 1 (ft), 1 (pt); LPNs
3 (ft), 4 (pt); Nurses aides 9 (ft), 3 (pt); Physical
therapists 1 (pt); Recreational therapists 1 (pt);
Occupational therapists 1 (pt); Speech therapists 1 (pt); Activities coordinators 1 (ft); Dietitians 1 (pt); Dentists 1 (pt).
Languages Spanish, French
Facilities Dining room; Activities room; Crafts
room; Laundry room.
Activities Arts and Crafts; Cards; Games; Prayer groups; Dances/Social or cultural gatherings.
Description This nursing home takes Medicaid
and county patients and has served the community 30 years.

Sunrise—Goulds*
22300 SW 16th Ave, Goulds, FL, 33170 (305)
245-6159

Licensure Intermediate Care for Mentally Retarded. *Beds* 120. *Certified* Medicaid. *Ownership* Proprietary.

Sunrise Group Home 1—Goulds*
1600 SW 216th St, Goulds, FL, 33170 (305) 248-3701
Licensure Intermediate Care for Mentally Retarded. *Beds* 15. *Certified* Medicaid. *Ownership* Proprietary.

GRACEVILLE

Jackson County Convalescent Center*
1002 Sanders Ave, Graceville, FL, 32440 (904) 263-4447
Licensure Skilled Care. *Beds* 99. *Certified* Medicaid. *Ownership* Proprietary.

GREEN COVE SPRINGS

Green Cove Springs Geriatric Center*
803 Oak St, Green Cove Springs, FL, 32043 (904) 284-5606
Licensure Skilled Care. *Beds* 120. *Certified* Medicaid; Medicare. *Ownership* Proprietary.
Staff RNs 5 (ft); LPNs 12 (ft); Nurses aides 37 (ft).
Languages Spanish, German

GREENVILLE

Pine Lake Nursing Home
Hwy 90 E, Greenville, FL, 32331 (904) 948-4601
Medical Dir/Dir of Nursing J M Durant MD. *Licensure* Skilled Care. *Beds* 58. *Certified* Medicaid. *Ownership* Proprietary.
Admissions Requirements Medical examination; Physician's request.
Staff Physicians 2 (pt); RNs 1 (ft), 2 (pt); LPNs 4 (ft), 6 (pt); Nurses aides 19 (ft), 5 (pt); Physical therapists 1 (pt); Activities coordinators 1 (ft); Dietitians 1 (pt); Dentists 1 (pt); Ophthalmologists 1 (pt); Podiatrists 1 (pt).
Facilities Dining room; Activities room; Laundry room; Barber/Beauty shop.
Activities Arts and Crafts; Cards; Games; Reading groups; Prayer groups; Movies; Shopping trips; Dances/Social or cultural gatherings.
Description Creative activities program held on Monday and Thursday, an opportunity for residents to develop any interests they may have or work on any interests they may have had earlier. Residents quilt, string beads and paint, as well as do woodworking.

GULFPORT

Gulfport Convalescent Center
1414 59th St S, Gulfport, FL, 33707 (813) 344-4608
Medical Dir/Dir of Nursing Robert Jenkins MD.
Licensure Skilled Care. *Beds* 120. *Certified* Medicaid; Medicare. *Ownership* Proprietary.

Staff Physicians; RNs; LPNs; Orderlies; Nurses aides; Physical therapists; Speech therapists; Activities coordinators; Dietitians; Dentists.
Languages Spanish
Facilities Dining room; Activities room; Barber/Beauty shop; Library.
Activities Arts and Crafts; Cards; Games; Prayer groups; Movies; Shopping trips; Dances/Social or cultural gatherings.

HALLANDALE

Hallandale Rehabilitation Center*
2400 E Hallandale Beach Blvd, Hallandale, FL, 33009 (305) 457-9717
Licensure Skilled Care. *Beds* 149. *Certified* Medicaid; Medicare. *Ownership* Proprietary.
Staff RNs 6 (ft); LPNs 19 (ft); Nurses aides 55 (ft).
Languages Spanish

HIALEAH

Hialeah Convalescent Home*
190 W 28th St, Hialeah, FL, 33010 (305) 885-2437
Licensure Skilled Care. *Beds* 276. *Certified* Medicaid; Medicare. *Ownership* Proprietary.
Staff RNs 29 (ft); LPNs 4 (ft); Nurses aides 88 (ft).
Languages Spanish

HOBE SOUND

Hobe Sound Geriatric Village
9555 SE Federal Hwy, Hobe Sound, FL, 33455 (305) 546-2911
Admin Milly Barry. *Medical Dir/Dir of Nursing* Maghraj Thanvi MD. *Licensure* Skilled Care. *Beds* 120. *Certified* Medicaid; Medicare. *Ownership* Proprietary.
Admissions Requirements Minimum age 16; Medical examination; Physician's request.
Staff Physicians 12 (pt); RNs 4 (ft), 4 (pt); LPNs 4 (ft), 11 (pt); Orderlies 1 (pt); Nurses aides 16 (ft), 32 (pt); Reality therapists 1 (pt); Recreational therapists 1 (ft); Activities coordinators 1 (ft).
Languages French, German, Spanish
Facilities Dining room; Physical therapy room; Activities room; Chapel; Crafts room; Laundry room; Barber/Beauty shop; Library.
Activities Arts and Crafts; Cards; Games; Reading groups; Prayer groups; Movies; Shopping trips; Dances/Social or cultural gatherings.
Description Facility is located in Hobe Sound on a beautifully wooded lot with a natural lake in front; a sprawling building all on one floor.

HOLLYWOOD

Golfcrest Nursing Home*
600 N 17th Ave, Hollywood, FL, 33020 (305) 927-2531
Licensure Skilled Care. *Beds* 67. *Certified* Medicaid; Medicare.

Ownership Proprietary.
Staff RNs 7 (ft); LPNs 5 (ft); Nurses aides 23 (ft).

Hollywood Hills Nursing Home
1200 N 35th Ave, Hollywood, FL, 33021 (305) 981-5511
Medical Dir/Dir of Nursing Dr Samuel Rand. *Licensure* Skilled Care. *Beds* 152. *Certified* Medicaid; Medicare. *Ownership* Proprietary.
Admissions Requirements Minimum age 30; Physician's request.
Staff Physicians; RNs; LPNs; Orderlies; Nurses aides; Physical therapists; Recreational therapists; Occupational therapists; Speech therapists; Activities coordinators; Dietitians; Dentists; Ophthalmologists; Podiatrists; Audiologists.
Languages Spanish
Facilities Dining room; Physical therapy room; Activities room; Chapel; Crafts room; Laundry room; Barber/Beauty shop; Library.
Activities Arts and Crafts; Cards; Games; Reading groups; Prayer groups; Movies; Shopping trips; Dances/Social or cultural gatherings.
Description Activities program second to none; unique trips taken and unusual events held.

Washington Manor Nursing and Rehabilitation Center
4200 Washington St, Hollywood, FL, 33021 (302) 981-6300
Medical Dir/Dir of Nursing Richard Reines MD.
Licensure Skilled Care; Intermediate Care. *Beds* 180.
Ownership Proprietary.
Admissions Requirements Minimum age 16; Medical examination.
Staff RNs 3 (ft), 3 (pt); LPNs 15 (ft), 10 (pt); Nurses aides 46 (ft), 23 (pt); Physical therapists; Recreational therapists 1 (ft); Occupational therapists; Speech therapists; Activities coordinators 3 (ft); Dietitians; Dentists; Ophthalmologists; Podiatrists.
Languages Spanish
Facilities Dining room; Physical therapy room; Activities room; Chapel; Crafts room; Laundry room; Barber/Beauty shop; Library; 2 Outdoor garden patios.
Activities Arts and Crafts; Cards; Games; Reading groups; Prayer groups; Movies; Shopping trips; Dances/Social or cultural gatherings; Outdoor barbecues and picnics.
Description Facility is exclusively for private pay residents only; entire home on ground floor surrounding 2 outdoor garden patios of one acre each. Reputation of home made it possible to withdraw from Medicare and Medicaid program years ago; home always has a waiting list.

HOMESTEAD

Homestead Manor Nursing Home
1330 NW 1st Ave, Homestead, FL, 33030 (305) 248-0271
Medical Dir/Dir of Nursing Dr Bankett and Dr Crump.
Licensure Skilled Care. *Beds* 54. *Certified* Medicaid; Medicare. *Ownership* Proprietary.

Staff Physicians; Dietitians; Nurses aides.
Languages Spanish, Italian, German, French
Facilities Dining room; Activities room; Crafts room; Laundry room; Barber/Beauty shop.
Activities Arts and Crafts; Games; Movies; Shopping trips; Dances/Social or cultural gatherings.

INVERNESS

Inverness Health Care Center
304 S Citrus Ave, Inverness, FL, 32650 (904) 726-3141
Licensure Skilled Care; Intermediate Care. *Beds* 104. *Certified* Medicaid; Medicare.
Ownership Proprietary.
Admissions Requirements Minimum age 17; Medical examination; Physician's request.
Staff Physicians; Dietitians; Nurses aides.
Facilities Dining room; Physical therapy room; Activities room; Chapel; Laundry room; Barber/Beauty shop.
Activities Arts and Crafts; Cards; Games; Reading groups; Prayer groups; Movies; Shopping trips; Dances/Social or cultural gatherings.

JACKSONVILLE

All Saints Catholic Nursing Home*
2040 Riverside Ave, Jacksonville, FL, 32204 (904) 389-4671
Licensure Skilled Care. *Beds* 57. *Certified* Medicaid.
Ownership Nonprofit.
Staff RNs 2 (ft); LPNs 6 (ft); Nurses aides 25 (ft); 11 (ft).
Languages Spanish, French, Italian, Tagalog

Americana Healthcare Center
3648 University Blvd S, Jacksonville, FL, 32216 (904) 733-7440
Admin David E Wodehouse. *Medical Dir/Dir of Nursing* Thomas E Michelsen DO.
Licensure Skilled Care. *Beds* 89. *Certified* Medicaid; Medicare.
Ownership Proprietary.
Admissions Requirements Medical examination; Physician's request.
Staff RNs 3 (ft), 3 (pt); LPNs 7 (ft), 6 (pt); Nurses aides 30 (ft), 8 (pt); Physical therapists 1 (ft), 1 (pt); Activities coordinators 1 (ft), 1 (pt).
Facilities Dining room; Physical therapy room; Activities room; Chapel; Crafts room; Laundry room; Barber/Beauty shop.
Activities Arts and Crafts; Cards; Games; Reading groups; Prayer groups; Movies; Shopping trips.

Arlington Manor Care Center
7723 Jasper Ave, Jacksonville, FL, 32211 (904) 725-8044
Medical Dir/Dir of Nursing Eduardo Cinca.
Licensure Skilled Care. *Beds* 100. *Certified* Medicaid.
Ownership Proprietary.
Admissions Requirements Medical examination; Physician's request.
Staff RNs 3 (ft); LPNs 6 (ft), 2 (pt); Orderlies 2 (ft); Nurses aides 24 (ft); Physical therapists 1 (ft); Reality therapists 1 (ft); Recreational therapists 1 (ft).

Languages Tagalog
Activities Prayer groups; Arts and Crafts; Shopping trips.

Cathedral Health and Rehabilitation Center*
333 E Ashley St, Jacksonville, FL, 32202 (904) 355-1761
Licensure Skilled Care. *Beds* 32. *Certified* Medicaid; Medicare.
Ownership Nonprofit.
Languages Spanish, Tagalog
Activities Prayer groups.

Cedar Hills Nursing Center
2061 Hyde Park Rd, Jacksonville, FL, 32210 (904) 786-7331
Medical Dir/Dir of Nursing Elias Mualem DO.
Licensure Skilled Care. *Beds* 180. *Certified* Medicaid; Medicare.
Ownership Proprietary.
Admissions Requirements Medical examination; Physician's request.
Staff Physicians 1 (ft); RNs 3 (ft), 3 (pt); LPNs 14 (ft), 6 (pt); Nurses aides 46 (ft), 10 (pt); Physical therapists 2 (pt); Occupational therapists 1 (pt); Speech therapists 1 (pt); Activities coordinators 3 (ft); Dietitians 1 (pt); Dentists 1 (pt); Ophthalmologists 1 (pt); Podiatrists 1 (pt); Audiologists 1 (pt).
Languages French, German, Spanish
Facilities Dining room; Physical therapy room; Activities room; Chapel; Crafts room; Laundry room; Barber/Beauty shop.
Activities Arts and Crafts; Games; Reading groups; Prayer groups; Movies; Shopping trips; Fishing.

Eartha M M White Nursing Home
5377 Moncrief Rd, Jacksonville, FL, 32209 (904) 768-1506
Admin S L Patterson.
Licensure Skilled Care. *Beds* 120. *Certified* Medicaid; Medicare.
Ownership Nonprofit.
Admissions Requirements Minimum age 18; Medical examination.
Staff Physicians 4 (pt); RNs 3 (ft), 4 (pt); LPNs 10 (ft), 7 (pt); Orderlies 2 (ft); Nurses aides 40 (ft), 1 (pt); Physical therapists 1 (ft); Reality therapists 1 (pt); Recreational therapists 1 (pt); Occupational therapists 1 (pt); Speech therapists 1 (pt); Activities coordinators 1 (ft); Dietitians 1 (pt); Dentists 1 (pt); Ophthalmologists 1 (pt); Podiatrists 1 (pt); Audiologists 1 (pt).
Languages Tagalog
Facilities Dining room; Physical therapy room; Activities room; Chapel; Crafts room; Laundry room; Barber/Beauty shop; Library.
Activities Arts and Crafts; Cards; Games; Reading groups; Prayer groups; Movies; Shopping trips; Dances/Social or cultural gatherings; Birthday parties.

Fannie E Taylor Home for the Aged
3937 Spring Park Rd, Jacksonville, FL, 32207 (904) 737-6777
Licensure Intermediate Care. *Beds* 24. *Certified* Medicaid.
Ownership Nonprofit.
Staff Physicians; Dietitians; Nurses aides.
Activities Arts and Crafts; Shopping trips.

Florida Christian Health Center
1827 Stockton St, Jacksonville, FL, 32204 (904) 384-3457
Medical Dir/Dir of Nursing Wayne Cartee MD.
Licensure Skilled Care. *Beds* 128. *Certified* Medicaid; Medicare.
Ownership Nonprofit.
Admissions Requirements Minimum age 17; Medical examination; Physician's request.
Staff Physicians 2 (pt); RNs 4 (ft), 2 (pt); LPNs 12 (ft), 6 (pt); Nurses aides 45 (ft), 7 (pt); Physical therapists 1 (pt); Activities coordinators 1 (ft).
Languages Spanish
Affiliation Disciples of Christ
Facilities Dining room; Physical therapy room; Activities room; Crafts room; Barber/Beauty shop.
Activities Arts and Crafts; Movies; Shopping trips; Dances/Social or cultural gatherings; Discussion groups; Sightseeing trips; Worship services.
Description Facility overlooks St Johns River; very active volunteer program with volunteers working in many areas.

Hodges Boulevard Cluster Homes*
3615 Hodges Blvd, RR 1, Jacksonville, FL, 32224 (904) 241-4173
Licensure Intermediate Care for Mentally Retarded. *Beds* 24.
Ownership Public.

Hospitality Care Center*
1504 Seabreeze Ave, Jacksonville, FL, 32250 (904) 249-7421
Licensure Skilled Care. *Beds* 120. *Certified* Medicaid.
Ownership Proprietary.
Staff RNs 7 (ft); LPNs 13 (ft); Nurses aides 26 (ft).
Languages Spanish

Jacksonville Convalescent Center*
730 College St, Jacksonville, FL, 32204 (904) 354-5589
Licensure Skilled Care. *Beds* 100. *Certified* Medicaid.
Ownership Proprietary.
Staff RNs 3 (ft); LPNs 8 (ft); Nurses aides 23 (ft).

Jacksonville Regency House*
33 W Adams St, Jacksonville, FL, 32202 (904) 358-1832
Licensure Skilled Care. *Beds* 35. *Certified* Medicaid; Medicare.
Ownership Nonprofit.
Languages German, Spanish
Affiliation Presbyterian

Mandarin Manor
10680 Old Saint Augustine Rd, Jacksonville, FL, 32223
Admin James L Dupes. *Medical Dir/Dir of Nursing* Jack E Giddings MD.
Licensure Skilled Care; Intermediate Care. *Beds* 120. *Certified* Medicaid; Medicare.
Ownership Proprietary.
Admissions Requirements Medical examination.
Staff RNs 5 (ft), 7 (pt); LPNs 6 (ft), 8 (pt);

Nurses aides 38 (ft); Physical therapists 1 (ft); Recreational therapists 1 (ft); Occupational therapists 1 (pt); Speech therapists 1 (pt); Activities coordinators 1 (ft); Dietitians 1 (pt).
Facilities Dining room; Physical therapy room; Activities room; Crafts room; Barber/Beauty shop; Library.
Activities Arts and Crafts; Cards; Games; Prayer groups; Movies; Shopping trips; Dances/Social or cultural gatherings.
Description Facility is situated on 5 acres of wooded land with a lake in front; setting provides first-hand contact with nature.

River Garden Hebrew Home for the Aged
1800 Stockton St, Jacksonville, FL, 32204 (904) 389-3665
Admin Elliott Palevsky. *Medical Dir/Dir of Nursing* Lawrence E Geeslin MD.
Licensure Skilled Care; Intermediate Care.
Beds SNF 182; ICF 10. *Certified* Medicaid; Medicare.
Ownership Nonprofit.
Admissions Requirements Medical examination; Physician's request.
Staff Physicians 1 (ft), 2 (pt); RNs 10 (ft), 2 (pt); LPNs 24 (ft); Nurses aides 87 (ft); Physical therapists 2 (ft), 2 (pt); Reality therapists 1 (ft); Recreational therapists 5 (ft); Occupational therapists 1 (pt); Speech therapists 2 (pt); Activities coordinators 1 (ft); Dietitians 1 (pt); Dentists 6 (pt); Ophthalmologists 4 (pt); Audiologists 2 (pt); Social workers 3 (ft).
Languages Spanish, German, Hebrew, Yiddish
Affiliation Jewish
Facilities Dining room; Physical therapy room; Activities room; Chapel; Crafts room; Laundry room; Barber/Beauty shop; Library; Landscaped river front garden with walks; Medical clinic.
Activities Arts and Crafts; Cards; Games; Reading groups; Prayer groups; Movies; Shopping trips; Dances/Social or cultural gatherings.
Description River Garden is a nonprofit geriatric center fully JCAH accredited. Long-term care programs create a rich prosthetic community within gracious surroundings; short-term care programs provide intense rehabilitative care to facilitate a return to independent community living. The full-time care team consists of physicians, nurses, social workers, and activity, and rehabilitation specialists.

Rosewood Haven Nursing Home*
12739 Dunns Creek Rd, Jacksonville, FL, 32218 (904) 757-1216
Licensure Skilled Care; Intermediate Care.
Beds SNF 14; ICF 41.
Ownership Proprietary.

Saint Catherine Laboure Manor
1717 Barrs St, Jacksonville, FL, 32204 (904) 387-0587
Medical Dir/Dir of Nursing Daniel F Fullmen MD.
Licensure Skilled Care. *Beds* 232. *Certified* Medicaid; Medicare.
Ownership Proprietary.
Admissions Requirements Medical examination; Physician's request.
Staff RNs 8 (ft); LPNs 26 (ft), 10 (pt); Orderlies 5 (ft); Nurses aides 89 (ft); Physical therapists 2

(ft); Recreational therapists 3 (ft), 1 (pt); Occupational therapists; Speech therapists; Activities coordinators; Dietitians; Podiatrists.
Languages Spanish, Vietnamese, Iranian
Affiliation Roman Catholic
Facilities Dining room; Physical therapy room; Activities room; Chapel; Crafts room; Laundry room; Barber/Beauty shop; Library.
Activities Arts and Crafts; Cards; Games; Reading groups; Prayer groups; Movies; Shopping trips; Dances/Social or cultural gatherings; Fishing.
Description Facility features full activity schedule, comprehensive rehabilitation, and a total caring atmosphere.

Saint Jude Manor Nursing Home*
2802 Parental Home Rd, Jacksonville, FL, 32216 (904) 721-0088
Licensure Skilled Care. *Beds* 238. *Certified* Medicaid; Medicare.
Ownership Proprietary.
Staff RNs 12 (ft); LPNs 17 (ft); Nurses aides 48 (ft).
Affiliation Roman Catholic

Southside Nursing Center*
40 Acme St, Jacksonville, FL, 32211 (904) 724-5933
Licensure Skilled Care. *Beds* 119. *Certified* Medicaid.
Ownership Proprietary.
Staff RNs 3 (ft); LPNs 5 (ft); Nurses aides 4 (ft); 11 (ft).

Turtle Creek Health Care Center*
11565 Harts Rd, Jacksonville, FL, 32218 (904) 751-1834
Licensure Skilled Care. *Beds* 180. *Certified* Medicaid; Medicare.
Ownership Proprietary.
Staff RNs 6 (ft); LPNs 10 (ft); Nurses aides 38 (ft).

Wesley Manor Nursing Home
State Rd 13 at Julington Creek Rd, Jacksonville, FL, 32223 (904) 262-7300
Medical Dir/Dir of Nursing Max Michael MD.
Licensure Skilled Care. *Beds* 57.
Ownership Nonprofit.
Admissions Requirements Minimum age 62; Medical examination.
Staff Physicians 3 (pt); Physical therapists 1 (pt); Recreational therapists 1 (pt); Occupational therapists 1 (pt); Speech therapists 1 (pt); Activities coordinators 1 (ft); Dietitians 1 (ft); Podiatrists 1 (pt); Audiologists 1 (pt).
Languages Italian
Affiliation Methodist
Facilities Dining room; Physical therapy room; Activities room; Chapel; Crafts room; Laundry room; Barber/Beauty shop; Library.
Activities Arts and Crafts; Cards; Games; Reading groups; Prayer groups; Movies; Shopping trips; Dances/Social or cultural gatherings.
Description Manor is primarily a residential retirement community in a beautiful garden setting on the banks of scenic Julington Creek; residency in the nursing home is provided for those who are residents of the retirement community; all apartments are ground level with their own private patio overlooking a garden.

JASPER

Suwannee Valley Nursing Center*
PO Drawer 1058, Jasper, FL, 32502 (904) 792-1868
Licensure Skilled Care. *Beds* 60. *Certified* Medicaid.
Ownership Proprietary.
Staff RNs 2 (ft); LPNs 6 (ft); Nurses aides 14 (ft).

JUNO BEACH

Waterford Health Center
601 S US Hwy 1, Juno Beach, FL, 33408
Admin Becky Viken.
Licensure Skilled Care. *Beds* 60. *Certified* Medicaid; Medicare.
Ownership Nonprofit.
Admissions Requirements Medical examination.
Staff Physicians 1 (ft); RNs 4 (ft), 1 (pt); LPNs 8 (ft), 1 (pt); Nurses aides 18 (ft), 3 (pt); Physical therapists 1 (ft); Recreational therapists 1 (ft); Activities coordinators 1 (ft); Dietitians 1 (ft).
Facilities Dining room; Physical therapy room; Activities room; Crafts room; Laundry room; Barber/Beauty shop; Library.
Activities Arts and Crafts; Cards; Games; Reading groups; Prayer groups; Movies; Shopping trips; Dances/Social or cultural gatherings.
Description This is a life care retirement community providing a wide range of activities for residents including a skilled nursing facility.

JUPITER

Convalescence Pavilion
1230 S Old Dixie Hwy, Jupiter, FL, 33458 (305) 746-4561
Admin Ann Monroe.
Licensure Skilled Care. *Beds* 120. *Certified* Medicaid; Medicare.
Ownership Nonprofit.
Admissions Requirements Minimum age 21; Medical examination; Physician's request.
Staff Physicians 3 (pt); RNs 12 (ft), 11 (pt); LPNs 7 (ft), 2 (pt); Nurses aides 46 (ft), 5 (pt); Physical therapists 1 (ft); Recreational therapists 1 (ft); Activities coordinators 2 (ft); Dietitians 1 (ft).
Facilities Dining room; Physical therapy room; Activities room; Chapel; Crafts room; Laundry room; Barber/Beauty shop; Library.
Activities Arts and Crafts; Cards; Games; Reading groups; Prayer groups; Movies; Shopping trips; Dances/Social or cultural gatherings.

KISSIMMEE

John Milton Nursing Home*
1120 W Donegan Ave, Kissimmee, FL, 32741 (305) 847-2854
Licensure Skilled Care. *Beds* 149. *Certified* Medicaid.
Ownership Proprietary.
Staff RNs 4 (ft); LPNs 10 (ft).
Languages Spanish

Kissimmee Good Samaritan Nursing Center
1500 Southgate Dr, Kissimmee, FL, 32741
(305) 846-7201
Medical Dir/Dir of Nursing Pedro Gonzales.
Licensure Skilled Care; Intermediate Care.
Beds SNF 142; ICF 28. *Certified* Medicaid.
Ownership Nonprofit.
Admissions Requirements Minimum age 21;
Medical examination; Physician's request.
Staff RNs 3 (ft), 6 (pt); LPNs 11 (ft), 3 (pt);
Orderlies 2 (ft); Nurses aides 66 (ft), 2 (pt);
Activities coordinators 3 (ft).
Languages Spanish, French, German
Affiliation Lutheran
Facilities Dining room; Physical therapy room;
Activities room; Crafts room; Laundry room.
Activities Arts and Crafts; Cards; Games;
Reading groups; Prayer groups; Movies; Shop-
ping trips; Dances/Social or cultural gatherings.

Kissimmee Health Care Center*
320 N Mitchell St, Kissimmee, FL, 32741 (305)
847-7200
Licensure Skilled Care. *Beds* 59. *Certified* Medicare.
Ownership Proprietary.
Staff Nurses aides 17 (ft).

LAKE ALFRED

Lake Alfred Restorium
350 W Haines Blvd, Lake Alfred, FL, 33850
(813) 956-1700
Medical Dir/Dir of Nursing Ernest DiLorenzo.
Licensure Skilled Care. *Beds* 31. *Cer-
tified* Medicaid.
Ownership Proprietary.
Admissions Requirements Minimum age 21;
Medical examination; Physician's request.
Staff RNs 2 (ft), 4 (pt); LPNs 2 (ft), 3 (pt);
Nurses aides 12 (ft), 2 (pt); Physical therapists 1
(pt); Activities coordinators 1 (ft); Dietitians 1
(pt).
Languages Polish
Facilities Dining room; Activities room; Laundry room; Library.
Activities Arts and Crafts; Cards; Games; Pray-
er groups; Movies; Dances/Social or cultural
gatherings.
Description Residents are encouraged to bring
favorite furnishings from home. We allow
choices in daily foods and activities within the
physicians orders. We like independent people.

LAKE CITY

Tanglewood Care Center
2400 S 1st St, Lake City, FL, 32055 (904)
752-7900
Admin Michael J Coretti. *Medical Dir/Dir of
Nursing* Dr L G Landrum.
Licensure Skilled Care; Intermediate Care.
Beds 95. *Certified* Medicaid; Medicare.
Admissions Requirements Minimum age 18;
Medical examination; Physician's request.
Staff RNs 2 (ft), 3 (pt); LPNs 7 (ft), 4 (pt);
Nurses aides 30 (ft), 6 (pt); Physical therapists;
Reality therapists; Recreational therapists;
Occupational therapists; Speech therapists;
Activities coordinators 1 (ft); Dietitians 1 (ft);
Dentists; Ophthalmologists; Podiatrists;

Audiologists.
Languages Russian, German
Affiliation Volunteers of America
Facilities Dining room; Physical therapy room;
Activities room; Chapel; Laundry room; Bar-
ber/Beauty shop; Library.
Activities Arts and Crafts; Cards; Games;
Reading groups; Prayer groups; Movies; Shop-
ping trips; Dances/Social or cultural gatherings.
Description Tanglewood is highly motivated in
community functions such as fair booths, gold-
en age projects, Olustee festival, fund raising,
health fair, and school volunteer programs.
Residents continue their vital link, being supportive members of society.

LAKE PARK

Helen Wilkes Nursing Home*
750 Bayberry Dr, Lake Park, FL, 33403 (305)
844-4396
Licensure Skilled Care. *Beds* 85. *Certified* Medicaid.
Ownership Proprietary.
Staff RNs 9 (ft); LPNs 8 (ft); Nurses aides 21
(ft); 16 (ft).

LAKE WALES

Lake Wales Convalescent Center
730 N Scenic Hwy, Lake Wales, FL, 33853
(813) 676-1512, 5751
Medical Dir/Dir of Nursing Fredrick M Rawl-
ings MD.
Licensure Skilled Care. *Beds* 60. *Cer-
tified* Medicaid.
Ownership Proprietary.
Admissions Requirements Minimum age 16;
Medical examination; Physician's request.
Staff Physicians 5 (pt); RNs 6 (ft); LPNs 8 (ft);
Nurses aides 35 (ft); Physical therapists 1 (pt);
Reality therapists 1 (pt); Recreational therapists
1 (pt); Speech therapists 1 (pt); Activities coordi-
nators 1 (ft); Dietitians 1 (pt); Dentists 1 (pt);
Ophthalmologists 1 (pt); Podiatrists 1 (pt);
Audiologists 1 (pt).
Affiliation Seventh-Day Adventist
Facilities Dining room; Activities room; Crafts
room; Laundry room; Barber/Beauty shop;
Library.
Activities Arts and Crafts; Cards; Games;
Reading groups; Prayer groups; Movies; Shopping trips.
Description Outstanding activities and volunteer program with sing-a-longs, ceramics, hand
crafts, presentations, and personal attention
given to all residents. Along with newly renovated rooms and dining areas, facility has a
courtyard where residents can garden in spring;
family council meeting hosted quarterly.

Ridge Convalescent Center
512 S 11th St, Lake Wales, FL, 33853 (813)
676-8502
Medical Dir/Dir of Nursing Dr Joseph A
Wiltshire.
Licensure Skilled Care. *Beds* 120. *Cer-
tified* Medicaid; Medicare.
Ownership Proprietary.
Admissions Requirements Medical examina-
tion.

Staff RNs 4 (ft); LPNs 9 (ft), 3 (pt); Nurses
aides 40 (ft), 10 (pt); Physical therapists 2 (pt);
Recreational therapists 1 (ft); Speech therapists
1 (pt); Activities coordinators 1 (ft); Dietitians
1 (pt); Podiatrists 1 (pt); Audiologists 1 (pt);
Social workers 1 (ft).
Facilities Dining room; Physical therapy room;
Activities room; Laundry room; Barber/Beauty
shop; Library.
Activities Arts and Crafts; Cards; Games;
Reading groups; Prayer groups; Shopping trips;
Dances/Social or cultural gatherings.

LAKE WORTH

**American Finnish Nursing Home, Finnish-
American Rest Home, Inc**
1800 South Dr, Lake Worth, FL, 33461 (305)
588-4333
Admin Paul P Halenda.
Licensure Intermediate Care. *Beds* 60. *Certi-
fied* Medicaid.
Ownership Nonprofit.
Admissions Requirements Minimum age 55;
Medical examination; Physician's request.
Staff RNs 5 (ft), 1 (pt); LPNs 8 (ft); Orderlies 2
(ft), 1 (pt); Nurses aides 21 (ft), 3 (pt); Physical
therapists 1 (ft); Recreational therapists 2 (ft);
Speech therapists 1 (ft); Activities coordinators
2 (ft); Dietitians 1 (pt).
Languages Finnish, Swedish, Spanish
Facilities Dining room; Physical therapy room;
Activities room; Chapel; Crafts room; Laundry
room; Barber/Beauty shop; Library; Recreation
hall.
Activities Arts and Crafts; Cards; Games;
Reading groups; Prayer groups; Movies; Shopping trips; Dances/Social or cultural gatherings;
Spontaneous and planned parties.
Description The recreation hall is a multipurpose room with a seating capacity of 400, used
for meetings of the corporation, large social
functions, staff meetings, and an occasional
rummage sale; large barbecue area adjoins.

Crest Manor Nursing Center
504 Third Ave S, Lake Worth, FL, 33460 (305)
585-4695
Medical Dir/Dir of Nursing David Kiner DO.
Licensure Skilled Care. *Beds* 71. *Cer-
tified* Medicaid; Medicare.
Ownership Proprietary.
Admissions Requirements Minimum age 16.
Staff RNs 4 (ft), 1 (pt); LPNs 4 (ft), 1 (pt);
Nurses aides 17 (ft), 5 (pt); Physical therapists 1
(pt); Speech therapists 1 (pt); Activities coordi-
nators 1 (ft); Dietitians 1 (pt); Podiatrists 1 (pt).
Languages Spanish, German, Tagalog
Facilities Dining room; Physical therapy room;
Activities room; Crafts room.
Activities Arts and Crafts; Cards; Games;
Reading groups; Movies; Shopping trips; Dan-
ces/Social or cultural gatherings.

Eason Nursing Home
1711 6th Ave S, Lake Worth, FL, 33460 (305)
582-1472
Admin T C Gervais. *Medical Dir/Dir of
Nursing* Robert J Miquel MD.
Licensure Skilled Care. *Beds* 99. *Cer-
tified* Medicaid; Medicare.
Ownership Proprietary.

Admissions Requirements Minimum age 65; Medical examination; Physician's request.
Staff RNs 6 (ft), 1 (pt); LPNs 5 (ft), 1 (pt); Nurses aides 30 (ft), 5 (pt); Activities coordinators 1 (ft), 1 (pt); Dietitians 1 (ft); Social workers 1 (ft).
Languages French, Spanish, Finnish
Facilities Dining room; Activities room; Crafts room; Laundry room; Barber/Beauty shop.
Activities Arts and Crafts; Cards; Games; Prayer groups; Movies; Shopping trips; Dances/Social or cultural gatherings; Picnics; Park outings.
Description Home has been in operation over 50 years; pride taken in having a homey atmosphere; many employees of between 5 and 24 years service. Facility motto is "love is the answer," and staff strives to put it into practice.

Lake Worth Health Care Center*
2501 N "A" St, Lake Worth, FL, 33460 (305) 585-9303
Licensure Skilled Care. *Beds* 162. *Certified* Medicaid.
Ownership Proprietary.
Staff RNs 8 (ft); LPNs 13 (ft); Nurses aides 34 (ft).
Languages Spanish

Mason's Nursing Home
3185 Boutwell Rd, Lake Worth, FL, 33461 (305) 585-6437
Admin Steven I Silverstein. *Medical Dir/Dir of Nursing* Allan Marcus.
Licensure Skilled Care; Intermediate Care. *Beds* 44.
Ownership Proprietary.
Admissions Requirements Minimum age 16; Medical examination; Physician's request.
Staff RNs; LPNs; Orderlies; Nurses aides; Activities coordinators; Dietitians.
Languages Spanish
Facilities Dining room; Physical therapy room; Activities room; Chapel; Crafts room; Laundry room; Barber/Beauty shop; Library.
Activities Arts and Crafts; Cards; Games; Reading groups; Prayer groups; Movies; Shopping trips; Dances/Social or cultural gatherings.
Description Center is a small private skilled nursing and intermediate care facility providing rehabilitation, psychiatric care, activities and social services in a warm suburban setting located in the Palm Beaches.

Medicana Nursing Center
1710 Lucerne Ave, Lake Worth, FL, 33460 (305) 582-5331
Medical Dir/Dir of Nursing Benedicto San Pedro DO.
Licensure Skilled Care. *Beds* 171. *Certified* Medicaid; Medicare.
Ownership Proprietary.
Admissions Requirements Minimum age 16; Medical examination; Physician's request.
Staff RNs 3 (ft), 2 (pt); LPNs 17 (ft), 2 (pt); Orderlies 1 (ft); Nurses aides 35 (ft), 10 (pt); Physical therapists 2 (pt); Recreational therapists 1 (ft); Occupational therapists 1 (ft); Speech therapists 1 (pt); Activities coordinators 1 (ft); Dietitians 1 (pt).
Languages Spanish, Finnish
Facilities Dining room; Physical therapy room; Activities room; Laundry room; Barber/Beauty

shop; Patio; TV lounge.
Activities Arts and Crafts; Cards; Games; Reading groups; Prayer groups; Movies; Shopping trips; Dances/Social or cultural gatherings; Music therapy.
Description Facility offers active participation in foster grandparent program with 4th and 5th grade classes at local school; color TV in every room; van with wheelchair lift for outings.

Palm Beach Care Nursing Home*
3599 Congress Ave, Lake Worth, FL, 33460 (305) 965-8876
Licensure Skilled Care; Intermediate Care. *Beds* SNF 110; ICF 58. *Certified* Medicaid.
Ownership Proprietary.
Staff RNs 6 (ft); LPNs 11 (ft); Nurses aides 32 (ft).
Languages Spanish, Japanese

LAKELAND

Florida United Presbyterian Homes Inc
1919 Lakeland Hills Blvd, Lakeland, FL, 33801 (813) 688-5612
Medical Dir/Dir of Nursing Sergio H Vallejo MD.
Licensure Skilled Care. *Beds* 120. *Certified* Medicaid; Medicare.
Ownership Nonprofit.
Admissions Requirements Physician's request.
Staff Physicians 1 (pt); RNs 9 (ft), 4 (pt); LPNs 7 (ft), 3 (pt); Orderlies 4 (ft); Nurses aides 53 (ft), 2 (pt); Physical therapists 1 (pt); Occupational therapists 1 (pt); Activities coordinators 1 (ft); Dietitians 1 (ft).
Affiliation Presbyterian
Facilities Dining room; Physical therapy room; Activities room; Chapel; Crafts room; Laundry room; Barber/Beauty shop.
Activities Arts and Crafts; Cards; Games; Reading groups; Prayer groups; Movies; Trips for luncheons.
Description Facility is located less than 2 miles from a hospital and in close proximity to the Watson Clinic and area doctors, operated by a Christian organization. Residents and staff treated with very much consideration.

Johnson Health Center—Florida United Presbyterian Homes Inc
16 Lake Hunter Dr, Lakeland, FL, 33803 (813) 688-5612
Medical Dir/Dir of Nursing Sergio Valleljo MD.
Licensure Skilled Care. *Beds* 120. *Certified* Medicaid.
Ownership Nonprofit.
Admissions Requirements Medical examination; Physician's request.
Staff RNs; LPNs; Orderlies; Nurses aides; Physical therapists; Reality therapists; Recreational therapists; Occupational therapists; Speech therapists; Activities coordinators.
Affiliation Presbyterian
Facilities Dining room; Physical therapy room; Activities room; Chapel; Barber/Beauty shop; Library.
Activities Arts and Crafts; Cards; Games; Reading groups; Prayer groups; Shopping trips.

Lakeland Convalescent Center*
610 E Bella Vista Dr, Lakeland, FL, 33805 (813) 688-8591
Licensure Skilled Care. *Beds* 120. *Certified* Medicaid; Medicare.
Ownership Proprietary.
Staff RNs 6 (ft); LPNs 10 (ft); Nurses aides 26 (ft); 15 (ft).

Lakeland Health Care Center*
1500 Kennedy Blvd, Lakeland, FL, 33802 (813) 858-4402
Licensure Skilled Care. *Beds* 240. *Certified* Medicaid; Medicare.
Ownership Proprietary.
Staff RNs 12 (ft); LPNs 10 (ft); Nurses aides 53 (ft); 46 (ft).

LANTANA

Atlantis Convalescent Center
6026 Old Congress Rd, Lantana, FL, 33462 (305) 964-4430
Admin Barry Cohen. *Medical Dir/Dir of Nursing* Richard Sulman DO.
Licensure Skilled Care. *Beds* 120. *Certified* Medicaid; Medicare.
Ownership Proprietary.
Admissions Requirements Minimum age 55; Medical examination; Physician's request.
Staff RNs 5 (ft); LPNs 20 (ft); Orderlies 3 (ft); Nurses aides 36 (ft); Physical therapists 3 (ft); Speech therapists 1 (ft); Activities coordinators 2 (ft); Dietitians 1 (ft); Dentists 1 (ft); Podiatrists 2 (ft); Audiologists 1 (ft).
Languages Spanish, German, French
Facilities Dining room; Physical therapy room; Activities room; Crafts room; Laundry room; Barber/Beauty shop; Library; Outdoor patios and enclosed patio; Pharmacy services.
Activities Arts and Crafts; Cards; Games; Reading groups; Prayer groups; Movies; Shopping trips; Dances/Social or cultural gatherings; Wheelchair exercises; Bingo; Music therapy; Reality orientation.
Description Modern 6-year-old facility owned and operated by National Health Care Affiliates, Buffalo, NY; expanded volunteer program; many community activities; country setting; therapeutic menus; nondenominational services provided for all religions.

LARGO

Oak Manor Nursing Center
3500 Oak Manor Ln, Largo, FL, 33540 (813) 581-9427
Medical Dir/Dir of Nursing Paul Straub MD.
Licensure Skilled Care. *Beds* 180. *Certified* Medicare.
Ownership Proprietary.
Admissions Requirements Physician's request.
Staff RNs 18 (ft), 3 (pt); LPNs 10 (ft), 4 (pt); Nurses aides 70 (ft), 13 (pt); Physical therapists 1 (ft), 1 (pt); Recreational therapists 1 (ft), 1 (pt); Occupational therapists 1 (ft); Speech therapists 1 (ft); Dietitians 1 (ft).
Facilities Dining room; Physical therapy room; Activities room; Crafts room; Laundry room; Barber/Beauty shop; Library.

Activities Arts and Crafts; Cards; Games; Reading groups; Prayer groups; Movies; Shopping trips; Dances/Social or cultural gatherings.

Tierra Pines Convalescent Center
7625 Ulmerton Rd, Largo, FL, 33540
Admin John P Williams.
Licensure Skilled Care. *Beds* 120. *Certified* Medicaid; Medicare.
Ownership Proprietary.
Admissions Requirements Minimum age 16; Medical examination; Physician's request.
Staff Physicians 2 (pt); RNs 6 (ft); LPNs 12 (ft); Nurses aides 43 (ft); Physical therapists; Reality therapists; Recreational therapists 2 (ft); Occupational therapists; Speech therapists; Activities coordinators 1 (ft); Dietitians; Dentists; Ophthalmologists; Podiatrists; Audiologists.
Facilities Dining room; Physical therapy room; Activities room; Crafts room; Laundry room; Barber/Beauty shop; Library.
Activities Arts and Crafts; Cards; Games; Movies; Dances/Social or cultural gatherings.

Wrights Nursing Home
11300 110th Ave N, Largo, FL, 33540 (813) 896-3651
Admin Darlene Kreuger. *Medical Dir/Dir of Nursing* Fred Leslie DO.
Licensure Skilled Care. *Beds* 60.
Ownership Proprietary.
Admissions Requirements Physician's request.
Staff RNs 5 (ft), 9 (pt); LPNs 2 (pt); Nurses aides 16 (ft), 9 (pt); Activities coordinators 1 (ft); Dietitians 1 (pt); Dentists 1 (pt); Podiatrists 1 (pt).
Languages Spanish
Facilities Dining room; Physical therapy room; Activities room; Chapel; Crafts room; Laundry room; Library.
Activities Arts and Crafts; Cards; Games; Reading groups; Shopping trips.
Description Staff has an unusually caring attitude. Yearly tea for volunteers and Thanksgiving dinner for families. Facility is decorated with antiques.

LAUDERDALE LAKES

Aviva Manor
3370 NW 47th Terrace, Lauderdale Lakes, FL, 33319 (305) 733-0655
Medical Dir/Dir of Nursing Arturo Blanco MD.
Licensure Skilled Care. *Beds* 120. *Certified* Medicare.
Ownership Proprietary.
Staff Physicians 4 (pt); RNs 3 (ft), 5 (pt); LPNs 6 (ft), 6 (pt); Nurses aides 43 (ft), 3 (pt); Reality therapists 1 (pt); Recreational therapists 2 (ft); Occupational therapists 1 (pt); Activities coordinators 1 (ft); Dietitians 1 (ft), 1 (pt); Dentists 1 (pt); Podiatrists 1 (pt).
Affiliation Jewish
Facilities Dining room; Physical therapy room; Activities room; Chapel; Crafts room; Laundry room; Barber/Beauty shop; Library; TV lounge.
Activities Arts and Crafts; Cards; Games; Reading groups; Prayer groups; Movies; Shopping trips; Dances/Social or cultural gatherings; Bread baking; Yiddish classes.

Description At Aviva Manor, we believe that nursing homes should be centers for learning and living. Our goal is to return our patients to their loved ones, better equipped to enjoy their days without being totally dependent on others. We do this through comprehensive rehabilitation, individual patient care, an intensive daily living training course, and specialized therapeutic activities, including all Jewish holidays. At Aviva Manor, we care.

Saint Johns Nursing and Rehabilitation Center
3075 NW 35th Ave, Lauderdale Lakes, FL, 33311 (305) 739-6233
Medical Dir/Dir of Nursing Mark Reiner MD.
Licensure Skilled Care. *Beds* 180. *Certified* Medicaid; Medicare.
Ownership Nonprofit.
Admissions Requirements Minimum age 18.
Staff RNs 16 (ft), 9 (pt); LPNs 18 (ft), 4 (pt); Nurses aides 73 (ft), 12 (pt); Physical therapists 7 (ft); Recreational therapists 3 (ft); Occupational therapists 5 (ft), 1 (pt); Activities coordinators 1 (ft); Dietitians 2 (ft).
Languages Spanish
Affiliation Roman Catholic
Facilities Dining room; Physical therapy room; Activities room; Chapel; Crafts room; Laundry room; Barber/Beauty shop; Library.
Activities Arts and Crafts; Cards; Games; Reading groups; Prayer groups; Movies; Dances/Social or cultural gatherings.

LECANTO

Franklin Cottage
Rt 1, Box 1000, Lecanto, FL, 32661 (904) 795-6808
Licensure Intermediate Care for Mentally Retarded. *Beds* 8.
Ownership Nonprofit.
Staff Physicians; Dietitians; Nurses aides.

Key Pine Village*
Rt 1, 1 Rainbow Circle, Lecanto, FL, 32661 (904) 746-3262
Licensure Intermediate Care for Mentally Retarded. *Beds* 48.
Ownership Proprietary.

LEESBURG

Lake Memorial Nursing Home*
400 E Dixie Ave, Leesburg, FL, 32748 (904) 787-2412
Licensure Skilled Care. *Beds* 36. *Certified* Medicaid.
Ownership Public.
Staff RNs 2 (ft); LPNs 3 (ft); Nurses aides 12 (ft).

Leesburg Healthcare Center
2000 Edgewood Ave, Leesburg, FL, 32748 (904) 787-3545
Medical Dir/Dir of Nursing Dr George Engelhard.
Licensure Skilled Care. *Beds* 116. *Certified* Medicaid; Medicare.
Ownership Proprietary.
Staff RNs; LPNs; Orderlies; Nurses aides; Physical therapists; Recreational therapists;

Speech therapists; Activities coordinators.
Facilities Dining room; Physical therapy room; Activities room; Laundry room; Barber/Beauty shop; Library.
Activities Arts and Crafts; Cards; Games; Reading groups; Prayer groups; Movies; Dances/Social or cultural gatherings.
Description Facility is dedicated to improving the quality of life for residents by offering quality nursing care, physical therapy, and speech therapy. Facility also has an active social services and activities department which is involved with programs such as adopt-a-grandparent.

Leesburg Nursing Center*
715 E Dixie Ave, Leesburg, FL, 33728 (904) 728-3020
Licensure Skilled Care. *Beds* 85. *Certified* Medicaid; Medicare.
Ownership Proprietary.
Staff Nurses aides 8 (ft); 9 (ft).

LONGWOOD

Longwood Health Care Center
1512 Grant St, Longwood, FL, 32750 (305) 339-9200
Medical Dir/Dir of Nursing David Parsons MD.
Licensure Skilled Care. *Beds* 120. *Certified* Medicaid; Medicare.
Ownership Proprietary.
Admissions Requirements Minimum age 18; Medical examination; Physician's request.
Staff Physicians 20 (ft); RNs 6 (ft); LPNs 9 (ft), 4 (pt); Nurses aides 33 (ft); Physical therapists 1 (ft); Speech therapists 1 (ft); Activities coordinators 1 (ft); Dentists 1 (ft); Ophthalmologists 1 (ft); Podiatrists 1 (ft); Audiologists 1 (ft).
Facilities Dining room; Physical therapy room; Activities room; Crafts room; Laundry room; Barber/Beauty shop.
Activities Arts and Crafts; Games; Reading groups; Prayer groups; Movies; Shopping trips.
Description Facility is located in a lovely section of Longwood directly across the street from Lake Daisy in a quiet section with light traffic.

LUTZ

Woodlands Nursing Center
13806 N 46th St, Lutz, FL, 33549 (813) 977-4214
Medical Dir/Dir of Nursing Dr Tim Seehausen.
Licensure Skilled Care. *Beds* 120. *Certified* Medicaid; Medicare.
Ownership Proprietary.
Admissions Requirements Minimum age 21; Medical examination; Physician's request.
Staff RNs 4 (ft), 1 (pt); LPNs 9 (ft), 2 (pt); Orderlies 2 (ft); Nurses aides 57 (ft), 6 (pt); Activities coordinators 1 (ft).
Facilities Dining room; Physical therapy room; Activities room; Crafts room; Laundry room; Barber/Beauty shop.
Activities Arts and Crafts; Cards; Games; Reading groups; Prayer groups; Movies; Shopping trips; Dances/Social or cultural gatherings.

MACCLENNY

Baker County Nursing Home*
159 N 3rd St, MacClenny, FL, 32063 (904)
259-3151
Licensure Skilled Care; Intermediate Care.
Beds 68. *Certified* Medicaid; Medicare.
Ownership Public.
Staff RNs 3 (ft); LPNs 9 (ft); Nurses aides 12
(ft); 13 (ft).
Languages Spanish, French, Tagalog

MARIANNA

Marianna Convalescent Center*
PO Drawer L, Marianna, FL, 32446 (904)
482-8091
Licensure Skilled Care. *Beds* 111. *Certified* Medicaid.
Ownership Public.
Staff RNs 8 (ft); LPNs 19 (ft); Nurses aides 38
(ft).

Sunland—Marianna Facility I*
PO Box 852, Hwy 71, Marianna, FL, 32446
(904) 526-2123
Licensure Intermediate Care for Mentally
Retarded. *Beds* 115.
Ownership Public.

Sunland—Marianna Facility II*
PO Box 852, Marianna, FL, 32446 (904)
526-2123
Licensure Intermediate Care for Mentally
Retarded. *Beds* 60. *Certified* Medicaid.
Ownership Public.
Staff RNs 3 (ft); LPNs 7 (ft); Nurses aides 32
(ft); 11 (ft).

MELBOURNE

Carnegie Gardens Nursing Home*
1415 S Hickory St, Melbourne, FL, 32901 (305)
723-1321
Licensure Skilled Care. *Beds* 138. *Certified* Medicaid; Medicare.
Ownership Proprietary.
Staff RNs 12 (ft); LPNs 11 (ft); Nurses aides 25
(ft); 24 (ft).

Florida Convalescent Home
516 E Sheridan Rd, Melbourne, FL, 32901
(305) 727-0984
Medical Dir/Dir of Nursing Timothy Povier
MD.
Licensure Skilled Care. *Beds* 60. *Certified* Medicaid; Medicare.
Ownership Nonprofit.
Admissions Requirements Minimum age 16.
Staff RNs 7 (ft); LPNs 5 (ft); Nurses aides 18
(ft); Activities coordinators 1 (ft); Dietitians 1
(ft).
Facilities Dining room; Activities room; Laundry room.
Activities Arts and Crafts; Games; Prayer
groups; Movies; Shopping trips.

Medic-Home Health Center of Melbourne
1420 S Oak St, Melbourne, FL, 32901 (305)
723-3215
Medical Dir/Dir of Nursing W S Lanford MD.

Licensure Skilled Care. *Beds* 110. *Certified* Medicaid.
Ownership Proprietary.
Staff Physicians 1 (ft), 2 (pt); RNs 9 (ft), 6 (pt);
LPNs 5 (ft), 2 (pt); Nurses aides 32 (ft), 7 (pt);
Physical therapists 1 (pt); Speech therapists 1
(pt); Activities coordinators 1 (ft); Dietitians 1
(ft); Dentists 1 (pt).
Facilities Dining room; Activities room; Chapel; Laundry room; Barber/Beauty shop.
Activities Arts and Crafts; Games; Reading
groups; Prayer groups; Movies; Shopping trips;
Dances/Social or cultural gatherings.

MERRITT ISLAND

Merritt Manor Nursing Home*
125 Alma Blvd, Merritt Island, FL, 32952
(305) 453-0202
Licensure Skilled Care. *Beds* 120. *Certified* Medicaid; Medicare.
Ownership Proprietary.
Staff RNs 4 (ft); LPNs 9 (ft); Nurses aides 12
(ft); 12 (ft).

MIAMI

Anne E Anderson Health Center*
8400 NW 25th Ave, Miami, FL, 33147 (305)
836-4382
Licensure Skilled Care. *Beds* 40. *Certified* Medicaid; Medicare.
Ownership Nonprofit.
Staff RNs 7 (ft); LPNs 6 (ft); Nurses aides 16
(ft).
Languages Spanish
Affiliation Evangelical Covenant Church

Arch Creek Nursing Home*
12505 NE 16th Ave, Miami, FL, 33161 (305)
891-1710
Licensure Skilled Care; Intermediate Care.
Beds 110. *Certified* Medicaid; Medicare.
Ownership Proprietary.
Staff RNs 5 (ft); LPNs 13 (ft); Nurses aides 26
(ft).
Languages Spanish, Russian, Yiddish, French

Ashley Manor Care Center
8785 NW 32nd Ave, Miami, FL, 33147 (305)
691-5711
Admin E Reneé Gibson. *Medical Dir/Dir of
Nursing* Ramon Alvarez MD.
Licensure Skilled Care. *Beds* 120. *Certified* Medicaid.
Ownership Proprietary.
Admissions Requirements Medical examination.
Staff RNs 5 (ft); LPNs 5 (ft), 8 (pt); Orderlies 1
(ft); Nurses aides 39 (ft), 3 (pt); Physical therapists 1 (pt); Reality therapists 1 (pt);
Recreational therapists 1 (ft); Speech therapists
1 (pt); Activities coordinators 1 (ft); Dietitians
1 (pt); Dentists 1 (pt); Ophthalmologists 1 (pt);
Podiatrists 1 (pt).
Languages French, Yiddish, Spanish, Creole
Facilities Dining room; Activities room; Crafts
room; Laundry room; Barber/Beauty shop.
Activities Arts and Crafts; Cards; Games;
Reading groups; Prayer groups; Movies; Shopping trips; Dances/Social or cultural gatherings.

Description Facility features enclosed and open
picnic and outside social areas, is easily accessible to shopping areas for those who are able to
go out on pass, and has large, ample parking
area that is lighted.

Coral Gables Convalescent Home
7060 SW 8th St, Miami, FL, 33144 (305)
261-1363
Licensure Skilled Care. *Beds* 87. *Certified* Medicare.
Ownership Proprietary.
Staff RNs 7 (ft), 4 (pt); LPNs 3 (ft), 3 (pt);
Nurses aides 31 (ft), 3 (pt); Physical therapists 1
(pt); Reality therapists 1 (pt); Recreational therapists 4 (pt); Speech therapists 1 (pt); Activities
coordinators 1 (ft); Dietitians 1 (pt).
Languages Spanish, German, Yiddish
Facilities Dining room; Physical therapy room;
Activities room; Crafts room; Laundry room;
Barber/Beauty shop; Library.
Activities Arts and Crafts; Cards; Games;
Reading groups; Prayer groups; Movies.
Description Facility has been family owned and
operated since 1958, the finest in individual
care; outdoor and indoor gardens; chefs make
cakes, soups, and meals from scratch.

East Ridge Retirement Village Health Center
19301 SW 87th Ave, Miami, FL, 33157 (305)
238-2623
Medical Dir/Dir of Nursing Chauncey Stone
MD.
Licensure Skilled Care. *Beds* 60.
Ownership Nonprofit.
Admissions Requirements Minimum age 62;
Medical examination.
Staff Physicians 4 (pt); RNs 3 (ft), 1 (pt); LPNs
8 (ft), 1 (pt); Nurses aides 15 (ft), 7 (pt); Speech
therapists 1 (pt); Activities coordinators 1 (ft);
Dietitians 1 (ft); Podiatrists 1 (pt); Audiologists
1 (pt); Dermatologist 1 (pt).
Languages Polish, Spanish
Facilities Dining room; Physical therapy room;
Activities room; Chapel; Crafts room; Laundry
room; Barber/Beauty shop; Library.
Activities Arts and Crafts; Cards; Games;
Reading groups; Prayer groups; Movies; Dances/Social or cultural gatherings.
Description Facility is part of a life care retirement village located 10 miles south of Coral
Gables in a 76 acre park-like setting. It is owned
by the residents and managed by Life Care Services Corp.

El Ponce De Leon Convalescent Center*
335 SW 12th Ave, Miami, FL, 33130 (305)
545-0673
Licensure Skilled Care. *Beds* 147. *Certified* Medicaid; Medicare.
Ownership Proprietary.
Staff RNs 21 (ft); LPNs 2 (ft); Nurses aides 32
(ft).
Languages Spanish, French

Fair Havens Center
201 Curtiss Pkwy, Miami, FL, 33166 (305)
887-1565
Medical Dir/Dir of Nursing Dr James Hudson.
Admissions Requirements Minimum age 18;
Medical examination.
Staff Physicians 10 (pt); RNs 12 (ft); LPNs 26
(ft); Orderlies 1 (ft); Nurses aides 90 (ft);

Physical therapists 4 (pt); Reality therapists 3 (ft); Recreational therapists 3 (ft); Occupational therapists 1 (pt); Speech therapists 1 (pt); Activities coordinators 1 (ft); Dietitians 2 (pt); Ophthalmologists 1 (pt); Podiatrists 3 (pt); Audiologists 1 (pt).
Affiliation Lutheran
Facilities Dining room; Physical therapy room; Activities room; Chapel; Crafts room; Laundry room; Barber/Beauty shop; Library.
Activities Arts and Crafts; Cards; Games; Reading groups; Movies; Shopping trips; Dances/Social or cultural gatherings.
Description This facility provides 3 levels of care in a historic building in Miami Springs; gardens are spacious and were originally landscaped by David Fairchild.

Floridean Nursing Home*
47 NW 32nd Pl, Miami, FL, 33125 (305) 649-2911
Licensure Skilled Care. *Beds* 52. *Certified* Medicaid.
Ownership Proprietary.
Staff RNs 3 (ft); LPNs 8 (ft); Nurses aides 19 (ft); 9 (ft).

Green Briar Nursing Center
9820 N Kendall Dr, Miami, FL, 33176 (305) 271-6311
Licensure Skilled Care. *Beds* 203. *Certified* Medicare.
Ownership Proprietary.
Staff Physicians; Dietitians; Nurses aides.
Languages Spanish, French, Yiddish
Activities Prayer groups; Arts and Crafts; Shopping trips.

Human Resources Health Center
2500 NW 22nd Ave, Miami, FL, 33142 (305) 638-6661
Medical Dir/Dir of Nursing John Cleveland.
Licensure Skilled Care. *Beds* 196. *Certified* Medicaid; Medicare.
Ownership Public.
Staff Physicians 3 (pt); RNs 14 (ft); LPNs 23 (ft); Nurses aides 64 (ft); Recreational therapists 1 (ft); Speech therapists 1 (pt); Dietitians 1 (ft); Podiatrists 1 (pt); Nurse practitioner 1 (ft); Psychiatrist 1 (ft).
Languages Spanish, French, Hebrew
Facilities Dining room; Physical therapy room; Activities room; Chapel; Crafts room; Laundry room; Barber/Beauty shop.
Activities Arts and Crafts; Cards; Games; Reading groups; Prayer groups; Movies; Shopping trips; Dances/Social or cultural gatherings; Adopt-a-grandparent.

Jackson Heights Nursing Home*
1404 NW 22nd St, Miami, FL, 33142 (305) 325-1050
Licensure Skilled Care. *Beds* 298. *Certified* Medicaid; Medicare.
Ownership Proprietary.
Staff RNs 12 (ft); LPNs 14 (ft); Nurses aides 14 (ft); Nurses aides 107 (ft); 41 (ft).
Languages Spanish, French, Tagalog

Jackson Manor Nursing Home
1861 NW 8th Ave, Miami, FL, 33136 (305) 324-0280
Licensure Skilled Care. *Beds* 168. *Certified* Medicaid; Medicare.
Ownership Proprietary.
Staff Physicians; Dietitians; Nurses aides.
Languages Spanish, French
Activities Prayer groups; Arts and Crafts; Shopping trips.

La Posada Convalescent Home
5271 SW 8th St, Miami, FL, 33134 (305) 448-4963
Licensure Skilled Care. *Beds* 54. *Certified* Medicaid.
Ownership Proprietary.
Admissions Requirements Minimum age 65.
Staff Nurses aides 8 (ft); Dietitians 4 (ft).
Languages Spanish
Facilities Dining room; Activities room.
Activities Arts and Crafts; Cards; Games; Reading groups; Prayer groups; Movies; Shopping trips; Dances/Social or cultural gatherings.

MACtown Inc
6250 NE 1st Pl, Miami, FL, 33138 (305) 758-2758
Medical Dir/Dir of Nursing Dr Hadley.
Licensure Intermediate Care for Mentally Retarded. *Beds* 56.
Ownership Nonprofit.
Admissions Requirements Minimum age 18; Medical examination.
Staff Physicians 2 (pt); RNs 1 (pt); LPNs 3 (ft), 1 (pt); Physical therapists 1 (pt); Reality therapists 1 (ft); Recreational therapists 3 (ft); Occupational therapists 1 (pt); Speech therapists 1 (ft); Dietitians 1 (pt); Podiatrists 1 (pt).
Facilities Dining room; Physical therapy room; Activities room; Laundry room; Workshop.
Activities Arts and Crafts; Cards; Games; Movies; Shopping trips; Dances/Social or cultural gatherings; Special Olympics.
Description MACtown creates an atmosphere where adults can live, learn, work, and preserve their individual dignity and integrity. They can grow and develop skills, the concept of self-achievement, and the rights of citizenship that lead to a more normal and self-fulfilling life.

Miami Jewish Home for the Aged*
151 NE 52nd St, Miami, FL, 33137 (305) 751-8626
Licensure Skilled Care; Intermediate Care.
Beds 332. *Certified* Medicaid; Medicare.
Ownership Nonprofit.
Staff RNs 12 (ft); LPNs 26 (ft); Nurses aides 89 (ft).
Languages Spanish, German, Yiddish, Russian, French
Affiliation Jewish

North Shore Nursing Home
9380 NW 7th Ave, Miami, FL, 33150 (305) 759-8711
Medical Dir/Dir of Nursing Stanley Roth MD.
Licensure Skilled Care. *Beds* 101. *Certified* Medicare.
Ownership Proprietary.
Staff RNs 2 (ft), 2 (pt); LPNs 12 (ft), 4 (pt); Nurses aides 26 (ft); Recreational therapists 1 (ft); Activities coordinators 1 (ft); Social workers 1 (ft).
Languages Spanish
Facilities Dining room; Physical therapy room; Barber/Beauty shop.

Activities Arts and Crafts; Cards; Games; Reading groups; Prayer groups; Movies; Shopping trips; Dances/Social or cultural gatherings; Picnics.
Description Facility has an outstanding program involving community personnel; involved with the Dade County public schools and several local churches.

Palmetto Extended Care Facility*
7600 SW 8th St, Miami, FL, 33144 (305) 261-2525
Licensure Skilled Care; Intermediate Care.
Beds 85. *Certified* Medicaid; Medicare.
Ownership Proprietary.
Staff RNs 3 (ft); LPNs 8 (ft); Nurses aides 21 (ft); 16 (ft).
Languages Spanish, Tagalog, Italian, Japanese

Palms Convalescent Home*
14601 NE 16th Ave, Miami, FL, 33161 (305) 945-7631
Licensure Skilled Care. *Beds* 85. *Certified* Medicaid.
Ownership Proprietary.
Staff RNs 3 (ft); LPNs 15 (ft); Nurses aides 18 (ft).
Languages Spanish, Hungarian, German, Yiddish, Polish

Perdue Medical Center*
2001 E Ridge Village Dr, Miami, FL, 33157 (305) 233-8931
Licensure Skilled Care. *Beds* 197. *Certified* Medicaid; Medicare.
Ownership Public.
Staff RNs 12 (ft); LPNs 10 (ft); Nurses aides 55 (ft).
Languages Spanish

Pines Nursing Home
301 NE 141st St, Miami, FL, 33161 (305) 893-1102
Medical Dir/Dir of Nursing Dr Mark A LaPorta.
Licensure Skilled Care. *Beds* 46. *Certified* Medicaid; Medicare.
Ownership Proprietary.
Staff Physicians 5 (pt); RNs 2 (ft); LPNs 5 (ft), 3 (pt); Nurses aides 42 (ft), 4 (pt); Physical therapists 1 (pt); Recreational therapists 1 (pt); Occupational therapists 1 (pt); Speech therapists 1 (pt); Activities coordinators 1 (pt); Dietitians 1 (ft); Dentists 1 (pt); Ophthalmologists 1 (pt); Podiatrists 1 (pt).
Languages French, Hatian, Hungarian, German, Russian, Polish, Spanish, Yiddish, Hebrew
Facilities Dining room; Activities room; Crafts room; Laundry room; Library.
Activities Arts and Crafts; Cards; Games; Reading groups; Prayer groups; Movies.

Riverside Care Center
899 NW 4th St, Miami, FL, 33128 (305) 326-1236
Medical Dir/Dir of Nursing Water J Demaio MD.
Licensure Skilled Care. *Beds* 80. *Certified* Medicaid; Medicare.
Ownership Proprietary.
Admissions Requirements Minimum age 21.
Staff RNs 2 (ft); LPNs 6 (ft), 6 (pt); Orderlies 1

(ft); Recreational therapists 1 (ft), 1 (pt); Activities coordinators 1 (ft), 1 (pt); Dietitians 1 (pt); Dentists 1 (pt); Podiatrists 1 (pt).
Languages Spanish
Facilities Dining room; Activities room; Crafts room; Laundry room; Barber/Beauty shop.
Activities Arts and Crafts; Cards; Games; Reading groups; Prayer groups; Movies; Shopping trips; Dances/Social or cultural gatherings; Special holiday dinners.
Description Our small 80-bed facility is involved in community resources. We offer a bilingual nursing services.

Snapper Creek Nursing Home*
9200 SW 87th Ave, Miami, FL, 33176 (305) 271 1313
Licensure Skilled Care. *Beds* 110. *Certified* Medicaid.
Ownership Proprietary.
Staff RNs 10 (ft); LPNs 7 (ft); Nurses aides 28 (ft).
Languages Spanish, Italian

MIAMI BEACH

Four Freedoms Manor*
42 Collins Ave, Miami Beach, FL, 33139 (305) 672-1771
Licensure Skilled Care. *Beds* 230. *Certified* Medicaid; Medicare.
Ownership Proprietary.
Staff RNs 14 (ft); LPNs 12 (ft); Nurses aides 51 (ft).

Miami Beach Hebrew Home for the Aged*
320 Collins Ave, Miami Beach, FL, 33139 (305) 672-6464
Licensure Skilled Care. *Beds* 104. *Certified* Medicaid; Medicare.
Ownership Nonprofit.
Staff RNs 8 (ft); LPNs 4 (ft); Nurses aides 53 (ft).
Languages Yiddish, Spanish, French
Affiliation Jewish

Miami Beach Nursing Home*
550 9th St, Miami Beach, FL, 33139 (305) 531-3321
Licensure Skilled Care. *Beds* 196. *Certified* Medicaid; Medicare.
Ownership Proprietary.
Staff RNs 5 (ft); LPNs 9 (ft); Nurses aides 57 (ft).
Languages French, Spanish

MILTON

Santa Rosa Convalescent Center
500 Broad St, Milton, FL, 32570 (904) 623-4661
Medical Dir/Dir of Nursing Rufus Thames.
Licensure Skilled Care. *Beds* 120. *Certified* Medicaid; Medicare.
Ownership Proprietary.
Admissions Requirements Minimum age 50; Medical examination; Physician's request.
Staff Physicians 6 (pt); RNs 4 (ft), 1 (pt); LPNs 8 (ft), 5 (pt); Nurses aides 36 (ft), 15 (pt); Physical therapists 1 (pt); Speech therapists 1 (pt); Activities coordinators 1 (ft); Dietitians 1

(pt); Dentists 1 (pt); Podiatrists 1 (pt).
Languages French
Facilities Dining room; Physical therapy room; Activities room; Chapel; Laundry room; Barber/Beauty shop; Library.
Activities Arts and Crafts; Games; Reading groups; Prayer groups; Dances/Social or cultural gatherings.

MONTICELLO

Jefferson Nursing Center
PO Box 477, Monticello, FL, 32344 (904) 997-2313
Licensure Skilled Care. *Beds* 60. *Certified* Medicaid.
Ownership Proprietary.
Staff RNs 1 (ft), 1 (pt); LPNs 3 (ft), 2 (pt); Nurses aides 15 (ft), 5 (pt); Recreational therapists 1 (ft), 1 (pt); Activities coordinators 1 (ft); Dietitians 1 (pt).
Facilities Dining room; Activities room; Crafts room; Laundry room; Barber/Beauty shop.
Activities Arts and Crafts; Games; Reading groups; Prayer groups; Movies; Shopping trips.

MOUNT DORA

Mount Dora Healthcare Center
1550 Brown St, Mount Dora, FL, 32757 (904) 383-4161
Medical Dir/Dir of Nursing C Robert Crow MD.
Licensure Skilled Care. *Beds* 116. *Certified* Medicaid; Medicare.
Ownership Proprietary.
Admissions Requirements Minimum age 16; Medical examination; Physician's request.
Staff RNs 4 (ft), 1 (pt); LPNs 14 (ft), 2 (pt); Nurses aides 37 (ft); Activities coordinators 1 (ft), 1 (pt).
Languages Spanish
Facilities Dining room; Physical therapy room; Activities room; Chapel; Crafts room; Laundry room; Barber/Beauty shop; Library.
Activities Arts and Crafts; Cards; Games; Reading groups; Prayer groups; Movies; Shopping trips; Dances/Social or cultural gatherings.
Description Facility features privacy areas, large covered patios, a 15-passenger van with lift for taking residents to appointments and outings, rooms facing a large atrium with all rooms having outside windows, and picnics and entertainment outside of the facility. Residents may have their own pets, if approved by veterinarians.

NAPLES

Americana Health Care Center*
3601 Lakewood Blvd, Naples, FL, 33940 (813) 261-2188
Beds 120.
Ownership Proprietary.

Golf Drive Residence*
777 9th St N, Naples, FL, 33940 (813) 261-8126
Licensure Skilled Care; Intermediate Care.
Beds SNF 83; ICF 31. *Certified* Medicaid; Medicare.

Ownership Proprietary.
Staff RNs 8 (ft); LPNs 11 (ft); Nurses aides 23 (ft).
Languages Spanish

Greater Naples Care Center*
2900 12th St N, Naples, FL, 33940 (813) 261-2554
Licensure Skilled Care. *Beds* 99. *Certified* Medicaid.
Ownership Proprietary.
Staff RNs 7 (ft); LPNs 7 (ft); Nurses aides 21 (ft).
Languages Spanish

The Moorings Park
111 Moorings Park Dr, Naples, FL, 33940
Admin Leo Fallon. *Medical Dir/Dir of Nursing* Maurice Lieker.
Licensure Skilled Care. *Beds* 60. *Certified* Medicare.
Ownership Nonprofit.
Admissions Requirements Medical examination; Physician's request.
Staff Physicians 1 (ft); RNs 3 (ft), 3 (pt); LPNs 3 (ft), 2 (pt); Orderlies 2 (ft); Nurses aides 20 (ft), 9 (pt); Physical therapists 1 (ft); Speech therapists 1 (pt); Activities coordinators 1 (ft); Dietitians 1 (pt); Dentists 1 (pt); Podiatrists 1 (pt).
Affiliation Presbyterian
Facilities Dining room; Physical therapy room; Activities room; Laundry room; Barber/Beauty shop.
Activities Arts and Crafts; Games; Reading groups; Prayer groups; Movies; Shopping trips; Dances/Social or cultural gatherings; Short trips.
Description Once a month approximately 15 patients enjoy a 2-hour luncheon cruise aboard the Tin City Queen through Naples Bay to the inlet of the Gulf of Mexico.

NEW PORT RICHEY

Heather Hill Nursing Home*
1151 E Kentucky Ave, New Port Richey, FL, 33552 (813) 849-6939
Licensure Skilled Care. *Beds* 120. *Certified* Medicaid; Medicare.
Ownership Proprietary.
Staff RNs 7 (ft); LPNs 11 (ft); Nurses aides 36 (ft).
Languages German, Greek, Spanish

Richey Manor Nursing Home
505 Indiana Ave, New Port Richey, FL, 33552 (813) 849-7555
Medical Dir/Dir of Nursing Dr Sells MD and Dr Montaldi DO.
Licensure Skilled Care. *Beds* 119. *Certified* Medicaid; Medicare.
Ownership Proprietary.
Admissions Requirements Minimum age 16; Medical examination; Physician's request.
Staff RNs 3 (ft), 2 (pt); Orderlies 2 (ft), 1 (pt); Nurses aides 29 (ft), 4 (pt); Activities coordinators 2 (ft); Dietitians 1 (ft).
Languages French, Italian, Polish, Spanish, Russian
Facilities Dining room; Physical therapy room; Activities room; Chapel; Crafts room; Laundry

room; Barber/Beauty shop.
Activities Arts and Crafts; Cards; Games; Reading groups; Prayer groups; Movies; Shopping trips; Dances/Social or cultural gatherings.
Description Facility offers 14-point guarantee of superior service; restaurant-style dining.

Southern Pines Nursing Center*
312 S Congress St, New Port Richey, FL, 33552 (813) 842-8402
Licensure Skilled Care. *Beds* 120. *Certified* Medicaid; Medicare.
Ownership Proprietary.
Staff RNs 7 (ft); LPNs 8 (ft); Nurses aides 25 (ft).
Languages Spanish

Whispering Pines Nursing Center Inc
25 Peggy Mac Ln, New Port Richey, FL, 33552 (305) 849-7205
Admin Nancy E Hall. *Medical Dir/Dir of Nursing* Malcolm Foster MD.
Licensure Skilled Care. *Beds* 56. *Certified* Medicaid; Medicare.
Ownership Proprietary.
Admissions Requirements Minimum age 16; Medical examination; Physician's request.
Staff Physicians 1 (pt); RNs 1 (ft), 2 (pt); LPNs 8 (ft), 2 (pt); Orderlies 3 (ft), 2 (pt); Nurses aides 15 (ft), 5 (pt); Physical therapists 2 (pt); Reality therapists 2 (pt); Occupational therapists 1 (pt); Speech therapists 1 (pt); Activities coordinators 1 (ft); Dietitians 1 (pt); Dentists 1 (pt); Ophthalmologists 1 (pt); Podiatrists 1 (pt); Audiologists 1 (pt).
Languages Spanish
Facilities Dining room; Activities room; Laundry room; Barber/Beauty shop; Library.
Activities Arts and Crafts; Cards; Games; Reading groups; Prayer groups; Movies; Shopping trips; Dances/Social or cultural gatherings.
Description Facility provides a home-like atmosphere being able to cater to each resident's individual needs as the smallest facility in the immediate area.

NEW SMYRNA BEACH

Ocean-View Nursing Home*
2810 S Atlantic Ave, New Smyrna Beach, FL, 32069 (904) 428-6424
Licensure Skilled Care. *Beds* 119. *Certified* Medicaid; Medicare.
Ownership Proprietary.
Staff RNs 7 (ft); LPNs 12 (ft); Nurses aides 22 (ft).
Languages Spanish, Korean, German

NORTH BAY VILLAGE

Treasure Isle Nursing Home
1735 N Treasure Dr, North Bay Village, FL, 33141 (305) 865-2383
Medical Dir/Dir of Nursing Dr Richard Jacobs.
Licensure Skilled Care. *Beds* 176. *Certified* Medicaid; Medicare.
Ownership Proprietary.
Admissions Requirements Minimum age 18.
Staff Physicians 10 (ft); RNs 20 (ft); LPNs 15 (ft); Nurses aides 50 (ft); Physical therapists 5

(ft); Recreational therapists 1 (ft); Occupational therapists 1 (ft); Speech therapists 1 (ft); Activities coordinators 1 (ft); Dietitians 1 (ft); Dentists 1 (ft); Ophthalmologists 1 (ft); Podiatrists 1 (ft); Audiologists 1 (ft).
Languages Spanish
Facilities Dining room; Physical therapy room; Activities room; Chapel; Crafts room; Laundry room; Library; Outside patio.
Activities Arts and Crafts; Cards; Games; Reading groups; Prayer groups; Movies; Shopping trips; Dances/Social or cultural gatherings; Trips to restaurants.
Description Home is situated in a beautiful community. Facility features a spacious courtyard, with chairs and umbrellas, large spacious dining areas and rooms and is located within minutes of the beach.

NORTH MIAMI

Bon Secours Hospital/Villa Maria Nursing Center
1050 NE 125th St, North Miami, FL, 33161 (305) 891-8850
Medical Dir/Dir of Nursing Dr Harold Weiner and Dr David Lipkin.
Licensure Rehabilitation; Nursing Center.
Beds Rehabilitation 60; Nursing Center 212.
Certified Medicaid; Medicare.
Ownership Proprietary.
Admissions Requirements Medical examination; Physician's request.
Staff Physicians 2 (ft); RNs 17 (ft), 6 (pt); LPNs 18 (ft), 7 (pt); Nurses aides 78 (ft), 12 (pt); Physical therapists 13 (ft); Recreational therapists 2 (ft) #13I 12 (ft); Speech therapists 2 (ft); Activities coordinators 1 (ft); Dietitians 1 (ft).
Languages Spanish, Hebrew, French, German, Greek, Polish, Tagalog, Yomba
Affiliation Roman Catholic
Facilities Dining room; Physical therapy room; Activities room; Chapel; Crafts room; Laundry room; Barber/Beauty shop; Library.
Activities Arts and Crafts; Cards; Games; Reading groups; Prayer groups; Movies; Shopping trips; Dances/Social or cultural gatherings.

Fountainhead Nursing and Convalescent Home*
390 NE 135th St, North Miami, FL, 33161 (305) 893-0660
Licensure Skilled Care. *Beds* 146. *Certified* Medicaid.
Ownership Proprietary.
Staff RNs 6 (ft); LPNs 10 (ft); Nurses aides 34 (ft).
Languages Spanish, French

North Miami Convalescent Home*
1255 NE 135th St, North Miami, FL, 33161 (305) 891-6850
Licensure Skilled Care. *Beds* 245. *Certified* Medicaid.
Ownership Proprietary.
Staff RNs 6 (ft); LPNs 17 (ft); Nurses aides 49 (ft); 36 (ft).

Pinecrest Convalescent Home
13650 NE 3rd Ct, North Miami, FL, 33161 (305) 893-1170

Medical Dir/Dir of Nursing Arthur Snyder.
Licensure Skilled Care. *Beds* 100. *Certified* Medicaid; Medicare.
Ownership Proprietary.
Admissions Requirements Minimum age 16.
Staff RNs 9 (ft); LPNs 7 (ft); Nurses aides 37 (ft); Physical therapists 2 (ft); Reality therapists 2 (ft); Recreational therapists 2 (ft); Occupational therapists 1 (pt); Speech therapists 1 (pt); Activities coordinators 2 (ft); Dietitians 1 (pt); Dentists 1 (pt); Ophthalmologists 1 (pt); Podiatrists 1 (pt); Audiologists 1 (pt).
Languages Spanish, French
Facilities Dining room; Physical therapy room; Activities room; Chapel; Crafts room; Laundry room; Barber/Beauty shop; Library.
Activities Arts and Crafts; Cards; Games; Reading groups; Prayer groups; Movies; Dances/Social or cultural gatherings.

NORTH MIAMI BEACH

Greynolds Park Manor
17400 W Dixie Hwy, North Miami Beach, FL, 33160 (305) 944-2361
Admin Martin E Casper. *Medical Dir/Dir of Nursing* Walter Demaio MD.
Licensure Skilled Care. *Beds* 324. *Certified* Medicaid; Medicare.
Ownership Proprietary.
Admissions Requirements Medical examination.
Staff RNs 28 (ft); LPNs 22 (ft); Nurses aides 109 (ft); Physical therapists 2 (ft); Occupational therapists 2 (ft); Activities coordinators 1 (ft), 3 (pt); Dietitians 1 (pt).
Languages Spanish, French, Hebrew, Yiddish
Facilities Dining room; Physical therapy room; Activities room; Chapel; Crafts room; Laundry room; Barber/Beauty shop; Library.
Activities Arts and Crafts; Cards; Games; Reading groups; Prayer groups; Movies; Shopping trips; Dances/Social or cultural gatherings; Candlelight dinners; Picnics in park.
Description This is a teaching nursing home in conjunction with Southeastern College of Osteopathic Medicine; accredited by the long-term care section of JCAH; 7-day-a-week rehabilitation offered.

Hebrew Home for the Aged—North Dade
1800 NE 168th St, North Miami Beach, FL, 33162 (305) 947-3445
Medical Dir/Dir of Nursing Dr Salvatore Certo.
Licensure Skilled Care. *Beds* 50. *Certified* Medicaid; Medicare.
Ownership Nonprofit.
Admissions Requirements Minimum age 40; Medical examination.
Staff Physicians 1 (pt); RNs 4 (ft); LPNs 3 (ft); Nurses aides 38 (ft); Physical therapists 1 (pt); Recreational therapists 1 (pt); Occupational therapists 1 (pt); Speech therapists 1 (pt); Activities coordinators 1 (ft); Dietitians 1 (pt); Dentists 1 (pt); Podiatrists 1 (pt); Audiologists 1 (pt).
Languages Spanish, Yiddish
Affiliation Jewish
Facilities Dining room; Activities room; Laun-

dry room.
Activities Arts and Crafts; Cards; Games; Reading groups; Movies; Shopping trips.

Heritage House Nursing and Rehabilitation Center
2201 NE 170th St, North Miami Beach, FL, 33160 (305) 945-1401
Admin Currie J Neville. *Medical Dir/Dir of Nursing* Dr Sheldon Staller.
Licensure Skilled Care. *Beds* 99. *Certified* Medicaid; Medicare.
Ownership Proprietary.
Staff Physicians 3 (ft); RNs 5 (ft); LPNs 6 (ft), 5 (pt); Orderlies 2 (ft); Nurses aides 31 (ft), 5 (pt); Physical therapists 1 (ft), 1 (pt); Speech therapists 1 (ft); Activities coordinators 1 (ft), 1 (pt); Dietitians 1 (ft); Social workers 1 (ft).
Languages Spanish, Creole
Facilities Dining room; Physical therapy room; Activities room; Crafts room; Laundry room; Barber/Beauty shop; Outdoor patio; Shade house.
Activities Arts and Crafts; Cards; Games; Reading groups; Prayer groups; Movies; Shopping trips; Dances/Social or cultural gatherings; Singing.
Description Center is a Unicare Health Facility offering a 14-point guarantee of superior services; provides home-like atmosphere with respect for dignity and quality of care. VA approved.

Kraver Institute
1800 NE 168th St, North Miami Beach, FL, 33162 (305) 947-3445
Licensure Intermediate Care for Mentally Retarded. *Beds* 20.
Ownership Nonprofit.
Staff Physicians; Dietitians; Nurses aides.
Languages Spanish
Activities Arts and Crafts; Shopping trips.

Royal Glades Convalescent Home*
16650 W Dixie Hwy, North Miami Beach, FL, 33160 (305) 945-7447
Licensure Skilled Care. *Beds* 150. *Certified* Medicaid; Medicare.
Ownership Proprietary.
Staff RNs 6 (ft); LPNs 14 (ft); Nurses aides 36 (ft); 27 (ft).
Languages Spanish, French, Hebrew, Yiddish

OCALA

New Horizon Rehabilitative Center*
635 SE 17th St, Ocala, FL, 32670 (904) 629-7921
Licensure Skilled Care. *Beds* 89. *Certified* Medicaid; Medicare.
Ownership Proprietary.
Staff RNs 6 (ft); LPNs 9 (ft); Nurses aides 28 (ft).
Languages German, French, Greek, Polish, Spanish

Ocala Geriatric Center Inc*
2333 SE Oakhurst Rd, Ocala, FL, 32670 (904) 732-2449
Licensure Skilled Care. *Beds* 180. *Certified* Medicaid; Medicare.
Ownership Proprietary.

Staff RNs 12 (ft); LPNs 13 (ft); Nurses aides 56 (ft); 28 (ft).
Languages Spanish

Ocala Health Care Center*
2021 SW 1st Ave, Ocala, FL, 32670 (904) 629-0063
Licensure Skilled Care. *Beds* 133. *Certified* Medicaid; Medicare.
Ownership Proprietary.
Staff RNs 9 (ft); LPNs 11 (ft); Nurses aides 29 (ft).

OLDSMAR

West Bay Nursing Home*
400 State Rd, Oldsmar, FL, 33557 (813) 855-4661
Beds 120.
Ownership Proprietary.

OPA LOCKA

Landmark Learning Center—Facility I*
PO Box 1898, Opa Locka, FL, 33055 (305) 624-9671
Licensure Intermediate Care for Mentally Retarded. *Beds* 120. *Certified* Medicaid.
Ownership Public.
Staff RNs 4 (ft); LPNs 7 (ft); Nurses aides 71 (ft).

Landmark Learning Center—Miami Facility II*
PO Box 1898, Opa Locka, FL, 33055 (305) 624-9671
Licensure Intermediate Care for Mentally Retarded. *Beds* 60.
Ownership Public.

Sunland Center—Miami Facility III*
PO Box 1898, OPA Locka, FL, 33055 (305) 624-9671
Licensure Intermediate Care for Mentally Retarded. *Beds* 60.
Ownership Public.

ORANGE CITY

John Knox Village Medical Center*
101 N Lake Dr, Orange City, FL, 32763 (904) 775-3840
Beds 60.
Ownership Nonprofit.

ORANGE PARK

Moosehaven Health Center
Hwy 17, PO Box 102, Orange Park, FL, 32073 (904) 264-9551
Medical Dir/Dir of Nursing H L Stephens MD.
Licensure Skilled Care; Intermediate Care.
Beds SNF 20; ICF 180.
Ownership Nonprofit.
Admissions Requirements Minimum age 65.
Staff Physicians 1 (ft), 3 (pt); Physical therapists 2 (ft); Activities coordinators 1 (ft); Dietitians 1 (ft); Dentists 1 (ft); Podiatrists 1 (ft); Audiologists 1 (ft).
Languages Spanish, Tagalog

Affiliation Royal Order of Moose
Facilities Dining room; Physical therapy room; Chapel; Crafts room; Laundry room; Barber-/Beauty shop; Library.
Activities Arts and Crafts; Cards; Games; Prayer groups; Shopping trips; Dances/Social or cultural gatherings; Aerobic exercises.
Description Moosehaven provides all social, physical, and medical needs at no cost to residents. Campus resembles a well groomed college campus with one-story housing with approximately 45 residents to each hall. Halls have "house mothers" for 24-hour supervision.

Orange Park Care Center
2019 Kingsley Ave, Drawer 896, Orange Park, FL, 32073 (904) 269-6194
Admin Amy H Roberts. *Medical Dir/Dir of Nursing* Charles Phillips MD and John Arnold MD.
Licensure Skilled Care; Intermediate Care.
Beds 105. *Certified* Medicaid; Medicare.
Ownership Proprietary.
Admissions Requirements Minimum age 16; Medical examination; Physician's request.
Staff RNs 6 (ft); LPNs 7 (ft); Orderlies 2 (ft); Nurses aides 35 (ft); Physical therapists 1 (pt); Speech therapists 1 (pt); Activities coordinators 1 (ft); Dietitians 1 (pt).
Facilities Dining room; Physical therapy room; Activities room; Crafts room; Laundry room; Barber/Beauty shop.
Activities Arts and Crafts; Cards; Games; Prayer groups; Movies; Shopping trips; Dances/Social or cultural gatherings.
Description Facility is located among pines adjacent to Humana Hospital and numerous physician offices; active community with volunteers interested in the facility.

ORLANDO

Americana Health Care Center of Orlando*
2414 Bedford Rd, Orlando, FL, 32803 (305) 898-5051
Licensure Skilled Care. *Beds* 102. *Certified* Medicare.
Ownership Proprietary.
Staff RNs 7 (ft); LPNs 10 (ft), 1 (pt); Nurses aides 23 (ft).
Languages German, Spanish, Italian

Barrington Terrace Nursing Home
215 Annie St, Orlando, FL, 32806 (305) 841-4371
Medical Dir/Dir of Nursing Dr Louis C Murry.
Licensure Skilled Care. *Beds* 60.
Ownership Proprietary.
Staff Physicians; Dietitians; Nurses aides.
Languages Spanish, Italian
Facilities Dining room; Activities room; Crafts room; Laundry room; Barber/Beauty shop.
Activities Arts and Crafts; Cards; Games; Prayer groups; Movies; Shopping trips.
Description This is the only family owned and operated nursing facility in central Florida; has provided quality care since 1963.

Florida Manor Nursing Home
830 W Michigan, Orlando, FL, 32805 (305) 843-3230
Medical Dir/Dir of Nursing John Royer MD.

Licensure Skilled Care. *Beds* 420. *Certified* Medicaid.
Ownership Nonprofit.
Admissions Requirements Minimum age 16; Medical examination.
Staff RNs 22 (ft), 3 (pt); LPNs 28 (ft), 2 (pt); Orderlies 2 (ft); Nurses aides 145 (ft), 3 (pt); Physical therapists 1 (ft); Reality therapists 1 (ft); Recreational therapists 6 (ft), 2 (pt); Speech therapists 1 (ft); Activities coordinators 2 (ft); Dietitians 1 (ft); Dentists 1 (pt).
Languages Spanish
Affiliation Roman Catholic
Facilities Dining room; Physical therapy room; Activities room; Chapel; Crafts room; Laundry room; Barber/Beauty shop.
Activities Arts and Crafts; Cards; Games; Reading groups; Prayer groups; Movies; Shopping trips; Dances/Social or cultural gatherings.

Guardian Care Convalescent Center
2500 W Church St, Orlando, FL, 32805 (305) 295-5371
Medical Dir/Dir of Nursing A L Bookhardt MD.
Licensure Skilled Care. *Beds* 76. *Certified* Medicaid.
Ownership Nonprofit.
Admissions Requirements Minimum age 16.
Staff Physicians 2 (pt); RNs 4 (ft), 1 (pt); LPNs 5 (ft), 6 (pt); Orderlies 2 (ft); Nurses aides 20 (ft), 6 (pt); Physical therapists 1 (pt); Reality therapists 1 (pt); Recreational therapists 1 (pt); Occupational therapists 1 (pt); Speech therapists 1 (pt); Activities coordinators 1 (ft); Dietitians 1 (pt); Dentists 1 (pt); Ophthalmologists 1 (pt); Podiatrists 1 (pt); Audiologists 1 (pt).
Languages Spanish
Facilities Dining room; Physical therapy room; Activities room; Crafts room; Laundry room; Barber/Beauty shop.
Activities Arts and Crafts; Cards; Games; Reading groups; Prayer groups; Movies; Shopping trips; Dances/Social or cultural gatherings.
Description Present plans call for expansion to 120 beds and refurbishing utilized basement wing to provide additional resident activities area and a chapel.

Loch Haven Lodge*
2250 Bedford Rd, Orlando, FL, 32803 (305) 898-4721
Licensure Skilled Care. *Beds* 50. *Certified* Medicaid.
Ownership Proprietary.
Staff RNs 3 (ft); LPNs 5 (ft); Nurses aides 15 (ft).

Orlando Health Care Center*
2000 N Semorian Blvd, Orlando, FL, 32807 (305) 671-5400
Licensure Skilled Care. *Beds* 118. *Certified* Medicaid.
Ownership Proprietary.
Staff RNs 3 (ft); LPNs 13 (ft); Nurses aides 26 (ft).

Orlando Lutheran Towers
300 E Church St, Orlando, FL, 32801 (305) 425-1033
Medical Dir/Dir of Nursing Dr Edwin O'Neal.
Licensure Skilled Care; Intermediate Care.
Beds SNF 30; ICF 30.

Ownership Nonprofit.
Admissions Requirements Minimum age 65; Medical examination.
Staff Physicians 1 (pt); RNs 2 (ft), 2 (pt); LPNs 5 (ft), 1 (pt); Orderlies 1 (ft); Nurses aides 9 (ft), 1 (pt); Physical therapists 1 (pt); Speech therapists; Activities coordinators 1 (ft); Dietitians 1 (pt); Dentists 1 (pt).
Languages German
Affiliation Lutheran
Facilities Dining room; Physical therapy room; Activities room; Chapel; Crafts room; Laundry room; Barber/Beauty shop; Library.
Activities Arts and Crafts; Cards; Games; Reading groups; Prayer groups; Movies; Shopping trips; Dances/Social or cultural gatherings.
Description Facility is located in downtown Orlando just 2 blocks from beautiful Lake Eola; offers full activities program and many opportunities for volunteer service.

Orlando Memorial Convalescent Center
1730 Lucerne Terrace, Orlando, FL, 32806 (305) 423-1612
Licensure Skilled Care. *Beds* 115. *Certified* Medicaid.
Ownership Proprietary.
Admissions Requirements Minimum age 21; Medical examination; Physician's request.
Staff Physicians 15 (pt); RNs 4 (ft), 1 (pt); LPNs 8 (ft), 3 (pt); Orderlies 3 (ft), 2 (pt); Nurses aides 28 (ft), 17 (pt); Physical therapists 1 (pt); Reality therapists 1 (pt); Recreational therapists 1 (pt); Occupational therapists 1 (pt); Speech therapists 1 (pt); Activities coordinators 2 (ft); Dietitians 1 (pt); Podiatrists 1 (pt); Audiologists 1 (pt).
Facilities Dining room; Physical therapy room; Activities room; Crafts room; Laundry room; Barber/Beauty shop.
Activities Arts and Crafts; Cards; Games; Reading groups; Prayer groups; Movies; Shopping trips.
Description Facility features excellent nursing care.

Westminster Towers*
70 Lucerne Circle, Orlando, FL, 32801 (305) 293-6557
Licensure Skilled Care. *Beds* 61.
Ownership Nonprofit.
Staff RNs 11 (ft); LPNs 4 (ft); Nurses aides 21 (ft); 25 (ft).
Affiliation Presbyterian

ORMOND BEACH

Bowmans Nursing Center
350 S Ridgewood Ave, Ormond Beach, FL, 32074 (904) 677-4545
Medical Dir/Dir of Nursing James Shoemaker DO.
Licensure Skilled Care. *Beds* 140. *Certified* Medicaid; Medicare.
Ownership Proprietary.
Admissions Requirements Minimum age 14; Medical examination; Physician's request.
Staff Physicians 1 (pt); RNs 5 (ft), 2 (pt); LPNs 8 (ft), 3 (pt); Orderlies 3 (ft); Nurses aides 39 (ft), 10 (pt); Physical therapists 3 (pt); Speech therapists 1 (pt); Activities coordinators 1 (ft), 1 (pt); Dietitians 1 (ft); Dentists 1 (pt); Podiatrists

1 (pt).
Languages Italian
Facilities Dining room; Physical therapy room; Activities room; Crafts room; Laundry room; Barber/Beauty shop; Library.
Activities Arts and Crafts; Cards; Games; Reading groups; Prayer groups; Movies; Shopping trips; Dances/Social or cultural gatherings; Monthly Catholic Mass; Monthly Episcopal Mass.
Description Facility features 4 outdoor patios and outdoor nature area, adopt-a-grandparent program, weekly ceramics classes, and monthly field trips.

Ormond Beach Health Care Center
170 N Kings Rd, Ormond Beach, FL, 32074 (904) 677-7955
Medical Dir/Dir of Nursing Roman Hendrickson.
Licensure Skilled Care. *Beds* 131. *Certified* Medicaid; Medicare.
Ownership Proprietary.
Admissions Requirements Minimum age 55; Physician's request.
Staff Physicians 30 (ft); RNs 10 (ft), 4 (pt); LPNs 7 (ft), 2 (pt); Nurses aides 38 (ft), 9 (pt); Physical therapists 3 (ft); Recreational therapists 2 (ft); Activities coordinators 1 (ft); Activities coordinators 1 (ft); Dietitians 1 (ft); Dentists 1 (ft); Podiatrists 1 (ft).
Languages Spanish, German
Facilities Dining room; Activities room; Chapel; Crafts room; Laundry room; Barber/Beauty shop.
Activities Arts and Crafts; Cards; Games; Reading groups; Prayer groups; Movies; Shopping trips; Dances/Social or cultural gatherings.

OVIEDO

Lutheran Haven*
Rt 3, Box 300, Hwy 426, Oviedo, FL, 32765 (305) 365-5676
Licensure Skilled Care. *Beds* 42.
Ownership Nonprofit.
Staff RNs 4 (ft); LPNs 7 (ft); Nurses aides 11 (ft).
Affiliation Lutheran

PALATKA

Putnam Memorial Nursing Home*
501 S Palm Ave, Palatka, FL, 32077 (904) 328-1472
Licensure Skilled Care. *Beds* 65. *Certified* Medicaid; Medicare.
Ownership Public.
Staff RNs 4 (ft); LPNs 11 (ft); Nurses aides 14 (ft).

PALM HARBOR

Baytree Nursing Center*
2600 Highlands Blvd N, Palm Harbor, FL, 33563
Beds 120.
Ownership Proprietary.

St Mark Village Inc
2655 Nebraska Ave, Palm Harbor, FL, 33563
(813) 785-2576
Medical Dir/Dir of Nursing James R Kinney
DO.
Licensure Skilled Care. *Beds* 60. *Certified* Medicare.
Ownership Nonprofit.
Staff RNs 3 (ft), 3 (pt); LPNs 1 (ft), 4 (pt);
Nurses aides 17 (ft), 7 (pt); Physical therapists;
Occupational therapists; Speech therapists;
Activities coordinators 1 (ft); Dietitians; Dentists; Podiatrists; Pharmacist; Music therapist.
Affiliation Lutheran
Facilities Dining room; Physical therapy room;
Activities room; Chapel; Crafts room; Laundry
room; Barber/Beauty shop; Library.
Activities Arts and Crafts; Cards; Games;
Reading groups; Prayer groups; Movies; Shopping trips; Dances/Social or cultural gatherings.

PANAMA CITY

Bay Convalescent Center*
1336 Saint Andrews Blvd, Panama City, FL,
32401 (904) 763-3911
Licensure Skilled Care; Intermediate Care.
Beds 160. *Certified* Medicaid; Medicare.
Ownership Proprietary.
Staff RNs 3 (ft); LPNs 15 (ft); Nurses aides 37
(ft).
Languages Spanish

Gulf Coast Convalescent Center
1937 Jenks Ave, Panama City, FL, 32401 (904)
769-7686
Medical Dir/Dir of Nursing James Shu MD.
Licensure Skilled Care. *Beds* 120. *Certified* Medicaid.
Ownership Proprietary.
Admissions Requirements Medical examination; Physician's request.
Staff Physicians 1 (pt); RNs 6 (ft), 4 (pt); LPNs
9 (ft), 8 (pt); Orderlies 4 (ft), 1 (pt); Nurses aides
46 (ft), 8 (pt); Physical therapists 1 (pt); Reality
therapists 1 (pt); Recreational therapists 1 (pt);
Occupational therapists 1 (pt); Speech therapists 1 (ft); Activities coordinators 1 (ft); Dietitians 1 (pt); Dentists 1 (pt).
Facilities Dining room; Physical therapy room;
Activities room; Chapel; Crafts room; Laundry
room; Barber/Beauty shop.
Activities Arts and Crafts; Cards; Games;
Reading groups; Prayer groups; Movies; Shopping trips; Dances/Social or cultural gatherings.
Description Facility features large covered
courtyard with small pool and fountain; ducks,
rabbits, and turtles run loose in courtyard; taste
committee for food items (food must receive
2/3 vote to remain); food preference survey
done annually with resident population.

Lelah G Wagner Nursing Home*
3409 W 19th St, Panama City, FL, 32401 (904)
763-3401
Licensure Skilled Care. *Beds* 66. *Certified* Medicaid; Medicare.
Ownership Proprietary.
Staff RNs 3 (ft); LPNs 7 (ft); Nurses aides 23
(ft).
Languages Spanish

Panama City Developmental Center
1407 Lincoln Dr, Panama City, FL, 32401
Admin Larry E Weishaar. *Medical Dir/Dir of
Nursing* Dr Zoran Yovanovich.
Licensure Intermediate Care for Mentally
Retarded. *Beds* 64. *Certified* Medicaid.
Ownership Nonprofit.
Staff Physicians 2 (pt); RNs 2 (ft); LPNs 3 (ft),
3 (pt); Nurses aides 48 (ft), 18 (pt); Physical
therapists 1 (pt); Recreational therapists 1 (ft);
Occupational therapists 1 (pt); Speech therapists 1 (pt); Dietitians 1 (ft); Dentists 1 (pt);
Ophthalmologists 1 (pt); Psychologists 2 (pt);
Recreational aides 1 (ft).
Facilities Dining room; Physical therapy room;
Activities room; Crafts room; Laundry room.
Activities Arts and Crafts; Cards; Games; Prayer groups; Movies; Shopping trips; Dances/Social or cultural gatherings; Training.
Description Clients live in one of 4 houses with
16 residents per house. Most time and effort is
focused on increasing their independence in all
areas such as self-care, daily living, basic
academics, human growth, recreation, physical
and occupational therapy, and special programs
as needed.

Panama City Nursing Center
924 W 13th St, Panama City, FL, 32401 (904)
763-8463
Medical Dir/Dir of Nursing Thomas G Merrill
DO.
Licensure Skilled Care. *Beds* 120. *Certified* Medicaid; Medicare.
Ownership Proprietary.
Admissions Requirements Medical examination; Physician's request.
Staff Physicians 23 (pt); RNs 9 (ft); LPNs 17
(ft); Nurses aides 48 (ft); Physical therapists 3
(pt); Occupational therapists 3 (pt); Speech therapists 1 (pt); Activities coordinators 1 (ft); Dietitians 1 (pt); Dentists 1 (pt); Ophthalmologists
3 (pt); Podiatrists 1 (pt); Audiologists 1 (pt).
Languages Spanish, German, Tagalog, Vietnamese, French
Facilities Dining room; Physical therapy room;
Activities room; Chapel; Crafts room; Laundry
room; Barber/Beauty shop; Library.
Activities Arts and Crafts; Cards; Games;
Reading groups; Prayer groups; Shopping trips;
Dances/Social or cultural gatherings.
Description VA approved.

PENNY FARMS

Mary M Olin Clinic
PO Box 483, Penny Farms, FL, 32079 (904)
529-9403
Licensure Skilled Care. *Beds* 40.
Ownership Nonprofit.
Staff Physicians; Dietitians; Nurses aides.
Activities Prayer groups; Arts and Crafts; Shopping trips.

PENSACOLA

Azalea Trace*
10100 Hillview, Pensacola, FL, 32504 (904)
478-5200
Beds 904.
Ownership Nonprofit.

The Bluffs Care Center*
4343 Langley Ave, Pensacola, FL, 32504 (904)
477-4550
Licensure Skilled Care. *Beds* 120. *Certified* Medicaid; Medicare.
Ownership Proprietary.
Staff RNs 3 (ft); LPNs 13 (ft); Nurses aides 27
(ft).

Escambia County Nursing Home
3107 N "H" St, Pensacola, FL, 32501 (904)
436-9300
Admin Shirley L Hoggard. *Medical Dir/Dir of
Nursing* Thomas L Hoyt MD.
Licensure Skilled Care. *Beds* 155. *Certified* Medicaid.
Ownership Public.
Admissions Requirements Medical examination; Physician's request.
Staff Physicians 2 (pt); RNs 3 (ft), 4 (pt); LPNs
15 (ft), 2 (pt); Orderlies 7 (ft); Nurses aides 43
(ft), 5 (pt); Physical therapists 2 (pt); Activities
coordinators 1 (ft); Dietitians 1 (pt); Dentists 1
(pt); Podiatrists 1 (pt).
Facilities Dining room; Physical therapy room;
Activities room; Crafts room; Laundry room;
Barber/Beauty shop; Library.
Activities Arts and Crafts; Games; Reading
groups; Prayer groups; Movies; Shopping trips;
Dances/Social or cultural gatherings.
Description We feel our activities program, as
well as our nursing care, are outstanding.
Patients enjoy, fishing trips, boat excursions,
shopping sprees, the "Lunch Bunch," our annual circus with clowns, jugglers, acrobats, etc.,
picnics at the beach, and much, much more.

Haven of Our Lady of Peace
5203 N 9th Ave, Pensacola, FL, 32504 (904)
477-0531
Medical Dir/Dir of Nursing Finley C Holmes
MD.
Licensure Skilled Care; Intermediate Care.
Beds SNF 47; ICF 42. *Certified* Medicaid.
Ownership Nonprofit.
Admissions Requirements Medical examination; Physician's request.
Staff RNs 2 (ft), 1 (pt); LPNs 10 (ft), 6 (pt);
Nurses aides 29 (ft), 3 (pt); Activities coordinators 1 (ft).
Languages Spanish
Affiliation Roman Catholic
Facilities Dining room; Activities room; Chapel; Crafts room; Laundry room; Barber/Beauty
shop; Library; Porches.
Activities Arts and Crafts; Cards; Games;
Reading groups; Prayer groups; Movies; Shopping trips; Dances/Social or cultural gatherings;
Picnics.
Description State licensed nursing home. "A
home away from home" for retired ladies, gentlemen, and couples; residential section and
infirmary wing.

Magnolias Nursing and Convalescent Center
600 W Gregory St, Pensacola, FL, 32501 (904)
438-4041
Admin Marion R Baldwin. *Medical Dir/Dir of
Nursing* William Balk MD.
Licensure Skilled Care. *Beds* 210. *Certified* Medicaid; Medicare.
Ownership Proprietary.
Admissions Requirements Minimum age 16;

Medical examination; Physician's request.
Staff Physicians 12 (pt); RNs 7 (ft), 8 (pt);
LPNs 15 (ft), 14 (pt); Orderlies 4 (ft), 1 (pt);
Nurses aides 59 (ft), 21 (pt); Physical therapists
1 (ft); Recreational therapists 1 (ft); Speech ther-
apists 1 (pt); Activities coordinators 1 (ft); Die-
titians 1 (pt); Dentists 1 (pt); Social workers 1
(ft); Physical therapy assistants 2 (pt).
Facilities Dining room; Physical therapy room;
Activities room; Crafts room; Laundry room;
Barber/Beauty shop.
Activities Arts and Crafts; Cards; Games;
Reading groups; Prayer groups; Movies; Shopping trips; Dances/Social or cultural gatherings.
Description Facility is in a central location with
large rooms and pleasant and attractive surroundings; 4 person activities department;
intensive nursing education enhances nursing
care.

Northview Community
10050 Hillview Rd, Pensacola, FL, 32504 (904)
438-1626
Medical Dir/Dir of Nursing Dr Tim Jordan.
Licensure Intermediate Care for Mentally
Retarded. *Beds* 30.
Ownership Proprietary.
Admissions Requirements Medical examina-
tion.
Staff Physicians 1 (pt); RNs 1 (ft); LPNs 3 (ft),
6 (pt); Nurses aides 40 (ft); Physical therapists 1
(pt); Recreational therapists 1 (ft); Occupational
therapists 1 (pt); Speech therapists 1 (pt);
Activities coordinators 1 (ft); Dietitians 1 (ft);
Dentists 1 (pt); Ophthalmologists 1 (pt).
Facilities Dining room; Physical therapy room;
Activities room; Crafts room; Laundry room.
Activities Arts and Crafts; Games; Reading
groups; Movies; Shopping trips; Dances/Social
or cultural gatherings.
Description We are a home for mentally
retarded children with good emphasis on programing for teaching self-help skills and red-
ucing behavior problems.

Pensacola Health Care Facility*
1717 W Avery St, Pensacola, FL, 32501 (904)
434-2355
Licensure Skilled Care. *Beds* 118. *Certified* Medicaid; Medicare.
Ownership Proprietary.
Staff RNs 5 (ft); LPNs 12 (ft); Nurses aides 25
(ft); 17 (ft).

PERRY

Perry Health Facility*
206 Forest Dr, Perry, FL, 32347 (904) 584-6334
Licensure Skilled Care. *Beds* 92. *Certified* Medicaid; Medicare.
Ownership Proprietary.
Staff RNs 1 (ft); LPNs 6 (ft); Nurses aides 21
(ft); 13 (ft).

PINELLAS PARK

Morningside
6770 102nd Ave N, Pinellas Park, FL, 33565
(813) 541-3561
Licensure Skilled Care; Intermediate Care.
Beds SNF 19; ICF 48. *Certified* Medicare.

Ownership Nonprofit.
Admissions Requirements Minimum age 18.
Staff RNs 8 (ft), 2 (pt); Nurses aides 10 (ft), 4
(pt); Activities coordinators 1 (pt); Dietitians 1
(pt).
Languages German
Affiliation Christian Science
Facilities Dining room; Activities room; Chap-
el; Crafts room; Laundry room; Barber/Beauty
shop; Library.
Activities Arts and Crafts; Cards; Games;
Reading groups; Prayer groups; Movies; Shop-
ping trips; Dances/Social or cultural gatherings.
Description Morningside is an accredited
Christian Science sanatorium; also licensed as a
nursing home by the state of Florida; all of the
nursing staff are trained Christian Science
nurses.

Parkway Nursing Home*
7575 65th Way N, Pinellas Park, FL, 33565
(813) 544-6673
Licensure Skilled Care. *Beds* 55. *Certified* Medicaid; Medicare.
Ownership Proprietary.
Staff RNs 6 (ft); LPNs 7 (ft); Nurses aides 23
(ft).

PLANT CITY

Community Convalescent Center*
2202 W Oak Ave, Plant City, FL, 33566 (813)
754-3761
Licensure Skilled Care. *Beds* 120. *Certified* Medicaid; Medicare.
Ownership Proprietary.
Staff RNs 9 (ft); LPNs 7 (ft); Nurses aides 29
(ft).
Languages Spanish

Forest Park Nursing Center
1702 W Oak Ave, Plant City, FL, 33566 (813)
752-4129
Admin Irene A Watson. *Medical Dir/Dir of
Nursing* Edgar Sapp MD.
Licensure Skilled Care. *Beds* 97. *Cer-
tified* Medicaid; Medicare.
Ownership Proprietary.
Staff RNs 6 (ft); LPNs 8 (ft); Orderlies 1 (ft);
Nurses aides 34 (ft); Physical therapists; Occu-
pational therapists; Speech therapists; Activities
coordinators 1 (ft); Podiatrists; Audiologists.
Facilities Dining room; Activities room; Crafts
room; Laundry room; Barber/Beauty shop.
Activities Arts and Crafts; Cards; Games;
Reading groups; Prayer groups; Movies; Shop-
ping trips.
Description VA approved.

PLANTATION

Covenant Care Center
7751 W Broward Blvd, Plantation, FL, 33314
(305) 473-8040
Licensure Skilled Care. *Beds* 100. *Cer-
tified* Medicaid; Medicare.
Ownership Nonprofit.
Staff Nurses aides 12 (ft); Dietitians 7 (ft).
Languages Spanish, Tagalog
Activities Dances/Social or cultural gatherings.

Plantation Nursing Home*
4250 NW 5th St, Plantation, FL, 33317 (305)
587-3296
Licensure Skilled Care. *Beds* 152. *Certified* Medicaid; Medicare.
Ownership Proprietary.
Staff RNs 12 (ft); LPNs 14 (ft); Nurses aides 33
(ft).
Languages Spanish

POMPANO BEACH

Colonial Palms
51 W Sample Rd, Pompano Beach, FL, 33064
(305) 942-5530
Medical Dir/Dir of Nursing Mike Solnik MD
and Dr Richman.
Licensure Skilled Care. *Beds* 81.
Ownership Proprietary.
Admissions Requirements Minimum age 16;
Medical examination.
Staff RNs 6 (ft); LPNs 9 (ft); Nurses aides 36
(ft), 9 (pt); Physical therapists 1 (pt); Recrea-
tional therapists 1 (pt); Occupational therapists
1 (pt); Speech therapists 1 (pt); Activities coor-
dinators 4 (ft); Dietitians 1 (pt); Dentists 1 (pt);
Podiatrists 1 (pt).
Languages Spanish
Facilities Dining room; Physical therapy room;
Activities room; Chapel; Crafts room; Barber-
/Beauty shop; Library.
Activities Arts and Crafts; Cards; Games;
Reading groups; Prayer groups; Movies; Dan-
ces/Social or cultural gatherings.
Description Colonial Palms provides luxurious
accommodations, superior nursing care, and an
outstanding activities program to meet the
needs of residents.

Colonial Palms East Nursing Home
3670 NE 3rd St, Pompano Beach, FL, 33064
(305) 941-4100
Medical Dir/Dir of Nursing Mike Solnik MD.
Licensure Skilled Care. *Beds* 120.
Ownership Proprietary.
Admissions Requirements Minimum age 16;
Medical examination.
Staff RNs 9 (ft); LPNs 13 (ft); Orderlies 1 (ft);
Nurses aides 44 (ft); Physical therapists; Occu-
pational therapists; Speech therapists; Activities
coordinators 7 (ft); Dietitians 1 (ft); Dentists;
Ophthalmologists; Podiatrists; Audiologists.
Facilities Dining room; Physical therapy room;
Activities room; Chapel; Crafts room; Laundry
room; Barber/Beauty shop; Library.
Activities Arts and Crafts; Cards; Games;
Reading groups; Prayer groups; Movies; Shop-
ping trips; Dances/Social or cultural gatherings.
Description Facility rated superior by the state
of Florida.

John Knox Village Medical Center
631 SW 6th St, Pompano Beach, FL, 33060
(305) 782-1300
Medical Dir/Dir of Nursing Jerome Froelich
MD.
Licensure Skilled Care. *Beds* 120. *Cer-
tified* Medicaid.
Ownership Proprietary.
Staff Physicians 1 (ft); RNs 5 (ft); LPNs 14 (ft);
Nurses aides 44 (ft); Physical therapists 1 (ft);
Activities coordinators 2 (ft); Dietitians 1 (ft);

Social service director 1 (ft).
Facilities Dining room; Physical therapy room; Activities room; Crafts room; Laundry room; Barber/Beauty shop; Library.
Activities Arts and Crafts; Cards; Games; Reading groups; Prayer groups; Movies; Shopping trips; Dances/Social or cultural gatherings.
Description Facility has a superior rating.

Pinehurst Convalescent Facility
2401 NE 2nd St, Pompano Beach, FL, 33062 (305) 943-5100
Medical Dir/Dir of Nursing Jerome Froelich MD.
Licensure Skilled Care. *Beds* 83. *Certified* Medicaid; Medicare.
Ownership Proprietary.
Admissions Requirements Medical examination; Physician's request.
Staff RNs 3 (ft); LPNs 7 (ft), 2 (pt); Orderlies 4 (ft); Nurses aides 26 (ft); Physical therapists 1 (pt); Recreational therapists 1 (ft); Activities coordinators 1 (ft); Dietitians 1 (ft); 15 (ft).
Languages Spanish, Italian
Facilities Dining room; Physical therapy room; Activities room; Laundry room; Barber/Beauty shop.
Activities Arts and Crafts; Cards; Games; Reading groups; Prayer groups; Movies; Shopping trips; Dances/Social or cultural gatherings.

PORT CHARLOTTE

Port Charlotte Care Center*
170 Beaver Ln, Port Charlotte, FL, 33952 (813) 625-3200
Licensure Skilled Care. *Beds* 103.
Ownership Proprietary.
Staff Nurses aides 5 (ft).

PORT SAINT LUCIE

Port Saint Lucie Convalescent Center*
7300 Oleander Ave, Port Saint Lucie, FL, 33452 (305) 466-4100
Beds 60.
Ownership Proprietary.

PUNTA GORDA

Life Care Center of Punta Gorda
733 E Olympia Ave, Punta Gorda, FL, 33950 (813) 639-8771
Medical Dir/Dir of Nursing Dr George Ponjikaran.
Licensure Skilled Care; Intermediate Care.
Beds 132. *Certified* Medicaid; Medicare.
Ownership Proprietary.
Admissions Requirements Minimum age 23; Medical examination.
Staff RNs 4 (ft), 13 (pt); LPNs 8 (ft), 4 (pt); Orderlies 3 (ft); Nurses aides 44 (ft), 6 (pt); Physical therapists 1 (ft); Occupational therapists 1 (ft); Speech therapists 1 (ft); Activities coordinators 1 (ft); Dietitians 1 (pt); Podiatrists 2 (pt); Audiologists 1 (pt).
Languages Spanish, German
Facilities Dining room; Physical therapy room; Activities room; Crafts room; Laundry room; Barber/Beauty shop.
Activities Arts and Crafts; Prayer groups; Movies; Dances/Social or cultural gatherings.
Description New 180-bed facility opened March 1, 1984, largest such facility in Charlotte County; only facility that will accept young adults and that uses total waterbeds for cure and prevention of decubitus ulcers.

QUINCY

Gadsden Nursing Home*
1621 Experiment Station Rd, Quincy, FL, 32351 (904) 627-9276
Licensure Skilled Care. *Beds* 60. *Certified* Medicaid.
Ownership Nonprofit.
Staff RNs 5 (ft); LPNs 11 (ft); Nurses aides 14 (ft); 14 (ft).

ROCKLEDGE

Adare Medical Center*
1175 Huntington Ln, Rockledge, FL, 32955 (305) 632-7341
Licensure Skilled Care. *Beds* 50. *Certified* Medicaid.
Ownership Proprietary.
Staff RNs 9 (ft); LPNs 12 (ft); Nurses aides 17 (ft); 24 (ft).
Languages Spanish

Sunnypines Convalescent Center*
587 Barton Blvd, Rockledge, FL, 32955 (305) 632-6300
Licensure Skilled Care. *Beds* 75. *Certified* Medicaid; Medicare.
Ownership Proprietary.
Languages Spanish

SAINT AUGUSTINE

Buckingham-Smith Memorial Home
169 Central Ave, Saint Augustine, FL, 32084 (904) 824-3638
Admin Lillian Gatlin. *Medical Dir/Dir of Nursing* Dr Julietta Alcontara.
Licensure Skilled Care. *Beds* 51. *Certified* Medicaid.
Ownership Nonprofit.
Staff RNs 4 (ft), 2 (pt); LPNs 2 (ft), 4 (pt); Orderlies 6 (ft); Nurses aides 15 (ft), 2 (pt); Recreational therapists 1 (ft); Activities coordinators.
Facilities Dining room; Activities room; Laundry room.
Activities Arts and Crafts; Cards; Games; Prayer groups; Shopping trips.

Gilmer Nursing Home
189 San Marco Ave, Saint Augustine, FL, 32084 (904) 824-3326
Licensure Skilled Care. *Beds* 68. *Certified* Medicaid.
Ownership Proprietary.
Admissions Requirements Minimum age 18; Medical examination; Physician's request.
Staff RNs 2 (ft); LPNs 5 (ft); Orderlies 1 (ft); Nurses aides 15 (ft); Recreational therapists 1 (ft).
Facilities Dining room; Activities room; Barber/Beauty shop.

Activities Arts and Crafts; Cards; Games; Reading groups; Prayer groups; Dances/Social or cultural gatherings.

Saint Augustine Center for Living
Rt 4, Box 180, Saint Augustine, FL, 32084 (904) 797-5027
Medical Dir/Dir of Nursing Michael Tessler MD.
Licensure Intermediate Care for Mentally Retarded. *Beds* 60. *Certified* Medicaid.
Ownership Proprietary.
Staff Nurses aides 3 (ft).
Activities Dances/Social or cultural gatherings.

Saint Augustine Geriatric Center
51 Sunrise Blvd, Saint Augustine, FL, 32084 (904) 824-4479
Medical Dir/Dir of Nursing Dr Micheal P Tessler.
Licensure Skilled Care. *Beds* 120. *Certified* Medicaid; Medicare.
Ownership Proprietary.
Admissions Requirements Medical examination; Physician's request.
Staff Physicians 21 (ft); RNs 3 (ft), 1 (pt); LPNs 15 (ft), 3 (pt); Nurses aides 48 (ft), 4 (pt); Physical therapists 2 (ft), 1 (pt); Speech therapists 1 (pt); Activities coordinators 1 (ft); Dietitians 1 (ft), 1 (pt); Dentists 1 (pt); Ophthalmologists 1 (pt); Podiatrists 2 (pt); Audiologists 1 (pt); Psychologist 1 (pt).
Facilities Dining room; Physical therapy room; Activities room; Crafts room; Laundry room; Barber/Beauty shop; 2 Covered, paved, fenced outdoor patios.
Activities Arts and Crafts; Cards; Games; Reading groups; Prayer groups; Movies; Shopping trips; Dances/Social or cultural gatherings; Sports events; Mass and Rosary; Pet therapy; Adopt-a-grandchild.
Description A VA approved facility with a superior rating from the state; 24-hour per day nursing staff; medical director also available 24 hours a day; within 5 minutes of a hospital and 2 minutes from county rescue service.

Saint Johns County Senior Citizens Home*
169 Marine St, Saint Augustine, FL, 32084 (904) 824-1755
Licensure Skilled Care. *Beds* 51. *Certified* Medicaid.
Ownership Public.
Staff RNs 8 (ft); LPNs 6 (ft); Nurses aides 15 (ft); 12 (ft).

SAINT CLOUD

Saint Cloud Health Care Center*
1301 Kansas Ave, Saint Cloud, FL, 32769 (305) 892-5121
Licensure Skilled Care. *Beds* 131. *Certified* Medicaid.
Ownership Proprietary.
Staff RNs 4 (ft); LPNs 11 (ft); Nurses aides 26 (ft).
Languages Spanish, French, German

SAINT PETERSBURG

Abbey Nursing Home
7101 9th St N, Saint Petersburg, FL, 33702
(813) 527-7231
Medical Dir/Dir of Nursing Dr Ernest Frierson.
Licensure Skilled Care. *Beds* 152. *Certified* Medicaid.
Ownership Proprietary.
Admissions Requirements Minimum age 21; Medical examination; Physician's request.
Staff RNs 11 (ft), 3 (pt); LPNs 8 (ft), 3 (pt); Orderlies 7 (ft); Nurses aides 54 (ft), 9 (pt); Activities coordinators 2 (ft); Dietitians 1 (ft).
Languages Italian, Hungarian, German, Spanish
Facilities Dining room; Activities room; Crafts room; Laundry room; Barber/Beauty shop.
Activities Arts and Crafts; Cards; Games; Reading groups; Movies.
Description We are a skilled nursing facility. We also have a special area for those residents who wander where they can walk about and not have to be restrained.

Alhambra Nursing Home
7501 38th Ave N, Saint Petersburg, FL, 33710
(813) 345-9307
Admin H Mary McKeown. *Medical Dir/Dir of Nursing* H P L'Heureux Jr.
Licensure Skilled Care. *Beds* 60.
Ownership Proprietary.
Staff Physicians; Dietitians; Nurses aides.
Facilities Dining room; Laundry room; Barber/Beauty shop.
Activities Arts and Crafts; Cards; Games; Reading groups; Movies; Dances/Social or cultural gatherings.

Alpine Nursing Center*
3456 21st Ave S, Saint Petersburg, FL, 33711
(813) 867-6573
Licensure Skilled Care. *Beds* 56. *Certified* Medicaid.
Ownership Proprietary.
Staff RNs 3 (ft); LPNs 6 (ft); Nurses aides 11 (ft); 8 (ft).

Bayou Manor
435 42nd Ave S, Saint Petersburg, FL, 33705
(813) 822-1871
Licensure Skilled Care. *Beds* 159. *Certified* Medicaid.
Ownership Proprietary.
Admissions Requirements Minimum age 16.
Staff RNs 6 (ft); LPNs 12 (ft); Nurses aides 48 (ft).
Languages Spanish
Facilities Dining room; Activities room; Crafts room; Laundry room; Barber/Beauty shop; Library.
Activities Arts and Crafts; Cards; Games; Reading groups; Prayer groups; Movies; Shopping trips; Dances/Social or cultural gatherings; Beach trips; Bowling.

Beach Convalescent Hotel*
8000 Blind Pasa Rd, Saint Petersburg, FL, 33706 (813) 367-3635
Licensure Skilled Care. *Beds* 38. *Certified* Medicaid.

Ownership Proprietary.
Staff RNs 5 (ft); LPNs 3 (ft); Nurses aides 10 (ft); 9 (ft).

Beverly Manor Convalescent Center*
550 9th Ave S, Saint Petersburg, FL, 33701
(813) 898-4105
Licensure Skilled Care; Intermediate Care.
Beds SNF 158; ICF 104. *Certified* Medicaid; Medicare.
Ownership Proprietary.
Staff RNs 8 (ft); LPNs 18 (ft); Nurses aides 79 (ft); 43 (ft).

Concordia Manor*
321 13th Ave S, Saint Petersburg, FL, 33701
(813) 822-3030
Licensure Skilled Care. *Beds* 39. *Certified* Medicaid.
Ownership Proprietary.
Staff RNs 2 (ft); LPNs 4 (ft); Nurses aides 9 (ft).

Convalescent Care Center*
550 62nd St S, Saint Petersburg, FL, 33707
(813) 347-6151
Licensure Skilled Care. *Beds* 120. *Certified* Medicaid; Medicare.
Ownership Proprietary.
Staff RNs 8 (ft); LPNs 8 (ft); Nurses aides 25 (ft).

Golfview Nursing Home*
3636 10th Ave N, Saint Petersburg, FL, 33713
(813) 894-7648
Licensure Skilled Care. *Beds* 56. *Certified* Medicaid; Medicare.
Ownership Proprietary.
Staff RNs 4 (ft); LPNs 5 (ft); Nurses aides 13 (ft).

Good Samaritan Nursing Home*
3127 57th Ave N, Saint Petersburg, FL, 33714
(813) 527-2171
Licensure Skilled Care. *Beds* 60. *Certified* Medicaid; Medicare.
Ownership Proprietary.
Staff RNs 5 (ft); LPNs 5 (ft); Nurses aides 14 (ft).
Languages German

Greenbrook Nursing Center
1000 24th St N, Saint Petersburg, FL, 33713
(813) 896-2109
Medical Dir/Dir of Nursing Dr Malcolm Fraser.
Licensure Skilled Care. *Beds* 120. *Certified* Medicaid; Medicare.
Ownership Proprietary.
Staff RNs 5 (ft), 2 (pt); LPNs 9 (ft), 4 (pt); Orderlies 4 (ft); Nurses aides 40 (ft), 8 (pt); Physical therapists 1 (ft); Reality therapists 1 (ft); Occupational therapists 1 (ft); Speech therapists 1 (ft); Activities coordinators 1 (ft); Dietitians 1 (ft), 1 (pt); Dentists 1 (pt); Ophthalmologists 1 (pt); Podiatrists 2 (pt); Audiologists 1 (pt).
Languages Spanish
Facilities Dining room; Physical therapy room; Activities room; Chapel; Crafts room; Barber/Beauty shop; Library.

Activities Arts and Crafts; Cards; Games; Reading groups; Prayer groups; Movies; Shopping trips; Dances/Social or cultural gatherings.

Huber Restorium
521 69th Ave N, Saint Petersburg, FL, 33702
(813) 527-7277
Medical Dir/Dir of Nursing Thirl Jarrett MD.
Licensure Skilled Care. *Beds* 96. *Certified* Medicare.
Ownership Proprietary.
Admissions Requirements Minimum age 21; Medical examination; Physician's request.
Staff Physicians 42 (pt); RNs 8 (ft), 3 (pt); LPNs 7 (ft), 4 (pt); Nurses aides 35 (ft), 35 (pt); Physical therapists 2 (pt); Reality therapists 1 (pt); Recreational therapists 1 (ft); Occupational therapists 1 (pt); Speech therapists 1 (pt); Activities coordinators 1 (ft); Dietitians 1 (ft); Dentists 1 (pt); Ophthalmologists 1 (pt); Podiatrists 1 (pt); Audiologists 1 (pt).
Facilities Dining room; Physical therapy room; Activities room; Chapel; Crafts room; Laundry room; Barber/Beauty shop; Library.
Activities Arts and Crafts; Cards; Games; Reading groups; Prayer groups; Movies; Shopping trips; Dances/Social or cultural gatherings.
Description Set in a park-like environment, recipient of "St Petersburg City Beautiful Commission Award"; rated a superior facility by State Licensure Board.

Jacaranda Manor*
4250 66th St N, Saint Petersburg, FL, 33709
(813) 546-2405
Licensure Skilled Care. *Beds* 299. *Certified* Medicare.
Ownership Proprietary.
Staff RNs 9 (ft); LPNs 12 (ft); Nurses aides 68 (ft); 46 (ft).
Languages Hebrew, Spanish, French, Tagalog

Jaylene Manor Nursing Home*
896 73rd Ave N, Saint Petersburg, FL, 33702
Licensure Skilled Care. *Beds* 63. *Certified* Medicaid.
Ownership Proprietary.
Staff RNs 4 (ft); LPNs 6 (ft); Nurses aides 20 (ft).
Languages Italian, Spanish

Lakeview Manor Nursing Home*
815 7th Ave S, Saint Petersburg, FL, 33701
(813) 898-3104
Licensure Skilled Care. *Beds* 39. *Certified* Medicaid.
Ownership Proprietary.
Staff RNs 1 (ft); LPNs 3 (ft); Nurses aides 8 (ft); 7 (ft).

Leisure Manor*
336 4th Ave N, Saint Petersburg, FL, 33701
(813) 896-4171
Licensure Skilled Care. *Beds* 24.
Ownership Proprietary.
Staff RNs 7 (ft); LPNs 4 (ft); Nurses aides 10 (ft).
Affiliation Presbyterian

Majestic Towers
1255 Pasadena Ave S, Saint Petersburg, FL, 33707 (813) 347-2160
Admin Virginia Dressler. *Medical Dir/Dir of*

Nursing Gilbert Pena MD.
Licensure Skilled Care. *Beds* 97.
Ownership Proprietary.
Staff RNs 5 (ft), 3 (pt); LPNs 9 (ft), 2 (pt); Orderlies 6 (ft); Nurses aides 27 (ft), 1 (pt); Physical therapists; Recreational therapists; Occupational therapists; Activities coordinators 2 (ft); Dietitians 1 (ft), 1 (pt); Dentists; Podiatrists; Audiologists; Social workers 1 (ft).
Facilities Dining room; Physical therapy room; Activities room; Chapel; Crafts room; Laundry room; Barber/Beauty shop; Library.
Activities Arts and Crafts; Cards; Games; Reading groups; Prayer groups; Movies; Shopping trips; Dances/Social or cultural gatherings.
Description This attractive facility is located on beautiful grounds within 100 feet of Boca Ciega Bay on one side, the Gulf of Mexico to the west, and Tampa Bay to the east. Health center is adjacent to 2 buildings of 20 stories each, 15 apartments per floor with cooking and generous living areas.

Maria Manor Health Care
10300 4th St N, Saint Petersburg, FL, 33702
(813) 576-1025
Admin Margaret R McDonald. *Medical Dir/Dir of Nursing* Julio Valdes MD.
Licensure Skilled Care. *Beds* 274. *Certified* Medicaid.
Ownership Nonprofit.
Admissions Requirements Minimum age 16; Medical examination; Physician's request.
Languages Spanish, Italian, Polish, Yugoslavian
Affiliation Roman Catholic
Facilities Dining room; Physical therapy room; Activities room; Chapel; Crafts room; Laundry room; Barber/Beauty shop; Library.
Activities Arts and Crafts; Cards; Games; Reading groups; Prayer groups; Movies; Shopping trips; Dances/Social or cultural gatherings.
Description Georgian-style older facility with 17 acres of beautiful landscaping; Mass served daily by resident chaplain.

Masonic Home of Florida
125 32nd Ave NE, Saint Petersburg, FL, 33704
(813) 822-3499
Medical Dir/Dir of Nursing Dr E Young.
Licensure Skilled Care. *Beds* 85.
Ownership Nonprofit.
Staff Physicians 2 (ft); RNs 12 (ft), 2 (pt); LPNs 9 (ft); Orderlies 1 (ft); Nurses aides 36 (ft), 4 (pt); Physical therapists 1 (pt); Reality therapists 1 (pt); Recreational therapists 1 (pt); Speech therapists 1 (pt); Activities coordinators 1 (ft); Dietitians 1 (ft); Dentists 2 (ft); Ophthalmologists 1 (ft); Podiatrists 1 (ft); Audiologists 1 (pt).
Affiliation Masons
Facilities Dining room; Physical therapy room; Activities room; Chapel; Crafts room; Laundry room; Barber/Beauty shop; Library.
Activities Arts and Crafts; Cards; Games; Prayer groups; Shopping trips; Dances/Social or cultural gatherings.
Description Resident must be a Mason in good standing by 60th birthday.

New Fern Restorium*
859 10th Ave N, Saint Petersburg, FL, 33701
(813) 896-8619

Licensure Skilled Care. *Beds* 116. *Certified* Medicaid; Medicare.
Ownership Proprietary.
Staff RNs 4 (ft); LPNs 13 (ft); Nurses aides 27 (ft).

North Horizon Health Care Center*
1301 16th St N, Saint Petersburg, FL, 33705
(813) 898-5119
Licensure Skilled Care. *Beds* 50. *Certified* Medicaid; Medicare.
Ownership Proprietary.
Staff RNs 2 (ft); LPNs 4 (ft); Nurses aides 11 (ft); 11 (ft).

North Shores Health Center*
939 Beach Dr, Saint Petersburg, FL, 33701
Beds 26.
Ownership Proprietary.

Palm Shores Retirement Center*
830 N Shore Dr, Saint Petersburg, FL, 33701
(813) 894-2102
Licensure Skilled Care. *Beds* 36.
Ownership Nonprofit.
Staff RNs 4 (ft); LPNs 3 (ft); Nurses aides 8 (ft); 30 (ft).
Languages Italian, German
Affiliation Baptist

Parc Center Apartments*
3190 75th St N, Saint Petersburg, FL, 33710
(813) 384-0607
Licensure Intermediate Care for Mentally Retarded. *Beds* 48.
Ownership Nonprofit.

Parc Cottage
3100 75th St N, Saint Petersburg, FL, 33710
(813) 345-9111
Licensure Intermediate Care for Mentally Retarded. *Beds* 16. *Certified* Medicaid.
Ownership Nonprofit.
Staff Physicians; Dietitians; Nurses aides.
Activities Arts and Crafts.

Rosedale Restorium*
3479 54th Ave N, Saint Petersburg, FL, 33714
(813) 527-7315
Licensure Skilled Care. *Beds* 192. *Certified* Medicaid.
Ownership Proprietary.
Staff RNs 8 (ft); LPNs 18 (ft); Nurses aides 40 (ft).

Saint Petersburg Cluster*
1101 102nd Ave N, Saint Petersburg, FL, 33702 (813) 536-5911
Licensure Intermediate Care for Mentally Retarded. *Beds* 8.

Shore Acres Nursing and Convalescent Home
4500 Indianapolis St NE, Saint Petersburg, FL, 33703 (813) 527-5801
Licensure Skilled Care. *Beds* 109. *Certified* Medicaid; Medicare.
Ownership Proprietary.
Staff Physicians; Dietitians; Nurses aides.
Languages Spanish, German, Polish, Italian, Slovak
Facilities Dining room; Physical therapy room; Activities room; Chapel; Crafts room; Laundry room; Barber/Beauty shop; Library.

Activities Arts and Crafts; Cards; Games; Reading groups; Prayer groups; Movies; Shopping trips; Dances/Social or cultural gatherings.

South Heritage Health Care Center
718 Lakeview Ave S, Saint Petersburg, FL, 33705 (813) 894-5125
Medical Dir/Dir of Nursing Dr Malcolm Fraser.
Licensure Skilled Care. *Beds* 75. *Certified* Medicaid; Medicare.
Ownership Proprietary.
Staff Physicians 1 (pt); RNs 3 (ft); LPNs 12 (ft); Nurses aides 27 (ft), 4 (pt); Physical therapists 1 (pt); Speech therapists 1 (pt); Activities coordinators 1 (ft); Dietitians 1 (pt); Dentists 1 (pt); Podiatrists 1 (pt); Audiologists 1 (pt).
Facilities Dining room; Activities room; Barber/Beauty shop.
Activities Arts and Crafts; Cards; Games; Reading groups; Prayer groups; Movies; Shopping trips; Dances/Social or cultural gatherings.
Description South Heritage has initiated a unique feature called a wheelchair garden; residents who are wheelchair-bound can continue to participate in gardening hobbies.

Suncoast Manor
6909 9th St S, Saint Petersburg, FL, 33705
(813) 867-1131
Medical Dir/Dir of Nursing Dr James West.
Licensure Skilled Care. *Beds* 161.
Ownership Nonprofit.
Admissions Requirements Minimum age 62; Medical examination; Physician's request.
Staff Physicians 3 (pt); RNs 10 (ft), 1 (pt); LPNs 10 (ft); Nurses aides 35 (ft), 1 (pt); Physical therapists 1 (ft); Speech therapists 1 (pt); Activities coordinators 1 (ft); Dietitians 1 (pt); Dentists 1 (pt); Ophthalmologists 1 (pt); Podiatrists 1 (pt); Audiologists 1 (pt); Private duty aides 40 (ft); Social workers 1 (pt).
Languages Spanish, German, French, Russian
Affiliation Episcopal
Facilities Dining room; Physical therapy room; Activities room; Chapel; Crafts room; Laundry room; Barber/Beauty shop; Library; Auditorium; Lounge; Gardens; Shuffleboard; Swimming.
Activities Arts and Crafts; Cards; Games; Reading groups; Prayer groups; Movies; Shopping trips; Dances/Social or cultural gatherings.
Description Unique in design and completely moderinized, facility provides the finest medical care; professionally staffed; registered nurses on duty 24 hours a day; cheerful, comfortable surroundings and genuine concerned attitude of staff guarantee peace of mind and security.

Suncoast Nursing Home*
2000 17th Ave S, Saint Petersburg, FL, 33712
(813) 823-1861
Licensure Skilled Care. *Beds* 59. *Certified* Medicaid.
Ownership Proprietary.
Staff RNs 2 (ft); LPNs 5 (ft); Nurses aides 9 (ft).

Sunny Shores Villas Health Center
125 5th Ave S, Saint Petersburg, FL, 33705
(813) 867-2131 ext 548
Admin S S McGlathery.

Licensure Skilled Care. *Beds* 108.
Ownership Nonprofit.
Admissions Requirements Minimum age 65;
Medical examination; Physician's request.
Staff Physicians 2 (pt); RNs 13 (ft); LPNs 11
(ft); Orderlies 1 (ft); Nurses aides 54 (ft);
Physical therapists; Reality therapists; Recreational therapists; Occupational therapists; Speech therapists; Activities coordinators 1 (ft);
Dietitians; Dentists; Ophthalmologists; Podiatrists; Audiologists; Social workers 1 (ft).
Affiliation Methodist
Facilities Dining room; Physical therapy room;
Activities room; Crafts room; Laundry room;
Barber/Beauty shop; Library.
Activities Arts and Crafts; Cards; Games;
Reading groups; Prayer groups; Movies; Shopping trips; Dances/Social or cultural gatherings.
Description This facility only serves the residents of the St Petersburg Methodist Home,
Inc, and does not accept patients from the general public; essentially a department in a life
care facility.

Swanholm Nursing Hotel*
6200 Central Ave, Saint Petersburg, FL, 33707
(813) 347-5196
Licensure Skilled Care. *Beds* 273. *Certified* Medicaid; Medicare.
Ownership Nonprofit.
Staff RNs 18 (ft); LPNs 13 (ft); Nurses aides 66
(ft).
Languages Spanish, Russian, Polish, French,
Yugoslavian, Czechoslavakian
Affiliation Lutheran

Tyrone Medical Inn
1100 66th St N, Saint Petersburg, FL, 33710
(813) 345-9331
Medical Dir/Dir of Nursing Douglas W Hood
MD.
Licensure Skilled Care. *Beds* 59. *Certified* Medicare.
Ownership Proprietary.
Staff RNs 2 (ft); LPNs 7 (ft); Nurses aides 22
(ft).
Facilities Dining room; Activities room; Barber/Beauty shop.
Activities Arts and Crafts; Games; Movies.

United Health Corporation
6300 46th Ave N, Saint Petersburg, FL, 33709
(813) 544-1444
Medical Dir/Dir of Nursing Dr George
Camarinos.
Licensure Skilled Care. *Beds* 102. *Certified* Medicaid; Medicare.
Ownership Proprietary.
Admissions Requirements Minimum age 16;
Medical examination; Physician's request.
Staff Physicians 3 (pt); RNs 4 (ft), 4 (pt); LPNs
7 (ft), 6 (pt); Orderlies 4 (ft), 1 (pt); Nurses aides
35 (ft), 6 (pt); Physical therapists; Speech therapists 1 (pt); Activities coordinators 1 (ft), 1 (pt);
Dietitians 1 (pt); Dentists 1 (pt); Podiatrists 1
(pt); Audiologists 1 (pt).
Languages French, Spanish
Facilities Dining room; Activities room; Crafts
room; Barber/Beauty shop.
Activities Arts and Crafts; Cards; Games;
Reading groups; Prayer groups; Movies; Shopping trips.

Victoria Martin Nursing Home
555 31st St S, Saint Petersburg, FL, 33712 (813)
821-0995
Medical Dir/Dir of Nursing Dr Orion T Ayer.
Licensure Skilled Care. *Beds* 38. *Certified* Medicaid.
Ownership Proprietary.
Admissions Requirements Medical examination; Physician's request.
Staff RNs 3 (ft), 5 (pt); LPNs 4 (pt); Nurses
aides 12 (ft), 2 (pt); Physical therapists; Activities coordinators 1 (ft).
Facilities Dining room; Activities room;
Laundry room.
Activities Arts and Crafts; Cards; Games;
Reading groups; Prayer groups; Movies; Dances/Social or cultural gatherings.
Description Facility offers home-like and
family-oriented atmosphere.

Wedgewood Health Care*
1735 9th St S, Saint Petersburg, FL, 33705
(813) 821-8866
Licensure Skilled Care; Intermediate Care.
Beds SNF 109; ICF 163. *Certified* Medicaid;
Medicare.
Ownership Proprietary.
Staff RNs 10 (ft); LPNs 21 (ft); Nurses aides 56
(ft).
Languages French, German

Whitehall Convalescent Home*
5601 31st St S, Saint Petersburg, FL, 33712
(813) 867-6955
Licensure Skilled Care. *Beds* 52.
Ownership Proprietary.
Staff RNs 4 (ft); LPNs 5 (ft); Nurses aides 18
(ft).
Languages French, Hindu, Spanish, Arabic

William and Mary Nursing Home*
811 Jackson St N, Saint Petersburg, FL, 33712
(813) 896-3651
Licensure Skilled Care. *Beds* 66. *Certified* Medicaid; Medicare.
Ownership Proprietary.
Staff RNs 5 (ft); LPNs 7 (ft); Nurses aides 21
(ft).
Languages Tagalog, Spanish

SAINT PETERSBURG BEACH

Crown Nursing Home*
5351 Gulf Blvd, Saint Petersburg Beach, FL,
33706 (813) 360-5548
Licensure Skilled Care. *Beds* 50. *Certified* Medicaid; Medicare.
Ownership Proprietary.
Staff LPNs 4 (ft); Nurses aides 13 (ft).
Languages Polish, German

SANFORD

Lakeview Nursing Center
919 E 2nd St, Sanford, FL, 32771 (305)
322-6707
Licensure Skilled Care. *Beds* 105.
Ownership Proprietary.
Staff RNs 3 (ft); LPNs 8 (ft); Nurses aides 29
(ft).
Languages Spanish, German

Sanford Nursing and Convalescent Center Inc*
950 Mellonville Ave, Sanford, FL, 32771 (305)
322-8566
Licensure Skilled Care. *Beds* 118. *Certified* Medicaid.
Ownership Proprietary.
Staff RNs 5 (ft); LPNs 5 (ft); Nurses aides 24
(ft); 15 (ft).
Languages Spanish, Swedish

SARASOTA

Bay Village of Sarasota*
8400 Vamo Rd, Sarasota, FL, 33581 (813)
966-5611
Licensure Skilled Care. *Beds* 107.
Ownership Nonprofit.
Staff RNs 19 (ft); LPNs 4 (ft); Nurses aides 30
(ft); 71 (ft).
Affiliation Presbyterian

Beneva Nursing Pavilion*
741 S Beneva Rd, Sarasota, FL, 35582 (813)
857-0310
Beds 120.
Ownership Proprietary.

Burzenski Nursing Home*
4450 8th St, Sarasota, FL, 33582 (813)
371-6430
Licensure Skilled Care. *Beds* 60.
Ownership Proprietary.

East Manor Medical Care Center*
1524 S East Ave, Sarasota, FL, 33579 (813)
365-2422
Licensure Skilled Care. *Beds* 171. *Certified* Medicaid; Medicare.
Ownership Proprietary.
Staff RNs 11 (ft); LPNs 13 (ft); Nurses aides 49
(ft); 25 (ft).
Languages Spanish

Hillhaven Convalescent Center*
1625 S Osprey Ave, Sarasota, FL, 33579 (813)
955-5741
Licensure Skilled Care. *Beds* 77. *Certified* Medicaid; Medicare.
Ownership Proprietary.
Staff RNs 13 (ft); LPNs 6 (ft); Nurses aides 17
(ft).

J H Floyd Sunshine Manor*
1755 18th St, Sarasota, FL, 33578 (813)
955-4915
Licensure Skilled Care. *Beds* 70. *Certified* Medicaid.
Ownership Nonprofit.
Staff RNs 4 (ft); LPNs 5 (ft); Nurses aides 24
(ft); 18 (ft).

Kennington Manor
3250 12th St, Sarasota, FL, 33577 (813)
365-4185
Medical Dir/Dir of Nursing Dr John Steele.
Licensure Skilled Care. *Beds* 147. *Certified* Medicaid.
Ownership Proprietary.
Admissions Requirements Minimum age 16.
Staff RNs 8 (ft), 3 (pt); LPNs 6 (ft), 4 (pt);
Orderlies 1 (ft), 1 (pt); Nurses aides 32 (ft);
Physical therapists 1 (pt); Speech therapists 1

(pt); Activities coordinators 1 (ft), 1 (pt); Dietitians 1 (pt); Dentists 1 (pt); Podiatrists 1 (pt); Audiologists 1 (pt).
Languages Spanish, Korean

Plymouth Harbor Inc
700 John Ringling Blvd, Sarasota, FL, 33577 (813) 365-2600
Licensure Skilled Care. *Beds* 43.
Ownership Nonprofit.
Staff RNs 10 (ft); LPNs 8 (ft); Orderlies 3 (ft); Nurses aides 12 (ft); Dietitians 1 (ft).
Affiliation Church of Christ
Facilities Dining room; Chapel; Laundry room; Barber/Beauty shop; Library.
Activities Arts and Crafts; Cards; Games; Reading groups; Prayer groups; Movies; Shopping trips.

Sarasota Nursing Pavilion
2600 Courtland St, Sarasota, FL, 33577 (813) 365-2926
Admin Claire Fellema. *Medical Dir/Dir of Nursing* Ernest Grochowski MD.
Licensure Skilled Care. *Beds* 180. *Certified* Medicaid; Medicare.
Ownership Proprietary.
Admissions Requirements Minimum age 16; Medical examination; Physician's request.
Staff LPNs 25 (ft), 8 (pt); Orderlies 3 (ft); Nurses aides 35 (ft), 20 (pt); Physical therapists 2 (ft); Recreational therapists 1 (ft); Occupational therapists 2 (ft); Speech therapists 1 (pt); Activities coordinators 1 (ft); Dietitians 1 (ft).
Languages Spanish, Vietnamese
Facilities Dining room; Physical therapy room; Activities room; Crafts room; Laundry room; Barber/Beauty shop; Library.
Activities Arts and Crafts; Cards; Games; Reading groups; Prayer groups; Movies; Shopping trips; Dances/Social or cultural gatherings.
Description VA approved facility offers skilled services including IV and oxygen therapy, Hickman and subclavian catheter care, tracheotomy, ileostomy, and colostomy care; 7-day-a-week restorative nursing and management of patients receiving treatment for cancer; excellent rehabilitative services provided.

Sarasota Welfare Home Inc
1501 N Orange Ave, Sarasota, FL, 33577 (813) 365-0250
Licensure Skilled Care; Intermediate Care. *Beds* 204. *Certified* Medicaid; Medicare.
Ownership Nonprofit.
Admissions Requirements Minimum age 65; Medical examination.
Staff Physicians; Dietitians; Nurses aides.
Languages Spanish
Facilities Dining room; Activities room; Chapel; Crafts room; Laundry room; Barber/Beauty shop; Library.
Activities Arts and Crafts; Cards; Games; Reading groups; Prayer groups; Movies; Shopping trips; Dances/Social or cultural gatherings.

Springwood Nursing Center Ltd*
4602 Northgate Court, Sarasota, FL, 33580 (813) 355-2913
Beds 120.
Ownership Proprietary.

Sunnyside Nursing Home
5201 Bahia Vista, Sarasota, FL, 33530 (813) 371-2729
Medical Dir/Dir of Nursing Dr Loren Zehr.
Licensure Skilled Care. *Beds* 60. *Certified* Medicaid.
Ownership Proprietary.
Staff RNs 4 (ft), 3 (pt); LPNs 3 (ft), 7 (pt); Orderlies 4 (ft), 3 (pt); Nurses aides 15 (ft), 10 (pt).
Languages German
Affiliation Mennonite
Facilities Dining room; Activities room; Laundry room; Barber/Beauty shop.
Activities Arts and Crafts; Cards; Games; Reading groups; Prayer groups; Movies; Dances/Social or cultural gatherings.

Wilhelms Nursing Home*
1507 S Tuttle Ave, Sarasota, FL, 33580 (813) 365-2737
Licensure Skilled Care. *Beds* 123. *Certified* Medicaid.
Ownership Proprietary.
Staff RNs 5 (ft); LPNs 11 (ft); Nurses aides 22 (ft).
Languages Spanish

SEBRING

Palms Health Care Center
306 S Ridgewood Dr, Sebring, FL, 33870 (813) 385-0161
Admin T R Newcomer. *Medical Dir/Dir of Nursing* Vinod Thakker MD.
Licensure Skilled Care. *Beds* 54. *Certified* Medicaid; Medicare.
Ownership Nonprofit.
Admissions Requirements Minimum age 62.
Staff RNs 1 (ft), 2 (pt); LPNs 8 (ft), 4 (pt); Orderlies 1 (ft), 1 (pt); Nurses aides 19 (ft), 10 (pt); Physical therapists 1 (pt); Activities coordinators 1 (ft); Dietitians 1 (ft), 1 (pt).
Affiliation Church of the Brethren
Facilities Dining room; Physical therapy room; Activities room; Chapel; Crafts room; Laundry room; Barber/Beauty shop; Library; Lobby; Social space.
Activities Arts and Crafts; Games; Movies; Shopping trips; Dances/Social or cultural gatherings.
Description The Palms is a church-related, not-for-profit retirement community located in a quiet noncongested area with an exceptional activities program and high quality care reputation; presently launching major new development project, ACLF, and healthcare additions.

Sebring Care Center*
3011 Kenilworth Blvd, Sebring, FL, 33870 (813) 382-2153
Licensure Skilled Care. *Beds* 103. *Certified* Medicaid; Medicare.
Ownership Proprietary.
Staff RNs 7 (ft); LPNs 7 (ft); Nurses aides 22 (ft).
Languages Spanish

SEMINOLE

Seminole Nursing Pavilion
10800 Temple Terrace, Seminole, FL, 33542
Admin Michael A Barody. *Medical Dir/Dir of Nursing* Mark F Franklin DO.
Licensure Skilled Care; Intermediate Care. *Beds* 120. *Certified* Medicaid; Medicare.
Ownership Proprietary.
Admissions Requirements Medical examination; Physician's request.
Staff Physicians; RNs; LPNs; Orderlies; Nurses aides; Physical therapists; Reality therapists; Recreational therapists; Occupational therapists; Speech therapists; Activities coordinators; Dietitians; Dentists; Ophthalmologists; Podiatrists; Audiologists.
Facilities Dining room; Physical therapy room; Activities room; Crafts room; Laundry room; Barber/Beauty shop; Library.
Activities Arts and Crafts; Games; Reading groups; Prayer groups; Movies; Shopping trips.
Description This is a newly built facility with all rooms individually decorated with wallpaper, carpet, and private baths; the Market Place is located on the property containing shops such as a general store, ice cream parlor, billards room, and dentist and doctor's office. There is a swimming pool and spa for the residents, as well as a town hall for meetings. VA approved.

SOUTH DAYTONA

Daytona Manor Nursing Home
650 Reed Canal St, South Daytona, FL, 32019 (904) 767-4831
Admin Elizabeth Peterson. *Medical Dir/Dir of Nursing* George B Powell DO.
Licensure Skilled Care. *Beds* 65. *Certified* Medicaid.
Ownership Proprietary.
Admissions Requirements Minimum age 16; Medical examination; Physician's request.
Staff Physicians; RNs; LPNs; Orderlies; Nurses aides; Physical therapists; Speech therapists; Activities coordinators; Dietitians; Dentists; Podiatrists.
Languages German, French, Spanish, Greek, Slavic
Facilities Dining room; Activities room; Barber/Beauty shop.
Activities Arts and Crafts; Cards; Games; Prayer groups; Movies.

SOUTH PASADENA

Deluxe Care Inn*
1820 Shore Dr S, South Pasadena, FL, 33707 (813) 384-9300
Licensure Skilled Care. *Beds* 58. *Certified* Medicare.
Ownership Proprietary.
Staff RNs 4 (ft); LPNs 9 (ft); Nurses aides 13 (ft).
Languages Spanish

Pasadena Manor*
1430 Pasadena Ave S, South Pasadena, FL, 33707 (813) 347-1257
Licensure Skilled Care. *Beds* 126. *Cer-*

tified Medicaid; Medicare.
Ownership Proprietary.
Staff RNs 6 (ft); LPNs 6 (ft); Nurses aides 28 (ft).
Languages Spanish, Tagalog

SPRING HILL

Evergreen Woods*
PO Box 3091, Spring Hill, FL, 33526 (904) 596-2055
Beds 60. *Certified* Medicaid; Medicare.
Ownership Nonprofit.

STARKE

Whispering Pines Care Center
808 S Colley Rd, Starke, FL, 32091 (904) 964-6220
Admin Patrick J Scanlin. *Medical Dir/Dir of Nursing* Pete G Felos MD.
Licensure Skilled Care. *Beds* 120. *Certified* Medicaid; Medicare.
Ownership Proprietary.
Admissions Requirements Minimum age 16; Medical examination.
Staff RNs 4 (ft); LPNs 4 (ft); Orderlies 1 (ft); Nurses aides 20 (ft), 8 (pt); Physical therapists 1 (pt); Activities coordinators 1 (ft), 1 (pt); Dietitians 1 (pt); Dentists 1 (pt); Podiatrists 1 (pt).
Facilities Dining room; Physical therapy room; Activities room; Chapel; Crafts room; Laundry room; Barber/Beauty shop; Library; Screened front patio; Wheelchair park/picnic area; Meditation room.
Activities Arts and Crafts; Cards; Games; Reading groups; Prayer groups; Movies; Dances/Social or cultural gatherings; Outings to restaurants, County Fair, Parades.
Description Facility renovated and added to in 1984.

STUART

Stuart Convalescent Center*
1500 Palm Beach Rd, Stuart, FL, 33494 (305) 283-5887
Licensure Skilled Care. *Beds* 182. *Certified* Medicaid; Medicare.
Ownership Proprietary.
Staff RNs 5 (ft); LPNs 7 (ft); Nurses aides 32 (ft); 15 (ft).

SUN CITY CENTER

Lake Towers Health Center
101 Trinity Lakes Dr, Sun City Center, FL, 33570 (813) 634-3347
Medical Dir/Dir of Nursing Gaspar Salvador MD.
Licensure Skilled Care. *Beds* 60. *Certified* Medicare.
Ownership Proprietary.
Staff RNs 2 (ft), 3 (pt); LPNs 7 (ft), 11 (pt); Nurses aides 13 (ft), 9 (pt); Activities coordinators 1 (ft).
Languages Spanish, French, Italian, Scottish
Facilities Dining room; Physical therapy room; Activities room; Crafts room; Barber/Beauty shop; Library.

Activities Arts and Crafts; Cards; Games; Reading groups; Prayer groups; Movies; Shopping trips; Dances/Social or cultural gatherings.

TALLAHASSEE

Capital Health Care Center
3333 Capital Medical Blvd, Tallahassee, FL, 32308 (904) 877-4115
Licensure Skilled Care. *Beds* 120. *Certified* Medicaid; Medicare.
Ownership Proprietary.
Admissions Requirements Minimum age 16; Medical examination; Physician's request.
Staff Dietitians; Nurses aides.
Facilities Dining room; Physical therapy room; Activities room; Crafts room; Laundry room; Barber/Beauty shop; Library.
Activities Arts and Crafts; Cards; Games; Reading groups; Prayer groups; Movies; Shopping trips; Dances/Social or cultural gatherings.
Description VA approved.

McCauley Cluster*
1385 McCauley Rd, Tallahassee, FL, 32308 (904) 487-1724
Licensure Intermediate Care for Mentally Retarded. *Beds* 24.
Ownership Proprietary.

Miracle Hill Nursing and Convalescent Home
1329 Abraham St, Tallahassee, FL, 32304 (904) 224-8486
Medical Dir/Dir of Nursing Dr Earl Britt and Dr Charlie Richardson.
Licensure Skilled Care. *Beds* 60. *Certified* Medicaid.
Ownership Nonprofit.
Admissions Requirements Minimum age 18; Medical examination.
Staff Physicians 3 (pt); RNs 2 (ft), 3 (pt); LPNs 5 (ft), 2 (pt); Orderlies 1 (ft); Nurses aides 24 (ft), 4 (pt); Physical therapists 1 (pt); Reality therapists 1 (pt); Recreational therapists 1 (pt); Speech therapists 1 (pt); Activities coordinators 1 (ft); Dietitians 1 (pt); Dentists 1 (pt); Podiatrists 1 (pt).
Facilities Dining room; Activities room; Crafts room; Laundry room; Barber/Beauty shop.
Activities Arts and Crafts; Games; Reading groups; Prayer groups; Movies; Shopping trips; Dances/Social or cultural gatherings.
Description Facility offers residents and family banquet, king and queen contest, Miracle Hill Day celebration, and volunteer recognition banquet.

Sunland Center—Tallahassee
2323 Phillips Rd, Tallahassee, FL, 32304 (904) 877-4161
Licensure Intermediate Care for Mentally Retarded. *Beds* 30.
Ownership Public.

Tallahassee Convalescent Home
2510 Miccosukee Rd, Tallahassee, FL, 32303 (904) 877-3131
Medical Dir/Dir of Nursing William T Kepper MD.
Licensure Skilled Care. *Beds* 72. *Certified* Medicaid.
Ownership Proprietary.

Admissions Requirements Medical examination.
Staff Physicians 1 (pt); RNs 4 (ft), 3 (pt); LPNs 4 (ft), 3 (pt); Nurses aides 22 (ft), 5 (pt); Reality therapists; Recreational therapists; Occupational therapists; Speech therapists; Activities coordinators; Dietitians; Podiatrists.
Languages French, Spanish
Facilities Dining room; Laundry room; Barber/Beauty shop; 2 Large TV rooms.
Activities Arts and Crafts; Cards; Games; Reading groups; Prayer groups; Movies; Shopping trips; Dances/Social or cultural gatherings.
Description A warm and friendly facility having many resident-oriented and family-oriented affairs during the year.

Tallahassee Developmental Center*
455 Appleyard Dr, Tallahassee, FL, 32304
Ownership Proprietary.

Westminister Oaks Nursing Home
4449 Meandering Way, Tallahassee, FL, 32308
Admin Robert F Wernet Jr. *Medical Dir/Dir of Nursing* Leslie S Emhof.
Licensure Skilled Care. *Beds* 60.
Ownership Nonprofit.
Admissions Requirements Minimum age 62; Medical examination; Physician's request.
Staff Physicians 1 (pt); RNs 5 (ft); LPNs 4 (ft); Orderlies 2 (ft); Nurses aides 15 (ft); Physical therapists 1 (pt); Reality therapists 1 (pt); Recreational therapists 1 (ft); Speech therapists 1 (pt); Activities coordinators 1 (ft); Dietitians 1 (ft); Dentists 1 (pt); Podiatrists 1 (pt); Audiologists 1 (pt).
Affiliation Presbyterian
Facilities Dining room; Physical therapy room; Activities room; Chapel; Crafts room; Laundry room; Barber/Beauty shop; Library.
Activities Arts and Crafts; Cards; Games; Reading groups; Prayer groups; Movies; Shopping trips; Dances/Social or cultural gatherings.
Description Facility is located on 96 wooded acres only 6 miles from downtown Tallahassee; full facilities and services available; continuing care retirement village.

TAMARAC

Tamarac Convalescent Center
7901 NW 88th Ave, Tamarac, FL, 33320 (305) 722-9330
Medical Dir/Dir of Nursing Juan Lopez.
Licensure Skilled Care; Intermediate Care.
Beds SNF 60; ICF 60. *Certified* Medicaid; Medicare.
Ownership Proprietary.
Admissions Requirements Physician's request.
Staff Physicians 6 (pt); RNs 2 (ft), 9 (pt); LPNs 7 (ft), 4 (pt); Orderlies 1 (ft); Nurses aides 40 (ft); Physical therapists 2 (ft); Reality therapists 1 (ft); Recreational therapists 1 (ft); Occupational therapists 1 (pt); Speech therapists 1 (pt); Activities coordinators 1 (ft); Dietitians 1 (pt); Dentists 1 (pt); Ophthalmologists 1 (pt); Podiatrists 1 (pt); Audiologists 1 (pt).
Languages German, Spanish, Italian
Facilities Dining room; Physical therapy room; Activities room; Crafts room; Laundry room; Barber/Beauty shop; Library.

Activities Arts and Crafts; Cards; Games; Reading groups; Prayer groups; Movies; Shopping trips; Dances/Social or cultural gatherings.

TAMPA

Ambrosia Home*
1709 Taliaferro Ave, Tampa, FL, 33602 (813) 223-4623
Licensure Skilled Care. *Beds* 80. *Certified* Medicaid.
Ownership Proprietary.
Staff RNs 4 (ft); LPNs 8 (ft); Nurses aides 24 (ft).
Languages Spanish, Italian

Bay to Bay Nursing Center*
3405 Bay to Bay Blvd, Tampa, FL, 33609 (813) 839-5325
Licensure Skilled Care. *Beds* 75. *Certified* Medicaid.
Ownership Proprietary.
Staff RNs 7 (ft); LPNs 6 (ft); Nurses aides 18 (ft); 17 (ft).

Cambridge Convalescent Center
9709 N Nebraska Ave, Tampa, FL, 33612 (813) 935-2121
Medical Dir/Dir of Nursing Henry Gomez MD.
Licensure Skilled Care. *Beds* 70. *Certified* Medicaid.
Ownership Proprietary.
Admissions Requirements Medical examination; Physician's request.
Staff Physicians 1 (pt); RNs 2 (ft), 1 (pt); LPNs 4 (ft), 2 (pt); Orderlies 1 (pt); Nurses aides 17 (ft), 2 (pt).
Languages Spanish
Facilities Dining room; Activities room; Crafts room; Laundry room; Barber/Beauty shop.
Activities Arts and Crafts; Games; Reading groups; Prayer groups; Movies; Dances/Social or cultural gatherings; Picnics.

Canterbury Towers*
3501 Bayshore Blvd, Tampa, FL, 33609 (813) 837-1083
Licensure Skilled Care. *Beds* 40. *Certified* Medicaid; Medicare.
Ownership Nonprofit.
Staff RNs 4 (ft); LPNs 5 (ft); Nurses aides 12 (ft).
Languages French, Spanish, German

Home Association
1203 22nd Ave, Tampa, FL, 33605 (813) 229-6901
Medical Dir/Dir of Nursing Aldo J Almaguer MD.
Licensure Skilled Care; Intermediate Care. *Beds* SNF 40; ICF 60. *Certified* Medicaid.
Ownership Nonprofit.
Admissions Requirements Minimum age 65; Medical examination.
Staff Physicians 3 (pt); RNs 4 (ft), 1 (pt); LPNs 9 (ft); Nurses aides 31 (ft); Activities coordinators 2 (ft), 3 (pt); Dietitians 1 (pt); Dentists 1 (pt).
Facilities Dining room; Activities room; Chapel; Crafts room; Laundry room; Barber/Beauty shop; Library.

Activities Arts and Crafts; Cards; Games; Reading groups; Prayer groups; Movies; Shopping trips; Dances/Social or cultural gatherings.
Description Old southern-style mansion located in 5-acre park setting; residents go on weekly outings to area attractions and restaurants; atmosphere of facility is very home-like.

John Knox Village Medical Center*
4100 E Fletcher Ave, Tampa, FL, 33612 (813) 971-7038
Licensure Skilled Care. *Beds* 60. *Certified* Medicare.
Ownership Nonprofit.
Staff RNs 3 (ft), 1 (pt); LPNs 1 (ft); Nurses aides 16 (ft); 10 (ft).
Languages Spanish

Manhattan Convalescent Center*
4610 S Manhattan Ave, Tampa, FL, 33611 (813) 839-5311
Licensure Skilled Care. *Beds* 179. *Certified* Medicaid.
Ownership Proprietary.
Staff RNs 7 (ft); LPNs 19 (ft); Nurses aides 36 (ft).
Languages Spanish, French

Medicenter of Tampa*
4411 N Habana St, Tampa, FL, 33614 (813) 872-2771
Licensure Skilled Care; Intermediate Care. *Beds* SNF 116; ICF 58. *Certified* Medicaid; Medicare.
Ownership Proprietary.
Staff RNs 12 (ft); LPNs 11 (ft).
Languages Spanish

Oakwood Park Su Casa*
1514 E Chelsea, Tampa, FL, 33610 (813) 238-6406
Licensure Skilled Care. *Beds* 240. *Certified* Medicaid; Medicare.
Ownership Proprietary.
Staff RNs 9 (ft); LPNs 23 (ft); Nurses aides 52 (ft).
Languages Spanish, Italian

Padgett Nursing Home*
5010 40th St, Tampa, FL, 33610 (813) 626-7109
Licensure Skilled Care. *Beds* 100. *Certified* Medicaid; Medicare.
Ownership Proprietary.
Staff RNs 4 (ft); LPNs 15 (ft); Nurses aides 24 (ft).
Languages Spanish

River Heights Nursing Home
2730 Ridgewood Ave, Tampa, FL, 33602 (813) 223-1303
Medical Dir/Dir of Nursing Dr Luis Crespo.
Licensure Skilled Care. *Beds* 42. *Certified* Medicaid.
Ownership Proprietary.
Admissions Requirements Minimum age 18; Medical examination; Physician's request.
Staff Physicians 1 (pt); RNs 4 (pt); LPNs 6 (pt); Orderlies 2 (pt); Nurses aides 10 (pt); Activities coordinators 1 (pt); Dietitians 1 (pt).
Languages Italian, Spanish, Czech
Facilities Dining room; Physical therapy room; Activities room; Crafts room; Laundry room; Barber/Beauty shop.

Activities Arts and Crafts; Cards; Games; Reading groups; Prayer groups; Movies; Shopping trips; Dances/Social or cultural gatherings.
Description Facility is situated on the Hillsborough River in a peaceful and quiet neighborhood.

Tampa Health Care Center
2916 Habana Way, Tampa, FL, 33614 (813) 876-5141
Medical Dir/Dir of Nursing Dr E A Perez.
Licensure Skilled Care. *Beds* 150. *Certified* Medicaid.
Ownership Proprietary.
Staff RNs 8 (ft), 8 (pt); LPNs 10 (ft), 6 (pt); Orderlies 5 (ft); Nurses aides 35 (ft), 20 (pt); Physical therapists 3 (pt); Reality therapists 1 (ft), 1 (pt); Recreational therapists 1 (pt); Occupational therapists 2 (pt); Speech therapists 1 (pt); Activities coordinators 1 (ft); Dietitians 1 (pt); Dentists 1 (pt); Ophthalmologists 1 (pt); Podiatrists 1 (pt); Audiologists 1 (pt).
Languages Spanish
Facilities Dining room; Physical therapy room; Activities room; Crafts room; Laundry room; Barber/Beauty shop; Library.
Activities Arts and Crafts; Cards; Games; Reading groups; Prayer groups; Movies; Shopping trips; Dances/Social or cultural gatherings.
Description Facility has association with a local colleges' nursing school for training of new nurses.

Town and County Convalescent Center*
8720 Jackson Springs Rd, Tampa, FL, 33615
Licensure Intermediate Care. *Beds* 120.
Ownership Proprietary.

University Park Convalescent Center
1818 E Fletcher Ave, Tampa, FL, 33612 (813) 977-2383
Medical Dir/Dir of Nursing Aldo J Almaguer MD.
Licensure Skilled Care. *Beds* 266. *Certified* Medicaid; Medicare.
Ownership Proprietary.
Admissions Requirements Minimum age 17; Medical examination; Physician's request.
Staff RNs 12 (ft), 3 (pt); LPNs 23 (ft), 2 (pt); Orderlies 9 (ft); Nurses aides 95 (ft); Physical therapists 1 (pt); Occupational therapists 1 (pt); Speech therapists 1 (pt); Activities coordinators 2 (ft); Dietitians 1 (pt); Dentists 1 (pt); Podiatrists 1 (pt); Audiologists 1 (pt).
Facilities Dining room; Physical therapy room; Activities room; Chapel; Barber/Beauty shop; Library.
Activities Arts and Crafts; Cards; Games; Reading groups; Prayer groups; Movies; Shopping trips; Dances/Social or cultural gatherings.
Description Special activities are carnivals in the spring and fall, rock and roll jamboree, wine and cheese parties, and New Years Eve party.

Wellington Manor*
10049 N Florida Ave, Tampa, FL, 33612 (813) 935-3185
Licensure Skilled Care. *Beds* 180. *Certified* Medicaid.
Ownership Proprietary.
Staff RNs 4 (ft); LPNs 17 (ft); Nurses aides 35 (ft).

TARPON SPRINGS

Tarpon Health Care Center*
501 S Walton Ave, Tarpon Springs, FL, 33589
(813) 938-2814
Licensure Skilled Care. *Beds* 120. *Certified* Medicaid.
Ownership Proprietary.
Staff RNs 2 (ft); LPNs 2 (ft); Nurses aides 26 (ft).

Tarpon Springs Convalescent Center
515 Chesapeake Dr, Tarpon Springs, FL, 33589
(813) 934-4629
Admin Mary J Love. *Medical Dir/Dir of Nursing* Thomas E Carson MD.
Licensure Skilled Care. *Beds* 120. *Certified* Medicaid; Medicare.
Ownership Proprietary.
Admissions Requirements Medical examination; Physician's request.
Staff RNs 2 (ft), 4 (pt); LPNs 7 (ft), 5 (pt); Nurses aides 40 (ft), 1 (pt); Physical therapists 1 (pt); Occupational therapists 1 (pt); Speech therapists 1 (pt); Activities coordinators 1 (ft); Dietitians 1 (pt); Dentists 1 (pt); Ophthalmologists 1 (pt); Podiatrists 1 (pt); Audiologists 1 (pt).
Languages Greek
Facilities Dining room; Physical therapy room; Activities room; Laundry room; Barber/Beauty shop.
Activities Arts and Crafts; Cards; Games; Reading groups; Prayer groups; Movies; Shopping trips; Dances/Social or cultural gatherings.
Description The rear of the center is located on a lovely bayou that curves into the yard. The facility has a screened back porch and patio area for walking and observing the lovely Florida sunsets. VA approved.

THONOTOSASSA

Lowe's Nursing and Convalescent Home*
Rt 1, Box 187, Thonotosassa, FL, 33592 (813) 228-9309
Medical Dir/Dir of Nursing E A Perez MD.
Licensure Skilled Care. *Beds* 120. *Certified* Medicaid; Medicare.
Ownership Proprietary.
Admissions Requirements Medical examination.
Staff RNs 3 (ft), 3 (pt); LPNs 11 (ft), 6 (pt); Nurses aides 60 (ft), 8 (pt); Activities coordinators 2 (ft); Dietitians 1 (pt).
Languages Spanish
Facilities Dining room; Physical therapy room; Activities room; Laundry room; Barber/Beauty shop.
Activities Arts and Crafts; Cards; Games; Reading groups; Prayer groups; Movies.
Description Facility is located in a very rural setting (next door to horse ranch) with many country activities, and many, many church groups.

TITUSVILLE

Titusville Nursing and Convalescent Center
1705 Jess Parrish Ct, Titusville, FL, 32796
(305) 269-5720
Medical Dir/Dir of Nursing Victor Boodhoo

MD.
Licensure Skilled Care. *Beds* 157. *Certified* Medicaid.
Ownership Proprietary.
Admissions Requirements Minimum age 21; Medical examination.
Staff Physicians 11 (pt); RNs 6 (ft), 8 (pt); LPNs 11 (ft), 5 (pt); Orderlies 5 (ft); Nurses aides 35 (ft), 15 (pt); Physical therapists 1 (pt); Occupational therapists 1 (pt); Speech therapists 1 (pt); Activities coordinators 2 (ft); Dietitians 1 (pt); Dentists 1 (pt); Podiatrists 2 (pt); Audiologists 1 (pt).
Languages French, Spanish
Facilities Dining room; Physical therapy room; Activities room; Chapel; Crafts room; Laundry room; Barber/Beauty shop.
Activities Arts and Crafts; Cards; Games; Prayer groups; Movies; Shopping trips.
Description VA approved.

TRENTON

Medic-Ayers Nursing Home*
RT 2, Box 32693, NE 7th St, Trenton, FL, 32693
Beds 60.
Ownership Proprietary.

VENICE

Venice Nursing Pavilion—North*
437 S Nokomis Ave, Venice, FL, 33595 (813) 488-9696
Licensure Skilled Care. *Beds* 120. *Certified* Medicaid; Medicare.
Ownership Proprietary.
Staff RNs 17 (ft); LPNs 3 (ft); Nurses aides 37 (ft).
Languages French, Italian, Spanish, Russian, Polish

Venice Nursing Pavilion—South*
200 Field Ave E, Venice, FL, 33595 (813) 484-2477
Licensure Skilled Care. *Beds* 120. *Certified* Medicaid; Medicare.
Ownership Proprietary.
Staff RNs 12 (ft); LPNs 6 (ft); Nurses aides 26 (ft); 23 (ft).
Languages Spanish

VERO BEACH

Florida Baptist Retirement Center*
1006 33rd St, Vero Beach, FL, 32960 (305) 567-5248
Licensure Skilled Care. *Beds* 24.
Ownership Nonprofit.
Staff RNs 2 (ft); LPNs 3 (ft); Nurses aides 6 (ft).
Affiliation Baptist

Mecca Convalescent Home
916 SW Hwy 1, Vero Beach, FL, 32960 (305) 562-3246
Admin Arvin A Okus. *Medical Dir/Dir of Nursing* R H Vinson MD.
Licensure Skilled Care. *Beds* 26. *Certified* Medicaid; Medicare.
Ownership Proprietary.

Admissions Requirements Physician's request.
Staff RNs 3 (ft), 1 (pt); LPNs 2 (ft), 1 (pt); Nurses aides 7 (ft), 4 (pt); Physical therapists; Reality therapists; Occupational therapists; Speech therapists; Activities coordinators 1 (ft); Dietitians; Dentists; Ophthalmologists; Podiatrists; Audiologists.
Facilities Dining room; Activities room; Laundry room.
Activities Arts and Crafts; Games; Shopping trips.

Royal Palm Convalescent Center
2180 10th Ave, Vero Beach, FL, 32960 (305) 567-5166
Medical Dir/Dir of Nursing Dr Donald Gold.
Licensure Skilled Care. *Beds* 72. *Certified* Medicare.
Ownership Proprietary.
Admissions Requirements Minimum age 16.
Staff Nurses aides 32 (ft); Dietitians 9 (ft).
Languages German
Facilities Dining room; Physical therapy room; Activities room; Crafts room; Laundry room; Barber/Beauty shop; Library.
Activities Arts and Crafts; Cards; Games; Reading groups; Prayer groups; Movies; Shopping trips; Dances/Social or cultural gatherings.

Vero Beach Care Center Inc*
3663 15th Ave, Vero Beach, FL, 32960 (305) 567-2552
Beds 103.
Ownership Proprietary.

WACHULA

Hardee Manor Nursing Home
401 Orange Pl, Wachula, FL, 33873 (813) 773-3231
Admin Ruth A Lewis. *Medical Dir/Dir of Nursing* Felix E Perez MD.
Licensure Skilled Care. *Beds* 60. *Certified* Medicaid; Medicare.
Ownership Proprietary.
Staff RNs 3 (ft); LPNs 6 (ft), 1 (pt); Orderlies 3 (ft), 1 (pt); Nurses aides 15 (ft), 6 (pt); Physical therapists; Speech therapists; Activities coordinators 1 (ft).
Languages Spanish
Facilities Dining room; Physical therapy room; Activities room; Chapel; Laundry room; Barber/Beauty shop.
Activities Arts and Crafts; Games; Prayer groups; Movies; Dances/Social or cultural gatherings.

WEST MELBOURNE

West Melbourne Health Care Center
2125 W New Haven Ave, West Melbourne, FL, 32901 (305) 725-7360
Medical Dir/Dir of Nursing Saul Dujovne MD.
Licensure Skilled Care; Intermediate Care.
Beds SNF 69; ICF 51. *Certified* Medicaid; Medicare.
Ownership Proprietary.
Admissions Requirements Minimum age 18; Medical examination; Physician's request.
Staff RNs 6 (ft), 7 (pt); LPNs 9 (ft), 3 (pt); Nurses aides 38 (ft), 7 (pt); Physical therapists;

Occupational therapists; Speech therapists.
Facilities Dining room; Physical therapy room;
Activities room; Laundry room; Barber/Beauty
shop; Library.
Activities Arts and Crafts; Cards; Games;
Reading groups; Prayer groups; Movies; Shopping trips; Dances/Social or cultural gatherings.

WEST PALM BEACH

Convalescent Center of the Palm Beaches
300 15th St, West Palm Beach, FL, 33401 (305)
832-6409
Medical Dir/Dir of Nursing Dr O L Kelley.
Licensure Skilled Care. *Beds* 99. *Certified* Medicaid; Medicare.
Ownership Proprietary.
Admissions Requirements Medical examination.
Staff RNs 4 (ft), 1 (pt); LPNs 11 (ft), 1 (pt);
Nurses aides 29 (ft), 6 (pt); Physical therapists 1
(ft); Occupational therapists 1 (pt); Speech therapists 1 (pt); Activities coordinators 1 (ft); Dietitians 1 (pt); Dentists 1 (pt); Ophthalmologists
1 (pt); Podiatrists 1 (pt); Audiologists 1 (pt).
Facilities Dining room; Physical therapy room;
Activities room; Crafts room; Laundry room;
Barber/Beauty shop.
Activities Arts and Crafts; Cards; Games;
Reading groups; Prayer groups; Movies.

Darcy Hall Nursing Home*
2170 Palm Beach Lakes Blvd, West Palm
Beach, FL, 33409 (305) 683-3333
Licensure Skilled Care. *Beds* 220. *Certified* Medicaid.
Ownership Proprietary.
Staff RNs 6 (ft); LPNs 20 (ft); Nurses aides 66
(ft).
Languages French, Spanish, Italian, German,
Tagalog

King David Center at Palm Beach*
1101 45th St, West Palm Beach, FL, 33407
(305) 844-4343
Licensure Skilled Care. *Beds* 191. *Certified* Medicaid; Medicare.
Ownership Proprietary.
Staff RNs 10 (ft); LPNs 10 (ft); Nurses aides 37
(ft).
Languages Italian, Spanish
Affiliation Jewish

Lakeside Health Center
2501 Australian Ave, West Palm Beach, FL,
33407 (305) 655-7780
Medical Dir/Dir of Nursing Dr Purcell.
Licensure Skilled Care. *Beds* 97. *Certified* Medicaid; Medicare.
Ownership Proprietary.
Staff RNs 5 (ft); LPNs 6 (ft); Nurses aides 32
(ft); Physical therapists 2 (pt); Occupational
therapists 1 (pt); Speech therapists 1 (pt);
Activities coordinators 1 (ft); Dietitians 1 (pt);
Dentists 1 (pt); Ophthalmologists 1 (pt); Podiatrists 1 (pt); Audiologists 1 (pt).
Facilities Dining room; Physical therapy room;
Activities room; Laundry room; Barber/Beauty
shop.
Activities Arts and Crafts; Cards; Games;
Reading groups; Prayer groups; Movies; Shopping trips; Dances/Social or cultural gatherings.

Lakeview Manor Nursing Home
208 Lake View Ave, West Palm Beach, FL,
33401 (305) 655-8322
Medical Dir/Dir of Nursing Dr Romano.
Licensure Skilled Care. *Beds* 102. *Certified* Medicaid.
Ownership Proprietary.
Admissions Requirements Minimum age 21;
Medical examination; Physician's request.
Staff RNs 5 (ft); LPNs 11 (ft); Orderlies 1 (ft);
Nurses aides 37 (ft); Physical therapists; Reality
therapists; Speech therapists; Activities coordinators 1 (ft); Dietitians 1 (ft); Dentists; Podiatrists; Pharmacists.
Languages Spanish, French, Yiddish
Facilities Dining room; Activities room; Crafts
room; Barber/Beauty shop.
Activities Arts and Crafts; Cards; Games;
Reading groups; Prayer groups; Movies; Shopping trips; Dances/Social or cultural gatherings.

**Lourdes-Noreen McKeen Residence for
Geriatric Care Inc**
315 S Flagler Dr, West Palm Beach, FL, 33401
(305) 655-8544
Medical Dir/Dir of Nursing Dr Thomas Murphy.
Licensure Skilled Care; Intermediate Care.
Beds SNF 40; ICF 80. *Certified* Medicaid;
Medicare.
Ownership Nonprofit.
Admissions Requirements Minimum age 65;
Medical examination.
Staff RNs 14 (ft), 4 (pt); LPNs 8 (ft), 2 (pt);
Nurses aides 48 (ft); Activities coordinators 1
(ft); Social workers 2 (ft).
Affiliation Roman Catholic
Facilities Dining room; Physical therapy room;
Activities room; Chapel; Laundry room; Barber/Beauty shop.
Activities Arts and Crafts; Cards; Games;
Reading groups; Movies; Dances/Social or cultural gatherings; Current events.

**Palm Beach County Home and General Care
Facility**
1200 45th St, West Palm Beach, FL, 33407
(305) 842-6111
Medical Dir/Dir of Nursing Dr Adil Sokmensuer.
Licensure Skilled Care; Intermediate Care.
Beds SNF 95; ICF 24. *Certified* Medicaid;
Medicare.
Ownership Public.
Admissions Requirements Minimum age 16;
Medical examination; Physician's request.
Staff Physicians 1 (ft); RNs 17 (ft), 1 (pt);
LPNs 19 (ft), 1 (pt); Orderlies 7 (ft); Nurses
aides 86 (ft); Physical therapists 1 (pt); Recreational therapists 1 (ft); Occupational therapists 1
(pt); Speech therapists 1 (pt); Activities coordinators 1 (ft); Dietitians 1 (pt); Dentists 1 (pt);
Ophthalmologists 1 (pt); Podiatrists 1 (pt);
Audiologists 1 (pt).
Languages Spanish
Facilities Dining room; Physical therapy room;
Activities room; Crafts room; Barber/Beauty
shop; Library.
Activities Arts and Crafts; Cards; Games;
Reading groups; Prayer groups; Movies; Shopping trips; Dances/Social or cultural gatherings;
Religious services for all denominations.
Description Facility features a complete

rehabilitation department including Hubbard
tank; also available are "Pet a Pet" program
and educational opportunities such as poetry
appreciation, creative expressions, course in
miracles, and provides for courses at local
junior college.

WILDWOOD

We Care
Rt 3, Box 490, Wildwood, FL, 32785
Admin Cathy Bowlin. *Medical Dir/Dir of
Nursing* Richard Wiley MD.
Licensure Skilled Care. *Beds* 120. *Certified* Medicaid.
Ownership Nonprofit.
Admissions Requirements Medical examination; Physician's request.
Staff RNs 9 (ft), 2 (pt); LPNs 10 (ft), 5 (pt);
Orderlies 4 (ft), 2 (pt); Nurses aides 44 (ft), 5
(pt); Physical therapists 1 (pt); Speech therapists
1 (pt); Activities coordinators 1 (ft); Dietitians
1 (pt); Dentists 1 (pt); Podiatrists 1 (pt);
Audiologists 1 (pt).
Facilities Dining room; Physical therapy room;
Activities room; Chapel; Laundry room; Barber/Beauty shop.
Activities Arts and Crafts; Cards; Games;
Reading groups; Prayer groups; Movies; Shopping trips; Dances/Social or cultural gatherings.
Description This facility, opened in May 1982,
is situated in a small town with a lot of community involvement; built on a very spacious
scale and located in a country-like setting, most
significant features of the facility are the personnel and care offered. Every effort is made to
reach each individual's needs from arranging
education programs to gardening and fishing
trips.

WILLISTON

Oakview Care Center*
301 3rd St, Williston, FL, 32696 (904)
528-3561
Licensure Skilled Care. *Beds* 180. *Certified* Medicaid.
Ownership Proprietary.
Staff RNs 6 (ft); LPNs 15 (ft); Nurses aides 44
(ft).
Languages Spanish, Vietnamese

WINTER GARDEN

West Orange Manor*
122 E Division St, Winter Garden, FL, 32787
(305) 656-3810
Licensure Skilled Care. *Beds* 118. *Certified* Medicaid.
Ownership Public.
Staff RNs 5 (ft); LPNs 10 (ft); Nurses aides 37
(ft).

WINTER HAVEN

Grovemont Nursing and Rehabilitation Center
2nd St and Ave "O" NE, Winter Haven, FL,
33880 (813) 293-3103
Medical Dir/Dir of Nursing Michael Carey.
Licensure Skilled Care. *Beds* 144. *Cer-*

tified Medicaid; Medicare.
Ownership Proprietary.
Admissions Requirements Medical examination; Physician's request.
Staff Physicians; RNs; LPNs; Nurses aides; Physical therapists; Recreational therapists; Occupational therapists; Speech therapists; Activities coordinators; Dietitians; Dentists; Ophthalmologists; Podiatrists; Audiologists.
Facilities Dining room; Physical therapy room; Activities room; Chapel; Crafts room; Barber-/Beauty shop; Library.
Activities Arts and Crafts; Reading groups; Prayer groups; Movies; Shopping trips; Dances-/Social or cultural gatherings.
Description Grovemont Nursing and Rehabilitation Center is the oldest nursing center in Winter Haven, servicing the needs of the community for 21 years. We offer speech, occupational, and physical therapies. We have the best physical therapy departments in the nursing home setting in the area. Eighty-five percent of our residents who are admitted for physical therapy are released in approximately 3 weeks. We have an outstanding activities either actively or passively.

WINTER PARK

Americana Health Care Center of Winter Park*
2075 Loch Lomond Dr, Winter Park, FL, 32792 (305) 628-5418
Licensure Skilled Care. *Beds* 138. *Certified* Medicaid; Medicare.
Ownership Proprietary.
Staff RNs 15 (ft); LPNs 10 (ft); Nurses aides 48 (ft).
Languages German

Howell Branch Court*
PO Box 4717, 3664 Howell Branch Rd, Winter Park, FL, 32794 (305) 671-1115
Licensure Intermediate Care for Mentally Retarded. *Beds* 64.
Ownership Proprietary.

Mary Lee Depugh Nursing Home
550 W Morse Blvd, Winter Park, FL, 32789 (305) 644-6634
Medical Dir/Dir of Nursing Dr Kenneth Richards.
Licensure Skilled Care. *Beds* 40. *Certified* Medicaid.
Ownership Nonprofit.
Admissions Requirements Minimum age 18; Medical examination; Physician's request.
Staff RNs 2 (ft); LPNs 5 (ft), 1 (pt); Nurses aides 12 (ft), 2 (pt); Activities coordinators 1 (ft); Dietitians 1 (pt).
Facilities Dining room; Activities room; Crafts room; Laundry room.
Activities Arts and Crafts; Cards; Games; Prayer groups; Movies; Shopping trips.

Winter Park Care Center*
2970 Scarlet Rd, Winter Park, FL, 32793 (305) 671-8030
Licensure Skilled Care. *Beds* 106. *Certified* Medicaid; Medicare.
Ownership Proprietary.

Staff RNs 7 (ft); LPNs 9 (ft); Nurses aides 22 (ft); 17 (ft).
Languages Spanish, Italian, Vietnamese

Winter Park Towers*
1111 S Lakemont Ave, Winter Park, FL, 32789 (305) 647-4083
Licensure Skilled Care. *Beds* 106.
Ownership Nonprofit.
Staff RNs 19 (ft); LPNs 2 (ft); Nurses aides 30 (ft).
Languages Polish, German, Italian, Russian, Hebrew, Spanish, French
Affiliation Presbyterian

ZEPHYRHILLS

Zephyr Haven Nursing Home*
310 Ave A, Zephyrhills, FL, 33599 (813) 782-5508
Licensure Skilled Care. *Beds* 60. *Certified* Medicaid.
Ownership Public.
Staff RNs 5 (ft); LPNs 8 (ft); Nurses aides 15 (ft); 18 (ft).

GEORGIA

ABBEVILLE

Abbeville Nursing Home Intermediate Care Facility
PO Box 445, Abbeville, GA, 31001 (912) 467-2515
Admin Homer S Fowler. *Medical Dir/Dir of Nursing* Dr William Hammond.
Licensure Intermediate Care. *Beds* 101. *Certified* Medicaid.
Admissions Requirements Medical examination; Physician's request.
Staff Physicians 1 (pt); RNs 1 (pt); LPNs 7 (ft); Orderlies 3 (ft); Nurses aides 18 (ft), 2 (pt); Physical therapists 1 (pt); Activities coordinators 2 (ft); Dietitians 1 (ft), 1 (pt); Dentists 1 (pt); Ophthalmologists 1 (pt).
Facilities Dining room; Physical therapy room; Activities room; Laundry room; Barber/Beauty shop.
Activities Games; Reading groups; Prayer groups; Movies; Shopping trips; Dances/Social or cultural gatherings.

ADEL

Memorial Convalescent Center*
PO Box 677, Adel, GA, 31620 (912) 896-3182
Admin James E Cunningham.
Licensure Skilled Care; Intermediate Care.
Beds 80. *Certified* Medicaid; Medicare.

ADRIAN

Johnson County Intermediate Care Home*
PO Box 207, Adrian, GA, 31002 (912) 668-3225
Admin Steve C Taylor.
Licensure Intermediate Care. *Beds* 59. *Certified* Medicaid.

ALBANY

Hospitality Care Center of Albany*
PO Box 2003, Albany, GA, 31701 (912) 435-0741
Admin James R Pitts.
Licensure Skilled Care; Intermediate Care.
Beds 168. *Certified* Medicaid; Medicare.

Palmyra Nursing Home*
1904 Palmyra Rd, Albany, GA, 31707 (912) 883-0500
Admin Davis W King.
Licensure Skilled Care; Intermediate Care.
Beds 250. *Certified* Medicaid; Medicare.

ALMA

Twin Oaks Convalescent Center
Worth St, Alma, GA, 31510 (912) 632-7293
Admin Betty Ann Stroud.
Licensure Skilled Care; Intermediate Care.
Beds 88. *Certified* Medicaid.

AMERICUS

Magnolia Manor Methodist Nursing Home
Box 346, S Lee St, Americus, GA, 31709 (912) 924-9352
Admin Mark Todd. *Medical Dir/Dir of Nursing* John H Robinson III.
Licensure Skilled Care; Intermediate Care.
Beds 238. *Certified* Medicaid; Medicare.
Admissions Requirements Medical examination; Physician's request.
Staff Physicians 2 (pt); RNs 13 (ft), 3 (pt); LPNs 25 (ft); Orderlies 5 (ft), 1 (pt); Nurses aides 68 (ft), 5 (pt); Physical therapists 1 (ft), 1 (pt); Speech therapists 1 (pt); Activities coordinators 3 (ft); Dietitians 1 (pt); Dentists 2 (pt).
Affiliation Methodist
Facilities Dining room; Physical therapy room; Activities room; Chapel; Crafts room; Laundry room; Barber/Beauty shop; Library.
Activities Arts and Crafts; Cards; Games; Reading groups; Prayer groups; Movies; Shopping trips; Dances/Social or cultural gatherings.
Description Facility is located on 375-acre campus, beautifully landscaped; all buildings are one story; only nursing home in Georgia with certified rehabilitation center designation.

ASHBURN

Ashburn Conver-Care Inc
Industrial Blvd, Box 629, Ashburn, GA, 31714 (912) 567-3473
Admin Brenda H Campbell. *Medical Dir/Dir of Nursing* Woodrow Gass MD.
Licensure Skilled Care. *Beds* 76. *Certified* Medicaid.

Admissions Requirements Medical examination; Physician's request.
Staff Physicians 2 (ft); RNs 2 (ft); LPNs 7 (ft); Orderlies 5 (ft); Nurses aides 30 (ft); Activities coordinators 1 (ft); Dietitians 1 (ft).
Facilities Dining room; Activities room; Chapel; Crafts room; Laundry room; Barber/Beauty shop.
Activities Arts and Crafts; Games; Prayer groups; Movies.
Description Facility offers good country living; residents receive a lot of tender loving care.

ATHENS

Athens Health Care Center Inc*
139 Alps Rd, Athens, GA, 30610 (404) 549-8020
Admin Mary Barnhart.
Licensure Skilled Care; Intermediate Care.
Beds 120. *Certified* Medicaid; Medicare.

Athens Heritage Home Inc
960 Hawthorne Ave, Athens, GA, 30610 (404) 549-1613
Admin Garnelle T Armour.
Licensure Skilled Care. *Beds* 104.
Admissions Requirements Minimum age 50; Medical examination; Physician's request.
Staff Physicians 8 (pt); RNs 2 (ft), 1 (pt); LPNs 8 (ft), 2 (pt); Physical therapists 1 (ft), 1 (pt); Activities coordinators 2 (ft); Dietitians 1 (pt); Dentists 1 (pt).
Facilities Dining room; Physical therapy room; Activities room; Chapel; Laundry room; Barber/Beauty shop; Library.
Activities Arts and Crafts; Cards; Games; Reading groups; Prayer groups; Movies; Shopping trips; Dances/Social or cultural gatherings.

Cedar Hill Nursing Home
PO Box E5676, Athens, GA, 30604 (404) 549-5382
Admin Corrie Pierce. *Medical Dir/Dir of Nursing* Dr A P Brooks.
Licensure Skilled Care; Intermediate Care.
Beds 122. *Certified* Medicaid.
Admissions Requirements Medical examination.
Staff Physicians 6 (pt); RNs 2 (ft), 1 (pt); LPNs 10 (ft), 2 (pt); Orderlies 5 (ft); Nurses aides 34 (ft), 5 (pt); Physical therapists 1 (pt); Recreational therapists 1 (ft); Dietitians 1 (pt); Dentists 1 (pt); Podiatrists 1 (pt).

Facilities Dining room; Physical therapy room; Activities room; Laundry room; Barber/Beauty shop.
Activities Arts and Crafts; Cards; Games; Reading groups; Prayer groups; Movies; Shopping trips.
Description Facility is located near University of Georgia; students from university come to facility for various types of clinical experiences.

Georgia Retardation Center—Athens
850 College Station Rd, Athens, GA, 30601 (404) 542-8970
Admin William M Riddle.
Licensure Intermediate Care for Mentally Retarded. *Beds* 40. *Certified* Medicare.
Admissions Requirements Minimum age 3–18.
Staff Physicians 1 (pt); RNs 2 (ft); LPNs 5 (ft); Physical therapists 1 (pt); Recreational therapists 1 (ft); Occupational therapists 1 (ft); Speech therapists 1 (ft); Dietitians 1 (pt); Audiologists 1 (pt).
Facilities Dining room; Physical therapy room; Activities room; Laundry room; Library.
Activities Arts and Crafts; Cards; Games; Movies; Shopping trips; Dances/Social or cultural gatherings.
Description Athens Unit-GRC is a childrens facility located on the campus of the University of Georgia. We are the University Affiliated Facility for Georgia.

Grandview Center Inc*
165 Winston Dr, Athens, GA, 30607 (404) 549-6013
Admin Coy C Williamson Jr.
Licensure Skilled Care; Intermediate Care.
Beds 100. *Certified* Medicaid; Medicare.

ATLANTA

A G Rhodes Home Inc*
350 Boulevard SE, Atlanta, GA, 30312 (404) 688-6731
Admin Harvey Baugess.
Licensure Skilled Care; Intermediate Care.
Beds 138. *Certified* Medicaid; Medicare.

Ansley Pavilion*
560 St Charles Ave, Atlanta, GA, 30308 (404) 874-2233
Admin Aaron Baranan.
Licensure Intermediate Care. *Beds* 90. *Certified* Medicaid.

Ashton Woods Convalescent Center*
3535 Ashton Woods Dr, Atlanta, GA, 30319 (404) 451-0236
Admin Elaine Carpenter.
Licensure Skilled Care. *Beds* 100. *Certified* Medicaid; Medicare.

Briarcliff Haven*
1000 Briarcliff Rd NE, Atlanta, GA, 30306 (404) 875-6456
Admin James I Kaufmann.
Licensure Skilled Care. *Beds* 103. *Certified* Medicaid.

Budd Terrace Intermediate Care Home*
1833 Clifton Rd NE, Atlanta, GA, 30329 (404) 325-2988
Admin Joan Carlson.
Licensure Intermediate Care. *Beds* 270. *Certified* Medicaid.

Camilla Street Intermediate Care Home
1011 Camilla St SW, Atlanta, GA, 30314 (404) 753-8839
Admin Fannie Hill. *Medical Dir/Dir of Nursing* Dr J B Ellison.
Licensure Intermediate Care. *Beds* 24. *Certified* Medicaid.
Admissions Requirements Medical examination; Physician's request.
Staff Physicians 1 (pt); RNs 1 (pt); LPNs 2 (ft), 4 (pt); Orderlies 1 (ft), 2 (pt); Nurses aides 4 (ft), 1 (pt); Activities coordinators 1 (pt); Dietitians 1 (pt).
Facilities Dining room; Activities room; Crafts room; Laundry room.
Activities Arts and Crafts; Games; Prayer groups; Dances/Social or cultural gatherings.

Canterbury Court Intermediate Care Unit*
3750 Peachtree Rd NE, Atlanta, GA, 30319 (404) 261-6611
Admin R A Lawrence.
Licensure Intermediate Care. *Beds* 16.

Christian City Convalescent Center
7300 Lester Rd, Atlanta, GA, 30349 (404) 964-3301
Admin Fred A Watson. *Medical Dir/Dir of Nursing* Robert Webster MD.
Licensure Skilled Care; Intermediate Care.
Beds 200. *Certified* Medicaid.
Admissions Requirements Minimum age 16; Medical examination.
Staff Physicians 5 (pt); RNs 13 (ft), 3 (pt); LPNs 5 (ft), 1 (pt); Nurses aides 80 (ft), 20 (pt); Physical therapists 1 (pt); Reality therapists 1 (ft); Recreational therapists 1 (pt); Occupational therapists 1 (pt); Speech therapists 1 (pt); Activities coordinators 1 (ft); Dietitians 1 (ft); Dentists 1 (pt); Ophthalmologists 1 (pt); Podiatrists 1 (pt).
Facilities Dining room; Physical therapy room; Activities room; Chapel; Laundry room; Barber/Beauty shop; Library.
Activities Arts and Crafts; Cards; Games; Reading groups; Prayer groups; Movies; Shopping trips; Dances/Social or cultural gatherings.
Description Resident council, family council, and large volunteer programs seem to benefit the residents the most.

Crestview Nursing Home
2800 Springdale Rd, Atlanta, GA, 30315 (404) 767-7407
Admin Arthur E Simpson. *Medical Dir/Dir of Nursing* Dr Phillip Benton.
Licensure Skilled Care; Intermediate Care.
Beds 388. *Certified* Medicaid; Medicare.
Staff Physicians 5 (pt); RNs 10 (ft); LPNs 47 (ft); Orderlies 35 (ft); Nurses aides 81 (ft); Physical therapists 4 (ft); Recreational therapists 3 (ft); Activities coordinators 3 (ft); Dietitians 2 (ft); Dentists 1 (ft); Podiatrists 2 (ft).
Facilities Dining room; Physical therapy room; Activities room; Chapel; Crafts room; Laundry room; Barber/Beauty shop; Library.
Activities Arts and Crafts; Cards; Games; Reading groups; Prayer groups.
Description Home is a full service long-term

heathcare facility; quality of care and physical environment offered to the residents are second to none.

Emory Convalescent Home
1466 Oxford Rd NE, Atlanta, GA, 30307 (404) 378-7339
Admin Bill M Provost. *Medical Dir/Dir of Nursing* Dr Tim Haroen.
Licensure Intermediate Care. *Beds* 41. *Certified* Medicare.
Admissions Requirements Medical examination; Physician's request.
Staff Physicians 5 (pt); RNs 1 (ft), 3 (pt); LPNs 3 (ft), 1 (pt); Orderlies 1 (ft), 1 (pt); Nurses aides 12 (ft), 4 (pt).
Facilities Dining room; Laundry room.
Activities Arts and Crafts; Games; Reading groups; Prayer groups; Movies; Shopping trips; Dances/Social or cultural gatherings.
Description VA approved.

Fountainview Convalescent Center*
1400 Briarcliff Rd, Atlanta, GA, 30306 (404) 378-2303
Admin Ms Taber B King.
Licensure Skilled Care. *Beds* 65.

Georgia Retardation Center
4770 N Peachtree Rd, Atlanta, GA, 30341 (404) 393-7157
Admin Bernard R Wagner. *Medical Dir/Dir of Nursing* Wiliam S Talley MD.
Licensure Skilled Care; Intermediate Care for Mentally Retarded. *Beds* SNF 94; ICF/MR 286. *Certified* Medicare.
Ownership Public.
Staff Physicians 6 (ft); RNs 40 (ft); LPNs 10 (ft); Nurses aides 480 (ft); Physical therapists 6 (ft); Recreational therapists 12 (ft); Occupational therapists 8 (ft); Speech therapists 6 (ft); Activities coordinators 21 (ft); Dietitians 6 (ft); Dentists 5 (ft); Ophthalmologists 1 (pt); Podiatrists 1 (pt); Audiologists 2 (ft), 1 (pt).
Facilities Dining room; Physical therapy room; Activities room; Chapel; Crafts room; Laundry room; Barber/Beauty shop; Library; Adaptive swimming pool.
Activities Arts and Crafts; Cards; Games; Reading groups; Prayer groups; Movies; Shopping trips; Dances/Social or cultural gatherings.
Description Center provides dental services for large number of outpatients; large campus-like setting; accredited by ACMR/DD; outstanding internal advocacy program; 2 to 1 staff to resident ratio; all admissions through regional placement centers; training center for area students in related fields.

Heritage Convalescent Center
54 Peachtree Park Dr, Atlanta, GA, 30309 (404) 351-6041
Admin Rose Marie Moore. *Medical Dir/Dir of Nursing* Dr Roy A Wiggins Jr.
Licensure Skilled Care; Intermediate Care.
Beds 180. *Certified* Medicaid; Medicare.
Admissions Requirements Medical examination; Physician's request.
Staff RNs 2 (ft), 2 (pt); LPNs 10 (ft); Orderlies 4 (ft); Nurses aides 53 (ft); Physical therapists 1 (pt); Activities coordinators 1 (ft); Dietitians 1 (ft).
Facilities Dining room; Physical therapy room;

Activities room; Chapel; Crafts room; Laundry room; Barber/Beauty shop; Library.
Activities Arts and Crafts; Cards; Games; Reading groups; Prayer groups; Movies; Shopping trips; Dances/Social or cultural gatherings.
Description Facility has recently been completely remodeled.

Imperial Health Care Inc*
2645 Whiting St NW, Atlanta, GA, 30318
(404) 799-9267
Admin Betty J F Hargrove.
Licensure Skilled Care; Intermediate Care.
Beds 120. *Certified* Medicaid; Medicare.

The Jewish Home for the Aged
3150 Howell Mill Rd NW, Atlanta, GA, 30327
(404) 351-8410
Admin Deborah Beards. *Medical Dir/Dir of Nursing* Sandford Shmerling.
Licensure Skilled Care; Intermediate Care.
Beds 120. *Certified* Medicaid; Medicare.
Admissions Requirements Minimum age 62; Medical examination.
Staff RNs 5 (ft); LPNs 14 (ft); Orderlies 35 (ft); Recreational therapists 2 (ft).
Affiliation Jewish
Facilities Activities room; Laundry room; Barber/Beauty shop; Library.
Activities Arts and Crafts; Cards; Games; Reading groups; Prayer groups; Movies; Shopping trips; Dances/Social or cultural gatherings.

Kathy Crawford Nursing Center
460 Auburn Ave NE, Atlanta, GA, 30312 (404) 523-1613
Admin James E Kinsey. *Medical Dir/Dir of Nursing* Dr Joseph Williams.
Licensure Intermediate Care. *Beds* 186. *Certified* Medicaid.
Staff Physicians 2 (pt); RNs 2 (ft); LPNs 11 (ft); Orderlies 11 (ft); Nurses aides 37 (ft); Reality therapists 2 (ft); Recreational therapists 2 (ft); Occupational therapists 1 (ft); Activities coordinators 1 (ft).
Facilities Dining room; Physical therapy room; Activities room; Chapel; Laundry room; Barber/Beauty shop.
Activities Arts and Crafts; Games; Reading groups; Prayer groups; Movies; Shopping trips; Dances/Social or cultural gatherings.

Northside Convalescent Center
993-E Johnson Ferry, Atlanta, GA, 30342 (404) 256-5131
Admin James R Fanger. *Medical Dir/Dir of Nursing* John McCoy MD.
Licensure Skilled Care. *Beds* 180. *Certified* Medicare.
Admissions Requirements Medical examination; Physician's request.
Staff Physicians 112 (pt); RNs 19 (ft), 4 (pt); LPNs 16 (ft), 7 (pt); Orderlies 9 (ft), 1 (pt); Nurses aides 90 (ft), 10 (pt); Physical therapists 3 (ft), 1 (pt); Reality therapists 4 (ft); Recreational therapists 2 (ft); Occupational therapists 1 (ft); Speech therapists 1 (ft); Dietitians 1 (ft); Dentists 1 (ft); Ophthalmologists 1 (ft); Podiatrists 2 (ft); Respiratory therapists 3 (ft), 2 (pt).
Facilities Dining room; Physical therapy room; Activities room; Crafts room; Laundry room; Barber/Beauty shop; Library; Bus and limo services.

Activities Arts and Crafts; Cards; Games; Reading groups; Prayer groups; Movies; Shopping trips; Dances/Social or cultural gatherings; Happy hour.
Description 18th century English hotel atmosphere with private and semi-private rooms available; selective menu with full-time waitress service in dining hall; private pay, Medicare, and VA accepted; approved for most insurance programs.

Nursecare Center of Atlanta
2920 Pharr Court Northwest, Atlanta, GA, 30305 (404) 261-9043
Admin John Flaxington.
Licensure Skilled Care; Intermediate Care.
Beds 200. *Certified* Medicaid; Medicare.
Facilities Dining room; Physical therapy room; Activities room; Chapel; Crafts room; Barber/Beauty shop.
Activities Arts and Crafts; Cards; Games; Prayer groups; Movies; Shopping trips; Dances/Social or cultural gatherings.

Our Lady of Perpetual Help
760 Washington St SW, Atlanta, GA, 30315
(404) 688-9515
Admin Sr Mary Peter. *Medical Dir/Dir of Nursing* Dr Thomas Lowry.
Licensure Skilled Care. *Beds* 48.
Staff Physicians 1 (ft); RNs 3 (ft); LPNs 4 (ft); Orderlies 2 (ft); Nurses aides 4 (ft); Dietitians 1 (ft); Dentists 1 (ft); Podiatrists 1 (ft).
Affiliation Roman Catholic
Facilities Chapel; Crafts room; Laundry room; Barber/Beauty shop; Library.
Activities Arts and Crafts; Cards; Games; Prayer groups; Movies.
Description A home established by the Hawthorne Dominicans for the care of incurable cancer patients without discrimination as to race, creed, or national origin. Seldom the destitute of Mother Alphonsa's day, they nevertheless are sufferers whose resources have been exhausted and who no longer have sufficient funds to provide for adequate nursing care.

Piedmont Hospital Extended Care Unit
1968 Peachtree Rd Northwest, Atlanta, GA, 30309 (404) 355-7611
Admin Hulett D Sumlin. *Medical Dir/Dir of Nursing* Dr Lloyd Timberlake.
Licensure Skilled Care. *Beds* 42. *Certified* Medicare.
Facilities Physical therapy room; Chapel; Barber/Beauty shop; Library.

Sadie G Mays Memorial Nursing Home
1821 W Anderson Ave, Atlanta, GA, 30314
(404) 794-2477
Admin William G Samples. *Medical Dir/Dir of Nursing* Dr A M Davis.
Licensure Skilled Care; Intermediate Care.
Beds 206. *Certified* Medicaid; Medicare.
Ownership Nonprofit.
Admissions Requirements Physician's request.
Staff Physicians; RNs; LPNs; Orderlies; Nurses aides; Physical therapists; Recreational therapists; Occupational therapists; Speech therapists; Activities coordinators; Dietitians; Dentists; Podiatrists.
Facilities Dining room; Physical therapy room; Activities room; Chapel; Crafts room; Laundry

room; Barber/Beauty shop; Library.
Activities Arts and Crafts; Cards; Games; Reading groups; Prayer groups; Movies; Shopping trips; Dances/Social or cultural gatherings.
Description Facility houses 206 elderly residents, the majority of whom resided in Fulton County; private and semi-private rooms; open patio and courtyard for sunning and outdoor activities; VA approved.

Sky Ranch Home
3700 Cascade Palmeto, Atlanta, GA, 30331
(404) 964-6950
Admin Matthew Dempsey. *Medical Dir/Dir of Nursing* Joe Cruise MD.
Licensure Intermediate Care. *Beds* 60. *Certified* Medicaid.
Staff Physicians; RNs 1 (ft); LPNs 4 (ft); Nurses aides 12 (ft), 4 (pt); Reality therapists 1 (ft); Recreational therapists 1 (ft); Activities coordinators 1 (ft); Dietitians 2 (ft); Dentists; Podiatrists.
Facilities Dining room; Physical therapy room; Activities room; Laundry room; Barber/Beauty shop; Library.
Activities Arts and Crafts; Games; Reading groups; Prayer groups; Movies; Shopping trips; Dances/Social or cultural gatherings.
Description This family-type facility is situated out in the country in a wooded area with a beautiful view.

Springdale Convalescent Center*
2850 Springdale Rd SW, Atlanta, GA, 30315
(404) 762-8672
Admin Cheri S Underwood.
Licensure Skilled Care; Intermediate Care.
Beds 109. *Certified* Medicaid.

Wesley Woods Health Center*
1841 Clifton Rd NE, Atlanta, GA, 30333 (404) 325-2988
Admin Bill Todd.
Licensure Skilled Care. *Beds* 171. *Certified* Medicaid; Medicare.

AUGUSTA

Augusta Health Care Facility
PO Box 5778, Augusta, GA, 30906 (404) 793-1057
Admin Paul Phillips. *Medical Dir/Dir of Nursing* Louis Scharff III MD.
Licensure Skilled Care. *Beds* 31. *Certified* Medicaid; Medicare.
Admissions Requirements Medical examination; Physician's request.
Staff Physicians 5 (pt); RNs 2 (ft), 1 (pt); LPNs 17 (ft), 7 (pt); Orderlies 5 (ft); Nurses aides 62 (ft), 4 (pt); Physical therapists 1 (ft), 1 (pt); Recreational therapists 2 (ft); Speech therapists 1 (pt); Activities coordinators 1 (ft); Dietitians 1 (ft), 1 (pt).
Facilities Dining room; Physical therapy room; Activities room; Chapel; Crafts room; Laundry room; Barber/Beauty shop; Library.
Activities Arts and Crafts; Cards; Games; Reading groups; Prayer groups; Movies; Shopping trips; Dances/Social or cultural gatherings.

Beverly Manor Convalescent Center
1600 Anthony Rd, Augusta, GA, 30904 (404)
738-3301
Admin Larry Swicegood. *Medical Dir/Dir of
Nursing* Dr Nathan Reeves.
Licensure Skilled Care; Intermediate Care.
Beds 99. *Certified* Medicaid; Medicare.
Admissions Requirements Medical examina-
tion; Physician's request.
Staff RNs 5 (ft); LPNs 15 (ft), 10 (pt); Orderlies
3 (ft), 1 (pt); Nurses aides 27 (ft), 15 (pt);
Physical therapists 1 (pt); Occupational thera-
pists 1 (pt); Speech therapists 1 (pt); Activities
coordinators 1 (ft); Dietitians 1 (ft); Dentists 1
(pt); Podiatrists 1 (pt).
Facilities Dining room; Physical therapy room;
Activities room; Chapel; Crafts room; Laundry
room; Barber/Beauty shop.
Activities Arts and Crafts; Games; Prayer
groups; Movies; Shopping trips.

Blair House
2541 Milledgville Rd, Augusta, GA, 30904
(404) 738-2581
Admin Frank Feltham. *Medical Dir/Dir of
Nursing* Luther M Thomas Jr.
Licensure Skilled Care; Intermediate Care.
Beds 100. *Certified* Medicaid.
Staff Physicians 1 (pt); RNs 2 (ft), 3 (pt); LPNs
8 (ft), 10 (pt); Orderlies 1 (ft); Nurses aides 20
(ft), 30 (pt); Physical therapists 1 (pt); Occupational therapists 1 (pt); Activities coordinators 1
(ft); Dietitians 1 (pt).
Facilities Dining room; Physical therapy room;
Activities room; Chapel; Laundry room; Bar-
ber/Beauty shop.
Activities Arts and Crafts; Games; Reading
groups; Prayer groups; Shopping trips; Dances-
/Social or cultural gatherings.
Description Blair House is locally owned and
operated, located in town on a major bus line.
A weekly happy hour (wine and cheese) is
enjoyed by many residents. Attends (disposable
diapers) are furnished at no additional charge
for those residents requiring them.

Bon Air Life Care Center*
873 Hickman Rd, Augusta, GA, 30904 (404)
737-8258
Admin Wanda J Hinton.
Beds 128.

Georgia War Veterans Nursing Home
1101 15th St, Augusta, GA, 30901 (404)
828-2531
Admin Judith A Guthrie. *Medical Dir/Dir of
Nursing* Arthur O Gelbart MD.
Licensure Skilled Care. *Beds* 192.
Description Admission limited to Georgia War
Veterans in need of skilled nursing home care
and a legal resident of the state for at least one
year at time of application.

Jennings Healthcare Inc
3235 Deans Bridge Rd, Augusta, GA, 30906
(404) 798-1430
Admin Kathleen Mixon. *Medical Dir/Dir of
Nursing* O L Gray.
Licensure Skilled Care; Intermediate Care.
Beds 76. *Certified* Medicaid; Medicare.
Admissions Requirements Medical examina-
tion; Physician's request.
Facilities Dining room; Physical therapy room;

Activities room; Laundry room; Barber/Beauty
shop; Library.
Activities Arts and Crafts; Cards; Games;
Reading groups; Prayer groups; Movies; Shop-
ping trips; Dances/Social or cultural gatherings.
Description VA approved.

University Hospital—Extended Care Facility
1355 Nelson St, Augusta, GA, 30910 (404)
724-4038
Admin Kathy Lesnevich. *Medical Dir/Dir of
Nursing* Joseph D Lee MD.
Licensure Skilled Care. *Beds* 60. *Cer-
tified* Medicaid; Medicare.
Admissions Requirements Physician's request.
Staff Physicians 1 (pt); RNs 9 (ft), 4 (pt); LPNs
15 (ft), 3 (pt); Nurses aides 11 (ft), 1 (pt);
Physical therapists 2 (ft); Recreational therapists
1 (ft); Occupational therapists 1 (ft); Speech
therapists 1 (pt); Dietitians 1 (ft), 1 (pt).
Facilities Dining room; Physical therapy room;
Activities room; Crafts room; Laundry room;
Barber/Beauty shop.
Description All physicians with admitting priv-
ileges at University Hospital may admit
patients.

West Lake Manor Health Care Center
820 Stevens Creek Rd, Augusta, GA, 30907
(404) 860-6622
Medical Dir/Dir of Nursing Richard E Melcher
MD.
Licensure Skilled Care; Intermediate Care.
Beds 100. *Certified* Medicaid; Medicare.
Staff RNs 4 (ft), 1 (pt); LPNs 7 (ft), 4 (pt);
Nurses aides 27 (ft), 10 (pt); Physical therapists
1 (pt); Recreational therapists 1 (ft); Speech
therapists 1 (pt); Activities coordinators 1 (ft);
Dietitians 1 (ft); Social workers 1 (ft).
Facilities Dining room; Physical therapy room;
Activities room; Chapel; Crafts room; Laundry
room; Barber/Beauty shop.
Activities Arts and Crafts; Cards; Games;
Reading groups; Prayer groups; Movies; Dan-
ces/Social or cultural gatherings.
Description Manor is fortunate to have a
caring staff that encourages resident governance
to maintain the home-like environment in
which they live.

Windermere*
2618 J Sewey Gray Circle, Augusta, GA, 30909
(404) 860-7572
Admin Charles Esposito.
Beds 120.

AUSTELL

Atlanta Health Care Center*
1700 Mulkey Rd, Austell, GA, 30001 (404)
941-5750
Admin Lloyd Schlegel.
Licensure Skilled Care; Intermediate Care.
Beds 62. *Certified* Medicaid; Medicare.

Brian Center of Nursing Care
2130 Anderson Mill Rd, Austell, GA, 30001
(404) 941-8813
Admin David D George. *Medical Dir/Dir of
Nursing* Robert S Trickland Jr DO.
Licensure Skilled Care; Intermediate Care.
Beds 170. *Certified* Medicaid; Medicare.

Staff Physicians 12 (pt); RNs 4 (ft); LPNs 15
(ft), 4 (pt); Orderlies 4 (ft), 2 (pt); Nurses aides
50 (ft), 10 (pt); Physical therapists 1 (ft); Occupational therapists 1 (pt); Speech therapists 1
(pt); Activities coordinators 1 (ft); Dietitians 1
(pt); Dentists 1 (pt); Podiatrists 1 (pt); Ophthalmologists 1 (pt); 1 (ft).
Facilities Dining room; Physical therapy room;
Activities room; Crafts room; Laundry room;
Barber/Beauty shop; Inner enclosed courtyard.
Activities Arts and Crafts; Cards; Games;
Reading groups; Prayer groups; Dances/Social
or cultural gatherings.
Description This a progressive facility which
provides both short-term rehabilitative care as
well as long-term placement. Hospice, respite
care, and physical therapy services are
available. VA approved.

BAINBRIDGE

Bainbridge Health Care Inc*
Rt 2, W College St, Box 20, Bainbridge, GA,
31717 (404) 243-0931
Admin Doris Grant.
Beds 100.

Memorial Manor Nursing Home*
1500 E Shotwell St, Bainbridge, GA, 31717
(912) 246-3500
Admin Raymond W Wright.
Licensure Skilled Care; Intermediate Care.
Beds 107. *Certified* Medicaid; Medicare.

Southwestern Developmental Center
PO Box 935, Bainbridge, GA, 31717 (912)
246-6750
Admin Sharon Haire. *Medical Dir/Dir of
Nursing* Dr Martin Bailey.
Licensure Intermediate Care for Mentally
Retarded. *Beds* 120. *Certified* Medicare.
Staff Physicians 2 (ft), 1 (pt); RNs 12 (ft);
LPNs 15 (ft); Physical therapists 2 (ft); Recrea-
tional therapists 6 (ft); Occupational therapists 2
(ft); Speech therapists 2 (ft); Activities coordi-
nators 1 (ft); Dietitians 2 (ft); Dentists 1 (ft), 1
(pt).
Facilities Dining room; Physical therapy room;
Activities room; Chapel; Crafts room; Laundry
room; Barber/Beauty shop; Library.
Activities Arts and Crafts; Cards; Games;
Reading groups; Prayer groups; Movies; Shopping trips; Dances/Social or cultural gatherings.

BALDWIN

Scenic View Health Care Center*
PO Box 288, Baldwin, GA, 30511 (404)
778-8377
Admin Sallie Y Powell.
Licensure Skilled Care; Intermediate Care.
Beds 112. *Certified* Medicaid.

BARNESVILLE

Heritage Inn—Barnesville*
Box 380, 148 Ft Valley, Barnesville, GA, 30204
(404) 358-2485
Admin Susan S Chapman.
Licensure Skilled Care; Intermediate Care.

Beds 117. *Certified* Medicaid.

BAXLEY

Appling County Nursing Home*
E Walnut St, Baxley, GA, 31513 (912) 367-4645
Admin Stanley Crews.
Licensure Skilled Care. *Beds* 31. *Certified* Medicaid; Medicare.

Baxley Manor Inc—Intermediate Care Facility
Donnie Lane, PO Box 507, Baxley, GA, 31513 (912) 367-4663
Admin Mary L Price. *Medical Dir/Dir of Nursing* A E Suarez MD.
Licensure Intermediate Care. *Beds* 70. *Certified* Medicaid; Medicare.
Admissions Requirements Physician's request.
Staff RNs 1 (ft), 1 (pt); LPNs 6 (ft), 2 (pt); Orderlies 7 (ft), 2 (pt); Nurses aides 13 (ft); Physical therapists 1 (pt); Activities coordinators 1 (ft); Dietitians 1 (pt); Podiatrists 1 (pt); Pharmacist 1 (pt).
Facilities Dining room; Physical therapy room; Activities room; Chapel; Crafts room; Laundry room; Barber/Beauty shop; Solarium.
Activities Arts and Crafts; Cards; Games; Reading groups; Prayer groups; Movies; Shopping trips; Dances/Social or cultural gatherings.

BLACKSHEAR

Pierce County Nursing Home
Carter Ave, Box 32, Blackshear, GA, 31516 (912) 449-6631
Admin Jim Goodman. *Medical Dir/Dir of Nursing* Don Waters MD.
Licensure Skilled Care. *Beds* 29. *Certified* Medicaid; Medicare.
Admissions Requirements Physician's request.
Staff Physicians 4 (ft); RNs 6 (ft), 2 (pt); LPNs 6 (ft); Orderlies 4 (ft); Nurses aides 12 (ft); Physical therapists 1 (ft); Activities coordinators 1 (ft); Dietitians 1 (ft).
Facilities Dining room; Physical therapy room; Activities room; Chapel; Crafts room; Laundry room; Barber/Beauty shop.
Activities Arts and Crafts; Cards; Games; Reading groups; Prayer groups; Movies; Shopping trips; Dances/Social or cultural gatherings.

BLAIRSVILLE

Union County Nursing Home
Rt 1, Box 1500, Blairsville, GA, 30512 (404) 745-2111
Admin Rebecca T Dyer. *Medical Dir/Dir of Nursing* George D Gowder Jr MD.
Licensure Skilled Care; Intermediate Care.
Beds 96. *Certified* Medicaid; Medicare.
Admissions Requirements Medical examination; Physician's request.
Staff Physicians 6 (pt); RNs 2 (ft), 1 (pt); LPNs 9 (ft), 2 (pt); Orderlies 6 (ft); Nurses aides 25 (ft); Recreational therapists 1 (ft); Dietitians 1 (pt).
Facilities Dining room; Physical therapy room; Chapel; Laundry room; Barber/Beauty shop.
Activities Arts and Crafts; Prayer groups; Movies.

BLAKLEY

Early Memorial Nursing Home*
630 Columbia Rd, Blakley, GA, 31723 (912) 723-3794
Admin Robert E Tiner.
Licensure Skilled Care; Intermediate Care.
Beds 127. *Certified* Medicaid; Medicare.

BLUE RIDGE

Fannin County Nursing Home
PO Box 1227, Blue Ridge, GA, 30513 (404) 632-2271
Admin Cecil Stuart. *Medical Dir/Dir of Nursing* Jack B Roof MD.
Licensure Skilled Care; Intermediate Care.
Beds 101. *Certified* Medicaid.
Admissions Requirements Minimum age 18; Medical examination; Physician's request.
Staff RNs 1 (ft), 1 (pt); LPNs 7 (ft), 1 (pt); Nurses aides 16 (ft), 6 (pt); Physical therapists 1 (pt); Recreational therapists 1 (ft); Activities coordinators 1 (ft); Dietitians 1 (pt); Podiatrists 1 (pt).
Facilities Dining room; Physical therapy room; Activities room; Chapel; Crafts room; Laundry room; Barber/Beauty shop.
Activities Arts and Crafts; Cards; Games; Reading groups; Prayer groups; Movies; Shopping trips; Dances/Social or cultural gatherings.

BREMEN

Haralson County Nursing Home*
Box 724, 315 Field St, Bremen, GA, 30110 (404) 537-4482
Admin Lettie D Wilson.
Licensure Skilled Care; Intermediate Care.
Beds 120. *Certified* Medicaid; Medicare.

BRUNSWICK

Goodwill Intermediate Care Home
2708 Lee St, Brunswick, GA, 31520 (912) 267-6771
Admin F B McKenzie. *Medical Dir/Dir of Nursing* Dr Mark T Pierce.
Licensure Intermediate Care. *Beds* 60. *Certified* Medicaid.
Staff Physicians 1 (ft); RNs 2 (ft); LPNs 3 (ft), 1 (pt); Nurses aides 9 (ft), 3 (pt); Physical therapists 1 (pt); Recreational therapists 1 (ft); Activities coordinators 1 (ft); Dietitians 1 (pt).
Facilities Dining room; Laundry room; Barber/Beauty shop.
Activities Arts and Crafts; Games; Reading groups; Prayer groups; Movies; Dances/Social or cultural gatherings.
Description A 60-bed facility providing intermediate nursing care for Glynn County and surrounding areas. Goodwill Home endeavors to meet the physical, social, and recreational needs of all its residents. Appropriate programs are developed and implemented with the assistance of community services and agencies to meet these needs. The total person is our responsibility therefore, the Goodwill Home is home away from home.

Medical Arts Center—Coastal Georgia*
2611 Wildwood Dr, Brunswick, GA, 31520 (912) 264-1434
Admin Thelma W Davis.
Licensure Skilled Care; Intermediate Care.
Beds 158. *Certified* Medicaid; Medicare.

Sears Manor*
3311 Lee St, Brunswick, GA, 31530 (912) 264-1826
Admin Claude G Sears.
Licensure Intermediate Care. *Beds* 60. *Certified* Medicaid.

BUCHANAN

Kimball Care Intermediate Care Home*
303 Carrollton St, Buchanan, GA, 30113 (404) 646-3868
Admin Roger D Kimball.
Licensure Intermediate Care. *Beds* 62. *Certified* Medicaid.

Resthaven Intermediate Care Home
PO Box 409, Buchanan, GA, 30113 (404) 646-5512
Admin Mary E Tucker. *Medical Dir/Dir of Nursing* Dr P J Kim.
Licensure Intermediate Care. *Beds* 60. *Certified* Medicaid.
Admissions Requirements Medical examination; Physician's request.
Staff RNs 1 (ft); LPNs 4 (ft), 3 (pt); Orderlies 2 (ft); Nurses aides 10 (ft), 4 (pt); Activities coordinators 1 (ft); Dietitians 1 (ft); 2 (ft).
Facilities Dining room; Activities room; Chapel; Crafts room; Laundry room; Barber/Beauty shop.
Activities Arts and Crafts; Games; Prayer groups; Shopping trips; Dances/Social or cultural gatherings.

BUENA VISTA

Marion Memorial Nursing Home
PO Box 197, Buena Vista, GA, 31803 (912) 649-7100
Admin David H Godwin. *Medical Dir/Dir of Nursing* Frank Catrett.
Licensure Skilled Care; Intermediate Care.
Beds 50. *Certified* Medicaid; Medicare.
Staff Physicians 2 (ft); RNs 2 (ft); LPNs 3 (ft), 3 (pt); Orderlies 3 (ft), 3 (pt); Nurses aides 12 (ft), 6 (pt); Physical therapists 1 (pt); Reality therapists 1 (pt); Recreational therapists 1 (pt); Occupational therapists 1 (pt); Speech therapists 1 (pt); Activities coordinators 1 (ft); Dietitians 1 (ft); Dentists 1 (pt); Ophthalmologists 1 (pt); Podiatrists 1 (pt); Audiologists 1 (pt).
Facilities Dining room; Physical therapy room; Activities room; Chapel; Crafts room; Laundry room; Barber/Beauty shop; Library.
Activities Arts and Crafts; Cards; Games; Movies; Shopping trips; Dances/Social or cultural gatherings.

BUFORD

Buford Manor Nursing Home*
2451 Peachtree Industrial Blvd, Buford, GA,

30518 (404) 945-6778
Admin Dana L Yon.
Licensure Skilled Care; Intermediate Care.
Beds 117. *Certified* Medicaid; Medicare.

BYROMVILLE

Rosewood Medical Nursing Center*
PO Box 24, Byromville, GA, 31007 (912)
433-5711
Admin Nancy Herndon.
Licensure Skilled Care. *Beds* 102. *Certified* Medicaid.

CALHOUN

Cherokee Nursing Home
1387 US Hwy 41 North, Calhoun, GA, 30701
(404) 629-1289
Admin Joyce L Crawford. *Medical Dir/Dir of Nursing* G W Brown MD.
Licensure Skilled Care. *Beds* 100. *Certified* Medicaid.
Admissions Requirements Medical examination; Physician's request.
Staff Physicians 1 (pt); RNs 2 (ft), 1 (pt); LPNs 7 (ft), 5 (pt); Nurses aides 20 (ft), 10 (pt); Activities coordinators 1 (ft), 1 (pt); Dietitians 1 (pt).
Facilities Dining room; Physical therapy room; Activities room; Crafts room; Laundry room; Barber/Beauty shop.
Activities Arts and Crafts; Cards; Games; Reading groups; Prayer groups; Movies; Shopping trips; Dances/Social or cultural gatherings.
Description Facility is located in the beautiful northern Georgia mountains, close to Interstate 75.

Gordon Health Care Inc*
PO Box 789, Calhoun, GA, 30701 (404)
625-0044
Admin Ben E Crawford.
Licensure Skilled Care; Intermediate Care.
Beds 117. *Certified* Medicaid; Medicare.

CAMILLA

Mitchell Convalescent Center
37 S Ellis St, Camilla, GA, 31730 (912)
336-8377
Admin Sue Rumble. *Medical Dir/Dir of Nursing* A A McNeill Jr.
Licensure Skilled Care; Intermediate Care.
Beds 35. *Certified* Medicaid; Medicare.
Admissions Requirements Medical examination; Physician's request.
Staff Physicians 3 (pt); RNs 1 (ft), 2 (pt); LPNs 4 (ft), 1 (pt); Orderlies 2 (ft), 1 (pt); Nurses aides 7 (ft), 4 (pt); Physical therapists 1 (ft), 1 (pt); Activities coordinators 1 (ft); Dentists 1 (pt); Podiatrists 1 (pt).
Facilities Dining room; Physical therapy room; Chapel; Laundry room; Barber/Beauty shop.
Activities Arts and Crafts; Games; Reading groups; Prayer groups; Shopping trips; Dances-/Social or cultural gatherings.

CANTON

Canton Intermediate Care Home
Rt 6, Box 18, Canton, GA, 30114 (404)
479-8791
Admin Betty Soriano. *Medical Dir/Dir of Nursing* Dr David Field.
Licensure Intermediate Care. *Beds* 36. *Certified* Medicaid.
Admissions Requirements Medical examination; Physician's request.
Staff RNs 1 (pt); LPNs 4 (ft), 3 (pt); Nurses aides 5 (ft), 4 (pt); Speech therapists 1 (pt); Activities coordinators 1 (ft); Dietitians 1 (pt); Dentists 1 (pt); Podiatrists 2 (pt).
Facilities Dining room; Activities room; Crafts room; Laundry room; Barber/Beauty shop.
Activities Arts and Crafts; Cards; Games; Reading groups; Shopping trips; Dances/Social or cultural gatherings.
Description New large outside covered recreational area for parties, bands, etc; Canton I Care Club (ladies' club) conducts weekly and monthly activities with all patients; volunteer club takes patients on trips and conducts regular programs and outings.

Coker Intermediate Care Home
150 Hospital Circle, Canton, GA, 30114 (404)
479-5649
Admin Melba G Coker. *Medical Dir/Dir of Nursing* Dr William Early.
Licensure Intermediate Care. *Beds* 81. *Certified* Medicaid.
Admissions Requirements Medical examination.
Staff RNs 1 (ft); LPNs 3 (ft), 2 (pt); Nurses aides 15 (ft), 4 (pt); Activities coordinators 1 (ft); Dietitians 6 (ft), 5 (pt).
Facilities Dining room; Activities room; Chapel; Crafts room; Laundry room; Barber/Beauty shop; Library.
Activities Arts and Crafts; Cards; Games; Prayer groups; Movies; Shopping trips; Dances/Social or cultural gatherings; Exercise groups; Adopt-a-grandparent program; Bible study groups; Sunday school; Rhythm band and music related activities.
Description Coker sits on a north Georgia hilltop overlooking the surrounding city of Canton; in the springtime it is noted for its beautiful flowers, especially the many dogwood trees. The furnishings, as well as the surrounding grounds, reflect the home-like atmosphere of the facility; well supported by community persons of all ages.

CARROLLTON

Bagwell Nursing Home Inc
443 Bagwell Rd, Carrollton, GA, 30117 (404)
834-3501
Admin Mrs Bill Bagwell. *Medical Dir/Dir of Nursing* Dr E C Bass Jr.
Licensure Skilled Care; Intermediate Care.
Beds 42. *Certified* Medicaid.
Admissions Requirements Medical examination; Physician's request.
Staff Physicians 1 (pt); RNs 1 (ft), 1 (pt); LPNs 3 (ft), 1 (pt); Nurses aides 10 (ft), 5 (pt); Activities coordinators 2 (ft); Dietitians 2 (ft), 4 (pt).
Facilities Dining room; Activities room; Laundry room; Barber/Beauty shop.
Activities Arts and Crafts; Games; Reading groups; Prayer groups; Shopping trips.

Carroll Convalescent Center
Rt 5, PO Box 292, 2327 N Hwy 27, Carrollton, GA, 30117 (404) 834-4404
Admin Edwin E Harman Jr. *Medical Dir/Dir of Nursing* Dr Dean B Talley.
Licensure Skilled Care; Intermediate Care.
Beds 159. *Certified* Medicaid.
Admissions Requirements Medical examination; Physician's request.
Staff RNs 3 (ft), 1 (pt); LPNs 18 (ft), 6 (pt); Orderlies 8 (ft), 4 (pt); Nurses aides 65 (ft), 15 (pt); Physical therapists 1 (ft), 1 (pt); Recreational therapists 1 (ft), 1 (pt); Speech therapists 1 (pt); Activities coordinators 1 (ft), 1 (pt).
Facilities Dining room; Physical therapy room; Activities room; Laundry room; Barber/Beauty shop; Library.
Activities Arts and Crafts; Cards; Games; Reading groups; Prayer groups; Shopping trips.

James C Polk Rest Home*
PO Box 1216, Carrollton, GA, 30117 (404)
832-6333
Admin Evelyn T Polk.
Licensure Intermediate Care. *Beds* 27. *Certified* Medicaid.

Pine Knoll Nursing Home*
PO Box 430, Carrollton, GA, 30117 (404)
832-8243
Admin Shirley Green.
Licensure Skilled Care; Intermediate Care.
Beds 122. *Certified* Medicaid.

CARTERSVILLE

Springdale Convalescent Center*
78 Opal St, Cartersville, GA, 30120 (404)
382-6120
Admin Elizabeth Russell.
Licensure Skilled Care; Intermediate Care.
Beds 118. *Certified* Medicaid.

CEDARTOWN

Cedartown Intermediate Care Center*
148 Carson Rd, Cedartown, GA, 30125 (404)
748-3622
Admin Edgar Gable Jr.
Licensure Intermediate Care. *Beds* 116. *Certified* Medicaid.

Polk County Nursing Home*
225 Philpot St, Cedartown, GA, 30125 (404)
748-4116
Admin Joan J Sanders.
Licensure Skilled Care; Intermediate Care.
Beds 100. *Certified* Medicaid.

CHATSWORTH

Chatsworth Health Care Center
PO Box 1126, Chatsworth, GA, 30705 (404)
695-8313
Admin Patricia W Haynes. *Medical Dir/Dir of Nursing* Dr Glenn Boyd.

COMER / GEORGIA / 213

Licensure Skilled Care; Intermediate Care.
Beds 120. *Certified* Medicaid; Medicare.
Admissions Requirements Medical examination; Physician's request.
Staff Physicians 9 (pt); RNs 3 (ft); LPNs 12 (ft), 4 (pt); Nurses aides 36 (ft), 8 (pt); Physical therapists 1 (ft); Reality therapists 1 (pt); Speech therapists 1 (pt); Activities coordinators 1 (ft); Dietitians 1 (pt); Ophthalmologists 2 (pt); Podiatrists 1 (pt).
Facilities Dining room; Physical therapy room; Activities room; Chapel; Crafts room; Laundry room; Barber/Beauty shop; Library.
Activities Arts and Crafts; Cards; Games; Reading groups; Prayer groups; Movies; Shopping trips; Dances/Social or cultural gatherings.
Description Facility features very active physical therapy department with a full-time registered physical therapist, 2 physical therapist aides, and one rehabilitation nurse. Hospice care and respite care are offered.

CLAXTON

Claxton Nursing Home*
PO Box 712, Claxton, GA, 30417 (912) 739-2245
Admin Judy Tippins.
Licensure Skilled Care; Intermediate Care.
Beds 87. *Certified* Medicaid; Medicare.

CLAYTON

Mountain View Convalescent Center
Box 865, Warwoman Rd, Clayton, GA, 30525 (404) 782-4276
Admin R P Carothers. *Medical Dir/Dir of Nursing* Gene Westmoreland.
Licensure Skilled Care; Intermediate Care.
Beds 117. *Certified* Medicaid.
Staff RNs 2 (ft); LPNs 6 (ft), 2 (pt); Orderlies 8 (ft), 1 (pt); Nurses aides 30 (ft), 8 (pt); Physical therapists 1 (ft); Activities coordinators 1 (ft); Dietitians 1 (ft); Dentists 1 (pt); Podiatrists 1 (pt).
Facilities Dining room; Physical therapy room; Activities room; Chapel; Crafts room; Laundry room; Barber/Beauty shop.
Activities Arts and Crafts; Cards; Games; Reading groups; Prayer groups; Movies; Shopping trips; Dances/Social or cultural gatherings.
Description Located in beautiful north Georgia mountains located in close proximity to North Carolina and South Carolina.

CLEVELAND

Cross Roads Intermediate Care Facility*
Rt 2, Cleveland, GA, 30528 (404) 865-3131
Admin Ed L Stephens.
Licensure Intermediate Care. *Beds* 60. *Certified* Medicaid.

Huntington Convalescent Home Inc*
Rt 2, Cleveland, GA, 30528 (404) 865-3131
Admin Ed L Stephens.
Licensure Skilled Care; Intermediate Care.
Beds 89. *Certified* Medicaid; Medicare.

COCHRAN

Bryant Nursing Center
PO Box 476, 6th St, Cochran, GA, 31014 (912) 934-7330
Admin Johnson Henson. *Medical Dir/Dir of Nursing* Dr Richard L Smith.
Licensure Skilled Care; Intermediate Care.
Beds 75. *Certified* Medicaid; Medicare.
Admissions Requirements Medical examination; Physician's request.
Staff Physicians 3 (pt); RNs 2 (ft); LPNs 5 (ft), 5 (pt); Orderlies 5 (ft), 3 (pt); Nurses aides 10 (ft), 9 (pt); Physical therapists 1 (pt); Activities coordinators 1 (ft); Dietitians 1 (ft); Dentists 1 (pt).
Facilities Dining room; Physical therapy room; Activities room; Chapel; Crafts room; Laundry room; Barber/Beauty shop.
Activities Arts and Crafts; Cards; Games; Reading groups; Prayer groups; Movies; Shopping trips; Dances/Social or cultural gatherings.
Description All programs are outstanding and provide the best quality of life possible; Middle Georgia College participates with rotation of prospective nurse students and Bleckley County High School rotates students from their health classes who hope to find occupation in the health field.

COLLEGE PARK

College Park Convalescent Home
1765 Temple Ave, College Park, GA, 30337 (404) 767-8600
Admin JoAnne Floyd. *Medical Dir/Dir of Nursing* Dr Reginald Smith.
Licensure Intermediate Care. *Beds* 100. *Certified* Medicaid.
Admissions Requirements Medical examination; Physician's request.
Staff Physicians 1 (ft); RNs 1 (pt); LPNs 6 (ft); Nurses aides 56 (ft); Physical therapists 1 (pt); Speech therapists 1 (pt); Activities coordinators 1 (ft); Dietitians 1 (ft); Dentists 1 (ft); Ophthalmologists 1 (pt); Podiatrists 1 (ft).
Facilities Dining room; Physical therapy room; Activities room; Laundry room; Barber/Beauty shop.
Activities Arts and Crafts; Cards; Games; Reading groups; Prayer groups; Movies; Shopping trips; Dances/Social or cultural gatherings.
Description Facility features a cookout monthly, eating out monthly, and a large resident council.

Oak Hill Intermediate Care Home*
4550 Janice Dr, College Park, GA, 30337 (404) 761-3817
Admin Annell Smith.
Licensure Intermediate Care. *Beds* 20.

COLQUITT

Miller Nursing Home*
209 N Cuthbert St, Colquitt, GA, 31737 (912) 758-2500
Admin Don Miller.
Licensure Skilled Care; Intermediate Care.
Beds 83. *Certified* Medicaid; Medicare.

COLUMBUS

Columbus Intermediate Care Home*
5131 Warm Springs Rd, Columbus, GA, 31904 (404) 561-1371
Admin William Levinsohn.
Licensure Intermediate Care. *Beds* 210. *Certified* Medicaid.

Hamilton House*
1911 Hamilton Rd, Columbus, GA, 31904 (404) 324-5194
Admin Jesse Martin.
Licensure Skilled Care. *Beds* 128. *Certified* Medicaid; Medicare.

Med Arts Health Facility*
910 Talbotton Rd, Columbus, GA, 31904 (404) 323-9513
Admin Pat Gray.
Licensure Skilled Care; Intermediate Care.
Beds 110. *Certified* Medicaid; Medicare.

Muscogee Manor
7150 Manor Rd, Columbus, GA, 31995 (404) 561-3218
Admin Joseph F Cobis. *Medical Dir/Dir of Nursing* Walker Rivers MD.
Licensure Skilled Care; Intermediate Care.
Beds 242. *Certified* Medicaid; Medicare.
Admissions Requirements Medical examination; Physician's request.
Staff Physicians 1 (pt); RNs 8 (ft); LPNs 15 (ft); Orderlies 3 (ft); Nurses aides 135 (ft); Physical therapists 1 (pt); Reality therapists 1 (pt); Recreational therapists 3 (ft); Occupational therapists 1 (pt); Speech therapists 1 (pt); Activities coordinators 1 (ft); Dietitians 1 (pt); Dentists 1 (pt); Ophthalmologists 1 (pt); Podiatrists 1 (pt); Audiologists 1 (pt).
Facilities Dining room; Physical therapy room; Activities room; Chapel; Crafts room; Laundry room; Barber/Beauty shop; Library; Dental office.
Activities Arts and Crafts; Cards; Games; Reading groups; Prayer groups; Movies; Shopping trips; Dances/Social or cultural gatherings.
Description Fully accredited by JCAH, outstanding ratings on all inspections for the past 13 years; owned by the Hospital Authority of Columbus, GA; certified gerontology registered nurses on staff.

Oak Manor Extended Care Facility*
2010 Warm Springs Rd, Columbus, GA, 31904 (404) 324-0387
Admin Clara K Brown.
Licensure Skilled Care; Intermediate Care.
Beds 210. *Certified* Medicaid; Medicare.

Pine Manor Nursing Home*
2000 Warm Springs Rd, Columbus, GA, 31904 (404) 324-2252
Admin Clara K Brown.
Licensure Skilled Care; Intermediate Care.
Beds 106. *Certified* Medicaid; Medicare.

COMER

Comer Health Care Inc*
200 Paoli Rd, Comer, GA, 31406 (404) 783-5116

Admin Evelyn Bevers.
Beds 100.

COMMERCE

Banks-Jackson-Commerce Nursing Home
Bolton Rd, Commerce, GA, 30539 (404)
335-3181
Admin Nancy Hinson. *Medical Dir/Dir of Nursing* Dr Joe Griffeth.
Licensure Skilled Care. *Beds* 72. *Certified* Medicaid; Medicare.
Admissions Requirements Medical examination; Physician's request.
Staff Physicians 5 (ft); LPNs 7 (ft), 2 (pt); Orderlies 5 (ft); Nurses aides 22 (ft), 6 (pt); Physical therapists 2 (ft); Activities coordinators 1 (ft); Dietitians 1 (ft); Dentists 1 (pt).
Facilities Dining room; Physical therapy room; Activities room; Chapel; Crafts room; Laundry room; Barber/Beauty shop; Library.
Activities Arts and Crafts; Cards; Games; Reading groups; Prayer groups; Movies; Shopping trips; Dances/Social or cultural gatherings; Cooking; Arranging flowers.
Description Hospital-based facility with emergency room physician always available. Formal physical therapy provided from hospital with physical therapy aides in nursing home under direction of physical therapist in hospital. Respiratory therapy available from the hospital. Two full-time treatment nurses. Excellent activity program.

Barrett Convalescent Home Inc
Ridgeway Rd, Commerce, GA, 30529 (404)
335-5118
Admin Johnny L Barrett.
Licensure Intermediate Care. *Beds* 50.
Staff Physicians 1 (pt); RNs 1 (ft); LPNs 6 (ft); Nurses aides 11 (ft); Physical therapists 1 (pt); Recreational therapists 1 (pt); Activities coordinators 2 (ft); Dietitians 1 (pt); Podiatrists 1 (pt).
Facilities Dining room; Physical therapy room; Activities room; Laundry room; Barber/Beauty shop.
Activities Games; Reading groups; Prayer groups; Movies; Dances/Social or cultural gatherings.
Description This is a very attractive, birth facility in convenient country-like setting with atmosphere of love and caring.

COMMING

Lanier Nursing Home
125 Samaritan Dr, Comming, GA, 30130
Medical Dir/Dir of Nursing Fred Boling MD.
Admissions Requirements Medical examination; Physician's request.
Staff RNs 3 (ft); LPNs 9 (ft), 1 (pt); Orderlies 1 (ft), 1 (pt); Nurses aides 40 (ft), 10 (pt); Physical therapists; Occupational therapists; Speech therapists; Activities coordinators 1 (ft); Dietitians; Podiatrists.
Facilities Dining room; Physical therapy room; Activities room; Laundry room; Barber/Beauty shop.
Activities Cards; Games; Prayer groups; Movies; Shopping trips; Dances/Social or cultural gatherings.

Description Facility is located in Forsyth County and nestled among the hills and trees surrounding Lake Lanier.

CONYERS

Starcrest Home of Conyers*
PO Box 438, Conyers, GA, 30207 (404)
483-3902
Admin Rachel B Athon.
Licensure Skilled Care; Intermediate Care.
Beds 164. *Certified* Medicaid.

CORDELE

Crane Retirement Home Inc*
902 Blackshear Rd, Cordele, GA, 31015 (912)
273-1481
Admin W B Crane.
Licensure Skilled Care; Intermediate Care.
Beds 143. *Certified* Medicaid; Medicare.

Crisp County Medical Nursing Center*
1106 N 4th Ave, Cordele, GA, 31015 (912)
273-1227
Admin Carolyn Kidd.
Licensure Skilled Care. *Beds* 100. *Certified* Medicaid; Medicare.

COVINGTON

Covington Manor Intermediate Care Home*
4148 Carroll St, Ex-C, Covington, GA, 30209
(404) 786-0428
Admin Joyce Bohanan.
Licensure Intermediate Care. *Beds* 71. *Certified* Medicaid.

Riverside Medical of Covington
5100 West St, Covington, GA, 30209 (404)
787-0211
Admin C L Johnson. *Medical Dir/Dir of Nursing* J W Purcell MD.
Licensure Skilled Care; Intermediate Care.
Beds 128. *Certified* Medicaid.
Admissions Requirements Medical examination.
Staff RNs 1 (ft), 1 (pt); LPNs 10 (ft), 2 (pt); Orderlies 4 (ft), 1 (pt); Nurses aides 36 (ft), 7 (pt); Physical therapists 1 (ft), 1 (pt); Dietitians 1 (ft), 1 (pt).
Facilities Dining room; Physical therapy room; Activities room; Chapel; Laundry room; Barber/Beauty shop; Library.
Activities Arts and Crafts; Games.

CUMMING

Cumming Convalescent Home*
PO Box 24, Cumming, GA, 30130 (404)
887-2308
Admin Irwin William Winter.
Licensure Intermediate Care. *Beds* 53. *Certified* Medicaid.

CUTHBERT

Joe Anne Burgin Nursing Home
203 Randolph St, Cuthbert, GA, 31740 (912)

732-2181
Admin Patricia Raines. *Medical Dir/Dir of Nursing* Carl E Sills MD.
Licensure Skilled Care; Intermediate Care.
Beds 80. *Certified* Medicaid; Medicare.
Admissions Requirements Physician's request.
Staff Physicians 3 (pt); RNs 2 (ft); LPNs 5 (ft), 4 (pt); Orderlies 3 (ft), 5 (pt); Nurses aides 18 (ft), 10 (pt); Physical therapists 1 (pt); Recreational therapists 1 (pt); Activities coordinators 1 (pt); Dietitians 1 (pt); Dentists 1 (pt).
Facilities Dining room; Physical therapy room; Activities room; Chapel; Crafts room; Laundry room; Barber/Beauty shop.
Activities Arts and Crafts; Cards; Games; Reading groups; Prayer groups; Movies; Shopping trips; Dances/Social or cultural gatherings.

DAHLONEGA

Gold City Convalescent Center
PO Box 96, Dahlonega, GA, 30533 (404)
864-3045
Admin Andrew J Morris. *Medical Dir/Dir of Nursing* Eugene Westmoreland MD.
Licensure Skilled Care; Intermediate Care.
Beds 102. *Certified* Medicaid.
Admissions Requirements Medical examination; Physician's request.
Staff Physicians 1 (pt); RNs 4 (ft), 1 (pt); LPNs 5 (ft), 2 (pt); Physical therapists 1 (ft), 1 (pt); Recreational therapists 1 (ft); Activities coordinators 1 (ft); Dietitians 1 (ft); Podiatrists 1 (pt); 58 (ft), 2 (pt).
Facilities Dining room; Physical therapy room; Activities room; Chapel; Crafts room; Laundry room; Barber/Beauty shop.
Activities Arts and Crafts; Cards; Games; Reading groups; Prayer groups; Movies; Shopping trips; Dances/Social or cultural gatherings.
Description Center is located in Dahlonega home of the first major gold rush in America and is surrounded by the foothills of the Blue Ridge Mountains and capable of facilitating 102 residents at any given time. Center utilizes the services of over 75 volunteer groups and individuals from the surrounding community and North Georgia College.

DALLAS

Paulding Medical Nursing
600 W Memorial Dr, Dallas, GA, 30132 (404)
445-4411
Admin Ray C Brees.
Licensure Skilled Care; Intermediate Care.
Beds 136. *Certified* Medicaid; Medicare.

DALTON

Quinton Memorial Health Center
1114 Burleyson Dr, Dalton, GA, 30720 (404)
226-4642
Admin Wayne Benson. *Medical Dir/Dir of Nursing* Neil Boggess MD.
Licensure Skilled Care; Intermediate Care.
Beds 120. *Certified* Medicaid.
Admissions Requirements Medical examination.
Staff RNs 3 (ft); LPNs 9 (ft), 4 (pt); Orderlies 1 (ft), 1 (pt); Nurses aides 34 (ft), 4 (pt); Physical

therapists 1 (ft), 1 (pt); Activities coordinators 1 (ft); Dietitians 1 (pt).
Facilities Dining room; Physical therapy room; Activities room; Chapel; Crafts room; Laundry room; Barber/Beauty shop.
Activities Arts and Crafts; Cards; Games; Prayer groups; Movies; Shopping trips; Birthday parties; Devotionals by multi-denominational leaders.
Description Facility, built in 1978, is a one-level structure with 2 wings of 60 beds each.

Ridgewood Manor
1110 Burleyson Dr, Dalton, GA, 30720 (404) 226-1021
Admin John S Driggers. *Medical Dir/Dir of Nursing* Dr Earl McGhee.
Licensure Intermediate Care. *Beds* 102. *Certified* Medicaid.
Admissions Requirements Medical examination; Physician's request.
Staff Physicians; RNs; LPNs; Nurses aides; Physical therapists; Activities coordinators; Dietitians; Dentists.
Facilities Dining room; Physical therapy room; Activities room; Chapel; Crafts room; Laundry room; Barber/Beauty shop.
Activities Arts and Crafts; Cards; Games; Prayer groups; Shopping trips; Dances/Social or cultural gatherings.

Wood Dale Health Care Center
1102 Burleyson Dr, Dalton, GA, 30720 (404) 226-1285
Admin Eugene P Harrison. *Medical Dir/Dir of Nursing* Robert L Raitz MD.
Licensure Skilled Care; Intermediate Care. *Beds* 108. *Certified* Medicaid.
Admissions Requirements Medical examination; Physician's request.
Staff Physicians 15 (pt); RNs 2 (ft), 1 (pt); LPNs 13 (ft), 6 (pt); Nurses aides 28 (ft), 12 (pt); Physical therapists 1 (pt); Speech therapists 1 (pt); Activities coordinators 1 (ft); Dietitians 1 (pt); Dentists 1 (pt).
Facilities Dining room; Physical therapy room; Activities room; Chapel; Crafts room; Laundry room; Barber/Beauty shop.
Activities Arts and Crafts; Cards.

DAWSON

Dawson Manor*
Box 607, 507 E Georgia Ave, Dawson, GA, 31742 (912) 995-5016
Admin Jimmy C Johns.
Licensure Skilled Care; Intermediate Care. *Beds* 74. *Certified* Medicaid.

DECATUR

Americana Health Care Center
2722 N Decatur Rd, Decatur, GA, 30033 (404) 296-5440
Admin Patricia Sheppard. *Medical Dir/Dir of Nursing* Dr Philip Jardina.
Licensure Skilled Care; Intermediate Care. *Beds* 141. *Certified* Medicare.
Admissions Requirements Minimum age 21; Medical examination.
Staff Physicians 3 (pt); RNs 7 (ft), 4 (pt); LPNs

10 (ft), 7 (pt); Nurses aides 47 (ft), 4 (pt); Physical therapists 2 (ft), 1 (pt); Reality therapists 2 (ft); Recreational therapists 2 (ft); Occupational therapists 1 (ft); Speech therapists 1 (pt); Activities coordinators 1 (ft); Dietitians 1 (ft); Dentists 1 (pt); Podiatrists 1 (pt); Audiologists 1 (pt).
Facilities Dining room; Physical therapy room; Activities room; Barber/Beauty shop; Occupational therapy room.
Activities Arts and Crafts; Cards; Games; Reading groups; Prayer groups; Movies; Shopping trips; Dances/Social or cultural gatherings.
Description Full rehabilitation services are available; respite and residential care are also provided.

Atlantacare Convalescent Center*
304 5th Ave, Decatur, GA, 30030 (404) 373-6231
Admin Roy Carter.
Licensure Intermediate Care. *Beds* 103. *Certified* Medicaid.

Beverly Manor Convalescent Center—53*
2787 N Decatur Rd, Decatur, GA, 30030 (404) 292-0626
Admin Joyce Byars.
Licensure Skilled Care. *Beds* 73. *Certified* Medicaid; Medicare.

DeKalb General Nursing Unit
2701 N Decatur Rd, Decatur, GA, 30033 (404) 292-4444
Admin Naomi Harman. *Medical Dir/Dir of Nursing* John A Harrel MD.
Licensure Skilled Care. *Beds* 50. *Certified* Medicaid; Medicare.
Admissions Requirements Medical examination; Physician's request.
Staff RNs 7 (ft), 7 (pt); Orderlies 2 (ft), 2 (pt); Nurses aides 10 (ft), 11 (pt); Physical therapists 1 (ft); Recreational therapists 1 (ft); Occupational therapists 1 (pt); Speech therapists 1 (pt); Activities coordinators 1 (pt); Dietitians 1 (pt).
Facilities Dining room; Physical therapy room; Activities room; Chapel; Crafts room; Barber/Beauty shop; Library; Patio; Garden space.
Activities Arts and Crafts; Cards; Games; Reading groups; Prayer groups; Movies; Shopping trips; Dances/Social or cultural gatherings; Garden groups.
Description Home is a 50-bed skilled unit within the hospital, whose patients have priority; extensive rehabilitative nursing program is provided with occupational, physical, and speech therapy and an acitivities program which is assisted by volunteers from the community.

Georgia Regional Development Learning Center
PO Box 32407, Decatur, GA, 30032 (404) 243-2160
Admin Stephen L Watson. *Medical Dir/Dir of Nursing* Tomas Naura MD.
Licensure Intermediate Care for Mentally Retarded. *Beds* 67. *Certified* Medicare.
Admissions Requirements Minimum age 1-17; Medical examination; Physician's request.
Staff Physicians 1 (ft); RNs 3 (ft); LPNs 14 (ft); Orderlies 52 (ft); Physical therapists 1 (ft); Recreational therapists 1 (ft); Occupational therapists 1 (ft); Speech therapists 1 (ft); Activities

coordinators 1 (ft); Dietitians 1 (ft); Dentists 1 (ft).
Facilities Dining room; Physical therapy room; Activities room; Chapel; Crafts room; Laundry room; Barber/Beauty shop; Library.
Activities Arts and Crafts; Cards; Games; Reading groups; Movies; Shopping trips; Dances/Social or cultural gatherings.

Glenwood Manor*
4115 Glenwood Rd, Decatur, GA, 30032 (404) 284-6414
Admin Lewis Brewer.
Licensure Skilled Care. *Beds* 185. *Certified* Medicaid.

Harvest Heights Baptist Home Center
3200 Panthersville Rd, Decatur, GA, 30034 (404) 243-8460
Admin Charlotte W Hunt. *Medical Dir/Dir of Nursing* Patricia Lloyd MD.
Licensure Skilled Care; Intermediate Care. *Certified* Medicaid; Medicare.
Ownership Nonprofit.
Admissions Requirements Minimum age 18; Medical examination.
Staff Physicians 10 (ft); RNs 5 (ft), 6 (pt); LPNs 7 (ft), 5 (pt); Nurses aides 45 (ft), 12 (pt); Physical therapists 1 (pt); Reality therapists 1 (pt); Recreational therapists 1 (pt); Occupational therapists 1 (pt); Speech therapists 1 (pt); Activities coordinators 2 (ft); Dietitians 2 (ft); Dentists 1 (pt); Ophthalmologists 2 (pt); Podiatrists 1 (pt); Audiologists 2 (pt); Social workers 1 (ft).
Affiliation Baptist
Facilities Dining room; Physical therapy room; Activities room; Chapel; Crafts room; Laundry room; Barber/Beauty shop; Library; Patios.
Activities Arts and Crafts; Cards; Games; Prayer groups; Movies; Shopping trips; Dances/Social or cultural gatherings.
Description Facility is located on 16 acres of grounds with fireplace in dining area, rose garden, varied activity programs; emphasis on residents maintaining all independence possible and dignity of the individual; active volunteer program.

DEMOREST

Habersham Home*
PO Box 37, Demorest, GA, 30535 (404) 754-2134
Admin John H Bridges Sr.
Licensure Skilled Care; Intermediate Care. *Beds* 84. *Certified* Medicaid; Medicare.

DONALSONVILLE

Seminole Manor*
PO Box 1006, Donalsonville, GA, 31745 (912) 524-2062
Admin Linda Abbott. *Medical Dir/Dir of Nursing* Dr Jacob Holley.
Licensure Intermediate Care. *Beds* 62. *Certified* Medicaid.
Admissions Requirements Medical examination; Physician's request.
Staff RNs 1 (ft); LPNs 5 (ft); Nurses aides 12 (ft); Activities coordinators 1 (ft); Dietitians 1

(ft).

Facilities Dining room; Activities room; Laundry room; Barber/Beauty shop.

Activities Arts and Crafts; Cards; Games; Reading groups; Prayer groups; Movies; Shopping trips; Dances/Social or cultural gatherings.

DOUGLAS

Fair Haven Convalescent Home Inc
210 Coffee Ave, Douglas, GA, 31533 (912) 384-3615
Admin Myrtle A Vickers. *Medical Dir/Dir of Nursing* Fred G Gilliard.
Licensure Skilled Care; Intermediate Care.
Beds 57. *Certified* Medicaid.
Admissions Requirements Medical examination; Physician's request.
Staff Physicians 5 (pt); RNs 1 (ft), 1 (pt); LPNs 3 (ft); Nurses aides 16 (ft); Activities coordinators 1 (ft); Dietitians 1 (pt); Podiatrists 1 (pt).
Facilities Dining room; Physical therapy room; Activities room; Laundry room; Barber/Beauty shop.
Activities Arts and Crafts; Cards; Games; Reading groups; Prayer groups; Movies; Shopping trips.

Shady Acres Convalescent Center Inc*
PO Box 1059, W Gordon, Douglas, GA, 31533 (912) 384-7811
Admin Myrtle A Vickers.
Licensure Skilled Care; Intermediate Care.
Beds 91. *Certified* Medicaid.

DOUGLASVILLE

Garden Terrace Nursing Center
PO Box 86, Hwy 5, Douglasville, GA, 30134 (912) 942-7111
Admin Peggy Beckett. *Medical Dir/Dir of Nursing* George Artress.
Licensure Skilled Care; Intermediate Care.
Beds 160. *Certified* Medicaid; Medicare.
Admissions Requirements Medical examination; Physician's request.
Staff Physicians 5 (pt); RNs 4 (ft), 3 (pt); LPNs 19 (ft), 6 (pt); Nurses aides 64 (ft), 18 (pt); Physical therapists 1 (ft); Speech therapists 1 (pt); Activities coordinators 2 (ft); Dietitians 1 (ft); Dentists 1 (pt); Ophthalmologists 1 (pt); Podiatrists 1 (pt); Audiologists 1 (pt).
Facilities Dining room; Physical therapy room; Activities room; Chapel; Laundry room; Barber/Beauty shop; Library; County book mobile.
Activities Arts and Crafts; Cards; Games; Reading groups; Prayer groups; Movies; Shopping trips.
Description Facility has a rural setting on 26-acres, 30 minutes from downtown Atlanta.

DUBLIN

Dublinaire Nursing Home*
Rt 4, Box 147, Dublin, GA, 31021 (912) 272-7437
Admin Kaye Bracewell.
Licensure Skilled Care; Intermediate Care.
Beds 149. *Certified* Medicaid; Medicare.

Laurens County Convalescent Center
PO Box 549, Dublin, GA, 31041 (912) 272-1666
Admin Mrs Freddie M Webb. *Medical Dir/Dir of Nursing* John A Bell MD.
Licensure Skilled Care; Intermediate Care.
Beds 130. *Certified* Medicaid.
Admissions Requirements Physician's request.
Staff Physicians 1 (ft), 10 (pt); RNs 1 (ft), 1 (pt); LPNs 9 (ft), 4 (pt); Orderlies 6 (ft), 4 (pt); Nurses aides 19 (ft), 10 (pt); Physical therapists 1 (pt); Activities coordinators 1 (ft); Dietitians 1 (pt); Dentists 1 (pt); Podiatrists 1 (pt).
Facilities Dining room; Physical therapy room; Activities room; Crafts room; Laundry room; Barber/Beauty shop.
Activities Arts and Crafts; Cards; Games; Reading groups; Prayer groups; Shopping trips; Dances/Social or cultural gatherings.
Description Services offered include speech therapy, physical therapy, social services, and scheduled activities; VA approved.

Southern Medical of Dublin Inc*
1634 Telfair St, Dublin, GA, 31021 (912) 272-3220
Admin Larry L Shriver.
Licensure Skilled Care; Intermediate Care.
Beds 108. *Certified* Medicaid; Medicare.

EAST POINT

Bonterra Nursing Center
2801 Felton Dr, East Point, GA, 30344 (404) 767-7591
Admin J Faye White. *Medical Dir/Dir of Nursing* Joe Cruise MD.
Licensure Skilled Care. *Beds* 118. *Certified* Medicaid.
Admissions Requirements Medical examination; Physician's request.
Staff Physicians 5 (pt); RNs 2 (ft), 3 (pt); LPNs 7 (ft), 6 (pt); Nurses aides 26 (ft), 10 (pt); Physical therapists 1 (pt); Recreational therapists 1 (ft); Occupational therapists 1 (pt); Speech therapists 1 (pt); Activities coordinators 1 (pt); Dietitians 1 (pt).

East Point Intermediate Care Home
1684 Ware Ave, East Point, GA, 30044 (404) 767-5874
Admin Willie E Smith. *Medical Dir/Dir of Nursing* Dr Robert Webbster.
Licensure Intermediate Care. *Beds* 21.
Admissions Requirements Minimum age 21; Medical examination; Physician's request.
Staff LPNs 1 (pt); Nurses aides 5 (pt).
Facilities Dining room; Crafts room; Laundry room.
Activities Cards; Games; Prayer groups; Shopping trips.
Description We are a small facility with a home-type atmosphere. We pride ourselves in a home-like setting.

South Fulton Hospital—Extended Care Facility
1170 Cleveland Ave, East Point, GA, 30044 (404) 763-5000
Admin Frank Conort.
Licensure Skilled Care. *Beds* 36. *Certified* Medicare.
Admissions Requirements Medical examina-

tion; Physician's request.
Staff RNs 5 (ft), 1 (pt); LPNs 3 (ft), 2 (pt); Nurses aides 11 (ft), 1 (pt); Physical therapists 4 (ft); Speech therapists 1 (ft); Activities coordinators 1 (pt); Dietitians 3 (ft).
Facilities Dining room; Physical therapy room; Activities room; Chapel; Barber/Beauty shop.
Activities Cards; Games; Birthday parties monthly; Parties special holidays.
Description Hospital-based unit; 90% of the patients are confined to bed.

EASTMAN

Heart of Georgia Nursing Home*
PO Box 493, Eastman, GA, 31023 (912) 374-5571
Admin Clifford Durden.
Licensure Skilled Care; Intermediate Care.
Beds 100. *Certified* Medicaid; Medicare.

Middle Georgia Nursing Home
PO Box 159, Eastman, GA, 31023 (912) 374-4733
Admin Betty Jean Sheffield. *Medical Dir/Dir of Nursing* Dr David H Conner.
Licensure Skilled Care; Intermediate Care.
Beds 100. *Certified* Medicaid; Medicare.
Staff RNs 1 (ft), 1 (pt); LPNs 9 (ft), 3 (pt); Orderlies 5 (ft), 2 (pt); Nurses aides 14 (ft), 4 (pt); Physical therapists 1 (ft); Activities coordinators 1 (ft); Dietitians 1 (ft); Podiatrists 1 (ft).
Facilities Dining room; Physical therapy room; Activities room; Chapel; Laundry room; Barber/Beauty shop.
Activities Arts and Crafts; Games; Reading groups; Prayer groups; Movies; Shopping trips.

EATONTON

Regency Health Care Center*
PO Box 541, Eatonton, GA, 31024 (404) 485-8573
Admin Robert Hudson.
Licensure Skilled Care; Intermediate Care.
Beds 92. *Certified* Medicaid; Medicare.

EDISON

Calhoun Nursing Home*
PO Box 387, Edison, GA, 31746 (912) 835-2251
Admin Newana C Williams.
Licensure Skilled Care; Intermediate Care.
Beds 40. *Certified* Medicaid; Medicare.

ELBERTON

Heardmont Health Care Center*
Route 6, Box 249, Elberton, GA, 30635 (404) 283-5429
Admin Aubrey T Fleming.
Licensure Skilled Care; Intermediate Care.
Beds 60. *Certified* Medicaid; Medicare.

Nancy Hart Memorial Medical Center*
PO Box 753, Elberton, GA, 30635 (404) 283-3335

Admin Lynn H Blackmon.
Licensure Intermediate Care. *Beds* 67. *Certified* Medicaid.

Spring Valley Health Care Center Inc*
651 Rhodes Dr, Elberton, GA, 30635 (404) 283-3880
Admin Wilma Castellaw.
Licensure Skilled Care; Intermediate Care. *Beds* 60. *Certified* Medicaid.

ELLIJAY

Gilmer Nursing Home*
PO Box 346, Ellijay, GA, 30540 (404) 635-4741
Admin S Cantey Gordon.
Licensure Skilled Care; Intermediate Care. *Beds* 50. *Certified* Medicaid; Medicare.

EVANS

Evans Health Care*
PO Box 338, Evans, GA, 30809 (404) 863-7514
Admin John Pulliam.
Beds 120.

FAIRBURN

Fairburn Health Care Center
178 Campbellton St West, Fairburn, GA, 30213 (404) 964-1320
Admin Richard E St Martin. *Medical Dir/Dir of Nursing* Bruno Denis MD.
Licensure Skilled Care; Intermediate Care. *Beds* 120. *Certified* Medicaid; Medicare.
Admissions Requirements Medical examination; Physician's request.
Staff RNs 2 (ft), 1 (pt); LPNs 10 (ft), 2 (pt); Orderlies 3 (ft); Nurses aides 40 (ft); Physical therapists 1 (ft); Recreational therapists 1 (ft).
Facilities Dining room; Physical therapy room; Activities room; Laundry room; Barber/Beauty shop.
Activities Arts and Crafts; Games; Reading groups; Prayer groups; Dances/Social or cultural gatherings.
Description Facility offers full-time physical therapy and outpatient physical therapy department; VA approved.

FITZGERALD

Fitzgerald Nursing Home*
Rt 1, Box 22, Fitzgerald, GA, 31750 (912) 423-4361
Admin Michael A Norkus.
Licensure Skilled Care; Intermediate Care. *Beds* 150. *Certified* Medicaid; Medicare.

Life Care Center Inc
PO Box 1289, Fitzgerald, GA, 31750 (912) 423-4353
Admin Edward M Coop. *Medical Dir/Dir of Nursing* Dr Roy Johnson.
Licensure Skilled Care; Intermediate Care. *Beds* 167. *Certified* Medicaid; Medicare.
Staff RNs 1 (ft), 5 (pt); LPNs 20 (ft), 10 (pt); Orderlies 3 (ft), 3 (pt); Nurses aides 40 (ft), 10 (pt); Physical therapists 2 (pt); Occupational therapists 1 (pt); Speech therapists 1 (pt);

Activities coordinators 2 (ft); Dietitians 1 (ft); Dentists 1 (pt); Ophthalmologists 1 (pt); Podiatrists 1 (pt).
Facilities Dining room; Physical therapy room; Activities room; Crafts room; Laundry room; Barber/Beauty shop.
Activities Arts and Crafts; Games; Reading groups; Prayer groups; Movies; Shopping trips; Dances/Social or cultural gatherings.
Description Facility features an in-house physician, large activity area, and field trips.

FOLKSTON

Mullis Manor II*
401 N Okefenokee, Folkston, GA, 31537 (912) 496-7396
Admin Jack R Mays.
Licensure Intermediate Care. *Beds* 92.

FORSYTH

Forsyth Nursing Home
PO Box 1067, Forsyth, GA, 31029 (912) 994-5671
Admin Kate Cotton. *Medical Dir/Dir of Nursing* Dr A W Bramblett.
Licensure Skilled Care; Intermediate Care. *Beds* 72. *Certified* Medicaid.
Admissions Requirements Medical examination; Physician's request.
Staff Physicians 7 (pt); RNs 1 (ft), 1 (pt); LPNs 6 (ft), 2 (pt); Nurses aides 17 (ft), 3 (pt); Physical therapists 1 (ft), 1 (pt); Recreational therapists 1 (ft); Activities coordinators 1 (ft).
Facilities Dining room; Physical therapy room; Activities room; Chapel; Crafts room; Laundry room; Barber/Beauty shop; Library.
Activities Arts and Crafts; Cards; Games; Reading groups; Prayer groups; Movies; Shopping trips; Dances/Social or cultural gatherings.
Description Home has a country setting, community involvement, and active resident and family council.

Hilltop Nursing Home
Rt 2, Box 619, Forsyth, GA, 31029 (912) 994-5662
Admin Rosalyn M Harbuck. *Medical Dir/Dir of Nursing* A W Bramblett.
Licensure Skilled Care; Intermediate Care. *Beds* 83. *Certified* Medicaid.
Admissions Requirements Medical examination; Physician's request.
Staff Physicians 7 (pt); RNs 2 (ft), 1 (pt); Orderlies 4 (ft), 2 (pt); Physical therapists 1 (pt); Occupational therapists 1 (pt); Activities coordinators 2 (ft); Dietitians 1 (ft), 1 (pt); Dentists 1 (pt); Ophthalmologists 1 (pt); Podiatrists 1 (pt).
Facilities Dining room; Physical therapy room; Activities room; Crafts room; Laundry room; Barber/Beauty shop.
Activities Arts and Crafts; Cards; Games; Prayer groups; Movies; Shopping trips; Dances/Social or cultural gatherings.

FORT GAINES

Clay County—Fort Gaines Nursing Home
PO Box 160, Fort Gaines, GA, 31751 (912) 768-2522
Admin Collier Mills. *Medical Dir/Dir of Nursing* Homer P Wood MD.
Licensure Skilled Care; Intermediate Care. *Beds* 49. *Certified* Medicaid; Medicare.
Admissions Requirements Minimum age 16; Medical examination; Physician's request.
Staff RNs 1 (ft), 1 (pt); LPNs 6 (ft); Orderlies 3 (ft); Nurses aides 17 (ft); Activities coordinators 1 (ft).
Facilities Dining room; Physical therapy room; Activities room; Crafts room; Laundry room; Barber/Beauty shop.
Activities Arts and Crafts; Games; Prayer groups; Movies; Shopping trips; Dances/Social or cultural gatherings.
Description Intermingled facility located in a rural area at the bluff of the Chattahoochee River in southwest Georgia at the Alabama state line.

FORT OGLETHORPE

Fort Oglethorpe Nursing Center*
528 Battlefield Pkwy, Fort Oglethorpe, GA, 30742 (404) 861-5154
Admin Martha Q Dunn.
Licensure Intermediate Care. *Beds* 120.

John L Hutcheson Extended Care Unit*
200 Gross Crescent, Fort Oglethorpe, GA, 30742 (404) 866-2121
Admin Pamela C Richards. *Medical Dir/Dir of Nursing* Dr David Winters.
Licensure Skilled Care. *Beds* 25. *Certified* Medicaid; Medicare.
Admissions Requirements Medical examination; Physician's request.
Staff RNs 3 (ft); LPNs 4 (ft), 1 (pt); Nurses aides 9 (ft); Physical therapists 1 (ft); Activities coordinators 1 (ft); Dietitians 1 (ft); Dentists 1 (ft).
Facilities Dining room; Physical therapy room; Activities room; Chapel; Crafts room; Barber/Beauty shop.
Activities Arts and Crafts; Cards; Games; Reading groups; Prayer groups.
Description Facility is a 25-bed, skilled-level facility that is hospital-based. Facility provides total nursing care and specialized services such as total parenteral nutrition, Hickman catheters, and stroke rehabilitation; all hospital services (X-ray, lab, respiratory therapy, speech and physical therapy) available in facility.

FORT VALLEY

Fort Valley Health Care Center*
PO Box 1237, Fort Valley, GA, 31030 (912) 825-2031
Admin Carolyn Wilson.
Licensure Intermediate Care. *Beds* 75. *Certified* Medicaid.

FRANKLIN

Franklin Health Care Center
PO Box 472, Franklin, GA, 30217 (404)
675-6674
Admin Jeanette Hammond. *Medical Dir/Dir
of Nursing* J L Robinson MD.
Licensure Skilled Care; Intermediate Care.
Beds 78. *Certified* Medicaid.
Admissions Requirements Medical examination; Physician's request.
Staff Physicians 10 (pt); RNs 4 (ft); LPNs 5
(ft), 1 (pt); Nurses aides 18 (ft), 5 (pt); Physical
therapists 1 (pt); Reality therapists 1 (ft); Recreational therapists 1 (ft); Occupational therapists
1 (pt); Speech therapists 1 (pt); Activities coordinators 1 (ft); Dietitians 1 (ft); Dentists 1 (pt);
Ophthalmologists 1 (pt); Podiatrists 1 (pt);
Audiologists 1 (pt).
Facilities Dining room; Physical therapy room;
Activities room; Crafts room; Laundry room;
Barber/Beauty shop.
Activities Arts and Crafts; Cards; Games;
Reading groups; Prayer groups; Movies; Shopping trips; Dances/Social or cultural gatherings.
Description Facility has a beautiful, enclosed
courtyard which allows residents to enjoy the
outdoors in a protective environment.

GAINESVILLE

Bell-Minor Home Inc*
447 Bradford St NW, Gainesville, GA, 30505
(404) 532-2066
Admin Doris G Bell.
Licensure Skilled Care; Intermediate Care.
Beds 92. *Certified* Medicaid; Medicare.

Camelot Care Intermediate Care Facility*
Rt 6, Gainesville, GA, 30501 (404) 983-3771
Admin Jo Stephens.
Licensure Intermediate Care. *Beds* 60. *Certified* Medicaid.

Gainesville Health Care Center
Box JJ, Dawsonville Hwy, Gainesville, GA,
30501 (404) 536-9835
Admin Jonathan Hitt. *Medical Dir/Dir of
Nursing* Terry Jones MD.
Licensure Intermediate Care. *Beds* 100. *Certified* Medicaid.
Staff RNs 2 (ft), 1 (pt); LPNs 8 (ft), 1 (pt);
Orderlies 1 (ft); Nurses aides 36 (ft); Physical
therapists 1 (ft); Recreational therapists 1 (ft);
Activities coordinators 1 (ft); Dietitians 1 (ft).
Facilities Dining room; Physical therapy room;
Activities room; Chapel; Crafts room; Laundry
room; Barber/Beauty shop; Library.
Activities Arts and Crafts; Cards; Games;
Reading groups; Movies; Shopping trips; Dances/Social or cultural gatherings; Church
groups.

Lakeshore Heights Nursing Care Center*
PO Box D, Gainesville, GA, 30501 (404)
536-3391
Admin Michael J Riemann.
Licensure Skilled Care; Intermediate Care.
Beds 104.

Lanier North Intermediate Care Facility*
103 Clarks Branch Rd, Gainesville, GA, 30501
(404) 534-3565
Admin Jack Head.
Licensure Intermediate Care. *Beds* 46. *Certified* Medicaid.

GIBSON

Gibson Rest and Convalescent Home*
Beall Springs Rd, Gibson, GA, 30810 (404)
598-3201
Admin J Dwight Todd.
Licensure Skilled Care; Intermediate Care.
Beds 104. *Certified* Medicaid; Medicare.

GLENVILLE

Glenvue Nursing Home
721 N Main St, Glenville, GA, 30427 (912)
654-2138
Admin Julian E Dutton. *Medical Dir/Dir of
Nursing* Charles H Drake.
Licensure Skilled Care; Intermediate Care.
Beds 160. *Certified* Medicaid; Medicare.
Admissions Requirements Medical examination; Physician's request.
Staff Physicians 1 (pt); RNs 3 (ft); LPNs 14
(ft), 1 (pt); Orderlies 8 (ft), 4 (pt); Nurses aides
23 (ft), 8 (pt); Physical therapists 1 (ft), 1 (pt);
Recreational therapists 1 (ft); Activities coordinators 1 (ft), 1 (pt); Dietitians 1 (pt); Dentists 1
(pt); Podiatrists 1 (pt).
Facilities Dining room; Physical therapy room;
Activities room; Chapel; Laundry room; Barber/Beauty shop; Library.
Activities Arts and Crafts; Games; Reading
groups; Prayer groups; Movies; Shopping trips;
Dances/Social or cultural gatherings.

GLENWOOD

Conner Nursing Home*
PO Box 128, Glenwood, GA, 30428 (912)
523-5597
Admin Peggy Yarborough.
Licensure Skilled Care; Intermediate Care.
Beds 62. *Certified* Medicaid; Medicare.

GRACEWOOD

Gracewood Developmental Center*
Gracewood State Hospital, Division B, Gracewood, GA, 30812 (404) 790-2254
Admin W Martin Peterson.
Beds 596.

Gracewood Developmental Center*
Gracewood State Hospital, Division A, Gracewood, GA, 30812 (404) 790-2254
Admin Phyllis S Ille.
Beds 554.

Gracewood Nursing Home*
Unit 9, Bldg 76, Ward 1–2, Gracewood, GA,
30812 (404) 30812
Admin Martin Peterson.
Beds 84.

GRAY

Gray Nursing Home
Dolly St, PO Box 175, Gray, GA, 31032 (912)
986-3151
Admin Mildred J Jiles. *Medical Dir/Dir of
Nursing* H B Jones Jr MD.
Licensure Skilled Care; Intermediate Care.
Beds 58. *Certified* Medicaid.
Staff Physicians 2 (pt); RNs 1 (ft), 1 (pt); LPNs
4 (ft), 1 (pt); Orderlies 2 (ft); Nurses aides 12
(ft), 2 (pt); Physical therapists 1 (pt); Activities
coordinators 1 (ft); Dietitians 1 (ft); Dentists 1
(pt); Podiatrists 1 (pt).
Facilities Dining room; Physical therapy room;
Activities room; Laundry room.
Activities Arts and Crafts; Cards; Games;
Reading groups; Prayer groups; Movies; Shopping trips; Dances/Social or cultural gatherings.
Description This smaller compact home can
provide more individualized attention.

Lynn Haven Nursing Home*
PO Box 356, Rt 1, Box 62, Gray, GA, 31032
(912) 986-3196
Admin William Repzynski.
Licensure Skilled Care; Intermediate Care.
Beds 104. *Certified* Medicaid; Medicare.

GREENVILLE

Alvista Care Home Inc
PO Box E, Greenville, GA, 30222 (404)
672-4241
Admin Aubrey Green. *Medical Dir/Dir of
Nursing* James W Smith MD.
Licensure Intermediate Care. *Beds* 113. *Certified* Medicaid.
Admissions Requirements Medical examination; Physician's request.
Staff Physicians 1 (ft); RNs 2 (ft); LPNs 6 (ft),
1 (pt); Orderlies 1 (ft); Activities coordinators 1
(ft); Dietitians 1 (pt).
Facilities Dining room; Physical therapy room;
Activities room; Chapel; Crafts room; Laundry
room; Barber/Beauty shop.
Activities Arts and Crafts; Games; Reading
groups; Prayer groups; Movies; Shopping trips;
Dances/Social or cultural gatherings.
Description Facility has a country setting
located in a 40-acre pecan orchard with an outside patio.

GRIFFIN

Brightmoor Medical Care Home*
Rt 3, Box 119M, Griffin, GA, 30223 (404)
228-8599
Admin R H Monkus.
Licensure Skilled Care; Intermediate Care.
Beds 133. *Certified* Medicaid; Medicare.

Living Center of Griffin
415 Airport Rd, Griffin, GA, 30223 (404)
227-8636
Admin Larry W Lawrence. *Medical Dir/Dir of
Nursing* Kenneth Reynolds MD.
Licensure Skilled Care; Intermediate Care.
Beds 146. *Certified* Medicaid; Medicare.
Staff Physicians 1 (pt); RNs 2 (ft), 1 (pt); LPNs
12 (ft), 2 (pt); Nurses aides 43 (ft), 4 (pt);

Physical therapists 1 (pt); Reality therapists 1 (pt); Activities coordinators 1 (ft); Dietitians 1 (pt); Dentists 1 (pt); Ophthalmologists 1 (pt); Podiatrists 1 (pt).
Facilities Dining room; Physical therapy room; Activities room; Chapel; Crafts room; Laundry room; Barber/Beauty shop.
Activities Arts and Crafts; Games; Reading groups; Prayer groups; Movies; Shopping trips.

Spalding Convalescent Center*
615 Northside Dr, Griffin, GA, 30223 (404) 228-4517
Admin Jim Pritchett.
Licensure Skilled Care; Intermediate Care.
Beds 69. *Certified* Medicaid; Medicare.

HARTWELL

Hart Care Center
127 Fairview Ave, Hartwell, GA, 30643 (404) 376-7121
Admin Theresa M Boteler. *Medical Dir/Dir of Nursing* B J Davis MD.
Licensure Skilled Care; Intermediate Care.
Beds 117. *Certified* Medicaid.
Admissions Requirements Physician's request.
Staff Physicians 5 (pt); RNs 1 (ft), 2 (pt); LPNs 7 (ft), 2 (pt); Orderlies 6 (ft), 10 (pt); Nurses aides 16 (ft), 15 (pt); Physical therapists 1 (pt); Activities coordinators 1 (ft); Dietitians 1 (ft); Dentists 1 (pt).
Facilities Dining room; Physical therapy room; Activities room; Crafts room; Laundry room; Barber/Beauty shop.
Activities Arts and Crafts; Cards; Games; Reading groups; Prayer groups; Movies; Shopping trips; Dances/Social or cultural gatherings.

Heritage Inn of Hartwell
108 Cade St, Hartwell, GA, 30643 (404) 376-3185
Admin Susan Walters. *Medical Dir/Dir of Nursing* L C Cauhioli.
Licensure Skilled Care; Intermediate Care.
Beds 92. *Certified* Medicaid; Medicare.
Admissions Requirements Physician's request.
Staff Physicians 5 (pt); RNs 1 (ft), 2 (pt); LPNs 8 (ft), 1 (pt); Orderlies 5 (ft), 3 (pt); Nurses aides 15 (ft), 12 (pt); Physical therapists 1 (pt); Activities coordinators 1 (ft); Dietitians 1 (pt); Dentists 1 (pt).
Facilities Dining room; Activities room; Crafts room; Laundry room; Barber/Beauty shop.
Activities Arts and Crafts; Cards; Games; Movies; Shopping trips; Dances/Social or cultural gatherings.
Description Recent report from *Medical Care*: "The overall environment in this facility appeared to be extremely home-like, and offered a great deal of personal attention to the residents. The overall staff/resident relationship appeared to be characterized by warmth and kindness."

HAWKINSVILLE

Pinewood Manor Inc*
PO Box 587, Hawkinsville, GA, 31036 (912) 892-7171
Admin Earl Ray Tripp.

Licensure Intermediate Care. *Beds* 102. *Certified* Medicaid.

HAZELHURST

Chapman Convalescent Home*
PO Box 754, Hazelhurst, GA, 31539 (912) 375-2539
Admin Phil Chapman.
Licensure Skilled Care; Intermediate Care.
Beds 73. *Certified* Medicaid; Medicare.

HIAWASSEE

Towns County Nursing Home
PO Box 395, Hiawassee, GA, 30546 (404) 896-2222
Admin Gerard R Hummel. *Medical Dir/Dir of Nursing* Dr James S Campbell.
Licensure Skilled Care; Intermediate Care.
Beds 30. *Certified* Medicaid; Medicare.
Admissions Requirements Medical examination; Physician's request.
Staff Physicians 7 (ft); RNs 1 (ft), 1 (pt); LPNs 3 (ft), 3 (pt); Orderlies 5 (ft), 2 (pt); Nurses aides 6 (ft); Physical therapists 1 (pt); Activities coordinators 1 (ft); Dietitians 1 (pt); Dentists 1 (pt); 1 (ft).
Facilities Dining room; Activities room; Chapel; Laundry room; Barber/Beauty shop.
Activities Arts and Crafts; Games; Reading groups; Prayer groups; Movies; Shopping trips; Dances/Social or cultural gatherings.
Description Home is located in the north Georgia mountains with a beautiful view of Lake Chatoge.

HIGH SHOALS

Family Life Enrichment*
Highshoals Rd, Biox 37A, High Shoals, GA, 30645 (404) 769-7738
Admin Magda D Bennett.
Beds 100.

HOMERVILLE

Mullis Manor Inc*
410 Sweat St, Homerville, GA, 31634 (912) 487-5328
Admin Barbara Mullis.
Licensure Intermediate Care. *Beds* 92. *Certified* Medicaid.

IDEAL

Ideal Intermediate Care Unit
PO Box 120, Ideal, GA, 31041 (912) 949-2270
Admin Charlie H Griffin Jr. *Medical Dir/Dir of Nursing* Richard Chase DO.
Licensure Intermediate Care. *Beds* 100. *Certified* Medicaid.
Admissions Requirements Medical examination.
Staff Physicians 1 (pt); RNs 1 (ft); LPNs 6 (ft); Orderlies 3 (ft); Nurses aides 22 (ft); Physical therapists 1 (ft); Recreational therapists 1 (ft); Activities coordinators 1 (ft); Dietitians 1 (ft); Dentists 1 (pt); Ophthalmologists 1 (pt); Podia-

trists 1 (pt); 18 (ft).
Facilities Dining room; Physical therapy room; Activities room; Crafts room; Laundry room; Barber/Beauty shop.
Activities Arts and Crafts; Games; Prayer groups; Movies; Shopping trips; Dances/Social or cultural gatherings.

JASPER

Grandview Health Care Center*
208 S Main St, Jasper, GA, 30143 (404) 692-5123
Admin Patton W Childers.
Licensure Intermediate Care. *Beds* 45. *Certified* Medicare.

Pickens General Nursing Center
1319 Church St, Jasper, GA, 30143 (404) 692-2441
Admin Fred Walker Jr. *Medical Dir/Dir of Nursing* E A Roper MD.
Licensure Skilled Care; Intermediate Care.
Beds 60. *Certified* Medicaid; Medicare.
Admissions Requirements Medical examination; Physician's request.
Staff Physicians 5 (ft), 2 (pt); RNs 2 (ft); LPNs 7 (ft), 2 (pt); Orderlies 2 (ft); Nurses aides 21 (ft), 3 (pt); Recreational therapists 1 (ft); Activities coordinators 1 (ft); Dietitians 1 (ft); Ophthalmologists 1 (pt); Podiatrists 1 (pt).
Facilities Dining room; Physical therapy room; Chapel; Laundry room; Barber/Beauty shop.
Activities Arts and Crafts; Games; Reading groups; Prayer groups; Movies; Shopping trips; Dances/Social or cultural gatherings.
Description Facility is located in a very pretty setting in a wooded area. Our inside decor is very bright and cheerful with large indoor planter and skylight.

JEFFERSONVILLE

Spring Valley Intermediate Care Facility*
PO Box 308, Jeffersonville, GA, 31044 (912) 945-3255
Admin Marcelle Hiatt.
Licensure Intermediate Care. *Beds* 131. *Certified* Medicaid.

JENKINSBURG

Westbury Nursing Home*
PO Box 38, Jenkinsburg, GA, 30234 (404) 775-7832
Admin James R Westbury.
Licensure Skilled Care; Intermediate Care.
Beds 197. *Certified* Medicaid.

JESUP

Altamaha Convalescent Center Inc*
Box 807, 1311 Cherry St, Jesup, GA, 31545 (912) 427-7792
Admin Rebecca T Darley.
Licensure Intermediate Care. *Beds* 62. *Certified* Medicaid.

Jesup Manor Nursing Center*
PO Box 917, Jesup, GA, 31545 (912) 427-6858
Admin Earl S Holcomb.
Licensure Skilled Care; Intermediate Care.
Beds 90. *Certified* Medicaid; Medicare.

Jesup Rest-A-While Nursing Home
PO Box 827, Jesup, GA, 31545 (912) 427-6873
Admin Madeline Houston. *Medical Dir/Dir of Nursing* Dr R A Pumpelly Jr.
Licensure Skilled Care; Intermediate Care.
Beds 72. *Certified* Medicaid.
Admissions Requirements Medical examination.
Staff Physicians 1 (ft); RNs 1 (ft), 1 (pt); LPNs 8 (ft), 1 (pt); Orderlies 1 (pt); Nurses aides 16 (ft), 4 (pt); Physical therapists 1 (ft); Activities coordinators 1 (ft); Dietitians 1 (pt); Dentists 1 (pt).
Facilities Dining room; Physical therapy room; Activities room; Crafts room; Laundry room; Barber/Beauty shop.
Activities Arts and Crafts; Games; Reading groups; Prayer groups; Movies; Shopping trips.

JONESBORO

Styrons Arrowhead Nursing Center*
239 Arrowhead Blvd, Jonesboro, GA, 30236 (404) 478-3013
Admin Marian Styron.
Licensure Skilled Care; Intermediate Care.
Beds 116. *Certified* Medicaid.

KENNESAW

Shady Grove Rest Home*
Rt 4, Box 84, Kennesaw, GA, 30144 (404) 427-7256
Admin James A Ross.
Licensure Intermediate Care. *Beds* 24. *Certified* Medicaid.

KEYSVILLE

Keysville Convalescent and Nursing Center*
Rt 1, Box 128, Keysville, GA, 30816 (404) 547-2591
Admin William C Harman.
Licensure Skilled Care; Intermediate Care.
Beds 64. *Certified* Medicaid; Medicare.

LA GRANGE

Florence Hand Home—Skilled Nursing Facility
200 Medical Dr, La Grange, GA, 30240 (404) 884-6131
Admin Chas L Foster Jr. *Medical Dir/Dir of Nursing* George McCrary MD.
Licensure Skilled Care; Intermediate Care.
Beds 150. *Certified* Medicaid; Medicare.
Admissions Requirements Medical examination; Physician's request.
Staff RNs 13 (ft), 1 (pt); LPNs 30 (ft); Orderlies 2 (ft); Nurses aides 32 (ft), 2 (pt); Physical therapists 1 (pt); Recreational therapists 1 (ft); Speech therapists 1 (pt); Activities coordinators 1 (pt); Dietitians 1 (ft), 1 (pt); Dentists 1 (pt); Ophthalmologists 1 (pt); Podiatrists 1 (pt).

Facilities Dining room; Activities room; Crafts room; Laundry room; Barber/Beauty shop; Library.
Activities Arts and Crafts; Cards; Games; Reading groups; Prayer groups; Movies; Shopping trips; Dances/Social or cultural gatherings; Picnics; Patio luncheons.
Description This "Hilton" of nursing homes looks like a fabulous hotel; each client in a semi-private room has own window, dresser, and closet. Currently there is a pet therapy program twice a week for clients with dementia to improve their social interactions; 3 reality orientation classes 5 days a week. This is a hospital-based extended care facility and shares all hospital services.

LAFAYETTE

LaFayette Health Care Inc*
Rt 4, Box 4, LaFayette, GA, 30728 (404) 30728
Admin David Currie.
Beds 100.

Shepherd Hills Health Care
Box 647, Patterson Rd, Lafayette, GA, 30728 (404) 638-4112
Admin Gladys Whiteside. *Medical Dir/Dir of Nursing* H C Derrick Jr MD.
Licensure Skilled Care; Intermediate Care.
Beds 106. *Certified* Medicaid.
Admissions Requirements Medical examination; Physician's request.
Staff Physicians 4 (pt); RNs 2 (ft), 1 (pt); LPNs 6 (ft), 5 (pt); Nurses aides 26 (ft), 5 (pt); Activities coordinators 1 (ft); Dentists 2 (pt); Podiatrists 1 (pt).
Facilities Dining room; Physical therapy room; Activities room; Chapel; Laundry room; Barber/Beauty shop.
Activities Arts and Crafts; Cards; Games; Movies; Shopping trips; Dances/Social or cultural gatherings; Annual "Rock 'N Roll fund raising for Heart Association; Annual "Miss Nursing Home Pageant".
Description Facility is on a hill overlooking LaFayette, the Queen City of the Highlands, providing a loving, home-like environment for those committed to care.

LAGRANGE

LaGrange Medcraft Nursing Home*
PO Box 280, LaGrange, GA, 30241 (404) 882-1405
Admin James L Ambrose.
Licensure Skilled Care; Intermediate Care.
Beds 138. *Certified* Medicaid; Medicare.

Negro Old Folks Home Inc*
609 Union St, LaGrange, GA, 30240 (404) 884-9466
Admin Mina B Wood.
Licensure Intermediate Care. *Beds* 12. *Certified* Medicaid.

Royal Elaine Intermediate Care Facility*
Box 1346, Hogansville Rd, LaGrange, GA, 30241 (404) 882-0121
Admin Eleanor S Neely.
Licensure Intermediate Care. *Beds* 116. *Certified* Medicaid.

LAKELAND

Lakeland Villa Convalescent Center
W Thigpen Rd, PO Box 86, Lakeland, GA, 31635 (912) 482-2229
Admin Ernest Yap. *Medical Dir/Dir of Nursing* Guy Mann MD.
Licensure Skilled Care; Intermediate Care.
Beds 62. *Certified* Medicaid; Medicare.
Staff Physicians 5 (pt); RNs 1 (ft), 2 (pt); LPNs 5 (ft), 2 (pt); Orderlies 2 (ft); Nurses aides 17 (ft), 8 (pt); Physical therapists 1 (pt); Activities coordinators 1 (ft); Dietitians 1 (pt); Podiatrists 1 (pt).
Affiliation Seventh-Day Adventist
Facilities Dining room; Physical therapy room; Activities room; Laundry room; Barber/Beauty shop.
Activities Cards; Games; Reading groups; Prayer groups; Movies.

LAWRENCEVILLE

Medical Arts Health Facility
213 Scenic Hwy, Lawrenceville, GA, 30245 (404) 963-5275
Admin Pat Tanner. *Medical Dir/Dir of Nursing* Dr Michael Lipsitt.
Licensure Skilled Care; Intermediate Care.
Beds 124. *Certified* Medicaid; Medicare.
Admissions Requirements Medical examination.
Staff Physicians 9 (pt); RNs 3 (ft), 4 (pt); LPNs 6 (ft), 2 (pt); Nurses aides 29 (ft), 30 (pt); Speech therapists 1 (pt); Activities coordinators 1 (ft).
Facilities Dining room; Physical therapy room; Activities room; Chapel; Crafts room; Laundry room; Barber/Beauty shop.
Activities Arts and Crafts; Cards; Games; Reading groups; Prayer groups; Movies; Shopping trips; Dances/Social or cultural gatherings.
Description This is a well-rounded medical facility that provides quality care for all residents through an organized plan; personal attention and a relaxed home-like atmosphere are trademarks.

LILBURN

Lilburn Health Care Center*
Box 488, 788 Indian Trail, Lilburn, GA, 30247 (404) 923-2020
Admin Janice Russell.
Licensure Skilled Care; Intermediate Care.
Beds 120. *Certified* Medicaid; Medicare.

LITHONIA

Starcrest of Lithonia*
PO Box 855, Lithonia, GA, 30058 (404) 482-2961
Admin Larry H Athon.
Licensure Skilled Care; Intermediate Care.
Beds 117. *Certified* Medicaid.

LOUISVILLE

Old Capital Inn Convalescent and Nursing Home
PO Box 32, Louisville, GA, 30434 (912) 625-3742
Admin Diane Rhodes. *Medical Dir/Dir of Nursing* W J Revell Sr MD.
Licensure Skilled Care; Intermediate Care.
Beds 143. *Certified* Medicaid.
Admissions Requirements Minimum age 16; Medical examination; Physician's request.
Staff Physicians 6 (pt); RNs 2 (ft); LPNs 8 (ft), 3 (pt); Orderlies 4 (ft); Nurses aides 32 (ft); Physical therapists 1 (pt); Activities coordinators 2 (ft); Dietitians 1 (ft).
Facilities Dining room; Physical therapy room; Activities room; Chapel; Crafts room; Laundry room; Barber/Beauty shop.
Activities Arts and Crafts; Cards; Games; Reading groups; Prayer groups; Movies; Shopping trips; Dances/Social or cultural gatherings.

LUMBER CITY

Lumber City Medcraft*
PO Box 336, Lumber City, GA, 31549 (912) 363-4356
Admin Jill Bowen.
Licensure Skilled Care; Intermediate Care.
Beds 87. *Certified* Medicaid; Medicare.

LYONS

Toombs Nursing and Intermediate Care Home
100 Oxley Dr, Lyons, GA, 30436 (912) 526-6336
Admin Herbert Conner.
Licensure Intermediate Care. *Beds* 104. *Certified* Medicaid.

MACON

Bel-Arbor Med-Care Nursing Home*
3468 Napier Ave, Macon, GA, 31204 (912) 477-4464
Admin W Charles Hampton.
Licensure Skilled Care; Intermediate Care.
Beds 130. *Certified* Medicaid; Medicare.

Eastview Nursing Home*
3020 Jeffersonville, Macon, GA, 31201 (912) 746-3547
Admin Beverly F Hardison.
Licensure Skilled Care; Intermediate Care.
Beds 92. *Certified* Medicaid; Medicare.

Good Will Nursing Home*
4373 Houston Ave, Macon, GA, 31206 (912) 788-4010
Admin Sandra Holton.
Licensure Skilled Care; Intermediate Care.
Beds 172. *Certified* Medicaid; Medicare.

Hospitality Care Center of Macon*
505 Coliseum Dr, Macon, GA, 31201 (912) 743-8687
Admin Wesley Vincent.
Licensure Skilled Care; Intermediate Care.
Beds 100. *Certified* Medicaid; Medicare.

Macon Healthcare Center
3051 Whiteside Rd, PO Box 10096, Macon, GA, 31206 (912) 788-1421
Admin Darrell Chisholm. *Medical Dir/Dir of Nursing* Dr William Brooks.
Licensure Skilled Care. *Beds* 147.
Admissions Requirements Medical examination; Physician's request.
Staff Physicians; RNs 2 (ft); LPNs 10 (ft), 7 (pt); Orderlies 6 (ft), 1 (pt); 26 (ft), 3 (pt).
Facilities Dining room; Physical therapy room; Activities room; Crafts room; Laundry room; Barber/Beauty shop.
Activities Arts and Crafts; Cards; Games; Movies; Shopping trips.
Description Facility activities include family nights, mothers day celebrations, picnics, ball games, and valentine parties.

Macon Medcraft
3520 Kenneth Dr, Macon, GA, 31206 (912) 781-9951
Admin Mildred Hollingshed. *Medical Dir/Dir of Nursing* Robert Nelson MD.
Licensure Intermediate Care. *Beds* 90.
Staff Physicians 1 (ft); RNs 1 (pt); LPNs 6 (ft); Orderlies 5 (ft), 1 (pt); Nurses aides 26 (ft); Physical therapists 1 (ft); Reality therapists 1 (ft); Recreational therapists 1 (ft); Speech therapists 1 (pt); Activities coordinators 1 (ft), 1 (pt); Dentists 1 (pt); Ophthalmologists 1 (pt); Podiatrists 1 (pt); Psychologist 1 (pt).
Facilities Dining room; Physical therapy room; Activities room; Chapel; Crafts room; Laundry room; Barber/Beauty shop.
Activities Arts and Crafts; Cards; Games; Reading groups; Prayer groups; Movies; Shopping trips; Dances/Social or cultural gatherings.
Description Trip every Tuesday to Center parks; every holiday and birthday celebrated; men and women's Christmas club.

Memorial Intermediate Care Home
1509 Cedar Ave, Macon, GA, 31208 (912) 743-4678
Admin Georgia Evans. *Medical Dir/Dir of Nursing* Dr C W James.
Licensure Intermediate Care. *Beds* 68. *Certified* Medicaid.
Staff RNs 1 (pt); LPNs 4 (ft), 3 (pt); Orderlies 3 (ft); Nurses aides 9 (ft), 9 (pt); Physical therapists 1 (pt); Reality therapists 1 (pt); Recreational therapists 1 (ft); Occupational therapists 1 (pt); Speech therapists 1 (pt); Activities coordinators 1 (ft); Dietitians 1 (pt).
Facilities Dining room; Physical therapy room; Activities room; Crafts room; Laundry room; Barber/Beauty shop.
Activities Arts and Crafts; Cards; Games; Reading groups; Prayer groups; Shopping trips; Dances/Social or cultural gatherings.

Oak Valley Nursing Home*
2795 Finney Circle, Macon, GA, 31201 (912) 745-4231
Admin Theo Fountain.
Licensure Skilled Care; Intermediate Care.
Beds 130. *Certified* Medicaid; Medicare.

Riverside of Macon
Rt 1, Pate Rd, Macon, GA, 31210 (912) 477-1720
Admin Joseph W Butler. *Medical Dir/Dir of Nursing* Dr J R Fountain.
Licensure Skilled Care; Intermediate Care.
Beds 121. *Certified* Medicaid.
Staff Physicians 2 (pt); RNs 1 (ft), 2 (pt); LPNs 6 (ft), 2 (pt); Orderlies 8 (ft); Nurses aides 40 (ft), 6 (pt); Physical therapists 1 (pt); Activities coordinators 1 (ft); Dietitians 1 (ft), 1 (pt); Dentists 1 (pt); Ophthalmologists 1 (pt); Podiatrists 1 (pt).
Facilities Dining room; Physical therapy room; Activities room; Chapel; Laundry room; Barber/Beauty shop.
Activities Arts and Crafts; Games; Prayer groups; Movies; Shopping trips.
Description Riverside of Macon is located 10 miles north of Macon in the beautiful rolling hills of Monroe county; situated on spacious, pine filled acres with home-like atmosphere in the quiet country with around the clock nursing. "There is a brighter tomorrow." VA approved.

Southern Medical of East Macon*
1060 Old Clinton Rd, Macon, GA, 31201 (912) 746-0266
Admin Paul R Noblitt.
Licensure Skilled Care; Intermediate Care.
Beds 122. *Certified* Medicaid.

Southern Medical Services of North Macon*
2255 Anthony Rd, Macon, GA, 31203 (912) 743-9347
Admin Susan Doreen Hansard.
Licensure Skilled Care; Intermediate Care.
Beds 228. *Certified* Medicaid; Medicare.

Three Oaks Intermediate Care Home
PO Box 7531, Macon, GA, 31204 (912) 986-6245
Admin Kenneth A Goings.
Licensure Intermediate Care. *Beds* 34. *Certified* Medicaid.

MADISON

Hospitality Care Center*
Box 228, Hwy 278, Madison, GA, 30650 (404) 342-3200
Admin Jeff Norton.
Licensure Intermediate Care. *Beds* 67. *Certified* Medicaid.

MARIETTA

Americana Healthcare Center
4360 Johnson Ferry Pl, Marietta, GA, 30067
Admin Barbara Baxter. *Medical Dir/Dir of Nursing* David Rearick DO.
Licensure Skilled Care; Intermediate Care.
Beds 120. *Certified* Medicare.
Ownership Proprietary.
Admissions Requirements Medical examination; Physician's request.
Staff RNs; LPNs; Orderlies; Nurses aides; Physical therapists; Reality therapists; Recreational therapists; Occupational therapists; Speech therapists; Activities coordinators; Dietitians.
Facilities Dining room; Physical therapy room; Activities room; Chapel; Crafts room; Laundry room; Barber/Beauty shop; Library; Rehabilita-

tive dining area.

Activities Arts and Crafts; Cards; Games; Reading groups; Prayer groups; Movies; Shopping trips; Dances/Social or cultural gatherings.
Description Facility is all on one floor and is decorated and designed for gracious living with the quality of life one deserves. Staff is professional and progressive and believes in giving quality care; rehabilitative services are outstanding.

Autumn Breeze Nursing Home
1480 Sandtown, Box 310, Marietta, GA, 30060 (404) 422-1755
Admin David Morgan. *Medical Dir/Dir of Nursing* George Artress MD.
Licensure Skilled Care; Intermediate Care.
Beds 127.
Admissions Requirements Medical examination; Physician's request.
Staff Physicians 13 (ft); RNs 4 (ft), 2 (pt); LPNs 8 (ft), 3 (pt); Orderlies 3 (ft); Nurses aides 45 (ft), 3 (pt); Physical therapists 1 (ft); Recreational therapists 1 (ft); Speech therapists 1 (pt); Activities coordinators 1 (ft); Dietitians 1 (ft).
Facilities Dining room; Physical therapy room; Activities room; Crafts room; Laundry room; Barber/Beauty shop.
Activities Arts and Crafts; Cards; Games; Reading groups; Prayer groups; Movies; Shopping trips; Dances/Social or cultural gatherings.
Description Facility features very active social and recreational programs.

Hillhaven Rehabilitation Convalescent Center*
26 Tower Rd, Marietta, GA, 30060 (404) 422-8913
Admin Romaine P Barnes.
Licensure Skilled Care. *Beds* 146. *Certified* Medicaid; Medicare.

Marietta Health Care Center
85 Saine Rd Southwest, Marietta, GA, 30060 (404) 429-8600
Admin Helen M Besal. *Medical Dir/Dir of Nursing* Gary Cowan MD.
Licensure Skilled Care; Intermediate Care.
Beds 119. *Certified* Medicaid; Medicare.
Admissions Requirements Medical examination; Physician's request.
Staff RNs 6 (ft), 1 (pt); LPNs 12 (ft), 4 (pt); Orderlies 2 (ft); Nurses aides 35 (ft), 8 (pt); Physical therapists 1 (ft); Speech therapists 1 (pt); Activities coordinators 1 (ft); Dietitians 1 (ft); Dentists 1 (pt); Social workers 1 (ft).
Facilities Dining room; Physical therapy room; Activities room; Crafts room; Barber/Beauty shop; Library.
Activities Arts and Crafts; Cards; Games; Reading groups; Prayer groups; Movies; Shopping trips; Dances/Social or cultural gatherings.
Description VA approved; adopt-a-grandparent program; family council; resident council.

Shoreham Convalescent Center*
811 Kennesaw Ave, Marietta, GA, 30060 (404) 422-2451
Admin Beulah Holmberg.
Licensure Skilled Care; Intermediate Care.
Beds 118. *Certified* Medicaid; Medicare.

MARSHALLVILLE

The Oaks Nursing Home Inc
Rt 1, Marshallville, GA, 31057 (912) 967-2223
Admin N Jule Windham.
Licensure Skilled Care. *Beds* 48.

MARTINEZ

Forrest Lake Manor Inc*
409 Pleasant Home Rd, Martinez, GA, 30907 (404) 863-6030
Admin Thema R Allgood.
Licensure Skilled Care; Intermediate Care.
Beds 92. *Certified* Medicaid; Medicare.

MCDONOUGH

Westbury Home*
PO Box 796, McDonough, GA, 30253 (404) 957-9081
Admin Phillip J Westbury.
Licensure Skilled Care; Intermediate Care.
Beds 180. *Certified* Medicaid.

MCRAE

McRae Manor Inc*
1104 S 1st Ave, McRae, GA, 31055 (912) 868-6473
Admin Buford T Cook.
Licensure Skilled Care; Intermediate Care.
Beds 133. *Certified* Medicaid; Medicare.

METTER

Metter Nursing Home*
PO Box 356, Metter, GA, 30439 (912) 685-5734
Admin William J Byrd.
Licensure Skilled Care; Intermediate Care.
Beds 89. *Certified* Medicaid; Medicare.

Pleasant View Nursing Home
303 Anderson, Box 576, Metter, GA, 30439 (912) 685-2168
Admin Cother Lee Hodges. *Medical Dir/Dir of Nursing* Dr J D Smith.
Licensure Skilled Care; Intermediate Care.
Beds SNF 58; ICF 62. *Certified* Medicaid.
Admissions Requirements Medical examination; Physician's request.
Staff Physicians 4 (ft); RNs 1 (ft), 2 (pt); LPNs 9 (ft), 1 (pt); Orderlies 7 (ft); Nurses aides 15 (ft), 7 (pt); Physical therapists 1 (ft); Activities coordinators 1 (ft); Dietitians 1 (ft); Dentists 1 (ft); Ophthalmologists 1 (ft); Podiatrists 1 (ft).
Facilities Dining room; Physical therapy room; Activities room; Chapel; Crafts room; Laundry room; Barber/Beauty shop.
Activities Arts and Crafts; Cards; Games; Reading groups; Prayer groups; Movies; Shopping trips; Dances/Social or cultural gatherings; Class programs; Community affairs.
Description Facility features mental retardation classes and reality orientation classes.

MIDWAY

Liberty Manor
PO Box 270, Midway, GA, 31320 (912) 884-3361
Admin Barbara Streetman. *Medical Dir/Dir of Nursing* Whitman Fraser.
Licensure Skilled Care; Intermediate Care.
Beds 169. *Certified* Medicaid.
Admissions Requirements Medical examination; Physician's request.
Staff Physicians 3 (ft), 2 (pt); RNs 3 (ft), 1 (pt); LPNs 11 (ft), 3 (pt); Orderlies 6 (ft); Nurses aides 24 (ft), 4 (pt); Physical therapists 1 (ft); Recreational therapists 1 (ft); Activities coordinators 1 (ft); Dietitians 1 (ft); Dentists 1 (ft); Ophthalmologists 1 (ft); Podiatrists 1 (ft).
Facilities Dining room; Physical therapy room; Activities room; Crafts room; Laundry room; Barber/Beauty shop; Library; Mental retardation room for skills teaching.
Activities Arts and Crafts; Games; Reading groups; Prayer groups; Movies; Shopping trips; Dances/Social or cultural gatherings.
Description Facility has a resident council group that meets weekly to give ideas and suggestions for betterment of the facility; monthly newspaper done by staff and residents. Magic Room for mentally retarded residents is a big success; wheelchair garden for the residents to plant and care for.

MILLEDGEVILLE

Allen Hall*
Central State Hospital, Milledgeville, GA, 31062 (912) 453-4145
Admin Lynne F Wright.
Licensure Intermediate Care. *Beds* 270. *Certified* Medicare.

Carl Vinson Skilled Nursing Home
Vinson Hwy, Milledgeville, GA, 31062 (912) 453-4547
Admin Alice K Paschal. *Medical Dir/Dir of Nursing* Ernesto Coligado MD.
Licensure Skilled Care. *Beds* 100.
Admissions Requirements Medical examination; Physician's request.
Staff Physicians 2 (ft); RNs 8 (ft); LPNs 12 (ft); Nurses aides 24 (ft); Physical therapists 1 (ft); Recreational therapists 1 (ft); Occupational therapists 1 (ft); Activities coordinators 1 (ft); Dietitians 1 (ft).
Facilities Dining room; Physical therapy room; Activities room; Chapel; Crafts room; Laundry room; Barber/Beauty shop; Library; Music; Vending machine room; Visiting room; Occupational therapy room.
Activities Arts and Crafts; Cards; Games; Reading groups; Prayer groups; Movies; Shopping trips; Dances/Social or cultural gatherings; Monthly birthday party; Overnight trips; Special event trips to baseball games and holiday events.
Description The Georgia War Veterans Home is a combination of 2 skilled nursing homes and one domiciliary, one of only 17 such homes in the U.S. Care and treatment is provided free of charge to residents who meet entry

criteria; veteran organizations statewide provide enormous support, such as activities, entertainment, and donations.

Central State Hospital
Milledgeville, GA, 31062 (912) 453-5043
Admin Bobby A Sheppard.
Licensure Intermediate Care. *Beds* 218. *Certified* Medicaid.

Chaplinwood Nursing Home*
Allen Memorial Dr, Milledgeville, GA, 31061 (912) 452-4596
Admin Troy Anthon.
Licensure Skilled Care; Intermediate Care. *Beds* 100. *Certified* Medicaid; Medicare.

Green Acres Intermediate Care Facility*
Allen Dr, Milledgeville, GA, 31061 (912) 452-4596
Admin Edward C Nelson.
Licensure Intermediate Care. *Beds* 95. *Certified* Medicaid.

Nursing Home Center*
Central State Hospital, Boone Bldg, Milledgeville, GA, 31062 (404) 453-4311
Admin Marion K Garland.
Beds 94.

Pecan Manor 1
Central State Hospital, Milledgeville, GA, 31062 (912) 452-3511
Admin Byron O Merritt III.
Licensure Intermediate Care for Mentally Retarded. *Beds* 30. *Certified* Medicare.

Pecan Manor 3*
Central State Hospital, Milledgeville, GA, 31061 (912) 452-5558
Admin Jerry T Bush.
Licensure Intermediate Care. *Beds* 134. *Certified* Medicare.

Piedmont Hall*
Central State Hospital, Milledgeville, GA, 31061 (912) 453-5776
Admin John Gates.
Licensure Intermediate Care for Mentally Retarded. *Beds* 149. *Certified* Medicare.

Richard B Russell Building*
PO Box 325, Milledgeville, GA, 31061 (404) 453-4128
Admin Sandra Wilder.
Beds 132.

Riverside Nursing Center*
Central State Hospital, Milledgeville, GA, 31062 (404) 453-4455
Admin Paul Mitchell.
Beds 75.

MILLEN

Bethany Home for Men
Gray St Exten, PO Box 600, Millen, GA, 30442 (912) 982-2531
Admin Raymond Vaughn. *Medical Dir/Dir of Nursing* J M Byne Jr MD.
Licensure Skilled Care; Intermediate Care. *Beds* 100. *Certified* Medicaid; Medicare.

Admissions Requirements Minimum age 16; Males only; Medical examination; Physician's request.
Staff Physicians 1 (ft); RNs 1 (ft), 1 (pt); LPNs 6 (ft), 5 (pt); Orderlies 5 (ft), 2 (pt); Nurses aides 20 (ft), 1 (pt); Physical therapists 1 (pt); Reality therapists 1 (ft); Recreational therapists 1 (ft); Activities coordinators 1 (ft); Dietitians 1 (ft); Dentists 1 (pt); Ophthalmologists 1 (pt); Podiatrists 1 (pt); Audiologists 1 (pt).
Affiliation Baptist
Facilities Dining room; Physical therapy room; Activities room; Chapel; Crafts room; Laundry room; Barber/Beauty shop; Library.
Activities Arts and Crafts; Cards; Games; Reading groups; Prayer groups; Movies; Shopping trips; Farm.
Description VA approved.

MOLENA

Molena Intermediate Care Home
PO Box 397, Molena, GA, 30258 (404) 495-5138
Admin Michael S Greene. *Medical Dir/Dir of Nursing* J W Smith Jr MD.
Licensure Intermediate Care. *Beds* 50. *Certified* Medicaid.
Admissions Requirements Medical examination.
Staff Physicians 1 (pt); RNs 1 (ft); LPNs 5 (ft); Orderlies 1 (ft); Nurses aides 18 (ft); Physical therapists 1 (pt); Reality therapists 1 (pt); Recreational therapists 1 (pt); Occupational therapists 1 (pt); Speech therapists 1 (pt); Activities coordinators 1 (ft); Dietitians 1 (ft); Dentists 1 (pt); Podiatrists 1 (pt); 1 (ft).
Facilities Dining room; Physical therapy room; Activities room; Chapel; Crafts room; Laundry room; Barber/Beauty shop; Library; Lobby; Sitting area.
Activities Arts and Crafts; Cards; Games; Reading groups; Prayer groups; Movies; Shopping trips; Dances/Social or cultural gatherings; Van trips.
Description Facility offers home-like atmosphere.

MONROE

Monroe Intermediate Care Facility
Rt 3, Monroe, GA, 30655 (404) 267-7541
Admin E Kenneth Murray. *Medical Dir/Dir of Nursing* Dr Phillip Enslen.
Licensure Intermediate Care. *Beds* 112. *Certified* Medicaid.
Admissions Requirements Minimum age 21; Medical examination; Physician's request.
Staff Physicians 5 (pt); RNs 1 (pt); LPNs 7 (ft), 1 (pt); Orderlies 1 (ft), 3 (pt); Physical therapists 1 (pt); Reality therapists 1 (pt); Recreational therapists 1 (ft), 1 (pt); Occupational therapists 1 (pt); Speech therapists 1 (pt); Activities coordinators 1 (ft); Dietitians 1 (ft), 1 (pt); Dentists 1 (pt); Ophthalmologists 1 (pt); Podiatrists 1 (pt); Audiologists 1 (pt).
Facilities Dining room; Physical therapy room; Activities room; Chapel; Crafts room; Laundry room.

Activities Arts and Crafts; Cards; Games; Reading groups; Prayer groups; Shopping trips; Dances/Social or cultural gatherings.

Walton County Hospital Convalescent Wing
330 Alcova St, PO Box 1346, Monroe, GA, 30655 (404) 267-8461
Admin Kenneth L Lowery. *Medical Dir/Dir of Nursing* Lynn M Hole MD.
Licensure Skilled Care. *Beds* 58. *Certified* Medicaid; Medicare.
Admissions Requirements Medical examination; Physician's request.
Facilities Dining room; Physical therapy room; Activities room; Crafts room; Barber/Beauty shop.
Activities Arts and Crafts; Cards; Games; Reading groups; Prayer groups; Movies; Shopping trips; Dances/Social or cultural gatherings; Outside programs by groups.

MONTEZUMA

Montezuma Health Care Center*
521 Sumter St, Box 639, Montezuma, GA, 31063 (912) 472-8168
Admin Lillian M Baggett.
Licensure Skilled Care; Intermediate Care. *Beds* 100. *Certified* Medicaid; Medicare.

MONTICELLO

The Retreat
898 College St, Monticello, GA, 31064 (404) 468-8826
Admin W Phillip Jordan Jr. *Medical Dir/Dir of Nursing* J Corbitt Kelly MD.
Licensure Intermingled. *Beds* 44. *Certified* Medicaid.
Ownership Nonprofit.
Admissions Requirements Medical examination; Physician's request.
Staff Physicians 2 (pt); RNs 1 (ft), 1 (pt); LPNs 3 (ft), 2 (pt); Orderlies 1 (ft), 1 (pt); Nurses aides 15 (ft), 12 (pt); Physical therapists 1 (pt); Activities coordinators 1 (ft); Activities coordinators 1 (ft); Dentists 2 (pt); Podiatrists 1 (pt).
Facilities Dining room; Physical therapy room; Activities room; Crafts room; Laundry room; Barber/Beauty shop.
Activities Cards; Games; Reading groups; Prayer groups; Movies; Shopping trips; Dances/Social or cultural gatherings.
Description The Retreat is a nonprofit nursing home operated by the Jasper County Hospital Authority; attached to the hospital with which it shares many departments.

MORROW

Lake City Health Care Center
2055 Rex Rd, Box 728, Morrow, GA, 30252 (404) 361-5114
Admin Margaret Griffin. *Medical Dir/Dir of Nursing* J Nam Lee MD.
Licensure Skilled Care; Intermediate Care. *Beds* 118. *Certified* Medicaid.
Admissions Requirements Medical examination; Physician's request.
Staff Physicians 3 (pt); RNs 1 (ft), 1 (pt); LPNs

7 (ft), 1 (pt); Nurses aides 41 (ft); Physical therapists 2 (ft); Recreational therapists 1 (ft); Activities coordinators 1 (ft); Dietitians 1 (ft).
Facilities Dining room; Physical therapy room; Activities room; Crafts room; Laundry room; Barber/Beauty shop; Library.
Activities Arts and Crafts; Cards; Games; Reading groups; Prayer groups; Movies; Shopping trips; Dances/Social or cultural gatherings.
Description Facility features a large outside landscaped area.

MOULTRIE

Brownwood Nursing Home
PO Box 2010, Moultrie, GA, 31768
Admin Jeffrey Jursik. *Medical Dir/Dir of Nursing* Odie Newborn.
Licensure Skilled Care; Intermediate Care.
Beds 100. *Certified* Medicaid; Medicare.
Ownership Proprietary.
Admissions Requirements Medical examination; Physician's request.
Staff Physicians 12 (pt); RNs 1 (ft), 2 (pt); LPNs 12 (ft); Orderlies 10 (ft); Nurses aides 20 (ft), 8 (pt); Physical therapists 1 (ft), 1 (pt); Speech therapists 1 (ft), 1 (pt); Activities coordinators 1 (ft); Dietitians 1 (ft), 1 (pt); Dentists 1 (pt); Podiatrists 1 (pt).
Facilities Dining room; Physical therapy room; Activities room; Crafts room; Laundry room; Barber/Beauty shop.
Activities Arts and Crafts; Cards; Games; Reading groups; Prayer groups; Movies; Shopping trips; Dances/Social or cultural gatherings.

Moultrie Rest-A-While Nursing Home*
PO Box 666, 2015 1st Ave, Moultrie, GA, 31768 (912) 985-4319
Admin Joann Turner.
Licensure Skilled Care; Intermediate Care.
Beds 68. *Certified* Medicaid; Medicare.

Rest Awhile Nursing Home*
422 5th Ave SE, Moultrie, GA, 31768 (912) 985-3637
Admin Eugene E Reid Jr.
Licensure Skilled Care; Intermediate Care.
Beds 59. *Certified* Medicaid.

Sunrise Nursing Home of Georgia Inc*
Rt 6, Thomasville Hwy, Moultrie, GA, 31768 (912) 985-4772
Admin P Z Clark Sr.
Licensure Skilled Care; Intermediate Care.
Beds 50. *Certified* Medicaid.

NASHVILLE

Berrien Nursing Center Inc
704 N Davis St, Nashville, GA, 31639 (912) 686-2034
Admin DeMaris P Hughes. *Medical Dir/Dir of Nursing* Dr James R Wilhoite.
Licensure Skilled Care; Intermediate Care.
Beds 54. *Certified* Medicaid; Medicare.
Admissions Requirements Medical examination; Physician's request.
Staff Physicians 5 (pt); RNs 1 (ft), 2 (pt); LPNs 4 (ft), 3 (pt); Orderlies 1 (ft); Nurses aides 11 (ft), 5 (pt); Physical therapists 1 (pt); Activities

coordinators 1 (ft); Dietitians 1 (pt); Dentists 1 (pt); Podiatrists 1 (pt).
Facilities Dining room; Activities room; Crafts room; Laundry room; Barber/Beauty shop.
Activities Arts and Crafts; Cards; Games; Reading groups; Prayer groups; Movies; Shopping trips; Dances/Social or cultural gatherings.

NEWNAN

Beaulieu Nursing Home*
Box 40, E Broad St, Newnan, GA, 30264 (404) 253-7160
Admin Kathleen Adams.
Licensure Skilled Care. *Beds* 66. *Certified* Medicaid; Medicare.

Newman Healthcare Center
120 Spring St, Newnan, GA, 30263 (404) 253-1475
Admin Carolyn Stenger. *Medical Dir/Dir of Nursing* John Wells MD.
Licensure Intermediate Care. *Beds* 50. *Certified* Medicaid.
Staff Physicians 10 (pt); RNs 1 (ft); LPNs 6 (ft); Orderlies 2 (ft); Nurses aides 10 (ft); Physical therapists 1 (pt); Activities coordinators 1 (ft); Dietitians 1 (pt); Dentists 1 (pt); Ophthalmologists 2 (ft); Podiatrists 1 (pt).

OCILLA

Osceola Nursing Home
8th and Alder, PO Box 505, Ocilla, GA, 31774 (912) 468-9431
Admin George Christopher Cook. *Medical Dir/Dir of Nursing* Dr W C Sams.
Licensure Skilled Care; Intermediate Care.
Beds 83. *Certified* Medicaid; Medicare.
Admissions Requirements Minimum age 35; Medical examination; Physician's request.
Staff Physicians 3 (ft); RNs 1 (ft), 2 (pt); LPNs 10 (ft), 4 (pt); Orderlies 6 (ft), 1 (pt); Nurses aides 14 (ft), 8 (pt); Physical therapists 1 (ft); Reality therapists 1 (ft); Recreational therapists 1 (ft); Speech therapists 1 (pt); Activities coordinators 1 (pt); Dietitians 1 (pt); Dentists 1 (pt); Ophthalmologists 1 (pt); Podiatrists 1 (pt).
Facilities Dining room; Physical therapy room; Activities room; Crafts room; Laundry room; Barber/Beauty shop.
Activities Arts and Crafts; Cards; Games; Reading groups; Prayer groups; Movies; Shopping trips; Dances/Social or cultural gatherings.
Description Facility features a home-like atmosphere with a very good staff relationship which contributes to good resident moral. Physio-social needs are met in a clean, orderly environment. Balanced therapeutic diets are served daily.

Palemon Gaskin Memorial Nursing Home
201 W Dismukes Ave, Ocilla, GA, 31774 (912) 468-7411
Admin Evelyn S Clark. *Medical Dir/Dir of Nursing* W C Sams MD.
Licensure Skilled Care; Intermediate Care.
Beds 30. *Certified* Medicaid; Medicare.
Staff RNs 1 (ft); LPNs 4 (ft), 2 (pt); Orderlies 1 (ft), 2 (pt); Nurses aides 10 (ft), 1 (pt); Physical therapists 1 (pt); Recreational therapists 1 (pt);

Activities coordinators 1 (ft); Dietitians 1 (ft).
Facilities Dining room; Chapel; Laundry room; Barber/Beauty shop.
Activities Arts and Crafts; Movies; Dances/Social or cultural gatherings.

OCONEE

Oconee Health Care Center*
PO Box 130, Oconee, GA, 31067 (912) 552-7381
Admin Laverne Bloodworth.
Licensure Intermediate Care. *Beds* 52. *Certified* Medicaid.

PELHAM

Pelham Parkway Nursing Home
601 Dogwood Dr, Pelham, GA, 31779 (912) 294-8602
Admin Voncille H Rumble. *Medical Dir/Dir of Nursing* W C Arwood Jr MD.
Licensure Skilled Care; Intermediate Care.
Beds 108. *Certified* Medicaid; Medicare.
Admissions Requirements Medical examination.
Staff Physicians 3 (pt); RNs 1 (ft), 1 (pt); LPNs 9 (ft), 3 (pt); Orderlies 6 (ft), 6 (pt); Nurses aides 24 (ft), 4 (pt); Physical therapists 1 (pt); Activities coordinators 1 (ft); Dietitians 1 (ft); Dentists 1 (pt); Podiatrists 1 (pt); 1 (ft).
Facilities Dining room; Physical therapy room; Activities room; Laundry room; Barber/Beauty shop.
Activities Arts and Crafts; Cards; Games; Prayer groups; Movies; Shopping trips; Dances/Social or cultural gatherings.
Description Home employees are proud of the reputation that they have because they care enough to do their best for your loved ones.

PERRY

Christ Sanctified Holy Church Home for the Aged
PO Box 1376, Perry, GA, 31069 (912) 987-1239
Admin Mariola Cosby. *Medical Dir/Dir of Nursing* Dr A G Hendricks.
Licensure Skilled Care; Intermediate Care.
Beds 31. *Certified* Medicaid.
Staff Physicians 6 (pt); RNs 1 (ft), 2 (pt); LPNs 1 (ft), 2 (pt); Nurses aides 11 (ft), 6 (pt); Physical therapists 1 (pt); Recreational therapists 1 (pt); Activities coordinators 1 (ft); Dietitians 1 (ft); Podiatrists 1 (pt).
Facilities Dining room; Laundry room; Barber/Beauty shop.
Activities Arts and Crafts; Prayer groups; Movies; Shopping trips; Dances/Social or cultural gatherings.
Description We try to have (or maintain), as near as possible, a home-like family atmosphere.

New Perry Nursing Home
PO Drawer P, Perry, GA, 31068 (912) 987-3251
Admin William C Davis Jr. *Medical Dir/Dir of Nursing* Dr J L Gallemore.

Licensure Skilled Care; Intermediate Care. *Beds* 73. *Certified* Medicaid.
Staff Physicians 4 (pt); RNs 3 (ft); LPNs 3 (ft), 2 (pt); Orderlies 2 (ft), 1 (pt); Nurses aides 27 (ft); Physical therapists 1 (pt); Recreational therapists 1 (ft); Activities coordinators 1 (ft); Dietitians 1 (pt); Podiatrists 1 (pt).
Facilities Dining room; Activities room; Chapel; Crafts room; Laundry room; Barber/Beauty shop; Library.
Activities Arts and Crafts; Cards; Games; Movies; Dances/Social or cultural gatherings.

PINEVIEW

Pineview Intermediate Care Home*
Box 148, Bay St, Pineview, GA, 31071 (912) 624-2432
Admin James M Stewart Jr.
Licensure Intermediate Care. *Beds* 103. *Certified* Medicaid.

PLAINS

Plains Convalescent Home*
PO Box 366, Plains, GA, 31780 (912) 824-7796
Admin Glenn Godwin.
Licensure Skilled Care; Intermediate Care. *Beds* 100. *Certified* Medicaid.

POOLER

Moss Oaks Health Care*
508 S Rogers St, Pooler, GA, 31322 (404) 748-6840
Admin John P Cowart.
Beds 122.

PORT WENTWORTH

Westview Medical Care Home*
PO Box 4134, Port Wentworth, GA, 31407 (912) 964-1515
Admin Cleveland J Fountain.
Licensure Skilled Care; Intermediate Care. *Beds* 101. *Certified* Medicaid.

PULASKI

Pulaski Nursing Home
PO Box 118, Pulaski, GA, 30451 (912) 685-5072
Admin Kay Hendricks. *Medical Dir/Dir of Nursing* Dorsey Smith MD.
Licensure Intermediate Care. *Beds* 89. *Certified* Medicaid.
Staff Physicians 4 (ft); RNs 1 (ft), 1 (pt); LPNs 7 (ft), 5 (pt); Orderlies 4 (ft), 2 (pt); Nurses aides 16 (ft), 6 (pt); Physical therapists 1 (pt); Activities coordinators 1 (ft); Dietitians 1 (pt); Dentists 1 (pt); Podiatrists 1 (pt).
Facilities Dining room; Physical therapy room; Activities room; Laundry room; Barber/Beauty shop.
Activities Arts and Crafts; Cards; Games; Reading groups; Prayer groups; Movies; Shopping trips; Dances/Social or cultural gatherings.

QUITMAN

Presbyterian Home Inc
PO Box 407, Quitman, GA, 31643 (912) 263-8633
Admin Frank H McElroy Jr. *Medical Dir/Dir of Nursing* L M Shealy MD.
Licensure Skilled Care; Intermediate Care. *Beds* 188. *Certified* Medicaid.
Admissions Requirements Medical examination; Physician's request.
Staff Physicians 4 (ft); RNs 3 (ft), 1 (pt); LPNs 24 (ft), 9 (pt); Orderlies 3 (ft), 1 (pt); Nurses aides 70 (ft), 12 (pt); Physical therapists 1 (ft); Occupational therapists 1 (pt); Speech therapists 1 (pt); Activities coordinators 1 (ft); Dietitians 1 (ft), 1 (pt); Dentists 1 (pt); Podiatrists 1 (pt).
Affiliation Presbyterian
Facilities Dining room; Physical therapy room; Activities room; Chapel; Crafts room; Laundry room; Barber/Beauty shop; Library.
Activities Arts and Crafts; Cards; Games; Reading groups; Prayer groups; Movies; Shopping trips; Dances/Social or cultural gatherings; Pond for fishing, etc.

REIDSVILLE

Tattnall Nursing Center
PO Box 860, Reidsville, GA, 30453 (912) 557-4345
Admin Kenneth Abbott. *Medical Dir/Dir of Nursing* H S Geiger Jr MD.
Licensure Skilled Care; Intermediate Care. *Beds* 92. *Certified* Medicaid.
Staff Physicians 1 (pt); RNs 2 (ft); LPNs 5 (ft), 1 (pt); Orderlies 8 (ft); Nurses aides 30 (ft), 3 (pt); Activities coordinators 1 (ft), 1 (pt).
Facilities Dining room; Physical therapy room; Activities room; Crafts room; Laundry room; Barber/Beauty shop.
Activities Arts and Crafts; Cards; Games; Movies; Shopping trips; Dances/Social or cultural gatherings.
Description Center is located in quiet rural area with excellent community involvement and has courteous and understanding personnel ready to serve.

RIVERDALE

Hospitality Care Center of Clayton*
PO Box 917, Riverdale, GA, 30274 (404) 478-1144
Admin Ken Carithers.
Licensure Skilled Care. *Beds* 100. *Certified* Medicaid; Medicare.

ROBERTA

Roberta Intermediate Care Home*
PO Box 146, Roberta, GA, 31078 (912) 836-3101
Admin Sally Aderhold.
Licensure Intermediate Care. *Beds* 100. *Certified* Medicaid.

ROCKMART

Rockmart Intermediate Care Center
528 Hunter St, Rockmart, GA, 30153 (404) 684-5491
Admin Ann Gober. *Medical Dir/Dir of Nursing* Umpon Sangmalee MD.
Licensure Intermediate Care. *Beds* 73. *Certified* Medicaid.
Admissions Requirements Medical examination; Physician's request.
Staff Physicians 1 (ft); RNs 1 (ft); LPNs 3 (ft), 2 (pt); Nurses aides 20 (ft), 4 (pt); Physical therapists 1 (pt); Activities coordinators 1 (ft); Dietitians 1 (pt); Dentists 1 (pt); Podiatrists 1 (pt).
Facilities Dining room; Physical therapy room; Activities room; Chapel; Crafts room; Laundry room; Barber/Beauty shop.
Activities Arts and Crafts; Cards; Games; Reading groups; Prayer groups; Movies; Shopping trips; Dances/Social or cultural gatherings.

ROME

Brentwood Park Nursing Home
PO Box 1441, Rome, GA, 30161 (404) 291-8212
Admin Louise K Houser. *Medical Dir/Dir of Nursing* Dr Joel Todino.
Licensure Skilled Care; Intermediate Care. *Beds* 100. *Certified* Medicaid.
Admissions Requirements Medical examination; Physician's request.
Staff Physicians 1 (pt); RNs 1 (ft), 1 (pt); LPNs 4 (ft), 3 (pt); Orderlies 3 (ft); Nurses aides 37 (ft); Physical therapists 1 (pt); Activities coordinators 1 (ft); Dietitians 1 (pt).
Facilities Dining room; Physical therapy room; Activities room; Chapel; Laundry room.
Activities Arts and Crafts; Cards; Games; Prayer groups; Movies; Shopping trips; Dances/Social or cultural gatherings.
Description Brentwood Park is beautifully located on a hillside with easy access to 2 hospitals, mental health facilities, and services; free county health services, and numerous other agencies.

Creswell Convalescent Center
1345 Redmond Rd, Rome, GA, 30161 (404) 234-8281
Admin Michael Coultas. *Medical Dir/Dir of Nursing* Grant Lewis.
Licensure Skilled Care; Intermediate Care. *Beds* 100. *Certified* Medicaid; Medicare.
Admissions Requirements Physician's request.
Staff RNs 2 (ft); LPNs 15 (ft); Orderlies 1 (ft); Nurses aides 40 (ft), 26 (pt); Physical therapists 1 (pt); Reality therapists 1 (ft); Recreational therapists 1 (ft); Occupational therapists 1 (pt); Speech therapists 1 (pt); Activities coordinators 1 (ft); Dietitians 1 (pt); Dentists 1 (pt); Podiatrists 1 (pt).
Facilities Dining room; Physical therapy room; Activities room; Crafts room; Laundry room; Barber/Beauty shop; Library; Gift shop.
Activities Arts and Crafts; Cards; Games; Reading groups; Prayer groups; Movies; Shopping trips; Dances/Social or cultural gatherings.

Fifth Avenue Health Care Center
505 N 5th Ave, Rome, GA, 30161 (404)
291-0521
Admin Clark H Peek. *Medical Dir/Dir of
Nursing* Dr Grant Lewis.
Licensure Skilled Care; Intermediate Care.
Beds 89. *Certified* Medicaid; Medicare.
Staff Physicians 1 (pt); LPNs 2 (ft), 1 (pt);
Orderlies 1 (ft), 1 (pt); Nurses aides 19 (ft), 14
(pt); Physical therapists 1 (pt); Recreational
therapists 1 (ft); Activities coordinators 1 (ft);
Dietitians 1 (pt); Dentists 1 (pt); Podiatrists 1
(pt).
Facilities Dining room; Physical therapy room;
Activities room; Chapel; Crafts room; Laundry
room; Barber/Beauty shop; Library.
Description All programs are outstanding.

Northwest Regional Intermediate Care Home*
400 Redmond Rd, Rome, GA, 30161 (404)
234-9481
Admin Susan J Gooch.
Licensure Intermediate Care. *Beds* 82. *Certified* Medicare.

Riverview Nursing Home*
809 S Broad St, Rome, GA, 30161 (404)
235-1337
Admin Annie Mae Langham.
Licensure Skilled Care; Intermediate Care.
Beds 100. *Certified* Medicaid.

Springwood Nursing Home*
109 Hemlock St, Rome, GA, 30161 (404)
235-8121
Admin Bruce Behner.
Licensure Skilled Care; Intermediate Care.
Beds 95. *Certified* Medicaid.

Valley View Health Care
158 Chulio Rd, Rome, GA, 30161 (404)
235-1132
Admin James L McAlpin. *Medical Dir/Dir of
Nursing* Dr Joel Todino.
Licensure Skilled Care; Intermediate Care.
Beds 77. *Certified* Medicaid.
Admissions Requirements Medical examination; Physician's request.
Staff Physicians 1 (ft); RNs 2 (ft); LPNs 3 (ft),
4 (pt); Orderlies 2 (ft), 1 (pt); Nurses aides 7 (ft),
12 (pt); Physical therapists 1 (ft), 1 (pt); Recreational therapists 1 (ft); Activities coordinators 1
(ft); Dietitians 1 (ft), 1 (pt); Dentists 1 (ft).
Facilities Dining room; Activities room; Chapel; Crafts room; Laundry room; Barber/Beauty
shop.
Activities Arts and Crafts; Cards; Games;
Reading groups; Prayer groups; Movies.

ROSSVILLE

Rossville Convalescent Center Inc
1425 McFarland Ave, Rossville, GA, 30741
(404) 861-0863
Admin Scott Adkison.
Licensure Skilled Care; Intermediate Care.
Beds 100. *Certified* Medicaid; Medicare.
Admissions Requirements Physician's request.
Staff Physicians 1 (pt); RNs 2 (ft); LPNs 6 (ft),
3 (pt); Orderlies 4 (ft).
Facilities Dining room; Physical therapy room;
Activities room; Crafts room; Laundry room;

Barber/Beauty shop; Library; Pharmacy.
Activities Arts and Crafts; Cards; Games;
Reading groups; Prayer groups; Movies; Dances/Social or cultural gatherings; Sewing group;
Entertainment.
Description Rossville Convalescent Center provides both short-term rehabilitation and long-term care; many patients come from the hospital for rehabilitation and then return home.
Family members of patients choose this as the
facility to go to if they themselves need this
type of service.

ROSWELL

Great Oaks Nursing Home*
Box 397, 1109 Green St, Roswell, GA, 30075
(404) 998-1802
Admin Doris A Jones.
Licensure Skilled Care; Intermediate Care.
Beds 269. *Certified* Medicaid; Medicare.

ROYSTON

Brown Memorial Convalescent Center*
PO Box 8, Royston, GA, 30662 (404) 245-5034
Admin Mrs Johnnie Escoe. *Medical Dir/Dir of
Nursing* William Ford MD.
Licensure Skilled Care; Intermediate Care.
Beds 144. *Certified* Medicaid; Medicare.
Admissions Requirements Medical examination; Physician's request.
Staff Physicians 5 (ft); RNs 2 (ft), 2 (pt); LPNs
9 (ft), 6 (pt); Orderlies 7 (ft), 9 (pt); Nurses aides
25 (ft), 25 (pt); Physical therapists 1 (ft), 1 (pt);
Speech therapists 1 (pt); Activities coordinators
2 (ft).
Facilities Dining room; Physical therapy room;
Activities room; Chapel; Crafts room; Laundry
room; Barber/Beauty shop; In house pharmacy.
Activities Arts and Crafts; Cards; Games;
Reading groups; Prayer groups; Movies; Shopping trips; Dances/Social or cultural gatherings.
Description We are hospital-based facility with
24-hour emergency room service, available to
the convalescent center. We also have a full-time MSW to help meet the residents' social
needs.

SAINT MARYS

Saint Mary's Convalescent Center*
805 Dilworth St, Saint Mary's, GA, 31558
(912) 882-4281
Admin Lois Cooper.
Licensure Skilled Care; Intermediate Care.
Beds 69. *Certified* Medicaid.

SAINT SIMONS ISLAND

Heritage Inn*
2255 Fredrica Rd, Saint Simons Island, GA,
31522 (912) 638-9988
Admin Tommy Stroud.
Licensure Skilled Care; Intermediate Care.
Beds 92. *Certified* Medicaid.

SANDERSVILLE

Rawlings Nursing Home
111 Brookins St, Sandersville, GA, 31082 (912)
552-3015
Admin Ruth Strange. *Medical Dir/Dir of
Nursing* Dr L R Harvey.
Licensure Skilled Care; Intermediate Care.
Beds 56. *Certified* Medicaid.
Admissions Requirements Medical examination; Physician's request.
Staff Physicians 7 (pt); RNs 2 (ft), 1 (pt); LPNs
5 (ft), 2 (pt); Orderlies 3 (ft); Nurses aides 27
(ft); Physical therapists 1 (pt); Reality therapists
1 (ft); Recreational therapists 1 (ft); Speech therapists 1 (pt); Activities coordinators 1 (ft); Dietitians 1 (pt).
Facilities Dining room; Physical therapy room;
Activities room; Crafts room; Laundry room;
Barber/Beauty shop.
Activities Arts and Crafts; Cards; Games;
Reading groups; Prayer groups; Movies; Shopping trips; Dances/Social or cultural gatherings.

Smith Medical Nursing Care Center
501 E McCarty St, Sandersville, GA, 31082
(912) 552-5155
Admin Katie Smith Poole. *Medical Dir/Dir of
Nursing* Dr William E Taylor.
Licensure Skilled Care; Intermediate Care.
Beds 56.
Admissions Requirements Medical examination; Physician's request.
Staff Physicians 1 (pt); RNs 1 (ft), 2 (pt); LPNs
6 (ft), 1 (pt); Orderlies 5 (ft); Nurses aides 8 (ft),
1 (pt); Physical therapists 1 (ft), 1 (pt); Activities coordinators 1 (ft), 2 (pt); Dietitians 1 (ft).
Facilities Dining room; Physical therapy room;
Activities room; Crafts room; Laundry room;
Barber/Beauty shop.
Activities Arts and Crafts; Cards; Games;
Reading groups; Prayer groups; Movies; Shopping trips; Dances/Social or cultural gatherings.
Description Facility serves Washington and
surrounding counties with skilled and intermediate care; motto is "where somebody cares."

Washington County Extended Care Facility
PO Box 636, Sandersville, GA, 31082 (912)
552-3901
Admin Charles E Hill. *Medical Dir/Dir of
Nursing* Dr Sandra Tinley.
Licensure Skilled Care. *Beds* 50. *Certified* Medicaid; Medicare.
Staff Physicians 8 (pt); RNs 1 (ft), 1 (pt); LPNs
7 (ft); Orderlies 1 (ft), 1 (pt); Nurses aides 11
(ft), 3 (pt); Physical therapists 1 (pt); Speech
therapists 1 (pt); Activities coordinators 1 (ft);
Dietitians 1 (pt); Audiologists 1 (pt).
Facilities Dining room; Physical therapy room;
Activities room; Chapel; Barber/Beauty shop.
Activities Arts and Crafts; Games; Reading
groups; Prayer groups; Movies; Shopping trips;
Dances/Social or cultural gatherings.

SAVANNAH

Azalealand Nursing Home Inc
2040 Colonial Dr, Savannah, GA, 31406 (912)
354-2752
Admin Chas L Von Waldner. *Medical Dir/Dir
of Nursing* Jules Victor Jr.

Licensure Skilled Care; Intermediate Care.
Beds 107.
Admissions Requirements Minimum age 65;
Medical examination; Physician's request.
Staff RNs 3 (ft), 2 (pt); LPNs 7 (ft), 2 (pt);
Nurses aides 20 (ft), 8 (pt); Physical therapists 1
(pt); Reality therapists 2 (pt); Recreational therapists 1 (ft), 1 (pt); Activities coordinators 1 (ft).
Facilities Dining room; Physical therapy room;
Activities room; Chapel; Laundry room; Barber/Beauty shop; Library.
Activities Cards; Games; Movies; Shopping
trips.

Chatham Nursing Home I*
6711 La Roche Ave, Savannah, GA, 31406
(912) 354-8225
Admin Harold C Sims II.
Licensure Skilled Care; Intermediate Care.
Beds 284. *Certified* Medicaid; Medicare.

Chatham Nursing Home II*
6711 La Roche Ave, Savannah, GA, 31406
(912) 354-8225
Admin Meredith H Smith.
Licensure Skilled Care; Intermediate Care.
Beds 100. *Certified* Medicaid; Medicare.

Cohen's Retreat
5715 Skidaway Rd, Savannah, GA, 31406
(912) 355-2873
Admin T'Lene Wilson. *Medical Dir/Dir of
Nursing* Lawrence J Lynch Jr MD.
Licensure Skilled Care; Intermediate Care.
Beds 31. *Certified* Medicaid.
Ownership Nonprofit.
Admissions Requirements Males only; Medical
examination; Physician's request.
Staff Physicians 1 (pt); RNs 1 (ft), 1 (pt); LPNs
3 (ft), 2 (pt); Orderlies 1 (ft), 2 (pt); Nurses aides
3 (ft), 3 (pt); Physical therapists 1 (pt); Reality
therapists 1 (ft); Recreational therapists 1 (ft);
Activities coordinators 1 (ft); Dietitians 1 (pt);
Dentists 1 (pt); Podiatrists 1 (pt).
Affiliation King's Daughters and Sons
Facilities Dining room; Laundry room; Barber/Beauty shop; Library.
Activities Cards; Games; Reading groups; Prayer groups; Movies; Shopping trips;
Dances/Social or cultural gatherings.
Description Home features private rooms, electric beds, home-cooked food, garden space,
picnic and parking areas within Victorian perspective; on a bus route and surrounded by 16
efficiency apartments for the retired, a little
league softball field, and a golf course within
walking distance.

Hillhaven Convalescent Center*
11800 Abercorn St, Savannah, GA, 31406
(912) 925-4402
Admin Betty J Hargrett.
Licensure Skilled Care. *Beds* 104. *Certified* Medicaid; Medicare.

Savannah Convalescent Center
815 E 63rd St, Savannah, GA, 31405 (912)
352-8015
Admin Mary Burroughs. *Medical Dir/Dir of
Nursing* John Fellingim MD.
Licensure Skilled Care. *Beds* 120. *Certified* Medicaid; Medicare.
Admissions Requirements Medical examina-

tion; Physician's request.
Staff Physicians 37 (pt); RNs 6 (ft), 2 (pt);
LPNs 17 (ft), 6 (pt); Orderlies 3 (ft), 3 (pt);
Nurses aides 22 (ft), 9 (pt); Physical therapists 1
(ft); Reality therapists 1 (ft); Recreational therapists 1 (ft); Occupational therapists 1 (pt); Speech therapists 1 (pt); Activities coordinators 1
(ft); Dietitians 1 (pt); Dentists 1 (pt); Ophthalmologists 1 (pt); Podiatrists 1 (pt); Audiologists
1 (pt).
Facilities Dining room; Physical therapy room;
Activities room; Crafts room; Laundry room;
Barber/Beauty shop.
Activities Arts and Crafts; Cards; Games;
Reading groups; Prayer groups; Movies; Shopping trips; Dances/Social or cultural gatherings.
Description Center has rehabilitative services
and progressive care concept.

Savannah Health Care*
12825 White Bluff Rd, Savannah, GA, 31406
(404) 925-5157
Admin Joe Hunt.
Beds 120.

SNELLVILLE

Snellville Nursing and Rehabilitation Center
3000 Lenora Ch Rd, Snellville, GA, 30278
(404) 972-2070
Admin M E Hill III. *Medical Dir/Dir of
Nursing* Dr R V Dronavalli.
Licensure Intermediate Care. *Beds* 117. *Certified* Medicaid.
Admissions Requirements Medical examination; Physician's request.
Staff Physicians; RNs; LPNs; Orderlies;
Nurses aides; Physical therapists; Occupational
therapists; Speech therapists; Activities coordinators; Dietitians; Dentists; Podiatrists.
Facilities Dining room; Physical therapy room;
Activities room; Crafts room; Laundry room;
Barber/Beauty shop; Library.
Activities Arts and Crafts; Cards; Games;
Reading groups; Prayer groups; Movies; Shopping trips; Dances/Social or cultural gatherings;
Bowling.
Description Facility is adjacent to Brisco Park
with a picnic area and a lake view; bus with lift
for wheelchairs; van; many special activities
stressed.

SOCIAL CIRCLE

Social Circle Intermediate Care Facility*
671 N Cherokee Rd, Social Circle, GA, 30279
(404) 464-2019
Admin Mary Ann Wood.
Licensure Intermediate Care. *Beds* 65. *Certified* Medicare.

SOPERTON

Treutlen County Nursing Home
PO Box 646, Soperton, GA, 30457 (912)
529-4418
Admin Aubrey Fleming.
Licensure Skilled Care; Intermediate Care.
Beds 50. *Certified* Medicaid.

SPARTA

Providence Health Care*
Box 86, Providence St, Sparta, GA, 31087 (404)
444-5153
Admin Joy A Hill.
Licensure Skilled Care; Intermediate Care.
Beds 71. *Certified* Medicaid.

Sparta Intermediate Care Center*
Rt 22, Sparta, GA, 31087 (404) 444-6057
Admin Carolyn Lovitz.
Licensure Intermediate Care. *Beds* 81. *Certified* Medicaid.

SPRINGFIELD

Effingham County Extended Care Facility
PO Box 386, Springfield, GA, 31329 (912)
754-6451
Admin Ramon Snyder. *Medical Dir/Dir of
Nursing* Ray Webb MD.
Licensure Skilled Care; Intermediate Care.
Beds 56. *Certified* Medicaid; Medicare.
Admissions Requirements Medical examination; Physician's request.
Staff RNs 2 (ft), 1 (pt); LPNs 4 (ft), 3 (pt);
Orderlies 3 (ft), 3 (pt); Nurses aides 9 (ft), 9 (pt).
Facilities Dining room; Physical therapy room;
Activities room; Chapel; Crafts room; Barber/Beauty shop; Library.
Activities Arts and Crafts; Cards; Games;
Reading groups; Prayer groups; Movies; Shopping trips; Dances/Social or cultural gatherings.
Description Hospital-based nursing home;
therefore, full medical services available on-site;
JCAH accredited.

STATESBORO

Browns Nursing Home*
226 College St, Statesboro, GA, 30458 (912)
764-9631
Admin Harold H Brown.
Licensure Skilled Care; Intermediate Care.
Beds 63. *Certified* Medicaid; Medicare.

Georgia Grace Memorial Home Inc*
PO Box 421, Statesboro, GA, 30458 (912)
764-6903
Admin Beatrice Riggs.
Licensure Skilled Care; Intermediate Care.
Beds 60. *Certified* Medicaid.

Nightingale Home Inc
Jones Mill Rd, Statesboro, GA, 30458 (912)
764-9011
Admin Martha A Firges. *Medical Dir/Dir of
Nursing* Dr Nellie Byne.
Licensure Skilled Care; Intermediate Care.
Beds 92. *Certified* Medicaid; Medicare.
Staff RNs 2 (ft), 4 (pt); LPNs 7 (ft), 5 (pt);
Orderlies 6 (ft), 2 (pt); Nurses aides 23 (ft), 5
(pt); Physical therapists 1 (pt); Recreational
therapists 1 (ft); Activities coordinators 1 (pt);
Dietitians 1 (pt).
Facilities Dining room; Physical therapy room;
Chapel; Laundry room; Barber/Beauty shop.
Activities Arts and Crafts; Games; Reading
groups; Prayer groups; Movies.
Description Facility is adjacent to high school,

near shopping mall, less than one mile from hospital. Cannot admit if primary diagnosis is a drug or alcohol abuse problem.

Statesboro Nursing Home
PO Box 746, Statesboro, GA, 30458 (912) 764-6108
Admin Roger W Popham. *Medical Dir/Dir of Nursing* Dr D Scarborough and Dr R Smith.
Licensure Skilled Care; Intermediate Care.
Beds 99. *Certified* Medicaid.
Admissions Requirements Medical examination; Physician's request.
Staff Physicians 5 (pt); RNs 2 (ft), 1 (pt); LPNs 9 (ft), 2 (pt); Orderlies 3 (ft), 4 (pt); Nurses aides 24 (ft), 6 (pt); Physical therapists 1 (pt); Speech therapists 1 (pt); Activities coordinators 1 (ft); Dietitians 1 (pt); Dentists 1 (pt); Podiatrists 1 (pt).
Facilities Dining room; Physical therapy room; Activities room; Laundry room; Barber/Beauty shop.
Activities Arts and Crafts; Games; Movies; Shopping trips; Dances/Social or cultural gatherings.

SUMMERVILLE

Oak View Nursing Home
PO Box 449, Summerville, GA, 30747 (404) 857-3419
Admin Randall Smith.
Licensure Skilled Care; Intermediate Care.
Beds 90. *Certified* Medicaid; Medicare.

SWAINSBORO

Emanuel County Nursing Home*
PO Box 7, Swainsboro, GA, 30401 (912) 237-9911
Admin Joe Tucker.
Licensure Skilled Care. *Beds* 47. *Certified* Medicaid; Medicare.

Swainsboro Nursing Home Inc*
Rt 4, Box 184, Swainsboro, GA, 30401 (912) 237-7022
Admin Dorothy Schrader.
Licensure Skilled Care; Intermediate Care.
Beds 103. *Certified* Medicaid.

SYLVANIA

Syl-View Health Care Center*
Box 199, 411 Pine St, Sylvania, GA, 30467 (912) 564-2015
Admin Karen Zeigler.
Licensure Skilled Care; Intermediate Care.
Beds 128. *Certified* Medicaid.

SYLVESTER

Sylvester Health Care Inc*
PO Box 406, Sylvester, GA, 31791 (912) 776-5541
Admin Douglas L Moody.
Licensure Skilled Care; Intermediate Care.
Beds 59. *Certified* Medicaid.

TALKING ROCK

Wildwood Intermediate Care Home*
Rt 2, Talking Rock, GA, 30175 (404) 692-6014
Admin Dee F Wilbanks.
Licensure Intermediate Care. *Beds* 44. *Certified* Medicaid.

THOMASTON

Clear View Nursing Care Center*
Box 1162, 310 Ave F, Thomaston, GA, 30286 (404) 647-6676
Admin Charles E Aspinwall.
Licensure Skilled Care; Intermediate Care.
Beds 119. *Certified* Medicaid; Medicare.

Providence Health Care*
Box 49, 1011 Green St, Thomaston, GA, 30286 (404) 647-6693
Admin Ann C Connell.
Licensure Skilled Care; Intermediate Care.
Beds 110. *Certified* Medicaid.

Riverside Medical Services of Thomaston
101 Old Talbotton Rd, Thomaston, GA, 30286 (404) 647-8161
Admin Sue G Estes. *Medical Dir/Dir of Nursing* H D Tyler MD.
Licensure Skilled Care; Intermediate Care.
Beds 73. *Certified* Medicaid; Medicare.
Admissions Requirements Medical examination; Physician's request.
Staff Physicians 16 (ft); RNs 1 (ft), 3 (pt); LPNs 9 (ft), 3 (pt); Orderlies 3 (ft), 3 (pt); Nurses aides 28 (ft); Recreational therapists 1 (ft), 1 (pt); Activities coordinators 1 (ft); Dietitians 1 (ft).
Facilities Dining room; Physical therapy room; Activities room; Chapel; Crafts room; Laundry room; Barber/Beauty shop.
Activities Arts and Crafts; Cards; Games; Reading groups; Prayer groups; Movies; Shopping trips; Dances/Social or cultural gatherings; "Kitchen Band".
Description Facility features an organized and chartered Multiple Sclerosis Support Group.

THOMASVILLE

Camellia Garden of Life Care
PO Box 1959, Thomasville, GA, 31792 (912) 226-0076
Admin Barbara C Riser. *Medical Dir/Dir of Nursing* Dr J Rawlings.
Licensure Intermediate Care. *Beds* 83.
Admissions Requirements Medical examination; Physician's request.
Staff RNs 1 (ft), 1 (pt); LPNs 7 (ft), 8 (pt); Orderlies 2 (pt); Nurses aides 16 (ft), 13 (pt); Activities coordinators 1 (ft); Dietitians 1 (ft).
Facilities Dining room; Activities room; Crafts room; Laundry room; Barber/Beauty shop.
Activities Arts and Crafts; Cards; Games; Reading groups; Prayer groups; Movies; Shopping trips; Dances/Social or cultural gatherings.
Description This is a totally private pay facility.

Glenn-Mor Home
Rt 1, PO Box 464, Thomasville, GA, 31792 (912) 226-8942
Admin Mary A Goodspeed. *Medical Dir/Dir of Nursing* Dr John Brinson.
Licensure Skilled Care; Intermediate Care.
Beds 64. *Certified* Medicaid; Medicare.
Admissions Requirements Medical examination.
Staff Physicians 7 (pt); RNs 1 (ft), 2 (pt); LPNs 4 (ft), 7 (pt); Orderlies 4 (ft); Nurses aides 15 (ft), 4 (pt); Physical therapists 1 (pt); Activities coordinators 1 (ft); Dietitians 1 (ft).
Facilities Dining room; Physical therapy room; Activities room; Crafts room; Laundry room; Barber/Beauty shop.
Activities Arts and Crafts; Games; Reading groups; Prayer groups; Movies; Shopping trips; Dances/Social or cultural gatherings; Rhythm band; Sing-a-longs; Music and motions; Painting/sketching classes.
Description Beautiful, large open grounds excellent for nature walks and outdoor activities including picnics, parties, fairs, and carnivals. A caring staff encourages as much independence as possible and is receptive to needs, whether physical or mental. Glenn-Mor's administrative body is interested in public participation, getting the community involved, and promoting patient activity through avid support of activities program.

Hospitality Care of Thomasville*
930 S Broad St, Thomasville, GA, 31792 (912) 226-9322
Admin James R Kallevig.
Licensure Skilled Care; Intermediate Care.
Beds 68. *Certified* Medicaid; Medicare.

Rosehaven Skilled Nursing Home
PO Box 1378, Thomasville, GA, 31792 (912) 228-2202
Admin Jean Morgan. *Medical Dir/Dir of Nursing* Nell Lane MD.
Licensure Intermediate Care for Mentally Retarded. *Beds* 20. *Certified* Medicaid.
Admissions Requirements Medical examination.
Staff Physicians 1 (ft), 1 (pt); RNs 7 (ft); LPNs 24 (ft); Nurses aides 86 (ft); Physical therapists 1 (pt); Recreational therapists 1 (ft); Occupational therapists 1 (pt); Speech therapists 2 (ft); Dietitians 1 (ft); Dentists 1 (pt).
Facilities Dining room; Physical therapy room; Activities room; Laundry room.

Thomasville Health Care Center
4 Skyline Dr, Thomasville, GA, 31792 (912) 226-4101
Admin Pat Reagan. *Medical Dir/Dir of Nursing* Dr Joe Rawlings.
Licensure Skilled Care; Intermediate Care.
Beds 52. *Certified* Medicaid.
Admissions Requirements Medical examination.
Facilities Dining room; Physical therapy room; Activities room; Laundry room; Barber/Beauty shop.
Activities Arts and Crafts; Cards; Games; Prayer groups; Movies; Shopping trips; Dances/Social or cultural gatherings.

THOMSON

Thomson Manor Nursing Home Inc*
PO Drawer 1080, Thomson, GA, 30824 (404)
595-5574
Admin William C McConnell.
Licensure Skilled Care; Intermediate Care.
Beds 150. *Certified* Medicaid.

TIFTON

Tift Health Care Inc*
215 20th St, Tifton, GA, 31794 (912) 382-7342
Admin Frances D Moody.
Licensure Skilled Care; Intermediate Care.
Beds 86. *Certified* Medicaid.

Tifton Nursing Home
1451 Newton Dr, Tifton, GA, 31794 (912)
382-1665
Admin R Vernon Bankston. *Medical Dir/Dir
of Nursing* Morris Davis MD.
Licensure Intermingled. *Beds* 100. *Certified* Medicaid.
Admissions Requirements Medical examination; Physician's request.
Staff Physicians 6 (pt); RNs 1 (ft), 1 (pt); LPNs
6 (ft), 6 (pt); Orderlies 5 (ft), 3 (pt); Nurses aides
16 (ft), 16 (pt); Physical therapists 1 (ft); Activities coordinators 1 (ft); Dietitians 1 (ft); Dentists 1 (pt); Ophthalmologists 1 (pt); Podiatrists
1 (pt); Audiologists 1 (pt).
Facilities Dining room; Physical therapy room;
Activities room; Crafts room; Laundry room;
Barber/Beauty shop; Library.
Activities Arts and Crafts; Cards; Games;
Reading groups; Prayer groups; Shopping trips;
Dances/Social or cultural gatherings.

TOCCOA

Toccoa Nursing Center*
PO Box 1129, Toccoa, GA, 30577 (404)
886-8491
Admin Frieda Weeks. *Medical Dir/Dir of
Nursing* Arthur Singer MD.
Licensure Skilled Care; Intermediate Care.
Beds 181. *Certified* Medicaid.
Admissions Requirements Medical examination.
Staff RNs 2 (ft), 3 (pt); LPNs 8 (ft), 8 (pt);
Orderlies 3 (ft), 2 (pt); Nurses aides 63 (ft), 19
(pt); Activities coordinators 1 (ft), 1 (pt).
Facilities Dining room; Physical therapy room;
Laundry room; Barber/Beauty shop.
Activities Arts and Crafts; Cards; Games;
Reading groups; Prayer groups; Movies; Shopping trips; Dances/Social or cultural gatherings.

TRENTON

Sandmont Gala Nursing Home*
Rt 2, Box 45, Trenton, GA, 30752 (404)
657-4171
Admin Shannon Tullis.
Licensure Skilled Care; Intermediate Care.
Beds 65. *Certified* Medicaid.

TUCKER

Briarwood Nursing Center Inc*
3888 LaVista Rd, Tucker, GA, 30084 (404)
938-5740
Admin Coralee Long.
Licensure Skilled Care. *Beds* 100.

Meadowbrook Nursing Home Inc
4608 Lawrenceville Hwy, Tucker, GA, 30084
(404) 491-9444
Admin Robert L Greene. *Medical Dir/Dir of
Nursing* Robert F Eaves Jr MD.
Licensure Skilled Care; Intermediate Care.
Beds 42. *Certified* Medicaid.
Staff RNs 1 (ft), 2 (pt); LPNs 3 (ft), 3 (pt);
Nurses aides 15 (ft), 3 (pt); Physical therapists 1
(pt); Activities coordinators 1 (ft); Dietitians 1
(ft).
Facilities Dining room; Physical therapy room;
Laundry room.
Activities Arts and Crafts; Cards; Games; Prayer groups; Movies.
Description This small 42-bed home offers
individualized, personal, skilled nursing care;
staff tends to "spoil" the residents; good as the
best, better than the rest.

Tucker Nursing Center
2165 Idlewood Rd, Tucker, GA, 30084 (404)
934-3172
Admin Michelle DesCarpenter. *Medical Dir-
/Dir of Nursing* Michael Lipsitt MD.
Licensure Skilled Care. *Beds* 120. *Certified* Medicaid.
Staff Physicians 3 (pt); RNs 6 (ft), 3 (pt); LPNs
4 (ft), 5 (pt); Nurses aides 28 (ft), 11 (pt);
Physical therapists 1 (pt); Activities coordinators 2 (ft).
Facilities Dining room; Activities room; Crafts
room; Laundry room; Barber/Beauty shop;
Library.
Activities Arts and Crafts; Cards; Games;
Movies; Dances/Social or cultural gatherings;
Atlanta Braves games; Bus trips.
Description Facility offers home-like atmosphere and furnishings.

TWIN CITY

Twin View Nursing Home
Box 128, Twin City, GA, 30471 (912) 763-2141
Admin Theo H Fountain.
Licensure Skilled Care; Intermediate Care.
Beds 110. *Certified* Medicaid.

TYBEE ISLAND

Oceanside Nursing Home
77 Van Horn, Box 870, Tybee Island, GA,
31328 (912) 786-4511
Admin Jewell S Towns. *Medical Dir/Dir of
Nursing* Carmen Gannon MD.
Licensure Skilled Care; Intermediate Care.
Beds 85. *Certified* Medicaid; Medicare.
Admissions Requirements Medical examination; Physician's request.
Staff Physicians 3 (pt); RNs 4 (ft), 1 (pt); LPNs
8 (ft), 2 (pt); Orderlies 2 (ft); Nurses aides 22
(ft); Recreational therapists 1 (ft); Activities
coordinators 1 (ft); Dietitians 1 (pt); Podiatrists

1 (pt).
Facilities Dining room; Physical therapy room;
Activities room; Crafts room; Laundry room;
Barber/Beauty shop.
Activities Arts and Crafts; Cards; Games;
Reading groups; Prayer groups; Movies; Shopping trips; Dances/Social or cultural gatherings.
Description Facility is situated 100 yards from
the ocean; 28 years experience in the same
locality.

Savannah Beach Nursing Home Inc
PO Box 870, Tybee Island, GA, 31328 (912)
786-5711
Admin Teresa Jackson. *Medical Dir/Dir of
Nursing* A P Phillips.
Licensure Skilled Care; Intermediate Care.
Beds 50. *Certified* Medicaid; Medicare.
Admissions Requirements Minimum age 18;
Medical examination; Physician's request.
Staff Physicians 3 (pt); RNs 2 (ft); LPNs 3 (ft),
1 (pt); Nurses aides 17 (ft), 1 (pt); Physical therapists 1 (pt); Activities coordinators 1 (ft); Dietitians 1 (ft); Dentists; Podiatrists; Music
therapist 1 (pt).
Facilities Dining room; Physical therapy room;
Activities room; Chapel; Crafts room; Laundry
room; Barber/Beauty shop; Library.
Activities Arts and Crafts; Cards; Games;
Reading groups; Prayer groups; Movies; Shopping trips; Dances/Social or cultural gatherings;
Ceramics.
Description Facility is located on beautiful
Tybee Island next to the ocean.

UNION POINT

Greene Point Health Care*
PO Box 312, Union Point, GA, 30669 (404)
486-2167
Admin Teresa Dyar.
Licensure Skilled Care; Intermediate Care.
Beds 71. *Certified* Medicaid; Medicare.

VALDOSTA

Crestwood Nursing Home*
PO Box 2999, Valdosta, GA, 31602 (912)
242-6868
Admin Charles O Templeton.
Licensure Skilled Care; Intermediate Care.
Beds 79. *Certified* Medicaid; Medicare.

Heritage House Nursing Home
PO Box 2999, Valdosta, GA, 31601 (912)
244-7368
Admin John H Eades. *Medical Dir/Dir of
Nursing* Joe C Stubb Jr MD.
Licensure Intermingled Care. *Beds* 98. *Certified* Medicaid.
Admissions Requirements Minimum age 21;
Medical examination; Physician's request.
Staff RNs 2 (ft); LPNs 9 (ft), 1 (pt); Orderlies 1
(pt); Nurses aides 28 (ft), 2 (pt); Activities coordinators 1 (ft); Dietitians 1 (pt).
Facilities Dining room; Physical therapy room;
Activities room; Chapel; Crafts room; Laundry
room; Barber/Beauty shop; Library.
Activities Arts and Crafts; Cards; Games;
Reading groups; Prayer groups; Movies; Shopping trips; Dances/Social or cultural gatherings.

Holly Hill Intermediate Care Facility*
PO Box 2999, Valdosta, GA, 31601 (912)
244-6968
Admin Charles O Templeton Jr.
Licensure Intermediate Care. *Beds* 100. *Certified* Medicaid.

Lakehaven Nursing Home
PO Box 2999, Valdosta, GA, 31601-2999 (912)
242-7368
Admin Quita T Baggett. *Medical Dir/Dir of Nursing* Joe C Stubbs MD.
Licensure Skilled Care; Intermediate Care.
Beds SNF 50; ICF 40. *Certified* Medicaid.
Admissions Requirements Medical examination; Physician's request.
Staff RNs 1 (ft), 2 (pt); LPNs 9 (ft); Activities coordinators 1 (ft); Social workers 1 (ft); Others 2 (ft).
Facilities Dining room; Physical therapy room; Activities room; Crafts room; Barber/Beauty shop; Library.
Activities Arts and Crafts; Cards; Games; Reading groups; Prayer groups; Movies; Shopping trips; Dances/Social or cultural gatherings; Yard sales; Rock-a-thons; Bible study; Sunday school.
Description This facility attempts to offer quality of living with meeting of medical/social related needs.

Parkwood Development Center
1501 N Lee St, Valdosta, GA, 31601 (912)
242-6268
Admin Ruth T Adkins. *Medical Dir/Dir of Nursing* Joseph C Stubbs MD.
Licensure Intermediate Care for Mentally Retarded. *Beds* 110. *Certified* Medicaid.
Ownership Proprietary.
Admissions Requirements Minimum age 6; Medical examination.
Staff Physicians 6 (ft); RNs 5 (ft); Nurses aides 95– 110 (ft); Physical therapists 1 (ft); Recreational therapists 1 (ft); Occupational therapists 1 (pt); Speech therapists 1 (ft); Activities coordinators 1 (ft); Dietitians 1 (ft); Dentists 3 (pt); Ophthalmologists 2 (pt); Podiatrists 1 (pt); Audiologists 1 (pt); Pharmacist 1 (pt); Psychologist 1 (ft); Psychiatrist 1 (ft); Social workers 1 (ft); Social work technicians 2 (ft); Teachers 4 (ft); QMRPs 2 (ft); Programming specialists 4 (ft).
Facilities Dining room; Physical therapy room; Chapel; Crafts room; Laundry room; Barber/Beauty shop; Library; Classrooms; Speech therapy; Activities center.
Activities Arts and Crafts; Cards; Games; Reading groups; Prayer groups; Movies; Shopping trips; Dances/Social or cultural gatherings.
Description Facility is a single-story structure designed to meet needs of residents including handicapped; each resident has an individual care plan.

VIDALIA

Bethany Home for Ladies*
PO Box 668, Vidalia, GA, 30474 (912)
537-7922
Admin Lonnie C Vaughn.

Licensure Skilled Care; Intermediate Care.
Beds 168. *Certified* Medicaid; Medicare.
Admissions Requirements Females only

Precious Intermediate Care Home
309 Mosley St, Box 89, Vidalia, GA, 30474
(912) 537-7532
Admin George H Yarbrough.
Licensure Intermediate Care. *Beds* 40. *Certified* Medicaid.

WADLEY

Glendale Nursing Home Inc*
PO Box 326, Wadley, GA, 30477 (912)
252-5254
Admin George T Harrison.
Licensure Skilled Care; Intermediate Care.
Beds 98. *Certified* Medicaid.

WARM SPRINGS

Meriwether Memorial Hospital Nursing Home*
PO Box 8, Warm Springs, GA, 31830 (404)
655-3331
Admin Jack W Smoot.
Licensure Skilled Care; Intermediate Care.
Beds 58. *Certified* Medicaid; Medicare.

WARNER ROBINS

Elberta Convalescent Home*
PO Box 1483, Warner Robins, GA, 31093
(912) 923-5922
Admin Mary R Drew.
Licensure Intermediate Care. *Beds* 66. *Certified* Medicaid.

Hallmark Nursing Home*
1601 Elberta Rd, Warner Robins, GA, 31093
(912) 922-2241
Admin Leah Swinford.
Licensure Skilled Care; Intermediate Care.
Beds 126. *Certified* Medicaid; Medicare.

Peachbelt Intermediate Care Home*
PO Drawer 2, Warner Robins, GA, 31093 (912)
923-3156
Admin Hallae Duncan.
Licensure Intermediate Care. *Beds* 106. *Certified* Medicaid.

WARRENTON

Providence Health Care
PO Box 69, Warrenton, GA, 30828 (404)
465-3328
Admin Marsha D Todd. *Medical Dir/Dir of Nursing* Dr John Lemley.
Licensure Skilled Care. *Beds* 110. *Certified* Medicaid; Medicare.
Admissions Requirements Medical examination; Physician's request.
Staff RNs 2 (ft), 1 (pt) 13C 8 (ft), 3 (pt); Orderlies 1 (ft); Nurses aides 30 (ft), 6 (pt); Physical therapists 1 (pt); Recreational therapists 1 (pt); Activities coordinators 1 (ft); Dietitians 1 (pt); Dentists 1 (pt); Podiatrists 1 (pt).
Facilities Dining room; Physical therapy room;

Activities room; Chapel; Crafts room; Laundry room; Barber/Beauty shop.
Activities Arts and Crafts; Cards; Games; Reading groups; Prayer groups; Movies; Shopping trips; Dances/Social or cultural gatherings.
Description VA approved.

WASHINGTON

Wilkes Health Care
112 Hospital Dr, PO Box 578, Washington,
GA, 30673 (404) 678-7804
Admin Joyce B Barden. *Medical Dir/Dir of Nursing* J E Pollock MD.
Licensure Skilled Care; Intermediate Care.
Beds 47. *Certified* Medicaid.
Admissions Requirements Medical examination; Physician's request.
Staff RNs 1 (ft), 1 (pt); LPNs 3 (ft); Nurses aides 10 (ft), 5 (pt); Physical therapists 1 (pt); Speech therapists 1 (pt); Activities coordinators 1 (ft); Dietitians 1 (pt); Dentists 1 (pt); Podiatrists 1 (pt).
Facilities Dining room; Physical therapy room; Laundry room; Barber/Beauty shop.
Activities Arts and Crafts; Games; Movies; Shopping trips; Dances/Social or cultural gatherings.

WAVERLY HALL

Oak View Intermediate Care Home
PO Box 468, Waverly Hall, GA, 31831 (404)
582-2117
Admin Theorde C Bowen. *Medical Dir/Dir of Nursing* Dr Thomas Blake.
Licensure Intermediate Care. *Beds* 100. *Certified* Medicaid.
Admissions Requirements Medical examination.
Staff Physicians 1 (pt); RNs 1 (ft); LPNs 3 (ft), 1 (pt); Orderlies 3 (ft), 2 (pt); Nurses aides 8 (ft), 3 (pt); Physical therapists 1 (pt); Activities coordinators 1 (ft), 2 (pt); Dietitians 1 (pt); Podiatrists 1 (pt).
Facilities Dining room; Physical therapy room; Activities room; Chapel; Crafts room; Laundry room; Barber/Beauty shop.
Activities Arts and Crafts; Cards; Games; Reading groups; Prayer groups; Movies; Shopping trips; Dances/Social or cultural gatherings.
Description Spacious country setting provides opportunity for outdoor activities such as nature walks, picnics, and barbecues; facility provides therapeutic baths and whirlpools; field excursions are available, such as going to various parks and attending the city fair.

WAYCROSS

Baptist Village Inc
PO Drawer 179, Waycross, GA, 31502 (912)
283-7050
Admin J Olan Jones. *Medical Dir/Dir of Nursing* W B Bates MD.
Licensure Skilled Care. *Beds* SNF 42; ICF 106. *Certified* Medicaid.
Admissions Requirements Minimum age 65; Medical examination; Physician's request.
Staff RNs 7 (ft), 5 (pt); LPNs 26 (ft), 7 (pt); Nurses aides 77 (ft), 12 (pt); Activities coordi-

nators 1 (ft).
Facilities Dining room; Physical therapy room; Activities room; Chapel; Crafts room; Laundry room; Barber/Beauty shop; Library.
Activities Arts and Crafts; Cards; Games; Reading groups; Prayer groups; Movies; Shopping trips; Dances/Social or cultural gatherings.
Description The ministry of Baptist Village is intended to receive older people who are in need. We have 3 levels of care: retirement area, intermediate care, and skilled care. Through the 26 years of its existence, the goal of Baptist Village has been able to provide a "gentle ministry to God's older children."

Riverside Nursing Home
1600 Riverside Ave, Waycross, GA, 31501
(912) 283-1185
Admin Alpha W Davis. *Medical Dir/Dir of Nursing* Dr D Richard Lynch.
Licensure Skilled Care. *Beds* 76. *Certified* Medicaid; Medicare.
Admissions Requirements Medical examination; Physician's request.
Staff RNs 3 (ft), 1 (pt); LPNs 10 (ft), 4 (pt); Orderlies 4 (ft), 1 (pt); Nurses aides 20 (ft), 5 (pt); Physical therapists 2 (pt); Recreational therapists 1 (ft), 1 (pt); Activities coordinators 1 (ft); Dietitians 1 (ft); Dentists 1 (pt); Podiatrists 1 (pt).
Facilities Dining room; Physical therapy room; Activities room; Laundry room; Barber/Beauty shop.
Activities Games; Reading groups; Prayer groups; Movies; Dances/Social or cultural gatherings.
Description The first Sunday in May the facility has open house for the residents; a special invitation is sent to each family representative.

Ware Manor Intermediate Care Facility
2210 Dorothy St, Waycross, GA, 31501 (912) 285-4721
Admin Barbara Aldridge. *Medical Dir/Dir of Nursing* Leo Sotirou MD.
Licensure Intermediate Care. *Beds* 92. *Certified* Medicaid.
Staff Physicians 1 (ft); RNs 1 (ft); LPNs 7 (ft); Orderlies 2 (ft); Nurses aides 20 (ft), 2 (pt); Physical therapists 1 (pt); Activities coordinators 1 (ft); Dietitians 1 (pt); Podiatrists 1 (pt).
Facilities Dining room; Physical therapy room; Chapel; Laundry room; Barber/Beauty shop.
Activities Arts and Crafts; Cards; Games; Reading groups; Prayer groups; Movies; Shopping trips.
Description Ware Manor has a cheery home-like atmosphere with sunlight-yellow corridors and colorful linens. Staff is particularly motivated toward developing self-help skills in mentally retarded residents.

WAYNESBORO

Brentwood Terrace Health Center*
PO Box 820, Waynesboro, GA, 30830 (404) 554-4425
Admin Shelia Weddon. *Medical Dir/Dir of Nursing* Joseph L Jackson.
Licensure Skilled Care; Intermediate Care. *Beds* 103. *Certified* Medicaid.

Admissions Requirements Minimum age 18; Medical examination; Physician's request.
Staff Physicians 8 (pt); RNs 2 (ft), 3 (pt); LPNs 6 (ft), 3 (pt); Orderlies 6 (ft), 3 (pt); Nurses aides 22 (ft), 4 (pt); Physical therapists 2 (pt); Speech therapists 1 (pt); Activities coordinators 1 (ft); Dietitians 1 (pt).
Facilities Dining room; Physical therapy room; Activities room; Chapel; Crafts room; Laundry room; Barber/Beauty shop.
Activities Arts and Crafts; Cards; Games; Reading groups; Prayer groups; Movies; Shopping trips; Dances/Social or cultural gatherings.

WHIGHAM

Heritage Inn of Whigham
PO Box 46, Whigham, GA, 31797 (912) 762-4121
Admin Edd W Johnson. *Medical Dir/Dir of Nursing* William J Morton MD.
Licensure Skilled Care; Intermediate Care. *Beds* 108. *Certified* Medicaid; Medicare.
Staff RNs 1 (ft), 2 (pt); LPNs 10 (ft), 3 (pt); Nurses aides 25 (ft), 7 (pt); Physical therapists 1 (pt); Activities coordinators 1 (ft); Dietitians 1 (pt).
Facilities Dining room; Physical therapy room; Activities room; Crafts room; Laundry room; Barber/Beauty shop.
Activities Arts and Crafts; Cards; Games; Reading groups; Prayer groups; Movies; Shopping trips; Dances/Social or cultural gatherings.

WINDER

Russell Nursing Home*
PO Box 588, Winder, GA, 30680 (404) 867-2108
Admin Sue Lane.
Licensure Skilled Care. *Beds* 120. *Certified* Medicaid.

WOODSTOCK

Boddy Nursing Center*
Drawer M, Arnold Mill, Woodstock, GA, 30188 (404) 926-0016
Admin Linda Morris.
Licensure Skilled Care; Intermediate Care. *Beds* 117. *Certified* Medicaid; Medicare.

WRIGHTSVILLE

Wrightsville Manor
PO Box 209, Wrightsville, GA, 31096 (912) 864-2286
Admin Shirley A Hall. *Medical Dir/Dir of Nursing* William A Dodd MD.
Licensure Intermediate Care. *Beds* 94. *Certified* Medicaid.
Admissions Requirements Medical examination; Physician's request.
Staff Physicians 1 (pt); RNs 1 (ft); LPNs 6 (ft), 3 (pt); Orderlies 1 (ft); Nurses aides 17 (ft), 2 (pt); Physical therapists 1 (ft); Activities coordinators 1 (ft); Dietitians 1 (pt); Dentists 1 (pt); Podiatrists 1 (pt); Social workers 1 (ft).
Facilities Dining room; Physical therapy room; Activities room; Crafts room; Laundry room;

Barber/Beauty shop.
Activities Arts and Crafts; Cards; Games; Reading groups; Prayer groups; Movies; Shopping trips; Dances/Social or cultural gatherings.

HAWAII

HALEIWA

Crawford's Convalescent Home
58-130 Kamehameha Hwy, Haleiwa, HI, 96712 (808) 638-8514
Admin Alice Lew.
Licensure Intermediate Care. *Beds* 68. *Certified* Medicaid.
Admissions Requirements Medical examination.
Staff RNs 3 (ft), 2 (pt); LPNs 1 (ft); Nurses aides 28 (ft); Physical therapists 1 (pt); Recreational therapists 1 (ft); Occupational therapists 1 (pt); Activities coordinators 1 (ft); Dietitians 1 (pt).
Facilities Dining room; Physical therapy room; Activities room; Crafts room; Laundry room.
Activities Arts and Crafts; Cards; Games; Prayer groups; Movies; Shopping trips; Dances/Social or cultural gatherings.

HILO

Hilo Hospital—Skilled Nursing Unit*
1190 Waianuenue Ave, Hilo, HI, 96720 (808) 961-4211
Admin Donald McGrath.
Licensure Skilled Care; Intermediate Care. *Beds* SNF 36; ICF 72. *Certified* Medicaid; Medicare.

Life Care Center of Hilo*
944 W Kawailani St, Hilo, HI, 96720 (808) 959-9151
Admin Kenneth F Raupach.
Licensure Intermediate Care. *Beds* 240. *Certified* Medicaid.

HONOKAA

Honokaa Hospital*
Box 37, Honokaa, HI, 96727 (808) 775-7211
Admin Jitsuo Kotake.
Licensure Skilled Care. *Beds* 8. *Certified* Medicaid; Medicare.

HONOLULU

Arcadia Retirement Residents
1434 Punahou St, Honolulu, HI, 96822 (808) 941-0941
Admin Helen E Meredith.

Licensure Skilled Care. *Beds* 54. *Certified* Medicare.
Admissions Requirements Minimum age 60; Medical examination.
Facilities Dining room; Physical therapy room; Activities room; Chapel; Crafts room; Laundry room; Barber/Beauty shop; Library.
Activities Arts and Crafts; Cards; Reading groups; Movies; Shopping trips.

Beverly Manor Convalescent Center*
1930 Kamehameha IV Rd, Honolulu, HI, 96819 (808) 847-4834
Admin Virginia Hueftle.
Licensure Skilled Care; Intermediate Care. *Beds* 108. *Certified* Medicaid; Medicare.

Convalescent Center of Honolulu
1900 Bachelot St, Honolulu, HI, 96817 (808) 531-5302
Admin Abe Sakai. *Medical Dir/Dir of Nursing* Dr Walter W Y Chang.
Licensure Skilled Care. *Beds* 182. *Certified* Medicaid; Medicare.
Admissions Requirements Medical examination; Physician's request.
Staff Physicians 1 (pt); RNs 16 (pt); LPNs 13 (pt); Nurses aides 80 (pt); Physical therapists 1 (pt); Reality therapists 1 (pt); Recreational therapists 2 (pt); Occupational therapists 1 (ft); Activities coordinators 1 (ft); Dietitians 1 (ft).
Facilities Dining room; Physical therapy room; Activities room; Laundry room; Library.
Activities Arts and Crafts; Cards; Games; Prayer groups; Movies; Shopping trips; Dances/Social or cultural gatherings.
Description The Center has a working agreement with Hospice Hawaii for hospice services.

Hale Ho Aloha
2630 Pacific Heights Rd, Honolulu, HI, 96813
Admin Lorraine Manayan.
Licensure Intermediate Care. *Beds* 73.
Admissions Requirements Medical examination.
Staff Physicians 3 (pt); RNs 3 (ft), 5 (pt); LPNs 2 (ft), 4 (pt); Nurses aides 41 (ft), 5 (pt); Physical therapists 1 (pt); Recreational therapists 1 (ft); Occupational therapists 1 (pt); Activities coordinators 1 (ft); Dietitians 1 (pt).
Facilities Dining room; Physical therapy room; Activities room; Crafts room; Laundry room; Barber/Beauty shop.

Activities Arts and Crafts; Cards; Games; Reading groups; Prayer groups; Movies; Shopping trips; Dances/Social or cultural gatherings.

Hale Malamalama
6163 Summer St, Honolulu, HI, 96821 (808) 396-0537
Admin Agnes Uyehara. *Medical Dir/Dir of Nursing* Dr George Seberg.
Licensure Intermediate Care. *Beds* 31. *Certified* Medicaid.
Admissions Requirements Minimum age 21; Medical examination; Physician's request.
Staff RNs 2 (ft), 1 (pt); LPNs 1 (ft); Nurses aides 13 (ft); Physical therapists 1 (pt); Recreational therapists 1 (pt); Occupational therapists 1 (pt).
Facilities Dining room; Physical therapy room; Activities room; Crafts room; Laundry room.
Activities Arts and Crafts; Cards; Games; Movies; Entertainment by clubs and groups.

Hale Nani Health Center
1677 Pensacola St, Honolulu, HI, 96822 (808) 537-3371
Admin Earl Baxendale. *Medical Dir/Dir of Nursing* Dr Gladys Fryer.
Licensure Skilled Care; Intermediate Care. *Beds* 232. *Certified* Medicaid; Medicare.
Admissions Requirements Medical examination; Physician's request.
Staff Physicians 1 (pt); RNs 10 (ft), 5 (pt); LPNs 10 (ft), 6 (pt); Physical therapists 1 (ft); Recreational therapists 2 (ft), 4 (pt); Occupational therapists 1 (ft); Speech therapists 1 (pt); Activities coordinators 1 (ft); Dietitians 2 (pt).
Facilities Dining room; Physical therapy room; Activities room; Chapel; Crafts room; Laundry room; Barber/Beauty shop; Library.
Activities Arts and Crafts; Cards; Games; Reading groups; Prayer groups; Movies.
Description We are licensed as "Swing Bed" which means a patient can change level of care, yet remain in the same room.

Island Nursing Home
1205 Alexander St, Honolulu, HI, 96826 (808) 946-5027
Admin Leland Yagi. *Medical Dir/Dir of Nursing* Doris Jasinski MD.
Licensure Skilled Care. *Beds* 42. *Certified* Medicaid; Medicare.
Admissions Requirements Physician's request.
Staff Physicians 1 (pt); RNs 6 (ft), 4 (pt);

Nurses aides 18 (ft), 4 (pt); Physical therapists 1 (pt); Occupational therapists 1 (pt); Activities coordinators 1 (ft), 1 (pt); Dietitians 1 (pt); Dentists 1 (pt).
Facilities Dining room; Physical therapy room; Activities room.
Activities Arts and Crafts; Games; Prayer groups; Movies; Shopping trips; Dances/Social or cultural gatherings.
Description Island Nursing Home is located near the Waikiki District of East Central Honolulu in proximity to public transportation, commercial, civic, educational, and recreational facilities. The facility is accredited by the Joint Commission on Accreditation of Hospitals providing excellent patient care, an extensive activity program, and a "home-like" atmosphere.

Kuakini Medical Center
347 N Kuakini St, Honolulu, HI, 96817 (808) 536-2236
Admin Masaichi Tasaka. *Medical Dir/Dir of Nursing* Dr Isaac Kawasaki.
Licensure Skilled Care; Intermediate Care. *Beds* SNF 50; ICF 100. *Certified* Medicaid; Medicare.
Admissions Requirements Medical examination; Physician's request.
Facilities Dining room; Physical therapy room; Activities room; Chapel; Crafts room; Laundry room; Barber/Beauty shop; Library.
Activities Arts and Crafts; Cards; Games; Reading groups; Prayer groups; Movies; Shopping trips; Dances/Social or cultural gatherings.

Leahi Hospital—Skilled Nursing Unit*
3675 Kilauea Ave, Honolulu, HI, 96816 (808) 734-0221
Admin Abraham Choy.
Licensure Skilled Care; Intermediate Care. *Beds* 184. *Certified* Medicaid; Medicare.

Maluhia Hospital
1027 Hala Dr, Honolulu, HI, 96817 (808) 845-2951
Admin Gilbert Gima. *Medical Dir/Dir of Nursing* Dr Yoshie Takagi.
Licensure Skilled Care; Intermediate Care. *Beds* 150. *Certified* Medicaid; Medicare.
Staff Physicians 1 (ft), 1 (pt); RNs 16 (ft); LPNs 15 (ft); Nurses aides 62 (ft); Physical therapists 1 (ft); Recreational therapists 1 (ft); Occupational therapists 2 (ft); Dietitians 2 (ft).
Facilities Dining room; Physical therapy room; Activities room; Chapel; Crafts room; Barber/Beauty shop; Library.
Activities Arts and Crafts; Cards; Games; Reading groups; Prayer groups; Movies; Shopping trips; Dances/Social or cultural gatherings.
Description Facility features a day hospital program, Monday through Friday.

Maunalani Hospital
5113 Maunalani Circle, Honolulu, HI, 96816 (808) 732-0771
Admin Kenneth Halpenny. *Medical Dir/Dir of Nursing* Dr George Mills.
Licensure Skilled Care. *Beds* 101. *Certified* Medicaid; Medicare.
Staff Physicians 1 (ft); RNs 9 (ft); LPNs 8 (ft); Nurses aides 43 (ft); Physical therapists 1 (ft); Recreational therapists 1 (ft); Occupational

therapists 1 (ft); Speech therapists 1 (ft); Activities coordinators 1 (ft); Dietitians 1 (ft).
Facilities Dining room; Physical therapy room; Activities room; Crafts room; Laundry room.
Activities Arts and Crafts; Cards; Games; Reading groups; Movies; Shopping trips.

Nuuanu Hale Hospital
2900 Pali Hwy, Honolulu, HI, 96817 (808) 595-6311
Admin Sallie Y Miyawaki. *Medical Dir/Dir of Nursing* Dr Dennis S Murakami.
Licensure Skilled Care. *Beds* 75. *Certified* Medicaid; Medicare.
Admissions Requirements Medical examination; Physician's request.
Staff Physicians 1 (pt); RNs 6 (ft), 5 (pt); LPNs 6 (pt); Nurses aides 32 (ft), 7 (pt); Physical therapists 1 (pt); Occupational therapists 1 (pt); Speech therapists 1 (pt); Activities coordinators 1 (ft); Dietitians 1 (pt); Dentists 1 (pt); Ophthalmologists 1 (pt); Podiatrists 1 (pt); Audiologists 1 (pt).
Facilities Dining room; Physical therapy room; Activities room; Crafts room.
Activities Arts and Crafts; Cards; Games; Reading groups; Prayer groups; Movies; Shopping trips; Dances/Social or cultural gatherings; Outings.
Description Hospital provides excellent care and service for the ill until both his/her health and rehabilitation potential are reached. The resident may then make the transitions necessary for a full, active life. JCAH accredited.

Saint Francis Hospital—Skilled Nursing Unit
2230 Liliha St, Honolulu, HI, 96817 (808) 547-6011
Admin Michael Matsuura. *Medical Dir/Dir of Nursing* Robert Ballard MD.
Licensure Skilled Care. *Beds* 52. *Certified* Medicaid; Medicare.
Admissions Requirements Medical examination; Physician's request.
Staff RNs 3 (ft), 2 (pt); LPNs 10 (ft); Nurses aides 19 (ft), 2 (pt); Physical therapists 1 (ft); Recreational therapists 1 (ft); Occupational therapists 1 (ft); Speech therapists 1 (pt); Activities coordinators 1 (ft), 1 (pt); Dietitians 1 (ft); Dentists 3 (ft); Podiatrists 1 (ft).
Affiliation Roman Catholic
Facilities Dining room; Physical therapy room; Activities room; Chapel; Crafts room; Laundry room; Library; Occupational therapy room.
Activities Arts and Crafts; Cards; Games; Prayer groups; Movies; Shopping trips; Dances/Social or cultural gatherings; Monthly luncheons.
Description Facility offers hospice program with hospice volunteers; patient socialization group that meets every Friday; patient teaching toward independent eating program; quality assurance audit done bi-monthly; special family dinners on certain holidays.

KAHUKU

Kahuku Hospital—Skilled Nursing Unit
Box 218, Kahuku, HI, 96731 (808) 293-9221
Admin Rikio Tanji.
Licensure Skilled Care. *Beds* 11. *Certified* Medicaid; Medicare.

KANEOHE

Ann Pearl Intermediate Care Facility*
45-181 Waikalua Rd, Kaneohe, HI, 96744 (808) 247-8558
Admin Clifford Miller Jr.
Licensure Intermediate Care. *Beds* 86. *Certified* Medicaid.

Kahanaola Convalescent Center
45-090 Namoku St, Kaneohe, HI, 96744 (808) 247-1670
Admin Larry P Van Hunning. *Medical Dir/Dir of Nursing* Glenn Stahl MD.
Licensure Skilled Care; Intermediate Care. *Beds* 42. *Certified* Medicaid; Medicare.
Admissions Requirements Medical examination; Physician's request.
Staff Physicians 1 (pt); RNs 4 (ft), 4 (pt); LPNs 1 (ft); Nurses aides 13 (ft), 5 (pt); Activities coordinators 1 (ft).
Affiliation Lutheran
Facilities Dining room; Physical therapy room; Activities room; Laundry room; Barber/Beauty shop; Lanai and Garden area.
Activities Arts and Crafts; Cards; Games; Reading groups; Prayer groups; Movies; Shopping trips; Dances/Social or cultural gatherings; Entertainment by community groups.
Description Kananaola sits nestled against a lush tropical background on the windward side of Oahu. The design of the facility allows residents the experience of a unique blend of nature, sun, and cool breezes.

KAPAA

Samuel Mahelona Memorial Hospital
4800 Kawaihau Rd, Kapaa, HI, 96746 (808) 822-4961
Admin John M English. *Medical Dir/Dir of Nursing* Dr Thomas E Harrison.
Licensure Skilled Care; Intermediate Care. *Beds* 56. *Certified* Medicaid; Medicare.
Admissions Requirements Medical examination; Physician's request.
Staff Physicians 1 (pt); RNs 17 (ft); LPNs 28 (ft); Nurses aides 20 (ft); Physical therapists 1 (pt); Occupational therapists 2 (ft); Activities coordinators 1 (ft); Dietitians 1 (ft).
Facilities Dining room; Physical therapy room; Activities room; Crafts room; Laundry room; Barber/Beauty shop; Library.
Activities Arts and Crafts; Cards; Games; Prayer groups; Movies; Shopping trips; Dances/Social or cultural gatherings.
Description Samuel Mahelona Memorial Hospital has been in existence in the same location since 1917 as a Tuberculosis Sanatorium. As decline in TB cases became evident, other types of cases were considered to fill the empty beds. Today the hospital provides skilled nursing, intermediate care, and psychiatric services in addition to tuberculosis care. The long-awaited, distinct psychiatric unit was completed and dedicated in 1983, a 9-bed unit.

KAPAAU

Kohala Hospital—Skilled Nursing Unit
Box 10, Kapaau, HI, 96755 (808) 889-6211
Admin Jitsuo Kotake.
Licensure Skilled Care; Intermediate Care.
Beds SNF 4; ICF 12. *Certified* Medicaid;
Medicare.
Admissions Requirements Medical examination; Physician's request.
Staff RNs 6 (ft); LPNs 5 (ft); Orderlies 6 (ft);
Physical therapists 1 (ft); Occupational therapists 1 (ft).
Facilities Activities room; Laundry room.
Activities Arts and Crafts; Prayer groups;
Movies.

KAUNAKAKAI

Molokai General Hospital—Skilled Nursing Unit*
Box 408, Kaunakakai, HI, 96748 (808)
553-5331
Admin Erma Mariano.
Licensure Intermediate Care. *Beds* 12. *Certified* Medicaid; Medicare.

KEALAKEKUA

Kona Hospital
Box 69, Kealakekua, HI, 96759 (808) 322-9311
Admin Jennie Wung.
Licensure Skilled Care; Intermediate Care.
Beds SNF 14; ICF 8. *Certified* Medicaid;
Medicare.
Staff RNs 4 (ft); LPNs 4 (ft); Orderlies 6 (ft);
Physical therapists 1 (ft); Occupational therapists 1 (ft); Activities coordinators 1 (ft); Dietitians 1 (ft).
Facilities Physical therapy room; Activities room.

KULA

Kula Hospital—Skilled Nursing Unit
Kula, HI, 96790 (808) 878-1221
Admin Richard F. Pittsinger. *Medical Dir/Dir of Nursing* John C Lewin MD.
Licensure Skilled Care; Intermediate Care;
Intermediate Care for Mentally Retarded.
Beds 105. *Certified* Medicaid; Medicare.
Admissions Requirements Medical examination.
Staff Physicians 1 (ft); RNs 18 (ft); LPNs 7 (ft);
Nurses aides 43 (ft); Physical therapists 1 (ft);
Occupational therapists 1 (ft); Dietitians 1 (ft).
Facilities Physical therapy room; Activities room; Chapel; Crafts room; Barber/Beauty shop; Library; A van for patient outings.
Activities Arts and Crafts; Cards; Games;
Reading groups; Prayer groups; Movies; Shopping trips; Dances/Social or cultural gatherings.
Description Special programs held on major holidays; monthly birthday parties; competition among nursing units patients on Easter, May Day, and Aloha Week with bonnets, leis, costumes, and more.

LANAI CITY

Lanai Community Hospital—Skilled Nursing Unit
Box 797, Lanai City, HI, 96763 (808) 565-6411
Admin Monica L Borges. *Medical Dir/Dir of Nursing* Richard Tesoro MD.
Licensure Skilled Care; Intermediate Care.
Beds 8. *Certified* Medicaid; Medicare.
Admissions Requirements Medical examination; Physician's request.
Staff Physicians 1 (ft); RNs 6 (ft); Nurses aides 5 (ft).
Facilities Dining room; Physical therapy room;
Activities room; Laundry room; Library;
Whirlpool.
Activities Arts and Crafts; Cards; Games;
Shopping trips; Parties for birthdays; Senior Citizen dining groups.
Description Hospital located around city with norfolk pine trees, elevation 1500 ft above sea level, cool temperature, building 15 years old; 6 nurses highly trained to do OB, medical, ER and pre-hospital nursing; open visitng hours for long-term care with children privileges; MSW, PT, OT, dietitian, dentist visits monthly as consultants.

LIHUE

G N Wilcox Memorial Hospital and Health Center
3420 Kuhio Hwy, Lihue, HI, 96766 (808)
245-1011
Admin Phillip Palmer. *Medical Dir/Dir of Nursing* William A Renti Cruz MD.
Licensure Skilled Care; Intermediate Care.
Beds 74. *Certified* Medicaid; Medicare.
Staff RNs 4 (ft), 3 (pt); LPNs 9 (ft), 1 (pt);
Nurses aides 21 (ft), 2 (pt); Physical therapists 1 (ft); Recreational therapists 3 (pt); Occupational therapists 1 (ft); Speech therapists 1 (pt); Activities coordinators 1 (ft); Dietitians 1 (ft); Dentists 1 (pt).
Facilities Physical therapy room; Activities room; Chapel; Crafts room; Library.
Activities Arts and Crafts; Cards; Games;
Movies; Shopping trips; Dances/Social or cultural gatherings.
Description Facility is attached to acute hospital so all ancillary services readily available; no psychiatric patients accepted.

PAHALA

Kau Hospital—Skilled Nursing Unit*
Box 248, Pahala, HI, 96777 (808) 928-8331
Admin Yoshito Iwamoto.
Licensure Skilled Care. *Beds* 8. *Certified* Medicaid; Medicare.

PEARL CITY

Waimano Training School and Hospital
Pearl City, HI, 96782 (808) 456-6211
Admin Kathleen Choy. *Medical Dir/Dir of Nursing* Louise Iwaishi MD.
Licensure Intermediate Care for Mentally Retarded. *Beds* 575. *Certified* Medicaid.
Admissions Requirements Medical examina-

tion; Physician's request.
Staff Physicians 3 (ft); RNs 74 (ft); LPNs 61 (ft); Nurses aides 174 (ft); Physical therapists 2 (ft); Recreational therapists 21 (ft); Occupational therapists 5 (ft); Speech therapists 3 (ft); Dietitians 2 (ft); Audiologists 1 (ft).
Facilities Dining room; Physical therapy room;
Laundry room.
Activities Arts and Crafts; Games; Movies;
Shopping trips; Dances/Social or cultural gatherings.
Description Facility has successful community placement program; outstanding location overlooking Pearl Harbor.

WAHIAWA

Wahiawa General Hospital*
128 Lehua St, Wahiawa, HI, 96786 (808)
621-8411
Admin Philip R Baltch.
Licensure Skilled Care. *Beds* 51. *Certified* Medicaid; Medicare.

WAIANAE

Leeward Nursing Home*
94-404 Jade St, Waianae, HI, 96792 (808)
695-9508
Admin Joseph Di Pardo.
Licensure Intermediate Care. *Beds* 50. *Certified* Medicaid.

WAILUKU

Hale Makua - Wailuku
1540 E Main St, Wailuku, HI, 96732 (808)
877-2761
Admin Anthony J Krieg. *Medical Dir/Dir of Nursing* Alice M Broadhurst MD.
Licensure Intermediate Care. *Beds* 124. *Certified* Medicaid; Medicare.
Admissions Requirements Medical examination; Physician's request.
Staff Physicians 1 (pt); RNs 20 (ft); Nurses aides 44 (ft); Physical therapists 1 (ft); Occupational therapists 1 (ft); Activities coordinators 1 (ft); Dietitians 1 (ft).
Facilities Dining room; Physical therapy room;
Activities room; Laundry room; Barber/Beauty shop; therapy room.
Activities Arts and Crafts; Games; Prayer groups; Movies; Shopping trips; Dances/Social or cultural gatherings; Programs put on by community clubs.
Description Hale Makua has an indoor-outdoor facility; nursing units are built around courtyards; each patient looks out to a garden setting.

WAILUKU MAUI

Hale Makua Home Health Care Agency
Saburo Bldg, 771 Alua St, Wailuku, Maui, HI,
(808) 877-2761
Admin Allan Robb. *Medical Dir/Dir of Nursing* Alice M Broardhurst MD.
Beds 120. *Certified* Medicaid; Medicare.
Admissions Requirements Physician's request.
Staff Physicians 1 (pt); RNs 20 (ft), 10 (pt);

Nurses aides 8 (ft); Physical therapists 2 (ft), 1 (pt); Occupational therapists 1 (pt).
Description Home Health Care Agency serves all the people of the isalnd of Maui except the Hana District; enables patients to remain in their own home rather than a nursing facility; has enabled infants to be discharged from hospital to the home.

WAIMEA

Kauai Veterans Memorial Hospital—Skilled Nursing Unit
Box 337, Waimea, HI, 96796 (808) 338-9431
Admin Richard Johnston. *Medical Dir/Dir of Nursing* Dr Yonemichi Miyashiro.
Licensure Skilled Care. *Beds* 6. *Certified* Medicaid; Medicare.
Admissions Requirements Medical examination; Physician's request.
Staff RNs 1 (ft); LPNs 4 (ft); Nurses aides 3 (ft); Physical therapists 1 (ft); Recreational therapists 1 (ft); Occupational therapists 1 (ft); Dietitians 1 (ft); Dentists 1 (ft).
Facilities Physical therapy room; Activities room; Crafts room; Library.
Activities Arts and Crafts; Cards; Games; Movies; Shopping trips; Monthly and holiday parties.

IDAHO

AMERICAN FALLS

Power County Nursing Home
Gifford at Roosevelt, American Falls, ID, 83211 (208) 226-2327
Admin Francis X McNamara. *Medical Dir/Dir of Nursing* Jiminie L Hutchison MD.
Licensure Skilled Care. *Beds* 20. *Certified* Medicaid; Medicare.
Facilities Dining room; Physical therapy room; Activities room; Crafts room; Laundry room.
Activities Arts and Crafts; Cards; Games; Reading groups; Prayer groups; Movies.

ARCO

Lost Rivers Nursing Home
551 Highland Dr, Arco, ID, 83213 (208) 527-8207
Admin Roger McLaughlin. *Medical Dir/Dir of Nursing* R F Barter MD.
Licensure Skilled Care. *Beds* 10. *Certified* Medicaid; Medicare.
Admissions Requirements Minimum age 25; Medical examination; Physician's request.
Staff Physicians 1 (ft), 1 (pt); RNs 3 (ft), 3 (pt); LPNs 2 (ft), 3 (pt); Nurses aides 3 (ft), 2 (pt); Activities coordinators 1 (pt); Dietitians 1 (pt); Dentists 1 (pt).
Facilities Dining room; Activities room.
Activities Arts and Crafts; Cards; Games; Reading groups; Prayer groups; Movies; Shopping trips; Dances/Social or cultural gatherings.
Description Facility size allows the providing of individual care; resultingly, staff spends alot of time with each client. Facility is located in the heart of the mountains on a hill looking down on the town.

ASHTON

Ashton Nursing Home*
Box 378, 801 Main St, Ashton, ID, 83420 (208) 652-7461
Admin Howard D Bergman.
Licensure Intermediate Care. *Beds* 12. *Certified* Medicaid.

BLACKFOOT

Bingham County Nursing Home
98 Poplar St, Blackfoot, ID, 83221 (208) 785-4100
Admin Carl Staley. *Medical Dir/Dir of Nursing* W G Hoge MD.
Licensure Skilled Care. *Beds* 50. *Certified* Medicaid; Medicare.
Admissions Requirements Medical examination; Physician's request.
Staff RNs 1 (ft); LPNs 4 (ft), 3 (pt); Orderlies 1 (ft); Nurses aides 12 (ft), 8 (pt); Physical therapists 1 (pt); Recreational therapists 1 (ft); Dietitians 1 (pt).
Facilities Dining room; Activities room; Crafts room; Laundry room; Barber/Beauty shop.
Activities Arts and Crafts; Cards; Games; Reading groups; Prayer groups; Movies; Shopping trips.
Description JCAH accredited.

Syrings Chalet*
Box 390, State Hospital South, Blackfoot, ID, 83221 (208) 785-1200
Admin Dwight J Petersen.
Licensure Intermediate Care. *Beds* 45. *Certified* Medicaid.

BOISE

Boise Group Home 1*
1736 N Five Mile Rd, Boise, ID, 83704 (208) 376-1861
Admin Richard Davis.
Licensure Intermediate Care for Mentally Retarded. *Beds* 12. *Certified* Medicaid.

Boise Group Home 2*
10528 Milclay St, Boise, ID, 83704 (208) 375-0450
Admin Richard Davis.
Licensure Intermediate Care for Mentally Retarded. *Beds* 6. *Certified* Medicaid.

Boise Group Home 3*
10349 Summerwind Dr, Boise, ID, 83704 (208) 376-1861
Admin Richard Davis.
Licensure Skilled Care; Intermediate Care. *Certified* Medicaid.

Boise Samaritan Village
3115 Sycamore Dr, Boise, ID, 83703 (208) 343-7726
Admin Dwight Wvenschel. *Medical Dir/Dir of Nursing* Dr Gene Dickey.
Licensure Skilled Care. *Beds* 215. *Certified* Medicaid.
Ownership Nonprofit.
Staff RNs 9 (ft), 10 (pt); LPNs 15 (ft), 7 (pt); Nurses aides 45 (ft), 57 (pt); Recreational therapists 1 (ft), 2 (pt).
Facilities Dining room; Physical therapy room; Activities room; Chapel; Crafts room; Laundry room; Barber/Beauty shop; Snack bar.
Activities Arts and Crafts; Cards; Games; Reading groups; Prayer groups; Movies; Shopping trips; Dances/Social or cultural gatherings.
Description We are a Christian nonprofit organization that offers a village concept of continuum care from apartments to our skilled care center to those who need our services. Our philosophy of care is centered around emphasizing the uniqueness and importance of each individual and how we can help each resident reach their optimum.

Capital Care Center
8211 Ustick, Boise, ID, 83704 (208) 375-3700
Admin Keith Holloway. *Medical Dir/Dir of Nursing* Edward Newcombe MD.
Licensure Skilled Care. *Beds* 108. *Certified* Medicaid; Medicare.
Staff Physicians 1 (pt); RNs 9 (ft), 3 (pt); LPNs 13 (ft), 2 (pt); Nurses aides 52 (ft), 8 (pt); Physical therapists 1 (ft); Occupational therapists 1 (pt); Speech therapists 1 (pt); Activities coordinators 1 (ft); Dietitians 1 (ft); Dentists 1 (pt); Podiatrists 1 (pt); Audiologists 1 (pt).
Facilities Dining room; Physical therapy room; Activities room; Crafts room; Laundry room; Barber/Beauty shop; Library.
Activities Arts and Crafts; Cards; Games; Reading groups; Prayer groups; Movies; Dances/Social or cultural gatherings.

Emerald Care Center
808 N Curtis Rd, Boise, ID, 83706 (208) 376-5273
Admin Ralph Chinchurreta. *Medical Dir/Dir of Nursing* Edward Newcombe MD.
Licensure Skilled Care. *Beds* 148. *Certified* Medicaid; Medicare.
Staff RNs 9 (ft), 1 (pt); LPNs 7 (ft), 2 (pt); Orderlies 3 (ft); Nurses aides 54 (ft), 2 (pt);

Physical therapists 3 (ft); Activities coordinators 2 (ft).
Facilities Dining room; Physical therapy room; Activities room; Crafts room; Laundry room; Barber/Beauty shop.
Activities Arts and Crafts; Cards; Games; Reading groups; Prayer groups; Movies; Shopping trips; Dances/Social or cultural gatherings.
Description Twenty-four hour skilled nursing care.

Gem State Homes Inc 3
2650 S Pond, Boise, ID, 83705 (208) 344-6683
Admin Jerry R Fowler.
Licensure Intermediate Care for Mentally Retarded. *Beds* 8. *Certified* Medicaid.
Admissions Requirements Minimum age 18.
Staff Physicians 2 (pt); RNs 1 (pt); LPNs 1 (pt); Physical therapists 1 (pt); Recreational therapists 1 (pt); Speech therapists 1 (pt); Activities coordinators 1 (pt); Dietitians 1 (pt); Dentists 1 (pt); Ophthalmologists 1 (pt); Podiatrists 1 (pt); Audiologists 1 (pt).
Facilities Dining room; Activities room; Crafts room.
Activities Arts and Crafts; Cards; Games; Movies; Shopping trips; Dances/Social or cultural gatherings.
Description Small community-based facility in residential neighborhood offering active treatment and day programing outside of living arrangements.

Gem State Homes Inc 4
4150 Leland Way, Boise, ID, 83709 (208) 362-3003
Admin Jerry R Fowler.
Licensure Intermediate Care for Mentally Retarded. *Beds* 8. *Certified* Medicaid.
Admissions Requirements Minimum age; Medical examination; Physician's request.
Staff Physicians 1 (pt); RNs 1 (pt); LPNs 1 (pt); Physical therapists 1 (pt); Recreational therapists 1 (pt); Speech therapists 1 (pt); Dietitians 1 (pt); Dentists 1 (pt); Audiologists 1 (pt).
Facilities Dining room; Activities room.
Activities Arts and Crafts; Games; Movies; Shopping trips; Dances/Social or cultural gatherings.
Description Facility provides small group, home-like atmosphere with active treatment programs; residents are provided day treatment programs outside of the living facility.

Grand Oaks Healthcare*
316 W Washington, Boise, ID, 83702 (208) 343-7755
Admin William J Scifres.
Licensure Skilled Care. *Beds* 88. *Certified* Medicaid; Medicare.

Hillcrest Care Center
1001 S Hilton St, Boise, ID, 83705 (208) 345-4464
Admin Steven H Schreiber. *Medical Dir/Dir of Nursing* Dr David Weeks.
Licensure Skilled Care. *Beds* 123. *Certified* Medicaid; Medicare.
Admissions Requirements Minimum age 16.
Staff Physicians 1 (pt); RNs 6 (ft), 5 (pt); LPNs 5 (ft), 4 (pt); Orderlies 2 (ft), 2 (pt); Nurses aides 27 (ft), 25 (pt); Physical therapists 1 (ft); Occupational therapists 1 (pt); Speech therapists 1

(pt); Activities coordinators 1 (ft); Dietitians 1 (pt).
Facilities Dining room; Physical therapy room; Activities room; Crafts room; Barber/Beauty shop; Greenhouse.
Activities Arts and Crafts; Cards; Games; Reading groups; Prayer groups; Movies; Shopping trips; Dances/Social or cultural gatherings.
Description Located in a quiet setting, Hillcrest Care Center presents a progressive approach to long- and short-term nursing care; combines quality nursing care, selective menu food service, rehabilitative activity and therapy programs, and a professional, caring staff. The center offers the foremost in skilled and intermediate nursing home care.

Idaho Veterans Home
320 Collins Rd, PO Box 7765, Boise, ID, 83707 (208) 334-5000
Admin Gary Bermessolo. *Medical Dir/Dir of Nursing* Dr Barry Cusack.
Licensure Skilled Care. *Beds* 218.
Ownership Public.
Admissions Requirements Medical examination; Physician's request.
Staff Physicians 12 (pt); RNs 7 (ft), 7 (pt); LPNs 6 (ft), 5 (pt); Nurses aides 25 (ft), 12 (pt); Physical therapists 1 (pt); Occupational therapists 1 (pt); Speech therapists 1 (pt); Activities coordinators 1 (ft); Dietitians 1 (pt); Dentists 3 (pt); Ophthalmologists 1 (pt); Podiatrists 1 (pt); Audiologists 7 (pt).
Facilities Dining room; Physical therapy room; Activities room; Chapel; Crafts room; Laundry room; Barber/Beauty shop; Library.
Activities Arts and Crafts; Cards; Games; Reading groups; Prayer groups; Movies; Shopping trips; Dances/Social or cultural gatherings.
Description Facility is currently enjoying a complete continuum of care including a 124-bed domiciliary, 10-bed shelter home, 80-bed skilled nursing care, and 4-bed rehabilitation unit. Contract with VA hospital for physician, pharmacy, dietician, and lab services.

Treasure Valley Manor*
909 Reserve, Boise, ID, 83702 (208) 343-7717
Admin Jean Heazle.
Licensure Skilled Care. *Beds* 165.
Certified Medicaid.

BONNERS FERRY

Boundary County Nursing Home
551 Kaniksu, Box 448, Bonners Ferry, ID, 83805 (208) 267-3141
Admin Donald M Johnstone.
Licensure Skilled Care. *Beds* 26. *Certified* Medicaid; Medicare.
Admissions Requirements Medical examination; Physician's request.
Staff Physicians 5 (ft), 1 (pt); RNs 2 (ft); LPNs 3 (ft), 2 (pt); Nurses aides 8 (ft), 6 (pt); Physical therapists 1 (pt); Activities coordinators 1 (ft); Dietitians 1 (pt).
Facilities Dining room; Physical therapy room; Activities room.
Activities Arts and Crafts; Games; Reading groups.
Description This nursing home is an extension of a hospital with the average patient age

around 70. We have an activities director who keeps residents as active as possible.

BUHL

Harral's Nursing Home Inc
820 Sprague Ave, Buhl, ID, 83316 (208) 543-6401
Admin Joyce Ellis.
Licensure Skilled Care. *Beds* 64. *Certified* Medicare.
Staff RNs 2 (ft), 2 (pt); LPNs 2 (ft), 4 (pt); Orderlies 1 (pt); Nurses aides 13 (ft), 25 (pt); Activities coordinators 2 (ft).
Facilities Dining room; Activities room; Crafts room; Laundry room.

BURLEY

Burley Care Center
1729 Miller St, Burley, ID, 83318 (208) 678-9474
Admin Phil Dieter. *Medical Dir/Dir of Nursing* H W Crawford MD.
Licensure Skilled Care. *Beds* 59. *Certified* Medicaid; Medicare.
Admissions Requirements Minimum age 21; Medical examination; Physician's request.
Staff RNs 3 (ft); LPNs 4 (ft), 5 (pt); Orderlies 1 (ft), 1 (pt); Nurses aides 12 (ft); Physical therapists 1 (pt); Speech therapists 1 (pt); Activities coordinators 1 (ft); Dietitians 1 (pt).
Facilities Dining room; Activities room; Crafts room; Barber/Beauty shop.
Activities Arts and Crafts; Games; Reading groups; Prayer groups; Movies; Shopping trips.

Cassia Memorial Hospital—Long Term Care Unit
2203 Parke Ave, Burley, ID, 83318 (208) 678-4444
Admin Fred W Schloss. *Medical Dir/Dir of Nursing* James Kircher MD.
Licensure Skilled Care. *Beds* 34. *Certified* Medicaid; Medicare.
Admissions Requirements Medical examination; Physician's request.
Staff Physicians 23 (ft); RNs 1 (ft), 1 (pt); LPNs 2 (ft), 2 (pt); Nurses aides 12 (ft), 6 (pt); Physical therapists 1 (ft), 1 (pt); Reality therapists 1 (ft); Recreational therapists 1 (ft); Occupational therapists 1 (pt); Speech therapists 1 (pt); Activities coordinators 1 (ft).
Facilities Dining room; Physical therapy room; Activities room; Barber/Beauty shop.
Activities Arts and Crafts; Cards; Games; Reading groups; Prayer groups; Movies; Shopping trips; Dances/Social or cultural gatherings.
Description This is a compact, progressive long-term care unit attached to an acute hospital, offering a wide range of services; located in rural community with hunting, fishing, and camping easily accessible.

CALDWELL

Caldwell Care Center*
210 Cleveland, Caldwell, ID, 83605 (208) 459-1522

Admin Claire Whitney.
Licensure Skilled Care. *Beds* 75. *Certified* Medicaid; Medicare.

Cascade Care Center*
2814 S Indiana Ave, Caldwell, ID, 83605 (208) 459-0808
Admin Cheryl Killian.
Licensure Skilled Care. *Beds* 112. *Certified* Medicaid; Medicare.

COEUR DALENE

Coeur d'Alene Convalescent Center*
2200 Ironwood Pl, Coeur d'Alene, ID, 83814 (208) 667-6486
Admin Keith Eitemiller.
Licensure Skilled Care. *Beds* 125. *Certified* Medicaid; Medicare.

Pinewood Care Center and Training Center
2514 N 7th St, Coeur d'Alene, ID, 83814 (208) 667-4511
Admin Taylor V Wallner. *Medical Dir/Dir of Nursing* Richard Eggleston MD and William Wood MD.
Licensure Skilled Care; Intermediate Care for Mentally Retarded. *Beds* SNF 89; ICF/MR 24. *Certified* Medicaid; Medicare.
Admissions Requirements Minimum age 16; Medical examination; Physician's request.
Staff Physicians 2 (pt); RNs 2 (ft), 2 (pt); LPNs 4 (ft), 2 (pt); Orderlies 3 (ft); Nurses aides 23 (ft), 8 (pt); Physical therapists 2 (pt); Reality therapists 1 (pt); Recreational therapists 1 (ft); Occupational therapists 1 (pt); Speech therapists 1 (pt); Activities coordinators 1 (ft); Dietitians 1 (pt); Dentists 1 (pt); Ophthalmologists 1 (pt); Podiatrists 1 (pt); Audiologists 1 (pt).
Facilities Dining room; Physical therapy room; Activities room; Crafts room; Laundry room; Barber/Beauty shop; Library.
Activities Arts and Crafts; Cards; Games; Reading groups; Prayer groups; Movies; Shopping trips; Dances/Social or cultural gatherings.
Description Facility features quest for quality instituted in March 1983: select-menu and salad bar; beautiful setting among very tall pine trees; located on serene boulevard intersection; excellent home away from home environment; meets all life/safety codes; excellent physical, occupational, speech therapy and social programs; sentry-security system throughout facility.

Pinewood Training Center*
2514 N 7th St, Coeur d'Alene, ID, 83814 (208) 667-4511
Admin Taylor "Vic" Wallner.
Licensure Intermediate Care for Mentally Retarded. *Beds* 24. *Certified* Medicaid.

Sunset Terrace Convalescent Center*
210 LaCrosse St, Coeur d'Alene, ID, 83814 (208) 664-2185
Admin Brian Morris.
Licensure Skilled Care. *Beds* 89. *Certified* Medicaid; Medicare.

EMMETT

Emmett Care Center
714 N Butte, Emmett, ID, 83617 (208) 365-4425
Admin Lisa W Briggs. *Medical Dir/Dir of Nursing* Dr Harmon Holverson.
Licensure Skilled Care. *Beds* 95. *Certified* Medicaid; Medicare.
Admissions Requirements Medical examination; Physician's request.
Staff Physicians 2 (pt); RNs 6 (ft), 2 (pt); LPNs 5 (ft), 4 (pt); Orderlies 1 (ft), 1 (pt); Nurses aides 23 (ft), 10 (pt); Physical therapists 1 (ft); Activities coordinators 1 (ft); Dietitians 1 (pt).
Facilities Dining room; Physical therapy room; Activities room; Crafts room; Laundry room; Barber/Beauty shop; Library.
Activities Arts and Crafts; Cards; Games; Reading groups; Prayer groups; Movies; Shopping trips; Dances/Social or cultural gatherings.
Description Located in a quiet setting adjacent to the hospital, center offers 24-hour skilled nursing care to its residents. Outstanding programs include selective menu food service and a physical therapy department staffed by a full-time registered physical therapist.

Holly Hills Care Center
501 W Idaho Blvd, Emmett, ID, 83617 (208) 365-3597
Admin Don Kinnaman. *Medical Dir/Dir of Nursing* Dr Harmon Holverson.
Licensure Intermediate Care. *Beds* 32. *Certified* Medicaid.
Admissions Requirements Physician's request.
Staff RNs 1 (ft), 2 (pt); LPNs 2 (ft), 4 (pt); Nurses aides 5 (ft), 3 (pt); Activities coordinators 1 (ft); Audiologists 1 (ft).
Facilities Dining room; Physical therapy room; Activities room; Crafts room; Laundry room; Barber/Beauty shop.
Activities Arts and Crafts; Cards; Games; Reading groups; Prayer groups; Shopping trips.
Description Holly Hills Care Center has applied, been surveyed, and has a verbal agreement for a skilled nursing facility. Professionalism, warmth, and friendliness are our keynotes; full activities program; licensed consultants in every department on contract.

GOODING

Green Acres Care Center*
1220 Montana St, Gooding, ID, 83330 (208) 934-5601
Admin David D Farnes.
Licensure Skilled Care. *Beds* 76. *Certified* Medicaid; Medicare.

Green Acres Community Training Center*
1220 Montana St, Gooding, ID, 83330 (208) 934-5603
Admin David D Farnes.
Licensure Intermediate Care for Mentally Retarded. *Beds* 24. *Certified* Medicaid.

GRANGEVILLE

Grangeville Convalescent Center
410 E N Second, Grangeville, ID, 83530 (208) 983-1131
Admin Ron Deeney. *Medical Dir/Dir of Nursing* Dr William Greenwood.
Licensure Skilled Care. *Beds* 50. *Certified* Medicaid; Medicare.
Admissions Requirements Minimum age 18; Medical examination; Physician's request.
Staff RNs 4 (ft), 1 (pt); LPNs 2 (ft); Nurses aides 21 (ft); Physical therapists 1 (pt); Recreational therapists 1 (ft); Activities coordinators 1 (ft); Dietitians 1 (pt).

Idaho County Nursing Home
W 722 North St, Grangeville, ID, 83530 (208) 983-1470
Admin Douglas A Winter. *Medical Dir/Dir of Nursing* Dr D Soltman.
Licensure Skilled Care. *Beds* 35. *Certified* Medicaid; Medicare.
Staff RNs 1 (ft), 2 (pt); LPNs 2 (ft), 3 (pt); Nurses aides 7 (ft), 8 (pt); Physical therapists 1 (pt); Speech therapists 1 (pt); Activities coordinators 1 (pt); Dietitians 6 (ft); Dentists 1 (pt); Ophthalmologists 1 (pt).
Facilities Dining room; Activities room; Laundry room; Barber/Beauty shop.
Activities Arts and Crafts; Games; Reading groups; Prayer groups; Movies; Dances/Social or cultural gatherings.
Description Facility provides a home-like setting due partly to its small size. Physical connection to Syringa General Hospital provides prompt, easy access to acute care and doctors.

HOMEDALE

Homedale Nursing Home Inc*
Box 96, 108 W Owyhee, Homedale, ID, 83628 (208) 337-3168
Admin Sid E Tucker.
Licensure Skilled Care. *Beds* 38. *Certified* Medicaid; Medicare.

IDAHO FALLS

Good Samaritan Center*
640 E Elva, Idaho Falls, ID, 83401 (208) 523-4795
Admin Kent Burgess.
Licensure Skilled Care. *Beds* 103. *Certified* Medicaid; Medicare.
Ownership Nonprofit.
Affiliation Lutheran

Idaho Falls Nursing Home*
900 Memorial Dr, Idaho Falls, ID, 83401 (208) 529-6111, Exten 6168
Admin Garnet Brown.
Licensure Skilled Care. *Beds* 92. *Certified* Medicaid; Medicare.

Valley Care Center*
2725 E 17th, Idaho Falls, ID, 83401 (208) 529-4567
Admin Jerry Klika.
Licensure Skilled Care. *Beds* 94. *Certified* Medicaid; Medicare.

Yellowstone Care Center*
2460 S Yellowstone, Idaho Falls, ID, 83401 (208) 523-9839

Admin Douglas B Christensen.
Licensure Intermediate Care for Mentally Retarded. *Beds* 30. *Certified* Medicaid.

JEROME

Saint Benedict's Long Term Care Unit
709 N Lincoln, Jerome, ID, 83338 (208) 324-4301
Admin Robert Campbell. *Medical Dir/Dir of Nursing* James Sloat MD.
Licensure Skilled Care. *Beds* 40. *Certified* Medicaid; Medicare.
Admissions Requirements Medical examination; Physician's request.
Staff RNs 2 (ft), 1 (pt); LPNs 3 (ft), 2 (pt); Nurses aides 17 (ft), 9 (pt); Physical therapists 1 (ft); Occupational therapists 1 (pt); Speech therapists 1 (pt); Activities coordinators 1 (ft); Dietitians 1 (pt).
Affiliation Roman Catholic
Facilities Dining room; Physical therapy room; Activities room; Chapel; Barber/Beauty shop.
Activities Arts and Crafts; Cards; Games; Reading groups; Prayer groups; Movies; Dances/Social or cultural gatherings.
Description Facility is in rural, irrigated farming area, attached to hospital, near Snake River Canyon and Thousand Springs.

KELLOGG

Shoshone Living Center
Box 689, 601 W Cameron, Kellogg, ID, 83837 (208) 784-1283
Admin Patsy Walker. *Medical Dir/Dir of Nursing* Frederick Haller MD.
Licensure Skilled Care. *Beds* 68. *Certified* Medicaid; Medicare.
Staff RNs 3 (ft), 4 (pt); LPNs 3 (ft), 2 (pt); Orderlies 2 (ft); Nurses aides 32 (ft), 12 (pt); Physical therapists 1 (pt); Recreational therapists 1 (pt); Occupational therapists 1 (pt); Speech therapists 1 (pt); Activities coordinators 1 (ft); Dietitians 1 (ft); Dentists 1 (pt); Podiatrists 1 (pt); 10 (ft), 4 (pt).
Facilities Dining room; Physical therapy room; Activities room; Crafts room; Laundry room; Barber/Beauty shop.
Activities Arts and Crafts; Cards; Games; Reading groups; Prayer groups; Movies; Shopping trips; Dances/Social or cultural gatherings.
Description The involvement of over 1000 local citizens, many organizations, and businesses towards facility continues to enhance the annual success of community involvement days.

KIMBERLY

Mountain View Care Center*
Rt 1, Box X, Polk St E, Kimberly, ID, 83341 (208) 423-5591
Admin Gary Morgan.
Licensure Skilled Care. *Beds* 64. *Certified* Medicaid; Medicare.

LEWISTON

Lewiston Care Center
3315 8th St, Lewiston, ID, 83501 (208) 743-9543
Admin Turid Reichert. *Medical Dir/Dir of Nursing* Richard M Alford MD.
Licensure Skilled Care. *Beds* 97. *Certified* Medicaid; Medicare.
Admissions Requirements Medical examination; Physician's request.
Staff RNs 7 (ft); LPNs 7 (ft); Orderlies 1 (ft); Nurses aides 28 (ft); Physical therapists 1 (pt); Reality therapists 1 (pt); Recreational therapists 1 (pt).
Facilities Dining room; Physical therapy room; Activities room; Crafts room; Laundry room; Barber/Beauty shop.
Activities Arts and Crafts; Cards; Games; Reading groups; Prayer groups; Movies; Shopping trips; Dances/Social or cultural gatherings; Bingo; Music; Exercises; Old time fiddlers (evenings).
Description Center is attractively furnished and decorated and is beautifully landscaped. Residents are served a selective menu with complimentary wine and other beverages by table service.

Orchards Villa Nursing Center*
1014 Burrell Ave, Lewiston, ID, 83501 (208) 743-4558
Admin Ron Preston.
Licensure Skilled Care. *Beds* 140. *Certified* Medicaid; Medicare.

MALAD

Oneida County Nursing Home*
Box 182, 150 N 200 W, Malad, ID, 83252 (208) 766-2231
Admin D Mahender Nath.
Licensure Skilled Care. *Beds* 24. *Certified* Medicaid; Medicare.
Ownership Public.

MCCALL

Payette Lakes Care Center*
PO Box P, 201 Floyd St, McCall, ID, 83638 (208) 634-2112
Admin Ronald D Nelson.
Licensure Skilled Care. *Beds* 64. *Certified* Medicaid; Medicare.

MERIDIAN

Gem State Homes Inc 2
40 W Franklin, Unit F, Meridian, ID, 83642 (208) 888-1155
Admin Martin Landholm. *Medical Dir/Dir of Nursing* Leslie Madsen RN.
Licensure Intermediate Care for Mentally Retarded. *Beds* 16. *Certified* Medicaid.
Admissions Requirements Minimum age 6; Medical examination.
Staff Physicians 1 (pt); RNs 1 (pt); LPNs 1 (pt); Physical therapists 1 (pt); Recreational therapists 1 (pt); Speech therapists 1 (pt); Dietitians 1 (pt); Dentists 1 (pt); Ophthalmologists 1

(pt); Podiatrists 1 (pt); Audiologists 1 (pt).
Activities Arts and Crafts; Games; Movies; Shopping trips; Dances/Social or cultural gatherings.
Description Facility features a home-like atmosphere in 8-bed home in community settings. Gem State Homes is a private corporation which was founded in 1980 to provide intermediate care services to persons with mental retardation in as normal an environment as possible.

Tomorrow's Hope Inc
4782 Armga, Meridian, ID, 83642
Admin Deborah A Pond.
Licensure Intermediate Care for Mentally Retarded. *Beds* 8. *Certified* Medicaid.
Ownership Nonprofit.
Admissions Requirements Minimum age 5; Medical examination; Physician's request.
Staff RNs 1 (ft); Physical therapists 1 (pt); Occupational therapists 1 (pt); Speech therapists 1 (pt); Dietitians 1 (pt).
Facilities Dining room; Activities room; Crafts room.
Activities Arts and Crafts; Movies; Shopping trips; Dances/Social or cultural gatherings.
Description Facility serves those in the moderate to severe range of mental retardation; offers intense self-help training with emphasis on progression to a less restrictive environment.

MONTPELIER

Bear Lake Memorial Nursing Home
164 S 5th, Montpelier, ID, 83254 (208) 847-1630
Admin D Mahender Nath. *Medical Dir/Dir of Nursing* R V Bjarnason DO.
Licensure Skilled Care. *Beds* 37. *Certified* Medicaid; Medicare.
Admissions Requirements Medical examination; Physician's request.
Staff Physicians 4 (ft); RNs 2 (ft), 1 (pt); LPNs 2 (ft), 2 (pt); Nurses aides 13 (ft), 2 (pt); Physical therapists 1 (ft); Activities coordinators 1 (ft); Dietitians 1 (pt); Dentists 3 (pt).
Facilities Dining room; Physical therapy room; Activities room; Crafts room; Laundry room; Barber/Beauty shop.
Activities Arts and Crafts; Cards; Games; Reading groups; Movies.

MOSCOW

Good Samaritan Village*
640 N Eisenhower St, Moscow, ID, 83843 (208) 882-6560
Admin Allan Tramel.
Licensure Skilled Care. *Beds* 60. *Certified* Medicaid; Medicare.
Ownership Nonprofit.
Affiliation Lutheran

Latah Care Center
W 510 Palouse River Dr, Moscow, ID, 83843 (208) 882-7586
Admin Verla Olson. *Medical Dir/Dir of Nursing* Frances Spain MD.
Licensure Skilled Care. *Beds* 76. *Certified* Medicaid; Medicare.

Ownership Nonprofit.
Admissions Requirements Minimum age 18; Medical examination; Physician's request.
Staff RNs 10 (ft); LPNs 3 (ft); Orderlies 10 (ft); Nurses aides 40 (ft); Physical therapists 7 (ft); Recreational therapists 2 (ft); Dietitians 1 (pt).
Facilities Dining room; Activities room; Crafts room; Laundry room; Barber/Beauty shop; Library.
Activities Arts and Crafts; Cards; Games; Reading groups; Movies; Shopping trips; Dances/Social or cultural gatherings.
Description Facility features high quality care, individually planned. VA approved.

Paradise Villa Convalescent Center*
420 Rowe St, Moscow, ID, 83843 (208) 882-4576
Admin George Wiemerslage.
Licensure Skilled Care. *Beds* 94. *Certified* Medicaid; Medicare.

Stepping Stones Inc*
922 N Grant St, Moscow, ID, 83843 (208) 83843
Admin Gene Christian.
Licensure Intermediate Care. *Beds* 8. *Certified* Medicaid.

MOUNTAIN HOME

Elmore Memorial Nursing Home*
PO Drawer H, Mountain Home, ID, 83647 (208) 587-8406
Admin John Kee.
Licensure Skilled Care. *Beds* 55. *Certified* Medicaid; Medicare.

NAMPA

Gem State Homes Inc 1*
512 Gem St, Nampa, ID, 83651 (208) 467-7589
Admin Martin Landholm.
Licensure Intermediate Care for Mentally Retarded. *Beds* 8. *Certified* Medicaid.

Holly Care Center*
472 Nampa-Caldwell Blvd, Nampa, ID, 83651 (208) 467-5721
Admin Rosemary Helms.
Licensure Skilled Care. *Beds* 49. *Certified* Medicaid; Medicare.

Idaho State School and Hospital—Intermediate Care Facility*
3100 11th Ave N, Nampa, ID, 83651 (208) 466-9255
Admin Dan Fazzini.
Licensure Intermediate Care for Mentally Retarded. *Beds* 388. *Certified* Medicaid.

Midland Manor Nursing Home
PO Box 397, 436 Midland Blvd, Nampa, ID, 83651 (208) 466-7803
Admin Velma Green. *Medical Dir/Dir of Nursing* Dr Harold Brown.
Licensure Skilled Care. *Beds* 111. *Certified* Medicaid; Medicare.
Admissions Requirements Physician's request.
Staff RNs 5 (ft), 3 (pt); LPNs 4 (ft), 5 (pt); Orderlies 2 (ft); Nurses aides 38 (ft), 4 (pt);

Activities coordinators 3 (ft); Dietitians 1 (pt).
Facilities Dining room; Activities room; Crafts room; Laundry room; Barber/Beauty shop; Library; Patio areas; Large backyard area.
Activities Arts and Crafts; Cards; Games; Reading groups; Prayer groups; Movies; Shopping trips; Dances/Social or cultural gatherings; Parties for staffs' children; Coffee hours.

Nampa Care Center
404 Horton, Nampa, ID, 83651 (208) 466-9292
Admin Betty J Heisch. *Medical Dir/Dir of Nursing* William B Ross MD.
Licensure Skilled Care. *Beds* 151. *Certified* Medicaid; Medicare.
Staff RNs 2 (ft), 8 (pt); Nurses aides 45 (ft), 15 (pt); Activities coordinators 3 (ft).
Facilities Dining room; Physical therapy room; Activities room; Laundry room; Barber/Beauty shop; TV lounge.
Activities Arts and Crafts; Cards; Games; Reading groups; Prayer groups; Movies; Shopping trips; Dances/Social or cultural gatherings.
Description Our social worker is also the activity director, providing a theoretical background for activities; also a young adult program designed to meet psychosocial needs of that specific population; program is overseen by in-house social worker and an MSW.

Sunny Ridge Manor
281 12th Ave Rd, Nampa, ID, 83651 (208) 467-7416
Admin Sharon Skilling.
Licensure Intermediate Care. *Beds* 30.
Admissions Requirements Minimum age 55; Medical examination.
Staff RNs; LPNs; Nurses aides; Recreational therapists; Dietitians.
Facilities Dining room; Activities room; Chapel; Crafts room; Laundry room; Barber/Beauty shop; Library.
Activities Arts and Crafts; Prayer groups.

OROFINO

Orofino Care Center Inc*
Box 1502, Ahsahka Rd, Orofino, ID, 83544 (208) 476-4568
Admin James Griffin.
Licensure Skilled Care. *Beds* 59. *Certified* Medicaid; Medicare.

PAYETTE

Casa Loma Convalescent Center*
1019 3rd Ave S, Payette, ID, 83661 (208) 642-4455
Admin Carol Ronk.
Licensure Skilled Care. *Beds* 103. *Certified* Medicaid; Medicare.

POCATELLO

Bannock County Nursing Home*
527 Memorial Dr, Pocatello, ID, 83201 (208) 232-8956
Admin Duane R Higer.

Licensure Skilled Care. *Beds* 56. *Certified* Medicaid; Medicare.
Ownership Public.

Eastgate Healthcare Associates Inc
2200 E Terry, Pocatello, ID, 83201 (208) 232-2570
Admin Jim Zeim. *Medical Dir/Dir of Nursing* Dr E F Hyde.
Licensure Skilled Care; Intermediate Care. *Beds* 121. *Certified* Medicaid; Medicare.
Admissions Requirements Medical examination; Physician's request.
Staff RNs 6 (ft), 4 (pt); LPNs 4 (ft), 6 (pt); Orderlies 1 (ft), 2 (pt); Nurses aides 42 (ft), 9 (pt); Physical therapists 1 (ft), 2 (pt); Recreational therapists 1 (ft), 1 (pt); Activities coordinators 1 (ft); Dietitians 1 (ft).
Facilities Dining room; Physical therapy room; Activities room; Laundry room; Barber/Beauty shop; Conference room.
Activities Arts and Crafts; Cards; Games; Reading groups; Prayer groups; Movies; Shopping trips.
Description Eastgate Healthcare specializes in the rehabilitation of the complete person with full-time physical therapy, social worker, dietitian, and registered nurses. Located less than one mile from 2 hospitals, we coordinate all available medical services to facilitate the patient.

Hillcrest Haven Convalescent Center*
1071 Renee Ave, Pocatello, ID, 83201 (208) 233-1411
Admin Gary Beasley.
Licensure Skilled Care. *Beds* 110. *Certified* Medicaid; Medicare.

South Park Group Home*
3625 Vaughn St, Pocatello, ID, 83201 (208) 233-6833
Admin Frances L Roberts.
Licensure Intermediate Care. *Beds* 15. *Certified* Medicaid.

PRESTON

Franklin County Nursing Home
44 N 1st St E, Preston, ID, 83263 (208) 852-0137
Admin D Mahender Nath. *Medical Dir/Dir of Nursing* Dr Rodney Grover.
Licensure Skilled Care. *Beds* 35. *Certified* Medicaid; Medicare.
Ownership Public.
Admissions Requirements Medical examination.
Staff Physicians 4 (ft); RNs 1 (ft), 1 (pt); LPNs 2 (ft), 5 (pt); Nurses aides 10 (ft), 9 (pt); Physical therapists 1 (ft); Activities coordinators 1 (ft); Dietitians 1 (pt); Dentists 1 (pt); Ophthalmologists 1 (pt).
Facilities Dining room; Physical therapy room; Activities room; Crafts room; Laundry room; Barber/Beauty shop; Library.
Activities Games; Reading groups; Movies.
Description Facility is located in a rural area in beautiful Cache Valley, is small and tries to give good care; expanding to 45 bed capacity.

RIGBY

Carson Nursing Home
Rt 2, Box 69, Rigby, ID, 83442 (208) 745-6285
Admin Gloria Carson Rhodehouse. *Medical
Dir/Dir of Nursing* Asael Tall.
Licensure Intermediate Care. *Beds* 23. *Certified* Medicaid.
Staff Physicians 1 (ft), 3 (pt); RNs 1 (ft), 4 (pt);
LPNs 2 (ft), 3 (pt); Nurses aides 6 (ft), 5 (pt);
Physical therapists 1 (pt); Dietitians 1 (pt);
Dentists 1 (pt); Podiatrists 1 (pt); Audiologists 1
(pt).
Facilities Dining room; Activities room; Crafts
room; Laundry room; Barber/Beauty shop.
Activities Arts and Crafts; Cards; Games;
Reading groups; Prayer groups; Movies.
Description Facility has country atmosphere;
also appropriate and directive programs.

RUPERT

Minidoka Memorial Hospital Geriatric Unit*
1224 8th St, Rupert, ID, 83350 (208) 436-0481
Admin Ed Richardson.
Licensure Skilled Care. *Beds* 79. *Certified* Medicaid; Medicare.
Ownership Nonprofit.

SAINT MARIES

Valley Vista Convalescent Center 59
820 Elm St, Saint Maries, ID, 83861 (208)
245-4576
Admin John Cordes. *Medical Dir/Dir of
Nursing* Thomas Richards.
Licensure Skilled Care. *Beds* 59. *Certified* Medicaid; Medicare.
Staff RNs 1 (ft), 2 (pt); LPNs 4 (ft), 2 (pt);
Orderlies 1 (ft); Nurses aides 23 (ft), 2 (pt);
Activities coordinators 1 (ft).
Facilities Dining room; Physical therapy room;
Activities room; Chapel; Crafts room; Laundry
room.
Activities Arts and Crafts; Cards; Games;
Reading groups; Prayer groups; Movies; Shopping trips; Pet therapy program.

SALMON

Casabello Estate Intermediate Care Facility
PO Box 1319, Salmon, ID, 83467 (208)
756-3543
Admin Joyce Hammond.
Licensure Intermediate Care. *Beds* 39. *Certified* Medicaid.
Admissions Requirements Physician's request.
Staff RNs 2 (ft), 1 (pt); LPNs 3 (ft); Nurses
aides 6 (ft), 2 (pt); Activities coordinators 1 (pt).
Facilities Dining room; Activities room; Chapel; Crafts room; Laundry room; Barber/Beauty
shop; Library; Garden room.
Activities Arts and Crafts; Cards; Games;
Reading groups; Prayer groups; Movies; Shopping trips; Dances/Social or cultural gatherings.
Description Facility enjoys a country setting in
high mountain valley with lovely view all four
seasons; over 2 acres of yard.

SANDPOINT

Sandpoint Manor
220 S Division, Sandpoint, ID, 83864 (208)
263-3933
Admin Craig A Johnson. *Medical Dir/Dir of
Nursing* Dr H Leedy.
Licensure Skilled Care; Intermediate Care.
Beds 89. *Certified* Medicaid; Medicare.
Staff RNs 5 (ft), 4 (pt); LPNs 2 (ft), 2 (pt);
Nurses aides 25 (ft), 18 (pt); Physical therapists
1 (ft), 1 (pt); Occupational therapists 1 (pt);
Speech therapists 1 (pt); Activities coordinators
1 (ft); Dietitians 1 (ft); Dentists 1 (pt).
Facilities Dining room; Physical therapy room;
Activities room; Chapel; Crafts room; Laundry
room; Barber/Beauty shop.
Activities Arts and Crafts; Cards; Games;
Movies; Shopping trips; Dances/Social or cultural gatherings.
Description Facility has a caring staff.

SHOSHONE

Wood River Convalescent Center
511 E 4th, Shoshone, ID, 83352 (208) 886-2228
Admin Helen Shewmaker. *Medical Dir/Dir of
Nursing* R G Neher MD.
Licensure Skilled Care. *Beds* 40. *Certified* Medicaid; Medicare.
Admissions Requirements Medical examination; Physician's request.
Staff Physicians 1 (pt); RNs 2 (ft), 1 (pt); LPNs
3 (ft), 1 (pt); Nurses aides 10 (ft), 3 (pt); Reality
therapists 2 (ft); Activities coordinators 1 (ft).
Facilities Dining room; Activities room; Crafts
room; Laundry room.
Activities Arts and Crafts; Cards; Games;
Reading groups; Prayer groups.
Description Resident crafts are entered in Lincoln County Fair so they receive recognition
and ribbons; they have decorated a bus and ridden in parade.

SILVERTON

Silverton County Good Samaritan Center
Box 358, Silverton, ID, 83867 (208) 556-1147
Admin Gary Bokelman. *Medical Dir/Dir of
Nursing* Thomas Prenger MD.
Licensure Skilled Care. *Beds* 59. *Certified* Medicaid; Medicare.
Admissions Requirements Medical examination; Physician's request.
Staff RNs 1 (ft), 2 (pt); LPNs 4 (ft), 4 (pt);
Nurses aides 10 (ft), 15 (pt); Physical therapists
1 (pt); Activities coordinators 1 (ft); Dietitians
1 (pt).
Affiliation Lutheran
Facilities Dining room; Physical therapy room;
Activities room; Chapel; Crafts room; Laundry
room; Barber/Beauty shop; Library; Resident
use kitchenette.
Activities Arts and Crafts; Cards; Games;
Reading groups; Prayer groups; Movies; Shopping trips; Dances/Social or cultural gatherings;
Fishing trips; Picnics; Bowling trips.
Description Facility is located in the mountains
of northern Idaho with much community
involvement, large volunteer program; residents have many opportunities to participate in

trips, concerts, and outings; facility has excellent reputation with the state for quality.

SODA SPRINGS

Caribou Memorial Nursing Home*
300 S Third W, Soda Springs, ID, 83276 (208)
547-3341
Admin Pearl S Fryar.
Licensure Skilled Care. *Beds* 37. *Certified* Medicaid; Medicare.

TWIN FALLS

Skyview—Hazeldel
640 Filer Ave W, Twin Falls, ID, 83301 (208)
734-8645
Admin Richard Drake. *Medical Dir/Dir of
Nursing* A C Emery MD.
Licensure Skilled Care. *Beds* 185. *Certified* Medicaid.
Admissions Requirements Medical examination; Physician's request.
Staff RNs 8 (ft), 4 (pt); LPNs 10 (ft), 5 (pt);
Orderlies 3 (ft); Nurses aides 80 (ft), 10 (pt);
Physical therapists 1 (ft); Activities coordinators 2 (ft), 2 (pt); Dietitians 1 (pt).
Facilities Dining room; Physical therapy room;
Activities room; Crafts room.
Activities Arts and Crafts; Cards; Games;
Reading groups; Movies; Dances/Social or cultural gatherings.

WEISER

Weiser Care Center
331 E Park St, Weiser, ID, 83672 (208)
549-2416
Admin Almeta Ingram. *Medical Dir/Dir of
Nursing* Dr Richard Giever.
Licensure Skilled Care. *Beds* 89. *Certified* Medicaid; Medicare.
Admissions Requirements Minimum age 18;
Physician's request.
Staff RNs 5 (ft), 2 (pt); LPNs 5 (ft), 1 (pt);
Nurses aides 25 (ft), 8 (pt); Physical therapists 1
(ft); Activities coordinators 1 (ft).
Facilities Dining room; Physical therapy room;
Activities room; Laundry room; Barber/Beauty
shop.
Activities Arts and Crafts; Cards; Games;
Reading groups; Prayer groups; Movies; Shopping trips; Dances/Social or cultural gatherings.
Description A very warm, friendly, odor-free
facility with very good nursing care. An excellent activity program is provided. Also, a selective menu is provided.

WENDELL

Magic Valley Manor
PO Box 306, N Idaho St, Wendell, ID, 83355
(208) 536-5571
Admin Kerry Arbuckle. *Medical Dir/Dir of
Nursing* Mark Spencer MD.
Licensure Skilled Care. *Beds* 40. *Certified* Medicaid.
Staff Physicians 1 (pt); RNs 1 (ft), 2 (pt); LPNs
1 (ft), 2 (pt); Nurses aides 6 (ft), 5 (pt); Physical
therapists 1 (pt); Occupational therapists 1 (pt);

Speech therapists 1 (pt); Activities coordinators 1 (ft); Dietitians 1 (pt); Dentists 1 (pt).
Facilities Dining room; Activities room; Laundry room.
Activities Arts and Crafts; Cards; Games; Prayer groups; Movies; Shopping trips; Dances/Social or cultural gatherings.
Description This small facility provides personal and individualized care; extensive activity program with good community involvement in a small town environment; day care and respite services available.

ILLINOIS

ABINGDON

Owen Care Center*
2000 W Martin St, Abingdon, IL, 61410 (309) 462-2356
Admin Debbie A Owen.
Licensure Skilled Care. *Beds* 74. *Certified* Medicaid.
Ownership Proprietary.

ADDISON

Iona Glos Specialized Living Center*
40 S Fairbank St, Addison, IL, 60101 (312) 543-2440
Admin Laura Abernathy.
Licensure Intermediate Care. *Beds* 100. *Certified* Medicaid.
Ownership Nonprofit.

ALBION

Rest Haven Manor Inc*
120 W Main, Albion, IL, 62806 (618) 445-2815
Admin Bernetta Daubs.
Licensure Intermediate Care. *Beds* 49. *Certified* Medicaid.
Ownership Proprietary.

ALEDO

Georgetown Manors
3rd Ave at 12th St SW, Aledo, IL, 61231 (309) 582-5376
Admin Evelyn J Pealstrom.
Licensure Intermediate Care. *Beds* SNF 100.
Certified Medicaid; Medicare.
Ownership Proprietary.

Mercer County Nursing Home*
NW 9th Ave and NW 3rd St, Aledo, IL, 61231 (309) 582-5361
Admin Frederick J Ehrenhart.
Licensure Intermediate Care. *Beds* 95. *Certified* Medicaid.
Ownership Public.

ALHAMBRA

Hampton Nursing Care Inc*
Main and Warsaw Sts, Alhambra, IL, 62001 (618) 488-3565
Admin Carolyn Gibbons.
Licensure Intermediate Care. *Beds* 86. *Certified* Medicaid.
Ownership Proprietary.

Hitz Memorial Home
Belle St, Alhambra, IL, 62001 (618) 488-2355
Admin Jon R Lyerla. *Medical Dir/Dir of Nursing* Dr Edward Hediger.
Licensure Intermediate Care. *Beds* 67. *Certified* Medicaid.
Ownership Nonprofit.
Admissions Requirements Minimum age 55; Medical examination; Physician's request.
Staff RNs 2 (ft), 2 (pt); LPNs 2 (ft), 1 (pt); Nurses aides 18 (ft), 7 (pt); Physical therapists 1 (pt); Speech therapists 1 (pt); Activities coordinators 1 (ft); Dietitians 1 (pt); Dentists 1 (pt); Audiologists 1 (pt).
Affiliation Church of Christ
Facilities Dining room; Physical therapy room; Activities room; Crafts room; Barber/Beauty shop; Library.
Activities Arts and Crafts; Cards; Games; Movies; Shopping trips; Dances/Social or cultural gatherings.
Description The church has seen fit to be in the business of operating nursing centers because of its concern for the well being of the elderly, the sick, and the infirm; attempts to provide a home with a Christian atmosphere.

ALTAMONT

Lutheran Care Center
US Hwy 40 W, Altamont, IL, 62411 (618) 483-6136
Admin Barbara Hamann. *Medical Dir/Dir of Nursing* Dr Delbert G Huelskoetter.
Licensure Skilled Care. *Beds* 97.
Ownership Nonprofit.
Admissions Requirements Minimum age 20; Medical examination; Physician's request.
Staff Physicians 1 (ft); RNs 4 (ft), 2 (pt); LPNs 8 (ft), 2 (pt); Orderlies 1 (ft), 1 (pt); Nurses aides 42 (ft), 5 (pt); Physical therapists 1 (pt); Recreational therapists 1 (ft); Dietitians 1 (ft).
Affiliation Lutheran
Facilities Dining room; Physical therapy room; Activities room; Chapel; Crafts room; Laundry room; Barber/Beauty shop; Library.
Activities Arts and Crafts; Cards; Games; Reading groups; Prayer groups; Movies; Shopping trips; Dances/Social or cultural gatherings.
Description Facility provides quality care for quality people; special emphasis is given to each residents' needs, returning them to their homes if possible; also offers day care, outpatient services, and free hospice program; respite care is encouraged.

ALTON

Burt Sheltered Care Home*
1414 Milton Rd, Alton, IL, 62002 (618) 465-1351
Admin Mary Jo Swengrosh.
Licensure Sheltered Care. *Beds* 29.
Ownership Nonprofit.

Eldercare of Alton*
3523 Wickenhauser, Alton, IL, 62002 (618) 465-8887
Admin Joyce A Wild.
Licensure Skilled Care; Intermediate Care.
Beds SNF 147; ICF 49. *Certified* Medicaid; Medicare.
Ownership Proprietary.

Eunice C Smith Nursing Home*
1251 College Ave, Alton, IL, 62002 (618) 462-7330
Admin Howard L Levitan.
Licensure Skilled Care. *Beds* 64. *Certified* Medicaid; Medicare.
Ownership Proprietary.

Northwoods Manor Inc
2349 Virden Dr, Alton, IL, 62002 (618) 466-5331
Admin David L Knoche.
Licensure Intermediate Care. *Beds* 43.
Ownership Proprietary.
Staff Physicians 1 (pt); RNs 1 (pt); LPNs 5 (ft); Nurses aides 1 (ft), 8 (pt); Physical therapists 1 (pt); Occupational therapists 1 (pt); Speech therapists 1 (pt); Activities coordinators 1 (ft); Dietitians 1 (pt).
Facilities Dining room; Activities room; Crafts room; Laundry room; Barber/Beauty shop.
Activities Arts and Crafts; Cards; Games; Reading groups; Prayer groups; Shopping trips; Dances/Social or cultural gatherings.
Description Northwoods Manor is family-owned and operated is very charming and very clean and tries to give patients a very nice, homey setting.

AMBOY

Mapleside Manor*
15 W Wasson Rd, Amboy, IL, 61310 (815)
857-2550
Admin Morris F Forman.
Licensure Intermediate Care. *Beds* 99. *Certified* Medicaid.
Ownership Proprietary.

ANNA

City Care Center*
Rt 1, Brady Mill Rd, Anna, IL, 62906 (618)
833-6343
Admin Patricia L Chamness.
Licensure Skilled Care. *Beds* 70. *Certified* Medicaid; Medicare.
Ownership Proprietary.

Mulberry Manor Inc
612 E Davie St, Anna, IL, 62906 (618)
833-6012
Admin James A Keller. *Medical Dir/Dir of Nursing* William H Whiting MD.
Licensure Intermediate Care. *Beds* 80. *Certified* Medicaid.
Ownership Nonprofit.
Admissions Requirements Minimum age 18; Medical examination; Physician's request.
Staff RNs 1 (ft); LPNs 4 (ft), 3 (pt); Orderlies 4 (ft); Nurses aides 7 (ft), 6 (pt); Recreational therapists 1 (pt); Activities coordinators 2 (ft).
Facilities Dining room; Physical therapy room; Activities room; Crafts room; Laundry room; Barber/Beauty shop.
Activities Arts and Crafts; Cards; Games; Reading groups; Prayer groups; Movies; Shopping trips; Dances/Social or cultural gatherings.
Description We pride ourselves on the worth and dignity of every individual that God creates. We believe that God doesn't make mistakes and expects the mentally handicapped to be developed into the human beings that it's possible for them to become.

Spanish Oaks Center*
223 W Vienna, Anna, IL, 62906 (618)
833-8013
Admin Connie L Jones.
Licensure Sheltered Care. *Beds* 37.
Ownership Proprietary.

Union County Skilled Nursing Home*
517 N Main St, Anna, IL, 62906 (618)
833-5155
Admin Eugene A Helfrich.
Licensure Skilled Care. *Beds* 60. *Certified* Medicaid.
Ownership Public.

ARCOLA

Clearbrook House*
420 S Walnut, Arcola, IL, 60005 (312)
259-6820
Admin Tracy Martin.
Licensure Intermediate Care. *Beds* 20.
Ownership Nonprofit.

We Care Nursing Facilities Inc*
422 E 4th South St, Arcola, IL, 61910 (217)
268-3555
Admin Nancy Gates.
Licensure Skilled Care. *Beds* 109. *Certified* Medicaid.
Ownership Proprietary.

ARLINGTON HEIGHTS

Americana Healthcare Center
715 W Central Rd, Arlington Heights, IL,
60005 (312) 392-2020
Admin Donna DeNardo. *Medical Dir/Dir of Nursing* Dr Cameron Thomson.
Licensure Skilled Care. *Beds* 151. *Certified* Medicare.
Ownership Proprietary.
Admissions Requirements Minimum age 18.
Staff Physicians 12 (pt); RNs 9 (ft), 4 (pt); LPNs 5 (ft), 7 (pt); Orderlies 2 (ft), 1 (pt); Nurses aides 26 (ft), 20 (pt); Physical therapists 2 (ft); Recreational therapists 1 (ft); Occupational therapists 2 (ft); Speech therapists 1 (ft), 1 (pt); Activities coordinators 1 (ft); Dietitians 1 (ft); Dentists 1 (pt); Podiatrists 1 (pt).
Facilities Dining room; Physical therapy room; Activities room; Crafts room; Laundry room; Barber/Beauty shop.
Activities Arts and Crafts; Cards; Games; Reading groups; Prayer groups; Movies; Shopping trips; Dances/Social or cultural gatherings.
Description Facility features a 24-bed luxury Williamsburg wing; specialized rehabilitation programs utilizing skills of staff physical therapists, occupational therapists, and speech pathologist; horticultural therapy; and video game therapy.

Lutheran Home and Service for Aged
800 W Oakton St, Arlington Heights, IL, 60005
(312) 253-3710
Admin Paul A Hauer. *Medical Dir/Dir of Nursing* T M Homa MD.
Licensure Skilled Care; Intermediate Care; Sheltered Care. *Beds* SNF 252; ICF; Sheltered Care 167. *Certified* Medicaid.
Ownership Nonprofit.
Admissions Requirements Minimum age 60; Medical examination.
Staff Physicians 3 (pt); RNs 15 (ft), 16 (pt); LPNs 5 (ft), 9 (pt); Orderlies 2 (ft); Nurses aides 52 (ft), 69 (pt); Physical therapists 1 (ft); Reality therapists 2 (ft); Recreational therapists 4 (ft); Occupational therapists 1 (pt); Speech therapists 1 (pt); Activities coordinators 2 (ft); Dietitians 2 (ft); Dentists 1 (pt); Ophthalmologists 1 (pt); Podiatrists 1 (pt); Audiologists 1 (pt).
Affiliation Lutheran
Facilities Dining room; Physical therapy room; Activities room; Chapel; Crafts room; Laundry room; Barber/Beauty shop; Library.
Activities Arts and Crafts; Cards; Games; Reading groups; Prayer groups; Movies; Shopping trips; Dances/Social or cultural gatherings.
Description Facility features all private rooms and continuum of care, located on an 80-acre campus in a residential community.

Magnus Farm Nursing Home
801 E Central Rd, Arlington Heights, IL, 60005
(312) 439-0018
Admin Alex B Magnus Jr.
Licensure Intermediate Care; Sheltered Care.
Beds ICF 15; Sheltered Care 96.
Ownership Proprietary.
Staff RNs 3 (ft); LPNs 1 (ft); Orderlies 1 (ft); Activities coordinators 1 (ft), 2 (pt).
Facilities Dining room; Activities room; Crafts room; Laundry room; Barber/Beauty shop.
Activities Arts and Crafts; Cards; Games; Reading groups; Prayer groups; Movies; Dances/Social or cultural gatherings.
Description Magnus Farm is a country estate for the elderly situated on 40 beautifully landscaped acres with a swimming pool. Facility has a warm, home-like atmosphere while also providing excellent care—the "personal touch," home-cooked meals, and stimulating activities.

AROMA PARK

Park View Manor*
103 W 4th St, Aroma Park, IL, 60910 (815)
932-4332
Admin Audrey Cook.
Licensure Sheltered Care. *Beds* 27.
Ownership Proprietary.

ARTHUR

The Arthur Home*
423 Eberhardt Dr, Arthur, IL, 61911 (217)
543-2103
Admin Leona M Hughes.
Licensure Skilled Care. *Beds* 69. *Certified* Medicaid; Medicare.
Ownership Nonprofit.

ASHMORE

Ashmore Estates
RFD Box 400, Ashmore, IL, 61912
Admin Roger David. *Medical Dir/Dir of Nursing* Dr Carl Johnson.
Licensure Intermediate Care for Mentally Retarded.
Admissions Requirements Minimum age 18.
Staff Physicians 2 (pt); RNs 1 (ft), 1 (pt); LPNs 3 (ft); Nurses aides 15 (ft); Activities coordinators 1 (ft).
Facilities Dining room; Activities room; Crafts room; Laundry room; Lounges; Multipurpose and motor development building.
Activities Arts and Crafts; Cards; Games; Movies; Shopping trips; Dances/Social or cultural gatherings; Special Olympics; Family nights; Church services; Softball games; Pizza nights.
Description Facility is located in a rural setting; many residents attend workshop programs in Charleston; staff has been able to help many mentally retarded persons with personal growth and with control of behavior.

ASTORIA

Astoria Care Center Inc*
1008 E Broadway, Astoria, IL, 61501 (309)
329-2136
Admin Caroline Stine.
Licensure Intermediate Care. *Beds* 57. *Certi-*

fied Medicaid.
Ownership Proprietary.

ATLANTA

Bartmann Nursing Home 2*
Rt 1, Atlanta, IL, 61723 (217) 642-5231
Admin Joyce O Conrady.
Licensure Intermediate Care. *Beds* 64.
Ownership Proprietary.

Bartmann Shelter Care Home*
Rt 1, Atlanta, IL, 61723 (217) 642-5231
Admin Sandra Allen.
Licensure Sheltered Care. *Beds* 29.
Ownership Proprietary.

AUBURN

Park's Memorial Convalescent Center
304 Maple Ave, Auburn, IL, 62615 (217) 438-6125
Admin Dave Lambert. *Medical Dir/Dir of Nursing* Kenneth Malmberg Md.
Licensure Skilled Care. *Beds* 70. *Certified* Medicaid; Medicare.
Ownership Proprietary.
Staff RNs 2 (ft), 1 (pt); LPNs 6 (ft), 2 (pt); Nurses aides 18 (ft), 6 (pt); Physical therapists 1 (ft); Recreational therapists 1 (ft); Occupational therapists 1 (pt); Speech therapists 1 (pt); Activities coordinators 1 (ft); Dietitians 1 (ft); Dentists 1 (pt); Ophthalmologists 1 (pt); Podiatrists 1 (pt); Audiologists 1 (pt); 1 (pt).
Facilities Dining room; Physical therapy room; Activities room; Laundry room; Barber/Beauty shop.
Activities Arts and Crafts; Cards; Games; Reading groups; Prayer groups; Movies.

AUGUSTA

Hancock County Sheltered Care
W Main St, Augusta, IL, 62311 (217) 392-2116
Admin Vicki S Carriger.
Licensure Sheltered Care. *Beds* 45.
Ownership Public.
Admissions Requirements Minimum age 18; Medical examination.
Staff RNs 1 (ft); LPNs 2 (ft); Nurses aides 8 (pt); Activities coordinators 1 (ft).
Facilities Dining room; Activities room; Laundry room.
Activities Arts and Crafts; Cards; Games; Reading groups; Prayer groups; Movies; Shopping trips; Dances/Social or cultural gatherings.
Description Facility is located at the edge of a rural community, an excellent small home of active ambulatory residents. Most residents are active in the local senior citizens group or the county's RSVP.

AURORA

Aurora Community Living Facility*
2080 Best Pl, Aurora, IL, 60506 (312) 896-5200
Admin Linda Dider.
Licensure Intermediate Care. *Beds* 20.
Ownership Nonprofit.

Aurora Manor*
1601 N Farnsworth, Aurora, IL, 60505 (312) 898-1180
Admin Mary E Sipla.
Licensure Skilled Care; Intermediate Care.
Beds SNF 112; ICF 96. *Certified* Medicaid; Medicare.
Ownership Proprietary.

Countryside Healthcare Center
2330 W Galena Blvd, Aurora, IL, 60506 (312) 896-4686
Admin Jerry Banks. *Medical Dir/Dir of Nursing* Marc Schlesinger MD.
Licensure Skilled Care; Intermediate Care.
Beds SNF 107; ICF 104. *Certified* Medicaid; Medicare.
Ownership Proprietary.
Admissions Requirements Medical examination.
Staff Physical therapists 1 (pt); Reality therapists 1 (pt); Recreational therapists 1 (pt); Occupational therapists 1 (pt); Speech therapists 1 (pt); Activities coordinators 1 (ft); Dietitians 1 (pt); Dentists 1 (pt); Ophthalmologists 1 (pt); Podiatrists 1 (pt).
Facilities Dining room; Physical therapy room; Activities room; Barber/Beauty shop.
Activities Arts and Crafts; Cards; Games; Reading groups; Prayer groups; Movies; Shopping trips; Dances/Social or cultural gatherings; Church services.
Description Facility is located in a quiet country setting on the west edge of Aurora; holds an annual country fair.

Elmwood Nursing Home*
1017 W Galena, Aurora, IL, 60506 (312) 897-3100
Admin Alvin E Martin.
Licensure Skilled Care. *Beds* 64.
Ownership Proprietary.

Jennings Terrace*
275 S LaSalle, Aurora, IL, 60505 (312) 897-6946
Admin Martin J Scarpetta.
Licensure Sheltered Care. *Beds* 104.
Ownership Nonprofit.

Parkview East Nursing and Convalescent Center
400 E New York, Aurora, IL, 60506 (312) 897-8714
Admin Ellen Boulnois. *Medical Dir/Dir of Nursing* William Weigel MD.
Licensure Skilled Care; Intermediate Care.
Beds SNF 80; ICF 41.
Ownership Proprietary.
Admissions Requirements Minimum age 22.
Staff Physicians 2 (pt); RNs 3 (ft), 2 (pt); LPNs 2 (ft), 3 (pt); Orderlies 2 (pt); Nurses aides 17 (ft), 8 (pt); Physical therapists 1 (pt); Occupational therapists 1 (pt); Speech therapists 1 (pt); Activities coordinators 1 (pt); Dietitians 1 (pt); Dentists 1 (pt); Ophthalmologists 1 (pt); Podiatrists 1 (pt).
Facilities Dining room; Physical therapy room; Activities room; Chapel; Crafts room; Laundry room; Barber/Beauty shop; Library; Ice cream parlour/snack shop.
Activities Arts and Crafts; Games; Reading groups; Movies; Dances/Social or cultural gath-erings; Baking.
Description Park View has a day care program structured to handle clients who need supervision and stimulation but who do not require institutionalization at present.

Sunnymere Inc*
925 6th Ave, Aurora, IL, 60505 (312) 898-7844
Admin Edith W Anderson.
Licensure Sheltered Care. *Beds* 49.
Ownership Nonprofit.

AVON

Avon Nursing Home Inc*
Box S, Avon, IL, 61415 (309) 465-3102
Admin Barbara L Kersh.
Licensure Intermediate Care. *Beds* 48. *Certified* Medicaid.
Ownership Proprietary.

BARRY

Barry Community Care Center*
1313 Pratt St, Barry, IL, 62312 (217) 335-2326
Admin Mark W Hubbard.
Licensure Skilled Care. *Beds* 76. *Certified* Medicaid; Medicare.
Ownership Proprietary.

BATAVIA

Michealsen Health Center
831 Batavia Ave, Batavia, IL, 60510 (312) 879-4300
Admin Richard K Waltmire. *Medical Dir/Dir of Nursing* Dr John O'Dwyer.
Licensure Skilled Care; Intermediate Care; Sheltered Care. *Beds* SNF 128; Sheltered Care 49. *Certified* Medicaid; Medicare.
Ownership Nonprofit.
Admissions Requirements Minimum age 18; Medical examination; Physician's request.
Facilities Dining room; Physical therapy room; Activities room; Chapel; Crafts room; Laundry room; Barber/Beauty shop.
Activities Arts and Crafts; Cards; Games; Reading groups; Prayer groups; Movies; Shopping trips; Dances/Social or cultural gatherings.

Roosevelt Square*
520 Fabyan Pkwy, Batavia, IL, 60510 (312) 879-5266
Admin Eileen Brandli.
Licensure Intermediate Care. *Beds* 63. *Certified* Medicaid.
Ownership Proprietary.

BEARDSTOWN

Elmwood Manor Inc*
1300 Grand Ave, Beardstown, IL, 62618 (217) 323-4055
Admin Eugene Pontius.
Licensure Intermediate Care. *Beds* 49. *Certified* Medicaid.
Ownership Proprietary.

Myers Nursing Home
1501 Canal St, Beardstown, IL, 62618 (217)
323-1900
Admin John W Myers. *Medical Dir/Dir of
Nursing* H C Zingher MD.
Licensure Skilled Care; Intermediate Care.
Beds 83. *Certified* Medicaid; Medicare.
Ownership Proprietary.
Admissions Requirements Minimum age 18;
Medical examination; Physician's request.
Staff Physicians 1 (pt); RNs 2 (ft), 3 (pt); LPNs
9 (ft), 1 (pt); Nurses aides 19 (ft), 13 (pt);
Physical therapists 2 (pt); Recreational thera-
pists 1 (pt); Speech therapists 1 (pt); Activities
coordinators 1 (ft); Dietitians 1 (pt); Dentists 1
(pt); Podiatrists 1 (pt); Audiologists 1 (pt).
Facilities Dining room; Activities room; Crafts
room; Barber/Beauty shop.
Activities Arts and Crafts; Cards; Games;
Reading groups; Prayer groups; Movies; Shopping trips.

BELLEVILLE

Belleville Nursing Center
900 Royal Heights, Belleville, IL, 62223 (618)
235-6133
Admin Susan M Franklin. *Medical Dir/Dir of
Nursing* Dr Paul Biedenharn.
Licensure Skilled Care. *Beds* 234. *Cer-
tified* Medicaid; Medicare.
Ownership Proprietary.
Admissions Requirements Medical examina-
tion.
Staff RNs 3 (ft); LPNs 14 (ft); Nurses aides 80
(ft), 20 (pt); Physical therapists 1 (pt); Recrea-
tional therapists 1 (pt); Speech therapists 1 (pt);
Activities coordinators 1 (ft); Dietitians 1 (pt);
Dentists 1 (pt).
Facilities Dining room; Physical therapy room;
Activities room; Crafts room; Laundry room;
Barber/Beauty shop.
Activities Arts and Crafts; Cards; Games;
Reading groups; Prayer groups; Movies; Shop-
ping trips; Dances/Social or cultural gatherings.

Calvin D Johnson Nursing Home
727 N 17th St, Belleville, IL, 62221 (618)
234-3323
Admin Annette B Bierchenk. *Medical Dir/Dir
of Nursing* Eric Lehr MD.
Licensure Skilled Care; Intermediate Care.
Beds SNF 196; ICF 51. *Certified* Medicaid;
Medicare.
Ownership Proprietary.
Admissions Requirements Medical examination; Physician's request.
Staff Physicians 1 (pt); RNs 4 (ft), 3 (pt); LPNs
8 (ft), 15 (pt); Orderlies 1 (ft); Nurses aides 51
(ft), 24 (pt); Physical therapists 1 (pt); Recrea-
tional therapists 1 (pt); Occupational therapists
1 (ft), 1 (pt); Speech therapists 1 (pt); Activities
coordinators 1 (ft); Dietitians 1 (pt); Dentists 1
(pt); Ophthalmologists 1 (pt); Podiatrists 1 (pt);
Audiologists 1 (pt).
Facilities Dining room; Physical therapy room;
Activities room; Chapel; Crafts room; Laundry
room; Barber/Beauty shop.
Activities Arts and Crafts; Cards; Games;
Reading groups; Prayer groups; Movies; Shopping trips; Dances/Social or cultural gatherings.
Description Facility features an outstanding

activity program and is involved in community
programs. Facility has a stroke club, RSVP, and
many others. Total redecorating completed
recently.

Castle Nursing Center
225 Castellano Dr, Belleville, IL, 62221 (618)
235-1300
Admin Lee Harvey. *Medical Dir/Dir of
Nursing* Dr H P Dexheimer.
Licensure Skilled Care; Intermediate Care.
Beds SNF 144; ICF 97. *Certified* Medicaid;
Medicare.
Ownership Proprietary.
Staff Physicians 1 (pt); RNs 7 (ft); LPNs 15
(ft); Orderlies 1 (ft); Nurses aides 66 (ft);
Physical therapists 1 (ft); Reality therapists 1
(ft); Occupational therapists 1 (pt); Speech ther-
apists 1 (pt); Activities coordinators 4 (ft); Die-
titians 1 (pt); Dentists 1 (pt); Audiologists 1
(pt).
Facilities Dining room; Physical therapy room;
Activities room; Chapel; Crafts room; Laundry
room; Barber/Beauty shop; Library; 5 living
rooms.
Activities Arts and Crafts; Cards; Games;
Reading groups; Prayer groups; Movies; Shopping trips; Dances/Social or cultural gatherings;
Excursions to ballgames, fishing, botanical gardens, zoo; inter-facility olympics.
Description Facility is conveniently located in
the heart of the quiet lakeside residential community of Castle Acres of Swamsea and is surrounded with an abundance of rhododendrons
and dogwood trees. Recently awarded the
highest recognition given by the State of Illinois
for quality of care.

Dammert Geriatric Center*
Rt 15, 9500 W Illinois, Belleville, IL, 62223
(618) 397-6700
Admin William P Clark.
Licensure Skilled Care; Sheltered Care.
Beds SNF 32; Sheltered Care 16. *Cer-
tified* Medicaid; Medicare.
Ownership Nonprofit.

Four Fountains Convalescent Center
101 S Belt West, Belleville, IL, 62220 (618)
277-7700
Admin Steven D Brant.
Licensure Skilled Care; Intermediate Care.
Beds 156. *Certified* Medicaid; Medicare.
Ownership Proprietary.
Staff Physicians 1 (pt); RNs 12 (ft); LPNs 10
(ft); Nurses aides 60 (ft), 10 (pt); Physical thera-
pists 3 (ft), 2 (pt); Occupational therapists 1 (pt);
Speech therapists 1 (pt); Activities coordinators
2 (ft); Dietitians 2 (pt); Dentists 1 (pt); Podiat-
rists 1 (pt); Audiologists 1 (pt).
Facilities Dining room; Physical therapy room;
Activities room; Crafts room; Laundry room;
Barber/Beauty shop; Library.
Activities Arts and Crafts; Cards; Games; Pray-
er groups; Movies; Shopping trips; Dances/So-
cial or cultural gatherings.
Description Alzheimer's support group meets
monthly; rehabilitation dining room daily.

Lincoln Home
150 N 27th St, Belleville, IL, 62223 (618)
235-6600
Admin Wilma D Seppi. *Medical Dir/Dir of*

Nursing Dr Paul Biedenharn.
Licensure Intermediate Care. *Beds* 152.
Ownership Proprietary.
Admissions Requirements Medical examina-
tion.
Staff RNs 3 (ft); LPNs 16 (pt); Orderlies 2 (ft),
1 (pt); Nurses aides 20 (ft), 6 (pt); Reality thera-
pists 1 (pt); Activities coordinators 1 (ft); Dieti-
tians 1 (pt).
Facilities Dining room; Activities room;
Chapel; Crafts room; Laundry room; Barber-
/Beauty shop.
Activities Arts and Crafts; Cards; Games;
Reading groups; Prayer groups; Movies; Shop-
ping trips; Dances/Social or cultural gatherings.

Memorial Convalescent Center
4315 Memorial Dr, Belleville, IL, 62220 (618)
233-7750
Admin Patricia Adams. *Medical Dir/Dir of
Nursing* Mathew Erscle.
Licensure Skilled Care. *Beds* 108. *Cer-
tified* Medicaid; Medicare.
Ownership Nonprofit.
Admissions Requirements Minimum age 18;
Medical examination; Physician's request.
Staff Physicians 1 (pt); RNs 7 (ft), 11 (pt);
LPNs 3 (ft), 2 (pt); Orderlies 1 (ft), 2 (pt);
Nurses aides 26 (ft), 29 (pt); Physical therapists
1 (pt); Recreational therapists 2 (ft).
Facilities Dining room; Physical therapy room;
Activities room; Chapel; Crafts room; Barber-
/Beauty shop; Library.
Activities Arts and Crafts; Cards; Games;
Reading groups; Prayer groups; Movies; Shop-
ping trips; Dances/Social or cultural gatherings.

Notre Dame Hills Convalescent Center
6401 W Main St, Belleville, IL, 62221 (618)
397-8400
Admin Lois J Snyder. *Medical Dir/Dir of
Nursing* Dr J T Tierney.
Licensure Skilled Care; Intermediate Care.
Beds SNF 61; ICF 61. *Certified* Medicaid;
Medicare.
Ownership Proprietary.
Admissions Requirements Minimum age 21;
Medical examination; Physician's request.
Staff RNs 4 (ft), 4 (pt); LPNs 4 (ft), 3 (pt);
Orderlies 2 (ft); Nurses aides 26 (ft), 14 (pt);
Physical therapists 3 (ft), 1 (pt); Recreational
therapists 1 (ft), 2 (pt); Speech therapists 1 (pt);
Dietitians 1 (pt); Dentists 1 (pt); Podiatrists 1
(pt).
Facilities Dining room; Physical therapy room;
Activities room; Laundry room; Barber/Beauty
shop; TV rooms.
Activities Arts and Crafts; Games; Prayer
groups; Movies; Shopping trips; Dances/Social
or cultural gatherings; Restaurant outings;
Cooking; Reality orientation classes.
Description Facility offers physical therapy 7
days a week.

Saint Clair County Special Living Center
1450 Caseyville Ave, Belleville, IL, 62221 (618)
277-7730
Admin Agnes Schloemann. *Medical Dir/Dir of
Nursing* Betty Daubauch RN.
Licensure Intermediate Care. *Beds* 100.
Ownership Proprietary.
Staff Physicians 1 (pt); RNs 2 (pt); LPNs 5 (ft),
4 (pt); Nurses aides 63 (ft), 38 (pt); Recreational

therapists 1 (ft), 1 (pt); Occupational therapists 1 (ft); Speech therapists 1 (pt); Activities coordinators 2 (ft); Dietitians 5 (ft), 5 (pt).
Facilities Dining room; Physical therapy room; Activities room; Crafts room; Laundry room; Barber/Beauty shop; Library.
Activities Arts and Crafts; Cards; Games; Reading groups; Prayer groups; Movies; Shopping trips; Dances/Social or cultural gatherings.
Description Center is an intermediate care residential facility that provides training and supervision for 100 severely and profoundly developmentally disabled adults in a home-like setting.

Saint Pauls Home*
1021 W "E" St, Belleville, IL, 62221 (618) 233-2095
Admin Warren W Peters.
Licensure Intermediate Care; Sheltered Care. *Beds* ICF 113; Sheltered Care 62. *Certified* Medicaid.
Ownership Nonprofit.

Weier Retirement Nursing Home*
5 Gundlach Pl, Belleville, IL, 62221 (618) 233-6625
Admin Roger W Hotson.
Licensure Intermediate Care. *Beds* 94. *Certified* Medicaid.
Ownership Proprietary.

BELLWOOD

Dale Johnson Center*
2614 Saint Charles Rd, Bellwood, IL, 60104 (312) 547-3550
Admin Catherine A Bachand.
Licensure Intermediate Care. *Beds* 20.
Ownership Nonprofit.

PARC Home
105 Eastern Ave, Bellwood, IL, 60104 (312) 547-3580
Admin Catherine A Bachand. *Medical Dir/Dir of Nursing* Raymond McDonald MD.
Licensure Intermediate Care; ICF/Developmentally Disabled. *Beds* 95.
Ownership Nonprofit.
Admissions Requirements Minimum age 18; Medical examination.
Staff Physicians 1 (pt); RNs 1 (pt); LPNs 4 (ft), 3 (pt); Nurses aides 20 (ft), 20 (pt); Reality therapists 3 (ft); Recreational therapists 1 (ft); Occupational therapists 1 (ft), 1 (pt); Speech therapists 1 (ft); Activities coordinators 1 (ft); Dietitians 1 (pt); Dentists 1 (pt); Ophthalmologists 1 (pt); Podiatrists 1 (pt); Audiologists 1 (pt).
Facilities Dining room; Activities room; Laundry room; Barber/Beauty shop.
Activities Arts and Crafts; Games; Prayer groups; Movies; Shopping trips; Dances/Social or cultural gatherings.

BELVIDERE

Fairview Manor
1701 W 5th Ave, Belvidere, IL, 61008 (815) 547-5451
Admin William A Johnston. *Medical Dir/Dir*

of Nursing Kent Hess MD.
Licensure Intermediate Care. *Beds* 79. *Certified* Medicaid.
Ownership Proprietary.
Admissions Requirements Medical examination; Physician's request.
Staff RNs 1 (ft); LPNs 4 (ft), 2 (pt); Nurses aides 16 (ft), 4 (pt); Physical therapists 1 (pt); Activities coordinators 1 (ft), 1 (pt); Dietitians 1 (ft).
Facilities Dining room; Physical therapy room; Activities room; Laundry room; Barber/Beauty shop; Library.
Activities Arts and Crafts; Cards; Games; Reading groups; Prayer groups; Movies; Shopping trips; Dances/Social or cultural gatherings.
Description Located in an easily accessible residential area, the one-story facility has smoke and fire detectors and a complete sprinkler system.

Maple Crest-Boone County Nursing Home*
4452 Squaw Prairie Rd, Belvidere, IL, 61008 (815) 547-6377
Admin William M Bersted.
Licensure Skilled Care. *Beds* 78. *Certified* Medicaid.
Ownership Public.

Northwoods Healthcare Center*
2250 S Pearl Street Rd, Belvidere, IL, 61008 (815) 544-0358
Admin Sue Blanchard.
Licensure Skilled Care. *Beds* 120. *Certified* Medicaid; Medicare.
Ownership Proprietary.

BEMENT

Bement Manor*
601 N Morgan, Bement, IL, 61813 (217) 678-4051
Admin Angela Cornell-Barr.
Licensure Intermediate Care. *Beds* 57. *Certified* Medicaid.
Ownership Proprietary.

BENSENVILLE

Anchorage Bensenville Home
111 E Washington, Bensenville, IL, 60106 (312) 766-5800
Admin Jane M Muller. *Medical Dir/Dir of Nursing* Dr P Kini.
Licensure Skilled Care; Intermediate Care. *Beds* SNF 89; ICF 142. *Certified* Medicaid.
Ownership Proprietary.
Admissions Requirements Medical examination.
Staff Physicians 1 (ft), 4 (pt); RNs 8 (ft), 17 (pt); LPNs 2 (ft), 5 (pt); Orderlies 3 (ft); Nurses aides 37 (ft), 21 (pt); Physical therapists 1 (ft); Reality therapists 1 (pt); Recreational therapists 4 (ft); Occupational therapists 1 (pt); Speech therapists 1 (pt); Activities coordinators 1 (ft); Dietitians 1 (ft); Dentists 1 (pt); Ophthalmologists 1 (pt); Podiatrists 1 (pt); Audiologists 1 (pt); 1 (ft).
Affiliation Church of Christ
Facilities Dining room; Physical therapy room; Activities room; Chapel; Crafts room; Laundry

room; Barber/Beauty shop; Library; Clinic area.
Activities Arts and Crafts; Cards; Games; Reading groups; Prayer groups; Movies; Shopping trips; Dances/Social or cultural gatherings.
Description Facility is certified for Medicare and Blue Cross; JCAH accredited.

BENTON

Cockrum Intermediate Care Facility*
1409 N Main St, Benton, IL, 62812 (618) 435-2712
Admin Mary B Cockrum.
Licensure Intermediate Care. *Beds* 71.
Ownership Proprietary.

Severin Intermediate Care Facility*
902 S McLeansboro St, Benton, IL, 62812 (618) 435-2442
Admin Paul D Leffler.
Licensure Intermediate Care. *Beds* 96. *Certified* Medicaid.
Ownership Proprietary.

BERWYN

Fairfax Health Care Center
3601 S Harlem Ave, Berwyn, IL, 60402 (312) 749-4160
Admin Rebecca L Lind. *Medical Dir/Dir of Nursing* Dr Alberto Saltiel.
Licensure Skilled Care. *Beds* 160. *Certified* Medicaid; Medicare.
Ownership Proprietary.
Admissions Requirements Minimum age 19; Medical examination; Physician's request.
Staff Physicians 3 (pt); RNs 8 (ft), 3 (pt); LPNs 6 (ft), 5 (pt); Orderlies 2 (ft); Nurses aides 43 (ft), 8 (pt); Physical therapists 1 (pt); Recreational therapists 4 (ft), 1 (pt); Occupational therapists 1 (pt); Speech therapists 1 (pt); Dietitians 1 (pt); Podiatrists 1 (pt).
Facilities Dining room; Physical therapy room; Activities room; Laundry room; Barber/Beauty shop; Sun rooms.
Activities Arts and Crafts; Cards; Games; Reading groups; Prayer groups; Movies; Shopping trips; Dances/Social or cultural gatherings.
Description Staff is educated, trained, and skilled in the highest quality care; professional nurses are on duty 24 hours a day, 7 days a week. Care is always given with honor and respect for the dignity of each individual.

Pershing Convalescent Home Inc*
3900 S Oak Park Ave, Berwyn, IL, 60402 (312) 484-7543
Admin Lucille R Engelsman.
Licensure Skilled Care. *Beds* 51. *Certified* Medicare.
Ownership Proprietary.

BETHALTO

Bethalto Care Center Inc*
815 S Prairie St, Bethalto, IL, 62010 (618) 377-2144
Admin Linda M Daniels.
Licensure Intermediate Care. *Beds* 98. *Certified* Medicaid.

Ownership Proprietary.

BLOOMINGDALE

Applewood Manor Convalescent Center*
275 Army Trail Rd, Bloomingdale, IL, 60108
(312) 893-9616
Admin Carol L Terrill.
Licensure Skilled Care. *Beds* 207. *Certified* Medicaid; Medicare.
Ownership Proprietary.

Bloomingdale Pavilion*
311 Edgewater Dr, Bloomingdale, IL, 60108
(312) 894-7400
Admin Linda L Pusateri.
Licensure Skilled Care. *Beds* 215. *Certified* Medicaid; Medicare.
Ownership Proprietary.

Elaine Boyd Creche Children's Nursing Home
267 E Lake St, Bloomingdale, IL, 60108 (312)
529-3350
Admin Chermaine Bell. *Medical Dir/Dir of Nursing* Oscar Novick MD.
Licensure Skilled Care. *Beds* 99. *Certified* Medicaid.
Ownership Proprietary.
Admissions Requirements Minimum age Birth; Medical examination.
Staff Physicians 1 (ft); RNs 4 (ft), 2 (pt); LPNs 4 (ft), 2 (pt); Nurses aides 50 (ft), 6 (pt); Physical therapists 1 (pt); Recreational therapists 1 (ft); Occupational therapists 1 (ft); Speech therapists 1 (ft); Activities coordinators 1 (ft); Dietitians 1 (ft), 1 (pt); Dentists 1 (pt); Audiologists 1 (ft).
Facilities Dining room; Physical therapy room; Activities room; Laundry room; Schoolrooms.
Activities Arts and Crafts; Games; Movies; Shopping trips; Special Olympics; Musical groups; Music aerobics.
Description The Creche is a multidisciplinary home offering education, residence, habilitative programing, water therapy, music therapy, all in a skilled care atmosphere for nurturing fragile lives. All staff members are certified or licensed to plan special highly individualized programs for the severely/profoundly retarded youth.

Marklund Home
164 S Prairie Ave, Bloomingdale, IL, 60108
(312) 529-2871
Admin Patricia Pearce. *Medical Dir/Dir of Nursing* Val Moller.
Licensure Skilled Care. *Beds* 98. *Certified* Medicaid; Medicare.
Ownership Nonprofit.
Admissions Requirements Medical examination; Physician's request.
Staff Physicians 1 (ft); RNs 4 (ft), 10 (pt); LPNs 1 (ft), 3 (pt); Orderlies 1 (ft); Nurses aides 30 (ft), 34 (pt); Physical therapists 1 (ft); Recreational therapists 1 (ft); Occupational therapists 1 (ft); Speech therapists 1 (ft); Activities coordinators 1 (pt); Dietitians 1 (pt); Dentists 2 (pt).
Facilities Dining room; Physical therapy room; Activities room; Crafts room; Laundry room; Library.
Activities Arts and Crafts; Games; Prayer groups; Movies; Shopping trips.
Description Facility features respite care, a spe-

cial education school, a park for the handicapped, swimming in outdoor pool, and recreational therapy.

BLOOMINGTON

Bloomington Manor
1925 S Main, Bloomington, IL, 61701 (309)
829-4348
Admin Mary W Leung. *Medical Dir/Dir of Nursing* Dr Ravi Kottoor.
Licensure Intermediate Care. *Beds* 77. *Certified* Medicaid.
Ownership Proprietary.
Admissions Requirements Medical examination.
Staff RNs 1 (ft); LPNs 3 (ft), 3 (pt); Orderlies 1 (pt); Nurses aides 6 (ft), 5 (pt); Physical therapists 1 (pt); Reality therapists 1 (ft), 1 (pt); Recreational therapists 1 (pt); Activities coordinators 1 (ft); Dietitians 1 (pt).
Facilities Dining room; Physical therapy room; Activities room; Crafts room; Laundry room; Barber/Beauty shop; Library.
Activities Arts and Crafts; Cards; Games; Reading groups; Prayer groups; Movies; Shopping trips; Dances/Social or cultural gatherings.
Description Horticultural therapy program is enhanced by a solarium and outdoor garden plots; pet therapy program; weaving program.

Bloomington Nursing and Rehabilitation Center
1509 N Calhoun St, Bloomington, IL, 61701
(309) 827-6046
Admin Thelma Wesle. *Medical Dir/Dir of Nursing* Dr Virgil Short.
Licensure Skilled Care. *Beds* 123.
Ownership Proprietary.
Admissions Requirements Minimum age 50; Medical examination.
Staff RNs 4 (ft), 1 (pt); LPNs 6 (ft), 3 (pt); Orderlies 6 (ft), 2 (pt); Nurses aides 30 (ft), 10 (pt); Physical therapists 1 (pt); Recreational therapists 1 (ft), 2 (pt); Speech therapists 1 (pt); Activities coordinators 1 (ft); Dietitians 1 (pt); Dentists 1 (pt); Ophthalmologists 1 (pt); Podiatrists 1 (pt); Audiologists 1 (pt).
Facilities Dining room; Physical therapy room; Activities room; Crafts room; Laundry room; Barber/Beauty shop.
Activities Arts and Crafts; Cards; Games; Reading groups; Prayer groups; Movies; Shopping trips; Dances/Social or cultural gatherings.
Description Center is a one-story brick building with a large fenced yard and a patio. The staff members are caring people who work very hard to make the facility a comfortable nursing center with a reputation for good patient care.

Hage House*
806 Four Seasons Rd, Bloomington, IL, 61701
(309) 827-6272
Admin Richard Reimers.
Licensure Intermediate Care. *Beds* 15.
Ownership Proprietary.

Heritage Manor Inc
700 E Walnut, Bloomington, IL, 61701 (309)
827-8004
Admin Jean Dulin. *Medical Dir/Dir of Nursing* Seymour R Goldberg MD.

Licensure Skilled Care; Intermediate Care.
Beds 110. *Certified* Medicaid; Medicare.
Ownership Proprietary.
Admissions Requirements Medical examination; Physician's request.
Staff Physicians 1 (pt); RNs 7 (ft), 2 (pt); LPNs 5 (ft), 7 (pt); Orderlies 2 (ft); Nurses aides 56 (ft); Physical therapists 1 (pt); Occupational therapists 1 (pt); Speech therapists 1 (pt); Activities coordinators 1 (ft), 2 (pt); Dietitians 1 (ft); Dentists 1 (pt); Podiatrists 1 (pt); Audiologists 1 (pt).
Facilities Dining room; Physical therapy room; Activities room; Chapel; Crafts room; Laundry room; Barber/Beauty shop; Library.
Activities Arts and Crafts; Cards; Games; Reading groups; Prayer groups; Movies; Shopping trips; Dances/Social or cultural gatherings.
Description Facility has volunteer coordinator with 200 plus volunteers; foster grandparent program; many large social parties; a Carribean cruise; county fair; cookouts; lots of involvement with families and community; best quality care is given.

Westminster Village Inc
2025 E Lincoln St, Bloomington, IL, 61701
(309) 663-6474
Admin Martha K Butler. *Medical Dir/Dir of Nursing* Dr James E Swanson.
Licensure Skilled Care; Intermediate Care.
Beds SNF 39; ICF 39.
Ownership Nonprofit.
Admissions Requirements Minimum age 18; Medical examination; Physician's request.
Staff RNs 2 (ft), 7 (pt); LPNs 5 (ft), 1 (pt); Orderlies 1 (ft); Nurses aides 20 (ft), 21 (pt); Activities coordinators 1 (ft); Dietitians 1 (ft).
Facilities Dining room; Physical therapy room; Activities room; Barber/Beauty shop; Library.
Activities Arts and Crafts; Cards; Games; Reading groups; Prayer groups; Movies; Shopping trips; Dances/Social or cultural gatherings.

BLUE ISLAND

Blue Island Nursing Home*
2427 W 127th St, Blue Island, IL, 60406 (312)
389-7799
Admin John A Heuser.
Licensure Intermediate Care. *Beds* 30. *Certified* Medicaid.
Ownership Proprietary.

BOURBONNAIS

Bourbonnais Terrace
133 Mohawk Dr, Bourbonnais, IL, 60914 (815)
937-4790
Admin Henrietta Chamness. *Medical Dir/Dir of Nursing* Samuel DeGuzman.
Licensure Skilled Care; Intermediate Care.
Beds SNF 100; ICF 97. *Certified* Medicaid.
Ownership Proprietary.
Admissions Requirements Minimum age 21.
Staff RNs 6 (ft); LPNs 7 (ft).
Facilities Dining room; Physical therapy room; Activities room; Laundry room; Barber/Beauty shop.

Activities Games; Prayer groups; Movies; Dances/Social or cultural gatherings; Community programs.

Kankakee Terrace Nursing Home
100 Belle Aire, Bourbonnais, IL, 60914 (815) 939-0910
Admin Barbara H Daum. *Medical Dir/Dir of Nursing* Dr Samuel DeGuzman.
Licensure Intermediate Care. *Beds* 126.
Ownership Proprietary.
Staff RNs 4 (pt); LPNs 2 (ft), 2 (pt); Nurses aides 13 (ft), 9 (pt); Activities coordinators 3 (ft), 1 (pt); Dietitians 1 (ft).
Facilities Dining room; Activities room; Laundry room; Barber/Beauty shop.
Activities Arts and Crafts; Cards; Games; Movies; Shopping trips; Dances/Social or cultural gatherings.
Description Facility features quiet residential area, pleasant home-like atmosphere, 24-hour nursing, restorative nursing program, semi-private rooms, recreational program, and short- and long-term care.

Our Lady of Victory Nursing Home
20 Briarcliff Ln, Bourbonnais, IL, 60914 (815) 939-3638
Admin Sr Magdalene Marcotte. *Medical Dir-/Dir of Nursing* Dr J M Dave.
Licensure Intermediate Care. *Beds* 81. *Certified* Medicaid.
Ownership Proprietary.
Admissions Requirements Medical examination; Physician's request.
Staff RNs 1 (ft), 3 (pt); LPNs 5 (ft), 3 (pt); Orderlies 1 (ft); Nurses aides 19 (ft), 8 (pt); Physical therapists 2 (ft), 1 (pt); Activities coordinators 1 (ft).
Affiliation Roman Catholic
Facilities Dining room; Physical therapy room; Activities room; Chapel; Crafts room; Laundry room; Library.
Activities Arts and Crafts; Cards; Games; Reading groups; Prayer groups; Movies; Shopping trips; Dances/Social or cultural gatherings.

BRADLEY

Bradley Royale Healthcare Centre*
650 Kinzie, Bradley, IL, 60915 (815) 933-1666
Admin Agnes M Streicher.
Licensure Skilled Care; Intermediate Care.
Beds SNF 48; ICF 50.
Ownership Proprietary.

BREESE

Breese Nursing Home
N 1st St E, Breese, IL, 62230 (618) 526-4521
Admin Joyce Haege. *Medical Dir/Dir of Nursing* Dr R J Sosa.
Licensure Skilled Care. *Beds* 123. *Certified* Medicaid; Medicare.
Ownership Proprietary.
Admissions Requirements Minimum age 18; Medical examination; Physician's request.
Staff Physicians 10 (pt); RNs 3 (ft), 2 (pt); LPNs 4 (ft), 3 (pt); Orderlies 1 (ft); Nurses aides 21 (ft), 20 (pt); Physical therapists 1 (pt); Speech therapists 1 (pt); Activities coordinators 1 (pt);

Dietitians 1 (pt); Dentists 2 (pt); Ophthalmologists 1 (pt); Audiologists 1 (pt).
Facilities Dining room; Physical therapy room; Activities room; Chapel; Crafts room; Laundry room; Barber/Beauty shop; Social services.
Activities Arts and Crafts; Cards; Games; Reading groups; Prayer groups; Movies; Shopping trips; Dances/Social or cultural gatherings.

BRIDGEPORT

Bridgeport Healthcare Center*
900 E Corporation St, Bridgeport, IL, 62417 (618) 945-2091
Admin Gwenda J Zellars.
Licensure Intermediate Care. *Beds* 94. *Certified* Medicare.
Ownership Proprietary.

BRIDGEVIEW

Bridgeview Convalescent Center
8100 S Harlem Ave, Bridgeview, IL, 60453 (312) 594-5440
Admin Lester E Okun. *Medical Dir/Dir of Nursing* Dr P Punjabi.
Licensure Skilled Care; Intermediate Care.
Beds SNF 101; ICF 51. *Certified* Medicaid; Medicare.
Ownership Proprietary.
Staff Physicians 6 (pt); RNs 8 (ft), 4 (pt); LPNs 6 (ft), 10 (pt); Orderlies 6 (ft); Nurses aides 77 (ft); Physical therapists 2 (pt); Reality therapists 1 (pt); Recreational therapists 1 (pt); Occupational therapists 1 (pt); Speech therapists 1 (pt); Activities coordinators 1 (ft); Dietitians 1 (pt); Dentists 1 (pt); Ophthalmologists 1 (pt); Podiatrists 1 (pt); Audiologists 1 (pt).
Facilities Dining room; Physical therapy room; Activities room; Crafts room; Laundry room; Barber/Beauty shop.
Activities Arts and Crafts; Cards; Games; Reading groups; Prayer groups; Movies; Shopping trips; Dances/Social or cultural gatherings.

BROOKFIELD

British Home
31st St and McCormick, Brookfield, IL, 60513 (312) 485-0135
Admin Robert Lytle. *Medical Dir/Dir of Nursing* Dr Richard Dirkes.
Licensure Intermediate Care; Sheltered Care.
Beds ICF 26; Sheltered Care 64.
Ownership Nonprofit.
Admissions Requirements Minimum age 70.
Staff RNs 6 (ft); LPNs 2 (pt); Nurses aides 8 (ft), 5 (pt); Activities coordinators 2 (ft); Dietitians 1 (ft).
Facilities Dining room; Activities room; Crafts room; Barber/Beauty shop; Library.
Activities Arts and Crafts; Cards; Games; Reading groups; Prayer groups; Movies; Shopping trips.

BUNKER HILL

South Lawn Shelter Care
512 S Franklin, Bunker Hill, IL, 62014 (618) 585-4875

Admin Gary G Rull.
Licensure Sheltered Care. *Beds* Sheltered Care 50.
Ownership Proprietary.
Admissions Requirements Minimum age 18; Medical examination.
Staff Physicians 1 (pt); RNs 1 (pt); Nurses aides 4 (ft); Recreational therapists 1 (pt); Activities coordinators 1 (pt); Dietitians 1 (pt).
Facilities Dining room; Activities room; Laundry room; Barber/Beauty shop.
Activities Arts and Crafts; Cards; Games; Reading groups; Prayer groups; Shopping trips.

BURBANK

Brentwood Nursing and Rehabilitation Center
5432 W 87th St, Burbank, IL, 60459 (312) 423-1200
Admin John D Kirby.
Licensure Skilled Care. *Beds* 124. *Certified* Medicare.
Ownership Proprietary.
Staff RNs; LPNs; Orderlies; Nurses aides; Physical therapists; Occupational therapists; Speech therapists; Activities coordinators; Dietitians.
Facilities Dining room; Physical therapy room; Activities room; Crafts room; Laundry room; Barber/Beauty shop.
Activities Arts and Crafts; Cards; Games; Reading groups; Prayer groups; Movies.
Description Center offers high degree of skilled nursing services and occupational and physical therapy rehabilitation programs.

Parkside Gardens
5701 W 79th St, Burbank, IL, 60459 (312) 636-3850
Admin Robin LeMasters.
Licensure Intermediate Care. *Beds* 78. *Certified* Medicaid.
Ownership Proprietary.
Facilities Dining room; Physical therapy room; Activities room; Laundry room; Barber/Beauty shop.
Activities Arts and Crafts; Cards; Games; Reading groups; Prayer groups; Movies.

BYRON

Neighbors Nursing Home
PO Box 585, Byron, IL, 61010 (815) 234-2511
Admin Grant Bullock. *Medical Dir/Dir of Nursing* P John Seward MD.
Licensure Skilled Care. *Beds* SNF 99. *Certified* Medicaid; Medicare.
Ownership Proprietary.
Admissions Requirements Medical examination.
Staff RNs 5 (ft), 2 (pt); LPNs 3 (ft), 4 (pt); Nurses aides 33 (ft), 6 (pt); Speech therapists 1 (pt); Activities coordinators 1 (ft), 1 (pt).
Facilities Dining room; Physical therapy room; Activities room; Laundry room; Barber/Beauty shop.
Activities Arts and Crafts; Cards; Games; Reading groups; Prayer groups; Movies; Shopping trips; Dances/Social or cultural gatherings.
Description Home offers a home atmosphere with care provided by people who truly care;

new primary care wing offers the latest in hi-tech treatment with nurses trained for these specific functions.

CAIRO

Greenbriar Manor
1100 Cedar St, Cairo, IL, 62914 (618) 734-1816
Admin Barbara Connell. *Medical Dir/Dir of Nursing* Gemo Wong MD.
Licensure Intermediate Care. *Beds* 64. *Certified* Medicaid.
Ownership Proprietary.
Admissions Requirements Minimum age 18; Medical examination.
Staff RNs 1 (ft); LPNs 5 (ft), 1 (pt); Orderlies 2 (ft); Nurses aides 17 (ft); Speech therapists; Activities coordinators; Dietitians.
Facilities Dining room; Activities room; Crafts room; Laundry room; Barber/Beauty shop.
Activities Arts and Crafts; Cards; Games; Reading groups; Prayer groups; Movies; Shopping trips; Dances/Social or cultural gatherings.

CAMP POINT

Grandview Manor
205 E Spring, Camp Point, IL, 62320 (217) 593-7734
Admin Larry E Ford. *Medical Dir/Dir of Nursing* Dr Frank Chamberlin.
Licensure Skilled Care; Intermediate Care. *Beds* 124. *Certified* Medicaid.
Ownership Proprietary.
Admissions Requirements Minimum age 21; Medical examination; Physician's request.
Staff RNs 3 (ft); LPNs 4 (ft), 5 (pt); Nurses aides 25 (ft), 4 (pt); Activities coordinators 2 (ft).
Facilities Dining room; Physical therapy room; Activities room; Laundry room; Barber/Beauty shop.
Activities Arts and Crafts; Cards; Games; Reading groups; Prayer groups; Movies; Shopping trips.

CANTON

Nursing Center of Canton
1675 E Ash St, Canton, IL, 61520 (309) 647-5631
Admin Shirley A Keithley. *Medical Dir/Dir of Nursing* Frantz Straub MD.
Licensure Skilled Care; Intermediate Care; Pediatric Care. *Beds* 190. *Certified* Medicaid; Medicare.
Ownership Proprietary.
Admissions Requirements Medical examination; Physician's request.
Staff RNs 10 (ft); LPNs 13 (ft); Orderlies 3 (ft); Nurses aides 90 (ft); Physical therapists 1 (pt); Speech therapists 1 (pt); Activities coordinators 3 (ft); Dietitians 1 (pt); Dentists 2 (pt); Ophthalmologists 1 (pt); Podiatrists 1 (pt); Audiologists 1 (pt).
Facilities Dining room; Physical therapy room; Activities room; Chapel; Crafts room; Laundry room; Barber/Beauty shop.
Activities Arts and Crafts; Cards; Games;

Reading groups; Prayer groups; Movies; Shopping trips; Dances/Social or cultural gatherings.
Description VA approved.

Sunset Nursing Home
129 S 1st, Canton, IL, 61520 (309) 647-4327
Admin Ronald P Wroblewski. *Medical Dir/Dir of Nursing* Dr Linda Forrestier.
Licensure Intermediate Care. *Beds* 98. *Certified* Medicaid.
Ownership Proprietary.
Admissions Requirements Medical examination.
Staff RNs 1 (pt); LPNs 4 (ft), 3 (pt); Nurses aides 13 (ft), 7 (pt); Physical therapists 2 (pt); Recreational therapists 1 (ft), 1 (pt).
Facilities Dining room; Physical therapy room; Activities room; Crafts room; Laundry room; Barber/Beauty shop.
Activities Arts and Crafts; Cards; Games; Reading groups; Prayer groups; Movies; Shopping trips; Dances/Social or cultural gatherings.
Description Facility is 2-story intermediate level building which was recently remodeled inside. Care offered is based on the potential for rehabilitation and reentry into community living.

CARBONDALE

Carbondale Manor*
500 Lewis Ln, Carbondale, IL, 62901 (618) 529-5355
Admin Bruce C Janssen.
Licensure Skilled Care; Intermediate Care. *Beds* SNF 90; ICF 119.
Ownership Proprietary.

Styrest Nursing Home*
Rt 4, Tower Rd, Carbondale, IL, 62901 (618) 549-3355
Admin Betty S Vick.
Licensure Skilled Care; Sheltered Care. *Beds* SNF 132; Sheltered Care 130. *Certified* Medicaid; Medicare.
Ownership Proprietary.

CARLINVILLE

Barry Care Center of Carlinville*
1200 University Ave, Carlinville, IL, 62626 (217) 854-2230
Admin Mary Owens.
Licensure Skilled Care. *Beds* 91.
Ownership Proprietary.

Doral Country Manor
RR 3, Carlinville, IL, 62626 (217) 854-4491
Admin Kathryn W Brockmiller.
Licensure Intermediate Care. *Beds* 71. *Certified* Medicaid.
Ownership Proprietary.
Admissions Requirements Minimum age 18; Medical examination.
Staff Physicians 2 (pt); RNs 1 (ft); LPNs 3 (ft), 3 (pt); Orderlies 1 (ft), 2 (pt); Nurses aides 11 (ft), 9 (pt); Physical therapists 1 (pt); Recreational therapists 1 (pt); Occupational therapists 1 (pt); Speech therapists 1 (pt); Activities coordinators 1 (pt); Dietitians 1 (pt); Dentists 1 (pt); Podiatrists 1 (pt); Audiologists 1 (pt).

Facilities Dining room; Physical therapy room; Activities room; Chapel; Crafts room; Laundry room; Barber/Beauty shop.
Activities Arts and Crafts; Games; Reading groups; Prayer groups; Movies; Shopping trips; Dances/Social or cultural gatherings; Orientation.

Friendship Home*
826 N High St, Carlinville, IL, 62626 (217) 854-9606
Admin Mary N Griffith.
Licensure Intermediate Care. *Beds* 49. *Certified* Medicaid.
Ownership Proprietary.

Weatherford Sunshine Manor*
318 Buchanan St, Carlinville, IL, 62626 (217) 854-2511
Admin J T Weatherford.
Licensure Skilled Care. *Beds* 98. *Certified* Medicaid.
Ownership Proprietary.

CARLYLE

Carlyle Healthcare Center Inc*
501 Clinton St, Carlyle, IL, 62231 (618) 594-3112
Admin Sr M Peter Altgilbers.
Licensure Intermediate Care. *Beds* 124. *Certified* Medicaid.
Ownership Proprietary.

CARMI

Wabash Christian Retirement Home*
College Blvd, Carmi, IL, 62821 (618) 382-4644
Admin John R Nelson.
Licensure Skilled Care. *Beds* 160. *Certified* Medicaid.
Ownership Nonprofit.

White County Nursing Home
Rt 3, Carmi, IL, 62821 (618) 382-7116
Admin Faye Frashie R Driggers.
Licensure Intermediate Care. *Beds* 72. *Certified* Medicaid.
Ownership Public.

CARRIER MILLS

Carrier Mills Nursing Home
US Rt 45 E, Carrier Mills, IL, 62917 (618) 994-2232
Admin George L Storms. *Medical Dir/Dir of Nursing* Grover G Sloan MD.
Licensure Skilled Care. *Beds* 68. *Certified* Medicaid; Medicare.
Ownership Proprietary.
Admissions Requirements Medical examination; Physician's request.
Staff Physicians 6 (pt); RNs 2 (ft), 1 (pt); LPNs 6 (ft), 3 (pt); Nurses aides 17 (ft), 3 (pt); Physical therapists 1 (ft), 1 (pt); Recreational therapists 1 (pt); Speech therapists 1 (pt); Activities coordinators 1 (ft), 1 (pt); Dietitians 1 (pt); Dentists 1 (pt); Ophthalmologists 1 (pt); Podiatrists 1 (pt); Audiologists 1 (pt).
Facilities Dining room; Physical therapy room;

Activities room; Crafts room; Laundry room; Barber/Beauty shop.
Activities Arts and Crafts; Cards; Games; Reading groups; Prayer groups; Movies; Shopping trips; Dances/Social or cultural gatherings.
Description Home has the best overall staff in southern Illinois. Outstanding programs in physical therpay and acute skilled care.

CARROLLTON

Mount Gilead Shelter Care Home
Rt 3, Box 53, Carrollton, IL, 62016 (217) 942-5362
Admin Alfreda Steinacher.
Licensure Sheltered Care. *Beds* Sheltered Care 28.
Ownership Proprietary.
Admissions Requirements Minimum age 19; Medical examination; Physician's request.
Facilities Dining room; Activities room.
Activities Arts and Crafts; Cards; Games; Prayer groups; Movies; Shopping trips; Dances/Social or cultural gatherings.
Description Facility is a country home with good country food, lots of tender loving care, and supervision 24-hours a day from local owners who care.

Reisch Memorial Nursing Home*
800 School St, Carrollton, IL, 62016 (217) 942-6946
Admin Thomas J McKula.
Licensure Skilled Care. *Beds* 40. *Certified* Medicaid.
Ownership Nonprofit.

CARTHAGE

Hancock County Nursing Home
S Adams St, Carthage, IL, 62321 (217) 357-3131
Admin Steven T Moburg.
Licensure Skilled Care; Intermediate Care.
Beds SNF 14; ICF 36. *Certified* Medicaid.
Ownership Nonprofit.
Admissions Requirements Physician's request.
Staff RNs 1 (ft), 2 (pt); LPNs 2 (ft), 2 (pt); Nurses aides 18 (ft), 4 (pt); Physical therapists 1 (pt); Speech therapists 1 (pt); Activities coordinators 1 (ft), 1 (pt); Dietitians 1 (pt).
Facilities Dining room; Physical therapy room; Activities room; Chapel; Crafts room; Laundry room; Barber/Beauty shop.
Activities Arts and Crafts; Cards; Games; Reading groups; Prayer groups; Movies; Dances/Social or cultural gatherings.

CASEY

Birchwood
100 NE 15th St, Casey, IL, 62420 (217) 932-5217
Admin Patricia J Bellinger.
Licensure Intermediate Care. *Beds* 73. *Certified* Medicaid.
Ownership Proprietary.
Staff RNs 1 (ft), 3 (pt); LPNs 1 (ft), 8 (pt); Nurses aides 4 (ft), 13 (pt); Activities coordinators 1 (ft), 1 (pt).

Facilities Dining room; Activities room; Crafts room; Laundry room; Barber/Beauty shop.
Activities Arts and Crafts; Cards; Games; Reading groups; Movies; Shopping trips; Dances/Social or cultural gatherings.
Description Birchwood is dedicated to the primary belief that the residents need a total care program—social, emotional, and spiritual as well as physical assistance is provided. Goals are set for each resident and a care plan is developed based on a medical estimate of his/her potential for physical and mental restoration. The plan is written as a Personal Care Plan and changes as the resident's condition changes. The plan is directed toward the resident's highest degree of functioning.

Casey Nursing Home
410 NW 3rd, Casey, IL, 62420 (217) 932-4081
Admin David J Sauer.
Licensure Skilled Care. *Beds* 92. *Certified* Medicaid; Medicare.
Ownership Nonprofit.
Admissions Requirements Medical examination; Physician's request.
Staff Physicians 3 (pt); RNs 3 (ft), 4 (pt); LPNs 4 (ft), 3 (pt); Orderlies 3 (ft); Nurses aides 24 (ft), 16 (pt); Physical therapists 1 (pt); Reality therapists 1 (pt); Recreational therapists 1 (pt); Occupational therapists 1 (pt); Speech therapists 1 (pt); Activities coordinators 1 (ft); Dietitians 1 (pt); Dentists 1 (pt); Audiologists 1 (pt).
Facilities Dining room; Activities room; Chapel; Crafts room; Laundry room; Barber/Beauty shop.
Activities Arts and Crafts; Games; Reading groups; Prayer groups; Movies; Shopping trips.
Description Facility has organized and sponsored a senior olympics competition with 3 other nursing centers for the past 4 years.

CENTRALIA

Brookside Manor Inc
2000 W Broadway, Centralia, IL, 62801 (618) 532-2428
Admin Paula J Ross. *Medical Dir/Dir of Nursing* Dr M A Junidi.
Licensure Intermediate Care. *Beds* 49. *Certified* Medicaid.
Ownership Proprietary.
Admissions Requirements Minimum age 18; Medical examination.
Staff RNs 1 (ft), 1 (pt); LPNs 3 (ft), 3 (pt); Nurses aides 12 (ft), 4 (pt); Speech therapists 1 (pt); Activities coordinators 1 (ft); Dietitians 3 (ft), 1 (pt).
Facilities Dining room; Activities room; Laundry room.
Activities Arts and Crafts; Cards; Games; Reading groups; Prayer groups; Movies; Shopping trips; Dances/Social or cultural gatherings.

Centralia Care Center*
1411 Frazier, Centralia, IL, 62801 (618) 533-1369
Admin Harold L Prather.
Licensure Skilled Care; Intermediate Care.
Beds SNF 16; ICF 43. *Certified* Medicaid.
Ownership Proprietary.

Centralia Fireside House*
1030 E McCord St, Centralia, IL, 62801 (618) 532-1833
Admin Charles L Hutson.
Licensure Skilled Care; Intermediate Care.
Beds SNF 51; ICF 47. *Certified* Medicaid.
Ownership Proprietary.

Centralia Friendship House Inc
1000 E McCord, Centralia, IL, 62801 (618) 532-3642
Admin Kyle C Moore. *Medical Dir/Dir of Nursing* Dr Aziz Rahman.
Licensure Intermediate Care. *Beds* 94. *Certified* Medicaid.
Ownership Proprietary.
Admissions Requirements Minimum age 30; Physician's request.
Staff RNs 2 (ft), 3 (pt); LPNs 4 (ft), 4 (pt); Nurses aides 10 (ft), 12 (pt); Activities coordinators 1 (ft); Dietitians 1 (ft).
Facilities Dining room; Physical therapy room; Activities room; Chapel; Laundry room; Barber/Beauty shop.
Activities Arts and Crafts; Cards; Games; Prayer groups; Movies; Shopping trips; Dances/Social or cultural gatherings; Bus trips.
Description Residents and staff together are like one big happy family sharing their everyday thoughts and happiness.

CHAMPAIGN

Americana Healthcare Center
309 E Springfield Ave, Champaign, IL, 61820 (217) 352-5135
Admin Dorothy Mikucki. *Medical Dir/Dir of Nursing* Dr Robert Bosler.
Licensure Skilled Care. *Beds* 102. *Certified* Medicaid; Medicare.
Ownership Proprietary.
Admissions Requirements Medical examination; Physician's request.
Staff RNs 8 (ft), 2 (pt); LPNs 9 (ft); Orderlies 4 (ft); Nurses aides 27 (ft), 4 (pt); Physical therapists 1 (ft); Reality therapists 1 (ft); Recreational therapists 1 (ft); Occupational therapists 1 (pt); Speech therapists 1 (pt); Activities coordinators 1 (ft); Dietitians 1 (ft).
Facilities Dining room; Physical therapy room; Activities room; Barber/Beauty shop; Outdoor patio - enclosed.
Activities Arts and Crafts; Cards; Games; Reading groups; Prayer groups; Movies; Shopping trips; Dances/Social or cultural gatherings.
Description We are designed to provide long-term nursing care and short-term rehabilitative convalescent care. Our goal is to provide quality service by trained and experienced staff in a home-like atmosphere. We strive to furnish appropriate care that restores and preserves health while safeguarding our patients' fundamental dignity.

Champaign Childrens Home
109 Kenwood Rd, Champaign, IL, 61820 (217) 356-5164
Admin Ellen R Morris. *Medical Dir/Dir of Nursing* William Farris MD.
Licensure Skilled Care; Intermediate Care.
Beds 85. *Certified* Medicaid.
Ownership Proprietary.

Admissions Requirements Minimum age 0–22; Medical examination.
Staff RNs 4 (ft), 2 (pt); LPNs 4 (ft), 1 (pt); Nurses aides 60 (ft); Physical therapists 1 (pt); Recreational therapists 4 (pt); Occupational therapists 2 (pt); Speech therapists 1 (pt); Activities coordinators 1 (pt); Dietitians 1 (ft); Dentists 1 (pt); Special education teachers 16 (ft), 2 (pt).
Activities Arts and Crafts; Games; Movies; Shopping trips; Education program.
Description Program is specifically for severely and profoundly handicapped children in need of skilled nursing. Also 24-hour nursing care is offered as well as a state approved special education program in-house. Only nonambulatory patients accepted.

Garwood Home
1515 N Market St, Champaign, IL, 61820 (217) 352-1412
Admin Carol Edwards. *Medical Dir/Dir of Nursing* Robert Atkins MD.
Licensure Sheltered Care. *Beds* 34.
Ownership Nonprofit.
Admissions Requirements Medical examination.
Staff LPNs 1 (ft), 3 (pt); Nurses aides 4 (pt); Activities coordinators 1 (ft); Dietitians 1 (pt).
Facilities Dining room; Activities room; Crafts room; Laundry room; Barber/Beauty shop.
Activities Arts and Crafts; Cards; Games; Reading groups; Prayer groups; Movies; Shopping trips; Dances/Social or cultural gatherings.
Description Garwood Home is one of the few facilities that houses only shelter care residents. Built in the early 1900s, a beautiful older home provides the residents a gracious and dignified atmosphere.

Greenbrier Nursing Center Inc
1915 S Mattis Ave, Champaign, IL, 61821 (217) 352-0516
Admin Edward J Haas. *Medical Dir/Dir of Nursing* Charles R Shepardson MD.
Licensure Skilled Care; Intermediate Care. *Beds* 118. *Certified* Medicaid; Medicare.
Ownership Proprietary.
Admissions Requirements Minimum age 21; Medical examination; Physician's request.
Staff Physicians 1 (pt); RNs 5 (ft), 3 (pt); LPNs 2 (ft), 1 (pt); Orderlies 2 (ft); Nurses aides 26 (ft), 9 (pt); Physical therapists 1 (ft), 2 (pt); Reality therapists 1 (pt); Recreational therapists 1 (ft); Occupational therapists 1 (pt); Speech therapists 1 (pt); Activities coordinators 1 (ft), 1 (pt); Dietitians 1 (ft); Dentists; Ophthalmologists; Podiatrists; Audiologists.
Facilities Dining room; Physical therapy room; Activities room; Crafts room; Laundry room; Barber/Beauty shop; Library.
Activities Arts and Crafts; Cards; Games; Reading groups; Prayer groups; Movies; Shopping trips; Dances/Social or cultural gatherings.

Heritage House 2
1315 Curt Dr, Champaign, IL, 61821 (217) 352-5707
Admin Thomas Lovenstein. *Medical Dir/Dir of Nursing* Dr Yardy.
Licensure Intermediate Care. *Beds* 60. *Certified* Medicaid.
Ownership Proprietary.

Staff Physicians 15 (pt); RNs 7 (ft); LPNs 1 (ft); Nurses aides 9 (ft), 5 (pt); Physical therapists 1 (pt); Reality therapists 1 (pt); Recreational therapists 1 (pt); Speech therapists 1 (pt); Activities coordinators 1 (pt); Dietitians 1 (pt); Dentists 1 (pt); Podiatrists 1 (pt); Audiologists 1 (pt).
Facilities Dining room; Physical therapy room; Activities room; Crafts room; Laundry room; Barber/Beauty shop.
Activities Arts and Crafts; Cards; Games; Reading groups; Prayer groups; Movies; Shopping trips; Dances/Social or cultural gatherings.
Description Small intermediate/skilled nursing home specializing in personal care, offering a home-like atmosphere and tender loving care.

Opportunity House
1315-A Curt Dr, Champaign, IL, 61820
Admin Patrick J Finn. *Medical Dir/Dir of Nursing* Dr Paul Yardy.
Licensure Intermediate Care for Mentally Retarded. *Beds* 60. *Certified* Medicaid.
Ownership Proprietary.
Admissions Requirements Minimum age 21; Medical examination; Physician's request.
Staff RNs 2 (ft); LPNs 4 (ft); Nurses aides 16 (ft); Activities coordinators 1 (pt).
Facilities Dining room; Laundry room; Barber/Beauty shop.
Activities Arts and Crafts; Cards; Games; Reading groups; Prayer groups; Movies; Shopping trips; Dances/Social or cultural gatherings.
Description Facility offers specialized programs to meet the educational and behavioral needs of mentally retarded; staff is trained to specialize in this type of resident and has an excellent track record in dealing with residents who can prove to be a problem in traditional facilities.

CHARLESTON

Brooking Park Geriatric Center—Charleston*
716 18th St, Charleston, IL, 61920 (217) 345-7054
Admin Marshall Grant.
Licensure Skilled Care; Intermediate Care. *Beds* SNF 45; ICF 94. *Certified* Medicaid.
Ownership Proprietary.

Charleston Manor
415 18th St, Charleston, IL, 61920 (217) 345-7048
Admin Helen Eckhoff.
Licensure Intermediate Care. *Beds* 62. *Certified* Medicaid.
Ownership Proprietary.
Admissions Requirements Medical examination.
Staff Physicians 1 (pt); RNs 1 (pt); LPNs 7 (ft); Nurses aides 16 (ft); Physical therapists 1 (pt); Dietitians 1 (pt).
Facilities Dining room; Activities room; Crafts room; Laundry room; Barber/Beauty shop.
Activities Arts and Crafts; Cards; Games; Reading groups; Prayer groups 14F; Shopping trips; Dances/Social or cultural gatherings.
Description Seniorama Pageant and rock n' roll jamboree are sponsored for heart and cancer funds. The Pageant is similar to a Miss America Pageant and includes contestants from other nursing homes which also includes a tea.

Heritage House of Charleston
738 18th St, Charleston, IL, 61920
Admin Robert Zabka.
Licensure Intermediate Care for Mentally Retarded. *Beds* 89. *Certified* Medicaid.
Ownership Proprietary.
Admissions Requirements Minimum age 18.
Facilities Dining room; Physical therapy room; Activities room; Chapel; Crafts room; Laundry room.
Activities Arts and Crafts; Cards; Games; Reading groups; Prayer groups; Movies; Shopping trips; Dances/Social or cultural gatherings.

Hilltop Convalescent Center*
910 W Polk St, Charleston, IL, 61920 (217) 345-7066
Admin Larry J Trigg.
Licensure Skilled Care; Intermediate Care. *Beds* SNF 36; ICF 72. *Certified* Medicaid; Medicare.
Ownership Proprietary.

CHENOA

Meadows Mennonite Home
Rt 1, Chenoa, IL, 61726 (309) 747-2702
Admin Catherine Beery.
Licensure Intermediate Care; Sheltered Care. *Beds* ICF 109; Sheltered Care 33. *Certified* Medicaid.
Ownership Nonprofit.
Admissions Requirements Minimum age 60; Medical examination.
Staff Physicians 1 (pt); Physical therapists 1 (pt); Recreational therapists 3 (pt); Occupational therapists 1 (pt); Speech therapists 1 (pt); Activities coordinators 1 (ft); Dietitians 1 (ft); Podiatrists 1 (pt).
Affiliation Mennonite
Facilities Dining room; Physical therapy room; Activities room; Chapel; Barber/Beauty shop.
Activities Arts and Crafts; Cards; Games; Reading groups; Prayer groups; Movies; Shopping trips; Dances/Social or cultural gatherings.

CHESTER

Saint Anns Healthcare Center Inc
770 State St, Chester, IL, 62233 (618) 826-2314
Admin J Michael Greer. *Medical Dir/Dir of Nursing* Dr John R Beck.
Licensure Skilled Care; Intermediate Care. *Beds* 102. *Certified* Medicaid; Medicare.
Ownership Proprietary.
Admissions Requirements Minimum age 21; Medical examination.
Staff Physicians 1 (pt); RNs 2 (ft), 3 (pt); LPNs 8 (pt); Nurses aides 12 (ft), 5 (pt); Physical therapists 1 (ft), 1 (pt); Reality therapists 1 (pt); Speech therapists 1 (pt); Activities coordinators 1 (ft), 2 (pt); Dietitians 1 (ft), 1 (pt).
Facilities Dining room; Activities room; Chapel; Crafts room; Laundry room; Barber/Beauty shop.
Activities Arts and Crafts; Cards; Games; Reading groups; Prayer groups; Movies; Shopping trips; Dances/Social or cultural gatherings.

Three Springs Lodge*
Rt 1, Chester, IL, 62233 (618) 826-3210
Admin Kenneth Rowold.
Licensure Intermediate Care. *Beds* 85. *Certified* Medicaid.
Ownership Proprietary.

CHICAGO

All American Nursing Home
5448 N Broadway St, Chicago, IL, 60640 (312) 334-2244
Admin Howard L Wengrow. *Medical Dir/Dir of Nursing* Riccardo Benvenuto MD.
Licensure Skilled Care; Intermediate Care. *Beds* SNF 48; ICF 96. *Certified* Medicaid.
Ownership Proprietary.
Admissions Requirements Minimum age 23.
Staff Physicians 4 (pt); RNs 5 (ft); LPNs 12 (ft); Nurses aides 38 (ft); Physical therapists 1 (pt); Reality therapists 1 (pt); Recreational therapists 1 (pt); Occupational therapists 1 (pt); Speech therapists 1 (pt); Activities coordinators 1 (ft); Dietitians 1 (pt); Dentists 1 (pt); Podiatrists 1 (pt).
Facilities Physical therapy room; Activities room; Chapel; Crafts room; Laundry room; Barber/Beauty shop; Library.
Activities Arts and Crafts; Cards; Games; Reading groups; Prayer groups; Movies; Shopping trips; Dances/Social or cultural gatherings.

Allshore House*
2840 W Foster Ave, Chicago, IL, 60625 (312) 561-2040
Admin Pamela Solomon.
Licensure Intermediate Care. *Beds* 48. *Certified* Medicaid.
Ownership Proprietary.

Ambassador Nursing Center Inc
4900 N Bernard, Chicago, IL, 60625 (312) 583-7130
Admin Fred Cantz. *Medical Dir/Dir of Nursing* Thomas Duffy.
Licensure Skilled Care. *Beds* 190. *Certified* Medicaid; Medicare.
Ownership Proprietary.
Admissions Requirements Minimum age 65; Medical examination; Physician's request.
Staff Physicians 4 (ft); RNs 11 (ft); LPNs 2 (ft); Nurses aides 40 (ft); Physical therapists 1 (ft); Reality therapists 1 (ft); Recreational therapists 3 (ft); Occupational therapists 3 (ft); Speech therapists 1 (ft); Activities coordinators 1 (ft); Dietitians 1 (ft); Dentists 1 (ft); Ophthalmologists 1 (ft); Podiatrists 1 (ft).
Facilities Dining room; Physical therapy room; Activities room; Chapel; Barber/Beauty shop; Library.
Activities Arts and Crafts; Cards; Games; Reading groups; Prayer groups; Movies; Shopping trips; Dances/Social or cultural gatherings.
Description All diets offered, as well as colostomy care provided.

Approved Home Inc
909 W Wilson Ave, Chicago, IL, 60640
Admin Laurie Hertz. *Medical Dir/Dir of Nursing* Brahma Gupta MD.
Licensure Intermediate Care for Mentally Retarded. *Beds* 151. *Certified* Medicaid.

Ownership Proprietary.
Admissions Requirements Minimum age 18; Medical examination; Physician's request.
Staff Physicians; RNs; LPNs; Recreational therapists; Occupational therapists; Speech therapists; Activities coordinators; Dietitians; Dentists; Ophthalmologists; Podiatrists; Audiologists.
Facilities Dining room; Activities room; Crafts room; Laundry room.
Activities Arts and Crafts; Cards; Games; Reading groups; Prayer groups; Movies; Shopping trips; Dances/Social or cultural gatherings.
Description Facility is located on the north side of Chicago only a few blocks from Lake Michigan and the surrounding park area; adult, ambulatory, developmentally disabled population is served with intensive and comprehensive programing focusing on habilitative training and behavioral programing.

Auburn Park Club*
7748 S Emerald, Chicago, IL, 60620 (312) 874-0012
Admin Mary Barney.
Licensure Intermediate Care. *Beds* 34.
Ownership Nonprofit.

Augustana Center for Developmentally Disabled Children
7464 N Sheridan Rd, Chicago, IL, 60626 (312) 973-5200
Admin Thomas Sullivan. *Medical Dir/Dir of Nursing* Herman B Lander MD.
Licensure Skilled Care. *Beds* 150. *Certified* Medicaid; Medicare.
Ownership Nonprofit.
Admissions Requirements Minimum age Birth; Medical examination.
Staff Physicians 4 (pt); LPNs 19 (ft), 1 (pt); Nurses aides 77 (ft), 1 (pt); Physical therapists 1 (ft); Recreational therapists 1 (ft); Occupational therapists 1 (ft); Speech therapists 1 (ft).
Affiliation Lutheran
Facilities Dining room; Physical therapy room; Activities room; Chapel.
Activities Games; Prayer groups.
Description Augustanta Center seeks to aid children and adults with developmental disabilities achieve their fullest potential in the least restrictive environment. The Center provides a full continuum of care to ensure that all persons served have the opportunity to live as normal lives as possible.

Balmoral Nursing Centre Inc*
2055 W Balmoral Ave, Chicago, IL, 60625 (312) 561-8661
Admin Herman Katz.
Licensure Skilled Care. *Beds* 213. *Certified* Medicaid.
Ownership Proprietary.

Belhaven Inc
11404 S Bell Ave, Chicago, IL, 60643 (312) 779-6400
Admin Nancy Angstrom.
Licensure Skilled Care; Intermediate Care. *Beds* SNF 27; ICF 66. *Certified* Medicaid; Medicare.
Ownership Proprietary.

Belmont Nursing Home Inc*
1936 W Belmont Ave, Chicago, IL, 60657 (312) 252-7176
Admin Eileen Conway.
Licensure Intermediate Care. *Beds* 61. *Certified* Medicaid.
Ownership Proprietary.

Bethany Home
4950 N Ashland, Chicago, IL, 60640 (312) 271-9040
Admin James R Born. *Medical Dir/Dir of Nursing* Dr Joseph Marin.
Licensure Sheltered Care. *Beds* Sheltered Care 269.
Ownership Nonprofit.
Admissions Requirements Minimum age 65; Medical examination.
Staff LPNs 6 (ft); Recreational therapists 2 (ft), 1 (pt); Dietitians 1 (ft).
Affiliation Methodist
Facilities Dining room; Activities room; Chapel; Crafts room; Laundry room; Barber/Beauty shop; Library.
Activities Arts and Crafts; Cards; Games; Reading groups; Prayer groups; Movies; Shopping trips; Dances/Social or cultural gatherings.
Description Residential living in an independent setting is offered by a supportive staff who care and render care and assistance when and if needed.

Bethune Plaza Inc*
4537 S Drexel, Chicago, IL, 60653 (312) 268-8950
Admin Jerome E Morgan Jr.
Licensure Intermediate Care. *Beds* 276.
Ownership Proprietary.

Beverly Hills Convalescent Center Inc
9628-32 S Vincennes, Chicago, IL, 60643 (312) 239-6515
Admin Herbert M Herman.
Licensure Intermediate Care. *Beds* 60. *Certified* Medicaid.
Ownership Nonprofit.

Beverly Nursing Home*
8001 S Western Ave, Chicago, IL, 60620 (312) 436-6600
Admin Jeanne B Connor.
Licensure Skilled Care. *Beds* 328. *Certified* Medicaid.
Ownership Proprietary.

Bohemian Home for the Aged
5061 N Pulaski Rd, Chicago, IL, 60650 (312) 588-1220
Admin Peter Z Brandler. *Medical Dir/Dir of Nursing* Stephen DuBala MD.
Licensure Intermediate Care. *Beds* 218. *Certified* Medicaid.
Ownership Nonprofit.
Admissions Requirements Minimum age 75; Medical examination.
Staff Physicians 1 (pt); RNs 9 (ft), 7 (pt); LPNs 2 (ft); Orderlies 1 (ft); Nurses aides 32 (ft); Physical therapists 1 (pt); Recreational therapists 2 (ft); Occupational therapists 1 (ft); Dietitians 1 (ft), 1 (pt); Dentists 1 (pt); Ophthalmologists 1 (pt); Podiatrists 1 (pt).
Facilities Dining room; Physical therapy room; Activities room; Crafts room; Laundry room;

Barber/Beauty shop; Library.
Activities Arts and Crafts; Games; Reading groups; Prayer groups; Movies; Shopping trips; Dances/Social or cultural gatherings.

Brightview Manor Convalescent Home*
4538 N Beacon, Chicago, IL, 60640 (312) 275-7200
Admin Judith M Silverstein.
Licensure Skilled Care. *Beds* 141. *Certified* Medicaid; Medicare.
Ownership Proprietary.

Buckingham Pavilion
2625 W Touhy Ave, Chicago, IL, 60645 (312) 764-6850
Admin Margaret Stern. *Medical Dir/Dir of Nursing* Dr H Kurz.
Licensure Skilled Care; Intermediate Care.
Beds 247. *Certified* Medicaid; Medicare.
Ownership Proprietary.
Admissions Requirements Minimum age 18.
Staff Physicians; RNs; Orderlies; Nurses aides; Physical therapists; Reality therapists; Recreational therapists; Occupational therapists; Speech therapists; Activities coordinators; Dietitians; Dentists; Ophthalmologists; Podiatrists; Audiologists.
Affiliation Jewish
Facilities Dining room; Physical therapy room; Activities room; Chapel; Crafts room; Laundry room; Barber/Beauty shop; Library.
Activities Arts and Crafts; Cards; Games; Reading groups; Prayer groups; Movies; Dances/Social or cultural gatherings.
Description Modern facility with activity areas, shopping mall, chapel, and 24-hour skilled nursing care.

Burnham Terrace Care Center*
14500 S Manistee, Chicago, IL, 60633 (312) 862-1260
Admin Herman W Frey.
Licensure Skilled Care; Intermediate Care.
Beds SNF 103; ICF 206.
Ownership Proprietary.

California Gardens Nursing Center*
2829 S California Blvd, Chicago, IL, 60608 (312) 847-8061
Admin Morton J Gelberd.
Licensure Skilled Care. *Beds* 306. *Certified* Medicaid; Medicare.
Ownership Proprietary.

CAM Center for Human Development*
5130 W Jackson Blvd, Chicago, IL, 60644 (312) 626-3300
Admin Rosie L Shelton.
Licensure Skilled Care. *Beds* 225. *Certified* Medicaid.
Ownership Nonprofit.

Carci Hall*
1735 W Taylor, Chicago, IL, 60612 (312) 942-1004
Admin Janet Conner.
Licensure Intermediate Care for Mentally Retarded. *Beds* 35.
Ownership Nonprofit.

Carlton House
725 W Montrose Ave, Chicago, IL, 60613 (312) 929-1700
Admin Marvin Needle. *Medical Dir/Dir of Nursing* Dr David Edelberg.
Licensure Skilled Care; Intermediate Care.
Beds 244. *Certified* Medicaid.
Ownership Proprietary.
Staff RNs 34 (ft); LPNs 5 (ft); Orderlies 2 (ft); Nurses aides 54 (ft); Physical therapists 2 (pt); Recreational therapists 2 (ft); Activities coordinators 1 (ft); Dietitians 1 (ft).
Facilities Dining room; Physical therapy room; Activities room; Crafts room; Laundry room; Barber/Beauty shop.
Activities Arts and Crafts; Games; Reading groups; Prayer groups; Movies; Shopping trips; Dances/Social or cultural gatherings.

Carmen Manor*
1470 W Carmen, Chicago, IL, 60640 (312) 878-7000
Admin Estelle B Gutman.
Licensure Intermediate Care. *Beds* 113. *Certified* Medicaid.
Ownership Proprietary.

Casa Central Center*
1401 N California Ave, Chicago, IL, 60622 (312) 278-1902
Admin Edgar I Morales.
Licensure Skilled Care; Intermediate Care.
Beds SNF 47; ICF 49. *Certified* Medicaid.
Ownership Nonprofit.

Central Nursing*
2450 N Central Ave, Chicago, IL, 60639 (312) 889-1333
Admin Henry O Mermelstein.
Licensure Skilled Care. *Beds* 245. *Certified* Medicaid.
Ownership Proprietary.

Central Plaza Residential Home
321-27 N Central, Chicago, IL, 60644 (312) 626-2300
Admin Marvara H Mims. *Medical Dir/Dir of Nursing* David Edelberg.
Licensure Intermediate Care. *Beds* 290. *Certified* Medicaid.
Ownership Proprietary.
Admissions Requirements Minimum age 18.
Staff Physicians; RNs; LPNs; Nurses aides; Physical therapists; Recreational therapists; Occupational therapists; Activities coordinators; Dietitians; Dentists; Ophthalmologists; Podiatrists; Audiologists.
Facilities Dining room; Physical therapy room; Activities room; Crafts room; Laundry room; Library.
Activities Arts and Crafts; Cards; Games; Reading groups; Movies; Shopping trips; Dances/Social or cultural gatherings.
Description Discharge planning, a comprehensive care program for those needing more structure is provided. The discharge planning program offers an apartment for a trial independent living situation where one can see if she/he is ready.

Chevy Chase Nursing Center*
3400 S Indiana Ave, Chicago, IL, 60616 (312) 842-5000

Admin Robert Hartman.
Licensure Skilled Care. *Beds* 314. *Certified* Medicaid.
Ownership Proprietary.

The Church Home*
5445 S Ingleside Ave, Chicago, IL, 60615 (312) 643-6483
Admin Ernest W Williams.
Licensure Intermediate Care; Sheltered Care.
Beds ICF 14; Sheltered Care 76.
Ownership Nonprofit.

Clark Manor Convalescent Center*
7433 N Clark St, Chicago, IL, 60626 (312) 338-8778
Admin Robert A Leavitt.
Licensure Skilled Care. *Beds* 273. *Certified* Medicaid; Medicare.
Ownership Proprietary.

Clayton Residential Home
2026 N Clark St, Chicago, IL, 60614 (312) 549-1840
Admin Robert B Baily. *Medical Dir/Dir of Nursing* Lester Baranov MD.
Licensure Intermediate Care. *Beds* 252. *Certified* Medicaid.
Ownership Proprietary.
Admissions Requirements Minimum age 18; Medical examination.
Staff Physicians 3 (pt); LPNs 9 (ft); Nurses aides 20 (ft); Physical therapists 1 (ft), 1 (pt); Reality therapists 2 (ft); Recreational therapists 1 (ft); Occupational therapists 1 (ft); Activities coordinators 1 (ft); Dietitians 1 (ft); Podiatrists 1 (pt).
Facilities Dining room; Physical therapy room; Activities room; Crafts room; Laundry room.
Activities Arts and Crafts; Games; Reading groups; Movies; Shopping trips; Dances/Social or cultural gatherings.
Description Clayton Residential Home can accommodate clients having a history of emotional illness. A comprehensive psychosocial program is offered to residents, which includes linkages with community-based socialization, day hospital, and vocational settings.

Cojeunaze Nursing Center
3311 S Michigan Ave, Chicago, IL, 60640 (312) 326-5700
Admin Faye H Nazon. *Medical Dir/Dir of Nursing* Pancho Degand MD.
Licensure Skilled Care; Intermediate Care.
Beds SNF 74; ICF 126. *Certified* Medicaid.
Ownership Proprietary.
Admissions Requirements Minimum age 19.
Staff Physicians 4 (pt); RNs 2 (ft), 5 (pt); LPNs 9 (ft), 4 (pt); Orderlies 1 (ft), 3 (pt); Nurses aides 45 (ft), 3 (pt); Physical therapists; Reality therapists; Recreational therapists 1 (pt); Occupational therapists 1 (pt); Speech therapists 1 (pt); Activities coordinators 1 (ft), 2 (pt); Dietitians 1 (pt); Dentists 1 (pt); Ophthalmologists 1 (pt); Podiatrists 1 (pt); Audiologists 23 (ft), 12 (pt).
Facilities Dining room; Physical therapy room; Activities room; Crafts room; Laundry room; Barber/Beauty shop; Library.
Activities Arts and Crafts; Cards; Games; Reading groups; Prayer groups; Movies; Shopping trips; Dances/Social or cultural gatherings.
Description Facility features retirement and

convalescence dedicated to community "new approach for the 80s"; new building of steel, masonry, and concrete, beautiful decor; registered nurses and trained personnel; excellent food; special diets; spacious lounges and patio; full-time social worker.

Columbus Manor Residential Care Home
5107-21 W Jackson Blvd, Chicago, IL, 60644 (312) 378-5490
Admin Daniel J O'Brien.
Licensure Intermediate Care. *Beds* 189. *Certified* Medicaid.
Ownership Proprietary.

Commodore Inn Inc*
5547 N Kenmore, Chicago, IL, 60640 (312) 561-7040
Admin Arthur Primack.
Licensure Intermediate Care. *Beds* 174. *Certified* Medicaid.
Ownership Proprietary.

Congress Care Center*
901 S Austin Ave, Chicago, IL, 60644 (312) 287-5959
Admin Barry Gans.
Licensure Skilled Care; Intermediate Care.
Beds SNF 70; ICF 70.
Ownership Proprietary.

Continental Care Center Inc
5336 N Western Ave, Chicago, IL, 60625 (312) 271-5600
Admin E Joseph Steinfeld. *Medical Dir/Dir of Nursing* Dr Abdul Sattar.
Licensure Skilled Care. *Beds* 208. *Certified* Medicaid.
Ownership Proprietary.
Admissions Requirements Minimum age 65.
Staff Physicians 38 (pt); RNs 13 (ft), 8 (pt); LPNs 3 (ft); Nurses aides 47 (ft); Activities coordinators 1 (ft).
Facilities Dining room; Physical therapy room; Activities room; Crafts room; Laundry room; Barber/Beauty shop; Library.
Activities Arts and Crafts; Cards; Games; Movies; Dances/Social or cultural gatherings; Current events.
Description Center is a skilled facility, mainly geriatric. Thrust is rehabilitation dedicated to upgrading and maintaining a resident's level of functioning when possible.

Convalescent Home of the First Church of Deliverance
4314 S Wabash Ave, Chicago, IL, 60653 (312) 538-8300
Admin Anna L Owens. *Medical Dir/Dir of Nursing* Carroll E Smith MD.
Licensure Skilled Care; Intermediate Care.
Beds SNF 143; ICF 56. *Certified* Medicaid.
Ownership Nonprofit.
Admissions Requirements Minimum age 21.
Staff Physicians 5 (pt); RNs 2 (ft); LPNs 16 (ft), 6 (pt); Orderlies 6 (ft), 2 (pt); Nurses aides 50 (ft), 3 (pt); Reality therapists 1 (pt); Activities coordinators 2 (ft); Dietitians 1 (ft), 1 (pt); Dentists 1 (pt); Ophthalmologists 1 (pt); Podiatrists 1 (pt).
Facilities Dining room; Physical therapy room; Activities room; Chapel; Crafts room; Laundry room; Barber/Beauty shop; Library.

Activities Arts and Crafts; Cards; Games; Reading groups; Prayer groups; Movies; Shopping trips; Dances/Social or cultural gatherings.

Covenant Home*
2725 W Foster Ave, Chicago, IL, 60625 (312) 878-8200
Admin H Thomas Hershberger.
Licensure Intermediate Care; Sheltered Care.
Beds ICF 52; Sheltered Care 105. *Certified* Medicaid.
Ownership Nonprofit.

Deauville Healthcare Center
7445 N Sheridan Rd, Chicago, IL, 60626 (312) 338-3300
Admin Mark Segal. *Medical Dir/Dir of Nursing* Dr Paul Vega.
Licensure Intermediate Care. *Beds* 149. *Certified* Medicaid.
Ownership Proprietary.
Admissions Requirements Minimum age 35; Medical examination; Physician's request.
Staff Physicians 4 (ft); RNs 3 (ft); LPNs 5 (ft); Orderlies 2 (ft); Nurses aides 25 (ft), 5 (pt); Physical therapists 1 (ft); Recreational therapists 1 (ft); Occupational therapists 1 (ft); Speech therapists 1 (ft); Activities coordinators 1 (ft); Dietitians 1 (ft); Dentists 1 (pt); Ophthalmologists 1 (pt); Podiatrists 1 (pt); Audiologists 1 (pt).
Facilities Dining room; Physical therapy room; Activities room; Crafts room; Laundry room; Barber/Beauty shop.
Activities Arts and Crafts; Cards; Games; Reading groups; Prayer groups; Movies; Shopping trips; Dances/Social or cultural gatherings.

Deborah House*
7428 N Rogers, Chicago, IL, 60626 (312) 761-0395
Admin William J Smith.
Licensure Intermediate Care. *Beds* 18.
Ownership Nonprofit.

Drexel Home Inc
6140 S Drexel Ave, Chicago, IL, 60637 (312) 643-2384
Admin Bernard S Pomerantz.
Licensure Skilled Care; Intermediate Care.
Beds SNF 25; ICF 203. *Certified* Medicaid; Medicare.
Ownership Proprietary.

Edgewater Nursing and Geriatric Center
5838 N Sheridan Rd, Chicago, IL, 60660 (312) 769-2230
Admin Steven Erenberg. *Medical Dir/Dir of Nursing* Solomon Dayan MD.
Licensure Skilled Care; Intermediate Care.
Beds SNF 61; ICF 127. *Certified* Medicaid; Medicare.
Ownership Proprietary.
Admissions Requirements Minimum age 18; Medical examination; Physician's request.
Staff RNs 14 (ft); LPNs 3 (ft); Nurses aides 28 (ft); Reality therapists 3 (ft); Recreational therapists 4 (ft); Activities coordinators 2 (ft).
Facilities Dining room; Physical therapy room; Activities room; Chapel; Crafts room; Laundry room; Barber/Beauty shop; Library; Examination room.

Activities Arts and Crafts; Cards; Games; Reading groups; Prayer groups; Movies; Shopping trips; Dances/Social or cultural gatherings.

Elston Home Inc*
4340 N Keystone, Chicago, IL, 60641 (312) 545-8700
Admin Steven Schayer.
Licensure Skilled Care. *Beds* 116. *Certified* Medicaid; Medicare.
Ownership Proprietary.

Fellowship House Inc
2601 N California, Chicago, IL, 60647 (312) 278-5300
Admin Alan M Squire.
Licensure Sheltered Care. *Beds* Sheltered Care 37.
Ownership Proprietary.
Admissions Requirements Minimum age 18; Medical examination.
Staff Recreational therapists; Activities coordinators; Dietitians.
Facilities Dining room; Laundry room; TV room.
Activities Arts and Crafts; Cards; Games.
Description The Fellowship House is aware of the need to supply the resident with quality basic care. Features a courteous staff 24 hours a day, spotlessly clean rooms, comfortable beds, 3 balanced meals served cafeteria-style, and activity program.

Garden View Home Inc
6450 N Ridge Ave, Chicago, IL, 60626 (312) 743-8700
Admin Howard D Geller. *Medical Dir/Dir of Nursing* A Sattar.
Licensure Skilled Care; Intermediate Care.
Beds SNF 110; ICF 26. *Certified* Medicaid.
Ownership Proprietary.
Staff Physicians; RNs; LPNs; Orderlies; Nurses aides; Physical therapists; Reality therapists; Recreational therapists; Occupational therapists; Speech therapists; Activities coordinators; Dietitians; Dentists; Ophthalmologists; Podiatrists; Audiologists.
Facilities Dining room; Physical therapy room; Activities room; Crafts room; Laundry room; Barber/Beauty shop; Library.
Activities Arts and Crafts; Cards; Games; Reading groups; Prayer groups; Movies; Shopping trips; Dances/Social or cultural gatherings.
Description VA approved.

Gracell Terrace Inc*
6410 S Kenwood Ave, Chicago, IL, 60637 (312) 752-8600
Admin Ida Smith.
Licensure Sheltered Care. *Beds* Sheltered Care 150.
Ownership Proprietary.

Grasmere Resident Home Inc
4621 N Sheridan Rd, Chicago, IL, 60640 (312) 334-6601
Admin Linda Peterson. *Medical Dir/Dir of Nursing* Dr David Edelberg.
Licensure Intermediate Care. *Beds* 216. *Certified* Medicaid.
Ownership Proprietary.
Admissions Requirements Minimum age 18.
Staff Physicians 6 (pt); RNs 1 (ft); LPNs 4 (ft),

4 (pt); Orderlies 5 (ft); Nurses aides 3 (ft); Occupational therapists 1 (pt); Activities coordinators 2 (ft); Dietitians 1 (pt).
Facilities Dining room; Activities room; Crafts room; Laundry room; Barber/Beauty shop; Library.
Activities Arts and Crafts; Cards; Games; Reading groups; Movies; Shopping trips; Dances/Social or cultural gatherings; Sensory integration; Reality orientation; Yoga.
Description Program is geared to the mentally ill, aged 18 and up. Features a very active program with a broad range of vocational programs available in and outside the home.

Greenview Pavilion
1425 W Estes, Chicago, IL, 60626 (312) 973-4780
Admin Ronald B Silver.
Licensure Skilled Care; Intermediate Care.
Beds 160. *Certified* Medicaid.
Ownership Proprietary.
Staff Physicians 8 (pt); RNs 16 (pt); Orderlies 6 (pt); Nurses aides 24 (pt); Physical therapists 2 (pt); Reality therapists 1 (pt); Recreational therapists 1 (pt); Occupational therapists 1 (pt); Speech therapists 1 (pt); Activities coordinators 1 (pt); Dietitians 1 (pt); Dentists 1 (pt); Ophthalmologists 1 (pt); Podiatrists 1 (pt); Audiologists 1 (pt).
Facilities Dining room; Physical therapy room; Activities room; Crafts room; Barber/Beauty shop.
Activities Arts and Crafts; Cards; Games; Reading groups; Prayer groups; Movies; Shopping trips.
Description Facility is dedicated to heavy skilled care, IVs, O2 gastric feeding IVAC food pumps, with a complete physical and occupational therapy program, as well as a speech and language rehabilitation program. VA approved.

Halsted Terrace Nursing Center
10935 S Halsted St, Chicago, IL, 60628 (312) 928-2000
Admin Annie R Sutton. *Medical Dir/Dir of Nursing* William London.
Licensure Skilled Care; Intermediate Care.
Beds 300. *Certified* Medicaid.
Ownership Proprietary.
Admissions Requirements Medical examination; Physician's request.
Staff Physicians 4 (pt); RNs 5 (ft), 3 (pt); LPNs 14 (ft), 6 (pt); Orderlies 2 (ft); Nurses aides 1 (ft); Physical therapists 2 (pt); Occupational therapists 2 (pt); Activities coordinators 1 (ft).
Facilities Dining room; Physical therapy room; Activities room; Crafts room; Laundry room; Barber/Beauty shop.
Activities Arts and Crafts; Cards; Games; Reading groups; Prayer groups; Movies; Shopping trips; Dances/Social or cultural gatherings.

Hazel Wilson Residential Care
4544 N Hazel, Chicago, IL, 60640 (312) 561-7241
Admin Ruth Levin. *Medical Dir/Dir of Nursing* Mitchell Sokoloff.
Licensure Intermediate Care. *Beds* 188. *Certified* Medicaid.
Ownership Proprietary.
Admissions Requirements Minimum age 21.
Staff Physicians 2 (pt); RNs 1 (ft); Orderlies 5

(ft); Nurses aides 21 (ft); Occupational therapists 2 (pt); Dietitians 1 (pt); Dentists 1 (pt); Podiatrists 1 (pt).

Hearthside Nursing Home Inc
1223 W 87th St, Chicago, IL, 60625 (312) 238-2019
Admin Mary Ann Conte. *Medical Dir/Dir of Nursing* Dr Cornelius Bolton.
Licensure Skilled Care; Intermediate Care.
Beds SNF 33; ICF 42. *Certified* Medicaid.
Ownership Proprietary.
Admissions Requirements Minimum age 18; Medical examination.
Staff Physicians 2 (pt); RNs 1 (ft), 1 (pt); LPNs 3 (ft), 4 (pt); Orderlies 1 (ft); Nurses aides 13 (ft), 7 (pt); Physical therapists 1 (pt); Reality therapists 1 (ft); Recreational therapists 1 (ft); Occupational therapists 1 (pt); Speech therapists 1 (pt); Activities coordinators 2 (ft); Dietitians 1 (pt); Dentists 1 (pt); Ophthalmologists 1 (pt); Podiatrists 1 (pt).
Facilities Dining room; Activities room; Crafts room; Laundry room; Barber/Beauty shop.
Activities Arts and Crafts; Cards; Games; Reading groups; Prayer groups; Movies; Shopping trips; Dances/Social or cultural gatherings.

Home Association Jewish Blind
3525 W Foster Ave, Chicago, IL, 60625 (312) 478-7040
Admin Fred I Oskin. *Medical Dir/Dir of Nursing* Dr Jerome Dalinka.
Licensure Sheltered Care. *Beds* Sheltered Care 53.
Ownership Nonprofit.
Admissions Requirements Minimum age 17; Medical examination.
Staff Physicians 1 (pt); RNs 4 (pt); Nurses aides 9 (ft); Occupational therapists 1 (pt); Activities coordinators 1 (pt); Ophthalmologists 1 (pt); Podiatrists 1 (pt).
Affiliation Jewish
Facilities Dining room; Activities room; Chapel; Crafts room; Laundry room; Barber/Beauty shop.
Activities Arts and Crafts; Games; Prayer groups; Dances/Social or cultural gatherings.

Hyde Park Nursing Center Inc*
4505 S Drexel Blvd, Chicago, IL, 60653 (312) 285-0550
Admin Jacquelyne A Petrie.
Licensure Skilled Care. *Beds* 155. *Certified* Medicaid.
Ownership Proprietary.

Illinois Masonic Warren N Barr Pavilion
66 W Oak St, Chicago, IL, 60610 (312) 337-5400
Admin Wetzel McCormick. *Medical Dir/Dir of Nursing* Bertrum Moss MD.
Licensure Skilled Care; Hospice; Adult Day Care. *Beds* 330. *Certified* Medicaid; Medicare.
Ownership Nonprofit.
Admissions Requirements Minimum age 18; Medical examination; Physician's request.
Staff Physicians 2 (ft), 5 (pt); RNs 34 (ft); LPNs 27 (ft); Orderlies 5 (ft); Nurses aides 140 (ft); Physical therapists 6 (ft); Recreational therapists 16 (ft); Occupational therapists 3 (ft); Speech therapists 3 (ft); Activities coordinators 1 (ft); Dietitians 2 (ft); Dentists 1 (pt); Ophthal-

mologists 1 (pt); Podiatrists 1 (pt); Audiologists 1 (ft).
Affiliation Masons
Facilities Dining room; Physical therapy room; Activities room; Crafts room; Laundry room; Barber/Beauty shop; Library; Solarium; Gift shop; Ice cream and soda fountain.
Activities Arts and Crafts; Cards; Games; Reading groups; Prayer groups; Movies; Shopping trips; Dances/Social or cultural gatherings; Art gallery.
Description Facility has hospice, 4 to 8 beds; adult day care for 15 people, Monday through Friday; and on-site medical support service; affiliated with 6 schools, colleges, and universities.

Jewish Peoples Convalescent Home
6512 N California Ave, Chicago, IL, 60645 (312) 743-8077
Admin Mike Applebaum. *Medical Dir/Dir of Nursing* Dr Dan Stockhammer.
Licensure Sheltered Care. *Beds* Sheltered Care 35.
Ownership Nonprofit.
Admissions Requirements Minimum age 60; Medical examination.
Staff Physicians 1 (pt); RNs 1 (pt); LPNs 2 (ft), 2 (pt); Nurses aides 4 (ft), 3 (pt); Recreational therapists 1 (pt); Occupational therapists 1 (pt); Activities coordinators 1 (pt); Dietitians 1 (pt).
Affiliation Jewish
Facilities Dining room; Activities room; Crafts room; Barber/Beauty shop.
Activities Arts and Crafts; Cards; Games.

Johnson Rehabilitation Nursing Home
3456 W Franklin Blvd, Chicago, IL, 60624 (312) 533-3033
Admin H Shirley Sneed. *Medical Dir/Dir of Nursing* Dorval R Carter MD.
Licensure Skilled Care; Intermediate Care.
Beds 76. *Certified* Medicaid; Medicare.
Ownership Proprietary.
Admissions Requirements Minimum age 18; Medical examination; Physician's request.
Staff Physicians 4 (pt); RNs 2 (ft); LPNs 8 (ft); Nurses aides 17 (ft); Physical therapists 1 (pt); Recreational therapists 1 (ft); Dietitians 1 (pt); Dentists 1 (pt); Podiatrists 1 (pt).
Facilities Dining room; Physical therapy room; Activities room; Laundry room.
Activities Arts and Crafts; Cards; Games; Reading groups; Prayer groups; Movies; Shopping trips; Dances/Social or cultural gatherings.

Kenwood Terrace*
6125 S Kenwood Ave, Chicago, IL, 60632 (312) 752-6000
Admin Ronald Glen Weiss.
Licensure Skilled Care; Intermediate Care.
Beds SNF 128; ICF 190. *Certified* Medicare.
Ownership Proprietary.

Kraus Home Inc
1620 W Chase, Chicago, IL, 60626 (312) 973-2100
Admin Lawrence Kraus.
Licensure Sheltered Care. *Beds* Sheltered Care 60.
Ownership Proprietary.
Admissions Requirements Medical examination.

Staff Physicians 1 (pt); RNs 1 (ft); LPNs 5 (ft); Nurses aides 5 (ft); Recreational therapists 1 (ft); Occupational therapists 1 (ft); Activities coordinators 1 (ft); Dietitians 1 (pt).
Facilities Dining room; Activities room; Crafts room; Laundry room; Barber/Beauty shop; Library.
Activities Arts and Crafts; Cards; Games; Reading groups; Movies; Shopping trips; Dances/Social or cultural gatherings.
Description The home tries to create more of a home- or club-like atmosphere, rather than that of an institution. Residents are ambulatory.

Lake Front Convalescent Center*
7618 N Sheridan, Chicago, IL, 60626 (312) 743-7711
Admin Frieda Bassman.
Licensure Skilled Care. *Beds* 99. *Certified* Medicaid; Medicare.
Ownership Proprietary.

Lake Shore Nursing Centre
7200-30 N Sheridan, Chicago, IL, 60626 (312) 973-7200
Admin Isadore Goldberg. *Medical Dir/Dir of Nursing* Dr Lester Baranou.
Licensure Skilled Care; Intermediate Care. *Beds* 324. *Certified* Medicaid; Medicare.
Ownership Proprietary.
Admissions Requirements Minimum age 21.
Staff RNs 36 (ft), 8 (pt); LPNs 2 (ft); Orderlies 1 (ft); Nurses aides 86 (ft), 13 (pt); Physical therapists 1 (pt); Reality therapists 1 (ft); Recreational therapists 3 (ft); Occupational therapists 1 (ft), 2 (pt); Speech therapists 1 (pt); Activities coordinators 1 (ft); Dietitians 1 (ft); Dentists 1 (pt); Ophthalmologists 1 (pt); Podiatrists 1 (pt); Audiologists 1 (pt).
Facilities Dining room; Physical therapy room; Activities room; Crafts room; Laundry room; Barber/Beauty shop; Library.
Activities Arts and Crafts; Cards; Games; Reading groups; Prayer groups; Movies; Shopping trips; Dances/Social or cultural gatherings.
Description Facility is geared for rehabilitation of CUAs, fractures, MIs, and post-operative residents who, after treatment, can return to the community and continue to function in all areas of adult life.

Lakeland Manor*
820 W Lawrence, Chicago, IL, 60640 (312) 769-2570
Admin Ann A Richards.
Licensure Skilled Care. *Beds* 310. *Certified* Medicaid; Medicare.
Ownership Proprietary.

Lakeside Boarding Home
6330 N Sheridan Rd, Chicago, IL, 60640 (312) 338-2811
Admin Hasmukh Gandhi. *Medical Dir/Dir of Nursing* Pareshkumar Jani MD.
Licensure Sheltered Care. *Beds* Sheltered Care 34.
Ownership Proprietary.
Admissions Requirements Minimum age 21.
Staff LPNs 1 (ft); Nurses aides 5 (ft); Activities coordinators 1 (ft).
Facilities Dining room; Activities room; Laundry room.
Activities Arts and Crafts; Cards; Games;

Reading groups; Prayer groups; Movies; Shopping trips; Dances/Social or cultural gatherings.
Description Transportation provided for residents' visits to hospitals and relatives. Facility has an excellent location on a lakefront. Personal care is given.

Lakeview Nursing and Geriatric Center
735 W Diversey Pkwy, Chicago, IL, 60614 (312) 348-4055
Admin Richard Schnitzer. *Medical Dir/Dir of Nursing* Dr T Kioutas.
Licensure Skilled Care; Intermediate Care. *Beds* SNF 63; ICF 117. *Certified* Medicaid.
Ownership Proprietary.
Admissions Requirements Minimum age 60.
Staff Physicians; RNs 12 (ft); LPNs 8 (ft); Orderlies 2 (ft); Nurses aides 52 (ft); Physical therapists 2 (ft); Recreational therapists 3 (ft); Occupational therapists; Speech therapists; Activities coordinators 1 (ft); Dietitians; Dentists; Ophthalmologists; Podiatrists; Audiologists.
Facilities Dining room; Physical therapy room; Activities room; Crafts room; Laundry room; Barber/Beauty shop; Library.
Activities Arts and Crafts; Cards; Games; Reading groups; Prayer groups; Movies; Shopping trips; Dances/Social or cultural gatherings.

Lincoln Park Terrace Inc
2732 N Hampden Ct, Chicago, IL, 60614 (312) 248-6000
Admin Dov Solomon. *Medical Dir/Dir of Nursing* Solomon Dayan.
Licensure Skilled Care. *Beds* 109.
Ownership Proprietary.
Admissions Requirements Minimum age 21.
Staff Physicians 6 (pt); RNs 5 (ft), 4 (pt); LPNs 8 (ft), 3 (pt); Nurses aides 25 (ft), 3 (pt); Physical therapists 1 (pt); Occupational therapists 1 (pt); Speech therapists 1 (pt); Activities coordinators 2 (ft); Dietitians 1 (pt); Dentists 1 (pt); Ophthalmologists 1 (pt); Podiatrists 1 (pt); Audiologists 1 (pt).
Facilities Dining room; Physical therapy room; Activities room; Crafts room; Laundry room; Barber/Beauty shop; Library.
Activities Arts and Crafts; Cards; Games; Reading groups; Movies; Shopping trips; Dances/Social or cultural gatherings.
Description Modern skilled care facility with a capacity of 109 specializing in individualized care. We are fully accredited and meet state and federal requirements. There is a sprinkler system throughout the facility. We have staff that strives hard to please and give lots of tender loving care to residents at all times.

Little Sisters of the Poor
2325 N Lakewood Ave, Chicago, IL, 60614 (312) 348-3232
Admin Sr Gertrude Mary. *Medical Dir/Dir of Nursing* Dr Dayan.
Licensure Skilled Care; Intermediate Care. *Beds* SNF 25; ICF 93. *Certified* Medicaid.
Ownership Nonprofit.
Admissions Requirements Minimum age 60.
Affiliation Roman Catholic
Facilities Dining room; Physical therapy room; Activities room; Chapel; Crafts room; Laundry room; Barber/Beauty shop; Library.

Activities Arts and Crafts; Cards; Games; Reading groups; Prayer groups; Movies; Shopping trips; Dances/Social or cultural gatherings.

Maple Terrace Shelter Care Home*
4743 W Washington, Chicago, IL, 60644 (312) 626-1439
Admin Pearl J Brooks.
Licensure Sheltered Care. *Beds* Sheltered Care 12.
Ownership Proprietary.

Margaret Manor*
1121 N Orleans, Chicago, IL, 60610 (312) 943-4300
Admin Della M McDonough.
Licensure Intermediate Care. *Beds* 135. *Certified* Medicaid.
Ownership Proprietary.

Margaret Manor-North Branch*
940 W Cullom Ave, Chicago, IL, 60613 (312) 525-9000
Admin Charles F Stumpf.
Licensure Intermediate Care. *Beds* 99. *Certified* Medicaid.
Ownership Proprietary.

Mayfield Manor Nursing Home
5901 W Washington Blvd, Chicago, IL, 60644 (312) 261-7074
Admin Robert M Nataupsky. *Medical Dir/Dir of Nursing* Dr Dayan.
Licensure Skilled Care; Intermediate Care. *Beds* 150. *Certified* Medicaid.
Ownership Proprietary.
Admissions Requirements Minimum age 21; Medical examination.
Staff Physicians 3 (pt); RNs 4 (ft); LPNs 18 (ft); Orderlies 7 (ft); Nurses aides 40 (ft); Physical therapists 3 (ft); Reality therapists 3 (ft); Recreational therapists 3 (ft); Occupational therapists 1 (pt); Speech therapists 1 (pt); Activities coordinators 1 (ft); Dietitians 1 (pt); Dentists 3 (pt); Ophthalmologists 3 (pt); Podiatrists 3 (pt); Audiologists 1 (pt).
Facilities Dining room; Physical therapy room; Activities room; Chapel; Crafts room; Laundry room; Barber/Beauty shop.
Activities Arts and Crafts; Cards; Games; Reading groups; Prayer groups; Movies; Shopping trips; Dances/Social or cultural gatherings.

Methodist Home
1415 W Foster Ave, Chicago, IL, 60625 (312) 769-5500
Admin Daniel A Ozelis.
Licensure Skilled Care; Intermediate Care; Sheltered Care. *Beds* SNF 23; ICF; Sheltered Care 23. *Certified* Medicaid.
Ownership Proprietary.
Affiliation Methodist
Facilities Dining room; Physical therapy room; Activities room; Chapel; Crafts room; Laundry room; Barber/Beauty shop; Library.
Activities Arts and Crafts; Cards; Games; Reading groups; Prayer groups; Movies; Dances/Social or cultural gatherings.

Michigan Terrace Nursing Center Inc
3405 S Michigan, Chicago, IL, 60616 (312) 791-0035
Admin Mark L Steinberg. *Medical Dir/Dir of*

Nursing Dr Sheldon Levine.
Licensure Skilled Care; Intermediate Care.
Beds 155. *Certified* Medicaid.
Ownership Proprietary.
Admissions Requirements Medical examination; Physician's request.
Staff Physicians 3 (pt); RNs 2 (ft), 2 (pt); LPNs 10 (ft), 4 (pt); Orderlies 5 (ft); Nurses aides 30 (ft), 5 (pt); Physical therapists 1 (pt); Recreational therapists 2 (ft); Occupational therapists 1 (pt); Speech therapists 1 (pt); Activities coordinators 1 (ft); Dietitians 1 (pt); Dentists 1 (pt); Ophthalmologists 1 (pt); Podiatrists 1 (pt).
Facilities Dining room; Physical therapy room; Activities room; Chapel; Crafts room; Laundry room; Barber/Beauty shop.
Activities Arts and Crafts; Cards; Games; Reading groups; Prayer groups; Dances/Social or cultural gatherings.

Mid-America Convalescent Centers Inc*
4920 N Kenmore, Chicago, IL, 60640 (312) 769-2700
Admin Paul Horvath.
Licensure Skilled Care. *Beds* 310. *Certified* Medicaid.
Ownership Proprietary.

Miller Nursing Home*
3256 W Douglas Blvd, Chicago, IL, 60623 (312) 521-6000
Admin Eula A Spinks.
Licensure Intermediate Care. *Beds* 43. *Certified* Medicare.
Ownership Proprietary.

Misericordia Home
2916 W 47th St, Chicago, IL, 60632 (312) 254-9595
Admin Rosemary Connelly. *Medical Dir/Dir of Nursing* Roseanne V Proteau MD.
Licensure Skilled Care. *Beds* 122. *Certified* Medicaid.
Ownership Nonprofit.
Admissions Requirements Minimum age Birth; Medical examination.
Staff Physicians 2 (ft); RNs 8 (ft), 6 (pt); LPNs 5 (ft), 3 (pt); Nurses aides 50 (ft), 30 (pt); Occupational therapists 1 (ft).
Affiliation Roman Catholic
Facilities Dining room; Physical therapy room; Activities room; Chapel; Crafts room; Laundry room; Library.
Activities Arts and Crafts; Reading groups; Prayer groups; Movies; Shopping trips.
Description Licensed skilled nursing facility for 122 mentally and/or physically disabled children. Excellent medical and nursing care is provided in a home-like atmosphere. Children also receive prespeech and feeding therapy, physical therapy, hydrotherapy, and music therapy. Children who are physically able participate in a classroom program which stresses pre-academic skills.

Monroe Pavilion Health Center Inc
1400 W Monroe St, Chicago, IL, 60607 (312) 666-4090
Admin Wayne J Hanik. *Medical Dir/Dir of Nursing* Robert Passovoy.
Licensure Intermediate Care. *Beds* 136.
Ownership Proprietary.
Staff Physicians 3 (ft); LPNs 9 (ft); Orderlies 5

(ft); Nurses aides 50 (ft); Physical therapists 1 (ft); Reality therapists 1 (ft); Occupational therapists 3 (ft); Speech therapists 1 (pt); Activities coordinators 3 (ft); Dietitians 1 (pt); Dentists 1 (pt); Ophthalmologists 1 (pt); Podiatrists 1 (pt).
Facilities Dining room; Physical therapy room; Activities room; Crafts room; Laundry room; Barber/Beauty shop; Library.
Activities Arts and Crafts; Cards; Games; Reading groups; Prayer groups; Movies; Shopping trips; Dances/Social or cultural gatherings.

Norridge Nursing Centre
7001 W Cullom, Chicago, IL, 60634 (312) 457-0700
Admin Barbara I Lyons. *Medical Dir/Dir of Nursing* Samuel Kruger MD.
Licensure Skilled Care; Intermediate Care.
Beds SNF 210; ICF 105.
Ownership Proprietary.
Admissions Requirements Minimum age 18.
Facilities Dining room; Physical therapy room; Activities room; Crafts room; Laundry room; Barber/Beauty shop; Library.
Activities Arts and Crafts; Cards; Games; Reading groups; Prayer groups; Movies; Shopping trips.

Northwest Home for the Aged
6300 N California Ave, Chicago, IL, 60659 (312) 973-1900
Admin Haim Perlstein. *Medical Dir/Dir of Nursing* Michael Preodor MD.
Licensure Skilled Care; Intermediate Care.
Beds SNF 100; ICF 50. *Certified* Medicaid.
Ownership Nonprofit.
Admissions Requirements Minimum age 65; Medical examination.
Staff Physicians 2 (ft); RNs 9 (ft), 11 (pt); LPNs 5 (ft); Orderlies 1 (ft); Nurses aides 49 (ft), 3 (pt); Physical therapists 1 (ft), 1 (pt); Recreational therapists 3 (ft); Occupational therapists 1 (pt); Speech therapists 1 (pt); Activities coordinators 1 (ft); Dietitians 1 (pt); Dentists 1 (pt); Ophthalmologists 1 (pt); Podiatrists 1 (pt); Audiologists 1 (pt).
Facilities Dining room; Physical therapy room; Activities room; Chapel; Crafts room; Laundry room; Barber/Beauty shop; Library.
Activities Arts and Crafts; Cards; Games; Reading groups; Prayer groups; Movies; Dances/Social or cultural gatherings.
Description Facility features beautifully decorated residents' rooms; full, varied activity program; newly expanded rehabilitation department with various equipment, including new modern whirlpool bathtubs; religious services provided on all floors; beauty shop, lovely dining room, lobby and day rooms; and a dedicated staff.

Norwegian Luther Bethesda Home
2833 N Nordica Ave, Chicago, IL, 60634 (312)622-6144
Admin Pamela K Seefurth.
Licensure Intermediate Care; Sheltered Care.
Beds ICF 50; Sheltered Care 100. *Certified* Medicaid.
Ownership Nonprofit.
Admissions Requirements Minimum age 70; Medical examination.
Affiliation Lutheran
Facilities Dining room; Activities room; Chap-

el; Crafts room; Barber/Beauty shop; Library.
Activities Arts and Crafts; Cards; Games; Prayer groups; Movies.

Norwood Park Home*
6016 N Nina Ave, Chicago, IL, 60631 (312) 631-4856
Admin James E Herbon.
Licensure Intermediate Care; Sheltered Care.
Beds ICF 125; Sheltered Care 140.
Ownership Nonprofit.

Oak Lawn Convalescent Home Inc*
9525 S Mayfield, Chicago, IL, 60643 (312) 636-7000
Admin Katherine Hartley.
Licensure Skilled Care; Intermediate Care.
Beds SNF 71; ICF 56. *Certified* Medicaid; Medicare.
Ownership Proprietary.

Old Peoples Home of the Church of Christ*
909 W Foster Ave, Chicago, IL, 60640 (312) 561-2900
Admin John M Yoder.
Licensure Intermediate Care; Sheltered Care.
Beds ICF 50; Sheltered Care 85.
Ownership Nonprofit.
Affiliation Church of Christ

Ora G Morrow Nursing Home
5001 S Michigan, Chicago, IL, 60615 (312) 924-9292
Admin Craig Caspurs. *Medical Dir/Dir of Nursing* Yrech Pardo MD.
Licensure Skilled Care; Intermediate Care.
Beds 192.
Ownership Nonprofit.
Admissions Requirements Minimum age 21.
Staff Physicians 12 (pt); RNs 6 (ft), 3 (pt); LPNs 13 (ft), 6 (pt); Orderlies 7 (ft); Nurses aides 43 (ft), 4 (pt); Physical therapists 1 (pt); Recreational therapists 4 (ft), 1 (pt); Occupational therapists 2 (pt); Speech therapists 2 (pt); Activities coordinators 1 (pt); Dietitians 1 (pt); Dentists 1 (pt); Ophthalmologists 2 (pt); Podiatrists 1 (pt).
Facilities Dining room; Physical therapy room; Activities room; Crafts room; Laundry room; Barber/Beauty shop.
Activities Arts and Crafts; Cards; Games; Prayer groups; Movies; Dances/Social or cultural gatherings.
Description Facility has 48 beds per nursing unit allowing for close licensed nurse observation and offers several out-of-the-building activities including barbecues, walk-a-thons for the heart association, bus trips, and more.

Palmer Terrace Nursing Center
2242 N Kedzie Ave, Chicago, IL, 60647 (312) 486-7700
Admin Maureen Gartland. *Medical Dir/Dir of Nursing* Arsenio Agngarayngay MD.
Licensure Skilled Care; Intermediate Care.
Beds 222. *Certified* Medicaid.
Ownership Proprietary.
Staff Physicians 8 (pt); RNs 9 (ft); LPNs 14 (ft); Nurses aides 44 (ft); Physical therapists 2 (ft), 1 (pt); Reality therapists 1 (pt); Occupational therapists 1 (ft), 1 (pt); Speech therapists 1 (ft), 1 (pt); Activities coordinators 5 (ft); Dietitians 1 (pt); Dentists 1 (pt); Ophthalmologists

1 (pt); Podiatrists 2 (pt); Audiologists 1 (pt).
Facilities Dining room; Physical therapy room;
Activities room; Crafts room; Laundry room;
Barber/Beauty shop.
Activities Arts and Crafts; Games; Reading
groups; Prayer groups; Movies; Shopping trips;
Dances/Social or cultural gatherings.

Park Nursing Home Inc
2320 S Lawndale, Chicago, IL, 60623 (312)
522-0400
Admin Beni Held. *Medical Dir/Dir of
Nursing* Ralph De Jesus.
Licensure Intermediate Care. *Beds* 105. *Certified* Medicaid.
Ownership Proprietary.
Admissions Requirements Minimum age 18;
Medical examination.
Staff RNs 1 (ft); LPNs 6 (ft); Nurses aides 24
(ft); Activities coordinators 1 (ft).
Facilities Dining room; Physical therapy room;
Activities room; Crafts room; Laundry room.
Activities Arts and Crafts; Cards; Games;
Reading groups; Prayer groups; Movies; Shopping trips; Dances/Social or cultural gatherings.

Peterson Park Health Care Center*
6141 N Pulaski Rd, Chicago, IL, 60646 (312)
478-2000
Admin Ronald N Shabat.
Licensure Skilled Care; Intermediate Care.
Beds SNF 96; ICF 92. *Certified* Medicaid.
Ownership Proprietary.

Renaissance House*
6050 N California Ave, Chicago, IL, 60659
(312) 761-4651
Admin John Gary.
Licensure Intermediate Care. *Beds* 20.
Ownership Nonprofit.

Rogers Park Manor Nursing Home
1512 W Fargo, Chicago, IL, 60626 (312)
465-7751
Admin Nancy A Snyder. *Medical Dir/Dir of
Nursing* Dr Aboul Sattar.
Licensure Skilled Care; Intermediate Care.
Beds SNF 70; ICF 29. *Certified* Medicaid.
Ownership Proprietary.
Admissions Requirements Minimum age 18.
Staff Physicians 4 (pt); RNs 4 (ft), 5 (pt); LPNs
7 (ft), 3 (pt); Orderlies 2 (ft), 3 (pt); Nurses aides
15 (ft), 3 (pt); Physical therapists 1 (pt); Recreational therapists 2 (ft), 1 (pt); Occupational therapists 1 (ft), 1 (pt); Speech therapists 1 (pt);
Activities coordinators 1 (ft); Dietitians 1 (pt);
Dentists 1 (pt); Ophthalmologists 1 (pt); Podiatrists 1 (pt); Audiologists 1 (pt).

Rosewood-Damen Nursing Home Inc*
6700-6710 N Damen Ave, Chicago, IL, 60645
(312) 465-5000
Admin Alan H Aron.
Licensure Skilled Care; Intermediate Care.
Beds SNF 51; ICF 76. *Certified* Medicaid.
Ownership Proprietary.

Sacred Heart Home*
1550 S Albany, Chicago, IL, 60623 (312)
277-6868
Admin Virginia E Barry.

Licensure Intermediate Care. *Beds* 172. *Certified* Medicaid.
Ownership Proprietary.

Saint Agnes Health Care Center*
60 E 18th St, Chicago, IL, 60610 (312)
922-2777
Admin Jaseph A Bonnah.
Licensure Skilled Care. *Beds* 107.
Ownership Proprietary.

Saint Joseph Home of Chicago Inc
2650 N Ridgeway Ave, Chicago, IL, 60647
(312) 235-8600
Admin Joseph A Bonnan. *Medical Dir/Dir of
Nursing* Salomon Dayan MD.
Licensure Skilled Care; Intermediate Care.
Beds SNF 54; ICF 119; Medicare 15.
Certified Medicaid; Medicare.
Ownership Nonprofit.
Admissions Requirements Minimum age 65;
Medical examination; Physician's request.
Staff Physicians 5 (pt); RNs 15 (ft); LPNs 10
(ft); Orderlies 2 (ft); Nurses aides 44 (ft);
Physical therapists 2 (ft); Reality therapists 1
(pt); Recreational therapists 1 (pt); Occupational therapists 1 (pt); Speech therapists 1 (pt);
Activities coordinators 4 (ft); Dietitians 1 (pt);
Dentists 1 (pt); Ophthalmologists 1 (pt); Podiatrists 1 (pt); Audiologists 1 (pt).
Affiliation Roman Catholic
Facilities Dining room; Physical therapy room;
Activities room; Chapel; Crafts room; Laundry
room; Barber/Beauty shop; Library; Lounges.
Activities Arts and Crafts; Cards; Games;
Reading groups; Prayer groups; Movies; Shopping trips; Dances/Social or cultural gatherings;
Pastoral services.

Saint Martha Manor
4621 N Racine Ave, Chicago, IL, 60640 (312)
784-2300
Admin Charles J Stumpf. *Medical Dir/Dir of
Nursing* Arsenio Agngarayngay.
Licensure Skilled Care. *Beds* 132. *Certified* Medicaid.
Ownership Nonprofit.
Admissions Requirements Minimum age 18.
Staff Physicians 5 (pt); RNs 17 (ft); LPNs 4
(ft); Orderlies 6 (ft); Nurses aides 20 (ft);
Physical therapists 3 (pt); Reality therapists 1
(ft); Recreational therapists 1 (ft); Occupational
therapists 1 (ft); Speech therapists 1 (ft), 1 (pt);
Activities coordinators 5 (ft); Dietitians 1 (pt);
Dentists 1 (pt); Podiatrists 1 (pt).
Facilities Dining room; Physical therapy room;
Activities room; Crafts room; Laundry room;
Barber/Beauty shop.
Activities Arts and Crafts; Cards; Games;
Reading groups; Prayer groups; Movies; Shopping trips; Dances/Social or cultural gatherings.

Saint Mary Square Living Center of Chicago*
7270 S Shore Dr, Chicago, IL, 60649 (312)
721-7700
Admin Mark Kammerer.
Licensure Intermediate Care; Developmentally
Disabled. *Beds* ICF 60; Developmental Disabled 100.
Ownership Nonprofit.

Saint Pauls House
3831 N Mozart St, Chicago, IL, 60618 (312)
478-4222
Admin Carol Zech and Dorothy Pipenhagen.
Medical Dir/Dir of Nursing Dr G M
Eduenson.
Licensure Skilled Care; Sheltered Care.
Beds SNF 90; Sheltered Care 79.
Ownership Nonprofit.
Staff Physicians 1 (pt); RNs 14 (ft); LPNs 2
(ft); Orderlies 6 (ft); Nurses aides 48 (ft);
Physical therapists 1 (ft), 1 (pt); Reality therapists 1 (ft); Recreational therapists 3 (ft); Occupational therapists 1 (pt); Speech therapists 1
(pt); Dietitians 1 (ft), 1 (pt); Dentists 1 (pt);
Ophthalmologists 1 (pt); Podiatrists 1 (pt);
Audiologists 1 (pt).
Affiliation Church of Christ
Facilities Dining room; Physical therapy room;
Activities room; Chapel; Crafts room; Laundry
room; Barber/Beauty shop; Library.
Activities Arts and Crafts; Cards; Games;
Reading groups; Prayer groups; Movies; Shopping trips; Dances/Social or cultural gatherings;
School classes.
Description Facility is contained in one square
block in city near transportation and shopping.
Employees have been at the facility for long
periods of time. Park is across the street. Religious services are held every Saturday and
Sunday. Facility is a member IAHA, Board of
Health and Human Services of United Church
of Christ.

Self Help Home for the Aged
908 W Argyle St, Chicago, IL, 60640 (312)
271-0300
Admin Dorothy Becker. *Medical Dir/Dir of
Nursing* Hyman Mackler MD.
Licensure Intermediate Care; Sheltered Care.
Beds Sheltered Care 26. *Certified* Medicaid.
Ownership Nonprofit.
Admissions Requirements Minimum age 65;
Medical examination; Physician's request.
Staff RNs 1 (ft); Physical therapists 1 (pt); Recreational therapists 1 (pt); Occupational therapists 1 (pt); Activities coordinators 1 (pt);
Dietitians 1 (pt); Dentists 1 (pt); Ophthalmologists 1 (pt); Podiatrists 1 (pt).
Affiliation Jewish
Facilities Dining room; Physical therapy room;
Activities room; Chapel; Crafts room; Laundry
room; Barber/Beauty shop; Library.
Activities Arts and Crafts; Cards; Games;
Reading groups; Movies; Shopping trips; Dances/Social or cultural gatherings.

Senn Park Nursing Center
5888 N Ridge Ave, Chicago, IL, 60626 (312)
769-2626
Admin Daniel Shabat.
Licensure Intermediate Care. *Beds* 128. *Certified* Medicaid.
Ownership Proprietary.
Staff RNs; LPNs; Orderlies; Nurses aides;
Physical therapists; Reality therapists; Occupational therapists; Speech therapists; Activities
coordinators; Dietitians; Dentists; Ophthalmologists; Podiatrists.
Facilities Dining room; Activities room; Crafts
room; Laundry room.
Activities Arts and Crafts; Cards; Games; Prayer groups; Movies; Shopping trips; Dances/So-

cial or cultural gatherings.
Description Facility has a young adult program (psychiatric unit) on one floor that prepares a resident to become as independent as possible. Counselors are available from 9 to 9; residents are taught independent living skills.

Sheridan Gardens Convalescent Home Inc*
1426 W Birchwood Ave, Chicago, IL, 60626 (312) 274-4405
Admin Dolores Lindenbaum.
Licensure Skilled Care. *Beds* 192. *Certified* Medicaid.
Ownership Proprietary.

Sherwin Manor Nursing Center*
7350 N Sheridan Rd, Chicago, IL, 60626 (312) 274-1000
Admin Joseph Osina.
Licensure Skilled Care. *Beds* 219. *Certified* Medicaid.
Ownership Proprietary.

Society for Danish Old Peoples Home*
5656 N Newcastle Ave, Chicago, IL, 60631 (312) 775-7383
Admin Ellyn Travi.
Licensure Intermediate Care; Sheltered Care.
Beds ICF 15; Sheltered Care 57.
Ownership Nonprofit.

Somerset House
5009 N Sheridan, Chicago, IL, 60640 (312) 561-0700
Admin Edward D Farmilant. *Medical Dir/Dir of Nursing* Dr David Edelberg.
Licensure Intermediate Care. *Beds* 450. *Certified* Medicaid.
Ownership Proprietary.
Admissions Requirements Minimum age 18.
Staff Physicians 4 (pt); RNs 3 (ft); LPNs 20 (ft), 2 (pt); Nurses aides 44 (ft); Recreational therapists 7 (ft); Occupational therapists 1 (ft), 2 (pt); Speech therapists 1 (pt); Activities coordinators 7 (ft); Dietitians 1 (pt); Dentists 1 (pt); Ophthalmologists 2 (pt); Podiatrists 1 (pt).
Facilities Dining room; Activities room; Crafts room; Laundry room; Barber/Beauty shop; Library.
Activities Arts and Crafts; Cards; Games; Reading groups; Prayer groups; Movies; Shopping trips; Dances/Social or cultural gatherings; Softball team.
Description Our philosophy of care is centered around the "Rehabilitation Model," the process of restoring a person to his/her maximum level of functioning through a developmental approach based on needs assessment and individual potential. The programs provide service for the physically handicapped, mentally handicapped, and functionally geriatric.

South Shore Kosher Rest Home Inc*
7325 S Exchange Ave, Chicago, IL, 60649 (312) 731-7300
Admin Andrew Phillps.
Licensure Intermediate Care. *Beds* 111. *Certified* Medicaid; Medicare.
Ownership Proprietary.

The Sovereign Home*
6159 N Kenmore Ave, Chicago, IL, 60640 (312) 761-9050

Admin David Stern.
Licensure Intermediate Care. *Beds* 55. *Certified* Medicaid.
Ownership Proprietary.

Touhy Terrace Nursing Center
2452 W Fitch Ave, Chicago, IL, 60660 (312) 338-6800
Admin Sioney J Glenner. *Medical Dir/Dir of Nursing* Dr Solomon Dayan.
Licensure Skilled Care; Intermediate Care.
Beds 307. *Certified* Medicaid; Medicare.
Ownership Proprietary.
Admissions Requirements Minimum age 50.
Facilities Dining room; Physical therapy room; Activities room; Crafts room; Laundry room; Barber/Beauty shop; Library.
Activities Arts and Crafts; Cards; Games; Reading groups; Prayer groups; Movies; Shopping trips; Dances/Social or cultural gatherings.
Description Facility features a basic living skills program for regressed males and females, a patio, a library and ice-cream socials.

Uptown Shelter Care Home Inc
4646 N Beacon St, Chicago, IL, 60640 (312) 561-7707
Admin Dinesh Gandhi. *Medical Dir/Dir of Nursing* Dr Paresh Jani.
Licensure Sheltered Care. *Beds* Sheltered Care 52.
Ownership Proprietary.
Admissions Requirements Minimum age 18.
Staff Physicians; RNs 1 (pt); LPNs 1 (ft), 1 (pt); Nurses aides 4 (ft), 2 (pt); Physical therapists; Recreational therapists; Occupational therapists 1 (pt); Activities coordinators 1 (ft), 1 (pt); Dietitians 1 (ft), 1 (pt); Dentists; Ophthalmologists; Podiatrists.
Facilities Dining room; Activities room; Crafts room; Laundry room; Library.
Activities Arts and Crafts; Cards; Games; Reading groups; Prayer groups; Shopping trips; Dances/Social or cultural gatherings.
Description All residents get personnel one-to-one base care. Facility provides transportation for any special medical or family visit.

Vista Laguna Aftercare Facility Inc*
449 W Winnecona Pkwy, Chicago, IL, 60620 (312) 224-3900
Admin Myrtle Martin.
Licensure Intermediate Care. *Beds* 164. *Certified* Medicaid.
Ownership Proprietary.

Washington and Jane Smith Home*
2340 W 113th Pl, Chicago, IL, 60643 (312) 238-8305
Admin Gary T Johanson.
Licensure Skilled Care; Sheltered Care.
Beds SNF 44; Sheltered Care 201.
Ownership Nonprofit.

Waterfront Terrace
7750 S Shore Dr, Chicago, IL, 60649 (312) 731-4200
Admin Maurice I Aaron. *Medical Dir/Dir of Nursing* Harry Crystal MD.
Licensure Intermediate Care. *Beds* 116. *Certified* Medicaid.
Ownership Proprietary.
Admissions Requirements Minimum age 30;

Physician's request.
Staff Physicians 3 (pt); RNs 1 (pt); LPNs 12 (ft); Nurses aides 28 (ft); Physical therapists 2 (pt); Occupational therapists 3 (pt); Activities coordinators 2 (ft); Dietitians 1 (pt); Dentists 2 (pt); Ophthalmologists 1 (pt); Podiatrists 1 (pt).
Facilities Dining room; Activities room; Crafts room; Laundry room; Barber/Beauty shop.
Activities Arts and Crafts; Cards; Games; Reading groups; Prayer groups; Movies; Shopping trips; Dances/Social or cultural gatherings; Outings.
Description Facility is a small, intermediate facility situated on Chicago's lakefront with a wonderful view and fabulous breeze. Outstanding activities program featuring many outside activities.

Wellington Plaza Therapy and Nursing Center
504 W Wellington St, Chicago, IL, 60657 (312) 281-6200
Admin Naftali Tzur. *Medical Dir/Dir of Nursing* Martin Ross MD.
Licensure Skilled Care. *Beds* 96.
Ownership Proprietary.
Admissions Requirements Medical examination; Physician's request.
Staff Physicians 3 (pt); RNs 7 (ft), 11 (pt); LPNs 5 (ft), 2 (pt); Orderlies 2 (ft); Nurses aides 28 (ft), 3 (pt); Physical therapists 1 (ft); Reality therapists 1 (pt); Recreational therapists 1 (ft); Occupational therapists 1 (ft); Speech therapists 1 (pt); Activities coordinators 1 (ft), 2 (pt); Dietitians 1 (ft); Dentists 1 (pt); Ophthalmologists 1 (pt); Podiatrists 1 (pt); Audiologists 1 (pt).
Facilities Dining room; Physical therapy room; Activities room; Chapel; Crafts room; Laundry room; Barber/Beauty shop.
Activities Arts and Crafts; Cards; Games; Reading groups; Prayer groups; Movies; Shopping trips; Dances/Social or cultural gatherings; College credit classes.
Description Nursing center offers a comprehensive restorative program which includes all residents, not just Medicare/Medicaid patients, provided by a multidisciplinary group and included in the daily room charge—the only one of its kind in the Chicago metropolitan region.

Wentworth Nursing Center*
201 W 69th St, Chicago, IL, 60637 (312) 487-1200
Admin Dorothy L Williams.
Licensure Skilled Care. *Beds* 300.
Ownership Proprietary.

Westwood Manor Inc
2444 W Touhy Ave, Chicago, IL, 60645 (312) 274-7705
Admin Meyer Liberman. *Medical Dir/Dir of Nursing* Dr Lawrence Mazur.
Licensure Skilled Care; Intermediate Care.
Beds SNF 9; ICF 106. *Certified* Medicaid.
Ownership Proprietary.
Admissions Requirements Minimum age 18.
Facilities Dining room; Physical therapy room; Activities room; Crafts room.
Activities Arts and Crafts; Cards; Games; Prayer groups; Movies; Shopping trips; Dances/Social or cultural gatherings.

Whitehall Convalescent Nursing Home
1901 N Lincoln Park W, Chicago, IL, 60614
(312) 943-2846
Admin Dorothy L Kleinhenz. *Medical Dir/Dir
of Nursing* Raja Khuri MD.
Licensure Skilled Care. *Beds* 91.
Ownership Proprietary.
Admissions Requirements Medical examina-
tion; Physician's request.
Staff Physicians; RNs; LPNs; Nurses aides;
Physical therapists; Recreational therapists;
Speech therapists; Activities coordinators; Die-
titians; Dentists; Ophthalmologists; Podiatrists.
Facilities Dining room; Physical therapy room;
Activities room; Barber/Beauty shop; Library.
Activities Arts and Crafts; Cards; Games;
Reading groups; Movies.

William L Dawson Nursing Home*
3500 S Giles Ave, Chicago, IL, 60653 (312)
326-2000
Admin Pamela M Orr.
Licensure Skilled Care. *Beds* 245. *Certified* Medicaid.
Ownership Proprietary.

Wincrest Nursing Home
6326 N Winthrop, Chicago, IL, 60660 (312)
338-7800
Admin C Shaps. *Medical Dir/Dir of Nur-
sing* Sidney Fieldman.
Licensure Intermediate Care. *Beds* 82. *Certi-
fied* Medicaid.
Ownership Proprietary.
Admissions Requirements Minimum age 50;
Medical examination; Physician's request.
Staff Physicians; RNs; LPNs; Orderlies;
Nurses aides; Physical therapists; Recreational
therapists; Occupational therapists; Activities
coordinators; Dietitians; Dentists; Podiatrists.
Facilities Dining room; Physical therapy room;
Activities room; Chapel; Laundry room; Bar-
ber/Beauty shop.
Activities Arts and Crafts; Cards; Games; Pray-
er groups; Movies.

**Winston Manor Convalescent and Nursing
Home***
2155 W Pierce Ave, Chicago, IL, 60622 (312)
252-2066
Admin Morton Stender.
Licensure Intermediate Care. *Beds* 180. *Certi-
fied* Medicaid.
Ownership Proprietary.

CHICAGO HEIGHTS

Chicago Heights Terrace
160 W 10th St, Chicago Heights, IL, 60411
(312) 754-2220
Admin Neal Kjos.
Licensure Intermediate Care. *Beds* 222. *Certi-
fied* Medicaid.
Ownership Proprietary.
Admissions Requirements Minimum age 18.
Facilities Dining room; Activities room; Crafts
room; Laundry room; Barber/Beauty shop;
Library.
Activities Arts and Crafts; Cards; Games;
Reading groups; Prayer groups; Movies; Shop-

ping trips; Dances/Social or cultural gatherings.
Description Facility primarily addresses its program to a young adult, psychiatric population.

Meridian Nursing Center—Suburban*
120 W 26th St, Chicago Heights, IL, 60411
(312) 756-5200
Admin Patrick L Saunders.
Licensure Skilled Care; Intermediate Care.
Beds SNF 63; ICF 48.
Ownership Proprietary.

Riviera Manor Inc*
490 W 16th Pl, Chicago Heights, IL, 60411
(312) 481-4444
Admin Gus G Potekin.
Licensure Skilled Care; Intermediate Care.
Beds SNF 150; ICF 50. *Certified* Medicaid;
Medicare.
Ownership Proprietary.

CHICAGO RIDGE

Chicago Ridge Nursing Center
10602 Southwest Hwy, Chicago Ridge, IL,
60415 (312) 448-1540
Admin Barry R Taerbaum. *Medical Dir/Dir of
Nursing* Sheldon Levine.
Licensure Skilled Care; Intermediate Care.
Beds 231. *Certified* Medicaid; Medicare.
Ownership Proprietary.
Admissions Requirements Minimum age 21.
Staff Physicians 4 (pt); RNs 12 (ft); LPNs 11
(ft); Orderlies 2 (ft); Nurses aides 43 (ft);
Physical therapists 2 (pt); Reality therapists 4
(ft), 2 (pt); Recreational therapists 4 (ft), 2 (pt);
Occupational therapists 1 (pt); Speech thera-
pists 1 (pt); Activities coordinators 4 (ft), 2 (pt);
Dietitians 1 (pt); Dentists 1 (pt); Ophthalmolo-
gists 1 (pt); Podiatrists 1 (pt); Audiologists 1
(pt).
Facilities Dining room; Physical therapy room;
Activities room; Chapel; Crafts room; Laundry
room; Barber/Beauty shop; Library.
Activities Arts and Crafts; Cards; Games;
Reading groups; Prayer groups; Movies; Shopping trips; Dances/Social or cultural gatherings;
Outings; Baseball games; Circus.
Description Facility features a highly developed
rehabilitation programs including physical, language, occupational, respiratory, and community integration. VA approved.

CHILLICOTHE

Parkhill Skilled Nursing Facility
Hillcrest Dr, Chillicothe, IL, 61523 (309)
274-2194
Admin John J Wachtel. *Medical Dir/Dir of
Nursing* Dr George A Hart.
Licensure Skilled Care; Intermediate Care.
Beds 75. *Certified* Medicaid; Medicare.
Ownership Nonprofit.
Admissions Requirements Medical examina-
tion; Physician's request.
Staff RNs 4 (ft), 5 (pt); LPNs 2 (ft), 6 (pt);
Nurses aides 17 (ft), 24 (pt); Activities coordi-
nators 1 (ft), 2 (pt).
Facilities Dining room; Physical therapy room;
Activities room; Laundry room; Barber/Beauty
shop.

Activities Arts and Crafts; Cards; Games;
Reading groups; Prayer groups; Movies; Dan-
ces/Social or cultural gatherings; Exercise
groups.

CHRISMAN

Pleasant Meadows Cristianvilo*
400 W Washington, Chrisman, IL, 61924 (217)
269-2396
Admin Robert Vincent.
Licensure Skilled Care. *Beds* 99. *Certified* Medicaid.
Ownership Nonprofit.

CICERO

Tower Pavilion
5825 W Cermak Rd, Cicero, IL, 60650 (312)
656-9120
Admin Michael T Dailey. *Medical Dir/Dir of
Nursing* Dr S Slodki.
Licensure Skilled Care; Intermediate Care.
Beds SNF 152; ICF 388. *Certified* Medicaid.
Ownership Proprietary.
Staff RNs 13 (ft), 3 (pt); LPNs 24 (ft), 1 (pt);
Orderlies 14 (ft); Nurses aides 82 (ft); Physical
therapists; Recreational therapists 1 (ft); Occu-
pational therapists; Speech therapists; Dentists
1 (pt); Podiatrists 1 (pt).
Facilities Dining room; Physical therapy room;
Activities room; Crafts room; Laundry room;
Barber/Beauty shop; Library.
Activities Arts and Crafts; Cards; Games; Pray-
er groups; Shopping trips; Dances/Social or cul-
tural gatherings; Cooking; Gardening.
Description Facility is centrally located near
Chicago's cultural and sports events, parks,
race tracks, and shopping.

CISNE

Cisne Manor Inc*
Watkins St, Cisne, IL, 62823 (618) 673-2177
Admin Carol A Lawler.
Licensure Intermediate Care. *Beds* 35. *Certi-
fied* Medicaid.
Ownership Proprietary.

CLIFTON

A Merkle-C Knipprath Nursing Home
Rt 1, Clifton, IL, 60927 (815) 694-2306
Admin Brother Damien.
Licensure Long-Term Care. *Beds* 99.
Ownership Nonprofit.
Admissions Requirements Medical examina-
tion; Physician's request.
Affiliation Roman Catholic
Facilities Dining room; Physical therapy room;
Activities room; Chapel; Crafts room; Laundry
room; Barber/Beauty shop; Library.
Activities Arts and Crafts; Cards; Games;
Reading groups; Prayer groups; Movies; Shop-
ping trips; Dances/Social or cultural gatherings.

CLINTON

Crest View Nursing Home
US Hwy 51 N, Clinton, IL, 61727 (217)
935-3826
Admin Douglas Graves. *Medical Dir/Dir of Nursing* Robert Myers MD.
Licensure Intermediate Care. *Beds* 108. *Certified* Medicaid.
Ownership Proprietary.
Admissions Requirements Minimum age 18; Medical examination.
Staff RNs 1 (pt); LPNs 5 (ft), 3 (pt); Nurses aides 24 (ft), 9 (pt); Recreational therapists 1 (pt); Occupational therapists 1 (pt); Activities coordinators 2 (ft); Dietitians 1 (pt).
Facilities Dining room; Physical therapy room; Activities room; Chapel; Crafts room; Laundry room; Barber/Beauty shop; Library.
Activities Arts and Crafts; Cards; Games; Reading groups; Prayer groups; Movies; Shopping trips; Dances/Social or cultural gatherings.
Description Privately owned and administered, the home has been serving Clinton and DeWitt counties for 29 years. It is located in a rural setting within the city limits.

Dewitt County Nursing Home
Rt 1, Clinton, IL, 61727 (217) 935-9418
Admin Norma G Reiman. *Medical Dir/Dir of Nursing* Selah Obasi MD.
Licensure Skilled Care; Intermediate Care; Sheltered Care. *Beds* SNF 30; ICF 60; Sheltered Care 25.
Ownership Public.
Admissions Requirements Minimum age 18; Medical examination; Physician's request.
Staff Physicians 7 (ft); RNs 2 (ft); LPNs 6 (ft), 1 (pt); Orderlies 1 (ft); Nurses aides 37 (ft); Physical therapists 1 (pt); Occupational therapists 1 (pt); Speech therapists 1 (pt); Activities coordinators 1 (ft); Dietitians 1 (pt); Dentists 1 (pt).
Facilities Dining room; Physical therapy room; Activities room; Crafts room; Laundry room; Barber/Beauty shop; Library.
Activities Arts and Crafts; Games; Reading groups; Prayer groups; Movies; Shopping trips; Dances/Social or cultural gatherings.

COAL VALLEY

Oak Glen Home
11210 95th St, Coal Valley, IL, 61240 (309)
799-3161
Admin David L Cray. *Medical Dir/Dir of Nursing* Alex J Pareigis MD.
Licensure Skilled Care; Intermediate Care. *Beds* 285. *Certified* Medicaid; Medicare.
Ownership Public.
Admissions Requirements Minimum age 18; Medical examination; Physician's request.
Staff Physicians 1 (pt); RNs 12 (ft); LPNs 20 (ft), 3 (pt); Orderlies 6 (ft); Nurses aides 47 (ft), 12 (pt); Activities coordinators 1 (ft); Dietitians 1 (pt).

COBDEN

Hillside Terrace*
Rt 3, Box 46, Cobden, IL, 62920 (618)

893-4214
Admin Donald H Lisch.
Licensure Skilled Care. *Beds* 74. *Certified* Medicaid.
Ownership Proprietary.

Tripp Shelter Care Home*
Box 336, Cobden, IL, 62920 (618) 893-2291
Admin Sylvia M Tripp.
Licensure Sheltered Care. *Beds* Sheltered Care 28.
Ownership Proprietary.

Village Sheltered Care Home*
114 Ash St, Cobden, IL, 62920 (618) 893-4122
Admin Henrietta Smith.
Licensure Sheltered Care. *Beds* Sheltered Care 22.
Ownership Proprietary.

COLCHESTER

Owen Care Center
22 N Hun, Colchester, IL, 62326 (309)
776-3236
Admin Mary E Garlick. *Medical Dir/Dir of Nursing* Stephan Roth MD.
Licensure Intermediate Care. *Beds* 49. *Certified* Medicaid.
Ownership Proprietary.
Admissions Requirements Minimum age 18; Medical examination.
Staff Physicians 6 (pt); RNs 3 (pt); LPNs 6 (pt); Orderlies 1 (pt); Nurses aides 3 (ft), 14 (pt); Physical therapists 1 (pt); Activities coordinators 1 (ft); Dietitians 1 (ft).
Facilities Dining room; Laundry room; Barber/Beauty shop.
Activities Arts and Crafts; Cards; Games; Reading groups; Prayer groups; Movies; Shopping trips; Dances/Social or cultural gatherings; Remotivation.
Description Free meals on wheels for community residents and a phone program to elderly shut-ins in community.

COLFAX

Octavia Manor Inc
402 S Harrison, Colfax, IL, 61728 (309)
723-2591
Admin Shirley K Geske. *Medical Dir/Dir of Nursing* Dr Marcus Que.
Licensure Intermediate Care. *Beds* 60. *Certified* Medicaid.
Ownership Proprietary.
Admissions Requirements Minimum age 60; Medical examination; Physician's request.
Staff Physicians 1 (pt); RNs 1 (ft), 1 (pt); LPNs 4 (ft), 4 (pt); Nurses aides 20 (ft), 15 (pt); Activities coordinators 1 (ft); Dietitians 1 (pt).
Facilities Dining room; Physical therapy room; Activities room; Crafts room; Laundry room; Barber/Beauty shop.
Activities Arts and Crafts; Cards; Games; Reading groups; Prayer groups; Movies; Shopping trips; Dances/Social or cultural gatherings.
Description Facility is located in a small town in a very remote, rural area; has a lot of community participation because facility is owned by a group of 30 local citizens.

COLLINSVILLE

Pleasant Rest Nursing Home*
614 N Summit, Collinsville, IL, 62234 (618)
344-8476
Admin Margaret M Myler.
Licensure Skilled Care. *Beds* 122. *Certified* Medicaid.
Ownership Proprietary.

CREAL SPRINGS

Creal Springs Nursing Home
S Line St, Creal Springs, IL, 62922 (618)
996-2313
Admin James F Avery. *Medical Dir/Dir of Nursing* Dr A Z Goldstein.
Licensure Skilled Care; Intermediate Care. *Beds* 80. *Certified* Medicaid.
Ownership Proprietary.
Admissions Requirements Minimum age 21; Medical examination; Physician's request.
Staff Physicians 3 (pt); RNs 1 (ft), 2 (pt); LPNs 7 (ft), 2 (pt); Orderlies 1 (ft); Nurses aides 19 (ft); Physical therapists 1 (pt); Reality therapists 1 (pt); Recreational therapists 1 (pt); Occupational therapists 1 (pt); Speech therapists 1 (pt); Activities coordinators 1 (ft); Dietitians 1 (pt); Dentists 1 (pt).
Facilities Dining room; Physical therapy room; Activities room; Crafts room; Laundry room; Barber/Beauty shop.
Activities Arts and Crafts; Cards; Games; Reading groups; Prayer groups; Movies; Shopping trips; Dances/Social or cultural gatherings.
Description Facility offers lakeside picnic area, boat rides, fishing, sightseeing tours, and a garden area for residents.

CRYSTAL LAKE

Crystal Pines*
335 Illinois St, Crystal Lake, IL, 60014 (815)
459-7791
Admin Jean C Lindquist.
Licensure Skilled Care. *Beds* 82. *Certified* Medicaid.
Ownership Proprietary.

Fair Oaks Nursing Home*
471 W Terra Cotta, Crystal Lake, IL, 60014
(815) 455-0550
Admin Carol A Louise.
Licensure Skilled Care. *Beds* 46.
Ownership Proprietary.

CUBA

Clayberg Fulton County Nursing Center
E Monroe St, Cuba, IL, 61427 (309) 785-5012
Admin Vicki S Hoke. *Medical Dir/Dir of Nursing* Dr Bruce Long.
Licensure Intermediate Care. *Beds* 49. *Certified* Medicaid.
Ownership Public.
Admissions Requirements Minimum age 62.
Facilities Dining room; Activities room; Crafts room; Laundry room; Barber/Beauty shop.
Activities Arts and Crafts; Cards; Games; Reading groups; Prayer groups; Movies; Dan-

ces/Social or cultural gatherings.

DANFORTH

Prairieview Lutheran Home
PO Box 4, Danforth, IL, 60930 (815) 269-2970
Admin Michael Royer.
Licensure Skilled Care; Intermediate Care.
Beds 60. *Certified* Medicaid.
Ownership Nonprofit.
Staff RNs 3 (ft), 2 (pt); LPNs 3 (ft), 3 (pt);
Orderlies 3 (ft); Nurses aides 15 (ft), 20 (pt);
Physical therapists 1 (pt); Speech therapists 1
(pt); Activities coordinators 2 (ft); Dietitians 1
(pt); Dentists 1 (pt); Podiatrists 1 (pt).
Affiliation Lutheran
Facilities Dining room; Physical therapy room;
Activities room; Chapel; Crafts room; Laundry
room; Barber/Beauty shop.
Activities Arts and Crafts; Cards; Games;
Reading groups; Prayer groups; Movies; Shop-
ping trips; Dances/Social or cultural gatherings;
Community college continuing education
classes.

DANVILLE

Americana Healthcare Center*
801 Logen Ave, Danville, IL, 61832 (217)
443-3106
Admin Maria S Meers.
Licensure Skilled Care. *Beds* 108. *Certified* Medicaid.
Ownership Proprietary.

Colonial Manor Inc
620 Warrington, Danville, IL, 61832 (217)
446-0660
Admin Richard W Black.
Licensure Skilled Care; Intermediate Care.
Beds 55. *Certified* Medicaid; Medicare.
Ownership Proprietary.
Staff RNs 3 (ft), 2 (pt); LPNs 2 (ft), 3 (pt);
Nurses aides 18 (ft), 2 (pt); Activities coordina-
tors 1 (ft); Dietitians 1 (pt).
Facilities Dining room; Laundry room; Barber-
/Beauty shop.
Activities Arts and Crafts; Cards; Games;
Reading groups; Prayer groups; Movies; Shop-
ping trips.

Danville Care Inc*
1701 N Bowman Ave, Danville, IL, 61832
(217) 443-2955
Admin Barbara Ann G Snapp.
Licensure Skilled Care; Intermediate Care.
Beds SNF 101; ICF 82. *Certified* Medicaid.
Ownership Proprietary.

Danville Manor*
1215 Holiday Dr, Danville, IL, 61832 (217)
443-4123
Admin Setsu Marks.
Licensure Intermediate Care; Developmentally
Disabled. *Beds* ICF 40; Developmentally
Disabled 43. *Certified* Medicaid.
Ownership Proprietary.

International Nursing Home of Danville*
207 S Buchanan, Danville, IL, 61832 (217)
446-1433

Admin Ruth Nance.
Licensure Intermediate Care. *Beds* 48. *Certi-
fied* Medicaid.
Ownership Nonprofit.

Vermillion Manor Nursing Home
RR 1, Box 13, Danville, IL, 61832 (217)
443-6430
Admin Brenda A Miller. *Medical Dir/Dir of
Nursing* E M Deuhirst MD.
Licensure Intermediate Care; Sheltered Care.
Beds 249. *Certified* Medicaid.
Ownership Public.
Admissions Requirements Medical examina-
tion; Physician's request.
Staff Physicians 1 (pt); RNs 2 (ft), 4 (pt); LPNs
11 (ft), 12 (pt); Nurses aides 96 (ft), 7 (pt).
Facilities Dining room; Physical therapy room;
Activities room; Chapel; Crafts room; Laundry
room; Barber/Beauty shop; Library.
Activities Arts and Crafts; Cards; Games;
Reading groups; Prayer groups; Movies; Shop-
ping trips; Dances/Social or cultural gatherings.
Description Recently license was converted to
249 intermediate; however, since the conver-
sion, sheltered care is still offered.

DE KALB

Community Center*
360 E Grand Ave, De Kalb, IL, 62526 (217)
428-6350
Admin Judy Weger.
Licensure Intermediate Care. *Beds* 58.
Ownership Proprietary.

De Kalb County Nursing Home*
2331 Sycamore Rd, De Kalb, IL, 60115 (815)
758-2477
Admin Stephen P Cichy.
Licensure Skilled Care. *Beds* 194. *Certified* Medicaid.
Ownership Public.

Oak Crest
2944 Greenwood Acres Dr, De Kalb, IL, 60115
(815) 756-8461
Admin Robert E Ash. *Medical Dir/Dir of
Nursing* Dr Stuart Olson.
Licensure Intermediate Care; Sheltered Care.
Beds ICF 30; Sheltered Care 36; Independent
73.
Ownership Nonprofit.
Admissions Requirements Minimum age 62;
Medical examination.
Staff RNs 3 (ft), 3 (pt); LPNs 2 (ft), 2 (pt);
Nurses aides 4 (ft), 18 (pt); Recreational thera-
pists 2 (ft); Activities coordinators 1 (ft).
Affiliation Methodist
Facilities Dining room; Physical therapy room;
Activities room; Chapel; Crafts room; Laundry
room; Barber/Beauty shop; Library.
Activities Arts and Crafts; Cards; Games;
Reading groups; Prayer groups; Movies; Shop-
ping trips; Dances/Social or cultural gatherings.

Pine Acres Retirement Center*
1212 S 2nd St, De Kalb, IL, 60115 (815)
758-8151
Admin Katherine A Keane.
Licensure Skilled Care. *Beds* 110. *Certified* Medicaid; Medicare.

Ownership Proprietary.

DECATUR

Americana Healthcare Center*
44 W Harrison St, Decatur, IL, 62526 (217)
877-7333
Admin G Edward Haywood Jr.
Licensure Skilled Care. *Beds* 96. *Certified* Medicaid; Medicare.
Ownership Proprietary.

Decatur Manor
136 S Dipper Ln, Decatur, IL, 62522 (217)
428-7767
Admin Candace J Carroll. *Medical Dir/Dir of
Nursing* Dr Kenneth J Rakowski.
Licensure Intermediate Care. *Beds* 49.
Ownership Proprietary.
Staff Physicians 1 (pt); RNs 1 (ft); LPNs 2 (ft),
3 (pt); Nurses aides 3 (ft), 3 (pt); Physical therapists 1 (pt); Recreational therapists 1 (pt); Occupational therapists 1 (pt); Speech therapists 1
(pt); Activities coordinators 1 (ft); Dietitians 2
(ft), 1 (pt); Dentists 1 (pt); Ophthalmologists 1
(pt); Podiatrists 1 (pt).
Facilities Dining room; Physical therapy room;
Activities room; Laundry room; Barber/Beauty
shop.
Activities Arts and Crafts; Games; Prayer
groups; Movies; Shopping trips; Dances/Social
or cultural gatherings.
Description Decatur Manor is a private pay,
intermediate care facility offering activities,
social services, nursing care, food services,
laundry services, and physical therapy by qualified, caring staff.

Fair Havens Christian Home
1790 S Fairview Ave, Decatur, IL, 62526 (217)
429-2551
Admin Norman E McCormick Jr. *Medical
Dir/Dir of Nursing* Dr Dale Sunderland.
Licensure Skilled Care. *Beds* 161. *Cer-
tified* Medicaid; Medicare.
Ownership Nonprofit.
Staff RNs 5 (ft), 5 (pt); LPNs 9 (ft), 9 (pt);
Orderlies 1 (ft); Nurses aides 35 (ft), 35 (pt);
Physical therapists 1 (pt).
Facilities Dining room; Physical therapy room;
Activities room; Chapel; Crafts room; Laundry
room; Barber/Beauty shop; Library.
Activities Arts and Crafts; Cards; Games;
Reading groups; Prayer groups; Movies; Shop-
ping trips; Dances/Social or cultural gatherings.

Lakeshore Manor Nursing Home*
1293 S 34th St, Decatur, IL, 62521 (217)
429-2313
Admin Shelley L and Warner Bennett.
Licensure Skilled Care. *Beds* 131. *Certified* Medicaid; Medicare.
Ownership Proprietary.

Lincoln Manor Inc*
438 W North St, Decatur, IL, 62522 (217)
429-7265
Admin Thomas W Booth.
Licensure Intermediate Care; Sheltered Care.
Beds ICF 126; Sheltered Care 5.
Ownership Proprietary.

Lincoln Manor—North Inc*
2650 N Monroe St, Decatur, IL, 62526 (217) 875-1973
Admin Shelba J Donoho.
Licensure Intermediate Care. *Beds* 121. *Certified* Medicaid.
Ownership Proprietary.

Monroe House*
2530 N Monroe St, Decatur, IL, 62526 (217) 875-0920
Admin Dwight L Miller.
Licensure Skilled Care; Intermediate Care.
Beds SNF 153; ICF 51.
Ownership Proprietary.

Northpark Manor
2601 N Union, Decatur, IL, 62526 (217) 877-5171
Admin Carol S Johnson. *Medical Dir/Dir of Nursing* Dr Rohidas Patil.
Licensure Intermediate Care. *Beds* 124. *Certified* Medicaid.
Ownership Proprietary.
Admissions Requirements Minimum age 18.
Staff RNs 1 (ft), 1 (pt); LPNs 4 (ft), 5 (pt); Nurses aides 9 (ft), 7 (pt); Activities coordinators 1 (ft).
Facilities Dining room; Activities room; Crafts room; Laundry room; Barber/Beauty shop.
Activities Arts and Crafts; Cards; Games; Shopping trips; Dances/Social or cultural gatherings.
Description Only ambulatory patients accepted. Let the Sun Shine, Inc a not-for-profit workshop where residents manufacture wooden items for retail sale; workers are paid based on production. Point system—residents earn points for performing daily living activities, attending activities, doing jobs; points redeemed weekly for many items.

Pershing Estates
1016 W Pershing Rd, Decatur, IL, 62526 (217) 875-0833
Admin Dennis Miller. *Medical Dir/Dir of Nursing* Dr R Patil.
Licensure Intermediate Care. *Beds* 127. *Certified* Medicaid.
Ownership Proprietary.
Staff Physicians 1 (pt); RNs 2 (pt); LPNs 8 (ft), 4 (pt); Orderlies 1 (pt); Nurses aides 38 (ft); Recreational therapists 1 (pt); Occupational therapists 1 (pt); Activities coordinators 2 (ft); Dietitians 1 (pt).

South Side Manor
729 S Webster, Decatur, IL, 62521
Admin Judy Busing.
Licensure Intermediate Care for Mentally Retarded. *Beds* 15. *Certified* Medicaid.
Ownership Proprietary.
Admissions Requirements Minimum age 18.
Staff Nurses aides 4 (ft), 6 (pt); Activities coordinators 1 (ft), 1 (pt).
Facilities Dining room; Laundry room.
Activities Arts and Crafts; Cards; Games; Movies; Shopping trips; Dances/Social or cultural gatherings.
Description Facility provides a comfortable home-like atmosphere for 15 developmentally disabled adults, programs of daily living skills, behavior/social areas, and leisure time activi-

ties. Personal goals are set up on an individual basis with an overall facility goal of providing these special people with a program to help them prepare for their transition into the community setting.

DEERFIELD

Brentwood North Nursing and Rehabilitation Center*
3705 Deerfield Rd, Deerfield, IL, 60015 (312) 459-1200
Admin Sheldon M Novoselsky.
Licensure Skilled Care; Intermediate Care.
Beds SNF 124; ICF 124.
Ownership Proprietary.

Golf View Developmental Center*
9555 W Golf Rd, Deerfield, IL, 60016 (312) 827-6628
Admin Anne L Tossi.
Licensure Intermediate Care. *Beds* 118.
Ownership Proprietary.

Whitehall North
300 Waukegan Rd, Deerfield, IL, 60015 (312) 945-4600
Admin Barbara Harms RN.
Licensure Skilled Care. *Beds* 170.
Ownership Proprietary.
Admissions Requirements Medical examination.
Staff RNs 40 (ft); LPNs 2 (ft); Orderlies 2 (ft); Nurses aides 80 (ft); Physical therapists 1 (ft); Recreational therapists 2 (ft), 3 (pt); Occupational therapists 1 (pt); Speech therapists 1 (pt); Dietitians 1 (ft); Dentists 1 (pt); Podiatrists 1 (pt).
Facilities Dining room; Physical therapy room; Activities room; Chapel; Crafts room; Laundry room; Barber/Beauty shop; Library.
Activities Arts and Crafts; Cards; Games; Reading groups; Prayer groups; Movies; Dances/Social or cultural gatherings.

DES PLAINES

Ballard Nursing Center Inc
9300 Ballard Rd, Des Plaines, IL, 60016 (312) 299-0182
Admin Mark Pick. *Medical Dir/Dir of Nursing* Dr Mazur.
Licensure Skilled Care; Intermediate Care.
Beds 231. *Certified* Medicaid; Medicare.
Ownership Proprietary.
Admissions Requirements Minimum age 60; Medical examination.
Staff RNs 12 (ft), 4 (pt); LPNs 6 (ft), 1 (pt); Orderlies 13 (ft); Nurses aides 39 (pt); Physical therapists 1 (ft); Reality therapists 1 (pt); Recreational therapists 1 (pt); Occupational therapists 1 (pt); Speech therapists 1 (pt); Activities coordinators 1 (ft); Dietitians 1 (pt); Dentists 1 (pt); Ophthalmologists 1 (pt); Podiatrists 1 (pt); Audiologists 1 (pt).
Facilities Dining room; Physical therapy room; Activities room; Crafts room; Laundry room; Barber/Beauty shop.
Activities Arts and Crafts; Cards; Games; Reading groups; Prayer groups; Movies; Dances/Social or cultural gatherings; Foster grand-

parents program; Pet therapy program.
Description Strong physical therapy department with full-time therapists; strong activities program with many activities geared towards different needs, i.e., stroke therapy class, exercise class, reality orientation class; strong social service department with 4 social workers providing support groups for residents and their families.

Holy Family Health Center
2380 Dempster St, Des Plaines, IL, 60016 (312) 296-3335
Admin Elizabeth Trembczynski. *Medical Dir/Dir of Nursing* Dr William Bagnuolo.
Licensure Skilled Care. *Beds* 372.
Ownership Nonprofit.
Admissions Requirements Medical examination.
Staff Physicians 1 (pt); RNs 33 (ft), 21 (pt); LPNs 5 (ft), 3 (pt); Orderlies 13 (ft), 5 (pt); Nurses aides 99 (ft), 18 (pt); Physical therapists 5 (ft); Recreational therapists 3 (ft), 2 (pt); Activities coordinators 1 (ft).
Affiliation Roman Catholic
Facilities Dining room; Physical therapy room; Activities room; Chapel; Barber/Beauty shop; Library.
Activities Arts and Crafts; Cards; Games; Reading groups; Movies; Dances/Social or cultural gatherings.
Description Facility has a full body whirlpool in which the resident is in a reclining position, used for the treatment of decubitus ulcers, contractures, and arthritic pain in joints.

Lee Manor*
1301 Lee St, Des Plaines, IL, 60016 (312) 827-9450
Admin Donald Plodzien.
Licensure Skilled Care. *Beds* 272. *Certified* Medicaid; Medicare.
Ownership Proprietary.

Nazarethville
300 N River Rd, Des Plaines, IL, 60016 (312) 297-5900
Admin RoseMarie Machalski. *Medical Dir/Dir of Nursing* Henry Niemeyer MD.
Licensure Intermediate Care; Sheltered Care.
Beds ICF 68; Sheltered Care 15. *Certified* Medicaid.
Ownership Nonprofit.
Admissions Requirements Minimum age 70; Medical examination; Physician's request.
Staff RNs 2 (ft), 10 (pt); LPNs 3 (pt); Nurses aides 20 (ft), 9 (pt); Activities coordinators 1 (ft).
Affiliation Roman Catholic
Facilities Dining room; Physical therapy room; Activities room; Chapel; Crafts room; Laundry room; Barber/Beauty shop; Library.
Activities Arts and Crafts; Cards; Games; Reading groups; Prayer groups; Movies; Dances/Social or cultural gatherings.

Oakton Pavilion Inc
1660 Oakton Pl, Des Plaines, IL, 60016 (312) 299-5588
Admin Jay Lewkowtiz. *Medical Dir/Dir of Nursing* R Levitan MD.
Licensure Skilled Care; Intermediate Care.
Beds 294. *Certified* Medicaid; Medicare.

Ownership Proprietary.
Admissions Requirements Minimum age 18; Medical examination; Physician's request.
Staff Physicians 3 (pt); RNs 28 (ft), 2 (pt); LPNs 7 (ft), 1 (pt); Orderlies 35 (ft); Nurses aides 110 (ft); Recreational therapists 8 (ft); Activities coordinators 1 (ft).
Facilities Dining room; Physical therapy room; Activities room; Chapel; Crafts room; Laundry room; Barber/Beauty shop; Library.
Activities Arts and Crafts; Cards; Games; Reading groups; Prayer groups; Movies; Shopping trips; Dances/Social or cultural gatherings; Intergenerational programs.
Description With community in mind, Oakton Pavillion sponsors tutorial programs for primary grades at 2 elementary schools; full-time chaplaincy program; seminars for the professional community; respite care; membership and provision of sites for community groups dealing with aging; support groups for families of residents. VA approved.

DIXON

Dixon Health Center
141 N Court, Dixon, IL, 61021 (815) 288-1477
Admin Gregory A Olson. *Medical Dir/Dir of Nursing* Dr Howard Edwards Jr.
Licensure Skilled Care; Intermediate Care.
Beds SNF 110; ICF 17. *Certified* Medicaid.
Ownership Proprietary.
Admissions Requirements Minimum age 18; Medical examination; Physician's request.
Staff Physicians 6 (pt); RNs 6 (ft), 3 (pt); LPNs 2 (ft), 1 (pt); Orderlies 1 (pt); Nurses aides 14 (ft), 7 (pt); Physical therapists 1 (ft); Reality therapists 1 (pt); Recreational therapists 1 (pt); Occupational therapists 1 (pt); Speech therapists 1 (pt); Activities coordinators 1 (ft); Dietitians 1 (ft); Dentists 1 (pt); Podiatrists 1 (pt).
Facilities Dining room; Physical therapy room; Activities room; Crafts room; Laundry room; Barber/Beauty shop; Library.
Activities Arts and Crafts; Cards; Games; Reading groups; Prayer groups; Movies; Shopping trips; Dances/Social or cultural gatherings.
Description Center is a newly remodeled 110-bed skilled nursing facility offering full-time registered physical therapist for both inpatient and outpatient services; also provides a 17-bed ICF wing that includes all private rooms and personal attention.

Heritage Square
620 N Ottawa Ave, Dixon, IL, 61021 (815) 288-2251
Admin Raymond W Bowman.
Licensure Intermediate Care; Sheltered Care.
Beds ICF 19; Sheltered Care 94. *Certified* Medicaid.
Ownership Nonprofit.
Admissions Requirements Minimum age 60; Medical examination; Physician's request.
Facilities Dining room; Physical therapy room; Activities room; Crafts room; Laundry room; Barber/Beauty shop; Library.
Activities Arts and Crafts; Cards; Games; Reading groups; Prayer groups; Movies; Shopping trips; Dances/Social or cultural gatherings.
Description The sheltered care design is such

that residents live in clusters of 4; this gives much freedom and a feeling of not living in a large group. All rooms are private.

Lee County Nursing Home
800 Division St, Dixon, IL, 61021 (815) 284-3393
Admin Sylvia E Montavon. *Medical Dir/Dir of Nursing* Gordon McFetridge MD.
Licensure Skilled Care; Intermediate Care.
Beds 92. *Certified* Medicaid.
Ownership Public.
Admissions Requirements Minimum age 18; Medical examination; Physician's request.
Staff RNs 4 (ft), 1 (pt); LPNs 4 (ft), 3 (pt); Orderlies 1 (ft); Nurses aides 21 (ft), 18 (pt); Activities coordinators 3 (ft), 2 (pt); Dietitians 6 (ft), 11 (pt).
Facilities Dining room; Physical therapy room; Activities room; Chapel; Crafts room; Laundry room; Barber/Beauty shop; Library.
Activities Arts and Crafts; Cards; Games; Reading groups; Prayer groups; Movies; Shopping trips; Dances/Social or cultural gatherings; Junior College classes.
Description Facility for county residents only with VA and Medicaid contracts; ongoing waiting list.

Village Inn*
135 N Court St, Dixon, IL, 61021 (815) 284-2253
Admin Karen O'Hare.
Licensure Intermediate Care. *Beds* 134.
Ownership Proprietary.

DOLTON

Country Manor Nursing Center*
1635 E 154th St, Dolton, IL, 60419 (312) 841-9550
Admin Isaac Begin.
Licensure Skilled Care; Intermediate Care.
Beds 192. *Certified* Medicaid.
Ownership Proprietary.

Dolton Terrace
14325 S Blackstone, Dolton, IL, 60419 (312) 849-5000
Admin Roxane Goad.
Licensure Skilled Care. *Beds* 61. *Certified* Medicaid; Medicare.
Ownership Proprietary.
Admissions Requirements Medical examination.
Staff Physicians 5 (pt); RNs 2 (ft), 3 (pt); LPNs 2 (ft), 3 (pt); Nurses aides 10 (ft), 13 (pt); Physical therapists 1 (ft), 1 (pt); Occupational therapists 1 (ft); Speech therapists 1 (ft); Activities coordinators 1 (ft), 1 (pt); Dietitians 1 (ft), 1 (pt); Dentists 1 (pt); Ophthalmologists 1 (pt); Podiatrists 1 (pt); Podiatrists 1 (pt); Audiologists 1 (pt).
Facilities Dining room; Physical therapy room; Laundry room; Barber/Beauty shop.
Activities Arts and Crafts; Cards; Games; Reading groups; Prayer groups; Shopping trips.
Description We are a very friendly facility of 67 beds. Our care is outstanding and our residents love it here. We have very few complaints. All of our programs are excellent.

DONGOLA

Keller Sheltered Care Home 1*
201 Cross St, Dongola, IL, 62926 (618) 827-4402
Admin Dorothy Henard.
Licensure Sheltered Care. *Beds* Sheltered Care 26.
Ownership Proprietary.

DOWNERS GROVE

Fairview Baptist Home
7S241 Fairview, Downers Grove, IL, 60516 (312) 852-4350
Admin Wesley P Ringdahl. *Medical Dir/Dir of Nursing* Farouk F Girgis MD.
Licensure Intermediate Care; Sheltered Care.
Beds ICF 65; Sheltered Care 124.
Ownership Nonprofit.
Admissions Requirements Minimum age 60; Medical examination.
Staff RNs 3 (ft), 9 (pt); LPNs 1 (pt); Orderlies 1 (ft); Nurses aides 22 (ft), 6 (pt); Activities coordinators 1 (ft), 2 (pt).
Affiliation Baptist
Facilities Dining room; Activities room; Chapel; Crafts room; Laundry room; Barber/Beauty shop; Library.
Activities Arts and Crafts; Cards; Games; Reading groups; Prayer groups; Movies; Shopping trips; Dances/Social or cultural gatherings.
Description Fairview Baptist Home is located on a tastefully landscaped 38-acre site in Downers Grove, a suburb 20 miles west of Chicago. Top priorities are to provide a Christian life style; physical, intellectual, and spiritual support; and an opportunity for active, productive living in a caring family setting.

Rest Haven West Nursing Home
3450 Saratoga Dr, Downers Grove, IL, 60515 (312) 963-2900
Admin Mary Busch. *Medical Dir/Dir of Nursing* Anthony Kotin.
Licensure Skilled Care. *Beds* 145.
Ownership Proprietary.
Admissions Requirements Minimum age 18.
Staff Physicians; RNs; LPNs; Orderlies; Nurses aides; Physical therapists; Reality therapists; Recreational therapists; Occupational therapists; Speech therapists; Activities coordinators; Dietitians; Dentists; Ophthalmologists; Podiatrists; Audiologists.
Affiliation Christian Reformed
Facilities Dining room; Physical therapy room; Activities room; Chapel; Crafts room; Laundry room; Barber/Beauty shop; Library.
Activities Arts and Crafts; Cards; Games; Reading groups; Prayer groups; Movies; Shopping trips.
Description Facility is a one-story building with very homey atmosphere. Also there is an Alzheimer's program.

DU QUOIN

Fair Acres Nursing Home Inc*
514 E Jackson, Du Quoin, IL, 62832 (618) 542-4731
Admin Virginia R Edwards.

Licensure Skilled Care; Intermediate Care.
Beds SNF 29; ICF 45. *Certified* Medicaid;
Medicare.
Ownership Proprietary.

Fairview Nursing Center*
602 E Jackson, Du Quoin, IL, 62832 (618)
542-3441
Admin Carol S Robinson.
Licensure Intermediate Care. *Beds* 77. *Certified* Medicaid.
Ownership Proprietary.

DURAND

Medina Nursing Center*
PO Box 538, Durand, IL, 61024 (815)
248-2151
Admin Holgeir J Oksnevad.
Licensure Skilled Care. *Beds* 81. *Certified* Medicaid.
Ownership Proprietary.

DWIGHT

Continental Manors Inc*
300 E Mazon, Dwight, IL, 60420 (815)
584-1240
Admin Rudy Michalek.
Licensure Skilled Care. *Beds* 92. *Certified* Medicaid.
Ownership Proprietary.

EAST MOLINE

East Moline Care Center
4700 10th St, East Moline, IL, 61244 (309)
796-0922
Admin Sharon F Carter. *Medical Dir/Dir of Nursing* John M Peterson MD.
Licensure Intermediate Care. *Beds* 97. *Certified* Medicaid.
Ownership Proprietary.
Admissions Requirements Minimum age 65;
Medical examination; Physician's request.
Staff RNs 4 (ft); LPNs 6 (ft); Orderlies 1 (ft);
Nurses aides 35 (ft); Physical therapists 1 (pt);
Recreational therapists 1 (pt); Occupational
therapists 1 (pt); Speech therapists 1 (pt);
Activities coordinators 1 (ft); Dietitians 1 (pt);
Dentists 1 (pt).
Facilities Dining room; Physical therapy room;
Activities room; Crafts room; Barber/Beauty
shop.
Activities Arts and Crafts; Cards; Games;
Reading groups; Movies; Shopping trips; Dances/Social or cultural gatherings.

East Moline Garden Plaza
430 30th Ave, East Moline, IL, 61244 (309)
755-3466
Admin Sharon Baraks. *Medical Dir/Dir of Nursing* Dr Gregory Motl.
Licensure Intermediate Care. *Beds* 120. *Certified* Medicaid.
Ownership Proprietary.
Admissions Requirements Minimum age 40;
Medical examination.
Staff RNs 1 (ft); LPNs 4 (ft), 3 (pt); Nurses
aides 8 (ft), 8 (pt); Reality therapists 2 (pt);

Activities coordinators 2 (ft), 1 (pt); Dietitians
1 (ft); Dentists 1 (pt); Physical therapy aides 2
(ft); Speech therapy aide 1 (pt).
Facilities Dining room; Physical therapy room;
Activities room; Chapel; Crafts room; Laundry
room; Barber/Beauty shop; Library; Speech
therapy room.
Activities Arts and Crafts; Cards; Games;
Reading groups; Prayer groups; Movies; Shopping trips; Dances/Social or cultural gatherings;
Money management; Cooking classes; Educational inservices.
Description Facility is all on one floor close to
bus line and shopping; library for the blind
nearby; some of the mentally handicapped
attend workshops with follow-ups by social
worker and activitiy director. Facility has a van
for outings.

EAST PEORIA

Fondulac Nursing Manor
901 Illini Dr, East Peoria, IL, 61611 (309)
694-6446
Admin Marsha Reardon. *Medical Dir/Dir of Nursing* Romona Brooks RN.
Licensure Skilled Care; Intermediate Care.
Beds 98. *Certified* Medicaid.
Ownership Proprietary.
Staff RNs 3 (ft); LPNs 5 (ft); Orderlies 2 (ft);
Nurses aides 18 (ft); Physical therapists 1 (ft), 1
(pt); Speech therapists 1 (pt); Activities coordinators 1 (ft), 2 (pt); Dietitians 1 (ft).
Facilities Dining room; Physical therapy room;
Activities room; Laundry room; Barber/Beauty
shop; Library.
Activities Arts and Crafts; Cards; Games;
Reading groups; Prayer groups; Movies; Dances/Social or cultural gatherings.

Good Samaritan Nursing Home*
1910 Springfield Rd, East Peoria, IL, 61611
(309) 694-1435
Admin Tommy E Wittekiend.
Licensure Intermediate Care. *Beds* 120. *Certified* Medicaid.
Ownership Proprietary.

EAST SAINT LOUIS

Briarcliff Health Care Center
3354 Jerome Ln, East Saint Louis, IL, 62206
(618) 337-9400
Admin Margie Guetterman. *Medical Dir/Dir of Nursing* Theo Bryan MD.
Licensure Skilled Care; Intermediate Care.
Beds SNF 51; ICF 89. *Certified* Medicaid;
Medicare.
Ownership Proprietary.
Admissions Requirements Physician's request.
Staff Physicians 2 (ft), 4 (pt); RNs 2 (ft); LPNs
10 (ft); Nurses aides 32 (ft); Physical therapists
2 (ft); Reality therapists 1 (ft); Recreational therapists 2 (ft); Speech therapists 1 (ft); Activities
coordinators 1 (ft); Dietitians 1 (ft); Dentists 1
(pt); Ophthalmologists 1 (pt); Podiatrists 1 (pt);
Audiologists 1 (pt).
Facilities Dining room; Physical therapy room;
Activities room; Laundry room; Barber/Beauty
shop.
Activities Arts and Crafts; Cards; Games;

Reading groups; Prayer groups; Movies; Shopping trips; Dances/Social or cultural gatherings.
Description Briarcliff is a progressive health
care center offering an environment reminiscent of past values while giving modern based
care. 24-hour professional staff continues to
maintain the trust that is foundation, motto is
"we care".

EDWARDSVILLE

Anna-Henry Nursing Home*
637 Hillsboro Ave, Edwardsville, IL, 62025
(618) 656-1136
Admin Mary Joann Gaertner.
Licensure Skilled Care; Intermediate Care.
Beds SNF 64; ICF 61. *Certified* Medicaid.
Ownership Proprietary.

Eden Village Care Center
400 S Station Rd, Edwardsville, IL, 62025 (618)
288-5016
Admin Linda S Hellenga. *Medical Dir/Dir of Nursing* Michael Rallo MD.
Licensure Skilled Care; Intermediate Care.
Beds 120. *Certified* Medicaid.
Ownership Nonprofit.
Admissions Requirements Minimum age 18;
Medical examination; Physician's request.
Affiliation Church of Christ
Facilities Dining room; Physical therapy room;
Activities room; Crafts room; Laundry room;
Barber/Beauty shop; Library.
Activities Arts and Crafts; Cards; Games;
Reading groups; Prayer groups; Movies; Shopping trips; Dances/Social or cultural gatherings.

Edwardsville Care Center
University Dr, Rt 8, Edwardsville, IL, 62025
(618) 656-1081
Admin Vincent A Aiello. *Medical Dir/Dir of Nursing* Robert Ayres.
Licensure Skilled Care; Intermediate Care.
Beds SNF 92; ICF 28. *Certified* Medicaid;
Medicare.
Ownership Proprietary.
Admissions Requirements Minimum age 21.
Staff RNs 3 (ft), 2 (pt); LPNs 8 (ft), 2 (pt);
Nurses aides 30 (ft), 3 (pt); Physical therapists 1
(ft); Recreational therapists 1 (ft); Occupational
therapists 1 (pt); Speech therapists 1 (pt);
Activities coordinators 1 (ft); Dietitians 1 (pt);
Dentists 1 (pt); Podiatrists 1 (pt); Audiologists 1
(pt).
Facilities Dining room; Physical therapy room;
Activities room; Crafts room; Laundry room;
Barber/Beauty shop.
Activities Arts and Crafts; Cards; Games;
Reading groups; Prayer groups; Movies; Shopping trips; Dances/Social or cultural gatherings.
Description Facility is professionally operated.
Staff is well trained in all aspects of their job.
Facility is odor-free. Physical therapy and
rehabilitation programs are very productive.

Madison County Nursing Home*
2121 Troy Rd, Edwardsville, IL, 62025 (618)
692-4556
Admin Billy L Rainwater.
Licensure Intermediate Care. *Beds* 100. *Certified* Medicaid.
Ownership Public.

Madison County Sheltered Care
S Main St, Box 441, Edwardsville, IL, 62025
(618) 692-4502
Admin Elizabeth M Agles.
Licensure Sheltered Care. *Beds* Sheltered Care
65.
Ownership Public.
Admissions Requirements Minimum age 18;
Medical examination.
Staff LPNs 1 (ft); Nurses aides 8 (ft), 9 (pt);
Activities coordinators 1 (ft); Dietitians 1 (pt).
Facilities Dining room; Activities room; Laundry room; Library.
Activities Arts and Crafts; Cards; Games;
Reading groups; Prayer groups; Movies; Shopping trips; Dances/Social or cultural gatherings;
Greenhouse; Vegetable garden for residents.
Description Facility is located on 11 acres of
large, spacious grounds 2 blocks from downtown Edwardsville.

EFFINGHAM

Effingham Care Center*
1600 W Lakewood, Effingham, IL, 62401 (217)
347-7781
Admin Joseph Edwards.
Licensure Intermediate Care. *Beds* 93.
Ownership Proprietary.

Lakeland Nursing Center*
800 W Temple, Effingham, IL, 62401 (217)
342-2171
Admin Karen S Wendt.
Licensure Skilled Care; Intermediate Care.
Beds SNF 154; ICF 48. *Certified* Medicaid;
Medicare.
Ownership Proprietary.

Marks Manor Nursing Home
1115 N Wenthe, Effingham, IL, 62401 (217)
347-7121
Admin Ernie Marks. *Medical Dir/Dir of
Nursing* Mary Ellen Siemer.
Licensure Skilled Care; Intermediate Care.
Beds 118. *Certified* Medicaid.
Ownership Proprietary.
Admissions Requirements Minimum age 18;
Medical examination.
Staff Physicians 3 (ft), 3 (pt); RNs 4 (ft); LPNs
7 (ft); Orderlies 4 (ft); Nurses aides 20 (ft);
Physical therapists 1 (pt); Speech therapists 1
(pt); Activities coordinators 1 (ft); Dietitians 1
(pt); Dentists 1 (pt).

EL PASO

El Paso Hawthorne Lodge*
850 E 2nd St, El Paso, IL, 61738 (309)
527-2700
Admin Becky Hall.
Licensure Skilled Care. *Beds* 123. *Certified* Medicaid; Medicare.
Ownership Proprietary.

McDaniel Nursing Home*
555 E Clay St, El Paso, IL, 61738 (309)
527-6240
Admin Mary McDaniel.
Licensure Skilled Care. *Beds* 49. *Certified* Medicaid; Medicare.

Ownership Proprietary.

ELDORADO

Eldorado Nursing Home Inc
3rd and Railroad Sts, Eldorado, IL, 62930
(618) 273-3318
Admin George W Baker.
Licensure Intermediate Care. *Beds* 74. *Certified* Medicaid.
Ownership Proprietary.

Fountainview Inc*
Rt 45, S Jefferson, Eldorado, IL, 62930 (618)
273-3353
Admin Mary F Watson.
Licensure Intermediate Care. *Beds* 123. *Certified* Medicaid.
Ownership Proprietary.

Good Shepherd Nursing Home 1*
1700 Jasper St, Eldorado, IL, 62930 (618)
273-2161
Admin Harold Finnie.
Licensure Intermediate Care. *Beds* 79. *Certified* Medicaid.
Ownership Proprietary.

Magnolia Manor Inc*
1100 Grant St, Eldorado, IL, 62930 (618)
273-5261
Admin Nigel Mibs.
Licensure Sheltered Care. *Beds* Sheltered Care
44.
Ownership Proprietary.

ELGIN

Americana Nursing Center
180 S State, Elgin, IL, 60120 (312) 742-3310
Admin Katherine Keane. *Medical Dir/Dir of
Nursing* Vikram Shuh MD.
Licensure Skilled Care; Intermediate Care.
Beds SNF 43; ICF 30. *Certified* Medicare.
Ownership Proprietary.
Admissions Requirements Minimum age 18;
Medical examination; Physician's request.
Staff Physicians 3 (pt); RNs 11 (ft); LPNs 2
(ft); Orderlies 1 (ft); Nurses aides 20 (ft), 3 (pt);
Physical therapists 1 (ft); Occupational therapists 1 (pt); Speech therapists 1 (pt); Activities
coordinators 1 (ft); Dietitians 1 (ft); Dentists 1
(pt); Ophthalmologists 1 (pt); Podiatrists 1 (pt);
Audiologists 1 (pt).
Facilities Dining room; Physical therapy room;
Activities room; Crafts room; Laundry room;
Barber/Beauty shop; Living rooms.
Activities Arts and Crafts; Cards; Games;
Reading groups; Prayer groups; Movies; Shopping trips; Dances/Social or cultural gatherings;
Country store.
Description Small, homey, comfortable, clean,
odor-free facility that offers professional, caring
staff; excellent rehabilitation program for all
patients; and an excellent activities program.
Admission and discharge planning offered;
community oriented volunteer group of
approximately 35-50 people.

Apostolic Christian Resthaven*
971 Bode Rd, Elgin, IL, 60120 (312) 695-9600
Admin William R Strackany.
Licensure Sheltered Care. *Beds* Sheltered Care
31.
Ownership Nonprofit.
Affiliation Apostolic Christian

Elgin Community Living Facility*
1640 Mark Ave, Elgin, IL, 60120 (312)
741-9175
Admin James W McNeil.
Licensure Intermediate Care. *Beds* 20.
Ownership Nonprofit.

**Ray Graham Elmhurst Convalescent Living
Facility***
188–192 E Park Ave, Elgin, IL, 60126 (312)
543-2400
Admin James Durnbaugh.
Licensure Intermediate Care. *Beds* 21.
Ownership Nonprofit.

Imperial Nursing Center of Elgin*
50 N Jane Dr, Elgin, IL, 60120 (312) 697-3750
Admin Richard J Payne.
Licensure Skilled Care. *Beds* 203. *Certified* Medicaid; Medicare.
Ownership Proprietary.

Little Angels Nursing Home Inc*
Rt 4, Box 304, Elgin, IL, 60120 (312) 741-1609
Admin Shelley C Wasmond.
Licensure Skilled Care; Intermediate Care.
Beds SNF 50; ICF 22. *Certified* Medicaid.
Ownership Proprietary.

Mary Margaret Manor Inc
134 N McLean Blvd, Elgin, IL, 60120 (312)
742-8822
Admin Gerald J Bowes.
Licensure Skilled Care; Intermediate Care.
Beds 106.
Ownership Proprietary.
Admissions Requirements Minimum age 55;
Medical examination; Physician's request.
Facilities Dining room; Physical therapy room;
Activities room; Crafts room; Barber/Beauty
shop.
Activities Arts and Crafts; Cards; Games;
Reading groups; Prayer groups; Movies; Shopping trips; Dances/Social or cultural gatherings.

Oak Crest Residence*
204 S State St, Elgin, IL, 60120 (312) 742-2255
Admin Dorcas Meissner.
Licensure Sheltered Care. *Beds* Sheltered Care
42.
Ownership Nonprofit.

Olivette Nursing Home
355 Raymond St, Elgin, IL, 60120 (312)
695-4300
Admin Michael A Calogero. *Medical Dir/Dir
of Nursing* Dr V Shah.
Licensure Skilled Care; Intermediate Care.
Beds SNF 72; ICF 18.
Ownership Nonprofit.
Facilities Dining room; Physical therapy room;
Activities room; Laundry room; Barber/Beauty
shop.
Activities Arts and Crafts; Cards; Games; Prayer groups; Movies; Dances/Social or cultural

gatherings.

ELIZABETH

Elizabeth Nursing Home Inc
540 Pleasant St, Elizabeth, IL, 61028 (815)
858-2275
Admin Nelson E Marks. *Medical Dir/Dir of
Nursing* Helen Reid.
Licensure Intermediate Care. *Beds* 49. *Certified* Medicaid.
Ownership Proprietary.
Admissions Requirements Minimum age 65;
Medical examination.
Staff RNs; LPNs; Nurses aides; Physical therapists; Reality therapists; Recreational therapists;
Occupational therapists; Activities coordinators; Dietitians; Dentists.
Facilities Dining room; Physical therapy room;
Activities room; Chapel; Crafts room; Laundry
room; Barber/Beauty shop.
Activities Arts and Crafts; Cards; Games; Prayer groups; Movies; Shopping trips; Dances/Social or cultural gatherings; Pet shows; Picnics;
Van rides; Active nursing home auxiliary.
Description Facility is located in a beautiful
rural setting; building is fireproof and air conditioned; approved activity program.

ELMHURST

Elmhurst Extended Care Center Inc
200 E Lake St, Elmhurst, IL, 60126 (312)
834-4337
Admin John Massard. *Medical Dir/Dir of
Nursing* Paul J Concepcion MD.
Licensure Skilled Care. *Beds* 112. *Certified* Medicaid; Medicare.
Ownership Proprietary.
Admissions Requirements Minimum age 18;
Medical examination; Physician's request.
Staff Physicians 4 (pt); RNs 9 (ft), 4 (pt); LPNs
5 (ft), 4 (pt); Orderlies 2 (ft), 1 (pt); Nurses aides
27 (ft), 28 (pt); Physical therapists 1 (pt); Recreational therapists 1 (pt); Occupational therapists
2 (pt); Speech therapists 1 (pt); Activities coordinators 4 (pt); Dietitians 1 (ft); Dentists 1 (pt);
Ophthalmologists 1 (pt); Podiatrists 1 (pt);
Audiologists 1 (pt).
Facilities Dining room; Physical therapy room;
Activities room; Chapel; Crafts room; Laundry
room; Barber/Beauty shop; Library.
Activities Arts and Crafts; Cards; Games;
Reading groups; Prayer groups; Movies; Shopping trips; Resident council.
Description Located on lovely grounds, Center
patients enjoy the warm months with outdoor
walkways and benches surrounding the facility;
24-hour nursing care provides security, and a
myriad of activities make for a rich and varied
life.

Elmhurst Terrace Convalescent Center*
127 W Diversey, Elmhurst, IL, 60126 (312)
530-5225
Admin Shirley A Holt.
Licensure Skilled Care; Intermediate Care.
Beds SNF 125; ICF 63. *Certified* Medicaid;
Medicare.
Ownership Proprietary.

ELMWOOD PARK

Royal Elm Inc*
7733 Grand Ave, Elmwood Park, IL, 60635
(312) 452-9200
Admin David J Tessler.
Licensure Skilled Care. *Beds* 245. *Certified* Medicaid.
Ownership Proprietary.

ENERGY

Mattingly Health Care Center
E College St, Energy, IL, 62933 (618) 942-7014
Admin Brenda J Loyd. *Medical Dir/Dir of
Nursing* Roger C Hendricks MD.
Licensure Intermediate Care; Intermediate
Care for Mentally Retarded. *Beds* ICF 86;
ICF/MR 73. *Certified* Medicaid.
Ownership Proprietary.
Admissions Requirements Minimum age 18;
Medical examination; Physician's request.
Staff RNs 1 (ft), 1 (pt); LPNs 10 (ft), 5 (pt);
Orderlies 6 (ft); Nurses aides 24 (ft), 9 (pt);
Activities coordinators 1 (ft).
Facilities Dining room; Physical therapy room;
Activities room; Crafts room; Laundry room;
Barber/Beauty shop.
Activities Arts and Crafts; Cards; Games;
Reading groups; Prayer groups; Movies; Shopping trips; Dances/Social or cultural gatherings.
Description Center is located in a rural setting
just 2 blocks east of Rt 148 and is just minutes
away from several primary medical facilities.
Building is divided into 3 wings to provide 3
levels of specialized care, activities, and social
rehabilitation, in order to return as many residents as possible to the community.

ENFIELD

Enfield Care Home*
N Walnut, Enfield, IL, 62835 (618) 963-2713
Admin A L Elledge.
Licensure Intermediate Care. *Beds* 49. *Certified* Medicaid.
Ownership Proprietary.

EUREKA

Eureka Apostolic Christian Home
610 Cruger, Eureka, IL, 61530 (309) 467-2311
Admin Joel E Banwart. *Medical Dir/Dir of
Nursing* Dr Robert Easton Jr.
Licensure Intermediate Care; Sheltered Care.
Beds ICF 46; Sheltered Care 54. *Certified* Medicaid.
Ownership Nonprofit.
Admissions Requirements Minimum age 55;
Medical examination; Physician's request.
Staff Physicians 5 (pt); RNs 4 (ft), 5 (pt); LPNs
5 (ft), 6 (pt); Orderlies 3 (pt); Nurses aides 18
(ft), 25 (pt); Physical therapists 1 (pt); Reality
therapists 1 (pt); Recreational therapists 1 (pt);
Activities coordinators 1 (ft); Dietitians 1 (pt).
Affiliation Apostolic Christian
Facilities Dining room; Physical therapy room;
Activities room; Crafts room; Laundry room;
Barber/Beauty shop; Library; Large community
room.

Activities Arts and Crafts; Games; Movies;
Shopping trips; Song worship; Church services.
Description Facility has private, intermediate
rooms.

Maple Lawn Health Center
Rt 2, Box 9, Eureka, IL, 61530 (309) 467-2337
Admin Clifford King. *Medical Dir/Dir of
Nursing* Ronald Meyer MD.
Licensure Skilled Care; Intermediate Care.
Beds SNF 62; ICF 18. *Certified* Medicaid.
Ownership Nonprofit.
Admissions Requirements Physician's request.
Staff Physicians 1 (pt); RNs 3 (ft); LPNs 9 (pt);
Nurses aides 42 (pt); Physical therapists 1 (ft), 1
(pt); Reality therapists 1 (ft); Recreational therapists 1 (pt); Occupational therapists 1 (pt); Speech therapists 1 (pt); Activities coordinators 1
(ft); Dietitians 1 (pt); Dentists 1 (pt); Ophthalmologists 1 (pt); Podiatrists 1 (pt); Audiologists
1 (pt).
Affiliation Mennonite
Facilities Dining room; Physical therapy room;
Activities room; Chapel; Crafts room; Laundry
room; Barber/Beauty shop; Library.
Activities Arts and Crafts; Cards; Games;
Reading groups; Prayer groups; Movies; Shopping trips; Dances/Social or cultural gatherings.
Description Facility combines the very best in
geriatric health care with innovative ideas. Presently facility has an intergenerational program
with a child day care center and an extensive
community outreach program including meals-on-wheels, chore/housekeeping, transportation
and supportive health services including a
licensed home health agency.

EVANSTON

American Plaza Nursing Center*
1406 N Chicago Ave, Evanston, IL, 60201
(312) 328-6503
Admin Jeffrey Joe Webster.
Licensure Intermediate Care. *Beds* 145. *Certified* Medicaid.
Ownership Proprietary.

Dobson Plaza Inc*
120 Dodge Ave, Evanston, IL, 60202 (312)
869-7744
Admin Charlotte Kohn.
Licensure Skilled Care. *Beds* 60. *Certified* Medicaid.
Ownership Proprietary.

Georgian Home
422 Davis St, Evanston, IL, 60201 (312)
475-4100
Admin Robert R Porter.
Licensure Skilled Care; Sheltered Care.
Beds SNF 22; Sheltered Care 223.
Ownership Nonprofit.

Homecrest Foundation*
1430 Chicago Ave, Evanston, IL, 60201 (312)
869-2162
Admin Mary Shelley.
Licensure Sheltered Care. *Beds* Sheltered Care
50.
Ownership Nonprofit.

James C King Home for the Aged*
1555 Oak Ave, Evanston, IL, 60201 (312)
864-5460
Admin James L McLelland.
Licensure Intermediate Care; Sheltered Care.
Beds ICF 20; Sheltered Care 90. *Certified* Medicaid.
Ownership Nonprofit.

Lake Crest Villa
2601 Central St, Evanston, IL, 60201 (312)
328-8700
Admin Blanche H Dunbar.
Licensure Sheltered Care. *Beds* Sheltered Care
25.
Ownership Nonprofit.

The Mather Home*
1615 Hinman Ave, Evanston, IL, 60201 (312)
328-3042
Admin Erna R Sperber.
Licensure Intermediate Care; Sheltered Care.
Beds ICF 32; Sheltered Care 166.
Ownership Nonprofit.

Oakwood Terrace Inc
1300 Oak Ave, Evanston, IL, 60201 (312)
869-1300
Admin Ross S Brown. *Medical Dir/Dir of
Nursing* John O'Donnell MD.
Licensure Intermediate Care. *Beds* 54. *Certified* Medicaid.
Ownership Proprietary.
Staff Physicians 1 (ft), 12 (pt); RNs 15 (ft), 6
(pt); LPNs 1 (ft); Nurses aides 22 (ft), 9 (pt);
Physical therapists 1 (ft); Reality therapists 1
(ft); Recreational therapists 2 (ft), 1 (pt); Occupational therapists 2 (ft), 1 (pt); Speech therapists 1 (ft); Activities coordinators 1 (ft);
Dietitians 1 (ft); Dentists 1 (ft); Ophthalmologists 1 (ft); Podiatrists 1 (ft); Audiologists 1 (ft).
Facilities Dining room; Physical therapy room;
Activities room; Chapel; Crafts room; Laundry
room; Barber/Beauty shop; Library.
Activities Arts and Crafts; Cards; Games;
Reading groups; Prayer groups; Movies; Shopping trips; Dances/Social or cultural gatherings.
Description Oakwood Terrace has a beautiful
porch and patio with flowers surrounded by a
garden that all the residents love. Activities
department plans outings and active programs;
Stouffers plans cookouts in the summertime
and prepares appetizing dishes for all the residents.

Pioneer Place*
2320 Pioneer Pl, Evanston, IL, 60201 (312)
328-8700
Admin Clare N Boehm.
Licensure Intermediate Care; Sheltered Care.
Beds ICF 50; Sheltered Care 116.
Ownership Nonprofit.

Presbyterian Home
3200 Grant St, Evanston, IL, 60201 (312)
492-4800
Admin Peter S Mulvey. *Medical Dir/Dir of
Nursing* Gerald Blandford.
Licensure Skilled Care; Intermediate Care;
Sheltered Care. *Beds* SNF 111; ICF 65; Sheltered Care 98. *Certified* Medicare.
Ownership Nonprofit.
Admissions Requirements Minimum age 65.

Staff Physicians 1 (ft), 2 (pt); RNs 18 (ft);
LPNs 5 (ft); Nurses aides 72 (ft); Physical therapists 2 (ft); Occupational therapists 2 (ft);
Activities coordinators 2 (ft), 1 (pt); Dietitians
1 (ft); Dentists 1 (pt); Ophthalmologists 1 (pt);
Podiatrists 1 (pt); Audiologists 1 (pt).
Affiliation Presbyterian
Facilities Dining room; Physical therapy room;
Activities room; Chapel; Crafts room; Laundry
room; Barber/Beauty shop; Library.
Activities Arts and Crafts; Cards; Games;
Reading groups; Prayer groups; Movies; Shopping trips; Dances/Social or cultural gatherings.

Ridgeview House Inc
901 Maple Ave, Evanston, IL, 60202 (312)
475-4000
Admin James Boyle.
Licensure Intermediate Care. *Beds* 437. *Certified* Medicaid.
Ownership Proprietary.
Activities Arts and Crafts; Cards; Games;
Reading groups; Prayer groups; Movies; Shopping trips; Dances/Social or cultural gatherings.
Description Facility specializes in service to
individuals needing care for psychiatric problems.

Ridgeview Pavilion*
820 Foster St, Evanston, IL, 60201 (312)
869-0142
Admin Bryan G Barrish.
Licensure Skilled Care. *Beds* 300. *Certified* Medicaid.
Ownership Proprietary.

Three Oaks Nursing Center
500 Asbury Ave, Evanston, IL, 60202 (312)
869-3600
Admin Herbert L Kellner. *Medical Dir/Dir of
Nursing* Lawrence Mazur MD.
Licensure Skilled Care; Intermediate Care.
Beds SNF 39; ICF 85. *Certified* Medicaid;
Medicare.
Ownership Proprietary.
Admissions Requirements Minimum age 40;
Medical examination; Physician's request.
Staff Physicians 1 (pt); RNs 3 (ft), 15 (pt);
LPNs 2 (ft), 1 (pt); Orderlies 3 (ft); Nurses aides
50 (ft); Physical therapists 2 (ft); Reality therapists 1 (ft); Recreational therapists 2 (ft); Occupational therapists 1 (ft); Speech therapists 1
(ft); Activities coordinators 2 (ft); Dietitians 1
(ft); Dentists 1 (pt); Ophthalmologists 1 (pt);
Podiatrists 1 (pt); Audiologists 1 (pt).
Facilities Dining room; Physical therapy room;
Activities room; Crafts room; Laundry room;
Barber/Beauty shop.
Activities Arts and Crafts; Cards; Games;
Reading groups; Prayer groups; Movies; Shopping trips; Dances/Social or cultural gatherings.
Description Licensed nurses 24 hours a day, 7
days a week. Owner directed. Facility offers
best care in the area.

EVERGREEN PARK

Diplomat Healthcare Center*
9125 S Pulaski Ave, Evergreen Park, IL, 60642
(312) 636-3080
Admin Loren B Levin.

Licensure Skilled Care. *Beds* 249. *Certified* Medicaid.
Ownership Proprietary.

Evergreen Manor Nursing Home
3327 W 95th St, Evergreen Park, IL, 60642
(312) 423-8020
Admin A H Helal.
Licensure Intermediate Care. *Beds* 21.
Ownership Proprietary.
Admissions Requirements Minimum age 18.
Staff Physicians 1 (ft), 1 (pt); RNs 1 (ft); LPNs
4 (ft); Nurses aides 3 (ft), 2 (pt); Activities coordinators 1 (ft), 1 (pt); Dietitians 1 (pt).
Facilities Dining room; Activities room; Laundry room.
Activities Arts and Crafts; Games; Prayer
groups.
Description Evergreen Manor is a small facility
which has the atmosphere of one large happy
family rather than an institution; due to size,
residents get more individual attention and care
than in a larger facility.

Gunderson's Retirement Home
2701 W 95th St, Evergreen Park, IL, 60642
(312) 422-5995
Admin Jerold E Gunderson. *Medical Dir/Dir
of Nursing* Dr Carballo.
Licensure Retirement Home. *Beds* Retirement
Home 12.
Ownership Proprietary.
Admissions Requirements Minimum age 35;
Medical examination; Physician's request.
Staff Nurses aides 1 (ft), 1 (pt); Activities coordinators.
Facilities Dining room; Activities room; Laundry room.
Activities Arts and Crafts; Cards; Games;
Movies.
Description This facility is designed to be
home-like.

Peace Memorial Home
10124 S Kedzie Ave, Evergreen Park, IL, 60642
(312) 636-9200
Admin Harold M Schoup. *Medical Dir/Dir of
Nursing* Dr John O'Brien.
Licensure Skilled Care; Intermediate Care.
Beds 242. *Certified* Medicaid.
Ownership Nonprofit.
Admissions Requirements Medical examination; Physician's request.
Staff Physicians 1 (pt); RNs 14 (ft); LPNs 11
(ft); Nurses aides 98 (ft); Physical therapists 1
(pt); Reality therapists 1 (ft); Recreational therapists 1 (pt); Speech therapists 1 (pt); Activities
coordinators 1 (ft); Dietitians 1 (pt); Dentists 1
(pt); Podiatrists 1 (pt).
Affiliation Church of Christ
Facilities Dining room; Physical therapy room;
Chapel; Laundry room; Barber/Beauty shop.
Activities Arts and Crafts; Cards; Games;
Reading groups; Prayer groups; Movies; Dances/Social or cultural gatherings.
Description Peace Memorial Home has always
stressed personalized nursing care; staffing ratio
is the best in the area.

FAIRBURY

Fairview Haven Inc
605-609 N 4th St, Fairbury, IL, 61739 (815) 692-2572
Admin Wayne Drayer. *Medical Dir/Dir of Nursing* Dr Kothari.
Licensure Intermediate Care. *Beds* 49. *Certified* Medicaid.
Ownership Nonprofit.
Admissions Requirements Minimum age 60; Medical examination.
Staff RNs 1 (pt); LPNs 4 (ft), 2 (pt); Orderlies 1 (pt); Nurses aides 10 (ft), 14 (pt); Activities coordinators 2 (pt).
Affiliation Apostolic Christian
Facilities Dining room; Activities room; Crafts room; Laundry room; Barber/Beauty shop.
Activities Arts and Crafts; Games; Reading groups; Movies; Shopping trips; Dances/Social or cultural gatherings.

Helen Lewis Smith Pavilion
519 S Fifth St, Fairbury, IL, 61739 (815) 692-2346
Admin Dereck Marshall. *Medical Dir/Dir of Nursing* Dr Vesselin Oreshkov.
Licensure Intermediate Care. *Beds* 49. *Certified* Medicaid.
Ownership Nonprofit.
Admissions Requirements Minimum age 21; Medical examination.
Staff Physicians 7 (ft); RNs 2 (ft), 3 (pt); LPNs 4 (ft), 2 (pt); Nurses aides 12 (ft), 12 (pt); Physical therapists 1 (ft); Recreational therapists 2 (pt); Speech therapists 1 (pt); Dietitians 1 (ft).
Facilities Dining room; Barber/Beauty shop.
Activities Arts and Crafts; Cards; Games; Reading groups; Prayer groups; Movies; Shopping trips; Dances/Social or cultural gatherings.
Description Facility is hospital based.

FAIRFIELD

Flora Manor*
E 12th St, Fairfield, IL, 62839 (618) 622-8494
Admin Dennis W Armbrust.
Licensure Intermediate Care. *Beds* 59.
Ownership Nonprofit.

Way Fair Restorium*
11th and Harding Sts, Fairfield, IL, 62837 (618) 842-2723
Admin Chalmers F Kerchner.
Licensure Skilled Care. *Beds* 104. *Certified* Medicaid; Medicare.
Ownership Nonprofit.

FARMER CITY

Jackson Heights Nursing Home
Brookview Dr and Crabtree Ct, Farmer City, IL, 61842 (217) 928-2118
Admin Velda M Swigart.
Licensure Intermediate Care. *Beds* 51. *Certified* Medicaid.
Ownership Nonprofit.
Admissions Requirements Minimum age 60; Medical examination; Physician's request.
Staff Physicians 6 (pt); RNs 1 (ft), 6 (pt); LPNs 1 (ft), 1 (pt); Nurses aides 14 (ft), 10 (pt); Activities coordinators 1 (ft).
Facilities Dining room; Activities room; Chapel; Crafts room; Laundry room; Barber/Beauty shop.
Activities Arts and Crafts; Cards; Games; Reading groups; Prayer groups; Movies.
Description Facility is small with home-like atmosphere.

FARMINGTON

Farmington Nursing Home Inc
Box 257, Farmington, IL, 61531 (309) 245-2408
Admin Arthalene Widger. *Medical Dir/Dir of Nursing* Dr James Reed.
Licensure Skilled Care; Intermediate Care. *Beds* 76. *Certified* Medicaid; Medicare.
Ownership Proprietary.
Admissions Requirements Medical examination; Physician's request.
Staff RNs 7 (ft); LPNs 7 (ft), 3 (pt); Orderlies 3 (ft); Nurses aides 30 (ft), 20 (pt); Physical therapists 1 (ft), 1 (pt); Reality therapists 1 (ft); Recreational therapists 1 (ft); Occupational therapists 1 (pt); Speech therapists 1 (pt); Activities coordinators 1 (ft); Dietitians 1 (pt); Dentists 1 (pt).
Facilities Dining room; Physical therapy room; Activities room; Crafts room; Laundry room; Barber/Beauty shop.
Activities Arts and Crafts; Cards; Games; Reading groups; Prayer groups; Movies; Dances/Social or cultural gatherings.

FLANAGAN

Beulah Land Christian Home
Rt 116, Flanagan, IL, 61740 (815) 796-2267
Admin Thomas A Novy.
Licensure Skilled Care; Intermediate Care Independent living. *Beds* SNF 15; ICF 28; Independent Living 32.
Ownership Nonprofit.
Affiliation Church of Christ
Facilities Dining room; Physical therapy room; Activities room; Chapel; Crafts room; Laundry room; Barber/Beauty shop; Library.
Description Livingston County's newest ICF and skilled home, a nonprofit facility sponsored by the independent Christian churches and Churches of Christ.

Good Samaritan Home of Flanagan
Box 308, Flanagan, IL, 61740 (815) 796-2288
Admin Mark Hovren. *Medical Dir/Dir of Nursing* Dr John Purnell.
Licensure Skilled Care; Intermediate Care. *Beds* 60. *Certified* Medicaid.
Ownership Nonprofit.
Admissions Requirements Medical examination.
Staff RNs 3 (ft), 4 (pt); LPNs 2 (ft), 4 (pt); Nurses aides 11 (ft), 18 (pt); Recreational therapists 2 (pt); Activities coordinators 1 (ft).
Affiliation Lutheran
Facilities Dining room; Physical therapy room; Activities room; Chapel; Crafts room; Laundry room; Barber/Beauty shop.
Activities Arts and Crafts; Cards; Games; Prayer groups; Shopping trips.

FLORA

Flora Care Center Inc
Frontage Rd W, Flora, IL, 62839 (618) 662-8381
Admin Kathryn A Blackwell. *Medical Dir/Dir of Nursing* Dr Eugene Foss MD.
Licensure Skilled Care; Intermediate Care. *Beds* 98. *Certified* Medicaid.
Ownership Proprietary.
Staff RNs 3 (ft), 5 (pt); LPNs 2 (ft), 3 (pt); Orderlies 2 (ft); Nurses aides 26 (ft), 4 (pt); Activities coordinators 1 (ft), 1 (pt).
Facilities Dining room; Physical therapy room; Activities room; Crafts room; Laundry room; Barber/Beauty shop; Library.
Activities Arts and Crafts; Cards; Games; Reading groups; Prayer groups; Movies; Shopping trips.
Description Classes arranged through Frontier College involving reality orientation, grooming, recreational and occupational therapy, cooking, crafts, and culture.

Flora Nursing Center
701 Shadwell, Flora, IL, 62839 (618) 662-8361
Admin Georgianna Feagans. *Medical Dir/Dir of Nursing* Dr Eugene Foss.
Licensure Skilled Care; Intermediate Care. *Beds* SNF 56; ICF 54. *Certified* Medicaid.
Ownership Proprietary.
Admissions Requirements Medical examination; Physician's request.
Staff RNs 5 (ft), 2 (pt); LPNs 3 (ft), 2 (pt); Nurses aides 25 (ft), 6 (pt); Physical therapists 1 (pt); Speech therapists 1 (pt); Activities coordinators 1 (ft); Dietitians 1 (pt); Dentists 1 (pt); Audiologists 1 (pt).
Facilities Dining room; Physical therapy room; Activities room; Laundry room; Barber/Beauty shop; Library.
Activities Arts and Crafts; Cards; Games; Reading groups; Movies; Shopping trips; Dances/Social or cultural gatherings.

FOREST PARK

Altenheim German Home
7824 W Madison St, Forest Park, IL, 60130 (312) 366-2206
Admin Diane M Mikes. *Medical Dir/Dir of Nursing* Donald Pochyly MD.
Licensure Intermediate Care; Sheltered Care. *Beds* ICF 90; Sheltered Care 53. *Certified* Medicaid.
Ownership Nonprofit.
Admissions Requirements Minimum age 65; Medical examination.
Staff Physicians 2 (pt); RNs 2 (ft), 8 (pt); LPNs 4 (ft), 2 (pt); Orderlies 2 (ft), 1 (pt); Nurses aides 32 (ft), 8 (pt); Speech therapists 1 (pt); Activities coordinators 1 (ft); Dietitians 1 (pt); Dentists 1 (pt); Ophthalmologists 1 (pt); Podiatrists 1 (pt); Audiologists 1 (pt); Audiologists 1 (pt).
Facilities Dining room; Physical therapy room; Activities room; Chapel; Crafts room; Laundry room; Barber/Beauty shop; TV room.
Activities Arts and Crafts; Cards; Games; Reading groups; Prayer groups; Movies; Shopping trips; Dances/Social or cultural gatherings; Educational programs.
Description Facility has provided 100 years of

caring. Beautiful 19th century structures surrounded by 14 acres of lush forestry, yards, and gardens.

Saint Vincent Community Living Facility*
659 E Jefferson, Forest Park, IL, 61032 (815) 232-6181
Admin Alria J Cole.
Licensure Intermediate Care. *Beds* 20.
Ownership Nonprofit.

FRANKFORT

Frankfort Terrace*
40 N Smith, Frankfort, IL, 60423 (815) 469-3156
Admin Wendy M Walsh.
Licensure Intermediate Care. *Beds* 118. *Certified* Medicaid.
Ownership Proprietary.

FRANKLIN GROVE

Franklin Grove Health Care Center*
409 N State St, Franklin Grove, IL, 61031 (815) 456-2374
Admin Michael N Fleming.
Licensure Skilled Care; Intermediate Care.
Beds SNF 70; ICF 51. *Certified* Medicaid; Medicare.
Ownership Proprietary.

FRANKLIN PARK

Leyden Community Extended Care Center*
10500 W Grand Ave, Franklin Park, IL, 60131 (312) 451-1520
Admin Theresa Gengler.
Licensure Skilled Care. *Beds* 154. *Certified* Medicaid; Medicare.
Ownership Nonprofit.

FREEBURG

Freeburg Care Center Inc*
Rt 2, Box 180M, Hwy 15E, Freeburg, IL, 62243 (618) 539-5856
Admin Robin Bozsa.
Licensure Intermediate Care. *Beds* 98. *Certified* Medicaid.
Ownership Proprietary.

FREEPORT

Freeport Manor Nursing Home
900 Kiwanis Dr, Freeport, IL, 61032 (815) 235-6196
Admin Dolores Currier. *Medical Dir/Dir of Nursing* Dr Lawrence Perlman.
Licensure Skilled Care; Intermediate Care.
Beds 116. *Certified* Medicaid; Medicare.
Ownership Proprietary.
Admissions Requirements Medical examination; Physician's request.
Staff RNs 5 (ft), 3 (pt); LPNs 6 (ft), 3 (pt); Nurses aides 27 (ft), 22 (pt); Activities coordinators 2 (ft).
Facilities Dining room; Physical therapy room; Activities room; Crafts room; Laundry room;

Barber/Beauty shop.
Activities Arts and Crafts; Cards; Games; Reading groups; Prayer groups; Movies; Dances/Social or cultural gatherings.

Parkview Home of Freeport Illinois Inc
1234 S Park Blvd, Freeport, IL, 61032 (815) 232-8385, 8612
Admin David B Conklin. *Medical Dir/Dir of Nursing* Allen W Workman MD.
Licensure Intermediate Care; Sheltered Care.
Beds ICF 16; Sheltered Care 49.
Ownership Nonprofit.
Admissions Requirements Minimum age 60; Medical examination.
Staff RNs 4 (ft), 2 (pt); LPNs 1 (ft), 3 (pt); Nurses aides 11 (ft), 6 (pt); Recreational therapists 1 (pt); Occupational therapists 1 (pt); Speech therapists 1 (pt); Activities coordinators 1 (ft); Dietitians 1 (pt); Dentists 1 (pt); Ophthalmologists 1 (pt); Podiatrists 1 (pt); Audiologists 1 (pt).
Facilities Dining room; Activities room; Crafts room; Laundry room; Barber/Beauty shop; Library; Multipurpose room; Game room; Lounge areas.
Activities Arts and Crafts; Cards; Games; Reading groups; Prayer groups; Movies; Shopping trips; Dances/Social or cultural gatherings; Exercise groups; Bowling; Singing groups.
Description Nursing care facility is retirement home oriented; all residents have voluntarily chosen this as their home for the rest of their lives; one lady has lived here for 23 years, one for 17, 44% for more than 10 years.

Saint Joseph Home for the Aged
649 E Jefferson St, Freeport, IL, 61032 (815) 232-6181
Admin Peter J Witynski.
Licensure Intermediate Care. *Beds* 106. *Certified* Medicaid.
Ownership Nonprofit.
Admissions Requirements Medical examination.
Staff Physicians 1 (pt); RNs 6 (ft), 1 (pt); LPNs 9 (ft); Orderlies 1 (ft); Nurses aides 29 (ft), 16 (pt); Occupational therapists 1 (pt); Activities coordinators 1 (ft), 2 (pt); Dietitians 1 (pt); Dentists 1 (pt).
Facilities Dining room; Physical therapy room; Activities room; Chapel; Crafts room; Laundry room; Barber/Beauty shop; Library.
Activities Arts and Crafts; Cards; Games; Reading groups; Prayer groups; Movies; Shopping trips; Dances/Social or cultural gatherings.
Description Staff provides music therapy, a fine motor program. Facility has qualified for IDPH quality incentive payment level II for several years.

Saint Mary Square Living Center Inc*
239 S Cherry, Freeport, IL, 61401 (309) 343-4101
Admin Gerald Dubois.
Licensure Intermediate Care. *Beds* 257.
Ownership Nonprofit.

Stephenson Nursing Home
2946 S Walnut Rd, Freeport, IL, 61032 (815) 235-6173
Admin R Douglas McCollum. *Medical Dir/Dir of Nursing* Dr William Metcalf.

Licensure Skilled Care; Intermediate Care.
Beds SNF 98; ICF 51. *Certified* Medicaid; Medicare.
Ownership Public.
Admissions Requirements Minimum age 18; Medical examination; Physician's request.
Staff RNs 7 (ft), 15 (pt); LPNs 2 (ft), 10 (pt); Orderlies 1 (ft), 3 (pt); Nurses aides 30 (ft), 20 (pt); Activities coordinators 1 (ft).
Facilities Dining room; Physical therapy room; Activities room; Laundry room; Barber/Beauty shop.
Activities Arts and Crafts; Cards; Games; Reading groups; Prayer groups; Movies; Shopping trips; Dances/Social or cultural gatherings.
Description The nursing home is used as a clinical site for Highland Community College and Stephenson Area Career Center.

FULTON

Harbor Crest Home Inc*
810 E 17th St, Fulton, IL, 61252 (815) 589-3411
Admin Ray W Rus.
Licensure Intermediate Care. *Beds* 84. *Certified* Medicaid.
Ownership Nonprofit.

GALATIA

Finnie Good Shepherd Nursing Home Inc*
Cross and Legion Sts, Galatia, IL, 62935 (618) 268-4631
Admin Bobby Joe Finnie.
Licensure Intermediate Care. *Beds* 73. *Certified* Medicaid.
Ownership Proprietary.

GALENA

Galena-Stauss Hospital and Nursing Care Facility
215 Summit St, Galena, IL, 61036 (815) 777-1340
Admin Roger D Hervey.
Licensure Skilled Care; Intermediate Care.
Beds 34. *Certified* Medicaid; Medicare.
Ownership Public.

GALESBURG

Applegate East
1145 Frank St, Galesburg, IL, 61401 (309) 342-2103
Admin Karen Cheline. *Medical Dir/Dir of Nursing* Dr Jerry Ramunis.
Licensure Intermediate Care; Sheltered Care.
Beds ICF 79; Sheltered Care 16.
Ownership Proprietary.
Admissions Requirements Medical examination.
Staff RNs 1 (ft); LPNs 5 (ft), 4 (pt); Nurses aides 20 (ft), 4 (pt); Activities coordinators 2 (ft).
Facilities Dining room; Activities room; Laundry room; Library.
Activities Arts and Crafts; Cards; Games; Reading groups; Prayer groups; Movies; Shopping trips; Dances/Social or cultural gatherings.
Description Facility encourages the area's

senior citizens and their clubs to eat meals here at holiday time and to participate in monthly dances and entertainment.

Galesburg Nursing and Rehabilitation Center*
280 E Losey St, Galesburg, IL, 61401 (309) 343-2166
Admin Benny Perkins.
Licensure Skilled Care. *Beds* 67. *Certified* Medicaid; Medicare.
Ownership Proprietary.

Knox Manor Inc
820 E 5th St, Galesburg, IL, 61401 (309) 342-5135
Admin Marjorie A Mahnesmith. *Medical Dir/Dir of Nursing* Dr Jerry Ramunis.
Licensure Intermediate Care. *Beds* 101. *Certified* Medicaid.
Ownership Proprietary.
Admissions Requirements Minimum age 18; Medical examination; Physician's request.
Staff Physicians 1 (pt); RNs 1 (ft); LPNs 5 (ft), 4 (pt); Orderlies 3 (ft), 2 (pt); Nurses aides 14 (ft), 7 (pt); Activities coordinators 2 (ft), 1 (pt).
Facilities Dining room; Physical therapy room; Activities room; Crafts room; Laundry room; Barber/Beauty shop.
Activities Arts and Crafts; Cards; Games; Reading groups; Movies; Shopping trips; Dances/Social or cultural gatherings; Worship service.
Description Facility has an excellent physical therapy program with 2 very qualified physical therapy orderlies and a registered physical therapist consultant.

The Marigold*
275 E Carl Sandburg Dr, Galesburg, IL, 61401 (309) 344-1151
Admin Richard D Erdman.
Licensure Intermediate Care. *Beds* 174.
Ownership Proprietary.

GENESEO

Geneseo Good Samaritan
704 S Illinois St, Geneseo, IL, 61254 (309) 944-6424
Admin Margaret Turner. *Medical Dir/Dir of Nursing* Marilyn Klundt.
Licensure Intermediate Care. *Beds* 72. *Certified* Medicaid.
Ownership Nonprofit.
Admissions Requirements Minimum age 21; Medical examination.
Staff RNs 5 (pt); LPNs 2 (pt); Nurses aides 15 (ft), 19 (pt); Activities coordinators 1 (ft), 1 (pt).
Facilities Dining room; Physical therapy room; Activities room; Chapel; Crafts room; Laundry room; Barber/Beauty shop.
Activities Arts and Crafts; Cards; Games; Reading groups; Prayer groups; Movies.
Description Nurses on duty 24-hours per day; very active activity department; large, active volunteer group; dietary department very conscious of special diets; in-house laundry for all residents, personal laundry; very clean home, friendly staff, and a pretty landscaped yard.

Hillcrest Home*
Rt 4, Geneseo, IL, 61254 (309) 944-6407
Admin Robert J Ruskin.
Licensure Skilled Care; Intermediate Care.
Beds SNF 106; ICF 102. *Certified* Medicaid.
Ownership Public.

GENEVA

Geneva Retirement Home
1101 E State St, Geneva, IL, 60134 (312) 232-7544
Admin Lise P Miller. *Medical Dir/Dir of Nursing* Dr J Nickless Fisher.
Licensure Skilled Care. *Beds* 107.
Ownership Proprietary.
Admissions Requirements Medical examination.
Staff RNs 4 (ft), 3 (pt); LPNs 1 (ft), 2 (pt); Nurses aides 5 (ft), 5 (pt); Activities coordinators 2 (ft); Dietitians 1 (pt); Podiatrists 1 (pt).
Facilities Dining room; Activities room; Chapel; Crafts room; Laundry room; Barber/Beauty shop; Library.
Activities Arts and Crafts; Cards; Games; Prayer groups; Movies; Shopping trips; Dances/Social or cultural gatherings.

GENOA

Ottawa Care Center
800 E Center St, Genoa, IL, 60135 (815) 434-7144
Admin Lois Kallstad.
Licensure Skilled Care. *Beds* 90.
Ownership Proprietary.

Sheltered Village*
Hwy 23 S, Genoa, IL, 60135 (815) 784-5146
Admin Heidi Hurl't A Kluga.
Licensure Intermediate Care. *Beds* 94.
Ownership Proprietary.

GIBSON CITY

Gibson Community Hospital Annex
430 E 19th, Gibson City, IL, 60936 (217) 784-4251
Admin Daniel J Marion. *Medical Dir/Dir of Nursing* Dr David Hagan.
Licensure Skilled Care. *Beds* 26.
Ownership Nonprofit.
Admissions Requirements Medical examination; Physician's request.
Staff Physicians 11 (ft); RNs 2 (ft), 4 (pt); LPNs 8 (ft); Orderlies 1 (pt); Nurses aides 16 (ft), 4 (pt); Physical therapists 1 (pt); Activities coordinators 1 (ft); Dietitians 1 (pt).
Facilities Dining room; Physical therapy room; Activities room; Chapel; Crafts room.
Activities Arts and Crafts; Cards; Games; Prayer groups; Movies; Shopping trips; Dances/Social or cultural gatherings.
Description Facility is located in a small midwestern farming community 120 miles south of Chicago.

Gibson Manor*
525 Hazel Dr, Gibson City, IL, 60936 (217) 784-4258

Admin Cecelia C Mitrione.
Licensure Intermediate Care. *Beds* 71. *Certified* Medicaid.
Ownership Proprietary.

GIFFORD

Country Health Inc
Rt 1, Box 14, Gifford, IL, 61847 (217) 568-7362
Admin La Von Heubrock. *Medical Dir/Dir of Nursing* Dr Tamara Mitchell.
Licensure Skilled Care; Intermediate Care.
Beds 89. *Certified* Medicaid.
Ownership Nonprofit.
Staff RNs 3 (ft), 3 (pt); LPNs 4 (ft), 3 (pt); Nurses aides 14 (ft), 24 (pt); Physical therapists 1 (pt); Activities coordinators 2 (ft); Dietitians 1 (pt).
Affiliation Lutheran
Facilities Dining room; Physical therapy room; Activities room; Chapel; Crafts room; Laundry room; Barber/Beauty shop.
Activities Arts and Crafts; Cards; Games; Reading groups; Prayer groups; Movies; Shopping trips; Dances/Social or cultural gatherings.
Description Country Health is located just north of Highway 136 in a lovely rural setting. A van takes residents on regular outings and shopping trips and activities of many varieties offered daily. Family meeting is conducted monthly with social service director, director of nursing, and administrator.

GILLESPIE

Barry Care Center of Gillespie*
RR 3, Gillespie, IL, 62033 (217) 839-2171
Admin Charlene Taylor.
Licensure Skilled Care. *Beds* 51.
Ownership Proprietary.

GILMAN

Gilman Nursing Center
Box 307, Rt 45 S, Gilman, IL, 60938 (217) 265-7200
Admin Judy Pree. *Medical Dir/Dir of Nursing* Dr Harry Barnett.
Licensure Skilled Care; Intermediate Care.
Beds 51. *Certified* Medicaid; Medicare.
Ownership Proprietary.
Admissions Requirements Minimum age 19.
Staff RNs 3 (ft), 2 (pt); LPNs 1 (ft), 1 (pt); Nurses aides 12 (ft), 10 (pt); Physical therapists 1 (pt); Recreational therapists 1 (ft); Occupational therapists 1 (pt); Speech therapists 1 (pt); Dietitians 1 (pt); Dentists 1 (pt); Ophthalmologists 1 (pt); Podiatrists 1 (pt); Audiologists 1 (pt).

GIRARD

Pleasant Hill Village
1010 W North St, Girard, IL, 62640 (217) 627-2181
Admin Philip E Flory. *Medical Dir/Dir of Nursing* David E Stevard MD.
Licensure Intermediate Care. *Beds* 92. *Certified* Medicaid.
Ownership Nonprofit.

Staff RNs 2 (ft); LPNs 8 (ft), 2 (pt); Nurses aides 30 (ft), 10 (pt); Activities coordinators 1 (ft).
Affiliation Church of the Brethren
Facilities Dining room; Physical therapy room; Activities room; Chapel; Crafts room; Laundry room; Barber/Beauty shop.
Activities Arts and Crafts; Cards; Games; Reading groups; Prayer groups; Movies; Shopping trips.

GLENVIEW

Glenview Terrace Nursing Center*
1511 Greenwood Rd, Glenview, IL, 60025 (312) 729-9090
Admin Sheldon Wolfe.
Licensure Skilled Care. *Beds* 253. *Certified* Medicaid; Medicare.
Ownership Proprietary.

Maryhaven Inc*
1700 E Lake Ave, Glenview, IL, 60025 (312) 729-1300
Admin Dennis G Lackie.
Licensure Skilled Care; Intermediate Care. *Beds* SNF 42; ICF 105. *Certified* Medicaid.
Ownership Nonprofit.

GLENWOOD

Glenwood Terrace Nursing Center
19330 S Cottage Grove, Glenwood, IL, 60425 (312) 758-6200
Admin Irene Glass. *Medical Dir/Dir of Nursing* Dr Kruger.
Licensure Skilled Care; Intermediate Care. *Beds* 184. *Certified* Medicaid.
Admissions Requirements Medical examination.
Facilities Dining room; Physical therapy room; Activities room; Crafts room; Laundry room; Barber/Beauty shop.
Activities Arts and Crafts; Cards; Games; Reading groups; Prayer groups; Movies; Shopping trips; Dances/Social or cultural gatherings.

GODFREY

Beverly Farm Foundation*
Humbert Rd, Godfrey, IL, 62035 (618) 466-0367
Admin Anthony L Jacobs.
Licensure Skilled Care; Intermediate Care. *Beds* SNF 20; ICF 384.
Ownership Nonprofit.

Blu-Fountain Manor
1623-29 W Delmar, Godfrey, IL, 62035 (618) 466-0443
Admin Arbedella A Carrico.
Licensure Skilled Care; Intermediate Care. *Beds* SNF 29; ICF 46. *Certified* Medicaid.
Ownership Proprietary.
Admissions Requirements Minimum age 16; Medical examination; Physician's request.
Facilities Dining room; Activities room; Crafts room; Laundry room; Barber/Beauty shop; Library.

Activities Arts and Crafts; Cards; Games; Reading groups; Prayer groups; Movies; Shopping trips; Dances/Social or cultural gatherings.

D'Adrian Convalescent Center*
1318 W Delmar, Godfrey, IL, 62035 (618) 466-0153
Admin Joseph H Cusic.
Licensure Skilled Care; Intermediate Care. *Beds* SNF 81; ICF 38. *Certified* Medicaid; Medicare.
Ownership Proprietary.

GOLCONDA

Pope County Care Center Inc*
Box 69, Rosalie St, Golconda, IL, 62938 (618) 683-7711
Admin Alan L Robbs.
Licensure Intermediate Care. *Beds* 53. *Certified* Medicaid.
Ownership Proprietary.

GOLDEN

Golden Good Shepherd Home Inc
Golden, IL, 62339 (217) 696-4421
Admin Lois B Albers. *Medical Dir/Dir of Nursing* Frank E Adrian MD.
Licensure Intermediate Care. *Beds* 42. *Certified* Medicaid.
Ownership Nonprofit.
Admissions Requirements Minimum age 65; Medical examination.
Staff RNs 1 (ft), 2 (pt); LPNs 2 (ft), 3 (pt); Nurses aides 22 (pt); Activities coordinators 2 (pt).
Facilities Dining room; Physical therapy room; Activities room; Chapel; Crafts room; Barber-/Beauty shop.
Activities Arts and Crafts; Cards; Games; Prayer groups; Movies.
Description Purpose is to provide a nursing home that doctors and relatives are proud to recommend, offering retirement living to which elderly people can look forward with pride and anticipation. Visits are welcome.

GRANITE CITY

Colonial Haven Nursing Home Inc
3900 Stearns Ave, Granite City, IL, 62040 (618) 931-3900
Admin Clarence Repp. *Medical Dir/Dir of Nursing* Dr Felicia Koch.
Licensure Skilled Care; Intermediate Care. *Beds* SNF 61; ICF 61. *Certified* Medicaid; Medicare.
Ownership Proprietary.
Admissions Requirements Medical examination; Physician's request.
Staff RNs 2 (ft), 1 (pt); LPNs 7 (ft), 4 (pt); Nurses aides 26 (ft), 19 (pt); Reality therapists 1 (ft); Recreational therapists 2 (pt); Activities coordinators 1 (ft).
Facilities Dining room; Physical therapy room; Activities room; Laundry room; Barber/Beauty shop.
Activities Arts and Crafts; Games; Reading groups; Prayer groups; Movies.

The Colonnades*
1 Colonial Dr, Granite City, IL, 62040 (618) 877-2700
Admin Charles J Goff.
Licensure Intermediate Care. *Beds* 90. *Certified* Medicaid.
Ownership Proprietary.

GRAYVILLE

Meadowood*
2nd and Commerce, Grayville, IL, 62844 (618) 375-2171
Admin Rebecca S Gubbins.
Licensure Skilled Care. *Beds* 104. *Certified* Medicaid.
Ownership Proprietary.

GREENUP

Cumberland Nursing Center
PO Box 755, Greenup, IL, 62428 (217) 923-3186
Admin Lee Markwell. *Medical Dir/Dir of Nursing* Joan Ettelbrick RN.
Licensure Intermediate Care. *Beds* 60. *Certified* Medicaid.
Ownership Proprietary.
Staff RNs 1 (ft); LPNs 5 (ft), 1 (pt); Nurses aides 19 (ft), 3 (pt); Activities coordinators 1 (ft); Dietitians 1 (pt).
Facilities Dining room; Activities room; Crafts room; Laundry room; Barber/Beauty shop.
Activities Arts and Crafts; Games; Reading groups; Prayer groups; Movies.

GREENVILLE

Fair Oaks
Hwy 140 and N Grigg St, Greenville, IL, 62246 (618) 664-1230
Admin Alan Harnetiaux.
Licensure Skilled Care. *Beds* 144. *Certified* Medicaid; Medicare.
Ownership Nonprofit.

Hillview Manor
S 4th St, Box 207, Greenville, IL, 62246 (618) 664-1622
Admin Margie M States. *Medical Dir/Dir of Nursing* James Goggin MD.
Licensure Skilled Care; Intermediate Care. *Beds* 98. *Certified* Medicaid.
Ownership Proprietary.
Admissions Requirements Minimum age 18.
Staff Physicians 4 (pt); RNs 2 (ft), 2 (pt); LPNs 4 (ft), 3 (pt); Nurses aides 11 (ft), 19 (pt); Physical therapists 1 (pt); Speech therapists 1 (pt); Activities coordinators 1 (ft); Dentists 1 (pt); Ophthalmologists 1 (pt); Podiatrists 1 (pt); Audiologists 1 (pt).

HAMILTON

Montebello Nursing Home
16th St and Keokuk, Hamilton, IL, 62341
Admin Thomas Wagner. *Medical Dir/Dir of Nursing* B C Kappmeyer MD.
Licensure Skilled Care; Intermediate Care. *Beds* 149. *Certified* Medicaid.

Ownership Proprietary.
Admissions Requirements Minimum age 18; Medical examination.
Staff Physicians 7 (pt); RNs 2 (ft), 4 (pt); LPNs 2 (ft), 4 (pt); Orderlies 1 (ft), 3 (pt); Nurses aides 17 (ft), 22 (pt); Physical therapists 2 (ft), 2 (pt); Reality therapists 2 (pt); Activities coordinators 2 (ft); Dietitians 1 (ft); Dentists 1 (pt); Podiatrists 1 (pt).
Facilities Dining room; Physical therapy room; Activities room; Laundry room; Barber/Beauty shop.
Activities Arts and Crafts; Cards; Games; Reading groups; Prayer groups; Movies; Shopping trips; Dances/Social or cultural gatherings.
Description Facility is located within the city yet with a country setting. Offers rooms for every taste with single and semi-private rooms available for the discriminating few. Single rooms include writing desk, love seat, cable TV, Levelor blinds, plants, and pictures (some rooms are carpeted).

HARDIN

Calhoun Care Center
908 S Park, Hardin, IL, 62047 (618) 576-9021
Admin Lualyce C Brown. *Medical Dir/Dir of Nursing* Bernard Baalman MD.
Licensure Skilled Care; Intermediate Care.
Beds 90. *Certified* Medicaid; Medicare.
Ownership Proprietary.
Admissions Requirements Minimum age 21.
Staff Physicians 3 (pt); RNs 3 (ft), 2 (pt); LPNs 4 (ft), 2 (pt); Orderlies 1 (ft); Nurses aides 35 (ft), 3 (pt); Physical therapists 2 (ft), 2 (pt); Reality therapists 1 (ft); Recreational therapists 1 (ft); Speech therapists 1 (ft); Activities coordinators 1 (ft); Dietitians 1 (ft).
Facilities Dining room; Physical therapy room; Activities room; Crafts room; Laundry room; Barber/Beauty shop.
Activities Arts and Crafts; Cards; Games; Reading groups; Prayer groups; Movies; Shopping trips; Dances/Social or cultural gatherings.
Description Facility offers total nursing care with physical therapy. Provided by a dedicated staff in a home-like atmosphere with personalized services and good food. Visits are welcome anytime.

HARRISBURG

Bacon Nursing Home Inc
N Land St, PO Box 296, Harrisburg, IL, 62946 (618) 252-6341
Admin Loretta W Turner. *Medical Dir/Dir of Nursing* Dr H Andrew Cserny.
Licensure Intermediate Care. *Beds* 50. *Certified* Medicaid.
Ownership Proprietary.
Admissions Requirements Minimum age 18; Medical examination; Physician's request.
Staff Physicians 1 (pt); RNs 1 (pt); LPNs 5 (ft), 1 (pt); Nurses aides 23 (ft), 3 (pt); Reality therapists 1 (ft); Occupational therapists 1 (pt); Speech therapists 1 (pt); Activities coordinators 1 (ft); Dietitians 1 (pt); Dentists 1 (pt); Ophthalmologists 1 (pt); Podiatrists 1 (pt); Audiologists 1 (pt).
Facilities Dining room; Physical therapy room;

Activities room; Crafts room; Laundry room; Barber/Beauty shop.
Activities Arts and Crafts; Cards; Games; Reading groups; Prayer groups; Movies; Shopping trips; Dances/Social or cultural gatherings.
Description Thirty beds for ICF/DD have been applied for; more programing is offered for preparation of these residents for living in the community in a less structured surrounding.

Harrisburg Manor Inc*
1000 W Sloan St, Harrisburg, IL, 62946 (618) 253-7807
Admin Patsy J Colson.
Licensure Intermediate Care. *Beds* 68. *Certified* Medicaid.
Ownership Proprietary.

Little Egypt Manor
901 N Webster, Harrisburg, IL, 62946 (618) 252-0576
Admin Wanda S Pavelonis. *Medical Dir/Dir of Nursing* Dr Carl Hauptmann.
Licensure Intermediate Care. *Beds* 48. *Certified* Medicaid.
Ownership Proprietary.
Admissions Requirements Minimum age 18; Medical examination; Physician's request.
Staff RNs 1 (pt); LPNs 3 (ft), 2 (pt); Nurses aides 9 (ft); Speech therapists 1 (pt); Activities coordinators 1 (ft); Dietitians 3 (ft), 3 (pt); Dentists 1 (pt).
Facilities Dining room; Activities room; Crafts room; Laundry room; Barber/Beauty shop.
Activities Arts and Crafts; Cards; Games; Reading groups; Prayer groups; Movies; Shopping trips; Dances/Social or cultural gatherings.

Saline Care Center*
120 S Land St, Harrisburg, IL, 62946 (618) 252-7405
Admin Larry M Field.
Licensure Intermediate Care. *Beds* 127. *Certified* Medicaid.
Ownership Proprietary.

HARVEY

Children's Haven Inc
121 W 154th St, Harvey, IL, 60426 (312) 596-2220
Admin Barbara J Thomas. *Medical Dir/Dir of Nursing* Lowell M Zoms MD.
Licensure Skilled Care; Intermediate Care.
Beds 130. *Certified* Medicaid.
Ownership Proprietary.
Admissions Requirements Minimum age 0-22; Medical examination.
Staff Physicians 6 (pt); RNs 7 (ft), 1 (pt); LPNs 2 (ft), 9 (pt); Nurses aides 45 (ft), 38 (pt); Physical therapists 1 (pt); Recreational therapists 1 (ft); Occupational therapists 1 (ft); Speech therapists 1 (pt); Activities coordinators 2 (ft); Dietitians 1 (pt).
Facilities Physical therapy room; Activities room.
Activities Arts and Crafts; Games; Movies; Dances/Social or cultural gatherings.
Description Skilled nursing for 130 pediatric multiply handicapped residents; provides

24-hour medical nursing care, physical therapy, occupational, speech, recreational, music, and corrective therapy, and special education.

Dixie Manor Sheltered Care*
15535 Dixie Hwy, Harvey, IL, 60426 (312) 339-6438
Admin Leona Thompson.
Licensure Sheltered Care. *Beds* Sheltered Care 23.
Ownership Proprietary.

Halsted Manor*
16048 S Halsted St, Harvey, IL, 60426 (312) 339-5311
Admin Diane H Starks.
Licensure Sheltered Care. *Beds* Sheltered Care 42.
Ownership Proprietary.

Heather Manor Nursing Center
15600 S Honore St, Harvey, IL, 60426 (312) 333-9550
Admin Mary Stanley. *Medical Dir/Dir of Nursing* Sheldon Levine DO.
Licensure Skilled Care; Intermediate Care.
Beds 172. *Certified* Medicaid; Medicare.
Ownership Proprietary.
Admissions Requirements Minimum age 18; Medical examination; Physician's request.
Staff Physicians 5 (pt); RNs 3 (ft); LPNs 12 (ft), 4 (pt); Orderlies 3 (ft), 1 (pt); Nurses aides 42 (ft), 3 (pt); Physical therapists 1 (ft); Recreational therapists 2 (ft); Occupational therapists 1 (pt); Speech therapists 1 (pt); Activities coordinators 1 (ft); Dietitians 1 (pt); Dentists 1 (pt); Ophthalmologists 1 (pt); Podiatrists 1 (pt); Audiologists 1 (pt).
Facilities Dining room; Physical therapy room; Activities room; Chapel; Crafts room; Laundry room; Barber/Beauty shop.
Activities Arts and Crafts; Cards; Games; Reading groups; Prayer groups; Movies; Shopping trips; Dances/Social or cultural gatherings; Field trips.
Description Manor is a clean, caring, family atmosphere home with every accreditation possible including JCAH. Every type of rehabilitation service is offered including full-time physical therapist on staff and speech and language rehabilitation. Activity program has a varied and stimulating full calendar of events. VA approved.

Kenniebrew Home*
14812 S Marshfield, Harvey, IL, 60426 (312) 339-9345
Admin Vondell L Kenniebrew.
Licensure Sheltered Care. *Beds* Sheltered Care 23.
Ownership Proprietary.

Starnes Nursing Home Inc*
14434 S Hoyne, Harvey, IL, 60426 (312) 389-2730
Admin Shirley Q White.
Licensure Intermediate Care. *Beds* 39. *Certified* Medicaid.
Ownership Proprietary.

HARWOOD HEIGHTS

Central Baptist Home for the Aged*
4750 N Orange, Harwood Heights, IL, 60656
(312) 452-8265
Admin Myron H Dudek.
Licensure Intermediate Care; Sheltered Care.
Beds ICF 113; Sheltered Care 23.
Ownership Nonprofit.
Affiliation Baptist

HAVANA

Martin Manor Nursing Home
609 N Harpham St, Havana, IL, 62644 (309)
543-6121
Admin Robert W Martin. *Medical Dir/Dir of
Nursing* N Khokhar MD.
Licensure Intermediate Care. *Beds* 89. *Certified* Medicaid.
Ownership Proprietary.
Admissions Requirements Minimum age 21;
Medical examination.
Staff Physicians 1 (pt); RNs 2 (ft); LPNs 4 (ft),
3 (pt); Nurses aides 19 (ft), 5 (pt); Physical therapists 1 (pt); Recreational therapists 1 (pt);
Occupational therapists 2 (ft); Speech therapists
1 (pt); Activities coordinators 1 (pt); Dietitians
1 (pt); Dentists 1 (pt); Podiatrists 1 (pt).
Facilities Dining room; Physical therapy room;
Activities room; Chapel; Crafts room; Laundry
room; Barber/Beauty shop; Library.
Activities Arts and Crafts; Cards; Games;
Reading groups; Prayer groups; Movies; Shopping trips; Dances/Social or cultural gatherings.

HAZEL CREST

Imperial Nursing Center of Hazel Crest
3300 W 175th St, Hazel Crest, IL, 60429 (312)
335-2400
Admin Barbara J Schubert.
Licensure Skilled Care; Intermediate Care.
Beds 204. *Certified* Medicaid; Medicare.
Ownership Proprietary.
Admissions Requirements Medical examination; Physician's request.
Staff Physicians 3 (ft); RNs 11 (ft), 4 (pt);
LPNs 5 (ft), 3 (pt); Nurses aides 45 (ft), 10 (pt);
Physical therapists 1 (ft); Recreational therapists
1 (ft); Occupational therapists 1 (pt); Speech
therapists 1 (pt); Activities coordinators 1 (ft);
Dietitians 1 (pt); Dentists 1 (pt); Ophthalmologists 1 (pt); Podiatrists 1 (pt); Audiologists 1
(pt).
Facilities Dining room; Physical therapy room;
Activities room; Crafts room; Laundry room;
Barber/Beauty shop.
Activities Arts and Crafts; Cards; Games;
Reading groups; Prayer groups; Movies; Shopping trips; Dances/Social or cultural gatherings.

HERRIN

Park Avenue Health Care Home*
PO Box 68, Herrin, IL, 62948 (618) 942-3928
Admin Julie Maschmann.
Licensure Intermediate Care. *Beds* 69. *Certified* Medicaid.
Ownership Proprietary.

Ray White Care Center*
1900 N Park Ave, Herrin, IL, 62948 (618)
942-2525
Admin C R White.
Licensure Intermediate Care. *Beds* 49. *Certified* Medicaid.
Ownership Proprietary.

Shawnee Christian Nursing Center*
1900 13th St, Herrin, IL, 62948 (618) 942-7391
Admin M Eileen Burberry.
Licensure Skilled Care. *Beds* 151.
Certified Medicaid; Medicare.
Ownership Nonprofit.

HIGHLAND

Chastains of Highland Inc*
2510 Lemon Street Rd, Highland, IL, 62249
(618) 654-2368
Admin Paul H McNalley.
Licensure Skilled Care; Intermediate Care.
Beds SNF 33; ICF 95. *Certified* Medicaid.
Ownership Proprietary.

Highland Manor
27th St and Azalea, Highland, IL, 62249 (618)
654-2393
Admin Marie Hoyt.
Licensure Intermediate Care. *Beds* 65. *Certified* Medicaid.
Ownership Nonprofit.
Staff RNs 2 (ft), 2 (pt); LPNs 2 (ft), 2 (pt);
Nurses aides 30 (ft), 10 (pt); Recreational therapists 1 (ft); Activities coordinators 1 (ft); Dietitians 1 (pt).
Facilities Dining room; Physical therapy room;
Activities room; Laundry room; Barber/Beauty
shop.
Activities Arts and Crafts; Cards; Games;
Reading groups; Prayer groups; Movies; Shopping trips; Dances/Social or cultural gatherings.

HIGHLAND PARK

Abbott House*
405 Central Ave, Highland Park, IL, 60035
(312) 432-6080
Admin Karla S Bishop.
Licensure Intermediate Care. *Beds* 104. *Certified* Medicaid.
Ownership Proprietary.

Villa Saint Cyril
1111 Saint Johns Ave, Highland Park, IL,
60035 (312) 432-9104
Admin Sr M Priscilla. *Medical Dir/Dir of
Nursing* Jules H Last MD.
Licensure Intermediate Care. *Beds* 82. *Certified* Medicaid.
Ownership Nonprofit.
Admissions Requirements Minimum age 65;
Medical examination.
Staff Physicians 2 (pt); RNs 7 (ft), 2 (pt); LPNs
1 (ft); Orderlies 3 (ft); Nurses aides 12 (ft), 4
(pt); Reality therapists 1 (ft); Recreational therapists 3 (ft), 1 (pt); Occupational therapists 1 (pt);
Activities coordinators 1 (ft); Dietitians 1 (ft);
Dentists 1 (pt); Podiatrists 1 (pt).
Affiliation Roman Catholic
Facilities Dining room; Activities room; Chapel; Crafts room; Laundry room; Barber/Beauty
shop; Library.
Activities Arts and Crafts; Cards; Games;
Reading groups; Prayer groups; Movies; Shopping trips; Dances/Social or cultural gatherings;
Luncheon; Concert outings; Children's outreach
program.
Description Facility features religious services
for various religious affiliations; activity program designed for individual needs; 3-story
building with individual nursing centers.

HIGHWOOD

Pavilion of Highland Park*
50 Pleasant, Highwood, IL, 60040 (312)
432-9142
Admin Contance B Zimmerman.
Licensure Skilled Care; Intermediate Care.
Beds SNF 82; ICF 13. *Certified* Medicaid.
Ownership Proprietary.

HILLSBORO

Hawthorne Lodge of Hillsboro
1300 E Treamont St, Hillsboro, IL, 62049 (217)
532-6191
Admin Wilma McCammack. *Medical Dir/Dir
of Nursing* Dr Walter Williams.
Licensure Skilled Care. *Beds* SNF 123. *Certified* Medicaid; Medicare.
Ownership Proprietary.
Admissions Requirements Minimum age 50;
Medical examination; Physician's request.
Staff RNs 2 (ft), 3 (pt); LPNs 8 (ft), 1 (pt);
Nurses aides 40 (ft), 6 (pt); Physical therapists 1
(ft), 1 (pt); Recreational therapists 2 (ft), 1 (pt);
Activities coordinators 2 (ft), 1 (pt); Dietitians
1 (ft).
Facilities Dining room; Physical therapy room;
Activities room; Chapel; Crafts room; Laundry
room; Barber/Beauty shop.
Activities Arts and Crafts; Cards; Games;
Reading groups; Prayer groups; Movies; Shopping trips; Dances/Social or cultural gatherings;
Quilting class; Cooking class.
Description Facility is next door to Hillsboro
Hospital and Hillsboro Medical Clinic. A local
school provides an adopt-a-grandparent program. The high school health class comes every
spring and spends one hour daily for 6 weeks.

Hillsboro Nursing Home*
S Route 127, Hillsboro, IL, 62049 (217)
532-6126
Admin Melvin L Zimmerman.
Licensure Intermediate Care. *Beds* 126. *Certified* Medicaid.

HINSDALE

Americana Healthcare Center
600 W Ogden Ave, Hinsdale, IL, 60521 (312)
325-9630
Admin Joseph D McGee.
Licensure Skilled Care. *Beds* 200. *Certified* Medicaid; Medicare.
Ownership Proprietary.

King Bruwaert House*
6101 County Line Rd, Hinsdale, IL, 60521
(312) 323-2250
Admin Muriel L Whybrow.
Licensure Intermediate Care; Sheltered Care.
Beds ICF 18; Sheltered Care 79.
Ownership Nonprofit.

Oak Brook Nursing Center*
2013 W Midwest Rd, Hinsdale, IL, 60521 (312)
495-0220
Admin Evelyn Underwood.
Licensure Skilled Care; Intermediate Care.
Beds SNF 110; ICF 28.
Ownership Proprietary.

West Suburban Shelter Care Center*
Rt 83 and 91st, Hinsdale, IL, 60521 (312)
323-0198
Admin Suresh R Mehta.
Licensure Sheltered Care. *Beds* Sheltered Care
48.
Ownership Proprietary.

HOMEWOOD

Mercy Health Care Rehabilitation Center*
19000 Halsted St, Homewood, IL, 60430 (312)
957-9200
Admin Sr Renee Humble.
Licensure Skilled Care. *Beds* 256. *Certified* Medicaid; Medicare.
Ownership Nonprofit.

HOOPESTON

**Hoopeston Community Memorial Nursing
Home**
701 E Orange St, Hoopeston, IL, 60942 (217)
283-5531
Admin Roy F Johnson. *Medical Dir/Dir of
Nursing* Dr T C Lee.
Licensure Skilled Care. *Beds* 50. *Certified* Medicaid; Medicare.
Ownership Nonprofit.
Staff RNs 1 (ft); LPNs 2 (ft), 2 (pt); Nurses
aides 12 (ft), 8 (pt); Physical therapists 1 (ft);
Activities coordinators 1 (ft), 1 (pt).
Facilities Dining room; Physical therapy room;
Activities room; Crafts room; Laundry room;
Barber/Beauty shop.
Activities Arts and Crafts; Cards; Games;
Reading groups; Prayer groups; Dances/Social
or cultural gatherings.
Description This is a comfortable nursing
home in a rural setting providing a variety of
activities for the elderly person.

HOPEDALE

Hopedale House*
2nd St, Hopedale, IL, 61747 (309) 449-3321
Admin William L Marshall.
Licensure Sheltered Care. *Beds* Sheltered Care
50.
Ownership Nonprofit.

Hopedale Nursing Home*
2nd St, Hopedale, IL, 61747 (309) 449-3321
Admin David W Britton.

Licensure Skilled Care. *Beds* 96. *Certified* Medicaid; Medicare.
Ownership Nonprofit.

HUTSONVILLE

Heritage Sheltered Care Home
207 Wood Ln, Hutsonville, IL, 62433 (618)
563-4806
Admin Rena A Smith.
Licensure Sheltered Care. *Beds* Sheltered Care
48.
Ownership Proprietary.
Admissions Requirements Minimum age 18;
Medical examination.
Facilities Dining room; Activities room; Crafts
room; Laundry room; Barber/Beauty shop;
Smoker.
Activities Arts and Crafts; Cards; Games;
Shopping trips; Dances/Social or cultural gatherings; Vacations.
Description Facility is set in wooded area and
quiet friendly surroundings. Trips throughout
the U.S. planned yearly as well as family reunions.

IRVINGTON

Country View Manor*
PO Box 189, Irvington, IL, 62848 (618)
249-6216
Admin Vincent B Campanella.
Licensure Intermediate Care. *Beds* 72.
Ownership Nonprofit.

ISLAND LAKE

Sheltering Oaks*
PO Box 367, Island Lake, IL, 60042 (312)
526-3636
Admin Robert A Bundy.
Licensure Intermediate Care. *Beds* 70. *Certified* Medicaid.
Ownership Proprietary.

ITASCA

The Arbor*
535 S Elm, Itasca, IL, 60143 (312) 773-9416
Admin John C Florina Jr.
Licensure Intermediate Care. *Beds* 80. *Certified* Medicaid.
Ownership Proprietary.

JACKSONVILLE

Barton W Stone Christian Home*
873 Grove St, Jacksonville, IL, 62650 (217)
243-3376
Admin Loren T Cline.
Licensure Intermediate Care; Sheltered Care.
Beds ICF 99; Sheltered Care 24. *Certified* Medicaid.
Ownership Nonprofit.

Ivanhoe Manor
1316 Tendick, Jacksonville, IL, 62650 (217)
243-6405
Admin Mary Shields.

Licensure Intermediate Care. *Beds* 93. *Certified* Medicaid.
Ownership Proprietary.
Admissions Requirements Minimum age 18;
Medical examination.
Facilities Dining room; Physical therapy room;
Activities room; Chapel; Crafts room; Laundry
room; Barber/Beauty shop.
Activities Arts and Crafts; Games; Reading
groups; Prayer groups; Movies; Shopping trips;
Dances/Social or cultural gatherings; Orientation.

Ivanhoe Manor Nursing Center
1313 Tendick, Jacksonville, IL, 62650 (217)
243-6405
Admin Mary W Shields.
Licensure Intermediate Care. *Beds* 93. *Certified* Medicaid.
Ownership Proprietary.

Jacksonville Convalescent Center*
1517 W Walnut St, Jacksonville, IL, 62650
(217) 243-6451
Admin David A Coble.
Licensure Skilled Care; Intermediate Care.
Beds SNF 61; ICF 27. *Certified* Medicaid;
Medicare.
Ownership Proprietary.

Meline Nursing Center*
1024 W Walnut St, Jacksonville, IL, 62650
(217) 245-5175
Admin William Rockmeir.
Licensure Skilled Care. *Beds* 138. *Certified* Medicaid; Medicare.
Ownership Proprietary.

Modern Care Convalescent and Nursing Home*
1500 W Walnut St, Jacksonville, IL, 62650
(217) 245-4183
Admin Marian E Chalcraft.
Licensure Skilled Care. *Beds* 68. *Certified* Medicaid; Medicare.
Ownership Proprietary.

Skyview Manor*
1021 N Church, Jacksonville, IL, 62650 (217)
245-4174
Admin Dennis Ferguson.
Licensure Intermediate Care. *Beds* 113. *Certified* Medicaid.

JERSEYVILLE

Garnets Chateau*
608 W Pearl St, Jerseyville, IL, 62052 (618)
498-4312
Admin Hilda G Day.
Licensure Intermediate Care. *Beds* 48. *Certified* Medicaid.
Ownership Proprietary.

Greenwood Manor Nursing Home*
410 Fletcher, Jerseyville, IL, 62052 (618)
498-6427
Admin Barbara Molloy.
Licensure Skilled Care. *Beds* 98. *Certified* Medicaid.
Ownership Proprietary.

Jerseyville Care Center*
923 S State St, Jerseyville, IL, 62052 (618)
498-6496
Admin Ray V Taylor.
Licensure Skilled Care. *Beds* 109. *Certified* Medicaid.
Ownership Proprietary.

JOHNSTON CITY

Lyn Wood Shelter Care Home
205 E 3rd St, Johnston City, IL, 62951 (618)
983-5731
Admin Nancy Whitson.
Licensure Sheltered Care. *Beds* Sheltered Care 23.
Ownership Proprietary.
Admissions Requirements Minimum age 18;
Medical examination.
Staff RNs 1 (pt); Activities coordinators 1 (ft);
Dietitians 1 (pt); Dentists 1 (pt); Ophthalmologists 1 (pt).
Facilities Dining room; Activities room; Laundry room.
Activities Arts and Crafts; Cards; Games;
Reading groups; Prayer groups; Movies; Shopping trips; Dances/Social or cultural gatherings.

JOLIET

Broadway Nursing Home
216 N Broadway, Joliet, IL, 60435 (815)
727-7672
Admin Alice J Connor.
Licensure Intermediate Care. *Beds* 60.
Ownership Proprietary.
Admissions Requirements Minimum age 55.
Staff RNs 1 (ft), 2 (pt); LPNs 4 (ft); Nurses
aides 12 (ft), 4 (pt); Activities coordinators 1
(pt); Dietitians 1 (pt).
Facilities Dining room; Activities room; Laundry room.
Activities Arts and Crafts; Cards; Games; Prayer groups; Movies; Cookouts; Picnics on patio;
Free concerts.

Deerbrook Nursing Centre*
306 N Larkin Ave, Joliet, IL, 60435 (815)
744-5560
Admin Hussain Siddique.
Licensure Skilled Care. *Beds* 224. *Certified* Medicaid; Medicare.
Ownership Proprietary.

Franciscan Nursing Home
300 N Madison St, Joliet, IL, 60435 (815)
725-3400
Admin Sr M Alexine Knotek. *Medical Dir/Dir
of Nursing* Anthony Razma MD.
Licensure Skilled Care. *Beds* 129. *Certified* Medicaid; Medicare.
Ownership Nonprofit.
Admissions Requirements Minimum age 18;
Medical examination; Physician's request.
Staff Physicians; RNs; LPNs; Nurses aides;
Physical therapists; Activities coordinators;
Dietitians.
Affiliation Roman Catholic
Facilities Dining room; Physical therapy room;
Activities room; Chapel; Barber/Beauty shop.
Activities Arts and Crafts; Cards; Games; Pray-

er groups; Movies; Shopping trips; Dances/Social or cultural gatherings.
Description Franciscan Nursing Home is a one-story, 129-bed skilled facility offering Intermediate and skilled care. in close proximity to
medical clinics and St Joseph Medical Center
with an enclosed patio and 2 interior court
yards.

Imperial Nursing Center of Joliet
222 N Hammes, Joliet, IL, 60435 (815)
725-0443
Admin Scott Gordon. *Medical Dir/Dir of
Nursing* Louis Minella.
Licensure Skilled Care; Intermediate Care.
Beds 203. *Certified* Medicaid; Medicare.
Ownership Proprietary.
Staff Physicians 3 (pt); RNs 10 (ft), 7 (pt);
LPNs 10 (ft), 12 (pt); Orderlies 3 (ft), 1 (pt);
Nurses aides 20 (ft), 8 (pt); Physical therapists 1
(ft); Reality therapists 3 (ft); Recreational therapists 4 (ft); Occupational therapists 2 (ft), 1 (pt);
Speech therapists 1 (ft); Activities coordinators
1 (ft); Dietitians 1 (ft), 1 (pt); Dentists 3 (pt);
Ophthalmologists 2 (pt); Podiatrists 1 (pt);
Audiologists 1 (pt).
Description VA approved.

Joliet Terrace*
2230 McDonough, Joliet, IL, 60436 (815)
729-3801
Admin Nancy De Young.
Licensure Intermediate Care. *Beds* 118. *Certified* Medicaid.
Ownership Proprietary.

Our Lady of Angels Retirement
1201 Wyoming Ave, Joliet, IL, 60435 (815)
725-6631
Admin Albert M Papesh.
Licensure Intermediate Care; Sheltered Care.
Beds ICF 50; Sheltered Care 50. *Certified* Medicaid.
Ownership Nonprofit.
Admissions Requirements Minimum age 65;
Medical examination.
Staff RNs 1 (ft), 5 (pt); LPNs 2 (pt); Nurses
aides 21 (ft), 12 (pt); Physical therapists 1 (pt);
Activities coordinators 1 (ft); Dietitians 1 (ft).
Affiliation Roman Catholic
Facilities Dining room; Physical therapy room;
Activities room; Chapel; Crafts room; Laundry
room; Barber/Beauty shop; Library.
Activities Arts and Crafts; Cards; Games;
Reading groups; Prayer groups; Movies; Shopping trips; Dances/Social or cultural gatherings.

Saint Patrick's Residence
22 E Clinton, Joliet, IL, 60431 (815) 727-5291
Admin Sr M Jacqueline Wagner. *Medical Dir/Dir of Nursing* Dr R Garcia.
Licensure Intermediate Care; Residential Care.
Beds ICF 107; Sheltered Care 90. *Certified* Medicaid.
Ownership Nonprofit.
Staff Physicians 1 (pt); RNs 3 (ft), 6 (pt); LPNs
5 (ft), 3 (pt); Nurses aides 49 (ft), 1 (pt);
Physical therapists 1 (pt); Recreational therapists 1 (pt); Occupational therapists 1 (pt); Speech therapists 1 (pt); Activities coordinators 1
(ft); Dietitians 1 (ft); Dentists 1 (pt); Ophthalmologists 1 (pt); Podiatrists 1 (pt); Audiologists
1 (pt).

Affiliation Roman Catholic
Facilities Dining room; Activities room; Chapel; Crafts room; Laundry room; Barber/Beauty
shop; Library.
Activities Arts and Crafts; Cards; Games;
Reading groups; Prayer groups; Movies; Shopping trips; Dances/Social or cultural gatherings.

Salem Village
1314 Rowell Ave, Joliet, IL, 60433 (815)
727-5451
Admin Ray W Hemphill. *Medical Dir/Dir of
Nursing* Mary E Jones RN.
Licensure Intermediate Care; Sheltered Care.
Beds ICF 236; Sheltered Care 77. *Certified* Medicare.
Ownership Nonprofit.
Admissions Requirements Minimum age 65;
Medical examination.
Staff Physicians 2 (pt); RNs 6 (ft), 7 (pt); LPNs
10 (ft), 11 (pt); Orderlies 1 (pt); Nurses aides 47
(ft), 32 (pt); Activities coordinators 1 (ft); Dietitians 1 (ft).
Facilities Dining room; Physical therapy room;
Activities room; Chapel; Crafts room; Laundry
room; Barber/Beauty shop; Library.
Activities Arts and Crafts; Cards; Games;
Reading groups; Prayer groups; Movies; Shopping trips; Dances/Social or cultural gatherings.
Description Salem Village's purpose as a not-for-profit care continuum is to provide a broad
choice of comfortable and secure living facilities, with care services where appropriate, for
retired and older persons whom for many reasons cannot or choose not to live in a competitive setting in the general community. As the
largest retirement community and the third
largest health care facility in Will County,
Salem Village has a natural leadership position
and a welcomed responsibility to prepare for
this future.

Sunny Hill Nursing Home
Doris and Neal Sts, Joliet, IL, 60433 (815)
727-8710
Medical Dir/Dir of Nursing Dr Kishor Ajmere.
Licensure Skilled Care; Intermediate Care.
Beds SNF 50; ICF 250. *Certified* Medicaid.
Ownership Public.
Admissions Requirements Minimum age 18;
Medical examination.
Staff RNs 7 (ft), 3 (pt); LPNs 27 (ft), 4 (pt);
Nurses aides 96 (ft), 8 (pt); Activities coordinators 1 (ft).
Facilities Dining room; Physical therapy room;
Activities room; Chapel; Crafts room; Laundry
room; Barber/Beauty shop; Library.
Activities Arts and Crafts; Cards; Games;
Reading groups; Prayer groups; Movies; Shopping trips; Dances/Social or cultural gatherings;
Resident council; Reality orientation; Exercises;
Service projects; Resident newsletter.
Description Located in a quiet, wooded,
pleasantly landscaped area on the southern edge
of Joliet. Facility offers
rehabilitative/restorative services for up to 300
predominately geriatric residents.

Will County Sheltered Workshop Community Living*
611 E Cass St, Joliet, IL, 60432 (815) 727-3627
Admin John Wimke.
Licensure Intermediate Care. *Beds* 58.
Ownership Nonprofit.

Woodside Nursing Center*
777 Draper, Joliet, IL, 60432 (815) 727-4794
Admin Jo Anne Fisher.
Licensure Skilled Care; Intermediate Care.
Beds 168. *Certified* Medicaid; Medicare.
Ownership Nonprofit.

JONESBORO

Gibbs and McRaven Sheltered Care Home
204 S Pecan, Jonesboro, IL, 62952 (618) 833-5740
Admin Howard H McRaven. *Medical Dir/Dir of Nursing* Burton E Rogby MD.
Licensure Sheltered Care. *Beds* Sheltered Care 25.
Ownership Proprietary.
Admissions Requirements Minimum age 18; Medical examination.
Staff Physicians 1 (pt); RNs 1 (pt); Orderlies 2 (ft); Nurses aides 4 (ft); Occupational therapists 1 (pt); Activities coordinators 1 (ft), 1 (pt); Dietitians 1 (pt); Dentists 1 (pt).
Facilities Dining room; Activities room; Crafts room; Laundry room; Library; Large sitting and visitors room.
Activities Arts and Crafts; Cards; Games; Reading groups; Prayer groups; Movies; Shopping trips; Dances/Social or cultural gatherings; Community outings to local restaurants and parks; Yearly trip to wild animal park.
Description Facility is a one-story building located in a residential part of town; family operated; complete activity program that includes community involvement.

Henard Sheltered Care Home*
204 S Main, Jonesboro, IL, 62952 (618) 833-6134
Admin Donna F Mansfield.
Licensure Sheltered Care. *Beds* Sheltered Care 16.
Ownership Proprietary.

Jonesboro Nursing Center Inc
PO Box B, Jonesboro, IL, 62952 (618) 833-7093
Admin Lonnie D Harvel. *Medical Dir/Dir of Nursing* Dr William H Whiting.
Licensure Intermediate Care. *Beds* 82. *Certified* Medicaid.
Ownership Proprietary.
Admissions Requirements Minimum age 18; Medical examination; Physician's request.
Staff Physicians 1 (pt); RNs 1 (ft); LPNs 7 (ft); Nurses aides 20 (ft), 4 (pt); Physical therapists 1 (pt); Reality therapists 1 (pt); Recreational therapists 1 (pt); Speech therapists 1 (pt); Activities coordinators 1 (ft), 1 (pt); Dietitians 1 (pt); Dentists 1 (pt); Ophthalmologists 1 (pt); Podiatrists 1 (pt); Audiologists 1 (pt).
Facilities Dining room; Activities room; Chapel; Crafts room; Laundry room; Barber/Beauty shop; Library.
Activities Arts and Crafts; Cards; Games;

Reading groups; Prayer groups; Movies; Shopping trips; Dances/Social or cultural gatherings.

JUSTICE

Rosary Hill Home
9000 W 81st St, Justice, IL, 60458
Admin Sr M Catherine. *Medical Dir/Dir of Nursing* James M Wall.
Licensure Intermediate Care; Sheltered Care.
Beds ICF 18; Sheltered Care 32.
Ownership Nonprofit.
Admissions Requirements Minimum age 65; Females only
Staff RNs 1 (ft); LPNs 1 (ft); Nurses aides 8 (ft); Activities coordinators 1 (pt); Dietitians 1 (pt); Podiatrists 1 (pt).
Affiliation Roman Catholic
Facilities Dining room; Activities room; Chapel; Laundry room; Barber/Beauty shop; Library.
Activities Arts and Crafts; Cards; Games; Prayer groups; Movies.

KANKAKEE

Americana Healthcare Center of Kankakee*
900 W River Pl, Kankakee, IL, 60901 (815) 933-1711
Admin Joy Rathe.
Licensure Skilled Care. *Beds* 88. *Certified* Medicaid; Medicare.
Ownership Proprietary.

The Heritage House*
901 N Entrance, Kankakee, IL, 60901 (815) 939-4500
Admin Harold A Wilken.
Licensure Skilled Care; Sheltered Care.
Beds SNF 31; Sheltered Care 99.
Ownership Nonprofit.

Westview Terrace*
1050 N Jeffrey St, Kankakee, IL, 60901 (815) 933-1660
Admin Henrietta Chamness.
Licensure Skilled Care; Intermediate Care.
Beds SNF 90; ICF 110. *Certified* Medicaid.
Ownership Proprietary.

KEWANEE

Kewanee Care Home*
144 Junior Ave, Kewanee, IL, 61443 (309) 853-4429
Admin Mark Goodwin.
Licensure Intermediate Care. *Beds* 65. *Certified* Medicaid.
Ownership Proprietary.

Kewanee Convalescent Center
605 E Church, Kewanee, IL, 61443 (309) 852-3389
Admin Vicky L Flack. *Medical Dir/Dir of Nursing* Sandor Apathy.
Licensure Skilled Care. *Beds* 200. *Certified* Medicaid; Medicare.
Ownership Proprietary.
Admissions Requirements Minimum age 18; Medical examination; Physician's request.

Staff RNs 7 (ft), 4 (pt); LPNs 10 (ft), 4 (pt); Orderlies 2 (ft); Nurses aides 40 (ft); Physical therapists 1 (ft); Activities coordinators 2 (ft).
Facilities Dining room; Physical therapy room; Activities room; Crafts room; Laundry room; Barber/Beauty shop.
Activities Arts and Crafts; Cards; Games; Reading groups; Prayer groups; Movies; Shopping trips; Dances/Social or cultural gatherings.

KNOXVILLE

Good Samaritan Nursing Home
407 N Hebard St, Knoxville, IL, 61448 (309) 289-2614
Admin Anna Wang. *Medical Dir/Dir of Nursing* Robert G Hickerson Jr MD.
Licensure Intermediate Care. *Beds* 49. *Certified* Medicaid.
Ownership Nonprofit.
Admissions Requirements Minimum age 18; Medical examination; Physician's request.
Staff RNs 1 (ft), 1 (pt); LPNs 4 (ft), 1 (pt); Nurses aides 24 (ft), 8 (pt); Reality therapists 1 (ft); Recreational therapists 1 (ft); Occupational therapists 1 (ft); Activities coordinators 1 (ft), 1 (pt); Dietitians 1 (ft).
Facilities Dining room; Physical therapy room; Activities room; Chapel; Crafts room; Laundry room; Library; Social hall.
Activities Arts and Crafts; Cards; Games; Reading groups; Prayer groups; Movies; Shopping trips; Dances/Social or cultural gatherings; Sunshine Singers.
Description Home features a licensed clinical psychologist who serves in the care plan and treatment team and who gives in-service training.

Knox County Nursing Home
N Market St, Knoxville, IL, 61448 (309) 289-2338
Admin Mary E Peterson.
Licensure Skilled Care. *Beds* 204. *Certified* Medicaid.
Ownership Public.
Admissions Requirements Physician's request.
Staff RNs 5 (ft), 3 (pt); LPNs 8 (ft), 10 (pt); Nurses aides 37 (ft), 64 (pt).
Facilities Dining room; Physical therapy room; Activities room; Chapel; Crafts room; Laundry room; Barber/Beauty shop; Library.
Activities Arts and Crafts; Cards; Games; Prayer groups; Movies; Dances/Social or cultural gatherings.
Description All ground level double rooms; country setting.

LA GRANGE

Fairview Health Care Center
701 N La Grange Rd, La Grange, IL, 60525 (312) 354-7300
Admin Stephanie Hart.
Licensure Skilled Care. *Beds* 131. *Certified* Medicare.
Ownership Proprietary.
Staff Physical therapists 1 (ft); Recreational therapists 1 (ft); Occupational therapists; Speech therapists; Activities coordinators; Dietitians; Dentists; Ophthalmologists; Podiatrists;

Audiologists 1 (ft).
Facilities Dining room; Physical therapy room; Activities room; Chapel; Crafts room; Laundry room; Barber/Beauty shop; Library.
Activities Arts and Crafts; Cards; Games; Reading groups; Prayer groups; Movies; Shopping trips.

La Grange Colonial Manor*
339 9th Ave, La Grange, IL, 60525 (312) 354-4660
Admin Don R Boyer.
Licensure Skilled Care; Intermediate Care.
Beds SNF 96; ICF 107. *Certified* Medicaid; Medicare.
Ownership Nonprofit.

Plymouth Place
315 N La Grange Rd, La Grange, IL, 60525 (312) 354-0340
Admin Donald E Clawson. *Medical Dir/Dir of Nursing* Dr Aubrey Moore.
Licensure Intermediate Care; Sheltered Care.
Beds ICF 76; Sheltered Care 134.
Ownership Nonprofit.
Admissions Requirements Minimum age 62; Medical examination.
Staff Physicians 3 (pt); RNs 7 (ft), 1 (pt); LPNs 2 (ft), 2 (pt); Nurses aides 20 (ft), 3 (pt); Physical therapists 1 (pt); Reality therapists 1 (pt); Recreational therapists 1 (pt); Occupational therapists 1 (pt); Speech therapists 1 (pt); Activities coordinators 1 (ft); Dietitians 1 (ft), 1 (pt); Dentists 1 (pt); Ophthalmologists 1 (pt); Podiatrists 1 (pt).
Affiliation Church of Christ
Facilities Dining room; Physical therapy room; Activities room; Chapel; Crafts room; Laundry room; Barber/Beauty shop; Library; Woodworking shop.
Activities Arts and Crafts; Cards; Games; Reading groups; Prayer groups; Movies; Shopping trips; Dances/Social or cultural gatherings; Exercises; Baseball team sponsorship.
Description Facility has convenient near-downtown location; major transportation readily available (20 minutes from Chicago O'Hare Airport, and one-quarter mile to Amtrak station); cottages, townhomes and apartments for a gracious lifestyle of resident's own choosing; major shopping center within easy walking distance.

White Oak Nursing Centre*
6800 W Joliet Rd, La Grange, IL, 60525 (312) 246-8500
Admin Jeanette Fox.
Licensure Skilled Care; Intermediate Care.
Beds SNF 88; ICF 157.
Ownership Proprietary.

LA ROSE

Evergreens
102 Locust St, La Rose, IL, 61541 (309) 399-7181
Admin Anna Stoens.
Licensure Sheltered Care. *Beds* 26.
Ownership Proprietary.
Admissions Requirements Minimum age 18.
Staff Physicians 1 (ft); RNs 1 (ft); Nurses aides 5 (ft); Activities coordinators 1 (ft); Dietitians 1

(ft), 1 (pt).
Facilities Dining room; Activities room; Laundry room.
Activities Games; Reading groups; Prayer groups; Dances/Social or cultural gatherings.
Description Facility is a small, 26-bed unit with a small town atmosphere.

LA SALLE

Care Inn Convalescent Center*
1445 Chartres St, La Salle, IL, 61301 (815) 223-4700
Admin Alice M Ghilino.
Licensure Skilled Care; Intermediate Care.
Beds SNF 50; ICF 49. *Certified* Medicaid; Medicare.
Ownership Proprietary.

LACON

Saint Joseph Nursing Home*
401 9th St, Lacon, IL, 61540 (309) 246-2175
Admin Sr Catherine Platte.
Licensure Intermediate Care. *Beds* 104. *Certified* Medicaid.
Ownership Nonprofit.

LAKE BLUFF

Hill Top
502 Waukegan Rd, Lake Bluff, IL, 60044 (312) 295-1550
Admin Marion W Tarbutton.
Licensure Skilled Care. *Beds* 26.
Ownership Nonprofit.
Affiliation Christian Science
Facilities Dining room; Activities room; Chapel; Crafts room; Laundry room; Barber/Beauty shop; Library.
Activities Arts and Crafts; Reading groups; Prayer groups; Movies.
Description Hill Top Sanitorium is mainly a short-term skilled care facility for those relying solely on prayer for healing; average patient stay is 17 days.

Lake Bluff Health Care Center
700 Jenkisson Ave, Lake Bluff, IL, 60044 (312) 295-3900
Admin James D Bowden. *Medical Dir/Dir of Nursing* David Schimel MD.
Licensure Skilled Care; Intermediate Care.
Beds 231. *Certified* Medicaid; Medicare.
Ownership Proprietary.
Admissions Requirements Minimum age 21; Medical examination; Physician's request.
Staff Physicians 8 (pt); RNs 18 (ft), 10 (pt); LPNs 12 (ft), 10 (pt); Orderlies 10 (ft); Nurses aides 95 (ft); Physical therapists 1 (ft); Recreational therapists 8 (ft); Occupational therapists 1 (pt); Speech therapists 1 (pt); Activities coordinators 1 (ft); Dietitians 1 (pt); Dentists 1 (pt); Ophthalmologists 1 (pt); Podiatrists 1 (pt); Audiologists 1 (pt).
Facilities Dining room; Physical therapy room; Activities room; Crafts room; Laundry room; Barber/Beauty shop; Library.
Activities Arts and Crafts; Cards; Games; Reading groups; Prayer groups; Movies; Shop-

ping trips.
Description Skilled nursing facility; extensive physical therapy and rehabilitation therapy are provided.

LAKE FOREST

Grove School Resident Center
40 E Old Mill Rd, Lake Forest, IL, 60045 (312) 234-5540
Admin Virginia F Matson. *Medical Dir/Dir of Nursing* Dr Shaku Chhabria.
Licensure Skilled Care; Intermediate Care.
Beds SNF 48; ICF 18. *Certified* Medicaid.
Ownership Nonprofit.
Admissions Requirements Minimum age 10; Medical examination; Physician's request.
Staff Physicians 1 (ft), 3 (pt); RNs 3 (ft), 1 (pt); LPNs 1 (ft), 2 (pt); Nurses aides 22 (ft); Physical therapists 1 (pt); Occupational therapists 1 (pt); Speech therapists 1 (ft); Activities coordinators 1 (ft); Dietitians 1 (pt).
Facilities Dining room; Physical therapy room; Activities room; Crafts room; Laundry room.
Activities Arts and Crafts; Games; Movies; Shopping trips.
Description An outstanding children's facility located on 27 wooded acres along Chicago's north shore. Easily accessible to national transportation.

Latham Estates*
Box 104, Lake Forest, IL, 62543 (217) 674-3738
Admin H D Henry.
Licensure Intermediate Care. *Beds* 139.
Ownership Proprietary.

Mount Saint Joseph*
24955 N Hwy 12, Lake Forest, IL, 60047 (312) 438-5050
Admin Margret M Vogel.
Licensure Intermediate Care. *Beds* 160.
Ownership Nonprofit.
Affiliation Roman Catholic

LANSING

Tri State Manor Nursing Home*
2500 E 175th St, Lansing, IL, 60438 (312) 474-7330
Admin Olive J Horeshimer.
Licensure Intermediate Care. *Beds* 56.
Ownership Proprietary.

LAWRENCEVILLE

United Methodist Village
1616 Cedar, Lawrenceville, IL, 62439 (618) 943-3347
Admin William C Carter. *Medical Dir/Dir of Nursing* Dr R T Kirkwood.
Licensure Skilled Care; Intermediate Care; Sheltered Care. *Beds* 248. *Certified* Medicaid.
Ownership Nonprofit.
Admissions Requirements Minimum age 65.
Staff Physicians 6 (pt); RNs 13 (ft), 17 (pt); LPNs 4 (ft), 6 (pt); Orderlies 2 (ft), 3 (pt); Nurses aides 33 (ft), 42 (pt); Physical therapists 1 (ft), 1 (pt); Speech therapists 1 (pt); Activities coordinators 1 (ft); Dietitians 1 (ft); Podiatrists

1 (pt).
Affiliation Methodist
Facilities Dining room; Physical therapy room; Activities room; Chapel; Crafts room; Laundry room; Barber/Beauty shop; Library.
Activities Arts and Crafts; Cards; Games; Reading groups; Prayer groups; Movies; Shopping trips; Dances/Social or cultural gatherings.

LEBANON

Bohannon Nursing Home Inc*
1201 N Alton, Lebanon, IL, 62254 (618) 537-4401
Admin Kenneth O Bohannon.
Licensure Intermediate Care. *Beds* 51. *Certified* Medicaid.
Ownership Proprietary.

LEHA

Broadway Arms Community Living Center*
1003 N Broadway, Leha, IL, 61542 (309) 686-3310
Admin Gail Leiby.
Licensure Intermediate Care. *Beds* 12.
Ownership Nonprofit.

LEMONT

Alvernia Manor
1598 Main St, Lemont, IL, 60439 (312) 257-7721
Admin Sr Cecilia M Adamic.
Licensure Sheltered Care. *Beds* 56.
Ownership Nonprofit.
Admissions Requirements Minimum age 65; Medical examination; Physician's request.
Staff RNs 1 (ft); LPNs 1 (pt); Activities coordinators 1 (ft); Dietitians 1 (pt); Podiatrists 1 (pt).
Affiliation Roman Catholic
Facilities Dining room; Activities room; Chapel; Crafts room; Laundry room; Barber/Beauty shop; Library.
Activities Arts and Crafts; Cards; Games; Reading groups; Prayer groups; Movies; Shopping trips; Dances/Social or cultural gatherings.
Description Alvernia Manor, operated by the Sisters of St Francis of Christ the King, is situated on low, undulating hills, amid giant oaks and large pine trees bounded on 2 sides by the famous Cog Hill Golf Course, 2 miles east of the small historic community of Lemon.

Holy Family Villa*
123rd St, Lemont, IL, 60439 (312) 257-2291
Admin Sr Grace C Wastak.
Licensure Intermediate Care. *Beds* 99. *Certified* Medicaid.
Ownership Nonprofit.
Affiliation Roman Catholic

Mother Teresa Home
1270 Main St, Lemont, IL, 60439 (312) 257-5801
Admin Mary Dorothea Micek.
Licensure Intermediate Care; Sheltered Care.
Beds ICF 46; Sheltered Care 11.
Ownership Nonprofit.
Admissions Requirements Minimum age 60;

Medical examination.
Staff RNs 3 (ft), 6 (pt); LPNs 2 (pt); Orderlies 1 (ft); Nurses aides 17 (ft), 5 (pt); Activities coordinators 1 (ft).
Affiliation Roman Catholic
Facilities Dining room; Activities room; Chapel; Crafts room; Laundry room; Barber/Beauty shop; Library.
Activities Arts and Crafts; Cards; Games; Reading groups; Prayer groups; Movies; Dances/Social or cultural gatherings.
Description Mother Theresa Home is located on very beautiful grounds in Lemont, approximately 25 miles southwest of Chicago; staff strives to give quality care to the residents who have chosen to make this their home.

LENA

Lena Continental Manor Nursing Home
1010 S Logan, Lena, IL, 61048 (815) 369-4561
Admin Lynn M Lyvers.
Licensure Intermediate Care. *Beds* 92. *Certified* Medicaid.
Ownership Proprietary.
Admissions Requirements Medical examination.
Staff RNs 3 (ft), 3 (pt); LPNs 3 (ft), 4 (pt); Nurses aides 17 (ft), 15 (pt); Activities coordinators 1 (ft), 1 (pt); Dietitians 1 (ft).
Facilities Dining room; Physical therapy room; Activities room; Chapel; Crafts room; Laundry room; Barber/Beauty shop.
Activities Arts and Crafts; Cards; Games; Reading groups; Prayer groups; Movies; Dances/Social or cultural gatherings.

LEWISTOWN

Clarytona Manor*
Sycamore Dr, Lewistown, IL, 61542 (309) 547-2267
Admin Kathryn S Demler.
Licensure Intermediate Care. *Beds* 99. *Certified* Medicaid.
Ownership Proprietary.

LEXINGTON

Three Oaks Nursing Center*
301 S Vine St, Lexington, IL, 61753 (309) 365-8016
Admin Gregory W Fears.
Licensure Intermediate Care. *Beds* 49. *Certified* Medicaid.
Ownership Proprietary.

LIBERTYVILLE

The Lambs Inc*
PO Box 520, Libertyville, IL, 60048 (312) 367-6100
Admin Jacqueline M Cohen.
Licensure Intermediate Care for Mentally Retarded. *Beds* 37.
Ownership Nonprofit.

Libertyville Manor Extended Care
610 Peterson Rd, Libertyville, IL, 60048 (312) 367-6100

Admin Slavko Stokovich. *Medical Dir/Dir of Nursing* Brenda Dahl.
Licensure Skilled Care; Intermediate Care.
Beds 129. *Certified* Medicaid; Medicare.
Ownership Proprietary.
Staff Physicians 6 (pt); RNs 8 (ft), 4 (pt); LPNs 1 (ft), 2 (pt); Orderlies 3 (ft); Nurses aides 28 (ft), 8 (pt); Physical therapists 1 (pt); Recreational therapists 3 (ft); Occupational therapists 1 (pt); Speech therapists 1 (pt); Dietitians 1 (pt); Dentists 1 (pt); Podiatrists 1 (pt).
Facilities Dining room; Physical therapy room; Activities room; Laundry room; Barber/Beauty shop; Library.
Activities Arts and Crafts; Cards; Games; Reading groups; Prayer groups; Movies; Shopping trips; Dances/Social or cultural gatherings.
Description New and modern facility is family owned and operated, with 35 years experience in geriatrics. Facility is situated in the country with private and semi-private rooms.

Winchester House
1125 N Milwaukee Ave, Libertyville, IL, 60048 (312) 362-4340
Admin Robert H Roiland.
Licensure Skilled Care; Intermediate Care.
Beds 359. *Certified* Medicaid.
Ownership Public.
Admissions Requirements Minimum age 18.
Staff RNs 30 (ft); LPNs 13 (ft); Nurses aides 146 (ft); Physical therapists 1 (pt); Recreational therapists 1 (ft); Occupational therapists 1 (pt); Speech therapists 1 (pt); Activities coordinators 1 (ft); Dietitians 1 (ft).
Facilities Dining room; Physical therapy room; Activities room; Chapel; Crafts room; Laundry room; Barber/Beauty shop; Library.
Activities Arts and Crafts; Cards; Games; Reading groups; Prayer groups; Movies; Shopping trips; Dances/Social or cultural gatherings.

LINCOLN

Christian Nursing Home Inc*
1507 7th St, Lincoln, IL, 62656 (217) 732-2189
Admin Timothy E Searby.
Licensure Skilled Care. *Beds* 99. *Certified* Medicaid.
Ownership Nonprofit.

Lincoln Land Nursing Home*
2202 N Kickapoo St, Lincoln, IL, 62656 (217) 735-1538
Admin Mabel M Myrick.
Licensure Skilled Care; Intermediate Care.
Beds SNF 59; ICF 25. *Certified* Medicaid.
Ownership Proprietary.

Mary Henry Nursing Home*
1800 5th St, Lincoln, IL, 62656 (217) 732-7990
Admin Emmett Luswald.
Licensure Intermediate Care. *Beds* 58. *Certified* Medicaid.
Ownership Proprietary.

Saint Clara's Manor
200 5th St, Lincoln, IL, 62656 (217) 735-1507
Admin George E Davis. *Medical Dir/Dir of Nursing* Dean A Hauter.
Licensure Skilled Care; Intermediate Care.
Beds SNF 70; ICF 70. *Certified* Medicaid.

Ownership Nonprofit.
Admissions Requirements Minimum age 65; Medical examination; Physician's request.

LISLE

Snow Valley Nursing Home
5000 Lincoln, Lisle, IL, 60532 (312) 852-5100
Admin Mary Anne Coburn. *Medical Dir/Dir of Nursing* Dr Timothy Brandt.
Licensure Skilled Care. *Beds* 49.
Ownership Proprietary.
Staff RNs 5 (ft), 4 (pt); Orderlies 1 (ft); Nurses aides 14 (ft), 8 (pt); Recreational therapists 1 (ft), 1 (pt); Dietitians 1 (pt).
Facilities Dining room; Activities room; Chapel; Crafts room; Laundry room; Barber/Beauty shop.
Activities Arts and Crafts; Cards; Games; Reading groups; Prayer groups; Movies; Shopping trips; Dances/Social or cultural gatherings.

LITCHFIELD

Allison Manor
yler & McKinley St, Litchfield, IL, 62056 (217) 324-5015
Admin Jill Spurgeon.
Licensure Intermediate Care. *Beds* 65. *Certified* Medicaid.
Ownership Proprietary.
Admissions Requirements Minimum age 18; Medical examination.
Facilities Dining room; Physical therapy room; Activities room; Chapel; Crafts room; Laundry room; Barber/Beauty shop.
Activities Arts and Crafts; Games; Reading groups; Prayer groups; Movies; Shopping trips; Dances/Social or cultural gatherings; Orientation.

Allison Manor Healthcare Center
Tyler and McKinley Sts, Litchfield, IL, 62056 (217) 324-3842
Admin Jill Spurgeon. *Medical Dir/Dir of Nursing* Dr R Somner.
Licensure Intermediate Care. *Beds* 65. *Certified* Medicaid.
Ownership Proprietary.
Admissions Requirements Minimum age 18.
Staff RNs 1 (pt); LPNs 6 (ft); Orderlies 3 (ft), 1 (pt); Nurses aides 20 (ft), 2 (pt); Physical therapists 1 (ft); Reality therapists 1 (ft); Recreational therapists 1 (ft); Speech therapists 1 (pt); Activities coordinators 1 (ft); Dietitians 1 (pt); Dentists 1 (pt); Ophthalmologists 1 (pt); Podiatrists 1 (pt); Audiologists 1 (pt).
Facilities Dining room; Physical therapy room; Activities room; Chapel; Crafts room; Laundry room; Barber/Beauty shop.
Activities Arts and Crafts; Cards; Games; Reading groups; Prayer groups; Movies; Shopping trips; Dances/Social or cultural gatherings.

Barry Care Center of Litchfield*
628 S Illinois St, Litchfield, IL, 62056 (217) 324-2153
Admin Sharon L Campbell.
Licensure Skilled Care. *Beds* 104. *Certified* Medicaid.
Ownership Proprietary.

Care Inn Convalescent Center
1285 E Union St, Litchfield, IL, 62056 (217) 324-3996
Admin Mary Coss. *Medical Dir/Dir of Nursing* J J Epplin MD.
Licensure Skilled Care; Intermediate Care.
Beds SNF 26; ICF 97. *Certified* Medicaid; Medicare.
Ownership Proprietary.
Admissions Requirements Minimum age 18; Physician's request.
Staff RNs 4 (ft); LPNs 8 (ft); Nurses aides 31 (ft); Physical therapists 1 (ft); Recreational therapists 1 (ft); Occupational therapists 1 (ft); Speech therapists 1 (pt); Activities coordinators 1 (ft); Dietitians 1 (ft); Dentists 1 (pt).
Facilities Dining room; Physical therapy room; Activities room; Chapel; Crafts room; Laundry room; Barber/Beauty shop; Library.
Activities Arts and Crafts; Cards; Games; Reading groups; Prayer groups; Movies; Shopping trips; Dances/Social or cultural gatherings.
Description Facility is accredited by JCAH.

LOMBARD

Ray Graham Lombard Community Living Center*
143 E Grove, Lombard, IL, 60148 (312) 543-2440
Admin James Durnbaugh.
Licensure Intermediate Care. *Beds* 18.
Ownership Nonprofit.

LONG GROVE

Maple Hill Nursing Home Ltd
Box 2308 RFD, Long Grove, IL, 60047 (312) 438-8275
Admin Liat Tzur. *Medical Dir/Dir of Nursing* Bijan Farah MD.
Licensure Intermediate Care. *Beds* 154. *Certified* Medicaid.
Ownership Proprietary.
Staff Physicians 8 (pt); RNs 7 (ft), 4 (pt); LPNs 1 (ft), 3 (pt); Orderlies 25 (ft); Nurses aides 3 (ft); Physical therapists 1 (pt); Recreational therapists 4 (ft); Occupational therapists 1 (pt); Dietitians 1 (ft), 1 (pt); Dentists 1 (pt); Podiatrists 1 (pt).
Facilities Dining room; Physical therapy room; Activities room; Chapel; Crafts room; Laundry room; Barber/Beauty shop; Library.
Activities Arts and Crafts; Cards; Games; Reading groups; Prayer groups; Movies; Shopping trips; Dances/Social or cultural gatherings.
Description Facility is located on 13 acres in rural Long Grove providing a beautiful outdoor setting and enjoyment for the residents. Activity department provides residents with creative and stimulating programs.

LOUISVILLE

Hill Crest Sheltered Care*
PO Box 119, Rt 45, Louisville, IL, 62858 (618) 686-4542
Admin Janice I Webb.
Licensure Sheltered Care. *Beds* Sheltered Care 23.
Ownership Proprietary.

Louisville Shelter Care Home*
Rt 45S, Box 307, Louisville, IL, 62858 (618) 665-3332
Admin Thomas J Pidgeon Jr.
Licensure Sheltered Care. *Beds* Sheltered Care 36.
Ownership Proprietary.

Twilight Haven Sheltered Care Home*
Rt 45 S, Box 307, Louisville, IL, 62858 (618) 665-3153
Admin Peggy L Pidgeon.
Licensure Sheltered Care. *Beds* Sheltered Care 22.
Ownership Proprietary.

LOVINGTON

Moultrie County Community Center
240 E State, PO Box 666, Lovington, IL, 61937
Admin Gayle Brown.
Licensure Intermediate Care for Mentally Retarded. *Beds* 15.
Ownership Proprietary.
Admissions Requirements Minimum age 18; Physician's request.
Staff Physicians 1 (pt); RNs 1 (pt); Nurses aides 11 (ft); Physical therapists 1 (pt); Reality therapists 1 (pt); Recreational therapists 1 (ft), 2 (pt); Occupational therapists 1 (pt); Speech therapists 1 (pt); Activities coordinators 1 (ft); Dietitians 1 (pt).
Facilities Dining room; Activities room; Crafts room; Laundry room.
Activities Arts and Crafts; Cards; Games; Reading groups; Movies; Shopping trips; Dances/Social or cultural gatherings; Family visits.

MACOMB

Elms
1212 Madelyn Ave, Macomb, IL, 61455 (309) 837-5482
Admin Charles Kneedy. *Medical Dir/Dir of Nursing* Dr Reem.
Licensure Skilled Care; Intermediate Care.
Beds 98. *Certified* Medicaid; Medicare.
Ownership Public.
Admissions Requirements Minimum age 18; Medical examination; Physician's request.
Facilities Dining room; Physical therapy room; Activities room; Crafts room; Laundry room; Barber/Beauty shop; Library.
Activities Arts and Crafts; Cards; Games; Reading groups; Prayer groups; Movies; Dances/Social or cultural gatherings.
Description Facility is rehabilitation oriented with quality care as our primary goal.

Macomb Manor Inc*
S Johnson and W Grant, Macomb, IL, 61455 (309) 837-2386
Admin Dianna M Fell.
Licensure Intermediate Care. *Beds* 65. *Certified* Medicaid.
Ownership Proprietary.

Macomb Nursing and Rehabilitation Center*
8 Doctors' Ln, Macomb, IL, 61455 (309) 833-5555
Admin Sandra Kendricks.

Licensure Skilled Care. *Beds* 58. Certified Medicaid; Medicare.
Ownership Proprietary.

Wesley Village Health Care Center*
1200 E Grant St, Macomb, IL, 61455 (309) 833-2123
Admin David Pease.
Licensure Intermediate Care; Sheltered Care.
Beds ICF 30; Sheltered Care 28.
Ownership Nonprofit.
Affiliation Methodist

MACON

Eastern Star Home
Macon, IL, 62544 (217) 764-3348
Admin Eleanor Davis. *Medical Dir/Dir of Nursing* Dr Robert Atz.
Licensure Intermediate Care; Sheltered Care.
Beds ICF 49; Sheltered Care 39.
Ownership Nonprofit.
Admissions Requirements Minimum age 62; Medical examination.
Staff Physicians 1 (pt); RNs 1 (ft); LPNs 6 (ft); Nurses aides 22 (ft); Physical therapists 1 (pt); Reality therapists 1 (pt); Recreational therapists 1 (pt); Occupational therapists 1 (pt); Activities coordinators 2 (ft); Dietitians 1 (pt).
Affiliation Order of Eastern Star
Facilities Dining room; Physical therapy room; Activities room; Chapel; Crafts room; Laundry room; Barber/Beauty shop.
Activities Arts and Crafts; Cards; Games; Reading groups; Prayer groups; Movies; Shopping trips; Dances/Social or cultural gatherings.
Description Home is located in a peaceful, countryside setting on 54 beautiful acres of private ground. Solariums and lounges provide a home-like atmosphere for entertainment and visits.

MARENGO

Florence Nursing Home
546 E Grant Hwy, Marengo, IL, 60152 (815) 568-8322
Admin Alice L Aumiller. *Medical Dir/Dir of Nursing* Charles J Lockwood MD.
Licensure Intermediate Care. *Beds* 49.
Ownership Proprietary.
Admissions Requirements Minimum age 18; Medical examination.
Facilities Dining room; Activities room; Crafts room; Laundry room; Barber/Beauty shop.
Activities Arts and Crafts; Cards; Games; Prayer groups; Movies; Shopping trips; Dances/Social or cultural gatherings; Exercise program; Pet visits.
Description Home has been owned and operated by the same family in the same location for over 50 years. "Caring matters most."

MARION

Fountains Nursing Home*
1301 E DeYoung St, Marion, IL, 62959 (618) 997-1365
Admin Joan W Baugher.

Licensure Intermediate Care. *Beds* 68. Certified Medicaid.
Ownership Proprietary.

Ray White Care Center Inc*
1101 Madison St, Marion, IL, 62959 (618) 993-8650
Admin Barbara L Phillips.
Licensure Intermediate Care. *Beds* 54. Certified Medicaid.
Ownership Proprietary.

MARSEILLES

Rivershores Nursing Home*
578 Commercial St, Marseilles, IL, 61341 (815) 795-5121
Admin Corda Fruendt.
Licensure Skilled Care. *Beds* 96.
Ownership Nonprofit.

MARSHALL

Burnside Nursing Home Inc*
410 N Second St, Marshall, IL, 62441 (217) 826-2358
Admin Donald B Smitley.
Licensure Skilled Care; Intermediate Care.
Beds SNF 50; ICF 64. *Certified* Medicaid.
Ownership Nonprofit.

MARYVILLE

Meadow View Care Center*
Interstate 70 and Rt 159, Maryville, IL, 62062 (618) 344-7750
Admin Kenneth Kabureck.
Licensure Intermediate Care. *Beds* 104. Certified Medicaid.
Ownership Proprietary.

MASCOUTAH

Grange Nursing Home
901 N 10th St, Mascoutah, IL, 62258 (618) 566-2183
Admin Charles L Conway. *Medical Dir/Dir of Nursing* Paul Biedenharn MD.
Licensure Intermediate Care. *Beds* 54. Certified Medicaid.
Ownership Nonprofit.
Admissions Requirements Minimum age 18.
Staff RNs 1 (ft), 1 (pt); LPNs 3 (ft), 2 (pt); Orderlies 1 (ft), 1 (pt); Nurses aides 12 (ft), 3 (pt); Activities coordinators 1 (ft).
Facilities Dining room; Physical therapy room; Laundry room.
Activities Arts and Crafts; Cards; Games; Movies; Dances/Social or cultural gatherings.

Mar-Ka Nursing Home
201 S 10th St, Mascoutah, IL, 62258 (618) 566-8000
Admin Harry C Poole. *Medical Dir/Dir of Nursing* Phillip J Koesterer MD.
Licensure Intermediate Care. *Beds* 76. Certified Medicaid.
Ownership Proprietary.
Admissions Requirements Minimum age 18.
Staff RNs 2 (ft); LPNs 6 (pt); Nurses aides 8

(ft), 10 (pt); Recreational therapists 1 (ft); Activities coordinators 1 (ft); Dietitians 1 (pt).
Facilities Dining room; Activities room; Chapel; Crafts room; Laundry room; Barber/Beauty shop; Library.
Activities Arts and Crafts; Cards; Games; Reading groups; Prayer groups; Movies; Shopping trips; Dances/Social or cultural gatherings.
Description The Mar-Ka is a one-story brick building, shaped like a wagon wheel with a large center rotunda, located on the outskirts of a small town; family owned and operated; giving superior nursing care for the lowest possible cost.

West Main Nursing Home*
1244 W Main St, Mascoutah, IL, 62258 (618) 566-7327
Admin Harold R Keenan.
Licensure Intermediate Care. *Beds* 34. Certified Medicaid.
Ownership Proprietary.

MATTESON

Applewood Nursing Home*
21020 S Kostner Ave, Matteson, IL, 60443 (312) 747-1300
Admin Robert J Patterson.
Licensure Skilled Care. *Beds* 96.
Ownership Proprietary.

MATTOON

Douglas Nursing Center*
W Rt 121, Mattoon, IL, 61938 (217) 234-6401
Admin Kenneth R Hedrick Sr.
Licensure Intermediate Care. *Beds* 51. Certified Medicaid.
Ownership Nonprofit.

Mattoon Health Care Center
2121 S 9th St, Mattoon, IL, 61938 (217) 235-7138
Admin Carl D Taniges. *Medical Dir/Dir of Nursing* L E McNiell MD.
Licensure Skilled Care; Intermediate Care.
Beds SNF 99. *Certified* Medicaid; Medicare.
Ownership Proprietary.
Admissions Requirements Minimum age 18; Medical examination; Physician's request.
Staff Physicians 12 (pt); RNs 1 (ft), 2 (pt); LPNs 7 (ft), 2 (pt); Nurses aides 3 (ft); Physical therapists 1 (pt); Recreational therapists 1 (pt); Occupational therapists 1 (pt); Speech therapists 1 (pt); Activities coordinators 1 (ft); Dietitians 1 (ft); Dentists 1 (pt); Podiatrists 1 (pt).
Facilities Dining room; Physical therapy room; Activities room; Crafts room; Laundry room; Barber/Beauty shop.
Activities Arts and Crafts; Cards; Games; Reading groups; Prayer groups; Movies; Shopping trips.
Description Our facility is located on one floor, therefore easily accessible to ambulatory and wheelchair patients alike. The residents rooms are either single or double rooms with their own bathrooms. Dining facilities are cheerful with food which is eye appealing while fulfilling patients dietary requirements. Our utmost concern is the welfare and health of our patients.

Mattoon Manor
1000 Palm, Mattoon, IL, 61938 (217) 234-7403
Admin Barbara J Clark. *Medical Dir/Dir of Nursing* Wilfred Brunswick MD.
Licensure Skilled Care; Intermediate Care.
Beds SNF 162; ICF 92. *Certified* Medicaid.
Ownership Proprietary.
Staff RNs 2 (ft), 2 (pt); LPNs 11 (ft); Nurses aides 46 (ft); Occupational therapists 1 (ft), 2 (pt); Speech therapists 2 (pt); Activities coordinators 1 (ft); Dentists 1 (ft); Physical therapist aides 2 (ft); Recreational therapist aides 3 (ft).
Facilities Dining room; Physical therapy room; Activities room; Chapel; Crafts room; Laundry room; Barber/Beauty shop; Library.
Activities Arts and Crafts; Cards; Games; Reading groups; Prayer groups; Movies; Shopping trips; Dances/Social or cultural gatherings.
Description Manor offers all rehabilitative services available. Physical setting is in a residential area with a park and shopping center within walking distance.

Odd Fellow-Rebekah Home
E Lafayette Ave, Mattoon, IL, 61938 (217) 235-5449
Admin S Lyle Jones. *Medical Dir/Dir of Nursing* Dr Robert F Swengel.
Licensure Skilled Care; Intermediate Care.
Beds 120. *Certified* Medicaid.
Ownership Proprietary.
Admissions Requirements Medical examination.
Staff RNs 2 (ft), 2 (pt); LPNs 8 (ft), 1 (pt); Orderlies 1 (ft); Nurses aides 34 (ft), 3 (pt); Activities coordinators 2 (ft); Dietitians 1 (ft).
Affiliation Independent Order of Odd Fellows
Facilities Dining room; Physical therapy room; Activities room; Chapel; Crafts room; Laundry room; Barber/Beauty shop.
Activities Arts and Crafts; Cards; Games; Reading groups; Prayer groups; Movies; Shopping trips; Dances/Social or cultural gatherings.
Description The Odd Fellow-Rebekah Home has many activities and programs for residents. The Gray family sings for birthday parties, chapel services, Bible studies, and other occasions.

MAYWOOD

Baptist Retirement Home
316 W Randolph, Maywood, IL, 60153 (312) 344-1541
Admin T Arthur Guscott. *Medical Dir/Dir of Nursing* Raymond J MacDonald MD.
Licensure Intermediate Care. *Beds* 178. *Certified* Medicaid.
Ownership Nonprofit.
Admissions Requirements Medical examination.
Staff Physicians 11 (pt); RNs 3 (ft); LPNs 5 (ft); Occupational therapists 1 (pt); Activities coordinators 2 (ft); Dietitians 1 (pt); Dentists 1 (pt); Ophthalmologists 1 (pt); Podiatrists 1 (pt); Audiologists 1 (pt).
Affiliation Baptist
Facilities Dining room; Physical therapy room; Activities room; Chapel; Crafts room; Laundry room; Barber/Beauty shop; Library.
Activities Arts and Crafts; Cards; Games; Reading groups; Prayer groups; Movies; Shop-

ping trips; Dances/Social or cultural gatherings.

MCHENRY

Royal Terrace
803 Royal Dr, PO Box 4, McHenry, IL, 60050 (815) 344-2600
Admin Catherine H Smith. *Medical Dir/Dir of Nursing* James Skopec MD.
Licensure Skilled Care; Intermediate Care.
Beds 315. *Certified* Medicaid; Medicare.
Ownership Proprietary.
Admissions Requirements Minimum age 18; Medical examination.
Staff Physicians 20 (pt); RNs 37 (ft); LPNs 20 (ft), Orderlies 10 (ft); Nurses aides 120 (ft); Physical therapists 3 (ft); Reality therapists 2 (ft); Recreational therapists 1 (ft); Occupational therapists 1 (pt); Speech therapists 1 (pt); Activities coordinators 1 (pt); Dietitians 1 (pt); Dentists 1 (pt); Ophthalmologists 1 (pt); Podiatrists 1 (pt); Audiologists 1 (pt).
Facilities Dining room; Physical therapy room; Activities room; Chapel; Crafts room; Laundry room; Barber/Beauty shop; Library; Greenhouse.
Activities Arts and Crafts; Cards; Games; Reading groups; Prayer groups; Movies; Shopping trips; Dances/Social or cultural gatherings; Concerts.
Description Facility is located in a rural setting, a 2-story building with spacious grounds including a greenhouse, large dining areas, and patio which has automatic doors to permit easy access. Clients participate in shopping, luncheons, and cultural trips. An active resident council assists in planning meals and foods for special occasions.

MCLEANSBORO

Oak View Manor
405 W Carpenter, McLeansboro, IL, 62859 (618) 643-3728
Admin John D Warner. *Medical Dir/Dir of Nursing* D I Tomaneng.
Licensure Intermediate Care. *Beds* 43. *Certified* Medicaid.
Ownership Proprietary.
Admissions Requirements Minimum age 18.
Staff Physicians 4 (pt); RNs 1 (pt); LPNs 5 (ft); Nurses aides 13 (ft); Recreational therapists 1 (pt); Occupational therapists 1 (pt); Activities coordinators 1 (ft); Dietitians 1 (ft); Dentists 1 (pt).
Facilities Dining room; Activities room; Chapel; Crafts room; Laundry room; Barber/Beauty shop.
Activities Arts and Crafts; Cards; Games; Reading groups; Prayer groups; Movies; Shopping trips.

MELROSE PARK

Oakridge Convalescent Home Inc*
323 Oakridge Ave, Melrose Park, IL, 60162 (312) 547-6595
Admin Lynn L Acerra.
Licensure Skilled Care. *Beds* 73.
Ownership Proprietary.

Villa Scalabrini*
480 N Wolf Rd, Melrose Park, IL, 60164 (312) 526-0040
Admin Lawrence Cozzi.
Licensure Skilled Care; Intermediate Care; Sheltered Care. *Beds* SNF 98; ICF 62; Sheltered Care 89. *Certified* Medicaid.
Ownership Proprietary.

MENDON

North Adams Home Inc*
Rt 2, Box 100, Mendon, IL, 62351 (217) 936-2137
Admin John D Bainum.
Licensure Intermediate Care. *Beds* 89. *Certified* Medicaid.
Ownership Nonprofit.

MENDOTA

Heritage Manor Nursing and Convalescent Home
1201 1st Ave, Mendota, IL, 61342 (815) 539-6745
Admin Marilee T Holzner. *Medical Dir/Dir of Nursing* J R Durham Md.
Licensure Skilled Care; Intermediate Care.
Beds SNF 49; ICF 27. *Certified* Medicaid; Medicare.
Ownership Proprietary.
Admissions Requirements Medical examination.
Staff RNs 5 (ft), 3 (pt); LPNs 4 (ft), 2 (pt); Orderlies 1 (ft); Nurses aides 22 (ft), 18 (pt); Physical therapists 1 (pt); Activities coordinators 1 (ft); Dietitians 1 (pt).
Facilities Dining room; Physical therapy room; Activities room; Crafts room; Laundry room; Barber/Beauty shop.
Activities Arts and Crafts; Cards; Games; Reading groups; Shopping trips; Dances/Social or cultural gatherings.
Description VA approved.

Mendota Lutheran Home
500 6th St, Mendota, IL, 61342 (815) 539-7439
Admin Earnest L Serr. *Medical Dir/Dir of Nursing* R Musick MD.
Licensure Intermediate Care; Sheltered Care.
Beds ICF 80; Sheltered Care 21.
Ownership Nonprofit.
Admissions Requirements Minimum age 65.
Staff Physicians 1 (pt); RNs 2 (ft), 3 (pt); LPNs 3 (ft), 4 (pt); Nurses aides 23 (ft), 19 (pt); Activities coordinators 1 (ft).
Affiliation Lutheran
Facilities Dining room; Activities room; Chapel; Laundry room; Barber/Beauty shop; Library.
Activities Arts and Crafts; Cards; Games; Reading groups; Prayer groups; Movies; Dances/Social or cultural gatherings.

METROPOLIS

Magnolia Manor*
2101 Metropolis St, Metropolis, IL, 62960 (618) 524-5677
Admin Denise Pippins.

Licensure Intermediate Care. *Beds* 61. *Certified* Medicaid.
Ownership Proprietary.

Metropolis Good Samaritan Home
2299 Metropolis St, Metropolis, IL, 62960
(618) 524-2634
Admin Ronald D Philips. *Medical Dir/Dir of Nursing* Dr Benito Bajuyo.
Licensure Skilled Care; Intermediate Care.
Beds 85. *Certified* Medicaid.
Ownership Nonprofit.
Staff RNs 2 (ft); LPNs 4 (ft), 3 (pt); Nurses aides 27 (ft), 5 (pt); Activities coordinators 1 (ft).
Affiliation Lutheran
Facilities Dining room; Physical therapy room; Activities room; Crafts room; Laundry room; Barber/Beauty shop.
Activities Arts and Crafts; Cards; Games; Reading groups; Prayer groups; Movies; Shopping trips; Dances/Social or cultural gatherings.

Southgate Health Care Center*
900 E 9th St, Metropolis, IL, 62960 (618) 524-2683
Admin Jane Ann P Henley.
Licensure Skilled Care; Intermediate Care.
Beds SNF 58; ICF 67. *Certified* Medicaid; Medicare.
Ownership Proprietary.

MIDLOTHIAN

Bowman Nursing Home
3249 W 147th St, Midlothian, IL, 60445 (312) 389-3141
Admin Frank Bozich. *Medical Dir/Dir of Nursing* Dr Adusamille.
Licensure Intermediate Care. *Beds* 92. *Certified* Medicaid.
Ownership Proprietary.
Admissions Requirements Minimum age 18.
Staff Physicians 3 (pt); RNs 2 (ft), 2 (pt); LPNs 7 (ft), 3 (pt); Nurses aides 31 (ft), 7 (pt); Physical therapists 2 (pt); Reality therapists 2 (pt); Recreational therapists 1 (ft), 1 (pt); Occupational therapists 1 (pt); Speech therapists 1 (pt); Activities coordinators 1 (pt); Dietitians 1 (pt); Dentists 1 (pt); Ophthalmologists 1 (pt); Podiatrists 1 (pt); Audiologists 1 (pt).
Facilities Dining room; Activities room; Crafts room; Laundry room; Barber/Beauty shop.
Activities Arts and Crafts; Cards; Games; Reading groups; Prayer groups; Movies; Shopping trips; Dances/Social or cultural gatherings.
Description Facility is on 3 acres of ground, 2 buildings on ground level with no stairs.

Crestwood Heights Nursing Center*
14255 S Cicero Ave, Midlothian, IL, 60445 (312) 371-0400
Admin Claude Bokor.
Licensure Skilled Care; Intermediate Care.
Beds SNF 108; ICF 216. *Certified* Medicaid.
Ownership Proprietary.

Crestwood Terrace
13301 S Central Ave, Midlothian, IL, 60445 (312) 597-5251
Admin Maureen M Skopick. *Medical Dir/Dir of Nursing* Dr A Noreiga.

Licensure Intermediate Care. *Beds* 120. *Certified* Medicaid.
Ownership Proprietary.
Admissions Requirements Medical examination.
Staff Physicians 1 (ft), 10 (pt); RNs 2 (ft), 2 (pt); LPNs 3 (ft), 6 (pt); Nurses aides 14 (ft), 10 (pt); Reality therapists 3 (ft); Recreational therapists 3 (ft); Occupational therapists 1 (pt); Speech therapists 1 (pt); Activities coordinators 1 (ft); Dietitians 1 (pt); Dentists 2 (pt); Ophthalmologists 1 (pt); Podiatrists 1 (pt).
Facilities Dining room; Physical therapy room; Activities room; Chapel; Crafts room; Laundry room; Barber/Beauty shop; Library; Van for outings.
Activities Arts and Crafts; Cards; Games; Reading groups; Prayer groups; Movies; Shopping trips; Dances/Social or cultural gatherings.
Description VA approved.

MILAN

Comfort Harbor Home*
114 W 2nd St, Milan, IL, 61264 (309) 787-2066
Admin J Michael Lavery.
Licensure Sheltered Care. *Beds* Sheltered Care 38.
Ownership Proprietary.

MILLSTADT

Mill Haven Care Center Inc*
415 Veterans Dr, Millstadt, IL, 62260 (618) 538-7290
Admin Dorothy M Davis.
Licensure Intermediate Care. *Beds* 101. *Certified* Medicaid.
Ownership Proprietary.

MINONK

Lida Home Nursing Home*
201 Locust, Minonk, IL, 61760 (309) 432-2557
Admin John C Kirkton.
Licensure Intermediate Care. *Beds* 49. *Certified* Medicaid.
Ownership Nonprofit.

MOLINE

Heritage 53*
4601 53rd St, Moline, IL, 61265 (309) 757-9540
Admin Timothy W Granet.
Licensure Intermediate Care. *Beds* 64.
Ownership Nonprofit.

Moline Nursing and Rehabilitation Center
833 16th Ave, Moline, IL, 61265 (309) 764-6744
Admin Leroy A Policky. *Medical Dir/Dir of Nursing* Dr Bruce Vesole.
Licensure Skilled Care; Intermediate Care.
Beds 119. *Certified* Medicaid; Medicare.
Ownership Proprietary.
Admissions Requirements Medical examination.
Staff RNs 4 (ft), 2 (pt); LPNs 4 (ft), 6 (pt); Nurses aides 6 (ft), 44 (pt); Physical therapists 1

(pt); Recreational therapists 1 (ft); Speech therapists 1 (pt); Activities coordinators 1 (pt); Dietitians 1 (pt).
Facilities Dining room; Physical therapy room; Activities room; Laundry room; Barber/Beauty shop.
Activities Arts and Crafts; Cards; Games; Reading groups; Prayer groups; Movies; Shopping trips; Dances/Social or cultural gatherings.
Description Center has a resident council, composed of residents elected by residents, who plan special meals, handle complaints, and help to make a happy home. Residents also belong to RSVP; which they help by stuffing envelopes, stapling letters, and other volunteer activities designated by RSVP.

MOMENCE

Good Shepherd Manor*
PO Box 260, Hwy 1, Momence, IL, 60954
(815) 472-6492
Admin Br Francis X Heisel.
Licensure Sheltered Care. *Beds* Sheltered Care 120.
Ownership Nonprofit.
Affiliation Roman Catholic

Momence Meadows Nursing Center Inc
500 S Walnut, Momence, IL, 60954 (815) 472-2423
Admin Teresa Thompson. *Medical Dir/Dir of Nursing* Dr Verapaneni.
Licensure Skilled Care; Intermediate Care.
Beds SNF 34; ICF 40. *Certified* Medicaid.
Ownership Proprietary.
Admissions Requirements Minimum age 21; Medical examination; Physician's request.
Staff Physicians 5 (pt); RNs 3 (ft), 2 (pt); LPNs 2 (ft), 4 (pt); Orderlies 1 (ft); Nurses aides 12 (ft), 7 (pt); Physical therapists 1 (pt); Reality therapists 1 (pt); Recreational therapists 1 (pt); Occupational therapists 1 (pt); Speech therapists 1 (pt); Activities coordinators 1 (ft), 1 (pt); Dietitians 1 (pt); Dentists 1 (pt); Ophthalmologists 1 (pt); Podiatrists 1 (pt).
Facilities Dining room; Physical therapy room; Activities room; Chapel; Crafts room; Laundry room; Barber/Beauty shop; Library.
Activities Arts and Crafts; Cards; Games; Reading groups; Prayer groups; Movies; Shopping trips; Dances/Social or cultural gatherings.
Description Facility is located in a small supportive community with many volunteers; very much involved in schools, church groups, and community related functions; offers occupational, physical, and speech therapy; wide variety of activities, both inside and outside of the building.

MONMOUTH

Applegate Inn Inc*
515 E Euclid Ave, Monmouth, IL, 61462 (309) 734-5163
Admin Richard Green.
Licensure Skilled Care; Intermediate Care.
Beds SNF 30; ICF 58. *Certified* Medicaid.
Ownership Proprietary.

Applegate Manor Inc*
515 E Euclid Ave, Monmouth, IL, 61462 (309)
734-5163
Admin Richard Green.
Licensure Skilled Care; Intermediate Care;
Sheltered Care. *Beds* SNF 30; ICF 58; Sheltered Care 30.
Ownership Proprietary.

Monmouth Nursing Home*
116 S "H" St, Monmouth, IL, 61462 (309)
734-3811
Admin John Clendenin.
Licensure Intermediate Care. *Beds* 35. *Certified* Medicaid.
Ownership Proprietary.

MONTICELLO

Piatt County Nursing Home
1111 N State St, Monticello, IL, 61856 (217)
762-2506
Admin Marilyn E Benedino.
Licensure Skilled Care; Intermediate Care.
Beds 99. *Certified* Medicaid.
Ownership Public.
Admissions Requirements Minimum age 55.
Facilities Dining room; Activities room; Crafts
room; Laundry room; Barber/Beauty shop.
Activities Arts and Crafts; Cards; Games;
Reading groups; Prayer groups; Movies; Shopping trips; Dances/Social or cultural gatherings.

MORRIS

Grundy County Home
Clay and Quarry Sts, PO Box 669, Morris, IL,
60450 (815) 942-3255
Admin S Morse.
Licensure Intermediate Care. *Beds* 143. *Certified* Medicaid.
Ownership Public.
Admissions Requirements Minimum age 18;
Medical examination; Physician's request.
Description Facility offers complete services;
admits only Grundy County residents.

Morris Lincoln Nursing Home
916 Fremont, Morris, IL, 60450 (815) 942-1202
Admin Marjorie D Johnson. *Medical Dir/Dir
of Nursing* Sandra Johnson RN.
Licensure Intermediate Care; Sheltered Care.
Beds ICF 47; Sheltered Care 34. *Certified* Medicaid.
Ownership Proprietary.
Admissions Requirements Minimum age 45;
Medical examination.
Staff RNs 2 (ft); LPNs 3 (ft), 2 (pt); Nurses
aides 14 (ft), 10 (pt); Physical therapists 1 (ft);
Recreational therapists 1 (pt); Speech therapists
1 (pt); Activities coordinators 1 (ft); Dietitians
1 (ft).
Facilities Dining room; Physical therapy room;
Activities room.
Activities Arts and Crafts.
Description Our facility is a family-type home
where residents and their families are well-
known and identified by staff. Personal attention is the key. A large wooded lawn surrounds
the facility where many activities are held in
appropriate weather.

MORRISON

**Morrison Community Hospital Skilled Nursing
Center**
303 N Jackson St, Morrison, IL, 61270 (815)
772-4003
Admin Douglas W Quick. *Medical Dir/Dir of
Nursing* I Vandermyde MD.
Licensure Skilled Care; Intermediate Care.
Beds 38. *Certified* Medicaid; Medicare.
Ownership Public.
Staff Physicians 1 (ft); RNs 8 (ft), 2 (pt); LPNs
3 (ft), 3 (pt); Orderlies 1 (ft); Nurses aides 15
(ft), 6 (pt); Physical therapists 2 (ft); Reality
therapists 1 (ft); Recreational therapists 1 (ft);
Occupational therapists 1 (ft); Speech therapists
1 (pt); Activities coordinators 1 (pt); Dietitians
1 (ft).
Facilities Dining room; Physical therapy room;
Activities room; Chapel; Crafts room; Laundry
room; Barber/Beauty shop; Library.
Activities Arts and Crafts; Cards; Games;
Reading groups; Prayer groups; Movies; Dances/Social or cultural gatherings; Educational.

Pleasant View Home*
N Jackson St, Morrison, IL, 61270 (815)
772-7288
Admin Mary K McKnight.
Licensure Intermediate Care. *Beds* 74. *Certified* Medicaid.
Ownership Public.

Resthaven Home
Maple Ave, Morrison, IL, 61270 (815)
772-4021
Admin Ronald L Garwick. *Medical Dir/Dir of
Nursing* Dr I Vandermyde.
Licensure Intermediate Care; Sheltered Care.
Beds ICF 49; Sheltered Care 27.
Ownership Nonprofit.
Staff RNs 1 (ft), 3 (pt); LPNs 1 (ft), 3 (pt);
Nurses aides 15 (ft), 11 (pt); Dietitians 1 (pt).
Facilities Dining room; Activities room; Laundry room; Barber/Beauty shop.
Activities Arts and Crafts; Cards; Games;
Reading groups; Prayer groups; Movies.

MORTON

Apostolic Christian Restmor I
935 E Jefferson St, Morton, IL, 61550 (309)
266-7141
Admin James L Metzger. *Medical Dir/Dir of
Nursing* Dr James Early.
Licensure Skilled Care; Sheltered Care.
Beds SNF 115; Sheltered Care 27.
Ownership Nonprofit.
Admissions Requirements Minimum age 18;
Medical examination.
Staff Physicians; RNs 5 (ft), 9 (pt); LPNs 4 (ft),
7 (pt); Orderlies 2 (ft); Nurses aides 42 (ft), 13
(pt); Physical therapists; Occupational therapists; Speech therapists; Activities coordinators
1 (ft); Dietitians; Dentists; Pharmacists 1 (ft), 2
(pt); Social workers 1 (ft).
Affiliation Apostolic Christian
Facilities Dining room; Physical therapy room;
Activities room; Chapel; Crafts room; Laundry
room; Barber/Beauty shop.

Activities Arts and Crafts; Cards; Games;
Reading groups; Prayer groups; Movies; Shopping trips; Dances/Social or cultural gatherings.

Apostolic Morton*
RR 3, Veterans Rd, Morton, IL, 61550 (309)
266-9781
Admin Robert Knobloch.
Licensure Intermediate Care. *Beds* 90.
Ownership Nonprofit.
Affiliation Apostolic Christian

Morton Healthcare Centre
190 E Queenwood Rd, Morton, IL, 61550
(309) 266-9741
Admin Katherine A Carson. *Medical Dir/Dir
of Nursing* Dr Phillip A Immesoete.
Licensure Skilled Care; Intermediate Care.
Beds 106. *Certified* Medicaid; Medicare.
Ownership Proprietary.
Admissions Requirements Minimum age 18.
Staff Physicians 1 (ft), 2 (pt); RNs 3 (ft), 2 (pt);
LPNs 2 (ft), 3 (pt); Orderlies 1 (pt); Nurses
aides 22 (ft), 1 (pt); Physical therapists 1 (pt);
Occupational therapists 1 (ft); Speech therapists
1 (pt); Activities coordinators 1 (pt); Dietitians
1 (pt); Dentists 1 (pt); Ophthalmologists 1 (pt);
Podiatrists 1 (pt).
Facilities Dining room; Physical therapy room;
Activities room; Crafts room; Laundry room;
Barber/Beauty shop; Library.
Activities Arts and Crafts; Cards; Games;
Reading groups; Prayer groups; Movies; Dances/Social or cultural gatherings.
Description Facility is in a beautiful rural setting close enough to town for all conveniences,
but out far enough to enjoy wide open surroundings. A skilled facility privileged to have a
large back area to enjoy many outside activities
in the summertime with staff, residents, and
families participating.

Morton Terrace
191 E Queenwood Rd, Morton, IL, 61550
(309) 266-5331
Admin Pat Chism. *Medical Dir/Dir of
Nursing* L S Patton DO.
Licensure Intermediate Care. *Beds* 144. *Certified* Medicaid.
Ownership Proprietary.
Admissions Requirements Minimum age 18.
Staff RNs 1 (ft); LPNs 5 (ft), 5 (pt); Orderlies 1
(ft), 1 (pt); Nurses aides 18 (ft), 9 (pt); Activities
coordinators 3 (ft).
Facilities Dining room; Physical therapy room;
Activities room; Laundry room; Barber/Beauty
shop.
Activities Arts and Crafts; Cards; Games;
Reading groups; Prayer groups; Movies; Shopping trips; Dances/Social or cultural gatherings.

MORTON GROVE

Bethany Terrace Nursing Home
8425 Waukegan Rd, Morton Grove, IL, 60053
(312) 965-8100
Admin Lorraine M Lukas. *Medical Dir/Dir of
Nursing* Paul Vega MD.
Licensure Skilled Care; Intermediate Care;
Sheltered Care. *Beds* SNF 103; ICF 150; Sheltered Care 12. *Certified* Medicaid; Medicare.
Ownership Nonprofit.

Admissions Requirements Minimum age 18; Medical examination; Physician's request.
Staff Physicians 3 (pt); RNs 15 (ft), 25 (pt); LPNs 8 (ft), 1 (pt); Orderlies 5 (ft), 2 (pt); Nurses aides 81 (ft), 26 (pt); Physical therapists 3 (ft); Reality therapists 4 (ft), 3 (pt); Occupational therapists 1 (pt); Activities coordinators 1 (ft); Dietitians 1 (ft).
Affiliation Methodist
Facilities Dining room; Physical therapy room; Activities room; Chapel; Crafts room; Laundry room; Barber/Beauty shop; Library; Occupational Therapy room; Rehab room; Enclosed patios.
Activities Arts and Crafts; Cards; Games; Reading groups; Prayer groups; Movies; Shopping trips; Dances/Social or cultural gatherings; Luncheons; Baseball; Community; Church; Botanical gardens; Tropical fish; Parrakeets; Rabbits; Baking; Resident council; Gardening; Mens' club; Parkinsons' group; Choral club; Community service projects.
Description Facility features our own bus with hydraulic lift, Alzheimer's Lane, Stroke Club and Parkinsons' Group, state approved Nurse's Aide Training Program, located in a one-story facility.

MOUNDS

Meridian Manor*
PO Box 216, 420 S Blanche St, Mounds, IL, 62964 (618) 745-6537
Admin Kirby Madden.
Licensure Intermediate Care. *Beds* 64. *Certified* Medicaid.
Ownership Proprietary.

MOUNT CARMEL

General Baptist Nursing Home
Rt 4, Mount Carmel, IL, 62863 (618) 263-4337
Admin Jack R Cole. *Medical Dir/Dir of Nursing* Dr R L Fuller.
Licensure Skilled Care; Intermediate Care. *Beds* 185. *Certified* Medicaid; Medicare.
Ownership Nonprofit.
Admissions Requirements Minimum age 18; Medical examination; Physician's request.
Staff RNs 3 (ft), 3 (pt); LPNs 11 (ft), 2 (pt); Orderlies 2 (ft); Nurses aides 41 (ft), 4 (pt); Activities coordinators 1 (ft), 3 (pt); Dietitians 6 (ft).
Affiliation Baptist
Facilities Dining room; Physical therapy room; Activities room; Chapel; Crafts room; Laundry room; Barber/Beauty shop; Library.
Activities Arts and Crafts; Cards; Games; Reading groups; Prayer groups; Movies; Shopping trips; Dances/Social or cultural gatherings; Senior citizens; Workshop.
Description General Baptist Nursing Home consists of 8 wings of patient rooms, 2 lobbies, and an open front porch with lawn chairs. Many residents attend Senior Citizens weekly for programs or games. Some are employed at a local workshop. Several participate in college classes taught in the facility through Wabash Valley College.

Shurtleff Manor
1527 N College Dr, Mount Carmel, IL, 62863 (618) 263-3511
Admin Helen R Lewis. *Medical Dir/Dir of Nursing* Dr C L Johns.
Licensure Intermediate Care. *Beds* 84. *Certified* Medicaid.
Ownership Proprietary.
Staff Physicians 7 (ft); RNs 1 (ft); LPNs 5 (ft); Nurses aides 15 (ft); Physical therapists 1 (ft); Reality therapists 1 (ft); Recreational therapists 2 (ft); Speech therapists 1 (ft); Activities coordinators 2 (ft); Dietitians 1 (ft); Dentists 2 (ft); Ophthalmologists 2 (ft); Podiatrists 1 (ft); Audiologists 1 (ft).
Facilities Dining room; Activities room; Crafts room; Laundry room; Barber/Beauty shop; Smoking and drinking lounge.
Activities Arts and Crafts; Cards; Games; Reading groups; Prayer groups; Movies; Shopping trips; Dances/Social or cultural gatherings.
Description Facility is one-story brick building completely with a sprinkler system. Our entire building is licensed by Dept of Public Health. Licensed personnel includes an RN on duty 24 hours a day and a registered therapist, registered dietician, and a speech therapist actively on duty 40 hours per week.

MOUNT CARROLL

Carroll County Good Samaritan Center*
N Washington St, Mount Carroll, IL, 61053 (815) 244-7715
Admin Arthur M Gustafson.
Licensure Intermediate Care. *Beds* 68. *Certified* Medicaid.
Ownership Nonprofit.

MOUNT MORRIS

Pinecrest Manor*
414 S McKendrie, Mount Morris, IL, 61054 (815) 734-4103
Admin Gary E Montel.
Licensure Skilled Care; Intermediate Care. *Beds* SNF 50; ICF 72. *Certified* Medicaid; Medicare.
Ownership Nonprofit.

MOUNT PULASKI

H J Vonderlieth Living Center
Rt 121 and Elkhart Rd, Mount Pulaski, IL, 62548 (217) 792-3218
Admin Steven E Evans. *Medical Dir/Dir of Nursing* James B Borgerson MD.
Licensure Skilled Care; Sheltered Care.
Beds SNF 88; Sheltered Care 2. *Certified* Medicaid.
Ownership Nonprofit.
Staff RNs 2 (ft), 2 (pt); LPNs 3 (ft), 7 (pt); Orderlies 1 (ft), 1 (pt); Nurses aides 24 (ft), 12 (pt); Physical therapists 1 (pt); Occupational therapists 1 (pt); Speech therapists 1 (pt); Activities coordinators 2 (ft); Dietitians 1 (ft); Dentists 1 (pt); Podiatrists 1 (pt); Audiologists 1 (pt).
Facilities Dining room.
Activities Arts and Crafts; Cards; Games; Reading groups; Prayer groups; Movies.

Description Facility is well built. Plan underway to allow residents to take more of a part in the decisions that are being made.

MOUNT STERLING

Modern Manor Inc
Camden Rd, Mount Sterling, IL, 62353 (217) 773-3377
Admin Marianna Pontius. *Medical Dir/Dir of Nursing* Russell R Dohner MD.
Licensure Skilled Care; Intermediate Care. *Beds* 87. *Certified* Medicaid; Medicare.
Ownership Proprietary.
Admissions Requirements Medical examination.
Staff RNs 4 (ft); LPNs 4 (ft), 1 (pt); Nurses aides 13 (ft), 16 (pt); Activities coordinators 1 (ft).
Facilities Dining room; Physical therapy room; Activities room; Chapel; Laundry room; Barber/Beauty shop.
Activities Arts and Crafts; Cards; Games; Prayer groups; Movies; Shopping trips; Dances/Social or cultural gatherings.
Description Modern Manor is located in a country setting, staffed with employees who extend a lot of love and care to the residents, and who have achieved very good results with patients who were considered terminal upon admission. Therapy program is also very good.

MOUNT VERNON

Casey Manor Nursing Home*
5 Doctors' Park, Mount Vernon, IL, 62864
Admin Bruce Flanigan.
Licensure Intermediate Care. *Beds* 113. *Certified* Medicaid.
Ownership Proprietary.

Jeffersonian Nursing Home
1700 White St, Mount Vernon, IL, 62864 (618) 242-4075
Admin Margaret K Setzekorn. *Medical Dir/Dir of Nursing* Dr C K Wells.
Licensure Skilled Care; Intermediate Care. *Beds* 64. *Certified* Medicaid.
Ownership Proprietary.
Admissions Requirements Minimum age 16; Medical examination; Physician's request.
Staff Physicians 6 (pt); RNs 2 (ft), 6 (pt); LPNs 2 (ft), 7 (pt); Nurses aides 6 (ft), 10 (pt); Physical therapists 1 (pt); Recreational therapists 1 (pt); Activities coordinators 1 (ft); Dietitians 1 (pt).
Facilities Dining room; Physical therapy room; Chapel; Laundry room; Barber/Beauty shop.
Activities Arts and Crafts; Cards; Games; Reading groups; Prayer groups; Movies; Shopping trips; Dances/Social or cultural gatherings.

Mount Vernon Care Facility Inc
1717 Jefferson St, Mount Vernon, IL, 62864 (618) 224-2861
Admin Darleen E Dycus.
Licensure Intermediate Care. *Beds* 64. *Certified* Medicaid.
Ownership Proprietary.
Admissions Requirements Minimum age 20; Medical examination; Physician's request.

Staff RNs 1 (pt); LPNs 6 (ft); Orderlies 4 (ft); Nurses aides 18 (ft); Dietitians 1 (pt).
Facilities Dining room; Activities room; Laundry room; Barber/Beauty shop.
Activities Arts and Crafts; Cards; Games; Reading groups; Prayer groups; Shopping trips; Dances/Social or cultural gatherings.

Nature Trail Home Inc*
1001 S 34th St, Mount Vernon, IL, 62864 (618) 242-5700
Admin Doris Brickey.
Licensure Intermediate Care. *Beds* 74. *Certified* Medicaid.
Ownership Proprietary.

MOUNT ZION

Woodland Inc Nursing Home
PO Box 310, Mount Zion, IL, 62549 (217) 428-0909
Admin Rhonda Komnick. *Medical Dir/Dir of Nursing* E J Boros MD.
Licensure Skilled Care. *Beds* 73. *Certified* Medicaid.
Ownership Proprietary.
Admissions Requirements Minimum age 18.
Staff Physicians 2 (pt); RNs 2 (ft), 1 (pt); LPNs 6 (ft), 4 (pt); Orderlies 1 (pt); Nurses aides 22 (ft), 17 (pt); Physical therapists 1 (ft), 2 (pt); Reality therapists 1 (pt); Recreational therapists 1 (ft), 1 (pt); Occupational therapists 1 (pt); Activities coordinators 1 (ft), 1 (pt); Dietitians 1 (pt); Dentists 1 (pt).
Facilities Dining room; Physical therapy room; Activities room; Crafts room; Laundry room; Barber/Beauty shop; Family visiting room.
Activities Arts and Crafts; Cards; Games; Reading groups; Prayer groups; Movies; Dances/Social or cultural gatherings; Current events.

MUNDELEIN

Glenkirk Campus South*
27219 N Owens Rd, Mundelein, IL, 60060 (312) 526-2176
Admin Wendell J Fry.
Licensure Intermediate Care. *Beds* 36.
Ownership Nonprofit.

Riverside Foundation*
14588 W Hwy 22, Mundelein, IL, 60060 (312) 634-3973
Admin Patricia T Weisser.
Licensure Intermediate Care. *Beds* 99. *Certified* Medicaid.
Ownership Nonprofit.

MURPHYSBORO

Jackson County Nursing Home*
1441 N 14th St, Murphysboro, IL, 62966 (618) 684-2136
Admin Richard A Ligon.
Licensure Skilled Care. *Beds* 260. *Certified* Medicaid; Medicare.
Ownership Public.

Roosevelt Square—Murphysboro*
1501 Shomaker Dr, Murphysboro, IL, 62966 (618) 684-2693
Admin B J Iubelt.
Licensure Intermediate Care. *Beds* 83.
Ownership Proprietary.

NAPERVILLE

American Nursing Center of Naperville
200 W Martin, Naperville, IL, 60540 (312) 355-4111
Admin Patrick Burke. *Medical Dir/Dir of Nursing* Dr Girgis.
Licensure Skilled Care; Intermediate Care. *Beds* 96. *Certified* Medicaid; Medicare.
Ownership Proprietary.
Admissions Requirements Physician's request.
Staff RNs; LPNs; Orderlies; Nurses aides; Physical therapists; Recreational therapists; Occupational therapists; Speech therapists; Activities coordinators; Dietitians.

Community Convalescent Center of Naperville
1136 Mill St, Naperville, IL, 60540 (312) 355-3300
Admin Cheryl E Roberts. *Medical Dir/Dir of Nursing* Dr William Perkins.
Licensure Skilled Care; Intermediate Care. *Beds* SNF 129; ICF 26. *Certified* Medicare.
Ownership Proprietary.
Admissions Requirements Minimum age 18; Medical examination; Physician's request.
Staff Physicians 4 (pt); RNs 10 (ft), 10 (pt); LPNs 5 (ft), 5 (pt); Orderlies 30 (ft), 20 (pt); Physical therapists 1 (ft); Occupational therapists 1 (pt); Speech therapists 1 (pt); Activities coordinators 1 (ft); Dietitians 1 (pt); Dentists 2 (pt); Ophthalmologists 1 (pt); Podiatrists 1 (pt).
Facilities Dining room; Physical therapy room; Activities room; Crafts room; Laundry room; Barber/Beauty shop; Library.
Activities Arts and Crafts; Cards; Games; Reading groups; Prayer groups; Movies; Shopping trips; Dances/Social or cultural gatherings.

Little Friends Inc*
140 W Wright, Naperville, IL, 60540 (312) 355-9858
Admin Deborah Martin.
Licensure Intermediate Care. *Beds* 40.
Ownership Nonprofit.

Oxford Lane Nursing Home
1525 S Oxford Ln, Naperville, IL, 60540 (312) 355-6420
Admin William Calliari. *Medical Dir/Dir of Nursing* Dr You.
Licensure Skilled Care; Intermediate Care. *Beds* 206. *Certified* Medicaid; Medicare.
Ownership Proprietary.
Admissions Requirements Minimum age 18.
Staff Physicians 8 (pt); RNs 12 (ft); LPNs 15 (ft); Orderlies 10 (ft); Nurses aides 70 (ft); Physical therapists 3 (ft); Reality therapists 2 (ft); Recreational therapists 10 (ft); Occupational therapists 1 (ft); Speech therapists 1 (ft); Activities coordinators 1 (ft); Dietitians 1 (ft); Dentists 1 (pt); Ophthalmologists 1 (pt); Podiatrists 4 (pt); Audiologists 1 (pt).
Facilities Dining room; Physical therapy room; Activities room; Crafts room; Laundry room;

Barber/Beauty shop; Library; Occupational therapy room.
Activities Arts and Crafts; Cards; Games; Reading groups; Prayer groups; Movies; Shopping trips; Dances/Social or cultural gatherings.
Description Facility has a 6-bed wing for residents on ventilators and for those becoming less dependent on ventilators. Facility goal is to improve the quality of the residents' lives.

NASHVILLE

Friendship Manor Inc*
305 Friendship Dr, Nashville, IL, 62263 (618) 327-3041
Admin Len R Hogan.
Licensure Skilled Care; Intermediate Care. *Beds* SNF 90; ICF 140. *Certified* Medicaid; Medicare.
Ownership Proprietary.

NEW ATHENS

New Athens Home*
203 S Johnson St, New Athens, IL, 62264 (618) 475-2550
Admin Richard Sutter.
Licensure Intermediate Care. *Beds* 64. *Certified* Medicaid.
Ownership Nonprofit.

NEW BADEN

Clinton Manor
111 E Illinois St, New Baden, IL, 62265 (618) 588-4924
Admin Dolores J Krebs. *Medical Dir/Dir of Nursing* Dr Paul Biedenharn.
Licensure Intermediate Care. *Beds* 69. *Certified* Medicaid.
Ownership Proprietary.
Admissions Requirements Minimum age 18; Medical examination.
Staff RNs 1 (ft), 1 (pt); LPNs 3 (ft), 2 (pt); Nurses aides 10 (ft), 7 (pt); Activities coordinators 2 (pt); Social workers.
Facilities Dining room; Activities room; Laundry room; Barber/Beauty shop.
Activities Arts and Crafts; Cards; Games; Reading groups; Prayer groups; Movies; Shopping trips; Dances/Social or cultural gatherings; Bingo.
Description Most of the residents are developmentally disabled, facility is in the process of changing license to ICF/DD.

NEWMAN

Continental Manor of Newman
PO Box 335, Newman, IL, 61942 (217) 837-2421
Admin Benjamina A Prince. *Medical Dir/Dir of Nursing* Dr Guinto.
Licensure Skilled Care; Intermediate Care. *Beds* 60. *Certified* Medicaid.
Ownership Proprietary.
Admissions Requirements Medical examination.
Staff Physicians 1 (pt); Physical therapists 1 (pt); Activities coordinators 1 (ft); Dietitians 1

(pt).
Facilities Dining room; Physical therapy room; Activities room; Crafts room; Laundry room; Barber/Beauty shop.
Activities Arts and Crafts; Games; Reading groups; Prayer groups; Movies; Shopping trips.

NEWTON

Newton Rest Haven Inc
300 S Scott St, PO Box 360, Newton, IL, 62448 (618) 783-2309
Admin William J Snyder and Karen E Kinder.
Licensure Skilled Care; Intermediate Care.
Beds 92. *Certified* Medicaid.
Ownership Proprietary.

NILES

Forest Villa
6840 W Touhy Ave, Niles, IL, 60648 (312) 647-8994
Admin Nancy Ashenbrenner. *Medical Dir/Dir of Nursing* David Edelberg MD.
Licensure Skilled Care; Intermediate Care.
Beds SNF 55; ICF 148. *Certified* Medicaid; Medicare.
Ownership Proprietary.
Admissions Requirements Minimum age 50.
Staff Physicians 3 (pt); RNs 20 (ft); Orderlies 7 (ft); Nurses aides 30 (ft); Physical therapists 1 (pt); Occupational therapists 1 (pt); Speech therapists 1 (pt); Activities coordinators 1 (ft); Dietitians 1 (pt); Dentists 1 (pt); Ophthalmologists 1 (pt); Podiatrists 1 (pt); Audiologists 1 (pt).
Facilities Dining room; Physical therapy room; Activities room; Crafts room; Laundry room; Barber/Beauty shop; Library.
Activities Arts and Crafts; Cards; Games; Reading groups; Prayer groups; Movies; Shopping trips; Dances/Social or cultural gatherings.
Description Most residents are Polish/Catholic, have a Catholic ministry program administered by 43 volunteers; average age of residents is 86; residents are medically stable and able to be up and about.

George J Goldman Memorial Home for the Aged*
6601 W Touhy Ave, Niles, IL, 60648 (312) 647-9875
Admin Ruth Cohen.
Licensure Skilled Care. *Beds* 99. *Certified* Medicaid.
Ownership Proprietary.

Golf Mill Plaza I
9777 Greenwood, Niles, IL, 60648 (312) 965-6300
Admin Corrine Lerman. *Medical Dir/Dir of Nursing* Jerome Podgers MD.
Licensure Skilled Care; Intermediate Care.
Beds SNF 99; ICF 88. *Certified* Medicaid.
Ownership Proprietary.
Admissions Requirements Minimum age 18.
Staff Physicians; RNs; LPNs; Orderlies; Nurses aides; Physical therapists; Reality therapists; Recreational therapists; Occupational therapists; Speech therapists; Activities coordinators; Dietitians; Dentists; Ophthalmologists; Podiatrists; Audiologists.

Facilities Dining room; Physical therapy room; Activities room; Crafts room; Laundry room; Barber/Beauty shop; Library.
Activities Arts and Crafts; Cards; Games; Reading groups; Prayer groups; Movies; Shopping trips; Dances/Social or cultural gatherings.
Description Facility is devoted to full-time care of the developmentally disabled including those with cerebral palsy, muscular dystrophy, multiple sclerosis, and severe/moderate mental retardation.

Golf Mill Plaza II*
8555 Maynard Rd, Niles, IL, 60648 (312) 967-7000
Admin Dwaine Douglas.
Licensure Skilled Care; Intermediate Care.
Beds SNF 188; ICF 112. *Certified* Medicaid.
Ownership Proprietary.

Miranda Manor Ltd*
8333 W Golf Rd, Niles, IL, 60648 (312) 966-9190
Admin Perla Rivera.
Licensure Skilled Care; Intermediate Care.
Beds SNF 148; ICF 148. *Certified* Medicaid.
Ownership Proprietary.

Regency Nursing Centre Inc*
6631 Milwaukee Ave, Niles, IL, 60648 (312) 647-7444
Admin Barbara Hecht.
Licensure Skilled Care. *Beds* 300. *Certified* Medicaid; Medicare.
Ownership Proprietary.

Saint Andrew Home for the Aged
7000 N Newark, Niles, IL, 60648 (312) 641-8332
Admin George A Gorski. *Medical Dir/Dir of Nursing* Conrad Wiet MD.
Licensure Intermediate Care; Sheltered Care.
Beds ICF 33; Sheltered Care 24. *Certified* Medicaid.
Ownership Nonprofit.
Admissions Requirements Minimum age 65; Medical examination.
Staff Physicians 1 (pt); RNs 3 (ft), 4 (pt).
Facilities Dining room; Physical therapy room; Activities room; Chapel; Crafts room; Laundry room; Barber/Beauty shop.
Activities Arts and Crafts; Cards; Games; Prayer groups; Movies; Shopping trips; Dances/Social or cultural gatherings.

Saint Benedict Home for Aged
6930 W Touhy Ave, Niles, IL, 60648 (312) 774-1440
Admin Sr Irene I Sebo. *Medical Dir/Dir of Nursing* Donald Quinlan MD.
Licensure Intermediate Care. *Beds* 52.
Ownership Nonprofit.
Admissions Requirements Minimum age 70; Medical examination.
Staff Physicians; RNs; LPNs 3 (ft), 2 (pt); Nurses aides 3 (ft), 2 (pt); Reality therapists 1 (pt); Occupational therapists 1 (pt); Dietitians 1 (ft); Dentists 1 (pt); Ophthalmologists 1 (pt); Podiatrists 1 (pt).
Affiliation Roman Catholic
Facilities Dining room; Activities room; Chapel; Laundry room; Barber/Beauty shop.
Activities Arts and Crafts; Cards; Games;

Reading groups; Prayer groups; Movies; Shopping trips; Dances/Social or cultural gatherings.

NOKOMIS

Nokomis Golden Manor
Stevens St, Nokomis, IL, 62075 (217) 563-7513
Admin Kenneth J Krebs. *Medical Dir/Dir of Nursing* Dr D Quizon.
Licensure Skilled Care; Intermediate Care.
Beds 79. *Certified* Medicaid; Medicare.
Ownership Proprietary.
Admissions Requirements Minimum age 18.
Staff Physicians 2 (pt); RNs 2 (ft), 2 (pt); LPNs 1 (ft), 5 (pt); Nurses aides 19 (ft), 12 (pt); Physical therapists 1 (pt); Occupational therapists 1 (pt); Speech therapists 1 (pt); Activities coordinators 1 (ft); Dietitians 1 (pt); Dentists 1 (pt); Podiatrists 1 (pt).
Facilities Dining room; Physical therapy room; Activities room; Chapel; Crafts room; Laundry room; Barber/Beauty shop; Library.
Activities Arts and Crafts; Cards; Games; Movies; Dances/Social or cultural gatherings.

NORMAL

Americana Healthcare Center*
610 Broadway, Normal, IL, 61761 (309) 452-4406
Admin Linda L Morrison.
Licensure Skilled Care. *Beds* 90. *Certified* Medicaid; Medicare.
Ownership Proprietary.

McLean County Nursing Home*
901 N Main, Normal, IL, 61761 (309) 452-8337
Admin Donald W Lee.
Licensure Skilled Care. *Beds* 150. *Certified* Medicaid.
Ownership Public.

Shamel Manor
509 N Adelaide St, Normal, IL, 61761 (309) 452-7468
Admin Rose M Stadel. *Medical Dir/Dir of Nursing* Dr P Sriratana.
Licensure Intermediate Care. *Beds* 180. *Certified* Medicaid.
Ownership Proprietary.
Admissions Requirements Medical examination.
Staff RNs 3 (ft); LPNs 12 (ft), 4 (pt); Orderlies 6 (ft); Nurses aides 25 (ft), 4 (pt); Recreational therapists 4 (ft); Activities coordinators 1 (ft).
Facilities Dining room; Activities room; Crafts room; Laundry room; Barber/Beauty shop.
Activities Arts and Crafts; Cards; Games; Reading groups; Prayer groups; Movies; Shopping trips; Dances/Social or cultural gatherings.
Description Facility offers quiet residential area, qualified for department of public health quality incentive Level II; beautiful retirement apartments; excellent nursing and volunteer program; individual and personalized care.

NORTH AURORA

North Aurora Manor
310 Banbury Rd, North Aurora, IL, 60542
(312) 892-7628
Admin Maggie E Czerwinski. *Medical Dir/Dir of Nursing* H Kim MD.
Licensure Intermediate Care. *Beds* 129. *Certified* Medicaid.
Ownership Proprietary.
Admissions Requirements Minimum age 55; Medical examination; Physician's request.
Staff RNs; LPNs; Orderlies; Nurses aides; Physical therapists; Activities coordinators; Dietitians.
Facilities Dining room; Activities room; Crafts room; Laundry room; Barber/Beauty shop.
Activities Arts and Crafts; Cards; Games; Reading groups; Prayer groups; Movies; Shopping trips; Dances/Social or cultural gatherings.

NORTHBROOK

Brandel Care Center
2155 Pfingsten Rd, Northbrook, IL, 60062
(312) 480-6350
Admin Beverly Z Smith. *Medical Dir/Dir of Nursing* Dr Russell Elmer.
Licensure Skilled Care; Intermediate Care. *Beds* 104. *Certified* Medicaid.
Ownership Nonprofit.
Admissions Requirements Minimum age 18.
Staff RNs 5 (ft), 15 (pt); LPNs 2 (ft), 1 (pt); Nurses aides 30 (ft), 30 (pt); Activities coordinators 2 (ft), 1 (pt).
Facilities Dining room; Physical therapy room; Activities room; Chapel; Crafts room; Laundry room; Barber/Beauty shop.
Activities Arts and Crafts; Cards; Games; Reading groups; Prayer groups; Movies.

Chateau Home
3410 Milwaukee Ave, Northbrook, IL, 60062
(312) 824-2010
Admin Jean J Olson.
Licensure Sheltered Care. *Beds* Sheltered Care 36.
Ownership Proprietary.

Glen Oaks Nursing Home Inc
270 Skokie Hwy, Northbrook, IL, 60062 (312) 835-4200
Admin Rita Steinback. *Medical Dir/Dir of Nursing* Dr Edward Sutoris.
Licensure Skilled Care; Intermediate Care. *Beds* SNF 164; ICF 130. *Certified* Medicaid; Medicare.
Ownership Proprietary.
Staff Physicians 7 (pt); RNs 38 (ft); LPNs 14 (ft); Orderlies 14 (ft); Nurses aides 64 (ft), 3 (pt); Physical therapists 5 (ft), 2 (pt); Reality therapists 2 (ft); Recreational therapists 7 (ft); Occupational therapists 1 (ft); Speech therapists 1 (pt); Activities coordinators 1 (ft); Dietitians 1 (pt); Dentists 1 (pt); Ophthalmologists 1 (pt); Podiatrists 2 (pt); Audiologists 1 (pt).
Facilities Dining room; Physical therapy room; Activities room; Crafts room; Laundry room; Barber/Beauty shop; Library.
Activities Arts and Crafts; Cards; Games; Reading groups; Prayer groups; Movies; Shopping trips; Dances/Social or cultural gatherings.

Description Special programs are "The Apartment," a reintegration program for geriatric residents to assist them in living on their own in the community; and "Art Therapy," a full art therapy program headed by an art therapist working with regressed adults; many other programs. VA approved.

Lake-Cook Terrace
222 Dennis Dr, Northbrook, IL, 60062 (312) 835-3700
Admin Flavia Ambrog. *Medical Dir/Dir of Nursing* Dr Jeffrey Leiblich.
Licensure Skilled Care. *Beds* 139. *Certified* Medicaid.
Ownership Proprietary.
Admissions Requirements Minimum age 40; Physician's request.
Staff Physicians 1 (ft), 1 (pt); RNs 3 (ft), 6 (pt); LPNs 3 (ft), 2 (pt); Orderlies 13 (ft), 1 (pt); Nurses aides 23 (ft), 2 (pt); Physical therapists 1 (pt); Reality therapists 1 (pt); Recreational therapists 1 (pt); Occupational therapists 1 (pt); Speech therapists 1 (pt); Activities coordinators 1 (ft); Dietitians 1 (pt); Dentists 1 (pt); Ophthalmologists 1 (pt); Podiatrists 1 (pt); Audiologists 1 (pt).
Facilities Dining room; Physical therapy room; Activities room; Crafts room; Laundry room; Barber/Beauty shop; Library.
Activities Arts and Crafts; Cards; Games; Reading groups; Prayer groups; Movies; Shopping trips; Dances/Social or cultural gatherings; Breakfast club; Lunch groups in-house; Luncheons.
Description During good weather many activities held away from the facility such as baseball games, trips to museums, and botanical gardens; shows put on by many agencies like vets, schools, etc. All rehabilitation is done in facility.

OAK FOREST

Kosary Home*
Box E, 6660 W 147th St, Oak Forest, IL, 60452
(312) 687-4300
Admin Julius Kosary.
Licensure Sheltered Care. *Beds* Sheltered Care 66.
Ownership Proprietary.

OAK LAWN

Americana Healthcare Center
9401 S Kostner Ave, Oak Lawn, IL, 60453
(312) 423-7882
Admin Leslie G Ohm. *Medical Dir/Dir of Nursing* Dr A Ricker.
Licensure Skilled Care. *Beds* 157. *Certified* Medicare.
Ownership Proprietary.
Admissions Requirements Minimum age 18; Medical examination; Physician's request.
Staff Physicians 3 (pt); RNs 4 (ft), 21 (pt); LPNs 7 (ft), 6 (pt); Orderlies 2 (pt); Nurses aides 35 (ft), 21 (pt); Physical therapists 1 (ft), 1 (pt); Recreational therapists 1 (ft); Occupational therapists 2 (pt); Speech therapists 1 (ft); Activities coordinators 1 (ft); Dietitians 1 (ft); Dentists 1 (pt); Podiatrists 1 (pt).

Facilities Dining room; Physical therapy room; Activities room; Crafts room; Laundry room; Barber/Beauty shop; Speech therapy room; Occupational therapy room; 4 lounge areas.
Activities Arts and Crafts; Cards; Games; Reading groups; Prayer groups; Movies; Shopping trips; Dances/Social or cultural gatherings; Happy hour; Exercise groups; R.O. classes; Baking classes; Social cart; "Green Thumb" plant club; Ceramics classes.
Description Americana Healthcare Center of Oak Lawn has a dual approach to extended care: a quality-long term care facility, focusing on the extention of our residents lifestyle, and a full-time rehabilitation program, which returns approximately 50% of our residents to their home environment.

Americana-Monticello Convalescent Center
6300 W 95th St, Oak Lawn, IL, 60453 (312) 735-5454
Admin Jeanne M Chiligiris. *Medical Dir/Dir of Nursing* Dr Stanley Ruzich.
Licensure Skilled Care; Intermediate Care. *Beds* 175. *Certified* Medicare.
Ownership Proprietary.
Facilities Dining room; Physical therapy room; Activities room; Laundry room; Barber/Beauty shop.
Activities Arts and Crafts; Cards; Games; Reading groups; Prayer groups; Movies; Shopping trips; Dances/Social or cultural gatherings.
Description Facility has Alzheimer's unit.

Concord Extended Care*
9401 S Ridgeland Ave, Oak Lawn, IL, 60453
(312) 599-6700
Admin Elsie Hoover.
Licensure Skilled Care. *Beds* 99. *Certified* Medicaid; Medicare.
Ownership Proprietary.

Greentree Nursing Center*
8540 S Harlem Ave, Oak Lawn, IL, 60455
(312) 598-2605
Admin Marshall A Mauer.
Licensure Skilled Care. *Beds* 404. *Certified* Medicaid.
Ownership Proprietary.

Hickory Hills Nursing Center Inc*
9246 S Roberts Rd, Oak Lawn, IL, 60457 (312) 598-4040
Admin Karen J Zarken.
Licensure Intermediate Care. *Beds* 74. *Certified* Medicaid.
Ownership Proprietary.

Robings Manor
502 N Main St, Oak Lawn, IL, 62012 (618) 372-3232
Admin Catherine D Hale.
Licensure Skilled Care. *Beds* 68. *Certified* Medicare.
Ownership Proprietary.

Rosary Hill Convalescent Center*
9000 W 81st St, Oak Lawn, IL, 60458 (312) 458-3040
Admin Catherine M Lasiewicki.
Licensure Skilled Care; Intermediate Care. *Beds* SNF 57; ICF 18.
Ownership Nonprofit.

OAK PARK

Oak Park Convalescent and Geriatric Center*
625 N Harlem Ave, Oak Park, IL, 60302 (312) 848-8484
Admin Kathy Maska.
Licensure Skilled Care; Intermediate Care.
Beds SNF 176; ICF 28. *Certified* Medicaid; Medicare.
Ownership Proprietary.

Oak Park Sheltered Care
637 S Maple Ave, Oak Park, IL, 60304 (312) 848-4400
Admin Jane F Silvestri.
Licensure Sheltered Care. *Beds* 26. *Certified* Medicaid.
Ownership Proprietary.
Staff RNs 1 (ft), 1 (pt); LPNs 1 (ft), 2 (pt); Physical therapists 1 (pt); Reality therapists 1 (pt); Recreational therapists 2 (pt).
Facilities Dining room; Activities room; Crafts room; Laundry room; Library.
Activities Arts and Crafts; Cards; Games; Reading groups; Prayer groups; Movies; Shopping trips; Dances/Social or cultural gatherings; Church services.
Description A small, beautifully decorated facility with lovely patios and yard; 24-hour nursing care; doctors' orders are strictly followed. Residents must be ambulatory.

Woodbine
6909 W North Ave, Oak Park, IL, 60302 (312) 386-1112
Admin Helen S Smith. *Medical Dir/Dir of Nursing* Peter Pulos MD.
Licensure Skilled Care; Intermediate Care.
Beds 68.
Ownership Proprietary.
Admissions Requirements Minimum age 21; Medical examination; Physician's request.
Staff Physicians 3 (pt); RNs 6 (ft), 5 (pt); LPNs 2 (ft), 4 (pt); Nurses aides 26 (ft); Physical therapists 3 (pt); Reality therapists 1 (pt); Recreational therapists 1 (pt); Occupational therapists 1 (ft), 1 (pt); Activities coordinators 1 (pt); Dietitians 1 (pt); Dentists 1 (pt); Ophthalmologists 1 (pt); Ophthalmologists 1 (pt); Podiatrists 1 (pt); Audiologists 1 (pt).
Facilities Dining room; Physical therapy room; Activities room; Crafts room; Laundry room; Barber/Beauty shop; Library.
Activities Arts and Crafts; Cards; Games; Reading groups; Prayer groups; Movies; Dances/Social or cultural gatherings.
Description Facility has been in Oak Park-River Forest area for 25 years and provides a social and recreational atmosphere as well as complete nursing care; spiritual program is nonsectarian; decor is New Orleans Colonial; facility is all on one floor.

OBLONG

Ridgeview Care Center*
1 Ridgeview Ln, Oblong, IL, 62449 (618) 592-4226
Admin Eileen W Cunningham.
Licensure Skilled Care. *Beds* 49. *Certified* Medicaid.
Ownership Proprietary.

ODIN

Odin Care Center Inc
Green St, Odin, IL, 62870 (618) 775-6444
Admin Opal Jolly. *Medical Dir/Dir of Nursing* P T Durion MD.
Licensure Skilled Care; Intermediate Care.
Beds 98. *Certified* Medicaid; Medicare.
Ownership Proprietary.
Admissions Requirements Minimum age 18; Medical examination; Physician's request.
Staff Physicians 11 (pt); RNs 3 (ft); LPNs 6 (ft); Orderlies 5 (ft); Nurses aides 30 (ft); Physical therapists 1 (pt); Occupational therapists 1 (ft); Speech therapists 1 (pt); Activities coordinators 2 (ft); Dietitians 1 (pt); Dentists 1 (pt); Ophthalmologists 1 (pt); Podiatrists 1 (pt); Audiologists 1 (pt).
Facilities Dining room; Physical therapy room; Activities room; Crafts room; Laundry room; Barber/Beauty shop; Library; Living room; Patio.
Activities Arts and Crafts; Cards; Games; Reading groups; Prayer groups; Movies; Shopping trips; Dances/Social or cultural gatherings; Remotivation group; Community affairs; Bingo.

OFALLON

Parkview Colonial Manor*
300 Weber Rd, O'Fallon, IL, 62269 (618) 632-3511
Admin Kenneth R Newell.
Licensure Skilled Care; Intermediate Care.
Beds SNF 108; ICF 41. *Certified* Medicaid; Medicare.
Ownership Proprietary.

OGLESBY

Horizon South Living Center
Pool Dr and Lehigh Ave, Oglesby, IL, 61348
Admin Gerlyn Koehler. *Medical Dir/Dir of Nursing* Dr W Y Kim.
Licensure Intermediate Care for Mentally Retarded. *Beds* 16.
Admissions Requirements Minimum age 18; Medical examination; Physician's request.
Staff RNs 3 (ft); LPNs 3 (ft); Recreational therapists 1 (ft); Activities coordinators 1 (ft); Training staff 15 (ft), 18 (pt).
Facilities Dining room; Activities room; Crafts room; Laundry room.
Activities Arts and Crafts; Cards; Games; Reading groups; Prayer groups; Movies; Shopping trips; Dances/Social or cultural gatherings.
Description This is an intermediate care facility for developmentally disabled adults; the program is designed to develop residents skills with goals to achieve their maximum potential of independence, so that as many as possible can move to less structured homes.

OLNEY

Burgin Manor
900-928 E Scott St, Olney, IL, 62450 (618) 393-2914
Admin Sue Burgin. *Medical Dir/Dir of*

Nursing Dr Thomas Summers.
Licensure Skilled Care; Intermediate Care.
Beds SNF 75; ICF 75. *Certified* Medicaid; Medicare.
Ownership Proprietary.
Admissions Requirements Medical examination.
Staff RNs 3 (ft), 4 (pt); LPNs 10 (ft), 7 (pt); Nurses aides 30 (ft), 18 (pt); Physical therapists 1 (pt); Occupational therapists 1 (pt); Speech therapists 1 (pt); Activities coordinators 3 (ft); Dietitians 1 (pt).
Facilities Dining room; Physical therapy room; Activities room; Chapel; Crafts room; Laundry room; Barber/Beauty shop; Occupational therapy room; Speech therapy room.
Activities Arts and Crafts; Cards; Games; Reading groups; Prayer groups; Movies; Shopping trips; Dances/Social or cultural gatherings; Bus tours; Fishing trips.
Description Facility features a superb activities program, an active adopt-a-grandparent program, outstanding physical therapy department with certified physical therapy assistant; excellent homemade food.

Marks Sunset Manor*
1044 Whittle, Olney, IL, 62450 (618) 392-0846
Admin Glen E Marks.
Licensure Sheltered Care. *Beds* 49.
Ownership Proprietary.

Olney Care Center*
410 E Mack Ave, Olney, IL, 62450 (618) 395-7421
Admin Alice Berger.
Licensure Skilled Care. *Beds* 98. *Certified* Medicaid; Medicare.
Ownership Proprietary.

OREGON

White Pines Manor
811 S 10th St, Oregon, IL, 61061 (815) 732-7994
Admin Thomas D Bowes Jr. *Medical Dir/Dir of Nursing* Dr Swan.
Licensure Skilled Care. *Beds* 63. *Certified* Medicaid; Medicare.
Staff RNs 2 (ft), 2 (pt); LPNs 2 (ft), 3 (pt); Nurses aides 20 (ft), 10 (pt); Physical therapists 1 (pt); Speech therapists 1 (pt); Activities coordinators 1 (ft); Dietitians 1 (pt).
Facilities Dining room; Physical therapy room; Activities room; Crafts room; Laundry room; Barber/Beauty shop; Library.
Activities Arts and Crafts; Cards; Games; Reading groups; Prayer groups; Movies; Shopping trips; Dances/Social or cultural gatherings.
Description Facility is located in a beautiful country setting; has exceptional physical therapy department, full rehabilitative services; all patients have rooms with private baths; received special recognition from the Illinois Department of Public Aid for quality of care.

OSWEGO

Tillers Nursing Home
Rt 71, PO Box 945, Oswego, IL, 60543 (312) 554-1001

Admin Robert M Saxon. *Medical Dir/Dir of Nursing* Michael R Saxon MD.
Licensure Skilled Care; Intermediate Care.
Beds 80.
Ownership Proprietary.
Admissions Requirements Medical examination.
Staff RNs 4 (ft), 8 (pt); Nurses aides 17 (ft), 18 (pt); Physical therapists 1 (ft); Recreational therapists 1 (ft); Occupational therapists 1 (pt); Speech therapists 1 (pt); Activities coordinators 1 (ft); Dietitians 1 (pt); Dentists 1 (pt); Ophthalmologists 1 (pt); Podiatrists 1 (pt); Audiologists 1 (pt).
Facilities Dining room; Physical therapy room; Activities room; Chapel; Crafts room; Laundry room; Barber/Beauty shop; TV room; Lounges; Patios; Screened porch.
Activities Arts and Crafts; Cards; Games; Reading groups; Prayer groups; Movies; Shopping trips; Dances/Social or cultural gatherings; Creative-type drama & poetry; Current events; Picnics; Mini-antique shows; Quilt shows; Style shows.
Description Facility is family owned and operated. The Tillers is managed with an unusual amount of alertness to the needs and desires of both residents and their families. Dr Michael R Saxon, Medical Director, and son Robert, Administrator, are committed to maintaining nursing care of the highest professional and humanitarian standards. They have a keen personal interest in the people they serve and are closely involved with all aspects of daily life at The Tillers.

OTTAWA

La Salle County Nursing Home
Rt 1, Ottawa, IL, 61350 (815) 433-0476
Admin Richard P Weber. *Medical Dir/Dir of Nursing* German Gonzalo MD.
Licensure Intermediate Care. *Beds* 104. *Certified* Medicaid.
Ownership Public.
Admissions Requirements Minimum age 18; Medical examination; Physician's request.
Staff Physicians 1 (pt); RNs 4 (ft), 4 (pt); LPNs 4 (ft), 4 (pt); Nurses aides 30 (ft), 6 (pt); Recreational therapists 2 (ft); Dietitians 1 (pt); Podiatrists 1 (pt).
Description Facility accepts La Salle County residents only.

Ottawa Care Center*
800 E Center St, Ottawa, IL, 61350 (815) 434-1130
Admin Lois Kallestad.
Licensure Skilled Care. *Beds* 93.
Ownership Nonprofit.

Pleasant View Lutheran Home
505 College Ave, Ottawa, IL, 61350 (815) 434-1130
Admin Karl O Norem. *Medical Dir/Dir of Nursing* Dr A G Giger.
Licensure Intermediate Care. *Beds* 235. *Certified* Medicaid.
Ownership Nonprofit.
Admissions Requirements Minimum age 60; Medical examination.
Staff Physicians 1 (pt); RNs 6 (ft), 6 (pt); LPNs

8 (ft), 6 (pt); Nurses aides 50 (ft), 23 (pt); Physical therapists 1 (pt); Recreational therapists 1 (pt); Occupational therapists 1 (pt); Speech therapists 1 (pt); Activities coordinators 1 (ft); Dietitians 1 (ft); Dentists 1 (pt); Podiatrists 1 (pt); Audiologists 1 (pt).
Affiliation Lutheran
Facilities Dining room; Physical therapy room; Activities room; Chapel; Crafts room; Laundry room; Barber/Beauty shop.
Activities Arts and Crafts; Cards; Games; Reading groups; Prayer groups; Movies; Shopping trips.

PALATINE

Little City Foundation*
1706 W Algonquin Rd, Palatine, IL, 60067 (312) 358-5510
Licensure Intermediate Care. *Beds* 80.
Ownership Nonprofit.

Plum Grove Nursing Home
24 S Plum Grove Rd, Palatine, IL, 60067 (312) 358-0311
Admin Gladys I Paine. *Medical Dir/Dir of Nursing* Daniel Schnuda MD.
Licensure Skilled Care; Intermediate Care. *Beds* 69.
Ownership Proprietary.
Staff RNs 6 (ft), 10 (pt); LPNs 1 (ft), 1 (pt); Orderlies 3 (ft); Nurses aides 16 (ft), 12 (pt); Activities coordinators 1 (ft), 1 (pt); Dietitians 1 (ft).
Facilities Dining room; Activities room; Crafts room; Laundry room; Barber/Beauty shop; Library; Dental facility.
Activities Arts and Crafts; Cards; Games; Reading groups; Prayer groups; Movies; Dances/Social or cultural gatherings; Baking group.
Description This is a private pay facility; patients are not separated as to their level of care or confusion; patients on ventilators are accepted; limited day care program available.

Saint Joseph's Home for the Elderly
80 W Northwest Hwy, Palatine, IL, 60067 (312) 358-5700
Admin Marguerite McCarthy. *Medical Dir/Dir of Nursing* Dr Andrew Cornejo.
Licensure Skilled Care; Intermediate Care. *Beds* SNF 50; ICF 34; 46. *Certified* Medicaid; Medicare.
Ownership Nonprofit.
Staff Physicians 4 (pt); RNs 20 (ft); LPNs 2 (pt); Orderlies 2 (pt); Nurses aides 40 (ft); Physical therapists 1 (pt); Occupational therapists 1 (pt); Activities coordinators 1 (ft); Dietitians 1 (pt); Dentists 1 (pt); Ophthalmologists 1 (pt); Podiatrists 2 (pt); Audiologists 1 (pt).
Affiliation Roman Catholic
Facilities Dining room; Physical therapy room; Activities room; Chapel; Crafts room; Laundry room; Barber/Beauty shop; Library.
Activities Arts and Crafts; Cards; Games; Reading groups; Prayer groups; Movies; Shopping trips; Dances/Social or cultural gatherings.
Description Complete overall program provides for total needs of the residents. Sisters care for the individuals who are poor and have limited resources, regardless of creed.

PALOS HEIGHTS

Rest Haven Illiana Christian Convalescent Home*
13259 S Central Ave, Palos Heights, IL, 60463 (312) 597-1000
Admin Peter J Schurman.
Licensure Skilled Care; Intermediate Care.
Beds SNF 96; ICF 99. *Certified* Medicaid.
Ownership Nonprofit.

Ridgeland Nursing Home Inc*
12500 S Ridgeland Ave, Palos Heights, IL, 60463 (312) 597-9300
Admin Edward Hogan.
Licensure Skilled Care. *Beds* 84. *Certified* Medicaid; Medicare.
Ownership Proprietary.

PALOS HILLS

Pine Manor Nursing Center
10426 S Roberts Rd, Palos Hills, IL, 60465 (312) 598-3460
Admin Mary R Walker. *Medical Dir/Dir of Nursing* Sam Kruger MD.
Licensure Skilled Care; Intermediate Care.
Beds SNF 120; ICF 83. *Certified* Medicaid.
Ownership Proprietary.
Admissions Requirements Minimum age 45; Medical examination.
Staff Physicians 5 (pt); RNs 7 (ft); LPNs 16 (ft), 2 (pt); Orderlies 3 (ft); Nurses aides 56 (ft), 8 (pt); Physical therapists 2 (ft); Speech therapists 1 (pt); Activities coordinators 3 (ft), 1 (pt); Dietitians 1 (ft); Dentists 1 (pt); Ophthalmologists 1 (pt); Podiatrists 1 (pt).
Facilities Dining room; Physical therapy room; Activities room; Crafts room; Laundry room; Barber/Beauty shop.
Activities Arts and Crafts; Cards; Games; Prayer groups; Movies; Shopping trips; Dances/Social or cultural gatherings.
Description Pine Manor Nursing Center is a one-level, 203-bed skilled facility located directly southwest of Chicago. Dedicated to the care and well being of every resident, Pine Manor offers modern medical and geriatric nursing care in a home-like atmosphere.

PANA

Barry Care Center of Pana*
1000 E 6th Street Rd, Pana, IL, 62557 (217) 562-2174
Admin Judith E White.
Licensure Skilled Care. *Beds* 166. *Certified* Medicaid; Medicare.
Ownership Proprietary.

Pana Hawthorne Lodge*
900 S Chestnut St, Pana, IL, 62557 (217) 562-3996
Admin Edward L Hastings.
Licensure Skilled Care. *Beds* 123. *Certified* Medicaid; Medicare.
Ownership Proprietary.

PARIS

Heritage Nursing Center*
310 S Eads Ave, Paris, IL, 61944 (217) 465-5395
Admin Elizabeth M Clark.
Licensure Intermediate Care. *Beds* 62. *Certified* Medicaid.
Ownership Proprietary.

Paris Healthcare Center*
1011 N Main St, Paris, IL, 61944 (217) 465-5376
Admin Nancy D Davis.
Licensure Intermediate Care. *Beds* 98. *Certified* Medicaid.
Ownership Proprietary.

PARK RIDGE

Clifton House*
100 N Clifton, Park Ridge, IL, 60068 (312) 825-6498
Admin Allan Litwack.
Licensure Intermediate Care. *Beds* 20.
Ownership Nonprofit.

Park Ridge Terrace
665 Busse Hwy, Park Ridge, IL, 60068 (312) 825-5517
Admin George G Davis. *Medical Dir/Dir of Nursing* Dr G Sarrafi.
Licensure Intermediate Care. *Beds* 55. *Certified* Medicaid.
Ownership Proprietary.
Admissions Requirements Minimum age 21; Medical examination.
Staff Physicians 1 (pt); RNs 1 (ft), 6 (pt); LPNs 2 (ft), 1 (pt); Orderlies 6 (ft); Nurses aides 11 (ft); Physical therapists 1 (pt); Recreational therapists 1 (pt); Occupational therapists 1 (pt); Speech therapists 1 (pt); Activities coordinators 2 (pt); Dietitians 1 (pt); Dentists 1 (pt); Ophthalmologists 1 (pt); Podiatrists 1 (pt); Social service consultant 1 (pt).
Facilities Dining room; Activities room; Laundry room; Sun room; Outdoor terrace.
Activities Arts and Crafts; Cards; Games; Reading groups; Prayer groups; Movies; Dances/Social or cultural gatherings; Musical entertainment; Parties.
Description Accredited by the Joint Commission on Accreditation of Hospitals, one floor facility with individual room air conditioning and heating controls. Celebrating our 23rd year. Limited to 55 residents.

Resurrection Nursing Pavilion*
1001 Greenwood Ave, Park Ridge, IL, 60068 (312) 692-5600
Admin Paul Crevis.
Licensure Skilled Care. *Beds* 298. *Certified* Medicaid; Medicare.
Ownership Nonprofit.

Saint Matthew Lutheran Home
1601 N Western Ave, Park Ridge, IL, 60068 (312) 825-5531
Admin Will C Rasmussen. *Medical Dir/Dir of Nursing* Dr S Shastri.
Licensure Skilled Care; Intermediate Care; Sheltered Care. *Beds* SNF 130; ICF 14; Sheltered Care 32.
Ownership Nonprofit.
Admissions Requirements Minimum age 62; Medical examination.
Staff RNs 15 (ft), 15 (pt); LPNs 3 (pt); Orderlies 20 (ft); Nurses aides 60 (ft); Physical therapists 1 (ft); Occupational therapists 1 (pt); Activities coordinators 1 (ft); Dietitians 1 (ft).
Affiliation Lutheran
Facilities Dining room; Physical therapy room; Activities room; Chapel; Crafts room; Laundry room; Barber/Beauty shop; Library.
Activities Arts and Crafts; Cards; Games; Reading groups; Movies; Shopping trips; Dances/Social or cultural gatherings.
Description St Matthew Lutheran Home is a program of Lutheran Social Services of Illinois. The agency serves over 170,000 persons each year through more than 100 programs located in Illinois. Lutheran Social Services of Illinois has acted as sponsor and manager of several retirement facilities.

PAXTON

Ford County Nursing Home
Rt 2, Paxton, IL, 60957 (217) 379-3261
Admin Judith L Ondercho. *Medical Dir/Dir of Nursing* Dr Richard Fuellner.
Licensure Skilled Care; Intermediate Care. *Beds* 69. *Certified* Medicaid.
Ownership Public.
Admissions Requirements Minimum age 18; Medical examination.
Staff Physicians 4 (ft), 3 (pt); RNs 5 (ft); LPNs 3 (ft); Orderlies 1 (ft); Physical therapists 1 (pt); Recreational therapists 2 (ft), 1 (pt); Speech therapists 1 (ft).
Facilities Dining room; Physical therapy room; Activities room; Laundry room; Barber/Beauty shop.
Activities Arts and Crafts; Cards; Games; Reading groups; Prayer groups; Movies; Shopping trips; Dances/Social or cultural gatherings; Community projects; Interhome outings; Special dinners; Baking/cooking sessions.
Description Facility features a small community, rural setting with large grounds.

Illinois Knights Templar Home for the Aged
450 Fulton St, Paxton, IL, 60957 (217) 379-3814
Admin John W Becker. *Medical Dir/Dir of Nursing* Robert C Basler MD.
Licensure Skilled Care; Intermediate Care. *Beds* SNF 37; ICF 12. *Certified* Medicaid.
Ownership Nonprofit.
Admissions Requirements Minimum age 60; Medical examination.
Staff Physicians; RNs; LPNs; Nurses aides; Physical therapists; Occupational therapists; Speech therapists; Activities coordinators; Dietitians; Dentists.
Affiliation Masons
Facilities Dining room; Physical therapy room; Activities room; Laundry room; Barber/Beauty shop; Library.
Activities Arts and Crafts; Cards; Games; Movies; Shopping trips; Dances/Social or cultural gatherings.
Description A banquet is held once a month for the residents in a special room with wine, hors d'oeuvres, and a special entree.

PEKIN

B J Perino Nursing Home Inc
601-603 Prince St, Pekin, IL, 61554 (309) 346l-1118
Admin Christena W Warren. *Medical Dir/Dir of Nursing* R Urban MD.
Licensure Intermediate Care. *Beds* 84. *Certified* Medicaid.
Ownership Proprietary.
Admissions Requirements Medical examination.
Staff Physicians 16 (pt); RNs 1 (ft); LPNs 8 (ft), 3 (pt); Orderlies 2 (ft); Nurses aides 15 (ft); Physical therapists 1 (ft), 1 (pt); Occupational therapists 1 (pt); Activities coordinators 1 (ft); Dietitians 1 (ft), 1 (pt); Dentists 1 (ft), 1 (pt); Podiatrists 1 (pt).
Facilities Dining room; Physical therapy room; Activities room; Crafts room; Laundry room; Barber/Beauty shop; Library.
Activities Arts and Crafts; Cards; Games; Reading groups; Prayer groups; Movies; Shopping trips; Dances/Social or cultural gatherings; Reality orientation; Remotivation.
Description VA approved.

Hallmark House Nursing Home*
2501 Allentown Rd, Pekin, IL, 61554 (309) 347-3121
Admin Mark L Leafgreen.
Licensure Intermediate Care. *Beds* 71. *Certified* Medicaid.
Ownership Proprietary.

Pekin Convalescent Center*
2220 State Rd, Pekin, IL, 61554 (309) 347-1110
Admin Jeffrey A Smith.
Licensure Skilled Care. *Beds* 202. *Certified* Medicaid; Medicare.
Ownership Proprietary.

Twin Oaks Community Living Facility*
2421 S 14th St, Pekin, IL, 61554 (309) 686-3310
Admin Joseph Budde.
Licensure Intermediate Care. *Beds* 12.
Ownership Nonprofit.

PEORIA

Americana Healthcare Center*
5600 Glen Elm Dr, Peoria, IL, 61614 (309) 688-8777
Admin Leroy Policky.
Licensure Skilled Care. *Beds* 104. *Certified* Medicaid; Medicare.
Ownership Proprietary.

Apostolic of Peoria*
7023 NE Skyline Dr, Peoria, IL, 61614 (309) 691-2816
Admin Roger D Herman.
Licensure Intermediate Care; Sheltered Care. *Beds* ICF 21; Sheltered Care 32.
Ownership Nonprofit.
Affiliation Apostolic Christian

Bel-Wood Nursing Home
6701 W Plank Rd, Peoria, IL, 61604 (309) 697-4541
Medical Dir/Dir of Nursing William R Nace MD.
Licensure Intermediate Care. *Beds* 300. *Certified* Medicaid.
Ownership Public.
Admissions Requirements Minimum age 18; Medical examination.
Staff RNs 16 (ft); LPNs 15 (ft); Nurses aides 72 (ft); Activities coordinators 1 (ft); Dietitians 1 (ft); Dentists 1 (pt); Podiatrists 1 (pt).
Facilities Dining room; Physical therapy room; Activities room; Chapel; Crafts room; Laundry room; Barber/Beauty shop; Library.
Activities Arts and Crafts; Cards; Games; Reading groups; Prayer groups; Movies; Shopping trips; Swimming; Bowling.

Christian Buehler Memorial Home*
3415 N Sheridan Rd, Peoria, IL, 61604 (309) 685-6236
Admin Louis E Amberg.
Licensure Skilled Care. *Beds* 71.
Ownership Nonprofit.

Galena Park Home*
5533 N Galena Rd, Peoria, IL, 61614 (309) 682-5428
Admin Julia K King.
Licensure Skilled Care; Sheltered Home.
Beds SNF 60; Sheltered Care 4. *Certified* Medicaid.
Ownership Nonprofit.

High View Nursing Center
2308 W Nebraska St, Peoria, IL, 61604 (309) 673-8251
Admin Arthur L Ott. *Medical Dir/Dir of Nursing* W S Newcomer MD.
Licensure Skilled Care. *Beds* 98. *Certified* Medicaid; Medicare.
Ownership Proprietary.
Admissions Requirements Minimum age 18; Medical examination.
Staff Physicians 1 (pt); RNs 8 (ft), 4 (pt); LPNs 4 (ft), 2 (pt); Orderlies 4 (ft); Nurses aides 30 (ft), 9 (pt); Physical therapists 1 (ft), 1 (pt); Reality therapists 1 (pt); Recreational therapists 1 (ft), 1 (pt); Occupational therapists 1 (ft), 1 (pt); Speech therapists 1 (pt); Activities coordinators 1 (ft); Dietitians 1 (pt); Dentists 1 (pt); Ophthalmologists 1 (pt); Podiatrists 1 (pt); Audiologists 1 (pt).
Facilities Dining room; Physical therapy room; Activities room; Chapel; Crafts room; Laundry room; Barber/Beauty shop; Library.
Activities Arts and Crafts; Cards; Games; Reading groups; Prayer groups; Movies; Dances/Social or cultural gatherings.

The Lutheran Home*
7019 N Galena Rd, Peoria, IL, 61614 (309) 692-4494
Admin G H Vander Schaaf.
Licensure Skilled Care. *Beds* 72. *Certified* Medicaid.
Ownership Nonprofit.
Affiliation Lutheran

Pavilion North
3111 Richwoods Blvd, Peoria, IL, 61614 (309) 688-2457
Admin Louise M Wilson. *Medical Dir/Dir of Nursing* Dr Maurer.
Licensure Intermediate Care. *Beds* 120. *Certified* Medicaid.
Ownership Proprietary.
Admissions Requirements Medical examination; Physician's request.
Facilities Dining room; Physical therapy room; Activities room; Crafts room; Laundry room; Barber/Beauty shop; Library.
Activities Arts and Crafts; Cards; Games; Reading groups; Prayer groups; Movies; Shopping trips; Dances/Social or cultural gatherings.
Description Complete rehabilitation program including occupational therapy and language rehabilitation offered.

Pavilion Oaks
3520 N Rochelle, Peoria, IL, 61604 (309) 688-0451
Admin Peggy Post. *Medical Dir/Dir of Nursing* Dr Phillip Immesoete.
Licensure Skilled Care. *Beds* 99. *Certified* Medicaid; Medicare.
Ownership Proprietary.
Admissions Requirements Physician's request.
Staff RNs 2 (ft), 2 (pt); LPNs 10 (ft), 4 (pt); Orderlies 3 (ft); Nurses aides 26 (ft), 5 (pt); Physical therapists 1 (pt); Reality therapists 1 (pt); Recreational therapists 1 (pt); Occupational therapists 1 (pt); Speech therapists 1 (ft); Activities coordinators 1 (ft); Dietitians 1 (ft); Dentists 1 (pt); Ophthalmologists 1 (pt); Podiatrists 1 (pt); Audiologists 1 (pt).
Facilities Dining room; Physical therapy room; Activities room; Crafts room; Laundry room; Barber/Beauty shop; Library.
Activities Arts and Crafts; Cards; Games; Reading groups; Prayer groups; Movies; Shopping trips; Dances/Social or cultural gatherings.
Description This is a care campus that is unique—3 intermediate facilities, one skilled facility, and one special programing for young adults with mental and emotional problems.

Pavilion South*
3614 N Rochelle Ln, Peoria, IL, 61604 (309) 688-0350
Admin Fred A Post.
Licensure Intermediate Care. *Beds* 120. *Certified* Medicaid.
Ownership Proprietary.

Pavilion West
3611 N Rochelle, Peoria, IL, 61614 (309) 688-4412
Admin Judy Williams. *Medical Dir/Dir of Nursing* Dr Phillip Immesoete.
Licensure Intermediate Care. *Beds* 98. *Certified* Medicaid.
Ownership Proprietary.
Admissions Requirements Medical examination; Physician's request.
Staff Physicians 2 (pt); RNs 1 (ft), 1 (pt); LPNs 2 (ft), 4 (pt); Orderlies 1 (ft); Physical therapists 1 (pt); Occupational therapists 1 (pt); Speech therapists 1 (pt); Activities coordinators 1 (ft), 1 (pt); Dietitians 1 (pt); Dentists 1 (pt); Ophthalmologists 1 (pt); Podiatrists 1 (pt).
Facilities Dining room; Physical therapy room; Activities room; Crafts room; Laundry room; Barber/Beauty shop; Library.
Description Pavilion West is one of 5 nursing homes offering a continuum of care ranging from full skilled care to intermediate care; offers 24-hour licensed professional nurses and a full program of therapy and activities.

Proctor J C Endowment Home*
2724 W Reservior, Peoria, IL, 61615 (309) 685-6580
Admin Robert Ziegenhagen.
Licensure Skilled Care. *Beds* 59.
Ownership Nonprofit.

Richwoods Terrace
3301 W Richwoods Blvd, Peoria, IL, 61604 (309) 685-5241
Admin Nancy J Smith.
Licensure Intermediate Care. *Beds* 152. *Certified* Medicaid.
Ownership Proprietary.
Admissions Requirements Minimum age 19.
Facilities Dining room; Physical therapy room; Activities room; Crafts room; Laundry room; Barber/Beauty shop; Gymnasium-auditorium.
Activities Arts and Crafts; Cards; Games; Reading groups; Prayer groups; Movies; Shopping trips; Dances/Social or cultural gatherings.
Description Richwoods Terrace has a mental health population of acute younger people; special programing aimed at this population such as a token program and rap groups.

Saint Joseph Home of Peoria*
2223 W Heading Ave, Peoria, IL, 61604 (309) 673-7425
Admin Sr Mary Dries.
Licensure Intermediate Care; Sheltered Care.
Beds ICF 35; Sheltered Care 159.
Ownership Nonprofit.
Affiliation Roman Catholic

Stuttle Community Living Facility*
201 Columbia Terrace, Peoria, IL, 61606 (309) 686-3300
Admin Joseph L Budde.
Licensure Intermediate Care. *Beds* 20.
Ownership Nonprofit.

PEOTONE

Peotone Bensenville Home
104 S West St, PO Box 668, Peotone, IL, 60468 (312) 258-9396
Admin Laura J Stone. *Medical Dir/Dir of Nursing* L W Jessen MD.
Licensure Intermediate Care. *Beds* 34. *Certified* Medicaid.
Ownership Nonprofit.
Admissions Requirements Minimum age 65; Medical examination.
Staff RNs 2 (ft), 4 (pt); LPNs 2 (ft), 1 (pt); Nurses aides 5 (ft), 6 (pt); Activities coordinators 1 (pt).
Affiliation Church of Christ
Facilities Dining room; Activities room; Crafts room; Laundry room; Barber/Beauty shop.
Activities Arts and Crafts; Games; Prayer groups; Movies.
Description Smallness of facility financially

limits the scope of services, but keeps emphasis on care, compassion, and concern; size and tender loving care make home special.

PERU

Heritage Manor Nursing and Convalescent Home and Apartments
22nd and Rock Sts, Peru, IL, 61354 (815) 223-4901
Admin Jean Dyer. *Medical Dir/Dir of Nursing* Dr J F Sickley.
Licensure Skilled Care. *Beds* 110. *Certified* Medicaid; Medicare.
Ownership Proprietary.
Admissions Requirements Minimum age 18; Medical examination.
Staff RNs 6 (ft), 7 (pt); LPNs 3 (ft), 4 (pt); Nurses aides 22 (ft), 27 (pt); Physical therapists 1 (pt); Activities coordinators 1 (ft).
Facilities Dining room; Physical therapy room; Activities room; Crafts room; Laundry room; Barber/Beauty shop.
Activities Arts and Crafts; Cards; Games; Prayer groups; Movies; Shopping trips.
Description Home offers a comfortable relaxing atmosphere with the 5-meal-a-day program made up of good food prepared well and served attractively; grounds are very attractive enhancing the whole setting; employees concern for the residents' welfare is unsurpassable.

PETERSBURG

Menard Convalescent Center
120 Antle St, Petersburg, IL, 62675 (217) 632-2249
Admin Clyde H Miller. *Medical Dir/Dir of Nursing* Dr Barry Free.
Licensure Skilled Care; Intermediate Care. *Beds* SNF 59; ICF 27. *Certified* Medicaid; Medicare.
Ownership Proprietary.
Staff Physicians 3 (pt); RNs 2 (ft), 1 (pt); LPNs 10 (ft); Nurses aides 50 (ft); Physical therapists 1 (pt); Activities coordinators 1 (ft); Dietitians 1 (pt); Dentists 1 (pt).
Facilities Dining room; Physical therapy room; Barber/Beauty shop.
Activities Arts and Crafts; Cards; Games; Prayer groups; Movies; Shopping trips.
Description Center located in a small town setting with many of the residents' relatives or close friends working within the facility.

Petersburg Manor*
Rt 3, Petersburg, IL, 62675 (217) 632-7442
Admin David L Pizzo.
Licensure Sheltered Care. *Beds* 59.
Ownership Proprietary.

Sunny Acres Nursing Home*
RR 3, Petersburg, IL, 62675 (217) 632-2334
Admin Dick R Warren.
Licensure Intermediate Care. *Beds* 96. *Certified* Medicaid.
Ownership Public.

PINCKNEYVILLE

Perry Manor Inc
708 Virginia Ct, Pinckneyville, IL, 62274 (618) 357-2493
Admin Hildren Secrease.
Licensure Intermediate Care. *Beds* 60. *Certified* Medicaid.
Ownership Proprietary.
Staff RNs 1 (ft); LPNs 2 (ft), 6 (pt); Nurses aides 10 (ft), 5 (pt); Activities coordinators 1 (ft).
Facilities Dining room; Activities room; Laundry room; Barber/Beauty shop.
Activities Arts and Crafts; Cards; Games; Reading groups; Prayer groups; Movies; Shopping trips; Dances/Social or cultural gatherings.

PIPER CITY

Greenbrier Lodge
600 Maple St, Piper City, IL, 60959 (815) 686-2277
Admin David L Beaver. *Medical Dir/Dir of Nursing* Dr A G Baxter.
Licensure Intermediate Care. *Beds* 60. *Certified* Medicaid.
Ownership Proprietary.
Admissions Requirements Minimum age 18.
Staff RNs 3 (ft), 1 (pt); LPNs 1 (ft), 3 (pt); Nurses aides 17 (ft), 10 (pt); Physical therapists 1 (pt); Activities coordinators 1 (ft); Dietitians 1 (ft); Podiatrists 1 (pt).
Facilities Dining room; Physical therapy room; Activities room; Crafts room; Laundry room; Barber/Beauty shop.
Activities Arts and Crafts; Cards; Games; Reading groups; Prayer groups; Movies; Shopping trips; Dances/Social or cultural gatherings.

PITTSFIELD

Owen Care Center—Pittsfield*
Box 24, Rt 36 E, Pittsfield, IL, 62363 (217) 285-4491
Admin Ann E Smith.
Licensure Intermediate Care. *Beds* 99. *Certified* Medicaid.
Ownership Proprietary.

PLAINFIELD

Lakewood Nursing Home*
1112 N Eastern Ave, Plainfield, IL, 60544 (815) 436-3400
Admin Wanda J Mattix.
Licensure Skilled Care. *Beds* 46. *Certified* Medicaid.
Ownership Proprietary.

POLO

Polo Continental Manor Inc
703 E Buffalo St, Polo, IL, 61064 (815) 946-2203
Admin Len L Huff. *Medical Dir/Dir of Nursing* Dr Franklin Swan.
Licensure Intermediate Care. *Beds* 81. *Certified* Medicaid.
Ownership Proprietary.

Admissions Requirements Medical examination.
Staff RNs 3 (ft), 2 (pt); LPNs 3 (ft), 4 (pt); Nurses aides 12 (ft), 6 (pt); Physical therapists 1 (pt); Activities coordinators 1 (ft), 2 (pt); Dietitians 1 (pt); Dentists 1 (pt); Ophthalmologists 1 (pt).
Description Facility is located in a rural area, characterized by exceptional community involvement.

PONTIAC

Evenglow Lodge*
215 E Washington, Pontiac, IL, 61764 (815) 844-6131
Admin Alexander Weinbender.
Licensure Intermediate Care; Shelter Care. *Beds* ICF 42; Shelter Care 128.
Ownership Nonprofit.

Humiston Haven
300 W Lowell, Pontiac, IL, 61764 (815) 842-1181
Admin Roberta S Doran. *Medical Dir/Dir of Nursing* Harold Schroder MD.
Licensure Intermediate Care. *Beds* ICF 90. *Certified* Medicaid.
Ownership Nonprofit.
Admissions Requirements Minimum age 60; Medical examination.
Staff RNs 4 (ft), 3 (pt); LPNs 3 (ft), 3 (pt); Orderlies 1 (pt); Nurses aides 28 (ft), 12 (pt); Activities coordinators 3 (ft).
Facilities Dining room; Physical therapy room; Chapel; Crafts room; Barber/Beauty shop; Library.
Activities Arts and Crafts; Cards; Games; Prayer groups; Movies; Dances/Social or cultural gatherings.
Description Facility features one-story construction with complete fire protection system of sprinklers and smoke detectors. Located in a rural community that is friendly and supportive. Highly qualified staff with all nursing assistants certified by education or experience by the Illinois Department of Public Health.

Livingston Manor
Rt 1, Pontiac, IL, 61764 (815) 844-5121
Admin Annevieve L Klien. *Medical Dir/Dir of Nursing* L S Lowenthal.
Licensure Intermediate Care. *Beds* 125. *Certified* Medicaid.
Ownership Public.
Admissions Requirements Minimum age 18; Medical examination.
Staff Physicians 1 (pt); RNs 2 (ft); LPNs 8 (ft), 3 (pt); Orderlies 2 (ft); Nurses aides 42 (ft), 10 (pt); Recreational therapists 2 (ft), 2 (pt).
Facilities Dining room; Physical therapy room; Activities room; Chapel; Crafts room; Laundry room; Barber/Beauty shop.
Activities Arts and Crafts; Cards; Games; Reading groups; Prayer groups; Movies; Shopping trips; Dances/Social or cultural gatherings.

PRAIRIE CITY

Prairie City Nursing Center*
Rt 2, Prairie City, IL, 61470 (309) 775-3313
Admin Jeanette A Rutherford.
Licensure Intermediate Care. *Beds* 49. *Certified* Medicaid.
Ownership Proprietary.

PRINCETON

Colonial Hall Nursing Home*
515 S 6th St, Princeton, IL, 61356 (815) 875-3347
Admin Larry R Patterson.
Licensure Skilled Care. *Beds* 72.
Ownership Proprietary.

Greenfield Home
508 Park Ave E, Princeton, IL, 61356 (815) 872-2261
Admin Barbara M Mueller. *Medical Dir/Dir of Nursing* Greg Davis.
Licensure Shelter Care. *Beds* 40.
Ownership Proprietary.
Admissions Requirements Minimum age 55; Medical examination.
Staff RNs 3 (pt); LPNs 2 (pt); Nurses aides 6 (ft), 4 (pt); Activities coordinators 1 (ft).
Facilities Dining room; Activities room.
Activities Arts and Crafts; Cards; Games; Reading groups; Prayer groups; Movies; Shopping trips.

Prairie View Nursing Home
Rt 5, Princeton, IL, 61356 (815) 875-1196
Admin George E Maupin. *Medical Dir/Dir of Nursing* Kent McQueen MD.
Licensure Skilled Care; Intermediate Care; Sheltered Care. *Beds* 160.
Ownership Public.
Admissions Requirements Minimum age 18; Medical examination; Physician's request.
Staff RNs 5 (ft), 2 (pt); LPNs 9 (ft), 3 (pt); Orderlies 2 (pt); Nurses aides 48 (ft), 13 (pt); Physical therapists 1 (pt); Recreational therapists 3 (ft); Occupational therapists 1 (pt); Activities coordinators 1 (ft); Dietitians 1 (pt); Dentists 1 (pt); Podiatrists 1 (pt).
Facilities Dining room; Physical therapy room; Activities room; Chapel; Crafts room; Laundry room; Barber/Beauty shop; Library.
Activities Arts and Crafts; Cards; Games; Reading groups; Prayer groups; Movies; Shopping trips.
Description Facility is a county-owned and operated nursing home located in a rural setting in Bureau County.

Roosevelt Square Princeton
1015 Park Ave E, Princeton, IL, 61356 (815) 875-1144
Admin Frank C Devantier. *Medical Dir/Dir of Nursing* E L Johnson MD.
Licensure Intermediate Care. *Beds* 63. *Certified* Medicaid.
Ownership Proprietary.
Staff RNs 1 (ft); LPNs 3 (ft), 3 (pt); Orderlies 3 (ft); Nurses aides 10 (ft), 8 (pt); Activities coordinators 1 (ft).

PROPHETSTOWN

Prophets Riverview
310 Mosher Dr, Prophetstown, IL, 61277 (815) 537-5175
Admin Shirley J Lintner. *Medical Dir/Dir of Nursing* Dr Bradley Meck.
Licensure Intermediate Care. *Beds* 68. *Certified* Medicaid.
Ownership Nonprofit.
Admissions Requirements Medical examination; Physician's request.
Staff RNs 1 (ft), 5 (pt); LPNs 1 (ft), 3 (pt); Nurses aides 10 (ft), 21 (pt); Activities coordinators 1 (ft).
Facilities Dining room; Physical therapy room; Activities room; Chapel; Crafts room; Laundry room; Barber/Beauty shop; Library.
Activities Arts and Crafts; Cards; Games; Reading groups; Prayer groups; Movies; Shopping trips; Dances/Social or cultural gatherings.
Description This is a long-term care facility in a Christian setting for intermediate care residents; holistic care, not only physical, but emotional, mental, social, and spiritual as well, given for more than 60 years. Believe that "In Christ's love, everyone is someone."

Winning Wheels Inc
Rt 3, Box 12A, Prophetstown, IL, 61277 (815) 537-5168
Admin Paul S Yackley. *Medical Dir/Dir of Nursing* Dr Joseph Neiweem.
Licensure Skilled Care. *Beds* 76. *Certified* Medicaid.
Ownership Proprietary.
Admissions Requirements Minimum age 18; Medical examination.
Staff Physicians 3 (pt); RNs 4 (ft); LPNs 8 (ft); Orderlies 6 (ft); Nurses aides 18 (ft), 6 (pt); Physical therapists 1 (pt); Recreational therapists 1 (pt); Occupational therapists 1 (pt); Speech therapists 1 (pt); Activities coordinators 1 (pt); Dietitians 1 (pt); Dentists 2 (pt); Podiatrists 1 (pt).
Facilities Dining room; Physical therapy room; Activities room; Chapel; Crafts room; Laundry room; Barber/Beauty shop; Library.
Activities Arts and Crafts; Cards; Games; Prayer groups; Movies; Shopping trips; Dances/Social or cultural gatherings.
Description Residents are mentally alert adults who are fully or partially confined to wheelchairs.

QUINCY

Christian Shelticenter
1340 N 10th St, Quincy, IL, 62301 (217) 222-0083
Admin Ruth A Lefoe.
Licensure Shelter Care. *Beds* 212.
Ownership Proprietary.
Admissions Requirements Minimum age 18; Medical examination.

Good Samaritan Home*
2130 Harrison St, Quincy, IL, 62301 (217) 223-8717
Admin Larry M Watson.

Licensure Intermediate Care; Shelter Care.
Beds ICF 102; Shelter Care 105.
Ownership Nonprofit.

Lincoln Hill Nursing Home
1440 N 10th St, Quincy, IL, 62301 (217) 224-3780
Admin Kenneth Newell. *Medical Dir/Dir of Nursing* Dr Laping.
Licensure Skilled Care; Intermediate Care. *Beds* 99. *Certified* Medicaid.
Ownership Proprietary.
Admissions Requirements Minimum age 18; Medical examination.
Staff RNs; LPNs; Orderlies; Nurses aides; Physical therapists; Recreational therapists; Speech therapists; Dietitians; Dentists; Podiatrists; Audiologists.
Facilities Dining room; Physical therapy room; Activities room; Barber/Beauty shop.
Activities Arts and Crafts; Cards; Games; Reading groups; Prayer groups; Movies; Shopping trips; Dances/Social or cultural gatherings.

Quinsippi Long Term Care Facility
720 Sycamore St, Quincy, IL, 62301 (217) 222-1480
Admin Theodore M DeBonis. *Medical Dir/Dir of Nursing* Theodore Stebbins.
Licensure Skilled Care; Intermediate Care. *Beds* SNF 94; ICF 120. *Certified* Medicaid; Medicare.
Ownership Proprietary.
Admissions Requirements Minimum age 18.
Staff Physicians 1 (ft); RNs 5 (ft), 3 (pt); LPNs 13 (ft), 9 (pt); Orderlies 2 (ft); Nurses aides 49 (ft), 16 (pt); Activities coordinators 3 (ft).
Facilities Dining room; Physical therapy room; Activities room; Chapel; Crafts room; Laundry room; Barber/Beauty shop.
Activities Arts and Crafts; Cards; Games; Reading groups; Prayer groups; Movies; Shopping trips; Dances/Social or cultural gatherings.
Description Facility is situated in a residential area on a beautiful landscaped city block; bright, cheerful interior and many talented employees to assist and care for residents makes Quinsippi a fine facility. Large physical therapy department dominates the area as one of the finest physical therapy service areas.

Sunset Home of the United Methodist Church
418 Washington St, Quincy, IL, 62301 (217) 223-2636
Admin Herbert A Crede. *Medical Dir/Dir of Nursing* Dr Theodore Stebbins.
Licensure Intermediate Care; Shelter Care.
Beds ICF 119; Shelter Care 129.
Ownership Nonprofit.
Admissions Requirements Minimum age 65; Medical examination.
Staff RNs 4 (ft); LPNs 21 (ft), 14 (pt); Physical therapists 1 (pt); Occupational therapists 1 (pt); Speech therapists 1 (pt); Activities coordinators 1 (ft); Dietitians 1 (pt); Dentists 1 (pt).
Affiliation Methodist
Facilities Dining room; Physical therapy room; Activities room; Chapel; Laundry room; Barber/Beauty shop; Library.
Activities Arts and Crafts; Cards; Games; Movies; Shopping trips; Dances/Social or cultural gatherings.
Description Perched on the bluff high over the

Mississippi, residents of Sunset Home enjoy a birds-eye view of river traffic between Memorial Bridge and lock and dam number 21. They also enjoy a program of activities within and outside facility, a protective environment planned for the fullest life of the senior.

RED BUD

Red Bud Care Center*
350 W South 1st St, Red Bud, IL, 62278 (618) 282-3891
Admin Judith A Horrell.
Licensure Skilled Care. *Beds* 112. *Certified* Medicaid.

RICHTON PARK

Richton Crossing Convalescent Center
Imperial Dr and Cicero Ave, Richton Park, IL, 60471 (312) 747-6120
Admin Roberta Magurany. *Medical Dir/Dir of Nursing* Dr David Jaffray.
Licensure Skilled Care. *Beds* 294.
Ownership Proprietary.
Admissions Requirements Medical examination.
Staff Physicians 7 (pt); RNs 9 (ft), 3 (pt); LPNs 10 (ft), 9 (pt); Orderlies 6 (ft), 2 (pt); Nurses aides 56 (ft), 16 (pt); Physical therapists 1 (ft); Reality therapists 1 (ft); Recreational therapists 5 (ft), 3 (pt); Occupational therapists 1 (ft); Speech therapists 1 (ft); Activities coordinators 1 (ft); Dietitians 1 (ft); Dentists 2 (pt); Ophthalmologists 1 (pt); Podiatrists 4 (pt); Audiologists 1 (ft).
Facilities Dining room; Physical therapy room; Activities room; Crafts room; Laundry room; Barber/Beauty shop; Library.
Activities Arts and Crafts; Cards; Games; Movies; Shopping trips; Dances/Social or cultural gatherings.
Description Understanding, caring, professional—these words form the cornerstone for the recuperation program that has been established for the Richton Crossing Convalescent Center. "Where Love Is."

RIDGWAY

Ridgway Manor Inc*
Rt 1, Box 181A, Ridgway, IL, 62979 (618) 272-8831
Admin Gennia S Canimore.
Licensure Intermediate Care. *Beds* 71. *Certified* Medicaid.
Ownership Proprietary.

RIVERSIDE

Scottish Home
28th and Des Plaines Rd, Riverside, IL, 60546 (312) 447-5092
Admin Delbertt M Carlson. *Medical Dir/Dir of Nursing* Howard Hane MD.
Licensure Intermediate Care; Sheltered Care. *Beds* ICF 14; Sheltered Care 48.
Ownership Nonprofit.
Admissions Requirements Minimum age 60; Medical examination.

Facilities Dining room; Physical therapy room; Activities room; Crafts room; Laundry room; Barber/Beauty shop; Library.
Activities Arts and Crafts; Cards; Movies; Shopping trips.

ROANOKE

Apostolic Christian Home*
1102 W Randolph, Roanoke, IL, 61561 (309) 923-5541
Admin Frank J Crawford.
Licensure Intermediate Care. *Beds* 75.
Ownership Nonprofit.
Affiliation Apostolic Christian

ROBBINS

Esma A Wright Pavilion
13901 Lydia Ave, Robbins, IL, 60472 (312) 385-8700
Admin Allen L Wright III.
Licensure Intermediate Care. *Beds* ICF 225. *Certified* Medicaid.
Ownership Proprietary.
Admissions Requirements Minimum age 18; Medical examination.
Staff Physicians 1 (ft), 6 (pt); RNs 2 (ft), 2 (pt); LPNs 18 (ft); Orderlies 8 (ft); Nurses aides 31 (ft); Physical therapists 1 (pt); Reality therapists 1 (pt); Recreational therapists 1 (ft); Occupational therapists 1 (pt); Activities coordinators 1 (ft); Dietitians 1 (ft); Dentists 1 (pt); Ophthalmologists 1 (pt); Podiatrists 1 (pt).
Facilities Dining room; Physical therapy room; Activities room; Chapel; Crafts room; Laundry room; Barber/Beauty shop; Library; Gift shop; Coffee shop; Boutique (free clothes); Pool hall.
Activities Arts and Crafts; Cards; Games; Reading groups; Prayer groups; Movies; Shopping trips; Dances/Social or cultural gatherings; Fashion shows; Private bus service.
Description Facility is oriented toward returning residents to independent community living.

ROBINSON

Cotillion Ridge Nursing Center
Rt 3, Robinson, IL, 62454 (618) 544-3192
Admin Gerald J Opiela.
Licensure Intermediate Care. *Beds* 69. *Certified* Medicaid.
Ownership Proprietary.
Admissions Requirements Minimum age 28; Medical examination.
Staff RNs 3 (ft), 1 (pt); LPNs 1 (ft), 2 (pt); Activities coordinators 1 (ft), 1 (pt).
Facilities Dining room; Physical therapy room; Laundry room; Barber/Beauty shop.
Activities Arts and Crafts; Cards; Games; Movies; Shopping trips.

Crawford County Convalescent Center Inc
902 W Mefford St, Robinson, IL, 62454 (618) 546-5638
Medical Dir/Dir of Nursing D J Pelley MD.
Licensure Intermediate Care. *Beds* 54. *Certified* Medicaid.
Ownership Proprietary.
Staff Physicians 4 (pt); RNs 3 (ft); LPNs 2 (ft),

1 (pt); Nurses aides 11 (ft), 3 (pt); Physical therapists 1 (pt); Recreational therapists 1 (pt); Speech therapists 1 (pt); Activities coordinators 1 (ft); Dietitians 1 (pt); Dentists 1 (pt); Podiatrists 1 (pt).
Facilities Dining room; Physical therapy room; Activities room; Laundry room; Barber/Beauty shop.
Activities Arts and Crafts; Cards; Games; Reading groups; Prayer groups; Shopping trips.

ROCHELLE

Rochelle Manor*
Caron Rd, Rochelle, IL, 61068 (815) 562-4047
Admin Mary Ann Hall.
Licensure Intermediate Care. *Beds* 74. *Certified* Medicaid.
Ownership Proprietary.

Rochelle Nursing and Rehabilitation Center
900 N 3rd St, Rochelle, IL, 61068 (815) 562-4111
Admin Nancy E Wolford. *Medical Dir/Dir of Nursing* L T Koritz MD.
Licensure Skilled Care; Intermediate Care. *Beds* 50. *Certified* Medicaid; Medicare.
Ownership Proprietary.
Admissions Requirements Minimum age 19.
Staff RNs 2 (ft), 4 (pt); LPNs 3 (pt); Nurses aides 10 (ft), 10 (pt); Recreational therapists 1 (ft); Activities coordinators 1 (ft).
Facilities Dining room; Physical therapy room; Activities room; Laundry room; Barber/Beauty shop.
Activities Arts and Crafts; Cards; Games; Reading groups; Prayer groups; Movies; Shopping trips; Dances/Social or cultural gatherings.
Description For the last 2 summers, rural area facility has had a "farm day"; staff dresses in overalls, buffet dinner is served, bales of straw and hay are set around facility, and posters of farm equipment are used for decoration; live animals such as horses, dogs, goats, ducks, rabbits, chickens, and cows are placed outside for patients to see and pet.

ROCK FALLS

Colonial Acres*
1000 Dixon Ave, Rock Falls, IL, 61071 (815) 625-8510
Admin Donna M Lattimer.
Licensure Skilled Care. *Beds* 55. *Certified* Medicaid; Medicare.
Ownership Proprietary.

Rock Falls Manor*
430 Martin Rd, Rock Falls, IL, 61071 (815) 626-4575
Admin William C Krzykowski.
Licensure Intermediate Care. *Beds* 57. *Certified* Medicaid.
Ownership Proprietary.

ROCK ISLAND

Friendship Manor
1209 21st Ave, Rock Island, IL, 61201 (309) 786-9667
Admin Larry G Howell. *Medical Dir/Dir of*

Nursing John M Peterson MD.
Licensure Skilled Care; Sheltered care.
Beds 60.
Ownership Nonprofit.
Admissions Requirements Minimum age 65; Medical examination.
Staff RNs 8 (ft); LPNs 5 (ft); Nurses aides 24 (ft); Physical therapists 1 (pt); Recreational therapists 1 (pt); Occupational therapists 1 (pt); Speech therapists 1 (pt); Activities coordinators 2 (ft), 2 (pt).
Facilities Dining room; Physical therapy room; Activities room; Chapel; Crafts room; Laundry room; Barber/Beauty shop; Library.
Activities Arts and Crafts; Cards; Games; Reading groups; Prayer groups; Movies; Shopping trips; Dances/Social or cultural gatherings.
Description Friendship Manor is a life-care facility with 231 independent nursing units, 30 sheltered care units, and a 60-bed skilled nursing home featuring full service—housekeeping, laundry, activities, security, transportation, emergency call system, dining room, maintenance, and other supportive residents services.

Rock Island Convalescent Center*
2545 24th St, Rock Island, IL, 61201 (309) 788-0458
Admin Tina Fehr.
Licensure Skilled Care. *Beds* 117. *Certified* Medicaid; Medicare.
Ownership Proprietary.

Rock Island County Health Care Center*
2122 25th Ave, Rock Island, IL, 61201 (309) 786-4429
Admin David W Johansen.
Licensure Skilled Care. *Beds* 83. *Certified* Medicaid.
Ownership Public.

Saint Anthonys Continuing Care Center*
767 30th St, Rock Island, IL, 61201 (309) 788-7631
Admin Mother Mary Anthony.
Licensure Skilled Care; Intermediate Care.
Beds SNF 143; ICF 46. *Certified* Medicaid; Medicare.
Ownership Nonprofit.
Affiliation Roman Catholic

ROCKFORD

Alma Nelson Manor*
550 S Mulford Rd, Rockford, IL, 61108 (815) 399-4914
Admin Barbara A Peterson.
Licensure Skilled Care. *Beds* 174. *Certified* Medicaid; Medicare.
Ownership Proprietary.

Alpine Fireside Health Center*
3650 N Alpine Rd, Rockford, IL, 61111 (815) 877-7408
Admin Kenneth E Alberts.
Licensure Intermediate Care; Shelter Care.
Beds ICF 47; Shelter Care 80.
Ownership Proprietary.

Amberwood Health Care Centre
2313 N Rockton Ave, Rockford, IL, 61103 (815) 964-4611
Admin Irene Y Johnson. *Medical Dir/Dir of Nursing* Dr Harry Darland.
Licensure Skilled Care. *Beds* 160. *Certified* Medicaid; Medicare.
Ownership Proprietary.
Staff RNs 6 (ft), 7 (pt); LPNs 3 (ft), 2 (pt); Nurses aides 15 (ft), 36 (pt); Physical therapists 1 (pt); Recreational therapists 4 (ft), 2 (pt); Occupational therapists 2 (pt); Speech therapists 1 (pt); Activities coordinators 1 (ft); Dietitians 1 (pt); Podiatrists 1 (pt).
Facilities Dining room; Physical therapy room; Activities room; Crafts room; Laundry room; Barber/Beauty shop.
Activities Arts and Crafts; Cards; Games; Reading groups; Prayer groups; Movies; Shopping trips; Dances/Social or cultural gatherings; Trips to zoo, Metro Centre.
Description Amberwood has a very active volunteer program with ages ranging from 10-70. The rehabilitation department consists of physical, occupational, and speech therapy department. Direct care is also provided in each of these areas. We also have the distinction of having a private section called Williamsburg Section. This section is elegantly decorated and serviced, includes both private and semi-private rooms, and a private dining room.

Briar Glen Healthcare Centre*
321 Arnold, Rockford, IL, 61108 (815) 397-5531
Admin Thomas A Drog.
Licensure Skilled Care; Intermediate Care.
Beds SNF 74; ICF 129. *Certified* Medicaid; Medicare.
Ownership Proprietary.

Deacon Home Ltd*
611 N Court St, Rockford, IL, 61103 (815) 964-0234
Admin Ivan Gibbs.
Licensure Shelter Care. *Beds* 16.
Ownership Proprietary.

Fairhaven Christian Home
3470 N Alpine Rd, Rockford, IL, 61111 (815) 877-1441
Admin Marvin E Johnson.
Licensure Intermediate Care; Sheltered Care.
Beds ICF 96; Sheltered Care 148.
Ownership Nonprofit.
Admissions Requirements Minimum age 65; Medical examination.
Staff RNs 10 (ft); LPNs 8 (ft); Nurses aides 60 (ft); Physical therapists 1 (ft); Recreational therapists 1 (ft); Activities coordinators 1 (ft); Dietitians 1 (ft).
Affiliation Evangelical Free Church
Facilities Dining room; Physical therapy room; Activities room; Chapel; Crafts room; Laundry room; Barber/Beauty shop; Library; Game room.
Activities Arts and Crafts; Games; Reading groups; Prayer groups; Movies; Shopping trips; Dances/Social or cultural gatherings.

Fountain Terrace*
6131 Park Ridge Rd, Rockford, IL, 61111 (815) 633-6810

Admin Larry Bingham.
Licensure Skilled Care. *Beds* 54.
Ownership Proprietary.

Highview Retirement Home*
4149 Safford Rd, Rockford, IL, 61103 (815) 964-3368
Admin Myrta J Smith.
Licensure Intermediate Care; Shelter Care.
Beds ICF 16; Shelter Care 33.
Ownership Nonprofit.

Maria Linden*
5360 Springbrook Rd, Rockford, IL, 61111 (815) 877-7416
Admin Sr Rose M Bushman.
Licensure Intermediate Care; Shelter Care.
Beds ICF 43; Shelter Care 65.
Ownership Nonprofit.

North Rockford Convalescent Home
1920 N Main St, Rockford, IL, 61103 (815) 964-6834
Admin Lloyd W Bower. *Medical Dir/Dir of Nursing* Karen Sloan.
Licensure Intermediate Care. *Beds* 97. *Certified* Medicaid.
Ownership Nonprofit.
Admissions Requirements Medical examination.
Staff RNs 6 (ft), 1 (pt); LPNs 8 (ft), 1 (pt); Orderlies 1 (ft); Nurses aides 34 (ft), 9 (pt); Physical therapists 1 (pt); Reality therapists 1 (pt); Activities coordinators 1 (ft); Dietitians 1 (pt); Dentists 1 (pt); Podiatrists 1 (pt).
Affiliation Methodist
Facilities Dining room; Physical therapy room; Activities room; Crafts room; Laundry room; Barber/Beauty shop; Library.
Activities Arts and Crafts; Cards; Games; Reading groups; Prayer groups; Movies; Shopping trips.
Description Very strong rehabilitation program; temporary placements welcome; excellent 24-hour nursing care; religious services for all faiths; family-oriented home has love and laughter.

P A Peterson Home for the Aging
1311 Parkview Ave, Rockford, IL, 61107 (815) 399-8832
Admin Elmer W Johnson. *Medical Dir/Dir of Nursing* William Gorski MD.
Licensure Intermediate Care; Sheltered Care.
Beds ICF 58; Sheltered Care 103.
Ownership Nonprofit.
Admissions Requirements Minimum age 62.
Staff RNs 3 (ft), 3 (pt); LPNs 5 (ft), 1 (pt); Nurses aides 19 (ft), 22 (pt); Activities coordinators 3 (ft); Dietitians 1 (ft).
Affiliation Lutheran
Facilities Dining room; Physical therapy room; Activities room; Chapel; Crafts room; Laundry room; Barber/Beauty shop; Library.
Activities Arts and Crafts; Cards; Games; Reading groups; Prayer groups; Movies; Shopping trips; Dances/Social or cultural gatherings.

Park Strathmoor*
5668 Strathmoor Dr, Rockford, IL, 61107 (815) 229-5200
Admin Charles N Debes.

Licensure Skilled Care; Intermediate Care. *Beds* 189. *Certified* Medicaid; Medicare. *Ownership* Proprietary.

Riverbluff Nursing Home
4401 N Main St, Rockford, IL, 61108 (815) 877-8061
Admin John M Ross. *Medical Dir/Dir of Nursing* Warren C Lewis MD.
Licensure Skilled Care; Intermediate Care. *Beds* 300. *Certified* Medicaid; Medicare. *Ownership* Public.
Admissions Requirements Minimum age 18; Medical examination; Physician's request.
Staff Physicians 2 (pt); RNs 18 (ft), 2 (pt); LPNs 18 (ft), 2 (pt); Nurses aides 100 (ft), 50 (pt); Physical therapists 1 (ft); Occupational therapists 1 (pt); Speech therapists 1 (pt); Activities coordinators 1 (ft); Dietitians 1 (pt); Dentists 1 (pt); Ophthalmologists 1 (pt); Podiatrists 1 (pt).
Facilities Dining room; Physical therapy room; Activities room; Chapel; Crafts room; Laundry room; Barber/Beauty shop; Library.
Activities Arts and Crafts; Cards; Games; Reading groups; Prayer groups; Movies; Shopping trips; Dances/Social or cultural gatherings.
Description Single-story brick structure with 4 76-bed units; skilled nursing care with 24-hour professional nurses in all 4 units; on-site pharmacy, physical therapy, dental unit, and X-ray department with priority admissions to public aid recipients.

Riverside Terrace Nursing Center Inc
707 W Riverside Blvd, Rockford, IL, 61103 (815) 877-5752
Admin Kimberly Vosmik. *Medical Dir/Dir of Nursing* Dr Mrizek.
Licensure Skilled Care; Intermediate Care. *Beds* 135. *Certified* Medicaid; Medicare. *Ownership* Proprietary.
Facilities Dining room; Physical therapy room; Activities room; Chapel; Crafts room; Laundry room; Barber/Beauty shop; Lounge areas; Pool table.
Activities Arts and Crafts; Cards; Games; Reading groups; Prayer groups; Movies; Shopping trips; Dances/Social or cultural gatherings.
Description Facility is near the Rock River in a beautiful wooded area; offers personable, friendly service and individualized programs. JCAH accredited.

Rockford Manor Inc
310 Arnold Ave, Rockford, IL, 61108 (815) 398-7954
Admin Marilyn Gibson. *Medical Dir/Dir of Nursing* Dr Warren Lewis.
Licensure Intermediate Care. *Beds* 81. *Certified* Medicaid. *Ownership* Proprietary.
Admissions Requirements Minimum age 55; Medical examination; Physician's request.
Staff RNs 1 (pt); LPNs 4 (ft), 2 (pt); Orderlies 1 (ft); Nurses aides 7 (ft), 12 (pt); Physical therapists 1 (pt); Activities coordinators 2 (ft); Dietitians 1 (pt); Dentists 1 (pt); Podiatrists 1 (pt).
Facilities Dining room; Activities room; Crafts room; Laundry room; Barber/Beauty shop.
Activities Arts and Crafts; Cards; Games; Reading groups; Prayer groups; Movies; Shopping trips; Dances/Social or cultural gatherings.

Description Facility is on one floor; all residents are geriatric. Facility gives heavier nursing care than most ICF in area and is applying for day care.

Roosevelt Square
3520 School St, Rockford, IL, 61103 (815) 968-4280
Admin Elizabeth J Lyons.
Licensure Intermediate Care. *Beds* 63. *Certified* Medicaid. *Ownership* Proprietary.
Admissions Requirements Minimum age 21; Medical examination; Physician's request.
Staff Physicians 1 (pt); RNs 2 (ft), 1 (pt); LPNs 2 (ft), 2 (pt); Nurses aides 7 (ft), 2 (pt); Activities coordinators; Dietitians; Dentists; Podiatrists.
Facilities Dining room; Activities room; Crafts room; Laundry room.
Activities Arts and Crafts; Cards; Games; Reading groups; Prayer groups; Movies; Shopping trips; Dances/Social or cultural gatherings; Daily exercises; Intellectural activities; Community involvement; Remotivation therapy; Reality orientation; Music therapy.
Description Facility provides intermediate nursing care in a retirement setting.

Walter J Lawson Memorial Home for Children*
1820 Walter Lawson Dr, Rockford, IL, 61111 (815) 654-2536
Admin Theo A Brandle.
Licensure Intermediate Care. *Beds* 83. *Ownership* Nonprofit.

Willows Health Center
4141 N Rockton Ave, Rockford, IL, 61103 (815) 654-2534
Admin Edwin S Hunt. *Medical Dir/Dir of Nursing* Dr Craig Rogers.
Licensure Skilled Care; Sheltered Care. *Beds* SNF 76; Sheltered Care 206. *Ownership* Nonprofit.
Admissions Requirements Minimum age 62; Medical examination.
Staff Physicians 1 (pt); RNs 21 (ft); LPNs 18 (ft); Nurses aides 32 (ft); Physical therapists 3 (ft); Recreational therapists 3 (ft); Occupational therapists 3 (ft); Speech therapists 1 (pt); Activities coordinators 7 (ft); Dietitians 1 (pt); Dentists 1 (pt); Podiatrists 1 (pt).
Affiliation Methodist
Facilities Dining room; Physical therapy room; Activities room; Chapel; Crafts room; Laundry room; Barber/Beauty shop; Library.
Activities Arts and Crafts; Cards; Games; Reading groups; Prayer groups; Movies; Shopping trips; Dances/Social or cultural gatherings.
Description Center is located in the fringe area of the city and is completely surrounded by country, over the crest of a hill so that the city is not visible. With the stately white pillars, facility has the appearance of colonial Williamsburg.

ROLLING MEADOWS

Americana Healthcare Center
4225 Kirchoff Rd, Rolling Meadows, IL, 60008 (312) 397-2400

Admin Joy P Rathe.
Licensure Skilled Care; Intermediate Care. *Beds* 155. *Certified* Medicaid; Medicare. *Ownership* Proprietary.
Admissions Requirements Medical examination.
Staff Physicians 2 (pt); RNs; LPNs; Orderlies; Nurses aides; Physical therapists 1 (ft), 2 (pt); Recreational therapists 1 (ft); Occupational therapists 1 (pt); Speech therapists 1 (pt); Activities coordinators 1 (ft); Dietitians 1 (pt); Dentists 1 (pt); Podiatrists 1 (pt).
Facilities Dining room; Physical therapy room; Activities room; Crafts room; Laundry room; Barber/Beauty shop.
Activities Arts and Crafts; Cards; Games; Reading groups; Prayer groups; Movies; Shopping trips; Dances/Social or cultural gatherings.

The Meadows
3250 S Plum Grove Rd, Rolling Meadows, IL, 60008
Admin Byrn Witt. *Medical Dir/Dir of Nursing* Dr Petel.
Licensure Intermediate Care for Mentally Retarded. *Certified* Medicaid. *Ownership* Proprietary.
Admissions Requirements Minimum age 18; Medical examination.
Staff Physicians 1 (pt); RNs 2 (ft), 2 (pt); LPNs 3 (ft), 4 (pt); Nurses aides 5 (ft); Physical therapists 1 (pt); Recreational therapists 1 (pt); Occupational therapists 1 (pt); Speech therapists 1 (pt); Activities coordinators 1 (ft); Dietitians 1 (pt); Dentists 1 (pt); Ophthalmologists 1 (pt); Podiatrists 1 (pt); Audiologists 1 (pt); Acting aides 8 (ft); Rehabilitation aides 10 (ft).
Facilities Dining room; Physical therapy room; Activities room; Crafts room; Laundry room; Barber/Beauty shop.
Activities Arts and Crafts; Games; Reading groups; Movies; Shopping trips; Dances/Social or cultural gatherings.
Description This facility serves developmentally disabled adults needing medical oversight; offers special programs for behaviorally handicapped people.

ROSELLE

Abbington House*
31 W Central, Roselle, IL, 60172 (312) 894-5058
Admin Marvin Struck.
Licensure Intermediate Care. *Beds* 75. *Certified* Medicaid. *Ownership* Proprietary.

ROSELLEADD

Sunrise Courts*
439 Lawrence, Roselle-Add, IL, 60172 (312) 543-2440
Admin James Durnbaugh.
Licensure Intermediate Care. *Beds* 20. *Ownership* Nonprofit.

ROSEVILLE

La Moine Christian Nursing Home
Box 347, Roseville, IL, 61473 (309) 426-2134
Admin James M Oliver. *Medical Dir/Dir of Nursing* Dr R E Icenogle.
Licensure Skilled Care; Intermediate Care.
Beds SNF 39; ICF 60. *Certified* Medicaid.
Ownership Nonprofit.
Admissions Requirements Minimum age 18.
Staff RNs 6 (ft), 4 (pt); LPNs 4 (ft), 3 (pt);
Nurses aides 26 (ft), 17 (pt); Physical therapists
1 (ft), 1 (pt); Speech therapists 1 (pt); Activities
coordinators 1 (ft), 2 (pt); Dietitians 5 (ft), 7
(pt).
Facilities Dining room; Physical therapy room;
Activities room; Chapel; Crafts room; Laundry
room; Barber/Beauty shop; Library.
Activities Arts and Crafts; Games; Reading
groups; Prayer groups; Movies; Shopping trips.
Description Facility is church sponsored and a
large number of staff are active church members; large church-related auxilary program.

ROSICLARE

Fairview House Nursing Home*
Fairview Rd, Rosiclare, IL, 62982 (618)
285-6613
Admin James C Stunson.
Licensure Intermediate Care. *Beds* 49. *Certified* Medicaid.
Ownership Proprietary.

ROUND LAKE

Hillcrest Retirement Village Inc*
1740 N Circuit Dr, Round Lake, IL, 60073
(312) 546-5301
Admin Shearon A Teaters.
Licensure Intermediate Care. *Beds* 93. *Certified* Medicaid.
Ownership Proprietary.

RUSHVILLE

Snyders Vaughn-Haven Inc*
135 S Morgan St, Rushville, IL, 62681 (217)
322-3420
Admin John R Snyder.
Licensure Intermediate Care. *Beds* 99. *Certified* Medicaid.
Ownership Proprietary.

SAINT CHARLES

Pine View Care Center*
611 Allen Ln, Saint Charles, IL, 60174 (312)
377-2211
Admin Mary Bowman.
Licensure Skilled Care. *Beds* 120.
Ownership Proprietary.

SAINT ELMO

Heritage Home Care Center
Rt 40, E Cumberland Rd, Saint Elmo, IL,
62458 (618) 829-5581
Admin Nancy L Pryor. *Medical Dir/Dir of*

Nursing Dr Hasin Shah.
Licensure Intermediate Care. *Beds* 49. *Certified* Medicaid.
Ownership Proprietary.
Admissions Requirements Minimum age 18.
Staff Physicians 5 (pt); RNs 5 (pt); LPNs 4
(pt); Nurses aides 10 (ft), 9 (pt); Physical therapists 1 (pt); Speech therapists 1 (pt); Activities
coordinators 1 (pt); Dietitians 1 (pt); Dentists 1
(pt); Podiatrists 1 (pt).
Facilities Dining room; Activities room; Crafts
room; Laundry room; Barber/Beauty shop.
Activities Arts and Crafts; Cards; Games;
Reading groups; Prayer groups; Movies; Shopping trips; Dances/Social or cultural gatherings.
Description Facility is located in a quiet, rural
setting surrounded by small, homey town.

SALEM

Bryan Manor*
PO Box 687, Rt 37 N, Salem, IL, 62881 (618)
548-4561
Admin Dennis K Headlee.
Licensure Intermediate Care. *Beds* 82.
Ownership Nonprofit.

Doctors Nursing Home*
Hawthorn Rd, Salem, IL, 62881
Admin Philip E Pennington.
Licensure Skilled Care. *Beds* 120. *Certified* Medicaid; Medicare.
Ownership Proprietary.

Twin Willow Nursing Center*
Rt 37 N, Salem, IL, 62881 (618) 548-0542
Admin Todd C Woodruff.
Licensure Intermediate Care. *Beds* 76. *Certified* Medicaid.
Ownership Proprietary.

SANDWICH

Roosevelt Square
902 E Arnold Ave, Sandwich, IL, 60548 (815)
786-8400
Admin Marie Vahl. *Medical Dir/Dir of
Nursing* Dr O H Fischer.
Licensure Intermediate Care. *Beds* 63. *Certified* Medicaid.
Ownership Proprietary.
Staff RNs 2 (ft), 3 (pt); LPNs 2 (ft); Nurses
aides 10 (ft), 10 (pt); Activities coordinators 1
(ft).
Facilities Dining room; Activities room; Crafts
room; Laundry room; Barber/Beauty shop.
Activities Arts and Crafts; Cards; Games;
Reading groups; Shopping trips; Dances/Social
or cultural gatherings.

Sandhaven Convalescent Center*
515 N Main, Sandwich, IL, 60548 (815)
786-8426
Admin Richard L Soule.
Licensure Skilled Care; Intermediate Care.
Beds SNF 58; ICF 58. *Certified* Medicaid;
Medicare.
Ownership Proprietary.

SAVANNA

Big Meadows
1000 Longmoor, Savanna, IL, 61074 (815)
273-2238
Admin Vincent R Arioso.
Licensure Intermediate Care. *Beds* 122. *Certified* Medicaid.
Ownership Proprietary.

SAVOY

Savoy Terrace*
203 W Burwash Ave, Savoy, IL, 61874 (217)
351-4111
Admin William J Heise.
Licensure Skilled Care. *Beds* 240. *Certified* Medicaid; Medicare.
Ownership Proprietary.

SCHAUMBURG

Friendship Village
350 W Schaumburg Rd, Schaumburg, IL,
60194 (312) 884-5005
Admin Raymond A Kane. *Medical Dir/Dir of
Nursing* Gregory Ostrom MD.
Licensure Skilled Care; Intermediate Care.
Beds 180. *Certified* Medicare.
Ownership Nonprofit.
Admissions Requirements Medical examination.
Staff RNs 12 (ft), 16 (pt); LPNs 3 (ft), 3 (pt);
Nurses aides 46 (ft), 36 (pt); Physical therapists
1 (ft), 3 (pt); Recreational therapists 2 (ft), 2 (pt);
Occupational therapists 2 (pt); Speech therapists 1 (pt); Activities coordinators 1 (ft); Dietitians 2 (ft); Dentists 1 (pt); Ophthalmologists 1
(pt); Podiatrists 1 (pt); Audiologists 1 (pt).
Facilities Dining room; Physical therapy room;
Activities room; Chapel; Crafts room; Laundry
room; Barber/Beauty shop; Library.
Activities Arts and Crafts; Cards; Games;
Reading groups; Prayer groups; Movies; Shopping trips; Dances/Social or cultural gatherings.
Description Goal is to treat each other with dignity and respect as an atmosphere is established
conducive to promoting each resident's maximum level of independence.

Moon Lake Convalescent Center*
1545 Barrington Rd, Schaumburg, IL, 60194
(312) 884-0011
Admin Behr W Burton.
Licensure Skilled Care; Intermediate Care.
Beds SNF 154; ICF 63. *Certified* Medicaid;
Medicare.
Ownership Proprietary.

SESSER

Redwood Manor
W Franklin St, Sesser, IL, 62884 (618)
625-5261
Admin Gloria Pasko. *Medical Dir/Dir of
Nursing* Dr L Kisle.
Licensure Intermediate Care. *Beds* 58. *Certified* Medicaid.
Ownership Proprietary.
Staff Physicians 1 (pt); RNs 1 (pt); LPNs 4 (ft),
2 (pt); Orderlies 3 (ft); Nurses aides 10 (ft);

Activities coordinators 1 (ft); Dietitians 1 (pt); Dentists 1 (pt); Podiatrists 1 (pt).
Facilities Dining room; Activities room; Laundry room; Barber/Beauty shop.
Activities Arts and Crafts; Games; Prayer groups; Movies; Shopping trips; Dances/Social or cultural gatherings.

SHABBONA

Shabbona Nursing Home Inc
W Comanche St, Shabbona, IL, 60550 (815) 824-2194
Admin Jackie Goken. *Medical Dir/Dir of Nursing* Dr Robert Purdy.
Licensure Skilled Care; Intermediate Care. *Beds* 91. *Certified* Medicaid.
Ownership Proprietary.
Admissions Requirements Minimum age 21; Medical examination; Physician's request.
Staff Physicians 6 (pt); RNs 6 (ft), 3 (pt); LPNs 1 (ft), 2 (pt); Orderlies 2 (ft); Nurses aides 19 (ft), 20 (pt); Physical therapists 1 (pt); Reality therapists 1 (pt); Recreational therapists 1 (pt); Occupational therapists 1 (pt); Speech therapists 1 (pt); Activities coordinators 1 (pt); Dietitians 1 (pt); Dentists 1 (pt); Ophthalmologists 1 (pt); Podiatrists 1 (pt); Audiologists 1 (pt).
Facilities Dining room; Physical therapy room; Activities room; Chapel; Crafts room; Laundry room; Barber/Beauty shop; Library.
Activities Arts and Crafts; Cards; Games; Reading groups; Prayer groups; Movies; Shopping trips; Dances/Social or cultural gatherings.
Description Facility is one-story brick building on the edge of a small town in a farming community with a patio between wings. Physical, occupational, and speech rehabilitation programs are outstanding.

SHANNON

Villas of Shannon Nursing Home*
418 S Ridge St, Shannon, IL, 61078 (815) 864-2425
Admin Blaine Fox.
Licensure Intermediate Care. *Beds* 73. *Certified* Medicaid.
Ownership Proprietary.

SHAWNEETOWN

Loretta Nursing Home
Logan and Lincoln Sts, Shawneetown, IL, 62984 (618) 269-3109
Admin Delbert H York. *Medical Dir/Dir of Nursing* Andrew Cserny MD.
Licensure Skilled Care; Intermediate Care. *Beds* 107. *Certified* Medicaid.
Ownership Proprietary.
Admissions Requirements Minimum age 18; Medical examination; Physician's request.
Staff RNs 2 (ft), 2 (pt); LPNs 5 (ft), 4 (pt); Nurses aides 27 (ft), 7 (pt); Activities coordinators 1 (ft); Dietitians 1 (pt).

SHELBYVILLE

Reservoir Manor*
419 E Main St, Shelbyville, IL, 62565 (217) 774-5113
Admin Charlotte Cohen.
Licensure Intermediate Care. *Beds* 15.
Ownership Proprietary.

Shelby Manor
2116 S 3rd and Dacey Dr, Shelbyville, IL, 62565 (217) 774-2128
Admin Charles L Austin. *Medical Dir/Dir of Nursing* Dr Edwin Sirov.
Licensure Intermediate Care. *Beds* 80. *Certified* Medicaid.
Ownership Proprietary.
Admissions Requirements Minimum age 21; Medical examination.
Staff Physicians 6 (ft); RNs 1 (pt); LPNs 5 (ft), 1 (pt); Nurses aides 9 (ft), 9 (pt); Occupational therapists 1 (pt); Activities coordinators 1 (ft), 1 (pt); Dietitians 1 (pt); Dentists 1 (pt); Podiatrists 1 (pt).
Facilities Dining room; Activities room; Crafts room; Laundry room; Barber/Beauty shop.
Activities Arts and Crafts; Games; Reading groups; Prayer groups; Movies; Shopping trips; Dances/Social or cultural gatherings.

Shelby Memorial Home*
Rt 128 N, Shelbyville, IL, 62565 (217) 774-2111
Admin Albert E Wimer.
Licensure Skilled Care. *Beds* 99. *Certified* Medicaid.
Ownership Proprietary.

Shelby Memorial Hospital Nursing Home*
S 1st and Cedar, Shelbyville, IL, 62565 (217) 774-3961
Admin Garland Strohl.
Licensure Skilled Care. *Beds* 20. *Certified* Medicaid.
Ownership Nonprofit.

SHELDON

Sheldon Healthcare Inc
170 W Concord St, PO Box 456, Sheldon, IL, 60966 (815) 429-3522
Admin Janice K Conrad. *Medical Dir/Dir of Nursing* Dr N D Hungness.
Licensure Intermediate Care. *Beds* 31. *Certified* Medicaid.
Ownership Proprietary.
Admissions Requirements Minimum age 70; Medical examination; Physician's request.
Staff RNs 1 (ft); LPNs 3 (ft), 4 (pt); Nurses aides 6 (ft), 6 (pt); Recreational therapists 1 (ft), 1 (pt); Activities coordinators 1 (ft); Dietitians 1 (ft).
Facilities Dining room; Laundry room; Barber/Beauty shop.
Activities Arts and Crafts; Cards; Games; Reading groups; Prayer groups; Movies; Dances/Social or cultural gatherings.
Description Facility is in a country farming community of 1400 residents, one block from business district, ball park, town park, and pavillion.

SILVIS

Roosevelt Square—Silvis*
1403 9th Ave, Silvis, IL, 61282 (309) 792-8998
Admin Margaret L Trousil.
Licensure Intermediate Care. *Beds* 63. *Certified* Medicaid.
Ownership Proprietary.

SIMPSON

Shawnee Shelter Care*
Rt 1, Simpson, IL, 62985 (618) 695-3321
Admin Georgia L Brown.
Licensure Shelter Care. *Beds* 13.
Ownership Proprietary.

SKOKIE

Old Orchard Manor
4660 Old Oarchard Rd, Skokie, IL, 60076 (312) 676-4800
Admin Jane Ionescu. *Medical Dir/Dir of Nursing* Arthur R Peterson MD.
Licensure Skilled Care. *Beds* 61.
Ownership Proprietary.
Admissions Requirements Minimum age 18; Medical examination; Physician's request.
Staff RNs 6 (ft), 7 (pt); Nurses aides 16 (ft), 2 (pt); Physical therapists 3 (pt); Reality therapists 1 (pt); Recreational therapists 1 (ft), 1 (pt); Activities coordinators 1 (ft); Dietitians 1 (ft).
Facilities Dining room; Physical therapy room; Activities room; Laundry room; Barber/Beauty shop.
Activities Arts and Crafts; Cards; Games; Reading groups; Prayer groups; Movies; Shopping trips; Dances/Social or cultural gatherings.
Description Facility features a five-meal-a-day program.

Orchard Village*
7671 Marmore, Skokie, IL, 60077 (312) 967-1800
Admin Eileen U Kroll.
Licensure Intermediate Care. *Beds* 55.
Ownership Nonprofit.

Skokie Meadows I
9615 N Knox, Skokie, IL, 60076 (312) 679-4161
Admin Doris E Teschner. *Medical Dir/Dir of Nursing* Dr Edward Sutoris.
Licensure Skilled Care; Intermediate Care. *Beds* SNF 55; ICF 58. *Certified* Medicaid; Medicare.
Ownership Proprietary.
Admissions Requirements Minimum age 20; Medical examination; Physician's request.
Staff RNs; Orderlies; Nurses aides; Physical therapists; Reality therapists; Recreational therapists; Occupational therapists; Speech therapists; Activities coordinators; Dietitians; Dentists; Ophthalmologists; Podiatrists; Audiologists.
Facilities Dining room; Physical therapy room; Activities room; Crafts room; Laundry room; Barber/Beauty shop.
Activities Arts and Crafts; Cards; Games; Reading groups; Prayer groups; Movies; Shopping trips; Dances/Social or cultural gatherings.

Description Three churches, the YMCA, and junior high school in the area make regularly scheduled visits in which all the residents are in some way involved. Also, there is a mails program between volunteers of the YMCA outreach program and residents.

Skokie Meadows II*
4600 W Golf Dr, Skokie, IL, 60076 (312) 679-1157
Admin Jacob M Graff.
Licensure Intermediate Care. *Beds* 111. *Certified* Medicaid.
Ownership Proprietary.

Village Nursing Home Inc*
9000 La Vergne Ave, Skokie, IL, 60077 (312) 679-2322
Admin Samuel Branman.
Licensure Skilled Care; Intermediate Care. *Beds* SNF 98; ICF 51. *Certified* Medicaid; Medicare.
Ownership Proprietary.

SMITHTON

Park Haven Care Center Inc*
107 S Lincoln, Smithton, IL, 62285 (618) 235-4600
Admin Georgia Listano.
Licensure Intermediate Care. *Beds* 101. *Certified* Medicaid.
Ownership Proprietary.

SOUTH BELOIT

Fair Oaks Nursing Home*
1515 Blackhawk Rd, South Beloit, IL, 61080 (815) 389-3911
Admin E H Pokorny.
Licensure Skilled Care. *Beds* 42.
Ownership Proprietary.

SOUTH ELGIN

Fox Valley Nursing Center*
759 Kane St, South Elgin, IL, 60177 (312) 697-3310
Admin Thomas J Dooley.
Licensure Skilled Care; Intermediate Care. *Beds* SNF 107; ICF 99. *Certified* Medicaid; Medicare.
Ownership Proprietary.

South Elgin Manor*
746 Spring, South Elgin, IL, 60177 (312) 697-0565
Admin Howard I James.
Licensure Intermediate Care. *Beds* 96. *Certified* Medicaid.
Ownership Proprietary.

SOUTH HOLLAND

Holland Home for the Aged*
16300 S Louis Ave, South Holland, IL, 60473 (312) 596-3050
Admin Lambert Wierenga.

Licensure Intermediate Care. *Beds* 326. *Certified* Medicaid.
Ownership Nonprofit.

Rest Haven South Nursing Home
16300 Wausau St, South Holland, IL, 60473 (312) 596-5500
Admin Richard Schutt. *Medical Dir/Dir of Nursing* Dr G Gnade.
Licensure Intermediate Care; Sheltered Care. *Beds* ICF 116; Sheltered Care 50.
Ownership Nonprofit.
Affiliation Christian Reformed

South Holland Nursing Home
16000 S Wabash Ave, South Holland, IL, 60473 (312) 339-0600
Admin Rita L Hochenbaum. *Medical Dir/Dir of Nursing* Dr Jai Arya.
Licensure Skilled Care. *Beds* 150. *Certified* Medicaid; Medicare.
Ownership Proprietary.
Admissions Requirements Minimum age 21; Medical examination.
Staff RNs 4 (ft), 1 (pt); LPNs 5 (ft), 2 (pt); Orderlies 5 (ft), 2 (pt); Nurses aides 45 (ft), 5 (pt); Activities coordinators 4 (ft), 2 (pt).
Facilities Dining room; Physical therapy room; Activities room; Chapel; Crafts room; Laundry room; Barber/Beauty shop.
Activities Arts and Crafts; Cards; Games; Movies; Shopping trips; Outings.
Description Facility is a one-story building having 3 wings of 50 beds each located in a suburban residential area on a closed-off street. The setting is quiet and a park is nearby. Excellent nursing and rehabilitative care is offered to all residents.

SPARTA

Randolph County Nursing Home
310 W Belmont, Sparta, IL, 62286 (618) 443-4351
Admin Paulette A Buch.
Licensure Skilled Care; Intermediate Care. *Beds* SNF 74; ICF 62. *Certified* Medicaid; Medicare.
Ownership Public.
Admissions Requirements Minimum age 18.
Staff RNs 3 (ft), 3 (pt); LPNs 5 (ft), 5 (pt); Nurses aides 30 (ft), 18 (pt).
Facilities Dining room; Physical therapy room; Activities room; Chapel; Crafts room; Laundry room; Barber/Beauty shop.
Activities Arts and Crafts; Cards; Games; Reading groups; Prayer groups; Movies; Shopping trips.

Senior Manor
223 E 4th, Sparta, IL, 62286 (618) 443-4411
Admin Ruth Jung. *Medical Dir/Dir of Nursing* Marilyn Anderson.
Licensure Intermediate Care. *Beds* 59. *Certified* Medicaid.
Ownership Proprietary.
Admissions Requirements Medical examination.
Staff RNs 1 (ft), 1 (pt); LPNs 3 (ft), 3 (pt); Nurses aides 5 (ft), 10 (pt); Physical therapists 1 (pt); Recreational therapists 1 (pt); Occupational therapists 1 (pt); Speech therapists 1 (pt);

Activities coordinators 1 (ft); Dietitians 1 (pt).
Facilities Dining room; Physical therapy room; Activities room; Chapel; Crafts room; Laundry room; Barber/Beauty shop; Library; Visitors lounge.
Activities Arts and Crafts; Cards; Games; Reading groups; Prayer groups; Movies; Shopping trips; Dances/Social or cultural gatherings.
Description Facility is located at edge of the city of Sparta in a very quiet part of town, 3 blocks from fire truck garage. It is a very clean, one-story nursing home with daily activities and regular church services conducted by the ministerial society.

SPRING VALLEY

Argyle House*
534 W Miller, Spring Valley, IL, 62702 (217) 786-2571
Admin John D Waltz.
Licensure Intermediate Care. *Beds* 20.
Ownership Nonprofit.

Spring Valley Nursing
1300 Greenwood Rd, Spring Valley, IL, 61362 (815) 664-4708
Admin Shirley Michelski. *Medical Dir/Dir of Nursing* Donald Gallagher,MD.
Licensure Intermediate Care. *Beds* 98. *Certified* Medicaid.
Ownership Proprietary.
Admissions Requirements Minimum age 18; Medical examination; Physician's request.
Staff RNs 7 (pt); LPNs 3 (ft), 2 (pt); Nurses aides 21 (ft), 20 (pt).
Facilities Dining room; Physical therapy room; Activities room; Crafts room; Laundry room; Barber/Beauty shop; Library.
Activities Arts and Crafts; Cards; Games; Reading groups; Prayer groups; Movies; Shopping trips; Dances/Social or cultural gatherings.
Description Large spacious day room is available that enables facility to hold large gatherings and community functions. Facility is easily accessible to downtown area including churches.

SPRINGFIELD

Brother James Court
Rt 1, Sangamon Ave Rd E, Springfield, IL, 62707
Admin Br David Sarnecki. *Medical Dir/Dir of Nursing* H B Henkel MD.
Licensure Intermediate Care for Mentally Retarded. *Beds* 96. *Certified* Medicaid.
Ownership Nonprofit.
Admissions Requirements Minimum age 18; Males only; Medical examination; Physician's request.
Staff RNs 3 (ft); LPNs 3 (ft), 1 (pt); Orderlies 7 (ft), 9 (pt); Recreational therapists 5 (ft); Occupational therapists 1 (pt); Speech therapists 1 (pt); Activities coordinators 1 (pt); Dietitians 1 (pt); Social workers 1 (ft), 1 (pt); Psychologists 1 (pt).
Affiliation Roman Catholic
Facilities Dining room; Activities room; Chapel; Crafts room; Laundry room; Barber/Beauty shop.

Activities Arts and Crafts; Games; Prayer groups; Movies; Shopping trips; Dances/Social or cultural gatherings; Practical skills class; Oral and written communications class; Music therapy class; Physical education class.
Description This facility is an ICF/DD for the care of adult mentally retarded men who are ambulatory and need long-term care; provides both residential and day programing geared specifically for the mentally retarded.

Capital Villa Nursing Center*
900 N Rutledge, Springfield, IL, 62702
Admin Ricardo L Thompson.
Licensure Skilled Care; Intermediate Care.
Beds SNF 127; ICF 26. *Certified* Medicaid; Medicare.
Ownership Proprietary.

Dirksen House Healthcare*
555 W Carpenter St, Springfield, IL, 62702
(217) 525-1880
Admin Donald D Adbouch.
Licensure Skilled Care; Intermediate Care.
Beds SNF 65; ICF 198. *Certified* Medicaid; Medicare.
Ownership Proprietary.

Eastgate Manor
525 S 18th, Springfield, IL, 62703 (217) 789-1680
Admin Mary Wade.
Licensure Intermediate Care. *Beds* 65. *Certified* Medicaid.
Ownership Proprietary.
Admissions Requirements Minimum age 18; Medical examination.
Facilities Dining room; Physical therapy room; Activities room; Chapel; Crafts room; Laundry room; Barber/Beauty shop.
Activities Arts and Crafts; Games; Reading groups; Prayer groups; Movies; Shopping trips; Dances/Social or cultural gatherings; Orientation.

Haven Retirement Center*
2301 W Monroe, Springfield, IL, 62704 (217) 546-0272
Admin James C Baur.
Licensure Skilled Care; Intermediate Care.
Beds SNF 61; ICF 133. *Certified* Medicaid.
Ownership Proprietary.

Illinois Presbyterian Home
2005 W Lawrence, Springfield, IL, 62704 (217) 546-5622
Admin Thomas P O'Fallon.
Licensure Intermediate Care; Sheltered Care.
Beds ICF 15; Sheltered Care 68. *Certified* Medicaid.
Ownership Nonprofit.
Admissions Requirements Minimum age 65; Medical examination.
Staff RNs 2 (ft), 2 (pt); LPNs 2 (ft), 3 (pt); Nurses aides 7 (ft), 3 (pt); Activities coordinators 1 (ft); Dietitians 1 (pt).
Affiliation Presbyterian
Facilities Dining room; Activities room; Crafts room; Laundry room; Library.
Activities Arts and Crafts; Cards; Games; Reading groups; Prayer groups; Movies; Shopping trips; Dances/Social or cultural gatherings.
Description Home for the elderly is situated on

west edge of Springfield surrounded by 21 acres of rolling meadows, trees, shrubs, and flowers. Nutritious and well-balanced meals are served family-style in the cheerful dining room. A wide variety of group and individual activities are provided.

Lewis Memorial Christian Village
3400 W Washington, Springfield, IL, 62702
(217) 787-9600
Admin Robert Florence. *Medical Dir/Dir of Nursing* Dr John Meyer.
Licensure Skilled Care; Intermediate Care.
Beds SNF 76; ICF 79. *Certified* Medicaid.
Ownership Nonprofit.
Admissions Requirements Medical examination.
Staff RNs 4 (ft), 6 (pt); LPNs 12 (ft), 8 (pt); Orderlies 3 (ft), 2 (pt); Nurses aides 48 (ft), 8 (pt); Physical therapists 1 (pt); Recreational therapists 3 (ft), 1 (pt); Speech therapists 1 (pt); Activities coordinators 1 (ft); Dietitians 10 (ft), 4 (pt); Dentists 1 (pt).
Facilities Dining room; Physical therapy room; Activities room; Chapel; Crafts room; Laundry room; Barber/Beauty shop.
Activities Arts and Crafts; Cards; Games; Reading groups; Prayer groups; Movies; Shopping trips.

Mary Bryant Home
2960 Stanton St, Springfield, IL, 62703 (217) 529-1611
Admin Frances Trees. *Medical Dir/Dir of Nursing* Dr Robert Nachtwey.
Licensure Shelter Care. *Beds* 36.
Ownership Nonprofit.
Admissions Requirements Minimum age 18 (Blind or legally blind); Medical examination.
Staff Nurses aides 3 (ft), 2 (pt); Activities coordinators 1 (ft).
Facilities Dining room; Activities room; Crafts room; Laundry room; Barber/Beauty shop; Library.
Activities Arts and Crafts; Cards; Games; Prayer groups; Shopping trips; Dances/Social or cultural gatherings.
Description Residents of facility visit School District 186 to teach second and third grade students how the blind cope with the activities of daily living.

Oak Terrace Retirement
1750 W Washington, Springfield, IL, 62702
(217) 787-6466
Admin Anasue L Haines. *Medical Dir/Dir of Nursing* Norman Scheibling.
Licensure Intermediate Care; Sheltered Care.
Beds ICF 58; Sheltered Care 40.
Ownership Proprietary.
Admissions Requirements Minimum age 18; Medical examination.
Staff RNs 1 (ft), 2 (pt); LPNs 4 (ft), 2 (pt); Orderlies 1 (pt); Nurses aides 4 (ft), 10 (pt); Activities coordinators 1 (ft), 1 (pt); Dietitians 1 (pt).
Facilities Dining room; Activities room; Crafts room; Laundry room; Barber/Beauty shop; Library.
Activities Arts and Crafts; Cards; Games; Reading groups; Prayer groups; Movies; Shopping trips.
Description Our retirement center, first opened

June, 1975 as a private facility, has maintained this status to the present. We are licensed by the State of Illinois as a combination shelter-intermediate care facility. Our total staff is committed to assisting the resident in maintaining or developing his/her maximum potential for continued independence to providing other services to enhance his/her well-being. The philosophy of nursing at our facility is the involvement of everyone in providing the highest standards of spiritual, mental, social, emotional, and physical care to our residents and families in accordance with the written policies and procedures of the administration and medical staff.

Roosevelt Square*
2120 W Washington St, Springfield, IL, 64704
(217) 546-1325
Admin Bill R Benedict.
Licensure Intermediate Care. *Beds* 77. *Certified* Medicaid.
Ownership Proprietary.

Rutledge Manor Care Home Inc*
913 N Rutledge St, Springfield, IL, 62702 (217) 525-1722
Admin Betty Hickman.
Licensure Intermediate Care; Shelter Care.
Beds ICF 155; Shelter Care 12.
Ownership Proprietary.

Saint Joseph Home of Springfield
S 6th St Rd, Springfield, IL, 62701 (217) 529-5596
Admin Sr Patricia Masterson.
Licensure Intermediate Care; Sheltered Care.
Beds ICF 21; Sheltered Care 100.
Ownership Proprietary.
Staff RNs 3 (ft); LPNs 5 (ft); Nurses aides 10 (ft); Recreational therapists 1 (ft); Dietitians 1 (pt).
Affiliation Roman Catholic
Facilities Dining room; Chapel; Laundry room; Barber/Beauty shop.
Activities Arts and Crafts; Cards; Games; Prayer groups; Movies; Shopping trips.

Springfield Manor
2800 W Lawrence St, Springfield, IL, 62703
(217) 787-1955
Admin Francis Greer.
Licensure Intermediate Care. *Beds* 160. *Certified* Medicaid.
Ownership Proprietary.

STAUNTON

Barry Care Center of Staunton*
215 W Pennsylvania Ave, Staunton, IL, 62088
(618) 635-5577
Admin Jamie Barry Verticchio.
Licensure Skilled Care. *Beds* 99. *Certified* Medicaid; Medicare.
Ownership Proprietary.

STERLING

Edgewild Health Center*
3601 16th Ave, Sterling, IL, 61081 (815) 626-0233

Admin Nola L Duffy.
Licensure Intermediate Care. *Beds* 70. *Certified* Medicaid.
Ownership Proprietary.

Exceptional Care and Training Center*
2601 Woodlawn Rd, Sterling, IL, 61081 (815)
626-5820
Admin Jarolyn B Fyhrlund.
Licensure Skilled Care; Intermediate Care.
Beds SNF 64; ICF 22. *Certified* Medicaid;
Medicare.
Ownership Proprietary.

Sterling Care Center*
105 E 23rd St, Sterling, IL, 61081 (815)
626-4264
Admin Jeanne E Radunz.
Licensure Skilled Care. *Beds* 102. *Certified* Medicaid; Medicare.
Ownership Proprietary.

STOCKTON

Morgan Memorial Home
501 E Front Ave, Stockton, IL, 61085 (815)
947-2215
Admin Genevieve Parker.
Licensure Intermediate Care. *Beds* 37. *Certified* Medicaid.
Ownership Proprietary.
Admissions Requirements Minimum age 18.
Staff RNs 1 (ft), 1 (pt); LPNs 3 (ft), 2 (pt);
Nurses aides 6 (ft), 13 (pt); Recreational therapists 1 (ft); Occupational therapists 1 (pt);
Activities coordinators 1 (pt); Dietitians 1 (ft),
5 (pt).
Facilities Dining room; Activities room; Crafts
room; Laundry room; Barber/Beauty shop.
Activities Arts and Crafts; Cards; Games;
Reading groups; Prayer groups; Movies; Dances/Social or cultural gatherings; Pet show
yearly; Flea market involving entire area; Bingo; Music.
Description We have a pet show yearly, anyone
having a pet is encouraged to participate; ribbons and trophies are awarded for winners of
each division. We feel we are treating the kids
in our community and at the same time our
residents enjoy seeing all the pets. We make it a
festive affair with balloons, cookies, punch, etc.
Adults from the community serve as judges
and emcee.

STREATOR

Camelot Manor
516 W Frech St, Streator, IL, 61364 (815)
672-9390
Admin R S Gomes.
Licensure Intermediate Care. *Beds* 100. *Certified* Medicaid.
Ownership Proprietary.
Admissions Requirements Minimum age 18;
Medical examination.
Staff RNs 1 (ft), 2 (pt); LPNs 3 (ft), 4 (pt);
Orderlies 2 (ft); Nurses aides 13 (ft), 3 (pt); Recreational therapists 1 (ft), 2 (pt); Activities coordinators 1 (ft); Podiatrists 1 (pt).
Facilities Dining room; Physical therapy room;
Activities room; Laundry room; Barber/Beauty

shop.
Activities Arts and Crafts; Cards; Games;
Reading groups; Prayer groups; Movies; Shopping trips; Dances/Social or cultural gatherings;
Bowling league.
Description Facility sponsors a monthly party
for all residents celebrating birthdays during
that month featuring musical entertainment
provided by volunteers. Families are invited
and cake, ice cream, and punch are served.
Every resident receives a gift donated by volunteers.

Heritage Manor Streator
1525 E Main St, Streator, IL, 61364 (815)
672-4516
Admin Cheryl L Lowney. *Medical Dir/Dir of
Nursing* Dr Luis Bachzo.
Licensure Skilled Care; Intermediate Care.
Beds 110. *Certified* Medicaid; Medicare.
Ownership Proprietary.
Admissions Requirements Minimum age 18.
Staff RNs; LPNs; Nurses aides; Physical therapists; Recreational therapists; Activities coordinators.
Facilities Dining room; Physical therapy room;
Activities room; Crafts room; Laundry room;
Barber/Beauty shop; Library.
Activities Arts and Crafts; Cards; Games;
Reading groups; Prayer groups; Movies; Shopping trips; Dances/Social or cultural gatherings.

SULLIVAN

Hawthorne Lodge of Sullivan*
11 Hawthorne Ln, Sullivan, IL, 61951 (217)
728-4327
Admin Denise A Land.
Licensure Skilled Care; Intermediate Care.
Beds 123. *Certified* Medicaid; Medicare.
Ownership Proprietary.

Illinois Masonic Home*
Rt 121 E, Sullivan, IL, 61951 (217) 728-4394
Admin James E Hart.
Licensure Skilled Care; Intermediate Care;
Shelter Care. *Beds* SNF 10; ICF 183; Shelter
Care 101.
Ownership Nonprofit.
Affiliation Masons

Sullivan Living Center
E View Pl, Sullivan, IL, 61951 (217) 728-7367
Admin John M Brinkoetter.
Licensure Intermediate Care. *Beds* 55. *Certified* Medicaid.
Ownership Proprietary.
Staff Physicians 1 (pt); RNs 1 (pt); LPNs 4 (ft);
Orderlies 2 (ft); Nurses aides 17 (ft), 6 (pt);
Physical therapists 1 (pt); Reality therapists 1
(pt); Recreational therapists 1 (pt); Occupational therapists 1 (pt); Speech therapists 1 (pt);
Activities coordinators 1 (ft), 1 (pt); Dietitians
1 (pt); Dentists 1 (pt); Ophthalmologists 1 (pt);
Podiatrists 1 (pt); Audiologists 1 (pt).
Facilities Dining room; Activities room; Chapel; Crafts room; Laundry room; Barber/Beauty
shop; Library.
Activities Arts and Crafts; Cards; Games;
Reading groups; Prayer groups; Movies; Shop-

ping trips; Dances/Social or cultural gatherings.
Description Private pay facility, family-owned
and operated, small single-story building.

Titus Memorial Presbyterian Home*
513 N Worth St, Sullivan, IL, 61951 (217)
728-4725
Admin Peggy Auten.
Licensure Shelter Care. *Beds* 14.
Ownership Nonprofit.
Affiliation Presbyterian

SUMNER

Pine Lawn Manor Care Center*
Box 186, Poplar and Maple, Sumner, IL, 62466
(618) 936-2703
Admin Peter B Narish.
Licensure Intermediate Care. *Beds* 93. *Certified* Medicaid.
Ownership Proprietary.

Red Hills Rest Haven*
1 Poplar Dr, Sumner, IL, 62466 (618) 936-2522
Admin Virgil Portwood.
Licensure Skilled Care. *Beds* 96. *Certified* Medicaid; Medicare.
Ownership Proprietary.

SYCAMORE

Opportunity House Inc*
PO Box 301, 202 Lucas St, Sycamore, IL,
60178 (815) 895-5108
Admin John Kroos.
Licensure Intermediate Care. *Beds* 17.
Ownership Nonprofit.

TAMMS

Tamms Sheltered Care
3rd St Near Carpenter, Tamms, IL, 62988 (618)
747-2613
Admin Jo Ann Benefield.
Licensure Sheltered Care. *Beds* 26.
Ownership Proprietary.
Admissions Requirements Minimum age 18;
Medical examination; Physician's request.
Staff Physicians 1 (pt); RNs 1 (pt); Nurses
aides 3 (ft), 4 (pt); Activities coordinators 1 (pt).
Facilities Dining room; Activities room; Laundry room.
Activities Arts and Crafts; Cards; Games;
Reading groups; Prayer groups; Shopping trips.
Description This is a small facility that can give
a lot of individual attention and direction in a
family setting.

TAYLORVILLE

Meadow Manor Inc*
Rt 48 N, Taylorville, IL, 62568 (217) 824-2277
Admin Corrine S Prehn.
Licensure Skilled Care; Intermediate Care.
Beds SNF 51; ICF 99. *Certified* Medicaid;
Medicare.
Ownership Proprietary.

Taylorville Care Center Inc*
600 S Houston, Taylorville, IL, 62568 (217)
824-9636
Admin Constance J Le Vault.
Licensure Intermediate Care. *Beds* 98. *Certified* Medicaid.
Ownership Proprietary.

TINLEY PARK

Mc Allister Nursing Home
183 and La Vergne, Tinley Park, IL, 60477
(312) 798-2272
Admin Theresa M Russo. *Medical Dir/Dir of Nursing* Bakul K Pankya MD.
Licensure Skilled Care; Intermediate Care.
Beds SNF 59; ICF 42. *Certified* Medicaid;
Medicare.
Ownership Proprietary.
Admissions Requirements Minimum age 18;
Medical examination; Physician's request.
Staff Physicians 2 (pt); RNs 6 (ft), 2 (pt); LPNs
5 (ft), 2 (pt); Orderlies 28 (ft), 4 (pt); Physical
therapists 1 (ft), 1 (pt); Reality therapists 1 (pt);
Recreational therapists 2 (ft); Occupational
therapists 1 (ft), 1 (pt); Speech therapists 1 (pt);
Activities coordinators 1 (pt); Dietitians 1 (ft),
1 (pt); Dentists 1 (pt); Ophthalmologists 1 (pt);
Ophthalmologists 1 (pt); Audiologists 1 (pt).
Facilities Dining room; Physical therapy room;
Activities room; Chapel; Crafts room; Laundry
room; Barber/Beauty shop; Library.
Activities Arts and Crafts; Cards; Games;
Reading groups; Prayer groups; Movies; Shopping trips; Dances/Social or cultural gatherings.
Description Facility is modern, family-owned
and family operated, in business 40 years.
Country-like setting on 7 acres. Single level, all
brick, fireproof, air conditioned building with
tastefully designed resident rooms. Medicaid
approved for intermediate and skilled levels of
care.

TOLUCA

Monte Cassino Healthcare Center*
101 E Via Ghiglieri, Toluca, IL, 61369 (815)
452-2321
Admin Betty Adolphson.
Licensure Skilled Care; Intermediate Care.
Beds SNF 71; ICF 33. *Certified* Medicaid.
Ownership Proprietary.

TOULON

Stark County Health Center
E Main St, Toulon, IL, 61483 (309) 286-2631
Admin Irwin F Malone. *Medical Dir/Dir of
Nursing* Josef Unhold MD.
Licensure Skilled Care; Intermediate Care.
Beds SNF 82; ICF 54. *Certified* Medicaid;
Medicare.
Ownership Proprietary.
Admissions Requirements Medical examination; Physician's request.
Facilities Dining room; Physical therapy room;
Activities room; Chapel; Crafts room; Laundry
room; Barber/Beauty shop; Library; TV rooms;
Greenhouse.
Activities Arts and Crafts; Cards; Games;
Reading groups; Prayer groups; Movies; Dan-

ces/Social or cultural gatherings; Nail care;
Cooking.
Description Facility features a single-story
building in a rural setting with individual
heating and air conditioning units in all rooms,
sprinkler system, and smoke alarms.

TROY

Professional Care
200 E Taylor, Troy, IL, 62294
Medical Dir/Dir of Nursing Richard C L Chen
MD.
Licensure Intermediate Care for Mentally
Retarded. *Beds* 149.
Admissions Requirements Minimum age 18;
Medical examination; Physician's request.
Staff Physicians 1 (ft), 11 (pt); RNs 1 (pt);
LPNs 12 (ft); Orderlies 4 (ft); Nurses aides 34
(ft); Physical therapists 2 (ft); Reality therapists
3 (ft); Recreational therapists 4 (ft); Occupational therapists 1 (pt); Speech therapists 1 (pt);
Dietitians 1 (pt); Dentists 1 (pt); Podiatrists 1
(pt); Audiologists 1 (pt).
Facilities Dining room; Physical therapy room;
Activities room; Chapel; Crafts room; Laundry
room; Barber/Beauty shop; Library.
Activities Arts and Crafts; Cards; Games; Prayer groups; Movies; Shopping trips; Dances/Social or cultural gatherings.

TUSCOLA

Douglas Manor Nursing Complex*
Rt 2, Tuscola, IL, 61953 (217) 253-2337
Admin George S Barnett.
Licensure Skilled Care; Intermediate Care.
Beds SNF 30; ICF 123. *Certified* Medicaid.
Ownership Proprietary.

URBANA

Americana Healthcare Center
600 N Coler, Urbana, IL, 61801 (217) 367-1191
Admin Darlena F Voegele. *Medical Dir/Dir of
Nursing* Dr Phillip Johnson.
Licensure Skilled Care; Intermediate Care.
Beds 100. *Certified* Medicaid; Medicare.
Ownership Proprietary.
Admissions Requirements Medical examination.
Staff Physicians; RNs; LPNs; Orderlies;
Nurses aides; Physical therapists; Reality therapists; Recreational therapists; Occupational
therapists; Speech therapists; Activities coordinators; Dietitians; Dentists; Ophthalmologists;
Podiatrists; Audiologists.
Facilities Dining room; Physical therapy room;
Activities room; Crafts room; Laundry room
19G.
Activities Arts and Crafts; Cards; Games;
Reading groups; Prayer groups; Movies; Shopping trips; Dances/Social or cultural gatherings.

Champaign County Nursing Home
1701 E Main, Urbana, IL, 61801 (217)
384-3784
Admin Joyce Ettensohn. *Medical Dir/Dir of
Nursing* Dr Paul Barton.
Licensure Skilled Care; Intermediate Care;
Sheltered Care. *Beds* SNF 153; ICF 56; Shel-

tered Care 79.
Ownership Public.
Admissions Requirements Minimum age 45;
Medical examination; Physician's request.
Staff Physicians 1 (pt); RNs 14 (ft), 10 (pt);
LPNs 7 (ft), 3 (pt); Nurses aides 80 (ft), 11 (pt);
Physical therapists 1 (pt); Reality therapists 1
(ft); Recreational therapists 6 (ft), 1 (pt); Occupational therapists 1 (pt); Activities coordinators 1 (pt); Dietitians 1 (pt); Dentists 1 (pt).
Facilities Dining room; Physical therapy room;
Activities room; Chapel; Crafts room; Barber/Beauty shop; Library.
Activities Arts and Crafts; Cards; Games;
Reading groups; Prayer groups; Movies; Shopping trips; Dances/Social or cultural gatherings.
Description Home offers an adult day care
program and respite care service to provide
temporary care of the frail, or disabled client.

Clark-Lindsey Village Inc*
101 W Windsor Rd, Urbana, IL, 61801 (217)
344-2144
Admin Benjamin F Vondracek.
Licensure Skilled Care; Intermediate Care;
Shelter Care. *Beds* SNF 40; ICF 8; Shelter Care
32.
Ownership Nonprofit.

Royal Fontana Nursing Center Inc*
907 N Lincoln, Urbana, IL, 61801 (217)
367-8421
Admin Leighton Collins.
Licensure Skilled Care. *Beds* 99. *Certified* Medicaid; Medicare.
Ownership Proprietary.

Urbana Nursing Home*
2006 S Philo Rd, Urbana, IL, 61801 (217)
344-0777
Admin Ruth M Engel.
Licensure Intermediate Care. *Beds* 48. *Certified* Medicaid.
Ownership Proprietary.

VANDALIA

Heritage House of Vandalia
Rt 185 W, Vandalia, IL, 62471 (618) 283-1434
Admin Rosalie Cox. *Medical Dir/Dir of
Nursing* Hans Rollinger MD.
Licensure Intermediate Care. *Beds* 79. *Certified* Medicaid.
Ownership Proprietary.
Admissions Requirements Minimum age 18;
Medical examination.
Staff RNs 2 (ft); LPNs 3 (ft), 2 (pt); Activities
coordinators 1 (ft).
Facilities Dining room; Physical therapy room;
Activities room; Laundry room; Barber/Beauty
shop.
Activities Cards; Games; Prayer groups;
Movies; Shopping trips; Dances/Social or cultural gatherings.
Description Facility was one of the first
involved in Evergreen Outreach Program.
Swimming pool is enjoyed by the residents
during the summer.

Sunnydale Acres*
1500 W Saint Louis, Vandalia, IL, 62471 (618)
283-4262

Admin Donna L Hannagan.
Licensure Intermediate Care. *Beds* 116. *Certified* Medicaid.
Ownership Proprietary.

VIENNA

Hillview Health Care Center*
PO Box 156, 11th St, Vienna, IL, 62995 (618) 658-2951
Admin Connie L Duncan.
Licensure Skilled Care; Intermediate Care.
Beds SNF 25; ICF 47. *Certified* Medicaid.
Ownership Proprietary.

Mount Shelter Care Home*
PO Box 215, Vienna, IL, 62995 (618) 695-2494
Admin Phyllis M Taylor.
Licensure Sheltered Care. *Beds* 29.
Ownership Proprietary.

VIRDEN

Hazle Memorial Baptist Home*
402 W Loud St, Virden, IL, 62690 (217) 965-4336
Admin Dorothy L Frigiola.
Licensure Intermediate Care. *Beds* 51. *Certified* Medicaid.
Ownership Nonprofit.
Affiliation Baptist

Sunrise Manor of Virden Inc
333 S Wrightsam St, Virden, IL, 62690 (217) 965-4715
Admin Patricia J Barnes. *Medical Dir/Dir of Nursing* Dr Zoltan Braun.
Licensure Skilled Care; Intermediate Care.
Beds SNF 53; ICF 46. *Certified* Medicaid; Medicare.
Ownership Proprietary.
Admissions Requirements Physician's request.
Staff RNs 2 (ft); LPNs 7 (ft), 5 (pt); Orderlies 2 (ft); Nurses aides 20 (ft), 25 (pt); Activities coordinators 2 (ft).
Facilities Dining room; Physical therapy room; Activities room; Chapel; Crafts room; Laundry room; Barber/Beauty shop; Library.
Activities Arts and Crafts; Cards; Games; Reading groups; Prayer groups; Movies; Shopping trips; Dances/Social or cultural gatherings.
Description Sunrise is a one-story, brick nursing facility set at the edge of town. We have 24-hour nursing care and a caring staff from a small caring community.

VIRGINIA

Walker Nursing Home Inc*
530 E Beardstown St, Virginia, IL, 62691 (217) 452-3218
Admin George W White.
Licensure Intermediate Care. *Beds* 55. *Certified* Medicaid.
Ownership Proprietary.

WALNUT

Walnut Manor*
308 S 2nd St, Walnut, IL, 61376 (815) 379-2131
Admin Dennis L Grobe.
Licensure Intermediate Care. *Beds* 62. *Certified* Medicaid.
Ownership Proprietary.

WASHINGTON

Washington Christian Village
1110 New Castle Rd, Washington, IL, 61571 (309) 444-3161
Admin Andrew Felix. *Medical Dir/Dir of Nursing* Dr Philip Immesoete.
Licensure Skilled Care. *Beds* 122. *Certified* Medicaid; Medicare.
Ownership Nonprofit.
Staff Physicians 8 (pt); RNs 6 (ft), 4 (pt); LPNs 6 (ft), 3 (pt); Nurses aides 31 (ft), 24 (pt); Physical therapists 1 (ft); Speech therapists 1 (pt); Activities coordinators 1 (ft); Dietitians 1 (ft); Dentists 1 (pt); Podiatrists 1 (pt); Audiologists 1 (pt).
Affiliation Church of Christ
Facilities Dining room; Physical therapy room; Activities room; Chapel; Crafts room; Laundry room; Barber/Beauty shop.
Activities Arts and Crafts; Cards; Games; Movies; Shopping trips.
Description Facility has a very extensive volunteer program with a volunteer coordinator on staff; Christian auxiliary donates items for a shopping cart, buys Christmas gifts for each resident, decorates tables, buys extras with yearly dues, and sends volunteers almost every day.

WATERLOO

Canterbury Manor
718 N Market, Waterloo, IL, 62298 (618) 939-8565
Admin Mary G Wood. *Medical Dir/Dir of Nursing* E F Maglasang.
Licensure Intermediate Care. *Beds* 74. *Certified* Medicaid.
Ownership Proprietary.
Admissions Requirements Minimum age 19.
Staff Physicians 6 (pt); RNs 1 (ft); LPNs 2 (ft), 4 (pt); Nurses aides 10 (ft), 15 (pt); Physical therapists 1 (pt); Recreational therapists 1 (pt); Occupational therapists 1 (pt); Activities coordinators 1 (ft), 1 (pt); Dietitians 1 (pt); Dentists 1 (pt).
Facilities Dining room; Physical therapy room; Activities room; Chapel; Crafts room; Laundry room; Barber/Beauty shop; Lounge.
Activities Arts and Crafts; Cards; Games; Reading groups; Prayer groups; Movies; Shopping trips; Dances/Social or cultural gatherings; Outings/picnics; Tours.
Description Canterbury Manor is a small, very home-like nursing home with an enclosed courtyard for many summer activities. Home is on one level with no steps and very close to restaurants and local merchants for easy shopping. A QUIP Level II home (highest recognition given the nursing home by Illinois Department of Public Health).

Monroe County Nursing Home
Illinois Ave, Waterloo, IL, 62298 (618) 939-3488
Admin Collette W Rau. *Medical Dir/Dir of Nursing* Russell W Jost MD.
Licensure Skilled Care; Intermediate Care.
Beds SNF 143; ICF 82. *Certified* Medicaid; Medicare.
Ownership Public.
Admissions Requirements Minimum age 16; Medical examination; Physician's request.
Staff Physicians 7 (pt); RNs 4 (ft), 8 (pt); LPNs 7 (ft), 11 (pt); Orderlies 2 (pt); Nurses aides 47 (ft), 60 (pt); Physical therapists 1 (pt); Reality therapists 1 (pt); Recreational therapists 1 (pt); Activities coordinators 1 (ft); Dietitians 1 (pt); Dentists 1 (pt); Podiatrists 1 (pt).
Facilities Dining room; Physical therapy room; Activities room; Chapel; Crafts room; Laundry room; Barber/Beauty shop.
Activities Arts and Crafts; Cards; Games; Reading groups; Prayer groups; Movies; Shopping trips; Dances/Social or cultural gatherings.
Description Special activities include "Home with Heart," a benefit for the American Heart Association; Easter Bonnet Parade, residents design and create hats to be modeled and judged; cooking and baking projects; annual bazaar dinner and bake sale, residents make crafts all year for this special day—as well as preparing their specialties, homemade stollen and candies.

WATSEKA

Iroquois Resident Home
200 Fairman St, Watseka, IL, 60970 (815) 432-5201
Admin Paul F Wenz. *Medical Dir/Dir of Nursing* S D Roeder and J M Roberts MD.
Licensure Skilled Care; Intermediate Care.
Beds 56.
Ownership Nonprofit.
Admissions Requirements Minimum age 22; Medical examination; Physician's request.
Staff Physicians 16 (ft); RNs 2 (ft), 2 (pt); LPNs 6 (ft), 1 (pt); Nurses aides 20 (ft), 1 (pt); Physical therapists 1 (ft); Speech therapists 1 (pt); Activities coordinators 1 (ft); Dietitians 1 (pt).
Facilities Dining room; Physical therapy room; Activities room; Laundry room; Barber/Beauty shop.
Activities Arts and Crafts; Cards; Games; Reading groups; Prayer groups; Movies; Dances/Social or cultural gatherings.

Watseka Hawthorne Lodge
715 E Raymond Rd, Watseka, IL, 60970 (815) 432-5476
Admin Becky Warlow. *Medical Dir/Dir of Nursing* Dr N D Hungness.
Licensure Skilled Care; Intermediate Care.
Beds 123. *Certified* Medicaid; Medicare.
Ownership Proprietary.
Admissions Requirements Minimum age 18.
Staff Physicians 10 (pt); RNs 2 (ft), 3 (pt); LPNs 5 (ft), 3 (pt); Nurses aides 16 (ft), 10 (pt); Physical therapists 1 (pt); Occupational therapists 1 (pt); Speech therapists 1 (pt); Activities coordinators 1 (ft); Dietitians 1 (pt); Dentists 1 (pt); Podiatrists 1 (pt).

Facilities Dining room; Physical therapy room; Activities room; Crafts room; Laundry room; Barber/Beauty shop.
Activities Arts and Crafts; Cards; Games; Reading groups; Prayer groups; Movies; Shopping trips; Dances/Social or cultural gatherings.

Watseka Manor Inc
900 Market St, Watseka, IL, 60970 (815) 432-5261
Admin Donna Carlson.
Licensure Skilled Care; Intermediate Care.
Beds SNF 13; ICF 63. *Certified* Medicaid.
Ownership Proprietary.
Admissions Requirements Minimum age 21.
Staff Physicians 7 (pt); RNs 2 (ft); LPNs 3 (ft), 2 (pt); Nurses aides 20 (ft); Physical therapists 1 (pt); Recreational therapists 1 (pt); Occupational therapists 1 (pt); Speech therapists 1 (pt); Dietitians 1 (pt); Dentists 1 (pt); Ophthalmologists 1 (pt); Podiatrists 1 (pt); Audiologists 1 (pt).
Facilities Dining room; Physical therapy room; Activities room; Crafts room; Laundry room; Barber/Beauty shop.
Activities Arts and Crafts; Cards; Games; Reading groups; Prayer groups; Movies; Shopping trips; Dances/Social or cultural gatherings.
Description At Watseka Manor, residents have the privilege of selecting their menus.

WAUCONDA

Town Hall Estates
176 Thomas Ct, Wauconda, IL, 60084 (312) 526-5551
Admin Mahlon W Pomeroy.
Licensure Intermediate Care. *Beds* 98. *Certified* Medicaid.
Ownership Nonprofit.
Staff RNs 3 (ft), 4 (pt); Nurses aides 23 (ft), 13 (pt); Dietitians 1 (pt); Dentists 1 (pt); Podiatrists 1 (pt).

WAUKEGAN

Bayside Terrace
1100 S Lewis Ave, Waukegan, IL, 60085 (312) 244-8196
Admin Betty A Satterfield. *Medical Dir/Dir of Nursing* Norberto J Martinez MD.
Licensure Intermediate Care. *Beds* 119. *Certified* Medicaid.
Ownership Proprietary.
Admissions Requirements Minimum age 21; Medical examination; Physician's request.
Staff RNs 2 (ft), 3 (pt); LPNs 3 (ft), 5 (pt); Orderlies 2 (ft); Nurses aides 6 (ft), 6 (pt); Reality therapists 1 (pt); Recreational therapists 3 (ft); Occupational therapists 1 (ft); Activities coordinators 1 (ft).

North Shore Geriatric Home
2222 W 14th St, Waukegan, IL, 60085 (312) 249-2400
Admin Alice E Volin. *Medical Dir/Dir of Nursing* Sam Krueger MD.
Licensure Skilled Care; Intermediate Care.
Beds SNF 123; ICF 138. *Certified* Medicaid; Medicare.
Ownership Proprietary.

Admissions Requirements Minimum age 30; Physician's request.
Staff Physicians 10 (pt); RNs 16 (ft); LPNs 8 (ft); Orderlies 12 (ft); Nurses aides 70 (ft), 8 (pt); Physical therapists 1 (pt); Reality therapists 1 (pt); Recreational therapists 1 (pt); Occupational therapists 1 (pt); Speech therapists 1 (pt); Activities coordinators 1 (ft); Dietitians 1 (ft); Dentists 1 (pt); Ophthalmologists 1 (pt); Podiatrists 1 (pt); Audiologists 1 (pt).
Facilities Dining room; Physical therapy room; Activities room; Chapel; Crafts room; Laundry room; Barber/Beauty shop.
Activities Arts and Crafts; Cards; Games; Reading groups; Prayer groups; Movies; Shopping trips; Dances/Social or cultural gatherings.
Description In addition to good nursing care, facility has very active social rehabilitation, activity, and physical rehabilitation program.

Terrace Nursing Home
1615 Sunset Ave, Waukegan, IL, 60087 (312) 244-6700
Admin George G Davis.
Licensure Skilled Care; Intermediate Care.
Beds 112. *Certified* Medicaid; Medicare.
Ownership Proprietary.
Admissions Requirements Minimum age 18; Medical examination; Physician's request.
Staff RNs 12 (ft); LPNs 4 (ft); Orderlies 3 (ft); Nurses aides 40 (ft); Physical therapists 1 (ft); Reality therapists 2 (ft); Recreational therapists 2 (ft); Occupational therapists 1 (pt); Speech therapists 1 (pt); Activities coordinators 1 (ft); Dietitians 1 (pt); Dentists 1 (pt); Ophthalmologists 1 (pt); Podiatrists 1 (pt); Audiologists 1 (pt).
Facilities Dining room; Physical therapy room; Activities room; Crafts room; Laundry room; Barber/Beauty shop; Library; Game room.
Activities Arts and Crafts; Cards; Games; Reading groups; Prayer groups; Movies; Shopping trips; Dances/Social or cultural gatherings.
Description JCAH accredited; Blue Cross and VA approved. Facility has patio, fenced-in garden, game room, and 2 hobby shops.

Waukegan Pavilion*
2217 Washington St, Waukegan, IL, 60085 (312) 244-1400
Admin James E Willcox.
Licensure Skilled Care. *Beds* 99. *Certified* Medicaid.
Ownership Proprietary.

Waukegan Terrace*
919 Washington Park, Waukegan, IL, 60085 (312) 623-9100
Admin Sidney Roberts.
Licensure Skilled Care; Intermediate Care.
Beds SNF 99; ICF 111.
Ownership Proprietary.

WEST CHICAGO

Christ the King
30 W 300 North Ave, West Chicago, IL, 60185 (312) 231-4050
Admin Charles A Trocchio.
Licensure Skilled Care; Intermediate Care. *Certified* Medicaid.
Ownership Proprietary.

Admissions Requirements Minimum age 21.
Staff Physicians 5 (pt); RNs 20 (ft); LPNs 12 (ft); Nurses aides 39 (ft), 20 (pt); Physical therapists 2 (ft); Recreational therapists 1 (ft); Occupational therapists 1 (pt); Speech therapists 1 (pt); Dietitians 1 (ft); Dentists 1 (pt); Podiatrists 2 (pt); Audiologists 1 (pt).
Facilities Dining room; Physical therapy room; Activities room; Chapel; Crafts room; Laundry room; Barber/Beauty shop; Library.
Activities Arts and Crafts; Cards; Games; Reading groups; Prayer groups; Movies; Shopping trips; Dances/Social or cultural gatherings.

West Chicago Terrace*
928 Joliet Rd, West Chicago, IL, 60185 (312) 231-9292
Admin Lois F O'Neill.
Licensure Intermediate Care. *Beds* 119. *Certified* Medicaid.
Ownership Proprietary.

WEST FRANKFORT

American Beauty Nursing Home
W 6th St at Columbia, West Frankfort, IL, 62896 (618) 932-2109
Admin Kennis H Wallace. *Medical Dir/Dir of Nursing* Dr Norman Chiou.
Licensure Skilled Care. *Beds* 96. *Certified* Medicaid.
Ownership Proprietary.
Staff Physicians 1 (pt); RNs 1 (ft); LPNs 8 (ft), 2 (pt); Nurses aides 20 (ft), 6 (pt); Recreational therapists 1 (pt); Activities coordinators 1 (pt); Audiologists 1 (pt).
Facilities Dining room; Activities room; Laundry room; Barber/Beauty shop.
Activities Arts and Crafts; Cards; Games; Reading groups; Prayer groups.
Description VA approved.

Frankfort Heights Manor*
2500 E Saint Louis St, West Frankfort, IL, 62896 (618) 932-3236
Admin Rosalie McNana.
Licensure Intermediate Care. *Beds* 57. *Certified* Medicaid.
Ownership Proprietary.

Parkview Nursing Home
301 E Garland, West Frankfort, IL, 62896 (618) 937-2428
Admin Jeanetta D Underwood.
Licensure Intermediate Care. *Beds* 51. *Certified* Medicaid.
Ownership Proprietary.
Admissions Requirements Minimum age 18; Medical examination.
Staff LPNs 4 (ft), 4 (pt); Nurses aides 8 (ft), 3 (pt); Reality therapists 1 (ft); Recreational therapists 1 (ft); Activities coordinators 1 (ft).

WEST SALEM

Golden Acres Inc*
Rt 1, West Salem, IL, 62476 (618) 456-8405
Admin Carol Bowen.
Licensure Shelter Care. *Beds* 33.
Ownership Proprietary.

WESTMONT

Americana Healthcare Center
512 E Ogden Ave, Westmont, IL, 60559 (312) 323-4400
Admin Stephen R Malcolm. *Medical Dir/Dir of Nursing* Azizar Arain MD.
Licensure Skilled Care; Intermediate Care.
Beds 155. *Certified* Medicaid; Medicare.
Ownership Proprietary.
Admissions Requirements Medical examination; Physician's request.
Staff Physicians 16 (pt); RNs 12 (ft), 6 (pt); LPNs 10 (ft), 8 (pt); Orderlies 3 (ft), 3 (pt); Nurses aides 50 (ft), 10 (pt); Physical therapists 1 (ft), 2 (pt); Recreational therapists 1 (ft), 3 (pt); Occupational therapists; Speech therapists; Dietitians; Dentists; Ophthalmologists; Podiatrists.
Facilities Dining room; Physical therapy room; Activities room; Crafts room; Laundry room; Barber/Beauty shop.
Activities Arts and Crafts; Cards; Games; Reading groups; Prayer groups; Movies; Shopping trips; Dances/Social or cultural gatherings.
Description Facility is participating in Manor Health Care's reach program designed to assist victims of catastrophic injuries (auto accidents, etc.).

Camelot Healthcare Centre*
5801 S Cass Ave, Westmont, IL, 60559 (312) 971-2645
Admin Arthur Rosenfeld.
Licensure Skilled Care; Intermediate Care.
Beds SNF 106; ICF 104. *Certified* Medicaid; Medicare.
Ownership Proprietary.

Westmont Terrace
6501 S Cass, Westmont, IL, 60559
Admin Chris Cherney. *Medical Dir/Dir of Nursing* Lawrence LaPalio.
Licensure Skilled Care; Intermediate Care.
Beds 215. *Certified* Medicaid; Medicare.
Ownership Proprietary.
Admissions Requirements Minimum age 60.
Staff Physicians 3 (ft); RNs 5 (ft), 4 (pt); LPNs 8 (ft), 8 (pt); Orderlies 5 (ft), 2 (pt); Nurses aides 35 (ft), 30 (pt); Physical therapists 1 (ft); Occupational therapists 1 (pt); Speech therapists 1 (ft); Activities coordinators 1 (pt); Dietitians 1 (pt); Dentists 1 (pt); Ophthalmologists 1 (pt); Podiatrists 1 (pt); Audiologists 1 (pt).
Facilities Dining room; Physical therapy room; Activities room; Laundry room; Barber/Beauty shop.
Activities Arts and Crafts; Games; Reading groups; Prayer groups; Movies; Shopping trips; Dances/Social or cultural gatherings.
Description The staff cares for residents as though they were their own parents.

WHEATON

Du Page Convalescent Center*
PO Box 708, 400 N County Farm Rd, Wheaton, IL, 60187 (312) 665-6400
Admin Ronald R Reinecke.
Licensure Skilled Care. *Beds* 408. *Certified* Medicaid.
Ownership Public.

Manchester Manor Convalescent Center
1325 Manchester Rd, Wheaton, IL, 60187 (312) 668-2500
Admin William E Waln. *Medical Dir/Dir of Nursing* Dr Sam Kreuger.
Licensure Skilled Care; Intermediate Care.
Beds SNF 70; ICF 37. *Certified* Medicaid; Medicare.
Ownership Proprietary.
Admissions Requirements Medical examination.
Staff Physicians 3 (pt); RNs 4 (ft), 2 (pt); LPNs 4 (ft), 2 (pt); Nurses aides 18 (ft), 14 (pt); Physical therapists 1 (pt); Reality therapists 1 (pt); Recreational therapists 1 (pt); Occupational therapists 2 (pt); Speech therapists 1 (pt); Activities coordinators 1 (ft); Dietitians 1 (pt); Dentists 1 (pt); Podiatrists 1 (pt).
Facilities Dining room; Physical therapy room; Activities room; Chapel; Crafts room; Laundry room; Barber/Beauty shop; Library.
Activities Arts and Crafts; Cards; Games; Reading groups; Prayer groups; Movies; Shopping trips; Dances/Social or cultural gatherings.
Description Center provides all levels of care; small enough to provide a homey (not institutional) environment; located in a beautiful, wooded suburban setting.

Parkway Terrace
219 E Parkway Dr, Wheaton, IL, 60187 (312) 668-4635
Admin Wayne Rethford. *Medical Dir/Dir of Nursing* Dr Clarance Wyngarden.
Licensure Skilled Care; Intermediate Care.
Beds 68. *Certified* Medicaid.
Ownership Nonprofit.
Admissions Requirements Minimum age 18.
Staff Physicians 1 (pt); RNs 6 (ft); LPNs 4 (ft); Orderlies 1 (ft); Nurses aides 16 (ft); Physical therapists 1 (pt); Occupational therapists 1 (pt); Speech therapists 1 (pt); Activities coordinators 2 (ft); Dietitians 1 (pt); Dentists 1 (pt); Ophthalmologists 1 (pt); Podiatrists 1 (pt); Audiologists 1 (pt).
Affiliation Assembly of God
Facilities Dining room; Activities room; Laundry room; Barber/Beauty shop.
Activities Arts and Crafts; Cards; Games; Reading groups; Prayer groups; Movies; Shopping trips; Dances/Social or cultural gatherings; Pet therapy.
Description Parkway Terrace is a very active facility located in a residential community not far from local shopping areas; much community involvement.

Sandalwood Healthcare Centre*
2180 W Manchester Rd, Wheaton, IL, 60187 (312) 665-4330
Admin Sarah Chamberlain.
Licensure Skilled Care; Intermediate Care.
Beds SNF 106; ICF 107. *Certified* Medicaid; Medicare.
Ownership Proprietary.

WHEELING

Addolorata Villa
555 McHenry Rd, Wheeling, IL, 60090 (312) 537-2900
Admin Sr Mary Roberta Prince. *Medical Dir-*

/Dir of Nursing Irwin Smith MD.
Licensure Intermediate Care; Sheltered Care.
Beds ICF 42; Sheltered Care 56.
Ownership Nonprofit.
Admissions Requirements Minimum age 60; Medical examination.
Staff RNs 4 (ft), 6 (pt); LPNs 1 (ft), 1 (pt); Nurses aides 12 (ft), 4 (pt); Activities coordinators 1 (ft), 3 (pt); Podiatrists 1 (pt).
Affiliation Roman Catholic
Facilities Dining room; Physical therapy room; Activities room; Chapel; Crafts room; Laundry room; Barber/Beauty shop; Library.
Activities Arts and Crafts; Cards; Games; Reading groups; Prayer groups; Movies; Shopping trips; Dances/Social or cultural gatherings.

WHITE HALL

Greene Meadows Nursing Home*
620 W Bridgeport, White Hall, IL, 62092 (217) 374-2144
Admin James A Febus.
Licensure Intermediate Care. *Beds* 126. *Certified* Medicaid.
Ownership Proprietary.

WILMETTE

Baha'i Home
401 Greenleaf Ave, Wilmette, IL, 60091 (312) 251-7000
Admin George T Walker.
Licensure Sheltered Care. *Beds* 22.
Ownership Nonprofit.
Admissions Requirements Minimum age 65; Medical examination.
Staff RNs 1 (pt); LPNs 1 (pt); Nurses aides 3 (ft), 3 (pt); Recreational therapists 1 (ft); Occupational therapists 1 (pt); Activities coordinators 1 (ft); Dietitians 1 (pt); Ophthalmologists 1 (pt); Podiatrists 1 (pt).
Affiliation Baha'i Faith
Facilities Dining room; Activities room; Crafts room; Laundry room; Barber/Beauty shop; Library; Large and small lounges.
Activities Arts and Crafts; Cards; Games; Reading groups; Prayer groups; Movies; Dances/Social or cultural gatherings; Discussion groups; Exercise groups; Sing-a-longs; Field trips.

Normandy House
432 Poplar Dr, Wilmette, IL, 60091 (312) 256-5000
Admin O E Lufkin. *Medical Dir/Dir of Nursing* A R Peterson MD.
Licensure Skilled Care; Intermediate Care.
Beds 80. *Certified* Medicaid; Medicare.
Ownership Proprietary.
Admissions Requirements Minimum age 22; Medical examination; Physician's request.
Staff Physicians 34 (pt); RNs 12 (ft); Nurses aides 20 (ft); Physical therapists 3 (pt); Speech therapists 1 (pt); Activities coordinators 1 (ft), 3 (pt); Dietitians 1 (pt); Dentists 1 (pt); Podiatrists 2 (pt).
Facilities Dining room; Physical therapy room; Activities room; Crafts room; Barber/Beauty shop; Library.
Activities Arts and Crafts; Cards; Games;

Reading groups; Prayer groups; Movies; Dances/Social or cultural gatherings.
Description Quiet, homey, fully-carpeted, private nursing care facility providing short-term restorative care, long-term care for chronic conditions, and supportive care for the terminally ill. JCAH accredited.

WILMINGTON

Royal Willows Nursing Care Center
555 Kahler Rd, Wilmington, IL, 60481 (815) 476-7931
Admin Philip S Mendelson. *Medical Dir/Dir of Nursing* Dr Richards.
Licensure Skilled Care; Intermediate Care.
Beds SNF 98; ICF 98. *Certified* Medicaid; Medicare.
Ownership Proprietary.
Admissions Requirements Medical examination.
Staff Physicians 6 (pt); RNs 3 (ft), 2 (pt); LPNs 7 (ft), 1 (pt); Orderlies 1 (ft); Nurses aides 28 (ft), 3 (pt); Physical therapists 1 (ft), 1 (pt); Recreational therapists 3 (ft); Occupational therapists 1 (pt); Speech therapists 1 (pt); Activities coordinators 1 (ft); Dietitians 1 (pt); Dentists 1 (pt); Ophthalmologists 1 (pt); Podiatrists 1 (pt); Audiologists 1 (pt).
Facilities Dining room; Physical therapy room; Activities room; Crafts room; Laundry room; Barber/Beauty shop; Library; Residents lounge; TV room.
Activities Arts and Crafts; Cards; Games; Reading groups; Prayer groups; Movies; Shopping trips; Dances/Social or cultural gatherings.
Description Rural setting with spacious grounds; large garden behind facility; covered patio with picnic tables.

WINCHESTER

Scott County Nursing Center
Rt 2, Winchester, IL, 62694 (217) 742-3101
Admin Inez M Holderman.
Licensure Intermediate Care. *Beds* 64. *Certified* Medicaid.
Ownership Public.
Admissions Requirements Minimum age 18; Medical examination.
Staff RNs 1 (ft); LPNs 6 (ft), 2 (pt); Nurses aides 18 (ft), 7 (pt); Recreational therapists 1 (ft); Activities coordinators 2 (ft); Dietitians 1 (pt).
Facilities Dining room; Physical therapy room; Activities room; Crafts room; Laundry room; Barber/Beauty shop.
Activities Arts and Crafts; Cards; Games; Movies; Shopping trips; Dances/Social or cultural gatherings; Family night.
Description Facility is located at the north edge of town; home-like farm setting. Family night each month with families of residents coming to the facility and sharing food, conversation, and programs.

WINFIELD

Zace Healthcare Center
28 W 141 Liberty St, Winfield, IL, 60190 (312) 668-2928

Admin Jackie Grant. *Medical Dir/Dir of Nursing* Dr J Oberhelman.
Licensure Skilled Care; Intermediate Care.
Beds SNF 67; ICF 32. *Certified* Medicaid.
Ownership Proprietary.
Admissions Requirements Minimum age 21; Medical examination.
Staff Physicians 1 (pt); RNs 5 (ft); LPNs 4 (ft), 4 (pt); Orderlies 5 (ft); Nurses aides 22 (ft); Physical therapists 1 (pt); Recreational therapists 2 (ft), 1 (pt); Occupational therapists 1 (ft), 1 (pt); Speech therapists 1 (ft), 1 (pt); Activities coordinators 1 (ft); Dietitians 1 (pt); Podiatrists 1 (pt).
Facilities Dining room; Physical therapy room; Activities room; Chapel; Crafts room; Laundry room; Barber/Beauty shop.
Activities Arts and Crafts; Cards; Games; Reading groups; Prayer groups; Movies; Shopping trips; Dances/Social or cultural gatherings.
Description This 99-bed facility is nestled among the towering trees high on top of a hill in the village of Winfield.

WOOD RIVER

Pioneer Center COmunity Living Facility*
1005 McHenry Ave, Wood River, IL, 60098 (815) 338-5584
Admin Connee Meschini.
Licensure Intermediate Care. *Beds* 20.
Ownership Nonprofit.

Wood River VIP Manor*
393 Edwardsville Rd, Wood River, IL, 62095 (618) 259-4111
Admin Linda L McGaughey.
Licensure Skilled Care; Intermediate Care.
Beds SNF 38; ICF 68. *Certified* Medicaid; Medicare.
Ownership Proprietary.

WOODSTOCK

Sheltered Village—Woodstock
600 Borden, Woodstock, IL, 60098
Medical Dir/Dir of Nursing Dr Mitra.
Licensure Intermediate Care for Mentally Retarded. *Beds* 94.
Admissions Requirements Minimum age 18; Medical examination; Physician's request.
Staff RNs 4 (ft), 3 (pt); Nurses aides 11 (ft), 2 (pt); Reality therapists 2 (pt); Recreational therapists 2 (ft); Occupational therapists 1 (ft); Speech therapists 1 (ft), 1 (pt); Activities coordinators 1 (ft); Dietitians 1 (pt); Dentists 1 (pt); Ophthalmologists 1 (pt); Podiatrists 1 (pt).
Facilities Dining room; Activities room; Crafts room; Laundry room; Barber/Beauty shop.
Activities Arts and Crafts; Cards; Games; Reading groups; Prayer groups; Movies; Shopping trips; Dances/Social or cultural gatherings.
Description Facility is located on 8 acres of well-landscaped grounds on the outskirts of a community of 10,000 people.

Sunset Manor (Division of Woodstock Christian Care Inc)
920 N Seminary, Woodstock, IL, 60098 (815) 338-1749
Admin R Douglas McGrew. *Medical Dir/Dir of Nursing* Dr Robin Purdy.
Licensure Skilled Care; Intermediate Care; Sheltered Care. *Beds* SNF 29; ICF 46; Sheltered Care 63. *Certified* Medicaid.
Ownership Nonprofit.
Admissions Requirements Minimum age 62; Medical examination.
Staff RNs 3 (ft), 14 (pt); LPNs 2 (ft), 3 (pt); Orderlies 2 (ft), 1 (pt); Nurses aides 15 (ft), 17 (pt); Physical therapists 1 (pt); Recreational therapists 1 (pt); Occupational therapists 1 (pt); Speech therapists 1 (pt); Activities coordinators 3 (ft); Dietitians 1 (pt).
Affiliation Methodist
Facilities Dining room; Physical therapy room; Activities room; Chapel; Crafts room; Laundry room; Barber/Beauty shop.
Activities Arts and Crafts; Cards; Games; Reading groups; Prayer groups; Movies; Shopping trips; Dances/Social or cultural gatherings.
Description Located in the quaint town of Woodstock, Sunset Manor offers retirement opportunity for those interested in independent living, semi-independent living, custodial care (sheltered care), intermediate nursing, or skilled nursing care.

Valley Hi Nursing Home
2406 Hartland Rd, Woodstock, IL, 60098 (815) 338-0312
Admin William Morefield. *Medical Dir/Dir of Nursing* Dr Leo A Reyes.
Licensure Skilled Care; Intermediate Care.
Beds SNF 47; ICF 43. *Certified* Medicaid.
Ownership Public.
Admissions Requirements Minimum age 18; Medical examination; Physician's request.
Staff RNs 9 (ft), 5 (pt); LPNs 3 (ft); Orderlies 1 (ft); Nurses aides 28 (ft), 4 (pt); Activities coordinators 1 (ft).
Facilities Dining room; Physical therapy room; Activities room; Chapel; Laundry room; Barber/Beauty shop.
Activities Arts and Crafts; Cards; Games; Movies; Shopping trips.

Woodstock Residence
309 McHenry Ave, Woodstock, IL, 60098 (815) 338-1700
Admin Marilyn A Johnson. *Medical Dir/Dir of Nursing* John C Paul MD.
Licensure Skilled Care. *Beds* 112. *Certified* Medicaid; Medicare.
Ownership Proprietary.
Admissions Requirements Minimum age 21; Medical examination; Physician's request.
Staff Physicians 1 (ft), 12 (pt); RNs 15 (ft); LPNs 1 (ft); Orderlies 2 (ft); Nurses aides 34 (ft), 4 (pt); Physical therapists 2 (ft), 1 (pt); Reality therapists 2 (ft), 1 (pt); Recreational therapists 2 (ft), 1 (pt); Occupational therapists 1 (pt); Speech therapists 1 (ft); Activities coordinators 1 (ft); Dietitians 1 (ft); Dentists 1 (pt); Ophthalmologists 1 (pt); Podiatrists 1 (pt); Audiologists 1 (pt).
Facilities Dining room; Physical therapy room; Activities room; Chapel; Crafts room; Laundry room; Barber/Beauty shop; Library; Covered patios; Gardens.
Activities Arts and Crafts; Cards; Games; Prayer groups; Movies; Shopping trips; Dances/Social or cultural gatherings.
Description Residence is a single-level structure

in a 5-acre park-like setting; cheerful, warm atmosphere; approved for Level II incentive program by Public Health Administration.

WORTH

Park Lawn Center*
5831 W 115th St, Worth, IL, 60482 (312) 396-1117
Admin Marjorie Chwastecki.
Licensure Intermediate Care. *Beds* 41.
Ownership Nonprofit.

YORKVILLE

Hillside Nursing and Convalescent Home
Rt 34 and Game Farm Rd, Yorkville, IL, 60560 (312) 553-5811
Admin Robert J Mahoney.
Licensure Skilled Care; Intermediate Care; Sheltered Care. *Beds* 79.
Ownership Proprietary.
Admissions Requirements Minimum age 18; Medical examination.
Staff RNs 8 (ft); LPNs 2 (ft); Orderlies 2 (ft); Nurses aides 19 (ft); Activities coordinators 1 (ft), 1 (pt); Dietitians 1 (ft).
Facilities Dining room; Activities room; Crafts room; Laundry room; Barber/Beauty shop; Library.
Activities Arts and Crafts; Cards; Games; Reading groups; Prayer groups; Movies; Shopping trips; Dances/Social or cultural gatherings.
Description This 21-year-old facility is located in a country setting, all on one floor; features restorative nursing.

ZEIGLER

Zeigler Colonial Manor Inc*
300 Church St, Zeigler, IL, 62999 (618) 596-6635
Admin Terra Potocki.
Licensure Intermediate Care; Developmentally Disabled. *Beds* SNF 27; Developmentally Disabled 22. *Certified* Medicaid.
Ownership Proprietary.

ZION

Crown Manor Nursing Home*
1805 27th St, Zion, IL, 60099 (312) 746-3736
Admin Wendell G Studebaker.
Licensure Skilled Care. *Beds* 113. *Certified* Medicaid; Medicare.
Ownership Proprietary.

Rolling Hills Manor
3615 16th St, Zion, IL, 60099 (312) 746-8382
Admin Katherine C Brown. *Medical Dir/Dir of Nursing* C David Engstrom MD.
Licensure Skilled Care. *Beds* 139. *Certified* Medicaid; Medicare.
Ownership Nonprofit.
Admissions Requirements Minimum age 65; Medical examination; Physician's request.
Staff RNs 5 (ft), 2 (pt); LPNs 5 (ft), 4 (pt); Nurses aides 27 (ft), 7 (pt); Physical therapists 1 (pt); Reality therapists 1 (ft); Recreational therapists 2 (ft), 2 (pt); Occupational therapists 1 (pt); Speech therapists 1 (pt); Activities coordinators 1 (ft); Dietitians 1 (pt); Dentists 1 (pt); Podiatrists 1 (pt); Audiologists 1 (pt).
Affiliation Slovak American Charitable Association
Facilities Dining room; Physical therapy room; Activities room; Crafts room; Laundry room; Barber/Beauty shop.
Activities Arts and Crafts; Cards; Games; Reading groups; Prayer groups; Movies; Shopping trips; Dances/Social or cultural gatherings.
Description Facility features wide screen TV with VCR to show good, color movies. Located in a rural setting with good clean air, this not-for-profit home is owned by the Slovak American Charitable Assoc, but open to all.

Sheridan Health Care Center
2534 Elim Ave, Zion, IL, 60099 (312) 746-8435
Admin Stanton F Aron. *Medical Dir/Dir of Nursing* Dr Thomas Engel.
Licensure Skilled Care; Intermediate Care. *Beds* SNF 95; ICF 191. *Certified* Medicaid.

INDIANA

ALBANY

Albany Nursing Care Inc
910 W Walnut, Albany, IN, 47320 (317)
789-4423
Admin Nicholas E Lefevre. *Medical Dir/Dir of
Nursing* Kay Starr RN.
Licensure Intermediate Care. *Beds* 101. *Certified* Medicaid.
Admissions Requirements Medical examination.
Staff RNs 1 (ft); LPNs 4 (ft); Nurses aides 37
(ft); Activities coordinators 2 (ft); Dietitians 1
(ft); Qualified medical assistants 3 (ft), 2 (pt).
Facilities Dining room; Activities room; Laundry room; Barber/Beauty shop; Library.
Activities Games; Reading groups; Prayer
groups; Movies; Shopping trips; Dances/Social
or cultural gatherings.

ALEXANDRIA

Alexandria Convalescent Center*
625 W Adams St, PO Box 209, Alexandria, IN,
46001 (317) 724-2496
Admin Bart Bingham.
Licensure Intermediate Care. *Beds* 16. *Certified* Medicaid.

The Willows*
Rt 4, Box 220, Alexandria, IN, 46001 (317)
724-4464
Admin Marian E Webb.
Licensure Intermediate Care. *Beds* 48. *Certi-
fied* Medicaid.

ANDERSON

Americana Healthcare Center—Anderson
1345 N Madison Ave, Anderson, IN, 46011
(317) 644-2888
Admin Betty Crum. *Medical Dir/Dir of
Nursing* Stephen J Wright MD.
Licensure Skilled Care; Intermediate Care.
Beds SNF 40; ICF 44. *Certified* Medicaid;
Medicare.
Admissions Requirements Minimum age 18;
Medical examination; Physician's request.
Staff RNs 6 (ft), 5 (pt); LPNs 5 (ft), 3 (pt);
Orderlies 1 (ft), 1 (pt); Nurses aides 34 (ft), 17
(pt); Physical therapists 1 (ft); Speech therapists
1 (pt); Activities coordinators 1 (ft).
Facilities Dining room; Physical therapy room;

Activities room; Chapel; Crafts room; Laundry
room; Barber/Beauty shop; Library.
Activities Arts and Crafts; Cards; Games;
Reading groups; Prayer groups; Movies; Shopping trips; Dances/Social or cultural gatherings.

Anderson Healthcare Center*
1809 N Madison Ave, Anderson, IN, 46012
(317) 644-0903
Admin Loretta G Folsom.
Licensure Skilled Care; Intermediate Care.
Beds SNF 83; ICF 92. *Certified* Medicaid;
Medicare.

The Family Tree Care Center*
1112 Monticello Dr, Anderson, IN, 46011 (317)
649-0496
Admin David Schmacher.
Licensure Intermediate Care. *Beds* 110. *Certified* Medicaid.

The Goble Home*
332 W 11th St, Anderson, IN, 46016 (317)
642-8156
Admin Dillard Marcum.
Licensure Intermediate Care. *Beds* 30. *Certified* Medicaid.

New Haven Nursing Home
1023 E 8th St, Anderson, IN, 46012 (317)
643-7391
Admin Josephine Wade.
Licensure Intermediate Care. *Beds* 14.

Rolling Hills Convalescent Center Inc
1821 Lindberg Rd, Anderson, IN, 46012 (317)
649-2532
Admin D J Wanders. *Medical Dir/Dir of
Nursing* Dr Linda Stropes.
Licensure Intermediate Care. *Beds* SNF 140;
ICF 26. *Certified* Medicaid; Medicare.
Admissions Requirements Medical examina-
tion; Physician's request.
Staff RNs 5 (ft), 2 (pt); LPNs 15 (ft), 4 (pt);
Nurses aides 58 (ft), 5 (pt); Physical therapists 1
(ft); Occupational therapists 1 (ft); Speech thera-
pists 1 (ft); Activities coordinators 1 (ft); Dieti-
tians 1 (ft).
Facilities Dining room; Physical therapy room;
Activities room; Crafts room; Laundry room;
Barber/Beauty shop.
Activities Arts and Crafts; Cards; Games;
Reading groups; Prayer groups; Movies; Shop-
ping trips; Dances/Social or cultural gatherings;

Family/New admission adjustment workshops.
Description Facility features a residents' council, educational classes, monthly residents'
newsletter, volunteer programs, adopt-
a-grandparent program, flower gardens, resident
parties and dances, vegetable garden, patio
areas with lawn furniture, and facility is located
on 11 acres of land.

ANGOLA

Angola Nursing Home
600 N Williams St, Angola, IN, 46703 (219)
665-6313
Admin L Marie Winebrenner.
Licensure Intermediate Care. *Beds* 40. *Certi-
fied* Medicaid.
Admissions Requirements Minimum age 18;
Medical examination; Physician's request.
Staff Physicians 1 (pt); RNs 1 (ft); LPNs 3 (ft),
1 (pt); Nurses aides 7 (ft), 7 (pt); Activities coordinators 1 (ft); Dietitians 1 (pt); Podiatrists 1
(pt).
Facilities Dining room; Activities room; Laundry room.
Activities Arts and Crafts; Cards; Games;
Reading groups; Prayer groups; Movies; Shopping trips; Dances/Social or cultural gatherings;
Picnics.
Description Twelve of the residents work at the
community sheltered workshop. Many outings
are planned for the year—trips to zoo, circuses,
fairs, swimming, and picnics.

Carlin Park Nursing Home Inc
PO Box 341, Angola, IN, 46703 (219) 665-9467
Admin Louis Crissman and Flo Shull. *Medical
Dir/Dir of Nursing* Floyd Coleman MD.
Licensure Intermediate Care. *Beds* 99. *Certi-
fied* Medicaid.
Admissions Requirements Minimum age 18;
Medical examination; Physician's request.
Staff Physicians 1 (pt); RNs 2 (ft), 1 (pt); LPNs
6 (ft), 2 (pt); Nurses aides 35 (ft), 7 (pt);
Physical therapists 1 (pt); Recreational thera-
pists 1 (ft); Activities coordinators 1 (ft); Dieti-
tians 1 (pt); Dentists 1 (pt); Ophthalmologists 1
(pt); Podiatrists 1 (pt).
Facilities Dining room; Physical therapy room;
Activities room; Chapel; Crafts room; Laundry
room; Barber/Beauty shop.
Activities Arts and Crafts; Cards; Games;
Reading groups; Prayer groups; Movies; Shopping trips; Dances/Social or cultural gatherings.

Lakeland Nursing Center
500 N Williams St, Angola, IN, 46703 (219)
665-2161
Admin Bobby R Scott.
Licensure Intermediate Care. *Beds* 60. *Certified* Medicaid.
Admissions Requirements Medical examination; Physician's request.
Staff RNs 2 (ft); LPNs 1 (ft), 4 (pt); Orderlies 2 (ft); Nurses aides 15 (ft), 2 (pt); Activities coordinators 1 (ft); Dietitians 1 (pt); Podiatrists 1 (pt).
Facilities Dining room; Physical therapy room; Activities room; Crafts room; Laundry room; Barber/Beauty shop; Library.
Activities Arts and Crafts; Cards; Games; Reading groups; Movies.

ARCADIA

Arcadia Children's Home*
303 Franklin Ave, Arcadia, IN, 46030 (317)
984-4528
Admin Leonard A Hall.
Licensure Intermediate Care. *Beds* 54. *Certified* Medicaid.

Hamilton Heights Health Center
706 W Main St, Arcadia, IN, 46030 (317)
984-3555
Admin Burl J Shinkle. *Medical Dir/Dir of Nursing* Dr Jerry Royer.
Licensure Intermediate Care. *Beds* 154. *Certified* Medicaid.
Admissions Requirements Minimum age 18; Medical examination; Physician's request.
Staff Physicians 3 (pt); RNs 3 (ft); LPNs 9 (ft), 2 (pt); Orderlies 2 (ft); Nurses aides 35 (ft), 6 (pt); Physical therapists 1 (pt); Recreational therapists 1 (ft); Occupational therapists 1 (pt); Speech therapists 1 (ft); Activities coordinators 1 (ft); Dietitians 1 (pt); Dentists 1 (pt); Podiatrists 1 (pt); Audiologists 1 (pt).
Facilities Dining room; Physical therapy room; Activities room; Chapel; Crafts room; Laundry room; Barber/Beauty shop; Library.
Activities Arts and Crafts; Cards; Games; Reading groups; Prayer groups; Movies; Shopping trips; Dances/Social or cultural gatherings.
Description Facility is a 154-bed ICF in a rural small town setting with swimming pool and recreational acres available.

ATTICA

Woodland Manor Nursing Center*
PO Box 166, Attica, IN, 47918 (317) 762-6133
Admin Linda Short.
Licensure Intermediate Care. *Beds* 53. *Certified* Medicaid.

AUBURN

Betz Nursing Home Inc
Rt 3, Auburn, IN, 46706 (219) 925-3814
Admin Doris Marshall. *Medical Dir/Dir of Nursing* Carol Marks RN.
Licensure Intermediate Care. *Beds* 102. *Certified* Medicaid.
Admissions Requirements Medical examination; Physician's request.

Staff RNs 1 (pt); LPNs 5 (pt); Nurses aides 75 (pt); Activities coordinators 5 (pt); Dietitians 1 (pt).
Facilities Dining room; Activities room; Crafts room; Laundry room; Barber/Beauty shop.
Activities Arts and Crafts; Cards; Games; Reading groups; Prayer groups; Movies; Dances/Social or cultural gatherings.
Description Facility is as near like home as possible; a beautician available 40 hours every week; facility is family owned and operated with a waiting list at all times.

Glen Oaks Nursing Home*
PO Box 544, E 7th St, Auburn, IN, 46706 (219)
925-1111
Admin Dennis Girardot.
Licensure Intermediate Care. *Beds* 73. *Certified* Medicaid.

AVILLA

Sacred Heart Home
Rt 2, Avilla, IN, 46710 (219) 897-2841
Admin Sr Bernadette Duman. *Medical Dir/Dir of Nursing* Dr Max Sneary.
Licensure Intermediate Care. *Beds* 133. *Certified* Medicaid.
Admissions Requirements Medical examination.
Staff Physicians 3 (pt); RNs 4 (ft), 1 (pt); LPNs 7 (ft), 2 (pt); Nurses aides 15 (ft), 26 (pt); Physical therapists 2 (pt); Recreational therapists 3 (pt); Activities coordinators 1 (ft); Dietitians 1 (pt); Podiatrists 1 (pt).
Affiliation Roman Catholic
Facilities Dining room; Physical therapy room; Activities room; Chapel; Laundry room; Barber/Beauty shop; Library.
Activities Arts and Crafts; Cards; Games; Reading groups; Prayer groups; Movies; Shopping trips; Dances/Social or cultural gatherings; Cooking sessions; Rhythm band; Choir.
Description This is a beautiful, fairly new facility nestled in the rural area of Avilla near Fort Wayne; has an excellent reputation and is known for quality care given; very active programs; home consists of 3 rather distinct units based on kind of care needed.

BATESVILLE

Dreyerhaus
958 E Hwy 46, Batesville, IN, 47006 (812)
934-2436
Admin Robert F Woods. *Medical Dir/Dir of Nursing* Michael Hansen MD.
Licensure Intermediate Care. *Beds* 132. *Certified* Medicaid.
Staff Physicians 1 (pt); RNs 4 (ft); LPNs 9 (ft); Orderlies 5 (ft); Nurses aides 40 (ft); Physical therapists 1 (ft); Activities coordinators 1 (ft); Dietitians 1 (pt).
Facilities Dining room; Physical therapy room; Activities room; Chapel; Crafts room; Laundry room; Barber/Beauty shop; Library.
Activities Arts and Crafts; Cards; Games; Reading groups; Prayer groups; Movies; Shopping trips; Dances/Social or cultural gatherings.

BEDFORD

Bedford Nursing Home
514 E 16th St, Bedford, IN, 47421 (812)
279-4611
Admin Nellie M Camp.
Licensure Intermediate Care. *Beds* 40. *Certified* Medicaid.
Admissions Requirements Minimum age 21.
Staff RNs 1 (pt); LPNs 3 (ft), 2 (pt); Nurses aides 10 (ft), 10 (pt); Activities coordinators 1 (pt); Dietitians 1 (ft), 4 (pt).
Facilities Dining room; Activities room; Laundry room.
Activities Arts and Crafts; Cards; Games; Reading groups; Prayer groups; Movies; Shopping trips; Dances/Social or cultural gatherings.
Description Facility offers open visiting hours, special diets, and free personal laundering.

Hospitality House
2111 Norton Ln, Bedford, IN, 47421 (812)
279-4437
Admin Albert Estes. *Medical Dir/Dir of Nursing* Dr Lawrence Benham.
Licensure Skilled Care; Intermediate Care; Pediatric Care. *Beds* SNF 32; ICF 95; Pediatric Care 40. *Certified* Medicaid; Medicare.
Admissions Requirements Medical examination; Physician's request.
Staff Physicians 14 (pt); RNs 7 (ft); LPNs 17 (ft); Nurses aides 40 (ft), 7 (pt); Physical therapists 1 (pt); Occupational therapists 2 (pt); Speech therapists 1 (pt); Activities coordinators 1 (ft); Dietitians 1 (ft).
Facilities Dining room; Physical therapy room; Activities room; Laundry room; Barber/Beauty shop; Speech therapy room.

Westview Manor Healthcare Center
1510 Clinic Dr, Bedford, IN, 47421 (812)
279-4494
Admin Marilyn Johnson. *Medical Dir/Dir of Nursing* Dr D J Kaderabek.
Licensure Skilled Care; Intermediate Care. *Beds* SNF 58; ICF 60. *Certified* Medicaid.
Admissions Requirements Minimum age 18; Medical examination; Physician's request.
Staff RNs 6 (ft); LPNs 8 (ft); Nurses aides 43 (ft); Physical therapists 1 (pt); Activities coordinators 2 (ft); Dietitians 1 (pt); Dentists 1 (pt); Podiatrists 1 (pt).
Facilities Dining room; Physical therapy room; Activities room; Crafts room; Laundry room; Barber/Beauty shop.
Activities Arts and Crafts; Cards; Games; Reading groups; Prayer groups; Movies; Shopping trips; Dances/Social or cultural gatherings.

BEECH GROVE

Beech Grove Healthcare Center
2002 Albany Ave, Beech Grove, IN, 46107
(317) 783-2911
Admin Tom Huckstep. *Medical Dir/Dir of Nursing* Dr Thomas Moran.
Licensure Skilled Care; Intermediate Care.
Beds SNF 77; ICF 122. *Certified* Medicaid; Medicare.
Admissions Requirements Medical examination; Physician's request.
Staff RNs 5 (ft), 2 (pt); LPNs 8 (ft), 3 (pt);

Nurses aides 46 (ft), 12 (pt); Physical therapists 2 (pt); Occupational therapists 2 (pt); Speech therapists 1 (pt); Activities coordinators 2 (ft); Dietitians 1 (ft); Dentists 2 (pt); Podiatrists 1 (pt).
Facilities Dining room; Physical therapy room; Activities room; Chapel; Laundry room; Barber/Beauty shop.
Activities Arts and Crafts; Cards; Games; Reading groups; Prayer groups; Movies; Shopping trips; Dances/Social or cultural gatherings.

Saint Paul Hermitage*
501 N 17th Ave, Beech Grove, IN, 46107 (317) 786-2261
Admin Sr Mary Gilbert Schipp.
Licensure Intermediate Care. *Beds* 48. *Certified* Medicaid.
Affiliation Roman Catholic

BERNE

Berne Nursing Home
906 W Main St, Berne, IN, 46711 (219) 589-2127
Admin Larry E Watkins.
Licensure Intermediate Care; Residential Care. *Beds* 25.
Admissions Requirements Minimum age 18; Medical examination.
Staff RNs 1 (pt); LPNs 1 (ft); Nurses aides 3 (ft), 15 (pt); Activities coordinators 1 (ft); Dietitians 1 (pt).
Facilities Dining room; Activities room; Laundry room; Barber/Beauty shop.
Activities Arts and Crafts; Cards; Games; Reading groups; Movies; Shopping trips; Dances/Social or cultural gatherings.

Swiss Village Inc*
W Main St, Berne, IN, 46711 (219) 589-3173
Admin Wayne Smith.
Licensure Intermediate Care. *Beds* 56.
Certified Medicaid.

BICKNELL

Bicknell Health Care Center
204 W 3rd St, Bicknell, IN, 47512 (812) 735-3021
Admin Cecil Perkins. *Medical Dir/Dir of Nursing* Dr B G O'Dell and Dr R W Rompf.
Licensure Intermediate Care. *Beds* 47. *Certified* Medicaid.
Admissions Requirements Medical examination.
Staff Physicians 2 (pt); RNs 1 (ft), 1 (pt); LPNs 3 (ft), 3 (pt); Nurses aides 13 (ft), 4 (pt); Physical therapists 1 (pt); Activities coordinators 1 (ft); Dietitians 1 (ft); Dentists 2 (pt); Ophthalmologists 2 (pt); Podiatrists 1 (pt).
Facilities Dining room; Physical therapy room; Activities room; Crafts room; Laundry room; Barber/Beauty shop; Library; Conference room; Supplementry nutrition room.
Activities Arts and Crafts; Cards; Games; Reading groups; Prayer groups; Movies; Shopping trips; Dances/Social or cultural gatherings; Birthday parties.
Description Facility is still small enough that a home-like atmosphere is still possible and

encouraged; family environment is prominent and patients are cared for on an individual basis. Licensed personnel are present 24 hours a day to provide professional care.

BLOOMFIELD

Bloomfield Nursing Center
150 N Seminary St, Bloomfield, IN, 47424 (812) 384-4448
Admin Janet B Teeple.
Licensure Intermediate Care. *Beds* 60. *Certified* Medicaid.
Admissions Requirements Minimum age 19; Medical examination.
Staff RNs 2 (ft); LPNs 4 (ft); Nurses aides 16 (ft); Physical therapists 1 (pt); Occupational therapists 1 (pt); Activities coordinators 1 (ft); Dietitians 1 (pt).
Facilities Dining room; Physical therapy room; Activities room; Laundry room; Barber/Beauty shop.
Activities Arts and Crafts; Cards; Games; Reading groups; Movies; Shopping trips; Dances/Social or cultural gatherings.
Description Located in a small town in south central Indiana, our friendly center has a very quiet and home-like atmosphere. We offer excellent dining, physical therapy, and 24-hour licensed nursing care.

BLOOMINGTON

Bloomington Convalescent Center
714 S Rogers St, Bloomington, IN, 47401 (812) 336-6893
Admin Mark S Fritz. *Medical Dir/Dir of Nursing* George Lewis MD.
Licensure Skilled Care; Intermediate Care. *Beds* SNF 26; ICF 143. *Certified* Medicaid; Medicare.
Admissions Requirements Minimum age 18; Medical examination; Physician's request.
Staff RNs 6 (ft), 5 (pt); LPNs 15 (ft), 14 (pt); Orderlies 10 (ft), 6 (pt); Nurses aides 25 (ft), 28 (pt); Physical therapists 1 (ft), 1 (pt); Occupational therapists 1 (pt); Speech therapists 1 (pt); Activities coordinators 1 (ft), 2 (pt); Dietitians 1 (pt); Dentists 1 (pt); Ophthalmologists 1 (pt); Podiatrists 1 (pt).
Facilities Dining room; Physical therapy room; Activities room; Crafts room; Barber/Beauty shop; Library.
Activities Arts and Crafts; Games; Reading groups; Prayer groups; Movies; Shopping trips; Dances/Social or cultural gatherings.

Bloomington Nursing Home
120 E Miller Dr, Bloomington, IN, 47401 (812) 336-1055
Admin William Doub.
Licensure Intermediate Care. *Beds* 40. *Certified* Medicaid.
Admissions Requirements Minimum age 18; Medical examination.
Staff RNs 1 (ft); LPNs 4 (pt); Orderlies 1 (pt); Nurses aides 7 (ft), 6 (pt); Activities coordinators 1 (ft); Dietitians 1 (pt).
Facilities Dining room; Activities room; Crafts room.

Activities Arts and Crafts; Games; Reading groups; Prayer groups; Movies; Shopping trips; Dances/Social or cultural gatherings.

Fontanbleu Nursing Center
3305 S Hwy 37, Bloomington, IN, 47401 (812) 332-4437
Admin L A Albright. *Medical Dir/Dir of Nursing* Dr Graham Schuler.
Licensure Intermediate Care. *Beds* 101. *Certified* Medicaid; Medicare.
Admissions Requirements Minimum age 18.

Hospitality House Inc
1100 S Curry Pike, PO Box 427, Bloomington, IN, 47402 (812) 339-1657
Admin Caroline Lin. *Medical Dir/Dir of Nursing* Dr LeWallen.
Licensure Skilled Care; Intermediate Care. *Beds* SNF 52; ICF 140. *Certified* Medicaid; Medicare.
Admissions Requirements Minimum age 18; Medical examination; Physician's request.
Staff Physicians 1 (pt); RNs 4 (ft), 3 (pt); LPNs 12 (ft), 5 (pt); Orderlies 2 (ft), 3 (pt); Nurses aides 50 (ft), 20 (pt); Physical therapists 1 (pt); Occupational therapists 2 (pt); Speech therapists 1 (pt); Activities coordinators 1 (ft), 4 (pt); Dietitians 1 (pt); Dentists 1 (pt); Ophthalmologists 1 (pt); Podiatrists 1 (pt); Audiologists 1 (pt).
Facilities Dining room; Physical therapy room; Activities room; Chapel; Crafts room; Laundry room; Barber/Beauty shop.
Activities Arts and Crafts; Cards; Games; Reading groups; Prayer groups; Movies; Shopping trips; Dances/Social or cultural gatherings.
Description One level facility is located on 17 acres; accredited by JCAH; 24 hours a day of fine nursing care; outstanding activities; reasonable costs; quality assurance program; full rehabilitation services; homemade meals; complete dietary services.

BLUFFTON

Cooper Community Care Center*
1509 Fort Wayne Rd, Bluffton, IN, 46714 (219) 824-2434
Admin Larry E Watkins.
Licensure Skilled Care; Intermediate Care. *Beds* SNF 30; ICF 53. *Certified* Medicaid; Medicare.

Davis Bluffton Nursing Home
1001 S Clark Ave, Bluffton, IN, 46714 (219) 824-0326
Admin Margaret Davis.
Licensure Intermediate Care. *Beds* 40. *Certified* Medicaid.
Admissions Requirements Minimum age 18; Medical examination.
Staff RNs 1 (ft), 1 (pt); LPNs 1 (ft); Nurses aides 9 (ft), 9 (pt); Activities coordinators 1 (ft); Dietitians 1 (pt).
Facilities Dining room; Activities room.
Activities Arts and Crafts; Cards; Games; Reading groups; Prayer groups; Movies; Dances/Social or cultural gatherings.
Description We are the oldest nursing home in

Wells County. Our purpose is to make it "home" for our residents and to give the best care possible.

Meadowvale Skilled Care Center
1529 W Lancaster St, Bluffton, IN, 46714 (219) 824-4320
Admin John R Siela. *Medical Dir/Dir of Nursing* Dr William Gitlin.
Licensure Intermediate Care. *Beds* 120. *Certified* Medicaid.
Admissions Requirements Medical examination; Physician's request.
Staff Physicians 1 (pt); RNs 2 (ft); LPNs 11 (ft), 1 (pt); Orderlies 1 (ft); Nurses aides 42 (ft), 13 (pt); Speech therapists 1 (pt); Activities coordinators 1 (ft); Dietitians 1 (pt); Dentists 1 (pt); Ophthalmologists 1 (pt); Podiatrists 1 (pt); Audiologists 1 (pt).
Facilities Dining room; Activities room; Chapel; Crafts room; Laundry room; Barber/Beauty shop.
Activities Arts and Crafts; Cards; Games; Reading groups; Prayer groups; Movies; Shopping trips; Dances/Social or cultural gatherings.

BOONVILLE

Baker's Rest Haven Inc*
305 E North St, Boonville, IN, 47601 (812) 897-2810
Admin Viola N Vance.
Licensure Intermediate Care. *Beds* 60. *Certified* Medicaid.

Boonville Convalescent Center Inc*
PO Box 72, 803 S 2nd St, Boonville, IN, 47601 (812) 897-1375
Admin Janet G Ludwyck.
Licensure Intermediate Care. *Beds* 91. *Certified* Medicaid.

BRAZIL

Clay County Health Center Inc
1408 E Hendrix St, Brazil, IN, 47834 (812) 433-4111
Admin Wilma I Ellison. *Medical Dir/Dir of Nursing* Rahim Farid.
Licensure Skilled Care; Intermediate Care. *Beds* SNF 39; ICF 60. *Certified* Medicaid; Medicare.
Facilities Dining room; Physical therapy room; Activities room; Crafts room; Laundry room; Barber/Beauty shop.
Activities Arts and Crafts; Cards; Games; Reading groups; Prayer groups; Movies.

BREMEN

R N Nursing Home Inc
316 Woodies Ln, Bremen, IN, 46506
Admin John D Pelzer. *Medical Dir/Dir of Nursing* Dr James Berndt.
Licensure Intermediate Care. *Beds* 82. *Certified* Medicaid.
Ownership Proprietary.
Admissions Requirements Medical examination; Physician's request.
Staff Physicians 6 (pt); RNs 4 (ft); LPNs 2 (ft); Nurses aides 27 (ft), 16 (pt); Physical therapists

1 (pt); Recreational therapists 1 (ft); Activities coordinators 1 (ft); Dietitians 2 (ft); Dentists 1 (ft); Podiatrists 1 (pt).
Facilities Dining room; Activities room; Chapel; Crafts room; Laundry room; Barber/Beauty shop; Library.
Activities Arts and Crafts; Cards; Games; Prayer groups; Movies; Dances/Social or cultural gatherings.
Description Facility is in a new building with a lovely patio with lots of flowers and a garden. Residents can participate in zoo trips, walk-o-rock, bowl-a-thon, cookouts, exercise classes, IHP program, work with Marshall Starke program.

TLC Nursing Home Inc*
8286 US West, Bremen, IN, 46506 (219) 546-4214
Admin Pauline Studt.
Licensure Intermediate Care. *Beds* 24. *Certified* Medicaid.

BROOKSTON

Archibald Memorial Home for Aged Deaf
Rt 2, Brookston, IN, 47923 (219) 563-3582
Admin Robert K Lewis.
Licensure Residential Care. *Beds* 16.
Staff Physicians 1 (pt); RNs 1 (pt); Recreational therapists 3 (pt); Activities coordinators 2 (pt); Dietitians 2 (ft); Dentists; Ophthalmologists; Podiatrists.
Facilities Dining room; Activities room; Crafts room; Laundry room; Barber/Beauty shop; Library.
Activities Arts and Crafts; Cards; Games; Prayer groups; Shopping trips; Dances/Social or cultural gatherings; Movies captioned for deaf.
Description Everything here is geared to and for the deaf.

BROOKVILLE

Elsie Dryer Nursing Home
273 Main St, Brookville, IN, 47012 (317) 647-6231
Admin Janet E Stevens. *Medical Dir/Dir of Nursing* Dr William Stitt.
Licensure Intermediate Care. *Beds* 49. *Certified* Medicaid.
Admissions Requirements Medical examination; Physician's request.
Staff Physicians 4 (pt); RNs 1 (pt); LPNs 3 (ft), 1 (pt); Orderlies 1 (ft); Nurses aides 7 (ft), 13 (pt); Activities coordinators 1 (ft).
Facilities Dining room.
Activities Arts and Crafts; Cards; Reading groups; Prayer groups; Movies.

BROWNSBURG

Golden Manor Health Care Center*
Hornaday Rd, Brownsburg, IN, 46112 (317) 852-3123
Admin Randy Hornstein.
Licensure Skilled Care; Intermediate Care. *Beds* 178. *Certified* Medicaid.

BROWNSTOWN

Hoosier Christian Village*
621 S Sugar, Brownstown, IN, 47220 (812) 358-2504
Admin William Way.
Licensure Skilled Care; Intermediate Care. *Beds* 97. *Certified* Medicaid; Medicare.

BUTLER

Butler Hotel Rest Home Inc
117 S Broadway St, Butler, IN, 46721 (219) 868-2076
Admin Phyllis Tittman. *Medical Dir/Dir of Nursing* William Goudy DO.
Licensure Intermediate Care. *Beds* 40. *Certified* Medicaid.
Admissions Requirements Minimum age 18; Medical examination.
Staff Physicians 1 (pt); RNs 1 (pt); LPNs 2 (ft), 1 (pt); Activities coordinators 1 (ft); Dietitians 1 (pt).
Facilities Dining room; Activities room; Crafts room; Laundry room.
Activities Arts and Crafts; Cards; Games; Prayer groups; Movies; Shopping trips; Dances/Social or cultural gatherings.

Meadowhaven Nursing Home*
300 W Liberty, Butler, IN, 46721 (219) 868-2164
Admin Robert W Shambaugh.
Licensure Intermediate Care. *Beds* 101. *Certified* Medicaid.

CARMEL

Carmel Care Center
118 Medical Dr, Carmel, IN, 46032 (317) 844-4211
Admin Stephen L Spaugh. *Medical Dir/Dir of Nursing* Norman Fogle MD.
Licensure Skilled Care; Intermediate Care. *Beds* SNF 99; ICF 163. *Certified* Medicaid; Medicare.
Admissions Requirements Minimum age 18; Medical examination; Physician's request.
Staff Physicians 30 (ft); RNs 10 (ft), 11 (pt); LPNs 14 (ft), 10 (pt); Orderlies 3 (ft); Nurses aides 72 (ft), 28 (pt); Physical therapists 1 (pt); Occupational therapists 1 (pt); Speech therapists 1 (pt); Activities coordinators 2 (ft); Dietitians 1 (pt); Dentists 1 (pt); Podiatrists 1 (pt); Audiologists 1 (pt).
Facilities Dining room; Physical therapy room; Activities room; Crafts room; Laundry room; Barber/Beauty shop; Library.
Activities Arts and Crafts; Cards; Games; Reading groups; Movies; Shopping trips; Dances/Social or cultural gatherings.

Lakeview Health Care Center
2907 E 136th St, Carmel, IN, 46032 (317) 846-0265
Admin Steven L Dehne. *Medical Dir/Dir of Nursing* Dr Robert Habig.
Licensure Comprehensive Care. *Beds* Comprehensive Care 22.
Staff Physicians 1 (pt); LPNs 2 (ft); Nurses aides 10 (ft); Recreational therapists 1 (pt);

Activities coordinators 1 (pt); Dietitians 1 (pt).
Facilities Dining room; Activities room; Laundry room.
Activities Arts and Crafts; Cards; Games; Reading groups; Prayer groups; Movies; Shopping trips; Dances/Social or cultural gatherings.
Description Nestled on a wooded hilltop overlooking rolling pasture land and grazing cattle and horses, small facility gives home-like feeling with good home cooking and a staff dedicated to service of love, laughter, and understanding.

CENTER POINT

Macanell Nursing Home Inc*
Rt 2, Box 139, Center Point, IN, 47840 (812) 835-3041
Admin Hugh W McCann.
Licensure Intermediate Care. *Beds* 67. *Certified* Medicaid.

CENTERVILLE

Pinehurst Nursing Home*
Box 145, Centerville, IN, 47330 (317) 855-3424
Admin Mary McClure.
Licensure Intermediate Care. *Beds* 72. *Certified* Medicaid.

CHANDLER

Medco Center of Chandler*
Rt 2, Chandler, IN, 47610 (812) 925-3381
Admin Rachel Ann Chambers.
Licensure Intermediate Care. *Beds* 74. *Certified* Medicaid.

CHARLESTOWN

Kentuckiana Christian Home Inc
Rt 2, Box 337, Charlestown, IN, 47111 (812) 256-3371
Admin Stanley Hunt.
Licensure Comprehensive Care. *Beds* 65. *Certified* Medicaid.
Admissions Requirements Minimum age 18; Medical examination.
Staff RNs 1 (pt); LPNs 2 (ft); Nurses aides 20 (ft), 3 (pt); Activities coordinators 1 (ft); Dietitians 1 (ft); 1 (ft).
Facilities Dining room; Activities room; Chapel; Crafts room; Laundry room; Barber/Beauty shop.
Activities Arts and Crafts; Cards; Games; Reading groups; Prayer groups; Movies; Shopping trips; Dances/Social or cultural gatherings.
Description There is a small park and 2 fishing lakes for residents.

CICERO

Cicero Children's Center Inc
69 N Harrison, PO Box 217, Cicero, IN, 46034 (317) 934-4393
Admin Lane Guttman.
Licensure Developmentally Disabled.
Beds 28.
Admissions Requirements Minimum age 0–21;

Medical examination.
Staff RNs 1 (pt); LPNs 1 (ft); Orderlies 2 (ft); Nurses aides 18 (pt); Activities coordinators 1 (ft); Dietitians 1 (pt).
Facilities Dining room; Activities room; Laundry room.
Description Resident children attend public school or participate in home bound school program; workshop facilities are nearby.

CLARKS HILL

Houston Health Care Inc—Clarks Hill*
Box 31, 602 Clark St, Clarks Hill, IN, 47930 (317) 523-2144
Admin Dave Ashbaugh.
Licensure Intermediate Care. *Beds* 34. *Certified* Medicaid.

CLARKSVILLE

Clarksville Healthcare Center
286 Eastern Blvd, Clarksville, IN, 47130 (812) 282-6663
Admin James Jester. *Medical Dir/Dir of Nursing* Dr Claude Meyer.
Licensure Skilled Care; Intermediate Care.
Beds SNF 87; ICF 108. *Certified* Medicaid; Medicare.
Admissions Requirements Minimum age 18.
Staff Physicians 1 (pt); RNs 3 (ft); LPNs 12 (ft), 4 (pt); Orderlies 3 (ft); Nurses aides 30 (ft), 15 (ft); Physical therapists 1 (ft); Recreational therapists 1 (ft), 1 (pt); Occupational therapists 1 (ft); Speech therapists 1 (ft); Activities coordinators 1 (ft); Dietitians 1 (ft); Dentists 1 (pt); Audiologists 1 (ft).
Facilities Dining room; Physical therapy room; Activities room; Crafts room; Laundry room; Barber/Beauty shop.
Activities Arts and Crafts; Cards; Games; Reading groups; Shopping trips; Dances/Social or cultural gatherings.
Description Facility is located in historical Clark County, Indiana, which is very scenic. One of the most modern facilities in the area.

Tendercare—Clarksville
517 N Hallmark Dr, Clarksville, IN, 47130 (812) 282-8406
Admin Donald G Pugh. *Medical Dir/Dir of Nursing* E'Austin B Johnson MD.
Licensure Skilled Care; Intermediate Care.
Beds SNF 61; ICF 62. *Certified* Medicaid; Medicare.
Admissions Requirements Medical examination.
Staff RNs 4 (ft), 1 (pt); LPNs 10 (ft), 2 (pt); Nurses aides 31 (ft), 1 (pt); Physical therapists; Occupational therapists; Speech therapists; Activities coordinators 2 (ft); Dietitians; Social workers; Qualified medical assistants 4 (ft), 1 (pt).
Facilities Dining room; Physical therapy room; Laundry room; Barber/Beauty shop; Living room; 2 TV lounges.
Activities Arts and Crafts; Cards; Games; Prayer groups; Movies; Shopping trips; Dances/Social or cultural gatherings.

Description Facility is close to 15 hospitals in Greater Louisville and Clark County area; hosts monthly meeting of Alzheimer's support group.

Westminster Health Care Center*
2200 Greentree N, Clarksville, IN, 47130 (812) 282-9691
Admin Carolyn Stuedli.
Licensure Skilled Care; Intermediate Care.
Beds 94. *Certified* Medicare.

CLINTON

Clinton Nursing Home
700 S Main St, Clinton, IN, 47842 (317) 832-8388
Admin Betty June Payton. *Medical Dir/Dir of Nursing* Margit Wilburn LPN.
Licensure Intermediate Care. *Beds* 40. *Certified* Medicaid.
Admissions Requirements Minimum age 16; Medical examination; Physician's request.
Staff RNs 1 (pt); LPNs 2 (ft), 2 (pt); Nurses aides 16 (ft), 3 (pt); Activities coordinators 1 (pt); Dietitians 1 (pt).

Vermillion Convalescent Center
Outer S Main St, Box 1A, Clinton, IN, 47842 (317) 832-3573
Admin David Olson. *Medical Dir/Dir of Nursing* S F Swaim MD.
Licensure Skilled Care; Intermediate Care.
Beds SNF 22; ICF 99. *Certified* Medicaid; Medicare.
Staff Physicians 6 (pt); RNs 5 (ft), 3 (pt); LPNs 13 (ft), 6 (pt); Orderlies 4 (ft); Nurses aides 35 (ft), 10 (pt); Physical therapists 1 (pt); Speech therapists 1 (pt); Activities coordinators 2 (ft); Dietitians 1 (pt); Dentists 1 (pt); Podiatrists 1 (pt); Audiologists 1 (pt).
Facilities Dining room; Physical therapy room; Activities room; Crafts room; Laundry room; Barber/Beauty shop; Library.
Activities Arts and Crafts; Cards; Games; Reading groups; Prayer groups; Movies; Shopping trips; Dances/Social or cultural gatherings.
Description JCAH approved.

CLOVERDALE

Houston Health Care Inc—Cloverdale
PO Box 247, 34 S Main, Cloverdale, IN, 46120 (317) 795-4260
Admin Judie C Martin.
Licensure Intermediate Care. *Beds* 40. *Certified* Medicaid.
Staff RNs 1 (pt); LPNs 3 (pt).

COLUMBIA CITY

Columbia City Community Care Center
Rt 9, Columbia City, IN, 46725 (219) 248-8141
Admin Jerry McClanahan. *Medical Dir/Dir of Nursing* Joe Mishler MD.
Licensure Skilled Care; Intermediate Care.
Beds SNF 40; ICF 42. *Certified* Medicaid; Medicare.
Admissions Requirements Medical examination.
Staff RNs 3 (ft), 1 (pt); LPNs 6 (ft), 3 (pt); Nurses aides 24 (ft), 10 (pt); Physical therapists

1 (pt); Activities coordinators 1 (ft), 1 (pt); Dietitians 1 (pt); Dentists 1 (pt); Podiatrists 1 (pt).
Facilities Dining room; Physical therapy room; Activities room; Laundry room; Barber/Beauty shop.
Activities Arts and Crafts; Games; Reading groups; Shopping trips; Dances/Social or cultural gatherings; Bowling; Church services.

Columbia City Nursing Home*
522 N Line St, Columbia City, IN, 46725 (219) 248-8216
Admin Jeanette Ellis.
Licensure Intermediate Care. *Beds* 40. *Certified* Medicaid.

Mary Farris Nursing Home
215 E Van Buren, Columbia City, IN, 46725 (219) 244-6316
Admin Mary Farris.
Licensure Intermediate Care. *Beds* 19. *Certified* Medicaid.

Miller's Merry Manor Inc*
710 W Ellsworth St, Columbia City, IN, 46725 (219) 248-8101
Admin Grace M Karst.
Licensure Skilled Care; Intermediate Care. *Beds* 114. *Certified* Medicaid; Medicare.

COLUMBUS

Bartholomew County Home*
2525 Illinois, Columbus, IN, 47201 (812) 372-7370
Admin Diane Burford.
Licensure Residential Care. *Beds* 31.

Columbus Convalescent Center*
PO Box 690, 2100 Midway St, Columbus, IN, 47201 (812) 372-8447
Admin Diane L Dodge.
Licensure Skilled Care; Intermediate Care. *Beds* 235. *Certified* Medicaid; Medicare.

Columbus Nursing Home*
5400 E 25th St, Columbus, IN, 47201 (812) 372-6136
Admin John Williams.
Licensure Intermediate Care. *Beds* 40. *Certified* Medicaid.

Four Seasons Home
1901 Taylor Rd, Columbus, IN, 47201 (812) 372-8481
Admin Robert W Banister.
Licensure Comprehensive Care; Residential Care. *Beds* 207.
Admissions Requirements Minimum age 62; Medical examination.
Staff RNs 4 (ft), 1 (pt); LPNs 5 (ft), 2 (pt); Nurses aides 21 (ft), 14 (pt); Activities coordinators 2 (ft), 1 (pt); Dietitians 1 (pt).
Facilities Dining room; Activities room; Chapel; Crafts room; Laundry room; Barber/Beauty shop; Library.
Activities Arts and Crafts; Cards; Games; Reading groups; Movies; Shopping trips; Dances/Social or cultural gatherings.

CONNERSVILLE

Heartland of Connersville
2500 Iowa St, Connersville, IN, 47331 (317) 825-7514
Admin Madge L Fosdick.
Licensure Intermediate Care. *Beds* 50. *Certified* Medicaid.
Admissions Requirements Minimum age 18; Medical examination.
Staff RNs 1 (ft); LPNs 3 (ft), 3 (pt); Activities coordinators 1 (ft); Dietitians 1 (pt).
Facilities Dining room; Activities room; Crafts room; Laundry room.
Activities Arts and Crafts; Cards; Games; Reading groups; Prayer groups; Movies; Shopping trips; Dances/Social or cultural gatherings; Family/resident dinners.
Description Facility is located on a quiet residential street with loving caring staff.

Lincoln Lodge Nursing Center*
PO Box 446, 1029 E 5th St, Connersville, IN, 47331 (317) 825-2121
Admin Goldie O'Neal.
Licensure Intermediate Care. *Beds* 51. *Certified* Medicaid.

Lincoln Manor Nursing Center*
PO Box 368, Connersville, IN, 47331 (317) 825-5551
Admin Chester O'Neal Jr.
Licensure Intermediate Care. *Beds* 100. *Certified* Medicaid.

CORYDON

Corydon Nursing Home
Rt 6, Box 147, Corydon, IN, 47112 (812) 738-2190
Admin Floyd A Shewmaker. *Medical Dir/Dir of Nursing* Thomas K Roberts MD.
Licensure Intermediate Care. *Beds* 40. *Certified* Medicaid.
Staff RNs 2 (pt); LPNs 3 (ft); Nurses aides 3 (ft), 8 (pt); Activities coordinators 1 (pt); Dietitians 1 (pt).
Facilities Dining room; Activities room; Crafts room; Laundry room; Barber/Beauty shop.
Activities Arts and Crafts; Cards; Games; Reading groups; Prayer groups; Movies; Shopping trips; Dances/Social or cultural gatherings.

Indian Creek Convalescent Center
240 Beechmont Dr, Corydon, IN, 47112
Admin William H Wallen. *Medical Dir/Dir of Nursing* Dr Bruce Burton.
Licensure Intermediate Care. *Beds* 100. *Certified* Medicaid.
Ownership Proprietary.
Admissions Requirements Minimum age 18.
Staff RNs 3 (ft); LPNs 5 (ft); Nurses aides 10 (ft), 19 (pt); Physical therapists 1 (pt); Activities coordinators 1 (ft); Dietitians 1 (pt).
Facilities Dining room; Physical therapy room; Activities room; Crafts room; Laundry room; Barber/Beauty shop.
Activities Arts and Crafts; Cards; Games; Reading groups; Prayer groups; Movies; Shopping trips; Dances/Social or cultural gatherings.

COVINGTON

Covington Manor Inc
1600 Liberty St E, Covington, IN, 47932 (317) 793-4818
Admin Edward Grogg. *Medical Dir/Dir of Nursing* Sarfraz A Mirza.
Licensure Skilled Care; Intermediate Care. *Beds* SNF 42; ICF 60. *Certified* Medicaid; Medicare.
Admissions Requirements Medical examination; Physician's request.
Staff RNs 8 (ft), 3 (pt); LPNs 7 (ft), 5 (pt); Nurses aides 30 (ft), 8 (pt); Physical therapists 2 (pt); Speech therapists 1 (pt); Activities coordinators 1 (ft); Dietitians 1 (pt); Dentists 1 (pt).
Facilities Dining room; Physical therapy room; Activities room; Crafts room; Laundry room; Barber/Beauty shop.
Activities Arts and Crafts; Cards; Games; Reading groups; Prayer groups; Movies; Shopping trips; Dances/Social or cultural gatherings.
Description This facility is situated in a country-type setting in a small town. We pride ourselves on the number of people we send home after their recuperative stay here. We have an excellent rehabilitative walk program which allows many of our residents to once again become ambulatory.

CRAWFORDSVILLE

Ben Hur Home Inc
1375 S Grant, Crawfordsville, IN, 47933 (317) 362-0905
Admin Sarah Houston Fox. *Medical Dir/Dir of Nursing* Carl B Howland MD.
Licensure Skilled Care; Intermediate Care. *Beds* SNF 54; ICF 121. *Certified* Medicaid; Medicare.
Staff RNs 5 (ft), 2 (pt); LPNs 5 (ft), 1 (pt); Orderlies 1 (ft), 1 (pt); Nurses aides 80 (ft), 6 (pt); Physical therapists 1 (ft); Occupational therapists 2 (ft); Speech therapists 1 (ft); Activities coordinators 2 (ft), 1 (pt); Dietitians 2 (ft); Audiologists 1 (pt).
Facilities Dining room; Physical therapy room; Activities room; Laundry room; Barber/Beauty shop; Library.
Activities Arts and Crafts; Cards; Games; Reading groups; Prayer groups; Movies; Shopping trips; Dances/Social or cultural gatherings.
Description Ben Hur Home is a unique health care facility serving adults of all ages. Situated on 6 lovely acres, the facility specializes in rehabilitative care, offering physical, occupational, and speech therapy in addition to active rehabilitative nursing techniques. Activity and social services departments offer a wide variety of services.

Carmen Nursing Home Inc
817 N Whitlock Ave, Crawfordsville, IN, 47933 (317) 362-8590
Admin Krista K Wright.
Licensure Intermediate Care. *Beds* 40.
Admissions Requirements Medical examination.
Staff RNs 1 (ft); LPNs 3 (pt); Nurses aides 9 (ft), 8 (pt); Activities coordinators 1 (pt); Dietitians 1 (pt).

Facilities Dining room; Laundry room.
Activities Arts and Crafts; Cards; Games; Dances/Social or cultural gatherings.

Houston Health Care Inc*
1371 S Grant Ave, Crawfordsville, IN, 47933
(317) 362-5365
Admin Caryl Barnes.
Licensure Intermediate Care. *Beds* 61. *Certified* Medicaid.

Lane House Inc
1000 Lane Ave, Crawfordsville, IN, 47933
(317) 362-4815
Admin Judith K Rauch.
Licensure Intermediate Care. *Beds* 60. *Certified* Medicaid.
Admissions Requirements Medical examination; Physician's request.
Staff RNs 2 (ft), 1 (pt); LPNs 2 (ft), 1 (pt); Nurses aides 18 (ft), 5 (pt); Activities coordinators 1 (ft), 1 (pt); Dietitians 1 (pt).
Facilities Dining room; Chapel; Laundry room; Barber/Beauty shop.
Activities Arts and Crafts; Cards; Games; Prayer groups; Movies; Shopping trips; Dances/Social or cultural gatherings.

CROWN POINT

Colonial Nursing Home Inc*
119 N Indiana Ave, Crown Point, IN, 46307
(219) 663-2532
Admin Laura Gumbiner and Barbara Slosson.
Licensure Intermediate Care. *Beds* 40. *Certified* Medicaid.

Lake County Convalescent Home
2900 W 93rd Ave, Crown Point, IN, 46307
(219) 633-5118
Admin Dorothy Gaski. *Medical Dir/Dir of Nursing* Dr J C Espino.
Licensure Intermediate Care. *Beds* 479. *Certified* Medicaid.
Admissions Requirements Minimum age 18; Medical examination; Physician's request.
Staff Physicians 1 (ft), 2 (pt); RNs 22 (ft), 18 (pt); LPNs 19 (ft), 3 (pt); Orderlies 4 (ft), 1 (pt); Nurses aides 161 (ft), 16 (pt); Occupational therapists 1 (pt); Activities coordinators 1 (ft); Dietitians 2 (ft).
Facilities Physical therapy room; Activities room; Chapel; Crafts room; Barber/Beauty shop; Library.
Activities Arts and Crafts; Cards; Games; Reading groups; Prayer groups; Movies; Shopping trips; Dances/Social or cultural gatherings.
Description Pet therapy program, twice monthly, arranged with local animal control shelter has been very effective for the residents; preschoolers visit on routine basis and perform by singing and dancing.

Lutheran Home of Northwest Indiana Inc
1200 E Luther Dr, Crown Point, IN, 46307-5099 (219) 633-3860, 769-1145
Admin Wayne A Hahn. *Medical Dir/Dir of Nursing* David Templin MD.
Licensure Intermediate Care; Residential and Respite Care. *Beds* 191. *Certified* Medicaid.
Staff Physicians 8 (pt); RNs 4 (ft), 6 (pt); LPNs 3 (ft); Nurses aides 9 (ft), 39 (pt); Physical thera-

pists 1 (pt); Reality therapists 1 (pt); Recreational therapists 1 (ft), 2 (pt); Occupational therapists 1 (pt); Speech therapists 1 (pt); Activities coordinators 1 (ft); Dietitians 1 (pt); Dentists 1 (pt); Ophthalmologists 1 (pt); Podiatrists 1 (pt); Audiologists 1 (pt).
Affiliation Lutheran
Facilities Dining room; Physical therapy room; Activities room; Chapel; Crafts room; Laundry room; Barber/Beauty shop; Library; Enclosed courtyard.
Activities Arts and Crafts; Cards; Games; Reading groups; Prayer groups; Movies; Shopping trips; Dances/Social or cultural gatherings; Dog lovers groups; Exercise classes.
Description Lutheran Retirement Village features colonial single-story buildings set in a rustic rural atmosphere; serves senior citizens offering care, security, and dignity in a loving family atmosphere. Village plan permits a support system to the spiritual, physical, and mental health of individuals assisting residents to retain their dignity while remaining mobile and independent just as long as possible.

Saint Anthony Home Inc*
201 Franciscan Rd, Crown Point, IN, 46307
(219) 738-2100
Admin Lawrence T Filosa.
Licensure Intermediate Care. *Beds* 144. *Certified* Medicaid.
Affiliation Roman Catholic

CULVER

Miller's Merry Manor Inc*
PO Box 498, 730 School St, Culver, IN, 46563
(219) 842-3337
Admin David Krizmanich.
Licensure Intermediate Care. *Beds* 66. *Certified* Medicaid.

CYNTHIANA

Merimac Nursing Home*
PO Box 275, Cynthiana, IN, 47612 (812) 845-2731
Admin Carlene Engelbright.
Licensure Intermediate Care. *Beds* 75. *Certified* Medicaid.

DALE

Golden Circle Nursing Center*
Hwy 68 W, Dale, IN, 47523 (812) 937-4442
Admin Donald R Thomason.
Licensure Intermediate Care. *Beds* 60. *Certified* Medicaid.

Professional Care Nursing Center Inc
Rt 2, Box 315, Dale, IN, 47523 (812) 937-4489
Admin Barbara K Miller. *Medical Dir/Dir of Nursing* Mario Leon MD.
Licensure Intermediate Care. *Beds* 60. *Certified* Medicaid.
Admissions Requirements Minimum age 18; Medical examination.
Staff Physicians 4 (pt); RNs 1 (ft), 2 (pt); Nurses aides 15 (ft), 5 (pt); Physical therapists 1 (pt); Activities coordinators 1 (ft); Dietitians 1 (pt); Dentists 1 (pt); Ophthalmologists 1 (pt);

Podiatrists 1 (pt).
Facilities Dining room; Activities room; Chapel; Crafts room; Laundry room; Barber/Beauty shop.
Activities Cards; Games; Reading groups; Prayer groups; Dances/Social or cultural gatherings.

DANVILLE

Danville Nursing Home*
337 W Lincoln St, Danville, IN, 46122 (317) 745-5861
Admin John W Lauth.
Licensure Intermediate Care. *Beds* 40. *Certified* Medicaid.

Golden Rule Nursing Home*
Rd 3S, 400 E, Danville, IN, 46122 (317) 745-5184
Admin Gary Michael.
Licensure Intermediate Care. *Beds* 100. *Certified* Medicaid.

Hendricks County Home
865 E Main, Danville, IN, 46122 (317) 745-9317
Licensure Residential Care. *Beds* 31.
Ownership Public.
Admissions Requirements Minimum age 18; Medical examination; Physician's request.
Staff Nurses aides 3 (ft), 1 (pt).
Facilities Dining room; Laundry room; Barber/Beauty shop.
Activities Arts and Crafts; Cards; Games.
Description We serve family-style meals. Residents may leave facility at any time to go to town, but are required to sign a release of responsibility prior to leaving. Rent is $275.00 per month.

Tendercare—Danville*
255 Meadow Dr, Danville, IN, 46122 (317) 745-5451
Admin Ronald C Hoffman.
Licensure Skilled Care; Intermediate Care. *Beds* SNF 58; ICF 45. *Certified* Medicaid; Medicare.

DECATUR

Decatur Community Care Center
1145 Mercer Ave, Decatur, IN, 46733 (219) 724-2191
Admin Melvin D Hamrick. *Medical Dir/Dir of Nursing* Dr Zwick.
Licensure Intermediate Care. *Beds* 101. *Certified* Medicaid.
Admissions Requirements Medical examination; Physician's request.
Staff RNs 1 (ft), 2 (pt); LPNs 5 (ft), 4 (pt); Nurses aides 13 (ft), 24 (pt); Activities coordinators 1 (ft), 1 (pt).
Facilities Dining room; Physical therapy room; Activities room; Laundry room; Barber/Beauty shop.
Activities Arts and Crafts; Cards; Games; Reading groups; Movies.

DELPHI

Delphi Nursing Home
1433 S Washington St, Delphi, IN, 46923 (317)
564-3123
Admin Gola Veach. *Medical Dir/Dir of
Nursing* Dr Seese.
Licensure Intermediate Care. *Beds* 40. *Certified* Medicaid.
Admissions Requirements Medical examination; Physician's request.
Staff RNs 2 (ft); LPNs 1 (ft), 1 (pt); Nurses
aides 8 (ft), 8 (pt); Activities coordinators 1 (pt);
Dietitians 1 (pt).

DEMOTTE

Lake Holiday Manor Nursing Home
10325 County Line Rd, DeMotte, IN, 46310
(219) 345-5211
Admin Eric L Borman.
Licensure Intermediate Care. *Beds* ICF 93;
Apartments 16. *Certified* Medicaid.
Admissions Requirements Medical examination.
Staff RNs 2 (ft); LPNs 6 (pt); Nurses aides 30
(ft), 30 (pt); Activities coordinators 1 (ft), 1 (pt);
Dietitians 1 (pt).
Facilities Dining room; Activities room; Chapel; Crafts room; Laundry room; Barber/Beauty
shop; Library.
Activities Arts and Crafts; Cards; Games;
Reading groups; Prayer groups; Movies; Shopping trips; Dances/Social or cultural gatherings.
Description Home is located in a rural area
with large oak trees where deer and wildlife
abound.

DILLSBORO

Dillsboro Manor*
Box 66, Dillsboro, IN, 47018 (812) 432-5226
Admin Dellas Ross.
Licensure Intermediate Care. *Beds* 47. *Certified* Medicaid.

DUNKIRK

Country Manor Nursing Home Inc*
Rt 2, Dunkirk, IN, 47336 (317) 768-7537
Admin Janellyn Antrim.
Licensure Intermediate Care. *Beds* 62. *Certified* Medicaid.

EARL PARK

Earl Park Nursing Home
402 Chestnut, Box 7, Earl Park, IN, 47942
(219) 474-6140
Admin Robert E McGinn.
Licensure Intermediate Care. *Beds* 14. *Certified* Medicaid.
Staff RNs 1 (pt); LPNs 2 (pt); Orderlies 1 (pt);
Nurses aides 4 (ft), 3 (pt); Activities coordinators 1 (ft); Dietitians 1 (pt).

EAST CHICAGO

**East Chicago Rehabilitation Convalescent
Center Inc**
5025 McCook Ave, East Chicago, IN, 46312
(219) 397-0380
Admin Beatrice Collins. *Medical Dir/Dir of
Nursing* Dr J P Mangahas.
Licensure Skilled Care. *Beds* 122. *Certified* Medicaid.
Admissions Requirements Medical examination; Physician's request.
Staff Physicians 5 (pt); RNs 5 (ft); LPNs 10
(ft); Orderlies 1 (ft), 4 (pt); Nurses aides 60 (ft);
Physical therapists 1 (pt); Reality therapists 1
(pt); Occupational therapists 1 (ft); Activities
coordinators 1 (ft); Dietitians 1 (pt); Dentists 1
(pt).
Facilities Dining room; Physical therapy room;
Activities room; Laundry room; Barber/Beauty
shop.
Activities Arts and Crafts; Cards; Games;
Reading groups; Prayer groups; Movies; Shopping trips; Dances/Social or cultural gatherings.

EDINBURG

Faith Home*
PO Box 218, Edinburg, IN, 46124 (812)
526-6390
Admin Raymond C Brown.
Licensure Intermediate Care. *Beds* 34. *Certified* Medicaid.

ELKHART

Americana Healthcare Center—Elkhart
343 S Nappanee St, Elkhart, IN, 46514 (219)
295-0096
Admin Michael Laudenslayer.
Licensure Skilled Care; Intermediate Care.
Beds SNF 46; ICF 53. *Certified* Medicaid;
Medicare.
Facilities Dining room; Physical therapy room;
Activities room; Chapel; Crafts room; Laundry
room; Barber/Beauty shop; Library.
Activities Arts and Crafts; Cards; Games;
Reading groups; Prayer groups; Movies; Shopping trips; Dances/Social or cultural gatherings.
Description This center has open visiting
hours; families and friends may visit at any
time.

Elkhart Healthcare Center
1400 W Franklin, Elkhart, IN, 46514 (219)
293-7556
Admin Ruth Brockman. *Medical Dir/Dir of
Nursing* Dr Horswell.
Licensure Skilled Care; Intermediate Care.
Beds SNF 42; ICF 125. *Certified* Medicaid;
Medicare.
Admissions Requirements Minimum age 19;
Medical examination.
Facilities Dining room; Physical therapy room;
Activities room; Crafts room; Laundry room;
Barber/Beauty shop.
Activities Arts and Crafts; Cards; Games;
Reading groups; Prayer groups; Movies; Dances/Social or cultural gatherings.

Fountainview Place
1001 W Hively Ave, Elkhart, IN, 46517 (219)
294-7641
Admin Carol Simmons. *Medical Dir/Dir of
Nursing* R G Harswell.
Licensure Skilled Care; Intermediate Care.
Beds SNF 116; ICF 182. *Certified* Medicaid;
Medicare.
Admissions Requirements Medical examination; Physician's request.
Staff RNs 17 (ft), 8 (pt); LPNs 16 (ft), 10 (pt);
Nurses aides 72 (ft), 11 (pt); Physical therapists
1 (ft), 1 (pt); Occupational therapists 1 (ft), 1
(pt); Speech therapists 1 (pt); Activities coordinators 2 (ft), 2 (pt); Dietitians 1 (pt); Dentists 1
(pt).
Facilities Dining room; Physical therapy room;
Activities room; Chapel; Crafts room; Laundry
room; Barber/Beauty shop; Library.
Activities Arts and Crafts; Cards; Games;
Reading groups; Prayer groups; Movies; Shopping trips; Dances/Social or cultural gatherings.

Hubbard Hill Estates Inc
28070 County Rd 24, Elkhart, IN, 46514 (219)
295-6260
Admin Floran Mast. *Medical Dir/Dir of
Nursing* Charlene Haines RN.
Licensure Intermediate Care. *Beds* 22.
Admissions Requirements Minimum age 62;
Medical examination.
Staff RNs 1 (ft); LPNs 2 (ft), 1 (pt); Nurses
aides 3 (ft), 6 (pt); Activities coordinators 1 (ft);
Dietitians 1 (pt).
Affiliation Missionary Church
Facilities Dining room; Activities room; Chapel; Crafts room; Laundry room; Barber/Beauty
shop; Library.
Activities Arts and Crafts; Cards; Games; Prayer groups; Movies; Shopping trips; Dances/Social or cultural gatherings.
Description Hubbard Hill Estates enjoys the
luxury of an 11 acre wooded campus in northern Indiana that provides a natural background
for the sprawling, one-level retirement facility;
85 residential apartments offer comfort, privacy, and independence while the 22-bed intermediate care unit provides security of professional
nursing care when needed.

Medco Center of Elkhart*
2600 Morehouse Ave, Elkhart, IN, 46514 (219)
295-8800
Admin Paul Ward.
Licensure Intermediate Care. *Beds* 74. *Certified* Medicaid.

ELWOOD

Dickey Nursing Home Inc
1007 N 9th St, Elwood, IN, 46036 (317)
552-7900
Admin Dianne E Blackford. *Medical Dir/Dir
of Nursing* Anita V Hanson MD.
Licensure Skilled Care; Intermediate Care.
Beds SNF 30; ICF 70. *Certified* Medicaid;
Medicare.
Admissions Requirements Minimum age 18;
Medical examination; Physician's request.
Staff Physicians 2 (pt); RNs 4 (ft), 2 (pt); LPNs
6 (ft), 4 (pt); Orderlies 1 (ft); Nurses aides 33
(ft), 11 (pt); Physical therapists 1 (pt); Speech

therapists 1 (pt); Activities coordinators 2 (ft); Dietitians 1 (pt); Dentists 1 (pt); Podiatrists 1 (pt); Audiologists 1 (pt); Optometrists 1 (pt).
Facilities Dining room; Physical therapy room; Activities room; Laundry room; Barber/Beauty shop; Library; Patios.
Activities Arts and Crafts; Cards; Games; Reading groups; Prayer groups; Movies; Shopping trips; Dances/Social or cultural gatherings; Exercise class.
Description Home began in 1960 with 17 beds in a remodeled house; new building constructed in 1967 and addition in 1975; remains in the family and retains much of the personal and individual handling of patients, families, and employees; present department heads have minimum of 10 years on the job, yet staff prides itself on continuing education and being up to date with regulations, and more.

Parkview Convalescent Centre*
N 19th St, Elwood, IN, 46036 (317) 552-9884
Admin Max Bingham.
Licensure Intermediate Care. *Beds* 92. *Certified* Medicaid.

EVANSVILLE

Bethel Sanitarium Inc
6015 Kratzville Rd, Evansville, IN, 47710 (812) 425-8182
Admin Louise Kuiken.
Licensure Intermediate Care. *Beds* 66. *Certified* Medicaid.
Admissions Requirements Medical examination.
Staff RNs 5 (ft); LPNs 4 (ft); Orderlies 1 (ft), 1 (pt); Nurses aides 21 (ft); Physical therapists 1 (pt); Reality therapists 1 (pt); Recreational therapists 1 (ft); Occupational therapists 1 (pt); Speech therapists 1 (pt); Activities coordinators 1 (ft); Dietitians 1 (ft), 1 (pt).
Affiliation Seventh-Day Adventist
Facilities Dining room; Physical therapy room; Activities room; Chapel; Laundry room; Barber/Beauty shop.
Activities Arts and Crafts; Games; Reading groups; Prayer groups; Movies; Shopping trips; Dances/Social or cultural gatherings.
Description King and Queen contest entered with all other nursing homes in this area; courtesy contest for this home only during February; birthdays honored each month and banquets held for special occasions.

Braun's Nursing Home Inc*
909 1st Ave, Evansville, IN, 47710 (812) 423-6214
Admin Ruth H Braun.
Licensure Intermediate Care. *Beds* 54. *Certified* Medicaid.

Columbia Health Care Facility*
1100 N Read St, Evansville, IN, 47710 (812) 424-8295
Admin Suzann K Dick.
Licensure Intermediate Care. *Beds* 34. *Certified* Medicaid.

Dellaren Nursing Care Center
816 N 1st Ave, Evansville, IN, 47710 (812) 426-2841

Admin George Arendell.
Licensure Intermediate Care. *Beds* 92. *Certified* Medicaid.
Admissions Requirements Minimum age 19.
Staff RNs 1 (ft); LPNs 4 (ft), 1 (pt); Nurses aides 16 (ft), 2 (pt); Activities coordinators 1 (ft).
Facilities Dining room; Activities room; Crafts room; Laundry room; Barber/Beauty shop; Library.
Activities Arts and Crafts; Cards; Games; Prayer groups; Movies; Shopping trips; Dances/Social or cultural gatherings.
Description We are keenly aware of the needs of our residents. We try to provide a wide variety of activities for them. We do resident shopping every week. We strive to allow our more ambulatory residents to do for themselves as much as possible.

Evansville Healthcare Center*
4301 Washington Ave, Evansville, IN, 47715 (812) 477-8971
Admin Jackie L Flowers.
Licensure Skilled Care; Intermediate Care. *Beds* 199. *Certified* Medicaid; Medicare.

Evansville Protestant Home Inc*
3701 Washington Ave, Evansville, IN, 47715 (812) 476-3360
Admin David H Roberts.
Licensure Intermediate Care; Residential Care. *Beds* ICF 102; Residential Care 144.

Gertha's Nursing Center Inc
605 Oakley St, Evansville, IN, 47710 (812) 423-4491
Admin Richard Gossman Sr. *Medical Dir/Dir of Nursing* Dr Richard Wagner.
Licensure Skilled Care; Intermediate Care. *Beds* SNF 45; ICF 110. *Certified* Medicaid; Medicare.
Admissions Requirements Minimum age 16; Medical examination; Physician's request.
Staff RNs 3 (ft), 1 (pt); LPNs 10 (ft), 4 (pt); Nurses aides 54 (ft), 8 (pt); Recreational therapists 3 (ft); Activities coordinators 1 (ft).
Facilities Dining room; Physical therapy room; Activities room; Crafts room; Laundry room; Barber/Beauty shop; Library.
Activities Arts and Crafts; Cards; Games; Reading groups; Prayer groups; Movies; Dances/Social or cultural gatherings.

Good Samaritan Home Inc*
PO Box 2788, 601 N Boeke, Evansville, IN, 47714 (812) 476-4912
Admin Charles J Warnick.
Licensure Intermediate Care. *Beds* 138. *Certified* Medicaid.

Holiday Home of Evansville
1201 W Buena Vista Rd, Evansville, IN, 47710 (812) 426-2221
Admin Donnie L Hester. *Medical Dir/Dir of Nursing* Dr William Gentry.
Licensure Skilled Care; Intermediate Care; Residential Care. *Beds* SNF 31; ICF 141; Residential Care 36. *Certified* Medicaid; Medicare.
Admissions Requirements Minimum age 65; Medical examination; Physician's request.
Staff RNs 10 (ft); LPNs 18 (ft); Nurses aides 60 (ft); Physical therapists 4 (ft); Activities coordi-

nators 1 (ft), 1 (pt); Dietitians 1 (ft); Audiologists 1 (pt); Speech pathologists 1 (ft).
Facilities Dining room; Physical therapy room; Activities room; Chapel; Crafts room; Laundry room; Barber/Beauty shop; Library.
Activities Arts and Crafts; Cards; Games; Reading groups; Prayer groups; Movies; Shopping trips; Dances/Social or cultural gatherings.

McCurdy Residential Center Inc
101 SE 1st St, Evansville, IN, 47708 (812) 425-1041
Admin Dorothy Zehner. *Medical Dir/Dir of Nursing* William Getty MD.
Licensure Intermediate Care. *Beds* 475. *Certified* Medicaid.
Admissions Requirements Medical examination.
Staff Physicians 1 (pt); RNs 6 (ft), 1 (pt); LPNs 26 (ft), 10 (pt); Orderlies 3 (ft); Nurses aides 24 (ft), 12 (pt); Activities coordinators 1 (ft); Dietitians 1 (ft); Dentists 1 (pt); Ophthalmologists 1 (pt); Podiatrists 1 (pt).
Facilities Dining room; Activities room; Chapel; Crafts room; Laundry room; Barber/Beauty shop; Library; Men's lounge.
Activities Arts and Crafts; Cards; Games; Reading groups; Movies; Shopping trips; Dances/Social or cultural gatherings; Ceramics; Chapel services; Current events.
Description Center is in a unique setting of a grand hotel overlooking the beautiful Ohio River, offering both residential and intermediate care; nursing staff around the clock. Since all residents are ambulatory, there is no feeling of "nursing home," and residents come and go as they wish.

Medco Center of Evansville—North
650 Fairway Dr, Evansville, IN, 47710 (812) 425-5243
Admin Michael L Taylor. *Medical Dir/Dir of Nursing* Dr William Gentry.
Licensure Skilled Care; Intermediate Care. *Beds* SNF 35; ICF 116. *Certified* Medicaid; Medicare.
Admissions Requirements Medical examination.
Staff Physicians; RNs; LPNs; Orderlies; Nurses aides; Physical therapists; Reality therapists; Recreational therapists; Occupational therapists; Speech therapists; Activities coordinators; Dietitians; Dentists; Ophthalmologists; Podiatrists; Audiologists.
Facilities Dining room; Physical therapy room; Activities room; Crafts room; Laundry room; Barber/Beauty shop; Library; Living room; Quiet rooms.
Activities Arts and Crafts; Cards; Games; Reading groups; Prayer groups; Movies; Shopping trips; Dances/Social or cultural gatherings; Baseball, basketball, and philharmonic tickets.
Description Facility features physicians on duty 24 hours a day; party rooms available for residents and families; strong activities program. Van is available for shopping and cultural events.

Parkview Convalescent Center Inc*
2819 N Saint Joseph Ave, Evansville, IN, 47712 (812) 424-2941
Admin Charles J Ludwyck.

Licensure Skilled Care; Intermediate Care. *Beds* SNF 31; ICF 77. *Certified* Medicaid; Medicare.

Pine Haven Nursing Home*
3401 Stocker Dr, Evansville, IN, 47712 (812) 424-8100
Admin Ruth Smith.
Licensure Intermediate Care. *Beds* 96. *Certified* Medicaid.

Rathbone Memorial Home*
1320 SE 2nd St, Evansville, IN, 47713 (812) 422-4254
Admin Eleanor White.
Licensure Residential Care. *Beds* 51.

Regina Pacis Home
3900 Washington Ave, Evansville, IN, 47715 (812) 479-4226
Admin Sr Mary Ellen Creedon. *Medical Dir/Dir of Nursing* Julian D Present MD.
Licensure Skilled Care; Intermediate Care. *Beds* SNF 86; ICF 50. *Certified* Medicaid; Medicare.
Admissions Requirements Minimum age 18; Medical examination.
Staff Physicians 1 (pt); RNs 4 (ft), 5 (pt); LPNs 8 (ft), 5 (pt); Nurses aides 37 (ft), 13 (pt); Physical therapists 1 (pt); Occupational therapists 1 (pt); Speech therapists 1 (pt); Activities coordinators 1 (pt); Dietitians 1 (pt); Dentists 1 (pt); Podiatrists 1 (pt).
Affiliation Roman Catholic
Facilities Dining room; Physical therapy room; Activities room; Chapel; Crafts room; Laundry room; Barber/Beauty shop; Library.
Activities Arts and Crafts; Cards; Games; Reading groups; Prayer groups; Movies; Dances/Social or cultural gatherings.
Description Regina Pacis Home is a 136-bed facility which is operated by St Mary's Medical Center of Evansville, Indiana, Daughters of Charity Institution. The facility is connected to the Medical Center by a tunnel; various services are provided by the Center, i.e., pharmacy, dietary, rehabilitation.

Saint John's Home for the Aged
1236 Lincoln Ave, Evansville, IN, 47714 (812) 464-3607
Admin Sr Amedee Maxwell.
Licensure Intermediate Care. *Beds* 130. *Certified* Medicaid.
Admissions Requirements Minimum age 60; Medical examination.
Staff RNs 3 (ft), 2 (pt); LPNs 11 (ft), 3 (pt); Orderlies 1 (pt); Nurses aides 22 (ft); Physical therapists 1 (pt); Recreational therapists 1 (ft); Occupational therapists 1 (pt); Speech therapists 1 (pt); Activities coordinators 1 (ft); Dietitians 1 (ft); Dentists 1 (pt); Ophthalmologists 1 (pt); Podiatrists 1 (pt).
Affiliation Roman Catholic
Facilities Dining room; Physical therapy room; Activities room; Chapel; Crafts room; Laundry room; Barber/Beauty shop; Library.
Activities Arts and Crafts; Cards; Games; Reading groups; Prayer groups; Movies; Shopping trips; Dances/Social or cultural gatherings; Exercise; Music therapy.

FAIRLAND

Ace Placid Home*
Rt 1, Box 350, Fairland, IN, 46126 (317) 835-2354
Admin Patsy R Ferguson.
Licensure Intermediate Care. *Beds* 18.

FLORA

Brethren's Home of Indiana Inc
Rt 2, Box 97, Flora, IN, 46929 (219) 967-4571
Admin Gene Geaslen.
Licensure Intermediate Care. *Beds* 86. *Certified* Medicaid.
Admissions Requirements Minimum age 65; Medical examination; Physician's request.
Staff RNs 2 (ft); LPNs 5 (pt); Orderlies 1 (pt); Nurses aides 19 (ft), 14 (pt); Activities coordinators 1 (ft), 1 (pt); Dietitians 1 (pt).
Affiliation Church of the Brethren
Facilities Dining room; Activities room; Chapel; Laundry room; Barber/Beauty shop.
Activities Arts and Crafts; Cards; Games; Reading groups; Prayer groups; Movies; Shopping trips; Dances/Social or cultural gatherings.
Description An intermediate care facility with independent living apartments located in a central Indiana rural setting; each room has individual climate control (heat and air conditioning) with large windows; a home-like atmosphere with daily activities.

FORT WAYNE

Byron Health Center
12101 Lima Rd, Fort Wayne, IN, 46808 (219) 637-3166
Admin Thomas Katsanis. *Medical Dir/Dir of Nursing* Dolores Espino MD.
Licensure Intermediate Care; Residential Care. *Beds* ICF 456; Residential Care 55. *Certified* Medicaid.
Ownership Public.
Admissions Requirements Minimum age 18; Medical examination; Physician's request.
Staff Physicians 1 (ft), 2 (pt); RNs 13 (ft); LPNs 32 (ft); Nurses aides 153 (ft), 12 (pt); Physical therapists 2 (pt); Recreational therapists 10 (ft); Occupational therapists 1 (ft); Speech therapists 1 (ft); Activities coordinators 2 (ft); Dietitians 3 (ft); Dentists 1 (pt); Ophthalmologists 1 (pt); Podiatrists 2 (pt); Audiologists 1 (pt).
Facilities Dining room; Physical therapy room; Activities room; Chapel; Crafts room; Laundry room; Barber/Beauty shop; Library.
Activities Arts and Crafts; Cards; Games; Reading groups; Prayer groups; Movies; Shopping trips; Dances/Social or cultural gatherings.
Description Byron Health Center has an all-inclusive per day rate that includes all services—room, meals, nursing care, physician services, medication, physical therapy, occupational therapy, podiatrist, optometrist, and dentist.

Covington Manor Nursing Center
5700 Wilkie Dr, Fort Wayne, IN, 46804 (219) 432-7556
Admin Rick Winkler. *Medical Dir/Dir of*

Nursing Bruce Hoppen MD.
Licensure Intermediate Care. *Beds* 115. *Certified* Medicaid.
Admissions Requirements Physician's request.
Staff Physicians 1 (pt); RNs 14 (ft); LPNs 3 (ft); Orderlies 5 (ft); Nurses aides 60 (ft), 11 (pt); Physical therapists 1 (pt); Reality therapists 1 (ft); Recreational therapists 1 (ft); Occupational therapists 1 (pt); Speech therapists 1 (pt); Activities coordinators 1 (ft); Dietitians 1 (pt); Dentists 1 (pt); Ophthalmologists 1 (pt); Podiatrists 1 (pt); Audiologists 1 (pt).
Facilities Dining room; Physical therapy room; Activities room; Chapel; Crafts room; Laundry room; Barber/Beauty shop; Library; Living rooms.
Activities Arts and Crafts; Cards; Games; Reading groups; Prayer groups; Movies; Shopping trips; Dances/Social or cultural gatherings.
Description The Nursing Center features a country atmosphere in an elite area of Fort Wayne; ultra-modern facilities with the latest in medical advances.

Crow's Haven Nursing Home
2440 Bowser Ave, Fort Wayne, IN, 46803 (219) 745-4508
Admin Arlene Thomas.
Licensure Intermediate Care. *Beds* ICF 58; Residential Care 22. *Certified* Medicaid.
Admissions Requirements Minimum age 18; Medical examination.
Staff RNs 1 (ft), 1 (pt); LPNs 1 (ft), 1 (pt); Nurses aides 10 (ft), 13 (pt); Activities coordinators 1 (ft); Dietitians 1 (pt).

Fairfield Healthcare Center*
2626 Fairfield Ave, Fort Wayne, IN, 46807 (219) 744-4211
Admin Michael Jackson.
Licensure Skilled Care; Intermediate Care. *Beds* SNF 63; ICF 63. *Certified* Medicaid; Medicare.

Fort Wayne Healthcare Center
2001 Hobson Rd, Fort Wayne, IN, 46805 (219) 484-9557
Admin Dennis M Lennartz. *Medical Dir/Dir of Nursing* Dr E Bolander.
Licensure Skilled Care; Intermediate Care. *Beds* SNF 89; ICF 90. *Certified* Medicaid; Medicare.
Admissions Requirements Minimum age 18; Medical examination.
Staff Physicians 4 (pt); RNs 8 (ft), 2 (pt); LPNs 10 (ft), 3 (pt); Nurses aides 34 (ft), 9 (pt); Physical therapists 1 (ft), 1 (pt); Recreational therapists 1 (ft); Occupational therapists 1 (pt); Speech therapists 1 (pt); Activities coordinators 1 (ft); Dietitians 1 (ft); Dentists 1 (pt); Ophthalmologists 1 (pt); Podiatrists 1 (pt); Audiologists 1 (pt).
Facilities Dining room; Physical therapy room; Activities room; Chapel; Crafts room; Laundry room; Barber/Beauty shop; Library.
Activities Arts and Crafts; Cards; Games; Reading groups; Prayer groups; Movies; Shopping trips; Dances/Social or cultural gatherings.

Fort Wayne Nursing Home
2402 N Beacon, Fort Wayne, IN, 46805 (219) 484-3415
Admin Susan K Schroeder. *Medical Dir/Dir of*

Nursing Carol Brockhouse RN.
Licensure Intermediate Care. *Beds* 40. *Certified* Medicaid.
Admissions Requirements Minimum age 19; Medical examination; Physician's request.
Staff Physicians; RNs; LPNs; Orderlies; Nurses aides; Activities coordinators; Dietitians.
Facilities Dining room; Activities room; Crafts room; Laundry room.
Activities Arts and Crafts; Cards; Games; Reading groups; Prayer groups; Shopping trips; Dances/Social or cultural gatherings.
Description Facility features comprehensive nursing care, licensed by State Board of Health, approved by state fire marshal, offers recreational activities, registered dietitian, special diets, personal laundry, 24-hour visiting hours, church services, and semi-private rooms.

Golden Years Homestead
8300 Maysville Rd, Fort Wayne, IN, 46815 (219) 749-9655
Admin Thomas G Garman. *Medical Dir/Dir of Nursing* Dr Philip Schubert.
Licensure Intermediate Care. *Beds* 61. *Certified* Medicaid.
Admissions Requirements Minimum age 62; Medical examination.
Staff RNs 1 (ft), 3 (pt); LPNs 6 (pt); Nurses aides 8 (ft), 14 (pt); Activities coordinators 1 (ft); Dietitians 1 (pt).
Affiliation Church of Christ
Facilities Dining room; Activities room; Chapel; Laundry room; Barber/Beauty shop; Library.
Activities Arts and Crafts; Cards; Games; Prayer groups; Movies.

Heritage Manor Health Care Center
7519 Winchester Rd, Fort Wayne, IN, 46819 (219) 747-7435
Admin James Snyder. *Medical Dir/Dir of Nursing* William Aeschlimen MD.
Licensure Intermediate Care. *Beds* 80. *Certified* Medicaid.
Admissions Requirements Medical examination; Physician's request.
Staff Physicians 1 (pt); RNs 2 (ft), 1 (pt); LPNs 3 (ft), 3 (pt); Orderlies 3 (ft), 2 (pt); Nurses aides 8 (ft), 14 (pt); Activities coordinators 1 (ft); Dietitians 1 (pt); Dentists 1 (pt); Podiatrists 1 (pt).
Facilities Dining room; Activities room; Laundry room; Barber/Beauty shop.
Activities Arts and Crafts; Cards; Games; Reading groups; Movies; Shopping trips.
Description Located at the southwest corner of Fort Wayne, facility is situated near scenic St Marys River. While not within the city limits, facility is conveniently located to medical centers, hospitals, shopping, and recreation.

Indian Village Health Center
2237 Engle Rd, Fort Wayne, IN, 46809 (219) 747-2353
Admin Ivaetta McCammon.
Licensure Intermediate Care. *Beds* 37.
Admissions Requirements Minimum age 60.
Staff RNs 1 (ft); LPNs 3 (ft); Orderlies 1 (ft); Nurses aides 13 (ft), 4 (pt); Reality therapists 1 (pt); Activities coordinators 1 (pt); Dietitians 1 (pt).
Facilities Dining room; Laundry room; Barber-

/Beauty shop.
Activities Arts and Crafts; Cards; Games; Movies; Shopping trips; Dances/Social or cultural gatherings.
Description Facility has quiet, home-like atmosphere in a residential setting with trees and shrubs gracing the building, 2 lounges with color TV, and dining room with lovely scenery. Residents have access to patio and garden area with lawn furniture.

Lawton Nursing Home
1649 Spy Run Ave, Fort Wayne, IN, 46805 (219) 422-8520
Admin Maribelle S Dyer. *Medical Dir/Dir of Nursing* L Bayazit MD.
Licensure Intermediate Care. *Beds* 100. *Certified* Medicaid.
Admissions Requirements Medical examination; Physician's request.
Staff RNs 5 (ft); LPNs 3 (ft), 3 (pt); Nurses aides 26 (ft), 3 (pt); Activities coordinators 1 (ft), 2 (pt); Dietitians 1 (pt); Dentists 1 (pt); Podiatrists 1 (pt).
Facilities Dining room; Activities room; Laundry room; Barber/Beauty shop.
Activities Arts and Crafts; Cards; Games; Reading groups; Prayer groups; Movies; Shopping trips; Dances/Social or cultural gatherings.
Description Home features dental facilities with dentist scheduled once per month.

Lutheran Homes Inc
6701 S Anthony Blvd, Fort Wayne, IN, 46806 (219) 447-1591
Admin Robert Scheimann.
Licensure Intermediate Care; Residential Care.
Beds ICF 276; Residential Care 120. *Certified* Medicaid.
Admissions Requirements Minimum age 62; Medical examination.
Affiliation Lutheran
Facilities Dining room; Physical therapy room; Activities room; Chapel; Crafts room; Laundry room; Barber/Beauty shop; Library.
Activities Arts and Crafts; Cards; Games; Reading groups; Prayer groups; Movies; Shopping trips; Dances/Social or cultural gatherings.

Parnell Park Nursing Home*
3811 Parnell Ave, Fort Wayne, IN, 46805 (219) 748-7155
Admin Lloyd White.
Licensure Skilled Care; Intermediate Care.
Beds SNF 47; ICF 157. *Certified* Medicaid; Medicare.

Riverview Care Center Inc
2827 Northgate Blvd, Fort Wayne, IN, 46815 (219) 485-9691
Admin Joseph Weingartner.
Licensure Skilled Care; Intermediate Care.
Beds SNF 30; ICF 30. *Certified* Medicaid.
Admissions Requirements Medical examination.
Facilities Dining room; Physical therapy room; Activities room; Chapel; Crafts room; Laundry room; Barber/Beauty shop.
Activities Arts and Crafts; Cards; Games; Reading groups; Prayer groups; Movies; Shopping trips; Dances/Social or cultural gatherings; Outings to plays; Bus trips.

Saint Anne Home*
1900 Randalia Dr, Fort Wayne, IN, 46805 (219) 484-5555
Admin John F Mauch.
Licensure Skilled Care; Intermediate Care.
Beds SNF 53; ICF 101. *Certified* Medicaid.

Three Rivers Convalescent Center
2940 N Clinton St, Fort Wayne, IN, 46805 (219) 484-0602
Admin Lora Thomas. *Medical Dir/Dir of Nursing* Dr Robert Vorhees.
Licensure Skilled Care; Intermediate Care.
Beds SNF 77; ICF 67. *Certified* Medicaid; Medicare.
Admissions Requirements Medical examination; Physician's request.
Staff Physicians 1 (ft); Physical therapists 1 (ft); Reality therapists 1 (ft); Recreational therapists 1 (ft); Occupational therapists 1 (ft); Speech therapists 1 (ft); Activities coordinators 1 (ft); Dietitians 1 (ft); Dentists 1 (ft); Podiatrists 1 (ft).
Facilities Dining room; Physical therapy room; Activities room; Crafts room; Laundry room; Barber/Beauty shop; Occupational therapy room.
Activities Arts and Crafts; Cards; Games; Reading groups; Prayer groups; Movies; Shopping trips; Dances/Social or cultural gatherings.
Description Facility specializes in rehabilitation with full-time physical, occupational, and speech therapy, Also has restorative nursing at all levels of care. VA approved.

Towne House Health Center*
2209 Saint Joe Center Rd, Fort Wayne, IN, 46815 (219) 749-9506
Admin Robert DeVoss.
Licensure Intermediate Care; Residential Care.
Beds ICF 77; Residential Care 210.

University Park Nursing Center
1400 Medical Park Dr, Fort Wayne, IN, 46825 (219) 484-1558
Admin Kevin L May. *Medical Dir/Dir of Nursing* Dr Jerry Dearth.
Licensure Intermediate Care. *Beds* 100.
Admissions Requirements Minimum age 21; Medical examination.
Staff Physicians 1 (pt); RNs 2 (ft), 2 (pt); LPNs 3 (ft), 3 (pt); Orderlies 1 (ft); Nurses aides 40 (ft); Physical therapists 1 (pt); Occupational therapists 1 (pt); Activities coordinators 1 (ft); Dietitians 1 (pt); Dentists 1 (pt); Ophthalmologists 1 (pt); Podiatrists 1 (pt); Audiologists 1 (pt).
Facilities Dining room; Physical therapy room; Activities room; Chapel; Crafts room; Laundry room; Barber/Beauty shop.
Activities Arts and Crafts; Cards; Games; Reading groups; Prayer groups; Movies; Shopping trips; Dances/Social or cultural gatherings.
Description Facility features warm, home-like setting, loving staff, and a park-like setting outside. Good meals and pleasant rooms and bathrooms.

Villa of the Woods*
5610 Noll Ave, Fort Wayne, IN, 46806 (219) 745-7039
Admin Janet H Lemler.
Beds 27.

Woodview Healthcare Center
3420 E State St, Fort Wayne, IN, 46805 (219)
483-2725
Admin John August.
Licensure Skilled Care; Intermediate Care.
Beds 94. *Certified* Medicaid; Medicare.
Facilities Dining room; Physical therapy room;
Activities room; Crafts room; Laundry room;
Barber/Beauty shop.
Activities Arts and Crafts; Cards; Games;
Reading groups; Movies; Shopping trips; Dan-
ces/Social or cultural gatherings.

FOWLER

Green-Hill Manor Inc*
501 N Lincoln Ave, Fowler, IN, 47944 (317)
884-1470
Admin E Dexter and C Brouillette.
Licensure Intermediate Care. *Beds* 23. *Certified* Medicaid.

FRANCESVILLE

Parkview Haven
PO Box 797, Francesville, IN, 47946 (219)
567-9149
Admin Elmer J Bucher.
Licensure Intermediate Care; Residential Care.
Beds 74.
Admissions Requirements Medical examina-
tion.
Staff RNs 1 (ft), 2 (pt); LPNs 1 (ft), 1 (pt);
Nurses aides 2 (ft), 12 (pt); Activities coordina-
tors 1 (ft); Dietitians 1 (pt).
Facilities Dining room; Crafts room; Laundry
room; Barber/Beauty shop; Library.
Activities Arts and Crafts; Games; Prayer
groups; Shopping trips.
Description Our endeavor is to provide a
Christian atmosphere. We realize that the spirit-
ual needs are of utmost importance when the
body begins to fail.

FRANKFORT

Clinton Center*
551 E Walnut St, Frankfort, IN, 46041 (317)
654-7869
Admin Rosemary Eddy.
Licensure Intermediate Care. *Beds* 40.

Clinton House Inc*
809 W Freeman St, Frankfort, IN, 46041 (317)
654-8783
Admin Laura L Peterson.
Licensure Intermediate Care. *Beds* 121. *Certified* Medicaid.

Frankfort Nursing Home
1234 Rossville Ave, Frankfort, IN, 46041 (317)
654-8118
Admin Robert D Lucas. *Medical Dir/Dir of
Nursing* Cheryl Moore RN.
Licensure Intermediate Care. *Beds* 40. *Certified* Medicaid.
Staff RNs 1 (ft), 1 (pt); LPNs 1 (pt); Nurses
aides 8 (ft), 10 (pt); Activities coordinators 1
(pt); Dietitians 1 (pt).
Facilities Dining room; Activities room; Laundry room.

Activities Arts and Crafts; Cards; Games;
Reading groups; Prayer groups; Movies; Dan-
ces/Social or cultural gatherings; Monthly
theme parties; Church services.
Description Facility is located on 6 acres of
land at the north edge of Frankfort; small size
enables the maintenance of an atmosphere of
home-like warmness and friendliness. Each resident is known personally by the administrator
and staff; relatives and friends of the residents
are encouraged to visit and become acquainted
with the facility.

Parkview Home
Rt 2, Frankfort, IN, 46041 (317) 659-3803
Admin Dorothy Schriefer.
Licensure Residential Care. *Beds* 40.
Admissions Requirements Medical examina-
tion; Physician's request.
Staff LPNs 1 (ft); Activities coordinators 1
(pt); Dietitians 1 (pt).
Facilities Dining room; Activities room; Chap-
el; Laundry room; Barber/Beauty shop;
Library.
Activities Games; Reading groups; Prayer
groups; Movies; Shopping trips.
Description Facility is out in the country across
from the park and golf course; 6 church buses
or transportation to other churches; several
school groups entertain.

**Wesley Manor—Northwest Indiana Methodist
Home Inc**
1555 N Main St, Frankfort, IN, 46041 (317)
659-1811
Admin E Thomas DeHaven.
Licensure Intermediate Care. *Beds* 550.
Affiliation Methodist

FRANKLIN

Franklin Healthcare Centre*
Rt 1, Franklin, IN, 46131 (317) 736-9113
Admin Virginia Gail Henry.
Licensure Skilled Care; Intermediate Care.
Beds SNF 63; ICF 60. *Certified* Medicaid;
Medicare.

Franklin Nursing Home
1130 N Main St, Franklin, IN, 46131 (317)
736-8214
Admin Mary L Johnson.
Licensure Intermediate Care. *Beds* 40. *Certi-
fied* Medicaid.
Admissions Requirements Minimum age 18.
Staff RNs 1 (pt); LPNs 1 (ft); Nurses aides 10
(ft), 9 (pt); Activities coordinators 1 (pt).
Facilities Dining room; Activities room; Laun-
dry room.
Activities Arts and Crafts; Cards; Games;
Reading groups; Prayer groups; Movies; Shop-
ping trips.

Franklin United Methodist Home
1070 W Jefferson, Franklin, IN, 46131 (317)
736-7185
Admin William T Murphy. *Medical Dir/Dir of
Nursing* William Provine II.
Licensure Residential Care. *Beds* 560.
Admissions Requirements Minimum age 62;
Medical examination.
Staff Physicians 1 (pt); RNs 2 (ft); LPNs 5 (ft);

Nurses aides 23 (ft); Physical therapists 2 (ft);
Recreational therapists 1 (ft); Activities coordi-
nators 1 (ft), 1 (pt); Dietitians 1 (ft); Podiatrists
1 (pt).
Affiliation Methodist
Facilities Dining room; Physical therapy room;
Activities room; Chapel; Crafts room; Laundry
room; Barber/Beauty shop; Library.
Activities Arts and Crafts; Cards; Games;
Reading groups; Prayer groups; Movies; Shop-
ping trips; Dances/Social or cultural gatherings.

Homeview Convalescent Center*
PO Box 464, 651 S State St, Franklin, IN,
46131 (317) 736-6414
Admin June Goodwin.
Licensure Intermediate Care. *Beds* 37. *Certi-
fied* Medicaid.

Indiana Masonic Home*
Old State Rd 31, Franklin, IN, 46131 (317)
736-6141
Admin Marvin Isley.
Licensure Residential Care. *Beds* 317.
Affiliation Masons

Welcome Nursing Home Inc
1109 N Main St, Franklin, IN, 46131 (317)
736-7041
Admin Mary Lou Ingle. *Medical Dir/Dir of
Nursing* William D Province.
Licensure Intermediate Care. *Beds* 69. *Certi-
fied* Medicaid.
Staff RNs 1 (ft); LPNs 2 (ft), 1 (pt); Orderlies 1
(ft); Nurses aides 18 (ft), 5 (pt); Activities coor-
dinators 1 (ft); Dietitians 1 (pt).
Facilities Dining room; Laundry room.
Activities Arts and Crafts; Cards; Games;
Reading groups; Prayer groups; Movies; Shop-
ping trips; Dances/Social or cultural gatherings.

FREELANDVILLE

Freelandville Community Home Inc
Hwy 58, Freelandville, IN, 47535 (812)
328-2134
Admin Mary Joyce Buescher. *Medical Dir/Dir
of Nursing* Barbara Burke.
Licensure Intermediate Care. *Beds* 50. *Certified* Medicaid.
Admissions Requirements Minimum age 50;
Medical examination.
Staff Physicians 1 (pt); RNs 2 (ft), 1 (pt); LPNs
3 (ft), 1 (pt); Orderlies 1 (ft); Nurses aides 9 (ft),
15 (pt); Activities coordinators 1 (ft); Dietitians
1 (ft); Podiatrists 1 (pt).
Facilities Dining room; Activities room; Chapel; Crafts room; Laundry room; Barber/Beauty
shop; Library.
Activities Arts and Crafts; Cards; Games;
Reading groups; Prayer groups; Movies; Shopping trips; Dances/Social or cultural gatherings.

FRENCH LICK

Medco Annex of French Lick*
Rt 2, French Lick, IN, 47432 (812) 936-9901
Admin Patricia Sanders.
Licensure Intermediate Care. *Beds* 58. *Certi-
fied* Medicaid.

Medco Center of French Lick*
PO Box 350, E College, French Lick, IN, 47432
(812) 936-9991
Admin Sheila Watts.
Licensure Skilled Care; Intermediate Care.
Beds SNF 42; ICF 42. *Certified* Medicaid;
Medicare.

GARRETT

Miller's Merry Manor Inc
1367 S Randolph, Garrett, IN, 46738
Admin P Carolyn Jacobs.
Licensure Intermediate Care. *Beds* 63. *Certified* Medicaid.
Ownership Proprietary.
Staff RNs 1 (ft), 5 (pt); LPNs 2 (ft), 1 (pt);
Orderlies 1 (pt); Nurses aides 5 (ft), 15 (pt);
Physical therapists 1 (pt); Speech therapists 1
(pt); Activities coordinators 3 (pt); Dietitians 1
(pt); Dentists 1 (pt); Podiatrists 1 (pt); Audiologists 1 (pt).
Facilities Dining room; Physical therapy room;
Activities room; Chapel; Crafts room; Laundry
room; Barber/Beauty shop; Library.
Activities Arts and Crafts; Cards; Games;
Reading groups; Prayer groups; Movies; Shopping trips; Dances/Social or cultural gatherings.
Description Facility offers a good neighbor
club—residents helping one another, Bible
study weekly, happy hour monthly, Valentine
secret pals involving residents and staff, friendship lunches and teas for residents and their
families, and a Christmas bazaar with crafts
and goodies made by residents.

GARY

Green's Geriatric Health Center Inc
2052 Delaware St, Gary, IN, 46407 (219)
886-1511
Admin Horace Brown.
Licensure Intermediate Care. *Beds* 35. *Certified* Medicaid.
Admissions Requirements Minimum age 70.
Staff Physicians 2 (pt); RNs 1 (pt); LPNs 1 (ft),
5 (pt); Orderlies 1 (ft), 1 (pt); Nurses aides 10
(ft), 13 (pt); Activities coordinators 1 (ft), 1 (pt);
Dietitians 1 (pt); Podiatrists 1 (pt).
Facilities Dining room; Activities room.
Activities Arts and Crafts; Cards; Games;
Reading groups; Prayer groups; Shopping trips.

Meridian Nursing Center—West Side*
353 Tyler St, Gary, IN, 46402 (219) 886-7070
Admin Gerald Rothenberg.
Licensure Intermediate Care. *Beds* 214. *Certified* Medicaid.

Miller Nursing Home Inc*
2301 Adams St, Gary, IN, 46407 (219)
882-5365
Admin Ida Miller Walker.
Licensure Intermediate Care. *Beds* 44. *Certified* Medicaid.

Mills Rest Home*
5011 Maryland St, Gary, IN, 46409 (219)
884-1712

Admin David L Mills and Audrey Mills.
Licensure Intermediate Care. *Beds* 34. *Certified* Medicaid.

Simmons Loving Care Health Facility*
PO Box 1675, 700 E 21st Ave, Gary, IN, 46407
(219) 882-2563
Admin Herberta B Miller and Anna L Simmons.
Licensure Intermediate Care. *Beds* 46. *Certified* Medicaid.

Wildwood Manor Inc
1964 Clark Rd, Gary, IN, 46404 (219)
949-9640
Admin A Joann Johnson. *Medical Dir/Dir of
Nursing* Daniel T Ramker.
Licensure Skilled Care. *Beds* 120. *Certified* Medicaid; Medicare.
Admissions Requirements Minimum age 21;
Medical examination; Physician's request.
Staff Physicians 4 (pt); RNs 3 (ft), 2 (pt); LPNs
11 (ft), 4 (pt); Nurses aides 36 (ft), 8 (pt);
Physical therapists 1 (ft); Occupational therapists 1 (ft); Speech therapists 1 (ft); Activities
coordinators 1 (ft); Dietitians 2 (pt); Dentists 1
(pt); Podiatrists 1 (pt).
Facilities Dining room; Physical therapy room;
Activities room; Chapel; Laundry room; Barber/Beauty shop.
Activities Arts and Crafts; Cards; Games;
Reading groups; Prayer groups; Movies.
Description Wildwood Manor is situated in the
center of a residential neighborhood but retains
the natural beauty of open woodland area;
grounds are highlighted by a natural pond and a
park-like atmosphere, where residents enjoy the
open spaces but retain the privacy many of
them enjoy.

Wildwood Manor Mount Inc
386 Mount St, Gary, IN, 46406 (219) 949-5600
Admin Estella Watkins. *Medical Dir/Dir of
Nursing* Daniel T Ramker.
Licensure Intermediate Care. *Beds* 69. *Certified* Medicaid.
Admissions Requirements Medical examination; Physician's request.
Staff Physicians 2 (pt); RNs 1 (ft); LPNs 3 (ft),
3 (pt); Nurses aides 16 (ft), 3 (pt); Physical therapists 1 (pt); Occupational therapists 1 (pt);
Speech therapists 1 (pt); Activities coordinators
1 (ft); Dietitians 1 (pt); Dentists 1 (pt); Ophthalmologists 1 (pt); Podiatrists 1 (pt); Audiologists
1 (pt).
Facilities Dining room; Activities room; Laundry room; Barber/Beauty shop.
Activities Arts and Crafts; Cards; Games; Prayer groups; Movies; Shopping trips;
Dances/Social or cultural gatherings.

GAS CITY

Twin City Nursing Home*
627 East-North H St, Gas City, IN, 46933 (317)
674-8516
Admin Margaret E Knox.
Licensure Intermediate Care. *Beds* 100. *Certified* Medicaid.

GASTON

ProCare Development Center*
502 N Madison St, Gaston, IN, 47342 (317)
358-3324
Admin Julie Maschman.
Licensure Intermediate Care. *Beds* 75. *Certified* Medicaid.

GOSHEN

Fountainview Place—Goshen*
2400 College Ave, Goshen, IN, 46526 (219)
533-0351
Admin Bill Van Offeren.
Licensure Skilled Care; Intermediate Care.
Beds SNF 49; ICF 78. *Certified* Medicaid;
Medicare.

Goshen Nursing Home
1101 W Lincoln Ave, Goshen, IN, 46526 (219)
533-8090
Admin Hugo Erickson. *Medical Dir/Dir of
Nursing* William Weybright.
Licensure Intermediate Care. *Beds* 40. *Certified* Medicaid.
Admissions Requirements Physician's request.
Staff Physicians 1 (pt); RNs 1 (pt); LPNs 1 (ft),
1 (pt); Nurses aides 13 (ft); Activities coordinators 1 (ft); Dietitians 1 (pt); Podiatrists 1 (pt).
Facilities Dining room; Activities room; Laundry room; Barber/Beauty shop.
Activities Arts and Crafts; Games; Reading
groups; Prayer groups; Movies; Shopping trips;
Dances/Social or cultural gatherings.

Greencroft Nursing Center
1225 Greencroft Dr, Goshen, IN, 46526 (219)
534-1546
Admin Wayne A Badskey. *Medical Dir/Dir of
Nursing* Donald L Minter MD.
Licensure Skilled Care; Intermediate Care.
Beds 180. *Certified* Medicaid; Medicare.
Admissions Requirements Minimum age 19;
Medical examination.
Staff RNs 10 (ft), 5 (pt); LPNs 7 (ft), 7 (pt);
Orderlies 1 (ft), 3 (pt); Nurses aides 53 (ft), 34
(pt); Physical therapists 1 (pt); Speech therapists
1 (pt); Activities coordinators 3 (ft); Dietitians
1 (pt).
Affiliation Mennonite
Facilities Dining room; Physical therapy room;
Activities room; Laundry room; Barber/Beauty
shop; Library.
Activities Arts and Crafts; Games; Reading
groups; Prayer groups; Movies; Exercise; Bible
study; Hymn sings; Current events.
Description Facility is located in strong Mennonite community near Goshen College; junior
and senior nursing students receive part of their
training here; social service students spend
practicum at Greencroft, the largest retirement
community of its kind in Indiana.

GOSPORT

Gosport Nursing Home*
27 S 7th St, Gosport, IN, 47433 (812) 879-4242
Admin Fred J Ponton.
Licensure Intermediate Care. *Beds* 74. *Certified* Medicaid.

GREENCASTLE

Asbury Towers
102 W Poplar St, Greencastle, IN, 46135 (317) 653-5148
Admin James L Ray.
Licensure Comprehensive Care; Residential Care. *Beds* 97.
Admissions Requirements Minimum age 65; Medical examination.
Affiliation Methodist

Eventide Rest Home
1306 S Bloomington St, Greencastle, IN, 46135 (317) 653-4570
Admin Kathie R Burns. *Medical Dir/Dir of Nursing* Gregory Larken MD.
Licensure Intermediate Care. *Beds* 40. *Certified* Medicaid.
Admissions Requirements Minimum age 18; Physician's request.
Staff RNs 1 (ft); LPNs 3 (pt); Orderlies 1 (ft); Nurses aides 4 (ft), 8 (pt); Activities coordinators 1 (ft), 2 (pt); Dietitians 1 (ft).
Facilities Dining room; Crafts room.
Activities Arts and Crafts; Reading groups; Prayer groups; Movies; Shopping trips; Dances-/Social or cultural gatherings.
Description Facility is a 40-bed ICF, primarily for young adult residents who are MR/DD; all of the daily nursing and activities are geared towards independent living; specializes in teaching basic adult living and survival skills.

Greencastle Nursing Home
815 E Tacoma Dr, Greencastle, IN, 46135 (317) 653-8280
Admin Maide Pierson. *Medical Dir/Dir of Nursing* Dr Macy.
Licensure Intermediate Care. *Beds* 40. *Certified* Medicaid.
Staff RNs 1 (pt); LPNs 2 (ft), 1 (pt); Orderlies 1 (ft), 1 (pt); Nurses aides 8 (ft), 2 (pt); Activities coordinators 1 (ft); Dietitians 1 (pt).
Facilities Dining room; Activities room; Laundry room.
Activities Arts and Crafts; Cards; Games; Reading groups; Prayer groups; Movies; Shopping trips; Dances/Social or cultural gatherings.

The Heritage House Convention Center of Putnam Company*
1601 Hospital Dr, Greencastle, IN, 46135 (317) 653-2602
Admin Sheryl Kern.
Beds 119.

Sunset Manor Nursing Home Inc
1109 S Indiana St, Greencastle, IN, 46135 (317) 653-3143
Admin Jack L Cross.
Licensure Intermediate Care. *Beds* 79. *Certified* Medicaid.
Staff RNs 2 (ft).
Facilities Dining room; Activities room; Laundry room.
Activities Cards; Games; Reading groups.

GREENFIELD

Brandywine Manor
745 N Swope St, Greenfield, IN, 46140 (317) 462-9221
Medical Dir/Dir of Nursing Hal Rhynearson MD.
Licensure Skilled Care; Intermediate Care.
Beds SNF 83; ICF 49. *Certified* Medicaid; Medicare.
Admissions Requirements Medical examination; Physician's request.
Staff RNs 7 (ft); LPNs 13 (ft); Nurses aides 40 (ft); Physical therapists 1 (ft); Recreational therapists 1 (ft); Occupational therapists 1 (ft), 1 (pt); Speech therapists 1 (pt); Activities coordinators 1 (ft); Dietitians 1 (pt); Dentists 1 (pt); Ophthalmologists 1 (pt); Podiatrists 1 (pt); Audiologists 1 (pt).
Facilities Dining room; Physical therapy room; Activities room; Chapel; Crafts room; Laundry room; Barber/Beauty shop; Lounge areas.
Activities Arts and Crafts; Cards; Games; Reading groups; Prayer groups; Movies; Shopping trips; Dances/Social or cultural gatherings.
Description This facility features outstanding physical, occupational, and speech therapy programs; accepts heavy skilled patients; excellent internal qualified aide programs in all areas.

Crescent Manor Nursing Home*
1310 E Main St, Greenfield, IN, 46140 (317) 462-4344
Admin Evelyn Walters.
Licensure Intermediate Care. *Beds* 40. *Certified* Medicaid.

Regency Place of Greenfield
200 Green Meadows Dr, Greenfield, IN, 46140 (317) 462-3311
Admin Homer Winans. *Medical Dir/Dir of Nursing* Ronald K Andrews MD.
Licensure Skilled Care; Intermediate Care.
Beds SNF 48; ICF 95; Residential 6. *Certified* Medicaid; Medicare.
Admissions Requirements Medical examination.
Staff RNs; LPNs; Nurses aides; Physical therapists; Recreational therapists; Occupational therapists; Speech therapists; Activities coordinators; Dietitians.
Facilities Dining room; Physical therapy room; Activities room; Chapel; Crafts room; Laundry room; Barber/Beauty shop; Library; Courtyard.
Activities Arts and Crafts; Cards; Games; Reading groups; Prayer groups; Movies; Shopping trips; Dances/Social or cultural gatherings.
Description JCAH accredited; home health care coordinator; VA approved.

Sugar Creek Convalescent Center Inc
Rt 7, Box 70, Greenfield, IN, 46140 (317) 894-3301
Admin Kenneth R Smith. *Medical Dir/Dir of Nursing* Joseph P Worley MD.
Licensure Skilled Care; Intermediate Care.
Beds SNF 40; ICF 30. *Certified* Medicaid.
Admissions Requirements Minimum age 18; Medical examination; Physician's request.
Staff Physicians 2 (pt); RNs 4 (ft), 3 (pt); LPNs 3 (ft), 3 (pt); Nurses aides 14 (ft), 11 (pt); Physical therapists 1 (pt); Reality therapists 1 (pt); Recreational therapists 1 (ft); Occupational

therapists 1 (pt); Speech therapists 1 (pt); Activities coordinators 1 (ft); Dietitians 1 (ft); Dentists 1 (pt); Podiatrists 1 (pt); Audiologists 1 (pt).
Facilities Dining room; Physical therapy room; Activities room; Chapel; Crafts room; Laundry room; Barber/Beauty shop; Library; Occupational therapy room.
Activities Arts and Crafts; Cards; Games; Reading groups; Prayer groups; Movies; Shopping trips; Dances/Social or cultural gatherings.
Description Those residents who are able are taken to the Indy 500 parade each year; annual resident/family, employee/family picnic. Nursing Health Care Home Association Heritage Award for excellence; member of Indiana and national nursing home associations.

GREENSBURG

Greensburg Nursing Home*
1420 Lincoln St, Greensburg, IN, 47240 (812) 663-7503
Admin Carol Sue Settles.
Licensure Intermediate Care. *Beds* 40. *Certified* Medicaid.

Heritage House of Greensburg*
410 Park Rd, Greensburg, IN, 47240 (812) 663-7543
Admin Elizabeth Kerns.
Licensure Intermediate Care. *Beds* 200. *Certified* Medicaid.

Odd Fellows Home
Rt 8, Greensburg, IN, 47240 (812) 663-8553
Admin Jon W Kohlmeier.
Licensure Intermediate Care; Residential Care. *Beds* 89. *Certified* Medicaid.
Admissions Requirements Medical examination.
Staff Physicians; RNs; LPNs; Orderlies; Nurses aides; Physical therapists; Speech therapists; Activities coordinators; Dietitians; Dentists; Ophthalmologists; Podiatrists; Audiologists.
Affiliation Independent Order of Odd Fellows
Facilities Dining room; Physical therapy room; Activities room; Chapel; Crafts room; Laundry room; Barber/Beauty shop.
Activities Arts and Crafts; Cards; Games; Reading groups; Prayer groups; Movies; Shopping trips; Dances/Social or cultural gatherings.
Description Facility is located on 150 very beautiful and serene acres in the community of Greensburg.

GREENWOOD

Fountainview Place of Greenwood
1400 W Main St, Greenwood, IN, 46142 (317) 888-4948
Admin Thomas L Kelly. *Medical Dir/Dir of Nursing* Dr Constance Van Valor.
Licensure Skilled Care; Intermediate Care.
Beds SNF 52; ICF 60. *Certified* Medicaid; Medicare.
Admissions Requirements Minimum age 21; Medical examination; Physician's request.
Facilities Dining room; Physical therapy room; Activities room; Chapel; Crafts room; Laundry

room; Barber/Beauty shop.
Activities Arts and Crafts; Cards; Games; Reading groups; Prayer groups; Movies; Shopping trips; Dances/Social or cultural gatherings.
Description Facility is JCAH accredited.

Greenwood Convalescent Center*
937 Fry Rd, Greenwood, IN, 46142 (317) 881-3610
Admin Patrica Blevins.
Licensure Intermediate Care. *Beds* 70.

Village Manor*
271 Village Ln, Greenwood, IN, 46142 (317) 888-3545
Admin George J Hill.
Beds 105.

Westminster Village
US Hwy 31 S, Greenwood, IN, 46142 (317) 881-2591
Admin Wayne A Badskey.
Licensure Skilled Care; Intermediate Care.
Beds SNF 43; ICF 48. *Certified* Medicaid; Medicare.

HAMMOND

Hammond Nursing Home*
1402 E 173rd St, Hammond, IN, 46320 (219) 844-4534
Admin Thelma Zabinski.
Licensure Intermediate Care. *Beds* 40. *Certified* Medicaid.

Saint Ann's Home*
5927 Columbia Ave, Hammond, IN, 46320 (219) 937-9400
Admin Ernest P Brister.
Licensure Residential Care. *Beds* 230.
Affiliation Roman Catholic

HANOVER

Hanover Nursing Center*
PO Box 47, State Rd 56 W, Hanover, IN, 47243 (812) 866-2625
Admin Kay Pitts.
Licensure Intermediate Care. *Beds* 151. *Certified* Medicaid.

HARTFORD CITY

Hartford City Community Care Center
PO Box 266, 715 N Mill St, Hartford City, IN, 47348 (317) 348-3310
Admin Kenneth W Seifferty. *Medical Dir/Dir of Nursing* Dr Thomas Lee.
Licensure Intermediate Care. *Beds* 52. *Certified* Medicaid.
Admissions Requirements Medical examination; Physician's request.
Staff Physicians 1 (pt); RNs 2 (ft), 1 (pt); LPNs 1 (ft), 2 (pt); Nurses aides 7 (ft), 11 (pt); Activities coordinators 1 (ft); Dietitians 1 (ft); Podiatrists 1 (pt).
Facilities Dining room; Activities room; Laundry room.
Activities Arts and Crafts; Cards; Games; Reading groups.
Description Facility is located in the heart of

the medical center of Hartford City. We have 4 doctors and a hospital within one-half block of the facility.

Miller's Merry Manor Inc
Rt 2, PO Box 266, Hartford City, IN, 47348 (317) 348-1072
Admin Dale Maryfield. *Medical Dir/Dir of Nursing* Roger Frazier DO.
Licensure Intermediate Care. *Beds* 86. *Certified* Medicaid.
Admissions Requirements Minimum age 18; Medical examination; Physician's request.
Staff RNs 3 (ft); LPNs 2 (ft), 2 (pt); Orderlies 1 (ft); Nurses aides 13 (ft), 3 (pt); Activities coordinators 1 (ft); Dietitians 1 (pt).
Facilities Dining room; Activities room; Chapel; Laundry room; Barber/Beauty shop.
Activities Arts and Crafts; Games; Reading groups; Prayer groups; Movies; Dances/Social or cultural gatherings.
Description Our facility is located in a rural setting on 10 acres of land on which a small creek flows across at the basin in the front of the property.

HIGHLAND

Highland Nursing Home
9630 5th St, Highland, IN, 46322 (219) 924-6953
Admin Richard E Meriwether. *Medical Dir/Dir of Nursing* Mona Stern MD.
Licensure Intermediate Care. *Beds* 40. *Certified* Medicaid.
Staff Physicians 1 (pt); RNs 1 (pt); LPNs 1 (ft), 2 (pt); Nurses aides 6 (ft), 20 (pt); Recreational therapists 1 (ft); Activities coordinators 1 (pt); Dietitians 1 (pt); Dentists 1 (pt).
Facilities Dining room; Activities room; Crafts room; Laundry room.
Activities Arts and Crafts; Cards; Games; Prayer groups; Dances/Social or cultural gatherings.
Description Quiet residential area setting in good neighborhood. Small facility of 40 beds, single-story construction with good nursing care.

HOBART

Millers Merry Manor
2901 W 37th Ave, Hobart, IN, 46342 (219) 942-2170
Admin Gary Brubaker.
Licensure Intermediate Care. *Beds* 101. *Certified* Medicaid.
Admissions Requirements Minimum age 18; Medical examination; Physician's request.
Staff RNs 4 (ft), 2 (pt); LPNs 2 (ft); Physical therapists 1 (pt); Speech therapists 1 (pt); Activities coordinators 1 (ft), 1 (pt); Dietitians 1 (pt); Dentists 1 (pt); Podiatrists 1 (pt).
Facilities Dining room; Physical therapy room; Activities room; Crafts room; Laundry room; Barber/Beauty shop.
Activities Arts and Crafts; Cards; Games; Reading groups; Prayer groups; Movies; Shopping trips; Dances/Social or cultural gatherings.
Description Facility has outdoor park-like courtyard; ongoing inservice program.

Sebo Heritage Manor Nursing Home*
4410 W 49th Ave, Hobart, IN, 46342 (219) 942-9422
Admin Wanda Sebo.
Licensure Intermediate Care. *Beds* 54. *Certified* Medicaid.

HOPE

Ken-Joy Convalescent Home
133 Maple St, Hope, IN, 47246 (812) 546-4814
Admin William H Muller.
Licensure Intermediate Care. *Beds* 34. *Certified* Medicaid.
Admissions Requirements Medical examination.
Staff RNs 1 (pt); LPNs 1 (ft), 1 (pt); Nurses aides 8 (ft), 6 (pt); Activities coordinators 1 (ft); Dietitians 1 (pt).
Facilities Dining room; Activities room; Laundry room.
Activities Arts and Crafts; Cards; Games; Reading groups.

Miller's Merry Manor Inc
PO Box 8, Hope, IN, 47246 (812) 546-4416
Admin Greg Spaulding. *Medical Dir/Dir of Nursing* Dr Kenneth Schneider.
Licensure Intermediate Care. *Beds* 74. *Certified* Medicaid.
Staff RNs 3 (ft); LPNs 5 (ft), 1 (pt); Nurses aides 22 (ft), 8 (pt); Activities coordinators 1 (ft), 1 (pt); Dietitians 1 (pt).
Facilities Dining room; Physical therapy room; Activities room; Crafts; Laundry room; Barber/Beauty shop.
Activities Arts and Crafts; Games; Reading groups; Prayer groups; Movies; Shopping trips; Dances/Social or cultural gatherings.
Description Facility sets in a beautiful rural setting overlooking Lake Schaefer.

HUNTINGBURG

Huntingburg Convalescent Center Inc
1712 Leland Dr, Huntingburg, IN, 47542 (812) 683-4090
Admin Martha Thewes. *Medical Dir/Dir of Nursing* Dr J G Ellison.
Licensure Skilled Care; Intermediate Care.
Beds 115. *Certified* Medicaid; Medicare.
Admissions Requirements Minimum age 18.
Staff Physicians 1 (pt); RNs 2 (ft), 6 (pt); LPNs 1 (ft), 6 (pt); Orderlies 1 (ft), 1 (pt); Nurses aides 32 (pt); Physical therapists 1 (pt); Occupational therapists 1 (pt); Activities coordinators 1 (ft); Dietitians 1 (pt); Dentists 1 (pt); Podiatrists 1 (pt).
Facilities Dining room; Physical therapy room; Activities room; Crafts room; Laundry room; Barber/Beauty shop.
Activities Arts and Crafts; Cards; Games; Reading groups; Prayer groups; Movies; Shopping trips; Dances/Social or cultural gatherings.

Medco Center of Huntingburg
530 4th St, Huntingburg, IN, 47542 (812) 683-2535
Admin Mary E Hoffhaus. *Medical Dir/Dir of Nursing* Theodore A Waflart.
Licensure Intermediate Care. *Beds* 82. *Certi-

fied Medicaid.
Admissions Requirements Minimum age 18;
Medical examination; Physician's request.
Staff Physicians 1 (ft), 5 (pt); RNs 3 (ft); LPNs
5 (pt); Nurses aides 9 (ft), 3 (pt); Physical thera-
pists 2 (pt); Occupational therapists 2 (pt);
Activities coordinators 1 (ft); Dietitians 1 (ft);
Dentists 1 (ft); Podiatrists 1 (ft).
Facilities Dining room; Physical therapy room;
Activities room; Chapel; Crafts room; Laundry
room; Barber/Beauty shop; Library; Meeting
rooms.
Activities Arts and Crafts; Cards; Games;
Reading groups; Prayer groups; Movies; Shopping trips; Dances/Social or cultural gatherings.
Description Facility features an outstanding
volunteer auxiliary, lovely garden and patio
area, beautiful lounges on each floor (3), Memorial Hall for community meeting rooms.

HUNTINGTON

Huntington Nursing Home
1425 Grant St, Huntington, IN, 46750 (219)
356-4867
Admin Sharon Andersen.
Licensure Intermediate Care. *Beds* 40. *Certified* Medicaid.
Admissions Requirements Minimum age 18.
Staff LPNs 2 (ft), 1 (pt); Nurses aides 7 (ft), 8
(pt); Activities coordinators 1 (ft); Dietitians 1
(pt).
Facilities Dining room; Laundry room.
Activities Arts and Crafts; Games; Reading
groups; Prayer groups; Shopping trips.
Description Small facility in a rural midwest
town; very comfortable home-like atmosphere;
menus and quality of food really keep residents
happy.

Miller's Merry Manor Inc
1500 Grant St, Huntington, IN, 46750 (219)
356-5713
Admin Patricia Dennis. *Medical Dir/Dir of
Nursing* S E Cape MD.
Licensure Skilled Care; Intermediate Care.
Beds SNF 37; ICF 132. *Certified* Medicaid;
Medicare.
Admissions Requirements Minimum age 18.
Staff Physicians 12 (pt); RNs 10 (ft), 4 (pt);
LPNs 5 (ft), 4 (pt); Nurses aides 38 (ft), 16 (pt);
Occupational therapists 1 (pt); Activities coor-
dinators 2 (ft); Dietitians 1 (ft).
Facilities Dining room; Physical therapy room;
Activities room; Crafts room; Laundry room;
Barber/Beauty shop.
Activities Arts and Crafts; Cards; Games;
Reading groups; Prayer groups; Movies; Shop-
ping trips; Dances/Social or cultural gatherings.

Norwood Nursing Center
Rt 8, Maple Grove Rd, Huntington, IN, 46750
(219) 356-1252
Admin Suzanne Whitted. *Medical Dir/Dir of
Nursing* Dr Richard Blair.
Licensure Intermediate Care. *Beds* 60. *Certi-
fied* Medicaid.
Staff RNs 2 (ft), 2 (pt); LPNs 3 (ft), 3 (pt);
Nurses aides 15 (ft), 23 (pt); Physical therapists
1 (pt); Activities coordinators 1 (pt); Dietitians
1 (pt); Dentists 1 (pt); Podiatrists 1 (pt).
Facilities Dining room; Physical therapy room;

Activities room; Laundry room; Barber/Beauty
shop.
Activities Arts and Crafts; Cards; Games;
Reading groups; Prayer groups; Movies; Shopping trips; Dances/Social or cultural gatherings.

INDIANAPOLIS

The Alpha Home*
1910 N Senate Ave, Indianapolis, IN, 46202
(317) 923-1518
Admin Sherlee Butler.
Licensure Intermediate Care. *Beds* 44. *Certified* Medicaid.

Altenheim Community
3525 E Hanna Ave, Indianapolis, IN, 46227
(317) 788-4261
Admin R Armstrong. *Medical Dir/Dir of
Nursing* Dr Ellsworth Stuckey.
Licensure Skilled Care; Intermediate Care.
Beds SNF 25; ICF 72; Social Care Units 25;
Independent Living Apartments 68. *Cer-
tified* Medicaid; Medicare.
Admissions Requirements Minimum age 60.
Affiliation Church of Christ
Facilities Dining room; Physical therapy room;
Activities room; Chapel; Crafts room; Laundry
room; Barber/Beauty shop; Library.
Activities Arts and Crafts; Cards; Games;
Reading groups; Prayer groups; Movies; Shop-
ping trips; Dances/Social or cultural gatherings;
Gardening; Foster grandparents program.
Description Facility is located on 32 acres on
the southeast side of Indianapolis near intersection of I-65 and I-465; sloping gently toward the
southeast, the location affords a clear view
across open countryside, and provides ample
space for outdoor activity. New home of modern design provides 3 ambulant wings, a residential care facility, a comprehensive care wing,
and 3-story center section; large rooms and
apartments accommodate 104 residents; comprehensive care wing and residential care
facility accommodate 72 residents.

Americana Healthcare Center—Indianapolis*
5600 E 16th St, Indianapolis, IN, 46218 (317)
356-0911
Admin Fred M Moon.
Licensure Skilled Care; Intermediate Care.
Beds 98. *Certified* Medicaid; Medicare.

**Americana Healthcare Center—Indianapolis
Midtown***
2010 N Capitol Ave, Indianapolis, IN, 46202
(317) 924-5821
Admin Eugene Caldwell.
Licensure Skilled Care; Intermediate Care.
Beds 153. *Certified* Medicaid; Medicare.

**Americana Healthcare Center—Indianapolis
North***
8350 Naab Rd, Indianapolis, IN, 46260 (317)
872-1110
Admin Rob Roy James.
Licensure Skilled Care; Intermediate Care.
Beds 201. *Certified* Medicaid; Medicare.

Anthony Hall Nursing Home
2135 N Alabama St, Indianapolis, IN, 46202
(317) 925-7917

Admin Larry Gray. *Medical Dir/Dir of
Nursing* Dr Linda Stropes.
Licensure Intermediate Care. *Beds* 23. *Certi-
fied* Medicaid.
Admissions Requirements Medical examina-
tion.
Staff RNs 1 (ft); LPNs 1 (ft), 2 (pt); Nurses
aides 10 (ft); Occupational therapists 1 (pt);
Dietitians 1 (pt); Dentists 1 (pt); Ophthalmolo-
gists 1 (pt); Podiatrists 1 (pt).
Facilities Dining room; Activities room; Laun-
dry room.
Activities Arts and Crafts; Cards; Games;
Prayer groups; Movies; Shopping trips; Dances-
/Social or cultural gatherings.
Description Anthony Hall is an old English
Tudor building with lawn; offers a special pro-
gram for the developmentally disabled and
mentally retarded residents. This is a full-
service facility with a family atmosphere.

The Barton House*
505 N Delaware St, Indianapolis, IN, 46204
(317) 634-9382
Admin Audrey Bonner.
Licensure Intermediate Care. *Beds* 120. *Certified* Medicaid.

Bel-Terrace Nursing Home Inc*
1629-1633 N College Ave, Indianapolis, IN,
46202 (317) 924-3239
Admin Bruce Clark.
Licensure Intermediate Care. *Beds* 68. *Certified* Medicaid.

Bethany Village
3518 Shelby St, Indianapolis, IN, 46227 (317)
786-0451
Admin Rosemary O'Brian.
Licensure Intermediate Care. *Beds* 48. *Certified* Medicaid.

Booker-Watts Nursing Home
2523 Central Ave, Indianapolis, IN, 46205
(317) 926-5919
Admin Herbert O Watts.
Licensure Intermediate Care. *Beds* 28. *Certified* Medicaid.

Broad Ripple Nursing Home
6127 N College, Indianapolis, IN, 46220 (317)
257-8392
Admin Linda Mead. *Medical Dir/Dir of
Nursing* Dr Jeff Salon.
Licensure Intermediate Care. *Beds* 50. *Certi-
fied* Medicaid.
Admissions Requirements Minimum age 19;
Medical examination.
Staff RNs 1 (ft); LPNs 2 (pt); Nurses aides 17
(ft), 5 (pt); Activities coordinators 1 (ft); Dieti-
tians 1 (pt).
Facilities Dining room.
Activities Arts and Crafts; Cards; Reading
groups; Prayer groups; Movies.
Description This is a small nursing home with
home-like atmosphere and a bright cheerful
decor.

Brookview Manor
7145 E 21st St, Indianapolis, IN, 46219 (317)
356-0977
Admin Arthur J Mirkin. *Medical Dir/Dir of
Nursing* Dr Fred Hendricks.

Licensure Skilled Care; Intermediate Care.
Beds SNF 94; ICF 50. *Certified* Medicaid;
Medicare.
Admissions Requirements Minimum age 18;
Medical examination.
Staff Physicians 1 (ft); RNs 7 (ft); LPNs 30 (ft);
Orderlies 1 (ft); Nurses aides 99 (ft); Physical
therapists 1 (ft), 3 (pt); Reality therapists 1 (ft);
Recreational therapists 1 (ft); Occupational
therapists 2 (ft); Speech therapists 1 (ft); Activi-
ties coordinators 2 (ft); Dietitians 1 (ft), 1 (pt);
Dentists 1 (pt); Ophthalmologists 1 (pt); Podia-
trists 1 (pt); Audiologists 1 (pt).
Facilities Dining room; Physical therapy room;
Activities room; Chapel; Crafts room; Laundry
room; Barber/Beauty shop; Library.
Activities Arts and Crafts; Cards; Games;
Reading groups; Prayer groups; Movies; Shop-
ping trips; Dances/Social or cultural gatherings.

Cedar Crest Health Center Inc
1924 Wellesley Blvd, Indianapolis, IN, 46219
(317) 353-6270
Admin J L Huffer. *Medical Dir/Dir of
Nursing* Roudolph Rouhana MD.
Licensure Skilled Care; Intermediate Care.
Beds SNF 70; ICF 70. *Certified* Medicaid;
Medicare.
Admissions Requirements Minimum age 18;
Medical examination; Physician's request.
Staff RNs 5 (ft), 1 (pt); LPNs 15 (ft), 5 (pt);
Orderlies 2 (ft); Nurses aides 47 (ft), 4 (pt);
Physical therapists 1 (ft); Recreational therapists
1 (ft); Occupational therapists 1 (pt); Speech
therapists 1 (pt); Activities coordinators 2 (ft);
Dietitians 1 (pt); Dentists 1 (pt); Podiatrists 1
(pt); Audiologists 1 (pt).
Facilities Dining room; Physical therapy room;
Activities room; Chapel; Crafts room; Barber-
/Beauty shop; Library.
Activities Arts and Crafts; Cards; Games;
Reading groups; Prayer groups; Movies; Shop-
ping trips; Dances/Social or cultural gatherings.
Description VA approved.

Central Healthcare Center*
55 W 33rd St, Indianapolis, IN, 46208 (317)
927-2461
Admin Roy L Anderson.
Licensure Skilled Care; Intermediate Care.
Beds 153. *Certified* Medicaid; Medicare.

Central Manor Health Care Center Inc*
2115 N Central, Indianapolis, IN, 46202 (317)
923-9844
Admin John L Coffey.
Licensure Intermediate Care. *Beds* 30. *Certified* Medicaid.

Churchman Manor*
2860 Churchman Ave, Indianapolis, IN, 46203
(317) 787-3451
Admin Mark R McCarroll.
Licensure Skilled Care; Intermediate Care.
Beds SNF 98; ICF 20. *Certified* Medicaid;
Medicare.

Continental Convalescent Center*
344 S Ritter Ave, Indianapolis, IN, 46219 (317)
359-5515
Admin Steven B Sanders.
Licensure Skilled Care. *Beds* 54. *Certified* Medicaid.

Courtney's Rest Home
3302-12 Washington Blvd, Indianapolis, IN,
46205 (317) 923-7760
Admin David Arbuckle.
Licensure Home for the Aged. *Beds* 23.

Crestview Health Care Facility Inc*
1118 E 46th St, Indianapolis, IN, 46205 (317)
257-1571
Admin Margaret Cronin.
Licensure Intermediate Care. *Beds* 50. *Certified* Medicaid.

Dailey's Convalescent Home Inc*
2926 N Capitol Ave, Indianapolis, IN, 46208
(317) 926-0254
Admin Anderson T Dailey.
Licensure Intermediate Care. *Beds* 40. *Certified* Medicaid.

Del Mar Nursing Home*
709 S Lynhurst Dr, Indianapolis, IN, 46241
(317) 243-3109
Admin Diane Bercovitz.
Licensure Intermediate Care. *Beds* 40. *Certified* Medicaid.

Delaware Health Care Facility Inc
1910 N Delaware, Indianapolis, IN, 46202
(317) 925-2393
Licensure Intermediate Care. *Beds* 42. *Certi-
fied* Medicaid.
Admissions Requirements Minimum age 18;
Medical examination; Physician's request.
Staff Physicians 3 (ft); RNs 1 (pt); LPNs 3 (ft);
Orderlies 1 (ft); Nurses aides 13 (ft); Activities
coordinators 1 (ft); Dietitians 1 (pt).
Facilities Dining room; Activities room; Laun-
dry room.
Activities Arts and Crafts; Cards; Games;
Reading groups; Prayer groups; Movies; Dan-
ces/Social or cultural gatherings.

Eagle Valley Healthcare Center
3017 Valley Farms Rd, Indianapolis, IN, 46224
Admin Don Finney. *Medical Dir/Dir of
Nursing* Dr Carl Otten.
Licensure Intermediate Care; Intermediate
Care for Mentally Retarded. *Beds* 120. *Certi-
fied* Medicaid.
Ownership Proprietary.
Admissions Requirements Minimum age 21.
Staff RNs 1 (ft); LPNs 5 (ft), 6 (pt); Orderlies 2
(ft); Physical therapists; Reality therapists 1
(pt); Occupational therapists; Speech therapists;
Activities coordinators 1 (ft); Dietitians 1 (pt);
Dentists; Podiatrists 2 (pt); Audiologists.
Facilities Dining room; Physical therapy room;
Activities room; Crafts room; Laundry room;
Barber/Beauty shop; Smoking lounge; Outside
fenced patio.
Activities Arts and Crafts; Cards; Games;
Reading groups; Prayer groups; Movies; Shop-
ping trips; Dances/Social or cultural gatherings.

Eastside Healthcare Center
1302 N Lesley Ave, Indianapolis, IN, 46219
(317) 353-8061
Admin Steve Harris. *Medical Dir/Dir of
Nursing* Linda Stropes MD.
Licensure Skilled Care; Intermediate Care.
Beds SNF 89; ICF 90. *Certified* Medicaid;
Medicare.

Admissions Requirements Minimum age 18.
Staff RNs 5 (ft); LPNs 10 (ft); Nurses aides 48
(ft), 10 (pt); Physical therapists 1 (ft); Occupa-
tional therapists 1 (ft); Speech therapists 1 (ft);
Activities coordinators 2 (ft); Dietitians 1 (ft);
Dentists 1 (ft); Podiatrists 1 (ft).
Facilities Dining room; Physical therapy room;
Activities room; Crafts room; Laundry room;
Barber/Beauty shop; Library.
Activities Arts and Crafts; Cards; Games;
Reading groups; Prayer groups; Movies; Shop-
ping trips; Dances/Social or cultural gatherings;
Reality orientation; Exercises.
Description Residents have euchre tourna-
ments and bowling tournaments with other
facilities; occupation therapy; respiration thera-
py; speech therapy; social service.

Emerson Nursing Home*
3420 N Emerson Ave, Indianapolis, IN, 46218
(317) 546-9567
Admin Sandra Perry.
Licensure Intermediate Care. *Beds* 40. *Certified* Medicaid.

Fairfield Health Care Facility Inc
3630 Central Ave, Indianapolis, IN, 46205
(317) 925-2317
Admin Marilyn D Connor. *Medical Dir/Dir of
Nursing* Dr LeBoux and Dr Stropes.
Licensure Intermediate Care. *Beds* 61. *Certi-
fied* Medicaid.
Admissions Requirements Minimum age 18;
Medical examination; Physician's request.
Staff Physicians 5 (pt); RNs 1 (ft); LPNs 3 (ft);
Nurses aides 12 (ft), 8 (pt); Physical therapists;
Occupational therapists; Speech therapists;
Activities coordinators 1 (ft), 1 (pt); Dietitians
1 (pt); Dentists; Ophthalmologists; Podiatrists;
Audiologists.
Facilities Dining room; Activities room; Laun-
dry room; Library.
Activities Arts and Crafts; Cards; Games;
Reading groups; Prayer groups; Movies; Shopping trips; Dances/Social or cultural gatherings.
Description Facility has large yard for cookouts
and activities; friendly activities department;
residents from other homes are invited to participate; active in community projects; in-
house shopping days; go to Indy 500 qualifica-
tions, ballet, circus, ballgames; resident council;
dietary input for menus; music in motion;
many schools share their programs with residents.

Fountainview Place of Indianapolis
5353 E Raymond St, Indianapolis, IN, 46203
(317) 353-8015
Admin Mike Taubenheim. *Medical Dir/Dir of
Nursing* Dr John Karedes.
Licensure Skilled Care; Intermediate Care.
Beds SNF 70; ICF 145. *Certified* Medicaid;
Medicare.
Admissions Requirements Minimum age 18;
Medical examination; Physician's request.
Staff Physicians; RNs; LPNs; Orderlies;
Nurses aides; Physical therapists; Recreational
therapists; Occupational therapists; Speech ther-
apists; Activities coordinators; Dietitians; Den-
tists; Podiatrists; Audiologists.
Facilities Dining room; Physical therapy room;
Activities room; Chapel; Crafts room; Laundry
room; Barber/Beauty shop; Library.

Activities Arts and Crafts; Cards; Games; Reading groups; Prayer groups; Movies; Shopping trips; Dances/Social or cultural gatherings. *Description* Fountainview Place of Indianapolis provides skilled and/or intermediate care to private pay as well as Medicare or Medicaid eligible patients. Wide variety of activities includes many that are planned by residents and funded by projects organized by them; facility tours are available on request.

Frame House Inc*
1316 N Tibbs, Indianapolis, IN, 46222 (317) 634-8330
Admin David L McCarroll.
Licensure Intermediate Care. *Beds* 62. *Certified* Medicaid.

Frame Nursing Home Inc*
373 N Holmes Ave, Indianapolis, IN, 46222 (317) 634-7846
Admin James R McCarroll.
Licensure Intermediate Care. *Beds* 75. *Certified* Medicaid.

Garfield Park Nursing Home*
2630 S Keystone Ave, Indianapolis, IN, 46203 (317) 787-5364
Admin Thelma B Bryant.
Licensure Intermediate Care. *Beds* 55.

Greenbriar Manor*
8181 Harcourt Rd, Indianapolis, IN, 46260 (317) 872-7261
Admin Arthur Mirkin.
Licensure Skilled Care; Intermediate Care. *Beds* SNF 130; ICF 20. *Certified* Medicaid; Medicare.

Hallmark Manor Nursing Home*
PO Box 301, 6851 E 10th St, Indianapolis, IN, 46219 (317) 357-5373
Admin James Thurston.
Beds 62.

Hoosier Village Retirement Center
5300 W 96th St, Indianapolis, IN, 46268 (317) 873-3349
Admin Terry Wilson.
Licensure Comprehensive Care; Residential Care. *Beds* Comprehensive Care 70; Residential Care 90.
Admissions Requirements Medical examination.
Staff RNs 6 (ft), 1 (pt); LPNs 2 (ft), 1 (pt); Nurses aides 30 (ft), 11 (pt); Physical therapists 1 (pt); Speech therapists 1 (pt); Podiatrists 1 (pt); Audiologists 1 (pt).
Facilities Dining room; Activities room; Chapel; Crafts room; Laundry room; Barber/Beauty shop; Library.
Activities Arts and Crafts; Cards; Games; Reading groups; Prayer groups; Movies; Shopping trips; Dances/Social or cultural gatherings.
Description Facility is situated on 160 beautifully landscaped acres, all one story with no steps; beautiful chapel, carports, and garages; limousine for transportation.

Hooverwood
7001 Hoover Rd, Indianapolis, IN, 46260 (317) 251-2261
Admin Jeffrey F Stern. *Medical Dir/Dir of*

Nursing Edward Steinmetz MD.
Licensure Skilled Care; Intermediate Care.
Beds SNF 93; ICF 70. *Certified* Medicaid; Medicare.
Ownership Nonprofit.
Admissions Requirements Medical examination.
Staff RNs 7 (ft), 10 (pt); LPNs 6 (ft), 2 (pt); Nurses aides 24 (ft), 37 (pt); Physical therapists 1 (ft); Recreational therapists 2 (ft), 1 (pt); Occupational therapists 1 (ft); Activities coordinators 1 (ft); Dietitians 1 (pt).
Affiliation Jewish
Facilities Dining room; Physical therapy room; Activities room; Chapel; Crafts room; Laundry room; Barber/Beauty shop; Library.
Activities Arts and Crafts; Cards; Games; Reading groups; Prayer groups; Movies; Shopping trips; Dances/Social or cultural gatherings; Sheltered workshop.
Description Hooverwood, a nonprofit agency of the Jewish Welfare Federation, operates on the basic premise of the dignity and worth of each individual. Programs and services are geared to continuing the self-esteem of each resident, and to help the residents become more productive, creative human beings within the framework of their potential; provides the opportunity and stimulus for continuing life with pride, dignity, companionship, and service.

Houston Village Inc
5055 W 52nd St, PO Box 229043, Indianapolis, IN, 46222
Admin Myna Kae Gallear. *Medical Dir/Dir of Nursing* Dr Clarence Thomas and Dr David Wallace.
Licensure Intermediate Care. *Beds* 39. *Certified* Medicaid.
Ownership Proprietary.
Staff Physicians 5 (pt); RNs 1 (pt); LPNs 1 (ft), 3 (pt); Orderlies 1 (pt); Nurses aides 2 (ft), 6 (pt); Dietitians 1 (pt); Dentists 1 (pt); Podiatrists 1 (pt).
Facilities Dining room; Activities room; Barber/Beauty shop.
Activities Arts and Crafts; Cards; Games; Reading groups; Prayer groups; Movies; Shopping trips.
Description This small facility is located on 6 acres of wooded area, a beautiful setting with a homey atmosphere; offers excellent care.

Independent Living Club
6038 W 25th St, Indianapolis, IN, 46224 (317) 291-5228
Admin Jack Roland.
Licensure Home for the Aged. *Beds* 31.
Admissions Requirements Medical examination.
Staff Nurses aides 1 (ft), 1 (pt); Activities coordinators 1 (ft); Dietitians 1 (pt); Podiatrists 1 (pt); Audiologists 1 (pt).
Facilities Dining room; Activities room; Crafts room; Laundry room; Barber/Beauty shop; Library.
Activities Cards; Games; Prayer groups; Shopping trips; Dances/Social or cultural gatherings; Church services.
Description The Club is an excellent setting for

senior citizens that want to maintain a sense of independence and dignity but have modest incomes; aid service available.

Indianapolis Retirement Home Inc*
1731 N Capitol Ave, Indianapolis, IN, 46202 (317) 924-5839
Admin Betty Sell.
Licensure Intermediate Care; Residential Care. *Beds* ICF 20; Residential Care 37.

Lakeview Manor Inc*
45 Beachway Dr, Indianapolis, IN, 46224 (317) 243-3721
Admin Thomas Tyson Jr.
Licensure Skilled Care; Intermediate Care. *Beds* SNF 43; ICF 144. *Certified* Medicaid; Medicare.

Lawrence Manor Nursing Home
8935 E 46th St, Indianapolis, IN, 46226 (317) 898-1515
Admin Mark R Feeser. *Medical Dir/Dir of Nursing* Karen Dawes.
Licensure Intermediate Care. *Beds* 60. *Certified* Medicaid.
Staff RNs 1 (ft); LPNs 2 (ft); Nurses aides 18 (ft), 7 (pt); Activities coordinators 1 (ft); Dietitians 1 (pt).
Facilities Dining room; Laundry room; Barber/Beauty shop.
Activities Arts and Crafts; Games; Reading groups; Prayer groups; Shopping trips.

Lynhurst Nursing Home*
5225 W Morris St, Indianapolis, IN, 46241 (317) 244-3251
Admin Kristina L Turner.
Licensure Intermediate Care. *Beds* 41. *Certified* Medicaid.

Mapleton Health Care Facility Inc
3650 Central Ave, Indianapolis, IN, 46205 (317) 925-1453
Admin Tena Blakemora. *Medical Dir/Dir of Nursing* Dr Lord, Dr Lebow, and Dr Strapts.
Licensure Intermediate Care. *Beds* 52. *Certified* Medicaid.
Admissions Requirements Minimum age 18; Medical examination; Physician's request.
Staff Physicians 3 (ft); RNs 1 (ft); LPNs 3 (ft), 1 (pt); Orderlies 1 (ft); Nurses aides 14 (ft); Activities coordinators 1 (ft); Dietitians 1 (pt); Dentists 1 (pt); Ophthalmologists 1 (pt); Podiatrists 1 (pt).
Facilities Dining room; Activities room; Laundry room; Barber/Beauty shop.
Activities Arts and Crafts; Cards; Games; Reading groups; Prayer groups; Movies; Shopping trips; Dances/Social or cultural gatherings.
Description Currently being remodeled. Will join with now existing Fairfield Health Care Facility. New facility will have 113 beds.

Marion County Home*
11850 Brookville Rd, Indianapolis, IN, 46239 (317) 862-6631
Admin Henry H Bahner.
Licensure Skilled Care; Intermediate Care; Residential Care. *Beds* 375. *Certified* Medicaid; Medicare.

Marquette Manor
8140 Township Line Rd, Indianapolis, IN, 46260 (317) 875-9700
Admin Donald M Blue. *Medical Dir/Dir of Nursing* Dr Thomas Lord.
Licensure Comprehensive Care. *Beds* 78.
Admissions Requirements Minimum age 62; Medical examination.
Staff Physicians 1 (pt); RNs 2 (ft), 2 (pt); LPNs 6 (ft), 3 (pt); Orderlies 4 (ft); Nurses aides 25 (ft), 9 (pt); Physical therapists 1 (pt); Occupational therapists 1 (pt); Speech therapists 1 (pt); Activities coordinators 1 (ft), 1 (pt); Dietitians 1 (ft); Dentists 1 (pt); Podiatrists 2 (pt); Audiologists 2 (pt).
Facilities Dining room; Physical therapy room; Activities room; Chapel; Crafts room; Laundry room; Barber/Beauty shop; Library; Dark rooms; Potting and planting room.
Activities Arts and Crafts; Cards; Games; Reading groups; Prayer groups; Movies; Shopping trips; Dances/Social or cultural gatherings; Travel groups; Exercise groups.
Description Facility features 249 apartments for independent living with housekeeping and dietary services available; 2 cottages are available on the grounds as well as a 78-bed comprehensive care facility.

Meridian Nursing Home*
2102 S Meridian St, Indianapolis, IN, 46225 (317) 786-9426
Admin Patricia Sue Sneed.
Licensure Intermediate Care. *Beds* 44. *Certified* Medicaid.

Miller's Community Health Care*
1651 N Campbell St, Indianapolis, IN, 46218 (317) 357-8040
Admin Michael A Butler.
Beds 80.

Millers Merry Manor
1700 N Illinois St, Indianapolis, IN, 46202 (317) 924-1325
Admin Rita L Fox. *Medical Dir/Dir of Nursing* Hugh Thatcher Jr MD.
Licensure Skilled Care; Intermediate Care. *Beds* SNF 102; ICF 51. *Certified* Medicaid; Medicare.
Admissions Requirements Minimum age 18; Medical examination; Physician's request.
Staff Physicians 15 (pt); RNs 6 (ft), 2 (pt); LPNs 11 (ft), 5 (pt); Orderlies 1 (ft); Nurses aides 49 (ft), 13 (pt); Physical therapists 1 (pt); Recreational therapists 2 (ft); Occupational therapists 1 (pt); Speech therapists 1 (pt); Activities coordinators 1 (ft); Dietitians 1 (pt); Dentists 1 (pt); Ophthalmologists 1 (pt); Podiatrists 1 (pt); Audiologists 1 (pt).
Facilities Dining room; Physical therapy room; Activities room; Chapel; Crafts room; Laundry room; Barber/Beauty shop.
Activities Arts and Crafts; Cards; Games; Reading groups; Prayer groups; Movies; Shopping trips; Dances/Social or cultural gatherings.

Mount Zion Geriatric Center*
3549 Boulevard Pl, Indianapolis, IN, 46208 (317) 925-9681
Admin Vera Duff.
Licensure Intermediate Care. *Beds* 104. *Certified* Medicaid.

New Hope Foundation of Indiana Inc*
8450 N Payne Rd, Indianapolis, IN, 46268 (317) 872-4210
Admin William T Habig.
Beds 60.

North Willow Center*
2002 W 86th St, Indianapolis, IN, 46260 (317) 844-8811
Admin Anna Hyden.
Licensure Intermediate Care for Mentally Retarded. *Beds* ICF/MR 208. *Certified* Medicaid; Medicare.

Northside Healthcare Center*
2140 W 86th St, Indianapolis, IN, 46260 (317) 844-7211
Admin Carole J Coats.
Licensure Skilled Care; Intermediate Care. *Beds* SNF 56; ICF 141. *Certified* Medicaid; Medicare.

Northwest Manor Nursing Home*
6640 W 34th St, Indianapolis, IN, 46224 (317) 293-4930
Admin Jennifer A Knoll.
Licensure Skilled Care; Intermediate Care. *Beds* 138. *Certified* Medicaid; Medicare.

Parkview Manor Nursing Home*
2424 E 46th St, Indianapolis, IN, 46205 (317) 253-3278
Admin Charles Bellus.
Licensure Intermediate Care. *Beds* 40. *Certified* Medicaid.

Pleasant View Lodge*
PO Box 36090C, Rt 12, Indianapolis, IN, 46236 (317) 335-2159
Admin Margaret McCreary.
Licensure Intermediate Care. *Beds* 28. *Certified* Medicaid.

Riley Health Care Facility Inc
901 N East St, Indianapolis, IN, 46202 (317) 635-2648
Admin Lena K Blakemore.
Licensure Intermediate Care. *Beds* 40. *Certified* Medicaid.
Admissions Requirements Minimum age 18; Medical examination; Physician's request.
Staff Physicians 3 (pt); RNs 1 (pt); LPNs 3 (pt); Orderlies 1 (pt); Nurses aides 9 (ft); Recreational therapists 1 (ft); Activities coordinators 1 (ft); Dietitians 1 (pt); Dentists 1 (pt); Ophthalmologists 1 (pt); Podiatrists 1 (pt); Audiologists 1 (pt).
Facilities Dining room; Activities room; Laundry room; Barber/Beauty shop.
Activities Arts and Crafts; Cards; Games; Movies; Shopping trips; Dances/Social or cultural gatherings.
Description Facility is convenient to public transportation and downtown Indianapolis featuring a one-story fire resistant building; home cooked meals; a member of IHCA. This is a small facility with home-like atmosphere.

Ritter Healthcare Center*
1301 N Ritter, Indianapolis, IN, 46219 (317) 353-9465
Admin Karyn Price.

Licensure Skilled Care; Intermediate Care. *Beds* SNF 33; ICF 198. *Certified* Medicaid; Medicare.

Rural Health Care Facility
1747 N Rural, Indianapolis, IN, 46218 (317) 635-1355
Admin Marilyn Conner.
Licensure Intermediate Care. *Beds* 50. *Certified* Medicaid.
Admissions Requirements Medical examination.
Staff RNs 1 (ft); LPNs 4 (ft), 1 (pt); Orderlies 1 (pt); Activities coordinators 1 (ft); Dietitians 1 (ft); Dentists 1 (pt); Ophthalmologists 1 (pt); Podiatrists 1 (pt); Audiologists 1 (pt).
Facilities Dining room; Activities room; Crafts room; Laundry room; Barber/Beauty shop.
Activities Arts and Crafts; Cards; Games; Prayer groups; Movies; Shopping trips; Dances/Social or cultural gatherings.

Saint Augustine Home for the Aged*
2345 W 86th St, Indianapolis, IN, 46260 (317) 872-6420
Admin Sr Agatha Sims.
Licensure Intermediate Care. *Beds* 109. *Certified* Medicaid.
Affiliation Roman Catholic

Saint Paul Baptist Church Home for the Aged
1141-45 N Sheffield Ave, Indianapolis, IN, 46222 (317) 637-2429
Admin James K Kinsey.
Licensure Intermediate Care. *Beds* 48. *Certified* Medicaid.
Admissions Requirements Minimum age 18; Medical examination; Physician's request.
Staff Physicians 2 (pt); RNs 1 (ft); LPNs 1 (ft), 2 (pt); Nurses aides 7 (ft), 12 (pt); Activities coordinators 1 (ft); Dietitians 1 (pt); Dentists 1 (pt); Ophthalmologists 1 (pt); Podiatrists 1 (pt).
Affiliation Baptist

Scott Manor Nursing Home Inc
3402 N Schofield, Indianapolis, IN, 46218 (317) 925-6038
Admin L Scott and B K Scott. *Medical Dir/Dir of Nursing* Martha M Tolbert.
Licensure Intermediate Care. *Beds* 40. *Certified* Medicaid.
Admissions Requirements Medical examination.
Staff RNs 1 (ft), 1 (pt); LPNs 2 (ft), 1 (pt); Orderlies 2 (ft), 2 (pt); Nurses aides 8 (ft), 2 (pt); Dietitians 4 (ft), 3 (pt).
Facilities Dining room; Laundry room; Barber/Beauty shop.
Activities Arts and Crafts; Games; Reading groups; Prayer groups; Movies; Dances/Social or cultural gatherings.

Sherwood Convalescent Home
3208 N Sherman Dr, Indianapolis, IN, 46218 (317) 545-6017
Admin Larry E Gray. *Medical Dir/Dir of Nursing* Dr Debra Carter Bluitt.
Licensure Intermediate Care. *Beds* 51. *Certified* Medicaid.
Admissions Requirements Minimum age 19; Medical examination.
Staff RNs 2 (ft); LPNs 3 (ft), 2 (pt); Orderlies 1 (ft), 1 (pt); Nurses aides 10 (ft), 2 (pt); Activities

coordinators 1 (ft); Dietitians 1 (pt).
Facilities Dining room; Activities room; Laundry room; Barber/Beauty shop.
Activities Arts and Crafts; Cards; Games; Prayer groups; Movies; Shopping trips; Dances/Social or cultural gatherings.

Southeastern Nursing Home*
4743 Southeastern Ave, Indianapolis, IN, 46203 (317) 356-0901
Admin Lucile Smith.
Licensure Intermediate Care. *Beds* 40. *Certified* Medicaid.

Southside Healthcare Center*
525 E Thompson Rd, Indianapolis, IN, 46227 (317) 787-8253
Admin Larry Allen.
Licensure Intermediate Care. *Beds* 156. *Certified* Medicaid.

Stone Manor Convalescent Center*
8201 W Washington St, Indianapolis, IN, 46231 (317) 244-6848
Admin Jeremy Carter.
Licensure Intermediate Care. *Beds* 65. *Certified* Medicaid.

Three Sisters Nursing Home Inc*
6130 N Michigan Rd, Indianapolis, IN, 46208 (317) 253-3486
Admin Mamie Beamon.
Licensure Intermediate Care. *Beds* 100. *Certified* Medicaid.

Warren Park Nursing Home
6855 E 10th St, Indianapolis, IN, 46229 (317) 353-9666
Admin Ruth E Denny. *Medical Dir/Dir of Nursing* Dr Clarence Thomas.
Licensure Intermediate Care. *Beds* 40. *Certified* Medicaid.
Admissions Requirements Minimum age 18; Medical examination; Physician's request.
Staff RNs 1 (pt); LPNs 3 (ft), 2 (pt); Orderlies 1 (pt); Nurses aides 4 (ft), 8 (pt); Recreational therapists 1 (ft); Activities coordinators 1 (ft); Dietitians 1 (pt).
Facilities Dining room; Activities room; Laundry room.
Activities Arts and Crafts; Cards; Games; Reading groups; Prayer groups; Movies; Shopping trips; Dances/Social or cultural gatherings.
Description Home is small, clean, newly redecorated, and comfortable; goal is to maintain the ultimate in personalized nursing care.

Westminster Village North Inc
11050 Presbyterian Dr, Indianapolis, IN, 46236 (317) 823-6841
Admin Judith L Stave. *Medical Dir/Dir of Nursing* A T Stone MD.
Licensure Skilled Care. *Beds* 77. *Certified* Medicare.
Admissions Requirements Minimum age 55.
Staff Physicians 1 (pt); RNs 6 (ft), 3 (pt); LPNs 5 (ft); Nurses aides 32 (ft), 6 (pt); Physical therapists 1 (ft); Activities coordinators 1 (ft); Dietitians 1 (ft).
Facilities Dining room; Physical therapy room; Activities room; Chapel; Crafts room; Laundry room; Barber/Beauty shop.
Activities Arts and Crafts; Cards; Games;

Reading groups; Prayer groups; Movies; Shopping trips.
Description Westminster Village North is located on a beautiful wooded acreage east of the city of Indianapolis; a companion living program (nonlicensed) is a step between residential and health center living; also a cottage program.

Westside Christian Village
8616 W 10th St, Indianapolis, IN, 46234
Admin Ronald E Davis. *Medical Dir/Dir of Nursing* Dr Joseph C Keslin.
Licensure Intermediate Care. *Beds* 59. *Certified* Medicaid.
Ownership Nonprofit.
Admissions Requirements Minimum age 65; Medical examination.
Staff Physicians 1 (pt); RNs 2 (ft); LPNs 6 (ft); Orderlies 4 (ft); Nurses aides 16 (ft), 5 (pt); Physical therapists 1 (pt); Recreational therapists 1 (pt); Occupational therapists 1 (pt); Activities coordinators 1 (ft); Dietitians 1 (ft).
Affiliation Church of the Nazarene
Facilities Dining room; Physical therapy room; Activities room; Chapel; Crafts room; Laundry room; Barber/Beauty shop; Library.
Activities Arts and Crafts; Cards; Games; Reading groups; Prayer groups; Movies; Shopping trips; Dances/Social or cultural gatherings.
Description Facility is nestled on 15 acres of secluded ground with wooded, park-like setting, yet just minutes away from shopping; apartment residents are offered 15 free days per year in the health center; offers dining hostess with seating as in a restaurant; excellent view from patient rooms in health center conducive to recovery.

Westview Nursing Home
5435 W 38th St, Indianapolis, IN, 46254 (317) 293-2266
Admin Elizabeth J Schwindler. *Medical Dir/Dir of Nursing* Dr Fred Brooks.
Licensure Intermediate Care. *Beds* 44. *Certified* Medicaid.
Admissions Requirements Medical examination.
Staff RNs 1 (ft), 1 (pt); LPNs 2 (ft), 2 (pt); Nurses aides 9 (ft), 6 (pt); Activities coordinators 1 (ft); Dietitians 1 (ft), 1 (pt).
Facilities Dining room; Activities room; Laundry room; Barber/Beauty shop.
Activities Arts and Crafts; Cards; Games; Reading groups; Prayer groups; Movies; Shopping trips; Dances/Social or cultural gatherings.
Description Westview Nursing Home is located one mile from I-465 for easy access, near shopping centers, restaurants, and movie houses; meals are well-prepared and planned by a registered dietician with attention to special diets; secure outdoor area; lounge area with color television.

JASONVILLE

Shakamak Good Samaritan Center
800 E Ohio St, Jasonville, IN, 47438 (812) 665-2226
Admin Lois I Jensen. *Medical Dir/Dir of Nursing* Carl Porter MD.
Licensure Intermediate Care. *Beds* 64. *Certi-

fied Medicaid.
Admissions Requirements Minimum age 18; Medical examination; Physician's request.
Staff RNs 1 (ft); LPNs 3 (ft), 5 (pt); Nurses aides 21 (ft), 6 (pt); Physical therapists 2 (pt); Activities coordinators 1 (ft).
Affiliation Lutheran
Facilities Dining room; Physical therapy room; Activities room; Chapel; Crafts room; Laundry room; Barber/Beauty shop; Library.
Activities Arts and Crafts; Cards; Games; Reading groups; Prayer groups; Movies; Shopping trips; Dances/Social or cultural gatherings.
Description Facility staff serves each resident emphasizing the development and care of the whole person, giving consideration to spiritual, social, and emotional needs as well as the residents' well being; all residents receive the care and services most appropriate to their individual needs; motto is "In Christ's Love Everyone is Someone."

JASPER

Jasper Nursing Center Inc
2909 Howard Dr, Jasper, IN, 47546 (812) 482-6161
Admin John L Wehrle.
Licensure Intermediate Care. *Beds* 112. *Certified* Medicaid.
Admissions Requirements Minimum age 18; Medical examination.
Staff RNs 4 (ft), 1 (pt); LPNs 7 (ft); Orderlies 1 (ft); Nurses aides 36 (ft), 3 (pt); Activities coordinators 1 (ft), 2 (pt); Dietitians 1 (pt).
Facilities Dining room; Activities room; Chapel; Crafts room; Laundry room; Barber/Beauty shop.
Activities Arts and Crafts; Cards; Games; Reading groups; Prayer groups; Movies; Shopping trips; Dances/Social or cultural gatherings.

Northwood Good Samaritan Center
PO Box 459, Jasper, IN, 47546 (812) 482-1722
Admin Kent J Brooks. *Medical Dir/Dir of Nursing* Dr Gootee.
Licensure Intermediate Care. *Beds* 107. *Certified* Medicaid.
Admissions Requirements Medical examination.
Staff RNs 2 (ft); LPNs 4 (ft), 2 (pt); Nurses aides 24 (ft), 11 (pt); Activities coordinators 2 (ft).
Facilities Dining room; Activities room; Chapel; Crafts room; Laundry room; Barber/Beauty shop; Library.
Activities Arts and Crafts; Cards; Games; Reading groups; Prayer groups; Movies; Dances/Social or cultural gatherings.

Providence Home*
520 W 9th St, Jasper, IN, 47546 (812) 482-6603
Admin Thaddeus Sztuczko.
Licensure Intermediate Care. *Beds* 66. *Certified* Medicaid.

JEFFERSONVILLE

Hillcrest Nursing Home Inc
203 Sparks Ave, Jeffersonville, IN, 47130 (812) 283-7918

Admin Jospeh M Higdon. *Medical Dir/Dir of Nursing* Leonardo Ramus MD.
Licensure Skilled Care; Intermediate Care. *Beds* SNF 51; ICF 177. *Certified* Medicaid; Medicare.
Admissions Requirements Minimum age 18; Medical examination; Physician's request.
Staff Physicians 3 (ft); RNs 6 (ft), 6 (pt); LPNs 18 (ft), 10 (pt); Nurses aides 31 (ft), 15 (pt); Physical therapists 2 (ft), 1 (pt); Recreational therapists 1 (ft), 3 (pt); Occupational therapists 1 (pt); Speech therapists 1 (pt); Activities coordinators 1 (ft); Dietitians 1 (ft); Dentists 1 (pt); Ophthalmologists 1 (pt); Podiatrists 1 (pt); Audiologists 1 (pt).
Facilities Dining room; Physical therapy room; Activities room; Chapel; Crafts room; Laundry room; Barber/Beauty shop; Library.
Activities Arts and Crafts; Cards; Games; Reading groups; Prayer groups; Movies; Shopping trips; Dances/Social or cultural gatherings.
Description Facility is located adjacent to hospital; full-time volunteer chaplain; van for outside trips and shopping; VA and JCAH approved.

Jeffersonville Nursing Home*
1720 E 8th St, Jeffersonville, IN, 47130 (812) 282-5102
Admin Patricia Ragland.
Licensure Intermediate Care. *Beds* 40. *Certified* Medicaid.

Ladies Home
330 W Market St, Jeffersonville, IN, 47130 (812) 283-6295
Admin Helen Haynes.
Licensure Residential Care. *Beds* 19.
Admissions Requirements Minimum age 50; Medical examination.
Staff RNs 1 (pt); Nurses aides 3 (ft); Recreational therapists 1 (pt); Activities coordinators 1 (pt); Dietitians 1 (pt).

Twilight Nursing Home Inc*
418 W Riverside Dr, Jeffersonville, IN, 47130 (812) 283-6401
Admin Delilah J Swaney.
Licensure Intermediate Care. *Beds* 11.

KENDALLVILLE

Kendallville Nursing Home
1433 S Main St, Kendallville, IN, 46755 (219) 347-3612
Admin Paula Rollins. *Medical Dir/Dir of Nursing* Dr C F Stallman.
Licensure Intermediate Care. *Beds* 40. *Certified* Medicaid.
Admissions Requirements Medical examination; Physician's request.
Staff RNs 1 (ft); LPNs 1 (ft), 1 (pt); Orderlies 1 (pt); Nurses aides 6 (ft), 10 (pt); Activities coordinators 1 (ft); Dietitians 1 (pt); Podiatrists 1 (pt).
Facilities Dining room; Activities room; Laundry room.
Activities Arts and Crafts; Cards; Games; Prayer groups; Movies; Field trips; Special outings; Picnics.
Description This is a small facility with a

home-like atmosphere and a very friendly staff well-qualified to meet the needs of the residents. Visits to facility are welcome.

Lutheran Homes Inc
612 E Mitchell St, Kendallville, IN, 46755 (219) 347-2256
Admin Paul Dobler. *Medical Dir/Dir of Nursing* Dr Warrener.
Licensure Intermediate Care. *Beds* 80. *Certified* Medicaid.
Admissions Requirements Minimum age 65; Medical examination.
Staff RNs 1 (ft), 2 (pt); LPNs 6 (ft), 4 (pt); Orderlies 2 (ft); Nurses aides 18 (ft), 10 (pt); Activities coordinators 1 (ft); Dietitians 1 (ft).
Affiliation Lutheran
Facilities Dining room; Activities room; Chapel; Crafts room; Laundry room; Barber/Beauty shop; Library.
Activities Arts and Crafts; Cards; Games; Reading groups; Prayer groups; Movies; Shopping trips; Dances/Social or cultural gatherings.
Description Facility has been located here for 50 years; "Meals in Motion" program; 8 residents in 8 years have reached 100 years of age.

KENTLAND

Kentland Nursing Home*
720 E Washington St, Kentland, IN, 47951 (219) 474-6741
Admin Inajean Goodwin.
Licensure Intermediate Care. *Beds* 40. *Certified* Medicaid.

KNIGHTSVILLE

Harty Nursing Home
PO Box D, Knightsville, IN, 47857 (812) 446-2309
Admin William E Harty.
Licensure Intermediate Care. *Beds* 71. *Certified* Medicaid.
Staff RNs 1 (ft); LPNs 3 (ft); Nurses aides 30 (ft); Activities coordinators 1 (ft); Dietitians 1 (pt).
Facilities Dining room; Activities room; Chapel; Crafts room; Laundry room; Barber/Beauty shop.
Activities Arts and Crafts; Cards; Games; Reading groups; Prayer groups; Movies; Shopping trips.

KNOX

Countryside Place
300 Culver Rd, Knox, IN, 46534 (219) 772-6248
Admin Brent Waymire. *Medical Dir/Dir of Nursing* Walter Fritz.
Licensure Skilled Care; Intermediate Care. *Beds* SNF 39; ICF 39. *Certified* Medicaid; Medicare.
Admissions Requirements Minimum age 18; Medical examination; Physician's request.
Staff RNs 4 (ft), 2 (pt); LPNs 3 (ft); Orderlies 1 (pt); Nurses aides 19 (ft), 9 (pt); Physical therapists 1 (pt); Speech therapists 1 (pt); Activities coordinators 2 (pt); Dietitians 1 (ft); Dentists 1 (pt); Podiatrists 1 (pt).

Facilities Dining room; Physical therapy room; Activities room; Crafts room; Laundry room; Barber/Beauty shop.
Activities Arts and Crafts; Cards; Games; Reading groups; Prayer groups; Movies; Shopping trips; Dances/Social or cultural gatherings.

KOKOMO

Americana Healthcare Center—Kokomo*
3518 S LaFountain St, Kokomo, IN, 46901 (317) 453-4666
Admin Dorothy Fordyce.
Licensure Skilled Care; Intermediate Care. *Beds* SNF 36; ICF 69. *Certified* Medicaid; Medicare.

Forest Park Healthcare Center*
2233 W Jefferson St, Kokomo, IN, 46901 (317) 457-9175
Admin Carolyn Siem.
Licensure Skilled Care; Intermediate Care. *Beds* SNF 123; ICF 72. *Certified* Medicaid; Medicare.

Kokomo Nursing Home*
1560 S Plate St, Kokomo, IN, 46901 (317) 452-8934
Admin Linda Crowe.
Licensure Intermediate Care. *Beds* 40. *Certified* Medicaid.

Sycamore Village Health Center*
2905 W Sycamore, Kokomo, IN, 46901 (317) 452-5491
Admin John Singleton.
Licensure Intermediate Care. *Beds* 173. *Certified* Medicaid.

Windsor Estates of Kokomo
429 Lincoln Rd W, Kokomo, IN, 46901 (317) 453-5600
Admin Linda Dishon. *Medical Dir/Dir of Nursing* James Whitfield.
Licensure Skilled Care; Intermediate Care. *Beds* 87. *Certified* Medicaid; Medicare.
Staff RNs 4 (ft), 1 (pt); LPNs 8 (ft), 2 (pt); Nurses aides 22 (ft), 2 (pt); Physical therapists 1 (pt); Speech therapists 1 (pt); Activities coordinators 1 (ft); Dietitians 1 (pt); Dentists 1 (pt); Ophthalmologists 1 (pt); Podiatrists 1 (pt).
Facilities Dining room; Physical therapy room; Activities room; Crafts room; Laundry room; Barber/Beauty shop.
Activities Arts and Crafts; Cards; Games; Reading groups; Prayer groups; Movies; Dances/Social or cultural gatherings.
Description Windsor Estates has a beautiful new addition and a redecorated original building; stresses a home-like environment and offers a full calendar of events to meet the needs of each individual resident. VA approved.

LADOGA

Golden Manor Health Care Center*
1001 E Main St, Ladoga, IN, 47954 (317) 942-2223

Admin David W Vice.
Licensure Intermediate Care. *Beds* 95. *Certified* Medicaid.

LAFAYETTE

Americana Healthcare Center—Lafayette
2201 Cason St, Lafayette, IN, 47901 (317) 447-4102
Admin Betty Montgomery.
Licensure Skilled Care; Intermediate Care. *Beds* SNF 19; ICF 38. *Certified* Medicaid; Medicare.
Admissions Requirements Medical examination; Physician's request.
Staff Physicians 1 (pt); RNs 6 (ft), 4 (pt); LPNs 3 (ft), 4 (pt); Nurses aides 25 (ft), 7 (pt); Physical therapists 1 (ft), 1 (pt); Occupational therapists 1 (ft), 1 (pt); Speech therapists 1 (pt); Activities coordinators 1 (ft); Dietitians 1 (ft).
Facilities Dining room; Physical therapy room; Activities room; Crafts room; Barber/Beauty shop.
Activities Arts and Crafts; Cards; Games; Reading groups; Prayer groups; Movies; Dances/Social or cultural gatherings.

Comfort Retirement and Nursing Home Inc*
312 N 8th St, Lafayette, IN, 47901 (317) 742-8455
Admin Richard E Linson.
Licensure Intermediate Care. *Beds* 46. *Certified* Medicaid.

Hillcrest Nursing Home
1123 South St, Lafayette, IN, 47901 (317) 742-6904
Admin Dan D Wheat. *Medical Dir/Dir of Nursing* Dr Mary Ade.
Licensure Intermediate Care. *Beds* 40. *Certified* Medicaid.
Admissions Requirements Medical examination; Physician's request.
Staff RNs 1 (pt); LPNs 3 (ft); Nurses aides 5 (ft), 8 (pt); Activities coordinators 1 (pt); Dietitians 1 (pt).
Facilities Dining room; Activities room; Laundry room.
Activities Arts and Crafts; Cards; Games; Reading groups; Prayer groups; Movies; Shopping trips; Dances/Social or cultural gatherings.
Description Our facility is a small, 40-bed home which gives personalized care to our residents. The staff is a good, caring group that care for the residents and are willing to give extra care when the need is there. Our rooms are nice and the place is, as a whole, clean, and odor-free.

Indiana Pythian Home
1501 S 18th St, Lafayette, IN, 47905 (317) 474-1405
Admin Bruce A Goodpaster. *Medical Dir/Dir of Nursing* Dr Eleanor Filmer.
Licensure Intermediate Care. *Beds* 75. *Certified* Medicaid.
Staff Physicians 1 (pt); RNs 1 (ft), 1 (pt); LPNs 2 (ft), 1 (pt); Nurses aides 23 (ft), 10 (pt); Activities coordinators 1 (ft).
Affiliation Knights of Pythias
Facilities Dining room; Activities room; Chapel; Crafts room; Laundry room; Barber/Beauty shop.
Activities Arts and Crafts; Cards; Reading groups; Prayer groups; Movies; Dances/Social or cultural gatherings.

Indiana Veterans Home
Rd 43 N, Lafayette, IN, 47901 (317) 463-1502
Admin Robert Hinds. *Medical Dir/Dir of Nursing* B E Fitzgerald MD.
Licensure Comprehensive Care; Residential Care; Boarding Home Care. *Beds* 648.
Ownership Public.
Admissions Requirements Medical examination; Physician's request.
Staff Physicians 1 (ft), 6 (pt); RNs 38 (ft); LPNs 29 (ft); Nurses aides 168 (ft); Physical therapists 4 (ft); Recreational therapists 12 (ft), 4 (pt); Occupational therapists 4 (ft); Speech therapists 1 (ft), 1 (pt); Activities coordinators 1 (ft); Dietitians 3 (ft); Dentists 1 (pt); Ophthalmologists 1 (pt); Podiatrists 1 (pt); Audiologists 1 (ft), 1 (pt).
Facilities Dining room; Physical therapy room; Activities room; Chapel; Crafts room; Laundry room; Barber/Beauty shop; Library.
Activities Arts and Crafts; Cards; Games; Reading groups; Prayer groups; Movies; Shopping trips; Dances/Social or cultural gatherings.
Description State nursing facility for veterans who served in wartime and their spouses. To be completed this year is a 152-bed nursing building which will bring total capacity to 800 beds; full service nursing facility; all medical services are included in per diem of $49.02—no extra charges for physicians, drugs, and the like.

Lafayette Healthcare Center
1903 Union St, Lafayette, IN, 47901 (317) 447-9431
Admin Samuel T Higdon. *Medical Dir/Dir of Nursing* Dr Eleanor Filmer.
Licensure Skilled Care; Intermediate Care. *Beds* SNF 69; ICF 133. *Certified* Medicaid; Medicare.
Admissions Requirements Medical examination.
Staff Physicians 1 (ft); RNs 2 (ft); LPNs 6 (ft), 3 (pt); Orderlies 4 (ft); Nurses aides 58 (ft), 3 (pt); Physical therapists 1 (ft); Occupational therapists 1 (pt); Speech therapists 1 (pt); Activities coordinators 1 (ft), 1 (pt); Dietitians 1 (ft); Dentists 1 (pt); Podiatrists 1 (pt); Audiologists 1 (pt).
Facilities Dining room; Physical therapy room; Activities room; Chapel; Crafts room; Laundry room; Barber/Beauty shop; Library.
Activities Arts and Crafts; Cards; Games; Reading groups; Prayer groups; Movies; Shopping trips; Dances/Social or cultural gatherings.
Description A lovely, newly remodeled facility within ¾ mile of 2 hospitals. A very indepth activity program which includes university students and animal science departments; active religious services several times a week are available. VA approved.

LAFONTAINE

Shangri-La Manor Inc
604 Rennaker St, LaFontaine, IN, 46940 (317) 981-2081

Admin Larrie L Falder. *Medical Dir/Dir of Nursing* Fred Poehler MD.
Licensure Intermediate Care. *Beds* 44. *Certified* Medicaid.
Admissions Requirements Medical examination.
Staff Physicians 1 (pt); RNs 1 (ft); LPNs 2 (ft); Orderlies 1 (ft); Nurses aides 25 (ft), 20 (pt); Activities coordinators 1 (ft); Dietitians 1 (pt).
Facilities Dining room; Activities room; Laundry room; Barber/Beauty shop; Lounges.
Activities Arts and Crafts; Cards; Games; Reading groups; Prayer groups; Movies; Shopping trips; Dances/Social or cultural gatherings.
Description Facility features individual care with a personal touch.

LAGRANGE

LaGrange Nursing Home
Rt 5, Box 74, LaGrange, IN, 46761 (219) 463-3822
Admin Sandra L Perry. *Medical Dir/Dir of Nursing* Debra Rose.
Licensure Intermediate Care. *Beds* 40. *Certified* Medicaid.
Admissions Requirements Medical examination; Physician's request.
Staff Physicians 1 (pt); RNs 1 (ft); LPNs 3 (pt); Nurses aides 7 (ft), 2 (pt); Activities coordinators 1 (ft); Dietitians 1 (pt); Dentists 1 (pt); Ophthalmologists 1 (pt); Podiatrists 1 (pt); Audiologists 1 (pt).
Facilities Dining room; Activities room; Crafts room; Laundry room.
Activities Arts and Crafts; Cards; Games; Reading groups; Prayer groups; Movies; Shopping trips; Dances/Social or cultural gatherings.
Description Residents are mainly mentally retarded and developmentally disabled. Facility strives to maintain their pride and dignity and to make their lives meaningful because they are special people.

Miller's Merry Manor Inc*
State Rd 9 N, LaGrange, IN, 46761 (219) 463-2172
Admin Phyllis A Miller.
Licensure Skilled Care; Intermediate Care. *Beds* 202. *Certified* Medicaid; Medicare.

LAPORTE

Countryside Place*
1700 I St, LaPorte, IN, 46350 (219) 362-6234
Admin Lorna Mamelson.
Licensure Skilled Care; Intermediate Care. *Beds* SNF 39; ICF 60. *Certified* Medicaid; Medicare.

Fountainview Terrace*
1900 Andrew Ave, LaPorte, IN, 46350 (219) 362-7014
Admin Howard Reiffteck.
Licensure Skilled Care; Intermediate Care. *Beds* SNF 64; ICF 114. *Certified* Medicaid; Medicare.

LAWRENCEBURG

Shady Nook Nursing Home*
607 Wilson Creek Rd, Lawrenceburg, IN,
47025 (812) 537-0930
Admin Daniel McMullen.
Licensure Intermediate Care. *Beds* 39. *Certified* Medicaid.

Terrace View Extended Care Facility*
403 Bielby Rd, Lawrenceburg, IN, 47025 (812)
537-1132
Admin Howard Goodman.
Licensure Skilled Care; Intermediate Care.
Beds SNF 41; ICF 82. *Certified* Medicaid;
Medicare.

LEAVENWORTH

Todd Dickey Medical Center*
PO Box 134, A East St, Leavenworth, IN,
47137 (812) 739-2292
Admin Jeffery Padgett.
Licensure Intermediate Care. *Beds* 78. *Certified* Medicaid; Medicare.

LEBANON

English Nursing Home Inc*
1015 N Lebanon St, Lebanon, IN, 46052 (317)
482-5880
Admin Frances E Kent.
Licensure Intermediate Care. *Beds* 36.

Golden Manor Health Care Center
1585 Perryworth Rd, PO Box 100, Lebanon,
IN, 46052 (317) 482-6391
Admin Sheila Andrews. *Medical Dir/Dir of
Nursing* Dr John Saalwaechter.
Licensure Skilled Care; Intermediate Care.
Beds SNF 65; ICF 65. *Certified* Medicaid;
Medicare.
Admissions Requirements Medical examination.
Staff Physicians 6 (pt); RNs 3 (ft); LPNs 6 (ft),
1 (pt); Orderlies 1 (ft); Nurses aides 24 (ft), 1
(pt); Physical therapists 1 (pt); Occupational
therapists 1 (pt); Speech therapists 1 (pt);
Activities coordinators 1 (ft); Dietitians 1 (pt);
Dentists 1 (pt); Podiatrists 1 (pt).
Facilities Dining room; Physical therapy room;
Activities room; Laundry room; Barber/Beauty
shop; Library.
Activities Arts and Crafts; Cards; Games;
Reading groups; Prayer groups; Movies; Shopping trips; Dances/Social or cultural gatherings.
Description Facility is located next to a large
pond amid willow and evergreen trees, yet
accessible from the interstate. An innovative
rehabilitation aid program was started in 1982.
There is a strong activity and social services
program including the Santa Hotline—
residents answer phone as Mr or Mrs Claus, listening to the children's Christmas wishes.

Lebanon Nursing Home
301 W Essex St, Lebanon, IN, 46052 (317)
482-1950
Admin Charlotte Elegere.
Licensure Intermediate Care. *Beds* 40. *Certified* Medicaid.

Admissions Requirements Medical examination.
Staff RNs 1 (ft), 1 (pt); LPNs 1 (pt); Nurses
aides 8 (ft), 6 (pt); Activities coordinators 2 (pt);
Dietitians 1 (pt).
Facilities Dining room; Laundry room.
Activities Cards; Games; Reading groups; Prayer groups; Shopping trips.

Parkwood Health Care Inc
1001 N Grant St, Lebanon, IN, 46052 (317)
482-6400
Admin Arthur O Dickerson.
Licensure Intermediate Care. *Beds* 133. *Certified* Medicaid.
Staff RNs 2 (ft), 3 (pt); LPNs 3 (ft), 2 (pt);
Nurses aides 29 (ft), 18 (pt); Physical therapists;
Speech therapists; Activities coordinators; Dietitians; Podiatrists; Audiologists; Qualified
medical assistants 11 (ft), 6 (pt).
Facilities Dining room; Physical therapy room;
Activities room; Laundry room; Barber/Beauty
shop.
Activities Arts and Crafts; Games; Reading
groups; Prayer groups; Movies.

LEWISVILLE

Homecare Center
State Rd 103, Lewisville, IN, 47352
Admin Christy Tompkins. *Medical Dir/Dir of
Nursing* Alice Grandon.
Licensure Intermediate Care. *Beds* 24.
Ownership Proprietary.
Admissions Requirements Minimum age 18;
Medical examination; Physician's request.
Staff RNs 1 (pt); LPNs 2 (ft), 1 (pt); Nurses
aides 8 (ft), 3 (pt); Activities coordinators 1 (pt);
Dietitians 1 (pt).
Facilities Dining room; Activities room; Crafts
room; Laundry room; Barber/Beauty shop.
Activities Arts and Crafts; Cards; Games;
Reading groups; Prayer groups; Movies; Dances/Social or cultural gatherings.
Description This small facility offers a homelike atmosphere in a rural community with a
large yard in which family gatherings are held;
most employees have been here several years
and are almost like family to the residents. VA
approved.

Lewisville Hotel for Senior Citizens*
Box 98, US 40, Lewisville, IN, 47352 (317)
987-7952
Admin Sarah Vollmer.
Licensure Residential Care. *Beds* 33.

LEXINGTON

Roe-Seal Memorial Home
Englishton Park, Lexington, IN, 47138 (812)
889-2681
Admin Janet A Heilman.
Licensure Residential Care. *Beds* 64.
Admissions Requirements Minimum age 60;
Medical examination; Physician's request.
Staff RNs 1 (pt); Nurses aides 2 (pt); Activities
coordinators 1 (pt); Dietitians 1 (pt).
Affiliation Presbyterian
Facilities Dining room; Activities room; Chapel; Crafts room; Laundry room; Barber/Beauty

shop; Library.
Activities Arts and Crafts; Cards; Games;
Reading groups; Prayer groups; Movies; Shopping trips; Dances/Social or cultural gatherings;
Field trips.
Description This state board of health licensed
residential care facility features 650 acres of
beautiful woodlands and 4 small lakes. A
unique part of the program is the interaction
between the residents and the children of the
community.

LIBERTY

Park Manor Nursing Home*
409 E Union St, Liberty, IN, 47353 (317)
458-6194
Admin Elaine Stubbs.
Licensure Intermediate Care. *Beds* 22. *Certified* Medicaid.

LIGONIER

**Heritage Manor Health Care Center of
Ligonier**
400 Pontiac St, Ligonier, IN, 46767 (219)
894-7118
Admin Carol A Reed. *Medical Dir/Dir of
Nursing* Pat Katsanis.
Licensure Intermediate Care. *Beds* 61. *Certified* Medicaid.
Admissions Requirements Medical examination.
Staff RNs 1 (ft); LPNs 2 (ft), 4 (pt); Orderlies 2
(pt); Nurses aides 8 (ft), 18 (pt); Physical therapists 1 (pt); Activities coordinators 1 (ft);
Dietitians 1 (pt); Podiatrists 1 (pt).
Facilities Dining room; Activities room; Laundry room; Barber/Beauty shop.
Activities Arts and Crafts; Cards; Games;
Reading groups; Prayer groups; Movies; Shopping trips; Dances/Social or cultural gatherings.
Description Facility is located in a very
pleasant picturesque country setting close to
Ligonier for shopping convenience as well as
physicians, medical supplies, churches, and
community groups.

LINTON

Glenburn Rest Haven Home Inc*
Rt #2, Glenburn Rd, Linton, IN, 47441 (812)
847-2221
Admin William T Fisher.
Licensure Intermediate Care. *Beds* 154. *Certified* Medicaid.

Linton Nursing Home
1501 E "A" St, Linton, IN, 47441 (812)
847-2988
Admin Ned K Cline. *Medical Dir/Dir of
Nursing* William Powers.
Licensure Intermediate Care. *Beds* 40. *Certified* Medicaid.
Admissions Requirements Minimum age 18;
Medical examination.
Staff Physicians 8 (pt); RNs 2 (pt); LPNs 2 (ft),
4 (pt); Nurses aides 8 (ft), 4 (pt); Physical therapists 1 (pt); Speech therapists 1 (pt); Activities
coordinators 1 (ft); Dietitians 1 (pt); Dentists 1
(pt); Ophthalmologists 2 (pt); Podiatrists 1 (pt);

Audiologists 1 (pt).
Facilities Dining room; Activities room; Laundry room.
Activities Arts and Crafts; Cards; Games; Reading groups; Prayer groups; Movies; Shopping trips; Dances/Social or cultural gatherings.

LOGANSPORT

Camelot Care Center
1555 Commerce St, Logansport, IN, 46947 (219) 753-0404
Admin Dorothy M Huston. *Medical Dir/Dir of Nursing* E R Luxenberg MD.
Licensure Intermediate Care. *Beds* 75. *Certified* Medicaid.
Admissions Requirements Medical examination.
Staff RNs; LPNs; Orderlies; Nurses aides; Physical therapists; Occupational therapists; Speech therapists; Activities coordinators; Dietitians.
Facilities Dining room; Activities room; Crafts room; Laundry room; Barber/Beauty shop.
Activities Arts and Crafts; Games; Reading groups; Movies; Shopping trips; Dances/Social or cultural gatherings; School programs; Sheltered workshop program.
Description This is a children's nursing home for MR/DDs.

Cass County Home
Perrysburg Rd, Logansport, IN, 46947 (219) 753-2791
Admin Mabel Frey.
Licensure Residential Care. *Beds* 24.

Chase Manor Nursing and Convalescent Center
1 Chase Park, Logansport, IN, 46947 (219) 753-4137
Admin David Krizmanich.
Licensure Skilled Care; Intermediate Care. *Beds* SNF 41; ICF 174. *Certified* Medicaid; Medicare.
Description Blue Cross and VA approved.

Neal Home
2518 George St, Logansport, IN, 46947 (219) 753-3920
Admin Mary L Strahle.
Licensure Home for the Aged. *Beds* 20.
Admissions Requirements Females only

LOOGOOTEE

Medco Center of Loogootee
Rt 4, Loogootee, IN, 47553 (812) 295-3624
Admin Donald G Pugh.
Licensure Intermediate Care. *Beds* 36. *Certified* Medicaid.
Admissions Requirements Medical examination; Physician's request.
Staff RNs 2 (ft), 1 (pt); LPNs 2 (ft); Nurses aides 6 (ft), 3 (pt); Activities coordinators 1 (pt).
Facilities Dining room; Laundry room.
Activities Arts and Crafts; Cards; Games; Reading groups; Prayer groups; Movies; Shopping trips; Dances/Social or cultural gatherings.
Description Medco Center of Loogootee is located in a beautiful, country setting in scenic

Martin County; meeting residents' needs and helping them to continue a dignified lifestyle is Medco's first responsibility; a home-like atmosphere, small enough to emphasize individual preferences in every detail.

LOWELL

Lowell Healthcare Center*
255 Burnham St, Lowell, IN, 46356 (219) 696-7791
Admin Gail Coffey.
Licensure Intermediate Care. *Beds* 56. *Certified* Medicaid.

LYNN

Parrott's Home
304 W Sherman St, PO Box 347, Lynn, IN, 47355 (317) 874-4281
Admin Maxine Parrott.
Licensure Residential Care. *Beds* 5.

MADISON

Clifty Falls Convalescent Center*
950 Cross Ave, Madison, IN, 47250 (812) 273-4640
Admin Aliene Breitenbach.
Licensure Intermediate Care. *Beds* 116. *Certified* Medicaid.

Madison Nursing Home
1945 Cragmont St, Madison, IN, 47250 (812) 273-4696
Admin Alice M Rogers.
Licensure Intermediate Care. *Beds* 40. *Certified* Medicaid.
Admissions Requirements Minimum age 18.
Staff RNs 1 (pt); LPNs 2 (ft), 1 (pt); Nurses aides 5 (ft), 5 (pt); Activities coordinators 1 (pt); Dietitians 1 (pt).
Facilities Dining room; Activities room; Laundry room.
Activities Arts and Crafts; Cards; Games; Movies.

Mayfield Nursing Home
702-710 Elm St, Madison, IN, 47250 (812) 265-2286
Admin George Mayfield and Susan Williamson. *Medical Dir/Dir of Nursing* Dr K Johnson.
Licensure Intermediate Care. *Beds* 32. *Certified* Medicaid.
Staff Physicians; RNs 2 (pt); LPNs 1 (ft), 1 (pt); Nurses aides 4 (ft), 10 (pt); Recreational therapists 1 (pt); Activities coordinators 1 (pt).
Facilities Dining room; Activities room; Laundry room; Barber/Beauty shop.
Activities Arts and Crafts; Cards; Games; Reading groups; Prayer groups; Movies; Shopping trips; Dances/Social or cultural gatherings; Picnics.
Description This is a family-owned facility specializing in tender loving care.

MARION

Bradner Village Residential Care Facility Inc*
PO Box 408, 505 Bradner Ave, Marion, IN, 46952 (317) 662-3981
Admin Jim J Walts.
Licensure Skilled Care; Intermediate Care.
Beds SNF 48; ICF 153. *Certified* Medicaid.

Colonial Oaks Health Care Center
4725 S Colonial Oaks Dr, Marion, IN, 46953
Admin Jeffrey M Evans. *Medical Dir/Dir of Nursing* Miles Donaldson MD.
Licensure Intermediate Care. *Beds* 60. *Certified* Medicaid.
Ownership Nonprofit.
Admissions Requirements Medical examination; Physician's request.
Staff Physicians 1 (pt); RNs 3 (ft); LPNs 2 (ft), 5 (pt); Nurses aides 16 (ft), 9 (pt); Physical therapists 3 (pt); Speech therapists 1 (pt); Activities coordinators 1 (ft), 1 (pt); Dietitians 1 (pt); Dentists 1 (pt); Podiatrists 1 (pt); Audiologists 1 (pt).
Facilities Dining room; Physical therapy room; Activities room; Laundry room; Barber/Beauty shop.
Activities Arts and Crafts; Cards; Games; Reading groups; Prayer groups; Movies; Shopping trips; Dances/Social or cultural gatherings.
Description This attractive, new health care center and retirement complex is located at the south edge of Marion in a country-like atmosphere; spacious grounds afford room for expansion as the need arises.

Emily E Flinn Home Inc
614 W 14th St, Marion, IN, 46953-2199 (317) 664-0618
Admin John L Andrae. *Medical Dir/Dir of Nursing* Dr Edward A Buhr.
Licensure Intermediate Care. *Beds* 78. *Certified* Medicaid.
Admissions Requirements Minimum age 70; Medical examination.
Staff Physicians 1 (pt); RNs 1 (ft); LPNs 4 (ft); Orderlies 2 (ft); Nurses aides 20 (ft); Physical therapists 1 (pt); Speech therapists 1 (pt); Activities coordinators 3 (ft); Dietitians 1 (pt); Audiologists 1 (pt).
Affiliation Disciples of Christ
Facilities Dining room; Physical therapy room; Activities room; Chapel; Crafts room; Laundry room; Barber/Beauty shop; Library.
Activities Arts and Crafts; Cards; Games; Reading groups; Prayer groups; Movies; Shopping trips.

Golden Age Nursing Home
1800 Kem Rd, Marion, IN, 46952 (317) 664-4573
Admin James R Hayes.
Licensure Intermediate Care. *Beds* 80. *Certified* Medicaid.
Staff RNs 2 (ft); LPNs 4 (ft); Nurses aides 30 (ft); Activities coordinators 2 (ft); Dietitians 1 (ft).
Facilities Dining room; Activities room; Crafts room; Laundry room; Barber/Beauty shop.
Activities Arts and Crafts; Cards; Games; Reading groups; Prayer groups; Movies; Shopping trips; Dances/Social or cultural gatherings.

Riverview Manor Nursing Home*
PO Box 1247, 221 N Washington St, Marion, IN, 46952 (317) 664-0612
Admin Suszane Gilliland.
Licensure Intermediate Care. *Beds* 103. *Certified* Medicaid.

Wesleyan Nursing Home
518 W 36th St, Marion, IN, 46952 (317) 674-3371
Admin Dave Clement. *Medical Dir/Dir of Nursing* Dr Charles Yale.
Licensure Skilled Care; Intermediate Care.
Beds SNF 58; ICF 96. *Certified* Medicaid; Medicare.
Admissions Requirements Medical examination.
Staff Physicians 23 (pt); RNs 4 (ft), 6 (pt); LPNs 5 (ft), 7 (pt); Orderlies 2 (ft); Nurses aides 41 (ft), 20 (pt); Physical therapists 2 (ft); Speech therapists 1 (ft); Activities coordinators 1 (ft); Dietitians 1 (ft); Dentists; Podiatrists; Audiologists.
Affiliation First Wesleyan Church
Facilities Dining room; Physical therapy room; Activities room; Chapel; Crafts room; Laundry room; Barber/Beauty shop; Library.
Activities Arts and Crafts; Cards; Games; Reading groups; Prayer groups; Movies; Shopping trips; Dances/Social or cultural gatherings.
Description Nursing home offers both skilled and intermediate levels of care with emphasis on rehabilitative nursing; will accept short- and long-term residents.

MARTINSVILLE

Dixon Home Care Center
60 E Harrison St, Martinsville, IN, 46151 (317) 342-1744
Admin Ruth E Denny.
Licensure Intermediate Care. *Beds* 17.

Grandview Manor Inc
2009 E Columbus St, Martinsville, IN, 46151 (317) 342-7115
Admin P Walker and S Shockley. *Medical Dir/Dir of Nursing* Gary Milda DO.
Licensure Intermediate Care. *Beds* 76. *Certified* Medicaid.
Staff Physicians 8 (pt); RNs 1 (ft); LPNs 3 (ft), 2 (pt); Orderlies 1 (ft); Nurses aides 15 (ft), 5 (pt); Recreational therapists 1 (pt); Activities coordinators 1 (ft), 1 (pt); Dietitians 1 (pt); Dentists 1 (pt); Ophthalmologists 1 (pt); Podiatrists 1 (pt); Social director 1 (ft).
Facilities Dining room; Activities room; Crafts room; Laundry room; Barber/Beauty shop.
Activities Arts and Crafts; Cards; Games; Reading groups; Prayer groups; Movies; Shopping trips; Dances/Social or cultural gatherings.
Description Facility offers learning facilities for family and friends for better understanding of geriatric and associated illnesses.

Heritage House Convalescent Center*
2055 Heritage Dr, Martinsville, IN, 46151 (317) 342-3305
Admin Timothy DeBruicker.
Licensure Skilled Care; Intermediate Care.
Beds SNF 59; ICF 60. *Certified* Medicaid; Medicare.

Kennedy Memorial Christian Home Inc
210 W Pike St, Martinsville, IN, 46151 (317) 342-6636
Admin Robert F Oldham. *Medical Dir/Dir of Nursing* Kathleen Brough Oldham MD.
Licensure Intermediate Care; Residential Care.
Beds ICF 58; Residential Care 100.
Admissions Requirements Minimum age 62; Medical examination.
Staff Physicians 1 (pt); RNs 1 (ft), 1 (pt); LPNs 3 (ft), 2 (pt); Recreational therapists 2 (ft); Activities coordinators 1 (pt); Dietitians 1 (pt).
Affiliation Disciples of Christ

MERRILLVILLE

Ross Care Center*
601 W 61st Ave, Merrillville, IN, 46410 (219) 980-5950
Admin Richard Shapiro.
Licensure Skilled Care; Intermediate Care.
Beds 180. *Certified* Medicaid; Medicare.

South Lake Care Center*
8800 Virginia Pl, Merrillville, IN, 46410 (219) 736-1310
Admin Alan Lien.
Beds 228.

MICHIGAN CITY

Beach Cliff Lodge Nursing Home
1001 Lake Shore Dr, Michigan City, IN, 46360 (219) 872-0120
Admin Janice Butcher. *Medical Dir/Dir of Nursing* Maurice Miller.
Licensure Intermediate Care. *Beds* 21. *Certified* Medicaid.
Admissions Requirements Minimum age 21; Medical examination; Physician's request.
Staff RNs 2 (ft), 1 (pt); Nurses aides 4 (ft), 3 (pt); Activities coordinators 1 (pt).
Facilities Dining room; Activities room; Laundry room.
Activities Arts and Crafts; Cards; Games; Reading groups; Prayer groups; Shopping trips.
Description Facility is on a hill overlooking Lake Michigan; in the summer residents can watch the sailboat races.

Lakeside Health Center Inc*
802 Hwy 20 E, Michigan City, IN, 46360 (219) 872-7251
Admin Dorothy Snavley.
Licensure Intermediate Care. *Beds* 64. *Certified* Medicaid.

Red Oaks Rehabilitation and Convalescent Center*
910 S Carroll Ave, Michigan City, IN, 46360 (219) 872-0696
Admin Maryann Oszuscik.
Licensure Skilled Care; Intermediate Care.
Beds SNF 58; ICF 58. *Certified* Medicaid; Medicare.

Wedow Private Home Care*
602 Spring St, Michigan City, IN, 46360 (219) 879-0140
Admin Wilbur Wedow.
Licensure Residential Care. *Beds* 17.

Woodview Rehabilitation Center*
1101 E Coolspring Ave, Michigan City, IN, 46360 (219) 874-5211
Admin Frank Estes.
Licensure Skilled Care; Intermediate Care.
Beds SNF 66; ICF 132. *Certified* Medicaid; Medicare.

MIDDLETOWN

Maple Village Nursing Home Inc
Box 135, Middletown, IN, 47356 (317) 354-4282
Admin F Richard King.
Licensure Intermediate Care. *Beds* 64. *Certified* Medicaid.
Admissions Requirements Minimum age 21.
Staff RNs 2 (ft); LPNs 3 (ft), 1 (pt); Nurses aides 10 (ft), 10 (pt); Activities coordinators 1 (ft); Dietitians 1 (pt).
Facilities Dining room; Activities room; Chapel; Crafts room; Laundry room; Barber/Beauty shop; Library.
Activities Arts and Crafts; Cards; Games; Reading groups; Prayer groups; Shopping trips; Dances/Social or cultural gatherings.

Middletown Nursing Center*
130 S 10th St, Middletown, IN, 47356 (317) 354-2223
Admin Larry A Jones.
Licensure Intermediate Care. *Beds* 39. *Certified* Medicaid.

MILAN

Milan Healthcare Center
Carr St, Milan, IN, 47031 (812) 654-2231
Admin T E Trumbauer.
Licensure Intermediate Care. *Beds* 65. *Certified* Medicaid.
Staff RNs; LPNs; Nurses aides; Activities coordinators.
Facilities Dining room; Activities room; Laundry room; Barber/Beauty shop.
Activities Arts and Crafts; Cards; Games; Prayer groups; Movies; Shopping trips; Dances/Social or cultural gatherings.
Description There is no place like home but facility is "home-like."

MILFORD

Lakeland Loving Care Center Inc
PO Box 767, Milford, IN, 46542 (219) 658-9554
Admin Barbara Rhodes. *Medical Dir/Dir of Nursing* Floyd Rheinheimer.
Licensure Intermediate Care. *Beds* 60. *Certified* Medicaid.
Staff RNs 2 (ft), 2 (pt); LPNs 1 (ft), 5 (pt); Nurses aides 9 (ft), 20 (pt); Physical therapists 1 (pt); Speech therapists 1 (pt); Activities coordinators 1 (ft); Dietitians 1 (pt); Podiatrists 1 (pt).
Facilities Dining room; Activities room; Crafts room; Laundry room; Barber/Beauty shop.
Activities Arts and Crafts; Cards; Games; Reading groups; Prayer groups; Movies; Shopping trips; Dances/Social or cultural gatherings.
Description Facility is located in a small town

in a largely farm area; proud of personal care, activity programs for everyone, crafts, coffee hour, religious groups, and trips to area malls.

MISHAWAKA

Countryside Place of Mishawaka
811 E 12th St, Mishawaka, IN, 46544 (219) 259-1917
Admin A W March. *Medical Dir/Dir of Nursing* Dr James Serwatka.
Licensure Skilled Care; Intermediate Care. *Beds* SNF 56; ICF 46. *Certified* Medicaid; Medicare.
Admissions Requirements Minimum age 65; Medical examination.
Staff Physicians 4 (ft); RNs 6 (ft); LPNs 6 (ft); Nurses aides 16 (ft); Physical therapists 2 (ft); Reality therapists 2 (ft); Occupational therapists 1 (ft); Speech therapists 1 (ft); Activities coordinators 1 (ft); Dietitians 1 (ft); Dentists 1 (ft); Podiatrists 1 (ft).
Facilities Dining room; Physical therapy room; Activities room; Crafts room; Laundry room; Barber/Beauty shop.
Activities Arts and Crafts; Cards; Games; Prayer groups; Movies; Dances/Social or cultural gatherings.
Description The social service department is a very capable and lucrative element of the home.

Fountainview Place of Mishawaka
609 W Tanglewood Ln, Mishawaka, IN, 46544 (219) 277-2500
Admin Catherine Gentry. *Medical Dir/Dir of Nursing* David Clayton MD.
Licensure Skilled Care; Intermediate Care. *Beds* SNF 44; ICF 84. *Certified* Medicaid; Medicare.
Staff RNs 1 (ft), 1 (pt); LPNs 10 (ft), 4 (pt); Orderlies 2 (ft); Nurses aides 22 (ft), 19 (pt); Physical therapists 1 (pt); Occupational therapists 1 (ft); Speech therapists 1 (pt); Activities coordinators 1 (ft); Qualified medication aides 3 (ft), 8 (pt).
Facilities Dining room; Physical therapy room; Activities room; Chapel; Crafts room; Barber/Beauty shop.
Activities Arts and Crafts; Cards; Games; Reading groups; Prayer groups; Movies; Shopping trips; Dances/Social or cultural gatherings.
Description Beautifully maintained one-story building in a lovely wooded setting; facility provides an outstanding level of quality of life; very extensive rehabilitation program which includes physical, occupational, and speech therapy; busy activity program includes Beverly Enterprises well-known adopt-a-grandparent program.

Melrose Manor
601 S Russell St, Mishawaka, IN, 46544 (219) 259-5050
Admin Judith Pauwels.
Licensure Intermediate Care. *Beds* 38. *Certified* Medicaid.
Admissions Requirements Minimum age 18; Medical examination; Physician's request.
Staff RNs 2 (ft); LPNs 2 (ft); Nurses aides 8 (ft), 23 (pt); Recreational therapists 1 (ft), 1 (pt); Activities coordinators 1 (ft).

Facilities Dining room; Activities room; Crafts room.
Activities Arts and Crafts; Cards; Games; Reading groups; Prayer groups; Shopping trips.

MITCHELL

Mitchell Manor*
Rt 4, Box 383, Mitchell, IN, 47446 (812) 849-2221
Admin Mary Williams.
Licensure Skilled Care; Intermediate Care. *Beds* SNF 21; ICF 63. *Certified* Medicaid.

Williams Health Facility*
Highway 37 S, Mitchell, IN, 47446 (812) 849-2221
Admin Wayne Williams.
Beds 44.

MONTICELLO

Lake View Home
800 W Norway Rd, Monticello, IN, 47960 (219) 583-3242
Admin Ora Rumple.
Licensure Residential Care. *Beds* 28.

Monticello Community Healthcare Center*
Rt 6, Monticello, IN, 47960 (219) 583-7073
Admin Michael Butler.
Licensure Skilled Care; Intermediate Care. *Beds* SNF 79; ICF 127. *Certified* Medicaid; Medicare.

MOORESVILLE

Millers Merry Manor
259 W Harrison, Mooresville, IN, 46158 (317) 831-6272
Licensure Intermediate Care. *Beds* 99. *Certified* Medicaid.

MORGANTOWN

Henderson Nursing Home Inc
140 W Washington St, Morgantown, IN, 46160 (812) 597-4418
Admin Karen Henderson. *Medical Dir/Dir of Nursing* Gary Midla DO.
Licensure Intermediate Care. *Beds* 41. *Certified* Medicaid.
Admissions Requirements Medical examination.
Staff Physicians 1 (ft); RNs 1 (pt); LPNs 3 (ft), 1 (pt); Orderlies 1 (pt); Nurses aides 15 (ft), 5 (pt); Activities coordinators 1 (ft); Dietitians 1 (pt).
Facilities Dining room; Activities room; Crafts room; Laundry room; Library.
Activities Arts and Crafts; Cards; Games; Reading groups; Prayer groups; Movies; Shopping trips; Dances/Social or cultural gatherings.

MORRISTOWN

Morristown Nursing Home*
Box 388, Morristown, IN, 46161 (317) 763-6525

Admin Martha Waltz.
Licensure Intermediate Care. *Beds* 64. *Certified* Medicaid.

MOUNT VERNON

Medco Center of Mount Vernon
1415 Country Club Rd, Mount Vernon, IN, 47620 (812) 838-6554
Admin Jim Ward.
Licensure Intermediate Care. *Beds* 123. *Certified* Medicaid.
Admissions Requirements Minimum age 18; Medical examination.
Facilities Dining room; Physical therapy room; Activities room; Chapel; Crafts room; Laundry room; Barber/Beauty shop.
Activities Arts and Crafts; Cards; Games; Reading groups; Prayer groups; Movies; Shopping trips; Dances/Social or cultural gatherings.

MULBERRY

Mulberry Lutheran Home
502 W Jackson St, Mulberry, IN, 46058 (317) 296-2911
Admin Mark Neubacher. *Medical Dir/Dir of Nursing* Grayson B Davis.
Licensure Intermediate Care. *Beds* 41. *Certified* Medicaid.
Admissions Requirements Medical examination.
Staff Physicians 1 (pt); RNs 3 (ft), 2 (pt); LPNs 3 (ft), 1 (pt); Orderlies 1 (ft), 1 (pt); Nurses aides 26 (ft), 26 (pt); Physical therapists 1 (pt); Activities coordinators 2 (ft), 1 (pt); Dietitians 1 (ft); Dentists 1 (pt).
Affiliation Lutheran
Facilities Dining room; Physical therapy room; Activities room; Chapel; Crafts room; Laundry room; Barber/Beauty shop; Library; Ceramics room.
Activities Arts and Crafts; Cards; Games; Reading groups; Prayer groups; Movies; Shopping trips; Bingo.
Description Facility is in a spacious, air-conditioned brick building in a pastoral setting with a beautiful campus. Services include special diet supervision, professional 24-hour nursing care, activities department, consultant pharmacist, open visiting, and a comfortable and spacious lounge area with fireplace and color television.

MUNCIE

Chateau Convalescent Centre*
2400 Chateau Dr, Muncie, IN, 47303 (317) 747-9044
Admin Betty J Hickey.
Licensure Intermediate Care. *Beds* 102. *Certified* Medicaid.

Delaware County Health Center*
Rt 5, Muncie, IN, 47302 (317) 747-7820
Admin Harold J Kwiatkowski.
Licensure Intermediate Care. *Beds* 84.

Fountainview Place of Muncie
2701 Lyn-Mar Dr, Muncie, IN, 47302 (317) 286-5979

Admin Pauline F Dailey. *Medical Dir/Dir of Nursing* Arnold Carter MD.
Licensure Skilled Care; Intermediate Care.
Beds SNF 71; ICF 78. *Certified* Medicaid; Medicare.
Admissions Requirements Medical examination.
Staff Physical therapists 1 (ft); Occupational therapists 1 (ft); Speech therapists 1 (pt); Activities coordinators 1 (ft).
Facilities Dining room; Physical therapy room; Activities room; Chapel; Crafts room; Laundry room; Barber/Beauty shop.
Activities Arts and Crafts; Cards; Games; Reading groups; Prayer groups; Movies; Shopping trips; Dances/Social or cultural gatherings.
Description Facility is situated in a wooded area; little traffic flow provides opportunity for many outside programs; several active residents involved with the Resident Service Volunteer Program. VA approved.

Friendly Hearth Nursing Center—Muncie*
505 N Gavin St, Muncie, IN, 47302 (317) 289-1915
Admin Terry Howard.
Licensure Intermediate Care. *Beds* 42. *Certified* Medicaid.

Muncie Health Care Center Inc*
PO Box 112, 4301 N Walnut St, Muncie, IN, 47405 (317) 282-0053
Admin David A Davis.
Licensure Intermediate Care. *Beds* 100. *Certified* Medicaid.

Parkview Nursing Home
2200 White River Blvd, Muncie, IN, 47303 (317) 289-3341
Admin Eileen E Page. *Medical Dir/Dir of Nursing* Dr Michael Seidle.
Licensure Skilled Care; Intermediate Care.
Beds SNF 53; ICF 48. *Certified* Medicaid; Medicare.
Admissions Requirements Minimum age 21; Medical examination; Physician's request.
Staff Physicians 1 (pt); RNs 5 (ft); LPNs 8 (ft); Nurses aides 34 (ft), 8 (pt); Physical therapists; Speech therapists; Activities coordinators 1 (ft); Podiatrists.
Facilities Dining room; Physical therapy room; Activities room; Crafts room; Laundry room; Barber/Beauty shop; Lounge area.
Activities Arts and Crafts; Cards; Reading groups; Prayer groups; Movies; Shopping trips; Bi-monthly newspaper; Exercise groups; Chapel twice weekly in lounge area.
Description Skilled center staffed on 24-hour basis by caring licensed professionals; in close proximity to hospital and other services, close to major interstate highways; many family activities are planned throughout the year such as family dinners, picnics, family nights; active family council and resident council; retired volunteer RSVP station.

Riverview Convalescent Home*
Rt 2, Box 89, Muncie, IN, 47302 (317) 288-5082
Admin Jessie Starks.
Licensure Intermediate Care. *Beds* 50. *Certified* Medicaid.

Sylvester Nursing Home
4400 Burlington Pike, Muncie, IN, 47302 (317) 284-8283
Admin Kevin S Jeffers. *Medical Dir/Dir of Nursing* Larry G Cole MD.
Licensure Intermediate Care. *Beds* 40. *Certified* Medicaid.
Admissions Requirements Medical examination.
Staff RNs 1 (pt); LPNs 2 (ft); Nurses aides 17 (ft), 3 (pt); Activities coordinators 1 (ft); Dietitians 1 (pt).
Facilities Dining room; Activities room; Laundry room; Barber/Beauty shop.
Activities Arts and Crafts; Games; Prayer groups; Movies; Shopping trips; Dances/Social or cultural gatherings.

Woodland Nursing Home*
3820 W Jackson St, Muncie, IN, 47304 (317) 289-3451
Admin Anna J Wilson.
Licensure Skilled Care; Intermediate Care.
Beds SNF 34; ICF 58. *Certified* Medicaid; Medicare.

MUNSTER

Munster Medical Inn
7935 Calumet Ave, Munster, IN, 46321 (219) 836-8300
Admin Jean T Robinson. *Medical Dir/Dir of Nursing* Dr William Heheman.
Licensure Skilled Care; Intermediate Care.
Beds SNF 158; ICF 48. *Certified* Medicaid; Medicare.
Admissions Requirements Minimum age 18.
Staff RNs 8 (ft), 12 (pt); LPNs 10 (ft), 6 (pt); Orderlies 3 (ft); Nurses aides 57 (ft), 23 (pt); Occupational therapists 1 (ft), 2 (pt); Speech therapists 1 (ft), 1 (pt); Activities coordinators 2 (ft), 3 (pt); Dietitians 1 (ft).
Facilities Dining room; Physical therapy room; Activities room; Chapel; Crafts room; Laundry room; Barber/Beauty shop; Library; Occupational therapy room; Speech therapy room.
Activities Arts and Crafts; Cards; Games; Reading groups; Prayer groups; Movies; Shopping trips; Dances/Social or cultural gatherings; Reality orientation.
Description Facility features grief counseling, in-house pharmacy, X-ray laboratory, EKG, nuclear medicine, 3 house physicians, hospice setting for terminal patients, and a high level of skilled care is offered. 5 meal-a-day plan.

NAPPANEE

Lu Ann Nursing Home*
952 W Walnut St, Nappanee, IN, 46550 (219) 773-4119
Admin John L Mellinger.
Licensure Intermediate Care. *Beds* 50. *Certified* Medicaid.

NASHVILLE

Brown County Community Care
Fred Henderson Dr, PO Box 667, Nashville, IN, 47448 (812) 988-6666
Admin Donna Moore. *Medical Dir/Dir of Nursing* Tim Alward.
Licensure Intermediate Care. *Beds* 70. *Certified* Medicaid.
Staff RNs 1 (ft), 1 (pt); LPNs 3 (ft), 1 (pt); Orderlies 2 (ft); Nurses aides 10 (ft), 9 (pt); Activities coordinators 1 (ft); Dietitians 1 (pt).
Facilities Dining room; Activities room; Laundry room; Barber/Beauty shop.
Activities Arts and Crafts; Cards; Games; Reading groups; Prayer groups; Shopping trips; Dances/Social or cultural gatherings.

NEW ALBANY

Green Valley Convalescent Center
3118 Green Valley Rd, New Albany, IN, 47150 (812) 945-2341
Admin Peter Graves. *Medical Dir/Dir of Nursing* J I Streepey MD.
Licensure Skilled Care; Intermediate Care.
Beds SNF 119; ICF 80. *Certified* Medicaid; Medicare.
Admissions Requirements Minimum age 18; Medical examination; Physician's request.
Staff RNs 10 (ft), 4 (pt); LPNs 12 (ft), 7 (pt); Nurses aides 70 (ft), 10 (pt); Physical therapists 1 (ft); Activities coordinators 2 (ft); Dietitians 1 (pt).
Facilities Dining room; Physical therapy room; Activities room; Barber/Beauty shop; Library.
Activities Arts and Crafts; Cards; Games; Reading groups; Prayer groups; Movies; Shopping trips; Dances/Social or cultural gatherings.

Lincoln Hills of New Albany*
326 Country Club Dr, New Albany, IN, 47150 (812) 948-1311
Admin Mary Lou Tindle.
Licensure Intermediate Care. *Beds* 100. *Certified* Medicaid.

New Albany Nursing Home*
1919 Bono Rd, New Albany, IN, 47150 (812) 944-4404
Admin Bobby R Dunn.
Licensure Intermediate Care. *Beds* 40. *Certified* Medicaid.

Providence Retirement Home
703 E Spring St, New Albany, IN, 47150 (812) 945-5221
Admin Sr Barbara Ann Zeller. *Medical Dir/Dir of Nursing* Eli Hallal.
Licensure Intermediate Care. *Beds* 85.
Admissions Requirements Medical examination.
Staff RNs 2 (ft); LPNs 2 (ft); Nurses aides 4 (ft), 3 (pt); Reality therapists 1 (ft); Activities coordinators 1 (ft), 1 (pt); Dietitians 1 (pt).
Affiliation Roman Catholic
Facilities Dining room; Activities room; Chapel; Crafts room; Laundry room; Barber/Beauty shop.
Activities Arts and Crafts; Cards; Games; Reading groups; Prayer groups; Movies; Shopping trips; Dances/Social or cultural gatherings.
Description Adult day care center is sponsored by Home.

NEW CARLISLE

Hamilton Grove
Chicago Trail, New Carlisle, IN, 46552 (219) 654-3118
Admin Ilah Hebner. *Medical Dir/Dir of Nursing* Robert Fenstermacher MD.
Licensure Intermediate Care; Residential Care. *Beds* 84. *Certified* Medicaid.
Admissions Requirements Minimum age 65.
Staff RNs 4 (ft); LPNs 12 (ft); Nurses aides 30 (ft), 8 (pt); Recreational therapists 2 (ft), 2 (pt); Activities coordinators 1 (ft); Dietitians 1 (pt).
Affiliation Methodist
Facilities Dining room; Physical therapy room; Activities room; Chapel; Crafts room; Laundry room; Barber/Beauty shop; Library; Commisary; Greenhouse.
Activities Arts and Crafts; Cards; Games; Reading groups; Prayer groups; Movies; Shopping trips; Dances/Social or cultural gatherings.
Description This is a retirement community in a rural setting midway between South Bend and Michigan City, offering the best in retirement living and excellent nursing care.

NEW CASTLE

Heritage House of New Castle*
PO Box 546, New Castle, IN, 47362 (317) 529-9694
Admin Sue Mervis.
Licensure Skilled Care; Intermediate Care. *Beds* SNF 21; ICF 90. *Certified* Medicaid; Medicare.

Holly Hill Nursing Home*
901 N 16th St, New Castle, IN, 47362 (317) 529-4695
Admin Giles Krupp.
Licensure Intermediate Care. *Beds* 40. *Certified* Medicaid.

New Castle Community Care Center*
115 N 10th St, New Castle, IN, 47362 (317) 529-2703
Admin Roger J Scheidler.
Licensure Intermediate Care. *Beds* 60. *Certified* Medicaid.

New Castle Healthcare Center*
990 N 16th St, New Castle, IN, 47362 (317) 529-0230
Admin Cecil Perkins.
Licensure Skilled Care; Intermediate Care. *Beds* SNF 87; ICF 108. *Certified* Medicaid; Medicare.

NEW HARMONY

Charles Ford Memorial Home
920 S Main St, New Harmony, IN, 47631 (812) 682-4685
Admin Dora Newman. *Medical Dir/Dir of Nursing* Dr Harrold Ropp.
Licensure Residential Care. *Beds* 25.
Admissions Requirements Minimum age 62; Females only; Medical examination.
Staff Physicians 1 (ft); LPNs 1 (ft); Nurses aides 5 (ft); Dietitians 1 (pt); Dentists 1 (pt); Ophthalmologists 1 (pt); Podiatrists 1 (pt).

NEW HAVEN

Brighton Hall Nursing Center*
1201 Daly Dr, New Haven, IN, 46774 (219) 482-3551
Admin Fred Webb.
Beds 120.

NEWBURGH

Medco Center of Newburgh*
4255 Medwel Dr, Newburgh, IN, 47630 (812) 853-2993
Admin Jim Scheller.
Licensure Intermediate Care. *Beds* 112. *Certified* Medicaid.

Newburgh Health Care and Residential Center*
10466 Pollack Ave, Newburgh, IN, 47630 (812) 853-2931
Admin Bruce Baker.
Licensure Intermediate Care. *Beds* 114. *Certified* Medicaid.

NOBLESVILLE

Noblesville Healthcare Center*
295 Westfield Rd, Noblesville, IN, 46060 (317) 773-3760
Admin Elizabeth J Schwindler.
Licensure Skilled Care; Intermediate Care. *Beds* SNF 97; ICF 98. *Certified* Medicaid; Medicare.

Noblesville Nursing Home
1391 Greenfield Pike, Noblesville, IN, 46060 (317) 773-1264
Admin Mary Jo Powers.
Licensure Intermediate Care. *Beds* 40. *Certified* Medicaid.
Staff RNs 1 (ft); LPNs 1 (ft), 1 (pt); Nurses aides 10 (ft), 7 (pt); Activities coordinators 1 (ft); Dietitians 1 (pt); Podiatrists 1 (pt).

NORTH MANCHESTER

The Estelle Peabody Memorial Home*
7th and Buffalo, North Manchester, IN, 47962 (219) 982-8616
Admin Richard M Craig.
Licensure Intermediate Care. *Beds* 150. *Certified* Medicaid.

Timbercrest—Church of the Brethren Home
East St, North Manchester, IN, 46962 (219) 982-2118
Licensure Intermediate Care. *Beds* 46. *Certified* Medicaid.
Admissions Requirements Minimum age 65; Medical examination.
Staff RNs 2 (ft); LPNs 3 (pt); Orderlies 1 (ft), 1 (pt); Nurses aides 12 (ft), 20 (pt); Activities coordinators 1 (ft); Dietitians 1 (ft), 3 (pt); Podiatrists 1 (pt).
Affiliation Church of the Brethren
Facilities Dining room; Activities room; Chapel; Crafts room; Laundry room; Barber/Beauty shop; Library.
Activities Arts and Crafts; Games; Reading groups; Prayer groups; Movies; Shopping trips;

Dances/Social or cultural gatherings.
Description Home is presently launching a 10-year building program to double capacity because of a 10-year waiting list.

NORTH VERNON

Hoosier Hills Healthcare Center*
PO Box 640, 1200 W O and M Ave, North Vernon, IN, 47265 (812) 346-7570
Admin Suzan J Russell.
Licensure Intermediate Care. *Beds* 64. *Certified* Medicaid.

North Vernon Nursing Home
801 N Elm St, North Vernon, IN, 47265 (812) 346-4942
Admin Frances J Cherry.
Licensure Intermediate Care. *Beds* 40. *Certified* Medicaid.
Admissions Requirements Physician's request.
Staff Physicians 3 (pt); RNs 2 (pt); LPNs 1 (ft), 2 (pt); Nurses aides 9 (ft), 6 (pt); Activities coordinators 1 (pt); Dietitians 1 (pt).
Facilities Dining room; Laundry room.
Activities Arts and Crafts; Cards; Games; Reading groups; Prayer groups; Shopping trips.
Description Facility creates a homey, loving atmosphere.

OAKLAND CITY

Good Samaritan Home Inc
210 N Gibson St, Oakland City, IN, 47560 (812) 749-4774
Admin Hovey Hedges and Donald Ingle.
Licensure Intermediate Care. *Beds* 85. *Certified* Medicaid.
Facilities Dining room; Activities room; Chapel; Laundry room; Barber/Beauty shop.
Activities Arts and Crafts; Games; Reading groups; Prayer groups; Movies.

Oakland City Rest Home*
114 Grove St, Oakland City, IN, 47560 (812) 749-3123
Admin Elaine Bacon.
Licensure Intermediate Care. *Beds* 18. *Certified* Medicaid.

ODON

Bertha D Garten Ketcham Meorial Center Inc
601 E Race St, Odon, IN, 47562 (812) 636-4920
Admin Betty Tolbert. *Medical Dir/Dir of Nursing* Barbara McMaster RN.
Licensure Intermediate Care. *Beds* 62. *Certified* Medicaid.
Admissions Requirements Minimum age 18; Medical examination.
Staff RNs 1 (ft); LPNs 4 (ft); Nurses aides 22 (ft), 2 (pt); Activities coordinators 1 (ft).
Facilities Dining room; Laundry room; Barber/Beauty shop.
Activities Arts and Crafts; Cards; Games; Reading groups; Prayer groups; Movies; Dances/Social or cultural gatherings; Shopping trips.

OSGOOD

Manderley Health Care Center
Hwy 421 S, Osgood, IN, 47037 (812) 689-4143
Admin Charles F Negangard. *Medical Dir/Dir
of Nursing* Janet Burdsall.
Licensure Intermediate Care. *Beds* 71. *Certi-
fied* Medicaid.
Admissions Requirements Minimum age 18;
Medical examination.
Staff RNs 1 (ft), 1 (pt); LPNs 4 (ft); Orderlies 1
(ft); Nurses aides 18 (ft), 8 (pt); Activities coor-
dinators 2 (ft); Dietitians 1 (pt).
Facilities Dining room; Activities room; Chapel; Laundry room; Barber/Beauty shop;
Library.
Activities Arts and Crafts; Cards; Games;
Reading groups; Prayer groups; Movies; Shopping trips; Dances/Social or cultural gatherings.
Description The Center is a beautiful, spacious
home whose doors are always open to families
and friends; educational program for residents
and outdoor activities are extraordinary; physicians visit regularly and are always on call;
house dentist and podiatrist also visit regularly.

OWENSVILLE

Owensville Convalescent Center Inc
Hwy 165 W, PO Box 368, Owensville, IN,
47565 (812) 729-7901
Admin Eugene Hall.
Licensure Intermediate Care. *Beds* 68. *Certi-
fied* Medicaid.

OXFORD

Edgewood View Nursing Home*
State Rd 55, Oxford, IN, 47971 (317) 385-2291
Admin Janet E Courtney.
Licensure Intermediate Care. *Beds* 54. *Certi-
fied* Medicaid.

PAOLI

Paoli Nursing Home
111 W Hospital View Rd, Paoli, IN, 47454
(812) 723-3000
Admin William Howard. *Medical Dir/Dir of
Nursing* Margaret McKnight.
Licensure Intermediate Care. *Beds* 40. *Certi-
fied* Medicaid.
Admissions Requirements Minimum age 19.
Staff RNs 1 (ft); LPNs 2 (ft); Nurses aides 10
(ft), 5 (pt); Recreational therapists 1 (pt); Activi-
ties coordinators 1 (pt); Dietitians 1 (pt); Podia-
trists 1 (pt).
Facilities Dining room; Activities room;
Chapel; Crafts room; Laundry room.
Activities Arts and Crafts; Cards; Games;
Reading groups; Prayer groups; Movies; Shop-
ping trips; Dances/Social or cultural gatherings.
Description The Home is located directly
across from hospital in a small-town setting.

PARKER CITY

Chrystal's Country Home Inc*
Randolph St, Parker City, IN, 47368 (317)
468-8280

Admin Robert E Steele.
Licensure Intermediate Care. *Beds* 99. *Certified* Medicaid.

PENDLETON

Rawlins House Inc
300 J H Walker Dr, PO Box 119, Pendleton,
IN, 46064
Admin Cindy L Costerison. *Medical Dir/Dir of
Nursing* Robert C Beeson MD.
Licensure Intermediate Care. *Beds* 134. *Certi-
fied* Medicaid.
Ownership Proprietary.
Admissions Requirements Physician's request.
Staff Physicians 1 (pt); RNs 2 (ft); LPNs 6 (ft),
5 (pt); Nurses aides 17 (ft), 22 (pt); Activities
coordinators 1 (ft), 2 (pt); Dietitians 1 (ft), 1
(pt).
Facilities Dining room; Activities room; Laundry room; Barber/Beauty shop; Sun room.
Activities Arts and Crafts; Cards; Games;
Reading groups; Shopping trips; Dances/Social
or cultural gatherings.
Description Facility has a very cheerful, homey
decor; residents and staff consider it to be very
personal; staff to resident ratio is very high
which enables a more attentive, personal
approach to each resident.

PERU

Miller's Merry Manor Inc*
317 Blair Pike, Peru, IN, 46970 (317) 473-4426
Admin Melody A Edwards.
Licensure Skilled Care; Intermediate Care.
Beds SNF 31; ICF 124. *Certified* Medicaid;
Medicare.

Peru Nursing Home*
390 West Blvd, Peru, IN, 46970 (317) 473-4900
Admin Jimmie Mae Lindley.
Licensure Intermediate Care. *Beds* 40. *Certified* Medicaid.

PETERSBURG

Petersburg Healthcare Center*
Box 100, Pike Ave, Petersburg, IN, 47567 (812)
354-8833
Admin Steve Harl.
Licensure Skilled Care; Intermediate Care.
Beds SNF 19; ICF 115. *Certified* Medicaid;
Medicare.

PLAINFIELD

Clark's Creek Health Care Center
3700 Clark's Creek Rd, PO Box 7, Plainfield,
IN, 46168 (317) 839-6577
Admin Margaret Hunley. *Medical Dir/Dir of
Nursing* Dr David M Hadley.
Licensure Skilled Care; Intermediate Care.
Beds SNF 50; ICF 140. *Certified* Medicaid;
Medicare.
Admissions Requirements Medical examina-
tion.
Staff Physicians 1 (ft); RNs 5 (ft), 1 (pt); LPNs
7 (ft), 2 (pt); Nurses aides 38 (ft), 26 (pt);
Physical therapists 1 (ft); Occupational thera-

pists 1 (ft); Speech therapists 1 (ft); Activities
coordinators 1 (ft), 3 (pt); Dietitians 1 (ft).
Facilities Dining room; Physical therapy room;
Activities room; Crafts room; Laundry room;
Barber/Beauty shop; Lounges.
Activities Arts and Crafts; Cards; Games;
Reading groups; Prayer groups; Movies; Shop-
ping trips; Dances/Social or cultural gatherings;
Outside activities such as parades and fairs;
Residents council.
Description Total wing in facility can accom-
modate 4 physicians; JCAH accreditation;
facility is in a country setting.

Vinewood Nursing Home*
404 N Vine St, Plainfield, IN, 46168 (317)
839-0154
Admin George W Petree.
Licensure Intermediate Care. *Beds* 27. *Certified* Medicaid.

PLYMOUTH

Kingston Nursing Home*
309 Kingston Dr, Plymouth, IN, 46563 (219)
936-9025
Admin Robert F Cox.
Licensure Intermediate Care. *Beds* 40. *Certified* Medicaid.

Miller's Merry Manor Inc*
PO Box 498, 600 W Oakhill Ave, Plymouth,
IN, 46563 (219) 936-9981
Admin Jane K Miller.
Licensure Skilled Care; Intermediate Care.
Beds SNF 33; ICF 106. *Certified* Medicaid;
Medicare.

**Pilgrim Manor Rehabilitation and Convalescent
Center***
222 Parkview St, Plymouth, IN, 46563 (219)
936-9943
Admin G Dean Byers.
Licensure Skilled Care; Intermediate Care.
Beds SNF 37; ICF 53. *Certified* Medicaid;
Medicare.

Shady Rest Home
10924 Lincoln Hwy E, Plymouth, IN, 46563
(219) 936-2635
Admin Steven M Kastner.
Licensure Residential Care. *Beds* 40.
Staff RNs 1 (pt); LPNs 1 (ft); Nurses aides 6
(ft); Activities coordinators 1 (ft); Dietitians 1
(pt).
Facilities Dining room; Activities room; Chapel; Crafts room; Laundry room; Barber/Beauty
shop.
Activities Arts and Crafts; Cards; Games;
Movies; Shopping trips; Dances/Social or cultural gatherings.
Description Home is located in a rural farm
setting in northern Indiana. Many residents
enjoy spending time outside.

PORTAGE

Fountainview Place Corp of Portage*
3175 Lancer Dr, Portage, IN, 46368 (219)
762-9571
Admin Vicki Curry.

Licensure Skilled Care; Intermediate Care. *Beds* SNF 48; ICF 95. *Certified* Medicaid; Medicare.

PORTLAND

Portland Community Care Center
200 N Park St, PO Box 1012, Portland, IN, 47371 (219) 726-9441
Admin Richard May. *Medical Dir/Dir of Nursing* Dr Eugene Gillum.
Licensure Intermediate Care. *Beds* 80. *Certified* Medicaid.
Admissions Requirements Minimum age 18; Medical examination.
Staff RNs; LPNs; Nurses aides; Speech therapists; Activities coordinators; Dietitians.
Facilities Dining room; Activities room; Crafts room; Laundry room; Barber/Beauty shop.
Activities Arts and Crafts; Cards; Games; Reading groups; Prayer groups; Movies.

Portland Community Care Center—East*
510 W High St, Portland, IN, 47371 (219) 726-9490
Admin Stephen Sharpe.
Beds 29.

POSEYVILLE

Allison Nursing Home Inc*
Locust St, Poseyville, IN, 47633 (812) 874-2814
Admin Debra Stoneberger Johnson.
Licensure Intermediate Care. *Beds* 39. *Certified* Medicaid.

PRINCETON

Forest Del Convalescent Home Inc
1020 W Vine St, Princeton, IN, 47670 (812) 385-5238
Admin L Phillip Roberts.
Licensure Intermediate Care. *Beds* 116. *Certified* Medicaid.
Admissions Requirements Minimum age 18; Medical examination; Physician's request.
Staff Physicians 1 (pt); Reality therapists 1 (pt); Recreational therapists 1 (pt); Activities coordinators 1 (ft); Dietitians 1 (pt); Dentists 1 (pt); Ophthalmologists 1 (pt); Podiatrists 1 (pt).
Facilities Dining room; Activities room; Crafts room; Laundry room; Barber/Beauty shop; TV lounge and entertainment center.
Activities Arts and Crafts; Cards; Games; Reading groups; Prayer groups; Movies; Shopping trips; Dances/Social or cultural gatherings; Trips out of facility.

Holiday Manor
Rt 4, 6th Ave, Princeton, IN, 47670 (812) 385-5288
Admin Robert Lovell.
Licensure Intermediate Care. *Beds* 91. *Certified* Medicaid.
Admissions Requirements Minimum age 18.
Staff RNs 3 (ft), 1 (pt); LPNs 4 (ft); Orderlies 2 (ft); Nurses aides 20 (ft), 4 (pt); Activities coordinators 1 (ft); Dietitians 1 (pt); Dentists 1 (pt); Ophthalmologists 1 (pt); Podiatrists 1 (pt).
Facilities Dining room; Activities room; Laundry room; Barber/Beauty shop.

Activities Arts and Crafts; Cards; Games; Reading groups; Prayer groups; Movies; Shopping trips; Dances/Social or cultural gatherings.

RENSSELEAR

Rensselaer Care Center*
1109 E Grace, Rensselear, IN, 47978 (219) 866-4181
Admin Larry Vanderwielen.
Licensure Intermediate Care. *Beds* 143. *Certified* Medicaid.

RICHMOND

Cherish Nursing Center
1811 S 9th St, Richmond, IN, 47374 (317) 962-8175
Admin Donald G Waggoner. *Medical Dir/Dir of Nursing* Dr James R Daggy.
Licensure Intermediate Care. *Beds* 29. *Certified* Medicaid.
Admissions Requirements Minimum age 16; Medical examination; Physician's request.
Staff Physicians 1 (pt); RNs 2 (pt); LPNs 3 (ft); Nurses aides 9 (ft), 3 (pt); Recreational therapists 1 (ft); Dietitians 1 (pt).
Facilities Dining room; Activities room; Laundry room.
Activities Arts and Crafts; Cards; Games; Reading groups; Prayer groups; Movies; Shopping trips; Dances/Social or cultural gatherings.

Friends Fellowship Community Inc*
2030 Chester Blvd, Richmond, IN, 47374 (317) 962-6546
Admin Merrill W Baxter.
Licensure Intermediate Care; Residential Care.
Beds ICF 38; Residential Care 218.

Golden Rule Nursing Center Inc*
2001 US 27 S, Richmond, IN, 47374 (317) 966-7681
Admin Sam Knobler.
Licensure Skilled Care; Intermediate Care.
Beds SNF 54; ICF 56. *Certified* Medicaid; Medicare.

Heritage House of Richmond Inc
2070 Chester Blvd, Richmond, IN, 47374 (317) 962-3543
Admin Janet Teeple. *Medical Dir/Dir of Nursing* Dr Glen Ramsdell.
Licensure Skilled Care; Intermediate Care.
Beds SNF 59; ICF 60. *Certified* Medicaid; Medicare.
Admissions Requirements Minimum age 19; Medical examination; Physician's request.
Staff RNs 5 (ft), 1 (pt); LPNs 7 (ft), 3 (pt); Nurses aides 49 (ft); Physical therapists 1 (ft); Activities coordinators 1 (ft), 1 (pt).
Facilities Dining room; Physical therapy room; Activities room; Crafts room; Laundry room; Barber/Beauty shop.
Activities Arts and Crafts; Cards; Games; Reading groups; Prayer groups; Movies; Dances/Social or cultural gatherings.
Description Heritage House has an outstanding reputation for quality patient care; physical therapy inpatient and outpatient programs are led by the outstanding physical therapist in the

region. The medical director is a noted specialist in respiratory care and geriatrics. Facility is located within a mile of the regional hospital.

Jenkins Hall-Reid Memorial Hospital
1401 Chester Blvd, Richmond, IN, 47374 (317) 962-4545
Admin Shirley Haley. *Medical Dir/Dir of Nursing* Paul S Runge MD.
Licensure Intermediate Care. *Beds* 58. *Certified* Medicaid.
Admissions Requirements Minimum age 18; Medical examination; Physician's request.
Staff RNs 4 (ft); LPNs 2 (ft), 3 (pt); Nurses aides 8 (ft), 13 (pt); Activities coordinators 1 (ft); Dentists; Podiatrists.
Facilities Dining room; Physical therapy room; Activities room; Chapel; Crafts room; Laundry room; Barber/Beauty shop; Library.
Activities Arts and Crafts; Cards; Games; Reading groups; Prayer groups; Movies; Shopping trips; Dances/Social or cultural gatherings.

Oak Ridge Convalescent Center
1042 Oak Dr, Richmond, IN, 47374 (317) 966-7788
Admin Paul Rhodes. *Medical Dir/Dir of Nursing* Francis B Warrick MD.
Licensure Skilled Care; Intermediate Care.
Beds SNF 100; ICF 22. *Certified* Medicaid; Medicare.
Admissions Requirements Minimum age 18; Medical examination; Physician's request.
Staff RNs 5 (ft); LPNs 11 (ft), 2 (pt); Orderlies 1 (ft); Nurses aides 37 (ft), 11 (pt); Physical therapists 2 (ft); Recreational therapists 1 (ft); Occupational therapists 2 (pt); Speech therapists 1 (pt); Activities coordinators 1 (ft); Dietitians 1 (pt); Dentists 1 (pt); Podiatrists 1 (pt).
Facilities Dining room; Physical therapy room; Activities room; Chapel; Crafts room; Laundry room; Barber/Beauty shop; Library; Occupational therapy room; Speech therapy room.
Activities Arts and Crafts; Cards; Games; Reading groups; Prayer groups; Movies; Shopping trips; Dances/Social or cultural gatherings.
Description Facility offers working independent resident council, community and staff volunteers, special room for family gatherings, 2 spacious resident lounges, garden space, 2 large atriums that are equipped with outdoor games adapted for wheelchair residents, and picnic tables provided for the convenience of the residents and their families.

Richmond Nursing Home*
2302 N Chester Blvd, Richmond, IN, 47374 (317) 962-0043
Admin Jeanne Krupp.
Licensure Intermediate Care. *Beds* 40. *Certified* Medicaid.

RISING SUN

Rising Sun Nursing Home*
Rio Vista Ave, Rising Sun, IN, 47040 (812) 438-2219
Admin Terry Miller.
Licensure Intermediate Care. *Beds* 58. *Certified* Medicaid.

ROCHESTER

Canterbury Manor*
Rt 6, Court Rd 50 N, Rochester, IN, 46975
(219) 223-4331
Admin Carl William Miller II.
Licensure Intermediate Care. *Beds* 117. *Certified* Medicaid.

Rochester Nursing Home*
240 E 18th St, Rochester, IN, 46975 (219)
223-5100
Admin Michael J Beach.
Licensure Intermediate Care. *Beds* 40. *Certified* Medicaid.

ROCKPORT

Miller's Merry Manor Inc*
815 Washington St, Rockport, IN, 47635 (812)
649-2276
Admin Marna Ames.
Licensure Intermediate Care. *Beds* 92. *Certified* Medicaid.

ROCKVILLE

Castle Shannon Nursing Home
Rt 3, Box 251, Rockville, IN, 47872 (317)
569-6526
Admin John C Bland.
Licensure Intermediate Care. *Beds* 40. *Certified* Medicaid.
Admissions Requirements Minimum age 18.

Lee Alan Bryant Health Care Facility Inc
Rt 1, Box 7, Rockville, IN, 47872 (317)
569-6654
Admin Bette A Hein. *Medical Dir/Dir of Nursing* Dr Richard Bloomer.
Licensure Intermediate Care; Residential Care.
Beds ICF 80; Residential Care 156. *Certified* Medicaid.
Admissions Requirements Medical examination.
Staff RNs 1 (ft); LPNs 4 (ft), 5 (pt); Orderlies 1 (ft), 1 (pt); Nurses aides 21 (ft), 7 (pt); Activities coordinators 2 (ft).
Facilities Dining room; Activities room; Crafts room; Laundry room; Barber/Beauty shop; Library.
Activities Arts and Crafts; Cards; Games; Reading groups; Prayer groups; Movies; Shopping trips; Dances/Social or cultural gatherings.

Parke County Nursing Home Inc
Rt 3, Box 259, Rockville, IN, 47872 (317)
569-6700
Admin Gerald Ball.
Licensure Intermediate Care. *Beds* 58. *Certified* Medicaid.
Admissions Requirements Minimum age 18; Medical examination.
Staff RNs 2 (pt); LPNs 3 (ft), 3 (pt); Orderlies 1 (ft); Nurses aides 30 (ft); Recreational therapists 1 (ft); Activities coordinators 1 (ft); Dietitians 1 (pt).
Facilities Dining room; Activities room; Crafts room; Laundry room; Barber/Beauty shop.
Activities Arts and Crafts; Cards; Games; Reading groups; Prayer groups; Movies; Shopping trips; Dances/Social or cultural gatherings.
Description Facility is in a rural setting adjacent to county golf course; 2-level brick colonial on several acres for outdoor activities such as gardening.

ROSSVILLE

Milner Community Health-Care Inc
Box 15, Rossville, IN, 46065 (317) 379-2112
Admin Ronald Kinnersley.
Licensure Intermediate Care. *Beds* 96. *Certified* Medicaid.
Ownership Nonprofit.
Admissions Requirements Minimum age 18; Medical examination.
Staff RNs 2 (ft), 6 (pt); LPNs 1 (ft), 2 (pt); Orderlies 1 (pt); Nurses aides 20 (ft), 16 (pt); Activities coordinators 1 (ft), 1 (pt); Dietitians 1 (pt).
Facilities Dining room; Activities room; Chapel; Crafts room; Laundry room; Barber/Beauty shop; Library; Century bathing units.
Activities Arts and Crafts; Cards; Games; Reading groups; Shopping trips; Dances/Social or cultural gatherings; Bible study; Religious services.

RUSHVILLE

Hillside Haven
424 N Perkins St, Rushville, IN, 46173 (317)
932-3024
Admin Mary Martha Todd.
Licensure Intermediate Care. *Beds* 28.
Admissions Requirements Medical examination; Physician's request.
Staff RNs 1 (pt); LPNs 1 (ft); Activities coordinators 1 (pt); Dietitians 1 (pt).
Facilities Dining room; Activities room; Laundry room.
Activities Arts and Crafts; Cards; Games; Shopping trips.
Description Hillside Haven is located in rural Rush County in the town of Rushville and has been in operation 21 years; a small facility with a home-like atmosphere, sewing, excellent food, and very personal care.

Jackson Nursing Home*
612 E 11th St, Rushville, IN, 46173 (317)
932-4127
Admin Marjorie Pearsey.
Licensure Skilled Care; Intermediate Care.
Beds SNF 50; ICF 120. *Certified* Medicaid; Medicare.

SALEM

Williams Convalescent Center Inc*
Homer and Anson Sts, Salem, IN, 47167 (812)
883-4681
Admin Wayne Williams and Kathleen Williams.
Licensure Skilled Care; Intermediate Care.
Beds SNF 39; ICF 79. *Certified* Medicaid; Medicare.

SAN PIERRE

Little Company of Mary Health Facility Inc*
Rt 1, Box 22A, San Pierre, IN, 46374 (219)
828-4111
Admin Thomas H Kramer.
Licensure Intermediate Care. *Beds* 200. *Certified* Medicaid.

SCOTTSBURG

Scott Villa Health Care Center Inc
Rt 6, US 31 S, Scottsburg, IN, 47170 (812)
752-3499
Admin Clara E McGinnis. *Medical Dir/Dir of Nursing* Marvin L McClain MD.
Licensure Intermediate Care. *Beds* 23. *Certified* Medicaid.
Admissions Requirements Medical examination.
Staff RNs 1 (ft); LPNs 2 (ft); Nurses aides 2 (ft), 7 (pt); Activities coordinators 1 (ft).
Facilities Dining room; Laundry room.
Activities Arts and Crafts; Cards; Games; Reading groups; Prayer groups; Shopping trips.
Description New facility is being constructed in another location with 70-bed capacity (20 skilled and 50 intermediate) scheduled for opening in early 1985.

Scottsburg Nursing Home*
1100 N Gardner St, Scottsburg, IN, 47170
(812) 752-5065
Admin Ollie M Blagrave.
Licensure Intermediate Care. *Beds* 40. *Certified* Medicaid.

Williams Manor
10 Todd Dr, Scottsburg, IN, 47170 (812)
752-5663
Admin Barbara K Fleener. *Medical Dir/Dir of Nursing* Dr William Scott.
Licensure Intermediate Care. *Beds* 84. *Certified* Medicaid.
Admissions Requirements Minimum age 18; Medical examination; Physician's request.
Staff Physicians 7 (pt); RNs 1 (ft), 1 (pt); LPNs 4 (ft), 3 (pt); Orderlies 1 (ft), 1 (pt); Recreational therapists 1 (ft); Activities coordinators 1 (pt); Dietitians 1 (pt).
Facilities Dining room; Physical therapy room; Activities room; Laundry room; Barber/Beauty shop; Conference room.
Activities Arts and Crafts; Cards; Games; Reading groups; Prayer groups; Movies; Shopping trips; Dances/Social or cultural gatherings; Picnics.
Description This is a family-owned home that has always put the residents first.

SELLERSBURG

Maple Manor Christian Home Inc—Adult Division
643 W Utica, Sellersburg, IN, 47172 (812)
246-4866
Admin Joseph Blansett.
Licensure Residential Care. *Beds* 36.
Admissions Requirements Minimum age 21; Medical examination.
Staff RNs 1 (pt); LPNs 1 (ft), 1 (pt); Nurses

aides 10 (ft), 2 (pt); Activities coordinators 1 (ft).
Affiliation Church of Christ
Facilities Dining room; Activities room; Crafts room; Laundry room; Barber/Beauty shop; Library; Lounge.
Activities Arts and Crafts; Games; Prayer groups; Movies.
Description Through church relationships, many of the residents and staff have known each other for years; a family-like Christian atmosphere prevails.

SEYMOUR

Jackson Park Convalescent Center Inc
707 Jackson Park Dr, Seymour, IN, 47274 (812) 522-2416
Admin Mary C Driver. *Medical Dir/Dir of Nursing* Dr Paul E Page.
Licensure Skilled Care; Intermediate Care. *Beds* SNF 25; ICF 91. *Certified* Medicaid.
Admissions Requirements Minimum age 18; Medical examination; Physician's request.
Staff Physicians 1 (pt); RNs 3 (ft), 2 (pt); LPNs 5 (ft), 3 (pt); Orderlies 1 (pt); Nurses aides 30 (ft), 15 (pt); Physical therapists 1 (pt); Activities coordinators 2 (ft); Dietitians 2 (pt); Dentists 1 (pt).
Facilities Dining room; Physical therapy room; Activities room; Chapel; Crafts room; Laundry room; Barber/Beauty shop.
Activities Arts and Crafts; Cards; Games; Reading groups; Prayer groups; Movies; Shopping trips; Dances/Social or cultural gatherings.

Lutheran Community Home Inc*
111 W Church Ave, Seymour, IN, 47274 (812) 522-5927
Admin Donald Bruce.
Licensure Intermediate Care. *Beds* 82. *Certified* Medicaid.
Affiliation Lutheran

SHELBYVILLE

The Heritage House Children's Center*
2325 S Miller St, Shelbyville, IN, 46176 (317) 392-3287
Admin Janet Coers.
Licensure Skilled Care; Intermediate Care. *Beds* 135. *Certified* Medicaid.

The Heritage House Convalescent Center*
2309 S Miller St, Shelbyville, IN, 46176 (317) 398-9781
Admin C Robert Norman.
Licensure Skilled Care; Intermediate Care. *Beds* 135. *Certified* Medicaid; Medicare.

Heritage Manor Inc*
2311 S Miller St, Shelbyville, IN, 46176 (317) 398-9777
Admin Diane L McNeely.
Licensure Intermediate Care. *Beds* 95.

SHERIDAN

Sheridan Health Care Center Inc*
903 Sheridan Ave, Sheridan, IN, 46069 (317) 758-5330

Admin Jeanne Roeder.
Licensure Intermediate Care. *Beds* 60. *Certified* Medicaid.

SOUTH BEND

Cardinal Manor
118 S William St, South Bend, IN, 46601 (219) 287-6501
Admin Delores J Polomskey.
Licensure Residential Care. *Beds* 59.
Admissions Requirements Minimum age 50; Medical examination.
Description This is a residential facility which cannot take any mentally ill or retarded residents; qualified medication aides licensed by the state.

Cardinal Nursing Home Inc*
1121 E LaSalle, South Bend, IN, 46601 (219) 287-6501
Admin Chris Mueller.
Licensure Skilled Care; Intermediate Care. *Beds* 291. *Certified* Medicaid; Medicare.

Carlyle Nursing Home*
5024 W Western Ave, South Bend, IN, 46625 (219) 288-1464
Admin Mary Banky. *Medical Dir/Dir of Nursing* Charles Myers MD.
Licensure Skilled Care; Intermediate Care. *Beds* SNF 52; ICF 191. *Certified* Medicaid; Medicare.
Admissions Requirements Minimum age 18; Medical examination; Physician's request.
Staff RNs 8 (ft), 4 (pt); LPNs 14 (ft), 4 (pt); Nurses aides 72 (ft), 5 (pt); Reality therapists 6 (ft), 1 (pt); Activities coordinators 2 (ft).
Facilities Dining room; Physical therapy room; Activities room; Chapel; Crafts room; Laundry room; Barber/Beauty shop.
Activities Arts and Crafts; Cards; Games; Reading groups; Prayer groups; Movies; Shopping trips; Dances/Social or cultural gatherings.
Description Facility ensures excellent professional nursing care and comfort for both the convalescent and the elderly. Profesional services and facilities are planned and administered by experienced, licensed personnel. Twenty-four hour registered nursing and physician care; liberal visiting hourscoupled with convenient public transportation make visiting easy. "Better care...because we care."

Healthwin Hospital*
20531 Darden Rd, South Bend, IN, 46637 (219) 272-0100
Admin Michael J Roman.
Licensure Skilled Care; Intermediate Care. *Beds* 110. *Certified* Medicaid; Medicare.

Morningside Nursing Home*
18325 Bailey Ave, South Bend, IN, 46637 (219) 272-6410
Admin Gregg Barkley.
Licensure Intermediate Care. *Beds* 35. *Certified* Medicaid.

Northwood Nursing Home
328 N Notre Dame Ave, South Bend, IN, 46617 (219) 232-4486
Admin Emma J Hawk.

Licensure Intermediate Care. *Beds* 40. *Certified* Medicaid.
Admissions Requirements Physician's request.
Staff Physicians 1 (ft), 1 (pt); RNs 2 (pt); LPNs 2 (ft); Nurses aides 18 (ft), 7 (pt); Activities coordinators 1 (ft); Dietitians 1 (pt); Dentists 1 (pt); Ophthalmologists 1 (pt); Podiatrists 1 (pt).
Facilities Dining room; Laundry room.
Activities Arts and Crafts; Cards; Games; Reading groups; Prayer groups; Movies; Shopping trips.
Description We give a great deal of love and good care.

Portage Manor
53308 Portage Rd, South Bend, IN, 46628 (219) 232-9100
Admin Damaris A Smith. *Medical Dir/Dir of Nursing* H O Foley MD.
Licensure Residential Care. *Beds* 120.
Ownership Public.
Facilities Dining room; Activities room; Chapel; Crafts room; Laundry room; Barber/Beauty shop.
Activities Arts and Crafts; Cards; Games; Reading groups; Prayer groups; Movies; Shopping trips; Dances/Social or cultural gatherings.
Description Facility is situated on the northwest edge of South Bend. In addition to the very large shaded grounds, facility has an 80-acre farm which produces the beef and pork eaten at the Manor. The bus stops at the front door making travel into South Bend convenient; activities department does personal shopping and takes the residents to stores.

Ridgedale Nursing Center
1950 E Ridgedale Rd, South Bend, IN, 46614 (219) 291-6722
Admin Lloyd White. *Medical Dir/Dir of Nursing* Dr Zia Chowhan.
Licensure Skilled Care; Intermediate Care. *Beds* SNF 21; ICF 225. *Certified* Medicaid; Medicare.
Admissions Requirements Medical examination; Physician's request.
Staff RNs 8 (ft), 15 (pt); LPNs 7 (ft), 5 (pt); Physical therapists 1 (pt); Activities coordinators 3 (ft), 1 (pt); Dietitians 1 (ft).
Facilities Dining room; Physical therapy room; Activities room; Laundry room; Barber/Beauty shop.
Activities Arts and Crafts; Cards; Games; Reading groups; Prayer groups; Movies; Shopping trips; Dances/Social or cultural gatherings.
Description Designed for pleasant, gracious living, Ridgedale is conveniently located in the beautiful Twyckenham Hills of South Bend, Indiana. Approximately 32 therapeutically planned diets are designed by Ridgedale's own registered dietician. Each resident's medical needs are reviewed individually, with emphasis on rehabilitation, and Ridgedale has its own physical therapist, and a speech therapist visits regularly.

River Park Nursing Home*
915 27th St, South Bend, IN, 46615 (219) 287-1016
Admin William Beghtel.
Licensure Intermediate Care. *Beds* 44. *Certified* Medicaid.

Riverbend Manor Inc
1024 N Notre Dame Ave, South Bend, IN,
46617 (219) 234-3179
Admin Ronald F Westman.
Licensure Intermediate Care. *Beds* 24. *Certified* Medicaid.

Riverside Center Inc
PO Box 2406, South Bend, IN, 46680 (219)
289-7871
Admin John D Pelzer.
Licensure Intermediate Care. *Beds* 81. *Certified* Medicaid.

Robert and Clara Milton Home Inc*
206 E Marion St, South Bend, IN, 46601 (219)
233-0165
Admin Rosemary Ward.
Licensure Intermediate Care; Residential Care.
Beds ICF 16; Residential Care 34.

St Paul's Retirement Community*
3602 S Ironwood Dr, South Bend, IN, 46614
(219) 291-8205
Admin Mark G Wimer.
Licensure Skilled Care; Intermediate Care.
Beds 554.

South Bend Convalescent Center Inc
4600 W Washington Ave, South Bend, IN,
46619 (219) 282-1294
Admin Rae D Leonard. *Medical Dir/Dir of Nursing* Zia Chowhan MD.
Licensure Intermediate Care. *Beds* 180. *Certified* Medicaid.
Admissions Requirements Minimum age 18;
Medical examination.
Staff Physicians 1 (pt); RNs 4 (ft), 1 (pt); LPNs
5 (ft), 1 (pt); Orderlies 7 (ft), 1 (pt); Nurses aides
48 (ft), 3 (pt); Recreational therapists 1 (ft);
Activities coordinators 2 (ft); Dietitians 1 (pt);
Dentists 1 (pt).
Facilities Dining room; Activities room; Crafts
room; Laundry room; Barber/Beauty shop.
Activities Arts and Crafts; Cards; Games;
Reading groups; Prayer groups; Movies; Shopping trips; Dances/Social or cultural gatherings.
Description Program for mentally retarded
includes in-house classroom.

SPENCER

Friendly Hearth Nursing Center of Spencer
Rt 2, Spencer, IN, 47460 (812) 879-4275
Admin Norman S Tirsway.
Licensure Intermediate Care. *Beds* 46. *Certified* Medicaid.
Admissions Requirements Minimum age 2;
Medical examination.
Staff RNs 1 (ft); LPNs 1 (pt); Nurses aides 11
(ft), 5 (pt); Activities coordinators 1 (ft); Dietitians 1 (pt).
Facilities Dining room; Activities room; Crafts
room; Laundry room.
Activities Arts and Crafts; Cards; Games;
Reading groups; Prayer groups; Movies; Shopping trips.
Description Facility is located in a rural setting
with large shaded yard and family-oriented
atmosphere; open visitation; meals planned by
registered dietician; church services and other
activities.

Owen County Home*
RR 3, Box 124, Spencer, IN, 47460 (812)
829-3492
Admin Ruthie Gray.
Beds 31.

SULLIVAN

Miller's Merry Manor*
PO Box 525, W Wolfe St, Sullivan, IN, 47882
(812) 268-6361
Admin Donald C Hunt.
Licensure Intermediate Care. *Beds* 175. *Certified* Medicaid.

Village Nursing Home
975 N Section St, Sullivan, IN, 47882 (812)
268-6810
Admin Richard W Bartnik. *Medical Dir/Dir of
Nursing* Betty Dukes MD.
Licensure Intermediate Care. *Beds* 40. *Certified* Medicaid.
Admissions Requirements Minimum age 18;
Medical examination; Physician's request.
Staff Physicians 1 (pt); LPNs 3 (ft), 2 (pt);
Nurses aides 6 (ft), 7 (pt); Physical therapists 1
(pt); Reality therapists 1 (pt); Recreational therapists 1 (pt); Speech therapists 1 (pt); Activities
coordinators 1 (ft), 1 (pt); Dietitians 1 (pt);
Dentists 1 (pt); Ophthalmologists 1 (pt); Podiatrists 1 (pt); Audiologists 1 (pt).
Facilities Dining room; Laundry room; Barber-
/Beauty shop.
Activities Arts and Crafts; Cards; Games;
Reading groups; Prayer groups; Movies; Shopping trips; Dances/Social or cultural gatherings.
Description Home features a specially trained
staff to handle mentally retarded and developmentally disabled residents.

SUMMITVILLE

Summit Convalescent Center Inc*
Rt 1, Box 348, Summitville, IN, 46070 (317)
536-2261
Admin William C Van Ness.
Licensure Intermediate Care. *Beds* 34. *Certified* Medicaid.

TELL CITY

Lincoln Hills Nursing Home Inc
19th and Pestalozzi, Tell City, IN, 47586 (812)
547-3427
Admin Roger Ambrose. *Medical Dir/Dir of
Nursing* Fred Smith MD.
Licensure Intermediate Care. *Beds* 165. *Certified* Medicaid.
Admissions Requirements Minimum age 18;
Medical examination; Physician's request.
Staff RNs 2 (ft), 1 (pt); LPNs 7 (ft); Nurses
aides 40 (ft), 27 (pt); Physical therapists 1 (ft);
Activities coordinators 1 (ft); Dietitians 1 (pt).
Facilities Dining room; Physical therapy room;
Activities room; Chapel; Crafts room; Laundry
room; Barber/Beauty shop.
Activities Arts and Crafts; Cards; Games;
Reading groups; Prayer groups; Movies; Shopping trips; Dances/Social or cultural gatherings.

TERRE HAUTE

Clara Fairbanks and Chauncey Rose Home Inc
721 8th Ave, Terre Haute, IN, 47804 (812)
232-3267
Admin Helen Cottrell.
Licensure Intermediate Care; Residential Care.
Beds 34.
Admissions Requirements Minimum age 68;
Females only; Medical examination.
Staff LPNs 5 (ft); Nurses aides 3 (ft); Activities
coordinators 1 (ft); Dietitians 1 (pt).
Facilities Dining room; Laundry room; Barber-
/Beauty shop.
Activities Arts and Crafts; Games; Reading
groups; Prayer groups; Movies; Shopping trips;
Dances/Social or cultural gatherings.
Description Private rooms are given to each
resident. The home is under endowment. No
Medicaid or Medicare funds are used. The residents are allowed $55.00 a month for shopping;
if more is needed they are allowed to have more
(to purchase a TV, for example).

Davis Gardens Health Center
1120 Davis Ave, Terre Haute, IN, 47802
Admissions Requirements Medical examination; Physician's request.
Staff Physicians 1 (pt); RNs 5 (ft), 1 (pt); LPNs
5 (ft), 3 (pt); Orderlies 1 (ft); Nurses aides 25
(ft), 8 (pt); Physical therapists 1 (ft); Occupational therapists 1 (ft); Speech therapists 1 (pt);
Activities coordinators 1 (ft); Dietitians 1 (ft).
Facilities Dining room; Physical therapy room;
Activities room; Laundry room; Barber/Beauty
shop.
Activities Arts and Crafts; Games; Reading
groups; Prayer groups; Movies; Shopping trips;
Dances/Social or cultural gatherings.

Ewing Nursing Home
504 S 15th St, Terre Haute, IN, 47807 (812)
232-3663
Admin Judith M Weathers. *Medical Dir/Dir of
Nursing* Selma M Mills RN.
Licensure Intermediate Care. *Beds* 18. *Certified* Medicaid.
Staff RNs 1 (ft); LPNs 2 (ft); Orderlies 1 (ft);
Nurses aides 4 (ft); Recreational therapists 1
(ft); Activities coordinators 1 (ft).
Facilities Dining room; Activities room; Laundry room.
Activities Arts and Crafts; Cards; Games;
Reading groups; Shopping trips; Dances/Social
or cultural gatherings.
Description Small facility with a home-like
atmosphere located in a residential setting.
Families are encouraged to come in on holidays
for dinner.

Maplewood Manor
500 Maple Ave, Terre Haute, IN, 47804 (812)
234-7702
Admin Betty Barber. *Medical Dir/Dir of
Nursing* H G Edwards.
Licensure Skilled Care; Intermediate Care.
Beds SNF 124; ICF 93. *Certified* Medicaid;
Medicare.
Admissions Requirements Minimum age 18.
Staff RNs 7 (ft); LPNs 23 (ft); Nurses aides 110
(ft), 10 (pt); Physical therapists 1 (ft), 1 (pt);
Recreational therapists 3 (ft), 1 (pt); Occupational therapists 1 (ft); Speech therapists 1 (pt);

Activities coordinators 1 (ft); Dietitians 1 (pt); Dentists 1 (pt); Podiatrists 1 (pt); Audiologists 1 (pt).
Facilities Dining room; Physical therapy room; Activities room; Chapel; Crafts room; Laundry room; Barber/Beauty shop.
Activities Arts and Crafts; Cards; Games; Reading groups; Prayer groups; Movies; Shopping trips; Dances/Social or cultural gatherings.
Description Facility is built around a beautiful fishing lake; maintains link with the community.

Meadows Manor*
3300 Poplar St, Terre Haute, IN, 47803 (812) 235-6281
Admin Vickie Curry.
Licensure Skilled Care; Intermediate Care.
Beds 103. *Certified* Medicaid.

Meadows Manor North Inc*
3150 N 7th St, Terre Haute, IN, 47804 (812) 466-5217
Admin Nancy Applegate.
Licensure Skilled Care; Intermediate Care.
Beds 100. *Certified* Medicaid.

Terre Haute Nursing Home*
830 S 6th St, Terre Haute, IN, 47808 (812) 232-7102
Admin Robert D Lau.
Licensure Intermediate Care. *Beds* 40. *Certified* Medicaid.

Vigo County Home
3500 Maple Ave, Terre Haute, IN, 47804 (812) 238-8375
Admin R Michael Cahill. *Medical Dir/Dir of Nursing* W L Loewenstein MD.
Licensure Intermediate Care. *Beds* 201. *Certified* Medicaid.
Ownership Public.
Admissions Requirements Medical examination; Physician's request.
Staff Physicians 1 (pt); RNs 6 (ft); LPNs 28 (ft); Nurses aides 66 (ft); Physical therapists 1 (pt); Reality therapists 1 (pt); Recreational therapists 3 (ft); Occupational therapists 1 (pt); Speech therapists 1 (pt); Activities coordinators 1 (ft); Dietitians 1 (ft); Dentists 1 (pt); Ophthalmologists 1 (pt); Podiatrists 1 (pt); Audiologists 1 (pt).
Facilities Dining room; Physical therapy room; Activities room; Chapel; Crafts room; Laundry room; Barber/Beauty shop.
Activities Arts and Crafts; Cards; Games; Reading groups; Prayer groups; Movies; Shopping trips; Dances/Social or cultural gatherings.
Description Facility offers nursing care which is second to none in a well kept building, not new; staff attitude overshadows any physical limitations.

Wallace Nursing Center Inc*
120 W Margaret Ave, Terre Haute, IN, 47802 (812) 232-3311
Admin Robert Wallace.
Licensure Intermediate Care. *Beds* 120. *Certified* Medicaid.

Webster's Rest Home*
513-515 N 14th St, Terre Haute, IN, 47807 (812) 232-4571

Admin Rachel Webster.
Licensure Intermediate Care. *Beds* 10. *Certified* Medicaid.

TIPTON

Millers Merry Manor
4-H Rd, PO Box 265, Tipton, IN, 46072 (317) 675-8791
Admin Roger L Gunther.
Licensure Intermediate Care. *Beds* 102. *Certified* Medicaid.
Admissions Requirements Minimum age 19; Medical examination; Physician's request.
Staff RNs 3 (ft); LPNs 3 (ft); Nurses aides 20 (ft), 15 (pt); Physical therapists 1 (pt); Speech therapists 1 (pt); Activities coordinators 1 (ft), 1 (pt); Dietitians 1 (pt); Audiologists 1 (pt).
Facilities Dining room; Physical therapy room; Activities room; Crafts room; Laundry room; Barber/Beauty shop; Library.
Activities Arts and Crafts; Cards; Games; Reading groups; Prayer groups; Movies; Dances/Social or cultural gatherings.
Description Facility features a home-like setting and courtyard for enjoyment of residents, staff, families, and visitors; next door to hospital and doctors park with 4 physicians that service the facility; also a conscientious and concerned staff.

Tipton Nursing Home
701 E Jefferson St, Tipton, IN, 46072 (317) 675-4024
Admin Margaret JoAnn Feeser.
Licensure Intermediate Care. *Beds* 40. *Certified* Medicaid.
Facilities Dining room; Activities room; Laundry room; Barber/Beauty shop.
Activities Arts and Crafts; Cards; Games; Reading groups; Prayer groups; Movies; Shopping trips; Dances/Social or cultural gatherings.

UPLAND

University Nursing Center
PO Box 3000, Upland, IN, 46989 (317) 998-2761
Admin Teresa Smucker. *Medical Dir/Dir of Nursing* F B Guevara MD.
Licensure Skilled Care; Intermediate Care.
Beds 81. *Certified* Medicaid; Medicare.
Staff Physicians 1 (pt); RNs 4 (ft), 1 (pt); LPNs 4 (ft), 3 (pt); Orderlies 1 (ft); Nurses aides 18 (ft), 9 (pt); Physical therapists 1 (pt); Speech therapists 1 (pt); Activities coordinators 1 (ft), 1 (pt); Dietitians 1 (pt).
Facilities Dining room; Physical therapy room; Activities room; Crafts room; Laundry room; Barber/Beauty shop.
Activities Arts and Crafts; Cards; Games; Reading groups; Prayer groups; Movies; Shopping trips; Dances/Social or cultural gatherings.
Description Center offers physical therapy and professional nursing care to all residents; located near 2 hospitals and near Taylor University, ensuring college student/resident interaction; social services, activities, and diet are disciplines included to contribute toward a well-rounded, resident oriented program.

VALPARAISO

Canterbury Place
251 East Dr, Valparaiso, IN, 46383 (219) 462-6158
Admin Glenn Wagner. *Medical Dir/Dir of Nursing* Dr Holwerda.
Licensure Skilled Care; Intermediate Care.
Beds SNF 51; ICF 51. *Certified* Medicaid; Medicare.
Admissions Requirements Minimum age 18; Medical examination.
Facilities Dining room; Physical therapy room; Laundry room; Barber/Beauty shop.
Activities Arts and Crafts; Cards; Games; Reading groups; Prayer groups; Movies; Dances/Social or cultural gatherings.

Vale View Convalescent Center
606 Wall St, Valparaiso, IN, 46383 (219) 464-4976
Admin C Jane Graves. *Medical Dir/Dir of Nursing* Joel L Hull MD and Owen H Lucas MD.
Licensure Skilled Care; Intermediate Care.
Beds SNF 96; ICF 96. *Certified* Medicaid; Medicare.
Admissions Requirements Minimum age 18; Medical examination; Physician's request.
Staff Physicians 1 (pt); RNs 11 (ft), 2 (pt); LPNs 2 (ft), 2 (pt); Nurses aides 61 (ft), 2 (pt); Physical therapists 1 (ft), 1 (pt), Recreational therapists 1 (ft); Occupational therapists 1 (ft); Speech therapists 1 (pt); Activities coordinators 3 (ft); Dietitians 1 (pt); Dentists 1 (pt); Podiatrists 1 (pt); Audiologists 1 (pt).
Facilities Dining room; Physical therapy room; Activities room; Crafts room; Laundry room; Barber/Beauty shop.
Activities Arts and Crafts; Cards; Games; Reading groups; Prayer groups; Movies; Shopping trips; Dances/Social or cultural gatherings; Cooking club.
Description Facility is fully serviced by a sprinkler system.

Whispering Pines Home for Senior Citizens
3301 N Calumet Ave, Valparaiso, IN, 46383 (219) 462-0508
Admin Jeanette Dolk. *Medical Dir/Dir of Nursing* Michael Weiss MD.
Licensure Intermediate Care. *Beds* 184. *Certified* Medicaid.
Admissions Requirements Minimum age 60; Medical examination.
Staff RNs 5 (ft), 7 (pt); LPNs 6 (ft), 5 (pt); Orderlies 58 (ft), 45 (pt); Activities coordinators 4 (ft), 1 (pt); Dietitians 1 (ft).
Facilities Dining room; Physical therapy room; Activities room; Chapel; Crafts room; Laundry room; Barber/Beauty shop; Library.
Activities Arts and Crafts; Cards; Games; Reading groups; Movies; Shopping trips; Dances/Social or cultural gatherings; Bible study.
Description Whispering Pines is located on 13 1/2 acres in 2 modern 2-story buildings. It is owned and operated by the Porter County Council of Church Women, a local nonprofit corporation which has been providing quality care for over 20 years. Its newest addition, the Pines Village Apartments, provides life care among its many services.

Willows Rehabilitation Center
1000 Elizabeth, Valparaiso, IN, 46383 (219)
464-4858
Admin LuAnn Nebelung. *Medical Dir/Dir of
Nursing* Dr Harry Holwerda.
Licensure Skilled Care; Intermediate Care.
Beds SNF 49; ICF 50. *Certified* Medicaid;
Medicare.
Admissions Requirements Medical examina-
tion; Physician's request.
Staff RNs 3 (ft), 1 (pt); LPNs 3 (ft), 2 (pt);
Nurses aides 50 (ft), 25 (pt); Physical therapists
2 (pt); Recreational therapists 1 (ft); Occupa-
tional therapists 1 (pt); Speech therapists 1 (pt);
Activities coordinators 1 (pt); Dietitians 1 (pt);
Dentists 1 (pt); Podiatrists 1 (pt); Audiologists 1
(pt).
Facilities Dining room; Physical therapy room;
Laundry room; Barber/Beauty shop.
Activities Arts and Crafts; Cards; Games;
Reading groups; Prayer groups; Movies; Shop-
ping trips; Dances/Social or cultural gatherings.

VERSAILLES

Silver Bell Nursing Home
Rt 2, Box 106, Versailles, IN, 47402 (812)
689-6222
Admin Walter Bradley Jr. *Medical Dir/Dir of
Nursing* Eula Busteed.
Licensure Intermediate Care. *Beds* 21. *Certi-
fied* Medicaid.
Admissions Requirements Medical examina-
tion.
Staff RNs 1 (pt); LPNs 1 (ft), 1 (pt); Orderlies 1
(pt); Nurses aides 7 (ft); Activities coordinators
1 (pt).
Facilities Dining room; Activities room; Laun-
dry room.
Activities Arts and Crafts; Cards; Games;
Reading groups; Prayer groups; Shopping trips;
Dances/Social or cultural gatherings.
Description Facility sets on a 3-acre lot with a
country atmosphere; 7 miles to shopping area; 5
semi-private rooms; one 3 bed ward and 2
4-bed wards; 24 hour nursing; a very homey
facility.

VEVAY

Jackson's Senior Citizens Home
501 W Pike St, Vevay, IN, 47043 (812)
427-3525
Admin Linda L McDole.
Licensure Residential Care. *Beds* 18.
Admissions Requirements Medical examina-
tion.
Staff Physicians 1 (pt); RNs 1 (pt); Activities
coordinators 1 (ft); Dietitians 1 (pt).
Facilities Dining room; Laundry room.
Activities Arts and Crafts; Games; Reading
groups; Dances/Social or cultural gatherings.

Swiss Villa Health Care Facility
Rt 3, Box 169A, Vevay, IN, 47043
Admin Steve Atwood and Joyce Atwood.
Medical Dir/Dir of Nursing Dr Ivan Lindgren.
Licensure Intermediate Care. *Beds* 60. *Certi-
fied* Medicaid.
Ownership Proprietary.
Admissions Requirements Medical examina-

tion; Physician's request.
Staff Physicians 2 (pt); RNs 2 (ft); LPNs 3 (ft),
2 (pt); Orderlies 4 (ft); Nurses aides 20 (ft);
Physical therapists 1 (pt); Reality therapists 1
(ft); Recreational therapists 2 (ft); Speech thera-
pists 1 (pt); Activities coordinators 1 (ft), 1 (pt);
Dietitians 1 (ft); Dentists 1 (pt).
Facilities Dining room; Physical therapy room;
Activities room; Laundry room; Barber/Beauty
shop.
Activities Arts and Crafts; Games; Reading
groups; Prayer groups; Shopping trips; Dances-
/Social or cultural gatherings.

VINCENNES

Crestview Convalescent Home*
Box 136, Old Bruceville Rd, Vincennes, IN,
47591 (812) 882-1783
Admin Richard Gossman Jr.
Licensure Skilled Care; Intermediate Care.
Beds SNF 29; ICF 137. *Certified* Medicaid;
Medicare.

Vincennes Nursing Home*
PO Box 903, 1202 S 16th St, Vincennes, IN,
47591 (812) 882-8292
Admin Frank Harrell.
Licensure Intermediate Care. *Beds* 66. *Certi-
fied* Medicaid.

Willow Manor Convalescent Center Inc*
1321 Willow St, Vincennes, IN, 47591 (812)
882-1136
Admin Roberta Kay Cresgy.
Licensure Skilled Care; Intermediate Care.
Beds SNF 43; ICF 99. *Certified* Medicaid;
Medicare.

WABASH

Manor Care, Division of Miller's Merry Manor
Rt 2, Wabash, IN, 46992
Admin Judy A Warner. *Medical Dir/Dir of
Nursing* James Haughn MD.
Licensure Intermediate Care. *Beds* 39. *Certi-
fied* Medicaid.
Ownership Proprietary.
Admissions Requirements Minimum age 18;
Medical examination; Physician's request.
Staff RNs 1 (ft); LPNs 2 (ft), 2 (pt); Nurses
aides 5 (ft), 6 (pt); Activities coordinators 1 (ft),
1 (pt).
Facilities Dining room; Activities room; Laun-
dry room; Barber/Beauty shop.
Activities Arts and Crafts; Games; Movies;
Shopping trips; Daily living classes.
Description Facility offers a sheltered workshop
arrangement with individual habilitation plans
plus patient care plans.

Miller's Merry Manor Inc*
1035 Manchester Ave, Wabash, IN, 46992
(219) 563-7427
Admin Ellen McAllister.
Licensure Skilled Care; Intermediate Care.
Beds SNF 27; ICF 75. *Certified* Medicaid;
Medicare.

Vernon Manor Children's Home*
PO Box 258, 1955 S Vernon St, Wabash, IN,
46992 (219) 563-8438
Admin Andris Ross.
Licensure Skilled Care; Intermediate Care.
Beds 136. *Certified* Medicaid.

Wabash Healthcare Center
600 Washington St, Wabash, IN, 46992 (219)
563-8402
Admin David Woods.
Licensure Skilled Care; Intermediate Care.
Beds SNF 54; ICF 54. *Certified* Medicaid;
Medicare.
Admissions Requirements Medical examina-
tion; Physician's request.
Staff Physicians 14 (pt); RNs 7 (ft), 3 (pt);
LPNs 4 (ft), 3 (pt); Nurses aides 35 (ft), 10 (pt);
Physical therapists 2 (pt); Reality therapists 2
(pt); Recreational therapists 2 (pt); Speech ther-
apists 1 (pt); Activities coordinators 1 (ft), 1
(pt); Dietitians 1 (pt); Dentists 1 (pt); Ophthal-
mologists 1 (pt); Podiatrists 1 (pt); Audiologists
1 (pt).
Facilities Dining room; Physical therapy room;
Activities room; Chapel; Crafts room; Laundry
room; Barber/Beauty shop; Library.
Activities Arts and Crafts; Cards; Games;
Reading groups; Prayer groups; Movies; Shopping trips; Dances/Social or cultural gatherings.
Description Facility provides meaningful
activities for all residents; van takes people to
outside functions and/or appointments; high
quality care dedicated to personal care.

WALDRON

Waldron Health Care Home Inc
Box 371, Waldron, IN, 46182 (317) 525-6332
Admin Charles D Kuhn.
Licensure Intermediate Care. *Beds* 51. *Certi-
fied* Medicaid.
Staff RNs 1 (ft); LPNs 1 (ft), 2 (pt); Nurses
aides 3 (ft), 20 (pt); Activities coordinators 1
(ft); Dietitians 1 (pt).
Facilities Dining room; Activities room; Laun-
dry room; Barber/Beauty shop.
Activities Arts and Crafts; Cards; Games;
Movies; Shopping trips.
Description Church services are held every
Sunday afternoon with 24 churches in commu-
nity taking turns; once a month a special day
(Hawaiian Day or A&W Day); open house in
May; picnic under tent in August; mother-
daughter tea and father-son breakfast.

WALKERTON

Miller's Merry Manor Inc*
Walkerton Trail, Walkerton, IN, 46574 (219)
586-3133
Admin William Gerlib.
Licensure Intermediate Care. *Beds* 116. *Certi-
fied* Medicaid.

WARREN

United Methodist Memorial Home
State Rd 5 N, Warren, IN, 46792 (219)
375-2201
Admin Philip E Souder. *Medical Dir/Dir of

Nursing Gerald Miller MD.
Licensure Residential Care; Comprehensive Nursing Care. *Beds* 655.
Admissions Requirements Minimum age 65; Medical examination; Physician's request.
Staff Physicians 7 (pt); RNs 14 (ft); LPNs 12 (ft); Nurses aides 112 (ft); Physical therapists 2 (ft), 1 (pt); Recreational therapists 2 (ft); Occupational therapists 5 (ft); Activities coordinators 2 (ft), 1 (pt); Dietitians 1 (pt); Dentists 1 (pt); Ophthalmologists 1 (pt); Podiatrists 1 (pt); Audiologists 1 (pt).
Affiliation Methodist
Facilities Dining room; Physical therapy room; Activities room; Chapel; Crafts room; Laundry room; Barber/Beauty shop; Library; Dentist office; Eye clinic; Post Office.
Activities Arts and Crafts; Cards; Games; Reading groups; Prayer groups; Movies; Shopping trips; Dances/Social or cultural gatherings.
Description Facility is in 74th year of providing total care for residents without ever being in debt; no Medicaid residents; have cared for over 2750 persons in this period of time.

WARSAW

Mason Health Care Facility
2501 E Center St, Warsaw, IN, 46580 (219) 267-6611
Admin Carlyle L Mason. *Medical Dir/Dir of Nursing* Harold Mason MD.
Licensure Skilled Care; Intermediate Care. *Beds* SNF 24; ICF 29. *Certified* Medicaid; Medicare.
Admissions Requirements Minimum age 18; Medical examination; Physician's request.
Staff RNs 3 (ft), 2 (pt); LPNs 1 (ft), 2 (pt); Nurses aides 11 (ft), 10 (pt); Physical therapists 1 (pt); Recreational therapists 1 (ft); Occupational therapists 1 (pt); Speech therapists 1 (pt); Activities coordinators 1 (ft); Dietitians 1 (pt).
Facilities Dining room; Physical therapy room; Activities room; Crafts room; Laundry room; Barber/Beauty shop.
Activities Arts and Crafts; Cards; Games; Reading groups; Shopping trips.

Miller's Merry Manor Inc
PO Box 377, County Farm Rd, Warsaw, IN, 46580 (219) 267-8196
Admin Mark A Peterson.
Licensure Skilled Care; Intermediate Care. *Beds* 103. *Certified* Medicaid; Medicare.
Admissions Requirements Minimum age 18; Medical examination; Physician's request.

Prairie View Rest Home Inc
300 Prairie St, Warsaw, IN, 46580 (219) 267-8922
Admin N Charlene Bradbury. *Medical Dir/Dir of Nursing* Michael P Dacquisto MD.
Licensure Intermediate Care. *Beds* 126. *Certified* Medicaid.
Admissions Requirements Minimum age 18; Medical examination; Physician's request.
Staff RNs 3 (ft), 3 (pt); LPNs 4 (ft); Nurses aides 40 (ft), 20 (pt); Activities coordinators 2 (ft); Dietitians 1 (pt).
Facilities Dining room; Physical therapy room; Activities room; Laundry room; Barber/Beauty shop.

Activities Arts and Crafts; Cards; Games; Reading groups; Prayer groups; Movies; Shopping trips; Dances/Social or cultural gatherings.
Description Home is a family owned and operated facility providing short-term and long-term care to the convalescent and aged. A recently completed expansion and remodeling project includes a beauty shop, activity room, physical therapy room, and exam room, plus private and semi-private accomodations.

Warsaw Nursing Home
2402 E Center St, Warsaw, IN, 46580 (219) 269-1152
Admin Ruth Muzzillo. *Medical Dir/Dir of Nursing* George A Ros MD.
Licensure Intermediate Care. *Beds* 40. *Certified* Medicaid.
Admissions Requirements Minimum age 18.
Staff RNs 1 (pt); LPNs 2 (pt); Orderlies 1 (ft); Nurses aides 14 (ft); Activities coordinators 1 (ft); Dietitians 1 (pt).
Facilities Dining room; Activities room; Laundry room.
Activities Arts and Crafts; Cards; Games; Shopping trips; Dances/Social or cultural gatherings.
Description Facility has all mentally retarded residents.

WASHINGTON

Eastgate Manor Nursing and Residential Center Inc
Hwy 50 E, PO Box 470, Washington, IN, 47501 (812) 254-3301
Admin Judith A Dreiman.
Licensure Intermediate Care. *Beds* 82. *Certified* Medicaid.
Admissions Requirements Minimum age 18; Medical examination; Physician's request.
Staff RNs 3 (ft), 2 (pt); LPNs 3 (ft), 6 (pt); Nurses aides 30 (ft), 10 (pt); Physical therapists 1 (pt); Activities coordinators 1 (ft); Dietitians 1 (pt); Dentists 1 (pt); Ophthalmologists 1 (pt).
Facilities Dining room; Physical therapy room; Activities room; Laundry room; Barber/Beauty shop.
Activities Arts and Crafts; Cards; Games; Reading groups; Prayer groups; Movies; Shopping trips; Dances/Social or cultural gatherings.
Description Center offers quality care at affordable prices.

Hillside Manor
1109 E National Hwy, Washington, IN, 47501 (812) 254-7159
Admin John F Helm. *Medical Dir/Dir of Nursing* Dr T W Davis.
Licensure Intermediate Care. *Beds* 27. *Certified* Medicaid.
Admissions Requirements Medical examination; Physician's request.
Staff RNs 1 (ft), 1 (pt); LPNs 1 (ft), 1 (pt); Nurses aides 7 (ft), 5 (pt); Physical therapists 1 (pt); Activities coordinators 1 (ft).
Facilities Dining room; Laundry room.
Activities Arts and Crafts; Cards; Games; Reading groups; Shopping trips.

Prairie Village Inc
1401 Hwy 57 S, Washington, IN, 47501 (812) 254-4516
Admin Georgia Atwood. *Medical Dir/Dir of Nursing* Donald Hall MD.
Licensure Intermediate Care. *Beds* 121. *Certified* Medicaid.
Admissions Requirements Minimum age 18.
Staff Physicians 5 (pt); RNs 3 (ft); LPNs 4 (ft); Orderlies 9 (ft); Nurses aides 39 (ft); Physical therapists 1 (pt); Activities coordinators 2 (ft); Dietitians 1 (pt); Dentists 1 (pt); Ophthalmologists 1 (pt); Podiatrists 1 (pt).
Facilities Dining room; Physical therapy room; Activities room; Laundry room; Barber/Beauty shop.
Activities Arts and Crafts; Cards; Games; Reading groups; Prayer groups; Shopping trips.

Washington Nursing Center Annex*
209 W Oak St, Washington, IN, 47501 (812) 254-0252
Admin David Snow.
Licensure Intermediate Care. *Beds* 17. *Certified* Medicaid.

Washington Nursing Center Inc
603 E National Hwy, Washington, IN, 47501 (812) 254-5117
Admin Jerome B Walker. *Medical Dir/Dir of Nursing* James P Beck MD.
Licensure Skilled Care; Intermediate Care. *Beds* 179. *Certified* Medicaid; Medicare.
Admissions Requirements Minimum age 18; Medical examination; Physician's request.
Staff Physicians 7 (pt); RNs 14 (ft); LPNs 6 (ft); Nurses aides 88 (ft); Physical therapists 1 (ft); Speech therapists 1 (pt); Activities coordinators 2 (ft); Dietitians 1 (pt); Dentists 1 (pt); Ophthalmologists 1 (pt); Podiatrists 1 (pt); Audiologists 1 (pt).
Facilities Dining room; Physical therapy room; Activities room; Laundry room; Barber/Beauty shop.
Activities Arts and Crafts; Cards; Games; Reading groups; Prayer groups; Movies; Shopping trips; Dances/Social or cultural gatherings.

WEST LAFAYETTE

Heritage Healthcare Inc
3400 Soldiers Home Rd, West Lafayette, IN, 47906 (317) 463-1541
Admin Lynn Smith. *Medical Dir/Dir of Nursing* Dr Tom Stolz.
Licensure Intermediate Care. *Beds* 127. *Certified* Medicaid.
Admissions Requirements Medical examination.
Staff RNs 10 (ft), 2 (pt); LPNs 6 (ft); Orderlies 5 (ft); Nurses aides 40 (ft), 6 (pt); Reality therapists 3 (pt); Recreational therapists 1 (ft), 3 (pt); Activities coordinators 1 (ft); Dietitians 1 (ft).
Facilities Dining room; Physical therapy room; Activities room; Crafts room; Laundry room; Barber/Beauty shop; Library.
Activities Arts and Crafts; Cards; Games; Reading groups; Prayer groups; Movies; Shopping trips; Dinner club.
Description This facility provides an adult day care center as an alternative to unnecessary institutionalization; also offers a flexible hour-

ly/weekly schedule of complete nursing assessment, therapies as needed, and recreational and educational programs.

Tippecanoe Villa*
5308 N 50 W, West Lafayette, IN, 47906 (317) 423-9240
Admin C Haan.
Licensure Residential Care. *Beds* 121.

Westminster Village West Lafayette
2741 N Salisbury St, West Lafayette, IN, 47906 (317) 463-3511
Admin Michael D Moore. *Medical Dir/Dir of Nursing* Eleanor H Filmer MD.
Licensure Skilled Care. *Beds* 38.
Admissions Requirements Minimum age 62; Medical examination.
Staff Physicians 1 (pt); RNs 4 (ft), 2 (pt); LPNs 1 (ft), 1 (pt); Nurses aides 13 (ft), 8 (pt); Physical therapists 1 (pt); Occupational therapists 1 (pt); Speech therapists 1 (pt); Activities coordinators 1 (ft); Dietitians 1 (pt); Dentists 1 (pt); Podiatrists 1 (pt); Audiologists 1 (pt); Qualified medication aides 6 (pt).
Facilities Dining room; Physical therapy room; Activities room; Chapel; Crafts room; Laundry room; Barber/Beauty shop; Library; Branch bank; General store.
Activities Arts and Crafts; Cards; Games; Reading groups; Prayer groups; Movies; Shopping trips; Dances/Social or cultural gatherings; Trips.
Description Westminster Village is a retirement community not affiliated or aligned with any other institution or organization; provides the optimal independent living environment for retirees and the elderly who still pursue an active life; it is a concept that allows residents to maintain their independent living style in an atmosphere that offers both security and socialization.

WESTFIELD

Westfield Village*
776 N Union, Westfield, IN, 46074 (317) 896-2515
Admin Marilyn Burris.
Licensure Intermediate Care. *Beds* 80. *Certified* Medicaid.

WHITING

Hammond-Whiting Convalescent Center
1000 114th St, Whiting, IN, 46394 (219) 659-2770
Admin William L McNiff. *Medical Dir/Dir of Nursing* Dr N Madarang.
Licensure Intermediate Care. *Beds* 80. *Certified* Medicaid.
Admissions Requirements Minimum age 18; Medical examination; Physician's request.
Staff RNs 2 (ft), 6 (pt); LPNs 1 (ft); Orderlies 1 (ft); Nurses aides 20 (ft), 12 (pt); Activities coordinators 1 (ft).
Facilities Dining room; Activities room; Laundry room; Barber/Beauty shop; TV lounge.
Activities Arts and Crafts; Cards; Games; Prayer groups; Movies; Dances/Social or cultural gatherings.

WILLIAMSPORT

Meadow Heights Nursing Center Inc
200 Short St, Williamsport, IN, 47993 (317) 762-6111
Admin Sara L Freeman. *Medical Dir/Dir of Nursing* Dr Hugo Brenner.
Licensure Intermediate Care. *Beds* 108. *Certified* Medicaid.
Facilities Dining room; Physical therapy room; Activities room; Chapel; Crafts room; Laundry room; Barber/Beauty shop.
Activities Arts and Crafts; Cards; Games; Reading groups; Prayer groups; Movies; Shopping trips; Dances/Social or cultural gatherings.

WINAMAC

Winamac Nursing Home*
515 E 13th St, Winamac, IN, 46996 (219) 946-6143
Admin Benjamin Crandall.
Licensure Intermediate Care. *Beds* 40. *Certified* Medicaid.

WINCHESTER

Randolph Nursing Home Inc*
701 S Oak St, Winchester, IN, 47394 (317) 584-2201
Admin Everett Rickert.
Licensure Intermediate Care. *Beds* 65. *Certified* Medicaid.

WINONA LAKE

Grace Village Health Care Facility
PO Box 337, Winona Lake, IN, 46590 (219) 269-2499
Admin Sherwood V Dunkee. *Medical Dir/Dir of Nursing* Nancy Derry RN.
Licensure Residential Care. *Beds* ICF 33; Residential Care 17.
Admissions Requirements Minimum age 60; Medical examination; Physician's request.
Staff RNs 2 (ft), 4 (pt); LPNs 1 (ft); Nurses aides 11 (ft), 9 (pt); Activities coordinators 1 (ft), 2 (pt); Dietitians 1 (ft).
Affiliation Church of the Brethren
Facilities Dining room; Physical therapy room; Activities room; Chapel; Crafts room; Laundry room; Barber/Beauty shop; Library.
Activities Arts and Crafts; Cards; Games; Reading groups; Prayer groups; Movies; Shopping trips; Dances/Social or cultural gatherings.
Description Facility is located in a residential area; one story multi-complex building on 18 1/2 acres.

ZIONSVILLE

Indiana Christian Retirement Park*
675 S Ford Rd, Zionsville, IN, 46077 (317) 873-5205
Admin William Muller.
Licensure Intermediate Care. *Beds* 43.

IOWA

ACKLEY

Ackley United Presbyterian Home*
1020 2nd Ave, Ackley, IA, 50601 (515)
847-2414
Admin Iva Griep.
Licensure Intermediate Care; Residential Care.
Beds ICF 55; Residential Care 40. *Certified* Medicaid.
Affiliation Presbyterian

ADAIR

Adair Community Health Center Inc*
608 North St, Adair, IA, 50002 (515) 742-3205
Admin Carolyn M Rabel.
Licensure Intermediate Care. *Beds* 48. *Certified* Medicaid.

ADEL

Adel Acres Care Center
1919 Greene St, Adel, IA, 50003 (515)
993-4511
Admin Shirley Clark.
Licensure Intermediate Care. *Beds* 59. *Certified* Medicaid.
Admissions Requirements Medical
examination.
Staff RNs 1 (ft); LPNs 2 (ft), 2 (pt); Nurses
aides 7 (ft), 18 (pt); Activities coordinators 1
(ft); Dietitians 1 (pt).
Facilities Dining room; Laundry room; Barber-
/Beauty shop.
Activities Arts and Crafts; Cards; Games;
Reading groups; Prayer groups; Movies; Shop-
ping trips; Dances/Social or cultural gatherings.
Description Facility has warm, family atmos-
phere.

AFTON

Afton Care Center Inc*
805 W Pearl, Afton, IA, 50830 (515) 347-8416
Admin Mary Cochran.
Licensure Intermediate Care. *Beds* 60.
Certified Medicaid.

AKRON

Akron City Hospital*
276 South St, Akron, IA, 51001 (712) 568-2422
Admin Jerold J Dykstra.
Licensure Intermediate Care. *Beds* 45.

ALBERT CITY

Pleasant View Home
410 S 3rd, Albert City, IA, 50510 (712)
843-2238
Admin Dorothy Nordlund RN.
Licensure Intermediate Care. *Beds* 50. *Certified* Medicaid.
Admissions Requirements Minimum age 18;
Medical examination; Physician's request.
Staff RNs 1 (ft), 5 (pt); LPNs 1 (pt); Nurses
aides 9 (ft), 10 (pt); Physical therapists 1 (pt);
Activities coordinators 1 (ft); Dietitians 1 (pt);
Dentists 1 (pt); Podiatrists 1 (pt); Audiologists 1
(pt).
Facilities Dining room; Activities room; Laun-
dry room; Barber/Beauty shop.
Activities Arts and Crafts; Cards; Games;
Reading groups; Prayer groups; Movies; Dan-
ces/Social or cultural gatherings.
Description Facility offers quality care; rehabilitation therapy under direction of a physical
therapist; excellent food; community involvement; daily activities.

ALBIA

Albia Care Center
116 Benton Ave W, Albia, IA, 52531
Admin Betty James.
Licensure Residential Care. *Beds* 50.
Certified Medicaid.
Ownership Proprietary.
Admissions Requirements Medical examina-
tion; Physician's request.
Staff LPNs 2 (ft); Orderlies 1 (ft); Nurses aides
12 (ft); Recreational therapists 1 (pt); Activities
coordinators 1 (ft); Dietitians.
Facilities Dining room; Activities room; Chap-
el; Crafts room; Laundry room; Barber/Beauty
shop; Library.
Activities Arts and Crafts; Cards; Games;
Reading groups; Prayer groups; Movies; Shop-
ping trips; Dances/Social or cultural gatherings.

Albia Manor
S Florence, Albia, IA, 52531 (515) 932-7105
Admin Connie Byrd.
Licensure Intermediate Care. *Beds* 94. *Certified* Medicaid.
Admissions Requirements Physician's request.
Staff RNs 3 (ft), 2 (pt); LPNs 5 (ft), 2 (pt);
Nurses aides 40 (ft), 15 (pt); Activities coordi-
nators 1 (ft), 1 (pt).
Facilities Dining room; Physical therapy room;
Activities room; Laundry room; Barber/Beauty
shop.
Activities Arts and Crafts; Cards; Games;
Reading groups; Prayer groups; Movies; Shop-
ping trips; Dances/Social or cultural gatherings.

ALGONA

Algona Good Samaritan Center*
214 W Kennedy St, Algona, IA, 50511 (515)
295-2414
Admin Lyman Bailey.
Licensure Intermediate Care. *Beds* 121. *Certified* Medicaid.

ALLISON

Allison Manor Nursing Home*
900 W 7th St, Allison, IA, 50602 (319)
267-2791
Admin Berdina Pulzier.
Licensure Intermediate Care. *Beds* 80. *Certified* Medicaid.

ALTOONA

Altoona Manor Care Center*
200 7th Ave SW, Altoona, IA, 50009 (515)
967-4267
Admin Norman Hjelmeland.
Licensure Intermediate Care. *Beds* 109. *Certified* Medicaid.

AMANA

Colonial Manors of Amana Inc
Box 160, Amana, IA, 52203 (319) 622-3131
Admin BH Otte. *Medical Dir/Dir of Nur-
sing* Dr Stacy Howell.
Licensure Intermediate Care. *Beds* 56.
Certified Medicaid.
Staff Physicians 1 (pt); RNs 1 (ft); LPNs 6 (ft),

3 (pt); Nurses aides 20 (ft), 8 (pt); Physical therapists 1 (pt); Speech therapists 1 (pt); Activities coordinators 1 (ft); Dietitians 1 (pt); Dentists 1 (pt); Podiatrists 1 (pt); Audiologists 1 (pt).
Facilities Dining room; Physical therapy room; Activities room; Chapel; Crafts room; Laundry room; Barber/Beauty shop.
Activities Arts and Crafts; Cards; Games; Reading groups; Prayer groups; Movies; Dances/Social or cultural gatherings.

AMES

Center for Personal Development
1008 Burnett, Ames, IA, 50010
Admin Donna J Ruden. *Medical Dir/Dir of Nursing* Dr Jack Dodd.
Licensure Residential Care.
Ownership Nonprofit.
Admissions Requirements Minimum age 18; Medical examination; Physician's request.
Staff Reality therapists 8 (ft); Activities coordinators 1 (ft).
Facilities Dining room; Activities room; Laundry room.
Activities Arts and Crafts; Cards; Games; Reading groups; Movies; Shopping trips; Dances/Social or cultural gatherings.
Description The center operates a residential care facility for adults who need assistance in becoming emotionally and economically self-sufficient; offers alternative and supplemental services; major goal is to help residents gain the awareness, self-knowledge, confidence, and skills which will enable them to function independently at a level which is both satisfying and enjoyable.

North Grand Care Center
3440 Grand Ave, Ames, IA, 50010 (515) 232-3426
Licensure Intermediate Care. *Beds* 100. *Certified* Medicaid.
Admissions Requirements Medical examination.
Staff RNs 5 (ft), 2 (pt); LPNs 3 (ft), 2 (pt); Orderlies 1 (ft); Nurses aides 25 (ft), 15 (pt); Physical therapists 1 (ft), 1 (pt); Reality therapists 1 (pt); Recreational therapists 1 (ft), 1 (pt); Occupational therapists 1 (pt); Speech therapists 1 (pt); Activities coordinators 1 (ft); Dietitians 11 (ft); Podiatrists 1 (pt); Audiologists 1 (pt).
Facilities Dining room; Physical therapy room; Activities room; Chapel; Crafts room; Laundry room; Barber/Beauty shop; Library; TV lounges.
Activities Arts and Crafts; Cards; Games; Reading groups; Prayer groups; Movies; Shopping trips; Dances/Social or cultural gatherings; Individualized activities.
Description Facility features people that care about the residents life and welfare, food that is unrivaled, outstanding rehabilitation program, individualized activities, 24-hour professional nursing care, and located in a progressive and experienced health care community.

Northcrest Health Care Center*
1801 20th St, Ames, IA, 50010 (515) 232-6760
Admin Larry L Allen.

Licensure Intermediate Care; Residential Care. *Beds* ICF 18; Residential Care 10. *Certified* Medicaid.

Riverside Manor*
1204 S 4th, Ames, IA, 50010 (515) 233-2903
Admin Lee V Livingston.
Licensure Intermediate Care. *Beds* 59. *Certified* Medicaid.

ANAMOSA

Anamosa Care Center
1209 E 3rd St, Anamosa, IA, 52205 (319) 462-4356
Licensure Intermediate Care. *Beds* 76. *Certified* Medicaid.

ANITA

Colonial Manor*
1000 Hillcrest Dr, Anita, IA, 50020 (712) 762-3219
Admin Brenda Euken.
Licensure Intermediate Care. *Beds* 65. *Certified* Medicaid.

ANKENY

Sunny View Care Center*
410 NW Ash Dr, Ankeny, IA, 50021 (515) 964-1101
Admin Bonnie Ballard.
Licensure Intermediate Care. *Beds* 74. *Certified* Medicaid.

APLINGTON

Maple Manor Nursing Home
345 Parrott, Aplington, IA, 50604 (319) 347-2309
Licensure Intermediate Care; Residential Care. *Beds* ICF 38; Residential Care 20. *Certified* Medicaid.
Admissions Requirements Medical examination.
Staff RNs 1 (pt); LPNs 4 (pt); Nurses aides 23 (pt); Physical therapists 1 (pt); Occupational therapists 1 (pt); Activities coordinators 2 (pt); Dietitians 1 (pt).
Facilities Dining room; Physical therapy room; Activities room; Laundry room; Barber/Beauty shop.
Activities Arts and Crafts; Cards; Games; Reading groups; Prayer groups; Movies; Shopping trips.

ARMSTRONG

Valley Vue Nursing Home*
2nd Ave, Armstrong, IA, 50514 (712) 864-3567
Admin Mary Tirevold.
Licensure Intermediate Care. *Beds* 50. *Certified* Medicaid.

ATLANTIC

Atlantic Care Center
1311 Sunnyside Ln, Atlantic, IA, 50022 (712) 243-3952
Medical Dir/Dir of Nursing Dr Keith Swanson.
Licensure Intermediate Care. *Beds* 123. *Certified* Medicaid.
Staff RNs 1 (ft); LPNs 8 (ft), 3 (pt); Nurses aides 18 (ft), 18 (pt); Physical therapists 1 (pt); Speech therapists 1 (pt); Activities coordinators 1 (ft), 1 (pt); Dietitians 1 (pt); Dentists 1 (pt); Ophthalmologists 1 (pt); Podiatrists 1 (pt); Audiologists 1 (pt).

Heritage House
1200 Brookridge Circle, Atlantic, IA, 50022 (712) 243-1850
Admin M Marie Harris.
Licensure Intermediate Care; Residential Care. *Beds* ICF 46; Residential Care 15. *Certified* Medicaid.
Staff RNs 1 (ft); LPNs 3 (ft), 6 (pt); Nurses aides 20 (ft), 9 (pt); Physical therapists 1 (ft); Activities coordinators 1 (ft); Dietitians 1 (pt).
Affiliation Methodist
Facilities Dining room; Physical therapy room; Activities room; Chapel; Crafts room; Laundry room; Barber/Beauty shop; Library.
Activities Arts and Crafts; Cards; Games; Reading groups; Prayer groups; Movies; Shopping trips; Dances/Social or cultural gatherings.
Description Facility features 4 levels of care; residents may progress up or down as health changes. Community organizations often meet here, keeping residents in touch; schools and churches bring musical groups to perform for residents; many activities planned by residents and their families.

AUDUBON

Friendship Home
714 N Division St, Audubon, IA, 50025 (712) 563-2651
Licensure Intermediate Care; Residential Care. *Beds* ICF 64; Residential Care 86. *Certified* Medicaid.
Admissions Requirements Medical examination.
Staff RNs 5 (ft), 4 (pt); LPNs 2 (ft), 4 (pt); Nurses aides 20 (ft), 20 (pt); Recreational therapists 1 (ft), 1 (pt).
Facilities Dining room; Physical therapy room; Activities room; Chapel; Crafts room; Laundry room; Barber/Beauty shop; Library; Social room; 3 large lounges.
Activities Arts and Crafts; Cards; Games; Reading groups; Prayer groups; Movies; Shopping trips; Dances/Social or cultural gatherings; Dining out; Visiting other homes; Morning devotions; Sunday workshop.
Description The Friendship Home offers a high level of staffing and excellent care in a cheerful setting at a low rate (one of the lowest in Iowa).

AURELIA

Sunset Knoll Inc
5th & Spruce, Aurelia, IA, 51005 (712) 434-2294

Admin O L Nelson. *Medical Dir/Dir of Nursing* Dr Richard Berge.
Licensure Intermediate Care; Residential Care. *Beds* ICF 48; Residential Care 20. *Certified* Medicaid.
Admissions Requirements Minimum age 50; Medical examination; Physician's request.
Staff RNs 2 (ft); Orderlies 3 (ft), 2 (pt); Nurses aides 19 (ft), 7 (pt); Physical therapists; Occupational therapists; Activities coordinators 2 (pt); Dietitians; Dentists; Podiatrists; Audiologists.
Facilities Dining room; Physical therapy room; Activities room; Chapel; Crafts room; Laundry room; Barber/Beauty shop.
Activities Arts and Crafts; Cards; Games; Reading groups; Prayer groups; Movies; Dances/Social or cultural gatherings.

AVOCA

Colonial Manors of Avoca
1100 Chestnut St, Avoca, IA, 51521 (712) 343-2665
Licensure Intermediate Care. *Beds* 46. *Certified* Medicaid.
Staff RNs 2 (ft); LPNs 4 (ft); Nurses aides 18 (ft); Activities coordinators 1 (ft); Dietitians 1 (ft).
Facilities Dining room; Laundry room.

BANCROFT

Heritage Home of Bancroft*
E Ramsey, Bancroft, IA, 50517 (515) 885-2463
Admin Jeanne M Kinney.
Licensure Intermediate Care. *Beds* 39. *Certified* Medicaid.

BATTLE CREEK

Willowdale Care Center
Hwy 175, Battle Creek, IA, 51006 (712) 365-4332
Admin Robert C Fortier.
Licensure Intermediate Care. *Beds* 61. *Certified* Medicaid.
Admissions Requirements Physician's request.
Staff RNs 2 (ft), 3 (pt); LPNs 1 (ft), 2 (pt); Nurses aides 14 (ft), 10 (pt); Physical therapists 1 (pt); Activities coordinators 1 (ft), 1 (pt); Dietitians 1 (pt).
Facilities Dining room; Physical therapy room; Activities room; Laundry room.
Activities Cards; Games; Movies; News presentations; Resident council.
Description Facility is located in a quiet, small town.

BAXTER

Colonial Manor*
PO Box 388, Baxter, IA, 50028 (515) 227-3602
Admin Glen Van Zante.
Licensure Intermediate Care. *Beds* 65. *Certified* Medicaid.

BAYARD

Bayard Care Center*
2nd Ave, Bayard, IA, 50029 (712) 651-2085
Admin Helen Andersen.
Licensure Intermediate Care. *Beds* 50. *Certified* Medicaid.

BEDFORD

Bedford Manor*
1005 W Pearl, Bedford, IA, 50833 (712) 523-2161
Admin Steven Fister.
Licensure Intermediate Care. *Beds* 64. *Certified* Medicaid.

BELLE PLAINE

Beverly Manor*
1505 Sunset Dr, Belle Plaine, IA, 52208 (319) 444-2500
Admin Geneva M Schutte.
Licensure Intermediate Care. *Beds* 70. *Certified* Medicaid.

BELLEVUE

Mill Valley Care Center
1201 Park St, Bellevue, IA, 52031 (319) 872-5521
Admin Joseph H Mazur.
Licensure Intermediate Care. *Beds* 68. *Certified* Medicaid.
Admissions Requirements Medical examination; Physician's request.
Staff RNs 1 (ft), 3 (pt); LPNs 3 (ft), 1 (pt); Nurses aides 9 (ft), 10 (pt); Activities coordinators 1 (ft); Dietitians 11 (pt).
Facilities Dining room; Physical therapy room; Activities room; Chapel; Crafts room; Laundry room; Barber/Beauty shop.
Activities Arts and Crafts; Cards; Games; Reading groups; Prayer groups; Movies; Shopping trips; Dances/Social or cultural gatherings.
Description The Mill Valley Care Center recently opened a new 17-bed addition.

BELMOND

Belmond Nursing Home*
1107 7th St NE, Belmond, IA, 50421 (515) 444-3195
Admin Opal M Ellingston.
Licensure Intermediate Care. *Beds* 86. *Certified* Medicaid.

BETTENDORF

Bettendorf Health Care Center*
2730 Crow Creek Rd, Bettendorf, IA, 52722 (319) 359-7463
Admin Steven Dowd.
Licensure Intermediate Care. *Beds* 100. *Certified* Medicaid.

Iowa Masonic Nursing Home
26th and State Sts, Bettendorf, IA, 52722 (319) 359-9171

Admin W Ross McCulla.
Licensure Intermediate Care. *Beds* 79. *Certified* Medicaid.
Admissions Requirements Minimum age 21; Medical examination; Physician's request.
Staff Physicians 1 (pt); RNs 3 (ft), 3 (pt); LPNs 3 (ft), 3 (pt); Nurses aides 20 (ft), 10 (pt); Physical therapists 1 (pt); Reality therapists 1 (pt); Occupational therapists 1 (pt); Speech therapists 1 (pt); Activities coordinators 2 (ft), 1 (pt); Dietitians 1 (pt); Dentists 1 (pt); Ophthalmologists 1 (pt); Podiatrists 1 (pt); Audiologists 1 (pt).
Affiliation Masons
Facilities Dining room; Physical therapy room; Activities room; Chapel; Crafts room; Laundry room; Barber/Beauty shop; Library; Game room.
Activities Arts and Crafts; Cards; Games; Reading groups; Prayer groups; Movies; Shopping trips; Dances/Social or cultural gatherings.
Description Facility sits on 22 acres on a hill overlooking the Mississippi River.

BLOOMFIELD

Bloomfield Manor Nursing Home*
800 N Davis St, Bloomfield, IA, 52537 (515) 664-2699
Admin Janet Schwieger.
Licensure Intermediate Care. *Beds* 104. *Certified* Medicaid.

BOONE

Eastern Star Masonic Home*
715 Mamie Eisenhower Ave, Boone, IA, 50036 (515) 432-5274
Admin Dennis Bock.
Licensure Intermediate Care; Residential Care. *Beds* ICF 50; Residential Care 98. *Certified* Medicaid.
Affiliation Order of Eastern Star

Evangelical Free Church Home*
112 W 4th St, Boone, IA, 50036 (515) 432-1393
Admin Ernest J Vick.
Licensure Intermediate Care. *Beds* 120. *Certified* Medicaid.
Affiliation Evangelical Free Church

Ledges Manor Corporation*
1400 22nd St, Boone, IA, 50036 (515) 432-5580
Admin Joe C Johnson.
Licensure Intermediate Care. *Beds* 94. *Certified* Medicaid.
Admissions Requirements Minimum age 18.
Staff RNs 2 (ft); LPNs 4 (ft), 3 (pt); Orderlies 1 (ft); Physical therapists 20 (ft), 14 (pt); Activities coordinators 1 (ft), 1 (pt).
Facilities Dining room; Activities room; Crafts room; Laundry room; Barber/Beauty shop.
Activities Arts and Crafts; Cards; Games; Reading groups; Prayer groups; Movies; Shopping trips.

BRITT

Westview Manor*
445 8th Ave SW, Britt, IA, 50423 (515) 843-3835

Admin Becky L Smit.
Licensure Intermediate Care. *Beds* 59. *Certified* Medicaid.

BROOKLYN

Brookhaven Nursing Home*
406 North St, Brooklyn, IA, 52211 (515) 522-9263
Admin Patricia Hilligas.
Licensure Intermediate Care. *Beds* 45. *Certified* Medicaid.

BUFFALO CENTER

Timely Mission Nursing Home*
109 Mission Dr, Buffalo Center, IA, 50424 (515) 562-2494
Admin Murray D Berggren.
Licensure Intermediate Care. *Beds* 51. *Certified* Medicaid.

BURLINGTON

Burlington Care Center
2610 S 5th St, Burlington, IA, 52601 (319) 753-2841
Admin Robert Richard.
Licensure Intermediate Care. *Beds* 101. *Certified* Medicaid.
Admissions Requirements Minimum age 18; Medical examination; Physician's request.
Staff RNs 2 (ft), 1 (pt); LPNs 4 (ft), 5 (pt); Nurses aides 22 (ft), 18 (pt); Physical therapists 1 (pt); Occupational therapists 1 (pt); Speech therapists 1 (pt); Activities coordinators 2 (ft); Dietitians 1 (pt); Dentists 1 (pt); Podiatrists 1 (pt); Audiologists 1 (pt).
Facilities Dining room; Physical therapy room; Activities room; Chapel; Laundry room; Barber/Beauty shop.
Activities Arts and Crafts; Cards; Games; Reading groups; Prayer groups; Movies; Shopping trips; Dances/Social or cultural gatherings.
Description Burlington Care Center is located between 2 beautiful parks. Car rides are a part of every nice day activity.

Burlington Medical Center*
602 N 3rd St, Burlington, IA, 52601 (319) 753-3011
Admin Heagle Glenn.
Licensure Skilled Care. *Beds* 16.
Ownership Public.

Elm View Care Center*
715 Shoquoquon Dr, Burlington, IA, 52601 (319) 752-4525
Admin Ronald Osby.
Licensure Intermediate Care. *Beds* 146. *Certified* Medicaid.

Saint Francis Continuation Center*
210 S 5th St, Burlington, IA, 52601 (319) 752-4564
Admin Sr M Jean Mill Meyer.
Licensure Skilled Care; Intermediate Care. *Beds* SNF 29; ICF 59. *Certified* Medicaid; Medicare.
Ownership Nonprofit.
Affiliation Roman Catholic

CARLISLE

Carlisle Care Center
680 Cole St, Carlisle, IA, 50047 (515) 989-0871
Licensure Intermediate Care; Residential Care. *Beds* ICF 68; Residential Care 33. *Certified* Medicaid.
Admissions Requirements Medical examination.
Staff RNs 1 (ft), 2 (pt); LPNs 3 (ft), 1 (pt); Orderlies 2 (ft); Nurses aides 18 (ft), 14 (pt); Activities coordinators 1 (ft), 1 (pt); Dietitians 1 (pt).
Facilities Dining room; Physical therapy room; Activities room; Laundry room; Barber/Beauty shop.
Activities Arts and Crafts; Games; Reading groups; Prayer groups; Movies; Shopping trips; Dances/Social or cultural gatherings.

CARROLL

Carroll Health Center*
2241 N West St, Carroll, IA, 51401 (712) 792-9284
Admin Edna Schluter.
Licensure Intermediate Care; Residential Care. *Beds* ICF 96; Residential Care 41. *Certified* Medicaid.

Carroll Manor*
500 Valley Dr, Carroll, IA, 51401 (712) 792-9281
Admin Lyle Hight.
Licensure Intermediate Care. *Beds* 51. *Certified* Medicaid.

New Hope Village Inc*
E 18th St, Carroll, IA, 51401 (712) 792-5500
Admin Frank Hermsen.
Licensure Intermediate Care for Mentally Retarded; Residential MR Care. *Beds* ICF/MR 32; Residential MR Care 72.

Saint Anthony Nursing Home
406 E Anthony St, Carroll, IA, 50058
Admin Robert Blincow.
Licensure Intermediate Care. *Beds* 80. *Certified* Medicaid.
Ownership Nonprofit.
Staff RNs 2 (ft), 2 (pt); LPNs 3 (ft), 4 (pt); Nurses aides 15 (ft), 12 (pt); Recreational therapists 1 (pt); Speech therapists; Activities coordinators 1 (ft); Dietitians 1 (ft); Dentists; Ophthalmologists; Podiatrists; Audiologists.
Affiliation Roman Catholic
Facilities Dining room; Physical therapy room; Activities room; Chapel; Crafts room; Laundry room; Barber/Beauty shop.
Activities Arts and Crafts; Cards; Games; Reading groups; Prayer groups; Movies; Shopping trips; Dances/Social or cultural gatherings.
Description Facility is an attached long-term unit of Saint Anthony Regional Hospital, which allows for easy access of hospital services such as lab, X-ray, physical therapy, emergency room, and other shared services.

CASCADE

Shady Rest Care Center
Johnson St NW, Cascade, IA, 52033 (319) 852-3277
Medical Dir/Dir of Nursing William J Mehrl.
Licensure Intermediate Care. *Beds* 50. *Certified* Medicaid.
Staff RNs 1 (ft), 4 (pt); LPNs 3 (pt); Nurses aides 4 (ft), 16 (pt); Activities coordinators 1 (ft); Dietitians 1 (pt).
Facilities Dining room; Physical therapy room; Activities room; Laundry room.
Activities Arts and Crafts; Cards; Games; Reading groups; Prayer groups; Movies; Dances/Social or cultural gatherings.

CEDAR FALLS

Cedar Falls Health Care Center*
1728 W 8th St, Cedar Falls, IA, 50613 (319) 277-2437
Admin Paul R Huffman.
Licensure Intermediate Care. *Beds* 100. *Certified* Medicaid.

Cedar Falls Lutheran Home*
7511 University Ave, Cedar Falls, IA, 50613 (319) 268-0401
Admin Karen Habenicht.
Licensure Intermediate Care; Residential Care. *Beds* ICF 103; Residential Care 81. *Certified* Medicaid.
Ownership Nonprofit.
Affiliation Lutheran

Western Home
420 11th St, Cedar Falls, IA, 50613 (319) 277-2141
Medical Dir/Dir of Nursing Dr Richard Frankhauser.
Licensure Intermediate Care; Residential Care. *Beds* ICF 68; Residential Care 76. *Certified* Medicaid.
Admissions Requirements Minimum age 60; Medical examination; Physician's request.
Staff RNs 2 (ft), 1 (pt); LPNs 6 (ft), 4 (pt); Orderlies 1 (ft); Nurses aides 19 (ft), 13 (pt); Activities coordinators 1 (ft); Dietitians 1 (ft); Social workers; activity assistants.
Affiliation Methodist
Facilities Dining room; Physical therapy room; Chapel; Crafts room; Laundry room; Barber/Beauty shop; Library; Large room with kitchen for family gatherings.
Activities Arts and Crafts; Cards; Games; Reading groups; Prayer groups; Movies; Shopping trips; Dances/Social or cultural gatherings; Special trips.
Description Home is a continuing care community that administers to the needs of the elderly; retirement residents live independently and are furnished 3 meals daily, weekly housekeeping, laundry services, and emergency nursing care; as their level of needs progress, further assistance is provided at the RCF and ICF levels of care.

Windsor Care Center
2305 Crescent Dr, Cedar Falls, IA, 50613 (319) 268-0489
Licensure Intermediate Care. *Beds* 100. *Certi-*

fied Medicaid.
Admissions Requirements Medical examination.
Staff RNs 1 (ft), 3 (pt); LPNs 4 (ft), 6 (pt); Orderlies 1 (ft), 1 (pt); Nurses aides 20 (ft), 15 (pt); Activities coordinators 1 (ft), 1 (pt); Dietitians 1 (ft).
Facilities Dining room; Physical therapy room; Activities room; Laundry room; Barber/Beauty shop.
Activities Arts and Crafts; Cards; Games; Reading groups; Prayer groups; Movies; Shopping trips; Dances/Social or cultural gatherings.
Description Facility is fully air-conditioned, adjacent to Thunderidge Shopping Mall.

CEDAR RAPIDS

Americana Healthcare Center*
1940 1st Ave NE, Cedar Rapids, IA, 52402 (319) 364-5151
Admin Jessie Diers.
Licensure Skilled Care. *Beds* 79. *Certified* Medicaid; Medicare.

Cedar Rapids Care Center
1220 5th Ave SE, Cedar Rapids, IA, 52403 (319) 366-8701
Licensure Intermediate Care; Intermediate Care for Mentally Retarded. *Beds* ICF 92; ICF/MR 26. *Certified* Medicaid.
Staff RNs 3 (ft); LPNs 3 (ft), 5 (pt); Orderlies 4 (ft); Nurses aides 12 (ft), 30 (pt); Occupational therapists 1 (pt); Speech therapists 1 (pt); Activities coordinators 1 (ft); Dietitians 1 (pt).
Facilities Dining room; Physical therapy room; Activities room; Barber/Beauty shop.
Activities Arts and Crafts; Cards; Games; Reading groups; Prayer groups; Movies; Shopping trips; Dances/Social or cultural gatherings.

Colbert Place
1312 1st Ave NW, Cedar Rapids, IA, 52405
Admin Cherie Clark.
Licensure Residental Care for Mentally Retarded.
Admissions Requirements Minimum age 18; Medical examination.
Staff Nurses aides 5 (pt); Activities coordinators 1 (ft).
Facilities Dining room; Activities room; Laundry room.
Activities Arts and Crafts; Cards; Games; Movies; Shopping trips; Dances/Social or cultural gatherings; Community outings.
Description Facility offers its residents skill development in socialization, personal grooming, housekeeping, cooking, laundry/clothing, money management, and recreation based on the needs of the individual.

Heritage Acres Care Center
200 Clive Dr SW, Cedar Rapids, IA, 52404 (319) 396-7171
Licensure Intermediate Care. *Beds* 201. *Certified* Medicaid.
Admissions Requirements Minimum age 55; Medical examination; Physician's request.
Staff RNs 3 (ft), 2 (pt); LPNs 10 (ft), 5 (pt); Orderlies 5 (ft), 2 (pt); Nurses aides 37 (ft), 17 (pt); Physical therapists; Occupational therapists; Speech therapists; Activities coordinators

3 (ft), 1 (pt); Dietitians; Dentists; Ophthalmologists; Podiatrists; Audiologists.
Facilities Dining room; Physical therapy room; Activities room; Barber/Beauty shop.
Activities Arts and Crafts; Cards; Games; Reading groups; Prayer groups; Movies; Shopping trips; Dances/Social or cultural gatherings.

Mercy Hospital*
701 10th St SE, Cedar Rapids, IA, 53403 (319) 398-6133
Admin A J Tinker.
Licensure Skilled Care. *Beds* 29.

Meth-Wick Manor
1224 13th St NW, Cedar Rapids, IA, 52405 (319) 365-9171
Medical Dir/Dir of Nursing Dr Joseph Galles.
Licensure Intermediate Care; Residential Care. *Beds* ICF 49; Residential Care 16. *Certified* Medicaid.
Admissions Requirements Minimum age 55; Medical examination.
Staff Physicians 1 (pt); RNs 1 (ft), 5 (pt); LPNs 6 (pt); Nurses aides 16 (ft), 11 (pt); Physical therapists 1 (pt); Occupational therapists 1 (pt); Speech therapists 1 (pt); Activities coordinators 1 (ft); Dietitians 1 (ft); Dentists 1 (pt); Podiatrists 1 (pt); Audiologists 1 (pt).
Affiliation Methodist
Facilities Dining room; Physical therapy room; Activities room; Chapel; Crafts room; Laundry room; Barber/Beauty shop; Library; Gift shop; Exercise room; Kitchen; Snack room; Patio; Garages; Numerous lounges..
Activities Arts and Crafts; Games; Prayer groups; Movies; Shopping trips; Dances/Social or cultural gatherings; Dining out; Exercise class; Weight control groups; Resident assemblies; Bake sales; Bazaars; Garage sales.
Description Meth-Wick Manor is located on 24-acre grounds overlooking the city of Cedar Rapids; outdoor patio features 2 shuffleboard courts, barbecue grill, and many private gardening plots. Meals are served in a gracious dining room; housekeeping, laundry, and maintenance are provided, while a health center is available for short- and long-term illnesses. Adult day services are also provided within the facility.

Northbrook Manor Care Center*
6420 Council St NE, Cedar Rapids, IA, 52402 (319) 393-1447
Admin Janice M Tague.
Licensure Intermediate Care. *Beds* 102. *Certified* Medicaid.

Saint Luke's Methodist Hospital*
1026 S Ave NE, Cedar Rapids, IA, 52402 (319) 369-7211
Admin Samuel T Wallace.
Licensure Skilled Care. *Beds* 12.
Affiliation Methodist

CENTERVILLE

Centerville Care Center Inc*
Box 447, 1208 Cross, Centerville, IA, 52544 (515) 856-8651

Admin Arthur W Schuttinga.
Licensure Intermediate Care. *Beds* 69. *Certified* Medicaid.

Golden Age Manor Inc*
1915 S 18th, Centerville, IA, 52544 (515) 856-2757
Admin Robert E Sacco.
Licensure Intermediate Care. *Beds* 100. *Certified* Medicaid.

Profitts Boarding Home*
615 W Washington, Centerville, IA, 52544 (319) 5856-8344
Admin Mary C Profitt.
Licensure Intermediate Care for Mentally Retarded. *Beds* 10.

CHARITON

Chariton Group Home
603 Court, Chariton, IA, 50049
Admin Alan Marshall.
Licensure Residential Care for Mentally Retarded. *Certified* Medicaid.
Ownership Nonprofit.
Admissions Requirements Minimum age 18; Males only; Medical examination; Physician's request.
Facilities Dining room; Activities room; Laundry room.
Activities Arts and Crafts; Games; Movies; Shopping trips; Dances/Social or cultural gatherings.
Description Facility provides a bridge between living in an institution and independent living; individuals are trained in several skills needed for survival in the real world—cooking, grooming, social, economic, and domestic life skills.

Chariton Manor*
N 7th St, Chariton, IA, 50049 (515) 774-5921
Admin Stanley Vanderwoude.
Licensure Intermediate Care. *Beds* 130. *Certified* Medicaid.

Remington Boarding Home
119 S 8th, Chariton, IA, 50049
Admin Ann L Remington.
Licensure Residential Care. *Beds* 10.
Ownership Proprietary.
Admissions Requirements Minimum age 19; Males only
Facilities Dining room.
Activities Cards; Games.
Description All residents must be able to be up and climb stairs; medicine is given, meals and laundry provided, and residents supervised; facility is one block from center of town.

CHARLES CITY

Chautauqua Avenue Guest Home 1*
120 Chautauqua Ave, Charles City, IA, 50616 (515) 228-6512
Admin David F Ayers.
Licensure Intermediate Care. *Beds* 84. *Certified* Medicaid.

Chautauqua Guest Home 2
602 11th St, Charles City, IA, 50616 (515)
228-2353
Medical Dir/Dir of Nursing D L Trefz MD.
Licensure Skilled Care. *Beds* 75. *Certified* Medicaid; Medicare.
Admissions Requirements Minimum age 16;
Medical examination; Physician's request.
Staff RNs 3 (ft), 1 (pt); LPNs 1 (ft), 3 (pt);
Nurses aides 11 (ft), 20 (pt); Activities coordinators 1 (ft), 1 (pt).
Facilities Dining room; Physical therapy room;
Activities room; Crafts room; Laundry room;
Barber/Beauty shop.
Activities Arts and Crafts; Cards; Games;
Reading groups; Prayer groups; Movies.
Description Facility is a member of the American and Iowa Health Care Associations. Also, the facility sponsors an annual scholarship for young aduts who plan to enter the health care field.

Chautauqua Guest Home 3*
302 9th St, Charles City, IA, 50616 (515)
228-5351
Admin Lyle H Koehler.
Licensure Intermediate Care. *Beds* 74. *Certified* Medicaid.

Comprehensive Systems Inc
1700 Clark St, Charles City, IA, 50616 (515)
228-4842
Medical Dir/Dir of Nursing Jane Quade.
Licensure Intermediate Care for Mentally Retarded. *Beds* 9.
Admissions Requirements Medical examination.
Staff LPNs 1 (ft); Orderlies 3 (pt); Nurses aides 8 (pt); Activities coordinators 1 (ft); Dietitians 1 (ft), 1 (pt).
Facilities Dining room; Physical therapy room;
Laundry room.
Activities Arts and Crafts; Games; Prayer groups; Movies; Shopping trips; Dances/Social or cultural gatherings.
Description Facility is very exceptional in that the size of the cottage and the close interaction of staff/resident contact offers a home-like atmosphere. The intense programs in domestic domain, community interaction, and behavioral/social domain are well taken care of for the residents; exceptional nursing care is offered.

Salsbury Baptist Home
807 5th St, Charles City, IA, 50616 (515)
228-1612
Admin John W Lusk.
Licensure Intermediate Care; Residential Care.
Beds ICF 51; Residential Care 39. *Certified* Medicaid.
Admissions Requirements Minimum age 55;
Medical examination; Physician's request.
Staff RNs 2 (ft), 2 (pt); LPNs 2 (ft), 2 (pt);
Orderlies 1 (ft), 2 (pt); Nurses aides 20 (ft), 15 (pt); Activities coordinators 1 (ft), 1 (pt); Dietitians 1 (pt).
Affiliation Baptist
Facilities Dining room; Physical therapy room;
Activities room; Chapel; Crafts room; Laundry room; Barber/Beauty shop; Library.
Activities Arts and Crafts; Cards; Games;
Reading groups; Prayer groups; Movies; Shopping trips; Reading program for school children.
Description This is a nicely furnished facility with cozy carpeted rooms in the residential section; open meal times to allow more leisure and relaxation for residents.

CHEROKEE

Cherokee Villa
1011 Roosevelt, Cherokee, IA, 51012 (712)
225-5180
Admin Ailene Shade.
Licensure Intermediate Care. *Beds* 72. *Certified* Medicaid.
Admissions Requirements Medical examination; Physician's request.
Staff RNs 1 (ft); LPNs 1 (ft); Nurses aides 1 (ft); Physical therapists 1 (pt); Occupational therapists 1 (pt); Speech therapists 1 (pt);
Activities coordinators 1 (ft); Dietitians 1 (pt).
Facilities Dining room; Physical therapy room;
Activities room; Chapel; Crafts room; Laundry room; Barber/Beauty shop.
Activities Arts and Crafts; Cards; Games;
Reading groups; Prayer groups; Movies; Shopping trips.

Country Side Estates
921 Riverview Rd, Cherokee, IA, 51012 (712)
225-5724
Licensure Intermediate Care. *Beds* 102. *Certified* Medicaid.
Admissions Requirements Medical examination.
Staff RNs 3 (ft); LPNs 5 (ft), 3 (pt); Orderlies 1 (ft); Nurses aides 25 (ft), 10 (pt); Physical therapists 1 (pt); Recreational therapists 1 (pt);
Occupational therapists 1 (pt); Speech therapists 1 (pt); Activities coordinators 1 (ft), 1 (pt);
Dietitians 1 (ft); Dentists 1 (pt); Podiatrists 1 (pt); Audiologists 1 (pt).
Facilities Dining room; Physical therapy room;
Activities room; Chapel; Crafts room; Laundry room; Barber/Beauty shop.
Activities Arts and Crafts; Cards; Games;
Reading groups; Prayer groups; Movies;
Humanities class.
Description We pride ourselves on quality care because we care. We have a 102-bed ICF facility, with 24-hour nursing service. Tender loving care prevails; our priorities are comfort, dignity, and love.

Hilltop Care Center
725 N 2nd St, Cherokee, IA, 51012 (712)
225-2561
Admin Robert C Fortier.
Licensure Intermediate Care. *Beds* 48. *Certified* Medicaid.
Admissions Requirements Physician's request.
Staff RNs 1 (ft), 1 (pt); LPNs 2 (ft), 2 (pt);
Activities coordinators 1 (ft), 1 (pt).
Facilities Dining room; Activities room; Laundry room.
Activities Arts and Crafts; Cards; Games; Prayer groups; Movies; Shopping trips.

CLARENCE

Clarence Nursing Home*
2nd & Smith, Clarence, IA, 52216 (319)
452-3262
Admin Joy D Mote.
Licensure Intermediate Care. *Beds* 46. *Certified* Medicaid.

CLARINDA

Bethesda Care Center*
600 Manor Dr, Clarinda, IA, 51632 (712)
542-5161
Admin Seth H Grafft.
Licensure Intermediate Care. *Beds* 117. *Certified* Medicaid.

Goldenrod Manor Care Center*
225 W Laperla Dr, Clarinda, IA, 51632 (712)
542-5621
Admin Marge Spry.
Licensure Intermediate Care. *Beds* 51. *Certified* Medicaid.

CLARION

Clarion Care Center
110 3rd Ave SW, Clarion, IA, 505235 (515)
532-2893
Admin Wayne Matthes.
Licensure Intermediate Care; Residential Care.
Beds ICF 72; Residential Care 21. *Certified* Medicaid.
Admissions Requirements Minimum age 16;
Medical examination; Physician's request.
Staff RNs 1 (ft), 5 (pt); LPNs 1 (ft), 4 (pt);
Orderlies 2 (ft); Nurses aides 13 (ft), 8 (pt);
Physical therapists 1 (pt); Occupational therapists 1 (pt); Speech therapists 1 (pt); Activities coordinators 1 (ft), 1 (pt); Dietitians 1 (pt);
Audiologists 1 (pt).
Facilities Dining room; Physical therapy room;
Activities room; Chapel; Laundry room; Barber/Beauty shop.
Activities Arts and Crafts; Cards; Games;
Reading groups; Prayer groups; Movies; Shopping trips; Dances/Social or cultural gatherings.
Description The beautiful 7-year new, single-level addition nestles between the community health center and clinic and senior citizen retirement apartments. Facility has an excellent record of residents returned to society, while less fortunate members have resided here for long periods of time, some since 1968.

CLARKSVILLE

Community Nursing Home Inc
115 N Hilton, Clarksville, IA, 50619 (319)
278-4900
Medical Dir/Dir of Nursing Dr James Rathe.
Licensure Intermediate Care; Residential Care.
Beds ICF 49; Residential Care 13. *Certified* Medicaid.
Admissions Requirements Minimum age 16;
Medical examination; Physician's request.
Staff RNs 1 (ft); LPNs 2 (ft), 3 (pt); Nurses aides 11 (ft), 9 (pt); Physical therapists 1 (pt);
Activities coordinators 1 (ft), 1 (pt); Dietitians 1 (pt); 1 (pt) Social worker.

Facilities Dining room; Physical therapy room; Activities room; Chapel; Crafts room; Laundry room; Barber/Beauty shop; Library.
Activities Arts and Crafts; Cards; Games; Reading groups; Prayer groups; Movies; Shopping trips; Dances/Social or cultural gatherings.
Description Community owned, community oriented facility located in a beautiful, wooded, residential setting; active auxilary and volunteers; quality care at reasonable rates.

CLEAR LAKE

Oakwood Manor Corporation*
400 Hwy 18 W, Clear Lake, IA, 50428 (515) 357-5244
Admin Paul G Klus.
Licensure Intermediate Care. *Beds* 89. *Certified* Medicaid.

CLEARFIELD

Clearview Home
Box 174, Clearfield, IA, 50840 (515) 336-2333
Admin Joe Ponth. *Medical Dir/Dir of Nursing* Vicky Leonard.
Licensure Intermediate Care. *Beds* 36. *Certified* Medicaid.
Staff Physicians 3 (pt); RNs 1 (ft); LPNs 2 (ft), 2 (pt); Nurses aides 10 (ft), 5 (pt); Physical therapists 1 (pt); Reality therapists 1 (pt); Occupational therapists 1 (pt); Activities coordinators 1 (ft); Dietitians 1 (pt); Dentists 1 (pt); Audiologists 1 (pt); 1 (pt) Pharmacist.
Facilities Dining room; Activities room; Laundry room; Barber/Beauty shop; Library.
Activities Arts and Crafts; Cards; Games; Reading groups; Prayer groups; Movies; Shopping trips; Dances/Social or cultural gatherings.
Description With an outstanding home-like atmosphere, facility is located in a rural area where staff and residents are usually friends and neighbors; small enough in size to give the residents the type of personalized care necessary for their compfort.

CLINTON

Alverno Health Care Facility
849 13th Ave N, Clinton, IA, 52732 (319) 242-1521
Admin Sr Ruth Cox.
Licensure Intermediate Care. *Beds* 136. *Certified* Medicaid.
Admissions Requirements Minimum age 60; Medical examination; Physician's request.
Staff RNs 9 (ft), 8 (pt); LPNs 4 (pt); Nurses aides 30 (ft), 8 (pt); Activities coordinators 1 (ft); Dietitians 1 (ft).
Affiliation Roman Catholic
Facilities Dining room; Physical therapy room; Activities room; Chapel; Crafts room; Laundry room; Barber/Beauty shop.
Activities Arts and Crafts; Cards; Games; Reading groups; Prayer groups; Movies; Shopping trips; Dances/Social or cultural gatherings.
Description Facility offers 7 suites for married couples and 103 private rooms.

Clinton Retirement Village
2604 N 4th St, Clinton, IA, 52732 (319) 243-6600
Admin Jill L Benthrup.
Licensure Intermediate Care. *Beds* 150. *Certified* Medicaid.
Admissions Requirements Medical examination; Physician's request.
Staff RNs 1 (ft), 2 (pt); LPNs 5 (ft), 3 (pt); Nurses aides 19 (ft), 16 (pt); Recreational therapists 1 (ft); Activities coordinators 1 (ft).
Facilities Dining room; Activities room; Chapel; Crafts room; Laundry room; Barber/Beauty shop.
Activities Arts and Crafts; Cards; Games; Reading groups; Prayer groups; Movies; Shopping trips; Dances/Social or cultural gatherings.
Description Facility is associated with the Hillhaven Corp. Our primary objective is to provide the finest patient care to each resident in the most dignified manner possible.

Gateway Intermediate Care
Bluff Terrace, 638 S Bluff Blvd, Clinton, IA, 52732
Admin Douglas Trembath.
Licensure Intermediate Care. *Beds* 64. *Certified* Medicaid.
Ownership Nonprofit.
Admissions Requirements Medical examination; Physician's request.
Staff RNs 3 (ft), 4 (pt); LPNs 1 (ft), 3 (pt); Orderlies 1 (pt); Nurses aides 9 (ft), 16 (pt); Physical therapists 3 (pt); Occupational therapists 1 (pt); Speech therapists 1 (pt); Activities coordinators 1 (ft); Dietitians 1 (ft); Audiologists 1 (pt).
Facilities Dining room; Activities room; Crafts room; Laundry room; Barber/Beauty shop.
Activities Arts and Crafts; Cards; Games; Reading groups; Prayer groups; Movies; Shopping trips; Dances/Social or cultural gatherings.
Description Facility ajoins Jane Lamb Health Center and has access to excellent physical therapy, X-ray, occupational therapy, respiratory therapy, and emergency rooms.

Wyndcrest Nursing Home*
600 14th Ave N, Clinton, IA, 52732 (319) 243-3200
Admin Brian Peterson.
Licensure Intermediate Care. *Beds* 95. *Certified* Medicaid.

COLUMBUS JUNCTION

Colonial Manor—Columbus Junction*
814 Springer Ave, Columbus Junction, IA, 52738 (319) 728-2276
Admin James T Keldgord.
Licensure Intermediate Care. *Beds* 60. *Certified* Medicaid.

CONRAD

Oakview Home*
511 Center St, Conrad, IA, 50621 (515) 366-2212
Admin Bonnie Switzer.

Licensure Intermediate Care; Residential.
Beds ICF 38; Residential 8. *Certified* Medicaid.

COON RAPIDS

Thomas Rest Haven*
217 Main St, Coon Rapids, IA, 50058 (712) 684-2253
Admin William McKinney.
Licensure Intermediate Care; Residential Care.
Beds ICF 44; Residential Care 18. *Certified* Medicaid.

CORALVILLE

Lantern Park Care Center*
915 N 20th Ave, Coralville, IA, 52241 (319) 351-8440
Admin Sydney Vanderwoude.
Licensure Intermediate Care. *Beds* 100. *Certified* Medicaid.

CORNING

Adams County Care Facility*
RFD 1, Corning, IA, 50841 (515) 322-3291
Admin Lois Wilkenson.
Licensure Intermediate Care for Mentally Retarded. *Beds* 51.

Colonial Manor of Corning*
Northgate Dr, Corning, IA, 50841 (515) 322-4061
Admin Roger Hinz.
Licensure Intermediate Care. *Beds* 64. *Certified* Medicaid.

CORRECTIONVILLE

Colonial Manors—Correctionville*
Box H, Correctionville, IA, 51016 (712) 372-4549
Admin Gregory A Andersen.
Licensure Intermediate Care. *Beds* 65. *Certified* Medicaid.

CORYDON

Corydon Care Center
745 E South St, Corydon, IA, 50060 (515) 872-1590
Admin Connie E White. *Medical Dir/Dir of Nursing* Paula Place RN.
Licensure Intermediate Care. *Beds* 79. *Certified* Medicaid.
Admissions Requirements Medical examination.
Staff Physicians 6 (pt); RNs 1 (ft), 1 (pt); LPNs 7 (pt); Nurses aides 12 (ft), 19 (pt); Physical therapists 1 (pt); Activities coordinators 2 (pt); Dietitians 1 (pt); Dentists 1 (pt); Audiologists 1 (pt).
Facilities Dining room; Physical therapy room; Activities room; Crafts room; Laundry room; Barber/Beauty shop.
Activities Arts and Crafts; Cards; Games; Reading groups; Prayer groups; Movies; Shopping trips; Dances/Social or cultural gatherings.

COUNCIL BLUFFS

Bethany Lutheran Home Inc
7 Elliott St, Council Bluffs, IA, 51501 (712) 328-9500
Licensure Intermediate Care. *Beds* 121. *Certified* Medicaid.
Admissions Requirements Medical examination.
Staff RNs 5 (ft), 5 (pt); LPNs 5 (ft), 4 (pt); Orderlies 2 (ft); Nurses aides 28 (ft), 22 (pt); Physical therapists 1 (ft), 1 (pt); Recreational therapists 1 (ft); Occupational therapists 1 (pt); Speech therapists 1 (pt); Activities coordinators 1 (ft), 1 (pt); Dietitians 1 (pt); Podiatrists 1 (pt); Audiologists 1 (pt).
Affiliation Lutheran
Facilities Dining room; Physical therapy room; Activities room; Chapel; Laundry room; Barber/Beauty shop.
Activities Arts and Crafts; Cards; Games; Reading groups; Prayer groups; Movies; Shopping trips; Dances/Social or cultural gatherings.
Description Facility has 3 residents who are teacher's aides at nearby Gunn School for 2 ½ hours each Wednesday. Also, we have a Bethany Teen Program with 14 youths ages 12–15.

Council Bluffs Care Center*
2452 N Broadway, Council Bluffs, IA, 51501 (712) 323-7135
Licensure Intermediate Care. *Beds* 150. *Certified* Medicaid.

Indian Hills Nursing Center*
1600 McPherson, Council Bluffs, IA, 51501 (712) 322-9285
Admin Lawrence R Cotton.
Licensure Intermediate Care. *Beds* 126. *Certified* Medicaid.

Northcrest Care Center*
34 Northcrest Dr, Council Bluffs, IA, 51501 (712) 328-2333
Admin Kenneth Opp.
Licensure Intermediate Care. *Beds* 102. *Certified* Medicaid.

Oakland Manor Nursing Home*
PO Box 487, Council Bluffs, IA, 51560 (712) 482-6404
Admin Carolee Hamblin.
Licensure Intermediate Care. *Beds* 64. *Certified* Medicaid.

CRESCO

Cresco Care Center Inc*
Rt 2, Vernon Rd, Cresco, IA, 52136 (319) 547-3580
Admin Barbara Neubaum.
Licensure Intermediate Care. *Beds* 73. *Certified* Medicaid.

Evans Memorial Home for the Aged Inc
1010 N Elm, Cresco, IA, 52136 (319) 547-2364
Medical Dir/Dir of Nursing Marge Overn RN.
Licensure Intermediate Care. *Beds* 61. *Certified* Medicaid.
Admissions Requirements Medical examination; Physician's request.

Staff RNs 1 (ft), 4 (pt); LPNs 2 (pt); Orderlies 1 (pt); Nurses aides 10 (ft), 18 (pt); Physical therapists 1 (pt); Reality therapists 1 (pt); Recreational therapists 1 (pt); Occupational therapists 1 (pt); Speech therapists 1 (pt); Activities coordinators 1 (ft), 1 (pt); Dietitians 1 (pt); Audiologists 1 (pt).
Facilities Dining room; Physical therapy room; Activities room; Chapel; Crafts room; Laundry room; Barber/Beauty shop.
Activities Arts and Crafts; Cards; Games; Reading groups; Prayer groups; Movies; Shopping trips; Dances/Social or cultural gatherings.
Description Facility offers a home away from home.

CRESTON

Care Center of Iowa Inc
1000 E Howard, Creston, IA, 50801 (515) 782-5012
Licensure Intermediate Care. *Beds* 71. *Certified* Medicaid.
Admissions Requirements Medical examination; Physician's request.
Staff RNs 2 (ft); LPNs 4 (ft); Nurses aides 24 (ft); Occupational therapists 1 (pt); Activities coordinators 1 (ft); Dietitians 1 (pt); Audiologists 1 (pt).
Facilities Dining room; Activities room; Chapel; Crafts room; Laundry room.
Activities Arts and Crafts; Cards; Games; Reading groups; Prayer groups; Movies; Shopping trips.

Creston Manor Nursing Home
1001 Cottonwood, Creston, IA, 50801 (515) 782-8511
Admin William Robinson.
Licensure Intermediate Care. *Beds* 74. *Certified* Medicaid.

DALLAS CENTER

Spurgeon Manor*
13th and Linden, Dallas Center, IA, 50063 (515) 992-3735
Admin Floyd J Haldeman.
Licensure Intermediate Care; Residential Care. *Beds* ICF 17; Residential Care 30. *Certified* Medicaid.

DANVILLE

Danville Care Center*
Birch and Seymour Sts, Danville, IA, 52623 (319) 392-4259
Licensure Intermediate Care. *Beds* 40. *Certified* Medicaid.

DAVENPORT

Americana Healthcare Center
815 E Locust St, Davenport, IA, 52803 (319) 324-3276
Licensure Skilled Care. *Beds* 110. *Certified* Medicaid; Medicare.

Davenport Good Samaritan
700 Waverly Rd, Davenport, IA, 52804 (319) 324-1651
Admin Karen Griggs.
Licensure Intermediate Care. *Beds* 211. *Certified* Medicaid.
Admissions Requirements Minimum age 16; Medical examination; Physician's request.
Staff Physicians 58 (pt); RNs 5 (ft), 6 (pt); LPNs 6 (ft), 5 (pt); Orderlies 4 (ft); Nurses aides 66 (ft), 22 (pt); Physical therapists 2 (pt); Recreational therapists 3 (ft), 2 (pt); Occupational therapists 1 (ft), 1 (pt); Speech therapists 1 (pt); Activities coordinators 1 (ft); Dietitians 1 (ft); Dentists 1 (pt).
Facilities Dining room; Physical therapy room; Activities room; Chapel; Crafts room; Laundry room; Barber/Beauty shop.
Activities Arts and Crafts; Cards; Games; Reading groups; Prayer groups; Movies; Shopping trips; Dances/Social or cultural gatherings; Bowling; Horticulture therapy.

Davenport Lutheran Home
1130 W 53rd St, Davenport, IA, 52806 (319) 391-5342
Admin Fern Werning.
Licensure Intermediate Care. *Beds* 80. *Certified* Medicaid.
Ownership Nonprofit.
Admissions Requirements Minimum age 65; Medical examination.
Staff RNs 1 (ft); LPNs 6 (ft), 1 (pt); Nurses aides 18 (ft), 13 (pt); Activities coordinators 1 (ft), 1 (pt); Dietitians 1 (pt).
Affiliation Lutheran
Facilities Dining room; Physical therapy room; Activities room; Chapel; Crafts room; Laundry room; Library.
Activities Arts and Crafts; Cards; Games; Reading groups; Prayer groups; Movies; Dances/Social or cultural gatherings.
Description Facility is located on 7 ½ acres in northwest Davenport, a church-related, nonprofit home; gives excellent individualized care and encourages residents to do as much for themselves as possible. Staff cares about the spiritual, emotional, and physical needs of residents.

Davenport Nursing Home*
326 E 29th St, Davenport, IA, 52806 (319) 323-8021
Admin Elizabeth Finkenhoefer.
Licensure Intermediate Care. *Beds* 41. *Certified* Medicaid.

Fejervary Health Care Center*
800 E Rusholme, Davenport, IA, 52803 (319) 322-1668
Admin Lawrence Campana.
Licensure Intermediate Care. *Beds* 118. *Certified* Medicaid.

Hy-Vue
4117 Eastern Ave, Davenport, IA, 52803 (319) 359-0474
Admin Arlene Jens. *Medical Dir/Dir of Nursing* Charles Andrews DO.
Licensure Intermediate Care for Mentally Retarded; Residential Care. *Beds* ICF/MR 51; Residential Care 14. *Certified* Medicaid.
Admissions Requirements Minimum age 18;

Medical examination.
Staff Physicians 3 (pt); RNs 2 (ft); LPNs 5 (pt); Orderlies 10 (ft); Nurses aides 15 (ft), 10 (pt); Physical therapists 3 (pt); Occupational therapists 1 (ft); Speech therapists 1 (pt); Activities coordinators 1 (ft); Dietitians 1 (pt); Dentists 2 (pt); Ophthalmologists 2 (pt); Podiatrists 1 (pt); Audiologists 1 (pt).
Facilities Dining room; Physical therapy room; Activities room.
Activities Arts and Crafts; Games; Reading groups; Movies; Shopping trips; Dances/Social or cultural gatherings.
Description All the residents are mentally retarded/developmentally disabled; our philosophy is to assist them in a normalization environment that will develop each individual's potential to the highest level of functioning possible.

Kahl Home for the Aged and Infirm
1101 W 9th St, Davenport, IA, 52804 (319) 324-1621
Licensure Intermediate Care. *Beds* 125. *Certified* Medicaid.
Admissions Requirements Minimum age 64; Medical examination.
Staff RNs 3 (ft), 4 (pt); LPNs 6 (ft), 3 (pt); Nurses aides 47 (ft), 4 (pt); Activities coordinators 1 (ft); Dietitians 1 (ft).
Affiliation Roman Catholic
Facilities Dining room; Physical therapy room; Activities room; Chapel; Crafts room; Laundry room; Barber/Beauty shop; Library.
Activities Arts and Crafts; Cards; Games; Reading groups; Prayer groups; Movies; Shopping trips; Dances/Social or cultural gatherings.

Meadow Lawn Nursing Center*
4656 W Kimberly Rd, Davenport, IA, 52806 (319) 391-5150
Admin Elizabeth Finkenhoefer.
Licensure Intermediate Care. *Beds* 65. *Certified* Medicaid.

Ridgecrest Retirement Village
4130 Northwest Blvd, Davenport, IA, 52806 (319) 391-3430
Medical Dir/Dir of Nursing John Collins MD.
Licensure Skilled Care; Intermediate Care; Residential Care. *Beds* SNF 14; ICF 70; Residential Care 14. *Certified* Medicaid; Medicare.
Ownership Nonprofit.
Facilities Dining room; Chapel; Laundry room; Barber/Beauty shop; Library.
Activities Arts and Crafts; Cards; Games; Reading groups; Prayer groups; Movies; Shopping trips.
Description We are an independent facility directed by an interdenomiational board of directors. Ridgecrest is a very reputable, 17-year-old facility operating with the life-care concept.

Royal Neighbor Home*
4760 Rockingham Rd, Davenport, IA, 52802 (319) 322-3591
Admin Helen A Meester.
Licensure Intermediate Care; Residential Care. *Beds* ICF 14; Residential Care 54.

DAYTON

Grandview of Dayton
2nd St NE, Dayton, IA, 50530 (515) 547-2288
Admin LaVon G Runkle. *Medical Dir/Dir of Nursing* Dr E DeHaan.
Licensure Intermediate Care. *Beds* 50. *Certified* Medicaid.
Staff Physicians 1 (ft); RNs 3 (ft); LPNs 3 (ft); Nurses aides 25 (ft); Physical therapists 1 (pt); Speech therapists 1 (ft); Activities coordinators 1 (ft); Dietitians 1 (ft); Dentists 1 (pt); Podiatrists 1 (pt); Audiologists 1 (pt).
Facilities Dining room; Physical therapy room; Activities room; Laundry room; Barber/Beauty shop.
Activities Arts and Crafts; Cards; Games; Reading groups; Prayer groups; Movies; Shopping trips; Dances/Social or cultural gatherings.
Description Spring Polka Fest held on March 25, 1984 with music provided by a well-known polka band from New Ulm, lunch was served by the faculty to approximately 200 residents and guests.

DECORAH

Aase Haugen Homes Inc*
4 Ohio St, Decorah, IA, 52101 (319) 382-3603
Admin Bernadean L Koehler.
Licensure Intermediate Care; Residential Care. *Beds* 146; Reidential Care 13. *Certified* Medicaid.

M A Barthell Order of Eastern Star Home
911 Ridgeway Dr, Decorah, IA, 52101 (319) 382-8787
Admin Gary Gavle. *Medical Dir/Dir of Nursing* Sharon Kidd.
Licensure Intermediate Care. *Beds* 46.
Admissions Requirements Physician's request.
Staff RNs 2 (ft), 1 (pt); LPNs 5 (pt); Orderlies 2 (pt); Nurses aides 6 (ft), 10 (pt); Activities coordinators 1 (ft), 1 (pt); Dietitians 1 (pt).
Affiliation Order of Eastern Star
Facilities Dining room; Physical therapy room; Activities room; Chapel; Crafts room; Laundry room; Barber/Beauty shop; Library.
Activities Arts and Crafts; Cards; Games; Reading groups; Prayer groups; Movies; Shopping trips; Dances/Social or cultural gatherings.
Description Our home is located on a hill overlooking the Iowa Bluffs, we have many lovely trees and flowers all spring and summer. Our activity program is outstanding. We all work closely with family and friends and encourage the new resident to bring personal belongings for their rooms.

Winneshiek County Health Care Facility
Rt 6, Decorah, IA, 52101 (319) 382-2518
Admin Maryl E Cook.
Licensure Intermediate Care; Residential Care. *Beds* ICF 12; Residential Care 80. *Certified* Medicaid.
Admissions Requirements Minimum age 18.
Staff Physicians 2 (pt); RNs 2 (ft); LPNs 1 (ft), 6 (pt); Nurses aides 10 (ft), 8 (pt); Physical therapists 1 (pt); Speech therapists 1 (pt); Activities coordinators 2 (ft), 1 (pt); Dietitians 1 (pt); Dentists 1 (pt); Ophthalmologists 1 (pt); Podiatrists 1 (pt); Audiologists 1 (pt).

Facilities Dining room; Activities room; Chapel; Crafts room; Laundry room; Barber/Beauty shop; Library.
Activities Arts and Crafts; Cards; Games; Reading groups; Prayer groups; Movies; Shopping trips; Dances/Social or cultural gatherings; Band; Camping.
Description Residents have an excellent band that travels all over Iowa and also entertains here at the facility.

DENISON

Denison Care Center*
Rt 1, Ridge Rd, Denison, IA, 51442 (712) 263-5611
Admin Helen Andersen.
Licensure Intermediate Care. *Beds* 50. *Certified* Medicaid.

Eventide Lutheran Home for the Aged
20th St and 1st Ave S, Denison, IA, 51442 (712) 263-3114
Licensure Intermediate Care; Residential Care. *Beds* ICF 71; Residential Care 69. *Certified* Medicaid.
Ownership Nonprofit.
Admissions Requirements Minimum age 60; Medical examination.
Staff RNs 1 (ft); LPNs 1 (ft); Orderlies 1 (ft); Nurses aides 1 (ft); Physical therapists 1 (pt); Speech therapists 1 (pt); Activities coordinators 1 (ft); Dietitians 1 (pt); Audiologists 1 (pt).
Affiliation Lutheran
Facilities Dining room; Physical therapy room; Activities room; Chapel; Laundry room; Barber/Beauty shop.
Activities Arts and Crafts; Cards; Games; Reading groups; Prayer groups; Movies; Shopping trips; Dances/Social or cultural gatherings.
Description Facility provides quality care.

DENVER

Denver Sunset Home*
235 N Mill St, Denver, IA, 50622 (319) 984-5372
Admin Janet Jessen.
Licensure Intermediate Care. *Beds* 21. *Certified* Medicaid.

DES MOINES

Bishop Drumm Care Center*
5837 Winwood Dr, Des Moines, IA, 50324 (515) 270-1100
Admin Sr Madeleva Comiskey.
Licensure Intermediate Care; Residential Care. *Beds* ICF 58; Residential Care 62. *Certified* Medicaid.
Affiliation Roman Catholic

Broadlawns West*
2501 24th St, Des Moines, IA, 50314 (515) 274-3566
Admin Jack Tharp.
Licensure Intermediate Care. *Beds* 80. *Certified* Medicaid.

Calvin Manor*
4210 Hickman Rd, Des Moines, IA, 50310
(515) 277-6141
Admin Richard J Shaffer.
Licensure Intermediate Care. *Beds* 59. *Certified* Medicaid.

Commonwealth Care Center*
5608 SW 9th St, Des Moines, IA, 50315 (515)
285-3070
Admin Barbara Kuhlken.
Licensure Intermediate Care. *Beds* 99. *Certified* Medicaid.

Convalescent Home for Children
5900 Pioneer Pkwy, Des Moines, IA, 50324
(515) 270-2205
Medical Dir/Dir of Nursing Sayeed Hussain
MD.
Licensure Skilled Care; Intermediate Care for
Mentally Retarded. *Beds* SNF 19; ICF/MR 44.
Certified Medicaid.
Admissions Requirements Minimum age Birth.
Staff RNs 9 (ft), 3 (pt); LPNs 8 (ft), 5 (pt);
Orderlies 1 (pt); Nurses aides 15 (ft), 22 (pt);
Physical therapists 1 (ft); Recreational therapists
1 (ft); Occupational therapists 1 (ft); Speech
therapists 1 (pt); Activities coordinators 1 (ft);
Dietitians 1 (pt); Dentists 2 (pt).
Facilities Dining room; Physical therapy room;
Activities room; Crafts room; Laundry room;
Barber/Beauty shop; Library; Game room.
Activities Arts and Crafts; Cards; Games;
Reading groups; Prayer groups; Movies; Shopping trips; Dances/Social or cultural gatherings;
Specific skill training in self-care, prevocational,
computers.

Craigmont Care Center*
2348 E 9th St, Des Moines, IA, 50316 (515)
262-9303
Admin Mary J Badgerow.
Licensure Intermediate Care. *Beds* 92. *Certified* Medicaid.

Crest Group Home
1316 22nd St, Des Moines, IA, 50311
Licensure Intermediate Care for Mentally
Retarded.
Ownership Nonprofit.
Admissions Requirements Minimum age 16;
Medical examination.
Staff Nurses aides 1 (pt); Occupational therapists 1 (ft); Activities coordinators 1 (pt); Medication managers 1 (ft); Medical aides 2 (ft).
Affiliation Baptist
Facilities Dining room; Activities room;
Laundry room.
Activities Arts and Crafts; Cards; Games;
Movies; Shopping trips; Dances/Social or cultural gatherings.
Description The main focus of this facility is to
assist mildly retarded adults to maintain or
improve their independent living skills.

Heather Manor
600 E 5th St, Des Moines, IA, 50316 (515)
243-6195
Admin Dean Schager. *Medical Dir/Dir of
Nursing* Lauretta Anderson DON.
Licensure Intermediate Care. *Beds* 31.
Admissions Requirements Minimum age 62;
Medical examination; Physician's request.

Staff Physicians 1 (pt); RNs 1 (ft), 3 (pt); LPNs
1 (ft), 4 (pt); Nurses aides 6 (ft), 8 (pt); Physical
therapists 1 (pt); Occupational therapists 1 (pt);
Speech therapists 1 (pt); Activities coordinators
1 (pt); Dietitians 1 (pt); Dentists 1 (pt); Podiatrists 1 (pt).
Facilities Dining room; Activities room; Chapel; Crafts room; Laundry room; Barber/Beauty
shop; Library.
Activities Arts and Crafts; Cards; Games;
Reading groups; Prayer groups; Movies; Shopping trips; Dances/Social or cultural gatherings.
Description We just purchased a new mini bus
which takes residents to the grocery store 3
times a week.

Hillhaven Convalescent Center
233 University, Des Moines, IA, 50314 (515)
284-1280
Admin Orville A Ballard. *Medical Dir/Dir of
Nursing* Roy W Overton MD.
Licensure Skilled Care; Intermediate Care.
Beds SNF 54; ICF 108. *Certified* Medicaid;
Medicare.
Admissions Requirements Medical examination; Physician's request.
Staff RNs 6 (ft), 4 (pt); LPNs 4 (ft), 3 (pt);
Orderlies 3 (ft), 2 (pt); Nurses aides 30 (ft), 10
(pt); Physical therapists 2 (ft); Occupational
therapists 1 (pt); Activities coordinators 1 (ft), 2
(pt).
Facilities Dining room; Physical therapy room;
Activities room; Crafts room; Laundry room;
Barber/Beauty shop.
Activities Arts and Crafts; Games; Reading
groups; Prayer groups; Shopping trips; Dances-
/Social or cultural gatherings.
Description Facility is centrally located within
easy access to freeway and 3 blocks from city
bus line, within minutes of hospitals and doctors' offices. All resident rooms have individually controlled heat and air conditioning.

Iowa Jewish Home
1620 Pleasant St, Des Moines, IA, 50314 (515)
288-1001
Admin Michael D Kelner. *Medical Dir/Dir of
Nursing* Stanton Danielson MD.
Licensure Skilled Care; Intermediate Care;
Residential Care. *Beds* SNF 42; ICF; Residential Care 5. *Certified* Medicaid; Medicare.
Admissions Requirements Minimum age 18;
Medical examination.
Staff Physicians 2 (pt); RNs 2 (ft), 8 (pt); LPNs
3 (ft), 1 (pt); Nurses aides 12 (ft), 15 (pt);
Physical therapists 1 (pt); Recreational therapists 1 (ft); Occupational therapists 1 (pt); Speech therapists 1 (pt); Activities coordinators 1
(ft); Dietitians 1 (ft), 1 (pt); Podiatrists 2 (pt).
Affiliation Jewish
Facilities Dining room; Chapel; Crafts room;
Laundry room; Barber/Beauty shop.
Activities Arts and Crafts; Games; Reading
groups; Prayer groups; Movies; Shopping trips;
Dances/Social or cultural gatherings; Theatre;
Restaurants; Bus rides; Pet visitation; Resident
council.
Description Facility is elated with the pet visitation program; residents, who react to little else,
respond warmly to controlled pets. Bus rides
and mall meandering are thoroughly enjoyed
by residents as it allows exposure to the community.

Luther Park Health Center
1555 Hull Ave, Des Moines, IA, 50316 (515)
262-5639
Medical Dir/Dir of Nursing Roy Overton MD.
Licensure Skilled Care; Intermediate Care.
Beds SNF 60; ICF 60. *Certified* Medicaid;
Medicare.
Admissions Requirements Minimum age 16.
Staff RNs 9 (ft), 3 (pt); LPNs 8 (ft), 4 (pt);
Nurses aides 37 (ft), 18 (pt); Physical therapists
1 (ft); Occupational therapists 1 (ft); Activities
coordinators 2 (ft); Dietitians 1 (ft).
Affiliation Lutheran
Facilities Dining room; Physical therapy room;
Activities room; Chapel; Crafts room; Laundry
room; Barber/Beauty shop; Library.
Activities Arts and Crafts; Cards; Games;
Reading groups; Prayer groups; Movies; Shopping trips; Dances/Social or cultural gatherings.

New Oaks Care Center*
3806 Easton Blvd, Des Moines, IA, 50317
(515) 265-1474
Admin Craig Ver Huel.
Licensure Intermediate Care. *Beds* 51. *Certified* Medicaid.

Normandy Hills Care Center*
721 16th St, Des Moines, IA, 50314 (515)
244-8131
Admin Carol J Smith.
Licensure Intermediate Care. *Beds* 50. *Certified* Medicaid.

Park Ridge Manor*
4755 Park Ridge, Des Moines, IA, 50317 (515)
265-5348
Admin Darrell D Hoefling.
Licensure Intermediate Care. *Beds* 74. *Certified* Medicaid.

Plainview Residential Care
1136 Harding Rd, Des Moines, IA, 50310
Admin Linda Pottorff.
Licensure Residential Care. *Beds* 11.
Certified Medicaid.
Ownership Proprietary.
Admissions Requirements Minimum age 30;
Females only; Medical examination; Physician's request.
Staff LPNs 1 (ft); Nurses aides 1 (ft).
Facilities Dining room; Activities room; Laundry room; Living room.
Activities Arts and Crafts; Games; Prayer
groups; Monthly birthday parties.
Description This is a small facility with a
Christian, home-like atmosphere; all residents
are ambulatory and care for themselves with
minimal supervision. Residents' families help
with shopping and trips outside of facility.

Ramsey Memorial Home
1611 27th St, Des Moines, IA, 50310 (515)
274-3612
Medical Dir/Dir of Nursing Robert Shires MD.
Licensure Intermediate Care; Residential Care.
Beds ICF 54; Residential Care 78. *Certified* Medicaid.
Admissions Requirements Minimum age 65;
Medical examination.
Staff RNs 2 (ft); LPNs 4 (ft), 5 (pt); Nurses
aides 19 (ft), 4 (pt); Physical therapists 1 (pt);
Activities coordinators 2 (ft); Dietitians 1 (pt).

Affiliation Disciples of Christ
Facilities Dining room; Activities room; Chapel; Crafts room; Laundry room; Barber/Beauty shop; Library.
Activities Arts and Crafts; Cards; Games; Reading groups; Prayer groups; Movies; Shopping trips; Dances/Social or cultural gatherings; Pet therapy program.

Riverview Manor*
701 Riverview, Des Moines, IA, 50316 (515) 266-1106
Admin Daniel R Schwieger.
Licensure Intermediate Care. *Beds* 138. *Certified* Medicaid.

Scottish Rite Park Health Care Center*
2909 Woodland, Des Moines, IA, 50310 (515) 274-4614
Admin Martha Mayr.
Licensure Intermediate Care; Residential Care. *Beds* ICF 40; Residential Care 19. *Certified* Medicaid.

Valborg Lutheran Home
1101 Grandview Ave, Des Moines, IA, 50316
Admin Eunice Knudsen.
Licensure Residential Care. *Beds* 50.
Certified Medicaid.
Ownership Nonprofit.
Admissions Requirements Medical examination; Physician's request.
Staff Nurses aides 5 (pt); Activities coordinators 1 (ft); Dietitians 1 (pt); Medical aides 4 (ft), 1 (pt).
Affiliation Lutheran
Facilities Dining room; Activities room; Chapel; Crafts room; Laundry room; Barber/Beauty shop; Library; Sewing room.
Activities Arts and Crafts; Cards; Games; Reading groups; Prayer groups; Movies; Shopping trips; Dances/Social or cultural gatherings.
Description Facility offers 3 meals a day, a room, activities of all kinds, resident council, assistance to residents in their daily living, family conferences, educational programs, community participation (helping families by giving them quilts made by residents, for instance), sharing with preschoolers in various ways.

Valley View Village*
2571 Guthrie Ave, Des Moines, IA, 50317 (515) 265-2571
Admin Dennis L Howe.
Licensure Intermediate Care. *Beds* 67. *Certified* Medicaid.

Villa Inn Home
1709 10th St, Des Moines, IA, 50314
Medical Dir/Dir of Nursing Cynthia Six.
Admissions Requirements Minimum age 18; Medical examination; Physician's request.
Staff RNs 1 (ft); LPNs 1 (pt); Nurses aides 8 (ft); Activities coordinators 1 (ft).
Facilities Dining room; Activities room; Crafts room; Laundry room; Library.
Activities Arts and Crafts; Cards; Games; Reading groups; Prayer groups; Movies; Shopping trips; Dances/Social or cultural gatherings.
Description Facility is well known for ability to care for more difficult mentally deficient or

emotionally unstable residents, average age 35-40 years. Residents are provided with many diverse activity programs.

Wesley Acres
3520 Grand, Des Moines, IA, 50312 (515) 274-3417
Medical Dir/Dir of Nursing Dr Robet Knox.
Licensure Intermediate Care; Residential Care. *Beds* ICF 59; Residential Care 62. *Certified* Medicaid.
Admissions Requirements Minimum age 60; Medical examination.
Staff Physicians 1 (pt); RNs 2 (ft), 14 (pt); LPNs 3 (pt); Orderlies 1 (ft), 2 (pt); Nurses aides 22 (ft), 16 (pt); Activities coordinators 2 (ft); Dietitians 1 (ft).
Affiliation Methodist
Facilities Dining room; Physical therapy room; Activities room; Chapel; Crafts room; Laundry room; Barber/Beauty shop; Library.
Activities Arts and Crafts; Games; Reading groups; Movies; Shopping trips.

DONNELLSON

Donnellson Manor Care Center*
901 State St, Donnellson, IA, 52625 (319) 835-5621
Admin David Dowell.
Licensure Intermediate Care. *Beds* 53. *Certified* Medicaid.

DOWS

Dows Care Center
909 Rowan Rd, Dows, IA, 50071 (515) 852-4147
Medical Dir/Dir of Nursing Charlotte Brim RN.
Licensure Intermediate Care. *Beds* 50. *Certified* Medicaid.
Admissions Requirements Medical examination; Physician's request.
Staff RNs 1 (ft), 2 (pt); LPNs 1 (ft), 3 (pt); Nurses aides 8 (ft), 13 (pt); Physical therapists 1 (pt); Recreational therapists 1 (pt); Occupational therapists 1 (pt); Speech therapists 1 (pt); Activities coordinators 1 (ft), 1 (pt); Dietitians 1 (pt); Podiatrists 1 (pt); Audiologists 1 (pt); Social worker 1 (pt).
Facilities Dining room; Physical therapy room; Activities room; Chapel; Laundry room; Barber/Beauty shop; Library.
Activities Arts and Crafts; Cards; Games; Reading groups; Prayer groups; Movies.
Description Dows Care Center is a 50-bed facility. Employees are friendly and caring and nursing care is excellent. Activity program is 5 days a week; many volunteer groups participate; church every Sunday and Bible Study each week with Communion each month, any denomination.

DUBUQUE

Americana Healthcare Center*
901 W 3rd St, Dubuque, IA, 52001 (319) 556-1163

Admin John Jackson.
Licensure Skilled Care. *Beds* 92. *Certified* Medicaid; Medicare.

Bethany Home*
1005 Lincoln Ave, Dubuque, IA, 52001 (319) 556-5233
Admin Paul G Gabrielson.
Licensure Intermediate Care; Residential Care. *Beds* ICF 56; Residential Care 32. *Certified* Medicaid.

Dubuque Health Care Center
2935 Kaufman, Dubuque, IA, 52001 (319) 566-0673
Licensure Intermediate Care. *Beds* 108. *Certified* Medicaid.
Admissions Requirements Minimum age 16; Physician's request.
Staff Recreational therapists 1 (ft); Activities coordinators 3 (pt).
Facilities Dining room; Physical therapy room; Activities room; Crafts room; Barber/Beauty shop.
Activities Arts and Crafts; Cards; Games; Reading groups; Prayer groups; Movies; Shopping trips; Dances/Social or cultural gatherings.

Ennoble Manor Care Center*
2000 Pasadena Dr, Dubuque, IA, 52001 (319) 557-1076
Admin Joan Sutherland.
Licensure Intermediate Care. *Beds* 102. *Certified* Medicaid.

Heritage Manor
4885 Asbury Rd, Dubuque, IA, 52001 (319) 583-6447
Medical Dir/Dir of Nursing Dr Brehm.
Licensure Intermediate Care. *Beds* 75. *Certified* Medicaid.
Staff RNs 4 (ft), 2 (pt); LPNs 2 (ft), 2 (pt); Orderlies 2 (ft), 1 (pt); Nurses aides 10 (ft), 14 (pt); Physical therapists; Occupational therapists; Speech therapists; Activities coordinators 1 (ft), 1 (pt); Dentists 1 (pt); Ophthalmologists 1 (pt); Podiatrists 1 (pt); Audiologists.
Facilities Dining room; Activities room; Chapel; Crafts room; Laundry room; Barber/Beauty shop; Covered patio; Living room; TV room; Activity van.
Activities Arts and Crafts; Cards; Games; Reading groups; Prayer groups; Movies; Shopping trips; Dances/Social or cultural gatherings.
Description Heritage Manor is located at the edge of Asbury in Dubuque; 2 wings are built to the south and west of the old St Philomena's church, with the church being used as a chapel or activity room at present.

Luther Manor*
3131 Hillcrest Rd, Dubuque, IA, 52001 (319) 588-1413
Licensure Intermediate Care. *Beds* 70. *Certified* Medicaid.
Affiliation Lutheran

Mercy Health Center*
Mercy Dr, Dubuque, IA, 52001 (319) 588-8400
Admin Mary Corita Hcid.
Licensure Intermediate Care. *Beds* 40.

Stonehill Care Center*
3485 Windsor Ave, Dubuque, IA, 52001 (319)
557-7180
Admin Sr Delores Ullrich.
Licensure Intermediate Care; Residential Care.
Beds ICF 126; Residential Care 124. *Certified* Medicaid.

Sunnycrest Manor*
2375 Roosevelt St, Dubuque, IA, 52001 (319)
583-1781
Admin Mitzi B Quick.
Licensure Intermediate Care for Mentally
Retarded. *Beds* 136. *Certified* Medicaid.

DUMONT

Dumont Nursing Home*
921 3rd St, Dumont, IA, 50625 (515) 857-3401
Admin Edna Reiners.
Licensure Intermediate Care; Residential Care.
Beds ICF 44; Residential Care 5. *Certified* Medicaid.

DUNLAP

Dunlap Care Center*
1403 Harrison Rd, Dunlap, IA, 51529 (712)
643-2121
Admin Rodney A Hirchert.
Licensure Intermediate Care. *Beds* 73. *Certified* Medicaid.

DYSART

Sunny Crest Nursing Center
401 Crisman St, Dysart, IA, 52224 (319)
476-2400
Licensure Intermediate Care. *Beds* 67. *Certified* Medicaid.

EAGLE GROVE

Rotary Ann Home Inc
620 SE 5th St, Eagle Grove, IA, 50533 (515)
448-5124
Medical Dir/Dir of Nursing Angelene Kappes
RN.
Licensure Intermediate Care. *Beds* 51. *Certified* Medicaid.
Admissions Requirements Medical examination.
Staff RNs 2 (ft), 3 (pt); LPNs 2 (ft), 2 (pt);
Nurses aides 10 (ft), 12 (pt); Activities coordinators 1 (ft).
Facilities Dining room; Physical therapy room;
Activities room; Chapel; Crafts room; Laundry
room; Barber/Beauty shop; Library.
Activities Arts and Crafts; Cards; Games;
Reading groups; Prayer groups; Movies; Shopping trips; Dances/Social or cultural gatherings.

EARLHAM

Earlham Manor Care Center*
201 Center St, Earlham, IA, 50072 (515)
758-2244

Admin Julia A Glass.
Licensure Intermediate Care. *Beds* 29. *Certified* Medicaid.

EARLING

Little Flower Haven*
Earling, IA, 51530 (712) 747-3301
Admin David Hoffmann.
Licensure Intermediate Care. *Beds* 61. *Certified* Medicaid.

EDGEWOOD

Edgewood Convalescent Home
Edgewood, IA, 52042 (319) 928-6461
Licensure Intermediate Care. *Beds* 33.
Certified Medicaid.
Admissions Requirements Medical examination.
Staff RNs 1 (ft), 1 (pt); LPNs 4 (pt); Nurses
aides 4 (ft), 12 (pt); Recreational therapists 1
(pt); Occupational therapists 1 (pt); Speech therapists 1 (pt); Activities coordinators 1 (ft); Dietitians 1 (ft), 1 (pt); Dentists 1 (pt);
Ophthalmologists 1 (pt); Podiatrists 1 (pt);
Audiologists 1 (pt).
Facilities Dining room; Physical therapy room;
Activities room; Chapel; Crafts room; Laundry
room; Barber/Beauty shop.
Activities Arts and Crafts; Cards; Games;
Reading groups; Prayer groups; Movies; Dances/Social or cultural gatherings.

ELDORA

Eldora Manor*
2213 16th Ave, Eldora, IA, 50627 (515)
858-3491
Admin Dale Moore.
Licensure Intermediate Care. *Beds* 70. *Certified* Medicaid.

Valley View Nursing Center*
2313 15th Ave, Eldora, IA, 50627 (515)
858-5422
Admin Dale Moore.
Licensure Intermediate Care; Residential Care.
Beds ICF 64; Residential Care 16. *Certified* Medicaid.

ELK HORN

Salem Lutheran Home*
2024 College St, Elk Horn, IA, 51531 (712)
764-4201
Admin Howard M Hansen.
Licensure Intermediate Care; Residential Care.
Beds ICF 100; Residential Care 62. *Certified* Medicaid.
Affiliation Lutheran

ELKADER

Elkader Care Center
116 Reimer St, Elkader, IA, 52043 (319)
245-1620
Admin Jean Westerbeck.
Licensure Intermediate Care. *Beds* 51. *Certi-*

fied Medicaid.
Admissions Requirements Minimum age 18;
Medical examination.
Staff RNs 1 (ft); LPNs 2 (ft), 3 (pt); Nurses
aides 4 (ft), 11 (pt); Activities coordinators 1
(ft); Dietitians 1 (pt).
Facilities Dining room; Chapel; Laundry
room; Barber/Beauty shop.
Activities Arts and Crafts; Cards; Games;
Reading groups; Prayer groups; Movies; Shopping trips.

ELMA

Colonial Manor
9th and Maple, Elma, IA, 51628 (515)
393-2134
Medical Dir/Dir of Nursing Dr Curtis Rainy.
Licensure Intermediate Care. *Beds* 62. *Certified* Medicaid.
Admissions Requirements Medical examination; Physician's request.
Staff Physicians 1 (pt); RNs 2 (ft), 1 (pt); LPNs
4 (pt); Nurses aides 10 (ft), 18 (pt); Physical
therapists 1 (pt); Recreational therapists 1 (pt);
Occupational therapists 1 (pt); Speech therapists 1 (pt); Activities coordinators 2 (ft); Dietitians 1 (pt); Dentists 1 (pt); Ophthalmologists 1
(pt); Podiatrists 1 (pt); Audiologists 1 (pt);
Social Workers 1 (pt); Activity Correspondents
1 (pt); Geriatric RN Consultants 1 (pt).
Facilities Dining room; Physical therapy room;
Activities room; Chapel; Crafts room; Laundry
room; Barber/Beauty shop; Library.
Activities Arts and Crafts; Cards; Games;
Reading groups; Prayer groups; Movies; Shopping trips; Dances/Social or cultural gatherings.
Description In 1982, 57% of all admissions
were rehabilitated and returned to a lesser care
home.

EMMETSBURG

Emmetsburg Care Center
2405 21st St, Emmetsburg, IA, 50536 (712)
852-4266
Medical Dir/Dir of Nursing Lyman Bailey.
Licensure Intermediate Care. *Beds* 88. *Certified* Medicaid.
Admissions Requirements Minimum age 16;
Medical examination; Physician's request.
Staff RNs 3 (ft), 7 (pt); LPNs 5 (ft), 10 (pt);
Orderlies 1 (pt); Nurses aides 20 (ft), 30 (pt);
Physical therapists 1 (pt); Reality therapists 2
(pt); Recreational therapists 2 (pt); Speech therapists 1 (pt); Activities coordinators 1 (ft); Dietitians 1 (pt); Audiologists 1 (pt).
Facilities Dining room; Physical therapy room;
Activities room; Chapel; Crafts room; Laundry
room; Barber/Beauty shop; Library.
Activities Arts and Crafts; Cards; Games;
Reading groups; Prayer groups; Movies; Shopping trips; Dances/Social or cultural gatherings.
Description This is a nursing center of beauty,
comfort, and dignity; offering professional
nursing care, with a home-like atmosphere
where care is facility's middle name and first
priority.

Lakeside Lutheran Home*
N Lawler St, Emmetsburg, IA, 50536 (712)
852-4060
Admin Robert Owen.
Licensure Intermediate Care. *Beds* 60. *Certified* Medicaid.
Ownership Nonprofit.
Affiliation Lutheran

ESTHERVILLE

Estherville Good Samaritan*
1646 5th Ave N, Estherville, IA, 51334 (712)
362-3522
Admin Thomas P Bonestroo.
Licensure Intermediate Care. *Beds* 141. *Certified* Medicaid.

Rosewood Manor*
1720 1st Ave N, Estherville, IA, 51334 (712)
362-2210
Admin Jeanne M Hofstader.
Licensure Intermediate Care. *Beds* 55. *Certified* Medicaid.

EXIRA

Exira Care Center*
409 S Carthage, Exira, IA, 50076 (712)
268-5393
Admin Curt B Mardesen.
Licensure Intermediate Care; Residential Care.
Beds ICF 46; Residential Care 16. *Certified* Medicaid.

FAIRFIELD

Nelson Nursing Home*
809 W Taylor, Fairfield, IA, 52556 (515)
472-6126
Admin Arlouine Trent.
Licensure Intermediate Care. *Beds* 63. *Certified* Medicaid.

Parkview Care Center*
Rt 1, PO Box 202A, Fairfield, IA, 52556 (515)
472-5022
Admin E Alberta Blough.
Licensure Intermediate Care. *Beds* 112. *Certified* Medicaid.

FAYETTE

Maple Crest Manor*
Box 339, Bolger Dr, Fayette, IA, 52142 (319)
425-3336
Admin Debra J Simmons.
Licensure Intermediate Care. *Beds* 60. *Certified* Medicaid.

FONDA

Fonda Care Center
6th and Queen Ave, Fonda, IA, 50540 (712)
288-4441
Medical Dir/Dir of Nursing Jane Bierstedt RN.
Licensure Intermediate Care. *Beds* 49. *Certified* Medicaid.
Admissions Requirements Minimum age 49;

Medical examination; Physician's request.
Staff Physicians 1 (pt); RNs 2 (ft); LPNs 1 (ft), 1 (pt); Orderlies 2 (ft), 1 (pt); Nurses aides 10 (ft), 10 (pt); Physical therapists 1 (pt); Occupational therapists 1 (pt); Speech therapists 1 (pt); Activities coordinators 1 (ft); Dietitians 1 (pt); Dentists 1 (pt); Podiatrists 1 (pt); Audiologists 1 (pt).
Facilities Dining room; Physical therapy room; Activities room; Laundry room; Barber/Beauty shop.
Activities Arts and Crafts; Cards; Games; Reading groups; Movies; Shopping trips.
Description This small facility provides personalized care for each individual according to their needs; your care needs are our highest priority.

FONTANELLE

Fontanelle Good Samaritan Center*
326 Summerset St, Fontanelle, IA, 50846 (515)
745-4201
Admin Bruce L Radike.
Licensure Intermediate Care. *Beds* 63. *Certified* Medicaid.

FOREST CITY

Good Samaritan Center*
606 S 7th, Forest City, IA, 50436 (515)
582-2232
Admin Randy Fitzgerald.
Licensure Intermediate Care. *Beds* 64. *Certified* Medicaid.

FORT DODGE

Ellen's Convalescent Health Center*
1305 N 22nd St, Fort Dodge, IA, 50501 (515)
955-4145
Admin James Kratovil.
Licensure Intermediate Care; Residential Care.
Beds ICF 80; Residential Care 18. *Certified* Medicaid.

Fort Dodge Group Home
525 S 15th St, Fort Dodge, IA, 50501
Admin Michael Wertz.
Licensure Intermediate Care for Mentally Retarded. *Beds* 12. *Certified* Medicaid; Medicare.
Ownership Nonprofit.
Admissions Requirements Minimum age 18; Medical examination.
Facilities Dining room; Activities room; Laundry room.
Activities Cards; Games; Movies; Shopping trips; Dances/Social or cultural gatherings.
Description Facility offers a supervised apartment program for mildly mentally retarded adults; staff assists residents when necessary.

Fort Dodge Villa Care Center
2721 10th Ave N, Fort Dodge, IA, 50501 (515)
576-7525
Licensure Intermediate Care; Residential Care.
Beds ICF 81; Residential Care 26. *Certified* Medicaid.
Admissions Requirements Medical examination; Physician's request.

Staff RNs 3 (ft), 7 (pt); LPNs 1 (ft), 2 (pt); Orderlies 1 (ft); Nurses aides 18 (ft), 17 (pt); Physical therapists; Reality therapists; Recreational therapists; Occupational therapists; Speech therapists; Activities coordinators 1 (ft); Dietitians 1 (pt).
Facilities Dining room; Physical therapy room; Activities room; Crafts room; Laundry room; Barber/Beauty shop.
Activities Arts and Crafts; Cards; Games; Reading groups; Prayer groups; Movies; Shopping trips; Dances/Social or cultural gatherings.
Description This 107-bed facility has the best of 2 worlds—RCF and ICF under one roof and on one floor.

Friendship Haven Inc
S Kenyon Rd, Fort Dodge, IA, 50501 (515)
572-2121
Admin Paul G Bousfield. *Medical Dir/Dir of Nursing* James Metzger.
Licensure Intermediate Care; Residential Care.
Beds ICF 208; Residential Care 300. *Certified* Medicaid.
Ownership Proprietary.
Admissions Requirements Minimum age 65; Medical examination.
Staff Physicians 1 (pt); RNs 21 (ft); LPNs 9 (ft); Nurses aides 130 (ft); Physical therapists 1 (ft); Activities coordinators 1 (ft); Dietitians 1 (ft); Dentists 1 (pt).
Affiliation Methodist
Facilities Dining room; Physical therapy room; Activities room; Chapel; Crafts room; Laundry room; Barber/Beauty shop; Library; Kitchen for baking activity; Coffee shop and small cafeteria; Gift shop and thrift shop.
Activities Arts and Crafts; Cards; Games; Reading groups; Prayer groups; Movies; Shopping trips; Dances/Social or cultural gatherings; Outside entertainment brought in; College classes of interest.
Description Located on 38 beautifully landscaped acres, Friendship Haven is a home where residents continue a full and rewarding life in a Christian atmosphere. It meets the standards established by the Certification Council, Health and Welfare Ministries of the United Methodist Church and the State of Iowa. Independent living units are available to those of retirement age or older. Health care is designed to accomodate those in need of supportive nursing in the same age group. The home operates on a a nonprofit basis and is debt-free.

Marian Home
2400 6th Ave N, Fort Dodge, IA, 50501 (515)
576-1138
Admin Gerald J Bruening.
Licensure Intermediate Care. *Beds* 97. *Certified* Medicaid.
Staff RNs 5 (ft), 7 (pt); LPNs 5 (pt); Nurses aides 15 (ft), 29 (pt); Physical therapists 2 (ft), 1 (pt); Speech therapists 1 (pt); Activities coordinators 2 (ft); Dietitians 1 (pt); Audiologists 1 (pt).
Affiliation Roman Catholic
Facilities Dining room; Physical therapy room; Activities room; Chapel; Crafts room; Laundry room; Barber/Beauty shop.
Activities Arts and Crafts; Cards; Games; Reading groups; Prayer groups; Movies; Shop-

ping trips; Dances/Social or cultural gatherings.
Description Home is a single floor facility with 12 apartments next to facility.

Villa Park Care Center*
728 14th Ave N, Fort Dodge, IA, 50501 (515) 576-7226
Admin Robert J Dahl.
Licensure Intermediate Care. *Beds* 100. *Certified* Medicaid.

FORT MADISON

Fort Madison Nursing Care Center
1702 41st St, Fort Madison, IA, 52627 (319) 372-8021
Admin Sr Donna Venteicher.
Licensure Intermediate Care. *Beds* 108. *Certified* Medicaid.
Admissions Requirements Minimum age 16; Medical examination.
Staff RNs 6 (ft), 2 (pt); LPNs 1 (ft), 3 (pt); Nurses aides 21 (ft), 15 (pt); Physical therapists; Occupational therapists; Speech therapists; Activities coordinators 1 (ft); Dietitians 1 (pt); Podiatrists; Audiologists.
Facilities Dining room; Physical therapy room; Chapel; Laundry room; Barber/Beauty shop.
Activities Arts and Crafts; Cards; Games; Reading groups; Prayer groups; Movies; Shopping trips; Dances/Social or cultural gatherings.
Description Facility offers 4-meal plan with selective menus, van for outings, and a quiet country atmosphere.

FREDERICKSBURG

Sunrise Guest Home*
Lions Rd, Fredericksburg, IA, 50630 (515) 237-5323
Admin Sharon Jan Ploeger.
Licensure Intermediate Care. *Beds* 37. *Certified* Medicaid.

GARNER

Concord Manor*
1375 Division St, Garner, IA, 50438 (515) 923-2677
Admin Becky L Smit.
Licensure Intermediate Care. *Beds* 66. *Certified* Medicaid.

GEORGE

George Community Good Samaritan Center*
400 N Washington, George, IA, 51237 (712) 475-3391
Admin Eugene R Mathison.
Licensure Intermediate Care. *Beds* 48. *Certified* Medicaid.

GLADBROOK

Westbrook Acres*
Hwy 69 W, Gladbrook, IA, 50635 (515) 473-2016

Admin Loretta L Larson.
Licensure Intermediate Care. *Beds* 33. *Certified* Medicaid.

GLENWOOD

Glen Haven Home*
302 6th St, Glenwood, IA, 51534 (712) 527-3101
Admin Monte L McVey.
Licensure Intermediate Care. *Beds* 90. *Certified* Medicaid.

Hillside Manor Corp
114 E Green St, Glenwood, IA, 51534 (712) 527-4841
Medical Dir/Dir of Nursing Robet K Fryzek.
Licensure Intermediate Care; Intermediate Care for Mentally Retarded. *Beds* ICF 67; ICF/MR 112. *Certified* Medicaid.
Staff Physicians 1 (pt); RNs 2 (ft); LPNs 12 (ft); Orderlies 7 (ft), 1 (pt); Nurses aides 63 (ft); Physical therapists 1 (pt); Recreational therapists 2 (ft); Occupational therapists 1 (pt); Speech therapists 1 (ft); Activities coordinators 1 (ft); Dietitians 1 (ft).
Facilities Dining room; Physical therapy room; Activities room; Crafts room; Laundry room; Barber/Beauty shop.
Activities Arts and Crafts; Games; Reading groups; Prayer groups; Movies; Shopping trips; Dances/Social or cultural gatherings.
Description Community based facility providing individualized programs, and specialty programs in rehabilitation and restorative care.

GOWRIE

Gowrie Manor*
1808 Main St, Gowrie, IA, 50543 (515) 352-3912
Admin William C Platts.
Licensure Intermediate Care. *Beds* 51. *Certified* Medicaid.

GRANGER

Granger Manor
2001 Kennedy, Granger, IA, 50109 (515) 999-2588
Licensure Intermediate Care. *Beds* 67. *Certified* Medicaid.

GREENE

Mathers Nursing Home
108 S High St, Greene, IA, 50636 (515) 823-4531
Admin Alberta Mathers.
Licensure Intermediate Care. *Beds* 25. *Certified* Medicaid.
Admissions Requirements Medical examination; Physician's request.
Staff LPNs 1 (ft), 3 (pt); Nurses aides 2 (ft), 10 (pt); Activities coordinators 1 (pt).
Facilities Dining room; Laundry room; Barber/Beauty shop.
Activities Arts and Crafts; Cards; Games; Reading groups; Prayer groups; Movies; Dances/Social or cultural gatherings.

GREENFIELD

Greenfield Manor Inc
615 SE Kent, Greenfield, IA, 50849 (515) 743-6131
Admin Helen L Martin.
Licensure Intermediate Care. *Beds* 57. *Certified* Medicaid.
Admissions Requirements Medical examination; Physician's request.
Staff RNs 3 (pt); LPNs 3 (ft), 3 (pt); Orderlies 1 (ft); Nurses aides 16 (ft), 9 (pt); Activities coordinators 3 (pt); Dietitians 1 (pt).
Facilities Dining room; Physical therapy room; Activities room.
Activities Arts and Crafts; Cards; Games; Reading groups; Prayer groups; Movies; Dances/Social or cultural gatherings.

GRINNELL

Friendship Manor Inc*
Rt 2, Grinnell, IA, 50112 (515) 236-6511
Admin Gordon Van Donselaar.
Licensure Intermediate Care. *Beds* 77. *Certified* Medicaid.

Mayflower Home
616 Broad, Grinnell, IA, 50112 (515) 236-6151
Medical Dir/Dir of Nursing Patricia Avalos RN.
Licensure Intermediate Care; Residential Care. *Beds* ICF 26; Residential Care 34. *Certified* Medicaid.
Admissions Requirements Medical examination.
Staff RNs 2 (ft), 4 (pt); LPNs 1 (ft), 1 (pt); Orderlies 1 (ft), 1 (pt); Nurses aides 7 (ft), 4 (pt); Activities coordinators 2 (pt).
Affiliation Church of Christ
Facilities Dining room; Physical therapy room; Activities room; Chapel; Crafts room; Laundry room; Barber/Beauty shop; Library.
Activities Arts and Crafts; Cards; Games; Reading groups; Prayer groups; Shopping trips; Dances/Social or cultural gatherings.
Description Mayflower Home consists of a campus with 5 buildings which provide independent living apartments and one building providing residential and intermediate care.

Saint Francis Manor Inc
2021 4th Ave, Grinnell, IA, 50112 (515) 236-7592
Licensure Intermediate Care. *Beds* 51. *Certified* Medicaid.
Admissions Requirements Physician's request.
Staff RNs 1 (ft); LPNs 2 (ft), 1 (pt); Nurses aides 25 (ft); Physical therapists 1 (pt); Speech therapists 1 (pt); Activities coordinators 1 (ft); Dietitians 1 (pt); Podiatrists 1 (pt); Audiologists 1 (pt).
Affiliation Roman Catholic
Facilities Dining room; Physical therapy room; Activities room; Crafts room; Laundry room; Barber/Beauty shop.
Activities Arts and Crafts; Cards; Games; Reading groups; Prayer groups; Movies; Shopping trips; Dances/Social or cultural gatherings.
Description Facility has a van which takes the

residents to the local hospital free of charge and which has a wheelchair lift for transporting nonambulatory residents.

GRISWOLD

Griswold Care Center Inc*
106 Harrison St, Griswold, IA, 51535 (712) 778-2534
Admin Joyce Hansen Shultz.
Licensure Intermediate Care; Residential Care. *Beds* ICF 40; Residential Care 6. *Certified* Medicaid.

GRUNDY CENTER

Beverly Manor Convalescent Center
1st St and J Ave, Grundy Center, IA, 50638 (319) 824-5436
Licensure Intermediate Care. *Beds* 47. *Certified* Medicaid.
Admissions Requirements Physician's request.
Staff LPNs 2 (ft), 2 (pt); Orderlies 1 (ft); Nurses aides 9 (ft), 5 (pt); Activities coordinators 1 (ft); 7 (ft), 11 (pt).
Facilities Dining room; Physical therapy room; Activities room; Laundry room; Barber/Beauty shop.
Activities Arts and Crafts; Games; Reading groups; Prayer groups; Movies; Shopping trips.

Grundy County Memorial Hospital—Nursing Home
E "J" Ave, Grundy Center, IA, 50638
Admin Ed Whitver.
Licensure Skilled Care; Intermediate Care. *Beds* 55. *Certified* Medicaid; Medicare.
Ownership Public.
Admissions Requirements Medical examination.
Staff Physicians 3 (ft); RNs 1 (ft), 1 (pt); LPNs 2 (ft), 1 (pt); Nurses aides 12 (ft), 5 (pt); Physical therapists 1 (pt); Occupational therapists 1 (pt); Speech therapists 1 (pt); Activities coordinators 1 (ft); Dietitians 1 (pt); Dentists 1 (pt); Podiatrists 1 (pt); Urologists 1 (pt).
Facilities Dining room; Physical therapy room; Activities room; Laundry room.
Activities Arts and Crafts; Games; Reading groups; Prayer groups; Movies; Dances/Social or cultural gatherings.
Description Facility is attached to a 33-bed hospital, making available the best medical services that may be needed by residents without leaving the building.

GUTHRIE CENTER

The New Homestead*
Rt 2, PO Box 13, Guthrie Center, IA, 50115 (515) 747-2204
Admin Keith A Jennings.
Licensure Intermediate Care. *Beds* 66. *Certified* Medicaid.

GUTTENBERG

Riverview Care Center Inc*
400 Acre St, Guttenberg, IA, 52052 (319) 252-2281

Admin Robert E Wooldridge.
Licensure Intermediate Care. *Beds* ICF 93.
Certified Medicaid.

HAMPTON

Franklin General Hospital*
1720 Central Ave E, Hampton, IA, 50441 (515) 456-4721
Admin Gary L Peterson.
Licensure Intermediate Care. *Beds* 52.

Franklin Nursing Home
105 1st Ave SW, Hampton, IA, 50441 (515) 456-4724
Licensure Intermediate Care. *Beds* 73. *Certified* Medicaid.

Hampton Nursing Home*
700 2nd St SE, Hampton, IA, 50441 (515) 456-4701
Admin Claudia Boeding.
Licensure Intermediate Care. *Beds* 97. *Certified* Medicaid.

HARLAN

Baptist Memorial Home*
2104 12th St, Harlan, IA, 51537 (712) 755-5174
Admin Warren Rippey.
Licensure Intermediate Care; Residential Care. *Beds* ICF 71; Residential Care 54. *Certified* Medicaid.
Affiliation Baptist

HARTLEY

Community Memorial Hospital*
8th Ave W, Hartley, IA, 51346 (712) 728-2428
Admin Madonna Towne.
Licensure Intermediate Care. *Beds* 43.

HAWARDEN

Hass Hillcrest Care Center*
2121 Ave L, Hawarden, IA, 51023 (712) 552-1074
Admin Vera M Dieck.
Licensure Intermediate Care. *Beds* 50. *Certified* Medicaid.

HILLS

Atrium Village*
Brady and 3rd, Hills, IA, 52235 (319) 679-2324
Admin Sharon K J Smith.
Licensure Intermediate Care. *Beds* 20.

HOLSTEIN

Holstein Good Samaritan Center*
505 W 2nd St, Holstein, IA, 51025 (712) 368-4323
Admin Cameron Liebenow.
Licensure Intermediate Care. *Beds* 60. *Certified* Medicaid.

HULL

Pleasant Acres of Hull*
309 Railroad, Hull, IA, 51239 (712) 439-2758
Admin John P Lienemann. *Medical Dir/Dir of Nursing* Helen DeStigter RN.
Licensure Intermediate Care. *Beds* 50. *Certified* Medicaid.
Admissions Requirements Medical examination; Physician's request.
Facilities Dining room; Physical therapy room; Laundry room; Barber/Beauty shop.
Activities Arts and Crafts; Cards; Games; Reading groups; Prayer groups; Movies; Shopping trips; Dances/Social or cultural gatherings; Bingo.

HUMBOLDT

Humboldt Care Center—North
1111 11th Ave N, Humboldt, IA, 50548 (515) 332-2623
Licensure Intermediate Care. *Beds* 100. *Certified* Medicaid.
Admissions Requirements Medical examination; Physician's request.
Staff RNs 4 (ft), 4 (pt); Orderlies 2 (ft), 3 (pt); Nurses aides 30 (ft), 20 (pt); Activities coordinators 1 (ft), 1 (pt); Dietitians 1 (pt).
Facilities Dining room; Physical therapy room; Activities room; Crafts room; Laundry room; Barber/Beauty shop.
Activities Arts and Crafts; Cards; Games; Reading groups; Prayer groups; Movies; Shopping trips; Dances/Social or cultural gatherings.
Description Goal of center is to provide a home for residents with not only decor and atmosphere in mind but also attitude of those who work and live here.

Humboldt Care Center—South
Hwy 169 S, Humboldt, IA, 50548 (515) 332-4104
Licensure Intermediate Care. *Beds* 50. *Certified* Medicaid.
Admissions Requirements Physician's request.
Facilities Dining room; Physical therapy room; Activities room; Crafts room; Laundry room; Barber/Beauty shop.
Activities Arts and Crafts; Cards; Games; Reading groups; Prayer groups; Movies; Shopping trips; Dances/Social or cultural gatherings.

IDA GROVE

Morningside Care Center
600 Morningside Ave, Ida Grove, IA, 51445 (712) 364-3327
Medical Dir/Dir of Nursing Jagne Harter.
Licensure Intermediate Care. *Beds* 52. *Certified* Medicaid.
Staff RNs 1 (ft); LPNs 3 (ft), 3 (pt); Physical therapists 1 (pt); Activities coordinators 1 (ft); Dietitians 1 (pt); Dentists 1 (pt); Audiologists 1 (pt).
Facilities Dining room; Physical therapy room; Activities room; Laundry room; Barber/Beauty shop.
Activities Arts and Crafts; Cards; Games; Reading groups; Prayer groups; Movies; Shopping trips; Dances/Social or cultural gatherings.

Description Facility is one-story, 2 wings all double rooms; 20 beds to be added this year, all ICF beds.

INDEPENDENCE

East Towne Manor
1700 3rd St, Independence, IA, 50644 (319) 334-7015
Licensure Intermediate Care. *Beds* 53. *Certified* Medicaid.
Staff RNs 1 (pt); LPNs 4 (ft), 3 (pt); Nurses aides 22 (pt); Physical therapists 1 (pt); Recreational therapists 1 (pt); Occupational therapists 1 (pt); Speech therapists 1 (pt); Activities coordinators 1 (ft); Dietitians 1 (pt); Dentists 1 (pt); Ophthalmologists 1 (pt); Podiatrists 1 (pt); Audiologists 1 (pt).
Facilities Dining room; Physical therapy room; Activities room; Laundry room; Barber/Beauty shop.
Activities Arts and Crafts; Cards; Games; Reading groups; Prayer groups; Movies; Shopping trips; Dances/Social or cultural gatherings.
Description We offer membership in the Pinicon Club—a new concept in intermediate health care. Residents receive 85 amenities absolutely free. All of these are included in one club rate. It is designed for the resident who wants more value for his or her health care dollar.

Independence Care Center*
1600 3rd St NE, Independence, IA, 50644 (319) 334-6039
Admin Lela J Barnes.
Licensure Intermediate Care. *Beds* 101. *Certified* Medicaid.

People's Memorial Hospital Nursing Care Center*
Hwy 20 E, Independence, IA, 50644 (319) 334-6071
Admin Betty Meehan.
Licensure Intermediate Care. *Beds* 59. *Certified* Medicaid.

INDIANOLA

Indianola Good Samaritan Center—East*
708 S Jefferson, Indianola, IA, 50125 (515) 961-2596
Admin Lanny Ward.
Licensure Intermediate Care. *Beds* 101. *Certified* Medicaid.

Indianola Good Samaritan Center—West*
709 S Jefferson, Indianola, IA, 50125 (515) 961-2596
Admin Lanny Ward.
Licensure Intermediate Care. *Beds* 41. *Certified* Medicaid.

Salem Manor
Box 318, Indianola, IA, 50125
Admin Pamela Rogers. *Medical Dir/Dir of Nursing* Ellen Emery.
Licensure Residential Care. *Beds* 33.
Certified Medicaid; Medicare.
Ownership Proprietary.
Admissions Requirements Males only; Medical

examination; Physician's request.
Staff LPNs 1 (ft); Nurses aides 4 (ft), 2 (pt); Recreational therapists 1 (ft); Activities coordinators 1 (ft).
Facilities Dining room; Activities room; Crafts room; Laundry room.
Activities Arts and Crafts; Cards; Games; Prayer groups; Shopping trips.

Westview Care Center Inc*
1900 W 3rd Pl, Indianola, IA, 50125 (515) 961-3189
Admin Maxine L Runyan.
Licensure Intermediate Care. *Beds* 74. *Certified* Medicaid.

IOWA CITY

Beverly Manor Convalescent Center
605 Greenwood Dr, Iowa City, IA, 52240 (319) 338-7912
Licensure Intermediate Care. *Beds* 87. *Certified* Medicaid.
Admissions Requirements Medical examination.
Staff RNs 5 (ft), 4 (pt); LPNs 2 (ft), 1 (pt); Orderlies 1 (pt); Nurses aides 16 (ft), 16 (pt); Physical therapists 1 (pt); Activities coordinators 1 (ft), 1 (pt); Dietitians 1 (pt).
Facilities Dining room; Physical therapy room; Activities room; Crafts room; Laundry room; Barber/Beauty shop; Library; Outside patio.
Activities Arts and Crafts; Cards; Games; Reading groups; Prayer groups; Movies; Shopping trips; Dances/Social or cultural gatherings; Pet days; Visits by school children; Outings to restaurants.
Description Beautiful physical plant surrounded by trees; services of a home health agency and a 16-unit congregate living complex available; excellent food and a well-rounded activities program; licensed nurses on staff 24-hours a day.

Iowa City Care Center
Rochester and Scott Rd, Iowa City, IA, 52240 (319) 351-7460
Licensure Intermediate Care. *Beds* 89. *Certified* Medicaid.
Admissions Requirements Medical examination; Physician's request.
Staff RNs 4 (ft), 3 (pt); LPNs 3 (ft), 3 (pt); Orderlies 1 (ft); Nurses aides 20 (ft), 11 (pt); Activities coordinators 1 (ft).
Facilities Dining room; Activities room; Crafts room; Laundry room; Barber/Beauty shop.
Activities Arts and Crafts; Cards; Games; Reading groups; Prayer groups; Movies; Shopping trips; Dances/Social or cultural gatherings.

Oaknoll Retirement Residence*
701 Oaknoll Dr, Iowa City, IA, 52240 (319) 351-1720
Admin Felicia Hope.
Licensure Skilled Care; Intermediate Care.
Beds SNF 32; ICF 16. *Certified* Medicare.

IOWA FALLS

Heritage Care Center
2320 Washington Ave, Iowa Falls, IA, 50126 (515) 648-4250
Licensure Intermediate Care. *Beds* 50. *Certified* Medicaid.
Admissions Requirements Minimum age 18; Medical examination; Physician's request.
Staff RNs 1 (ft); LPNs 3 (ft); Nurses aides 11 (ft), 7 (pt); Physical therapists 1 (pt); Recreational therapists 1 (ft); Occupational therapists 1 (pt); Speech therapists 1 (pt); Activities coordinators 1 (ft); Dietitians 1 (pt).
Facilities Dining room; Physical therapy room; Activities room; Laundry room; Barber/Beauty shop; Library.
Activities Arts and Crafts; Cards; Games; Reading groups; Prayer groups; Movies; Shopping trips; Dances/Social or cultural gatherings.

Scenic Manor*
Manor Dr and Fremont, Iowa Falls, IA, 50126 (515) 648-4671
Admin Glenn O Doupe.
Licensure Intermediate Care. *Beds* 61. *Certified* Medicaid.

JEFFERSON

Greene County Medical Center*
1000 W Lincolnway, Jefferson, IA, 50129 (515) 386-2114
Admin James E Bagley.
Licensure Intermediate Care. *Beds* 75.

Jefferson Manor*
100 E Sunset, Jefferson, IA, 50129 (515) 386-4107
Admin Lyle Hight.
Licensure Intermediate Care. *Beds* 93. *Certified* Medicaid.

KALONA

Pleasant View Home
811 3rd St, Kalona, IA, 52247 (319) 656-2421
Licensure Intermediate Care. *Beds* 49. *Certified* Medicaid.
Admissions Requirements Medical examination.
Affiliation Mennonite
Facilities Dining room; Physical therapy room; Activities room; Chapel; Barber/Beauty shop.
Activities Games; Reading groups; Prayer groups; Shopping trips.

KANAWHA

Kanawha Community Home
130 W 6th St, Kanawha, IA, 50447 (515) 762-3302
Licensure Intermediate Care. *Beds* 44. *Certified* Medicaid.
Staff RNs 2 (ft), 1 (pt); LPNs 1 (ft), 2 (pt); Nurses aides 5 (ft), 15 (pt); Activities coordinators 1 (ft).
Facilities Dining room; Activities room; Laundry room; Barber/Beauty shop.
Activities Arts and Crafts; Games; Reading

groups; Prayer groups; Movies.
Description This is a good place to live when you can't live alone.

KEOKUK

Keokuk Convalescent Center*
500 Mesenger Rd, Keokuk, IA, 52632 (319) 524-5321
Admin Ralph Roberts.
Licensure Skilled Care; Intermediate Care. *Beds* SNF 21; ICF 105. *Certified* Medicaid; Medicare.

River Hills in Keokuk*
3140 Plank Rd, Keokuk, IA, 52632 (319) 524-5772
Admin Joyce L Post.
Licensure Intermediate Care. *Beds* 62. *Certified* Medicaid.

KEOSAUQUA

Van Buren Good Samaritan Center
Dodge and Country Rd, Keosauqua, IA, 52565 (319) 293-3761
Medical Dir/Dir of Nursing Dr Kiyoshi Furumoto.
Licensure Intermediate Care. *Beds* 75. *Certified* Medicaid.
Admissions Requirements Minimum age 16; Medical examination; Physician's request.
Staff RNs 1 (ft), 7 (pt); LPNs 1 (ft), 3 (pt); Orderlies 2 (pt); Nurses aides 9 (ft), 35 (pt).
Facilities Dining room; Physical therapy room; Activities room; Chapel; Crafts room; Laundry room; Barber/Beauty shop.
Activities Arts and Crafts; Cards; Games; Reading groups; Prayer groups; Movies; Shopping trips; Dances/Social or cultural gatherings.

KEOTA

Maplewood Manor Inc*
County Line Rd, Keota, IA, 52248 (515) 636-3400
Admin Bernadette Adams.
Licensure Intermediate Care. *Beds* 54. *Certified* Medicaid.

KEYSTONE

Keystone Nursing Care Center*
5th St E, Keystone, IA, 52249 (319) 442-3234
Admin Susan Rieck.
Licensure Intermediate Care. *Beds* 45.

KINGSLEY

Colonial Manors of Kingsley*
Box 407, Kingsley, IA, 51028 (712) 378-2400
Admin Donna Enderlin.
Licensure Intermediate Care. *Beds* 43. *Certified* Medicaid.

KNOXVILLE

Griffin Nursing Center*
606 N 7th St, Knoxville, IA, 50138 (515) 842-2187
Admin Hazel M Griffin.
Licensure Intermediate Care. *Beds* 60. *Certified* Medicaid.

Knoxville Rest Home
205 N Iowa St, Knoxville, IA, 50138 (515) 842-4618
Licensure Intermediate Care. *Beds* 34. *Certified* Medicaid.
Staff RNs 1 (ft), 1 (pt); LPNs 2 (ft); Nurses aides 26 (pt); Physical therapists 1 (pt); Recreational therapists 1 (ft); Occupational therapists 1 (pt); Speech therapists 1 (pt); Activities coordinators 1 (ft); Dietitians 1 (pt); Podiatrists 1 (pt); Audiologists 1 (pt).
Facilities Dining room; Laundry room.
Activities Arts and Crafts; Cards; Games; Reading groups; Prayer groups; Movies; Shopping trips; Dances/Social or cultural gatherings.
Description Knoxville Rest Home gives quality care in a home-like atmosphere.

Marion County Care Facility
Rt 2, Knoxville, IA, 50138
Admin K V Orr.
Licensure Residential Care. *Beds* 50.
Ownership Nonprofit.
Admissions Requirements Minimum age 18; Medical examination; Physician's request.
Staff LPNs 1 (ft); Nurses aides 5 (ft), 1 (pt); Activities coordinators 1 (ft); Dietitians 1 (ft); Medical aides 5 (ft), 1 (pt).
Facilities Dining room; Activities room; Chapel; Crafts room; Barber/Beauty shop.
Activities Arts and Crafts; Cards; Games; Reading groups; Prayer groups; Movies; Shopping trips; Dances/Social or cultural gatherings.
Description Facility has a workshop where the residents work and are paid for each piece they do.

West Ridge Manor*
1201 W Jackson St, Knoxville, IA, 50138 (515) 842-3153
Admin Denna M Ford.
Licensure Intermediate Care. *Beds* 78. *Certified* Medicaid.

LAKE CITY

Shady Oaks*
Lake City, IA, 51449 (712) 464-3106
Admin Lois Nadine Lindsay.
Licensure Skilled Care; Intermediate Care. *Beds* SNF 12; ICF 127. *Certified* Medicaid; Medicare.

LAKE MILLS

Lake Mills Nursing Home Inc*
406 S 10th Ave E, Lake Mills, IA, 50450 (515) 592-4900
Admin Robert Helgeson.
Licensure Intermediate Care. *Beds* 101. *Certified* Medicaid.

LAKE PARK

Lake Park Care Center*
1304 Market St, Lake Park, IA, 51347 (712) 832-3691
Admin Robert J Hinz.
Licensure Intermediate Care. *Beds* 51. *Certified* Medicaid.

LAMONI

Lamoni Manor
215 S Oak St, Lamoni, IA, 50140 (515) 784-3388
Medical Dir/Dir of Nursing Velma Gleason RN.
Licensure Intermediate Care. *Beds* 51. *Certified* Medicaid.
Admissions Requirements Minimum age 16; Medical examination; Physician's request.
Staff RNs 2 (ft), 1 (pt); LPNs 2 (ft); Orderlies 2 (pt); Nurses aides 13 (ft), 9 (pt); Physical therapists 1 (pt); Speech therapists 1 (pt); Activities coordinators 1 (ft); Dietitians 1 (pt); Dentists 1 (pt); Audiologists 1 (pt).
Facilities Dining room; Activities room; Laundry room; Barber/Beauty shop; Library.
Activities Arts and Crafts; Cards; Games; Prayer groups; Movies; Shopping trips.
Description Lamoni Manor is licensed as an intermediate care facility (ICF) and has been serving the area since 1973; every effort is made to provide a home-like atmosphere both in comfort and privacy.

LANSING

Thornton Manor*
1329 Main, Lansing, IA, 52151 (319) 533-4236
Admin Stephen H Haas.
Licensure Intermediate Care. *Beds* 60. *Certified* Medicaid.

LAPORTE CITY

Colonial Manor
Hwy 218 N, LaPorte City, IA, 50651 (319) 342-2125
Licensure Intermediate Care. *Beds* 46. *Certified* Medicaid.
Admissions Requirements Minimum age 18; Medical examination; Physician's request.
Staff RNs 1 (ft); LPNs 3 (ft); Nurses aides 5 (ft), 5 (pt); Physical therapists 1 (pt); Occupational therapists 1 (pt); Speech therapists 1 (pt); Activities coordinators 1 (ft); Dietitians 1 (pt); Dentists 1 (pt); Podiatrists 1 (pt); Audiologists 1 (pt).
Facilities Dining room; Laundry room; Barber/Beauty shop.
Activities Arts and Crafts; Cards; Games; Reading groups; Prayer groups; Movies; Shopping trips; Dances/Social or cultural gatherings; Weekly music therapy.
Description Weight reduction classes offered to the community by facility dietician; 100 member volunteer auxiliary.

LAURENS

Hovenden Memorial Good Samaritan Home*
304 E Veterans Rd, Laurens, IA, 50554 (712)
845-4915
Admin Vergene Bailey.
Licensure Intermediate Care; Residential Care.
Beds ICF 42; Residential Care 9. *Certified* Medicaid.

LEMARS

Brentwood Good Samaritan Center*
Hwy 3 E, Lemars, IA, 51031 (712) 546-4101
Admin Larry D Sieler.
Licensure Intermediate Care. *Beds* 65. *Certified* Medicaid.

Plymouth Manor Care Center*
954 7th Ave SE, Lemars, IA, 51031 (712)
546-7831
Admin Patricia A McDougall.
Licensure Intermediate Care. *Beds* 83. *Certified* Medicaid.

LENOX

Lenox Care Center*
111 E Van Buren, Lenox, IA, 50851 (515)
333-2226
Admin Virginia Bennett.
Licensure Intermediate Care. *Beds* 53. *Certified* Medicaid.

LEON

Leon Care Center*
200 Northern Ave, Leon, IA, 50144 (515)
446-4833
Admin Gary A Martin.
Licensure Intermediate Care. *Beds* 61. *Certified* Medicaid.

Westview Acres
Jct 2 and 69 W, Leon, IA, 50144 (515)
446-4165
Licensure Intermediate Care. *Beds* 91. *Certified* Medicaid.
Admissions Requirements Minimum age 16.
Staff RNs 1 (ft); LPNs 7 (ft); Nurses aides 27
(ft), 5 (pt); Speech therapists 1 (pt); Activities
coordinators 2 (ft); Dietitians 1 (pt); Dentists 1
(pt).
Facilities Dining room; Physical therapy room;
Activities room; Crafts room; Laundry room;
Barber/Beauty shop.
Activities Arts and Crafts; Cards; Games;
Reading groups; Prayer groups; Movies; Shopping trips; Dances/Social or cultural gatherings.

LOGAN

Westmont Care Center
314 S Elm, Logan, IA, 51546 (712) 644-2922
Licensure Intermediate Care; Residential Care.
Beds ICF 73; Residential Care 26. *Certified* Medicaid.

LONE TREE

Lone Tree Health Care Center*
Pioneer Rd, Lone Tree, IA, 52755 (319)
629-4255
Admin Dale Van Dewater.
Licensure Intermediate Care. *Beds* 46. *Certified* Medicaid.

MADRID

Madrid Home for the Aging*
613 W North St, Madrid, IA, 50156 (515)
795-3007
Admin William R Thayer.
Licensure Intermediate Care; Residential Care.
Beds ICF 109; Residential Care 39. *Certified* Medicaid.

MALVERN

Nishna Care Center Inc*
902 2nd Ave, Malvern, IA, 51551 (712)
624-8300
Admin Geraldine A Reid.
Licensure Intermediate Care. *Beds* 51. *Certified* Medicaid.

MANCHESTER

Delaware County Memorial Hospital*
709 W Main, Manchester, IA, 52057 (319)
927-3232
Admin Paul Albright.
Licensure Intermediate Care. *Beds* 37.

Good Neighbor Home*
105 McCarren Dr, Manchester, IA, 52057 (319)
927-3907
Admin Paul C Wenske.
Licensure Intermediate Care. *Beds* 106. *Certified* Medicaid.

Memorial Care Center
709 W Main, Manchester, IA, 52057 (319)
927-2626
Medical Dir/Dir of Nursing Larry Severidt
MD.
Licensure Intermediate Care. *Beds* 37. *Certified* Medicaid.
Admissions Requirements Minimum age 16;
Medical examination; Physician's request.
Staff Physicians 9 (ft), 1 (pt); RNs 1 (ft); LPNs
1 (ft), 4 (pt); Nurses aides 4 (ft), 15 (pt);
Physical therapists 1 (pt); Speech therapists 1
(pt); Activities coordinators 1 (pt); Activities
coordinators 1 (pt); Dentists 5 (pt); Podiatrists
1 (pt); Audiologists 1 (pt).
Facilities Dining room; Physical therapy room;
Activities room; Crafts room; Laundry room;
Barber/Beauty shop.
Activities Arts and Crafts; Cards; Games;
Reading groups; Prayer groups; Movies; Dances/Social or cultural gatherings.

MANILLA

Manilla Manor*
158 N 5th St, Manilla, IA, 51454 (712)
654-6812

Admin Dana Jorgensen.
Licensure Intermediate Care. *Beds* 63. *Certified* Medicaid.

MANLY

Manly Care Center
Hwy 9 E, Manly, IA, 50456 (515) 454-2223
Admin Delores Denney. *Medical Dir/Dir of
Nursing* Dr Richard Munns.
Licensure Intermediate Care. *Beds* 69. *Certified* Medicaid.
Admissions Requirements Minimum age 21;
Medical examination; Physician's request.
Staff RNs 2 (ft), 3 (pt); LPNs 2 (ft), 2 (pt);
Orderlies 1 (ft), 1 (pt); Nurses aides 16 (ft), 10
(pt); Activities coordinators 1 (ft); Dietitians 1
(pt).
Facilities Dining room; Physical therapy room;
Activities room; Crafts room; Laundry room;
Barber/Beauty shop; Library.
Activities Arts and Crafts; Cards; Games;
Movies; Dances/Social or cultural gatherings.
Description Quality of care is high; ancillary
services contracted through nearby hospitals;
family practice makes routine visits to the
nursing home. Transportation is provided by
Easter Seal Society. Spiritual needs are met by
local pastors.

MANNING

Manning General Hospital*
410–412 Main St, Manning, IA, 51455 (712)
653-2072
Admin Darrell E Vondrak.
Licensure Intermediate Care. *Beds* 58.

Manning Plaza
402 Main St, Manning, IA, 51455 (712)
653-6441
Licensure Intermediate Care. *Beds* 46. *Certified* Medicaid.

MANSON

Manson Good Samaritan Center*
1402 Main St, Manson, IA, 50563 (712)
469-3908
Admin June V Eno.
Licensure Intermediate Care. *Beds* 50. *Certified* Medicaid.

MAPLETON

Maple Heights Inc*
Sunrise Ave, Mapleton, IA, 51034 (712)
882-1680
Admin Richard Feauto.
Licensure Intermediate Care. *Beds* 64. *Certified* Medicaid.

MAQUOKETA

Crestridge Inc
1015 Wesley Dr, Maquoketa, IA, 52060 (319)
652-4968
Licensure Intermediate Care. *Beds* 101. *Certified* Medicaid.

Admissions Requirements Medical examination.
Staff RNs 3 (ft), 4 (pt); LPNs 1 (ft), 4 (pt); Orderlies 1 (pt); Nurses aides 10 (ft), 33 (pt); Activities coordinators 2 (pt); Dietitians 1 (pt).
Facilities Dining room; Physical therapy room; Activities room; Chapel; Crafts room; Laundry room; Barber/Beauty shop; Library.
Activities Arts and Crafts; Cards; Games; Prayer groups; Movies; Dances/Social or cultural gatherings.

Jackson County Public Hospital*
700 W Grove St, Maquoketa, IA, 52060 (319) 652-2474
Admin Jon L Jensen.
Licensure Skilled Care. *Beds* 18.
Ownership Public.

Manning Residential Care Center
601 W Summit St, Maquoketa, IA, 52060
Admin Cleo Manning.
Licensure Intermediate Care. *Beds* 15.
Ownership Proprietary.
Admissions Requirements Minimum age 50; Physician's request.
Staff LPNs 1 (pt); Nurses aides 4 (ft); Activities coordinators 1 (pt).
Facilities Dining room; Activities room; Laundry room.
Activities Arts and Crafts; Cards; Games; Prayer groups; Movies; Shopping trips.
Description Facility is a very small, brick home; personal care given to residents; church groups provide activities.

Maquoketa Care Center
McKinsey Dr, Maquoketa, IA, 52060 (319) 652-5195
Admin Uda Coon.
Licensure Intermediate Care. *Beds* 50. *Certified* Medicaid.
Admissions Requirements Minimum age 18; Medical examination; Physician's request.
Staff RNs 2 (pt); LPNs 1 (ft), 2 (pt); Orderlies 1 (ft); Nurses aides 6 (ft), 18 (pt); Activities coordinators 2 (pt).
Facilities Dining room; Physical therapy room; Activities room; Crafts room; Laundry room; Barber/Beauty shop.
Activities Arts and Crafts; Cards; Games; Reading groups; Prayer groups; Movies; Shopping trips; Dances/Social or cultural gatherings.
Description The Center offers trips into the community in the van, poetry and current events, spelling bees, weaving, and quilt making; family meals are provided with outdoor barbecues in summer; gifts given to residents on their birthdays and at Christmas.

MARENGO

Rose Haven Nursing Home Inc
1500 N Franklin Ave, Marengo, IA, 52301 (319) 642-3221
Medical Dir/Dir of Nursing Mary Ellen Montrose.
Licensure Intermediate Care. *Beds* 58. *Certified* Medicaid.
Admissions Requirements Minimum age 16; Medical examination.
Staff RNs 2 (ft); LPNs 2 (ft), 3 (pt); Nurses

aides 10 (ft), 14 (pt); Recreational therapists 1 (ft); Activities coordinators 1 (ft).
Facilities Dining room; Activities room; Chapel; Crafts room; Laundry room; Barber/Beauty shop.
Activities Arts and Crafts; Cards; Games; Reading groups; Prayer groups; Movies; Shopping trips; Dances/Social or cultural gatherings.

MARION

Crestview Acres Inc
1485 Grand Ave, Marion, IA, 52302 (319) 377-4823
Licensure Intermediate Care. *Beds* 101. *Certified* Medicaid.
Staff RNs 2 (ft); LPNs 9 (ft); Nurses aides 20 (ft), 10 (pt).

Linn County Care Facility
1860 County Home Rd, Marion, IA, 52302 (319) 398-3534
Medical Dir/Dir of Nursing Alfred Brendel.
Licensure Intermediate Care; Residential Care. *Beds* ICF 32; Residential Care 248. *Certified* Medicaid.
Admissions Requirements Minimum age 16; Medical examination; Physician's request.
Staff Physicians 1 (pt); RNs 2 (ft); LPNs 3 (ft), 3 (pt); Nurses aides 20 (ft), 15 (pt); Activities coordinators 5 (ft); Dietitians 1 (pt).
Facilities Dining room; Activities room; Crafts room; Laundry room; Barber/Beauty shop.
Activities Arts and Crafts; Cards; Games; Reading groups; Movies; Shopping trips; Dances/Social or cultural gatherings.

Linn Manor*
1140 Elim Dr, Marion, IA, 52302 (319) 377-4611
Admin Grant L Hagen.
Licensure Intermediate Care. *Beds* 44. *Certified* Medicaid.

Maple Lawn Home for Aged
7607 Council St, Marion, IA, 52302
Admin Nadine Trachta.
Licensure Residential Care. *Beds* 18.
Ownership Proprietary.
Admissions Requirements Minimum age 18; Medical examination; Physician's request.
Staff Nurses aides 6 (ft).
Facilities Dining room; Activities room; Laundry room; Barber/Beauty shop.
Activities Arts and Crafts; Cards; Games; Reading groups; Prayer groups.
Description Facility offers a home-like atmosphere with home cooked meals.

Willow Gardens*
455 31st St, Marion, IA, 52302 (319) 377-7363
Admin Donald Chensvold.
Licensure Intermediate Care. *Beds* 91. *Certified* Medicaid.

Winslow House*
3456 Indian Creek Rd, Marion, IA, 52302 (319) 377-8296
Admin Barry Morrissey.
Licensure Intermediate Care. *Beds* 50. *Certified* Medicaid.

MARSHALLTOWN

Grandview Heights*
910 E Olive St, Marshalltown, IA, 50158 (515) 752-4581
Admin Charles H Koonce.
Licensure Intermediate Care. *Beds* 129. *Certified* Medicaid.

Iowa Veterans Home
13th and Summitt St, Marshalltown, IA, 50158 (515) 752-1501
Medical Dir/Dir of Nursing Carroll E Kern MD.
Licensure Intermediate Care; Residential Care. *Beds* SNF 327; ICF 391; Residential Care 113.
Admissions Requirements Medical examination.
Staff Physicians 5 (ft), 12 (pt); RNs 63 (ft), 10 (pt); LPNs 64 (ft), 4 (pt); Nurses aides 214 (ft), 9 (pt); Physical therapists 2 (ft); Recreational therapists 25 (ft); Occupational therapists 3 (ft); Speech therapists 2 (ft); Activities coordinators 1 (ft); Dietitians 4 (ft); Dentists 1 (pt); Podiatrists 1 (pt); Audiologists 1 (ft); Optometrist 1 (pt) Dermatologist 1 (pt) Psychologist 1 (pt) X-Ray Tech 1 (ft) Lab Tech 4 (ft), 2 (pt) Respiratory Therapists 2 (ft) Social Workers 11 (ft) Drug Abuse Counselors 2 (ft) Pharmacist 4 (ft) Pharmacist Asst 4 (ft).
Facilities Dining room; Physical therapy room; Activities room; Chapel; Crafts room; Laundry room; Barber/Beauty shop; Library; Speech Clinic; Respiratory therapy clinic; Hearing clinic; Clinical laboratory X-ray; Dental office.
Activities Arts and Crafts; Cards; Games; Reading groups; Prayer groups; Movies; Shopping trips; Dances/Social or cultural gatherings.
Description Veterans and their spouses are eligible for admission.

Marshall County Care Facility
Rt 3, Marshalltown, IA, 50158 (515) 752-3694
Admin Marian Malloy.
Licensure Intermediate Care; Residential Care. *Beds* ICF 80; Residential Care 64. *Certified* Medicaid.
Admissions Requirements Minimum age 16; Medical examination; Physician's request.
Staff RNs 4 (ft); LPNs 6 (ft), 1 (pt); Orderlies 3 (ft), 2 (pt); Nurses aides 40 (ft), 9 (pt); Physical therapists; Recreational therapists 2 (ft); Occupational therapists; Speech therapists; Activities coordinators 1 (ft); Dietitians; Dentists; Audiologists.
Facilities Dining room; Physical therapy room; Activities room; Chapel; Crafts room; Laundry room; Barber/Beauty shop; Library.
Activities Arts and Crafts; Cards; Games; Reading groups; Prayer groups; Movies; Shopping trips; Dances/Social or cultural gatherings; Bowling; Flea markets; Fishing; Cooking; Kitchen band; School.

Marshalltown Manor Care Center*
2206 S Center, Marshalltown, IA, 50158 (515) 752-4553
Admin Diane Sarich.
Licensure Intermediate Care. *Beds* 82. *Certified* Medicaid.

Villa Del Sol*
2401 S 2nd St, Marshalltown, IA, 50158 (515) 752-1553
Admin Jan Plahn.
Licensure Intermediate Care; Residential Care.
Beds ICF 88; Residential Care 29. *Certified* Medicaid.

MASON CITY

Americana Healthcare Center*
222 S Pierce Ave, Mason City, IA, 50401 (515) 423-3355
Admin Barbara D Beirbaum.
Licensure Skilled Care. *Beds* 77. *Certified* Medicaid; Medicare.

Good Shepherd Geriatric Center*
302 2nd St NE, Mason City, IA, 50401 (515) 424-1740
Admin Joseph C Kempf.
Licensure Skilled Care; Intermediate Care; Residential Care. *Beds* SNF 20; ICF 236; Residential Care 10. *Certified* Medicaid; Medicare.

Heritage Nursing Center*
501 S Kentucky, Mason City, IA, 50401 (515) 432-2121
Admin Angela A Klus.
Licensure Intermediate Care. *Beds* 92. *Certified* Medicaid.

Iowa Odd Fellows Home
1037 19th St NW, Mason City, IA, 50401 (515) 432-0428
Admin Glen E Bandel. *Medical Dir/Dir of Nursing* Sylvia Lloyd.
Licensure Intermediate Care; Residential Care. *Beds* ICF 64; Residential Care 82. *Certified* Medicaid.
Ownership Nonprofit.
Admissions Requirements Medical examination; Physician's request.
Staff Physicians 5 (pt); RNs 1 (ft), 1 (pt); LPNs 10 (ft); Nurses aides 30 (ft), 12 (pt); Physical therapists 1 (pt); Reality therapists 1 (pt); Recreational therapists 1 (pt); Occupational therapists 1 (pt); Speech therapists 1 (pt); Activities coordinators 2 (ft), 1 (pt); Dietitians 1 (pt); Dentists 2 (pt); Ophthalmologists 1 (pt); Podiatrists 1 (pt); Audiologists 1 (pt).
Affiliation Independent Order of Odd Fellows
Facilities Dining room; Physical therapy room; Activities room; Crafts room; Laundry room; Barber/Beauty shop; Library.
Activities Arts and Crafts; Cards; Games; Reading groups; Prayer groups; Movies; Shopping trips.
Description This home is located on a 230-acre farm within the city of Mason City owned by the Grand Lodge of Iowa. The Odd Fellow and Rebekah Lodges provide nursing, residential care, and retirement living in the spirit of friendship, love, and truth.

MCGREGOR

Great River Care Center
PO Box E, McGregor, IA, 52044 (319) 873-3527
Admin Jean Westerbeck.

Licensure Intermediate Care. *Beds* 51. *Certified* Medicaid.
Admissions Requirements Minimum age 18; Medical examination.
Staff RNs 1 (ft), 2 (pt); LPNs 2 (pt); Nurses aides 4 (ft), 18 (pt); Activities coordinators 1 (ft); Dietitians 1 (pt).
Facilities Dining room; Physical therapy room; Laundry room; Barber/Beauty shop.
Activities Arts and Crafts; Cards; Games; Prayer groups; Shopping trips; Dances/Social or cultural gatherings.

MECHANICSVILLE

Mechanicsville Care Center*
206 4th St, Mechanicsville, IA, 52306 (319) 432-7235
Admin Helen B Sheldon.
Licensure Intermediate Care. *Beds* 69. *Certified* Medicaid.

MEDIAPOLIS

Bethesda Care Center
608 Prairie St, Mediapolis, IA, 52637 (319) 394-3991
Medical Dir/Dir of Nursing Cynthia Olsen.
Licensure Intermediate Care. *Beds* 61. *Certified* Medicaid.
Admissions Requirements Medical examination; Physician's request.
Staff RNs 2 (ft); LPNs 3 (ft), 6 (pt); Nurses aides 14 (ft), 4 (pt); Activities coordinators 1 (ft); Dietitians 1 (pt); 8 (ft), 6 (pt).
Facilities Dining room; Physical therapy room; Activities room; Crafts room; Laundry room; Barber/Beauty shop; 2 Resident TV lounges.
Activities Arts and Crafts; Cards; Games; Reading groups; Prayer groups; Movies; Shopping trips; Dances/Social or cultural gatherings.
Description Facility features fenced patio area with seating; van with hydro-lift; facility monthly newsletter; therapies on contract; community physicians, active with personal touch; growing corporation with progressive ideas on quality care for mental, physical and spiritual well being.

MILFORD

Milford Nursing Home
1600 13th, Milford, IA, 51351 (712) 338-4742
Admin Sandra Bertelson. *Medical Dir/Dir of Nursing* Joni Mitchell.
Licensure Intermediate Care. *Beds* 50. *Certified* Medicaid.
Admissions Requirements Medical examination.
Staff Physicians 10 (pt); RNs 2 (ft); LPNs 1 (ft), 3 (pt); Orderlies 1 (pt); Nurses aides 5 (ft), 12 (pt); Physical therapists 1 (pt); Activities coordinators 1 (ft); Dietitians 1 (pt); Dentists 1 (pt); Ophthalmologists 1 (pt); Podiatrists 1 (pt); Audiologists 1 (pt).
Facilities Dining room; Physical therapy room; Activities room; Chapel; Laundry room; Barber/Beauty shop.
Activities Arts and Crafts; Cards; Games; Reading groups; Prayer groups; Movies; Shopping trips; Dances/Social or cultural gatherings.

Description Facility offers activities such as movies, attending theaters, bus rides, boat rides, and special parties; nursing home king and queen chosen once a year.

MISSOURI VALLEY

Longview Home Inc*
1010 Longview Rd, Missouri Valley, IA, 51555 (712) 642-2264
Admin Eugene Sherer.
Licensure Intermediate Care. *Beds* 69. *Certified* Medicaid.

MITCHELLVILLE

Mitchell Village Center of Care*
114 Gay St, Mitchellville, IA, 50169 (515) 967-3726
Admin Mary Vanderpool.
Licensure Intermediate Care. *Beds* 65. *Certified* Medicaid.

MONTEZUMA

Senior Home*
Meadow Lane Dr, Montezuma, IA, 50171 (515) 623-5497
Admin Millie R Meixner.
Licensure Intermediate Care. *Beds* 51. *Certified* Medicaid.

MONTICELLO

Senior Home
500 Pine Haven Dr, Monticello, IA, 52310 (319) 465-5415
Licensure Intermediate Care. *Beds* 100. *Certified* Medicaid.
Admissions Requirements Medical examination; Physician's request.
Staff RNs 2 (ft), 3 (pt); LPNs 2 (ft), 4 (pt); Nurses aides 10 (ft), 24 (pt); Physical therapists; Occupational therapists; Speech therapists; Activities coordinators 1 (ft), 1 (pt); Dietitians; Dentists; Audiologists; Social worker.
Facilities Dining room; Physical therapy room; Activities room; Chapel; Laundry room; Barber/Beauty shop; Library.
Activities Arts and Crafts; Cards; Games; Reading groups; Prayer groups; Movies; Shopping trips; Dances/Social or cultural gatherings.

MONTROSE

Montrose Health Center
7th St, Montrose, IA, 52639 (319) 463-5438
Admin Donna Venteicher.
Licensure Intermediate Care; Residential Care. *Beds* ICF 60; Residential Care 20. *Certified* Medicaid.
Admissions Requirements Minimum age 16; Medical examination.
Staff RNs 2 (ft), 3 (pt); LPNs 1 (ft), 2 (pt); Nurses aides 16 (ft), 6 (pt); Activities coordinators 2 (ft).
Facilities Dining room; Activities room; Crafts room; Laundry room; Barber/Beauty shop; Examination room.

Activities Arts and Crafts; Cards; Games; Reading groups; Prayer groups; Movies; Shopping trips; Dances/Social or cultural gatherings.
Description Facility offers 4-meal plan with selective menus, van for outings, and a friendly, small towm atmosphere.

MORNING SUN

Morning Sun Manor
Washington-Manor Rd, Morning Sun, IA, 52640 (319) 868-7751
Licensure Intermediate Care. *Beds* 60. *Certified* Medicaid.
Staff RNs 2 (ft), 1 (pt); LPNs 2 (ft); Nurses aides 10 (ft), 7 (pt); Activities coordinators 1 (ft); Dietitians 1 (pt).
Facilities Dining room; Activities room; Barber/Beauty shop.
Activities Arts and Crafts; Cards; Games; Reading groups; Movies; Shopping trips; Dances/Social or cultural gatherings.
Description Located in a quiet rural community with a relaxed atmosphere where quality care is our tradition.

MOUNT AYR

Clearview Home*
406 W Washington St, Mount Ayr, IA, 50854 (515) 464-2240
Admin Richard C Routh.
Licensure Intermediate Care. *Beds* 97. *Certified* Medicaid.

Mount Ayr Health Care Center
PO Box 547, Mount Ayr, IA, 50854 (515) 464-3204
Admin L W Gobar.
Licensure Intermediate Care. *Beds* 53. *Certified* Medicaid.
Admissions Requirements Minimum age 18; Medical examination; Physician's request.
Staff Physicians; RNs; LPNs; Orderlies; Nurses aides; Physical therapists; Activities coordinators; Dietitians; Dentists; Ophthalmologists; Audiologists.
Facilities Dining room; Physical therapy room; Activities room; Chapel; Crafts room; Laundry room; Barber/Beauty shop; Library; Woodworking shop.
Activities Arts and Crafts; Cards; Games; Reading groups; Prayer groups; Movies; Shopping trips; Dances/Social or cultural gatherings.

MOUNT PLEASANT

Henry County Memorial Hospital*
Saunders Pk, Mount Pleasant, IA, 52341 (319) 385-3141
Admin Robert A Miller.
Licensure Intermediate Care. *Beds* 29.

Mapleleaf Health Care Center
701 Mapleleaf Dr, Mount Pleasant, IA, 52641 (319) 385-2293
Admin Dale Showalter.
Licensure Intermediate Care. *Beds* 63. *Certified* Mcdicaid.
Admissions Requirements Minimum age 16; Medical examination; Physician's request.

Staff RNs 2 (ft); LPNs 2 (ft), 4 (pt); Nurses aides 14 (ft), 6 (pt); Physical therapists 1 (pt); Occupational therapists 1 (pt); Speech therapists 1 (pt); Activities coordinators 1 (ft); Dietitians 1 (pt); Dentists 1 (pt); Podiatrists 1 (pt); Audiologists 1 (pt).
Facilities Dining room; Physical therapy room; Activities room; Chapel; Laundry room; Barber/Beauty shop.
Activities Arts and Crafts; Cards; Games; Reading groups; Movies; Shopping trips; Dances/Social or cultural gatherings.
Description This is a model, long-term care campus for older adults with innovative concepts that are comprehensive for the whole person—physically, mentally, socially, and spiritually.

Pleasant Manor Care Center*
413 Broadway, Mount Pleasant, IA, 52641 (319) 385-8095
Admin Edward Matney.
Licensure Intermediate Care. *Beds* 50. *Certified* Medicaid.

MOUNT VERNON

Hallmark Care Center
Hwys 30 and 1, Mount Vernon, IA, 52314 (319) 895-8891
Admin Diane M Sarich. *Medical Dir/Dir of Nursing* Robert Sautter MD.
Licensure Intermediate Care. *Beds* 68. *Certified* Medicaid.
Admissions Requirements Minimum age 18; Medical examination; Physician's request.
Staff Physical therapists; Reality therapists; Recreational therapists; Occupational therapists; Speech therapists; Activities coordinators 1 (ft); Dietitians 1 (ft).
Facilities Dining room; Physical therapy room; Activities room; Crafts room; Laundry room; Barber/Beauty shop; Library.
Activities Arts and Crafts; Cards; Games; Reading groups; Prayer groups; Movies; Dances/Social or cultural gatherings.

MUSCATINE

Benjamin Hershey Memorial Convalescent Home*
1810 Mulberry Ave, Muscatine, IA, 52761 (319) 263-8304
Admin Grace E Meerdink.
Licensure Intermediate Care. *Beds* 67. *Certified* Medicaid.

Bethesda Care Center*
3440 Mulberry Ave, Muscatine, IA, 52761 (319) 263-2194
Admin Joseph H Schulte.
Licensure Intermediate Care. *Beds* 71. *Certified* Medicaid.

Lutheran Homes Society
Hershey Ave, Muscatine, IA, 52761 (319) 263-1241
Licensure Intermediate Care; Residential Care. *Beds* ICF 146; Residential Care 15. *Certified* Medicaid.
Admissions Requirements Medical examina-

tion; Physician's request.
Staff RNs 4 (ft), 2 (pt); LPNs 7 (ft); Nurses aides 70 (ft), 30 (pt); Occupational therapists 1 (ft); Activities coordinators 1 (ft).
Affiliation Lutheran
Facilities Dining room; Physical therapy room; Activities room; Chapel; Crafts room; Laundry room; Barber/Beauty shop; Library.
Activities Arts and Crafts; Cards; Games; Reading groups; Movies; Shopping trips; Dances/Social or cultural gatherings; Bible study.

Muscatine Care Center*
2002 Cedar St, Muscatine, IA, 52761 (319) 264-2023
Admin Richard L Mathiot.
Licensure Intermediate Care. *Beds* 100. *Certified* Medicaid.

NEVADA

Oak Park Care Center
100 6th St, Nevada, IA, 50201 (515) 382-6556
Medical Dir/Dir of Nursing Marlene Bennink.
Licensure Intermediate Care. *Beds* 69. *Certified* Medicaid.
Admissions Requirements Medical examination; Physician's request.
Staff RNs 2 (ft); LPNs 3 (ft), 3 (pt); Nurses aides 10 (ft), 10 (pt); Activities coordinators 1 (ft); Dietitians 1 (pt).

Story County Hospital*
630 6th, Nevada, IA, 50201 (515) 382-2111
Admin John J Kaduce.
Licensure Intermediate Care. *Beds* 80.

NEW HAMPTON

Health Care Manor
S 4th St, New Hampton, IA, 50659 (515) 394-4153
Licensure Intermediate Care; Residential Care. *Beds* ICF 51; Residential Care 16. *Certified* Medicaid.
Admissions Requirements Medical examination; Physician's request.
Staff RNs 1 (ft), 1 (pt); LPNs 1 (ft), 5 (pt); Nurses aides 15 (ft), 10 (pt); Physical therapists 1 (pt); Occupational therapists 1 (pt); Speech therapists 1 (pt); Activities coordinators 1 (ft), 1 (pt); Dietitians 1 (ft).
Facilities Dining room; Physical therapy room; Activities room; Crafts room; Laundry room; Barber/Beauty shop; Separate lounge area.
Activities Arts and Crafts; Cards; Games; Reading groups; Prayer groups; Shopping trips; Dances/Social or cultural gatherings.
Description Facility bases work on good patient care and is known for outstanding rehabilitation program and superb dietary kitchen.

New Hampton Care Center Inc*
530 S Linn, New Hampton, IA, 50659 (515) 394-3151
Admin Bonnie L Hubka.
Licensure Intermediate Care. *Beds* 50. *Certified* Medicaid.

NEW LONDON

New London Care Center*
Pine St, New London, IA, 52645 (319)
367-5753
Admin Thomas J Wage.
Licensure Intermediate Care. *Beds* 51. *Certified* Medicaid.

NEW SHARON

New Sharon Care Center
Park and Cherry, New Sharon, IA, 50207 (515)
637-4031
Medical Dir/Dir of Nursing Norma Patterson.
Licensure Intermediate Care. *Beds* 63. *Certified* Medicaid.
Admissions Requirements Medical examination; Physician's request.
Staff Physicians 2 (pt); RNs 2 (ft); LPNs 3 (ft), 1 (pt); Physical therapists 1 (pt); Occupational therapists 1 (pt); Speech therapists 1 (pt); Activities coordinators 1 (ft); Dietitians 1 (pt); Dentists 1 (pt); Ophthalmologists 1 (pt); Podiatrists 1 (pt); Audiologists 1 (pt).
Facilities Dining room; Physical therapy room; Activities room; Crafts room; Laundry room; Barber/Beauty shop.
Activities Arts and Crafts; Cards; Games; Reading groups; Prayer groups; Movies; Shopping trips; Dances/Social or cultural gatherings.

NEWELL

Newell Good Samaritan Center*
PO Box 395, Newell, IA, 50568 (712) 272-3327
Admin Debra L Jensen.
Licensure Intermediate Care. *Beds* 50. *Certified* Medicaid.

NEWTON

Embassy Manor Care Center*
200 S 8th Ave E, Newton, IA, 50208 (515)
792-7440
Admin Vivian Degreef.
Licensure Intermediate Care. *Beds* 101. *Certified* Medicaid.

Heritage Manor Care Center
1743 S 8th Ave E, Newton, IA, 50208 (515)
792-5680
Licensure Intermediate Care. *Beds* 62. *Certified* Medicaid.

Jasper County Care Facility
Rt 4, Newton, IA, 50208 (515) 792-2000
Medical Dir/Dir of Nursing Marvin Moles MD.
Licensure Intermediate Care; Residential Care. *Beds* ICF 44; Residential Care 66. *Certified* Medicaid.
Admissions Requirements Minimum age 18; Physician's request.
Staff Physicians 1 (pt); RNs 2 (ft), 2 (pt); LPNs 3 (ft), 6 (pt); Orderlies 3 (pt); Nurses aides 10 (ft), 11 (pt); Physical therapists 1 (ft), 1 (pt); Recreational therapists 1 (ft), 5 (pt); Occupational therapists 1 (ft), 1 (pt); Speech therapists 1 (pt); Activities coordinators 1 (ft); Dietitians 1 (ft); Dentists 6 (pt); Ophthalmologists 1 (pt);

Podiatrists 1 (pt); Audiologists 1 (pt).
Facilities Dining room; Physical therapy room; Activities room; Chapel; Crafts room; Laundry room; Barber/Beauty shop; Library; Occupational therapy room.
Activities Arts and Crafts; Cards; Games; Reading groups; Prayer groups; Movies; Shopping trips; Dances/Social or cultural gatherings; Bell choir.
Description The facility's bell choir is gaining an excellent reputation and beginning to travel statewide.

Mary Frances Skilled Memorial Hospital*
204 N 4th Ave E, Newton, IA, 50208 (515)
792-1273
Admin Marc Ihm.
Licensure Skilled Care. *Beds* 21.

Nelson Manor Nursing Home*
1500 1st Ave E, Newton, IA, 50208 (515)
792-1443
Admin Mary Ann Shaw.
Licensure Intermediate Care. *Beds* 36. *Certified* Medicaid.

NORA SPRINGS

Nora Springs Manor*
Hwy 18 W, Nora Springs, IA, 50458 (515)
749-5331
Admin Kenneth E Davis.
Licensure Intermediate Care. *Beds* 60. *Certified* Medicaid.

NORTH ENGLISH

English Valley Nursing Care Center*
Box 156, North English, IA, 52316 (319)
664-3257
Admin Audrey Weldon.
Licensure Intermediate Care. *Beds* 67. *Certified* Medicaid.

NORTHWOOD

Lutheran Retirement Home*
700 10th St N, Northwood, IA, 50459 (515)
324-1712
Admin James Tweeten.
Licensure Intermediate Care. *Beds* 81. *Certified* Medicaid.
Affiliation Lutheran

NORWALK

Norwalk Manor Care Center*
921 Sunset, Norwalk, IA, 50211 (515) 981-0604
Admin Theodora Q Kracht.
Licensure Intermediate Care. *Beds* 51. *Certified* Medicaid.

Regency Care Center*
815 High Rd, Norwalk, IA, 50211 (515)
981-4269
Admin Lou Ann Cooper.
Licensure Intermediate Care. *Beds* 51. *Certified* Medicaid.

ODEBOLT

Colonial Manor of Odebolt*
Hwy 39, Odebolt, IA, 51458 (712) 668-2731
Admin Jack Lavelle.
Licensure Intermediate Care. *Beds* 64. *Certified* Medicaid.

OELWEIN

Grandview Nursing Center*
800 5th St SE, Oelwein, IA, 50662 (319)
283-1908
Admin Randall L Parks.
Licensure Intermediate Care. *Beds* 83. *Certified* Medicaid.

Oelwein Care Center
600 7th Ave, Oelwein, IA, 50662 (319)
283-3057
Admin Betty J Baum.
Licensure Intermediate Care. *Beds* 61. *Certified* Medicaid.
Admissions Requirements Minimum age 18; Medical examination.
Staff RNs 2 (ft); LPNs 4 (ft); Nurses aides 15 (ft), 10 (pt); Physical therapists 1 (pt); Occupational therapists 1 (pt); Speech therapists 1 (pt); Activities coordinators 1 (ft); Dietitians 1 (pt); Audiologists 1 (pt).
Facilities Dining room; Physical therapy room; Activities room; Chapel; Crafts room; Laundry room; Barber/Beauty shop.
Activities Arts and Crafts; Cards; Games; Reading groups; Prayer groups; Movies; Shopping trips; Dances/Social or cultural gatherings.
Description A beautiful park surrounds the facility; van available for outside activities; large patio available with comfortable furniture; organized activities; entire staff is comprised of high quality people to care for high quality people.

OGDEN

Ogden Manor*
625 E Oak, Ogden, IA, 50212 (515) 275-2481
Admin Joe C Johnson.
Licensure Intermediate Care. *Beds* 57. *Certified* Medicaid.

ONAWA

Onawa Home for the Aged Inc*
222 N 15th St, Onawa, IA, 51040 (712)
423-2510
Admin Richard J Feauto.
Licensure Intermediate Care. *Beds* 98. *Certified* Medicaid.

ORANGE CITY

Heritage House
519 Albany Ave SE, Orange City, IA, 51041
(712) 737-4811
Admin Beth Haarsma.
Licensure Intermediate Care. *Beds* 50. *Certified* Medicaid.
Admissions Requirements Medical examination.

Staff RNs 2 (ft), 2 (pt); LPNs 2 (ft), 1 (pt); Orderlies 1 (pt); Nurses aides 5 (ft), 22 (pt); Physical therapists 1 (pt); Recreational therapists 2 (pt); Activities coordinators 1 (ft); Dietitians 1 (pt).
Facilities Dining room; Physical therapy room; Activities room; Chapel; Laundry room; Barber/Beauty shop; Library.
Activities Arts and Crafts; Cards; Games; Reading groups; Prayer groups; Movies; Shopping trips; Dances/Social or cultural gatherings.
Description Residents receive kind and loving care by capable staff in a clean and pleasant atmosphere.

OSAGE

Faith Lutheran Home Inc*
914 Cherry St, Osage, IA, 50461 (515) 732-4863
Admin Irving J Kemp.
Licensure Intermediate Care. *Beds* 60. *Certified* Medicaid.
Affiliation Lutheran

White House of Osage*
830 S 5th St, Osage, IA, 50461 (515) 732-5520
Admin Jo Post.
Licensure Intermediate Care. *Beds* 77. *Certified* Medicaid.

OSCEOLA

Osceola Leisure Manor*
Hwy 69 N, Osceola, IA, 50213 (515) 342-6061
Admin Ruth Stephens.
Licensure Intermediate Care. *Beds* 101. *Certified* Medicaid.

OSKALOOSA

Mahaska Manor*
914 N 12th St, Oskaloosa, IA, 52577 (515) 673-6577
Admin Donna Johnson.
Licensure Intermediate Care. *Beds* 103. *Certified* Medicaid.

Pleasant Park Manor*
1510 High Ave, Oskaloosa, IA, 52577 (515) 673-7032
Admin Myrna Schutjer.
Licensure Intermediate Care. *Beds* 92. *Certified* Medicaid.

Siesta Park Manor
1302 High Ave W, Oskaloosa, IA, 52577 (515) 672-2474
Admin Becky Ruschman.
Licensure Intermediate Care. *Beds* 37.

OSSIAN

Ossian Senior Hospice Inc
PO Box 98, Ossian, IA, 52161 (319) 532-9440
Licensure Intermediate Care. *Beds* 38. *Certified* Medicaid.
Admissions Requirements Minimum age 21; Medical examination; Physician's request.
Staff Physicians 2 (pt); RNs 2 (ft), 2 (pt); LPNs 3 (pt); Nurses aides 5 (ft), 14 (pt); Physical ther-

apists 1 (pt); Activities coordinators 1 (pt).
Facilities Dining room; Physical therapy room; Activities room; Chapel; Laundry room; Barber/Beauty shop.
Activities Arts and Crafts; Cards; Games; Reading groups; Prayer groups; Movies; Dances/Social or cultural gatherings.
Description Meals on wheels program available.

OTTUMWA

Crest Group Home
433 N Weller St, Ottumwa, IA, 52501
Admin David Godby.
Licensure Residential Care. *Beds* 15.
Certified Medicaid; Medicare.
Ownership Nonprofit.
Admissions Requirements Minimum age 18; Medical examination.
Staff Activities coordinators 1 (pt).
Affiliation Baptist
Facilities Dining room; Activities room; Laundry room; Living room.
Activities Games; Movies; Shopping trips; Dances/Social or cultural gatherings.
Description Facility features an independent living skills training program.

Ottumwa Good Samaritan Center*
2035 W Chester, Ottumwa, IA, 52501 (515) 682-8041
Admin Ronald Moegenburg.
Licensure Intermediate Care. *Beds* 126. *Certified* Medicaid.

Ottumwa Manor Nursing Home*
927 E Pennsylvania, Ottumwa, IA, 52501 (515) 684-4594
Admin Helen Jo Broerman.
Licensure Intermediate Care. *Beds* 101. *Certified* Medicaid.

Ridgewood Care Center Inc*
1977 Albia Rd, Ottumwa, IA, 52501 (515) 683-3111
Admin Kay Dudycha.
Licensure Intermediate Care; Residential Care.
Beds ICF 54; Residential Care 16. *Certified* Medicaid.

River Hills Care Center
606 E Penn Ave, Ottumwa, IA, 52501 (515) 682-8175
Admin Robert Davis.
Licensure Intermediate Care. *Beds* 146. *Certified* Medicaid.
Staff RNs 4 (pt); LPNs 12 (pt); Orderlies 4 (pt); Nurses aides 51 (pt); Recreational therapists 3 (pt); Occupational therapists 1 (pt); Speech therapists 1 (pt); Activities coordinators 1 (ft); Dietitians 1 (pt); Dentists 1 (pt); Ophthalmologists 1 (pt); Podiatrists 1 (pt); Audiologists 1 (pt).
Facilities Dining room; Physical therapy room; Activities room; Chapel; Laundry room; Barber/Beauty shop.
Activities Arts and Crafts; Cards; Games; Reading groups; Prayer groups; Movies; Shopping trips; Dances/Social or cultural gatherings.
Description Facility features home-style cooking including a home-style bakery. Extensive physical therapy program.

Sunnyslope Care Center*
Rt 1, E Steller, Ottumwa, IA, 52501 (515) 684-6523
Admin John J Coler.
Licensure Intermediate Care. *Beds* 61. *Certified* Medicaid.

PANORA

Craft Care Center*
805 E Main, Panora, IA, 50216 (515) 755-2700
Admin Janet Proctor.
Licensure Intermediate Care. *Beds* 108. *Certified* Medicaid.

PAULLINA

Wide View Rest Home*
423 Willow St, Paullina, IA, 51046 (712) 448-3455
Admin Tom V Nelson.
Licensure Intermediate Care. *Beds* 41. *Certified* Medicaid.

PELLA

Christian Opportunity Center
1553 Broadway, Pella, IA, 50219 (515) 628-1162
Medical Dir/Dir of Nursing Jane Klyn RN.
Licensure Intermediate Care for Mentally Retarded. *Beds* 15. *Certified* Medicaid.
Admissions Requirements Minimum age 18; Medical examination; Physician's request.
Staff RNs 1 (ft), 1 (pt); Orderlies 5 (ft), 10 (pt); Activities coordinators 1 (pt); Dietitians 1 (pt).
Facilities Dining room; Physical therapy room; Activities room; Crafts room; Laundry room.
Activities Arts and Crafts; Cards; Games; Reading groups; Prayer groups; Movies; Shopping trips; Dances/Social or cultural gatherings.
Description Christian Opportunity Center is an organization dedicated to providing quality services to handicapped people; it provides work experiences, activities, and residential living in a number of different environments.

Pella Community Hospital*
404 Jefferson St, Pella, IA, 50219 (515) 628-3150
Admin John Harmeling.
Licensure Intermediate Care. *Beds* 61.

PERRY

Lutheran Home for the Aged*
2323 E Willis Ave, Perry, IA, 50220 (515) 465-5342
Admin Michael Bonello.
Licensure Intermediate Care; Residential Care.
Beds ICF 66; Residential Care 47. *Certified* Medicaid.
Affiliation Lutheran

Perry Manor*
2625 Iowa St, Perry, IA, 50220 (515) 465-5349
Admin Randall Lange.
Licensure Intermediate Care. *Beds* 54. *Certified* Medicaid.

Rowley Memorial Masonic Home
3000 E Willis Ave, Perry, IA, 50220 (515)
465-5316
Medical Dir/Dir of Nursing Arvis Gross.
Licensure Intermediate Care; Residential Care.
Beds ICF 24; ResidentiaL Care 50. *Certified* Medicaid.
Admissions Requirements Medical examination.
Staff RNs 1 (ft), 2 (pt); LPNs 5 (ft), 1 (pt); Nurses aides 15 (ft), 13 (pt); Physical therapists 1 (pt); Recreational therapists 2 (ft); Occupational therapists 1 (pt); Speech therapists 1 (pt); Activities coordinators 1 (ft); Dietitians 1 (pt).
Affiliation Masons
Facilities Dining room; Activities room; Chapel; Crafts room; Laundry room; Barber/Beauty shop; Library.
Activities Arts and Crafts; Cards; Games; Reading groups; Prayer groups; Movies; Shopping trips; Dances/Social or cultural gatherings.

PLEASANT VALLEY

Riverview Manor Nursing Home
Spencer Rd, Pleasant Valley, IA, 52767 (319)
332-4600
Admin Robert C Fortier.
Licensure Intermediate Care. *Beds* 51. *Certified* Medicaid.

PLEASANTVILLE

Pleasant Care Inc*
908 N State St, Pleasantville, IA, 50225 (515)
848-5718
Admin Max W Shook.
Licensure Skilled Care; Intermediate Care.
Beds SNF 37; ICF 20. *Certified* Medicaid; Medicare.

POCAHONTAS

Pocahontas Manor*
700 NW 7th, Pocahontas, IA, 50574 (712)
335-3386
Admin J D Shepard.
Licensure Intermediate Care. *Beds* 92. *Certified* Medicaid.

POLK CITY

Polk City Manor
1002 NW 114th Ave, Rt 2, Polk City, IA,
50226 (515) 984-6201
Admin Betty Marshall. *Medical Dir/Dir of Nursing* Etha Seronko RN.
Licensure Intermediate Care. *Beds* 68. *Certified* Medicaid.
Admissions Requirements Minimum age 18; Medical examination; Physician's request.
Staff RNs 1 (ft); LPNs 3 (ft), 1 (pt); Orderlies 1 (ft); Nurses aides 16 (ft), 7 (pt); Activities coordinators 1 (ft), 1 (pt).
Facilities Dining room; Activities room; Crafts room; Laundry room; Barber/Beauty shop; Library; Wine and cheese.
Activities Arts and Crafts; Cards; Games; Reading groups; Prayer groups; Movies; Shopping trips; Dances/Social or cultural gatherings;

Van rides.
Description Friendly, clean, small-town setting allows for caring for loved ones on a short-term or long-term basis. We encourage each resident's room to be decorated in a home-like setting.

POMEROY

Pomeroy Care Center
303 E 7th St, Pomeroy, IA, 50575 (712)
468-2241
Admin Susan Juilfs. *Medical Dir/Dir of Nursing* Lloyd Holm DO.
Licensure Intermediate Care. *Beds* 48. *Certified* Medicaid.
Admissions Requirements Medical examination; Physician's request.
Staff Physicians 1 (pt); RNs 1 (ft); LPNs 2 (ft), 2 (pt); Nurses aides 2 (ft), 24 (pt); Physical therapists 1 (pt); Activities coordinators 2 (pt); Dietitians 1 (pt); Dentists 1 (pt); Ophthalmologists 1 (pt); Audiologists 1 (pt).
Facilities Dining room; Physical therapy room; Activities room; Laundry room; Barber/Beauty shop; Library.
Activities Arts and Crafts; Cards; Games; Reading groups; Prayer groups; Movies; Shopping trips; Dances/Social or cultural gatherings; Bible study.
Description Center is a community-oriented facility which provides quality care on a nondiscriminatory basis.

POSTVILLE

Community Memorial Hospital*
Oak Dr and Hospital Rd, Postville, IA, 52162
(319) 864-7431
Admin John C Meyer.
Licensure Intermediate Care. *Beds* 8.

Good Samaritan Center
Hospital Rd, Postville, IA, 52162 (319)
864-7425
Licensure Intermediate Care. *Beds* 60. *Certified* Medicaid.
Admissions Requirements Minimum age 18; Medical examination; Physician's request.
Staff RNs 1 (ft), 1 (pt); LPNs 3 (ft); Nurses aides 10 (ft), 17 (pt); Physical therapists; Reality therapists; Recreational therapists; Occupational therapists; Speech therapists; Activities coordinators 1 (ft), 1 (pt); Dietitians 1 (pt); Dentists; Ophthalmologists; Podiatrists; Audiologists.
Affiliation Lutheran
Facilities Dining room; Activities room; Chapel; Crafts room; Laundry room; Barber/Beauty shop; Library; Several nice lounges.
Activities Arts and Crafts; Cards; Games; Prayer groups; Shopping trips; Dances/Social or cultural gatherings; Conversation hour; Thursday night entertainment; Walking program.
Description Facility has a clean, home-like atmosphere, 2 activity areas, one large gathering room, and a smaller crafts room.

PRAIRIE CITY

Clearview Manor*
501 N Sherman, Prairie City, IA, 50228 (515)
994-2173
Admin Linda Garza.
Licensure Intermediate Care. *Beds* 80. *Certified* Medicaid.

PRIMGHAR

Primghar Care Center*
980 Cedar St, Primghar, IA, 51245 (712)
757-3655
Admin Robert W Richardson.
Licensure Intermediate Care. *Beds* 40. *Certified* Medicaid.

RED OAK

Red Oak Good Samaritan Center*
201 Alix Ave, Red Oak, IA, 51566 (712)
623-3170
Admin Stephen Hohbach.
Licensure Intermediate Care. *Beds* 75. *Certified* Medicaid.

Vista Gardens Nursing Home
1600 Summit, Red Oak, IA, 51566 (712)
623-5156
Admin Dale Waldemer. *Medical Dir/Dir of Nursing* Ruth Waldemer RN.
Licensure Intermediate Care. *Beds* 68. *Certified* Medicaid.
Staff RNs 3 (ft); LPNs 7 (ft), 1 (pt); Nurses aides 14 (ft), 5 (pt); Physical therapists 1 (ft); Activities coordinators 1 (ft); Dietitians 1 (pt).
Facilities Dining room; Physical therapy room; Activities room; Laundry room; Barber/Beauty shop; Sitting area/lounge.
Activities Arts and Crafts; Cards; Games; Reading groups; Prayer groups; Movies; Music programs.
Description Home is a nondiscriminatory facility, well staffed with the main concern being quality care; physical therapy aide; activity coordinator plans daily events to benefit residents; home cooked meals are enjoyed by the residents with special attention given to those on special diets.

REINBECK

Parkview Manor Inc*
1009 3rd St, Reinbeck, IA, 50669 (319)
345-2221
Admin Jeanne Hoeppner.
Licensure Intermediate Care. *Beds* 56. *Certified* Medicaid.

REMSEN

Happy Siesta Nursing Home
424 Roosevelt, Remsen, IA, 51050 (712)
786-1117
Admin Sandy Anderson. *Medical Dir/Dir of Nursing* Debbie Steffen.
Licensure Intermediate Care. *Beds* 61. *Certified* Medicaid.
Staff RNs 1 (ft), 2 (pt); LPNs 5 (pt); Nurses

aides 7 (ft), 16 (pt); Activities coordinators 1 (ft).
Facilities Dining room; Chapel; Laundry room; Barber/Beauty shop.
Activities Arts and Crafts; Cards; Games; Reading groups; Prayer groups; Movies; Shopping trips.
Description Staff at Happy Siesta Nursing Home provides an atmosphere of caring; 24-hour nursing care, special diets, planned activities, and an air conditioned, clean environment makes this one of the best homes in northwest Iowa.

RICEVILLE

Riceville Community Rest Home*
Rt 1, Box 40, Riceville, IA, 50466 (515) 985-2606
Admin Lavonne M Mayer.
Licensure Intermediate Care. *Beds* 49. *Certified* Medicaid.

ROCK RAPIDS

Lyon Manor Care Center*
1010 S Union, Rock Rapids, IA, 51246 (712) 472-3748
Admin Mildred Robinson.
Licensure Intermediate Care. *Beds* 50. *Certified* Medicaid.

Rock Rapids Health Centre*
703 S Union, Rock Rapids, IA, 51246 (712) 472-2585
Admin Daniel Boyle.
Licensure Intermediate Care; Residential Care. *Beds* ICF 50; Residential Care 39. *Certified* Medicaid.

ROCK VALLEY

Valley Manor Nursing Home Division
1300 21st Ave, Rock Valley, IA, 51247 (712) 476-2831
Licensure Intermediate Care. *Beds* 94. *Certified* Medicaid.
Admissions Requirements Medical examination; Physician's request.
Staff Physicians 3 (ft); RNs 1 (ft), 1 (pt); LPNs 4 (ft), 7 (pt); Nurses aides 11 (ft), 28 (pt); Recreational therapists 3 (pt); Activities coordinators 1 (ft), 2 (pt); Dietitians 1 (pt).
Facilities Dining room; Activities room; Chapel; Laundry room; Barber/Beauty shop.
Activities Arts and Crafts; Cards; Games; Reading groups; Prayer groups; Movies; Dances/Social or cultural gatherings.
Description Physical therapists are shared with hospital.

ROCKWELL

Rockwell Community Nursing Home*
707 Elm St, Rockwell, IA, 50469 (515) 822-3203
Admin Richard Blake.
Licensure Intermediate Care. *Beds* 52. *Certified* Medicaid.

ROCKWELL CITY

Sunny Knoll Care Center Inc
700 E Lake St, Rockwell City, IA, 50579 (712) 297-8022
Licensure Intermediate Care. *Beds* 41. *Certified* Medicaid.
Admissions Requirements Minimum age 18; Medical examination; Physician's request.
Staff RNs 1 (ft), 1 (pt); LPNs 2 (pt); Nurses aides 4 (ft), 10 (pt); Physical therapists 1 (pt); Activities coordinators 1 (pt).
Facilities Dining room; Physical therapy room; Activities room; Laundry room; Barber/Beauty shop.
Activities Arts and Crafts; Games; Reading groups; Prayer groups; Movies; Shopping trips.
Description Facility is all on ground level. Facility wants this to be the residents' "home" whether it is for a week, a month, or the rest of their lives.

ROLFE

Rolfe Care Center
303 2nd St, Rolfe, IA, 50581 (712) 848-3351
Licensure Intermediate Care. *Beds* 33. *Certified* Medicaid.
Admissions Requirements Medical examination; Physician's request.
Staff RNs 1 (ft); LPNs 2 (pt); Nurses aides 1 (ft), 16 (pt); Physical therapists 1 (pt); Reality therapists 1 (pt); Recreational therapists 1 (pt); Activities coordinators 1 (pt); Dietitians 1 (pt); Dentists 1 (pt); Audiologists 1 (pt).
Facilities Dining room; Physical therapy room; Activities room; Laundry room; Library.
Activities Arts and Crafts; Cards; Games; Reading groups; Prayer groups.
Description The back entrance of the facility has a ramp to the lower level of the basement and a ramp and stairway to the upper level.

SAC CITY

Loring Hospital*
Highland Ave, Sac City, IA, 50583 (712) 662-7105
Admin Terry J DeJong.
Licensure Intermediate Care. *Beds* 21.

Park View Manor*
Park Ave, Sac City, IA, 50583 (712) 662-7174
Admin Kent Mertens.
Licensure Intermediate Care. *Beds* 76. *Certified* Medicaid.

SAINT ANSGAR

Saint Ansgar Good Samaritan*
701 E 4th St, Saint Ansgar, IA, 50472 (515) 736-4912
Admin David C Schmidt.
Licensure Intermediate Care. *Beds* 76. *Certified* Medicaid.

SANBORN

Prairie View Home*
Hwy 18, Sanborn, IA, 51248 (712) 729-3228
Admin Victor E Vogelaar.
Licensure Intermediate Care. *Beds* 73. *Certified* Medicaid.

SEYMOUR

Seymour Care Center*
E 4th and Morgan, Seymour, IA, 52590 (515) 898-2294
Admin R Alan Griffith.
Licensure Intermediate Care. *Beds* 51. *Certified* Medicaid.

SHEFFIELD

Sheffield Care Center*
100 Bennett Dr, Sheffield, IA, 50475 (515) 892-4691
Admin Alice J Miller.
Licensure Intermediate Care; Residential Care. *Beds* ICF 45; Residential Care 15. *Certified* Medicaid.

SHELDON

Community Memorial Hospital—Long-Term Care Unit*
118 N 7th, Sheldon, IA, 51201 (712) 324-2541
Admin Mark Dagoberg.
Licensure Intermediate Care. *Beds* 54.

Handicap Village of Northwest Iowa*
330 Village Circle, Sheldon, IA, 51201 (712) 324-4873
Admin Robert Hoogeveen.
Licensure Intermediate Care for Mentally Retarded; Residential MR Care. *Beds* ICF/MR 48; Residential MR Care 50. *Certified* Medicaid.

SHELL ROCK

Shell Rock Care Center*
Kelly & Waverly Rds, Shell Rock, IA, 50670 (319) 885-4341
Admin Darrell Ferry.
Licensure Intermediate Care. *Beds* 56. *Certified* Medicaid.

SHENANDOAH

Elm Heights Care Center*
1203 S Elm, Shenandoah, IA, 51601 (717) 246-4627
Admin Dennis DeWild.
Licensure Intermediate Care. *Beds* 47.

Garden View Care Center
1200 W Nishna Rd, Shenandoah, IA, 51601 (712) 246-4515
Licensure Intermediate Care. *Beds* 101. *Certified* Medicaid.
Staff Physicians 8 (pt); RNs 1 (ft); LPNs 12 (ft); Nurses aides 23 (ft), 11 (pt); Physical therapists 4 (pt); Speech therapists 1 (pt); Activities

coordinators 1 (pt); Dietitians 1 (pt); Dentists 2 (pt); Podiatrists 1 (pt); Audiologists 1 (pt).
Facilities Dining room; Physical therapy room; Activities room; Laundry room; Barber/Beauty shop.
Activities Arts and Crafts; Cards; Games; Reading groups; Prayer groups; Movies; Shopping trips; Dances/Social or cultural gatherings.
Description Physician referrals are received from the surrounding area because of our physical therapy program.

SIBLEY

Country View Manor Inc
100 Cedar Ln, Sibley, IA, 51249 (712) 754-2568
Licensure Intermediate Care. *Beds* 64. *Certified* Medicaid.
Admissions Requirements Medical examination; Physician's request.
Staff RNs 2 (ft), 2 (pt); LPNs 1 (ft), 3 (pt); Nurses aides 11 (ft), 16 (pt); Activities coordinators 2 (pt).
Facilities Dining room; Activities room; Chapel; Crafts room; Laundry room; Barber/Beauty shop.
Activities Arts and Crafts; Cards; Games; Reading groups; Prayer groups; Movies; Shopping trips; Dances/Social or cultural gatherings; Bingo; Memorial services.
Description Country View Manor provides 24-hour professional nursing care in a home-like setting. Strives to put the "home" in nursing home. Facility is surrounded by spacious grounds and has a large front porch for summer use; the coffee pot is always on.

Sibley Care Center*
700 9th Ave N, Sibley, IA, 51249 (712) 754-3629
Admin Mildred Robinson.
Licensure Intermediate Care. *Beds* 51. *Certified* Medicaid.

SIDNEY

Sidney Health Center*
Hwy 275 S, Sidney, IA, 51652 (712) 374-2693
Admin Robert Riggs.
Licensure Intermediate Care. *Beds* 100. *Certified* Medicaid.

SIGOURNEY

Manor House*
1212 S Stuart St, Sigourney, IA, 52591 (515) 622-2142
Admin David O Yearian.
Licensure Intermediate Care. *Beds* 80. *Certified* Medicaid.

Sigourney Care Center
900 S Stone, Sigourney, IA, 52591 (515) 622-2971
Admin Mary F Greiner.
Licensure Intermediate Care; Residential Care. *Beds* ICF 51; Residential Care 10. *Certified* Medicaid.
Admissions Requirements Medical examination.
Staff RNs 2 (ft), 1 (pt); LPNs 2 (ft); Orderlies 1

(pt); Nurses aides 6 (ft), 11 (pt); Physical therapists 1 (pt); Occupational therapists 1 (pt); Speech therapists 1 (pt); Activities coordinators 1 (ft); Dietitians 1 (pt).
Facilities Dining room; Activities room; Laundry room; Barber/Beauty shop.
Activities Arts and Crafts; Cards; Games; Reading groups; Prayer groups; Movies; Shopping trips; Dances/Social or cultural gatherings; Tours; Picnics; Sing-a-longs.
Description Sigourney Care Center is one of the cleanest and most active nursing homes in the area, located in the county seat of Keokuk County with a choice of 2 pharmacies and 6 to 7 doctors that will make nursing home calls; many volunteer groups call on the facility as do all the churches in the community. Staff endeavors to create a home-like atmosphere for all residents.

SIOUX CENTER

Community Hospital and Health Center*
605 S Main, Sioux Center, IA, 51250 (712) 722-1271
Admin Erikson Lee P.
Licensure Intermediate Care. *Beds* 59.

SIOUX CITY

Casa De Paz*
2121 W 19th St, Sioux City, IA, 51103 (712) 233-3127
Admin Jerry Wood.
Licensure Intermediate Care. *Beds* 95. *Certified* Medicaid.

Countryside Retirement Home
6120 Morningside Ave, Sioux City, IA, 51106 (712) 276-3000
Licensure Intermediate Care. *Beds* 160. *Certified* Medicaid.
Admissions Requirements Minimum age 55; Medical examination; Physician's request.
Facilities Dining room; Physical therapy room; Activities room; Chapel; Crafts room; Laundry room; Barber/Beauty shop; Library.
Activities Arts and Crafts; Cards; Games; Reading groups; Prayer groups; Shopping trips; Dances/Social or cultural gatherings.

Holy Spirit Retirement Home*
1701 W 25th St, Sioux City, IA, 51103 (712) 252-2726
Admin Phyllis J Peters.
Licensure Intermediate Care. *Beds* 94. *Certified* Medicaid.

Indian Hills Care Center*
1800 Indian Hills Dr, Sioux City, IA, 51104 (712) 329-4582
Admin R C Caruso.
Licensure Intermediate Care. *Beds* 160. *Certified* Medicaid.

Julia's Valley Manor
3901 Green Ave, Sioux City, IA, 51106 (712) 252-0114
Medical Dir/Dir of Nursing Sandy Hunter.
Licensure Intermediate Care. *Beds* 50. *Certified* Medicaid.

Admissions Requirements Medical examination; Physician's request.
Staff RNs 2 (ft); LPNs 3 (ft); Nurses aides 10 (ft), 1 (pt); Activities coordinators 1 (ft); Dietitians 1 (pt).
Facilities Dining room; Physical therapy room; Activities room; Chapel; Crafts room; Laundry room; Barber/Beauty shop.
Activities Arts and Crafts; Cards; Games; Reading groups; Prayer groups; Movies; Shopping trips; Dances/Social or cultural gatherings; Bingo.
Description Facility offers the benefits of a small home (50 Beds) with personalized care, a country environment with modern furnishings, plus 30 years of quality care and experience. Nursing department recognizes special medical needs of the elderly and encourages them to maintain their strengths and abilities as long as possible.

Matney's Morningside Manor
3420 S Lakeport Rd, Sioux City, IA, 51106 (712) 276-4311
Admin Linda K Halber.
Licensure Intermediate Care. *Beds* 103. *Certified* Medicaid.
Admissions Requirements Medical examination.
Staff RNs 2 (ft), 3 (pt); LPNs 1 (ft), 9 (pt); Orderlies 1 (ft), 2 (pt); Nurses aides 16 (ft), 16 (pt); Activities coordinators 1 (ft), 1 (pt); Dietitians 1 (pt).
Facilities Dining room; Physical therapy room; Activities room; Crafts room; Laundry room; Barber/Beauty shop.
Activities Arts and Crafts; Cards; Games; Reading groups; Prayer groups; Movies; Shopping trips; Dances/Social or cultural gatherings.
Description We pride ourselves on the individual care given our residents, our activity programs and the family atmosphere maintained by the staff while providing professional care.

Matney's Westside Manor
1414 Casselman, Sioux City, IA, 51103 (712) 258-0896
Licensure Intermediate Care. *Beds* 104. *Certified* Medicaid.
Admissions Requirements Medical examination; Physician's request.
Staff RNs 16 (ft), 2 (pt); LPNs 2 (ft), 2 (pt); Nurses aides 24 (ft), 14 (pt); Activities coordinators 1 (ft), 1 (pt); Dietitians 1 (pt).
Facilities Dining room; Physical therapy room; Activities room; Crafts room; Laundry room; Barber/Beauty shop.
Activities Arts and Crafts; Cards; Games; Reading groups; Prayer groups; Movies; Shopping trips; Dances/Social or cultural gatherings.

New Horizons Care Center*
3800 Indian Hills, Sioux City, IA, 51104 (712) 239-5025
Admin Lamar Jones.
Licensure Intermediate Care. *Beds* 50. *Certified* Medicaid.

Sunrise Manor*
5501 Gordon Dr E, Sioux City, IA, 51106 (712) 276-3821
Admin John Gerwulf.

Licensure Intermediate Care; Residential Care. *Beds* 68; Residential Care 130. *Certified* Medicaid.

Westwood Convalescent and Rest Home*
3201 Stone Park Blvd, Sioux City, IA, 51104 (712) 258-0135
Admin Steve Lockwood.
Licensure Intermediate Care. *Beds* 85. *Certified* Medicaid.

Woodbury Country Care Facility*
RFD 2, Box 202, Sioux City, IA, 51103 (712) 943-5093
Admin George J Hemness.
Licensure Intermediate Care for Mentally Retarded. *Beds* 120.

SIOUX RAPIDS

Sioux Care Center*
702 Blake St, Sioux Rapids, IA, 50585 (712) 283-2302
Admin Sandra Tielber.
Licensure Intermediate Care. *Beds* 35. *Certified* Medicaid.

SOLON

Solon Nursing Care Center*
523 E 5th St, Solon, IA, 52333 (319) 644-2752
Admin N Evelyn Edwards.
Licensure Intermediate Care. *Beds* 67. *Certified* Medicaid.

SPENCER

Longhouse Residence
711 W 11th St, Spencer, IA, 51301 (712) 262-2344
Licensure Intermediate Care; Residential Care. *Beds* ICF 93; Residential Care 60. *Certified* Medicaid.
Staff RNs 6 (ft), 2 (pt); LPNs 4 (ft), 2 (pt); Orderlies 2 (ft); Nurses aides 30 (ft), 10 (pt); Physical therapists 1 (pt); Activities coordinators 4 (pt); Dietitians 1 (pt); Audiologists 1 (pt).
Facilities Dining room; Physical therapy room; Activities room; Chapel; Crafts room; Laundry room; Barber/Beauty shop.
Activities Arts and Crafts; Cards; Games; Reading groups; Prayer groups; Movies; Shopping trips; Dances/Social or cultural gatherings.

Saint Luke Lutheran Home
Saint Luke Dr, Box 4128, Spencer, IA, 51301 (712) 262-5931
Medical Dir/Dir of Nursing Dr Frink and Dr Fieselmann.
Licensure Intermediate Care. *Beds* 116. *Certified* Medicaid.
Staff Physicians 9 (ft); RNs 2 (ft), 7 (pt); LPNs 3 (ft), 5 (pt); Orderlies 6 (ft); Nurses aides 30 (ft), 19 (pt); Physical therapists 1 (pt); Recreational therapists 3 (pt); Speech therapists 1 (pt); Activities coordinators 1 (ft); Dietitians 1 (pt); Dentists 1 (pt); Audiologists 1 (pt).
Affiliation Lutheran
Facilities Dining room; Physical therapy room; Activities room; Chapel; Crafts room; Laundry room; Barber/Beauty shop; Library.

Activities Arts and Crafts; Cards; Games; Reading groups; Prayer groups; Movies; Shopping trips; Dances/Social or cultural gatherings.

SPIRIT LAKE

Dickinson County Care Facility
RFD Box 6090, Spirit Lake, IA, 51360
Admin Colleen Van Dee.
Licensure Residential Care. *Beds* 38.
Ownership Public.
Admissions Requirements Minimum age 18; Medical examination.
Staff LPNs 1 (ft); Nurses aides 9 (ft); Recreational therapists 1 (ft); Activities coordinators 1 (ft); Dietitians 1 (ft); Social workers 1 (ft).
Facilities Dining room; Physical therapy room; Laundry room; Barber/Beauty shop; Lounges.
Activities Arts and Crafts; Cards; Games; Reading groups; Prayer groups; Movies; Shopping trips; Dances/Social or cultural gatherings.
Description This county-owned facility serves the mentally ill and mentally retarded; located in a grove of oak trees in the lakes area of Iowa, a superior setting for rehabilitation of residents to return them to the community.

Hilltop Care Center*
1901 Zenith Ave, Spirit Lake, IA, 51360 (712) 336-3300
Admin Jon T Neubaum.
Licensure Intermediate Care. *Beds* 51. *Certified* Medicaid.

STACYVILLE

Stacyville Community Nursing Home
Rt 1, Box 4C, Stacyville, IA, 50476 (515) 737-2215
Admin Anita Adams.
Licensure Intermediate Care. *Beds* 47. *Certified* Medicaid.
Ownership Nonprofit.
Admissions Requirements Medical examination.
Staff RNs 1 (ft); LPNs 4 (pt); Nurses aides 10 (ft), 12 (pt); Activities coordinators 1 (ft), 1 (pt).
Facilities Dining room; Physical therapy room; Activities room; Laundry room; Barber/Beauty shop.
Activities Arts and Crafts; Cards; Games; Prayer groups; Movies; Dances/Social or cultural gatherings; Flower gardens.

STANTON

Stanton Care Center
213 Holland Ave, Stanton, IA, 51573 (712) 829-2727
Medical Dir/Dir of Nursing Allen and Louise Hart.
Licensure Intermediate Care. *Beds* 30. *Certified* Medicaid.
Admissions Requirements Minimum age 18; Medical examination; Physician's request.
Staff Physicians; RNs; LPNs; Nurses aides; Physical therapists; Recreational therapists; Speech therapists; Activities coordinators; Dietitians; Ophthalmologists; Podiatrists; Audiologists.
Facilities Dining room; Physical therapy room;

Activities room; Chapel; Crafts room; Laundry room; Barber/Beauty shop; Library.
Activities Arts and Crafts; Cards; Games; Prayer groups; Movies; Dances/Social or cultural gatherings.
Description Facility has 30 residential beds with sheltered or supervised living.

STATE CENTER

State Center Manor*
State Center, IA, 50247 (515) 483-2812
Admin Barbara Lawson.
Licensure Intermediate Care. *Beds* 51. *Certified* Medicaid.

STORM LAKE

Buena Vista Manor Care Center
1325 N Lake Ave, Storm Lake, IA, 50588 (712) 732-3254
Licensure Intermediate Care. *Beds* 100. *Certified* Medicaid.
Admissions Requirements Minimum age 17; Medical examination; Physician's request.
Staff RNs 5 (ft), 1 (pt); LPNs 3 (ft); Nurses aides 26 (ft), 13 (pt); Physical therapists 1 (pt); Activities coordinators 1 (ft), 1 (pt); Dietitians 1 (pt); Podiatrists 1 (pt); Audiologists 1 (pt).
Facilities Dining room; Physical therapy room; Activities room; Chapel; Crafts room; Laundry room; Barber/Beauty shop.
Activities Arts and Crafts; Cards; Games; Reading groups; Prayer groups; Movies; Shopping trips; Dances/Social or cultural gatherings.

Methodist Manor
4th at Larchwood, Storm Lake, IA, 50588 (712) 732-1120
Admin B Donaldson.
Licensure Intermediate Care; Residential Care. *Beds* ICF 93; Residential Care 88. *Certified* Medicaid.
Admissions Requirements Minimum age 55; Medical examination.
Staff Physicians 14 (pt); RNs 4 (ft), 3 (pt); LPNs 5 (ft), 4 (pt); Nurses aides 19 (ft), 16 (pt); Physical therapists 1 (ft), 1 (pt); Recreational therapists 1 (ft); Speech therapists 1 (pt); Activities coordinators 1 (ft); Dietitians 1 (pt); Dentists 2 (pt); Podiatrists 2 (pt); Audiologists 1 (pt).
Affiliation Methodist
Facilities Dining room; Physical therapy room; Activities room; Chapel; Crafts room; Laundry room; Barber/Beauty shop; Library.
Activities Arts and Crafts; Cards; Games; Reading groups; Prayer groups; Movies; Shopping trips; Dances/Social or cultural gatherings.

STORY CITY

Bethany Manor Inc*
814 Cedar St, Story City, IA, 50248 (515) 733-4328
Licensure Intermediate Care. *Beds* 167. *Certified* Medicaid.

STRATFORD

Stratford Care Center
Hwy 175 E, Stratford, IA, 50249 (515)
838-2795
Licensure Intermediate Care. *Beds* 70. *Certified* Medicaid.
Admissions Requirements Minimum age 21;
Medical examination.
Staff LPNs 7 (ft); Orderlies 3 (ft); Nurses aides
16 (ft), 7 (pt); Activities coordinators 1 (ft), 1
(pt); Dietitians 1 (pt).
Facilities Dining room; Physical therapy room;
Activities room; Crafts room; Laundry room;
Barber/Beauty shop.
Activities Arts and Crafts; Cards; Games;
Reading groups; Movies; Shopping trips; Dances/Social or cultural gatherings.

STRAWBERRY POINT

Strawberry Point Lutheran Home*
313 Elkader St, Strawberry Point, IA, 52076
(319) 933-6037
Admin Joan Kelley.
Licensure Intermediate Care. *Beds* 92. *Certified* Medicaid.
Ownership Nonprofit.
Affiliation Lutheran

STUART

Community Care Center Inc
1603 S 7th St, Stuart, IA, 50250 (515) 523-2815
Admin Mary Ellen Gilman.
Licensure Intermediate Care. *Beds* 50. *Certified* Medicaid.
Staff RNs 10 (ft), 1 (pt); LPNs 1 (ft), 9 (pt);
Nurses aides 5 (ft), 17 (pt); Physical therapists 1
(pt); Speech therapists 1 (pt); Activities coordinators 2 (pt); Dietitians 1 (pt); Audiologists 1
(pt).
Facilities Dining room; Physical therapy room;
Activities room; Laundry room; Barber/Beauty
shop.
Activities Arts and Crafts; Cards; Games;
Reading groups; Prayer groups; Movies; Shopping trips; Dances/Social or cultural gatherings.
Description Facility sponsors an annual, very
successful quilt show; a tremendous volunteer
program; and 24-hour nursing care in a family
atmosphere. Facility is community owned.

SUMNER

Hillcrest Rest Home Inc
915 W 1st St, Sumner, IA, 50674 (319)
578-8591
Admin Eunice A Neil.
Licensure Intermediate Care. *Beds* 86. *Certified* Medicaid.
Admissions Requirements Medical examination.
Staff Physicians 3 (pt); RNs 2 (ft), 1 (pt); LPNs
2 (ft), 3 (pt); Nurses aides 15 (ft), 19 (pt);
Physical therapists 1 (pt); Reality therapists 1
(ft), 1 (pt); Activities coordinators 1 (ft).
Facilities Dining room; Physical therapy room;
Activities room; Chapel; Crafts room; Laundry
room; Barber/Beauty shop.

Activities Arts and Crafts; Games; Reading
groups; Prayer groups; Movies; Shopping trips;
Dances/Social or cultural gatherings.
Description Facility features a very outstanding
activity program. Facility is located next door
to the local hospital on the edge of town. Residents have a rural view and many long-time
employees have known residents prior to
employment.

SUTHERLAND

Millie's Rest Home*
506 4th St, Sutherland, IA, 51058 (712)
446-3857
Admin Tom V Nelson.
Licensure Intermediate Care. *Beds* 44. *Certified* Medicaid.

TABOR

Tabor Manor Care Center*
400 Main St, Tabor, IA, 51653 (712) 629-2645
Admin Leonard B Worchester.
Licensure Intermediate Care. *Beds* 63. *Certified* Medicaid.

TAMA

Sunny Hill Retirement and Nursing Home
Hwy 63 N, Tama, IA, 52339 (515) 484-4061
Admin Rosemary Schrach.
Licensure Intermediate Care. *Beds* 51.
Certified Medicaid.
Staff RNs 2 (pt); LPNs 1 (ft), 4 (pt); Nurses
aides 13 (ft), 7 (pt); Activities coordinators 1
(ft); Dietitians 1 (pt).
Facilities Dining room; Laundry room; Barber/Beauty shop.
Activities Arts and Crafts; Cards; Games;
Reading groups; Prayer groups; Movies; Shopping trips; Dances/Social or cultural gatherings.
Description Facility is a family-type nursing
home of 51 residents. We are able to give more
personalized care in our family atmosphere.
Very little turnover in staff. Most employees
have been here 10 years or more. If possible we
start discharging on the day of admittance. We
are known as the nursing home "That Cares."

TIPTON

Cedar County Care Facility
Rt 2, Tipton, IA, 52772
Admin Elsie E Walter. *Medical Dir/Dir of
Nursing* Marlene Evers.
Licensure Residential Care. *Beds* 54.
Certified Medicare.
Ownership Public.
Admissions Requirements Minimum age 18;
Medical examination; Physician's request.
Staff LPNs 2 (ft); Nurses aides 7 (ft), 3 (pt);
Activities coordinators 2 (pt); Dietitians 1 (ft).
Facilities Dining room; Activities room; Chapel; Crafts room; Laundry room; Barber/Beauty
shop; Library.
Activities Arts and Crafts; Games; Reading
groups; Prayer groups; Movies; Shopping trips;
Dances/Social or cultural gatherings.
Description Facility is located in a rural setting

with many opportunities to enjoy the great outdoors; many activities involve the outside community; residents have the opportunity to
continue education and/or obtain their GED.

Cedar Manor
1200 Mulberry, Tipton, IA, 52772 (319)
886-2133
Admin David R Juhl. *Medical Dir/Dir of
Nursing* Joanne Beckley.
Licensure Intermediate Care. *Beds* 55. *Certified* Medicaid.
Admissions Requirements Physician's request.
Staff RNs 2 (ft), 3 (pt); LPNs 1 (ft), 2 (pt);
Nurses aides 12 (ft), 7 (pt); Physical therapists 1
(pt); Recreational therapists 1 (pt); Activities
coordinators 1 (pt); Dietitians 1 (pt).
Facilities Dining room; Laundry room; Barber-/Beauty shop; Library.
Activities Arts and Crafts; Cards; Games;
Reading groups; Prayer groups; Movies; Dances/Social or cultural gatherings; Bowling; Volley ball; Shuffleboard.

TITONKA

Titonka Care Center*
Hwy 226, Titonka, IA, 50480 (515) 928-2600
Admin Murray D Berggren.
Licensure Intermediate Care. *Beds* 51.
Certified Medicaid.

TOLEDO

Bethesda Care Center
PO Box 135, Toledo, IA, 52342 (515) 484-5080
Licensure Intermediate Care. *Beds* 98. *Certified* Medicaid.

TRAER

Sunrise Hill Care Center*
909 6th St, Traer, IA, 50675 (319) 478-2730
Admin Harold Lynch.
Licensure Intermediate Care. *Beds* 64.
Certified Medicaid.

TRIPOLI

Tripoli Nursing Home
604 3rd St SW, Tripoli, IA, 50676 (319)
882-4269
Licensure Intermediate Care. *Beds* 22. *Certified* Medicaid.
Admissions Requirements Physician's request.
Staff Physicians 4 (pt); RNs 3 (pt); LPNs 2
(pt); Nurses aides 4 (ft), 11 (pt); Activities coordinators 1 (pt); Dietitians 1 (pt).
Facilities Dining room; Activities room; Crafts
room; Laundry room; Main lobby.
Activities Arts and Crafts; Cards; Games;
Reading groups; Movies; Shopping trips;
Church groups.
Description Facility is a small home in a small
community with a home-like atmosphere.

URBANDALE

Karen Acres Rest Home*
3605 Elm Dr, Urbandale, IA, 50322 (515)
276-4969
Admin Bernadine Elifrits.
Licensure Intermediate Care. *Beds* 37. *Certified* Medicaid.

Quality Health Care Center
4614 NW 84th St, Urbandale, IA, 50322 (515)
244-0321
Medical Dir/Dir of Nursing Dr Roy Overton.
Licensure Intermediate Care. *Beds* 120. *Certified* Medicaid.
Admissions Requirements Medical examination.
Staff RNs 3 (ft), 1 (pt); LPNs 5 (ft), 2 (pt);
Orderlies 4 (ft), 2 (pt); Nurses aides 25 (ft); Recreational therapists 2 (ft); Activities
coordinators 1 (ft); Dietitians 1 (pt).
Facilities Dining room; Physical therapy room;
Activities room; Chapel; Crafts room; Laundry
room; Barber/Beauty shop.
Activities Arts and Crafts; Cards; Games;
Reading groups; Prayer groups; Movies.
Description The Center opened a brand new
120-bed facility in Urbandale in April of 1984,
to be followed by a community center and
approximately 75 retirement townhomes.

VILLISCA

Villisca Good Samaritan Center*
Central Ave and Redmond, Villisca, IA, 50864
(712) 826-9591
Admin Loren H Clayton.
Licensure Intermediate Care. *Beds* 65. *Certified* Medicaid.

VINTON

Benton County Care Facility
Rt 2, Vinton, IA, 52349
Admin Helen Corcran.
Licensure Residential Care. *Beds* 50.
Certified Medicaid; Medicare.
Ownership Nonprofit.
Admissions Requirements Minimum age 18;
Medical examination; Physician's request.
Staff RNs 1 (ft); LPNs 2 (pt); Orderlies 1 (ft);
Nurses aides 5 (ft), 5 (pt); Activities coordinators 1 (ft); Dietitians 1 (pt).
Facilities Dining room; Activities room; Crafts
room; Laundry room; Barber/Beauty shop;
Library.
Activities Arts and Crafts; Cards; Games;
Reading groups; Prayer groups; Movies; Shopping trips; Dances/Social or cultural gatherings.
Description Facility has an active group of residents, with woodworking as one of the most
outstanding projects.

Lutheran Home for the Aged*
1301 2nd Ave, Vinton, IA, 52349 (319)
472-4751
Admin Leon Hodges.
Licensure Intermediate Care. *Beds* 61. *Certified* Medicaid.
Ownership Nonprofit.
Affiliation Lutheran

Virginia Gay Hospital*
N 9th Ave, Vinton, IA, 52349 (319) 472-4751
Admin Leon Hodges.
Licensure Intermediate Care. *Beds* 58.

WALL LAKE

Twilight Acres Inc
Melrose Ave, Wall Lake, IA, 51466 (712)
664-2488
Admin Lauretta Skarin.
Licensure Intermediate Care; Residential Care.
Beds ICF 44; Residential Care 31. *Certified* Medicaid.
Admissions Requirements Medical examination.
Staff RNs 1 (ft), 6 (pt); LPNs 3 (ft), 2 (pt);
Nurses aides 13 (ft), 17 (pt); Physical therapists
1 (pt); Activities coordinators 2 (ft).
Facilities Dining room; Physical therapy room;
Activities room; Chapel; Crafts room; Laundry
room; Barber/Beauty shop.
Activities Arts and Crafts; Cards; Games;
Reading groups; Prayer groups; Movies; Shopping trips; Dances/Social or cultural gatherings.
Description Facility features fire works display
and homemade ice cream for July 4th, fishing
trips, and is known locally as the nursing home
that is so clean because the floors are scrubbed
on hands and knees.

WAPELLO

Wapello Nursing Home*
Hwy 61 S, Wapello, IA, 52653 (319) 523-2001
Admin C W Keldgord.
Licensure Intermediate Care. *Beds* 40. *Certified* Medicaid.

WASHINGTON

Halcyon House*
1015 S Iowa Ave, Washington, IA, 52353 (319)
653-3523
Admin Lillian Dehne.
Licensure Intermediate Care; Residential Care.
Beds ICF 22; Residential Care 20. *Certified* Medicaid.

United Presbyterian Home
1203 E Washington, Washington, IA, 52353
(319) 653-5473
Licensure Intermediate Care; Residential Care.
Beds ICF 36; Residential Care 11. *Certified* Medicaid.
Admissions Requirements Minimum age 62;
Medical examination.
Staff RNs 3 (ft), 2 (pt); LPNs 2 (ft), 1 (pt);
Nurses aides 16 (ft), 4 (pt); Physical therapists 1
(pt); Activities coordinators 1 (ft), 1 (pt); Dietitians 1 (pt).
Affiliation Presbyterian
Facilities Dining room; Physical therapy room;
Activities room; Chapel; Crafts room; Laundry
room; Barber/Beauty shop; Library.
Activities Arts and Crafts; Cards; Games;
Reading groups; Prayer groups; Movies; Dances/Social or cultural gatherings.
Description Home has 52 2-bedroom cottages,
18 apartments, 38 single rooms, 16-bed residen-

tial care center, and 36-bed intermediate care
center, all on a large campus in a small city in a
great agricultural area of Iowa.

Washington Care Center
601 E Polk St, Washington, IA, 52353 (319)
653-6526
Licensure Intermediate Care. *Beds* 101. *Certified* Medicaid.
Staff RNs 4 (ft), 4 (pt); LPNs 2 (ft), 2 (pt);
Nurses aides 21 (ft), 17 (pt); Physical therapists
1 (ft), 1 (pt); Recreational therapists 1 (ft), 1 (pt);
Activities coordinators 1 (ft), 1 (pt).
Facilities Dining room; Physical therapy room;
Activities room; Crafts room; Laundry room;
Barber/Beauty shop.
Activities Movies; Dances/Social or cultural
gatherings.

WATERLOO

Americana Healthcare Center
201 W Ridgeway Ave, Waterloo, IA, 50701
(319) 234-7777
Admin Richard Parades. *Medical Dir/Dir of
Nursing* Dr Ronald Roth.
Licensure Skilled Care; Intermediate Care.
Beds SNF 20; ICF 47. *Certified* Medicare.
Facilities Dining room; Physical therapy room;
Activities room; Crafts room; Laundry room;
Barber/Beauty shop.
Activities Arts and Crafts; Cards; Games;
Reading groups; Prayer groups; Movies; Shopping trips; Dances/Social or cultural gatherings.

Black Hawk County Health Care
1407 Independence Ave, Waterloo, IA, 50703
(319) 291-2567
Licensure Intermediate Care. *Beds* 120. *Certified* Medicaid.
Admissions Requirements Medical examination; Physician's request.
Staff RNs 2 (ft); LPNs 12 (ft), 2 (pt); Orderlies
2 (ft); Nurses aides 40 (ft); Physical therapists 1
(pt); Reality therapists 1 (pt); Recreational therapists 1 (ft); Occupational therapists 1 (pt);
Speech therapists 1 (pt); Activities coordinators
1 (ft); Dietitians 1 (ft); Dentists 2 (pt); Podiatrists 1 (pt).
Facilities Dining room; Activities room; Chapel; Crafts room; Laundry room; Barber/Beauty
shop.
Activities Arts and Crafts; Cards; Games;
Reading groups; Prayer groups; Movies; Shopping trips; Dances/Social or cultural gatherings.

Fairway Group Home*
2221 Fairway Ln, Waterloo, IA, 50702 (319)
236-1033
Admin Bob Bowen.
Licensure Intermediate Care for Mentally
Retarded. *Beds* 12.

Friendship Village Retirement Center*
600 Park Ln, Waterloo, IA, 50702 (319)
291-8100
Admin Mary B O'Brien.
Licensure Skilled Care; Intermediate Care.
Beds SNF 17; ICF 33. *Certified* Medicaid;
Medicare.

Harmony House Health Care Center
2950 W Shaulis, Waterloo, IA, 50703 (319)
234-4495
Admin Daniel M Larmore. *Medical Dir/Dir of Nursing* Ronald Roth MD.
Licensure Intermediate Care; Intermediate
Care for Mentally Retarded. *Beds* ICF 46;
ICF/MR 68. *Certified* Medicaid.
Admissions Requirements Minimum age 16;
Medical examination; Physician's request.
Staff Physicians 18 (pt); RNs 2 (ft); LPNs 12
(ft), 6 (pt); Orderlies 9 (ft), 3 (pt); Nurses aides
54 (ft), 16 (pt); Physical therapists 1 (pt); Recreational therapists 3 (ft); Occupational therapists
1 (ft); Speech therapists 1 (ft); Activities coordinators 1 (ft); Dietitians 1 (ft); Dentists 1 (pt);
Ophthalmologists 1 (pt); Podiatrists 1 (pt).
Facilities Dining room; Physical therapy room;
Activities room; Crafts room; Laundry room;
Barber/Beauty shop; Living rooms.
Activities Arts and Crafts; Cards; Games;
Reading groups; Prayer groups; Movies; Shopping trips; Dances/Social or cultural gatherings.
Description Facility offers innovative programing and rehabilitation training for
mentally/physically handicapped, geriatric, and
traumatically head-injured individuals in 3 distinct living units.

Parkview Gardens Care Center*
310 Upland Dr, Waterloo, IA, 50701 (319)
234-4423
Admin Robert F Davis.
Licensure Intermediate Care. *Beds* 160. *Certified* Medicaid.

Ravenwood Health Care Center*
2951 Saint Francis Dr, Waterloo, IA, 50702
(319) 232-6808
Admin Gordon Kline.
Licensure Intermediate Care. *Beds* 196. *Certified* Medicaid.

WAUKON

Allamakee County Care Center*
RR 2, Waukon, IA, 52172 (319) 568-4251
Admin Harry B Banta.
Licensure Intermediate Care for Mentally
Retarded. *Beds* 75.

Northgate Care Center
10th Ave NW, Waukon, IA, 52172 (319)
568-3494
Admin LouAnn Wikan. *Medical Dir/Dir of
Nursing* Maxine Connor.
Licensure Intermediate Care. *Beds* 51. *Certified* Medicaid.
Admissions Requirements Minimum age 18;
Medical examination.
Staff RNs 2 (ft); LPNs 2 (ft), 2 (pt); Orderlies 1
(ft); Nurses aides 10 (ft), 9 (pt); Activities coordinators 1 (ft); Dietitians 2 (pt).
Facilities Dining room; Activities room; Laundry room; Barber/Beauty shop.
Activities Arts and Crafts; Cards; Games;
Reading groups; Prayer groups; Movies; Dances/Social or cultural gatherings.

Waukon Good Samaritan Center*
21 E Main St, Waukon, IA, 52172 (319)
568-3447

Admin Jay E Johnson.
Licensure Intermediate Care; Residential Care.
Beds ICF 100; Residential Care 11. *Certified* Medicaid.

WAVERLY

Bartels Lutheran Home Inc
1922 5th Ave NW, Waverly, IA, 50677 (319)
352-4540
Licensure Intermediate Care; Residential Care.
Beds ICF 141; Residential Care 96. *Certified* Medicaid.
Staff RNs 5 (ft), 1 (pt); LPNs 9 (ft), 11 (pt);
Orderlies 2 (pt); Nurses aides 29 (ft), 64 (pt);
Activities coordinators 1 (ft); Dietitians 1 (pt).
Affiliation Lutheran
Facilities Dining room; Activities room; Chapel; Crafts room; Laundry room; Barber/Beauty
shop; Library.
Activities Arts and Crafts; Cards; Games;
Reading groups; Prayer groups; Movies; Shopping trips; Dances/Social or cultural gatherings.

WAYLAND

Parkview Home
102 N Jackson, Wayland, IA, 52654 (319)
256-3525
Medical Dir/Dir of Nursing Marie Widmer
RN.
Licensure Intermediate Care; Residential Care.
Beds ICF 27; Residential Care 22. *Certified* Medicaid.
Staff RNs 1 (ft); LPNs 2 (ft), 4 (pt); Nurses
aides 4 (ft), 11 (pt); Activities coordinators 1
(ft); Dietitians 1 (pt).
Affiliation Mennonite
Facilities Dining room; Physical therapy room;
Activities room; Chapel; Crafts room; Laundry
room; Barber/Beauty shop; Library.
Activities Arts and Crafts; Games; Reading
groups; Prayer groups; Movies; Shopping trips.

WEBSTER CITY

Crestview Manor
2401 S Des Moines St, Webster City, IA, 50595
(515) 832-2727
Admin Joe H Sherman.
Licensure Intermediate Care. *Beds* 84. *Certified* Medicaid.
Admissions Requirements Medical examination.
Staff RNs 3 (ft), 4 (pt); LPNs 2 (ft), 2 (pt);
Nurses aides 10 (ft), 26 (pt); Physical therapists;
Activities coordinators 1 (ft), 1 (pt); Dietitians
1 (ft); Podiatrists; Audiologists.
Facilities Dining room; Physical therapy room;
Activities room; Laundry room; Barber/Beauty
shop.
Activities Arts and Crafts; Cards; Games;
Reading groups; Prayer groups; Movies.

Southfield Care Center*
2416 S Des Moines St, Webster City, IA, 50595
(515) 832-3881
Admin Diana Shefveland.
Licensure Intermediate Care. *Beds* 52. *Certified* Medicaid.

WELLMAN

Parkview Manor
516 13th St, Wellman, IA, 52356 (319)
646-2911
Medical Dir/Dir of Nursing Dr Dwight
Kauffman.
Licensure Intermediate Care. *Beds* 94. *Certified* Medicaid.
Admissions Requirements Medical examination; Physician's request.
Staff RNs 4 (ft), 4 (pt); LPNs 1 (ft), 1 (pt);
Orderlies 1 (ft); Nurses aides 21 (ft), 10 (pt);
Physical therapists 1 (pt); Activities coordinators 1 (ft), 2 (pt); Dietitians 1 (pt).
Facilities Dining room; Physical therapy room;
Activities room; Laundry room; Barber/Beauty
shop.
Activities Arts and Crafts; Games; Reading
groups; Prayer groups; Movies; Shopping trips;
Dances/Social or cultural gatherings.

WEST BEND

West Bend Care Center*
203 4th St NW, West Bend, IA, 50597 (515)
887-4071
Admin Phyllis Fandel.
Licensure Intermediate Care. *Beds* 40. *Certified* Medicaid.

WEST BRANCH

Crestview Care Center*
Oliphant and Northside Dr, West Branch, IA,
52358 (319) 643-2551
Admin Regina Abel.
Licensure Intermediate Care. *Beds* 65. *Certified* Medicaid.

WEST DES MOINES

Fountain West Health Center*
1501 Office Park Rd, West Des Moines, IA,
50265 (515) 223-1223
Admin Gary A Tiemeyer.
Licensure Intermediate Care; Residential Care.
Beds ICF 156; Residential Care 38. *Certified* Medicaid.

West Park Care Center*
1211 Vine St, West Des Moines, IA, 50265
(515) 233-1251
Admin Bert M Elder.
Licensure Intermediate Care. *Beds* 214. *Certified* Medicaid.

WEST LIBERTY

Simpson Memorial Home*
1001 N Miller St, West Liberty, IA, 52776 (319)
627-4775
Admin Jack L McIntosh.
Licensure Intermediate Care. *Beds* 63. *Certified* Medicaid.

WEST POINT

West Point Care Center*
N 6th and Ave G, West Point, IA, 52656 (319)
837-6117
Admin Edward Matney.
Licensure Intermediate Care. *Beds* 51. *Certified* Medicaid.

WEST UNION

Good Samaritan Center*
300 Hall St, West Union, IA, 52175 (319)
422-3814
Admin David L Sorbel.
Licensure Intermediate Care. *Beds* 71. *Certified* Medicaid.

WHEATLAND

Colonial Manor Nursing and Care Center*
515 E Lincolnway, Wheatland, IA, 52777 (319)
374-2951
Admin Connie Byrd.
Licensure Intermediate Care. *Beds* 50. *Certified* Medicaid.

WHITING

Pleasant View Inc
200 Shannon Dr, Whiting, IA, 51063 (712)
458-2417
Medical Dir/Dir of Nursing Dr John L Garred.
Licensure Intermediate Care. *Beds* 106. *Certified* Medicaid.
Admissions Requirements Minimum age 16;
Medical examination.
Staff Physicians 6 (pt); RNs 1 (ft), 7 (pt); LPNs
1 (ft), 3 (pt); Nurses aides 15 (ft), 20 (pt);
Physical therapists 1 (pt); Activities coordinators 1 (ft), 2 (pt); Dietitians 1 (pt).
Facilities Dining room; Physical therapy room;
Activities room; Chapel; Crafts room; Laundry
room; Barber/Beauty shop; Library.
Activities Arts and Crafts; Cards; Games;
Reading groups; Prayer groups; Movies; Shopping trips; Dances/Social or cultural gatherings.
Description Professional care in a home-like
atmosphere. Numerous varied activities, excellent community support, super volunteer program.

WILLIAMSBURG

Williamsburg Care Center*
104 Court St, Williamsburg, IA, 52361 (319)
668-2311
Admin David O Yearian.
Licensure Intermediate Care. *Beds* 44. *Certified* Medicaid.

WILTON

Wilton Memorial Home*
415 E Prairie, Wilton, IA, 52778 (319)
732-2086
Admin L R Buroker.
Licensure Intermediate Care. *Beds* 34.

WINFIELD

Sunrise Terrace
W Central Ave, Winfield, IA, 52659 (319)
257-3303
Licensure Intermediate Care. *Beds* 62. *Certified* Medicaid.
Admissions Requirements Medical examination.
Staff RNs 2 (ft), 5 (pt); LPNs 1 (ft), 1 (pt);
Nurses aides 12 (ft), 7 (pt); Activities coordinators 1 (ft).
Facilities Dining room; Physical therapy room;
Activities room; Chapel; Laundry room; Barber/Beauty shop.
Activities Arts and Crafts; Cards; Games;
Reading groups; Prayer groups; Movies; Shopping trips; Dances/Social or cultural gatherings.

WINTERSET

Bethesda Care Center
1015 W Summitt, Winterset, IA, 50273 (515)
462-1711
Admin Eva McDonald.
Licensure Intermediate Care; Residential Care.
Beds ICF 80; Residential Care 19. *Certified* Medicaid.
Ownership Nonprofit.
Admissions Requirements Minimum age 16;
Medical examination; Physician's request.
Staff RNs 1 (ft), 2 (pt); LPNs 6 (ft), 3 (pt);
Orderlies 2 (pt); Nurses aides 22 (ft), 12 (pt);
Activities coordinators 2 (ft).
Facilities Dining room; Physical therapy room;
Activities room; Chapel; Crafts room; Laundry
room; Barber/Beauty shop; Library.
Activities Arts and Crafts; Cards; Games;
Reading groups; Prayer groups; Movies; Shopping trips; Dances/Social or cultural gatherings;
Baking and cooking classes.
Description Bethesda Care Center is within
easy access to shopping, churches of all denominations, a medical clinic, hospital, dental
offices, optometrists' offices, and banking. It is
an ideal spot to enjoy the "take-it-easy" atmosphere of small town life and the grounds are
beautifully landscaped to enhance Iowa's ever-changing seasons. The modern one-story brick
building is of fireproof materials and has a
complete sprinkler system throughout; accommodations are in private or semi-private rooms
each with its own or adjoining bath. Lounge
areas are available to entertain guests and there
is ample parking. Chapel is quiet, peaceful area
designed to meet the spiritual needs of residents
and families. There is a good area around the
home for daily walks, a patio for sitting in the
sun, and flower boxes and a garden plot are
provided for interested gardeners.

Winterset Care Center—North*
411 E Lane St, Winterset, IA, 50273 (515)
462-1571
Admin Alberta R Little.
Licensure Intermediate Care. *Beds* 98. *Certified* Medicaid.

Winterset Care Center—South*
715 S 2nd Ave, Winterset, IA, 50273 (515)
462-4040

Admin Alberta R Little.
Licensure Intermediate Care. *Beds* 98. *Certified* Medicaid.

WOODBINE

Rose Vista Home Inc*
1109 Normal St, Woodbine, IA, 51579 (712)
647-2010
Admin Esther L Sherer.
Licensure Intermediate Care. *Beds* 56. *Certified* Medicaid.

WOODWARD

Parkview Manor Care Center*
700 S 3rd Ave, Woodward, IA, 50276 (525)
438-2568
Admin Julia A Glass.
Licensure Intermediate Care. *Beds* 39. *Certified* Medicaid.

ZEARING

Colonial Manor of Zearing*
401 E Garfield, Zearing, IA, 50278 (515)
487-7631
Admin Kent Jorgensen.
Licensure Intermediate Care. *Beds* 56. *Certified* Medicaid.

KANSAS

ABILENE

Abilene Nursing Center
705 N Brady, Abilene, KS, 67410 (913)
263-1431
Admin Sue Jirkovsky. *Medical Dir/Dir of
Nursing* J Dennis Biggs MD.
Licensure Intermediate Care. *Beds* 108. *Certified* Medicaid.
Admissions Requirements Minimum age 16;
Medical examination.
Staff RNs 2 (ft), 1 (pt); LPNs 3 (ft), 1 (pt);
Nurses aides 25 (ft), 10 (pt); Activities coordinators 1 (ft).
Facilities Dining room; Physical therapy room;
Activities room; Chapel; Crafts room; Laundry
room; Barber/Beauty shop; Library.
Activities Arts and Crafts; Games; Reading
groups; Prayer groups; Movies; Dances/Social
or cultural gatherings.

Highland Care Home
1601 W 1st St, Abilene, KS, 67410 (913)
263-2070
Admin Joyce Watts. *Medical Dir/Dir of
Nursing* Viola Aker.
Licensure Intermediate Care. *Beds* 42. *Certified* Medicaid.
Admissions Requirements Minimum age 18;
Medical examination.
Staff RNs 1 (ft); LPNs 1 (ft), 1 (pt); Orderlies 1
(ft); Nurses aides 8 (ft), 8 (pt); Physical therapists 1 (pt); Reality therapists 1 (pt); Recreational therapists 1 (pt); Occupational therapists
1 (pt); Speech therapists 1 (pt); Activities coordinators 1 (ft); Dietitians 1 (pt); Audiologists 1
(pt).
Facilities Dining room; Physical therapy room;
Activities room; Chapel; Crafts room; Laundry
room; Barber/Beauty shop.
Activities Arts and Crafts; Cards; Games;
Reading groups; Prayer groups; Movies; Shopping trips.

ALMA

Alma Manor Nursing Home*
234 Manor Circle, Alma, KS, 66401 (913)
765-3318
Admin Robert W Stoufer.
Licensure Intermediate Care. *Beds* 100. *Certified* Medicaid.
Ownership Proprietary.

ALTAMONT

Retirement Acres*
Rt 1, Box 150, 32nd and 96 Hwy, Altamont,
KS, 67330 (316) 784-5346
Admin Florence Stockton.
Licensure Intermediate Care. *Beds* 46. *Certified* Medicaid.
Ownership Proprietary.

ANTHONY

Cedar Crest Inc
212 N 5th, Anthony, KS, 67003 (316) 842-5103
Admin Carole Eggert. *Medical Dir/Dir of
Nursing* Dr Jeff Bond.
Licensure Intermediate Care. *Beds* 50. *Certified* Medicaid.
Admissions Requirements Minimum age 16;
Medical examination.
Staff RNs 1 (pt); LPNs 1 (ft), 1 (pt); Nurses
aides 12 (ft), 5 (pt); Recreational therapists 1
(ft); Activities coordinators 1 (ft).
Facilities Dining room; Physical therapy room;
Activities room; Crafts room; Laundry room;
Barber/Beauty shop.
Activities Arts and Crafts; Cards; Games;
Reading groups; Prayer groups; Movies; Dances/Social or cultural gatherings; Sightseeing
trips.
Description Facility offers large, tastefully decorated centers; single level, fire-resistant construction; family-style dining; special occupational,
restorative, and speech therapy rooms provided; RN & LPN supervision, physician on call;
fully licensed by Kansas State Board of Health;
major emphasis on medical, social, and
physical rehabilitation.

ARKANSAS CITY

Arkansas City Presbyterian Manor
1711 N 4th St, Arkansas City, KS, 67005 (316)
442-8700
Admin Robert J Pletcher. *Medical Dir/Dir of
Nursing* Judy Hershberger.
Licensure Intermediate Care. *Beds* 53.
Admissions Requirements Minimum age 65;
Medical examination; Physician's request.
Staff RNs 2 (ft), 2 (pt); LPNs 2 (ft); Nurses
aides 24 (ft), 3 (pt); Occupational therapists 1
(ft), 1 (pt); Activities coordinators 1 (ft); Dietitians 1 (ft).

Affiliation Presbyterian
Facilities Dining room; Physical therapy room;
Activities room; Chapel; Crafts room; Laundry
room; Barber/Beauty shop; Library.
Activities Arts and Crafts; Cards; Games;
Reading groups; Prayer groups; Movies; Dances/Social or cultural gatherings.
Description Facility features a walking course.

Medicalodge East of Arkansas City*
203 E Osage, Arkansas City, KS, 67005 (316)
442-9300
Admin Bruce Struble.
Licensure Intermediate Care. *Beds* 91. *Certified* Medicaid.
Ownership Proprietary.

Medicalodge North of Arkansas City
2575 Greenway, Arkansas City, KS, 67005
(316) 442-1120
Admin Edward A Long Jr.
Licensure Intermediate Care. *Beds* 96. *Certified* Medicaid.
Admissions Requirements Minimum age 16;
Medical examination; Physician's request.
Staff RNs 1 (ft); LPNs 5 (ft); Orderlies 1 (ft);
Nurses aides 14 (ft); Physical therapists 1 (ft);
Activities coordinators 1 (ft).
Facilities Dining room; Physical therapy room;
Activities room; Chapel; Crafts room; Laundry
room; Barber/Beauty shop; Library.
Activities Games; Reading groups; Prayer
groups; Movies.

ARMA

Crestview Lodge*
Box 789, 3rd and Melvin Sts, Arma, KS, 66712
(316) 347-4103
Admin Raymond T Stazzoni.
Licensure Intermediate Care. *Beds* 100. *Certified* Medicaid.
Ownership Proprietary.

ASHLAND

Fountain View Villa
528 W 8th St, Ashland, KS, 67831 (316)
635-2311
Admin Sandra Butler.
Licensure Intermediate Care. *Beds* 36. *Certified* Medicaid.

ATCHISON

Atchison County Nursing Home
1419 N 6th St, Atchison, KS, 66002 (913)
367-1905
Medical Dir/Dir of Nursing Vonda Young.
Licensure Intermediate Care. *Beds* 50. *Certified* Medicaid.
Ownership Public.
Admissions Requirements Minimum age 16;
Medical examination.
Staff RNs 1 (pt); LPNs 4 (ft), 1 (pt); Nurses
aides 18 (ft), 1 (pt); Activities coordinators 1
(ft); Dietitians 1 (ft).
Facilities Dining room; Physical therapy room;
Activities room; Chapel; Crafts room; Laundry
room; Barber/Beauty shop.
Activities Arts and Crafts; Games; Reading
groups; Prayer groups; Movies; Shopping trips;
Dances/Social or cultural gatherings.
Description Our entire staff is certified. We are
minutes from a hospital and doctor's offices
and close to downtown shopping areas.

Medicalodge of Atchison*
1637 Riley, Atchison, KS, 66002 (913)
367-6066
Admin Kathleen Crosswhite.
Licensure Skilled Care; Intermediate Care.
Beds 100. *Certified* Medicaid.
Ownership Proprietary.

ATWOOD

Good Samaritan Center
650 Lake Rd, Box 216, Atwood, KS, 67730
(913) 626-3253
Admin Howard R Goehring.
Licensure Intermediate Care. *Beds* 48. *Certified* Medicaid.
Admissions Requirements Medical examination; Physician's request.
Staff RNs 1 (pt); LPNs 4 (ft); Orderlies 1 (ft);
Nurses aides 14 (ft), 6 (pt); Occupational therapists 1 (pt); Activities coordinators 1 (ft);
Dietitians 1 (pt).
Facilities Dining room; Physical therapy room;
Activities room; Chapel; Crafts room; Laundry
room; Barber/Beauty shop.
Activities Arts and Crafts; Cards; Games;
Reading groups; Prayer groups; Movies; Shopping trips; Dances/Social or cultural gatherings.

AUGUSTA

Walnut Valley Manor
2100 N Ohio, Augusta, KS, 67010 (316)
775-6333
Admin Margarite Dodson.
Licensure Intermediate Care. *Beds* 50. *Certified* Medicaid.
Admissions Requirements Minimum age 18;
Medical examination; Physician's request.
Staff Physicians 6 (pt); RNs 1 (pt); LPNs 1 (ft);
Nurses aides 19 (ft), 1 (pt); Physical therapists 1
(pt); Reality therapists 1 (pt); Recreational therapists 1 (pt); Occupational therapists 1 (pt);
Speech therapists 1 (pt); Activities coordinators
1 (ft); Dietitians 2 (ft); Dentists 1 (pt); Ophthalmologists 1 (pt); Podiatrists 1 (pt); Audiologists
1 (pt).

Facilities Dining room; Physical therapy room;
Activities room; Crafts room; Laundry room;
Barber/Beauty shop.
Activities Arts and Crafts; Cards; Games;
Reading groups; Prayer groups; Movies; Shopping trips; Dances/Social or cultural gatherings.

BALDWIN CITY

Baldwin City Nursing Facility*
1223 Orchard Ln, Baldwin City, KS, 66006
(913) 594-6492
Admin Ronald E Nelson.
Licensure Intermediate Care. *Beds* 48. *Certified* Medicaid.
Ownership Public.

BAXTER SPRINGS

Midwest Nursing Center Inc
217 E 14th St, Baxter Springs, KS, 66713 (316)
856-2662
Admin Shirley Ellsworth. *Medical Dir/Dir of
Nursing* C B Smith DO.
Licensure Intermediate Care. *Beds* 50. *Certified* Medicaid.
Admissions Requirements Medical examination; Physician's request.
Staff Physicians; RNs; LPNs; Physical
therapists; Reality therapists; Recreational therapists; Occupational therapists; Speech
therapists; Activities coordinators; Dietitians;
Dentists; Ophthalmologists; Podiatrists;
Audiologists.
Facilities Dining room; Physical therapy room;
Activities room; Chapel; Crafts room; Laundry
room; Barber/Beauty shop; Library.
Activities Arts and Crafts; Cards; Games;
Reading groups; Prayer groups; Movies; Shopping trips; Dances/Social or cultural gatherings.
Description Facility is located near town shopping district; brick structure with a large living
room. Staff is friendly, courteous, and kind.
Community is very supportive—church services available 3 times per week.

Quaker Hill Manor
Rt 1, Baxter Springs, KS, 66713 (316) 848-3797
Admin Betty R Haner. *Medical Dir/Dir of
Nursing* Zina Hopkins.
Licensure Intermediate Care. *Beds* 36. *Certified* Medicaid.
Admissions Requirements Minimum age 16;
Medical examination.
Staff LPNs 3 (ft); Nurses aides 12 (ft), 1 (pt).
Facilities Dining room; Physical therapy room;
Activities room; Laundry room.
Activities Arts and Crafts; Reading groups;
Prayer groups; Movies; Shopping trips.
Description Facility is a home away from
home. We have a large yard and circle drive for
walks. Located 4 miles from a town. Supplies
much tender loving care.

BELLE PLAINE

Eastview Manor
801 N Logan, Belle Plaine, KS, 67013 (316)
488-2228
Admin George Livingston.
Licensure Intermediate Care. *Beds* 50. *Certi-*

fied Medicaid.
Admissions Requirements Medical examination; Physician's request.
Staff RNs 1 (pt); LPNs 3 (ft); Nurses aides 20
(ft); Physical therapists 1 (pt); Reality therapists
1 (pt); Recreational therapists 1 (ft); Occupational therapists 1 (pt); Speech therapists 1 (pt);
Activities coordinators 1 (ft); Dietitians 1 (pt);
Dentists 1 (pt); Podiatrists 1 (pt); Audiologists 1
(pt).
Facilities Dining room; Physical therapy room;
Activities room; Chapel; Crafts room; Laundry
room; Barber/Beauty shop.
Activities Arts and Crafts; Games; Reading
groups; Prayer groups; Shopping trips; Dances-
/Social or cultural gatherings.
Description Facility features a small town setting with caring employees.

BELLEVILLE

Belleville Health Care Center*
2626 Wesleyan Dr, Belleville, KS, 66935 (913)
527-5636
Admin Philip W Caldwell.
Licensure Intermediate Care. *Beds* 78. *Certified* Medicaid.

Heartland Care Center—Belleville*
Box 524, 500 W 23rd St, Belleville, KS, 66935
(913) 527-2242
Admin Carmen Kesler.
Licensure Intermediate Care. *Beds* 99. *Certified* Medicaid.
Ownership Proprietary.

BELOIT

Hilltop Lodge Inc Nursing Home
815 N Independence, Beloit, KS, 67420 (913)
738-3516
Admin Harold E Heidrick.
Licensure Intermediate Care. *Beds* 100. *Certified* Medicaid.
Admissions Requirements Minimum age 18;
Medical examination; Physician's request.
Staff Physicians 6 (pt); RNs 5 (pt); LPNs 5
(pt); Orderlies 3 (pt); Nurses aides 20 (ft), 15
(pt); Physical therapists 1 (pt); Recreational
therapists 1 (ft); Occupational therapists 1 (pt);
Speech therapists 1 (pt); Activities coordinators
1 (ft); Dietitians 1 (pt); Dentists 1 (pt); Ophthalmologists 1 (pt); Podiatrists 1 (pt); Audiologists
1 (pt).
Facilities Dining room; Physical therapy room;
Activities room; Chapel; Crafts room; Laundry
room; Barber/Beauty shop; Library.
Activities Arts and Crafts; Cards; Games;
Reading groups; Prayer groups; Movies; Shopping trips; Dances/Social or cultural gatherings.
Description Facility is fully carpeted, has 3
dining rooms, full-time nursing coverage, and
is close to hospital, clinic, and shopping center.

BLUE RAPIDS

Blue Valley Nursing Home*
710 Southwest Ave, Blue Rapids, KS, 66411
(913) 226-7777
Admin Doris J Neis.

Licensure Intermediate Care. *Beds* 53. *Certified* Medicaid.
Ownership Proprietary.

BONNER SPRINGS

Bonner Health Center
520 E Morse, Bonner Springs, KS, 66012 (913) 441-2515
Admin Donna B Foster.
Licensure Intermediate Care. *Beds* 50. *Certified* Medicaid.
Admissions Requirements Minimum age 16; Medical examination; Physician's request.
Staff RNs 1 (ft); LPNs 2 (ft); Nurses aides 14 (ft), 3 (pt); Physical therapists 1 (ft); Activities coordinators 1 (ft).
Facilities Dining room; Physical therapy room; Activities room; Crafts room; Laundry room; Barber/Beauty shop.
Activities Arts and Crafts; Cards; Games; Reading groups; Prayer groups; Movies; Shopping trips; Dances/Social or cultural gatherings.
Description Facility is a small nursing home with a very comfortable, homey atmosphere; emphasis is in offering good patient care, along with many activities to occupy minds and time.

Kaw Valley Manor*
510 E Morse, Bonner Springs, KS, 66012 (913) 441-2444
Admin John S May.
Licensure Intermediate Care. *Beds* 108. *Certified* Medicaid.
Ownership Proprietary.

BUCKLIN

Hill Top House*
PO Box 248, 505 W Elm, Bucklin, KS, 67834 (316) 826-3202
Admin Bert L Earls.
Licensure Intermediate Care. *Beds* 50. *Certified* Medicaid.
Ownership Nonprofit.

BUHLER

Buhler Sunshine Home Inc*
412 W "C" Ave, Buhler, KS, 67522 (316) 543-2251
Admin Richard Heim.
Licensure Intermediate Care. *Beds* 43. *Certified* Medicaid.
Ownership Proprietary.

BURLINGAME

Santa Fe Trail Nursing Center
401 Prospect Pl, Burlingame, KS, 66413 (913) 654-3391
Admin Marion E Smith.
Licensure Intermediate Care. *Beds* 50. *Certified* Medicaid.
Admissions Requirements Minimum age 21; Medical examination.
Staff RNs 1 (pt); LPNs 1 (ft), 1 (pt); Nurses aides 15 (ft); Physical therapists 1 (pt); Occupational therapists 1 (pt); Speech therapists 1 (pt);

Dietitians 1 (pt); Dentists 1 (pt).
Facilities Dining room; Physical therapy room; Activities room; Chapel; Laundry room; Barber/Beauty shop.
Activities Arts and Crafts; Cards; Games; Reading groups; Prayer groups; Shopping trips; Dances/Social or cultural gatherings.
Description Center sets on the west side of town, high on a hill overlooking pastures and ponds.

BURLINGTON

Golden Age Lodge of Burlington*
Box 43, Cross and Jarboe, Burlington, KS, 66839 (316) 364-2117
Admin Rosalee Garrett.
Licensure Intermediate Care. *Beds* 102. *Certified* Medicaid.
Ownership Proprietary.

CALDWELL

Leisure Center*
415 S Osage, Caldwell, KS, 67022 (316) 845-6495
Admin Roberta L Childers.
Licensure Intermediate Care. *Beds* 57. *Certified* Medicaid.
Ownership Proprietary.

CANEY

Caney Rest Home
615 S High, Caney, KS, 67333 (316) 879-2929
Admin Beulah Robinson. *Medical Dir/Dir of Nursing* Dr R F Moore.
Licensure Intermediate Care. *Beds* 45. *Certified* Medicaid.
Admissions Requirements Minimum age 16; Medical examination; Physician's request.
Staff LPNs 1 (ft), 1 (pt); Orderlies 1 (ft); Nurses aides 12 (ft); Activities coordinators 1 (ft).
Facilities Dining room; Physical therapy room; Activities room; Crafts room; Laundry room; Barber/Beauty shop.
Activities Arts and Crafts; Games; Reading groups; Prayer groups; Humanities program through Coffeyville Community College.

CANTON

Shiloh Manor*
Box 67, 601 S Kansas, Canton, KS, 67428 (316) 628-4404
Admin Dale K Kohlman.
Licensure Intermediate Care. *Beds* 60. *Certified* Medicaid.
Ownership Nonprofit.
Affiliation Lutheran

CEDAR VALE

Cedar Vale Manor
100 River Rd, PO Box 307, Cedar Vale, KS, 67024 (316) 758-2248
Admin Marjorie R Lampson.
Licensure Intermediate Care. *Beds* 50. *Certified* Medicaid.

Staff LPNs 2 (ft), 1 (pt); Orderlies 3 (ft); Nurses aides 10 (ft), 2 (pt); Activities coordinators 1 (ft), 1 (pt).
Facilities Dining room; Physical therapy room; Activities room; Chapel; Laundry room; Barber/Beauty shop.
Activities Arts and Crafts; Cards; Games; Reading groups; Prayer groups; Movies; Shopping trips; Dances/Social or cultural gatherings.
Description Facility has a well-rounded activity program; provides good nursing care and an abundance of tender loving care.

CHANUTE

Arolyn Heights Home
1709 W 7th, Chanute, KS, 66720 (316) 431-9200
Admin Mary J Williams. *Medical Dir/Dir of Nursing* Judy Golay RN.
Licensure Intermediate Care. *Beds* 49. *Certified* Medicaid.
Staff RNs 1 (ft); LPNs 5 (ft); Nurses aides 16 (ft), 1 (pt); Physical therapists 1 (pt); Recreational therapists 1 (pt); Occupational therapists 1 (pt); Speech therapists 1 (pt); Activities coordinators 1 (ft); Dietitians 1 (pt); Dentists 1 (pt); Podiatrists 1 (pt); Audiologists 1 (pt).
Facilities Dining room; Physical therapy room; Activities room; Chapel; Crafts room; Laundry room; Barber/Beauty shop.
Activities Arts and Crafts; Cards; Games; Reading groups; Prayer groups; Dances/Social or cultural gatherings.

Bethesda Nursing Center
530 W 14th St, Chanute, KS, 66720 (316) 431-4940
Admin David J Reynolds. *Medical Dir/Dir of Nursing* Robert Haskins.
Licensure Intermediate Care. *Beds* 90. *Certified* Medicaid.
Staff RNs 1 (ft); LPNs 6 (ft), 1 (pt); Nurses aides 30 (ft); Physical therapists 1 (pt); Occupational therapists 1 (pt); Speech therapists 1 (pt); Activities coordinators 1 (ft); Dietitians 1 (pt); Dentists 1 (pt); Podiatrists 1 (pt); Audiologists 1 (pt).
Facilities Dining room; Physical therapy room; Activities room; Chapel; Crafts room; Laundry room; Barber/Beauty shop.
Activities Arts and Crafts; Cards; Games; Reading groups; Prayer groups; Movies; Shopping trips; Dances/Social or cultural gatherings.
Description Completely remodeled facility, has now joined the Hillhaven Corporation.

Colonial Acres
1630 W 2nd, Chanute, KS, 66720 (316) 431-4151
Admin Sonja Ann Emerson. *Medical Dir/Dir of Nursing* Edith Cowan RN.
Licensure Intermediate Care. *Beds* 105. *Certified* Medicaid.
Admissions Requirements Minimum age 16; Medical examination; Physician's request.
Staff RNs 1 (ft); LPNs 5 (ft), 3 (pt); Nurses aides 25 (ft), 7 (pt); Physical therapists 1 (ft); Occupational therapists 1 (pt); Speech therapists 1 (pt); Activities coordinators 1 (ft); Dietitians 1 (ft); Podiatrists 1 (pt).
Facilities Dining room; Physical therapy room;

Activities room; Chapel; Laundry room; Barber/Beauty shop.
Activities Arts and Crafts; Cards; Games; Reading groups; Prayer groups; Movies; Shopping trips.

Westview Nursing Home
1720 W 2nd St, Chanute, KS, 66720 (316) 431-0800
Admin Patricia Ann Weiner.
Licensure Intermediate Care. *Beds* 52. *Certified* Medicaid.

CHAPMAN

Chapman Valley Manor*
1009 N Marshall St, Chapman, KS, 67431 (913) 922-6594
Admin Thomas L Canfield.
Licensure Intermediate Care. *Beds* 50. *Certified* Medicaid.
Ownership Proprietary.

CHENEY

Cheney Golden Age Home Inc
724 N Jefferson, Cheney, KS, 67025 (316) 542-3691
Admin George W Ball Jr. *Medical Dir/Dir of Nursing* Randall Fahrenholtz MD.
Licensure Intermediate Care. *Beds* 48. *Certified* Medicaid.
Admissions Requirements Minimum age 18; Medical examination.
Staff RNs; LPNs; Nurses aides; Physical therapists; Reality therapists; Recreational therapists; Activities coordinators.
Facilities Dining room; Physical therapy room; Activities room; Crafts room; Laundry room; Barber/Beauty shop.
Activities Arts and Crafts; Cards; Games; Reading groups; Prayer groups; Movies; Shopping trips; Dances/Social or cultural gatherings.
Description An overall community involvement provides a homey atmosphere for residents.

CHERRYVALE

Cherryvale Medi-Lodge
1001 W Main, Cherryvale, KS, 67335 (316) 336-2102
Admin Wylene A Nibarger.
Licensure Intermediate Care. *Beds* 51. *Certified* Medicaid.
Admissions Requirements Medical examination; Physician's request.
Staff Physicians 1 (pt); RNs 1 (pt); LPNs 2 (ft); Nurses aides 19 (ft), 1 (pt); Activities coordinators 1 (ft).
Facilities Dining room; Physical therapy room; Activities room; Chapel; Crafts room; Laundry room; Barber/Beauty shop; Library.
Activities Arts and Crafts; Cards; Games; Reading groups; Prayer groups; Movies; Shopping trips; Dances/Social or cultural gatherings.

CHETOPA

Chetopa Nursing Home
814 Walnut, Chetopa, KS, 67336 (316) 236-7248
Admin Gail Gallo. *Medical Dir/Dir of Nursing* Judy Fromm RN.
Licensure Intermediate Care. *Beds* 41. *Certified* Medicaid.
Admissions Requirements Minimum age 18; Medical examination; Physician's request.
Staff RNs 1 (ft); LPNs 1 (pt); Nurses aides 12 (ft), 2 (pt); Physical therapists 1 (pt); Reality therapists 1 (pt); Recreational therapists 1 (pt); Occupational therapists 1 (pt); Speech therapists 1 (pt); Activities coordinators 1 (ft); Dietitians 1 (pt); Podiatrists 1 (pt).
Facilities Dining room; Physical therapy room; Activities room; Chapel; Crafts room; Laundry room; Barber/Beauty shop; Library.
Activities Arts and Crafts; Cards; Games; Reading groups; Prayer groups; Movies; Shopping trips; Dances/Social or cultural gatherings.
Description This is an older facility.

CIMARRON

Heritage of Cimarron*
706 N Main, Cimarron, KS, 67835 (316) 855-3498
Admin Sharon G Frantz.
Licensure Intermediate Care. *Beds* 48. *Certified* Medicaid.
Ownership Nonprofit.

CLAY CENTER

Clay Center Presbyterian Manor*
924 8th St, Clay Center, KS, 67432 (913) 632-5646
Admin Mariel Kolle.
Licensure Intermediate Care. *Beds* 25. *Certified* Medicaid.
Ownership Nonprofit.
Affiliation Presbyterian

Medicalodge of Clay Center
715 Liberty, Clay Center, KS, 67432 (913) 632-5696
Admin Rosemary Gonser.
Licensure Intermediate Care. *Beds* 96. *Certified* Medicaid.
Admissions Requirements Minimum age 16; Medical examination; Physician's request.
Staff RNs 1 (ft), 2 (pt); LPNs 4 (ft); Orderlies 2 (ft); Nurses aides 25 (ft), 5 (pt); Physical therapists 1 (pt); Reality therapists 1 (ft); Occupational therapists 1 (pt); Speech therapists 1 (pt); Activities coordinators 1 (ft); Dietitians 1 (pt).
Facilities Dining room; Physical therapy room; Activities room; Crafts room; Laundry room; Barber/Beauty shop; 2 Quiet rooms which serve many purposes including chapel.
Activities Arts and Crafts; Cards; Games; Prayer groups; Movies; Dances/Social or cultural gatherings.
Description One outstanding program during nursing home week: we have a family reunion where we invite back all discharged residents.

CLEARWATER

Ninnescah Manor Inc
620 Wood St, Clearwater, KS, 67026 (316) 584-2271
Admin Marlis J Felber.
Licensure Intermediate Care. *Beds* 60. *Certified* Medicaid.
Admissions Requirements Medical examination; Physician's request.
Staff RNs 1 (ft); LPNs 2 (ft); Nurses aides 13 (ft), 6 (pt); Activities coordinators 1 (ft).
Facilities Dining room; Physical therapy room; Activities room; Crafts room; Laundry room; Barber/Beauty shop; Library.
Activities Arts and Crafts; Cards; Games; Reading groups; Prayer groups; Movies; Shopping trips; Dances/Social or cultural gatherings.
Description Facility is located in rural community with active volunteer program.

CLIFTON

Estelle's Nursing Home
RR 1, Box 218, Clifton, KS, 66937 (913) 455-3522
Admin Eva L Schwab. *Medical Dir/Dir of Nursing* Judy Chaput LPN.
Licensure Intermediate Care. *Beds* 32. *Certified* Medicaid.
Admissions Requirements Medical examination.
Staff RNs 1 (pt); LPNs 1 (ft), 2 (pt); Nurses aides 10 (ft), 4 (pt); Physical therapists 1 (ft), 1 (pt); Reality therapists 1 (ft); Occupational therapists 1 (pt); Speech therapists 1 (pt); Activities coordinators 1 (ft); Dietitians 1 (pt); Dentists 1 (pt); Audiologists 1 (pt).
Facilities Dining room; Physical therapy room; Activities room; Crafts room; Laundry room; Barber/Beauty shop.
Activities Arts and Crafts; Cards; Games; Reading groups; Prayer groups; Movies; Shopping trips; Dances/Social or cultural gatherings; Volunteer parties.
Description Facility has been family-owned for 25 years, home-like atmosphere, local workers, local residents making good public relationships, very little personnel turnover. Small, well run facilty.

CLYDE

Park Villa
114 S High, Clyde, KS, 66938 (913) 446-2818
Admin Dorothy Koch. *Medical Dir/Dir of Nursing* Dr Freeborn.
Licensure Intermediate Care. *Beds* 50. *Certified* Medicaid.
Admissions Requirements Physician's request.
Staff LPNs 1 (ft), 2 (pt); Nurses aides 13 (ft), 9 (pt); Activities coordinators 1 (ft).
Facilities Dining room; Physical therapy room; Activities room; Chapel; Crafts room; Laundry room; Barber/Beauty shop.
Activities Arts and Crafts; Cards; Games; Prayer groups; Movies; Bible study.
Description Facility offers therapy daily; whirlpool bath.

COFFEYVILLE

Medicalodge East of Coffeyville*
720 W 1st, Coffeyville, KS, 67337 (316)
251-3705
Admin Zelda Stanley.
Licensure Intermediate Care. *Beds* 44. *Certified* Medicaid.
Ownership Proprietary.

Medicalodge West of Coffeyville*
2910 Midland Ave, Coffeyville, KS, 67337
(316) 251-2420
Admin Russell Loyd.
Licensure Skilled Care; Intermediate Care.
Beds 189. *Certified* Medicaid.
Ownership Proprietary.

Sunny View Nursing Home
14th and Roosevelt, Coffeyville, KS, 67337
(316) 251-4032
Admin Jane Guy. *Medical Dir/Dir of Nursing* G W Banks.
Licensure Intermediate Care. *Beds* 49. *Certified* Medicaid.
Admissions Requirements Minimum age 21;
Medical examination; Physician's request.
Staff RNs 1 (ft); LPNs 1 (pt); Orderlies 1 (ft);
Nurses aides 20 (ft), 5 (pt); Physical therapists 1
(pt); Activities coordinators 1 (ft); Dietitians 1
(pt).
Facilities Dining room; Physical therapy room;
Activities room; Laundry room; Barber/Beauty
shop.
Activities Arts and Crafts; Games; Reading
groups; Movies; Shopping trips; Dances/Social
or cultural gatherings.
Description Facility features a beautiful country
setting. Although this is not a religious affiliated
institution, it does have a strong Bible study
program which seems to be appreciated by all
denominations.

COLBY

Good Samaritan Home
Rt 1, Box 1, Colby, KS, 67701 (913) 462-7564
Admin Kenneth H Wagner.
Licensure Intermediate Care. *Beds* 46. *Certified* Medicaid.

Lantern Park Manor
Franklin Ave and College Dr, Colby, KS, 67701
(913) 462-6721
Admin Wanda I Carter. *Medical Dir/Dir of Nursing* Asher Dahl MD.
Licensure Intermediate Care. *Beds* 70. *Certified* Medicaid.
Admissions Requirements Minimum age 18.
Staff RNs 2 (ft), 2 (pt); LPNs 1 (ft).
Facilities Dining room; Physical therapy room;
Activities room; Crafts room; Laundry room;
Barber/Beauty shop.
Activities Cards; Games; Prayer groups;
Movies; Shopping trips; Dances/Social or cultural gatherings.
Description Residents have rhythm band with
approximately 40 members; 20 residents make
up the Sunflower Swingers, a group that entertains in surrounding areas.

Thomas County Care Center*
PO Box 606, 350 S Range, Colby, KS, 67701
(913) 462-8296
Admin James J O'Leary.
Licensure Intermediate Care. *Beds* 46. *Certified* Medicaid.
Ownership Public.

COLDWATER

Pioneer Lodge
3rd and Frisco, Coldwater, KS, 67029 (316)
582-2123
Admin Ernest K Parker.
Licensure Intermediate Care. *Beds* 52. *Certified* Medicaid.
Staff RNs 1 (ft); LPNs 1 (pt); Nurses aides 20
(ft); Physical therapists 1 (pt); Activities coordinators 1 (ft).
Facilities Dining room; Physical therapy room;
Activities room; Chapel; Crafts room; Laundry
room; Barber/Beauty shop.
Activities Arts and Crafts; Games; Reading
groups; Prayer groups; Movies.
Description The Lodge offers family-type
atmosphere of a small town nursing home,
gives quality nursing care at reasonable rates.

COLUMBUS

Medicalodge of Columbus*
101 N Lee St, Columbus, KS, 66725 (316)
429-2134
Admin Wilma D Van Houten.
Licensure Intermediate Care. *Beds* 100. *Certified* Medicaid.
Ownership Proprietary.

COLWICH

Colwich Health Center
5th and Colwich, Colwich, KS, 67030 (316)
796-0919
Admin Donald E Schmidt. *Medical Dir/Dir of Nursing* Dr Mary Goodwin.
Licensure Intermediate Care. *Beds* 60. *Certified* Medicaid.
Admissions Requirements Medical examination.
Staff RNs 1 (ft), 3 (pt); LPNs 1 (ft), 3 (pt);
Nurses aides 10 (ft), 7 (pt); Recreational therapists 1 (ft); Activities coordinators 1 (ft).
Facilities Dining room; Physical therapy room;
Activities room; Crafts room; Laundry room;
Barber/Beauty shop; Library.
Activities Arts and Crafts; Cards; Games;
Reading groups; Prayer groups; Movies; Shopping trips.
Description Facility is located in a small community 12 miles from Wichita, Kansas, which
cares about people.

CONCORDIA

Concordia Rest Home
825 E 7th, Concordia, KS, 66901 (913)
243-3497
Admin Carol Ann Saint.
Licensure Intermediate Care. *Beds* 48. *Certified* Medicaid.

Admissions Requirements Medical examination; Physician's request.
Staff RNs 1 (pt); LPNs 1 (ft); Nurses aides 20
(ft), 2 (pt); Activities coordinators 1 (pt).
Facilities Dining room; Physical therapy room;
Activities room; Chapel; Laundry room; Barber/Beauty shop; Library.
Activities Arts and Crafts; Cards; Games;
Reading groups; Prayer groups; Movies; Shopping trips.
Description A clean, neat home with staff that
offers tender loving care located between 2
grade schools. Young people are encouraged to
visit the home often. Residents feel as if this is
their home.

Mount Joseph
Rt 1, Concordia, KS, 66901 (913) 243-1347
Admin Gerald Gallagher. *Medical Dir/Dir of Nursing* Donita Copple.
Licensure Intermediate Care. *Beds* 100. *Certified* Medicaid.
Ownership Nonprofit.
Admissions Requirements Physician's request.
Staff RNs 4 (ft), 3 (pt); LPNs 3 (ft), 2 (pt);
Nurses aides 40 (ft), 15 (pt); Physical therapists
1 (pt); Recreational therapists 1 (pt); Activities
coordinators 2 (ft).
Affiliation Roman Catholic
Facilities Dining room; Physical therapy room;
Activities room; Chapel; Crafts room; Barber/Beauty shop; Library.
Activities Arts and Crafts; Cards; Games; Prayer groups; Movies.

Sunset Nursing Center
620 Second Ave, Concordia, KS, 66901 (913)
243-2720
Admin Dennis W Knapp.
Licensure Intermediate Care. *Beds* 58.
Ownership Nonprofit.
Admissions Requirements Minimum age 65;
Medical examination.
Staff RNs 2 (ft); LPNs 4 (ft); Nurses aides 15
(ft), 7 (pt); Activities coordinators 2 (ft).
Affiliation Baptist
Facilities Dining room; Physical therapy room;
Activities room; Laundry room; Barber/Beauty
shop; Library.
Activities Arts and Crafts; Games; Reading
groups; Prayer groups; Movies; Shopping trips;
Dances/Social or cultural gatherings.

CONWAY SPRINGS

Spring View Manor Inc
500 S 8th, Conway Springs, KS, 67031 (316)
465-2285
Admin Virginia C Winter.
Licensure Intermediate Care. *Beds* 47. *Certified* Medicaid.
Staff Physicians 1 (pt); RNs 1 (pt); LPNs 1 (ft);
Nurses aides 10 (ft), 4 (pt); Physical therapists 1
(ft), 1 (pt); Recreational therapists 1 (ft), 1 (pt);
Occupational therapists 1 (pt); Speech therapists 1 (pt); Activities coordinators 1 (ft); Dietitians 1 (ft); Dentists 1 (pt); Ophthalmologists 1
(pt); Podiatrists 1 (pt); Audiologists 1 (pt).

COTTONWOOD FALLS

Chase County Nursing Center*
612 Walnut, Cottonwood Falls, KS, 66845
(316) 273-6360
Admin Earlene Lind.
Licensure Intermediate Care. *Beds* 73. *Certified* Medicaid.
Ownership Proprietary.

COUNCIL GROVE

Country Club Home*
PO Box 319, 400 Sunset Dr, Council Grove,
KS, 66846 (316) 767-6114
Admin Ierryll H Brown.
Licensure Intermediate Care. *Beds* 100. *Certified* Medicaid.
Ownership Proprietary.

CUNNINGHAM

Hilltop Manor Inc
Saint Leo Rd, PO Box 8, Cunningham, KS,
67035 (316) 298-2781
Admin Izena Beckenholdt.
Licensure Intermediate Care. *Beds* 76. *Certified* Medicaid.
Staff RNs 2 (ft), 2 (pt); LPNs 1 (ft); Nurses aides 32 (ft); Physical therapists 1 (pt); Occupational therapists 1 (pt); Speech therapists 1 (pt); Dietitians 1 (pt); Dentists 1 (pt); Podiatrists 1 (pt); Audiologists 1 (pt).
Facilities Dining room; Physical therapy room; Activities room; Crafts room; Laundry room; Barber/Beauty shop; Library.
Activities Arts and Crafts; Cards; Games; Reading groups; Prayer groups; Movies; Shopping trips; Dances/Social or cultural gatherings.
Description Facility features an excellent physical therapy program, and is a small-town, locally-owned family home.

DELPHOS

Delphos Rest Home Inc
405 Custer St, Box 347, Delphos, KS, 67436
(913) 523-4234
Admin Carmelita Berndt.
Licensure Intermediate Care. *Beds* 34. *Certified* Medicaid.
Admissions Requirements Medical examination.
Staff Physicians; RNs; Nurses aides; Physical therapists; Recreational therapists; Occupational therapists; Speech therapists; Activities coordinators; Dietitians.
Facilities Dining room; Physical therapy room; Activities room; Laundry room; Barber/Beauty shop.
Activities Arts and Crafts; Cards; Games; Prayer groups.

DERBY

Westview Manor
445 N Westview, Derby, KS, 67037 (316)
788-3739
Admin John A Nicholas. *Medical Dir/Dir of Nursing* Roger L Thomas DO.
Licensure Skilled Care; Intermediate Care.
Beds 116. *Certified* Medicaid.
Admissions Requirements Minimum age 21; Medical examination; Physician's request.
Staff Physicians 30 (pt); RNs 4 (ft), 2 (pt); LPNs 3 (ft), 4 (pt); Orderlies 2 (ft), 1 (pt); Nurses aides 30 (ft), 25 (pt); Physical therapists 1 (pt); Reality therapists 1 (pt); Recreational therapists 1 (ft); Occupational therapists 1 (pt); Speech therapists 1 (pt); Activities coordinators 1 (ft); Dietitians 1 (ft); Dentists 1 (pt); Ophthalmologists 1 (pt); Podiatrists 1 (pt); Audiologists 1 (pt).
Facilities Dining room; Physical therapy room; Activities room; Crafts room; Laundry room; Barber/Beauty shop; Library.
Activities Arts and Crafts; Cards; Games; Reading groups; Prayer groups; Movies; Shopping trips; Dances/Social or cultural gatherings.
Description Facility specializes in activity programs for geriatric citizens of all abilities. Westview Manor has the oldest ongoing adopt-a-grandparent program in the area.

DESOTO

DeSoto Rest Home Inc
5th and Willow Ln, DeSoto, KS, 66018 (913)
585-1845
Admin Karen Rockers. *Medical Dir/Dir of Nursing* Dr Ron LaHae.
Licensure Intermediate Care. *Beds* 50. *Certified* Medicaid.
Admissions Requirements Minimum age 21; Medical examination; Physician's request.
Staff Physicians; RNs; LPNs 3 (ft); Orderlies 3 (ft); Nurses aides 12 (ft); Physical therapists; Recreational therapists; Occupational therapists; Speech therapists; Activities coordinators 1 (ft); Dietitians; Dentists; Ophthalmologists; Podiatrists; Audiologists.
Activities Arts and Crafts; Cards; Games; Reading groups; Prayer groups; Movies; Shopping trips; Dances/Social or cultural gatherings.
Description Facility is located in a small town with community involvement; has a hardworking, dedicated staff. Half of the facility is designated for mental health.

DEXTER

Grouse Valley Manor*
PO Box 98, S Main and Grouse, Dexter, KS,
67038 (316) 876-5421
Admin Pearl Coon.
Licensure Intermediate Care. *Beds* 50. *Certified* Medicaid.
Ownership Proprietary.

DODGE CITY

Good Samaritan Center*
501 Beeson Rd, Dodge City, KS, 67801 (316)
227-7512
Admin Royce L Rall.
Licensure Intermediate Care. *Beds* 85. *Certified* Medicaid.
Ownership Nonprofit.
Affiliation Lutheran

Trinity Manor*
Hwy 50 Bypass and 6th, Dodge City, KS,
67801 (316) 227-8551
Admin Barbara Schroeder.
Licensure Intermediate Care. *Beds* 53. *Certified* Medicaid.
Ownership Nonprofit.
Affiliation Methodist

DOUGLASS

Douglass Nursing Center*
9541 S Hwy 77, Douglass, KS, 67039 (316)
746-2157
Admin Edith L Cox.
Licensure Intermediate Care. *Beds* 67. *Certified* Medicaid.
Ownership Proprietary.

DOWNS

Downs Nursing Center
1218 Kansas Ave, Rt 2, Downs, KS, 67437
(913) 454-3321
Admin Jacqueline A Williams. *Medical Dir/Dir of Nursing* Burton Cox DO.
Licensure Intermediate Care. *Beds* 60. *Certified* Medicaid.
Staff RNs 2 (ft), 1 (pt); LPNs 2 (ft), 1 (pt).
Facilities Dining room; Physical therapy room; Activities room; Crafts room; Laundry room; Barber/Beauty shop.
Activities Arts and Crafts; Cards; Games; Prayer groups; Movies; Shopping trips; Dances/Social or cultural gatherings.
Description Home health services are available.

EASTON

Easton Manor
PO Box 216, Easton, KS, 66020 (913) 773-8254
Admin Madge L Bordon. *Medical Dir/Dir of Nursing* Lawrence W Wilson.
Licensure Intermediate Care. *Beds* 59. *Certified* Medicaid.
Staff Physicians 4 (pt); RNs 1 (ft); LPNs 4 (ft), 2 (pt); Physical therapists 1 (ft); Recreational therapists 1 (ft).
Facilities Dining room; Physical therapy room; Activities room; Crafts room; Laundry room; Barber/Beauty shop.
Activities Arts and Crafts; Games; Reading groups; Dances/Social or cultural gatherings.
Description Facility actively participates in the rock and roll jamboree and Nursing Home Week. Also has an annual dinner for residents and their families just before Thanksgiving.

EDWARDSVILLE

Edwardsville Convalescent Center*
750 Blake St, Edwardsville, KS, 66111 (913)
422-5832
Admin Bucella Hurd.
Licensure Intermediate Care. *Beds* 50. *Certified* Medicaid.
Ownership Proprietary.

Edwardsville Manor Inc*
751 Blake St, Edwardsville, KS, 66111 (913) 441-1900
Admin Diana L Jones.
Licensure Intermediate Care. *Beds* 100. *Certified* Medicaid.
Ownership Proprietary.

Parkway Care Home*
749 Blake St, Edwardsville, KS, 66111 (913) 422-5952
Admin Orus J Jones.
Licensure Intermediate Care. *Beds* 50. *Certified* Medicaid.
Ownership Proprietary.

EL DORADO

El Dorado Nursing Center
900 Country Club Ln, El Dorado, KS, 67042 (316) 321-4444
Admin John E Steinhaus.
Licensure Intermediate Care. *Beds* 93. *Certified* Medicaid.
Ownership Proprietary.
Admissions Requirements Medical examination; Physician's request.
Staff RNs 2 (ft), 1 (pt); LPNs 3 (ft); Nurses aides 16 (ft), 4 (pt); Activities coordinators 1 (ft).
Facilities Dining room; Physical therapy room; Activities room; Laundry room; Barber/Beauty shop.
Activities Arts and Crafts; Cards; Games; Movies; Shopping trips; Dances/Social or cultural gatherings; Adopt-a-grandparent; Resident council; Family council.

Knutson Manor Nursing Center*
1313 S High, El Dorado, KS, 67042 (316) 321-4140
Admin Elizabeth L Heinrich.
Licensure Skilled Care; Intermediate Care. *Beds* 116. *Certified* Medicaid; Medicare.

ELLINWOOD

Woodhaven Inc
510 W 7th St, Ellinwood, KS, 67526 (316) 564-2337
Admin Judith White.
Licensure Intermediate Care. *Beds* 54. *Certified* Medicaid.
Staff RNs 1 (ft); LPNs 1 (ft); Nurses aides 15 (ft), 5 (pt); Physical therapists 1 (pt); Occupational therapists 1 (pt); Speech therapists 1 (pt); Activities coordinators 1 (ft); Dietitians 1 (pt); Audiologists 1 (pt).
Facilities Dining room; Physical therapy room; Activities room; Crafts room; Laundry room; Barber/Beauty shop; Quiet room.
Activities Arts and Crafts; Cards; Games; Reading groups; Prayer groups; Movies; Shopping trips; Dances/Social or cultural gatherings.

ELLIS

Good Samaritan Center*
1100 Spruce, Ellis, KS, 67637 (913) 726-3101
Admin John R Binder Jr.
Licensure Intermediate Care. *Beds* 59. *Certified* Medicaid.
Ownership Nonprofit.
Affiliation Lutheran

ELLSWORTH

Ellsworth Good Samaritan Center—Villa Hope*
Box D, Ellsworth, KS, 67439 (913) 472-3167
Admin Janyce J Larsen.
Licensure Intermediate Care. *Beds* 49. *Certified* Medicaid.
Ownership Nonprofit.
Affiliation Lutheran

Good Samaritan Center—Villa Grace
Hwy K-14 S, Box D, Ellsworth, KS, 67439 (913) 472-3167
Admin Virgil Larsen. *Medical Dir/Dir of Nursing* Margaret Long RN.
Licensure Intermediate Care. *Beds* 68. *Certified* Medicaid.
Admissions Requirements Minimum age 55; Medical examination; Physician's request.
Staff RNs 3 (ft), 1 (pt); LPNs 2 (ft); Orderlies 1 (pt); Nurses aides 12 (ft), 10 (pt); Physical therapists 1 (ft); Reality therapists 1 (ft); Recreational therapists 1 (ft); Occupational therapists 1 (pt); Speech therapists 1 (pt); Activities coordinators 1 (ft); Dietitians 1 (ft); Audiologists 1 (pt).
Facilities Dining room; Physical therapy room; Activities room; Chapel; Crafts room; Laundry room; Barber/Beauty shop; Library.
Activities Arts and Crafts; Cards; Games; Reading groups; Prayer groups; Movies; Shopping trips; Dances/Social or cultural gatherings.
Description A Christian organization, committed to meeting the total needs of people; a very good physical therapy program and many people are restored and able to return to their homes; a very caring, dedicated staff that treats people with respect and a desire to preserve their dignity.

EMPORIA

Emporia Rest Home
221 W Logan, PO Box G, Emporia, KS, 66801 (316) 342-4212
Admin Gary Waite. *Medical Dir/Dir of Nursing* Lucille Stovall LPN.
Licensure Intermediate Care. *Beds* 46. *Certified* Medicaid.
Admissions Requirements Minimum age 18.
Staff LPNs 3 (ft), 1 (pt); Nurses aides 22 (ft); Activities coordinators 1 (ft).
Facilities Dining room; Physical therapy room; Activities room; Chapel; Crafts room; Laundry room; Barber/Beauty shop.
Activities Arts and Crafts; Cards; Games; Reading groups; Prayer groups; Movies; Shopping trips; Dances/Social or cultural gatherings.

Flint Hills Manor*
1620 Wheeler, Emporia, KS, 66801 (316) 342-3280
Admin Ann M Kelly and Brian J Raydo.
Licensure Intermediate Care. *Beds* 100. *Certified* Medicaid.
Ownership Proprietary.

Regency Health Care Center East
217 W Logan, Emporia, KS, 66801 (316) 342-8611
Admin Lillian Ghramm.
Licensure Intermediate Care. *Beds* 50. *Certified* Medicaid.
Admissions Requirements Medical examination; Physician's request.
Staff LPNs 2 (ft), 1 (pt); Orderlies 1 (ft); Nurses aides 14 (ft), 4 (pt).
Facilities Dining room; Physical therapy room; Activities room; Laundry room; Barber/Beauty shop.
Activities Arts and Crafts; Games; Reading groups; Prayer groups; Movies; Dances/Social or cultural gatherings.
Description We set high standards to have the best nursing and personal care in town.

Shady Lawn Manor Inc*
315 S Commercial, Emporia, KS, 66801 (316) 342-3656
Admin Elizabeth May Grossenbacher.
Licensure Intermediate Care. *Beds* 60. *Certified* Medicaid.
Ownership Proprietary.

ENTERPRISE

Enterprise Estates Nursing Center
502 Gallery, Enterprise, KS, 67441 (913) 934-2278
Admin William C Steinkamp. *Medical Dir/Dir of Nursing* Dr Charles Svabada.
Licensure Intermediate Care. *Beds* 52. *Certified* Medicaid.
Admissions Requirements Minimum age 16; Medical examination; Physician's request.
Staff RNs 1 (ft); LPNs 2 (ft); Nurses aides 1 (ft), 3 (pt); Activities coordinators 1 (ft).
Facilities Dining room; Physical therapy room; Activities room; Barber/Beauty shop.
Activities Arts and Crafts; Cards; Games; Reading groups; Prayer groups; Movies.

ERIE

Arkhaven at Erie
330 N Main, Erie, KS, 66733 (316) 224-5301
Admin Ernestine C Anselmi. *Medical Dir/Dir of Nursing* Carole A Hastong RN.
Licensure Intermediate Care. *Beds* 43. *Certified* Medicaid.
Staff RNs 1 (ft); LPNs 1 (pt); Nurses aides 10 (ft), 6 (pt).
Facilities Dining room; Physical therapy room; Activities room; Chapel; Crafts room; Laundry room; Barber/Beauty shop; Library.
Activities Arts and Crafts; Cards; Games; Reading groups; Prayer groups; Movies; Shopping trips; Dances/Social or cultural gatherings.
Description Facility is small and very clean; has a great caring and loving staff that cares about residents as individuals.

ESKRIDGE

Heritage Village
E Hwy 4, Eskridge, KS, 66432 (913) 449-2294
Admin Richard S Lundgren. *Medical Dir/Dir of Nursing* Dr William H Walker.

Licensure Intermediate Care. *Beds* 66. *Certified* Medicaid.
Admissions Requirements Minimum age 18; Medical examination; Physician's request.
Staff Physicians 1 (pt); RNs 1 (ft); LPNs 4 (ft); Orderlies 2 (ft); Nurses aides 15 (ft), 4 (pt); Physical therapists 1 (pt); Recreational therapists 1 (pt); Occupational therapists 1 (pt); Speech therapists 1 (pt); Activities coordinators 1 (ft); Dietitians 1 (pt); Dentists 1 (pt); Ophthalmologists 1 (pt); Podiatrists 1 (pt); Audiologists 1 (pt).
Facilities Dining room; Physical therapy room; Activities room; Chapel; Crafts room; Laundry room; Barber/Beauty shop; Library.
Activities Arts and Crafts; Cards; Games; Reading groups; Prayer groups; Movies; Shopping trips; Dances/Social or cultural gatherings.

EUDORA

Eudora Nursing Center
1415 Maple, Eudora, KS, 66025 (913) 542-2176
Admin Civil Gray.
Licensure Intermediate Care. *Beds* 100. *Certified* Medicaid.
Admissions Requirements Medical examination.
Staff RNs 2 (ft); LPNs 4 (ft); Orderlies 1 (pt); Nurses aides 38 (ft); Activities coordinators 1 (ft); Dietitians 1 (pt).
Facilities Dining room; Physical therapy room; Activities room; Chapel; Crafts room; Laundry room; Barber/Beauty shop; Library.
Activities Arts and Crafts; Cards; Games; Reading groups; Prayer groups; Movies; Cooking.

EUREKA

Eureka Rest Home
1406 N Elm, Eureka, KS, 67045 (316) 583-5630
Admin Rosalie Garrison. *Medical Dir/Dir of Nursing* Pauline Bone.
Licensure Intermediate Care. *Beds* 48. *Certified* Medicaid.
Admissions Requirements Minimum age 16; Medical examination.
Staff RNs 1 (pt); LPNs 2 (ft); Nurses aides 18 (ft), 3 (pt); Physical therapists 1 (pt); Recreational therapists 1 (ft); Occupational therapists 1 (pt); Speech therapists 1 (pt); Activities coordinators 1 (ft); Dietitians 1 (pt); Dentists 1 (pt); Ophthalmologists 1 (pt); Audiologists 1 (pt).
Facilities Dining room; Physical therapy room; Activities room; Laundry room; Barber/Beauty shop.
Activities Arts and Crafts; Cards; Games; Reading groups; Prayer groups; Movies; Shopping trips; Dances/Social or cultural gatherings.

Medicalodge of Eureka
1020 N School, Rt 2, Box 94C, Eureka, KS, 67045 (316) 583-7418
Admin Martha Speer.
Licensure Intermediate Care. *Beds* 90. *Certified* Medicaid.
Ownership Proprietary.
Admissions Requirements Minimum age 16; Medical examination.
Staff RNs 1 (ft); LPNs 5 (ft); Activities coordi-

nators 1 (ft), 1 (pt).
Facilities Dining room; Physical therapy room; Activities room; Chapel; Laundry room; Barber/Beauty shop; Library.
Activities Arts and Crafts; Cards; Games; Reading groups; Prayer groups; Movies; Shopping trips; Dances/Social or cultural gatherings.
Description Local Historical Society brings small items to show and "guess what this is." They also show enlarged photographs, mounted on large posters, of the old days.

FLORENCE

Regency Health Care Center
9th and Marion, Florence, KS, 66851 (316) 878-4440 and (316) 878-4631
Admin Massie Teufel.
Licensure Intermediate Care; Intermediate Care for Mentally Retarded. *Beds* 60. *Certified* Medicaid.
Admissions Requirements Minimum age 21.
Staff RNs 1 (pt); LPNs 1 (ft); Orderlies 2 (pt); Nurses aides 16 (ft); Physical therapists 1 (pt); Recreational therapists 1 (pt); Occupational therapists 2 (ft); Activities coordinators 1 (ft); Dietitians 1 (ft).
Facilities Dining room; Physical therapy room; Activities room; Chapel; Crafts room; Laundry room; Barber/Beauty shop; Library.
Activities Arts and Crafts; Cards; Games; Prayer groups; Movies; Shopping trips; Dances/Social or cultural gatherings.
Description Regency Health Care Center of Florence is dedicated to the extension, and improvement of the quality of life of the chronically mentally ill adult, through compassionate consideration, and caring concern.

FORT SCOTT

Arkhaven at Fort Scott*
737 Heylman, Fort Scott, KS, 66701 (316) 223-1620
Admin Cynthia Lipe.
Licensure Intermediate Care. *Beds* 60. *Certified* Medicaid.
Ownership Proprietary.

Fort Scott Manor
736 Heylman, Fort Scott, KS, 66701 (316) 223-3120
Admin Debby Jackson. *Medical Dir/Dir of Nursing* Idella Brown.
Licensure Intermediate Care. *Beds* 53. *Certified* Medicaid.
Ownership Proprietary.
Staff RNs 1 (pt); LPNs 2 (ft), 2 (pt); Physical therapists 1 (pt); Occupational therapists 1 (pt); Speech therapists 1 (pt); Activities coordinators 1 (ft); Dietitians 1 (pt); Dentists 1 (pt); Podiatrists 1 (pt); Audiologists 1 (pt).
Facilities Dining room; Physical therapy room; Activities room; Crafts room; Laundry room; Barber/Beauty shop.
Activities Arts and Crafts; Cards; Games; Reading groups; Prayer groups; Shopping trips; Dances/Social or cultural gatherings.

Medicalodge of Fort Scott*
915 S Horton, Fort Scott, KS, 66701 (316) 223-0210
Admin Kathleen A Ballbeck.
Licensure Intermediate Care. *Beds* 132. *Certified* Medicaid.
Ownership Proprietary.

FOWLER

Fowler Nursing Home*
512 E 5th, Fowler, KS, 67844 (316) 646-5215
Admin Gary E Turner.
Licensure Intermediate Care. *Beds* 33. *Certified* Medicaid.
Ownership Nonprofit.

FRANKFORT

Frankfort Community Care Home Inc
510 Walnut, Frankfort, KS, 66427 (913) 292-4442
Admin Dorothy Lindeen.
Licensure Intermediate Care. *Beds* 50. *Certified* Medicaid.
Staff RNs 1 (ft), 1 (pt); Physical therapists 1 (pt); Recreational therapists 1 (ft); Activities coordinators 1 (ft).
Facilities Dining room; Physical therapy room; Activities room; Chapel; Crafts room; Laundry room; Barber/Beauty shop; Library.
Activities Arts and Crafts; Cards; Games; Movies.

FREDONIA

Hillcrest Manor*
240 N 19th St, Fredonia, KS, 66736 (316) 378-4163
Admin Mildred J Hubbard.
Licensure Intermediate Care. *Beds* 50. *Certified* Medicaid.
Ownership Proprietary.

FRONTENAC

Sunset Manor*
206 S Dittmann, Frontenac, KS, 66762 (316) 231-7340
Admin Raymond R Knaup.
Licensure Intermediate Care. *Beds* 116. *Certified* Medicaid.
Ownership Proprietary.

GALENA

Barker Rest Home*
109 W Empire, Galena, KS, 66739 (316) 783-5048
Admin Barbara Link.
Licensure Intermediate Care. *Beds* 50. *Certified* Medicaid.
Ownership Proprietary.

Galena Manor Health Center
8th and Keller, Galena, KS, 66739 (316) 783-1383
Admin Marjorie A Abraham. *Medical Dir/Dir of Nursing* Stephen J Bazzano DO.

Licensure Intermediate Care. *Beds* 65. *Certified* Medicaid.
Admissions Requirements Minimum age 16; Medical examination.
Staff LPNs 3 (ft), 2 (pt); Orderlies 2 (ft); Activities coordinators 1 (ft); Dietitians 1 (ft).
Facilities Dining room; Physical therapy room; Activities room; Crafts room; Laundry room; Barber/Beauty shop; Library; Quiet room; Day room.
Activities Arts and Crafts; Cards; Games; Reading groups; Prayer groups; Movies; Shopping trips; Dances/Social or cultural gatherings.
Description Facility features dedicated, caring staff offering the best in care, good food, and a family-type atmosphere.

GARDEN CITY

Briar Hill Manor Inc
2308 E 3rd St, Garden City, KS, 67846 (316) 276-7643
Admin Shirley Klotz.
Licensure Intermediate Care. *Beds* 104. *Certified* Medicaid.
Admissions Requirements Minimum age 18; Medical examination; Physician's request.
Facilities Dining room; Physical therapy room; Activities room; Laundry room; Barber/Beauty shop.
Activities Arts and Crafts; Cards; Games; Reading groups; Prayer groups; Movies; Shopping trips; Dances/Social or cultural gatherings.
Description Manor has an excellent physical therapy and activity program, good food, good care, located in a safe, clean atmosphere; has reasonable rates.

Garden Valley Retirement Village
1505 E Spruce, Garden City, KS, 67846 (316) 275-9651
Admin Floyd E Born.
Licensure Intermediate Care. *Beds* 70. *Certified* Medicaid.
Admissions Requirements Medical examination; Physician's request.
Staff RNs 2 (ft), 5 (pt); LPNs 2 (ft), 2 (pt); Nurses aides 28 (ft), 4 (pt); Activities coordinators 2 (ft), 1 (pt).
Affiliation Mennonite
Facilities Dining room; Physical therapy room; Activities room; Chapel; Crafts room; Laundry room; Barber/Beauty shop; Library.
Activities Arts and Crafts; Cards; Games; Reading groups; Prayer groups; Movies; Shopping trips; Dances/Social or cultural gatherings.

GARDNER

Bedford Manor*
223 Bedford St, Gardner, KS, 66030 (913) 884-6520
Admin Betty Mestagh.
Licensure Intermediate Care. *Beds* 82. *Certified* Medicaid.
Ownership Proprietary.

GARNETT

Arkhaven at Garnett
Rt 2, W 77th, Garnett, KS, 66032 (913) 448-6884
Admin Barbara Watkins. *Medical Dir/Dir of Nursing* Mildred Dysart.
Licensure Intermediate Care. *Beds* 49. *Certified* Medicaid.
Admissions Requirements Minimum age 16.
Staff RNs 1 (pt); LPNs 3 (ft); Orderlies 2 (ft); Nurses aides 9 (ft), 2 (pt); Physical therapists 1 (pt); Reality therapists 1 (pt); Occupational therapists 1 (pt); Speech therapists 1 (pt); Activities coordinators 1 (ft); Dietitians 1 (pt); Dentists 1 (pt); Audiologists 1 (pt).
Facilities Dining room; Physical therapy room; Activities room; Chapel; Crafts room; Laundry room; Barber/Beauty shop.
Activities Arts and Crafts; Cards; Games; Movies; Shopping trips; Dances/Social or cultural gatherings.
Description Arkhaven is an intermediate care facility which specializes in geriatric and convalescent care with a friendly atmosphere. Residents are urged to make their rooms as homelike as possible; they may use their own furniture. Outings with family, friends, and groups are encouraged.

Parkview Estate*
101 N Pine, Garnett, KS, 66032 (913) 448-5521
Admin Deborah A Curry.
Licensure Intermediate Care. *Beds* 60. *Certified* Medicaid.
Ownership Proprietary.

GIRARD

The Heritage*
PO Box 66, 511 N Western, Girard, KS, 66743 (316) 724-8288
Admin John Twarog.
Licensure Intermediate Care. *Beds* 100. *Certified* Medicaid.
Ownership Proprietary.

GLASCO

Nicol Home Inc
Spears and Buffalo, PO Box 68, Glasco, KS, 67445 (913) 568-2251
Admin Sunnie Z Brooks.
Licensure Intermediate Care. *Beds* 32. *Certified* Medicaid.
Staff RNs; LPNs; Nurses aides; Physical therapists; Occupational therapists; Speech therapists; Activities coordinators; Dietitians; Audiologists.
Facilities Dining room; Physical therapy room; Activities room; Laundry room; Barber/Beauty shop; Library.
Activities Arts and Crafts; Cards; Games; Reading groups; Movies.

GODDARD

Medicalodge of Goddard*
501 Easy St, Goddard, KS, 67052 (316) 794-8635
Admin Yvonne Cummins.

Licensure Intermediate Care. *Beds* 50. *Certified* Medicaid.
Ownership Proprietary.

GOODLAND

Golden West Skills Center*
108 Aspen Rd, Goodland, KS, 67735 (913) 899-2322
Admin Glendon L Horn.
Licensure Intermediate Care for Mentally Retarded. *Beds* 53. *Certified* Medicaid.
Ownership Proprietary.

Sherman County Good Samaritan Center
208 W 2nd St, Goodland, KS, 67735 (913) 899-3521
Admin James G Mertz.
Licensure Intermediate Care. *Beds* 60. *Certified* Medicaid.
Admissions Requirements Medical examination.
Staff RNs 1 (pt); LPNs 4 (ft); Nurses aides 23 (ft); Activities coordinators 1 (ft).
Facilities Dining room; Physical therapy room; Activities room; Chapel; Crafts room; Laundry room; Barber/Beauty shop.
Activities Arts and Crafts; Cards; Games; Reading groups; Movies; Shopping trips; Dances/Social or cultural gatherings.

GREAT BEND

Cherry Village
1401 Cherry Ln, Great Bend, KS, 67530 (316) 792-2165
Admin Pamla Johansen. *Medical Dir/Dir of Nursing* Pamla S Kern.
Licensure Skilled Care. *Beds* 90. *Certified* Medicaid; Medicare.
Admissions Requirements Minimum age 21; Medical examination; Physician's request.
Staff RNs 5 (ft); LPNs 4 (ft); Nurses aides 32 (ft); Physical therapists 1 (ft); Recreational therapists 1 (pt); Occupational therapists 1 (pt); Speech therapists 1 (pt); Activities coordinators 1 (ft); Dietitians 1 (pt); Dentists 1 (pt); Podiatrists 1 (pt); Audiologists 1 (pt).
Facilities Dining room; Physical therapy room; Activities room; Crafts room; Laundry room; Barber/Beauty shop.
Activities Arts and Crafts; Cards; Games; Reading groups; Prayer groups; Movies; Dances/Social or cultural gatherings.

Great Bend Manor*
1560 K-96 Hwy, Great Bend, KS, 67530 (316) 792-2448
Admin Tom A Hermansen.
Licensure Intermediate Care. *Beds* 160. *Certified* Medicaid.
Ownership Proprietary.

GREENSBURG

Cedar Crest at Greensburg
723 S Elm, Greensburg, KS, 67054 (316) 723-2633
Admin Bonnie Brozek. *Medical Dir/Dir of Nursing* Dr Thomas Hicklin DO.
Licensure Intermediate Care. *Beds* 50. *Certi-

fied Medicaid.
Ownership Proprietary.
Admissions Requirements Minimum age 16.
Staff Physicians 1 (pt); RNs 1 (pt); LPNs 2 (ft),
1 (pt); Nurses aides 15 (ft); Physical therapists 1
(ft); Recreational therapists 1 (pt); Occupational
therapists 1 (pt); Activities coordinators 1 (ft);
Dietitians 1 (ft).
Facilities Dining room; Physical therapy room;
Activities room; Chapel; Crafts room; Barber-
/Beauty shop.
Activities Arts and Crafts; Cards; Games;
Reading groups; Prayer groups; Movies; Shop-
ping trips; Dances/Social or cultural gatherings.

HALSTEAD

Halstead Nursing Center*
10th and Walnut, Halstead, KS, 67056 (316)
835-2277
Admin Thomas A Nevills.
Licensure Intermediate Care. *Beds* 100. *Certified* Medicaid.
Ownership Proprietary.

HARDTNER

Achenbach Learning Center*
Box 38, Hardtner, KS, 67057 (316) 296-4421
Admin Bernard Turnbaugh.
Licensure Intermediate Care for Mentally
Retarded. *Beds* 51. *Certified* Medicaid.
Ownership Proprietary.

HARPER

Harper Community Care Home*
615 W 12th, Harper, KS, 67058 (316) 896-2914
Admin Robert A Morgan Sr.
Licensure Intermediate Care. *Beds* 57. *Certi-
fied* Medicaid.
Ownership Proprietary.

HARTFORD

Hartford Manor
Rt 2, Box 139, Hartford, KS, 66854 (316)
392-5523
Admin Linda M Slead. *Medical Dir/Dir of
Nursing* K R Hunter MD.
Licensure Intermediate Care for Mentally
Retarded. *Beds* 50. *Certified* Medicaid.
Admissions Requirements Minimum age 18;
Medical examination.
Staff RNs 2 (pt); LPNs 1 (ft); Recreational
therapists 1 (ft); Dietitians 1 (pt).
Facilities Dining room; Physical therapy room;
Activities room; Chapel; Laundry room; Bar-
ber/Beauty shop.
Activities Arts and Crafts; Cards; Games;
Reading groups; Prayer groups; Movies; Shop-
ping trips; Dances/Social or cultural gatherings.

HAVEN

Heartland Development Center—Haven
216 N Topeka, Haven, KS, 67543 (316)
465-2249
Admin William Kesler. *Medical Dir/Dir of
Nursing* Gerald Albright.
Licensure Intermediate Care for Mentally
Retarded. *Beds* 89. *Certified* Medicaid.
Admissions Requirements Minimum age 18;
Medical examination; Physician's request.
Staff RNs 2 (ft); LPNs 3 (ft); Orderlies 8 (ft);
Nurses aides 40 (ft); Physical therapists 1 (pt);
Reality therapists 1 (pt); Recreational therapists
1 (pt); Occupational therapists 1 (pt); Speech
therapists 1 (pt); Activities coordinators 3 (ft);
Dietitians 1 (ft); Dentists 1 (pt); Ophthalmolo-
gists 1 (pt); Podiatrists 1 (pt); Audiologists 1
(pt).
Facilities Dining room; Physical therapy room;
Activities room; Laundry room; Barber/Beauty
shop.
Activities Arts and Crafts; Cards; Games;
Reading groups; Prayer groups; Movies; Shop-
ping trips; Dances/Social or cultural gatherings.
Description Center is the only ICF/MR with an
attached work training program in Kansas.

HAVILAND

Cedar Crest at Haviland*
Main St, Haviland, KS, 67059 (316) 862-5233
Admin Virginia A Hammond.
Licensure Intermediate Care. *Beds* 50. *Certi-
fied* Medicaid.
Ownership Proprietary.

HAYS

Hays Good Samaritan Center
27th and Canal, Hays, KS, 67601 (913)
625-7331
Admin Virginia Langston.
Licensure Intermediate Care. *Beds* 84. *Certified* Medicaid.
Admissions Requirements Medical examination; Physician's request.
Staff RNs 1 (ft), 1 (pt); LPNs 2 (ft), 2 (pt);
Orderlies 2 (ft), 2 (pt); Nurses aides 14 (ft), 23
(pt); Activities coordinators 1 (ft); Dietitians 1
(ft).
Facilities Dining room; Physical therapy room;
Activities room; Laundry room; Barber/Beauty
shop.
Activities Arts and Crafts; Cards; Reading
groups; Prayer groups; Movies; Dances/Social
or cultural gatherings.
Description Facility features MOOR Therapy
program (a combination of music, remotivation
and reality orientation).

St John's of Hays
24th and Canterbury Rd, Hays, KS, 67601
(913) 628-3243
Admin Donald D Curl. *Medical Dir/Dir of
Nursing* Russell Cramm MD.
Licensure Skilled Care. *Beds* 60. *Cer-
tified* Medicaid; Medicare.
Admissions Requirements Medical examina-
tion; Physician's request.
Staff Physicians 1 (pt); RNs 3 (ft), 2 (pt); LPNs
3 (ft), 2 (pt); Nurses aides 20 (ft), 10 (pt);
Physical therapists 1 (ft); Activities coordina-
tors 1 (ft).
Affiliation Roman Catholic
Facilities Dining room; Physical therapy room;
Activities room; Chapel; Laundry room; Bar-

ber/Beauty shop.
Activities Arts and Crafts; Cards; Games;
Reading groups; Prayer groups; Movies; Shop-
ping trips; Dances/Social or cultural gatherings.

HAYSVILLE

Green Meadows Nursing Center Inc
215 Lamar St, Haysville, KS, 67060 (316)
524-3211
Admin Pat Smith. *Medical Dir/Dir of
Nursing* Nova L Morgan MD.
Licensure Skilled Care. *Beds* 150. *Cer-
tified* Medicaid.
Ownership Proprietary.
Admissions Requirements Minimum age;
Medical examination; Physician's request.
Staff Physicians 3 (pt); RNs 2 (ft), 2 (pt); LPNs
6 (ft), 7 (pt); Orderlies 5 (ft); Nurses aides 35
(ft), 22 (pt); Physical therapists 1 (pt); Occupa-
tional therapists 1 (pt); Speech therapists 1 (pt);
Activities coordinators 1 (ft); Dietitians 1 (pt);
Dentists 1 (pt); Podiatrists 1 (pt); Audiologists 1
(pt).
Facilities Dining room; Physical therapy room;
Activities room; Chapel; Crafts room; Laundry
room; Barber/Beauty shop; Library.
Activities Arts and Crafts; Cards; Games;
Reading groups; Prayer groups; Movies; Shopping trips; Dances/Social or cultural gatherings;
Reality orientation; Remotivation groups; Music therapy.
Description Our activity program is very active
and progressive and our reputation for nursing
care is good. We are very successful with residents who have had placement problems.

HERINGTON

Lutheran Home Inc*
2 E Ash St, Herington, KS, 67449 (913)
258-2283
Admin William D Peterson.
Licensure Intermediate Care. *Beds* 100. *Certi-
fied* Medicaid.
Ownership Nonprofit.
Affiliation Lutheran

HESSTON

Schowalter Villa
200 W Cedar, Hesston, KS, 67062 (316)
327-4261
Admin Leo G Schmidt. *Medical Dir/Dir of
Nursing* Paul Franson MD.
Licensure Intermediate Care. *Beds* 57. *Certi-
fied* Medicaid.
Admissions Requirements Medical examina-
tion; Physician's request.
Staff Physicians 3 (pt); RNs 3 (ft), 3 (pt); LPNs
1 (ft); Orderlies 1 (ft); Nurses aides 9 (ft), 18
(pt); Physical therapists 1 (pt); Occupational
therapists 1 (pt); Speech therapists 1 (pt);
Activities coordinators 1 (ft); Dietitians 1 (pt);
Dentists 1 (pt); Podiatrists 1 (pt); Audiologists 1
(pt).
Affiliation Mennonite
Facilities Dining room; Physical therapy room;
Activities room; Crafts room; Laundry room;
Barber/Beauty shop; Library.
Activities Arts and Crafts; Games; Reading

groups; Prayer groups; Movies; Shopping trips; Dances/Social or cultural gatherings.
Description Church-operated retirement center with a full range of services in a Christian community environment; adjacent to Hesston College and the Dyck Arboretum of the Plains.

HIAWATHA

Oak Ridge Acres
200 Sioux Ave, Hiawatha, KS, 66434 (913) 742-2149
Admin Lois Birt.
Licensure Intermediate Care. *Beds* 49. *Certified* Medicaid.
Admissions Requirements Minimum age 16; Medical examination; Physician's request.
Staff RNs 1 (ft); LPNs 3 (ft); Nurses aides 13 (ft), 3 (pt); Physical therapists 1 (pt); Recreational therapists 1 (ft), 1 (pt); Occupational therapists 1 (pt); Speech therapists 1 (pt); Activities coordinators 1 (ft); Dietitians 1 (pt).
Facilities Dining room; Physical therapy room; Activities room; Laundry room; Barber/Beauty shop.
Activities Arts and Crafts; Cards; Games; Reading groups; Movies; Dances/Social or cultural gatherings; Bible study; One-to-one individualized activities.
Description Facility is small and home-like. Staff is caring and supportive, involved as friends with residents, who are treated as unique, special individuals; with high quality programing and stability.

Pleasant View Nursing Center*
Rt 4, Hiawatha, KS, 66434 (913) 742-2175
Admin Jerry W Johnson.
Licensure Intermediate Care. *Beds* 60. *Certified* Medicaid.
Ownership Public.

Regency Health Care Center
Rt 2, Iowa St, Hiawatha, KS, 66434 (913) 742-7465
Admin Irene Kindig. *Medical Dir/Dir of Nursing* Dr Larson.
Licensure Skilled Care; Intermediate Care. *Beds* ICF 100. *Certified* Medicaid; Medicare.
Admissions Requirements Minimum age 16; Physician's request.
Staff RNs 1 (ft), 1 (pt); LPNs 5 (ft); Physical therapists 2 (ft); Activities coordinators 1 (ft).
Facilities Dining room; Physical therapy room; Activities room; Chapel; Crafts room; Laundry room; Barber/Beauty shop; Library.
Activities Arts and Crafts; Games; Prayer groups; Movies.
Description Full program of activities with assistance of volunteers; a good rehabilitation program; staff offers loving care. Home is located on 10 acres, peaceful, quiet, and offering a relaxed atmosphere.

HIGHLAND

Collier Manor*
Box 117, South Ave, Highland, KS, 66035 (913) 442-3816
Admin Bette J Fritch.

Licensure Intermediate Care. *Beds* 50. *Certified* Medicaid.
Ownership Proprietary.

HILL CITY

Dawson Place Inc*
208 W Prout, Hill City, KS, 67642 (913) 674-3414
Admin Ladonna Hensley.
Licensure Intermediate Care. *Beds* 55. *Certified* Medicaid.
Ownership Proprietary.

HILLSBORO

Parkside Homes Inc
200 Willow Rd, Hillsboro, KS, 67063 (316) 947-5700
Admin Luella Janzen.
Licensure Intermediate Care. *Beds* 50. *Certified* Medicaid.
Staff Physicians 6 (pt); RNs 2 (pt); LPNs 3 (ft); Nurses aides 7 (ft), 18 (pt); Physical therapists 1 (pt); Reality therapists 1 (pt); Recreational therapists 1 (pt); Occupational therapists 1 (pt); Speech therapists 1 (pt); Activities coordinators 1 (pt); Dietitians 1 (pt); Dentists 1 (pt); Podiatrists 1 (pt); Audiologists 1 (pt).
Affiliation Mennonite
Facilities Dining room; Physical therapy room; Activities room; Chapel; Crafts room; Laundry room; Barber/Beauty shop; Library.
Activities Arts and Crafts; Cards; Games; Reading groups; Prayer groups; Movies; Shopping trips; Dances/Social or cultural gatherings.
Description Facility features Christian retirement living.

HOISINGTON

Homestead Villa Inc
272 W Cheyenne, Hoisington, KS, 67544 (316) 653-4141
Admin Jack H Farrer.
Licensure Intermediate Care. *Beds* 70. *Certified* Medicaid.
Admissions Requirements Medical examination; Physician's request.
Staff Physicians; RNs 3 (ft), 1 (pt); LPNs 1 (pt); Nurses aides 30 (ft); Physical therapists 1 (pt); Reality therapists 1 (ft); Recreational therapists 1 (ft); Occupational therapists 1 (pt); Speech therapists 1 (pt); Activities coordinators 1 (ft); Dietitians 7 (ft); Dentists 1 (pt); Ophthalmologists 1 (pt); Audiologists 1 (pt).
Facilities Dining room; Physical therapy room; Activities room; Laundry room; Barber/Beauty shop.
Activities Arts and Crafts; Games; Reading groups; Prayer groups; Movies; Dances/Social or cultural gatherings.

HOLTON

Jackson County Nursing Home Inc
1121 W 7th, Holton, KS, 66436 (913) 364-3164
Admin Suzanne Misenhelter.
Licensure Intermediate Care. *Beds* 64. *Certified* Medicaid.

Merry Manor Inc
100 Topeka, Holton, KS, 66439 (913) 364-3840
Admin Mary Ann Kirk.
Licensure Intermediate Care. *Beds* 47. *Certified* Medicaid.
Admissions Requirements Medical examination.
Staff RNs 1 (pt); LPNs 2 (ft), 1 (pt); Nurses aides 7 (ft), 7 (pt); Activities coordinators 1 (ft); Dietitians 1 (pt).
Facilities Dining room; Physical therapy room; Activities room; Laundry room; Barber/Beauty shop.
Activities Arts and Crafts; Cards; Games; Reading groups; Prayer groups; Shopping trips; Dances/Social or cultural gatherings.
Description Residents and staff are one big happy family with everyone helping the other one.

HORTON

Tri-County Manor Nursing Center
1890 Euclid, Horton, KS, 66439 (913) 486-2697
Admin Robert Rison. *Medical Dir/Dir of Nursing* Dr Edgardo Francisco.
Licensure Intermediate Care. *Beds* 110. *Certified* Medicaid; Medicare.
Admissions Requirements Minimum age 16; Medical examination; Physician's request.
Staff Physicians 5 (pt); RNs 2 (pt); LPNs 6 (ft), 2 (pt); Orderlies 3 (ft), 1 (pt); Nurses aides 34 (ft), 6 (pt); Physical therapists 1 (pt); Occupational therapists 1 (pt); Speech therapists 1 (pt); Activities coordinators 1 (ft); Dietitians 1 (pt); Dentists 1 (pt); Ophthalmologists 1 (pt); Podiatrists 1 (pt); Audiologists 1 (pt).
Facilities Dining room; Physical therapy room; Activities room; Crafts room; Laundry room; Barber/Beauty shop; Library.
Activities Arts and Crafts; Cards; Games; Reading groups; Prayer groups; Shopping trips; Dances/Social or cultural gatherings; Musical programs; Scenic bus rides.
Description Facility offers restorative therapy program and outpatient care.

HOWARD

Howard Twilight Manor*
PO Box 237, Hwy 99, Howard, KS, 67349 (316) 374-2495
Admin Mary J Smith.
Licensure Intermediate Care. *Beds* 50. *Certified* Medicaid.

HUGOTON

Pioneer Manor
6th and Polk, Box 9, Hugoton, KS, 67951 (316) 544-2023
Admin Hazel L Timken. *Medical Dir/Dir of Nursing* Roger W Ihrig MD.
Licensure Intermediate Care. *Beds* 56. *Certified* Medicaid.
Admissions Requirements Medical examination; Physician's request.
Staff Physicians 6 (pt); RNs 2 (ft); LPNs 5 (ft); Nurses aides 8 (ft), 9 (pt); Physical therapists 1 (pt); Reality therapists 2 (ft); Recreational therapists 2 (pt); Occupational therapists 2 (pt); Spee-

ch therapists 1 (pt); Activities coordinators 1 (ft); Dietitians 4 (ft), 5 (pt); Audiologists 1 (pt).
Facilities Dining room; Physical therapy room; Activities room; Chapel; Crafts room; Laundry room; Barber/Beauty shop.
Activities Arts and Crafts; Games; Reading groups; Prayer groups; Movies; Shopping trips; Dances/Social or cultural gatherings; Make floats for county fair; Make Chamber of Commerce annual banquet decorations.
Description Facility features good meals, good music program, and parties. Residents entertain their clubs or church groups when their turn to host.

HUMBOLDT

Pinecrest Nursing Home
1020 Pine, Humboldt, KS, 66748 (316) 473-2393
Admin Carolyn J Moore.
Licensure Intermediate Care. *Beds* 51. *Certified* Medicaid.
Admissions Requirements Medical examination.
Staff RNs 1 (ft); LPNs 4 (ft), 1 (pt); Nurses aides 14 (ft), 2 (pt); Physical therapists 1 (pt); Recreational therapists 1 (ft); Occupational therapists 1 (pt); Speech therapists 1 (pt); Activities coordinators 1 (ft); Dietitians 1 (pt); Dentists 1 (pt); Podiatrists 1 (pt); Audiologists 1 (pt).
Facilities Dining room; Physical therapy room; Activities room; Chapel; Crafts room; Laundry room; Barber/Beauty shop; Library.
Activities Arts and Crafts; Cards; Games; Reading groups; Prayer groups; Movies; Shopping trips; Dances/Social or cultural gatherings.
Description Facility features a home-like, family atmosphere.

HUTCHINSON

Countryside Villa
Rt 1, Box 275, Hutchinson, KS, 67501 (316) 663-2829
Admin Darlene Thiessen. *Medical Dir/Dir of Nursing* Dr Albright.
Licensure Intermediate Care. *Beds* 50. *Certified* Medicaid.
Admissions Requirements Medical examination; Physician's request.
Staff LPNs 2 (ft), 1 (pt); Physical therapists 1 (ft); Reality therapists 1 (ft); Occupational therapists 1 (ft); Speech therapists 1 (ft); Activities coordinators 1 (ft); Dietitians 1 (ft); Dentists 1 (ft).
Facilities Dining room; Physical therapy room; Activities room; Crafts room; Laundry room; Barber/Beauty shop.
Activities Arts and Crafts; Cards; Games; Reading groups; Movies.
Description Countryside Villa is an intermediate care facility in a country setting with a self-care apartment unit nearby. The residents are offered a number of activities and when weather permits, outside walks, and trips.

Golden Plains Convalescent Center
1202 E 23rd St, Hutchinson, KS, 67501 (316) 669-9393

Admin Marilyn S Luman. *Medical Dir/Dir of Nursing* W C Goodpasture MD.
Licensure Skilled Care. *Beds* 120. *Certified* Medicaid; Medicare.
Admissions Requirements Minimum age 16; Medical examination; Physician's request.
Staff Physicians 1 (ft); RNs 8 (ft), 4 (pt); LPNs 4 (ft), 2 (pt); Nurses aides 45 (ft), 10 (pt); Physical therapists 1 (ft); Speech therapists 1 (ft); Activities coordinators 1 (ft); Dietitians 1 (pt); Dentists 1 (pt); Ophthalmologists 1 (pt); Podiatrists 1 (pt); Audiologists 1 (pt).
Facilities Dining room; Physical therapy room; Activities room; Laundry room; Barber/Beauty shop; Library.
Activities Arts and Crafts; Cards; Games; Reading groups; Prayer groups; Movies; Dances/Social or cultural gatherings.

Hutchinson Good Samaritan Center
810 E 30th Ave, Hutchinson, KS, 67501 (316) 663-1189
Admin Dennis Beeman.
Licensure Intermediate Care. *Beds* 90. *Certified* Medicaid.
Admissions Requirements Minimum age 21.
Staff RNs 3 (ft); LPNs 3 (ft); Nurses aides 30 (ft); Activities coordinators 1 (ft), 1 (pt).
Affiliation Lutheran
Facilities Dining room; Physical therapy room; Activities room; Chapel; Crafts room; Laundry room; Barber/Beauty shop; Library.
Activities Arts and Crafts; Cards; Games; Reading groups; Prayer groups; Movies; Shopping trips; Bell choir; Adopt-a-grandparent program.
Description The Center plans to build 18 duplexes as needed.

Oakwood Villa
2301 N Severance, Hutchinson, KS, 67501 (316) 662-0597
Admin Patrick Hutchens. *Medical Dir/Dir of Nursing* Dr Savage.
Licensure Intermediate Care. *Beds* 100. *Certified* Medicaid.
Admissions Requirements Minimum age 18; Medical examination.
Staff RNs 4 (ft); LPNs 8 (ft); Orderlies 5 (ft); Nurses aides 30 (ft); Reality therapists 1 (ft); Recreational therapists 1 (ft); Activities coordinators 1 (ft); Dietitians 1 (ft).
Facilities Dining room; Physical therapy room; Activities room; Chapel; Crafts room; Laundry room; Barber/Beauty shop.
Activities Arts and Crafts; Cards; Games; Reading groups; Prayer groups; Movies; Shopping trips; Dances/Social or cultural gatherings; Fishing; Barbecues; Shuffleboard; Horseshoes.

Wesley Towers Inc
700 Monterey Pl, Hutchinson, KS, 67502 (316) 663-9175
Admin Eva D Gruver.
Licensure Intermediate Care. *Beds* 66.
Admissions Requirements Medical examination.
Staff RNs 8 (ft), 6 (pt); LPNs 3 (pt); Nurses aides 16 (ft), 5 (pt); Activities coordinators.
Affiliation Methodist
Facilities Dining room; Activities room; Chapel; Crafts room; Laundry room; Barber/Beauty shop; Library; Mens woodwork shop; Weaving

room.
Activities Arts and Crafts; Cards; Games; Reading groups; Prayer groups; Movies; Shopping trips; Dances/Social or cultural gatherings; Swimming and fishing outings.
Description This is a multi-service facility, 2 apartment buildings with services, one apartment for complete independent living; duplexes and cluster apartments for the younger elderly that wish to live independently and yet have emergency help; health care and community service of meals-on-wheels.

INDEPENDENCE

Colonial Lodge—Independence
1000 W Mulberry, Independence, KS, 67301 (316) 331-8420
Admin James Pollock. *Medical Dir/Dir of Nursing* Dr Charles Empson.
Licensure Intermediate Care. *Beds* 55. *Certified* Medicaid.
Staff RNs 2 (ft), 1 (pt); LPNs 1 (ft), 1 (pt); Nurses aides 19 (ft), 4 (pt).
Facilities Dining room; Physical therapy room; Activities room; Chapel; Crafts room; Laundry room; Barber/Beauty shop.
Activities Arts and Crafts; Cards; Prayer groups.

Glenwood Estate
621 S 2nd, Independence, KS, 67301 (316) 331-2260
Admin Marilyn Botts.
Licensure Intermediate Care. *Beds* 43. *Certified* Medicaid.
Admissions Requirements Minimum age 16; Medical examination; Physician's request.
Staff RNs; LPNs; Nurses aides; Physical therapists; Recreational therapists; Occupational therapists; Speech therapists; Activities coordinators; Dietitians; Dentists; Ophthalmologists; Podiatrists; Audiologists.
Facilities Dining room; Physical therapy room; Crafts room; Laundry room; Barber/Beauty shop.
Activities Arts and Crafts; Cards; Games; Reading groups; Prayer groups; Movies; Dances/Social or cultural gatherings.

Heartland Terrace—Independence*
1101 Donald Ave, Independence, KS, 67301 (316) 331-8432
Admin Les A Tallman.
Licensure Intermediate Care. *Beds* 50. *Certified* Medicaid.
Ownership Proprietary.

Manor Nursing Home*
614 S 8th, Independence, KS, 67301 (316) 331-0511
Admin James N Riddles.
Licensure Intermediate Care. *Beds* 60. *Certified* Medicaid.
Ownership Nonprofit.
Affiliation Lutheran

INMAN

Pleasant View Home*
108 N Walnut, Inman, KS, 67546 (316) 585-6411
Admin Edward J Wiebe.
Licensure Intermediate Care. *Beds* ICF 87.
Certified Medicaid.

IOLA

Arkhaven of Iola*
1336 N Walnut, Iola, KS, 66749 (316) 365-6989
Admin Luella Weems.
Licensure Intermediate Care. *Beds* 120. *Certified* Medicaid.
Ownership Proprietary.

Countryside Estates*
600 E Garfield St, Iola, KS, 66749 (316) 365-5221
Admin Margaret R Barnett.
Licensure Intermediate Care. *Beds* 100. *Certified* Medicaid.
Ownership Proprietary.

Sterling Heights Manor
1110 E Carpenter, Iola, KS, 66749 (319) 365-3107
Admin Velma R Ballard. *Medical Dir/Dir of Nursing* Rosemary Davis LPN.
Licensure Intermediate Care. *Beds* 45. *Certified* Medicaid.
Admissions Requirements Minimum age 16.
Staff RNs 1 (pt); LPNs 2 (ft); Nurses aides 10 (ft); Physical therapists 1 (pt); Reality therapists 1 (pt); Recreational therapists 1 (pt); Occupational therapists 1 (pt); Speech therapists 1 (pt); Activities coordinators 1 (pt); Dietitians 1 (pt); Podiatrists 1 (pt); Audiologists 1 (pt).
Facilities Dining room; Physical therapy room; Activities room; Chapel; Crafts room; Laundry room; Barber/Beauty shop.
Activities Arts and Crafts; Cards; Games; Reading groups; Prayer groups; Movies; Shopping trips.

JAMESTOWN

Cheyenne Lodge Nursing Home
716 Cedar, Jamestown, KS, 66948 (913) 439-6211
Admin Ella Thurston.
Licensure Intermediate Care. *Beds* 60. *Certified* Medicaid.
Admissions Requirements Minimum age 16; Medical examination.
Staff RNs 2 (ft), 1 (pt); LPNs 4 (ft); Nurses aides 12 (ft), 6 (pt); Activities coordinators 1 (ft), 2 (pt).
Facilities Dining room; Physical therapy room; Chapel; Laundry room; Barber/Beauty shop.
Activities Arts and Crafts; Cards; Games; Reading groups; Prayer groups; Movies; Shopping trips; Dances/Social or cultural gatherings.

JUNCTION CITY

Good Samaritan Center
416 W Spruce, Junction City, KS, 66441 (913) 238-1187
Admin Dorothy Frederick.
Licensure Intermediate Care. *Beds* 46. *Certified* Medicaid.
Staff RNs 1 (ft); LPNs 2 (ft), 2 (pt); Nurses aides 18 (ft); Activities coordinators 1 (ft).
Affiliation Lutheran
Facilities Dining room; Physical therapy room; Activities room; Laundry room; Barber/Beauty shop.
Activities Arts and Crafts; Cards; Games; Reading groups; Prayer groups; Movies; Shopping trips; Dances/Social or cultural gatherings.

Valley View Professional Care Center
1417 W Ash St, PO Box 107, Junction City, KS, 66441 (913) 762-2162
Admin Howard J Funston. *Medical Dir/Dir of Nursing* Dr Alex Scott.
Licensure Skilled Care. *Beds* 125. *Certified* Medicaid; Medicare.
Admissions Requirements Medical examination; Physician's request.
Staff RNs 6 (ft), 2 (pt); LPNs 6 (ft); Nurses aides 46 (ft), 4 (pt); Physical therapists 1 (pt); Speech therapists 1 (pt); Activities coordinators 1 (ft); Dietitians 1 (pt).
Facilities Dining room; Physical therapy room; Activities room; Chapel; Crafts room; Laundry room; Barber/Beauty shop.
Activities Arts and Crafts; Cards; Games; Reading groups; Prayer groups; Movies; Shopping trips; Dances/Social or cultural gatherings.
Description Valley View Professional Care Center is a skilled nursing home dedicated to serving the community through compassionate care of the infirm and aged of all races, nationalities, and creeds. We specialize in social, emotional, and spiritual care as well as medical and nursing care. We are ideally located in a beautiful rural setting.

Valley Vista Care Center
1115 W 14th St, Junction City, KS, 66441 (913) 238-2128
Admin Richard Jung. *Medical Dir/Dir of Nursing* Alex Scott MD.
Licensure Intermediate Care. *Beds* 51. *Certified* Medicaid.
Admissions Requirements Medical examination; Physician's request.
Staff RNs 1 (ft), 1 (pt); LPNs 6 (ft); Orderlies 1 (pt); Nurses aides 10 (ft); Activities coordinators 3 (ft).
Facilities Dining room; Physical therapy room; Activities room; Chapel; Crafts room; Laundry room; Barber/Beauty shop.
Activities Arts and Crafts; Cards; Games; Reading groups; Prayer groups; Movies; Shopping trips; Dances/Social or cultural gatherings.
Description We have all-certified nursing staff. We are minutes from hospital and doctor's offices. Close to downtown shopping areas.

KANSAS CITY

Bryant-Butler-Kitchen Nursing Home*
3500 N 27th St, Kansas City, KS, 66104 (913) 342-6960
Admin Raymond Handy Sr.
Licensure Intermediate Care. *Beds* 100. *Certified* Medicaid.
Ownership Nonprofit.

Kansas City Presbyterian Manor
7850 Freeman St, Kansas City, KS, 66112 (913) 334-3666
Medical Dir/Dir of Nursing John O Mallory.
Licensure Intermediate Care; Personal Care.
Beds ICF 107; Personal Care 43. *Certified* Medicaid.
Admissions Requirements Minimum age 65.
Staff RNs 1 (ft), 5 (pt); LPNs 7 (ft); Nurses aides 36 (ft), 4 (pt); Activities coordinators 1 (ft), 1 (pt).
Affiliation Presbyterian
Facilities Dining room; Physical therapy room; Activities room; Chapel; Crafts room; Laundry room; Barber/Beauty shop; Library.
Activities Arts and Crafts; Cards; Games; Reading groups; Prayer groups; Movies; Shopping trips; Dances/Social or cultural gatherings; Dinner theatre.

The Manor of Kansas City*
3231 N 61st St, Kansas City, KS, 66104 (913) 299-1770
Admin Helen S Hundley.
Licensure Intermediate Care. *Beds* 80. *Certified* Medicaid.
Ownership Proprietary.

Medicalodge East of Kansas City
6261 Leavenworth Rd, Kansas City, KS, 66104 (913) 299-9722
Admin Debbie Frazier.
Licensure Intermediate Care. *Beds* 75.
Ownership Proprietary.

Medicalodge North of Kansas City
6500 Greeley, Kansas City, KS, 66104 (913) 334-0200
Admin Richard O Retrum. *Medical Dir/Dir of Nursing* Norman Marvin MD.
Licensure Skilled Care; Intermediate Care.
Beds SNF 30; ICF 70. *Certified* Medicaid.
Staff RNs 5 (ft), 2 (pt); LPNs 8 (ft), 4 (pt); Orderlies 4 (ft); Nurses aides 40 (ft), 15 (pt); Physical therapists 1 (ft); Occupational therapists 1 (pt); Speech therapists 1 (pt); Activities coordinators 1 (ft); Dietitians 1 (pt); Podiatrists 1 (pt); Audiologists 1 (pt).
Facilities Dining room; Physical therapy room; Activities room; Laundry room; Barber/Beauty shop.
Activities Arts and Crafts; Cards; Games; Prayer groups; Movies; Dances/Social or cultural gatherings; Sporting events.

Medicalodge South of Kansas City
6501 Greeley, Kansas City, KS, 66104 (913) 334-5252
Admin Doug Frihart.
Licensure Intermediate Care. *Beds* 100. *Certified* Medicaid.
Admissions Requirements Medical examination; Physician's request.
Staff Physicians 2 (pt); RNs 1 (ft), 1 (pt); LPNs 5 (ft); Nurses aides 22 (ft), 1 (pt); Physical therapists 1 (pt); Reality therapists 1 (pt); Recreational therapists 1 (pt); Occupational therapists 1 (pt); Speech therapists 1 (pt); Activities coordinators 1 (ft), 1 (pt); Dietitians 1 (pt); Dentists 1 (pt); Podiatrists 1 (pt); Audiologists 1 (pt).
Facilities Dining room; Physical therapy room; Activities room; Chapel; Crafts room; Laundry

room; Barber/Beauty shop; Library.
Activities Arts and Crafts; Cards; Games; Reading groups; Prayer groups; Movies; Shopping trips.

Saint Joseph Home*
759 Vermont Ave, Kansas City, KS, 66101 (913) 621-6800
Admin Bernard B Brown Jr.
Licensure Skilled Care; Intermediate Care. *Beds* SNF 65; ICF 136. *Certified* Medicaid; Medicare.
Ownership Nonprofit.
Affiliation Roman Catholic

KENSINGTON

Prairie Haven Inc
Box 248, N Hwy 36, Kensington, KS, 66951 (913) 476-2623
Admin Bobbie L Hodge.
Licensure Intermediate Care. *Beds* 58. *Certified* Medicaid.
Ownership Proprietary.
Admissions Requirements Medical examination; Physician's request.
Staff RNs 2 (ft), 1 (pt); Orderlies 1 (ft); Nurses aides 15 (ft), 1 (pt); Activities coordinators 1 (ft).
Facilities Dining room; Physical therapy room; Activities room; Laundry room; Barber/Beauty shop.
Activities Arts and Crafts; Cards; Games; Reading groups; Prayer groups; Shopping trips; Dances/Social or cultural gatherings.
Description Our selective menu is nutritionally and therapeutically appetizing. Our residents make decisions at meal time as to what choice sounds good to them each day. They eat better and exercise freedom.

KINGMAN

Cedar Crest Inc of Kingman*
310 W Copeland, Kingman, KS, 67068 (316) 532-2223
Admin James Prichard.
Licensure Intermediate Care. *Beds* 96. *Certified* Medicaid.
Ownership Proprietary.

KINSLEY

Medicalodge of Kinsley*
Box 65-A, 6th and Winchester, Kinsley, KS, 67547 (316) 659-3506
Admin Carolyn Walker.
Licensure Intermediate Care. *Beds* 76. *Certified* Medicaid.
Ownership Proprietary.

KIOWA

Kiowa Manor Inc*
1020 Main, Kiowa, KS, 67070 (316) 825-4732
Admin John G Stickel.
Licensure Intermediate Care. *Beds* 50. *Certified* Medicaid.
Ownership Proprietary.

LACROSSE

Rush County Nursing Home*
6th and Locust, LaCrosse, KS, 67548 (913) 222-2574
Admin John E Kern.
Licensure Intermediate Care. *Beds* 60. *Certified* Medicaid.

LACYGNE

Swan Manor Inc
215 N Broadway, Lacygne, KS, 66040 (913) 757-4414
Admin Daniel F Widner. *Medical Dir/Dir of Nursing* Robert Banks MD.
Licensure Intermediate Care. *Beds* 36. *Certified* Medicaid.
Staff Physicians 1 (pt); RNs 1 (pt); LPNs 1 (ft), 1 (pt); Physical therapists 1 (pt); Reality therapists 1 (pt); Recreational therapists 1 (pt); Occupational therapists 1 (pt); Speech therapists 1 (pt); Activities coordinators 1 (pt); Dietitians 1 (pt); Dentists 1 (pt); Podiatrists 1 (pt); Audiologists 1 (pt).
Facilities Dining room; Physical therapy room; Activities room; Crafts room; Laundry room; Barber/Beauty shop.
Activities Arts and Crafts; Cards; Games; Reading groups; Prayer groups; Movies.

LANSING

Colonial Manor Nursing and Health Care Center
Holiday Plaza Ctr, PO Box 250, Lansing, KS, 66043 (913) 727-1284
Admin Dale K Grunewald.
Licensure Intermediate Care. *Beds* 60. *Certified* Medicaid.
Ownership Proprietary.
Admissions Requirements Minimum age 16; Medical examination.
Staff RNs 1 (ft); LPNs 2 (ft), 1 (pt); Orderlies 1 (ft); Nurses aides 20 (ft); Activities coordinators 1 (ft).
Facilities Dining room; Physical therapy room; Activities room; Laundry room; Barber/Beauty shop.
Activities Cards; Games; Reading groups; Prayer groups; Movies; Shopping trips; Dances/Social or cultural gatherings; Bingo.

LARNED

Hammond Holiday Home Inc
1114 W 11th St, Larned, KS, 67550 (316) 285-6914
Admin Michael Burke.
Licensure Intermediate Care. *Beds* 100. *Certified* Medicaid.
Admissions Requirements Minimum age 16; Medical examination.
Staff RNs 5 (ft); Orderlies 1 (ft), 1 (pt); Nurses aides 21 (ft), 23 (pt); Physical therapists 1 (pt); Occupational therapists 1 (pt); Speech therapists 1 (pt); Activities coordinators 1 (pt); Dietitians 1 (pt); Dentists 1 (pt); Podiatrists 1 (pt); Audiologists 1 (pt).
Facilities Dining room; Physical therapy room;

Activities room; Chapel; Crafts room; Laundry room; Barber/Beauty shop.
Activities Arts and Crafts; Cards; Games; Reading groups; Prayer groups; Movies; Dances/Social or cultural gatherings.
Description Our facility's major emphasis is rehabilitation. Physical therapy, occupational therapy, recreational, and religious service are all part of our holistic and therapeutic program. We try to treat the whole person and in doing so allow that individual to build upon his/her positive points.

LAWRENCE

Autumn Manor of Lawrence
1800 W 27th St, Lawrence, KS, 66044 (913) 842-4383
Admin Felizitas Bright.
Licensure Intermediate Care. *Beds* 100. *Certified* Medicaid.

Lawrence Manor Nursing Home
PO Box 946, 345 Florida, Lawrence, KS, 66044 (913) 843-6868
Admin Anna C Flory.
Licensure Intermediate Care. *Beds* 36. *Certified* Medicaid.

Lawrence Presbyterian Manor
1429 Kasold Dr, Lawrence, KS, 66044 (913) 841-4262
Admin Phillip M Levi Jr. *Medical Dir/Dir of Nursing* .
Licensure Intermediate Care. *Beds* 43. *Certified* Medicaid.
Admissions Requirements Minimum age 65; Medical examination.
Staff RNs 2 (ft), 1 (pt); Orderlies 3 (ft); Nurses aides 24 (pt); Physical therapists 2 (pt); Occupational therapists 2 (pt); Speech therapists 2 (pt); Activities coordinators 1 (ft); Dietitians 1 (ft); Dentists 1 (pt); Podiatrists 1 (pt).
Affiliation Presbyterian
Facilities Dining room; Physical therapy room; Activities room; Chapel; Crafts room; Laundry room; Barber/Beauty shop; Library.
Activities Cards.

Samaritan Lodge
205 N Michigan, Lawrence, KS, 66044 (913) 843-8934
Medical Dir/Dir of Nursing Carl Inzarello MD.
Licensure Intermediate Care. *Beds* 50. *Certified* Medicaid.
Ownership Proprietary.
Admissions Requirements Minimum age 14; Medical examination.
Staff LPNs; Orderlies; Nurses aides; Reality therapists; Activities coordinators.
Facilities Dining room; Physical therapy room; Activities room; Chapel; Crafts room; Laundry room; Barber/Beauty shop; Library; Lounge.
Activities Arts and Crafts; Cards; Games; Reading groups; Prayer groups; Movies; Shopping trips; Dances/Social or cultural gatherings.

Valley View Care Home*
2518 Ridge Ct, Lawrence, KS, 66044 (913) 842-2610
Admin Ruth Foster.

Licensure Intermediate Care. *Beds* 61. *Certified* Medicaid.
Ownership Public.

LEAVENWORTH

Leavenworth County Convalescent Infirmary
Broadway and Rees, Leavenworth, KS, 66048
(913) 682-4501
Admin Thomas V McEvoy. *Medical Dir/Dir of Nursing* Sami Duysak MD.
Licensure Skilled Care; Intermediate Care.
Beds SNF 47; ICF 34. *Certified* Medicaid.
Ownership Public.
Admissions Requirements Minimum age 18;
Medical examination; Physician's request.
Staff Physicians 1 (pt); RNs 4 (ft), 2 (pt); LPNs
4 (ft); Orderlies 3 (ft), 1 (pt); Nurses aides 23
(ft), 5 (pt); Occupational therapists 1 (pt); Speech therapists 2 (pt); Activities coordinators 1
(ft); Dietitians 1 (pt); Audiologists 1 (pt).
Facilities Dining room; Physical therapy room;
Activities room; Laundry room; Barber/Beauty
shop.
Activities Arts and Crafts; Cards; Games; Prayer groups; Movies.

Medicalodge of Leavenworth*
1503 Ohio, Leavenworth, KS, 66048 (913)
682-1844
Admin Donita Simons.
Licensure Intermediate Care. *Beds* 120. *Certified* Medicaid.
Ownership Proprietary.

LENEXA

Delmar Gardens of Lenexia
9701 Monrovia, Lenexa, KS, 66215 (913)
492-1130
Admin Richard L Carlson. *Medical Dir/Dir of Nursing* Dr Lawrence Steffen.
Licensure Skilled Care; Intermediate Care.
Beds SNF 32; ICF 158. *Certified* Medicare.
Admissions Requirements Medical examination; Physician's request.
Staff RNs 5 (ft), 3 (pt); LPNs 3 (ft), 2 (pt);
Nurses aides 50 (ft); Physical therapists 1 (ft), 1
(pt); Recreational therapists 2 (ft); Occupational
therapists 1 (pt); Speech therapists 1 (pt); Dietitians 1 (pt).
Facilities Dining room; Physical therapy room;
Activities room; Chapel; Crafts room; Laundry
room; Barber/Beauty shop; Library.
Activities Arts and Crafts; Cards; Games;
Reading groups; Prayer groups; Movies; Shopping trips; Dances/Social or cultural gatherings.
Description Ultra-modern facility with spacious rooms and outstanding dietary
department; caters to individual needs.

Lakeview Village Inc
9100 Park, Lenexa, KS, 66215 (913) 888-1900
Admin Lowell E Strahan.
Licensure Intermediate Care. *Beds* 21.
Admissions Requirements Minimum age 62;
Medical examination.
Staff RNs 1 (ft), 1 (pt); LPNs 1 (ft), 2 (pt);
Orderlies 1 (ft); Nurses aides 12 (ft); Recreational therapists 1 (ft); Activities coordinators 1
(ft); Dietitians 1 (pt); Dentists 1 (pt); Podiatrists

1 (pt).
Facilities Dining room; Physical therapy room;
Activities room; Chapel; Crafts room; Laundry
room; Barber/Beauty shop; Library.
Activities Arts and Crafts; Cards; Games;
Reading groups; Prayer groups; Movies; Shopping trips; Dances/Social or cultural gatherings.
Description Facility has a 5-story highrise with
159 apartments and 47 fourplexes with 188
apartments. Offers continuing care to own
retirement residents only; does not accept direct
admission to nursing facility. Offers broad
range of programs and activities including
charter bus tours.

LEONARDVILLE

Leonardville Nursing Home*
Box 148, Hwy 24, Leonardville, KS, 66449
(913) 293-5246
Admin Kathryn Whitley.
Licensure Intermediate Care. *Beds* 50. *Certified* Medicaid.
Ownership Proprietary.

LEOTI

Golden Acres Nursing Home
Earl and 7th, Leoti, KS, 67861 (316) 375-4600
Admin Jerry Korbe.
Licensure Intermediate Care. *Beds* 30. *Certified* Medicaid.
Ownership Public.
Admissions Requirements Minimum age 65.
Staff RNs 1 (pt); LPNs 1 (ft), 1 (pt); Nurses
aides 13 (ft), 2 (pt); Physical therapists 1 (pt);
Activities coordinators 1 (ft).
Facilities Dining room; Physical therapy room;
Activities room; Chapel; Barber/Beauty shop.
Activities Arts and Crafts; Games; Reading
groups; Prayer groups; Movies.
Description Golden Acres is a county-owned,
nonprofit facility in rural Western Kansas. The
emphasis is in maintaining quality care to the
residents and families of Wichita County.

LIBERAL

Liberal Good Samaritan Center
2160 Zennia Ln, Liberal, KS, 67901 (316)
624-3831
Admin Roger K Thompson.
Licensure Intermediate Care. *Beds* 100. *Certified* Medicaid.
Admissions Requirements Medical examination; Physician's request.
Staff RNs 4 (ft); LPNs 3 (ft), 1 (pt); Nurses
aides 21 (ft), 20 (pt); Physical therapists 1 (pt);
Occupational therapists 1 (pt); Speech therapists 1 (pt); Activities coordinators 2 (ft); Dietitians 1 (pt); Dentists 1 (pt); Podiatrists 1 (pt).
Affiliation Lutheran
Facilities Dining room; Physical therapy room;
Activities room; Chapel; Crafts room; Laundry
room; Barber/Beauty shop.
Activities Arts and Crafts; Cards; Games;
Reading groups; Prayer groups; Movies; Shopping trips; Dances/Social or cultural gatherings.

LINCOLN

Mid-America Nursing Center of Lincoln*
922 N 5th St, Lincoln, KS, 67455 (913)
524-4428
Admin Theressa Lesley Simpson.
Licensure Intermediate Care. *Beds* 73. *Certified* Medicaid.
Ownership Proprietary.

LINDSBORG

Bethany Home Association of Lindsborg
321 N Chestnut, Lindsborg, KS, 67456 (913)
227-2721
Admin William P Carlson. *Medical Dir/Dir of Nursing* Jeanie Holwenda RN.
Licensure Intermediate Care. *Beds* 132. *Certified* Medicaid.
Admissions Requirements Minimum age 65.
Staff RNs 1 (ft), 2 (pt); LPNs 5 (ft); Nurses
aides 40 (ft), 35 (pt); Physical therapists 1 (ft);
Activities coordinators 1 (ft); Dietitians 1 (ft).
Affiliation Lutheran
Facilities Dining room; Physical therapy room;
Chapel; Laundry room; Barber/Beauty shop.
Activities Arts and Crafts; Cards; Games;
Reading groups; Prayer groups; Movies.
Description Bethany Home is an ICF with a
Christ-like atmosphere of love and caring, felt
by all who enter its doors. Residents live in a
home-like arrangement rather than institutional; they care about each other and staff
members as well, and in turn are looked upon
as family by staff.

LINN

Linn Community Nursing Home Inc
W 3rd, Linn, KS, 66953 (913) 348-5551
Admin Sonia DeRusseau.
Licensure Intermediate Care. *Beds* 77. *Certified* Medicaid.
Ownership Public.
Staff RNs 1 (pt); LPNs 4 (ft); Nurses aides 13
(ft), 23 (pt); Activities coordinators 2 (ft).
Facilities Dining room; Physical therapy room;
Activities room; Crafts room; Laundry room;
Barber/Beauty shop; Quiet room.
Activities Arts and Crafts; Cards; Games; Prayer groups; Movies; Shopping trips; Dances/Social or cultural gatherings; Birthday parties;
Bingo.

LITTLE RIVER

Sandstone Heights*
State St, Little River, KS, 67457 (316) 897-6266
Admin Shirley Granger.
Licensure Intermediate Care. *Beds* 56. *Certified* Medicaid.
Ownership Public.

LOGAN

Logan Manor Nursing Home*
Main St and 3rd, Logan, KS, 67646 (913)
689-4201
Admin Carol L Greene.

Licensure Intermediate Care. *Beds* 50. *Certified* Medicaid.
Ownership Public.

LOUISBURG

Southridge Manor Care Home
N 12th and Broadway, Louisburg, KS, 66053
(913) 837-2611
Admin David J Mercier. *Medical Dir/Dir of Nursing* Barborah Spies MD.
Licensure Intermediate Care. *Beds* 55. *Certified* Medicaid.
Admissions Requirements Physician's request.
Staff RNs 1 (ft); LPNs 2 (ft), 1 (pt); Nurses aides 8 (ft), 5 (pt); Physical therapists 1 (pt); Occupational therapists 1 (pt); Speech therapists 1 (pt); Activities coordinators 1 (ft); Dietitians 1 (pt); Dentists 1 (pt).
Facilities Dining room; Physical therapy room; Activities room; Chapel; Laundry room; Barber/Beauty shop.
Activities Arts and Crafts; Cards; Games; Reading groups; Prayer groups; Shopping trips; Dances/Social or cultural gatherings.
Description Small town setting with good community participation and relaxed country atmosphere. Home-style meals available with all meals made from scratch. Beautician on staff for personal grooming.

LUCAS

Lucas Rest Home*
Johnson and Main, Lucas, KS, 67648 (316) 525-6215
Admin Celia Anschutz.
Licensure Intermediate Care. *Beds* 50. *Certified* Medicaid.
Ownership Proprietary.

LYNDON

Hilltop Home*
131 W 14th St, Lyndon, KS, 66451 (913) 828-4842
Admin Vona P Price.
Licensure Intermediate Care. *Beds* 54. *Certified* Medicaid.
Ownership Proprietary.

LYONS

Lyons Good Samaritan Center
1311 S Douglas, Lyons, KS, 67554 (316) 257-5163
Admin John Carlberg.
Licensure Intermediate Care. *Beds* 85. *Certified* Medicaid.
Admissions Requirements Medical examination; Physician's request.
Staff RNs 1 (ft), 3 (pt); LPNs 1 (ft), 3 (pt); Nurses aides 20 (ft); Physical therapists 1 (ft); Occupational therapists 1 (ft); Activities coordinators 1 (ft).
Affiliation Lutheran
Facilities Dining room; Physical therapy room; Chapel; Laundry room; Barber/Beauty shop.
Activities Arts and Crafts; Cards; Games; Reading groups; Movies.

Description A junior high school class elects to spend their activity time at the center visiting an adopted resident. A garden is planted and cared for by residents willing to spend time outdoors, along with staff that are off duty.

MACKSVILLE

Parkview Manor*
Box 128, Hwy 50, Macksville, KS, 67557 (316) 348-3665
Admin John Steinhaus.
Licensure Intermediate Care. *Beds* 59. *Certified* Medicaid.

MADISON

Madison Manor
Bluestem Dr, Box 277, Madison, KS, 66860
(316) 437-2470
Admin Andrew Johnson.
Licensure Intermediate Care. *Beds* 55. *Certified* Medicaid.
Ownership Proprietary.
Staff RNs 1 (pt); LPNs 4 (ft); Orderlies 1 (ft); Nurses aides 15 (ft), 5 (pt).
Facilities Dining room; Physical therapy room; Activities room; Chapel; Laundry room; Barber/Beauty shop.
Activities Arts and Crafts; Cards; Games; Reading groups; Prayer groups; Movies; Shopping trips.

MANHATTAN

College Hill Skilled Nursing Center
2423 Kimball, Manhattan, KS, 66502 (913) 539-7671
Admin Brian S Warren.
Licensure Skilled Care. *Beds* 106. *Certified* Medicaid; Medicare.
Staff Physicians 2 (pt); RNs 2 (ft); LPNs 8 (ft), 8 (pt); Orderlies 3 (ft); Nurses aides 25 (ft), 5 (pt); Physical therapists 1 (ft); Occupational therapists 1 (pt); Activities coordinators 1 (ft); Dietitians 1 (pt).
Facilities Dining room; Physical therapy room; Activities room; Chapel; Crafts room; Laundry room; Barber/Beauty shop.
Activities Arts and Crafts; Cards; Games; Reading groups; Prayer groups; Movies; Shopping trips; Dances/Social or cultural gatherings; Bus rides; Cooking class; Field trips.
Description Facility features specialized rehabilitation facilities with occupational and physical therapy; social workers on staff. Facility specializes in post-operative hip fracture and stroke rehabilitation.

Meadowlark Hills
2121 Meadowlark Rd, Manhattan, KS, 66502
(913) 537-4610
Admin John R Grace. *Medical Dir/Dir of Nursing* Dr P Meek and Dr W Durkee.
Licensure Skilled Care. *Beds* 53. *Certified* Medicaid; Medicare.
Admissions Requirements Minimum age 65; Medical examination; Physician's request.
Staff RNs 1 (ft), 5 (pt); LPNs 2 (ft), 1 (pt); Orderlies 1 (pt); Nurses aides 13 (ft), 6 (pt); Activities coordinators 2 (ft), 1 (pt).

Facilities Dining room; Physical therapy room; Activities room; Crafts room; Laundry room; Barber/Beauty shop; Library.
Activities Arts and Crafts; Cards; Games; Reading groups; Prayer groups; Movies; Dances/Social or cultural gatherings.
Description Facility features health care; 53 resident capacity; independent apartment living; 115 at present; and a day care program for adults 7 days a week.

Wharton Manor Inc
2101 Claflin Rd, Manhattan, KS, 66502 (913) 776-0636
Admin Norman Wallace. *Medical Dir/Dir of Nursing* Dr S Mosier.
Licensure Intermediate Care. *Beds* 60. *Certified* Medicaid.
Admissions Requirements Minimum age 16; Medical examination; Physician's request.
Staff RNs 1 (ft); LPNs 4 (pt); Nurses aides 23 (ft); Physical therapists 1 (ft); Activities coordinators 1 (ft); Dietitians 5 (ft), 3 (pt).
Facilities Dining room; Physical therapy room; Activities room; Chapel; Barber/Beauty shop; Library.
Activities Arts and Crafts; Cards; Games; Reading groups; Prayer groups; Movies; Shopping trips; Dances/Social or cultural gatherings; Cooking; Pet days.
Description Many residents are involved with horticultural therapy programs which benefit the nursing home and the community. There are flower beds, vegetable gardens, outdoor flower boxes, and numerous indoor plants. It is very satisfying to work with soil and watch seeds grow and bloom.

MARION

Marion Manor Inc
1500 E Lawrence St, Marion, KS, 66861 (316) 382-2191
Admin Ken Vanduska.
Licensure Intermediate Care. *Beds* 80. *Certified* Medicaid.
Staff RNs 1 (ft), 3 (pt); LPNs 1 (ft), 1 (pt); Nurses aides 10 (ft), 10 (pt); Physical therapists 1 (pt); Reality therapists 1 (pt); Recreational therapists 1 (pt); Occupational therapists 1 (pt); Speech therapists 1 (pt); Activities coordinators 1 (ft), 1 (pt); Dietitians 1 (pt).
Facilities Dining room; Physical therapy room; Activities room; Crafts room; Laundry room; Barber/Beauty shop.
Activities Arts and Crafts; Cards; Games; Reading groups; Prayer groups; Movies; Shopping trips; Dances/Social or cultural gatherings.

MARQUETTE

Riverview Estates Inc
202 S Washington St, Marquette, KS, 67464
(316) 546-2211
Admin Barbara Lindquist.
Licensure Intermediate Care. *Beds* 50. *Certified* Medicaid.
Staff RNs 3 (pt); LPNs 1 (pt); Orderlies 1 (ft), 1 (pt); Nurses aides 10 (ft), 9 (pt); Physical therapists 1 (pt); Occupational therapists 1 (pt); Speech therapists 1 (pt); Activities coordinators 1

(ft); Dietitians 1 (pt); Dentists 1 (pt); Ophthalmologists 1 (pt); Audiologists 1 (pt).
Facilities Dining room; Physical therapy room; Activities room; Chapel; Crafts room; Laundry room; Barber/Beauty shop.
Activities Arts and Crafts; Cards; Games; Reading groups; Prayer groups; Movies; Shopping trips; Dances/Social or cultural gatherings.

MARYSVILLE

Marshall County Nursing Center*
1906 North St, Marysville, KS, 66508 (913) 562-5321
Admin Georgeanna Sohl.
Licensure Intermediate Care. *Beds* 49. *Certified* Medicaid.
Ownership Proprietary.

Mary Marshall Manor Inc*
810 N 18th, Marysville, KS, 66508 (913) 562-5325
Admin Dorothy L Welch.
Licensure Intermediate Care. *Beds* 94. *Certified* Medicaid.

MCPHERSON

Cedars—Church of the Bretheren Home
1111 E Kansas Ave, McPherson, KS, 67460 (316) 241-0919
Admin LeRoy C Weddle.
Licensure Intermediate Care. *Beds* 69. *Certified* Medicaid.
Admissions Requirements Minimum age 62; Medical examination.
Staff RNs 2 (ft), 1 (pt); LPNs 3 (ft), 4 (pt); Nurses aides 11 (ft), 12 (pt); Activities coordinators 1 (ft); Dietitians 1 (ft).
Affiliation Church of the Brethren
Facilities Dining room; Physical therapy room; Activities room; Chapel; Laundry room; Barber/Beauty shop; Library.
Activities Cards; Games; Reading groups; Prayer groups; Movies; Dances/Social or cultural gatherings.
Description Facility features very clean, private rooms (83%), and skilled-care level staff.

E and M Rainbow Home Inc
606 E Ave B, McPherson, KS, 67460 (316) 241-3414
Admin Edna R Bruce.
Licensure Personal Care. *Beds* 20.

Heartland—McPherson
1601 N Main, McPherson, KS, 67460 (316) 241-5360
Admin Arden L Gray. *Medical Dir/Dir of Nursing* Dr Tom Billings.
Licensure Intermediate Care. *Beds* 100. *Certified* Medicaid.
Staff LPNs 17 (ft); Nurses aides 19 (ft); Physical therapists 1 (pt); Occupational therapists 1 (pt); Speech therapists 1 (pt); Activities coordinators 1 (ft); Dietitians 1 (pt); Audiologists 1 (pt).
Facilities Dining room; Physical therapy room; Activities room; Chapel; Crafts room; Laundry room; Barber/Beauty shop.
Activities Arts and Crafts; Games; Reading groups; Prayer groups.

Mac House
225 S Hickory, McPherson, KS, 67460 (316) 241-6780
Admin S K Duffee.
Licensure Intermediate Care for Mentally Retarded. *Beds* 13. *Certified* Medicaid.
Admissions Requirements Minimum age 18.
Staff RNs 1 (pt); Nurses aides 5 (ft), 4 (pt).
Facilities Dining room; Crafts room.
Activities Arts and Crafts; Cards; Games; Movies; Shopping trips; Dances/Social or cultural gatherings.
Description Mac House emphasis is on developing independence in life skills of residents through training. Living arrangements emphasize family atmosphere. Residents also receive quality medical care.

MEADE

Lone Tree Lodge
407 E Rainbelt, Meade, KS, 67864 (316) 873-2146
Admin B B Reimer. *Medical Dir/Dir of Nursing* Agnes Wiens.
Licensure Intermediate Care. *Beds* 56. *Certified* Medicaid.
Ownership Nonprofit.
Admissions Requirements Medical examination.
Staff RNs 1 (ft), 2 (pt); LPNs 2 (ft), 1 (pt); Nurses aides 14 (ft), 4 (pt); Physical therapists 1 (pt); Reality therapists 1 (pt); Recreational therapists 1 (pt); Occupational therapists 1 (pt); Activities coordinators 1 (ft); Dietitians 1 (ft); Dentists 1 (pt).
Affiliation Mennonite
Facilities Dining room; Physical therapy room; Activities room; Chapel; Laundry room; Barber/Beauty shop.
Activities Arts and Crafts; Movies.

MEDICINE LODGE

Medicine Valley Lodge Inc*
106 W Stolp, Medicine Lodge, KS, 67104 (316) 886-3425
Admin James J Williams.
Licensure Intermediate Care for Mentally Retarded. *Beds* 48. *Certified* Medicaid.
Ownership Proprietary.

MERRIAM

Trinity Lutheran Manor
9700 W 62nd St, Merriam, KS, 66203 (913) 384-0800
Admin Willa Hughes. *Medical Dir/Dir of Nursing* Mohan Gollerkeri.
Licensure Skilled Care; Intermediate Care. *Beds* SNF 60; ICF 60. *Certified* Medicaid; Medicare.
Admissions Requirements Minimum age 18.
Staff RNs; LPNs; Orderlies; Nurses aides; Physical therapists; Recreational therapists; Occupational therapists; Speech therapists; Dietitians; Dentists; Ophthalmologists; Podiatrists;

Audiologists.
Affiliation Lutheran
Facilities Dining room; Physical therapy room; Activities room; Chapel; Crafts room; Laundry room; Barber/Beauty shop.
Activities Arts and Crafts; Cards; Games; Reading groups; Prayer groups; Movies; Shopping trips; Dances/Social or cultural gatherings.

MINNEAPOLIS

Minneapolis Good Samaritan Center
816 Argyle, Minneapolis, KS, 67467 (913) 392-2162
Admin Richard Elliott.
Licensure Intermediate Care. *Beds* 100. *Certified* Medicaid.
Staff RNs 1 (ft), 4 (pt); LPNs 6 (ft); Nurses aides 30 (pt); Occupational therapists 1 (pt); Activities coordinators 2 (ft).
Affiliation Lutheran
Facilities Dining room; Physical therapy room; Activities room; Chapel; Crafts room; Laundry room; Barber/Beauty shop.
Activities Arts and Crafts; Cards; Games; Reading groups; Prayer groups; Movies; Shopping trips; Dances/Social or cultural gatherings.
Description We are a small community nursing home where care and concern of each resident is a daily function. In God's love everyone is someone.

MINNEOLA

Minneola Nursing Home*
Box 396, 205 Chestnut, Minneola, KS, 67865 (316) 885-4238
Admin Lou A Esplund.
Licensure Intermediate Care. *Beds* 50. *Certified* Medicaid.
Ownership Nonprofit.

MOLINE

Elk Manor Home*
Rt 1, Box 7, Walnut St, Moline, KS, 67353 (316) 647-3336
Admin June E Gillespie.
Licensure Intermediate Care. *Beds* 41. *Certified* Medicaid.
Ownership Public.

MONTEZUMA

Bethel Home Inc
Aztec St, Montezuma, KS, 67867 (316) 846-2241
Admin Marion D Becker. *Medical Dir/Dir of Nursing* Alma Wiens.
Licensure Intermediate Care. *Beds* 48. *Certified* Medicaid.
Admissions Requirements Physician's request.
Staff RNs 1 (ft); LPNs 1 (ft), 5 (pt); Nurses aides 10 (ft), 11 (pt); Physical therapists 2 (pt); Recreational therapists 1 (pt); Activities coordinators 1 (ft), 1 (pt); Dietitians 3 (ft), 4 (pt).
Affiliation Mennonite
Facilities Dining room; Physical therapy room; Activities room; Chapel; Crafts room; Laundry room; Barber/Beauty shop; Library.

Activities Arts and Crafts; Games; Reading groups; Prayer groups; Shopping trips; Dances-/Social or cultural gatherings.
Description Facility believes in providing quality care, pleasant surroundings, and activities in a spiritual atmosphere.

MORAN

Moran Manor
Rt 1, Moran, KS, 66755 (316) 237-4309
Admin Sandra Northcutt.
Licensure Intermediate Care. *Beds* 50. *Certified* Medicaid.
Admissions Requirements Minimum age 16; Medical examination.
Staff RNs 1 (ft); LPNs 1 (ft), 2 (pt); Nurses aides 11 (ft), 6 (pt); Physical therapists 1 (ft), 1 (pt); Occupational therapists 1 (pt); Speech therapists 1 (pt); Activities coordinators 1 (ft), 1 (pt); Dietitians 1 (pt); Dentists 1 (pt); Podiatrists 1 (pt); Audiologists 1 (pt).
Facilities Dining room; Physical therapy room; Activities room; Laundry room; Barber/Beauty shop.
Activities Arts and Crafts; Cards; Games; Reading groups; Prayer groups; Movies; Shopping trips; Dances/Social or cultural gatherings.
Description The Century II tub is very beneficial to residents; good activity program; good nursing care; facility cleanliness excellent.

MOUND CITY

Sugar Valley Home Inc*
W Main, Mound City, KS, 66056 (913) 795-2231
Admin Wes W Worthington.
Licensure Intermediate Care. *Beds* 56. *Certified* Medicaid.
Ownership Proprietary.

MOUNDRIDGE

Memorial Home for the Aged
Box 29, Moundridge, KS, 67107 (316) 345-2341
Admin David D Schrag. *Medical Dir/Dir of Nursing* Dr W E Kaufman.
Licensure Intermediate Care. *Beds* 42. *Certified* Medicaid.
Admissions Requirements Medical examination.
Staff RNs 1 (ft), 2 (pt); LPNs 1 (pt); Nurses aides 3 (ft), 21 (pt).
Affiliation Mennonite
Facilities Dining room; Physical therapy room; Activities room; Chapel; Crafts room; Laundry room; Barber/Beauty shop; Library.
Activities Arts and Crafts; Reading groups.
Description A new nursing home was completed in November, 1983. The old nursing home is now assisted self-care; also have duplexes, sixplexes, and cottages for independent retirement living. Facility is supported by 9 local congregations. Many of the activities have a religious or local ethnic flavor.

Moundridge Manor
710 N Christian Ave, Moundridge, KS, 67107 (316) 345-6364

Admin Bernard Regehr. *Medical Dir/Dir of Nursing* Dr W Kauffman.
Licensure Intermediate Care. *Beds* 66. *Certified* Medicaid.
Ownership Nonprofit.
Admissions Requirements Minimum age 16; Medical examination; Physician's request.
Staff RNs 1 (ft), 1 (pt); LPNs 4 (ft), 3 (pt); Nurses aides 23 (ft); Speech therapists 1 (pt); Activities coordinators 1 (ft); Audiologists 1 (pt).
Affiliation Mennonite
Facilities Dining room; Physical therapy room; Activities room; Crafts room; Laundry room; Barber/Beauty shop.
Activities Arts and Crafts; Games; Reading groups; Prayer groups.
Description We have a minister or lay person coming in every morning for devotions; singalong weekly; short church service every Sunday morning; singing group every Thursday night, and Sunday School every Saturday night.

MOUNT HOPE

Mount Hope Nursing Center
704 E Main, Mount Hope, KS, 67108 (316) 667-2431
Admin Patricia J Elliott. *Medical Dir/Dir of Nursing* J M Steck MD.
Licensure Intermediate Care. *Beds* 62. *Certified* Medicaid.
Admissions Requirements Minimum age 16; Medical examination; Physician's request.
Staff RNs 1 (ft), 1 (pt); LPNs 1 (ft), 1 (pt); Activities coordinators 1 (ft).
Facilities Dining room; Physical therapy room; Activities room; Chapel; Crafts room; Laundry room; Barber/Beauty shop.
Activities Arts and Crafts; Cards; Games; Reading groups; Prayer groups; Movies; Shopping trips; Dances/Social or cultural gatherings.

MULVANE

Villa Maria
116 SE Central, Mulvane, KS, 67110 (316) 777-1129
Admin Sr M Magdalen Giaretta. *Medical Dir/Dir of Nursing* Leslie H Cobb MD.
Licensure Intermediate Care. *Beds* 66. *Certified* Medicaid.
Admissions Requirements Medical examination; Physician's request.
Staff RNs; LPNs; Nurses aides; Reality therapists; Recreational therapists; Occupational therapists; Speech therapists; Activities coordinators; Dietitians; Dentists; Ophthalmologists; Podiatrists; Audiologists.
Affiliation Roman Catholic
Facilities Dining room; Physical therapy room; Activities room; Chapel; Laundry room; Barber/Beauty shop; Library.
Activities Arts and Crafts; Cards; Games; Reading groups; Prayer groups; Movies; Dances/Social or cultural gatherings.
Description Facility's dietary department prepares meals-on-wheels for the local citizens 7 days a week.

NEODESHA

Golden Keys Nursing Home
221 Mill St, Neodesha, KS, 66757 (316) 325-2639
Admin Phyllis C Cunningham. *Medical Dir/Dir of Nursing* Bert Chronister MD.
Licensure Intermediate Care. *Beds* 64. *Certified* Medicaid.
Admissions Requirements Minimum age 18; Medical examination; Physician's request.
Staff RNs 2 (ft), 1 (pt); LPNs 2 (ft), 3 (pt); Nurses aides 18 (ft), 3 (pt); Reality therapists 2 (pt); Recreational therapists 1 (ft); Activities coordinators 1 (ft).
Facilities Dining room; Physical therapy room; Activities room; Laundry room; Barber/Beauty shop.
Activities Arts and Crafts; Cards; Games; Reading groups; Prayer groups; Movies; Shopping trips; Dances/Social or cultural gatherings.
Description The Golden Keys Nursing Home was established to provide nursing care and related medical services to the aged and infirm. We are adjacent to our local hospital, with a walk-thru tunnel attaching each facility. We care for both the long-term and the convalescent resident. We meet the total needs of each individual by providing spiritual, social, and divisional recreational activities and opportunities.

Neodesha Nursing Home*
1626 N 8th, Neodesha, KS, 66757 (316) 325-3088
Admin Lois Ann Gulick.
Licensure Intermediate Care. *Beds* 50. *Certified* Medicaid.
Ownership Proprietary.

NEWTON

Bethel Home for the Aged
222 S Pine, Newton, KS, 67114 (316) 283-4014
Admin Alvin I Penner.
Licensure Intermediate Care. *Beds* 67. *Certified* Medicaid.
Admissions Requirements Medical examination.
Staff RNs 2 (ft), 4 (pt); LPNs 4 (pt); Orderlies 1 (ft), 1 (pt); Nurses aides 14 (ft), 19 (pt); Physical therapists 2 (pt); Occupational therapists 1 (pt); Speech therapists 1 (pt); Activities coordinators; Dietitians 1 (pt); Dentists 2 (pt); Audiologists 1 (pt).
Affiliation Mennonite
Facilities Dining room; Physical therapy room; Activities room; Chapel; Crafts room; Laundry room; Barber/Beauty shop; Library.
Activities Arts and Crafts; Games; Prayer groups; Movies; Shopping trips.
Description Facility is located adjacent to a general hospital and physicians' offices and is near churches.

Friendly Acres
200 SW 14th, Box 648, Newton, KS, 67114 (316) 283-4770
Admin James L White.
Licensure Intermediate Care; Personal Care. *Beds* ICF 144; Personal Care 46. *Certified* Medicaid.

Admissions Requirements Minimum age 65; Medical examination.
Affiliation Methodist
Facilities Dining room; Physical therapy room; Activities room; Chapel; Crafts room; Laundry room; Barber/Beauty shop; Library.
Activities Arts and Crafts; Games; Reading groups; Prayer groups; Shopping trips; Dances-/Social or cultural gatherings; Ceramics.

Kansas Christian Home Inc
1035 SE 3rd St, PO Box 627, Newton, KS, 67114 (316) 283-6600
Admin Jeff Loane.
Licensure Intermediate Care. *Beds* 115. *Certified* Medicaid.

Newton Presbyterian Manor Inc
1200 E 7th, Box 255, Newton, KS, 67114 (316) 283-5400
Admin Patricia A Curtis.
Licensure Intermediate Care. *Beds* 120. *Certified* Medicaid.
Admissions Requirements Minimum age 65; Medical examination; Physician's request.
Staff RNs 2 (ft); LPNs 4 (ft); Recreational therapists 1 (ft), 1 (pt).
Affiliation Presbyterian
Facilities Dining room; Physical therapy room; Activities room; Chapel; Crafts room; Laundry room; Barber/Beauty shop; Library; Greenhouse.
Activities Arts and Crafts; Cards; Games; Prayer groups; Movies; Shopping trips; Dances/Social or cultural gatherings.
Description Campus consists of 13 cottages, 30 apartment units, and the main building which accomodates from 110 to 120 residents. Facility offers 4 levels of service.

NORTON

Andbe Home Inc
201 W Crane, Norton, KS, 67654 (913) 877-2601
Admin Wilma Winder.
Licensure Intermediate Care. *Beds* 100. *Certified* Medicaid.
Admissions Requirements Medical examination.
Staff RNs 2 (ft); LPNs 7 (ft); Orderlies 1 (ft); Nurses aides 36 (ft); Physical therapists 1 (pt); Activities coordinators 1 (ft); Dietitians 1 (pt); 1 (ft).
Facilities Dining room; Physical therapy room; Activities room; Chapel; Crafts room; Laundry room; Barber/Beauty shop.
Activities Arts and Crafts; Cards; Games; Reading groups; Prayer groups; Movies; Shopping trips; Bus rides.

NORTONVILLE

Village Villa
Walnut and Taggert, Nortonville, KS, 66060 (913) 886-6400
Admin Martha Madison. *Medical Dir/Dir of Nursing* Dr Willard Madison.
Licensure Intermediate Care. *Beds* 50. *Certified* Medicaid.
Ownership Proprietary.

Admissions Requirements Minimum age 18; Medical examination; Physician's request.
Staff RNs 1 (ft), 1 (pt); Nurses aides 16 (ft), 5 (pt).
Facilities Dining room; Physical therapy room; Activities room; Chapel; Laundry room; Barber/Beauty shop; Sunroom with TV; Quiet room.
Activities Arts and Crafts; Cards; Games; Reading groups; Movies; Bible study by volunteers; News time and visiting; Music time and singing.
Description Village Villa is located in Jefferson County, Kansas in the quiet little rural town of Nortonville. Village Villa offers a real caring staff, planned activities, excellent food, and pleasant, clean surroundings. We provide a physician on call for emergencies and RN's are on duty daily.

OAKLEY

Oakley Manor
615 Price, Oakley, KS, 67748 (913) 672-3115
Admin Nancy Riggs. *Medical Dir/Dir of Nursing* Rosemary Davis LPN.
Licensure Intermediate Care. *Beds* 45. *Certified* Medicaid.
Admissions Requirements Minimum age 16.
Staff RNs 1 (pt); LPNs 2 (ft), 1 (pt); Orderlies 1 (ft); Nurses aides 16 (ft), 4 (pt); Physical therapists 1 (ft); Activities coordinators 1 (ft).
Facilities Dining room; Physical therapy room; Laundry room; Barber/Beauty shop.
Activities Arts and Crafts; Games; Prayer groups; Movies; Shopping trips; Dances/Social or cultural gatherings.

OBERLIN

Decatur County Good Samaritan Center
108 E Ash, Oberlin, KS, 67749 (913) 475-2245
Admin Richard D Kjelland. *Medical Dir/Dir of Nursing* Dr Ren Whitacker.
Licensure Intermediate Care. *Beds* 79. *Certified* Medicaid.
Admissions Requirements Minimum age 35; Medical examination; Physician's request.
Staff Physicians 4 (pt); RNs 3 (pt); LPNs 4 (pt); Nurses aides 35 (pt); Physical therapists 1 (pt); Activities coordinators 1 (ft), 2 (pt).
Affiliation Lutheran
Facilities Dining room; Physical therapy room; Activities room; Chapel; Laundry room; Barber/Beauty shop.
Activities Arts and Crafts; Cards; Games; Reading groups; Prayer groups; Movies; Shopping trips; Dances/Social or cultural gatherings.
Description Medical day care is available.

OLATHE

Good Samaritan Center
572 E Park, Olathe, KS, 66061 (913) 782-1372
Admin Russell Hilderbrand.
Licensure Intermediate Care. *Beds* 162. *Certified* Medicaid.
Ownership Nonprofit.
Admissions Requirements Minimum age 18; Medical examination; Physician's request.
Staff RNs 4 (ft); LPNs 10 (ft); Orderlies 1 (ft);

Nurses aides 50 (ft), 20 (pt); Activities coordinators 1 (ft).
Affiliation Lutheran
Facilities Dining room; Physical therapy room; Activities room; Chapel; Crafts room; Laundry room; Barber/Beauty shop; Library; Plant room.
Activities Arts and Crafts; Cards; Games; Reading groups; Prayer groups; Movies; Shopping trips; Dances/Social or cultural gatherings.

Johnson County Nursing Center*
1125 W Spruce, Olathe, KS, 66061 (913) 782-0272
Admin Kenneth F Betterton.
Licensure Intermediate Care. *Beds* 99. *Certified* Medicaid.
Ownership Public.

Olathe Nursing Home
625 N Lincoln, Olathe, KS, 66061 (913) 782-1311
Admin Bertha Jane Harden. *Medical Dir/Dir of Nursing* Ronald LaHue DO.
Licensure Intermediate Care. *Beds* 54. *Certified* Medicaid.
Admissions Requirements Minimum age 60; Medical examination.
Staff LPNs 2 (ft), 1 (pt); Orderlies 2 (ft); Nurses aides 13 (ft); Physical therapists 1 (ft); Activities coordinators 1 (ft).
Facilities Dining room; Physical therapy room; Activities room; Chapel; Laundry room; Barber/Beauty shop.
Activities Arts and Crafts; Cards; Prayer groups; Movies; Shopping trips.
Description Facility has a home-type atmosphere.

Regency Health Care Center
400 S Rogers Rd, Olathe, KS, 66062 (913) 782-3350
Admin Judy Powell. *Medical Dir/Dir of Nursing* Tom Williams MD.
Licensure Skilled Care. *Beds* 109. *Certified* Medicaid; Medicare.
Admissions Requirements Minimum age 16; Medical examination; Physician's request.
Staff Physicians 13 (pt); RNs 3 (ft), 1 (pt); LPNs 3 (ft); Orderlies 1 (ft); Nurses aides 31 (ft), 1 (pt); Physical therapists 1 (pt); Reality therapists 1 (pt); Recreational therapists 1 (ft); Occupational therapists 1 (pt); Speech therapists 1 (pt); Activities coordinators 1 (pt); Dietitians 1 (pt); Dentists 1 (pt); Podiatrists 1 (pt); Audiologists 1 (pt).
Facilities Dining room; Physical therapy room; Activities room; Crafts room; Laundry room; Barber/Beauty shop.
Activities Arts and Crafts; Cards; Games; Reading groups; Movies; Shopping trips; Dances/Social or cultural gatherings.
Description Facility offers a balanced program meeting the physical, social, emotional, and spiritual needs of each resident. Rehabilitation is an integral part of the resident's plan of care. Physical, occupational and speech therapies are offered on a regular basis. Facility offers specialized care and is dedicated to providing appropriate care to meet the needs of each resident.

ONAGA

Golden Acres Inc*
500 Western St, Onaga, KS, 66521 (913) 889-4227
Admin Barbara Eddy.
Licensure Intermediate Care. *Beds* 55. *Certified* Medicaid.
Ownership Proprietary.

OSAGE CITY

Osage Manor Inc
10th and Main, Osage City, KS, 66523 (913) 528-4262
Admin George L Meisner. *Medical Dir/Dir of Nursing* Irene Hasenbank.
Licensure Intermediate Care. *Beds* 67. *Certified* Medicaid.
Admissions Requirements Medical examination.
Staff RNs 1 (ft); LPNs 3 (ft); Nurses aides 20 (ft), 15 (pt); Occupational therapists 1 (ft); Activities coordinators 1 (ft).
Facilities Dining room; Physical therapy room; Activities room; Chapel; Crafts room; Laundry room; Barber/Beauty shop.
Activities Arts and Crafts; Cards; Games; Reading groups; Prayer groups; Movies; Shopping trips; Dances/Social or cultural gatherings; Fishing trips with picnic; Watermelon feeds; Ice cream social; Pot luck suppers; Country/western bands; Balloon lift offs; Movies.

Peterson Nursing Home
630 Holliday, Osage City, KS, 66523 (913) 528-4420
Admin Iris Peterson.
Licensure Intermediate Care. *Beds* 60. *Certified* Medicaid.
Staff RNs 1 (ft); LPNs 1 (ft); Nurses aides 16 (ft); Physical therapists 1 (pt); Recreational therapists 1 (pt); Occupational therapists 1 (pt); Speech therapists 1 (pt); Activities coordinators 1 (pt); Dietitians 1 (pt); Audiologists 1 (pt).
Facilities Dining room; Physical therapy room; Activities room; Chapel; Crafts room; Laundry room; Barber/Beauty shop.
Activities Arts and Crafts; Cards; Games; Reading groups; Prayer groups; Movies; Shopping trips; Dances/Social or cultural gatherings; Resident council.

OSAWATOMIE

Osawatomie Rest Home*
PO Box 309, 514 Leroy, Osawatomie, KS, 66064 (913) 755-3519
Admin Martha Frazier.
Licensure Intermediate Care. *Beds* 24. *Certified* Medicaid.
Ownership Proprietary.

Regency Health Care Center—Osawatomie
1615 Parker Ave, Osawatomie, KS, 66064 (913) 755-4165
Admin William P Sinclair. *Medical Dir/Dir of Nursing* W O Appenfeller MD.
Licensure Skilled Care; Intermediate Care. *Beds* SNF 47; ICF 95. *Certified* Medicaid; Medicare.

Ownership Proprietary.
Admissions Requirements Minimum age 16; Medical examination; Physician's request.
Staff Physicians 4 (pt); RNs 5 (ft), 2 (pt); LPNs 6 (ft), 4 (pt); Orderlies 12 (ft); Nurses aides 45 (ft); Physical therapists 1 (pt); Recreational therapists 3 (ft); Occupational therapists 1 (pt); Speech therapists 1 (pt); Activities coordinators 1 (pt); Dietitians 1 (pt); Dentists 1 (pt).
Facilities Dining room; Physical therapy room; Activities room; Chapel; Crafts room; Laundry room; Barber/Beauty shop; Library.
Activities Arts and Crafts; Cards; Games; Reading groups; Prayer groups; Movies; Shopping trips; Dances/Social or cultural gatherings.

OSBORNE

Parkview Manor I
811 N 1st St, Osborne, KS, 67473 (913) 346-2114
Admin Gladys Cunningham.
Licensure Intermediate Care. *Beds* 58. *Certified* Medicaid.
Admissions Requirements Minimum age 16; Medical examination.
Staff RNs 2 (pt); LPNs 1 (ft); Nurses aides 16 (ft), 4 (pt).
Facilities Dining room; Physical therapy room; Activities room; Laundry room; Barber/Beauty shop.
Activities Arts and Crafts; Cards; Games; Reading groups; Prayer groups; Shopping trips; Dances/Social or cultural gatherings; Sunday school; Church services; Bible study.
Description Facility offers residents and guests coffee weekly, memorial services, and exercises.

Parkview Manor II
811 N 1st St, Osborne, KS, 67473 (913) 346-2116
Licensure Intermediate Care. *Beds* 60. *Certified* Medicaid.
Staff RNs 2 (ft); LPNs 2 (ft); Nurses aides 22 (ft); Recreational therapists 1 (ft); Activities coordinators 1 (ft); Dietitians 1 (ft).

OSKALOOSA

Cherokee Lodge Adult Care*
Box 307, 700 Cherokee, Oskaloosa, KS, 66066 (913) 863-2108
Admin James H Tenpenny.
Licensure Intermediate Care. *Beds* 100. *Certified* Medicaid.
Ownership Proprietary.

OSWEGO

Oswego Guest Home
College Rd, PO Box 26, Oswego, KS, 67356 (316) 795-4429
Admin Janice K Schertz.
Licensure Intermediate Care. *Beds* 50. *Certified* Medicaid.
Admissions Requirements Minimum age 18; Medical examination; Physician's request.
Staff RNs 1 (pt); LPNs 3 (ft); Orderlies 1 (ft), 1 (pt); Physical therapists 1 (pt); Reality therapists 1 (pt); Occupational therapists 1 (pt); Activities coordinators 1 (ft); Dietitians 1 (pt); Podiatrists

1 (pt).
Facilities Dining room; Physical therapy room; Activities room; Crafts room; Laundry room; Barber/Beauty shop.
Activities Arts and Crafts; Cards; Games; Reading groups; Prayer groups; Movies; Shopping trips; Dances/Social or cultural gatherings.
Description Facility with homey atmosphere is located in a rural community 2 blocks from Oswego Hospital; doctors make rounds daily; variety of special activities.

OTTAWA

Cedar House Inc
15th and Hickory, Ottawa, KS, 66067 (913) 242-5399
Admin Tom H Keller.
Licensure Intermediate Care. *Beds* 113. *Certified* Medicaid.
Staff RNs 2 (ft), 1 (pt); LPNs 3 (ft), 1 (pt); Orderlies 1 (ft); Nurses aides 20 (ft), 3 (pt); Physical therapists 1 (pt); Recreational therapists 1 (ft); Occupational therapists 1 (pt); Speech therapists 1 (pt); Activities coordinators 1 (ft); Dentists 1 (pt); Audiologists 1 (pt).
Facilities Dining room; Physical therapy room; Activities room; Laundry room; Barber/Beauty shop.
Activities Arts and Crafts; Cards; Games; Prayer groups; Movies; Dances/Social or cultural gatherings.
Description Facility features friendly, personal care.

Crestview Nursing Home*
1002 W 7th St Terrace, Ottawa, KS, 66067 (913) 242-3454
Admin Dorothy M Ubelaker.
Licensure Intermediate Care. *Beds* 51. *Certified* Medicaid.
Ownership Proprietary.

OVERBROOK

Bookside Manor
Hwy 56, Box 327, Overbrook, KS, 66524 (913) 665-7124
Admin Elaine Wells. *Medical Dir/Dir of Nursing* Dr James Ruble Jr.
Licensure Intermediate Care. *Beds* 100. *Certified* Medicaid.
Admissions Requirements Minimum age 16.
Staff Physicians 1 (ft); RNs 4 (ft); LPNs 4 (ft), 2 (pt); Orderlies 4 (ft); Nurses aides 30 (ft), 10 (pt); Physical therapists 1 (pt); Occupational therapists 1 (pt); Speech therapists 1 (pt); Activities coordinators 1 (ft); Dietitians 1 (pt); Dentists 1 (pt).
Facilities Dining room; Physical therapy room; Activities room; Chapel; Crafts room; Laundry room; Barber/Beauty shop; Visitors lounge.
Activities Arts and Crafts; Cards; Games; Reading groups; Prayer groups; Movies; Shopping trips; Dances/Social or cultural gatherings; School programs.
Description Brookside offers professional 24-hour licensed care in a beautiful, rural setting. Low staff turnover and excellent physician coverage are 2 of the best attributes. Located just 30 miles south of Topeka makes it con-

venient for families and friends to visit and shop. Facility's only business is people business and greatest assets are kindness, gentleness, honesty, firmness, and the greatest of all, love.

OVERLAND PARK

Conser House
7829 Conser, Overland Park, KS, 66204
Admin Laurie L Thomeczek.
Licensure Intermediate Care for Mentally Retarded. *Beds* 10. *Certified* Medicaid.
Ownership Nonprofit.
Admissions Requirements Minimum age 18; Medical examination; Physician's request.
Staff RNs 1 (pt); LPNs 2 (ft); Nurses aides 9 (ft).
Facilities Dining room; Activities room; Laundry room.
Activities Arts and Crafts; Cards; Games; Prayer groups; Movies; Shopping trips; Dances/Social or cultural gatherings.
Description This facility is a group home for severely and profoundly retarded adults. Each resident has a specific, individualized training program used both at the residence and at day program site away from the facility.

Heritage House Nursing Center Inc
7541 Switzer, Overland Park, KS, 66214 (913) 631-2200
Admin G Perry Stonebraker. *Medical Dir/Dir of Nursing* Dr Philip Boyer.
Licensure Skilled Care; Intermediate Care.
Beds SNF 49; ICF 150. *Certified* Medicaid; Medicare.
Admissions Requirements Medical examination.
Staff RNs 4 (ft), 1 (pt); LPNs 8 (ft), 3 (pt); Nurses aides 52 (ft), 3 (pt); Physical therapists 1 (pt); Occupational therapists 1 (pt); Speech therapists 1 (pt); Activities coordinators 1 (ft); Dietitians 1 (ft); Dentists 1 (pt); Podiatrists 1 (pt); Audiologists 1 (pt).
Facilities Dining room; Physical therapy room; Activities room; Crafts room; Laundry room; Barber/Beauty shop; Library.
Activities Arts and Crafts; Cards; Games; Reading groups; Movies; Dances/Social or cultural gatherings; Zoo.
Description Heritage House Nursing Center is an extremely attractive, safe, modern, 200-bed, complete health care facility designed to provide skilled care for our residents. Our programs include physical, occupational, and speech therapy, as well as a full array of activities, social services, a dietician, and volunteers.

Indian Creek Nursing Center Inc*
6515 W 103rd, Overland Park, KS, 66212 (913) 642-5545
Admin Ruth McCune.
Licensure Skilled Care. *Beds* 110.
Ownership Proprietary.

Indian Meadows Nursing Center Inc*
6505 W 103rd, Overland Park, KS, 66212 (913) 649-5110
Admin Judith M Wolff.
Licensure Skilled Care. *Beds* 100.
Ownership Proprietary.

OXFORD

Riverview Manor Inc*
200 S Ohio, Oxford, KS, 67119 (319) 455-2214
Admin Carol Sue Wilkerson.
Licensure Intermediate Care. *Beds* 50. *Certified* Medicaid.
Ownership Proprietary.

PAOLA

Country Haven*
908 N Pearl St, Paola, KS, 66071 (913) 294-4309
Admin Richard McKinney.
Licensure Intermediate Care. *Beds* 80. *Certified* Medicaid.
Ownership Proprietary.

Medicalodge of Paola*
Box C, 501 Assembly Ln, Paola, KS, 66071 (913) 294-3345
Admin Bill Crego.
Licensure Intermediate Care. *Beds* 88. *Certified* Medicaid.

Pine Crest Haven*
1004 N Pearl, Paola, KS, 66071 (913) 294-2404
Admin Rufus Turner Jr.
Licensure Intermediate Care. *Beds* 50. *Certified* Medicaid.
Ownership Proprietary.

PARSONS

Elmhaven*
1315 S 15th, Parsons, KS, 67357 (316) 421-1320
Admin Patricia L Woodworth.
Licensure Intermediate Care. *Beds* 49. *Certified* Medicaid.
Ownership Proprietary.

Heritage Home
1400 S 15th, Parsons, KS, 67357 (316) 421-1430
Admin Jeannie Nichols. *Medical Dir/Dir of Nursing* F N Stephens DO.
Licensure Intermediate Care. *Beds* 50. *Certified* Medicaid.
Admissions Requirements Minimum age 18; Medical examination; Physician's request.
Staff RNs 1 (ft), 1 (pt); LPNs 1 (pt); Nurses aides 11 (ft), 2 (pt); Activities coordinators 2 (ft).
Facilities Dining room; Physical therapy room; Activities room; Chapel; Crafts room; Laundry room; Barber/Beauty shop.
Activities Arts and Crafts; Cards; Games; Reading groups; Prayer groups; Movies; Shopping trips; Dances/Social or cultural gatherings.

Parsons Good Samaritan Center
709 Leawood Dr, Parsons, KS, 67357 (316) 421-1110
Admin John M Rook.
Licensure Intermediate Care. *Beds* 69. *Certified* Medicaid.
Admissions Requirements Minimum age 21; Medical examination; Physician's request.
Staff RNs 1 (ft); LPNs 3 (ft), 2 (pt); Orderlies 1

(ft); Nurses aides 20 (ft), 8 (pt); Recreational therapists 1 (pt); Activities coordinators 1 (ft).
Facilities Dining room; Physical therapy room; Activities room; Chapel; Crafts room; Laundry room; Barber/Beauty shop; Library; Smoke room.
Activities Arts and Crafts; Games; Movies; Shopping trips; Dances/Social or cultural gatherings.
Description Facility has van with wheelchair lift.

Parsons Presbyterian Manor
3501 Dirr, Parsons, KS, 67353 (316) 421-1450
Admin Thomas Gengler. *Medical Dir/Dir of Nursing* Dr Dan Pauls.
Licensure Intermediate Care; Personal Care.
Beds ICF 41; Personal Care 25. *Certified* Medicaid.
Admissions Requirements Minimum age 65; Medical examination.
Staff RNs 1 (ft); LPNs 2 (ft); Nurses aides 7 (ft), 3 (pt); Activities coordinators 1 (ft).
Affiliation Presbyterian
Facilities Dining room; Physical therapy room; Activities room; Chapel; Crafts room; Laundry room; Barber/Beauty shop; Library.
Activities Arts and Crafts; Cards; Games; Prayer groups; Movies; Shopping trips; Dances/Social or cultural gatherings.

Westbrook Manor Nursing Center*
3500 W Broadway, Parsons, KS, 67357 (316) 421-4180
Admin Wade Patton.
Licensure Intermediate Care. *Beds* 100. *Certified* Medicaid.
Ownership Proprietary.

PEABODY

Peabody Memorial Nursing Home Inc*
407 N Locust, Peabody, KS, 66866 (316) 983-2152
Admin Cheryl Blaken.
Licensure Intermediate Care. *Beds* 98. *Certified* Medicaid.
Ownership Proprietary.

Westview Manor
4th and Peabody, Peabody, KS, 66866 (316) 983-2165
Admin Joleen R Hasker. *Medical Dir/Dir of Nursing* Dorothy Rhodes.
Licensure Intermediate Care. *Beds* 52. *Certified* Medicaid.
Ownership Proprietary.
Staff RNs 3 (ft); Nurses aides 10 (ft), 3 (pt).
Facilities Dining room; Physical therapy room; Activities room; Laundry room; Barber/Beauty shop.
Activities Arts and Crafts; Cards; Games; Reading groups; Prayer groups; Movies; Shopping trips; Dances/Social or cultural gatherings.

PHILLIPSBURG

Phillips County Home
784 6th St, Phillipsburg, KS, 67661 (913) 543-2131
Admin Sondra Kester.

Licensure Intermediate Care. *Beds* 31. *Certified* Medicaid.
Staff LPNs 1 (ft), 2 (pt); Recreational therapists 1 (pt); Activities coordinators 1 (ft).
Facilities Dining room; Laundry room; Barber-/Beauty shop.

Southview Manor
E Hwy US 36, Box 628, Phillipsburg, KS, 67661 (913) 543-5209
Admin Marcia Mullis.
Licensure Intermediate Care. *Beds* 99. *Certified* Medicaid.
Admissions Requirements Medical examination.
Staff RNs 2 (pt); LPNs 2 (ft), 1 (pt); Nurses aides 27 (ft); Physical therapists 1 (ft); Activities coordinators 1 (ft).
Facilities Dining room; Physical therapy room; Activities room; Crafts room; Laundry room; Barber/Beauty shop.
Activities Arts and Crafts; Cards; Games; Prayer groups; Movies; Shopping trips; Dances/Social or cultural gatherings.

PITTSBURG

Medicalodge North of Pittsburg
2614 N Joplin, Pittsburg, KS, 66762 (316) 231-3970
Admin Dana Dugger.
Licensure Intermediate Care. *Beds* 80. *Certified* Medicaid.
Admissions Requirements Medical examination.
Staff RNs 2 (ft); LPNs 5 (ft); Orderlies 1 (ft); Nurses aides 25 (ft); Activities coordinators 1 (ft).
Facilities Dining room; Physical therapy room; Activities room; Chapel; Crafts room; Laundry room; Barber/Beauty shop.
Activities Arts and Crafts; Cards; Games; Reading groups; Prayer groups; Movies; Shopping trips; Dances/Social or cultural gatherings.
Description Facility features home-type atmosphere with activities daily. Many types of programs and outings are enjoyed by our residents.

Medicalodge South of Pittsburg
2520 S Rouse, Pittsburg, KS, 66762 (316) 231-0300
Admin Jacqueline England. *Medical Dir/Dir of Nursing* Dr G W Pogson.
Licensure Skilled Care; Intermediate Care. *Beds* SNF 24; ICF 76. *Certified* Medicaid; Medicare.
Admissions Requirements Minimum age 16; Medical examination; Physician's request.
Staff Physicians 1 (pt); RNs 5 (ft), 1 (pt); LPNs 8 (ft), 1 (pt); Orderlies 1 (ft); Nurses aides 36 (ft), 4 (pt); Recreational therapists 1 (ft); Activities coordinators 1 (ft), 1 (pt); Dietitians 1 (pt).
Facilities Dining room; Physical therapy room; Activities room; Chapel; Crafts room; Laundry room; Barber/Beauty shop; Library.
Activities Arts and Crafts; Cards; Games; Reading groups; Prayer groups; Movies; Dances/Social or cultural gatherings; Shopping trips.
Description Facility is extra clean with an excellent activity program.

New Horizons of Pittsburg*
2702 N Joplin, Pittsburg, KS, 66762 (316) 231-3910
Admin Ruth Post.
Licensure Intermediate Care for Mentally Retarded. *Beds* 88. *Certified* Medicaid.

Regency Health Care of Pittsburg
1005 Centennial, Pittsburg, KS, 66762 (316) 231-1120
Admin Wilma Van Houten.
Licensure Intermediate Care. *Beds* 100. *Certified* Medicaid.
Admissions Requirements Minimum age 16; Medical examination; Physician's request.
Staff RNs 2 (ft); LPNs 8 (ft); Orderlies 4 (ft); Nurses aides 42 (ft); Physical therapists 1 (ft); Reality therapists 1 (ft); Recreational therapists 1 (ft); Occupational therapists 1 (ft); Speech therapists 1 (ft); Activities coordinators 1 (ft); Dietitians 1 (ft); Dentists 1 (ft); Podiatrists 1 (ft); Audiologists 1 (ft).
Facilities Dining room; Physical therapy room; Activities room; Crafts room; Laundry room; Barber/Beauty shop; Library.
Activities Arts and Crafts; Cards; Games; Reading groups; Prayer groups; Movies; Shopping trips; Dances/Social or cultural gatherings.
Description Regency is a professional nursing care center. Under recent change of ownership, now offering more services, and complete changes in dietary, restorative and nursing programs.

Shields Adult Care Home Inc
2420 S Rouse, Pittsburg, KS, 66762 (316) 231-5590
Admin Wilfred C Shields. *Medical Dir/Dir of Nursing* D M Halsinger MD.
Licensure Intermediate Care for Mentally Retarded. *Beds* 50. *Certified* Medicaid.
Admissions Requirements Minimum age 18; Medical examination.
Staff Physicians 1 (pt); RNs 1 (ft); LPNs 1 (ft); Orderlies 2 (ft); Nurses aides 16 (ft); Physical therapists 1 (pt); Recreational therapists 1 (ft); Occupational therapists 1 (pt); Speech therapists 1 (pt); Activities coordinators 1 (ft); Dietitians 1 (pt); Dentists 1 (pt); Ophthalmologists 1 (pt); Podiatrists 1 (pt); Audiologists 1 (pt); Psychologists 1 (ft), 1 (pt).
Facilities Dining room; Physical therapy room; Activities room; Chapel; Crafts room; Laundry room; Barber/Beauty shop; Library.
Activities Arts and Crafts; Cards; Games; Reading groups; Prayer groups; Movies; Shopping trips; Dances/Social or cultural gatherings.
Description For 27 years, Shields Adult Care Home has offered the community a facility with a home-like atmosphere and professionals to meet the needs of our residents. Individualized programs are designed and implemented by our psychologist to train the residents to function independently. Our goal is to return our residents to the community to live as normal lives as possible.

PLAINVILLE

Rooks County Home*
1000 S Washington, Plainville, KS, 67663 (913) 434-2846

Admin Forrest A Burkholder Jr.
Licensure Intermediate Care. *Beds* 52. *Certified* Medicaid.
Ownership Public.

PLEASANTON

Pleasant View Manor Inc
1005 W 15th, Box 22, Pleasanton, KS, 66075 (913) 352-8455
Admin Mary K Smith. *Medical Dir/Dir of Nursing* Dr Fred Dunlap.
Licensure Intermediate Care. *Beds* 50. *Certified* Medicaid.
Admissions Requirements Minimum age 16; Medical examination.
Staff Physicians 1 (pt); RNs 1 (pt); LPNs 2 (ft); Nurses aides 20 (ft); Physical therapists 1 (pt); Occupational therapists 1 (pt); Speech therapists 1 (pt); Activities coordinators 1 (pt); Dietitians 1 (pt); Dentists 1 (pt); Ophthalmologists 1 (pt); Podiatrists 1 (pt); Audiologists 1 (pt).
Facilities Dining room; Physical therapy room; Activities room; Chapel; Crafts room; Laundry room; Barber/Beauty shop; Library.
Activities Arts and Crafts; Cards; Games; Reading groups; Prayer groups; Movies; Shopping trips; Dances/Social or cultural gatherings.
Description Facility is located on 9 acres overlooking city lake and grade school playground; swimming pool is within one block. Facility offers restful rural living, 70 miles south of Kansas City on US 69.

PRATT

Cedar Crest at Pratt*
1221 Larimer, Pratt, KS, 67124 (316) 672-6541
Admin Robert K Doolittle.
Licensure Intermediate Care. *Beds* 95. *Certified* Medicaid.
Ownership Proprietary.

Siesta Home of Pratt Inc
227 S Howard, Pratt, KS, 67124 (316) 672-5971
Admin Linda M Young.
Licensure Intermediate Care. *Beds* 60. *Certified* Medicaid.
Admissions Requirements Medical examination.
Staff RNs 1 (ft), 1 (pt); LPNs 1 (ft); Nurses aides 15 (ft), 5 (pt); Physical therapists 1 (pt); Occupational therapists 1 (pt); Speech therapists 1 (pt); Activities coordinators 1 (ft); Dietitians 1 (pt); Dentists 1 (pt); Audiologists 1 (pt).
Facilities Dining room; Physical therapy room; Activities room; Chapel; Laundry room; Barber/Beauty shop.
Activities Arts and Crafts; Cards; Games; Reading groups; Prayer groups; Movies; Shopping trips.

PRESCOTT

Prescott Country View Nursing Home
Hwy 69, Box 37, Prescott, KS, 66767 (913) 471-4315
Admin Betty S Keiser.
Licensure Intermediate Care. *Beds* 50. *Certified* Medicaid.
Staff RNs 1 (ft), 1 (pt); LPNs 2 (ft), 1 (pt);

Orderlies 1 (ft); Nurses aides 14 (ft), 2 (pt); Physical therapists 1 (pt); Reality therapists 1 (pt); Occupational therapists 1 (pt); Speech therapists 1 (pt); Activities coordinators 1 (ft), 1 (pt); Dietitians 1 (pt); Dentists 1 (pt); Ophthalmologists 1 (pt); Podiatrists 1 (pt); Audiologists 1 (pt).
Facilities Dining room; Physical therapy room; Activities room; Chapel; Laundry room; Barber/Beauty shop; Quiet room.
Activities Arts and Crafts; Cards; Games; Reading groups; Prayer groups; Movies.

PRETTY PRAIRIE

Prairie Sunset Home*
601 E Main, Pretty Prairie, KS, 67570 (316) 459-6822
Admin Della Ann Towse.
Licensure Intermediate Care. *Beds* 45. *Certified* Medicaid.
Ownership Proprietary.

PROTECTION

Protection Valley Manor
600 S Broadway, PO Box 448, Protection, KS, 67127 (316) 622-4261
Admin Walter Rex Maris.
Licensure Intermediate Care. *Beds* 50. *Certified* Medicaid.
Admissions Requirements Medical examination.
Staff LPNs 1 (ft), 1 (pt); Nurses aides 6 (ft), 4 (pt); Activities coordinators 1 (ft); Dietitians 1 (ft).
Facilities Dining room; Physical therapy room; Activities room; Chapel; Crafts room; Laundry room; Barber/Beauty shop; Library.
Activities Arts and Crafts; Games; Reading groups; Prayer groups; Movies; Shopping trips.

RICHMOND

Oakhaven Nursing Center
340 South St, Richmond, KS, 66080 (913) 835-6135
Admin Mary Sue Cox.
Licensure Intermediate Care. *Beds* 53. *Certified* Medicaid.
Admissions Requirements Minimum age 16; Medical examination; Physician's request.
Staff RNs 1 (ft); LPNs 1 (ft), 1 (pt); Nurses aides 1 (pt); Physical therapists 1 (pt); Reality therapists 1 (ft); Recreational therapists 1 (pt); Occupational therapists 1 (pt); Speech therapists 1 (pt); Activities coordinators 1 (ft); Dietitians 1 (pt); Audiologists 1 (pt).
Facilities Dining room; Physical therapy room; Activities room; Chapel; Crafts room; Laundry room; Barber/Beauty shop; Library; Greenhouse.
Activities Arts and Crafts; Cards; Games; Reading groups; Prayer groups; Movies; Shopping trips; Dances/Social or cultural gatherings.

ROSE HILL

Heritage Village of Rose Hill*
601 N Rose Hill Rd, Rose Hill, KS, 67133 (316) 776-2194
Admin Cheryl Galyardt.
Licensure Intermediate Care. *Beds* 60. *Certified* Medicaid.
Ownership Proprietary.

ROSSVILLE

Rossville Valley Manor*
Box 328, 600 Perry, Rossville, KS, 66533 (913) 584-6104
Admin Aaron D Kelley Jr.
Licensure Intermediate Care. *Beds* 65. *Certified* Medicaid.
Ownership Proprietary.

RUSSELL

Ala Fern Nursing Home
225 E Jewell, Russell, KS, 67665 (913) 483-2868
Admin Edward Mefford. *Medical Dir/Dir of Nursing* Jerald Starkey MD.
Licensure Intermediate Care for Mentally Retarded. *Beds* 46. *Certified* Medicaid.
Admissions Requirements Minimum age 21; Medical examination; Physician's request.
Staff Physicians 4 (pt); RNs 1 (pt); LPNs 3 (ft); Nurses aides 15 (ft), 15 (pt); Physical therapists 1 (ft); Reality therapists 1 (ft); Recreational therapists 1 (ft); Occupational therapists 1 (ft); Speech therapists 1 (ft); Activities coordinators 1 (ft); Dietitians 1 (ft); Dentists 1 (ft); Ophthalmologists 1 (ft); Podiatrists 1 (ft); Audiologists 1 (ft).
Facilities Dining room; Physical therapy room; Activities room; Chapel; Crafts room; Laundry room; Barber/Beauty shop; Library.
Activities Arts and Crafts; Cards; Games; Reading groups; Prayer groups; Movies; Shopping trips; Dances/Social or cultural gatherings.

Russell Kare Center*
320 S Lincoln, Russell, KS, 67665 (913) 483-5364
Admin Patrick Burke.
Licensure Intermediate Care. *Beds* 80. *Certified* Medicaid.
Ownership Proprietary.

SABETHA

Apostolic Christian Home
511 Paramount St, Sabetha, KS, 66534 (913) 294-3471
Admin John E Lehman. *Medical Dir/Dir of Nursing* Kevin Kennally MD.
Licensure Intermediate Care. *Beds* 80. *Certified* Medicaid.
Staff RNs 2 (ft), 6 (pt); LPNs 1 (ft), 3 (pt); Nurses aides 24 (ft), 27 (pt); Physical therapists 2 (ft); Recreational therapists 1 (ft).
Affiliation Apostolic Christian
Facilities Dining room; Physical therapy room; Activities room; Chapel; Crafts room; Laundry room; Barber/Beauty shop; Library.
Activities Arts and Crafts; Cards; Games; Reading groups; Prayer groups; Movies.
Description Constructed a $1,200,000 congregate retirement facility in 1983 with 22 living units and large ancillary area including greenhouse, living and dining areas, country store, and craft room. Eight-unit addition to be added in 1984.

Fountain Villa Care Center
913 Dakota, Sabetha, KS, 66534 (913) 284-2124
Admin Terri Watkins.
Licensure Intermediate Care. *Beds* 60. *Certified* Medicaid.
Admissions Requirements Medical examination.
Staff RNs 1 (ft); LPNs 1 (ft); Nurses aides 19 (ft), 9 (pt); Physical therapists 2 (pt); Reality therapists 1 (ft); Occupational therapists 1 (pt); Speech therapists 1 (pt); Activities coordinators 1 (ft); Dietitians 1 (ft), 1 (pt); Dentists 1 (pt).
Facilities Dining room; Physical therapy room; Activities room; Crafts room; Laundry room; Barber/Beauty shop; Library.
Activities Arts and Crafts; Cards; Games; Reading groups; Prayer groups; Movies; Shopping trips; Dances/Social or cultural gatherings.
Description Facility features weekly Bible study group, dinner out monthly, and lots of window area providing light and cheerfulness.

Sabetha Manor Inc
1441 Oregon, Sabetha, KS, 66534 (913) 284-3411
Admin Jim Nye.
Licensure Intermediate Care. *Beds* 60. *Certified* Medicaid.
Staff RNs 1 (ft), 2 (pt); Nurses aides 15 (ft), 5 (pt); Physical therapists 1 (ft), 1 (pt); Occupational therapists 1 (pt); Speech therapists 1 (pt); Activities coordinators 1 (ft), 1 (pt); Dietitians 1 (pt); Dentists 1 (pt); Ophthalmologists 1 (pt); Podiatrists 1 (pt); Audiologists 1 (pt).
Facilities Dining room; Physical therapy room; Activities room; Crafts room; Laundry room; Barber/Beauty shop.
Activities Arts and Crafts; Cards; Games; Reading groups; Shopping trips; Dances/Social or cultural gatherings.
Description Sabetha Manor is located on 3 beautiful acres; well known for top quality tender loving care. Our restorative department is known as one of the best in the area.

SAINT FRANCIS

Good Samaritan Village*
Box 747, S Side Hwy 36, Saint Francis, KS, 67756 (913) 332-2531
Admin Michael H Fleming.
Licensure Intermediate Care. *Beds* 57. *Certified* Medicaid.
Ownership Nonprofit.
Affiliation Lutheran

SAINT JOHN

Hearthstone Nursing Center
4th and Sante Fe, Saint John, KS, 67576 (316) 549-3541
Admin Phil D England.

Licensure Intermediate Care. *Beds* 68. *Certified* Medicaid.
Admissions Requirements Medical examination; Physician's request.
Staff RNs 1 (ft), 1 (pt); LPNs 2 (ft), 2 (pt); Nurses aides 18 (ft), 3 (pt); Activities coordinators 1 (ft).
Facilities Dining room; Physical therapy room; Activities room; Laundry room; Barber/Beauty shop.
Activities Arts and Crafts; Cards; Games; Reading groups; Prayer groups; Movies; Shopping trips; Dances/Social or cultural gatherings; Family interaction groups.
Description Facility features individual selectivity of AOL and Manus in a family atmosphere.

SAINT MARYS

Saint Marys Manor*
206 Grand Ave, Saint Marys, KS, 66536 (913) 437-2286
Admin Michael E McCrite.
Licensure Intermediate Care. *Beds* 50. *Certified* Medicaid.
Ownership Proprietary.

SAINT PAUL

Living Skills Center
PO Box 278, Saint Paul, KS, 66771 (316) 449-2277
Admin Roman K Freundorfer. *Medical Dir-/Dir of Nursing* Asha Verma MD.
Licensure Intermediate Care for Mentally Retarded. *Beds* 63. *Certified* Medicaid.
Admissions Requirements Minimum age 18; Medical examination; Physician's request.
Staff Physicians 1 (pt); RNs 1 (ft); LPNs 1 (ft); Nurses aides 25 (ft), 15 (pt); Physical therapists 1 (pt); Recreational therapists 1 (ft); Occupational therapists 1 (pt); Speech therapists 1 (pt); Activities coordinators 1 (ft); Dietitians 1 (pt); Dentists 1 (pt); Ophthalmologists 1 (pt); Podiatrists 1 (pt); Audiologists 1 (pt).
Facilities Dining room; Physical therapy room; Activities room; Crafts room; Laundry room; Barber/Beauty shop.
Activities Arts and Crafts; Cards; Games; Reading groups; Prayer groups; Movies; Shopping trips; Dances/Social or cultural gatherings; Special Olympics.
Description This is a training center for mentally retarded adults.

SALINA

Kenwood View Nursing Home*
Box 569, 900 Elmhurst Blvd, Salina, KS, 67401 (913) 825-5471
Admin George Erwin.
Licensure Skilled Care. *Beds* 94. *Certified* Medicaid.
Ownership Proprietary.

Salina Nursing Center
1007 Johnston, Salina, KS, 67401 (713) 823-7107

Admin Phyllis M Franklin.
Licensure Skilled Care; Intermediate Care.
Beds SNF 28; ICF 78. *Certified* Medicaid.

Salina Presbyterian Manor
2601 E Crawford, Salina, KS, 67401 (913) 825-1366
Admin Martha L Carter.
Licensure Intermediate Care. *Beds* 60.
Admissions Requirements Minimum age 65; Medical examination.
Staff RNs 3 (ft), 4 (pt); LPNs 1 (ft), 3 (pt) #13E 18 (ft), 11 (pt); Activities coordinators 1 (ft); Dietitians 1 (ft).
Affiliation Presbyterian
Facilities Dining room; Physical therapy room; Activities room; Chapel; Crafts room; Laundry room; Barber/Beauty shop; Library.
Activities Arts and Crafts; Cards; Games; Reading groups; Prayer groups; Movies; Shopping trips; Dances/Social or cultural gatherings.

Shalimar Plaza Nursing Home
2054 Lambertson Ln, Salina, KS, 674011 (913) 827-5589
Admin Dorothy L Caswell. *Medical Dir/Dir of Nursing* Dr Thomas Taylor.
Licensure Intermediate Care. *Beds* 46. *Certified* Medicaid.
Admissions Requirements Minimum age 21; Medical examination; Physician's request.
Staff RNs 1 (ft); LPNs 2 (ft), 1 (pt); Orderlies 1 (ft); Nurses aides 10 (ft), 6 (pt); Physical therapists 1 (pt); Reality therapists 1 (pt); Recreational therapists 1 (pt); Occupational therapists 1 (pt); Speech therapists 1 (pt); Activities coordinators 1 (pt); Dietitians 1 (pt); Dentists 1 (pt); Audiologists 1 (pt).
Facilities Dining room; Physical therapy room; Activities room; Crafts room; Laundry room; Barber/Beauty shop.
Activities Arts and Crafts; Cards; Games; Reading groups; Prayer groups; Movies; Shopping trips; Dances/Social or cultural gatherings; Exercise class.
Description Facility is above staffing requirements ensuring quality care. It is located in a residential neighborhood with friendly neighbors. Barrier free, residents can maneuver a 4-block area in wheelchairs with no difficulty.

Windsor Estates of Salina
623 S 3rd, Salina, KS, 67401 (913) 825-6757
Admin Ann McCall. *Medical Dir/Dir of Nursing* Dr Lou Forster.
Licensure Skilled Care. *Beds* 60. *Certified* Medicare.
Facilities Dining room; Physical therapy room; Activities room; Crafts room; Laundry room; Barber/Beauty shop.
Activities Arts and Crafts; Cards; Games; Reading groups; Prayer groups; Movies; Shopping trips; Dances/Social or cultural gatherings.

SCOTT CITY

Park Lane Nursing Home
13th and College, Scott City, KS, 67871 (316) 872-2148
Admin Greg Uhruh.
Licensure Intermediate Care. *Beds* 84. *Certified* Medicaid.

Admissions Requirements Medical examination; Physician's request.
Staff RNs 2 (ft), 1 (pt); LPNs 2 (ft), 1 (pt); Nurses aides 21 (ft), 9 (pt); Physical therapists 1 (pt); Activities coordinators 1 (ft); Dietitians 1 (pt).
Facilities Dining room; Physical therapy room; Activities room; Chapel; Crafts room; Laundry room; Barber/Beauty shop.
Activities Arts and Crafts; Cards; Games; Reading groups; Prayer groups; Movies; Shopping trips; Dances/Social or cultural gatherings.

SEDAN

Pleasant Valley Manor Inc
623 E Elm St, Box 40, Sedan, KS, 67361 (3216) 725-3154
Admin Carmaleta Lorenz.
Licensure Intermediate Care. *Beds* 72. *Certified* Medicaid.
Admissions Requirements Physician's request.
Staff RNs 1 (pt); LPNs 3 (ft); Orderlies 5 (ft); Nurses aides 18 (ft); Physical therapists 1 (pt); Reality therapists 1 (pt); Recreational therapists 1 (pt); Occupational therapists 1 (pt); Speech therapists 1 (pt); Activities coordinators 1 (ft); Dietitians 1 (pt); Dentists 1 (pt).
Facilities Dining room; Physical therapy room; Activities room; Chapel; Crafts room; Laundry room; Barber/Beauty shop.
Activities Arts and Crafts; Cards; Games; Reading groups; Prayer groups; Movies; Shopping trips; Dances/Social or cultural gatherings; Bowling.
Description Facility features a pleasant atmosphere and is very clean with good nursing all performed by people who care.

SEDGWICK

Sedgwick Convalescent Center Inc
712 Monroe, Box 49, Sedgwick, KS, 67135 (316) 772-5185
Admin Jerry W Johnson.
Licensure Intermediate Care. *Beds* 100. *Certified* Medicaid.
Admissions Requirements Medical examination; Physician's request.
Staff Physicians 1 (pt); RNs 1 (ft), 1 (pt); LPNs 3 (ft), 3 (pt); Nurses aides 28 (ft), 7 (pt); Physical therapists 1 (pt); Reality therapists 1 (pt); Occupational therapists 1 (pt); Speech therapists 1 (pt); Activities coordinators 1 (ft); Dietitians 1 (pt); Dentists 1 (pt); Podiatrists 1 (pt); Audiologists 1 (pt).
Facilities Dining room; Physical therapy room; Activities room; Crafts room; Laundry room; Barber/Beauty shop.
Activities Arts and Crafts; Games; Reading groups; Prayer groups; Movies.

SENECA

Country View Estates
512 Community Dr, Seneca, KS, 66538 (913) 336-3528
Admin Edna Jane Werner.
Licensure Intermediate Care. *Beds* 75. *Certified* Medicaid.
Admissions Requirements Minimum age 16;

Medical examination; Physician's request.
Staff RNs 1 (ft), 1 (pt); LPNs 5 (pt); Nurses aides 11 (ft), 20 (pt); Activities coordinators 2 (pt).
Facilities Dining room; Physical therapy room; Activities room; Laundry room; Barber/Beauty shop; Living room.
Activities Arts and Crafts; Cards; Games; Reading groups; Prayer groups.
Description Residents are accepted as individuals and are respected and cared for to the best of the staff's ability to make their stay as near home-like as possible. Individual birthdays are celebrated with the other residents and staff singing happy birthday while the celebrant is presented a cake. Holidays are celebrated with a party.

Crestview Manor*
808 N 8th, Seneca, KS, 66538 (913) 336-2156
Admin Paul H Bergman.
Licensure Intermediate Care. *Beds* 50. *Certified* Medicaid.
Ownership Proprietary.

SHARON SPRINGS

Prairie Manor
408 E 6th St, Box 129, Sharon Springs, KS, 67758 (913) 852-4244
Admin Roberta O'Leary.
Licensure Intermediate Care. *Beds* 28. *Certified* Medicaid.
Admissions Requirements Medical examination.
Staff RNs 1 (ft), 1 (pt); LPNs 1 (pt); Orderlies 1 (pt); Nurses aides 8 (ft), 8 (pt); Activities coordinators 1 (ft).

SHAWNEE

Sharonlane Inc*
10315 Johnson Dr, Shawnee, KS, 66203 (913) 631-8200
Admin Marjory L Dwight.
Licensure Intermediate Care. *Beds* 66.
Ownership Proprietary.

SHAWNEE MISSION

Faith Handicap Village*
14155 W 113th St, Shawnee Mission, KS, 66215 (913) 888-4446
Admin Gary Condra.
Licensure Intermediate Care for Mentally Retarded. *Beds* 15. *Certified* Medicaid.

Faith Handicap Village 2
14175 W 113, Shawnee Mission, KS, 66215
Admin Steven V Miller.
Licensure Intermediate Care for Mentally Retarded. *Beds* 45. *Certified* Medicaid.
Admissions Requirements Minimum age 18; Medical examination.
Staff Physicians 1 (pt); RNs 1 (ft), 1 (pt); Nurses aides 27 (ft), 6 (pt); Physical therapists 1 (pt); Recreational therapists 1 (ft); Occupational therapists 1 (pt); Speech therapists 1 (pt); Activities coordinators 1 (pt); Dietitians 1 (pt); Dentists 1 (pt); Ophthalmologists 1 (pt); Podiatrists 1 (pt); Audiologists 1 (pt); Social workers

1 (ft); QMRPs 1 (ft).
Facilities Dining room; Activities room; Crafts room; Laundry room; Living room.
Activities Arts and Crafts; Cards; Games; Movies; Shopping trips; Dances/Social or cultural gatherings; Special Olympics.
Description Mentally retarded adults are given the programs and encouragement to develop mentally, physically, socially, and spiritually to their fullest potential; each resident is given the opportunity to reach his/her individual goal of independent living in a dignified and meaningful way.

Faith Handicap Village 3
14235 W 113th, Shawnee Mission, KS, 66215
Admin Steven V Miller.
Licensure Intermediate Care for Mentally Retarded. *Beds* 45. *Certified* Medicaid.
Ownership Nonprofit.
Admissions Requirements Minimum age 18; Medical examination.
Staff Physicians 1 (pt); RNs 1 (ft), 1 (pt); Nurses aides 27 (ft), 6 (pt); Recreational therapists 1 (ft); Occupational therapists 1 (pt); Speech therapists 1 (pt); Activities coordinators 1 (pt); Dietitians 1 (pt); Dentists 1 (pt); Ophthalmologists 1 (pt); Podiatrists 1 (pt); Audiologists 1 (pt); Social workers 1 (ft); QMRPs.
Facilities Dining room; Activities room; Crafts room; Laundry room; Living room.
Activities Arts and Crafts; Cards; Games; Movies; Shopping trips; Dances/Social or cultural gatherings; Special Olympics.
Description Facility offers a horticultural therapy program for the mentally handicapped.

SMITH CENTER

Bethesda Care Center
117 W 1st, Smith Center, KS, 66967 (913) 382-6696
Admin James D Smith. *Medical Dir/Dir of Nursing* V W Steinkruger.
Licensure Intermediate Care. *Beds* 66. *Certified* Medicaid.
Ownership Nonprofit.
Admissions Requirements Minimum age 21.
Staff RNs 1 (ft); LPNs 2 (ft); Nurses aides 40 (ft); Physical therapists 1 (pt); Occupational therapists 1 (pt); Speech therapists 1 (pt); Activities coordinators 1 (ft); Dietitians 1 (pt); Dentists 1 (pt).
Facilities Dining room; Physical therapy room; Activities room; Chapel; Laundry room; Barber/Beauty shop; Library.
Activities Arts and Crafts; Cards; Games; Reading groups; Prayer groups; Movies; Shopping trips; Dances/Social or cultural gatherings.
Description Facility is rehabilitation oriented using a holistic approach to health care. That approach cares for the physical, psychological, social, and spiritual aspects of residents.

SMOLAN

White Cross Health Center*
Rt 1, Smolan, KS, 67479 (913) 668-2251
Admin Betty Ade.

Licensure Intermediate Care. *Beds* 53. *Certified* Medicaid.
Ownership Proprietary.

SOUTH HAVEN

Wheatland Lodge
PO Box 198, South Haven, KS, 67140 (316) 892-5513
Admin Walter O Egli. *Medical Dir/Dir of Nursing* Denise Showman.
Licensure Intermediate Care. *Beds* 50. *Certified* Medicaid.
Ownership Proprietary.
Admissions Requirements Physician's request.
Staff RNs 1 (ft); LPNs 2 (pt); Nurses aides 19 (ft), 7 (pt); Physical therapists 1 (ft); Occupational therapists 1 (ft); Activities coordinators 1 (ft).
Facilities Dining room; Physical therapy room; Activities room; Chapel; Crafts room; Laundry room; Barber/Beauty shop.

SOUTH HUTCHISON

Mennonite Friendship Manor Inc
600 W Blanchard, South Hutchison, KS, 67505 (316) 663-7175
Admin Lowell Guengerin.
Licensure Intermediate Care. *Beds* 120. *Certified* Medicaid.
Admissions Requirements Medical examination.
Affiliation Mennonite
Facilities Dining room; Physical therapy room; Activities room; Barber/Beauty shop; Library.
Activities Arts and Crafts; Games; Prayer groups.

SPRING HILL

Spring Hill Manor
251 Wilson Ave, Spring Hill, KS, 66083 (913) 686-3100
Admin Shirley Newson.
Licensure Intermediate Care. *Beds* 50. *Certified* Medicaid.
Admissions Requirements Medical examination; Physician's request.
Staff RNs; LPNs; Nurses aides; Physical therapists; Recreational therapists; Occupational therapists; Speech therapists; Activities coordinators; Dietitians; Dentists; Podiatrists; Audiologists.
Facilities Dining room; Physical therapy room; Activities room; Chapel; Crafts room; Laundry room; Barber/Beauty shop; Library.
Activities Arts and Crafts; Games; Prayer groups; Movies; Shopping trips.
Description Local middle school 5th grade visits several times a week and has adopted residents as foster grandparents. This is enjoyed by residents and children alike and has been ongoing for 2 school years.

STAFFORD

Leisure Homestead Association
405 E Grand, Stafford, KS, 67578 (316) 234-5208

Admin Jennifer Younie.
Licensure Intermediate Care. *Beds* 55. *Certified* Medicaid.
Ownership Nonprofit.
Admissions Requirements Physician's request.
Staff RNs 1 (ft); LPNs 2 (ft); Nurses aides 12 (ft), 3 (pt); Physical therapists 1 (pt); Occupational therapists 1 (pt); Speech therapists 1 (pt); Activities coordinators 1 (ft); Dietitians 1 (pt).
Facilities Dining room; Physical therapy room; Activities room; Crafts room; Laundry room; Barber/Beauty shop.
Activities Arts and Crafts; Cards; Games; Reading groups; Prayer groups; Movies; Shopping trips; Dances/Social or cultural gatherings.
Description Leisure Homestead is a nonprofit corporation. We have an excellent activities program with lots of support from the community. We have excellent food and people say we are very clean.

STERLING

Sterling Presbyterian Manor*
204 W Washington, Sterling, KS, 67579 (319) 278-3651
Admin Sadie P Goodwin.
Licensure Intermediate Care. *Beds* ICF 57.
Certified Medicaid.
Affiliation Presbyterian

STOCKTON

Solomon Valley Manor*
315 S Ash, Stockton, KS, 67669 (913) 425-6109
Admin Lloyd L Hollern.
Licensure Intermediate Care. *Beds* 50. *Certified* Medicaid.
Ownership Proprietary.

SYRACUSE

Hamilton County Rest Home
E Gate St, PO Box L, Syracuse, KS, 67878 (316) 384-7780
Admin Kathryn D Zimmett. *Medical Dir/Dir of Nursing* Dr C E Petterson.
Licensure Intermediate Care. *Beds* 21. *Certified* Medicaid.
Admissions Requirements Minimum age 21; Medical examination; Physician's request.
Staff Physicians 2 (pt); RNs 2 (pt); LPNs 2 (ft); Nurses aides 7 (ft), 8 (pt); Physical therapists 1 (pt); Activities coordinators 1 (ft), 1 (pt); Dietitians 1 (pt); Dentists 1 (pt); Ophthalmologists 1 (pt); Podiatrists 1 (pt).
Facilities Dining room; Physical therapy room; Activities room; Chapel; Crafts room; Laundry room; Barber/Beauty shop.
Activities Arts and Crafts; Cards; Games; Reading groups; Prayer groups; Movies; Shopping trips; Dances/Social or cultural gatherings.
Description Facility is oriented to giving the resident a feeling of continuing importance in the community and a feeling that this is his/her home, not an institution. Picnics and parties that include their families are held several times a year. Residents are involved with Boy and Girl Scouts, county fairs, parades, and local school activities.

TOPEKA

Aldersgate Village Health Unit
7220 Asbury Dr, Topeka, KS, 66614 (913) 478-9440
Admin James Emerson. *Medical Dir/Dir of Nursing* Michael Laccheo MD.
Licensure Intermediate Care. *Beds* 50.
Admissions Requirements Minimum age 16; Medical examination; Physician's request.
Staff Physicians 2 (pt); RNs 4 (ft), 4 (pt); LPNs 5 (ft), 1 (pt); Orderlies 2 (ft); Nurses aides 10 (ft), 8 (pt); Physical therapists 1 (pt); Occupational therapists 1 (pt); Speech therapists 1 (pt); Activities coordinators 1 (ft), 1 (pt); Dietitians 2 (ft); Dentists 1 (pt); Podiatrists 1 (pt); Audiologists 1 (pt).
Affiliation Methodist
Facilities Dining room; Physical therapy room; Activities room; Chapel; Crafts room; Laundry room; Barber/Beauty shop; Library; Outpatient clinic rooms; Dental office; Sundries shop; Wood shop; Spa.
Activities Arts and Crafts; Cards; Games; Reading groups; Prayer groups; Movies; Shopping trips; Dances/Social or cultural gatherings; Pet therapy; Music therapy; Men's breakfast; Ladies tea; Creative cooking; Exercise classes; Spelling bee; Quizical quizzes; Play reading; Gardening.
Description Through exercise classes, lectures, informational bulletin boards, nature/exercise trail, a sense of wellness and health promotion is fostered.

Brewster Place—The Congregational Home*
1205 W 29th, Topeka, KS, 66611 (913) 267-1666
Admin Ronald A Schmoller.
Licensure Skilled Care. *Beds* 77. *Certified* Medicaid; Medicare.

Briarcliff Care Center
3224 W 29th St, Topeka, KS, 66614 (913) 272-2601
Admin Mary Anne Warren. *Medical Dir/Dir of Nursing* Dr William Wade.
Licensure Intermediate Care. *Beds* 50. *Certified* Medicaid.
Admissions Requirements Medical examination; Physician's request.
Staff RNs 1 (pt); LPNs 4 (ft), 2 (pt); Nurses aides 15 (ft), 4 (pt); Physical therapists 1 (pt); Activities coordinators 1 (ft); Dietitians 1 (pt).
Facilities Dining room; Physical therapy room; Activities room; Crafts room; Laundry room; Barber/Beauty shop; TV room; Quiet room; Sitting room.
Activities Arts and Crafts; Cards; Games; Reading groups; Prayer groups; Movies; Shopping trips; Dances/Social or cultural gatherings; Community speakers.
Description Facility is a small care center with a home-like atmosphere. Excellent activities, physical therapy, and therapeutic diets; also offers respite care and day care services.

Countryside Health Center*
3501 Seward, Topeka, KS, 66616 (913) 234-6147
Admin Floyd Eaton.
Licensure Intermediate Care. *Beds* 60. *Certified* Medicaid.
Ownership Proprietary.

Eventide Convalescent Center Inc
2015 E 10th, Topeka, KS, 66607 (913) 233-8918
Admin M Mac Austin. *Medical Dir/Dir of Nursing* Dr Robert Jacoby.
Licensure Skilled Care. *Beds* 100. *Certified* Medicaid; Medicare.
Admissions Requirements Medical examination; Physician's request.
Staff Physicians 1 (pt); RNs 2 (ft); LPNs 7 (ft), 1 (pt); Orderlies 9 (ft); Nurses aides 25 (ft); Physical therapists 1 (pt); Occupational therapists 1 (pt); Speech therapists 1 (pt); Activities coordinators 2 (ft); Dietitians 1 (ft), 1 (pt); Dentists 1 (pt); Ophthalmologists 1 (pt); Podiatrists 1 (pt); Audiologists 1 (pt).
Facilities Dining room; Physical therapy room; Activities room; Chapel; Crafts room; Laundry room; Barber/Beauty shop; Library.
Activities Arts and Crafts; Cards; Games; Reading groups; Prayer groups; Shopping trips; Dances/Social or cultural gatherings.

Fairlawn Heights Nursing Home
5400 W 7th, Topeka, KS, 66606 (913) 272-65880
Admin Deardee G Klausman. *Medical Dir/Dir of Nursing* Joan Sehder MD.
Licensure Intermediate Care. *Beds* 70. *Certified* Medicaid.
Admissions Requirements Medical examination; Physician's request.
Staff RNs 1 (ft); LPNs 4 (ft); Orderlies 4 (ft); Nurses aides 19 (ft); Physical therapists 1 (pt); Occupational therapists 1 (pt); Speech therapists 1 (pt); Activities coordinators 1 (ft); Dietitians 1 (pt).
Facilities Dining room; Physical therapy room; Activities room; Crafts room; Laundry room; Barber/Beauty shop.
Activities Arts and Crafts; Cards; Games; Reading groups; Prayer groups; Movies; Shopping trips; Dances/Social or cultural gatherings; Reminiscence therapy.
Description Facility's beautiful hillside setting overlooks the Menninger Farms and the Kansas governors mansion. Emphasis is placed on maintaining and motivating residents. Activity therapy and social services are stressed; member of Kansas Health Care Association and the American Health Care Association.

Glendale Manor
1334 Buchanan, Topeka, KS, 66604 (913) 235-6258
Admin Brenda Bauman Swank. *Medical Dir/Dir of Nursing* Hazel Craig.
Licensure Intermediate Care. *Beds* 53. *Certified* Medicaid.
Staff RNs 1 (pt); LPNs 2 (ft); Orderlies 5 (ft), 1 (pt); Nurses aides 8 (ft), 4 (pt); Physical therapists 1 (pt); Activities coordinators; Dietitians.
Facilities Dining room; Physical therapy room; Activities room; Crafts room; Laundry room; Barber/Beauty shop; Library.
Activities Arts and Crafts; Cards; Games; Reading groups; Prayer groups; Movies; Shopping trips; Dances/Social or cultural gatherings.

Highland Villa
1821 E 21st St, Topeka, KS, 66607 (913)
233-9626
Admin Milly Ann Briggs.
Licensure Intermediate Care. *Beds* 100. *Certified* Medicaid.
Admissions Requirements Minimum age 21;
Medical examination; Physician's request.
Staff RNs 1 (ft); LPNs 7 (ft); Orderlies 3 (ft);
Nurses aides 37 (ft); Activities coordinators 1
(ft).
Facilities Dining room; Physical therapy room;
Activities room; Laundry room; Barber/Beauty
shop.
Activities Arts and Crafts; Cards; Games; Prayer groups; Movies; Shopping trips; Dances/Social or cultural gatherings.

Hillhaven of Topeka
711 Garfield, Topeka, KS, 66606
Medical Dir/Dir of Nursing Jorge Herrera.
Licensure Skilled Care; Intermediate Care.
Certified Medicare.
Admissions Requirements Minimum age 16;
Medical examination; Physician's request.
Staff RNs 8 (ft), 4 (pt); LPNs 10 (ft); Orderlies
5 (ft); Nurses aides 50 (ft); Physical therapists 1
(ft); Occupational therapists 1 (pt); Activities
coordinators 2 (ft); Dietitians 1 (pt).
Facilities Dining room; Physical therapy room;
Activities room; Crafts room; Laundry room;
Barber/Beauty shop.
Activities Arts and Crafts; Cards; Games; Prayer groups; Movies; Shopping trips; Dances/Social or cultural gatherings.
Description This facility focuses on
rehabilitation with professional nurses available
around the clock; respite care also available.

Howe Care Center
1301 N Jefferson, Topeka, KS, 66608 (913)
233-5127
Admin Robert Hickey. *Medical Dir/Dir of
Nursing* Glenn O Bair MD.
Licensure Intermediate Care. *Beds* 34. *Certified* Medicaid.
Admissions Requirements Medical examination; Physician's request.
Staff Physicians 2 (ft); RNs 1 (pt); LPNs 2 (ft);
Orderlies 1 (pt); Nurses aides 2 (ft), 2 (pt);
Activities coordinators 1 (ft); Dietitians 1 (pt).
Facilities Dining room; Physical therapy room;
Activities room; Laundry room; Barber/Beauty
shop; Library.
Activities Arts and Crafts; Cards; Games;
Reading groups; Prayer groups; Movies; Shopping trips; Dances/Social or cultural gatherings.
Description Center has an agreement at the
YWCA for swimming and exercises each week.
During the summer, residents swim at the city
pool.

Indian Trail Nursing Center*
1112 Republican, Topeka, KS, 66607 (913)
233-0588
Admin Alice Priestley.
Licensure Intermediate Care. *Beds* 82. *Certified* Medicaid.
Ownership Proprietary.

Manor of Topeka
4101 Martin Dr, Topeka, KS, 66619 (913)
267-3100

Admin Sharon L Durrell.
Licensure Intermediate Care. *Beds* 80. *Certified* Medicaid.
Staff LPNs 6 (ft); Nurses aides 24 (ft); Activities coordinators 1 (ft); Dietitians 1 (pt).
Facilities Dining room; Activities room;
Chapel; Crafts room; Laundry room; Barber/Beauty shop.
Activities Arts and Crafts; Cards; Games;
Reading groups; Prayer groups; Movies; Shopping trips; Dances/Social or cultural gatherings.
Description The Manor is an 80-bed facility
divided into 2 40-bed units. Each unit is complete with private and semi-private rooms,
central bathing rooms, living room, dining
room, laundry room, and nurse station. One
main kitchen serves both units as does the
activities-therapy room, beauty shop and
administration offices. The office of the director
of nursing is located in the south unit. The
Manor program is designed to meet the residents nursing, as well as social needs. A comprehensive activities and social program is
provided under the direction of qualified personnel. Dietary department provides 3
balanced meals each day, as well as evening
nourishments. Housekeeping, laundry, and
maintenance is also provided to ensure the residents clean, pleasant surroundings.

McCrite Care Center—Southwest*
1610 W 37th St, Topeka, KS, 66611 (913)
267-2960
Admin Jacqueline Hays.
Licensure Intermediate Care. *Beds* 80. *Certified* Medicaid.
Ownership Proprietary.

The Oaks
331 Oakley, Topeka, KS, 66606 (913) 232-1212
Admin Karen Jones. *Medical Dir/Dir of
Nursing* David Warrick MD.
Licensure Intermediate Care. *Beds* 50. *Certified* Medicaid.
Admissions Requirements Minimum age 50.
Staff LPNs 3 (ft); Orderlies 2 (ft) Nurses aides
11 (ft); Physical therapists 1 (pt); Activities
coordinators 2 (ft).
Facilities Dining room; Physical therapy room;
Activities room; Crafts room; Laundry room;
Barber/Beauty shop; Library.
Activities Arts and Crafts; Cards; Games;
Reading groups; Movies; Shopping trips; Dances/Social or cultural gatherings.
Description Facility features specialized care for
geriatric residents needing psychiatric care; contract with famed Menninger Foundation to provide necessary consultation and/or treatments.
Day care as well as long-term care provided in
an atmosphere of empathy and acceptance. Ongoing training to give staff tools necessary to
maintain the therapeutic milieu.

Pioneer Village 1*
431 Arter, Topeka, KS, 66607 (913) 233-1922
Admin Marlene Putnam and Dean Duermier.
Licensure Intermediate Care for Mentally
Retarded. *Beds* 15. *Certified* Medicaid.
Ownership Proprietary.

Pioneer Village 2
430 Winfield, Topeka, KS, 66607
Admin Marlene Putnam. *Medical Dir/Dir of*

Nursing Lori Huntoon.
Licensure Intermediate Care for Mentally
Retarded. *Beds* 60. *Certified* Medicaid.
Ownership Nonprofit.
Admissions Requirements Minimum age 16;
Medical examination.
Staff Physicians 1 (pt); RNs 1 (ft); LPNs 2 (ft);
Nurses aides 30 (ft); Physical therapists 1 (pt);
Recreational therapists 1 (pt); Occupational
therapists 1 (pt); Speech therapists 1 (pt);
Activities coordinators 1 (ft); Dietitians 1 (pt);
Dentists 1 (pt); Ophthalmologists 1 (pt); Podiatrists 1 (pt); Audiologists 1 (pt).
Description Facility strives for normalization
through programs in self-help skills and work
activity.

Pioneer Village 3*
441 Arter, Topeka, KS, 66607 (913) 233-1922
Admin Marlene Putnam and Dean Duemeier.
Licensure Intermediate Care for Mentally
Retarded. *Beds* 15. *Certified* Medicaid.

Pioneer Village 4
441 Winfield, Topeka, KS, 66607
Admin Marlene Putnam. *Medical Dir/Dir of
Nursing* William Wade DO.
Licensure Intermediate Care for Mentally
Retarded. *Beds* 15. *Certified* Medicaid; Medicare.
Ownership Nonprofit.
Admissions Requirements Minimum age 16.
Staff Physicians 1 (pt); RNs 1 (ft); LPNs 2 (ft);
Nurses aides 30 (ft); Physical therapists 1 (pt);
Recreational therapists 1 (ft); Occupational
therapists 1 (pt); Speech therapists 1 (pt);
Activities coordinators 1 (ft); Dietitians 1 (pt);
Dentists 1 (pt); Ophthalmologists 1 (pt); Podiatrists 1 (pt); Audiologists 1 (pt); Pharmacists 1
(pt); Psychologists 1 (pt).

Samaritan Home Inc
2075 Fillmore, Topeka, KS, 66604 (913)
234-0548
Admin Raymond E Briggs. *Medical Dir/Dir of
Nursing* Joan Sehdeu MD.
Licensure Intermediate Care. *Beds* 77. *Certified* Medicaid.
Admissions Requirements Minimum age 22;
Medical examination; Physician's request.
Staff RNs 1 (pt); LPNs 4 (ft); Orderlies 3 (ft);
Nurses aides 23 (ft); Physical therapists 1 (pt);
Occupational therapists 1 (pt); Activities coordinators 1 (ft); Dietitians 1 (pt).
Facilities Dining room; Physical therapy room;
Activities room; Chapel; Crafts room; Laundry
room; Library.
Activities Arts and Crafts; Cards; Games;
Reading groups; Prayer groups; Movies; Shopping trips; Dances/Social or cultural gatherings.
Description Facility specializes almost entirely
in geriatrics with chronic illness. Samaritan
Home has a relatively large number of private
rooms, and is equiped to assist handicapped
residents with transportation to and from many
doctor and hospital appointments.

Tanner Care Home Inc
504 E Paramore, Topeka, KS, 66608 (913)
357-0365
Admin Susan Y Parry.
Licensure Intermediate Care. *Beds* 53. *Certified* Medicaid.

Topeka Convalescent Center
515 Horne St, Topeka, KS, 66606 (913) 233-2321
Admin Jim Klausman. *Medical Dir/Dir of Nursing* William Nice MD.
Licensure Intermediate Care. *Beds* 100. *Certified* Medicaid.
Staff Physicians 1 (pt); RNs 3 (ft); LPNs 6 (ft); Nurses aides 22 (ft), 5 (pt); Physical therapists 1 (ft); Occupational therapists 1 (pt); Speech therapists 1 (pt); Activities coordinators 1 (ft); Dietitians 1 (pt); Dentists 1 (pt); Ophthalmologists 1 (pt); Podiatrists 1 (pt); Audiologists 1 (pt).
Facilities Dining room; Physical therapy room; Activities room; Crafts room; Laundry room; Barber/Beauty shop; Library.
Activities Arts and Crafts; Cards; Games; Reading groups; Prayer groups; Movies; Shopping trips; Dances/Social or cultural gatherings.
Description Topeka Convalescent Center is a 100-bed facility located adjacent to 2 general hospitals. Twenty-four hour licensed nursing coverage is provided for convalescent and long-term residents.

Topeka Presbyterian Manor Inc
4712 W 6th St, Topeka, KS, 66606 (913) 272-6510
Admin Ted A Nickell. *Medical Dir/Dir of Nursing* Julia A Self.
Licensure Skilled Care; Intermediate Care; Personal Care. *Beds* SNF 62; ICF 65; Personal Care 80. *Certified* Medicaid.
Admissions Requirements Minimum age 65; Medical examination.
Staff RNs 7 (ft), 6 (pt); LPNs 10 (ft), 4 (pt); Nurses aides 30 (ft), 17 (pt); Physical therapists; Activities coordinators 2 (ft); Dietitians 1 (ft).
Affiliation Presbyterian
Facilities Dining room; Physical therapy room; Activities room; Chapel; Crafts room; Laundry room; Barber/Beauty shop; Library.
Activities Arts and Crafts; Cards; Games; Reading groups; Prayer groups; Movies; Shopping trips; Dances/Social or cultural gatherings.

United Methodist Home
1135 College Ave, Topeka, KS, 66604 (913) 234-0421
Admin A Lowell Geelan. *Medical Dir/Dir of Nursing* Dr Michael Laccheo.
Licensure Intermediate Care; Personal Care. *Beds* ICF 100; Personal Care 10. *Certified* Medicaid.
Ownership Nonprofit.
Admissions Requirements Minimum age 65; Medical examination; Physician's request.
Staff Physicians 2 (pt); RNs 4 (ft), 2 (pt); LPNs 8 (ft), 4 (pt); Nurses aides 27 (ft); Physical therapists 1 (pt); Reality therapists 1 (pt); Recreational therapists 1 (ft); Occupational therapists 1 (pt); Speech therapists 1 (pt); Activities coordinators 1 (ft); Dietitians 1 (ft); Dentists 1 (pt); Ophthalmologists 1 (pt); Podiatrists 1 (pt); Audiologists 1 (pt).
Affiliation Methodist
Facilities Dining room; Physical therapy room; Activities room; Chapel; Crafts room; Laundry room; Barber/Beauty shop; Library.
Activities Arts and Crafts; Cards; Games; Reading groups; Prayer groups; Movies; Shopping trips; Dances/Social or cultural gatherings.
Description The United Methodist Home in

Topeka offers many services to residents which make retirement living more rewarding and enjoyable including 3 delicious, balanced meals daily; nursing care immediately available, 24 hours a day, 7 days a week; thorough room cleaning once every 2 weeks; complete laundry service available; Mulvance Chapel and The Upper Room Chapel with 4 worship services weekly; post office; banking service available; transportation services; in-house doctors and pharmacy; comfortable guest room for visitors; relaxed, comfortable library; public library bookmobile visits every other week; a sundry and gift shop; and whirlpool bathing unit.

Westwood Manor*
5015 W 28th St, Topeka, KS, 66614 (913) 273-0886
Admin Andrea Fusaro.
Licensure Intermediate Care. *Beds* 54. *Certified* Medicaid.
Ownership Proprietary.

Woodland Health Center
440 Woodland, Topeka, KS, 66607 (913) 233-0544
Admin Faye McAfee. *Medical Dir/Dir of Nursing* Kent Palmberg MD.
Licensure Skilled Care; Intermediate Care. *Beds* SNF 27; ICF 80. *Certified* Medicaid.
Admissions Requirements Minimum age 16; Medical examination; Physician's request.
Staff RNs 2 (ft), 1 (pt); LPNs 5 (ft), 1 (pt); Nurses aides 27 (ft); Recreational therapists 1 (ft); Activities coordinators 1 (ft).
Facilities Dining room; Physical therapy room; Activities room; Laundry room; Barber/Beauty shop; Living room.
Activities Arts and Crafts; Games; Reading groups; Movies; Shopping trips; Dances/Social or cultural gatherings.

TRIBUNE

Helmwood Care Home
317 E Harper, Box 190, Tribune, KS, 67879 (316) 376-4225
Admin Gilbert Booker. *Medical Dir/Dir of Nursing* W F Werner MD.
Licensure Intermediate Care. *Beds* 32. *Certified* Medicaid.
Admissions Requirements Minimum age 18; Medical examination.
Staff Physicians 1 (ft); RNs 2 (ft); LPNs 1 (ft); Nurses aides 10 (ft), 3 (pt); Reality therapists; Occupational therapists; Speech therapists; Activities coordinators 1 (pt); Dentists 1 (pt); Ophthalmologists; Podiatrists; Audiologists; Social workers 2 (ft), 1 (pt); Certified dietician assistant 1 (ft).
Facilities Dining room; Physical therapy room; Activities room; Chapel; Crafts room; Laundry room; Barber/Beauty shop.
Activities Arts and Crafts; Cards; Games; Reading groups; Prayer groups; Movies; Shopping trips; Dances/Social or cultural gatherings.
Description Facility offers hot meals for the senior citizens in the community; day care program.

ULYSSES

Western Prairie Care Home*
300 E Maize, Ulysses, KS, 67880 (316) 356-3331
Admin Paul A Florquist.
Licensure Intermediate Care. *Beds* 75. *Certified* Medicaid.
Ownership Public.

UNIONTOWN

Marmaton Valley Home*
Box 22, Hwy K-3 and 54, Uniontown, KS, 66779 (316) 756-4661
Licensure Intermediate Care. *Beds* 40. *Certified* Medicaid.

VALLEY CENTER

New Horizons of Valley Center
821 3rd St Terrace, Valley Center, KS, 67147 (316) 755-1288
Admin Helen E Janes.
Licensure Intermediate Care for Mentally Retarded. *Beds* 100. *Certified* Medicaid.
Admissions Requirements Minimum age 18.

VALLEY FALLS

Valley View Nursing Home Inc*
12th and Sycamore, Valley Falls, KS, 66088 (913) 945-3832
Admin Albert J Klausman.
Licensure Intermediate Care. *Beds* 80. *Certified* Medicaid.
Ownership Proprietary.

VICTORIA

Saint John Rest Home
701 7th St, Victoria, KS, 67671 (913) 735-2208
Admin Donald D Curl.
Licensure Intermediate Care. *Beds* 60. *Certified* Medicaid.
Admissions Requirements Medical examination; Physician's request.
Staff RNs 1 (ft); LPNs 2 (ft), 3 (pt); Orderlies 1 (pt); Nurses aides 4 (ft), 11 (pt); Physical therapists 1 (ft); Recreational therapists 1 (ft); Occupational therapists 1 (pt); Activities coordinators 1 (ft); Dietitians 1 (pt).
Affiliation Roman Catholic
Facilities Dining room; Physical therapy room; Activities room; Chapel; Laundry room; Barber/Beauty shop; Library.
Activities Arts and Crafts; Cards; Games; Reading groups; Prayer groups; Movies; Shopping trips; Dances/Social or cultural gatherings.

WAKEENY

Heartland Manor*
Box 427, 320 South Ave, Wakeeny, KS, 67672 (913) 743-2913
Admin Irma G Ell.
Licensure Intermediate Care. *Beds* 50. *Certified* Medicaid.
Ownership Proprietary.

WAKEFIELD

Heritage Village of Wakefield
6th and Grove, Wakefield, KS, 67487 (913)
461-5417
Admin Mary Jane Istas.
Licensure Intermediate Care. *Beds* 50. *Certified* Medicaid.
Admissions Requirements Medical examination; Physician's request.
Staff Physicians; RNs; LPNs; Nurses aides; Physical therapists; Occupational therapists; Speech therapists; Activities coordinators; Dietitians; Dentists; Ophthalmologists; Audiologists.
Facilities Dining room; Physical therapy room; Activities room; Chapel; Crafts room; Laundry room; Barber/Beauty shop; Library.
Activities Arts and Crafts; Games; Reading groups; Prayer groups; Shopping trips; Dances-/Social or cultural gatherings.
Description Wakefield is nestled on the west side of Milford Lake Reservoir. Heritage Village is built on a knoll overlooking the high school athletic field, residential area, and city park, with a beautiful view of the lake stretching to the hills beyond.

WAMEGO

Valley Vista Good Samaritan Center*
2011 Grandview Dr, Wamego, KS, 66547 (913)
456-9482
Admin Michael D Adkins.
Licensure Intermediate Care. *Beds* 50. *Certified* Medicaid.
Ownership Nonprofit.
Affiliation Lutheran

WASHINGTON

Centennial Homestead
311 E 2nd, Washington, KS, 66968 (913)
325-2361
Admin Pauline Wells.
Licensure Intermediate Care. *Beds* 50. *Certified* Medicaid.
Admissions Requirements Minimum age 16; Medical examination; Physician's request.
Staff RNs 1 (ft), 1 (pt); LPNs 1 (pt); Nurses aides 23 (ft), 4 (pt); Physical therapists 1 (pt); Speech therapists 1 (pt); Activities coordinators 1 (ft); Dietitians 1 (pt); Audiologists 1 (pt).
Facilities Dining room; Physical therapy room; Activities room; Laundry room; Barber/Beauty shop.
Activities Arts and Crafts; Cards; Games; Movies; Dances/Social or cultural gatherings.
Description Facility has outstanding physical therapy program; all aides are trained to be resorative aides. Activity program is special because of the discussion groups and the freedom of expression.

WATHENA

Colonial Manor of Wathena*
PO Box 559, Wathena, KS, 66090 (913)
989-3141
Admin Sheila Todaro.

Licensure Intermediate Care. *Beds* 60. *Certified* Medicaid.
Ownership Proprietary.

WAVERLY

Sunset Manor
128 S Pearson Ave, Box 246, Waverly, KS,
66871 (913) 733-2744
Admin Melinda J Arb.
Licensure Intermediate Care. *Beds* ICF 25; ICF/MR 25. *Certified* Medicaid.
Ownership Proprietary.
Admissions Requirements Medical examination.
Staff RNs 1 (ft), 1 (pt); LPNs 1 (pt); Orderlies 1 (pt); Nurses aides 12 (ft), 6 (pt).
Facilities Dining room; Physical therapy room; Activities room; Laundry room; Barber/Beauty shop.
Activities Arts and Crafts; Cards; Games; Reading groups; Prayer groups; Movies; Shopping trips; Dances/Social or cultural gatherings.

WELLINGTON

Cedar View Good Samaritan Center
Rt 4, 1600 W 8th, Wellington, KS, 67152 (316)
326-2232
Admin Helen K Dreyer.
Licensure Intermediate Care. *Beds* 97. *Certified* Medicaid.
Ownership Nonprofit.
Admissions Requirements Medical examination; Physician's request.
Affiliation Lutheran
Facilities Dining room; Physical therapy room; Activities room; Chapel; Crafts room; Laundry room; Barber/Beauty shop.
Activities Arts and Crafts; Cards; Games; Reading groups; Prayer groups; Movies; Shopping trips.

Lakeside Lodge*
102 W Botkin, Wellington, KS, 67152 (316)
326-7437
Admin David L Scott.
Licensure Intermediate Care. *Beds* 69. *Certified* Medicaid.
Ownership Proprietary.

WELLSVILLE

Wellsville Manor*
304 W 7th, Wellsville, KS, 66092 (913)
883-4101
Admin Joe A Collins.
Licensure Intermediate Care. *Beds* 60. *Certified* Medicaid.
Ownership Proprietary.

WESTMORELAND

Westy Community Care Home
Hwy 99 and Main St, Westmoreland, KS,
66549 (913) 457-3666
Admin Virginia Roggenkamp. *Medical Dir-/Dir of Nursing* Dr Thomas Dechairo.
Licensure Intermediate Care. *Beds* 52. *Certified* Medicaid.

Admissions Requirements Medical examination; Physician's request.
Staff RNs 1 (ft); LPNs 1 (ft), 3 (pt); Orderlies 1 (pt); Nurses aides 14 (ft), 8 (pt); Physical therapists 1 (pt); Occupational therapists 1 (pt); Speech therapists 1 (pt); Activities coordinators 1 (ft); Dietitians 1 (pt); Dentists 1 (pt); Ophthalmologists 1 (pt); Audiologists 1 (pt).
Facilities Dining room; Physical therapy room; Activities room; Crafts room; Laundry room; Barber/Beauty shop.
Activities Arts and Crafts; Cards; Games; Reading groups; Prayer groups; Movies; Shopping trips; Dances/Social or cultural gatherings.
Description Since there is not a meals-on-wheels program in the community, the nursing home provides meals to the homebound in the area. In order to delay institutional placement, the home works closely with county home health.

WHITEWATER

Wheat State Manor Inc
601 S Main, Whitewater, KS, 67154 (316)
799-2182
Admin Iva F Rutenbeck.
Licensure Intermediate Care. *Beds* 66. *Certified* Medicaid.
Admissions Requirements Medical examination; Physician's request.
Staff Physicians 1 (pt); RNs 3 (ft), 3 (pt); LPNs 1 (ft), 1 (pt); Physical therapists 1 (pt); Occupational therapists 1 (pt); Speech therapists 1 (pt); Activities coordinators 1 (ft); Dietitians 1 (pt); Dentists 1 (pt); Podiatrists 1 (pt); Audiologists 1 (pt).
Facilities Dining room; Physical therapy room; Activities room; Crafts room; Laundry room; Barber/Beauty shop.
Activities Arts and Crafts; Games; Movies; Dances/Social or cultural gatherings.
Description Facility is owned by 9 local churches of the following denominations: Methodist, Mennonite, Baptist, and Federated Christian.

WICHITA

Catholic Center for the Aging*
3411 E Zimmerly, Wichita, KS, 67218 (316)
681-2118
Admin J Timothy Allin.
Licensure Skilled Care; Intermediate Care.
Beds 100. *Certified* Medicaid.
Ownership Nonprofit.
Affiliation Roman Catholic

Cherry Creek Village
8100 E Pawnee, Wichita, KS, 67207 (316)
684-1313
Admin Richard McKinney. *Medical Dir/Dir of Nursing* Dr Robert Fowler.
Licensure Skilled Care. *Beds* 120. *Certified* Medicaid.
Admissions Requirements Medical examination; Physician's request.
Facilities Dining room; Physical therapy room; Activities room; Crafts room; Laundry room; Barber/Beauty shop; Ceramics area.
Activities Arts and Crafts; Cards; Games;

Reading groups; Prayer groups; Movies.
Description A combined health care and retirement apartment building that provides a continuum of care geriatric age residents. Special emphasis on convalescence and planned placement at apartment/independent care.

Christ Villa Nursing Center*
1555 N Meridian, Wichita, KS, 67203 (316) 942-8471
Admin Jimmie Linville.
Licensure Skilled Care. *Beds* 100. *Certified* Medicaid.
Ownership Nonprofit.
Affiliation Church of Christ

Heartland Rehabilitation Center
3410 E Funston St, Wichita, KS, 67218 (316) 685-1341
Admin Marcia Mullis.
Licensure Intermediate Care. *Beds* ICF/MR 81. *Certified* Medicaid.
Admissions Requirements Minimum age 18; Medical examination.
Staff RNs 1 (ft), 1 (pt); LPNs 7 (ft); Nurses aides 15 (ft), 4 (pt); Recreational therapists 1 (ft); Activities coordinators 2 (ft).
Facilities Dining room; Physical therapy room; Activities room; Crafts room; Laundry room; Barber/Beauty shop.
Activities Arts and Crafts; Cards; Games; Reading groups; Prayer groups; Shopping trips; Dances/Social or cultural gatherings.
Description Facility is carpeted; located in a quiet residential area; psychologists on retainer—visit facility almost daily at no cost to the residents; many activities daily.

Homestead Health Center Inc*
2133 S Elizabeth, Wichita, KS, 67213 (316) 262-4473
Admin Bill Lee Shook.
Licensure Intermediate Care. *Beds* 60. *Certified* Medicaid.
Ownership Proprietary.

Kansas Masonic Home*
401 S Seneca, Wichita, KS, 67213 (316) 267-0271
Admin Jerry B Lindenbaum.
Licensure Skilled Care. *Beds* 60. *Certified* Medicaid; Medicare.
Affiliation Masons

Keen Agers Home Inc
2840 S Hillside, Wichita, KS, 67216 (316) 684-7777
Admin Ray Huber and Audry Huber.
Licensure Intermediate Care. *Beds* 57. *Certified* Medicaid.
Admissions Requirements Minimum age 18.
Staff Physicians 3 (pt); RNs 1 (ft); LPNs 2 (ft); Orderlies 1 (ft); Nurses aides 14 (ft), 2 (pt); Physical therapists 1 (pt); Reality therapists 1 (pt); Occupational therapists 1 (pt); Activities coordinators 1 (ft); Dietitians 1 (pt).
Facilities Dining room; Physical therapy room; Activities room; Chapel; Laundry room; Barber/Beauty shop.
Activities Arts and Crafts; Cards; Games; Reading groups; Prayer groups; Movies; Shopping trips; Dances/Social or cultural gatherings.

Description This is the smallest facility in Wichita and the only one locally owned and operated.

Lakewood Village Nursing Center*
1319 Seville, Wichita, KS, 67209 (316) 722-6916
Admin Iva Jo Bradley.
Licensure Intermediate Care. *Beds* 72. *Certified* Medicaid.
Ownership Proprietary.

Lincoln East Nursing Home
4007 E Lincoln, Wichita, KS, 67218 (316) 683-7588
Admin Jane E Smith. *Medical Dir/Dir of Nursing* Daniel Thompson.
Licensure Intermediate Care. *Beds* 60. *Certified* Medicaid.
Admissions Requirements Medical examination; Physician's request.
Staff RNs 1 (ft); LPNs 1 (ft), 1 (pt); Orderlies 1 (ft); Nurses aides 19 (ft), 3 (pt); Activities coordinators 1 (ft).
Facilities Dining room; Physical therapy room; Activities room; Laundry room; Barber/Beauty shop; Library.
Activities Arts and Crafts; Cards; Games; Reading groups; Prayer groups; Quilting; Ceramics.

Meadows Hillside Home Inc
2800 N Hillside, Wichita, KS, 67219 (316) 682-1350
Admin Judith C Garrett. *Medical Dir/Dir of Nursing* Dr Wray.
Licensure Intermediate Care. *Beds* 100. *Certified* Medicaid.
Admissions Requirements Medical examination; Physician's request.
Staff RNs 1 (ft); LPNs 5 (ft), 2 (pt); Nurses aides 25 (ft), 3 (pt); Activities coordinators 1 (ft).
Facilities Dining room; Physical therapy room; Activities room; Chapel; Crafts room; Laundry room; Barber/Beauty shop.
Activities Arts and Crafts; Games; Prayer groups; Movies; Shopping trips; Dances/Social or cultural gatherings.

Medicalodge of Wichita*
2280 S Minneapolis, Wichita, KS, 67211 (216) 265-5693
Admin Nadene Oller.
Licensure Skilled Care; Intermediate Care. *Beds* 100. *Certified* Medicaid; Medicare.

Northeast Health Care Center
5005 E 21st St N, Wichita, KS, 67208 (316) 685-9291
Admin Ronald D Mathis. *Medical Dir/Dir of Nursing* Dr Robert Fowler.
Licensure Skilled Care. *Beds* 100. *Certified* Medicare.
Admissions Requirements Medical examination; Physician's request.
Staff RNs 6 (ft); LPNs 8 (ft); Nurses aides 30 (ft); Physical therapists 1 (pt); Occupational therapists 1 (pt); Speech therapists 1 (pt); Activities coordinators 1 (ft); Dietitians 1 (ft), 1 (pt); Dentists 1 (pt); Podiatrists 1 (pt); Audiologists 1 (pt).

Regency Health Care Center
1432 N Waco, Wichita, KS, 67203 (316) 262-8481
Admin Norman Durmaskin. *Medical Dir/Dir of Nursing* Dr A J Wray.
Licensure Skilled Care. *Beds* 119. *Certified* Medicaid.
Admissions Requirements Medical examination; Physician's request.
Facilities Dining room; Physical therapy room; Activities room; Chapel; Crafts room; Laundry room; Barber/Beauty shop; Library.
Activities Arts and Crafts; Games; Reading groups; Prayer groups; Movies; Dances/Social or cultural gatherings.
Description Quality skilled care is provided by well-trained nursing personnel. Special emphasis is placed on physical therapy rehabilitation. Nutritious, appetizing meals are considered a significant contribution to good health.

Terrace Gardens Nursing Center Inc
1315 N West St, Wichita, KS, 67203 (316) 943-1294
Admin Chester R West. *Medical Dir/Dir of Nursing* Dr Jon Kardatzke.
Licensure Intermediate Care; Personal Care. *Beds* ICF 110; Personal Care 106.
Admissions Requirements Medical examination; Physician's request.
Staff Physicians 1 (pt); RNs 2 (ft); LPNs 7 (ft); Nurses aides 50 (ft); Physical therapists 1 (pt); Recreational therapists 2 (ft), 1 (pt); Occupational therapists 1 (pt); Speech therapists 1 (pt); Activities coordinators 1 (ft); Dietitians 1 (pt); Podiatrists 1 (pt).
Facilities Dining room; Physical therapy room; Activities room; Chapel; Crafts room; Laundry room; Barber/Beauty shop; Library.
Activities Arts and Crafts; Cards; Games; Reading groups; Prayer groups; Movies; Shopping trips; Dances/Social or cultural gatherings.
Description Apartment living where we provide the noon meal weekly; maid and laundry service, and 24-hour available nursing services with 2 levels of care. Patients are located according to personality and disposition.

Wichita Care Center*
1319 W May, Wichita, KS, 67213 (316) 262-1155
Admin Sonny Ellis Sprick.
Licensure Skilled Care; Intermediate Care. *Beds* SNF 35; ICF 114. *Certified* Medicaid.
Ownership Proprietary.

Wichita Presbyterian Manor Inc
4700 W 13th, Wichita, KS, 67212 (316) 942-7456
Admin Adaline B Farrell.
Licensure Intermediate Care. *Beds* 60. *Certified* Medicaid.
Admissions Requirements Medical examination.
Staff Physicians 1 (pt); RNs 3 (ft); LPNs 4 (ft), 1 (pt); Nurses aides 14 (ft), 1 (pt); Physical therapists 1 (pt); Reality therapists 1 (ft); Recreational therapists 1 (ft); Occupational therapists 1 (pt); Speech therapists 1 (pt); Activities coordinators 1 (ft); Dietitians 1 (pt); Dentists 1 (pt); Ophthalmologists 1 (pt); Podiatrists 1 (pt); Audiologists 1 (pt).
Affiliation Presbyterian

Facilities Dining room; Physical therapy room; Activities room; Chapel; Crafts room; Laundry room; Barber/Beauty shop; Library.
Activities Arts and Crafts; Cards; Games; Reading groups; Prayer groups; Movies; Shopping trips; Dances/Social or cultural gatherings.
Description Apartments built in garden-style 6-plexes; family support group programs; life enrichment program by chaplain; large, excellent dining rooms with outstanding menus and special diets of many types.

Woodlawn Nursing Home Inc
1600 S Woodlawn, Wichita, KS, 67218 (316) 683-4628
Admin John T Wills.
Licensure Skilled Care; Intermediate Care. *Beds* SNF 58; ICF 67. *Certified* Medicaid; Medicare.

WILSON

Wilson Nursing Home*
5th St and Colorado, Wilson, KS, 67490 (913) 658-2505
Admin Barbara J Hladek.
Licensure Intermediate Care. *Beds* 50. *Certified* Medicaid.
Ownership Proprietary.

WINFIELD

Directions Unlimited*
2802 E Hwy 160, Winfield, KS, 67156 (316) 221-3335
Admin Anne V Robinson.
Licensure Intermediate Care for Mentally Retarded. *Beds* 81. *Certified* Medicaid.
Ownership Proprietary.

Good Samaritan Center*
1320 Wheat Rd, Winfield, KS, 67156 (316) 221-4660
Admin Robert T Bloom.
Licensure Intermediate Care. *Beds* 135. *Certified* Medicaid.
Ownership Nonprofit.
Affiliation Lutheran

Heritage House of Winfield
2720 E 12th St, Winfield, KS, 67156 (316) 221-9120
Admin Charley Barr. *Medical Dir/Dir of Nursing* Seavard Denkke MD.
Licensure Intermediate Care. *Beds* 50. *Certified* Medicaid.
Admissions Requirements Physician's request.
Staff RNs 2 (ft); LPNs 1 (ft); Orderlies 1 (ft); Nurses aides 28 (ft); Physical therapists 1 (ft); Reality therapists 1 (ft); Recreational therapists 1 (ft); Occupational therapists 1 (ft); Speech therapists 1 (pt); Activities coordinators 1 (ft); Dietitians 1 (pt); Dentists 1 (pt); Ophthalmologists 1 (pt); Podiatrists 1 (pt); Audiologists 1 (pt).

Winfield Rest Haven Inc
1611 Ritchie, Winfield, KS, 67156 (316) 221-9290
Admin Linda Voth. *Medical Dir/Dir of Nursing* Dr S S Daehnke.

Licensure Intermediate Care. *Beds* 48.
Admissions Requirements Medical examination; Physician's request.
Staff RNs 1 (ft), 1 (pt); LPNs 1 (ft), 1 (pt); Physical therapists 1 (pt); Occupational therapists 1 (pt); Speech therapists 1 (pt); Dietitians 1 (pt).
Affiliation Church of Christ
Facilities Dining room; Physical therapy room; Activities room; Crafts room; Laundry room; Barber/Beauty shop.
Activities Arts and Crafts; Cards; Games; Reading groups; Prayer groups; Movies; Shopping trips.

YATES CENTER

Autumn Manor Inc 1*
801 S Fry St, Yates Center, KS, 66783 (316) 625-2111
Admin Nellie W Chapman.
Licensure Intermediate Care. *Beds* 50. *Certified* Medicaid.
Ownership Proprietary.

Autumn Manor Inc 2*
801 S Fry St, Yates Center, KS, 66783 (316) 625-2111
Admin Dorothy V Kester.
Licensure Intermediate Care. *Beds* 50. *Certified* Medicaid.
Ownership Proprietary.

KENTUCKY

ALBANY

Albany Personal Care Home
404 Washington St, Albany, KY, 42602 (606)
387-5737
Admin Terill Wilson.
Licensure Personal Care. *Beds* 52.

ASHLAND

Artrips Personal Care Home
3000 Central Ave, Ashland, KY, 41101 (606)
325-3244
Admin Maggie Artrip.
Licensure Personal Care. *Beds* 16.
Admissions Requirements Minimum age 20;
Females only; Medical examination.
Staff RNs 1 (pt); Orderlies 2 (ft); Nurses aides
3 (ft); Activities coordinators 1 (ft), 1 (pt); Die-
titians 3 (ft).
Facilities Dining room; Activities room; Crafts
room; Laundry room.
Activities Cards; Games; Reading groups; Pray-
er groups.

Elmwood Village of Ashland
5400 Apple Blossom Ln, Ashland, KY, 41101
(606) 324-2161
Admin Charles Myron Bates. *Medical Dir/Dir
of Nursing* W R Duff MD.
Licensure Skilled Care; Intermediate Care; Personal Care. *Beds* SNF 56; ICF 95; Personal
Care 14. *Certified* Medicaid; Medicare.
Admissions Requirements Medical examination; Physician's request.
Staff Physicians 5 (pt); RNs 1 (ft), 2 (pt); LPNs
20 (ft), 4 (pt); Nurses aides 70 (ft), 10 (pt);
Reality therapists 1 (ft), 1 (pt); Recreational
therapists 3 (ft); Speech therapists 1 (pt); Activities coordinators 1 (ft); Dietitians 1 (pt); Dentists 1 (pt); Ophthalmologists 1 (pt); Podiatrists
1 (pt).
Facilities Dining room; Physical therapy room;
Activities room; Chapel; Crafts room; Laundry
room; Barber/Beauty shop; Library.
Activities Arts and Crafts; Cards; Games;
Reading groups; Prayer groups; Movies; Dan-
ces/Social or cultural gatherings.

Hamilton's Personal Care Home
250 W Central Ave, Ashland, KY, 41101 (606)
324-3252
Admin Ann Hamilton.
Licensure Personal Care. *Beds* 22.

Admissions Requirements Minimum age 18;
Medical examination.
Staff RNs 1 (pt); Orderlies 1 (ft); Nurses aides
2 (ft), 5 (pt); Activities coordinators 1 (pt).
Facilities Dining room; Activities room; Crafts
room; Laundry room.
Activities Cards; Games; Reading groups;
Shopping trips.

King's Daughters and Sons Home for the Aged
1100 Bath Ave, Ashland, KY, 41101 (606)
324-0343
Admin William F Ramsdell.
Licensure Personal Care. *Beds* 36.
Staff Nurses aides 3 (ft); Activities coordina-
tors 1 (pt); Dietitians 1 (pt).
Affiliation King's Daughters and Sons
Facilities Dining room; Activities room; Chap-
el; Laundry room; Barber/Beauty shop;
Library.
Activities Cards; Games; Prayer groups.

Riverview Homes
38 Russell Rd, Ashland, KY, 41101 (606)
836-3551
Admin Sheila Lemaster.
Licensure Personal Care. *Beds* 78.
Staff Physicians 2 (ft); Nurses aides 18 (ft);
Speech therapists 1 (pt); Activities coordinators
1 (ft); Dietitians 1 (pt); Podiatrists 1 (pt).
Facilities Dining room; Activities room; Crafts
room; Laundry room.
Activities Arts and Crafts; Games; Prayer
groups; Shopping trips; Dances/Social or cultural gatherings.

AUBURN

Auburn Nursing Center
121 Pearl St, Auburn, KY, 42206 (502)
542-4111
Admin Grover A Corum. *Medical Dir/Dir of
Nursing* Dr Dewey Wood.
Licensure Skilled Care; Intermediate Care.
Beds SNF 30; ICF 36. *Certified* Medicaid;
Medicare.
Admissions Requirements Medical examina-
tion; Physician's request.
Staff RNs 2 (ft), 1 (pt); LPNs 5 (ft), 1 (pt);
Nurses aides 20 (ft), 3 (pt); Activities coordina-
tors 1 (ft); Dietitians 1 (ft).
Facilities Dining room; Activities room; Laun-
dry room; Barber/Beauty shop; Library.
Activities Arts and Crafts; Cards; Games;

Movies; Shopping trips; Dances/Social or cultural gatherings.
Description Facility is made as near like home
as possible under the circumstances. Each
employee knows residents and family members
so total communication is possible.

AUGUSTA

Bracken Center
Rt 1, PO Box 418, Augusta, KY, 41002 (606)
756-3162
Admin Madeline Ruf. *Medical Dir/Dir of
Nursing* Milton Brindley MD.
Licensure Intermediate Care; Personal Care.
Beds ICF 32; Personal Care 50. *Cer-
tified* Medicaid.
Admissions Requirements Physician's request.
Staff RNs 1 (ft); LPNs 4 (ft); Nurses aides 24
(ft); Speech therapists 1 (pt); Activities coordi-
nators 1 (ft); Dietitians 1 (pt).
Facilities Dining room; Activities room; Laun-
dry room; Barber/Beauty shop.
Activities Arts and Crafts; Cards; Games;
Shopping trips.

BARBOURVILLE

Barbourville Nursing Home
117 Shelby St, Barbourville, KY, 40906 (606)
546-5136
Admin Judy Scott. *Medical Dir/Dir of
Nursing* Dr Harold Bushey.
Licensure Skilled Care; Intermediate Care; Per-
sonal Care. *Beds* SNF 21; ICF 67; Personal
Care 25. *Certified* Medicaid.
Admissions Requirements Medical examina-
tion; Physician's request.
Staff Physicians 7 (ft); RNs 5 (ft); LPNs 11 (ft);
Nurses aides 45 (ft); Physical therapists 1 (pt);
Speech therapists 1 (pt); Activities coordinators
2 (ft); Dietitians 12 (ft); Dentists 1 (ft).
Facilities Dining room; Physical therapy room;
Activities room; Laundry room; Barber/Beauty
shop.
Activities Arts and Crafts; Games; Reading
groups; Prayer groups; Shopping trips.

BARDSTOWN

Colonial House*
708 Bartley Ave, Bardstown, KY, 40004 (502) 348-9260
Admin Mary Clark.
Licensure Personal Care. *Beds* 96.
Ownership Proprietary.

Federal Hill Manor Nursing and Convalescent Center*
Box 349, Old Bloomfield Rd, Bardstown, KY, 40004 (502) 348-4220
Admin James B Walsh.
Licensure Skilled Care; Intermediate Care; Personal Care. *Beds* SNF 15; ICF 79; Personal Care 6. *Certified* Medicaid; Medicare.
Ownership Proprietary.

BEATTYVILLE

Lee County Personal Care Home Inc
Lumber St, PO Box 245, Beattyville, KY, 41311 (606) 464-3611
Admin Fred Austin. *Medical Dir/Dir of Nursing* Dr J M Smith and Dr A L Taulbee.
Licensure Intermediate Care; Personal Care.
Beds ICF 87; Personal Care 18. *Certified* Medicaid.
Ownership Public.
Staff RNs 2 (ft), 1 (pt); LPNs 2 (ft); Nurses aides 25 (ft), 2 (pt); Activities coordinators 2 (ft); Dietitians 1 (pt).
Facilities Dining room; Activities room; Crafts room; Laundry room; Barber/Beauty shop.
Activities Arts and Crafts; Games; Reading groups; Movies; Shopping trips; Dances/Social or cultural gatherings.

BEAVER DAM

Parkway Nursing Center
Rt 4, Beaver Dam, KY, 42320 (502) 274-3502
Admin Barbara Dillehay.
Licensure Intermediate Care; Personal Care.
Beds 108.
Admissions Requirements Medical examination; Physician's request.
Staff LPNs 4 (ft); Nurses aides 38 (ft).
Facilities Dining room; Activities room; Chapel; Crafts room; Laundry room; Barber/Beauty shop; Library.
Activities Arts and Crafts; Games; Reading groups; Prayer groups; Movies; Shopping trips; Dances/Social or cultural gatherings.
Description The first long-term care facility in Ohio County to receive the "Superior" rating; has an excellent staff who emphasize quality patient care and pride in seeing residents reach their highest living potential.

BEDFORD

Trimble Nursing Center*
Box 27, Hwy 42, Bedford, KY, 40006 (502) 255-3244
Admin Ann Breitenbach.
Licensure Intermediate Care; Personal Care.
Beds ICF 42; Personal Care 18. *Certified* Medicaid.
Ownership Proprietary.

BENTON

Lake Haven Health Care Center
US 641, PO Box 203, Benton, KY, 42025-0203 (502) 527-3296
Admin William R Watson II. *Medical Dir/Dir of Nursing* C R Freeman MD.
Licensure Intermediate Care; Personal Care.
Beds ICF 76; Personal Care 24. *Certified* Medicaid.
Admissions Requirements Medical examination; Physician's request.
Staff LPNs 2 (ft); Orderlies 28 (ft); Physical therapists 1 (pt); Reality therapists 1 (pt); Speech therapists 1 (pt); Activities coordinators 1 (pt); Dietitians 1 (pt); Dentists 1 (pt); Podiatrists 1 (pt); Audiologists 1 (pt).
Facilities Dining room; Activities room; Laundry room; Barber/Beauty shop.
Activities Arts and Crafts; Cards; Games; Reading groups; Shopping trips.
Description Facility specializes in geriatric care; located in a desirable retirement area; far enough away from a large metropolitan area to give the care found in rural areas, but close enough to major medical centers to ensure high quality care.

Marshall County Hospital—Skilled Nursing Facility
E 9th St, Benton, KY, 42025 (502) 527-1336
Admin Jeff Buckley. *Medical Dir/Dir of Nursing* David Compton MD.
Licensure Skilled Care. *Beds* 34. *Certified* Medicaid; Medicare.
Ownership Public.
Staff Physicians 1 (pt); RNs 2 (ft); LPNs 6 (ft); Orderlies 1 (ft); Nurses aides 9 (ft), 1 (pt); Physical therapists 1 (ft); Speech therapists 1 (pt); Activities coordinators 1 (ft); Dietitians 1 (pt); Dentists 1 (pt); Podiatrists 1 (pt).
Facilities Dining room; Physical therapy room; Activities room; Chapel; Crafts room; Barber-/Beauty shop; Library.
Activities Arts and Crafts; Cards; Games; Reading groups; Movies; Dances/Social or cultural gatherings.

BEREA

Berea Health Care Center
Rt 1, Berea, KY, 40403 (606) 986-4710
Admin Audrey Runda. *Medical Dir/Dir of Nursing* Clifford Kerby MD.
Licensure Intermediate Care. *Beds* 40. *Certified* Medicaid.
Admissions Requirements Medical examination; Physician's request.
Staff Physicians 6 (pt); RNs 1 (ft); LPNs 1 (ft), 2 (pt); Orderlies 3 (ft), 1 (pt); Nurses aides 16 (ft), 3 (pt); Recreational therapists 2 (pt); Activities coordinators 2 (pt); Dietitians 1 (pt).
Facilities Dining room; Activities room.
Activities Arts and Crafts; Cards; Games; Prayer groups; Movies; Dances/Social or cultural gatherings.
Description Small facility with home-like atmosphere; personal relationships among residents, family, and staff encouraged. Residents' pets (dog and bird) are enjoyed by all.

Berea Hospital—Skilled Nursing Facility*
PO Box 128, Estill St, Berea, KY, 40403 (606) 986-3151
Admin David E Burgio.
Licensure Skilled Care. *Beds* 37. *Certified* Medicaid; Medicare.
Ownership Nonprofit.

BOONEVILLE

Owsley County Health Care Center
Hwy 11, PO Box 539, Booneville, KY, 41314 (606) 593-6302
Admin Judy Terry. *Medical Dir/Dir of Nursing* Dr Larry Mason.
Licensure Intermediate Care; Personal Care.
Beds ICF 91; Personal Care 10. *Certified* Medicaid.
Staff Physicians 4 (pt); RNs 1 (ft), 1 (pt); LPNs 3 (ft); Orderlies 3 (ft), 2 (pt); Nurses aides 21 (ft), 5 (pt); Activities coordinators 1 (ft); Dietitians 1 (pt).
Facilities Dining room; Activities room; Crafts room; Laundry room; Barber/Beauty shop.
Activities Arts and Crafts; Cards; Games; Reading groups; Prayer groups; Movies; Shopping trips; Dances/Social or cultural gatherings.
Description This is a beautifully constructed 101-bed facility with a countryside location.

BOWLING GREEN

Bowling Green Health Care Center*
4079 Scottsville Rd, Bowling Green, KY, 42101 (502) 782-1125
Admin Mary Outlaw.
Licensure Skilled Care; Intermediate Care; Personal Care. *Beds* SNF 30; ICF 88; Personal Care 58. *Certified* Medicaid; Medicare.
Ownership Proprietary.

Colonial Manor Nursing Home
2365 Nashville Rd, Bowling Green, KY, 42101 (502) 842-1641
Admin Mary P Williams. *Medical Dir/Dir of Nursing* Harold West MD.
Licensure Skilled Care; Intermediate Care.
Beds SNF 38; ICF 10. *Certified* Medicaid; Medicare.
Staff RNs 3 (ft), 3 (pt); LPNs 2 (ft), 3 (pt); Orderlies 1 (ft); Nurses aides 21 (ft), 3 (pt); Physical therapists 1 (pt); Speech therapists 1 (pt); Activities coordinators 1 (pt); Dietitians 1 (pt).
Facilities Dining room; Activities room.
Activities Arts and Crafts; Cards; Games; Movies.
Description Small facility maintains a caring, home-like atmosphere.

Fairview Health Center*
550 High St, Bowling Green, KY, 42101 (502) 843-3296
Admin Jerry Rogers.
Licensure Skilled Care; Intermediate Care.
Beds SNF 29; ICF 157. *Certified* Medicaid; Medicare.
Ownership Proprietary.

Fern Terrace Lodge of Bowling Green
1030 Shive Ln, Bowling Green, KY, 42101
(502) 781-6784
Admin Dorothy Stinnett. *Medical Dir/Dir of
Nursing* Evelyn Towe.
Licensure Personal Care. *Beds* 68.
Admissions Requirements Minimum age 18;
Medical examination; Physician's request.
Staff Nurses aides 9 (ft), 2 (pt); Activities coor-
dinators 1 (ft).
Facilities Dining room; Activities room; Laun-
dry room; Barber/Beauty shop.
Activities Cards; Games; Reading groups;
Prayer groups; Shopping trips; Dances/Social
or cultural gatherings.

Medco Center of Bowling Green
1561 Newton Ave, Bowling Green, KY, 42101
(502) 842-1611
Admin Rose F Moss.
Licensure Intermediate Care. *Beds* 66. *Certi-
fied* Medicaid.
Ownership Proprietary.
Admissions Requirements Medical examina-
tion.
Staff Physicians 23 (ft); RNs 1 (ft), 1 (pt);
LPNs 5 (ft), 3 (pt); Nurses aides 26 (ft); Speech
therapists 1 (ft); Activities coordinators 1 (ft);
Dietitians 1 (ft); Dentists 1 (ft); Podiatrists 1
(ft); Audiologists 1 (ft).
Facilities Dining room; Laundry room; Barber-
/Beauty shop.
Activities Arts and Crafts; Cards; Games;
Reading groups; Movies; Shopping trips; Dan-
ces/Social or cultural gatherings.

Panorama*
PO Box 1113, US 231 W, Morgantown Rd,
Bowling Green, KY, 42101 (502) 782-7770
Admin Jane Artis.
Licensure Intermediate Care for Mentally
Retarded. *Beds* 58.
Ownership Proprietary.

BRANDENBURG

Medco Center of Brandenburg*
814 Old Ekron Rd, Brandenburg, KY, 40108
(502) 422-2148
Admin Sandy Bashem.
Licensure Intermediate Care; Personal Care.
Beds ICF 51; Personal Care 13. *Cer-
tified* Medicaid.
Ownership Proprietary.

BRODHEAD

Sowder Nursing Home
Rt 1, Box 91-A, Brodhead, KY, 40409 (606)
758-8711
Admin Linda L Whitt.
Licensure Intermediate Care; Personal Care.
Beds ICF 81; Personal Care 10. *Cer-
tified* Medicaid.
Admissions Requirements Minimum age 16.
Staff RNs 1 (pt); LPNs 5 (ft), 1 (pt); Orderlies 3
(ft), 3 (pt); Nurses aides 38 (ft), 3 (pt); Activities
coordinators 1 (ft); Dietitians 1 (pt); Social
workers 1 (ft).
Facilities Dining room; Activities room; Bar-
ber/Beauty shop.

Activities Arts and Crafts; Games; Reading
groups; Prayer groups; Dances/Social or cultural gatherings.

BROWNSVILLE

Joywells*
PO Box 372, Brownsville, KY, 42210 (502)
597-2159
Admin Marie Pasley.
Licensure Personal Care. *Beds* 37.
Ownership Nonprofit.

BURKESVILLE

Cumberland Valley Manor
S Main St, PO Box 433, Burkesville, KY,
42717 (502) 864-4315
Admin Tim Hicks. *Medical Dir/Dir of
Nursing* Dr Robert Flowers.
Licensure Intermediate Care; Personal Care.
Beds ICF 52; Personal Care 8.
Admissions Requirements Medical examina-
tion; Physician's request.
Staff Physicians 4 (ft); RNs 1 (ft); LPNs 5 (ft),
4 (pt); Orderlies 7 (ft), 5 (pt); Nurses aides 13
(ft), 8 (pt); Activities coordinators 1 (ft), 1 (pt);
Dietitians 1 (pt).
Facilities Dining room; Activities room; Chap-
el; Crafts room; Laundry room; Barber/Beauty
shop.
Activities Arts and Crafts; Cards; Games;
Reading groups; Prayer groups; Movies; Shop-
ping trips; Dances/Social or cultural gatherings.
Description We have a country store. For the
past 3 years we have hosted the Cumberland
River Arts and Crafts Festival. In 1983 we were
judged "Facility of the Year" by the KAHCF.

BUTLER

Butler Rest Home*
PO Box 131, Front and Main Sts, Butler, KY,
41006 (606) 472-6011
Admin Anne Combs.
Licensure Personal Care. *Beds* 19.
Ownership Proprietary.

Grants Lake Rest Home*
PO Box 231, Taylor St, Butler, KY, 41006 (606)
472-2217
Admin Anne Combs.
Licensure Intermediate Care. *Beds* 32.
Ownership Proprietary.

CADIZ

Shady Lawn Nursing Home
Rt 1, Box 22, Cadiz, KY, 42211 (502) 522-3236
Admin Ray Lafser. *Medical Dir/Dir of
Nursing* Dr William Anderson.
Licensure Skilled Care; Intermediate Care.
Beds SNF 15; ICF 35. *Certified* Medicaid;
Medicare.
Admissions Requirements Medical examina-
tion; Physician's request.
Staff RNs 2 (ft), 2 (pt); LPNs 4 (ft), 2 (pt);
Nurses aides 12 (ft), 9 (pt); Activities coordina-
tors 1 (pt); Dietitians 1 (ft).
Facilities Dining room; Activities room; Chap-

el; Crafts room; Laundry room; Barber/Beauty
shop; Lobby; Movie room; TV room.
Activities Arts and Crafts; Games; Prayer
groups; Movies; Dances/Social or cultural gatherings; Social get-togethers; Birthday parties;
Holiday parties.
Description Facility has 3-4 acres covered beautifully with trees. Has achieved 13 superior
goals of state, though only 6 are required for
"Superior" rating. Staff is caring, sharing, and
kind; touch residents with love.

Trigg County Manor Personal Care Home
Shelby St, Rt 6, Box 298, Cadiz, KY, 42211
(502) 522-3711
Admin Dorothy Tooke.
Licensure Personal Care. *Beds* 68.
Admissions Requirements Minimum age 15;
Medical examination; Physician's request.
Staff LPNs 1 (ft); Nurses aides 23 (ft); Activi-
ties coordinators 1 (ft).
Facilities Dining room; Activities room; Laun-
dry room; Barber/Beauty shop; Library.
Activities Arts and Crafts; Cards; Games;
Reading groups; Prayer groups; Movies; Shop-
ping trips; Dances/Social or cultural gatherings.
Description Facility has a beautiful setting with
lots of space for outside activities. Blessed with
many Christian and social groups who come to
entertain patients.

CALHOUN

Golden Years*
PO Box 35, Hwy 136, Calhoun, KY, 42327
(502) 273-5289
Admin Larry Hamer.
Licensure Intermediate Care; Personal Care.
Beds ICF 51; Personal Care 33. *Cer-
tified* Medicaid.
Ownership Proprietary.

**McLean County General Hospital—Skilled
Nursing Unit***
Hwy 81 N, Calhoun, KY, 42347 (502)
273-5252
Admin Ron Ferguson.
Licensure Skilled Care. *Beds* 8. *Cer-
tified* Medicaid; Medicare.
Ownership Nonprofit.

Sunny Acres*
Rt 1, Calhoun, KY, 42327 (502) 273-3113
Admin Janette M Ferguson.
Licensure Personal Care. *Beds* 20.
Ownership Proprietary.

CALVERT CITY

Calvert City Convalescent Center*
PO Box 7, 5th Ave, Calvert City, KY, 42029
(502) 395-4124
Admin Omer Hille.
Licensure Intermediate Care; Personal Care.
Beds ICF 95; Personal Care 5. *Certified* Medi-
caid.
Ownership Nonprofit.

Cedar Crest Senior Citizens Home*
Rt 1, Box 125, Calvert City, KY, 42029 (502)
898-6288

Admin Alan D Sims.
Licensure Intermediate Care; Personal Care.
Beds ICF 83; Personal Care 35. *Certified* Medicaid.
Ownership Proprietary.

CAMPBELLSVILLE

Medco Center of Campbellsville*
Rt 4, Campbellsville, KY, 42718 (502) 465-3506
Admin Marlene Morgan.
Licensure Intermediate Care. *Beds* 67. *Certified* Medicaid.
Ownership Proprietary.

Metzmeier Nursing Home
700 N Central Ave, Campbellsville, KY, 42718 (502) 465-4321
Admin Don Metzmeier. *Medical Dir/Dir of Nursing* Roy E Wilson MD.
Licensure Skilled Care; Intermediate Care.
Beds SNF 55; ICF 16. *Certified* Medicaid; Medicare.
Staff Physicians 14 (pt); RNs 2 (ft), 1 (pt); LPNs 7 (ft), 1 (pt); Orderlies 3 (ft); Nurses aides 24 (ft), 12 (pt); Speech therapists 1 (pt); Activities coordinators 1 (ft); Dietitians; Dentists 5 (pt); Ophthalmologists.
Facilities Dining room; Physical therapy room; Activities room; Laundry room; Barber/Beauty shop.
Activities Arts and Crafts; Cards; Games; Reading groups; Prayer groups; Movies; Shopping trips; Dances/Social or cultural gatherings.

CARLISLE

Johnson-Mathers Nursing Home
Paris Rd, Box 232, Carlisle, KY, 40311 (606) 289-7181
Admin Robert W Hester Jr. *Medical Dir/Dir of Nursing* Allen Hamon MD.
Licensure Skilled Care; Intermediate Care; Personal Care. *Beds* SNF 17; ICF; Personal Care 4. *Certified* Medicaid; Medicare.
Admissions Requirements Medical examination; Physician's request.
Staff RNs 3 (ft), 2 (pt); LPNs 2 (ft), 3 (pt); Orderlies 4 (ft), 2 (pt); Nurses aides 16 (ft), 8 (pt); Physical therapists 1 (pt); Speech therapists 1 (pt); Activities coordinators 1 (pt); Dietitians 1 (pt).
Facilities Dining room; Physical therapy room; Activities room; Chapel; Crafts room; Barber/Beauty shop.
Activities Arts and Crafts; Cards; Games; Reading groups; Prayer groups; Dances/Social or cultural gatherings; Residents council.
Description One-level facility offers excellent personalized care; very active activities program with much family involvement; unit-dose pharmacy adjoining an acute care facility; has earned Kentucky Department of Human Resources rating of Superior.

CARROLLTON

Carrollton Nursing Home*
205 5th St, Carrollton, KY, 41008 (502) 732-5528

Admin Vernice Tuttle.
Licensure Personal Care. *Beds* 32.
Ownership Proprietary.

Green Valley Health Care Center
Rt 1, PO Box 342, Carrollton, KY, 41008 (502) 732-6683
Admin Sandra Martin. *Medical Dir/Dir of Nursing* Valecia Penick RN.
Licensure Intermediate Care; Personal Care.
Beds ICF 55; Personal Care 8.
Staff RNs 1 (ft); LPNs 1 (ft); Orderlies 20 (ft); Physical therapists 1 (ft); Speech therapists 1 (ft); Activities coordinators 1 (ft); Dietitians 1 (pt); Dentists 1 (pt); Ophthalmologists 1 (pt); Audiologists 1 (pt).
Facilities Dining room; Activities room; Laundry room; Library.
Activities Arts and Crafts; Cards; Games; Reading groups; Prayer groups; Dances/Social or cultural gatherings.

CENTRAL CITY

Sparks Rest Home*
PO Box 387, 5th and Noffsinger Sts, Central City, KY, 42330 (502) 754-4838
Admin Lorene Sparks.
Licensure Personal Care. *Beds* 88.
Ownership Proprietary.

CLINTON

Clinton-Hickman County Hospital—Intermediate Care Facility*
359 Washington St, Clinton, KY, 42031 (502) 653-2461
Admin William B Little.
Licensure Intermediate Care. *Beds* 46. *Certified* Medicaid.
Ownership Nonprofit.

West Kentucky Manor
106 Padgett Dr, Clinton, KY, 42031 (502) 653-2011
Admin Sharon Boaz.
Licensure Intermediate Care; Personal Care.
Beds ICF 86; Personal Care 10. *Certified* Medicaid.
Staff RNs 1 (ft), 2 (pt); LPNs 1 (pt); Orderlies 2 (ft); Nurses aides 35 (ft), 2 (pt); Physical therapists 1 (pt); Recreational therapists 1 (ft); Speech therapists 1 (pt); Dietitians 1 (ft).
Facilities Dining room; Physical therapy room; Activities room; Crafts room; Laundry room; Barber/Beauty shop.
Activities Arts and Crafts; Cards; Games; Reading groups; Prayer groups; Movies; Shopping trips; Dances/Social or cultural gatherings; Pet therapy.

CLOVERPORT

Tindles Personal Care Home*
Hwy 105, Cloverport, KY, 40111 (502) 788-3723
Admin Sue Tindle and Ray Tindle.
Licensure Personal Care. *Beds* 40.
Ownership Proprietary.

COLUMBIA

Goodin's Rest Home
Rt 3, Columbia, KY, 42728 (502) 384-2630
Admin Bertha Goodin.
Licensure Personal Care. *Beds* 5.

Summit Manor*
400 Bomar Heights, Columbia, KY, 42728 (502) 384-2153
Admin George H Webb.
Licensure Skilled Care; Intermediate Care.
Beds SNF 50; ICF 54. *Certified* Medicaid; Medicare.
Ownership Proprietary.

CORBIN

Christian Health Center*
PO Box 1304, Master St and Commonwealth Ave, Corbin, KY, 40701 (606) 528-2886
Admin Betty S Corey.
Licensure Intermediate Care; Personal Care.
Beds ICF 92; Personal Care 23.
Ownership Nonprofit.

Hillcrest Nursing Home
Rt 7, Box 365, Corbin, KY, 40701 (606) 528-8917
Admin Carolyn Smith. *Medical Dir/Dir of Nursing* Elmer G Prewitt MD.
Licensure Skilled Care; Intermediate Care.
Beds SNF 41; ICF 79. *Certified* Medicaid; Medicare.
Ownership Proprietary.
Admissions Requirements Medical examination.
Staff Physicians 8 (ft); RNs 5 (ft); LPNs 9 (ft); Orderlies 2 (ft); Nurses aides 44 (ft); Physical therapists 1 (ft); Speech therapists 1 (pt); Activities coordinators 1 (ft); Dietitians 1 (pt); Dentists 3 (pt).
Facilities Dining room; Physical therapy room; Activities room; Crafts room; Barber/Beauty shop.
Activities Arts and Crafts; Cards; Games; Reading groups; Prayer groups; Movies; Dances/Social or cultural gatherings.
Description Superior rating 1984 by Licensure Board. Facility of the Year 1976, 1978, for State of Kentucky.

Mountain Laurel Manor
Rt 7, Box 349, Corbin, KY, 40701 (606) 528-8822
Admin Cathy J Willis. *Medical Dir/Dir of Nursing* Dr Elmer G Prewitt.
Licensure Intermediate Care. *Beds* 50. *Certified* Medicaid.
Staff Physicians 7 (ft); RNs 1 (pt); LPNs 4 (ft), 1 (pt); Nurses aides 8 (ft), 9 (pt); Activities coordinators 1 (ft); Dietitians 1 (ft).
Facilities Dining room; Laundry room.
Activities Arts and Crafts; Games; Prayer groups; Dances/Social or cultural gatherings.
Description Mountain Laurel Manor provides quality nursing care in a home-like atmosphere; offers therapeutic diets, laundry service, and planned activities.

COVINGTON

Covington Ladies Home Inc
702 Garrard St, Covington, KY, 41011 (606) 431-6913
Admin Virginia Johnson.
Licensure Personal Care. *Beds* 36.
Admissions Requirements Minimum age 65; Females only; Medical examination.
Staff LPNs 3 (ft); Nurses aides 6 (ft), 3 (pt); Activities coordinators 1 (ft).
Facilities Dining room; Activities room; Chapel; Laundry room.
Activities Arts and Crafts; Cards; Games; Prayer groups; Movies; Shopping trips.
Description Facility features a home-like atmosphere, not institutional. Each resident has her private room. Matron is resident of home and is available 24 hours daily. Beautician makes weekly visits.

Garrard Convalescent Home
425 Garrard St, Covington, KY, 41011 (606) 581-9393
Admin Ralph Stacy. *Medical Dir/Dir of Nursing* Dr F B Rodriquez.
Licensure Skilled Care; Intermediate Care.
Beds SNF 46; ICF 17. *Certified* Medicaid; Medicare.
Staff RNs 2 (ft), 1 (pt); LPNs 6 (ft); Physical therapists 1 (ft); Recreational therapists 1 (ft); Speech therapists 1 (pt); Activities coordinators 1 (ft); Dietitians 1 (pt); Dentists 1 (pt); Podiatrists 1 (pt); Audiologists 1 (pt).
Facilities Dining room; Activities room; Laundry room.
Activities Arts and Crafts; Cards; Reading groups; Prayer groups; Dances/Social or cultural gatherings; Trips to zoo.
Description This small facility has created a home-like environment instead of an institutional one; maximizes community resources. State has given facility superior rating.

Ridgeview Nursing Home*
800 Highland Ave, Covington, KY, 41011 (606) 491-3800
Admin Earl V Visse.
Licensure Skilled Care; Intermediate Care; Personal Care. *Beds* SNF 58; ICF 249; Personal Care 83. *Certified* Medicaid; Medicare.
Ownership Nonprofit.

Rosedale Manor
4250 Glenn Ave, Covington, KY, 41015-1699 (606) 431-2244
Admin Arthur W Urlage. *Medical Dir/Dir of Nursing* Kathy Knight.
Licensure Intermediate Care; Personal Care.
Beds ICF 142; Personal Care 66. *Certified* Medicaid.
Admissions Requirements Medical examination.
Staff RNs 1 (ft); LPNs 9 (ft); Orderlies 56 (ft), 10 (pt); Recreational therapists 2 (ft); Activities coordinators 1 (ft); Dietitians 1 (pt); Audiologists 1 (ft).
Facilities Dining room; Activities room; Chapel; Crafts room; Laundry room; Barber/Beauty shop; Library.
Activities Arts and Crafts; Cards; Games;

Reading groups; Prayer groups; Movies; Shopping trips; Dances/Social or cultural gatherings; Field trips; Shuffleboard; Picnics; Fishing.

Saint Charles Nursing Home*
500 Farrell Dr, Covington, KY, 41011 (606) 331-3224
Admin Sr Mary Luann Bender.
Licensure Skilled Care; Intermediate Care.
Beds SNF 54; ICF 93. *Certified* Medicaid; Medicare.
Ownership Nonprofit.

CYNTHIANA

Edgemont Manor Nursing Home*
Monticello Heights, Cynthiana, KY, 41031 (606) 234-4595
Admin Joseph Franks.
Licensure Intermediate Care; Personal Care.
Beds ICF 68; Personal Care 2.
Ownership Proprietary.

Grand Haven
Rodgers Park, Cynthiana, KY, 41031 (606) 234-2050
Admin Martha Brown.
Licensure Intermediate Care. *Beds* 50. *Certified* Medicaid.
Admissions Requirements Medical examination; Physician's request.
Staff RNs 1 (ft), 2 (pt); LPNs 1 (ft), 2 (pt); Nurses aides 10 (ft), 10 (pt); Physical therapists 1 (pt); Speech therapists 1 (pt); Activities coordinators 1 (ft).
Facilities Dining room; Activities room; Laundry room; Barber/Beauty shop.
Activities Cards; Games; Prayer groups; Dances/Social or cultural gatherings.
Description The activity director is one of the specialities; also have a lot of outside entertainment.

Harrison Memorial Extended Care Facility
PO Box 250, Cynthiana, KY, 41031 (606) 234-2300
Admin Patrick Romano. *Medical Dir/Dir of Nursing* Richard Allen MD.
Licensure Skilled Care. *Beds* 10. *Certified* Medicaid; Medicare.
Ownership Proprietary.
Admissions Requirements Medical examination; Physician's request.
Staff RNs 27 (ft), 8 (pt); LPNs 14 (ft), 1 (pt); Nurses aides 28 (ft); Physical therapists 1 (ft); Activities coordinators 1 (ft); Dietitians 1 (ft).
Facilities Dining room; Activities room.
Activities Cards; Games; Reading groups; Prayer groups.
Description Facility is attached to acute facility so patients have benefits that free-standing nursing homes may not offer (physical portable X-ray, respiratory therapy, c/c planning). In addition to 11 staff physicians, also has 12 consulting physicians that specialize in a variety of fields of medicine; will provide speech therapist when required.

Martin's Rest Home
321 Oddville Ave, Cynthiana, KY, 41031 (606) 234-1683
Admin Martha R Brown.

Licensure Personal Care. *Beds* 51.
Staff Nurses aides 10 (ft), 4 (pt); Dietitians 1 (pt).
Facilities Dining room; Activities room; Laundry room.
Activities Games; Shopping trips; Dances/Social or cultural gatherings.

Shady Lawn Home*
108 Miller St, Cynthiana, KY, 41031 (606) 234-2606
Admin Martha Brown.
Licensure Personal Care. *Beds* 75.
Ownership Proprietary.

DANVILLE

Fellowship Home
642 N 3rd St, Danville, KY, 40422 (606) 236-3352
Admin Nell S Jones. *Medical Dir/Dir of Nursing* R Quinn Bailey MD.
Licensure Intermediate Care; Personal Care.
Beds ICF 54; Personal Care 6. *Certified* Medicaid.
Admissions Requirements Minimum age 18; Medical examination; Physician's request.
Facilities Dining room; Activities room; Crafts room; Laundry room.
Activities Arts and Crafts; Cards; Games; Reading groups; Prayer groups; Movies; Shopping trips; Dances/Social or cultural gatherings.

Friendship House
642 N 3rd St, Danville, KY, 40422 (606) 236-3972
Admin Nell S Jones. *Medical Dir/Dir of Nursing* R Quinn Bailey MD.
Licensure Skilled Care. *Beds* 50. *Certified* Medicaid; Medicare.
Admissions Requirements Minimum age 18; Medical examination; Physician's request.
Facilities Dining room; Activities room; Crafts room; Laundry room.
Activities Arts and Crafts; Cards; Games; Reading groups; Prayer groups; Movies; Shopping trips; Dances/Social or cultural gatherings.

Golden Living Center*
203 Bruce Ct, Danville, KY, 40422 (606) 236-9292
Admin Shirley Quisenberry.
Licensure Intermediate Care; Personal Care.
Beds ICF 74; Personal Care 16.
Ownership Proprietary.

DAWSON SPRINGS

Dawson Springs Health Care Center*
PO Box 338, 100 Ramsey St, Dawson Springs, KY, 42408 (502) 797-8131
Admin Deborah Markham.
Licensure Skilled Care; Intermediate Care.
Beds SNF 20; ICF 60. *Certified* Medicaid; Medicare.

New Dawson Springs Nursing Home
213 Water St, PO Box 36, Dawson Springs, KY, 42408 (502) 797-2025
Admin Linda S Thomas.
Licensure Intermediate Care; Personal Care.

Beds ICF 69; Personal Care 35. *Certified* Medicaid.
Staff LPNs 3 (ft), 1 (pt); Activities coordinators 1 (ft).
Facilities Dining room; Laundry room.
Activities Arts and Crafts; Cards; Games; Reading groups; Prayer groups; Movies; Shopping trips; Dances/Social or cultural gatherings.
Description Facility features warm, friendly atmosphere.

Outwood ICF-MR
Hwy 109, Dawson Springs, KY, 42408 (502) 797-3771
Admin Earl Harris. *Medical Dir/Dir of Nursing* Sophia Logan RN.
Licensure Intermediate Care for Mentally Retarded. *Beds* 80. *Certified* Medicaid.
Admissions Requirements Minimum age 6; Medical examination.
Staff Physicians 1 (pt); RNs 4 (ft), 1 (pt); LPNs 3 (ft), 1 (pt); Nurses aides 78 (ft), 6 (pt); Physical therapists 1 (pt); Recreational therapists 1 (ft); Occupational therapists 1 (ft); Speech therapists 1 (ft); Dietitians 1 (pt); Dentists 1 (pt); Audiologists 1 (pt).
Facilities Dining room; Physical therapy room; Activities room; Chapel; Crafts room; Laundry room; Barber/Beauty shop; Library; Classrooms.
Activities Arts and Crafts; Games; Movies; Shopping trips; Dances/Social or cultural gatherings.
Description Effective September 7, 1983, moved into a new 80-bed facility with 5 cottages housing 16 residents, 16 classrooms, and a multi-purpose building featuring medical therapy, recreational, and adminsitrative support.

DRY RIDGE

Carlsbad Nursing Home*
Main St, Dry Ridge, KY, 41035 (606) 823-8201
Admin James Burcham.
Licensure Intermediate Care; Personal Care.
Beds ICF 32; Personal Care 15.
Ownership Proprietary.

Dry Ridge Personal Care Home*
Taft Hwy, Dry Ridge, KY, 41035 (606) 824-6164
Admin Ronald B Bennett.
Licensure Personal Care. *Beds* 64.
Ownership Proprietary.

EDMONTON

Harper Home for the Aged
Rt 2, Box 43, Edmonton, KY, 42129 (502) 432-5202
Admin Betty B Higginbotham.
Licensure Personal Care. *Beds* 29.
Admissions Requirements Minimum age 16; Medical examination.
Staff Nurses aides 5 (ft); Activities coordinators 1 (ft).
Facilities Dining room; Laundry room.
Activities Arts and Crafts; Cards; Games; Movies; Shopping trips; Dances/Social or cultural gatherings; Church services; Activities for

visually handicapped and hard of hearing.
Description Facility has a country setting, about 3 miles from Edmonton. One goal is to make facility a "home away from home". Employees are genuinely interested in the residents. Community is involved and interested in making the residents still feel a part of the community.

Metcalfe County Nursing Home
Box 125, Edmonton, KY, 42129 (502) 432-2921
Admin Teresa G Lewis.
Licensure Intermediate Care; Personal Care.
Beds ICF 71; Personal Care 30. *Certified* Medicaid.
Staff Physicians 2 (pt); RNs 1 (ft); LPNs 5 (ft); Nurses aides 24 (ft), 6 (pt); Activities coordinators 1 (ft); Dietitians 1 (ft); Dentists 1 (pt); Ophthalmologists 1 (pt).
Facilities Dining room; Physical therapy room; Activities room; Crafts room; Laundry room; Barber/Beauty shop.
Activities Arts and Crafts; Cards; Games; Reading groups; Prayer groups; Movies; Shopping trips; Dances/Social or cultural gatherings.
Description Located in the heart of south central Kentucky, this 101-bed personal and intermediate care facility offers the finest in rehibilitative care. Staffed by highly-trained professionals, all energy is directed toward a common goal of spiritual and physical wellness. Modern, progressive ideas and old-fashioned care combine to provide unsurpassable standards.

ELIZABETHTOWN

Elizabethan Home
510 Pennsylvania Ave, Elizabethtown, KY, 42701 (502) 769-3314
Admin Margaret Jones.
Licensure Intermediate Care. *Beds* 67. *Certified* Medicaid.
Admissions Requirements Physician's request.
Staff RNs 1 (pt); LPNs 4 (ft); Nurses aides 25 (ft), 5 (pt); Physical therapists 1 (pt); Speech therapists 1 (pt); Activities coordinators 1 (ft); Dietitians 1 (pt); Dentists 1 (pt).
Facilities Dining room; Activities room; Crafts room.
Activities Games; Prayer groups; Dances/Social or cultural gatherings.

Medco Center of Elizabethtown*
PO Box 604, 108 Laymon Ln, Elizabethtown, KY, 42701 (502) 765-6106
Admin Dorothy Dile.
Licensure Intermediate Care; Personal Care.
Beds ICF 50; Personal Care 16. *Certified* Medicaid.
Ownership Proprietary.

Woodland Terrace Health Care Facility*
PO Box 1, 1117 Woodland Dr, Elizabethtown, KY, 42701 (502) 769-2363
Admin Norman Seese.
Licensure Skilled Care; Intermediate Care; Personal Care. *Beds* SNF 56; ICF 62; Personal Care 6. *Certified* Medicaid.
Ownership Proprietary.

ELKHORN CITY

Mountain View Health Care Center*
PO Box 650, US Hwy 197, Elkhorn City, KY, 41522 (606) 754-4134
Admin Sharon K Hall.
Licensure Intermediate Care; Personal Care.
Beds ICF 106; Personal Care 20. *Certified* Medicaid.
Ownership Proprietary.

ELKTON

Country Manor of Todd County*
PO Box 4004, Allensville St, Elkton, KY, 54220 (502) 265-5321
Admin Ada Spurlin.
Licensure Personal Care. *Beds* 94.

FALMOUTH

Falmouth Rest Home*
406 Barkley St, Falmouth, KY, 41040 (606) 654-4341
Admin James F Smith.
Licensure Personal Care. *Beds* 28.
Ownership Proprietary.

Sharp's Rest Home*
307 Maple Ave, Falmouth, KY, 41040 (606) 654-8294
Admin Ruth Sharp.
Licensure Personal Care. *Beds* 22.
Ownership Proprietary.

FLATWOODS

Oakmont Manor*
1100 Grandview Dr, Flatwoods, KY, 41139 (606) 836-3187
Admin June Setser.
Licensure Intermediate Care. *Beds* 60. *Certified* Medicaid.
Ownership Proprietary.

FLEMINGSBURG

Pioneer Trace Nursing Home*
Box 275C, Pioneer Trace Dr, Flemingsburg, KY, 41041 (606) 845-2131
Admin Mary Ann Campbell.
Licensure Intermediate Care; Personal Care.
Beds ICF 89; Personal Care 6. *Certified* Medicaid.
Ownership Proprietary.

FLORENCE

Woodspoint Nursing Home
7300 Woodspoint Dr, Florence, KY, 41042 (606) 371-5731
Admin Pravin C Shah.
Licensure Skilled Care; Intermediate Care.
Beds SNF 50; ICF 101. *Certified* Medicaid; Medicare.
Ownership Nonprofit.
Facilities Dining room; Physical therapy room; Activities room; Chapel; Laundry room; Barber/Beauty shop.

Activities Arts and Crafts; Cards; Games; Reading groups; Prayer groups; Movies; Shopping trips; Dances/Social or cultural gatherings.
Description Facility is situated on the Mall Road exit of I-75, and is located near Boothe Memorial Hospital.

FORDSVILLE

Medco Center of Fordsville*
PO Box 205, Fordsville, KY, 42343 (502) 276-5173
Admin Lavine Terry.
Licensure Intermediate Care. *Beds* 67. *Certified* Medicaid.
Ownership Proprietary.

FORT THOMAS

Carmel Manor
Carmel Manor Rd, Fort Thomas, KY, 41075 (606) 781-5111
Admin Sr Maureen Hughes. *Medical Dir/Dir of Nursing* Dr Edward Stratman.
Licensure Personal Care. *Beds* 99.
Admissions Requirements Minimum age 65; Medical examination.
Staff Physicians 2 (pt); RNs 2 (ft); LPNs 6 (pt); Nurses aides 55 (ft), 7 (pt); Activities coordinators 1 (ft); Dietitians 1 (pt).
Affiliation Roman Catholic
Facilities Dining room; Physical therapy room; Activities room; Chapel; Crafts room; Laundry room; Barber/Beauty shop; Library; Coffee shop.
Activities Arts and Crafts; Cards; Games; Prayer groups; Movies; Shopping trips; Dances/Social or cultural gatherings.
Description A facility with a large outdoor patio overlooking the beautiful Ohio River.

Horizon House II*
435 River Rd, Fort Thomas, KY, 41075 (606) 441-9060, 491-2752
Admin Donna Denniston.
Ownership Nonprofit.

FRANKFORT

Capital Hall
1040 US 127 S, Frankfort, KY, 40601 (502) 875-5600
Admin Kelley F Owens. *Medical Dir/Dir of Nursing* James T Ramsey MD.
Licensure Skilled Care; Intermediate Care; Personal Care. *Beds* SNF 25; ICF; Personal Care 25. *Certified* Medicaid; Medicare.
Facilities Dining room; Physical therapy room; Activities room; Crafts room; Laundry room; Barber/Beauty shop.
Activities Arts and Crafts; Cards; Games; Reading groups; Prayer groups; Movies; Shopping trips; Dances/Social or cultural gatherings.

Franklin Manor
Old Soldiers Ln, Frankfort, KY, 40601 (502) 875-7272
Admin Steve A Rose. *Medical Dir/Dir of Nursing* Dr William McElwain.
Licensure Skilled Care; Intermediate Care.
Beds SNF 50; ICF 50. *Certified* Medicaid;

Medicare.
Admissions Requirements Medical examination.
Staff RNs 2 (ft), 3 (pt); LPNs 7 (ft), 1 (pt); Orderlies 4 (ft); Nurses aides 30 (ft), 1 (pt); Physical therapists 1 (ft), 1 (pt); Speech therapists 1 (pt); Activities coordinators 1 (ft); Dietitians 1 (ft).
Facilities Dining room; Physical therapy room; Activities room; Crafts room; Laundry room; Barber/Beauty shop; Lobby/lounge.
Activities Arts and Crafts; Games; Reading groups; Prayer groups; Dances/Social or cultural gatherings.

Green's Rest Home*
214 Holmes St, Frankfort, KY, 40601 (502) 227-4689
Admin William A Green.
Licensure Personal Care. *Beds* 24.
Ownership Proprietary.

FRANKLIN

Franklin Rest Home*
214 S College St, Franklin, KY, 42134 (502) 586-5995
Admin Karla White.
Licensure Personal Care. *Beds* 28.
Ownership Proprietary.

Lewis Memorial Methodist Home*
US 31 W North, Franklin, KY, 42134 (502) 586-3461
Admin Edward D Brandeberry.
Licensure Personal Care. *Beds* 15.
Ownership Nonprofit.
Affiliation Methodist

Medco Center of Franklin
414 Robey St, PO Box 367, Franklin, KY, 42134 (502) 586-7141
Admin Brenda Dye. *Medical Dir/Dir of Nursing* Dr J M Pulliam.
Licensure Intermediate Care. *Beds* 98. *Certified* Medicaid.
Staff RNs 2 (ft); LPNs 4 (pt); Orderlies 2 (pt); Nurses aides 30 (ft), 15 (pt); Physical therapists 1 (pt); Activities coordinators 1 (ft), 1 (pt); Dietitians 1 (pt).
Facilities Dining room; Physical therapy room; Activities room; Laundry room; Barber/Beauty shop.
Activities Arts and Crafts; Cards; Games; Reading groups; Prayer groups; Movies; Dances/Social or cultural gatherings.
Description Center is located in a rural setting, bordered by farmland on two sides, a beautiful lake on one side, and a residential section on the other, plenty of outdoor space available for residents' enjoyment; full-time staff dedicated to quality care and enhancing the residents' self image.

FULTON

Haws Memorial Nursing Home
Holiday Ln, Fulton, KY, 42041 (502) 472-1971
Admin Joe Brownlow.
Licensure Skilled Care. *Beds* 60. *Certified* Medicaid; Medicare.

Facilities Dining room; Physical therapy room; Activities room; Crafts room; Barber/Beauty shop; Library.
Activities Arts and Crafts; Games; Reading groups; Movies; Dances/Social or cultural gatherings.

Parkway Manor Nursing Home
309 N Highland Dr, Fulton, KY, 42041 (502) 472-3386
Admin Joanne L Harper.
Licensure Intermediate Care. *Beds* 20. *Certified* Medicaid.
Staff Physicians 4 (ft); RNs 2 (pt); LPNs 1 (ft), 1 (pt); Nurses aides 8 (ft), 2 (pt); Activities coordinators 1 (ft); Dietitians 1 (pt).
Facilities Dining room; Laundry room; Barber/Beauty shop.
Activities Arts and Crafts; Cards; Games; Dances/Social or cultural gatherings.
Description Parkway Manor, Inc is a home-like facility with a family-like atmosphere. The staff and management put forth all possible effort to give tender, loving care to all residents, and comply strictly to physicians' orders and all federal, state, and local requirements and guidelines.

GEORGETOWN

Cardome*
US 25, Georgetown, KY, 40324 (502) 863-1578
Admin Sr J Mary Milet.
Licensure Personal Care. *Beds* 35.
Ownership Nonprofit.

Dover Manor Nursing Home*
Scotland Wood Dr, Georgetown, KY, 40324 (502) 863-9529
Admin Nedra Devine.
Licensure Intermediate Care; Personal Care. *Beds* ICF 85; Personal Care 10. *Certified* Medicaid.
Ownership Proprietary.

Geneva's Geriatric Center*
814 Bourbon St, Georgetown, KY, 40324 (502) 863-0291
Admin Geneva R Taylor.
Licensure Personal Care. *Beds* Personal Care 10.
Ownership Proprietary.

Springhaven Nursing Care*
102 Pocahontas Trail, Georgetown, KY, 40324-1196 (502) 254-3696, 3983
Admin Gary Hitchings.
Licensure Skilled Care; Intermediate Care. *Beds* SNF 15; ICF 35. *Certified* Medicaid; Medicare.
Ownership Proprietary.

GLASGOW

Barren County Health Care Center*
300 Westwood St, Glasgow, KY, 42141 (502) 651-9131
Admin Steve Brown.
Licensure Intermediate Care. *Beds* 94. *Certified* Medicaid.
Ownership Proprietary.

Glasgow Rest Home*
220 Westwood St, Glasgow, KY, 42141 (602)
651-6661
Admin Steve Brown.
Licensure Personal Care. *Beds* 74.
Ownership Proprietary.

Glasgow State—Intermediate Care Facility*
Box 199, State Ave, Glasgow, KY, 42141 (502)
651-2151
Admin John Broadbent.
Licensure Intermediate Care. *Beds* 100. *Certified* Medicaid.
Ownership Nonprofit.

Glenview Manor
1002 Glenview Dr, Glasgow, KY, 42141 (502)
651-8332
Admin Alex Mitchell. *Medical Dir/Dir of Nursing* Dr David Fant.
Licensure Intermediate Care. *Beds* 52. *Certified* Medicaid; Medicare.
Admissions Requirements Medical examination; Physician's request.
Staff RNs 1 (ft); LPNs 1 (ft); Orderlies 3 (ft); Nurses aides 12 (ft); Activities coordinators 1 (ft); Dietitians 1 (ft).
Facilities Dining room; Activities room; Crafts room; Laundry room; Barber/Beauty shop.
Activities Arts and Crafts; Cards; Games; Reading groups; Prayer groups; Movies; Shopping trips.
Description Facility has professional nursing staff 24 hours per day; VA approved; daily planned activities and special diets approved.

Homewood Health Care Center*
PO Box 297, Homewood Blvd, Glasgow, KY, 42141 (502) 651-6126
Admin Emogene C Stephens.
Licensure Skilled Care; Intermediate Care; Personal Care. *Beds* SNF 98; ICF 86; Personal Care 22. *Certified* Medicaid; Medicare.
Ownership Proprietary.

GREENSBURG

Green Hill Manor
213 Industrial Rd, Greensburg, KY, 42743
(502) 932-4241
Admin Geneva Marcum. *Medical Dir/Dir of Nursing* Dr Robert Shuffert.
Licensure Intermediate Care; Personal Care.
Beds ICF 118; Personal Care 8. *Certified* Medicaid.
Admissions Requirements Medical examination.
Staff RNs 3 (ft); LPNs 8 (ft); Orderlies 3 (ft); Nurses aides 38 (ft); Activities coordinators 2 (ft); Dietitians 1 (pt).
Facilities Dining room; Activities room; Laundry room; Barber/Beauty shop.
Activities Arts and Crafts; Cards; Games; Movies; Shopping trips; Dances/Social or cultural gatherings.
Description Facility features a family night each quarter, licensed nurses 24 hours per day, and special activities at the Green River Art and Craft Festival.

McDowell Skilled Nursing Facility
202-206 Milby, Greensburg, KY, 42743 (502)
932-4211
Admin William E Dowe. *Medical Dir/Dir of Nursing* Dr Robert Shuffett.
Licensure Skilled Care. *Beds* SNF 26. *Certified* Medicaid; Medicare.
Admissions Requirements Physician's request.
Staff RNs 2 (ft), 1 (pt); LPNs 4 (ft), 6 (pt); Orderlies 3 (ft), 2 (pt); Nurses aides 7 (ft), 8 (pt); Physical therapists 1 (ft); Speech therapists 1 (pt); Activities coordinators 1 (ft); Dietitians 1 (ft).
Facilities Dining room; Physical therapy room; Activities room; Crafts room; Laundry room; Barber/Beauty shop; Patio.
Activities Arts and Crafts; Cards; Games; Reading groups; Movies; Shopping trips; Dances/Social or cultural gatherings.
Description Residents are participants in rock-a-thon for Heart Fund, a valentine banquet with king/queen and prince/princess, yard sales twice yearly, and nursing open house during National Nursing Home week. Facility is round, well lighted with a warm, friendly atmosphere.

GREENVILLE

Belle Meade Home
521 Greene Dr, PO Box 565, Greenville, KY, 42345 (502) 338-1523
Admin Marlin K Sparks.
Licensure Intermediate Care; Personal Care.
Beds ICF 62; Personal Care 30. *Certified* Medicaid.
Staff RNs 5 (ft); LPNs 6 (ft); Nurses aides 24 (ft); Activities coordinators 1 (ft); Dietitians 1 (ft).
Facilities Dining room; Activities room; Laundry room; Barber/Beauty shop.
Activities Arts and Crafts; Cards; Games; Reading groups; Prayer groups; Shopping trips; Dances/Social or cultural gatherings.

Maple Manor Healthcare Center
515 Greene Dr, Greenville, KY, 42345 (502)
338-5400
Admin Joy M Knight. *Medical Dir/Dir of Nursing* C J Shipp MD.
Licensure Intermediate Care; Personal Care.
Beds ICF 88; Personal Care 18. *Certified* Medicaid.
Ownership Nonprofit.
Staff RNs 2 (ft); LPNs 5 (ft), 4 (pt); Nurses aides 33 (ft), 5 (pt); Physical therapists 1 (pt); Speech therapists 1 (pt); Activities coordinators 1 (ft); Dietitians 1 (pt).
Facilities Dining room; Activities room; Chapel; Crafts room; Laundry room; Barber/Beauty shop.
Activities Arts and Crafts; Cards; Games; Reading groups; Prayer groups; Movies; Shopping trips; Dances/Social or cultural gatherings.

Muhlenberg Community Hospital—Skilled Nursing Facility
440 Hopkinsville St, Greenville, KY, 42345
(502) 338-4211
Admin Charles J Perry.
Licensure Skilled Care. *Beds* 30. *Certified* Medicaid; Medicare.

Admissions Requirements Medical examination; Physician's request.
Staff Physicians 30 (ft); RNs 2 (ft); LPNs 10 (ft); Orderlies 1 (ft); Nurses aides 7 (ft); Physical therapists 1 (ft); Speech therapists 1 (pt); Activities coordinators 1 (pt); Dietitians 1 (ft).
Facilities Physical therapy room; Activities room; Chapel; Laundry room.
Activities Arts and Crafts.
Description This is a hospital-based service.

Poplar Grove Rest Home Inc
512 W Campbell St, Greenville, KY, 42345
(502) 338-4592
Admin Ken L Jones. *Medical Dir/Dir of Nursing* Dr King.
Licensure Personal Care. *Beds* 42.
Admissions Requirements Minimum age 18; Medical examination.
Staff LPNs 1 (ft); Nurses aides 9 (ft); Activities coordinators 1 (pt); Dietitians 1 (pt).
Facilities Dining room; Laundry room.
Activities Arts and Crafts; Cards; Games; Reading groups; Prayer groups; Movies; Shopping trips; Dances/Social or cultural gatherings.

HARDINSBURG

Medco Center of Hardinsburg*
Rt 1, Box 134, Hardinsburg, KY, 40143 (502)
756-2159
Admin Ann Snyder.
Licensure Intermediate Care. *Beds* 63. *Certified* Medicaid.
Ownership Proprietary.

HARLAN

Harlan Appalachian Regional Hospital—Extended Care Facility*
PO Box 960, Martin Fork Rd, Harlan, KY, 40831 (606) 573-1400
Admin Ray G Roberts.
Licensure Skilled Care. *Beds* 24. *Certified* Medicaid; Medicare.

Harlan Health Care Center*
Mounted Rt 1, Hwy 421-S, Harlan, KY, 40831
(606) 573-7250
Admin Ronald A Spatafora.
Licensure Skilled Care; Intermediate Care.
Beds SNF 24; ICF 119. *Certified* Medicaid.
Ownership Proprietary.

Laurels*
Star Rt, Box 216, Harlan, KY, 40831 (606)
573-5105
Admin Claude White.
Licensure Personal Care. *Beds* 50.
Ownership Nonprofit.

HARRODSBURG

Harrodsburg Health Care Center
853 Lexington Rd, Harrodsburg, KY, 40330
(606) 734-7791
Admin T W Struttmann.
Licensure Intermediate Care; Personal Care.
Beds ICF 102; Personal Care 10. *Certified* Medicaid.
Staff RNs; LPNs; Orderlies; Nurses aides;

Physical therapists; Reality therapists; Recreational therapists; Activities coordinators; Dietitians.
Facilities Dining room; Activities room; Chapel; Crafts room; Laundry room; Barber/Beauty shop.
Activities Arts and Crafts; Cards; Games; Reading groups; Prayer groups; Movies.

HARTFORD

Professional Care Home
McMurty St, Hartford, KY, 42347 (502) 298-7437
Admin Brewier Welch.
Licensure Intermediate Care; Personal Care. *Beds* ICF 118; Personal Care 11. *Certified* Medicaid.
Staff RNs 1 (ft); LPNs 5 (ft), 2 (pt); Nurses aides 43 (ft), 4 (pt); Speech therapists 1 (pt); Activities coordinators 1 (ft); Dietitians 1 (ft).
Facilities Dining room; Activities room; Laundry room; Barber/Beauty shop.
Activities Arts and Crafts; Games; Prayer groups; Shopping trips; Dances/Social or cultural gatherings.

HAZARD

Hazard Nursing Home
Rt 3 Box 650, Airport Industrial Site, Hazard, KY, 41701 (606) 439-2306
Admin Debra K Reynolds. *Medical Dir/Dir of Nursing* Cordell Williams MD.
Licensure Skilled Care; Intermediate Care. *Beds* SNF 40; ICF 110. *Certified* Medicaid; Medicare.
Facilities Dining room; Physical therapy room; Activities room; Crafts room; Laundry room; Barber/Beauty shop.
Activities Arts and Crafts; Games; Reading groups; Prayer groups.

HENDERSON

Henderson Rest Home
201 Watson Ln, Henderson, KY, 42420 (502) 826-2394
Admin Christie Shelton. *Medical Dir/Dir of Nursing* Dr Jack Bland.
Licensure Personal Care. *Beds* 64.
Admissions Requirements Medical examination.
Staff RNs 1 (ft); Nurses aides 1 (ft); Recreational therapists 1 (ft).
Facilities Dining room; Laundry room.
Activities Arts and Crafts; Cards; Games; Reading groups; Prayer groups; Movies; Shopping trips; Dances/Social or cultural gatherings.
Description In the fall of 1983, adopt-a-grandparent program was started; all residents have been adopted at least twice. Volunteers are meeting many otherwise unmet needs.

Medco Center of Henderson*
2500 N Elm St, Henderson, KY, 42420 (502) 826-9794
Admin Jerry Akin.
Licensure Intermediate Care. *Beds* ICF 100.
Certified Medicaid; Medicare.
Ownership Proprietary.

Redbanks*
851 Kimsey Ln, Henderson, KY, 42420 (502) 826-6436
Admin Georgene Fraley.
Licensure Skilled Care; Intermediate Care; Personal Care. *Beds* SNF 76; ICF 146; Personal Care 49. *Certified* Medicaid; Medicare.
Ownership Nonprofit.

HIGHLAND HEIGHTS

Lakeside Place
3510 Alexandria Pike, Highland Heights, KY, 41076 (606) 441-1100
Admin Robert D Williams. *Medical Dir/Dir of Nursing* Dr Donald Stevens.
Licensure Skilled Care; Intermediate Care; Personal Care. *Beds* SNF 50; ICF; Personal Care 48. *Certified* Medicaid; Medicare.
Admissions Requirements Minimum age 5; Physician's request.
Staff Physicians 26 (pt); RNs 3 (ft), 7 (pt); LPNs 20 (ft), 4 (pt); Orderlies 11 (ft), 4 (pt); Nurses aides 111 (ft), 9 (pt); Physical therapists 3 (pt); Speech therapists 1 (pt); Activities coordinators 1 (ft); Dietitians 1 (ft); Dentists 1 (pt); Ophthalmologists 1 (pt); Podiatrists 1 (pt); Audiologists 1 (pt).
Facilities Dining room; Physical therapy room; Activities room; Chapel; Laundry room; Barber/Beauty shop; Library; 5 TV rooms/solariums.
Activities Arts and Crafts; Cards; Games; Prayer groups; Movies; Shopping trips; Monthly birthday party's; Special event banquets; Annual resident/family picnic; Pet therapy.
Description Community hearing service offered.

HODGENVILLE

Sunrise Manor Nursing Home
Phillips Ln, Rt 3, Hodgenville, KY, 42748 (502) 358-3103
Admin Hilda Harned. *Medical Dir/Dir of Nursing* Glenn Catlett MD.
Licensure Skilled Care; Intermediate Care. *Beds* SNF 50; ICF 72. *Certified* Medicaid; Medicare.
Admissions Requirements Medical examination.
Staff Physicians 1 (pt); RNs 5 (ft); LPNs 5 (ft), 3 (pt); Orderlies 1 (ft); Nurses aides 40 (ft), 8 (pt); Physical therapists 1 (ft); Occupational therapists; Speech therapists; Activities coordinators 1 (ft); Dietitians.
Facilities Dining room; Physical therapy room; Activities room; Chapel; Laundry room; Barber/Beauty shop; TV room.
Activities Arts and Crafts; Cards; Games; Reading groups; Prayer groups; Dances/Social or cultural gatherings.
Description Sunrise Manor has established a widely known long-standing reputation for providing quality care at reasonable costs. Residents favorite areas include a beautifully landscaped courtyard and a chapel which contains a simple wooden cross made from the famous boundary oak tree at Lincoln National Park. VA contracts.

HOPKINSVILLE

Brookfield Manor
Box 711, Hopkinsville, KY, 42240 (502) 886-8185
Admin Sue Winders.
Licensure Personal Care. *Beds* 78.
Staff LPNs 1 (ft); Nurses aides 14 (ft); Activities coordinators 1 (ft); Dietitians 1 (ft).
Facilities Dining room; Activities room; Laundry room; Barber/Beauty shop.
Activities Arts and Crafts; Cards; Games; Reading groups; Prayer groups.

Christian Health Care Center
200 Sterling Dr, Hopkinsville, KY, 42240 (502) 885-1166
Admin Ronald Moss. *Medical Dir/Dir of Nursing* Guinn Cost MD.
Licensure Skilled Care; Intermediate Care. *Beds* SNF 30; ICF 86. *Certified* Medicaid; Medicare.
Staff RNs 3 (ft), 3 (pt); LPNs 11 (ft), 5 (pt); Nurses aides 24 (ft), 19 (pt); Physical therapists 1 (pt); Recreational therapists 1 (ft); Speech therapists 1 (pt); Activities coordinators 1 (ft); Dietitians 1 (pt); Dentists 1 (pt); Podiatrists 1 (pt).
Facilities Dining room; Physical therapy room; Activities room; Chapel; Crafts room; Laundry room; Barber/Beauty shop.
Activities Arts and Crafts; Cards; Games; Reading groups; Prayer groups; Movies; Shopping trips; Dances/Social or cultural gatherings.

Covington's Convalescent Center*
115 Cayce St, Hopkinsville, KY, 42240 (502) 886-4403, 6773
Admin Gwen Covington.
Licensure Intermediate Care; Personal Care. *Beds* ICF 32; Personal Care 25. *Certified* Medicaid.
Ownership Proprietary.

Gainesville Manor
Rt 9, PO Box 4004, Hopkinsville, KY, 42240 (502) 886-0258
Admin Ida Woodard. *Medical Dir/Dir of Nursing* Dr J W Frazier.
Licensure Personal Care. *Beds* 102.
Admissions Requirements Minimum age 18; Medical examination; Physician's request.
Staff Physicians; LPNs 1 (ft), 1 (pt); Orderlies 1 (ft); Nurses aides 20 (ft), 2 (pt); Activities coordinators 1 (ft); Dietitians 1 (pt); Dentists 1 (pt); Ophthalmologists 2 (pt); Audiologists 1 (pt).
Facilities Dining room; Activities room; Crafts room; Laundry room; Library.
Activities Arts and Crafts; Cards; Games; Reading groups; Prayer groups; Shopping trips; Dances/Social or cultural gatherings.
Description Facility has large spacious grounds with basketball court and volleyball court; picnic tables in park area, benches around facility, and a large garden area.

Pennyrile Home*
502 Noel Dr, Hopkinsville, KY, 42240 (502) 885-9100
Admin Elizabeth Everett.
Licensure Personal Care. *Beds* 94.
Ownership Proprietary.

Pinecrest Manor
Highpoint Dr, Hopkinsville, KY, 42240 (502)
885-1151
Admin Joseph Robertson. *Medical Dir/Dir of
Nursing* Dr Robert Rose.
Licensure Skilled Care; Intermediate Care.
Beds SNF 16; ICF 79. *Certified* Medicaid;
Medicare.
Admissions Requirements Minimum age 21;
Physician's request.
Staff Physicians 19 (pt); RNs 3 (ft), 2 (pt);
LPNs 7 (ft), 12 (pt); Orderlies 2 (ft), 3 (pt);
Nurses aides 26 (ft), 14 (pt); Physical therapists
1 (ft); Speech therapists 1 (pt); Activities coordi-
nators 1 (ft); Dietitians 1 (ft).
Affiliation Seventh-Day Adventist
Facilities Dining room; Physical therapy room;
Activities room; Crafts room; Laundry room;
Barber/Beauty shop.
Activities Arts and Crafts; Games; Reading
groups; Prayer groups; Movies; Dances/Social
or cultural gatherings.
Description Pinecrest Manor is nestled atop a
rolling hillside of 19 acres with beautiful surroundings. We provide excellent nursing care
and activities for our patients. Only area facility
with a full-time, certified physical therapist.

INDEPENDENCE

Regency Manor
5716 Madison Pike, Independence, KY, 41051
(606) 356-9294
Admin Patricia C Schroer. *Medical Dir/Dir of
Nursing* Sharon Strause.
Licensure Personal Care. *Beds* 50.
Admissions Requirements Minimum age 18.
Staff Nurses aides 9 (ft); Activities coordina-
tors 1 (ft).
Facilities Dining room; Activities room; Crafts
room; Barber/Beauty shop.
Activities Arts and Crafts; Cards; Games; Pray-
er groups; Movies; Dances/Social or cultural
gatherings.

IRVINE

Irvine Health Care
Bertha St, Irvine, KY, 40336 (606) 723-5153
Admin Ruth M Pasley.
Licensure Intermediate Care; Personal Care.
Beds ICF 78; Personal Care 18. *Cer-
tified* Medicaid.
Staff Physicians 4 (pt); RNs 2 (ft); LPNs 2 (ft);
Nurses aides 22 (ft), 8 (pt); Activities coordina-
tors 1 (ft); Podiatrists 1 (pt).
Facilities Dining room; Activities room; Laun-
dry room; Barber/Beauty shop.
Activities Games; Prayer groups; Movies;
Shopping trips.

JACKSON

Nim Henson Geriatric Center
PO Box 636, Jackson, KY, 41339 (606)
666-2456
Admin Gordon Combs. *Medical Dir/Dir of
Nursing* Emanuel C Turner MD.
Licensure Skilled Care; Intermediate Care.
Beds SNF 30; ICF 92. *Certified* Medicaid;
Medicare.

Admissions Requirements Medical examination.
Staff Physicians 1 (pt); RNs 1 (ft), 3 (pt); LPNs
7 (ft), 3 (pt); Orderlies 2 (ft); Nurses aides 44
(ft), 3 (pt); Physical therapists 1 (pt); Activities
coordinators 1 (ft); Dietitians 1 (pt).
Facilities Dining room; Laundry room; Barber-
/Beauty shop.
Activities Arts and Crafts; Games; Movies;
Religious services; Entertainment.
Description Located in a lovely mountain river
valley at Jackson, KY, the Nim Henson Geriatric Center provides excellent patient care by a
concerned, trained, experienced staff.

JAMESTOWN

Fair Oaks Personal Care Home*
PO Box 140, Hwy 127, Jamestown, KY, 42629
(502) 343-2101
Admin Wayne Reid.
Licensure Intermediate Care. *Beds* 94. *Certi-
fied* Medicaid.
Ownership Proprietary.

JEFFERSONTOWN

Louisville Lutheran Home Inc
10617 E Watterson Trail, Jeffersontown, KY,
40299 (502) 267-7403
Admin Mary Lou Dearner. *Medical Dir/Dir of
Nursing* Dr Ken Peters.
Licensure Intermediate Care; Personal Care.
Beds ICF 60; Personal Care 38. *Cer-
tified* Medicaid.
Admissions Requirements Medical examina-
tion; Physician's request.
Staff Physicians 2 (ft); RNs 2 (ft); LPNs 5 (ft);
Nurses aides 26 (ft); Physical therapists 1 (pt);
Activities coordinators 1 (ft); Dietitians 1 (ft), 1
(pt); Dentists 1 (pt); Podiatrists 1 (pt).
Affiliation Lutheran
Facilities Dining room; Physical therapy room;
Laundry room; Barber/Beauty shop.
Activities Arts and Crafts; Cards; Games;
Reading groups; Prayer groups; Movies; Shop-
ping trips; Dances/Social or cultural gatherings.
Description Facility features hospice trained
volunteers, outpatient physical therapy ser-
vices, on-campus senior citizens center, and
was established in 1926. Entire staff CPR-
trained.

JENKINS

Letcher County Golden Years Rest Home*
PO Box 867, Lakeside Dr, Jenkins, KY, 41537
(606) 832-2123
Admin James F Tackett.
Licensure Personal Care. *Beds* 44.
Ownership Public.

JONESVILLE

Jonesville Rest Home*
Rt 36, Jonesville, KY, 41052 (606) 824-4610
Admin Leon Tuttle and Wanda Sue Tuttle.
Licensure Personal Care. *Beds* 26.
Ownership Proprietary.

KINDMAN

Knott County Health Care Center
Perkins Branch Rd, PO Box 436, Kindman,
KY, 41822 (606) 785-5011
Admin O J Simpson. *Medical Dir/Dir of
Nursing* George A Sullivan MD.
Licensure Skilled Care; Intermediate Care.
Beds SNF 29; ICF 53. *Certified* Medicaid;
Medicare.
Staff Physicians 5 (ft); RNs 3 (ft); LPNs 12 (ft);
Orderlies 4 (ft); Nurses aides 28 (ft); Activities
coordinators 1 (ft); Dietitians 1 (ft); Dentists 1
(ft).
Facilities Dining room; Physical therapy room;
Activities room; Crafts room; Laundry room;
Barber/Beauty shop; Library.
Activities Arts and Crafts; Cards; Games;
Reading groups; Prayer groups; Movies; Shop-
ping trips.

KUTTAWA

Hilltop Nursing Home
Lake Barkley Dr, Kuttawa, KY, 42055 (502)
388-7611 and 388-2291
Admin Nancy J Adams and Clyde S Adams.
Licensure Intermediate Care; Personal Care.
Beds ICF 96; Personal Care 32. *Cer-
tified* Medicaid.
Admissions Requirements Medical examina-
tion.
Staff RNs 2 (ft); LPNs 6 (ft), 1 (pt); Orderlies 2
(ft); Nurses aides 54 (ft), 2 (pt); Speech thera-
pists 1 (pt); Activities coordinators 1 (pt);
Dietitians 1 (pt).
Facilities Dining room; Activities room; Crafts
room; Laundry room; Barber/Beauty shop.
Activities Arts and Crafts; Cards; Games;
Reading groups; Prayer groups; Movies; Dan-
ces/Social or cultural gatherings.
Description Hilltop Nursing Home, Inc in Old
Kuttawa, KY is the midpoint between New
Eddyville and New Kuttawa. It is a quiet rural
community with Barkley Lake as the southern-
most city limit. Facility is less than 200 feet
from the lake's edge. The lake and countryside
give residents a wonderful view all year long.

LACENTER

Life Care Center of LaCenter
5th and Pine Sts, LaCenter, KY, 42056 (502)
665-5681
Admin Marilyn D Ingram.
Licensure Intermediate Care; Personal Care.
Beds ICF 70; Personal Care 21. *Cer-
tified* Medicaid.
Staff Physicians 4 (pt); RNs 1 (ft); LPNs 4 (ft);
Nurses aides 33 (ft); Recreational therapists 1
(pt); Speech therapists 1 (pt); Activities coordi-
nators 1 (ft); Dietitians 1 (pt).
Facilities Dining room; Laundry room; Barber-
/Beauty shop.
Activities Arts and Crafts; Games; Movies;
Shopping trips; Dances/Social or cultural gath-
erings.

LACKEY

Golden Years Rest Home
Rt 80, Lackey, KY, 41643 (606) 946-2220
Admin Loveda L Snyder. *Medical Dir/Dir of Nursing* Alberta G Deaton.
Licensure Personal Care. *Beds* 84.
Admissions Requirements Minimum age 18; Medical examination; Physician's request.
Staff Physicians 3 (ft), 1 (pt); LPNs 1 (ft); Orderlies 2 (ft); Nurses aides 16 (ft), 4 (pt); Activities coordinators 1 (ft), 1 (pt); Dietitians 1 (ft), 1 (pt); Dentists 1 (pt); Ophthalmologists 1 (pt); Audiologists 1 (pt).
Facilities Dining room; Activities room; Laundry room; Barber/Beauty shop.
Activities Arts and Crafts; Cards; Games; Reading groups; Prayer groups; Movies; Shopping trips; Dances/Social or cultural gatherings.
Description Facility features family-type atmosphere.

LAGRANGE

Cedar Lake Lodge*
PO Box 286, Jericho Rd, LaGrange, KY, 40031 (502) 222-7157
Admin Jim Richardson.
Licensure Intermediate Care for Mentally Retarded. *Beds* 76. *Certified* Medicaid.
Ownership Nonprofit.

LANCASTER

Garrard County Home for Senior Citizens
308 W Maple St, Lancaster, KY, 40444 (606) 792-2112
Admin W David MacCool. *Medical Dir/Dir of Nursing* Paul J Sides MD.
Licensure Personal Care. *Beds* 48.
Admissions Requirements Minimum age 21; Medical examination.
Staff RNs 1 (pt); LPNs 2 (ft), 2 (pt); Nurses aides 6 (ft); Activities coordinators 1 (ft); Dietitians 1 (pt); Social worker 1 (pt).
Facilities Dining room; Activities room; Laundry room; Barber/Beauty shop.
Activities Arts and Crafts; Games; Reading groups; Prayer groups; Movies; Shopping trips.
Description Our 46-bed personal care facility is located in rural south central Kentucky. Nursing supervision and care is available 24 hours a day by licensed nursing staff. The facility is hospital-based and multiple diagnostic facilities are available to residents.

Garrard County Memorial Hospital—Skilled Nursing Facility*
308 W Maple St, Lancaster, KY, 40444 (606) 792-2112
Admin Robert R Hagan.
Licensure Skilled Care. *Beds* 34. *Certified* Medicaid; Medicare.
Ownership Nonprofit.

LAWRENCEBURG

Heritage Hall*
Box 349, 331 S Main, Lawrenceburg, KY, 40342 (502) 839-7261
Admin Rebecca Collins.
Licensure Intermediate Care; Personal Care.
Beds ICF 57; Personal Care 15. *Certified* Medicaid.
Ownership Proprietary.

Sunset Hill Home for the Aged and Infirm*
Rt 2, Lawrenceburg, KY, 40342 (502) 839-6383
Admin William Crabb.
Licensure Personal Care. *Beds* 16.
Ownership Nonprofit.

LEBANON

Cedars of Lebanon Rest Home*
S Harrison, Lebanon, KY, 40033 (502) 692-3121
Admin Marion Hilton.
Licensure Intermediate Care; Personal Care.
Beds ICF 81; Personal Care 13. *Certified* Medicaid.
Ownership Proprietary.

Spring View Hospital*
353 W Walnut St, Lebanon, KY, 40033 (502) 692-6051
Admin Evelyn P Anderson.
Licensure Skilled Care. *Beds* 38.
Ownership Proprietary.

LEITCHFIELD

Aid Acres*
PO Box 186, Wallace Ave, Leitchfield, KY, 42754 (502) 259-4036
Admin Sharon Perkins.
Licensure Intermediate Care; Personal Care.
Beds ICF 50; Personal Care 18. *Certified* Medicaid.
Ownership Proprietary.

Grayson Manor
349 E Lake Dr, Leitchfield, KY, 42754 (502) 259-4028
Admin Greg Wells. *Medical Dir/Dir of Nursing* Suzanne Givan.
Licensure Intermediate Care; Personal Care.
Beds ICF 66; Personal Care 36. *Certified* Medicaid.
Staff RNs 2 (ft), 1 (pt); LPNs 3 (ft), 3 (pt); Orderlies 3 (ft), 1 (pt); Nurses aides 14 (ft), 4 (pt); Activities coordinators 1 (ft); Dietitians 1 (ft); Dentists 1 (ft).

LEWISPORT

Hancock County Rest Haven
Drawer G, Lewisport, KY, 42351 (502) 295-6825
Admin Kaye Jones. *Medical Dir/Dir of Nursing* Dr B P Smith.
Licensure Personal Care. *Beds* 78.
Admissions Requirements Minimum age 18; Medical examination.
Staff Physicians 1 (ft), 1 (pt); Nurses aides 11 (ft); Recreational therapists 2 (pt); Activities coordinators 1 (ft).
Facilities Dining room; Laundry room.
Activities Arts and Crafts; Cards; Games; Reading groups; Prayer groups; Movies; Shopping trips; Dances/Social or cultural gatherings.
Description Facility is located in a rural community, close to shopping center. Mental health service in the facility 5 days per week. Churches of various denominations hold services each week.

LEXINGTON

Arnett Pritchett Foundation Home
319 Duke Rd, Lexington, KY, 40502 (606) 266-6031
Admin Victoria Kangas. *Medical Dir/Dir of Nursing* Mary Rogers Hay.
Licensure Personal Care. *Beds* 14.
Admissions Requirements Minimum age 65; Females only
Staff Physicians 1 (ft); Nurses aides 5 (ft); Activities coordinators 1 (ft); Dietitians 1 (ft).
Facilities Dining room; Activities room; Laundry room; Library.
Activities Arts and Crafts; Cards; Games; Reading groups; Prayer groups; Movies; Shopping trips; Dances/Social or cultural gatherings.

Ashland Terrace*
475 S Ashland Ave, Lexington, KY, 40502 (606) 266-2581
Admin Leona Coleman.
Licensure Personal Care. *Beds* 22.
Ownership Nonprofit.

Excepticon—Lexington Campus
1321 Trent Blvd, Lexington, KY, 40502 (606) 272-3496
Admin Nona M Bush.
Licensure Intermediate Care for Mentally Retarded. *Beds* 180. *Certified* Medicaid.
Admissions Requirements Minimum age 18; Medical examination.
Staff Physicians 2 (pt); RNs 2 (pt); LPNs 7 (pt); Nurses aides 45 (ft), 9 (pt); Physical therapists 1 (pt); Recreational therapists 3 (ft); Occupational therapists 2 (ft); Speech therapists 1 (ft); Dietitians 1 (ft); Dentists 1 (pt).
Facilities Dining room; Activities room; Crafts room; Laundry room.
Activities Arts and Crafts; Games; Movies; Shopping trips; Dances/Social or cultural gatherings.
Description Physicians are on campus 4 days per week; 24-hour nursing coverage; professional nurse instruction in health and hygiene and sex education; 30-day medication reviews; CPR certification for nursing staff; easy accessibility to 4 major general hospitals. Facility is located in a residential setting in an apartment-type complex with double- and single-room accommodations.

Glen Haven Personal Care Home
444 Glen Arvin Ave, Lexington, KY, 40508 (606) 233-1833
Admin Hazel Ulrey.
Licensure Personal Care. *Beds* 25.

Harrison's Sanatorium
1537 N Limestone, Lexington, KY, 40504 (606) 252-6673
Admin Elaine Kniffen. *Medical Dir/Dir of Nursing* John H Prewitt MD.
Licensure Skilled Care. *Beds* 77. *Certified* Medicaid; Medicare.
Admissions Requirements Physician's request.

Staff RNs 5 (ft); LPNs 9 (ft); Orderlies 3 (ft); Nurses aides 24 (ft); Physical therapists 1 (pt); Reality therapists 1 (ft); Recreational therapists 1 (ft); Speech therapists 1 (pt); Dietitians 1 (pt).
Facilities Dining room; Physical therapy room; Activities room; Chapel; Crafts room; Laundry room; Barber/Beauty shop.
Activities Arts and Crafts; Cards; Games; Reading groups; Prayer groups; Movies; Shopping trips; Dances/Social or cultural gatherings.

Hayden's Personal Care Home*
553 E 3rd St, Lexington, KY, 40508 (606) 233-1944
Admin Lulu Hayden.
Licensure Personal Care. *Beds* 36.
Ownership Proprietary.

Homestead Nursing Center*
1608 Versailles Rd, Lexington, KY, 40504 (606) 252-0871
Admin Betty Wells.
Licensure Skilled Care; Intermediate Care.
Beds SNF 101; ICF 25. *Certified* Medicaid; Medicare.
Ownership Proprietary.

Julius Marks Home
866 Georgetown St, Lexington, KY, 40505 (606) 253-2558
Admin Patricia A Taylor.
Licensure Intermediate Care; Personal Care.
Beds ICF 73; Personal Care 34. *Certified* Medicaid.
Admissions Requirements Medical examination; Physician's request.
Staff RNs 1 (ft); LPNs 6 (ft), 1 (pt); Nurses aides 63 (ft); Reality therapists 1 (pt); Recreational therapists 1 (ft); Activities coordinators 1 (ft).
Facilities Dining room; Activities room; Laundry room; Barber/Beauty shop; Library.
Activities Arts and Crafts; Cards; Games; Reading groups; Prayer groups; Movies; Shopping trips; Dances/Social or cultural gatherings.
Description Daily reality orientation and monthly gourmet club (residents dine at local restaurants) offered. Facility has 4 buildings located on 11 acres of well-landscaped property.

Lexington Country Place
700 Mason Headley Rd, Lexington, KY, 40504 (606) 259-3486
Admin David K Rice. *Medical Dir/Dir of Nursing* Kenneth C Tufts MD.
Licensure Skilled Care. *Beds* 111. *Certified* Medicaid; Medicare.
Admissions Requirements Minimum age 16; Medical examination; Physician's request.
Staff RNs 6 (ft), 1 (pt); Orderlies 4 (ft); Nurses aides 42 (ft); Physical therapists 1 (ft); Recreational therapists 1 (ft); Speech therapists 1 (pt); Dietitians 1 (ft); Podiatrists 1 (pt).
Facilities Dining room; Physical therapy room; Activities room; Crafts room; Laundry room; Barber/Beauty shop; Library.
Activities Arts and Crafts; Cards; Games; Reading groups; Prayer groups; Movies; Shopping trips; Dances/Social or cultural gatherings.

Lexington Manor Health Care Facility
353 Waller Ave, Lexington, KY, 40504 (606) 252-3558
Admin Steve E Robison.
Licensure Skilled Care; Intermediate Care.
Beds SNF 52; ICF 128. *Certified* Medicaid; Medicare.
Admissions Requirements Medical examination; Physician's request.
Staff Physicians 3 (pt); RNs 7 (ft), 3 (pt); LPNs 18 (ft), 2 (pt); Orderlies 3 (ft); Nurses aides 63 (ft); Physical therapists 2 (pt); Speech therapists 1 (pt); Activities coordinators 1 (ft), 1 (pt); Dietitians 1 (pt); Dentists 1 (pt); Podiatrists 1 (pt).
Facilities Dining room; Physical therapy room; Activities room; Laundry room; Barber/Beauty shop.
Activities Arts and Crafts; Cards; Games; Reading groups; Prayer groups; Movies; Shopping trips; Dances/Social or cultural gatherings.
Description A Hill Haven facility, features 24-hour licensed nursing care, planned recreational program, staff chaplain; VA approved; conveniently located to hospitals.

Margaret Lily Home
160 Constitution St, Lexington, KY, 40508 (606) 252-3676
Admin Nancy Washbaugh.
Licensure Personal Care. *Beds* 28.

Mayfair Manor
3300 Tates Creek Rd, Lexington, KY, 40502 (606) 266-2126
Admin Danny E Hays. *Medical Dir/Dir of Nursing* Kenneth Tufts MD.
Licensure Skilled Care. *Beds* 100. *Certified* Medicaid; Medicare.
Admissions Requirements Physician's request.
Staff RNs 4 (ft), 2 (pt); LPNs 10 (ft), 4 (pt); Nurses aides 25 (ft), 20 (pt); Physical therapists 1 (ft), 1 (pt); Activities coordinators 1 (ft); Dietitians 1 (ft).
Facilities Dining room; Physical therapy room; Activities room; Laundry room; Barber/Beauty shop; Library.
Activities Arts and Crafts; Cards; Games; Reading groups; Prayer groups; Movies; Shopping trips; Dances/Social or cultural gatherings.
Description Awarded "Facility of the Year" recognition for Kentucky's Eastern District by KAHCF, facility has unique dental program, organized medical staff, a vast array of activities, and a registered dietician in charge of food service.

Meadowbrook Personal and Intermediate Care Home
2020 Cambridge Dr, Lexington, KY, 40504 (606) 252-6747
Admin Beatrice E Hood.
Licensure Intermediate Care; Personal Care.
Beds ICF 106; Personal Care 34. *Certified* Medicaid.
Admissions Requirements Medical examination.
Staff Physicians 10 (pt); RNs 1 (ft), 1 (pt); LPNs 5 (ft), 2 (pt); Orderlies 2 (ft), 2 (pt); Nurses aides 40 (ft), 9 (pt); Physical therapists 2 (pt); Speech therapists 1 (pt); Activities coordinators 1 (ft); Dietitians 1 (ft); Dentists 1 (pt); Podiatrists 1 (pt).
Facilities Dining room; Activities room; Crafts room; Laundry room; Barber/Beauty shop; Library; Sun rooms.
Activities Arts and Crafts; Cards; Games; Reading groups; Prayer groups; Movies; Shopping trips; Dances/Social or cultural gatherings.
Description Warm, comfortably furnished home with 4 large, inviting sun rooms decorated with rattan furniture, lamps, and many plants. Each bedroom is wallpapered, roomy, and cozy; private rooms offered. The home has a van that is used to take the residents on picnics, fishing, shopping, for rides in the country, and ice cream.

Miller's Nursing Home
1122 Oak Hill Dr, Lexington, KY, 40505 (606) 252-2055
Admin Nina R Baker. *Medical Dir/Dir of Nursing* Dr Taylor.
Licensure Nursing Home. *Beds* 34.
Admissions Requirements Minimum age 16; Physician's request.
Staff Physicians 3 (pt); RNs 1 (ft), 2 (pt); LPNs 2 (ft), 2 (pt); Orderlies 1 (ft); Nurses aides 10 (ft), 4 (pt); Activities coordinators 1 (pt).

Rose Manor Intermediate Care Facility
3057 Cleveland Pike, Lexington, KY, 40505 (606) 299-4117
Admin Alfred E McGregor. *Medical Dir/Dir of Nursing* Nickie Kerr.
Licensure Intermediate Care. *Beds* 34. *Certified* Medicaid.
Admissions Requirements Medical examination.
Staff RNs 2 (ft), 5 (pt); LPNs 1 (ft); Activities coordinators 1 (ft); Dietitians 1 (ft).
Facilities Dining room; Barber/Beauty shop.
Activities Arts and Crafts; Games; Reading groups.

Saint Margaret of Cortona Home
1310 Leestown Pike, Lexington, KY, 40508 (606) 255-4855
Admin Rose Francis Schifferli.
Licensure Personal Care. *Beds* 24.
Ownership Nonprofit.
Admissions Requirements Minimum age 55; Females only; Medical examination; Physician's request.
Staff RNs 1 (ft); Dietitians 1 (ft).
Affiliation Roman Catholic
Facilities Dining room; Chapel; Laundry room; Library.
Activities Cards; Games; Prayer groups; Movies.
Description Residents must be ambulatory and able to care for themselves physically. A friendly, home atmosphere prevails. All rooms are private.

Stephens Nursing Home
PO Box 11746, 909 Georgetown St, Lexington, KY, 40577-1746 (606) 254-9602
Admin Susan Lawson.
Licensure Intermediate Care; Personal Care.
Beds ICF 52; Personal Care 44. *Certified* Medicaid.
Ownership Proprietary.

Tates Creek Personal and Intermediate Care Facility
3576 Pimlico Pkwy, Lexington, KY, 40502 (606) 272-0608
Admin Beatrice E Hood. *Medical Dir/Dir of Nursing* Dr Richard French.
Licensure Intermediate Care; Personal Care.
Beds ICF 100; Personal Care 36. *Certified* Medicaid.
Admissions Requirements Physician's request.
Staff Physicians 15 (pt); RNs 1 (ft), 1 (pt); LPNs 5 (ft), 4 (pt); Orderlies 3 (ft); Nurses aides 37 (ft), 8 (pt); Physical therapists 2 (pt); Activities coordinators 1 (ft), 1 (pt); Dietitians 1 (ft); Dentists 1 (pt); Podiatrists 1 (pt).
Facilities Dining room; Activities room; Crafts room; Laundry room; Barber/Beauty shop; Library; Florida rooms; Van.
Activities Arts and Crafts; Cards; Games; Reading groups; Prayer groups; Movies; Shopping trips; Dances/Social or cultural gatherings.
Description Tates Creek is a resident oriented home. The decor is comfortable and cozy, with wallpaper in every bedroom, plants, good food, and continual activities, including going to shops, fishing, outside movies, restaurants, and hairdressers.

LIBERTY

Green River Rest Home*
PO Box G, Liberty, KY, 42539 (606) 787-9256
Admin Anna Lee Tasker.
Licensure Personal Care. *Beds* 24.
Ownership Nonprofit.

LONDON

Laurel Heights Home for the Elderly*
208 W 12th St, London, KY, 40741 (606) 864-4155
Admin John Osborne.
Licensure Skilled Care; Intermediate Care; Personal Care. *Beds* SNF 47; ICF 68; Personal Care 82. *Certified* Medicaid; Medicare.
Ownership Nonprofit.

LOUISA

J J Jordan Geriatric Center
Carpet Mill Rd, PO Box 726, Louisa, KY, 41230 (606) 638-4586
Admin David McKenzie. *Medical Dir/Dir of Nursing* Lloyd Browning MD and Norman Edwards MD.
Licensure Skilled Care; Intermediate Care; Personal Care. *Beds* SNF 34; ICF; Personal Care 16. *Certified* Medicaid; Medicare.
Admissions Requirements Physician's request.
Staff Physicians 2 (pt); RNs 3 (ft); LPNs 5 (ft); Orderlies 3 (ft); Nurses aides 40 (ft); Physical therapists 1 (ft); Speech therapists 1 (pt); Activities coordinators 1 (ft); Dietitians 1 (pt); Dentists 1 (pt).
Facilities Dining room; Physical therapy room; Activities room; Laundry room; Barber/Beauty shop.
Activities Arts and Crafts; Cards; Games; Movies; Shopping trips.

LOUISVILLE

Baptist Home East*
3001 Hounz Lane, Louisville, KY, 40222 (502) 426-5531
Admin Larry Jack Butler.
Licensure Intermediate Care; Personal Care.
Beds ICF 90; Personal Care 20. *Certified* Medicaid.
Ownership Nonprofit.
Affiliation Baptist

Bashford East Health Care Facility
3535 Bardstown Rd, Louisville, KY, 40218 (502) 459-1400
Admin C J Prater. *Medical Dir/Dir of Nursing* Dr L Perlstein.
Licensure Skilled Care; Intermediate Care.
Beds SNF 42; ICF 90. *Certified* Medicaid.
Staff RNs 6 (ft); LPNs 13 (ft); Orderlies 2 (ft); Nurses aides 50 (ft); Activities coordinators 1 (ft); Dietitians 1 (pt).
Facilities Dining room; Physical therapy room; Laundry room; Barber/Beauty shop.
Activities Arts and Crafts; Cards; Games; Reading groups; Prayer groups; Movies; Shopping trips; Dances/Social or cultural gatherings.

Bethesda Manor Nursing Home*
1252 Forest Dr, Louisville, KY, 40219 (502) 964-3381
Admin Homer F Rodgers.
Licensure Skilled Care; Intermediate Care.
Beds SNF 19; ICF 121. *Certified* Medicaid; Medicare.
Ownership Nonprofit.

Briarwood Nursing and Convalescent Center*
4300 Hazelwood Ave, Louisville, KY, 40215 (502) 367-6139
Admin Carol Ann Bottoms.
Licensure Skilled Care; Intermediate Care.
Beds SNF 39; ICF 39. *Certified* Medicaid; Medicare.
Ownership Proprietary.

Brownsboro Hills Nursing Home*
2141 Sycamore Ave, Louisville, KY, 40206 (502) 895-5417
Admin Harold V Bomar Jr.
Licensure Skilled Care. *Beds* 96.
Ownership Proprietary.

Charles P Moorman Home for Women*
966 Cherokee Rd, Louisville, KY, 40204 (502) 451-4424
Admin Vivienne Stanz.
Licensure Personal Care. *Beds* 81.
Ownership Nonprofit.
Admissions Requirements Females only

Christian Church Home of Louisville
942 S 4th St, Louisville, KY, 40203 (502) 583-6533
Admin Kim W Williams. *Medical Dir/Dir of Nursing* Dr Kenneth Holtzapple and Dr John C Wright.
Licensure Skilled Care; Intermediate Care; Personal Care. *Beds* SNF 27; ICF 137; Personal Care 70. *Certified* Medicaid; Medicare.
Admissions Requirements Medical examination.
Staff RNs 5 (ft), 4 (pt); LPNs 8 (ft), 6 (pt);

Nurses aides 44 (ft), 34 (pt); Physical therapists 1 (ft); Activities coordinators 1 (ft).
Facilities Dining room; Physical therapy room; Activities room; Chapel; Laundry room; Barber/Beauty shop; Library; Board room.
Activities Arts and Crafts; Games; Prayer groups.
Description Currently in the process of building a new $4.8 million facility with 120 beds to be completed in April, 1985.

Christopher—East*
4200 Browns Ln, Louisville, KY, 40220 (502) 459-8900
Admin J Edward Brown.
Licensure Intermediate Care; Personal Care; Nursing Home. *Beds* ICF 50; Personal Care 50; Nursing Home 100.
Ownership Proprietary.

Eastern Star Home of Kentucky*
923 Cherokee Rd, Louisville, KY, 40204 (502) 451-3535
Admin Thula Herrington.
Licensure Personal Care. *Beds* 30.
Ownership Nonprofit.
Affiliation Order of Eastern Star

Episcopal Church Home
1201 Lyndon Ln, Louisville, KY, 40222 (502) 425-8840
Admin J T Horton.
Licensure Intermediate Care; Personal Care.
Beds ICF 93; Personal Care 127. *Certified* Medicaid.
Affiliation Episcopal

Fair Lodge Health Care Center*
4522 Winnrose Way, Louisville, KY, 40211 (502) 778-5063
Admin O Howard Silvers.
Licensure Personal Care. *Beds* 141.
Ownership Proprietary.

Four Courts Inc
2100 Millvale Rd, Louisville, KY, 40205 (502) 451-0990
Admin Peggy Howe. *Medical Dir/Dir of Nursing* Dr Harold Kramer.
Licensure Skilled Care; Intermediate Care; Personal Care. *Beds* SNF 10; ICF 43; Personal Care 22. *Certified* Medicaid; Medicare.
Facilities Dining room; Physical therapy room; Activities room; Chapel; Crafts room; Laundry room; Barber/Beauty shop; Library.
Activities Arts and Crafts; Games; Reading groups; Movies; Shopping trips; Dances/Social or cultural gatherings.

Georgetown Manor Health Care Services
900 Gagel Ave, Louisville, KY, 40216 (502) 368-5827
Admin David E Wren. *Medical Dir/Dir of Nursing* E J Brockman MD.
Licensure Skilled Care. *Beds* 120. *Certified* Medicaid; Medicare.
Admissions Requirements Minimum age 16; Medical examination; Physician's request.
Staff RNs 7 (ft), 3 (pt); LPNs 13 (ft), 6 (pt); Nurses aides 34 (ft), 40 (pt); Physical therapists 2 (ft); Recreational therapists 3 (ft), 1 (pt); Occupational therapists 1 (pt); Speech therapists 1 (pt); Activities coordinators 1 (pt); Dieti-

tians 1 (ft), 2 (pt); Podiatrists 1 (pt).
Facilities Dining room; Physical therapy room; Activities room; Chapel; Laundry room; Barber/Beauty shop.
Activities Arts and Crafts; Cards; Games; Prayer groups; Movies.

Hazelwood Intermediate Care Facility*
PO Box 14506, 1800 Bluegrass Ave, Louisville, KY, 40214 (502) 361-2301
Admin Reuben M Thomas.
Licensure Intermediate Care for Mentally Retarded. *Beds* 220. *Certified* Medicaid.
Ownership Nonprofit.

Hillcreek Manor Convalescent Center
3116 Breckinridge Ln, Louisville, KY, 40220 (502) 459-9120
Admin Shirley Roederer. *Medical Dir/Dir of Nursing* Dr Kenneth Hodge.
Licensure Skilled Care; Intermediate Care; Personal Care. *Beds* SNF 28; ICF; Personal Care 30. *Certified* Medicaid; Medicare.
Admissions Requirements Medical examination; Physician's request.
Staff RNs 7 (ft), 1 (pt); LPNs 12 (ft), 7 (pt); Nurses aides 42 (ft), 26 (pt); Physical therapists 1 (ft); Speech therapists 1 (pt); Activities coordinators 2 (ft).
Facilities Dining room; Physical therapy room; Activities room; Chapel; Crafts room; Laundry room; Barber/Beauty shop; Library.
Activities Arts and Crafts; Cards; Games; Reading groups; Prayer groups; Movies; Dances/Social or cultural gatherings.
Description The highly trained staff of Hillcreek Manor is dedicated to providing a very special quality of life for all residents. Offers a complete restorative program in a warm and caring, home-like atmosphere. The high standards set have merited a superior rating by Kentucky's Cabinet for Human Resources.

Hillhaven Convalescent Center
432 E Jefferson St, Louisville, KY, 40202 (502) 583-2851
Admin Narda G Silon. *Medical Dir/Dir of Nursing* James Redmon MD.
Licensure Skilled Care; Intermediate Care. *Beds* SNF 60; ICF 120. *Certified* Medicaid; Medicare.
Admissions Requirements Minimum age 18; Medical examination.
Staff RNs 5 (ft), 2 (pt); LPNs 16 (ft), 6 (pt); Nurses aides 60 (ft), 20 (pt); Physical therapists 1 (ft); Speech therapists 1 (pt); Activities coordinators 11 (ft); Dietitians 1 (ft).
Facilities Dining room; Physical therapy room; Activities room; Chapel; Laundry room; Barber/Beauty shop.
Activities Arts and Crafts; Cards; Games; Reading groups; Prayer groups; Movies; Shopping trips; Dances/Social or cultural gatherings.
Description A very nice 4-story building, on bus lines convenient to hospital, expressway system, and downtown shopping. Fully-staffed with 24-hour nursing service to give quality care.

Home of the Innocents
485 E Gray St, Louisville, KY, 40202 (502) 582-3769
Admin David A Graves. *Medical Dir/Dir of*

Nursing Elsa Roe MD.
Licensure Skilled Care; Intermediate Care.
Beds 30. *Certified* Medicaid; Medicare.
Admissions Requirements Minimum age 3 days.
Staff Physicians 1 (pt); RNs 1 (ft), 5 (pt); LPNs 6 (ft), 2 (pt); Nurses aides 10 (ft), 8 (pt); Physical therapists 1 (pt); Activities coordinators 1 (ft); Dietitians 1 (pt); Dentists 1 (pt).
Affiliation Episcopal
Facilities Dining room; Laundry room.
Description Pediatric nursing care facility provides an in-house child development and infant stimulation program. In addition, one-third of the patients attend special education programs in the public schools.

Jefferson Manor
1801 Lynn Way, Louisville, KY, 40222 (502) 426-4513
Admin D C Bell. *Medical Dir/Dir of Nursing* Robert L Nold Sr MD.
Licensure Intermediate Care.
Admissions Requirements Medical examination; Physician's request.
Staff RNs 5 (ft), 3 (pt); LPNs 7 (ft), 7 (pt); Nurses aides 25 (ft), 25 (pt); Physical therapists 2 (pt); Speech therapists 1 (pt); Activities coordinators 2 (ft); Dietitians 1 (pt); Dentists 1 (pt); Podiatrists 1 (pt); Respiration therapists 4 (ft), 2 (pt).
Facilities Dining room; Physical therapy room; Activities room; Crafts room; Laundry room; Barber/Beauty shop; Library.
Activities Arts and Crafts; Cards; Games; Reading groups; Prayer groups; Movies; Shopping trips; Dances/Social or cultural gatherings; Wine and cheese parties; Family dinners; Guest luncheons.
Description Facility is located on 4 acres in a quiet residential area easily accessible from Interstate 264, designed for those who desire an elegant lifestyle combined with excellence in health care; provides for residents' physical, psychological, social, and spiritual needs.

Keeling Home for Care*
236 E Kentucky St, Louisville, KY, 40203 (502) 584-2191
Admin Louis Best.
Licensure Personal Care. *Beds* 126.
Ownership Proprietary.

Kings Daughters and Sons Home
1705 Stevens Ave, Louisville, KY, 40205 (502) 451-7330
Admin Edward L Holley. *Medical Dir/Dir of Nursing* Harold M Kramer MD.
Licensure Skilled Care; Intermediate Care; Personal Care. *Beds* SNF 94; ICF 60; Personal Care 15. *Certified* Medicaid; Medicare.
Admissions Requirements Medical examination; Physician's request.
Staff Physicians 2 (pt); RNs 4 (ft); LPNs 12 (ft); Orderlies 3 (ft); Nurses aides 65 (ft); Physical therapists 1 (ft); Speech therapists 1 (pt); Activities coordinators 1 (ft); Dietitians 1 (ft); Dentists 1 (pt); Ophthalmologists 1 (pt); Podiatrists 1 (pt).
Affiliation King's Daughters and Sons
Facilities Dining room; Physical therapy room; Activities room; Chapel; Crafts room; Laundry room; Barber/Beauty shop; Library.

Activities Arts and Crafts; Cards; Games; Reading groups; Prayer groups; Movies; Dances/Social or cultural gatherings.
Description Facility is 75 years old in service to mankind; it is a ministry of people in need in the name of Jesus Christ.

Klondike Manor*
3802 Klondike Ln, Louisville, KY, 40218 (502) 452-1579
Admin Deborah Haering.
Licensure Intermediate Care. *Beds* 62. *Certified* Medicaid.
Ownership Proprietary.

Louisville Birthing Center*
1101 S Second St, Louisville, KY, 40203 (502) 581-9477
Admin Judith Davenport.
Ownership Proprietary.

Louisville Protestant Althenheim*
936 Barrett Ave, Louisville, KY, 40204 (502) 584-7417
Admin Joan Walcutt.
Licensure Personal Care. *Beds* 58.
Ownership Nonprofit.

Lyndon Lane Nursing Center*
1101 Lyndon Ln, Louisville, KY, 40222 (502) 425-0331
Admin Lanny Harvey.
Licensure Skilled Care; Intermediate Care.
Beds SNF 29; ICF 136. *Certified* Medicaid; Medicare.
Ownership Proprietary.

Marian Home
3105 Lexington Rd, Louisville, KY, 40206 (502) 893-0121
Admin M Adelaide Fackler. *Medical Dir/Dir of Nursing* Walter L Thompson MD.
Licensure Intermediate Care; Personal Care.
Beds ICF 55; Personal Care 15. *Certified* Medicaid.
Ownership Nonprofit.
Admissions Requirements Females only; Medical examination; Physician's request.
Staff Physicians 1 (pt); RNs 5 (pt); LPNs 1 (ft), 4 (pt); Nurses aides 13 (ft), 10 (pt); Recreational therapists 3 (pt); Activities coordinators 1 (pt); Dietitians 5 (ft), 8 (pt); Podiatrists 1 (pt).
Affiliation Roman Catholic
Facilities Dining room; Physical therapy room; Activities room; Chapel; Crafts room; Laundry room; Barber/Beauty shop; Library.
Activities Arts and Crafts; Cards; Games; Reading groups; Prayer groups; Movies; Shopping trips; Dances/Social or cultural gatherings.
Description Marian Home is a special purpose facility. Admissions are limited to religious women.

Meadows—East*
2529 6 Mile Ln, Louisville, KY, 40220 (502) 491-5560
Admin Debra Finneran.
Licensure Intermediate Care; Personal Care.
Beds ICF 128; Personal Care 70. *Certified* Medicaid.
Ownership Proprietary.

Meadows—South*
1120 Christland Rd, Louisville, KY, 40214
(502) 367-0104
Admin Kathy Fellonneau.
Licensure Intermediate Care; Personal Care.
Beds ICF 100; Personal Care 32. *Certified* Medicaid.
Ownership Proprietary.

Meadowview Nursing and Convalescent Center
9701 Whipps Mill Rd, Louisville, KY, 40223
(502) 426-2778
Admin Mary Campbell. *Medical Dir/Dir of Nursing* A J Perez MD.
Licensure Intermediate Care; Personal Care.
Beds ICF 100; Personal Care 32. *Certified* Medicaid.
Admissions Requirements Minimum age 21; Medical examination; Physician's request.

Melrose Manor
4331 Churchman Ave, Louisville, KY, 40215
(502) 367-6489
Admin William M Pierce.
Licensure Nursing Home. *Beds* 45.
Admissions Requirements Minimum age 18; Medical examination.
Staff Physicians 1 (pt); RNs 1 (ft); LPNs 2 (ft), 6 (pt); Orderlies 2 (ft); Nurses aides 16 (ft), 6 (pt); Physical therapists; Activities coordinators 1 (ft); Dietitians 1 (pt); Audiologists.
Facilities Dining room; Activities room; Laundry room; Barber/Beauty shop; Library.
Activities Arts and Crafts; Games; Reading groups; Shopping trips; Dances/Social or cultural gatherings.
Description Small private facility elects not to participate in Title 18 and 19 programs.

Mount Holly Nursing Home
446 Mount Holly Ave, Louisville, KY, 40206
(502) 897-1646
Admin Nancy Bale. *Medical Dir/Dir of Nursing* Dr Eric Hilgeford.
Licensure Nursing Home. *Beds* 109.
Admissions Requirements Medical examination; Physician's request.
Staff RNs 7 (ft), 5 (pt); LPNs 1 (ft), 1 (pt); Nurses aides 27 (ft); Physical therapists 1 (pt); Occupational therapists 1 (pt); Speech therapists 1 (pt); Activities coordinators 1 (pt); Dietitians 1 (pt); Dentists 4 (pt); Podiatrists 2 (pt).
Facilities Dining room; Physical therapy room; Activities room; Crafts room; Laundry room; Barber/Beauty shop.
Activities Arts and Crafts; Cards; Games; Reading groups; Prayer groups; Movies; Dances/Social or cultural gatherings.
Description Home-like 19-year old facility is nestled in a beautiful older section of town surrounded by trees and hills; recently completed a major internal renovation.

Mount Lebanon Personal Care Home*
1015 Magazine St, Louisville, KY, 40203 (502) 589-0727
Admin Antoinette O Taylor.
Licensure Intermediate Care. *Beds* 117.
Ownership Nonprofit.

Nazareth Home
2000 Newburg Rd, Louisville, KY, 40205 (502) 459-9681

Admin Sr Philip Maria Fuhs. *Medical Dir/Dir of Nursing* Russell May MD.
Licensure Skilled Care; Intermediate Care; Personal care. *Beds* SNF 32; ICF 86; Personal Care 50. *Certified* Medicaid; Medicare.
Staff Physicians 2 (pt); RNs 7 (ft); LPNs 9 (ft), 7 (pt); Orderlies 1 (ft); Nurses aides 41 (ft), 15 (pt); Physical therapists 1 (pt); Speech therapists 1 (pt); Activities coordinators 3 (ft); Dietitians 1 (pt); Dentists 2 (pt); Podiatrists 1 (pt).
Affiliation Roman Catholic
Facilities Dining room; Physical therapy room; Activities room; Chapel; Crafts room; Laundry room; Barber/Beauty shop; Library.
Activities Arts and Crafts; Cards; Games; Reading groups; Prayer groups; Movies; Shopping trips; Dances/Social or cultural gatherings
Description Facility has initiated validation programs for disoriented residents which has aided greatly in calming them.

Northfield Manor Health Care Facility
6000 Hunting Rd, Louisville, KY, 40222 (502) 426-1425
Admin Carolyn Kottak. *Medical Dir/Dir of Nursing* Terry Hagan MD.
Licensure Skilled Care. *Beds* 120. *Certified* Medicaid.
Staff Physicians 20 (pt); RNs 4 (ft), 2 (pt); LPNs 4 (ft), 6 (pt); Orderlies 1 (ft); Nurses aides 32 (ft), 8 (pt); Activities coordinators 1 (ft); Dietitians 1 (ft); Dentists 1 (pt); Podiatrists 1 (pt).
Facilities Dining room; Physical therapy room; Activities room; Laundry room; Barber/Beauty shop.
Activities Arts and Crafts; Cards; Games; Prayer groups; Movies; Dances/Social or cultural gatherings.

Parkway Medical Center
1155 Eastern Pkwy, Louisville, KY, 40217 (502) 636-5241
Admin Joseph Okruhlica. *Medical Dir/Dir of Nursing* Dr Donne DeMunbrun.
Licensure Skilled Care; Intermediate Care.
Beds 252. *Certified* Medicaid; Medicare.
Admissions Requirements Physician's request.
Staff Physicians 2 (ft); RNs 15 (ft); LPNs 33 (ft); Nurses aides 112 (ft); Physical therapists 1 (ft), 1 (pt); Speech therapists 1 (pt); Activities coordinators 1 (ft); Dietitians 1 (pt); Dentists 2 (pt); Podiatrists 1 (pt).
Facilities Dining room; Physical therapy room; Activities room; Chapel; Crafts room; Barber/Beauty shop; Dental office; X-ray facility; Coffee shop; Pharmacy; Gift shop.
Activities Arts and Crafts; Cards; Games; Prayer groups; Movies; Dances/Social or cultural gatherings; Annual outings.

Parr's Rest Home
969 Cherokee Rd, Louisville, KY, 40204 (502) 451-5440
Admin Dorothy Cable. *Medical Dir/Dir of Nursing* Doris Pipkin MD.
Licensure Personal Care. *Beds* 80.
Admissions Requirements Minimum age 65; Medical examination.
Staff Physicians; RNs; Nurses aides 8 (ft), 1 (pt); Activities coordinators 1 (pt); Podiatrists 1 (pt).
Facilities Dining room; Activities room; Chapel; Crafts room; Laundry room; Barber/Beauty

shop.
Activities Arts and Crafts; Cards; Games; Reading groups; Prayer groups; Movies; Shopping trips; Dances/Social or cultural gatherings.

Pine Tree Villa
4604 Lowe Rd, Louisville, KY, 40220 (502) 451-1401
Admin James T Sleadd.
Licensure Intermediate Care; Personal Care.
Beds ICF 70; Personal Care 133. *Certified* Medicaid.
Admissions Requirements Medical examination; Physician's request.
Staff RNs; LPNs; Nurses aides; Recreational therapists; Activities coordinators; Dietitians.
Facilities Dining room; Physical therapy room; Activities room; Chapel; Laundry room; Barber/Beauty shop.
Activities Arts and Crafts; Cards; Games; Reading groups; Prayer groups; Movies; Shopping trips; Dances/Social or cultural gatherings.

Pleasant Place*
12800 Dixie Hwy, Louisville, KY, 40272 (502) 937-4965
Admin Ken L Jones.
Licensure Personal Care. *Beds* 58.
Ownership Proprietary.

Rose Anna Hughes Presbyterian Home*
1402 Saint James Court, Louisville, KY, 40208 (502) 637-3639
Admin Margaret Vaughn.
Licensure Personal Care. *Beds* 32.
Ownership Nonprofit.
Affiliation Presbyterian

Sacred Heart Home
2120 Payne St, Louisville, KY, 40206 (502) 895-9425
Admin Mary Julius Voelz.
Licensure Personal Care. *Beds* 64.
Admissions Requirements Minimum age 65; Medical examination.
Staff RNs 1 (ft); LPNs 1 (ft); Nurses aides 10 (pt); Activities coordinators 1 (ft).
Affiliation Roman Catholic
Facilities Dining room; Activities room; Chapel; Laundry room; Barber/Beauty shop; Library.
Activities Cards; Games; Reading groups; Prayer groups; Movies; Dances/Social or cultural gatherings.
Description This is a personal care/congregate living facility with spacious lawns and ample walking area; located on a car line near downtown but far enough out that suburban shopping centers are easily accessible.

Saint Matthews Manor
227 Browns Ln, Louisville, KY, 40207 (502) 893-2595
Admin Earle Goff.
Licensure Nursing Home. *Beds* 125.
Admissions Requirements Medical examination.
Staff RNs 12 (ft), 12 (pt); LPNs 1 (ft); Orderlies 2 (pt); Nurses aides 45 (ft), 6 (pt); Physical therapists 1 (pt); Activities coordinators 1 (ft); Dietitians 1 (ft); Podiatrists 1 (pt).
Facilities Dining room; Activities room; Crafts room; Laundry room; Barber/Beauty shop;

Library.
Activities Arts and Crafts; Cards; Games; Prayer groups; Movies; Shopping trips; Dances/Social or cultural gatherings; Field trips.
Description Recently renovated; RNs around the clock; respite care provided; waitress service in dining room; adjacent to 2 major hospitals.

Summerfield Manor Nursing Home*
1877 Farnsley Rd, Louisville, KY, 40216 (502) 448-8622
Admin Donald D Irwin.
Licensure Intermediate Care. *Beds* 179. *Certified* Medicaid.
Ownership Proprietary.

Twinbrook Nursing Home*
3526 Dutchmans Ln, Louisville, KY, 40205 (502) 452-6331
Admin Bryan S McCoy Jr.
Licensure Skilled Care; Nursing Home. *Beds* SNF 25; Nursing Home 62. *Certified* Medicaid; Medicare.
Ownership Proprietary.

W W Spradling Rest Home*
726 S Preston, Louisville, KY, 40203 (502) 585-2426
Admin William H Brown Sr.
Licensure Personal Care. *Beds* 24.
Ownership Nonprofit.

Wesley Manor Nursing Center and Retirement Home*
PO Box 19258, 5012 E Manslick Rd, Louisville, KY, 40219 (502) 969-3277
Admin Edward D Brandeberry.
Licensure Skilled Care; Intermediate Care; Personal Care. *Beds* SNF 10; ICF 58; Personal Care 39. *Certified* Medicaid; Medicare.
Ownership Nonprofit.

Westminster Terrace
2116 Buechel Bank Rd, Louisville, KY, 40218 (502) 499-9383
Admin Robert Elliott. *Medical Dir/Dir of Nursing* Dr Harold Haller.
Licensure Skilled Care; Intermediate Care. *Beds* SNF 31; ICF 81. *Certified* Medicaid; Medicare.
Admissions Requirements Minimum age 65; Physician's request.
Staff RNs 7 (ft), 4 (pt); LPNs 10 (ft), 1 (pt); Nurses aides 21 (ft), 25 (pt); Physical therapists 1 (ft); Speech therapists 1 (pt); Activities coordinators 2 (ft); Dietitians 1 (ft); Dentists 1 (pt); Podiatrists 1 (pt).
Affiliation Presbyterian
Facilities Dining room; Physical therapy room; Activities room; Chapel; Crafts room; Laundry room; Barber/Beauty shop; Library.
Activities Arts and Crafts; Cards; Games; Reading groups; Prayer groups; Movies; Shopping trips; Dances/Social or cultural gatherings.
Description Westminster Terrace is the first continuing care retirement community in Kentucky. It is more than just a comfortable, secure, and maintenance-free place to live; features individual garden plots and private balconies, and the security of knowing one of the most modern and well-run nursing centers in the area is adjacent.

Windsor Health Care*
9600 Lambourne Blvd, Louisville, KY, 40272 (502) 935-6153
Admin Marietta Preston.
Licensure Intermediate Care. *Beds* 128. *Certified* Medicaid.
Ownership Proprietary.

Woodhaven Medical Services
8101 Dixie Hwy, Louisville, KY, 40258 (502) 937-2700
Admin David B Wilson.
Licensure Skilled Care; Intermediate Care. *Beds* SNF 94; ICF 161. *Certified* Medicaid.

LUDLOW

Madonna Manor*
2344 Amsterdam Rd, Ludlow, KY, 41016 (606) 341-3981
Admin Sr M Charles Wolking.
Licensure Intermediate Care. *Beds* 38. *Certified* Medicaid.
Ownership Nonprofit.

MADISONVILLE

Brown's Rest Home
384 Thompson Ave, Madisonville, KY, 42431 (502) 821-5294
Admin Larry Brown.
Licensure Intermediate Care; Personal Care. *Beds* ICF 100; Personal Care 48. *Certified* Medicaid.
Admissions Requirements Medical examination.
Staff RNs 1 (pt); LPNs 6 (ft); Orderlies 3 (ft); Nurses aides 50 (ft), 20 (pt); Speech therapists 1 (pt); Dietitians 1 (pt).
Facilities Dining room; Activities room; Crafts room; Laundry room.
Activities Arts and Crafts; Cards; Games; Prayer groups; Movies; Shopping trips; Dances/Social or cultural gatherings.

Clinic Convalescent Center*
55 E North St, Madisonville, KY, 42431 (502) 821-1492
Admin Coleen Lovell.
Licensure Skilled Care. *Beds* 66. *Certified* Medicaid; Medicare.
Ownership Proprietary.

Kentucky Rest Haven*
419 N Seminary St, Madisonville, KY, 42431 (502) 821-5564
Admin Danny Belcher.
Licensure Skilled Care; Intermediate Care. *Beds* SNF 59; ICF 35. *Certified* Medicaid; Medicare.
Ownership Proprietary.

Senior Citizen Nursing Home
US Rt 41A and Pride Ave, Madisonville, KY, 42431 (502) 821-1813
Admin Sandra Higgins. *Medical Dir/Dir of Nursing* Dr Richard Dodds.
Licensure Skilled Care; Intermediate Care. *Beds* SNF 32; ICF 54. *Certified* Medicaid; Medicare.
Admissions Requirements Medical examina-

tion; Physician's request.
Facilities Dining room; Physical therapy room; Laundry room; Barber/Beauty shop; Library.
Activities Cards; Games; Movies; Shopping trips; Dances/Social or cultural gatherings.
Description Teaching facility.

Watkins Rest Home*
Franklin and Givens Sts, Madisonville, KY, 42431 (502) 821-7232
Admin Frank Ramsey.
Licensure Personal Care. *Beds* 86.
Ownership Proprietary.

MANCHESTER

Laurel Creek Health Care Center*
Rt 2, Box 254, Manchester, KY, 40962 (606) 598-6163
Admin Deborah Fannin.
Licensure Intermediate Care; Personal Care. *Beds* ICF 98; Personal Care 20. *Certified* Medicaid.
Ownership Proprietary.

Memorial Hospital—Skilled Nursing Facility
401 Memorial Dr, Manchester, KY, 40962 (606) 598-5104
Admin Robert W Burchard. *Medical Dir/Dir of Nursing* Dr Cecil Taylor.
Licensure Skilled Care. *Beds* 11. *Certified* Medicaid; Medicare.
Admissions Requirements Physician's request.
Staff RNs 2 (ft); LPNs 3 (ft), 2 (pt); Orderlies 2 (ft); Nurses aides 3 (ft), 2 (pt); Physical therapists 1 (ft); Recreational therapists 1 (pt); Activities coordinators 1 (pt); Dietitians 1 (pt).
Affiliation Seventh-Day Adventist
Facilities Physical therapy room; Activities room; Chapel; Laundry room.
Activities Arts and Crafts; Games; Movies; Individual activities as needed.

MARION

Best Care Nursing Home*
Moore and Watson Sts, Marion, KY, 42064 (502) 965-2218
Admin Marie Yates.
Licensure Intermediate Care; Personal Care. *Beds* ICF 83; Personal Care 24. *Certified* Medicaid.
Ownership Proprietary.

MASONIC HOME

Masonic Widows and Orphans Home and Infirmary
Masonic Home, KY, 40041 (502) 897-3344
Admin Ronald Mundy. *Medical Dir/Dir of Nursing* Dr Rodney Veitschegger.
Licensure Skilled Care; Personal Care; Nursing Home. *Beds* SNF 38; Personal Care 129; Nursing Home 130. *Certified* Medicaid; Medicare.
Admissions Requirements Minimum age 60; Females only; Medical examination; Physician's request.
Staff Physicians 4 (pt); RNs 9 (ft), 5 (pt); LPNs 8 (ft), 4 (pt); Nurses aides 48 (ft), 6 (pt); Physical therapists 1 (pt); Activities coordina-

tors 2 (ft), 1 (pt); Dietitians 1 (ft).
Affiliation Masons
Facilities Dining room; Physical therapy room;
Activities room; Chapel; Crafts room; Laundry
room; Barber/Beauty shop.
Activities Arts and Crafts; Cards; Games;
Reading groups; Prayer groups; Movies; Shopping trips; Dances/Social or cultural gatherings.
Description The Masonic Widows and
Orphans Home and Infirmary, Inc, is a fraternal organization which provides nursing care to
widows of Masons. The widow must be at least
65 years old and her husband been a member
of a Kentucky lodge.

MAYFIELD

Care Inn of Mayfield*
4th and Indiana Ave, Mayfield, KY, 42066
(502) 247-0200
Admin Floyd D Beard.
Licensure Skilled Care; Intermediate Care.
Beds SNF 42; ICF 58. *Certified* Medicaid;
Medicare.
Ownership Proprietary.

Green Acres Personal Care Home*
402 W Farthing St, Mayfield, KY, 42066 (502)
247-6477
Admin Samuel Gray.
Licensure Personal Care. *Beds* 73.
Ownership Proprietary.

Mayfield Personal Care Home*
Hwy 45, Box 325, Mayfield, KY, 42066 (502)
247-3259
Admin Dianne DeSpain.
Licensure Personal Care. *Beds* 140.
Ownership Proprietary.

Meadowview Retirement Home*
Rt 7, Box 64, Mayfield, KY, 42066 (502)
345-2116
Admin Joseph M Shellman.
Licensure Personal Care. *Beds* 24.
Ownership Proprietary.

Mill's Manor*
Mill's Manor Dr, Mayfield, KY, 42066 (502)
247-7890
Admin Lowell Beck.
Licensure Intermediate Care. *Beds* 98. *Certified* Medicaid.
Ownership Proprietary.

Skyview Personal Care Home*
Rt 4, Mayfield, KY, 42066 (502) 623-6696
Admin Nancy Riley.
Licensure Personal Care. *Beds* 40.
Ownership Proprietary.

MAYSVILLE

Maysville Extended Care Facility*
Rt 2, Maysville, KY, 41056 (606) 564-4085
Admin Marion Russell.
Licensure Skilled Care; Intermediate Care.
Beds SNF 18; ICF 82. *Certified* Medicaid;
Medicare.
Ownership Proprietary.

MELBER

Melber Rest Home
General Delivery, Melber, KY, 42069 (502)
856-3210
Admin Anna L Parks.
Licensure Personal Care. *Beds* 10.
Admissions Requirements Minimum age 16;
Medical examination.
Staff Nurses aides 2 (ft); Dietitians 1 (ft).
Facilities Dining room; Activities room; Laundry room.
Activities Arts and Crafts; Cards; Games; Prayer groups; Shopping trips; Dances/Social or
cultural gatherings.
Description Melber Rest Home is just like your
own home. People at this home do what they
want so long as it pleases state rules.

MIDDLESBORO

Ruby's Rest Home
504 S 24th St, Middlesboro, KY, 40965 (606)
248-1540
Admin Ruby Lake. *Medical Dir/Dir of
Nursing* Dr C L Kinpatrick.
Licensure Personal Care. *Beds* 64.
Admissions Requirements Minimum age 16;
Females only; Medical examination; Physician's request.
Staff Physicians 1 (pt); RNs 1 (pt); LPNs 2
(pt); Orderlies 13 (pt); Activities coordinators 1
(ft); Dietitians 1 (ft).
Facilities Dining room; Activities room; Crafts
room; Laundry room; TV lounges.
Activities Arts and Crafts; Cards; Games;
Reading groups; Prayer groups; Movies; Shopping trips; Dances/Social or cultural gatherings.
Description Facility features worship services
and planned activities.

MONTICELLO

Dishman Personal Care Home*
Warsham Ln, Monticello, KY, 42633 (606)
348-6201
Admin Christine Goff.
Licensure Personal Care. *Beds* 49.
Ownership Proprietary.

Hicks Golden Years Nursing Home
Rt 4, Box 121, Monticello, KY, 42633 (606)
348-6034
Admin Charlotte Anderson.
Licensure Intermediate Care; Personal Care.
Beds ICF 55; Personal Care 5. *Certified* Medicaid.
Staff RNs 3 (ft); LPNs 2 (ft); Orderlies 2 (ft);
Nurses aides 20 (ft), 2 (pt); Physical therapists 1
(pt); Activities coordinators 1 (ft); Dietitians 1
(ft).
Facilities Dining room; Activities room; Chapel; Laundry room; Barber/Beauty shop.
Activities Arts and Crafts; Cards; Games;
Reading groups; Prayer groups; Movies; Shopping trips; Dances/Social or cultural gatherings.
Description Golden Years provides up-to-date
medical care to all residents. The atmosphere is
very home-like. Each resident is treated
according to individual needs and personality.
Staff is very dedicated and caring.

MOREHEAD

Life Care Center of Morehead
933 N Tolliver Rd, PO Box 298, Morehead,
KY, 40351 (606) 784-7518
Admin Virginia H Saunders. *Medical Dir/Dir
of Nursing* J Hunter Black MD.
Licensure Skilled Care; Intermediate Care; Personal Care. *Beds* SNF 30; ICF 67; Personal
Care 14. *Certified* Medicaid; Medicare.
Admissions Requirements Minimum age 16;
Medical examination; Physician's request.
Staff RNs 2 (ft), 2 (pt); LPNs 6 (ft), 5 (pt);
Nurses aides 38 (ft), 8 (pt); Activities coordinators 1 (ft); Dietitians 1 (pt); Dentists 1 (pt).
Facilities Dining room; Chapel; Laundry
room; Barber/Beauty shop.
Activities Arts and Crafts; Cards; Games; Prayer groups; Dances/Social or cultural gatherings.
Description This is the only nursing home in
Rowan County. As a result, we service the area
within a 50-mile radius. Our facility serves as
the practicum site for the county vocational
school (nursing assistant and LPN programs)
and Morehead State University (RN program).

MORGANFIELD

Grove Center Rest Home
Rt 3, Box 118, Morganfield, KY, 42437 (502)
389-2874
Admin Marcus Logsdon.
Licensure Personal Care. *Beds* 44.

Higgins Learning Center
PO Box 374, Morganfield, KY, 42437 (502)
389-0822
Admin Robert R Rupsch. *Medical Dir/Dir of
Nursing* Joel Haffner.
Licensure Intermediate Care for Mentally
Retarded. *Beds* 56. *Certified* Medicaid.
Admissions Requirements Minimum age 7.
Staff Physicians 1 (ft); RNs 4 (pt); LPNs 4 (ft);
Orderlies 26 (ft), 3 (pt); Physical therapists 1
(pt); Recreational therapists 1 (ft); Occupational
therapists 1 (pt); Speech therapists 1 (pt);
Activities coordinators 1 (ft); Dietitians 1 (pt).
Facilities Dining room; Physical therapy room;
Activities room; Crafts room; Laundry room;
Library.
Activities Arts and Crafts; Cards; Games;
Reading groups; Prayer groups; Movies; Shopping trips; Dances/Social or cultural gatherings.
Description The Higgins Learning Center is a
56-bed ICF-MR established by Res-Care, Inc to
provide quality, residential care for MR/DD
clients. Higgins was one of the first proprietary
facilities to undergo and obtain voluntary
accreditation status (ACMRDD).

Medco Center of Morganfield*
Rt 5, Box 24A, Morganfield, KY, 42437 (502)
389-3513
Admin Wanda J Jones.
Licensure Intermediate Care. *Beds* 60. *Certified* Medicaid.
Ownership Proprietary.

MORGANTOWN

Lakeview Nursing Home
Warren St, Box 159, Morgantown, KY, 42261
(502) 526-3368
Admin Ralph Eaton. *Medical Dir/Dir of
Nursing* Dr Robert Johnson.
Licensure Skilled Care; Intermediate Care; Personal Care. *Beds* SNF 38; ICF 96; Personal
Care 35. *Certified* Medicaid; Medicare.
Admissions Requirements Medical examination; Physician's request.
Staff Physicians 4 (pt); RNs 4 (ft), 3 (pt); LPNs
4 (ft), 1 (pt); Orderlies 1 (ft); Nurses aides 58
(ft), 16 (pt); Physical therapists 1 (pt); Speech
therapists 1 (pt); Activities coordinators 1 (ft);
Dietitians 1 (pt); Dentists 1 (pt).
Facilities Dining room; Physical therapy room;
Activities room; Chapel; Laundry room; Barber/Beauty shop.
Activities Arts and Crafts; Cards; Games;
Reading groups; Prayer groups; Movies; Shopping trips; Dances/Social or cultural gatherings.
Description Facility is located one block from
business section of town; superior license rating
for all 3 levels of care.

MOUNT STERLING

Annie Walker Nursing Home*
PO Box 639, Bridgett Dr, Mount Sterling, KY,
40353 (606) 498-6397
Admin Dila Walker.
Licensure Intermediate Care; Personal Care.
Beds ICF 32; Personal Care 18.
Ownership Proprietary.

Mary Chiles Hospital*
PO Box 520, Sterling Ave, Mount Sterling, KY,
40353 (606) 498-1220
Admin Larry Unroe.
Licensure Skilled Care. *Beds* 30. *Certified* Medicaid; Medicare.
Ownership Nonprofit.

Windsor Care Center*
PO Box 251, Rt 460, Widsor Square, Mount
Sterling, KY, 40353 (606) 498-3343
Admin James R Stephens.
Licensure Intermediate Care; Personal Care.
Beds ICF 52; Personal Care 8. *Certified* Medicaid.
Ownership Nonprofit.

MOUNT VERNON

**Rockcastle County Hospital—Skilled Nursing
Facility***
Rt 4, Box 36, Mount Vernon, KY, 40456 (606)
256-2195
Admin Rober Cromer.
Licensure Skilled Care. *Beds* 32. *Certified* Medicaid; Medicare.
Ownership Nonprofit.

MUNFORDVILLE

Hart County Personal Care Home
Riverview Ct, Munfordville, KY, 42765 (502)
524-4194
Admin Dan Tullock.

Licensure Personal Care. *Beds* 54.
Admissions Requirements Minimum age 16;
Medical examination.
Staff Nurses aides 11 (ft).
Facilities Dining room; Laundry room; Barber/Beauty shop.
Activities Recreation in afternoon.
Description Facility sits on a beautiful lot, well-kept, with mature shade trees, overlooking scenic Green River (hence the name Riverview
Court). Our facility has a religious service every
Sunday p.m. conducted by various churches in
the community.

MURRAY

Fern Terrace Lodge of Murray*
1505 Stadium View Dr, Murray, KY, 42071
(502) 753-7109
Admin Laverne Tapp.
Licensure Personal Care. *Beds* 103.
Ownership Proprietary.

**Murray-Calloway County Hospital Long Term
Care Unit**
803 Poplar St, Murray, KY, 42071 (502)
753-5131
Admin J Stuart Poston.
Licensure Skilled Care; Intermediate Care.
Beds SNF 20; ICF 20. *Certified* Medicaid;
Medicare.
Staff Physicians 35 (ft); RNs 1 (ft), 1 (pt);
LPNs 8 (ft), 1 (pt); Orderlies 1 (ft), 1 (pt);
Nurses aides 12 (ft); Physical therapists 1 (ft);
Speech therapists 1 (pt); Activities coordinators
1 (ft); Dietitians 2 (ft); Dentists 1 (ft); Ophthalmologists 3 (ft).
Facilities Dining room; Physical therapy room;
Activities room; Chapel; Laundry room; Barber/Beauty shop; Library.
Activities Arts and Crafts; Cards; Games; Prayer groups; Movies; Shopping trips;
Dances/Social or cultural gatherings; Pet therapy; Cooking club.

Westview Nursing Home*
PO Box 165, 1401 S 16th St, Murray, KY,
42071 (502) 753-1304
Admin Harold G Beaman.
Licensure Skilled Care; Intermediate Care.
Beds SNF 56; ICF 118. *Certified* Medicaid;
Medicare.
Ownership Proprietary.

NAZARETH

Nazareth Infirmary
Nazareth, KY, 40048 (502) 348-5931
Admin Patricia Farrell.
Licensure Personal Care. *Beds* 42.

NERINX

Loretto Motherhouse Infirmary
Nerinx, KY, 40049 (502) 865-5811
Admin R A Schuler.
Licensure Intermediate Care; Personal Care.
Beds ICF 63; Personal Care 22. *Certified* Medicaid.
Admissions Requirements Females only;
Medical examination; Physician's request.

Staff RNs 1 (ft); LPNs 4 (ft); Nurses aides 17
(ft), 9 (pt); Activities coordinators 1 (ft), 1 (pt).
Affiliation Roman Catholic
Facilities Dining room; Physical therapy room;
Activities room; Chapel; Crafts room; Laundry
room; Barber/Beauty shop; Library.
Activities Arts and Crafts; Games; Reading
groups; Prayer groups; Movies; Shopping trips.
Description Loretto Motherhouse Infirmary is
a special purpose facility primarily for retired
and infirmed Sisters of Loretto.

NEW CASTLE

Homestead Nursing Center of New Castle
Box 329, New Castle, KY, 40050 (502)
845-2861
Admin Marilyn Perry. *Medical Dir/Dir of
Nursing* Dr R Houston.
Licensure Intermediate Care. *Beds* 60. *Certified* Medicaid.
Admissions Requirements Minimum age 16.
Staff Physicians 4 (ft); RNs 2 (ft); LPNs 2 (ft);
Nurses aides 22 (ft); Physical therapists 1 (ft);
Recreational therapists 1 (ft); Activities coordinators 1 (ft); Dietitians 1 (ft); Dentists 1 (ft).
Facilities Dining room; Activities room; Crafts
room; Laundry room; Barber/Beauty shop;
Library.
Activities Arts and Crafts; Cards; Games;
Reading groups; Prayer groups; Movies; Dances/Social or cultural gatherings.

NEWPORT

Baptist Convalescent Center
120 Main St, Newport, KY, 41071 (606)
581-1938
Admin Lee Hopkins. *Medical Dir/Dir of
Nursing* Dr W V Pierce.
Licensure Skilled Care; Intermediate Care.
Beds 167. *Certified* Medicaid; Medicare.
Staff Physicians 1 (ft); RNs 3 (ft), 7 (pt); LPNs
7 (ft), 6 (pt); Nurses aides 39 (ft), 36 (pt);
Physical therapists 2 (ft); Activities coordinators 1 (ft); Dietitians 1 (ft); Dentists 1 (pt).
Affiliation Baptist
Facilities Dining room; Physical therapy room;
Activities room; Chapel; Crafts room; Laundry
room; Barber/Beauty shop; Parlor.
Activities Arts and Crafts; Cards; Games; Prayer groups; Movies; Shopping trips; Exercise
class; Birthday parties; Sing-a-longs; Discussion
group; Bookmobile; Rhythm band.
Description Facility is located on a beautiful
5-acre tract on the brow of the hill in south
Newport with a splendid view of the basin area,
especially downtown Cincinnati. There is room
to stroll, or just sit in a quiet shaded area.

Salvation Army Adult Day Care Center*
10th and Patterson Sts, Newport, KY, 41071
(606) 291-8107
Admin Alice Skirtz.
Licensure Intermediate Care.
Ownership Nonprofit.
Affiliation Salvation Army

NICHOLASVILLE

Rose Terrace Lodge*
401 N 2nd St, Nicholasville, KY, 40356 (606) 885-3821
Admin Lucille H Layell.
Licensure Personal Care. *Beds* 36.
Ownership Proprietary.

Royal Manor
100 Sparks Ave, Nicholasville, KY, 40356 (606) 885-4171
Admin Olive Peel.
Licensure Intermediate Care; Personal Care.
Beds ICF 73; Personal Care 10. *Certified* Medicaid.
Admissions Requirements Medical examination.
Staff Physicians 1 (pt); RNs 1 (ft), 1 (pt); LPNs 3 (ft); Nurses aides 25 (ft); Physical therapists 1 (pt); Recreational therapists 1 (pt); Occupational therapists 1 (pt); Speech therapists 1 (pt); Activities coordinators 1 (pt); Dietitians 1 (pt).
Facilities Dining room; Activities room; Laundry room; Barber/Beauty shop.
Activities Arts and Crafts; Cards; Games; Reading groups; Prayer groups; Movies; Shopping trips; Dances/Social or cultural gatherings.
Description Facility located on 3 beautiful rolling acres, with a rural atmosphere in a suburban area; features a dedicated staff with positive community involvement.

NORTH MIDDLETOWN

Lovely's Rest Home*
PO Box 114, North Middletown, KY, 40357 (606) 362-4560
Admin Allean Platt.
Licensure Personal Care. *Beds* 11.
Ownership Proprietary.

OWENSBORO

Carmel Home
2501 Old Hartford Rd, Owensboro, KY, 42301 (502) 683-0227
Admin Sister M Andrea.
Licensure Intermediate Care; Personal Care.
Beds ICF 30; Personal Care 54. *Certified* Medicaid.
Admissions Requirements Minimum age 65.
Staff RNs 1 (pt); LPNs 5 (ft), 3 (pt); Nurses aides 10 (ft), 11 (pt); Recreational therapists 1 (ft); Activities coordinators 1 (ft).
Facilities Dining room; Activities room; Chapel; Crafts room; Laundry room; Barber/Beauty shop; Library; Medical services.
Activities Arts and Crafts; Cards; Games; Reading groups; Prayer groups; Movies; Shopping trips; Dances/Social or cultural gatherings; Validation therapy groups.

Davco Rest Home*
2526 W 10th St, Owensboro, KY, 42301 (502) 684-1705
Admin Audrey Mason Williams.
Licensure Personal Care. *Beds* 92.
Ownership Proprietary.

Fern Terrace Lodge*
45 Woodford Ave, Owensboro, KY, 42301 (502) 684-7171
Admin Gertrude P Cagle.
Licensure Personal Care. *Beds* 68.
Ownership Proprietary.

Hermitage Manor
1614 Parrish Ave, Owensboro, KY, 42301 (502) 684-4559
Admin Jack T Wells. *Medical Dir/Dir of Nursing* Sarah Kamuf.
Licensure Skilled Care; Intermediate Care.
Beds SNF 22; ICF 28.
Staff RNs 1 (ft), 1 (pt); LPNs 3 (ft), 3 (pt); Nurses aides 13 (ft), 12 (pt); Activities coordinators 1 (ft); Dietitians 1 (ft).
Facilities Dining room; Activities room; Crafts room; Laundry room; Barber/Beauty shop.
Activities Arts and Crafts; Cards; Games; Reading groups; Prayer groups; Movies; Shopping trips; Dances/Social or cultural gatherings.
Description Facility has large private rooms, a home-like atmosphere, friendly employees, and quality care; also a whirlpool bath available to all residents. Facility is very clean and has many social activities for residents.

Hillcrest Healthcare Center*
3740 Old Hartford Rd, Owensboro, KY, 42301 (502) 684-7259
Admin Betty R Wimmer.
Licensure Skilled Care; Intermediate Care.
Beds SNF 32; ICF 124. *Certified* Medicaid; Medicare.
Ownership Proprietary.

Leisure Years Nursing Home Inc
1205 Leitchfield Rd, Owensboro, KY, 42301 (502) 684-0464
Admin Flora J Norsworthy.
Licensure Intermediate Care; Personal Care.
Beds ICF 88; Personal Care 96. *Certified* Medicaid.
Staff Physicians 45 (pt); RNs 1 (pt); LPNs 13 (ft); Orderlies 5 (ft); Nurses aides 43 (ft), 5 (pt); Physical therapists 2 (ft); Reality therapists 2 (ft); Recreational therapists 2 (ft); Speech therapists 1 (pt); Activities coordinators 1 (ft); Dietitians 1 (pt); Dentists 1 (pt).
Facilities Dining room; Activities room; Laundry room; Barber/Beauty shop.
Activities Arts and Crafts; Cards; Games; Reading groups; Prayer groups; Movies; Shopping trips; Dances/Social or cultural gatherings.
Description Facility features in-house speech therapy and physical therapy.

Mary Harding Home Inc
1314 W 7th St, Owensboro, KY, 42301 (502) 684-5459
Admin Mrs Ernestine Smith.
Licensure Personal Care. *Beds* 12.
Ownership Nonprofit.
Admissions Requirements Medical examination; Physician's request.
Staff Physicians 1 (pt); Nurses aides 4 (ft), 2 (pt); Dietitians 1 (pt).
Facilities Dining room; Activities room; Laundry room.
Activities Arts and Crafts; Cards; Games; Prayer groups; Dances/Social or cultural gatherings.

Mary Kendall Home
199 Phillips Ct, Owensboro, KY, 42301 (502) 683-5044
Admin Donna C Anderson.
Licensure Personal Care. *Beds* 22.
Admissions Requirements Females only; Medical examination.
Staff Nurses aides 4 (ft), 4 (pt); Activities coordinators 1 (pt); Dietitians 1 (pt).
Facilities Dining room; Laundry room.
Activities Arts and Crafts; Cards; Games; Reading groups; Prayer groups; Shopping trips; Weekly church service; Sunday school.

Medco Center of Owensboro*
2420 W 3rd St, Owensboro, KY, 42301 (502) 685-3141
Admin Richard Tobin.
Licensure Skilled Care; Intermediate Care.
Beds SNF 60; ICF 72. *Certified* Medicaid; Medicare.
Ownership Proprietary.

Rosedale
415 Sutton Ln, Owensboro, KY, 42301 (502) 684-6753
Admin Juanita Kaelin.
Licensure Personal Care. *Beds* 50.
Admissions Requirements Minimum age 21; Medical examination; Physician's request.
Staff RNs 1 (ft); Nurses aides 13 (ft), 2 (pt); Activities coordinators 1 (pt); Dietitians 1 (ft), 2 (pt).
Facilities Dining room; Activities room; Laundry room.
Activities Arts and Crafts; Cards; Games; Reading groups; Prayer groups; Movies; Shopping trips; Dances/Social or cultural gatherings.
Description Facility is the oldest nursing home in Owensboro, has received a "Superior Rating" from the state of Kentucky; excel in individualized attention and home-like atmosphere; highly complimented on home-cooked meals and activity department.

Wendell Foster Center
815 Triplett St, Owensboro, KY, 42301 (502) 683-4517
Admin Robert G Mobley. *Medical Dir/Dir of Nursing* Anne H Hopwood MD.
Licensure Intermediate Care for Mentally Retarded. *Beds* 63.
Admissions Requirements Medical examination; Physician's request.
Staff Physicians 1 (pt); RNs 1 (ft); LPNs 7 (ft), 2 (pt); Nurses aides 3 (ft); Physical therapists 2 (ft); Occupational therapists 1 (ft); Speech therapists 1 (ft); Activities coordinators 1 (ft); Dietitians 1 (ft).
Facilities Dining room; Physical therapy room; Activities room; Chapel; Crafts room; Laundry room; Barber/Beauty shop; Library.
Activities Arts and Crafts; Cards; Games; Reading groups; Prayer groups; Movies; Shopping trips; Dances/Social or cultural gatherings.

OWENTON

Owenton Manor
Hwy 127 N, Owenton, KY, 40359 (502) 484-5721
Admin Bernard Poe.

Licensure Intermediate Care; Personal Care. *Beds* ICF 60; Personal Care 20. *Certified* Medicaid.
Admissions Requirements Minimum age 18; Medical examination; Physician's request.
Staff RNs 1 (ft), 1 (pt); LPNs 4 (ft), 1 (pt); Orderlies 3 (ft), 3 (pt); Nurses aides 42 (ft), 12 (pt); Physical therapists 1 (pt); Speech therapists 1 (pt); Activities coordinators 1 (ft); Dietitians 1 (pt).
Facilities Dining room; Activities room; Crafts room; Laundry room; Barber/Beauty shop.
Activities Arts and Crafts; Cards; Games; Reading groups; Prayer groups; Movies; Dances/Social or cultural gatherings.
Description All nursing aides and medication aides are taught and trained by the facility by an RN on staff who is certified by the state as an instructor. Each course is 72 hours with certification through Northern Kentucky Vocational Technical School. Classes are taught twice yearly and are also open to others throughout the community and surrounding counties.

OWINGSVILLE

Colonial Rest Home*
E Main St, Owingsville, KY, 40360 (606) 674-2222
Admin Emery V Goodpaster and Joetta Y Goodpaster.
Licensure Personal Care. *Beds* 26.
Ownership Proprietary.

Hilltop Lodge*
Box 448, E High St, Owingsville, KY, 40360 (606) 674-6062
Admin Jerry Maze.
Licensure Intermediate Care. *Beds* 39. *Certified* Medicaid.
Ownership Proprietary.

Ridgeway Manor*
PO Box 38, Owingsville, KY, 40360 (606) 674-6613
Admin Thomas Maze.
Licensure Intermediate Care. *Beds* 60. *Certified* Medicaid.
Ownership Proprietary.

PADUCAH

Life Care Center of Paducah
600 N 4th St, Paducah, KY, 42001 (502) 442-3568
Admin Tim Herber. *Medical Dir/Dir of Nursing* C F Sullivan MD.
Licensure Intermediate Care; Personal Care. *Beds* ICF 102; Personal Care 40. *Certified* Medicaid.
Staff RNs 3 (ft); LPNs 6 (ft), 3 (pt); Orderlies 3 (ft); Nurses aides 35 (ft), 15 (pt); Physical therapists 1 (pt); Activities coordinators 1 (ft); Dietitians 1 (pt); Podiatrists 2 (pt).
Facilities Dining room; Activities room; Chapel; Crafts room; Barber/Beauty shop; Library.
Activities Arts and Crafts; Cards; Games; Prayer groups; Movies; Shopping trips; Dances/Social or cultural gatherings.

McElrath Rest Home*
517 S 5th St, Paducah, KY, 42001 (502) 442-2600
Admin Anna Mae McElrath.
Licensure Personal Care. *Beds* 11.
Ownership Proprietary.

Medco Center of Paducah*
867 McGuire Ave, Paducah, KY, 42001 (502) 442-6168
Admin Jim Kennedy.
Licensure Intermediate Care. *Beds* 108. *Certified* Medicaid.
Ownership Proprietary.

Parkview Convalescent Center*
544 Lone Oak Rd, Paducah, KY, 42001 (502) 443-6543
Admin Paul D Borders.
Licensure Skilled Care; Intermediate Care. *Beds* SNF 114; ICF 12. *Certified* Medicaid; Medicare.
Ownership Proprietary.

Riverfront Terrace Healthcare Facility
501 N 3rd St, PO Box 1137, Paducah, KY, 42001-1137 (502) 444-9661
Admin Billie J Tabb. *Medical Dir/Dir of Nursing* Dr Curtis E Bippert.
Licensure Intermediate Care. *Beds* 100. *Certified* Medicaid.
Admissions Requirements Medical examination; Physician's request.
Staff Physicians 8 (pt); RNs 3 (ft), 2 (pt); LPNs 5 (ft), 3 (pt); Nurses aides 30 (ft), 15 (pt); Physical therapists 1 (ft); Speech therapists 1 (pt); Activities coordinators 1 (ft); Dietitians 1 (pt); Dentists 1 (pt); Ophthalmologists 1 (pt); Podiatrists 1 (pt); Audiologists 1 (pt).
Facilities Dining room; Physical therapy room; Activities room; Laundry room; Barber/Beauty shop.
Activities Arts and Crafts; Cards; Games; Reading groups; Prayer groups; Shopping trips; Dances/Social or cultural gatherings; Reality orientation classes.
Description Riverfront Terrace is located in the heart of downtown Paducah across the street from Executive Inn Riverfront on the downtown loop of Interstate 24. Provides 3 outstanding rehabilitative programs: 24-hour reality orientation, restorative feeding, and bladder and bowel retraining, to provide residents with a sense of dignity and personal value.

Superior Care Home*
310 Clay St, Paducah, KY, 42001 (502) 442-6884
Admin Barbara Davis.
Licensure Intermediate Care. *Beds* 85. *Certified* Medicaid.
Ownership Proprietary.

Virginia's Rest Home
1104 Jefferson St, Paducah, KY, 42001 (502) 442-2312
Admin Marie Morris.
Licensure Personal Care. *Beds* 18.

PAINTSVILLE

Jennie Wiley Rest Home
PO Box 391, Paintsville, KY, 40202 (606) 789-5558
Admin Lawrence G Brown.
Licensure Personal Care. *Beds* 51.

Shree Ji Health Care Center*
1258 Stafford Ave, Paintsville, KY, 41240 (606) 789-3523
Admin Arun Agrawal.
Licensure Personal Care. *Beds* 56.
Ownership Proprietary.

PARIS

Bourbon Heights Nursing Home*
2000 S Main St, Paris, KY, 40361 (606) 987-5750
Admin Emmett R Davis Jr.
Licensure Skilled Care; Intermediate Care; Personal Care; Nursing Home. *Beds* SNF 10; ICF 30; Personal Care 17; Nursing Home 32. *Certified* Medicaid; Medicare.
Ownership Nonprofit.

Hopewell Home
611 High St, Paris, KY, 40361 (606) 987-5495
Admin Anna Lail.
Licensure Personal Care. *Beds* 32.

PARKERS LAKE

Cumberland Manor Rest Home
Rt 2, Box 232, Parker's Lake, KY, 42634 (606) 376-5951
Admin Mary A Gordon.
Licensure Personal Care. *Beds* 49.
Admissions Requirements Minimum age 16; Medical examination.
Staff LPNs 1 (ft); Orderlies 2 (ft); Nurses aides 8 (ft).
Facilities Dining room; Laundry room.
Activities Games; Prayer groups; Dances/Social or cultural gatherings.

PEMBROKE

Medco Center of Pembroke
Hwy 41, Pembroke, KY, 42266 (502) 475-4227
Admin Mollie Banksfry. *Medical Dir/Dir of Nursing* J C Woodall.
Licensure Intermediate Care. *Beds* 64. *Certified* Medicaid.
Staff LPNs 7 (ft); Orderlies 4 (ft); Nurses aides 20 (ft); Speech therapists 1 (pt); Activities coordinators 1 (ft); Dietitians 1 (pt); Dentists 1 (pt).
Facilities Dining room; Activities room; Laundry room.
Activities Arts and Crafts; Cards; Games; Reading groups; Prayer groups; Movies; Shopping trips; Dances/Social or cultural gatherings.
Description Facility features very active residents council, choice of desserts for lunch and dinner, and residents choose holiday meals. Very loving atmosphere and caring staff.

PEWEE VALLEY

Friendship Manor Nursing Home
LaGrange Rd, Pewee Valley, KY, 40056 (502) 241-8821
Admin Beth Pearman.
Licensure Intermediate Care; Nursing Home.
Beds ICF 40; Nursing Home 54. *Certified* Medicaid.
Admissions Requirements Medical examination; Physician's request.
Staff Physicians 5 (pt); RNs 2 (ft); LPNs 6 (ft), 2 (pt); Orderlies 5 (ft); Nurses aides 24 (ft), 5 (pt) #13F 1 (pt); Speech therapists 1 (pt); Activities coordinators 1 (ft), 1 (pt); Dietitians 1 (pt); Dentists 1 (pt); Podiatrists 1 (pt).
Affiliation Seventh-Day Adventist
Facilities Dining room; Activities room; Crafts room; Laundry room; Barber/Beauty shop.
Activities Arts and Crafts; Cards; Games; Reading groups; Prayer groups; Movies; Shopping trips.
Description Facility has own ombudsman for beneficial pilot program.

PHELPS

Phelps Community Medical Center*
PO Box 424, Phelps, KY, 41553 (606) 456-8725
Admin Homer R Spears.
Licensure Intermediate Care; Personal Care.
Beds ICF 100; Personal Care 24. *Certified* Medicaid.
Ownership Proprietary.

PHILPOT

Knottsville Home*
Rt 1, Philpot, KY, 42366 (502) 281-4881
Admin Sr Raymond Carrot.
Licensure Personal Care. *Beds* 68.
Ownership Nonprofit.

PIKEVILLE

Mountain Manor Nursing Home
182 S Mayo Trail, Pikeville, KY, 41501 (606) 437-7327
Admin Jack W Thacker. *Medical Dir/Dir of Nursing* Dr J D Adams and Dr M L Wiss.
Licensure Skilled Care; Intermediate Care.
Beds SNF 95; ICF 11. *Certified* Medicaid; Medicare.
Staff RNs 3 (ft), 3 (pt); LPNs 13 (ft), 6 (pt); Orderlies 2 (ft); Nurses aides 29 (ft), 2 (pt); Physical therapists 2 (ft); Activities coordinators 1 (ft); Dietitians 1 (ft); Dentists 2 (ft).
Facilities Dining room; Physical therapy room; Activities room; Crafts room; Laundry room; Barber/Beauty shop.
Activities Arts and Crafts; Cards; Games; Reading groups; Prayer groups; Movies; Dances/Social or cultural gatherings.
Description Mountain Manor Nursing Home is an ultra-modern, spacious nursing home nestled among the beautiful mountains of eastern Kentucky. Facility is covered by licensed nursing personnel around the clock, with RNs on call if not in the facility. Medical staff

includes 32-licensed physcans with services ranging from pediatrics to orthopedics. Offers a full-range of activities from movies to church services; active rehabilitation and respiratory programs. JCAH accredited.

PINEVILLE

Pineville Health Care Center
Rt 1, US 25 E, Pineville, KY, 40977 (606) 337-7091
Admin Frances Thomas. *Medical Dir/Dir of Nursing* Emanuel Rader MD.
Licensure Intermediate Care; Personal Care.
Beds ICF 100; Personal Care 22. *Certified* Medicaid.
Admissions Requirements Minimum age 18; Medical examination; Physician's request.
Staff Physicians 4 (ft); RNs 1 (ft); LPNs 7 (ft), 3 (pt); Orderlies 4 (ft); Nurses aides 16 (ft), 7 (pt); Activities coordinators 1 (ft); Social workers 1 (ft).
Facilities Dining room; Activities room; Laundry room; Barber/Beauty shop; Library.
Activities Arts and Crafts; Games; Reading groups; Prayer groups; Movies; Shopping trips.
Description Facility is fully air conditioned; has scenic view of the eastern Kentucky mountains; sprinkler system throughout; physician in house weekly; unit dose medication; restorative nursing program; volunteer program; chaplaining program; and picnic/park area in rear of nursing home.

PRESTONSBURG

Mountain Manor Nursing Home
17 College Ln, Prestonsburg, KY, 41653 (606) 886-2378
Admin Goldie Rorrer.
Licensure Intermediate Care. *Beds* 56. *Certified* Medicaid.
Admissions Requirements Medical examination; Physician's request.
Staff Physicians 5 (ft); RNs 1 (ft); LPNs 2 (ft), 1 (pt); Nurses aides 16 (ft); Activities coordinators 1 (ft); Dietitians 1 (pt); Dentists 5 (pt).
Facilities Dining room; Physical therapy room; Activities room; Crafts room; Laundry room; Barber/Beauty shop.
Activities Arts and Crafts; Cards; Games; Reading groups; Prayer groups; Movies; Shopping trips; Dances/Social or cultural gatherings.

Riverview Manor*
1020 Circle Dr, Prestonsburg, KY, 41653 (606) 886-9178
Admin Eleanor Robinson.
Licensure Skilled Care; Intermediate Care.
Beds SNF 56; ICF 60. *Certified* Medicaid; Medicare.
Ownership Proprietary.

PRINCETON

Highlands Homes
Stevens Ave, PO Box 590, Princeton, KY, 42445 (502) 365-3254
Admin Bonnie McGregory.
Licensure Personal Care. *Beds* 88.
Staff LPNs 2 (ft); Nurses aides 22 (ft), 4 (pt);

Recreational therapists 1 (ft).
Facilities Dining room; Activities room; Laundry room.
Activities Arts and Crafts; Games; Prayer groups.

Princeton Health Care Manor Inc*
1333 W Main, Princeton, KY, 42445 (502) 365-3541
Admin Mary Jewel Alexander.
Licensure Intermediate Care; Personal Care.
Beds ICF 104; Personal Care 8.
Ownership Proprietary.

PROSPECT

Beachland Intermediate Care Home*
PO Box 147, 6301 Bass Rd, Prospect, KY, 40059 (502) 228-8359
Admin Bettie L Taylor.
Licensure Intermediate Care. *Beds* 100. *Certified* Medicaid.
Ownership Proprietary.

PROVIDENCE

Country Meadows Rest Haven*
Rt 1, Box 98, Providence, KY, 42450 (502) 667-2682
Admin Loeta Tow.
Licensure Personal Care. *Beds* 50.
Ownership Proprietary.

Shemwell Nursing Home*
805 Princeton St, Providence, KY, 42450 (502) 667-5472
Admin Billie C Cole.
Licensure Skilled Care. *Beds* 22.
Ownership Proprietary.

RICHMOND

Crestview Personal Care Home*
S Meadowlark Dr, Richmond, KY, 40475 (606) 623-5031
Admin Grover C Fish Jr.
Licensure Personal Care. *Beds* 50.
Ownership Proprietary.

Kenwood House*
S Meadowlark Dr, Richmond, KY, 40475 (606) 623-9472
Admin Grover C Fish Jr.
Licensure Skilled Care; Intermediate Care.
Beds SNF 42; ICF 46. *Certified* Medicaid; Medicare.
Ownership Proprietary.

Madison Manor*
S Meadowlark Dr, Richmond, KY, 40475 (606) 623-3564
Admin Mary Ousley.
Licensure Intermediate Care. *Beds* 101. *Certified* Medicaid.
Ownership Proprietary.

RUSSELL

Russell Convalescent Home*
407 Ferry Rd, Russell, KY, 41169 (606) 836-5616
Admin Carolyn Baumgarden and Oscar Baumgarden.
Licensure Personal Care. *Beds* 28. *Certified* Medicaid.
Ownership Proprietary.

RUSSELLVILLE

Benton's Personal Care Home
635 E 5th St, Russellville, KY, 42276 (502) 726-9467
Admin Jettie Benton.
Licensure Personal Care. *Beds* 26.

Russellville Health Care Manor*
683 E 3rd St, Russellville, KY, 42276 (502) 726-9049
Admin Altricia Carol Harrell.
Licensure Intermediate Care; Personal Care.
Beds ICF 92; Personal Care 20. *Certified* Medicaid.
Ownership Proprietary.

SAINT CATHERINE

Sansbury Memorial Infirmany
Saint Catherine Motherhouse, Saint Catherine, KY, 40061 (606) 336-3974
Admin Sr Anne Robert Gray.
Licensure Intermediate Care; Personal Care.
Beds ICF 36; Personal Care 28. *Certified* Medicaid.
Admissions Requirements Females only
Staff Physicians 2 (pt); RNs 1 (ft); LPNs 5 (ft); Nurses aides 18 (ft); Dietitians 1 (ft).
Affiliation Roman Catholic
Description Facility is a nursing home for retired Sisters; does not accept lay people.

SALEM

Salem Nursing Home
PO Box 216, Salem, KY, 42078 (502) 988-2388
Admin Carol Roberts. *Medical Dir/Dir of Nursing* Stephen Burkhart MD.
Licensure Skilled Care. *Beds* 50. *Certified* Medicaid; Medicare.
Staff RNs 2 (ft), 1 (pt); LPNs 4 (ft), 2 (pt); Physical therapists 1 (ft); Speech therapists 1 (pt); Activities coordinators 1 (ft); Dietitians 1 (ft).
Facilities Dining room; Activities room; Crafts room.
Activities Arts and Crafts; Cards; Games; Reading groups; Prayer groups.

SALYERSVILLE

Mountain Valley Rest Home*
PO Box 445, Salyersville, KY, 41465 (606) 349-2014
Admin Mary Bandy.
Licensure Personal Care. *Beds* 32.
Ownership Proprietary.

Salyersville Health Care Center*
PO Box 819, Hwy 460, Salyersville, KY, 41465 (606) 349-6181
Admin Clarence Shackelford.
Licensure Intermediate Care; Personal Care.
Beds ICF 147; Personal Care 21. *Certified* Medicaid.
Ownership Proprietary.

SANDERS

Valley Haven Rest Home
McDaniel St, Sanders, KY, 41083 (502) 347-5739
Admin Violet M Koutoulas.
Licensure Personal Care. *Beds* 45.
Admissions Requirements Minimum age 16; Males only; Medical examination.
Staff Nurses aides 4 (ft); Dietitians 1 (pt).
Facilities Dining room; Activities room; Laundry room.
Activities Arts and Crafts; Cards; Games.
Description Facility is in a country setting in a rural area.

SCIENCE HILL

Hilltop Rest Home*
Rt 2, Science Hill, KY, 42553 (606) 423-2555
Admin Ida M Dick.
Licensure Personal Care. *Beds* 40.
Ownership Proprietary.

SCOTTSVILLE

Hillcrest Home*
515 Water St, Scottsville, KY, 42164 (502) 237-3485
Admin May Foster.
Licensure Personal Care. *Beds* 36.
Ownership Proprietary.

Hillview Manor
Rt 1, Hillview Dr, Scottsville, KY, 42164 (502) 237-4164
Admin Rebecca Christian.
Licensure Personal Care. *Beds* 84.
Admissions Requirements Minimum age 16; Medical examination; Physician's request.
Staff RNs 1 (pt); Nurses aides 35 (ft); Activities coordinators 1 (ft), 2 (pt).
Facilities Dining room; Laundry room.
Activities Arts and Crafts; Cards; Games; Reading groups; Prayer groups; Movies; Shopping trips; Dances/Social or cultural gatherings.
Description Facility is in a home-like environment, providing individualized attention. The recreation program is a favorite with the residents due to its diversity. The staff is friendly and accepts all residents as a part of their family.

Opal's Home for the Aged*
711 N 7th St, Scottsville, KY, 42164 (502) 237-3444
Admin Carol Graves.
Licensure Personal Care. *Beds* 8.
Ownership Proprietary.

Scottsville Rest Home*
PO Box 186, N 4th St, Scottsville, KY, 42164 (502) 237-4671
Admin Keith Schmalzbauer.
Licensure Personal Care. *Beds* 40.
Ownership Proprietary.

SEBREE

Colonial Terrace Intermediate Care
S Church St, Sebree, KY, 42455 (502) 835-2533
Admin Kathy Crowley. *Medical Dir/Dir of Nursing* Jason Samuel MD.
Licensure Intermediate Care; Personal Care.
Beds ICF 80; Personal Care 23. *Certified* Medicaid.
Admissions Requirements Minimum age 20; Medical examination; Physician's request.
Staff Physicians 6 (pt); RNs 1 (pt); LPNs 2 (ft), 1 (pt); Nurses aides 35 (ft); Recreational therapists 1 (pt); Speech therapists 1 (pt); Activities coordinators 1 (ft), 2 (pt); Dietitians 1 (pt); Dentists 1 (pt); Audiologists 1 (pt).
Facilities Dining room; Activities room; Chapel; Crafts room; Laundry room; Barber/Beauty shop; Library.
Activities Arts and Crafts; Cards; Games; Reading groups; Prayer groups; Movies; Shopping trips; Dances/Social or cultural gatherings.
Description Facility has an enclosed courtyard and is beautifully landscaped including strawberry bed; to the rear of facility is an active garden spot and several fruit trees; presently papering rooms for a homey atmosphere; numerous outings for residents and community involvement programs monthly; excellent nursing care and community and staff volunteer programs.

SHELBYVILLE

Colonial Halls Property's Inc
920 Henry Clay St, Shelbyville, KY, 40065 (502) 633-4762
Admin Frank E Kees.
Licensure Personal Care. *Beds* 57.
Staff RNs 1 (ft); LPNs 1 (pt); Orderlies 1 (ft); Nurses aides 18 (ft); Activities coordinators 1 (ft); Dietitians 1 (pt).
Facilities Dining room; Activities room; Chapel; Crafts room; Laundry room; Library.
Activities Arts and Crafts; Cards; Games; Reading groups; Prayer groups; Movies; Shopping trips.

Crestview Nursing Home
Rt 6, Box 382, Shelbyville, KY, 40065 (502) 633-2454
Admin Jeanette Pope. *Medical Dir/Dir of Nursing* Donald Chatham MD.
Licensure Nursing Home. *Beds* 58.
Admissions Requirements Physician's request.
Staff Physicians 10 (pt); RNs 2 (ft), 1 (pt); LPNs 5 (ft), 3 (pt); Orderlies 1 (ft), 1 (pt); Nurses aides 20 (ft), 20 (pt); Recreational therapists 1 (ft); Activities coordinators 1 (ft); Dietitians 1 (pt); Podiatrists 1 (pt).
Facilities Dining room; Physical therapy room; Activities room; Crafts room; Laundry room; Barber/Beauty shop.
Activities Arts and Crafts; Cards; Games;

Reading groups; Prayer groups; Movies; Shopping trips; Dances/Social or cultural gatherings.
Description We have licensed nurses 24 hours a day.

Old Masons Home of Kentucky*
US 60 E, Shelbyville, KY, 40065 (502) 633-3486
Admin Thomas Scott.
Licensure Intermediate Care; Personal Care.
Beds ICF 20; Personal Care 130. *Certified* Medicaid.
Ownership Nonprofit.
Affiliation Masons

Shelby Manor*
PO Box 219, US 60 W, Shelbyville, KY, 40065 (502) 633-2691
Admin Thomas R Hower.
Licensure Intermediate Care; Personal Care.
Beds ICF 63; Personal Care 90. *Certified* Medicaid.
Ownership Proprietary.

SHEPHERDSVILLE

Colonial House of Shepherdsville*
Star Rt, Box 64, Shepherdsville, KY, 40165 (502) 543-7042
Admin Sarah M Simpson.
Licensure Personal Care. *Beds* 62.
Ownership Proprietary.

Patterson's Pleasant View Personal Care Home*
Hwy 44 E and Loyd's Ln, Shepherdsville, KY, 40165 (502) 543-7995
Admin Marie Sublett Carter.
Licensure Personal Care. *Beds* 13.
Ownership Proprietary.

SHIVELY

Rockford Manor*
4700 Quinn Dr, Shively, KY, 40216 (502) 448-5850
Admin James Morris.
Licensure Intermediate Care. *Beds* 120. *Certified* Medicaid.
Ownership Proprietary.

SMITHLAND

Livingston County Rest Home
PO Box 216, Smithland, KY, 42081 (502) 928-2137
Admin Nora E Ramage. *Medical Dir/Dir of Nursing* Eva Lee Ramage.
Licensure Personal Care. *Beds* 38.
Ownership Public.
Admissions Requirements Minimum age 16; Medical examination.
Staff Orderlies 1 (ft), 2 (pt); Nurses aides 7 (ft); Activities coordinators 1 (pt); Dietitians 2 (ft), 2 (pt).
Facilities Dining room; Activities room; Chapel; Laundry room; Barber/Beauty shop.
Activities Arts and Crafts; Games; Reading groups; Movies; Shopping trips; Dances/Social or cultural gatherings.

SOMERSET

Colonial Care Home
202 N Main St, Somerset, KY, 42501 (606) 679-1504
Admin Joan O Johnson.
Licensure Personal Care. *Beds* 50.
Admissions Requirements Minimum age 45; Medical examination; Physician's request.
Staff Nurses aides 7 (ft), 4 (pt); Dietitians 2 (ft), 2 (pt).
Facilities Dining room; Activities room; Laundry room.
Activities Arts and Crafts; Games; Reading groups; Prayer groups; Shopping trips.

Crestview Care Home*
235 S Richardson, Somerset, KY, 42501 (606) 678-8927
Admin Olga Wilson.
Licensure Personal Care. *Beds* 28.
Ownership Proprietary.

Midtown*
106 Gover St, Somerset, KY, 42501 (606) 679-8331
Admin Brenda Hardgrove.
Licensure Intermediate Care. *Beds* 123. *Certified* Medicaid.
Ownership Proprietary.

Oakwood Intermediate Care Facility
US 27 S, Somerset, KY, 42501 (606) 679-4361
Admin Mary Warman. *Medical Dir/Dir of Nursing* Alberto Jayme MD.
Licensure Intermediate Care for Mentally Retarded. *Beds* 420. *Certified* Medicaid.
Admissions Requirements Minimum age 6.
Staff Physicians 1 (ft), 1 (pt); RNs 13 (ft), 2 (pt); LPNs 15 (ft); Nurses aides; Physical therapists 1 (ft); Recreational therapists 1 (ft); Occupational therapists 1 (ft); Speech therapists 2 (ft); Dietitians 2 (ft); Dentists 1 (pt); Audiologists 1 (pt); Patient aides 341 (ft), 67 (pt).
Facilities Dining room; Physical therapy room; Activities room; Laundry room; Barber/Beauty shop; Library; Residential cottages; Habilitative classrooms; Gym.
Activities Arts and Crafts; Cards; Games; Movies; Shopping trips; Dances/Social or cultural gatherings.
Description Facility offers daily living training, habilitative training, and community living experiences and training.

Somerset Center*
Bourne Ave and Central Ave, Somerset, KY, 42501 (606) 679-7421
Admin Mary Creekmore.
Licensure Skilled Care; Intermediate Care; Personal Care. *Beds* SNF 36; ICF 116; Personal Care 12. *Certified* Medicaid; Medicare.
Ownership Proprietary.

Sunrise Manor*
200 Norfleet Dr, Somerset, KY, 42501 (606) 678-5104
Admin Terrill A Wilson.
Licensure Skilled Care; Intermediate Care.
Beds SNF 64; ICF 29. *Certified* Medicaid; Medicare.
Ownership Proprietary.

SOUTH SHORE

Voiers Convalescent Center*
James E Hannah Dr, South Shore, KY, 41175 (606) 932-6266
Admin Clarence Voiers.
Licensure Intermediate Care. *Beds* 30. *Certified* Medicaid.
Ownership Proprietary.

SOUTH WILLIAMSON

Williamson Appalachian Regional Hospital*
2000 Central Ave, South Williamson, KY, 41503 (606) 237-1010
Admin W D Crosely.
Licensure Skilled Care; Rehabilitation.
Beds 193.
Ownership Nonprofit.

SPRINGFIELD

Medco Center of Springfield
120 E Grundy Ave, Springfield, KY, 40069 (606) 336-7771
Admin Violet Elliott.
Licensure Intermediate Care. *Beds* 70. *Certified* Medicaid.
Admissions Requirements Minimum age 21; Medical examination.
Staff LPNs 4 (ft), 3 (pt); Orderlies 2 (ft); Nurses aides 24 (ft), 2 (pt); Activities coordinators 1 (ft).
Facilities Dining room; Activities room; Laundry room; Barber/Beauty shop.
Activities Arts and Crafts; Cards; Games; Reading groups; Prayer groups; Movies; Shopping trips; Dances/Social or cultural gatherings.
Description Facility is located in beautiful, quiet neighborhood with religious activities and a beautiful living area.

STANFORD

Fort Logan Hospital—Extended Care Facility*
124 Portman Ave, Stanford, KY, 40484 (606) 365-2187
Admin Terry C Powers.
Licensure Skilled Care. *Beds* 30. *Certified* Medicaid; Medicare.
Ownership Nonprofit.

Stanford House
Harmon Heights, Stanford, KY, 40484 (606) 365-2141
Admin Brenda Williams. *Medical Dir/Dir of Nursing* Dr Joseph Middleton.
Licensure Intermediate Care. *Beds* 98. *Certified* Medicaid.
Staff Physicians 5 (pt); RNs 1 (pt); LPNs 6 (ft), 1 (pt); Nurses aides 23 (ft); Activities coordinators 1 (ft); Dietitians 1 (pt); Dentists 1 (pt).
Facilities Dining room; Physical therapy room; Activities room; Laundry room; Barber/Beauty shop.
Activities Arts and Crafts; Cards; Games; Reading groups; Movies; Shopping trips; Dances/Social or cultural gatherings.

STANTON

Stanton Nursing Center*
Derickson Rd, Stanton, KY, 40380 (606)
663-2846
Admin Debra Dennis.
Licensure Intermediate Care; Personal Care.
Beds ICF 81; Personal Care 9. *Certified* Medicaid.
Ownership Proprietary.

STURGIS

Sturgis Community Rest Home
7th and Main Sts, Sturgis, KY, 42459 (502)
333-5508
Admin Minnie S Thompson.
Licensure Personal Care. *Beds* 27.
Admissions Requirements Medical examination.
Staff Physicians 1 (pt); Nurses aides 3 (ft), 3
(pt); Activities coordinators 1 (ft); Dietitians 1
(pt).
Facilities Dining room; Activities room; Chapel; Crafts room; Laundry room; Barber/Beauty
shop.
Activities Arts and Crafts; Games; Prayer
groups; Movies; Shopping trips; Dances/Social
or cultural gatherings.
Description Facility is community oriented,
very homey in atmosphere and very accessible
to the community as it is located in downtown
Sturgis.

TOMPKINSVILLE

Monroe Health Care Facility*
706 N Magnolia, Tompkinsville, KY, 42167
(502) 487-6135
Admin Brewier Welch.
Licensure Skilled Care; Intermediate Care; Personal Care. *Beds* SNF 32; ICF 70; Personal
Care 18. *Certified* Medicaid; Medicare.
Ownership Proprietary.

VANCEBURG

Vanceburg Health Care*
PO Box 297, Vanceburg, KY, 41179 (606)
796-3046
Admin Richard Heaton.
Licensure Intermediate Care; Personal Care.
Beds ICF 94; Personal Care 16. *Certified* Medicaid.
Ownership Proprietary.

VERSAILLES

Taylor Manor Nursing Home
Berry Ave, PO Drawer D, Versailles, KY,
40383 (606) 873-4201
Admin Francis Edward Stone.
Licensure Personal Care. *Beds* 42.
Admissions Requirements Medical examination.
Staff Physicians 6 (ft); RNs 3 (ft); LPNs 2 (ft);
Orderlies 1 (ft); Nurses aides 30 (ft); Recreational therapists 1 (ft), 1 (pt).
Affiliation Roman Catholic

Facilities Dining room; Activities room; Chapel; Crafts room; Barber/Beauty shop.
Activities Cards; Games; Prayer groups.

WAYNESBURG

Waynesburg Rest Home
PO Box 68, Waynesburg, KY, 40489 (606)
379-2614
Admin Reva Reynolds.
Licensure Personal Care. *Beds* 28.
Ownership Proprietary.
Admissions Requirements Minimum age 30;
Physician's request.
Staff Nurses aides 10 (ft); Recreational therapists 3 (pt); Activities coordinators 2 (pt); Dietitians 1 (pt).
Facilities Dining room; Activities room;
Laundry room; Barber/Beauty shop.

WEST LIBERTY

Allen's Rest Home
Rt 1, Box 6, West Liberty, KY, 41472 (606)
743-3846
Admin Pamela Burton. *Medical Dir/Dir of
Nursing* Loretta Fyffe.
Licensure Intermediate Care. *Beds* 29. *Certified* Medicaid.
Staff Physicians 1 (ft); RNs 1 (pt); LPNs 3 (ft);
Nurses aides 10 (ft), 3 (pt); Recreational therapists 1 (ft); Activities coordinators 1 (ft); Dietitians 2 (ft), 2 (pt); Dentists 1 (pt).
Facilities Dining room; Activities room;
Laundry room.
Activities Arts and Crafts; Cards; Games;
Reading groups; Movies.

**Morgan County Appalachian Regional
Hospital**
PO Box 545, West Liberty, KY, 41472 (606)
743-3186
Admin Raymond Rowlett. *Medical Dir/Dir of
Nursing* Morris L Peyton MD.
Licensure Skilled Care; Intermediate Care.
Beds SNF 15. *Certified* Medicaid; Medicare.
Admissions Requirements Physician's request.
Staff RNs 12 (ft); LPNs 5 (ft); Nurses aides 14
(ft); Activities coordinators 1 (pt); Dietitians 1
(ft).
Facilities Dining room; Activities room; Crafts
room; Barber/Beauty shop.
Activities Arts and Crafts; Games.

WILLIAMSBURG

Williamsburg Nursing Home*
Rt 4, Box 733, Williamsburg, KY, 40769 (606)
549-4321
Admin Connie Moren.
Licensure Skilled Care; Intermediate Care.
Beds SNF 30; ICF 70. *Certified* Medicaid;
Medicare.
Ownership Proprietary.

WINCHESTER

Glenway Lodge*
Rt 7, Van Meter Rd, Winchester, KY, 40391
(606) 744-1800

Admin A G White.
Licensure Skilled Care; Intermediate Care; Personal Care. *Beds* SNF 50; ICF 131; Personal
Care 15. *Certified* Medicaid; Medicare.
Ownership Proprietary.

WOODBURN

Hopkins Nursing Home*
College St, Woodburn, KY, 42170 (502)
529-2853
Admin Scarlotte Freeman.
Licensure Skilled Care; Intermediate Care.
Beds SNF 21; ICF 29. *Certified* Medicaid;
Medicare.
Ownership Proprietary.

Twilight Personal Care Home
Clark St, Woodburn, KY, 42170 (502)
529-2962
Admin Jack Wofford.
Licensure Personal Care. *Beds* 25.

Wofford Personal Care Home*
Clark St, Woodburn, KY, 42170 (502)
529-2962
Admin Jack Wofford.
Licensure Personal Care. *Beds* Personal Care
25.
Ownership Proprietary.

WURTLAND

Wurtland Manor*
100 Wurtland Ave, Wurtland, KY, 41144 (606)
836-1956
Admin Carl W Cotton.
Licensure Intermediate Care. *Beds* 96. *Certified* Medicaid.
Ownership Proprietary.

LOUISIANA

ABBEVILLE

Heritage Manor of Abbeville*
2403 Alonzo St, Abbeville, LA, 70510 (318)
893-6140
Admin Freddie Bossley.
Licensure Intermediate Care. *Beds* 60. *Certified* Medicaid.

ALEXANDRIA

Annie Mae Matthews Memorial Nursing Home*
5100 Jackson St, Alexandria, LA, 71301 (318)
445-5215
Admin Gloria Carmouche.
Licensure Intermediate Care. *Beds* 116. *Certified* Medicaid.

Heritage Manor of Alexandria 1*
5115 McArthur Dr, Alexandria, LA, 71301
(318) 442-2340
Admin Bill Blacksher.
Licensure Intermediate Care. *Beds* 56. *Certified* Medicaid.

Heritage Manor of Alexandria 2
3343 Masonic Dr, Alexandria, LA, 71301 (318)
445-6508
Admin Wayne L Morris. *Medical Dir/Dir of Nursing* Dr William Brown.
Licensure Intermediate Care. *Beds* 124. *Certified* Medicaid.
Admissions Requirements Medical examination; Physician's request.
Staff Physicians; RNs; LPNs; Orderlies; Nurses aides; Physical therapists; Reality therapists; Recreational therapists; Occupational therapists; Activities coordinators; Dietitians; Dentists; Podiatrists.
Facilities Dining room; Activities room; Chapel; Crafts room; Laundry room; Barber/Beauty shop.
Activities Arts and Crafts; Cards; Games; Reading groups; Prayer groups; Movies; Shopping trips; Dances/Social or cultural gatherings.
Description Centrally located in Alexandria, immediately adjacent to the largest hospital. Conveniently located close to shopping center and residential areas.

Heritage Manor of Alexandria—North
1709 Odom St, Alexandria, LA, 71301 (318)
445-6355
Admin Otey Dear. *Medical Dir/Dir of Nursing* Dr M Khokhar.
Licensure Intermediate Care. *Beds* 75. *Certified* Medicaid.
Staff RNs 1 (ft); LPNs 3 (ft), 3 (pt); Orderlies 2 (ft), 1 (pt); Nurses aides 35 (ft), 12 (pt); Activities coordinators 1 (ft); Dietitians 1 (ft).
Facilities Dining room; Laundry room; Barber/Beauty shop.
Activities Arts and Crafts; Cards; Games; Reading groups; Prayer groups; Movies; Shopping trips; Dances/Social or cultural gatherings.

Louisiana Special Education Center
PO Drawer 7797, Alexandria, LA, 71037 (318)
487-5484
Admin Aline Cicardo. *Medical Dir/Dir of Nursing* Dr L J Credeur.
Licensure Intermediate Care for Orthopedically Handicapped. *Beds* 75. *Certified* Medicaid.
Admissions Requirements Minimum age 3; Medical examination.
Staff Physicians 4 (pt); RNs 6 (ft); LPNs 5 (ft); Nurses aides 44 (ft); Physical therapists 1 (pt); Occupational therapists 1 (ft); Speech therapists 3 (ft); Activities coordinators 1 (ft); Dietitians 1 (ft); Dentists 1 (ft); Audiologists 1 (pt).
Facilities Dining room; Physical therapy room; Activities room; Crafts room; Laundry room; Barber/Beauty shop; Library.
Activities Arts and Crafts; Cards; Games; Reading groups; Movies; Shopping trips; Dances/Social or cultural gatherings.
Description The goal of the Center is to develop and operate a program in education and treatment to care for the needs of orthopedically handicapped students ranging in age from 3 through 21 years. Center is under the jurisdiction of the state board of elementary and secondary education.

Naomi Heights Nursing Home
2421 E Texas Ave, Alexandria, LA, 71301 (318)
443-5638
Admin Finley C Matthews Jr.
Licensure Intermediate Care. *Beds* 97. *Certified* Medicaid.
Staff RNs 3 (ft); LPNs 7 (ft), 1 (pt); Orderlies 5 (ft); Nurses aides 26 (ft); Dietitians 1 (pt).
Facilities Dining room; Activities room; Laundry room; Barber/Beauty shop.

Activities Arts and Crafts; Prayer groups; Movies; Shopping trips; Dances/Social or cultural gatherings.

Pecan Grove Training Center
5000 Lower 3rd St, Alexandria, LA, 71301
(318) 448-0291
Admin C L Miller.
Licensure Intermediate Care for Mentally Retarded. *Beds* 120. *Certified* Medicaid.

Pleasant Manor*
5908 Skye St, Alexandria, LA, 71301 (318)
445-5984
Admin Ernest M Smith.
Licensure Intermediate Care. *Beds* 160. *Certified* Medicaid.

Saint Mary's Training School
Hwy 1 N, PO Drawer 7768, Alexandria, LA,
71301 (318) 443-6443
Admin Antoinette Baroncini. *Medical Dir/Dir of Nursing* Dr L J Credeur.
Licensure Intermediate Care for Mentally Retarded. *Beds* 152. *Certified* Medicaid.
Admissions Requirements Minimum age 3; Medical examination.
Staff Physicians 4 (pt); RNs 1 (ft); LPNs 2 (ft); Nurses aides 5 (ft); Physical therapists 1 (pt); Recreational therapists 2 (ft); Occupational therapists 1 (ft); Speech therapists 1 (ft), 2 (pt); Activities coordinators 2 (ft); Dietitians 1 (ft); Dentists 1 (pt); Audiologists 1 (pt).
Affiliation Roman Catholic
Facilities Dining room; Activities room; Chapel; Crafts room; Laundry room; Barber/Beauty shop; Library.
Activities Arts and Crafts; Games; Movies; Shopping trips; Dances/Social or cultural gatherings.
Description St Mary's Training School is a private, licensed, Catholic residential facility for the mentally retarded who are ambulatory and within the severe, moderate, or mild range of mental retardation between the ages of 3 and 22. Pre-vocational training is emphasized; a home-like atmosphere is maintained; certified to receive Title XIX payments.

Wilshire Manor Nursing Home*
PO Box 1286, 1200 Windsor Pl, Alexandria,
LA, 71301 (318) 445-9356

Admin Bob Marshall.
Licensure Intermediate Care. *Beds* 110. *Certified* Medicaid.

ALGIERS

Touro Shakespeare Home*
2621 General Meyer Ave, Algiers, LA, 70114
(504) 366-9881
Admin Russell J Henry.
Licensure Intermediate Care. *Beds* 119. *Certified* Medicaid.

Willow Wood—New Orleans Home for Jewish Aged*
PO Box 6024, 3700 Behrman Pl, Algiers, LA, 70114 (504) 367-5640
Admin Byron S Arbeit.
Licensure Skilled Care; Intermediate Care. *Beds* 101. *Certified* Medicaid; Medicare.
Affiliation Jewish

AMITE

Amite Nursing Home Inc*
709 E North Pl, Amite, LA, 70422 (504) 748-9473
Admin Preston J Broussard.
Licensure Intermediate Care. *Beds* 100. *Certified* Medicaid.

ARABI

Maison Orleans Nursing Home*
PO Box 234, 2310 Mehle Ave, Arabi, LA, 70032 (504) 279-0401
Admin Frank T Stewart Jr.
Licensure Intermediate Care. *Beds* 110. *Certified* Medicaid.

Saint Ann's Convalescent Home*
PO Box 236, 633 Mehle St, Arabi, LA, 70032 (504) 279-4461
Admin Hilman Mendoza.
Licensure Intermediate Care. *Beds* 70. *Certified* Medicaid.

ARCADIA

Arcadia Baptist Home*
PO Box 599, 1109 6th St, Arcadia, LA, 71001 (318) 263-8468
Admin L T Stringer.
Licensure Intermediate Care. *Beds* 80. *Certified* Medicaid.
Affiliation Baptist

BAKER

Baker Manor*
PO Box 409, 36121 Baker Blvd, Baker, LA, 70714 (504) 778-0573
Admin Kathryn E Hoover.
Licensure Intermediate Care. *Beds* 136. *Certified* Medicaid.

BASILE

Basile Care Center Inc*
PO Box 38, Chambers St, Basile, LA, 70515 (318) 432-6663
Admin Joseph Young.
Licensure Intermediate Care. *Beds* 78. *Certified* Medicaid.

BASTROP

Cherry Ridge Nursing Home
PO Box 941, Bastrop, LA, 71220 (318) 281-6933
Admin Claudia Winkler. *Medical Dir/Dir of Nursing* Jack Noble Md.
Licensure Intermediate Care. *Beds* 110. *Certified* Medicaid.
Admissions Requirements Physician's request.
Staff Physicians 1 (pt); RNs 1 (ft); LPNs 10 (ft); Orderlies 6 (ft); Nurses aides 34 (ft); Physical therapists 1 (pt); Activities coordinators 1 (ft); Dietitians 1 (pt); Dentists 1 (pt).
Facilities Dining room; Activities room; Chapel; Crafts room; Laundry room; Barber/Beauty shop.
Activities Arts and Crafts; Cards; Games; Reading groups; Prayer groups; Shopping trips; Dances/Social or cultural gatherings.

Hickory Manor Nursing Home Inc
360 W Hickory, Bastrop, LA, 71220 (318) 281-6523
Admin John B Williams. *Medical Dir/Dir of Nursing* Dr Bruce Wheeler.
Licensure Intermediate Care. *Beds* 106. *Certified* Medicaid.
Admissions Requirements Minimum age 21.
Staff Physicians 10 (pt); RNs 1 (ft); LPNs 9 (ft), 3 (pt); Orderlies 5 (ft); Nurses aides 20 (ft); Physical therapists 1 (pt); Activities coordinators 1 (ft); Dietitians 1 (ft); Dentists 2 (pt); Ophthalmologists 2 (pt).
Facilities Dining room; Physical therapy room; Activities room; Chapel; Crafts room; Laundry room; Barber/Beauty shop.
Activities Arts and Crafts; Cards; Games; Prayer groups; Movies; Shopping trips; Dances/Social or cultural gatherings.
Description Facility is located near Morehouse General Hospital. Christian staff in pleasant surroundings; 70% of staff here 5 years or longer.

Hillview Nursing Home
Alvin St, PO Box 667, Bastrop, LA, 71220 (318) 281-0322
Admin Doris V Johnston. *Medical Dir/Dir of Nursing* Patrica Watson.
Licensure Intermediate Care. *Beds* 120. *Certified* Medicaid.
Staff RNs 1 (ft); LPNs 10 (ft); Orderlies 4 (ft); Nurses aides 40 (ft); Physical therapists 1 (pt); Dietitians 1 (ft).
Facilities Dining room; Physical therapy room; Activities room; Crafts room; Laundry room.
Activities Arts and Crafts; Cards; Games; Reading groups; Prayer groups; Movies; Shopping trips; Dances/Social or cultural gatherings.

Summerlin Lane Nursing Home*
1408 Summerlin Ln, Bastrop, LA, 71220 (318) 281-5188
Admin Don Temple.
Licensure Intermediate Care. *Beds* 99. *Certified* Medicaid.

BATON ROUGE

Baton Rouge Extensive Care Facility*
4914 McClelland Dr, Baton Rouge, LA, 70805 (504) 356-3551
Admin Cornelia H Swayze.
Licensure Intermediate Care. *Beds* 123. *Certified* Medicaid.

Baton Rouge General Hospital Annex*
3888 North Blvd, Baton Rouge, LA, 70806 (504) 387-7900
Admin Tom Alexander.
Licensure Skilled Care. *Beds* 49. *Certified* Medicare.

Capitol Nursing Home
11546 Florida Blvd, Baton Rouge, LA, 70815 (504) 275-0474
Admin Mary Alice Latil. *Medical Dir/Dir of Nursing* Kathy Hagan.
Licensure Intermediate Care. *Beds* 85. *Certified* Medicaid.
Admissions Requirements Physician's request.
Staff RNs 1 (ft), 1 (pt); LPNs 7 (ft); Nurses aides 25 (ft); Activities coordinators 1 (ft); Dietitians 1 (ft), 1 (pt).
Facilities Dining room; Activities room; Chapel; Crafts room; Laundry room; Barber/Beauty shop; Library.
Activities Arts and Crafts; Cards; Games; Reading groups; Prayer groups; Movies; Shopping trips; Dances/Social or cultural gatherings.

Care Center
11188 Florida Blvd, Baton Rouge, LA, 70815 (504) 275-7570
Medical Dir/Dir of Nursing Helen Lancaster.
Licensure Intermediate Care. *Beds* 106. *Certified* Medicaid.
Admissions Requirements Medical examination.
Staff RNs 1 (ft); LPNs 5 (ft), 3 (pt); Nurses aides 64 (ft), 6 (pt); Activities coordinators 1 (ft); Dietitians 1 (pt).
Facilities Dining room; Laundry room; Barber/Beauty shop.
Activities Arts and Crafts; Games; Reading groups; Prayer groups; Shopping trips; Dances/Social or cultural gatherings.
Description We strive to create a loving and home-like atmosphere; also to maintain a high level of nursing care.

Convention Street Nursing Center*
PO Box 65274, 4660 Convention St, Baton Rouge, LA, 70896 (504) 926-5884
Admin Alan Barnett.
Licensure Intermediate Care. *Beds* 54. *Certified* Medicaid.

Fountain Lodge Nursing Home*
4005 North Blvd, Baton Rouge, LA, 70806 (504) 387-5934

Admin Muriel L Bates.
Licensure Intermediate Care. *Beds* 184. *Certified* Medicaid.

Guest House of Baton Rouge
10145 Florida Blvd, Baton Rouge, LA, 70815
(504) 272-0111
Admin J M Powell and Mary N Powell.
Medical Dir/Dir of Nursing Dr O P McCutchen.
Licensure Intermediate Care. *Beds* 126.
Admissions Requirements Medical examination; Physician's request.
Staff RNs 3 (ft), 2 (pt); LPNs 5 (ft), 3 (pt); Orderlies 5 (ft), 3 (pt); Nurses aides 40 (ft), 8 (pt); Physical therapists 1 (pt); Occupational therapists 1 (ft); Activities coordinators 1 (ft); Dietitians 1 (pt).
Facilities Dining room; Physical therapy room; Activities room; Chapel; Crafts room; Laundry room; Barber/Beauty shop; Library.
Activities Arts and Crafts; Games; Reading groups; Prayer groups; Shopping trips; Dances-/Social or cultural gatherings.
Description Facility offers a good activities program; location is very convenient.

Hillhaven Rest Home 1*
170 W Washington St, Baton Rouge, LA, 70802
(504) 343-8770
Admin Elaine S Wells.
Licensure Intermediate Care. *Beds* 89. *Certified* Medicaid.

Hillhaven Rest Home 2*
4100 North Blvd, Baton Rouge, LA, 70806
(504) 387-6704
Admin Marion Cangelosi.
Licensure Intermediate Care. *Beds* 123. *Certified* Medicaid.

Jefferson Manor
9919 Jefferson Hwy, Baton Rouge, LA, 70809
(504) 293-1434
Admin Danny Brown.
Licensure Intermediate Care. *Beds* 120. *Certified* Medicaid.
Staff RNs 1 (ft); LPNs 6 (ft); Nurses aides 26 (ft); Physical therapists 1 (pt); Reality therapists 1 (pt); Recreational therapists 1 (pt); Occupational therapists 1 (pt); Speech therapists 1 (pt); Activities coordinators 1 (ft), 1 (pt); Dietitians 1 (pt); Dentists 1 (pt); Ophthalmologists 1 (pt); Podiatrists 1 (pt).
Facilities Dining room; Physical therapy room; Activities room; Chapel; Crafts room; Laundry room; Barber/Beauty shop; Library.
Activities Arts and Crafts; Cards; Games; Prayer groups; Movies; Shopping trips; Dances/Social or cultural gatherings.

Ollie Steele Burden Manor*
4200 Essen Ln, Baton Rouge, LA, 70809 (504) 926-0091
Admin Sr Rose M Fitzgerald.
Licensure Intermediate Care. *Beds* 60.
Ownership Nonprofit.

Patio Lodge Nursing Home*
4363 Convention St, Baton Rouge, LA, 70806
(504) 383-6134

Admin Gordon Jeansonne.
Licensure Intermediate Care. *Beds* 141. *Certified* Medicaid.

BELLE CHASSE

Belle Chasse State School
Rt 1, PO Box 680, Belle Chasse, LA, 70037
(504) 394-1200
Admin Wayne Greenleaf. *Medical Dir/Dir of Nursing* Dr Norman Leslie.
Licensure Intermediate Care for Mentally Retarded. *Beds* 420. *Certified* Medicaid.
Admissions Requirements Minimum age 3; Medical examination.
Staff Physicians 3 (ft), 6 (pt); RNs 5 (ft); LPNs 14 (ft); Physical therapists 2 (ft), 2 (pt); Recreational therapists 6 (ft); Occupational therapists 5 (ft); Speech therapists 6 (ft); Activities coordinators 1 (ft); Dietitians 2 (ft), 1 (pt); Dentists 1 (ft), 4 (pt); Ophthalmologists 1 (pt); Audiologists 1 (ft).
Facilities Dining room; Physical therapy room; Activities room; Crafts room; Laundry room; Barber/Beauty shop; Library.
Activities Arts and Crafts; Cards; Games; Reading groups; Prayer groups; Movies; Shopping trips; Dances/Social or cultural gatherings.
Description Highly specialized, MR/DD residential training services for clients who are medically and/or behaviorally (psychiatrically) involved.

BERNICE

Pine Crest Manor Nursing Home
101 Reeves St, Bernice, LA, 71222 (318) 285-7600
Admin Helen Campbell. *Medical Dir/Dir of Nursing* W C Reeves MD.
Licensure Intermediate Care. *Beds* 126. *Certified* Medicaid.
Staff Physicians 1 (pt); RNs 1 (ft); LPNs 10 (ft), 1 (pt); Orderlies 4 (ft); Nurses aides 33 (ft), 4 (pt); Activities coordinators 1 (ft), 1 (pt); Dietitians 1 (pt).
Facilities Dining room; Physical therapy room; Activities room; Chapel; Crafts room; Laundry room; Barber/Beauty shop.
Activities Arts and Crafts; Games; Reading groups; Prayer groups; Movies; Shopping trips; Dances/Social or cultural gatherings.

BOGALUSA

Rest Haven Nursing Home*
1301 Harrison St, Bogalusa, LA, 70427 (504) 732-3909
Admin James E Morris.
Licensure Intermediate Care. *Beds* 204. *Certified* Medicaid.

BOSSIER CITY

Bossier Health Care Center*
2901 Douglas Dr, Bossier City, LA, 71010
(318) 747-2700
Admin Josey Nelson.
Licensure Intermediate Care. *Beds* 138. *Certified* Medicaid.

Heritage Manor of Bossier City
2575 N Airline Dr, Bossier City, LA, 71010
(318) 746-7466
Admin Josey H Nelson.
Licensure Intermediate Care. *Beds* 63. *Certified* Medicaid.

Northwest Louisiana State School
5401 Shed Rd B, Bossier City, LA, 71010 (318) 742-6220
Admin Cecil N Colwell.
Licensure Intermediate Care for Mentally Retarded. *Beds* 228. *Certified* Medicaid.

Pilgrim Manor of Bossier City—North*
1524 Doctors Dr, Bossier City, LA, 71010 (318) 742-1623
Admin William V Hines.
Licensure Intermediate Care. *Beds* 177. *Certified* Medicaid.

Pilgrim Manor of Bossier City—South*
1525 Fullilove Dr, Bossier City, LA, 71112
(318) 742-5420
Admin Byron Neal Hines.
Licensure Intermediate Care. *Beds* 96. *Certified* Medicaid.

BUNKIE

Bayou Vista Manor Nursing Home*
PO Box 270, 323 Evergreen Rd, Bunkie, LA, 71322 (318) 346-2080
Admin Ray Buckner.
Licensure Intermediate Care. *Beds* 170. *Certified* Medicaid.

CENTERPOINT

Oak Haven Nursing Home
PO Box 198, Centerpoint, LA, 71323 (318) 253-6219
Admin Linda Scanlan.
Licensure Intermediate Care. *Beds* 104. *Certified* Medicaid.
Staff Physicians 1 (pt); RNs 1 (ft), 1 (pt); LPNs 5 (ft), 3 (pt); Orderlies 1 (pt); Nurses aides 25 (ft), 11 (pt); Activities coordinators 1 (ft); Dietitians 1 (pt); Dentists 1 (pt).
Facilities Dining room; Crafts room; Laundry room; Barber/Beauty shop.
Activities Arts and Crafts; Cards; Games; Prayer groups; Shopping trips; Dances/Social or cultural gatherings.
Description Facility is located in the country on 10 acres with a fenced-in yard and features many activities, a home-like atmosphere, and excellent nursing care.

CHURCH POINT

Acadia—Saint Landry Guest Home*
830 S Broadway St, Church Point, LA, 70525
(318) 684-6316
Admin Carole L Thibodaux.
Licensure Intermediate Care. *Beds* 118. *Certified* Medicaid.

CLINTON

Grace Nursing Home
PO Drawer 945, Clinton, LA, 70722 (504) 683-8533
Admin Ben J Wimbertcy. *Medical Dir/Dir of Nursing* Dr John Piker.
Licensure Intermediate Care. *Beds* 128. *Certified* Medicaid.
Staff Physicians 1 (pt); RNs 1 (ft), 1 (pt); LPNs 6 (ft), 3 (pt); Orderlies 2 (ft); Nurses aides 30 (ft), 5 (pt); Physical therapists 1 (pt); Reality therapists 1 (pt); Recreational therapists 1 (pt); Occupational therapists 1 (pt); Speech therapists 1 (pt); Activities coordinators 1 (ft); Dietitians 1 (pt).
Facilities Dining room; Physical therapy room; Activities room; Crafts room; Laundry room; Barber/Beauty shop.
Activities Arts and Crafts; Movies; Shopping trips; Dances/Social or cultural gatherings.
Description Facility is located on 10-acres in East Felicidad Parish about 2 miles south of Clinton; beautiful country with lots of rolling hills and trees.

COLFAX

Grant Manor Care Center
Rt 3, Box 227, Webb Smith Dr, Colfax, LA, 71417 (318) 627-3207
Admin Colene D Bankston. *Medical Dir/Dir of Nursing* Dr G C Bohm.
Licensure Intermediate Care. *Beds* 140. *Certified* Medicaid.
Admissions Requirements Medical examination; Physician's request.
Staff Physicians 4 (ft), 6 (pt); RNs 2 (ft); LPNs 6 (ft), 4 (pt); Nurses aides 30 (ft), 10 (pt); Physical therapists 2 (ft), 1 (pt); Activities coordinators 1 (ft); Dietitians 1 (ft); Dentists 1 (pt).
Facilities Dining room; Physical therapy room; Activities room; Crafts room; Laundry room; Barber/Beauty shop.
Activities Arts and Crafts; Games; Reading groups; Prayer groups; Shopping trips.

COLUMBIA

Columbia Heights Nursing Home*
PO Box 398, Columbia, LA, 71418 (318) 649-2702
Admin Robin Causey.
Licensure Intermediate Care. *Beds* 130. *Certified* Medicaid.

Columbia State School
Hwy 850, PO Box B, Columbia, LA, 71418 (318) 649-2385
Admin Gene I Barrow.
Licensure Intermediate Care for Mentally Retarded. *Beds* 32. *Certified* Medicaid.
Admissions Requirements Minimum age 3; Medical examination.
Staff Physicians 3 (pt); RNs 1 (ft); LPNs 1 (pt); Physical therapists 1 (pt); Occupational therapists 1 (pt); Speech therapists 1 (ft); Dietitians 1 (ft); Dentists 1 (pt).
Facilities Dining room; Physical therapy room; Activities room; Laundry room; Library; Adaptive physical education and diagnostic areas.

Activities Cards; Games; Reading groups; Movies; Shopping trips; Dances/Social or cultural gatherings.
Description Intermediate care facility providing short-term intensive training concentrating on teaching basic self-help skills with use of positive reinforcement to severely and profoundly mentally retarded.

COUSHATTA

Senior Citizens Center
Box 768, Coushatta, LA, 71019 (318) 932-5202
Admin Len Stephens. *Medical Dir/Dir of Nursing* Elsie Madden RN.
Licensure Intermediate Care. *Beds* 83. *Certified* Medicaid.
Admissions Requirements Medical examination.
Staff RNs 1 (ft); LPNs 4 (ft), 1 (pt); Nurses aides 18 (ft), 5 (pt); Physical therapists 1 (pt); Activities coordinators 1 (ft); Dietitians 1 (pt).
Facilities Dining room; Activities room; Laundry room; Barber/Beauty shop.
Activities Cards; Games; Prayer groups; Movies; Shopping trips; Dances/Social or cultural gatherings.
Description Facility offers residents a home-like atmosphere and serves them with tender loving care.

Springville Nursing Center
Springville Rd, PO Box 469, Coushatta, LA, 71019 (318) 932-5688
Admin Len W Stephens. *Medical Dir/Dir of Nursing* Loyce V Plunkett RN.
Licensure Intermediate Care. *Beds* 74. *Certified* Medicaid.
Admissions Requirements Medical examination.
Staff RNs 1 (ft); LPNs 4 (ft), 1 (pt); Orderlies 3 (ft), 2 (pt); Nurses aides 18 (ft), 3 (pt); Physical therapists 1 (pt); Activities coordinators 1 (ft); Dietitians 1 (pt).
Facilities Dining room; Activities room; Laundry room; Barber/Beauty shop.
Activities Arts and Crafts; Games; Prayer groups; Movies; Shopping trips; Dances/Social or cultural gatherings; Field trips.
Description Residents' families encouraged to participate in the daily living of the residents. Residents are urged to participate in community activities and affairs as much as their individual conditions will allow.

COVINGTON

Forest Manor*
PO Box 779, Madisonville Hwy, Covington, LA, 70433 (504) 892-6900
Admin Jack Bossier.
Licensure Intermediate Care. *Beds* 192. *Certified* Medicaid.

CROWLEY

Bayou Village Nursing Center*
PO Brawer 387, 1101 S Eastern Ave, Crowley, LA, 70526 (318) 783-2740

Admin Allen Carrier.
Licensure Intermediate Care. *Beds* 97. *Certified* Medicaid.

Christian Villa
1120 W Hutchinson, Crowley, LA, 70526 (318) 783-5533
Admin Willie Maynard Jr. *Medical Dir/Dir of Nursing* J C Dauphin MD.
Licensure Intermediate Care. *Beds* 73. *Certified* Medicaid.
Admissions Requirements Medical examination; Physician's request.
Staff Physicians 1 (ft), 1 (pt); RNs 1 (ft); LPNs 4 (ft), 2 (pt); Orderlies 3 (ft); Nurses aides 41 (ft); Physical therapists 1 (pt); Recreational therapists 1 (ft); Occupational therapists 1 (pt); Activities coordinators 1 (ft); Dietitians 1 (ft); Dentists 1 (pt); Ophthalmologists 1 (pt).
Facilities Dining room; Laundry room; Lounge.
Activities Arts and Crafts; Cards; Games; Reading groups; Prayer groups; Movies; Shopping trips; Dances/Social or cultural gatherings.
Description Facility is open to people of all faiths and race, color, or creed. Mindful of the past, grateful for the present, and knowing that He holds the future in His hand. "Not by might, nor by power, but by my spirit, saith the Lord."

Crowley Town and Country Nursing Center Inc
1400 E Elm St, PO Box 1274, Crowley, LA, 70526 (318) 783-8101
Admin Cynthia Lege. *Medical Dir/Dir of Nursing* H Lawrence Gardiner MD.
Licensure Intermediate Care. *Beds* 124. *Certified* Medicaid.
Admissions Requirements Medical examination; Physician's request.
Staff Physicians 1 (ft); RNs 1 (ft); LPNs 9 (ft), 1 (pt); Orderlies 1 (ft); Nurses aides 20 (ft), 5 (pt); Physical therapists 1 (pt); Activities coordinators 1 (ft).
Facilities Dining room; Activities room; Chapel; Crafts room; Laundry room; Library.
Activities Arts and Crafts; Cards; Games; Prayer groups; Movies; Dances/Social or cultural gatherings.
Description A family activity group has been formed to handle all major socials, totally organized by the families. They contact the activity department if anything is needed. This frees the activity department to do other needed activities and stimulation.

Heritage Manor of Crowley
1526 N Ave I, PO Drawer 1547, Crowley, LA, 70526 (318) 783-2363
Admin Marian A Trahan.
Licensure Intermediate Care. *Beds* 57. *Certified* Medicaid.
Admissions Requirements Medical examination.
Staff RNs 1 (ft); LPNs 3 (ft), 4 (pt); Nurses aides 40 (ft), 3 (pt); Activities coordinators 1 (ft); Dietitians 1 (pt).
Facilities Dining room; Laundry room; Barber/Beauty shop.
Activities Arts and Crafts; Cards; Games; Reading groups; Prayer groups; Movies; Shopping trips; Dances/Social or cultural gatherings.

CUT OFF

South Lafourche Nursing Center
PO Box 338, Cut Off, LA, 70345 (504)
693-8677
Admin Lou Gaspard. *Medical Dir/Dir of Nursing* Dr Seludd.
Licensure Intermediate Care. *Beds* 122. *Certified* Medicaid.
Admissions Requirements Medical examination.
Staff Physicians 1 (ft); RNs 1 (ft); LPNs 6 (ft); Orderlies 3 (ft); Nurses aides 26 (ft); Physical therapists 1 (ft); Occupational therapists 1 (pt); Speech therapists 1 (pt); Activities coordinators 1 (ft); Dietitians 1 (pt); Dentists 1 (pt); Ophthalmologists 1 (pt); Podiatrists 1 (pt); Audiologists 1 (pt).
Facilities Dining room; Physical therapy room; Activities room; Chapel; Crafts room; Laundry room; Barber/Beauty shop; Library.
Activities Arts and Crafts; Games; Prayer groups; Movies; Shopping trips; Dances/Social or cultural gatherings.

DELHI

Delhi Guest Home
203 Rancher St, Delhi, LA, 71232 (318)
878-5106
Admin Archie B Clayton Jr.
Licensure Intermediate Care for Mentally Retarded. *Beds* 145. *Certified* Medicaid.

Richland Nursing Home
504 N Charter St, Delhi, LA, 71232 (318)
878-2417
Admin Allen S Brown.
Licensure Intermediate Care. *Beds* 87. *Certified* Medicaid.
Staff RNs 1 (ft); LPNs 6 (ft); Orderlies 1 (ft); Nurses aides 18 (ft); Physical therapists; Activities coordinators; Dentists; Ophthalmologists.
Facilities Dining room; Barber/Beauty shop.
Activities Arts and Crafts; Cards; Games; Reading groups; Prayer groups; Movies.

DENHAM SPRINGS

Golden Age Nursing Home
Rt 5, 4-H Club Rd, Box 574, Denham Springs, LA, 70726 (504) 665-5544
Admin Cindy Quirk. *Medical Dir/Dir of Nursing* Louise Corkern.
Licensure Intermediate Care. *Beds* 175. *Certified* Medicaid.
Staff Physicians 9 (pt); RNs 1 (ft), 1 (pt); LPNs 10 (ft), 3 (pt); Nurses aides 27 (ft), 23 (pt); Physical therapists 1 (pt); Occupational therapists 1 (pt); Speech therapists 1 (pt); Activities coordinators 1 (ft), 1 (pt); Dietitians 1 (pt); Dentists 1 (pt); Ophthalmologists 1 (pt); Podiatrists 1 (pt).
Facilities Dining room; Physical therapy room; Activities room; Crafts room; Laundry room; Barber/Beauty shop; Sunroom.
Activities Arts and Crafts; Cards; Games; Reading groups; Prayer groups; Movies; Shopping trips; Dances/Social or cultural gatherings; Field trips.
Description Situated in a lovely country setting, shaded by tall pine and oak trees, Golden Age Nursing Home has the advantage of country environment close to Baton Rouge and the excellent medical facilities and cultural entertainment available there.

Harvest Manor Nursing Home
PO Box 847, 1625 Cockerham Rd, Denham Springs, LA, 70726 (504) 665-8946
Admin Barbara Stephenson.
Licensure Intermediate Care. *Beds* 177. *Certified* Medicaid.
Staff RNs 2 (ft), 2 (pt); LPNs 8 (ft), 2 (pt); Nurses aides 19 (ft); Activities coordinators 1 (ft); Dietitians 1 (ft).
Facilities Dining room; Activities room; Crafts room; Laundry room; Barber/Beauty shop.
Activities Arts and Crafts; Prayer groups; Movies.

DEQUINCY

Greenhills Nursing Home*
PO Box 1219, 602 N Division, DeQuincy, LA, 70633 (318) 786-2466
Admin Sidney O Sanders.
Licensure Intermediate Care. *Beds* 76. *Certified* Medicaid.

DERIDDER

Beauregard Nursing Home*
PO Box 230, 1420 Blankenship Dr, DeRidder, LA, 70630 (318) 463-9022
Admin George Mitchell.
Licensure Intermediate Care. *Beds* 142. *Certified* Medicaid.

Westwood Manor Nursing Home*
810 High School Dr, DeRidder, LA, 70634 (318) 463-6293
Admin Benson W Sylvest.
Licensure Intermediate Care. *Beds* 76. *Certified* Medicaid.

DONALDSONVILLE

D'Ville House*
PO Box 799, Vatican Dr, Donaldsonville, LA, 70346 (504) 473-8614
Admin Barbara Ourso.
Licensure Intermediate Care. *Beds* 133. *Certified* Medicaid.

ERATH

Morris Lahasky Nursing Home
501 E Conrad St, Erath, LA, 70533 (318)
937-6752
Admin Hazel Hebert. *Medical Dir/Dir of Nursing* Dr Bernard Lahasky.
Licensure Intermediate Care. *Beds* 128. *Certified* Medicaid.
Staff Physicians 6 (ft); RNs 1 (ft), 1 (pt); Orderlies 2 (ft), 1 (pt); Nurses aides 32 (ft), 5 (pt); Physical therapists 1 (pt); Activities coordinators 1 (ft); Dietitians 1 (pt).
Languages French
Facilities Dining room; Physical therapy room; Activities room; Chapel; Crafts room; Laundry room; Barber/Beauty shop.
Activities Arts and Crafts; Cards; Games; Reading groups; Prayer groups; Movies; Shopping trips; Dances/Social or cultural gatherings.
Description Facility has a country-type setting on the outskirts of a very small town; building in the shape of a windmill sits on 5 acres of land with several old pecan trees. People are very friendly and speak a lot of French.

EUNICE

Nursing Home of Eunice
1100 Nile St, Eunice, LA, 70535 (318)
457-2681
Admin June Dupuis. *Medical Dir/Dir of Nursing* Dr Brian Heinen.
Licensure Intermediate Care. *Beds* 146. *Certified* Medicaid.
Admissions Requirements Medical examination; Physician's request.
Staff Physicians 1 (pt); RNs 1 (ft); LPNs 12 (ft), 4 (pt); Nurses aides 54 (ft), 14 (pt); Physical therapists 1 (pt); Activities coordinators 2 (ft); Dietitians 1 (pt); Dentists 1 (pt).
Facilities Dining room; Activities room; Crafts room; Laundry room; Barber/Beauty shop.
Activities Arts and Crafts; Cards; Games; Reading groups; Prayer groups; Movies; Shopping trips; Dances/Social or cultural gatherings.

FARMERVILLE

Lakeview Nursing Home
110 W Hill St, Farmerville, LA, 71241 (318)
368-3103
Admin Donnice Reynolds. *Medical Dir/Dir of Nursing* Carol Kennedy RN.
Licensure Intermediate Care. *Beds* 115. *Certified* Medicaid.
Admissions Requirements Medical examination.
Staff RNs 2 (ft); LPNs 10 (ft); Orderlies 1 (ft); Nurses aides 35 (ft); Physical therapists 1 (pt); Recreational therapists 1 (ft); Activities coordinators 1 (ft); Dietitians 1 (ft).
Facilities Dining room; Physical therapy room; Activities room; Crafts room; Laundry room; Barber/Beauty shop.
Activities Arts and Crafts; Cards; Games; Reading groups; Prayer groups; Movies; Shopping trips; Dances/Social or cultural gatherings.

FERRIDAY

Concordia Parish Rest Home*
411 N 4th St, Ferriday, LA, 71334 (318)
757-2181
Admin Floyd Thornhill.
Licensure Intermediate Care. *Beds* 60. *Certified* Medicaid.

Heritage Manor of Ferriday*
PO Box 392, Hwy 65 N, Ferriday, LA, 71334 (318) 757-8671
Admin Tommy L Massey.
Licensure Intermediate Care. *Beds* 60. *Certified* Medicaid.

FRANKLIN

Franklin Nursing Home*
PO Box 1229, 1907 Chinaberry St, Franklin, LA, 70538 (318) 828-1918
Admin Amanda Landry.
Licensure Intermediate Care. *Beds* 120. *Certified* Medicaid.

FRANKLINTON

Heritage Manor of Franklinton*
Rt 7, Box 31, Franklinton, LA, 70438 (504) 839-4491
Admin Cletus Solar.
Licensure Intermediate Care. *Beds* 59. *Certified* Medicaid.

GONZALES

Gonzales Health Care Center*
711 W Cornerview Rd, Gonzales, LA, 70737 (504) 644-6581
Admin Preston Broussard.
Licensure Intermediate Care. *Beds* 102. *Certified* Medicaid.

Heritage Manor of Gonzales*
PO Box 518, 905 W Cornerview Rd, Gonzales, LA, 70737 (504) 644-5358
Admin Dick Bagwell.
Licensure Intermediate Care. *Beds* 104. *Certified* Medicaid.

HAMMOND

Belle Maison Nursing Home
301 7th Ward Medical Plaza, Hammond, LA, 70401 (504) 542-0110
Admin E P Guitreau Jr. *Medical Dir/Dir of Nursing* Collins P Lipcomb MD.
Licensure Intermediate Care. *Beds* 132. *Certified* Medicaid.
Admissions Requirements Medical examination.
Staff Physicians; RNs 3 (ft); LPNs 10 (ft); Nurses aides 65 (ft); Physical therapists; Reality therapists; Recreational therapists 1 (ft); Speech therapists; Activities coordinators 1 (ft); Dietitians; Podiatrists; Audiologists.
Facilities Dining room; Physical therapy room; Activities room; Chapel; Crafts room; Laundry room; Barber/Beauty shop; Library.
Activities Arts and Crafts; Cards; Games; Reading groups; Prayer groups; Movies; Dances/Social or cultural gatherings.

Hammond Nursing Home*
501 Old Covington Hwy, Hammond, LA, 70401 (504) 542-1200
Admin Ray Naquin.
Licensure Intermediate Care. *Beds* 120. *Certified* Medicaid.

Hammond State School
Rt 3, Box 165-P, Hammond, LA, 70401 (504) 567-3111
Admin Austin H Glass.
Licensure Intermediate Care for Mentally Retarded. *Beds* 750. *Certified* Medicaid.

Heritage Manor of Hammond*
800 S Oak St, Hammond, LA, 70401 (504) 345-7210
Admin Mike Wunnenberg.
Licensure Intermediate Care. *Beds* 108. *Certified* Medicaid.

HARRISONBURG

Harrisonburg Nursing Center*
PO Box 307, Sicily St, Harrisonburg, LA, 71340 (318) 744-5954
Admin Beth Willis.
Licensure Intermediate Care. *Beds* 104. *Certified* Medicaid.

HARVEY

Manhattan Manor Extended Care Facility
1020 Manhattan Blvd, Harvey, LA, 70058 (504) 362-2020
Admin Minette McCurley. *Medical Dir/Dir of Nursing* David Euans.
Licensure Skilled Care; Intermediate Care. *Beds* 102. *Certified* Medicaid; Medicare.
Admissions Requirements Medical examination; Physician's request.
Staff RNs 2 (ft); LPNs 12 (ft), 4 (pt); Orderlies 1 (ft); Nurses aides 35 (ft); Physical therapists 1 (pt); Speech therapists 1 (pt); Activities coordinators 1 (pt); Dietitians 1 (pt); Dentists 1 (pt); Podiatrists 1 (pt).
Facilities Dining room; Activities room; Barber/Beauty shop.
Activities Arts and Crafts; Cards; Games; Reading groups; Prayer groups.

Manhattan Manor Guest House*
2233 8th St, Harvey, LA, 70058 (504) 362-9522
Admin Geneva B Pettiford.
Licensure Intermediate Care. *Beds* 104. *Certified* Medicaid.

HAYNESVILLE

Heritage Nursing Center
114 Bailey St, Haynesville, LA, 71038 (318) 624-1166
Admin John L Savagge Jr. *Medical Dir/Dir of Nursing* Dr E Butler.
Licensure Intermediate Care. *Beds* 38. *Certified* Medicaid.
Staff RNs 1 (ft); LPNs 5 (ft); Orderlies 1 (ft); Nurses aides 13 (ft); Activities coordinators 1 (ft); Dietitians 1 (ft).
Facilities Dining room; Activities room; Laundry room; Barber/Beauty shop.
Activities Cards; Games; Reading groups; Prayer groups; Movies.

HESSMER

Hessmer Nursing Home
Rt 1, Box 61, Hessmer, LA, 71341 (318) 563-8416
Admin Nell Oliver. *Medical Dir/Dir of Nursing* Dr F P Bordelon.
Licensure Intermediate Care. *Beds* 92. *Certified* Medicaid.
Admissions Requirements Minimum age 18;

Medical examination; Physician's request.
Staff RNs 1 (ft); LPNs 5 (ft), 6 (pt); Orderlies 2 (ft); Nurses aides 25 (ft), 5 (pt); Activities coordinators 1 (ft); Dietitians 1 (pt).
Facilities Dining room; Activities room; Chapel; Crafts room; Laundry room.
Activities Arts and Crafts; Cards; Games; Prayer groups; Movies; Shopping trips.

HINESTON

Fair Oaks Nursing Home*
PO Box 32, Hwy 121, Hineston, LA, 71438 (318) 793-2368
Admin Lois Carruth.
Licensure Intermediate Care. *Beds* 66. *Certified* Medicaid.

HOMER

Presbyterian Village of Homer
PO Box 149, Homer, LA, 71040 (318) 927-3352
Admin Robert L McGaha. *Medical Dir/Dir of Nursing* Betty Smith.
Licensure Intermediate Care. *Beds* 79. *Certified* Medicaid.
Admissions Requirements Physician's request.
Staff Physicians 3 (pt); RNs 2 (ft); LPNs 7 (ft); Orderlies 5 (ft); Nurses aides 20 (ft); Recreational therapists 1 (ft), 1 (pt); Activities coordinators 1 (ft); Dietitians 1 (pt); Dentists 1 (pt).
Affiliation Presbyterian

HOUMA

Inez Sako Nursing Home II*
107 S Hollywood Rd, Houma, LA, 70360 (504) 876-3250
Admin Robert E Dill III.
Licensure Intermediate Care. *Beds* 105. *Certified* Medicaid.

Maranatha Care Center*
1395 W Tunnel Blvd, Houma, LA, 70360 (504) 872-4553
Admin Mary Klein.
Licensure Intermediate Care. *Beds* 201. *Certified* Medicaid.

IOTA

Southwest Louisiana State School
PO Box 218, Iota, LA, 70543 (318) 824-6250
Admin James A Austin.
Licensure Intermediate Care for Mentally Retarded. *Beds* 32. *Certified* Medicaid.

JACKSON

Villa Feliciana Geriatric Hospital*
PO Box 438, Jackson, LA, 70748 (504) 634-7793
Admin John A London.
Licensure Skilled Care; Intermediate Care. *Beds* 610. *Certified* Medicaid; Medicare.

JEFFERSON

Jefferson Health Care Center*
2200 Jefferson Hwy, Jefferson, LA, 70121 (504)
837-3144
Admin John Robert Laster.
Licensure Intermediate Care. *Beds* 288. *Certified* Medicaid.

JENA

Golden Age Nursing Center
PO Drawer S, Jena, LA, 71342 (318) 992-4175
Admin William Phelps. *Medical Dir/Dir of Nursing* Dr I C Turnley.
Licensure Intermediate Care. *Beds* 88. *Certified* Medicaid.
Admissions Requirements Medical examination.
Staff Physicians 1 (ft), 10 (pt); RNs 1 (pt); LPNs 8 (ft), 4 (pt); Activities coordinators 1 (ft); Dietitians 1 (ft), 2 (pt); Dentists 1 (ft), 1 (pt); Ophthalmologists 1 (ft); Podiatrists 1 (ft); Audiologists 1 (ft).
Facilities Dining room; Activities room; Crafts room; Laundry room; Barber/Beauty shop.
Activities Arts and Crafts; Games; Reading groups; Prayer groups; Movies; Shopping trips; Dances/Social or cultural gatherings.
Description One of the first homes to begin the foster grandparents program as well as a very active group of auxiliary volunteers. Each quarter, all families and friends are invited out to share an evening of food and fellowship as well as see a program planned and performed by the residents.

La Salle Nursing Home Inc
PO Drawer 1510, Jena, LA, 71342 (318)
992-6627
Admin W J Nunnally.
Licensure Intermediate Care. *Beds* 103. *Certified* Medicaid.
Admissions Requirements Medical examination.
Staff Physicians 4 (pt); RNs 2 (ft), 1 (pt); LPNs 10 (ft); Orderlies 2 (ft); Nurses aides 50 (ft), 7 (pt); Physical therapists 1 (pt); Activities coordinators 1 (ft); Dietitians 1 (ft); Dentists 1 (pt).
Facilities Dining room; Activities room; Crafts room; Laundry room; Barber/Beauty shop.
Activities Arts and Crafts; Cards; Games; Reading groups; Prayer groups; Movies; Shopping trips; Dances/Social or cultural gatherings; Field trips.
Description Facility has 5-acre park designed for the elderly and handicapped. Modern facility is connected to La Salle General Hospital. A nonprofit facility dedicated to the total care of the aged and handicapped.

JENNINGS

Jefferson Davis Nursing Home
1338 N Cutting Ave, PO Box 757, Jennings, LA, 70546 (318) 824-3165
Admin Thomas L Qualey Jr. *Medical Dir/Dir of Nursing* Louis Shirley MD.
Licensure Intermediate Care. *Beds* 135. *Certified* Medicaid.
Staff RNs 1 (ft); LPNs 11 (ft); Orderlies 2 (ft);

Nurses aides 38 (ft), 15 (pt); Physical therapists 1 (pt); Recreational therapists 1 (pt); Activities coordinators 1 (ft); Dietitians 1 (ft); Dentists 1 (pt).
Facilities Dining room; Physical therapy room; Activities room; Crafts room; Laundry room; Barber/Beauty shop; Library.
Activities Arts and Crafts; Cards; Games; Reading groups; Prayer groups; Movies; Shopping trips; Dances/Social or cultural gatherings; Trips outside city.
Description Situated in a pastoral community, yet a short drive from major metropolitan centers, the nursing home offers an excellent blend of nursing care services and social events that have proved to be most beneficial in developing a total patient care program.

Jennings Guest House*
203 S Louise St, Jennings, LA, 70546 (318)
824-2466
Admin Bobby R Linscomb.
Licensure Intermediate Care. *Beds* 152. *Certified* Medicaid.

JONESBORO

Carter Nursing Home*
503 W Main St, Jonesboro, LA, 71251 (318)
259-2729
Admin Catherine Walsworth.
Licensure Intermediate Care. *Beds* 51. *Certified* Medicaid.

Jackson Manor Nursing Home*
PO Box 669, Hwy 167 S, Jonesboro, LA, 71251 (318) 259-7386
Admin Charles E Pogue.
Licensure Intermediate Care. *Beds* 84. *Certified* Medicaid.

Wyatt Manor Nursing Home*
Rt 3, Box 200, Jonesboro, LA, 71251 (318)
259-3290
Admin Harold Hickey.
Licensure Intermediate Care. *Beds* 62. *Certified* Medicaid.

JONESVILLE

Homage Manor*
300 Nasif St, Jonesville, LA, 71343 (318)
339-7374
Admin Floyd Thornhill.
Licensure Intermediate Care. *Beds* 54. *Certified* Medicaid.

KAPLAN

Heritage Manor of Kaplan*
1300 W 8th St, Kaplan, LA, 70548 (318)
643-7302
Admin Barbara B Hair.
Licensure Intermediate Care. *Beds* 120. *Certified* Medicaid.

Vermillion Health Care Center*
Rt 2, Box 100, Kaplan, LA, 70548 (318)
643-2949

Admin Vern Pleasant.
Licensure Intermediate Care. *Beds* 60. *Certified* Medicaid.

KENNER

Waldon Healthcare Center
2401 Idaho St, Kenner, LA, 70062 (504)
466-0222
Admin Regina Danner. *Medical Dir/Dir of Nursing* Dr Paez.
Licensure Intermediate Care. *Beds* 205. *Certified* Medicaid.
Admissions Requirements Medical examination; Physician's request.
Staff RNs 4 (ft), 2 (pt); LPNs 12 (ft), 5 (pt); Nurses aides 60 (ft); Activities coordinators 2 (ft); Dietitians 2 (ft).
Facilities Dining room; Activities room; Crafts room; Laundry room; Barber/Beauty shop.
Activities Arts and Crafts; Cards; Games; Reading groups; Prayer groups; Movies; Shopping trips; Dances/Social or cultural gatherings; Field trips.
Description Residents are really involved in the arts and crafts program; enjoy tending to the needs of their 2 dogs Pal and Midnight. They have formed their own public action committee and are very active in community affairs.

KENTWOOD

Kentwood Manor Nursing Home*
PO Box 67, Kentwood, LA, 70444 (504)
229-2112
Admin Herbert M Hart Jr.
Licensure Intermediate Care. *Beds* 132. *Certified* Medicaid.

KINDER

Kinder Nursing Home
PO Drawer 1270, Kinder, LA, 70648 (318)
738-5671
Admin Ronnie Smith.
Licensure Intermediate Care. *Beds* 100. *Certified* Medicaid.
Admissions Requirements Minimum age 30; Medical examination; Physician's request.
Staff RNs 1 (ft), 1 (pt); LPNs 8 (ft), 2 (pt); Orderlies 2 (ft); Nurses aides 25 (ft), 8 (pt); Activities coordinators 1 (ft); Dietitians 1 (pt).
Facilities Dining room; Activities room; Laundry room; Barber/Beauty shop.
Activities Arts and Crafts; Games; Prayer groups; Movies.

LACOMBE

Lacombe Nursing Home
Hwy 190, PO Box 6, Lacombe, LA, 70445
(504) 882-5417
Admin Ronald Goux. *Medical Dir/Dir of Nursing* Dr Gerald Keller.
Licensure Intermediate Care. *Beds* 97. *Certified* Medicaid.
Admissions Requirements Medical examination.
Staff Physicians 1 (ft); RNs 2 (ft); LPNs 3 (ft). 3 (pt); Nurses aides 15 (ft), 9 (pt); Activities

coordinators.
Facilities Dining room; Activities room; Chapel; Crafts room; Laundry room; Barber/Beauty shop.
Activities Arts and Crafts; Cards; Games; Reading groups; Prayer groups; Shopping trips; Dances/Social or cultural gatherings.
Description Facility is set among the rustic, shady oaks of Lacombe; has a 24-hour security system. Accomodations for social, dietary, and occupational therapies available, which also includes barber and beauty salon services; also has nurses on duty 24 hours.

LAFAYETTE

Acadiana Nursing Home
408 SE Evangeline Thruway, Lafayette, LA, 70501 (318) 235-9976
Admin Lonnie Sarver. *Medical Dir/Dir of Nursing* Dr Donald Reed.
Licensure Intermediate Care. *Beds* 92. *Certified* Medicaid.
Admissions Requirements Minimum age 40; Medical examination.
Staff Physicians 1 (ft); RNs 1 (ft); LPNs 5 (ft), 3 (pt); Orderlies 1 (ft); Nurses aides 35 (ft), 4 (pt); Activities coordinators 1 (ft); Dietitians 1 (ft); Podiatrists 1 (pt).
Facilities Crafts room.

Amelia Manor Nursing Home
903 Center St, Lafayette, LA, 70501 (318) 234-7331
Admin J B Sarver. *Medical Dir/Dir of Nursing* William Melencon.
Licensure Intermediate Care. *Beds* 150. *Certified* Medicaid.
Admissions Requirements Minimum age 40; Medical examination; Physician's request.
Staff Physicians 3 (pt); RNs 1 (ft); LPNs 10 (ft), 3 (pt); Nurses aides 50 (ft), 5 (pt); Physical therapists 1 (pt); Recreational therapists 1 (ft); Occupational therapists 1 (pt); Speech therapists 1 (pt); Activities coordinators 1 (ft); Dietitians 1 (pt); Dentists 2 (pt).
Facilities Dining room; Activities room; Crafts room; Laundry room; Barber/Beauty shop.
Activities Arts and Crafts; Cards; Games; Prayer groups; Movies; Shopping trips; Dances/Social or cultural gatherings.

Bethany MHS Health Care Center
Saint Julien St, PO Box 2308, Lafayette, LA, 70502 (318) 234-2459
Licensure Intermediate Care. *Beds* 42.
Affiliation Roman Catholic
Facilities Dining room; Chapel; Crafts room; Laundry room; Barber/Beauty shop.
Activities Arts and Crafts; Cards; Games; Prayer groups; Movies.

Heritage Manor of Lafayette
325 Bacque Crescent Dr, Lafayette, LA, 70501 (318) 232-0299
Admin David Reaves.
Licensure Intermediate Care. *Beds* 60. *Certified* Medicaid.
Admissions Requirements Medical examination.
Staff Physicians 1 (pt); RNs 1 (ft); LPNs 7 (ft), 2 (pt); Nurses aides 20 (ft), 3 (pt); Physical ther-

apists 1 (pt); Reality therapists 1 (pt); Recreational therapists 1 (pt); Occupational therapists 1 (pt); Speech therapists 1 (pt); Activities coordinators 1 (ft); Dietitians 1 (pt); Dentists 1 (pt); Podiatrists 1 (pt); Audiologists 1 (pt).
Facilities Dining room; Activities room; Laundry room; Barber/Beauty shop.
Activities Arts and Crafts; Cards; Games; Reading groups; Prayer groups; Movies; Shopping trips; Dances/Social or cultural gatherings.

Lafayette Guest House
431 E Lillian Rd, Lafayette, LA, 70501 (318) 233-6855
Admin Cecel P Manuel. *Medical Dir/Dir of Nursing* Dr Charles Dugal.
Licensure Intermediate Care. *Beds* 206. *Certified* Medicaid.
Admissions Requirements Physician's request.
Staff Physicians 1 (ft); RNs 1 (ft), 1 (pt); LPNs 16 (ft); Orderlies 2 (ft); Nurses aides 21 (ft); Physical therapists; Reality therapists; Dietitians 1 (pt); Dentists 1 (pt); Ophthalmologists 1 (pt); Podiatrists 1 (pt); Audiologists 1 (pt).

Lafayette Health Care Center*
433 E Lillian Rd, Lafayette, LA, 70501 (318) 233-7235
Admin Greg Store.
Licensure Intermediate Care. *Beds* 130. *Certified* Medicaid.

Landry Road Nursing Home
1005 Landry Rd, Lafayette, LA, 70506 (318) 232-6370
Admin Barbara King. *Medical Dir/Dir of Nursing* Anita Conner RN.
Licensure Intermediate Care. *Beds* 101. *Certified* Medicaid.
Admissions Requirements Medical examination; Physician's request.
Staff RNs 1 (ft); LPNs 4 (ft), 5 (pt); Nurses aides 18 (ft), 10 (pt); Physical therapists 1 (pt); Speech therapists 1 (pt); Activities coordinators 1 (ft); Dietitians 1 (pt).
Facilities Dining room; Activities room; Crafts room; Laundry room; Barber/Beauty shop; Solarium.
Activities Arts and Crafts; Cards; Games; Reading groups; Prayer groups; Movies; Dances/Social or cultural gatherings.
Description Facility is located in a beautiful setting in the center of many green oak trees which provide beautiful and cool outdoor recreation; easy access with main roads passing facility; loving care for the elderly.

Oakwood Village Nurse Care Center
2500 E Simcoe St, Lafayette, LA, 70501 (318) 233-7115
Admin Gordon Doine.
Licensure Intermediate Care. *Beds* 160. *Certified* Medicaid.
Admissions Requirements Medical examination; Physician's request.
Staff RNs 1 (ft); LPNs 13 (ft); Nurses aides 42 (ft); Recreational therapists 1 (ft); Activities coordinators 1 (ft); Dietitians 1 (ft).
Facilities Dining room; Laundry room; Barber/Beauty room.
Activities Arts and Crafts; Cards; Games; Prayer groups; Movies.

LAKE CHARLES

Casa de Vida
200 Ave C, PO Box 1422, Lake Charles, LA, 70602 (318) 436-6664
Admin Kenneth Istre.
Licensure Intermediate Care for Mentally Retarded. *Beds* 120. *Certified* Medicaid.

Green Acres Rest Home*
Rt 1, Box 1310, Lake Charles, LA, 70601 (318) 436-9527
Admin Jimmy W White.
Licensure Intermediate Care. *Beds* 90. *Certified* Medicaid.

Lake Charles Care Center*
2701 Ernest St, Lake Charles, LA, 70601 (318) 439-0336
Admin Jane R Grimes.
Licensure Intermediate Care. *Beds* 136. *Certified* Medicaid.

Martin de Porres Nursing Home*
PO Box 1294, 200 Teal St, Lake Charles, LA, 70601 (318) 439-5761
Admin Robert Leonards.
Licensure Intermediate Care. *Beds* 235. *Certified* Medicaid.
Affiliation Roman Catholic

Oak Park Care Center*
PO Box 1851, 2714 1st Ave, Lake Charles, LA, 70601 (318) 478-2920
Admin Stan Barnett.
Licensure Intermediate Care. *Beds* 175. *Certified* Medicaid.

Resthaven Nursing Center*
4532 Sale Ln, Lake Charles, LA, 70605 (318) 477-6371
Admin Fred F Doolittle.
Licensure Intermediate Care. *Beds* 126. *Certified* Medicaid.

Rosewood Nursing Home*
543 15th St, Lake Charles, LA, 70601 (318) 439-8338
Admin Jimmy W White.
Licensure Intermediate Care. *Beds* 90. *Certified* Medicaid.

LAKE PROVIDENCE

Shady Lake Nursing Home
Mill St, PO Box 426, Lake Providence, LA, 71254 (318) 559-2248
Admin Doris Johnston. *Medical Dir/Dir of Nursing* Virginia Ratcliff.
Licensure Intermediate Care. *Beds* 100. *Certified* Medicaid.
Staff RNs 1 (ft); LPNs 8 (ft); Orderlies 4 (ft); Nurses aides 22 (ft); Activities coordinators 1 (ft); Dietitians 1 (ft).
Facilities Dining room; Physical therapy room; Activities room; Laundry room; Barber/Beauty shop.
Activities Arts and Crafts; Cards; Games; Prayer groups; Movies; Shopping trips; Dances/Social or cultural gatherings.

LAPLACE

Twin Oaks Nursing and Convalescent Home
1881 W 5th St, LaPlace, LA, 70068 (504) 652-9538
Admin Janet Beaman. *Medical Dir/Dir of Nursing* S J St Martin MD.
Licensure Intermediate Care. *Beds* 152. *Certified* Medicaid.
Admissions Requirements Medical examination; Physician's request.
Staff Physicians 1 (pt); RNs 1 (ft); LPNs 15 (ft); Nurses aides 45 (ft); Physical therapists 1 (pt); Activities coordinators 1 (ft); Dietitians 1 (pt); Dentists 1 (pt); Podiatrists 1 (pt).
Facilities Dining room; Activities room; Barber/Beauty shop.
Activities Arts and Crafts; Games; Dances/Social or cultural gatherings.

LEESVILLE

Kurthwood Manor Nursing Home*
PO Box 270, Leesville, LA, 71446 (318) 239-6578
Admin Jerry L Wilson.
Licensure Intermediate Care. *Beds* 142. *Certified* Medicaid.

Leesville State School*
401 W Texas St, Leesville, LA, 71446 (318) 239-2687
Admin Joseph Martinez.
Licensure Intermediate Care for Mentally Retarded. *Beds* 96. *Certified* Medicaid.

Pine Haven Nursing Home*
Rt 2, Box 145, Leesville, LA, 71446 (318) 463-8778
Admin Lilly Allen.
Licensure Intermediate Care. *Beds* 38. *Certified* Medicaid.

LULING

Luling Nursing Home
PO Box 1098, Paul Maillard Rd, Luling, LA, 70070 (504) 785-8271
Admin T E McConnell. *Medical Dir/Dir of Nursing* Irene Ham.
Licensure Intermediate Care. *Beds* 189. *Certified* Medicaid.
Admissions Requirements Medical examination; Physician's request.
Staff Physicians 1 (pt); RNs 2 (ft), 3 (pt); LPNs 10 (ft); Nurses aides 37 (ft), 13 (pt); Activities coordinators 1 (ft).
Facilities Dining room; Laundry room; Barber/Beauty shop.
Activities Arts and Crafts; Cards; Games; Prayer groups; Movies; Dances/Social or cultural gatherings.

LUTCHER

Riverlands Health Care Center*
PO Drawer CC, Lutcher, LA, 70071 (504) 869-5029
Admin Sam E Narrow Jr.
Licensure Intermediate Care. *Beds* 66. *Certified* Medicaid.

MAMOU

Savoy Care Center*
801 Poinciana Ave, Mamou, LA, 70554 (318) 468-2495
Admin Gertrude Guillory.
Licensure Intermediate Care. *Beds* 42. *Certified* Medicaid.

MANDEVILLE

Pontchartrain Guest House
Hwy 190 and Atlin St, Mandeville, LA, 70448 (504) 626-8581
Admin Ronald A Goux.
Licensure Intermediate Care. *Beds* 182. *Certified* Medicaid.

MANSFIELD

Heritage Manor of Mansfield*
102 E Schley St, Mansfield, LA, 71052 (318) 872-0276
Admin Vaughn G Gilbert.
Licensure Intermediate Care. *Beds* 135. *Certified* Medicaid.

MANSURA

Rio-Sol Nursing Home*
PO Box 85, Privot and Zelynne Sts, Mansura, LA, 71350 (318) 964-2198
Admin Laura Spruill.
Licensure Intermediate Care. *Beds* 92. *Certified* Medicaid.

MANY

Heritage Manor of Many 1
PO Box 112, Natchitoches Hwy, Many, LA, 71449 (318) 256-5250
Admin Edwin Teal Sr. *Medical Dir/Dir of Nursing* Dr R J Qorta.
Licensure Intermediate Care. *Beds* 128. *Certified* Medicaid.
Admissions Requirements Medical examination.
Staff RNs 1 (ft); LPNs 8 (ft); Nurses aides 46 (ft); Physical therapists 1 (pt); Activities coordinators 1 (ft); Dietitians 1 (pt); Dentists 1 (pt).
Facilities Dining room; Physical therapy room; Activities room; Crafts room; Laundry room; Barber/Beauty shop.
Activities Arts and Crafts; Games; Reading groups; Movies; Dances/Social or cultural gatherings.

Heritage Manor of Many 2*
PO Box 112, Hwy 6 E, Many, LA, 71449 (318) 256-9233
Admin Judy May.
Licensure Intermediate Care. *Beds* 60. *Certified* Medicaid.

MARION

Marion Nursing Home*
PO Box 306, Marion, LA, 71260 (318) 292-4514

Admin Dorothy Allen.
Licensure Intermediate Care. *Beds* 81. *Certified* Medicaid.

MARKSVILLE

Colonial Nursing Home
PO Box 216, 413 N Washington St, Marksville, LA, 71351 (318) 253-4556
Admin R Nell Oliver. *Medical Dir/Dir of Nursing* F P Bordelon Jr MD.
Licensure Intermediate Care. *Beds* 104. *Certified* Medicaid.
Admissions Requirements Minimum age 18.
Staff RNs 1 (ft); LPNs 7 (ft), 3 (pt); Orderlies 4 (ft); Nurses aides 24 (ft), 6 (pt); Activities coordinators 1 (ft); Dietitians 1 (pt).
Facilities Dining room; Activities room; Chapel; Crafts room; Laundry room.
Activities Arts and Crafts; Cards; Games; Prayer groups; Movies; Shopping trips; Dances/Social or cultural gatherings.

Valley View Health Care Facility
PO Box 535, Marksville, LA, 71351 (318) 253-6553
Admin Donna Caubarreaux.
Licensure Intermediate Care. *Beds* 100. *Certified* Medicaid.
Staff Physicians; RNs; LPNs; Orderlies; Nurses aides; Activities coordinators; Dietitians.
Facilities Dining room; Activities room; Laundry room; Barber/Beauty shop.
Activities Arts and Crafts; Cards; Games; Prayer groups; Movies; Shopping trips; Dances/Social or cultural gatherings.

MARRERO

Heritage Manor of Marrero*
5301 August Ln, Marrero, LA, 70072 (504) 341-3658
Admin Michael J Ford.
Licensure Intermediate Care. *Beds* 134. *Certified* Medicaid.

MER ROUGE

Oak Woods Home for the Elderly
Hwy W 165, PO Box 263, Mer Rouge, LA, 71261 (318) 647-3691
Admin Henry C Bullock. *Medical Dir/Dir of Nursing* Cupid Maroney RN.
Licensure Intermediate Care. *Beds* 110. *Certified* Medicaid.
Admissions Requirements Medical examination; Physician's request.
Staff RNs 1 (ft); LPNs 14 (ft), 2 (pt); Orderlies 7 (ft), 1 (pt); Nurses aides 34 (ft), 2 (pt); Physical therapists 1 (pt); Activities coordinators 2 (ft); Dietitians 1 (ft).
Facilities Dining room; Physical therapy room; Activities room; Chapel; Crafts room; Laundry room; Barber/Beauty shop; Library.
Activities Arts and Crafts; Cards; Games; Reading groups; Prayer groups; Movies; Shopping trips; Dances/Social or cultural gatherings.

MERRYVILLE

Merryville Nursing Center*
PO Drawer C, Bryan St, Merryville, LA, 70653
(318) 825-6181
Admin Benson Slyvest.
Licensure Intermediate Care. *Beds* 50. *Certified* Medicaid.

METAIRIE

Colonial Oaks Nursing and Convalescent Home
4312 Ithaca St, Metairie, LA, 70002 (504)
887-6414
Admin Kathy McEnaney. *Medical Dir/Dir of Nursing* Dr Samuel E Greenburg.
Licensure Intermediate Care. *Beds* 100.
Admissions Requirements Medical examination.
Staff Physicians 1 (ft); RNs 2 (ft), 1 (pt); LPNs 5 (ft), 4 (pt); Orderlies 1 (ft); Nurses aides 33 (ft), 7 (pt); Physical therapists 1 (pt); Activities coordinators 1 (ft); Dietitians 1 (ft); Dentists 1 (pt); Ophthalmologists 1 (pt); Podiatrists 1 (pt).
Facilities Dining room; Activities room; Laundry room; Barber/Beauty shop.
Activities Arts and Crafts; Cards; Games; Prayer groups; Movies; Dances/Social or cultural gatherings.
Description Facility features easy access to other medical facilities (hospital across the street). Doctors offices are also across from facility. X-ray and lab work performed in the facility.

Metairie Healthcare Center*
6401 Ackel St, Metairie, LA, 70003 (504)
885-8611
Admin David Hargrave.
Licensure Intermediate Care. *Beds* 196. *Certified* Medicaid.

Saint Anthony's Nursing Home*
6001 Airline Hwy, Metairie, LA, 70003 (504)
733-8448
Admin H L Mendoza.
Licensure Intermediate Care. *Beds* 102. *Certified* Medicaid.
Affiliation Roman Catholic

MINDEN

Evergreen Manor
PO Box 1177, Rt 3, Minden, LA, 71058-1177
(318) 377-5405
Admin James A Brigham. *Medical Dir/Dir of Nursing* Judy Pittman RN.
Licensure Intermediate Care for Mentally Retarded. *Beds* 96. *Certified* Medicaid.
Admissions Requirements Minimum age 15; Medical examination.
Staff RNs 1 (ft); LPNs 6 (ft); Nurses aides 50 (ft); Physical therapists 1 (pt); Recreational therapists 1 (ft); Occupational therapists 1 (pt); Speech therapists 1 (ft); Activities coordinators 1 (ft); Dietitians 1 (ft); Dentists 1 (pt); 12 (ft).
Affiliation Presbyterian
Facilities Dining room; Physical therapy room; Activities room; Chapel; Crafts room; Laundry room; Barber/Beauty shop.

Activities Arts and Crafts; Games; Prayer groups; Movies; Shopping trips; Dances/Social or cultural gatherings.

Meadowview Nursing Home*
400 Meadowview Dr, Minden, LA, 71055
(318) 377-1011
Admin Larry Penix.
Licensure Intermediate Care. *Beds* 228. *Certified* Medicaid.

Town and Country Nursing Center*
614 Weston St, Minden, LA, 71055 (318)
377-5148
Admin Walter Ledig.
Licensure Intermediate Care. *Beds* 128. *Certified* Medicaid.

MONROE

Georgia Street Nursing Home
2700 Georgia St, Monroe, LA, 71202 (318)
323-9671
Admin John Parnell. *Medical Dir/Dir of Nursing* David Barnes MD.
Licensure Intermediate Care. *Beds* 94. *Certified* Medicaid.
Admissions Requirements Medical examination.
Staff Physicians 1 (ft), 4 (pt); RNs 1 (ft), 2 (pt); LPNs 10 (ft), 3 (pt); Orderlies 8 (ft), 2 (pt); Nurses aides 20 (ft), 4 (pt); Physical therapists 1 (ft), 1 (pt); Reality therapists 1 (ft); Recreational therapists 1 (ft); Occupational therapists 1 (pt); Speech therapists 1 (pt); Activities coordinators 1 (ft), 1 (pt); Dietitians 1 (ft), 1 (pt); Dentists 1 (pt); Ophthalmologists 1 (pt); Podiatrists 1 (pt); Audiologists 1 (pt).
Facilities Dining room; Physical therapy room; Activities room; Chapel; Crafts room; Laundry room; Barber/Beauty shop; Library.
Activities Arts and Crafts; Cards; Games; Reading groups; Prayer groups; Movies; Shopping trips; Dances/Social or cultural gatherings; Field trips.
Description Family owned and operated facility with highest "track record" per nursing and staff standards per state and federal guidelines/surveys in Louisiana; a rarely seen family atmosphere.

Lincoln Park Nursing Home*
PO Box 4252, 4600 Berg Jones Rd, Monroe, LA, 71201 (318) 387-0683
Admin John T Parnell.
Licensure Intermediate Care. *Beds* 96. *Certified* Medicaid.

Mary Goss Nursing Home*
PO Box 4509, 3404 White St, Monroe, LA, 71201 (318) 323-9013
Admin Louise G Tucker.
Licensure Intermediate Care. *Beds* 91. *Certified* Medicaid.

Monroe Manor Nursing Home*
4201 S Grand St, Monroe, LA, 71201 (318)
325-8244
Admin Jacqueline Burnette.
Licensure Intermediate Care. *Beds* 108. *Certified* Medicaid.

Riverside Nursing Home Inc*
3001 S Grand St, Monroe, LA, 71201 (318)
388-3200
Admin James C Houston.
Licensure Intermediate Care. *Beds* 166. *Certified* Medicaid.

Saint Joseph's Home for Infirm and Aged
2301 Sterlington Rd, Monroe, LA, 71201 (318)
323-3426
Admin H Werner Wolf.
Licensure Intermediate Care. *Beds* 126. *Certified* Medicaid.
Admissions Requirements Medical examination.
Staff RNs 2 (ft); LPNs 16 (ft); Nurses aides 30 (ft); Activities coordinators 1 (ft).
Affiliation Roman Catholic
Facilities Dining room; Activities room; Chapel; Crafts room; Laundry room; Barber/Beauty shop.
Activities Arts and Crafts; Cards; Games; Prayer groups; Movies; Shopping trips.

Shady Oaks Nursing Home
4310 S Grand St, Monroe, LA, 71201 (318)
322-2616
Admin Jacob O Strickland. *Medical Dir/Dir of Nursing* Dr Doyle Hamilton.
Licensure Intermediate Care. *Beds* 108. *Certified* Medicaid.
Admissions Requirements Medical examination; Physician's request.
Staff Physicians 10 (pt); RNs 1 (ft); LPNs 7 (ft), 1 (pt); Orderlies 2 (ft); Nurses aides 28 (ft), 2 (pt); Physical therapists 1 (pt); Occupational therapists 1 (pt); Speech therapists 1 (pt); Activities coordinators 1 (ft); Dietitians 1 (pt); Dentists 1 (pt); Podiatrists 1 (pt).
Facilities Dining room; Activities room; Chapel; Crafts room; Laundry room; Barber/Beauty shop.
Activities Arts and Crafts; Cards; Games; Reading groups; Prayer groups; Shopping trips; Dances/Social or cultural gatherings.
Description Shady Oaks Nursing Home is located on beautiful Ouachita River amid giant oak trees in a quiet, rural setting. Our goal for our residents is always to give them the best care at all times in order to keep them happy and healthy.

MORGAN CITY

Saint Mary's Guest Home*
PO Box 2563, Justa St, Morgan City, LA, 70380 (504) 384-1726
Admin Nolan Ledet.
Licensure Intermediate Care. *Beds* 87. *Certified* Medicaid.

NAPOLEONVILLE

Assumption Health Care
PO Box 351, Napoleonville, LA, 70390
Admin A O Arnold. *Medical Dir/Dir of Nursing* Dr Charles Bolotte.
Admissions Requirements Medical examination.
Staff RNs 1 (ft), 1 (pt); LPNs 12 (ft); Nurses aides 30 (ft); Physical therapists 1 (pt); Speech

therapists 1 (pt); Activities coordinators 1 (ft); Dietitians 1 (pt); Dentists 1 (pt).
Facilities Dining room; Activities room; Chapel; Laundry room; Barber/Beauty shop; Library.
Activities Arts and Crafts; Cards; Games; Movies; Shopping trips; Dances/Social or cultural gatherings.
Description Facility is located a quarter mile from General Hospital and Kidney Dialysis Center; features a private pay section with special benefits.

NATCHITOCHES

Natchitoches Manor Nursing Home
720 Keyser Ave, PO Box 2158, Natchitoches, LA, 71457 (318) 352-8296
Admin Charles L Watson. *Medical Dir/Dir of Nursing* Dr I L Campbell.
Licensure Intermediate Care. *Beds* 160. *Certified* Medicaid.
Staff RNs 2 (ft), 1 (pt); LPNs 6 (ft); Orderlies 5 (ft); Nurses aides 25 (ft); Activities coordinators 1 (ft); Dietitians 1 (pt).
Facilities Dining room; Physical therapy room; Activities room; Crafts room; Laundry room; Barber/Beauty shop.
Activities Arts and Crafts; Cards; Games; Reading groups; Prayer groups; Movies; Shopping trips; Dances/Social or cultural gatherings.
Description Facility is close to hospital and town.

Natchitoches Parish Hospital—Long Term Care Unit
501 Keyser Ave, PO Box 2038, Natchitoches, LA, 71457 (318) 352-1200
Admin Eugene Spillman.
Licensure Intermediate Care. *Beds* 108. *Certified* Medicaid.
Ownership Public.
Staff Physicians 5 (ft); RNs 9 (ft); LPNs 9 (ft); Orderlies 5 (ft); Nurses aides 10 (ft); Speech therapists 1 (ft); Activities coordinators 2 (ft); Dietitians 1 (ft).
Facilities Dining room; Physical therapy room; Activities room; Chapel; Barber/Beauty shop.
Activities Arts and Crafts; Games; Reading groups.

Riverside Guest Care Center*
650 Keyser Ave, Natchitoches, LA, 71457 (318) 352-8779
Admin Billy P Plunkett.
Licensure Intermediate Care. *Beds* 102. *Certified* Medicaid.

NEW IBERIA

Azalea Villa Nursing Home
1002 Admiral Doyle, PO Box 777, New Iberia, LA, 70560 (318) 364-5472
Admin Norma D Dupre. *Medical Dir/Dir of Nursing* Dr J C Musso.
Licensure Intermediate Care. *Beds* 150. *Certified* Medicaid.
Admissions Requirements Medical examination; Physician's request.
Facilities Dining room; Activities room; Laundry room; Barber/Beauty shop.

Activities Arts and Crafts; Cards; Games; Reading groups; Prayer groups; Movies; Shopping trips; Dances/Social or cultural gatherings.

Consolata Home
2319 E Main St, New Iberia, LA, 70560 (318) 365-8226
Admin David Landry. *Medical Dir/Dir of Nursing* Dr Oscar Alvarez.
Licensure Intermediate Care. *Beds* 94. *Certified* Medicaid.
Admissions Requirements Medical examination.
Staff Physicians 1 (pt); RNs 1 (ft), 2 (pt); LPNs 7 (ft), 6 (pt); Nurses aides 25 (ft), 10 (pt); Activities coordinators 1 (ft); Dietitians 1 (pt).
Affiliation Roman Catholic
Facilities Dining room; Activities room; Chapel; Crafts room; Laundry room; Barber/Beauty shop.
Activities Arts and Crafts; Cards; Games; Prayer groups; Movies; Dances/Social or cultural gatherings.
Description A 94-bed nonprofit facility expanding to meet the needs of community; located along Bayou Teche next to Iberia General Hospital. Activities include: daily Mass, Rosary, exercise and bingo; open coffee and visiting hours; resident of the month party; meal planning by residents with wine served; meal of the month; semi-annual barbecue, annual boucherie.

Heritage Manor of New Iberia—North*
PO Box 957, 1803 Jane St, New Iberia, LA, 70560 (318) 365-2466
Admin Larry Viator.
Licensure Intermediate Care. *Beds* 121. *Certified* Medicaid.

Heritage Manor of New Iberia—South*
PO Box 967, 600 Bayard St, New Iberia, LA, 70560 (318) 365-3441
Admin Harvey W Koenig II.
Licensure Intermediate Care. *Beds* 80. *Certified* Medicaid.

NEW ORLEANS

Audubon Health Care Center
13500 Chef Menteur Hwy, New Orleans, LA, 70129 (504) 254-9431
Admin John Coats Jr. *Medical Dir/Dir of Nursing* Dr Gordon McHardy.
Licensure Intermediate Care. *Beds* 207. *Certified* Medicaid.

Chateau de Notre Dame*
2832 Burdette St, New Orleans, LA, 70125 (504) 866-2741
Admin Dolly More.
Beds 180.
Ownership Nonprofit.

Coliseum Medical Center*
3601 Coliseum St, New Orleans, LA, 70115 (504) 897-3381
Admin Fredrick R Mirmelstein.
Licensure Skilled Care. *Beds* 78. *Certified* Medicare.

Covenant Home
5919 Magazine St, New Orleans, LA, 70115 (504) 897-6216
Admin Timothy A Bains. *Medical Dir/Dir of Nursing* Howard Russell MD.
Licensure Intermediate Care. *Beds* 84. *Certified* Medicaid.
Admissions Requirements Minimum age 65; Medical examination; Physician's request.
Staff RNs 2 (ft); LPNs 7 (ft), 3 (pt); Nurses aides 25 (ft), 3 (pt); Activities coordinators 1 (ft).
Facilities Dining room; Physical therapy room; Activities room; Chapel; Crafts room; Laundry room; Barber/Beauty shop; Library.
Activities Arts and Crafts; Cards; Games; Prayer groups; Movies.

F Edward Hebert
1 Sanctuary Dr, New Orleans, LA, 70114 (504) 363-2200
Admin Patricia Miller. *Medical Dir/Dir of Nursing* Frank Wagner MD.
Licensure Skilled Care. *Beds* 44. *Certified* Medicare.
Admissions Requirements Medical examination.
Facilities Physical therapy room; Activities room; Chapel; Crafts room.
Activities Arts and Crafts; Cards; Games; Reading groups; Prayer groups; Movies.

Lafon Home of the Holy Family
6900 Chef Menteur Hwy, New Orleans, LA, 70126 (504) 246-1100
Admin Augustine McDaniel.
Licensure Intermediate Care. *Beds* 171. *Certified* Medicaid.
Admissions Requirements Medical examination; Physician's request.
Staff RNs 4 (ft), 2 (pt); LPNs 12 (ft), 10 (pt); Orderlies 1 (ft); Nurses aides 24 (ft), 20 (pt); Physical therapists 2 (pt); Speech therapists 1 (pt); Activities coordinators 2 (ft), 2 (pt); Dietitians 1 (ft); Dentists 1 (pt); Podiatrists 1 (pt).
Affiliation Roman Catholic
Facilities Dining room; Physical therapy room; Activities room; Chapel; Crafts room; Laundry room; Barber/Beauty shop; Library.
Activities Arts and Crafts; Cards; Games; Prayer groups; Movies; Shopping trips; Dances/Social or cultural gatherings.

Lutheran Home of New Orleans*
6400 Hayne Blvd, New Orleans, LA, 70126 (504) 246-7900
Admin Harry Franatovich.
Licensure Intermediate Care. *Beds* 208. *Certified* Medicaid.
Affiliation Lutheran

Maison Hospitaliere*
822 Barracks St, New Orleans, LA, 70116 (504) 524-4309
Admin Joyce Flynn.
Licensure Intermediate Care. *Beds* 87. *Certified* Medicaid.

Mary-Joseph Residence for the Elderly
4201 Woodland Dr, New Orleans, LA, 70114 (504) 394-2200
Admin Sr Marcelle Slabinski.
Licensure Intermediate Care. *Beds* 122. *Certi-*

fied Medicaid.
Admissions Requirements Minimum age 60; Medical examination.
Staff Physicians 3 (ft); RNs 4 (pt); LPNs 8 (ft), 6 (pt); Nurses aides 30 (ft); Physical therapists 1 (ft); Activities coordinators 1 (ft); Dietitians 1 (pt); Dentists 1 (pt); Ophthalmologists 1 (pt); Podiatrists 1 (pt).
Affiliation Roman Catholic
Facilities Dining room; Physical therapy room; Activities room; Chapel; Crafts room; Laundry room; Barber/Beauty shop.
Activities Arts and Crafts; Cards; Games; Prayer groups; Movies; Shopping trips; Dances/Social or cultural gatherings.

New Orleans Home and Rehabilitation Center
612 Henry Clay Ave, New Orleans, LA, 70178 (504) 895-4833
Admin Gary A Fontenot. *Medical Dir/Dir of Nursing* Henry Rothschild MD.
Licensure Skilled Care; Intermediate Care.
Beds SNF 101; ICF 101. *Certified* Medicaid.
Admissions Requirements Minimum age 18; Medical examination; Physician's request.
Staff RNs 6 (ft); LPNs 23 (ft); Nurses aides 73 (ft), 4 (pt); Recreational therapists 1 (ft); Speech therapists 1 (ft).
Facilities Dining room; Physical therapy room; Activities room; Chapel; Crafts room; Laundry room; Barber/Beauty shop; Library.
Activities Arts and Crafts; Cards; Games; Reading groups; Prayer groups; Movies; Shopping trips; Dances/Social or cultural gatherings.

Poydras Home
5354 Magazine St, New Orleans, LA, 70115 (504) 897-0535
Admin Phyllis Maness. *Medical Dir/Dir of Nursing* Dr John Phillips.
Licensure Intermediate Care. *Beds* 44.
Admissions Requirements Medical examination.
Staff RNs 1 (ft), 3 (pt); LPNs 2 (ft), 6 (pt); Nurses aides 8 (ft), 3 (pt); Activities coordinators 1 (pt); Dietitians 1 (pt).
Facilities Dining room; Activities room; Chapel; Crafts room; Laundry room; Barber/Beauty shop; Library.
Activities Arts and Crafts; Cards; Movies.

Prayer Tower Rest Home
3316 Pine St, New Orleans, LA, 70125 (504) 486-1235
Admin Thelma Harper.
Licensure Intermediate Care. *Beds* 104. *Certified* Medicaid.
Admissions Requirements Medical examination; Physician's request.
Staff Physicians 1 (pt); RNs 1 (ft); LPNs 7 (ft), 2 (pt); Orderlies 2 (ft); Nurses aides 30 (ft); Activities coordinators 2 (ft), 1 (pt); Dietitians 1 (pt); Dentists 1 (pt).
Affiliation Church of God
Facilities Dining room; Activities room; Chapel; Crafts room; Laundry room; Barber/Beauty shop.
Activities Arts and Crafts; Cards; Games; Reading groups; Prayer groups; Movies; Shopping trips.
Description This is a facility born out of love; renders professional nursing service for the elderly with tender love and care for all.

Protestant Bethany Home*
2535 Esplanade Ave, New Orleans, LA, 70119 (504) 949-1738
Admin Timothy A Bains.
Licensure Intermediate Care. *Beds* 37. *Certified* Medicaid.

Provident House
1539 Delachaise, New Orleans, LA, 70115 (504) 895-3953
Admin Peggy Resor.
Licensure Skilled Care; Intermediate Care.
Beds 115. *Certified* Medicaid; Medicare.

Saint Anna's Asylum*
1823 Prytania St, New Orleans, LA, 70130 (504) 523-3466
Admin Barbara S Nicolas.
Beds 88.
Ownership Nonprofit.

Saint Margaret's Daughters' Home*
6220 Chartres St, New Orleans, LA, 70117 (504) 279-6414
Admin Mercedes Diecidue.
Licensure Intermediate Care. *Beds* 111. *Certified* Medicaid.
Affiliation Roman Catholic

NEW ROADS

Lakeview Manor Nursing Home Inc*
Rt 2, Box 275, New Roads, LA, 70760 (504) 638-4404
Admin Myron Chatelain.
Licensure Intermediate Care. *Beds* 120. *Certified* Medicaid.

Pointe Coupes Parish Nursing Home
2202-A Hospital Rd, New Roads, LA, 70760
Admin Mary Ann Gustin.
Licensure Intermediate Care. *Beds* 120. *Certified* Medicaid.
Ownership Nonprofit.
Staff RNs 2 (ft), 1 (pt); LPNs 10 (ft); Orderlies 1 (ft); Nurses aides 35 (ft); Physical therapists 1 (pt); Reality therapists 1 (pt); Recreational therapists 1 (pt); Speech therapists 1 (pt); Activities coordinators 1 (ft); Dietitians 1 (ft); Dentists 1 (pt); Ophthalmologists 1 (pt); Audiologists 1 (pt).
Facilities Dining room; Physical therapy room; Activities room; Crafts room; Laundry room; Barber/Beauty shop; Library.
Activities Games; Prayer groups; Movies; Shopping trips; Dances/Social or cultural gatherings.

NEWELLTON

Saint Charles Nursing Home
PO Box 508, Hwy 4, Newellton, LA, 71357 (318) 467-5121
Admin Louise Crane.
Licensure Intermediate Care. *Beds* 56. *Certified* Medicaid.

OAK GROVE

Carroll Nursing Home
N Castleman St, Oak Grove, LA, 71263 (318) 428-3249
Admin Elvyn N Dumas.
Licensure Intermediate Care. *Beds* 106. *Certified* Medicaid.
Admissions Requirements Medical examination; Physician's request.
Staff Physicians 1 (pt); RNs 1 (ft); LPNs 7 (ft), 1 (pt); Orderlies 1 (ft), 1 (pt); Nurses aides 40 (ft), 3 (pt); Recreational therapists 1 (ft); Activities coordinators 1 (ft); Dietitians 1 (pt); Dentists 1 (pt).
Facilities Dining room; Activities room; Crafts room; Laundry room; Barber/Beauty shop; Library.
Activities Arts and Crafts; Cards; Games; Reading groups; Prayer groups; Movies; Shopping trips; Dances/Social or cultural gatherings.

OAKDALE

Care Nursing Home Inc
PO Box 683, S 16th St and 6th Ave, Oakdale, LA, 71463 (318) 335-1469
Admin Don Lindig. *Medical Dir/Dir of Nursing* Dr George B Mowad.
Licensure Intermediate Care. *Beds* 77. *Certified* Medicaid.
Staff Physicians 3 (pt); RNs 1 (ft), 2 (pt); LPNs 5 (ft), 3 (pt); Orderlies 6 (ft), 2 (pt); Nurses aides 21 (ft), 7 (pt); Physical therapists 1 (pt); Recreational therapists 1 (pt); Activities coordinators 1 (ft); Dietitians 1 (pt); Dentists 1 (pt); Ophthalmologists 1 (pt).
Facilities Dining room; Physical therapy room; Activities room; Chapel; Crafts room; Laundry room; Barber/Beauty shop; Library.
Activities Arts and Crafts; Cards; Games; Prayer groups; Movies; Shopping trips.

OPELOUSAS

Opelousas Health Care Inc
328 W Grolee St, Opelousas, LA, 70570 (318) 942-7588
Admin Ruth Stelly. *Medical Dir/Dir of Nursing* N C Lafleur MD.
Licensure Intermediate Care. *Beds* 71. *Certified* Medicaid.
Admissions Requirements Medical examination; Physician's request.
Staff Physicians 1 (ft), 7 (pt); RNs 1 (ft); LPNs 9 (ft), 2 (pt); Nurses aides 17 (ft), 11 (pt); Activities coordinators 1 (ft); Dietitians 1 (pt).
Affiliation VFW Womens' Auxiliary
Facilities Dining room; Activities room; Chapel; Crafts room; Laundry room; Barber/Beauty shop.
Activities Arts and Crafts; Cards; Games; Prayer groups; Movies; Shopping trips; Dances/Social or cultural gatherings.

Our Lady of Prompt Succor Nursing Home
751 Prudhomme Ln, Opelousas, LA, 70570 (318) 948-3634
Admin Sr Margaret M Lafleur. *Medical Dir/Dir of Nursing* Dr Donald Gremillion.
Licensure Skilled Care. *Beds* 80.

Certified Medicare.
Staff RNs 4 (ft); LPNs 6 (ft), 2 (pt); Nurses aides 30 (ft), 4 (pt); Physical therapists 1 (pt); Speech therapists 1 (pt); Activities coordinators 1 (pt); Dietitians 1 (pt); Dentists 1 (pt); Audiologists 1 (pt).
Affiliation Roman Catholic
Facilities Dining room; Activities room; Chapel; Laundry room; Barber/Beauty shop.
Activities Arts and Crafts; Cards; Games; Reading groups; Prayer groups; Shopping trips; Dances/Social or cultural gatherings.

Senior Village Nursing Home*
160 Ducharme Rd, Opelousas, LA, 70570 (318) 948-4486
Admin Susan Bourgogne.
Licensure Intermediate Care. *Beds* 208. *Certified* Medicaid.

PINEVILLE

Camellia Garden Nursing Home*
701 Bayou Marie Rd, Pineville, LA, 71360 (318) 445-4251
Admin Georgia O West.
Licensure Intermediate Care. *Beds* 93. *Certified* Medicaid.

Hilltop Nursing Center 2
1100 Bayou Marie Rd, Pineville, LA, 71360 (318) 487-9400
Admin Doris Leland. *Medical Dir/Dir of Nursing* Carrie Graves.
Licensure Intermediate Care. *Beds* 102. *Certified* Medicaid.
Admissions Requirements Minimum age 21; Medical examination; Physician's request.
Staff RNs 1 (ft), 2 (pt); LPNs 6 (ft), 4 (pt); Orderlies 1 (ft); Nurses aides 28 (ft); Activities coordinators 1 (ft); Dietitians 1 (ft).
Facilities Dining room; Activities room; Laundry room; Barber/Beauty shop; Library.
Activities Arts and Crafts; Cards; Games; Prayer groups; Movies; Shopping trips; Dances/Social or cultural gatherings.
Description Facility has activities daily including rhythm band, sing-a-longs, RSVP programs for eligible residents, annual domino contest inviting other nuring homes to participate, yearly fund raising events, monthly birthday party and other special parties, special fishing trips, picnics, beautiful trees in fenced yard with swings and chairs, and a home-like atmosphere.

Hilltop Nursing Home
500 Dupree St, PO Box 67, Pineville, LA, 71360 (318) 442-9552
Admin Juanita B Kelley. *Medical Dir/Dir of Nursing* Dr Grover Bahm.
Licensure Intermediate Care. *Beds* 98. *Certified* Medicaid.
Admissions Requirements Medical examination; Physician's request.
Staff Physicians 1 (ft), 6 (pt); RNs 2 (ft); LPNs 10 (ft); Orderlies 2 (ft); Nurses aides 25 (ft), 4 (pt); Physical therapists 1 (pt); Activities coordinators 1 (ft); Dietitians 1 (pt).
Facilities Dining room; Activities room; Laundry room; Barber/Beauty shop.
Activities Arts and Crafts; Cards; Games;

Prayer groups; Movies; Shopping trips; Dances/Social or cultural gatherings.
Description Facility is very active in raising funds for the American Heart Association.

Lakeland Nursing Home*
PO Box 933, Hillsdale Dr, Pineville, LA, 71360 (318) 448-0141
Admin Herman P Marshall.
Licensure Intermediate Care. *Beds* 140. *Certified* Medicaid.

Pilgrim Manor of Pineville*
200 Gordon St, Pineville, LA, 71360 (318) 442-4364
Admin Edward E Rose.
Licensure Intermediate Care. *Beds* 152. *Certified* Medicaid.

Pinecrest State School
PO Drawer 191, Pineville, LA, 71360 (318) 640-0754
Admin Coates Stuckey.
Licensure Intermediate Care for Mentally Retarded. *Beds* 1688. *Certified* Medicaid.

PLAIN DEALING

Whispering Pines*
Hwy 3 S, PO Box 147, Plain Dealing, LA, 71064 (318) 326-4259
Admin Louis A Dye Sr.
Licensure Intermediate Care. *Beds* 77. *Certified* Medicaid.

PLAQUEMINE

Plaquemine Nursing Home*
PO Box 487, 1202 Ferdinand St, Plaquemine, LA, 70764 (504) 387-1345
Admin Bruno E Egros Jr.
Licensure Intermediate Care. *Beds* 106. *Certified* Medicaid.

PLAUCHEVILLE

Avoyelles Manor Nursing Home*
Rt 1, Box 215, LA Hwy 107, Plaucheville, LA, 71362 (318) 922-3404
Admin Donald Scallan.
Licensure Intermediate Care. *Beds* 104. *Certified* Medicaid.

PLEASANT HILL

North Sabine Nursing Home*
PO Box 245, Hwy 174, Pleasant Hill, LA, 71065 (318) 796-3357
Admin Elizabeth Durr.
Licensure Intermediate Care. *Beds* 90. *Certified* Medicaid.

PORT ALLEN

Port Allen Care Center*
403 15th St, Port Allen, LA, 70767 (504) 346-8581

Admin Barbara Anne King.
Licensure Intermediate Care. *Beds* 50. *Certified* Medicaid.

POYDRAS

Poydras Manor*
Rt 3, Box 132, Massicot St, Poydras, LA, 70085 (504) 682-5771
Admin Vallie B White.
Licensure Intermediate Care. *Beds* 36. *Certified* Medicaid.

QUITMAN

Pine Hill Senior Citizens*
Rt 2, Box 54, Quitman, LA, 71268 (318) 259-4829
Admin Billy M Roberson.
Licensure Intermediate Care. *Beds* 80. *Certified* Medicaid.

RACELAND

Inez Sako Nursing Home I*
PO Box 389, Sako Dr, Hwy 1, Raceland, LA, 70394 (504) 537-3569
Admin Dolly Terrebonne.
Licensure Intermediate Care. *Beds* 87. *Certified* Medicaid.

RAYNE

Rayne Guest House
PO Box 54, 308 Amelia St, Rayne, LA, 70578 (318) 334-5111
Admin Leroy Richard.
Licensure Intermediate Care. *Beds* 80. *Certified* Medicaid.

RAYVILLE

Colonial Manor Guest House*
505 E 4th St, Rayville, LA, 71269 (318) 728-3291
Admin David E Barr.
Licensure Intermediate Care. *Beds* 130. *Certified* Medicaid.

Community Comfort Cottage*
PO Box 60, 717 Madeline St, Rayville, LA, 71269 (318) 728-5373
Admin Claude H Minor.
Licensure Intermediate Care. *Beds* 85. *Certified* Medicaid.

Rayville Guest House Inc*
PO Box 875, Rayville, LA, 71269 (318) 728-2089
Admin Edmond Boudreaux.
Licensure Intermediate Care. *Beds* 125. *Certified* Medicaid.

RUSTON

Alpine Guest Care Center*
PO Box 1385, Hwy 80 E, Ruston, LA, 71270 (318) 255-6492

Admin Elton Dugan.
Licensure Intermediate Care. *Beds* 117. *Certified* Medicaid.

Longleaf Nursing Home*
PO Box 849, Hwy 80 E, Ruston, LA, 71270
(318) 255-5001
Admin Henry S Roane III.
Licensure Intermediate Care. *Beds* 92. *Certified* Medicaid.

Ruston State School
PO Box 907, Ruston, LA, 71270 (318)
247-3721
Admin William A Lybargar. *Medical Dir/Dir of Nursing* Allen Herbert MD.
Licensure Intermediate Care for Mentally Retarded. *Beds* 192. *Certified* Medicaid.
Admissions Requirements Minimum age 16.
Facilities Dining room; Activities room; Crafts room; Library.
Activities Arts and Crafts; Games; Reading groups; Movies; Shopping trips; Dances/Social or cultural gatherings.
Description All 8 cottages at Ruston State School have recently been renovated. We have a very good behavior management program in operation.

Towne Oaks Nursing Center*
1405 White St, Ruston, LA, 71270 (318)
255-4400
Admin Bill Copeland.
Licensure Intermediate Care. *Beds* 119. *Certified* Medicaid.

SAINT BERNARD

Fernandez Nursing Home*
Rt 2, Box 251, Saint Bernard, LA, 70085 (504)
682-0131
Admin M R Fernandez.
Licensure Intermediate Care. *Beds* 30. *Certified* Medicaid.

SAINT FRANCISVILLE

Idlewood Nursing Center*
PO Box 249, Hwy 10, Saint Francisville, LA,
70775 (504) 635-3346
Admin Tom McVea.
Licensure Intermediate Care. *Beds* 128. *Certified* Medicaid.

SAINT MARTINVILLE

Saint Martinville Guest House*
PO Box 787, 200 Claire Dr, Saint Martinville,
LA, 70582 (318) 394-6044
Admin Larry Baker.
Licensure Intermediate Care. *Beds* 94. *Certified* Medicaid.

SHREVEPORT

Booker T Washington Nursing Home*
PO Box 6021, 610 Turner Ln, Shreveport, LA,
71106 (318) 861-1951

Admin Hattie Mae Scott.
Licensure Intermediate Care. *Beds* 54. *Certified* Medicaid.

Eden Gardens Nursing Center
PO Box 6045, 7923 Line Ave, Shreveport, LA,
71106 (318) 865-0261
Admin Elaine B Rhinehart.
Licensure Intermediate Care. *Beds* 74. *Certified* Medicaid.
Admissions Requirements Medical examination.

Glen Oaks Home
1524 Glen Oak St, Shreveport, LA, 71103 (318)
221-0911
Admin Peggy R Newell.
Licensure Intermediate Care. *Beds* 61. *Certified* Medicaid.
Admissions Requirements Minimum age 65; Medical examination.
Staff Physicians 1 (pt); RNs 1 (ft), 1 (pt); LPNs 5 (ft); Nurses aides 20 (ft); Physical therapists 1 (pt); Reality therapists 1 (pt); Activities coordinators 2 (ft); Dietitians 1 (pt); Dentists 1 (pt); Podiatrists 1 (pt).
Facilities Dining room; Activities room; Laundry room; Barber/Beauty shop.
Activities Arts and Crafts; Cards; Games; Reading groups; Prayer groups; Movies; Shopping trips; Dances/Social or cultural gatherings; Field trips.
Description The unique thing about facility is the residential-style physical plant. Residents are allowed to bring in their own furniture, and of 61 residents, 40 have private dorm-type rooms. Upon admission all must be ambulatory, alert, and capable of handling their personal grooming; 10 semi-private infirmary rooms available if more care is needed.

The Guest House*
9225 Normandie Dr, Shreveport, LA, 71118
(318) 686-0515
Admin A T Birkelbach.
Licensure Intermediate Care. *Beds* 117. *Certified* Medicaid.

Harmony House Nursing Home
1825 Laurel St, Shreveport, LA, 71103 (318)
424-5251
Admin G Wayne Hopper.
Licensure Intermediate Care. *Beds* 115. *Certified* Medicaid.
Staff Physicians 2 (pt); RNs 1 (ft); LPNs 6 (ft), 2 (pt); Orderlies 2 (ft), 1 (pt); Nurses aides 30 (ft); Physical therapists 1 (pt); Speech therapists 1 (ft), 1 (pt); Activities coordinators 1 (ft); Dietitians 1 (ft); Dentists 1 (ft); Ophthalmologists 1 (pt); Audiologists 1 (pt).

Heritage Manor of Shreveport*
1536 Claiborne Ave, Shreveport, LA, 71103
(318) 631-3426
Admin Sandra Elliott.
Licensure Intermediate Care. *Beds* 86. *Certified* Medicaid.

Heritage Manor of Westwood*
PO Box 9289, 1 Westwood Circle, Shreveport,
LA, 71109 (318) 631-1846

Admin Betty Stuart.
Licensure Intermediate Care. *Beds* 82. *Certified* Medicaid.

Highland Guest Care Center*
453 Jordan St, Shreveport, LA, 71101 (318)
222-2261
Admin Kathryn C Gamble.
Licensure Intermediate Care. *Beds* 38. *Certified* Medicaid.

Live Oak Retirement Center
600 E Flournoy Lucas Rd, Shreveport, LA,
71115
Admin Donald W James. *Medical Dir/Dir of Nursing* Dr David T Henry.
Licensure Intermediate Care. *Beds* 130. *Certified* Medicaid.
Ownership Nonprofit.
Admissions Requirements Minimum age 62; Medical examination; Physician's request.
Staff Physicians; RNs 2 (ft), 1 (pt); LPNs 14 (ft), 5 (pt); Orderlies 3 (ft); Nurses aides 26 (ft), 12 (pt); Activities coordinators 4 (ft).
Facilities Dining room; Physical therapy room; Activities room; Chapel; Crafts room; Laundry room; Barber/Beauty shop; Library; Convenience store; Gift shop.
Activities Arts and Crafts; Cards; Games; Reading groups; Prayer groups; Movies; Shopping trips; Dances/Social or cultural gatherings.
Description Facility is located in southeast Shreveport on 36 acres; beautiful lake stocked with fish surrounds the garden apartments and gives a scenic view from the windows; a quarter-mile track by the lake is used by residents for jogging or strolling; covered walkways lead from the garden apartments to the main community building. Residents place their handcrafted items for sale in the gift shop.

Louisiana Nursing Home
225 Wyandotte St, Shreveport, LA, 71101 (318)
221-3591
Admin Debbie Brooks. *Medical Dir/Dir of Nursing* Dr T Reilly and Dr Hawkins.
Licensure Intermediate Care. *Beds* 101. *Certified* Medicaid.
Admissions Requirements Medical examination.
Staff Physicians 2 (ft); RNs 1 (ft); LPNs 9 (ft), 3 (pt); Nurses aides 28 (ft), 6 (pt); Physical therapists 1 (pt); Recreational therapists 1 (ft); Speech therapists 1 (pt); Activities coordinators 1 (ft); Dietitians 1 (ft).
Facilities Dining room; Laundry room; Barber/Beauty shop.
Activities Arts and Crafts; Cards; Games; Reading groups; Prayer groups; Movies; Shopping trips; Dances/Social or cultural gatherings.

Magnolia Manor Nursing Home*
1411 Claiborne Ave, Shreveport, LA, 71103
(318) 861-2526
Admin John L Colvin.
Licensure Intermediate Care. *Beds* 98. *Certified* Medicaid.

Meadowpark Nursing Center*
3050 Baird Rd, Shreveport, LA, 71118 (318)
688-1010

Admin Claude Pasquier.
Licensure Intermediate Care. *Beds* 120. *Certified* Medicaid.

Midway Manor Nursing Home
2150 Midway St, Shreveport, LA, 71108 (318) 635-5314
Admin Jean S McCarty. *Medical Dir/Dir of Nursing* Dr J F Hawkins.
Licensure Intermediate Care. *Beds* 212. *Certified* Medicaid.
Admissions Requirements Medical examination.
Staff RNs 4 (ft); LPNs 16 (ft), 2 (pt); Orderlies 8 (ft), 2 (pt); Nurses aides 58 (ft), 12 (pt); Activities coordinators 2 (ft); Dietitians 2 (ft).
Facilities Dining room; Activities room; Crafts room; Laundry room; Barber/Beauty shop.
Activities Arts and Crafts; Cards; Games; Prayer groups; Movies; Shopping trips; Dances/Social or cultural gatherings.

Nursecare of Shreveport*
1736 Irving Pl, Shreveport, LA, 71101 (318) 221-1983
Admin Jay M Burkhart Jr.
Licensure Intermediate Care. *Beds* 182. *Certified* Medicaid.

Pierremont Heritage Manor
725 Mitchell Ln, Shreveport, LA, 71106 (318) 868-2789
Admin Carolyn Fultz. *Medical Dir/Dir of Nursing* Dr David Henry.
Licensure Intermediate Care. *Beds* 196. *Certified* Medicaid.
Admissions Requirements Medical examination.
Staff Physicians 1 (pt); RNs 2 (ft), 1 (pt); LPNs 18 (ft); Nurses aides 54 (ft), 4 (pt); Activities coordinators 1 (ft), 1 (pt); Dietitians 1 (pt).
Facilities Dining room; Activities room; Laundry room; Barber/Beauty shop.
Activities Arts and Crafts; Cards; Games; Reading groups; Prayer groups; Movies; Dances/Social or cultural gatherings.

Roseview Nursing Center*
3405 Mansfield Rd, Shreveport, LA, 71103 (318) 222-3100
Admin Mary Ann Schaefer.
Licensure Intermediate Care. *Beds* 124. *Certified* Medicaid.

Shreveport Manor Nursing Home*
3302 Mansfield Rd, Shreveport, LA, 71103 (318) 222-9482
Admin Ralph Balentine.
Licensure Intermediate Care. *Beds* 124. *Certified* Medicaid.

Virginia Hall*
2715 Virginia Ave, Shreveport, LA, 71103 (318) 425-3247
Admin Rosalind B Foster.
Licensure Skilled Care; Intermediate Care. *Beds* 155. *Certified* Medicaid; Medicare.

SIMMESPORT

Bayou Chateau Nursing Center
Rt 1, PO Box 390, Simmesport, LA, 71369 (318) 941-2294
Admin Dorothy Anne Lacour. *Medical Dir/Dir of Nursing* Leon F Beridon MD.
Licensure Intermediate Care. *Beds* 104. *Certified* Medicaid.
Admissions Requirements Physician's request.
Staff Physicians 1 (pt); RNs 1 (ft); LPNs 8 (ft); Nurses aides 30 (ft), 15 (pt); Recreational therapists 1 (ft); Activities coordinators 1 (ft); Dietitians 1 (pt).
Facilities Dining room; Activities room; Laundry room; Barber/Beauty shop; Sun lounges.
Activities Arts and Crafts; Cards; Games; Reading groups; Prayer groups; Movies; Shopping trips; Dances/Social or cultural gatherings.
Description Centrally located nurses station overlooks all 4 wings and dining area for maximum observation and control. Facility has 2 whirlpools (ladies and mens) and 4 spacious sun lounges; very warm and friendly atmosphere.

SLIDELL

Greenbriar Nursing and Convalescent Home*
505 Robert Rd, Slidell, LA, 70458 (504) 643-6900
Admin Jon W Franzke.
Licensure Intermediate Care. *Beds* 124. *Certified* Medicaid.

Guest House of Slidell*
1051 Robert Rd, Slidell, LA, 70458 (504) 643-5630
Admin Thomas G Beck Jr.
Licensure Intermediate Care. *Beds* 90. *Certified* Medicaid.

SPRINGHILL

Fountain View Nursing Home*
215 1st St NE, Springhill, LA, 71075 (318) 539-3956
Admin L M Cadenhead Jr.
Licensure Intermediate Care. *Beds* 93. *Certified* Medicaid.

SULPHUR

High Hope Care Center
PO Box 46, Sulphur, LA, 70663
Admin Paul C Reed. *Medical Dir/Dir of Nursing* Dr H B Lovejoy.
Licensure Intermediate Care. *Beds* 101. *Certified* Medicaid.
Ownership Proprietary.
Admissions Requirements Minimum age 18; Medical examination.
Staff Physicians; RNs; LPNs; Nurses aides; Physical therapists; Activities coordinators; Dietitians; Dentists; Social workers.
Facilities Dining room; Activities room; Crafts room; Laundry room; Barber/Beauty shop.
Activities Arts and Crafts; Cards; Games; Prayer groups; Movies; Shopping trips.
Description Facility is situated in a rural setting with plenty of outside activities offered, centrally located to serve all of Western Calcasien Parish; owner operated to ensure proper care of residents. VA approved.

Holly Hill House
100 Kingston Rd, Sulphur, LA, 70663 (318) 625-5843
Admin Ray Green. *Medical Dir/Dir of Nursing* C L Fellows MD.
Licensure Skilled Care. *Beds* 235. *Certified* Medicaid; Medicare.
Admissions Requirements Medical examination; Physician's request.
Staff Physicians 1 (pt); RNs 4 (ft), 1 (pt); LPNs 18 (ft), 5 (pt); Orderlies 1 (ft); Nurses aides 40 (ft), 10 (pt); Physical therapists 1 (pt); Occupational therapists 1 (pt); Speech therapists 1 (pt); Activities coordinators 2 (ft); Dietitians 1 (ft); Dentists 1 (pt); Podiatrists 1 (pt); Audiologists 1 (pt).
Facilities Dining room; Activities room; Chapel; Crafts room; Laundry room; Barber/Beauty shop; Library.
Activities Arts and Crafts; Cards; Games; Reading groups; Prayer groups; Movies; Shopping trips; Dances/Social or cultural gatherings; Pet therapy.

TALLULAH

Delta Haven Nursing Home*
201 Lee St, Tallulah, LA, 71282 (318) 574-4621
Admin Donald W Henderson.
Licensure Intermediate Care. *Beds* 146. *Certified* Medicaid.

Madison Parish Home for the Aged
701 N Chestnut St, Tallulah, LA, 71282 (318) 574-1541
Admin Georgia Mae C Johnson. *Medical Dir/Dir of Nursing* Reba Rinicker.
Licensure Intermediate Care. *Beds* 43. *Certified* Medicaid.
Admissions Requirements Medical examination; Physician's request.
Staff Physicians 5 (pt); RNs 1 (ft); LPNs 6 (ft), 1 (pt); Nurses aides 6 (ft), 6 (pt); Activities coordinators 1 (ft); Dietitians 1 (pt).
Affiliation Baptist
Facilities Dining room; Activities room; Laundry room.
Activities Arts and Crafts; Cards; Games; Prayer groups; Shopping trips.

THIBODAUX

Heritage Manor of Thibodaux*
1300 Lafourche St, Thibodaux, LA, 70301 (504) 446-1332
Admin Ollie Hymel.
Licensure Intermediate Care. *Beds* 58. *Certified* Medicaid.

Lafourche Home for the Aged
1002 Tiger Dr, Thibodaux, LA, 70301 (504) 447-2205
Admin Ann Howell. *Medical Dir/Dir of Nursing* Richard A Morvant MD.
Licensure Intermediate Care. *Beds* 64. *Certified* Medicaid.
Ownership Nonprofit.

Admissions Requirements Medical examination.
Staff RNs 1 (ft), 1 (pt); LPNs 4 (ft), 3 (pt); Nurses aides 35 (ft), 15 (pt); Activities coordinators 1 (ft); Dietitians 1 (ft).
Facilities Dining room; Activities room; Crafts room; Laundry room; Barber/Beauty shop.
Activities Arts and Crafts; Cards; Games; Prayer groups; Movies; Shopping trips; Dances/Social or cultural gatherings.

TIOGA

Tioga Manor Nursing Center*
PO Box 1097, Hope Ln, Tioga, LA, 71477 (318) 640-3010
Admin Iris Winegeart.
Licensure Intermediate Care. *Beds* 120. *Certified* Medicaid.

VILLE PLATTE

Maison de Sante*
220 S Thompson St, Ville Platte, LA, 70586 (318) 363-4048
Admin Matthus M West Sr.
Licensure Intermediate Care. *Beds* 171. *Certified* Medicaid.

VIVIAN

Heritage Manor of Vivian
Rt 1, Box 111, Camp Rd, Vivian, LA, 71082 (318) 375-2203
Admin Ben T Stogsdill. *Medical Dir/Dir of Nursing* John Haymes MD.
Licensure Intermediate Care. *Beds* 80. *Certified* Medicaid.
Admissions Requirements Medical examination; Physician's request.
Staff Physicians 2 (pt); RNs 1 (ft); LPNs 6 (ft), 1 (pt); Orderlies 3 (ft); Nurses aides 16 (ft); Activities coordinators 1 (ft); Dietitians 1 (pt); Dentists 1 (pt).
Facilities Dining room; Activities room; Laundry room; Barber/Beauty shop.
Activities Arts and Crafts; Cards; Games; Reading groups.

WELSH

Welsh Nursing Facility*
PO Box 626, 410 Simmons St, Welsh, LA, 70591 (318) 734-2550
Admin Jean Paul LeJeune.
Licensure Intermediate Care. *Beds* 60. *Certified* Medicaid.

WEST MONROE

G B Cooley Hospital for Mentally Retarded
Rt 8, Box 93, West Monroe, LA, 71291 (318) 387-4371
Admin Larry Parks.
Licensure Intermediate Care for Mentally Retarded. *Beds* 48. *Certified* Medicaid.

Ridgecrest Nursing Home
100 Landrum Dr. West Monroe, LA, 71291 (318) 387-2577
Admin Carolyn Jeansonne. *Medical Dir/Dir of Nursing* Cathy Goatley D.O.N..
Licensure Intermediate Care. *Beds* 114. *Certified* Medicaid.
Admissions Requirements Medical examination; Physician's request.
Staff RNs 1 (ft); LPNs 8 (ft), 1 (pt); Orderlies 2 (ft); Nurses aides 34 (ft); Activities coordinators 1 (ft); Dietitians 1 (pt).
Facilities Dining room; Activities room; Crafts room; Laundry room; Barber/Beauty shop; Sun porch.
Activities Arts and Crafts; Cards; Games; Reading groups; Prayer groups; Movies; Shopping trips; Dances/Social or cultural gatherings; Fishing; Picnics; Senior Olympics.

West Monroe Guest House*
1007 Glenwood Dr, West Monroe, LA, 71291 (318) 387-3900
Admin Virginia B Coplin.
Licensure Intermediate Care. *Beds* 182. *Certified* Medicaid.

WINNFIELD

Autumn Leaves Nursing Home*
PO Box 591, 1400 W Court St, Winnfield, LA, 71483 (318) 628-6171
Admin Jimmy Dale Zimmerman.
Licensure Intermediate Care. *Beds* 114. *Certified* Medicaid.

Parkview Guest Care Center*
PO Box 948, 701 1st St, Winnfield, LA, 71483 (318) 628-3533
Admin Ron Frazier.
Licensure Intermediate Care. *Beds* 88. *Certified* Medicaid.

WINNSBORO

Franklin Guest Home*
2400 Ellis St, Winnsboro, LA, 71295 (318) 435-5026
Admin Lois J Evans.
Licensure Intermediate Care. *Beds* 108. *Certified* Medicaid.

King's Guest Home*
1216 Prairie Rd, Winnsboro, LA, 71295 (318) 435-5194
Admin A A Kelley Jr.
Licensure Intermediate Care. *Beds* 67. *Certified* Medicaid.

Winnsboro Manor Nursing Center*
PO Box 879, Lone Cedar Rd, Winnsboro, LA, 71295 (318) 435-4536
Admin James D Sikes.
Licensure Intermediate Care. *Beds* 111. *Certified* Medicaid.

WISNER

Mary Anna Nursing Home*
PO Drawer B, Wisner, LA, 71378 (318) 724-7244
Admin Carl D Batey.
Licensure Intermediate Care. *Beds* 80. *Certified* Medicaid.

Rosalie Nursing Home
Hwy 15, PO Box 190, Wisner, LA, 71378 (318) 724-7493
Admin Thelma G Sanders. *Medical Dir/Dir of Nursing* Nita Karen Sanders RN.
Licensure Intermediate Care. *Beds* 75. *Certified* Medicaid.
Admissions Requirements Medical examination.
Staff RNs 1 (ft); LPNs 4 (ft), 2 (pt); Orderlies 1 (ft); Nurses aides 22 (ft), 3 (pt); Activities coordinators 1 (pt); Dietitians 1 (pt).
Facilities Dining room; Activities room; Crafts room; Laundry room.
Activities Arts and Crafts; Cards; Games; Prayer groups; Movies; Shopping trips; Dances/Social or cultural gatherings.

ZACHARY

Lane Memorial Hospital—Geriatric Unit
6300 Main St, Zachary, LA, 70791 (504) 654-4511
Admin Charlie L Massey.
Licensure Intermediate Care. *Beds* 39. *Certified* Medicaid.
Admissions Requirements Physician's request.
Staff Physicians 30 (ft), 50 (pt); RNs 1 (ft), 3 (pt); LPNs 4 (ft), 2 (pt); Orderlies 1 (ft), 2 (pt); Nurses aides 8 (ft), 4 (pt); Physical therapists 1 (ft), 1 (pt); Occupational therapists 1 (pt); Activities coordinators 1 (pt); Dietitians 1 (ft).
Facilities Dining room; Physical therapy room; Activities room; Chapel; Crafts room; Laundry room; Barber/Beauty shop.
Activities Arts and Crafts; Cards; Games; Reading groups.
Description Hospital and nursing home are attached, and both the hospital and nursing home merit JCAH accreditation.

Zachary Manor*
PO Drawer C, 6161 Main St, Zachary, LA, 70791 (504) 654-6893
Admin Billie F Dean.
Licensure Intermediate Care. *Beds* 110. *Certified* Medicaid.

MAINE

ABBOT

Abbot Group Home*
West Rd, Abbot, ME, 04406 (207) 876-3703
Admin Steve Aaltonen.
Licensure Intermediate Care for Mentally
Retarded. *Beds* 6.

ALBION

Bethany Inc*
Hussey Rd, Albion, ME, 04910 (207) 437-2761
Admin Kathryn Sawtelle.
Licensure Intermediate Care. *Beds* 25. *Certified* Medicaid.

ATHENS

Athens Group Home*
Brighton Rd, PO Box 142, Athens, ME, 04912
(207) 654-2629
Admin Carla Ring.
Licensure Intermediate Care for Mentally
Retarded. *Beds* 6.

AUBURN

Auburn Nursing Home Inc*
185 Summer St, Auburn, ME, 04210 (207)
786-0676
Admin Donald Powers.
Licensure Intermediate Care. *Beds* 42. *Certified* Medicaid.

Bolster Heights Health Care Facility*
26 Bolster St, Auburn, ME, 04210 (207)
784-1364
Admin Gailene Buckley.
Licensure Intermediate Care. *Beds* 70. *Certified* Medicaid.

Bon Air Nursing Home*
109 Davis Ave, Auburn, ME, 04210 (207)
783-0550
Admin Pauline Robertson.
Licensure Intermediate Care. *Beds* 13. *Certified* Medicaid.

Clover Healthcare
440 Minot Ave, Auburn, ME, 04210 (207)
784-3573
Admin William Gillis. *Medical Dir/Dir of*

Nursing Dr John Milazo.
Licensure Intermediate Care. *Beds* 120. *Certified* Medicaid.
Staff Physicians 2 (pt); RNs 7 (ft), 5 (pt); LPNs
6 (ft), 3 (pt); Nurses aides 52 (ft), 33 (pt);
Physical therapists 1 (ft); Occupational therapists 1 (pt); Speech therapists 1 (pt); Activities
coordinators 1 (ft); Dietitians 1 (ft), 1 (pt).
Facilities Dining room; Physical therapy room;
Activities room; Crafts room; Laundry room;
Barber/Beauty shop; Greenhouse.
Activities Arts and Crafts; Cards; Games;
Reading groups; Prayer groups; Movies; Shopping trips; Dances/Social or cultural gatherings;
Cocktail party.

High Street Health Care Facility*
10 High St, Auburn, ME, 04210 (702) 782-9878
Admin Rachel Alward.
Licensure Intermediate Care. *Beds* 25. *Certified* Medicaid.

Lovelett Health Care Center*
392 Turner St, Auburn, ME, 04210 (207)
784-4773
Admin Ann Lally.
Licensure Intermediate Care. *Beds* 22. *Certified* Medicaid.

Promenade Health Care Facility*
27 Charles St, Auburn, ME, 04210 (207)
782-1621
Admin Gailene Buckley.
Licensure Intermediate Care. *Beds* 29. *Certified* Medicaid.

AUGUSTA

Augusta Convalescent Center*
187 Eastern Ave, Augusta, ME, 04330 (207)
622-3121
Admin Rosemary Rowe.
Licensure Intermediate Care. *Beds* 78. *Certified* Medicaid.

Augusta Mental Health Institute
Arsenal St, PO Box 724, Augusta, ME, 04330
(207) 622-3751
Admin Garrell Mullaney. *Medical Dir/Dir of
Nursing* Jose Castellanos MD.
Licensure Intermediate Care for Mentally
Retarded. *Beds* 70. *Certified* Medicaid.
Staff Physicians 1 (ft); RNs 3 (ft), 1 (pt); LPNs
6 (ft); Nurses aides 39 (ft); Physical therapists 1

(pt); Recreational therapists 1 (ft); Dietitians 1
(pt).
Facilities Dining room; Physical therapy room;
Chapel; Crafts room; Laundry room; Barber/Beauty shop; Library; Gift shop; Canteen.
Activities Arts and Crafts; Cards; Games;
Reading groups; Movies; Shopping trips; Dances/Social or cultural gatherings.
Description The nursing home unit is a certified intermediate care facility licensed for 105
patients. It is an integral part of the Augusta
Mental Health Institute and does not admit
directly from the community, only from the
AMHI psychiatric population. It meets all standards as an ICF Unit for Title 19. The population is, by definition, not acute but requires
professional nursing care and rehabilitation
activities. Age is not a standard measurement
for admission, rather physical deterioration
which requires 24 hours a day of medically
supervised care.

Maine Veterans Home*
Cony Rd, Augusta, ME, 04330 (207) 622-2454
Admin William Carney.
Licensure Intermediate Care. *Beds* 120.

Williams Health Care Facility—Glenridge*
Glenridge Dr, Augusta, ME, 04330 (207)
623-2593
Admin Shirley Williams.
Licensure Intermediate Care. *Beds* 120. *Certified* Medicaid.

Williams Health Care Facility—Gray Birch
Gray Birch Dr, Augusta, ME, 04330 (207)
622-6226
Admin Kenneth Williams. *Medical Dir/Dir of
Nursing* Roy Miller MD.
Licensure Skilled Care; Intermediate Care.
Beds SNF 20; ICF 100. *Certified* Medicaid;
Medicare.
Staff RNs 6 (ft), 5 (pt); LPNs 5 (ft), 4 (pt);
Orderlies 5 (ft), 3 (pt); Nurses aides 42 (ft), 22
(pt); Physical therapists 1 (pt); Reality therapists
1 (pt); Recreational therapists 1 (ft), 4 (pt);
Activities coordinators 1 (ft); Dietitians 1 (pt).
Facilities Dining room; Physical therapy room;
Activities room; Chapel; Crafts room; Laundry
room; Barber/Beauty shop; Library.
Activities Arts and Crafts; Cards; Games;
Reading groups; Prayer groups; Movies; Shopping trips; Dances/Social or cultural gatherings.

BANGOR

Bangor City Nursing Facility
103 Texas Ave, Bangor, ME, 04401 (207)
947-4557
Admin Judith B Roscetti. *Medical Dir/Dir of
Nursing* Edward Babcock MD.
Licensure Skilled Care. *Beds* 54. *Certified* Medicaid; Medicare.
Staff Physicians 1 (pt); RNs 4 (ft), 5 (pt); LPNs
4 (ft), 3 (pt); Nurses aides 18 (ft), 10 (pt);
Physical therapists 1 (pt); Activities coordinators 1 (ft); Social workers 1 (ft).
Facilities Dining room; Physical therapy room;
Activities room; Crafts room; Laundry room;
Barber/Beauty shop; Library.
Activities Arts and Crafts; Cards; Games; Prayer groups; Movies; Shopping trips; Dances/Social or cultural gatherings; Bowling; Birthday
parties; Religious services for all denominations.
Description Dance groups come in to entertain.

Bangor Convalescent Center
516 Mount Hope Ave, Bangor, ME, 04401
(207) 947-6131
Admin Penelope Sargent. *Medical Dir/Dir of
Nursing* Michael Bruhel MD.
Licensure Intermediate Care. *Beds* 80. *Certified* Medicaid.
Admissions Requirements Medical examination.
Staff Physicians 12 (pt); RNs 2 (ft), 1 (pt);
LPNs 8 (ft), 2 (pt); Nurses aides 25 (ft), 10 (pt);
Physical therapists 1 (pt); Occupational therapists 1 (pt); Speech therapists 1 (pt); Activities
coordinators 1 (ft), 1 (pt); Dietitians 1 (ft), 1
(pt).
Facilities Dining room; Physical therapy room;
Activities room; Crafts room; Laundry room;
Barber/Beauty shop; Library; Living rooms.
Activities Arts and Crafts; Cards; Games;
Reading groups; Prayer groups; Movies; Shopping trips; Dances/Social or cultural gatherings;
Field trips; Family dinners.
Description Individual care plans developed
with the resident if able or family on admission
with goal setting on individual needs and
potential for return to the community.

Bangor Mental Health Institute
PO Box 926, Bangor, ME, 04401 (207)
947-6981
Admin Patricia Oulton. *Medical Dir/Dir of
Nursing* Roger M Wilson MD.
Licensure Intermediate Care. *Beds* 130. *Certified* Medicaid.
Staff Physicians 5 (ft), 5 (pt); RNs 46 (ft);
LPNs 27 (ft); Nurses aides 226 (ft); Physical
therapists 1 (ft); Reality therapists 1 (ft); Recreational therapists 2 (ft); Occupational therapists 1
(ft).
Facilities Dining room; Physical therapy room;
Activities room; Chapel; Crafts room; Barber-
/Beauty shop; Library.
Activities Arts and Crafts; Cards; Games;
Movies; Shopping trips; Dances/Social or cultural gatherings.
Description Facility features the following programs: pet therapy, gym programs, cooking
class, individual assistance, physical therapy
training ward staff to do on-ward programs,
wine and cheese party, on-ward leathercraft E-3,

bi-weekly trips to Together Place, bowling banquet, winter carnival, Sunbeam Cruise (once
during summer months), gingerbread house
program, adopt-a-grandparent, music, and
movement.

**Eastern Maine Medical Center—Ross Skilled
Nursing Division**
489 State St, Bangor, ME, 04401 (207)
947-3711
Admin Robert Brandow. *Medical Dir/Dir of
Nursing* Dr Phillip Mossman.
Licensure Skilled Care. *Beds* 15. *Certified* Medicaid; Medicare.
Admissions Requirements Medical examination; Physician's request.
Staff RNs 4 (ft), 4 (pt); Nurses aides 7 (ft), 8
(pt); Physical therapists 2 (ft); Occupational
therapists 1 (pt); Speech therapists 1 (pt);
Activities coordinators 1 (ft); Dietitians 1 (pt);
Audiologists 1 (pt).
Facilities Dining room; Physical therapy room;
Activities room; Chapel; Crafts room; Laundry
room; Barber/Beauty shop.
Activities Arts and Crafts; Cards; Games;
Reading groups; Movies; Dances/Social or cultural gatherings.
Description The Ross Division is a distinct
part of a 416-bed acute-care hospital.

Elizabeth Levinson Center
159 Hogan Rd, Bangor, ME, 04401 (207)
947-6136
Admin Dr Robert Durgan.
Licensure Intermediate Care for Mentally
Retarded. *Beds* 33. *Certified* Medicaid.
Admissions Requirements Medical examination; Physician's request.
Staff RNs 5 (ft); LPNs 4 (ft); Physical therapists 1 (ft); Recreational therapists 1 (ft);
Occupational therapists 1 (ft); Activities coordinators 1 (ft).
Facilities Dining room; Physical therapy room;
Activities room; Laundry room.
Activities Arts and Crafts; Games; Movies;
Shopping trips; Dances/Social or cultural gatherings.
Description The Elizabeth Levinson Center
serves severely and profoundly retarded children, birth through twenty. Residents come
from throughout the state of Maine. The center
provides a variety of services: emergency respite care, respite care, short-term evaluation
program, contracted training, and a preschool
program. All referrals for admission to the center must be made through one of the regional
offices of the Bureau of Mental Retardation.

James A Taylor Osteopathic Hospital
268 Stillwater Ave, Bangor, ME, 04401 (207)
942-5286
Admin James R Kelly Jr. *Medical Dir/Dir of
Nursing* Koster K Peter DO.
Licensure Intermediate Care. *Beds* 38. *Certified* Medicaid.
Admissions Requirements Physician's request.
Staff RNs 2 (ft); LPNs 5 (ft); Nurses aides 14
(ft); Physical therapists 1 (pt); Activities coordinators 1 (pt); Dietitians 1 (ft).
Facilities Dining room; Activities room; Chapel; Laundry room.
Activities Arts and Crafts; Cards; Games;
Movies; Shopping trips.

Description Facility is connected to a 60-bed
acute care hospital located in a nice residential
area close to the interstate.

Pine Street Group Home*
188 Pine St, Bangor, ME, 04401 (207)
947-2739
Admin Bonnie Jean Brooks.
Licensure Intermediate Care for Mentally
Retarded. *Beds* 6. *Certified* Medicaid.

Stillwater Health Care
335 Stillwater Ave, Bangor, ME, 04401 (207)
947-1111
Admin Gail Cote. *Medical Dir/Dir of Nursing* Dr Henry Atkins.
Licensure Intermediate Care. *Beds* 65. *Certified* Medicaid.
Staff RNs 3 (ft), 2 (pt); LPNs 3 (ft), 3 (pt);
Nurses aides 16 (ft), 21 (pt); Activities coordinators 1 (ft).
Facilities Dining room; Physical therapy room;
Activities room; Chapel; Laundry room; Barber/Beauty shop.
Activities Arts and Crafts; Cards; Games;
Reading groups; Prayer groups; Movies; Shopping trips; Dances/Social or cultural gatherings.
Description Nondenominational chapel service
for staff and residents every day helps to
impress upon everyone the motto "Living is
loving and caring".

Westgate Manor
750 Union St, Bangor, ME, 04401 (207)
942-7336
Admin Susan C Cirone. *Medical Dir/Dir of
Nursing* Charles Burger MD.
Licensure Intermediate Care. *Beds* 113. *Certified* Medicaid.
Admissions Requirements Medical examination; Physician's request.
Staff RNs 6 (ft), 3 (pt); LPNs 6 (ft), 3 (pt);
Nurses aides 20 (ft), 10 (pt); Activities coordinators 1 (ft).
Facilities Dining room; Physical therapy room;
Activities room; Chapel; Crafts room; Laundry
room; Barber/Beauty shop; Library.
Activities Arts and Crafts; Cards; Games;
Reading groups; Prayer groups; Movies; Shopping trips; Dances/Social or cultural gatherings.
Description Facility is located on a tree-studded
lot within minutes of 2 hospitals and with
access to all types of medical specialists and
cultural aspects of the city.

BAR HARBOR

Sonogee Estages*
Eden St, Bar Harbor, ME, 04609 (207)
288-5800
Admin Richard Collier.
Licensure Intermediate Care. *Beds* 82. *Certified* Medicaid.

Summit House Health Care Center*
Norman Rd, Bar Harbor, ME, 04609 (207)
288-5856
Admin David Waldron.
Licensure Intermediate Care. *Beds* 88. *Certified* Medicaid.

BATH

Bath Nursing Home
Winship St, PO Box 286, Bath, ME, 04530
(207) 443-9772
Admin Carol Sharp. *Medical Dir/Dir of
Nursing* Anthony Keating MD.
Licensure Intermediate Care. *Beds* 72. *Certi-
fied* Medicaid.
Admissions Requirements Medical examina-
tion; Physician's request.
Staff Physicians 16 (pt); RNs 3 (ft), 4 (pt);
LPNs 3 (ft), 2 (pt); Nurses aides 22 (ft), 12 (pt);
Physical therapists; Occupational therapists;
Speech therapists; Activities coordinators 1 (ft),
1 (pt); Dietitians 1 (pt); Dentists 3 (pt);
Ophthalmologists 3 (pt); Podiatrists 1 (pt).
Facilities Dining room; Physical therapy room;
Activities room; Chapel; Crafts room; Laundry
room; Barber/Beauty shop.
Activities Arts and Crafts; Cards; Games;
Reading groups; Prayer groups; Movies; Shop-
ping trips; Dances/Social or cultural gatherings.
Description Students from Voc 10 come for
part of their training; great volunteer program
with many activities; home works closely with
the youth in the area and has many programs
involving all ages.

Hillhouse Convalescent Home*
Box 98, Whiskeag Rd, Bath, ME, 04530 (207)
443-6301
Admin Marjorie Voorhees.
Licensure Intermediate Care. *Beds* 37. *Certi-
fied* Medicaid.

BELFAST

Bradbury Memorial Nursing Home*
32 High St, Belfast, ME, 04915 (207) 338-3666
Admin Edward A Bonefant.
Licensure Intermediate Care. *Beds* 60. *Certified* Medicaid.

BIDDEFORD

Good Shepherd Villa Health Care Facility
173 South St, Biddeford, ME, 04005 (207)
282-4138
Admin Ralph Ham. *Medical Dir/Dir of
Nursing* M P Houle MD.
Licensure Intermediate Care. *Beds* 124. *Certified* Medicaid.
Staff RNs 5 (ft); LPNs 11 (ft); Nurses aides 36
(ft); Activities coordinators 2 (ft); Dietitians 2
(ft).
Facilities Dining room; Physical therapy room;
Activities room; Chapel; Crafts room; Laundry
room; Barber/Beauty shop.
Activities Arts and Crafts; Cards; Games;
Reading groups; Prayer groups; Movies; Shopping trips; Dances/Social or cultural gatherings.
Description Facility features ongoing bus rides
in area (to beaches in season), special events,
restaurant trips once-a-month, ball games (AAA
League), outside barbecues every other week
during summer months—June 5 to September
5.

Greenhill Residence
1 Green St, Biddeford, ME, 04005 (207)
282-3741
Admin Amy Levasseur.
Licensure Intermediate Care for Mentally
Retarded. *Beds* 6.
Admissions Requirements Minimum age 16;
Medical examination; Physician's request.
Staff RNs 1 (pt); Activities coordinators 1 (ft).
Facilities Dining room; Activities room; Laun-
dry room.
Activities Arts and Crafts; Cards; Games;
Movies; Shopping trips; Dances/Social or cul-
tural gatherings.
Description Greenhill is a group home for
mentally retarded adults which takes a holistic
approach within the realms of normalization.
Residents are working towards a less supervised
living situation whenever possible. Programing
focuses on adult daily living skills, social skills,
recreation, and personal growth.

Sacco River Health Care Center*
355 Pool Rd, Biddeford, ME, 04005 (207)
283-3646
Admin William Allaire.
Licensure Skilled Care; Intermediate Care.
Beds SNF 20; ICF 51. *Certified* Medicaid;
Medicare.

Saint Andre Health Care Facility
407 Pool St, Biddeford, ME, 04005 (207)
282-5171
Admin Sr Jeannette Labrecque. *Medical Dir-
/Dir of Nursing* Dr Sarah Moore MD.
Licensure Intermediate Care. *Beds* 96. *Certi-
fied* Medicaid.
Staff RNs 4 (ft), 9 (pt); LPNs 3 (ft), 5 (pt);
Nurses aides 25 (ft), 33 (pt); Activities coordi-
nators 2 (ft), 1 (pt).
Affiliation Roman Catholic
Facilities Dining room; Physical therapy room;
Activities room; Chapel; Laundry room; Bar-
ber/Beauty shop; Library.
Activities Arts and Crafts; Games; Movies;
Shopping trips; Dances/Social or cultural gatherings.
Description Beautifully situated on a sprawling
40-acre site along the Saco River, St. Andre's is
easily accessible from the main highways. Residents receive long-term intermediate care while
enjoying warm, home-like surroundings in
modern facility. A gracious independent lifestyle is achieved through cheerfully decorated
private and semi-private rooms. Each room
features comfortable furnishings, closet and
drawer space, television and telephone jacks,
adjustable bed, sink, adjoining half-bath, and
an electronic nurse call for prompt attention.

Trull Nursing Home*
15 May St, Biddeford, ME, 04005 (207)
284-4507
Admin Marion Stickney.
Licensure Intermediate Care. *Beds* 49. *Certified* Medicaid.

BINGHAM

Somerset Manor*
Owen St, Bingham, ME, 04920 (207) 672-4041
Admin Elmer Blaine Hale.
Licensure Intermediate Care. *Beds* 34. *Certi-
fied* Medicaid.

BREWER

Brewer Convalescent Center
174 Parkway S, Brewer, ME, 04412 (207)
989-7300
Admin Linda Kaine. *Medical Dir/Dir of
Nursing* Richard Sagall.
Licensure Intermediate Care. *Beds* 116. *Certi-
fied* Medicaid.
Staff Physicians 1 (ft); RNs 5 (ft), 2 (pt); LPNs
9 (ft), 1 (pt); Nurses aides 30 (ft), 20 (pt);
Physical therapists 1 (pt); Speech therapists 1
(pt); Activities coordinators 2 (ft), 1 (pt); Dieti-
tians 1 (ft); Podiatrists 1 (pt).
Facilities Dining room; Physical therapy room;
Activities room; Crafts room; Laundry room;
Barber/Beauty shop; Library.
Activities Arts and Crafts; Cards; Games;
Reading groups; Prayer groups; Movies; Shopping trips; Dances/Social or cultural gatherings;
Fund raising; Resident council.
Description Built in 1974, this one-story home
nestles among birches on beautifully landscaped grounds on Parkway South. Facilities
include the most modern health care equipment and services with a wide range of social
activities designed to encourage each resident's
personal growth and fulfillment.

Penobscot Valley Nursing Home
23 Holyoke St, Brewer, ME, 04412 (207)
989-3100
Admin Sally Lord.
Licensure Intermediate Care. *Beds* 26. *Certified* Medicaid.

BRIDGETON

Good Neighbors Inc*
S High St, Bridgeton, ME, 04009 (207)
647-8244
Admin Rebecca Shanor.
Licensure Intermediate Care for Mentally
Retarded. *Beds* 12. *Certified* Medicaid.

BRUNSWICK

Brunswick Convalescent Center
Baribeau Dr, Brunswick, ME, 04011 (207)
725-4379
Admin Jacquelyn Moser. *Medical Dir/Dir of
Nursing* E Schmidt MD.
Licensure Intermediate Care. *Beds* 82. *Certi-
fied* Medicaid.
Admissions Requirements Medical examina-
tion.
Staff RNs 3 (ft), 4 (pt); LPNs 1 (ft), 7 (pt);
Orderlies 1 (ft); Nurses aides 21 (ft), 28 (pt);
Activities coordinators 1 (ft); Dietitians 1 (ft).
Facilities Dining room; Activities room; Crafts
room; Laundry room; Barber/Beauty shop;
Library.
Activities Arts and Crafts; Reading groups;

Prayer groups; Movies; Shopping trips; Dances-/Social or cultural gatherings.
Description Center is located near Bowdoin College, Regional Memorial Hospital, and a variety of historic landmarks.

Brunswick Manor Inc*
26-28 Cumberland Ave, Brunswick, ME, 04011 (207) 725-5801
Admin Jane Colarusso.
Licensure Intermediate Care. *Beds* 51. *Certified* Medicaid.

Mere Point Nursing Home*
Mere Point Rd, Brunswick, ME, 04011 (207) 725-2870
Admin Eleanor Bullett.
Licensure Intermediate Care. *Beds* 26. *Certified* Medicaid.

Regional Memorial Hosptial
58 Baribeau Dr, Brunswick, ME, 04011 (207) 729-0181
Admin Herbert Paris. *Medical Dir/Dir of Nursing* Dr Carson.
Licensure Skilled Care. *Beds* 8. *Certified* Medicaid; Medicare.
Admissions Requirements Medical examination.
Staff RNs 1 (ft), 2 (pt); LPNs 1 (ft), 3 (pt); Nurses aides 3 (ft), 3 (pt); Physical therapists 2 (ft), 2 (pt); Occupational therapists 1 (ft); Speech therapists; Activities coordinators 1 (ft); Dietitians 1 (ft).
Facilities Dining room; Physical therapy room; Activities room; Library.
Activities Arts and Crafts; Games.

CALAIS

Barnard Nursing Home Inc*
Palmer St Extension, Calais, ME, 04619 (207) 454-2366
Admin Valarie Barnard.
Licensure Intermediate Care. *Beds* 100. *Certified* Medicaid.

CAMDEN

Camden Health Care Center
108 Elm St, Camden, ME, 04843 (207) 236-8381
Admin Jefferson D Ackor.
Licensure Skilled Care; Intermediate Care. *Beds* SNF 20; ICF 140. *Certified* Medicaid; Medicare.
Admissions Requirements Medical examination; Physician's request.
Staff Physicians 2 (pt); RNs 5 (ft), 10 (pt); LPNs 20 (ft), 20 (pt); Nurses aides 75 (ft), 50 (pt); Physical therapists 2 (pt); Recreational therapists 2 (pt); Occupational therapists 2 (pt); Speech therapists 2 (pt); Activities coordinators 1 (ft); Dietitians 2 (pt); Dentists 1 (pt); Audiologists 1 (ft).
Facilities Dining room; Physical therapy room; Activities room; Chapel; Crafts room; Laundry room; Barber/Beauty shop; Library; Living center.
Activities Arts and Crafts; Cards; Games; Reading groups; Prayer groups; Movies; Shop-ping trips; Dances/Social or cultural gatherings.
Description Located on the edge of the town of Camden, one of Maine's prettiest villages, center looks out on Mount Megunticook in a rural village environment.

Camden Nursing Home Inc*
19 Mountain St, Camden, ME, 04843 (207) 236-2900
Admin Kenneth Weber.
Licensure Intermediate Care. *Beds* 29. *Certified* Medicaid.

CANTON

Victorian Villa
Pleasant St, Canton, ME, 04221 (207) 597-2071
Admin Aiden E Redding. *Medical Dir/Dir of Nursing* Pat Coyne DN.
Licensure Intermediate Care. *Beds* 36. *Certified* Medicaid.
Staff RNs 2 (ft); LPNs 3 (ft); Nurses aides 10 (ft), 12 (pt); Recreational therapists 1 (pt); Activities coordinators 1 (pt).
Facilities Dining room; Physical therapy room; Laundry room; Barber/Beauty shop.
Activities Arts and Crafts; Games; Reading groups; Prayer groups; Movies; Shopping trips; Dances/Social or cultural gatherings.

CAPE ELIZABETH

The Viking Intermediate Care Facility*
Scott Dyer Rd, Cape Elizabeth, ME, 04107 (207) 767-3373
Admin Duane Rancourt.
Licensure Intermediate Care. *Beds* 60. *Certified* Medicaid.

CARIBOU

Caribou Nursing Home
10 Bernadette St, Caribou, ME, 04736 (207) 498-3102
Admin Philip Cyr.
Licensure Intermediate Care. *Beds* 110. *Certified* Medicaid.
Admissions Requirements Medical examination.
Staff RNs 1 (ft), 7 (pt); LPNs 1 (ft), 10 (pt); Nurses aides 16 (ft), 67 (pt); Physical therapists 1 (ft); Activities coordinators 2 (ft); Dietitians 6 (ft), 9 (pt).
Facilities Dining room; Physical therapy room; Activities room; Crafts room; Laundry room; Barber/Beauty shop.
Activities Arts and Crafts; Cards; Games; Prayer groups; Movies; Dances/Social or cultural gatherings.
Description Facility offers day care on an hourly basis for mentally incompetent; also offers respite care for 3 or more days. Modern, safe, clean facility with caring staff.

COOPERS MILLS

Country Manor Nursing Home*
Coopers Mills, ME, 04341 (207) 549-7471
Admin Donald Lemar.
Licensure Intermediate Care. *Beds* 53. *Certified* Medicaid.

Sheepscot Valley Health Center*
Main St, Coopers Mills, ME, 04341 (207) 549-7581
Admin David N Fenton.

DANFORTH

Danforth Nursing Home
Depot St, Danforth, ME, 04424 (207) 448-2383
Admin Pamela DeWitt. *Medical Dir/Dir of Nursing* John Madigan MD.
Licensure Intermediate Care. *Beds* 18. *Certified* Medicaid.
Staff Physicians 2 (pt); RNs 1 (ft), 1 (pt); Nurses aides 6 (ft), 8 (pt); Physical therapists 1 (pt); Occupational therapists 1 (pt); Activities coordinators 1 (pt); Dietitians 1 (pt).
Facilities Dining room; Activities room; Crafts room; Laundry room.
Activities Arts and Crafts; Cards; Games; Reading groups.

Still Waters Nursing Home Inc*
Main St, Danforth, ME, 04424 (207) 448-2327
Admin Gertrude Ripley.
Licensure Intermediate Care. *Beds* 21. *Certified* Medicaid.

DEER ISLE

Island Nursing Home
Rt 15, Deer Isle, ME, 04627
Medical Dir/Dir of Nursing Dan Rissi MD.
Admissions Requirements Physician's request.
Staff Physicians; RNs 3 (ft); LPNs 3 (ft); Nurses aides 9 (ft), 16 (pt); Physical therapists; Activities coordinators; Podiatrists; Social workers.
Facilities Dining room; Physical therapy room; Activities room; Crafts room; Laundry room; Barber/Beauty shop; Library.
Activities Arts and Crafts; Cards; Games; Reading groups; Prayer groups; Movies; Shopping trips; Cooking groups; Happy hour.
Description Facility is located in a wooded setting on an island whose year-round population is 3500.

DEXTER

Dexter Nursing Home*
64 Park St, Dexter, ME, 04930 (207) 924-5516
Admin Gerard Cyr.
Licensure Intermediate Care. *Beds* 66. *Certified* Medicaid.

DIXFIELD

Dixfield Health Care Center Inc*
100 Weld St, Dixfield, ME, 04224 (207) 562-4922

Admin Paula Varney.
Licensure Intermediate Care. *Beds* 55. *Certified* Medicaid.

DOVERFOXCROFT

Hibbard Nursing Home
Guilford Rd, Dover-Foxcroft, ME, 04426 (207) 564-8129
Admin Jane M Hibbard. *Medical Dir/Dir of Nursing* L J Stitham MD.
Licensure Skilled Care; Intermediate Care.
Beds SNF 12; ICF 66. *Certified* Medicaid; Medicare.
Staff Physicians 10 (ft), 3 (pt); RNs 3 (ft), 3 (pt); LPNs 4 (ft), 2 (pt); Nurses aides 31 (ft), 13 (pt); Physical therapists 1 (ft); Speech therapists 1 (pt); Activities coordinators 2 (ft); Dietitians 1 (pt); Dentists 1 (pt); Ophthalmologists 1 (pt); Podiatrists 1 (pt).
Facilities Dining room; Physical therapy room; Activities room; Crafts room; Laundry room; Barber/Beauty shop; Library.
Activities Arts and Crafts; Cards; Games; Reading groups; Prayer groups; Movies; Shopping trips; Dances/Social or cultural gatherings.

EAGLE LAKE

Eagle Lake Nursing Home*
Church St, Eagle Lake, ME, 04739 (207) 444-5152
Admin Gerald Frenette.
Licensure Intermediate Care. *Beds* 60. *Certified* Medicaid.

EAST LEBANON

Greenwood Nursing Care Center Inc*
Little River Rd, East Lebanon, ME, 04027 (207) 457-1033
Admin Christine Boisvert.
Licensure Intermediate Care. *Beds* 31. *Certified* Medicaid.

EASTPORT

Eastport Memorial Hospital—Intermediate Care Unit
23 Boynton St, Eastport, ME, 04631 (207) 853-2531
Admin Inez Mills.
Licensure Intermediate Care. *Beds* 26. *Certified* Medicaid.
Admissions Requirements Medical examination.
Staff RNs 1 (ft); LPNs 3 (ft), 1 (pt); Nurses aides 10 (ft), 1 (pt); Activities coordinators 1 (pt); Dietitians 1 (pt).
Facilities Dining room; Activities room; Crafts room; Barber/Beauty shop.
Activities Arts and Crafts; Cards; Games; Reading groups; Prayer groups; Shopping trips; Exercise.
Description Facility features an auxiliary tea (2 times a year); fair (annual); special open house to celebrate birthdays (102 years and 2 100 years); musical groups (community and school children).

EDDINGTON

Eddington Group Home*
Rts 9 and 178, Eddington, ME, 04428 (207) 989-1303
Admin Jacqueline Turner.
Licensure Intermediate Care for Mentally Retarded. *Beds* 6. *Certified* Medicaid.

ELLSWORTH

Agape House
360 E Main St, Ellsworth, ME, 04605
Medical Dir/Dir of Nursing Charles Alexander Md.
Licensure Intermediate Care for Mentally Retarded. *Beds* 20. *Certified* Medicaid.
Ownership Nonprofit.
Admissions Requirements Minimum age 20.
Staff RNs 2 (ft), 1 (pt); LPNs 2 (ft), 2 (pt); Nurses aides 20 (ft), 10 (pt); Speech therapists 1 (pt); Activities coordinators 1 (pt); Dietitians 1 (pt).
Facilities Dining room; Laundry room.
Activities Arts and Crafts; Games; Shopping trips; Dances/Social or cultural gatherings.
Description Newly constructed facility designed with 2 living areas for 10 residents each. Day program offers 5 hours a day Monday through Friday outside of facility. Van and bus equipped for transportation of handicapped. Therapeutic park to be built in 1984.

Collier's Nursing Home*
33 Birch Ave, Ellsworth, ME, 04605 (207) 667-9336
Admin Lawrence Collier.
Licensure Intermediate Care. *Beds* 40. *Certified* Medicaid.

Ellsworth Convalescent Center
38 Court St, Ellsworth, ME, 04605 (207) 667-9036
Admin Belle Chandler. *Medical Dir/Dir of Nursing* Charles Alexander MD.
Licensure Intermediate Care. *Beds* 94. *Certified* Medicaid.
Admissions Requirements Medical examination; Physician's request.
Staff RNs 4 (ft), 1 (pt); LPNs 5 (ft), 2 (pt); Nurses aides 39 (ft); Physical therapists 1 (pt); Speech therapists 1 (pt); Activities coordinators 1 (ft); Dietitians 1 (ft).
Facilities Dining room; Physical therapy room; Activities room; Laundry room; Barber/Beauty shop; Library.
Activities Arts and Crafts; Cards; Games; Reading groups; Prayer groups; Movies; Shopping trips; Dances/Social or cultural gatherings.

FAIRFIELD

Klearview Manor*
RFD 1, Shawmut Rd, Fairfield, ME, 04937 (207) 453-2112
Admin Joan Clough.
Licensure Intermediate Care for Mentally Retarded. *Beds* 29.

Pleasant Hill Health Facility
Mountain Rd, Fairfield, ME, 04937 (207) 453-2511
Admin John Lane. *Medical Dir/Dir of Nursing* Marion Strickland MD.
Licensure Intermediate Care. *Beds* 95. *Certified* Medicaid.
Staff RNs 3 (ft); LPNs 11 (ft), 3 (pt); Orderlies 5 (ft), 3 (pt); Nurses aides 34 (ft), 8 (pt); Activities coordinators 1 (ft), 1 (pt); Dietitians 1 (pt); Podiatrists 1 (pt).
Facilities Dining room; Physical therapy room; Activities room; Laundry room; Barber/Beauty shop.
Activities Arts and Crafts; Cards; Games; Reading groups; Prayer groups; Movies; Shopping trips; Dances/Social or cultural gatherings.
Description Facility is set off by itself on top of a beautifully landscaped hill overlooking the town; offers a wide range of services from rehabilitation to the care of the terminally ill, provided by a professional staff that cares.

FALMOUTH

Falmouth Convalescent Center*
191 Foreside Rd, Falmouth, ME, 04105 (207) 781-4714
Admin Sandra Tate.
Licensure Intermediate Care. *Beds* 70. *Certified* Medicaid.

FARMINGTON

Franklin Manor I
N Main St, Farmington, ME, 04938 (207) 778-3386
Admin Carl D Gagnon. *Medical Dir/Dir of Nursing* K Gooch MD.
Licensure Intermediate Care. *Beds* 53. *Certified* Medicaid.
Admissions Requirements Medical examination; Physician's request.
Staff RNs 4 (ft), 2 (pt); LPNs 6 (ft), 2 (pt); Orderlies 2 (ft); Nurses aides 23 (ft), 16 (pt); Physical therapists 1 (pt); Recreational therapists 1 (ft); Activities coordinators 1 (ft); Dietitians 1 (pt).
Facilities Dining room; Activities room; Chapel; Crafts room; Laundry room; Barber/Beauty shop; Library.
Activities Arts and Crafts; Cards; Games; Reading groups; Prayer groups; Movies; Shopping trips; Dances/Social or cultural gatherings.
Description Facility features a beautiful rural location, large lawn areas with bedded, wheelchair accessible raised gardens for resident use.

Franklin Manor II
18 Orchard St, Farmington, ME, 04938 (207) 778-4416
Admin Valerie House. *Medical Dir/Dir of Nursing* Paul Taylor MD.
Licensure Intermediate Care. *Beds* 32. *Certified* Medicaid.
Admissions Requirements Medical examination.
Staff RNs 1 (ft), 1 (pt); LPNs 3 (ft), 3 (pt); Nurses aides 10 (ft), 8 (pt); Activities coordinators 1 (pt).
Facilities Dining room; Laundry room.

Activities Arts and Crafts; Cards; Games; Reading groups; Prayer groups; Movies; Shopping trips; Dances/Social or cultural gatherings. *Description* Facility is located in a small town residential setting with a home-like atmosphere.

Our House
8 Anson St, Farmington, ME, 04938 (207) 778-2602
Admin William Whyte.
Licensure Intermediate Care for Mentally Retarded. *Beds* 6. *Certified* Medicaid.
Admissions Requirements Minimum age 18.
Staff Nurses aides 4 (ft), 6 (pt).
Facilities Dining room; Laundry room.
Activities Arts and Crafts; Movies; Shopping trips; Dances/Social or cultural gatherings.
Description All clients attend a structured day program outside of facility. All staff members have sign language abilities and use this all through the day. Clients are encouraged to be independent in activities and skills made available at this facility.

Sandy River Nursing Care Center
PO Box 404, Farmington, ME, 04938
Admin Leon Bresloff. *Medical Dir/Dir of Nursing* Paul Brinkman MD.
Licensure Intermediate Care. *Beds* 95. *Certified* Medicaid.
Ownership Proprietary.
Admissions Requirements Minimum age 16; Medical examination; Physician's request.
Staff Physicians 1 (pt); RNs 5 (ft), 3 (pt); LPNs 4 (ft), 1 (pt); Nurses aides 20 (ft), 30 (pt); Physical therapists 1 (pt); Recreational therapists 2 (pt); Occupational therapists 1 (pt); Speech therapists 1 (pt); Activities coordinators 1 (pt); Podiatrists 1 (pt).
Facilities Dining room; Physical therapy room; Activities room; Barber/Beauty shop.
Activities Arts and Crafts; Cards; Games; Reading groups; Prayer groups; Movies; Shopping trips; Dances/Social or cultural gatherings.
Description Management philosophy is to provide holistic health care in a warm, safe, caring, and supportive environment so residents are free to integrate their life energy in constructive and creative ways.

FORT FAIRFIELD

Community General Hospital
3 Green St, Fort Fairfield, ME, 04742 (207) 472-3811
Admin Theodore Gagnon.
Licensure Skilled Care. *Beds* 12. *Certified* Medicaid; Medicare.

FORT KENT

Forest Hill Manor*
Bolduc Ave, Fort Kent, ME, 04743 (207) 834-3915
Admin James LeVasseur.
Licensure Intermediate Care. *Beds* 45. *Certified* Medicaid.

FREEPORT

Freeport Convalescent Center*
Old County Rd, Freeport, ME, 04032 (207) 865-4782
Admin Vicki White.
Licensure Intermediate Care. *Beds* 82. *Certified* Medicaid.

Freeport Nursing Home*
East St, Freeport, ME, 04032 (207) 865-4713
Admin Elaine Hicks.
Licensure Intermediate Care. *Beds* 60. *Certified* Medicaid.

Freeport Town Square I*
Lower Main St, Freeport, ME, 04032 (207) 865-4876
Admin Samuel Parker.
Licensure Intermediate Care for Mentally Retarded. *Beds* 6.

Freeport Town Square II*
Lower Main St, Freeport, ME, 04032 (207) 865-6060
Admin Samuel Parker.
Licensure Intermediate Care for Mentally Retarded. *Beds* 8.

FRYEBURG

Fryeburg Health Care Center*
Fairview Dr, Fryeburg, ME, 04037 (207) 935-3351
Admin David Hicks.
Licensure Intermediate Care. *Beds* 82. *Certified* Medicaid.

Hicks Nursing Home*
27 Oxford St, Fryeburg, ME, 04037 (207) 935-2985
Admin Erna Hicks.
Licensure Intermediate Care. *Beds* 27. *Certified* Medicaid.

GARDINER

Gardiner Group Home*
23 River St, Gardiner, ME, 04345 (207) 582-7355
Admin Deborah Dixon.
Licensure Intermediate Care for Mentally Retarded. *Beds* 6.

Merrill Memorial Manor Inc*
146 Dresden Ave, Gardiner, ME, 04345 (207) 582-2114
Admin Donald Lemar.
Licensure Intermediate Care. *Beds* 64. *Certified* Medicaid.

Robinson Health Care Facility
284 Brunswick Ave, Gardiner, ME, 04345 (207) 582-6250
Admin Kenneth Robinson. *Medical Dir/Dir of Nursing* John Hussey MD.
Licensure Intermediate Care. *Beds* 50. *Certified* Medicaid.
Staff RNs 2 (ft), 2 (pt); LPNs 2 (ft), 2 (pt); Nurses aides 10 (ft), 17 (pt); Activities coordinators 1 (ft); Dietitians 1 (pt); Podiatrists 1 (pt);

Social workers 1 (ft).
Facilities Dining room; Physical therapy room; Activities room; Laundry room.
Activities Arts and Crafts; Cards; Games; Reading groups; Prayer groups; Movies; Shopping trips; Birthday parties.
Description Facility offers a family oriented environment where staff, residents, and management all work together as a family; residents are encouraged to bring articles from home for their living area so they are surrounded by familiar objects.

Willowcrest Home Inc
Rt 4, Gardiner, ME, 04345 (207) 582-3632
Admin Donald Palleschi. *Medical Dir/Dir of Nursing* Maurice Guillemette MD.
Licensure Intermediate Care. *Beds* 42. *Certified* Medicaid.
Admissions Requirements Minimum age 16.
Staff Physicians 1 (pt); RNs 1 (ft); LPNs 2 (ft), 2 (pt); Orderlies 11 (ft), 14 (pt); Physical therapists 1 (pt); Speech therapists 1 (pt); Activities coordinators 1 (ft); Dietitians 1 (pt); Dentists 1 (pt); Podiatrists 1 (pt).
Facilities Dining room; Activities room.
Activities Arts and Crafts; Cards; Games; Reading groups; Prayer groups; Movies; Shopping trips; Dances/Social or cultural gatherings; Outside trips.
Description Facility has an excellent activities program—outside trips and country setting.

GORHAM

Gorham Manor
30 New Portland Rd, Gorham, ME, 04038 (207) 839-3732
Admin Arlene Cooper.
Licensure Intermediate Care. *Beds* 24. *Certified* Medicaid.
Admissions Requirements Minimum age 16; Medical examination.
Staff RNs 1 (ft); LPNs 2 (ft), 1 (pt); Nurses aides 5 (ft), 9 (pt); Activities coordinators 1 (ft); Social workers 1 (ft).
Facilities Dining room; Activities room; Crafts room; Laundry room.
Activities Arts and Crafts; Cards; Games; Reading groups; Prayer groups; Movies; Shopping trips; Dances/Social or cultural gatherings.
Description Small one-story facility is in a country setting and in a college town; very home-like with very supportive families who actively participate in their relatives' care and activities.

GREENE

Greene Acres Manor Inc*
Rt 202, Greene, ME, 04236 (207) 946-5225
Admin Rachel Alward.
Licensure Intermediate Care. *Beds* 59. *Certified* Medicaid.

GREENVILLE

Charles A Dean Memorial Hospital—Intermediate Care Unit*
Pritham Ave, Greenville, ME, 04442 (207) 695-2223

Admin Ralph Gabarro.
Licensure Intermediate Care. *Beds* 28. *Certified* Medicaid.

HALLOWELL

Hayden House*
Winthrop St, Hallowell, ME, 04347 (207)
622-6712
Admin Charlene Kinnelly.
Licensure Intermediate Care for Mentally
Retarded. *Beds* 15. *Certified* Medicaid.

HARTLAND

Sanfield Manor Inc
Main St, Hartland, ME, 04943 (207) 938-4455
Admin Rita R Low. *Medical Dir/Dir of
Nursing* Marion Strickland MD.
Licensure Intermediate Care. *Beds* 47. *Certified* Medicaid.
Staff RNs 1 (ft), 1 (pt); LPNs 3 (ft); Nurses
aides 26 (ft); Activities coordinators 1 (ft);
Social workers 1 (ft).
Facilities Dining room; Physical therapy room;
Laundry room.
Activities Arts and Crafts; Cards; Games; Prayer groups.
Description Facility is dedicated to the individual physical, emotional, and social needs of the
residents.

HOULTON

Crest View Manor Inc
Rt 2, Calais Rd, Houlton, ME, 04730 (207)
532-3498
Admin Cecil Williams. *Medical Dir/Dir of
Nursing* Dr Ted Sussman.
Licensure Intermediate Care; Boarding Care.
Beds ICF 20; Boarding Care 17. *Certified* Medicaid.
Admissions Requirements Medical examination.
Staff RNs 1 (ft), 1 (pt); LPNs 1 (ft); Nurses
aides 10 (ft), 15 (pt); Activities coordinators 1
(ft).
Facilities Activities room; Laundry room.
Activities Arts and Crafts; Cards; Games;
Movies; Shopping trips; Dances/Social or cultural gatherings.

Gardiner Nursing Home Inc
Box 520, Houlton, ME, 04730 (702) 532-3323
Admin Mark A Anderson.
Licensure Intermediate Care. *Beds* 55. *Certified* Medicaid.
Staff RNs 1 (ft); LPNs 4 (ft), 3 (pt); Nurses
aides 30 (ft), 4 (pt); Activities coordinators 1
(ft); Dietitians 1 (pt).
Facilities Dining room; Activities room; Laundry room; Barber/Beauty shop; Library.
Activities Arts and Crafts; Cards; Games;
Reading groups; Prayer groups; Movies; Dances/Social or cultural gatherings.

Houlton Regional Hospital*
20 Hartford St, Houlton, ME, 04730 (207)
532-9471

Admin Bradley C Bean.
Licensure Skilled Care. *Beds* 11. *Certified* Medicaid; Medicare.

Houlton Residential Center*
45 School St, Houlton, ME, 04730 (207)
532-9446
Admin William Barnes.
Licensure Intermediate Care for Mentally
Retarded. *Beds* 34. *Certified* Medicaid.

Madigan Estates
Military St, Houlton, ME, 04730 (207)
532-6593
Admin Brenda L Brown.
Licensure Intermediate Care. *Beds* 50. *Certified* Medicaid.
Admissions Requirements Medical examination.
Staff Physicians 8 (pt); RNs 3 (ft), 1 (pt); LPNs
6 (ft); Nurses aides 25 (ft); Physical therapists 1
(pt); Reality therapists 1 (pt); Recreational therapists 1 (ft); Speech therapists 1 (pt); Activities
coordinators 1 (pt); Dietitians 1 (pt); Dentists 1
(pt); Ophthalmologists 1 (pt); Podiatrists 1 (pt);
Audiologists 1 (pt).
Facilities Dining room; Activities room; Laundry room; Barber/Beauty shop.
Activities Arts and Crafts; Cards; Games;
Reading groups; Prayer groups; Movies; Shopping trips; Dances/Social or cultural gatherings.

Park Street Group Home*
7 Park St, Houlton, ME, 04730 (207) 532-7150
Admin Mary Carbone.
Licensure Intermediate Care for Mentally
Retarded. *Beds* 6.

HOWLAND

Riverview Nursing Home Inc*
River St, Howland, ME, 04448 (207) 732-4121
Admin Fern Cummings.
Licensure Intermediate Care. *Beds* 35. *Certified* Medicaid.

ISLAND FALLS

Green Valley Group Home*
Box 127, Sewall St, Island Falls, ME, 04747
(207) 463-2156
Admin Dale Lowe.
Licensure Intermediate Care for Mentally
Retarded. *Beds* 6. *Certified* Medicaid.

JACKMAN

Jackman Region Health Center
HCR 64, Box 155, Jackman, ME, 04945-9609
(207) 668-2691
Admin Ralph Gabarro. *Medical Dir/Dir of
Nursing* Neil Karsen MD.
Licensure Intermediate Care. *Beds* 18. *Certified* Medicaid.
Staff Physicians 1 (ft); RNs 1 (ft), 3 (pt); LPNs
1 (ft), 2 (pt); Nurses aides 4 (ft), 11 (pt);
Physical therapists 1 (pt); Activities coordinators 1 (pt); Dietitians 1 (pt).
Languages French
Facilities Dining room; Activities room; Laundry room; Barber/Beauty shop; Library.

Activities Cards; Games; Prayer groups;
Movies; Shopping trips; Dances/Social or cultural gatherings; Senior citizen events.
Description Senior citizen bus available for
local senior citizen activities; bilingual facility
(French and English).

Northland Manor
Main St, Jackman, ME, 04945 (207) 668-3221
Admin George R Petty.
Licensure Intermediate Care for Mentally
Retarded. *Beds* 25.
Admissions Requirements Minimum age 18;
Medical examination.
Staff RNs 1 (ft); LPNs 3 (ft); Nurses aides 10
(ft), 3 (pt); Activities coordinators 1 (ft); Dietitians 1 (pt).
Facilities Dining room; Activities room; Laundry room.
Activities Arts and Crafts; Cards; Games;
Reading groups; Prayer groups; Movies; Shopping trips.
Description Northland Manor receives, cares
for, and has active programs for the profoundly
retarded.

JONESPORT

Resthaven Nursing Home Inc*
Ocean St, Jonesport, ME, 04649 (207)
497-2363
Admin Peter Marshall.
Licensure Intermediate Care. *Beds* 22. *Certified* Medicaid.

KENNEBUNK

Beach Wood
77 Brown St, Kennebunk, ME, 04043 (207)
985-7959
Admin Karen Miller.
Licensure Intermediate Care for Mentally
Retarded. *Beds* 6.
Admissions Requirements Medical examination.
Staff RNs 1 (pt); Physical therapists 1 (pt);
Occupational therapists 1 (pt); Speech therapists 1 (pt); Activities coordinators 1 (ft); Dietitians 1 (pt).
Facilities Dining room; Laundry room.
Activities Arts and Crafts; Games; Movies;
Shopping trips; Dances/Social or cultural gatherings.
Description Facility is an intermediate care
facility for mentally retarded adults. All attend
day programs; each has an individual program
plan reviewed by an interdisciplinary team
quarterly (or more often if necessary) and each
has a primary trainer whose responsibility
includes monitoring these plans.

Kennebunk Nursing Home Inc
Ross Rd, Kennebunk, ME, 04043 (207)
985-7141
Admin Patricia Small.
Licensure Intermediate Care. *Beds* 70. *Certified* Medicaid.
Admissions Requirements Medical examination; Physician's request.
Staff RNs 3 (ft), 4 (pt); LPNs 2 (ft), 3 (pt);
Nurses aides 17 (ft), 16 (pt); Physical therapists

1 (pt); Recreational therapists 1 (ft); Speech therapists 1 (pt); Activities coordinators 1 (ft); Dietitians 1 (pt); Podiatrists 1 (pt).
Facilities Dining room; Physical therapy room; Activities room; Crafts room; Laundry room; Barber/Beauty shop; Library.
Activities Arts and Crafts; Cards; Games; Reading groups; Prayer groups; Movies; Shopping trips.

KITTERY

Homestead
US Rt 1, Kittery, ME, 03904 (207) 439-2100
Admin David Sowerby. *Medical Dir/Dir of Nursing* Dr William Gilbert.
Licensure Intermediate Care. *Beds* 56. *Certified* Medicaid.
Admissions Requirements Minimum age 55; Medical examination.
Staff RNs 2 (ft), 2 (pt); LPNs 2 (ft), 3 (pt); Orderlies 1 (pt); Nurses aides 13 (ft), 17 (pt); Physical therapists; Reality therapists 1 (ft); Occupational therapists; Speech therapists; Activities coordinators 1 (ft); Social workers 1 (ft).
Facilities Dining room; Activities room; Barber/Beauty shop.
Activities Arts and Crafts; Prayer groups; Movies; Shopping trips; Dances/Social or cultural gatherings; Happy hour; Church service; Bingo; Cooking club; Exercise.

LEWISTON

d'Youville Pavilion Nursing Home
102 Campus Ave, Lewiston, ME, 04240 (207) 783-1471
Admin Sr Yvonne Pouliout. *Medical Dir/Dir of Nursing* Dr Betty Keneddy.
Licensure Intermediate Care. *Beds* 280. *Certified* Medicaid.
Admissions Requirements Minimum age 16; Medical examination.
Staff Physicians 1 (pt); RNs 11 (ft), 9 (pt); LPNs 17 (ft), 4 (pt); Nurses aides 1 (ft), 1 (pt); Nurses aides 88 (ft), 119 (pt); Physical therapists 1 (pt); Recreational therapists 3 (ft); Occupational therapists 1 (pt); Speech therapists 1 (pt); Activities coordinators 1 (ft); Dietitians 1 (ft); Podiatrists 1 (pt).
Affiliation Roman Catholic
Facilities Dining room; Physical therapy room; Activities room; Chapel; Crafts room; Laundry room; Barber/Beauty shop; Library.
Activities Arts and Crafts; Cards; Games; Reading groups; Prayer groups; Movies; Shopping trips; Dances/Social or cultural gatherings.

Good Shepherd Health Care Facility*
67 Webster St, Lewiston, ME, 04240 (207) 782-3922
Admin Sarto Sasseville.
Licensure Intermediate Care. *Beds* 20. *Certified* Medicaid.

Marshwood Health Care Facility*
Roger Ave, Lewiston, ME, 04240 (207) 784-0108

Admin Barbara Barker.
Licensure Intermediate Care. *Beds* 120. *Certified* Medicaid.

Montello Manor Nursing Home
540 College St, Lewiston, ME, 04240 (207) 783-2039
Admin Doris L Orestis. *Medical Dir/Dir of Nursing* John Mendros.
Licensure Skilled Care; Intermediate Care. *Beds* SNF 71; ICF 72. *Certified* Medicaid; Medicare.
Staff Physicians 1 (pt); RNs 15 (ft), 5 (pt); LPNs 9 (ft), 2 (pt); Orderlies 3 (ft), 1 (pt); Nurses aides 30 (ft), 20 (pt); Physical therapists 2 (pt); Occupational therapists 1 (pt); Speech therapists 1 (pt); Activities coordinators 2 (pt); Dietitians 1 (pt); Dentists 1 (pt); Ophthalmologists 1 (pt); Podiatrists 1 (pt); Audiologists 1 (pt).
Facilities Dining room; Physical therapy room; Activities room; Crafts room; Laundry room; Barber/Beauty shop.
Activities Arts and Crafts; Cards; Games; Reading groups; Prayer groups; Movies; Shopping trips; Dances/Social or cultural gatherings; Newsletter.
Description Facility is all on one floor. Several patient rooms available with living rooms and patios.

Russell Park Manor*
158–178 Russell St, Lewiston, ME, 04240 (207) 786-0691
Admin Maurice Labbe.
Licensure Skilled Care; Intermediate Care. *Beds* 30; ICF 90.

Saint Casimir Health Care Facility
69 Horton St, Lewiston, ME, 04240 (207) 784-5273
Admin Charles Cook.
Licensure Intermediate Care. *Beds* 21. *Certified* Medicaid.
Staff LPNs 3 (ft), 2 (pt); Nurses aides 7 (ft), 5 (pt); Activities coordinators 1 (ft).
Affiliation Roman Catholic
Facilities Dining room; Activities room; Crafts room; Laundry room.
Activities Arts and Crafts; Cards; Games; Prayer groups; Movies; Shopping trips; Dances/Social or cultural gatherings; Various outings.
Description St Casimir Health Care Facility (due partly because building was once a family residence) does offer a very home-like atmosphere. We are very orientated to meeting individual and group needs. We are proud of the involvement of family and friends of the residents. Besides having a wide variety of activities, our activities director has developed a very extensive exercise program which has been very well accepted and participated in by the residents.

LINCOLN

Colonial Acres Nursing Home
Workman Terrace, Lincoln, ME, 04457 (207) 794-6534
Admin R Eugene Libby. *Medical Dir/Dir of Nursing* Bourcard Nesin MD.
Licensure Intermediate Care. *Beds* 78. *Certi-*

fied Medicaid.
Admissions Requirements Medical examination; Physician's request.
Staff RNs 3 (ft), 3 (pt); LPNs 4 (ft), 2 (pt); Nurses aides 23 (ft), 25 (pt); Activities coordinators 1 (ft).
Facilities Dining room; Physical therapy room; Activities room; Chapel; Crafts room; Laundry room; Barber/Beauty shop.
Activities Arts and Crafts; Cards; Games; Reading groups; Prayer groups; Movies; Shopping trips; Dances/Social or cultural gatherings.
Description The facility is located in beautiful surroundings atop a hill overlooking town, lakes, and Mt Katahdin with well maintained lawns and flowers. A home-like atmosphere is provided within colonial brick and white pillar facility. Staff works well with one another for the comfort and ease of residents.

LISBON FALLS

Lamp Nursing Home
Lisbon Rd, Lisbon Falls, ME, 04252 (207) 353-4318
Admin Shirley Quinlan. *Medical Dir/Dir of Nursing* Joseph M Mendes MD.
Licensure Intermediate Care. *Beds* 37. *Certified* Medicaid.
Admissions Requirements Medical examination.
Staff RNs 3 (ft); LPNs 1 (pt); Nurses aides 13 (ft), 6 (pt); Physical therapists; Speech therapists; Activities coordinators 1 (ft); Dietitians 1 (pt); Dentists; Podiatrists.
Facilities Dining room; Activities room; Crafts room; Barber/Beauty shop; Library.
Activities Arts and Crafts; Cards; Games; Reading groups; Prayer groups; Movies; Shopping trips; Dances/Social or cultural gatherings.

LIVERMORE FALLS

Pomeroy Hill Nursing Home
Firoica Rd, Livermore Falls, ME, 04254 (207) 897-6748
Admin Arthur Upton. *Medical Dir/Dir of Nursing* Dr Joseph DeGrinney.
Licensure Intermediate Care. *Beds* 60. *Certified* Medicaid.
Staff RNs 5 (ft), 2 (pt); LPNs 3 (ft), 4 (pt); Nurses aides 17 (ft), 17 (pt); Physical therapists 1 (pt); Reality therapists 1 (ft); Recreational therapists 1 (ft); Occupational therapists 1 (pt); Activities coordinators 1 (ft); Dietitians 1 (pt); Podiatrists 1 (pt).
Facilities Dining room; Physical therapy room; Activities room; Crafts room; Laundry room; Barber/Beauty shop.
Activities Arts and Crafts; Cards; Games; Reading groups; Prayer groups; Movies; Shopping trips; Dances/Social or cultural gatherings; Outside trips.
Description Facility has outdoor covered patio overlooking duck pond; individual living rooms for every 4 rooms; specializes in reality therapy and pet therapy.

LUBEC

Oceanview Nursing Home
48 Washington St, Lubec, ME, 04652 (207) 733-4374
Admin Margaret Brown. *Medical Dir/Dir of Nursing* Dr Robert G MacBride.
Licensure Intermediate Care. *Beds* 50. *Certified* Medicaid.
Admissions Requirements Physician's request.
Staff Physicians 1 (ft); RNs 2 (ft); LPNs 3 (ft), 1 (pt); Orderlies 1 (ft); Physical therapists 1 (pt); Activities coordinators 1 (ft); Dietitians 1 (pt); Podiatrists 1 (pt).
Facilities Dining room; Activities room; Barber/Beauty shop.
Activities Arts and Crafts; Cards; Games; Reading groups; Prayer groups; Movies; Shopping trips; Dances/Social or cultural gatherings; Potluck dinners with families; Picnics; Restaurant dinners.
Description Facility overlooks the ocean; the warm, loving, sensitive care-givers provide residents with a home away from home. Rehabilitation and restorative care set the priority to facilitate each resident reaching maximum potential and function as independently as possible.

MACHIAS

Marshall Health Care Facility
High St Ext, Machias, ME, 04654 (207) 255-3387
Admin Vaughn Marshall. *Medical Dir/Dir of Nursing* Karl V Larson MD.
Licensure Intermediate Care. *Beds* 62. *Certified* Medicaid.
Admissions Requirements Medical examination.
Staff Physicians 4 (pt); RNs 4 (ft), 3 (pt); LPNs 2 (ft), 1 (pt); Nurses aides 42 (ft).
Facilities Dining room; Activities room; Chapel; Crafts room; Laundry room; Barber/Beauty shop; Library.
Activities Arts and Crafts; Cards; Games; Reading groups; Prayer groups; Movies.
Description Facility is located in Machias, Maine, a small village in "down east" Maine. University of Maine campus is nearby. Facility is only 5 years old with spacious grounds.

MADAWASKA

Highview Manor*
40 Riverview St, Madawaska, ME, 04756 (207) 728-3338
Admin George Dugal.
Licensure Intermediate Care. *Beds* 78. *Certified* Medicaid.

MADISON

Maplecrest Center Inc*
174 Main St, Madison, ME, 04950 (207) 696-3033
Admin Donald Currier.
Licensure Intermediate Care. *Beds* 58. *Certified* Medicaid.

MARS HILL

Aroostook Health Center
Highland Ave, Mars Hill, ME, 04758 (207) 768-4900
Admin Paul H Schreiber. *Medical Dir/Dir of Nursing* Eric Nicolas MD.
Licensure Skilled Care; Intermediate Care. *Beds* SNF 14; ICF 50. *Certified* Medicaid; Medicare.
Staff Physicians 2 (ft); RNs 2 (ft), 3 (pt); LPNs 7 (ft), 8 (pt); Nurses aides 17 (ft), 37 (pt); Physical therapists 1 (ft); Occupational therapists 1 (pt); Speech therapists 1 (pt); Activities coordinators 1 (ft), 1 (pt); Dietitians 1 (ft).
Facilities Dining room; Physical therapy room; Activities room; Barber/Beauty shop.
Activities Arts and Crafts; Cards; Games; Reading groups; Prayer groups; Shopping trips; Dances/Social or cultural gatherings.
Description Beautiful setting overlooking the mountains and the ski slope in Mars Hill.

MILBRIDGE

Marchalin
Main St, Milbridge, ME, 04658 (207) 546-2371
Admin Janice G Dyer. *Medical Dir/Dir of Nursing* Carl Aselton MD.
Licensure Intermediate Care. *Beds* 65. *Certified* Medicaid.
Admissions Requirements Medical examination.
Staff RNs 1 (ft); LPNs 2 (ft), 6 (pt); Orderlies 1 (pt); Nurses aides 12 (ft), 20 (pt); Physical therapists; Speech therapists; Activities coordinators 1 (ft); Dietitians.
Facilities Dining room; Physical therapy room; Activities room; Crafts room; Laundry room; Barber/Beauty shop.
Activities Arts and Crafts; Cards; Games; Reading groups; Prayer groups; Movies; Shopping trips; Dances/Social or cultural gatherings.

MILLINOCKET

Kathahdin Nursing Home*
22 Walnut St, Millinocket, ME, 04462 (207) 723-4711
Admin Michael Cyr.
Licensure Intermediate Care. *Beds* 50. *Certified* Medicaid.

MINOT

Woodman Hill ICF/MR
PO Box 87, Minot, ME, 04258 (207) 345-9752
Admin Bryan Erskine.
Licensure Intermediate Care for Mentally Retarded. *Beds* 6. *Certified* Medicaid.
Admissions Requirements Minimum age 20.
Staff Physicians 1 (pt); RNs 1 (pt); Nurses aides 5 (ft), 5 (pt).
Facilities Dining room; Activities room; Crafts room; Laundry room.
Activities Arts and Crafts; Cards; Games; Shopping trips; Dances/Social or cultural gatherings.
Description Woodman Hilll is a behavior stabilization facility for mentally retarded adults in

the severe-profound range. Behavior modificaton programs are used, and some include aversive techniques for dangerous behavior.

NORTH BERWICK

North Berwick Nursing Home*
Elm St, North Berwick, ME, 03906 (207) 676-2242
Admin Frances Lacourse.
Licensure Intermediate Care. *Beds* 48. *Certified* Medicaid.

NORTH VASSALBORO

Volmer Nursing Home Inc
Rt 1, Box 1190, North Vassalboro, ME, 04962 (207) 872-6089
Admin Roland E Drovin.
Licensure Intermediate Care. *Beds* 32. *Certified* Medicaid.
Staff RNs 1 (ft); LPNs 2 (ft); Nurses aides 9 (ft), 6 (pt); Activities coordinators 1 (ft); Dietitians 1 (ft), 1 (pt).
Facilities Dining room; Activities room; Crafts room; Laundry room; Barber/Beauty shop; Library.
Activities Arts and Crafts; Cards; Games; Prayer groups; Shopping trips.

NORTH WINDHAM

Ledgewood Manor*
Rt 115, Box 760, North Windham, ME, 04062 (702) 892-2261
Admin Edison Bennett.
Licensure Intermediate Care. *Beds* 60. *Certified* Medicaid.

NORWAY

Norway Nursing Home
Marion Ave, Norway, ME, 04268 (207) 743-7075
Admin Julie Hermans.
Licensure Intermediate Care. *Beds* 70. *Certified* Medicaid.
Admissions Requirements Minimum age 16; Medical examination.
Staff RNs 4 (ft), 2 (pt); LPNs 3 (ft), 3 (pt); Nurses aides 15 (ft), 23 (pt); Physical therapists 1 (pt); Activities coordinators 1 (ft), 1 (pt); Dietitians 1 (pt).
Facilities Dining room; Physical therapy room; Activities room; Laundry room; Barber/Beauty shop.
Activities Arts and Crafts; Cards; Games; Reading groups; Prayer groups; Movies; Shopping trips; Dances/Social or cultural gatherings.

OLD ORCHARD BEACH

Elms Residence Nursing Home
28 Portland Ave, Old Orchard Beach, ME, 04604 (207) 934-2174
Admin Roger Painchaud.
Licensure Intermediate Care. *Beds* 26. *Certified* Medicaid.
Staff RNs 3 (ft); LPNs 2 (ft); Nurses aides 6

(ft), 10 (pt); Activities coordinators 1 (ft).
Facilities Dining room; Activities room; Crafts room; Laundry room.
Activities Arts and Crafts; Cards; Games; Reading groups; Movies; Dances/Social or cultural gatherings.

ORONO

Orono Nursing Home Inc
Bennoch Rd, Orono, ME, 04473 (207) 866-4914
Admin William Shirley. *Medical Dir/Dir of Nursing* Michael Bruehl MD.
Licensure Skilled Care; Intermediate Care.
Beds SNF 12; ICF 60. *Certified* Medicaid; Medicare.
Staff Physicians 6 (pt); RNs 10 (ft), 6 (pt); LPNs 1 (ft), 2 (pt); Nurses aides 30 (ft), 25 (pt); Physical therapists 1 (pt); Activities coordinators 1 (ft), 1 (pt); Dietitians 1 (pt); Podiatrists 1 (pt).
Facilities Dining room; Physical therapy room; Activities room; Laundry room; Barber/Beauty shop.
Activities Arts and Crafts; Cards; Games; Reading groups; Prayer groups; Movies; Shopping trips; Dances/Social or cultural gatherings.
Description Facility features a lovely rural setting, landscaped lawns, flowers, and an outstanding activity program emphasizing quality of life involvement and satisfaction.

Treats Falls
2 Hill St, Orono, ME, 04473 (207) 866-3769
Admin R Valentine.
Licensure Intermediate Care for Mentally Retarded. *Beds* 20. *Certified* Medicaid.
Admissions Requirements Minimum age 18; Medical examination.
Staff Physicians 1 (pt); RNs 1 (pt); LPNs 1 (pt); Nurses aides 23 (ft); Physical therapists 1 (pt); Occupational therapists 1 (pt); Activities coordinators 1 (pt); Dietitians 1 (pt).
Facilities Dining room; Activities room; Crafts room; Laundry room.
Activities Arts and Crafts; Cards; Games; Movies; Shopping trips; Dances/Social or cultural gatherings.

ORRINGTON

Orrington Group Home*
Rt 15, Orrington, ME, 04474 (207) 825-3557
Admin Melinda Ward.
Licensure Intermediate Care for Mentally Retarded. *Beds* 6. *Certified* Medicaid.

PARSONFIELD

Greenhill Farm
Old Middle Rd, Parsonfield, ME, 04005 (207) 625-8644
Admin Doug DuBois.
Licensure Intermediate Care for Mentally Retarded. *Beds* 6.
Admissions Requirements Minimum age 18; Medical examination; Physician's request.
Staff RNs; Activities coordinators 1 (ft).
Facilities Dining room; Activities room; Crafts room; Laundry room.

Activities Arts and Crafts; Cards; Games; Reading groups; Shopping trips; Dances/Social or cultural gatherings.
Description Greenhill Farm is located in rural north Parsonfield, overlooking the White Mountains. The farm has 6 acres of land, a barn, and a basketball court. Provides developmentally disabled persons an opportunity for personal development and growth, privacy, enhancement of self-esteem and dignity, within a home-like environment.

PATTEN

Resthaven Nursing Home
Houlton St, Patten, ME, 04765 (207) 528-2200
Admin Justine Michaud. *Medical Dir/Dir of Nursing* Ronald Blum.
Licensure Intermediate Care. *Beds* 25. *Certified* Medicaid.
Staff RNs 1 (ft), 2 (pt); LPNs 2 (pt); Nurses aides 3 (ft), 4 (pt); Activities coordinators 1 (ft); Dietitians 1 (pt); Audiologists 5 (ft), 2 (pt).
Facilities Dining room; Activities room; Laundry room.
Activities Arts and Crafts; Cards; Games; Prayer groups; Movies; Shopping trips.

PENOBSCOT

Penobscot Nursing Home
Main St, Penobscot, ME, 04476 (207) 326-4344
Admin Wendell Dennison. *Medical Dir/Dir of Nursing* Dr Walker.
Licensure Intermediate Care. *Beds* 91. *Certified* Medicaid.
Staff RNs 2 (ft); LPNs 6 (ft); Nurses aides 26 (ft); Physical therapists 1 (pt); Activities coordinators 1 (ft), 1 (pt).
Facilities Dining room; Activities room; Crafts room; Laundry room; Barber/Beauty shop.
Activities Arts and Crafts; Cards; Games; Reading groups; Prayer groups; Movies; Shopping trips; Wine therapy.
Description Modern low-cost facility with the largest nursing home solar hot water system in the state.

PITTSFIELD

Pittsfield Convalescent Center*
Leighton St, Pittsfield, ME, 04967 (207) 487-3182
Admin Pamela Meservey.
Licensure Intermediate Care. *Beds* 30. *Certified* Medicaid.

Sebasticook Valley Health Care Facility
Leighton St, Pittsfield, ME, 04967 (207) 487-3131
Admin Carey C Davis.
Licensure Intermediate Care. *Beds* 64. *Certified* Medicaid.
Admissions Requirements Physician's request.
Staff RNs 2 (ft), 1 (pt); LPNs 5 (ft), 1 (pt); Nurses aides 25 (ft), 13 (pt); Activities coordinators 1 (ft).
Facilities Dining room; Activities room; Laundry room; Barber/Beauty shop; Library.

Activities Arts and Crafts; Cards; Games; Reading groups; Prayer groups; Movies; Shopping trips; Dances/Social or cultural gatherings.

PORTLAND

Barron Center
1145 Brighton Ave, Portland, ME, 04102 (207) 774-2623
Admin Anthony Forgione. *Medical Dir/Dir of Nursing* Benjamin Zolou MD.
Licensure Skilled Care; Intermediate Care.
Beds SNF 20; ICF 160. *Certified* Medicaid; Medicare.
Admissions Requirements Medical examination; Physician's request.
Staff Physicians 4 (ft); RNs 16 (ft); LPNs 12 (ft); Nurses aides 78 (ft); Physical therapists 4 (ft); Recreational therapists 3 (ft); Occupational therapists 1 (pt); Speech therapists 1 (pt); Dietitians 1 (pt); Dentists 1 (pt); Ophthalmologists 1 (pt); Podiatrists 2 (pt).
Facilities Dining room; Physical therapy room; Activities room; Chapel; Crafts room; Laundry room; Barber/Beauty shop.
Activities Arts and Crafts; Cards; Games; Reading groups; Prayer groups; Movies; Shopping trips; Dances/Social or cultural gatherings.
Description Facility has been city-owned and operated for 80 years. Features a new physical plant, front park with pond, fountain and gazebo; in-house laboratory and radiology units; organized medical staff.

Devonshire Manor*
68 Devonshire St, Portland, ME, 04101 (207) 772-2893
Admin Betty Edwards.
Licensure Intermediate Care. *Beds* 149. *Certified* Medicaid.

Emery Street Community Residence*
72 Emery St, Portland, ME, 04103 (207) 772-6332
Admin Jean Millen.
Licensure Intermediate Care for Mentally Retarded. *Beds* 6. *Certified* Medicaid.

Jewish Home for the Aged*
158 North St, Portland, ME, 04101 (207) 772-5456
Admin C Gail MacLean.
Licensure Skilled Care; Intermediate Care.
Beds SNF 18; ICF 70. *Certified* Medicaid; Medicare.
Affiliation Jewish

Saint Joseph's Manor*
1133 Washington Ave, Portland, ME, 04101 (207) 797-0600
Admin Ronald Tardif.
Licensure Intermediate Care. *Beds* 200. *Certified* Medicaid.

Seaside Nursing and Retirement Home*
850 Baxter Blvd, Portland, ME, 04101 (207) 774-7878
Admin Eleanor Matterson.
Licensure Skilled Care; Intermediate Care.
Beds SNF 38; ICF 76. *Certified* Medicaid.

Woodfords Group Home I*
342 Woodfords St, Portland, ME, 04103 (207)
773-3557
Admin Melvin Richards.
Licensure Intermediate Care for Mentally
Retarded. *Beds* 6. *Certified* Medicaid.

Woodfords Group Home II*
388 Woodfords St, Portland, ME, 04103 (207)
774-3331
Admin Melvin Richards.
Licensure Intermediate Care for Mentally
Retarded. *Beds* 4. *Certified* Medicaid.

POWNAL

Pineland Center*
PO Box C, Pownal, ME, 04069 (207) 688-4811
Admin George Zitnay.
Licensure Intermediate Care for Mentally
Retarded. *Beds* 340. *Certified* Medicaid.

PRESQUE ISLE

Presque Isle Nursing Home Inc*
162 Academy St, Presque Isle, ME, 04769 (207)
764-0145
Admin Albert G Cyr.
Licensure Intermediate Care. *Beds* 82. *Certified* Medicaid.

RICHMOND

Walton Nursing Home
67 S Front St, Richmond, ME, 04357 (207)
737-4371
Admin Barbara Walton.
Licensure Intermediate Care. *Beds* 18. *Certified* Medicaid.

ROCKLAND

Knox Division—Intermediate Care Facility
2 Maple St, Rockland, ME, 04841 (207)
594-2841
Admin Alan S Kinne. *Medical Dir/Dir of
Nursing* David Bradeen MD.
Licensure Intermediate Care. *Beds* 44. *Certified* Medicaid.
Admissions Requirements Medical examination.
Staff RNs 2 (ft), 4 (pt); LPNs 2 (pt); Nurses
aides 6 (ft), 21 (pt); Recreational therapists 1
(ft).
Facilities Dining room; Physical therapy room;
Activities room; Crafts room; Laundry room;
Barber/Beauty shop.
Activities Arts and Crafts; Cards; Games; Prayer groups; Movies; Shopping trips; Dances/Social or cultural gatherings.
Description Facility has an outside screened-in
building where residents have meals and activities during the summer; active resident council;
CNA restorative aide 5 days per week.

Rockland Convalescent Center*
201 Camden St, Rockland, ME, 04841 (207)
596-6423

Admin Paul L Gerry.
Licensure Intermediate Care. *Beds* 64. *Certified* Medicaid.

RUMFORD

Cozy Inn Nursing Home
Eaton Hill Rd, Rumford, ME, 04276 (207)
364-7863
Admin John Ford. *Medical Dir/Dir of
Nursing* David Phillips MD.
Licensure Intermediate Care. *Beds* 57. *Certified* Medicaid.
Staff RNs 6 (ft); LPNs 3 (ft); Nurses aides 27
(ft); Activities coordinators 1 (ft); Dietitians 1
(pt).
Facilities Dining room; Activities room; Chapel; Crafts room; Laundry room; Barber/Beauty
shop.
Activities Arts and Crafts; Cards; Games; Prayer groups; Movies.
Description Facility features a brick veneer
building situated in the Appalachian Mountains in Maine overlooking the Androscoggin
River with a beautiful view of the river and Mt
Zircon on the southern side.

SACO

Beane Nursing Home
15 Nott St, Saco, ME, 04072 (207) 284-6443
Admin Robert R Goodrow. *Medical Dir/Dir of
Nursing* Andre Fortier MD.
Licensure Intermediate Care. *Beds* 15. *Certified* Medicaid.
Admissions Requirements Medical examination; Physician's request.
Staff RNs 1 (ft), 1 (pt); LPNs 2 (ft), 3 (pt);
Nurses aides 5 (ft), 3 (pt); Activities coordinators 1 (pt); Dietitians 1 (ft), 2 (pt).
Facilities Dining room; Physical therapy room;
Activities room; Chapel; Crafts room; Laundry
room; Barber/Beauty shop; Library.
Activities Arts and Crafts; Cards; Games;
Reading groups; Prayer groups; Movies; Shopping trips; Dances/Social or cultural gatherings.
Description Established in 1944, the Home is a
small facility whose total staff have the empathy to care for the residents' needs 24 hours a
day. The home has remained a very personal
and family oriented facility with flexible visiting hours.

Evergreen Manor
328 North St, Saco, ME, 04072 (207) 282-5161
Admin Robert E Wolter. *Medical Dir/Dir of
Nursing* Andre Fortier MD.
Licensure Intermediate Care. *Beds* 42. *Certified* Medicaid.
Staff RNs 3 (ft), 1 (pt); LPNs 3 (ft), 2 (pt);
Nurses aides 19 (ft), 6 (pt); Recreational therapists 1 (ft); Activities coordinators 1 (ft); Dietitians 1 (pt).
Facilities Dining room; Activities room;
Chapel; Crafts room; Laundry room; Barber/Beauty shop; Library.
Activities Arts and Crafts; Cards; Games;
Reading groups; Prayer groups; Movies; Shopping trips; Dances/Social or cultural gatherings.

SAINT ALBANS

Square Road Farm*
Square Rd, Saint Albans, ME, 04971 (207)
948-2046
Admin Patricia Ross.
Licensure Intermediate Care for Mentally
Retarded. *Beds* 6.

SANFORD

Hillcrest Skilled Care Division
Hillcrest Dr, Sanford, ME, 04073 (207)
324-2056
Admin Peter Booth. *Medical Dir/Dir of
Nursing* Carl E Richards MD.
Licensure Skilled Care; Intermediate Care.
Beds SNF 25; ICF 77. *Certified* Medicaid;
Medicare.
Admissions Requirements Medical examination; Physician's request.
Staff RNs 3 (ft), 6 (pt); LPNs 9 (ft), 8 (pt);
Nurses aides 27 (ft), 12 (pt); Physical therapists
3 (pt); Recreational therapists 1 (ft); Occupational therapists 1 (pt); Speech therapists 1 (pt);
Activities coordinators 1 (ft); Dietitians 1 (pt);
Audiologists 1 (pt).
Facilities Dining room; Physical therapy room;
Activities room; Laundry room; Barber/Beauty
shop.
Activities Arts and Crafts; Cards; Games;
Reading groups; Movies; Shopping trips; Dances/Social or cultural gatherings.
Description Facility features community
bowling, National Audubon Society Club
membership, video disc machine, pool tables,
outside patio, and barbecue facilities.

Maine Stay Nursing Home
291 Main St, Sanford, ME, 04073 (207)
324-7999
Admin Doyle T Sowerby.
Licensure Intermediate Care; Lodging Care.
Beds ICF 45; Lodging Care 11. *Certified* Medicaid.
Staff RNs 3 (ft); LPNs 2 (ft), 2 (pt); Orderlies 1
(ft); Nurses aides 17 (ft); Activities coordinators
1 (ft), 1 (pt); Dietitians 1 (pt); Podiatrists 1 (pt).
Facilities Dining room; Activities room; Chapel; Crafts room; Laundry room; Barber/Beauty
shop.
Activities Arts and Crafts; Cards; Games;
Reading groups; Prayer groups; Movies; Shopping trips; Dances/Social or cultural gatherings.
Description Licensed personnel on duty round
the clock; special diets readily available;
dynamic activity and social service programs.
Facility is within easy walking distance of the
library, senior citizens center, shopping plaza,
theatres, and restaurants.

Sanford Nursing Home*
179 Main St, Sanford, ME, 04073 (207)
324-6818
Admin Doyle Sowerby.
Licensure Intermediate Care. *Beds* 31. *Certified* Medicaid.

SCARBOROUGH

Casa Inc*
148 Gorham Rd, Scarborough, ME, 04074
(207) 883-6333
Admin Anne D Walsh.
Licensure Intermediate Care for Mentally
Retarded. *Beds* 8.

SKOWHEGAN

Cedar Ridge Inc
234 Maidson Ave, Skowhegan, ME, 04976
(207) 474-9686
Admin David Sylvester. *Medical Dir/Dir of
Nursing* Robert Kaschub MD.
Licensure Intermediate Care. *Beds* 50. *Certi-
fied* Medicaid.
Admissions Requirements Medical examina-
tion.
Staff RNs 3 (ft), 1 (pt); LPNs 3 (ft); Nurses
aides 35 (ft); Physical therapists 1 (pt); Recrea-
tional therapists 1 (ft); Activities coordinators 1
(ft); Dietitians 1 (ft).
Facilities Dining room; Physical therapy room;
Activities room; Crafts room; Laundry room;
Barber/Beauty shop.
Activities Arts and Crafts; Cards; Games;
Reading groups; Prayer groups; Movies; Shop-
ping trips; Dances/Social or cultural gatherings.

Woodlawn Nursing Home*
91 W Front St, Skowhegan, ME, 04976 (207)
474-9300
Admin Anthony Belliveau.
Licensure Intermediate Care. *Beds* 50. *Certified* Medicaid.

SOUTH PARIS

Market Square Health Care Facility
Box 280 12 Market Square, South Paris, ME,
04281 (207) 743-7086
Admin Richard H Charloff.
Licensure Intermediate Care. *Beds* 99. *Certi-
fied* Medicaid.
Staff Physicians 6 (pt); RNs 6 (ft); LPNs 12
(ft); Orderlies 42 (ft); Occupational therapists 1
(pt); Speech therapists 1 (pt); Activities coordi-
nators 1 (ft); Dietitians 1 (ft); Dentists 1 (pt);
Ophthalmologists 1 (pt); Podiatrists 1 (pt);
Audiologists 1 (pt).
Facilities Dining room; Physical therapy room;
Activities room; Crafts room; Laundry room;
Library.
Activities Arts and Crafts; Cards; Games;
Reading groups; Prayer groups; Movies; Shop-
ping trips; Dances/Social or cultural gatherings.

SOUTH PORTLAND

Hillside Rest and Nursing Home
161 Preble St, South Portland, ME, 04106 (207)
799-2245
Admin Sarah L MacDuffie. *Medical Dir/Dir of
Nursing* Douglas Hill MD.
Licensure Intermediate Care. *Beds* 18. *Certi-
fied* Medicaid.
Staff RNs 1 (ft); LPNs 2 (ft), 2 (pt); Nurses
aides 4 (ft), 6 (pt); Activities coordinators 1 (pt);
Dietitians 1 (pt); Podiatrists 1 (pt).

Facilities Dining room; Activities room; Crafts
room; Laundry room.
Activities Arts and Crafts; Cards; Games;
Reading groups; Prayer groups; Movies.
Description Facility is in 18-bed home-style setting located on a beautiful, tree-lined street. We
try to maintain a family atmosphere with
home-cooked meals, spacious porches, and
cable television.

Manden Nursing Home
1060 Broadway, South Portland, ME, 04106
(207) 799-1945
Admin Dawn Wursthorne.
Licensure Intermediate Care. *Beds* 10. *Certified* Medicaid.

South Portland Nursing Home Inc*
42 Anthoine St, South Portland, ME, 04106
(207) 799-8561
Admin Donald Johnson.
Licensure Intermediate Care. *Beds* 73. *Certified* Medicaid.

SOUTH WINDHAM

Swampscotta Nursing Home
Rt 302, South Windham, ME, 04082 (207)
892-6922
Admin Florence Y Mayberry. *Medical Dir/Dir
of Nursing* Walter Penta MD.
Licensure Intermediate Care. *Beds* 36. *Certified* Medicaid.

STRONG

Strong Children's Home
Main St, Strong, ME, 04983 (207) 684-3341
Admin Glenna Barden. *Medical Dir/Dir of
Nursing* Mary E Gregor.
Licensure Intermediate Care for Mentally
Retarded. *Beds* 20. *Certified* Medicaid.
Admissions Requirements Medical examina-
tion.
Staff RNs 3 (ft); LPNs 2 (ft), 3 (pt); Nurses
aides 20 (ft), 10 (pt); Physical therapists 1 (pt);
Recreational therapists 1 (pt) 13K 1 (ft).
Facilities Dining room; Physical therapy room;
Activities room; Laundry room.
Activities Arts and Crafts; Games; Reading
groups; Movies; Shopping trips; Dances/Social
or cultural gatherings.
Description The children aged 4-20 attend a
school program run by S.A.D. 58, and the over
20-year-old children attend Sandy River
Rehabilitation program. During the summer
we have a riding therapy program at a nearby
stable and a physical therapy assistant.

SULLIVAN

Maplecrest Nursing Home
Rt 1, Sullivan, ME, 04689 (207) 422-3345
Admin Martha Scott.
Licensure Intermediate Care. *Beds* 34. *Certi-
fied* Medicaid.
Staff RNs 1 (ft), 1 (pt); LPNs 3 (ft), 1 (pt);
Nurses aides 14 (ft); Activities coordinators 1
(ft), 1 (pt).
Facilities Dining room; Activities room; Crafts
room; Laundry room.

Activities Arts and Crafts; Cards; Games;
Reading groups; Prayer groups; Movies; Shopping trips.

TOPSHAM

Amenity Manor*
29 Elm St, Topsham, ME, 04086 (207)
725-7495
Admin Robert Colarusso.
Licensure Intermediate Care. *Beds* 69. *Certified* Medicaid.

Gregory Home
1 Middlesex Rd, Topsham, ME, 04086 (207)
729-8251
Admin Rebecca Murray.
Licensure Intermediate Care for Mentally
Retarded. *Beds* 8. *Certified* Medicaid.
Admissions Requirements Minimum age 18.
Activities Arts and Crafts; Cards; Games;
Reading groups; Prayer groups; Movies; Shop-
ping trips; Dances/Social or cultural gatherings.
Description Facility attempts to meet the indi-
vidual needs of clients rather than forfeit those
needs for the group.

UPPER FRENCHVILLE

Saint Joseph Nursing Home
PO Box K, Upper Frenchville, ME, 04784 (207)
543-6648
Admin Clovis Daigle. *Medical Dir/Dir of
Nursing* Dr Zui Sun Tao.
Licensure Intermediate Care. *Beds* 37. *Certified* Medicaid.
Admissions Requirements Medical examination; Physician's request.
Staff Physicians 1 (pt); RNs 1 (ft), 2 (pt); LPNs
3 (ft), 1 (pt); Orderlies 1 (pt); Nurses aides 12
(ft), 8 (pt); Activities coordinators 1 (pt); Dietitians 1 (ft).
Affiliation Roman Catholic
Facilities Dining room; Activities room; Chapel; Crafts room; Laundry room; Barber/Beauty
shop.
Activities Arts and Crafts; Cards; Games; Prayer groups; Movies; Dances/Social or cultural
gatherings.
Description Facility features recent renovations,
whirlpool, volunteer program, and pet therapy.

VAN BUREN

Borderview Manor
State St, Van Buren, ME, 04785 (207) 868-5211
Admin John B Pelletier. *Medical Dir/Dir of
Nursing* William Chan MD.
Licensure Intermediate Care; Boarding Care.
Beds ICF 82; Boarding Care 36. *Cer-
tified* Medicaid.
Staff RNs 6 (ft), 4 (pt); LPNs 1 (ft), 1 (pt);
Nurses aides 40 (ft), 11 (pt); Activities coordi-
nators 2 (ft); Dietitians 1 (ft); 41 (ft), 10 (pt).
Facilities Dining room; Physical therapy room;
Activities room; Chapel; Crafts room; Laundry
room; Barber/Beauty shop.
Activities Arts and Crafts; Cards; Games;
Reading groups; Prayer groups; Movies; Shop-
ping trips; Dances/Social or cultural gatherings.

WALDOBORO

Fieldcrest Manor Inc
RFD 1, Box 34, Waldoboro, ME, 04572 (207) 832-5343
Admin Wayde Rankin. *Medical Dir/Dir of Nursing* Jack Waterman MD.
Licensure Intermediate Care. *Beds* 70. *Certified* Medicaid.
Staff Physicians 9 (pt); RNs 2 (ft), 2 (pt); LPNs 3 (ft), 2 (pt); Nurses aides 20 (ft), 23 (pt); Activities coordinators 1 (ft); Dietitians 1 (pt); Podiatrists 1 (pt).
Facilities Dining room; Activities room; Laundry room; Barber/Beauty shop.
Activities Arts and Crafts; Games; Prayer groups; Movies; Shopping trips.

WATERVILLE

Colonial House Manor
110 College Ave, Waterville, ME, 04901 (207) 873-0641
Admin Bruce Alexander. *Medical Dir/Dir of Nursing* Joseph Michaud MD and John M Szala DO.
Licensure Intermediate Care. *Beds* 74. *Certified* Medicaid.
Admissions Requirements Medical examination; Physician's request.
Staff Physicians 19 (pt); RNs 2 (ft), 5 (pt); LPNs 2 (ft), 3 (pt); Nurses aides 18 (ft), 20 (pt).
Facilities Dining room; Activities room; Chapel; Crafts room; Laundry room; Barber/Beauty shop; Library.
Activities Arts and Crafts; Cards; Games; Reading groups; Prayer groups; Movies; Shopping trips; Dances/Social or cultural gatherings.

Lakewood Manor
220 Kennedy Memorial Dr, Waterville, ME, 04901 (207) 873-5125
Admin Norma Pearl. *Medical Dir/Dir of Nursing* Dr Stanley Beckerman.
Licensure Intermediate Care. *Beds* 75. *Certified* Medicaid.
Staff Physicians 14 (pt); RNs 5 (ft), 1 (pt); LPNs 4 (ft), 4 (pt); Orderlies 2 (ft); Nurses aides 26 (ft), 5 (pt); Physical therapists 1 (pt); Reality therapists 1 (pt); Recreational therapists 1 (pt); Occupational therapists 1 (pt); Speech therapists 1 (pt); Activities coordinators 1 (ft); Dietitians 1 (pt); Dentists 1 (pt); Ophthalmologists 1 (pt); Podiatrists 1 (pt); Audiologists 1 (pt).
Facilities Dining room; Physical therapy room; Activities room; Chapel; Crafts room; Laundry room; Barber/Beauty shop; Library; Living rooms.
Activities Arts and Crafts; Cards; Games; Reading groups; Prayer groups; Movies; Shopping trips; Dances/Social or cultural gatherings; Bean and cheese parties.
Description Home is in a country-like setting with wooded areas on 3 sides.

Mount Saint Joseph Nursing Home*
Highwood St, Waterville, ME, 04901 (207) 873-0705
Admin Sr Cecile Chagnon.
Licensure Intermediate Care. *Beds* 77. *Certified* Medicaid.

Waterville Convalescent Center*
Cool St, Waterville, ME, 04901 (207) 873-0721
Admin Thelma Cushman.
Licensure Intermediate Care. *Beds* 78. *Certified* Medicaid.

Western Avenue Residence*
101 Western Ave, Waterville, ME, 04901 (207) 872-8195
Admin Donna Moore.
Licensure Intermediate Care for Mentally Retarded. *Beds* 6.

WEST PARIS

Ledgeview Memorial Homeᴬ
West Paris, ME, 04289 (207) 674-2250
Admin Lawrence Wilday. *Medical Dir/Dir of Nursing* Thomas Nangle MD.
Licensure Intermediate Care. *Beds* 124. *Certified* Medicaid.
Admissions Requirements Medical examination; Physician's request.
Staff RNs 2 (ft), 5 (pt); LPNs 8 (ft), 4 (pt); Orderlies 1 (ft); Nurses aides 34 (ft), 27 (pt); Physical therapists 1 (pt); Speech therapists 1 (pt); Activities coordinators 2 (ft); Dietitians 1 (pt); Dentists 1 (pt); Podiatrists 1 (pt); Audiologists 1 (pt).
Affiliation Seventh-Day Adventist
Facilities Dining room; Physical therapy room; Activities room; Chapel; Crafts room; Laundry room; Barber/Beauty shop; Library; Dental.
Activities Arts and Crafts; Cards; Games; Reading groups; Prayer groups; Movies; Shopping trips; Dances/Social or cultural gatherings; Day trips; Cookouts.

WEST SCARBOROUGH

Pine Point Manor*
Pine Point Rd, West Scarborough, ME, 04074 (207) 883-2468
Admin Beverly Malpass.
Licensure Intermediate Care. *Beds* 62. *Certified* Medicaid.

WINTHROP

Heritage Home
Rt 3, Old Lewiston Rd, Winthrop, ME, 04364 (207) 377-8453
Admin Richard Merrill. *Medical Dir/Dir of Nursing* Dr R E Barron.
Licensure Intermediate Care. *Beds* 56. *Certified* Medicaid.
Staff RNs 2 (ft), 6 (pt); LPNs 2 (ft), 3 (pt); Nurses aides 17 (ft), 15 (pt); Recreational therapists 1 (ft), 1 (pt); Activities coordinators 1 (ft), 1 (pt); Dietitians 1 (pt).
Facilities Dining room; Activities room; Laundry room; Barber/Beauty shop; Library.
Activities Arts and Crafts; Cards; Games; Reading groups; Prayer groups; Movies; Shopping trips; Dances/Social or cultural gatherings.
Description Facility offers rural early American setting and decor; practices restorative nursing; provides the kind of quality care each resident requires.

Nicholson's Nursing Home*
11 Western Ave, Winthrop, ME, 04364 (207) 377-8184
Admin Geraldine Nicholson.
Licensure Intermediate Care. *Beds* 45. *Certified* Medicaid.

YARMOUTH

Brentwood Manor*
122 Portland St, Yarmouth, ME, 04096 (207) 846-9021
Admin William Cullen.
Licensure Intermediate Care. *Beds* 73. *Certified* Medicaid.

Coastal Manor*
10 W Main St, Yarmouth, ME, 04096 (207) 846-5013
Admin Georgene Marshall.
Licensure Intermediate Care. *Beds* 46. *Certified* Medicaid.

YORK

York Hospital—Henry Stratter Extended Care Wing*
15 Hospital Dr, York, ME, 03909 (207) 363-4321
Admin Jud Knox.
Licensure Skilled Care. *Beds* 18. *Certified* Medicaid; Medicare.

YORK HARBOR

Harbor Home
Norwood Farms Rd, York Harbor, ME, 03911 (207) 363-2422
Admin Daniel Sowerby.
Licensure Intermediate Care. *Beds* 79. *Certified* Medicaid.

MARYLAND

ADELPHI

Adelphi Manor*
1801 Metzerott Rd, Adelphi, MD, 20783 (301) 434-0500
Admin George Vascellaro. *Medical Dir/Dir of Nursing* Paul DeVore MD.
Licensure Skilled Care; Intermediate Care.
Beds 218. *Certified* Medicaid; Medicare.
Ownership Proprietary.

Hillhaven Nursing Home
3210 Powder Mill Rd, Adelphi, MD, 20783 (301) 937-3939
Admin Joyce A Malin. *Medical Dir/Dir of Nursing* Robert Irey MD.
Licensure Intermediate Care. *Beds* 18. *Certified* Medicaid.
Ownership Proprietary.
Staff RNs 1 (ft), 4 (pt); LPNs 6 (pt); Nurses aides 3 (ft), 8 (pt); Physical therapists 1 (pt); Recreational therapists 1 (pt); Occupational therapists; Speech therapists; Activities coordinators 1 (pt); Dietitians; Dentists; Podiatrists.
Facilities Dining room; Activities room.
Activities Arts and Crafts; Cards; Games; Prayer groups; Movies.
Description Smallness of facility creates extended family between residents and staff. No smoking is allowed and no pork products are served.

ANNAPOLIS

Annapolis Convalescent Center
Bay Ridge Ave and Van Buren St, Annapolis, MD, 21403 (301) 269-0444
Admin Laurie Davis. *Medical Dir/Dir of Nursing* Richard Hochman MD.
Licensure Skilled Care; Intermediate Care.
Beds 91. *Certified* Medicaid; Medicare.
Ownership Proprietary.
Admissions Requirements Minimum age 54; Medical examination; Physician's request.
Staff Physicians 22 (pt); RNs 3 (ft), 3 (pt); LPNs 5 (ft), 4 (pt); Nurses aides 26 (ft), 16 (pt); Physical therapists 2 (ft), 2 (pt); Speech therapists 1 (pt); Activities coordinators 1 (ft); Dietitians 1 (pt); Dentists 1 (pt); Podiatrists 3 (pt).
Facilities Dining room; Physical therapy room; Activities room; Crafts room; Laundry room; Barber/Beauty shop.
Activities Arts and Crafts; Games; Reading groups; Movies; Shopping trips; Dances/Social

or cultural gatherings.
Description The Annapolis Convalescent Center, due to its small size, is very family oriented. Our home is an extension of the residents' own, and has a good family involvement. Our activities are stimulating and the residents especially enjoy mind benders.

Bay Manor Nursing Home
509 Revell Hwy, Annapolis, MD, 21401 (301) 757-2069
Admin Jean M Buccheri. *Medical Dir/Dir of Nursing* Dr C V Cyriac.
Licensure Intermediate Care. *Beds* 74. *Certified* Medicaid.
Ownership Proprietary.
Staff Physicians 1 (ft); RNs 2 (ft), 4 (pt); LPNs 5 (pt); Nurses aides 28 (ft); Recreational therapists 1 (ft); Activities coordinators 2 (pt).
Facilities Dining room; Activities room; Laundry room; TV room.
Activities Arts and Crafts; Cards; Games; Reading groups; Prayer groups; Movies; Shopping trips; Dances/Social or cultural gatherings; Music; Resident council; Cooking; Exercise.
Description Facility offers pleasant surroundings, home-like atmosphere, special diets, moderate rates, 24-hour professional nursing service.

BALTIMORE

Ardleigh Nursing Home Inc
2095 Rockrose Ave, Baltimore, MD, 21211 (301) 243-7458
Admin Benjamin H Roffman. *Medical Dir/Dir of Nursing* Dr L Kemper Owens.
Licensure Intermediate Care. *Beds* 33. *Certified* Medicaid.
Ownership Proprietary.
Admissions Requirements Minimum age 14; Medical examination.
Staff Physicians; RNs; LPNs; Nurses aides; Activities coordinators; Dietitians.
Activities Arts and Crafts; Cards; Games; Reading groups; Prayer groups; Movies; Shopping trips; Dances/Social or cultural gatherings.
Description Facility is located on a beautiful 2 acre parcel of land, condusive to old manor setting; historical building creates a homey atmosphere. Small patient population adds to the family feeling.

Arlington Baptist Nursing Center
7600 Clays Ln, Baltimore, MD, 21207 (301) 298-1400
Admin Y T Allen. *Medical Dir/Dir of Nursing* Dr Darold Beard.
Licensure Domiciliary Care; Comprehensive Care. *Beds* Domiciliary Care 60; Comprehensive Care 60.
Ownership Nonprofit.
Staff RNs 5 (ft), 3 (pt); LPNs 3 (ft), 1 (pt); Orderlies 1 (ft), 2 (pt); Nurses aides 22 (ft), 13 (pt); Physical therapists; Activities coordinators 1 (ft); Dietitians 1 (ft); Dentists; Ophthalmologists; Podiatrists.
Affiliation Baptist
Facilities Dining room; Activities room; Chapel; Crafts room; Laundry room; Barber/Beauty shop.
Activities Arts and Crafts; Games; Prayer groups; Movies; Shopping trips; Bible study.
Description Very beautiful facility built in 1980, located in a rural setting all on one floor with no steps.

Armacost Nursing Home
812 Regester Ave, Baltimore, MD, 21239 (301) 377-5225
Admin Ira Dennis Greene.
Licensure Intermediate Care. *Beds* 45. *Certified* Medicaid.
Ownership Proprietary.

Ashburton Nursing Home
3520 N Hilton Rd, Baltimore, MD, 21215 (301) 466-2400
Admin Theresa M Kelly. *Medical Dir/Dir of Nursing* Allan H Macht MD.
Licensure Intermediate Care. *Beds* 37. *Certified* Medicaid.
Ownership Proprietary.
Admissions Requirements Minimum age 21; Medical examination; Physician's request.
Staff Physicians 1 (ft); RNs 2 (ft); LPNs 1 (ft), 3 (pt); Nurses aides 7 (ft), 4 (pt); Physical therapists 1 (ft); Reality therapists 1 (ft); Recreational therapists 1 (ft); Speech therapists 1 (pt); Activities coordinators 1 (ft); Dietitians 1 (pt); Dentists 1 (pt); Ophthalmologists 1 (pt); Podiatrists 1 (pt).
Facilities Dining room; Physical therapy room; Activities room; Laundry room.
Activities Arts and Crafts; Cards; Games; Reading groups; Prayer groups; Shopping trips; Dances/Social or cultural gatherings; Outdoor

picnics; Various trips.
Description We are a 37-bed facility situated in a beautiful old converted mansion. We have lovely surroundings (trees, shrubbery, etc.) conducive to lots of outdoor activities for our residents.

The Belair Convalesarium*
6116 Belair Rd, Baltimore, MD, 21206 (301) 426-1424
Admin Robert R Ross. *Medical Dir/Dir of Nursing* Luis E Rivera MD.
Licensure Skilled Care; Intermediate Care.
Beds 196. *Certified* Medicaid; Medicare.
Ownership Proprietary.

Blancaflor Nursing Home*
1802 Eutaw Pl, Baltimore, MD, 21217 (301) 523-7820
Admin Henry Goldbaum. *Medical Dir/Dir of Nursing* Richard Tyson.
Licensure Intermediate Care. *Beds* 50. *Certified* Medicaid.
Ownership Proprietary.

Century Home Inc
102 N Paca St, Baltimore, MD, 21201 (301) 727-2050
Admin Oscar Newman. *Medical Dir/Dir of Nursing* Hollis Seunarine MD.
Licensure Intermediate Care. *Beds* 82. *Certified* Medicaid.
Ownership Proprietary.
Facilities Dining room; Activities room.
Activities Arts and Crafts; Cards; Games; Prayer groups; Movies.
Description Facility features good patient care—no odors, catheters, or bed-ridden patients.

Crawford Retreat Inc*
2117 Denison St, Baltimore, MD, 21216 (301) 566-0160
Admin Marie A Fox. *Medical Dir/Dir of Nursing* Edward Hunt Jr MD.
Licensure Intermediate Care. *Beds* 23. *Certified* Medicaid.
Ownership Proprietary.

Dukeland Nursing Home and Convalescent Center
1501 N Dukeland St, Baltimore, MD, 21216 (301) 945-7433
Admin Jerry Washington. *Medical Dir/Dir of Nursing* Dr Arthur Lebson.
Licensure Intermediate Care. *Beds* 104. *Certified* Medicaid.
Ownership Proprietary.
Staff RNs 2 (ft), 2 (pt); LPNs 8 (ft), 5 (pt); Orderlies 5 (ft), 3 (pt); Nurses aides 40 (ft), 20 (pt); Physical therapists 1 (pt); Recreational therapists 1 (ft); Speech therapists 1 (pt); Dietitians 1 (pt); Dentists 1 (pt); Ophthalmologists 1 (pt); Podiatrists 1 (pt).
Facilities Dining room; Physical therapy room; Activities room; Crafts room; Laundry room; Barber/Beauty shop.
Activities Arts and Crafts; Cards; Games; Reading groups; Prayer groups; Movies.

Edgewood Nursing Home*
6000 Bellona Ave, Baltimore, MD, 21212 (301) 323-4223

Admin Jeffrey Berenbach. *Medical Dir/Dir of Nursing* Anthony Cazozza MD.
Licensure Skilled Care; Intermediate Care.
Beds 127. *Certified* Medicaid; Medicare.
Ownership Proprietary.

Federal Hill Nursing Center
1213 Light St, Baltimore, MD, 21230 (301) 727-1600
Admin Michael E Morin. *Medical Dir/Dir of Nursing* Dr Thomas C Folkemer.
Licensure Intermediate Care. *Beds* 314. *Certified* Medicaid.
Ownership Proprietary.
Admissions Requirements Medical examination; Physician's request.
Staff Physicians 12 (pt); RNs 9 (ft), 2 (pt); LPNs 15 (ft), 5 (pt); Orderlies 3 (ft); Nurses aides 90 (ft), 20 (pt); Physical therapists 3 (pt); Recreational therapists 1 (ft); Speech therapists 1 (pt); Activities coordinators 6 (ft); Dietitians 1 (pt); Dentists 1 (pt); Ophthalmologists 1 (pt); Podiatrists 1 (pt).
Facilities Dining room; Physical therapy room; Activities room; Chapel; Crafts room; Laundry room; Barber/Beauty shop; Library.
Activities Arts and Crafts; Cards; Games; Reading groups; Prayer groups; Movies; Shopping trips; Dances/Social or cultural gatherings.
Description Candlelight dinners for families and residents are featured. Facility located near Baltimore's new harborplace.

Friedler's Guest House*
2449 Shirley Ave, Baltimore, MD, 21215 (301) 466-0061
Admin Nathan Rofsky. *Medical Dir/Dir of Nursing* Manuel Levin MD.
Licensure Intermediate Care. *Beds* 31. *Certified* Medicaid.
Ownership Proprietary.

Garden Village*
5837 Belair Rd, Baltimore, MD, 21206 (301) 483-5800
Admin Norman W Ward. *Medical Dir/Dir of Nursing* Albert Bradley MD.
Licensure Skilled Care; Intermediate Care.
Beds 100. *Certified* Medicaid; Medicare.
Ownership Proprietary.

Garrison Nursing Home Inc*
2803 Garrison Blvd, Baltimore, MD, 21216 (301) 367-6726
Admin Teresa Friend. *Medical Dir/Dir of Nursing* Edward O Hunt Jr MD.
Licensure Intermediate Care. *Beds* 21. *Certified* Medicaid.
Ownership Proprietary.
Admissions Requirements Minimum age 45; Medical examination.
Staff Physicians 1 (ft); RNs 1 (ft); LPNs 4 (ft); Orderlies 1 (pt); Nurses aides 4 (ft), 2 (pt); Activities coordinators 1 (pt); Dietitians 1 (pt); Dentists 1 (pt); Ophthalmologists 1 (pt); Podiatrists 1 (pt).
Facilities Dining room; Laundry room.
Activities Arts and Crafts; Cards; Games; Reading groups; Prayer groups; Shopping trips.
Description Facility features a home-like atmosphere.

General German Aged People's Home of Baltimore
22 S Athol Ave, Baltimore, MD, 21229 (301) 566-3600
Admin Herbert E Stuenkel. *Medical Dir/Dir of Nursing* Dr William J Bryson.
Licensure Skilled Care; Domiciliary Care.
Beds 114.
Ownership Nonprofit.
Admissions Requirements Minimum age 65; Medical examination.
Staff Physicians 1 (pt); RNs 2 (ft); LPNs 6 (ft), 8 (pt); Nurses aides 20 (ft), 5 (pt); Physical therapists 1 (pt); Occupational therapists 1 (pt); Speech therapists 1 (pt); Activities coordinators 1 (ft); Dietitians 2 (pt); Dentists 1 (pt); Ophthalmologists 1 (pt); Podiatrists 2 (pt).
Languages German
Facilities Dining room; Chapel; Crafts room; Laundry room; Barber/Beauty shop.
Activities Arts and Crafts; Cards; Games; Movies; Shopping trips.

Granada Nursing Home Inc*
4017 Liberty Heights Ave, Baltimore, MD, 21207 (301) 542-5306
Admin Robert T DeFontes. *Medical Dir/Dir of Nursing* Hollis Seunaring MD.
Licensure Intermediate Care. *Beds* 112. *Certified* Medicaid.
Ownership Proprietary.

Greater Pennsylvania Ave Nursing Center Inc
607 Pennsylvania Ave, Baltimore, MD, 21201 (301) 728-3344
Admin John Murphy. *Medical Dir/Dir of Nursing* Richard Tyson.
Licensure Intermediate Care. *Beds* 124. *Certified* Medicaid.
Ownership Proprietary.
Admissions Requirements Minimum age 21; Medical examination; Physician's request.
Staff Physicians 5 (pt); RNs 4 (ft), 1 (pt); LPNs 10 (ft), 3 (pt); Nurses aides 43 (ft); Physical therapists 2 (pt); Speech therapists 1 (pt); Activities coordinators 1 (ft); Dietitians 1 (pt); Dentists 1 (pt); Ophthalmologists 1 (pt); Podiatrists 1 (pt).
Facilities Dining room; Physical therapy room; Activities room; Barber/Beauty shop.
Activities Arts and Crafts; Cards; Games; Reading groups; Prayer groups; Movies; Shopping trips; Dances/Social or cultural gatherings.
Description In addition to providing the highest quality 24-hour nursing care, we strive to maintain the social interaction of our residents. We provide many outstanding programs for their enjoyment. Among these are music therapy, creative skills activities, horticultural and spiritual programs, and community orientated activities.

Greenwood Acres Nursing Home*
3706 Nortonia Rd, Baltimore, MD, 21216 (301) 947-1444
Admin Delzora S Johnson. *Medical Dir/Dir of Nursing* Shaukat Y Kahn MD.
Licensure Intermediate Care. *Beds* 23. *Certified* Medicaid.
Ownership Proprietary.

Harford Gardens Convalescent Center Inc*
4700 Harford Rd, Baltimore, MD, 21214 (301) 254-3012
Admin Sonya Dwyer. *Medical Dir/Dir of Nursing* E Ellsworth Cook MD.
Licensure Intermediate Care. *Beds* 58. *Certified* Medicaid.
Ownership Proprietary.

Haven Nursing Home
3939 Penhurst Ave, Baltimore, MD, 21215 (301) 664-9535
Admin Evelyn Bennett. *Medical Dir/Dir of Nursing* Richard Bennett MD.
Licensure Intermediate Care. *Beds* 22. *Certified* Medicaid.
Ownership Proprietary.
Admissions Requirements Minimum age 45; Medical examination; Physician's request.
Staff Physicians 1 (pt); RNs 1 (ft), 1 (pt); LPNs 3 (ft), 2 (pt); Nurses aides 6 (ft); Recreational therapists 1 (ft); Activities coordinators 1 (ft); Dietitians 1 (pt); Podiatrists 1 (pt).
Facilities Dining room; Activities room; Crafts room; Laundry room.
Activities Arts and Crafts; Cards; Games; Reading groups; Prayer groups; Movies; Shopping trips; Dances/Social or cultural gatherings.
Description Facility is small and home-like.

Hayes Care Home*
3001 Garrison Blvd, Baltimore, MD, 21216 (301) 542-9694
Admin Queen E Hayes.
Licensure Intermediate Care; Domiciliary Care. *Beds* ICF 11; Domiciliary Care 4. *Certified* Medicaid.
Ownership Proprietary.

Highland Health Facility Mental Retardation Unit
5200 Eastern Ave, Bldg D, Baltimore, MD, 21224 (301) 276-7000
Admin Deloris M Miller. *Medical Dir/Dir of Nursing* Patricia Mildvan MD.
Licensure Intermediate Care for Mentally Retarded. *Beds* 99. *Certified* Medicaid.
Ownership Public.
Staff Physicians 1 (ft), 2 (pt); RNs 2 (ft); LPNs 14 (ft); Nurses aides 59 (ft); Physical therapists 1 (ft); Recreational therapists 1 (ft); Occupational therapists 1 (ft); Speech therapists 1 (pt); Activities coordinators 1 (pt); Dietitians 1 (ft); Dentists 1 (pt).
Facilities Dining room; Physical therapy room; Activities room; Crafts room; Laundry room.
Activities Arts and Crafts; Games; Movies; Shopping trips; Dances/Social or cultural gatherings.

Hurwitz House
133 Slade Ave, Baltimore, MD, 21208 (301) 466-8700
Admin Louis M Balk. *Medical Dir/Dir of Nursing* Steven Levinson.
Licensure Intermediate Care. *Beds* 23. *Certified* Medicaid.
Ownership Nonprofit.
Admissions Requirements Minimum age 60; Medical examination.
Staff LPNs 3 (ft), 3 (pt); Nurses aides 3 (ft), 3 (pt).
Affiliation Jewish

Facilities Dining room; Activities room; Laundry room.
Activities Arts and Crafts; Cards; Games; Reading groups; Movies; Shopping trips.
Description Licensed nursing home incorporating residential concepts best described as a group living arrangement with health services.

Jenkins Memorial Nursing Home
1000 S Caton Ave, Baltimore, MD, 21229 (301) 644-7100
Admin Sr Catherine Sanders. *Medical Dir/Dir of Nursing* John F Hartman MD.
Licensure Skilled Care; Comprehensive Care. *Beds* SNF 83; Comprehensive Care 43. *Certified* Medicaid; Medicare.
Ownership Nonprofit.
Admissions Requirements Medical examination.
Staff RNs 3 (ft); LPNs 10 (ft), 4 (pt); Nurses aides 45 (ft), 22 (pt); Physical therapists 1 (ft), 1 (pt); Activities coordinators 2 (ft), 1 (pt); Dietitians 1 (pt); Dentists 1 (pt); Ophthalmologists 1 (pt); Podiatrists 1 (pt).
Affiliation Roman Catholic
Facilities Dining room; Physical therapy room; Activities room; Chapel; Crafts room; Laundry room; Barber/Beauty shop; Library.
Activities Arts and Crafts; Cards; Games; Prayer groups; Movies; Shopping trips; Dances/Social or cultural gatherings; Exercises.

Jewish Convalescent Center—Scotts Level*
7920 Scotts Level Rd, Baltimore, MD, 21208 (301) 521-3600
Admin Robert Hansen. *Medical Dir/Dir of Nursing* A A Silver MD.
Licensure Skilled Care; Intermediate Care. *Beds* 151. *Certified* Medicaid; Medicare.
Ownership Proprietary.
Affiliation Jewish

John L Deaton Medical Center Inc*
611 S Charles St, Baltimore, MD, 21230 (301) 547-8500
Admin Wallace M Dow. *Medical Dir/Dir of Nursing* Julian W Reed MD.
Licensure Skilled Care; Intermediate Care. *Beds* SNF 140; ICF 80. *Certified* Medicaid; Medicare.
Ownership Nonprofit.

Katherine Robb Nursing Home
4105 Essex Rd, Baltimore, MD, 21207 (301) 486-7226
Admin Alesia Tomassetti. *Medical Dir/Dir of Nursing* Dr Robert Kroopnick.
Licensure Intermediate Care. *Beds* 15. *Certified* Medicaid.
Ownership Proprietary.
Staff Recreational therapists 1 (pt).

Kenesaw Nursing Home Inc*
2601 Roslyn Ave, Baltimore, MD, 21216 (301) 466-3900
Admin Doris P Gordon. *Medical Dir/Dir of Nursing* Edward Hunt Jr MD.
Licensure Intermediate Care. *Beds* 27. *Certified* Medicaid.
Ownership Proprietary.

Kenson Nursing Home
2922 Arunah Ave, Baltimore, MD, 21216 (301) 947-3566
Admin Lucille Kennedy. *Medical Dir/Dir of Nursing* Dr S Liau MD.
Licensure Intermediate Care. *Beds* 38. *Certified* Medicaid.
Ownership Proprietary.
Admissions Requirements Minimum age 12.
Staff Physicians 2 (ft); RNs 2 (ft); LPNs 11 (ft); Orderlies 4 (ft); Nurses aides 10 (ft); Physical therapists 1 (ft); Reality therapists 1 (ft); Recreational therapists 1 (ft); Occupational therapists 1 (ft); Speech therapists 1 (ft); Activities coordinators 2 (ft); Dietitians 1 (ft); Dentists 1 (ft); Ophthalmologists 1 (ft); Podiatrists 1 (ft); Audiologists 1 (ft).
Facilities Dining room; Activities room; Chapel; Crafts room; Laundry room.
Activities Arts and Crafts; Cards; Games; Reading groups; Prayer groups; Movies; Shopping trips; Dances/Social or cultural gatherings.

Keswick Home for Incurables of Baltimore City*
700 W 40th St, Baltimore, MD, 21211 (301) 235-8860
Admin Brooks Major. *Medical Dir/Dir of Nursing* Aubrey Richardson MD.
Licensure Skilled Care; Intermediate Care. *Beds* SNF 176; ICF 40. *Certified* Medicaid; Medicare.
Ownership Nonprofit.

Key Circle Hospice Inc
1214 Eutaw Pl, Baltimore, MD, 21217 (301) 523-7800
Admin S D Selenski. *Medical Dir/Dir of Nursing* Richard R Rigler.
Licensure Intermediate Care. *Beds* 121. *Certified* Medicaid.
Ownership Proprietary.
Facilities Dining room; Physical therapy room; Activities room; Laundry room; Barber/Beauty shop.
Activities Arts and Crafts; Cards; Games; Prayer groups; Movies; Shopping trips; Dances/Social or cultural gatherings.

Lafayette Square Nursing Center Inc
140 W Lafayette Ave, Baltimore, MD, 21217 (301) 523-3400
Admin Kay Perkins. *Medical Dir/Dir of Nursing* Dr Richard Tyson.
Licensure Intermediate Care. *Beds* 264. *Certified* Medicaid.
Ownership Proprietary.
Staff Physicians 9 (pt); RNs 5 (ft), 1 (pt); LPNs 20 (ft), 3 (pt); Nurses aides 140 (ft), 20 (pt); Physical therapists 4 (pt); Recreational therapists 5 (ft); Speech therapists 1 (pt); Activities coordinators 1 (ft); Dietitians 1 (ft); Dentists 1 (pt); Ophthalmologists 1 (pt); Podiatrists 1 (pt); Audiologists 1 (pt).
Facilities Dining room; Physical therapy room; Activities room; Chapel; Crafts room; Laundry room; Barber/Beauty shop; Library; Art gallery.
Activities Arts and Crafts; Cards; Games; Reading groups; Prayer groups; Movies; Dances/Social or cultural gatherings; Outside activities trips.
Description Lafayette Square Nursing Center is

located in the Bolton Hill area of Baltimore. The staff is dedicated to meeting the individual needs of each resident.

Lake Drive Nursing Home Inc*
2401 Eutaw Place, Baltimore, MD, 21217 (301) 669-4444
Admin Herman Kodeck. *Medical Dir/Dir of Nursing* Arthur Lebson MD.
Licensure Intermediate Care. *Beds* 50. *Certified* Medicaid.
Ownership Proprietary.

Levindale Hebrew Geriatric Center and Hospital
Greenspring and Belvedere Aves, Baltimore, MD, 21215 (301) 466-8700
Admin Stanford A Alliker. *Medical Dir/Dir of Nursing* Steven A Levenson MD.
Licensure Skilled Care; Intermediate Care; Special Hospital. *Beds* SNF 65; ICF 165; Special Hospital 53. *Certified* Medicaid; Medicare.
Ownership Nonprofit.
Staff Physicians 4 (ft), 5 (pt); RNs 19 (ft), 8 (pt); LPNs 33 (ft), 28 (pt); Orderlies 16 (ft), 5 (pt); Nurses aides 84 (ft), 9 (pt); Physical therapists 4 (ft); Recreational therapists 4 (ft), 2 (pt); Occupational therapists 1 (ft); Activities coordinators 1 (ft).
Affiliation Jewish
Facilities Dining room; Physical therapy room; Activities room; Chapel; Crafts room; Laundry room; Barber/Beauty shop.
Activities Arts and Crafts; Cards; Games; Reading groups; Prayer groups; Movies; Shopping trips; Dances/Social or cultural gatherings.
Description Levindale provides more than just long-term geriatric care. As a specialty hospital, services include a rehabilitation unit, general medical unit, a hospice program; offers an adult day care program, group home arrangement, and community based personal care program.

Lincoln Convalescent Center Inc*
1217 W Fayette St, Baltimore, MD, 21223 (301) 727-3947
Admin Mildred L Pipkin. *Medical Dir/Dir of Nursing* Ali Baykaler MD.
Licensure Skilled Care; Intermediate Care. *Beds* 224. *Certified* Medicaid.
Ownership Proprietary.

Little Sisters of the Poor—Saint Martin's
601 Maiden Choice Ln, Baltimore, MD, 21228 (301) 744-9367
Admin Sr Margaret R Halloran. *Medical Dir/Dir of Nursing* Stanley Ankudas MD.
Licensure Intermediate Care; Domiciliary Care. *Beds* ICF 157; Domiciliary Care 103.
Certified Medicaid.
Ownership Nonprofit.
Affiliation Roman Catholic

Manor Care—Rossville*
6600 Ridge Rd, Baltimore, MD, 21237 (301) 574-4950
Admin Charles Tendrow. *Medical Dir/Dir of Nursing* Walter Kees MD.
Licensure Intermediate Care. *Beds* 204. *Certified* Medicaid.
Ownership Proprietary.

Maryland Baptist Aged Home
2801 Rayner Ave, Baltimore, MD, 21216 (301) 945-7650
Admin Angeline Byrd. *Medical Dir/Dir of Nursing* Dr Hollis Sevnarine.
Licensure Intermediate Care. *Beds* 33. *Certified* Medicaid.
Ownership Nonprofit.
Admissions Requirements Minimum age 14.
Staff Physicians 1 (ft); RNs 1 (ft), 1 (pt); LPNs 3 (ft), 3 (pt); Orderlies 1 (ft), 1 (pt); Nurses aides 6 (ft), 3 (pt); Activities coordinators 1 (ft); Dietitians 1 (ft); Ophthalmologists 1 (pt); Podiatrists 1 (pt).
Affiliation Baptist
Facilities Dining room; Activities room; Chapel; Laundry room; Library.
Activities Arts and Crafts; Cards; Games; Reading groups; Prayer groups; Movies; Shopping trips.
Description Facility is all on one floor, located in a residential area around the corner from an acute care hospital that contracts for residents; birthday club; constant flow of church-oriented activities from the community.

Mason F Lord Chronic Hospital and Nursing Facility
5200 Eastern Ave, Baltimore, MD, 21224 (301) 396-8741
Admin Cleve Laub. *Medical Dir/Dir of Nursing* Edmund G Beacham MD.
Licensure Chronic Hospital; Comprehensive Care. *Beds* Chronic Hospital 45; Comprehensive Care 168. *Certified* Medicare.
Ownership Public.
Admissions Requirements Minimum age 14; Physician's request.
Staff Physicians 1 (ft), 5 (pt); RNs 15 (ft), 1 (pt); LPNs 20 (ft); Nurses aides 96 (ft); Physical therapists 1 (ft); Recreational therapists 1 (ft); Occupational therapists 2 (ft); Speech therapists 1 (ft); Dietitians 1 (ft); Podiatrists 1 (pt).
Facilities Dining room; Physical therapy room; Activities room; Chapel; Crafts room; Laundry room; Library.
Activities Arts and Crafts; Games; Reading groups; Prayer groups; Movies; Shopping trips; Dances/Social or cultural gatherings.
Description Mason F Lord has a 30-slot medical day care center, 10 bed short-term respite program, 10 Clinitron beds for treatment of severe skin breakdowns such as burns, and decubitus ulcers; affiliated and owned by an acute hospital which provides intensive consultative services in all medical specialties.

Melchor Nursing Home
2327 N Charles St, Baltimore, MD, 21218 (301) 235-8997
Admin P Ramona Fearins.
Licensure Intermediate Care. *Beds* 50. *Certified* Medicaid.
Ownership Proprietary.
Admissions Requirements Minimum age 18; Medical examination; Physician's request.
Facilities Dining room; Activities room; Laundry room.
Activities Arts and Crafts; Cards; Games; Reading groups; Prayer groups; Movies; Shopping trips; Dances/Social or cultural gatherings.

Meridian Nursing Center—Caton Manor
3330 Wilkens Ave, Baltimore, MD, 21229 (301) 525-1544
Admin Michael R Barker. *Medical Dir/Dir of Nursing* Herbert Levickas.
Licensure Skilled Care; Intermediate Care. *Beds* SNF 184; ICF 150. *Certified* Medicaid; Medicare.
Admissions Requirements Minimum age 14; Medical examination.
Facilities Dining room; Activities room; Laundry room; Barber/Beauty shop.
Activities Arts and Crafts; Cards; Games; Reading groups; Prayer groups; Movies; Shopping trips; Dances/Social or cultural gatherings.
Description Meridian Caton Manor has an excellent quality of life program that meets the pyscho-social needs of the residents. More importantly, however, it has trained, experienced staff who believe in "the basics" of nursing care. Meridian Caton Manor is convenient to quality hospitals, public transportation, and only minutes away from Baltimore's new Inner Harbor.

Meridian Nursing Center—Hamilton*
6040 Harford Rd, Baltimore, MD, 21214 (301) 426-8855
Admin Rick Kincaid. *Medical Dir/Dir of Nursing* Ingeborg Fromm MD.
Licensure Skilled Care; Intermediate Care. *Beds* 104. *Certified* Medicaid; Medicare.
Ownership Proprietary.

Meridian Nursing Center—Heritage
7232 German Hill Rd, Baltimore, MD, 21222
Admin Pamela E Fisher. *Medical Dir/Dir of Nursing* Theodore C Patterson MD.
Licensure Skilled Care; Intermediate Care. *Beds* 180. *Certified* Medicaid; Medicare.
Ownership Proprietary.
Facilities Dining room; Physical therapy room; Activities room; Laundry room; Barber/Beauty shop.
Activities Arts and Crafts; Games; Prayer groups; Movies; Dances/Social or cultural gatherings.
Description Facility features a hospice program in conjunction with church hospital.

Meridian Nursing Center—Long Green*
115 E Melrose Ave, Baltimore, MD, 21212 (301) 435-9073
Admin Karen P Pressmann. *Medical Dir/Dir of Nursing* William Helfrich MD.
Licensure Skilled Care; Intermediate Care. *Beds* 140. *Certified* Medicaid; Medicare.
Ownership Proprietary.

Midtown Home
808 Saint Paul St, Baltimore, MD, 21202 (301) 685-6766
Admin Julia Perle. *Medical Dir/Dir of Nursing* Alex Enrique MD.
Licensure Intermediate Care. *Beds* 137. *Certified* Medicaid.
Ownership Proprietary.
Admissions Requirements Minimum age 26; Medical examination.
Staff Physicians 4 (ft); RNs 4 (pt); LPNs 11 (ft); Orderlies 8 (ft); Nurses aides 64 (ft); Physical therapists 1 (ft), 1 (pt); Reality therapists 1 (ft); Speech therapists 1 (pt); Activities

coordinators 1 (ft); Dietitians 1 (ft); Dentists 1 (pt); Ophthalmologists 1 (pt); Podiatrists 1 (pt); Audiologists 1 (pt).
Facilities Dining room; Physical therapy room; Activities room; Library.
Activities Arts and Crafts; Cards; Games; Reading groups; Prayer groups; Movies; Dances/Social or cultural gatherings.
Description Facility has been providing quality nursing care for over 25 years in the heart of Baltimore.

Milford Manor Nursing Home
4204 Milford Mill Rd, Baltimore, MD, 21208 (301) 486-1500
Admin Bruce Raffel. *Medical Dir/Dir of Nursing* Dr Cutler/Lebson.
Licensure Skilled Care. *Beds* 99. *Certified* Medicaid; Medicare.
Ownership Proprietary.
Admissions Requirements Medical examination.
Staff RNs 3 (ft), 1 (pt); LPNs 7 (ft), 1 (pt); Nurses aides 42 (ft); Physical therapists; Recreational therapists; Speech therapists; Activities coordinators; Dietitians; Dentists; Podiatrists.
Affiliation Jewish
Facilities Dining room; Physical therapy room; Activities room; Chapel; Crafts room; Laundry room; Barber/Beauty shop; TV lounges.
Activities Arts and Crafts; Cards; Games; Reading groups; Prayer groups; Movies; Shopping trips; Dances/Social or cultural gatherings.
Description Milford Manor is family owned, family operated, providing a variety of health services on a personal basis to the elderly in the area; modern facility is centrally located between hospitals and the Pikesville community.

Mount Sinai Nursing Home Inc*
4613 Park Heights Ave, Baltimore, MD, 21215 (301) 367-5300
Admin Maury J Leibowtiz. *Medical Dir/Dir of Nursing* Arthur Lebson MD.
Licensure Intermediate Care. *Beds* 59. *Certified* Medicaid.
Ownership Proprietary.

Pall Mall Nursing Center
4601 Pall Mall Rd, Baltimore, MD, 21215 (301) 664-5551
Admin Jo Sargent-Forbes. *Medical Dir/Dir of Nursing* Arthur Lebson MD.
Licensure Skilled Care; Intermediate Care.
Beds SNF 82; ICF 82. *Certified* Medicaid; Medicare.
Ownership Nonprofit.
Admissions Requirements Minimum age 14; Physician's request.
Staff RNs 3 (ft), 1 (pt); LPNs 7 (ft), 6 (pt); Nurses aides 18 (ft), 25 (pt); Physical therapists; Recreational therapists 1 (ft); Occupational therapists; Speech therapists; Dietitians 1 (pt).
Facilities Dining room; Physical therapy room; Activities room.
Activities Arts and Crafts; Cards; Games; Reading groups; Prayer groups; Movies; Shopping trips.

Perring Parkway Nursing Home Inc*
1801 Wentworth Rd, Baltimore, MD, 21234 (301) 661-5717

Admin Lucy Monninger. *Medical Dir/Dir of Nursing* Anthony Carozza MD.
Licensure Skilled Care; Intermediate Care.
Beds 130. *Certified* Medicaid; Medicare.
Ownership Proprietary.

Pimlico Manor*
2525 W Belvedere Ave, Baltimore, MD, 21215 (301) 367-9100
Admin Gary Waitt. *Medical Dir/Dir of Nursing* Leon Kochman MD.
Licensure Skilled Care; Intermediate Care.
Beds 70. *Certified* Medicaid; Medicare.
Ownership Proprietary.

Pleasant Manor Nursing and Convalescent Center*
4615 Park Heights Ave, Baltimore, MD, 21215 (301) 542-4800
Admin Isaac Goldman. *Medical Dir/Dir of Nursing* Jamie Punzalan MD.
Licensure Skilled Care; Intermediate Care.
Beds 137. *Certified* Medicaid; Medicare.
Ownership Proprietary.

Poplar Manor Nursing Home
3313 Poplar St, Baltimore, MD, 21216 (301) 566-1300
Admin Philip Greene. *Medical Dir/Dir of Nursing* Dr Mark Davis.
Licensure Intermediate Care. *Beds* 157. *Certified* Medicaid.
Ownership Proprietary.
Staff Physicians 1 (ft), 1 (pt); RNs 6 (ft), 1 (pt); LPNs 8 (ft), 3 (pt); Orderlies 6 (ft), 1 (pt); Nurses aides 36 (ft), 6 (pt); Speech therapists 1 (pt); Activities coordinators 1 (ft); Dietitians 1 (ft), 1 (pt); Dentists 1 (pt); Ophthalmologists 1 (pt); Podiatrists 1 (pt).
Facilities Dining room; Laundry room.
Activities Arts and Crafts; Games; Prayer groups; Movies; Dances/Social or cultural gatherings.

Seton Hill Manor*
501 W Franklin St, Baltimore, MD, 21201 (301) 837-4990
Admin Lorraine Raffel. *Medical Dir/Dir of Nursing* Jamie Punzalan MD.
Licensure Skilled Care; Intermediate Care.
Beds 300. *Certified* Medicaid.
Ownership Proprietary.

Uplands Home for Church Women
4501 Old Frederick Rd, Baltimore, MD, 21229 (301) 945-1900
Admin Carol A Baker. *Medical Dir/Dir of Nursing* Dr Alva Baker.
Licensure Domiciliary Care; Comprehensive Care. *Beds* 48.
Ownership Nonprofit.
Admissions Requirements Minimum age 65; Females only; Medical examination; Physician's request.
Staff Physicians 1 (pt); RNs 1 (ft); LPNs 2 (ft), 2 (pt); Nurses aides 6 (ft), 5 (pt); Activities coordinators 1 (pt); Dietitians 1 (pt).
Affiliation Episcopal
Facilities Dining room; Activities room; Chapel; Crafts room; Laundry room; Barber/Beauty shop; Library.
Activities Arts and Crafts; Cards; Games;

Movies; Shopping trips; Dances/Social or cultural gatherings.
Description Home-like atmosphere is offered.

Valley Nursing and Convalescent Center Inc*
8710 Emge Rd, Baltimore, MD, 21234 (301) 661-5995
Admin Orlando Orsino. *Medical Dir/Dir of Nursing* Marion Kowaleski MD.
Licensure Skilled Care; Intermediate Care.
Beds 173. *Certified* Medicaid; Medicare.
Ownership Proprietary.

Valley View Nursing Home*
8720 Emge Rd, Baltimore, MD, 21234 (301) 668-1961
Admin Ronald Sohl. *Medical Dir/Dir of Nursing* Anthony Carozza MD.
Licensure Skilled Care; Intermediate Care.
Beds 130. *Certified* Medicaid; Medicare.
Ownership Proprietary.

Walter P Carter Center—Mental Retardation Unit
630 W Fayette St, Baltimore, MD, 21201 (301) 528-2139
Admin Robert G Jacobs.
Licensure Intermediate Care for Mentally Retarded. *Beds* 20. *Certified* Medicaid.
Ownership Public.
Description Facility is a special diagnostic evaluation short-term treatment unit of the Mental Retardation Administation of the state of Maryland. Admissions are for adults with behavioral problems and are short-term.

Wesley Home Inc
2211 W Rogers Ave, Baltimore, MD, 21209 (301) 664-4006
Admin Anne H Schisler. *Medical Dir/Dir of Nursing* Phyllis Foster.
Licensure Domiciliary Care. *Beds* 224.
Ownership Nonprofit.
Admissions Requirements Minimum age 65; Medical examination; Physician's request.
Staff Physical therapists 1 (pt); Recreational therapists 1 (pt); Speech therapists 1 (pt); Activities coordinators 1 (ft).
Affiliation Methodist
Facilities Dining room; Physical therapy room; Activities room; Chapel; Crafts room; Laundry room; Barber/Beauty shop; Library.
Activities Arts and Crafts; Cards; Games; Reading groups; Prayer groups; Movies; Shopping trips.
Description Located in the Mount Washington section of Baltimore since 1931, Wesley Home is a nonprofit Christian home under the guidance of member churches of the United Methodist Church.

BEL AIR

Bel Air Convalescent Center Inc
410 MacPhail Rd, Bel Air, MD, 21014 (301) 879-1120
Admin Amy J Rothert. *Medical Dir/Dir of Nursing* Dr Andrew Nowakowski.
Licensure Skilled Care; Intermediate Care.
Beds 150. *Certified* Medicaid; Medicare.
Ownership Proprietary.
Staff Physicians 14 (pt); RNs 11 (pt); Nurses

aides 80 (ft); Physical therapists 3 (pt); Recreational therapists 2 (pt); Speech therapists 1 (pt); Activities coordinators 1 (pt); Dietitians 1 (pt); Dentists 1 (pt); Podiatrists 1 (pt).
Facilities Dining room; Physical therapy room; Laundry room; Barber/Beauty shop; Lounges.
Activities Arts and Crafts; Cards; Games; Reading groups; Prayer groups; Movies; Shopping trips; Dances/Social or cultural gatherings.
Description 150-bed skilled facility located in suburban area of Bel Air, Maryland with 24-hour licensed nursing care in a home-like atmosphere.

BERLIN

Berlin Nursing Home
US Rt 346 at Rt 113, Berlin, MD, 21811 (301) 641-4400
Admin Philip Lang. *Medical Dir/Dir of Nursing* Federico Arthes MD.
Licensure Comprehensive Care; Domiciliary Care. *Beds* Comprehensive Care 143; Domiciliary Care 28. *Certified* Medicaid; Medicare.
Ownership Proprietary.
Admissions Requirements Minimum age 15; Medical examination; Physician's request.
Staff Physicians 1 (ft), 3 (pt); RNs 8 (ft), 5 (pt); LPNs 8 (ft), 2 (pt); Orderlies 7 (ft), 2 (pt); Nurses aides 37 (ft), 15 (pt); Physical therapists 1 (pt); Recreational therapists 1 (pt); Occupational therapists 1 (pt); Activities coordinators 1 (ft); Dietitians 1 (pt); Dentists 1 (pt); Ophthalmologists 1 (pt); Podiatrists 1 (pt); Audiologists 1 (pt).
Facilities Dining room; Physical therapy room; Activities room; Chapel; Crafts room; Laundry room; Barber/Beauty shop; Library; Enclosed outdoor patio.
Activities Arts and Crafts; Cards; Games; Reading groups; Prayer groups; Shopping trips; Dances/Social or cultural gatherings.
Description A luxury nursing home designed from the ground up for congenial living in the safety and comfort of modern masonry construction. Dignified residential atmosphere surrounded by spacious lawns—a quiet and enjoyable "home away from home."

BETHESDA

Bethesda Health Care Center Inc*
5721 Grosvenor Ln, Bethesda, MD, 20014 (301) 530-1600
Admin Larry White. *Medical Dir/Dir of Nursing* Hadi Bahar MD.
Licensure Skilled Care; Intermediate Care.
Beds 180. *Certified* Medicaid; Medicare.
Ownership Proprietary.

Carriage Hill—Bethesda Inc*
5215 Cedar Lane Ave, Bethesda, MD, 20014 (301) 897-5500
Admin Ruth Reynolds. *Medical Dir/Dir of Nursing* John Umhau MD.
Licensure Skilled Care; Intermediate Care.
Beds 74.
Ownership Proprietary.

Fernwood House Retirement and Nursing Center*
6530 Democracy Blvd, Bethesda, MD, 20817 (301) 530-9000
Admin Karen J Jones. *Medical Dir/Dir of Nursing* J Blaine Fitzgerald MD.
Licensure Skilled Care; Intermediate Care.
Beds 100. *Certified* Medicaid; Medicare.
Ownership Proprietary.

BOONSBORO

Fahrney-Keedy Memorial Home Inc
Rt 2, Box 78, Boonsboro, MD, 21713 (301) 733-6284
Admin Richard A Bowman.
Licensure Intermediate Care; Domiciliary Care. *Beds* 100; Domiciliary Care 40.
Certified Medicaid.
Ownership Nonprofit.
Admissions Requirements Minimum age 62; Medical examination.
Staff Physicians 1 (pt); RNs 2 (ft); LPNs 11 (ft); Orderlies 1 (ft); Nurses aides 51 (ft), 20 (pt); Physical therapists 1 (pt); Reality therapists 1 (ft); Recreational therapists 2 (ft); Activities coordinators 1 (ft); Dietitians 1 (pt); Dentists 1 (pt); Podiatrists 1 (pt).
Affiliation Church of the Brethren
Facilities Dining room; Physical therapy room; Activities room; Chapel; Crafts room; Laundry room; Barber/Beauty shop.
Activities Arts and Crafts; Games; Reading groups; Prayer groups; Movies; Shopping trips; Dances/Social or cultural gatherings.
Description Fahrney-Keedy is a church-related nursing home with cottages and apartments (independent living), and domiciliary care rooms as well as a nursing care area. Home has been in operation 80 years; located in a rural setting 70 miles from Washington, DC and less than 10 miles from Hagerstown, MD.

Reeders Memorial Home*
141 S Main St, Boonsboro, MD, 21713 (301) 432-5457
Admin Nancy E Stocks. *Medical Dir/Dir of Nursing* R Lawrence Kugler MD.
Licensure Skilled Care; Intermediate Care.
Beds 150. *Certified* Medicaid.
Ownership Nonprofit.

BRADDOCK HEIGHTS

Vindobona Nursing Home Inc
6012 Jefferson Blvd, Braddock Heights, MD, 21714 (301) 371-7160
Admin Nayoda E Kefauver. *Medical Dir/Dir of Nursing* Dr Wayne Allgier.
Licensure Comprehensive Care. *Beds* 61. *Certified* Medicaid.
Ownership Proprietary.
Admissions Requirements Minimum age 16; Medical examination.
Staff RNs 5 (ft), 3 (pt); LPNs 2 (ft), 4 (pt); Nurses aides 15 (ft), 20 (pt); Recreational therapists 1 (ft); Activities coordinators 1 (ft); Dietitians 1 (pt).
Facilities Dining room; Activities room; Crafts room; Barber/Beauty shop; Library; Examining and treatment room.

Activities Arts and Crafts; Cards; Games; Reading groups; Prayer groups; Movies; Shopping trips; Dances/Social or cultural gatherings; Monthly parties; Group band; Croquet; Horseshoes; Picnics; Family style dinners; Sing-a-longs; Bingo; Resident council.
Description Vindobona Nursing Home is situated in a rural setting with professional, long-term employees dedicated to giving quality care; home-like environment is indicative of personal loving care rendered by the staff.

BROOKLYN PARK

Meridian Nursing Center—Hammonds Lane
Hammonds Ln and Robinswood Rd, Brooklyn Park, MD, 21225 (301) 636-3400
Admin David C Almquist. *Medical Dir/Dir of Nursing* Dr Michael Schwartz.
Licensure Skilled Care; Intermediate Care.
Beds SNF 79; ICF 50. *Certified* Medicaid; Medicare.
Ownership Proprietary.
Admissions Requirements Medical examination.
Staff Physicians 1 (pt); RNs 10 (ft); LPNs 10 (ft); Nurses aides 50 (ft), 20 (pt); Physical therapists 1 (pt); Occupational therapists 1 (pt); Speech therapists 1 (pt); Activities coordinators 2 (ft); Dietitians 1 (pt); Dentists 1 (pt); Ophthalmologists 1 (pt); Podiatrists 1 (pt).
Facilities Dining room; Physical therapy room; Activities room; Laundry room; Barber/Beauty shop; Library.
Activities Arts and Crafts; Cards; Games; Reading groups; Prayer groups; Movies; Shopping trips; Dances/Social or cultural gatherings.
Description Hammonds Lane is a modern, attractive, 129-bed, skilled nursing facility. It offers progressive rehabilitation services and has a large variety of activities in which the residents may participate. The highly trained and compassionate staff is its biggest asset.

CAMBRIDGE

Cambridge House
520 Glenburn Ave, Cambridge, MD, 21613 (301) 228-9191
Admin Cynthia L Woodard. *Medical Dir/Dir of Nursing* Dr Eyup Tanman.
Licensure Skilled Care; Intermediate Care.
Beds 180. *Certified* Medicaid; Medicare.
Ownership Proprietary.
Staff Physicians 2 (pt); RNs 5 (ft), 1 (pt); LPNs 14 (ft), 6 (pt); Orderlies 5 (ft); Nurses aides 55 (ft), 5 (pt); Physical therapists 2 (pt); Speech therapists 1 (pt); Activities coordinators 2 (ft); Dietitians 1 (pt); Audiologists 2 (pt).
Facilities Dining room; Physical therapy room; Activities room; Laundry room; Barber/Beauty shop.
Activities Arts and Crafts; Cards; Games; Reading groups; Prayer groups; Movies; Shopping trips; Dances/Social or cultural gatherings; Country rides; Outdoor theater; Picnics; Barbecues.
Description Modern facility offers in-house pharmacy, physical and speech therapists, out-

standing activities department to meet every resident's hobby or favorite pastime. VA approved.

Glasgow Nursing Home*
311 Glenburn Ave, Cambridge, MD, 21613 (301) 228-3780
Admin Shirley M Smith. *Medical Dir/Dir of Nursing* Michael Moskewicz MD.
Licensure Intermediate Care. *Beds* 32. *Certified* Medicaid.
Ownership Proprietary.

CATONSVILLE

Breightonwood
1917 Powers Lane, Catonsville, MD, 21228 (301) 747-0689
Admin Kathy Gelzhiser. *Medical Dir/Dir of Nursing* David Moseman.
Licensure Intermediate Care. *Beds* 34. *Certified* Medicaid.
Ownership Proprietary.
Admissions Requirements Minimum age 14; Medical examination; Physician's request.
Staff Physicians 1 (pt); RNs 1 (ft), 1 (pt); LPNs 3 (ft), 3 (pt); Orderlies 1 (pt); Nurses aides 8 (ft); Activities coordinators 1 (ft); Dietitians 1 (pt).
Facilities Dining room; Activities room.
Activities Arts and Crafts; Games; Reading groups; Prayer groups.
Description We have an excellent activities program, beautiful grounds, small home-type setting, and excellent nursing care.

Forest Haven Nursing Home
315 Ingleside Ave, Catonsville, MD, 21228 (301) 747-7425
Admin Faye L Maguire. *Medical Dir/Dir of Nursing* Allan Mock.
Licensure Skilled Care; Intermediate Care.
Beds SNF 172; ICF 15. *Certified* Medicaid; Medicare.
Ownership Proprietary.
Admissions Requirements Medical examination.
Facilities Dining room; Physical therapy room; Activities room; Chapel; Crafts room; Laundry room; Barber/Beauty shop; Library.
Activities Arts and Crafts; Cards; Games; Reading groups; Prayer groups; Movies; Shopping trips; Dances/Social or cultural gatherings.
Description Facility is located in beautiful Baltimore County with spacious, wide porches and patios in beautiful woods. Good home-cooked meals.

Frederick Villa Nursing Center*
711 Academy Rd, Catonsville, MD, 21228 (301) 788-3300
Admin Jack Tucker. *Medical Dir/Dir of Nursing* Elmo Gayoso MD.
Licensure Intermediate Care. *Beds* 125. *Certified* Medicare.
Ownership Proprietary.

Inglenook*
333 Harlem Ln, Catonsville, MD, 21228 (301) 744-1020
Admin Sandra Mennerick. *Medical Dir/Dir of Nursing* James McPhillips.

Licensure Skilled Care; Intermediate Care.
Beds 96. *Certified* Medicaid; Medicare.
Ownership Proprietary.

Meridian Nursing Center—Catonsville
16 Fusting Ave, Catonsville, MD, 21228 (301) 747-1800
Admin Pamela E Fisher. *Medical Dir/Dir of Nursing* Herbert J Levickas.
Licensure Skilled Care; Intermediate Care.
Beds SNF 37; ICF 160. *Certified* Medicaid; Medicare.
Ownership Proprietary.
Staff Physicians 1 (pt); RNs 5 (ft), 5 (pt); LPNs 8 (ft), 4 (pt); Nurses aides 58 (ft), 20 (pt); Speech therapists; Activities coordinators 2 (ft); Dietitians 1 (pt); Dentists; Ophthalmologists; Podiatrists.
Facilities Dining room; Physical therapy room; Activities room; Crafts room; Laundry room; Barber/Beauty shop.
Activities Arts and Crafts; Cards; Games; Prayer groups; Movies; Shopping trips; Dances/Social or cultural gatherings.
Description Facility features cheerful atmosphere, professional caring staff who believe in promoting independence and social interaction; strong activities program; quality nursing and rehabilitative care.

Ridgeway Manor Nursing Home
5743 Edmondson Ave, Catonsville, MD, 21228 (301) 747-5250
Admin John E Burleigh Jr.
Licensure Intermediate Care. *Beds* 45. *Certified* Medicaid.
Ownership Proprietary.
Staff Physicians 2 (pt); RNs 1 (ft), 3 (pt); LPNs 1 (ft), 8 (pt); Nurses aides 7 (ft), 15 (pt); Physical therapists 1 (pt); Reality therapists 1 (pt); Recreational therapists 3 (pt); Occupational therapists 1 (pt); Speech therapists 1 (pt); Activities coordinators 1 (pt); Dietitians 1 (pt); Dentists 1 (pt); Ophthalmologists 1 (pt); Podiatrists 1 (pt); Audiologists 1 (pt).
Facilities Dining room; Physical therapy room; Activities room; Crafts room; Laundry room; Barber/Beauty shop; Library.
Activities Arts and Crafts; Cards; Games; Reading groups; Prayer groups; Movies; Shopping trips.
Description Manor offers a homey atmosphere with the care of an excellent nursing staff; large porches for outside walking, rocking, bird watching and listening, and enjoying the beautiful changes in landscape as the 4 seasons evolve.

Saint Joseph's Nursing Home
1222 Tugwell Dr, Catonsville, MD, 21228 (301) 747-0026
Admin Sr Carolyn Carne. *Medical Dir/Dir of Nursing* Dr J Nelson McKay MD.
Licensure Intermediate Care. *Beds* 40. *Certified* Medicaid.
Ownership Nonprofit.
Admissions Requirements Medical examination.
Staff Physicians 1 (ft), 4 (pt); RNs 2 (ft), 2 (pt); LPNs 1 (ft), 2 (pt); Nurses aides 10 (ft), 13 (pt); Recreational therapists 1 (ft); Activities coordinators 1 (ft); Dietitians 1 (ft); Dentists 1 (pt).
Affiliation Roman Catholic

Facilities Dining room; Activities room; Chapel; Crafts room; Laundry room; Barber/Beauty shop; Library.
Activities Arts and Crafts; Cards; Games; Reading groups; Prayer groups; Movies; Dances/Social or cultural gatherings.

Summit Nursing Home Inc*
98 Smithwood Ave, Catonsville, MD, 21228 (301) 747-3287
Admin Lawrence J Repetti. *Medical Dir/Dir of Nursing* James E Rowe MD.
Licensure Skilled Care. *Beds* 141. *Certified* Medicare.
Ownership Proprietary.
Staff RNs 7 (ft), 20 (pt); LPNs 2 (ft), 9 (pt); Nurses aides 103 (ft), 24 (pt); Physical therapists 1 (pt); Recreational therapists 1 (ft); Speech therapists 1 (pt); Activities coordinators 1 (ft); Dietitians 1 (pt); Dentists 1 (pt); Podiatrists 1 (pt).
Facilities Dining room; Physical therapy room; Activities room; Chapel; Crafts room; Laundry room; Barber/Beauty shop.
Activities Arts and Crafts; Games; Reading groups; Prayer groups; Movies; Dances/Social or cultural gatherings.

Tawes/Bland Bryant Nursing Center*
Wade Ave, Spring Grove Hospital, Catonsville, MD, 21228 (301) 455-7603
Admin Haywood R Ammons. *Medical Dir/Dir of Nursing* Carl Fischer MD.
Licensure Skilled Care. *Beds* 296. *Certified* Medicaid; Medicare.
Ownership Public.

CENTREVILLE

Meridian Nursing Center—Corsica Hills*
PO Box 50, Rt 213, Centreville, MD, 21617 (301) 758-2323
Admin Michael R Baker. *Medical Dir/Dir of Nursing* John Smith Jr MD.
Licensure Skilled Care; Intermediate Care.
Beds 139. *Certified* Medicaid; Medicare.
Ownership Proprietary.

CHESTERTOWN

Magnolia Hall Inc
Morgnec Rd, Chestertown, MD, 21620 (301) 778-4550
Admin Pauline E Lindauer. *Medical Dir/Dir of Nursing* Harry P Ross MD.
Licensure Intermediate Care. *Beds* 74. *Certified* Medicaid.
Ownership Nonprofit.
Admissions Requirements Minimum age 16; Medical examination; Physician's request.
Staff RNs 3 (ft), 2 (pt); LPNs 6 (ft), 2 (pt); Nurses aides 40 (ft), 20 (pt); Recreational therapists 1 (pt); Activities coordinators 1 (ft); Dietitians 1 (pt); Podiatrists 1 (pt).
Facilities Dining room; Physical therapy room; Activities room; Chapel; Laundry room; Barber/Beauty shop.
Activities Arts and Crafts; Cards; Games; Prayer groups; Movies; Dances/Social or cultural gatherings.
Description Facility is located in a rural home-

like setting in a small town and offers general nursing care, recreational activities, special diets, and all necessary treatments including, if necessary, assistance with bathing, feeding, and incontinency care. There are additional charges for physical therapy, laboratory, equipment rental, pharmacy, and certain medical supplies; consultation is also available for dental, podiatry, and optometric services.

CHEVERLY

Prince George's Nursing Care Center
3035 Hospital Dr, Cheverly, MD, 20785 (301) 341-3350
Admin James A Hotchkiss Jr.
Licensure Skilled Care; Intermediate Care; Chronic Care. *Beds* SNF 80; ICF 80; Chronic Care 20. *Certified* Medicaid; Medicare.
Ownership Public.

CHEVY CHASE

Bethesda Retirement Nursing Center
8700 Jones Mill Rd, Chevy Chase, MD, 20015 (301) 657-8686
Admin Jeanetta M Manuel. *Medical Dir/Dir of Nursing* J Blaine Fitzgerald.
Beds 166. *Certified* Medicare.
Ownership Proprietary.
Admissions Requirements Minimum age 16; Medical examination.
Staff RNs 19 (ft); LPNs 3 (ft); Orderlies 3 (pt); Nurses aides 55 (ft); Physical therapists 1 (pt); Recreational therapists 3 (ft); Occupational therapists 1 (pt); Speech therapists 1 (pt); Activities coordinators 1 (ft); Dietitians 1 (pt); Dentists 1 (pt); Podiatrists 1 (pt); Audiologists 1 (pt).
Facilities Dining room; Physical therapy room; Activities room; Chapel; Crafts room; Barber-/Beauty shop; Library; Lounges; Lobbies; Patios.
Activities Arts and Crafts; Cards; Games; Reading groups; Prayer groups; Movies; Shopping trips; Dances/Social or cultural gatherings.
Description Primary goal of staff is to provide quality care; in addition, caring and sensitive staff are concerned about the quality of life for residents; environment reflects this with the warm and friendly atmosphere.

CLINTON

Clinton Convalescent Center
9211 Stuart Ln, Clinton, MD, 20735 (301) 868-3600
Admin Owen Schwartz. *Medical Dir/Dir of Nursing* Frank Ryan MD.
Licensure Skilled Care; Intermediate Care.
Beds 275. *Certified* Medicaid; Medicare.
Ownership Proprietary.
Staff RNs 15 (pt); LPNs 24 (pt); Nurses aides 150 (pt); Physical therapists 2 (pt); Speech therapists 1 (ft); Activities coordinators 4 (ft), 1 (pt); Dietitians 1 (ft).
Facilities Dining room; Physical therapy room; Activities room; Chapel; Crafts room; Laundry room; Barber/Beauty shop.

Activities Arts and Crafts; Cards; Games; Reading groups; Prayer groups; Movies; Dances/Social or cultural gatherings.

COCKEYSVILLE

Broadmead
13801 York Rd, Cockeysville, MD, 21030 (301) 628-6900
Admin Amelia Gerst. *Medical Dir/Dir of Nursing* Charles E Ellicott.
Licensure Skilled Care. *Beds* 97. *Certified* Medicare.
Ownership Nonprofit.
Admissions Requirements Minimum age 65; Medical examination.
Staff Physicians 4 (pt); RNs 8 (ft), 11 (pt); LPNs 5 (ft), 1 (pt); Physical therapists 3 (pt); Occupational therapists 1 (pt); Speech therapists 1 (pt); Activities coordinators 1 (ft); Dietitians 1 (pt); Dentists 1 (pt); Ophthalmologists 2 (pt); Podiatrists 2 (pt).
Affiliation Society of Friends
Facilities Dining room; Physical therapy room; Activities room; Crafts room; Laundry room; Barber/Beauty shop; Library.
Activities Arts and Crafts; Movies; Shopping trips; Dances/Social or cultural gatherings.
Description Broadmead is a community of 240 residential units built around a community center providing a wide range of services and functions including dining, crafts, recreation, medical services, nursing care, and administrative support.

Maryland Masonic Homes
Shawan Rd, Cockeysville, MD, 21030 (301) 666-2222
Admin Wilma L Stone. *Medical Dir/Dir of Nursing* Anthony Vetere.
Licensure Intermediate Care; Domiciliary Care. *Beds* 200.
Ownership Nonprofit.
Admissions Requirements Minimum age 60; Medical examination.
Staff Physicians 3 (pt); RNs 3 (ft), 6 (pt); LPNs 10 (ft); Nurses aides 46 (ft); Physical therapists 1 (pt); Recreational therapists 1 (pt); Speech therapists 1 (pt); Activities coordinators 1 (ft); Activities coordinators 1 (pt); Dentists 1 (pt); Podiatrists 1 (pt); Social workers 1 (ft).
Affiliation Masons
Facilities Dining room; Physical therapy room; Activities room; Chapel; Crafts room; Laundry room; Barber/Beauty shop; Library.
Activities Arts and Crafts; Cards; Games; Reading groups; Movies; Shopping trips; Dances/Social or cultural gatherings.

COLUMBIA

Lorien Nursing and Convalescent Home
334 Cedar Ln, Columbia, MD, 21044 (301) 531-5151
Admin David Harans. *Medical Dir/Dir of Nursing* Jerome Hantman MD.
Licensure Intermediate Care. *Beds* 120. *Certified* Medicaid; Medicare.
Ownership Proprietary.
Staff Physicians 60 (pt); RNs 15 (ft), 8 (pt); LPNs 18 (ft), 4 (pt); Orderlies 2 (ft), 4 (pt);

Nurses aides 76 (ft), 18 (pt); Physical therapists 1 (pt); Recreational therapists 2 (pt); Occupational therapists 1 (pt); Speech therapists 1 (pt); Activities coordinators 1 (ft), 1 (pt); Dietitians 2 (ft); Dentists 1 (pt); Ophthalmologists 1 (pt); Podiatrists 1 (pt); Audiologists 1 (pt).
Facilities Dining room; Physical therapy room; Activities room; Chapel; Laundry room; Barber/Beauty shop.
Activities Arts and Crafts; Games; Reading groups; Prayer groups; Movies.

CRISFIELD

Alice Byrd Tawes Nursing Home
Halls Hwy, Crisfield, MD, 21817 (301) 968-1200
Admin Melvyn R Creeley. *Medical Dir/Dir of Nursing* James Sterling MD.
Licensure Skilled Care; Intermediate Care.
Beds 64. *Certified* Medicaid; Medicare.
Ownership Nonprofit.
Admissions Requirements Minimum age 14.
Staff Physicians 2 (pt); RNs 1 (ft), 2 (pt); LPNs 6 (ft), 2 (pt); Nurses aides 15 (ft), 10 (pt); Physical therapists 1 (pt); Activities coordinators 1 (ft); Dietitians 1 (ft); Dentists 1 (pt); Podiatrists 1 (pt).
Facilities Dining room; Physical therapy room; Activities room; Crafts room; Laundry room; Barber/Beauty shop.
Activities Arts and Crafts; Games; Reading groups; Prayer groups; Shopping trips; Dances/Social or cultural gatherings.
Description The Alice Byrd Tawes Nursing Home is characterized by its location on the eastern shore of Maryland overlooking the Chesapeake Bay; situated adjacent to the Edward W McCready Hospital.

CROFTON

Crofton Convalescent Center
2500 Davidsonville Rd, Crofton, MD, 21114 (301) 721-1000
Admin Celeste T Phelps. *Medical Dir/Dir of Nursing* Max C Frank MD.
Licensure Skilled Care; Intermediate Care.
Beds 110. *Certified* Medicaid; Medicare.
Ownership Proprietary.
Admissions Requirements Minimum age 14; Medical examination.
Staff Physicians 2 (pt); RNs 8 (ft), 8 (pt); LPNs 6 (pt); Nurses aides 43 (ft), 13 (pt); Physical therapists 2 (pt); Activities coordinators 1 (ft).
Facilities Dining room; Physical therapy room; Activities room; Chapel; Laundry room; Barber/Beauty shop; Library.
Activities Arts and Crafts; Cards; Games; Reading groups; Prayer groups; Movies; Shopping trips; Dances/Social or cultural gatherings.
Description Center was conceived as a means to provide much needed professional and personalized care to the expanding population of citizens in the metropolitan area. Organized in 1975 responding to the need for a facility intended not only to provide modern and sophisticated care, but more importantly a sincere commitment on the part of the staff to render a personal service with love and concern.

CROWNSVILLE

Crownsville Hospital Center-Phillips Building*
Crownsville, MD, 21032 (601) 987-6200
Admin Dennis Bryne. *Medical Dir/Dir of Nursing* Olmpia Aybar.
Beds 100.
Ownership Public.

Fairfield Nursing Center
1454 Fairfield Loop Rd, Crownsville, MD, 21032 (301) 987-6338
Admin Calvin W Parker. *Medical Dir/Dir of Nursing* Richard Hochman MD.
Licensure Skilled Care; Intermediate Care.
Beds 140. *Certified* Medicaid; Medicare.
Ownership Nonprofit.
Admissions Requirements Minimum age 19.
Staff Physicians 1 (pt); RNs 12 (ft), 7 (pt); LPNs 9 (ft), 3 (pt); Nurses aides 63 (ft), 33 (pt); Physical therapists 1 (ft); Occupational therapists 1 (pt); Speech therapists 2 (pt); Activities coordinators 1 (ft); Dietitians 2 (pt).
Facilities Dining room; Physical therapy room; Activities room; Crafts room; Laundry room; Barber/Beauty shop; Library.
Activities Arts and Crafts; Cards; Games; Reading groups; Movies; Shopping trips; Dances/Social or cultural gatherings.
Description Satellites of this nursing center are the Fairfield Community Therapy Center, Fairfield Social Adult Day Care Center, Fairfield Medical Adult Day Care Center, Case Managers, Personal Care in Home, and Fairfield Home Health Agency.

CUMBERLAND

Allegany County Nursing Home
Furnace St Ext, PO Box 599, Cumberland, MD, 21502 (301) 777-5941
Admin Bertie M Stotler. *Medical Dir/Dir of Nursing* Dr Robustiano J Barrera.
Licensure Intermediate Care. *Beds* 153. *Certified* Medicaid.
Ownership Public.
Staff Physicians 1 (ft), 1 (pt); RNs 4 (ft), 2 (pt); LPNs 10 (ft), 9 (pt); Orderlies 9 (ft), 9 (pt); Nurses aides 29 (ft), 27 (pt); Physical therapists 1 (ft); Activities coordinators 1 (ft), 1 (pt); Dietitians 1 (ft); Dentists 1 (ft); Podiatrists 1 (ft).
Facilities Dining room; Physical therapy room; Activities room; Crafts room; Laundry room; Barber/Beauty shop.
Activities Arts and Crafts; Cards; Games; Prayer groups; Movies; Dances/Social or cultural gatherings; Birthday parties.

Cumberland Villa Nursing Center*
510 Winifred Rd, Cumberland, MD, 21502 (301) 724-6066
Admin Shirley E Paulus. *Medical Dir/Dir of Nursing* Peter B Halmos.
Licensure Skilled Care; Intermediate Care.
Beds 135. *Certified* Medicaid.
Ownership Proprietary.

Joseph D Brandenburg Center
Country Club Rd, PO Box 1722, Cumberland, MD, 21502 (301) 777-2250
Admin Carolyn K Brown. *Medical Dir/Dir of Nursing* Dr Gary Wagoner.

Licensure Intermediate Care for Mentally Retarded. *Beds* 50. *Certified* Medicaid.
Ownership Public.
Admissions Requirements Minimum age 18.
Staff Physicians 1 (pt); RNs 6 (ft); LPNs 3 (ft); Physical therapists 1 (pt); Recreational therapists 2 (ft); Occupational therapists 1 (ft); Speech therapists 1 (ft), 1 (pt); Audiologists 2 (pt).
Facilities Dining room; Physical therapy room; Activities room; Crafts room; Laundry room; Barber/Beauty shop; Library.
Activities Arts and Crafts; Games; Movies; Shopping trips; Dances/Social or cultural gatherings.

Lions Manor Nursing Home
Seton Dr Ext, Cumberland, MD, 21502 (301) 722-6272
Admin Leo J Bechtold. *Medical Dir/Dir of Nursing* Ralph P Erdly MD.
Licensure Skilled Care; Intermediate Care.
Beds 101. *Certified* Medicaid; Medicare.
Ownership Nonprofit.
Admissions Requirements Minimum age 14; Medical examination.
Staff Physicians 3 (pt); RNs 6 (ft), 2 (pt); LPNs 8 (ft); Orderlies 3 (ft), 1 (pt); Nurses aides 35 (ft), 5 (pt); Physical therapists 1 (pt); Activities coordinators 2 (ft), 1 (pt); Dietitians 1 (pt).
Facilities Dining room; Physical therapy room; Activities room; Crafts room; Laundry room; Barber/Beauty shop; Library.
Activities Arts and Crafts; Cards; Games; Reading groups; Prayer groups; Movies; Shopping trips; Dances/Social or cultural gatherings; Birthday and holiday parties; Resident Council; Outings in handicap vehicle; Religious services; Volunteer Corps.
Description Lions Manor is located on spacious, landscaped grounds in a residential area atop Haystack Mountain and is adjacent to Sacred Heart Hospital. Lions Manor is an independent, nonprofit facility, established and governed by the Nursing Home Board of Allegany County, which is composed of volunteer members selected from the local community.

DENTON

Caroline Nursing Home Inc
520 Kerr Ave, Denton, MD, 21629 (301) 479-2130
Admin Karen L Potter. *Medical Dir/Dir of Nursing* Cynthia Lipsitz MD.
Licensure Skilled Care; Intermediate Care.
Beds 76. *Certified* Medicaid; Medicare.
Ownership Nonprofit.
Admissions Requirements Minimum age 18.
Staff Physicians 6 (pt); RNs 4 (ft), 4 (pt); LPNs 4 (ft), 5 (pt); Nurses aides 24 (ft), 26 (pt); Physical therapists 1 (pt); Occupational therapists 1 (pt); Speech therapists 1 (pt); Activities coordinators 1 (ft); Dietitians 1 (pt); Dentists 1 (pt); Ophthalmologists 1 (pt); Podiatrists 1 (pt).
Facilities Dining room; Physical therapy room; Activities room; Chapel; Crafts room; Laundry room; Barber/Beauty shop.
Activities Arts and Crafts; Cards; Games; Reading groups; Prayer groups; Movies; Shopping trips.

Wesleyan Health Care Center Inc*
280 Camp Rd, Denton, MD, 21629 (601) 479-4400
Admin Anthony Grieco. *Medical Dir/Dir of Nursing* Philip Felipe MD.
Beds 120.
Ownership Nonprofit.

EASTON

Memorial Hospital—Easton
219 S Washington St, Easton, MD, 21601 (301) 822-1000
Admin Nick Rajacich. *Medical Dir/Dir of Nursing* Albert T Dawkins MD.
Licensure Skilled Care; Intermediate Care.
Beds 33. *Certified* Medicaid; Medicare.
Ownership Nonprofit.
Admissions Requirements Minimum age 14; Physician's request.
Staff RNs 4 (ft), 2 (pt); LPNs 1 (ft), 3 (pt); Nurses aides 15 (ft).

Meridian Nursing Center—The Pines
Rt 50 and Dutchman's Ln, Easton, MD, 21601 (301) 822-4000
Admin Bruce Levin. *Medical Dir/Dir of Nursing* Stephen P Carney MD.
Licensure Skilled Care; Intermediate Care; Domiciliary Care. *Beds* SNF 181; ICF 42; Domiciliary Care 22. *Certified* Medicaid; Medicare.
Ownership Proprietary.

William Hill Manor
501 Dutchman's Ln, Easton, MD, 21601
Admin Esther L Russell. *Medical Dir/Dir of Nursing* Dr Albert Dawkins.
Licensure Skilled Care; Intermediate Care.
Beds 60. *Certified* Medicaid; Medicare.
Ownership Proprietary.
Admissions Requirements Minimum age 55; Medical examination; Physician's request.
Staff Physicians 1 (pt); RNs 2 (ft), 4 (pt); LPNs 3 (ft), 4 (pt); Orderlies 1 (ft); Nurses aides 17 (ft), 9 (pt); Physical therapists 2 (pt); Occupational therapists 1 (pt); Speech therapists 1 (pt); Activities coordinators 2 (ft); Dietitians 1 (pt); Dentists 1 (pt); Ophthalmologists 1 (pt); Podiatrists 1 (pt).
Facilities Dining room; Physical therapy room; Activities room; Crafts room; Laundry room; Barber/Beauty shop; Library; Cocktail lounge/bar; Gift shop; Post office/mail room; Full service bank.
Activities Arts and Crafts; Cards; Games; Reading groups; Prayer groups; Movies; Shopping trips; Dances/Social or cultural gatherings; Guest speakers; Special dinners and parties; Exercise classes.
Description Facility is located on the beautiful eastern shore of Maryland lending itself to a variety of beautiful settings; easy access to Baltimore, Washington, Annapolis, Chesapeake Bay, and ocean resort areas make available many in-house or outside activities.

EDGEWATER

Pleasant Living Convalescent Center
144 Washington Rd, Edgewater, MD, 21037
Admin Howard Waltz Jr. *Medical Dir/Dir of Nursing* Charles W Kinzer MD.
Licensure Skilled Care; Intermediate Care.
Beds 120. *Certified* Medicaid; Medicare.
Ownership Proprietary.
Admissions Requirements Minimum age 14; Medical examination; Physician's request.
Staff Physicians 17 (pt); RNs 6 (ft), 4 (pt); LPNs 5 (ft), 7 (pt); Orderlies 6 (ft); Nurses aides 37 (ft), 28 (pt); Physical therapists 1 (pt); Recreational therapists 1 (ft); Speech therapists 1 (pt); Activities coordinators 2 (ft); Dietitians 1 (pt); Dentists 1 (pt); Ophthalmologists 1 (pt); Podiatrists 1 (pt); Audiologists 1 (pt).
Facilities Dining room; Physical therapy room; Activities room; Chapel; Crafts room; Laundry room; Barber/Beauty shop; Library.
Activities Arts and Crafts; Cards; Games; Reading groups; Prayer groups; Movies; Shopping trips; Dances/Social or cultural gatherings; Picnic outings.
Description This facility offers selected menus 3 times weekly; set in a wooded area with outside recreation facilities, fish pond, gazebo, huge arbor with flowered vines for shade and summer comfort.

ELKTON

Devine Haven Convalescent Home*
224 E Main St, Elkton, MD, 21921 (301) 398-4550
Admin William J Clark. *Medical Dir/Dir of Nursing* S Ralph Andrews Jr MD.
Licensure Intermediate Care. *Beds* 43. *Certified* Medicaid.
Ownership Proprietary.

Laurelwood Nursing Center*
100 Laurel Dr, Elkton, MD, 21921 (301) 398-8800
Admin Carole McMullen. *Medical Dir/Dir of Nursing* Joseph Lanzi MD.
Licensure Skilled Care; Intermediate Care.
Beds 130. *Certified* Medicaid.
Ownership Proprietary.

ESSEX

Riverview Nursing Centre
One Eastern Blvd, Essex, MD, 21221 (301) 574-1400
Admin Wayne K DeFontes. *Medical Dir/Dir of Nursing* Morris Rainess MD.
Licensure Intermediate Care. *Beds* 305. *Certified* Medicaid.
Ownership Proprietary.
Admissions Requirements Minimum age 14; Medical examination.
Staff Physicians 2 (pt); RNs 8 (ft), 2 (pt); LPNs 20 (ft), 10 (pt); Orderlies 8 (ft), 4 (pt); Nurses aides 150 (ft), 30 (pt); Physical therapists 2 (ft); Recreational therapists 3 (ft), 2 (pt); Speech therapists 1 (pt); Activities coordinators 1 (ft), 2 (pt); Dietitians 1 (pt); Dentists 1 (pt); Ophthalmologists 1 (pt); Podiatrists 1 (pt); Audiologists 1 (pt).

Facilities Dining room; Physical therapy room; Activities room; Chapel; Crafts room; Laundry room; Barber/Beauty shop; Library.
Activities Arts and Crafts; Cards; Games; Reading groups; Prayer groups; Movies; Shopping trips; Dances/Social or cultural gatherings.

FORESTVILLE

Regency Nursing and Rehabilitation Treatment Center
7420 Marlboro Pike, Forestville, MD, 20028 (301) 736-0240
Admin Jean R Rock. *Medical Dir/Dir of Nursing* Kelvin L Minchin MD.
Licensure Skilled Care; Intermediate Care.
Beds 160. *Certified* Medicaid; Medicare.
Ownership Proprietary.
Admissions Requirements Minimum age 14; Medical examination.
Staff RNs 4 (ft), 6 (pt); LPNs 5 (ft), 4 (pt); Orderlies 61 (ft), 11 (pt); Recreational therapists 1 (ft); Activities coordinators 1 (ft).
Facilities Dining room; Physical therapy room; Activities room; Crafts room; Laundry room; Barber/Beauty shop; Library.
Activities Arts and Crafts; Cards; Games; Reading groups; Prayer groups; Movies; Shopping trips; Dances/Social or cultural gatherings.

FORT WASHINGTON

Fort Washington Rehabilitation Center
12021 Livingston Rd, Fort Washington, MD, 20744
Admin Lois A McGovern. *Medical Dir/Dir of Nursing* William Furst MD.
Licensure Skilled Care; Intermediate Care.
Beds 150. *Certified* Medicaid; Medicare.
Ownership Proprietary.
Admissions Requirements Minimum age 14; Medical examination.
Staff Physicians 16 (pt); RNs 6 (ft), 14 (pt); LPNs 14 (ft), 8 (pt); Nurses aides 120 (ft); Physical therapists 2 (ft); Reality therapists 1 (ft); Recreational therapists 1 (ft); Occupational therapists 1 (ft); Speech therapists 1 (ft); Activities coordinators 1 (ft); Dietitians 1 (ft); Dentists 1 (pt); Ophthalmologists 1 (pt); Podiatrists 1 (pt); Audiologists 1 (pt).
Facilities Dining room; Physical therapy room; Activities room; Crafts room; Laundry room; Barber/Beauty shop.
Activities Arts and Crafts; Cards; Games; Reading groups; Prayer groups; Movies; Shopping trips; Dances/Social or cultural gatherings; Adult education.
Description Facility offers a coordinated rehabilitation program of occupational, speech, and physical therapy.

FREDERICK

Citizens Nursing Home of Frederick County
2200 Rosemont Ave, Frederick, MD, 21701 (301) 694-1550
Admin William P Hill Jr. *Medical Dir/Dir of Nursing* B O Thomas Jr MD.
Licensure Skilled Care; Intermediate Care.
Beds 170. *Certified* Medicaid; Medicare.
Ownership Public.

Staff Physicians 1 (pt); RNs 12 (ft), 8 (pt); LPNs 7 (ft), 10 (pt); Nurses aides 50 (ft), 35 (pt); Physical therapists 2 (pt); Speech therapists 1 (pt); Activities coordinators 1 (ft); Dietitians 1 (ft), 1 (pt).
Facilities Dining room; Physical therapy room; Activities room; Chapel; Crafts room; Laundry room; Barber/Beauty shop; Library.
Activities Arts and Crafts; Cards; Games; Reading groups; Prayer groups; Movies; Shopping trips.

Home for the Aged—Frederick*
115 Record St, Frederick, MD, 21701 (301) 663-6822
Admin Dorothy A Stamm. *Medical Dir/Dir of Nursing* Timothy Hicky MD.
Licensure Intermediate Care; Domiciliary Care. *Beds* ICF 6; Domiciliary Care 23.
Ownership Nonprofit.

Homewood Retirement Center—Frederick
31 W Patrick St, Frederick, MD, 21701 (301) 694-7292
Admin Joseph H Clem. *Medical Dir/Dir of Nursing* George I Smith Jr MD.
Licensure Skilled Care; Domiciliary Care.
Beds 93. *Certified* Medicaid.
Ownership Nonprofit.
Admissions Requirements Minimum age 60; Medical examination; Physician's request.
Staff RNs 5 (ft), 6 (pt); LPNs 10 (ft), 4 (pt); Nurses aides 34 (ft), 11 (pt); Physical therapists 1 (pt); Speech therapists 1 (pt); Activities coordinators 1 (ft); Dietitians 1 (pt); Dentists 1 (pt); Podiatrists 1 (pt).
Affiliation Church of Christ
Facilities Dining room; Physical therapy room; Activities room; Chapel; Crafts room; Laundry room; Barber/Beauty shop; Library; Game room; Sunshine room.
Activities Arts and Crafts; Cards; Games; Reading groups; Prayer groups; Movies; Shopping trips; Dances/Social or cultural gatherings; Bingo; Birthday parties.
Description Downtown location, very convenient to stores and restaurants.

Meridian Nursing Center—Frederick
400 North Ave, Frederick, MD, 21701 (301) 663-5181
Admin Bruce Boyer. *Medical Dir/Dir of Nursing* Gilcin Meadors MD.
Licensure Skilled Care; Intermediate Care.
Beds 166. *Certified* Medicaid; Medicare.
Ownership Proprietary.
Admissions Requirements Minimum age 14; Physician's request.
Staff Physicians 1 (pt); RNs 5 (ft), 6 (pt); LPNs 7 (ft), 5 (pt); Nurses aides 54 (ft), 11 (pt); Physical therapists 1 (pt); Activities coordinators 1 (ft), 1 (pt); Dietitians 1 (pt).
Facilities Dining room; Physical therapy room; Activities room; Chapel; Crafts room; Laundry room; Barber/Beauty shop; Library; Patio garden.
Activities Arts and Crafts; Games; Reading groups; Prayer groups; Movies; Shopping trips; Dances/Social or cultural gatherings; Daylong bus trips; Pet therapy.
Description Facility is conveniently located near the hospital, doctors offices, and shopping.

FROSTBURG

Frostburg Village Nursing Home of Allegany County*
Corner Rts 36 and 40, 1 Kaylor Circle, Frostburg, MD, 21532 (301) 689-2425
Admin Leo J Cyr. *Medical Dir/Dir of Nursing* S L Sanshir MD.
Licensure Skilled Care; Intermediate Care.
Beds 170. *Certified* Medicaid; Medicare.
Ownership Nonprofit.

GAITHERSBURG

Herman M Wilson Health Care Center*
201-301 Russell Ave, Gaithersburg, MD, 20760 (301) 926-4900
Admin Alan W Porterfield. *Medical Dir/Dir of Nursing* Henry Scruggs MD.
Licensure Skilled Care; Intermediate Care.
Beds 279. *Certified* Medicaid; Medicare.
Ownership Nonprofit.

GARRISON

Garrison Valley Center Inc
Reisterstown and Greenspring Valley Rd, Garrison, MD, 21055 (301) 363-3337
Admin Ida M Campanella. *Medical Dir/Dir of Nursing* Allan H Macht.
Licensure Intermediate Care. *Beds* 76. *Certified* Medicaid.
Ownership Proprietary.
Admissions Requirements Minimum age 16.
Staff RNs 1 (ft), 3 (pt); LPNs 1 (ft); Orderlies 3 (ft); Nurses aides 24 (ft); Physical therapists 1 (pt); Activities coordinators 1 (ft); Dietitians 1 (pt).
Facilities Dining room; Activities room; Laundry room; Library.
Activities Arts and Crafts; Games; Reading groups; Movies; Parties.

GLEN BURNIE

Maryland Manor of Glen Burnie
7575 E Howard St, Glen Burnie, MD, 21061 (301) 768-8200
Admin Paul J Robertson. *Medical Dir/Dir of Nursing* Peter Rheinstein MD.
Licensure Skilled Care. *Beds* 99. *Certified* Medicaid; Medicare.
Ownership Proprietary.
Admissions Requirements Minimum age 18; Medical examination.
Staff Physicians; RNs; LPNs; Orderlies; Nurses aides; Physical therapists; Speech therapists; Activities coordinators; Dietitians; Dentists; Ophthalmologists; Podiatrists; Audiologists.
Facilities Dining room; Physical therapy room; Activities room; Chapel; Crafts room; Laundry room; Barber/Beauty shop; Library.
Activities Arts and Crafts; Cards; Games; Reading groups; Prayer groups; Movies; Shopping trips; Dances/Social or cultural gatherings.

North Arundel Nursing and Convalescent Center Inc*
313 Hospital Dr, Glen Burnie, MD, 21061 (301) 761-1222

Admin Shirley McKnight. *Medical Dir/Dir of Nursing* Mustafa C Oz MD.
Licensure Skilled Care; Intermediate Care.
Beds 101. *Certified* Medicaid; Medicare.
Ownership Proprietary.

Plaza Manor Nursing Home*
7355 Furnace Branch Rd E, Glen Burnie, MD, 21061 (301) 766-3460
Admin Brenda Watson. *Medical Dir/Dir of Nursing* Edward Hunt Jr MD.
Licensure Skilled Care; Intermediate Care.
Beds 115. *Certified* Medicaid.
Ownership Proprietary.

GRANTSVILLE

Goodwill Mennonite Home Inc
Dorsey Hotel Rd, Grantsville, MD, 21536 (301) 895-5194
Admin R Henry Diller. *Medical Dir/Dir of Nursing* George Stoltzfus MD.
Licensure Intermediate Care. *Beds* 81. *Certified* Medicaid.
Ownership Nonprofit.
Admissions Requirements Medical examination.
Staff RNs 1 (ft); LPNs 5 (ft); Orderlies 4 (ft), 1 (pt); Nurses aides 20 (ft); Activities coordinators 1 (ft).
Affiliation Mennonite
Facilities Dining room; Physical therapy room; Activities room; Chapel; Crafts room; Laundry room; Barber/Beauty shop.
Activities Arts and Crafts; Games; Movies.

GREENBELT

Greenbelt Nursing Center*
7010 Greenbelt Rd, Greenbelt, MD, 20770 (301) 345-9595
Admin Carol A Powell. *Medical Dir/Dir of Nursing* David Granite MD.
Licensure Skilled Care; Intermediate Care.
Beds 132. *Certified* Medicaid; Medicare.
Ownership Proprietary.

HAGERSTOWN

Avalon Manor
Rt 8, Box 35, Hagerstown, MD, 21740 (301) 739-9360
Admin Stuart Ricker. *Medical Dir/Dir of Nursing* Dr William Lesh.
Licensure Intermediate Care. *Beds* 211. *Certified* Medicaid.
Ownership Proprietary.
Admissions Requirements Medical examination.
Staff Physicians 3 (pt); RNs 7 (ft), 2 (pt); LPNs 16 (ft), 2 (pt); Nurses aides 96 (ft), 1 (pt); Recreational therapists 2 (ft); Activities coordinators 2 (pt); Dietitians 1 (pt); Dentists 1 (pt); Podiatrists 1 (pt).
Facilities Dining room; Activities room; Crafts room; Laundry room; Barber/Beauty shop; Lounges.
Activities Arts and Crafts; Cards; Games; Prayer groups; Movies; Shopping trips; Dances/Social or cultural gatherings.
Description Manor is situated on 26 acres just

north of Hagerstown, catering to short-term convalescing and long-term residency; quality nursing care is administered with the goal of rehabilitating those in need.

Clearview Nursing Home Inc*
Rt 3, Box 144, Hagerstown, MD, 21740 (301) 582-1654
Admin Willa Jean Vaters. *Medical Dir/Dir of Nursing* John D Wilson MD.
Licensure Intermediate Care. *Beds* 49. *Certified* Medicaid.
Ownership Proprietary.

Coffman Home for the Aging Inc*
1304 Pennsylvania Ave, Hagerstown, MD, 21740 (301) 733-2914
Admin Ruth Yvonne Eyler. *Medical Dir/Dir of Nursing* J D Wilson MD.
Licensure Intermediate Care. *Beds* 51. *Certified* Medicaid.
Ownership Public.

Colton Villa Nursing Center
750 Dual Hwy, Hagerstown, MD, 21740 (301) 797-4020
Admin Margaret V Saylor. *Medical Dir/Dir of Nursing* Dr Abdul Waheed.
Licensure Skilled Care; Intermediate Care.
Beds 160. *Certified* Medicaid; Medicare.
Ownership Proprietary.
Admissions Requirements Minimum age 18; Medical examination; Physician's request.
Staff Physicians 1 (pt); RNs 8 (ft), 3 (pt); LPNs 9 (ft), 3 (pt); Nurses aides 60 (ft), 4 (pt); Physical therapists 1 (pt); Speech therapists 2 (pt); Activities coordinators 2 (ft); Dietitians 1 (pt); Podiatrists 1 (pt).
Facilities Dining room; Activities room; Laundry room; Barber/Beauty shop.
Activities Arts and Crafts; Cards; Games; Reading groups; Prayer groups; Movies; Shopping trips; Dances/Social or cultural gatherings.
Description Facility provides speech therapy and audiological services, physical therapy, Adopt-a-grandparent program, and active volunteer program. This is a Beverly Enterprise nursing facility.

Garlock Memorial Convalescent Home Inc*
241 S Prospect St, Hagerstown, MD, 21740 (301) 733-3310
Admin David L Brown. *Medical Dir/Dir of Nursing* Sidney Novenstein MD.
Licensure Intermediate Care. *Beds* 37. *Certified* Medicaid.
Ownership Proprietary.

Potomac Center*
1380 Marshall St, Hagerstown, MD, 21740 (301) 791-4650
Admin Steven J Smith. *Medical Dir/Dir of Nursing* J Ramsey Farah MD.
Licensure Intermediate Care for Mentally Retarded. *Beds* 150. *Certified* Medicaid.
Ownership Public.

Ravenwood Lutheran Village Nursing Home
1183 Luther Dr, Hagerstown, MD, 21740 (301) 790-1000
Admin Carole L Malin.
Licensure Skilled Care; Intermediate Care.

Beds 86. *Certified* Medicaid; Medicare.
Ownership Nonprofit.
Affiliation Lutheran

Western Maryland Center*
1500 Pennsylvania Ave, Hagerstown, MD,
21740 (301) 791-4430
Admin Wilfred T Tumbusch. *Medical Dir/Dir
of Nursing* F U Porciumcula MD.
Licensure Skilled Care; Intermediate Care.
Beds SNF 62; ICF 92. *Certified* Medicaid;
Medicare.
Ownership Public.

HAVRE DE GRACE

Brevin Nursing Home Inc
421 S Union Ave, Havre de Grace, MD, 21078
(301) 935-1740
Admin Jerrold F Bress.
Licensure Intermediate Care. *Beds* 40. *Certified* Medicaid.
Ownership Proprietary.

Citizens Nursing Home of Harford County
415 S Market St, Havre de Grace, MD, 21078
(301) 939-5500
Admin John C Fisher. *Medical Dir/Dir of
Nursing* John D Yun MD.
Licensure Skilled Care; Intermediate Care.
Beds 200. *Certified* Medicaid; Medicare.
Ownership Public.
Admissions Requirements Minimum age 14;
Medical examination; Physician's request.
Staff RNs 4 (ft), 6 (pt); LPNs 14 (ft), 11 (pt);
Nurses aides 48 (ft), 42 (pt); Activities coordinators 1 (ft); Dietitians 1 (ft).
Facilities Dining room; Physical therapy room;
Activities room; Chapel; Crafts room; Laundry
room; Barber/Beauty shop; Enclosed courtyard.
Activities Arts and Crafts; Cards; Games; Prayer groups; Movies; Shopping trips; Dances/Social or cultural gatherings; Outside
entertainment; College programs.
Description Facility is situated on the Susquehanna River 2 blocks from Harford
Memorial Hospital; air conditioned throughout; cable TV is provided at no additional cost;
telephone jacks are located in each patient's
room.

HENRYTON

Henryton Center*
8000 Henryton Rd, Henryton, MD, 21080
(301) 795-2400
Admin Charles Leight. *Medical Dir/Dir of
Nursing* Ella Sutton-Soliman MD.
Licensure Intermediate Care for Mentally
Retarded. *Beds* 330. *Certified* Medicaid.
Ownership Public.

HYATTSVILLE

Carroll Manor Nursing Home
4922 LaSalle Rd, Hyattsville, MD, 20782 (301)
864-2333
Admin Mother Margaret Patrick. *Medical Dir-
/Dir of Nursing* Dr Thomas E Curtin.
Licensure Skilled Care; Intermediate Care.
Beds 232. *Certified* Medicaid; Medicare.

Ownership Nonprofit.
Admissions Requirements Minimum age 60;
Medical examination; Physician's request.
Staff Physicians 2 (pt); RNs 10 (ft), 9 (pt);
LPNs 12 (ft), 4 (pt); Orderlies 1 (ft); Nurses
aides 85 (ft), 10 (pt); Physical therapists 2 (pt);
Recreational therapists 2 (ft); Activities coordinators 1 (ft); Dietitians 1 (ft); Dentists 1 (pt);
Podiatrists 2 (pt).
Affiliation Roman Catholic
Facilities Dining room; Physical therapy room;
Activities room; Chapel; Crafts room; Laundry
room; Barber/Beauty shop; Library; Cocktail
lounge; Auditorium.
Activities Arts and Crafts; Cards; Games;
Reading groups; Prayer groups; Movies; Shopping trips; Dances/Social or cultural gatherings.
Description In collaboration with the Catholic
University of America, Carroll Manor is a
teaching nursing home in the Robert Wood
Johnson Foundation Grant Program.

Hyattsville Manor*
6500 Riggs Rd, Hyattsville, MD, 20783 (301)
559-0300
Admin Steven Hatlestad. *Medical Dir/Dir of
Nursing* Myron Lenkin MD.
Licensure Skilled Care; Intermediate Care.
Beds 151. *Certified* Medicaid; Medicare.
Ownership Proprietary.

Madison Manor Nursing Home*
5801 42nd Ave, Hyattsville, MD, 20781 (301)
864-8800
Admin Collette Storck. *Medical Dir/Dir of
Nursing* B Arora MD.
Licensure Intermediate Care. *Beds* 27. *Certified* Medicaid.
Ownership Proprietary.

Sacred Heart Home*
5805 Queens Chapel Rd, Hyattsville, MD,
20782 (301) 277-6500
Admin Eugene Zibrat. *Medical Dir/Dir of
Nursing* Ibrahim Khatri MD.
Licensure Skilled Care; Intermediate Care.
Beds 102. *Certified* Medicaid.
Ownership Nonprofit.

KENSINGTON

Circle Manor Nursing Home
10231 Carroll Pl, Kensington, MD, 20795 (301)
949-0222
Admin Ellis J Duke. *Medical Dir/Dir of
Nursing* Dr Avrunin, Dr Rosenbaum, and Dr
Shargel.
Licensure Intermediate Care. *Beds* 86. *Certified* Medicaid.
Ownership Proprietary.
Staff RNs 3 (ft), 1 (pt); LPNs 3 (ft), 3 (pt);
Nurses aides 34 (ft), 3 (pt); Activities coordinators 2 (ft); Dietitians 1 (pt).
Facilities Dining room; Activities room; Crafts
room; Laundry room; Barber/Beauty shop.
Activities Arts and Crafts; Cards; Games;
Reading groups; Prayer groups; Movies; Shopping trips; Dances/Social or cultural gatherings.
Description Facility features an old Victorian
mansion set on 5 acres of lawn. Beautiful country atmosphere in the middle of town.

Kensington Gardens Nursing Home
3000 McComas Ave, Kensington, MD, 20795
(301) 933-0060
Admin Faye Lucas. *Medical Dir/Dir of
Nursing* David Kessler.
Licensure Intermediate Care; Comprehensive
Care. *Beds* 170. *Certified* Medicaid; Medicare.
Ownership Proprietary.
Admissions Requirements Minimum age 17;
Medical examination.
Staff RNs 16 (ft), 4 (pt); LPNs 8 (ft), 1 (pt);
Orderlies 22 (ft); Nurses aides 16 (ft); Physical
therapists 1 (ft); Recreational therapists 4 (ft);
Speech therapists 1 (pt); Activities coordinators
1 (ft); Dietitians 1 (pt); Dentists 1 (pt); Podiatrists 1 (pt).
Facilities Dining room; Physical therapy room;
Activities room; Crafts room; Laundry room;
Barber/Beauty shop.
Activities Arts and Crafts; Cards; Games;
Reading groups; Prayer groups; Movies; Shopping trips; Dances/Social or cultural gatherings.
Description Facility is located on 19 acres with
pond; offers family-style dining.

LA PLATA

Charles County Nursing Home*
Rt 488, Box 1320, La Plata, MD, 20646 (301)
934-1900
Admin Lester E Clough. *Medical Dir/Dir of
Nursing* Paul Prichard MD.
Licensure Skilled Care; Intermediate Care.
Beds 105. *Certified* Medicaid; Medicare.
Ownership Public.

LANHAM

Magnolia Gardens Nursing Home*
8200 Good Luck Rd, Lanham, MD, 20801
(301) 552-2000
Admin William R Greco. *Medical Dir/Dir of
Nursing* Leon Levitsky MD.
Licensure Skilled Care; Intermediate Care.
Beds 104. *Certified* Medicaid; Medicare.
Ownership Proprietary.

LAUREL

Greater Laurel Nursing Home*
14200 Laurel Pk Dr, Laurel, MD, 20707 (601)
792-4717
Admin Margaret Sybert. *Medical Dir/Dir of
Nursing* Gregory Compton MD.
Beds 131.
Ownership Proprietary.

LEONARDTOWN

Saint Mary's Nursing Home
PO Box 418, Leonardtown, MD, 20650 (301)
475-5681
Admin George E Smith. *Medical Dir/Dir of
Nursing* J Roy Guyther MD.
Licensure Skilled Care; Intermediate Care.
Beds SNF 36; ICF 30. *Certified* Medicaid;
Medicare.
Ownership Nonprofit.
Admissions Requirements Minimum age 14;
Physician's request.

Staff RNs 3 (ft), 2 (pt); LPNs 8 (ft), 1 (pt); Nurses aides 19 (ft), 14 (pt); Physical therapists 1 (pt); Activities coordinators 1 (ft); Dietitians 1 (pt); Dentists 1 (pt); Podiatrists 1 (pt). *Facilities* Dining room; Activities room; Chapel; Laundry room; Barber/Beauty shop. *Activities* Arts and Crafts; Cards; Games; Reading groups; Prayer groups; Dances/Social or cultural gatherings.

LEXINGTON PARK

Amber House
Great Mills Rd, PO Box 620, Lexington Park, MD, 20653
Admin Jack Upchurch Jr. *Medical Dir/Dir of Nursing* Dr James Boyd.
Licensure Skilled Care; Intermediate Care. *Beds* 123. *Certified* Medicaid; Medicare. *Ownership* Proprietary.
Admissions Requirements Minimum age 14; Physician's request.
Staff Physicians 1 (pt); RNs 5 (ft); LPNs 12 (ft), 6 (pt); Orderlies 3 (ft); Nurses aides 45 (ft), 13 (pt); Physical therapists 1 (pt); Speech therapists 1 (pt); Activities coordinators 1 (ft), 2 (pt); Dietitians 1 (ft); Dentists 1 (pt); Ophthalmologists 1 (pt); Podiatrists 1 (pt).
Facilities Dining room; Physical therapy room; Activities room; Crafts room; Laundry room; Barber/Beauty shop; Library.
Activities Arts and Crafts; Cards; Games; Reading groups; Prayer groups; Movies; Shopping trips; Dances/Social or cultural gatherings.
Description Facility is located in a rural community completely surrounded by trees; a very active volunteer program complements the activities program to provide a wide range of daily activities, outings, and crafts. VA approved.

LONACONING

Egle Nursing Home
57 Jackson St, Lonaconing, MD, 21539 (301) 463-5451
Admin Vera Clark Egle. *Medical Dir/Dir of Nursing* Donald Manger MD.
Licensure Intermediate Care. *Beds* 24. *Certified* Medicaid.
Ownership Proprietary.
Admissions Requirements Minimum age 16.
Staff Physicians; RNs; LPNs; Nurses aides; Physical therapists; Reality therapists; Recreational therapists; Occupational therapists; Speech therapists; Activities coordinators; Dietitians; Dentists; Ophthalmologists; Podiatrists.
Facilities Dining room; Activities room; Crafts room; Laundry room.
Activities Arts and Crafts; Cards; Games; Reading groups; Prayer groups; Movies; Shopping trips; Dances/Social or cultural gatherings.

MANCHESTER

Long View Nursing Home*
128 N Main St, Manchester, MD, 21101 (301) 239-7139
Admin Martha J Tarutis. *Medical Dir/Dir of Nursing* Wilbur Foard MD.

Licensure Skilled Care; Intermediate Care. *Beds* 58. *Certified* Medicaid; Medicare. *Ownership* Proprietary.

MAUGANSVILLE

Mennonite Old People's Home*
Maugansville Rd, Maugansville, MD, 21767 (301) 733-5899
Admin Allen Martin.
Licensure Intermediate Care. *Beds* 17. *Ownership* Nonprofit.
Affiliation Mennonite

MIDDLE RIVER

Ivy Hall
19 Harrison Ave, Middle River, MD, 21220 (301) 687-1383
Admin Darell R Cammack Jr.
Licensure Intermediate Care. *Beds* 22. *Certified* Medicaid.
Ownership Proprietary.
Staff Physicians 3 (pt); RNs 2 (ft); LPNs 4 (ft), 2 (pt); Nurses aides 10 (ft); Activities coordinators 1 (ft); Dietitians 1 (pt).
Facilities Dining room; Activities room.
Activities Arts and Crafts; Games; Prayer groups; Movies; Bingo.
Description Activities program and nursing services are individualized; outside activities are encouraged for all residents. New building with complete facilities will be completed before 1985.

MILLERSVILLE

Knollwood Manor Inc
899 Cecil Ave, PO Box 8, Millersville, MD, 21108 (301) 987-1644
Admin John H Lloyd Jr. *Medical Dir/Dir of Nursing* Paul S Rhodes MD.
Licensure Skilled Care; Intermediate Care. *Beds* 97. *Certified* Medicaid; Medicare. *Ownership* Proprietary.
Admissions Requirements Minimum age 21; Medical examination; Physician's request.
Staff RNs 3 (ft), 3 (pt); LPNs 3 (ft), 3 (pt); Orderlies 2 (ft); Nurses aides 30 (ft), 16 (pt); Activities coordinators 2 (ft).
Description VA approved.

MITCHELLVILLE

Villa Rosa Nursing Home*
3800 Lottsford Vista Rd, Mitchellville, MD, 20716 (301) 459-4700
Admin Anthony Dal Balcon. *Medical Dir/Dir of Nursing* Ciro Montanez MD.
Licensure Skilled Care; Intermediate Care. *Beds* 100.
Ownership Nonprofit.

MOUNT AIRY

Pleasant View Nursing Home of Mount Airy
4101 Baltimore, National Pike, Mount Airy, MD, 21771 (301) 829-0800
Admin Eugene E Jackson. *Medical Dir/Dir of*

Nursing Dr Melvin Kordon.
Licensure Intermediate Care. *Beds* 104. *Certified* Medicaid.
Ownership Proprietary.
Admissions Requirements Minimum age 14; Medical examination.
Staff RNs 2 (ft); LPNs 6 (ft), 4 (pt); Orderlies 1 (ft), 2 (pt); Nurses aides 20 (ft), 20 (pt); Physical therapists 1 (pt); Recreational therapists 1 (ft), 1 (pt); Occupational therapists 1 (pt); Activities coordinators 1 (ft); Dietitians 1 (pt); Dentists 1 (pt); Ophthalmologists 1 (pt); Podiatrists 1 (pt).
Facilities Dining room; Activities room; Crafts room; Laundry room; Barber/Beauty shop; Library.
Activities Arts and Crafts; Cards; Games; Reading groups; Prayer groups; Movies; Shopping trips; Dances/Social or cultural gatherings.

OAKLAND

Cuppett and Weeks Nursing Home Inc
706 E Alder, Oakland, MD, 21550 (301) 334-2333
Admin James Cuppett. *Medical Dir/Dir of Nursing* Dr B L Grant.
Licensure Intermediate Care. *Beds* 155. *Certified* Medicaid.
Ownership Proprietary.
Admissions Requirements Medical examination.
Staff Physicians 1 (pt); RNs 3 (ft), 2 (pt); LPNs 10 (ft), 1 (pt); Nurses aides 55 (ft), 7 (pt); Physical therapists 1 (pt); Occupational therapists 1 (pt); Activities coordinators 1 (ft); Dietitians 2 (pt); Dentists 1 (pt).
Facilities Dining room; Activities room; Laundry room; Barber/Beauty shop.
Activities Arts and Crafts; Cards; Games; Prayer groups; Shopping trips; Dances/Social or cultural gatherings.

Dennett Road Manor Inc
1113 Mary Dr, Oakland, MD, 21550 (301) 334-8346
Admin Thomas U Cuppett. *Medical Dir/Dir of Nursing* James H Feaster Jr MD.
Licensure Intermediate Care. *Beds* 100. *Certified* Medicaid.
Ownership Proprietary.
Admissions Requirements Minimum age 60; Medical examination; Physician's request.
Staff Physicians 10 (pt); RNs 5 (ft), 1 (pt); LPNs 5 (ft), 2 (pt); Nurses aides 23 (ft), 27 (pt); Activities coordinators 2 (ft); Dietitians 1 (ft), 1 (pt); Dentists 1 (pt); Podiatrists 1 (pt).
Facilities Dining room; Activities room; Crafts room; Laundry room; Barber/Beauty shop; Library.
Activities Arts and Crafts; Games; Reading groups; Prayer groups; Movies.

OLNEY

Brooke Grove Nursing Home*
18201 Marden Ln, Olney, MD, 20832 (301) 924-4475
Admin Eleanore L Nanson. *Medical Dir/Dir of Nursing* Charles Ligon MD.

Licensure Skilled Care; Intermediate Care.
Beds 99. *Certified* Medicaid.
Ownership Nonprofit.

Sharon Nursing Home*
18201 Marden Ln, Olney, MD, 20832 (301)
924-4475
Admin Carl E Howe. *Medical Dir/Dir of
Nursing* Charles Ligon MD.
Licensure Intermediate Care. *Beds* 45. *Certified* Medicaid.
Ownership Nonprofit.

OWINGS MILLS

Baptist Home of Maryland
10729 Park Heights Ave, Owings Mills, MD,
21117 (301) 484-3324
Admin Vlasta A Stadler. *Medical Dir/Dir of
Nursing* Dr John H Lavin.
Licensure Intermediate Care; Domiciliary
Care. *Beds* ICF 17; Domiciliary Care 47.
Ownership Nonprofit.
Admissions Requirements Minimum age 65;
Medical examination.
Staff Physicians; RNs; LPNs; Nurses aides;
Physical therapists; Activities coordinators;
Dietitians; Dentists; Ophthalmologists; Podiatrists.
Affiliation Baptist
Facilities Dining room; Activities room; Chapel; Crafts room; Laundry room; Barber/Beauty
shop.
Activities Arts and Crafts; Games; Prayer
groups; Movies; Shopping trips.
Description Facility is a converted mansion
built in 1915 on a 42-acre estate in Greenspring
Valley area, north of Baltimore; can accomodate couples.

Rosewood Center*
Rosewood Ln, Owings Mills, MD, 21117 (301)
363-0300
Admin Linda Gustaf. *Medical Dir/Dir of
Nursing* Barbara Hudson MD.
Licensure Intermediate Care for Mentally
Retarded. *Beds* 1204. *Certified* Medicaid.
Ownership Public.

PIKESVILLE

Augsburg Lutheran Home of Maryland Inc
6811 Campfeild Rd, Pikesville, MD, 21207
(301) 486-4573
Admin Norman O Payne. *Medical Dir/Dir of
Nursing* Arthur M Lebson MD.
Licensure Intermediate Care. *Beds* 78. *Certified* Medicaid.
Ownership Nonprofit.
Admissions Requirements Minimum age 65;
Medical examination.
Staff Physicians 1 (ft); RNs 2 (ft), 5 (pt); LPNs
6 (ft), 5 (pt); Nurses aides 22 (ft), 15 (pt);
Physical therapists 1 (ft); Reality therapists 1
(ft); Recreational therapists 1 (ft); Speech therapists 1 (ft); Activities coordinators 1 (ft); Dietitians 1 (ft); Dentists 2 (ft); Ophthalmologists 1
(ft); Podiatrists 1 (ft).
Affiliation Lutheran
Facilities Dining room; Activities room; Chapel; Crafts room; Laundry room; Barber/Beauty

shop; Library.
Activities Arts and Crafts; Cards; Games;
Reading groups; Prayer groups; Movies; Shopping trips; Dances/Social or cultural gatherings.

Pikesville Nursing and Convalescent Center
7 Sudbrook Ln, Pikesville, MD, 21208 (301)
486-8771
Admin Fred DiBartolo. *Medical Dir/Dir of
Nursing* Dr Harold Bob.
Licensure Skilled Care; Intermediate Care.
Beds 174. *Certified* Medicaid; Medicare.
Ownership Proprietary.
Admissions Requirements Minimum age 14;
Medical examination.
Staff RNs 6 (ft); LPNs 12 (ft), 5 (pt); Orderlies
5 (ft); Nurses aides 60 (ft), 23 (pt); Physical
therapists 1 (pt); Recreational therapists 1 (ft);
Activities coordinators 1 (ft).
Affiliation Jewish
Facilities Dining room; Physical therapy room;
Activities room; Chapel; Barber/Beauty shop;
Library; Four separate TV lounges (one on each
unit).
Activities Arts and Crafts; Prayer groups;
Movies; Numerous volunteer groups provide
entertainment.
Description Pikesville Nursing and Convalescent Center was not planned to be an ordinary nursing home. It isn't. It's a place of
dignity and encouragement. It's a place where
all are welcome. It's a place to be comfortable,
relaxed, and secure. It's a place anyone would
be proud to call home.

POCOMOKE CITY

Hartley Hall Inc
1006 Market St, Pocomoke City, MD, 21851
(301) 957-2252
Admin George W Anderson. *Medical Dir/Dir
of Nursing* Dr Paul Fleury.
Licensure Comprehensive Care. *Beds* 50. *Certified* Medicaid; Medicare.
Ownership Nonprofit.
Admissions Requirements Minimum age 16.
Staff Physicians 1 (pt); RNs 3 (ft), 2 (pt); LPNs
3 (ft), 3 (pt); Orderlies 1 (ft); Nurses aides 17
(ft), 7 (pt); Physical therapists 1 (pt); Speech
therapists 1 (pt); Activities coordinators 1 (ft);
Dietitians 1 (pt); Dentists 1 (pt); Podiatrists 1
(pt).
Facilities Dining room; Physical therapy room;
Activities room; Chapel; Crafts room; Laundry
room; Barber/Beauty shop.
Activities Arts and Crafts; Cards; Games;
Reading groups; Prayer groups; Movies.
Description All patients are charged the same
daily rate based on level of care; no additional
charge for a private room.

PRINCE FREDERICK

Calvert County Nursing Center Inc
RR 2, Box 274, Prince Frederick, MD, 20678
(301) 535-2300
Admin John A Olmstead. *Medical Dir/Dir of
Nursing* Thomas Lusby MD.
Licensure Intermediate Care. *Beds* 98. *Certified* Medicaid.
Ownership Nonprofit.

Calvert House Corp
Rt 1, Box 1, Prince Frederick, MD, 20678 (301)
535-0984
Admin Helen P Marsellas. *Medical Dir/Dir of
Nursing* George J Weems MD.
Licensure Intermediate Care. *Beds* 50. *Certified* Medicaid.
Ownership Proprietary.
Admissions Requirements Minimum age 14;
Medical examination; Physician's request.
Staff Physicians 3 (pt); RNs 3 (ft); LPNs 2 (ft);
Nurses aides 22 (ft), 2 (pt); Physical therapists 1
(pt); Activities coordinators 1 (ft); Dietitians 1
(pt); Dentists 1 (pt); Podiatrists 1 (pt).
Facilities Dining room; Physical therapy room;
Laundry room.
Activities Arts and Crafts; Cards; Games; Prayer groups; Movies.

RANDALLSTOWN

Chapel Hill Convalescent Home
4511 Roboson Rd, Randallstown, MD, 21133
(301) 922-2443
Admin Frances Gosnay. *Medical Dir/Dir of
Nursing* Dr Renzo Ricci.
Licensure Intermediate Care. *Beds* 71. *Certified* Medicaid.
Ownership Proprietary.
Admissions Requirements Minimum age 14;
Medical examination; Physician's request.
Staff Physicians 8 (pt); RNs 1 (ft), 1 (pt); LPNs
4 (ft), 3 (pt); Orderlies 2 (ft); Nurses aides 29
(ft), 10 (pt); Physical therapists 1 (pt); Speech
therapists 1 (pt); Activities coordinators 1 (ft);
Dietitians 1 (pt); Dentists 1 (pt); Ophthalmologists 1 (pt); Podiatrists 1 (pt).
Facilities Dining room; Physical therapy room;
Activities room; Crafts room; Laundry room;
Barber/Beauty shop; Library.
Activities Arts and Crafts; Cards; Games; Prayer groups; Dances/Social or cultural gatherings.
Description Facility features excellent daily
activities, beautiful country setting, home-like
atmosphere, and a good staff who cares.

Meridian Nursing Center—Randallstown
9109 Liberty Rd, Randallstown, MD, 21133
(301) 655-7373
Admin Richard Hanauer. *Medical Dir/Dir of
Nursing* H Gerald Oster MD.
Licensure Skilled Care; Intermediate Care.
Beds 250. *Certified* Medicaid; Medicare.
Ownership Proprietary.
Admissions Requirements Medical examination.
Staff Physicians 46 (pt); RNs 7 (ft), 5 (pt);
LPNs 12 (ft), 18 (pt); Nurses aides 67 (ft), 42
(pt); Physical therapists 2 (ft); Speech therapists
1 (pt); Activities coordinators 3 (ft), 2 (pt); Dietitians 2 (ft); Dentists 1 (pt); Podiatrists 1 (ft);
Optomitrist 1 (pt); Social workers 1 (ft), 1 (pt).
Facilities Dining room; Physical therapy room;
Activities room; Crafts room; Laundry room;
Barber/Beauty shop; Library.
Activities Arts and Crafts; Cards; Games;
Reading groups; Prayer groups; Movies; Shopping trips; Dances/Social or cultural gatherings;
Overnight outings; Special functions.
Description Facility offers a quality of life program designed to meet all residents' needs
including in-room individualized activity pro-

grams, daily craft classes, exercise class, discussion groups, religious services, adult education, and biannual overnight mini-vacations to nearby resorts.

Old Court Nursing Center
5412 Old Court Rd, Randallstown, MD, 21133 (301) 922-3200
Admin Patricia Doherty. *Medical Dir/Dir of Nursing* Michael Pearlman MD.
Licensure Skilled Care; Intermediate Care.
Beds 144. *Certified* Medicaid; Medicare.
Ownership Proprietary.

REISTERSTOWN

Bent Nursing Home Inc
12020 Reisterstown Rd, Reisterstown, MD, 21136 (301) 833-3141
Admin Dennis R Melchor. *Medical Dir/Dir of Nursing* Dr C E McWilliams.
Licensure Intermediate Care. *Beds* 51. *Certified* Medicaid.
Ownership Proprietary.
Admissions Requirements Minimum age 21; Medical examination; Physician's request.
Staff Physicians 1 (ft), 1 (pt); RNs 4 (ft), 2 (pt); LPNs 6 (ft), 3 (pt); Nurses aides 21 (ft), 8 (pt); Physical therapists 1 (pt); Recreational therapists 1 (ft); Occupational therapists 1 (pt); Speech therapists 1 (pt); Dietitians 1 (pt); Dentists 1 (pt); Ophthalmologists 1 (pt); Podiatrists 1 (pt); Audiologists 1 (pt).

RISING SUN

Calvert Manor Nursing Home Inc*
1881 Telegraph Rd, Rising Sun, MD, 21911 (301) 658-6555
Admin Ruth N Graybeal. *Medical Dir/Dir of Nursing* Neil Taylor Jr MD.
Licensure Skilled Care; Intermediate Care.
Beds 93. *Certified* Medicaid.
Ownership Proprietary.

ROCKVILLE

Collingswood Nursing Center*
299 Hurley Ave, Rockville, MD, 20850 (301) 762-8900
Admin Carol Mulligan. *Medical Dir/Dir of Nursing* Walter Goozh MD.
Licensure Skilled Care; Intermediate Care.
Beds 157. *Certified* Medicaid; Medicare.
Ownership Proprietary.

Hebrew Home of Greater Washington
6121 Montrose Rd, Rockville, MD, 20852 (301) 881-0300
Admin Samuel Roberts. *Medical Dir/Dir of Nursing* Dr Dan Patel.
Licensure Skilled Care; Intermediate Care.
Beds 550. *Certified* Medicaid; Medicare.
Ownership Nonprofit.
Staff Physicians 2 (ft), 4 (pt); Physical therapists 4 (ft); Reality therapists 5 (ft); Occupational therapists 3 (ft); Speech therapists 1 (ft); Activities coordinators 5 (ft); Dietitians 3 (ft); Dentists 24 (pt); Ophthalmologists 10 (pt); Podiatrists 30 (pt); Audiologists 1 (pt).
Affiliation ewish

National Lutheran Home for the Aged*
9701 Viers Dr, Rockville, MD, 20850 (301) 424-9560
Admin Richard Reichard. *Medical Dir/Dir of Nursing* Harold McCann MD.
Licensure Skilled Care; Intermediate Care.
Beds 300. *Certified* Medicaid; Medicare.
Ownership Nonprofit.
Affiliation Lutheran

Potomac Valley Nursing Home*
1235 Potomac Valley Rd, Rockville, MD, 20850 (301) 762-0700
Admin Roxanne Stigers. *Medical Dir/Dir of Nursing* Henry Scruggs MD.
Licensure Skilled Care; Intermediate Care.
Beds 168. *Certified* Medicaid.
Ownership Proprietary.

Rockville Nursing Home Inc*
303 Adclare Rd, Rockville, MD, 20850 (301) 279-9000
Admin Ray Cromwell. *Medical Dir/Dir of Nursing* Frauke Westphal MD.
Licensure Skilled Care; Intermediate Care.
Beds 100. *Certified* Medicaid; Medicare.
Ownership Nonprofit.

SABILLASVILLE

Victor Cullen Center
6000 Cullen Dr, Sabillasville, MD, 21780 (301) 241-3131
Admin Steven Haigh. *Medical Dir/Dir of Nursing* Robert Brull MD.
Licensure . *Beds* 90. *Certified* Medicaid; Medicare.
Ownership Public.

SALISBURY

Deer's Head Center
PO Box 2018, Salisbury, MD, 21801 (301) 742-2164
Admin Edward G Phoebus. *Medical Dir/Dir of Nursing* Nancy W Tustin MD.
Licensure Skilled Care; Intermediate Care.
Beds 33. *Certified* Medicaid; Medicare.
Ownership Public.
Admissions Requirements Physician's request.
Staff Physicians 1 (ft); RNs 8 (ft); LPNs 3 (ft); Orderlies 4 (ft); Nurses aides 2 (ft); Physical therapists 1 (ft); Recreational therapists 1 (ft); Occupational therapists 1 (ft); Speech therapists 1 (pt); Activities coordinators 1 (ft); Dietitians 1 (ft); Dentists 1 (pt); Ophthalmologists 1 (pt); Podiatrists 1 (pt); Audiologists 1 (pt).
Facilities Dining room; Physical therapy room; Activities room; Chapel; Crafts room; Laundry room; Barber/Beauty shop; Library.
Activities Arts and Crafts; Cards; Games; Reading groups; Prayer groups; Movies; Shopping trips; Dances/Social or cultural gatherings.

Holly Center*
PO Box 2358, Snow Hill Rd, Salisbury, MD, 21801 (301) 546-2181
Admin Frank Gibson. *Medical Dir/Dir of Nursing* Hilda Houlihan MD.

Licensure Intermediate Care for Mentally Retarded. *Beds* 250. *Certified* Medicaid.
Ownership Public.

River Walk Manor
105 Times Square, Salisbury, MD, 21801 (301) 749-2474
Admin Joseph M Rando. *Medical Dir/Dir of Nursing* Thomas C Hill Jr MD.
Licensure Skilled Care; Intermediate Care.
Beds 150. *Certified* Medicaid; Medicare.
Ownership Proprietary.
Facilities Dining room; Physical therapy room; Activities room; Crafts room; Laundry room; Barber/Beauty shop.
Activities Arts and Crafts; Cards; Games; Reading groups; Prayer groups; Movies; Shopping trips; Dances/Social or cultural gatherings.

Salisbury Nursing Home
US 50 at Civic Ave, Salisbury, MD, 21801 (301) 749-1466
Admin Dennis Nooner. *Medical Dir/Dir of Nursing* Dr Earl Beardsley.
Licensure Intermediate Care. *Beds* 310. *Certified* Medicaid; Medicare.
Ownership Proprietary.
Admissions Requirements Minimum age 14; Physician's request.
Staff Physicians 2 (pt); RNs 23 (pt); LPNs 12 (pt); Orderlies 20 (pt); Nurses aides 80 (pt); Physical therapists 1 (pt); Activities coordinators 1 (pt); Dietitians 1 (pt).
Facilities Dining room; Physical therapy room; Activities room; Crafts room; Laundry room; Barber/Beauty shop; Library.
Activities Arts and Crafts; Cards; Games; Reading groups; Prayer groups; Movies; Shopping trips.

Wicomico Nursing Home
Booth St, PO Box 2378, Salisbury, MD, 21801 (301) 742-8896
Admin Mary E Schwartz. *Medical Dir/Dir of Nursing* A C Mitchell MD.
Licensure Skilled Care; Intermediate Care.
Beds 82. *Certified* Medicaid; Medicare.
Ownership Public.
Admissions Requirements Minimum age 14; Medical examination; Physician's request.
Staff RNs 4 (ft), 2 (pt); LPNs 5 (ft), 1 (pt); Orderlies 2 (ft); Nurses aides 20 (ft), 9 (pt); Physical therapists 1 (pt); Activities coordinators 1 (ft); Dietitians 1 (ft).
Facilities Dining room; Physical therapy room; Activities room; Laundry room; Barber/Beauty shop.
Activities Arts and Crafts; Cards; Games; Reading groups; Prayer groups; Movies; Shopping trips; Dances/Social or cultural gatherings.
Description Facility is located just outside a lovely rural community; building is all on one level; offers a wide variety of services and activities geared to individual needs. A full-time registered dietitian plans menus reflecting the cuisine of the area.

SANDY SPRING

Friends Nursing Home Inc
17340 Quaker Ln, Sandy Spring, MD, 20860 (301) 924-4900

Admin Frank Bailey. *Medical Dir/Dir of Nursing* Charles Ligon MD.
Licensure Intermediate Care. *Beds* 80. *Certified* Medicaid.
Ownership Nonprofit.
Staff Physicians 1 (pt); RNs 2 (ft), 12 (pt); LPNs 2 (ft); Nurses aides 35 (ft), 10 (pt); Physical therapists 1 (pt); Recreational therapists 1 (ft), 2 (pt); Speech therapists 1 (pt); Dietitians 1 (pt); Podiatrists 1 (pt).
Affiliation Society of Friends
Facilities Dining room; Physical therapy room; Activities room; Crafts room; Laundry room; Barber/Beauty shop; Library.
Activities Arts and Crafts; Cards; Games; Reading groups; Prayer groups; Movies; Shopping trips.

SEVERNA PARK

Meridian Nursing Center—Severna Park*
24 Truck House Rd, Severna Park, MD, 21146 (301) 544-4220
Admin Martha Clingman. *Medical Dir/Dir of Nursing* Thomas Walsh MD.
Beds 141.
Ownership Proprietary.

SILVER SPRING

Althea Woodland Nursing Home
1000 Daleview Dr, Silver Spring, MD, 20901 (301) 434-2646
Admin Ron G Carsell. *Medical Dir/Dir of Nursing* Bernard Fitzgerald.
Licensure Skilled Care; Intermediate Care.
Beds 52.
Ownership Proprietary.
Staff Physicians 5 (pt); RNs 6 (ft); LPNs 1 (ft); Nurses aides 25 (ft); Physical therapists 2 (pt); Recreational therapists 1 (pt); Speech therapists 1 (pt); Activities coordinators 1 (pt); Dietitians 1 (pt); Dentists 1 (pt); Podiatrists 1 (pt); Social workers 1 (pt).
Facilities Dining room; Activities room; Chapel; Crafts room; Laundry room; Barber/Beauty shop.
Activities Arts and Crafts; Cards; Games; Reading groups; Prayer groups; Movies; Shopping trips; Dances/Social or cultural gatherings.
Description Facility is licensed for music therapy interns.

Bel Pre Health Care Center
2601 Bel Pre Rd, Silver Spring, MD, 20906 (301) 598-6000
Admin Kathleen Dollymore. *Medical Dir/Dir of Nursing* Raymond Benack MD.
Licensure Skilled Care; Intermediate Care.
Beds 100. *Certified* Medicaid.
Ownership Proprietary.
Admissions Requirements Minimum age 18; Medical examination.
Staff RNs 7 (ft), 6 (pt); LPNs 1 (ft), 2 (pt); Nurses aides 43 (ft); Physical therapists 2 (pt); Recreational therapists 1 (ft); Speech therapists 1 (pt); Activities coordinators 1 (ft); Dietitians 1 (pt); Podiatrists 1 (pt).
Facilities Dining room; Activities room; Crafts room; Laundry room; Barber/Beauty shop.

Activities Arts and Crafts; Cards; Games; Reading groups; Prayer groups; Movies; Shopping trips; Dances/Social or cultural gatherings.

Carriage Hill Nursing Center—Silver Spring*
9101 2nd Ave, Silver Spring, MD, 20910 (301) 588-5544
Admin Flora Luckett. *Medical Dir/Dir of Nursing* John Umhau MD.
Licensure Skilled Care; Intermediate Care.
Beds 97. *Certified* Medicare.
Ownership Proprietary.

Chevy Chase Retirement and Nursing Center*
2015 East-West Hwy, Silver Spring, MD, 20910 (301) 587-2400
Admin Sandra Wood. *Medical Dir/Dir of Nursing* J Blaine Fitzgerald.
Licensure Skilled Care; Intermediate Care.
Beds 87. *Certified* Medicaid; Medicare.
Ownership Proprietary.

Colonial Villa Nursing Home*
12325 New Hampshire Ave, Silver Spring, MD, 20904 (301) 622-4600
Admin Donna R Gordon. *Medical Dir/Dir of Nursing* Marian Chung MD.
Licensure Skilled Care; Intermediate Care.
Beds 92. *Certified* Medicaid; Medicare.
Ownership Proprietary.

Fairland Nursing Home*
2101 Fairland Rd, Silver Spring, MD, 20904 (301) 384-6161
Admin Deidre Rye. *Medical Dir/Dir of Nursing* Thomas Ward MD.
Licensure Skilled Care; Intermediate Care.
Beds 83. *Certified* Medicaid; Medicare.
Ownership Proprietary.

Great Oaks Center*
12001 Cherry Hill Rd, Silver Spring, MD, 20904 (301) 595-5000
Admin Clifford P Lockyer. *Medical Dir/Dir of Nursing* Stefano Kenessey MD.
Licensure Intermediate Care for Mentally Retarded. *Beds* 500. *Certified* Medicaid.
Ownership Public.

Sylvan Manor Health Care Center
2700 Barker St, Silver Spring, MD, 20910 (301) 565-0300
Admin Barbara McKenna. *Medical Dir/Dir of Nursing* Martin Shargel MD.
Licensure Skilled Care; Intermediate Care.
Beds 137. *Certified* Medicaid.
Ownership Proprietary.

SMITHSBURG

Kemp Horn Home
Rt 1, Box 39, Smithsburg, MD, 21783 (301) 824-3121
Admin Doug Kent. *Medical Dir/Dir of Nursing* Ramsey Farah MD.
Licensure Intermediate Care for Mentally Retarded. *Beds* 17. *Certified* Medicaid.
Ownership Nonprofit.
Staff Physicians 1 (ft), 1 (pt); RNs 2 (ft); LPNs 2 (ft); Orderlies 6 (ft); Physical therapists 1 (ft); Occupational therapists 1 (ft); Speech therapists 1 (ft); Dietitians 1 (ft).

Facilities Dining room; Activities room.
Activities Arts and Crafts; Cards; Games; Reading groups; Movies; Shopping trips; Dances/Social or cultural gatherings.

SNOW HILL

Harrison House
430 W Market St, Snow Hill, MD, 21863 (301) 632-3755
Admin Jeannine C Aydelotte. *Medical Dir/Dir of Nursing* Dorothy C Holzworth MD.
Licensure Skilled Care; Intermediate Care.
Beds 58. *Certified* Medicaid; Medicare.
Ownership Proprietary.
Admissions Requirements Minimum age 14; Medical examination; Physician's request.
Staff Physicians 2 (pt); RNs 1 (ft), 5 (pt); LPNs 6 (ft); Nurses aides 18 (ft), 10 (pt); Activities coordinators 1 (ft).
Facilities Dining room; Physical therapy room; Activities room; Laundry room; Barber/Beauty shop.
Activities Arts and Crafts; Cards; Games; Reading groups; Prayer groups; Movies; Shopping trips.
Description Facility is small with a home-like atmosphere. Activities reflect residents, staff, and community involvement. Located near Atlantic seashore.

SUITLAND

Suitland Nursing Home Inc
2405 Whitehall St, Suitland, MD, 20023 (301) 736-8210
Admin Barbara McKenna.
Licensure Intermediate Care. *Beds* 34. *Certified* Medicaid.
Ownership Proprietary.

SYKESVILLE

Fairhaven Nursing Home*
7200 3rd Ave, Sykesville, MD, 21784 (301) 795-8800
Admin James Melhorn. *Medical Dir/Dir of Nursing* Alva Baker MD.
Licensure Skilled Care; Intermediate Care.
Beds 99.
Ownership Nonprofit.

Golden Age Guest Home
1442 Buckhorn Rd, Sykesville, MD, 21784 (301) 795-2737
Admin James C Talbott. *Medical Dir/Dir of Nursing* J H Caricofe MD.
Licensure Intermediate Care. *Beds* 20. *Certified* Medicaid.
Ownership Proprietary.
Staff Physicians 2 (pt); RNs 1 (ft), 1 (pt); LPNs 2 (ft), 4 (pt); Nurses aides 5 (ft), 2 (pt); Activities coordinators 1 (ft); Dietitians 1 (pt).
Facilities Dining room.
Activities Arts and Crafts; Cards; Games; Prayer groups; Movies.
Description Facility is located in a country setting.

Sykesville Eldercare Center
7312 1st Ave, Sykesville, MD, 21784 (301)
795-0800
Admin Robert L Killett. *Medical Dir/Dir of Nursing* José Chapulle MD.
Licensure Skilled Care; Intermediate Care.
Beds 75. *Certified* Medicaid; Medicare.
Ownership Proprietary.
Admissions Requirements Minimum age 21.
Staff RNs 2 (ft), 5 (pt); LPNs 2 (ft), 4 (pt);
Nurses aides 31 (ft), 2 (pt); Activities coordinators 1 (ft).
Facilities Dining room; Activities room; Laundry room; Barber/Beauty shop.
Activities Arts and Crafts; Cards; Games;
Reading groups; Prayer groups; Movies; Shopping trips.
Description Facility established and family operated since 1955, features a country atmosphere and is currently expanding to 125 beds with new kitchen, laundry, physical therapy room, occupational therapy room, 2 more dining rooms, 2 more activity rooms; to be ready for occupancy February 1985.

TAKOMA PARK

Heritage Health Care Center
7525 Carroll Ave, Takoma Park, MD, 20012
(301) 270-4200
Admin Lauren Rock. *Medical Dir/Dir of Nursing* Dr Mark Li.
Licensure Skilled Care; Intermediate Care.
Beds 102. *Certified* Medicaid; Medicare.
Ownership Proprietary.
Staff Physicians; RNs; LPNs; Orderlies;
Nurses aides; Physical therapists; Reality therapists; Recreational therapists; Occupational therapists; Speech therapists; Activities coordinators; Dietitians; Dentists; Podiatrists; Audiologists.
Facilities Dining room; Physical therapy room; Activities room; Crafts room; Laundry room; Barber/Beauty shop.
Activities Arts and Crafts; Cards; Games;
Reading groups; Prayer groups; Movies; Shopping trips; Dances/Social or cultural gatherings.
Description Heritage Health Care is a unique facility that offers many special programs that enhance the health of the elderly and prevent disease; offers an outstanding rehabilitation program that specializes in treating fractured hips and strokes.

TOWSON

Dulaney Towson Nursing and Convalescent Center
111 West Rd, Towson, MD, 21204 (301)
828-6500
Admin Albert H Radtke. *Medical Dir/Dir of Nursing* Charles O'Donnell MD.
Licensure Skilled Care; Intermediate Care.
Beds 151. *Certified* Medicaid; Medicare.
Ownership Proprietary.

Holly Hill Manor Inc*
531 Stevenson Ln, Towson, MD, 21204 (301)
823-5310
Admin M L Cursey Jr. *Medical Dir/Dir of Nursing* Stephen Laiken.

Licensure Intermediate Care. *Beds* 55. *Certified* Medicaid.
Ownership Proprietary.

Manor Care—Ruxton
7001 Charles St, Towson, MD, 21204 (301)
821-9600
Admin Thomas A Keiser. *Medical Dir/Dir of Nursing* Walter T Kees MD.
Licensure Intermediate Care. *Beds* 200. *Certified* Medicaid; Medicare.
Ownership Proprietary.
Staff Physicians; RNs; LPNs; Orderlies;
Nurses aides; Physical therapists 1 (ft); Reality therapists 3 (ft); Recreational therapists 3 (ft);
Occupational therapists 2 (ft); Speech therapists 1 (ft); Activities coordinators 3 (ft); Dietitians 2 (ft); Dentists 1 (ft); Podiatrists 1 (ft); Audiologists 1 (ft).
Facilities Dining room; Physical therapy room; Activities room; Crafts room; Laundry room; Barber/Beauty shop; Library.
Activities Arts and Crafts; Cards; Games;
Reading groups; Prayer groups; Movies; Shopping trips; Dances/Social or cultural gatherings.
Description Facility features a specialized garden raised for handicapped access to wheelchair height; projected plans for shaded portico overlooking spacious wooded area; innovative recreation program with discussion groups, team events, and portable VCR and color television for group or individual use.

Manor Care—Towson
509 E Joppa Rd, Towson, MD, 21204 (301)
828-9494
Admin Vida Sullivan. *Medical Dir/Dir of Nursing* Walter T Kees MD.
Licensure Skilled Care; Comprehensive Care.
Beds 115. *Certified* Medicaid; Medicare.
Ownership Proprietary.
Admissions Requirements Medical examination.
Staff Physicians 1 (pt); RNs 7 (ft), 10 (pt);
LPNs 3 (ft), 2 (pt); Nurses aides 28 (ft), 23 (pt);
Recreational therapists 1 (ft), 1 (pt); Audiologists 8 (ft), 8 (pt).
Facilities Dining room; Physical therapy room; Activities room; Crafts room; Laundry room; Barber/Beauty shop.
Activities Arts and Crafts; Cards; Games;
Reading groups; Prayer groups; Movies; Shopping trips; Dances/Social or cultural gatherings.
Description Facility offers small family-like atmosphere.

Multi-Medical Convalescent and Nursing Center*
7700 York Rd, Towson, MD, 21204 (301)
821-5500
Admin Rose B Burkoff. *Medical Dir/Dir of Nursing* Henry I Babbitt MD.
Licensure Skilled Care; Intermediate Care.
Beds 120. *Certified* Medicare.
Ownership Proprietary.

Pickersgill Inc
615 Chestnut Ln, Towson, MD, 21204 (301)
825-7423
Admin Richard B Buck. *Medical Dir/Dir of Nursing* Dr Keith Manley.
Licensure Intermediate Care. *Beds* 169. *Certified* Medicaid.

Ownership Nonprofit.
Admissions Requirements Minimum age 65;
Medical examination.
Staff Physicians 1 (pt); RNs 4 (ft), 7 (pt); LPNs 2 (ft); Orderlies 3 (ft); Nurses aides 45 (ft); Physical therapists 1 (pt); Recreational therapists 1 (ft); Speech therapists 1 (pt); Activities coordinators 1 (ft); Dietitians 1 (ft); Dentists 1 (pt); Podiatrists 1 (pt).
Facilities Dining room; Physical therapy room; Activities room; Crafts room; Laundry room; Barber/Beauty shop; Library.
Activities Arts and Crafts; Cards; Games;
Reading groups; Prayer groups; Movies; Shopping trips; Dances/Social or cultural gatherings.

Presbyterian Home of Maryland Inc*
400 Georgia Ct, Towson, MD, 21204 (301)
823-4622
Admin Rosa Lee Robertson.
Licensure Intermediate Care; Domiciliary Care. *Beds* ICF 22; Domiciliary Care 80.
Ownership Nonprofit.
Affiliation Presbyterian

Stella Maris/The Cardinal Shehan Center for the Aging
Dulaney Valley Rd, Towson, MD, 21204 (301)
252-4500
Admin Sr Louise Mary Battle. *Medical Dir/Dir of Nursing* Dr Eddie Nakhuda and Dr Kendall R Faulkner.
Licensure Skilled Care; Intermediate Care;
Hospice. *Beds* SNF 432; ICF 46; Hospice 13.
Certified Medicaid; Medicare.
Ownership Nonprofit.
Admissions Requirements Medical examination.
Staff Physicians 2 (ft), 38 (pt); RNs 14 (ft), 38 (pt); LPNs 3 (ft), 3 (pt); Orderlies 16 (ft); Nurses aides 104 (ft), 55 (pt); Physical therapists 2 (ft); Recreational therapists 2 (ft); Occupational therapists 1 (ft); Speech therapists 1 (pt); Activities coordinators 1 (ft); Dietitians 3 (ft).
Affiliation Roman Catholic
Facilities Dining room; Physical therapy room; Activities room; Chapel; Crafts room; Laundry room; Barber/Beauty shop; Library; Thrift shop; Gift shop; Kitchen.
Activities Arts and Crafts; Cards; Games;
Reading groups; Prayer groups; Movies; Shopping trips; Dances/Social or cultural gatherings.
Description Facility currently offers the only federally certified hospice program in the state of Maryland, along with the only inpatient unit in the area. Outpatient speech and physical therapy are available to the general public.

Towson Convalescent Home Inc
301 W Chesapeake Ave, Towson, MD, 21204
(301) 823-8181
Admin Maryland C Gore.
Licensure Intermediate Care. *Beds* 34.
Ownership Proprietary.
Staff RNs 2 (ft), 1 (pt); LPNs 4 (pt); Nurses aides 24 (ft), 3 (pt); Activities coordinators 1 (pt); Dietitians 1 (pt).
Facilities Dining room; Activities room.
Activities Arts and Crafts; Games; Prayer groups; Movies.

UPPER MARLBORO

Manor Care of Largo Inc
600 Largo Rd, Upper Marlboro, MD, 20870
(301) 350-5555
Admin Helen J Edwards. *Medical Dir/Dir of Nursing* Norton Elson.
Licensure Skilled Care; Intermediate Care.
Beds 120. *Certified* Medicaid; Medicare.
Ownership Proprietary.
Admissions Requirements Minimum age 16.
Staff Physicians; RNs; LPNs; Orderlies; Nurses aides; Physical therapists; Reality therapists; Recreational therapists; Occupational therapists; Speech therapists; Activities coordinators; Dietitians; Dentists; Ophthalmologists; Podiatrists; Audiologists.
Facilities Dining room; Physical therapy room; Activities room; Barber/Beauty shop; Library.
Activities Arts and Crafts; Cards; Games; Reading groups; Prayer groups; Movies; Shopping trips; Dances/Social or cultural gatherings.

WESTMINSTER

Fairhaven Nursing Home*
200 St Luke's Circle, Westminster, MD, 21157
(601) 795-8800
Admin Lyle E Peters. *Medical Dir/Dir of Nursing* John Lehigh MD.
Beds 99.
Ownership Nonprofit.

Westminster Villa Nursing and Convalescent Center
234 Washington Blvd, Westminster, MD, 21157 (301) 848-0700
Admin Lorrie Custudio. *Medical Dir/Dir of Nursing* Daniel Welliver MD.
Licensure Skilled Care; Intermediate Care.
Beds 170. *Certified* Medicaid; Medicare.
Ownership Proprietary.

WHEATON

Manor Care—Wheaton
11901 Georgia Ave, Wheaton, MD, 20902
(301) 942-2500
Admin Kathryn Heflin. *Medical Dir/Dir of Nursing* Walter Goozh MD.
Licensure Skilled Care; Intermediate Care.
Beds 102. *Certified* Medicare.
Ownership Proprietary.
Admissions Requirements Minimum age 16; Medical examination.
Facilities Dining room; Physical therapy room; Activities room; Laundry room; Barber/Beauty shop; Library; Living room; Lobby.
Activities Arts and Crafts; Cards; Games; Reading groups; Prayer groups; Movies; Shopping trips; Dances/Social or cultural gatherings; Resident council; Monthly newsletter.
Description The facility has an excellent rehabilitative program offering physical therapy, occupational therapy, and speech therapy. We have recently refurnished the entire facility with carpeting, new wallcovering, draperies, and furniture. The atmosphere in the facility is very home-like.

Randolph Hills Nursing Home
4011 Randolph Rd, Wheaton, MD, 20902
(301) 933-2500
Admin Harvey R Wertlieb. *Medical Dir/Dir of Nursing* Dr Barry Rosenbahm.
Licensure Skilled Care; Intermediate Care.
Beds 95. *Certified* Medicaid; Medicare.
Ownership Proprietary.
Admissions Requirements Minimum age 14; Medical examination; Physician's request.
Staff RNs 13 (ft); LPNs 2 (ft); Nurses aides 33 (ft); Physical therapists 1 (ft); Recreational therapists 1 (ft); Occupational therapists 1 (pt); Speech therapists 1 (pt); Activities coordinators 2 (ft); Dietitians 1 (pt); Dentists 1 (pt); Ophthalmologists 1 (pt); Podiatrists 1 (pt); Audiologists 1 (pt).
Facilities Dining room; Physical therapy room; Activities room; Crafts room; Laundry room; Barber/Beauty shop; Library.
Activities Arts and Crafts; Cards; Games; Reading groups; Prayer groups; Movies; Shopping trips; Dances/Social or cultural gatherings.

University Nursing Home Inc
901 Arcola Ave, Wheaton, MD, 20902 (301) 649-2400
Admin Robert N Hagerman Jr and Anne M Souders. *Medical Dir/Dir of Nursing* Myron L Lenkin MD.
Licensure Skilled Care; Intermediate Care.
Beds 150. *Certified* Medicaid; Medicare.
Ownership Proprietary.
Admissions Requirements Minimum age 16; Medical examination.
Staff RNs 25 (ft), 8 (pt); LPNs 10 (ft), 2 (pt); Nurses aides 65 (ft), 5 (pt); Physical therapists 1 (ft).
Facilities Dining room; Physical therapy room; Activities room; Crafts room; Barber/Beauty shop.
Activities Arts and Crafts; Cards; Games; Reading groups; Prayer groups; Movies; Dances/Social or cultural gatherings; Resident Council.

WILLIAMSPORT

Homewood Retirement Center—Williamsport*
2750 Virginia Ave, Williamsport, MD, 21795
(301) 582-1628
Admin Donald E Lewis.
Licensure Intermediate Care; Domiciliary.
Beds ICF 93; Domiciliary Care 43. *Certified* Medicaid.
Ownership Nonprofit.

Williamsport Nursing Home
154 N Artizan St, Williamsport, MD, 21795
(301) 223-7971
Admin David Benton. *Medical Dir/Dir of Nursing* John Melnick MD.
Licensure Intermediate Care. *Beds* 96. *Certified* Medicaid.
Ownership Nonprofit.
Admissions Requirements Minimum age 14.
Staff Physicians 2 (pt); RNs 6 (ft), 3 (pt); LPNs 6 (ft), 3 (pt); Nurses aides 60 (ft), 8 (pt); Physical therapists 1 (pt); Speech therapists 1 (pt); Activities coordinators 2 (ft); Dietitians 1 (pt); Podiatrists 1 (pt).
Facilities Dining room; Activities room; Crafts room; Laundry room; Barber/Beauty shop.
Activities Arts and Crafts; Cards; Games; Movies; Rides in wheelchair accessible van.

MASSACHUSETTS

ABINGTON

Colony House Healthcare Nursing Home
277 Washington St, Abington, MA, 02351 (617)
871-0200
Admin Mark O'Flaherty.
Licensure Skilled Care; Intermediate Care.
Beds 102. *Certified* Medicaid.
Admissions Requirements Medical examination.
Staff RNs 4 (ft), 17 (pt); LPNs 1 (ft), 7 (pt);
Nurses aides 8 (ft), 54 (pt); Recreational therapists 1 (pt); Activities coordinators 1 (ft).
Facilities Dining room; Physical therapy room;
Activities room; Crafts room; Laundry room;
Barber/Beauty shop.
Activities Arts and Crafts; Cards; Games;
Reading groups; Prayer groups; Movies; Dances/Social or cultural gatherings.

Mildred Alford Nursing Home*
81 Birch St, Abington, MA, 02351 (617)
878-4660
Admin Gilbert Rocha.
Licensure Skilled Care; Intermediate Care.
Beds 99. *Certified* Medicaid.

ACTON

**Suburban Manor Convalescent and Nursing
Home***
1 Great Rd, Acton, MA, 01720 (617) 263-9101
Admin Vincent M Polo.
Licensure Skilled Care; Intermediate Care.
Beds 122. *Certified* Medicaid; Medicare.

ACUSHNET

Acushnet Nursing Home*
127 S Main St, Acushnet, MA, 02740 (617)
995-1857
Admin Mary Loughlin.
Licensure Intermediate Care. *Beds* 28. *Certified* Medicaid.

ADAMS

Adams Rest Home Inc*
17 Commercial St, Adams, MA, 01220 (413)
743-1132
Admin Harold Stein.
Licensure Rest Home. *Beds* 45.

Rest Haven Rest Home*
395 Old Columbia St, Adams, MA, 01220
(413) 743-2115
Admin Gladys M Hall.
Licensure Rest Home. *Beds* 29.

AGAWAM

Heritage Hall Nursing Home*
100 Harvey Johnson Dr, Agawam, MA, 01001
(413) 786-8000
Admin Richard L Circosta.
Licensure Skilled Care; Intermediate Care.
Beds 122. *Certified* Medicaid; Medicare.

Heritage Hall Nursing Home—West*
61 Cooper St, Agawam, MA, 01001 (413)
786-8000
Admin Richard Circosta.
Licensure Skilled Care. *Beds* 164. *Certified* Medicaid; Medicare.

Heritage Hall Retirement and Nursing Home*
55 Cooper St, Agawam, MA, 01001 (413)
786-8000
Admin James Clifford.
Licensure Intermediate Care. *Beds* 124. *Certified* Medicaid.

Kelley Rest Home
808 Suffield St, Agawam, MA, 01001 (413)
786-2177
Admin C Burns.
Licensure Rest Home. *Beds* 10.

AMESBURY

Amesbury Nursing and Retirement Home
22 Maple St, Amesbury, MA, 01913 (617)
388-4682
Admin Thomas H Daley.
Licensure Skilled Care; Intermediate Care.
Beds 124. *Certified* Medicaid.

Eastwood Rest Home Inc
39 High St, Amesbury, MA, 01913 (617)
388-1749
Admin Jane E Rochon.
Licensure Rest Home. *Beds* 33.
Admissions Requirements Medical examination.
Facilities Dining room; Activities room; Laundry room.

Activities Cards; Games; Prayer groups;
Shopping trips; Dances/Social or cultural gatherings.

Hillside Rest Home*
29 Hillside Ave, Amesbury, MA, 01913 (617)
388-1010
Admin William E Ring.
Licensure Rest Home. *Beds* 28.

Maplewood Manor Nursing Home
Morrill Pl, Amesbury, MA, 01913 (617)
388-3500
Admin Robert M Shaughnessy. *Medical Dir-/Dir of Nursing* Charles J Schissel MD.
Licensure Skilled Care; Intermediate Care.
Beds 120. *Certified* Medicaid; Medicare.
Facilities Dining room; Physical therapy room;
Activities room; Chapel; Crafts room; Laundry
room; Barber/Beauty shop; TV rooms.
Activities Arts and Crafts; Cards; Games;
Reading groups; Prayer groups; Movies; Shopping trips; Dances/Social or cultural gatherings.

North Eastwood Rest Home*
276 Main St, Amesbury, MA, 01913 (617)
388-0083
Admin Jane E Rochon.
Licensure Rest Home. *Beds* 27.

Parkside Rest Home*
Sparhawk St, Amesbury, MA, 01913 (617)
388-2446
Admin William L Twomey.
Licensure Rest Home. *Beds* 30.

AMHERST

Amherst Home for Aged Women*
1165 N Pleasant St, Amherst, MA, 01002 (413)
549-0115
Admin Walter C Jones.
Licensure Charitable Home. *Beds* 6.
Admissions Requirements Females only

Amherst Nursing Home Inc
150 University Dr, Amherst, MA, 01002 (413)
256-8185
Admin Bettie S Kravetz and Sharon E Meyers.
Licensure Skilled Care; Intermediate Care.
Beds 81. *Certified* Medicaid.
Facilities Dining room; Physical therapy room;
Activities room; Chapel; Crafts room; Laundry
room; Barber/Beauty shop; Rotunda.

Activities Arts and Crafts; Cards; Games; Reading groups; Prayer groups; Movies; Dances/Social or cultural gatherings.

ANDOVER

Academy Manor of Andover
89 Morton St, Andover, MA, 01810 (617) 475-0944
Admin David Solomont. *Medical Dir/Dir of Nursing* Dr Edward Broddus.
Licensure Skilled Care; Intermediate Care. *Beds* 87. *Certified* Medicaid.
Admissions Requirements Medical examination; Physician's request.
Staff RNs 11 (ft); LPNs 7 (ft); Nurses aides 16 (ft), 10 (pt); Physical therapists 1 (pt); Recreational therapists 2 (ft); Occupational therapists 1 (pt); Speech therapists 2 (pt); Activities coordinators 2 (ft); Dietitians 1 (pt); Dentists 1 (pt); Ophthalmologists 1 (pt); Podiatrists 1 (pt).
Facilities Dining room; Physical therapy room; Activities room; Chapel; Crafts room; Laundry room; Barber/Beauty shop; Library.
Activities Arts and Crafts; Cards; Games; Reading groups; Prayer groups; Movies; Shopping trips; Dances/Social or cultural gatherings.
Description Facility prides itself on the homelike atmosphere and quality of care; innovative in field with the establishment of an extensive selective dining program for residents and staff. Two full-time activities personnel and a full-time social worker provide the residents with a well-rounded recreational and social program.

Randolph Nursing Home*
102 Burnham Rd, Andover, MA, 01810 (617) 475-2092
Admin Frank Andreoli.
Licensure Intermediate Care. *Beds* 17. *Certified* Medicaid.

ARLINGTON

Arlington Rest Home Inc
129 Lake St, Arlington, MA, 02174 (617) 643-8761
Admin Eloise C Milligan.
Licensure Rest Home. *Beds* 19.
Admissions Requirements Minimum age 21; Females only; Medical examination; Physician's request.
Staff RNs 1 (pt); LPNs 2 (ft); Nurses aides 4 (pt); Recreational therapists 1 (pt); Activities coordinators 1 (pt); Dietitians 1 (pt).
Facilities Dining room; Activities room; Laundry room; Barber/Beauty shop.
Activities Arts and Crafts; Games; Reading groups; Prayer groups; Movies; Shopping trips.
Description All residents are a part of the large family-like setting.

Hillside House Rest Home
163 Hillside Ave, Arlington, MA, 02174 (617) 648-0086
Admin Armand R Baldinelli. *Medical Dir/Dir of Nursing* Dr David Gersh.
Licensure Intermediate Care. *Beds* 50. *Certified* Medicaid.
Admissions Requirements Medical examination; Physician's request.

Staff RNs 1 (pt); LPNs 1 (ft); Nurses aides 5 (ft), 3 (pt); Activities coordinators 1 (ft); Dietitians 1 (pt); Podiatrists 1 (pt).
Facilities Dining room; Activities room; Crafts room; Laundry room.
Activities Arts and Crafts; Cards; Games; Reading groups; Prayer groups; Movies; Shopping trips; Dances/Social or cultural gatherings.

Jefferson Rest Home
149 Hillside Ave, Arlington, MA, 02174 (617) 648-0085
Admin Vasco Lima.
Licensure Rest Home. *Beds* 23.

Park Avenue Nursing, Convalescent and Retirement Home*
146 Park Ave, Arlington, MA, 02174 (617) 648-9530
Admin Joseph J Alessandroni.
Licensure Skilled Care; Intermediate Care. *Beds* 80. *Certified* Medicaid.

Park Circle Nursing Home
15 Park Circle, Arlington, MA, 02174 (617) 643-9275
Admin Gloria Marzocchi.
Licensure Intermediate Care. *Beds* 25. *Certified* Medicaid.
Admissions Requirements Minimum age 21; Females only; Medical examination.
Facilities Dining room; Activities room; Crafts room; Laundry room; Barber/Beauty shop; Library.
Activities Arts and Crafts; Cards; Games; Reading groups; Prayer groups; Movies; Shopping trips; Dances/Social or cultural gatherings.

Wellington Manor Nursing Home*
8 Wellington St, Arlington, MA, 02174 (617) 648-7300
Admin Mary A Carroll.
Licensure Intermediate Care. *Beds* 42. *Certified* Medicaid.

ASHBURNHAM

Big G Rest Home
97 Platts Rd, Ashburnham, MA, 01466 (617) 827-4561
Admin Eino Oja.
Licensure Rest Home. *Beds* 17.

Collins Rest Home Inc*
10 Lawrence St, Ashburnham, MA, 01430 (617) 827-4351
Admin Louise A Gilligan.
Licensure Rest Home. *Beds* 20.

Sunnyvale Rest Home
10 Central St, Ashburnham, MA, 01430 (617) 827-4212
Admin Donald G Desmarais. *Medical Dir/Dir of Nursing* Curtis Clayman MD.
Licensure Rest Home. *Beds* 16.
Admissions Requirements Minimum age 21; Medical examination.
Staff Physicians 1 (pt); RNs 1 (pt); Activities coordinators 1 (pt); Dietitians 1 (pt); Dentists 1 (pt).
Facilities Dining room; Activities room; Laundry room.

Activities Arts and Crafts; Cards; Games; Reading groups; Prayer groups; Movies; Shopping trips; Dances/Social or cultural gatherings.
Description Facility is nestled in a small New England town, circa 1785; within a 2-minute walk to town are antique shops, coffee shop, library, and senior citizen center.

ASHFIELD

Ashfield House Rest Home
Main St, Ashfield, MA, 01330 (413) 881-1360
Admin Mary T Corbott.
Licensure Rest Home. *Beds* 40.
Admissions Requirements Minimum age 21; Medical examination.
Staff LPNs 1 (ft); Nurses aides 13 (ft); Recreational therapists 1 (pt); Dietitians 1 (pt); Podiatrists 1 (pt).

ASHLAND

Ashland Manor Nursing Home*
25 Central St, Ashland, MA, 01721 (617) 881-1044
Admin Sabina Milman.
Licensure Intermediate Care. *Beds* 29. *Certified* Medicaid.

Mill Pond Rest Home
84 Myrtle St, Ashland, MA, 01721 (617) 881-1360
Admin A Bridget Trainor.
Licensure Rest Home. *Beds* 27.
Admissions Requirements Minimum age 50; Medical examination.
Staff LPNs 1 (ft); Orderlies 3 (ft), 1 (pt); Nurses aides 1 (ft); Activities coordinators 1 (pt); Dietitians 1 (pt).
Facilities Dining room; Activities room; Laundry room; Barber/Beauty shop.
Activities Arts and Crafts; Cards; Games; Prayer groups; Movies; Shopping trips; Dances/Social or cultural gatherings.
Description Residents live in a relaxed homelike atmosphere. Restrictions are few and only imposed if and when the behavior of one resident impinges on the comfort or privacy of another.

ATHOL

Fleetwood Nursing Home*
821 Daniel Shay Hwy, Athol, MA, 01331 (617) 249-3717
Admin Francis F Krupa.
Licensure Skilled Care; Intermediate Care. *Beds* 126. *Certified* Medicaid.

Tully Brook Rest Home*
232 N Orange Rd, Athol, MA, 01331 (617) 249-4482
Admin Helen M Bisbee.
Licensure Rest Home. *Beds* 9.

ATTLEBORO

Bristol Nursing Home
1000 Oak Hill Ave, Attleboro, MA, 02703 (617) 222-6400

Admin David Morrall. *Medical Dir/Dir of Nursing* J Allen Bryer MD.
Licensure Intermediate Care. *Beds* 68. *Certified* Medicaid.
Staff RNs 7 (pt); LPNs 3 (ft), 7 (pt); Nurses aides 10 (ft), 17 (pt); Physical therapists 1 (pt); Activities coordinators 1 (ft).

Morin's Retirement Home Inc
144 Pleasant St, Attleboro, MA, 02703 (617) 222-1532
Admin Normand J Morin.
Licensure Rest Home. *Beds* 60.
Admissions Requirements Minimum age 50; Medical examination; Physician's request.
Staff RNs 2 (ft); LPNs 2 (ft); Nurses aides 4 (ft); Activities coordinators 1 (pt); Dietitians 1 (pt).
Facilities Dining room; Activities room; Laundry room; Library.
Activities Arts and Crafts; Games; Prayer groups; Movies; Shopping trips.
Description We practice preventive medicine. Our residential care facility does not require nurses, but we find they are very helpful for our 60 residents, to monitor their health, and prevent needless doctor and hospital visits.

Pleasant Manor Nursing Home*
193-195 Pleasant St, Attleboro, MA, 02703 (617) 222-4950
Admin Milton V Thibeault.
Licensure Skilled Care; Intermediate Care.
Beds 133. *Certified* Medicaid.

Ridgewood Court Nursing Home*
27 George St, Attleboro, MA, 02703 (617) 226-1650
Admin Larry A Lencz.
Licensure Skilled Care; Intermediate Care.
Beds 120. *Certified* Medicaid; Medicare.

Victorian Mansion Retirement Home*
574 Newport Ave, Attleboro, MA, 02703 (617) 761-5115
Admin Jodie Seidl.
Licensure Rest Home. *Beds* 18.

AYER

Shady Glade Rest Home*
44 E Main St, Ayer, MA, 01432 (617) 772-2330
Admin Barbara A Rice.
Licensure Rest Home. *Beds* 16.

Woodford of Ayer Long Term Care Facility
15 Winthrop St, Ayer, MA, 01432 (617) 772-0409
Admin Harold Schwartz. *Medical Dir/Dir of Nursing* Dr Barttleson.
Licensure Intermediate Care. *Beds* 71. *Certified* Medicaid.
Admissions Requirements Medical examination.
Staff RNs 1 (ft), 3 (pt); LPNs 8 (ft), 3 (pt); Orderlies 1 (ft); Nurses aides 30 (ft), 10 (pt).
Facilities Dining room; Activities room; Laundry room; Barber/Beauty shop; Whirlpools.
Activities Arts and Crafts; Cards; Games; Reading groups; Prayer groups; Movies; Shopping trips.

BARNSTABLE

Cape Regency Nursing Home*
120 S Main St, Barnstable, MA, 02630 (617) 387-6560
Admin Charles Peterman.
Licensure Skilled Care; Intermediate Care.
Beds SNF 80; ICF 40.

Fraser Rest Home of Hyannis*
349 Sea St, Hyannis, Barnstable, MA, 02601 (617) 775-4881
Admin Charles R Fraser.
Licensure Rest Home. *Beds* 37. *Certified* Medicare.

Harbor View Rest Home*
3401 Main St, Barnstable, MA, 02630 (617) 362-3042
Admin Robert McCubrey.
Licensure Rest Home. *Beds* 24.

Lewis Bay Convalescent Home
89 Lewis Bay Rd, Barnstable, MA, 02601 (617) 775-7601
Admin Michael T Kelly. *Medical Dir/Dir of Nursing* Arthur Bickford MD.
Licensure Skilled Care; Intermediate Care.
Beds 142. *Certified* Medicaid; Medicare.
Admissions Requirements Minimum age 21; Medical examination; Physician's request.
Facilities Dining room; Physical therapy room; Activities room; Laundry room; Barber/Beauty shop; Library.
Activities Arts and Crafts; Cards; Games; Reading groups; Prayer groups; Movies; Shopping trips; Dances/Social or cultural gatherings; Remotivation; Sensitivity stimulation; Exercise to music; Radio interviews; Annual fair.
Description On a regular basis, there is an Alcoholics Anonymous meeting, also a club for some high level 3 residents to give them support and increase their independent living skills. Wisdom College, a community service, is offered in literature and creative writing. Intergenerational experience is shared with an elementary school and bluebirds.

Resthaven Nursing Home*
82 School St, Barnstable, MA, 02601 (617) 775-3616
Admin Nicholas H Thisse.
Licensure Skilled Care. *Beds* 44. *Certified* Medicaid.

BARRE

Christian Hill Rest Home*
Christian Hill Dr, Barre, MA, 01005 (617) 355-4491
Admin May E Danahy.
Licensure Rest Home. *Beds* 18.

BEDFORD

Carleton-Willard Retirement and Nursing Center
100 Old Billerica Rd, Bedford, MA, 01730 (617) 275-8700
Admin Barbara A Doyle. *Medical Dir/Dir of Nursing* John W Bergin MD.
Licensure Charitable Home. *Beds* 337.
Ownership Nonprofit.
Admissions Requirements Minimum age 65; Medical examination; Physician's request.
Staff Physicians 1 (ft); RNs 6 (ft), 16 (pt); LPNs 10 (ft), 15 (pt); Nurses aides 46 (ft), 23 (pt); Physical therapists 2 (ft); Recreational therapists 1 (ft); Occupational therapists; Activities coordinators 2 (ft); Dietitians 1 (ft).
Facilities Dining room; Physical therapy room; Activities room; Crafts room; Laundry room; Barber/Beauty shop; Library.
Activities Arts and Crafts; Cards; Games; Reading groups; Prayer groups; Movies; Shopping trips; Dances/Social or cultural gatherings; Day trips; Workshop; Ceramics.
Description Carleton-Willard Village is the first nonprofit residential life care community for people 65 years of age and older in Massachusetts. Facility evolved from the merged interests of the Elizabeth Carleton House of Boston and the Frances E Willard Homes of Boston, Waltham, and Bedford. These 2 nonprofit predecessor organizations have been offering a variety of housing, nursing, and social services to the elderly for nearly 100 years.

BELCHERTOWN

Belchertown State School
Box 446, Belchertown, MA, 01007 (413) 326-3111
Admin William Jones. *Medical Dir/Dir of Nursing* Aran Kasparyan MD.
Licensure Intermediate Care for Mentally Retarded. *Beds* 415. *Certified* Medicaid.
Ownership Public.
Admissions Requirements Minimum age 6.
Staff Physicians 3 (ft); RNs 50 (ft), 2 (pt); LPNs 52 (ft), 10 (pt); Nurses aides 243 (ft), 9 (pt); Physical therapists 4 (ft); Recreational therapists 27 (ft), 15 (pt); Occupational therapists 6 (ft), 1 (pt); Speech therapists 14 (ft); Dietitians 4 (ft); Dentists 1 (ft).
Facilities Dining room; Physical therapy room; Activities room; Chapel; Crafts room; Laundry room; Barber/Beauty shop; Library.
Activities Arts and Crafts; Cards; Games; Reading groups; Prayer groups; Movies; Shopping trips; Dances/Social or cultural gatherings.
Description This is a residential facility for individuals with mental retardation. Goal is normalization through individualized developmental programs structured to help the residents attain their maximum potential and to enable them to function in the least restrictive environment.

BELMONT

Belmont Manor Nursing Home*
34 Agassiz Ave, Belmont, MA, 02178 (617) 489-1200
Admin Edgar Karger.
Licensure Skilled Care; Intermediate Care.
Beds 119. *Certified* Medicaid.

BEVERLY

Beverly Nursing Home*
40 Heather St, Beverly, MA, 01915 (617) 927-6220
Admin James F Smith.
Licensure Skilled Care; Intermediate Care.
Beds 160. *Certified* Medicaid; Medicare.

Blueberry Hill Healthcare Nursing Home
75 Brimbal Ave, Beverly, MA, 01915 (617) 927-2020
Admin Philip S Sher. *Medical Dir/Dir of Nursing* F Carbone MD.
Licensure Skilled Care; Intermediate Care.
Beds 94. *Certified* Medicaid; Medicare.
Staff Physicians 19 (pt); RNs 6 (ft), 10 (pt); LPNs 2 (ft), 8 (pt); Nurses aides 16 (ft), 28 (pt); Physical therapists 1 (pt); Occupational therapists 1 (pt); Speech therapists 1 (pt); Activities coordinators 2 (ft); Dietitians 1 (pt); Dentists 1 (pt); Ophthalmologists 1 (pt); Podiatrists 2 (pt); Audiologists 1 (pt).
Facilities Dining room; Physical therapy room; Activities room; Chapel; Crafts room; Laundry room; Barber/Beauty shop; Library.
Activities Arts and Crafts; Cards; Games; Reading groups; Prayer groups; Movies; Shopping trips; Dances/Social or cultural gatherings.
Description Accredited by JCAH and a member AHCA, MFHF, and National Council of Health Centers.

Girdler House
78 Lothrop St, Beverly, MA, 01915 (617) 922-0346
Admin Margaret Shea. *Medical Dir/Dir of Nursing* Sadie Reid.
Licensure Rest Home. *Beds* 11.
Admissions Requirements Minimum age 65; Females only; Medical examination; Physician's request.
Staff RNs 3 (pt); LPNs 1 (pt); Nurses aides 1 (pt).

Mediplex of Beverly: A Long-Term Care Facility
265 Essex St, Beverly, MA, 01915 (617) 927-3260
Admin Carolyn Renaud. *Medical Dir/Dir of Nursing* Dr Gregory Bazylewicz.
Licensure Skilled Care. *Beds* 190. *Certified* Medicaid; Medicare.
Admissions Requirements Minimum age 16; Medical examination.
Staff RNs 3 (ft), 13 (pt); LPNs 6 (ft), 17 (pt); Orderlies 1 (ft), 1 (pt); Nurses aides 29 (ft), 40 (pt); Physical therapists; Recreational therapists 2 (ft); Occupational therapists; Activities coordinators 1 (ft); Dietitians 1 (pt); Social Workers 2 (ft).
Facilities Dining room; Physical therapy room; Activities room; Chapel; Crafts room; Barber/Beauty shop; Library.
Activities Arts and Crafts; Cards; Games; Reading groups; Prayer groups; Movies; Shopping trips; Dances/Social or cultural gatherings.
Description Mediplex of Beverly is a modern, spacious, skilled care facility offering quality care. Facility is located in quiet residential area enhanced by beautiful grounds and patio for outdoor enjoyment. A respite care program is available for families caring for elderly at home who need relief on a short-term basis.

BILLERICA

Bay State Rehabilitation Care*
78 Boston Rd, Billerica, MA, 01862 (617) 667-5123
Admin Charles W Merriam Jr.
Licensure Intermediate Care. *Beds* 80. *Certified* Medicaid.

Country View Nursing Home*
Boston Rd, Rt 3A, Billerica, MA, 01821 (617) 667-2166
Admin Carl E Moeller.
Licensure Intermediate Care. *Beds* 121. *Certified* Medicaid.

Simmons Nursing Home Inc
317 Boston Rd, Billerica, MA, 01862 (617) 663-3538
Admin Cristine Silva. *Medical Dir/Dir of Nursing* Dr J Marshall and Dr L Neuman.
Licensure Intermediate Care. *Beds* 44. *Certified* Medicaid.
Admissions Requirements Females only
Staff Physicians 3 (pt); RNs 1 (ft), 3 (pt); LPNs 2 (pt); Nurses aides 12 (pt); Physical therapists 1 (pt); Recreational therapists 1 (pt); Occupational therapists 1 (pt); Activities coordinators 1 (pt); Dietitians 1 (pt).
Facilities Dining room; Activities room; Crafts room; Laundry room.
Activities Arts and Crafts; Cards; Games; Reading groups; Prayer groups; Movies; Shopping trips; Dances/Social or cultural gatherings.
Description Facility features home-like atmosphere with dynamic caring nurses; 3 acres of lawn for outside activities, cookouts, etc; home-cooked fresh foods served; outings such as lunches, foliage tours, and seaside trips are regularly scheduled.

BLACKSTONE

Blackstone Nursing Home*
Butler St, Blackstone, MA, 01504 (617) 883-5818
Admin Davis E Perlmutter.
Licensure Intermediate Care. *Beds* 33. *Certified* Medicaid.

BOSTON

Allston Manor Nursing Home
533 Cambridge St, Boston, MA, 02134 (617) 782-2053
Admin John E Gerety Jr. *Medical Dir/Dir of Nursing* Herbert Leventhall MD.
Licensure Intermediate Care. *Beds* 150. *Certified* Medicaid.
Admissions Requirements Minimum age 21; Medical examination; Physician's request.
Staff Physicians 12 (pt); RNs 5 (ft), 10 (pt); LPNs 2 (ft), 10 (pt); Nurses aides 5 (ft), 60 (pt); Physical therapists 1 (pt); Recreational therapists 1 (ft), 3 (pt); Occupational therapists 1 (pt); Speech therapists 1 (pt); Activities coordinators 1 (ft); Dietitians 1 (pt); Dentists 1 (pt); Ophthal-mologists 1 (pt); Podiatrists 1 (pt); Audiologists 1 (pt).
Facilities Dining room; Physical therapy room; Activities room; Crafts room; Laundry room; Barber/Beauty shop; Library.
Activities Arts and Crafts; Cards; Games; Reading groups; Prayer groups; Movies; Shopping trips; Dances/Social or cultural gatherings.
Description Home offers an outstanding activity program both in the facility and in the metropolitan Boston area; residents in groups visit other nursing homes, museums, sporting events, and cultural events.

Almeida Rest Home*
69 Robinson St, Jamaica Plain, Boston, MA, 02130 (617) 522-1904
Admin Vernard N Granderson.
Licensure Rest Home. *Beds* 30.

Ann's Rest Home
66 Bowdoin Ave, Boston, MA, 02121 (617) 825-1793
Admin Willard L Basler.
Licensure Rest Home. *Beds* 13.
Admissions Requirements Minimum age 21.
Facilities Dining room.
Activities Arts and Crafts; Cards; Games; Movies.
Description Facility features a setting that provides family care to all. Food is served family-style and not institutionally with portion control.

Arborway Manor Convalescent Home
55 Burroughs St, Boston, MA, 02130 (617) 524-2155
Admin Marilyn M Maher. *Medical Dir/Dir of Nursing* Arlene Rego.
Licensure Intermediate Care. *Beds* 32.
Admissions Requirements Medical examination; Physician's request.
Facilities Dining room; Activities room; Crafts room; Laundry room; Barber/Beauty shop.
Activities Arts and Crafts; Cards; Games; Reading groups; Prayer groups; Movies; Shopping trips; Dances/Social or cultural gatherings.
Description Facility is conveniently located on MBTA lines and close to shopping areas and restaurants and overlooks Jamaica Pond. Small intimate atmosphere with lots of tender loving care; beautiful grounds.

Armenian Nursing Home*
431 Pond St, Boston, MA, 02130 (617) 552-2600
Admin N Paul Ajemian.
Licensure Skilled Care. *Beds* 83. *Certified* Medicaid.

Auburn House Nursing Home
9 Revere St, Boston, MA, 02130 (617) 524-2822
Admin Jane G Spear.
Licensure Intermediate Care. *Beds* 71. *Certified* Medicaid.
Admissions Requirements Minimum age 21; Medical examination; Physician's request.
Staff Physicians 2 (pt); RNs 1 (ft), 3 (pt); LPNs 2 (ft), 4 (pt); Nurses aides 14 (ft), 4 (pt); Physical therapists 1 (pt); Recreational therapists 1 (ft), 1 (pt); Occupational therapists 1 (pt); Speech therapists 1 (pt); Dietitians 1 (pt); Den-

tists 1 (pt); Podiatrists 1 (pt).
Facilities Dining room; Activities room; Crafts room; Laundry room; Library.
Activities Arts and Crafts; Cards; Games; Reading groups; Prayer groups; Movies; Shopping trips; Dances/Social or cultural gatherings.
Description Home has a strong musical program, a staff which is very active in all aspects of nursing home life (including special luncheons prepared by staff), activities for families, counseling, and a rich spiritual life.

Bayside Nursing Home*
804 E 7th St, Boston, MA, 02127 (617) 268-1833
Admin Joseph Vilimas Jr.
Licensure Intermediate Care. *Beds* 103. *Certified* Medicaid.

Beatrice Catherine Rest Home
47 Ocean St, Boston, MA, 02124 (617) 825-4862
Admin Marguerite I Munster.
Licensure Rest Home. *Beds* 18.
Admissions Requirements Minimum age 75; Females only
Staff RNs 2 (ft); Nurses aides 4 (ft), 1 (pt); Activities coordinators 1 (pt).
Facilities Activities room; Laundry room.
Activities Arts and Crafts; Cards; Games; Movies; Exercises.
Description Facility is a beautiful, clean, oak, Victorian home.

Beatrice Marie Nursing Home
337 Neponset Ave, Boston, MA, 02122 (617) 265-2350
Admin Thomas F Healy. *Medical Dir/Dir of Nursing* John Jainchill MD.
Licensure Skilled Care; Intermediate Care. *Beds* 109. *Certified* Medicaid.
Admissions Requirements Minimum age 21; Medical examination; Physician's request.
Staff RNs 4 (ft), 2 (pt); LPNs 10 (ft), 7 (pt); Orderlies 3 (ft), 1 (pt); Nurses aides 24 (ft), 26 (pt); Activities coordinators 2 (ft), 2 (pt).
Facilities Dining room; Activities room; Crafts room; Barber/Beauty shop.
Activities Arts and Crafts; Cards; Games; Reading groups; Prayer groups; Movies; Shopping trips; Dances/Social or cultural gatherings; Ceramics; Cooking.
Description All rooms are 1 and 2 bed; can also accommodate married couples.

Boston Home Inc
2049-61 Dorchester Ave, Boston, MA, 02124 (617) 825-3905
Admin Cletus A Carr. *Medical Dir/Dir of Nursing* Eugene F McAuliffe.
Licensure Skilled Care. *Beds* 42. *Certified* Medicaid.
Ownership Nonprofit.
Admissions Requirements Minimum age 21; Females only; Medical examination; Physician's request.
Staff Physicians 2 (pt); RNs 2 (ft), 4 (pt); LPNs 2 (ft), 2 (pt); Nurses aides 16 (ft), 20 (pt); Physical therapists 1 (pt); Occupational therapists 1 (pt); Speech therapists 1 (pt); Activities coordinators 1 (pt); Dietitians 1 (pt); Dentists 1 (pt); Ophthalmologists 1 (pt); Podiatrists 1 (pt); Audiologists 1 (pt).

Facilities Physical therapy room; Activities room; Chapel; Laundry room; Barber/Beauty shop; Library.
Activities Arts and Crafts; Cards; Games; Reading groups; Prayer groups; Movies; Shopping trips; Dances/Social or cultural gatherings.
Description Facility is located on 16 acres of beautiful grounds creating a home-like atmosphere for patients; heavy care patients welcome; staff physician coverage provided at facility's expense.

Bradegan Manor Rest Home*
11 Revere St, Jamaica Plain, Boston, MA, 02130 (617) 524-5070
Licensure Rest Home. *Beds* 44. *Certified* Medicaid.

Bradford Convalescent Home
214 Harvard St, Boston, MA, 02124 (617) 265-2333
Admin Jonathan M Shadovitz.
Licensure Intermediate Care. *Beds* 91. *Certified* Medicaid.

Bradlee Rest Home*
33 Bradlee St, Boston, MA, 02124 (617) 436-3560
Admin Toni L Bullock.
Licensure Rest Home. *Beds* 17.

Bradley Nursing Home*
495 Walnut Ave, Boston, MA, 02130 (617) 522-0660
Admin Joseph C Novak.
Licensure Intermediate Care. *Beds* 26. *Certified* Medicaid.

Burgoyne Rest Home
53 Hartford St, Boston, MA, 02125 (617) 445-1868
Admin Willard L Basler.
Licensure Rest Home. *Beds* 11.
Admissions Requirements Minimum age 21.
Facilities Activities room.
Activities Movies.
Description Home specializes in a family setting that provides family care. Food is prepared and served family-style with no portion control; historically has provided care to blind residents as well as others.

Centre Manor Nursing Home
45 Centre St, Roxbury, Boston, MA, 02119 (617) 427-2624
Admin Ethel Peters. *Medical Dir/Dir of Nursing* John Jainchill.
Licensure Intermediate Care. *Beds* 84. *Certified* Medicaid.
Admissions Requirements Medical examination.
Staff Physicians 3 (ft); RNs 3 (ft); LPNs 8 (ft); Orderlies 5 (ft); Nurses aides 30 (ft); Recreational therapists 1 (ft); Activities coordinators 1 (ft); Dietitians 1 (pt); Dentists 1 (pt); Ophthalmologists 1 (pt); Podiatrists 1 (pt).
Facilities Dining room; Activities room; Laundry room; Barber/Beauty shop.
Activities Arts and Crafts; Cards; Games; Reading groups; Prayer groups; Movies; Shopping trips; Dances/Social or cultural gatherings; Bowling.

Description This is an 84-bed, urban nursing home that services the surrounding community with an energetic, multi-cultural staff.

Charles House Convalescent Home*
10 Bellamy St, Boston, MA, 02135 (617) 782-8113
Admin David Potvin.
Licensure Skilled Care; Intermediate Care. *Beds* 121. *Certified* Medicaid.

Circle Manor Nursing Home
29 Chestnut Hill Ave, Boston, MA, 02135 (617) 254-7655
Admin Clifford Blake. *Medical Dir/Dir of Nursing* Margaret Brennan RN.
Licensure Intermediate Care. *Beds* 64. *Certified* Medicaid.
Admissions Requirements Medical examination.
Staff Physicians; RNs 1 (ft), 3 (pt); LPNs 6 (pt); Nurses aides 11 (ft), 9 (pt); Physical therapists; Recreational therapists 1 (ft); Dietitians.
Facilities Dining room; Activities room; Chapel; Crafts room; Laundry room; Barber/Beauty shop.
Activities Arts and Crafts; Cards; Games; Reading groups; Prayer groups; Movies; Shopping trips; Dances/Social or cultural gatherings.

Columbus Nursing Home
910 Sartoga St, Boston, MA, 02128 (617) 569-1159
Admin Tom Dresser. *Medical Dir/Dir of Nursing* Dr William Kanish.
Licensure Skilled Care. *Beds* 110. *Certified* Medicaid; Medicare.
Admissions Requirements Minimum age 18.
Facilities Dining room; Physical therapy room; Activities room; Crafts room; Laundry room; Barber/Beauty shop.
Activities Arts and Crafts; Cards; Games; Reading groups; Prayer groups; Movies; Shopping trips; Dances/Social or cultural gatherings.
Description Facility offers psychosocial program aimed at assisting clients with chronic psychiatric disorders who show potential for eventual discharge to a lower level of care and/or into the community.

Corey Hill Nursing Home
249 Corey Rd, Boston, MA, 02135 (617) 734-7138
Admin Louis Dronge. *Medical Dir/Dir of Nursing* Dr Herbert Leventhal.
Licensure Intermediate Care. *Beds* 43. *Certified* Medicaid.
Admissions Requirements Minimum age 60; Medical examination; Physician's request.
Staff RNs 2 (ft), 1 (pt); LPNs 2 (ft), 1 (pt); Nurses aides 14 (ft), 6 (pt); Activities coordinators 1 (ft); Dietitians 1 (pt).

Cushing Manor Rest Home*
20 Cushing Ave, Dorchester, Boston, MA, 02125 (617) 436-9608
Admin Natalie I Batchelder.
Licensure Rest Home. *Beds* 36. *Certified* Medicaid.

Deutsches Altenheim
2222 Centre St, Boston, MA, 02132 (617) 325-1230

Admin Donna Lee McLean. *Medical Dir/Dir of Nursing* Dr Robert Mullins.
Licensure Intermediate Care. *Beds* 40. *Certified* Medicaid.
Admissions Requirements Minimum age 65.
Staff RNs 4 (ft); LPNs 3 (ft); Orderlies 1 (ft); Nurses aides 4 (ft), 8 (pt); Recreational therapists 1 (ft); Dietitians 1 (pt); Dentists 1 (pt); Podiatrists 1 (pt).
Affiliation German Ladies Aid Society
Facilities Dining room; Activities room; Chapel; Crafts room; Laundry room; Barber/Beauty shop; Library.
Activities Arts and Crafts; Cards; Games; Reading groups; Prayer groups; Movies; Shopping trips; Dances/Social or cultural gatherings.
Description Built in 1914, the home provides private rooms for all residents and is set on 12 acres of beautifully landscaped land.

Don Orione Nursing Home*
111 Orient Ave, Boston, MA, 02128 (617) 569-2100
Admin Rocco Crescenzi.
Licensure Intermediate Care. *Beds* 197. *Certified* Medicaid.

Duplex Nursing Home Inc
12 Harris Ave, Boston, MA, 02130 (617) 522-0588
Admin Janet C Murphy.
Licensure Intermediate Care. *Beds* 46. *Certified* Medicaid.
Admissions Requirements Minimum age 21; Males only
Staff RNs 1 (ft), 3 (pt); LPNs 2 (ft), 2 (pt); Nurses aides 7 (ft), 3 (pt); Activities coordinators 1 (pt); Dietitians 1 (pt); Dentists 1 (pt); Ophthalmologists 1 (pt); Podiatrists 1 (pt).
Facilities Dining room; Activities room.
Activities Arts and Crafts; Cards; Games; Reading groups; Prayer groups; Movies; Shopping trips; Dances/Social or cultural gatherings.
Description Facility has small home-like atmosphere with heavy concentration on personalized health care delivery.

Elizabeth Carelton House*
2055 Columbus Ave, Boston, MA, 02119 (617) 522-2100
Admin Hilda Jane Miller.
Licensure Intermediate Care. *Beds* 110. *Certified* Medicaid.

Ellen James Rest Home*
42 Elm Hill Ave, Roxbury, Boston, MA, 02121 (617) 427-7464
Admin Jeanette Savoie.
Licensure Rest Home. *Beds* 40.

Elm Hill Nursing Home*
237-241 Walnut Ave, Boston, MA, 02119 (617) 427-4798
Admin Jeanette Savoie.
Licensure Intermediate Care. *Beds* 55. *Certified* Medicaid.

Englewood Nursing Home*
27 Howland St, Boston, MA, 02121 (617) 427-2332
Admin Lillian B Granderson.
Licensure Intermediate Care. *Beds* 35. *Certified* Medicaid.

Fairfax Rest Home
15 Fairfax St, Boston, MA, 02124 (617) 265-8431
Admin Andrew Basler.
Licensure Rest Home. *Beds* 17.

Fairmount Rest Home Inc*
172 Fairmount Ave, Hyde Park, Boston, MA, 02136 (617) 361-5150
Admin Mildred Marden.
Licensure Rest Home. *Beds* 32.

Forest Hills Nursing Home*
101 Brookley Rd, Boston, MA, 02130 (617) 524-4700
Admin Charles J O'Malley.
Licensure Intermediate Care. *Beds* 110. *Certified* Medicaid.

Frances Merry Barnard Home
50 Beacon St, Boston, MA, 02136 (617) 361-0156
Admin Elizabeth Haley.
Licensure Rest Home. *Beds* 11.

Franida House Nursing Home*
65 Glen Rd, Boston, MA, 02130 (617) 522-8714
Admin Barbara A Smith.
Licensure Intermediate Care. *Beds* 22. *Certified* Medicaid.

Frank Wood Convalescent Home*
1135 Morton St, Boston, MA, 02126 (617) 298-8003
Admin Dennis F Sullivan.
Licensure Skilled Care. *Beds* 58. *Certified* Medicaid; Medicare.

Gardner House Rest Home
47 Centre St, Boston, MA, 02119 (617) 445-1727
Admin Phillip P Cohen. *Medical Dir/Dir of Nursing* Dr Rubin.
Licensure Rest Home. *Beds* 24.
Admissions Requirements Minimum age 40; Physician's request.
Facilities Activities room; Crafts room; Laundry room.
Activities Arts and Crafts; Cards; Games; Reading groups; Prayer groups; Movies; Shopping trips.

Gardner Pierce Nursing and Rest Home
333 Commonwealth Ave, Boston, MA, 02115 (617) 266-3300
Admin Edward M Levitt.
Licensure Intermediate Care. *Beds* 38. *Certified* Medicaid.

Grampian Nursing Home
33 Grampian Way, Boston, MA, 02125 (617) 436-3331
Admin Louis Furash. *Medical Dir/Dir of Nursing* Kathleen Maffie.
Licensure Intermediate Care. *Beds* 26. *Certified* Medicaid.
Admissions Requirements Females only; Medical examination; Physician's request.
Staff Physicians 4 (pt); RNs 1 (pt); LPNs 3 (ft), 3 (pt); Nurses aides 10 (ft), 4 (pt); Physical therapists 1 (pt); Activities coordinators 1 (ft); Dietitians 1 (pt); Dentists 1 (pt); Ophthalmologists

1 (pt); Podiatrists 1 (pt); Audiologists 1 (pt).
Facilities Activities room; Laundry room; Barber/Beauty shop.
Activities Arts and Crafts; Cards; Games; Reading groups; Movies; Shopping trips; Dances/Social or cultural gatherings.
Description Facility is located on Saven Hill by the Sea overlooking Boston Harbor and features home-type atmosphere, "we care" attitude, and lots of tender loving care.

Greenery Nursing Home
99-111 Chestnut Hill Ave, Boston, MA, 02135 (617) 787-3390
Admin George M Ferenick. *Medical Dir/Dir of Nursing* Dr William Garvin.
Licensure Skilled Care; Intermediate Care. *Beds* 198. *Certified* Medicaid; Medicare.
Staff Physicians 3 (pt); RNs 49 (pt); LPNs 42 (pt); Nurses aides 144 (ft); Physical therapists 16 (ft); Recreational therapists 10 (ft); Occupational therapists 16 (ft); Speech therapists 7 (ft); Activities coordinators 1 (ft); Dietitians 1 (ft).
Facilities Dining room; Physical therapy room; Activities room; Crafts room; Laundry room; Barber/Beauty shop; Library.
Activities Arts and Crafts; Cards; Games; Prayer groups; Movies; Shopping trips; Dances/Social or cultural gatherings.
Description The Greenery's program goal is to provide comprehensive rehabilitation milieu to young adults who have physical and cognitive disabilities resulting from traumatic and non-traumatic head injury for the purpose of increasing their level of functioning to the maximum extent.

Hale-Barnard Home
273 Clarendon St, Boston, MA, 02116 (617) 536-3726
Admin Rebekah Richardson. *Medical Dir/Dir of Nursing* Christine Wolford.
Licensure Charitable Home. *Beds* 60.
Admissions Requirements Minimum age 65; Medical examination.
Staff RNs 2 (ft); LPNs 6 (pt); Nurses aides 1 (ft), 1 (pt); Activities coordinators 1 (pt).
Facilities Dining room; Activities room; Laundry room; Barber/Beauty shop; Library.
Activities Cards; Games; Reading groups; Movies; Shopping trips; Dances/Social or cultural gatherings.
Description All rooms are private. Weekly outings are planned and a sherry hour occurs each Friday. Currently developing a homecare project.

Harbor Inn Nursing Home Inc
1380 Columbia Rd, Boston, MA, 02127 (617) 268-5450
Admin Lillian Ruth Talcof. *Medical Dir/Dir of Nursing* Veronica Boderick MD.
Licensure Intermediate Care. *Beds* 107. *Certified* Medicaid.
Admissions Requirements Minimum age 50.
Staff Physicians 4 (pt); RNs 1 (ft), 1 (pt); LPNs 6 (ft), 1 (pt); Nurses aides 18 (ft), 4 (pt); Recreational therapists 1 (ft); Dietitians 1 (pt); Dentists 1 (pt); Ophthalmologists 1 (pt); Podiatrists 1 (pt).
Facilities Dining room; Activities room; Crafts room; Barber/Beauty shop.
Activities Arts and Crafts; Cards; Games;

Reading groups; Prayer groups; Movies; Shopping trips; Dances/Social or cultural gatherings; Dining out.
Description Facility has ideal setting, facing the ocean with an excellent view of sunrise and sunset; all on one floor.

Harris Avenue Rest Home*
7 Harris Ave, Jamaica Plain, Boston, MA, 02130 (617) 524-9796
Admin Dianne Lilis.
Licensure Rest Home. *Beds* 23. *Certified* Medicaid.

Haven Nursing Home*
44 Peter Parley Rd, Boston, MA, 02130 (617) 524-3150
Admin Donald J MacQuarrie.
Licensure Intermediate Care. *Beds* 20. *Certified* Medicaid.

Highland Rest Home
516 Warren St, Boston, MA, 02121 (617) 427-6640
Admin Jeanette Savoie. *Medical Dir/Dir of Nursing* Frances Valentine.
Licensure Rest Home. *Beds* 41.
Admissions Requirements Minimum age 40; Medical examination.
Staff LPNs 1 (ft); Nurses aides 3 (ft), 8 (pt); Activities coordinators 1 (pt); Activities coordinators 1 (pt).
Facilities Dining room; Laundry room.
Activities Arts and Crafts; Cards; Games; Prayer groups; Movies; Shopping trips; Dances/Social or cultural gatherings.

Hill Top Manor Nursing Home*
30 Hilltop St, Dorchester, Boston, MA, 02124 (617) 288-3410
Admin Bruce J Bedard.
Licensure Intermediate Care. *Beds* 90. *Certified* Medicaid.

Hodgdon Rest Home*
95 Moreland St, Roxbury, Boston, MA, 02121 (617) 445-8864
Admin Adolphus G Bullock.
Licensure Rest Home. *Beds* 60.

Home for Aged Women
201-05 S Huntington Ave, Boston, MA, 02130 (617) 522-3080
Admin Andrew J Comeau. *Medical Dir/Dir of Nursing* Kim Bowman MD.
Licensure Intermediate Care. *Beds* 145. *Certified* Medicaid.
Ownership Nonprofit.
Admissions Requirements Minimum age 60; Females only; Medical examination.
Staff RNs 1 (ft); LPNs 5 (ft), 1 (pt); Nurses aides 29 (ft), 6 (pt); Activities coordinators 2 (ft).
Facilities Dining room; Physical therapy room; Activities room; Crafts room; Laundry room; Barber/Beauty shop; Library.
Activities Arts and Crafts; Cards; Games; Reading groups; Prayer groups; Movies; Shopping trips; Dances/Social or cultural gatherings.
Description Established in 1849, the Home for Aged Women is Massachusetts' oldest and largest nonprofit facility for senior women. The present building was designed in 1927 by the renowned architectual firm of Coolidge, Shepley, Bulfinch and Abbot and embodies a spirit of grace, serenity, and independence which is the hallmark of home tradition.

Hyde Park Convalescent Home
113 Central Ave, Boston, MA, 02136 (617) 361-2388
Admin Arthur D Kruskall.
Licensure Skilled Care; Intermediate Care. *Beds* 53. *Certified* Medicaid.
Staff RNs 1 (ft), 3 (pt); LPNs 4 (ft), 4 (pt); Nurses aides 13 (ft), 18 (pt); Activities coordinators 1 (ft); 1 (ft).
Facilities Dining room; Activities room; Crafts room; Laundry room; Barber/Beauty shop.
Activities Arts and Crafts; Cards; Games; Reading groups; Prayer groups; Movies; Shopping trips; Dances/Social or cultural gatherings; Mens club; Cooking club; Garden club; Exercise bike club.

Jamaica Towers Nursing Home
174 Forest Hills St, Boston, MA, 02130 (617) 522-6675
Admin Alfred J Souza. *Medical Dir/Dir of Nursing* Saripalli V Subbaraju MD.
Licensure Skilled Care; Intermediate Care. *Beds* 120. *Certified* Medicaid; Medicare.
Admissions Requirements Minimum age 21; Physician's request.
Staff Physicians 18 (pt); RNs 5 (ft), 2 (pt); LPNs 7 (ft), 9 (pt); Orderlies 4 (ft); Nurses aides 60 (ft), 1 (pt); Physical therapists 1 (pt); Occupational therapists 1 (pt); Speech therapists 1 (pt); Activities coordinators 2 (ft); Dietitians 1 (pt); Dentists 1 (pt); Ophthalmologists 1 (pt); Podiatrists 1 (pt); Audiologists 1 (pt).
Facilities Dining room; Physical therapy room; Activities room; Crafts room; Laundry room; Barber/Beauty shop.
Activities Arts and Crafts; Cards; Games; Reading groups; Prayer groups; Movies; Shopping trips; Dances/Social or cultural gatherings.
Description Facility is a modern, fire protected, city home close to public transportation offering Level I, II and III care.

Johnson Nursing Home
46 Wren St, Boston, MA, 02132 (617) 325-5006
Admin Louis J Furash.
Licensure Intermediate Care. *Beds* 32. *Certified* Medicaid.

Long Term Care at Neponset—Ashmont Manor
45 Coffey St, Neponset, Boston, MA, 02122 (617) 282-9700
Admin Peter S Gordon.
Licensure Intermediate Care. *Beds* 77. *Certified* Medicaid.
Staff RNs 1 (ft), 1 (pt); LPNs 5 (ft), 6 (pt); Nurses aides 20 (ft), 20 (pt); Physical therapists 1 (pt); Reality therapists 2 (ft); Recreational therapists 2 (ft); Occupational therapists 1 (pt); Activities coordinators 1 (ft); Dietitians 1 (pt).
Facilities Dining room; Activities room; Chapel; Crafts room; Laundry room.
Activities Arts and Crafts; Cards; Games; Reading groups; Prayer groups; Movies; Shopping trips; Dances/Social or cultural gatherings.
Description Located on an acre of land, Ashmont Manor offers country setting in the middle of the city. Newly constructed addition offers air conditioned, semi-private and private accomodations with private bath and balcony.

Long Term Care at Neponset—Neponset Hall
35 Coffey St, Neponset, Boston, MA, 02122 (617) 282-3600
Admin Peter S Gordon.
Licensure Intermediate Care. *Beds* 98. *Certified* Medicaid.
Staff RNs 2 (ft), 2 (pt); LPNs 5 (ft), 6 (pt); Nurses aides 20 (ft), 25 (pt); Physical therapists 1 (pt); Recreational therapists 1 (ft), 1 (pt); Occupational therapists 1 (pt); Activities coordinators 1 (ft); Dietitians 1 (pt).
Facilities Dining room; Activities room; Chapel; Crafts room; Laundry room.
Activities Arts and Crafts; Cards; Games; Reading groups; Prayer groups; Movies; Shopping trips; Dances/Social or cultural gatherings.

Lynmark Nursing Home Inc
15 Robinwood Ave, Boston, MA, 02130 (617) 522-9044
Admin Marilyn Maher.
Licensure Intermediate Care. *Beds* 20. *Certified* Medicaid.

Marco Polo Rest Home Inc
Box 501, Boston, MA, 02128 (617) 567-7500
Admin Richard J Diamond. *Medical Dir/Dir of Nursing* Glenn Rothfeld MD.
Licensure Rest Home. *Beds* 62.
Admissions Requirements Minimum age 45; Medical examination.
Staff Nurses aides 4 (ft), 6 (pt); Activities coordinators 1 (pt).
Facilities Dining room; Activities room; Laundry room.
Activities Arts and Crafts; Cards; Games; Dances/Social or cultural gatherings.
Description We are a long-term, Level IV psychiatric facility with a median age of 69. Our residents are chronically disabled, but stable. We are not involved in nursing care nor rehabilitation. Applicants must be Level IV eligible.

Marian Manor
130 Dorchester St, Boston, MA, 02127 (617) 268-3333
Admin Sr M Mark Louis. *Medical Dir/Dir of Nursing* Ernesté Waingortin MD.
Licensure Skilled Care; Intermediate Care; Residential Care. *Beds* 376. *Certified* Medicaid.
Admissions Requirements Minimum age 65; Physician's request.
Affiliation Roman Catholic
Facilities Dining room; Physical therapy room; Activities room; Chapel; Crafts room; Laundry room; Barber/Beauty shop; Library.
Activities Arts and Crafts; Cards; Games; Prayer groups; Movies; Shopping trips; Dances/Social or cultural gatherings.

Martin Nursing Home*
415 Columbia Rd, Boston, MA, 02125 (617) 436-4170
Admin Susanna Sheppard.
Licensure Intermediate Care. *Beds* 150. *Certified* Medicaid.

Mary Murphy Nursing Home
70 Rockview St, Boston, MA, 02130 (617)
524-6200
Admin Ethel Peters. *Medical Dir/Dir of
Nursing* Dr Louis Kassler.
Licensure Intermediate Care. *Beds* 91. *Certified* Medicaid.
Admissions Requirements Minimum age 21;
Medical examination; Physician's request.
Staff Physicians 4 (pt); RNs 2 (ft), 2 (pt); LPNs
4 (ft), 2 (pt); Orderlies 1 (ft); Nurses aides 18
(ft), 8 (pt); Physical therapists 1 (pt); Recreational therapists 1 (pt); Speech therapists 1 (pt);
Activities coordinators 1 (ft), 1 (pt); Dietitians
1 (pt); Dentists 1 (pt); Ophthalmologists 1 (pt);
Podiatrists 1 (pt).
Activities Arts and Crafts; Cards; Games;
Reading groups; Prayer groups; Movies; Shopping trips.

Melville Rest Home
3 Melville Ave, Boston, MA, 02124 (617)
288-5816
Admin Margaret T Murray. *Medical Dir/Dir of
Nursing* Dr Boderick.
Licensure Rest Home. *Beds* 23.
Admissions Requirements Minimum age 18;
Medical examination.
Staff LPNs 1 (pt); Activities coordinators 1
(pt).
Facilities Dining room; Activities room; Laundry room; Kitchen.
Activities Arts and Crafts; Cards; Games;
Reading groups; Prayer groups; Movies; Shopping trips; Dances/Social or cultural gatherings.
Description Facility is a rest home with all residents needing no nursing care; home-like
setting provided with people's ages ranging
from 24 to 84 averaging 40-50.

Milton View Nursing Home*
150 River St, Mattapan, Boston, MA, 02126
(617) 296-0140
Admin Thomas B Dresser.
Licensure Intermediate Care. *Beds* 64. *Certified* Medicaid.

Monroe Rest Home*
72 Robinwood Ave, Jamaica Plain, Boston,
MA, 02130 (617) 524-6900
Admin John H Keeney Jr.
Licensure Rest Home. *Beds* 33.

Mount Pleasant Home*
301 S Huntington Ave, Boston, MA, 02130
(617) 522-7600
Admin Harriet H Caton.
Licensure Rest Home. *Beds* 44.

Nelson Manor Nursing Home*
3 Aspinwall Rd, Dorchester, Boston, MA,
02124 (617) 288-4100
Admin Barbara Cohen.
Licensure Intermediate Care. *Beds* 47. *Certified* Medicaid.

Norwegian Old Peoples Home*
1205 Centre St, Boston, MA, 02131 (617)
325-9439
Admin Olaf A Ness.
Licensure Charitable Home. *Beds* 18.

Oak Haven Nursing Home*
74 Howland St, Boston, MA, 02121 (617)
427-8080
Admin Loretta Murphy.
Licensure Intermediate Care. *Beds* 38. *Certified* Medicaid.

Park Dale Rest Home*
36 Elm Hill Ave, Boston, MA, 02121 (617)
427-9649
Admin L B Granderson.
Licensure Rest Home. *Beds* 27.

Parker Hill Manor Rest Home
18-20 Parker Hill Ave, Boston, MA, 02120
(617) 232-0725
Admin David Jacob Lawson.
Licensure Rest Home. *Beds* 26.
Admissions Requirements Minimum age 18;
Medical examination.
Staff Physicians; RNs; Nurses aides; Activities
coordinators; Dietitians; Dentists; Ophthalmologists; Podiatrists; Audiologists.
Facilities Dining room; Activities room; Crafts
room; Laundry room.
Activities Arts and Crafts; Cards; Games;
Reading groups; Prayer groups; Movies; Shopping trips; Dances/Social or cultural gatherings;
Field trips.
Description Facility has implemented a "pet
therapy" program that has been covered on
television with news stories featuring therapeutic benefits in that type of activity.

Parkway Nursing Home*
1190 VFW Pkwy, Boston, MA, 02132 (617)
325-1688
Admin Burton K Lipsky.
Licensure Intermediate Care. *Beds* 140. *Certified* Medicaid.

Parkwell Nursing Home*
745 Truman Hwy, Boston, MA, 02136 (617)
361-8300
Admin Patrick O'Connor.
Licensure Skilled Care; Intermediate Care.
Beds 124. *Certified* Medicaid; Medicare.

Parley Vale Rest Home
3 Parley Vale, Boston, MA, 02130 (617)
524-4223
Admin E E Osborn.
Licensure Rest Home. *Beds* 27.

Provident Nursing Home*
1501 Commonwealth Ave, Boston, MA, 02135
(617) 782-1320
Admin Stephen J Kelly.
Licensure Intermediate Care. *Beds* 146. *Certified* Medicaid.

The Recuperative Center
1245 Centre St, Boston, MA, 02131 (617)
325-5400
Admin Gregory C Karr.
Licensure Skilled Care. *Beds* 81. *Certified* Medicaid; Medicare.
Admissions Requirements Minimum age 20.
Staff Physicians; RNs; LPNs; Orderlies;
Nurses aides; Physical therapists; Reality therapists; Recreational therapists; Occupational
therapists; Speech therapists; Activities coordinators.

Facilities Dining room; Physical therapy room;
Activities room; Chapel; Crafts room; Barber-/Beauty shop.
Activities Arts and Crafts; Cards; Games;
Reading groups; Prayer groups; Movies.
Description A skilled facility specializing in
short-term rehabilitation; over 85% of patients
admitted return to independent community
living. The center offers respite care as well as
care for the terminally ill.

Regent Nursing Home*
74 Corey Rd, Brighton, Boston, MA, 02146
(617) 277-2782
Admin Janina Elmaleh.
Licensure Intermediate Care. *Beds* 41. *Certified* Medicaid.

Resthaven Corporation*
120 Fisher Ave, Boston, MA, 02120 (617)
738-1500
Admin Felix F Albano.
Licensure Skilled Care; Intermediate Care.
Beds 240. *Certified* Medicaid.

Riverside Nursing Home*
405 River St, Boston, MA, 02126 (617)
296-5585
Admin James E Brady.
Licensure Intermediate Care. *Beds* 85. *Certified* Medicaid.

Riverview Nursing Home*
142 Bigelow St, Boston, MA, 02135 (617)
782-3424
Admin Barry Chiler.
Licensure Intermediate Care. *Beds* 143. *Certified* Medicaid.

Robinwood II Rest Home
87 Robinwood Ave, Boston, MA, 02130 (617)
524-2804
Admin Francis E Quillard.
Licensure Rest Home. *Beds* 31.
Admissions Requirements Minimum age 21;
Males only
Staff Physicians 3 (pt); Nurses aides 7 (ft); Recreational therapists 1 (pt); Dietitians 1 (pt).
Facilities Activities room.
Activities Cards; Games; Prayer groups;
Movies; Shopping trips.

Rodger Rest Home*
54 Bowdoin St, Dorchester, Boston, MA, 02124
(617) 825-1771
Admin Lillian B Granderson.
Licensure Rest Home. *Beds* 20.

Rodgerson House
434 Jamaica Way, Jamaica Plain, Boston, MA,
02130 (617) 522-7230
Admin James F Seagle Jr. *Medical Dir/Dir of
Nursing* Dr Amnon Wachman.
Licensure Intermediate Care; Charitable
Home. *Beds* 56. *Certified* Medicaid.
Admissions Requirements Minimum age 55;
Males only; Medical examination.
Staff Physicians 1 (pt); RNs 1 (pt); LPNs 3 (ft),
3 (pt); Nurses aides 5 (ft), 4 (pt); Activities coordinators 1 (ft); Dietitians 1 (pt).
Facilities Dining room; Physical therapy room;
Activities room; Crafts room; Laundry room;
Pub; Billiard room; Smoking lounges; TV

room.
Activities Arts and Crafts; Games; Reading groups; Movies; Dances/Social or cultural gatherings; Lunch trips; Overnight sightseeing trips.
Description Facility features private rooms, walking and exercise path, and spacious grounds with vegetable and flower gardens.

Saint Joseph's Manor
321 Centre St, Boston, MA, 02122 (617) 825-6320
Admin Sr James Frances Powers.
Licensure Charitable Home. *Beds* 77.
Admissions Requirements Minimum age 70; Females only; Medical examination; Physician's request.
Staff RNs 1 (pt); LPNs 1 (ft); Orderlies 3 (ft), 5 (pt); Activities coordinators 1 (ft); Dietitians 1 (pt); Podiatrists 1 (pt).
Affiliation Roman Catholic
Facilities Dining room; Activities room; Chapel; Laundry room; Barber/Beauty shop.
Activities Arts and Crafts; Cards; Games; Reading groups; Prayer groups; Movies; Shopping trips; Dances/Social or cultural gatherings.
Description The principal purpose of the facility is to provide a home to care for the health, safety, and comfort of retired ladies. Nursing services are provided 24 hours a day giving the residents physical and mental security.

Sheriff Manor Nursing Home
176 Humboldt, Boston, MA, 02121 (617) 445-5224
Admin Roger T Dillingham.
Licensure Intermediate Care. *Beds* 60. *Certified* Medicaid.

Sherrill House Inc
135 S Huntington Ave, Boston, MA, 02130 (617) 731-2400
Admin Donald M Powell. *Medical Dir/Dir of Nursing* Dr Jens Touborg.
Licensure Skilled Care; Intermediate Care; Charitable Home. *Beds* 160. *Certified* Medicaid; Medicare.
Staff RNs 25 (ft); LPNs 10 (ft); Orderlies 5 (ft); Nurses aides 50 (ft); Physical therapists 1 (ft), 2 (pt); Recreational therapists 2 (ft); Occupational therapists 1 (ft); Speech therapists 1 (pt); Activities coordinators 1 (ft); Dietitians 1 (pt).
Facilities Dining room; Physical therapy room; Activities room; Chapel; Crafts room; Laundry room; Barber/Beauty shop; Library.
Activities Arts and Crafts; Cards; Games; Reading groups; Prayer groups; Movies; Shopping trips.

Stadium Manor Nursing Home*
461 Walnut Ave, Boston, MA, 02130 (617) 522-1170
Admin James D Regan.
Licensure Intermediate Care. *Beds* 120. *Certified* Medicaid.

Star of David Convalescent Home
1100 VFW Parkway, Boston, MA, 02132 (617) 325-8100
Admin Richard Sabounjiam. *Medical Dir/Dir of Nursing* Dr Joseph Pines.
Licensure Intermediate Care. *Beds* 146. *Certified* Medicaid.

Admissions Requirements Medical examination.
Staff RNs 18 (ft); LPNs 6 (ft); Orderlies 4 (ft); Nurses aides 38 (ft); Physical therapists 2 (ft), 1 (pt); Reality therapists 2 (ft); Occupational therapists 1 (pt); Speech therapists 1 (pt); Activities coordinators 1 (ft), 2 (pt); Dietitians 1 (pt).
Facilities Dining room; Physical therapy room; Activities room; Chapel; Crafts room; Laundry room; Barber/Beauty shop; Library; Lounges; Auditorium.
Activities Arts and Crafts; Cards; Reading groups; Prayer groups; Movies; Shopping trips; Dances/Social or cultural gatherings.
Description Facility features observance of all Jewish religious holidays in addition to regular daily and sabbath services, and all regular American and secular celebrations; kosher kitchen.

Stonehedge Nursing Home*
5 Redlands Rd, Boston, MA, 02132 (617) 327-6325
Admin Lawrence E Warner.
Licensure Intermediate Care. *Beds* 79. *Certified* Medicaid.

Tara Nursing Home
52 Alban St, Boston, MA, 02124 (617) 436-5048
Admin Robert D Wilkins. *Medical Dir/Dir of Nursing* Dr G Bonderman.
Licensure Intermediate Care. *Beds* 22. *Certified* Medicaid.
Admissions Requirements Females only; Medical examination.
Staff RNs 1 (ft); LPNs 1 (ft), 2 (pt); Nurses aides 5 (ft), 3 (pt); Activities coordinators 1 (ft).
Facilities Dining room; Activities room; Laundry room.
Activities Arts and Crafts; Cards; Games; Reading groups; Prayer groups; Movies; Shopping trips.
Description Facility features a bright, cheery home-like atmosphere with excellent food and kindly nurses who give loving care.

Townsend Nursing Home*
135 Townsend St, Boston, MA, 02121 (617) 445-0420
Admin Lillian Granderson.
Licensure Intermediate Care. *Beds* 128. *Certified* Medicaid.

Village Manor Nursing Home
25 Alpine St, Boston, MA, 02126 (617) 361-5400
Admin Melanie Kosich. *Medical Dir/Dir of Nursing* Thomas Monahan Jr MD.
Licensure Skilled Care; Intermediate Care. *Beds* 123. *Certified* Medicaid.
Admissions Requirements Minimum age 21; Medical examination.
Staff Physicians 1 (pt); RNs 7 (ft), 3 (pt); LPNs 11 (ft), 3 (pt); Orderlies 3 (ft), 2 (pt); Nurses aides 40 (ft), 4 (pt); Physical therapists 1 (pt); Reality therapists 1 (pt); Occupational therapists 1 (pt); Speech therapists 1 (pt); Activities coordinators 1 (ft), 2 (pt); Dietitians 1 (pt); Dentists 1 (pt); Ophthalmologists 1 (pt); Podiatrists 1 (pt); Audiologists 1 (pt).
Facilities Dining room; Physical therapy room; Activities room; Crafts room; Laundry room;

Barber/Beauty shop; TV rooms.
Activities Arts and Crafts; Cards; Games; Reading groups; Prayer groups; Movies; Shopping trips; Dances/Social or cultural gatherings.
Description This facility is affiliated with the Faulkner Hospital, a community teaching hospital, through common ownership. Services offered are enhanced by hospital staff, including social services, occupational therapy, dietary, and administration. Located within Boston, the facility is atop a hill with spacious grounds and landscaping.

Wayne Manor Nursing Home*
133 Hancock St, Boston, MA, 02125 (617) 265-5220
Admin Barbara Cohen.
Licensure Intermediate Care. *Beds* 78. *Certified* Medicaid.

West Roxbury Manor Nursing Home
5060 Washington St, Boston, MA, 02132 (617) 323-5440
Admin Burton K Lipsky. *Medical Dir/Dir of Nursing* James Harrison MD.
Licensure Skilled Care; Intermediate Care. *Beds* 76. *Certified* Medicaid.
Admissions Requirements Minimum age 50; Medical examination; Physician's request.
Staff Physicians 12 (pt); RNs 5 (ft); LPNs 8 (ft); Orderlies 1 (ft); Nurses aides 25 (ft); Physical therapists 1 (pt); Reality therapists 1 (pt); Recreational therapists 1 (ft), 1 (pt); Occupational therapists 1 (pt); Speech therapists 1 (pt); Activities coordinators 1 (ft); Dietitians 1 (pt); Dentists 1 (pt); Ophthalmologists 1 (pt); Podiatrists 1 (pt); Audiologists 1 (pt).
Facilities Dining room; Laundry room; Library.
Activities Arts and Crafts; Cards; Games; Reading groups; Movies; Shopping trips; Dances/Social or cultural gatherings.
Description This home specializes in providing a warm, loving atmosphere; excellent rehabilitation programs.

BRAINTREE

Braintree Manor Nursing and Retirement Center*
1102 Washington St, Braintree, MA, 02185 (617) 848-3100
Admin Francis J Pattavina.
Licensure Skilled Care; Intermediate Care. *Beds* 247. *Certified* Medicaid; Medicare.

Elihu White Nursing and Rehabilitation Center*
95 Commercial St, Braintree, MA, 02184 (617) 848-3678
Admin Florence E Logan.
Licensure Skilled Care; Intermediate Care. *Beds* 189. *Certified* Medicaid; Medicare.

Franklin Nursing Home
149 Franklin St, Braintree, MA, 02185 (617) 843-3136
Admin Beverly Singer. *Medical Dir/Dir of Nursing* Dr Max Pearlstein.
Licensure Intermediate Care. *Beds* 72. *Certified* Medicaid.
Admissions Requirements Minimum age 50;

Medical examination.
Staff RNs 4 (pt); LPNs 2 (ft), 3 (pt); Nurses aides 5 (ft), 9 (pt); Recreational therapists 1 (pt).
Facilities Dining room; Laundry room.
Activities Arts and Crafts; Cards; Games; Reading groups; Prayer groups; Shopping trips.
Description Facility offers warm home-like atmosphere with a caring staff.

Franvale Nursing Home*
20 Pond St, Braintree, MA, 02185 (617) 848-1616
Admin Thomas H Daley.
Licensure Skilled Care; Intermediate Care.
Beds 88. *Certified* Medicaid; Medicare.

Hollingsworth House Nursing and Retirement Center*
1120 Washington St, Braintree, MA, 02185 (617) 848-3100
Admin Vincent Pattavina.
Licensure Intermediate Care. *Beds* 120. *Certified* Medicaid.

John Scott House Nursing and Rehabilitation Center*
233 Middle St, Braintree, MA, 02184 (617) 843-1860
Admin Michael Welch.
Licensure Skilled Care; Intermediate Care.
Beds 200. *Certified* Medicaid; Medicare.

Resthaven Nursing Home*
155 Quincy Ave, Braintree, MA, 02184 (617) 843-2155
Admin Ruth E Houde.
Licensure Skilled Care. *Beds* 69. *Certified* Medicaid.

BREWSTER

Brewster Manor Nursing and Retirement Home
873 Harwich Rd, Brewster, MA, 02631 (617) 896-7046
Admin Dorothea L Maloney. *Medical Dir/Dir of Nursing* John Horgan MD.
Licensure Skilled Care; Intermediate Care.
Beds 129. *Certified* Medicaid; Medicare.
Staff RNs 5 (ft), 18 (pt); LPNs 2 (ft), 5 (pt); Orderlies 2 (ft), 2 (pt); Nurses aides 26 (ft), 45 (pt); Physical therapists 1 (pt); Reality therapists 1 (pt); Occupational therapists 1 (pt); Speech therapists 1 (pt); Activities coordinators 1 (ft), 1 (pt); Dietitians 1 (pt); Dentists 1 (pt); Ophthalmologists 1 (pt); Podiatrists 1 (pt).
Facilities Dining room; Physical therapy room; Activities room; Chapel; Crafts room; Laundry room; Barber/Beauty shop.
Activities Arts and Crafts; Cards; Games; Reading groups; Prayer groups; Movies; Shopping trips; Dances/Social or cultural gatherings.

BRIDGEWATER

Bridgewater Nursing Home*
16 Pleasant St, Bridgewater, MA, 02324 (617) 697-4616
Admin William Gold.
Licensure Intermediate Care. *Beds* 43. *Certified* Medicaid.

BROCKTON

Braemoor Nursing Home Inc*
34 N Pearl St, Brockton, MA, 02401 (617) 586-3696
Admin William A Roland.
Licensure Skilled Care; Intermediate Care.
Beds 120. *Certified* Medicaid; Medicare.

Embassy House Healthcare Nursing Home
2 Beaumont Ave, Brockton, MA, 02402 (617) 588-8550
Admin Lewis B Rosen. *Medical Dir/Dir of Nursing* Dr Elliot Korim.
Licensure Skilled Care; Intermediate Care.
Beds 123. *Certified* Medicaid; Medicare.
Admissions Requirements Minimum age 21; Medical examination; Physician's request.
Staff Physicians 15 (pt); RNs 14 (ft), 18 (pt); LPNs 5 (ft), 8 (pt); Orderlies 1 (pt); Nurses aides 14 (ft), 38 (pt); Physical therapists 1 (pt); Recreational therapists 1 (pt); Occupational therapists 1 (pt); Speech therapists 1 (pt); Activities coordinators 1 (ft), 1 (pt); Dietitians 1 (pt); Dentists 1 (pt); Podiatrists 1 (pt); Audiologists 1 (pt).
Facilities Dining room; Physical therapy room; Activities room; Crafts room; Laundry room; Barber/Beauty shop; Library; TV rooms; Solariums.
Activities Arts and Crafts; Cards; Games; Reading groups; Prayer groups; Movies; Shopping trips; Dances/Social or cultural gatherings; Fishing for men; Bus tours.
Description Facility is well known for rehabilitation services including self-feeding program, active programs offered in physical and occupational therapy, and reality orientation.

Fairview Rest Home
197 W Chestnut St, Brockton, MA, 02401 (617) 586-7704
Admin Marguerite Donato.
Licensure Rest Home. *Beds* 14.
Admissions Requirements Minimum age 40; Females only; Medical examination; Physician's request.
Staff Nurses aides 1 (ft), 4 (pt); Dietitians 1 (pt); Podiatrists 1 (pt).
Facilities Dining room; Laundry room.
Activities Cards; Games; Prayer groups; Church groups.
Description Fairview is a small home-like facility which enables the elderly to live in the same manner they were accustomed to before residing here.

Green Oak Nursing Home
947 N Main St, Brockton, MA, 02401 (617) 587-9367
Admin Shirley Lajoie.
Licensure Intermediate Care. *Beds* 83. *Certified* Medicaid.
Admissions Requirements Minimum age 40.
Staff RNs 3 (ft), 1 (pt); LPNs 3 (ft), 4 (pt); Nurses aides 14 (ft), 10 (pt); Recreational therapists 1 (ft), 1 (pt); Activities coordinators 1 (ft); Dietitians 1 (pt).
Facilities Dining room; Activities room; Crafts room; Laundry room; Barber/Beauty shop; Library.
Activities Arts and Crafts; Cards; Games; Reading groups; Prayer groups; Movies; Shop-

ping trips; Dances/Social or cultural gatherings.
Description Facility features monthly trips to restaurant for lunches; bazaars 3 times a year.

Lutheran Home of Brockton
888 N Main St, Brockton, MA, 02401 (617) 587-6556
Admin William S Eaton. *Medical Dir/Dir of Nursing* Francis A Kincus MD.
Licensure Skilled Care; Intermediate Care.
Beds SNF 82; ICF 41. *Certified* Medicaid.
Admissions Requirements Minimum age 65; Medical examination.
Staff Physicians 1 (pt); RNs 6 (ft), 15 (pt); LPNs 5 (ft), 9 (pt); Orderlies 2 (pt); Nurses aides 28 (ft), 26 (pt); Physical therapists 3 (pt); Reality therapists 1 (pt); Recreational therapists 2 (ft); Occupational therapists 1 (pt); Speech therapists 1 (pt); Activities coordinators 1 (ft); Dietitians 1 (pt).
Affiliation Lutheran
Facilities Dining room; Physical therapy room; Activities room; Chapel; Crafts room; Laundry room; Barber/Beauty shop; Library.
Activities Arts and Crafts; Cards; Games; Reading groups; Prayer groups; Movies; Shopping trips; Dances/Social or cultural gatherings.
Description Facility is in a very modern building, with a very dedicated staff, set in a residential area of a city which makes it very accessible to hospitals and other services.

Madalawn Nursing Home*
1330 Main St, Brockton, MA, 02401 (617) 583-1070
Admin Thomas F Shields.
Licensure Intermediate Care. *Beds* 50. *Certified* Medicaid.

Quincy Adams Nursing Home*
130 Quincy Ave, Brockton, MA, 02402 (617) 588-4700
Admin Martha A Munies.
Licensure Skilled Care; Intermediate Care.
Beds 125. *Certified* Medicaid.

Regent Park Nursing and Retirement Home*
41 Libby St, Brockton, MA, 02402 (617) 588-1450
Admin Arther E Quilty.
Licensure Intermediate Care. *Beds* 180. *Certified* Medicaid.

Saint John Rest Home*
25 Simmons Ave, Brockton, MA, 02401 (617) 586-2746
Admin John H Keeney.
Licensure Rest Home. *Beds* 21.

Saint Joseph Manor*
215 Thatcher St, Brockton, MA, 02402 (617) 583-5834
Admin Sr Geraldine Nevaras.
Licensure Skilled Care; Intermediate Care.
Beds 120. *Certified* Medicaid.

West Acres Nursing Home*
804 Pleasant St, Brockton, MA, 02401 (617) 583-6000
Admin Emanuel Freddura.
Licensure Skilled Care; Intermediate Care.
Beds 109. *Certified* Medicaid; Medicare.

West Elm Nursing Home
227 W Elm St, Brockton, MA, 02401 (617) 583-2203
Admin Mary J Tomlinson.
Licensure Intermediate Care. *Beds* 54. *Certified* Medicaid.
Admissions Requirements Minimum age 21; Medical examination; Physician's request.
Staff RNs 2 (ft), 1 (pt); LPNs 1 (ft), 2 (pt); Nurses aides 10 (ft), 4 (pt); Recreational therapists 1 (pt); Dietitians 1 (pt).
Facilities Dining room; Activities room; Laundry room.
Activities Arts and Crafts; Cards; Games; Reading groups; Prayer groups; Movies; Shopping trips; Dances/Social or cultural gatherings; Outside dinners.
Description Excellent intermediate care facility is a home away from home.

Woodridge House Nursing Home*
596 Summer St, Brockton, MA, 02402 (617) 586-1467
Admin John G Soule.
Licensure Skilled Care; Intermediate Care. *Beds* 123. *Certified* Medicaid; Medicare.

BROOKLINE

Brentwood Nursing Home Inc*
34-36 Francis St, Brookline, MA, 02146 (617) 277-0722
Admin Mary K Bittner.
Licensure Intermediate Care. *Beds* 23. *Certified* Medicaid.

Chamberlain Nursing Home
123 Gardner Rd, Brookline, MA, 02146 (617) 277-0225
Admin Barbara A Smith.
Licensure Intermediate Care. *Beds* 27. *Certified* Medicaid.
Staff RNs 2 (ft), 1 (pt); LPNs 1 (ft); Nurses aides 4 (ft), 2 (pt); Activities coordinators 1 (ft); Dietitians 1 (pt).
Facilities Dining room; Activities room; Laundry room.
Activities Arts and Crafts; Games; Movies; Shopping trips; Dances/Social or cultural gatherings; Overnight trips.
Description Located in a lovely residential section, facility aims to maintain as "normal" a home setting as possible; hosts relatives and friends for a turkey dinner the Sunday before Thanksgiving. Residents feel they have some control over their lives and that staff are friends as well as attendants.

City View Nursing Home Inc*
232 Summit Ave, Brookline, MA, 02146 (617) 232-8266
Admin Leon Backenroth.
Licensure Intermediate Care. *Beds* 80. *Certified* Medicaid.

Coolidge Street Rest Home
41 Coolidge St, Brookline, MA, 02146 (617) 566-6636
Admin Nancy A Winer.
Licensure Rest Home. *Beds* 24.
Admissions Requirements Minimum age 21; Females only

Staff Physicians; RNs; Orderlies 1 (pt); Nurses aides 2 (ft), 5 (pt); Activities coordinators; Dietitians; Dentists; Podiatrists.
Facilities Dining room; Activities room; Library.
Activities Arts and Crafts; Cards; Games; Reading groups; Prayer groups; Movies; Shopping trips; Dances/Social or cultural gatherings.
Description Facility is located close to stores and restaurants, a very convenient place to live. Provides a home-like atmosphere and residents become an extended family unit.

Mason Terrace Rest Home
12 Mason Terrace, Brookline, MA, 02146 (617) 277-0655
Admin Herbert A Porter.
Licensure Rest Home. *Beds* 26.
Admissions Requirements Minimum age 20; Medical examination; Medical examination.
Staff LPNs 1 (pt); Orderlies 1 (pt); Nurses aides 5 (pt); Activities coordinators 1 (pt); Dietitians 1 (pt); Podiatrists 1 (pt).
Facilities Dining room; Activities room; Crafts room; Laundry room.
Activities Arts and Crafts; Cards; Games; Reading groups.
Description Home has a nice yard with trees and redwood tables with benches; separate dining rooms for males and females; serves good, nutritious meals.

Park Marion Nursing Center*
99 Park St, Brookline, MA, 02146 (617) 731-1050
Admin Alan Richman.
Licensure Skilled Care. *Beds* 120. *Certified* Medicaid.

Wellman House Rest Home*
35-37 Winchester St, Brookline, MA, 02146 (617) 277-4081
Admin Albert V Reynolds.
Licensure Rest Home. *Beds* 20.

Winthrop Road Rest Home*
24 Winthrop Rd, Brookline, MA, 02146 (617) 277-5504
Admin Arthur V Reynolds.
Licensure Rest Home. *Beds* 31.

CAMBRIDGE

Cambridge Home for Aged People
360 Mount Auburn St, Cambridge, MA, 02138 (617) 876-0369
Admin Miriam S Klapper. *Medical Dir/Dir of Nursing* r Arum Tumnsian.
Licensure Intermediate Care. *Beds* Level III 12; Level IV 38.
Admissions Requirements Minimum age 65; Medical examination.
Staff Physicians 1 (pt); RNs 1 (ft), 4 (pt); LPNs 3 (pt); Orderlies 1 (pt); Nurses aides 2 (ft), 6 (pt); Activities coordinators 1 (pt); Dietitians 1 (pt); Dentists 1 (pt); Ophthalmologists 1 (pt); Podiatrists 1 (pt).
Facilities Dining room; Activities room; Laundry room; Barber/Beauty shop; Library.
Activities Cards; Games; Prayer groups; Movies; Shopping trips; Dances/Social or cultural gatherings.

Cambridge Nursing Home*
1 Russell St, Cambridge, MA, 02140 (617) 491-6110
Admin Madelyn Dolliver.
Licensure Skilled Care; Intermediate Care. *Beds* 119. *Certified* Medicaid.

Chester Manor Rest Home
10 Chester St, Cambridge, MA, 02140 (617) 876-1863
Admin Richard D Pacifico.
Licensure Rest Home. *Beds* 36.

Harvard Manor Nursing Home*
273 Harvard St, Cambridge, MA, 02139 (617) 547-4291
Admin Saul Tobias.
Licensure Intermediate Care. *Beds* 95. *Certified* Medicaid.

The Jane Elizabeth House Nursing Home*
6 Prentiss St, Cambridge, MA, 02140 (617) 354-9018
Admin Bradley McDermott.
Licensure Intermediate Care. *Beds* 53. *Certified* Medicaid.

Neville Manor
650 Concord Ave, Cambridge, MA, 02138 (617) 492-6310
Admin Gerald L MacDonald. *Medical Dir/Dir of Nursing* Ira Mintzer.
Licensure Skilled Care; Intermediate Care. *Beds* 155. *Certified* Medicaid.
Admissions Requirements Minimum age 21; Medical examination.
Staff Physicians 1 (pt); RNs 7 (ft), 5 (pt); LPNs 6 (ft), 6 (pt); Orderlies 6 (ft), 4 (pt); Nurses aides 36 (ft), 18 (pt); Reality therapists 1 (pt); Occupational therapists 1 (pt); Speech therapists 1 (pt); Activities coordinators 3 (ft); Dietitians 1 (pt); Dentists 1 (pt); Ophthalmologists 1 (pt); Podiatrists 1 (pt); Audiologists 1 (pt).
Facilities Dining room; Physical therapy room; Activities room; Crafts room; Laundry room; Barber/Beauty shop; Library; Gift shop.
Activities Arts and Crafts; Cards; Games; Reading groups; Prayer groups; Movies; Shopping trips; Dances/Social or cultural gatherings; Bus trips.

Prospect Street Nursing Home
195 Prospect St, Cambridge, MA, 02139 (617) 491-6363
Admin Barry Chiler.
Licensure Skilled Care; Intermediate Care. *Beds* 100. *Certified* Medicaid.
Admissions Requirements Minimum age 21.
Facilities Dining room; Activities room; Crafts room; Laundry room; Barber/Beauty shop.
Activities Arts and Crafts; Cards; Games; Reading groups; Prayer groups; Movies; Shopping trips; Dances/Social or cultural gatherings.

Vernon Hall Inc*
8 Dana St, Cambridge, MA, 02138 (617) 864-4267
Admin Joseph G Pallotta.
Licensure Skilled Care; Intermediate Care. *Beds* 83. *Certified* Medicaid.

CANTON

Hellenic Nursing Home for Aged
601 Sherman St, Canton, MA, 02021 (617)
828-7450
Admin Mary Jarvis. *Medical Dir/Dir of
Nursing* George A Hasiotis.
Licensure Skilled Care; Intermediate Care.
Beds 120. *Certified* Medicaid.
Admissions Requirements Minimum age 65.
Staff RNs 6 (ft), 6 (pt); LPNs 6 (ft), 6 (pt);
Orderlies 1 (pt); Nurses aides 29 (ft), 25 (pt);
Physical therapists 2 (pt); Reality therapists 1
(ft), 1 (pt); Activities coordinators 1 (ft).
Affiliation Hellenic Women's Benevolent
Society
Facilities Dining room; Physical therapy room;
Activities room; Chapel; Crafts room; Laundry
room; Barber/Beauty shop.
Activities Arts and Crafts; Cards; Games;
Reading groups; Prayer groups; Movies; Shop-
ping trips; Dances/Social or cultural gatherings.

CARVER

Hilltop Rest Home
Lakeview St, Carver, MA, 02330 (617)
866-4548
Admin Mildred D Weeden.
Licensure Rest Home. *Beds* 14.
Admissions Requirements Medical examina-
tion; Physician's request.
Staff Physicians 1 (ft), 1 (pt); RNs 1 (pt);
Nurses aides 1 (ft); Dietitians 1 (pt); Dentists 1
(pt); Ophthalmologists 1 (pt); Podiatrists 1 (pt);
Audiologists 1 (pt).
Facilities Dining room; Activities room; Chap-
el; Laundry room.
Activities Cards; Games; Prayer groups; Shop-
ping trips; Dances/Social or cultural gatherings.
Description Residents may come and go as
they wish. When not socializing they are content staying within grounds because the view
and vicinity are so beautiful.

CENTERVILLE

Centerville Nursing Home
22 Richardson Rd, Centerville, MA, 02632
(617) 775-5050
Admin Alice K Forbes. *Medical Dir/Dir of
Nursing* Dr John F Berry.
Licensure Skilled Care. *Beds* 75. *Cer-
tified* Medicaid.
Admissions Requirements Minimum age 21;
Medical examination; Physician's request.
Staff RNs 5 (ft), 9 (pt); LPNs 1 (ft), 3 (pt);
Orderlies 3 (ft); Nurses aides 22 (ft), 8 (pt);
Activities coordinators 1 (ft).
Facilities Dining room; Physical therapy room;
Activities room; Crafts room.
Activities Arts and Crafts; Cards; Games;
Reading groups; Prayer groups; Movies; Shop-
ping trips; Dances/Social or cultural gatherings.
Description Seventy-five-bed Level II skilled
nursing facility. Intravenous therapy, naso-
gastric feeding, and gastrostomy feeding are
available.

CHARLTON

Charlton Manor Rest Home*
Town Farm Rd, Charlton, MA, 01507 (617)
248-5136
Admin Caroline G Iandoli.
Licensure Rest Home. *Beds* 35.

Masonic Home
Masonic Home Rd, Charlton, MA, 01507 (617)
248-7344
Admin James L Parker. *Medical Dir/Dir of
Nursing* I Gerald Shelby MD.
Licensure Intermediate Care. *Beds* 207. *Certi-
fied* Medicaid.
Admissions Requirements Minimum age 65;
Medical examination.
Staff Physicians 2 (pt); RNs 7 (ft), 5 (pt); LPNs
5 (ft), 2 (pt); Nurses aides 40 (ft), 20 (pt);
Reality therapists 1 (ft); Recreational therapists
1 (ft), 1 (pt); Occupational therapists 1 (pt);
Activities coordinators 1 (ft); Dietitians 1 (ft);
Dentists 1 (pt); Podiatrists 1 (pt).
Affiliation Masons
Facilities Dining room; Physical therapy room;
Activities room; Chapel; Crafts room; Laundry
room; Barber/Beauty shop; Library.
Activities Arts and Crafts; Cards; Games;
Reading groups; Prayer groups; Movies; Shop-
ping trips; Dances/Social or cultural gatherings.

CHELMSFORD

Alpine Nursing Home
83 Middlesex St, Chelmsford, MA, 01863 (617)
251-3472
Admin John G Metcalf Jr. *Medical Dir/Dir of
Nursing* Susan Black MD.
Licensure Intermediate Care. *Beds* 23.
Admissions Requirements Medical examination.
Staff RNs 1 (ft); LPNs 1 (ft), 3 (pt); Orderlies 1
(ft); Nurses aides 2 (ft), 6 (pt); Physical therapists 1 (pt); Occupational therapists 1 (pt); Speech therapists 1 (pt); Activities coordinators 1
(ft); Dietitians 1 (pt); Dentists 1 (pt); Ophthalmologists 1 (pt); Podiatrists 1 (pt); Audiologists
1 (pt).
Facilities Dining room; Activities room; Crafts
room; Laundry room; Barber/Beauty shop;
Library.
Activities Arts and Crafts; Cards; Games; Prayer groups; Movies; Shopping trips; Dances/So-
cial or cultural gatherings.

Palm Manor Nursing Home Inc
40 Parkhurst Rd, Chelmsford, MA, 01824
(617) 256-3151
Admin Nels A Palm III. *Medical Dir/Dir of
Nursing* Dr Thomas Fitzpatrick.
Licensure Skilled Care; Intermediate Care.
Beds 120. *Certified* Medicaid.
Facilities Dining room; Physical therapy room;
Activities room; Chapel; Laundry room; Bar-
ber/Beauty shop; Library.
Activities Arts and Crafts; Cards; Games;
Reading groups; Prayer groups; Movies; Shop-
ping trips; Dances/Social or cultural gatherings.

Serenity Rest Home*
146 Tynsboro Rd, Chelmsford, MA, 01863
(617) 251-4420
Admin Henry H Martell.
Licensure Rest Home. *Beds* 21.

Sunny Acres Nursing Home*
254 Billerica Rd, Chelmsford, MA, 01824 (617)
256-0231
Admin Shirley Schwartz.
Licensure Intermediate Care. *Beds* 40. *Certified* Medicaid.

CHELSEA

Chelsea Jewish Nursing Home*
17 Lafayette Ave, Chelsea, MA, 02150 (617)
884-6766
Admin Barry Berman.
Licensure Intermediate Care; Charitable
Home. *Beds* 94. *Certified* Medicaid.
Affiliation Jewish

Cottage Manor Nursing Home
148 Shawmut St, Chelsea, MA, 02150 (617)
889-2250
Admin Marjorie A Minichello.
Licensure Intermediate Care. *Beds* 34. *Certi-
fied* Medicaid.
Admissions Requirements Minimum age 21;
Medical examination.
Staff RNs 2 (ft); LPNs 4 (pt); Orderlies 1 (pt);
Nurses aides 9 (ft), 4 (pt); Recreational thera-
pists 1 (ft); Activities coordinators 1 (ft); Dieti-
tians 1 (pt).
Facilities Dining room; Activities room; Crafts
room; Laundry room; Barber/Beauty shop.
Activities Arts and Crafts; Cards; Games;
Reading groups; Prayer groups; Movies; Shop-
ping trips; Dances/Social or cultural gatherings.

**L F Quigley Memorial Skilled Nursing
Facility***
100 Summit Ave, Chelsea, MA, 02150 (617)
884-5660
Admin John L Quigley.
Licensure Skilled Care. *Beds* 82. *Certified* Medicaid; Medicare.

CHICOPEE

Birch Manor Nursing Home*
44 New Lombard Rd, Chicopee, MA, 01020
(413) 592-7738
Admin Barbara M Austin.
Licensure Intermediate Care. *Beds* 56. *Certified* Medicaid.

Chicopee Municipal Home
820 Front St, Chicopee, MA, 01020 (413)
598-8455
Admin David F Leitl. *Medical Dir/Dir of
Nursing* Dr Raymond Gagnon.
Licensure Intermediate Care. *Beds* 74. *Certified* Medicaid.
Admissions Requirements Minimum age 65;
Medical examination.
Staff Physicians 3 (pt); RNs 4 (ft), 2 (pt); LPNs
5 (ft), 1 (pt); Nurses aides 22 (ft), 10 (pt); Recreational therapists 1 (ft); Occupational therapists
1 (pt); Speech therapists 1 (pt); Activities coor-

dinators 1 (ft); Dietitians 1 (pt); Podiatrists 1 (pt).
Facilities Dining room; Activities room; Chapel; Crafts room; Laundry room; Barber/Beauty shop; Library.
Activities Arts and Crafts; Cards; Games; Reading groups; Prayer groups; Movies; Shopping trips; Dances/Social or cultural gatherings.

Chicopee Rest Home
12 Dallaire Ave, Chicopee, MA, 01020 (413) 532-4004
Admin Ruth I Mercer.
Licensure Rest Home. *Beds* 38.
Admissions Requirements Minimum age 16; Medical examination.
Staff RNs 1 (pt); Nurses aides 1 (ft), 9 (pt); Activities coordinators 1 (pt); Dietitians 1 (pt).
Facilities Dining room; Barber/Beauty shop.
Activities Arts and Crafts; Cards; Games; Reading groups; Prayer groups; Movies; Shopping trips; Dances/Social or cultural gatherings.
Description Facility offers a home away from home, enabling residents to maintain their independence while having 24-hour support.

Elms Manor Nursing Home
269 Moore St, Chicopee, MA, 01013 (413) 592-7736
Admin Jeffrey Kline.
Licensure Intermediate Care. *Beds* 85. *Certified* Medicaid.
Admissions Requirements Minimum age 21.
Staff RNs 2 (ft); LPNs 2 (ft), 5 (pt); Nurses aides 10 (ft), 8 (pt); Physical therapists 1 (pt); Reality therapists 1 (pt); Recreational therapists 1 (ft); Occupational therapists 1 (pt); Speech therapists 1 (pt); Activities coordinators 1 (ft); Dietitians 1 (pt); Podiatrists 1 (pt).
Facilities Dining room; Activities room; Laundry room; Barber/Beauty shop.
Activities Arts and Crafts; Cards; Games; Reading groups; Prayer groups; Movies; Shopping trips; Dances/Social or cultural gatherings.

Terrace Manor Nursing Home
180 Beauchamp Terrace, Chicopee, MA, 01020 (413) 594-6910
Admin Mary C O'Neill.
Licensure Intermediate Care. *Beds* 58. *Certified* Medicaid.

Williamsett Nursing Home Inc*
11 Saint Anthony St, Chicopee, MA, 01013 (413) 536-2540
Admin Jean M. Clifford.
Licensure Skilled Care. *Beds* 85. *Certified* Medicaid; Medicare.

Williamsett Nursing Home—West*
545 Chicopee St, Chicopee, MA, 01013 (413) 536-2540
Admin Jean M Clifford.
Licensure Skilled Care; Intermediate Care. *Beds* 101. *Certified* Medicaid; Medicare.

CLINTON

Clinton Home for Aged People
271 Church St, Clinton, MA, 01510 (617) 365-4872
Admin Bertha M Huentler.

Licensure Rest Home. *Beds* 12.
Admissions Requirements Minimum age 65; Medical examination.
Staff RNs 1 (pt).
Facilities Dining room; Living room.
Description Home is a beautiful residence overlooking a beautiful park, located in the center of town just a few minutes walk to the shopping area.

Clinton Manor Nursing Home*
250 Main St, Clinton, MA, 01510 (617) 368-0171
Admin Harvey A Hoffman.
Licensure Intermediate Care. *Beds* 80. *Certified* Medicaid.

Ferguson Rest Home
88 Walnut St, Clinton, MA, 01510 (617) 365-3552
Admin Duncan Ferguson. *Medical Dir/Dir of Nursing* Dr William Jacobson.
Licensure Rest Home. *Beds* 17.
Admissions Requirements Minimum age 50; Females only; Medical examination; Physician's request.
Staff LPNs 1 (pt); Nurses aides 6 (pt).
Facilities Dining room; Laundry room; Barber/Beauty shop; Library.
Activities Arts and Crafts; Games; Movies; Shopping trips.
Description Facility is located one-half block from Central Park, library, and town hall, one and one-half blocks from downtown shopping; bus service to Worcester and other cities.

COHASSET

Cohasset Knoll Nursing Home
Rt 3A, Cohasset, MA, 02025 (617) 383-9060
Admin Arthur C Taylor. *Medical Dir/Dir of Nursing* Albert Cline.
Licensure Skilled Care. *Beds* 80. *Certified* Medicare.
Ownership Nonprofit.
Admissions Requirements Minimum age 21; Medical examination; Physician's request.
Staff Physicians 16 (pt); RNs 5 (ft), 4 (pt); LPNs 2 (ft), 3 (pt); Nurses aides 21 (ft), 20 (pt); Physical therapists 1 (pt); Occupational therapists 1 (pt); Speech therapists 1 (pt); Activities coordinators 1 (ft), 1 (pt); Dietitians 1 (pt); Dentists 1 (pt); Podiatrists 2 (pt).
Facilities Dining room; Physical therapy room; Activities room; Crafts room; Laundry room; Barber/Beauty shop; Library; Sitting rooms.
Activities Arts and Crafts; Cards; Games; Reading groups; Prayer groups; Movies; Shopping trips; Dances/Social or cultural gatherings.

Ripley Road Nursing Home Inc*
25 Ripley Rd, Cohasset, MA, 02025 (617) 383-0419
Admin Kathleen R Logan.
Licensure Intermediate Care. *Beds* 22. *Certified* Medicaid.

CONCORD

Rivercrest Long Term Care Facility
Deaconess Rd, Concord, MA, 01742 (617) 369-5151
Admin Cathy B Smith. *Medical Dir/Dir of Nursing* Dr Henry Vaillant.
Licensure Skilled Care; Intermediate Care. *Beds* 175. *Certified* Medicaid; Medicare.
Admissions Requirements Minimum age 65; Medical examination.
Staff RNs 39 (ft); LPNs 17 (ft); Nurses aides 55 (ft); Physical therapists 1 (ft); Reality therapists 1 (ft); Recreational therapists 2 (ft); Occupational therapists 1 (pt); Speech therapists 1 (pt); Dietitians 3 (ft); Dentists 1 (pt); Ophthalmologists 1 (pt); Podiatrists 2 (pt); Audiologists 1 (pt).
Affiliation Methodist
Facilities Dining room; Physical therapy room; Activities room; Chapel; Crafts room; Laundry room; Barber/Beauty shop; Library.
Activities Arts and Crafts; Cards; Games; Reading groups; Prayer groups; Movies; Shopping trips; Dances/Social or cultural gatherings.
Description Facility in the heart of America's birthplace offers countless daily opportunities for every resident; located in the midst of numerous communities rich in their colonial heritage.

Walden House Healthcare Nursing Home
785 Main St, Concord, MA, 01742 (617) 369-6889
Admin Michon M Reiling. *Medical Dir/Dir of Nursing* Mary Donald MD.
Licensure Skilled Care; Intermediate Care. *Beds* 123. *Certified* Medicaid; Medicare.
Staff RNs 6 (ft), 18 (pt); LPNs 4 (ft), 5 (pt); Orderlies 2 (ft), 1 (pt); Nurses aides 30 (ft), 20 (pt); Physical therapists 1 (ft); Reality therapists 1 (ft); Recreational therapists 1 (ft); Occupational therapists 1 (pt); Activities coordinators 1 (ft); Dietitians 1 (ft).
Facilities Dining room; Physical therapy room; Activities room; Chapel; Crafts room; Laundry room; Barber/Beauty shop; Library.
Activities Arts and Crafts; Cards; Games; Reading groups; Prayer groups; Movies; Shopping trips; Dances/Social or cultural gatherings.

DALTON

Curtis Manor Retirement Home*
83 Curtis Ave, Dalton, MA, 01226 (413) 684-0218
Admin Bradford Jameson.
Licensure Rest Home. *Beds* 23.

Dalton Nursing Home Inc
265 Main St, Dalton, MA, 01226 (413) 684-3212
Admin Harry S Chapman. *Medical Dir/Dir of Nursing* Wilfren A Blais MD.
Licensure Skilled Care. *Beds* 77. *Certified* Medicaid.
Staff RNs 3 (ft), 4 (pt); LPNs 5 (ft), 5 (pt); Orderlies 2 (ft); Nurses aides 14 (ft), 19 (pt); Physical therapists 2 (ft); Activities coordinators 1 (ft); Dietitians 1 (pt); Podiatrists 1 (pt).
Facilities Dining room; Physical therapy room; Activities room; Crafts room; Laundry room;

Barber/Beauty shop.
Activities Arts and Crafts; Games; Reading groups; Prayer groups; Movies; Shopping trips; Dances/Social or cultural gatherings.

DANVERS

Blakedale Rest Home*
49 Coolidge Rd, Danvers, MA, 01923 (617) 774-4391
Admin Christine D Deschenes.
Licensure Rest Home. *Beds* 13.

Cedar Glen Nursing Home*
44 Summer St, Danvers, MA, 01923 (617) 774-6955
Admin Audrey Aschiero.
Licensure Skilled Care; Intermediate Care.
Beds 100. *Certified* Medicaid.

Charles V Hogan Regional Center
PO Box A, Danvers, MA, 01937 (617) 774-5000
Admin Karl De Haas.
Licensure Intermediate Care for Mentally Retarded. *Beds* 325.
Staff Physicians; RNs; LPNs; Orderlies; Nurses aides; Physical therapists; Reality therapists; Recreational therapists; Occupational therapists; Speech therapists; Activities coordinators; Dietitians; Dentists; Ophthalmologists; Podiatrists; Audiologists.
Facilities Dining room; Physical therapy room; Activities room; Chapel; Crafts room; Laundry room; Barber/Beauty shop; Library.
Activities Arts and Crafts; Cards; Games; Reading groups; Prayer groups; Movies; Shopping trips; Dances/Social or cultural gatherings.
Description Patients must be referred by a DMH area office in District III.

Danvers Twin Oaks Nursing Home
63 Locust St, Danvers, MA, 01923 (617) 777-0011
Admin Steven J Farrow. *Medical Dir/Dir of Nursing* John Hazelton MD.
Licensure Skilled Care; Intermediate Care.
Beds 101. *Certified* Medicaid; Medicare.
Staff RNs.
Facilities Dining room; Physical therapy room; Activities room; Crafts room; Barber/Beauty shop; Library.
Activities Arts and Crafts; Cards; Games; Reading groups; Prayer groups; Movies; Shopping trips; Dances/Social or cultural gatherings.

Heritage House Nursing Home*
11 Sylvan St, Danvers, MA, 01923 (617) 774-1763
Admin David W Bittner.
Licensure Intermediate Care. *Beds* 42. *Certified* Medicaid.

Hunt Nursing and Retirement Home Inc
90 Lindall St, Danvers, MA, 01923 (617) 777-3740
Admin Daniel Micherone. *Medical Dir/Dir of Nursing* B Geoffrey Piken MD.
Licensure Skilled Care; Intermediate Care.
Beds 120. *Certified* Medicaid.
Admissions Requirements Minimum age 60.
Staff Physicians 3 (pt); RNs 18 (pt); LPNs 6

(pt); Orderlies 5 (pt); Nurses aides 65 (pt); Physical therapists 1 (pt); Recreational therapists 1 (pt); Occupational therapists 1 (pt); Speech therapists 1 (pt); Activities coordinators 2 (pt); Dietitians 1 (pt); Dentists 1 (pt); Ophthalmologists 1 (pt); Podiatrists 1 (pt); Audiologists 1 (pt).
Facilities Dining room; Physical therapy room; Activities room; Crafts room; Laundry room; Barber/Beauty shop; Library; Patios.
Activities Arts and Crafts; Cards; Games; Reading groups; Prayer groups; Movies; Shopping trips; Dances/Social or cultural gatherings; Community program.
Description Facility offers a hotel-like atmosphere in an elegant environment. Staff provides a high level of professionalism and congeniality, making the elderly residents' quality of life a source of pride.

Liberty Pavilion Nursing Home
56 Liberty St, Danvers, MA, 01923 (617) 777-2700
Admin Jean Heffernan. *Medical Dir/Dir of Nursing* John Hazelton MD.
Licensure Skilled Care; Intermediate Care.
Beds 160. *Certified* Medicaid; Medicare.
Admissions Requirements Minimum age 18; Medical examination; Physician's request.
Staff Physicians; RNs; LPNs; Orderlies; Nurses aides; Physical therapists; Occupational therapists; Speech therapists; Activities coordinators; Dietitians; Dentists; Ophthalmologists; Podiatrists; Audiologists.
Facilities Dining room; Physical therapy room; Activities room; Chapel; Crafts room; Laundry room; Barber/Beauty shop.
Activities Arts and Crafts; Cards; Games; Reading groups; Prayer groups; Movies; Shopping trips; Dances/Social or cultural gatherings.

New England Home for the Deaf*
154 Water St, Danvers, MA, 01923 (617) 774-0445
Admin Alleyne Alvarez.
Licensure Intermediate Care for Mentally Retarded. *Beds* 40.

DARTMOUTH

Country Rest Home*
263 Bakerville Rd, Dartmouth, MA, 02174 (617) 992-9280
Admin Elsie M Niemac.
Licensure Rest Home. *Beds* 25.

Dartmouth House Nursing Home*
567 Dartmouth St, Dartmouth, MA, 02748 (617) 997-0797
Admin Kathleen A Delsordo.
Licensure Intermediate Care. *Beds* 108. *Certified* Medicaid.

Dartmouth Manor Rest Home*
70 State Rd, Dartmouth, MA, 02747 (617) 993-9255
Admin James Casey.
Licensure Rest Home. *Beds* 25.

Harborview Manor Nursing Home*
173 Smith Neck Rd, Dartmouth, MA, 02748 (617) 992-8901

Admin Kathleen McKenna.
Licensure Intermediate Care. *Beds* 29. *Certified* Medicaid.

DEDHAM

Eastwood at Dedham Convalescent Center
1007 East St, Dedham, MA, 02026 (617) 329-1520
Admin Julie A Secord.
Licensure Skilled Care; Intermediate Care.
Beds 142. *Certified* Medicaid.

DEERFIELD

Hillside Nursing Home*
N Hillside Rd, Deerfield, MA, 01373 (413) 665-2200
Admin Robert S Page Jr.
Licensure Intermediate Care. *Beds* 54. *Certified* Medicaid.

DIGHTON

Dighton Nursing and Convalescent Home*
907 Centre St, Dighton, MA, 02764 (617) 669-6741
Admin Henry J Keenan.
Licensure Intermediate Care. *Beds* 30. *Certified* Medicaid.

DORCHESTER

Edgewood Convalescent Home
637 Washington St, Dorchester, MA, 02124 (617) 436-6210
Admin Brian T Hurley. *Medical Dir/Dir of Nursing* Mark Ostrem MD.
Licensure Skilled Care; Intermediate Care.
Beds SNF 48; ICF 50. *Certified* Medicaid.
Admissions Requirements Physician's request.
Staff RNs 5 (ft); LPNs 5 (ft); Orderlies 2 (ft); Nurses aides 30 (ft), 15 (pt); Physical therapists 1 (pt); Recreational therapists 1 (ft), 1 (pt); Occupational therapists 1 (pt); Speech therapists 1 (pt); Dietitians 1 (pt); Dentists 1 (pt); Ophthalmologists 1 (pt); Podiatrists 1 (pt).
Facilities Dining room; Physical therapy room; Activities room; Crafts room; Laundry room; Barber/Beauty shop.
Activities Arts and Crafts; Cards; Games; Reading groups; Prayer groups; Movies; Shopping trips.
Description Facility is in very close proximity to major teaching hospitals in Boston on a public transportation line; a Hillhaven facility.

DUXBURY

Duxbury House Nursing Home*
298 Kings Town Way, Duxbury, MA, 02332 (617) 585-2397
Admin Ruth St John.
Licensure Intermediate Care. *Beds* 23. *Certified* Medicaid.

EAST BRIDGEWATER

Hallmark Nursing Home
66 Central St, East Bridgewater, MA, 02333
(617) 378-7227
Admin Patrick J O'Connor. *Medical Dir/Dir of Nursing* Albert Dunn MD.
Licensure Skilled Care; Intermediate Care.
Beds 123. *Certified* Medicaid.
Admissions Requirements Minimum age 21;
Medical examination.
Staff Physicians 1 (ft), 2 (pt); RNs 3 (ft), 5 (pt);
LPNs 3 (ft), 10 (pt); Orderlies 1 (ft); Nurses
aides 29 (ft), 31 (pt); Physical therapists 1 (pt);
Occupational therapists 1 (pt); Speech thera-
pists 1 (pt); Activities coordinators 1 (ft), 1 (pt);
Dietitians 1 (pt); Podiatrists 1 (pt).
Facilities Dining room; Physical therapy room;
Activities room; Crafts room; Laundry room;
Barber/Beauty shop; Library.
Activities Arts and Crafts; Games; Prayer
groups; Movies; Shopping trips; Dances/Social
or cultural gatherings.
Description Nestled in a small community,
Hallmark Nursing Home offers excellent care
and a dynamic activities program in a warm,
comfortable setting.

Westview Rest Home*
446 West St, East Bridgewater, MA, 02333
(617) 378-2451
Admin Robert W Carey Jr.
Licensure Rest Home. *Beds* 18.

EAST LONGMEADOW

East Longmeadow Nursing Home*
305 Maple St, East Longmeadow, MA, 01028
(413) 525-6361
Admin George B Glass.
Licensure Intermediate Care. *Beds* 119. *Certified* Medicaid.

EASTHAMPTON

Hampshire Manor Nursing Home*
Rt 10, Easthampton, MA, 01027 (413)
584-2213
Admin David LaBroad.
Licensure Intermediate Care. *Beds* 42. *Certi-
fied* Medicaid.

EASTON

Easton-Lincoln Nursing Home*
184 Lincoln St, Easton, MA, 02356 (617)
238-7053
Admin Wendy D Stein.
Licensure Skilled Care; Intermediate Care.
Beds 87. *Certified* Medicaid; Medicare.

Village Rest Home
22 Main St, Easton, MA, 02356 (617) 238-7262
Admin Carol L Audette.
Licensure Rest Home. *Beds* 14.
Admissions Requirements Females only;
Medical examination; Physician's request.
Staff LPNs 1 (pt); Nurses aides 5 (pt); Dieti-
tians 1 (pt).
Facilities Dining room; Activities room; Laun-
dry room.

Activities Arts and Crafts; Cards; Games;
Movies; Shopping trips; Dances/Social or cultural gatherings.

EVERETT

Parkway Manor Nursing Home
13 School St, Everett, MA, 02149 (617)
387-1200
Admin Lillian M Murray.
Licensure Intermediate Care. *Beds* 57. *Certi-
fied* Medicaid.
Admissions Requirements Minimum age 21;
Medical examination; Physician's request.
Staff RNs 2 (ft), 2 (pt); LPNs 5 (ft), 3 (pt);
Nurses aides 16 (ft), 9 (pt); Activities coordina-
tors 1 (ft); Dietitians 1 (pt).
Facilities Dining room; Activities room.
Activities Arts and Crafts; Cards; Games;
Reading groups; Prayer groups; Movies; Dan-
ces/Social or cultural gatherings.

Robert Appleton Nursing Home
153 Linden St, Everett, MA, 02149 (617)
389-3699
Admin Miriam S Clapper.
Licensure Intermediate Care. *Beds* 23. *Certified* Medicaid.

Woodlawn Manor Nursing Home*
289 Elm St, Everett, MA, 02149 (617) 387-6560
Admin James R Plunkett.
Licensure Skilled Care; Intermediate Care.
Beds 144. *Certified* Medicaid.

FAIRHAVEN

Bailie's Rest Home
125 New Boston Rd, Fairhaven, MA, 02719
(617) 993-4106
Admin Eleanor M Charpentier.
Licensure Rest Home. *Beds* 12.

Center Green Rest Home*
109 Green St, Fairhaven, MA, 02719 (617)
994-7653
Licensure Rest Home. *Beds* 27.

McCormack Rest Home*
88 Fort St, Fairhaven, MA, 02719 (617)
993-3277
Admin Teresa Ann Vieira.
Licensure Rest Home. *Beds* 13.

Nichols House Nursing Home
184 Main St, Fairhaven, MA, 02719 (617)
997-3193
Admin W B Glass. *Medical Dir/Dir of
Nursing* Edward D Mackler MD.
Licensure Skilled Care; Intermediate Care.
Beds 107. *Certified* Medicaid; Medicare.
Staff RNs 8 (ft), 5 (pt); LPNs 6 (ft), 3 (pt);
Nurses aides 31 (ft), 17 (pt); Reality therapists 1
(ft); Occupational therapists 1 (pt); Speech therapists 1 (pt); Activities coordinators 2 (ft), 1
(pt); Dietitians 1 (pt); Dentists 1 (pt); Ophthalmologists 1 (pt); Podiatrists 1 (pt); Audiologists
1 (pt).
Facilities Dining room; Physical therapy room;
Activities room; Laundry room; Barber/Beauty
shop; Library.

Activities Arts and Crafts; Cards; Games;
Reading groups; Prayer groups; Movies; Shopping trips; Dances/Social or cultural gatherings.
Description Home specializes in rehabilitative
services, particularly dealing with mental confusion.

Our Lady's Haven
71 Center St, Fairhaven, MA, 02719 (617)
999-4561
Admin M A Bade.
Licensure Intermediate Care. *Beds* 38. *Certi-
fied* Medicaid.
Admissions Requirements Minimum age 65.
Staff RNs 5 (ft), 7 (pt); LPNs 3 (ft); Nurses
aides 27 (ft), 21 (pt); Physical therapists 1 (pt);
Occupational therapists 1 (pt); Speech thera-
pists 1 (pt); Activities coordinators 1 (ft); Dieti-
tians 1 (pt); Dentists 1 (pt); Podiatrists 1 (pt).
Affiliation Roman Catholic
Facilities Dining room; Physical therapy room;
Activities room; Chapel; Crafts room; Barber-
/Beauty shop; Library.
Activities Arts and Crafts; Cards; Games;
Prayer groups; Movies; Shopping trips.

FALL RIVER

Catholic Memorial Home
2446 Highland Ave, Fall River, MA, 02720
(617) 679-0011
Admin Mother M C Regina. *Medical Dir/Dir
of Nursing* Dr Anne Higgins.
Licensure Skilled Care; Intermediate Care.
Beds 288. *Certified* Medicaid.
Admissions Requirements Minimum age 65;
Medical examination.
Affiliation Roman Catholic
Facilities Dining room; Physical therapy room;
Activities room; Chapel; Crafts room; Laundry
room; Barber/Beauty shop; Library.
Activities Arts and Crafts; Cards; Games;
Reading groups; Prayer groups.
Description In dedication to the care and digni-
ty of the whole person, Catholic Memorial
Home offers a wide range of fine facilities and
services. Residents receive 24-hour nursing care
under the supervision of the director of nurses,
with physician on call at all times; provided are
dental, podiatry, speech, eye, hearing, and orthopedic services, as well as laboratory, X-ray,
EKG, ambulance, and pharmacy services. The
Home has transfer agreements with area hospitals for in-patient and out-patient services as
needed. Physical therapy room is equipped
with parallel bars, stairs, walkers, and traction
machines.

Cliff Gables Nursing Home*
423 Middle St, Fall River, MA, 02724 (617)
687-4855
Admin Linda Valenzano.
Licensure Intermediate Care. *Beds* 39. *Certified* Medicaid.

Cliff Haven Nursing Home*
745 Highland Ave, Fall River, MA, 02720 (617)
674-3354
Admin Linda Valenzano.
Licensure Intermediate Care. *Beds* 31. *Certified* Medicaid.

Cliff Heights Nursing Home*
635 Rock St, Fall River, MA, 02720 (617) 674-7509
Admin Linda Valenzano.
Licensure Intermediate Care. *Beds* 34. *Certified* Medicaid.

Cliff Lawn Nursing Home*
851 Highland Ave, Fall River, MA, 02720 (617) 678-6100
Admin Linda Valenzano.
Licensure Intermediate Care. *Beds* 26. *Certified* Medicaid.

Cliff Manor Nursing Home*
431 Rock St, Fall River, MA, 02720 (617) 678-8011
Admin Linda Valenzano.
Licensure Intermediate Care. *Beds* 37. *Certified* Medicaid.

Crawford House Convalescent Home*
273 Oak Grove Ave, Fall River, MA, 02723 (617) 679-4866
Admin Gilberto Reis.
Licensure Skilled Care; Intermediate Care. *Beds* 123. *Certified* Medicaid.

Crestwood Convalescent Home*
170 Oak Grove Ave, Fall River, MA, 02723 (617) 678-5234
Admin Joyce Pinto.
Licensure Skilled Care; Intermediate Care. *Beds* 102. *Certified* Medicaid.

Fall River Jewish Home for the Aged
538 Robeson St, Fall River, MA, 02720 (617) 679-6172
Admin Ellen Feldman.
Licensure Skilled Care; Intermediate Care. *Beds* 60. *Certified* Medicaid.
Affiliation Jewish

Fall River Nursing Home Inc
1748 Highland Ave, Fall River, MA, 02720 (617) 675-1131
Admin James A Jackson. *Medical Dir/Dir of Nursing* N Kenneth Shand MD.
Licensure Skilled Care; Intermediate Care. *Beds* 164. *Certified* Medicaid.
Admissions Requirements Minimum age 16.
Staff Physicians 1 (pt); RNs 14 (ft), 5 (pt); LPNs 11 (ft), 5 (pt); Orderlies 2 (ft); Nurses aides 48 (ft), 31 (pt); Physical therapists 1 (ft), 1 (pt); Recreational therapists 1 (ft), 2 (pt); Occupational therapists 1 (pt); Dietitians 1 (pt); Dentists 1 (pt); Podiatrists 2 (pt).
Facilities Dining room; Physical therapy room; Activities room; Chapel; Crafts room; Laundry room; Barber/Beauty shop; Library.
Activities Arts and Crafts; Cards; Games; Reading groups; Prayer groups; Movies; Shopping trips; Dances/Social or cultural gatherings.
Description Facility has an adult day health center 5 days per week.

Hanover House Retirement Facility*
391 Hanover St, Fall River, MA, 02720 (617) 675-7583
Admin Irma Lentenore.
Licensure Rest Home. *Beds* 35.

Highland Manor Nursing Home Inc
761 Highland Ave, Fall River, MA, 02720 (617) 679-1411
Admin Michael F Cummings.
Licensure Intermediate Care. *Beds* 26. *Certified* Medicaid.

Home for Aged People in Fall River
1168 Highland Ave, Fall River, MA, 02720 (617) 679-0144
Admin Yolanda E McAuliffe.
Licensure Rest Home. *Beds* 59.
Admissions Requirements Minimum age 68; Medical examination; Physician's request.

Kimwell Nursing Home
495 New Boston Rd, Fall River, MA, 02720 (617) 679-0106
Admin Jack Booth. *Medical Dir/Dir of Nursing* N Kenneth Shard MD.
Licensure Skilled Care; Intermediate Care. *Beds* 124. *Certified* Medicaid; Medicare.
Admissions Requirements Medical examination.
Staff Physicians 3 (pt); RNs 3 (ft), 8 (pt); LPNs 5 (ft), 5 (pt); Orderlies 2 (ft); Nurses aides 21 (ft), 36 (pt); Physical therapists 1 (pt); Reality therapists 1 (pt); Occupational therapists 1 (pt); Speech therapists 1 (pt); Activities coordinators 1 (ft); Dietitians 1 (pt); Dentists 1 (pt); Ophthalmologists 1 (pt); Podiatrists 1 (pt); Audiologists 1 (pt).
Facilities Dining room; Physical therapy room; Activities room; Chapel; Crafts room; Laundry room; Barber/Beauty shop; Library.
Activities Arts and Crafts; Cards; Games; Reading groups; Prayer groups; Movies; Shopping trips; Dances/Social or cultural gatherings.
Description This is the only Level I facility located in Fall River.

Rose Hawthorne Lathrop Home*
1600 Bay St, Fall River, MA, 02724 (617) 673-2322
Admin Sr Marie Cordis.
Licensure Intermediate Care. *Beds* 35. *Certified* Medicaid.

Rosewood Manor Rest Home
547 Highland Ave, Fall River, MA, 02720 (617) 678-6075
Licensure Rest Home. *Beds* 60.
Admissions Requirements Minimum age 21; Medical examination.
Staff Nurses aides 6 (ft), 6 (pt); Activities coordinators 1 (ft); Dietitians 1 (pt); Dentists 1 (pt); Ophthalmologists 1 (pt); Podiatrists 1 (pt).
Facilities Dining room; Activities room; Laundry room; Barber/Beauty shop.
Activities Arts and Crafts; Cards; Games; Reading groups; Prayer groups; Movies; Shopping trips; Dances/Social or cultural gatherings.

FALMOUTH

Falmouth Nursing Home*
545 Main St, Falmouth, MA, 02541 (617) 548-3800
Admin John J Hedderson.
Licensure Skilled Care; Intermediate Care. *Beds* 121. *Certified* Medicaid.

Fraser Rest Home of Falmouth*
17 Pine St, Falmouth, MA, 02540 (617) 563-3522
Admin Caleb Fraser.
Licensure Rest Home. *Beds* 23.

Royal Megansett Nursing Home*
209 County Rd, Falmouth, MA, 02556 (617) 563-5913
Admin Robert H Warner.
Licensure Intermediate Care. *Beds* 85. *Certified* Medicaid.

FITCHBURG

Birchwood Manor Nursing Home*
1199 John Fitch Hwy, Fitchburg, MA, 01420 (617) 345-0146
Admin Angelino J Rollo.
Licensure Skilled Care; Intermediate Care. *Beds* 160. *Certified* Medicaid; Medicare.

Cedar Street Home Inc
30 Cedar St, Fitchburg, MA, 01420 (617) 342-0527
Admin B Hollows.
Licensure Retirement Home. *Beds* 22.
Ownership Nonprofit.
Admissions Requirements Minimum age 62; Medical examination.
Staff Physicians 1 (pt); RNs 1 (pt); LPNs 1 (pt); Nurses aides 8 (pt); Activities coordinators 1 (pt); Dietitians 1 (pt); Audiologists 1 (pt).
Facilities Dining room; Activities room; Crafts room; Laundry room; Barber/Beauty shop; Library.
Activities Arts and Crafts; Cards; Games; Reading groups; Prayer groups; Movies; Shopping trips; Dances/Social or cultural gatherings; Recreational outings.
Description Facility features private rooms and 2-room suites; 24-hour nurses aide staff; home cooked meals, housekeeping, and laundry service; activities designed to meet residents interests. Area college students serve semester-long internships.

Grand View Rest Home
55 Garnet St, Fitchburg, MA, 01420 (617) 342-3030
Admin Donald and Claudette Richards. *Medical Dir/Dir of Nursing* Dr Parnes.
Licensure Rest Home. *Beds* 21.
Admissions Requirements Minimum age 30; Medical examination.
Staff RNs 1 (pt); Nurses aides 4 (ft), 3 (pt); Activities coordinators 1 (pt); Dietitians 1 (pt).
Facilities Dining room; Activities room; Laundry room.
Activities Arts and Crafts; Cards; Games; Reading groups; Prayer groups; Movies; Shopping trips; Dances/Social or cultural gatherings.
Description Old Victorian Home within walking distance to downtown. Bingo and Bible readings are currently very popular, as are singing and music.

High Street Rest Home*
69 High St, Fitchburg, MA, 01420 (617) 342-7962
Admin Kathryn E Salafia.
Licensure Rest Home. *Beds* 16.

Hillcrest Nursing Home
94 Summer St, Fitchburg, MA, 01420 (617)
343-3374
Admin Anita M Cox. *Medical Dir/Dir of
Nursing* Joseph M Silver.
Licensure Skilled Care; Intermediate Care.
Beds 96. *Certified* Medicaid.
Admissions Requirements Minimum age 21;
Medical examination; Physician's request.
Staff RNs 6 (ft), 4 (pt); LPNs 5 (ft), 5 (pt);
Nurses aides 20 (ft), 25 (pt); Physical therapists
1 (pt); Occupational therapists 1 (pt); Speech
therapists 1 (pt); Activities coordinators 1 (ft), 1
(pt); Dietitians 1 (pt); Dentists 1 (pt); Ophthal-
mologists 1 (pt); Podiatrists 4 (pt); Audiologists
1 (pt).
Facilities Dining room; Physical therapy room;
Activities room; Chapel; Crafts room; Laundry
room; Barber/Beauty shop; Library.
Activities Arts and Crafts; Cards; Games;
Reading groups; Prayer groups; Movies; Shopping trips; Dances/Social or cultural gatherings.
Description Our home is a one-story, colonial
building with a large backyard which is shady
and provides a pleasant change of scenery in
the summer months. We feature musical presentations frequently.

James Manor Rest Home*
222 South St, Fitchburg, MA, 01420 (617)
342-5041
Admin Ann Dumont.
Licensure . *Beds* 28.

Magnolia Rest Home
159 Summer St, Fitchburg, MA, 01420 (617)
342-5372
Admin Anthony W Sciabarrasi. *Medical Dir-
/Dir of Nursing* Eric L Knutson.
Licensure Rest Home. *Beds* 16.
Admissions Requirements Minimum age 50.
Staff Physicians 1 (ft); LPNs 1 (pt); Nurses
aides 6 (pt); Dietitians 2 (pt); Dentists 1 (ft);
Podiatrists 1 (ft).
Facilities Dining room; Activities room; Crafts
room; Laundry room.
Activities Arts and Crafts; Cards; Games;
Reading groups.

Mount Elam Nursing Home
360 Electric Ave, Fitchburg, MA, 01420 (617)
342-3242
Admin Ruhie L Thompson. *Medical Dir/Dir
of Nursing* Philip A Isaacson MD.
Licensure Skilled Care. *Beds* 99. *Certified* Medicaid; Medicare.
Admissions Requirements Minimum age 21;
Medical examination; Physician's request.
Staff Physicians 2 (pt); RNs 7 (ft), 7 (pt); LPNs
9 (ft), 4 (pt); Orderlies 1 (pt); Nurses aides 35
(ft), 34 (pt); Physical therapists 1 (pt); Occupa-
tional therapists 1 (pt); Speech therapists 1 (pt);
Activities coordinators 1 (ft); Dietitians 1 (pt);
Dentists 1 (pt); Podiatrists 2 (pt); Audiologists 1
(pt); Recreational assistants 5 (ft), 2 (pt);
Rehabilitation assistants 3 (ft).
Facilities Dining room; Physical therapy room;
Activities room; Laundry room; Barber/Beauty
shop.
Activities Arts and Crafts; Cards; Games;
Reading groups; Prayer groups; Movies; Dan-
ces/Social or cultural gatherings.
Description All 99 beds are certified for Level I

Medicare residents if needed and no resident
higher than a Level III is permitted; 3 sepa-
rately staffed units each with restorative nursing
included.

New Bunker Rest Home*
82 Mechanic St, Fitchburg, MA, 01420 (617)
345-5701
Admin Esther E Ogilvie.
Licensure Rest Home. *Beds* 17.

Tower Hill Rest Home
20 Myrtle Ave, PO Box 943, Fitchburg, MA,
01420 (617) 342-4242
Admin John B Picard. *Medical Dir/Dir of
Nursing* Dr Babineau.
Licensure Rest Home. *Beds* 21.
Staff RNs 1 (pt); Nurses aides 3 (ft), 5 (pt);
Dietitians 1 (pt); Podiatrists 1 (pt).
Affiliation Roman Catholic
Facilities Dining room; Activities room; Laun-
dry room; Barber/Beauty shop.
Activities Arts and Crafts; Cards; Games;
Reading groups; Prayer groups; Dances/Social
or cultural gatherings.

Wright Rest Home*
10 Prospect St, Fitchburg, MA, 01420 (617)
345-5827
Admin James J Worth.
Licensure Rest Home. *Beds* 28.

FOXBORO

Doolittle Universalist Home
16 Bird St, Foxboro, MA, 02035 (617)
543-2131
Admin Ruth C Mulkey. *Medical Dir/Dir of
Nursing* Dr John MacDonald.
Licensure Charitable Home. *Beds* 33.
Admissions Requirements Minimum age 65;
Medical examination; Physician's request.
Staff Physicians; RNs 2 (ft), 5 (pt); LPNs 2 (ft),
2 (pt); Nurses aides 3 (ft), 9 (pt); Physical therapists; Activities coordinators; Dietitians; Dentists; Ophthalmologists; Podiatrists;
Audiologists.
Affiliation Unitarian Universalist
Facilities Dining room; Activities room; Laun-
dry room; Barber/Beauty shop.
Activities Arts and Crafts; Games; Reading
groups; Prayer groups; Shopping trips.
Description Home is located approximately ½
block from the town green and directly adjacent
to the library; within easy walking distance to
shopping, theater, and community services;
home has a family atmosphere.

Van Dora Nursing Home Inc
67 Central St, Foxboro, MA, 02035 (617)
543-8000
Admin Joseph G Ranieri.
Licensure Intermediate Care. *Beds* 67. *Certified* Medicaid.

FRAMINGHAM

Clearview Nursing Home*
162 Old Connecticut Path, Framingham, MA,
01701 (617) 875-5096

Admin Sarah M Katz.
Licensure Intermediate Care. *Beds* 18. *Certified* Medicaid.

Countryside Nursing Home Inc
153 Winter St, Framingham, MA, 01701 (617)
872-5250
Admin John Steacie.
Licensure Intermediate Care. *Beds* 30. *Certified* Medicaid.
Admissions Requirements Females only
Staff RNs 1 (ft); LPNs 4 (pt); Nurses aides 30
(pt); Physical therapists 1 (pt); Occupational
therapists 1 (pt); Speech therapists 1 (pt);
Activities coordinators 1 (ft); Dietitians 1 (pt).
Facilities Dining room; Activities room; Laundry room.
Activities Arts and Crafts; Cards; Games; Prayer groups; Shopping trips.
Description Facility features a very home-like
setting located on beautiful grounds.

Edgell Rest Home*
248 Edgell Rd, Framingham, MA, 01701 (617)
875-5454
Admin James J Battles.
Licensure Rest Home. *Beds* 14.

Framingham Nursing Home
517 Winter St, Framingham, MA, 01701 (617)
875-0607
Admin Beverly McIntyre. *Medical Dir/Dir of
Nursing* Pramod Chira MD.
Licensure Skilled Care. *Beds* 43. *Cer-
tified* Medicaid.
Admissions Requirements Minimum age 21;
Medical examination.
Staff Physicians 1 (pt); RNs 4 (ft); LPNs 4 (ft);
Nurses aides 20 (ft); Physical therapists 1 (pt);
Reality therapists 1 (pt); Recreational therapists
1 (ft), 1 (pt); Occupational therapists 1 (pt);
Speech therapists 1 (pt); Activities coordinators
1 (pt); Dietitians 1 (pt); Dentists 1 (pt);
Ophthalmologists 1 (pt); Podiatrists 1 (pt);
Audiologists 1 (pt).
Facilities Dining room; Activities room; Crafts
room; Laundry room.
Activities Arts and Crafts; Cards; Games;
Reading groups; Prayer groups; Movies; Shop-
ping trips; Dances/Social or cultural gatherings.
Description Facility is a small homey facility in
an older home setting with a large yard and
screen porch.

Hilltop Manor Nursing Home Inc
11 Arbetter Dr, Framingham, MA, 01701 (617)
877-3300
Admin Armand R Balinelli. *Medical Dir/Dir
of Nursing* Dr John Whitcomb.
Licensure Intermediate Care. *Beds* 33. *Certified* Medicaid.
Admissions Requirements Minimum age 45;
Medical examination; Physician's request.
Staff Physicians 1 (pt); RNs 4 (ft); LPNs 8 (pt);
Orderlies 1 (ft); Nurses aides 8 (ft); Physical
therapists 1 (pt); Reality therapists 1 (pt); Recreational therapists 1 (pt); Occupational therapists
1 (pt); Speech therapists 1 (pt); Activities coor-
dinators 1 (pt); Dietitians 1 (pt); Dentists 1 (pt);
Ophthalmologists 1 (pt); Podiatrists 1 (pt).
Facilities Dining room; Activities room; Laun-
dry room; Library.
Activities Arts and Crafts; Cards; Games;

Reading groups; Prayer groups; Movies; Shopping trips; Dances/Social or cultural gatherings. *Description* Facility is located on 8 ½ acres of land by the Nobscott Mountain of Framingham.

Kathleen Daniel Health Care Center
485 Franklin St, Framingham, MA, 01701 (617) 872-8801
Admin Robert D Whitkin. *Medical Dir/Dir of Nursing* Arthur Freedman MD.
Licensure Skilled Care; Intermediate Care.
Beds 124. *Certified* Medicaid; Medicare.
Staff Physicians 20 (pt); RNs 10 (ft), 4 (pt); LPNs 6 (ft), 6 (pt); Orderlies 2 (ft); Nurses aides 35 (ft), 17 (pt), Physical therapists 1 (pt); Reality therapists 2 (ft); Recreational therapists 2 (ft), 2 (pt); Occupational therapists 1 (pt); Speech therapists 1 (pt); Activities coordinators 1 (ft); Dietitians 1 (pt); Dentists 1 (pt); Ophthalmologists 1 (pt); Podiatrists 1 (pt); Audiologists 1 (pt); Psychologist 1 (pt).
Facilities Dining room; Physical therapy room; Activities room; Chapel; Crafts room; Laundry room; Barber/Beauty shop.
Activities Arts and Crafts; Cards; Games; Reading groups; Prayer groups; Movies; Shopping trips; Dances/Social or cultural gatherings. *Description* The Center is a modern multilevel skilled nursing facility serving the metro-west area of Greater Boston. In addition to the finest in nursing and medical care, also available are physical and occupational therapy, dietary evaluation, psychiatric evaluation and counseling, and recreation therapy. We offer pleasant surroundings and spacious living quarters.

Middlesex Manor Nursing Home
228 Concord St, Framingham, MA, 01701 (617) 237-2799
Admin Robert D Brennan.
Licensure Intermediate Care. *Beds* 97. *Certified* Medicaid.
Staff RNs 4 (ft), 2 (pt); LPNs 4 (ft), 4 (pt); Nurses aides 15 (ft), 10 (pt); Physical therapists 1 (pt); Recreational therapists 1 (pt); Activities coordinators 1 (ft), 1 (pt); Dietitians 1 (pt); Dentists 1 (pt); Ophthalmologists 1 (pt); Podiatrists 1 (pt); Audiologists 1 (pt).

Saint Patricks Manor*
863 Central Ave, Framingham, MA, 01701 (617) 873-7407
Admin Mother Catherine M Joseph.
Licensure Skilled Care; Intermediate Care.
Beds 292. *Certified* Medicaid.
Affiliation Roman Catholic

Tara Nursing Home Inc
9 Arbetter Dr, Framingham, MA, 01701 (617) 877-3300
Admin Armand R Baldinelli. *Medical Dir/Dir of Nursing* Dr John Whitcomb.
Licensure Skilled Care; Intermediate Care.
Beds 80. *Certified* Medicaid.
Admissions Requirements Minimum age 45; Medical examination.
Staff Physicians 4 (pt); RNs 6 (ft); Nurses aides 10 (ft); Physical therapists 1 (pt); Reality therapists 1 (pt); Recreational therapists 1 (ft); Occupational therapists 1 (pt); Speech therapists 1

(pt); Activities coordinators 1 (ft); Dietitians 1 (pt); Dentists 1 (ft); Ophthalmologists 1 (pt); Podiatrists 1 (pt); Audiologists 1 (pt).

Vernon House Inc*
20 Vernon St, Framingham, MA, 01701 (617) 873-7556
Admin Sadie Mayo.
Licensure Rest Home. *Beds* 14.

Winter Gables Nursing Home*
342 Winter St, Framingham, MA, 01701 (617) 879-6100
Admin Caroline M Kreshpane.
Licensure Intermediate Care. *Beds* 43. *Certified* Medicaid.

Winter Gables Rest Home
340 Winter St, Framingham, MA, 01701 (617) 879-6100
Admin Caroline M Kreshpane.
Licensure Rest Home. *Beds* 30.

FRANKLIN

Ben Franklin Nursing Home Inc*
45 Union St, Franklin, MA, 02038 (617) 528-0905
Admin Joseph G Ranieri.
Licensure Intermediate Care. *Beds* 18. *Certified* Medicaid.

Franklin House Healthcare Nursing Home
Chestnut St, Franklin, MA, 02038 (617) 528-4600
Admin Sharon R Kellegrew. *Medical Dir/Dir of Nursing* Leslie Silverstone MD.
Licensure Skilled Care. *Beds* 82. *Certified* Medicaid.
Facilities Dining room; Physical therapy room; Activities room; Crafts room; Laundry room; Barber/Beauty shop; Library.
Activities Arts and Crafts; Cards; Games; Reading groups; Prayer groups; Movies; Shopping trips; Dances/Social or cultural gatherings.

GARDNER

Eastwood Pines Nursing Home*
Eastwood Circle, Gardner, MA, 01440 (617) 632-8776
Admin Abe Treshinsky.
Licensure Skilled Care; Intermediate Care.
Beds 128. *Certified* Medicaid; Medicare.

Gallant Rest Home
381 E Broadway, Gardner, MA, 01440 (617) 632-6175
Admin Robert W LeBlanc. *Medical Dir/Dir of Nursing* Dr John Denman.
Licensure Rest Home. *Beds* 13.
Admissions Requirements Minimum age 18.
Staff Physicians 1 (ft); LPNs 1 (ft); Dentists 1 (pt); Podiatrists 1 (pt).
Facilities Dining room; Activities room; Laundry room.
Activities Arts and Crafts; Cards; Games; Prayer groups; Movies; Shopping trips.
Description Facility is located in a country setting one mile from shopping center offering home cooking and an activity program.

Gardner Manor Nursing Home*
155 Green St, Gardner, MA, 01440 (617) 632-2900
Admin Annie Green.
Licensure Skilled Care; Intermediate Care.
Beds 74. *Certified* Medicaid.

Wachusett Manor Nursing Home*
32 Hospital Hll Rd, Gardner, MA, 01440 (617) 632-5477
Admin Charlene Ferreira.
Licensure Intermediate Care. *Beds* 89. *Certified* Medicaid.

GLOUCESTER

Gloucester Manor Rest Home
46 Summer St, Gloucester, MA, 01930 (617) 283-4208
Admin Jack Pearlman.
Licensure Rest Home. *Beds* 36.
Staff LPNs 1 (ft), 1 (pt); Nurses aides 12 (ft), 8 (pt); Activities coordinators 1 (ft); Dietitians 1 (pt).
Facilities Dining room; Crafts room; Laundry room.
Activities Arts and Crafts; Cards; Games; Reading groups; Prayer groups; Movies; Shopping trips.
Description Facility is located high over Atlantic Ocean with a great view, pure air, walking and exercise grounds.

Greycliff at Cape Ann Nursing Home
272 Washington St, Gloucester, MA, 01930 (617) 281-0333
Admin Thomas B Dresser. *Medical Dir/Dir of Nursing* Dr Douglas Fiero.
Licensure Skilled Care; Intermediate Care.
Beds 101. *Certified* Medicaid.
Admissions Requirements Medical examination.
Staff RNs 5 (ft), 2 (pt); LPNs 3 (ft), 3 (pt); Nurses aides 20 (ft), 25 (pt); Physical therapists 1 (pt); Occupational therapists 1 (pt); Activities coordinators 2 (ft); Dietitians 1 (pt); Podiatrists 1 (pt).
Facilities Dining room; Activities room; Crafts room; Laundry room; Barber/Beauty shop; Library.
Activities Arts and Crafts; Cards; Games; Reading groups; Prayer groups; Movies; Shopping trips; Dances/Social or cultural gatherings. *Description* Greycliff at Cape Ann is a progressive nursing home dedicated to quality patient care in a picturesque environment.

Hillcrest Rest Home
374 Washington St, Gloucester, MA, 01930 (617) 283-1032
Admin June B Cahoon. *Medical Dir/Dir of Nursing* David Cohen MD.
Licensure Rest Home. *Beds* 14.
Admissions Requirements Minimum age 50; Females only; Medical examination; Physician's request.
Staff RNs 2 (ft), 1 (pt); LPNs 3 (ft), 1 (pt); Nurses aides 4 (ft), 3 (pt); Recreational therapists 1 (pt); Occupational therapists; Speech therapists; Activities coordinators; Dietitians; Podiatrists.

Shore Cliff
Cliff Rd, Gloucester, MA, 01930 (617)
525-3456
Admin Mary L Barnett.
Licensure Charitable Home. *Beds* 34.
Admissions Requirements Minimum age 65;
Medical examination.
Staff RNs 2 (ft); LPNs 5 (pt); Nurses aides 1
(ft), 3 (pt); Activities coordinators 1 (pt).
Facilities Dining room; Activities room; Laundry room; Barber/Beauty shop; Library.
Activities Arts and Crafts; Cards; Games;
Reading groups; Prayer groups; Movies; Shopping trips; Dances/Social or cultural gatherings;
Field trips; Exercise program.
Description Facility offers gracious Level IV
retirement living beside the sea in a traditionally
furnished, family environment; dining room,
terraces, and porches enjoy a sweeping panorama of the Atlantic Ocean near historic
Gloucester, Manchester, and Marblehead. A
quaint shopping area is within easy walking distance.

GRAFTON

Crescent Manor Rest Home*
5 Crescent St, Grafton, MA, 01519 (617)
839-2124
Admin Robert Waters.
Licensure Rest Home. *Beds* 58.

Edgewood Nursing Home Inc
23 N Brigham Hill Rd, Grafton, MA, 01536
(617) 839-4980
Admin Mark Awed.
Licensure Intermediate Care. *Beds* 36. *Certified* Medicaid.
Admissions Requirements Minimum age 16.
Staff RNs 1 (pt); LPNs 2 (ft), 4 (pt); Nurses
aides 4 (ft), 4 (pt); Activities coordinators 1 (pt);
Dietitians 1 (pt).
Facilities Dining room; Activities room; Laundry room; Barber/Beauty shop.
Activities Arts and Crafts; Cards; Games;
Reading groups; Prayer groups; Movies; Dances/Social or cultural gatherings.

Keith Hill Nursing Home Inc*
44 Old Upton Rd, Grafton, MA, 01519 (617)
839-2195
Admin Richard J Carlson.
Licensure Skilled Care; Intermediate Care.
Beds 43. *Certified* Medicaid.

GREAT BARRINGTON

Great Barrington Healthcare Nursing Home*
148 Maple Ave, Great Barrington, MA, 01230
(413) 528-3320
Admin Robert Schwenk.
Licensure Skilled Care; Intermediate Care.
Beds 106. *Certified* Medicaid; Medicare.

Pines Nursing Home Inc
320 Maple Ave, Great Barrington, MA, 01230
(413) 528-2650
Admin Lloyd R Berkey.
Licensure Skilled Care; Intermediate Care.
Beds 78. *Certified* Medicaid.
Facilities Dining room; Physical therapy room;

Activities room; Chapel; Laundry room; Barber/Beauty shop.
Activities Arts and Crafts; Cards; Games;
Reading groups; Prayer groups; Movies; Shopping trips; Dances/Social or cultural gatherings.

Willowood Nursing and Retirement Facility*
Christian Hill Rd, Great Barrington, MA,
01230 (413) 528-4560
Admin Curtis L Ivey.
Licensure Skilled Care; Intermediate Care.
Beds 130. *Certified* Medicaid; Medicare.

GREENFIELD

Franklin Nursing & Rehabilitation Center
329 Conway St, Greenfield, MA, 01301 (413)
772-0811
Admin Doris Garbose.
Licensure Skilled Care; Intermediate Care.
Beds 250. *Certified* Medicaid.
Facilities Dining room; Physical therapy room;
Activities room; Laundry room; Barber/Beauty
shop.
Activities Arts and Crafts; Cards; Games;
Reading groups; Prayer groups; Movies; Shopping trips; Dances/Social or cultural gatherings.

Pioneer Valley Manor Rest Home*
148 Montague City Rd, Greenfield, MA, 01301
(413) 773-8589
Admin Simone McDonald.
Licensure Rest Home. *Beds* 37.

Poet's Seat Nursing Home*
359 High St, Greenfield, MA, 01301 (413)
774-2253
Admin Mary L Harris.
Licensure Skilled Care. *Beds* 63. *Certified* Medicaid.

Turner Rest Home
1110 Bernardston Rd, Greenfield, MA, 01301
(413) 772-6219
Admin Evelyn L Eareckson.
Licensure Rest Home. *Beds* 8.

GROTON

Hale Convalescent and Nursing Home Inc*
58 Main St, Groton, MA, 01472 (617)
448-6802
Admin Paul R Chernov.
Licensure Intermediate Care. *Beds* 36. *Certified* Medicaid.

Montrath Pediatric Nursing Center
22 Hillside Ave, Groton, MA, 01450 (617)
448-3388
Admin Francis M Anoneoli. *Medical Dir/Dir
of Nursing* Richard V Straub.
Licensure Intermediate Care. *Beds* 76. *Certified* Medicaid.
Staff Physicians 1 (pt); RNs 2 (ft), 13 (pt);
LPNs 4 (ft), 11 (pt); Nurses aides 36 (ft), 50
(pt); Physical therapists 1 (ft); Occupational
therapists 1 (ft); Speech therapists 1 (pt); Dietitians 1 (pt); Dentists 1 (pt); Ophthalmologists 1
(pt); Podiatrists 1 (pt); Audiologists 1 (pt).
Facilities Dining room; Physical therapy room;
Activities room; Laundry room; Barber/Beauty

shop; Special Education program rooms.
Activities Movies; Field trips.
Description Mountrath is a skilled Level II
facility for children ages birth to 21 years with
severe injuries to the central nervous system
and multiple handicaps.

HADLEY

Shady Lawn Rest Home Inc
90 Middle St, Hadley, MA, 01035 (413)
584-4018
Admin Anna Thompson. *Medical Dir/Dir of
Nursing* David Artzerounian.
Licensure Rest Home. *Beds* 20.
Admissions Requirements Minimum age 20;
Medical examination.
Staff LPNs 2 (pt); Nurses aides 6 (pt); Dietitians 2 (pt).
Facilities Dining room; Laundry room.
Activities Arts and Crafts; Cards; Games;
Shopping trips; Lunch trips.
Description This is a caring family-style
facility.

HAMPDEN

Mary Lyon Nursing Home*
34 W Main St, Hampden, MA, 01036 (413)
566-3431
Admin C L Verrill.
Licensure Skilled Care. *Beds* 60. *Certified* Medicaid.

HANOVER

Mill Pond Rest Home
974 Main St, Hanover, MA, 02339 (617)
871-0171
Admin Edward R Hammond Jr. *Medical Dir-/Dir of Nursing* Donna Buckley RN.
Licensure Rest Home. *Beds* 38.
Admissions Requirements Minimum age 55;
Medical examination; Physician's request.
Staff Orderlies 1 (pt); Nurses aides 10 (ft), 4
(pt); Recreational therapists 1 (pt); Activities
coordinators 1 (pt); Dietitians 1 (pt).
Facilities Dining room; Activities room; Chapel; Barber/Beauty shop.
Activities Cards; Games; Movies; Shopping
trips; Dances/Social or cultural gatherings.
Description Home is situated on a 3-acre lot in
north Hanover with a pond in its back yard;
best known for homey atmosphere with a very
personable staff.

North River Nursing Home*
Box 11, Washington St, Hanover, MA, 02339
(617) 826-4521
Admin Maryanne Sullivan.
Licensure Intermediate Care. *Beds* 39. *Certified* Medicaid.

HARDWICK

Hilltop Rest Home*
31 Prospect St, Gilbertville, Hardwick, MA,
01031 (413) 477-6601
Admin Richard J Muise.
Licensure Rest Home. *Beds* 22.

HARWICH

Rambling Rose Rest Home*
Main St, Harwich, MA, 02645 (617) 432-0135
Admin Harry E Daley.
Licensure Rest Home. *Beds* 37.

HAVERHILL

Baker Katz Nursing Home*
194 Boardman St, Haverhill, MA, 01830 (617) 375-5697
Admin David M Baker.
Licensure Intermediate Care. *Beds* 77. *Certified* Medicaid.

Churchview Health Center Retirement Home
35-37 Arlington St, Box 150, Haverhill, MA, 01830 (617) 372-3675
Admin Ann Azzarito. *Medical Dir/Dir of Nursing* Arnold George MD.
Licensure Rest Home. *Beds* 22.
Admissions Requirements Minimum age 21; Medical examination; Physician's request.
Facilities Dining room; Activities room; Laundry room.
Activities Arts and Crafts; Prayer groups.

Glynn Memorial Home*
61 Brown St, Haverhill, MA, 01830 (617) 374-7511
Admin Elizabeth Benoit.
Licensure Intermediate Care. *Beds* 48. *Certified* Medicaid.

Griffin White Home*
170 Main St, Haverhill, MA, 01830 (617) 372-1501
Admin Harold MacFarlane.
Licensure Charitable Home. *Beds* 16.
Admissions Requirements Males only

Hannah Duston Long Term Health Care Facility
126 Monument St, Haverhill, MA, 01830 (617) 373-1747
Admin Robert Bastck. *Medical Dir/Dir of Nursing* Homode Habhab MD.
Licensure Skilled Care; Intermediate Care. *Beds* 80. *Certified* Medicaid; Medicare.
Admissions Requirements Minimum age 50; Medical examination; Physician's request.
Staff Physicians 3 (ft), 7 (pt); RNs 5 (ft), 3 (pt); LPNs 5 (ft), 6 (pt); Orderlies 1 (ft); Nurses aides 20 (ft), 17 (pt); Physical therapists 1 (ft), 1 (pt); Reality therapists 1 (ft); Recreational therapists 1 (ft), 1 (pt); Occupational therapists 1 (pt); Speech therapists 1 (pt); Activities coordinators 1 (ft), 1 (pt); Dietitians 1 (pt); Dentists 1 (pt); Ophthalmologists 1 (pt); Podiatrists 1 (pt); Audiologists 1 (pt).
Facilities Dining room; Physical therapy room; Activities room; Chapel; Crafts room; Laundry room; Barber/Beauty shop; Library.
Activities Arts and Crafts; Cards; Games; Reading groups; Prayer groups; Movies; Shopping trips; Dances/Social or cultural gatherings.
Description Facility features a selective menu for dining.

Haverhill Manor Nursing Home
100 Lawrence St, Haverhill, MA, 01830 (617) 374-0356
Admin Robert J Cantwell. *Medical Dir/Dir of Nursing* Charles Chaput.
Licensure Skilled Care; Intermediate Care. *Beds* 100. *Certified* Medicaid.
Staff RNs 8 (ft); LPNs 14 (ft); Nurses aides 43 (ft); Activities coordinators 2 (ft).
Facilities Dining room; Physical therapy room; Activities room; Laundry room; Barber/Beauty shop.
Activities Arts and Crafts; Cards; Games; Reading groups; Prayer groups; Movies; Shopping trips; Dances/Social or cultural gatherings.

Kenoza Hillcrest Nursing Home*
186 North Ave, Haverhill, MA, 01830 (617) 373-5121
Admin Leo Curtin.
Licensure Intermediate Care. *Beds* 21. *Certified* Medicaid.

Kenoza Manor Convalescent Home
190 North Ave, Haverhill, MA, 01830 (617) 372-7700
Admin Robert S Pike.
Licensure Skilled Care; Intermediate Care. *Beds* 100. *Certified* Medicaid.
Staff Physicians; RNs; LPNs; Orderlies; Nurses aides; Physical therapists; Reality therapists; Recreational therapists; Occupational therapists; Speech therapists; Activities coordinators; Dietitians; Dentists; Ophthalmologists; Podiatrists; Audiologists.
Facilities Dining room; Physical therapy room; Activities room; Chapel; Crafts room; Laundry room; Barber/Beauty shop; Library.
Activities Arts and Crafts; Cards; Games; Reading groups; Prayer groups; Movies; Shopping trips; Dances/Social or cultural gatherings.

Kenoza Nursing Home*
87 Shattuck Rd, Haverhill, MA, 01830 (617) 372-1081
Admin Jon R Guarino.
Licensure Skilled Care. *Beds* 87. *Certified* Medicaid.

Lenox Nursing Home Inc*
378 S Main St, Haverhill, MA, 01830 (617) 374-7953
Admin Marion A Thisse.
Licensure Intermediate Care. *Beds* 27. *Certified* Medicaid.

Oxford Manor Nursing Home
689 Main St, Haverhill, MA, 01830 (617) 373-1131
Admin Charlene K Dolan. *Medical Dir/Dir of Nursing* David Byrne MD.
Licensure Skilled Care; Intermediate Care. *Beds* 120. *Certified* Medicaid; Medicare.
Admissions Requirements Minimum age 21.
Facilities Dining room; Physical therapy room; Activities room; Laundry room; Barber/Beauty shop.
Activities Arts and Crafts; Cards; Games; Reading groups; Prayer groups; Movies; Shopping trips; Dances/Social or cultural gatherings.

Scott's Rest Home
69 Keeley St, Haverhill, MA, 01830-6694 (617) 374-4535
Admin Eva M Scott.
Licensure Rest Home. *Beds* 10.
Facilities Dining room; Activities room; Laundry room; Barber/Beauty shop.
Description Facility is a home away from home where, if hungry or needing anything, if capable, they may help themselves.

Stevens-Bennett Home Inc
337 Main St, Haverhill, MA, 01830 (617) 374-8861
Admin Hilda M Carleton. *Medical Dir/Dir of Nursing* Dr David Byrne.
Licensure Retirement home. *Beds* 30.
Admissions Requirements Minimum age 65; Females only; Medical examination; Physician's request.
Staff RNs 1 (pt); Nurses aides 1 (ft), 5 (pt); Activities coordinators 1 (pt); Dietitians 1 (pt).
Facilities Dining room; Activities room; Crafts room; Laundry room; Barber/Beauty shop; Library.
Activities Arts and Crafts; Games; Movies; Shopping trips; Dances/Social or cultural gatherings.
Description Each resident has private room and own furniture. Facility located less than ¼ mile from stores and is on a bus line; very low rates.

Union Mission Nursing Home Inc
150 Water St, Haverhill, MA, 01830 (617) 374-0707
Admin Dr Eugene Tillock. *Medical Dir/Dir of Nursing* Melvin Tribeman MD.
Licensure Skilled Care; Intermediate Care. *Beds* 160. *Certified* Medicaid.
Admissions Requirements Medical examination; Physician's request.
Staff Physicians 15 (pt); RNs 8 (ft); LPNs 6 (ft); Nurses aides 48 (ft); Physical therapists 1 (pt); Recreational therapists 1 (ft); Occupational therapists 1 (pt); Speech therapists 1 (pt); Activities coordinators 1 (ft); Dietitians 1 (pt); Dentists 2 (pt); Ophthalmologists 1 (pt); Podiatrists 3 (pt); Audiologists 1 (pt).
Facilities Dining room; Physical therapy room; Activities room; Crafts room; Barber/Beauty shop; Library; Lounges.
Activities Arts and Crafts; Cards; Games; Reading groups; Prayer groups; Movies; Shopping trips; Dances/Social or cultural gatherings; Continuing education.
Description Facility is fully accredited by the JCAH; an international award winner from the NFPA in fire safety and prevention; professional affiliations for training health professionals.

HINGHAM

Deering Nursing Home Inc*
1192 Main St, Hingham, MA, 02043 (617) 749-2285
Admin Lorraine A Starr.
Licensure Intermediate Care. *Beds* 54. *Certified* Medicaid.

New England Friends Home
Turkey Hill Ln, Hingham, MA, 02043 (617) 749-3556
Admin Brian Drayton.
Licensure Rest Home. *Beds* 15.
Affiliation Society of Friends
Facilities Dining room; Activities room; Library.
Activities Cards; Games; Prayer groups; Movies; Dances/Social or cultural gatherings.
Description With our small size, and the Quaker tradition of service, we offer a family-like atmosphere amidst much natural beauty. We are alert to needs on all levels: physical, emotional, and spiritual, and try to provide real community for all who are here.

Queen Anne Nursing Home*
50 Recreation Park Dr, Hingham, MA, 02043 (617) 749-4983
Admin Peter H Starr.
Licensure Skilled Care; Intermediate Care.
Beds 94. *Certified* Medicaid; Medicare.

HINSDALE

Ashmere Manor Nursing Center
George Schnopp Rd, Hinsdale, MA, 01235 (413) 655-2920
Admin Michael T Casey. *Medical Dir/Dir of Nursing* David W Morrison DO.
Licensure Intermediate Care. *Beds* 82. *Certified* Medicaid.
Staff Physicians 1 (ft); RNs 6 (ft); LPNs 6 (ft), 4 (pt); Orderlies 2 (ft), 1 (pt); Nurses aides 23 (ft), 15 (pt); Physical therapists 2 (ft); Reality therapists 1 (ft); Recreational therapists 1 (ft); Occupational therapists 1 (pt); Speech therapists 1 (pt); Activities coordinators 1 (ft); Dietitians 1 (ft); Dentists 1 (pt); Ophthalmologists 1 (pt); Podiatrists 1 (pt); Audiologists 1 (pt).
Facilities Dining room; Physical therapy room; Activities room; Chapel; Crafts room; Laundry room; Barber/Beauty shop.
Activities Arts and Crafts; Cards; Games; Reading groups; Prayer groups; Movies; Shopping trips; Dances/Social or cultural gatherings; Fall and Spring tours.

HOLBROOK

Holbrook Nursing Home*
45 S Franklin St, Holbrook, MA, 02343 (617) 767-1915
Admin Margaret Pomeroy.
Licensure Intermediate Care. *Beds* 43. *Certified* Medicaid.

HOLDEN

Holden Nursing Home Inc
32 Mayo Rd, Holden, MA, 01520 (617) 829-4327
Admin John L Knight. *Medical Dir/Dir of Nursing* Henry Kramer.
Licensure Intermediate Care. *Beds* 88. *Certified* Medicaid.
Admissions Requirements Minimum age 21; Medical examination; Physician's request.
Staff Physicians 1 (pt); RNs 6 (ft), 6 (pt); LPNs 4 (ft), 5 (pt); Nurses aides 23 (ft), 18 (pt);

Physical therapists 1 (ft); Recreational therapists 1 (ft); Occupational therapists 1 (pt); Dietitians 2 (ft), 1 (pt).
Facilities Dining room; Physical therapy room; Activities room; Chapel; Laundry room; Barber/Beauty shop; Library.
Activities Arts and Crafts; Cards; Games; Reading groups; Prayer groups; Movies; Shopping trips; Dances/Social or cultural gatherings; Church services.
Description The Holden Nursing Home was formed for the purpose of meeting the needs of the geriatric individual. We endeavor to identify the elderly person as an individual with individual rights which include security and shelter. We are located in a beautiful country setting. The nursing home offers its residents a 5-meal plan.

Stone House Hill*
Stone House Hill Rd, Holden, MA, 01520 (617) 755-5345
Admin Arthur Penny.
Licensure Intermediate Care. *Beds* 49. *Certified* Medicaid.

HOLLISTON

Dolly Madison Rest Home
1432 Washington St, Holliston, MA, 01746 (617) 429-4764
Admin Charles H Tule.
Licensure Rest Home. *Beds* 10.
Admissions Requirements Medical examination.
Staff RNs; Nurses aides; Activities coordinators; Dietitians.
Facilities Dining room; Activities room; Laundry room.
Activities Cards; Games; Shopping trips.
Description This is an old farmhouse in a small town with a very quiet setting.

Holliston Manor Nursing Home
84 Elm St, Holliston, MA, 01746 (617) 429-4566
Admin V Jean Cohen. *Medical Dir/Dir of Nursing* John LaRossa MD.
Licensure Intermediate Care. *Beds* 40. *Certified* Medicaid.
Admissions Requirements Minimum age 21.
Staff Physicians 3 (pt); RNs 1 (ft), 4 (pt); LPNs 1 (ft), 3 (pt); Orderlies 1 (pt); Nurses aides 7 (ft), 6 (pt); Physical therapists 1 (pt); Activities coordinators 1 (ft); Dietitians 1 (pt); Podiatrists 1 (pt).
Facilities Dining room; Activities room.
Activities Arts and Crafts; Games; Prayer groups; Movies; Shopping trips; Dances/Social or cultural gatherings.

HOLYOKE

Beaven Kelly Home
1245 Main St, Holyoke, MA, 01040 (413) 532-4892
Admin Sr Mary.
Licensure Rest Home. *Beds* 55.
Admissions Requirements Minimum age 60; Males only; Medical examination; Physician's request.

Staff RNs 1 (ft); LPNs 2 (ft); Nurses aides 3 (ft), 3 (pt); Activities coordinators 1 (ft); Dietitians 1 (pt); Podiatrists 2 (pt).
Affiliation Roman Catholic
Facilities Dining room; Chapel; Laundry room; Barber/Beauty shop.
Activities Arts and Crafts; Cards; Games; Reading groups; Prayer groups; Movies; Shopping trips; Dances/Social or cultural gatherings.
Description Facility is located on beautiful grounds providing outdoor activities, picnics, walks, quiet time; swimming facilities available; near bus lines.

Brookwood Court Nursing Home
260 Easthampton Rd, Holyoke, MA, 01040 (413) 538-9733
Admin Mary Jane Roeder. *Medical Dir/Dir of Nursing* Thomas Gartman MD.
Licensure Skilled Care; Intermediate Care.
Beds 164. *Certified* Medicaid; Medicare.
Admissions Requirements Physician's request.
Staff Physicians 1 (pt); RNs 8 (ft), 8 (pt); LPNs 9 (ft), 5 (pt); Orderlies 2 (ft), 1 (pt); Nurses aides 48 (ft), 27 (pt); Physical therapists 1 (pt); Occupational therapists 1 (pt); Speech therapists 1 (pt); Activities coordinators 1 (ft), 2 (pt); Dietitians 1 (pt); Dentists 1 (pt); Podiatrists 1 (pt).
Facilities Dining room; Physical therapy room; Activities room; Chapel; Crafts room; Laundry room; Barber/Beauty shop.
Activities Arts and Crafts; Cards; Games; Reading groups; Prayer groups; Movies; Shopping trips; Dances/Social or cultural gatherings.
Description Facility features elegant dining with waitress service and selective menu; high staff to resident ratio, varied plus innovative 7 days per week activity program; 7 days per week administrative coverage.

Buckley Nursing and Retirement Home*
282 Cabot St, Holyoke, MA, 01040 (413) 538-7470
Admin William Hartt.
Licensure Skilled Care; Intermediate Care.
Beds 136. *Certified* Medicaid; Medicare.

Chapel Hill Nursing Home*
100 Locust St, Holyoke, MA, 01040 (413) 536-3435
Admin Rosemary Dubuc.
Licensure Skilled Care. *Beds* 61. *Certified* Medicaid.

Holyoke Geriatric and Convalescent Center
45 Lower Westfield Rd, Holyoke, MA, 01040 (413) 536-8110
Admin Timothy V Cotz. *Medical Dir/Dir of Nursing* Robert Mausel MD.
Licensure Skilled Care; Intermediate Care.
Beds 240. *Certified* Medicaid; Medicare.
Admissions Requirements Medical examination.
Staff Physicians 14 (pt); RNs 20 (ft); LPNs 14 (ft); Nurses aides 100 (ft); Physical therapists 1 (ft); Recreational therapists 7 (ft); Occupational therapists 1 (ft); Speech therapists 1 (pt); Activities coordinators 7 (ft); Dietitians 1 (ft); Dentists 1 (pt); Ophthalmologists 1 (pt); Podiatrists 3 (pt).
Facilities Dining room; Physical therapy room; Activities room; Chapel; Crafts room; Laundry room; Barber/Beauty shop; Library; Bar; Gift

shop.
Activities Arts and Crafts; Cards; Games;
Reading groups; Prayer groups; Movies; Shopping trips; Dances/Social or cultural gatherings.
Description Facility features a unique rehabilitation program (over 40% of all admissions are discharged back to the community).

Holyoke Nursing Home*
1913 Northampton St, Holyoke, MA, 01040
(413) 536-7110
Admin Douglas P Ferguson.
Licensure Skilled Care; Intermediate Care.
Beds 100. *Certified* Medicaid; Medicare.

Loomis House Retirement Community
298 Jarvis Ave, Holyoke, MA, 01040 (413)
538-7551
Admin Richard Heath. *Medical Dir/Dir of
Nursing* Dr Brian Akers and Dr David Clinton.
Licensure Rest Home. *Beds* 28.
Staff RNs; LPNs; Nurses aides; Physical therapists; Reality therapists; Recreational therapists;
Occupational therapists; Speech therapists;
Activities coordinators; Dietitians; Dentists;
Podiatrists.
Facilities Dining room; Physical therapy room;
Activities room; Crafts room; Barber/Beauty
shop; Library.
Activities Arts and Crafts; Cards; Prayer
groups; Movies; Shopping trips.

Mount Saint Vincent Home
Holy Family Rd, Holyoke, MA, 01040 (413)
532-3246
Admin Ann Marie Mahoney. *Medical Dir/Dir
of Nursing* Michael A Rosner MD.
Licensure Skilled Care; Intermediate Care.
Beds 120. *Certified* Medicaid.
Admissions Requirements Medical examination; Physician's request.
Staff RNs 8 (ft), 6 (pt); LPNs 5 (ft), 8 (pt);
Orderlies 1 (ft); Nurses aides 23 (ft), 28 (pt);
Recreational therapists 1 (ft), 1 (pt); Activities
coordinators 1 (ft); Dietitians 1 (ft).
Affiliation Roman Catholic
Facilities Dining room; Physical therapy room;
Activities room; Chapel; Crafts room; Laundry
room; Barber/Beauty shop; Library.
Activities Arts and Crafts; Cards; Games;
Reading groups; Prayer groups; Movies; Shopping trips; Dances/Social or cultural gatherings.

Oak Manor Nursing Home*
19 Quirk Ave, Holyoke, MA, 01040 (413)
532-1415
Admin Beth McCauley-Dupre.
Licensure Intermediate Care. *Beds* 60. *Certified* Medicaid.

HOPEDALE

Hopedale Garden Nursing Home*
325 S Main St, Hopedale, MA, 01747 (617)
473-9600
Admin Sidney Croll.
Licensure Intermediate Care. *Beds* 70. *Certified* Medicaid.

**Oakledge Manor Convalescent and Retirement
Home**
34 Adin St, Hopedale, MA, 01747 (617)
473-0171
Admin James F Tracy. *Medical Dir/Dir of
Nursing* Faheem Farooq MD.
Licensure Skilled Care; Intermediate Care.
Beds 56. *Certified* Medicaid.
Admissions Requirements Medical examination; Physician's request.
Staff Physicians 3 (pt); RNs 5 (ft); LPNs 2 (ft),
2 (pt); Nurses aides 20 (ft); Physical therapists 1
(pt); Reality therapists 1 (pt); Recreational therapists 1 (pt); Occupational therapists 1 (pt);
Speech therapists 1 (pt); Activities coordinators
1 (ft); Dietitians 1 (pt); Dentists 1 (pt); Podiatrists 2 (pt); Audiologists 1 (pt).
Facilities Dining room; Activities room; Crafts
room; Laundry room; Library.
Activities Arts and Crafts; Cards; Games;
Reading groups; Prayer groups; Movies; Shopping trips; Dances/Social or cultural gatherings.

HUDSON

Saint Jude Convalescent Home
53 Church St, Hudson, MA, 01749 (617)
562-6906
Admin Beverly Singer. *Medical Dir/Dir of
Nursing* Dr Michelle Ricaro.
Licensure Intermediate Care. *Beds* 43. *Certified* Medicaid.
Admissions Requirements Minimum age 50.
Staff RNs 4 (ft), 3 (pt); LPNs 2 (pt); Nurses
aides 6 (ft), 10 (pt); Activities coordinators 1
(pt).
Facilities Laundry room.
Activities Arts and Crafts; Cards; Games;
Reading groups; Prayer groups; Shopping trips;
Dances/Social or cultural gatherings.
Description This small nursing home provides
a warm home-like atmosphere assisted by a
caring staff; excellent multi-faceted activities
program.

HYANNIS

Whitehall Health Care Facilities
Falmouth Rd, PO Box 979, Hyannis, MA,
02601 (617) 775-6662
Admin Allen J White and Dr David K White.
Medical Dir/Dir of Nursing Dr Forrest Beame.
Licensure Skilled Care; Intermediate Care.
Beds 187. *Certified* Medicaid; Medicare.
Staff Physicians; RNs 25 (ft); LPNs 6 (ft);
Orderlies 6 (ft); Nurses aides 60 (ft); Physical
therapists; Reality therapists 1 (ft); Recreational
therapists 4 (ft); Occupational therapists 2 (pt);
Speech therapists 1 (pt); Activities coordinators
2 (ft); Dietitians 1 (ft); Dentists 1 (ft); Ophthalmologists 1 (pt); Podiatrists 1 (pt); Audiologists
1 (pt).
Facilities Dining room; Physical therapy room;
Activities room; Chapel; Crafts room; Laundry
room; Barber/Beauty shop; Library.
Activities Arts and Crafts; Cards; Games;
Reading groups; Prayer groups; Movies; Shopping trips; Dances/Social or cultural gatherings.
Description Facility has been awarded excellent
rating by the Massachusetts Federation of
Nursing Homes; JCAH approved.

IPSWICH

Coburn Charitable Society
20 N Main St, Ipswich, MA, 01938 (617)
356-3571
Admin Helen Fraga.
Licensure Rest Home. *Beds* 9.
Admissions Requirements Minimum age 60;
Medical examination.
Staff Nurses aides 2 (pt); Podiatrists 1 (pt).

**Stephen Caldwell Memorial Convalescent
Home**
16 Green St, Ipswich, MA, 01938 (617)
356-5460
Admin Jeannette D Connor. *Medical Dir/Dir
of Nursing* Dr Thomas Sullivan.
Licensure Skilled Care. *Beds* 36. *Certified* Medicaid.
Admissions Requirements Minimum age 21.
Staff LPNs 4 (ft); Nurses aides 12 (ft), 8 (pt);
Occupational therapists 1 (pt); Speech therapists 1 (pt); Activities coordinators 1 (ft); Dietitians 1 (pt); Dentists 1 (pt); Ophthalmologists 1
(pt); Podiatrists 1 (pt); Audiologists 1 (pt).
Facilities Dining room; Physical therapy room;
Activities room; Crafts room; Laundry room.
Activities Arts and Crafts; Cards; Games;
Reading groups; Prayer groups; Movies.
Description Facility has small family-like
atmosphere; provides skilled nursing care.

JAMAICA PLAIN

Tudor House Nursing Home
81 S Huntington Ave, Jamaica Plain, MA,
02130 (617) 277-2633
Admin Herbert D Fisher.
Licensure Intermediate Care. *Beds* 43. *Certified* Medicaid.

KINGSTON

Shady Breeze Rest Home*
15 Foster Ln, Kingston, MA, 02360 (617)
585-3657
Admin Phyllis H Mehrman.
Licensure Rest Home. *Beds* 15.

LAKEVILLE

Island Terrace Nursing Home
Long Point Rd, PO Box 232, Lakeville, MA,
02346 (617) 947-0151
Admin Lucille Tolles. *Medical Dir/Dir of
Nursing* Bernard Beuthner MD.
Licensure Skilled Care 10B. *Beds* 73.
Certified Medicaid.
Staff RNs 3 (ft); LPNs 6 (ft); Nurses aides 23
(ft); Physical therapists 1 (pt); Occupational
therapists 1 (pt); Activities coordinators 1 (ft);
Dietitians 1 (pt); Podiatrists 1 (pt).
Facilities Dining room; Physical therapy room;
Activities room; Crafts room; Laundry room;
Barber/Beauty shop; Library.
Activities Arts and Crafts; Games; Reading
groups; Prayer groups; Movies; Shopping trips.
Description Facility is located in a quiet country setting, 12 miles north of New Bedford,
overlooking Great Quittaeur Pond.

Meadow View Nursing Home*
18 Crooked Ln, Lakeville, MA, 02346 (617)
947-2793
Admin Ora Mae Torres.
Licensure Intermediate Care. *Beds* 29. *Certified* Medicaid.

LANCASTER

River Terrace Healthcare Nursing Home
Ballard Hill, Lancaster, MA, 01523 (617)
365-4538
Admin Philip Quillard.
Licensure Skilled Care; Intermediate Care.
Beds 82. *Certified* Medicaid.

LAWRENCE

Anlaw Nursing Home*
555 S Union St, Lawrence, MA, 01843 (617)
682-5281
Admin Carmella M Mancini.
Licensure Skilled Care; Intermediate Care.
Beds 90. *Certified* Medicaid; Medicare.

Berkley Retirement Home
150 Berkley St, Lawrence, MA, 01841 (617)
682-1614
Admin Nancy J Herrmann. *Medical Dir/Dir of Nursing* Edward Broaddus MD.
Licensure Rest Home. *Beds* 32.
Admissions Requirements Minimum age 65;
Medical examination.
Staff Physicians 1 (pt); RNs 1 (ft); LPNs 5 (pt);
Nurses aides 5 (pt); Recreational therapists 1
(pt); Activities coordinators 1 (pt); Dietitians 1
(pt); Podiatrists 1 (pt).
Facilities Dining room; Activities room; Chapel; Crafts room; Laundry room; Barber/Beauty
shop; Library.
Activities Arts and Crafts; Cards; Games;
Reading groups; Prayer groups; Movies; Shopping trips; Dances/Social or cultural gatherings.
Description Facility provides a home-like setting, but with nursing supervision in the
background, a retirement home with a small
nursing unit which handles only residents; out
of town dining to various restaurants with
transportation provided by owned van.

German Old Folks Home Inc
374 Howard St, Lawrence, MA, 01841 (617)
682-5593
Admin Valerie Emerton.
Licensure Rest Home. *Beds* 31.
Admissions Requirements Medical examination; Physician's request.
Staff Orderlies 1 (pt); Nurses aides 6 (pt);
Reality therapists 1 (pt); Recreational therapists;
Activities coordinators 1 (pt).
Facilities Dining room; Activities room; Crafts
room; Laundry room.
Activities Arts and Crafts; Cards; Games; Prayer groups; Movies; Shopping trips; Dances/Social or cultural gatherings.
Description Facility features private rooms
except for 5 doubles; boarding-house atmosphere; bus stop at door.

Mary Immaculate Nursing Home
0 Bennington St, Lawrence, MA, 01841 (617)
685-6321
Admin Richard J Hamilton. *Medical Dir/Dir
of Nursing* Alan Miller MD.
Licensure Skilled Care; Intermediate Care.
Beds 250. *Certified* Medicaid; Medicare.
Admissions Requirements Minimum age 21.
Staff Physicians 28 (pt); RNs 20 (ft), 5 (pt);
LPNs 35 (ft), 25 (pt); Orderlies 2 (ft), 2 (pt);
Nurses aides 70 (ft), 35 (pt); Physical therapists
2 (ft), 1 (pt); Recreational therapists 4 (ft); Occupational therapists 1 (ft), 1 (pt); Speech therapists 1 (pt); Activities coordinators 1 (ft);
Dietitians 3 (ft), 1 (pt); Dentists 1 (pt); Podiatrists 1 (pt); Audiologists 1 (pt).
Affiliation Roman Catholic
Facilities Dining room; Physical therapy room;
Activities room; Chapel; Crafts room; Laundry
room; Barber/Beauty shop; Library; Outside
patio; Wheelchair garden; Patient bar.
Activities Arts and Crafts; Cards; Games;
Reading groups; Prayer groups; Movies; Shopping trips; Dances/Social or cultural gatherings.
Description Mary Immaculate Nursing Home
was the first charitable institution in the city of
Lawrence, established in 1868, and has continued uninterrupted services to the community since that time under sponsorship and
leadership of the Grey Nuns of Montreal. In
response to the needs of the elderly, a comprehensive geriatric health care delivery system
is provided through a 250-bed multilevel skilled
nursing home, an adult day health care center,
and 305 units of congregate housing for the
elderly/handicapped.

Town Manor Nursing Home Inc*
55 Lowell St, Lawrence, MA, 01840 (617)
688-6056
Admin Robert F Belluche.
Licensure Skilled Care; Intermediate Care.
Beds 111. *Certified* Medicaid.

Winfield House Convalescent Home*
800 Essex St, Lawrence, MA, 01841 (617)
686-2994
Admin Richard P Blinn.
Licensure Skilled Care; Intermediate Care.
Beds 94. *Certified* Medicaid.

LEE

Berkshire Hills Nursing Home—North
19 Prospect St, Lee, MA, 01238 (413) 243-2010
Admin Paul R Chernov. *Medical Dir/Dir of
Nursing* Charles W Stratton MD.
Licensure Intermediate Care. *Beds* 73. *Certified* Medicaid.
Staff Physicians; RNs; LPNs; Orderlies;
Nurses aides; Physical therapists; Recreational
therapists; Occupational therapists; Speech therapists; Dietitians; Dentists; Ophthalmologists;
Podiatrists; Audiologists.
Facilities Dining room; Physical therapy room;
Activities room; Laundry room; Barber/Beauty
shop.
Activities Arts and Crafts; Cards; Games;
Reading groups; Prayer groups; Movies; Shopping trips.

LENOX

Edgecombe Nursing and Convalescent Home
40 Sunset Ave, Lenox, MA, 01240 (413)
637-0622
Admin James Bednarski.
Licensure Skilled Care; Intermediate Care.
Beds 124. *Certified* Medicaid.
Admissions Requirements Minimum age 21;
Physician's request.
Staff Physicians 1 (pt); RNs 6 (ft), 4 (pt); LPNs
5 (ft), 1 (pt); Orderlies 3 (ft); Nurses aides 40
(ft), 9 (pt); Physical therapists 1 (pt); Recreational therapists 2 (ft); Occupational therapists 1
(pt); Speech therapists 1 (pt); Dietitians 1 (pt);
Dentists 1 (pt); Podiatrists 2 (pt).
Facilities Dining room; Physical therapy room;
Activities room; Chapel; Crafts room; Laundry
room; Barber/Beauty shop.
Activities Arts and Crafts; Cards; Games;
Reading groups; Prayer groups; Movies; Dances/Social or cultural gatherings.

Valley View Nursing Home
540 Pittsfield Rd, Lenox, MA, 01240 (413)
637-1221
Admin Kim P Murphy.
Licensure Intermediate Care. *Beds* 140. *Certified* Medicaid.
Staff Physicians 2 (pt); RNs 3 (ft), 2 (pt); LPNs
6 (ft), 4 (pt); Nurses aides 25 (ft), 17 (pt); Occupational therapists 1 (pt); Activities coordinators 1 (ft); Dietitians 1 (pt); Dentists 1 (pt);
Ophthalmologists 1 (pt); Podiatrists 1 (pt).
Facilities Dining room; Physical therapy room;
Activities room; Chapel; Crafts room; Laundry
room; Barber/Beauty shop; Library.
Activities Arts and Crafts; Cards; Games;
Reading groups; Prayer groups; Movies; Shopping trips; Dances/Social or cultural gatherings;
Exercise program.
Description Facility features visits from children's organizations (scouts, church youth, etc);
private courtyards surrounded by building,
beautiful gardens, and wooded areas; and an
excellent volunteer program.

LEOMINSTER

Fairlawn Nursing Home Inc
370 West St, Leominster, MA, 01453 (617)
537-0774
Admin Theodore F Willruth. *Medical Dir/Dir
of Nursing* Knute Alfredson MD.
Licensure Skilled Care; Intermediate Care.
Beds 121. *Certified* Medicaid; Medicare.
Staff RNs 4 (ft), 11 (pt); LPNs 3 (ft), 15 (pt);
Orderlies 2 (ft), 3 (pt); Nurses aides 15 (ft), 33
(pt); Physical therapists 1 (pt); Occupational
therapists 1 (pt); Speech therapists 1 (pt);
Activities coordinators 2 (ft); Dietitians 1 (pt);
Dentists 1 (pt); Podiatrists 2 (pt).
Facilities Dining room; Physical therapy room;
Activities room; Crafts room; Library.
Activities Arts and Crafts; Cards; Games;
Reading groups; Prayer groups; Movies; Shopping trips; Dances/Social or cultural gatherings.
Description Home has light, airy rooms all on
one level; very active activity program; licensed
nurses giving direct care on all levels of care;
accredited by JCAH and member AHCA and
MFNH; holder of the "E" award for Excellence.

Fairmount Rest Home*
34 Fairmount St, Leominster, MA, 01453 (617) 537-5472
Admin Mary A Gagne.
Licensure Rest Home. *Beds* 20.

Homestead Rest Home
226 Main St, Leominster, MA, 91453 (617) 537-7202
Admin Richard Ryan.
Licensure Rest Home. *Beds* 21.
Admissions Requirements Medical examination; Physician's request.
Facilities Dining room; Laundry room; Barber/Beauty shop.
Activities Arts and Crafts; Cards; Games; Movies; Shopping trips.

Keystone Nursing Home Inc
Keystone Dr, Leominster, MA, 01453 (617) 537-9327
Admin Doris R Garbose. *Medical Dir/Dir of Nursing* John J Murphy MD.
Licensure Skilled Care; Intermediate Care. *Beds* 106. *Certified* Medicaid.

Leominster Home for Old Ladies*
16 Pearl St, Leominster, MA, 01453 (617) 537-3022
Admin Myrtle Bean.
Licensure Charitable Home. *Beds* 11.
Admissions Requirements Females only

Village Rest Home
446 Main St, Leominster, MA, 01453 (617) 534-6270
Admin Matilda Iandoli.
Licensure Rest Home. *Beds* 25.
Admissions Requirements Minimum age 32; Medical examination; Physician's request.
Staff LPNs 1 (ft); Nurses aides 3 (ft), 3 (pt); Reality therapists 1 (pt); Recreational therapists 1 (pt); Activities coordinators 1 (pt); Dentists 1 (pt); Podiatrists 1 (pt).
Facilities Dining room; Activities room; Crafts room; Laundry room; Barber/Beauty shop; Library.
Activities Arts and Crafts; Cards; Games; Reading groups; Prayer groups; Movies; Shopping trips; Dances/Social or cultural gatherings.
Description Private car service free of charge to visit beauty parlor or doctors' offices; facility has beautiful yard with a garden; all personnel give close supervision.

LEXINGTON

Dana Home of Lexington*
2027 Massachusetts Ave, Lexington, MA, 02173 (617) 861-0131
Admin Audrea Murphy.
Licensure Charitable Home. *Beds* 15.

East Village Nursing Home*
140 Emerson St, Lexington, MA, 02173 (617) 861-8630
Admin Robert Cataldo.
Licensure Skilled Care; Intermediate Care. *Beds* 162. *Certified* Medicaid.

Fairlawn Nursing Home Inc
265 Lowell St, Lexington, MA, 02173 (617) 862-7640
Admin Thomas R Walsh. *Medical Dir/Dir of Nursing* Robert Stewart MD.
Licensure Intermediate Care. *Beds* 104.

Mediplex at Lexington—Long Term Care Facility*
178 Lowell St, Lexington, MA, 02173 (617) 862-7400
Admin Sylvia J Chiasson.
Licensure Intermediate Care. *Beds* 120. *Certified* Medicaid.

Pine Knoll Nursing Home*
30 Watertown St, Lexington, MA, 02173 (617) 862-8151
Admin Edward F Cataldo.
Licensure Skilled Care. *Beds* 81. *Certified* Medicaid; Medicare.

LINCOLN

Lincoln Rest Home
Farrar Rd, Lincoln, MA, 01773 (617) 259-8128
Admin Joseph S Sulomont.
Licensure Rest Home. *Beds* 12.

LITTLETON

Littleton House Nursing Home*
191 Foster St, Littleton, MA, 01460 (617) 486-3512
Admin Andrew MacLeod.
Licensure Intermediate Care. *Beds* 120. *Certified* Medicaid.

LONGMEADOW

Jewish Nursing Home of Western Massachusetts*
770 Converse St, Longmeadow, MA, 01106 (413) 567-6211
Admin Ralph Wener.
Licensure Skilled Care; Intermediate Care. *Beds* 200. *Certified* Medicaid; Medicare.
Affiliation Jewish

LOWELL

Arcadia Nursing Home*
841 Merrimack St, Lowell, MA, 01854 (617) 459-0546
Admin Isabel R Donovan.
Licensure Skilled Care; Intermediate Care. *Beds* 142. *Certified* Medicaid.

Battles Home
236 Fairmount St, Lowell, MA, 01852 (617) 453-2531
Admin Clifford R Jennings.
Licensure Rest Home. *Beds* 12.
Admissions Requirements Males only; Medical examination.
Facilities Dining room; Activities room; Laundry room; Library Living room; Pool room.
Description The Battles Home is an endowed men's retirement home organized in 1901, classified as a Class IV home. Potential residents

are approved by a board of trustees. When the resident is unable to take care of himself, he is required to be transferred to his family or a Class III or Class II nursing home.

Beaconcrest Nursing Home*
500 Wentworth Ave, Lowell, MA, 01850 (617) 458-1271
Admin Arthur Rublinder.
Licensure Skilled Care; Intermediate Care. *Beds* 103. *Certified* Medicaid.

Christian Hill Convalescent Home*
19 Varnum St, Lowell, MA, 01850 (617) 454-5644
Admin Frank P Miller.
Licensure Skilled Care; Intermediate Care. *Beds* 160. *Certified* Medicaid; Medicare.

Colonial Rest Home
945 Middlesex St, Lowell, MA, 01851 (617) 454-5644
Admin Elliott C Williams.
Licensure Rest Home. *Beds* 22.

D'Youville Manor
981 Varum Ave, Lowell, MA, 01854 (617) 454-5681
Admin Pauline Beauchesne. *Medical Dir/Dir of Nursing* Stephen R Brovender MD.
Licensure Skilled Care; Intermediate Care; Adult Day Care. *Beds* 196. *Certified* Medicaid.
Admissions Requirements Minimum age 55; Medical examination; Physician's request.
Staff RNs 3 (ft), 8 (pt); LPNs 12 (ft), 14 (pt); Orderlies 3 (ft), 2 (pt); Nurses aides 38 (ft), 29 (pt); Physical therapists 2 (ft), 1 (pt); Recreational therapists 1 (ft); Occupational therapists 1 (ft), 1 (pt); Activities coordinators 1 (ft); Dietitians 1 (ft); Podiatrists 7 (pt).
Affiliation Roman Catholic
Facilities Dining room; Physical therapy room; Activities room; Chapel; Crafts room; Laundry room; Barber/Beauty shop; Library.
Activities Arts and Crafts; Cards; Games; Prayer groups; Movies; Shopping trips; Dances/Social or cultural gatherings.
Description The goals of the facility are to provide comprehensive nursing care to Level II and Level III patients; to rehabilitate patients with restorative potential; and to provide for the elderly patients an atmosphere of peace, love, and security.

Fairhaven Nursing Home*
476 Varnum Ave, Lowell, MA, 01854 (617) 458-3388
Admin Margaret H Larkin.
Licensure Skilled Care; Intermediate Care. *Beds* 166. *Certified* Medicaid.

Glenwood Manor Convalescent Home
577 Varnum Ave, Lowell, MA, 01854 (617) 455-5444
Admin Scott Elsass. *Medical Dir/Dir of Nursing* Dr Susan Black.
Licensure Intermediate Care. *Beds* 101. *Certified* Medicaid.
Admissions Requirements Minimum age 21; Medical examination; Physician's request.
Staff RNs; LPNs; Orderlies; Nurses aides; Physical therapists; Reality therapists; Recrea-

tional therapists; Occupational therapists; Speech therapists; Activities coordinators; Dietitians; Dentists; Ophthalmologists; Podiatrists; Audiologists.
Facilities Dining room; Activities room; Crafts room; Barber/Beauty shop.
Activities Arts and Crafts; Cards; Games; Reading groups; Prayer groups; Movies; Shopping trips; Dances/Social or cultural gatherings.
Description Facility offers quality patient care while maintaining competitive prices. Facility has a very active activities program with rehabilitation service connected to the program; serves well-balanced nutritional meals in a centrally located dining room.

Horn Home for Aged
98 Smith St, Lowell, MA, 01851 (617) 452-9571
Admin Margaret O Knutson. *Medical Dir/Dir of Nursing* Dr Douglas E Bragdon.
Licensure Rest Home. *Beds* 14.
Admissions Requirements Minimum age 65; Females only; Medical examination; Physician's request.
Staff RNs 1 (pt); Podiatrists 1 (pt).
Facilities Dining room; Laundry room.
Description Small home offers supervisory care, meals, and laundry in a quiet setting.

Merrimack Valley Retirement Home
360 Pawtucket St, Lowell, MA, 01854 (617) 453-6412
Admin Yale Canter.
Licensure Rest Home. *Beds* 19.

Northwood Convalescent Center
1010 Varnum Ave, Lowell, MA, 01854 (617) 458-8773
Admin Richard Wallace. *Medical Dir/Dir of Nursing* John Korbowniczak MD.
Licensure Skilled Care; Intermediate Care. *Beds* 123. *Certified* Medicaid; Medicare.
Admissions Requirements Medical examination.
Staff Physicians 5 (pt); RNs; LPNs; Orderlies; Physical therapists 1 (pt); Recreational therapists 2 (ft), 1 (pt); Occupational therapists 1 (pt); Speech therapists 1 (pt); Activities coordinators 1 (ft); Dietitians 1 (pt); Dentists 1 (pt); Podiatrists 1 (pt).
Facilities Dining room; Physical therapy room; Activities room; Crafts room; Laundry room; Barber/Beauty shop.
Activities Arts and Crafts; Cards; Games; Reading groups; Prayer groups; Movies; Shopping trips; Dances/Social or cultural gatherings.
Description Facility offers a comprehensive recreational program involving residents' strengths. In addition, offers a varied and "tasteful" dietary program with residents having choices concerning meals.

Princeton House Rest Home*
94-100 Priceton Blvd, Lowell, MA, 01853 (617) 458-4056
Admin Jeanette F Savoie.
Licensure Rest Home. *Beds* 56.

River Valley House
5320 Fletcher St, Lowell, MA, 01854 (617) 452-6071
Admin Harry Councilman. *Medical Dir/Dir of Nursing* Dr Benjamin Gaieski.
Licensure Rest Home. *Beds* 36.
Ownership Nonprofit.
Admissions Requirements Minimum age 62; Females only; Medical examination.
Staff Physicians 1 (pt); LPNs 1 (ft); Nurses aides 6 (ft), 6 (pt); Activities coordinators 1 (ft); Dietitians 1 (pt).
Facilities Dining room; Activities room; Crafts room; Laundry room; Barber/Beauty shop; Library.
Activities Arts and Crafts; Cards; Games; Prayer groups; Movies; Shopping trips; Dances/Social or cultural gatherings.
Description River Valley House was incorporated in July, 1867 as a nonprofit, charitable retirement home for Protestant, female mill workers, who were without families and unable to work. The present building is 102 years old and remains in appearance much the same as when it was built.

Town and Country Nursing Home*
915 Westford St, Lowell, MA, 01851 (617) 459-7262
Admin Alexander E Struzziero.
Licensure Intermediate Care. *Beds* 50. *Certified* Medicaid.

Willow Manor Nursing Home*
30 Princeton Blvd, Lowell, MA, 01851 (617) 454-8086
Admin S Joseph S Solomont.
Licensure Skilled Care; Intermediate Care. *Beds* 84. *Certified* Medicaid.

LYNN

Abbott House Nursing Home*
28 Essex St, Lynn, MA, 01902 (617) 595-5500
Admin George H Bane.
Licensure Skilled Care. *Beds* 47. *Certified* Medicaid; Medicare.
Ownership Proprietary.

Alba Nursing Home*
12 Park St, Lynn, MA, 01905 (617) 599-3993
Admin William A Sherman, Jr.
Licensure Intermediate Care. *Beds* 34. *Certified* Medicaid.

Alden Manor Nursing Home
94 Franklin St, Lynn, MA, 91902 (617) 592-7758
Admin William Mantzoukas. *Medical Dir/Dir of Nursing* James Gottschall.
Licensure Intermediate Care. *Beds* 62. *Certified* Medicaid.
Staff RNs 2 (pt); LPNs 1 (ft), 2 (pt); Nurses aides 9 (ft), 11 (pt); Physical therapists 1 (pt); Recreational therapists 1 (pt); Activities coordinators 1 (pt); Dietitians 1 (pt).
Facilities Dining room; Activities room; Crafts room; Laundry room.
Activities Arts and Crafts; Cards; Games; Prayer groups; Movies.
Description Facility is associated with Health System Management Corporation

Atlantic Rest Home
60 Atlantic St, Lynn, MA, 01902 (617) 598-0609
Admin David J Solimine Jr.
Licensure Rest Home. *Beds* 21.
Admissions Requirements Minimum age 60; Females only; Medical examination; Physician's request.
Staff Nurses aides 3 (ft), 5 (pt); Podiatrists.
Facilities Dining room.
Activities Cards; Games.
Description Located one block from ocean and downtown shopping areas, Atlantic Rest Home is close to many churches and close to public transportation.

Avalon Nursing Home*
24 Baker St, Lynn, MA, 01902 (617) 498-1142
Admin George H Bane.
Licensure Intermediate Care. *Beds* 29. *Certified* Medicaid.

Baker Manor Rest Home*
16 Baker St, Lynn, MA, 01902 (617) 592-7033
Admin Richard F Truax.
Licensure Rest Home. *Beds* 15. *Certified* Medicaid.

Crestview Manor Nursing Home*
72 Nahant St, Lynn, MA, 01902 (617) 598-6363
Admin William A Sherman Jr.
Licensure Intermediate Care. *Beds* 29. *Certified* Medicaid.

Family Rest Home
13 Essex St, Lynn, MA, 01902 (617) 595-7644
Admin James B Kerwin.
Licensure Intermediate Care. *Beds* 22. *Certified* Medicaid.
Admissions Requirements Medical examination.
Facilities Dining room; Activities room; Laundry room.
Activities Arts and Crafts; Cards; Games; Shopping trips.

Joseph P Devlin Nursing Home*
179 Holyoke St, Lynn, MA, 01905 (617) 595-3743
Admin Ann Gauvain.
Licensure Skilled Care. *Beds* 54. *Certified* Medicaid.
Ownership Public.

Karlson Rest Home Inc
73 Baker St, Lynn, MA, 01902 (617) 595-8931
Admin Maureen Callahan.
Licensure Rest Home. *Beds* 15.
Staff Physicians 1 (pt); RNs 1 (pt); Nurses aides 1 (ft), 6 (pt); Activities coordinators 1 (pt); Dietitians 1 (pt); Dentists 1 (pt); Ophthalmologists 1 (pt); Podiatrists 1 (pt).

Lawrence Manor Nursing Home*
26 Henry Ave, Lynn, MA, 01902 (617) 595-2941
Admin Albert Dukatz.
Licensure Intermediate Care. *Beds* 39. *Certified* Medicaid.

Lenox Hill Nursing and Rehabilitation Care Facility*
70 Granite St, Lynn, MA, 01904 (617) 581-2400

Admin Robert N Murphy.
Licensure Skilled Care; Intermediate Care.
Beds 218. *Certified* Medicaid; Medicare.

Lynn Home and Infirmary
655 Boston St, Lynn, MA, 01905 (617)
593-4347
Admin Donald P Dixon. *Medical Dir/Dir of Nursing* Dr Milton Helsel.
Licensure Intermediate Care. *Beds* 105. *Certified* Medicaid.
Admissions Requirements Medical examination; Physician's request.
Staff Physicians 1 (pt); RNs 9 (ft); LPNs 4 (ft); Nurses aides 30 (ft); Physical therapists 1 (pt); Occupational therapists 1 (pt); Activities coordinators 1 (ft), 1 (pt); Dietitians 1 (pt).
Facilities Activities room; Laundry room.
Activities Arts and Crafts; Games; Prayer groups; Movies.

Lynn Home for Elderly Persons
Atlantic Terrace, Lynn, MA, 01902 (617)
593-8099
Admin Barbara L Reagan. *Medical Dir/Dir of Nursing* G Fred Jackson MD.
Licensure Rest Home. *Beds* 39.
Admissions Requirements Minimum age 65; Medical examination.
Staff RNs 1 (pt); LPNs 1 (ft), 4 (pt); Nurses aides 3 (ft), 5 (pt); Activities coordinators 1 (ft).
Facilities Dining room; Activities room; Crafts room; Laundry room; Barber/Beauty shop; Library; Sewing room; Card room; Ceramic shop.
Activities Arts and Crafts; Cards; Games; Reading groups; Prayer groups; Movies; Shopping trips; Dances/Social or cultural gatherings; Ceramics; Cooking.
Description Facility features all private rooms, van for transportation to outside activities, resident dog and cat. Religious services held in home every Sunday.

Lynn Shore Rest Home
37 Breed St, Lynn, MA, 01902 (617) 595-7110
Admin David J Solimine Jr.
Licensure Rest Home. *Beds* 32.
Admissions Requirements Minimum age 60; Medical examination; Physician's request.
Staff Nurses aides 3 (ft), 3 (pt); Podiatrists.
Facilities Dining room; Activities room.
Activities Cards; Games.
Description Lynn Shore Rest Home is located one block from the ocean and near public transportation, churches, and shopping areas.

Pariseau Nursing Home Inc
66 Johnson St, Lynn, MA, 01902 (615)
592-5849
Admin Margaret T Murray. *Medical Dir/Dir of Nursing* Lois Stone.
Licensure Intermediate Care. *Beds* 28. *Certified* Medicaid.
Admissions Requirements Females only; Medical examination; Physician's request.
Staff Physicians 3 (pt); RNs 1 (ft), 1 (pt); LPNs 5 (pt); Nurses aides 4 (ft), 5 (pt); Physical therapists 1 (pt); Recreational therapists 1 (pt); Occupational therapists 1 (pt); Speech therapists 1 (pt); Activities coordinators 1 (pt); Dietitians 1 (pt); Dentists 1 (pt); Ophthalmologists 1 (pt); Podiatrists 1 (pt).

Facilities Dining room; Laundry room.
Activities Arts and Crafts; Cards; Games; Reading groups; Prayer groups; Shopping trips; Dances/Social or cultural gatherings.

Phillips Manor Nursing Home*
28 Linwood Rd, Lynn, MA, 01905 (617)
592-8000
Admin Anna Freehling. *Beds* 20. *Certified* Medicaid.
Licensure Intermediate Care. *Beds* 20. *Certified* Medicaid.

Pine Hill Rest Home*
341 Linwood St, Lynn, MA, 01905 (617)
598-6256
Admin Charles Dandaneau.
Licensure Rest Home. *Beds* 12.

Twomey Rest Home
54 Tudor St, Lynn, MA, 01902 (617) 593-4567
Admin Timothy Twomey.
Licensure Rest Home. *Beds* 30.

MALDEN

Bartlett Manor Nursing Home
180 Summer St, Malden, MA, 02148 (617)
324-7800
Admin Susan Dorenbaum.
Licensure Intermediate Care. *Beds* 41. *Certified* Medicaid.

Buchanan Nursing Home Inc
190 Summer St, Malden, MA, 02148 (617)
324-7800
Admin Stanley Kotce. *Medical Dir/Dir of Nursing* S Olans.
Licensure Intermediate Care. *Beds* 35. *Certified* Medicaid.
Staff RNs; LPNs 2 (ft); Nurses aides 8 (ft), 4 (pt); Activities coordinators 1 (pt).
Facilities Dining room; Activities room; Crafts room; Laundry room.
Activities Arts and Crafts; Games; Prayer groups; Movies; Shopping trips; Dances/Social or cultural gatherings.
Description Residents receive excellent nursing care.

Care Well Manor Nursing Home
203 Summer St, Malden, MA, 02148 (617)
324-3663
Admin Neil B McCole.
Licensure Intermediate Care. *Beds* 23. *Certified* Medicaid.
Admissions Requirements Minimum age 21; Females only; Medical examination.
Staff RNs 1 (ft); LPNs 1 (ft), 2 (pt); Nurses aides 3 (ft), 4 (pt); Activities coordinators; Dietitians.
Facilities Dining room; Activities room; Crafts room; Laundry room.
Activities Arts and Crafts; Cards; Games; Reading groups; Prayer groups; Movies; Shopping trips; Dances/Social or cultural gatherings; Outings for lunches and dinners.

Davenport Memorial Home*
70 Salem St, Malden, MA, 02148 (617)
324-0150
Admin Beth E Walsh.
Licensure Charitable Home. *Beds* 20.

Dexter House Nursing Facility
120 Main St, Malden, MA, 02148 (617)
324-5600
Admin Gerald A Sohn.
Licensure Skilled Care; Intermediate Care.
Beds 130. *Certified* Medicaid.
Admissions Requirements Minimum age 21; Medical examination; Physician's request.
Staff Physicians 1 (pt); RNs 13 (ft); LPNs 9 (ft); Nurses aides 55 (ft); Physical therapists 1 (ft); Reality therapists 1 (ft); Recreational therapists 1 (ft); Occupational therapists 1 (pt); Speech therapists 1 (pt); Dietitians 1 (ft); Dentists 1 (pt); Ophthalmologists 1 (pt); Podiatrists 1 (pt); Audiologists 1 (pt); Social workers 1 (ft).
Facilities Dining room; Physical therapy room; Activities room; Crafts room; Barber/Beauty shop; Library.
Activities Arts and Crafts; Cards; Games; Reading groups; Prayer groups; Movies; Shopping trips; Dances/Social or cultural gatherings.
Description Transitional motivation is a comprehensive program made up of doctor, nurses, social worker, and pharmacist to deal with the Alzheimer's patient.

Forestdale Nusing Home*
342 Forest St, Malden, MA, 02148 (617)
322-1716
Admin Clyde L Tyler Jr.
Licensure Intermediate Care. *Beds* 69. *Certified* Medicaid.

Malden Home for Aged Persons
578 Main St, Malden, MA, 02148 (617)
321-3740
Admin Bridget Berk. *Medical Dir/Dir of Nursing* H Portman MD.
Licensure Intermediate Care. *Beds* 25.
Ownership Nonprofit.
Admissions Requirements Minimum age 65; Females only; Medical examination.
Staff RNs 2 (ft), 1 (pt); LPNs 4 (pt); Nurses aides 2 (ft), 4 (pt); Activities coordinators 1 (pt); Dietitians 1 (pt).
Facilities Dining room; Activities room; Crafts room; Laundry room; Barber/Beauty shop; Store.
Activities Arts and Crafts; Cards; Games; Shopping trips; Annual fair.
Description Facility has private rooms for level IV residents.

Malden Nursing Home*
255 Clifton St, Malden, MA, 02148 (617)
324-2620
Admin Clyde L Tyler Jr.
Licensure Intermediate Care. *Beds* 52. *Certified* Medicaid.

Mansion Rest Home*
14 Rockland Ave, Malden, MA, 02148 (617)
322-4634
Admin Reta C Mackinnon.
Licensure Rest Home. *Beds* 27. *Certified* Medicaid.

McFadden Memorial Manor*
341 Forest St, Malden, MA, 02148 (617)
322-1700
Admin Harry E Munro.
Licensure Intermediate Care. *Beds* 61. *Certified* Medicaid.

San Fillipe Rest Home
53 James St, Malden, MA, 02148 (617) 324-7233
Admin Carol A Wallace.
Licensure Rest Home. *Beds* 17.
Staff LPNs 2 (pt); Nurses aides 2 (ft), 5 (pt); Activities coordinators 1 (pt); Dietitians 1 (pt).
Facilities Activities room.
Activities Arts and Crafts; Cards; Games; Reading groups; Prayer groups; Shopping trips; Dances/Social or cultural gatherings.

MANCHESTER

Oakwood Nursing Home*
601 Summer St, Manchester, MA, 01944 (617) 526-4653
Admin Joanne E O'Day.
Licensure Intermediate Care. *Beds* 29. *Certified* Medicaid.

White Gables Rest Home
807 Summer St, Manchester, MA, 01944 (617) 526-4905
Admin Kevin J Grady.
Licensure Rest Home. *Beds* 25.
Staff RNs 1 (pt); LPNs 1 (pt); Nurses aides 4 (ft), 6 (pt); Recreational therapists 1 (pt); Activities coordinators 1 (pt); Dietitians 1 (pt).
Facilities Dining room; Activities room; Chapel; Crafts room; Laundry room; Barber/Beauty shop; Library; Living rooms.
Activities Arts and Crafts; Cards; Games; Reading groups; Prayer groups; Movies; Shopping trips; Dances/Social or cultural gatherings; Sightseeing bus tours; Gardening, flower and vegetable.
Description The facility is located in the seaside community of Manchester by the Sea with direct ocean views from many of our private and semi-private rooms; well-manicured grounds with extensive flowering trees, flower beds, and vegetable gardens.

MARBLEHEAD

Devereux Nursing Home Inc
39 Lafayette St, Marblehead, MA, 01945 (617) 631-6120
Admin Everett M Hoffman. *Medical Dir/Dir of Nursing* Dr Elliot Strauss.
Licensure Skilled Care. *Beds* 64. *Certified* Medicaid; Medicare.
Admissions Requirements Minimum age 25; Medical examination; Physician's request.
Staff Physicians 13 (pt); RNs 9 (ft); LPNs 7 (ft); Nurses aides 19 (ft), 18 (pt); Physical therapists 1 (pt); Reality therapists 1 (ft), 2 (pt); Recreational therapists 1 (ft), 2 (pt); Occupational therapists 1 (pt); Speech therapists 1 (pt); Dietitians 1 (pt); Dentists 4 (pt); Ophthalmologists 2 (pt); Podiatrists 3 (pt).
Facilities Dining room; Physical therapy room; Activities room; Chapel; Crafts room; Laundry room; Barber/Beauty shop; Library; Patio.
Activities Arts and Crafts; Cards; Games; Reading groups; Prayer groups; Movies; Shopping trips.
Description This facility is approved for Medicare, Medicaid, BC/BS, and PIC. Also, approved by JCAH.

Lafayette Convalescent Home*
25 Lafayette St, Marblehead, MA, 01945 (617) 631-4535
Admin Beatrice G Breitstein.
Licensure Skilled Care; Intermediate Care.
Beds 62. *Certified* Medicaid.

MARLBOROUGH

Braemoor East of Marlboro Nursing Home
400 Bolton St, Marlborough, MA, 01752 (617) 481-6123
Admin Richard B Plasmati. *Medical Dir/Dir of Nursing* Prakash Patel MD.
Licensure Skilled Care; Intermediate Care.
Beds 160. *Certified* Medicaid.
Admissions Requirements Medical examination; Physician's request.
Facilities Dining room; Physical therapy room; Activities room; Chapel; Crafts room; Laundry room; Barber/Beauty shop.
Activities Arts and Crafts; Cards; Games; Reading groups; Movies; Shopping trips.

Braemoor of Marlborough Nursing Home
121 Northboro Rd, Marlborough, MA, 01752 (617) 485-4040
Admin Scott D Ullrich. *Medical Dir/Dir of Nursing* A Michele Ricard MD.
Licensure Skilled Care; Intermediate Care.
Beds 196. *Certified* Medicaid; Medicare.
Admissions Requirements Minimum age 21; Medical examination; Physician's request.
Staff RNs 10 (ft), 5 (pt); LPNs 15 (ft), 10 (pt); Orderlies 4 (ft), 2 (pt); Nurses aides 50 (ft), 25 (pt); Physical therapists 1 (ft); Recreational therapists 1 (ft), 3 (pt); Activities coordinators 1 (ft); Dietitians 1 (pt).
Facilities Dining room; Physical therapy room; Activities room; Chapel; Crafts room; Laundry room; Barber/Beauty shop; Library.
Activities Arts and Crafts; Cards; Games; Reading groups; Prayer groups; Movies; Shopping trips; Dances/Social or cultural gatherings.
Description At Braemoor, the emphasis is on rehabilitation. Physical, occupational, and speech therapy programs and restorative nursing programs help residents reach their fullest potential, even if they cannot go home.

Pine Grove Rest Home
455 Northboro Rd, Marlborough, MA, 01752 (617) 481-6562
Admin Alice M McGee. *Medical Dir/Dir of Nursing* Dr C Levin.
Licensure Rest Home. *Beds* 28.
Admissions Requirements Minimum age 25; Males only; Medical examination; Physician's request.
Staff RNs 1 (ft); Nurses aides 4 (ft); Recreational therapists 1 (pt).
Languages French, Spanish
Facilities Dining room; Activities room; Crafts room; Laundry room; Library.
Activities Arts and Crafts; Cards; Games; Movies; Shopping trips; Dances/Social or cultural gatherings; Holiday parties; Bingo.
Description Facility has a clean home-like environment; residents may have a regular garden with flowers; swimming pool; nice dining area; trips out to dinners and special events; bowling; shopping center nearby.

MASHPEE

Pilgrim's Pride Nursing Home
Rt 28 at Noisy Hole Rd, Mashpee, MA, 02649 (617) 477-1310
Admin Shirley Nadelman. *Medical Dir/Dir of Nursing* Mary A Ravin MD.
Licensure Intermediate Care. *Beds* 120. *Certified* Medicaid.
Admissions Requirements Minimum age 21; Medical examination; Physician's request.
Staff Physicians 1 (pt); RNs 5 (ft), 1 (pt); LPNs 6 (ft), 5 (pt); Nurses aides 30 (ft), 15 (pt); Activities coordinators 2 (ft); Dietitians 1 (pt); Podiatrists 1 (pt).
Facilities Dining room; Physical therapy room; Activities room; Chapel; Crafts room; Laundry room; Barber/Beauty shop; Library; Dental office.
Activities Arts and Crafts; Cards; Games; Reading groups; Prayer groups; Movies; Shopping trips; Dances/Social or cultural gatherings; Field trips.
Description Besides providing excellent nursing care, Pilgrims Pride Nursing Home has won numerous awards for outstanding activities program with forty active volunteers, emphasis is put on having the residents participate in activities in the community as much as possible.

MATTAPOISETT

Mattapoisett Nursing Home
79 North St, Mattapoisett, MA, 02739 (617) 758-2512
Admin Norman L Turcotte.
Licensure Intermediate Care. *Beds* 42. *Certified* Medicaid.
Admissions Requirements Minimum age 21; Medical examination; Physician's request.
Staff RNs 1 (ft), 5 (pt); LPNs 1 (ft), 1 (pt); Nurses aides 10 (ft), 14 (pt); Activities coordinators 1 (pt); Dietitians 1 (pt).
Facilities Dining room; Activities room; Laundry room.
Activities Arts and Crafts; Cards; Games; Reading groups; Prayer groups; Movies; Shopping trips; Dances/Social or cultural gatherings.
Description Facility offers excellent nursing care, good food, and clean environment in a family setting.

MEDFIELD

Med-Vale Nursing Home*
519 Main St, Medfield, MA, 02052 (617) 359-6050
Admin Frances Perlmutter.
Licensure Intermediate Care. *Beds* 49. *Certified* Medicaid.
Facilities Activities room; Laundry room.
Activities Arts and Crafts; Cards; Games; Prayer groups; Movies; Dances/Social or cultural gatherings; Dinner out; Foliage trips; Trips to the beach; Bowling.
Description Facility features a pet therapy program.

MEDFORD

Emery Retirement and Convalescent Home*
34 Grove St, Medford, MA, 02155 (617)
488-7117
Admin Thomas J McNulty Jr.
Licensure Intermediate Care. *Beds* 31. *Certified* Medicaid.

Magoun Manor Nursing Home
68 Magoun Ave, Medford, MA, 02155 (617)
488-7117
Admin Mary J Tomlinson.
Licensure Intermediate Care. *Beds* 29. *Certified* Medicaid.
Admissions Requirements Medical examination; Physician's request.
Staff RNs; LPNs; Nurses aides; Recreational therapists; Activities coordinators; Dietitians.
Facilities Dining room; Activities room; Crafts room; Laundry room.
Activities Arts and Crafts; Cards; Games; Reading groups; Prayer groups; Movies; Shopping trips; Dances/Social or cultural gatherings; Bowling; Life program.
Description Excellent intermediate care offered in a safe and comfortable home for men and women.

Medford Rest Home
2 Central St, Medford, MA, 02155 (617)
391-4741
Admin Mary Jane Allen.
Licensure Rest Home. *Beds* 28. *Certified* Medicaid.
Staff Physicians 3 (pt); RNs 1 (pt); Activities coordinators 1 (pt); Dietitians 1 (pt).
Facilities Dining room; Crafts room; Laundry room.
Activities Arts and Crafts; Movies.

Rest Haven Nursing Home*
96 Mystic St, Medford, MA, 02155 (617)
396-3632
Admin David A Niles.
Licensure Intermediate Care. *Beds* 33. *Certified* Medicaid.

Winthrop House Nursing Home*
300 Winthrop St, Medford, MA, 02155 (617)
396-4400
Admin Martha B Armstrong.
Licensure Skilled Care; Intermediate Care. *Beds* 142. *Certified* Medicaid.

MEDWAY

Mary-land Rest Home
17 Holliston St, Medway, MA, 02053 (617)
533-2900
Admin Gertrude A O'Connor.
Licensure Intermediate Care. *Beds* 32. *Certified* Medicaid.
Admissions Requirements Minimum age 35; Medical examination.
Staff RNs 1 (pt); Nurses aides 3 (ft), 7 (pt); Activities coordinators 1 (pt).
Facilities Dining room.
Activities Arts and Crafts; Cards; Games; Reading groups; Prayer groups; Movies; Shopping trips; Parties; Cookouts.

Medway Country Manor Nursing Home*
Holliston St, Medway, MA, 02053 (617)
533-6634
Admin John Peters.
Licensure Skilled Care; Intermediate Care. *Beds* 82. *Certified* Medicaid.

MELROSE

Elmhurst Nursing and Retirement Home*
743 Main St, Melrose, MA, 02176 (617)
622-7500
Admin Joanne E O'Day.
Licensure Intermediate Care. *Beds* 43. *Certified* Medicaid.

The Fitch Home Inc
75 Lake Ave, Melrose, MA, 02176 (617)
665-0521 and 665-0522
Admin Joyce M Lamb.
Licensure Rest Home. *Beds* 30.
Admissions Requirements Minimum age 65; Medical examination.
Staff Physicians 1 (pt); RNs 1 (ft); LPNs 4 (pt); Nurses aides 1 (ft), 4 (pt); Activities coordinators 1 (pt); Dietitians 1 (pt); Podiatrists 1 (pt).
Facilities Dining room; Activities room; Crafts room; Laundry room; Barber/Beauty shop; Library.
Activities Games; Movies; Shopping trips.
Description Facility offers retirement living accomodations for those who are not able or do not wish to maintain their own private residence; provides meals, laundry, housekeeping and emergency nursing care. Home is maintained as a private residence with all rooms private.

Mackenzie Nursing Home Inc*
24 Vine St, Melrose, MA, 02176 (617)
665-4419
Admin Melvin Silverman.
Licensure Intermediate Care. *Beds* 29. *Certified* Medicaid.

Middlesex Fells Nursing Home
40 Martin St, Melrose, MA, 02176 (617)
665-7050
Admin Charles A Holden Jr. *Medical Dir/Dir of Nursing* Dr Robert Holden.
Licensure Skilled Care; Intermediate Care. *Beds* 106. *Certified* Medicaid; Medicare.
Admissions Requirements Medical examination.
Staff Physicians 3 (pt); RNs 13 (ft), 10 (pt); LPNs 4 (ft), 2 (pt); Orderlies 1 (ft); Nurses aides 20 (ft), 26 (pt); Physical therapists 2 (pt); Occupational therapists 1 (pt); Speech therapists 1 (pt); Activities coordinators 1 (ft), 1 (pt); Dietitians 1 (pt); Dentists 1 (pt); Podiatrists 1 (pt); Audiologists 1 (pt).
Facilities Dining room; Physical therapy room; Activities room; Crafts room; Laundry room; Barber/Beauty shop.
Activities Arts and Crafts; Cards; Games; Reading groups; Prayer groups; Movies; Shopping trips.
Description Facility offers respite care services in a new program called the Visiting Resident Program.

Normandy House Nursing Home*
15 Green St, Melrose, MA, 02176 (617)
665-3950
Admin Bonnie-Jean McLean.
Licensure Skilled Care; Intermediate Care. *Beds* 82. *Certified* Medicaid.

Oosterman Rest Home*
93 Laurel St, Melrose, MA, 02176 (617)
665-3188
Admin Troy Oosterman.
Licensure Rest Home. *Beds* 20.

Tuell Nursing Home Inc
92 Franklin St, Melrose, MA, 02176 (617)
665-0764
Admin Francis J Cummings.
Licensure Intermediate Care. *Beds* 28. *Certified* Medicaid.
Admissions Requirements Females only
Staff RNs 11 (ft), 2 (pt); LPNs 1 (ft), 3 (pt); Nurses aides 5 (ft), 14 (pt); Physical therapists 1 (pt); Activities coordinators 1 (pt); Dietitians 1 (pt).
Facilities Dining room; Activities room.

METHUEN

Blenwood Nursing Home*
302 Broadway, Methuen, MA, 01844 (617)
682-8113
Admin Marion A Thisse.
Licensure Intermediate Care. *Beds* 41. *Certified* Medicaid.

Broadway Convalescent Home*
281 Broadway, Methuen, MA, 01844 (617)
682-5373
Admin Linda E Weldon.
Licensure Skilled Care; Intermediate Care. *Beds* 52. *Certified* Medicaid.

Halcyon House Rest Home
175 Berkeley St, Methuen, MA, 01844 (617)
685-5505
Admin Elizabeth L Bonde.
Licensure Rest Home. *Beds* 20.
Staff LPNs 1 (pt); Nurses aides 10 (ft); Physical therapists 1 (pt); Speech therapists 1 (pt); Activities coordinators 1 (pt); Dietitians 1 (pt); Podiatrists 1 (pt).
Facilities Dining room; Activities room.
Activities Arts and Crafts; Cards; Games; Reading groups; Movies; Shopping trips.

Henry C Nevins Home Inc*
10 Ingalls Ct, Methuen, MA, 01844 (617)
682-7611
Admin Kenneth C Mermer.
Licensure Charitable Home. *Beds* 133. *Certified* Medicaid.

McGowan Nursing Home*
489 Prospect St, Methuen, MA, 01844 (617)
682-4342
Admin Mary R Kim.
Licensure Intermediate Care. *Beds* 41. *Certified* Medicaid.

Methuen House Nursing and Convalescent Center*
480 Jackson St, Methuen, MA, 01844 (617) 686-3906
Admin Joseph O'Rourke.
Licensure Skilled Care; Intermediate Care.
Beds 101. *Certified* Medicaid.

MIDDLEBORO

Fair Havens Rest Home
334 Marion Rd, Middleboro, MA, 02346 (617) 947-1660
Admin Ann Potwin.
Licensure Rest Home. *Beds* 28.
Admissions Requirements Minimum age 21.
Staff LPNs 2 (ft); Nurses aides 10 (ft), 10 (pt); Reality therapists 1 (ft); Recreational therapists 1 (ft); Activities coordinators 1 (ft).
Affiliation Lutheran
Facilities Dining room; Activities room; Chapel; Crafts room; Laundry room; Barber/Beauty shop; Library.
Activities Arts and Crafts; Cards; Games; Reading groups; Prayer groups; Movies; Shopping trips; Dances/Social or cultural gatherings.
Description Facility offers unique opportunity for full-time pet therapy with both cats and dogs; family-style dining. Residents are encouraged to maintain independence and individuality.

Greenlawn Nursing Home
14 E Grove St, Middleboro, MA, 02346 (617) 947-1172
Admin Shirley and Warren Dionne.
Licensure Intermediate Care. *Beds* 47. *Certified* Medicaid.
Admissions Requirements Medical examination.
Staff Physicians; RNs; LPNs; Nurses aides; Physical therapists; Reality therapists; Recreational therapists; Occupational therapists; Speech therapists; Activities coordinators; Dietitians; Dentists; Ophthalmologists; Podiatrists; Audiologists.
Facilities Dining room; Activities room; Laundry room; Barber/Beauty shop.
Activities Arts and Crafts; Cards; Games; Reading groups; Prayer groups; Movies; Shopping trips; Dances/Social or cultural gatherings.
Description Greenlawn is a "home with a heart" which is shown in the individual care given to all residents.

MIDDLEBOROUGH

Alpha Village Long Term Care Facility*
312 Marion Rd, Middleborough, MA, 02346 (617) 947-0095
Admin Ora Mae Torres.
Licensure Intermediate Care. *Beds* 50. *Certified* Medicaid.

Forest Manor Long Term Care Facility
Isaac St, Middleborough, MA, 02346 (617) 947-9295
Admin Peter B Brown Jr. *Medical Dir/Dir of Nursing* Sylvio Landry MD.
Licensure Skilled Care; Intermediate Care.
Beds 124. *Certified* Medicaid; Medicare.

Facilities Dining room; Physical therapy room; Activities room; Crafts room; Laundry room; Barber/Beauty shop.
Activities Arts and Crafts; Cards; Games; Reading groups; Prayer groups; Dances/Social or cultural gatherings.

Hannah B G Shaw Home for the Aged Inc
299 Wareham St, PO Box 390, Middleborough, MA, 02346 (617) 947-0332
Admin Lenore Baldwin.
Licensure Home for the Aged. *Beds* 50.

Middleboro Rest Home
5 Barrows St, Middleborough, MA, 02346 (617) 947-4120
Admin Roger L Plante.
Licensure Rest Home. *Beds* 17.
Staff Physicians 1 (pt); RNs 6 (pt); Nurses aides 2 (ft), 2 (pt); Recreational therapists 1 (pt); Dietitians 1 (pt); Dentists 1 (pt); Podiatrists 1 (pt).
Facilities Dining room; Activities room; Laundry room.
Activities Arts and Crafts; Cards; Games; Reading groups; Prayer groups; Shopping trips; Dances/Social or cultural gatherings.
Description Residents treated as family by dedicated staff. Facility is located ¼ mile from the downtown area and residents may walk as often as desired. Activities director plans outings where all residents go outside the home twice a month.

Oak Hill Nursing Home*
76 North St, Middleborough, MA, 02346 (617) 947-4775
Admin Frances G Comeau. *Medical Dir/Dir of Nursing* Bernard Beuthner.
Licensure Skilled Care; Intermediate Care.
Beds 126. *Certified* Medicaid; Medicare.
Facilities Dining room; Physical therapy room; Activities room; Crafts room; Laundry room; Barber/Beauty shop; Library.
Activities Arts and Crafts; Cards; Games; Reading groups; Prayer groups; Movies; Dances/Social or cultural gatherings.

Susan Welch Rest Home
98 S Main St, Middleborough, MA, 02346 (617) 947-2155
Admin Marion F Pattison.
Licensure Rest Home. *Beds* 24.
Admissions Requirements Medical examination; Physician's request.
Staff LPNs 1 (ft), 3 (pt); Activities coordinators 1 (pt); Dietitians 1 (pt).
Facilities Dining room; Activities room; Laundry room.
Activities Arts and Crafts; Cards; Games; Prayer groups; Movies; Shopping trips.

MILFORD

Blair House LTCF of Milford
20 Claflin St, Milford, MA, 01757 (617) 473-1272
Admin Eileen M Hegarty. *Medical Dir/Dir of Nursing* Dr Faheem Farooq.
Licensure Skilled Care. *Beds* 61. *Certified* Medicaid; Medicare.
Admissions Requirements Minimum age 21;

Medical examination; Physician's request.
Staff RNs 4 (ft), 4 (pt); LPNs 3 (ft), 2 (pt); Nurses aides 11 (ft), 14 (pt); Physical therapists 1 (pt); Occupational therapists 1 (pt); Speech therapists 1 (pt); Activities coordinators 1 (ft); Dietitians 1 (pt); Dentists 1 (pt); Podiatrists 1 (pt).
Facilities Dining room; Physical therapy room; Activities room; Barber/Beauty shop.
Activities Cards; Games; Prayer groups; Movies; Dances/Social or cultural gatherings; Bowling; Cookouts.

Milford Manor Rest Home Inc
16 Claflin St, Milford, MA, 01757 (617) 473-2896
Admin Kalidas R Patel.
Licensure Rest Home. *Beds* 27.
Admissions Requirements Minimum age 30; Medical examination; Physician's request.
Staff Physicians 2 (pt); LPNs 1 (pt); Nurses aides 4 (ft), 4 (pt); Activities coordinators 1 (ft); Dietitians 1 (pt); Podiatrists 1 (pt).
Facilities Dining room; Activities room; Crafts room; Laundry room.
Activities Arts and Crafts; Cards; Games; Reading groups; Prayer groups; Shopping trips; Dances/Social or cultural gatherings.
Description Milford Manor is a rest home converted from the old Harris Mansion. It sits on a hill overlooking the town with 13 lovely patients rooms and a large backyard picnic area, close to town; offers a good activity program and home-style cooking.

Milford PMI
Countryside Dr, Milford, MA, 01757 (617) 473-0435
Admin Michael R Smith.
Licensure Skilled Care; Intermediate Care.
Beds 73. *Certified* Medicaid.

MILLBURY

Pine Grove Villa Nursing Home*
Rhodes St, Millbury, MA, 01527 (617) 865-2572
Admin Ruth M Duplisea.
Licensure Intermediate Care. *Beds* 41. *Certified* Medicaid.

Smith Nursing Home*
29 Main St, Millbury, MA, 01527 (617) 865-6825
Admin Anthony E Penny.
Licensure Skilled Care; Intermediate Care.
Beds 44. *Certified* Medicaid.

MILLIS

Four Seasons Rest Home*
71 Union St, Millis, MA, 02054 (617) 376-5083
Admin Gabriel Gabrielli.
Licensure Rest Home. *Beds* 34.

MILTON

Milton Health Care Facility*
1200 Brush Mill Rd, Milton, MA, 02186 (617) 333-0600

Admin Donald Gresh.
Licensure Skilled Care; Intermediate Care.
Beds SNF 40; ICF 40.

MONSON

Buckwell Rest Home*
300 Main St, Monson, MA, 01057 (413)
267-9285
Admin Donna Swist.
Licensure Rest Home. *Beds* 17.

MONTGOMERY

Mountain View Nursing Home
Rt 1, Montgomery, MA, 01085 (413) 562-0097
Admin Mary Uschmann.
Licensure Intermediate Care. *Beds* 27. *Certified* Medicaid.

NAHANT

Jesmond Nursing Home*
271 Nahant Rd, Nahant, MA, 01908 (617)
581-0420
Admin Rosemary C Costin.
Licensure Skilled Care; Intermediate Care.
Beds 57. *Certified* Medicaid.

Rockledge Manor Nursing Home
162 Willow Rd, Nahant, MA, 01908 (617)
581-0249
Admin Robert D Brennan.
Licensure Intermediate Care. *Beds* 43. *Certified* Medicaid.

NANTUCKET

Our Island Home*
E Creek Rd, Nantucket, MA, 02554 (617)
228-0462
Admin Mark R Ellsworth.
Licensure Intermediate Care. *Beds* 45. *Certified* Medicaid.

NATICK

Brittany Convalescent Home
168 W Central St, Natick, MA, 01760 (617)
655-1000
Admin Jonathan Shadovitz. *Medical Dir/Dir of Nursing* Edward Hoffer.
Licensure Skilled Care; Intermediate Care.
Beds 120. *Certified* Medicaid.
Admissions Requirements Minimum age 65; Medical examination; Physician's request.
Staff RNs 3 (ft), 8 (pt); LPNs 3 (ft), 2 (pt); Orderlies 1 (pt); Nurses aides 16 (ft), 14 (pt); Physical therapists 1 (pt); Reality therapists 1 (pt); Recreational therapists 1 (pt); Occupational therapists 1 (pt); Speech therapists 1 (pt); Activities coordinators 1 (ft), 2 (pt); Dietitians 1 (pt); Dentists 1 (pt); Ophthalmologists 1 (pt); Podiatrists 1 (pt); Audiologists 1 (pt).
Facilities Dining room; Physical therapy room; Activities room; Crafts room; Laundry room; Barber/Beauty shop; Library.
Activities Arts and Crafts; Cards; Games; Reading groups; Prayer groups; Movies; Shop-

ping trips; Dances/Social or cultural gatherings.
Description Facility provides multi-level care, skilled, intermediate, and retirement care; in-house psycho-neurological services; modern physical plant, access to public transportation and convenient to shopping centers; corporate professional consulting services; volunteer training program; clergy involvement; rotating seasonal menu schedules; 3 miles equidistant to 2 major hospitals.

Hanson Nursing Home*
30 Pleasant St, Natick, MA, 01760 (617)
653-1543
Admin Robert L Douglas.
Licensure Intermediate Care. *Beds* 13. *Certified* Medicaid.

Natick Nursing Home
34 Lincoln St, Natick, MA, 01760 (617)
653-8330
Admin Marilyn H Morgan.
Licensure Intermediate Care. *Beds* 56. *Certified* Medicaid.
Staff RNs 1 (ft), 1 (pt); LPNs 4 (ft); Nurses aides 15 (ft); Activities coordinators 1 (ft), 1 (pt); Dietitians 1 (pt).
Facilities Dining room; Activities room; Laundry room.
Activities Arts and Crafts; Cards; Games; Reading groups; Movies; Shopping trips; Dances/Social or cultural gatherings; Drama Club takes musicals to other homes and hospitals.
Description Facility staff believes in and supports residents' continued inner growth through community spirit, which encourages their giving of their renewed and newly developing talents (in drama, creative poetry, etc.) to one another and the outside community.

Nims Rest Home
38 Fiske St, Natick, MA, 01760 (617) 653-0382
Admin Helen Nims. *Medical Dir/Dir of Nursing* Muriel Baim.
Licensure Rest Home. *Beds* 21.
Admissions Requirements Minimum age 35; Medical examination; Physician's request.
Staff RNs 1 (pt); Nurses aides 4 (ft); Dietitians 1 (ft); Podiatrists 1 (pt).
Facilities Dining room; Activities room; Laundry room.
Activities Arts and Crafts; Cards; Games; Prayer groups; Shopping trips; Dances/Social or cultural gatherings; A group comes the first of every month for singing and prayers.
Description Residents' swim June through September in supervised pool; also, weekly visits to senior center to have lunch, play bingo, and enjoy arts and crafts. We plan trips to different parks and amusements, all expenses paid by owner.

Phillips House Nursing Home
10 Phillips St, Natick, MA, 01760 (617)
653-1543
Admin Robert L Douglas.
Licensure Intermediate Care. *Beds* 9.

White Gables Rest Home of Natick*
50 Pleasant St, Natick, MA, 01760 (617)
653-2733
Admin Jean Sprague.
Licensure Rest Home. *Beds* 12.

NEEDHAM

Briarwood Healthcare Nursing Home*
26 Garfield St, Needham, MA, 02192 (617)
449-4040
Admin Shirley Platt.
Licensure Skilled Care; Intermediate Care.
Beds 120. *Certified* Medicaid.

Daystar Home
1180 Great Plain Ave, Needham, MA, 02192
(617) 449-1149
Admin Ethel F Blettner.
Licensure Rest Home. *Beds* 20.

Hamilton House Nursing Home*
141 Chestnut St, Needham, MA, 02192 (617)
444-9114
Admin Anita M Chevrette. *Medical Dir/Dir of Nursing* John Fernald MD and Asha Wallace MD.
Licensure Skilled Care; Intermediate Care.
Beds 80. *Certified* Medicaid; Medicare.
Admissions Requirements Minimum age 21.
Staff RNs 6 (ft), 9 (pt); LPNs 2 (ft), 2 (pt); Orderlies 1 (ft); Nurses aides 18 (ft), 34 (pt).
Facilities Dining room; Physical therapy room; Activities room; Chapel; Crafts room; Laundry room; Barber/Beauty shop.
Activities Arts and Crafts; Cards; Games; Reading groups; Prayer groups; Movies; Shopping trips; Dances/Social or cultural gatherings.

NEW BEDFORD

Arbourway Rest Home*
875 Plainville Rd, New Bedford, MA, 02745
(617) 995-8229
Admin James A Casey.
Licensure Rest Home. *Beds* 24.

Blaire House LTCF of New Bedford*
397 County St, New Bedford, MA, 02740 (617)
997-9396
Admin John R Swanson.
Licensure Skilled Care; Intermediate Care.
Beds 123. *Certified* Medicaid; Medicare.

Bristol Nursing and Convalescent Home*
9 Pope St, New Bedford, MA, 02740 (617)
997-3358
Admin Ashley Clark.
Licensure Intermediate Care. *Beds* 73. *Certified* Medicaid.

The Cottage Rest Home*
434 Cottage St, New Bedford, MA, 02740 (617)
997-7678
Admin Teresa Ann Vieira.
Licensure Intermediate Care. *Beds* 13. *Certified* Medicaid.

Hallmark Nursing Home of New Bedford*
1123 Rockdale Ave, New Bedford, MA, 02740
(617) 997-7448
Admin William Moloney.
Licensure Skilled Care; Intermediate Care.
Beds 121. *Certified* Medicaid.

Havenwood Rest Home
251 Walnut St, New Bedford, MA, 02740 (617)
994-3120

Admin Donald L Di Santi.
Licensure Rest Home. *Beds* 41.
Admissions Requirements Minimum age 25; Medical examination.
Staff Physicians 2 (pt); LPNs 1 (pt); Nurses aides 4 (ft); Activities coordinators 1 (pt); Dietitians 1 (pt); Dentists 1 (pt); Podiatrists 1 (pt).
Facilities Dining room; Activities room; Laundry room.
Activities Arts and Crafts; Cards; Games; Shopping trips; Dances/Social or cultural gatherings.

Kristen Beth Nursing Home Inc
713 Shawmut Ave, New Bedford, MA, 02746 (617) 999-6456
Admin Irene C Awed. *Medical Dir/Dir of Nursing* Dr John Barnes.
Licensure Skilled Care; Intermediate Care.
Beds 93. *Certified* Medicaid.
Admissions Requirements Minimum age 21.
Staff RNs 6 (ft); LPNs 5 (ft), 2 (pt); Nurses aides 37 (ft); Physical therapists 1 (pt); Occupational therapists 1 (pt); Speech therapists 1 (pt); Dietitians 1 (pt); Dentists 1 (pt); Ophthalmologists 1 (pt); Podiatrists 1 (pt).
Facilities Dining room; Physical therapy room; Activities room; Crafts room; Laundry room; Barber/Beauty shop.
Activities Arts and Crafts; Cards; Games; Reading groups; Prayer groups; Movies; Shopping trips; Dances/Social or cultural gatherings.

New Bedford Jewish Convalescent Home*
200 Hawthorn St, New Bedford, MA, 02740 (617) 997-9314
Admin Estelle R Shanbrun.
Licensure Skilled Care; Intermediate Care.
Beds 80. *Certified* Medicaid; Medicare.
Affiliation Jewish

Rita's Rest Home*
49 Desautels St, New Bedford, MA, 02745 (617) 992-6074
Admin Rita Rouke.
Licensure Rest Home. *Beds* 10.

Rol-Ann Rest Home*
31 7th St, New Bedford, MA, 02740 (617) 996-1730
Admin Florence T Tavano.
Licensure Rest Home. *Beds* 17.

Sacred Heart Nursing Home
359 Summer St, New Bedford, MA, 02740 (617) 996-6751
Admin Beatrice Duchesne. *Medical Dir/Dir of Nursing* Dr William A Jeffrey.
Licensure Skilled Care; Intermediate Care.
Beds 217. *Certified* Medicaid.
Admissions Requirements Minimum age 65; Medical examination; Physician's request.
Staff Physicians 1 (pt); RNs 12 (ft), 4 (pt); LPNs 19 (ft), 8 (pt); Orderlies 1 (ft); Nurses aides 73 (ft), 25 (pt); Physical therapists 3 (ft), 1 (pt); Reality therapists 1 (ft), 2 (pt); Recreational therapists 3 (ft); Occupational therapists 1 (pt); Speech therapists 1 (pt); Activities coordinators 1 (pt); Dietitians 1 (pt); Dentists 1 (ft); Podiatrists 2 (pt).
Affiliation Roman Catholic
Facilities Dining room; Physical therapy room; Activities room; Chapel; Crafts room; Laundry

room; Barber/Beauty shop; Library.
Activities Arts and Crafts; Cards; Games; Reading groups; Prayer groups; Movies; Shopping trips; Dances/Social or cultural gatherings.
Description Facility has been recognized as being outstanding. Has had a data processing center for 3 years, in the process of implementing the total patient care plan on the system. Dental clinic installed in 1983.

Sassaquin Convalescent Home*
4586 Acushnet Ave, New Bedford, MA, 02745 (617) 998-1188
Admin Kenneth E Strong Jr.
Licensure Skilled Care; Intermediate Care.
Beds 120. *Certified* Medicaid.

Savoy Convalescent Home*
670 County St, New Bedford, MA, 02743 (617) 994-2400
Admin Nancy A Winer.
Licensure Skilled Care. *Beds* 39. *Certified* Medicaid.

Taber Street Nursing Home
19 Taber St, New Bedford, MA, 02740 (617) 997-0791
Admin Robin Churray. *Medical Dir/Dir of Nursing* Dr Barnes.
Licensure Intermediate Care. *Beds* 55. *Certified* Medicaid.
Staff RNs 4 (ft), 1 (pt); LPNs 3 (ft), 2 (pt); Nurses aides 17 (ft), 6 (pt); Activities coordinators 1 (pt); Dietitians 1 (pt).
Facilities Dining room; Activities room; Laundry room; Barber/Beauty shop.
Activities Arts and Crafts; Games; Movies; Dances/Social or cultural gatherings.

NEWBURYPORT

Brigham Manor Convalescent Home*
77 High St, Newburyport, MA, 01950 (617) 462-4221
Admin Brenda J Page.
Licensure Intermediate Care. *Beds* 64. *Certified* Medicaid.

Country Manor Convalescent Home
180 Low St, Newburyport, MA, 01950 (617) 465-5361
Admin James R Thomason.
Licensure Skilled Care; Intermediate Care.
Beds 123. *Certified* Medicaid.
Facilities Dining room; Physical therapy room; Activities room; Chapel; Laundry room; Barber/Beauty shop.
Activities Arts and Crafts; Games; Reading groups; Prayer groups; Movies; Shopping trips.

Newburyport Manor Nursing Home
351 High St, Newburyport, MA, 01950 (617) 462-6669
Admin Sidney Bleeker.
Licensure Intermediate Care. *Beds* 68. *Certified* Medicaid.

Newburyport Society Home for Aged Men
361 High St, Newburyport, MA, 01950 (617) 465-7091
Admin Patricia C Messinger.
Licensure Rest Home. *Beds* 9.

Admissions Requirements Minimum age 65; Males only; Medical examination.
Staff RNs; Nurses aides; Dietitians.
Facilities Dining room; Activities room; Laundry room.
Description Facility serves the area giving supportive care; residents must be ambulatory and come to dining room for meals; family-like atmosphere.

Newburyport Society Home for Aged Women*
75 High St, Newburyport, MA, 01950 (617) 465-7102
Admin Edna Roaf.
Licensure Charitable Home. *Beds* 10.

Port Manor Nursing Home*
Hale and Low Sts, Newburyport, MA, 01950 (617) 462-7373
Admin David Madigan.
Licensure Skilled Care. *Beds* 102.

NEWTON

Baptist Home of Massachusetts
66 Commonwealth Ave, Newton, MA, 02167 (617) 969-9380
Admin Cathy B Smith. *Medical Dir/Dir of Nursing* Allen Ergel MD.
Licensure Intermediate Care. *Beds* 131. *Certified* Medicaid.
Admissions Requirements Minimum age 65; Medical examination.
Staff Physicians 1 (pt); RNs 7 (ft), 1 (pt); LPNs 3 (ft), 4 (pt); Orderlies 1 (pt); Nurses aides 21 (ft), 4 (pt); Physical therapists 1 (pt); Recreational therapists 1 (ft); Occupational therapists 1 (pt); Activities coordinators 1 (ft), 1 (pt); Dietitians 1 (pt); Dentists 1 (pt); Ophthalmologists 1 (pt); Podiatrists 1 (pt); Audiologists 1 (pt).
Affiliation Baptist
Facilities Dining room; Activities room; Chapel; Crafts room; Laundry room; Barber/Beauty shop; Library.
Activities Arts and Crafts; Games; Reading groups; Prayer groups; Movies; Shopping trips; Dances/Social or cultural gatherings; Field trips.

Braeburn Nursing Home
20 Kinmonth Rd, Newton, MA, 02168 (617) 332-8481
Admin Peter H DiFoggio. *Medical Dir/Dir of Nursing* Roberta S Golledge.
Licensure Intermediate Care. *Beds* 84. *Certified* Medicaid.
Admissions Requirements Minimum age 40; Medical examination.
Staff RNs 4 (ft), 3 (pt); LPNs 2 (ft), 4 (pt); Nurses aides 23 (ft), 9 (pt); Recreational therapists 1 (ft); Activities coordinators 1 (ft); Dietitians 1 (pt); Dentists 1 (pt); Ophthalmologists 1 (pt); Podiatrists 2 (pt).
Facilities Dining room; Physical therapy room; Activities room; Chapel; Crafts room; Laundry room; Barber/Beauty shop; Library.
Activities Arts and Crafts; Cards; Games; Reading groups; Prayer groups; Movies; Dances/Social or cultural gatherings.
Description Outstanding patient care in a moderatly-priced facility.

Burton Convalescent Home Corp*
11 Washington St, Newton, MA, 02158
(617)964-9342
Licensure Intermediate Care. *Beds* 30. *Certified* Medicaid.

Chetwynde Convalescent Home*
1660 Washington St, Newton, MA, 02165 (617)
244-1137
Admin Charlene B Ferriera.
Licensure Intermediate Care. *Beds* 27. *Certified* Medicaid.

Chetwynde Nursing Home*
1650 Washington St, Newton, MA, 02165 (617)
244-5407
Admin Eleanor B Lanoa.
Licensure Skilled Care; Intermediate Care.
Beds 75. *Certified* Medicaid.

Elliot Manor Nursing Home
25 Mechanic St, Newton, MA, 02164 (617)
527-1750
Admin Carl E Mueller. *Medical Dir/Dir of Nursing* Dr Carl Levison.
Licensure Intermediate Care. *Beds* 49. *Certified* Medicaid.
Admissions Requirements Minimum age 21;
Medical examination; Medical examination.
Staff RNs 2 (ft), 3 (pt); LPNs 1 (ft), 2 (pt);
Nurses aides 10 (ft), 12 (pt); Activities coordinators; Dietitians.

Garland Rest Home*
217 Bellevue St, Newton, MA, 02158 (617)
527-0381
Admin Rosemary Omelite.
Licensure Rest Home. *Beds* 9.

Heathwood Nursing Home*
188 Florence St, Newton, MA, 02167 (617)
332-4730
Admin Janet S Urdang.
Licensure Intermediate Care. *Beds* 74. *Certified* Medicaid.

Lakeview Rest Home
38 Lake Ave, Newton, MA, 02159 (617)
244-9179
Admin Joan Sterndale.
Licensure Rest Home. *Beds* 12.
Admissions Requirements Medical examination.
Staff Physicians 1 (pt); RNs 1 (pt); Nurses aides 12 (ft); Recreational therapists 1 (pt);
Activities coordinators 1 (pt); Dentists 1 (pt);
Podiatrists 1 (pt).
Activities Cards; Games; Movies.

Mediplex of Newton—Long Term Care Facility*
2101 Washington St, Newton, MA, 02162 (617)
969-4660
Admin Gerald S LaBourene.
Licensure Skilled Care; Intermediate Care.
Beds 190. *Certified* Medicaid.

Mount Ida Rest Home
32 Newtonville Ave, Newton, MA, 02158 (617)
527-5657
Admin Rita Casey.
Licensure Rest Home. *Beds* 18.
Admissions Requirements Minimum age 21;

Males only; Medical examination; Physician's request.
Staff Physicians; RNs; Orderlies; Nurses aides;
Activities coordinators; Dietitians.
Facilities Activities room; Laundry room.
Activities Cards; Games; Reading groups;
Movies; Shopping trips.
Description Facility features home-like atmosphere, excellent food, and loving care.

Newton Convalescent Home*
25 Armory St, Newton, MA, 02165 (617)
969-2300
Admin Annette Blackman.
Licensure Skilled Care; Intermediate Care.
Beds 123. *Certified* Medicaid.

Pelham House Nursing Home
45 Pelham St, Newton, MA, 02159 (617)
527-5833
Licensure Intermediate Care. *Beds* 18.
Staff RNs 3 (ft); LPNs 2 (ft), 2 (pt); Nurses aides 1 (ft), 2 (pt); Physical therapists 1 (pt);
Recreational therapists 1 (pt); Occupational therapists 1 (pt); Speech therapists 1 (pt);
Activities coordinators 1 (ft); Dietitians 1 (pt);
Dentists 1 (pt); Podiatrists 1 (pt).
Facilities Dining room; Activities room; Crafts room; Laundry room; Barber/Beauty shop;
Library.
Activities Arts and Crafts; Cards; Games;
Reading groups; Prayer groups; Movies; Shopping trips; Dances/Social or cultural gatherings.
Description Facility is community based in a home-like setting.

Stone Institution and Newton Home for Aged People
277 Elliott St, Newton, MA, 02164 (617)
527-0023
Admin Joan McMullin Luthy.
Licensure Rest Home. *Beds* 23.
Admissions Requirements Minimum age 65;
Medical examination.
Staff Physicians 1 (pt); RNs 1 (pt); LPNs 1
(pt); Nurses aides 5 (ft), 2 (pt); Dietitians 1 (pt);
Podiatrists 1 (pt).
Facilities Dining room; Activities room; Laundry room; Barber/Beauty shop; Library.
Activities Games; Movies; Teas.

Swedish Home for the Aged
206 Waltham St, Newton, MA, 02165 (617)
527-6566
Admin Mildred Lundstrom. *Medical Dir/Dir of Nursing* David W Duhone MD.
Licensure Charitable Home. *Beds* 30.
Admissions Requirements Minimum age 65.
Staff RNs 1 (pt); LPNs 1 (pt); Nurses aides 1 (ft), 2 (pt).
Facilities Dining room; Activities room; Barber/Beauty shop.
Activities Movies; Shopping trips; Exercise class.
Description This is a level IV retirement home.

Vanderklish Hall Nursing Home*
929 Beacon St, Newton, MA, 02159 (617)
244-5063
Admin Duncan Vanderklish.
Licensure Intermediate Care. *Beds* 22. *Certified* Medicaid.

NORTH ADAMS

Adams Nursing Home of North Adams*
Franklin St, North Adams, MA, 02147 (413)
664-6691
Admin Lucy C Bass.
Licensure Skilled Care; Intermediate Care.
Beds 83. *Certified* Medicaid.

Homestead Rest Home*
215 E Main St, North Adams, MA, 01247 (413)
663-6885
Admin Henry Dargie.
Licensure Rest Home. *Beds* 36.

Richardson Rest Home Inc*
767 S Church St, North Adams, MA, 01247
(413) 663-8035
Admin Ruth M Richardson.
Licensure Rest Home. *Beds* 26.

NORTH ANDOVER

Prescott House Nursing Home
140 Prescott St, North Andover, MA, 01845
(617) 685-8086
Admin Alan D Solomont. *Medical Dir/Dir of Nursing* Martin J Melia MD.
Licensure Skilled Care; Intermediate Care.
Beds 130. *Certified* Medicaid.
Admissions Requirements Minimum age 21.
Staff Physicians 1 (pt); RNs 5 (ft), 23 (pt);
LPNs 2 (ft), 11 (pt); Nurses aides 25 (ft), 21
(pt); Physical therapists 1 (pt); Recreational therapists 2 (ft); Occupational therapists 1 (pt);
Activities coordinators 1 (ft); Dietitians 1 (pt);
Podiatrists 1 (pt).
Facilities Dining room; Physical therapy room;
Activities room; Crafts room; Laundry room;
Barber/Beauty shop; Library.
Activities Arts and Crafts; Cards; Games;
Reading groups; Prayer groups; Movies; Shopping trips; Dances/Social or cultural gatherings.

Stevens Hall Long Term Care Facility
75 Park St, North Andover, MA, 01845 (617)
685-3372
Admin Timothy Barry. *Medical Dir/Dir of Nursing* Matthew Cushing MD.
Licensure Skilled Care; Intermediate Care.
Beds 122. *Certified* Medicaid; Medicare.
Admissions Requirements Minimum age 21.
Staff Physicians 1 (ft), 4 (pt); RNs 7 (ft), 12
(pt); LPNs 5 (ft), 4 (pt); Orderlies 2 (ft); Nurses aides 27 (ft), 13 (pt); Physical therapists 1 (ft);
Recreational therapists 1 (ft); Occupational therapists 1 (pt); Speech therapists 1 (pt);
Activities coordinators 1 (ft); Dietitians 1 (pt);
Dentists 1 (pt); Ophthalmologists 2 (pt); Podiatrists 2 (pt); Audiologists 1 (pt).
Facilities Dining room; Physical therapy room;
Activities room; Crafts room; Laundry room;
Barber/Beauty shop; Library; TV rooms; Sitting rooms.
Activities Arts and Crafts; Cards; Games;
Reading groups; Prayer groups; Movies; Shopping trips; Dances/Social or cultural gatherings;
Bowling; Happy hour; Traveling store; Various bus trips; Sunday ice cream; Parties; Morning coffee, tea, hot chocolate and donuts, English muffins.

NORTH ATTLEBORO

Madonna Manor
N Washington St, North Attleboro, MA, 02760
(617) 699-2740
Admin Sr M Thomas More. *Medical Dir/Dir of Nursing* J Allen Bryer MD.
Licensure Skilled Care; Intermediate Care.
Beds 121. *Certified* Medicaid.
Admissions Requirements Minimum age 65; Medical examination.
Staff RNs 6 (ft), 9 (pt); LPNs 4 (ft), 10 (pt); Orderlies 2 (ft); Nurses aides 10 (ft), 30 (pt); Physical therapists 1 (ft); Recreational therapists 1 (ft), 3 (pt); Activities coordinators 1 (ft), 3 (pt); Dietitians 4 (ft), 12 (pt).
Affiliation Roman Catholic
Facilities Dining room; Physical therapy room; Activities room; Chapel; Laundry room; Barber/Beauty shop; Library.
Activities Arts and Crafts; Cards; Games; Reading groups; Prayer groups; Movies; Shopping trips; Dances/Social or cultural gatherings.

NORTH EASTON

Stonehill Manor Nursing and Retirement Home
231 Main St, North Easton, MA, 02356 (617) 238-6511
Admin Ruth M St John. *Medical Dir/Dir of Nursing* Marilyn Sasserson.
Licensure Intermediate Care. *Beds* 26. *Certified* Medicaid.
Admissions Requirements Minimum age 21; Females only; Medical examination.
Staff Physicians 5 (pt); RNs 2 (pt); LPNs 5 (pt); Nurses aides 12 (pt); Physical therapists 1 (pt); Activities coordinators 1 (pt); Dietitians 1 (pt); Dentists 1 (pt); Ophthalmologists 1 (pt); Podiatrists 1 (pt).
Facilities Dining room; Activities room; Laundry room.
Activities Arts and Crafts; Cards; Games; Reading groups; Prayer groups; Movies; Shopping trips; Dances/Social or cultural gatherings.
Description Facility is on 1.7 gorgeous acres in beautiful, historic, small town; extremely family oriented, homey atmosphere; compassionate, loving care of all residents by a top notch staff.

NORTH HAMPTON

Hampshire Charitable Hospital*
Off River Rd, North Hampton, MA, 01053
(413) 584-8457
Admin Edwin Warner.
Licensure Skilled Care.

NORTH READING

Green Grove Convalescent Home*
134 North St, North Reading, MA, 01864 (617) 944-1107
Admin Donald Moody.
Licensure Skilled Care; Intermediate Care.
Beds 101. *Certified* Medicaid.

NORTHAMPTON

Florence Rest Home
29 N Main St, Northampton, MA, 01060 (413) 584-2418
Admin Marguerite Tuperkeizsis.
Licensure Rest Home. *Beds* 26.
Admissions Requirements Minimum age 21; Medical examination; Physician's request.
Staff Activities coordinators 1 (ft).
Facilities Dining room; Activities room; Laundry room; Porch/enclosed in winter with glass, screened in summer.
Activities Arts and Crafts; Cards; Games; Reading groups; Prayer groups; Movies; Shopping trips; Dances/Social or cultural gatherings.
Description Facilty features a suburban setting within walking distance to center of town and public transportation, a home-like atmosphere, and home cooking. Daily guidance and supervision routinely given as needed and quality supportive care provided 24 hours daily including medication and dietary supervision as well as assistance with personal hygiene and medical care plan.

Lathrop Home for Aged Women
215 South St, Northampton, MA, 01060 (413) 584-2865
Admin Elizabeth Gallant.
Licensure Rest Home. *Beds* 40.
Admissions Requirements Minimum age 65; Females only; Medical examination.
Staff RNs 2 (ft), 1 (pt); LPNs 4 (pt); Nurses aides 4 (ft), 3 (pt); Activities coordinators 1 (pt); Podiatrists 1 (pt).
Facilities Dining room; Activities room; Crafts room; Laundry room; Barber/Beauty shop; Library; Screened porch.
Activities Arts and Crafts; Games; Prayer groups; Shopping trips; Dances/Social or cultural gatherings.
Description Facility features private rooms in a lovely Victorian building within walking distance of Smith College and downtown Northampton.

Northampton Nursing Home Inc
737 Bridge Rd, Northampton, MA, 01060 (413) 586-3300
Admin A Benson Walen. *Medical Dir/Dir of Nursing* Bernard St John DO.
Licensure Skilled Care; Intermediate Care.
Beds 123. *Certified* Medicaid.
Admissions Requirements Minimum age 6 months; Medical examination; Physician's request.
Staff Physicians 1 (pt); RNs 16 (ft), 15 (pt); LPNs 12 (ft), 17 (pt); Nurses aides 20 (ft), 23 (pt); Physical therapists 3 (pt); Occupational therapists 2 (pt); Speech therapists 1 (pt); Activities coordinators 1 (ft), 1 (pt); Dietitians 1 (pt); Dentists 1 (pt); Podiatrists 3 (pt).
Facilities Dining room; Physical therapy room; Activities room; Chapel; Crafts room; Laundry room; Barber/Beauty shop; Library.
Activities Arts and Crafts; Cards; Games; Reading groups; Prayer groups; Movies; Shopping trips; Dances/Social or cultural gatherings.
Description Facility motto is "people caring for people."

PINE REST / NORTHBOROUGH

Pine Rest Nursing Home
5 Franklin St, Northampton, MA, 01060 (413) 584-2369
Admin Leon L Dickinson. *Medical Dir/Dir of Nursing* Donald B Rogers MD.
Licensure Intermediate Care. *Beds* 47. *Certified* Medicaid.
Staff RNs 1 (ft); LPNs 3 (ft), 2 (pt); Orderlies 2 (ft); Nurses aides 12 (ft), 6 (pt); Activities coordinators 1 (ft); Dietitians 1 (pt).
Facilities Dining room; Activities room; Library.
Activities Arts and Crafts; Cards; Games; Reading groups; Movies; Shopping trips; Dances/Social or cultural gatherings.

Pioneer Valley Nursing Home*
548 Elm St, Northampton, MA, 01060 (413) 586-3150
Admin John Mahoney.
Licensure Skilled Care; Intermediate Care.
Beds 123. *Certified* Medicaid; Medicare.

River Valley Rest Home
159 Pine St, Northampton, MA, 01060 (413) 584-3776
Admin Anita L Thompson. *Medical Dir/Dir of Nursing* Anna W Thompson.
Licensure Rest Home. *Beds* 29.
Admissions Requirements Medical examination.
Staff Nurses aides 1 (ft), 5 (pt); Activities coordinators 1 (ft).
Activities Arts and Crafts; Cards; Games.
Description Facility is situated in a small suburban village which provides for a quiet atmosphere as well as being close to many cultural events, medical facilities, and shopping centers. In support of these outside activities, River Valley is continually developing and expanding the activity program.

Rockridge—Laurel Park
25 Coles Meadow Rd, Northampton, MA, 01060 (413) 586-2902
Admin Dorothea Y Munro.
Licensure Rest Home. *Beds* 63.
Admissions Requirements Minimum age 65; Medical examination.
Staff RNs 2 (ft), 5 (pt); LPNs 1 (pt); Nurses aides 2 (ft), 7 (pt); Activities coordinators 1 (ft); Dietitians 1 (pt); Podiatrists 1 (pt).
Facilities Dining room; Activities room; Chapel; Crafts room; Laundry room; Barber/Beauty shop; Library.
Activities Arts and Crafts; Cards; Games; Reading groups; Prayer groups; Movies; Shopping trips; Dances/Social or cultural gatherings.
Description Situated on 12 acres of scenic woodlands, Rockridge provides outstanding retirement accomodations for men and women. Residents enjoy easy access to varied cultural and educational opportunities sponsored by Smith, Mount Holyoke, Amherst, and Hampshire Colleges, and the University of Massachusetts.

NORTHBOROUGH

Grangers Nursing Home
112 W Main St, Northborough, MA, 01532
(617) 393-2382

Admin Kathryn E Whitman. *Medical Dir/Dir of Nursing* Christian W Aussenheimer.
Licensure Skilled Care; Intermediate Care.
Beds 33. *Certified* Medicaid.
Admissions Requirements Minimum age 16.
Staff Physicians; RNs; LPNs; Nurses aides; Physical therapists; Reality therapists; Recreational therapists; Occupational therapists; Speech therapists; Activities coordinators; Dietitians; Dentists; Ophthalmologists; Podiatrists; Audiologists.
Facilities Dining room; Physical therapy room; Activities room; Crafts room; Laundry room; Barber/Beauty shop; Library.
Activities Arts and Crafts; Cards; Games; Reading groups; Prayer groups; Movies; Shopping trips; Dances/Social or cultural gatherings.

Northboro Rest Home*
238 W Main St, Northborough, MA, 01532
(617) 393-3304
Admin Edward F Thorton Jr.
Licensure Rest Home. *Beds* 20.

Thornton Nursing Home*
238 1/2 W Main St, Northborough, MA, 01532
(617) 393-2368
Admin Edward F Thornton Jr.
Licensure Skilled Care; Intermediate Care.
Beds 84. *Certified* Medicaid.

NORTHBRIDGE

Beaumont Nursing Home
85 Beaumont Dr, Northbridge, MA, 01534
(617) 234-9771
Admin Daniel J Salmon. *Medical Dir/Dir of Nursing* James Kuehan MD.
Licensure Skilled Care; Intermediate Care.
Beds 142. *Certified* Medicaid; Medicare.
Staff Physicians; RNs; LPNs; Orderlies; Nurses aides; Physical therapists; Recreational therapists; Occupational therapists; Speech therapists; Activities coordinators; Dietitians; Dentists; Ophthalmologists; Podiatrists; Audiologists.
Facilities Dining room; Physical therapy room; Activities room; Crafts room; Laundry room; Barber/Beauty shop; Library.

Northbridge Nursing and Retirement Home*
2356 Providence Rd, Northbridge, MA, 01534
(617) 234-8778
Admin Charles M Daley.
Licensure Intermediate Care. *Beds* 118. *Certified* Medicaid.

NORTON

Country Haven Nursing Home*
184 Mansfield Ave, Norton, MA, 02766 (617)
285-7745
Admin Thomas D Ward.
Licensure Skilled Care; Intermediate Care.
Beds 94. *Certified* Medicaid.

Daggett-Crandall-Newcomb Home
55 Newland St, Norton, MA, 02766 (617)
285-7944
Admin Cheryl J Larson. *Medical Dir/Dir of Nursing* Dr Craig Hobson.

Licensure Retirement Home. *Beds* 30.
Admissions Requirements Minimum age 65; Medical examination.
Staff Physicians 1 (ft); RNs 1 (ft), 2 (pt); LPNs 1 (ft), 4 (pt); Nurses aides 3 (ft), 5 (pt).
Facilities Dining room; Activities room; Laundry room; Barber/Beauty shop; Library.
Activities Arts and Crafts; Cards; Games; Shopping trips; Slides.

Old Colony Road Rest Home*
377 Old Colony Rd, Norton, MA, 02766 (617)
222-1074
Admin Robert J Devlin.
Licensure Rest Home. *Beds* 50.

NORWELL

Norwell Knoll Nursing Home
329 Washington St, Norwell, MA, 02061 (617)
659-4901
Admin Brian G Geany. *Medical Dir/Dir of Nursing* Dr Clifford Ward.
Licensure Skilled Care; Intermediate Care.
Beds 80. *Certified* Medicaid.
Admissions Requirements Medical examination; Physician's request.
Staff Physicians 22 (pt); RNs 7 (ft); LPNs 2 (ft); Nurses aides 32 (ft), 6 (pt); Physical therapists 1 (pt); Recreational therapists 1 (ft); Occupational therapists 1 (pt); Speech therapists 1 (pt); Activities coordinators 1 (ft); Dietitians 1 (pt); Dentists 1 (pt); Ophthalmologists 1 (pt); Podiatrists 1 (pt); Audiologists 1 (pt).
Facilities Dining room; Physical therapy room; Activities room; Chapel; Crafts room; Laundry room; Barber/Beauty shop.
Activities Arts and Crafts; Cards; Games; Reading groups; Prayer groups; Movies; Shopping trips; Dances/Social or cultural gatherings; Fashion shows.

Stetson Manor Nursing Home*
12 Barstow Ave, Norwell, MA, 02061 (617)
826-2311
Admin Martha Mello.
Licensure Intermediate Care. *Beds* 17. *Certified* Medicaid.

NORWOOD

Charlwell House Nursing Home
305 Walpole St, Norwood, MA, 02062 (617)
762-7700
Admin Lorraine M Ryan. *Medical Dir/Dir of Nursing* Prya Nandi MD.
Licensure Skilled Care; Intermediate Care.
Beds 124. *Certified* Medicaid; Medicare.
Staff RNs 10 (ft), 15 (pt); LPNs 15 (ft), 10 (pt); Orderlies 1 (ft); Nurses aides 60 (ft), 20 (pt); Physical therapists 1 (pt); Reality therapists 2 (pt); Recreational therapists 1 (ft); Occupational therapists 1 (pt); Activities coordinators 1 (ft); Dietitians 1 (pt); Dentists 1 (pt); Ophthalmologists 1 (pt); Podiatrists 1 (pt).
Facilities Dining room; Physical therapy room; Activities room; Chapel; Crafts room; Laundry room; Barber/Beauty shop; Library; Gift shop; Meeting room; Porch and patios.
Activities Arts and Crafts; Cards; Games; Reading groups; Prayer groups; Movies; Shop-

ping trips; Dances/Social or cultural gatherings; Gardening outside; Greenhouse gardening; Exercise and walk clubs; Cooking clubs.
Description Charlwell provides a warm, home-like atmosphere, encouraging residents independence to challenge their physical and mental limitations; staff-provides needed physical and nursing care, and applauds and supports all self-care activity.

Denny House Nursing Home*
86 Saunders Rd, Norwood, MA, 02062 (617)
762-4426
Admin Maurice M Denny.
Licensure Intermediate Care. *Beds* 38. *Certified* Medicaid.

The Ellis Nursing Home*
Ellis Ave, Norwood, MA, 02062 (617)
762-6880
Admin George W Seabrook.
Licensure Skilled Care; Intermediate Care.
Beds 191. *Certified* Medicaid; Medicare.

Maple Grove Manor Convalescent Home*
460 Washington St, Norwood, MA, 02062 (617)
769-2200
Admin Francis C Sybil.
Licensure Skilled Care; Intermediate Care.
Beds 185. *Certified* Medicaid; Medicare.

Norwood Nursing and Retirement Home*
767 Washington St, Norwood, MA, 02062 (617)
769-3704
Admin Kathleen M McGregor.
Licensure Intermediate Care. *Beds* 48. *Certified* Medicaid.

Victoria Haven Nursing Facility*
137 Nichols St, Norwood, MA, 02062 (617)
762-0858
Admin William Gold.
Licensure Intermediate Care. *Beds* 31. *Certified* Medicaid.

OAK BLUFFS

Marthas Vineyard Hospital—Skilled and Intermediate Care Facility*
Linton Ln, Oak Bluffs, MA, 02557 (617)
693-0410
Admin Robert L Langlois.
Licensure Skilled Care; Intermediate Care.
Beds 40. *Certified* Medicaid.

ORANGE

Eastern Star Home*
75 E Main St, Orange, MA, 01364 (617)
544-6695
Admin Dorothy E Stackhouse.
Licensure Rest Home. *Beds* 17.
Affiliation Order of Eastern Star

ORLEANS

Orleans Convalescent and Retirement Home*
Daley Terrace, Orleans, MA, 02563 (617)
255-2328

Admin Peter J Meade.
Licensure Skilled Care. *Beds* 50. *Certified* Medicaid.

OXBRIDGE

Sunnyside Rest Home*
Old Millville Rd, Oxbridge, MA, 01569 (617) 278-3357
Admin Dorothy F Moore.
Licensure Intermediate Care for Mentally Retarded. *Beds* 37.

OXFORD

Sandalwood Convalescent Home*
3 Pine St, Oxford, MA, 01540 (617) 987-8417
Admin Mary A Graham.
Licensure Skilled Care; Intermediate Care. *Beds* 77. *Certified* Medicaid.

PALMER

Monson State Hospital*
Box F, Palmer, MA, 01069 (413) 283-3411
Admin Ron Rosen.
Licensure Intermediate Care for Mentally Retarded. *Beds* 851. *Certified* Medicaid. *Ownership* Public.

Palmer House Healthcare Nursing Home
Shearer St, Palmer, MA, 01069 (413) 283-8361
Admin Bonnie J Davis.
Licensure Intermediate Care. *Beds* 61. *Certified* Medicaid.

PEABODY

Farnsworth Nursing Home*
28 Bowditch St, Peabody, MA, 01960 (617) 532-0768
Admin Gerald Swartz.
Licensure Intermediate Care. *Beds* 74. *Certified* Medicaid.

Pilgrim House-at-Peabody Nursing Home*
96 Forest St, Peabody, MA, 01960 (617) 532-0303
Admin John C Wrightson.
Licensure Skilled Care. *Beds* 144. *Certified* Medicaid; Medicare.

Rainbow Nursing Home
210 Lowell St, Peabody, MA, 01960 (617) 531-2499
Admin Stanley Kotce. *Medical Dir/Dir of Nursing* W Nalnesnik MD.
Licensure Intermediate Care. *Beds* 31. *Certified* Medicaid.
Admissions Requirements Medical examination.
Staff Physicians; RNs; LPNs; Nurses aides; Recreational therapists; Activities coordinators; Dietitians; Audiologists.
Facilities Dining room; Activities room; Crafts room; Laundry room.
Activities Arts and Crafts; Cards; Games; Reading groups; Prayer groups; Movies; Shop-

ping trips; Dances/Social or cultural gatherings.
Description Facility features excellent medical and psychological care.

Shirling Manor Rest Home*
45 Washington St, Peabody, MA, 01960 (617) 531-2192
Admin Shirley E Steeves.
Licensure Rest Home. *Beds* 29. *Certified* Medicaid.

PEPPERELL

Freeman Nursing Home
Main St, Pepperell, MA, 01463 (617) 433-2461
Admin Esther P Elliott.
Licensure Intermediate Care. *Beds* 20. *Certified* Medicaid.
Staff RNs 1 (ft), 3 (pt); LPNs 3 (pt); Orderlies 3 (ft); Nurses aides 2 (ft), 7 (pt); Reality therapists 1 (pt); Recreational therapists 1 (pt); Activities coordinators 1 (ft); Dietitians 1 (pt).
Facilities Dining room; Activities room; Crafts room; Laundry room.
Activities Arts and Crafts; Cards; Games; Prayer groups; Movies; Dances/Social or cultural gatherings.
Description Facility provides home-like atmosphere and family-style care.

Park Manor Nursing Home Inc
13 Park St, Pepperell, MA, 01463 (617) 433-2490
Admin Esther P Elliott.
Licensure Intermediate Care. *Beds* 32. *Certified* Medicaid.
Staff RNs 2 (pt); LPNs 2 (ft), 3 (pt); Nurses aides 5 (ft), 12 (pt); Recreational therapists 1 (ft); Activities coordinators 1 (ft); Dietitians 1 (pt).
Facilities Dining room; Activities room; Laundry room.
Activities Arts and Crafts; Cards; Games; Reading groups; Prayer groups; Movies; Dances/Social or cultural gatherings.
Description Residents receive home-like, family-style care.

PITTSFIELD

Berkshire Nursing Home Inc*
360 W Housatonic St, Pittsfield, MA, 01201 (413) 442-4841
Admin Michael Stroetzel.
Licensure Skilled Care; Intermediate Care. *Beds* 84. *Certified* Medicaid.

Berkshire Place
89 South St, Pittsfield, MA, 01201 (413) 445-4056
Admin Marion Nielsen.
Licensure Intermediate Care; Charitable Home. *Beds* 38. *Certified* Medicaid.
Admissions Requirements Minimum age 65; Females only; Medical examination.
Staff RNs 8 (pt); LPNs 4 (ft); Nurses aides 1 (ft), 4 (pt); Physical therapists 1 (pt); Recreational therapists 1 (pt); Activities coordinators 1 (ft); Dietitians 1 (pt); Podiatrists 1 (pt).
Facilities Dining room; Laundry room; Barber-/Beauty shop.

Activities Arts and Crafts; Cards; Games; Shopping trips; Dances/Social or cultural gatherings.
Description This is a rest home with infirmary connected for residents' use.

Bertha M Young Rest Home*
261 South St, Pittsfield, MA, 01201 (413) 448-8801
Admin Doris T Hogan.
Licensure Rest Home. *Beds* 20.

Edgewood Rest Home*
50 Edgewood Rd, Pittsfield, MA, 01201 (413) 442-1004
Admin Dorothy E Studley.
Licensure Rest Home. *Beds* 13.

Springside of Pittsfield Long Term Care Facility*
255 Lebanon Ave, Pittsfield, MA, 01201 (413) 499-2334
Admin David Carlson.
Licensure Intermediate Care. *Beds* 100. *Certified* Medicaid.

Willow Manor Rest Home Inc*
800 North St, Pittsfield, MA, 01201 (413) 443-6385
Admin Edward J Cristiano.
Licensure Rest Home. *Beds* 19.

PLAINVILLE

Plainville Nursing Home
62 South St, Plainville, MA, 02762 (617) 695-1434
Admin Robert D Brennan.
Licensure Intermediate Care. *Beds* 60. *Certified* Medicaid.
Admissions Requirements Physician's request.
Facilities Dining room.
Activities Arts and Crafts; Cards; Games; Reading groups; Prayer groups; Movies; Shopping trips; Dances/Social or cultural gatherings.

PLYMOUTH

Happiness House Rest Home
3 Chilton St, Plymouth, MA, 02360 (617) 746-2982
Admin Harry McCabe.
Licensure Rest Home. *Beds* 36.
Admissions Requirements Medical examination; Physician's request.
Staff LPNs 2 (pt); Orderlies 2 (ft), 7 (pt); Recreational therapists 1 (pt); Activities coordinators 1 (pt).
Facilities Dining room; Activities room; Crafts room.
Activities Arts and Crafts; Cards; Games; Prayer groups; Movies; Shopping trips.
Description Facility is located one-tenth of a mile from historic Plymouth Harbor with easy access to downtown Plymouth and the historical features of the town.

Mayflower House Nursing Home and Child Center*
123 South St, Plymouth, MA, 02360 (617) 746-4343

Admin Valmai D Hilton.
Licensure Skilled Care; Intermediate Care.
Beds 124. *Certified* Medicaid; Medicare.

Newfield House Inc Convalescent Home
19 Newfield St, Plymouth, MA, 02360 (617)
746-2912
Admin Elizabeth Longhi.
Licensure Intermediate Care. *Beds* 100.

Pilgrim Manor Nursing Home
60 Stafford St, Plymouth, MA, 02360 (617)
746-7016
Admin Bonnie A Burke. *Medical Dir/Dir of
Nursing* John T O'Neil MD.
Licensure Skilled Care; Intermediate Care.
Beds 176. *Certified* Medicaid.
Admissions Requirements Minimum age 50.
Staff Physicians 1 (pt); RNs 8 (ft), 9 (pt); LPNs
5 (ft), 11 (pt); Nurses aides 40 (ft), 49 (pt);
Physical therapists 2 (pt); Recreational thera-
pists 2 (ft), 1 (pt); Occupational therapists 1 (pt);
Speech therapists 1 (pt); Activities coordinators
1 (ft); Dietitians 1 (pt); Podiatrists 2 (pt).
Facilities Dining room; Physical therapy room;
Activities room; Chapel; Crafts room; Barber-
/Beauty shop.
Activities Arts and Crafts; Cards; Games; Pray-
er groups; Movies; Shopping trips;
Dances/Social or cultural gatherings.
Description JCAH accredited facility.

Plymouth Nursing Home
35 Warren Ave, Plymouth, MA, 02360 (617)
746-2085
Admin Lorrine Kerrigan.
Licensure Intermediate Care. *Beds* 37. *Certified* Medicaid.

PROVINCETOWN

Cape End Manor*
100 Alden St, Provincetown, MA, 02657 (617)
487-0235
Admin David M Maloney.
Licensure Intermediate Care. *Beds* 40. *Certified* Medicaid.

QUINCY

Almana Rest Home*
8 Old Colony Ave, Quincy, MA, 02170 (617)
479-5912
Admin Jackelene M Walton.
Licensure Rest Home. *Beds* 22.
Admissions Requirements Medical examina-
tion; Physician's request.
Staff RNs 1 (pt); Orderlies 2 (ft), 3 (pt); Dieti-
tians 1 (pt).
Facilities Activities room.
Activities Cards; Games; Prayer groups;
Shopping trips.
Description We at Almana Rest Home hope to
allow older people to maintain their independ-
ence and dignity while gaining social support
by sharing some living space with others.

Crestview Nursing Home
86 Greenleaf St, Quincy, MA, 02169 (617)
472-9721
Admin Stephen J Clinton.

Licensure Intermediate Care. *Beds* 49. *Certi-
fied* Medicaid.
Admissions Requirements Medical examina-
tion; Physician's request.
Staff RNs 1 (ft), 1 (pt); LPNs 5 (ft), 4 (pt);
Nurses aides 8 (ft), 20 (pt); Activities coordina-
tors 1 (ft), 1 (pt); Dietitians 1 (pt).
Facilities Dining room; Activities room;
Laundry room; Barber/Beauty shop; 2 Living
rooms.
Activities Arts and Crafts; Cards; Games;
Reading groups; Prayer groups; Movies; Shop-
ping trips; Dances/Social or cultural gatherings;
Auto drives; Corsages on Mother's Day; Daily
walks by those able, on nice days.
Description Facility features cookouts (1 per
month, weather permitting) and international
dinners (1 per month).

Friel Nursing Home Inc*
58 Beach St, Quincy, MA, 02170 (617)
479-7722
Admin Isabel Friel.
Licensure Intermediate Care. *Beds* 29. *Certified* Medicaid.

John Adams Nursing Home*
211 Franklin St, Quincy, MA, 02169 (617)
479-0837
Admin Muriel F Finn.
Licensure Skilled Care. *Beds* 49. *Certified* Medicaid.

Merrymount Manor Nursing Home
38 Edgemere Rd, Quincy, MA, 02169 (617)
472-1704
Admin John G Murphy.
Licensure Intermediate Care. *Beds* 24. *Certi-
fied* Medicaid.
Staff RNs 1 (ft), 1 (pt); LPNs 2 (ft), 2 (pt);
Nurses aides 4 (ft), 8 (pt); Dietitians 1 (pt).
Facilities Dining room; Laundry room;
Library.
Activities Arts and Crafts; Cards; Games;
Reading groups; Movies; Shopping trips; Dan-
ces/Social or cultural gatherings.

Oceanside Nursing Home*
445 Quincy Shore Dr, Quincy, MA, 02171
(617) 472-4618
Admin Harry J Minassian.
Licensure Intermediate Care. *Beds* 25. *Certified* Medicaid.

Presidential Convalescent Home Inc
43 Old Colony Ave, Quincy, MA, 02170 (617)
471-0155
Admin Carl A Awed. *Medical Dir/Dir of
Nursing* Dr Joseph Carella.
Licensure Skilled Care; Intermediate Care.
Beds 89. *Certified* Medicaid.
Staff RNs 8 (ft), 3 (pt); LPNs 3 (ft), 4 (pt);
Nurses aides 27 (ft); Physical therapists 1 (pt);
Occupational therapists 1 (pt); Speech thera-
pists 1 (pt); Activities coordinators 1 (ft), 1 (pt);
Dietitians 1 (pt); Dentists 1 (pt); Ophthalmolo-
gists 1 (pt); Podiatrists 1 (pt).
Facilities Dining room; Activities room; Crafts
room; Laundry room; Barber/Beauty shop.
Activities Arts and Crafts; Cards; Games;
Reading groups; Prayer groups; Movies; Shop-
ping trips; Dances/Social or cultural gatherings.
Description This facility has a full-time

physiotherapy aide who works under the direction of a physiotherapy consultant and occupational therapy consultant. Activities department
is very active with a versitile program to fit all
residents needs.

Quincy Nursing Home*
11 Thomas J McGrath Hwy, Quincy, MA,
02169 (617) 479-2820
Admin Mabel S Hurley.
Licensure Skilled Care; Intermediate Care.
Beds 139. *Certified* Medicaid; Medicare.

Robbin House Convalescent Home*
205 Elm St, Quincy, MA, 02169 (617)
471-1750
Admin Leon D Hinman.
Licensure Skilled Care; Intermediate Care.
Beds 114. *Certified* Medicaid.

William B Rice Eventide Home*
215 Adams St, Quincy, MA, 02169 (617)
472-8300
Admin Priscilla Urann.
Licensure Intermediate Care. *Beds* 53. *Certified* Medicaid.

Wollaston Nursing and Retirement Home*
210 Arlington St, Quincy, MA, 02170 (617)
773-6362
Admin Edna F Rand.
Licensure Intermediate Care. *Beds* 21. *Certified* Medicaid.

RANDOLPH

Hollywell Nursing Home*
975 N Main St, Randolph, MA, 02368 (617)
963-8800
Admin William F Lee.
Licensure Skilled Care; Intermediate Care.
Beds 139. *Certified* Medicaid; Medicare.

Seth Mann II Home for the Aged*
349 N Main St, Randolph, MA, 02368 (617)
963-9116
Admin Evelyn McLeer.
Licensure Charitable Home. *Beds* 5.

READING

Daniel's Nursing Home Inc
59 Middlesex Ave, Reading, MA, 01867 (617)
944-0198
Admin D Lee Rorick.
Beds 30. *Certified* Medicaid.

REVERE

Annemark Nursing Home Inc
133 Salem St, Revere, MA, 02151 (617)
322-4861
Admin Elena A Bean.
Licensure Intermediate Care. *Beds* 140. *Certi-
fied* Medicaid.
Admissions Requirements Minimum age 50.
Facilities Dining room; Physical therapy room;
Activities room; Crafts room; Laundry room;
Barber/Beauty shop; Day rooms.
Activities Arts and Crafts; Cards; Games;
Reading groups; Prayer groups; Movies; Shop-

ping trips; Dances/Social or cultural gatherings.
Description This is a new facility with 80 beds
Level II and 60 Level III.

Ocean View Manor Nursing Home*
400 Revere Beach Blvd, Revere, MA, 02151
(617) 284-1958
Admin Edward A Christopher.
Licensure Intermediate Care. *Beds* 150. *Certified* Medicaid.

ROCKLAND

Del Manor Nursing Home Inc*
54 Webster St, Rockland, MA, 02370 (617)
871-0555
Admin Edmond L Delprete.
Licensure Skilled Care. *Beds* 110. *Certified* Medicaid.

Linden Nursing and Retirement Home*
167 W Water St, Rockland, MA, 02370 (617)
878-3728
Admin Arthur S Logan.
Licensure Intermediate Care. *Beds* 19. *Certified* Medicaid.

Rockland Nursing Home*
384 Union St, Rockland, MA, 02370 (617)
878-4405
Admin Janet M Williams.
Licensure Intermediate Care. *Beds* 21. *Certified* Medicaid.

South Shore Nursing Facility
115 North Ave, Rockland, MA, 02370 (617)
878-3309
Admin Charles O Williams. *Medical Dir/Dir
of Nursing* John Carpenter MD.
Licensure Skilled Care; Intermediate Care.
Beds 84. *Certified* Medicaid; Medicare.
Staff RNs 6 (ft), 12 (pt); LPNs 2 (ft), 1 (pt);
Orderlies 2 (pt); Nurses aides 14 (ft), 23 (pt);
Physical therapists 1 (pt); Occupational therapists 1 (pt); Speech therapists 1 (pt); Activities
coordinators 1 (ft), 1 (pt); Dietitians 1 (pt);
Dentists 1 (pt); Ophthalmologists 1 (pt); Podiatrists 1 (pt); Audiologists 1 (pt).
Facilities Dining room; Physical therapy room;
Activities room; Crafts room; Laundry room;
Barber/Beauty shop.
Activities Arts and Crafts; Cards; Games;
Movies; Shopping trips; Dances/Social or cultural gatherings.

Tiffany Rest and Retirement Home*
5 Union St, Rockland, MA, 02370 (617)
878-3757
Admin Diane B Gillis.
Licensure Rest Home. *Beds* 43.

Tiffany II Rest Home*
56 W Water St, Rockland, MA, 02370 (617)
878-0676
Admin Donna M Zaccardi.
Licensure Rest Home. *Beds* 16.

ROCKPORT

Den-Mar Nursing Home*
44 South St, Rockport, MA, 01966 (617)
546-6311
Admin William E Ring Jr.
Licensure Skilled Care; Intermediate Care.
Beds 80. *Certified* Medicaid.

ROSLINDALE

Roxbury Home for Aged Women
1215 Centre St, Roslindale, MA, 02131 (617)
323-0373
Admin Alice Runci. *Medical Dir/Dir of
Nursing* Dr Alice Rogado.
Licensure Intermediate Care; Charitable
Home. *Beds* 24.
Admissions Requirements Minimum age 65;
Females only; Medical examination.
Staff Physicians 1 (pt); RNs 1 (pt); LPNs 1 (ft),
1 (pt); Nurses aides 7 (pt); Activities coordinators 1 (pt); Dietitians 1 (pt); Dentists 1 (pt);
Ophthalmologists 1 (pt); Podiatrists 1 (pt);
Audiologists 1 (pt).

ROWLEY

Sea View Convalescent and Nursing Home
Mansion Dr, Rowley, MA, 01969 (617)
948-7440
Admin Stephen B Comley. *Medical Dir/Dir of
Nursing* Dr William Wigglesworth.
Licensure Intermediate Care. *Beds* 61. *Certified* Medicaid.
Admissions Requirements Minimum age 45;
Physician's request.
Staff RNs 2 (ft), 4 (pt); LPNs 6 (pt); Nurses
aides 14 (ft), 8 (pt); Physical therapists 1 (pt);
Recreational therapists 1 (pt); Activities coordinators 1 (ft), 1 (pt); Dietitians 1 (pt); Podiatrists
1 (pt); Social workers 1 (pt).
Facilities Dining room; Physical therapy room;
Activities room; Chapel; Crafts room; Laundry
room; Barber/Beauty shop; Library; Classroom;
Garden; Greenhouse; Elevator; Residents'
kitchen; Kiln and pottery workshop.
Activities Arts and Crafts; Cards; Games;
Reading groups; Prayer groups; Movies; Shopping trips; Dances/Social or cultural gatherings;
Outings in van; Gardening and plant care;
Ceramics.
Description Sea View is located in a rural setting 30 miles north of Boston in a small New
England town; offers residents many special
programs and activities designed to make their
lives more productive and meaningful.

ROXBURY

Saint Monica's Home
17 Highland Park St, Roxbury, MA, 02119
(617) 445-8961
Admin Donald S Lindsay.
Licensure Skilled Care. *Beds* 42. *Certified* Medicaid.
Admissions Requirements Females only
Affiliation Episcopal

RUTLAND

**Rutland Heights Hospital—Skilled Nursing
Facility***
Maple Ave, Rutland, MA, 01543 (413)
886-4711
Admin William R Goyelte.
Licensure Skilled Care. *Beds* 36. *Certified* Medicaid; Medicare.

SALEM

Bertran Home for Aged Men*
29 Washington Square, Salem, MA, 01970
(617) 744-1002
Admin Eugene M Mater.
Licensure Charitable Home. *Beds* 61.
Admissions Requirements Males only

**Doctor Robert Shaughnessy—Skilled Nursing
Facility**
Dove Ave, Salem, MA, 01970 (617) 745-9000
Admin Evangeline R Dumont. *Medical Dir/Dir of Nursing* Frederic O Buckley Jr MD.
Licensure Skilled Care. *Beds* 40. *Certified* Medicaid; Medicare.
Admissions Requirements Minimum age 45;
Medical examination.
Staff Physicians 1 (pt); RNs 5 (ft), 1 (pt); LPNs
5 (ft), 4 (pt); Nurses aides 16 (ft), 5 (pt);
Physical therapists 1 (ft); Reality therapists 1
(ft), 1 (pt); Recreational therapists 1 (ft); Occupational therapists 1 (ft); Speech therapists 1
(ft); Activities coordinators 1 (ft); Dietitians 1
(ft); Dentists 1 (ft).
Facilities Dining room; Physical therapy room;
Activities room; Chapel; Crafts room; Barber-
/Beauty shop; Sitting room.
Activities Arts and Crafts; Cards; Games;
Reading groups; Prayer groups; Movies; Shopping trips; Dances/Social or cultural gatherings;
Concerts.
Description Facility features semi-private
rooms, each with bathroom facilities, a closet,
well windowed and air conditioned; individual
shower and tub rooms. Each patient has a TV
free of charge. All rooms and corridors are done
in pastel colors. Families are encouraged to visit
daily.

Home for Aged Women in Salem
180 Derby St, Salem, MA, 01970 (617)
744-0219
Admin Arthur Webster.
Licensure Rest Home. *Beds* 36.

Ivy Manor Rest Home*
204 Lafayette St, Salem, MA, 01970 (617)
745-2920
Admin Shirley A Phillips.
Licensure Rest Home. *Beds* 17.

Newhall Nursing Home
7 Carpenter St, Salem, MA, 01970 (617)
744-3844
Admin Betsey D Marcus.
Licensure Intermediate Care. *Beds* 47. *Certified* Medicaid.
Admissions Requirements Minimum age 21;
Medical examination; Physician's request.
Staff RNs 3 (pt); LPNs 4 (ft), 2 (pt); Nurses
aides 13 (ft), 6 (pt); Activities coordinators;

Dietitians.
Facilities Dining room; Activities room.
Activities Arts and Crafts; Cards; Games;
Reading groups; Prayer groups; Movies; Shopping trips.

SALISBURY

Greenleaf House Nursing Home*
Elm St, Salisbury, MA, 01950 (617) 462-3111
Admin Marcella A Costin.
Licensure Intermediate Care. *Beds* 60. *Certified* Medicaid.

SANDISFIELD

New Boston Nursing Home Inc*
Rt 57, Sandisfield, MA, 01255 (413) 258-4731
Admin Brian J Foohey.
Licensure Intermediate Care. *Beds* 49.
Certified Medicaid.

SANDWICH

Fraser Rest Home of Sandwich*
125 Old Maine St, Sandwich, MA, 02563 (617) 888-0880
Admin David P Fraser.
Licensure Rest Home. *Beds* 20.

SAUGUS

Abbey Hill Nursing Home
163 Hamilton St, Saugus, MA, 01906 (617) 233-2522
Admin Patrick J Fahy. *Medical Dir/Dir of Nursing* Dr J Stanley Carp.
Licensure Intermediate Care. *Beds* 30. *Certified* Medicaid.
Admissions Requirements Minimum age 55.
Staff RNs 1 (ft), 4 (pt); LPNs 4 (pt); Nurses aides 3 (ft), 6 (pt); Physical therapists 1 (pt); Activities coordinators 1 (ft); Dietitians 1 (pt); Dentists 1 (ft); Ophthalmologists 1 (ft); Podiatrists 1 (ft); Social workers 1 (pt).
Facilities Dining room; Activities room; Laundry room.
Activities Arts and Crafts; Cards; Games; Reading groups; Prayer groups; Movies; Shopping trips; Dances/Social or cultural gatherings.

Louise Caroline Rehabilitation and Nursing Center
266 Lincoln Ave, Saugus, MA, 01906 (617) 233-6830
Admin George F Hayden. *Medical Dir/Dir of Nursing* Terrance O'Malley MD.
Licensure Skilled Care; Intermediate Care.
Beds 80. *Certified* Medicaid; Medicare.
Admissions Requirements Minimum age 65.
Staff Physicians 6 (pt); RNs 5 (ft), 9 (pt); LPNs 4 (ft), 2 (pt); Nurses aides 22 (ft), 19 (pt); Physical therapists 1 (pt); Recreational therapists 1 (pt); Occupational therapists 1 (pt); Speech therapists 1 (pt); Activities coordinators 1 (ft); Dietitians 2 (pt).
Facilities Dining room; Physical therapy room; Activities room; Crafts room; Laundry room; Barber/Beauty shop.

Activities Arts and Crafts; Cards; Games; Reading groups; Prayer groups; Movies; Shopping trips; Restaurant outings.

North Shore Convalescent Home
73 Chestnut St, Saugus, MA, 01906 (617) 233-8123
Admin Edward Y Serro. *Medical Dir/Dir of Nursing* J Stanley Carp MD.
Licensure Skilled Care; Intermediate Care.
Beds 100. *Certified* Medicaid.
Admissions Requirements Minimum age 21.
Staff Nurses aides 60 (ft); Physical therapists 1 (pt); Reality therapists 1 (pt); Recreational therapists 2 (ft), 1 (pt); Occupational therapists 1 (pt); Speech therapists 1 (pt); Activities coordinators 1 (ft); Dietitians 1 (ft); Dentists 1 (pt); Ophthalmologists 1 (pt); Podiatrists 1 (pt); Audiologists 1 (pt).
Facilities Dining room; Physical therapy room; Activities room; Chapel; Crafts room; Laundry room; Barber/Beauty shop.
Activities Arts and Crafts; Cards; Games; Reading groups; Prayer groups; Movies; Shopping trips; Dances/Social or cultural gatherings.

SCITUATE

Cardigan Nursing Home*
59 Country Way, Scituate, MA, 02040 (617) 545-9477
Admin John H Hilton Jr.
Licensure Intermediate Care. *Beds* 65. *Certified* Medicaid.

Scituate Ocean Manor
309 Driftway, Scituate, MA, 02066 (617) 545-1370
Admin James Oliver. *Medical Dir/Dir of Nursing* Tod Forman MD.
Licensure Skilled Care; Intermediate Care.
Beds 113. *Certified* Medicaid.
Staff Physicians 2 (pt); RNs 5 (ft), 12 (pt); LPNs 6 (ft), 9 (pt); Orderlies 2 (ft); Nurses aides 22 (ft), 53 (pt); Physical therapists 2 (ft), 1 (pt); Recreational therapists 2 (ft); Occupational therapists 1 (pt); Speech therapists 1 (pt); Activities coordinators 1 (ft), 1 (pt); Dietitians 1 (pt); Dentists 1 (pt); Ophthalmologists 1 (pt); Podiatrists 1 (pt); Audiologists 1 (pt).
Facilities Dining room; Physical therapy room; Activities room; Chapel; Crafts room; Laundry room; Barber/Beauty shop; Library.
Activities Arts and Crafts; Cards; Games; Reading groups; Prayer groups; Movies; Shopping trips; Dances/Social or cultural gatherings.

SHARON

Sharon Manor Nursing Home*
259 Norwood St, Sharon, MA, 02067 (617) 784-6781
Admin John J Ribeiro.
Licensure Skilled Care. *Beds* 58. *Certified* Medicaid; Medicare.

SHELBURNE

Anchorage Nursing Home*
Mohawk Trail, Rt 2, Shelburne, MA, 01370 (413) 625-2305

Admin Franics B Caldwell.
Licensure Intermediate Care. *Beds* 35. *Certified* Medicaid.

La Belle's Rest Home*
3 High St, Shelburne, MA, 01370 (413) 625-6560
Admin Clive D Human.
Licensure Rest Home. *Beds* 32.

Mohawk Manor Rest Home Inc
45 Water St, Shelburne, MA, 01370 (413) 625-6860
Admin Gail A Bissell.
Licensure Rest Home. *Beds* 24.
Admissions Requirements Minimum age 35; Medical examination; Physician's request.
Staff RNs 1 (pt); LPNs 1 (ft); Nurses aides 9 (pt); Activities coordinators 1 (pt); Dietitians 1 (pt); 5 (pt).
Facilities Dining room; Laundry room.
Activities Arts and Crafts; Cards; Games; Prayer groups; Movies; Shopping trips.

SHREWSBURY

Shrewsbury Nursing Home Inc*
66 South St, Shrewsbury, MA, 01545 (617) 845-6786
Admin Betty L Stratford.
Licensure Skilled Care; Intermediate Care.
Beds 123. *Certified* Medicaid.

SOMERSET

Clifton Geriatric Center Long Term Care Facility*
500 Wilbur Ave, Somerset, MA, 02725 (617) 675-7589
Admin Clifton O Greenwood.
Licensure Skilled Care; Intermediate Care.
Beds 130. *Certified* Medicaid.

SOMERVILLE

Chandler Manor Rest Home*
38 Chandler St, Somerville, MA, 02144 (617) 666-1519
Admin Janina Elmaleh.
Licensure Rest Home. *Beds* 21.

Clarendon Hill Nursing Home*
1323 Broadway, Somerville, MA, 02144 (617) 623-6700
Admin Burton F Faulkner Jr.
Licensure Intermediate Care. *Beds* 58. *Certified* Medicaid.

Jeanne Jugan Residence
186 Highland Ave, Somerville, MA, 02143 (617) 776-4420
Admin Angelique Roth.
Licensure Skilled Care; Intermediate Care.
Beds 120. *Certified* Medicaid.

Mary Ellen Nursing Home*
170 Highland Ave, Somerville, MA, 02143 (617) 625-7764
Admin Martha L Ditucci.
Licensure Intermediate Care. *Beds* 23. *Certified* Medicaid.

Prospect Hill Manor Nursing Home*
37 Munroe St, Somerville, MA, 02143 (617)
666-9891
Admin Richard Percoco.
Licensure Intermediate Care. *Beds* 40. *Certified* Medicaid.

Reagan's Resident Care Facility*
174 Morrison Ave, Somerville, MA, 02144
(617) 666-0380
Admin Dorothy E Edwards.
Licensure Rest Home. *Beds* 42.

Somerville Home for the Aged
117 Summer St, Somerville, MA, 02143 (617)
776-0260
Admin Elsa E Lewis.
Licensure Rest Home. *Beds* 59.
Admissions Requirements Minimum age 65;
Medical examination.
Staff RNs 1 (pt); LPNs 1 (pt); Activities coordinators 1 (pt); Dietitians 1 (pt).
Facilities Dining room; Activities room; Chapel; Crafts room; Laundry room; Barber/Beauty shop; Library.
Activities Arts and Crafts; Cards; Games;
Reading groups; Prayer groups; Movies; Shopping trips; Dances/Social or cultural gatherings.

Sunrise Nursing Home*
26 Adams St, Somerville, MA, 02145 (617)
625-2233
Admin Jacob M Volensky.
Licensure Intermediate Care. *Beds* 40. *Certified* Medicaid.

Winter Hill Nursing Home
50 Evergreen Ave, Somerville, MA, 02145
(617) 628-0110
Admin Robert D Brennan. *Medical Dir/Dir of Nursing* Dr Herbert Leventhal.
Licensure Intermediate Care. *Beds* 78. *Certified* Medicaid.
Admissions Requirements Minimum age 21;
Medical examination; Physician's request.
Staff RNs 1 (ft), 1 (pt); LPNs 4 (ft), 4 (pt);
Nurses aides 21 (ft), 10 (pt); Recreational therapists 1 (ft), 1 (pt); Dietitians 1 (pt).
Facilities Dining room; Activities room; Laundry room.
Activities Arts and Crafts; Cards; Games;
Reading groups; Prayer groups; Movies; Shopping trips; Dances/Social or cultural gatherings.
Description Foster grandchild program activities are held on a weekly basis.

SOUTH HADLEY

Falls Nursing Home*
18 Hartford St, South Hadley, MA, 01075 (413)
538-8403
Admin Angelina T Savko.
Licensure Intermediate Care. *Beds* 44. *Certified* Medicaid.

SOUTH YARMOUTH

Windsor Nursing Home
265 N Main St, South Yarmouth, MA, 02664
(617) 394-3514
Admin Judith A Welling. *Medical Dir/Dir of Nursing* Dr Charles Derrick.
Licensure Intermediate Care. *Beds* 120. *Certified* Medicaid.
Admissions Requirements Minimum age 21.
Staff Physicians 1 (pt); RNs 4 (ft), 13 (pt);
LPNs 1 (ft), 4 (pt); Nurses aides 17 (ft), 25 (pt);
Physical therapists 1 (pt); Occupational therapists 1 (pt); Activities coordinators 2 (ft); Dietitians 1 (pt); Dentists 1 (pt); Podiatrists 1 (pt).
Facilities Dining room; Physical therapy room;
Activities room; Chapel; Crafts room; Laundry room; Barber/Beauty shop; Library.
Activities Arts and Crafts; Cards; Games;
Reading groups; Prayer groups; Movies; Shopping trips; Dances/Social or cultural gatherings.
Description Facility offers an adult day health program with capacity of 18 per day; family life program.

SOUTHBRIDGE

Liberty House Nursing Home*
84 Chapin St, Southbridge, MA, 01550 (617)
765-9133
Admin James A Neustadt.
Licensure Skilled Care; Intermediate Care.
Beds 246. *Certified* Medicaid.

SPENCER

Coventry Hall Nursing Home
500 Main St, Spencer, MA, 01562 (617)
885-2277
Admin Glynes Hunter.
Licensure Intermediate Care. *Beds* 31. *Certified* Medicaid.

Lincoln Hill Manor Rest Home
53 Lincoln St, Spencer, MA, 01562 (617)
885-3338
Admin Joan M Lynds. *Medical Dir/Dir of Nursing* Dr Richard Fowler.
Licensure Rest Home. *Beds* 30.
Admissions Requirements Minimum age 30;
Medical examination; Physician's request.
Staff Physicians 5 (ft); RNs 1 (pt); Recreational therapists 1 (ft); Dietitians 1 (pt); Podiatrists 1 (pt).
Facilities Dining room; Laundry room.
Activities Cards; Games; Reading groups; Prayer groups.

SPRINGFIELD

Beech Manor Rest Home*
38 Warner St, Springfield, MA, 01103 (413)
733-7162
Admin Ellen N Rice.
Licensure Rest Home. *Beds* 12.

Blue Spruce Rest Home
175 Bowdoin St, Springfield, MA, 01109 (413)
739-2373
Admin Nathan H Rice.
Licensure Rest Home. *Beds* 19.
Admissions Requirements Medical examination; Physician's request.
Facilities Dining room; Activities room; Laundry room; Barber/Beauty shop.
Activities Arts and Crafts; Cards; Games;
Shopping trips.

Campbell's Ingersoll Rest Home*
29 Ingersoll Grove St, Springfield, MA, 01109
(413) 732-1068
Admin Collin A Campbell.
Licensure Rest Home. *Beds* 36.

Chapin Center Skilled Nursing Facility
200 Kendall St, Springfield, MA, 01104 (413)
737-4756
Admin Robert Denson. *Medical Dir/Dir of Nursing* Alphonse Calvanese MD.
Licensure Skilled Care; Intermediate Care.
Beds 160. *Certified* Medicaid.
Admissions Requirements Minimum age 55;
Medical examination; Physician's request.
Staff Physicians 13 (pt); RNs 5 (ft), 10 (pt);
LPNs 7 (ft), 8 (pt); Orderlies 1 (ft), 1 (pt);
Nurses aides 31 (ft), 22 (pt); Physical therapists 1 (pt); Occupational therapists 1 (pt); Speech therapists 1 (pt); Activities coordinators 1 (ft);
Dietitians 1 (pt); Dentists 1 (pt); Ophthalmologists 1 (pt); Podiatrists 1 (pt).
Facilities Dining room; Physical therapy room;
Activities room; Crafts room; Barber/Beauty shop.
Activities Arts and Crafts; Cards; Games;
Reading groups; Prayer groups; Movies; Dances/Social or cultural gatherings; Reality orientation.
Description Facility features buildings equipped with fire-resistant construction, complete with sprinkler system, smoke alarms, fire doors, and extinquishers; daily housekeeping and laundry service; and is located in a residential area conveniently near 2 interstate highways.

Chestnut Knoll
471 Chestnut St, Springfield, MA, 01107 (413)
732-7817
Admin Alice Marsian.
Licensure Intermediate Care; Charitable Home. *Beds* 48. *Certified* Medicaid.
Admissions Requirements Minimum age 65;
Females only; Medical examination.
Staff Physicians 1 (pt); RNs 1 (ft), 2 (pt); LPNs 3 (ft), 3 (pt); Nurses aides 4 (ft), 5 (pt); Dietitians 1 (pt).
Facilities Dining room; Chapel; Laundry room; Barber/Beauty shop; Library.
Activities Cards; Games; Movies; Shopping trips.

Crescent Hill Nursing Center
370 Pine St, Springfield, MA, 01105 (413)
781-5290
Admin David Johnson. *Medical Dir/Dir of Nursing* Jack Skelskie MD.
Licensure Skilled Care; Intermediate Care.
Beds SNF 41; ICF 129. *Certified* Medicaid.
Admissions Requirements Minimum age 16.
Staff Physicians 21 (pt); RNs 6 (ft), 2 (pt);
LPNs 8 (ft), 8 (pt); Orderlies 2 (ft), 1 (pt);
Nurses aides 24 (ft), 27 (pt); Physical therapists 2 (ft), 1 (pt); Reality therapists 1 (ft), 1 (pt);
Occupational therapists 1 (pt); Speech therapists 1 (pt); Activities coordinators 2 (ft); Dietitians 1 (pt); Dentists 1 (pt); Ophthalmologists 1 (pt); Podiatrists 1 (pt); Audiologists 1 (pt).
Facilities Dining room; Physical therapy room;
Activities room; Crafts room; Laundry room;
Barber/Beauty shop.
Activities Arts and Crafts; Cards; Games;

Reading groups; Prayer groups; Movies; Shopping trips; Dances/Social or cultural gatherings.
Description Facility features a self-supporting ceramics program with in-house kiln, large screen TV/VCR in activities room for current films, documentaries, and inservices.

Hahn Rest Home*
178 Thompson St, Springfield, MA, 01109
(413) 737-5124
Admin Kathleen M Hahn.
Licensure Rest Home. *Beds* 13.

Hampden House Retirement Home
190 Kendall St, Springfield, MA, 01104 (413) 733-6617
Admin Richard A Fertal Jr. *Medical Dir/Dir of Nursing* Alphonse Calvanese.
Licensure Rest Home. *Beds* 160.
Ownership Proprietary.
Admissions Requirements Minimum age 50; Medical examination.
Staff LPNs 3 (ft), 2 (pt); Nurses aides 9 (ft), 1 (pt); Activities coordinators 1 (ft); Dietitians 1 (ft).
Facilities Dining room; Activities room; Laundry room; Barber/Beauty shop.
Activities Arts and Crafts; Games; Reading groups; Prayer groups; Movies; Shopping trips; Dances/Social or cultural gatherings.
Description Our 160-bed facility is easily accessible to stores, banks, library, and bus line. Complete banking, postal, and dry cleaning services ares are provided. The variety of activities offered, such as monthly chartered bus trips, adult classes, bowling, square dancing, bingo, religious services, theater, and luncheons are designed to meet the specific needs and interests of all residents.

Hilltop Rest Home*
103 Bowdoin St, Springfield, MA, 01109 (413) 739-6377
Admin Edith Gibby.
Licensure Rest Home. *Beds* 19.

Hodges Rest Home*
69 Bowdoin St, Springfield, MA, 01109 (413) 788-4850
Admin Della M Hodges.
Licensure Rest Home. *Beds* 14.

Hurstdale Rest Home
181 Acorn St, Springfield, MA, 01109 (413) 734-0177
Admin M Z Barksdale. *Medical Dir/Dir of Nursing* Dr Jack Skelskie.
Licensure Rest Home. *Beds* 15.
Admissions Requirements Minimum age 21; Medical examination; Physician's request.
Staff Physicians 1 (pt); RNs 1 (pt); LPNs 2 (pt); Orderlies 1 (pt); Nurses aides 2 (pt); Recreational therapists 1 (pt); Occupational therapists 1 (pt); Activities coordinators 1 (pt); Dietitians 1 (pt); Podiatrists 1 (pt).
Affiliation Afro-American
Facilities Dining room; Activities room; Crafts room; Laundry room; Library.
Activities Arts and Crafts; Cards; Games; Reading groups; Prayer groups; Shopping trips; Dances/Social or cultural gatherings.

Description Facility is located in a country setting yet close to town, surrounded by a park and a college.

Ivy Manor Rest Home*
368 St James Ave, Springfield, MA, 01109 (413) 788-6783
Admin Roger F Thomas.
Licensure Rest Home. *Beds* 12.

Maple Hill Rest Home*
156 Mill St, Springfield, MA, 01108 (413) 737-2148
Admin Michael H Joseph.
Licensure Rest Home. *Beds* 32.

Pine Manor Nursing Home
1190 Liberty St, Springfield, MA, 01104 (413) 781-0831
Admin Joseph P Kennedy Jr.
Licensure Intermediate Care. *Beds* 101. *Certified* Medicaid.
Admissions Requirements Minimum age 21; Medical examination.
Facilities Dining room; Activities room; Laundry room; Barber/Beauty shop.
Activities Arts and Crafts; Cards; Games; Movies; Shopping trips; Dances/Social or cultural gatherings.

Primus Mason Manor
74 Walnut St, Springfield, MA, 01105 (413) 733-1517
Admin Ronald J Slosek.
Licensure Rest Home. *Beds* 20.
Admissions Requirements Minimum age 60; Medical examination; Physician's request.
Staff Physicians 1 (pt); LPNs 1 (pt); Nurses aides 2 (pt); Activities coordinators 1 (pt); Dietitians 1 (pt); Dentists 1 (pt); Ophthalmologists 1 (pt); Podiatrists 1 (pt); Audiologists 1 (pt).
Facilities Dining room; Activities room; Laundry room; Barber/Beauty shop; Library.
Activities Arts and Crafts; Cards; Games; Movies; Shopping trips; Dances/Social or cultural gatherings.
Description Mason Manor is composed of 20 private beds and has recently added a respite program.

Reno's Rest Home*
175 Mill St, Springfield, MA, 01108 (413) 737-5964
Admin Edith M Bellucci.
Licensure Rest Home. *Beds* 18.

Ring Nursing Home—Ridgewood
22 Ridgewood Pl, Springfield, MA, 01105 (413) 781-1141
Admin Sheila M Leahey.
Licensure Intermediate Care. *Beds* 126. *Certified* Medicaid.
Staff RNs 1 (ft), 1 (pt); LPNs 7 (ft), 7 (pt); Nurses aides 25 (ft), 18 (pt); Activities coordinators 1 (ft), 1 (pt); Dietitians 1 (pt).
Facilities Dining room; Physical therapy room; Activities room; Chapel; Laundry room; Barber/Beauty shop.
Activities Arts and Crafts; Cards; Games; Reading groups; Prayer groups; Movies; Dances/Social or cultural gatherings.

Ring Nursing Home—South
155 Mill St, Springfield, MA, 01105 (413) 732-1126
Admin Matthew J Leahy.
Licensure Intermediate Care. *Beds* 110. *Certified* Medicaid.
Staff RNs 6 (ft), 2 (pt); LPNs 4 (ft), 2 (pt); Nurses aides 28 (ft), 30 (pt); Physical therapists 1 (pt); Recreational therapists 2 (ft); Dietitians 1 (pt).

Saint Lukes Home
79-85 Spring St, Springfield, MA, 01105 (413) 736-5494
Admin Sr Mary of Providence.
Licensure Rest Home. *Beds* 92.
Admissions Requirements Minimum age 60; Medical examination; Physician's request.
Staff Physicians 1 (pt); RNs 2 (ft); LPNs 1 (ft), 1 (pt); Nurses aides 8 (ft), 8 (pt); Activities coordinators 1 (ft); Dietitians 1 (pt); Podiatrists 1 (pt).
Affiliation Roman Catholic
Facilities Dining room; Activities room; Chapel; Laundry room; Barber/Beauty shop.
Activities Arts and Crafts; Cards; Games; Reading groups; Prayer groups; Movies; Shopping trips; Dances/Social or cultural gatherings.
Description Facility is located close to downtown area, library, civic center, parks, many restaurants, theaters, and other recreational areas; within walking of Amtrak and bus lines.

Springfield Municipal Hospital
1400 State St, Springfield, MA, 01109 (413) 787-6700
Admin George H Lane.
Licensure Skilled Care; Intermediate Care. *Beds* 438. *Certified* Medicaid.
Admissions Requirements Medical examination; Physician's request.
Facilities Dining room; Physical therapy room; Activities room; Chapel; Crafts room; Laundry room; Barber/Beauty shop; Library.
Activities Arts and Crafts; Cards; Games; Prayer groups; Movies; Shopping trips; Dances/Social or cultural gatherings.
Description Springfield Municipal Hospital is a multilevel facility caring for the following categories of patients: chronic disease, rehabilitative, skilled nursing facility, intermediate care facility. On the campus is also an apartment complex for the frail elderly and handicapped, not operated by Springfield Municipal Hospital.

Spruce Manor Nursing Home*
388 Central St, Springfield, MA, 01105 (413) 734-4986
Admin Amelia Fournier.
Licensure Intermediate Care. *Beds* 150. *Certified* Medicaid.

Stone Acre Rest Home Inc
120 Mill St, Springfield, MA, 01108 (413) 734-3054
Admin Conrad E Wertheim.
Licensure Rest Home. *Beds* 26.
Admissions Requirements Minimum age 21; Medical examination.
Staff Physicians 1 (pt); LPNs 1 (ft); Nurses aides 3 (ft), 1 (pt); Activities coordinators 1 (pt); Dietitians 1 (pt).

Facilities Dining room; Activities room; Crafts room; Laundry room; Barber/Beauty shop.
Activities Cards; Games; Movies; Shopping trips.
Description Facility features a home-like setting and dedicated staff.

STONEHAM

Arnold House Nursing Home
490 William St, Stoneham, MA, 02180 (617) 438-1116
Admin Marjorie R Cook. *Medical Dir/Dir of Nursing* Dr Frank Hinnendael.
Licensure Intermediate Care. *Beds* 20.
Admissions Requirements Females only
Staff RNs 1 (ft), 4 (pt); LPNs 1 (ft), 1 (pt); Nurses aides 2 (ft), 11 (pt); Activities coordinators 1 (pt); Dietitians 1 (pt); Podiatrists 1 (pt).
Facilities Dining room.
Activities Arts and Crafts; Cards; Games; Prayer groups; Movies; Shopping trips; Dances/Social or cultural gatherings.
Description Facility features gracious living in a spacious, personal, home-like setting located on a golf course.

Bear Hill Nursing Center at Wakefield
Enter 11 North St, Stoneham, MA, 02180
Medical Dir/Dir of Nursing John Danis MD.
Admissions Requirements Minimum age 21; Physician's request.
Staff Physicians; RNs 10 (ft); LPNs 10 (ft); Orderlies 2 (ft); Nurses aides 30 (ft); Physical therapists 1 (pt); Reality therapists 1 (pt); Recreational therapists 2 (ft); Occupational therapists 1 (pt); Speech therapists 1 (pt); Activities coordinators 1 (ft); Dietitians 1 (pt); Dentists 1 (pt); Ophthalmologists 1 (pt); Podiatrists 1 (pt); Audiologists 1 (pt).
Facilities Dining room; Physical therapy room; Activities room; Chapel; Crafts room; Laundry room; Barber/Beauty shop; Library; Pub; Greenhouse; Cinema.
Activities Arts and Crafts; Cards; Games; Reading groups; Prayer groups; Movies; Shopping trips; Dances/Social or cultural gatherings.
Description Built in 1983, the center boasts a quality of life found in only the most innovative health care facilities. The setting was designed to combine elements of a garden-style apartment building, a hotel, and a nursing home.

Home for Aged People
32 Franklin St, Stoneham, MA, 02180 (617) 438-0580
Licensure Rest Home. *Beds* 11.
Admissions Requirements Minimum age 65; Medical examination; Physician's request.
Staff Dietitians 1 (pt); Podiatrists 1 (pt).
Facilities Dining room; Laundry room.

Sunshine Nursing Home Inc
12 Benton St, Stoneham, MA, 02180 (617) 438-9305
Admin Lillian I Price. *Medical Dir/Dir of Nursing* Dr Hinnendael.
Licensure Intermediate Care. *Beds* 33. *Certified* Medicaid.
Admissions Requirements Minimum age 18; Medical examination; Physician's request.

Staff RNs 2 (ft); LPNs 1 (ft), 2 (pt); Nurses aides 5 (ft), 12 (pt); Activities coordinators 1 (pt); Dietitians 1 (pt).
Facilities Dining room; Activities room; Crafts room; Laundry room; Barber/Beauty shop.
Activities Arts and Crafts; Cards; Games; Reading groups; Movies; Shopping trips.
Description Home is a small, family-type facility with a very strong activities program. Staff is very loving and caring.

STOUGHTON

Blue Hills Convalescent Home*
1044 Park St, Stoughton, MA, 02072 (617) 344-7300
Admin John Omeara.
Licensure Skilled Care; Intermediate Care.
Beds 101. *Certified* Medicaid.

Francis T Crimmins Rest Home
239 Pleasant St, Stoughton, MA, 02072 (617) 344-2451
Admin Lorraine Roche.
Licensure Rest Home. *Beds* 20.
Admissions Requirements Females only; Medical examination.

Norfolk Nursing Home*
94 Prospect St, Stoughton, MA, 02072 (617) 344-3645
Admin Catherine Warner.
Licensure Intermediate Care. *Beds* 59. *Certified* Medicaid.

STOW

Stow Rest Home*
Wheeler Rd, Stow, MA, 01775 (617) 897-7923
Admin Charles L Alves.
Licensure Rest Home. *Beds* 18.

Whitney Homestead Rest Home*
Great Rd, Stow, MA, 01775 (617) 756-1515
Admin Bonnie Fredette.
Licensure Skilled Care; Intermediate Care.
Beds SNF 40; ICF 40.

SUDBURY

Sudbury Pines Nursing Home
642 Boston Post Rd, Sudbury, MA, 01776 (617) 443-9000
Admin Ernest Henderson III. *Medical Dir/Dir of Nursing* Dr Melvin Kramer.
Licensure Skilled Care; Intermediate Care.
Beds 80. *Certified* Medicaid.
Admissions Requirements Minimum age 16.
Staff Physicians 3 (pt); RNs 3 (ft), 9 (pt); LPNs 6 (pt); Nurses aides 15 (ft), 33 (pt); Physical therapists 1 (ft), 1 (pt); Reality therapists 1 (ft), 1 (pt); Recreational therapists 1 (ft), 1 (pt); Occupational therapists 1 (pt); Speech therapists 1 (pt); Dietitians 1 (pt); Dentists 1 (pt); Podiatrists 1 (pt).
Facilities Dining room; Physical therapy room; Activities room; Chapel; Crafts room; Laundry room; Barber/Beauty shop; Library.
Activities Arts and Crafts; Cards; Games; Reading groups; Prayer groups; Movies; Shopping trips.

Description Facility's greatest pride is to have assembled a team of people who like each other and work well together, for that rubs off in better attitudes toward the patients and the giving of loving care. Pride also taken in food and various activities and programs offered.

SUNDERLAND

Cozy Corner Nursing Home Inc
Old Amherst Rd, PO Box 405, Sunderland, MA, 01375 (413) 665-2740
Admin I James Bednarski III. *Medical Dir/Dir of Nursing* Samuel Hunter MD.
Licensure Intermediate Care. *Beds* 57. *Certified* Medicaid.
Admissions Requirements Minimum age 21; Medical examination.
Staff Physicians 14 (pt); RNs 4 (ft), 3 (pt); LPNs 1 (ft), 1 (pt); Nurses aides 12 (ft), 8 (pt); Physical therapists 1 (pt); Recreational therapists 1 (pt); Occupational therapists 1 (pt); Speech therapists 1 (pt); Activities coordinators 1 (ft); Dietitians 1 (pt); Dentists 1 (pt); Podiatrists 1 (pt).
Facilities Dining room; Activities room; Chapel; Crafts room; Laundry room; Barber/Beauty shop.
Activities Arts and Crafts; Cards; Games; Reading groups; Prayer groups; Movies; Shopping trips.

SWAMPSCOTT

Jewish Rehabilitation Center for the Aged
330 Paradise Rd, Swampscott, MA, 01907 (617) 598-5310
Admin Julian Rich. *Medical Dir/Dir of Nursing* David Levy MD.
Licensure Skilled Care; Intermediate Care.
Beds 171. *Certified* Medicaid.
Admissions Requirements Minimum age 65; Medical examination; Physician's request.
Staff Physicians 1 (pt); RNs 12 (ft), 6 (pt); LPNs 7 (ft), 9 (pt); Orderlies 2 (ft), 1 (pt); Nurses aides 58 (ft), 15 (pt); Physical therapists 1 (pt); Recreational therapists 3 (ft), 2 (pt); Occupational therapists 1 (pt); Speech therapists 1 (pt); Activities coordinators 1 (ft); Dietitians 1 (ft); Dentists 1 (pt); Ophthalmologists 1 (pt); Podiatrists 1 (pt); Audiologists 1 (pt).
Affiliation Jewish
Facilities Dining room; Physical therapy room; Activities room; Chapel; Laundry room; Barber/Beauty shop; Library.
Activities Arts and Crafts; Cards; Games; Prayer groups; Movies; Dances/Social or cultural gatherings.
Description Adult day center opened in December, 1982; capacity for 30 senior day program participants.

SWANSEA

Country Gardens Nursing Home*
2045 Grand Army Hwy, Swansea, MA, 02777 (617) 379-9700
Admin Elizabeth Wood.
Licensure Skilled Care. *Beds* 82. *Certified* Medicaid; Medicare.

Gardner's Grove Nursing Home*
924 Gardner's Neck Rd, Swansea, MA, 02777
(617) 674-1717
Admin Evelyn H Purdy.
Licensure Intermediate Care. *Beds* 27. *Certified* Medicaid.

Swansea Rest Home Inc
115 Wilbur Ave, Swansea, MA, 02777 (617)
678-8661
Admin Marion G Albritton. *Medical Dir/Dir
of Nursing* Dr Mouded.
Licensure Rest Home. *Beds* 16.
Staff Physicians; RNs; Nurses aides; Activities
coordinators; Dietitians; Dentists; Ophthalmologists; Podiatrists.
Facilities Dining room; Activities room; Laundry room.
Activities Arts and Crafts; Cards; Games;
Shopping trips; Dances/Social or cultural gatherings.

TAUNTON

Longmeadow Nursing Home*
68 Dean St, Taunton, MA, 02780 (617)
822-0070
Licensure Intermediate Care. *Beds* 51. *Certified* Medicaid.

Marian Manor of Taunton*
33 Summer St, Taunton, MA, 02780 (617)
822-4885
Admin Sr Marie Therese.
Licensure Intermediate Care. *Beds* 83. *Certified* Medicaid.

Paul A Dever State School*
1380 Bay St, Box 631, Taunton, MA, 02780
(617) 824-5881
Admin Anne Lewis.
Licensure Skilled Care. *Beds* 20.
Ownership Public.

Taunton Female Charity Association Inc*
96 Broadway, Taunton, MA, 02780 (617)
824-7747
Admin Mary A Conteras.
Licensure Charitable Home. *Beds* 12.
Admissions Requirements Females only

Taunton Nursing Home*
350 Norton Ave, Taunton, MA, 02780 (617)
822-6404
Admin Peter F Tardo.
Licensure Intermediate Care. *Beds* 39. *Certified* Medicaid.

Wedgemere Convalescent Home
146 Dean St, Taunton, MA, 02780 (617)
823-0767
Admin Joseph J Polizzotti.
Licensure Skilled Care. *Beds* 80. *Certified* Medicaid; Medicare.

TEMPLETON

Baldwinville Nursing Home*
Hospital Rd, Baldwinville, Templeton, MA,
01436 (617) 939-2196

Admin Leighton S Cheney.
Licensure Skilled Care; Intermediate Care.
Beds 82. *Certified* Medicaid.

TEWKSBURY

Casa Grande Long Term Care Facility*
10 Erlin Terrace, Tewksbury, MA, 01876 (617)
851-3121
Admin Richard T Forsley.
Licensure Skilled Care; Intermediate Care.
Beds 124. *Certified* Medicaid; Medicare.

Castle Nursing Home
553 North St, Tewksbury, MA, 01876 (617)
851-9621
Admin Benjamin L Benson. *Medical Dir/Dir
of Nursing* Dr Ralph LePase.
Licensure Intermediate Care. *Beds* 26. *Certi-
fied* Medicaid.
Admissions Requirements Minimum age 21;
Females only
Staff Physicians 2 (pt); LPNs 3 (ft), 3 (pt);
Nurses aides 7 (ft), 6 (pt); Activities coordina-
tors 2 (pt); Dietitians 1 (ft); Dentists 1 (ft).
Facilities Dining room; Activities room.
Activities Arts and Crafts; Cards; Games;
Reading groups; Prayer groups; Movies; Shop-
ping trips; Dances/Social or cultural gatherings.
Description Facility features beautiful grounds,
summertime cookouts, and all types of lawn
parties.

UPTON

Knowlton Manor Nursing Home
145 Main St, Upton, MA, 01587 (617)
529-6983
Admin Anthony D'Amore. *Medical Dir/Dir of
Nursing* Barbara Sperry.
Licensure Intermediate Care. *Beds* 37. *Certi-
fied* Medicaid.
Staff RNs 2 (ft), 2 (pt); LPNs 1 (ft), 2 (pt);
Orderlies 1 (ft); Nurses aides 8 (ft), 4 (pt); Rec-
reational therapists 1 (pt); Occupational thera-
pists 1 (pt); Dietitians 1 (pt).
Facilities Dining room; Activities room;
Laundry room.
Activities Arts and Crafts; Cards; Games;
Reading groups; Prayer groups; Movies; Shop-
ping trips; Dances/Social or cultural gatherings.
Description Excellent care in a small, home-
like, noninstitutional setting.

WAKEFIELD

Elizabeth E Boit Home
5 Bennett St, Wakefield, MA, 01880 (617)
245-0008
Admin Muriel Ellis.
Licensure Rest Home. *Beds* 12.
Admissions Requirements Minimum age 65;
Females only; Medical examination; Physi-
cian's request.
Facilities Dining room; Laundry room;
Library.
Activities Cards; Games; Shopping trips.
Description Facility features all private rooms;
residents bring own furniture if desired; meals
served in the dining room.

Forest Manor Nursing Home*
8 Parker Rd, Wakefield, MA, 01880 (617)
245-0444
Admin Marta Carney.
Licensure Intermediate Care. *Beds* 39. *Certified* Medicaid.

Greenview Manor Nursing Home
Bathol St, Wakefield, MA, 01880 (617)
245-7600
Admin Kenneth Bane. *Medical Dir/Dir of
Nursing* Alexander Latty MD.
Licensure Skilled Care; Intermediate Care.
Beds 108. *Certified* Medicaid.
Staff Physicians 25 (pt); RNs 6 (ft), 9 (pt);
LPNs 3 (ft), 5 (pt); Orderlies 1 (pt); Nurses
aides 27 (ft), 35 (pt); Physical therapists 1 (pt);
Reality therapists 1 (ft), 2 (pt); Recreational
therapists 1 (ft), 2 (pt); Occupational therapists
1 (pt); Speech therapists 1 (pt); Activities coor-
dinators 1 (pt); Dietitians 1 (pt); Dentists 1 (pt);
Ophthalmologists 1 (pt); Podiatrists 2 (pt).
Facilities Dining room; Physical therapy room;
Activities room; Crafts room; Laundry room;
Barber/Beauty shop; Library.
Activities Arts and Crafts; Cards; Games;
Reading groups; Prayer groups; Movies; Shop-
ping trips; Dances/Social or cultural gatherings;
Minibus trips.
Description Facility owns wheelchair-lift bus,
used for residents trips; offers an extraordinary
therapeutic recreation program.

Greenwood Nursing Home
90 Greenwood St, Wakefield, MA, 01880 (617)
246-0211
Admin Merna E Morse.
Licensure Intermediate Care. *Beds* 36. *Certified* Medicaid.
Staff RNs 1 (ft); LPNs 2 (ft), 2 (pt); Nurses
aides 6 (ft), 9 (pt); Activities coordinators 1 (ft);
Dietitians 1 (pt).
Facilities Dining room; Activities room; Laundry room.
Activities Arts and Crafts; Cards; Games;
Reading groups; Prayer groups; Dances/Social
or cultural gatherings.
Description The Greenwood Nursing Home is
a small facility that caters to the individual
needs of residents. Staff has become an
extended family to residents.

Guardian Nursing Home*
105 Chestnut St, Wakefield, MA, 01880 (617)
245-2483
Admin Stephen Scapicchio.
Licensure Intermediate Care. *Beds* 24. *Certified* Medicaid.

Kirkwood Nursing Home*
202 Main St, Wakefield, MA, 01880 (617)
245-4129
Admin Bettiann Wells.
Licensure Intermediate Care. *Beds* 32. *Certified* Medicaid.

Oosterman's Rest Home
706 Main St, Wakefield, MA, 01880 (617)
245-4778
Admin Gladys Foster.
Licensure Rest Home. *Beds* 19.
Admissions Requirements Females only;
Medical examination; Physician's request.

Facilities Dining room.
Activities Cards; Games.
Description Oosterman's is a small home-like facility.

WALTHAM

Abbey Forest Nursing Home*
50 Forest St, Waltham, MA, 02154 (617) 893-3453
Admin Patrick J Fahy.
Licensure Intermediate Care. *Beds* 40. *Certified* Medicaid.

Doctor C Benjamin Fuller Home
250 South St, Waltham, MA, 02154 (617) 893-4229
Admin Gregory Karr.
Licensure Intermediate Care. *Beds* 28. *Certified* Medicaid.

Hopkins Nursing Home*
508 Lexington St, Waltham, MA, 02154 (617) 893-7841
Admin Paul G Hopkins.
Licensure Intermediate Care. *Beds* 19. *Certified* Medicaid.

Larchwood Lodge Nursing Home*
221 Worcester Lane, Waltham, MA, 02154 (617) 894-4720
Admin G Paul Hopkins.
Licensure Intermediate Care. *Beds* 32. *Certified* Medicaid.

Lee Rest Home*
222 Bacon St, Waltham, MA, 02154 (617) 894-0645
Admin William F Lee.
Licensure Rest Home. *Beds* 27.

Leland Home
21 Newton St, Waltham, MA, 02154 (617) 893-2557
Admin Eleanor M Larkin. *Medical Dir/Dir of Nursing* David Duhme MD.
Licensure Intermediate Care. *Beds* 41. *Certified* Medicaid.
Admissions Requirements Minimum age 65; Medical examination; Physician's request.
Staff Physicians 1 (pt); RNs 1 (ft), 4 (pt); LPNs 2 (ft), 3 (pt); Nurses aides 2 (ft), 4 (pt); Recreational therapists 1 (pt); Activities coordinators 1 (pt); Dietitians 1 (pt); Dentists 1 (pt); Ophthalmologists 1 (pt); Podiatrists 1 (pt); Audiologists 1 (pt).
Facilities Dining room; Physical therapy room; Activities room; Chapel; Crafts room; Laundry room; Barber/Beauty shop; Library.
Activities Arts and Crafts; Cards; Games; Reading groups; Prayer groups; Movies; Shopping trips.
Description Home is most unique in that it houses 41 residents and maintains a homey atmosphere; residents act as a family and are part of decision making; meals in common dining room served home-style; special functions at request of family; English high tea; family cookouts.

Maristhill Nursing Home*
66 Newton St, Waltham, MA, 02154 (617) 893-0240
Admin Phyllis Rooney Sr.
Licensure Skilled Care; Intermediate Care; Charitable Home. *Beds* 123. *Certified* Medicaid.

Piety Corner Nursing Home*
325 Bacon St, Waltham, MA, 02154 (617) 894-5264
Admin Guy D'Amore.
Licensure Intermediate Care. *Beds* 34. *Certified* Medicaid.

Prospect Hill Nursing Home
31 Woodland Rd, Waltham, MA, 02154 (617) 893-6916
Admin Vasco A Lima Jr. *Medical Dir/Dir of Nursing* Albert Levinson.
Licensure Intermediate Care. *Beds* 28. *Certified* Medicaid.
Admissions Requirements Females only; Medical examination; Physician's request.
Staff RNs 1 (ft); LPNs 4 (ft); Nurses aides 6 (ft); Physical therapists 1 (pt); Reality therapists 1 (pt); Recreational therapists 1 (pt); Occupational therapists 1 (pt); Speech therapists 1 (pt); Activities coordinators 1 (ft); Dietitians 1 (pt); Dentists 1 (pt); Podiatrists 1 (pt).
Facilities Dining room; Activities room; Crafts room; Laundry room.
Activities Arts and Crafts; Cards; Games; Reading groups; Prayer groups; Movies; Shopping trips; Dances/Social or cultural gatherings.

Reservoir Nursing Home Inc*
1841 Trapelo Rd, Waltham, MA, 02154 (617) 890-5000
Admin Dorothy S Hill.
Licensure Skilled Care; Intermediate Care. *Beds* 120. *Certified* Medicaid; Medicare.

Ross-Worthen Home
90 Worcester Ln, Waltham, MA, 02154 (617) 893-4250
Admin Marjorie McKeon.
Licensure Intermediate Care. *Beds* 22. *Certified* Medicaid.

Varnum Park Rest Home*
249 Bacon St, Waltham, MA, 02154 (617) 894-3320
Admin Doris M Lee.
Licensure Rest Home. *Beds* 31.

Waltham Nursing Home Inc*
91 Summer St, Waltham, MA, 02154 (617) 893-6944
Admin Deborah A Hagar.
Licensure Intermediate Care. *Beds* 29. *Certified* Medicaid.

WAREHAM

Cape Cod Nursing and Retirement Home*
Lewis Point Rd, Buzzards Bay, Wareham, MA, 02532 (617) 759-5752
Admin Kathleen McGregor.
Licensure Intermediate Care. *Beds* 97. *Certified* Medicaid.

Lake View Rest Home*
2 Depot St, Wareham, MA, 02538 (617) 295-1440
Admin Sandra McCubrey.
Licensure Rest Home. *Beds* 16.

Roland Thatcher Nursing Home*
Main St, Wareham, MA, 02571 (617) 295-1040
Admin Charlotte A Strong.
Licensure Skilled Care; Intermediate Care. *Beds* 108. *Certified* Medicaid.

WASHINGTON

Maple View Nursing Home*
Lover's Lane Rd, Washington, MA, 01201 (413) 623-8936
Admin Elizabeth Jones.
Licensure Intermediate Care. *Beds* 57. *Certified* Medicaid.

WATERTOWN

Charlesgate Manor Convalescent Home Inc
590 Main St, Watertown, MA, 02172 (617) 924-1966
Medical Dir/Dir of Nursing Dr Eli Jacobs.
Licensure Skilled Care; Intermediate Care. *Beds* 102. *Certified* Medicaid.
Staff Physicians 3 (pt); RNs 5 (ft), 4 (pt); LPNs 3 (ft), 4 (pt); Orderlies 2 (ft), 1 (pt); Nurses aides 20 (ft), 36 (pt); Physical therapists 1 (pt); Reality therapists 1 (pt); Occupational therapists 1 (pt); Speech therapists 1 (pt); Activities coordinators 1 (ft), 1 (pt); Dietitians 1 (pt); Dentists 1 (pt); Ophthalmologists 1 (pt); Podiatrists 1 (pt).
Facilities Dining room; Physical therapy room; Activities room; Chapel; Crafts room; Laundry room; Barber/Beauty shop.
Activities Arts and Crafts; Cards; Games; Reading groups; Prayer groups; Movies; Shopping trips; Dances/Social or cultural gatherings.

Emerson Convalescent Home Inc
59 Coolidge Hill Rd, Watertown, MA, 02172 (617) 924-1130
Admin Norman J Duffy. *Medical Dir/Dir of Nursing* Alan M Barron MD.
Licensure Skilled Care; Intermediate Care. *Beds* 163. *Certified* Medicaid.
Admissions Requirements Minimum age 60; Medical examination.
Staff RNs 8 (ft), 5 (pt); LPNs 10 (ft), 11 (pt); Orderlies 3 (ft), 3 (pt); Nurses aides 60 (ft), 58 (pt); Physical therapists 1 (pt); Reality therapists 1 (pt); Recreational therapists 1 (ft), 2 (pt); Occupational therapists 1 (ft); Activities coordinators 1 (ft); Dietitians 1 (pt); Social workers 2 (ft).
Facilities Dining room; Physical therapy room; Activities room; Chapel; Crafts room; Laundry room; Barber/Beauty shop.
Activities Arts and Crafts; Cards; Games; Reading groups; Prayer groups; Movies; Shopping trips; Dances/Social or cultural gatherings.
Description A 6-story building, the basement includes all storage and laundry, the first floor all department offices, activities; the 4 other floors are resident floors with all being laid out the same.

Marshall House
120 Mount Auburn St, Watertown, MA, 02172
(617) 924-4510
Admin Julie Brandlen.
Licensure Rest Home. *Beds* 18.
Admissions Requirements Minimum age 65;
Medical examination.
Staff RNs 1 (pt); Nurses aides 2 (ft), 4 (pt);
Recreational therapists 1 (pt).
Facilities Dining room; Activities room; Crafts
room; Laundry room; Living rooms; Patio.
Activities Arts and Crafts; Cards; Movies; Exercise class.
Description All residents have private rooms
with shared bathroom (with one other resident). Residents are given the option of participating in any or all of the activities provided by
Marshall Home while still respecting personal
privacy needs. Complete laundry service is
available to all residents.

WAYLAND

Cochituate Nursing Home Inc*
188 Commonwealth Rd, Wayland, MA, 01778
(617) 653-8500
Admin Philip R Guidrey.
Licensure Intermediate Care. *Beds* 40. *Certified* Medicaid.

Kathryn Barton Nursing Home
373 Commonwealth Rd, Wayland, MA, 01778
(617) 653-5401
Admin Susan Corman Burnett. *Medical Dir-/Dir of Nursing* Joyce Vettraino MD.
Licensure Skilled Care. *Beds* 55. *Certified* Medicaid; Medicare.
Staff Physicians 1 (pt); RNs 4 (ft), 3 (pt); LPNs
2 (ft), 6 (pt); Nurses aides 24 (ft), 12 (pt);
Physical therapists 1 (pt); Speech therapists 1
(pt); Activities coordinators 1 (ft); Dietitians 1
(pt); Dentists 1 (pt); Podiatrists 1 (pt).
Facilities Dining room; Physical therapy room;
Crafts room; Laundry room; Barber/Beauty
shop.
Activities Arts and Crafts; Games; Prayer
groups; Movies; Shopping trips; Dances/Social
or cultural gatherings; Sculpture group; Painting
class; Weekly cookout in summer; Musical
group; Exercise aerobics.
Description Facility is one level, accessible to
the handicapped. Provides many choices in the
areas of activities; one outstanding program is
the exercise aerobics for the elderly. It is offered
under the direction of a physical therapist and
conducted by a trained physical therapy assistant.

WEBSTER

Oakwood Convalescent Home
86 Hartley St, Webster, MA, 01570-1699 (617)
943-3889
Admin Daniel A O'Neil.
Licensure Skilled Care; Intermediate Care.
Beds 81. *Certified* Medicaid.
Admissions Requirements Minimum age 21.
Staff Physicians; RNs 4 (ft), 2 (pt); LPNs 3 (ft),
4 (pt); Orderlies; Nurses aides; Physical therapists; Occupational therapists; Speech therapists; Activities coordinators; Dietitians;

Dentists; Ophthalmologists; Podiatrists;
Audiologists.
Facilities Dining room; Activities room; Chapel; Laundry room; Barber/Beauty shop.
Activities Arts and Crafts; Cards; Games;
Reading groups; Movies; Shopping trips; Dances/Social or cultural gatherings.

Webster House LTCF
749 School St, Webster, MA, 01570 (617)
949-0111
Admin Richard A Wentzel.
Licensure Skilled Care; Intermediate Care.
Beds 43. *Certified* Medicaid.

Webster Manor LTCF
749 School St, Webster, MA, 10570 (617)
949-0644
Admin Richard Wentzel.
Licensure Skilled Care; Intermediate Care.
Beds 123. *Certified* Medicaid.
Admissions Requirements Minimum age 21.
Staff Physicians 1 (pt); Orderlies 2 (ft);
Physical therapists 1 (ft), 1 (pt); Reality therapists 1 (pt); Recreational therapists 1 (pt); Occupational therapists 1 (ft), 1 (pt); Speech
therapists 1 (pt); Activities coordinators 1 (ft);
Dietitians 1 (pt); Dentists 1 (pt); Ophthalmologists 1 (pt); Podiatrists 1 (pt); Audiologists 1
(pt).
Facilities Dining room; Physical therapy room;
Activities room; Chapel; Crafts room; Laundry
room; Barber/Beauty shop; Library.
Activities Arts and Crafts; Cards; Games;
Reading groups; Prayer groups; Movies; Shopping trips; Dances/Social or cultural gatherings.

WELLESLEY

Elizabeth Seton Residence*
125 Oakland St, Wellesley, MA, 02181 (617)
251-2161
Admin Joan Cassidy.
Licensure Skilled Care. *Beds* 41.

Newton-Wellesley Nursing Home
694 Worcester Rd, Wellesley, MA, 02181 (617)
237-6400
Admin Sharyn Zimmerman.
Licensure Skilled Care; Intermediate Care.
Beds 120. *Certified* Medicaid; Medicare.
Staff RNs 8 (ft), 10 (pt); LPNs 6 (ft), 4 (pt);
Orderlies 4 (ft); Nurses aides 20 (ft), 35 (pt);
Physical therapists 1 (pt); Occupational therapists 1 (pt); Speech therapists 1 (pt); Activities
coordinators 3 (ft); Dietitians 1 (pt); Dentists 1
(pt); Ophthalmologists 1 (pt); Podiatrists 1 (pt);
Resorative therapists 3 (ft).
Facilities Dining room; Physical therapy room;
Activities room; Laundry room; Barber/Beauty
shop.
Activities Arts and Crafts; Cards; Games;
Reading groups; Prayer groups; Movies; Shopping trips; Dances/Social or cultural gatherings;
Luncheon trips; Movie trips.
Description Facility specializes in Alzheimer's;
planning, a special care unit for patients with
Alzheimer's disease and related disorders.

Wellesley Manor Nursing Home
878 Worcester St, Wellesley, MA, 02181 (617)
235-6699

Admin Mark Berman.
Licensure Skilled Care. *Beds* 97. *Certified* Medicare.
Facilities Dining room; Physical therapy room;
Activities room; Crafts room; Laundry room;
Barber/Beauty shop.
Activities Arts and Crafts; Cards; Games;
Reading groups; Prayer groups; Movies.

WEST BOYLSTON

Oakdale Nursing Home*
86 N Main St, West Boylston, MA, 01539 (617)
835-6076
Admin Stanley E Andriski.
Licensure Skilled Care; Intermediate Care.
Beds 80. *Certified* Medicaid.

WEST BROOKFIELD

Brook Haven Rest Home*
Main St, West Brookfield, MA, 01585 (617)
867-3325
Admin Madaline D Smith-Papison.
Licensure Rest Home. *Beds* 22.

Quaboag Nursing Home*
32 Main St, West Brookfield, MA, 01585 (617)
867-7716
Admin James J Moran.
Licensure Skilled Care; Intermediate Care.
Beds 129. *Certified* Medicaid.

Westbrook Heights Rest Home
Brookfield Rd, West Brookfield, MA, 01585
(617) 867-2062
Admin Annette Dorman. *Medical Dir/Dir of
Nursing* R Fowler MD.
Licensure Rest Home. *Beds* 26.
Admissions Requirements Minimum age 35;
Medical examination; Physician's request.
Staff Physicians 2 (pt); RNs 1 (pt); LPNs 1
(pt); Orderlies 3 (ft); Nurses aides 2 (ft); Activities coordinators 2 (pt); Dietitians 2 (ft), 1 (pt);
Dentists 1 (pt); Podiatrists 1 (pt).
Facilities Dining room; Activities room; Crafts
room; Laundry room; Barber/Beauty shop.
Activities Arts and Crafts; Cards; Games; Prayer groups; Shopping trips; Dances/Social or cultural gatherings.
Description Facility is located in a country
setting within walking distance to center of
town with bandstand entertainment in the
summer months and close to shopping area;
offers residents gardening and picnic areas.

WEST SPRINGFIELD

Riverdale Gardens Nursing Home*
42 Prospect Ave, West Springfield, MA, 01089
(413) 733-3151
Admin George A McNeill.
Licensure Skilled Care; Intermediate Care.
Beds 125. *Certified* Medicaid; Medicare.

West Springfield Nursing Home
217 Westfield St, West Springfield, MA, 01089
(413) 788-6126
Admin Leo A Gadoua. *Medical Dir/Dir of
Nursing* James J Visconti MD.
Licensure Skilled Care. *Beds* 120. *Cer-*

tified Medicaid.
Admissions Requirements Minimum age 21.
Staff RNs 9 (ft), 5 (pt); LPNs 3 (ft), 4 (pt); Orderlies 1 (ft), 1 (pt); Nurses aides 40 (ft), 20 (pt); Reality therapists 1 (pt); Recreational therapists 1 (ft), 1 (pt); Occupational therapists 1 (pt); Speech therapists 1 (pt); Activities coordinators 1 (ft); Dietitians 1 (pt).
Facilities Dining room; Activities room; Crafts room; Laundry room; Barber/Beauty shop; Library.
Activities Arts and Crafts; Cards; Games; Prayer groups; Movies; Shopping trips; Dances/Social or cultural gatherings; Bingo.
Description One-floor facility with a very active activity department and very dedicated volunteer group.

WESTBOROUGH

Westborough Nursing Home
Colonial Dr, Westborough, MA, 01581 (617) 366-9131
Admin Anthony J Penny. *Medical Dir/Dir of Nursing* Robert Klugman MD.
Licensure Skilled Care; Intermediate Care.
Beds 123. *Certified* Medicaid; Medicare.
Staff RNs 6 (ft), 14 (pt); LPNs 4 (ft), 5 (pt); Nurses aides 28 (ft), 28 (pt); Activities coordinators 2 (ft), 1 (pt).
Facilities Dining room; Physical therapy room; Activities room; Crafts room; Laundry room; Barber/Beauty shop.
Activities Arts and Crafts; Cards; Games; Reading groups; Prayer groups; Movies; Shopping trips; Dances/Social or cultural gatherings.

WESTFIELD

Barnard Rest Home*
160 Franklin St, Westfield, MA, 01085 (413) 562-2931
Admin Ivan K Barnard.
Licensure Rest Home. *Beds* 84.

Governor's House Nursing Home
66 Broad St, Westfield, MA, 01085 (413) 562-5464
Admin Rosemary Debuc. *Medical Dir/Dir of Nursing* Paul Bothnen MD.
Licensure Skilled Care; Intermediate Care.
Beds 100. *Certified* Medicaid.
Ownership Proprietary.
Facilities Dining room; Physical therapy room; Activities room; Chapel; Crafts room; Laundry room; Barber/Beauty shop; Library.
Activities Arts and Crafts; Cards; Games; Movies; Shopping trips; Dances/Social or cultural gatherings.
Description Facility was designed by an award winning architect.

Valley View Nursing Home Inc
Feeding Hills Rd, Westfield, MA, 01085 (413) 568-2341
Admin Joseph H Smith Jr. *Medical Dir/Dir of Nursing* James J Visconti MD.
Licensure Skilled Care. *Beds* 80. *Certified* Medicaid.
Admissions Requirements Minimum age 21.
Staff Occupational therapists 1 (pt); Speech

therapists 1 (pt); Activities coordinators 1 (ft); Dietitians 1 (pt); Dentists 1 (pt); Podiatrists 1 (pt).
Facilities Dining room; Physical therapy room; Activities room; Crafts room; Laundry room; Barber/Beauty shop; Library.
Activities Arts and Crafts; Cards; Games; Dances/Social or cultural gatherings.

Westfield Manor Nursing Home*
E Silver Rd, Westfield, MA, 01085 (413) 562-5122
Admin Richard E Furlong.
Licensure Skilled Care; Intermediate Care.
Beds 104. *Certified* Medicaid.

WESTFORD

Westford Nursing Home Inc
15 Main St, Westford, MA, 01886 (617) 692-4787
Admin Carol A Fortier. *Medical Dir/Dir of Nursing* Dr Thomas Fitzpatrick.
Licensure Intermediate Care. *Beds* 58. *Certified* Medicaid.
Admissions Requirements Medical examination.
Staff Physicians; RNs 4 (pt); LPNs 2 (ft), 5 (pt); Nurses aides 14 (ft), 11 (pt); Activities coordinators 1 (pt); Dietitians 1 (pt); Podiatrists 1 (pt).
Activities Arts and Crafts; Cards; Games; Reading groups; Prayer groups; Movies; Shopping trips; Dances/Social or cultural gatherings.
Description Facility is located in a picturesque country-like setting. Westford's only intermediate care facility provides 24-hour nursing care.

WESTMINISTER

Maranatha Rest Home
99 State Rd, Westminister, MA, 01473 (617) 632-0985
Admin Richard R Boucher.
Licensure Rest Home. *Beds* 12.
Admissions Requirements Medical examination; Physician's request.
Staff Nurses aides 8 (ft); Recreational therapists 1 (ft); Activities coordinators 1 (ft); Dietitians 1 (pt).
Facilities Dining room; Activities room; Laundry room; Library.
Activities Cards; Games; Reading groups; Prayer groups; Shopping trips.
Description Facility features home-like atmosphere.

WESTON

Campion Residence and Renewal Center
319 Concord Rd, Weston, MA, 02193 (617) 894-0751
Admin Richard T Cleary. *Medical Dir/Dir of Nursing* Dr John E Doherty.
Licensure Rest Home. *Beds* 15.
Admissions Requirements Males only
Staff Physicians 1 (pt); RNs 4 (ft), 4 (pt); LPNs 3 (ft); Nurses aides 4 (ft), 7 (pt); Physical therapists 1 (pt); Activities coordinators 1 (pt); Dietitians 1 (ft); Dentists 1 (pt).
Affiliation Roman Catholic

Facilities Dining room; Physical therapy room; Activities room; Chapel; Crafts room; Laundry room; Barber/Beauty shop; Library.
Activities Arts and Crafts; Cards; Games; Prayer groups; Movies.
Description Center admits only members of own religious order (Society of Jesus). A retreat and renewal center is part of overall operation and up to 100 people can be accomodated for such activities. It is a beautiful rural setting with extensive grounds.

Weston Manor Nursing and Retirement
75 Norumbega Rd, Weston, MA, 02193 (617) 891-6100
Admin Benjamin Shuman. *Medical Dir/Dir of Nursing* Jerome Tanzer MD.
Licensure Intermediate Care. *Beds* 120. *Certified* Medicaid.
Staff Physicians 1 (pt); RNs 8 (ft), 9 (pt); LPNs 4 (ft), 3 (pt); Orderlies 3 (ft), 2 (pt); Nurses aides 25 (ft), 35 (pt); Physical therapists 2 (pt); Recreational therapists 2 (ft); Occupational therapists 1 (pt); Speech therapists 1 (pt); Activities coordinators 1 (ft); Dietitians 1 (pt); Dentists 1 (pt); Ophthalmologists 1 (pt); Podiatrists 1 (pt); Audiologists 1 (pt).
Facilities Dining room; Physical therapy room; Activities room; Chapel; Crafts room; Laundry room; Barber/Beauty shop.
Activities Arts and Crafts; Cards; Games; Reading groups; Movies; Shopping trips; Dances/Social or cultural gatherings.
Description Weston Manor also has a day care center for senior citizens; close to the major highway, but in a very quiet setting with a lovely duck pond.

WEYMOUTH

Bradley Manor Nursing Home
861 Main St, Weymouth, MA, 02190 (617) 337-0678
Admin Joseph Aristide.
Licensure Skilled Care; Intermediate Care.
Beds 72. *Certified* Medicaid.

Brookbend Rest Home*
27 Front St, Weymouth, MA, 02188 (617) 335-2596
Admin Alice L Chappel.
Licensure Rest Home. *Beds* 33.

Colonial Nursing and Rehabilitation Center*
125 Broad St, Weymouth, MA, 02188 (617) 337-3121
Admin Rita M Welch.
Licensure Skilled Care; Intermediate Care.
Beds 211. *Certified* Medicaid; Medicare.

Pope Nursing Home*
140 Webb St, Weymouth, MA, 02188 (617) 335-4352
Admin Margaret Pomerdy.
Licensure Intermediate Care. *Beds* 37. *Certified* Medicaid.

Samuel Marcus Nursing and Retirement Home*
28 Front St, Weymouth, MA, 02188 (617) 337-9074

Admin Arthur S Logan.
Licensure Intermediate Care. *Beds* 22. *Certified* Medicaid.

Weymouth Manor Nursing Home*
188 Summer St, Weymouth, MA, 02188 (617) 337-6900
Admin Patrick O'Connor.
Licensure Skilled Care; Intermediate Care. *Beds* 84. *Certified* Medicaid.

Whittaker Rest Home*
46 Union St, Weymouth, MA, 02190 (617) 335-5885
Admin Robert S Whittaker.
Licensure Rest Home. *Beds* 34.

WHITMAN

Brae Burn Nursing Home*
146 South Ave, Whitman, MA, 02382 (617) 447-5541
Admin Francis J Cummings.
Licensure Intermediate Care. *Beds* 60. *Certified* Medicaid.

WILLIAMSBURG

Colonial Rest Home*
18 S Main St, Williamsburg, MA, 01039 (413) 268-7321
Admin Collin S Campbell.
Licensure Rest Home. *Beds* 18.

Sunny Acres Nursing Home*
Rt 9, Haydenville, Williamsburg, MA, 01039 (413) 268-7291
Admin James R Wade.
Licensure Intermediate Care. *Beds* 30. *Certified* Medicaid.

WILLIAMSTOWN

Adams Nursing Home*
Adams Rd, Williamstown, MA, 01267 (413) 458-4353
Admin Earle O Brown Jr.
Licensure Skilled Care. *Beds* 72. *Certified* Medicaid.

Sweetbrook Nursing Home*
Cold Spring Rd, Williamstown, MA, 01267 (413) 458-8127
Admin K Elaine Neely.
Licensure Skilled Care. *Beds* 122. *Certified* Medicaid; Medicare.

WINCHENDON

Hillside Rest Home*
547 Central St, Winchendon, MA, 01475 (617) 297-2333
Admin Stanley S Smith.
Licensure Rest Home. *Beds* 27.

Open Arms Nursing Home
163 Brown St, Winchendon, MA, 01475 (617) 297-2458
Admin Edith A Hallet.
Licensure Intermediate Care. *Beds* 39. *Certi-*

fied Medicaid.
Staff Physicians; RNs 2 (ft), 1 (pt); LPNs 2 (ft), 1 (pt); Nurses aides 8 (ft), 3 (pt); Physical therapists 1 (ft); Occupational therapists 1 (pt); Speech therapists 1 (pt); Activities coordinators 1 (ft), 1 (pt); Dietitians 1 (pt); Dentists 1 (pt); Ophthalmologists 1 (pt); Podiatrists 1 (pt).
Facilities Dining room; Physical therapy room; Activities room; Crafts room; Laundry room; Barber/Beauty shop; Library.
Activities Arts and Crafts; Cards; Games; Reading groups; Prayer groups; Movies; Dances/Social or cultural gatherings; Feeding groups.
Description Facility provides a "home" for patients until, hopefully, they can return to their own home as functional alert persons. Their physical well-being, self-esteem, and maximum daily function are staff's ultimate goals.

Pleasant View Rest Home
271 High St, Winchendon, MA, 01475 (617) 297-0325
Admin Robert J Grady. *Medical Dir/Dir of Nursing* John Harrington MD.
Licensure Rest Home. *Beds* 19.
Admissions Requirements Minimum age 18; Medical examination; Physician's request.
Staff Physicians 1 (pt); LPNs 1 (ft); Nurses aides 13 (pt); Dietitians 1 (pt); Dentists 1 (pt); Podiatrists 1 (pt); Audiologists 1 (pt).
Facilities Dining room; Activities room; Crafts room; Laundry room; Library.
Activities Arts and Crafts; Cards; Games; Reading groups; Prayer groups; Movies; Shopping trips.
Description This facility is in a country setting where animals are prominent. Flowers and vegatable gardens are planted and maintained. Nature walks with residents are held for an understanding of our environment. A young medical staff oriented to care of geriatric residents is always available.

WINCHESTER

Aberjona Nursing Home Inc*
Box 490, 184 Swanton St, Winchester, MA, 01890 (617) 729-9370
Admin Robert Salter.
Licensure Skilled Care; Intermediate Care. *Beds* 123. *Certified* Medicaid.

Home for Aged People
110 Mount Vernon St, Winchester, MA, 01890 (617) 729-0497
Admin Grace P Phillips.
Licensure Rest Home. *Beds* 17.
Admissions Requirements Minimum age 65; Medical examination.
Staff RNs 1 (ft).
Facilities Dining room; Activities room; Crafts room; Laundry room; Barber/Beauty shop; Library.
Activities Games; Movies.
Description Facility has home-like atmosphere with private rooms furnished by residents; 3 home cooked meals a day; hobby room for any activities; lounge for social gatherings, musical programs, and more.

Winchester Convalescent and Nursing Home*
Box 490, 223 Swanton St, Winchester, MA, 01890 (617) 729-9595
Admin Gershon Salter.
Licensure Skilled Care; Intermediate Care. *Beds* 120. *Certified* Medicaid; Medicare.

WINDSOR

Elizabeth Seton Residence
125 Oakland St, Windsor, MA, 02181 (617) 251-2161
Admin Margaret Coyle.
Licensure Skilled Care. *Beds* 32. *Certified* Medicaid.

WINTHROP

Bay View Nursing Home*
26 Sturgis St, Winthrop, MA, 02152 (617) 846-1326
Admin Mary V Keniston.
Licensure Intermediate Care. *Beds* 78. *Certified* Medicaid.

Cliff House Nursing Home Inc
170 Cliff Ave, Winthrop, MA, 02152 (617) 846-0500
Admin C H Anderson. *Medical Dir/Dir of Nursing* John Coyle MD.
Licensure Skilled Care; Intermediate Care. *Beds* 88. *Certified* Medicaid.
Staff RNs; LPNs; Orderlies; Nurses aides; Physical therapists; Reality therapists; Occupational therapists; Speech therapists; Activities coordinators; Dietitians; Dentists; Podiatrists; Audiologists.
Facilities Dining room; Activities room; Crafts room; Laundry room; Barber/Beauty shop.
Activities Arts and Crafts; Cards; Games; Shopping trips.
Description Facility features an ocean view and is minutes from downtown Boston.

Governor Winthop Nursing Home
142 Pleasant St, Winthrop, MA, 02152 (617) 846-7750
Admin Robert D Wilkins. *Medical Dir/Dir of Nursing* Dr George Bonderman.
Licensure Intermediate Care. *Beds* 87. *Certified* Medicaid.
Admissions Requirements Physician's request.
Staff Physicians 7 (pt); RNs 4 (ft), 6 (pt); LPNs 4 (ft), 4 (pt); Orderlies 1 (pt); Nurses aides 25 (ft), 10 (pt); Physical therapists 1 (ft); Recreational therapists 2 (pt); Speech therapists 1 (pt); Activities coordinators 1 (ft); Dietitians 1 (pt); Dentists 1 (pt); Ophthalmologists 1 (pt); Podiatrists 1 (pt); Audiologists 1 (pt).
Facilities Dining room; Physical therapy room; Activities room; Laundry room; Barber/Beauty shop.
Activities Arts and Crafts; Games; Reading groups; Prayer groups; Movies; Shopping trips; Ceramics.
Description Truly outstanding physical plant with an excellent caring staff; very active activities program; superior food; facility immaculately clean.

WOBURN

Glendale Nursing Home*
171 Cambridge Rd, Woburn, MA, 01801 (617) 933-7080
Admin Mary Carroll.
Licensure Intermediate Care. *Beds* 49. *Certified* Medicaid.

New England Rehabilitation Hospital*
Rehabilitation Way, Woburn, MA, 01801 (617) 935-5050
Admin Sr Joan Cassidy.
Licensure Skilled Care. *Beds* 120. *Certified* Medicaid; Medicare.

Tidd Home
74 Elm St, Woburn, MA, 01801 (617) 933-0248
Admin Beverly Whalen.
Licensure Charitable Home. *Beds* 14.
Admissions Requirements Minimum age 65; Females only; Medical examination.
Facilities Dining room; Laundry room.
Activities Cards; Movies; Shopping trips.
Description Facility is a home for ladies that are able to look after themselves. Residential nurses and doctors are not needed; residents are taken to doctor, dentist, and shopping.

Woburn Nursing Home Inc*
18 Frances St, Woburn, MA, 01801 (617) 933-8175
Admin Edith Salter.
Licensure Skilled Care; Intermediate Care.
Beds 110. *Certified* Medicaid.

WORCESTER

Anna Maria Rest Home
1398 Main St, Worcester, MA, 01603 (617) 756-1515
Admin Florence Stearns.
Licensure Rest Home. *Beds* 64.
Facilities Dining room; Activities room; Crafts room; Laundry room; Barber/Beauty shop; Reading room; 2 Lounges with color TVs.
Activities Arts and Crafts; Games; Reading groups; Prayer groups; Movies; Shopping trips; Dances/Social or cultural gatherings; Planned trips; Entertainment groups.
Description Modern building adheres to all safety codes; air changes every 12 minutes; elevator serves all 3 floors; experienced attendants are on duty with stations on each floor.

Armstrong Nursing Home
119 Forest St, Worcester, MA, 01609 (617) 754-6190
Admin James M Meola. *Medical Dir/Dir of Nursing* Dr Arthur Ward.
Licensure Intermediate Care. *Beds* 17. *Certified* Medicaid.
Admissions Requirements Minimum age 50; Males only; Medical examination; Physician's request.
Staff Physicians 1 (pt); RNs 1 (ft), 2 (pt); LPNs 1 (ft), 5 (pt); Nurses aides 1 (ft), 2 (pt); Activities coordinators 1 (pt); Dietitians 1 (pt).
Facilities Dining room; Laundry room.
Activities Arts and Crafts; Cards; Games; Movies; Shopping trips.

Bancroft House Healthcare Nursing Home
835 Main St, Worcester, MA, 01610 (617) 757-6311
Admin John Mahoney. *Medical Dir/Dir of Nursing* Carl Marsh MD.
Licensure Skilled Care; Intermediate Care.
Beds 120. *Certified* Medicaid; Medicare.
Admissions Requirements Minimum age 18.
Staff RNs 4 (ft), 13 (pt); LPNs 3 (ft), 6 (pt); Nurses aides 19 (ft), 26 (pt); Activities coordinators 1 (ft), 1 (pt); 14 (ft), 16 (pt).
Facilities Dining room; Physical therapy room; Activities room; Crafts room; Laundry room; Barber/Beauty shop.
Activities Arts and Crafts; Cards; Games; Reading groups; Prayer groups; Movies; Shopping trips; Dances/Social or cultural gatherings.

Beechaven Nursing Home*
133 Paine St, Worcester, MA, 01605 (617) 752-3029
Admin Leo H Roberge Jr.
Licensure Intermediate Care. *Beds* 19. *Certified* Medicaid.

Belmont Home*
255 Belmont St, Worcester, MA, 01605 (617) 799-1554
Admin Arthur Firella.
Licensure Skilled Care; Intermediate Care.
Beds 184. *Certified* Medicaid.

Blaire House of Worcester
116 Houghton St, Worcester, MA, 01604 (617) 791-5543
Admin Robert E Arsenaunt. *Medical Dir/Dir of Nursing* Dr Thomas Walsh.
Licensure Skilled Care; Intermediate Care.
Beds 75. *Certified* Medicaid.
Staff Physicians 11 (pt); RNs 4 (ft), 8 (pt); LPNs 2 (ft), 2 (pt); Orderlies 4 (ft), 1 (pt); Nurses aides 13 (ft), 15 (pt); Physical therapists 1 (pt); Recreational therapists 1 (ft); Occupational therapists 1 (ft), 1 (pt); Activities coordinators 1 (ft); Dietitians 1 (pt); Dentists 1 (pt); Ophthalmologists 1 (pt); Podiatrists 1 (pt).
Facilities Dining room; Activities room; Crafts room; Laundry room; Barber/Beauty shop; Library.
Activities Arts and Crafts; Cards; Games; Reading groups; Prayer groups; Movies; Shopping trips; Dances/Social or cultural gatherings.

Burncoat Plains Rest Home*
572 Burncoat St, Worcester, MA, 01606 (617) 853-0021
Admin William J Lange.
Licensure Rest Home. *Beds* 35.

Castle Park Nursing Home*
22-24 King St, Worcester, MA, 01610 (617) 752-8910
Admin Janet P Waller.
Licensure Intermediate Care. *Beds* 30. *Certified* Medicaid.

Catherine Rest Home
27 Catherine St, Worcester, MA, 01610 (617) 756-3954
Admin George H Gross.
Licensure Rest Home. *Beds* 26.
Admissions Requirements Minimum age 21; Medical examination; Physician's request.

Staff LPNs 1 (ft); Orderlies 1 (ft), 1 (pt); Nurses aides 1 (ft), 3 (pt); Recreational therapists 1 (pt); Activities coordinators 1 (pt); Dietitians 1 (pt).
Facilities Dining room; Activities room; Laundry room.
Activities Arts and Crafts; Cards; Games; Reading groups; Movies.
Description Facility is a 27-bed, Level IV facility located close to shopping center and on bus route. Registered dietician and registered nurses on call 24 hours daily.

Catherine Windsor Rest Home
25 Catherine St, Worcester, MA, 01606 (617) 791-5166
Admin Richard F Alarie.
Licensure Rest Home. *Beds* 34.
Admissions Requirements Minimum age 21; Medical examination.
Staff RNs 1 (pt); Orderlies 2 (pt); Nurses aides 4 (ft); Recreational therapists 1 (pt); Dietitians 1 (pt).
Facilities Dining room; Laundry room.
Activities Arts and Crafts; Cards; Games; Reading groups; Movies.

Charstelle Nursing Home
39 Queen St, Worcester, MA, 01610 (617) 753-4791
Admin Myrtle F Cram. *Medical Dir/Dir of Nursing* Dr Jeffrey Burl.
Licensure Skilled Care; Intermediate Care.
Beds 160. *Certified* Medicaid.
Admissions Requirements Minimum age 21.
Staff RNs 5 (ft), 11 (pt); LPNs 9 (ft), 4 (pt); Orderlies 3 (ft), 2 (pt); Nurses aides 50 (ft), 7 (pt); Physical therapists 1 (pt); Recreational therapists 2 (ft); Occupational therapists 1 (pt); Activities coordinators 2 (ft); Dietitians 1 (pt); Podiatrists 1 (pt).
Facilities Dining room; Physical therapy room; Activities room; Chapel; Crafts room; Laundry room; Barber/Beauty shop; Library.
Activities Arts and Crafts; Cards; Games; Reading groups; Prayer groups; Movies; Shopping trips; Dances/Social or cultural gatherings.

Clark Manor Nursing Home*
1350 Main St, Worcester, MA, 01603 (617) 791-4200
Admin Morris Sibulkin Jr.
Licensure Skilled Care; Intermediate Care.
Beds 162. *Certified* Medicaid.

Dalton Rest Home*
453 Cambridge St, Worcester, MA, 01610 (617) 756-7310
Admin William J Lange.
Licensure Rest Home. *Beds* 34.

Dodge Park Rest Home*
101 Randolph Rd, Worcester, MA, 01606 (617) 853-8180
Admin Anthony E Penny.
Licensure Rest Home. *Beds* 32.

Donna Kay Rest Home Inc
16 Marble St, Worcester, MA, 01603 (617) 755-6667
Admin Barbara J Duffy.
Licensure Rest Home. *Beds* 60.
Admissions Requirements Physician's request.
Staff LPNs 1 (pt); Nurses aides 10 (ft), 8 (pt);

Recreational therapists 1 (pt); Activities coordinators 1 (pt); Dietitians 1 (pt).
Facilities Dining room; Activities room; Crafts room; Laundry room; Barber/Beauty shop; Library.
Activities Arts and Crafts; Cards; Games; Reading groups; Prayer groups; Movies; Shopping trips; Dances/Social or cultural gatherings.
Description Facility is caring and loving.

Elmwood Manor Nursing Home*
21 Catherine St, Worcester, MA, 01610 (617) 756-4875
Admin John G Bastille.
Licensure Intermediate Care. *Beds* 31. *Certified* Medicaid.

Evamor Manor
23 May St, Worcester, MA, 01610 (617) 799-4043
Admin Josephine M Morrow.
Licensure Intermediate Care. *Beds* 28. *Certified* Medicaid.
Admissions Requirements Minimum age 21; Medical examination; Physician's request.
Staff RNs 1 (pt); LPNs 1 (pt); Orderlies 1 (pt); Nurses aides 3 (ft), 3 (pt); Activities coordinators 1 (pt); Dietitians 1 (pt).
Facilities Dining room; Activities room; Crafts room; Laundry room; Barber/Beauty shop; Library.
Activities Arts and Crafts; Cards; Games; Reading groups; Prayer groups; Movies; Shopping trips; Dances/Social or cultural gatherings.

Evans Manor Nursing Home*
27 Tirrell St, Worcester, MA, 01603 (617) 755-4255
Admin Clifton N LaFrenier.
Licensure Intermediate Care. *Beds* 18. *Certified* Medicaid.

Goddard House Home for Aged Men*
1199 Main St, Worcester, MA, 01602 (617) 753-4890
Admin Margaret P Naylor.
Licensure Rest Home. *Beds* 32.
Admissions Requirements Males only

Hammond House Convalescent Home*
18 Hammond St, Worcester, MA, 01610 (617) 799-7991
Admin Esther Travers.
Licensure Intermediate Care. *Beds* 70. *Certified* Medicaid.

Harvard Nursing Home Inc*
14 John St, Worcester, MA, 01609 (619) 755-7268
Admin Frithiof B Carlson.
Licensure Intermediate Care. *Beds* 42. *Certified* Medicaid.

Hermitage Nursing Home*
383 Mill St, Worcester, MA, 01602 (617) 791-8131
Admin Stephen C Warner.
Licensure Skilled Care; Intermediate Care. *Beds* 101. *Certified* Medicaid; Medicare.

Heywood Valley Nursing Home
59 Acton St, Worcester, MA, 01604 (617) 791-3147

Admin William J McGinley Jr. *Medical Dir/Dir of Nursing* Dr Robert McGan.
Licensure Skilled Care; Intermediate Care.
Beds 157. *Certified* Medicaid; Medicare.
Staff Physicians 4 (pt); Physical therapists 5 (ft); Recreational therapists 5 (ft); Occupational therapists 4 (ft); Speech therapists 1 (ft); Activities coordinators 1 (ft); Dietitians 1 (pt); Dentists 1 (pt).
Facilities Dining room; Physical therapy room; Activities room; Barber/Beauty shop; Library.
Activities Arts and Crafts; Cards; Games; Reading groups; Prayer groups; Movies; Shopping trips; Dances/Social or cultural gatherings.
Description Facility features special programs for the care and rehabilitation of young adults and a special coma treatment program.

Highland Manor Rest Home*
41 Lancaster St, Worcester, MA, 01608 (617) 753-0184
Admin Edward C Bastille.
Licensure Rest Home. *Beds* 30.

Home For Aged Women*
1183 Main St, Worcester, MA, 01603 (617) 752-4628
Admin Dorothy H Eldridge.
Licensure Intermediate Care. *Beds* 48. *Certified* Medicaid.
Admissions Requirements Females only

Homestead Hall*
10 Homestead Ave, Worcester, MA, 01610 (617) 755-7915
Admin D Patricia Johnson.
Licensure Rest Home. *Beds* 30.

Jewish Home for the Aged*
629 Salisbury St, Worcester, MA, 01609 (617) 798-8653
Admin Marvin A Goldberg.
Licensure Skilled Care; Intermediate Care.
Beds 141. *Certified* Medicaid; Medicare.
Affiliation Jewish

Knollwood Nursing Home Inc*
271 E Mountain St, Worcester, MA, 01606 (617) 853-6912
Admin Charles G Padula Jr.
Licensure Skilled Care. *Beds* 70. *Certified* Medicaid; Medicare.

Lincoln Nursing Home*
299 Lincoln St, Worcester, MA, 01605 (617) 852-2001
Admin Sarli J Battista.
Licensure Skilled Care; Intermediate Care.
Beds 130. *Certified* Medicaid; Medicare.

Linda Lee Rest Home
30 Institute Rd, Worcester, MA, 01609 (617) 753-3718
Admin Olga Burdett. *Medical Dir/Dir of Nursing* Arthur Ward.
Licensure Rest Home. *Beds* 11.
Admissions Requirements Minimum age 21; Females only; Medical examination; Physician's request.
Staff Nurses aides 2 (ft), 4 (pt); Dietitians 1 (pt); Podiatrists 1 (pt).
Facilities Dining room; Activities room; Laundry room.

Activities Cards; Games; Reading groups; Movies; Shopping trips.
Description Bus goes right by door; 2 parks within walking distance; art museum located in the next block from rest home.

Lutheran Home of Worcester Inc
26 Harvard St, Worcester, MA, 01609 (617) 754-8877
Admin Rev Richard E Olson. *Medical Dir/Dir of Nursing* Lorenzo Campos MD.
Licensure Skilled Care; Intermediate Care.
Beds 141. *Certified* Medicaid.
Admissions Requirements Minimum age 65; Medical examination.
Staff Physicians 1 (pt); RNs 6 (ft), 12 (pt); LPNs 4 (ft), 8 (pt); Orderlies 1 (ft), 1 (pt); Nurses aides 17 (ft), 48 (pt); Physical therapists 2 (pt); Reality therapists 2 (ft); Recreational therapists 1 (ft); Occupational therapists 2 (pt); Speech therapists 1 (pt); Dietitians 1 (pt).
Affiliation Lutheran
Facilities Dining room; Physical therapy room; Activities room; Chapel; Crafts room; Laundry room; Barber/Beauty shop; Outdoor gazebo.
Activities Arts and Crafts; Cards; Games; Reading groups; Prayer groups; Movies; Shopping trips; Dances/Social or cultural gatherings.
Description Facility is located on north edge of downtown Worcester; public transportation at door; active program of volunteer services under professional direction.

Maple Hall Nursing Home
19 King St, Worcester, MA, 01610 (617) 753-4380
Admin Lloyd W Buckley.
Licensure Intermediate Care. *Beds* 56. *Certified* Medicaid.

Meadowbrook Manor
856 Main St, Worcester, MA, 01610 (617) 756-7822
Admin Anne Jette.
Licensure Rest Home. *Beds* 25.

Mill Hill Nursing Home Inc*
215 Mill St, Worcester, MA, 01602 (617) 791-3168
Admin F E Kuzdzal.
Licensure Skilled Care; Intermediate Care.
Beds 101. *Certified* Medicaid.

Newton Manor Rest Home*
M10 Pleasant St, Worcester, MA, 01602 (617) 753-4024
Admin Marie Callahan.
Licensure Rest Home. *Beds* 25.

Odd Fellows Home of Massachusetts
104 Randolph Rd, Worcester, MA, 01606 (617) 853-6687
Admin George E Shaw. *Medical Dir/Dir of Nursing* Dr Robert Anderson.
Licensure Intermediate Care. *Beds* 75. *Certified* Medicaid.
Admissions Requirements Medical examination.
Staff Physicians; RNs; LPNs; Orderlies; Nurses aides; Physical therapists; Reality therapists; Recreational therapists; Occupational therapists; Speech therapists; Activities coordinators; Dietitians; Dentists; Ophthalmologists;

Podiatrists; Audiologists.
Affiliation Independent Order of Odd Fellows
Facilities Dining room; Activities room; Chapel; Crafts room; Laundry room; Barber/Beauty shop; Barber/Beauty shop.
Activities Arts and Crafts; Cards; Games; Reading groups; Prayer groups; Movies; Shopping trips; Dances/Social or cultural gatherings.
Description Building has beautiful architectural design reminiscent of the 1890s with spacious rooms of distinctive design; located near museums and many other cultural facilities; offers a panoramic view of the city and Indian Lake. Home rests high on a hill, where there's always a cool breeze in the summer. There's much to do, and many to fellowship with. The personnel and furnishings project a home-like atmosphere. Both members and nonmembers are welcomed.

Park Hill Manor Nursing Home*
1 Gorham St, Worcester, MA, 01605 (617) 825-1267
Admin Edward MacLeod.
Licensure Intermediate Care. *Beds* 101. *Certified* Medicaid.

Pleasant Acres Rest Home*
107 E Mountain St, Worcester, MA, 01606 (617) 853-8333
Admin Bernadette Wilcox.
Licensure Rest Home. *Beds* 10.

Providence House Nursing Home*
119 Providence St, Worcester, MA, 01604 (617) 791-7881
Admin Eugene L Oriol.
Licensure Skilled Care; Intermediate Care. *Beds* 160. *Certified* Medicaid; Medicare.

Roselawn Manor Rest Home*
60 Randolph Rd, Worcester, MA, 01606 (617) 853-5140
Admin Ruth G Bopp.
Licensure Rest Home. *Beds* 12.

Saint Francis Home
37 Thorne St, Worcester, MA, 01604 (617) 755-8605
Admin Sr Jacquelyn Alix.
Licensure Intermediate Care. *Beds* 66. *Certified* Medicaid.
Admissions Requirements Minimum age 65; Medical examination.
Staff RNs 1 (ft); LPNs 4 (ft); Nurses aides 10 (ft), 6 (pt); Recreational therapists 1 (ft); Activities coordinators 1 (ft).
Affiliation Roman Catholic
Facilities Dining room; Activities room; Chapel; Crafts room; Laundry room; Barber/Beauty shop; Library.
Activities Arts and Crafts; Cards; Games; Reading groups; Prayer groups; Movies; Dances/Social or cultural gatherings.
Description Remotivation therapy offered for those losing touch with reality; adult day health center for people living at home who need supervision, nutritional assistance, socialization, and health monitoring.

Salisbury Nursing Home*
25 Oriol Dr, Worcester, MA, 01605 (617) 852-3330

Admin Donald F Flanagan.
Licensure Skilled Care; Intermediate Care. *Beds* 160. *Certified* Medicaid.

Schussler Rest Home*
1 Schussler Rd, Worcester, MA, 01609 (617) 757-6759
Admin George H Gross.
Licensure Rest Home. *Beds* 25.

Smiths Rest Home*
25 Sturgis St, Worcester, MA, 01605 (617) 755-8711
Admin George H Gross.
Licensure Rest Home. *Beds* 27.

Spring Valley Convalescent Home*
81 Chatham St, Worcester, MA, 01069 (617) 754-3276
Admin Jeffrey Kline.
Licensure Skilled Care; Intermediate Care. *Beds* 82. *Certified* Medicaid.

Wayside Nursing Home Inc*
751 Grove St, Worcester, MA, 01605 (617) 852-4365
Admin Edith C Cobb.
Licensure Skilled Care. *Beds* 69. *Certified* Medicaid; Medicare.

West Side Nursing Home
35 Fruit St, Worcester, MA, 01609 (617) 752-6763
Admin Jeanne M Care. *Medical Dir/Dir of Nursing* Merle Ingraham.
Licensure Skilled Care; Intermediate Care. *Beds* 90. *Certified* Medicaid.
Admissions Requirements Minimum age 65.
Staff Physicians 6 (pt); RNs 24 (ft); LPNs 18 (ft); Orderlies 10 (ft); Nurses aides 50 (ft); Physical therapists 1 (ft); Reality therapists 2 (pt); Recreational therapists 4 (pt); Occupational therapists 1 (pt); Speech therapists 1 (pt); Activities coordinators 1 (ft); Dietitians 1 (ft); Dentists 1 (pt); Ophthalmologists 1 (pt); Audiologists 1 (pt).
Facilities Dining room; Activities room; Crafts room; Laundry room; Barber/Beauty shop.
Activities Arts and Crafts; Cards; Games; Reading groups; Movies; Shopping trips; Dances/Social or cultural gatherings; Therapy groups.
Description Facility features first pilot program in the state of Massachussetts for psychiatric-geriatric program.

Winter Hill Rest Home
24 Chester St, Worcester, MA, 01605 (617) 852-2438
Admin William J Lange. *Medical Dir/Dir of Nursing* Dr Carl Marsh.
Licensure Rest Home. *Beds* 15.
Admissions Requirements Females only; Medical examination; Physician's request.
Facilities Dining room; Activities room.
Activities Arts and Crafts; Cards; Games; Reading groups; Movies; Shopping trips; Dances/Social or cultural gatherings.

WRENTHAM

Kings Daughters and Sons Home for the Aged in Norfolk County
289 East St, Wrentham, MA, 02093 (617) 384-3531
Admin DeAnna E Willis.
Licensure Intermediate Care. *Beds* 31. *Certified* Medicaid.
Admissions Requirements Minimum age 65; Medical examination; Physician's request.
Staff Physicians 1 (pt); LPNs 1 (ft), 8 (pt); Nurses aides 3 (ft); Physical therapists 1 (pt); Activities coordinators 1 (ft); Dietitians 1 (pt); Dentists 2 (pt); Ophthalmologists 1 (pt); Podiatrists 1 (pt).
Affiliation King's Daughters and Sons
Facilities Dining room; Laundry room; Barber/Beauty shop; Library.
Activities Arts and Crafts; Cards; Games; Movies; Shopping trips; Dances/Social or cultural gatherings.
Description This is a Level IV facility with a Level III infirmary, a gracious old home with 10 acres of land to stroll through three-quarters of a mile from the center of town; independent living with staffing to provide care when necessary; private rooms (a place to be alone) and large dining room seating 4 to a table.

Maples Convalescent Home*
24 Common St, Wrentham, MA, 02093 (617) 384-3481
Admin Caroline F Capachin.
Licensure Intermediate Care. *Beds* 50. *Certified* Medicaid.

Serenity Hill Nursing Home
655 Dedham St, Wrentham, MA, 02093 (617) 384-3400
Admin Deanna Willis.
Licensure Intermediate Care. *Beds* 44. *Certified* Medicaid.
Admissions Requirements Minimum age 60; Medical examination; Physician's request.
Staff RNs 1 (ft), 2 (pt); LPNs 5 (pt); Nurses aides 5 (ft), 22 (pt); Recreational therapists 1 (ft); Dietitians 1 (pt).
Facilities Dining room; Activities room; Crafts room; Laundry room.
Activities Arts and Crafts; Cards; Games; Reading groups; Prayer groups; Movies; Shopping trips; Dances/Social or cultural gatherings.
Description Facility features gourmet class; band and music therapy; van for out-of-facility programs; a country per month study group.

Sheldonville Nursing Home
1022 West St, Wrentham, MA, 02070 (617) 384-2421
Admin Barbara Horowitz.
Licensure Intermediate Care. *Beds* 50. *Certified* Medicaid.
Staff Physicians; RNs; LPNs; Nurses aides; Physical therapists; Reality therapists; Recreational therapists; Occupational therapists; Speech therapists; Activities coordinators; Dietitians; Dentists; Ophthalmologists; Podiatrists; Audiologists.
Facilities Dining room; Activities room; Chapel; Crafts room; Barber/Beauty shop; TV sitting room.
Activities Arts and Crafts; Cards; Games;

Reading groups; Prayer groups; Movies; Shopping trips; Dances/Social or cultural gatherings. *Description* Small 50 bed, Level III facility on a lovely old estate in rural setting; 24-hour licensed personnel; award winning activities program.

MICHIGAN

ADRIAN

Hillhaven Convalescent Center
730 Kimole Ln, Adrian, MI, 49221 (517)
263-6771
Medical Dir/Dir of Nursing Richard Burns
DO.
Licensure Skilled Care; Intermediate Care.
Beds 99. *Certified* Medicaid; Medicare.
Admissions Requirements Minimum age 13;
Medical examination; Physician's request.
Staff Physical therapists 1 (pt); Activities coordinators 1 (ft).
Facilities Dining room; Physical therapy room;
Activities room; Chapel; Crafts room; Laundry
room; Barber/Beauty shop; Library.
Activities Arts and Crafts; Cards; Games;
Reading groups; Prayer groups; Movies; Shopping trips; Bingo; Craft classes; Current events.
Description In September 1984 adult education
classes began for those residents wishing to earn
credits towards their high school diploma; other
residents may participate.

Lenawee County Medical Care Facility*
200 Sandcreek, Adrian, MI, 49221 (517)
263-6794
Licensure Skilled Care; Intermediate Care.
Beds 136. *Certified* Medicaid; Medicare.
Ownership Public.

Provincial House—Adrian
700 Lakeshire Trail, Adrian, MI, 49221 (517)
263-0781
Medical Dir/Dir of Nursing Dr Michael Worzniak.
Licensure Skilled Care; Intermediate Care.
Beds 117. *Certified* Medicaid; Medicare.
Admissions Requirements Medical examination; Physician's request.
Staff RNs 5 (ft), 1 (pt); LPNs 8 (ft); Orderlies
65 (ft); Physical therapists 1 (pt); Occupational
therapists 1 (pt); Speech therapists 1 (pt);
Activities coordinators 1 (ft); Dietitians 1 (pt);
Audiologists 1 (pt).
Facilities Dining room; Physical therapy room;
Activities room; Barber/Beauty shop.
Activities Arts and Crafts; Cards; Games;
Reading groups; Prayer groups; Movies; Shopping trips; Dances/Social or cultural gatherings.

ALBION

Albion Manor
1000 W Erie St, Albion, MI, 49224 (517)
629-5501
Medical Dir/Dir of Nursing Dr Horace Davis.
Licensure Skilled Care; Intermediate Care.
Beds 80. *Certified* Medicaid.
Admissions Requirements Minimum age 15;
Medical examination; Physician's request.
Staff Physicians 8 (pt); RNs 1 (ft), 2 (pt); LPNs
4 (ft), 5 (pt); Orderlies 1 (ft); Nurses aides 26
(ft), 11 (pt); Physical therapists 1 (pt); Occupational therapists 1 (pt); Speech therapists 1 (pt);
Activities coordinators 1 (ft); Dietitians 1 (pt);
Dentists 1 (pt).
Facilities Dining room; Physical therapy room;
Activities room; Crafts room; Laundry room;
Barber/Beauty shop.
Activities Arts and Crafts; Cards; Games;
Reading groups; Prayer groups; Movies; Shopping trips; Dances/Social or cultural gatherings.
Description Albion Manor is located in a quiet
rural area designed to provide each resident
with the life style they wish to continue; a promoter of quality of life through tender loving
care.

ALLEGAN

Allegan County Medical Care Facility
3265 122nd Ave, Allegan, MI, 49010 (616)
673-2102
Admin Keith M Miller.
Licensure Skilled Care. *Beds* 60. *Certified* Medicaid; Medicare.

Pine Oaks Nursing Center*
1200 Ely St, Allegan, MI, 49010
Licensure Intermediate Care. *Beds* 123. *Certified* Medicaid; Medicare.

ALLEN PARK

Allen Park Convalescent Home*
9150 Allen Rd, Allen Park, MI, 48101 (313)
386-2150
Licensure Skilled Care; Intermediate Care.
Beds 180.

ALLEN PK

Inter-City Christ Manor*
4600 Allen Rd, Allen Pk, MI, 48101
Licensure Intermediate Care. *Beds* 17.

ALLENDALE

West Michigan Care Center
11007 Radcliff Dr, Allendale, MI, 49401 (616)
895-6688
Medical Dir/Dir of Nursing Roger Holman
DO.
Licensure Intermediate Care. *Beds* 60. *Certified* Medicaid.
Admissions Requirements Minimum age 17.
Staff RNs 1 (ft); LPNs 3 (ft), 7 (pt); Nurses
aides 9 (ft), 24 (pt); Activities coordinators 1
(ft).
Facilities Dining room; Barber/Beauty shop.
Activities Arts and Crafts; Cards; Games;
Reading groups; Prayer groups; Dances/Social
or cultural gatherings.
Description Facility has quiet country atmosphere located in a combination area of residential homes and farm land.

ALMA

Gratiot County Medical Care Facility
312 Warwick Rd, Alma, MI, 48801 (517)
463-4952
Licensure Skilled Care; Intermediate Care.
Beds 50. *Certified* Medicaid; Medicare.

Michigan Masonic Home
1200 Wright Ave, Alma, MI, 48801 (517)
463-3141
Admin Blaine Henry. *Medical Dir/Dir of
Nursing* Dr Jack Sanders.
Licensure Skilled Care; Intermediate Care.
Beds 204. *Certified* Medicaid; Medicare.
Admissions Requirements Medical examination.
Staff Physicians 1 (ft), 1 (pt); RNs 2 (ft), 7 (pt);
LPNs 20 (ft), 25 (pt); Nurses aides 25 (ft), 40
(pt); Physical therapists 2 (ft), 1 (pt); Recreational therapists 1 (ft); Occupational therapists 6
(ft); Dietitians 1 (pt); Dentists 1 (pt); Ophthalmologists 1 (pt); Podiatrists 1 (pt); Audiologists
1 (pt).
Affiliation Masons
Facilities Dining room; Physical therapy room;

Activities room; Chapel; Crafts room; Laundry room; Barber/Beauty shop; Library.
Activities Arts and Crafts; Cards; Games; Reading groups; Prayer groups; Movies.
Description This is a home with dignity.

Wilcox Nursing Home*
525 N State St, Alma, MI, 48801 (517) 463-4000
Licensure Intermediate Care. *Beds* 45. *Certified* Medicaid.

ALPENA

Pierce Nursing Home*
1234 Golf Course Rd, Alpena, MI, 49707 (517) 356-1030
Licensure Intermediate Care. *Beds* 36.

Provincial House—Alpena*
301 Long Rapids Rd, Alpena, MI, 49707 (517) 356-2194
Licensure Skilled Care; Intermediate Care. *Beds* 117. *Certified* Medicaid; Medicare.

ANN ARBOR

Glacier Hills Nursing Center
1200 Earhart Rd, Ann Arbor, MI, 48105 (313) 769-6410
Admin Margaret Wolf. *Medical Dir/Dir of Nursing* F S Van Reesema MD.
Licensure Skilled Care; Intermediate Care. *Beds* 89. *Certified* Medicaid; Medicare.
Admissions Requirements Minimum age 15; Physician's request.
Staff RNs 7 (ft), 9 (pt); LPNs 6 (ft), 2 (pt); Nurses aides 34 (ft), 5 (pt); Physical therapists 3 (pt); Occupational therapists 1 (pt); Speech therapists 1 (pt); Activities coordinators 2 (ft), 1 (pt); Dietitians 1 (ft).
Facilities Dining room; Physical therapy room; Activities room; Crafts room; Laundry room; Barber/Beauty shop; Library.
Activities Arts and Crafts; Cards; Games; Reading groups; Prayer groups; Movies; Dances/Social or cultural gatherings.
Description Facility offers progressive, intensive rehabilitation program for CUA, hip fractures, MI; actively particpates in hospice care.

Hillside Terrace Retirement Home*
1939 Jackson, Ann Arbor, MI, 48103 (313) 761-4451
Licensure Intermediate Care. *Beds* 23. *Certified* Medicaid.

Huron View Lodge*
355 Huron View Blvd, Ann Arbor, MI, 48103 (313) 761-3800
Licensure Skilled Care; Intermediate Care. *Beds* 71. *Certified* Medicaid; Medicare.

Whitehall Convalescent Home
3370 Morgan Rd, Ann Arbor, MI, 48104 (313) 971-3230
Medical Dir/Dir of Nursing W E Dolfin MD.
Licensure Intermediate Care. *Beds* 102. *Certified* Medicaid.
Admissions Requirements Minimum age 18;

Medical examination; Physician's request.
Staff RNs 6 (ft), 2 (pt); LPNs 8 (ft), 2 (pt); Nurses aides 60 (ft), 14 (pt); Physical therapists 1 (pt); Recreational therapists 1 (ft); Activities coordinators 1 (ft); Dietitians 1 (pt).
Facilities Dining room; Physical therapy room; Activities room; Crafts room; Laundry room; Barber/Beauty shop.
Activities Arts and Crafts; Cards; Games; Reading groups; Prayer groups; Movies.
Description Home is located in beautiful country setting on the outskirts of Ann Arbor. Home has operated since 1958 under the same ownership and has been recognized for its excellent care.

ARMADA

Fair Acres Nursing Home*
22600 Armada Ride, Armada, MI, 48005 (313) 784-5322
Licensure Intermediate Care. *Beds* 49. *Certified* Medicaid.

ASHLEY

Maple Valley Nursing Home*
211 W Wallace, Ashley, MI, 48806 (517) 847-2011
Licensure Intermediate Care. *Beds* 49. *Certified* Medicaid.

BAD AXE

Huron County Medical Care Facility
1116 S Van Dyke Rd, Bad Axe, MI, 48413 (517) 269-6425
Medical Dir/Dir of Nursing R A Lockard MD.
Licensure Skilled Care; Intermediate Care. *Beds* 109. *Certified* Medicaid; Medicare.
Admissions Requirements Medical examination; Physician's request.
Staff Physicians 2 (pt); RNs 6 (ft), 8 (pt); LPNs 5 (ft), 3 (pt); Nurses aides 42 (ft), 20 (pt); Physical therapists 1 (pt); Recreational therapists 1 (pt); Occupational therapists 1 (pt); Speech therapists 1 (pt); Activities coordinators 1 (ft); Dietitians 1 (ft).
Facilities Dining room; Physical therapy room; Activities room; Laundry room; Barber/Beauty shop.
Activities Arts and Crafts; Cards; Games; Reading groups; Prayer groups; Movies; Dances/Social or cultural gatherings.

Sunny Acres Nursing Center*
2762 Pigeon Rd, Bad Axe, MI, 48413 (517) 269-9138
Licensure Intermediate Care. *Beds* 30. *Certified* Medicaid.

BALDWIN

Oak Village Care Center*
4153 S M-37, Baldwin, MI, 49304 (616) 745-4648d
Licensure Skilled Care; Intermediate Care. *Beds* 90. *Certified* Medicaid; Medicare.

BATTLE CREEK

Arrowood Nursing Center*
270 N Bedford at US 37, Battle Creek, MI, 49017 (616) 968-2296
Licensure Skilled Care; Intermediate Care. *Beds* 123. *Certified* Medicaid; Medicare.

Calhoun County Medical Care Facility*
1150 E Michigan Ave, Battle Creek, MI, 49017 (616) 962-5458
Licensure Skilled Care; Intermediate Care. *Beds* 120. *Certified* Medicaid; Medicare.
Ownership Public.

Provincial House of Battle Creek
111 Evergreen Rd, Battle Creek, MI, 49017
Admin Helen Gastian. *Medical Dir/Dir of Nursing* Gerald Rutledge DO.
Licensure Skilled Care. *Beds* 117. *Certified* Medicaid; Medicare.
Ownership Proprietary.
Admissions Requirements Medical examination; Physician's request.
Staff RNs 5 (ft), 1 (pt); LPNs 6 (ft), 4 (pt); Orderlies 3 (ft), 3 (pt); Nurses aides 32 (ft), 15 (pt); Activities coordinators 1 (ft); Dietitians 1 (ft).
Facilities Dining room; Physical therapy room; Activities room; Chapel; Crafts room; Laundry room; Barber/Beauty shop; Library.
Activities Arts and Crafts; Cards; Games; Reading groups; Prayer groups; Movies; Shopping trips; Dances/Social or cultural gatherings.
Description This facility, situated on the outskirts of Battle Creek, is a leader in the health care community, offering excellent resident care and outstanding activities and social programing; provides multiple opportunities for self-help and involvement in the community through swimming sessions and campout/cookouts, all of which enhance the quality of life for residents.

Riverside Manor
675 Wagner Dr, Battle Creek, MI, 49015 (616) 962-6244
Licensure Intermediate Care. *Beds* 88. *Certified* Medicaid.
Admissions Requirements Minimum age 15.
Staff RNs 1 (ft); LPNs 7 (ft), 2 (pt); Orderlies 1 (ft); Nurses aides 19 (ft), 15 (pt); Activities coordinators 2 (ft).
Facilities Dining room; Activities room; Barber/Beauty shop.
Activities Arts and Crafts; Cards; Games; Prayer groups; Movies; Shopping trips; Dances/Social or cultural gatherings.
Description Facility provides a clean, caring, supportive, rehabilitative environment.

Springhill
200 Roosevelt Ave, Battle Creek, MI, 49017 (616) 965-3327
Medical Dir/Dir of Nursing Paul Diamante MD.
Licensure Skilled Care; Intermediate Care. *Beds* 65. *Certified* Medicaid; Medicare.
Admissions Requirements Medical examination; Physician's request.
Staff RNs 4 (ft), 4 (pt); LPNs 2 (ft), 9 (pt); Nurses aides 15 (ft), 27 (pt); Activities coordinators 1 (pt).

Facilities Dining room; Physical therapy room; Activities room; Crafts room; Laundry room; Barber/Beauty shop.
Activities Arts and Crafts; Cards; Games; Reading groups; Prayer groups; Movies; Shopping trips; Dances/Social or cultural gatherings.
Description Our building is expressly designed to accomodate the physically incapacitated. Hallways are wide with a call system at the nursing station. Patient rooms are pleasant. Lounge areas are bright and cheery. Decor of the building is tasteful. Sensitive fire alarm system and staff well trained for emergencies. We have an emergency power supply. Television is available for viewing in the lounges. Community telephones are accessible to patients. Rooms are available for married couples as well as for single adults. We have activities daily. Medicare, BC/BS, and Medicaid approved. There are on-going inservice and care conferences for the staff, thus keeping abreast of the latest advances in professional nursing care. We provide quality nursing care and an atmosphere of compassion and kindness.

BAY CITY

Colonial Rest Home*
2394 Midland Rd, Bay City, MI, 48706 (517) 684-2303
Licensure Intermediate Care. *Beds* 52.

Hampton Manor
800 Mulholland St, Bay City, MI, 48706 (517) 895-8539
Medical Dir/Dir of Nursing L Berta DO.
Licensure Skilled Care; Intermediate Care.
Beds 51. *Certified* Medicaid; Medicare.
Admissions Requirements Minimum age 16.
Staff RNs 2 (ft), 3 (pt); LPNs 1 (ft), 2 (pt); Nurses aides 15 (ft), 11 (pt); Activities coordinators 1 (ft).
Facilities Dining room; Laundry room; Barber/Beauty shop.
Activities Arts and Crafts; Cards; Games; Reading groups; Prayer groups; Movies; Shopping trips; Dances/Social or cultural gatherings.

Rach Sovereign Memorial Home
1014 Center Ave, Bay City, MI, 48706 (517) 892-8493
Licensure Intermediate Care. *Beds* 7. *Certified* Medicaid.

Tri-City Nursing Center
3254 E Midland Rd, Bay City, MI, 48706 (517) 686-3770
Medical Dir/Dir of Nursing Ronald Koehler DO.
Licensure Skilled Care; Intermediate Care.
Beds 126. *Certified* Medicaid; Medicare.
Admissions Requirements Minimum age 15; Medical examination; Physician's request.
Staff RNs 6 (ft), 2 (pt); LPNs 12 (ft), 6 (pt); Nurses aides 80 (ft), 60 (pt); Physical therapists 1 (ft); Recreational therapists 1 (ft); Speech therapists 1 (pt); Activities coordinators 1 (ft); Dietitians 1 (pt).

BELDING

Belding Christian Home*
414 E State St, Belding, MI, 48809 (616) 794-0406
Licensure Skilled Care; Intermediate Care.
Beds 123. *Certified* Medicaid; Medicare.

BELLAIRE

Meadow Brook Medical Care Facility
4543 Scenic Hwy, Bellaire, MI, 49615 (616) 533-8661
Medical Dir/Dir of Nursing Donald Bills DO.
Licensure Skilled Care; Intermediate Care.
Beds 113. *Certified* Medicaid.
Admissions Requirements Physician's request.
Staff RNs 8 (ft); LPNs 7 (ft), 2 (pt); Orderlies 3 (ft); Nurses aides 45 (ft), 12 (pt); Physical therapy aides 2 (ft); Recreational therapy aides 2 (ft).
Facilities Dining room; Physical therapy room; Chapel; Crafts room; Laundry room; Barber/Beauty shop.
Activities Arts and Crafts; Cards; Games; Movies; Dances/Social or cultural gatherings.
Description Facility has a trout pond for summer fishing and a picnic pavilion.

BELLEVILLE

Van Buren Convalescent Center*
44401 Willow Run Expwy, Belleville, MI, 48111 (313) 697-8051
Licensure Skilled Care; Intermediate Care.
Beds 222. *Certified* Medicaid; Medicare.

BENTON HARBOR

Blossom Care Center*
1385 Empire Ave, Benton Harbor, MI, 49022 (616) 925-0033
Licensure Skilled Care; Intermediate Care.
Beds 123. *Certified* Medicaid; Medicare.

BERRIEN CENTER

Berrien General Hospital
1250 Deanshill Rd, Berrien Center, MI, 49102 (616) 471-7761
Medical Dir/Dir of Nursing Dwain Silvernale MD.
Licensure Skilled Care; Intermediate Care.
Beds 189. *Certified* Medicaid; Medicare.
Admissions Requirements Minimum age 18; Physician's request.
Staff Physicians 14 (ft), 1 (pt); RNs 7 (ft), 3 (pt); LPNs 13 (ft), 7 (pt); Orderlies 51 (ft), 18 (pt); Physical therapists 2 (ft); Recreational therapists 1 (ft); Speech therapists 1 (pt); Activities coordinators 1 (ft); Dietitians 1 (ft); Dentists 1 (pt); Ophthalmologists 1 (pt).
Facilities Dining room; Physical therapy room; Activities room; Chapel; Crafts room; Laundry room; Barber/Beauty shop; Living center.
Activities Arts and Crafts; Games; Reading groups; Prayer groups; Movies; Shopping trips; Dances/Social or cultural gatherings.
Description Facility is a hospital-based, long-term care unit.

Bry Fern Care Center
Deanis Hill, PO Box 68, Berrien Center, MI, 49102 (616) 473-4911
Medical Dir/Dir of Nursing Dr Richard Roach.
Licensure Intermediate Care. *Beds* 62. *Certified* Medicaid.
Admissions Requirements Minimum age 15; Medical examination.
Staff RNs 3 (ft); LPNs 5 (ft); Orderlies 2 (pt); Nurses aides 12 (ft), 18 (pt); Physical therapists; Occupational therapists; Speech therapists; Activities coordinators 1 (ft); Dietitians 1 (ft); Ophthalmologists.
Facilities Dining room; Activities room; Crafts room; Laundry room; Barber/Beauty shop; Library.
Activities Arts and Crafts; Cards; Games; Reading groups; Prayer groups; Movies; Shopping trips; Dances/Social or cultural gatherings.
Description Bry Fern Care Center is a serene basic care facility located in the relaxing farm community of Berrien Center, Michigan. From the shaded wooden deck many patients enjoy observing the activities of the animals as they graze in the fields.

BIG RAPIDS

Greenridge Nursing Center
725 Fuller, Big Rapids, MI, 49307 (616) 796-2631
Licensure Skilled Care; Intermediate Care.
Beds 126. *Certified* Medicaid; Medicare.
Admissions Requirements Minimum age 15; Medical examination; Physician's request.
Staff RNs 4 (ft), 2 (pt); LPNs 3 (ft), 8 (pt); Nurses aides 45 (ft), 50 (pt); Physical therapists 1 (ft); Recreational therapists 1 (ft); Activities coordinators 1 (ft); Dietitians 1 (ft).
Facilities Dining room; Physical therapy room; Activities room; Crafts room; Laundry room; Barber/Beauty shop.
Activities Arts and Crafts; Cards; Games; Reading groups; Prayer groups; Movies; Shopping trips; Dances/Social or cultural gatherings.
Description Greenridge Nursing Center is heavily committed to the maximum rehabilitation of our patients. We have developed a full-time physical therapy department. We have also contracted for speech and occupational therapists.

BIRMINGHAM

Cambridge Nursing Center—South*
18200 W 13 Mile Rd, Birmingham, MI, 48009 (313) 647-6500
Licensure Skilled Care; Intermediate Care.
Beds 102. *Certified* Medicaid; Medicare.

BLOOMFIELD HILLS

Bloomfield Hills Care Center*
50 Square Lake Rd, Bloomfield Hills, MI, 48013 (313) 338-0345
Licensure Skilled Care; Intermediate Care.
Beds 366. *Certified* Medicaid; Medicare.

Brae Burn*
1312 N Woodward Ave, Bloomfield Hills, MI, 48013 (313) 644-8015
Licensure Intermediate Care. *Beds* 115. *Certified* Medicaid.

Georgian—Bloomfield
2975 N Adams Rd, Bloomfield Hills, MI, 48013 (313) 645-2900
Medical Dir/Dir of Nursing Dr John Dzuiba.
Licensure Skilled Care; Intermediate Care.
Beds 274. *Certified* Medicaid; Medicare.
Staff Physicians 7 (pt); RNs 16 (ft), 9 (pt); LPNs 8 (ft), 5 (pt); Orderlies 6 (ft); Nurses aides 60 (ft), 18 (pt); Recreational therapists 1 (ft), 1 (pt); Activities coordinators 1 (ft); Dietitians 1 (ft), 1 (pt).
Facilities Dining room; Physical therapy room; Activities room; Chapel; Laundry room; Barber/Beauty shop.
Activities Arts and Crafts; Cards; Games; Reading groups; Prayer groups; Movies; Dances/Social or cultural gatherings.
Description Facility offers the unique opportunity of attending a main dining room for lunch and dinner, with waiters and waitresses taking orders and serving meals in a distinctive setting.

BLOOMINGDALE

Bethany Nursing Home
42235 C R 665, Bloomingdale, MI, 49026 (616) 521-3383
Medical Dir/Dir of Nursing Daniel Ekkens MD.
Licensure Skilled Care; Intermediate Care.
Beds 78. *Certified* Medicaid; Medicare.
Admissions Requirements Minimum age 15; Medical examination; Physician's request.
Staff RNs 3 (ft), 1 (pt); LPNs 3 (ft), 2 (pt); Orderlies 2 (pt); Nurses aides 19 (ft), 19 (pt); Activities coordinators 1 (ft); Dietitians 1 (pt).
Facilities Dining room; Physical therapy room; Activities room; Crafts room; Laundry room; Barber/Beauty shop; Library.
Activities Arts and Crafts; Cards; Games; Reading groups; Prayer groups; Movies; Shopping trips; Dances/Social or cultural gatherings.

BRIDGMAN

Jordans Nursing Home
9935 Red Arrow Hwy, Bridgman, MI, 49106 (616) 465-3017
Admin Larry Olson.
Licensure Intermediate Care. *Beds* 105. *Certified* Medicaid.
Admissions Requirements Minimum age 15; Medical examination; Physician's request.
Staff Physicians 4 (pt); RNs 1 (ft), 4 (pt); LPNs 2 (ft), 4 (pt); Nurses aides 31 (ft), 28 (pt); Reality therapists 1 (ft); Recreational therapists 1 (ft); Activities coordinators 1 (ft), 1 (pt); Dietitians 1 (ft); Dentists 1 (pt).
Facilities Dining room; Activities room; Chapel; Crafts room; Laundry room; Barber/Beauty shop.
Activities Arts and Crafts; Games; Prayer groups; Movies.
Description Facility is a modern, well-maintained brick building with enclosed courtyard; partially air conditioned; plenty of parking; beautifully landscaped; 99% occupancy with waiting list.

CADILLAC

Lakeview Manor Nursing Home
460 Pearl St, Cadillac, MI, 49601 (313) 775-0101
Medical Dir/Dir of Nursing Wendell Hyink MD.
Licensure Skilled Care; Intermediate Care.
Beds 218. *Certified* Medicaid; Medicare.
Admissions Requirements Minimum age 16; Medical examination; Physician's request.
Staff Physicians 1 (pt); RNs 7 (ft), 4 (pt); LPNs 16 (ft), 13 (pt); Nurses aides 66 (ft), 24 (pt); Physical therapists; Activities coordinators 1 (ft); Dietitians 1 (ft).
Facilities Dining room; Physical therapy room; Activities room; Crafts room; Barber/Beauty shop; 5 lounges.
Activities Arts and Crafts; Cards; Games; Reading groups; Prayer groups; Movies; Shopping trips; Dances/Social or cultural gatherings.

CANTON

Whispering Willow Manor*
49650 Warren Rd, Canton, MI, 48170 (313) 459-7060
Licensure Intermediate Care. *Beds* 39. *Certified* Medicaid.

CARO

Tuscola County Medical Care Facility
1285 Cleaver Rd, Caro, MI, 48723 (517) 673-4117
Admin Darlene Davidson. *Medical Dir/Dir of Nursing* Edward N Elmendorf MD.
Licensure Skilled Care; Intermediate Care.
Beds 123. *Certified* Medicaid; Medicare.
Admissions Requirements Minimum age 15; Medical examination; Physician's request.
Staff Physicians 1 (ft); RNs 4 (ft), 3 (pt); LPNs 4 (ft), 5 (pt); Orderlies 6 (ft), 2 (pt); Nurses aides 41 (ft), 18 (pt); Physical therapists 1 (pt); Occupational therapists 1 (pt); Speech therapists 1 (pt); Activities coordinators 1 (ft); Dietitians 1 (pt); Dentists 1 (pt); Podiatrists 1 (pt); Audiologists 1 (pt).
Facilities Dining room; Physical therapy room; Activities room; Chapel; Crafts room; Laundry room; Barber/Beauty shop.
Activities Arts and Crafts; Cards; Games; Reading groups; Prayer groups; Movies; Shopping trips; Dances/Social or cultural gatherings.

CASS CITY

Provincial House—Cass City
Hospital Dr, Cass City, MI, 48726 (517) 872-2174
Admin Alan J Sward. *Medical Dir/Dir of Nursing* Dr Zuzga.
Licensure Skilled Care; Intermediate Care.
Beds 117. *Certified* Medicaid; Medicare.
Staff Physicians 5 (pt); RNs 4 (ft), 2 (pt); LPNs 7 (ft), 2 (pt); Nurses aides 57 (ft), 18 (pt); Physical therapists 1 (pt); Occupational therapists 1 (pt); Speech therapists 1 (pt); Activities coordinators 1 (ft); Dietitians 1 (pt); Dentists 1 (pt); Ophthalmologists 1 (pt); Podiatrists 1 (pt).
Facilities Dining room; Physical therapy room; Activities room; Crafts room; Laundry room; Barber/Beauty shop.
Activities Arts and Crafts; Cards; Games; Reading groups; Movies; Shopping trips; Dances/Social or cultural gatherings.

CASSOPOLIS

Cass County Medical Care Facility
Rt 2, 23770 Hospital St, Cassopolis, MI, 49031 (616) 445-3801
Admin Norma J Weaver. *Medical Dir/Dir of Nursing* Aaron K Warren MD.
Licensure Skilled Care; Intermediate Care.
Beds 80. *Certified* Medicaid; Medicare.
Admissions Requirements Minimum age 16; Physician's request.
Staff RNs 4 (ft), 1 (pt); LPNs 4 (ft), 4 (pt); Nurses aides 35 (ft), 10 (pt); Activities coordinators 2 (ft).
Facilities Dining room; Physical therapy room; Activities room; Chapel; Crafts room; Laundry room; Barber/Beauty shop.
Activities Arts and Crafts; Cards; Games; Reading groups; Prayer groups; Movies; Dances/Social or cultural gatherings.

CEDAR SPRINGS

Cedar Springs Nursing Center*
400 Jeffrey, Cedar Springs, MI, 49319 (616) 696-0170
Licensure Skilled Care; Intermediate Care.
Beds 77. *Certified* Medicaid; Medicare.

CENTERLINE

Father Murray Nursing Center
8444 Engleman, Centerline, MI, 48015 (313) 755-2400
Medical Dir/Dir of Nursing Barry Szczesny DO.
Licensure Skilled Care; Intermediate Care.
Beds 234. *Certified* Medicaid; Medicare.
Admissions Requirements Minimum age 16; Medical examination; Physician's request.
Facilities Dining room; Physical therapy room; Activities room; Crafts room; Laundry room; Barber/Beauty shop.
Activities Arts and Crafts; Cards; Games; Reading groups; Prayer groups; Movies; Shopping trips; Dances/Social or cultural gatherings.

CENTREVILLE

Fairview Medical Care Facility*
441 E Main, Centreville, MI, 49032 (616) 467-9575
Licensure Skilled Care; Intermediate Care.
Beds 64. *Certified* Medicaid; Medicare.
Ownership Public.

CHARLOTTE

Eaton County Medical Care Facility*
530 W Beech St, Charlotte, MI, 48813 (517)
543-2940
Licensure Skilled Care; Intermediate Care.
Beds 100. *Certified* Medicaid; Medicare.
Ownership Public.

Immanuel Nursing Home*
511 E Sheperd, Charlotte, MI, 48813 (517)
543-4750
Licensure Intermediate Care. *Beds* 49. *Certified* Medicaid.

CHEBOYGAN

Community Memorial*
748 S Main St, Cheboygan, MI, 49721
Licensure Skilled Care. *Beds* 50. *Certified* Medicaid; Medicare.

Green Meadows Nursing Home*
824 S Huron, Cheboygan, MI, 49721
Licensure Intermediate Care. *Beds* 98.

CHELSEA

Chelsea United Methodist
W Middle St, Chelsea, MI, 48118 (313)
475-8633
Admin Catherine M Durkin. *Medical Dir/Dir of Nursing* James Peggs MD.
Licensure Skilled Care; Intermediate Care.
Beds 62. *Certified* Medicaid; Medicare.
Admissions Requirements Minimum age 62;
Medical examination.
Staff Physical therapists; Reality therapists;
Recreational therapists; Occupational therapists; Speech therapists; Dentists; Ophthalmologists; Podiatrists; Audiologists.
Affiliation Methodist
Facilities Dining room; Activities room;
Chapel; Crafts room; Laundry room; Barber-/Beauty shop; Library; Ice cream parlor;
Ceramic shop; Woodworking shop.
Activities Arts and Crafts; Cards; Games;
Reading groups; Prayer groups; Movies; Shopping trips; Dances/Social or cultural gatherings;
Outside groups with socials and entertainment;
Special dinners; Girl Scout troop.
Description Multilevel care facility on 25 acres
in rural setting; accommodations include 26
totally independent apartments, 173 beds HFA,
62 beds nursing (to be expanded to 110 beds),
Alzheimer's and related dementias unit.

CHESANING

Chesaning Rest Home
201 S Front St, Chesaning, MI, 48616 (517)
845-6602
Licensure Intermediate Care. *Beds* 39. *Certified* Medicaid.
Admissions Requirements Minimum age 18;
Medical examination; Physician's request.
Staff Physicians 3 (pt); RNs 1 (ft), 2 (pt); LPNs
3 (ft), 4 (pt); Nurses aides 6 (ft), 15 (pt); Recreational therapists 2 (pt); Dietitians 1 (pt).
Facilities Dining room; Activities room; Laundry room; Barber/Beauty shop.

Activities Arts and Crafts; Cards; Games;
Reading groups; Prayer groups; Movies; Shopping trips; Dances/Social or cultural gatherings.
Description Facility is a homey, close-knit,
39-bed, basic care facility with a caring staff,
located in a rural, small town. Facility is in
accordance with all rules and regulations of
Michigan Department of Public Health.

CLARE

Clare Nursing Home
600 SE 4th St, Clare, MI, 48617 (517) 386-7723
Admin Wilma Shurlow. *Medical Dir/Dir of
Nursing* Dr E C Shurlow.
Licensure Skilled Care; Intermediate Care.
Beds 129. *Certified* Medicaid; Medicare.
Staff RNs 2 (ft), 4 (pt); LPNs 12 (ft), 4 (pt);
Orderlies 3 (ft), 1 (pt); Nurses aides 41 (ft), 36
(pt); Physical therapists 1 (pt); Speech therapists; Activities coordinators 1 (ft); Dietitians 1
(pt); Dentists.
Facilities Dining room; Physical therapy room;
Activities room; Chapel; Crafts room; Laundry
room; Barber/Beauty shop; 3 Day rooms.
Activities Arts and Crafts; Cards; Games;
Reading groups; Prayer groups; Movies; Shopping trips; Dances/Social or cultural gatherings.
Description Nice facility located in a small
town with lots of friendly caring people; community college uses facility for 6-week nurse's
aide training program 4 times a year; associate
degree nursing workshop; area schools use
facility for a co-op program for about 18 students.

CLAWSON

Cambridge Nursing Center—North*
525 N Main, Clawson, MI, 48017 (313)
435-5200
Licensure Skilled Care; Intermediate Care.
Beds 120. *Certified* Medicaid; Medicare.

CLIO

Clio Convalescent Center
13137 N Clio Rd, Clio, MI, 48420 (313)
686-2600
Medical Dir/Dir of Nursing Siva V Sankaran
MD.
Licensure Intermediate Care. *Beds* 101. *Certified* Medicaid.
Admissions Requirements Minimum age 15;
Medical examination.
Staff Physicians 4 (pt); RNs 2 (ft), 4 (pt); LPNs
3 (ft), 7 (pt); Nurses aides 23 (ft), 27 (pt); Activities coordinators 1 (ft); Dietitians 1 (pt); Dentists 1 (pt); Podiatrists 1 (pt).
Facilities Dining room; Activities room;
Chapel; Crafts room; Laundry room; Barber-/Beauty shop.
Activities Arts and Crafts; Cards; Games;
Reading groups; Prayer groups; Dances/Social
or cultural gatherings.
Description Clio Convalescent Center is a currently licensed 101-bed intermediate care
facility; services under the direction of an MD
Medical Director and an RN Director of
Nursing; continuous professional nursing staff

provided; wide range of restorative, social, recreational, nutritional, and personal services are
available.

COLDWATER

Carriage Inn Convalescent Center*
90 N Michigan Ave, Coldwater, MI, 49036
(517) 279-9808
Licensure Skilled Care; Intermediate Care.
Beds 169. *Certified* Medicaid; Medicare.

Maple Lawn Medical Care Facility*
841 Marshall Rd, Coldwater, MI, 49036 (517)
279-9587
Licensure Skilled Care; Intermediate Care.
Beds 114. *Certified* Medicaid; Medicare.
Ownership Public.

CORUNNA

Shiawassee Medical Care Facility*
729 S Norton St, Corunna, MI, 48817 (517)
743-3491
Licensure Skilled Care; Intermediate Care.
Beds 151. *Certified* Medicaid; Medicare.
Ownership Nonprofit.

CRYSTAL FALLS

Crystal Manor*
400 Superior Ave, Crystal Falls, MI, 49920
(906) 875-6663
Licensure Intermediate Care. *Beds* 71. *Certified* Medicaid.

Iron County Medical Care Facility
1523 W US 2, Crystal Falls, MI, 49920 (906)
875-6671
Medical Dir/Dir of Nursing Dr Robert F Han.
Licensure Skilled Care; Intermediate Care.
Beds 109. *Certified* Medicaid; Medicare.
Admissions Requirements Physician's request.
Staff Physicians 2 (pt); RNs 4 (pt); LPNs 8 (ft),
3 (pt); Orderlies 3 (ft), 2 (pt); Nurses aides 31
(ft), 19 (pt); Physical therapists 1 (pt); Activities
coordinators 1 (pt); Dietitians 1 (pt); Audiologists 6 (ft).
Facilities Dining room; Physical therapy room;
Activities room; Chapel; Crafts room; Laundry
room; Barber/Beauty shop; Library; Smoking
and TV areas.
Activities Arts and Crafts; Cards; Games;
Reading groups; Prayer groups; Movies; Dances/Social or cultural gatherings.
Description Iron County Medical Care Facility,
constructed in 1976, is located 2 miles west of
Crystall Falls and is visible from the highway in
a setting of trees. Beautiful patient pavilion was
employee sponsored and community funded,
and is enjoyed immensely by the patients.

DEARBORN HEIGHTS

Dearborn Heights Convalescent Center*
26001 Ford Rd, Dearborn Heights, MI, 48127
Licensure Intermediate Care. *Beds* 151. *Certified* Medicaid.

DETROIT

Alpha Annex Nursing Center*
609 E Grand Blvd, Detroit, MI, 48207 (313)
923-0300
Licensure Skilled Care; Intermediate Care.
Beds 103. *Certified* Medicaid; Medicare.

Alpha Manor Nursing Home*
440 E Grand Blvd, Detroit, MI, 48207 (313)
579-2900
Licensure Intermediate Care. *Beds* 100.

Ambassador Nursing Center*
9146 Woodward Ave, Detroit, MI, 48203 (313)
875-1263
Licensure Skilled Care. *Beds* 195. *Certified* Medicaid; Medicare.

Americare Convalescent Center*
19211 Anglin St, Detroit, MI, 48234 (313)
893-9745
Licensure Intermediate Care. *Beds* 139. *Certified* Medicaid.

Anchorage Convalescent Center*
13850 Grand River Ave, Detroit, MI, 48226
(313) 273-2470
Licensure Intermediate Care. *Beds* 53. *Certified* Medicaid.

Arnold Home
18520 W 7 Mile Rd, Detroit, MI, 48219 (313)
531-4001
Medical Dir/Dir of Nursing Meyer J Elman
MD.
Licensure Skilled Care; Intermediate Care.
Beds 256. *Certified* Medicaid; Medicare.
Ownership Nonprofit.
Admissions Requirements Minimum age 15;
Medical examination; Physician's request.
Staff Physicians 3 (pt); RNs 5 (ft), 7 (pt); LPNs
12 (ft), 9 (pt); Nurses aides 87 (ft); Physical
therapists 1 (pt); Reality therapists 1 (pt); Recreational therapists 2 (ft); Occupational therapists
1 (ft), 1 (pt); Speech therapists 1 (pt); Activities
coordinators 1 (ft); Dietitians 1 (ft); Dentists 1
(pt); Ophthalmologists 1 (pt); Podiatrists 1 (pt);
Audiologists 1 (pt).
Facilities Dining room; Physical therapy room;
Activities room; Chapel; Crafts room; Laundry
room; Barber/Beauty shop; Library.
Activities Arts and Crafts; Cards; Games; Prayer groups; Movies; Shopping trips; Dances/Social or cultural gatherings.
Description The Arnold Home, a nonprofit
nursing home since 1901, offers three levels of
residency: apartments for those who enjoy
active, independent retirement; intermediate
nursing care for those requiring some medical
attention; and skilled nursing for those
requiring comprehensive nursing care.

Avonside Nursing Home*
791 E Grand Blvd, Detroit, MI, 48207 (313)
9211-1332
Licensure Intermediate Care. *Beds* 42. *Certified* Medicaid.

Barton Nursing Home*
722 E Grand Blvd, Detroit, MI, 48207 (313)
923-8080
Licensure Intermediate Care. *Beds* 50. *Certified* Medicaid.

Boulevard Temple Methodist Home
2567 W Grand Blvd, Detroit, MI, 48208 (313)
895-5340
Admin R Kevin McFeely. *Medical Dir/Dir of
Nursing* Mary Martinen MD.
Licensure Intermediate Care. *Beds* 124. *Certified* Medicaid.
Admissions Requirements Medical examination.
Staff Physicians 3 (ft); RNs 4 (ft); LPNs 10 (ft),
6 (pt); Nurses aides 42 (ft), 16 (pt); Physical
therapists 1 (ft); Activities coordinators 1 (ft);
Dietitians 1 (ft); Dentists 1 (pt); Podiatrists 1
(pt).
Affiliation Methodist
Facilities Dining room; Physical therapy room;
Activities room; Chapel; Crafts room; Laundry
room; Barber/Beauty shop; Library.
Activities Arts and Crafts; Games; Reading
groups; Prayer groups; Movies; Shopping trips;
Dances/Social or cultural gatherings.
Description Facility is affiliated with Henry
Ford Hospital's geriatric outreach program.

Broadstreet Medical*
12040 Broadstreet, Detroit, MI, 48204 (313)
931-2800
Licensure Skilled Care; Intermediate Care.
Beds 97. *Certified* Medicare.

Cadillac Nursing Home*
1533 Cadillac Blvd, Detroit, MI, 48214 (313)
823-0435
Licensure Skilled Care; Intermediate Care.
Beds 97. *Certified* Medicaid; Medicare.

Coplin Manor Convalescent Home
4721 Coplin, Detroit, MI, 48215 (313)
823-0330
Medical Dir/Dir of Nursing Arthur Cooper
DO.
Licensure Intermediate Care. *Beds* 38. *Certified* Medicaid.
Admissions Requirements Minimum age 18;
Females only; Medical examination; Physician's request.
Staff RNs; LPNs; Orderlies; Nurses aides;
Physical therapists; Reality therapists; Recreational therapists; Occupational therapists; Speech therapists; Activities coordinators;
Dietitians; Dentists; Ophthalmologists; Podiatrists; Audiologists.
Facilities Dining room; Physical therapy room;
Activities room; Crafts room; Laundry room;
Barber/Beauty shop.
Activities Arts and Crafts; Cards; Games;
Reading groups; Prayer groups; Movies; Shopping trips; Dances/Social or cultural gatherings.

Cranbrook Nursing Home
5000 E 7 Mile Rd, Detroit, MI, 48234 (313)
366-8500
Licensure Skilled Care; Intermediate Care.
Beds 91. *Certified* Medicaid; Medicare.
Admissions Requirements Minimum age 15;
Medical examination; Physician's request.
Staff RNs; LPNs; Orderlies; Nurses aides;

Physical therapists 1 (pt); Occupational therapists 1 (pt); Activities coordinators 1 (ft); Dietitians 1 (pt).
Facilities Dining room; Physical therapy room;
Activities room; Crafts room; Barber/Beauty
shop.
Activities Arts and Crafts; Cards; Games;
Reading groups; Prayer groups; Movies; Shopping trips; Dances/Social or cultural gatherings.

David Nursing Home*
13241 W Chicago, Detroit, MI, 48228 (313)
834-6670 and 834-1192
Licensure Skilled Care. *Beds* 57. *Certified* Medicaid.

Detroiter Residence
2560 Woodward, Detroit, MI, 48201 (313)
963-3545
Licensure Intermediate Care. *Beds* 300. *Certified* Medicaid.
Staff Physicians 5 (pt); RNs 3 (ft); LPNs 18
(ft); Orderlies 12 (ft); Nurses aides 150 (ft);
Physical therapists 4 (ft); Reality therapists 2
(ft); Recreational therapists 4 (ft); Occupational
therapists 1 (pt); Speech therapists 1 (pt);
Activities coordinators 1 (ft); Dietitians 3 (ft), 1
(pt); Dentists 1 (pt); Ophthalmologists 1 (pt);
Podiatrists 1 (pt).
Facilities Dining room; Physical therapy room;
Activities room; Chapel; Crafts room; Laundry
room; Barber/Beauty shop; Library.
Activities Arts and Crafts; Games; Reading
groups; Prayer groups; Shopping trips; Dances-
/Social or cultural gatherings.
Description The Detroiter features private
rooms with baths, suites are available, outdoor
garden area, spacious dining room.

East Grand Nursing Home*
130 E Grand Blvd, Detroit, MI, 48207 (313)
824-8224
Licensure Skilled Care; Intermediate Care.
Beds 94.

Eastwood Nursing Center*
626 E Grand Blvd, Detroit, MI, 48207
Licensure Skilled Care; Intermediate Care.
Beds 86. *Certified* Medicaid; Medicare.

Elmwood Geriatric Village*
1881 E Grand Blvd, Detroit, MI, 48211 (313)
571-5552
Licensure Skilled Care; Intermediate Care.
Beds 120. *Certified* Medicaid; Medicare.

Evangelical Home*
6700 W Outer Dr, Detroit, MI, 48235 (313)
836-1700
Licensure Skilled Care; Intermediate Care.
Beds 121. *Certified* Medicaid; Medicare.

Fairlane Memorial Convalescent Home
15750 Joy Rd, Detroit, MI, 48228 (313)
273-6850
Medical Dir/Dir of Nursing J Mayer DO.
Licensure Skilled Care; Intermediate Care.
Beds SNF 180; ICF 145. *Certified* Medicaid.
Staff Physicians 5 (pt); RNs 10 (ft); LPNs 15
(ft); Orderlies 7 (ft); Nurses aides 100 (ft);
Physical therapists 3 (ft); Reality therapists 5
(ft); Recreational therapists 1 (ft); Occupational
therapists 1 (ft); Speech therapists 1 (ft); Activi-

ties coordinators 1 (ft); Dietitians 2 (ft); Dentists 1 (ft); Ophthalmologists 1 (ft); Podiatrists 1 (ft); Audiologists 1 (ft).
Facilities Dining room; Physical therapy room; Activities room; Chapel; Laundry room; Barber/Beauty shop.
Activities Arts and Crafts; Cards; Games; Reading groups; Prayer groups; Movies; Shopping trips; Dances/Social or cultural gatherings.

Friendship Manor Nursing Home*
3950 Beaubien Ave, Detroit, MI, 48201 (313) 833-7600
Licensure Skilled Care; Intermediate Care. *Beds* 170. *Certified* Medicaid; Medicare.

Grace Convalescent Center*
18901 Meyers Rd, Detroit, MI, 48235 (313) 864-8481
Licensure Skilled Care; Intermediate Care. *Beds* 226. *Certified* Medicaid; Medicare.

Great Lakes Convalescent Center*
12900 W Chicago, Detroit, MI, 48228 (313) 491-6400
Licensure Skilled Care; Intermediate Care. *Beds* 164. *Certified* Medicaid; Medicare.

Hadley Manor
535 E Grand Blvd, Detroit, MI, 48207 (313) 932-2020
Medical Dir/Dir of Nursing Dr William Silverstone.
Licensure Intermediate Care. *Beds* 38. *Certified* Medicaid.
Staff RNs 1 (ft), 2 (pt); LPNs 2 (ft), 3 (pt); Nurses aides 9 (ft); Activities coordinators 1 (pt); Dietitians 1 (pt).
Facilities Dining room; Activities room.
Activities Cards; Games; Prayer groups.

Hamilton Nursing Home*
590 E Grand Blvd, Detroit, MI, 48207 (313) 921-1580
Licensure Skilled Care. *Beds* 55. *Certified* Medicaid; Medicare.

Hillcrest Convalescent Center*
E12535 Harper, Detroit, MI, 48213 (313) 371-5520
Licensure Skilled Care; Intermediate Care. *Beds* 79. *Certified* Medicaid; Medicare.

Ingleside Convalescent Center*
9155 Woodward Ave, Detroit, MI, 48202 (313) 872-1420
Licensure Intermediate Care. *Beds* 141.

Jessie Thompson Convalescent Home
650 E Grand Blvd, Detroit, MI, 48207 (313) 925-6651
Medical Dir/Dir of Nursing Frederick Gold.
Licensure Intermediate Care. *Beds* 42. *Certified* Medicaid.
Admissions Requirements Minimum age 21; Medical examination; Physician's request.
Staff Physicians 3 (ft); RNs 1 (ft); LPNs 4 (ft); Nurses aides 22 (ft); Recreational therapists 1 (ft); Activities coordinators 1 (ft); Dietitians 2 (ft); Dentists 1 (ft); Podiatrists 1 (ft).

Jewish Home for the Aged 2
19100 W 7 Mile Rd, Detroit, MI, 48219 (313) 532-7112
Medical Dir/Dir of Nursing William Solomon MD.
Licensure Skilled Care; Intermediate Care. *Beds* 212. *Certified* Medicaid; Medicare.
Staff Physicians 1 (ft), 3 (pt); RNs 5 (ft), 4 (pt); LPNs 10 (ft), 3 (pt); Nurses aides 77 (ft), 24 (pt); Physical therapists 1 (pt); Occupational therapists 4 (ft); Speech therapists 1 (pt); Activities coordinators 1 (ft); Dietitians 1 (pt); Dentists 1 (pt); Ophthalmologists 1 (pt); Podiatrists 1 (pt).
Affiliation Jewish
Facilities Dining room; Physical therapy room; Activities room; Chapel; Crafts room; Laundry room; Barber/Beauty shop; Library.
Activities Arts and Crafts; Cards; Games; Reading groups; Prayer groups; Movies; Shopping trips; Dances/Social or cultural gatherings.
Description In addition to excellent nursing care, the home offers a complete array of medical and social services including clinics, physical therapy, occupational therapy with an emphasis on ADL, art therapy, dance therapy, drama and discussion groups, and semi-annual vacations.

La Villa Convalescent Center*
660 E Grand Blvd, Detroit, MI, 48207
Licensure Skilled Care; Intermediate Care. *Beds* 95. *Certified* Medicaid; Medicare.

Lakeland Convalescent Center*
751 E Grand Blvd, Detroit, MI, 48207 (313) 921-0998
Licensure Intermediate Care. *Beds* 92. *Certified* Medicaid.

Lasalle Nursing Home*
2411 W Grand Blvd, Detroit, MI, 48208 (313) 897-5144
Licensure Skilled Care. *Beds* 100. *Certified* Medicaid; Medicare.

Law-Den Nursing Home*
1640 Webb Ave, Detroit, MI, 48206 (313) 867-1719
Licensure Intermediate Care. *Beds* 100. *Certified* Medicaid.

Lincoln Convalescent Center*
13001 W Chicago Blvd, Detroit, MI, 48228 (313) 834-1204
Licensure Skilled Care; Intermediate Care. *Beds* 118. *Certified* Medicaid; Medicare.

Little Sisters of the Poor
17550 Southfield Rd, Detroit, MI, 48235 (313) 531-1565
Medical Dir/Dir of Nursing Frank Prokop MD.
Licensure Skilled Care; Intermediate Care. *Beds* 76. *Certified* Medicaid; Medicare.
Affiliation Roman Catholic
Facilities Dining room; Physical therapy room; Activities room; Chapel; Crafts room; Laundry room; Barber/Beauty shop; Library; Kitchen; Gift shop; Auditorium.
Activities Arts and Crafts; Cards; Games; Reading groups; Prayer groups; Movies; Shopping trips; Dances/Social or cultural gatherings;

Occupational therapy.
Description Facility offers skilled nursing home, senior center, independent living, licensed nursing care beds, medical clinic, convent, and day care program of socialization and guidance for the aged poor. There is a separate building with private bedrooms for those elderly poor who are capable of caring for themselves.

Luther Haven*
474 E Grand Blvd, Detroit, MI, 48207 (313) 579-2255
Licensure Skilled Care. *Beds* 89. *Certified* Medicaid; Medicare.
Affiliation Lutheran

Madonna Nursing Center*
15311 Schaefer St, Detroit, MI, 48227 (313) 835-4775
Licensure Skilled Care; Intermediate Care. *Beds* 138. *Certified* Medicaid.

Medicos Recovery Care Center*
22355 W 8 Mile, Detroit, MI, 48219 (313) 255-6450
Licensure Skilled Care. *Beds* 180. *Certified* Medicaid; Medicare.

Moroun Nursing Home*
8045 E Jefferson, Detroit, MI, 48214 (313) 821-3525
Licensure Skilled Care; Intermediate Care. *Beds* 189. *Certified* Medicaid; Medicare.

New Detroit Nursing Center*
716 E Grand Blvd, Detroit, MI, 48207 (313) 923-0300
Licensure Intermediate Care. *Beds* 50. *Certified* Medicaid.

Newlight Nursing Home*
9520 Grand River Ave, Detroit, MI, 48204 (313) 491-7920
Licensure Skilled Care; Intermediate Care. *Beds* 189. *Certified* Medicaid; Medicare.

Northland Nursing Center*
21630 Hessel, Detroit, MI, 48219 (313) 534-8400
Licensure Skilled Care; Intermediate Care. *Beds* 110. *Certified* Medicaid; Medicare.

Northwest Care Center*
16181 Hubbell, Detroit, MI, 48235 (313) 273-8764
Licensure Skilled Care; Intermediate Care. *Beds* 154. *Certified* Medicaid; Medicare.

Presbyterian Village*
17383 Garfield Ave, Detroit, MI, 48240 (313) 531-6874, 6875
Licensure Skilled Care; Intermediate Care. *Beds* 88. *Certified* Medicaid; Medicare.
Affiliation Presbyterian

Qualicare Nursing Center*
695 E Grand Blvd, Detroit, MI, 48207 (313) 925-6655
Licensure Skilled Care. *Beds* 115. *Certified* Medicaid; Medicare.

Redford Geriatric Village
22811 W 7 Mile Rd, Detroit, MI, 48219 (313)
534-1440
Medical Dir/Dir of Nursing Sudhir Walavalkar
MD.
Licensure Skilled Care; Intermediate Care.
Beds 106. *Certified* Medicaid; Medicare.
Admissions Requirements Minimum age 18.
Staff Physicians 1 (pt); RNs 2 (ft), 5 (pt); LPNs
5 (ft), 9 (pt); Nurses aides 30 (ft), 12 (pt);
Physical therapists 1 (pt); Occupational thera-
pists 1 (pt); Speech therapists 1 (pt); Activities
coordinators 1 (ft); Dietitians 1 (pt); Dentists 1
(pt); Ophthalmologists 1 (pt); Podiatrists 1 (pt);
Audiologists 1 (pt).

Regency Park Convalescent Center*
5201 Conner Ave, Detroit, MI, 48213 (313)
571-5555
Licensure Intermediate Care. *Beds* 234. *Certified* Medicaid.

Renaissance Continuing Care
746 Collingwood, Detroit, MI, 48202 (313)
883-6200
Licensure Skilled Care; Intermediate Care.
Beds 473. *Certified* Medicaid; Medicare.

Saint Annes Convalescent Home*
6232 Cadioux Rd, Detroit, MI, 48224 (313)
886-2500
Licensure Skilled Care. *Beds* 105. *Certified* Medicaid; Medicare.

Saint Benedict Nursing Home*
281 W Grand Blvd, Detroit, MI, 48216 (313)
554-2700
Licensure Skilled Care; Intermediate Care.
Beds 258. *Certified* Medicaid; Medicare.

Saint Clare Convalescent Center*
15063 Gratiot, Detroit, MI, 48205 (313)
372-4065
Licensure Skilled Care; Intermediate Care.
Beds 150. *Certified* Medicaid; Medicare.

Saint Josephs Home for the Aged
4800 Cadieux Rd, Detroit, MI, 48224 (313)
882-3800
Licensure Home for Aged.

Saint Martin Deporres Nursing Home*
1880 E Grand Blvd, Detroit, MI, 48211 (313)
925-6868
Licensure Skilled Care; Intermediate Care.
Beds 81. *Certified* Medicaid; Medicare.
Affiliation Roman Catholic

Westwood Nursing Center*
16588 Schaefer, Detroit, MI, 48235 (313)
925-6655
Licensure Skilled Care; Intermediate Care.
Beds 139. *Certified* Medicaid; Medicare.

DEWITT

Avon Nursing Home
477 Solon Rd, Dewitt, MI, 48820 (517)
484-0164
Licensure Intermediate Care. *Beds* 24. *Certified* Medicaid.

DIMONDALE

Saint Lawrence Diamondale Center
4000 N Michigan Rd, Dimondale, MI, 48821
(517) 646-6258
Medical Dir/Dir of Nursing William Meade
MD.
Licensure Skilled Care; Intermediate Care.
Beds 163. *Certified* Medicaid; Medicare.
Admissions Requirements Medical examina-
tion; Physician's request.
Staff RNs; LPNs; Orderlies; Nurses aides;
Physical therapists; Recreational therapists;
Occupational therapists; Speech therapists;
Activities coordinators; Dietitians; Dentists;
Ophthalmologists; Podiatrists; Audiologists.
Affiliation Roman Catholic
Facilities Dining room; Physical therapy room;
Activities room; Chapel; Crafts room; Laundry
room; Barber/Beauty shop; Lobby.
Activities Arts and Crafts; Cards; Games;
Reading groups; Prayer groups; Movies; Shop-
ping trips; Dances/Social or cultural gatherings.

DOWAGIAC

Dowagiac Nursing Home*
611 N Colby St, Dowagiac, MI, 49047 (616)
782-3471
Licensure Skilled Care; Intermediate Care.
Beds 150. *Certified* Medicaid; Medicare.

DURAND

Durand Convalescent Center*
8750 E Monroe Rd, Durand, MI, 48429 (517)
288-3166
Licensure Skilled Care; Intermediate Care.
Beds 119. *Certified* Medicaid; Medicare.

EAST JORDAN

Grandvue Medical Care Facility
East Jordan, MI, 49727 (616) 536-2286
Licensure Skilled Care; Intermediate Care.
Beds 73. *Certified* Medicaid; Medicare.

EAST LANSING

Burcham Hills Retirement Center*
2700 Burcham Dr, East Lansing, MI, 48823
(517) 351-8377
Licensure Skilled Care; Intermediate Care.
Beds 89. *Certified* Medicaid; Medicare.

Provincial House—East
2815 Northwind Dr, East Lansing, MI, 48823
(517) 332-0817
Medical Dir/Dir of Nursing E Rittenhouse
DO.
Licensure Intermediate Care. *Beds* 113. *Certi-
fied* Medicaid.
Admissions Requirements Minimum age 21;
Medical examination; Physician's request.
Staff RNs 3 (ft), 2 (pt); LPNs 4 (ft), 6 (pt);
Orderlies 4 (ft), 1 (pt); Nurses aides 38 (ft), 10
(pt); Activities coordinators 1 (ft).
Facilities Dining room; Activities room; Laun-
dry room; Barber/Beauty shop.
Activities Arts and Crafts; Cards; Games;
Reading groups; Prayer groups; Movies; Shop-
ping trips; Dances/Social or cultural gatherings.
Description Facility has a monthly luncheon
outing to a nearby restaurant; large, enclosed
patio in the center of the building for enjoying
the sunshine, birds, squirrels, and flowers.

Provincial House—Whitehills*
1843 N Hagadorn Rd, East Lansing, MI, 48823
(517) 332-5061
Licensure Skilled Care; Intermediate Care.
Beds 115. *Certified* Medicaid; Medicare.

ESCANABA

Bishop Noa Home*
624 Ludington St, Escanaba, MI, 49829 (906)
786-5810
Licensure Intermediate Care. *Beds* 81.
Affiliation Roman Catholic

Northwoods Manor*
2415 5th Ave S, Escanaba, MI, 49829 (906)
786-5810
Licensure Skilled Care; Intermediate Care.
Beds 99. *Certified* Medicaid; Medicare.

Northwoods Manor Annex*
2525 5th Ave S, Escanaba, MI, 49829 (906)
786-0408
Licensure Skilled Care; Intermediate Care.
Beds 59. *Certified* Medicaid; Medicare.

ESSEXVILLE

Bay County Medical Care Facility*
564 W Hampton Rd, Essexville, MI, 48732
(517) 894-3000
Licensure Skilled Care; Intermediate Care.
Beds 206. *Certified* Medicaid; Medicare.

FAIRVIEW

Ausable Valley Home*
Box 2000, Maple Dr, Fairview, MI, 48621
(517) 848-2241
Licensure Skilled Care; Intermediate Care.
Beds 62. *Certified* Medicaid; Medicare.

FARMINGTON

Oak Hill Nursing Home*
34225 Grand River, Farmington, MI, 48024
(313) 477-7373
Licensure Skilled Care; Intermediate Care.
Beds 137. *Certified* Medicaid; Medicare.

Oak Hill Nursing Home Annex*
34225 Grand River, Farmington, MI, 48024
(313) 474-6750
Licensure Intermediate Care. *Beds* 16. *Certified* Medicaid.

FARMINGTON HILLS

Farmington Nursing Home*
30405 Folsom Rd, Farmington Hills, MI,
48204 (313) 477-7400
Licensure Skilled Care; Intermediate Care.
Beds 179. *Certified* Medicaid; Medicare.

FARMINGTON TOWNSHIP

Williamsburg Convalescent Center
21017 Middlebelt Rd, Farmington Township,
MI, 48024 (313) 476-8300
Admin Ruth Bard. *Medical Dir/Dir of
Nursing* Richard Knight DO.
Licensure Skilled Care; Intermediate Care.
Beds 112. *Certified* Medicaid; Medicare.
Admissions Requirements Minimum age 18;
Medical examination; Physician's request.
Staff Physicians 9 (pt); RNs 6 (ft); LPNs 7 (ft);
Orderlies 6 (ft); Nurses aides 37 (ft); Physical
therapists 1 (pt); Recreational therapists 1 (pt);
Occupational therapists 1 (pt); Speech thera-
pists 1 (pt); Activities coordinators 1 (ft); Dieti-
tians 1 (ft); Dentists 1 (pt); Ophthalmologists 1
(pt); Podiatrists 1 (pt); Audiologists 1 (pt).
Facilities Dining room; Physical therapy room;
Activities room; Crafts room; Laundry room;
Barber/Beauty shop; Library.
Activities Arts and Crafts; Cards; Games;
Reading groups; Prayer groups; Movies; Shopping trips; Dances/Social or cultural gatherings.
Description Facility features a nail clinic, beauty consultant, stroke club, and men's and
women's nights.

FARWELL

Ardis Nursing Home*
Box 389, 2532 Cadillac, Farwell, MI, 48622
(517) 588-9928
Licensure Intermediate Care. *Beds* 71. *Certified* Medicaid.

FENTON

Crestmont Medical Care Facility
111 Trealout, Fenton, MI, 48430 (313) 629-4105
Medical Dir/Dir of Nursing W Buchanan MD.
Licensure Skilled Care; Intermediate Care.
Beds 136. *Certified* Medicaid; Medicare.
Staff Physicians 6 (pt); RNs 8 (ft), 5 (pt); LPNs
5 (ft); Orderlies 3 (ft); Nurses aides 51 (ft), 14
(pt); Physical therapists 1 (pt); Occupational
therapists 1 (pt); Speech therapists 1 (pt);
Activities coordinators 2 (ft); Dietitians 1 (pt);
Dentists 1 (pt); Podiatrists 1 (pt); Physical therapy assistants 1 (ft).
Facilities Dining room; Physical therapy room;
Activities room; Chapel; Crafts room; Laundry
room; Barber/Beauty shop; Family room; Day
room; Classroom.
Activities Arts and Crafts; Cards; Games; Prayer groups; Movies; Shopping trips; Dances/So-
cial or cultural gatherings; Picnics; Happy hour.
Description New 44-bed wing added in 1984
with emphasis on providing a home environment.

Elder House
202 Shiawassee Ave, Fenton, MI, 48430 (313)
629-6391
Licensure Home for Aged. *Beds* 36.
Admissions Requirements Minimum age 60;
Medical examination; Physician's request.
Staff RNs 1 (pt); Nurses aides 6 (ft); Activities
coordinators 1 (ft); Dietitians 1 (pt).
Facilities Dining room; Activities room; Crafts
room; Barber/Beauty shop; Library; Outdoor
activity area.
Activities Arts and Crafts; Cards; Games;
Reading groups; Prayer groups; Movies; Shop-
ping trips; Dances/Social or cultural gatherings;
Cookouts; Bowling.
Description A home for gracious living with
excellent food and privacy, and individuality
always respected.

Fenton Extended Care Center*
512 Beach St, Fenton, MI, 48430 (313)
629-4117
Licensure Intermediate Care. *Beds* 121. *Certified* Medicaid.

Hammond Rest Home*
700 S Adelaide St, Fenton, MI, 48430 (313)
629-9641
Licensure Intermediate Care. *Beds* 25. *Certified* Medicaid.

FERNDALE

Hilton Convalescent Home*
3161 Hilton Rd, Ferndale, MI, 48220 (313)
547-6227
Licensure Skilled Care; Intermediate Care.
Beds 78. *Certified* Medicaid; Medicare.

FLINT

Briarwood Manor Nursing Home
3011 N Center Rd, Flint, MI, 48506 (313)
736-0600
Medical Dir/Dir of Nursing Thomas E Lewis
MD.
Licensure Skilled Care; Intermediate Care.
Beds 97. *Certified* Medicaid; Medicare.
Admissions Requirements Minimum age 15;
Medical examination; Physician's request.
Staff RNs 3 (ft), 1 (pt); LPNs 6 (ft), 14 (pt);
Nurses aides 26 (ft), 26 (pt); Physical therapists
1 (pt); Speech therapists 1 (pt); Activities coor-
dinators 1 (ft); Dietitians 1 (ft).
Facilities Dining room; Physical therapy room;
Activities room; Laundry room; Barber/Beauty
shop.
Activities Arts and Crafts; Cards; Games;
Reading groups; Prayer groups; Movies; Dan-
ces/Social or cultural gatherings.
Description Newsletter is published monthly;
resident council and family council meet periodically.

Chateau Gardens
627 Begole St, Flint, MI, 48503 (313) 234-1667
Medical Dir/Dir of Nursing Richard Dykewicz
MD.
Licensure Skilled Care; Intermediate Care.
Beds 222. *Certified* Medicaid; Medicare.
Admissions Requirements Physician's request.

Staff RNs 6 (ft), 8 (pt); LPNs 13 (ft), 3 (pt);
Orderlies 1 (ft), 3 (pt); Nurses aides 60 (ft), 33
(pt); Physical therapists 1 (pt); Occupational
therapists 1 (pt); Speech therapists 1 (pt);
Activities coordinators 1 (ft); Dietitians 1 (pt).
Facilities Dining room; Physical therapy room;
Activities room; Chapel; Crafts room; Laundry
room; Barber/Beauty shop; Library.
Activities Arts and Crafts; Cards; Games;
Reading groups; Prayer groups; Movies; Shop-
ping trips; Dances/Social or cultural gatherings.

Clara Barton Terrace
1801 E Atherton Rd, Flint, MI, 48507 (313)
742-5850
Admin Diane Blick. *Medical Dir/Dir of
Nursing* Maurice Chapin MD.
Licensure Intermediate Care. *Beds* 149. *Certi-
fied* Medicaid.
Admissions Requirements Minimum age 15;
Medical examination.
Staff RNs 4 (ft), 3 (pt); LPNs 9 (ft), 10 (pt);
Nurses aides 50 (ft), 40 (pt); Activities coordi-
nators 1 (ft).
Facilities Dining room; Physical therapy room;
Activities room; Chapel; Crafts room; Laundry
room; Barber/Beauty shop; Library.
Activities Arts and Crafts; Cards; Games;
Reading groups; Prayer groups; Movies; Shop-
ping trips; Dances/Social or cultural gatherings;
Pet therapy; Video games.
Description Lovely landscaped large inner
courtyard with lighted, garden pool ideal for
shuffleboard and many outdoor activities.

Genesee Care Center*
G-4436 Beecher Rd, Flint, MI, 48504 (313)
733-0290
Licensure Skilled Care; Intermediate Care.
Beds 101. *Certified* Medicaid.

Heritage Manor Convalescent Center
G-3201 Beecher Rd, Flint, MI, 48504 (313)
732-9200
Medical Dir/Dir of Nursing Kenneth Jordan
MD.
Licensure Skilled Care; Intermediate Care.
Beds 180. *Certified* Medicaid; Medicare.
Admissions Requirements Minimum age 17;
Medical examination; Physician's request.
Facilities Dining room; Physical therapy room;
Activities room; Library.
Activities Arts and Crafts; Cards; Games;
Reading groups; Prayer groups; Movies; Shop-
ping trips; Dances/Social or cultural gatherings.

Kith Haven*
G-1069 Ballenger Hwy, Flint, MI, 48505 (313)
235-6676
Licensure Skilled Care; Intermediate Care.
Beds 167. *Certified* Medicaid; Medicare.

FLUSHING

Fostrian Manor*
540 Sunnyside Dr, Flushing, MI, 48433 (313)
659-5695
Licensure Skilled Care; Intermediate Care.
Beds 101. *Certified* Medicaid; Medicare.

FRANKENMUTH

Frankenmuth Convalescent Center*
500 W Genesee, Frankenmuth, MI, 48734
(517) 652-6101
Licensure Skilled Care; Intermediate Care.
Beds 126. *Certified* Medicaid; Medicare.

Lutheran Home
725 W Genesee, Frankenmuth, MI, 48734
(517) 652-9951
Medical Dir/Dir of Nursing J F Shetlar MD.
Licensure Skilled Care; Intermediate Care.
Beds 112. *Certified* Medicaid; Medicare.
Admissions Requirements Minimum age 65;
Medical examination.
Staff RNs 7 (ft), 14 (pt); LPNs 4 (pt); Nurses
aides 24 (ft), 30 (pt); Physical therapists 1 (pt);
Activities coordinators 1 (ft), 2 (pt); Dietitians
1 (ft).
Affiliation Lutheran
Facilities Dining room; Physical therapy room;
Activities room; Chapel; Crafts room; Laundry
room; Barber/Beauty shop; Library.
Activities Arts and Crafts; Cards; Games;
Reading groups; Prayer groups; Movies; Shop-
ping trips; Dances/Social or cultural gatherings.
Description Facility has excellent physical
plant, homey atmosphere, over 100 regular volunteers, Class I rating with state surveyors,
excellent community involvement and support.

FRANKFORT

Benzie County Medical Care Facility
210 W Maple, Frankfort, MI, 49635 (616)
352-9674
Admin Esther Bosscher. *Medical Dir/Dir of
Nursing* James N Kaufman MD.
Licensure Skilled Care; Intermediate Care.
Beds 42. *Certified* Medicaid; Medicare.
Admissions Requirements Minimum age 16;
Physician's request.
Staff Physicians 1 (pt); RNs 2 (ft), 9 (pt); LPNs
2 (ft); Orderlies 1 (ft); Nurses aides 21 (ft), 5
(pt); Activities coordinators 1 (ft); Dietitians 1
(pt).
Facilities Dining room; Physical therapy room;
Activities room; Crafts room; Laundry room;
Barber/Beauty shop.
Activities Arts and Crafts; Cards; Games;
Reading groups; Prayer groups; Movies.

FREMONT

Meadows Nursing Home*
4554 48th St, Fremont, MI, 49412 (616)
924-3990
Licensure Skilled Care; Intermediate Care.
Beds 129. *Certified* Medicaid; Medicare.

Newaygo County Medical Care Facility
4465 W 48th St, Rt 1, Fremont, MI, 49412
(616) 924-2020
Medical Dir/Dir of Nursing Alicia Pedelty
MD.
Licensure Skilled Care; Intermediate Care.
Beds 116. *Certified* Medicaid; Medicare.
Admissions Requirements Physician's request.
Staff Physicians 1 (pt); RNs 4 (ft), 6 (pt); LPNs

6 (ft), 5 (pt); Nurses aides 35 (ft), 23 (pt);
Physical therapists 1 (pt); Recreational thera-
pists 1 (ft); Occupational therapists 1 (pt); Spee-
ch therapists 1 (pt); Activities coordinators 1
(ft); Dietitians 1 (pt); Dentists 1 (pt); Ophthal-
mologists 1 (pt); Podiatrists 1 (pt); Audiologists
1 (pt).
Facilities Dining room; Physical therapy room;
Activities room; Crafts room; Laundry room;
Barber/Beauty shop; Library.
Activities Arts and Crafts; Cards; Games;
Reading groups; Prayer groups; Movies; Dan-
ces/Social or cultural gatherings; Music therapy;
Exercise classes.
Description Facility is located rurally on 30
acres; much landscaping; JCAH accredited.
Facility schedules groups and in-house pro-
grams.

GALESBURG

Matheson Nursing Home*
1080 N 35th St, Galesburg, MI, 49503 (616)
665-7043
Licensure Skilled Care; Intermediate Care.
Beds 93. *Certified* Medicaid; Medicare.

GAYLORD

**Otsego County Memorial—Intermediate Care
Facility***
825 N Center St, Gaylord, MI, 49735 (517)
732-1731
Licensure Skilled Care; Intermediate Care.
Beds 34. *Certified* Medicaid; Medicare.

Provincial House—Gaylord
508 Random Ln, Gaylord, MI, 49735 (517)
732-3508
Medical Dir/Dir of Nursing Kim Waterfall
MD.
Licensure Skilled Care; Intermediate Care.
Beds 120. *Certified* Medicaid; Medicare.
Admissions Requirements Medical examina-
tion.
Staff Physicians 2 (ft); RNs 4 (ft), 1 (pt); LPNs
5 (ft), 3 (pt); Orderlies 2 (ft); Nurses aides 30
(ft), 3 (pt); Physical therapists 1 (pt); Recrea-
tional therapists 1 (ft); Speech therapists 1 (ft);
Activities coordinators 1 (ft); Dietitians 1 (ft);
Dentists 1 (pt); Ophthalmologists 1 (pt); Podia-
trists 1 (pt).
Facilities Dining room; Physical therapy room;
Activities room; Crafts room; Laundry room;
Barber/Beauty shop; Library; 2 Day rooms.
Activities Arts and Crafts; Cards; Games;
Reading groups; Prayer groups; Movies; Shopping trips; Dances/Social or cultural gatherings;
Family nights; Picnics.
Description Provincial House—Gaylord is a
beautifully designed and decorated 120-bed
skilled nursing facility, which is set in the beautiful Alpine Village of Gaylord. We offer highly
trained professionals to care for the very skilled
patients and a variety of diversional activities
for our more basic patients. Besides being
highly-trained, our staff is exceptionally kind
and caring.

GLADWIN

Gladwin Nursing Home
3270 Pratt Lake Rd, Gladwin, MI, 48624 (517)
426-7275
Medical Dir/Dir of Nursing H A Timreck MD.
Licensure Skilled Care; Intermediate Care.
Beds 60. *Certified* Medicaid; Medicare.
Admissions Requirements Minimum age 15;
Medical examination; Physician's request.
Staff RNs 4 (ft), 3 (pt); LPNs 2 (ft), 4 (pt);
Nurses aides 15 (ft), 7 (pt).
Facilities Dining room; Physical therapy room;
Activities room.
Activities Arts and Crafts; Cards; Games;
Reading groups; Dances/Social or cultural gath-
erings.

GOODELLS

Saint Clair County Medical Center
8332 County Park Dr, Goodells, MI, 48027
(313) 325-1291
Admin Cora M Urgdart. *Medical Dir/Dir of
Nursing* Frederick E Ludwig MD.
Licensure Skilled Care; Intermediate Care.
Beds 75. *Certified* Medicaid; Medicare.
Admissions Requirements Minimum age 15;
Medical examination; Physician's request.
Staff Physicians 1 (pt); RNs 3 (ft), 4 (pt); LPNs
4 (ft), 2 (pt); Nurses aides 19 (ft), 20 (pt);
Physical therapists 1 (pt); Occupational thera-
pists 1 (pt); Speech therapists 1 (pt); Activities
coordinators 1 (ft); Dietitians 1 (pt).
Facilities Dining room; Physical therapy room;
Activities room; Crafts room; Laundry room;
Barber/Beauty shop; Library.
Activities Arts and Crafts; Cards; Games;
Reading groups; Prayer groups; Movies; Dan-
ces/Social or cultural gatherings.
Description Center is located in rural setting
with spacious grounds and long porches.

GRAND BLANC

Grand Blanc Convalescent Center
8481 Holly Rd, Grand Blanc, MI, 48439 (313)
694-1711
Admin Paul N Wright. *Medical Dir/Dir of
Nursing* Dr Joseph T Batdorf.
Licensure Skilled Care. *Beds* 95. *Cer-
tified* Medicaid; Medicare.
Admissions Requirements Minimum age 18;
Medical examination; Physician's request.
Staff RNs 2 (ft), 10 (pt); LPNs 2 (ft), 5 (pt);
Nurses aides 25 (ft), 26 (pt); Physical therapists
1 (pt); Reality therapists 1 (ft); Recreational
therapists 1 (ft); Occupational therapists 1 (pt);
Speech therapists 1 (pt); Activities coordinators
1 (ft); Dietitians 1 (ft); Dentists 1 (pt); Ophthal-
mologists 1 (pt); Podiatrists 1 (pt); Audiologists
1 (pt).
Affiliation Roman Catholic
Facilities Dining room; Physical therapy room;
Activities room; Chapel; Crafts room; Laundry
room; Barber/Beauty shop; Library; Patient
lounges.
Activities Arts and Crafts; Cards; Games;
Reading groups; Prayer groups; Movies; Shopping trips; Dances/Social or cultural gatherings;
Music and cooking classes; Gardening.

Description Facility is located in a homey, country-like setting with woods and ponds near a medical complex of physicians, X-ray, diagnostic laboratory, dentists, pharmacy, and cardiovascular diagnostic center, 10 miles from all major hospitals in Flint.

Riverbend Nursing Home
11941 Belsay Rd, Grand Blanc, MI, 48439 (313) 694-1970
Admin M Ellen Knickerbocker. *Medical Dir-/Dir of Nursing* Thomas B Marwil MD.
Licensure Skilled Care; Intermediate Care. *Beds* 127. *Certified* Medicaid; Medicare.
Staff Physicians 3 (pt); RNs 6 (ft), 7 (pt); LPNs 5 (ft), 4 (pt); Orderlies 1 (pt); Nurses aides 39 (ft), 17 (pt); Physical therapists 1 (ft); Occupational therapists 1 (pt); Speech therapists 1 (pt); Activities coordinators 1 (ft); Dietitians 1 (pt); Dentists 1 (pt); Ophthalmologists 1 (pt).
Facilities Dining room; Physical therapy room; Activities room; Crafts room; Laundry room; Barber/Beauty shop; Library.
Activities Arts and Crafts; Cards; Games; Reading groups; Prayer groups; Movies; Shopping trips; Dances/Social or cultural gatherings.
Description Riverbend Nursing Home is located in a beautiful country setting in Grand Blanc, Michigan. Spacious grounds and sparkling rooms lend all the comforts of home, and caring staff is dedicated to maintaining an environment of concern and dignity for all residents.

GRAND HAVEN

Riverside Nursing Home*
415 Friant, Grand Haven, MI, 49417 (616) 842-4120
Licensure Intermediate Care. *Beds* 34. *Certified* Medicaid.

Shore Haven Nursing Home*
900 S Beacon, Grand Haven, MI, 49417 (616) 846-1850
Licensure Skilled Care; Intermediate Care. *Beds* 126. *Certified* Medicaid; Medicare.

Sylvan Dell Nursing Home*
1615 S Despelder St, Grand Haven, MI, 49417 (616) 842-0770
Licensure Skilled Care. *Beds* 64. *Certified* Medicaid; Medicare.

GRAND RAPIDS

Cascade Care Center
1095 Medical Park SE, Grand Rapids, MI, 49506 (616) 949-7220
Licensure Skilled Care; Intermediate Care. *Beds* 123. *Certified* Medicaid; Medicare.

Christian Nursing Center*
801 College SE, Grand Rapids, MI, 49507 (616) 452-8992 and 452-7206
Licensure Intermediate Care. *Beds* 42. *Certified* Medicaid.

Christian Rest Home Association
1000 Edison Ave NW, Grand Rapids, MI, 49504 (616) 453-2475

Admin John Rurter. *Medical Dir/Dir of Nursing* John Vander Molen MD.
Licensure Skilled Care; Intermediate Care.
Beds 153. *Certified* Medicaid; Medicare.
Admissions Requirements Minimum age 15; Medical examination; Physician's request.
Staff RNs 1 (ft), 12 (pt); LPNs 1 (ft), 10 (pt); Orderlies 1 (pt); Nurses aides 45 (ft), 45 (pt); Physical therapists 1 (ft); Recreational therapists 2 (ft), 1 (pt); Occupational therapists 1 (pt).
Facilities Dining room; Physical therapy room; Activities room; Chapel; Crafts room; Laundry room; Barber/Beauty shop; Library.
Activities Arts and Crafts; Cards; Games; Reading groups; Prayer groups; Movies; Shopping trips; Dances/Social or cultural gatherings.

Faith Nursing Home*
845 Jefferson SE, Grand Rapids, MI, 49507 (616) 452-9198
Licensure Intermediate Care. *Beds* 30. *Certified* Medicaid.

Grand Valley Nursing Center
4118 Kalamazoo Ave SE, Grand Rapids, MI, 49508 (616) 455-7300
Medical Dir/Dir of Nursing Dr Dirk Mouw.
Licensure Skilled Care; Intermediate Care.
Beds 165. *Certified* Medicaid; Medicare.
Admissions Requirements Minimum age 3; Medical examination; Physician's request.
Staff RNs 9 (ft), 15 (pt); LPNs 10 (ft), 10 (pt); Nurses aides 46 (ft), 38 (pt); Physical therapists 1 (ft); Recreational therapists 1 (ft); Occupational therapists 1 (ft); Speech therapists 1 (ft); Activities coordinators 1 (ft); Dietitians 1 (ft); Dentists 1 (pt); Ophthalmologists 1 (pt); Podiatrists 1 (pt); Social workers 2 (ft), 1 (pt); Psychologists 1 (ft).
Facilities Dining room; Physical therapy room; Activities room; Chapel; Crafts room; Barber/Beauty shop; Library.
Activities Arts and Crafts; Cards; Games; Reading groups; Prayer groups; Movies; Shopping trips; Dances/Social or cultural gatherings; Luncheon trips.
Description This center specializes in long-term rehabilitation; has a spinal cord unit funded by Crippled Children and a brain impaired unit where patients are accepted from level II through level VIII.

Greenview Nursing Home*
1708 Leonard St NE, Grand Rapids, MI, 49505 (616) 456-7243
Licensure Skilled Care; Intermediate Care. *Beds* 69. *Certified* Medicaid; Medicare.

Holland Home*
1450 E Fulton, Grand Rapids, MI, 49503 (616) 459-3495
Licensure Intermediate Care. *Beds* 79. *Certified* Medicaid.

Holland Home—Brown Home*
1435 E Fulton, Grand Rapids, MI, 49503 (616) 459-2717
Licensure Intermediate Care. *Beds* 11. *Certified* Medicaid.

Holland Home—Raybrook Manor*
2121 Raybrook Ave SE, Grand Rapids, MI, 49506 (616) 949-6656
Licensure Intermediate Care. *Beds* 50. *Certified* Medicaid.

Kent Community Hospital Complex*
750 Fuller Ave NE, Grand Rapids, MI, 49503 (616) 774-3300
Licensure Skilled Care; Intermediate Care. *Beds* 338. *Certified* Medicaid; Medicare.

Lafayette Christian Nursing Home*
1001 Lafayette SE, Grand Rapids, MI, 49507 (616) 452-9673
Licensure Intermediate Care. *Beds* 61. *Certified* Medicaid.

Luther Home*
1706 Division Ave S, Grand Rapids, MI, 49507 (616) 243-0252
Licensure Intermediate Care. *Beds* 52. *Certified* Medicaid.
Affiliation Lutheran

M J Clark Memorial Home*
1546 Sherman SE, Grand Rapids, MI, 49506 (616) 452-7206
Licensure Skilled Care; Intermediate Care. *Beds* 111. *Certified* Medicaid; Medicare.

Michigan Christian Home*
1845 Boston St SE, Grand Rapids, MI, 49506 (616) 245-9179
Licensure Skilled Care; Intermediate Care. *Beds* 29. *Certified* Medicaid; Medicare.

Olds Manor
201 Michigan NW, Grand Rapids, MI, 49502 (616) 429-0101
Medical Dir/Dir of Nursing John N Campbell MD.
Licensure Intermediate Care. *Beds* 44. *Certified* Medicaid.
Admissions Requirements Medical examination; Physician's request.
Staff Physicians 2 (pt); RNs 2 (ft); LPNs 10 (ft); Orderlies 3 (ft); Nurses aides 11 (ft), 15 (pt); Activities coordinators 1 (ft); Dietitians 1 (ft); Ophthalmologists 1 (ft); Podiatrists 1 (ft).
Facilities Dining room; Activities room; Chapel; Crafts room; Laundry room; Barber/Beauty shop; Library.
Activities Arts and Crafts; Games; Prayer groups; Movies; Shopping trips.

Pilgrim Manor
2000 Leonard Ave, Grand Rapids, MI, 49505 (616) 458-1133
Medical Dir/Dir of Nursing Dr Keith Crane.
Licensure Skilled Care; Intermediate Care.
Beds 42. *Certified* Medicaid; Medicare.
Admissions Requirements Minimum age 62.
Staff Physicians 1 (pt); RNs 2 (ft), 4 (pt); LPNs 4 (ft), 5 (pt); Nurses aides 21 (ft), 10 (pt); Activities coordinators 1 (ft); Dietitians 1 (pt); Podiatrists 1 (pt).
Affiliation Congregational
Facilities Dining room; Activities room; Chapel; Crafts room; Laundry room; Barber/Beauty shop; Library.

Activities Arts and Crafts; Cards; Games; Reading groups; Prayer groups; Movies; Shopping trips; Dances/Social or cultural gatherings.

Porter Hills Presbyterian Village*
3600 Fulton St E, Grand Rapids, MI, 49506
(616) 949-4971
Licensure Skilled Care. *Beds* 51. *Certified* Medicaid; Medicare.
Affiliation Presbyterian

Rest Haven Homes
1424 Union Ave NE, Grand Rapids, MI, 49505
(616) 363-6819
Licensure Intermediate Care. *Beds* 25.
Admissions Requirements Minimum age 15; Medical examination.
Staff Physicians 1 (pt); RNs 2 (pt); LPNs 2 (ft), 3 (pt); Orderlies 1 (pt); Nurses aides 10 (pt); Activities coordinators 1 (pt); Dietitians 1 (pt).
Facilities Dining room; Physical therapy room; Laundry room; Barber/Beauty shop; Library.
Activities Arts and Crafts; Games; Reading groups; Prayer groups; Movies; Shopping trips; Dances/Social or cultural gatherings.

Saint Ann's Home
2161 Leonard NW, Grand Rapids, MI, 49503
(616) 453-7715
Medical Dir/Dir of Nursing Jerome Mancewicz MD.
Licensure Intermediate Care. *Beds* 37. *Certified* Medicaid.
Admissions Requirements Minimum age 65; Medical examination; Physician's request.
Staff RNs 1 (ft), 1 (pt); LPNs 3 (ft), 7 (pt); Nurses aides 8 (ft), 11 (pt); Activities coordinators 1 (ft); Dietitians 1 (ft).
Affiliation Roman Catholic
Facilities Dining room; Activities room; Chapel; Crafts room; Laundry room; Barber/Beauty shop; Library.
Activities Arts and Crafts; Cards; Games; Reading groups; Prayer groups; Movies; Shopping trips; Dances/Social or cultural gatherings.

Sherbrooke Nursing Home*
1157 Medical Park Dr, Grand Rapids, MI, 49506 (616) 949-7310
Licensure Skilled Care. *Beds* 71.

Springbrook Manor*
2320 E Beltline SE, Grand Rapids, MI, 49506
(616) 949-3000
Licensure Skilled Care; Intermediate Care.
Beds 205. *Certified* Medicaid; Medicare.

Villa Elizabeth
2100 Leonard NE, Grand Rapids, MI, 49505
(616) 454-8273
Medical Dir/Dir of Nursing Dr Maskill.
Licensure Skilled Care; Intermediate Care.
Beds 136. *Certified* Medicaid; Medicare.
Admissions Requirements Minimum age 65; Medical examination.
Staff RNs 4 (ft), 9 (pt); LPNs 1 (ft), 5 (pt); Nurses aides 29 (ft), 52 (pt); Activities coordinators 2 (ft).
Affiliation Roman Catholic
Facilities Dining room; Physical therapy room; Activities room; Chapel; Crafts room; Laundry

room; Barber/Beauty shop.
Activities Arts and Crafts; Cards; Games; Reading groups; Prayer groups; Movies.

Walker Care Center
1050 4 Mile Rd NW, Grand Rapids, MI, 49504
(616) 784-0646
Medical Dir/Dir of Nursing Dr James O'Brien.
Licensure Skilled Care; Intermediate Care.
Beds 207. *Certified* Medicaid; Medicare.
Admissions Requirements Minimum age 17; Medical examination; Physician's request.
Staff Physicians 3 (pt); RNs 8 (ft), 4 (pt); LPNs 4 (ft), 11 (pt); Orderlies 1 (ft), 2 (pt); Nurses aides 52 (ft), 30 (pt); Physical therapists 1 (ft); Reality therapists 1 (ft); Recreational therapists 1 (ft).
Facilities Dining room; Physical therapy room; Activities room; Chapel; Crafts room; Laundry room; Barber/Beauty shop; Library; Cooking kitchen; Men's workshop.
Activities Arts and Crafts; Cards; Games; Reading groups; Prayer groups; Movies; Shopping trips; Dances/Social or cultural gatherings; Outside visits to community functions; Bowling; Pet shows; Education class.

GRANDVILLE

Brookcrest Nursing Home*
3400 Wilson Ave SW, Grandville, MI, 49418
(616) 534-5487
Licensure Skilled Care. *Beds* 153. *Certified* Medicaid; Medicare.

GRASS LAKE

Cedar Knoll Rest Home
9230 Cedar Knoll Dr, Grass Lake, MI, 49240
(517) 522-8471
Medical Dir/Dir of Nursing E E Vivirski MD.
Licensure Skilled Care; Intermediate Care.
Beds 169. *Certified* Medicaid; Medicare.
Admissions Requirements Minimum age 16; Medical examination; Physician's request.
Staff RNs 6 (ft), 2 (pt); LPNs 12 (ft), 2 (pt); Orderlies 14 (ft); Nurses aides 64 (ft), 1 (pt); Recreational therapists 2 (ft).
Facilities Dining room; Physical therapy room; Activities room; Crafts room; Laundry room; Barber/Beauty shop.
Activities Arts and Crafts; Cards; Games; Reading groups; Prayer groups; Movies; Shopping trips.
Description Lovely rural setting; home-like atmosphere with happy and contented residents cared for by concerned employees.

GRAYLING

Mercy Hospital*
1100 Michigan Ave, Grayling, MI, 49738 (517) 348-5461
Licensure Skilled Care; Intermediate Care.
Beds 40. *Certified* Medicaid; Medicare.

GREENVILLE

Christensen's Nursing Home
828 E Washington Ave, Greenville, MI, 48838
(616) 754-7186
Medical Dir/Dir of Nursing Gerald L Tovatt DO.
Licensure Skilled Care; Intermediate Care.
Beds 106. *Certified* Medicaid; Medicare.
Admissions Requirements Minimum age 18; Medical examination; Physician's request.
Staff RNs 4 (ft), 2 (pt); LPNs 6 (ft), 4 (pt); Nurses aides 40 (ft), 20 (pt); Physical therapists 1 (ft), 1 (pt); Recreational therapists 1 (ft), 1 (pt); Activities coordinators 1 (ft), 1 (pt); Dietitians 1 (pt).
Facilities Dining room; Physical therapy room; Activities room; Crafts room; Laundry room; Barber/Beauty shop.
Activities Arts and Crafts; Cards; Games; Reading groups; Prayer groups; Movies; Shopping trips; Dances/Social or cultural gatherings.

United Memorial Hospital*
615 S Bower St, Greenville, MI, 48838 (616) 754-4691
Licensure Skilled Care; Intermediate Care.
Beds 40. *Certified* Medicaid; Medicare.

GROSSE POINTE WOODS

Georgian East*
21401 Mack Ave, Grosse Pointe Woods, MI, 48236 (313) 778-0800
Licensure Intermediate Care. *Beds* 80. *Certified* Medicare.

HAMTRAMCK

Saint Joseph Nursing Home*
9400 Conant, Hamtramck, MI, 48212 (313) 874-4500
Licensure Skilled Care; Intermediate Care.
Beds 170. *Certified* Medicaid; Medicare.
Affiliation Roman Catholic

HANCOCK

Cypress Manor
1400 Poplar St, Hancock, MI, 49930 (906) 482-6644
Licensure Intermediate Care. *Beds* 63. *Certified* Medicaid.
Admissions Requirements Minimum age 18; Medical examination; Physician's request.
Staff Physicians 4 (ft); RNs 2 (ft); LPNs 4 (ft); Nurses aides 25 (ft); Physical therapists 1 (pt); Reality therapists 1 (pt); Recreational therapists 1 (pt); Occupational therapists 1 (pt); Speech therapists 1 (pt); Activities coordinators 1 (ft); Dietitians 1 (pt); Dentists 1 (pt); Ophthalmologists 1 (pt); Podiatrists 1 (pt); Audiologists 1 (pt).
Facilities Dining room; Physical therapy room; Activities room; Laundry room; Barber/Beauty shop.
Activities Arts and Crafts; Cards; Games; Reading groups; Prayer groups; Movies; Shopping trips; Dances/Social or cultural gatherings.
Description Cypress Manor is nestled on a beautifully landscaped lot in Hancock, Michi-

gan, in the heart of the Copper Country. The facility has grounds that encompass 5 acres, 3 of which are wooded.

Houghton County Medical Care Facility
1100 Quincy St, Hancock, MI, 49930 (906) 482-5050
Medical Dir/Dir of Nursing Hororatio Barrios MD.
Licensure Skilled Care; Intermediate Care.
Beds 197. *Certified* Medicaid; Medicare.
Admissions Requirements Minimum age 18; Medical examination; Physician's request.
Staff Physicians 9 (pt); RNs 8 (ft), 6 (pt); LPNs 7 (ft), 4 (pt); Orderlies 5 (ft), 4 (pt); Nurses aides 66 (ft), 14 (pt); Physical therapists 1 (pt); Speech therapists 1 (pt); Activities coordinators 2 (ft); Dietitians 1 (pt); Dentists 1 (pt); Ophthalmologists 1 (pt).
Facilities Dining room; Physical therapy room; Activities room; Chapel; Crafts room; Barber-/Beauty shop; Library.
Activities Arts and Crafts; Cards; Games; Reading groups; Movies; Shopping trips; Dances/Social or cultural gatherings.

Portage View Hospital
200-10 Michigan St, Hancock, MI, 49930 (517) 482-1122
Medical Dir/Dir of Nursing Marko V Beley.
Licensure Skilled Care. *Beds* 30. *Certified* Medicare.
Admissions Requirements Minimum age 15; Medical examination; Physician's request.
Staff Physicians 9 (pt); RNs 1 (ft); LPNs 2 (ft), 6 (pt); Nurses aides 6 (ft), 9 (pt); Physical therapists 2 (ft), 1 (pt); Speech therapists 1 (pt); Activities coordinators 1 (pt); Dietitians 2 (ft); Dentists 5 (pt); Ophthalmologists 2 (ft).
Facilities Activities room; Crafts room.
Activities Arts and Crafts; Cards; Games; Movies; Shopping trips.
Description We try to provide as much of a home-like environment as possible within the hospital setting. We take our patients to the mall, circus, ice show, picnics.

HARBOR BEACH

Harbor Beach Community Hospital*
1st and Broad Sts, Harbor Beach, MI, 48441 (517) 479-3201
Licensure Skilled Care; Intermediate Care.
Beds 40. *Certified* Medicaid; Medicare.

HARBOR SPRINGS

Emmet County Medical Care Facility
750 E Main St, Harbor Springs, MI, 49740 (616) 526-2161
Medical Dir/Dir of Nursing Richard A Knecht MD.
Licensure Skilled Care; Intermediate Care.
Beds 110. *Certified* Medicaid; Medicare.
Admissions Requirements Minimum age 16; Medical examination; Physician's request.
Staff Physicians 3 (pt); RNs 2 (pt); LPNs 1 (ft), 1 (pt); Orderlies 1 (ft); Nurses aides 42 (ft), 8 (pt); Reality therapists 1 (pt); Occupational therapists 1 (pt); Speech therapists 1 (pt); Activities coordinators 1 (ft); Dietitians 1 (ft);

Dentists 1 (pt); Podiatrists 1 (pt).
Facilities Dining room; Physical therapy room; Activities room; Chapel; Crafts room; Laundry room; Barber/Beauty shop.
Activities Arts and Crafts; Cards; Games; Reading groups; Prayer groups; Movies.

HARPER WOODS

Cottage-Belmont Nursing Center*
19840 Harper Ave, Harper Woods, MI, 48236 (313) 881-9556
Licensure Skilled Care; Intermediate Care.
Beds 103.

HARRISVILLE

Jamieson Nursing Home
790 S US 23, Harrisville, MI, 48740 (517) 724-6889
Admin Sally J Smith.
Licensure Intermediate Care. *Beds* 51. *Certified* Medicaid.
Admissions Requirements Minimum age 15; Physician's request.
Staff Physicians; RNs; LPNs; Nurses aides; Recreational therapists; Occupational therapists; Speech therapists; Activities coordinators; Dietitians; Dentists; Ophthalmologists; Podiatrists; Audiologists.
Facilities Dining room; Activities room; Chapel; Crafts room; Laundry room; Barber/Beauty shop; Library.
Activities Arts and Crafts; Cards; Games; Reading groups; Prayer groups; Movies; Shopping trips; Dances/Social or cultural gatherings; Gardening.
Description The nursing home that cares—located in a beautiful 9 ½ acre wooded setting off US 23.

HART

Oceana County Medical Care Facility*
701 E Main St, Hart, MI, 49420 (313) 873-2148
Licensure Skilled Care; Intermediate Care.
Beds 113. *Certified* Medicaid; Medicare.
Ownership Public.

HASTINGS

Barry County Medical Care Facility*
2700 Nashville Rd, Hastings, MI, 49058 (616) 945-9564
Licensure Skilled Care; Intermediate Care.
Beds 138. *Certified* Medicaid; Medicare.

Provincial House—Hastings
240 E North St, Hastings, MI, 49058 (616) 945-9564
Medical Dir/Dir of Nursing James Hogan DO.
Licensure Skilled Care; Intermediate Care.
Beds 111. *Certified* Medicaid; Medicare.
Admissions Requirements Medical examination; Physician's request.
Staff Physicians 17 (pt); RNs 4 (ft), 5 (pt); LPNs 5 (ft), 3 (pt); Nurses aides 35 (ft), 31 (pt); Physical therapists 1 (pt); Occupational therapists 1 (pt); Speech therapists 1 (pt); Activities coordinators 2 (pt); Dietitians 2 (pt); Dentists 1

(pt); Ophthalmologists 1 (pt); Podiatrists 1 (pt); Audiologists 1 (pt).
Facilities Dining room; Physical therapy room; Activities room; Crafts room; Laundry room; Barber/Beauty shop.
Activities Arts and Crafts; Cards; Games; Reading groups; Prayer groups; Movies; Shopping trips; Dances/Social or cultural gatherings.
Description Facility has total patient care planning; skilled nursing care; respirator patient care; mental health services; in-house optometrist services.

HIGHLAND PARK

Park Geriatric Village
111 Ford Ave, Highland Park, MI, 48203 (313) 883-3585
Admin D J Bortz III. *Medical Dir/Dir of Nursing* S Walavalkar MD.
Licensure Skilled Care; Intermediate Care.
Beds 134. *Certified* Medicaid; Medicare.
Admissions Requirements Minimum age 18.
Staff Physicians 2 (ft); RNs 3 (ft), 3 (pt); LPNs 7 (ft), 10 (pt); Orderlies 6 (ft), 8 (pt); Nurses aides 36 (ft), 25 (pt); Physical therapists 1 (ft); Reality therapists 1 (ft); Recreational therapists 1 (ft), 1 (pt); Occupational therapists 1 (ft); Speech therapists 1 (ft); Activities coordinators 1 (ft); Dietitians 1 (ft); Dentists 1 (ft); Ophthalmologists 1 (ft); Podiatrists 2 (ft); Audiologists 1 (ft).
Facilities Dining room; Physical therapy room; Activities room; Laundry room; Barber/Beauty shop.
Activities Arts and Crafts; Cards; Games; Reading groups; Prayer groups; Movies.

Royal Nursing Center*
91 Glendale Ave, Highland Park, MI, 48203 (313) 869-7711
Licensure Skilled Care; Intermediate Care.
Beds 183. *Certified* Medicaid; Medicare.

Saint Lukes Episcopal Home
224 Highland Ave, Highland Park, MI, 48203 (313) 868-1445
Licensure Intermediate Care. *Beds* 22. *Certified* Medicaid.
Admissions Requirements Minimum age 65; Medical examination.
Staff Physicians 3 (ft); RNs 2 (ft), 4 (pt); LPNs 3 (ft), 2 (pt); Nurses aides 12 (ft), 8 (pt); Activities coordinators 1 (ft), 1 (pt); Dietitians 1 (pt); Dentists 1 (pt); Podiatrists 1 (pt).
Affiliation Episcopal
Facilities Dining room; Activities room; Chapel; Crafts room; Barber/Beauty shop; Library.
Activities Arts and Crafts; Cards; Games; Reading groups; Prayer groups; Movies; Shopping trips.
Description The purpose of the house is to offer life-long security with the knowledge that different levels of care are available.

HILLMAN

Pineview of Hillman*
631 Caring St, Hillman, MI, 49746
Licensure Intermediate Care. *Beds* 70. *Certified* Medicaid; Medicare.

HILLSDALE

Hillsdale County Medical Care Facility
140 W Mechanic St, Hillsdale, MI, 49242 (517) 439-9341
Medical Dir/Dir of Nursing Dr Frank Monti.
Licensure Skilled Care; Intermediate Care. *Beds* 160. *Certified* Medicaid; Medicare.
Admissions Requirements Minimum age 15; Medical examination; Physician's request.
Staff Physicians 1 (ft), 1 (pt); RNs 6 (ft), 2 (pt); LPNs 20 (ft), 10 (pt); Nurses aides 50 (ft), 50 (pt); Physical therapists 1 (pt); Recreational therapists 2 (ft); Occupational therapists 1 (pt); Speech therapists 1 (pt); Activities coordinators 1 (ft); Dietitians 1 (ft); Dentists 1 (pt); Ophthalmologists 1 (pt); Podiatrists 1 (pt).
Facilities Dining room; Physical therapy room; Activities room; Chapel; Crafts room; Laundry room; Barber/Beauty shop.
Activities Arts and Crafts; Cards; Games; Reading groups; Prayer groups; Movies; Dances/Social or cultural gatherings.
Description Facility is located in a rural setting with nice scenery. Residents are able to enjoy warm weather on patio and fall trips to local fair. Patient Concerns Committee formed to voice all problems.

HOLLAND

Birchwood Manor*
493 W 32nd St, Holland, MI, 49423 (616) 396-1438
Licensure Skilled Care; Intermediate Care. *Beds* 111. *Certified* Medicaid; Medicare.

Meadowbrook Care Center*
280 W 40th, Holland, MI, 49423 (616) 392-7161
Licensure Skilled Care; Intermediate Care. *Beds* 125. *Certified* Medicaid; Medicare.

HOLLY

Sunday Convalescent and Rest Home
313 Sherwood St, Holly, MI, 48442 (313) 634-9281
Medical Dir/Dir of Nursing G S Buchanan MD.
Licensure Intermediate Care. *Beds* 66. *Certified* Medicaid.
Admissions Requirements Medical examination.
Staff Physicians; RNs; LPNs; Nurses aides; Recreational therapists; Activities coordinators; Dietitians; Dentists; Ophthalmologists; Podiatrists; Audiologists.
Facilities Dining room; Activities room; Crafts room; Barber/Beauty shop; Library.
Activities Arts and Crafts; Cards; Games; Reading groups; Prayer groups; Movies.

HOLT

Martin Luther—Holt Home*
5091 Willoughby Rd, Holt, MI, 48842 (517) 694-2144
Licensure Skilled Care; Intermediate Care. *Beds* 84. *Certified* Medicaid; Medicare.
Affiliation Lutheran

HOUGHTON LAKE

King Nursing Home*
206 Tower Hill Rd, Houghton Lake, MI, 48629 (517) 422-5153
Licensure Intermediate Care. *Beds* 49. *Certified* Medicaid.

HOWELL

Greenbriar Convalescent Center*
3003 W Grand River, Howell, MI, 48843 (517) 546-4210
Licensure Skilled Care; Intermediate Care. *Beds* 121. *Certified* Medicaid; Medicare.

Livingston Care Center
1333 W Grand River, Howell, MI, 48843 (517) 548-1900
Medical Dir/Dir of Nursing Edwin C Blumberg DO.
Licensure Skilled Care; Intermediate Care. *Beds* 200. *Certified* Medicaid; Medicare.
Admissions Requirements Minimum age 17; Medical examination.
Staff Physicians 17 (pt); RNs 3 (ft), 4 (pt); LPNs 8 (ft), 11 (pt); Orderlies 3 (ft), 1 (pt); Nurses aides 72 (ft), 18 (pt); Physical therapists 1 (ft); Occupational therapists 1 (pt); Speech therapists 1 (pt); Activities coordinators 1 (ft), 2 (pt); Dietitians 1 (pt); Podiatrists 1 (pt); Respiration therapists 1 (pt).
Facilities Dining room; Physical therapy room; Activities room; Chapel; Laundry room; Barber/Beauty shop; Library.
Activities Arts and Crafts; Cards; Games; Reading groups; Prayer groups; Movies; Shopping trips; Dances/Social or cultural gatherings.
Description Facility supplies home-bound meals, ventilator (respiratory) unit, hospice program, and 10-bed lockup unit; home care; JCAH and AHCA approved, HCAM certified.

HUBBELL

Our Lady of Mercy Convalescent Home Inc
1201 Grant St, Box 369, Hubbell, MI, 49934 (906) 296-3301 and 296-9601
Medical Dir/Dir of Nursing B H Nanavati MD.
Licensure Intermediate Care. *Beds* 45. *Certified* Medicaid.
Admissions Requirements Minimum age 15.
Staff Physicians 1 (pt); RNs 2 (ft), 1 (pt); LPNs 3 (ft), 1 (pt); Nurses aides 12 (ft), 8 (pt); Activities coordinators 1 (ft); Dietitians 1 (pt).
Affiliation Roman Catholic
Facilities Dining room; Activities room; Chapel; Crafts room; Laundry room; Barber/Beauty shop.
Activities Arts and Crafts; Cards; Games; Prayer groups; Movies; Dances/Social or cultural gatherings; Library services.
Description Our Lady of Mercy is a small personalized facility located on the Keweenaw Peninsula of Michigan's upper peninsula. Residents and fifth graders from Lake Linden-Hubbell enjoy the Foster Grandparents program. Excellent loving nursing care is the pride of our staff. Consultant services are available on request.

HUDSONVILLE

Hudsonville Christian Nursing Home*
3650 Van Buren, Hudsonville, MI, 49426 (616) 669-1520
Licensure Skilled Care; Intermediate Care. *Beds* 113. *Certified* Medicaid; Medicare.

INKSTER

Advance Nursing Center*
2936 S John Daley Rd, Inkster, MI, 48141 (313) 278-7272
Licensure Skilled Care; Intermediate Care. *Beds* 92. *Certified* Medicaid; Medicare.

Geriatric Health Center
28355 Michigan Ave, Inkster, MI, 48141 (313) 274-0310
Medical Dir/Dir of Nursing Lawrence Usher DO.
Licensure Intermediate Care. *Beds* 79. *Certified* Medicaid.
Admissions Requirements Minimum age 18; Medical examination; Physician's request.
Staff Physicians 1 (pt); RNs 1 (ft); LPNs 3 (ft).
Facilities Dining room; Activities room; Crafts room; Laundry room; Barber/Beauty shop.
Activities Arts and Crafts; Cards; Games; Reading groups; Prayer groups; Movies; Shopping trips; Dances/Social or cultural gatherings.

IONIA

Ionia Manor*
814 Lincoln, Ionia, MI, 48846 (616) 527-0080
Licensure Skilled Care; Intermediate Care. *Beds* 120. *Certified* Medicaid; Medicare.

IRON MOUNTAIN

Freeman Convalescent Home*
Box 130, Star Rt 3, Iron Mountain, MI, 49801 (906) 774-1530
Licensure Intermediate Care. *Beds* 45. *Certified* Medicaid.

Hyland Convalescent Home*
601 E "G" St, Iron Mountain, MI, 49801 (906) 774-9333
Licensure Intermediate Care. *Beds* 51.

IRON RIVER

Iron River Nursing Home*
Lincoln St, Iron River, MI, 49935 (906) 265-5168
Licensure Intermediate Care. *Beds* 69. *Certified* Medicaid.

IRONWOOD

Hautamaki Westgate Rest Home*
1500 N Lowell St, Ironwood, MI, 49938 (906) 932-3867
Licensure Intermediate Care. *Beds* 65. *Certified* Medicaid.

Josephson Nursing Home
634 E Ayer St, Ironwood, MI, 49938 (906) 932-2006
Medical Dir/Dir of Nursing Allen C Gorrilca MD.
Licensure Intermediate Care. *Beds* 47. *Certified* Medicaid.
Staff Physicians 9 (pt); RNs 1 (ft); LPNs 8 (ft); Nurses aides 20 (ft), 30 (pt); Physical therapists 1 (pt); Reality therapists 1 (pt); Recreational therapists 1 (pt); Activities coordinators 1 (ft); Dietitians 1 (pt); Dentists 1 (pt); Ophthalmologists 1 (pt); Podiatrists 1 (pt); Audiologists 1 (pt).
Facilities Dining room; Activities room; Laundry room.
Activities Arts and Crafts; Cards; Games; Reading groups; Prayer groups; Movies; Shopping trips; Dances/Social or cultural gatherings; Fishing trips; Picnics; Swimming.
Description A new addition finished autumn 1984.

ISHPEMING

Mather Nursing Center
435 Stoneville Rd, Ishpeming, MI, 49849 (906) 485-1073
Medical Dir/Dir of Nursing Dr Barbara Lyons.
Licensure Skilled Care; Intermediate Care.
Beds 122. *Certified* Medicaid; Medicare.
Staff Physicians; RNs; LPNs; Orderlies; Nurses aides; Physical therapists; Reality therapists; Recreational therapists; Occupational therapists; Speech therapists; Activities coordinators; Dietitians; Podiatrists.
Facilities Dining room; Physical therapy room; Activities room; Chapel; Crafts room; Laundry room; Barber/Beauty shop; Library.
Activities Arts and Crafts; Cards; Games; Reading groups; Prayer groups; Movies; Shopping trips; Dances/Social or cultural gatherings.
Description Nursing students train on site; facility has very active auxiliary group; local bus service comes to front door.

JACKSON

Faith Haven Care Center*
6531 W Michigan Ave, Jackson, MI, 49201 (517) 750-3822
Licensure Skilled Care; Intermediate Care.
Beds 88. *Certified* Medicaid; Medicare.

Jackson County Medical Care Facility*
1715 Lansing Ave, Jackson, MI, 49202 (517) 783-2726
Licensure Skilled Care; Intermediate Care.
Beds 194. *Certified* Medicaid; Medicare.
Ownership Public.

Marlin Manor*
434 W North St, Jackson, MI, 49202 (517) 787-3250
Licensure Skilled Care. *Beds* 100. *Certified* Medicaid; Medicare.

Odd Fellow and Rebekah Home
2388 W Michigan Ave, Jackson, MI, 49202 (517) 787-5140
Medical Dir/Dir of Nursing Micheal Grebner

MD and Bruce Bigelow MD.
Licensure Intermediate Care. *Beds* 50.
Admissions Requirements Minimum age 16; Medical examination.
Staff Physicians 2 (ft); RNs 2 (ft), 1 (pt); LPNs 3 (ft), 1 (pt); Orderlies 1 (ft), 1 (pt); Nurses aides 19 (ft), 9 (pt); Recreational therapists 1 (ft); Activities coordinators 2 (pt); Dietitians 1 (pt).
Affiliation Independent Order of Odd Fellows
Facilities Dining room; Physical therapy room; Activities room; Chapel; Crafts room; Laundry room; Barber/Beauty shop.
Activities Arts and Crafts; Cards; Reading groups; Prayer groups; Movies; Shopping trips; Dances/Social or cultural gatherings.

Vista Grande Villa
2251 Springport Rd, Jackson, MI, 49202 (517) 787-0222
Medical Dir/Dir of Nursing Dr F I Van-Wagnen.
Licensure Skilled Care; Intermediate Care.
Beds 60. *Certified* Medicaid; Medicare.
Admissions Requirements Minimum age 62; Medical examination; Physician's request.
Staff Physicians 1 (pt); RNs 4 (ft), 4 (pt); LPNs 3 (ft), 10 (pt); Orderlies 1 (ft); Nurses aides 15 (ft), 15 (pt); Physical therapists 1 (pt); Speech therapists 1 (pt); Activities coordinators 1 (ft), 2 (pt); Dietitians 1 (pt); Dentists 1 (pt); Podiatrists 1 (pt).
Facilities Dining room; Physical therapy room; Activities room; Chapel; Crafts room; Laundry room; Barber/Beauty shop; Library.
Activities Arts and Crafts; Cards; Games; Reading groups; Prayer groups; Movies; Shopping trips; Dances/Social or cultural gatherings.
Description Life care retirement and skilled nursing care; private apartments in 4 sizes; modern rehabilitative nursing facility; numerous services furnished; located in south central Michigan.

KALAMAZOO

Alamo Nursing Home
8290 W "C" Ave, Kalamazoo, MI, 49001 (616) 343-2587
Medical Dir/Dir of Nursing R E Topp.
Licensure Skilled Care; Intermediate Care.
Beds 100. *Certified* Medicaid; Medicare.
Staff RNs 4 (ft), 9 (pt); LPNs 5 (ft), 3 (pt); Orderlies 1 (pt); Nurses aides 45 (ft), 10 (pt); Occupational therapists 1 (pt); Activities coordinators 1 (ft), 1 (pt); Dietitians 1 (pt).
Facilities Dining room; Physical therapy room; Activities room; Crafts room; Laundry room; Barber/Beauty shop.
Activities Arts and Crafts; Cards; Games; Reading groups; Prayer groups; Movies; Shopping trips.
Description Home is located in a rural setting free from city traffic and noise.

Birch Manor
537 Chicago Ave, Kalamazoo, MI, 49001 (616) 382-2392
Medical Dir/Dir of Nursing Frank Harrell MD.
Licensure Skilled Care; Intermediate Care.
Beds 121. *Certified* Medicaid; Medicare.
Admissions Requirements Minimum age 15; Medical examination; Physician's request.

Staff RNs 14 (ft); LPNs 8 (ft); Orderlies 4 (ft); Nurses aides 100 (ft); Reality therapists 1 (pt); Recreational therapists 4 (ft); Occupational therapists 1 (pt); Activities coordinators 1 (ft); Dietitians 1 (pt).
Facilities Dining room; Physical therapy room; Activities room; Chapel; Crafts room; Laundry room; Barber/Beauty shop; Library.
Activities Arts and Crafts; Cards; Games; Reading groups; Prayer groups; Movies; Dances/Social or cultural gatherings; Outdoor picnics; Tours by bus.
Description Birch Manor Nursing Home enjoys a very good reputation in the community and has a high ratio of private pay residents. Many activities are offered at Birch Manor that are not offered at other facilities. Unique nursing staff offers first-rate nursing care with a 60-hour nursing assistant program to all nursing employees before employment and ongoing inservice programs held twice weekly for nursing personnel.

Brookhaven Care Facility*
1701 Olmstead Rd, Kalamazoo, MI, 49001 (616) 349-9694
Licensure Intermediate Care. *Beds* 50. *Certified* Medicaid.

Friendship Village
1400 N Drake Rd, Kalamazoo, MI, 49007 (616) 381-0560
Medical Dir/Dir of Nursing Dr Bennard Dowd.
Licensure Skilled Care; Intermediate Care.
Beds 57. *Certified* Medicaid; Medicare.
Admissions Requirements Minimum age 62; Medical examination; Physician's request.
Staff Physicians 3 (pt); RNs 1 (ft), 6 (pt); LPNs 4 (ft), 3 (pt); Nurses aides 22 (ft), 8 (pt); Physical therapists 1 (pt); Speech therapists 1 (pt); Activities coordinators 1 (ft); Dietitians 1 (pt); Dentists 1 (pt); Ophthalmologists 1 (pt); Podiatrists 1 (pt); Audiologists 1 (pt).
Facilities Dining room; Physical therapy room; Activities room; Chapel; Crafts room; Laundry room; Barber/Beauty shop; Library.
Activities Arts and Crafts; Cards; Games; Reading groups; Prayer groups; Movies; Shopping trips; Dances/Social or cultural gatherings.
Description In-house home health for apartment residents.

Provincial House*
1701 S 11th St, Kalamazoo, MI, 49009 (616) 375-2020
Licensure Skilled Care; Intermediate Care.
Beds 117. *Certified* Medicaid; Medicare.

Provincial House—Kalamazoo Total Living Center*
2575 N Drake Rd, Kalamazoo, MI, 49008 (616) 342-0206
Licensure Skilled Care; Intermediate Care.
Beds 117. *Certified* Medicaid.

Provincial House—Portage
7855 Currier Dr, Kalamazoo, MI, 49002 (616) 323-7748
Medical Dir/Dir of Nursing Dr Simon Hoogendyk.
Licensure Skilled Care; Intermediate Care.
Beds 120. *Certified* Medicaid; Medicare.

Admissions Requirements Medical examination; Physician's request.
Staff RNs 8 (ft), 3 (pt); LPNs 6 (ft), 2 (pt); Orderlies 2 (ft), 2 (pt); Nurses aides 40 (ft), 30 (pt); Physical therapists 1 (pt); Recreational therapists 1 (ft); Occupational therapists 1 (pt); Speech therapists 1 (pt); Activities coordinators 1 (ft); Dietitians 1 (ft); Dentists 1 (pt); Podiatrists 1 (pt); Audiologists 1 (pt).
Facilities Dining room; Physical therapy room; Activities room; Crafts room; Laundry room; Barber/Beauty shop; Library.
Activities Arts and Crafts; Games; Reading groups; Prayer groups; Movies; Shopping trips.
Description Facility will be 5 years old in 1984. It is carpeted throughout and color coordinated beautifully. A full-time director of nursing oversees the nursing staff and works closely with the social service coordinator, activities coordinator, dietary supervisor, and administrator to provide a quality of life for residents.

Ridgeview Manor
3625 W Michigan, Kalamazoo, MI, 49007 (616) 375-4550
Medical Dir/Dir of Nursing Dr J T Cerovski.
Licensure Skilled Care; Intermediate Care.
Beds 180. *Certified* Medicaid; Medicare.
Admissions Requirements Medical examination; Physician's request.
Facilities Dining room; Physical therapy room; Activities room; Crafts room; Laundry room; Barber/Beauty shop.
Activities Arts and Crafts; Cards; Games; Reading groups; Prayer groups; Movies; Shopping trips; Dances/Social or cultural gatherings.

Upjohn Community Nursing Home
2400 Portage St, Kalamazoo, MI, 49001 (616) 381-4290
Admin Francis J Blaise. *Medical Dir/Dir of Nursing* William T Bateman MD.
Licensure Skilled Care; Intermediate Care.
Beds 130. *Certified* Medicaid; Medicare.
Admissions Requirements Minimum age 62; Medical examination; Physician's request.
Staff Physicians 1 (pt); RNs 6 (ft), 10 (pt); LPNs 5 (ft), 6 (pt); Orderlies 2 (ft), 3 (pt); Nurses aides 38 (ft), 61 (pt); Physical therapists 1 (pt); Reality therapists 1 (ft); Occupational therapists 1 (ft); Speech therapists; Activities coordinators 1 (ft).
Facilities Dining room; Physical therapy room; Activities room; Chapel; Crafts room; Laundry room; Barber/Beauty shop; Library.
Activities Arts and Crafts; Cards; Games; Reading groups; Prayer groups; Movies; Shopping trips; Dances/Social or cultural gatherings.

Verdries Nursing Home*
1430 Alamo Ave, Kalamazoo, MI, 49007 (616) 349-2661
Licensure Skilled Care; Intermediate Care.
Beds 140. *Certified* Medicaid; Medicare.

KALKASKA

Kalkaska Memorial Health Center*
Box 37, 419 S Coral, Kalkaska, MI, 49646 (616) 258-9142
Licensure Skilled Care; Intermediate Care.
Beds 8. *Certified* Medicaid; Medicare.

KAWKAWLIN

Huron Woods Nursing Home*
1395 S Huron, Kawkawlin, MI, 48631 (517) 684-3213
Licensure Intermediate Care. *Beds* 51. *Certified* Medicaid.

KINGSFORD

Americana Healthcare Center
1225 Woodward Ave, Kingsford, MI, 49801 (906) 774-4805
Medical Dir/Dir of Nursing Dr Donald Jacobs.
Licensure Skilled Care; Intermediate Care.
Beds 101. *Certified* Medicaid; Medicare.
Admissions Requirements Minimum age 18; Medical examination; Physician's request.
Staff RNs 1 (ft), 5 (pt); LPNs 2 (ft), 7 (pt); Nurses aides 23 (ft), 32 (pt); Physical therapists 1 (pt); Speech therapists 1 (pt); Activities coordinators 1 (ft); Dietitians 1 (pt); Dentists 1 (pt).
Facilities Dining room; Physical therapy room; Activities room; Chapel; Crafts room; Laundry room; Barber/Beauty shop.
Activities Arts and Crafts; Cards; Games; Reading groups; Prayer groups; Movies; Shopping trips; Dances/Social or cultural gatherings.
Description Facility is situated on 5 acres; in spring, summer, and fall residents watch several deer which come to graze in field behind the center.

LAKEVIEW

Kelsey Memorial Hospital
418 Washington, Lakeview, MI, 48850 (517) 352-7211
Medical Dir/Dir of Nursing James Fleming DO.
Licensure Skilled Care; Intermediate Care.
Beds 42. *Certified* Medicaid; Medicare.
Admissions Requirements Medical examination; Physician's request.
Staff Physicians 7 (ft); RNs 1 (ft), 3 (pt); Nurses aides 11 (ft), 7 (pt); Physical therapists 1 (ft), 1 (pt); Activities coordinators 1 (ft); Dentists 1 (ft), 1 (pt); Ophthalmologists 1 (pt); Podiatrists 1 (pt).
Facilities Dining room; Physical therapy room; Activities room; Barber/Beauty shop.
Activities Arts and Crafts; Cards; Games; Reading groups; Prayer groups; Movies; Shopping trips; Dances/Social or cultural gatherings; Parties; Picnics; Museum trips.
Description Yearly the residents decorate a float for town's festival; senior olympics held in fall with a family picnic following. Entire hospital is working together to raise money for a van with a lift to take residents out to flea markets, senior citizen picnics, museums, and color tours.

LAMONT

Glenwood Christian Nursing Home
13030 44th Ave, Lamont, MI, 49430 (616) 677-1243
Medical Dir/Dir of Nursing Mary S Kitchel MD.

Licensure Skilled Care; Intermediate Care.
Beds 66. *Certified* Medicaid; Medicare.
Admissions Requirements Minimum age 17; Medical examination; Physician's request.
Staff Physicians 7 (ft); RNs 11 (ft); LPNs 5 (ft); Nurses aides 50 (ft); Physical therapists 1 (ft); Recreational therapists 1 (ft); Occupational therapists 1 (pt); Speech therapists 1 (pt); Activities coordinators 1 (ft); Dietitians 1 (ft); Dentists 1 (pt); Ophthalmologists 1 (pt); Podiatrists 1 (pt).
Facilities Dining room; Physical therapy room; Activities room; Crafts room; Laundry room; Barber/Beauty shop.
Activities Arts and Crafts; Cards; Games; Reading groups; Prayer groups; Movies; Shopping trips.
Description Quiet relaxed setting located on the Grand River; strong activity department; active volunteers; and full-time physical therapist.

LANSE

Baraga County Memorial Hospital*
770 N Main St, Lanse, MI, 49946 (906) 524-6166
Licensure Skilled Care; Intermediate Care.
Beds 14. *Certified* Medicaid; Medicare.

Winkler Nursing Home*
833 Sicotte Ave, Lanse, MI, 49946 (906) 524-6531
Licensure Skilled Care; Intermediate Care.
Beds 59. *Certified* Medicaid; Medicare.

LANSING

NHE—Lansing
1313 Mary Ave, Lansing, MI, 48910 (517) 393-6130
Medical Dir/Dir of Nursing Willard J Miller MD.
Licensure Skilled Care; Intermediate Care.
Beds 134. *Certified* Medicaid; Medicare.
Admissions Requirements Minimum age 17; Medical examination; Physician's request.
Staff Physicians 2 (ft), 4 (pt); LPNs 6 (ft), 6 (pt); Nurses aides 42 (ft), 16 (pt); Activities coordinators 1 (ft); Dietitians 1 (ft).
Facilities Dining room; Physical therapy room; Activities room; Laundry room.
Activities Arts and Crafts; Reading groups; Movies; Dances/Social or cultural gatherings.
Description A Hillhaven facility, one of the oldest facilities in Lansing; active staff development program.

Provincial House—South
2100 Provincial Dr, Lansing, MI, 48910 (517) 882-2458
Medical Dir/Dir of Nursing Stephen TePastte MD.
Licensure Skilled Care; Intermediate Care.
Beds 120. *Certified* Medicaid; Medicare.
Admissions Requirements Minimum age 16; Medical examination.
Staff Physicians 1 (pt); RNs 8 (ft), 2 (pt); LPNs 7 (ft), 5 (pt); Nurses aides 45 (ft), 11 (pt); Physical therapists 1 (pt); Occupational therapists 1 (pt); Speech therapists 1 (pt); Activities coordinators 1 (ft); Dietitians 1 (pt); Dentists 1

(pt); Ophthalmologists 1 (pt); Podiatrists 1 (pt); Audiologists 1 (pt).
Facilities Dining room; Physical therapy room; Activities room; Crafts room; Laundry room; Barber/Beauty shop; Library.
Activities Arts and Crafts; Cards; Games; Reading groups; Prayer groups; Movies; Shopping trips; Dances/Social or cultural gatherings.
Description Facility has both resident and family councils, which act as both support groups and advisory councils; everyone is encouraged to participate.

Provincial House—West
731 Starkweather Dr, Lansing, MI, 48917 (517) 323-9133
Medical Dir/Dir of Nursing Dr John Neuman.
Licensure Skilled Care; Intermediate Care.
Beds 117. *Certified* Medicaid; Medicare.
Admissions Requirements Medical examination.
Staff Physicians 1 (ft), 14 (pt); RNs 4 (ft), 4 (pt); LPNs 4 (ft), 4 (pt); Nurses aides 30 (ft), 35 (pt); Physical therapists 1 (pt); Occupational therapists 1 (pt); Speech therapists 1 (pt); Activities coordinators 1 (ft); Dietitians 1 (ft); Dentists 1 (pt); Podiatrists 1 (pt).
Facilities Dining room; Physical therapy room; Activities room; Laundry room; Barber/Beauty shop; TV lounge.
Activities Arts and Crafts; Cards; Games; Reading groups; Prayer groups; Movies; Shopping trips; Dances/Social or cultural gatherings; Musical programs.
Description Facility stresses rehabilitative nursing care, striving to maximize the potential of residents to do what they can for themselves; approach this goal through progressive therapy programs and quality of care.

Roselawn Manor
707 Armstrong Rd, Lansing, MI, 48910 (517) 393-5680
Licensure Skilled Care. *Beds* 234. *Certified* Medicaid; Medicare.
Staff Physicians 4 (pt); RNs 8 (pt); LPNs 14 (pt); Physical therapists 1 (pt); Recreational therapists 3 (ft), 3 (pt); Occupational therapists 1 (pt); Speech therapists 1 (pt); Activities coordinators 1 (ft); Dietitians 2 (ft); Dentists 1 (pt); Ophthalmologists 1 (pt); Podiatrists 1 (pt); Audiologists 1 (pt).
Facilities Dining room; Physical therapy room; Activities room; Crafts room; Laundry room; Barber/Beauty shop.
Activities Arts and Crafts; Cards; Games; Reading groups; Prayer groups; Movies; Shopping trips; Dances/Social or cultural gatherings.
Description Roselawn is a facility of Beverly Enterprises, located in the south Lansing, Michigan area. The facility is staffed with a competent, energetic, properly trained and commited group of individuals. Roselawn is committed to the improvement of quality of life of its residents/patients.

LAPEER

Ferguson Convalescent Home*
239 S Main, Lapeer, MI, 48446 (313) 664-6611
Licensure Intermediate Care. *Beds* 91. *Certified* Medicaid.

Lapeer County Medical Care Facility
1455 Suncrest Dr, Lapeer, MI, 48446 (313) 664-8571
Medical Dir/Dir of Nursing Jules Reinhardt DO.
Licensure Skilled Care; Intermediate Care.
Beds 162. *Certified* Medicaid; Medicare.
Ownership Public.
Admissions Requirements Minimum age 16; Physician's request.
Staff Physicians 2 (pt); RNs 10 (ft), 1 (pt); LPNs 17 (ft), 12 (pt); Physical therapists 1 (pt); Recreational therapists 1 (ft); Occupational therapists 1 (pt); Speech therapists 1 (pt); Activities coordinators 1 (ft); Dietitians 1 (pt); Dentists 1 (pt); Ophthalmologists 1 (pt); Podiatrists 1 (pt).
Facilities Dining room; Physical therapy room; Activities room; Chapel; Laundry room; Barber/Beauty shop.
Activities Arts and Crafts; Cards; Games; Reading groups; Prayer groups; Movies; Shopping trips; Dances/Social or cultural gatherings.
Description In October 1983, our Adult Day Care program began. As of April 1984, this program has become an ongoing service. This serves as a transition period for those who may need long-term care in the future and as a practical discharge plan for those who return home or home with relatives. These individuals have the option of returning back for further recreation programing.

LAWTON

Hope Nursing Home*
99 Walker St, Lawton, MI, 49065 (616) 624-4311
Licensure Intermediate Care. *Beds* 93. *Certified* Medicaid.

LINCOLN

Lincoln Haven Rest Home*
950 Barlow Rd, Lincoln, MI, 48742 (517) 736-8481
Licensure Intermediate Care. *Beds* 36. *Certified* Medicaid.

LINDEN

Stanmarie*
9051 Silver Lake Rd, Linden, MI, 48451 (313) 735-7413
Licensure Intermediate Care. *Beds* 50. *Certified* Medicaid.

LITCHFIELD

Litchfield Manor Care Center*
527 Marshall Rd, Litchfield, MI, 49252 (517) 542-2323
Licensure Intermediate Care. *Beds* 81. *Certified* Medicaid.

LIVONIA

Camelot Hall Convalescent Centre
35100 Ann Arbor Trail, Livonia, MI, 48150 (313) 522-1444
Admin Nancy J Nix. *Medical Dir/Dir of Nursing* Dr David Miller.
Licensure Skilled Care. *Beds* 166. *Certified* Medicaid; Medicare.
Admissions Requirements Minimum age 45; Physician's request.
Staff Physicians 2 (ft); RNs 10 (ft); LPNs 12 (ft); Orderlies 4 (ft); Nurses aides 60 (ft); Physical therapists 1 (ft); Reality therapists 2 (ft); Recreational therapists 4 (ft); Occupational therapists 1 (ft); Speech therapists 1 (pt); Activities coordinators 1 (ft); Dietitians 1 (ft); Dentists 2 (pt); Podiatrists 1 (pt).
Facilities Dining room; Physical therapy room; Activities room; Crafts room; Laundry room; Barber/Beauty shop; Library.
Activities Arts and Crafts; Cards; Games; Reading groups; Prayer groups; Movies; Shopping trips; Dances/Social or cultural gatherings.
Description Facility is located behind Edward Hines Park in peaceful surroundings. Very active reality-orientation program. Very large activities program.

Dorvin Convalescent and Nursing Center*
29270 Morlock, Livonia, MI, 48152 (313) 476-0550
Licensure Skilled Care; Intermediate Care.
Beds 132. *Certified* Medicaid; Medicare.

Livonia Nursing Center*
28910 Plymouth Rd, Livonia, MI, 48150 (313) 522-8970
Licensure Intermediate Care. *Beds* 88. *Certified* Medicaid.

Marycrest Manor*
15475 Middlebelt Rd, Livonia, MI, 48154 (313) 427-9175
Licensure Skilled Care; Intermediate Care.
Beds 55. *Certified* Medicaid; Medicare.

Middlebelt Nursing Centre
14900 Middlebelt Rd, Livonia, MI, 48154 (313) 425-4200
Admin Charles A Gutkowski. *Medical Dir/Dir of Nursing* Donald Albert MD.
Licensure Skilled Care; Intermediate Care.
Beds 162. *Certified* Medicaid; Medicare.
Admissions Requirements Minimum age 16; Medical examination; Physician's request.
Staff Physicians 4 (pt); RNs 4 (ft), 6 (pt); LPNs 6 (ft), 4 (pt); Orderlies 2 (ft); Nurses aides 70 (ft), 20 (pt); Reality therapists 2 (ft); Recreational therapists 2 (ft); Occupational therapists 1 (pt); Speech therapists 1 (pt); Activities coordinators 1 (ft); Dietitians 1 (ft), 1 (pt); Dentists 1 (pt); Ophthalmologists 1 (pt); Podiatrists 1 (pt); Audiologists 1 (pt).
Facilities Dining room; Physical therapy room; Activities room; Chapel; Crafts room; Laundry room; Barber/Beauty shop; Library.
Activities Arts and Crafts; Cards; Games; Reading groups; Prayer groups; Movies; Shopping trips; Dances/Social or cultural gatherings; Sports; Entertainment events; Fishing - outside facility; Marching in parades.
Description We stress community involve-

ment. We offer learning opportunities for "health care" students, in conjunction with local high schools and colleges. Middlebelt Nursing Center has sponsored blood drives and blood pressure clinics. Residents are involved through sponsorship of little league teams, volunteer service to the Cancer Society, Heart Association. An atrium, located in the center of the building, provides enjoyment for residents during all seasons. We have a large fenced yard with a gazebo and umbrella tables and chairs where many of our activities and special events are held.

Saint Jude Convalescent Center*
34350 Ann Arbor Trail, Livonia, MI, 48150 (313) 261-4800
Licensure Skilled Care; Intermediate Care. *Beds* 64. *Certified* Medicaid; Medicare. *Affiliation* Roman Catholic

University Convalescent and Nursing Home*
28550 5 Mile Rd, Livonia, MI, 48154 (313) 427-8270
Licensure Skilled Care; Intermediate Care. *Beds* 184. *Certified* Medicaid; Medicare.

LOWELL

Lowell Medical Care Center*
350 N Center St, Lowell, MI, 49331 (616) 897-8473
Licensure Skilled Care; Intermediate Care. *Beds* 153. *Certified* Medicaid; Medicare.

LUDINGTON

Baywood Nursing Home*
1000 Tinkham Ave, Ludington, MI, 49431 (616) 845-6291
Licensure Skilled Care; Intermediate Care. *Beds* 126. *Certified* Medicaid; Medicare.

Oakview Medical Care Facility
1000 Diana St, Ludington, MI, 49431 (616) 845-5185
Admin Jeffery L Welch. *Medical Dir/Dir of Nursing* William Sutter MD.
Licensure Skilled Care; Intermediate Care. *Beds* 76. *Certified* Medicaid; Medicare. *Ownership* Public.
Admissions Requirements Minimum age 14; Medical examination; Physician's request.
Staff Physicians 3 (pt); RNs 3 (ft), 4 (pt); LPNs 5 (ft), 7 (pt); Nurses aides 27 (ft), 27 (pt); Physical therapists 3 (ft); Occupational therapists 1 (ft); Speech therapists 1 (pt); Activities coordinators 1 (ft); Dietitians 1 (pt); Dentists 1 (pt); Ophthalmologists; Podiatrists; Audiologists.
Facilities Dining room; Physical therapy room; Activities room; Crafts room; Laundry room; Barber/Beauty shop; Library.
Activities Arts and Crafts; Cards; Games; Prayer groups; Movies; Dances/Social or cultural gatherings.
Description Rehabilitative program stressed; high percentage of patients are returned to their own homes.

MADISON HEIGHTS

Cambridge Nursing Center—East*
31155 DeQuindre, Madison Heights, MI, 48071 (313) 585-7070
Licensure Skilled Care; Intermediate Care. *Beds* 160. *Certified* Medicaid; Medicare.

MANISTEE

Manistee Heights Care Center*
300 Care Center Dr, Manistee, MI, 49660 (313) 723-6262
Licensure Intermediate Care. *Beds* 119. *Certified* Medicaid.

Manistee Medical Care Facility*
1505 E Parkdale Ave, Manistee, MI, 49660 (313) 723-2543
Licensure Skilled Care; Intermediate Care. *Beds* 102. *Certified* Medicaid; Medicare. *Ownership* Public.

MANISTIQUE

Schoolcraft Medical Care Facility*
520 Main St, Manistique, MI, 49854
Licensure Intermediate Care. *Beds* 75. *Certified* Medicaid; Medicare.

MAPLE CITY

Maple Valley Nursing Home
Rt 2, Box 7, Maple City, MI, 49664 (616) 228-5895
Medical Dir/Dir of Nursing Joseph Steffey.
Licensure Intermediate Care. *Beds* 25. *Certified* Medicaid.
Admissions Requirements Minimum age 16; Medical examination; Physician's request.
Staff Physicians 2 (pt); RNs 1 (ft), 1 (pt); LPNs 2 (ft), 3 (pt); Nurses aides 3 (ft), 6 (pt); Recreational therapists 1 (ft); Activities coordinators 1 (ft); Dietitians 1 (pt); Dentists 1 (pt); Ophthalmologists 1 (pt); Podiatrists 1 (pt).
Facilities Dining room; Activities room; Crafts room; Laundry room.
Activities Arts and Crafts; Cards; Games; Prayer groups; Movies; Recreational rides via bus.

MARLETTE

Marlette Community Hospital
2770 Main St, Marlette, MI, 48453 (517) 635-7491
Medical Dir/Dir of Nursing Dr James Cripps.
Licensure Skilled Care; Intermediate Care. *Beds* 43. *Certified* Medicaid; Medicare.
Admissions Requirements Medical examination.
Facilities Dining room; Physical therapy room; Activities room; Chapel; Crafts room; Laundry room; Barber/Beauty shop; Library.
Activities Arts and Crafts; Cards; Games; Movies.

MARNE

Beacon Light Christian Nursing Home*
15140 16th Ave, Marne, MI, 49435 (616) 667-1215
Licensure Skilled Care; Intermediate Care. *Beds* 198. *Certified* Medicaid; Medicare.

MARQUETTE

Acocks Medical Facility
Acocks Dr, Marquette, MI, 49855 (906) 226-3586
Medical Dir/Dir of Nursing Douglas Sherk MD.
Licensure Skilled Care; Intermediate Care. *Beds* 98. *Certified* Medicaid; Medicare.
Staff RNs 6 (ft), 1 (pt); LPNs 3 (ft), 7 (pt); Orderlies 8 (ft), 2 (pt); Nurses aides 38 (ft), 6 (pt); Activities coordinators 1 (ft); Dentists 1 (pt); Podiatrists 1 (pt).
Facilities Dining room; Physical therapy room; Activities room; Chapel; Crafts room; Laundry room.
Activities Arts and Crafts; Cards; Games; Reading groups; Prayer groups; Movies; Shopping trips; Dances/Social or cultural gatherings.

Brooks Center Health Care Facility
S Rt 41, Marquette, MI, 49855
Admin Grace E McCarthy. *Medical Dir/Dir of Nursing* Benjamin T Ulep.
Licensure Skilled Care; Intermediate Care. *Beds* 11. *Certified* Medicaid; Medicare.
Admissions Requirements Males only; Medical examination; Physician's request.
Staff Physicians 1 (ft); RNs 10 (ft); LPNs 4 (ft); Physical therapists; Reality therapists; Recreational therapists; Occupational therapists; Speech therapists; Activities coordinators; Dietitians 1 (pt); Dentists 1 (pt); Ophthalmologists; Podiatrists; Audiologists; Laboratory workers 1 (ft); Physical aides 1 (ft).
Description This is a nontypical setting; all patients/residents are from the prison population.

Norlite Nursing Center*
701 Homestead St, Marquette, MI, 49855 (906) 228-9252
Licensure Skilled Care; Intermediate Care. *Beds* 99. *Certified* Medicaid; Medicare.

MARSHALL

Marshall Manor
575 N Madison St, Marshall, MI, 49068 (616) 781-4281
Medical Dir/Dir of Nursing M A Tazelaar MD.
Licensure Skilled Care; Intermediate Care. *Beds* 71. *Certified* Medicaid; Medicare.
Staff RNs 4 (ft), 1 (pt); LPNs 2 (ft), 4 (pt); Orderlies 1 (ft); Nurses aides 25 (ft), 10 (pt); Physical therapists 1 (pt); Recreational therapists 2 (pt); Speech therapists 1 (pt); Activities coordinators 1 (ft); Dietitians 1 (pt).
Facilities Dining room; Physical therapy room; Activities room; Chapel; Crafts room; Barber/Beauty shop.
Activities Arts and Crafts; Cards; Games;

Reading groups; Prayer groups; Movies.
Description We are a skilled nursing facility and offer all skilled care and observations.

Provincial House—Marshall
879 E Michigan Ave, Marshall, MI, 49068 (616) 781-4251
Licensure Intermediate Care. *Beds* 114. *Certified* Medicaid.
Admissions Requirements Minimum age 15; Medical examination; Physician's request.
Staff Physicians 16 (pt); RNs 3 (ft), 3 (pt); LPNs 1 (ft), 9 (pt); Orderlies 2 (pt); Nurses aides 24 (ft), 42 (pt); Physical therapists 1 (pt); Reality therapists 1 (pt); Recreational therapists 1 (ft); Occupational therapists 1 (pt); Speech therapists 1 (pt); Activities coordinators 1 (ft); Dietitians 1 (ft); Dentists 1 (pt); Ophthalmologists 1 (pt); Podiatrists 1 (pt); Audiologists 1 (pt).
Facilities Dining room; Physical therapy room; Activities room; Crafts room; Laundry room; Barber/Beauty shop.
Activities Arts and Crafts; Cards; Games; Reading groups; Prayer groups; Movies; Dances/Social or cultural gatherings.

MAYVILLE

Fisher Convalescent Home*
521 Ohmer Rd, M-24, Mayville, MI, 48744 (517) 843-6185
Licensure Intermediate Care. *Beds* 38. *Certified* Medicaid.

MCMILLAN

Applewood Manor Inc*
Rt 3, Box 2347, McMillan, MI, 49853 (906) 586-9641
Licensure Intermediate Care. *Beds* 30. *Certified* Medicaid.

MENOMINEE

Menominee Nursing Home
501 2nd St, Menominee, MI, 49858 (906) 863-9941
Admin Gerard A Buser.
Licensure Intermediate Care. *Beds* 32. *Certified* Medicaid.
Admissions Requirements Minimum age 16; Medical examination; Physician's request.
Staff RNs 1 (ft), 3 (pt); LPNs 1 (ft), 4 (pt); Nurses aides 4 (ft), 15 (pt); Recreational therapists 1 (pt); Activities coordinators 1 (pt); Dietitians 1 (ft).
Facilities Dining room; Activities room.
Activities Arts and Crafts; Cards; Games; Reading groups; Prayer groups; Movies; Shopping trips; Dances/Social or cultural gatherings.
Description Facility will add 15 beds this year.

MIDLAND

Midland Hospital Center—Skilled Nursing Unit
4005 Orchard Dr, Midland, MI, 48640 (517) 839-3000
Medical Dir/Dir of Nursing Christopher

Hough MD.
Licensure Skilled Care; Intermediate Care. *Beds* 48. *Certified* Medicaid; Medicare.
Admissions Requirements Medical examination; Physician's request.
Staff Physicians 1 (pt); RNs 6 (ft), 4 (pt); LPNs 4 (ft), 3 (pt); Nurses aides 15 (ft), 2 (pt); Physical therapists 8 (ft); Recreational therapists 1 (pt); Occupational therapists 3 (ft), 1 (pt); Speech therapists 2 (ft), 1 (pt); Dietitians 3 (ft), 2 (pt); Audiologists 1 (pt).
Facilities Dining room; Physical therapy room; Activities room; Chapel; Laundry room; Barber/Beauty shop.
Activities Arts and Crafts; Cards; Games; Reading groups; Prayer groups; Movies.
Description The unit serves as a transitional facility for patients discharged from the hospital's acute-care setting; primarily serving patients requiring skilled nursing services. All hospital ancillary services available as ordered by the patient's personal physician.

Midland Kings Daughters*
2410 Rodd St, Midland, MI, 48640
Licensure Intermediate Care. *Beds* 31.

Provincial House—Midland*
4900 Hedgewood, Midland, MI, 48640 (517) 631-9670
Licensure Skilled Care; Intermediate Care. *Beds* 120. *Certified* Medicaid; Medicare.

Town and Country Nursing Home
3615 E Ashman St, Midland, MI, 48640 (517) 631-0460
Medical Dir/Dir of Nursing John E Vargas DO.
Licensure Skilled Care; Intermediate Care. *Beds* 153. *Certified* Medicaid; Medicare.
Admissions Requirements Medical examination; Physician's request.
Staff RNs 6 (ft), 1 (pt); LPNs 5 (ft), 8 (pt); Orderlies 4 (ft), 6 (pt); Nurses aides 17 (ft), 64 (pt); Activities coordinators 1 (ft); Dietitians 1 (pt).
Facilities Dining room; Activities room; Crafts room; Laundry room; Barber/Beauty shop.
Activities Arts and Crafts; Cards; Games; Reading groups; Prayer groups; Shopping trips; Dances/Social or cultural gatherings.
Description Twenty acres of secure grounds allow space for picnics and walks. In this peaceful atmosphere, patients enjoy companionship, comfort, and the friendly personal care of excellent nursing staff; volunteers from the community visit residents regularly and assist in many lively activities.

MILFORD

West Hickory Haven*
3310 W Commerce Rd, Milford, MI, 48042 (313) 684-6635
Licensure Skilled Care; Intermediate Care. *Beds* 101. *Certified* Medicaid; Medicare.

MIO

Whiteoak Manor*
PO Box 466, Mio, MI, 48647 (517) 826-3983
Licensure Intermediate Care. *Beds* 28. *Certified* Medicaid.

MONROE

Beach Nursing Home
1215 N Telegraph Rd, Monroe, MI, 48161 (517) 242-4848
Licensure Skilled Care; Intermediate Care. *Beds* 192. *Certified* Medicaid; Medicare.

Frenchtown Convalescent Center*
3250 N Monroe, Monroe, MI, 48161 (517) 243-5100
Licensure Skilled Care; Intermediate Care. *Beds* 229. *Certified* Medicaid; Medicare.

The Lutheran Home*
1236 S Monroe St, Monroe, MI, 48161 (517) 241-9533
Licensure Skilled Care; Intermediate Care. *Beds* 102. *Certified* Medicaid; Medicare.
Ownership Nonprofit.
Affiliation Lutheran

Monroe Care Center*
481 Village Green Ln, Monroe, MI, 48161 (517) 242-6282
Licensure Skilled Care. *Beds* 103. *Certified* Medicare.

Monroe Convalescent Center
120 Maple Blvd, Monroe, MI, 48161 (313) 242-5656
Admin Jessie T Joyner Jr. *Medical Dir/Dir of Nursing* Lawrence Usher DO.
Licensure Intermediate Care. *Beds* 70. *Certified* Medicaid.
Admissions Requirements Minimum age 16; Medical examination; Physician's request.
Staff Physicians 1 (pt); RNs 1 (ft), 2 (pt); LPNs 6 (ft), 3 (pt); Orderlies 4 (ft), 2 (pt); Nurses aides 19 (ft), 11 (pt); Physical therapists 1 (pt); Recreational therapists 1 (pt); Occupational therapists 1 (pt); Activities coordinators 1 (ft); Dietitians 1 (pt); Dentists 1 (pt); Ophthalmologists 1 (pt); Podiatrists 1 (pt).
Facilities Dining room; Physical therapy room; Activities room; Barber/Beauty shop.
Activities Arts and Crafts; Cards; Games; Prayer groups; Movies; Dances/Social or cultural gatherings.
Description Local organizations provide activities, education, and entertainment to patients throughout the year; these events combined with those planned by activities director ensure that residents realize their full personal potential and pass time in a pleasant and meaningful atmosphere; staff members are often the "family members" for patients. No patient need ever feel alone in this small, family-oriented atmosphere.

MONTROSE

Mary James Nursing Home
13476 Duffield Rd, Montrose, MI, 48457 (313) 639-6113
Medical Dir/Dir of Nursing John T Block DO.
Licensure Skilled Care; Intermediate Care.
Beds 63. *Certified* Medicaid; Medicare.
Admissions Requirements Minimum age 18; Medical examination; Physician's request.
Staff Physicians 2 (pt); RNs 3 (ft), 1 (pt); LPNs 1 (ft), 3 (pt); Nurses aides 19 (ft), 17 (pt); Recreational therapists 1 (ft); Activities coordinators 1 (ft); Dietitians 1 (ft); Podiatrists 1 (pt).
Facilities Dining room.
Activities Arts and Crafts; Cards; Games; Reading groups; Prayer groups; Movies; Shopping trips; Dances/Social or cultural gatherings.
Description As administration wants good therapeutic/recreational programs/activities, they make transportation available. We tour at least twice a month. We have at least ⅓ of the patients attend each tour. Five of our 63 patients are not in wheelchairs.

Montrose Nursing Home
9317 W Vienna Rd, Montrose, MI, 48457
Admin Gale E Neff.
Licensure Intermediate Care. *Beds* 71. *Certified* Medicaid.
Ownership Proprietary.
Admissions Requirements Minimum age 15; Medical examination.
Staff RNs 1 (ft), 1 (pt); LPNs 3 (ft), 5 (pt); Orderlies 1 (pt); Nurses aides 20 (ft), 12 (pt); Activities coordinators 1 (ft); Dietitians 1 (pt).
Facilities Dining room; Activities room; Laundry room; Barber/Beauty shop.
Activities Arts and Crafts; Cards; Games; Reading groups; Prayer groups; Movies; Shopping trips; Dances/Social or cultural gatherings.

MOUNT CLEMENS

Church of Christ Care Center
23575 15 Mile Rd, Mount Clemens, MI, 48043 (313) 791-2470
Medical Dir/Dir of Nursing Francis Komaro DO.
Licensure Intermediate Care. *Beds* 130. *Certified* Medicaid.
Admissions Requirements Physician's request.
Staff Physicians 1 (pt); RNs 6 (ft), 4 (pt); LPNs 3 (ft), 3 (pt); Nurses aides 40 (ft), 30 (pt); Activities coordinators 1 (ft); Dietitians 1 (pt).
Affiliation Church of Christ
Facilities Dining room; Activities room; Laundry room; Barber/Beauty shop.
Activities Arts and Crafts; Cards; Games; Reading groups; Prayer groups; Movies; Shopping trips; Dances/Social or cultural gatherings.
Description Nursing facility is surrounded by 52-bed senior housing units which are contained in 8 separate apartment-type buildings situated on approximately 8 acres of property.

Clinton Aire Nursing Center
17001 17 Mile Rd, Mount Clemens, MI, 48043 (313) 286-7100
Medical Dir/Dir of Nursing Sonjai Poonpanij MD.
Licensure Skilled Care; Intermediate Care.

Beds 150. *Certified* Medicaid; Medicare.
Admissions Requirements Minimum age 15.
Staff RNs 3 (ft), 6 (pt); LPNs 3 (ft), 11 (pt); Orderlies 5 (ft), 2 (pt); Nurses aides 37 (ft), 19 (pt); Physical therapists 1 (pt); Recreational therapists 1 (ft); Occupational therapists 1 (pt); Speech therapists 1 (pt); Activities coordinators 1 (ft); Dietitians 1 (ft); Dentists 1 (pt); Ophthalmologists 1 (pt); Podiatrists 1 (pt); Audiologists 1 (pt).
Facilities Dining room; Physical therapy room; Activities room; Chapel; Laundry room; Barber/Beauty shop.
Activities Arts and Crafts; Cards; Games; Reading groups; Prayer groups; Movies; Shopping trips.

Clintonview Care
37700 Harper Ave, Mount Clemens, MI, 48043 (313) 468-0827
Medical Dir/Dir of Nursing M Shiffman MD.
Licensure Skilled Care; Intermediate Care.
Beds 264. *Certified* Medicaid; Medicare.
Admissions Requirements Minimum age 17; Medical examination; Physician's request.
Staff Physicians 4 (pt); RNs 16 (ft), 4 (pt); LPNs 10 (ft), 3 (pt); Orderlies 6 (ft); Nurses aides 120 (ft), 5 (pt); Physical therapists 1 (ft); Recreational therapists 1 (ft); Occupational therapists 1 (ft); Speech therapists 1 (pt); Activities coordinators 1 (ft); Dietitians 1 (pt); Dentists 3 (pt); Ophthalmologists 2 (pt); Podiatrists 1 (pt); Audiologists 1 (pt).
Facilities Dining room; Physical therapy room; Activities room; Chapel; Crafts room; Laundry room; Barber/Beauty shop; Library.
Activities Arts and Crafts; Cards; Games; Reading groups; Prayer groups; Movies; Shopping trips; Dances/Social or cultural gatherings.

Martha T Berry Medical Care Facility
43533 Elizabeth Rd, Mount Clemens, MI, 48043 (313) 469-5265
Medical Dir/Dir of Nursing Patrick K McClellan DO.
Licensure Skilled Care; Intermediate Care.
Beds 218. *Certified* Medicaid; Medicare.
Admissions Requirements Minimum age 17; Physician's request.
Staff Physicians 1 (ft), 1 (pt); RNs 23 (ft), 3 (pt); LPNs 12 (ft), 1 (pt); Orderlies 3 (ft), 1 (pt); Nurses aides 75 (ft), 29 (pt); Physical therapists 1 (ft); Reality therapists 3 (ft); Recreational therapists 1 (ft); Occupational therapists 1 (ft); Speech therapists 1 (pt); Dietitians 1 (ft).
Facilities Dining room; Physical therapy room; Activities room; Crafts room; Barber/Beauty shop.
Activities Arts and Crafts; Cards; Games; Reading groups; Prayer groups; Movies; Shopping trips; Dances/Social or cultural gatherings; Community parties; Musical groups; Basic adult education; Horticultural therapy; Exercise program; One-to-one contacts; Patient council; Picnics; Barbeques; Monthly newspaper and calendar.

MOUNT PLEASANT

Isabella County Medical Care Facility
1222 N Drive, Mount Pleasant, MI, 48858 (517) 772-2957

Medical Dir/Dir of Nursing John J Minster MD.
Licensure Skilled Care. *Beds* 80. *Certified* Medicaid; Medicare.
Admissions Requirements Medical examination; Physician's request.
Staff Physicians 30 (pt); RNs 5 (ft), 9 (pt); LPNs 4 (ft), 7 (pt); Orderlies 1 (ft); Nurses aides 31 (ft), 15 (pt); Physical therapists 3 (ft); Occupational therapists 1 (ft); Speech therapists 1 (pt); Activities coordinators 1 (pt); Dietitians 1 (pt).
Facilities Dining room; Physical therapy room; Activities room; Chapel; Crafts room; Laundry room; Barber/Beauty shop.
Activities Arts and Crafts; Cards; Games; Reading groups; Prayer groups; Movies; Shopping trips; Dances/Social or cultural gatherings.

Pleasant Manor
400 S Crapo St, Mount Pleasant, MI, 48858 (517) 773-5918
Admin Sandra Caul. *Medical Dir/Dir of Nursing* Dr Leo Wickert.
Licensure Skilled Care; Intermediate Care.
Beds 112. *Certified* Medicaid; Medicare.
Admissions Requirements Minimum age 15; Medical examination; Physician's request.
Staff Physicians 15 (pt); RNs 5 (ft), 4 (pt); LPNs 5 (ft), 4 (pt); Nurses aides 30 (ft), 24 (pt); Physical therapists 1 (pt); Recreational therapists 1 (pt); Occupational therapists 1 (pt); Speech therapists 1 (pt); Dietitians 1 (ft), 1 (pt); Podiatrists 1 (pt); Audiologists 1 (pt).
Facilities Dining room; Activities room; Barber/Beauty shop.
Activities Arts and Crafts; Cards; Games; Reading groups; Prayer groups; Movies; Shopping trips; Dances/Social or cultural gatherings; Exercise class; Stroke club; Monthly special event; Outings each week.
Description Deisolation is the key theme of this progressive nursing center incorporating admission family conferences, effective and efficient care plans, and aggressive discharge planning system returning residents to home care, foster care, or independent living.

Provincial House—Total Living Center*
1524 Portabella Rd, Mount Pleasant, MI, 48858 (517) 772-2967
Licensure Skilled Care; Intermediate Care.
Beds 117. *Certified* Medicaid.

MUNISING

Superior Shores Nursing Center
300 W City Park Dr, Munising, MI, 49862 (906) 387-2273
Licensure Skilled Care; Intermediate Care.
Beds 106. *Certified* Medicaid; Medicare.
Admissions Requirements Minimum age 18; Medical examination; Physician's request.
Facilities Dining room; Physical therapy room; Activities room; Laundry room; Barber/Beauty shop.
Activities Arts and Crafts; Cards; Games; Reading groups; Prayer groups; Movies; Shopping trips; Dances/Social or cultural gatherings.

MUSKEGON

Brookhaven Medical Care Facility
1890 Apple Ave, Muskegon, MI, 49442 (616)
773-9146
Medical Dir/Dir of Nursing Erwin Grasman
MD.
Licensure Skilled Care; Intermediate Care.
Beds 218. *Certified* Medicaid; Medicare.
Admissions Requirements Minimum age 18;
Physician's request.
Staff Physicians 3 (pt); RNs 6 (ft), 2 (pt); LPNs
19 (ft), 11 (pt); Nurses aides 51 (ft), 39 (pt);
Physical therapists 1 (pt); Reality therapists 1
(pt); Occupational therapists 1 (pt); Speech ther-
apists 1 (pt); Activities coordinators 1 (ft); Die-
titians 1 (ft); Podiatrists 1 (pt).
Facilities Dining room; Physical therapy room;
Activities room; Chapel; Crafts room; Barber-
/Beauty shop.
Activities Arts and Crafts; Cards; Games;
Reading groups; Prayer groups; Movies; Shop-
ping trips; Dances/Social or cultural gatherings.

Christian Convalescent Home*
1275 Kenneth Ave, Muskegon, MI, 49442
(616) 722-7165
Licensure Intermediate Care. *Beds* 49.

Deboer Nursing Home*
1684 Vulcan, Muskegon, MI, 49442 (616)
777-2511
Licensure Skilled Care. *Beds* 90. *Certified* Medicaid; Medicare.

Knollview Manor Nursing Home*
1061 W Hackley Ave, Muskegon, MI, 49441
(616) 755-2255
Licensure Skilled Care. *Beds* 107. *Certified* Medicaid; Medicare.

Muskegon Correctional Facility
2400 S Sheridan, Muskegon, MI, 49442
Admin Diane Haynor. *Medical Dir/Dir of
Nursing* Richard G Huff DO.
Licensure Skilled Care. *Beds* 7.
Ownership Public.
Admissions Requirements Minimum age 18;
Males only; Medical examination; Physician's
request.
Staff Physicians 1 (pt); RNs 8 (ft); Dietitians 1
(ft); Dentists 1 (ft); Physician's aides 1 (ft).
Facilities Physical therapy room; Activities
room; Crafts room; Laundry room; Barber-
/Beauty shop; Library.
Activities Games; Movies.
Description This inpatient care facility is with-
in a medium security prison which is a
vocational and learning facility with a popula-
tion of 589 men whose average age is 28.

Seaway Care Center*
1300 Broadway, Muskegon, MI, 49441 (616)
755-2221
Licensure Intermediate Care. *Beds* 69. *Certified* Medicaid.

Sherman Oaks Care Center*
1380 E Sherman Blvd, Muskegon, MI, 49444
(616) 733-2578
Licensure Skilled Care. *Beds* 98. *Certified* Medicaid; Medicare.

University Park Care Center*
570 S Harvey St, Muskegon, MI, 49442 (616)
773-9121
Licensure Intermediate Care. *Beds* 99. *Certified* Medicaid.

MUSKEGON HEIGHTS

Park Manor Convalescent Home*
2333 Jarmon, Muskegon Heights, MI, 49444
(616) 733-9423
Licensure Intermediate Care. *Beds* 27. *Certified* Medicaid.

NEWBERRY

Helen Newberry Joy Hospital*
502 W Harrie, Newberry, MI, 49868 (906)
293-5181
Licensure Skilled Care; Intermediate Care.
Beds 31. *Certified* Medicaid.

NILES

Michigan Skilled Care*
Box 417, 911 S 3rd St, Niles, MI, 49120 (616)
684-4320
Licensure Skilled Care; Intermediate Care.
Beds 100. *Certified* Medicaid; Medicare.

Oak Grove Manor
1217 State Line Rd, Niles, MI, 49120 (616)
683-4143
Medical Dir/Dir of Nursing Kent D Hassan
MD.
Licensure Intermediate Care. *Beds* 15. *Certi-
fied* Medicaid.
Admissions Requirements Minimum age 15;
Medical examination; Physician's request.
Staff RNs 1 (ft), 1 (pt); LPNs 2 (ft), 2 (pt);
Nurses aides 3 (ft), 3 (pt); Physical therapists 1
(pt); Recreational therapists 1 (pt) Speech ther-
apists 1 (pt); Activities coordinators 1 (ft); Die-
titians 1 (pt); Dentists 1 (pt); Podiatrists 1 (pt).
Facilities Dining room; Activities room; Crafts
room; Barber/Beauty shop.
Activities Arts and Crafts; Cards; Games; Prayer groups; Movies; Shopping trips.

Riveridge Manor*
1333 N Wells St, Niles, MI, 49120 (616)
684-1111
Licensure Intermediate Care. *Beds* 84.

Stateline Care Center
1211 State Line Rd, Niles, MI, 49120 (616)
684-2810
Medical Dir/Dir of Nursing Kent D Hassan
MD.
Licensure Skilled Care; Intermediate Care.
Beds 89. *Certified* Medicaid; Medicare.
Admissions Requirements Minimum age 15;
Medical examination; Physician's request.
Staff Physicians 1 (pt); RNs 3 (ft), 1 (pt); LPNs
4 (ft), 4 (pt); Orderlies 2 (ft); Nurses aides 20
(ft), 10 (pt); Physical therapists 1 (pt); Occupa-
tional therapists 1 (pt); Speech therapists 1 (pt);
Activities coordinators 1 (ft), 2 (pt); Dietitians
1 (pt); Dentists 1 (pt); Podiatrists 1 (pt).
Facilities Dining room; Activities room; Crafts
room; Laundry room; Barber/Beauty shop.

Activities Arts and Crafts; Cards; Games;
Movies; Shopping trips; Dances/Social or cultural gatherings.

NORTH MUSKEGON

Hillcrest Nursing Home*
695 Mitzi Dr, North Muskegon, MI, 49445
(616) 744-1641
Licensure Intermediate Care. *Beds* 63. *Certified* Medicaid.

NORTHPORT

Leelanau Memorial Hospital*
High St, Northport, MI, 49670 (616) 386-5101
Licensure Skilled Care; Intermediate Care.
Beds 61. *Certified* Medicaid; Medicare.

NORTHVILLE

Wishing Well Manor*
520 W Main St, Northville, MI, 48167 (313)
349-4290
Licensure Intermediate Care. *Beds* 37. *Certified* Medicaid.

NOVI

Beverly Manor Convalescent Center*
24500 Meadowbrook Rd, Novi, MI, 48050
(313) 447-2000
Licensure Skilled Care; Intermediate Care.
Beds 144. *Certified* Medicaid; Medicare.

Whitehall Convalescent Home 2
43455 W 10 Mile Rd, Novi, MI, 48050 (313)
349-2200
Medical Dir/Dir of Nursing R M Atchison
MD.
Licensure Intermediate Care. *Beds* 82. *Certi-
fied* Medicaid.
Admissions Requirements Minimum age 18;
Medical examination; Physician's request.
Staff RNs 4 (ft), 2 (pt); LPNs 2 (ft), 4 (pt);
Nurses aides 50 (ft), 6 (pt); Recreational thera-
pists 1 (ft); Activities coordinators 1 (ft); Dieti-
tians 1 (pt).
Affiliation Royal Order of Moose
Facilities Dining room; Activities room; Crafts
room; Laundry room; Barber/Beauty shop;
Library.
Activities Arts and Crafts; Cards; Games;
Reading groups; Prayer groups; Movies.
Description Home has been in operation since
1956 and has a reputation for giving excellent
nursing care.

OKEMOS

Ingham County Medical Care Facility
3860 Dobie Rd, Okemos, MI, 48864 (517)
349-1050
Admin D Vande Vare. *Medical Dir/Dir of
Nursing* John Strandmark MD.
Licensure Skilled Care; Intermediate Care.
Beds 204. *Certified* Medicaid; Medicare.
Admissions Requirements Minimum age 12;
Medical examination; Physician's request.

Staff Physicians 3 (pt); RNs 15 (ft); LPNs 20 (ft); Nurses aides 145 (ft); Physical therapists 1 (pt); Recreational therapists 2 (ft), 1 (pt); Occupational therapists 1 (pt); Speech therapists 3 (pt); Activities coordinators 1 (ft); Dietitians 1 (ft); Dentists 1 (pt); Ophthalmologists 1 (pt); Podiatrists 1 (pt); Audiologists 2 (pt).
Facilities Dining room; Physical therapy room; Activities room; Crafts room; Laundry room; Barber/Beauty shop; Library.
Activities Arts and Crafts; Cards; Games; Reading groups; Prayer groups; Movies; Shopping trips; Dances/Social or cultural gatherings.
Description Home is set in a beautiful suburban/country setting, and is built around a large atrium; rooms are large and open onto 10 foot wide corridors.

ONTONAGON

Maple Manor Nursing Center*
102 2nd St, Ontonagon, MI, 49953
Licensure Intermediate Care. *Beds* 64. *Certified* Medicaid.

Ontonagon Memorial Hospital*
601 7th St, Ontonagon, MI, 49953 (906) 884-2811
Licensure Skilled Care; Intermediate Care. *Beds* 46. *Certified* Medicaid; Medicare.

ORTONVILLE

Ortonville Nursing Home*
330 Sherman Ct, Ortonville, MI, 48462 (313) 627-2420
Licensure Intermediate Care. *Beds* 51. *Certified* Medicaid.

OSHTEMO

Oshtemo Care Center*
6203 W Michigan Ave, Oshtemo, MI, 49009 (616) 375-1204
Licensure Skilled Care; Intermediate Care. *Beds* 101. *Certified* Medicaid.

OVID

Ovid Convalescent Manor*
9480 M 21 W, Ovid, MI, 48866 (517) 834-2228
Licensure Intermediate Care. *Beds* 63. *Certified* Medicaid.

PERRINTON

Brown Nursing Home*
Rt 1, Perrinton, MI, 48871 (517) 236-7348
Licensure Intermediate Care. *Beds* 50. *Certified* Medicaid.

PETOSKEY

Petosky Nursing Center*
1500 Spring St, Petoskey, MI, 49770
Licensure Skilled Care; Intermediate Care. *Beds* 123. *Certified* Medicaid; Medicare.

PIGEON

Scheuber Hospital*
170 N Caseville Rd, Pigeon, MI, 48755 (517) 453-3223
Licensure Intermediate Care. *Beds* 19. *Certified* Medicaid.

PLAINWELL

Beverly Manor Convalescent Center
3260 E "B" Ave, Plainwell, MI, 49080 (616) 349-6649
Medical Dir/Dir of Nursing Richard Kik DO.
Licensure Intermediate Care. *Beds* 58. *Certified* Medicaid.
Admissions Requirements Minimum age 21; Medical examination; Physician's request.
Staff RNs 3 (ft), 1 (pt); LPNs 4 (ft), 1 (pt); Nurses aides 30 (ft), 6 (pt); Recreational therapists 1 (ft); Activities coordinators 1 (ft); Dietitians 1 (ft).
Facilities Dining room; Activities room; Laundry room.
Activities Arts and Crafts; Cards; Games; Reading groups; Prayer groups; Movies; Shopping trips; Dances/Social or cultural gatherings; Exercises.
Description Facility features resident council, monthly newsletter, resident of the month, and a monthly family night potluck.

Bridgewood Manor Inc
320 Brigham St, Box 28, Plainwell, MI, 49080 (616) 685-5390
Licensure Intermediate Care. *Beds* 124. *Certified* Medicaid.

PLYMOUTH

Hendry Convalescent Center*
105 Haggerty Rd, Plymouth, MI, 48170 (313) 455-0510
Licensure Skilled Care. *Beds* 129. *Certified* Medicare.

West Trail Nursing Home
395 W Ann Arbor Trail, Plymouth, MI, 48170 (313) 453-3983
Medical Dir/Dir of Nursing Joseph Gadbaw MD.
Licensure Intermediate Care. *Beds* 46. *Certified* Medicaid.
Admissions Requirements Medical examination; Physician's request.
Staff Physicians 1 (pt); RNs 2 (ft); LPNs 3 (ft); Nurses aides 14 (ft); Recreational therapists 1 (ft); Activities coordinators 1 (ft); Dietitians 1 (ft); Dentists 1 (pt); Podiatrists 1 (pt).
Facilities Dining room; Activities room; Laundry room; Barber/Beauty shop; Library.
Activities Arts and Crafts; Cards; Games; Reading groups; Prayer groups; Movies; Shopping trips; Dances/Social or cultural gatherings.
Description Facility offers a warm, cozy atmosphere with excellent patient care.

PONTIAC

Grovecrest Convalescent Center
1121 Prall St, Pontiac, MI, 48053 (313) 334-4732
Licensure Skilled Care; Intermediate Care. *Beds* 57. *Certified* Medicare.

Lourdes
2300 Watkins Lake Rd, Pontiac, MI, 48054 (313) 674-2241
Medical Dir/Dir of Nursing W P Richards MD.
Licensure Skilled Care; Intermediate Care. *Beds* 108. *Certified* Medicaid; Medicare.
Admissions Requirements Minimum age 65; Medical examination; Physician's request.
Staff Physicians 4 (pt); RNs 4 (ft), 13 (pt); LPNs 6 (ft), 6 (pt); Nurses aides 36 (ft), 19 (pt); Physical therapists 1 (pt); Activities coordinators 1 (ft), 1 (pt); Dentists 1 (pt); Podiatrists 1 (pt).
Affiliation Roman Catholic
Facilities Dining room; Physical therapy room; Activities room; Chapel; Crafts room; Laundry room; Barber/Beauty shop.
Activities Arts and Crafts; Cards; Games; Reading groups; Prayer groups; Movies; Dances/Social or cultural gatherings; Pet therapy; Bowling; Music, sing-a-longs, entertainment; Resident council; Current events; Library on wheels; Quarterly newsletter.
Description The facility is surrounded by woods and overlooks Scott Lake; each room looks out on scenic view. To meet spiritual needs of residents, a pastoral minister and a resident chaplain are available 7 days a week. Adult classes are conducted each day with subject matter varying from American government, science and mathamatics, to cooking. Ethnic dinners and entertainment are planned by residents.

Oakland County Medical Care Facility
2200 N Telegraph Rd, Pontiac, MI, 48053 (313) 858-1415
Medical Dir/Dir of Nursing Antonio Nucum MD.
Licensure Skilled Care; Intermediate Care. *Beds* 120. *Certified* Medicaid; Medicare.
Admissions Requirements Physician's request.
Staff Physicians 1 (ft); RNs 8 (ft), 7 (pt); LPNs 8 (ft), 6 (pt); Nurses aides 33 (ft), 35 (pt); Physical therapists 1 (ft); Occupational therapists 1 (ft); Speech therapists 1 (ft); Activities coordinators 1 (ft); Dietitians 1 (ft); Dentists 1 (pt).
Facilities Dining room; Physical therapy room; Activities room; Chapel; Crafts room; Laundry room; Barber/Beauty shop; Library.
Activities Arts and Crafts; Cards; Games; Reading groups; Prayer groups; Shopping trips.
Description Facility offers extremely highly skilled acuity level.

Oakland Geriatric Village
1255 Silver Bell, Pontiac, MI, 48057 (313) 391-0900
Medical Dir/Dir of Nursing Dr Janicke DO.
Licensure Skilled Care; Intermediate Care. *Beds* 106. *Certified* Medicaid; Medicare.
Admissions Requirements Medical examination; Physician's request.

Staff Physicians 6 (pt); RNs 2 (ft), 7 (pt); LPNs 3 (ft), 14 (pt); Nurses aides 60 (pt); Physical therapists 1 (pt); Recreational therapists 1 (ft); Occupational therapists 1 (pt); Speech therapists 1 (pt); Activities coordinators 1 (ft); Dietitians 1 (ft); Dentists 1 (pt); Ophthalmologists 1 (pt); Podiatrists 1 (pt).
Facilities Dining room; Physical therapy room; Activities room; Crafts room; Laundry room; Barber/Beauty shop.
Activities Arts and Crafts; Cards; Reading groups; Prayer groups; Movies; Shopping trips; Dances/Social or cultural gatherings; Bowling; Senior citizens' center visited weekly.
Description The outstanding characteristic of this facility is the warm, friendly approach to delivering total nursing care in a family-like atmosphere; individual consideration in meeting patient needs and wants.

Pontiac Nursing Center*
532 Orchard Lake Rd, Pontiac, MI, 48053 (313) 338-7151
Licensure Skilled Care; Intermediate Care.
Beds 360. *Certified* Medicaid; Medicare.

PORT HURON

The Evangelical Home—Port Huron
5635 Lakeshore Rd, Port Huron, MI, 48060
Admin Thomas H Hoewisch. *Medical Dir/Dir of Nursing* Doughlas A Krause MD.
Licensure Skilled Care. *Beds* 129. *Certified* Medicaid; Medicare.
Ownership Nonprofit.
Admissions Requirements Medical examination; Physician's request.
Staff RNs 4 (ft), 3 (pt); LPNs 6 (ft), 5 (pt); Orderlies 3 (ft), 2 (pt); Nurses aides 36 (ft), 31 (pt); Activities coordinators 1 (ft).
Affiliation Church of Christ
Facilities Dining room; Physical therapy room; Activities room; Barber/Beauty shop.
Activities Arts and Crafts; Cards; Games; Prayer groups; Movies; Dances/Social or cultural gatherings.
Description Facility, located on spacious landscaped grounds that provide a pleasant view, offers a well rounded activity program that complements a terrific nursing staff.

Marwood Manor
1300 Beard St, Port Huron, MI, 48060 (313) 982-8591
Admin Peter Cangemi. *Medical Dir/Dir of Nursing* Frederick E Ludwig MD.
Licensure Skilled Care; Intermediate Care.
Beds 252. *Certified* Medicaid; Medicare.
Admissions Requirements Minimum age 17; Medical examination; Physician's request.
Staff RNs 2 (ft), 5 (pt); LPNs 13 (ft), 11 (pt); Orderlies 2 (pt); Nurses aides 84 (ft), 17 (pt); Physical therapists 1 (ft); Occupational therapists 1 (pt); Speech therapists 1 (pt); Activities coordinators 1 (ft), 1 (pt).
Facilities Dining room; Physical therapy room; Activities room; Chapel; Crafts room; Laundry room; Barber/Beauty shop; Library.
Activities Arts and Crafts; Cards; Games; Prayer groups; Movies; Dances/Social or cultural gatherings; Live bands; Cookouts; Christmas

teas; Popcorn parties; Ice cream socials; Bingo.
Description Facility has an outstanding state health and citizens group rating.

POWERS

Pinecrest Medical Care Facility
Sheridan Rd, Powers, MI, 49874 (906) 497-5244
Medical Dir/Dir of Nursing Francis Dewane MD.
Licensure Skilled Care; Intermediate Care.
Beds 160. *Certified* Medicaid; Medicare.
Admissions Requirements Minimum age 14; Physician's request.
Staff Physicians 1 (ft); RNs 3 (ft), 2 (pt); LPNs 17 (ft), 10 (pt); Orderlies 2 (ft); Nurses aides 57 (ft), 43 (pt); Physical therapists; Activities coordinators 1 (ft); Dietitians; Dentists; Podiatrists.
Facilities Dining room; Physical therapy room; Activities room; Chapel; Crafts room; Laundry room; Barber/Beauty shop.
Activities Arts and Crafts; Games; Prayer groups; Movies; Shopping trips; Dances/Social or cultural gatherings.

REDFORD TOWNSHIP

Cambridge Nursing Center—West*
18633 Beech Daly Rd, Redford Township, MI, 48240 (313) 255-1010
Licensure Skilled Care; Intermediate Care.
Beds 121. *Certified* Medicaid; Medicare.

REED CITY

Reed City Hospital*
7665 Patterson Rd, Reed City, MI, 49677 (616) 832-5511
Licensure Skilled Care; Intermediate Care.
Beds 50. *Certified* Medicaid; Medicare.

RICHMOND

Medilodge of Richmond
34901 Division Rd, Richmond, MI, 48062 (313) 727-7562
Licensure Intermediate Care. *Beds* 126. *Certified* Medicaid.

RIVERVIEW

Marian Manor Medical Center*
18591 Quarry Rd, Riverview, MI, 48192 (313) 282-2100
Licensure Skilled Care; Intermediate Care.
Beds 140. *Certified* Medicaid; Medicare.

Rivergate Convalescent Center*
14041 Pennsylvania, Riverview, MI, 48192 (313) 284-7200
Licensure Skilled Care; Intermediate Care.
Beds 223. *Certified* Medicaid; Medicare.

The Rivergate Terrace—Intermediate Care Facility*
14141 Pennsylvania, Riverview, MI, 48192 (313) 284-8000, 283-6244
Licensure Intermediate Care. *Beds* 221. *Certified* Medicaid.

ROCHESTER

Avondale Nursing Center
1480 Walton Blvd, Rochester, MI, 48063
Medical Dir/Dir of Nursing C E Hendershott DO.
Licensure Skilled Care; Intermediate Care.
Beds 124. *Certified* Medicaid; Medicare.
Admissions Requirements Minimum age 15; Medical examination; Physician's request.
Staff RNs 2 (ft), 25 (pt); LPNs 4 (pt); Orderlies 1 (ft); Nurses aides 60 (ft), 14 (pt); Physical therapists 1 (ft); Activities coordinators 1 (ft).
Facilities Dining room; Physical therapy room; Activities room; Chapel; Crafts room; Laundry room; Barber/Beauty shop; Library.
Activities Arts and Crafts; Cards; Games; Reading groups; Prayer groups; Movies; Dances/Social or cultural gatherings.

ROGERS CITY

Rogers City Hospital Long-Term Care Unit
555 N Bradley Hwy, Rogers City, MI, 49779 (517) 734-2151
Medical Dir/Dir of Nursing R M Foley MD.
Licensure Skilled Care; Intermediate Care.
Beds 49. *Certified* Medicaid; Medicare.
Admissions Requirements Physician's request.
Staff Physicians 6 (ft); RNs 2 (ft); LPNs 3 (ft), 6 (pt); Nurses aides 6 (ft), 30 (pt); Physical therapists 1 (ft); Recreational therapists 1 (ft), 1 (pt); Speech therapists 1 (pt); Activities coordinators 1 (ft), 1 (pt); Dietitians 1 (ft); Dentists 1 (pt).
Facilities Dining room; Physical therapy room; Activities room; Chapel; Crafts room; Barber/Beauty shop; Library; TV room.
Activities Arts and Crafts; Cards; Games; Reading groups; Prayer groups; Movies; Shopping trips; Special dinners; Band concerts; Color tours; Bus rides; Bingo.
Description The motto of Rogers City Hospital is "We Care" and the entire staff of the long-term care unit provides personalized, high-quality care in a family-like atmosphere.

ROMEO

Romeo Nursing Center
250 Denby St, PO Box 306, Romeo, MI, 48065 (313) 752-3571
Licensure Intermediate Care. *Beds* 35. *Certified* Medicaid.
Admissions Requirements Minimum age 18; Medical examination.
Staff Physicians 1 (ft); RNs 1 (ft), 2 (pt); LPNs 4 (pt); Nurses aides 8 (ft), 6 (pt); Activities coordinators 1 (ft); Dietitians 1 (pt); Dentists 1 (pt); Ophthalmologists 1 (pt); Podiatrists 1 (pt).
Facilities Dining room; Activities room.
Activities Arts and Crafts; Cards; Games; Dances/Social or cultural gatherings.

Woodwards Rest Home 1
309 S Bailey, Romeo, MI, 48065 (313)
752-2581
Licensure Intermediate Care. *Beds* 34. *Certi-
fied* Medicaid.
Admissions Requirements Minimum age 21.
Staff RNs 1 (ft), 1 (pt); LPNs 3 (ft), 2 (pt);
Nurses aides 11 (ft), 5 (pt); Activities coordina-
tors 1 (pt); Dietitians 1 (pt).
Facilities Dining room; Activities room; Crafts
room; Laundry room; Barber/Beauty shop.
Activities Arts and Crafts; Cards; Games;
Reading groups; Prayer groups; Shopping trips.

ROMULUS

Apple Tree Lane Convalescent Home*
39000 Chase Rd, Romulus, MI, 48174 (313)
941-1142
Licensure Intermediate Care. *Beds* 43. *Certified* Medicaid.

ROSE CITY

Ogemaw Valley Medical Facility*
517 W Page St, Rose City, MI, 48654 (313)
685-25656
Licensure Skilled Care; Intermediate Care.
Beds 140. *Certified* Medicaid; Medicare.

ROSEVILLE

Rose Villa Nursing Center*
25375 Kelly Rd, Roseville, MI, 48066 (313)
773-6022
Licensure Skilled Care; Intermediate Care.
Beds 172. *Certified* Medicaid; Medicare.

ROYAL OAK

Alexander Continuing Care Center
718 W 4th St, Royal Oak, MI, 48067 (313)
545-0571
Medical Dir/Dir of Nursing James Lesser MD.
Licensure Skilled Care; Intermediate Care.
Beds 96. *Certified* Medicare.
Admissions Requirements Minimum age 18;
Medical examination; Physician's request.
Staff Physicians 2 (ft), 3 (pt); RNs 3 (ft); LPNs
6 (pt); Orderlies 2 (ft); Nurses aides 28 (ft), 4
(pt); Physical therapists 1 (ft), 1 (pt); Speech
therapists 1 (pt); Activities coordinators 1 (ft), 1
(pt); Dietitians 1 (ft); Ophthalmologists 1 (pt);
Podiatrists 1 (pt); Audiologists 1 (pt).
Facilities Dining room; Physical therapy room;
Activities room; Laundry room; Barber/Beauty
shop.
Activities Arts and Crafts; Cards; Games; Prayer groups; Movies.
Description Facility is located in a quiet, residential area providing services to a special
closed head injury population in addition to
usual skilled and basic care.

Oakland Care Center
3030 Greenfield, Royal Oak, MI, 48072 (313)
288-6610
Medical Dir/Dir of Nursing Edwin Blumberg
DO.
Licensure Skilled Care; Intermediate Care.

Beds 151. *Certified* Medicaid; Medicare.
Admissions Requirements Minimum age 15.
Staff Physicians 1 (ft), 8 (pt); RNs 1 (ft), 6 (pt);
LPNs 10 (ft), 6 (pt); Nurses aides 36 (ft), 27
(pt); Physical therapists 1 (ft); Reality therapists
1 (pt); Recreational therapists 1 (pt); Occupa-
tional therapists 1 (pt); Speech therapists 1 (pt);
Activities coordinators 1 (ft), 1 (pt); Dietitians
1 (ft); Dentists 2 (pt); Ophthalmologists 2 (pt);
Podiatrists 1 (pt); Audiologists 1 (pt).
Facilities Dining room; Physical therapy room;
Activities room; Crafts room; Laundry room;
Barber/Beauty shop; Library.
Activities Arts and Crafts; Cards; Games;
Reading groups; Prayer groups; Movies; Shopping trips; Dances/Social or cultural gatherings;
Sightseeing.
Description Facility pushes hard for fun, whole-
some activities that range from in-house day to
day activities to trips out for sightseeing, fun,
fishing, shopping, or whatever else suits the res-
idents fancy; also sponsors art exhibits, garden
exhibits, pets, and other events.

SAGINAW

Hoyt Nursing Home*
1202 Weiss St, Saginaw, MI, 48602
Licensure Intermediate Care. *Beds* 69. *Certified* Medicaid; Medicare.

Luther Manor
3161 Davenport, Saginaw, MI, 48602 (517)
799-1902
Licensure Skilled Care; Intermediate Care.
Beds 98. *Certified* Medicaid; Medicare.
Admissions Requirements Medical examina-
tion; Physician's request.
Affiliation Lutheran
Facilities Dining room; Activities room; Chap-
el; Crafts room; Laundry room; Barber/Beauty
shop; Library.
Activities Arts and Crafts; Cards; Games;
Reading groups; Prayer groups; Movies; Shop-
ping trips; Dances/Social or cultural gatherings.
Description Facility features in-house daily tele-
vision programing; field trips.

Maccabee Gardens Extended Care*
2160 N Center Rd, Saginaw, MI, 48603 (517)
799-2996
Licensure Skilled Care; Intermediate Care.
Beds 98. *Certified* Medicaid; Medicare.

Martin Luther Saginaw Home
4322 Mackinaw Rd, Saginaw, MI, 48602 (517)
792-8729
Medical Dir/Dir of Nursing James Brasseur
DO.
Licensure Skilled Care; Intermediate Care.
Beds 71. *Certified* Medicaid; Medicare.
Staff RNs 4 (ft), 1 (pt); LPNs 3 (ft), 5 (pt);
Orderlies 2 (ft), 1 (pt); Nurses aides 15 (ft), 12
(pt); Physical therapists 1 (pt); Speech thera-
pists; Activities coordinators 1 (ft); Dietitians;
Dentists.
Affiliation Lutheran
Facilities Dining room; Physical therapy room;
Activities room; Laundry room; Barber/Beauty
shop.
Activities Arts and Crafts; Cards; Games;
Reading groups; Prayer groups; Movies; Shop-

ping trips; Dances/Social or cultural gatherings.
Description Motto "Christian Care for Aging
Christians" reflects purpose in providing
quality nursing care through a friendly and professional atmosphere.

Saginaw Community Hospital*
Box 2089, 3340 Hospital Rd, Saginaw, MI,
48605 (517) 790-1234
Licensure Skilled Care; Intermediate Care.
Beds 208. *Certified* Medicaid; Medicare.

Saginaw Geriatric Home*
1413 Gratiot, Saginaw, MI, 48602 (517)
793-3471
Licensure Intermediate Care. *Beds* 55. *Certified* Medicaid.

Saint Francis Home
915 N River Rd, Saginaw, MI, 48603 (517)
781-3150
Admin Sr Jane Marie. *Medical Dir/Dir of
Nursing* Dr Ron Jensen.
Licensure Skilled Care; Intermediate Care.
Beds 100. *Certified* Medicaid; Medicare.
Admissions Requirements Medical examina-
tion.
Staff RNs 13 (pt); LPNs 7 (pt); Nurses aides 10
(ft), 45 (pt); Physical therapists 1 (pt); Recrea-
tional therapists 1 (ft), 3 (pt); Occupational ther-
apists 1 (ft), 3 (pt); Activities coordinators 1 (ft);
Dietitians 1 (ft); Podiatrists 1 (pt).
Affiliation Roman Catholic
Facilities Dining room; Physical therapy room;
Activities room; Chapel; Crafts room; Laundry
room; Barber/Beauty shop.
Activities Arts and Crafts; Cards; Games; Prayer groups; Movies; Dances/Social or cultural
gatherings.

Sun Valley Manor*
2901 Galaxie Dr, Saginaw, MI, 48601 (517)
777-5110
Licensure Skilled Care; Intermediate Care.
Beds 103. *Certified* Medicaid; Medicare.

SAINT CLAIR

Faith Medical Care Center
4220 S Hospital Dr, Saint Clair, MI, 48079
(313) 329-4736
Medical Dir/Dir of Nursing Gordon H Webb
MD.
Licensure Skilled Care; Intermediate Care.
Beds 125. *Certified* Medicaid; Medicare.
Admissions Requirements Minimum age 16;
Medical examination.
Staff Physicians 14 (pt); RNs 4 (ft), 2 (pt);
LPNs 6 (ft), 4 (pt); Orderlies 1 (ft); Nurses aides
39 (ft), 10 (pt); Recreational therapists 2 (ft);
Activities coordinators 1 (ft); Dietitians 2 (ft);
Dentists 1 (pt); Podiatrists 1 (pt); Auxiliaries 50
(pt).
Facilities Dining room; Activities room; Crafts
room; Laundry room; Barber/Beauty shop.
Activities Arts and Crafts; Cards; Games;
Reading groups; Prayer groups; Movies; Dan-
ces/Social or cultural gatherings.
Description Physical, occupational, speech, and
audio-respiratory therapy are available from
River District Hospital, to which facility is

physically connected. Facility has a beautiful patio for picnics and cookouts; home-cooked meals; very family-oriented, very loving staff.

SAINT CLAIR SHORES

Saint Mary Nursing Home
22601 E 9 Mile Rd, Saint Clair Shores, MI, 48080 (313) 772-4300
Admin C T Bertolini. *Medical Dir/Dir of Nursing* Harry Latos DO.
Licensure Skilled Care; Intermediate Care.
Beds SNF 103; ICF 4. *Certified* Medicaid; Medicare.
Admissions Requirements Minimum age 15; Medical examination; Physician's request.
Staff Physicians 13 (pt); RNs 5 (ft), 1 (pt); LPNs 1 (ft), 6 (pt); Orderlies 2 (ft), 1 (pt); Nurses aides 30 (ft), 10 (pt); Physical therapists; Recreational therapists; Occupational therapists; Speech therapists; Dietitians; Dentists; Ophthalmologists; Podiatrists.
Facilities Dining room; Physical therapy room; Activities room; Laundry room; Barber/Beauty shop.
Activities Arts and Crafts; Cards; Games; Reading groups; Prayer groups; Movies; Shopping trips; Dances/Social or cultural gatherings.

SAINT IGNACE

Mackinac County Medical Care Facility*
Hombach St, Saint Ignace, MI, 49781 (906) 643-7788
Licensure Skilled Care; Intermediate Care.
Beds 60. *Certified* Medicaid; Medicare.
Ownership Public.

SAINT JOHNS

Hazel I Findlay Country*
1101 S Scott Rd, Saint Johns, MI, 48879
Licensure Intermediate Care. *Beds* 65.

Rivard Nursing Home
311-13 E Higham, Saint Johns, MI, 48879 (517) 224-2985
Licensure Intermediate Care. *Beds* 32. *Certified* Medicaid.

SAINT JOSEPH

Shoreham Terrace*
3425 Lake Shore Dr, Saint Joseph, MI, 49085 (616) 983-6501
Licensure Skilled Care; Intermediate Care.
Beds 112. *Certified* Medicaid; Medicare.

SAINT LOUIS

Schnepps Convalescent Home*
4527 E Washington Ave, Saint Louis, MI, 48880 (517) 681-5721
Licensure Skilled Care; Intermediate Care.
Beds 73. *Certified* Medicaid; Medicare.

Westgate Manor Nursing Home*
1149 W Monroe Rd, Saint Louis, MI, 48880 (517) 681-3852
Licensure Skilled Care; Intermediate Care.
Beds 81. *Certified* Medicaid; Medicare.

SALINE

Evangelical Home*
440 W Russell, Saline, MI, 48176 (313) 429-9401
Licensure Skilled Care; Intermediate Care.
Beds 215. *Certified* Medicaid; Medicare.

SANDUSKY

Sanilac Medical Care Facility*
137 N Elk St, Sandusky, MI, 48471 (313) 648-3017
Licensure Skilled Care; Intermediate Care.
Beds 84. *Certified* Medicaid; Medicare.

SAULT SAINTE MARIE

Chippewa County War Memorial
500 Osborn Blvd, Sault Sainte Marie, MI, 49783 (906) 632-3331
Medical Dir/Dir of Nursing E J Ranta MD.
Licensure Skilled Care; Intermediate Care.
Beds 51. *Certified* Medicaid; Medicare.
Admissions Requirements Medical examination; Physician's request.
Staff Physicians 12 (pt); RNs 1 (ft); LPNs 5 (ft); Orderlies 1 (pt); Nurses aides 13 (ft); Physical therapists 1 (pt); Speech therapists 1 (pt); Activities coordinators 1 (ft); Dietitians 1 (ft); Dentists 1 (pt).
Facilities Dining room; Physical therapy room; Activities room; Chapel; Crafts room; Barber-/Beauty shop; Library.
Activities Arts and Crafts; Cards; Games; Reading groups; Prayer groups; Movies; Shopping trips; Dances/Social or cultural gatherings; Senior living classes through the community schools.
Description Facility is attached to a general hospital so emergency medical care is immediately available.

Provincial House—Sault Sainte Marie*
1011 Meridian, Sault Sainte Marie, MI, 49783 (906) 635-1518
Licensure Skilled Care. *Beds* 117. *Certified* Medicaid; Medicare.

SOUTH HAVEN

Countryside Nursing Home
120 Baseline Rd, South Haven, MI, 49090 (616) 637-8411
Medical Dir/Dir of Nursing Thomas Burns MD.
Licensure Intermediate Care. *Beds* 63. *Certified* Medicaid.
Admissions Requirements Medical examination.
Staff RNs 3 (pt); LPNs 6 (ft), 2 (pt); Orderlies 9 (ft); Nurses aides 25 (ft), 20 (pt); Recreational therapists 1 (ft), 2 (pt); Activities coordinators 1 (ft); Dietitians 1 (pt).

Facilities Dining room; Activities room; Laundry room; Barber/Beauty shop.
Activities Arts and Crafts; Cards; Games; Reading groups; Prayer groups; Movies; Shopping trips; Dances/Social or cultural gatherings.
Description Fully carpeted facility located on the shore of Lake Michigan in a wooded area.

Martin Luther—South Haven*
850 Phillips St, South Haven, MI, 49090
Licensure Skilled Care; Intermediate Care.
Beds 125. *Certified* Medicaid; Medicare.
Affiliation Lutheran

SOUTH LYON

Martin Luther Memorial Home
307 Elm Place, South Lyon, MI, 48178 (313) 437-2048
Medical Dir/Dir of Nursing Dr Barbara Mercer.
Licensure Skilled Care; Intermediate Care.
Beds 44. *Certified* Medicaid; Medicare.
Admissions Requirements Medical examination.
Staff RNs 4 (pt); LPNs 2 (ft), 2 (pt); Orderlies 1 (pt); Nurses aides 24 (ft), 10 (pt); Activities coordinators 2 (pt).
Affiliation Lutheran
Facilities Dining room; Physical therapy room; Crafts room; Laundry room; Barber/Beauty shop.
Activities Arts and Crafts; Games; Reading groups; Prayer groups; Movies.
Description Christian care for the aging Christian is not just a nice theme but is actually provided in home for the aged and nursing home. Facility has been privileged to care for people for nearly 20 years.

SOUTHFIELD

Bedford Villa Nursing Center
16240 W 12 Mile Rd, Southfield, MI, 48075 (313) 557-3333
Medical Dir/Dir of Nursing Dr Knauff.
Licensure Skilled Care; Intermediate Care.
Beds 61.
Admissions Requirements Physician's request.
Staff Physicians 1 (ft); Physical therapists 1 (pt); Reality therapists 1 (pt); Recreational therapists 1 (pt); Occupational therapists 1 (pt); Speech therapists 1 (pt); Activities coordinators 1 (pt); Dietitians 1 (ft); Dentists 1 (pt); Podiatrists 1 (pt).
Facilities Dining room; Activities room; Crafts room; Laundry room; Barber/Beauty shop; Library; TV room.
Activities Arts and Crafts; Cards; Games; Reading groups; Prayer groups; Movies; Dances/Social or cultural gatherings; Outings; Pet on premises.
Description Small facility is close to many hospitals, on one floor with family atmosphere; family is welcomed and encouraged to participate in daily living and activities; personalization of rooms encouraged; 24-hour professional staff and physician; extraordinary dietary service with personal dietary preferences available; religious and social activities ongoing.

Franklin Manor Convalescent Center*
26900 Franklin Rd, Southfield, MI, 48034 (313) 352-7390
Licensure Intermediate Care. *Beds* 107. *Certified* Medicaid.

Hospice of Southeastern Michigan*
22401 Foster Winter, Southfield, MI, 48075 (313) 569-1500
Licensure Skilled Care. *Beds* 42. *Certified* Medicaid.

Jewish Home for the Aged 1*
26051 Lahser Rd, Southfield, MI, 48034 (313) 352-2336
Licensure Skilled Care; Intermediate Care. *Beds* 100. *Certified* Medicaid; Medicare. *Affiliation* Jewish

Lahser Hills Nursing Center*
25300 Lahser Rd, Southfield, MI, 48034 (313) 354-3222
Licensure Skilled Care; Intermediate Care. *Beds* 161. *Certified* Medicaid; Medicare.

Mount Vernon Nursing Center*
26715 Greenfield Rd, Southfield, MI, 48075 (313) 557-0050
Licensure Skilled Care; Intermediate Care. *Beds* 228. *Certified* Medicaid; Medicare.

Southfield Center*
22401 Foster Winter, Southfield, MI, 48075
Licensure Intermediate Care. *Beds* 150. *Certified* Medicaid; Medicare.

SOUTHGATE

Beverly Manor*
15400 Trenton Rd, Southgate, MI, 48195 (313) 284-4620
Licensure Skilled Care; Intermediate Care. *Beds* 100. *Certified* Medicaid; Medicare.

SPRING ARBOR

Arbor Manor Care Center
151 2nd St, Spring Arbor, MI, 49283 (517) 750-1900
Medical Dir/Dir of Nursing Howard Hoffman MD.
Licensure Skilled Care; Intermediate Care; Home for the Aged. *Beds* 115. *Certified* Medicaid; Medicare.
Admissions Requirements Medical examination; Physician's request.
Staff RNs 5 (ft), 1 (pt); LPNs 4 (ft), 7 (pt); Orderlies 1 (ft), 1 (pt); Nurses aides 26 (ft), 38 (pt); Activities coordinators 1 (ft).
Facilities Dining room; Physical therapy room; Activities room; Crafts room; Laundry room; Barber/Beauty shop; Library.
Activities Arts and Crafts; Games; Reading groups; Prayer groups; Movies; Shopping trips; Dances/Social or cultural gatherings.

SPRINGFIELD

Provincial House—Battle Creek
111 Evergreen Rd, Springfield, MI, 49017 (616) 965-1308

Medical Dir/Dir of Nursing Dr Gerald Rutledge.
Licensure Skilled Care; Intermediate Care. *Beds* 117. *Certified* Medicaid; Medicare.
Admissions Requirements Minimum age 17; Physician's request.
Staff RNs 5 (ft), 1 (pt); LPNs 6 (ft), 4 (pt); Nurses aides 26 (ft), 25 (pt); Activities coordinators 1 (ft); Dietitians 1 (ft).
Facilities Dining room; Physical therapy room; Activities room; Crafts room; Laundry room; Barber/Beauty shop.
Activities Arts and Crafts; Cards; Games; Reading groups; Prayer groups; Movies; Shopping trips; Dances/Social or cultural gatherings.
Description Facility is clean, pretty with nice rural setting, and alive with activity.

STANDISH

Standish Community Hospital
805 W Cedar, Standish, MI, 48658 (616) 846-4521
Admin Gordon Tolodziecki. *Medical Dir/Dir of Nursing* Edward G Papp DO.
Licensure Skilled Care; Intermediate Care. *Beds* 44. *Certified* Medicaid; Medicare.
Staff Physicians 6 (pt); RNs 1 (ft); LPNs 8 (ft), 3 (pt); Nurses aides 18 (ft), 8 (pt); Physical therapists 1 (pt); Recreational therapists 1 (pt); Speech therapists 1 (pt); Dietitians 1 (pt); Dentists 2 (pt); Podiatrists 1 (pt).
Facilities Dining room; Physical therapy room; Activities room; Crafts room; Laundry room; Barber/Beauty shop.
Activities Arts and Crafts; Cards; Games; Reading groups; Prayer groups; Movies; Shopping trips; Dances/Social or cultural gatherings.

STEPHENSON

Roubals Nursing Home
Rt 1, Box 32, Stephenson, MI, 49887 (906) 753-2231
Licensure Intermediate Care. *Beds* 73. *Certified* Medicaid.
Admissions Requirements Minimum age 18; Medical examination; Physician's request.
Staff RNs 1 (ft); LPNs 3 (ft), 4 (pt); Nurses aides 42 (ft), 12 (pt); Activities coordinators 1 (ft), 2 (pt); Dietitians 1 (pt).
Facilities Dining room; Activities room; Crafts room; Laundry room; Barber/Beauty shop.
Activities Arts and Crafts; Cards; Games; Reading groups; Prayer groups; Movies; Shopping trips; Dances/Social or cultural gatherings.
Description Facility is located in a small rural town with many long-term residents of the area as staff; this highly dedicated staff have many of their own relations in the home.

STERLING

Greenbriar Nursing Home
500 School Rd, Sterling, MI, 48659
Admin John H Swaffield. *Medical Dir/Dir of Nursing* Gordon A Page Jr MD.
Licensure Skilled Care; Intermediate Care. *Beds* 104. *Certified* Medicaid; Medicare. *Ownership* Proprietary.
Admissions Requirements Minimum age 15.

Staff Physical therapists 1 (pt); Occupational therapists 1 (pt); Speech therapists 1 (pt); Activities coordinators 1 (ft); Dietitians 1 (ft).
Facilities Dining room; Physical therapy room; Activities room; Chapel; Crafts room; Laundry room; Barber/Beauty shop.
Activities Arts and Crafts; Cards; Games; Reading groups; Prayer groups; Movies; Shopping trips.

STERLING HEIGHTS

Nightingale North*
14151 15 Mile, Sterling Heights, MI, 48077 (313) 939-0200
Licensure Skilled Care; Intermediate Care. *Beds* 257. *Certified* Medicaid; Medicare.

STOCKBRIDGE

Geriatric Center—Stockbridge*
406 W Main St, Stockbridge, MI, 49285 (517) 851-7700
Licensure Intermediate Care. *Beds* 53. *Certified* Medicaid.

STURGIS

Froh Community Home
308 Spruce, Sturgis, MI, 49091 (616) 651-8661
Medical Dir/Dir of Nursing Dr Olin Lepard.
Licensure Skilled Care; Intermediate Care. *Beds* 118. *Certified* Medicaid; Medicare.
Admissions Requirements Minimum age 16; Medical examination; Physician's request.
Staff RNs 1 (ft), 2 (pt); LPNs 5 (ft), 3 (pt); Orderlies 3 (ft); Nurses aides 38 (ft), 15 (pt); Activities coordinators 1 (ft).
Affiliation Mennonite
Facilities Dining room; Physical therapy room; Activities room; Chapel; Laundry room; Barber/Beauty shop.
Activities Movies.
Description Facility prepares float for Michigan Week; rocking chair for American Heart Association.

TAWAS CITY

Iosco County Medical Care Facility*
1201 Harris Ave, Tawas City, MI, 48763 (517) 362-4424
Licensure Skilled Care; Intermediate Care. *Beds* 64. *Certified* Medicaid; Medicare. *Ownership* Public.

Provinical House—Tawas City*
400 W North St, Tawas City, MI, 48763 (517) 362-8645
Licensure Skilled Care; Intermediate Care. *Beds* 120. *Certified* Medicaid; Medicare.

TAYLOR

Park Nursing Center Inc*
12575 Telegraph Rd, Taylor, MI, 48180 (313) 287-4710
Licensure Skilled Care; Intermediate Care. *Beds* 265. *Certified* Medicaid; Medicare.

Pine Knoll Convalescent Center*
23600 Northline Rd, Taylor, MI, 48180 (313)
287-8580
Licensure Skilled Care; Intermediate Care.
Beds 142. *Certified* Medicaid; Medicare.

Taylor Total Living Center*
22950 Northline Rd, Taylor, MI, 48180
Licensure Intermediate Care. *Beds* 150. *Certified* Medicaid.

TECUMSEH

Herrick Nursing Home
500 E Pottawatomie, Tecumseh, MI, 49286
(517) 423-2141
Medical Dir/Dir of Nursing George Promstaller DO.
Licensure Intermediate Care. *Beds* 25. *Certified* Medicaid.
Staff RNs; LPNs; Orderlies; Nurses aides;
Physical therapists; Occupational therapists;
Speech therapists; Activities coordinators; Dietitians.
Facilities Dining room; Activities room; Chapel; Laundry room; Barber/Beauty shop.
Activities Arts and Crafts; Cards; Games;
Reading groups; Prayer groups.
Description Home includes a 6-bed rehabilitation program for intensive daily therapeutic
regimen, primarily for closed head injury
patients.

THREE RIVERS

River Forest Nursing Care*
55378 Wilbur Rd, Three Rivers, MI, 49093
(616) 273-8385
Licensure Skilled Care; Intermediate Care.
Beds 87. *Certified* Medicaid; Medicare.

Three Rivers Manor
517 Erie St, Three Rivers, MI, 49093 (616)
273-8661
Medical Dir/Dir of Nursing B Mutnal MD.
Licensure Skilled Care; Intermediate Care.
Beds 100. *Certified* Medicaid; Medicare.
Admissions Requirements Minimum age 17.
Facilities Dining room; Physical therapy room;
Activities room; Chapel; Crafts room; Laundry
room; Barber/Beauty shop.
Activities Arts and Crafts; Cards; Games;
Reading groups; Prayer groups; Movies; Dances/Social or cultural gatherings.

TRAVERSE CITY

Birchwood Nursing Center*
2950 LaFranier Rd, Traverse City, MI, 49684
(616) 947-0506
Licensure Skilled Care; Intermediate Care.
Beds 155. *Certified* Medicaid; Medicare.

Grand Traverse County Medical Care Facility
410 S Elwood, Traverse City, MI, 49684 (616)
947-4750
Medical Dir/Dir of Nursing Robert Johnson
MD.
Licensure Skilled Care; Intermediate Care.
Beds 181. *Certified* Medicaid; Medicare.
Staff Physicians 1 (pt); RNs 10 (ft), 5 (pt);

LPNs 10 (ft), 10 (pt); Orderlies 5 (ft), 5 (pt);
Nurses aides 75 (ft), 25 (pt).
Facilities Dining room; Physical therapy room;
Activities room; Chapel; Crafts room; Laundry
room; Barber/Beauty shop; Library.
Activities Arts and Crafts; Cards; Games;
Reading groups; Prayer groups; Movies; Shopping trips; Dances/Social or cultural gatherings.

Provincial House—Traverse City*
2585 S LaFranier Rd, Traverse City, MI, 49684
(616) 947-9511
Licensure Skilled Care; Intermediate Care.
Beds 120. *Certified* Medicaid; Medicare.

Traverse Geriatric Village*
2828 Concord, Traverse City, MI, 49684 (616)
941-1200
Licensure Intermediate Care. *Beds* 96. *Certified* Medicaid; Medicare.

TRENTON

Balmoral Skilled Nursing Home
5500 Fort St, Trenton, MI, 48183 (313)
675-1600
Medical Dir/Dir of Nursing Dr S Kwasiborski.
Licensure Skilled Care; Intermediate Care.
Beds 209. *Certified* Medicaid; Medicare.
Admissions Requirements Minimum age 16.
Staff Physicians 50 (pt); RNs 5 (ft), 6 (pt);
LPNs 7 (ft), 7 (pt); Nurses aides 51 (ft), 14 (pt);
Physical therapists 1 (ft); Occupational therapists 1 (pt); Speech therapists 1 (pt); Activities
coordinators 1 (ft); Dietitians 1 (ft); Dentists 1
(pt); Ophthalmologists 1 (pt); Podiatrists 1 (pt).
Facilities Dining room; Physical therapy room;
Activities room; Laundry room; Barber/Beauty
shop; Library.
Activities Arts and Crafts; Cards; Games; Prayer groups; Movies; Dances/Social or cultural
gatherings; Classes; Cooking.
Description There is a courtyard enjoyed all
year round; day care children in facility interact
with residents; family night programs for each
station; dinners for new residents and 2 members of family.

Trenton Convalescent Center*
406 Elm St, Trenton, MI, 48183 (313) 676-3232
Licensure Intermediate Care. *Beds* 51. *Certified* Medicaid.

UNION LAKE

Orchard Lake Resthaven*
Box 317, 4260 Forbush, Union Lake, MI,
48085 (313) 363-7161
Licensure Intermediate Care. *Beds* 40. *Certified* Medicaid.

Orchard Lake Resthaven*
4260 Forbush, Box 317, Union Lake, MI,
48085
Licensure Intermediate Care. *Beds* 40.

West Winds Nursing Home
10765 Bogie Lake Rd, Union Lake, MI, 48085
(313) 363-9400
Admin Daniel C Page. *Medical Dir/Dir of
Nursing* J J Johnstone DO.

Licensure Intermediate Care. *Beds* 50. *Certified* Medicaid.
Admissions Requirements Minimum age 60.
Staff Physicians 2 (pt); RNs 7 (ft); LPNs 3 (ft);
Nurses aides 13 (ft), 24 (pt); Physical therapists;
Reality therapists; Recreational therapists;
Occupational therapists; Speech therapists;
Activities coordinators 1 (ft); Dietitians 1 (pt);
Dentists; Ophthalmologists; Podiatrists;
Audiologists.
Facilities Dining room; Activities room; Crafts
room; Laundry room; Barber/Beauty shop.
Activities Arts and Crafts; Cards; Games;
Reading groups; Prayer groups; Movies; Dances/Social or cultural gatherings.

UTICA

Wil Mar Convalescent Home*
45305 Cass Ave, Utica, MI, 48087
Licensure Intermediate Care. *Beds* 52. *Certified* Medicaid.

WAKEFIELD

Gogebic County Medical Care Facility
Rt 1, Box 3, Wakefield, MI, 49968 (906)
224-9811
Medical Dir/Dir of Nursing Bruce D Gordon
MD.
Licensure Skilled Care; Intermediate Care.
Beds 109. *Certified* Medicaid; Medicare.
Admissions Requirements Minimum age 15;
Medical examination; Physician's request.
Staff Physicians 6 (pt); RNs 3 (ft), 5 (pt); LPNs
5 (ft), 7 (pt); Orderlies 1 (ft), 1 (pt); Nurses aides
42 (ft), 18 (pt); Physical therapists 1 (ft), 1 (pt);
Reality therapists 2 (ft); Recreational therapists
1 (ft), 2 (pt); Activities coordinators 1 (ft); Dietitians 1 (ft); Dentists 1 (ft), 1 (pt); Ophthalmologists 1 (pt); Podiatrists 1 (pt); Audiologists
1 (pt).
Facilities Dining room; Physical therapy room;
Activities room; Chapel; Crafts room; Laundry
room; Barber/Beauty shop; Library.
Activities Arts and Crafts; Games; Reading
groups; Prayer groups; Movies; Shopping trips;
Dances/Social or cultural gatherings.

WARREN

Abbey Convalescent and Nursing Home
12250 E 12 Mile Rd, Warren, MI, 48093 (313)
751-6200
Admin Juanita A Majishe. *Medical Dir/Dir of
Nursing* Barry Szczesny DO.
Licensure Skilled Care; Intermediate Care.
Beds 201. *Certified* Medicaid; Medicare.
Admissions Requirements Minimum age 21;
Medical examination; Physician's request.
Staff Physicians; RNs 12 (ft); LPNs 14 (ft);
Nurses aides 40 (ft), 25 (pt); Physical therapists
1 (pt); Recreational therapists 2 (ft); Speech
therapists 1 (pt); Activities coordinators 1 (ft);
Dietitians 1 (pt); Dentists 1 (pt); Ophthalmologists 1 (pt); Podiatrists 1 (pt); Audiologists 1
(pt).
Facilities Dining room; Physical therapy room;
Activities room; Laundry room; Barber/Beauty
shop.
Activities Arts and Crafts; Cards; Games;

Reading groups; Prayer groups; Movies; Shopping trips; Dances/Social or cultural gatherings. *Description* Facility is located in a suburban area, newly renovated, situated all on one floor; offers pet program and family night for residents.

Nightingale East Nursing Home*
11525 E 10 Mile Rd, Warren, MI, 48089 (313) 759-0700
Licensure Skilled Care; Intermediate Care. *Beds* 185. *Certified* Medicaid; Medicare.

Saint Anthony Nursing Center*
31830 Ryan Rd, Warren, MI, 48092 (313) 977-6700
Licensure Skilled Care; Intermediate Care. *Beds* 72. *Certified* Medicaid; Medicare. *Affiliation* Roman Catholic

Warren Village*
11700 E 10 Mile Rd, Warren, MI, 48089 (313) 759-5960
Licensure Skilled Care; Intermediate Care. *Beds* 304. *Certified* Medicaid; Medicare.

WAYLAND

Sandy Creek Nursing Center
425 E Elm St, Wayland, MI, 49348 (616) 792-2249
Admin Evelyn Hampel. *Medical Dir/Dir of Nursing* Dale Kniper DO.
Licensure Skilled Care; Intermediate Care. *Beds* 99. *Certified* Medicaid; Medicare. *Admissions Requirements* Minimum age 16; Medical examination.
Staff RNs 4 (ft), 5 (pt); LPNs 4 (ft), 4 (pt); Nurses aides 38 (ft), 37 (pt); Activities coordinators 3 (ft).
Facilities Dining room; Physical therapy room; Activities room; Laundry room; Barber/Beauty shop; TV lounges.
Activities Arts and Crafts; Games; Reading groups; Prayer groups; Movies.

WAYNE

Venoy Continued Care Center*
3999 Venoy Rd, Wayne, MI, 48184 (313) 326-6600
Licensure Skilled Care; Intermediate Care. *Beds* 210. *Certified* Medicaid; Medicare.

Wayne Convalescent Center
34330 Van Born Rd, Wayne, MI, 48184 (313) 721-0740
Medical Dir/Dir of Nursing Fredrick Kroot DO.
Licensure Intermediate Care. *Beds* 53. *Certified* Medicaid.
Admissions Requirements Minimum age 15; Medical examination; Physician's request.
Staff RNs 2 (ft); LPNs 4 (ft), 2 (pt); Orderlies 3 (ft); Nurses aides 30 (ft), 10 (pt); Recreational therapists 1 (ft), Speech therapists; Activities coordinators 1 (ft); Dietitians; Dentists; Ophthalmologists; Podiatrists.

Wayne Total Living Center*
4427 Venoy Rd, Wayne, MI, 48184
Licensure Intermediate Care. *Beds* 150. *Certified* Medicaid.

WEST BLOOMFIELD

West Bloomfield Geriatric Center
6470 Alden Dr, West Bloomfield, MI, 48033 (313) 363-4121
Admin F Taker. *Medical Dir/Dir of Nursing* Dr J Janicke.
Licensure Intermediate Care. *Beds* 56. *Certified* Medicaid.
Admissions Requirements Minimum age 21.
Staff Physicians 1 (ft); RNs 1 (ft), 3 (pt), LPNs 2 (ft), 4 (pt); Nurses aides 35 (ft); Activities coordinators 1 (ft); Dietitians 1 (pt); Dentists 1 (pt); Ophthalmologists 1 (pt); Podiatrists 1 (pt).
Facilities Dining room; Barber/Beauty shop.
Activities Arts and Crafts; Games; Reading groups; Prayer groups; Movies.
Description Facility is located on 10 acres, gently rolling, heavily wooded lot across street from lake. Provides quality care, diversional activities, all in gentle atmosphere.

WEST BRANCH

West Branch Geriatric Village*
445 S Valley St, West Branch, MI, 48661 (313) 345-3600
Licensure Intermediate Care. *Beds* 93. *Certified* Medicaid.

WESTLAND

Four Chaplains Convalescent Home
28349 Joy Rd, Westland, MI, 48185 (313) 261-9500
Medical Dir/Dir of Nursing Dr Jack Mayer.
Licensure Skilled Care; Intermediate Care. *Beds* 111. *Certified* Medicaid; Medicare.
Admissions Requirements Medical examination; Physician's request.
Staff Physicians 3 (pt); RNs 4 (ft), 2 (pt); LPNs 5 (ft), 11 (pt); Orderlies 4 (ft), 2 (pt); Nurses aides 39 (ft), 12 (pt); Physical therapists 4 (pt); Occupational therapists 2 (pt); Speech therapists 2 (pt); Activities coordinators 3 (pt); Dietitians 1 (pt); Dentists 1 (pt); Ophthalmologists 1 (pt); Podiatrists 1 (pt); Audiologists 1 (pt).
Facilities Dining room; Physical therapy room; Activities room; Chapel; Crafts room; Laundry room; Barber/Beauty shop; Library.
Activities Arts and Crafts; Cards; Games; Reading groups; Prayer groups; Movies; Shopping trips; Dances/Social or cultural gatherings; Exercises; Current events; Cooking classes.
Description Facility has very large, beautifully manicured grounds; elegantly furnished; separate dining facilities for alert; silver tea cart for service of snacks to room-bound; in-house laundry; certified nurses aides; limousine service for outpatient dentistry, ophthalmology, and x-ray; van for transportation; pet therapy, resident cat.

Middlebelt-Hope Nursing Center
38410 Cherry Hill Rd, Westland, MI, 48184 (313) 326-1200

Admin Patricia Ostland. *Medical Dir/Dir of Nursing* J Mobladi MD.
Licensure Skilled Care; Intermediate Care. *Beds* 142. *Certified* Medicaid; Medicare.
Admissions Requirements Minimum age 15; Physician's request.
Staff Physicians 2 (ft); RNs 6 (ft), 2 (pt); LPNs 7 (ft), 5 (pt); Orderlies 2 (ft); Nurses aides 54 (ft), 27 (pt); Physical therapists 1 (ft); Reality therapists 3 (ft); Recreational therapists 3 (ft); Occupational therapists 1 (ft); Speech therapists 1 (ft); Activities coordinators 1 (ft); Dietitians 1 (pt); Dentists 1 (pt); Podiatrists 1 (pt).
Facilities Dining room; Physical therapy room; Activities room; Crafts room; Laundry room; Barber/Beauty shop; TV room.
Activities Arts and Crafts; Cards; Games; Reading groups; Prayer groups; Movies; Dances/Social or cultural gatherings; Picnics.
Description Facility offers personal and individualized care to meet each resident's lifestyle and preferences.

Nightingale West*
8365 Newburgh Rd, Westland, MI, 48185 (313) 261-5300
Licensure Skilled Care; Intermediate Care. *Beds* 236. *Certified* Medicaid; Medicare.

Westland Convalescent Center
36137 W Warren, Westland, MI, 48185 (313) 728-6100
Medical Dir/Dir of Nursing Leonard Rosenberg.
Licensure Skilled Care; Intermediate Care. *Beds* 230. *Certified* Medicaid; Medicare.
Admissions Requirements Minimum age 15; Medical examination; Physician's request.
Staff RNs 20 (ft), 6 (pt); LPNs 16 (ft), 4 (pt); Orderlies 10 (ft); Nurses aides 150 (ft); Physical therapists 1 (ft); Reality therapists 4 (ft); Occupational therapists 1 (ft); Speech therapists 1 (ft); Activities coordinators 3 (ft); Dietitians 2 (ft); Dentists 1 (pt); Ophthalmologists 1 (pt); Podiatrists 2 (pt); Audiologists 1 (pt).
Facilities Dining room; Physical therapy room; Activities room; Crafts room; Laundry room; Barber/Beauty shop; Library.
Activities Arts and Crafts; Reading groups; Prayer groups; Movies; Shopping trips; Dances/Social or cultural gatherings.

WHITEHALL

Whitehall Manor
916 Lewis St, Whitehall, MI, 49461 (616) 894-4056
Medical Dir/Dir of Nursing Albert Engstrom MD.
Licensure Skilled Care; Intermediate Care. *Beds* 125. *Certified* Medicaid; Medicare.
Admissions Requirements Minimum age 15; Medical examination; Physician's request.
Staff Physicians 7 (pt); RNs 3 (ft), 4 (pt); LPNs 7 (ft), 16 (pt); Orderlies 2 (pt); Nurses aides 43 (ft), 25 (pt); Physical therapists 1 (pt); Occupational therapists 1 (pt); Speech therapists 1 (pt); Activities coordinators 1 (ft); Dietitians 1 (pt); Dentists 1 (pt); Podiatrists 1 (pt); Audiologists 1 (pt).
Facilities Dining room; Physical therapy room; Activities room; Crafts room; Laundry room;

Barber/Beauty shop.
Activities Arts and Crafts; Cards; Games; Reading groups; Prayer groups; Movies; Shopping trips; Dances/Social or cultural gatherings.
Description Facility is located in a lovely country setting on the outskirts of a small community; includes 15 acres surrounded by trees and a stream.

WHITMORE LAKE

Whitmore Lake Convalescent Center
8633 N Main St, Whitmore Lake, MI, 48189 (313) 449-4431
Medical Dir/Dir of Nursing George Fischmann MD.
Licensure Skilled Care; Intermediate Care. *Beds* 212. *Certified* Medicaid; Medicare.
Staff RNs 3 (ft), 5 (pt); LPNs 12 (ft), 7 (pt); Orderlies 12 (ft); Nurses aides 47 (ft), 17 (pt); Activities coordinators 1 (ft), 2 (pt); Dietitians 10 (ft), 10 (pt).
Facilities Dining room; Physical therapy room; Activities room; Chapel; Crafts room; Laundry room; Barber/Beauty shop; Library; Privacy room.
Activities Arts and Crafts; Cards; Games; Reading groups; Prayer groups; Movies; Dances/Social or cultural gatherings; GED program.
Description Facility features an excellent activities program; beds all on main floor; picnic area which is wheelchair accessible; full-time social worker; gift shop; full-time physical and occupational therapists on staff.

WOODHAVEN

Applewood Nursing Center
18500 Van Horn Rd, Woodhaven, MI, 48183 (313) 676-7575
Medical Dir/Dir of Nursing Craig Kwalton DO.
Licensure Skilled Care; Intermediate Care. *Beds* 150. *Certified* Medicaid; Medicare.
Admissions Requirements Medical examination; Physician's request.
Facilities Dining room; Physical therapy room; Activities room; Crafts room; Laundry room; Barber/Beauty shop.
Activities Arts and Crafts; Cards; Games; Reading groups; Prayer groups; Movies; Dances/Social or cultural gatherings.

WYOMING

Holland Home—Crestview Nursing Center*
625 36th St, Wyoming, MI, 49509 (616) 531-0200
Licensure Intermediate Care. *Beds* 120. *Certified* Medicaid.

YALE

Medilodge of Yale*
90 Jean St, Yale, MI, 48097 (313) 387-3226
Licensure Skilled Care. *Beds* 88. *Certified* Medicaid; Medicare.

YPSILANTI

Evergreen Hills Nursing Center*
1045 Ware Court, Ypsilanti, MI, 48197 (313) 483-5421
Licensure Intermediate Care. *Beds* 108. *Certified* Medicaid.

Gilbert Old People's Home
203 S Huron St, Ypsilanti, MI, 48197 (313) 482-9498
Medical Dir/Dir of Nursing William Barss MD.
Licensure Intermediate Care. *Beds* 32. *Certified* Medicaid.
Admissions Requirements Minimum age 65; Medical examination.
Facilities Dining room; Activities room; Laundry room; Barber/Beauty shop; Library.
Activities Arts and Crafts; Games; Prayer groups; Movies; Shopping trips.

Huron Valley Mens Facility*
3201 Bemis Rd, Ypsilanti, MI, 48197
Licensure Intermediate Care. *Beds* 16.

Kith Haven—Ypsilanti*
28 S Prospect St, Ypsilanti, MI, 48197 (313) 483-6125
Licensure Skilled Care; Intermediate Care. *Beds* 180. *Certified* Medicaid; Medicare.

ZEELAND

Haven Park Nursing Center*
285 N State St, Zeeland, MI, 49464 (616) 772-4641
Licensure Skilled Care; Intermediate Care. *Beds* 153. *Certified* Medicaid; Medicare.

Wood Haven Nursing Home
320 E Central Ave, Zeeland, MI, 49464 (616) 772-9191
Licensure Intermediate Care. *Beds* 45. *Certified* Medicaid.
Admissions Requirements Medical examination; Physician's request.
Staff RNs 1 (ft); LPNs 2 (ft), 8 (pt); Nurses aides 10 (ft), 25 (pt); Activities coordinators 1 (ft); Dietitians 1 (ft).
Facilities Dining room; Activities room; Crafts room; Laundry room; Library.
Activities Arts and Crafts; Cards; Games; Reading groups; Prayer groups; Movies; Dances/Social or cultural gatherings.

MINNESOTA

ADA

Ada Municipal Hospital*
405 E 2nd Ave, Ada, MN, 56510 (218) 784-2561
Admin Robert Cameron.
Licensure Intermediate Care. *Beds* 53. *Certified* Medicaid; Medicare.
Ownership Public.

Project New Hope-Ada 2*
21 E 4th Ave, Ada, MN, 58510 (218) 784-2217
Admin Glenn Medicraft.
Licensure Intermediate Care for Mentally Retarded. *Beds* 6. *Certified* Medicaid.
Ownership Nonprofit.

Project New Hope-Ada I*
207 Jamison Dr, Ada, MN, 56510 (218) 784-2717
Admin Glenn Medicraft.
Licensure Intermediate Care for Mentally Retarded. *Beds* 6. *Certified* Medicaid.
Ownership Nonprofit.

ADAMS

Adams Group Home*
PO Box 344, 407 6th St NW, Adams, MN, 55909 (507 582-3482
Admin Roy Harley.
Licensure Intermediate Care. *Beds* 16. *Certified* Medicaid.
Ownership Nonprofit.

Adams Health Care Center*
Rt 2, Box 300, Adams, MN, 55909 (507) 582-3263
Admin James Thalberg.
Licensure Skilled Care; Intermediate Care.
Beds SNF 55; ICF 11. *Certified* Medicaid.
Ownership Public.

ADRIAN

Arnold Memorial Hospital
601 Louisiana Ave, Adrian, MN, 56110
Admin Charlotte Heitkamp. *Medical Dir/Dir of Nursing* L A Laikola MD.
Licensure Intermediate Care. *Certified* Medicaid.
Ownership Nonprofit.
Admissions Requirements Medical examina-

tion; Physician's request.
Staff RNs 1 (pt); LPNs 2 (ft), 2 (pt); Nurses aides 3 (ft), 15 (pt); Recreational therapists 2 (pt); Activities coordinators 1 (ft).
Facilities Dining room; Activities room; Chapel; Crafts room; Laundry room; Barber/Beauty shop; Library.
Activities Arts and Crafts; Cards; Games; Reading groups; Prayer groups; Movies.

AH GWAH CHING

Ah Gwah Ching Nursing Home*
Ah Gwah Ching, MN, 56430 (218) 547-1250
Admin James R Wall.
Licensure Skilled Care; Intermediate Care.
Beds SNF 179; ICF 164. *Certified* Medicaid.
Ownership Public.

AITKIN

Aicota Nursing Home
820 2nd St SW, Aitkin, MN, 56431 (218) 927-2164
Admin Jere Cluff.
Licensure Skilled Care; Intermediate Care.
Beds 106. *Certified* Medicaid.
Ownership Proprietary.

ALBANY

Mother of Mercy Nursing Home*
Box R, Albany, MN, 56307 (612) 845-2195
Admin Patrick F Mitchell.
Licensure Skilled Care; Intermediate Care.
Beds SNF 57; ICF 5. *Certified* Medicaid.
Ownership Nonprofit.
Affiliation Roman Catholic

ALBERT LEA

Albert Lea Boarding Care Home
315 Park Ave, Albert Lea, MN, 56007 (507) 373-9616
Admin Myrtly Dahl.
Licensure Boarding Care. *Beds* 21.
Ownership Proprietary.
Admissions Requirements Medical examination; Physician's request.
Staff RNs 1 (ft); LPNs 1 (ft); Nurses aides 13 (ft); Activities coordinators 1 (pt); Dietitians 1 (pt).

Facilities Dining room; Laundry room.
Activities Arts and Crafts; Cards; Games; Reading groups; Prayer groups; Movies; Shopping trips.

Albert Lea Good Samaritan Center
Rt 2, PO Box 217, Albert Lea, MN, 56007 (507) 373-0684
Admin Dan L Hanson. *Medical Dir/Dir of Nursing* Dr Thoburn Thompson.
Licensure Skilled Care; Intermediate Care; Boarding Care. *Beds* 182. *Certified* Medicaid.
Ownership Nonprofit.
Admissions Requirements Minimum age 16; Medical examination; Physician's request.
Staff RNs 2 (ft), 9 (pt); LPNs 4 (ft), 7 (pt); Orderlies 1 (pt); Nurses aides 21 (ft), 83 (pt); Physical therapists 1 (pt); Recreational therapists 4 (ft); Activities coordinators 1 (ft); Dietitians 1 (ft).
Affiliation Lutheran
Facilities Dining room; Physical therapy room; Activities room; Chapel; Crafts room; Laundry room; Barber/Beauty shop; Library.
Activities Arts and Crafts; Cards; Games; Reading groups; Prayer groups; Movies; Shopping trips; Dances/Social or cultural gatherings.
Description Facility features an active volunteer program; religious services each Sunday; daily devotions; bus and van with wheelchair lift; several outings and outdoor activities for all residents. Adult day-care, hospice programs are available. Excellent physical therapy program.

Albert Lea Health Care Center*
617 10th St, Albert Lea, MN, 56007 (507) 373-7600
Admin David J Blum.
Licensure Skilled Care. *Beds* 28. *Certified* Medicaid.
Ownership Proprietary.

Broadway Care Home
512 S Broadway, Albert Lea, MN, 56007
Admin A Frazier.
Licensure Boarding Care. *Beds* 11.
Ownership Proprietary.
Admissions Requirements Medical examination; Physician's request.
Staff RNs 1 (pt); LPNs 1 (ft); Nurses aides 5 (ft); Dietitians 1 (pt).
Facilities Dining room; Activities room; Laundry room.
Activities Arts and Crafts; Cards; Games;

Reading groups; Prayer groups; Movies; Shopping trips; Dances/Social or cultural gatherings. *Description* Home is like a large family with emphasis on each individual and one-to-one relationships; residents are catered to with regard to their preferences in food servings and social activities.

Crest Home of Albert Lea*
1205 Garfield Ave, Albert Lea, MN, 56007 (507) 373-0188
Admin Irene Scott.
Licensure Intermediate Care for Mentally Retarded. *Beds* 15. *Certified* Medicaid.
Ownership Nonprofit.

Norstrude Guest Home*
601 E 5th St, Albert Lea, MN, 56007 (507) 373-3691
Admin Ellen N Evans.
Licensure Boarding Care. *Beds* 9.
Ownership Proprietary.

Saint Johns Lutheran Home
901 Luther Place, Albert Lea, MN, 56007 (507) 373-8226
Admin Clifford R Paulsen. *Medical Dir/Dir of Nursing* L E Shelhamer MD.
Licensure Skilled Care; Intermediate Care.
Beds 206. *Certified* Medicaid.
Ownership Nonprofit.
Admissions Requirements Minimum age 21; Medical examination; Physician's request.
Staff RNs 7 (ft), 9 (pt); LPNs 4 (ft), 13 (pt); Orderlies 1 (pt); Nurses aides 45 (ft), 60 (pt); Physical therapists 3 (ft); Occupational therapists 2 (ft), 2 (pt); Speech therapists 1 (pt); Activities coordinators 1 (pt); Dietitians 1 (ft).
Affiliation Lutheran
Facilities Dining room; Physical therapy room; Activities room; Chapel; Crafts room; Laundry room; Barber/Beauty shop; Library.
Activities Arts and Crafts; Cards; Games; Reading groups; Prayer groups; Movies; Shopping trips; Dances/Social or cultural gatherings.

Thorne Crest Retirement Center
1201 Garfield Ave, Albert Lea, MN, 56007 (507) 373-2311
Admin Dale L Rippey.
Licensure Skilled Care; Intermediate Care.
Beds 52. *Certified* Medicaid.
Ownership Nonprofit.
Admissions Requirements Medical examination.
Staff RNs 3 (ft), 5 (pt); LPNs 2 (ft), 4 (pt); Orderlies 1 (pt); Nurses aides 10 (ft), 20 (pt); Activities coordinators 1 (ft), 2 (pt).
Affiliation Baptist
Facilities Dining room; Physical therapy room; Activities room; Chapel; Crafts room; Laundry room; Barber/Beauty shop; Library.
Activities Arts and Crafts; Cards; Games; Reading groups; Prayer groups; Movies; Shopping trips; Dances/Social or cultural gatherings.
Description Facility includes 98 apartments for independent living with 52-bed health care center attached.

Woodvale V*
1204 Plainview Ln, Albert Lea, MN, 56007 (507) 373-7629
Admin Walter Baldus.

Licensure Intermediate Care for Mentally Retarded. *Beds* 32. *Certified* Medicaid.
Ownership Proprietary.

Woodvale VII*
PO Box 650, 1432 Spartan Ave, Albert Lea, MN, 56007 (507) 373-7629
Admin Walter Baldus.
Licensure Skilled Care; Intermediate Care.
Beds SNF 10; ICF 10. *Certified* Medicaid.
Ownership Proprietary.

ALEXANDRIA

Bethany Home*
1020 Lark St, Alexandria, MN, 56308 (612) 763-3105
Admin Ervin C Malm.
Licensure Skilled Care; Intermediate Care.
Beds SNF 90; ICF 91. *Certified* Medicaid.
Ownership Nonprofit.

Knute Nelson Memorial Home*
420 12th Ave E, Alexandria, MN, 56308 (612) 763-6653
Admin T Arnold Thompson.
Licensure Skilled Care; Intermediate Care.
Beds SNF 97; ICF 70. *Certified* Medicaid.
Ownership Nonprofit.

Project New Hope 6*
3401 S Broadway, Alexandria, MN, 56308 (612) 762-2349
Admin Glenn Medicraft.
Licensure Intermediate Care for Mentally Retarded. *Beds* 6. *Certified* Medicaid.
Ownership Nonprofit.

Project New Hope 7*
3401 S Broadway, Alexandria, MN, 56308 (612) 762-2349
Admin Glenn Medicraft.
Licensure Intermediate Care for Mentally Retarded. *Beds* 6. *Certified* Medicaid.
Ownership Nonprofit.

Project New Hope Inc*
3401 S Broadway, Alexandria, MN, 56308 (612) 762-2349
Admin Glenn Medicraft.
Licensure Intermediate Care for Mentally Retarded. *Beds* 30. *Certified* Medicaid.
Ownership Nonprofit.

ANNANDALE

Annandale Care Center*
RR 4, Box 57, Hwy 24 E, Annandale, MN, 55302 (612) 274-3737
Admin John Nelson.
Licensure Skilled Care; Intermediate Care.
Beds SNF 41; ICF 19. *Certified* Medicaid; Medicare.
Ownership Proprietary.

ANOKA

Anoka Maple Manor Care Center*
1040 Madison St, Anoka, MN, 55303 (612) 421-2311
Admin Eunice Taylor.

Licensure Skilled Care; Intermediate Care.
Beds SNF 71; ICF 54. *Certified* Medicaid; Medicare.
Ownership Proprietary.

Anoka State Hospital
Box 511, Anoka, MN, 55303 (612) 421-3940
Admin W Lightburn.
Licensure Intermediate Care for Mentally Retarded. *Beds* 147. *Certified* Medicaid.
Ownership Public.

Twin Rivers Care Center
305 Fremont St, Anoka, MN, 55303 (612) 421-5660
Admin B Christen. *Medical Dir/Dir of Nursing* K M Kubasch.
Licensure Skilled Care; Intermediate Care.
Beds 66. *Certified* Medicaid.
Ownership Proprietary.
Admissions Requirements Minimum age 16; Medical examination.
Staff Physicians; RNs 4 (ft), 2 (pt); LPNs 1 (ft), 3 (pt); Nurses aides 13 (ft), 13 (pt); Physical therapists 1 (ft); Recreational therapists 2 (pt); Occupational therapists 1 (ft); Speech therapists 1 (pt); Activities coordinators 1 (ft); Dietitians 1 (pt); Dentists; Ophthalmologists 2 (pt); Podiatrists 1 (pt); Audiologists 1 (pt).
Facilities Dining room; Physical therapy room; Activities room; Crafts room; Laundry room; Barber/Beauty shop.
Activities Arts and Crafts; Cards; Games; Reading groups; Prayer groups; Movies; Shopping trips; Dances/Social or cultural gatherings.
Description Twin Rivers is located 5 blocks west of downtown Anoka. Provides physical, occupational, speech, and recreational therapy as well as skilled and intermediate nursing care.

APPLETON

Appleton Municipal Hospital*
300 S Behl St, Appleton, MN, 56208 (612) 189-2422
Admin Genevieve Robbins.
Licensure Skilled Care; Intermediate Care.
Beds SNF 40; ICF 44. *Certified* Medicaid.
Ownership Public.

ARDEN HILLS

Acr Homes on Cummings*
1385 Cummings Ln, Arden Hills, MN, 55112 (612) 636-7537
Admin James Nelson.
Licensure Intermediate Care for Mentally Retarded. *Beds* 6. *Certified* Medicaid.
Ownership Proprietary.

Presbyterian Homes
3220 Lake Johanna Blvd, Arden Hills, MN, 55112 (612) 631-1024
Admin William Hagstrom. *Medical Dir/Dir of Nursing* Robert Blomberg MD.
Licensure Skilled Care; Intermediate Care; Boarding Care. *Beds* SNF 158; ICF 50; Boarding Care 18. *Certified* Medicaid; Medicare.
Ownership Nonprofit.
Admissions Requirements Medical examina-

tion.
Staff Physicians 9 (pt); RNs 13 (ft), 29 (pt); LPNs 4 (ft), 6 (pt); Nurses aides 45 (ft), 49 (pt); Physical therapists 1 (ft), 1 (pt); Recreational therapists 1 (ft); Occupational therapists 1 (pt); Speech therapists 1 (pt); Activities coordinators 1 (ft); Dietitians 1 (ft); Dentists 3 (pt); Podiatrists 1 (pt); Audiologists 1 (pt).
Affiliation Presbyterian
Facilities Dining room; Physical therapy room; Activities room; Chapel; Crafts room; Laundry room; Barber/Beauty shop; Library.
Activities Arts and Crafts; Cards; Games; Reading groups; Prayer groups; Movies; Shopping trips; Dances/Social or cultural gatherings.

ARLINGTON

Arlington Good Samaritan Center
411 7th Ave NW, Arlington, MN, 55307 (612) 964-2252
Admin Dale Miller.
Licensure Intermediate Care. *Beds* 63. *Certified* Medicaid.
Ownership Nonprofit.
Affiliation Lutheran

ASHBY

Pelican Lake Nursing Home
Ashby, MN, 56309 (218) 747-2929
Admin Roger Odell. *Medical Dir/Dir of Nursing* Larry Rapp DO.
Licensure Skilled Care; Intermediate Care. *Beds* 78. *Certified* Medicaid.
Ownership Proprietary.
Admissions Requirements Medical examination.
Staff Physicians 1 (pt); RNs 3 (ft); LPNs 2 (ft), 5 (pt); Nurses aides 4 (ft), 30 (pt); Activities coordinators 1 (ft), 1 (pt).
Facilities Dining room; Activities room; Crafts room; Laundry room; Barber/Beauty shop.
Activities Arts and Crafts; Cards; Games; Reading groups; Prayer groups; Movies; Dances/Social or cultural gatherings.

ATWATER

Atwater House*
5th and Minnesota Ave, Atwater, MN, 56209 (612) 974-8070
Admin Beverly Helgeson.
Licensure Intermediate Care for Mentally Retarded. *Beds* 15. *Certified* Medicaid.
Ownership Nonprofit.

AURORA

Salmi Boarding Home*
Rt 1, Box 237-B, Aurora, MN, 55705 (218) 638-2990
Admin Clyde E Salmi.
Licensure Intermediate Care for Mentally Retarded. *Beds* 15. *Certified* Medicaid.
Ownership Proprietary.

White Community Hospital*
320 Hwy 110 E, Aurora, MN, 55705 (218) 229-2211

Admin Bernice Stevens.
Licensure Skilled Care; Intermediate Care. *Beds* SNF 28; ICF 43. *Certified* Medicaid; Medicare.
Ownership Nonprofit.

AUSTIN

Agape Halfway House*
200 SW 5th St, Austin, MN, 55912 (507) 433-8819
Admin Robert C Marxen.
Licensure Supervised Living Facility. *Beds* 15.
Ownership Nonprofit.

Burr Oak Manor
400 10th Ave NW, Austin, MN, 55912 (507) 433-7391
Admin Patrick J Rafferty. *Medical Dir/Dir of Nursing* Dr C Jones.
Licensure Skilled Care; Intermediate Care. *Beds* SNF 106; ICF 31. *Certified* Medicaid.
Ownership Proprietary.
Admissions Requirements Minimum age 18.
Staff RNs 3 (ft), 9 (pt); LPNs 2 (ft), 8 (pt); Nurses aides 6 (ft), 69 (pt); Physical therapists 1 (pt); Occupational therapists 1 (pt); Activities coordinators 1 (ft); Dietitians 1 (pt); Dentists 1 (pt).
Facilities Dining room; Physical therapy room; Activities room; Chapel; Crafts room; Laundry room; Barber/Beauty shop.
Activities Arts and Crafts; Cards; Games; Reading groups; Prayer groups; Movies.

Cedar I*
207 SW 1st Ave, Austin, MN, 55912 (507) 433-7301
Admin Walter Baldus.
Licensure Intermediate Care for Mentally Retarded. *Beds* 10. *Certified* Medicaid.
Ownership Proprietary.

Cedar II*
601 13th Ave SE, Austin, MN, 55912 (507) 433-7301
Admin Walter Baldus.
Licensure Intermediate Care for Mentally Retarded. *Beds* 9. *Certified* Medicaid.
Ownership Proprietary.

Cedar III*
1921 6th Ave NW, Austin, MN, 55912 (507) 433-7301
Admin Walter Baldus.
Licensure Intermediate Care for Mentally Retarded. *Beds* 6. *Certified* Medicaid.
Ownership Proprietary.

Cedar IV*
108 16th St SE, Austin, MN, 55912 (507) 433-7301
Admin Walter Baldus.
Licensure Intermediate Care for Mentally Retarded. *Beds* 6. *Certified* Medicaid.
Ownership Proprietary.

Comforcare Center*
205 14th St NW, Austin, MN, 55912 (507) 437-4526
Admin Joe Stanislav.

Licensure Skilled Care; Intermediate Care. *Beds* SNF 43; ICF 2. *Certified* Medicaid.
Ownership Proprietary.

Sacred Heart Hospice
1200 12th St SW, Austin, MN, 55912 (507) 433-1808
Admin Madonna Waletzke. *Medical Dir/Dir of Nursing* Dr Thomas Seery.
Licensure Skilled Care; Intermediate Care. *Beds* SNF 49; ICF 10. *Certified* Medicaid.
Ownership Nonprofit.
Admissions Requirements Physician's request.
Staff RNs 1 (ft), 6 (pt); LPNs 13 (pt); Orderlies 1 (pt); Nurses aides 34 (pt); Recreational therapists 2 (ft); Occupational therapists 1 (ft).
Affiliation Roman Catholic
Description Facility also offers home health care and adult day care.

Saint Marks Lutheran Home
400 15th Ave SW, Austin, MN, 55912 (507) 437-4594
Admin Glenn E Mair. *Medical Dir/Dir of Nursing* Dr Thomas Seery.
Licensure Skilled Care; Intermediate Care. *Beds* SNF 96; ICF 25. *Certified* Medicaid.
Admissions Requirements Minimum age 18; Medical examination; Physician's request.
Staff Physicians 1 (pt); RNs 1 (ft), 14 (pt); LPNs 2 (ft), 13 (pt); Nurses aides 125 (pt); Physical therapists 1 (pt); Recreational therapists 1 (pt); Activities coordinators 1 (pt); Dietitians 1 (pt).
Affiliation Lutheran
Facilities Dining room; Physical therapy room; Activities room; Chapel; Crafts room; Laundry room; Barber/Beauty shop; Library.
Activities Arts and Crafts; Cards; Games; Reading groups; Prayer groups; Movies; Shopping trips; Dances/Social or cultural gatherings.
Description Facility added 48 beds in 1982 within a "house-type" concept with 3 houses of 16 beds each.

Woodvale III
1209 1st St NE, Austin, MN, 55912 (507) 437-7621
Admin Walter A Baldus.
Licensure Supervised Living Facility. *Beds* 41. *Certified* Medicaid.
Ownership Proprietary.
Admissions Requirements Minimum age 18; Medical examination.
Staff RNs 1 (pt); LPNs 1 (ft), 1 (pt); Orderlies 8 (ft), 13 (pt); Recreational therapists 1 (ft).
Facilities Dining room; Laundry room.
Activities Arts and Crafts; Cards; Games; Reading groups; Movies; Shopping trips; Dances/Social or cultural gatherings.

BAGLEY

Greenview Nursing Home
Rt 1, Bagley, MN, 56621 (218) 694-6552
Admin Jan Otness. *Medical Dir/Dir of Nursing* Fred Martin MD.
Licensure Skilled Care. *Beds* 70. *Certified* Medicaid.
Ownership Proprietary.
Admissions Requirements Medical examination; Physician's request.

Staff RNs 5 (ft); LPNs 8 (ft); Nurses aides 20 (ft).
Facilities Dining room; Activities room; Crafts room; Barber/Beauty shop.
Activities Arts and Crafts; Cards; Games; Reading groups; Prayer groups; Movies; Shopping trips; Dances/Social or cultural gatherings.

Pine Ridge Residence*
Box 291, 8th St and Hallan Ave, Bagley, MN, 56621 (218) 694-6716
Admin Don Blooflat.
Licensure Intermediate Care for Mentally Retarded. *Beds* ICF/MR 15. *Certified* Medicaid.
Ownership Nonprofit.

BALATON

Colonial Manor of Balaton*
PO Box 375, Hwy 14 E, Balaton, MN, 56115 (507) 734-3511
Admin Gary L Brink.
Licensure Intermediate Care. *Beds* 78. *Certified* Medicaid.
Ownership Proprietary.

BARNESVILLE

Barnesville Care Center
600 5th St SE, Barnesville, MN, 56514 (218) 354-2254
Admin Betsy Freedland.
Licensure Skilled Care; Intermediate Care. *Beds* 76. *Certified* Medicaid.
Ownership Proprietary.

BARRETT

Barrett Care Center
Barrett, MN, 56311 (612) 528-2527
Admin Betty De Clercq. *Medical Dir/Dir of Nursing* Dr Larry Rapp.
Licensure Intermediate Care. *Beds* 60. *Certified* Medicaid.
Ownership Proprietary.
Admissions Requirements Medical examination; Physician's request.
Facilities Dining room; Physical therapy room; Activities room; Crafts room; Laundry room; Barber/Beauty shop; Library.
Activities Arts and Crafts; Cards; Games; Reading groups; Prayer groups; Movies; Shopping trips; Dances/Social or cultural gatherings.
Description Facility offers small town, home-like atmosphere; dedicated staff; individualized programs and diets; reasonable rates.

Steffen Group Home
Barrett, MN, 56311 (218) 528-2533
Admin Ronna Steffen.
Licensure Supervised Living Facility.
Beds ICF/MR 6. *Certified* Medicaid.
Ownership Proprietary.
Admissions Requirements Minimum age 18; Females only; Medical examination.
Staff LPNs 1 (ft).
Facilities Dining room; Activities room; Crafts room; Laundry room.

Activities Arts and Crafts; Cards; Games; Reading groups; Movies; Shopping trips; Dances/Social or cultural gatherings.

BATTLE LAKE

Battle Lake Nursing Home
Box 68, Battle Lake, MN, 56515 (218) 864-5231
Admin Eveline Lykken. *Medical Dir/Dir of Nursing* Charles McGraw.
Licensure Intermediate Care. *Beds* 65. *Certified* Medicaid.
Ownership Public.
Admissions Requirements Medical examination; Physician's request.

Ottertail Nursing Home
Rt 2, Battle Lake, MN, 56515 (218) 495-2993
Admin Mark Tysver. *Medical Dir/Dir of Nursing* John Myhre MD.
Licensure Intermediate Care. *Beds* 62. *Certified* Medicaid.
Ownership Proprietary.
Admissions Requirements Medical examination; Physician's request.
Staff RNs 2 (ft), 3 (pt); LPNs 3 (pt); Orderlies 1 (ft); Nurses aides 8 (ft), 19 (pt).
Facilities Dining room; Activities room; Crafts room; Laundry room; Barber/Beauty shop.
Activities Arts and Crafts; Cards; Games; Reading groups; Prayer groups; Movies; Shopping trips.
Description Modern facility is located in a scenic setting on the shores of beautiful Otter Tail Lake. Our 18 acres make it perfect for the person who likes to be outdoors.

BAUDETTE

Pioneer Nursing Home
410 3rd Ave SE, Baudette, MN, 56623 (218) 634-1588
Admin Scott Wordelman.
Licensure Intermediate Care. *Beds* 52. *Certified* Medicaid.
Staff RNs 1 (ft), 1 (pt); LPNs 2 (ft), 4 (pt); Orderlies 1 (pt); Nurses aides 9 (ft), 11 (pt); Physical therapists 2 (ft); Activities coordinators 1 (ft); Dietitians 1 (ft).
Facilities Dining room; Physical therapy room; Activities room; Crafts room.
Activities Arts and Crafts; Cards; Games; Reading groups; Prayer groups; Movies; Shopping trips; Dances/Social or cultural gatherings.

BAXTER

Brainerd Group Home II*
Birchwood Dr, RR 2, Baxter, MN, 56401 (218) 828-4383
Admin John Peterson.
Licensure Skilled Care; Intermediate Care.
Beds SNF 12; ICF 12. *Certified* Medicaid.
Ownership Nonprofit.

BAYPORT

Croixdale Residence
334 N 7th Ave, Bayport, MN, 55003 (612) 439-4946
Admin Margaret Juhl.
Licensure Boarding Care. *Beds* 50.
Ownership Nonprofit.

BELGRADE

Belgrade Nursing Home
Box 340, Belgrade, MN, 56312 (612) 254-8215
Admin Philip Lord. *Medical Dir/Dir of Nursing* G R Savelkoul MD.
Licensure Skilled Care; Intermediate Care.
Beds 64. *Certified* Medicaid.
Ownership Nonprofit.
Admissions Requirements Minimum age 16; Medical examination; Physician's request.
Staff Physicians 1 (pt); RNs 1 (ft), 3 (pt); LPNs 1 (ft), 7 (pt); Physical therapists 1 (pt); Speech therapists 1 (pt); Activities coordinators 1 (ft), 2 (pt); Dietitians 1 (pt); Dentists 1 (pt).
Facilities Dining room; Physical therapy room; Activities room; Chapel; Crafts room; Laundry room; Barber/Beauty shop; TV/Day room.
Activities Arts and Crafts; Cards; Games; Reading groups; Prayer groups; Movies; Shopping trips; Dances/Social or cultural gatherings; Outside entertainment groups.
Description Large enough to serve, small enough to be personal and home-like, providing high quality 24-hour care.

BELLE PLAINE

The Lutheran Home*
611 W Main St, Belle Plaine, MN, 56011 (612) 873-2215
Admin Robert W Schlicht.
Licensure Intermediate Care; Intermediate Care for Mentally Retarded. *Beds* ICF 128; ICF/MR 52. *Certified* Medicaid.
Ownership Nonprofit.
Affiliation Lutheran

BELVIEW

Parkview Home
401 County State Aid Hwy 9, Belview, MN, 56214 (507) 938-4151
Admin Madonna Keavney. *Medical Dir/Dir of Nursing* Steve Medrud MD.
Licensure Skilled Care; Intermediate Care.
Beds SNF 40; ICF 22. *Certified* Medicaid.
Ownership Public.
Admissions Requirements Medical examination.
Facilities Dining room; Physical therapy room; Activities room; Chapel; Crafts room; Laundry room; Barber/Beauty shop; Library; Conference rooms.
Activities Arts and Crafts; Cards; Games; Reading groups; Prayer groups; Movies; Shopping trips; Dances/Social or cultural gatherings; Community interaction; Remotivation.

BEMIDJI

Beltrami Nursing Home
1633 Delton Ave, Bemidji, MN, 56601 (218) 751-1024
Admin L Schuette. *Medical Dir/Dir of Nursing* Dr Gary Winkler.
Licensure Skilled Care; Intermediate Care; Boarding Care. *Beds* SNF 81; ICF 32; Boarding Care 20. *Certified* Medicaid.
Ownership Public.
Admissions Requirements Medical examination; Physician's request.
Staff RNs 5 (ft), 4 (pt); LPNs 8 (ft), 8 (pt); Nurses aides 25 (ft), 27 (pt); Physical therapists 1 (pt); Recreational therapists 3 (ft), 2 (pt); Occupational therapists 1 (pt); Speech therapists 1 (pt); Activities coordinators 1 (ft); Dietitians 1 (pt); Dentists 1 (pt); Audiologists 1 (pt).
Facilities Dining room; Physical therapy room; Activities room; Chapel; Crafts room; Laundry room; Barber/Beauty shop; Library.
Activities Arts and Crafts; Cards; Games; Reading groups; Prayer groups; Movies; Shopping trips; Dances/Social or cultural gatherings.
Description Facility features staff quality circles and chaplain on staff.

Mississippi Home
1001 Mississippi Ave, Bemidji, MN, 56601 (218) 751-0957
Admin Carson Stensland.
Licensure Supervised Living Facility. *Beds* 8. *Certified* Medicaid.
Ownership Proprietary.
Admissions Requirements Minimum age 18; Medical examination.
Facilities Dining room.
Activities Arts and Crafts; Shopping trips; Dances/Social or cultural gatherings.
Description Home is located in a residential setting with access to city buses; home-like atmosphere; staff 24-hours a day; many group and individual activities in and around area; due to size, most professional needs are met on a consultant basis.

North Country Nursing and Rehabilitation
109 E 8th St, Bemidji, MN, 56601 (218) 751-0220
Admin Eunice Ulshafer. *Medical Dir/Dir of Nursing* James F Hatch MD.
Licensure Skilled Care; Intermediate Care. *Beds* 60. *Certified* Medicaid; Medicare.
Ownership Nonprofit.
Staff RNs 2 (ft), 6 (pt); LPNs 2 (ft), 9 (pt); Nurses aides 9 (ft), 30 (pt); Physical therapists 1 (pt); Occupational therapists 1 (pt); Speech therapists 1 (pt); Activities coordinators 1 (ft); Dietitians 1 (pt); Dentists 1 (pt); Audiologists 1 (pt).
Facilities Dining room; Physical therapy room; Activities room; Chapel; Barber/Beauty shop.
Activities Arts and Crafts; Cards; Games; Movies.
Description Facility's goal is to restore and/or maintain each resident to his or her fullest possible physical, mental, and emotional health. Facility is oriented toward rehabilitation and convalescent care.

North Star Homes
2528 Park Ave, Bemidji, MN, 56601
Admin Judith M Thorson. *Medical Dir/Dir of Nursing* Grant Christopher.
Licensure Intermediate Care for Mentally Retarded. *Beds* 14. *Certified* Medicare.
Ownership Nonprofit.
Admissions Requirements Minimum age 18; Medical examination; Physician's request.
Staff LPNs 1 (pt); House parents 10 (ft), 10 (pt).
Facilities Dining room; Activities room; Laundry room.
Activities Arts and Crafts; Cards; Games; Reading groups; Movies; Shopping trips; Dances/Social or cultural gatherings.
Description This is a small community-based residential home for multiply handicapped adults with a family setting providing training on an individual basis to reach goals of greater independence; building is barrier-free to accommodate wheelchairs.

REM Beltrami*
Rt 5, Box 197-E, Bemidji, MN, 56601 (218) 586-2573
Admin Thomas Miller.
Licensure Intermediate Care for Mentally Retarded. *Beds* 10. *Certified* Medicaid.
Ownership Proprietary.

BENSON

Meadow Lane Healthcare Center
W Hwy 9, Benson, MN, 56215 (612) 843-2225
Admin Greg Carlson. *Medical Dir/Dir of Nursing* Steve Honibrink MD.
Licensure Skilled Care; Intermediate Care. *Beds* SNF 32; ICF 62.
Ownership Public.
Admissions Requirements Minimum age 16; Medical examination; Physician's request.
Staff RNs 2 (ft), 4 (pt); LPNs 3 (ft), 3 (pt); Nurses aides 15 (ft), 26 (pt); Physical therapists 2 (pt); Recreational therapists 1 (ft), 2 (pt); Occupational therapists 1 (ft); Speech therapists 1 (pt); Activities coordinators 1 (ft); Dietitians 1 (pt); Dentists 1 (pt); Ophthalmologists 1 (pt); Podiatrists 1 (pt); Audiologists 1 (pt).
Facilities Dining room; Physical therapy room; Activities room; Chapel; Crafts room; Laundry room; Barber/Beauty shop.
Activities Arts and Crafts; Cards; Games; Reading groups; Prayer groups; Movies; Shopping trips; Dances/Social or cultural gatherings.

Swift County Home*
1650 Stone Ave, Benson, MN, 56215 (612) 843-3509
Admin Marg Demarce.
Licensure Skilled Care; Intermediate Care for Mentally Retarded. *Beds* SNF 10; ICF/MR 10. *Certified* Medicaid.
Ownership Nonprofit.

BERTHA

Memorial Community Hospital*
Box 97, Bertha, MN, 56437 (218) 924-2700
Admin Richard L Scott.

Licensure Skilled Care; Intermediate Care. *Beds* SNF 10; ICF 16. *Certified* Medicaid.
Ownership Public.

BIGFORK

Northern Itasca*
Bigfork, MN, 56628 (218) 743-3177
Admin Lillian M Krueger.
Licensure Skilled Care. *Beds* 62. *Certified* Medicaid.
Ownership Public.

BIRD ISLAND

Bird Island Manor Healthcare Center*
421 S 11th St, Bird Island, MN, 55310 (612) 365-4141
Admin Lamberta Doll.
Licensure Intermediate Care. *Beds* 24. *Certified* Medicaid.
Ownership Proprietary.

BLACKDUCK

Northern Pines Good Samaritan
Blackduck, MN, 56630 (218) 835-4218
Admin Don W Toft. *Medical Dir/Dir of Nursing* Dr G W Mouser.
Licensure Intermediate Care. *Beds* 70. *Certified* Medicaid.
Ownership Nonprofit.
Admissions Requirements Medical examination; Physician's request.
Staff RNs 1 (ft), 1 (pt); LPNs 3 (ft), 2 (pt); Nurses aides 15 (ft), 15 (pt).
Affiliation Lutheran
Facilities Dining room; Physical therapy room; Activities room; Crafts room; Laundry room.
Activities Arts and Crafts; Cards; Games; Reading groups; Prayer groups; Movies; Shopping trips; Dances/Social or cultural gatherings.
Description Choir of residents performs at center and functions of churches in nearby town; a walking program where residents walk distances equivalent to prescribed destinations.

BLAINE

Louis House North*
1000 Paul Parkway, Blaine, MN, 55343 (612) 757-2906
Admin Don F Benson.
Licensure Skilled Care. *Beds* 22.
Ownership Proprietary.

BLOOMING PRAIRIE

Prairie Manor*
220 3rd St NW, Blooming Prairie, MN, 55917 (507) 583-4434
Admin Larry Peak.
Licensure Skilled Care. *Beds* 82. *Certified* Medicaid.
Ownership Nonprofit.

BLOOMINGTON

Bloomington Maple Manor Care Center
8916 Lyndale Ave S, Bloomington, MN, 55420
(612) 881-5803
Admin Pamela Guyer.
Licensure Skilled Care; Intermediate Care.
Beds 63. *Certified* Medicaid.
Ownership Proprietary.

Bloomington Nursing Home
9200 Nicollet Ave S, Bloomington, MN, 55420
(612) 881-8676
Admin Beverly Baago. *Medical Dir/Dir of Nursing* Dr Lorraine Kretchman.
Licensure Skilled Care; Intermediate Care.
Beds 80. *Certified* Medicaid.
Ownership Proprietary.
Admissions Requirements Minimum age 18; Medical examination.
Staff Physicians 2 (pt); RNs 2 (ft), 8 (pt); LPNs 6 (pt); Nurses aides 9 (ft), 26 (pt); Physical therapists 1 (pt); Recreational therapists 1 (ft); Occupational therapists 1 (pt); Speech therapists 1 (pt); Dietitians 1 (ft); Dentists 1 (pt); Podiatrists 1 (pt); Audiologists 1 (pt); Respiratory aides 2 (pt); Social workers 1 (ft); Others 15 (ft), 19 (pt).
Facilities Dining room; Physical therapy room; Activities room; Laundry room.
Activities Arts and Crafts; Cards; Games; Reading groups; Prayer groups; Movies; Shopping trips; Dances/Social or cultural gatherings.

Bloomington Outreach Home
10633 Kell Ave S, Bloomington, MN, 55437
(612) 881-2848
Admin Eileen L Harris.
Licensure Supervised Care Facility. *Beds* 6.
Certified Medicaid.
Facilities Dining room; Activities room; Crafts room; Laundry room.
Activities Arts and Crafts; Cards; Games; Movies; Shopping trips; Dances/Social or cultural gatherings.

Eagle Nursing Home*
401 W 95th St, Bloomington, MN, 55420 (612) 888-9461
Admin William J Eagle.
Licensure Intermediate Care. *Beds* 80. *Certified* Medicaid.
Ownership Proprietary.

Forestview Sunlen*
400 E 99th St, Bloomington, MN, 55420 (612) 888-0897
Admin William Koski.
Licensure Intermediate Care for Mentally Retarded. *Beds* 6. *Certified* Medicaid.
Ownership Proprietary.

Friendship Village
8100 Highwood Dr, Bloomington, MN, 55438
(612) 831-2232
Medical Dir/Dir of Nursing Paul Kaldor MD.
Licensure Skilled Care. *Beds* 66. *Certified* Medicare.
Ownership Proprietary.
Admissions Requirements Minimum age 62; Medical examination; Physician's request.
Staff Physicians 1 (ft); RNs 3 (ft), 4 (pt); LPNs 6 (ft), 4 (pt); Nurses aides 21 (ft), 8 (pt);

Physical therapists 1 (pt); Activities coordinators 1 (ft), 2 (pt); Dietitians 1 (ft); Podiatrists 1 (pt).
Facilities Dining room; Physical therapy room; Activities room; Chapel; Crafts room; Laundry room; Barber/Beauty shop; Library.
Activities Arts and Crafts; Cards; Games; Reading groups; Prayer groups; Movies; Shopping trips; Dances/Social or cultural gatherings.
Description Life Care Retirement Community with attached 66-bed, long-term care facility.

Gerarda House*
6001 W 106th St, Bloomington, MN, 55438
(612) 888-9741
Admin John Miller.
Licensure Supervised Care Facility. *Beds* 6.
Ownership Proprietary.

Martin Luther Manor*
1401 E 100th St, Bloomington, MN, 55420
(612) 888-7751
Admin Joyce M Underkofler.
Licensure Skilled Care; Intermediate Care.
Beds SNF 40; ICF 80. *Certified* Medicaid.
Ownership Nonprofit.
Affiliation Lutheran

Minnesota Masonic Home*
11400 Normandale Blvd, Bloomington, MN, 55437 (612) 881-8665
Admin Edwin A Martini.
Licensure Skilled Care; Intermediate Care.
Beds SNF 157; ICF 249. *Certified* Medicaid.
Ownership Nonprofit.
Affiliation Masons

REM Bloomington*
9201 Cedar Ave S, Bloomington, MN, 55420
(612) 854-1800
Admin Thomas Miller.
Licensure Skilled Care; Intermediate Care.
Beds SNF 15; ICF 15. *Certified* Medicaid.
Ownership Proprietary.

Saint Stephen Group Home
8450 France Ave S, Bloomington, MN, 55431
(612) 831-1011
Admin Norman Doeden.
Licensure Supervised Care Facility. *Beds* 24.
Certified Medicaid.
Ownership Nonprofit.
Admissions Requirements Minimum age 18; Medical examination.
Staff RNs 1 (pt); Resident counselors 10 (ft), 10 (pt).
Affiliation Lutheran
Facilities Dining room; Activities room; Laundry room.
Activities Arts and Crafts; Cards; Games; Movies; Shopping trips; Dances/Social or cultural gatherings.
Description Our residents demand a developmental model stressing normalization concepts; therefore, they are away from the residence 30 hours weekly, Monday through Friday, in day programs such as sheltered workshops, developmental achievement centers, or public schools.

BLUE EARTH

Assisi Residence I*
218 S Linton, Blue Earth, MN, 56013 (507) 526-5629
Admin Lila Holdsworth.
Licensure Intermediate Care for Mentally Retarded. *Beds* 12. *Certified* Medicaid.
Ownership Nonprofit.

Assisi Residence II
325 W 2nd, Blue Earth, MN, 56013 (507) 526-5629
Admin Lila Holdsworth.
Licensure Intermediate Care for Mentally Retarded. *Beds* 7. *Certified* Medicaid.
Ownership Nonprofit.

Saint Lukes Lutheran Home*
1217 S Ramsey, Blue Earth, MN, 56013 (507) 526-2184
Admin Charles E Carlson.
Licensure Skilled Care; Intermediate Care.
Beds SNF 131; ICF 49. *Certified* Medicaid.
Ownership Nonprofit.
Affiliation Lutheran

BOVEY

Hawthorne House*
Rt 1, Box 189, Bovey, MN, 55709 (218) 245-1853
Admin Gregory A White.
Licensure Intermediate Care for Mentally Retarded. *Beds* 23. *Certified* Medicaid.
Ownership Proprietary.

BRAINERD

Bethany Good Samaritan Center
804 Wright St, Brainerd, MN, 56401 (218) 829-1407
Admin Dale Backhaus. *Medical Dir/Dir of Nursing* Dr Donald Gunderson.
Licensure Skilled Care; Intermediate Care.
Beds 160. *Certified* Medicaid.
Ownership Nonprofit.
Admissions Requirements Minimum age 16.
Staff RNs 6 (ft), 7 (pt); LPNs 6 (ft), 7 (pt); Orderlies 6 (ft), 3 (pt); Nurses aides 30 (ft), 60 (pt); Physical therapists 1 (pt); Recreational therapists 1 (pt); Activities coordinators 1 (ft); Dietitians 1 (ft).
Affiliation Lutheran
Facilities Dining room; Physical therapy room; Activities room; Crafts room; Laundry room; Barber/Beauty shop; Library.
Activities Cards; Games; Reading groups; Prayer groups; Movies; Shopping trips; Dances/Social or cultural gatherings.
Description Bethany is a 160-resident facility, highly skilled with a licensed nursing staff of 26 plus support people. Spiritual well-being is highly thought of as well as the family setting. The Brainerd community is involved in the total resident care.

Brainerd Good Samaritan Center
803 Kingwood St, Brainerd, MN, 56401 (218) 829-8711
Admin Michael Hinson. *Medical Dir/Dir of*

Nursing Dr Peter Dunphy.
Licensure Skilled Care; Intermediate Care;
Boarding Care. *Beds* SNF 24; ICF; Boarding
Care 32. *Certified* Medicaid.
Ownership Nonprofit.
Admissions Requirements Medical examina-
tion; Physician's request.
Staff RNs 1 (ft), 4(pt); LPNs 2 (ft), 7 (pt);
Nurses aids 6 (ft), 14 (pt); Activities coordina-
tors 1 (ft), 2 (pt); Dietitians 1 (ft), 1 (pt).
Affiliation Lutheran
Facilities Dining room; Activities room; Chap-
el; Crafts room; Laundry room; Barber/Beauty
shop; Library.
Activities Arts and Crafts; Cards; Games;
Reading groups; Prayer groups; Movies; Shop-
ping trips; Dances/Social or cultural gatherings.
Description "In Christ's love, everyone is
someone."

Charis House*
1008 S 10th St, Brainerd, MN, 58401 (218)
828-4823
Admin John D Peterson.
Licensure Skilled Care; Intermediate Care.
Beds SNF 12; B 12. *Certified* Medicaid.
Ownership Nonprofit.

BRECKENRIDGE

St Frances Home for the Aged*
501 Oak St, Breckenridge, MN, 56520 (218)
643-6661
Admin Siena Wald.
Licensure Skilled Care; Intermediate Care.
Beds SNF 85; ICF 39. *Certified* Medicaid;
Medicare.
Ownership Public.
Affiliation Roman Catholic

BRIANERD

Woodland Acres Health Care Center
1933 Buffalo Hills Ln, Brianerd, MN, 56401
Admin Gary Hjelmstad. *Medical Dir/Dir of
Nursing* Dr S Hanska.
Licensure Skilled Care. *Beds* 80. *Cer-
tified* Medicaid.
Ownership Proprietary.
Admissions Requirements Minimum age 16;
Medical examination; Physician's request.
Staff RNs; LPNs; Nurses aids 10 (ft); Occupa-
tional therapists 1 (ft); Activities coordinators 2
(ft); Social workers 1 (ft); Physical therapy
aides 1 (ft).
Facilities Dining room; Physical therapy room;
Activities room; chapel; Crafts room; Laundry
room; Barber/Beauty shop; Library.
Activities Arts and Crafts; Cards; Games;
Reading groups; Prayer groups; Movies; Shop-
ping trips; Dances/Social or cultural gatherings.

BROOKLYN CENTER

Brooklyn Center Outreach Home*
507 69th Ave N, Brooklyn Center, MN, 55430
(612) 561-9030
Admin Eileen Harris.
Licensure Intermediate Care for Mentally
Retarded. *Beds* 6. *Certified* Medicaid.
Ownership Nonprofit.

Maranatha Conservative Baptist Home Inc
5401 69th Ave N, Brooklyn Center, MN, 55429
(612) 561-0477
Admin Robert Lindstrom. *Medical Dir/Dir of
Nursing* Michael Ruegsegger MD.
Licensure Skilled Care; Intermediate Care.
Beds 98. *Certified* Medicaid.
Ownership Nonprofit.
Admissions Requirements Minimum age 60;
Medical examination; Physician's request.
Staff RNs 4 (ft), 12 (pt); LPNs 6 (ft), 8 (pt);
Orderlies 2 (pt); Nurses aides 10 (ft), 26 (pt);
Activities coordinators 2 (ft), 2 (pt); Dietitians
1 (ft).
Affiliation Baptist
Facilities Dining room; Physical therapy room;
Activities room; Chapel; Crafts room; Laundry
room; Barber/Beauty shop; Library.
Activities Arts and Crafts; Games; Reading
groups; Prayer groups; Movies; Shopping trips;
Dances/Social or cultural gatherings.

Residential Alternatives II*
5449 Lyndale Ave N, Brooklyn Center, MN,
55430 (612) 560-2220
Admin Peter Jacobson.
Licensure Intermediate Care for Mentally
Retarded. *Beds* 8. *Certified* Medicaid.

BROOKLYN PARK

Homeward Bound—Brooklyn Park*
6745 77th Ave N, Brooklyn Park, MN, 55429
(612) 566-7860
Admin James Glasoe.
Licensure Intermediate Care for Mentally
Retarded. *Beds* 32. *Certified* Medicaid.
Ownership Nonprofit.

Residential Alternatives III*
6525 Edgewood Ave N, Brooklyn Park, MN,
55428 (612) 533-5104
Admin Peter Jacobson.
Licensure Intermediate Care for Mentally
Retarded. *Beds* 8. *Certified* Medicaid.
Ownership Proprietary.

BROOKSTON

Hilltop Manor
338, Brookston, MN, 55711 (218) 453-5622
Admin M Gunderson.
Licensure Supervised Living Facility. *Beds* 10.
Certified Medicaid.
Ownership Proprietary.
Admissions Requirements Minimum age 18;
Medical examination.
Staff RNs 1 (pt); Activities coordinators 1 (pt).
Facilities Dining room; Activities room; Crafts
room; Laundry room.
Activities Arts and Crafts; Cards; Games;
Reading groups; Prayer groups; Movies; Shop-
ping trips; Dances/Social or cultural gatherings.

Maki Home Inc*
Star Rt, Box 630, Brookston, MN, 55711 (218)
879-3296
Admin Helen Maki.
Licensure Intermediate Care for Mentally
Retarded; Supervised Living Facility. *Bed-*

s ICF/MR 28; Supervised Living Facility 28.
Certified Medicaid.
Ownership Proprietary.

BROWNS VALLEY

Browns Valley Community Nursing Home
PO Box 340, Browns Valley, MN, 56219 (612)
695-2165
Admin Ronald Butler. *Medical Dir/Dir of
Nursing* Colleen Peickert RN. *Beds* 63. *Certi-
fied* Medicaid.
Licensure Intermediate Care. *Beds* 63. *Certi-
fied* Medicaid.
Ownership Proprietary.
Admissions Requirements Minimum age 18;
Medical examination; Physician's request.
Staff Physicians 12 (pt); RNs 1 (ft), 2 (pt);
LPNs 1 (ft), 4 (pt); Nurses aides 16 (ft), 12 (pt);
Physical therapists 1 (pt); Recreational thera-
pists 1 (ft), 2 (pt); Occupational therapists 1 (pt);
Activities coordinators 1 (ft); Dietitians 1 (pt).
Facilities Dining room; Physical therapy room;
Activities room; Crafts room; Laundry room;
Barber/Beauty shop; Garden; Workshop.
Activities Arts and Crafts; Cards; Games; Pray-
er groups; Shopping trips; Dances/Social or cul-
tural gatherings; Outings.
Description A small-town facility with an
experienced staff that knows and cares for residents. Facility enjoys a good, regional
reputation as a quality care center.

BUFFALO

Buffalo Group Home*
914 3rd Ave NE, Buffalo, MN, 55313 (612)
682-3960
Admin Terry Nelson.
Licensure Intermediate Care for Mentally
Retarded. *Beds* 15. *Certified* Medicaid.
Ownership Proprietary.

Ebenezer Covenant Home
310 Lake Blvd, Buffalo, MN, 55313 (612)
682-1434
Admin J Daniel Engels. *Medical Dir/Dir of
Nursing* Dr Waldo Anderson.
Licensure Skilled Care; Intermediate Care.
Beds SNF 51; ICF 14. *Certified* Medicaid.
Ownership Nonprofit.
Admissions Requirements Medical examina-
tion.
Staff RNs 4 (ft), 2 (pt); LPNs 2 (ft), 5 (pt);
Nurses aides 10 (ft), 32 (pt); Activities coordi-
nators 1 (ft).
Affiliation Evangelical Covenant Church
Activities Arts and Crafts; Cards; Games;
Reading groups; Prayer groups; Movies; Shop-
ping trips.

Residential Alternatives 1*
303 Douglas Dr, Buffalo, MN, 55313 (612)
682-4588
Admin Peter Jacobson.
Licensure Intermediate Care for Mentally
Retarded. *Beds* 6. *Certified* Medicaid.
Ownership Proprietary.

Residential Alternatives I*
1804 Sakenda Rd, Buffalo, MN, 55313 (612)
682-5868

Admin Peter Jacobson.
Licensure Intermediate Care. *Beds* 8. *Certified* Medicaid.
Ownership Proprietary.

Retirement Center of Wright County*
200 Park Ln, Buffalo, MN, 55313 (612) 682-3030
Admin Roger E Lundeen.
Licensure Skilled Care; Intermediate Care.
Beds SNF 107; ICF 47. *Certified* Medicaid.
Ownership Nonprofit.

BUFFALO LAKE

Buffalo Lake Nursing Home
703 W Yellowstone Trail, Buffalo Lake, MN, 55314 (612) 833-2181
Admin Stan Gallup. *Medical Dir/Dir of Nursing* C A Anderson MD.
Licensure Intermediate Care. *Beds* 66. *Certified* Medicaid.
Ownership Proprietary.
Admissions Requirements Medical examination; Physician's request.
Staff Physicians 2 (pt); RNs 1 (ft), 1 (pt); LPNs 5 (pt); Nurses aides 10 (ft), 40 (pt); Activities coordinators 1 (pt); Dietitians 1 (pt).
Facilities Dining room; Activities room; Laundry room.
Activities Arts and Crafts; Cards; Games; Reading groups; Prayer groups; Movies; Shopping trips; Dances/Social or cultural gatherings.
Description Facility features a beautiful rural setting with spacious grounds.

BUHL

Mesabi Home
Jones Ave, Buhl, MN, 55713 (218) 258-3253
Admin Betty Holmes.
Licensure Intermediate Care. *Beds* 31. *Certified* Medicaid.
Ownership Nonprofit.
Admissions Requirements Medical examination; Physician's request.
Staff RNs 1 (ft), 3 (pt); LPNs 2 (pt); Nurses aides 2 (ft), 7 (pt); Activities coordinators 1 (pt); Dietitians 1 (pt); Audiologists 8 (pt).
Facilities Dining room; Laundry room.
Activities Arts and Crafts; Cards; Games; Reading groups; Prayer groups; Movies; Shopping trips; Dances/Social or cultural gatherings.

BURNSVILLE

Ebenezer Ridges
13820 Community Dr, Burnsville, MN, 55337 (218) 534-3121
Admin Robert Held. *Medical Dir/Dir of Nursing* Dr Brian Ebeling.
Licensure Skilled Care. *Beds* 104. *Certified* Medicaid; Medicare.
Ownership Nonprofit.
Admissions Requirements Medical examination.
Staff Physical therapists 1 (ft), 1 (pt); Recreational therapists 1 (ft); Occupational therapists 1 (pt); Speech therapists 1 (pt).
Affiliation Lutheran
Facilities Dining room; Physical therapy room;

Activities room; Crafts room; Barber/Beauty shop.
Activities Arts and Crafts; Cards; Games; Reading groups; Prayer groups; Movies; Shopping trips.
Description Facility offers an adult day care program, 9am to 4pm Monday through Friday.

CALEDONIA

Houston County Group Home
109 S Winnebago St, Caledonia, MN, 55921 (507) 724-2000
Admin Dennis Theede.
Licensure Intermediate Care for Mentally Retarded. *Beds* 28. *Certified* Medicaid.
Ownership Nonprofit.
Admissions Requirements Minimum age 18; Medical examination; Physician's request.
Staff RNs 1 (pt); LPNs 1 (pt); Speech therapists 1 (pt).
Facilities Dining room; Activities room; Laundry room.
Activities Arts and Crafts; Cards; Games; Reading groups; Prayer groups; Movies; Shopping trips; Dances/Social or cultural gatherings.
Description Home is a community based facility for 13 mentally handicapped adults who function in the severe to mild range of retardation. Program emphasis includes developmental training in self-help skills to ensure greater independence in a warm, home-like environment close to their families.

CAMBRIDGE

Cambridge Care Center
548 W 1st Ave, Cambridge, MN, 55008 (612) 689-2323
Admin Dale Thompson. *Medical Dir/Dir of Nursing* P S Sanders MD.
Licensure Skilled Care; Intermediate Care.
Beds SNF 110; ICF 47. *Certified* Medicaid; Medicare.
Ownership Proprietary.
Admissions Requirements Medical examination; Physician's request.
Staff RNs 8 (ft); LPNs 5 (ft); Nurses aides 40 (ft); Physical therapists 1 (ft); Occupational therapists 1 (ft); Speech therapists 1 (pt); Activities coordinators 1 (ft); Dietitians 1 (pt); Dentists 1 (pt); Podiatrists 1 (pt); Audiologists 1 (pt).
Facilities Dining room; Physical therapy room; Activities room; Chapel; Crafts room; Laundry room; Barber/Beauty shop; Library.
Activities Arts and Crafts; Cards; Games; Reading groups; Prayer groups; Movies; Shopping trips; Dances/Social or cultural gatherings; Resident council; Family council.

Cambridge State Hospital*
Cambridge, MN, 55008 (612) 689-2121
Admin Jonathan Balk.
Licensure Intermediate Care for Mentally Retarded. *Beds* 588. *Certified* Medicaid.
Ownership Public.

Grandview Christian Home*
800 NW 2nd Ave, Cambridge, MN, 55008 (612) 689-1474

Admin Dan Bolhouse.
Licensure Skilled Care; Intermediate Care.
Beds SNF 58; ICF 122. *Certified* Medicaid.
Ownership Nonprofit.

Residential Alternatives VI*
Central at E Rum River D, Cambridge, MN, 55008 (612) 689-3794
Admin Peter Jacobson.
Licensure Skilled Care; Intermediate Care.
Beds SNF 6; ICF 6. *Certified* Medicaid.
Ownership Proprietary.

CANBY

Canby Community Hospital
112 Saint Olaf Ave S, Canby, MN, 56220
Admin Robert Salmon. *Medical Dir/Dir of Nursing* Robert Snortum.
Licensure Skilled Care; Intermediate Care.
Beds 75. *Certified* Medicaid.
Ownership Nonprofit.
Admissions Requirements Minimum age 16; Medical examination.
Staff Physicians 3 (ft); RNs 1 (ft), 3 (pt); LPNs 3 (ft), 10 (pt); Nurses aides 9 (ft), 32 (pt); Physical therapists 1 (pt); Speech therapists 1 (pt); Activities coordinators 1 (ft), 2 (pt); Dietitians 1 (ft); Dentists 2 (ft); Audiologists 1 (pt).
Facilities Dining room; Physical therapy room; Activities room; Chapel; Crafts room; Laundry room; Barber/Beauty shop; Library.
Activities Arts and Crafts; Cards; Games; Reading groups; Prayer groups; Movies; Dances/Social or cultural gatherings.

REM II A and B*
1201 Haarfagar St N, Canby, MN, 56220 (507) 223-7186
Admin Craig Miller.
Licensure Intermediate Care for Mentally Retarded. *Beds* 30. *Certified* Medicaid.
Ownership Proprietary.

CANNON FALLS

Cannon Falls Manor Nursing Home
300 N Dow St, Cannon Falls, MN, 55009 (507) 263-4658
Admin Bonnie Campeau. *Medical Dir/Dir of Nursing* Lloyd Klefstad.
Licensure Skilled Care; Intermediate Care; Boarding Care Home. *Beds* SNF 76; ICF 10; Boarding Care 2. *Certified* Medicaid.
Ownership Proprietary.
Admissions Requirements Minimum age 16.
Staff Physicians 2 (ft); RNs 1 (ft), 6 (pt); LPNs 3 (ft), 6 (pt); Nurses aides 7 (ft), 45 (pt); Physical therapists 1 (pt); Dietitians 1 (pt).
Facilities Dining room; Physical therapy room; Activities room; Crafts room; Laundry room; Barber/Beauty shop; Conference room.
Activities Arts and Crafts; Cards; Games; Reading groups; Prayer groups; Movies; Shopping trips; Dances/Social or cultural gatherings.
Description Our facility offers a homey atmosphere to the area's residents in need of nursing care. Since we are located in a small, farming community, most of our residents are quite

well known locally. Every effort is made to keep the quality of life as updated as possible while preserving individual dignity.

Cannon Valley Center
PO Box 21, Cannon Falls, MN, 55009 (507) 263-4271
Admin Bob Klaus.
Licensure Supervised Living Facility. *Beds* 75.
Ownership Proprietary.

CARLTON

Carlton Nursing Home
810 3rd St, Carlton, MN, 55718 (218) 384-4258
Admin Larry C Penk. *Medical Dir/Dir of Nursing* Dr Vickie Anderson.
Licensure Skilled Care; Intermediate Care.
Beds 96. *Certified* Medicaid; Medicare.
Ownership Nonprofit.
Admissions Requirements Minimum age 16; Medical examination.
Staff Physicians 2 (pt); RNs 1 (ft), 3 (pt); LPNs 10 (pt); Orderlies 1 (pt); Nurses aides 42 (pt); Physical therapists 1 (ft); Speech therapists 1 (pt); Activities coordinators 1 (ft); Dietitians 1 (pt); Dentists 1 (pt); Ophthalmologists 1 (pt); Podiatrists 1 (pt).
Facilities Dining room; Physical therapy room; Activities room; Crafts room; Laundry room; Barber/Beauty shop.
Activities Arts and Crafts; Cards; Games; Reading groups; Prayer groups; Movies; Shopping trips; Dances/Social or cultural gatherings.
Description Carlton Nursing Home is located in a beautifully wooded area of northwestern Minnesota; recently completed Pineview Apartments, an attached apartment complex for the elderly, with services for renters available through the nursing home.

CENTER CITY

Hazelden Foundation*
Box II, Center City, MN, 55012 (612) 257-4010
Admin Harold A Swift.
Licensure Skilled Care; Intermediate Care.
Beds SNF 15; ICF 15. *Certified* Medicaid.
Ownership Proprietary.

South Center Manor Inc*
Park Island, Center City, MN, 55012 (612) 257-1686
Admin Lowell J Petersen.
Licensure Intermediate Care for Mentally Retarded. *Beds* 15.
Ownership Proprietary.

CEYLON

Schmidtke Rest Home
Ceylon, MN, 56121 (507) 632-4348
Admin Clark Schmidtke.
Licensure Boarding Care. *Beds* 11.
Ownership Proprietary.
Admissions Requirements Medical examination.
Staff RNs 1 (pt); Nurses aides 3 (ft), 1 (pt); Activities coordinators 1 (ft); Dietitians 1 (pt).
Facilities Dining room; Laundry room.

Activities Cards; Games; Reading groups; Prayer groups; Movies; Dances/Social or cultural gatherings.

CHANHASSEN

Chanhassen Center*
7701 Arboretum Blvd, Chanhassen, MN, 55317 (612) 934-3264
Admin William J Gregg.
Licensure Supervised Living Facility. *Beds* 70.
Ownership Nonprofit.

Dungarvin VI*
7226 Frontier Trail, Chanhassen, MN, 55317
Admin Diane Madden.
Licensure Supervised Living Facility. *Beds* 6.
Ownership Proprietary.

CHATFIELD

Chosen Valley Care Center*
1102 Liberty St SE, Chatfield, MN, 55923 (507) 867-4220
Admin Ruth Jensen.
Licensure Skilled Care. *Beds* 86. *Certified* Medicaid.
Ownership Public.

CHISAGO CITY

Linnea Residential Home*
28770 Old Town Rd, Chisago City, MN, 55013 (612) 257-2211
Admin Donna Hoverman.
Licensure Intermediate Care for Mentally Retarded. *Beds* 12. *Certified* Medicaid.
Ownership Nonprofit.

The Margaret S Parmly Residence*
28210 Old Towne Rd, Chisago City, MN, 55013 (612) 257-5620
Admin David J Kaasa.
Licensure Skilled Care; Intermediate Care.
Beds SNF 77; ICF 24. *Certified* Medicaid.
Ownership Nonprofit.

CHISHOLM

Buchanan Nursing Home*
30 1st St NW, Chisholm, MN, 55719 (218) 254-3614
Admin John Buchanan.
Licensure Intermediate Care. *Beds* 39. *Certified* Medicaid.
Ownership Proprietary.

Chisholm Memorial Nursing Home
Park Addition, Chisholm, MN, 55719 (218) 254-3367
Admin Allen Rosenow. *Medical Dir/Dir of Nursing* Dr Jack B Greene.
Licensure Nursing Home. *Beds* 21.
Ownership Public.
Admissions Requirements Minimum age 21; Medical examination; Physician's request.
Staff RNs 2 (ft), 5 (pt); LPNs 1 (ft), 8 (pt); Nurses aides 12 (ft), 24 (pt); Physical therapists 3 (pt); Occupational therapists 1 (pt); Speech therapists 1 (pt); Activities coordinators 2 (ft);

Dietitians 1 (ft).
Facilities Dining room; Physical therapy room; Activities room; Chapel; Crafts room; Laundry room; Barber/Beauty shop; Library.
Activities Arts and Crafts; Cards; Games; Reading groups; Prayer groups; Movies; Shopping trips; Dances/Social or cultural gatherings.
Description We are located on Longyear Lake in a park setting. We have a beautiful home atmosphere and strive to bring many new ideas so the residents may reminisce about their past.

Heritage Manor Health Care Center
321 NE 6th St, Chisholm, MN, 55719
Admin Robert Koepcke. *Medical Dir/Dir of Nursing* Dr Jack Greene.
Licensure Skilled Care. *Beds* 76. *Certified* Medicaid; Medicare.
Ownership Nonprofit.
Admissions Requirements Medical examination; Physician's request.
Staff Physicians 1 (pt); RNs 2 (ft), 5 (pt); LPNs 2 (ft), 5 (pt); Orderlies 5 (pt); Nurses aides 11 (ft), 22 (pt); Physical therapists 2 (pt); Occupational therapists 1 (pt); Speech therapists 1 (pt); Activities coordinators 1 (pt); Dietitians 1 (pt); Dentists 1 (pt); Podiatrists 1 (pt).
Facilities Dining room; Physical therapy room; Activities room; Chapel; Crafts room; Laundry room; Barber/Beauty shop.
Activities Arts and Crafts; Cards; Games; Movies; Shopping trips; Dances/Social or cultural gatherings; Field trips; Outings to restaurants.
Description This is a community-based, community-involved facility located in a convenient and beautiful spot next to Longyear Lake.

Range Center*
1001 8th Ave NW, Chisholm, MN, 55719 (218) 254-3347
Admin James Mickelson.
Licensure Intermediate Care for Mentally Retarded. *Beds* 29. *Certified* Medicaid.
Ownership Nonprofit.

Range Center—Oakwood Home
28 NE 11th St, Chisholm, MN, 55719 (218) 254-2932
Admin James Mickelson.
Licensure Supervised Living Facility. *Beds* 6. *Certified* Medicaid.
Ownership Nonprofit.
Admissions Requirements Minimum age 3.
Staff RNs 1 (pt).
Facilities Dining room; Activities room; Laundry room; Typical family living home.
Activities Arts and Crafts; Cards; Games; Reading groups; Movies; Shopping trips; Dances/Social or cultural gatherings.

CLARA CITY

Clara City Community Nursing Home
1012 Division St N, Clara City, MN, 56222 (612) 847-3553
Admin Mark Rossi.
Licensure Intermediate Care. *Beds* 95. *Certified* Medicaid.
Ownership Public.
Admissions Requirements Medical examina-

tion; Physician's request.
Staff Physicians 3 (pt); RNs 2 (ft); LPNs 3 (ft), 6 (pt); Orderlies 1 (ft); Physical therapists 1 (pt); Activities coordinators 1 (ft); Dietitians 1 (pt).
Facilities Dining room; Physical therapy room; Activities room; Chapel; Crafts room; Laundry room; Barber/Beauty shop.
Activities Arts and Crafts; Cards; Games; Reading groups; Movies; Shopping trips; Dances/Social or cultural gatherings.

CLARISSA

Central Todd County Care Center*
Hwy 71 Near Oak St, Clarissa, MN, 56440 (218) 756-3636
Admin Margaret Taggert.
Licensure Skilled Care; Intermediate Care.
Beds SNF 58; ICF 20. *Certified* Medicaid.
Ownership Nonprofit.

CLARKFIELD

Clarkfield Care Center*
805 5th Ave, Clarkfield, MN, 56223 (612) 669-7561
Admin Dennis Kamstra.
Licensure Intermediate Care. *Beds* 86. *Certified* Medicaid.
Ownership Public.

CLEAR LAKE

High Point Lodge Nursing Home
Rt 1, Clear Lake, MN, 55319 (612) 743-2695
Admin Hazel L Bollinger. *Medical Dir/Dir of Nursing* Jill Lake.
Licensure Intermediate Care. *Beds* 26. *Certified* Medicaid.
Ownership Proprietary.
Admissions Requirements Minimum age 18; Medical examination; Physician's request.
Staff RNs 1 (ft); LPNs 1 (ft), 2 (pt); Nurses aides 3 (ft), 8 (pt); Activities coordinators 1 (pt).
Facilities Dining room; Activities room; Laundry room.
Activities Arts and Crafts; Cards; Games; Shopping trips; Bowling; Boating; Fishing.
Description Facility located on shore of beautiful Briggs Lake.

CLEARBROOK

Good Samaritan Center
Clearbrook, MN, 56634 (218) 776-3157
Admin Collin Eid. *Medical Dir/Dir of Nursing* Sherry Torgerson.
Licensure Intermediate Care. *Beds* 96. *Certified* Medicaid.
Ownership Nonprofit.
Admissions Requirements Medical examination.
Staff RNs 1 (ft), 2 (pt); LPNs 6 (ft), 5 (pt); Nurses aides 9 (ft), 29 (pt); Physical therapists 1 (ft), 1 (pt); Activities coordinators 1 (ft); Dietitians 1 (pt).
Affiliation Lutheran
Facilities Dining room; Activities room; Chapel; Crafts room; Laundry room; Barber/Beauty

shop.
Activities Arts and Crafts; Cards; Games; Reading groups; Prayer groups; Movies; Shopping trips; Dances/Social or cultural gatherings.
Description Facility features dedicated staff, excellent care, in a predominately Scandanavian area.

CLINTON

Clinton Good Samaritan Center
Clinton, MN, 56225 (612) 325-5414
Admin Luella Rupp.
Licensure Intermediate Care. *Beds* 54. *Certified* Medicaid.
Ownership Nonprofit.
Staff RNs 1 (ft); LPNs 2 (ft), 1 (pt); Orderlies 1 (ft); Nurses aides 9 (ft), 11 (pt); Activities coordinators 1 (ft), 1 (pt).
Affiliation Lutheran
Facilities Dining room; Activities room; Laundry room.
Activities Arts and Crafts; Cards; Games; Reading groups.
Description Facility offers beachball, basketball, and group exercise every morning.

CLOQUET

Pine Ridge Home 1*
413 Broadway, Cloquet, MN, 55720 (218) 879-1168
Admin David Felske.
Licensure Intermediate Care for Mentally Retarded. *Beds* 6. *Certified* Medicaid.
Ownership Nonprofit.

Pine Ridge Home 2*
16 11th St, Cloquet, MN, 55720 (218) 879-1168
Admin David Felske.
Licensure Intermediate Care for Mentally Retarded. *Beds* 6. *Certified* Medicaid.
Ownership Nonprofit.

Pine Ridge Home 3*
1509 14th St, Cloquet, MN, 55720 (218) 879-1168
Admin David Felske.
Licensure Intermediate Care for Mentally Retarded. *Beds* 13. *Certified* Medicaid.
Ownership Nonprofit.

COKATO

Cokato Manor
W Hwy 12, Cokato, MN, 55321 (612) 286-2158
Admin Larry S Petersen. *Medical Dir/Dir of Nursing* John Bersstrom MD.
Licensure Skilled Care; Intermediate Care.
Beds 66. *Certified* Medicaid.
Ownership Proprietary.
Admissions Requirements Medical examination; Physician's request.
Staff RNs 1 (ft), 3 (pt); LPNs 3 (ft), 2 (pt); Orderlies 2 (ft); Nurses aides 24 (ft), 20 (pt); Physical therapists 1 (pt); Reality therapists 1 (pt); Activities coordinators 2 (ft), 1 (pt); Dietitians 1 (pt).
Facilities Dining room; Physical therapy room; Activities room; Laundry room; Barber/Beauty

shop.
Activities Arts and Crafts; Cards; Games; Prayer groups; Dances/Social or cultural gatherings.

Warner Care Home 1*
325 Swanson Ave, Cokato, MN, 55321 (612) 286-2185
Admin Charles Kroeger.
Licensure Intermediate Care for Mentally Retarded. *Beds* 15. *Certified* Medicaid.
Ownership Proprietary.

Warner Care Home 2*
180 6th St W, Cokato, MN, 55321 (612) 286-2185
Admin Charles Kroeger.
Licensure Intermediate Care for Mentally Retarded. *Beds* 7. *Certified* Medicaid.
Ownership Proprietary.

Warner Care Home 3*
370 W 3rd St, Cokato, MN, 55321 (612) 286-2185
Admin Charles Kroeger.
Licensure Intermediate Care for Mentally Retarded. *Beds* 7. *Certified* Medicaid.
Ownership Proprietary.

COLD SPRING

Assumption Home
715 N 1st St, Cold Spring, MN, 56320 (612) 685-3693
Admin Robert McCardle. *Medical Dir/Dir of Nursing* Dr John Kelly.
Licensure Skilled Care; Intermediate Care.
Beds SNF 71; ICF 24. *Certified* Medicaid.
Ownership Nonprofit.
Staff RNs 2 (ft), 5 (pt); LPNs 1 (ft), 6 (pt); Nurses aides 18 (ft), 21 (pt); Physical therapists 1 (pt); Reality therapists 1 (pt); Recreational therapists 3 (ft); Activities coordinators 1 (ft); Dietitians 1 (pt).
Affiliation Roman Catholic
Facilities Dining room; Physical therapy room; Activities room; Chapel; Crafts room; Laundry room; Barber/Beauty shop; Library.
Activities Arts and Crafts; Cards; Games; Reading groups; Prayer groups; Movies; Shopping trips; Dances/Social or cultural gatherings.

Mother Teresa Home*
101 10th Ave, Cold Spring, MN, 56320 (612) 685-6626
Admin Rev Richard Leisen.
Licensure Skilled Care; Intermediate Care for Mentally Retarded. *Beds* SNF 14; ICF/MR 14. *Certified* Medicaid; Medicare.
Ownership Public.
Affiliation Roman Catholic

COLUMBIA HEIGHTS

Crest View Lutheran Home*
4444 Reservoir Blvd NE, Columbia Heights, MN, 55421 (612) 788-1678
Admin Thomas W Paul.
Licensure Skilled Care. *Beds* 122. *Certified* Medicaid; Medicare.
Ownership Nonprofit.
Affiliation Lutheran

COOK

Cook Community Hospital*
3rd St and Cedar Ave, Cook, MN, 55723 (218)
666-5945
Admin Lineta Scott.
Licensure Skilled Care. *Beds* 41. *Certified* Medicaid.
Ownership Public.

COON RAPIDS

Camila Rose Group Home
11800 Xeon Blvd, Coon Rapids, MN, 55433
(612) 775-8489
Admin Mary Tjosvold.
Licensure Intermediate Care for Mentally
Retarded. *Beds* ICF/MR 35. *Certified* Medicaid.
Ownership Proprietary.
Admissions Requirements Minimum age 18;
Medical examination.
Staff RNs 1 (pt); LPNs 2 (ft), 1 (pt); Recreational therapists 1 (pt); Occupational therapists
1 (pt); Speech therapists 1 (pt); Activities coordinators 1 (pt); Dietitians 1 (ft); Social workers
1 (pt); Advisors 20 (ft).
Facilities Dining room; Physical therapy room;
Activities room; Chapel; Crafts room; Laundry
room; Barber/Beauty shop; Library.
Activities Arts and Crafts; Cards; Games;
Reading groups; Movies; Shopping trips; Dances/Social or cultural gatherings.
Description Home is composed of 2 houses
and 2 apartments joined under one roof by a
multipurpose activities room. Goal is to provide an environment for mentally handicapped
adults that maximizes each person's capabilities; an individualized program plan is used to
assist them in gaining the skills necessary to
achieve maximum potential.

Camilia Rose Convalescent Center
11800 Xeon Blvd NW, Coon Rapids, MN,
55433 (612) 755-8400
Admin N Brendle. *Medical Dir/Dir of
Nursing* William Rodman MD.
Licensure Skilled Care; Intermediate Care.
Beds SNF 39; ICF 55. *Certified* Medicaid.
Ownership Proprietary.
Admissions Requirements Minimum age 16;
Medical examination; Physician's request.
Staff RNs 1 (ft), 10 (pt); LPNs 13 (pt); Nurses
aides 10 (ft), 29 (pt); Physical therapists 1 (ft);
Recreational therapists 3 (ft); Occupational
therapists 2 (ft); Speech therapists 1 (pt); Dietitians 1 (pt).
Facilities Dining room; Physical therapy room;
Activities room; Chapel; Crafts room; Laundry
room; Barber/Beauty shop; Library; Artist studio.
Description Facility is set in a grove of trees
with 2 creeks nearby; has a day-care program
for seniors. Philosophy is one of wellness and
reaching each individuals highest level of
independent functioning physically, mentally,
socially, emotionally, and spiritually.

Community Living*
2483 109th Ave NW, Coon Rapids, MN,
55431 (612) 443-2048
Admin Jerry Gross.

Licensure Intermediate Care for Mentally
Retarded. *Beds* 24. *Certified* Medicaid.
Ownership Proprietary.

Demar Childrens Home
11777 Xeon Blvd, Coon Rapids, MN, 55433
Licensure Intermediate Care for Mentally
Retarded.
Admissions Requirements Medical examination; Physician's request.
Staff RNs 1 (ft); LPNs 2 (ft); Nurses aides 25
(ft); Physical therapists; Recreational therapists
1 (ft); Occupational therapists 1 (ft); Dietitians.
Facilities Dining room; Physical therapy room;
Activities room; Crafts room; Laundry room.
Activities Arts and Crafts; Cards; Games;
Reading groups; Movies; Shopping trips; Dances/Social or cultural gatherings.
Description Facility is for children under 18
years of age who have a primary diagnosis of
mental retardation, secondary diagnosis of
physical handicaps; seizures, cerebal palsy, and
behavior problems are accepted; staff incorporates learning groups; communication groups;
art, music, and dance therapy; and a varied
activities program.

Park River Estates
1371 98th Ln NW, Coon Rapids, MN, 55433
(612) 757-2320
Admin Steven Chies. *Medical Dir/Dir of
Nursing* Dr Mark Brakke.
Licensure Skilled Care; Intermediate Care.
Beds SNF 81; ICF 13. *Certified* Medicaid.
Admissions Requirements Medical examination; Physician's request.
Facilities Dining room; Physical therapy room;
Activities room; Chapel; Crafts room; Laundry
room; Barber/Beauty shop; Library.
Activities Arts and Crafts; Cards; Games;
Reading groups; Prayer groups; Movies; Shopping trips; Dances/Social or cultural gatherings.
Description Facility is newly expanded and
remodeled; has a foster grandparent program
with the local schools.

COSMOS

Cosmos Healthcare Center*
Cosmos, MN, 56228 (612) 877-7227
Admin Margaret Stauder.
Licensure Skilled Care; Intermediate Care.
Beds SNF 29; ICF 29. *Certified* Medicaid.
Ownership Proprietary.

COTTAGE GROVE

Forestview Hemingway*
8045 Hemingway Ave S, Cottage Grove, MN,
55016 (612) 459-7747
Admin William Koski.
Licensure Intermediate Care for Mentally
Retarded. *Beds* 6. *Certified* Medicaid.
Ownership Proprietary.

CROMWELL

Villa Vista
Cromwell, MN, 55726 (218) 644-3331
Admin Ebba E Hedin. *Medical Dir/Dir of
Nursing* Dr B R Puumala.

Licensure Boarding Care. *Beds* 51. *Certified* Medicaid.
Ownership Proprietary.
Admissions Requirements Medical examination.
Staff RNs 1 (ft); LPNs 1 (ft), 1 (pt); Nurses
aides 10 (ft), 4 (pt); Activities coordinators 1
(ft); Dietitians 1 (pt).

CROOKSTON

Crookston Group Home
315 Summit Ave, Crookston, MN, 56716 (218)
281-5113
Admin Vernon Nordmark.
Licensure Supervised Living Facility. *Beds* 10.
Certified Medicaid.
Ownership Nonprofit.
Admissions Requirements Minimum age 18.
Activities Arts and Crafts; Cards; Games;
Movies; Shopping trips; Dances/Social or cultural gatherings.
Description Provides residential programs and
services for developmentally disabled persons.

Crookston Group Home 2*
1423 Forskett, Crookston, MN, 56716 (218)
281-1904
Admin Vernon Nordmard.
Licensure Intermediate Care for Mentally
Retarded. *Beds* 10. *Certified* Medicaid.
Ownership Nonprofit.

Riverview Hospital
323 S Minnesota, Crookston, MN, 56716
Admin Thomas Lenertz. *Medical Dir/Dir of
Nursing* Dr Howard Wikoff.
Licensure Skilled Care; Intermediate Care.
Beds 100. *Certified* Medicare.
Ownership Nonprofit.
Admissions Requirements Medical examination; Physician's request.
Staff Physicians 10 (ft); RNs 2 (ft), 1 (pt);
LPNs 8 (ft), 5 (pt); Orderlies 2 (ft), 1 (pt);
Nurses aides 13 (ft), 29 (pt); Physical therapists
2 (ft), 1 (pt); Occupational therapists 2 (ft), 1
(pt); Speech therapists 1 (pt); Activities coordinators 1 (ft); Dietitians 2 (ft); Ophthalmologists
1 (ft); Podiatrists 2 (pt); Audiologists 1 (pt).
Facilities Dining room; Physical therapy room;
Activities room; Chapel; Crafts room; Barber-
/Beauty shop; Woodworking room.
Activities Arts and Crafts; Cards; Games;
Reading groups; Prayer groups; Movies; Shopping trips; Dances/Social or cultural gatherings.

Villa Saint Vincent
516 Walsh, Crookston, MN, 56716 (218)
281-3424
Admin Mike Siekas. *Medical Dir/Dir of
Nursing* Dr John K Wood.
Licensure Skilled Care; Intermediate Care.
Beds SNF 80; ICF 95. *Certified* Medicaid;
Medicare.
Ownership Nonprofit.
Staff RNs 4 (ft), 4 (pt); LPNs 7 (ft), 2 (pt);
Nurses aides 55 (ft), 32 (pt); Physical therapists
1 (pt); Recreational therapists 5 (ft); Occupational therapists 1 (pt); Dietitians 1 (pt); Dentists 1 (pt).
Facilities Dining room; Activities room;
Chapel; Crafts room; Laundry room; Barber-

/Beauty shop; Library; Woodworking shop; Darkroom; Kiln for ceramics.
Activities Arts and Crafts; Cards; Games; Prayer groups; Movies; Dances/Social or cultural gatherings.

CRYSTAL

Crystal Care Center
3245 Vera Cruz Ave N, Crystal, MN, 55422 (612) 535-6260
Admin Patricia Kalaidis. *Medical Dir/Dir of Nursing* Dr Keith Kubasch.
Licensure Skilled Care; Intermediate Care.
Beds 192. *Certified* Medicaid.
Ownership Nonprofit.
Admissions Requirements Minimum age 40; Medical examination; Physician's request.
Staff Physicians; RNs 25 (ft); LPNs 25 (ft); Nurses aides 50 (ft), 20 (pt); Physical therapists 1 (ft), 2 (pt); Recreational therapists 3 (ft), 2 (pt); Occupational therapists 1 (ft); Activities coordinators 1 (ft).
Affiliation Volunteers of America
Facilities Dining room; Physical therapy room; Activities room; Chapel; Crafts room; Laundry room; Barber/Beauty shop; Library.
Activities Arts and Crafts; Cards; Games; Reading groups; Prayer groups; Movies; Shopping trips; Dances/Social or cultural gatherings.
Description Excellent rehabilitation programs with an emphasis on having the resident be as independent as possible. Home-like, family atmosphere, featuring high-quality nursing and extended care services.

Dungarvin V
3157 Douglas Dr, Crystal, MN, 55422 (612) 545-55422
Admin Diane Madden.
Licensure Supervised Living Facility. *Beds* 12.
Certified Medicaid.
Ownership Proprietary.
Staff RNs 1 (pt); Activities coordinators 1 (ft).
Facilities Laundry room.
Activities Games; Movies; Shopping trips; Dances/Social or cultural gatherings.
Description This is an apartment training program facility for 12 mildly developmentally disabled adults offering formal and informal programing in areas of domestic skills, personal hygiene, vocational growth and placement, sexuality, socialization, leisure and recreation, problem solving, and also mechanical skills.

Forestview—Kentucky*
4806 Kentucky Ave N, Crystal, MN, 55428 (612) 535-3116
Admin William Koski.
Licensure Intermediate Care for Mentally Retarded. *Beds* 6. *Certified* Medicaid.
Ownership Proprietary.

DASSEL

Dassel Lakeside Community Home
441 William Ave, Dassel, MN, 55325 (612) 275-3433
Admin W Ward.
Licensure Intermediate Care. *Beds* 63. *Certified* Medicaid.

Ownership Public.
Admissions Requirements Medical examination; Physician's request.
Staff RNs 1 (ft), 2 (pt); LPNs 3 (ft), 5 (pt); Nurses aides 11 (ft), 25 (pt); Physical therapists 1 (pt); Recreational therapists 3 (pt); Activities coordinators 1 (ft); Dietitians 1 (pt).
Facilities Dining room; Physical therapy room; Activities room; Chapel; Crafts room; Laundry room; Barber/Beauty shop; Library.
Activities Arts and Crafts; Cards; Games; Reading groups; Prayer groups; Movies; Shopping trips; Dances/Social or cultural gatherings.
Description Facility features a lake shore setting in a very scenic area and has lower than average room rates with a reputation for high quality care.

DAWSON

Johnson Memorial Hospital Home
Walnut Memorial Pl, Dawson, MN, 56232
Admin Leigh Hantho. *Medical Dir/Dir of Nursing* Dr P W Maus.
Licensure Skilled Care; Intermediate Care.
Beds 70. *Certified* Medicaid.
Ownership Nonprofit.
Admissions Requirements Medical examination.
Staff Physicians 2 (ft); RNs 1 (ft), 3 (pt); LPNs 4 (ft), 5 (pt); Nurses aides 17 (ft), 22 (pt); Physical therapists 1 (pt); Occupational therapists 1 (pt); Activities coordinators 1 (ft); Dietitians 1 (pt); Dentists 2 (pt); Activity assistants 5 (ft).
Facilities Dining room; Physical therapy room; Activities room; Chapel; Barber/Beauty shop; Day room.
Activities Arts and Crafts; Cards; Games; Reading groups; Prayer groups; Dances/Social or cultural gatherings; Weekly bingo.
Description Facility offers outstanding rehabilitation and social life programs.

DEER RIVER

Community Memorial Hospital and Homestead*
1002 Comstock Dr, Deer River, MN, 56636 (218) 246-8295
Admin David McClure.
Licensure Skilled Care; Intermediate Care.
Beds SNF 70; ICF 55. *Certified* Medicaid.
Ownership Nonprofit.

DEERWOOD

Cedarbrook Manor Nursing Home
Rt 1, Box 633, Deerwood, MN, 56444 (218) 534-3121
Admin Martha Gant.
Licensure Skilled Care; Intermediate Care.
Beds 77. *Certified* Medicaid.
Ownership Public.

DELANO

Delano Healthcare Center
433 County Rd 30, Delano, MN, 55328 (612) 972-2987

Admin Joanne Gilbertson. *Medical Dir/Dir of Nursing* Dr Glen Deutsch.
Licensure Skilled Care; Intermediate Care.
Beds SNF 56; ICF 8. *Certified* Medicaid.
Ownership Proprietary.
Admissions Requirements Physician's request.
Staff RNs 3 (ft), 1 (pt); LPNs 2 (ft), 3 (pt); Nurses aides 9 (ft), 31 (pt); Physical therapists 1 (ft); Recreational therapists 2 (ft); Occupational therapists 1 (ft); Speech therapists 1 (pt).
Facilities Dining room; Physical therapy room; Activities room; Barber/Beauty shop; Library.
Activities Arts and Crafts; Cards; Games; Reading groups; Prayer groups; Movies; Shopping trips; Dances/Social or cultural gatherings.

Dells Place
235 S 2nd St, Delano, MN, 55328 (612) 972-3664
Admin Vern Wahlstrom.
Licensure Intermediate Care for Mentally Retarded. *Beds* ICF/MR 9. *Certified* Medicaid.
Ownership Nonprofit.

DENT

Peleske Group Home*
Rt 1, Dent, MN, 56528 (218) 758-2570
Admin Mary Peleske.
Licensure Intermediate Care for Mentally Retarded. *Beds* 8.
Ownership Proprietary.

DETROIT LAKES

Emmanuel Nursing Home
Madison Ave, Detroit Lakes, MN, 56501 (218) 847-9215
Admin Mark Hoplin. *Medical Dir/Dir of Nursing* Dr Robert Hodap.
Licensure Skilled Care; Intermediate Care.
Beds 144. *Certified* Medicaid.
Ownership Nonprofit.
Staff RNs 6 (ft); LPNs 12 (ft); Orderlies 2 (ft); Nurses aides 50 (ft), 40 (pt); Physical therapists 1 (pt); Speech therapists 1 (pt); Activities coordinators 1 (ft); Dietitians 1 (pt).
Affiliation Lutheran
Facilities Dining room; Physical therapy room; Activities room; Chapel; Crafts room; Laundry room; Barber/Beauty shop; Library.
Activities Arts and Crafts; Cards; Games; Reading groups; Prayer groups; Movies; Shopping trips; Dances/Social or cultural gatherings.

Saint Marys Nursing Center*
1014 Lincoln Ave, Detroit Lakes, MN, 56501 (218) 847-5611
Admin Gary Greenquist.
Licensure Skilled Care. *Beds* 103. *Certified* Medicaid; Medicare.
Ownership Proprietary.

Summit Home*
920 Summit Ave, Detroit Lakes, MN, 56501 (218) 847-7176
Admin Thomas Reiffenberger.
Licensure Intermediate Care for Mentally Retarded. *Beds* 9. *Certified* Medicaid.
Ownership Nonprofit.

West Home*
1118 West Ave, Detroit Lakes, MN, 56501
(218) 847-7176
Admin Thomas Reiffenberger.
Licensure Intermediate Care for Mentally
Retarded. *Beds* 9. *Certified* Medicaid.
Ownership Nonprofit.

DODGE CENTER

Dodge Residence*
PO Box 208, 503 5th Ave NW, Dodge Center,
MN, 55927 (507) 374-2836
Admin Ron Davis.
Licensure Intermediate Care for Mentally
Retarded. *Beds* 8. *Certified* Medicaid.
Ownership Proprietary.

Fairview Nursing Home
Rt 1, PO Box 334, Dodge Center, MN, 55927
(507) 374-2578
Admin Donald W Bakke. *Medical Dir/Dir of
Nursing* O S Kulstad.
Licensure Skilled Care. *Beds* 72. *Certified* Medicaid; Medicare.
Ownership Public.
Admissions Requirements Minimum age 16;
Medical examination.
Staff RNs 3 (ft), 4 (pt); LPNs 3 (ft), 4 (pt);
Nurses aides 15 (ft), 23 (pt); Physical therapists
1 (pt); Occupational therapists 1 (pt); Activities
coordinators 1 (ft); Dietitians 1 (ft).
Facilities Dining room; Physical therapy room;
Activities room; Chapel; Laundry room; Barber/Beauty shop.
Activities Arts and Crafts; Cards; Games; Prayer groups; Movies.

DULUTH

Aftenro Home
1425 N 19th Ave E, Duluth, MN, 55811 (218)
724-7755
Admin H Ricci. *Medical Dir/Dir of Nursing* Catherine Watt.
Licensure Boarding Care. *Beds* 66.
Certified Medicaid.
Ownership Nonprofit.
Admissions Requirements Medical examination.
Staff Physicians 1 (ft); RNs 1 (pt); LPNs 9 (pt);
Nurses aides 9 (pt); Activities coordinators 1
(ft); Dietitians 1 (pt).
Affiliation Lutheran
Facilities Dining room; Activities room; Chapel; Crafts room; Laundry room; Barber/Beauty shop.
Activities Arts and Crafts; Games; Prayer groups; Movies; Shopping trips; Dances/Social or cultural gatherings.
Description Facility features a family-like atmosphere where everyone is friendly and each resident gets personal individual attention.

Caromin House—Dodge
4620 Dodge St, Duluth, MN, 55804 (218)
525-6995
Admin Trudy Carlson.
Licensure Supervised Living Facility. *Beds* 6.
Certified Medicaid.
Ownership Proprietary.

Admissions Requirements Minimum age 18.
Description Facility has home-like environment; residents are retarded adults.

Caromin House—Tioga
6009 Tioga St, Duluth, MN, 55804 (218)
525-5650
Admin Trudy Carlson.
Licensure Supervised Living Facility. *Beds* 15.
Certified Medicaid.
Ownership Proprietary.
Admissions Requirements Minimum age 18;
Females only
Description A facility for retarded adults with a home-like environment.

Champion Childrens Home
1889 Lester River Rd, Duluth, MN, 55804
(218) 525-1165
Admin Judy Johnson.
Licensure Supervised Living Facility. *Beds* 16.
Certified Medicaid.
Ownership Proprietary.
Admissions Requirements Medical examination.
Staff RNs 1 (pt); LPNs 1 (ft), 1 (pt); Nurses
aides 2 (ft), 15 (pt); Dietitians 1 (pt).
Facilities Dining room; Activities room; Laundry room; Music room; Living room.
Activities Arts and Crafts; Games; Reading
groups; Movies; Shopping trips; Dances/Social
or cultural gatherings.
Description Champion Home is located on 15
acres of land. The land is used for recreational
purposes throughout the year. Specializes in
working with the severely and profoundly mentally retarded, and in working with children
with autistic tendencies or behavioral problems.
Age range of residents is 0-25 years.

Cliff House*
1707 Cliff Ave, Duluth, MN, 55803 (218)
724-8005
Admin Judy Johnson.
Licensure Intermediate Care for Mentally
Retarded. *Beds* 6. *Certified* Medicaid.
Ownership Proprietary.

Duluth Regional Care Center I
2232 E 1st St, Duluth, MN, 55812 (218)
728-4347
Admin Clyde Johnson.
Licensure Supervised Living Facility. *Beds* 10.
Certified Medicaid.
Ownership Nonprofit.
Admissions Requirements Minimum age 17.
Facilities Dining room; Activities room; Laundry room.
Activities Cards; Games; Movies; Shopping
trips; Dances/Social or cultural gatherings.
Description Baldwin facility addresses those
needs of residents that will further their independence in the community. The house sits in
the east end of Duluth on a public bus line
making community mobility quite accessible.

Duluth Regional Care Center II
323 90th Ave W, Duluth, MN, 55808 (218)
626-1784
Admin Clyde Johnson.
Licensure Supervised Living Facility. *Beds* 6.
Certified Medicaid.
Ownership Nonprofit.

Admissions Requirements Minimum age 17;
Medical examination.
Facilities Dining room; Activities room; Laundry room.
Activities Arts and Crafts; Cards; Games;
Movies; Shopping trips; Dances/Social or cultural gatherings.
Description We are a residential facility serving
the needs of 6 retarded adults (assessing level of
independence and development of goals
directed towards greater independence of
living).

Duluth Regional Care Center III
631 W Skyline Blvd, Duluth, MN, 55806 (218)
727-5984
Admin Clyde Johnson.
Licensure Supervised Living Facility. *Beds* 10.
Certified Medicaid.
Ownership Nonprofit.
Admissions Requirements Minimum age 18;
Medical examination.
Staff RNs.
Activities Cards; Games; Movies; Shopping
trips; Dances/Social or cultural gatherings.
Description Duluth Regional Care Center III,
also known as the DRCC Triplex, is a large
white brick building surrounded by tall pine
trees overlooking the harbor city of Duluth; the
triplex is 3 apartments shared by mentally
retarded adults who are learning to become
more independent.

Duluth Regional Care Center IV*
2502 W 2nd St, Duluth, MN, 55807 (218)
727-4423
Admin Clyde Johnson.
Licensure Intermediate Care for Mentally
Retarded. *Beds* 6. *Certified* Medicaid.
Ownership Nonprofit.

Lake Haven Manor Nursing Center
7700 Grand Ave, Duluth, MN, 55807 (218)
628-2341
Admin A J Newby.
Licensure Intermediate Care. *Beds* 132. *Certified* Medicaid.
Ownership Proprietary.
Admissions Requirements Minimum age 18;
Medical examination; Physician's request.
Staff RNs 3 (ft), 7 (pt); LPNs 3 (ft), 8 (pt);
Nurses aides 31 (ft), 30 (pt); Physical therapists
1 (ft), 1 (pt); Activities coordinators 1 (ft); Dietitians 1 (pt); Social service coordinator 1 (ft).
Facilities Dining room; Physical therapy room;
Activities room; Chapel; Crafts room; Laundry
room; Barber/Beauty shop.
Activities Arts and Crafts; Cards; Games; Prayer groups; Movies; Shopping trips; Dances/Social or cultural gatherings.
Description Quality care for individuals' needs
in a home-like atmosphere geared for life and
living.

Lakeshore Lutheran Home*
4002 London Rd, Duluth, MN, 55804 (218)
525-1951
Admin Alden G Adams.
Licensure Skilled Care; Intermediate Care.
Beds SNF 160; ICF 69. *Certified* Medicaid;
Medicare.
Ownership Nonprofit.
Affiliation Lutheran

Nekton on Greysolon
3518 Greysolon Rd, Duluth, MN, 55803 (218) 724-9373
Admin Joe Modec.
Licensure Supervised Living Facility. *Beds* 6.
Certified Medicaid.
Ownership Proprietary.
Admissions Requirements Minimum age 4; Medical examination; Physician's request.
Staff Physicians 4 (pt); RNs 1 (pt); Physical therapists 1 (pt); Recreational therapists 2 (pt); Occupational therapists 1 (pt); Speech therapists 1 (pt); Activities coordinators 1 (pt); Dietitians 1 (pt); Dentists 1 (pt); Ophthalmologists 1 (pt); Podiatrists 1 (pt); Audiologists 1 (pt).
Facilities Dining room; Activities room; Laundry room; Library.
Activities Arts and Crafts; Cards; Games; Reading groups; Movies; Shopping trips; Dances/Social or cultural gatherings.
Description Nekton-Greysolon is a group home for 6 developmentally disabled teenagers. Most of our emphasis is put on "family-type" activities and creating an atmosphere to live and work with others.

Nekton on London Road*
4515 London Rd, Duluth, MN, 55804 (218) 525-3632
Admin Joe Modec.
Licensure Intermediate Care for Mentally Retarded. *Beds* 6. *Certified* Medicaid.
Ownership Proprietary.

Nekton on Springvale*
2214 Springvale Rd, Duluth, MN, 55811 (218) 722-7280
Admin Joe Modec.
Licensure Intermediate Care for Mentally Retarded. *Beds* 6. *Certified* Medicaid.
Ownership Proprietary.

Nekton on Wallace*
1702 Wallace Ave, Duluth, MN, 55803 (218) 726-6224
Admin Joe Modec.
Licensure Intermediate Care for Mentally Retarded. *Beds* 6. *Certified* Medicaid.
Ownership Proprietary.

Park Point Manor
1601 St Louis Ave, Duluth, MN, 55802 (218) 727-8651
Admin Joanne Susens. *Medical Dir/Dir of Nursing* Doug Hiza MD.
Licensure Skilled Care; Intermediate Care.
Beds SNF 216; ICF 24. *Certified* Medicaid; Medicare.
Ownership Proprietary.
Admissions Requirements Minimum age 16; Medical examination; Physician's request.
Staff Physicians 1 (pt); RNs 8 (ft), 10 (pt); LPNs 10 (ft), 20 (pt); Nurses aides 20 (ft), 90 (pt); Physical therapists 1 (ft); Recreational therapists 3 (ft); Activities coordinators 1 (ft); Speech therapists 1 (pt); Activities coordinators 1 (ft); Dietitians 1 (pt); Dentists 1 (pt); Podiatrists 1 (pt).
Facilities Dining room; Physical therapy room; Activities room; Crafts room; Laundry room; Barber/Beauty shop; Library.
Activities Arts and Crafts; Cards; Games; Reading groups; Prayer groups; Movies; Shop-

ping trips; Dances/Social or cultural gatherings.
Description Facility includes a 24-bed unit for young handicapped adults.

Residential Services of Northeast Minnesota I*
2048 E 8th St, Duluth, MN, 55812 (218) 728-6810
Admin Timothy S Mowbray.
Licensure Intermediate Care for Mentally Retarded. *Beds* 13. *Certified* Medicaid.
Ownership Nonprofit.

Residential Services of Northeastern Minnesota II*
707 Arrowhead Rd, Duluth, MN, 55811 (218) 728-6823
Admin Tim Mowbray.
Licensure Skilled Care; Intermediate Care for Mentally Retarded. *Beds* SNF 13; ICF/MR 13.
Certified Medicaid.
Ownership Nonprofit.

Saint Louis County Medical Care Facility*
2501 Rice Lake Rd, Duluth, MN, 55811 (218) 722-6646
Admin Ronald Johnson.
Licensure Skilled Care; Intermediate Care.
Beds SNF 238; ICF 77. *Certified* Medicaid.
Ownership Public.

Surf and Sand Nursing Home
3910 Minnesota Ave, Duluth, MN, 55802 (218) 727-8933
Admin W Buchanan.
Licensure Skilled Care; Intermediate Care.
Beds SNF 42; ICF 14. *Certified* Medicaid; Medicare.
Ownership Proprietary.

Thunderbird House*
229 N 4th Ave W, Duluth, MN, 55806 (218) 727-1476
Admin Edwin J Benton.
Licensure Supervised Living Facility. *Beds* 10.
Ownership Nonprofit.

Viewcrest Nursing Home*
3111 Church St, Duluth, MN, 55811 (218) 727-8801
Admin Gerald Buchanan.
Licensure Skilled Care; Intermediate Care.
Beds SNF 98; ICF 40. *Certified* Medicaid.
Ownership Proprietary.

EAGAN

Orvilla Inc*
3430 Westcott Hills Dr, Eagan, MN, 55123 (612) 454-8501
Admin James Driscoll.
Licensure Intermediate Care for Mentally Retarded. *Beds* 54. *Certified* Medicaid.
Ownership Proprietary.

Warren P Eustis House*
720 Blue Gentian Rd, Eagan, MN, 55121 (612) 452-6908
Admin Dagny Christianson.
Licensure Skilled Care; Intermediate Care.
Beds SNF 34; ICF 15. *Certified* Medicaid.
Ownership Nonprofit.

EAST GRAND FORKS

East Grand Forks Group Home
1924 5th Ave NW, East Grand Forks, MN, 56716 (218) 773-7439
Admin Vernon Nordmark.
Licensure Supervised Living Facility. *Beds* 10.
Certified Medicaid.
Ownership Nonprofit.
Admissions Requirements Minimum age 15; Medical examination.
Staff RNs.
Activities Arts and Crafts; Cards; Games; Reading groups; Movies; Shopping trips; Dances/Social or cultural gatherings.

Good Samaritan Nursing Center
1414 20th St NW, East Grand Forks, MN, 56721 (218) 773-7484
Admin David J Horazdovsky. *Medical Dir/Dir of Nursing* Dr Dale Moquist.
Licensure Skilled Care; Intermediate Care.
Beds SNF 107; ICF 22; Apartments 20. *Certified* Medicaid.
Ownership Nonprofit.
Admissions Requirements Minimum age 16; Medical examination; Physician's request.
Staff RNs 5 (ft), 2 (pt); LPNs 8 (ft), 9 (pt); Orderlies 2 (ft), 5 (pt); Nurses aides 21 (ft), 55 (pt); Activities coordinators 1 (ft).
Affiliation Lutheran
Facilities Dining room; Physical therapy room; Activities room; Chapel; Crafts room; Laundry room; Barber/Beauty shop; Library.
Activities Arts and Crafts; Cards; Games; Reading groups; Prayer groups; Movies; Shopping trips; Dances/Social or cultural gatherings.
Description Center is located in the heartland of the Red River Valley in northwestern Minnesota; primary area industry is farming. Center tends to the emotional, social, and physical well-being of each resident.

EDEN PRAIRIE

Castle Ridge Care Center
625 Prairie Center, Eden Prairie, MN, 55344
Admin Daniel R Mohler. *Medical Dir/Dir of Nursing* David Olson MD.
Licensure Skilled Care. *Beds* 60. *Certified* Medicaid.
Ownership Nonprofit.
Admissions Requirements Medical examination; Physician's request.
Staff RNs 3 (ft), 8 (pt); LPNs 2 (ft), 3 (pt); Nurses aides 10 (ft), 33 (pt).
Affiliation Baptist
Facilities Dining room; Physical therapy room; Activities room; Chapel; Crafts room; Laundry room; Barber/Beauty shop; Library.
Activities Arts and Crafts; Cards; Games; Reading groups; Prayer groups; Movies; Dances/Social or cultural gatherings.

Mauriel Humphrey Residence-Fraser*
8761 Preserve Blvd, Eden Prairie, MN, 55344 (612) 941-5376
Admin Steven Haill.
Licensure Skilled Care; Intermediate Care.
Beds 24. *Certified* Medicaid.
Ownership Nonprofit.

Muriel Humphrey Residence-Charlson*
8751 Preserve Blvd, Eden Prairie, MN, 55344
(612) 941-5376
Admin Steven Naill.
Licensure Skilled Care; Intermediate Care.
Beds SNF 12; ICF 12. *Certified* Medicaid.
Ownership Nonprofit.

Muriel Humphry Residence—Westby*
8771 Preserve Blvd, Eden Prairie, MN, 55344
(612) 941-5361
Admin Steven Naill.
Licensure Skilled Care; Intermediate Care.
Beds SNF 12; ICF 12. *Certified* Medicaid.
Ownership Nonprofit.

EDEN VALLEY

Valley Rest Home
Eden Valley, MN, 55329 (612) 453-6747
Admin Maryann Ruhland.
Licensure Boarding Care. *Beds* 21.
Ownership Proprietary.

EDGERTON

Edgebrook Rest Center Inc*
505 Trosky Rd W, Edgerton, MN, 56128 (507)
442-7121
Admin Larry Oberloh.
Licensure Intermediate Care. *Beds* 61. *Certified* Medicaid.
Ownership Nonprofit.

EDINA

Edina Care Center*
6200 Xerxes Ave S, Edina, MN, 55423 (612)
925-4810
Admin Leila E Campbell.
Licensure Skilled Care; Intermediate Care.
Beds SNF 120; ICF 41. *Certified* Medicaid.
Ownership Nonprofit.

Heritage of Edina
3456 Heritage Dr, Edina, MN, 66435 (612)
927-5656
Admin Gregg Getchell. *Medical Dir/Dir of Nursing* Dr Albert Petzek.
Licensure Nursing Home. *Beds* 121.
Ownership Proprietary.
Staff RNs 3 (ft), 12 (pt); LPNs 2 (ft), 8 (pt); Orderlies 5 (ft), 6 (pt); Nurses aides 17 (ft), 32 (pt); Physical therapists 2 (ft); Speech therapists 1 (pt); Activities coordinators 1 (ft); Dietitians 1 (ft); Dentists 1 (pt); Podiatrists 1 (pt).
Facilities Dining room; Physical therapy room; Activities room; Chapel; Crafts room; Laundry room; Barber/Beauty shop.
Activities Arts and Crafts; Cards; Games; Reading groups; Prayer groups; Movies; Shopping trips; Dances/Social or cultural gatherings.
Description Heritage of Edina is a one-story brick nursing home, located in the lovely suburb of Edina. It is close to Fairview Southdale Hospital, Southdale Shopping Center, and Southdale Medical Building. It serves private intermediate and skilled patients and has 3 lovely retirement apartments for independent elderly.

Nekton on William*
5100 William Ave, Edina, MN, 55436 (612)
644-7680
Admin Mike Seiwert.
Licensure Intermediate Care for Mentally Retarded. *Beds* 6. *Certified* Medicaid.
Ownership Proprietary.

ELK RIVER

Elk River Nursing Home*
400 Evans Ave, Elk River, MN, 55330 (612)
441-1213
Admin Timothy J O'Brien.
Licensure Skilled Care; Intermediate Care.
Beds SNF 60; ICF 60. *Certified* Medicaid; Medicare.
Ownership Nonprofit.

The Shire—Dungarvin IV*
9607 201st Ave NE, Elk River, MN, 55330
(612) 441-6043
Admin Diane Jones Madden.
Licensure Intermediate Care for Mentally Retarded. *Beds* 12. *Certified* Medicaid.
Ownership Proprietary.

ELLSWORTH

Parkview Manor Nursing Home
Ellsworth, MN, 56129 (507) 967-2482
Admin Jane Davidson.
Licensure Intermediate Care. *Beds* 60. *Certified* Medicaid.
Ownership Public.
Admissions Requirements Medical examination; Physician's request.
Staff RNs 1 (ft), 1 (pt); LPNs 3 (pt); Nurses aides 11 (ft), 22 (pt); Activities coordinators 1 (ft), 2 (pt); Dietitians 1 (pt).
Facilities Dining room; Activities room; Crafts room; Laundry room.
Activities Arts and Crafts; Cards; Games; Reading groups; Prayer groups; Movies; Baking.
Description Once a week, residents play bingo which they enjoy very much with fruit for prizes. They also have bowling once a week with a traveling trophy.

ERSKINE

Johnson Rest Home*
Vance Ave N, Erskine, MN, 56535 (218)
687-3955
Admin Palma C Johnson.
Licensure Intermediate Care. *Beds* 8.
Ownership Proprietary.

Pioneer Memorial Home*
Box 189, Hwy 59 and 2, Erskine, MN, 56535
(218) 687-2365
Admin Dorothy Sundahl.
Licensure Skilled Care; Intermediate Care.
Beds SNF 37; ICF 32. *Certified* Medicaid.
Ownership Nonprofit.

EVANSVILLE

Crestview Manor
PO Box 176, Evansville, MN, 56326 (218)
948-2210
Admin Rick Andresen. *Medical Dir/Dir of Nursing* Dr James Lueders.
Licensure Skilled Care; Intermediate Care.
Beds 70. *Certified* Medicaid.
Ownership Proprietary.
Staff Physicians 1 (pt); RNs 1 (ft), 2 (pt); LPNs 2 (ft), 6 (pt); Nurses aides 9 (ft), 24 (pt); Activities coordinators 1 (ft).
Facilities Dining room; Physical therapy room; Crafts room; Laundry room; Barber/Beauty shop.
Activities Arts and Crafts; Cards; Games; Reading groups; Prayer groups; Movies; Shopping trips; Dances/Social or cultural gatherings.
Description Facility offers adult day care and respite care.

EVELETH

Arrowhead Nursing Home*
601 Grant Ave, Eveleth, MN, 55734 (218)
741-2550
Admin Phyllis J King.
Licensure Skilled Care; Intermediate Care.
Beds SNF 85; ICF 37. *Certified* Medicaid.
Ownership Proprietary.

Eveleth Fitzgerald Community Hospital— Nursing Home
227 McKinley Ave, Eveleth, MN, 55734
Admin Rosalyn Karosich. *Medical Dir/Dir of Nursing* R M Martinson MD.
Licensure Skilled Care. *Beds* 24. *Certified* Medicaid; Medicare.
Ownership Nonprofit.
Admissions Requirements Minimum age 18; Medical examination.
Staff Physicians 7 (ft); RNs 5 (ft), 3 (pt); LPNs 2 (ft), 3 (pt); Nurses aides 3 (ft), 3 (pt); Physical therapists 1 (pt); Recreational therapists 1 (pt); Activities coordinators 1 (pt); Dietitians 1 (pt); Ophthalmologists 1 (pt); Podiatrists 1 (pt).
Facilities Dining room; Activities room; Crafts room; Laundry room; Barber/Beauty shop.
Activities Arts and Crafts; Cards; Games; Reading groups; Prayer groups; Movies.
Description This hospital attached facility makes available laboratory and X-ray services.

Range Center—Birchwood Home*
1016 W 1st St, Eveleth, MN, 55734 (218)
744-3915
Admin James Mickelson.
Licensure Intermediate Care for Mentally Retarded. *Beds* 6. *Certified* Medicaid.
Ownership Nonprofit.

EXCELSIOR

Excelsior Nursing Home*
515 Division St, Excelsior, MN, 55331 (612)
464-5488
Admin Ruth Hauge.
Licensure Skilled Care. *Beds* 66. *Certified* Medicaid.
Ownership Proprietary.

Lake Auburn Home for Aged
7555 Victoria Dr, Excelsior, MN, 55331 (612) 443-2421
Admin Marvel Heath.
Licensure Boarding Care. *Beds* 22.
Ownership Nonprofit.
Admissions Requirements Minimum age 45; Medical examination.
Staff RNs 2 (pt); Nurses aides 9 (pt); Recreational therapists 1 (pt); Activities coordinators 1 (pt).
Affiliation Moravian
Facilities Dining room; Activities room; Laundry room; Library.
Activities Arts and Crafts; Cards; Games; Movies; Shopping trips.
Description Home is in a tranquil rural setting caring for semi-independent residents who need a place between independent living and a skilled or intermediate care facility; a loving home-like atmosphere provided by a caring staff that centers on individual needs and gives the residents a sense of belonging.

Minnetonka Health Care Center
20395 Summerville Rd, Excelsior, MN, 55331 (612) 474-4474
Admin Ramona Beckman. *Medical Dir/Dir of Nursing* Dr Milton Seifert.
Licensure Intermediate Care. *Beds* 21. *Certified* Medicaid.
Ownership Proprietary.
Admissions Requirements Minimum age 18; Medical examination; Physician's request.
Staff RNs 1 (ft), 1 (pt); LPNs 1 (ft), 2 (pt); Nurses aides 2 (ft), 4 (pt); Recreational therapists 1 (pt); Activities coordinators 1 (pt); Dietitians 1 (pt).
Facilities Dining room; Activities room.
Activities Arts and Crafts; Cards; Games; Reading groups; Prayer groups; Movies; Shopping trips; Dances/Social or cultural gatherings.
Description We are primarily interested in the care of older, mental health patients. We are small and organize our care and programs to help patients feel they are living as a family and have some small responsibilities towards the family unit.

Mount Olivet Rolling Acres*
7200 Rolling Acres Rd, Excelsior, MN, 55331 (612) 474-5974
Admin Gerald F Walsh.
Licensure Intermediate Care for Mentally Retarded. *Beds* 74. *Certified* Medicaid.
Ownership Nonprofit.

FAIRFAX

Fairfax Nursing Home
10th Ave, SE, Fairfax, MN, 55332 (507) 426-8241
Medical Dir/Dir of Nursing Dr Thomas Gillis.
Licensure Intermediate Care. *Beds* 65. *Certified* Medicaid.
Ownership Proprietary.
Staff Physicians 1 (pt); RNs 3 (ft), 3 (pt); LPNs 3 (ft), 3 (pt); Nurses aides 10 (ft), 15 (pt); Physical therapists 1 (pt); Occupational therapists 1 (ft), 1 (pt); Speech therapists 1 (pt); Activities coordinators 1 (ft); Dietitians 1 (pt); Dentists 1 (pt); Podiatrists 1 (pt); Audiologists 1

(pt).
Facilities Dining room; Physical therapy room; Activities room; Chapel; Crafts room; Laundry room; Barber/Beauty shop.
Activities Arts and Crafts; Cards; Games; Reading groups; Prayer groups; Movies; Shopping trips; Dances/Social or cultural gatherings.

FAIRMONT

Fairmont Community Hospital*
835 Johnson St, Fairmont, MN, 56031 (507) 238-4259
Admin Tom A Doherty.
Licensure Skilled Care; Intermediate Care. *Beds* 74.
Ownership Nonprofit.

Lakeview Methodist Health Care Center
610 Summit Dr, Fairmont, MN, 56031 (507) 235-6606
Admin George W Klus. *Medical Dir/Dir of Nursing* Dr H A Williamson.
Licensure Skilled Care; Intermediate Care; Boarding Care. *Beds* SNF 81; ICF 60; Boarding Care 18. *Certified* Medicaid.
Ownership Nonprofit.
Admissions Requirements Medical examination; Physician's request.
Staff RNs 5 (ft), 7 (pt); LPNs 8 (ft), 6 (pt); Orderlies 1 (ft), 3 (pt); Nurses aides 17 (ft), 36 (pt); Physical therapists 2 (ft); Reality therapists 1 (ft); Recreational therapists 2 (ft); Activities coordinators 1 (ft); Dietitians 1 (ft).
Affiliation Methodist
Facilities Dining room; Physical therapy room; Activities room; Chapel; Laundry room; Barber/Beauty shop; Library.
Activities Arts and Crafts; Cards; Games; Reading groups; Prayer groups; Movies; Shopping trips; Dances/Social or cultural gatherings.

REM Fairmont 8*
111 Dorothy St, Fairmont, MN, 56031 (507) 238-4751
Admin Thomas Miller.
Licensure Skilled Care; Intermediate Care. *Beds* SNF 15; ICF 15. *Certified* Medicaid.
Ownership Proprietary.

REM-Fairmont Inc
107 Dorothy St, Fairmont, MN, 56031 (507) 238-4751
Admin Thomas Miller.
Licensure Supervised Living Facility. *Beds* 30. *Certified* Medicaid.
Ownership Proprietary.
Admissions Requirements Minimum age 16; Medical examination.
Staff Direct care 10 (ft), 14 (pt).
Facilities Dining room; Activities room; Crafts room; Laundry room.
Activities Arts and Crafts; Cards; Games; Reading groups; Movies; Shopping trips; Dances/Social or cultural gatherings.
Description REM-Fairmont Inc is apartment-style living for adults, men and women, who are mentally retarded. REM-Fairmont Inc provides 24-hour supervision and staff that are trained to teach the residents skills that will enable them to do more for themselves.

FARIBAULT

Constance Bultman Wilson Center
PO Box 917, Faribault, MN, 55021 (507) 334-5561
Admin M R Wilson.
Licensure Supervised Living Facility. *Beds* 50.
Ownership Nonprofit.

Faribault Manor Nursing Home
1738 Hulett Ave, Faribault, MN, 55021 (507) 334-3919
Admin Dave Westbrook. *Medical Dir/Dir of Nursing* Dr Goode.
Licensure Skilled Care. *Beds* 94. *Certified* Medicaid; Medicare.
Ownership Proprietary.
Admissions Requirements Minimum age 18.
Staff Physicians 1 (pt); RNs 3 (ft), 4 (pt); LPNs 6 (ft), 3 (pt); Nurses aides 23 (ft), 19 (pt); Physical therapists 1 (pt); Reality therapists 1 (pt); Occupational therapists 1 (pt); Speech therapists 1 (pt); Activities coordinators 2 (ft), 1 (pt); Dietitians 1 (pt); Dentists 1 (pt); Ophthalmologists 1 (pt); Podiatrists 1 (pt); Audiologists 1 (pt).
Facilities Dining room; Physical therapy room; Activities room; Laundry room; Barber/Beauty shop.
Activities Arts and Crafts; Cards; Games; Reading groups; Prayer groups; Movies; Shopping trips; Dances/Social or cultural gatherings.

Faribault State Hospital*
Faribault, MN, 55021 (507) 332-3000
Admin Charles V Turnbull.
Licensure Skilled Care; Intermediate Care for Mentally Retarded. *Beds* SNF 35; ICF/MR 775. *Certified* Medicaid.
Ownership Public.

Pleasant Manor
27 Brand Ave, Faribault, MN, 55021 (507) 334-2036
Admin David Meillier. *Medical Dir/Dir of Nursing* Dr Robert C Speckhals.
Licensure Skilled Care; Intermediate Care. *Beds* SNF 63; ICF 40. *Certified* Medicaid; Medicare.
Ownership Proprietary.
Admissions Requirements Minimum age 18; Medical examination.
Staff Physicians 12 (ft); RNs 2 (ft), 7 (pt); LPNs 9 (ft), 7 (pt); Nurses aides 19 (ft), 44 (pt); Physical therapists 1 (pt); Recreational therapists 3 (ft); Occupational therapists 1 (pt); Speech therapists 1 (pt); Activities coordinators 1 (pt); Dietitians 1 (pt); Dentists 1 (pt); Podiatrists 1 (pt); Audiologists 1 (pt).
Facilities Dining room; Physical therapy room; Activities room; Crafts room; Laundry room; Barber/Beauty shop.
Activities Arts and Crafts; Cards; Games; Reading groups; Prayer groups; Movies; Shopping trips; Dances/Social or cultural gatherings.

Region Park Hall
1150 SW 3rd St, Faribault, MN, 55021 (507) 334-6292
Admin Charles A Kroeger.
Licensure Intermediate Care for Mentally Retarded. *Beds* 12. *Certified* Medicaid.
Ownership Proprietary.

Resident Homes-Harmony
611 NW 5th St, Faribault, MN, 55021 (507) 334-5262
Admin Brad Reddeman. *Medical Dir/Dir of Nursing* Helen Dahlstedt.
Licensure Supervised Living Facility. *Beds* ICF/MR 8. *Certified* Medicaid.
Ownership Nonprofit.
Admissions Requirements Minimum age 18; Females only
Staff RNs 1 (pt); Activities coordinators 1 (pt).
Facilities Dining room; Laundry room.
Activities Arts and Crafts; Cards; Games; Reading groups; Movies; Shopping trips; Dances/Social or cultural gatherings.

Resident Homes-Haven
538 NW 2nd St, Faribault, MN, 55021 (507) 332-8320
Admin Brad Reddeman. *Medical Dir/Dir of Nursing* Helen Dahlstedt.
Licensure Supervised Living Facility. *Beds* 9. *Certified* Medicaid.
Ownership Nonprofit.
Admissions Requirements Minimum age 18; Medical examination; Physician's request.
Staff RNs 1 (pt); Recreational therapists 1 (ft).
Facilities Dining room; Laundry room.
Activities Arts and Crafts; Cards; Games; Reading groups; Movies; Shopping trips; Dances/Social or cultural gatherings.

Saint Lucan Convalescent Center*
503 E Division St, Faribault, MN, 55021 (507) 334-4314
Admin David Erickson.
Licensure Skilled Care. *Beds* 148. *Certified* Medicaid; Medicare.
Ownership Public.
Affiliation Roman Catholic

St Lucas Convalescent and Geriatric Care
503 E Division St, Faribault, MN, 55021 (507) 334-4314
Admin Linda Ripka. *Medical Dir/Dir of Nursing* Robert P Meyer MD.
Licensure Skilled Care. *Beds* 148. *Certified* Medicaid; Medicare.
Ownership Nonprofit.
Admissions Requirements Medical examination; Physician's request.
Staff RNs 5 (ft), 1 (pt); LPNs 7 (ft), 12 (pt); Nurses aides 22 (ft), 49 (pt); Physical therapists 1 (ft); Occupational therapists 1 (pt); Speech therapists 1 (pt); Activities coordinators 1 (ft); Dietitians 1 (pt); Physical therapy assistants 2 (pt).
Affiliation Church of Christ
Facilities Dining room; Physical therapy room; Activities room; Chapel; Crafts room; Laundry room; Barber/Beauty shop.
Activities Arts and Crafts; Cards; Games; Reading groups; Prayer groups; Movies; Shopping trips; Dances/Social or cultural gatherings.
Description Facility has adult day care program.

Seventh Street House*
216 7th St NW, Faribault, MN, 55021 (507) 334-8985
Admin Russell Kennedy.

Licensure Intermediate Care for Mentally Retarded. *Beds* 15. *Certified* Medicaid.
Ownership Proprietary.

214 Park Avenue Home*
214 Park Ave, Faribault, MN, 55021 (507) 334-7808
Admin George Johnson.
Licensure Intermediate Care for Mentally Retarded. *Beds* 15.
Ownership Proprietary.

FARMINGTON

Sanford Nursing Home
913 Main St, Farmington, MN, 55024 (612) 463-7825
Admin Gretchen M Dahlen. *Medical Dir/Dir of Nursing* T W Lai MD.
Licensure Skilled Care. *Beds* 65. *Certified* Medicaid; Medicare.
Ownership Nonprofit.
Admissions Requirements Minimum age 50; Medical examination; Physician's request.
Staff RNs 2 (ft), 4 (pt); LPNs 2 (ft), 6 (pt); Nurses aides 6 (ft), 30 (pt); Physical therapists 1 (pt); Activities coordinators 1 (ft), 1 (pt); Dietitians 3 (pt).
Facilities Dining room; Physical therapy room; Activities room; Chapel; Crafts room; Laundry room; Barber/Beauty shop; Library.
Activities Arts and Crafts; Cards; Games; Reading groups; Prayer groups; Movies; Shopping trips; Dances/Social or cultural gatherings; Luncheon trips; Daytime trips (other than shopping).
Description Sanford Nursing Home provides quality care in a home-like setting and caring atmosphere.

FERGUS FALLS

Broen Memorial Home*
420 Alcott Ave E, Fergus Falls, MN, 56537 (218) 736-5441
Admin Ina M Larson.
Licensure Intermediate Care. *Beds* 232. *Certified* Medicaid.

Fergus Falls State Hospital*
Corner Fir and Union, Fergus Falls, MN, 56537 (218) 739-7200
Admin Robert F Hoffman.
Licensure Intermediate Care for Mentally Retarded. *Beds* 270. *Certified* Medicaid.
Ownership Public.

Koep Group Home*
Rt 3, Box 220, Fergus Falls, MN, 56537 (218) 736-6312
Admin Ione Koep.
Licensure Intermediate Care for Mentally Retarded. *Beds* 8. *Certified* Medicaid.
Ownership Proprietary.

Lake Park-Wild Rice Residential Treatment Center for Children
S Maybelle, Fergus Falls, MN, 56537 (218) 736-7549
Admin Terry Denley.
Licensure Supervised Living Facility. *Beds* 46.

Certified Medicaid.
Ownership Nonprofit.
Admissions Requirements Minimum age 7; Medical examination.
Staff RNs 1 (ft); LPNs 1 (ft), 3 (pt).
Affiliation Lutheran
Facilities Dining room; Activities room; Crafts room; Laundry room; Library.
Activities Arts and Crafts; Cards; Games; Movies; Shopping trips; Dances/Social or cultural gatherings.
Description Facility features a working relationship with Fergus Falls Public School, Lakeland Mental Health Center, Fergus Falls Medical Group, Fergus Falls Park & Recreation, and other community services.

Pioneer Home
1006 S Sheridan St, Fergus Falls, MN, 56537 (218) 739-3361
Admin Carmon Jackson. *Medical Dir/Dir of Nursing* David Bjork MD.
Licensure Intermediate Care; Boarding Care. *Beds* ICF 112; Boarding Care 26. *Certified* Medicaid.
Ownership Nonprofit.
Admissions Requirements Minimum age 16; Medical examination.
Staff RNs 3 (ft); LPNs 5 (ft), 2 (pt); Orderlies 3 (ft); Nurses aides 31 (ft), 21 (pt); Recreational therapists 2 (ft), 1 (pt); Activities coordinators 1 (ft).
Affiliation Lutheran
Facilities Dining room; Physical therapy room; Activities room; Chapel; Crafts room; Laundry room; Barber/Beauty shop; Library; Therapy park.
Activities Arts and Crafts; Cards; Games; Reading groups; Prayer groups; Movies; Shopping trips; Dances/Social or cultural gatherings; Music groups.
Description This facility is oriented toward wellness with emphasis on activity for physical, mental, and spiritual well-being.

Piper Group Home
Rt 6, Box 167, Fergus Falls, MN, 56537 (218) 736-6612
Admin Catherine Piper.
Licensure Supervised Living Facility. *Beds* 6. *Certified* Medicaid.
Ownership Proprietary.
Admissions Requirements Minimum age 18; Females only; Medical examination; Physician's request.
Facilities Dining room; Crafts room; Laundry room.
Activities Arts and Crafts; Cards; Games; Movies; Shopping trips; Dances/Social or cultural gatherings.
Description Facility serves 6 mentally retarded adults. Program emphasizes independent living skills towards community independence and living.

Project New Hope 1*
527 W Cedar, Fergus Falls, MN, 56308 (612) 739-3293
Admin Glenn Medicraft.
Licensure Intermediate Care for Mentally Retarded. *Beds* 6. *Certified* Medicaid.
Ownership Nonprofit.

Project New Hope 2*
1505 S Arlington, Fergus Falls, MN, 56308
(612) 739-3293
Admin Glenn Medicraft.
Licensure Intermediate Care for Mentally
Retarded. *Beds* 6. *Certified* Medicaid.
Ownership Nonprofit.

Project New Hope 3*
720 W Douglas, Fergus Falls, MN, 56308 (612)
736-3293
Admin Glenn Medicraft.
Licensure Intermediate Care for Mentally
Retarded. *Beds* 6. *Certified* Medicaid.
Ownership Nonprofit.

FERTILE

Fair Meadow Nursing Home*
Box 8, Fertile, MN, 56540 (218) 945-6194
Admin Barry J Robertson.
Licensure Intermediate Care. *Beds* 83. *Certified* Medicaid.
Ownership Public.

FOLEY

Foley Nursing Center*
10 Pine St, Foley, MN, 56329 (612) 968-7268
Admin Richard Jokinen.
Licensure Skilled Care; Intermediate Care.
Beds SNF 97; ICF 20. *Certified* Medicaid.
Ownership Proprietary.

FOREST LAKE

Birchwood Health Care Center
604 NE 1st St, Forest Lake, MN, 55025 (612)
464-5600
Admin Thomas Goeritz. *Medical Dir/Dir of
Nursing* Carl Pikert.
Licensure Skilled Care; Intermediate Care.
Beds SNF 40; ICF 121. *Certified* Medicaid;
Medicare.
Ownership Proprietary.
Admissions Requirements Minimum age 16;
Medical examination; Physician's request.
Staff Physicians 3 (pt); RNs 7 (ft), 10 (pt);
LPNs 2 (ft), 15 (pt); Orderlies 2 (ft); Nurses
aides 20 (ft), 55 (pt); Physical therapists 1 (ft), 1
(pt); Occupational therapists 2 (ft); Speech therapists 1 (pt); Activities coordinators 2 (ft), 3
(pt); Dietitians 1 (pt); Dentists 1 (pt); Ophthalmologists 1 (pt); Podiatrists 1 (pt); Audiologists
1 (pt).
Facilities Dining room; Physical therapy room;
Activities room; Chapel; Crafts room; Laundry
room; Barber/Beauty shop.
Activities Arts and Crafts; Cards; Games;
Reading groups; Prayer groups; Movies; Shopping trips; Dances/Social or cultural gatherings.
Description Center offers hospice and respite
care; CASA; home health care program.

FOSSTON

Fosston Group Home*
N Mark Ave, Fosston, MN, 56542 (218)
435-6088
Admin Vernon C Nordmark.

Licensure Intermediate Care for Mentally
Retarded. *Beds* 10. *Certified* Medicaid.
Ownership Nonprofit.

Fosston Municipal Hospital*
900 Hilligoss, Fosston, MN, 56542 (218)
435-1494
Admin Dale Jackson.
Licensure Intermediate Care. *Beds* 50.
Ownership Nonprofit.

Johnson Rest Home
516 2nd St NE, Fosston, MN, 56542 (218)
435-1494
Admin Palma C Johnson. *Medical Dir/Dir of
Nursing* Dr Haven.
Licensure Intermediate Care; Boarding Care.
Beds ICF 20; Boarding Care 20. *Certified* Medicaid.
Ownership Proprietary.
Admissions Requirements Medical examination; Physician's request.
Staff RNs 1 (ft), 1 (pt); LPNs 1 (pt); Nurses
aides 10 (pt); Recreational therapists 1 (ft); Dietitians 1 (pt).
Facilities Dining room; Activities room; Crafts
room.
Activities Arts and Crafts; Cards; Games;
Reading groups; Prayer groups; Movies; Shopping trips; Dances/Social or cultural gatherings.
Description We are a small privately owned
home-like facility located between Grand
Forks, North Dakota and Bemidji, Minnesota
where the prairie meets the pine. Due to our
size, we are able to give individualized care and
cater to special requests.

Midway Care Center
114 2nd St NE, Fosston, MN, 56542 (218)
435-1272
Admin Allen G Potvin.
Licensure Boarding Care. *Beds* 32. *Certified* Medicaid.
Ownership Proprietary.
Admissions Requirements Minimum age 16;
Medical examination; Physician's request.
Staff Physicians 1 (pt); RNs 1 (ft); LPNs 1 (ft),
1 (pt); Nurses aides 2 (ft), 5 (pt); Physical therapists 1 (pt); Recreational therapists 2 (ft); Dietitians 1 (pt); Dentists 1 (pt); Podiatrists 1 (pt).
Facilities Dining room; Activities room; Crafts
room; Laundry room; Barber/Beauty shop.
Activities Arts and Crafts; Cards; Games;
Reading groups; Prayer groups; Movies; Shopping trips; Dances/Social or cultural gatherings.
Description Facility provides 3 licensure
catagories—nursing home, boarding care, and
board and lodging; facility located right off U.S.
Highway 2 and uptown Fosston, making it easy
to get to and convenient for visitors.

FRANKLIN

Franklin Healthcare Center
900 E 3rd St, Franklin, MN, 55333 (507)
557-2211
Admin Lamberta Doll. *Medical Dir/Dir of
Nursing* Dr Buhr and Dr Thompson.
Licensure Skilled Care; Intermediate Care;
Boarding Care. *Beds* SNF 24; ICF 34. *Certified* Medicaid.
Ownership Proprietary.

Admissions Requirements Minimum age 16;
Medical examination.
Staff RNs 1 (ft), 3 (pt); LPNs 1 (ft), 10 (pt);
Nurses aides 11 (ft), 40 (pt); Physical therapists
1 (pt); Occupational therapists 1 (pt); Activities
coordinators 1 (ft), 1 (pt); Dietitians 1 (ft).
Facilities Dining room; Physical therapy room;
Activities room; Chapel; Crafts room; Laundry
room; Barber/Beauty shop.
Activities Arts and Crafts; Cards; Games;
Reading groups; Prayer groups; Movies; Shopping trips; Dances/Social or cultural gatherings;
International days; Adopt-a-grandparent program.
Description Facility is situated on a bluff overlooking the Minnesota River valley's
spectacular view; features a family council and
a resident council.

FRAZEE

Frazee Retirement Center*
Box 96, 2nd St SW, Frazee, MN, 56544 (218)
334-4501
Admin Robert B McTaggert.
Licensure Skilled Care; Intermediate Care.
Beds SNF 76; ICF 26. *Certified* Medicaid.
Ownership Proprietary.

Smith Group Home
Rt 1, Box 17A, Frazee, MN, 56544 (218)
334-5651
Admin Leona Smith.
Licensure Supervised Living Facility. *Beds* 7.
Certified Medicaid.
Ownership Proprietary.

FRIDLEY

Fridley Convalescent Home*
7590 Lyric Ln, Fridley, MN, 55432 (612)
786-7700
Admin Jackie Jedlicki.
Licensure Skilled Care. *Beds* 129. *Certified* Medicaid.
Ownership Nonprofit.

Lynwood Healthcare Center
5700 E River Rd, Fridley, MN, 55432 (612)
571-3150
Admin Gary Larson. *Medical Dir/Dir of
Nursing* Dr C E Turbak.
Licensure Skilled Care. *Beds* 55. *Certified* Medicaid; Medicare.
Staff Physicians 1 (pt); RNs 2 (ft), 1 (pt); LPNs
2 (ft), 5 (pt); Nurses aides 10 (ft), 15 (pt);
Physical therapists 1 (ft); Occupational therapists 1 (ft); Speech therapists 1 (pt); Activities
coordinators 1 (ft), 1 (pt); Dietitians 1 (pt).

FULDA

Maple Lawn Nursing Home
400 7th St, Fulda, MN, 56131 (507) 425-2571
Admin Mariann K Kroshus.
Licensure Intermediate Care. *Beds* 62. *Certified* Medicaid.
Ownership Nonprofit.

New Dawn Inc*
307 S Lafayette Ave, Fulda, MN, 56131 (507) 425-3278
Admin Louis R Nelson.
Licensure Intermediate Care for Mentally Retarded. *Beds* 15. *Certified* Medicaid.
Ownership Nonprofit.

GAYLORD

Gaylord Community Hospital and Nursing Home
640 3rd St, Gaylord, MN, 55334
Admin David DeMars. *Medical Dir/Dir of Nursing* Dr Waldo Munderovski
Licensure Skilled Care. *Beds* 58. *Certified* Medicaid.
Ownership Public.
Admissions Requirements Minimum age 16; Medical examination; Physician's request.
Staff Physicians 5 (pt); RNs 1 (ft), 1 (pt); LPNs 10 (pt); Nurses aides 26 (pt); Physical therapists 1 (pt); Reality therapists 1 (ft); Recreational therapists 1 (ft), 2 (pt); Occupational therapists 1 (pt); Activities coordinators 1 (ft); Dietitians 1 (pt).
Facilities Dining room; Physical therapy room; Activities room; Crafts room; Laundry room; Barber/Beauty shop; Library.
Activities Arts and Crafts; Cards; Games; Prayer groups; Movies; Shopping trips; Dances/Social or cultural gatherings.
Description This beautiful facility offers excellent nursing care and a picturesque view of Lake Titloe and its islands from both upper and lower decks.

GLENCOE

Glenhaven Nursing Home
705 E 18th St, Glencoe, MN, 55336 (612) 864-3158
Admin John C Doidge. *Medical Dir/Dir of Nursing* Dr Donald Rudy.
Licensure Skilled Care; Intermediate Care.
Beds SNF 88; ICF 22. *Certified* Medicaid; Medicare.
Ownership Public.
Staff RNs 3 (ft), 3 (pt); LPNs 3 (ft), 8 (pt); Nurses aides 11 (ft), 28 (pt); Occupational therapists 1 (pt); Speech therapists 1 (pt); Activities coordinators 2 (ft), 2 (pt).
Facilities Dining room; Physical therapy room; Activities room; Chapel; Crafts room; Laundry room; Barber/Beauty shop; Library.
Activities Arts and Crafts; Cards; Games; Reading groups; Prayer groups; Movies; Shopping trips; Dances/Social or cultural gatherings.

GLENWOOD

Glenwood Retirement Home Inc*
719 SE 2nd St, Glenwood, MN, 56334 (612) 634-5131
Admin Gordon H Amble.
Licensure Skilled Care; Intermediate Care.
Beds SNF 53; ICF 47. *Certified* Medicaid.
Ownership Nonprofit.

Lakeview Care Center
Franklin at Lakeshore Dr, Glenwood, MN, 56334 (612) 634-4552
Admin Ruth Gunderson. *Medical Dir/Dir of Nursing* Dr Jeffrey Schlueter.
Licensure Skilled Care; Intermediate Care.
Beds 66. *Certified* Medicaid; Medicare.
Ownership Proprietary.
Admissions Requirements Minimum age 16; Medical examination.
Staff RNs 2 (ft), 2 (pt); LPNs 2 (ft), 2 (pt); Nurses aides 10 (ft), 20 (pt); Physical therapists 1 (ft); Activities coordinators 1 (ft).
Facilities Dining room; Activities room; Laundry room.
Activities Arts and Crafts; Cards; Games; Reading groups; Prayer groups; Movies; Shopping trips; Dances/Social or cultural gatherings.

GOLDEN VALLEY

Colonial Acres Health Care Center
5825 Saint Croix Ave, Golden Valley, MN, 55422 (612) 544-1555
Admin Timothy Wenberg. *Medical Dir/Dir of Nursing* Dr Roger Grimm.
Licensure Skilled Care; Intermediate Care.
Beds 151. *Certified* Medicaid.
Ownership Nonprofit.
Admissions Requirements Medical examination; Physician's request.
Staff Physicians 1 (pt); RNs 7 (ft), 13 (pt); LPNs 8 (ft), 8 (pt); Orderlies 5 (ft), 13 (pt); Nurses aides 21 (ft), 42 (pt); Physical therapists 1 (ft); Occupational therapists 1 (ft); Speech therapists 1 (pt); Activities coordinators 1 (ft); Dietitians 1 (pt).
Affiliation Evangelical Covenant Church
Facilities Dining room; Physical therapy room; Activities room; Chapel; Crafts room; Laundry room; Barber/Beauty shop; Library.
Activities Arts and Crafts; Games; Reading groups; Prayer groups; Movies; Shopping trips; Dances/Social or cultural gatherings.
Description Colonial Acres is a Christian skilled nursing home that has 2 levels of a 4-level life care center located in western Minneapolis. Shopping is nearby and the facility is located in a park-like setting with major freeways within blocks.

Courage Residence
3915 Golden Valley Rd, Golden Valley, MN, 55422 (612) 588-0811
Admin Aileen Baesemann. *Medical Dir/Dir of Nursing* Dr Alan Bensman.
Licensure Skilled Care. *Beds* 64. *Certified* Medicaid.
Ownership Nonprofit.
Admissions Requirements Minimum age 18.
Staff Physicians 5 (pt); RNs 4 (ft), 6 (pt); LPNs 1 (ft), 6 (pt); Orderlies and; Nurses aides 11 (ft), 20 (pt); Physical therapists 2 (ft), 1 (pt); Recreational therapists 2 (ft); Occupational therapists 3 (ft), 1 (pt); Speech therapists 1 (ft), 1 (pt); Activities coordinators 2 (ft); Dietitians 1 (pt); Audiologists 1 (pt).
Facilities Dining room; Physical therapy room; Laundry room; Library.
Activities Arts and Crafts; Cards; Games; Reading groups; Prayer groups; Movies; Shopping trips; Dances/Social or cultural gatherings.

Description Courage Residence is a transitional rehabilitation facility for physically disabled young adults. Clients are admitted for a specific period of time with the goal of moving to a more independent living situation in the community. Programs are individualized and clients can participate in physical, occupational, and speech therapy, recreational therapy, driver's education, vocational and personal counseling, family counseling, discharge planning, nursing education, and follow-up services.

Trevilla of Golden Valley*
7505 Country Club Rd, Golden Valley, MN, 55427 (612) 545-0416
Admin Sharon Bertsch.
Licensure Skilled Care; Intermediate Care.
Beds SNF 218; ICF 35. *Certified* Medicaid; Medicare.
Ownership Proprietary.

Weldwood Health Care Center
5411 Circle Downs, Golden Valley, MN, 55416 (612) 545-5633
Admin Joyce Scott. *Medical Dir/Dir of Nursing* William Shimp MD.
Licensure Skilled Care; Intermediate Care.
Beds SNF 66; ICF 22. *Certified* Medicaid.
Ownership Proprietary.
Admissions Requirements Minimum age 18; Medical examination; Physician's request.
Staff RNs 6 (ft), 2 (pt); LPNs 5 (ft), 2 (pt); Nurses aides 30 (ft), 15 (pt); Recreational therapists 2 (ft); Activities coordinators 1 (ft); Dietitians 1 (pt); Dentists 1 (pt); Podiatrists 1 (pt); Social services 1 (ft), 1 (pt).
Facilities Dining room; Activities room; Crafts room; Laundry room; Barber/Beauty shop.
Activities Arts and Crafts; Cards; Games; Reading groups; Prayer groups; Movies; Shopping trips; Dances/Social or cultural gatherings; Camping trips.
Description Facility is located in a western suburb of Minneapolis.

GRACEVILLE

Grace Home*
116 W 2nd St, Graceville, MN, 56240 (612) 748-7261
Admin Charles E Lund.
Licensure Intermediate Care. *Beds* 60. *Certified* Medicaid.
Ownership Nonprofit.

GRAND MARAIS

Cook County Northshore Hospital—Care and Nursing Center
Gunflint Train, Grand Marais, MN, 55604
Admin William R Allen. *Medical Dir/Dir of Nursing* Dr Michael DeBevec.
Beds 47.
Ownership Nonprofit.
Staff RNs 2 (ft), 4 (pt); LPNs 1 (ft), 1 (pt); Nurses aides 10 (ft), 10 (pt); Activities coordinators 1 (ft); Dietitians 1 (pt).
Facilities Dining room; Physical therapy room; Activities room; Laundry room; Barber/Beauty shop; Library.
Activities Arts and Crafts; Cards; Games;

Reading groups; Shopping trips.
Description This nursing home, attached to a small rural hospital, offers complete services—laboratory, X-ray, pharmacy, dietary, activities, surgery, emergency room, ambulance, nursing, and much more care.

GRAND MEADOW

Meadow Manor Nursing Home
210 E Grand Ave, Grand Meadow, MN, 55936
(507) 754-5212
Admin Robert A Lamp. *Medical Dir/Dir of Nursing* B D Westra MD.
Licensure Skilled Care. *Beds* 50. *Certified* Medicaid.
Ownership Nonprofit.
Admissions Requirements Minimum age 18; Medical examination; Physician's request.
Facilities Dining room; Physical therapy room; Activities room; Chapel; Crafts room; Laundry room; Barber/Beauty shop 19H.
Activities Arts and Crafts; Cards; Games; Reading groups; Prayer groups; Movies; Shopping trips; Dances/Social or cultural gatherings.
Description Facility features new experience in living including 24-hour professional nursing care; physician directed medical services; therapeutic diets; rehabilitation therapy; activities programs with community involvement; volunteer services; social services for patients and families; spiritual guidance; weekly chapel services; nonprofit city-owned; fire resistant building; insurance policy analysis; state licensed and certified.

GRAND RAPIDS

Christus Group Home
510 13th St SE, Grand Rapids, MN, 55744
(218) 326-8095
Admin Sandra Johnson. *Medical Dir/Dir of Nursing* Carolyn Lorbiecki RN.
Licensure Supervised Care Facility. *Beds* 12. *Certified* Medicaid.
Ownership Nonprofit.
Admissions Requirements Minimum age 18; Medical examination.
Staff RNs 1 (pt); Dietitians 1 (pt); Counselors 5 (ft), 4 (pt).
Affiliation Lutheran
Facilities Dining room; Crafts room; Laundry room.
Activities Arts and Crafts; Cards; Games; Movies; Shopping trips; Dances/Social or cultural gatherings.
Description This is a group home for 12 mentally retarded adults.

Itasca Nursing Home
Hale Lake Rd, Grand Rapids, MN, 55744
(218) 326-0542
Admin Donald R Davis. *Medical Dir/Dir of Nursing* Dr L E Karges.
Licensure Skilled Care; Intermediate Care; Boarding Home. *Beds* SNF 60; ICF 58; Boarding Home 58. *Certified* Medicaid.
Ownership Public.
Staff RNs 4 (pt); LPNs 6 (ft), 8 (pt); Orderlies 2 (pt); Nurses aides 17 (ft), 21 (pt); Physical therapists 1 (pt); Recreational therapists 2 (pt);

Activities coordinators 1 (ft); Dietitians 1 (ft); Social workers 1 (pt).
Facilities Dining room; Physical therapy room; Activities room; Chapel; Crafts room; Laundry room; Barber/Beauty shop.
Activities Arts and Crafts; Cards; Games; Prayer groups; Movies; Shopping trips; Dances/Social or cultural gatherings.
Description Facility offers a respite program—3-day minimum, 30-day maximum stay.

Leisure Hills Inc*
2801 S Pokegama, Grand Rapids, MN, 55744
(218) 326-3431
Admin Ronald Evensen.
Licensure Skilled Care. *Beds* 124. *Certified* Medicaid.
Ownership Proprietary.

GRANITE FALLS

Municipal Hospital and Granite Manor*
345 10th Ave, Granite Falls, MN, 56241 (612) 564-3111
Admin Jay Eckersly.
Licensure Skilled Care; Intermediate Care.
Beds 58. *Certified* Medicaid; Medicare.
Ownership Public.

Project Turnabout
660 18th St, Granite Falls, MN, 56241 (612) 564-4911
Admin William C Anderson.
Licensure Supervised Living Facility. *Beds* 38.
Ownership Nonprofit.

HALLOCK

Kittson County Nursing Home
410 Cedar Ave S, Hallock, MN, 56728 (218) 843-2633
Admin John A Nelson.
Licensure Intermediate Care. *Beds* 36. *Certified* Medicaid.
Ownership Public.

Kittson Memorial Hospital*
1010 S Birch, Hallock, MN, 56728 (218) 843-3612
Admin Bruce Berg.
Licensure Skilled Care; Intermediate Care.
Beds 95. *Certified* Medicaid.
Ownership Nonprofit.

HALSTAD

Halstad Lutheran Memorial Home
147 E County Hwy, Halstad, MN, 56548 (218) 456-2105
Admin Michael S Ackley. *Medical Dir/Dir of Nursing* Dr G Brown.
Licensure Intermediate Care. *Beds* 68. *Certified* Medicaid.
Ownership Nonprofit.
Admissions Requirements Medical examination; Physician's request.
Staff Physicians; RNs; LPNs 8 (ft); Nurses aides 26 (ft), 14 (pt); Physical therapists 1 (pt); Activities coordinators 1 (ft).
Affiliation Lutheran
Facilities Dining room; Physical therapy room;

Activities room; Chapel; Crafts room; Laundry room; Barber/Beauty shop; Library; Meeting room.
Activities Arts and Crafts; Cards; Games; Reading groups; Prayer groups; Movies; Shopping trips; Dances/Social or cultural gatherings.

HARMONY

Harmony Community Hospital
815 S Main St, Harmony, MN, 55939
Admin Greg Braun. *Medical Dir/Dir of Nursing* T S Kalidindi.
Licensure Skilled Care; Intermediate Care.
Beds 45. *Certified* Medicaid.
Ownership Nonprofit.
Staff Physicians 1 (ft); RNs 1 (ft); LPNs 2 (ft), 9 (pt); Nurses aides 5 (ft), 28 (pt); Physical therapists 1 (pt); Activities coordinators 1 (ft), 1 (pt).
Facilities Dining room; Physical therapy room; Activities room; Crafts room; Laundry room; Barber/Beauty shop.
Activities Arts and Crafts; Cards; Games; Reading groups; Prayer groups; Movies; Dances/Social or cultural gatherings.

Sunshine Place*
135 Center St E, Harmony, MN, 55939 (507) 886-2220
Admin Luwayne Ommen.
Licensure Intermediate Care for Mentally Retarded. *Beds* 12. *Certified* Medicaid.
Ownership Nonprofit.

HASTINGS

Haven Homes Health Center
930 W 16th St, Hastings, MN, 55033 (612) 437-6176
Admin Lester Fair. *Medical Dir/Dir of Nursing* Dr David Ecker.
Licensure Skilled Care; Intermediate Care.
Beds 107. *Certified* Medicaid; Medicare.
Ownership Proprietary.
Admissions Requirements Minimum age 18; Medical examination; Physician's request.
Staff Physicians; RNs; LPNs; Orderlies; Nurses aides; Physical therapists 1 (ft); Recreational therapists 1 (ft); Occupational therapists 1 (ft); Speech therapists 1 (pt); Dietitians 1 (ft).
Facilities Dining room; Physical therapy room; Activities room; Chapel; Crafts room; Laundry room; Barber/Beauty shop.
Activities Arts and Crafts; Cards; Games; Reading groups; Prayer groups; Movies; Dances/Social or cultural gatherings.
Description Facility is very strongly oriented to rehabilitation through nursing care, occupational therapy, physical therapy, and speech therapy; excellent activity program.

Henry Hagen Residence*
19845 Lillehei Ave, Hastings, MN, 55033 (612) 437-9363
Admin Henry Hagen.
Licensure Intermediate Care for Mentally Retarded. *Beds* 6. *Certified* Medicaid.
Ownership Proprietary.

Micoll Residence*
926 W 2nd St, Hastings, MN, 55033 (612)
437-1967
Admin James Driscoll.
Licensure Skilled Care; Intermediate Care.
Beds 12. *Certified* Medicaid.
Ownership Proprietary.

Minnesota Veterans Home
Hastings, MN, 55033 (612) 437-3111
Admin Robert J Strunk. *Medical Dir/Dir of Nursing* Ralph D Rayner MD.
Licensure Boarding Care. *Beds* 200.
Ownership Public.
Admissions Requirements Medical examination.
Staff Physicians 1 (pt); RNs 3 (ft); LPNs 5 (ft); Recreational therapists 1 (ft); Activities coordinators 1 (ft); Dietitians 1 (pt); Dentists 1 (pt); Ophthalmologists 1 (pt); Podiatrists 1 (pt); Chiropractors 1 (pt); Social workers 2 (ft); CD counselors 2 (ft).
Facilities Dining room; Physical therapy room; Activities room; Chapel; Crafts room; Laundry room; Barber/Beauty shop; Library.
Activities Arts and Crafts; Cards; Games; Reading groups; Prayer groups; Movies; Shopping trips; Dances/Social or cultural gatherings; Sports activities; Fishing trips; Golf.
Description Very active woodworking shop, ceramics, and print shop enable residents to learn new skills and improve on old skills; excellent form of rehabilitation therapy to develop confidence and self-reliability.

Regina Memorial Hospital*
Nininger Rd, Hastings, MN, 55033 (612)
437-8435
Admin John W Junkman.
Licensure Skilled Care. *Beds* 80. *Certified* Medicaid; Medicare.
Ownership Nonprofit.

HAWLEY

Clay County Residence
1358 Main St, Hawley, MN, 56549 (218)
236-2673
Admin Doug Johnson.
Licensure Supervised Living Facility. *Beds* 8.
Certified Medicaid.
Ownership Nonprofit.
Admissions Requirements Minimum age 18; Medical examination.
Staff RNs 1 (pt).
Facilities Dining room; Activities room; Crafts room; Laundry room.
Activities Arts and Crafts; Cards; Games; Movies; Shopping trips.

HAYFIELD

Field Crest Nursing Home
Rt 2, Box 6A, Hayfield, MN, 55940 (507)
477-3266
Admin Paul Rengstorf. *Medical Dir/Dir of Nursing* Dr Larry Grubbs.
Licensure Skilled Care. *Beds* 84. *Certified* Medicaid.
Ownership Public.
Admissions Requirements Medical examina-

tion.
Staff RNs 4 (ft), 5 (pt); LPNs 4 (ft), 6 (pt); Nurses aides 27 (ft), 16 (pt); Occupational therapists 3 (pt); Activities coordinators 1 (ft).
Facilities Dining room; Activities room; Laundry room; Barber/Beauty shop; Library.
Activities Arts and Crafts; Cards; Games; Reading groups; Prayer groups; Movies; Shopping trips; Dances/Social or cultural gatherings.

HENDRICKS

Hendricks Community Hospital*
E Lincoln St, Hendricks, MN, 56136 (507)
275-3134
Admin Steven L Midtaune.
Licensure Skilled Care; Intermediate Care.
Beds SNF 40; ICF 30. *Certified* Medicaid.
Ownership Nonprofit.

HENNING

Henning Nursing Home
907 Marshall Ave, Henning, MN, 56551 (218)
583-2359
Admin Richard Cloeter. *Medical Dir/Dir of Nursing* Dr Jon Wigert.
Licensure Intermediate Care. *Beds* 64. *Certified* Medicaid.
Ownership Proprietary.
Admissions Requirements Minimum age 16.
Staff RNs 1 (ft), 1 (pt); LPNs 2 (ft), 3 (pt); Nurses aides 5 (ft), 30 (pt); Recreational therapists 1 (ft), 1 (pt); Activities coordinators 1 (ft).
Facilities Dining room; Activities room; Crafts room; Laundry room.
Activities Arts and Crafts; Cards; Games; Reading groups; Prayer groups; Movies; Shopping trips; Dances/Social or cultural gatherings.
Description Facility features 26 festive meals per year including a restaurant night with linens, crystal, wine, steak, and shrimp. Also the facility offers specialized rehabilitation services including short-term convalescence.

HIBBING

Golden Crest Nursing Home
2413 1st Ave, Hibbing, MN, 55746 (218)
262-1081
Admin Michael V Schultz. *Medical Dir/Dir of Nursing* Dr Ahola.
Licensure Skilled Care; Intermediate Care.
Beds SNF 76; ICF 8. *Certified* Medicaid.
Ownership Proprietary.
Staff RNs 4 (ft), 5 (pt); LPNs 5 (ft), 4 (pt); Nurses aides 20 (ft), 14 (pt); Recreational therapists 1 (ft); Occupational therapists 1 (ft); Activities coordinators 1 (ft).
Facilities Dining room; Physical therapy room; Activities room; Crafts room; Laundry room; Barber/Beauty shop; Library.
Activities Arts and Crafts; Cards; Games; Reading groups; Prayer groups; Movies; Shopping trips; Dances/Social or cultural gatherings.

Leisure Hills Healthcare Center*
1500 3rd Ave E, Hibbing, MN, 55746 (218)
263-7583
Admin Kenneth W Steiger.

Licensure Skilled Care; Intermediate Care.
Beds SNF 203; ICF 12. *Certified* Medicaid.
Ownership Proprietary.

Range Center—Mapleview*
506 W 47th St, Hibbing, MN, 55748 (218)
263-4573
Admin James Mickelson.
Licensure Skilled Care; Intermediate Care for Mentally Retarded. *Beds* SNF 6; ICF/MR 6.
Certified Medicaid.
Ownership Nonprofit.

HILLS

Tuff Memorial Home*
Hills, MN, 56138 (507) 962-3276
Admin James D Iverson.
Licensure Intermediate Care. *Beds* 52. *Certified* Medicaid.
Ownership Nonprofit.

HOFFMAN

Hoffman Care Center
104 6th St S, Hoffman, MN, 56339 (612)
986-2048
Admin Daniel Waage. *Medical Dir/Dir of Nursing* R Sampson DO.
Licensure Skilled Care; Intermediate Care.
Beds 54. *Certified* Medicaid; Medicare.
Ownership Proprietary.
Staff Physicians 1 (pt); RNs 1 (ft), 2 (pt); LPNs 3 (ft), 3 (pt); Orderlies 1 (ft); Nurses aides 20 (ft), 30 (pt); Physical therapists 1 (pt); Activities coordinators 1 (ft); Dietitians 1 (pt).
Facilities Dining room; Physical therapy room; Activities room; Chapel; Crafts room; Laundry room; Day room in conjunction with Chapel.
Activities Arts and Crafts; Cards; Games; Reading groups; Prayer groups; Movies; Shopping trips; Dances/Social or cultural gatherings; Discussion groups.
Description We have a weekly "kids day" where mothers in our community can bring in preschool children during morning hours. This is for the enjoyment of residents, and to provide a community service.

HOPKINS

Chapel View Inc*
615 Minnetonka Mills Rd, Hopkins, MN, 55343 (612) 938-2761
Admin Roger M Jewett.
Licensure Skilled Care; Intermediate Care.
Beds SNF 104; ICF 24. *Certified* Medicaid.
Ownership Nonprofit.

Hopkins Nursing Home
724 Country Rd 18, Hopkins, MN, 55343 (612)
935-3338
Admin Marie Nelson.
Licensure Skilled Care; Intermediate Care.
Beds SNF 120; ICF 63. *Certified* Medicaid.
Ownership Proprietary.

HOUSTON

Valley View Nursing Home*
510 E Cedar St, Houston, MN, 55943 (507)
895-3125
Admin Arthur J Miller.
Licensure Intermediate Care. *Beds* 68. *Certified* Medicaid.
Ownership Nonprofit.

HOWARD LAKE

Howard Lake Care Center
Box CC, Howard Lake, MN, 55349 (612)
543-3800
Admin Timothy Ryden. *Medical Dir/Dir of Nursing* Dr Bergstrom.
Licensure Skilled Care; Intermediate Care.
Beds SNF 52; ICF 21. *Certified* Medicaid.
Ownership Proprietary.
Facilities Dining room; Physical therapy room;
Activities room; Crafts room; Laundry room;
Barber/Beauty shop.
Activities Arts and Crafts; Cards; Games;
Reading groups; Movies; Shopping trips; Dances/Social or cultural gatherings; Bible studies.

HUTCHINSON

Aveyron Homes Inc
851 Dale St, Hutchinson, MN, 55350 (612)
587-6277
Admin William L Everett. *Medical Dir/Dir of Nursing* Jan Luthens RN and Dr Carl Bretzke.
Licensure Supervised Living Facility. *Beds* 14.
Certified Medicaid.
Ownership Nonprofit.
Admissions Requirements Minimum age 18;
Medical examination; Physician's request.
Staff Physicians 1 (pt); RNs 1 (pt); LPNs 1
(pt); Recreational therapists 1 (pt); Activities
coordinators 1 (pt).
Facilities Dining room; Activities room; Crafts
room; Laundry room; Library.
Activities Arts and Crafts; Cards; Games;
Reading groups; Movies; Shopping trips; Dances/Social or cultural gatherings; Cultural gatherings.
Description Aveyron stresses the importance of
community orientation and involvement to
offer dignity and opportunity to its residents.

Burns Manor Nursing Home*
N High Dr, Hutchinson, MN, 55350 (612)
587-4919
Admin Mavis Geier.
Licensure Skilled Care; Intermediate Care.
Beds SNF 65; ICF 64. *Certified* Medicaid;
Medicare.
Ownership Public.

INTERNATIONAL FALLS

Falls Nursing Home
Hwy 11-71, International Falls, MN, 56649
(218) 283-8313
Admin Rose M Matthews. *Medical Dir/Dir of Nursing* Dr Charles Helleloid.
Licensure Skilled Care; Intermediate Care.
Beds SNF 90; ICF 10. *Certified* Medicaid;
Medicare.

Ownership Public.
Admissions Requirements Minimum age 18;
Medical examination; Physician's request.
Staff RNs 2 (ft), 2 (pt); LPNs 4 (ft), 7 (pt);
Nurses aides 26 (ft), 28 (pt); Activities coordinators 1 (ft); Dietitians 1 (pt); Dentists 1 (pt).
Facilities Dining room; Activities room; Chapel; Crafts room; Barber/Beauty shop.
Activities Arts and Crafts; Cards; Games;
Reading groups; Prayer groups; Movies; Shopping trips; Dances/Social or cultural gatherings.
Description Facility is attached by 2 breezeways
to the Falls Memorial Hospital; shared service
agreement with hospital.

International Falls Group Home*
2000 Spruce St, International Falls, MN, 56649
(218) 285-7264
Admin Sandra Johnson.
Licensure Skilled Care; Intermediate Care.
Beds SNF 11; ICF 12. *Certified* Medicaid.
Ownership Nonprofit.

INVER GROVE HEIGHTS

Inver Grove Care Center*
4700 S Robert Trail, Inver Grove Heights, MN,
55075 (612) 451-1853
Admin Steven Foster.
Licensure Skilled Care; Intermediate Care.
Beds SNF 70; ICF 6. *Certified* Medicaid.
Ownership Proprietary.

Wedgewood Health Care Center
2060 Upper 55th St E, Inver Grove Heights,
MN, 55075 (612) 451-1881
Admin Edward Lehmann. *Medical Dir/Dir of Nursing* Mary Wangsness MD.
Licensure Skilled Care; Intermediate Care.
Beds 140. *Certified* Medicaid.
Ownership Proprietary.
Admissions Requirements Minimum age 16;
Medical examination; Physician's request.
Staff RNs 4 (ft), 9 (pt); LPNs 3 (ft), 7 (pt);
Nurses aides 23 (ft), 32 (pt); Physical therapists;
Recreational therapists 1 (ft); Activities coordinators 1 (pt).
Facilities Dining room; Physical therapy room;
Activities room; Chapel; Crafts room; Laundry
room; Barber/Beauty shop.
Activities Arts and Crafts; Cards; Games;
Reading groups; Prayer groups; Movies; Shopping trips; Dances/Social or cultural gatherings;
Music therapy groups; Resident council.

IVANHOE

Divne Providence Hospital*
312 E George St, Ivanhoe, MN, 56142 (507)
694-1414
Admin Mariette Ketterer.
Licensure Skilled Care. *Beds* 51. *Certified* Medicaid.
Ownership Nonprofit.

JACKSON

Good Samaritan Sunset Home*
600 West St, Jackson, MN, 56143 (507)
847-3100
Admin William E Brown.

Licensure Skilled Care; Intermediate Care.
Beds SNF 71; ICF 18. *Certified* Medicaid.
Ownership Nonprofit.

Jackson Municipal Hospital—Nursing Home
Northern Hwy, Jackson, MN, 56143
Admin Sr Patricia Glowski. *Medical Dir/Dir of
Nursing* Dr Paul Wright.
Licensure Intermediate Care. *Beds* 21. *Certified* Medicaid.
Ownership Nonprofit.
Admissions Requirements Minimum age 50;
Medical examination; Physician's request.
Staff RNs 1 (pt); LPNs 1 (ft), 3 (pt); Nurses
aides 4 (ft), 4 (pt); Physical therapists 1 (ft);
Activities coordinators 1 (ft); Dietitians 1 (pt).
Facilities Dining room; Physical therapy room;
Activities room; Crafts room; Laundry room.
Activities Arts and Crafts; Cards; Games;
Reading groups; Movies; Dances/Social or cultural gatherings.
Description This hospital affiliated nursing
home has an adult day care program for those
in the community who cannot care for themselves 24 hours a day.

JANESVILLE

Janesville Nursing Home
102 E North St, Janesville, MN, 56048 (507)
234-5113
Admin Bradley Gauger. *Medical Dir/Dir of Nursing* David Pope MD.
Licensure Skilled Care; Intermediate Care.
Beds SNF 34; ICF 11. *Certified* Medicaid.
Ownership Public.
Admissions Requirements Medical examination.
Staff RNs 1 (ft), 3 (pt); LPNs 2 (ft), 3 (pt);
Nurses aides 5 (ft), 14 (pt); Activities coordinators 2 (ft); Dietitians 1 (ft).
Facilities Dining room; Activities room; Laundry room; Barber/Beauty shop.
Activities Cards; Games; Reading groups;
Movies.
Description We now have a primary care concept and an open breakfast policy that includes
all residents. Residents now wake up when they
want to and are fed breakfast until 10:30 am.

JORDAN

Lynnville Treatment Center
17706 Valley View Dr, Jordan, MN, 55352
(612) 492-6650
Admin Phil Hansen.
Licensure Supervised Living Facility. *Beds* 65.
Ownership Nonprofit.
Admissions Requirements Minimum age 14.
Staff RNs 6 (ft); LPNs 1 (ft); Nurses aides 1
(ft); Dietitians 1 (pt).

Valleyview Nursing Home Inc
4061 W 173rd St, Jordan, MN, 55352 (612)
492-6160
Admin Ralph Olinger. *Medical Dir/Dir of Nursing* Dr W N Amra.
Licensure Skilled Care; Intermediate Care.
Beds SNF 60; ICF 42. *Certified* Medicaid.
Ownership Proprietary.
Admissions Requirements Medical examina-

tion.
Staff Physicians 17 (pt); RNs 4 (ft), 3 (pt);
LPNs 4 (ft), 10 (pt); Orderlies 1 (pt); Nurses
aides 21 (ft), 37 (pt); Physical therapists 1 (ft);
Speech therapists 1 (pt); Activities coordinators
1 (ft); Dietitians 1 (pt); Dentists 1 (pt); Podiatr-
ists 1 (pt).
Facilities Dining room; Physical therapy room;
Activities room; Chapel; Laundry room; Bar-
ber/Beauty shop.
Activities Arts and Crafts; Cards; Games;
Reading groups; Movies 14G; Dances/Social or
cultural gatherings.
Description Facility is located in the country on
150 acres.

KARLSTAD

Karlstad Memorial Nursing Center*
3rd and Washington, Karlstad, MN, 56732
(218) 436-2161
Admin Jerry Peak.
Licensure Skilled Care; Intermediate Care.
Beds SNF 51; ICF 20. *Certified* Medicaid.
Ownership Public.

Valley Group Home 2*
Box 240, Main St S, Karlstad, MN, 56732 (218)
436-2518
Admin Mark Richardson.
Licensure Intermediate Care for Mentally
Retarded. *Beds* 10. *Certified* Medicaid.
Ownership Proprietary.

KASSON

Fourth Street House*
17 4th St SW, Kasson, MN, 55944 (507)
634-4121
Admin Ronald Davis.
Licensure Intermediate Care for Mentally
Retarded. *Beds* 14. *Certified* Medicaid.
Ownership Proprietary.

KELLIHER

Good Samaritan Center*
PO Box 189, Main St, Kelliher, MN, 56650
(218) 647-8258
Admin Duane J Delaney.
Licensure Intermediate Care. *Beds* 40. *Certi-
fied* Medicaid.
Ownership Nonprofit.

KENYON

Kenyon Sunset Home
127 2nd St, Kenyon, MN, 55946 (507)
789-6134
Admin Mark R Robinson. *Medical Dir/Dir of
Nursing* Dr William Walter.
Licensure Skilled Care; Intermediate Care;
Boarding Care. *Beds* 79. *Certified* Medicaid.
Ownership Nonprofit.
Affiliation Lutheran
Facilities Dining room; Physical therapy room;
Activities room; Chapel; Crafts room; Laundry
room; Barber/Beauty shop.

Activities Arts and Crafts; Cards; Games;
Reading groups; Prayer groups; Movies; Shopping trips; Dances/Social or cultural gatherings.

KERKHOVEN

Lindberg Rest Home*
Kerkhoven, MN, 56252 (612) 264-2601
Admin Florence E Lindberg.
Licensure Boarding Care. *Beds* 26.
Ownership Proprietary.

KIMBALL

Madden Kimball Home*
Box 129, Kimball, MN, 55353 (612) 398-5678
Admin Dolores Madden.
Licensure Intermediate Care for Mentally
Retarded. *Beds* 32. *Certified* Medicaid.
Ownership Proprietary.

LA CRESCENT

Houston Company Home-Lacrescent*
1700 Lancer Blvd, La Crescent, MN, 55947
(507) 895-8111
Admin Dennis Theede.
Licensure Skilled Care; Intermediate Care.
Beds 15. *Certified* Medicaid.
Ownership Nonprofit.

La Crescent Nursing Center
701 Main St, La Crescent, MN, 55947 (507)
895-4445
Admin Gale A Bruessel. *Medical Dir/Dir of
Nursing* Dr Phillip Utz.
Licensure Skilled Care; Intermediate Care.
Beds SNF 70; ICF 7. *Certified* Medicaid.
Ownership Proprietary.
Admissions Requirements Medical examina-
tion; Physician's request.
Staff Physicians 2 (pt); RNs 2 (ft), 3 (pt); LPNs
9 (pt); Orderlies 2 (pt); Nurses aides 2 (ft), 30
(pt); Physical therapists 1 (pt); Recreational
therapists 1 (ft); Occupational therapists 1 (pt);
Speech therapists 1 (pt); Respiratory aides 2
(pt).
Facilities Dining room; Physical therapy room;
Activities room; Chapel; Crafts room; Laundry
room; Barber/Beauty shop.
Activities Arts and Crafts; Cards; Games; Prayer groups; Movies; Shopping trips; Dances/So-
cial or cultural gatherings; Birthday parties;
Bingo; Happy hours; Memorial services.
Description Facility offers an extensive volunteer program; volunteers perform many duties
such as meal deliveries, directing games, one-
on-one visitations, Bible study, shopping cart,
hair care and beauty shop, music. Staff is very
aware of residents' needs and provides loving
care. Facility is set in the bluffs overlooking the
west side of the Mississippi River valley. VA
approved.

LAFAYETTE

Lafayette Good Samaritan Center
19 Esther St, Lafayette, MN, 56054 (507)
228-8238
Admin John C Ashton.

Licensure Intermediate Care. *Beds* 40. *Certi-
fied* Medicaid.
Staff Physicians 1 (pt); RNs 2 (ft); LPNs 4 (ft);
Orderlies 1 (ft); Nurses aides 20 (ft); Physical
therapists 1 (ft); Reality therapists 1 (ft); Recrea-
tional therapists 1 (ft); Activities coordinators 1
(ft); Dietitians 1 (ft); Dentists 1 (pt).
Affiliation Lutheran
Facilities Dining room; Physical therapy room;
Activities room; Chapel; Crafts room; Laundry
room; Barber/Beauty shop; Library.
Activities Arts and Crafts; Cards; Games;
Reading groups; Prayer groups; Movies; Shop-
ping trips; Dances/Social or cultural gatherings.

LAKE CITY

Lake City Nursing Home
405 W Grant St, Lake City, MN, 55041 (612)
345-5366
Admin B McRoy.
Licensure Skilled Care. *Beds* 115. *Cer-
tified* Medicaid; Medicare.
Ownership Public.
Staff Physicians 4 (pt); RNs 2 (ft), 4 (pt); LPNs
2 (ft), 9 (pt); Nurses aides 10 (ft), 55 (pt);
Physical therapists 1 (pt); Speech therapists 1
(pt); Activities coordinators 1 (ft); Dietitians 1
(pt); Dentists 1 (pt).
Facilities Dining room; Physical therapy room;
Activities room; Crafts room; Laundry room;
Barber/Beauty shop.
Activities Arts and Crafts; Cards; Games;
Reading groups; Prayer groups; Movies; Shop-
ping trips; Dances/Social or cultural gatherings.

River Oaks Health Care Center
815 N High St, Lake City, MN, 55041 (612)
345-2713
Admin J E Range.
Licensure Nursing Home. *Beds* 36.
Ownership Proprietary.
Admissions Requirements Minimum age 21;
Medical examination.
Staff RNs 1 (ft), 1 (pt); LPNs 3 (ft), 3 (pt);
Nurses aides 10 (ft), 12 (pt); Recreational thera-
pists 1 (pt); Activities coordinators 1 (pt); Dieti-
tians 1 (pt).
Facilities Dining room; Activities room;
Chapel; Crafts room; Family room.
Activities Arts and Crafts; Cards; Games; Pray-
er groups; Movies; Shopping trips.

Seven Eleven North High*
711 N High St, Lake City, MN, 55041 (612)
345-2625
Admin Michael Weinandt.
Licensure Skilled Care; Intermediate Care for
Mentally Retarded. *Beds* SNF 8; ICF/MR 8.
Certified Medicaid.
Ownership Nonprofit.

LAKE CRYSTAL

Lake Crystal Health Care Center*
202 Laclaire, Lake Crystal, MN, 56055 (507)
726-2669
Admin Adella Scheuneman.
Licensure Skilled Care; Intermediate Care.
Beds SNF 40; ICF 24. *Certified* Medicaid.
Ownership Proprietary.

LAKE ELMO

Nekton on Stillwater Lane*
10092 Stillwater Ln, Lake Elmo, MN, 55042
(612) 777-1907
Admin Steve Kodulboy.
Licensure Intermediate Care for Mentally
Retarded. *Beds* 6. *Certified* Medicaid.
Ownership Proprietary.

LAKE PARK

Sunnyside Nursing Home*
Rt 2, Lake Park, MN, 56544 (218) 238-5944
Admin Gary Ask.
Licensure Intermediate Care. *Beds* 63. *Certified* Medicaid.
Ownership Public.

LAKEFIELD

Colonial Manor
Manor Dr, Lakefield, MN, 56150 (507)
662-6155
Admin Jack Burgess. *Medical Dir/Dir of
Nursing* Dr M Rath.
Licensure Intermediate Care. *Beds* 54. *Certified* Medicaid.
Ownership Public.
Staff Physicians 1 (pt); RNs 5 (ft); LPNs 6 (pt);
Nurses aides 12 (ft), 11 (pt); Physical therapists
1 (pt); Activities coordinators 1 (ft); Dietitians
1 (pt).
Facilities Activities room; Crafts room; Laundry room; Barber/Beauty shop.
Activities Arts and Crafts; Cards; Games;
Reading groups; Prayer groups; Movies; Shopping trips; Dances/Social or cultural gatherings.

LAKEVILLE

Zenith Apartments*
20345, Lakeville, MN, 55044 (612) 452-4264
Admin James Driscoll.
Licensure Skilled Care; Intermediate Care.
Beds SNF 15; ICF 15. *Certified* Medicaid.
Ownership Proprietary.

LAMBERTON

Valley View Manor*
Box 126, Lamberton, MN, 56152 (507)
752-7346
Admin James W Pederson.
Licensure Skilled Care; Intermediate Care.
Beds SNF 65; ICF 15. *Certified* Medicaid.
Ownership Public.

LE CENTER

Central Nursing Home
444 N Cordova, Le Center, MN, 56057 (612)
357-2275
Admin Phil Buckman. *Medical Dir/Dir of
Nursing* Dr Michael Wilcox.
Licensure Skilled Care; Intermediate Care.
Beds SNF 90; ICF 20. *Certified* Medicaid.
Ownership Proprietary.
Admissions Requirements Medical examina-
tion; Physician's request.
Staff RNs 2 (ft), 2 (pt); LPNs 4 (ft), 9 (pt);
Nurses aides 20 (ft), 36 (pt); Activities coordinators 1 (ft); Dietitians 1 (ft).
Facilities Dining room; Activities room; Chapel; Barber/Beauty shop; Library.
Activities Arts and Crafts; Cards; Games;
Reading groups; Prayer groups; Movies; Shopping trips; Dances/Social or cultural gatherings.

LESTER PRAIRIE

Alice Haney Annex*
1st Ave & Maple St, Lester Prairie, MN, 55354
(612) 395-2518
Admin Tom Bettendorf.
Licensure Intermediate Care for Mentally
Retarded. *Beds* 15. *Certified* Medicaid.
Ownership Proprietary.

Alice Haney Home*
100 S Maple, Lester Prairie, MN, 55354 (612)
395-2517
Admin Tom Bettendorf.
Licensure Intermediate Care for Mentally
Retarded. *Beds* 40. *Certified* Medicaid.
Ownership Proprietary.

LEWISTON

Lewiston Villa
505 E Main St, Lewiston, MN, 55952 (507)
523-2123
Admin Patrick A Taylor. *Medical Dir/Dir of
Nursing* Dr Morris.
Licensure Skilled Care; Intermediate Care.
Beds 58. *Certified* Medicaid.
Ownership Proprietary.
Admissions Requirements Minimum age 16;
Medical examination; Physician's request.
Staff RNs 2 (ft), 2 (pt); LPNs 3 (ft), 2 (pt);
Orderlies 2 (pt); Nurses aides 10 (ft), 6 (pt);
Activities coordinators 1 (ft).
Facilities Dining room; Physical therapy room;
Activities room; Chapel; Crafts room; Laundry
room; Barber/Beauty shop; Library.
Activities Arts and Crafts; Cards; Games;
Reading groups; Prayer groups; Movies; Shopping trips; Dances/Social or cultural gatherings;
Outings.
Description Facility is a new 58-bed HUD
approved facility.

LEXINGTON

Forestview—Lexington
9329 Dunlap Ave N, Lexington, MN, 55112
(612) 546-1969
Admin W Koski.
Licensure Supervised Living Facility. *Beds* ICF/MR 6. *Certified* Medicaid.
Staff RNs 1 (pt).
Facilities Laundry room.
Activities Arts and Crafts; Cards; Games;
Movies; Shopping trips; Dances/Social or cultural gatherings; Camping and other outdoor
activities.

LITCHFIELD

Bethany Home
203 N Armstrong, Litchfield, MN, 55355 (612)
693-2423
Admin Michael Boyle. *Medical Dir/Dir of
Nursing* Cecil Leitch.
Licensure Boarding Care. *Beds* 52.
Ownership Nonprofit.
Admissions Requirements Medical examina-
tion; Physician's request.
Staff RNs; LPNs; Orderlies; Nurses aides;
Physical therapists; Activities coordinators;
Dietitians.
Affiliation Lutheran
Facilities Dining room; Activities room; Chapel; Laundry room; Barber/Beauty shop.
Activities Arts and Crafts; Cards; Games;
Reading groups; Prayer groups; Movies; Shopping trips; Dances/Social or cultural gatherings.

Emmanuel Home
600 S Davis, Litchfield, MN, 55355 (612)
693-2472
Admin Michael Boyle. *Medical Dir/Dir of
Nursing* Cecil Leitch MD.
Licensure Skilled Care. *Beds* 120. *Certified* Medicaid.
Ownership Nonprofit.
Staff RNs 10 (ft); LPNs 18 (ft); Nurses aides 90
(ft); Physical therapists 1 (ft); Activities coordinators 1 (ft).
Affiliation Lutheran
Facilities Dining room; Physical therapy room;
Activities room; Chapel; Crafts room; Laundry
room; Barber/Beauty shop.
Activities Arts and Crafts; Cards; Games;
Reading groups; Prayer groups; Movies; Shopping trips; Dances/Social or cultural gatherings.

Meeker County Community Home
504 S Litchfield, Litchfield, MN, 55355 (612)
693-2418
Admin Carol Marchant.
Licensure Supervised Care Facility. *Beds* 15.
Certified Medicaid.
Ownership Nonprofit.
Admissions Requirements Minimum age 18.
Staff RNs 1 (pt).
Facilities Dining room; Activities room; Laundry room; Living room; Kitchen.
Activities Arts and Crafts; Cards; Games;
Reading groups; Movies; Shopping trips; Dances/Social or cultural gatherings.
Description Our home is an education/training
program for mentally retarded adults. The
emphasis is on teaching daily living skills, with
the goal of helping each resident become as
independent as possible.

LITTLE CANADA

Nekton on Sextant
332 Sextant, Little Canada, MN, 55117 (612)
483-3093
Admin Milt Conrath.
Licensure Intermediate Care for Mentally
Retarded. *Beds* 6. *Certified* Medicaid.
Ownership Proprietary.

LITTLE FALLS

Christus Group Home*
315 SW 6th St, Little Falls, MN, 56345 (612)
632-2240
Admin John D Peterson.
Licensure Intermediate Care for Mentally
Retarded. *Beds* 13. *Certified* Medicaid.
Ownership Nonprofit.

Lutheran Senior Citizen Home
1200 1st Ave NE, Little Falls, MN, 56345 (612)
632-9211
Admin H Zyvoloski. *Medical Dir/Dir of
Nursing* Dr Royden Belcher.
Licensure Skilled Care; Intermediate Care.
Beds SNF 100; ICF 18. *Certified* Medicaid.
Ownership Nonprofit.
Admissions Requirements Minimum age 21;
Medical examination; Physician's request.
Staff Physicians 1 (pt); RNs 2 (ft), 7 (pt); LPNs
8 (ft), 1 (pt); Orderlies 4 (ft); Nurses aides 33
(ft), 25 (pt); Reality therapists 2 (pt); Recrea-
tional therapists 6 (ft); Activities coordinators 1
(ft); Dietitians 1 (ft); Physical therapy aides 3
(ft).
Affiliation Lutheran
Facilities Dining room; Physical therapy room;
Activities room; Chapel; Crafts room; Laundry
room; Barber/Beauty shop; Library.
Activities Arts and Crafts; Cards; Games;
Reading groups; Prayer groups; Movies; Shopping trips; Dances/Social or cultural gatherings.
Description Facility offers family-type atmosphere at all times; has been operating at full
capacity for 20 years.

Saint Ottos Home*
920 SE 4th St, Little Falls, MN, 56345 (612)
632-9281
Admin Mary Latonna Kalis.
Licensure Intermediate Care. *Beds* 134. *Certified* Medicaid; Medicare.
Ownership Nonprofit.

LONG LAKE

Long Lake Nursing Home*
345 Browns Rd S, Long Lake, MN, 55356 (612)
473-2527
Admin Jane V Hutar.
Licensure Skilled Care. *Beds* 52. *Certified* Medicaid.
Ownership Proprietary.

LONG PRAIRIE

Long Prairie Memorial Hospital*
20 9th St SE, Long Prairie, MN, 56347 (612)
732-2141
Admin Kevin Smith.
Licensure Skilled Care; Intermediate Care.
Beds SNF 64; ICF 29. *Certified* Medicaid;
Medicare.
Ownership Nonprofit.

LUVERNE

Mary J Brown Good Samaritan Center
110 S Walnut Ave, Luverne, MN, 56156 (507)
283-2375

Admin Susan E Borg. *Medical Dir/Dir of
Nursing* Dr Larry Lyon.
Licensure Intermediate Care; Boarding Care.
Beds ICF 70; Boarding Care 4. *Certified* Medi-
caid.
Ownership Nonprofit.
Admissions Requirements Medical examina-
tion.
Staff RNs 1 (ft), 2 (pt); LPNs 3 (ft), 2 (pt);
Nurses aides 10 (ft), 15 (pt); Physical therapists
2 (ft), 1 (pt); Activities coordinators 1 (ft), 1
(pt); Dietitians 1 (pt).
Affiliation Lutheran
Facilities Dining room; Physical therapy room;
Activities room; Chapel; Crafts room; Laundry
room; Barber/Beauty shop.
Activities Arts and Crafts; Cards; Games;
Reading groups; Prayer groups; Movies; Shop-
ping trips; Dances/Social or cultural gatherings.

MABEL

Green Lea Manor*
Box 306, Mabel, MN, 55954 (507) 493-5436
Admin Roland M Torgerson.
Licensure Intermediate Care. *Beds* 79. *Certi-
fied* Medicaid.
Ownership Public.

MADELIA

Luther Memorial Home
221 6th St SW, Madelia, MN, 56062 (507)
642-3271
Admin Kyle Nordine. *Medical Dir/Dir of
Nursing* William Halverson MD.
Licensure Intermediate Care. *Beds* 89. *Certi-
fied* Medicaid.
Ownership Nonprofit.
Admissions Requirements Medical examina-
tion.
Staff RNs 1 (ft), 3 (pt); LPNs 6 (ft); Activities
coordinators 1 (ft), 1 (pt); Dietitians 1 (pt).
Affiliation Lutheran
Facilities Dining room; Activities room; Chap-
el; Crafts room; Barber/Beauty shop; Library.
Activities Arts and Crafts; Cards; Games;
Reading groups; Prayer groups; Movies; Shop-
ping trips; Dances/Social or cultural gatherings.
Description Facility is a single-level, spacious
facility with large campus grounds.

MADISON

Madison Lutheran Home
900 2nd Ave, Madison, MN, 56256 (612)
598-7536
Admin Curtis C Legwold. *Medical Dir/Dir of
Nursing* Dr Westby and Dr Camp.
Licensure Skilled Care; Intermediate Care;
Boarding Care. *Beds* SNF 80; ICF 96;
Boarding Care 36. *Certified* Medicaid.
Ownership Nonprofit.
Affiliation Lutheran
Facilities Dining room; Physical therapy room;
Activities room; Chapel; Laundry room; Bar-
ber/Beauty shop.
Activities Arts and Crafts; Cards; Games;
Reading groups; Prayer groups; Movies; Shop-
ping trips; Dances/Social or cultural gatherings.

MANKATO

Family House
328 N 6th St, Mankato, MN, 56001 (507)
345-1652
Admin Paul Hagen.
Licensure Supervised Living Facility. *Beds* 7.
Ownership Nonprofit.
Admissions Requirements Minimum age 5.
Facilities Dining room; Activities room; Crafts
room; Laundry room.
Activities Arts and Crafts; Cards; Games;
Reading groups; Prayer groups; Movies; Shop-
ping trips; Dances/Social or cultural gatherings.

Harry Meyering Center
109 Homestead Dr, Mankato, MN, 56001
(507) 387-8281
Admin Carol Lee.
Licensure Supervised Living Facility. *Bed-
s* ICF/MR 44. *Certified* Medicaid.
Ownership Nonprofit.
Admissions Requirements Minimum age 18;
Medical examination.
Staff LPNs 1 (ft), 1 (pt); Activities coordina-
tors 1 (ft).
Facilities Laundry room.
Activities Arts and Crafts; Cards; Games;
Reading groups; Movies; Shopping trips; Dan-
ces/Social or cultural gatherings.
Description Center has 11 individual apart-
ments for developmentally disabled adults;
focus is on independent living skills.

Hillcrest Health Care Center*
Rt 9, Box 3, Mankato, MN, 56001 (507)
387-3491
Admin Helen L Johnson.
Licensure Skilled Care; Intermediate Care.
Beds SNF 98; ICF 60. *Certified* Medicaid.
Ownership Proprietary.

Mankato House Health Care Center
700 James Ave, Mankato, MN, 56001 (507)
345-4631
Admin Dorothy Leduc. *Medical Dir/Dir of
Nursing* Dr Harry Brauer.
Licensure Skilled Care; Intermediate Care.
Beds 97. *Certified* Medicaid.
Ownership Proprietary.
Admissions Requirements Minimum age 18;
Medical examination; Physician's request.
Staff Physicians 1 (pt); RNs 4 (ft), 11 (pt);
LPNs 6 (ft), 14 (pt); Orderlies 2 (pt); Nurses
aides 23 (ft), 26 (pt); Physical therapists 1 (pt);
Recreational therapists 2 (ft); Occupational
therapists 1 (pt); Activities coordinators 1 (ft);
Dietitians 1 (pt).

Mankato Lutheran Home For the Aged
718 Mound Ave, Mankato, MN, 56001 (507)
345-4576
Admin Charles Zimmerman. *Medical Dir/Dir
of Nursing* John J Heimark MD.
Licensure Skilled Care; Boarding Care.
Beds SNF 45; Boarding Care 24. *Cer-
tified* Medicaid.
Ownership Nonprofit.
Admissions Requirements Minimum age 16;
Medical examination; Physician's request.
Staff RNs 1 (ft), 4 (pt); LPNs 2 (ft), 7 (pt);
Orderlies 3 (pt); Nurses aides 7 (ft), 17 (pt);
Recreational therapists 1 (ft); Activities coordi-

nators 2 (pt); Dietitians 1 (ft).
Affiliation Lutheran
Facilities Dining room; Physical therapy room; Activities room; Chapel; Crafts room; Laundry room; Barber/Beauty shop; Library; Resident lounge.
Activities Arts and Crafts; Cards; Games; Reading groups; Prayer groups; Movies; Shopping trips; Dances/Social or cultural gatherings.
Description Mankato Lutheran Home is a stately facility on grounds overlooking an expansive city park along the confluence of the Minnesota and Blue Earth Rivers; offers residential skilled nursing care and boarding care services; community-based outreach programs provided, including adult day care, in-home respite, and home health care services.

Oaklawn Health Care Center*
1112 Mulberry, Mankato, MN, 56001 (507) 388-2913
Admin John Thro.
Licensure Skilled Care; Intermediate Care.
Beds SNF 52; ICF 11. *Certified* Medicaid.
Ownership Proprietary.

REM-Mankato Inc
210 Thomas Dr, Mankato, MN, 56001 (612) 387-3181
Admin Thomas Miller.
Licensure Supervised Living Facility. *Beds* 45. *Certified* Medicaid.
Ownership Proprietary.
Admissions Requirements Minimum age 18; Medical examination.
Staff RNs 1 (ft); LPNs 1 (pt).
Facilities Dining room; Activities room; Laundry room.
Activities Arts and Crafts; Cards; Games; Movies; Shopping trips; Dances/Social or cultural gatherings; Sporting and other community events.
Description REM-Mankato, Inc is a supervised living residence for 45 adults who are mentally retarded. REM is a complex of 3 apartment buildings wherein residents learn daily living skills to increase their independence.

MAPLE PLAIN

Haven Homes of Maple Plain
1520 Wyman Avenue, Maple Plain, MN, 55359 (612) 479-1993
Admin Daniel Fair. *Medical Dir/Dir of Nursing* Jo Berger MD.
Licensure Skilled Care; Intermediate Care.
Beds 67. *Certified* Medicaid.
Ownership Proprietary.
Admissions Requirements Medical examination; Physician's request.
Staff Physicians 4 (pt); RNs 2 (ft), 4 (pt); LPNs 5 (pt); Nurses aides 6 (ft), 23 (pt); Physical therapists 1 (pt); Recreational therapists 1 (ft); Occupational therapists 1 (pt); Speech therapists 1 (pt); Dietitians 1 (pt); Dentists 1 (pt); Podiatrists 1 (pt); Audiologists 1 (pt).
Facilities Dining room; Physical therapy room; Barber/Beauty shop.
Activities Arts and Crafts; Cards; Games; Reading groups; Movies.

MAPLETON

Mapleton Community Home
301 Troendel St, Mapleton, MN, 56065 (507) 524-3315
Admin Calvin Ward. *Medical Dir/Dir of Nursing* Dr John Lester.
Licensure Skilled Care; Intermediate Care.
Beds 80. *Certified* Medicaid.
Ownership Nonprofit.
Admissions Requirements Medical examination; Physician's request.
Staff RNs 2 (ft), 5 (pt); LPNs 10 (pt); Nurses aides 14 (ft), 38 (pt); Activities coordinators 1 (ft), 2 (pt); Dietitians 1 (pt).
Facilities Dining room; Activities room; Chapel; Crafts room; Laundry room; Barber/Beauty shop; Library.
Activities Arts and Crafts; Cards; Games; Reading groups; Prayer groups; Movies; Shopping trips.
Description Home is located next to the city park in a quiet and restful part of town; has bus with wheelchair lift to transport residents to lakes for picnics and shopping centers for relaxation.

MAPLEWOOD

Maplewood Maple Manor Care Center
550 E Roselawn Ave, Maplewood, MN, 55117 (612) 774-9765
Admin Leon Rotering. *Medical Dir/Dir of Nursing* Leon Nesvicil MD.
Licensure Skilled Care; Intermediate Care.
Beds SNF 112; ICF 47. *Certified* Medicaid; Medicare.
Ownership Proprietary.
Admissions Requirements Medical examination; Physician's request.
Staff RNs 7 (ft), 15 (pt); LPNs 3 (ft), 10 (pt); Nurses aides 31 (ft), 49 (pt); Physical therapists 1 (ft); Recreational therapists 4 (ft); Occupational therapists 1 (pt); Dietitians 2 (pt); Volunteer coordinator 1 (ft); Social services 2 (ft).
Facilities Dining room; Physical therapy room; Activities room; Crafts room; Laundry room; Barber/Beauty shop; Library; Meeting rooms.
Activities Arts and Crafts; Cards; Games; Reading groups; Prayer groups; Movies; Shopping trips; Dances/Social or cultural gatherings; Poetry; Art; Camping; Exercise.
Description Maplewood Maple Manor Care Center offers residents a wide range of services in a home-like environment and an atmosphere of mutual respect, consideration, and friendship. Facility has 3 separate nursing stations with a spacious lounge and dining room at each station. The lounge areas are often used for entertainment programs, parties, family education, and church services as well as for visiting and watching television. Outside grounds provide private areas for walking and bird watching. During the warm months, residents and families gather on the patio and cedar deck to enjoy the sunshine, fresh air, and beautiful surroundings.

Nekton on Frost*
1695 Frost Ave, Maplewood, MN, 55109 (612) 770-2531
Admin Milt Conrath.

Licensure Intermediate Care for Mentally Retarded. *Beds* 6. *Certified* Medicaid.
Ownership Proprietary.

Ramsey Nursing Home*
2000 White Bear Ave, Maplewood, MN, 55109 (612) 777-7486
Admin Einar Soberg.
Licensure Skilled Care; Intermediate Care.
Beds SNF 120; ICF 60. *Certified* Medicaid.
Ownership Public.

Sur La Rue de Skillman*
373 Skillman Ave, Maplewood, MN, 55117 (612) 488-6956
Admin Peter Sajevic.
Licensure Intermediate Care for Mentally Retarded. *Beds* 6. *Certified* Medicaid.
Ownership Proprietary.

MARSHALL

REM Marshall A, B, C*
1003 N 4th St, Marshall, MN, 56258 (507) 532-1458
Admin Robert Miller.
Licensure Intermediate Care for Mentally Retarded. *Beds* 45. *Certified* Medicaid.
Ownership Proprietary.

Wiener Memorial Medical Center*
300 S Bruce St, Marshall, MN, 56258 (507) 532-9661
Admin Ronald L Jensen.
Licensure Skilled Care. *Beds* 76. *Certified* Medicaid; Medicare.
Ownership Public.

MCINTOSH

McIntosh Nursing Home Inc*
245 N State, McIntosh, MN, 56556 (218) 563-2713
Admin Manda Lunds.
Licensure Skilled Care; Intermediate Care.
Beds SNF 38; ICF 38. *Certified* Medicaid; Medicare.
Ownership Proprietary.

Riverside Board and Care Home*
240 1st St NE, McIntosh, MN, 56556 (218) 563-4451
Admin Dennis Ekeberg.
Licensure Boarding Care. *Beds* 11.
Ownership Proprietary.

MENAHGA

Green Pine Acres Nursing Home*
PO Box 130, Menahga, MN, 56464 (218) 564-4101
Admin Clair Erickson.
Licensure Intermediate Care. *Beds* 91. *Certified* Medicaid.
Ownership Public.

MENDOTA HIGHTS

DCI Dakota Adults*
2031 S Victoria Rd, Mendota Hights, MN,
55118 (612) 455-1286
Admin Kathleen Pine.
Licensure Skilled Care; Intermediate Care.
Beds SNF 12; ICF 12. *Certified* Medicaid.
Ownership Nonprofit.

MILACA

Elim Home
730 2nd St SE, Milaca, MN, 56353 (612)
983-2185
Admin Volnie O'Brien. *Medical Dir/Dir of
Nursing* Dr Bruce Gersterkorn.
Licensure Skilled Care. *Beds* 119. *Certified* Medicaid.
Ownership Nonprofit.
Admissions Requirements Medical examination; Physician's request.
Staff RNs 2 (ft), 8 (pt); LPNs 1 (ft), 5 (pt);
Nurses aides 8 (ft), 57 (pt); Physical therapists 1
(ft); Reality therapists 1 (ft); Activities coordinators 1 (ft), 2 (pt); Dietitians 1 (ft).
Affiliation Evangelical Free Church
Facilities Dining room; Physical therapy room;
Activities room; Chapel; Crafts room; Laundry
room; Barber/Beauty shop; Library.
Activities Arts and Crafts; Cards; Games;
Reading groups; Prayer groups; Movies; Shopping trips; Dances/Social or cultural gatherings.
Description Facility is fully air conditioned.
Residents are served by in-house chaplain.

Stepping Stones Group Home*
560 SE 3rd St, Milaca, MN, 56353 (612)
983-2550
Admin Glenn Anderson.
Licensure Skilled Care; Intermediate Care.
Beds SNF 4; ICF 8. *Certified* Medicaid.
Ownership Nonprofit.

MINNEAPOLIS

Aldrich Boarding Care Home*
3101 Aldrich Ave S, Minneapolis, MN, 55408
(612) 825-4488
Admin D W Thistlewood.
Licensure Boarding Care. *Beds* 25.
Ownership Proprietary.

Andrew Care Home
1215 S 9th St, Minneapolis, MN, 55404 (612)
336-6321
Admin Karen M Foy.
Licensure Intermediate Care; Boarding Care.
Beds ICF 228; Boarding Care 228. *Certified* Medicaid.
Ownership Proprietary.
Admissions Requirements Minimum age 18;
Medical examination.
Staff LPNs 4 (ft), 1 (pt); Recreational therapists
8 (ft); Dietitians 1 (pt).
Facilities Dining room; Activities room; Crafts
room; Laundry room.
Activities Arts and Crafts; Cards; Games;
Reading groups; Movies; Shopping trips; Dances/Social or cultural gatherings.
Description Andrew is a community-based

mental health residential facility. Its purpose
and philosophy is to maximize the independence and integration into the community, and
enhance the quality of life for those individuals
with mental health needs.

Angelus Convalescent Home*
4544 4th Ave S, Minneapolis, MN, 55409 (612)
827-3526
Admin Steven E Felsenberg.
Licensure Skilled Care; Intermediate Care.
Beds SNF 62; ICF 22. *Certified* Medicaid.
Ownership Proprietary.

Augustana Home
1007 E 14th St, Minneapolis, MN, 55404 (612)
333-1551
Admin John Palmquist. *Medical Dir/Dir of
Nursing* Dr Henry Quist.
Licensure Skilled Care; Intermediate Care;
Boarding Care. *Beds* 262. *Certified* Medicaid;
Medicare.
Ownership Nonprofit.
Admissions Requirements Minimum age 65;
Medical examination; Physician's request.
Staff RNs 17 (ft), 18 (pt); LPNs 12 (ft), 8 (pt);
Nurses aides 58 (ft), 125 (pt); Physical therapists 3 (ft); Reality therapists 2 (ft); Recreational
therapists 8 (ft); Activities coordinators 1 (ft).
Affiliation Lutheran
Facilities Dining room; Physical therapy room;
Activities room; Chapel; Crafts room; Laundry
room; Barber/Beauty shop; Library.
Activities Arts and Crafts; Cards; Games;
Reading groups; Prayer groups; Movies; Shopping trips; Dances/Social or cultural gatherings.

Bannochie Nursing Home*
3515 2nd Ave S, Minneapolis, MN, 55408
(612) 822-3600
Admin Douglas W Bannochie.
Licensure Intermediate Care. *Beds* 43. *Certified* Medicaid.
Ownership Proprietary.

Baptist Residence*
512 49th Ave N, Minneapolis, MN, 55430
(612) 529-7747
Admin Warren Rippey.
Licensure Intermediate Care. *Beds* 87. *Certified* Medicaid.
Ownership Nonprofit.

Bethany Covenant Home*
2309 Hayes St NE, Minneapolis, MN, 55418
(612) 781-2691
Admin Mark Cairns.
Licensure Intermediate Care. *Beds* 66. *Certified* Medicaid.
Ownership Nonprofit.

Birchwood Care Home*
715 W 31st St, Minneapolis, MN, 55408 (612)
823-7286
Admin Donald E Fowler.
Licensure Intermediate Care. *Beds* 60. *Certified* Medicaid.
Ownership Proprietary.

Boreen Nursing Home*
2100 1st Ave S, Minneapolis, MN, 55404 (612)
874-1101
Admin Scott S Cooper.

Licensure Intermediate Care. *Beds* 35. *Certified* Medicaid.
Ownership Proprietary.

Bryn Mawr Nursing Home*
275 Penn Ave N, Minneapolis, MN, 55405
(612) 377-4723
Admin Dorothy M Rifenrath.
Licensure Skilled Care; Intermediate Care.
Beds SNF 129; ICF 49. *Certified* Medicaid;
Medicare.
Ownership Proprietary.

Bywood East
3427 Central Ave NE, Minneapolis, MN,
55418 (612) 788-9757
Admin Richard Werner.
Licensure Intermediate Care. *Beds* 105. *Certified* Medicaid.
Ownership Proprietary.
Admissions Requirements Minimum age 17.
Staff RNs 1 (ft), 2 (pt); LPNs 12 (ft), 6 (pt);
Nurses aides 3 (ft), 1 (pt); Recreational therapists 1 (ft); Occupational therapists 1 (ft); Dietitians 1 (pt); Dentists 1 (pt); Podiatrists 1 (pt).
Facilities Dining room; Activities room;
Barber/Beauty shop; Library.
Activities Arts and Crafts; Cards; Games;
Reading groups; Prayer groups; Movies; Shopping trips; Dances/Social or cultural gatherings.
Description Our facility has a noninstitutional
look; it is fully carpeted and totally air conditioned. Residents are able to choose their meals
from our cafeteria-style of food service. All
activities and recreation are handled by the
facility and are provided with no additional
cost to our residents.

Careview Home Inc*
5517 Lyndale Ave S, Minneapolis, MN, 55419
(612) 827-5677
Admin James Kaiser.
Licensure Skilled Care. *Beds* 150. *Certified* Medicaid; Medicare.
Ownership Nonprofit.

Cedar Pines Nursing Home*
2739 Cedar Ave, Minneapolis, MN, 55407
(612) 724-5491
Admin Merle V Nugent.
Licensure Skilled Care; Intermediate Care.
Beds SNF 95; ICF 36. *Certified* Medicaid;
Medicare.
Ownership Proprietary.

Central Nursing Home
1828 Central Ave NE, Minneapolis, MN,
55418 (612) 781-3118
Admin Joanne Gilbertson. *Medical Dir/Dir of
Nursing* Dr John Doyle.
Licensure Skilled Care; Intermediate Care.
Beds SNF 101; ICF 48. *Certified* Medicaid.
Ownership Proprietary.
Admissions Requirements Minimum age 16;
Medical examination; Physician's request.
Staff RNs 5 (ft), 2 (pt); LPNs 3 (ft), 10 (pt);
Nurses aides 19 (ft), 39 (pt); Physical therapists
1 (ft); Recreational therapists 4 (pt); Occupational therapists 1 (ft); Speech therapists 1 (pt);
Activities coordinators 1 (ft); Dietitians 1 (ft).
Facilities Dining room; Physical therapy room;
Activities room; Laundry room; Barber/Beauty
shop.

Activities Arts and Crafts; Cards; Games; Reading groups; Prayer groups; Movies; Shopping trips; Dances/Social or cultural gatherings.

Charles Bronstien Home
2644 Fremont Ave S, Minneapolis, MN, 55408
(612) 377-3710
Admin Norman Doeden.
Licensure Supervised Living Facility. *Beds* ICF/MR 10. *Certified* Medicaid.
Ownership Nonprofit.

Chateau Healthcare Center*
2106 2nd Ave S, Minneapolis, MN, 55404
(612) 874-1603
Admin Sheryl Osburn.
Licensure Skilled Care; Intermediate Care.
Beds SNF 80; ICF 13. *Certified* Medicaid; Medicare.
Ownership Proprietary.

Christian Union Home
1507 Lowry Ave NE, Minneapolis, MN, 55418
(612) 781-4871
Admin Dave Bredenberg.
Licensure Boarding Care. *Beds* 52.
Ownership Nonprofit.
Admissions Requirements Medical examination.
Staff RNs 1 (ft); LPNs 1 (ft); Nurses aides 8 (pt); Recreational therapists 2 (pt); Activities coordinators 1 (pt); Dietitians 1 (pt); Dentists 1 (pt).
Facilities Dining room; Activities room; Chapel; Crafts room; Laundry room; Barber/Beauty shop; Library.
Activities Arts and Crafts; Cards; Games; Reading groups; Prayer groups; Movies; Shopping trips; Dances/Social or cultural gatherings.
Description Facility has a very homey atmosphere with an abundance of antiques and traditional decor; located near center of Minneapolis but on spacious grounds in very nice neighborhood; excellent home cooked food, and a courteous well-qualified staff.

Clara Doerr-Lindley Hall*
1717 2nd Ave S, Minneapolis, MN, 55403
(612) 870-4440
Admin David Wiencke.
Licensure Intermediate Care for Mentally Retarded. *Beds* 103. *Certified* Medicaid.
Ownership Nonprofit.

Clifton House
301 Clifton Ave, Minneapolis, MN, 55403
(612) 870-8111
Admin Neal H Frank Jr.
Licensure Skilled Care. *Beds* 13.
Ownership Nonprofit.
Affiliation Christian Science
Facilities Dining room; Laundry room; Barber/Beauty shop; Library.
Activities Arts and Crafts; Reading groups.

David Herman Health Center
2401 Chicago Ave S, Minneapolis, MN, 55404
(612) 871-3661
Admin Marion Resnick. *Medical Dir/Dir of Nursing* Thomas J Bloss MD.
Licensure Skilled Care; Intermediate Care.
Beds SNF 130; ICF 17. *Certified* Medicaid.
Ownership Proprietary.

Admissions Requirements Minimum age 18; Medical examination; Physician's request.
Staff Physicians 3 (pt); RNs 9 (ft); LPNs 12 (ft), 2 (pt); Nurses aides 51 (ft), 6 (pt); Physical therapists 3 (ft); Recreational therapists 3 (ft), 1 (pt); Occupational therapists 1 (ft), 1 (pt); Speech therapists 1 (pt); Activities coordinators 4 (ft); Dietitians 1 (pt); Dentists 1 (pt); Ophthalmologists 1 (pt); Podiatrists 1 (pt); Audiologists 1 (pt); Clinical psychologist 1 (pt).
Facilities Dining room; Physical therapy room; Activities room; Chapel; Crafts room; Barber/Beauty shop; Library.
Activities Arts and Crafts; Cards; Games; Movies; Dances/Social or cultural gatherings; Birthday parties.
Description Beautiful facility is centrally located and surrounded by hospitals and medical buildings; on 2 bus lines; central air conditioning, enclosed patio, excellent food, and bright, cheerful rooms.

Ebenezer Hall
2545 Portland Ave S, Minneapolis, MN, 55404
(612) 879-2200
Admin Susan O'Shea. *Medical Dir/Dir of Nursing* Dr Robert Tierney.
Licensure Intermediate Care; Boarding Care.
Beds ICF 172; Boarding Care 139. *Certified* Medicaid.
Ownership Nonprofit.
Admissions Requirements Minimum age 65.
Affiliation Lutheran
Facilities Dining room; Physical therapy room; Activities room; Chapel; Crafts room; Laundry room; Barber/Beauty shop; Library.
Activities Arts and Crafts; Cards; Games; Reading groups; Prayer groups; Movies; Shopping trips; Dances/Social or cultural gatherings.

Ebenezer Society/Luther Hall
2636 Park Ave S, Minneapolis, MN, 55407
(612) 879-2200
Admin Kevin Gerber. *Medical Dir/Dir of Nursing* Robert Tierney MD.
Licensure Skilled Care; Intermediate Care.
Beds SNF 179; ICF 131. *Certified* Medicaid; Medicare.
Ownership Nonprofit.
Admissions Requirements Minimum age 62.
Affiliation Lutheran
Facilities Dining room; Physical therapy room; Activities room; Chapel; Crafts room; Laundry room; Barber/Beauty shop.
Activities Arts and Crafts; Cards; Games; Reading groups; Prayer groups; Movies; Shopping trips; Dances/Social or cultural gatherings.

Elliot Avenue Boarding Care Home*
1500 Elliot Ave S, Minneapolis, MN, 55404
(612) 339-2291
Admin Muriel Ganje.
Licensure Intermediate Care. *Beds* 15. *Certified* Medicaid.
Ownership Proprietary.

Emerson Boarding Care Home*
2708 Emerson Ave S, Minneapolis, MN, 55408
(612) 872-7100
Admin Muriel Ganje.
Licensure Intermediate Care. *Beds* 10. *Certified* Medicaid.
Ownership Proprietary.

Fair Oaks Nursing Home*
321 E 25th St, Minneapolis, MN, 55404 (612) 874-1701
Admin Margaret Hellman.
Licensure Skilled Care. *Beds* 114. *Certified* Medicaid.
Ownership Proprietary.

First Christian Church Residence*
2300 Stevens Ave S, Minneapolis, MN, 55404
(612) 870-1811
Admin Ernest L Midthun.
Licensure Intermediate Care. *Beds* 65. *Certified* Medicaid.
Ownership Nonprofit.

Flambeau-Aneskarn 1*
1446 W 34th St, Minneapolis, MN, 55408
(612) 823-3927
Admin Sandra Schweich.
Licensure Intermediate Care for Mentally Retarded. *Beds* 7.
Ownership Nonprofit.

Forestview James*
1616 James Ave N, Minneapolis, MN, 55411
(612) 521-6115
Admin William Koski.
Licensure Intermediate Care for Mentally Retarded. *Beds* 6.
Ownership Proprietary.

Franklin Nursing Home*
501 Franklin Ave W, Minneapolis, MN, 55405
(612) 871-7112
Admin Kevin Gerber.
Licensure Skilled Care. *Beds* 69. *Certified* Medicaid; Medicare.
Ownership Nonprofit.

Grand Avenue Rest Home*
3956 Grand Ave S, Minneapolis, MN, 55409
(612) 824-1434
Admin Richard Johnson.
Licensure Intermediate Care. *Beds* 21. *Certified* Medicaid; Medicare.
Ownership Proprietary.

Horizon West Health Care*
1620 Oak Park Ave N, Minneapolis, MN, 55411 (612) 588-0804
Admin Dave Westbrook.
Licensure Skilled Care; Intermediate Care.
Beds SNF 44; ICF 52. *Certified* Medicaid.
Ownership Proprietary.

Hyland Park Nursing Home
2304 Emerson Ave N, Minneapolis, MN, 55411 (612) 521-3679
Admin Thomas D Fauskee.
Licensure Intermediate Care. *Beds* 68. *Certified* Medicaid.
Admissions Requirements Physician's request.
Staff Physicians 2 (pt); RNs 3 (ft); LPNs 3 (ft); Nurses aides 16 (ft), 16 (pt); Physical therapists 1 (pt); Recreational therapists 4 (ft); Occupational therapists 1 (ft), 2 (pt); Speech therapists 1 (pt); Dietitians 1 (pt); Dentists 1 (pt); Ophthalmologists 1 (pt); Podiatrists 1 (pt).
Facilities Dining room; Activities room; Crafts room; Laundry room; Occupational therapy room.
Activities Arts and Crafts; Cards; Games;

Reading groups; Prayer groups; Movies; Shopping trips; Dances/Social or cultural gatherings. *Description* Intermediate care facility featuring excellent recreation and occupational therapy programing housed in a warm, friendly home-like atmosphere.

Jones-Harrison Home
3700 Cedar Lake Ave, Minneapolis, MN, 55416 (612) 920-2030
Admin E J Hein. *Medical Dir/Dir of Nursing* Dr John Cardle.
Licensure Intermediate Care; Boarding Care.
Beds ICF 163; Boarding Care 123. *Certified* Medicaid.
Ownership Nonprofit.
Admissions Requirements Minimum age 62; Medical examination; Physician's request.
Staff Physicians 1 (pt); RNs 3 (ft), 5 (pt); LPNs 4 (ft), 4 (pt); Nurses aides 9 (ft), 19 (pt); Physical therapists 1 (pt); Reality therapists 1 (ft); Recreational therapists 1 (ft); Occupational therapists 1 (pt); Speech therapists 1 (pt); Activities coordinators 1 (ft); Dietitians 1 (pt); Dentists 1 (pt); Ophthalmologists 1 (pt); Podiatrists 1 (pt); Audiologists 1 (pt).
Facilities Dining room; Physical therapy room; Activities room; Chapel; Crafts room; Laundry room; Barber/Beauty shop; Library; Resident store; Garden space and plant rooms; Van.
Activities Arts and Crafts; Cards; Games; Reading groups; Prayer groups; Movies; Shopping trips; Dances/Social or cultural gatherings; Educational opportunities.
Description Jones-Harrison Home provides elegant and spacious surroundings for the board and care resident. Our excellent health care center offers intermediate and skilled nursing, temporary and respite care, and a complete therapy program. Concern for the total resident and his/her family is expressed at Jones-Harrison Home.

LaSalle Convalescent Home*
1920 Lasalle Ave, Minneapolis, MN, 55403 (612) 870-8611
Admin Wayne Olson.
Licensure Skilled Care; Intermediate Care.
Beds SNF 106; ICF 33. *Certified* Medicaid.
Ownership Proprietary.

Loring Nursing Home
2327 Pillsbury Ave S, Minneapolis, MN, 55404 (612) 871-1713
Admin Steve Tjeltveit. *Medical Dir/Dir of Nursing* Dr Robert Tierney.
Licensure Intermediate Care. *Beds* 45. *Certified* Medicaid.
Ownership Nonprofit.
Admissions Requirements Medical examination; Physician's request.
Staff Physical therapists; Occupational therapists; Speech therapists; Activities coordinators 1 (ft); Dietitians 1 (ft); Dentists; Ophthalmologists; Podiatrists.
Affiliation Lutheran
Facilities Dining room; Activities room; Chapel; Crafts room; Laundry room; Barber/Beauty shop; Library.
Activities Arts and Crafts; Cards; Games; Reading groups; Movies; Shopping trips; Dances/Social or cultural gatherings.

Description Loring is a converted mansion featuring 3 lounges, a 5-meal program, and an extremely committed staff.

Maria Home
420 Ridgewood Ave S, Minneapolis, MN, 55403 (612) 871-0805
Admin Sheldon Schneider.
Licensure Supervised Living Facility. *Beds* ICF/MR 9. *Certified* Medicaid.
Ownership Proprietary.
Admissions Requirements Minimum age 18; Medical examination.
Staff RNs 1 (pt); Activities coordinators 1 (pt); Counselors 2 (ft), 1 (pt).
Facilities Dining room; Activities room; Laundry room.
Activities Arts and Crafts; Cards; Games; Movies; Shopping trips; Dances/Social or cultural gatherings.

Medallion II Board & Lodge Home
2430 Pillsbury Ave S, Minneapolis, MN, 55404 (612) 871-8306
Admin Robert Servold.
Licensure Intermediate Care. *Beds* 25. *Certified* Medicaid.
Ownership Proprietary.
Admissions Requirements Minimum age 18.
Staff Cook/Mgr 1 (ft), 1 (pt); Housekeepers 2 (pt).
Facilities Dining room; Laundry room.

Minneapolis Outreach Home
5304 Stevens Ave S, Minneapolis, MN, 55419 (612) 823-9241
Admin Eileen Harris.
Licensure Supervised Living Facility. *Beds* 6. *Certified* Medicaid.
Ownership Nonprofit.
Admissions Requirements Minimum age 18; Medical examination.
Staff Physicians 1 (pt); RNs 1 (pt).
Affiliation Presbyterian
Facilities Dining room; Activities room; Laundry room.
Activities Arts and Crafts; Cards; Games; Prayer groups; Movies; Shopping trips; Dances/Social or cultural gatherings.
Description Facility care based on family oriented philosophy striving for normalization.

Minnesota Veterans Home*
51st St at Minnehaha, Minneapolis, MN, 55417 612) 729-9325
Admin Jean Donaldson.
Licensure Intermediate Care. *Beds* 346.
Ownership Public.

Mount Olivet Homes Inc*
5517 Lyndale Ave S, Minneapolis, MN, 55419 (612) 827-5677
Admin James Kaiser.
Licensure Intermediate Care. *Beds* 97. *Certified* Medicaid.
Ownership Nonprofit.

Nekton on Minnehaha Park*
3822 E 49th St, Minneapolis, MN, 55417 (612) 729-5526
Admin Mike Seiwert.
Licensure Intermediate Care for Mentally Retarded. *Beds* 6. *Certified* Medicaid.

Nekton on Queen*
614 Queen Ave S, Minneapolis, MN, 55404 (612) 377-5587
Admin Mike Seiwert.
Licensure Intermediate Care for Mentally Retarded. *Beds* 6. *Certified* Medicaid.
Ownership Proprietary.

Nicollet Health Care Center Inc
4429 Nicollet Ave S, Minneapolis, MN, 55409 (612) 827-5667
Admin Joan Bangasser. *Medical Dir/Dir of Nursing* Stuart Lancer MD.
Licensure Skilled Care; Intermediate Care.
Beds SNF 88; ICF 59. *Certified* Medicaid; Medicare
Admissions Requirements Minimum age 16; Medical examination; Physician's request.
Facilities Dining room; Physical therapy room; Activities room; Crafts room; Laundry room; Barber/Beauty shop; Library.
Activities Arts and Crafts; Cards; Games; Reading groups; Prayer groups; Movies; Shopping trips; Dances/Social or cultural gatherings.

Northeast House Inc
1918 NE 19th Ave, Minneapolis, MN, 55418 (612) 789-8841
Admin Donald G Levin. *Medical Dir/Dir of Nursing* Dr V K Arora.
Licensure Supervised Living Facility. *Beds* 24. *Certified* Medicaid.
Ownership Proprietary.
Admissions Requirements Minimum age 40; Medical examination.
Staff Physicians 2 (pt); RNs 1 (ft); LPNs 2 (pt); Physical therapists 1 (pt); Reality therapists 3 (ft); Recreational therapists 1 (ft); Occupational therapists 1 (pt); Speech therapists 1 (pt); Activities coordinators 2 (ft); Dietitians 1 (pt); Dentists 1 (pt); Ophthalmologists 1 (pt); Podiatrists 1 (pt); Audiologists 1 (pt).
Facilities Dining room; Activities room; Crafts room; Laundry room; Library.
Activities Arts and Crafts; Cards; Games; Reading groups; Prayer groups; Movies; Shopping trips; Dances/Social or cultural gatherings.
Description Facility is located in a beautiful setting on spacious grounds in a quiet residential area, yet just 10 minutes to downtown Minneapolis.

Oak Grove Care Center
131 Oak Grove, Minneapolis, MN, 55403 (612) 871-5800
Admin Kariann Nelson.
Licensure Boarding Care. *Beds* 21.
Ownership Proprietary.
Admissions Requirements Minimum age 30; Medical examination.
Staff LPNs 1 (ft), 2 (pt); Nurses aides 1 (ft), 2 (pt); Reality therapists 2 (ft); Recreational therapists 1 (ft); Dietitians 1 (pt).
Facilities Dining room; Activities room; Crafts room; Laundry room.
Activities Arts and Crafts; Cards; Games; Movies; Shopping trips; Dances/Social or cultural gatherings.
Description The facility, located in a turn-of-the-century mansion, is fully carpeted and provides a home-like atmosphere. The facility

has a contract with Hennepin County Social Services and provides services to adult mentally ill clients.

Oak Ridge Care Center*
1300 Olson Memorial Hwy, Minneapolis, MN, 55411 (612) 374-5660
Admin Mark Mandel.
Licensure Skilled Care; Intermediate Care.
Beds SNF 128; ICF 8. *Certified* Medicaid.
Ownership Proprietary.

One Hundred Eighty Degrees Inc*
236 Clifton Ave, Minneapolis, MN, 55403 (612) 870-7227
Admin Barbara Emer.
Licensure Supervised Living Facility. *Beds* 27.
Certified Medicaid.
Ownership Nonprofit.

Outreach Northeast Group Home
729 Adams St NE, Minneapolis, MN, 55403 (612) 379-8897
Admin J Neil Tift.
Licensure Supervised Living Facility. *Beds* 7.
Certified Medicaid.
Ownership Nonprofit.
Admissions Requirements Minimum age 18; Medical examination.
Staff RNs.
Facilities Dining room; Laundry room.
Activities Arts and Crafts; Cards; Games; Movies; Shopping trips; Dances/Social or cultural gatherings.
Description This is a group home serving 7 mentally retarded adults.

Pillsbury Board and Care Home
2500 Pillsbury Ave S, Minneapolis, MN, 55404 (612) 872-8363
Admin Lona Mason. *Medical Dir/Dir of Nursing* Diane Page.
Licensure Intermediate Care. *Beds* 22. *Certified* Medicaid.
Ownership Proprietary.
Admissions Requirements Minimum age 21; Medical examination; Physician's request.
Staff RNs 1 (ft); LPNs 3 (pt); Activities coordinators 1 (ft); Dietitians 1 (pt).
Facilities Dining room.
Activities Arts and Crafts; Cards; Games; Reading groups; Prayer groups; Shopping trips; Dances/Social or cultural gatherings.
Description Facility features personal homelike care; health care services are available through contracts with outside providers; convenient to stores and downtown Minneapolis; large yard for outdoor activities.

Portland Residence
1619 Portland Ave S, Minneapolis, MN, 55404 (612) 332-8300
Admin L Jankowski.
Licensure Supervised Living Facility.
Beds 101. *Certified* Medicaid.
Ownership Proprietary.
Admissions Requirements Minimum age 18; Medical examination; Physician's request.
Staff RNs 3 (pt); Recreational therapists 1 (pt); Speech therapists 1 (ft).
Facilities Dining room; Activities room; Crafts room; Laundry room; Auditorium; Exercise patio; Weight room; Gym; Kitchen.

Activities Arts and Crafts; Cards; Games; Reading groups; Prayer groups; Movies; Shopping trips; Dances/Social or cultural gatherings.
Description Portland provides service for 101 mentally retarded ambulatory adults. We provide services, specifically, for retirement age and hearing-impaired mentally retarded residents.

Queen Treatment Center
300 Queen Ave N, Minneapolis, MN, 55405 (612) 374-3380
Admin Dan Halvorsen. *Medical Dir/Dir of Nursing* Kenneth Kubasch.
Licensure Skilled Care; Intermediate Care; Boarding Care. *Beds* SNF 58; ICF 5; Boarding Care 12. *Certified* Medicaid; Medicare.
Ownership Proprietary.
Staff Physicians 1 (pt); RNs 4 (ft); LPNs 10 (ft); Orderlies 6 (ft); Nurses aides 24 (ft); Physical therapists 1 (ft); Reality therapists 1 (ft); Recreational therapists 4 (ft); Occupational therapists 1 (ft); Speech therapists 1 (ft); Activities coordinators 1 (ft); Dietitians 1 (ft); Dentists 1 (pt); Ophthalmologists 1 (pt); Podiatrists 1 (pt); Audiologists 1 (pt).
Facilities Dining room; Activities room; Laundry room; Barber/Beauty shop.
Activities Arts and Crafts; Cards; Games; Prayer groups; Movies; Shopping trips; Dances/Social or cultural gatherings; AA meetings.
Description Facility specializes in chronic alcoholic patients who also have associated behavioral problems; a history of chronic alcoholism is a requirement for admission; physical therapy is provided by staff of nursing home across the street.

Redeemer Residence*
3111 Lyndale Ave S, Minneapolis, MN, 55408 (612) 827-2555
Admin Fred Strandberg.
Licensure Skilled Care; Intermediate Care.
Beds SNF 54; ICF 109. *Certified* Medicaid.
Ownership Nonprofit.

REM Lyndale*
2210 Lyndale Ave N, Minneapolis, MN, 55411 (612) 522-6689
Admin Thomas Miller.
Licensure Intermediate Care for Mentally Retarded. *Beds* 10. *Certified* Medicaid.
Ownership Proprietary.

REM Pillsbury*
2311 Pillsbury Ave S, Minneapolis, MN, 55404 (612) 871-1954
Admin Douglas Miller.
Licensure Intermediate Care for Mentally Retarded. *Beds* 34. *Certified* Medicaid.
Ownership Proprietary.

REM Pleasant*
2548 Pleasant Ave S, Minneapolis, MN, 55404 (612) 872-7800
Admin Thomas Miller.
Licensure Intermediate Care for Mentally Retarded. *Beds* 15. *Certified* Medicaid.
Ownership Proprietary.

REM Southeast*
1307 6th St SE, Minneapolis, MN, 55414 (612) 378-1556

Admin Thomas Miller.
Licensure Intermediate Care for Mentally Retarded. *Beds* 10. *Certified* Medicaid.
Ownership Proprietary.

Riverview Nursing Home*
4659 Lyndale Ave N, Minneapolis, MN, 55412 (612) 529-9152
Admin Richard Johnson.
Licensure Intermediate Care. *Beds* 44. *Certified* Medicaid.
Ownership Proprietary.

Saint Anns Residence
2120 Clinton Ave S, Minneapolis, MN, 55404 (612) 871-0666
Admin Annette Rowland.
Licensure Supervised Living Facility. *Beds* 30.
Certified Medicaid.
Ownership Nonprofit.

Saint Olafs Residence
2912 Fremont Ave N, Minneapolis, MN, 55411 (612) 522-6561
Admin Richard Holy.
Licensure Skilled Care; Boarding Care.
Beds SNF 63; Boarding Care 122. *Certified* Medicaid.
Ownership Nonprofit.

Sentinel Care Home
2122 Portland Ave S, Minneapolis, MN, 55404 (612) 874-8845
Admin Harold Garvin.
Licensure Boarding Care. *Beds* 16.
Ownership Proprietary.

Shanti House
4954 Upton Ave S, Minneapolis, MN, 55410 (612) 374-9740
Admin Janice Folsom.
Licensure Supervised Living Facility. *Beds* 40.
Ownership Nonprofit.
Admissions Requirements Minimum age 14; Medical examination.
Staff Reality therapists 5 (ft); Live-in parent/counselors 2 (ft).

Southside Care Center
2644 Aldrich Ave S, Minneapolis, MN, 55408 (612) 872-4233
Admin March Kronfeld.
Licensure Boarding Care. *Beds* ICF 20; Boarding Care 20. *Certified* Medicaid.
Admissions Requirements Medical examination.
Staff RNs 1 (pt); LPNs 2 (ft), 1 (pt); Nurses aides 2 (ft), 2 (pt); Recreational therapists 1 (ft); Activities coordinators 1 (pt); Dietitians 1 (pt).
Facilities Dining room; Activities room; Laundry room; Barber/Beauty shop.
Activities Arts and Crafts; Cards; Games; Prayer groups.

Stevens Square*
101 E 32nd St, Minneapolis, MN, 55408 (612) 823-5201
Admin Rachel Rustad.
Licensure Skilled Care; Intermediate Care.
Beds SNF 15; ICF 51. *Certified* Medicaid.
Ownership Nonprofit.

Summit House*
1004 Summit Ave, Minneapolis, MN, 55403
(612) 377-1350
Admin Carol Robson.
Licensure Intermediate Care for Mentally
Retarded. *Beds* 6. *Certified* Medicaid.
Ownership Proprietary.

Three Thirty-Five Ridgewood
335 Ridgewood Ave S, Minneapolis, MN,
55403 (612) 871-0805
Admin Sheldon Schneider.
Licensure Supervised Living Facility. *Bed-
s* ICF/MR 9. *Certified* Medicaid.
Ownership Proprietary.
Admissions Requirements Minimum age 18;
Medical examination.
Staff RNs 1 (pt); Activities coordinators 1 (pt);
Counselors 1 (ft), 2 (pt).
Facilities Dining room; Activities room; Laun-
dry room.
Activities Arts and Crafts; Cards; Games;
Movies; Shopping trips; Dances/Social or cul-
tural gatherings.

University Health Care Center*
22 27th Ave SE, Minneapolis, MN, 55414
(612) 332-4262
Admin David Briscoe.
Licensure Skilled Care. *Beds* 345. *Certified* Medicaid.
Ownership Proprietary.

Villa Maria
719 E 16th St, Minneapolis, MN, 55404 (612)
339-7281
Admin K Howland.
Licensure Skilled Care; Intermediate Care.
Beds SNF 154; ICF 16. *Certified* Medicaid.
Ownership Proprietary.
Admissions Requirements Minimum age 16;
Medical examination; Physician's request.
Description Facility offers short-term and res-
pite care.

Walker Methodist Health Center Inc
3707 Bryant Ave S, Minneapolis, MN, 55409
(612) 827-5931
Admin Paul Mikelson. *Medical Dir/Dir of
Nursing* Wayne Hagen MD.
Licensure Skilled Care; Intermediate Care.
Beds SNF 244; ICF 246. *Certified* Medicaid;
Medicare.
Ownership Nonprofit.
Admissions Requirements Minimum age 65.
Staff Physicians 1 (pt); RNs 29 (ft), 14 (pt);
LPNs 23 (ft), 14 (pt); Nurses aides 115 (ft), 95
(pt); Recreational therapists 6 (ft), 1 (pt); Activi-
ties coordinators 1 (ft); Dietitians 1 (ft).
Affiliation Methodist
Facilities Dining room; Physical therapy room;
Activities room; Chapel; Crafts room; Laundry
room; Barber/Beauty shop; Library.
Activities Arts and Crafts; Cards; Games;
Reading groups; Prayer groups; Movies; Shopping trips; Dances/Social or cultural gatherings.
Description In the process of building a 7-story
independent living facility (apartments) on
campus which will enable occupants to have
emergency nursing care. In addition, we have
respite care and are looking into and implementing adult day care and home health care.

Willows Central Nursing Home
625 E 16th St, Minneapolis, MN, 55404 (612)
332-3541
Admin Kristi Olmanson. *Medical Dir/Dir of
Nursing* Henry Smith MD.
Licensure Intermediate Care; Boarding Care.
Beds ICF 150; Boarding Care 22. *Cer-
tified* Medicaid.
Ownership Proprietary.
Admissions Requirements Minimum age 16;
Medical examination.
Staff RNs 10 (ft), 1 (pt); LPNs 6 (ft), 8 (pt);
Orderlies 11 (ft), 3 (pt); Nurses aides 22 (ft), 14
(pt); Physical therapists 1 (ft); Recreational ther-
apists 1 (ft); Occupational therapists 2 (ft); Spee-
ch therapists 1 (pt); Activities coordinators 2
(ft); Dietitians 1 (pt); Audiologists 1 (pt); Social
workers 3 (ft).
Facilities Dining room; Physical therapy room;
Activities room; Chapel; Crafts room; Laundry
room; Barber/Beauty shop; Library.
Activities Arts and Crafts; Cards; Games;
Reading groups; Prayer groups; Movies; Shopping trips; Dances/Social or cultural gatherings.
Description Facility is convenient to downtown, senior citizen center, and on mainline
bus service, all rooms have double occupancy
with attached bathrooms, special program
emphasis for boarding care residents includes
giving attention to mental health needs, clients
needing physical rehabilitation, and arrangement of support services to return to community living are welcome.

Willows Convalescent Center South*
6130 Lyndale Ave S, Minneapolis, MN, 55419
(612) 866-3095
Admin Phebe Givens.
Licensure Skilled Care. *Beds* 144. *Certified* Medicaid.
Ownership Proprietary.

Yorkshire Manor*
2200 Park Ave S, Minneapolis, MN, 55404
(612) 871-2200
Admin Jenean Erickson.
Licensure Skilled Care; Intermediate Care.
Beds SNF 31; ICF 53. *Certified* Medicaid.
Ownership Proprietary.

MINNEOTA

Minneota Manor
700 N Monroe St, Minneota, MN, 56264 (507)
872-6166
Admin R Erickson. *Medical Dir/Dir of
Nursing* Dr Charles VanDersluis.
Licensure Skilled Care; Intermediate Care.
Beds SNF 51; ICF 36. *Certified* Medicaid.
Ownership Proprietary.
Staff RNs 1 (ft), 5 (pt); LPNs 2 (ft), 4 (pt);
Nurses aides 12 (ft), 35 (pt); Speech therapists 1
(pt); Activities coordinators 1 (ft), 1 (pt); Dieti-
tians 1 (pt).
Facilities Dining room; Activities room; Laun-
dry room; Barber/Beauty shop; Library.
Activities Arts and Crafts; Cards; Games;
Reading groups; Movies; Shopping trips; Small
group meals.

MINNETONKA

Forestview Minnetonka*
14212 Excelsior Blvd, Minnetonka, MN, 55343
(612) 938-7203
Admin William Koski.
Licensure Intermediate Care for Mentally
Retarded. *Beds* 6. *Certified* Medicaid.
Ownership Proprietary.

Hammer Residence Group Home 1
16325 County Rd 15, Minnetonka, MN, 55391
(612) 473-1261
Admin Merlyn Larson.
Licensure Supervised Care Facility. *Beds* 6.
Certified Medicaid.
Ownership Nonprofit.

Oak Terrace Nursing Home*
County Rds 4 and 67, Minnetonka, MN, 55343
(612) 934-4100
Admin Maurice A Treberg.
Licensure Skilled Care. *Beds* 350. *Cer-
tified* Medicaid; Medicare.
Ownership Public.

REM Minnetonka*
21 Westwood Rd, Minnetonka, MN, 55435
(612) 541-9421
Admin Thomas Miller.
Licensure Skilled Care; Intermediate Care.
Beds SNF 15; ICF 15. *Certified* Medicaid.
Ownership Proprietary.

Resa On Eden Prarie Rd
5601 Eden Prairie Rd, Minnetonka, MN,
55343 (612) 933-3348
Admin Jean Searles.
Licensure Supervised Living Facility. *Bed-
s* ICF/MR 6.
Ownership Proprietary.
Admissions Requirements Minimum age 45.
Staff RNs 1 (pt); 11 (pt).
Activities Arts and Crafts; Cards; Games;
Movies; Shopping trips; Dances/Social or cul-
tural gatherings.

MONTEVIDEO

Luther Haven Nursing Home*
E Hwy 7, Montevideo, MN, 56265 (612)
269-6517
Admin James Flaherty.
Licensure Skilled Care; Intermediate Care.
Beds SNF 65; ICF 55. *Certified* Medicaid.
Ownership Nonprofit.
Affiliation Lutheran

REM-Montevideo Inc
585 Gravel Rd, Montevideo, MN, 56265 (612)
269-6479
Admin R E Miller.
Licensure Supervised Living Facility. *Bed-
s* ICF/MR 15. *Certified* Medicaid.
Ownership Proprietary.
Admissions Requirements Minimum age 16;
Medical examination; Physician's request.
Staff RNs 1 (pt); Nurses aides 3 (ft), 8 (pt);
Recreational therapists 1 (pt); Activities coordi-
nators 1 (pt).
Facilities Dining room; Activities room; Laun-
dry room.

Activities Arts and Crafts; Cards; Games; Reading groups; Movies; Shopping trips; Dances/Social or cultural gatherings; Camping; Bowling; Swimming; Fishing.
Description An independent living unit (like an efficiency apartment) to enhance normalized living skills—houses 3 residents who also take part in all in house activities.

MONTGOMERY

Siemers Boarding Care Home
211 Spruce Ave, Montgomery, MN, 56069 (612) 364-8831
Admin David Mann.
Licensure Boarding Care. *Beds* 12. *Certified* Medicaid.
Ownership Proprietary.
Staff RNs 1 (pt); LPNs 1 (ft); Nurses aides 5 (pt); Dietitians 1 (pt).
Facilities Dining room; Activities room; Laundry room.
Activities Arts and Crafts; Cards; Games; Shopping trips; Dances/Social or cultural gatherings.

MONTICELLO

Monticello Big Lake Community Nursing Home*
E 4th and Washington, Monticello, MN, 55362 (612) 295-5116
Admin Wayne Ward.
Licensure Skilled Care; Intermediate Care.
Beds SNF 40; ICF 34. *Certified* Medicaid.
Ownership Public.

MOORHEAD

Clay County Residence II
2842 Village Green Dr, Moorhead, MN, 56560
Admin Douglas Johnson.
Licensure Intermediate Care for Mentally Retarded. *Beds* 6. *Certified* Medicaid; Medicare.
Ownership Nonprofit.
Admissions Requirements Minimum age 16; Medical examination.
Staff RNs 1 (pt).
Facilities Dining room; Activities room; Crafts room; Laundry room.
Activities Arts and Crafts; Cards; Games; Movies; Shopping trips.

Eventide Lutheran Home
1405 S 7th St, Moorhead, MN, 56560 (218) 233-7508
Admin Mark A Broman. *Medical Dir/Dir of Nursing* Dr John R Holten.
Licensure Skilled Care; Intermediate Care.
Beds 195. *Certified* Medicaid.
Ownership Nonprofit.
Admissions Requirements Medical examination.
Staff RNs 8 (ft), 5 (pt); LPNs 5 (ft), 12 (pt); Nurses aides 40 (ft), 65 (pt); Physical therapists 1 (ft), 1 (pt); Recreational therapists 5 (pt); Activities coordinators 1 (ft); Dietitians 1 (ft).
Affiliation Lutheran
Facilities Dining room; Physical therapy room; Activities room; Chapel; Crafts room; Laundry

room; Barber/Beauty shop; Library.
Activities Arts and Crafts; Cards; Games; Prayer groups; Movies; Shopping trips; Dances/Social or cultural gatherings.
Description Eventide is currently organizing adult day care and home health care programs within the Fargo-Moorhead area; full-time physical therapist is on staff. Eventide is a relatively new modern building, centrally located, with proximity to Concordia College and Moorhead State University.

Moorhead Healthcare Center
2810 N 2nd Ave, Moorhead, MN, 56560 (218) 233-7578
Admin Roger Paulsberg. *Medical Dir/Dir of Nursing* Dr Craychee.
Licensure Skilled Care; Intermediate Care.
Beds 89. *Certified* Medicaid; Medicare.
Ownership Proprietary.
Admissions Requirements Medical examination; Physician's request.
Facilities Dining room; Physical therapy room; Activities room; Chapel; Crafts room; Laundry room; Barber/Beauty shop.
Activities Arts and Crafts; Cards; Games; Reading groups; Prayer groups; Movies; Shopping trips; Dances/Social or cultural gatherings.

Valley Group Home 1*
1330 2nd Ave N, Moorhead, MN, 56560 (218) 236-9805
Admin Helen Young.
Licensure Intermediate Care for Mentally Retarded. *Beds* 10. *Certified* Medicaid.
Ownership Proprietary.

MOOSE LAKE

Moose Lake State Hospital*
1000 Lakeshore Dr, Moose Lake, MN, 55767 (618) 485-4411
Admin Frank R Milczard.
Licensure Skilled Care; Intermediate Care.
Beds SNF 245; ICF/MR 203. *Certified* Medicaid; Medicare.
Ownership Public.

MORA

Brighter Day Residence*
620 N Wood St, Mora, MN, 55051 (612) 679-3840
Admin Kathy La Combe.
Licensure Intermediate Care for Mentally Retarded. *Beds* 8. *Certified* Medicaid.
Ownership Nonprofit.

Fireside Foster Inn
114 W Maple St, Mora, MN, 55051 (612) 679-2822
Admin Robert Sandberg.
Licensure Board Care and Board Lodging.
Beds 29. *Certified* Medicaid.
Ownership Proprietary.
Staff LPNs 1 (ft), 2 (pt); Nurses aides 9 (pt); Activities coordinators 1 (pt); Dietitians 1 (pt).

Sunshine Villa
Birch Mor Medical Park, Mora, MN, 55051 (612) 679-1411

Admin R Sundberg. *Medical Dir/Dir of Nursing* Larry Brettingen.
Licensure Skilled Care; Intermediate Care.
Beds SNF 58; ICF 29. *Certified* Medicaid.
Ownership Proprietary.
Facilities Dining room; Physical therapy room; Activities room; Crafts room; Laundry room; Barber/Beauty shop.
Activities Arts and Crafts; Cards; Games; Reading groups; Prayer groups; Movies; Shopping trips.

MORGAN

Gil Mor Manor
Morgan, MN, 56266 (507) 249-3144
Admin Rita Sabatino. *Medical Dir/Dir of Nursing* C M Galvin.
Licensure Intermediate Care. *Beds* 49. *Certified* Medicaid.
Ownership Nonprofit.
Admissions Requirements Physician's request.
Staff RNs 1 (ft); LPNs 4 (ft), 1 (pt); Nurses aides 10 (ft), 10 (pt); Activities coordinators 1 (ft); Dietitians 1 (pt).
Facilities Dining room; Activities room; Chapel; Crafts room; Laundry room; Barber/Beauty shop; Library.
Activities Arts and Crafts; Cards; Games; Reading groups; Prayer groups; Movies; Shopping trips.
Description Facility is located in a rural setting with 25 private rooms on one floor with a clinic connected; there are no steps for residents.

MORRIS

Inisteige-Aneskarn 3*
210 W 7th, Morris, MN, 56267 (612) 589-2057
Admin Janice Krings.
Licensure Intermediate Care for Mentally Retarded. *Beds* 10. *Certified* Medicaid.
Ownership Nonprofit.

Villa of Saint Francis Nursing Home*
1001 Scott Ave, Morris, MN, 56267 (612) 589-1133
Admin Luverne Hoffman.
Licensure Skilled Care; Intermediate Care.
Beds SNF 98; ICF 46. *Certified* Medicaid.
Ownership Nonprofit.

MOUNTAIN LAKE

Eventide Home*
810 3rd Ave, Mountain Lake, MN, 56159 (507) 427-3221
Admin Jane Schiefelbein.
Licensure Intermediate Care. *Beds* 50. *Certified* Medicaid.
Ownership Nonprofit.

Good Samaritan Village
745 Basinger Memorial Dr, Mountain Lake, MN, 56159 (507) 427-2464
Admin G R Baumgartner.
Licensure Intermediate Care. *Beds* 80. *Certified* Medicaid.
Ownership Nonprofit.
Affiliation Lutheran

NEW BRIGHTON

Innsbruck Healthcare Center
2800 Hwy 694, New Brighton, MN, 55112
(612) 633-1686
Admin Deborah Barnes.
Licensure Skilled Care. *Beds* 130. *Certified* Medicaid.
Ownership Proprietary.

New Brighton Care Center*
550 8th St NW, New Brighton, MN, 55112
(612) 633-7200
Admin Michael Chies.
Licensure Skilled Care; Intermediate Care.
Beds SNF 6; ICF 58. *Certified* Medicaid.
Ownership Proprietary.

Trevilla of New Brighton
825 1st Ave NW, New Brighton, MN, 55112
(612) 633-7875
Admin Charlotte Samuelson.
Licensure Skilled Care; Intermediate Care.
Beds SNF 177; ICF 12. *Certified* Medicaid;
Medicare.
Ownership Proprietary.

NEW HOPE

Ambassador Nursing Home
8100 Medicine Lake Rd, New Hope, MN,
55427 (612) 544-4171
Admin Larry Loecker. *Medical Dir/Dir of Nursing* Diane Dahl MD.
Licensure Skilled Care; Intermediate Care.
Beds SNF 84; ICF 30. *Certified* Medicaid;
Medicare.
Ownership Proprietary.
Admissions Requirements Medical examination.
Staff RNs 5 (ft), 7 (pt); LPNs 3 (ft), 12 (pt);
Nurses aides 21 (ft), 20 (pt); Physical therapists
1 (ft); Activities coordinators 1 (ft), 1 (pt);
Social workers 1 (ft), 1 (pt).
Facilities Dining room; Physical therapy room;
Activities room; Crafts room; Laundry room;
Barber/Beauty shop; Library; Gazebo; Large
patio.
Activities Arts and Crafts; Cards; Games;
Reading groups; Prayer groups; Movies; Shopping trips; Dances/Social or cultural gatherings.
Description Facility offers individualized care
with skill and kindness, careful attention to personal needs, comfort and safety as paramount
concerns, comprehensive care, pleasant surroundings, reasonable costs—everything for the
aged and convalescing.

Homeward Bound
4741 Zealand Ave N, New Hope, MN, 55427
(612) 535-6171
Admin James Glasoe. *Medical Dir/Dir of Nursing* Arnold Anderson MD.
Licensure Supervised Living Facility. *Beds* 64.
Certified Medicaid.
Ownership Nonprofit.
Staff RNs 3 (ft); LPNs 6 (ft), 12 (pt); Nurses
aides 14 (ft), 30 (pt); Physical therapists 1 (ft);
Recreational therapists 1 (ft); Occupational
therapists 2 (ft); Speech therapists 1 (ft); Activities coordinators 1 (ft).
Description Facility offers home-like atmosphere plus quality health care for multihandicapped youth featuring a developmental
model utilizing community services including
educational programs outside facility.

North Ridge Care Center
5430 Boone Ave N, New Hope, MN, 55428
(612) 536-7000
Admin Charles Thompson. *Medical Dir/Dir of Nursing* Dr James J Pattee.
Licensure Skilled Care; Intermediate Care.
Beds 559. *Certified* Medicaid; Medicare.
Ownership Proprietary.
Admissions Requirements Medical examination.
Staff Physicians 1 (pt); RNs 18 (ft), 20 (pt);
LPNs 27 (ft), 33 (pt); Nurses aides 74 (ft), 138
(pt); Physical therapists 3 (pt); Occupational
therapists 2 (pt); Activities coordinators 1 (ft);
Recreational aides 7 (ft), 15 (pt).
Facilities Dining room; Physical therapy room;
Activities room; Chapel; Crafts room; Laundry
room; Barber/Beauty shop; Occupational therapy room.
Activities Arts and Crafts; Cards; Games;
Reading groups; Prayer groups; Movies; Shopping trips; Dances/Social or cultural gatherings;
Bazaars.
Description This multi-level facility offers full
range of long-term care services including congregate apartments, home health, adult day
care, educational programs, and nutritional programs.

Saint Therese Home*
8000 Bass Lake Rd, New Hope, MN, 55428
(612) 537-4503
Admin Richard B Ludwig.
Licensure Skilled Care; Intermediate Care.
Beds SNF 202; ICF 100. *Certified* Medicaid.
Ownership Nonprofit.

NEW LONDON

Glen Oaks Nursing and Retirement Centers
207 N Main, New London, MN, 56273 (612)
354-2231
Admin Larry Juhl. *Medical Dir/Dir of Nursing* Jock A Guy MD.
Licensure Skilled Care. *Beds* 62. *Certified* Medicaid.
Ownership Proprietary.
Admissions Requirements Minimum age 16;
Medical examination.
Staff Physicians 1 (pt); RNs 2 (ft), 7 (pt); LPNs
9 (pt); Nurses aides 3 (ft), 27 (pt); Physical therapists 1 (pt); Reality therapists 1 (pt); Recreational therapists 1 (pt); Occupational therapists
1 (pt); Dietitians 1 (pt); Dentists 1 (pt).
Facilities Dining room; Physical therapy room;
Activities room; Chapel; Crafts room; Laundry
room; Barber/Beauty shop; Library.
Activities Arts and Crafts; Cards; Games;
Reading groups; Prayer groups; Movies; Shopping trips; Dances/Social or cultural gatherings.
Description Glen Oaks is a 62-bed skilled
nursing facility physically attached to a 30-unit
apartment complex located in picturesque New
London, an outstanding physical plant located
on 20 beautifully landscaped acres complete
with gardens and duck ponds.

NEW PRAGUE

Mala Strana Health Care Center
1001 Columbus Ave N, New Prague, MN,
56071 (612) 758-2511
Admin Jacqueline J Henle. *Medical Dir/Dir of Nursing* Michael Wilcox MD.
Licensure Skilled Care. *Beds* 120. *Certified* Medicaid.
Ownership Proprietary.
Admissions Requirements Medical examination; Physician's request.
Languages Czech
Facilities Dining room; Physical therapy room;
Activities room; Chapel; Crafts room; Laundry
room; Barber/Beauty shop; Library.
Activities Arts and Crafts; Cards; Games;
Reading groups; Prayer groups; Movies; Shopping trips; Dances/Social or cultural gatherings.
Description Located on a beautiful hilltop less
than a mile from the local hospital, Mala Strana
(Czech for little village) offers quality nursing
care, physical and occupational therapy, social
services, and varied therapeutic and social
activities; respite care, audiology and podiatry
services, speech therapy, and psychological
counseling.

NEW RICHLAND

New Richland Care Center
312 NE 1st St, New Richland, MN, 56072
(507) 465-3292
Admin Obie L Reese Jr.
Licensure Skilled Care. *Beds* 60. *Certified* Medicaid.
Ownership Public.
Facilities Dining room; Physical therapy room;
Activities room; Chapel; Crafts room; Laundry
room; Barber/Beauty shop.
Activities Arts and Crafts; Cards; Games;
Reading groups; Prayer groups; Movies; Shopping trips; Dances/Social or cultural gatherings.

NEW ULM

Eleven Seven*
117 S Minnesota, New Ulm, MN, 56073 (612)
359-7812
Admin Mark Wiger.
Licensure Skilled Care; Intermediate Care for
Mentally Retarded. *Beds* 16. *Certified* Medicaid.
Ownership Proprietary.

Highland Manor*
405 N Highland Ave, New Ulm, MN, 56073
(507) 359-2026
Admin Elroy E Ubl.
Licensure Skilled Care; Intermediate Care.
Beds SNF 62; ICF 36. *Certified* Medicaid.
Ownership Nonprofit.

MBW on Center*
801 Center St, New Ulm, MN, 56073 (507)
354-3522
Admin Mark Wiger.
Licensure Intermediate Care for Mentally
Retarded. *Beds* 8. *Certified* Medicaid.
Ownership Proprietary.

New Ulm CRF I*
327 N Germany, New Ulm, MN, 56073 (507)
359-2892
Admin D Bill Olson.
Licensure Skilled Care; Intermediate Care for
Mentally Retarded. *Beds* 12. *Certified* Medicaid.
Ownership Proprietary.

New Ulm CRF II*
1708 N Garden, New Ulm, MN, 56073 (507)
359-2892
Admin D Bill Olson.
Licensure Skilled Care; Intermediate Care for
Mentally Retarded. *Beds* 12. *Certified* Medicaid.
Ownership Proprietary.

NEW YORK MILLS

Elders Home
New York Mills, MN, 56567 (218) 385-2005
Admin Andrew Tumberg. *Medical Dir/Dir of
Nursing* Kenneth Muckala MD.
Licensure Intermediate Care. *Beds* 70. *Certified* Medicaid.
Ownership Nonprofit.
Admissions Requirements Medical examination.
Staff RNs 1 (ft); LPNs 5 (ft), 5 (pt); Nurses
aides 14 (ft), 12 (pt); Activities coordinators 1
(ft), 1 (pt).
Affiliation Lutheran
Facilities Dining room; Activities room; Chapel; Crafts room; Laundry room; Barber/Beauty
shop; Rehab therapy room.
Activities Arts and Crafts; Games; Reading
groups; Prayer groups; Movies; Shopping trips;
Music appreciation; Local sporting events;
Monthly birthday parties.

NOPEMING

Nopeming Nursing Home*
Nopeming, MN, 55770 (218) 628-2381
Admin Thomas T Kuzas.
Licensure Skilled Care; Intermediate Care.
Beds SNF 166; ICF 45. *Certified* Medicaid;
Medicare.
Ownership Public.

NORTH BRANCH

Green Acres Nursing Home*
North Branch, MN, 55056 (612) 674-7068
Admin Ellis R Johnson.
Licensure Skilled Care; Intermediate Care.
Beds SNF 67; ICF 68. *Certified* Medicaid.
Ownership Public.

NORTH MANKATO

Theresa K Sexton Home*
2050 Haughton Ave N, North Mankato, MN,
56001 (507) 345-1652
Admin Paul Hagen.
Licensure Skilled Care. *Beds* 10. *Certified* Medicaid.
Ownership Proprietary.

Theresa K Sexton Home-North*
2080 Haughton Ave N, North Mankato, MN,
56001 (507) 345-1652
Admin Paul Hagen.
Licensure Intermediate Care. *Beds* 8. *Certified* Medicaid.
Ownership Proprietary.

NORTH SAINT PAUL

Maplewood Care Center
1900 Sherren Ave E, North Saint Paul, MN,
55109 (612) 770-1365
Admin Angeline Sewall. *Medical Dir/Dir of
Nursing* Dr James Nolin.
Licensure Skilled Care; Intermediate Care.
Beds SNF 132; ICF 44. *Certified* Medicaid.
Ownership Nonprofit.
Admissions Requirements Minimum age 65;
Physician's request.
Staff RNs 16 (ft), 24 (pt); LPNs 5 (ft), 9 (pt);
Nurses aides 65 (ft), 97 (pt); Physical therapists
1 (ft); Recreational therapists 4 (ft); Occupational therapists 1 (ft); Dietitians 1 (ft).
Facilities Dining room; Physical therapy room;
Activities room; Chapel; Laundry room; Barber/Beauty shop; Library.
Activities Arts and Crafts; Cards; Games;
Reading groups; Prayer groups; Movies; Shopping trips; Dances/Social or cultural gatherings;
Live music; Outside entertainment.
Description Center is located at the intersection
of Highway 26 and White Bear Avenue. Onsite or contracted services include dental care,
podiatrist, ophthamologist, speech and
audiology therapists; religious services (Protestant and Catholic) are held at regularly
scheduled times; a monthly memorial service is
held by the facility chaplain in the third-floor
chapel area.

North Saint Paul Nursing Home
2375 Skillman Ave E, North Saint Paul, MN,
55109 (612) 777-7435
Admin Joanne Jankowski.
Licensure Skilled Care. *Beds* 47. *Certified* Medicaid.
Ownership Proprietary.

NORTHFIELD

Minnesota Odd Fellows Home*
815 Forest Ave, Northfield, MN, 55057 (507)
645-6611
Admin Carlton Sather.
Licensure Skilled Care; Intermediate Care.
Beds SNF 60; ICF 60. *Certified* Medicaid.
Ownership Nonprofit.
Affiliation Independent Order of Odd Fellows

Northfield Retirement Center
900 Cannon Valley Dr, Northfield, MN, 55057
(507) 645-9511
Admin Gerhard Nygaard.
Licensure Intermediate Care. *Beds* 80. *Certified* Medicaid.
Ownership Nonprofit.
Admissions Requirements Medical examination.
Staff RNs 1 (ft), 2 (pt); LPNs 4 (ft), 1 (pt);
Nurses aides 7 (ft), 18 (pt); Physical therapists 1

(pt); Recreational therapists 2 (pt); Occupational therapists 1 (pt); Activities coordinators 1
(ft); Dietitians 1 (pt).
Affiliation Lutheran
Facilities Dining room; Activities room; Chapel; Crafts room; Laundry room; Barber/Beauty
shop; Library.
Activities Arts and Crafts; Cards; Games;
Reading groups; Prayer groups; Movies; Shopping trips; Dances/Social or cultural gatherings.

NORTHOME

Northome Nursing Home
PO Box 138, Northome, MN, 56661 (218)
897-5235
Admin Paul Raygor.
Licensure Skilled Care; Intermediate Care;
Intermediate Care for Mentally Retarded.
Beds SNF 20; ICF 22; ICF/MR 16. *Certified* Medicaid.
Ownership Proprietary.
Staff RNs 3 (ft), 1 (pt); LPNs 4 (ft); Nurses
aides 20 (ft), 3 (pt); Physical therapists 1 (ft), 1
(pt); Activities coordinators 1 (ft), 2 (pt).
Facilities Dining room; Physical therapy room;
Activities room; Crafts room; Laundry room.
Activities Arts and Crafts; Cards; Games;
Reading groups; Prayer groups; Movies; Shopping trips.

OLIVIA

Olivia Healthcare Center*
1003 W Maple, Olivia, MN, 56277 (612)
523-1652
Admin Lynn Hanson.
Licensure Skilled Care; Intermediate Care.
Beds SNF 76; ICF 18. *Certified* Medicaid.
Ownership Proprietary.

ONAMIA

Community Mercy Hospital*
200 N Elm St, Onamia, MN, 56359 (612)
532-3154
Admin Gene M Helle.
Licensure Skilled Care; Intermediate Care.
Beds SNF 20; ICF 20. *Certified* Medicaid;
Medicare.
Ownership Nonprofit.

ORTONVILLE

Monarch Heights
501 Burdick Ave, Ortonville, MN, 56278
Admin Myron Wee. *Medical Dir/Dir of
Nursing* Arloa Lewis.
Licensure Intermediate Care for Mentally
Retarded. *Beds* 12. *Certified* Medicaid.
Ownership Nonprofit.
Admissions Requirements Minimum age 18;
Medical examination; Physician's request.
Staff Physicians 1 (pt); RNs 1 (pt); Nurses
aides 12 (ft), 7 (pt); Physical therapists 1 (pt);
Reality therapists 1 (pt); Speech therapists 1
(pt); Activities coordinators 1 (ft); Dietitians 1
(pt); Dentists 1 (pt).
Facilities Dining room; Activities room; Crafts
room; Laundry room; Training kitchen.

Activities Arts and Crafts; Cards; Games; Reading groups; Prayer groups; Movies; Shopping trips; Dances/Social or cultural gatherings. *Description* Facility provides individual program plans for the residents, including but not limited to independent skill training, personal hygiene, social skills, and recreation skills. All residents are involved in day programs outside the facility such as special education, and some are involved in behavior programs.

Northridge Residence
1075 Roy St, Ortonville, MN, 56278 (612) 839-6113
Admin Richard Slieter. *Medical Dir/Dir of Nursing* Robert Ross MD.
Licensure Skilled Care; Intermediate Care. *Beds* 74. *Certified* Medicaid.
Ownership Public.
Admissions Requirements Medical examination; Physician's request.
Staff Physicians 4 (pt); RNs 2 (ft), 2 (pt); LPNs 4 (ft), 3 (pt); Orderlies and; Nurses aides 20 (ft), 20 (pt); Physical therapists 1 (pt); Speech therapists 1 (pt); Activities coordinators 2 (pt), 2 (pt); Dietitians 1 (ft); Audiologists 1 (pt).
Facilities Dining room; Physical therapy room; Activities room; Chapel; Crafts room; Laundry room; Barber/Beauty shop.
Activities Arts and Crafts; Cards; Games; Reading groups; Prayer groups; Movies; Shopping trips; Dances/Social or cultural gatherings.

OSAKIS

Community Memorial Home
410 Main St SW, Osakis, MN, 56360 (612) 859-2142
Admin Evelyn Graf. *Medical Dir/Dir of Nursing* Paul E Van Garp MD.
Licensure Skilled Care. *Beds* 62. *Certified* Medicaid.
Ownership Nonprofit.
Admissions Requirements Medical examination; Physician's request.
Staff Physicians 13 (pt); RNs 1 (ft), 6 (pt); LPNs 2 (ft), 5 (pt); Nurses aides 8 (ft), 21 (pt); Physical therapists 1 (pt); Activities coordinators 1 (ft); Dietitians 1 (ft); Dentists 2 (pt).
Facilities Dining room; Physical therapy room; Activities room; Crafts room; Laundry room.
Activities Arts and Crafts; Cards; Games; Reading groups; Prayer groups; Movies; Shopping trips; Dances/Social or cultural gatherings; Music; Pet show; Flower show.
Description We have a physical rehabilitation nursing program. The Osakis community provides attention to the people living in the home by offering a variety of volunteer services.

Osakis Group Home*
405 Lake St, Osakis, MN, 56360 (612) 859-4200
Admin Terry Nelson.
Licensure Intermediate Care for Mentally Retarded. *Beds* 13. *Certified* Medicaid.
Ownership Proprietary.

OSSEO

Berkshire Residence*
501 2nd St SE, Osseo, MN, 55369 (612) 425-3939
Admin Sonja Johnson.
Licensure Intermediate Care. *Beds* 150. *Certified* Medicaid.
Ownership Proprietary.

Monterey Inn of Osseo*
525 2nd St SE, Osseo, MN, 53369 (612) 425-2128
Admin Robert Jenkins.
Licensure Skilled Care; Intermediate Care. *Beds* SNF 96; ICF 41. *Certified* Medicaid.
Ownership Proprietary.

OSTRANDER

Ostrander Nursing Home
PO Box 36, Ostrander, MN, 55961 (507) 657-2231
Admin Faye M Sonju. *Medical Dir/Dir of Nursing* Dr R Matson and Dr B Westra.
Licensure Skilled Care; Intermediate Care. *Beds* 57. *Certified* Medicaid.
Ownership Proprietary.
Admissions Requirements Medical examination; Physician's request.
Staff RNs 1 (ft), 5 (pt); LPNs 2 (ft), 5 (pt); Nurses aides 9 (ft), 15 (pt); Activities coordinators 1 (ft); Dietitians 1 (pt).
Facilities Dining room; Activities room; Laundry room; Barber/Beauty shop.
Activities Arts and Crafts; Cards; Games; Reading groups; Prayer groups; Movies; Shopping trips; Dances/Social or cultural gatherings.
Description Facility adjoins a park with easy access to town. Hospital facilities are conveniently available.

OWATONNA

Cedarview Nursing Home
1409 S Cedar St, Owatonna, MN, 55060 (507) 451-7240
Admin Roger Whitcomb. *Medical Dir/Dir of Nursing* Dr A J Olson.
Licensure Skilled Care; Intermediate Care. *Beds* SNF 94; ICF 14. *Certified* Medicaid.
Ownership Public.
Admissions Requirements Minimum age 16; Medical examination.
Staff Physicians 1 (pt); RNs 3 (ft), 6 (pt); LPNs 12 (pt); Orderlies 1 (pt); Nurses aides 12 (ft), 43 (pt); Physical therapists 1 (pt); Reality therapists 3 (pt); Recreational therapists 2 (ft); Speech therapists 1 (pt); Activities coordinators 1 (ft); Dietitians 1 (pt); Dentists 1 (pt); Ophthalmologists 1 (pt); Podiatrists 1 (pt); Audiologists 1 (pt).

Oak Hill Rest Home
343 E Pearl St, Owatonna, MN, 55060 (507) 451-4564
Admin Gordon Tulberg.
Licensure Boarding Care. *Beds* 28.
Ownership Proprietary.

Owatonna Health Care Center*
201 SW 18th St, Owatonna, MN, 55060 (507) 451-6800
Admin Karl Pelovsky.
Licensure Skilled Care; Intermediate Care. *Beds* SNF 90; ICF 20. *Certified* Medicaid.
Ownership Proprietary.

West Hills Lodge*
545 Florence Ave, Owatonna, MN, 55060 (507) 451-1172
Admin W H Taylor.
Licensure Supervised Living Facility. *Beds* 14.
Ownership Nonprofit.

Westside Boarding Care Home*
Rt 1, Owatonna, MN, 55060 (507) 451-0823
Admin Margaret Striemer.
Licensure Boarding Care. *Beds* 13.

Woodvale VI*
592 Adams St, Owatonna, MN, 55060 (507) 451-1296
Admin Walter Baldus.
Licensure Intermediate Care for Mentally Retarded. *Beds* 15. *Certified* Medicaid.
Ownership Proprietary.

PARK RAPIDS

Heartland Home*
Box 214, 609 W 7th St, Park Rapids, MN, 56470 (218) 732-4572
Admin Jim Loving.
Licensure Intermediate Care for Mentally Retarded. *Beds* 8. *Certified* Medicaid.
Ownership Nonprofit.

Sunset Nursing Home*
W 5th St, Park Rapids, MN, 56470 (218) 732-3329
Admin Delbert G Clark.
Licensure Skilled Care. *Beds* 130. *Certified* Medicaid.
Ownership Public.
Admissions Requirements Medical examination; Physician's request.
Facilities Dining room; Physical therapy room; Activities room; Chapel; Crafts room; Laundry room; Barber/Beauty shop.
Activities Arts and Crafts; Cards; Games; Reading groups; Prayer groups; Movies; Dances/Social or cultural gatherings.
Description We also offer adult day care.

PARKERS PRAIRIE

Saint Williams Nursing Home*
Soo St, Parkers Prairie, MN, 56361 (218) 338-4671
Admin Cyrilla Bitzan.
Licensure Intermediate Care. *Beds* 70. *Certified* Medicaid.
Ownership Nonprofit.

PAYNESVILLE

Paynesville Community Hospital*
200 1st St W, Paynesville, MN, 56382 (612) 243-3767
Admin William Lacroix.

Licensure Skilled Care. *Beds* 57. *Certified* Medicaid; Medicare.
Ownership Public.

Paynesville Good Samaritan Home
311 Washburn Ave, Paynesville, MN, 56362
(612) 243-7451
Admin Elizabeth Crusoe.
Licensure Boarding Care. *Beds* 48. *Certified* Medicaid.
Ownership Nonprofit.
Admissions Requirements Medical examination.
Staff RNs 1 (ft), 1 (pt); LPNs 4 (pt); Nurses aides 3 (ft), 9 (pt); Activities coordinators 1 (ft); Dietitians 1 (pt).
Affiliation Lutheran
Facilities Dining room; Activities room; Chapel; Crafts room; Laundry room.
Activities Arts and Crafts; Cards; Games; Reading groups; Prayer groups; Movies; Shopping trips; Dances/Social or cultural gatherings.

PELICAN RAPIDS

Good Samaritan Center
119 N Broadway, Box Z, Pelican Rapids, MN, 56572 (218) 863-2401
Admin Mark Bichler. *Medical Dir/Dir of Nursing* Richard Lysre MD.
Licensure Intermediate Care. *Beds* 70. *Certified* Medicaid.
Ownership Nonprofit.
Admissions Requirements Medical examination.
Staff Physicians 3 (pt); RNs 1 (ft), 1 (pt); LPNs 4 (ft); Orderlies 2 (pt); Nurses aides 15 (ft), 20 (pt); Physical therapists 1 (pt); Recreational therapists 2 (ft); Activities coordinators 1 (ft); Dietitians 1 (ft); Dentists 3 (pt); Audiologists 1 (pt).
Affiliation Lutheran
Facilities Dining room; Activities room; Chapel; Crafts room; Laundry room; Barber/Beauty shop; Smoking day room with TV.
Activities Arts and Crafts; Cards; Games; Reading groups; Prayer groups; Movies; Shopping trips; Dances/Social or cultural gatherings.
Description Facility is located one block from downtown on main highway. Transportation is provided for doctor and other appointments; meals on wheels program serving the community; active volunteers program; old-time music programs twice monthly; family dinners and picnics.

Pelican Valley Health Center
211 E Mill St, Pelican Rapids, MN, 56572
Medical Dir/Dir of Nursing Owen Thompson MD.
Ownership Nonprofit.
Staff Physicians 3 (pt); RNs 2 (ft), 4 (pt); LPNs 3 (ft), 8 (pt); Orderlies 1 (ft); Nurses aides 5 (ft), 19 (pt); Physical therapists 3 (pt); Recreational therapists 1 (pt); Speech therapists 1 (pt); Activities coordinators 1 (ft); Dietitians 1 (ft), 1 (pt); Dentists 3 (pt); Audiologists 1 (pt); Rehabilitation aides 2 (ft), 3 (pt).
Affiliation Lutheran
Facilities Dining room; Physical therapy room; Activities room; Laundry room; Barber/Beauty shop; Library.

Activities Arts and Crafts; Cards; Games; Reading groups; Prayer groups; Movies; Dances/Social or cultural gatherings.
Description Facility aims toward holistic health care of the members of the community; presently provides hospital and skilled nursing home services; plans include expansion with home health, respite care, and retirement services.

PERHAM

Perham Memorial Hospital and Home*
665 3rd St SW, Perham, MN, 56573 (218) 346-4500
Admin Robert D Johnson.
Licensure Skilled Care; Intermediate Care.
Beds SNF 68; ICF 42. *Certified* Medicaid.
Ownership Public.

PIERZ

Saint Marys Villa Nursing Home
1st Ave S, Pierz, MN, 56364 (612) 468-6405
Admin K Pipho. *Medical Dir/Dir of Nursing* Dr David Howard.
Licensure Skilled Care; Intermediate Care; Boarding Care. *Beds* SNF 75; ICF 26; Boarding Care 7. *Certified* Medicaid.
Ownership Nonprofit.
Staff Physicians 1 (pt); RNs 7 (ft), 7 (pt); LPNs 4 (ft), 5 (pt); Nurses aides 12 (ft), 16 (pt); Physical therapists 1 (pt); Speech therapists 1 (pt); Activities coordinators 1 (ft); Dietitians 1 (pt); Dentists 1 (pt); Ophthalmologists 1 (pt); Podiatrists 1 (pt); Audiologists 1 (pt).
Affiliation Roman Catholic
Facilities Dining room; Physical therapy room; Activities room; Chapel; Crafts room; Laundry room; Barber/Beauty shop.
Activities Arts and Crafts; Cards; Games; Reading groups; Prayer groups; Movies; Shopping trips; Dances/Social or cultural gatherings.

PINE CITY

Lakeside Nursing Home*
129 E 6th St, Pine City, MN, 55063 (612) 629-2542
Admin Mary Blaufuss. *Medical Dir/Dir of Nursing* R F Mach MD.
Licensure Skilled Care; Intermediate Care.
Beds SNF 93; ICF 42. *Certified* Medicaid.
Ownership Proprietary.
Admissions Requirements Minimum age 16; Medical examination.
Staff RNs 2 (ft), 4 (pt); LPNs 3 (ft), 9 (pt); Nurses aides 17 (ft), 40 (pt); Physical therapists 1 (pt); Recreational therapists 1 (ft); Dietitians 1 (ft).
Facilities Dining room; Physical therapy room; Activities room; Chapel; Crafts room; Laundry room; Barber/Beauty shop.
Activities Arts and Crafts; Reading groups; Movies; Dances/Social or cultural gatherings; Reality orientation and remotivation.
Description Facility is JCAH accredited with a quality assurance program implemented and functioning. Resident, family, and church councils have been organized and are functioning.

PINE ISLAND

Pine Haven Nursing Home
210 NW 3rd St, Pine Island, MN, 55963 (507) 356-8304
Admin A Murray. *Medical Dir/Dir of Nursing* O E H Larson MD.
Licensure Skilled Care. *Beds* 74. *Certified* Medicaid.
Ownership Nonprofit.
Admissions Requirements Physician's request.
Staff RNs 1 (ft), 3 (pt); LPNs 1 (ft), 7 (pt); Nurses aides 10 (ft), 25 (pt); Physical therapists 1 (pt); Occupational therapists 1 (pt); Activities coordinators 1 (pt).
Facilities Dining room; Physical therapy room; Activities room; Crafts room; Barber/Beauty shop.
Activities Arts and Crafts; Cards; Games; Reading groups; Movies; Shopping trips; Dances/Social or cultural gatherings; Bible studies.

PINE RIVER

Good Samaritan Home
PO Box 27, Pine River, MN, 56474 (218) 587-4423
Admin Jim Wolf. *Medical Dir/Dir of Nursing* Dr C R Pelzl.
Licensure Skilled Care; Intermediate Care.
Beds 93. *Certified* Medicaid.
Ownership Nonprofit.
Admissions Requirements Medical examination.
Staff RNs 3 (ft), 3 (pt); LPNs 6 (ft), 3 (pt); Orderlies 1 (pt); Nurses aides 30 (ft), 15 (pt); Physical therapists 1 (pt); Activities coordinators 1 (ft); Dietitians 1 (pt); Dentists 1 (pt).
Facilities Dining room; Physical therapy room; Activities room; Chapel; Crafts room; Laundry room; Barber/Beauty shop; Library.
Activities Arts and Crafts; Cards; Games; Reading groups; Prayer groups; Movies; Shopping trips; Dances/Social or cultural gatherings.
Description Home is nestled comfortably among the Norway pines in a quaint little resort community in north central Minnesota, the heartland area.

Pine River Group Home*
PO Box 96, Pine River, MN, 56474 (218) 587-4888
Admin Bruce Winder.
Licensure Intermediate Care for Mentally Retarded. *Beds* 11. *Certified* Medicaid.
Ownership Nonprofit.

PIPESTONE

Good Samaritan Village
Rt 1, Pipestone, MN, 56164 (507) 825-4697
Admin Bruce Stratman.
Licensure Intermediate Care; Boarding Care.
Beds ICF 96; Boarding Care 30. *Certified* Medicaid.
Ownership Nonprofit.
Admissions Requirements Medical examination.
Affiliation Lutheran
Facilities Dining room; Physical therapy room; Activities room; Chapel; Crafts room; Laundry

room; Barber/Beauty shop; Library.
Activities Arts and Crafts; Cards; Games; Reading groups; Prayer groups; Movies; Shopping trips; Dances/Social or cultural gatherings; Art therapy; Music therapy.

Hiawatha Manor
107 5th Ave NE, Pipestone, MN, 56164 (507) 825-5697
Admin Frank C Robinson.
Licensure Supervised Living Facility. *Beds* 10.
Certified Medicaid.
Ownership Nonprofit.
Admissions Requirements Minimum age 18.
Staff Nurses aides 9 (pt).
Facilities Dining room; Laundry room.
Activities Cards; Games; Reading groups; Prayer groups; Movies; Shopping trips.

Pipestone County Hospital
911 5th Ave SW, Pipestone, MN, 56164
Admin Malcolm P Cole. *Medical Dir/Dir of Nursing* Dr R W Keyes.
Licensure Skilled Care. *Beds* 40. *Certified* Medicaid.
Ownership Public.
Admissions Requirements Medical examination; Physician's request.
Staff Physicians 9 (pt); RNs 2 (ft), 5 (pt); LPNs 2 (ft); Nurses aides 7 (ft), 15 (pt); Physical therapists 1 (pt); Activities coordinators 1 (ft); Dietitians 1 (pt); Dentists 5 (pt).
Facilities Dining room; Physical therapy room; Activities room; Chapel; Barber/Beauty shop.
Activities Arts and Crafts; Cards; Games; Movies; Dances/Social or cultural gatherings.
Description This hospital has recently moved into a new building.

PLAINVIEW

Hillcrest Nursing and Retirement Home*
800 2nd Ave NW, Plainview, MN, 55964 (507) 534-3191
Admin Edwin Rud.
Licensure Skilled Care. *Beds* 71. *Certified* Medicaid.
Ownership Public.

PLYMOUTH

Hazelden Pioneer House*
11505 36th Ave N, Plymouth, MN, 55441 (612) 559-2022
Admin Damian McElrath.
Licensure Supervised Living Facility. *Beds* 67.
Ownership Nonprofit.

Louis House Treatment Center*
115 Forestview Ln, Plymouth, MN, 55441 (612) 546-8008
Admin Don F Benson.
Licensure Supervised Care Facility. *Beds* 15.
Ownership Proprietary.

Mission Farms Nursing Home
3401 Medicine Lake Blvd, Plymouth, MN, 55441 (612) 559-3123
Admin James Pearson.
Licensure Intermediate Care; Boarding Care.
Beds ICF 104; Boarding Care 32. *Cer-*

tified Medicaid.
Ownership Nonprofit.
Admissions Requirements Males only; Medical examination; Physician's request.
Facilities Dining room; Activities room; Chapel; Library.
Activities Arts and Crafts; Cards; Games; Reading groups; Prayer groups; Movies; Shopping trips; Special tours and field trips for bowling, pool, circus, ball games, treats, special music programs, church services.

Outreach Group Home
2735 Olive Ln North, Plymouth, MN, 55391 (612) 473-7182
Admin Eileen Harris.
Licensure Supervised Living Facility. *Beds* 6.
Certified Medicaid.
Ownership Nonprofit.
Admissions Requirements Minimum age 16.
Staff Physicians; RNs; Physical therapists; Recreational therapists; Occupational therapists; Speech therapists; Dietitians; Dentists; Ophthalmologists; Podiatrists; Audiologists.
Facilities Dining room; Activities room; Laundry room.
Activities Arts and Crafts; Games; Movies; Shopping trips; Dances/Social or cultural gatherings.
Description Residential facility for mentally retarded adults requiring 24-hour care.

Vanguard Extended Care
3401 E Medicine Lake Blvd, Plymouth, MN, 55441 (612) 559-4249
Admin Leonard Boche.
Licensure Supervised Living Facility. *Beds* 65.
Ownership Nonprofit.

PRESTON

Preston Care Center
608 Winona, Preston, MN, 55965 (507) 765-3837
Admin Thomas Rislow. *Medical Dir/Dir of Nursing* Dr John Nehring.
Licensure Skilled Care; Intermediate Care.
Beds 79. *Certified* Medicaid.
Ownership Proprietary.
Staff RNs 4 (ft), 2 (pt); LPNs 9 (ft), 6 (pt); Nurses aides 20 (ft), 20 (pt); Recreational therapists 1 (ft); Activities coordinators 1 (ft), 1 (pt).
Facilities Dining room; Physical therapy room; Activities room; Chapel; Crafts room; Laundry room; Barber/Beauty shop.
Activities Arts and Crafts; Cards; Games; Reading groups; Prayer groups; Movies; Shopping trips; Dances/Social or cultural gatherings.
Description We also provide meals and emergency nursing service to an apartment house for the elderly which is about 5 blocks away.

PRINCETON

Elim Home*
101 S 7th Ave, Princeton, MN, 55371 (612) 389-1171
Admin Dwight Schmidt.
Licensure Skilled Care. *Beds* 140. *Certified* Medicaid; Medicare.
Ownership Nonprofit.

Sahara House*
407 5th Ave S, Princeton, MN, 55371 (612) 389-4503
Admin William Kerwin.
Licensure Supervised Living Facility. *Beds* 13.
Ownership Nonprofit.

RED LAKE FALLS

Hillcrest Nursing Home*
311 Broadway, Red Lake Falls, MN, 56750 (218) 253-2157
Admin L W Larson.
Licensure Intermediate Care. *Beds* 74. *Certified* Medicaid.
Ownership Public.

RED WING

Haven Home of Red Wing
213 Pioneer Rd, Red Wing, MN, 55066 (612) 338-3059
Admin F Marie Fair. *Medical Dir/Dir of Nursing* Dr Charles Roth.
Licensure Skilled Care; Intermediate Care.
Beds 60. *Certified* Medicaid.
Ownership Nonprofit.
Staff RNs 1 (ft), 3 (pt); LPNs 3 (ft), 2 (pt); Orderlies 1 (ft); Nurses aides 9 (ft), 15 (pt); Activities coordinators 1 (ft); Dietitians 1 (ft); Social workers 1 (pt).
Facilities Dining room; Activities room; Laundry room; Barber/Beauty shop; Library.
Activities Arts and Crafts; Cards; Games; Reading groups; Prayer groups; Movies; Shopping trips; Activities for mentally retarded occasionally; Cooking classes for residents.

Red Wing Group Home*
4911 W Hwy 61, Red Wing, MN, 55066 (612) 388-9446
Admin Roy A Harley.
Licensure Intermediate Care for Mentally Retarded. *Beds* 12. *Certified* Medicaid.
Ownership Nonprofit.

Red Wing Health Center
4th and Jackson, Red Wing, MN, 55066 (612) 388-2843
Admin Donna Van Loon. *Medical Dir/Dir of Nursing* Dr Charles Roth.
Licensure Skilled Care; Intermediate Care.
Beds 220. *Certified* Medicaid; Medicare.
Ownership Proprietary.
Staff Physicians 10 (pt); RNs 5 (ft), 7 (pt); LPNs 10 (ft), 11 (pt); Nurses aides 44 (ft), 86 (pt); Physical therapists 1 (ft); Recreational therapists 7 (ft); Occupational therapists 2 (ft), 3 (pt); Speech therapists 1 (pt); Activities coordinators 1 (ft); Dietitians 1 (pt).
Facilities Dining room; Physical therapy room; Activities room; Chapel; Crafts room; Laundry room; Barber/Beauty shop; Library; Child day care.
Activities Arts and Crafts; Cards; Games; Reading groups; Prayer groups; Movies; Shopping trips; Dances/Social or cultural gatherings; Adopt-a-grandparent.
Description Located on a hill overlooking the Mississippi River, facility has one of the few rehabilitation programs for disabled young

adults in the upper Midwest. This program offers extensive occupational, physical, and recreational therapy geared to the needs of this group; the program draws residents from several states.

Seminary Memorial Home
906 College Ave, Red Wing, MN, 55066 (612) 388-6769
Admin W C Sundberg. *Medical Dir/Dir of Nursing* Dr D R Bruns.
Licensure Skilled Care; Intermediate Care.
Beds 112. *Certified* Medicaid.
Ownership Nonprofit.
Affiliation Lutheran
Facilities Dining room; Physical therapy room; Activities room; Chapel; Crafts room; Barber-/Beauty shop.
Activities Arts and Crafts; Cards; Games; Prayer groups; Movies; Shopping trips; Dances/Social or cultural gatherings.
Description Facility is located on a bluff overlooking the Mississippi.

Vasa Lutheran Home for Children
5225 W Hwy 61, Red Wing, MN, 55066 (612) 388-4727
Admin Roy Harley.
Licensure Supervised Living Facility. *Beds* 55.
Certified Medicaid.
Ownership Nonprofit.
Admissions Requirements Minimum age 5; Medical examination.
Staff RNs 1 (ft); LPNs 2 (pt); Recreational therapists 2 (ft); Activities coordinators 1 (ft).
Affiliation Lutheran
Facilities Dining room; Activities room; Crafts room; Laundry room; Library.
Activities Arts and Crafts; Games; Reading groups; Movies; Shopping trips; Dances/Social or cultural gatherings.

REDWOOD FALLS

REM-Redwood Falls Inc
1011 E Elm St, Redwood Falls, MN, 56283 (507) 637-3541
Admin R E Miller.
Licensure Supervised Living Facility.
Beds 132. *Certified* Medicaid.
Ownership Proprietary.
Admissions Requirements Minimum age 18.
Staff RNs 1 (ft); LPNs 2 (ft); Recreational therapists 1 (ft); Occupational therapists 1 (pt); Speech therapists 1 (pt); Activities coordinators 1 (ft).
Facilities Dining room; Laundry room; Barber-/Beauty shop.
Activities Arts and Crafts; Cards; Games; Movies; Shopping trips; Dances/Social or cultural gatherings.
Description Facility offers developmental programs for developmentally disabled adults.

Sunwood Care Center*
200 S DeKalb, Redwood Falls, MN, 56283 (507) 637-5711
Admin Vernon Junker.
Licensure Skilled Care; Intermediate Care.
Beds SNF 49; ICF 43. *Certified* Medicaid.
Ownership Proprietary.

Wood-Dale Home
600 Sunrise Blvd, Redwood Falls, MN, 56283 (507) 637-3587
Admin Alma J Little. *Medical Dir/Dir of Nursing* Dr J B Flinn.
Licensure Skilled Care; Intermediate Care.
Beds SNF 56; ICF 4. *Certified* Medicaid.
Ownership Proprietary.
Staff Physicians 5 (pt); RNs 2 (ft), 10 (pt); LPNs 6 (ft), 8 (pt); Orderlies 4 (pt); Nurses aides 15 (ft), 15 (pt); Physical therapists 1 (pt); Reality therapists 1 (pt); Recreational therapists 1 (pt); Occupational therapists 2 (pt); Speech therapists 1 (pt); Activities coordinators 2 (pt); Dietitians 1 (pt); Dentists 1 (pt); Ophthalmologists 1 (pt); Podiatrists 1 (pt); Audiologists 1 (pt).
Facilities Dining room; Physical therapy room; Activities room; Chapel; Crafts room; Laundry room; Barber/Beauty shop.
Activities Arts and Crafts; Cards; Games; Reading groups; Prayer groups; Movies; Shopping trips; Dances/Social or cultural gatherings; Seasonal sightseeing trips.

RENVILLE

Ren-Villa
205 SE Elm St, Renville, MN, 56284 (612) 329-8304
Admin Craig Doughty.
Licensure Intermediate Care. *Beds* 76. *Certified* Medicaid.
Ownership Public.
Staff RNs 1 (ft), 1 (pt); LPNs 1 (ft), 9 (pt); Nurses aides 6 (ft), 35 (pt).
Facilities Dining room; Activities room; Crafts room; Laundry room; Residents park.
Activities Arts and Crafts; Cards; Games; Reading groups; Prayer groups; Movies; Dances/Social or cultural gatherings.

REVERE

Revere Home
202 S Main, Revere, MN, 56166 (507) 752-7182
Admin Maxine Olson.
Licensure Boarding Care. *Beds* 22.
Ownership Proprietary.
Admissions Requirements Minimum age 18; Medical examination.
Staff LPNs 1 (ft), 1 (pt); Nurses aides 10 (pt); Activities coordinators 1 (pt); Dietitians 1 (pt).
Facilities Dining room; Activities room; Crafts room; Laundry room.
Activities Arts and Crafts; Cards; Games; Movies; Shopping trips; Bingo; Sightseeing trips.
Description Facility is located in a quiet, peaceful rural area.

RICHFIELD

Forestview Vincent*
7615 Vincent Ave S, Richfield, MN, 55423 (612) 861-4373
Admin William Koski.
Licensure Intermediate Care for Mentally Retarded. *Beds* 6. *Certified* Medicaid.
Ownership Proprietary.

Progress Valley II
308 E 78th St, Richfield, MN, 55423 (612) 869-3223
Admin Don Stuhlman.
Licensure Supervised Living Facility. *Beds* 24.
Ownership Nonprofit.

Richfield Outreach Group Home*
7425 4th Ave S, Richfield, MN, 55423 (612) 866-2035
Admin Eileen Harris.
Licensure Intermediate Care for Mentally Retarded. *Beds* 6. *Certified* Medicaid.
Ownership Nonprofit.

Richview
7727 Portland Ave S, Richfield, MN, 55423 (612) 861-1691
Admin C A Peterson. *Medical Dir/Dir of Nursing* John Lamey MD.
Licensure Skilled Care; Intermediate Care.
Beds SNF 126; ICF 49. *Certified* Medicaid.
Ownership Proprietary.
Admissions Requirements Medical examination; Physician's request.
Staff RNs 8 (ft), 5 (pt); LPNs 6 (ft), 6 (pt); Nurses aides 36 (ft), 36 (pt); Physical therapists 1 (ft); Occupational therapists 1 (ft); Speech therapists 1 (pt); Activities coordinators 1 (ft); Dietitians 1 (pt); Audiologists 1 (pt).
Facilities Dining room; Physical therapy room; Activities room; Chapel; Crafts room; Laundry room; Barber/Beauty shop.
Activities Arts and Crafts; Cards; Games; Reading groups; Prayer groups; Movies; Shopping trips; Dances/Social or cultural gatherings; Sightseeing outings.
Description Facility is conveniently located for shopping and public transportation, has company bus with wheelchair lifts for outings to theatre and other places, offers complete daily rehabilitation program for all residents, and free day care offered as a community service.

RICHVILLE

Shelton Group Home*
Rt 1, Richville, MN, 56576 (218) 758-2438
Admin Carol Shelton.
Licensure Intermediate Care for Mentally Retarded. *Beds* 8. *Certified* Medicaid.
Ownership Proprietary.

ROBBINSDALE

Crystal Lake Health Care Center
3815 W Broadway, Robbinsdale, MN, 55422 (612) 588-4635
Admin Ruth E Kureth. *Medical Dir/Dir of Nursing* Roger Grimm MD.
Licensure Skilled Care; Intermediate Care.
Beds SNF 108; ICF 58. *Certified* Medicaid; Medicare.
Ownership Proprietary.
Admissions Requirements Medical examination; Physician's request.
Staff RNs 5 (ft), 18 (pt); LPNs 8 (ft), 5 (pt); Orderlies 3 (pt); Nurses aides 35 (ft), 48 (pt); Physical therapists 3 (pt); Recreational therapists 2 (ft), 2 (pt); Occupational therapists 2 (pt); Activities coordinators 1 (ft).

Facilities Dining room; Physical therapy room; Activities room; Crafts room; Laundry room; Barber/Beauty shop; Occupational therapy room.
Activities Arts and Crafts; Cards; Games; Reading groups; Prayer groups; Movies; Shopping trips; Dances/Social or cultural gatherings.
Description CLHCC is a Medicare cerfitied facility offering services to meet residents' psychosocial and physical needs; speech, recreational, remotivation, and music therapy; social, psychological, inpatient and outpatient physical therapy; barber and beauty services; occupational therapy, audiology, podiatry; van; kitchen, garden, and flower beds for handicapped residents.

Erinkay-Aneskarn 2*
3349 Chowen Ave N, Robbinsdale, MN, 55422 (612) 529-7480
Admin Sandra Schweich.
Licensure Intermediate Care for Mentally Retarded. *Beds* 6. *Certified* Medicaid.
Ownership Nonprofit.

Residential Alternatives IV*
2759 France Ave N, Robbinsdale, MN, 55422 (612) 521-0367
Admin Peter Jacobson.
Licensure Intermediate Care for Mentally Retarded. *Beds* 6. *Certified* Medicaid.
Ownership Proprietary.

Residential ALternatives VIII*
3801 W Broadway, Robbinsdale, MN, 55422 (612) 522-6363
Admin Peter Jacobson.
Licensure Skilled Care; Intermediate Care for Mentally Retarded. *Beds* 9. *Certified* Medicaid.
Ownership Proprietary.

Trevilla of Robbinsdale*
3130 Grimes Ave N, Robbinsdale, MN, 55422 (612) 588-0771
Admin Michael Evans.
Licensure Skilled Care; Intermediate Care for Mentally Retarded. *Beds* SNF 259; ICF/MR 132. *Certified* Medicaid.
Ownership Proprietary.

ROCHESTER

Bear Creek House*
812 10th Ave SE, Rochester, MN, 55901 (507) 288-0531
Admin Steven Larson.
Licensure Intermediate Care for Mentally Retarded. *Beds* 6. *Certified* Medicaid.
Ownership Nonprofit.

Bethany Samaritain Heights*
1530 11th Ave NW, Rochester, MN, 55901 (507) 289-3336
Admin L E Bliese.
Licensure Skilled Care; Intermediate Care.
Beds SNF 100; ICF 20. *Certified* Medicaid; Medicare.
Ownership Public.

Gray Gables Recovery Home*
604 5th St SW, Rochester, MN, 55901 (507) 282-2500
Admin Joan Witry.
Licensure Skilled Care. *Beds* 22.
Ownership Public.

Guest House*
PO Box 954, Rochester, MN, 55901 (507) 288-4693
Admin Howard J Thompson.
Licensure Boarding Care. *Beds* 35.
Ownership Nonprofit.

Hiawatha Childrens Home*
1820 Valkyrie Dr NW, Rochester, MN, 55901 (507) 289-7222
Admin Douglas H Butler.
Licensure Intermediate Care for Mentally Retarded. *Beds* 44. *Certified* Medicaid.
Ownership Nonprofit.

Madonna Towers
4001 19th Ave NW, Rochester, MN, 55901 (507) 288-3911
Admin Steve Wuitschick. *Medical Dir/Dir of Nursing* Guy Daugherty MD.
Licensure Skilled Care; Intermediate Care.
Beds SNF 24; ICF 36; Apartments 139. *Certified* Medicaid; Medicare.
Ownership Nonprofit.
Admissions Requirements Minimum age 62; Medical examination.
Staff Physicians 1 (pt); RNs; LPNs; Orderlies; Nurses aides; Physical therapists; Speech therapists; Activities coordinators; Dietitians; Dentists; Podiatrists.
Affiliation Roman Catholic
Facilities Dining room; Physical therapy room; Activities room; Chapel; Crafts room; Laundry room; Barber/Beauty shop; Library.
Activities Arts and Crafts; Cards; Games; Reading groups; Prayer groups; Movies; Shopping trips; Dances/Social or cultural gatherings.
Description Facility is located on 12 acres and includes an art room, game room, theatre, and solarium.

Maple Manor Nursing Home
1875 19th St NW, Rochester, MN, 55901 (507) 282-9449
Admin Earl J Schillo.
Licensure Skilled Care; Intermediate Care; Boarding Care. *Beds* SNF 63; ICF 37; Boarding Care 9. *Certified* Medicaid.
Ownership Proprietary.

Meadow Park House*
1605 8th Ave SE, Rochester, MN, 55901 (507) 288-3893
Admin Steven Larson.
Licensure Intermediate Care for Mentally Retarded. *Beds* 6. *Certified* Medicaid.
Ownership Nonprofit.

Pine Circle Community Living Center*
1612 E Center Ct, Rochester, MN, 55901 (507) 289-2819
Admin Debra Langer.
Licensure Supervised Living Facility. *Beds* 18.
Ownership Nonprofit.

REM Rochester NW
2509 55th St NW, Rochester, MN, 55901
Admin Thomas Miller. *Medical Dir/Dir of Nursing* Jack Priggen.
Licensure Intermediate Care for Mentally Retarded. *Beds* 30. *Certified* Medicaid.
Ownership Proprietary.
Admissions Requirements Minimum age 16; Medical examination; Physician's request.
Staff RNs 1 (pt); Nurses aides 10 (ft), 10 (pt); Activities coordinators 1 (pt).
Facilities Dining room; Activities room; Laundry room.
Activities Arts and Crafts; Cards; Games; Movies; Shopping trips; Dances/Social or cultural gatherings.
Description Facility consists of 2 15-bed units. To be accepted, residents must have a diagnosis of mental retardation and must be ambulatory or mobile nonambulatory and capable of existing independently in emergency situations.

Rochester Health Care Center
2215 Hwy 52 N, Rochester, MN, 55901 (507) 288-1818
Admin John Julius. *Medical Dir/Dir of Nursing* C R Holland MD.
Licensure Skilled Care. *Beds* 68. *Certified* Medicaid.
Ownership Proprietary.
Admissions Requirements Minimum age 18.
Staff RNs 3 (ft), 2 (pt); LPNs 3 (ft), 3 (pt); Orderlies 2 (pt); Nurses aides 20 (ft); Physical therapists 1 (pt); Reality therapists 1 (pt); Recreational therapists 1 (pt); Occupational therapists 1 (pt); Speech therapists 1 (pt); Activities coordinators 1 (ft); Dietitians 1 (pt); Dentists 1 (pt); Ophthalmologists 1 (pt); Podiatrists 1 (pt); Audiologists 1 (pt).
Facilities Dining room; Physical therapy room; Activities room; Crafts room; Laundry room; Barber/Beauty shop.
Activities Arts and Crafts; Cards; Games; Reading groups; Prayer groups; Movies; Shopping trips; Dances/Social or cultural gatherings.
Description Facility serves 26 festive meals per year including restaurant night with linen and crystal, wine, steak, and shrimp. Specialized rehabilitation services involving short-term convalescents.

Rochester State Hospital
2110 E Center St, Rochester, MN, 55901 (507) 285-7008
Admin R F Rosenthal.
Licensure Supervised Living Facility. *Beds* ICF/MR 159. *Certified* Medicaid.
Ownership Public.

Samaritan Bethany Home
24 8th St NW, Rochester, MN, 55901 (507) 289-4031
Admin Lorraine A Peterson. *Medical Dir/Dir of Nursing* Peter Cross MD.
Licensure Skilled Care. *Beds* 122. *Certified* Medicaid.
Ownership Nonprofit.
Admissions Requirements Minimum age 16; Medical examination; Physician's request.
Staff RNs; LPNs; Nurses aides; Physical therapists; Recreational therapists; Speech therapists; Activities coordinators; Dietitians.
Affiliation Church of Christ

Facilities Dining room; Physical therapy room; Activities room; Chapel; Crafts room; Laundry room; Barber/Beauty shop.
Activities Arts and Crafts; Cards; Games; Reading groups; Prayer groups; Movies; Shopping trips; Dances/Social or cultural gatherings.
Description Facility is a church related, not-for-profit organization dedicated to providing quality care in a home-like environment, utilizing modern concepts in programing for residents.

Sixth Street House*
805 6th St SE, Rochester, MN, 55901 (507) 288-4138
Admin Steven Larson.
Licensure Intermediate Care for Mentally Retarded. *Beds* 6. *Certified* Medicaid.
Ownership Nonprofit.

Southside House*
1418 4th St SE, Rochester, MN, 55901 (507) 281-2523
Admin Steven Larson.
Licensure Intermediate Care for Mentally Retarded. *Beds* 6.
Ownership Nonprofit.

Town Hall Estates*
607 E Center St, Rochester, MN, 55901 (507) 288-3615
Admin Arnold C Swanson.
Licensure Boarding Care. *Beds* 75.
Ownership Nonprofit.

Woodside Convalescent Center*
501 8th Ave SE, Rochester, MN, 55904 (507) 288-6514
Admin Barry Jacobson.
Licensure Skilled Care; Intermediate Care.
Beds SNF 129; ICF 30. *Certified* Medicaid; Medicare.
Ownership Proprietary.

ROSEAU

Eventide Home
307 3rd Ave NW, Roseau, MN, 56751 (218) 463-1447
Admin Alice Halvorson.
Licensure Boarding Care. *Beds* 26.
Ownership Nonprofit.
Admissions Requirements Minimum age 18; Medical examination.
Staff RNs; Nurses aides; Activities coordinators; Dietitians.
Facilities Dining room; Activities room; Chapel; Crafts room; Laundry room; Library.
Activities Arts and Crafts; Cards; Games; Reading groups; Prayer groups; Movies; Shopping trips; Dances/Social or cultural gatherings.
Description Facility provides clean, home-like atmosphere, excellent meals, and daily activities.

REM Roseau*
208 2nd Ave NE, Roseau, MN, 56751 (218) 463-1031
Admin Douglas Miller.
Licensure Intermediate Care for Mentally Retarded. *Beds* ICF/MR 33. *Certified* Medicaid.
Ownership Proprietary.

Roseau County Nursing Center*
216 Center St, Roseau, MN, 56750 (218) 463-3211
Admin Joanne Thompson.
Licensure Skilled Care. *Certified* Medicare.
Ownership Public.

ROSEVILLE

Dungarvin II*
3101 W Owasso Blvd, Roseville, MN, 55112 (612) 483-8377
Admin Diane Jones Madden.
Licensure Intermediate Care for Mentally Retarded. *Beds* 6. *Certified* Medicaid.
Ownership Proprietary.

Golden Age Health Care Center*
1415 W County Rd B, Roseville, MN, 55113 (612) 631-1616
Admin Robert Hysjulien.
Licensure Skilled Care; Intermediate Care.
Beds SNF 118; ICF 23. *Certified* Medicaid; Medicare.
Ownership Proprietary.

Lake Ridge Health Care Center
2727 N Victoria, Roseville, MN, 55113 (612) 483-5431
Admin Lynne Glasrud. *Medical Dir/Dir of Nursing* Dr Timothy F Lane.
Licensure Skilled Care. *Beds* 240. *Certified* Medicare.
Ownership Proprietary.
Admissions Requirements Minimum age 18; Medical examination; Physician's request.
Staff RNs 10 (ft), 35 (pt); LPNs 5 (ft), 7 (pt); Orderlies 1 (ft), 8 (pt); Nurses aides 34 (ft), 75 (pt); Physical therapists 1 (ft); Speech therapists 1 (pt); Activities coordinators 1 (ft); Dietitians 1 (pt); Dentists 1 (pt); Podiatrists 1 (pt); Audiologists 1 (pt).
Facilities Dining room; Physical therapy room; Activities room; Chapel; Crafts room; Barber-/Beauty shop; Library; Dental office.
Activities Arts and Crafts; Cards; Games; Reading groups; Prayer groups; Movies; Shopping trips; Dances/Social or cultural gatherings; Exploration activities outside facility.
Description Facility has respite/vacation, short-term, post operative, and long-term programs. Facility has achieved an "E" for excellence award and is accredited by the Joint Commission on Accreditation of Hospitals. Facility is fully carpeted, 100% fireproof, and air conditioned with private and semi-private rooms, new wing rooms have remote control television, sitting area for private meals, electric beds, and ceramic-tiled bathrooms.

Rose of Sharon Manor
1000 Lovell Ave, Roseville, MN, 55113 (612) 484-3378
Admin Marjorie Johnson. *Medical Dir/Dir of Nursing* J Richard Burton MD.
Licensure Skilled Care. *Beds* 85.
Ownership Proprietary.
Admissions Requirements Minimum age 18.

Staff Physicians 1 (pt); RNs 5 (ft), 5 (pt); LPNs 2 (ft), 6 (pt); Orderlies 1 (ft), 3 (pt); Nurses aides 9 (ft), 36 (pt); Physical therapists 1 (ft); Recreational therapists 1 (ft), 2 (pt); Occupational therapists 1 (pt); Speech therapists 1 (pt); Activities coordinators 1 (ft); Dietitians 1 (pt); Dentists 1 (pt); Ophthalmologists 1 (pt); Podiatrists 1 (pt); Audiologists 1 (pt).
Facilities Dining room; Physical therapy room; Activities room; Crafts room; Barber/Beauty shop.
Activities Arts and Crafts; Cards; Games; Reading groups; Prayer groups; Movies; Shopping trips; Dances/Social or cultural gatherings.
Description Facility features bingo, bowling and birthday parties.

Whitehouse Nursing Home
563 W County Rd B, Roseville, MN, 55113 (612) 489-8851
Admin D Lundberg. *Medical Dir/Dir of Nursing* David Gilbertson DO.
Licensure Skilled Care; Intermediate Care.
Beds SNF 64; ICF 15. *Certified* Medicaid.
Ownership Proprietary.
Admissions Requirements Medical examination; Physician's request.
Staff RNs 2 (ft), 8 (pt); LPNs 4 (pt); Nurses aides 11 (ft), 33 (pt); Physical therapists 1 (pt); Recreational therapists 1 (ft), 1 (pt); Activities coordinators 1 (ft), 1 (pt); Dietitians 1 (ft).
Facilities Dining room; Laundry room; Barber-/Beauty shop; Multipurpose room used for activities, chapel, crafts, and day room; Activity kitchen.
Activities Arts and Crafts; Cards; Games; Reading groups; Prayer groups; Movies; Shopping trips; Dances/Social or cultural gatherings.
Description Facility offers strong volunteer program; close relationship with nearby private school; have developed some intergenerational curriculum to use with residents and 5th and 6th graders from school.

RUSH CITY

Hillcrest Healthcare Center
650 Bremer Ave S PO Box 606, Rush City, MN, 55069 (612) 358-4765
Admin Patricia A Behrendt.
Licensure Skilled Care; Intermediate Care.
Beds 65.
Ownership Proprietary.

RUSHFORD

Good Shepherd Lutheran Home
Rushford, MN, 55971 (507) 864-7714
Admin Virgil Lacey. *Medical Dir/Dir of Nursing* Dr John R Peterson.
Licensure Skilled Care; Intermediate Care.
Beds 98. *Certified* Medicaid.
Ownership Nonprofit.
Admissions Requirements Medical examination.
Staff RNs; LPNs; Orderlies; Nurses aides; Physical therapists; Reality therapists; Recreational therapists; Occupational therapists; Speech therapists; Activities coordinators; Dietitians; Dentists; Audiologists.
Affiliation Lutheran

Facilities Dining room; Physical therapy room; Activities room; Chapel; Crafts room; Laundry room; Barber/Beauty shop.
Activities Arts and Crafts; Cards; Games; Reading groups; Prayer groups; Movies; Shopping trips; Dances/Social or cultural gatherings.
Description Facility has 50 private rooms with private bathrooms at no additional cost; also offers boarding care, respite and adult day care.

SAINT ANTHONY VILLAGE

Saint Anthony Health Center*
3700 Foss Rd NE, Saint Anthony Village, MN, 55421 (612) 788-9673
Admin Marian Post.
Licensure Skilled Care; Intermediate Care.
Beds SNF 128; ICF 26. *Certified* Medicaid.
Ownership Proprietary.

SAINT CHARLES

Whitewater Manor Health Care Center*
525 Bluff Ave, Saint Charles, MN, 55972 (507) 932-3283
Admin Deborah Barnes.
Licensure Skilled Care. *Beds* 79. *Certified* Medicaid.
Ownership Proprietary.

SAINT CLOUD

Dan's Boarding Care Home
1101 3rd St N, Saint Cloud, MN, 56301 (612) 251-6567
Admin Doreen Murphy.
Licensure Boarding Care. *Beds* 12.
Ownership Proprietary.
Admissions Requirements Minimum age 18; Males only; Medical examination; Physician's request.
Staff Orderlies; Nurses aides; Dietitians.
Facilities Dining room; Laundry room.
Activities Cards; Games; Movies; Shopping trips.
Description Facility features a cozy, family setting.

REM Saint Cloud*
1506 33rd Ave N, Saint Cloud, MN, 56301 (612) 252-8875
Admin Craig Miller.
Licensure Skilled Care; Intermediate Care for Mentally Retarded. *Beds* SNF 15; ICF/MR 15. *Certified* Medicaid.
Ownership Proprietary.

Saint Benedicts Center
1810 Minnesota Blvd SE, Saint Cloud, MN, 56301 (612) 252-0010
Admin Sr Rita Budig.
Licensure Skilled Care; Intermediate Care.
Beds SNF 167; ICF 55. *Certified* Medicaid.
Ownership Nonprofit.
Admissions Requirements Medical examination; Physician's request.
Staff RNs 7 (ft), 7 (pt); LPNs 8 (ft), 16 (pt); Nurses aides 45 (ft), 75 (pt); Physical therapists 1 (ft); Occupational therapists 1 (ft); Activities coordinators 1 (ft).
Affiliation Roman Catholic

Facilities Dining room; Physical therapy room; Activities room; Chapel; Crafts room; Laundry room; Barber/Beauty shop; Library.
Activities Arts and Crafts; Cards; Games; Reading groups; Prayer groups; Movies; Shopping trips; Dances/Social or cultural gatherings.
Description Hospice care provided within the Center, respite care (short term), adult day care, and home health care.

Saint Cloud Manor*
1717 Michigan Ave SE, Saint Cloud, MN, 56301 (612) 251-9120
Admin Darwin Schwantes.
Licensure Skilled Care. *Beds* 108. *Certified* Medicaid.
Ownership Proprietary.

Saint Elizabeth Home*
306 15th Ave N, Saint Cloud, MN, 56301 (612) 252-8350
Admin Richard Leisen.
Licensure Intermediate Care for Mentally Retarded. *Beds* 14. *Certified* Medicaid.
Ownership Nonprofit.

SAINT JAMES

Pleasant View Good Samaritan Center
1000 S 2nd St, Saint James, MN, 56081 (507) 375-3286
Admin Jeris M Tangen.
Licensure Intermediate Care. *Beds* 79. *Certified* Medicaid.
Ownership Nonprofit.
Admissions Requirements Minimum age 18.
Staff RNs 1 (ft), 1 (pt); LPNs 3 (ft), 1 (pt); Nurses aides 10 (ft), 24 (pt); Activities coordinators 1 (ft).
Affiliation Lutheran
Facilities Dining room; Activities room; Chapel; Crafts room; Laundry room; Barber/Beauty shop; Library.
Activities Arts and Crafts; Cards; Games; Reading groups; Prayer groups; Movies; Shopping trips.

SAINT LOUIS PARK

Greenwood Residence West
6019 W 39th St, Saint Louis Park, MN, 55416 (612) 929-4681
Admin Norman Bollinger. *Medical Dir/Dir of Nursing* Dorothy Prickeril.
Licensure Intermediate Care for Mentally Retarded. *Beds* 14. *Certified* Medicaid.
Ownership Proprietary.
Admissions Requirements Minimum age 18; Medical examination; Physician's request.
Staff RNs 1 (ft), 1 (pt); LPNs 2 (ft), 2 (pt); Nurses aides 1 (ft), 1 (pt); Recreational therapists 1 (ft); Dietitians 1 (pt); 6 (pt).

Minnesota Jewish Group Home 1*
8101 Westwood Hills Dr, Saint Louis Park, MN, 55426 (612) 544-7030
Admin Sandra Schweich.
Licensure Intermediate Care for Mentally Retarded. *Beds* 6. *Certified* Medicaid.
Ownership Nonprofit.
Affiliation Jewish

Park Nursing and Convalescent Center*
4415 W 36½ St, Saint Louis Park, MN, 55416 (612) 927-9717
Admin Rosemary Holt.
Licensure Skilled Care; Intermediate Care.
Beds SNF 102; ICF 19. *Certified* Medicaid; Medicare.
Ownership Proprietary.

Park Plaza Healthcare Center*
3201 Virginia Ave South, Saint Louis Park, MN, 55426 (612) 935-0333
Admin Phyllis Winters.
Licensure Skilled Care; Intermediate Care.
Beds SNF 214; ICF 86. *Certified* Medicaid; Medicare.
Ownership Proprietary.

Parkview Treatment Center
3705 Park Center Blvd, Saint Louis Park, MN, 55416 (612) 929-5531
Admin Brenda Griffin. *Medical Dir/Dir of Nursing* David Mersy MD.
Licensure Supervised Living Facility. *Beds* 35.
Ownership Proprietary.
Admissions Requirements Minimum age 18.
Staff Physicians 1 (ft), 1 (pt); RNs 2 (ft); LPNs 10 (ft); Physical therapists 1 (pt); Dietitians 1 (pt).

Summit House II*
4600 Minnetonka Blvd, Saint Louis Park, MN, 55426 (612) 926-5553
Admin Carol Robson.
Licensure Intermediate Care for Mentally Retarded. *Beds* 6. *Certified* Medicaid.
Ownership Proprietary.

Texas Terrace Convalescent
7900 W 28th St, Saint Louis Park, MN, 55426 (612) 920-8380
Admin Loren Collman. *Medical Dir/Dir of Nursing* Jesse Barron MD.
Licensure Skilled Care; Intermediate Care.
Beds SNF 187; ICF 7. *Certified* Medicaid; Medicare.
Ownership Proprietary.
Admissions Requirements Minimum age 18; Medical examination; Physician's request.
Facilities Dining room; Physical therapy room; Activities room; Chapel; Crafts room; Laundry room; Barber/Beauty shop; Library.
Activities Arts and Crafts; Cards; Games; Reading groups; Prayer groups; Movies; Shopping trips; Dances/Social or cultural gatherings.

Westwood Nursing Home
7500 W 22nd St, Saint Louis Park, MN, 55426 (612) 546-4261
Admin Cheryl Nybo and Kerri Ronny.
Medical Dir/Dir of Nursing Dr Keith Kubash.
Licensure Skilled Care; Intermediate Care.
Beds SNF 165; ICF 47. *Certified* Medicaid; Medicare.
Ownership Proprietary.
Admissions Requirements Minimum age 16; Medical examination; Physician's request.
Staff RNs 9 (ft), 10 (pt); LPNs 10 (ft), 10 (pt); Orderlies 8 (ft), 3 (pt); Nurses aides 56 (ft), 29 (pt); Physical therapists 1 (ft); Recreational therapists 7 (ft), 1 (pt); Occupational therapists 1 (ft); Speech therapists 1 (ft); Activities coordinators 1 (ft); Dietitians 1 (ft).

Facilities Dining room; Physical therapy room; Activities room; Crafts room; Barber/Beauty shop; Several smoking and nonsmoking lounges.

Activities Arts and Crafts; Cards; Games; Reading groups; Prayer groups; Movies; Shopping trips; Dances/Social or cultural gatherings; Annual camping trip; Ceramics; Woodshop; Music, pet, occupational, and speech therapies.

Description Westwood is a progressive suburban facility which accepts private pay, Medicaid and Veterans Administration contracts. Westwood offers several programs that meet the needs of residents—stroke club, arthritic group, COPD support group, and family orientation sessions. Dentists and opticians visit monthly.

SAINT PAUL

Amy Johnson Residence*
89 Virginia St, Saint Paul, MN, 55102 (612) 225-0574
Admin Joanne Martinez.
Licensure Boarding Care. *Beds* 25.
Ownership Proprietary.

Aurora House
2134 Marshall Ave, Saint Paul, MN, 55104 (612) 645-8622
Admin Terry Forss.
Licensure Supervised Living Facility. *Beds* ICF/MR 6. *Certified* Medicaid.
Ownership Proprietary.
Admissions Requirements Minimum age 18; Medical examination; Physician's request.
Staff RNs; Reality therapists; Recreational therapists.

Bethel Care Center*
420 Marshall Ave, Saint Paul, MN, 55102 (612) 224-2368
Admin Ona Orth.
Licensure Skilled Care; Intermediate Care. *Beds* SNF 127; ICF 22. *Certified* Medicaid.
Ownership Proprietary.

Bethesda Lutheran Infirmary*
558 Capitol Blvd, Saint Paul, MN, 55103 (612) 221-2347
Admin Richard Mellen.
Licensure Skilled Care. *Beds* 138. *Certified* Medicaid; Medicare.
Ownership Nonprofit.
Affiliation Lutheran

Chez Nous*
2248 Carter Ave, Saint Paul, MN, 55108 (612) 644-2346
Admin Dan Kastrul.
Licensure Skilled Care; Intermediate Care for Mentally Retarded. *Beds* SNF 6; ICF/MR 6. *Certified* Medicaid.
Ownership Proprietary.

Commonwealth Healthcare Center*
2237 Commonwealth Ave, Saint Paul, MN, 55108 (612) 646-7486
Admin Michael Goblirsch.
Licensure Skilled Care; Intermediate Care.

Beds SNF 86; ICF 22. *Certified* Medicaid; Medicare.
Ownership Proprietary.

Dayton Boarding Care Home*
740 Dayton Ave, Saint Paul, MN, 55104 (612) 226-1051
Admin Stephen R Scalzo.
Licensure Boarding Care. *Beds* 26.
Ownership Proprietary.

Dayton House of People Inc*
565 Dayton Ave, Saint Paul, MN, 55102 (612) 222-1009
Admin Rachel Feldman.
Licensure Supervised Living Facility. *Beds* 15.
Ownership Nonprofit.

Dungarvin
1086 Como Place, Saint Paul, MN, 55103 (612) 489-0745
Admin Diane Jones. *Medical Dir/Dir of Nursing* Dr D Current.
Licensure Intermediate Care for Mentally Retarded. *Beds* 15. *Certified* Medicaid.
Ownership Proprietary.
Admissions Requirements Minimum age 18; Medical examination; Physician's request.
Staff RNs 1 (pt); Activities coordinators 1 (ft); Dietitians 1 (pt).
Facilities Dining room; Crafts room; Laundry room; Library.
Activities Arts and Crafts; Cards; Games; Reading groups; Movies; Shopping trips; Dances/Social or cultural gatherings.
Description We are a licensed ICF/MR facility. We house 15 mentally retarded adults. We provide programs and supervision in socialization, budgeting (financial), recreation, behavior, and self-care skills. We provide a life experience which is conducive to optimal growth consistent with the normalization principle as set forth by Wolfensberger.

Dungarvin III
1270 Larpenteur Ave E, Saint Paul, MN, 55109 (612) 776-2044
Admin Diane Jones. *Medical Dir/Dir of Nursing* Dr D Current.
Licensure Supervised Living Facility. *Beds* 6. *Certified* Medicaid.
Ownership Proprietary.
Admissions Requirements Minimum age 18.
Facilities Dining room; Laundry room.
Activities Arts and Crafts; Games; Movies; Shopping trips; Dances/Social or cultural gatherings; Wide variety of activities as per resident interest.
Description People in this program are currently working on developing more independent skills in the following areas: grooming, domestic skills, social skills, communication skills, leisure skills, community skills, self-expression skills, and assertiveness skills.

Episcopal Church Home of Minnesota
1879 Feronia Ave, Saint Paul, MN, 55104 (612) 646-4061
Admin Thomas V Moss. *Medical Dir/Dir of Nursing* Kenneth Lerdahl MD.
Licensure Skilled Care; Intermediate Care; Boarding Care. *Beds* SNF 10; ICF 41; Boarding Care 80. *Certified* Medicaid.

Ownership Nonprofit.
Admissions Requirements Minimum age 70.
Staff Physicians 2 (pt); RNs 5 (ft), 2 (pt); LPNs 2 (ft), 1 (pt); Nurses aides 16 (ft), 7 (pt); Recreational therapists 1 (ft); Occupational therapists 1 (pt); Speech therapists 1 (pt); Activities coordinators 2 (pt); Dietitians 1 (pt); Dentists 1 (pt); Podiatrists 1 (pt); Audiologists 1 (pt).
Affiliation Episcopal
Facilities Dining room; Activities room; Chapel; Crafts room; Laundry room; Barber/Beauty shop; Library.
Activities Arts and Crafts; Cards; Games; Reading groups; Prayer groups; Movies; Shopping trips; Dances/Social or cultural gatherings.

Familystyle Homes
398 Duke St, Saint Paul, MN, 55102 (612) 291-2612
Admin Roger Valentine. *Medical Dir/Dir of Nursing* James Janecek MD.
Licensure Boarding Care. *Beds* 21.
Ownership Proprietary.
Admissions Requirements Minimum age 18; Medical examination; Physician's request.
Staff RNs 1 (ft); LPNs 2 (ft); Nurses aides 3 (ft); Activities coordinators 1 (ft); Dietitians 1 (ft); Mental health counselors 4 (ft); Mental health workers 15 (ft).
Facilities Dining room; Activities room; Crafts room; Laundry room; Library; 23 Residential houses and duplexes.
Activities Arts and Crafts; Cards; Games; Prayer groups; Movies; Shopping trips; Dances/Social or cultural gatherings; Camping; Jogging.
Description Facility offers residential living for adult mentally ill; married couples accepted; chemical dependency counseling; support groups available; case management services; resident work program; independent living skills training.

Fellowship Club*
680 Stewart Ave, Saint Paul, MN, 55102 (612) 227-7637
Admin Harold Swift.
Licensure Supervised Living Facility. *Beds* 55.
Ownership Nonprofit.

Frances Residence*
1735 Arlington Ave E, Saint Paul, MN, 55106 (612) 774-9014
Admin Jeffrey T Boston.
Licensure Skilled Care; Intermediate Care for Mentally Retarded. *Beds* SNF 6; ICF/MR 6. *Certified* Medicaid.
Ownership Proprietary.

Good Neighbor Home—Fairmount*
1081 Fairmount Ave, Saint Paul, MN, 55104 (612) 292-1929
Admin Gerald Glomb.
Licensure Intermediate Care for Mentally Retarded. *Beds* 6. *Certified* Medicaid.
Ownership Proprietary.

Greenbrier Home Inc*
941 Birmingham, Saint Paul, MN, 55106 (612) 771-5531
Admin Bob Van Slyke.
Licensure Intermediate Care for Mentally Retarded. *Beds* 165. *Certified* Medicaid.
Ownership Nonprofit.

Greenwood Residence East
1609 Jackson St, Saint Paul, MN, 55117 (612)
488-2561
Admin Norman Bollinger. *Medical Dir/Dir of
Nursing* Connie Halloff.
Licensure Supervised Living Facility. *Beds* ICF/MR 16. *Certified* Medicaid.
Ownership Proprietary.
Admissions Requirements Minimum age 18;
Medical examination; Physician's request.
Staff RNs 1 (ft), 1 (pt); LPNs 3 (ft), 2 (pt);
Nurses aides 1 (ft), 2 (pt); Recreational therapists 1 (ft).
Facilities Dining room; Physical therapy room;
Activities room; Crafts room; Laundry room.
Activities Arts and Crafts; Cards; Games;
Movies; Shopping trips; Dances/Social or cultural gatherings.

Harmony Nursing Home*
135 Geranium Ave, Saint Paul, MN, 55117
(612) 488-6658
Admin Dolores Watters.
Licensure Skilled Care. *Beds* 150. *Certified* Medicaid.
Ownership Proprietary.

Hayes Residence
1620 Randolph Ave, Saint Paul, MN, 55105
(612) 690-4458
Admin Helen Jennen.
Licensure Intermediate Care. *Beds* 40. *Certified* Medicaid.
Ownership Proprietary.
Admissions Requirements Medical examination; Physician's request.
Staff RNs 2 (pt); LPNs 3 (ft); Nurses aides 2
(ft), 5 (pt); Recreational therapists 1 (ft); Dietitians 1 (pt).
Facilities Dining room; Activities room; Crafts
room; Laundry room.
Activities Arts and Crafts; Cards; Games;
Reading groups; Prayer groups; Movies; Shopping trips; Dances/Social or cultural gatherings;
Parties.
Description Residence is a 40-bed board and
care home, also certified as an ICF II, currently
applying for licensure under rule 36; may eventually limit population to those residents
having mental illness as a diagnosis.

Hewitt House of People Inc*
1593 Hewitt Ave, Saint Paul, MN, 55102 (612)
645-9424
Admin Dorothy Berger.
Licensure Intermediate Care for Mentally
Retarded. *Beds* 22.
Ownership Nonprofit.

Highland Chateau
2319 W 7th St, Saint Paul, MN, 55116 (612)
698-0793
Admin Jerry Sansby. *Medical Dir/Dir of
Nursing* Fred Wilson MD.
Licensure Skilled Care. *Beds* 111. *Certified* Medicaid; Medicare.
Ownership Proprietary.
Admissions Requirements Minimum age 18;
Medical examination; Physician's request.
Staff RNs 5 (ft), 8 (pt); LPNs 4 (ft), 3 (pt);
Nurses aides 26 (ft), 24 (pt); Physical therapists
1 (ft); Recreational therapists 2 (ft); Activities
coordinators 1 (ft); Dietitians 1 (ft).

Facilities Dining room; Physical therapy room;
Activities room; Laundry room; Barber/Beauty
shop.
Activities Arts and Crafts; Cards; Games;
Reading groups; Prayer groups; Movies; Shopping trips.

Hoikka House
238 Pleasant Ave, Saint Paul, MN, 55102 (612)
222-7491
Admin Rhoda Miller. *Medical Dir/Dir of
Nursing* Dr Thomas Smith.
Licensure Intermediate Care. *Beds* 117.
Ownership Proprietary.
Admissions Requirements Minimum age 18;
Medical examination.
Staff Physicians; RNs; LPNs; Recreational
therapists; Activities coordinators; Dietitians.
Facilities Dining room; Activities room; Crafts
room; Laundry room.
Activities Arts and Crafts; Cards; Games;
Reading groups; Movies; Shopping trips; Dances/Social or cultural gatherings.
Description Hoikka House has an in-house
sheltered work program which employs 25 residents. Jobs range from laundry aides to dishwashers, coffee servers, housekeepers, and light
janitorial duties.

Hope Transition Center Inc*
1471 Como Ave, Saint Paul, MN, 55108 (612)
644-7961
Admin Harriet J Grinstead.
Licensure Supervised Living Facility. *Beds* 40.
Ownership Nonprofit.

Kent House of People
197 N Kent St, Saint Paul, MN, 55102 (612)
222-0752
Admin Bobby Russell.
Licensure Supervised Living Facility. *Beds* 14.
Ownership Nonprofit.

Little Sisters of the Poor
330 S Exchange St, Saint Paul, MN, 55102
(612) 227-0336
Admin Sr Gonzague. *Medical Dir/Dir of
Nursing* Dr Cecil Warren.
Licensure Skilled Care; Intermediate Care.
Beds SNF 64; ICF 56. *Certified* Medicaid.
Ownership Nonprofit.
Admissions Requirements Minimum age 62;
Medical examination.
Affiliation Roman Catholic
Facilities Dining room; Physical therapy room;
Activities room; Chapel; Crafts room; Laundry
room; Barber/Beauty shop; Library.
Activities Arts and Crafts; Cards; Games;
Reading groups; Prayer groups; Movies; Shopping trips; Dances/Social or cultural gatherings.

Lyngblomsten Care Center
1415 Almond Ave, Saint Paul, MN, 55108
(612) 646-2941
Admin Wallace Hauge. *Medical Dir/Dir of
Nursing* Dr Donald Severson.
Licensure Skilled Care; Intermediate Care.
Beds SNF 184; ICF 72. *Certified* Medicaid.
Ownership Nonprofit.
Admissions Requirements Medical examination.
Staff Physical therapists 1 (ft), 1 (pt); Occupational therapists 1 (ft); Activities coordinators 1

(ft); Dietitians 3 (ft).
Affiliation Lutheran
Facilities Dining room; Physical therapy room;
Activities room; Chapel; Crafts room; Laundry
room; Barber/Beauty shop; Library.
Activities Arts and Crafts; Cards; Games;
Reading groups; Prayer groups; Movies; Shopping trips; Dances/Social or cultural gatherings.
Description Lyngblomsten was founded in
1903 and upholds a reputation for quality
Christian care. Our services and programs
include 256-bed care center, 105-unit independent living apartment complex, and Community Senior Center offering a variety of health,
educational and social programs.

Lynhurst Healthcare Centerᴬ
471 Lynnhurst Ave W, Saint Paul, MN, 55104
(612) 645-6453
Admin Darlene Noreen.
Licensure Skilled Care. *Beds* 84. *Certified* Medicaid.
Ownership Proprietary.

Midway Manor
375 N Lexington Pkwy, Saint Paul, MN, 55104
(612) 645-0577
Admin Allan Swartz. *Medical Dir/Dir of
Nursing* Fred Webber MD.
Licensure Skilled Care; Intermediate Care.
Beds SNF 128; ICF 58. *Certified* Medicaid.
Ownership Proprietary.
Admissions Requirements Minimum age 18;
Medical examination; Physician's request.
Staff RNs 8 (ft), 4 (pt); LPNs 4 (ft), 2 (pt);
Nurses aides 45 (ft), 45 (pt); Physical therapists
2 (ft); Occupational therapists 2 (ft); Speech
therapists 1 (pt); Activities coordinators 1 (ft);
Dietitians 1 (ft).
Facilities Dining room; Physical therapy room;
Activities room; Chapel; Laundry room; Barber/Beauty shop; Library.
Activities Arts and Crafts; Cards; Games;
Reading groups; Prayer groups; Movies; Shopping trips; Dances/Social or cultural gatherings.
Description Morning rehabilitation sessions
held on all floors for all residents every day of
the week.

Minnesota Jewish Group Home II*
1778 Rome Ave, Saint Paul, MN, 55103 (612)
690-1566
Admin Sandra Schweich.
Licensure Skilled Care; Intermediate Care for
Mentally Retarded. *Beds* SNF 6; ICF/MR 6.
Certified Medicaid.
Ownership Nonprofit.
Affiliation Jewish

Mounds Park Residence
908 Mound St, Saint Paul, MN, 55106 (612)
776-7170
Admin Frederick Brumm. *Medical Dir/Dir of
Nursing* Dr Paul Dyrdal.
Licensure Boarding Care. *Beds* 37.
Ownership Proprietary.
Admissions Requirements Minimum age 18;
Medical examination.
Staff Physicians 3 (pt); LPNs 2 (ft), 1 (pt);
Nurses aides 5 (ft), 1 (pt); Recreational therapists 1 (ft), 1 (pt); Speech therapists 1 (ft);
Activities coordinators 1 (ft), 1 (pt); Dietitians
1 (pt); Dentists 1 (pt); Ophthalmologists 1 (pt);

Podiatrists 1 (pt); Audiologists 1 (pt).
Facilities Dining room; Activities room; Crafts room; Barber/Beauty shop; Library; 2 Lounges.
Activities Arts and Crafts; Cards; Games; Reading groups; Prayer groups; Movies; Shopping trips; Dances/Social or cultural gatherings; Resident council.
Description Facility has unique setting in historic home, 5 minutes from downtown St Paul on bus line, overlooking Mississippi River with spacious park-like grounds; reasonable rates.

Nekton on Goodrich*
917 Goodrich Ave, Saint Paul, MN, 55105 (612) 221-0180
Admin Milt Conrath.
Licensure Intermediate Care for Mentally Retarded. *Beds* 8. *Certified* Medicaid.
Ownership Proprietary.

Nekton on Mississippi*
1866 Mississippi Blvd, Saint Paul, MN, 55116 (612) 699-9348
Admin Steve Kodleboy.
Licensure Intermediate Care for Mentally Retarded. *Beds* 6. *Certified* Medicaid.
Ownership Proprietary.

Nekton on Wheeler*
148 Wheeler Ave S, Saint Paul, MN, 55105 (612) 690-0120
Admin Mike Seiwert.
Licensure Intermediate Care for Mentally Retarded. *Beds* 6. *Certified* Medicaid.
Ownership Proprietary.

Nekton on Wyoming*
445 E Wyoming, Saint Paul, MN, 55107 (612) 291-8054
Admin Milt Conrath.
Licensure Intermediate Care for Mentally Retarded. *Beds* 6.
Ownership Proprietary.

New Connection A*
444 Lynnhurst Ave, Saint Paul, MN, 55104 (612) 645-8810
Admin Patrick Stevens.
Licensure Intermediate Care for Mentally Retarded. *Beds* 15.
Ownership Nonprofit.

Norhaven*
1394 Jackson St, Saint Paul, MN, 55117 (612) 488-0275
Admin Peter Sajevic.
Licensure Intermediate Care for Mentally Retarded. *Beds* 108. *Certified* Medicaid.
Ownership Proprietary.

Our House of Minnesota I and II
1846 Dayton Ave and 1846 Portland Ave, Saint Paul, MN, 55104 (612) 646-1104
Admin Lynn R Megan.
Licensure Supervised Living Facility. *Beds* 6.
Certified Medicaid.
Ownership Nonprofit.
Admissions Requirements Minimum age 18; Medical examination; Physician's request.
Facilities Dining room; Laundry room.
Activities Arts and Crafts; Cards; Games; Reading groups; Prayer groups; Movies; Shopping trips; Dances/Social or cultural gatherings;

Adult education.
Description Our House of Minnesota, Inc operates 2 group homes for adults who are mentally retarded; provide community integration for residents as well as a home-like environment.

Our Lady of Good Counsel
2076 St Anthony Ave, Saint Paul, MN, 55104 (612) 646-2797
Admin Mary Daniel King. *Medical Dir/Dir of Nursing* Dr Wayne H Thalhuber and Dr LeRoy Geis.
Licensure Nursing Home. *Beds* 40.
Ownership Nonprofit.
Admissions Requirements Minimum age 16.
Staff Physicians 2 (pt); RNs 2 (ft), 1 (pt); LPNs 5 (ft); Orderlies 3 (ft), 2 (pt); Nurses aides 2 (ft); Dietitians 1 (pt); Dentists 1 (pt).
Affiliation Roman Catholic
Facilities Activities room; Chapel; Laundry room; Barber/Beauty shop; Library.
Activities Dances/Social or cultural gatherings.
Description Ours is a free home for incurable cancer patients exclusively. Residents able to do crafts are encouraged by the nursing staff of Sisters. We have a large dayroom and patio for those patients able to use wheelchair or ambulate. TVs and radios available for all patients are free. We have a 4th of July picnic where all are invited. The home also has a Christmas party where all gather in dayroom with families and friends.

Parkway Manor*
324 Johnson Pkwy, Saint Paul, MN, 55106 (612) 774-9737
Admin Mark Thomas.
Licensure Skilled Care. *Beds* 239. *Certified* Medicaid; Medicare.
Ownership Proprietary.

Peoples Child Care Residence*
1611 Ames Ave, Saint Paul, MN, 55106 (612) 774-5940
Admin MaryKay McJilton.
Licensure Intermediate Care for Mentally Retarded. *Beds* 32. *Certified* Medicaid.
Ownership Nonprofit.

Phoenix Residence
135 Colorado St E, Saint Paul, MN, 55107 (612) 227-7655
Admin Judy Witherspoon.
Licensure Supervised Living Facility. *Beds* 48.
Certified Medicaid.
Ownership Nonprofit.
Admissions Requirements Minimum age 18; Medical examination.
Staff RNs 5 (pt); LPNs 1 (ft), 3 (pt); Nurses aides 38 (ft), 30 (pt); Recreational therapists 2 (ft); Occupational therapists 1 (pt); Activities coordinators 1 (pt).
Facilities Dining room; Physical therapy room; Activities room; Crafts room; Laundry room; Library.
Activities Arts and Crafts; Cards; Games; Reading groups; Movies; Shopping trips; Dances/Social or cultural gatherings.
Description Specialized facility for developmentally disabled, multiple handicapped young adults; full complement of formed daytime

developmental programs; respite care; emphasis on normal, home-like atmosphere with 4 units of 12 residents each.

Pineview Residence Inc
69 N Milton, Saint Paul, MN, 55104 (612) 227-1333
Admin Joanne Chapman.
Licensure Boarding Care. *Beds* 22.
Ownership Proprietary.
Admissions Requirements Minimum age 55; Medical examination.
Staff Physicians; RNs; Nurses aides; Recreational therapists; Activities coordinators; Dietitians.
Facilities Dining room; Activities room; Crafts room; Laundry room; Barber/Beauty shop.
Activities Arts and Crafts; Cards; Games; Prayer groups; Movies; Shopping trips; Dances/Social or cultural gatherings.
Description Facility gives residents a real sense of family; residents and staff stay a long time. Individual activity programing is offered.

Pleasant Hill Care Center*
391 Pleasant Ave, Saint Paul, MN, 55102 (612) 224-3837
Admin Mona Meinke.
Licensure Skilled Care; Intermediate Care.
Beds SNF 79; ICF 11. *Certified* Medicaid.
Ownership Proprietary.

Quinlan Home
233 W 5th St, Saint Paul, MN, 55102 (612) 222-7200
Admin Laura Reynolds.
Licensure Boarding Care. *Beds* 26.
Ownership Proprietary.

Regency Manor Inc*
445 Galtier St, Saint Paul, MN, 55103 (612) 224-1848
Admin James Laine.
Licensure Skilled Care; Intermediate Care.
Beds SNF 94; ICF 51. *Certified* Medicaid.
Ownership Proprietary.

Residence III
1968 Foxridge Rd, Saint Paul, MN, 55106 (612) 631-2672
Admin Ann Carey.
Licensure Supervised Living Facility. *Beds* 6.
Certified Medicaid.
Ownership Nonprofit.
Admissions Requirements Minimum age 15.
Facilities Dining room; Laundry room.
Description This is a group home for mentally retarded cerebral palsy teenagers.

Saint Marys Home
1925 Norfolk Ave, Saint Paul, MN, 55116 (612) 698-5508
Admin homas Fauskee.
Licensure Skilled Care; Intermediate Care.
Beds SNF 110; ICF 30. *Certified* Medicaid.
Ownership Nonprofit.

Saint Pauls Church Home Inc
484 Ashland Ave, Saint Paul, MN, 55102 (612) 227-8351
Admin Lionel Jadoo. *Medical Dir/Dir of Nursing* Dr Mario Garcia.
Licensure Skilled Care; Intermediate Care.

Beds SNF 89; ICF 23. *Certified* Medicaid.
Ownership Nonprofit.
Admissions Requirements Medical examination.
Staff Physicians; RNs 4 (ft), 2 (pt); LPNs 7 (ft), 18 (pt); Nurses aides 19 (ft), 22 (pt); Physical therapists 2 (pt); Recreational therapists 1 (ft), 1 (pt); Occupational therapists 2 (ft); Speech therapists 1 (pt); Activities coordinators 1 (ft); Dietitians 1 (pt); Dentists 1 (pt); Ophthalmologists 1 (pt); Podiatrists 1 (pt); Audiologists 1 (pt).
Affiliation Church of Christ
Facilities Dining room; Physical therapy room; Activities room; Chapel; Crafts room; Laundry room; Barber/Beauty shop; Library.
Activities Arts and Crafts; Cards; Games; Reading groups; Prayer groups; Movies; Shopping trips; Dances/Social or cultural gatherings.

Sholom Home
1554 Midway Pkwy, Saint Paul, MN, 55108
(612) 646-6311
Admin Marshall Silberstein. *Medical Dir/Dir of Nursing* Joseph Geller MD.
Licensure Skilled Care; Intermediate Care.
Beds SNF 274; ICF 28. *Certified* Medicaid.
Ownership Nonprofit.
Affiliation Jewish
Facilities Dining room; Physical therapy room; Activities room; Chapel; Crafts room; Laundry room; Barber/Beauty shop; Library.
Activities Arts and Crafts; Cards; Games; Reading groups; Prayer groups; Movies; Shopping trips; Dances/Social or cultural gatherings; Choir; Horticulture; Exercise.
Description Facility provides meals on wheels and day adult care.

Stevencroft*
1436 Ashland Ave, Saint Paul, MN, 55104
(612) 644-2514
Admin Sandra Bump.
Licensure Skilled Care; Intermediate Care for Mentally Retarded. *Beds* SNF 6; ICF/MR 11. *Certified* Medicaid.
Ownership Proprietary.

Summit Manor Health Care Center*
80 Western Ave N, Saint Paul, MN, 55102
(612) 227-8988
Admin William R Reese.
Licensure Skilled Care; Intermediate Care.
Beds SNF 109; ICF 11. *Certified* Medicaid.
Ownership Proprietary.

Sur La Rue de Breen*
1174 Breen St, Saint Paul, MN, 55106 (612) 488-6956
Admin Peter Sajevic.
Licensure Intermediate Care for Mentally Retarded. *Beds* 6. *Certified* Medicaid.
Ownership Proprietary.

Sur La Rue De Wheelock Ridge
1561 Wheelock Ridge, Saint Paul, MN, 55102
(612) 488-6956
Admin Peter Sajevic.
Licensure Supervised Living Facility. *Beds* 6. *Certified* Medicaid.
Ownership Proprietary.

Twin City Linnea Home*
2040 W Como Ave, Saint Paul, MN, 55108
(612) 646-2544
Admin Keith Johnson.
Licensure Intermediate Care. *Beds* 73. *Certified* Medicaid.
Ownership Nonprofit.

Twin Town Treatment Center
1706 University Ave, Saint Paul, MN, 55104
(612) 645-3661
Admin Robert Harty.
Licensure Supervised Living Facility. *Beds* 50.
Ownership Proprietary.

Wicklough*
905 E 7th St, Saint Paul, MN, 55106 (612) 774-1165
Admin Diane Jones Madden.
Licensure Intermediate Care for Mentally Retarded. *Beds* 100. *Certified* Medicaid.
Ownership Proprietary.

Wilder Health Care Center*
512 Humboldt Ave, Saint Paul, MN, 55107
(612) 227-8091
Admin Susan Kiley.
Licensure Skilled Care. *Beds* 147. *Certified* Medicaid; Medicare.
Ownership Nonprofit.

Wilder Residence East
696 Dellwood Pl, Saint Paul, MN, 55106 (612) 776-4107
Admin Barbara Halper. *Medical Dir/Dir of Nursing* Madeline Adcock.
Licensure Skilled Care; Intermediate Care; Boarding Care. *Beds* 108. *Certified* Medicaid.
Ownership Nonprofit.
Admissions Requirements Minimum age 60; Medical examination; Physician's request.
Staff RNs 8 (ft); LPNs 12 (ft); Orderlies 2 (ft); Nurses aides 98 (ft); Physical therapists 1 (pt); Recreational therapists 1 (ft), 2 (pt); Occupational therapists; Speech therapists; Activities coordinators; Dietitians.
Facilities Dining room; Physical therapy room; Activities room; Chapel; Crafts room; Laundry room; Barber/Beauty shop; Library; Solarium.
Activities Arts and Crafts; Cards; Games; Reading groups; Prayer groups; Movies; Shopping trips; Dances/Social or cultural gatherings.
Description Facility features private rooms with respite beds available for stays less than 30 days.

Wilder Residence West*
514 Humboldt Ave, Saint Paul, MN, 55107
(612) 227-6684
Admin Rick T Johnson.
Licensure Skilled Care; Intermediate Care.
Beds SNF 9; ICF 41. *Certified* Medicaid; Medicare.
Ownership Nonprofit.

Wilson Apartments*
1975 Wilson Ave, Saint Paul, MN, 55106 (612) 738-6603
Admin James Driscoll.
Licensure Skilled Care; Intermediate Care for Mentally Retarded. *Beds* SNF 15; ICF/MR 15. *Certified* Medicaid.
Ownership Proprietary.

SAINT PETER

Community Hospital*
618 W Broadway, Saint Peter, MN, 56082
(507) 931-2200
Admin David Larson.
Licensure Skilled Care; Intermediate Care.
Beds SNF 71; ICF 17. *Certified* Medicaid; Medicare.
Ownership Public.

Grandview Care Center
830 N Sunrise Dr, Saint Peter, MN, 56082
(507) 931-9021
Admin Linda Nelsen. *Medical Dir/Dir of Nursing* M D Olmanson.
Licensure Skilled Care; Intermediate Care.
Beds SNF 74; ICF 2. *Certified* Medicaid.
Ownership Proprietary.
Admissions Requirements Minimum age 17; Medical examination; Physician's request.
Staff Physicians 7 (pt); RNs 2 (ft), 3 (pt); LPNs 4 (ft), 6 (pt); Nurses aides 15 (ft), 25 (pt); Physical therapists 1 (pt); Recreational therapists 1 (ft), 1 (pt); Occupational therapists 1 (pt); Speech therapists 1 (pt); Activities coordinators 1 (ft); Dietitians 1 (pt); Dentists 1 (pt); Podiatrists 1 (pt); Audiologists 1 (pt).
Facilities Dining room; Physical therapy room; Activities room; Laundry room; Barber/Beauty shop; Library; Lounge.
Activities Arts and Crafts; Cards; Games; Reading groups; Prayer groups; Movies; Shopping trips; Dances/Social or cultural gatherings.

Minnesota Supervised Living Facility*
100 Freeman Dr, Saint Peter, MN, 56082 (507) 931-7115
Admin Joseph Solien.
Licensure Skilled Care. *Beds* 184.
Ownership Public.

Saint Peter State Hospital*
100 Freeman Dr, Saint Peter, MN, 56082 (507) 931-7115
Admin Joseph W Solien.
Licensure Intermediate Care for Mentally Retarded. *Beds* 204. *Certified* Medicaid; Medicare.
Ownership Public.

SANDSTONE

Sandstone Area Nursing Home*
Washington St, Sandstone, MN, 55072 (612) 245-2224
Admin Max Blaufuss.
Licensure Skilled Care. *Beds* 46. *Certified* Medicaid.
Ownership Nonprofit.

SARTELL

Country Manor Nursing Home*
520 1st St NE, Sartell, MN, 56377 (812) 253-1920
Admin Hollis Helgeson.
Licensure Skilled Care. *Beds* 187. *Certified* Medicaid.
Ownership Proprietary.

SAUK CENTRE

Dorothe Lane Home
205 6th St, Sauk Centre, MN, 56378 (612) 352-3653
Admin Joseph M Bartsh.
Licensure Supervised Living Facility. *Beds* 8.
Certified Medicaid.
Ownership Proprietary.
Admissions Requirements Minimum age 13;
Medical examination.
Staff RNs 1 (pt); LPNs 1 (pt); Activities coordinators 1 (ft).
Facilities Dining room; Activities room; Laundry room.
Activities Arts and Crafts; Cards; Games;
Movies; Shopping trips; Dances/Social or cultural gatherings.
Description The Dorothe Lane Home provides varied programs for moderately mentally retarded teenagers and young adults.

Lakeview Childrens Home
Lincoln and W 2nd St, Sauk Centre, MN, 56378 (612) 352-3081
Admin Joseph M Bartsh.
Licensure Supervised Living Facility. *Beds* 7.
Certified Medicaid.
Ownership Proprietary.
Admissions Requirements Minimum age 3;
Medical examination.
Staff RNs 1 (pt); LPNs 1 (ft).
Facilities Dining room; Activities room; Laundry room.
Activities Arts and Crafts; Games; Movies;
Shopping trips; Dances/Social or cultural gatherings.
Description The Lakeview Childrens Home provides a varied program for profoundly retarded children and teens.

Pettit Childrens Home*
812 S Main St, Sauk Centre, MN, 56378 (612) 352-2844
Admin Cathy Marthaler.
Licensure Intermediate Care for Mentally Retarded. *Beds* 15. *Certified* Medicaid.
Ownership Proprietary.

Saint Michaels Hospital and Nursing Home*
425 N Elm St, Sauk Centre, MN, 56378 (612) 352-2221
Admin Roy Provo.
Licensure Skilled Care; Intermediate Care.
Beds SNF 56; ICF 4. *Certified* Medicaid;
Medicare.
Ownership Public.

SAUK RAPIDS

Good Shepherd Lutheran Home
1115 4th Ave N, Sauk Rapids, MN, 56379 (612) 252-6525
Admin Tim Steller. *Medical Dir/Dir of Nursing* Dr Vernon E Neils.
Licensure Skilled Care. *Beds* 174. *Certified* Medicaid.
Ownership Nonprofit.
Admissions Requirements Minimum age 16;
Medical examination; Physician's request.
Staff RNs 7 (ft), 7 (pt); LPNs 15 (ft), 9 (pt);
Orderlies 2 (ft), 5 (pt); Nurses aides 24 (ft), 39

(pt); Activities coordinators 1 (ft).
Affiliation Lutheran
Facilities Dining room; Physical therapy room;
Activities room; Chapel; Crafts room; Laundry room; Barber/Beauty shop.
Activities Arts and Crafts; Cards; Games;
Reading groups; Prayer groups; Movies; Shopping trips; Dances/Social or cultural gatherings.

Granite Care Home*
202 2nd Ave S, Sauk Rapids, MN, 56379 (612) 251-4736
Admin Quinton W Hommerding.
Licensure Intermediate Care for Mentally Retarded. *Beds* 23. *Certified* Medicaid.
Ownership Proprietary.

SHAKOPEE

Delphi*
1411 E Shakopee Ave, Shakopee, MN, 55379 (612) 445-1680
Admin Betsy Nelson.
Licensure Intermediate Care for Mentally Retarded. *Beds* 10. *Certified* Medicaid.
Ownership Proprietary.

Shakopee Friendship Manor*
1340 3rd Ave W, Shakopee, MN, 55379 (612) 445-4155
Admin Terry A Riffe.
Licensure Skilled Care. *Beds* 116. *Certified* Medicaid.
Ownership Proprietary.

SHERBURN

Friendship Haven I*
Fox Lake Rd, Sherburn, MN, 56171 (507) 764-2391
Admin Michael Hennessey.
Licensure Intermediate Care for Mentally Retarded. *Beds* 14. *Certified* Medicaid.
Ownership Nonprofit.

Friendship Haven II*
Fox Lake Rd, Sherburn, MN, 56171 (507) 764-2391
Admin Michael Hennessey.
Licensure Intermediate Care for Mentally Retarded. *Beds* 6. *Certified* Medicaid.
Ownership Nonprofit.

SHOREVIEW

Dungarvin VI*
3490 N Victoria, Shoreview, MN, 55112 (612) 482-8029
Admin Diane Jones Madden.
Licensure Intermediate Care for Mentally Retarded. *Beds* 6. *Certified* Medicaid.
Ownership Public.

Lake Owasso Residence*
210 Owasso Blvd N, Shoreview, MN, 55112 (612) 484-2234
Admin Roger O Larson.
Licensure Intermediate Care for Mentally Retarded. *Beds* 64. *Certified* Medicaid.
Ownership Public.

Nekton on Hodgson Rd*
5091 Hodgson Rd, Shoreview, MN, 55112 (612) 483-4024
Admin Steve Kodulboy.
Licensure Intermediate Care for Mentally Retarded. *Beds* 6. *Certified* Medicaid.
Ownership Proprietary.

Residence I
935 Amble Rd, Shoreview, MN, 55112 (612) 484-0985
Admin Ann Carey.
Licensure Supervised Living Facility. *Beds* ICF/MR 8. *Certified* Medicaid.
Ownership Nonprofit.
Admissions Requirements Medical examination; Physician's request.
Staff RNs 1 (pt); Activities coordinators 2 (ft); 5 (pt).
Facilities Dining room; Activities room.
Activities Cards; Games; Reading groups; Prayer groups; Movies; Shopping trips;
Dances/Social or cultural gatherings.

Residence II
925 Amble Rd, Shoreview, MN, 51122 (612) 484-6718
Admin Ann Carey.
Licensure Supervised Living Facility. *Beds* ICF/MR 8. *Certified* Medicaid.
Ownership Nonprofit.
Staff RNs 1 (pt); Activities coordinators 2 (ft).
Facilities Dining room; Activities room; Laundry room.
Activities Cards; Games; Reading groups;
Prayer groups; Shopping trips; Dances/Social or cultural gatherings.

SLAYTON

Slayton Manor
2957 Redwood Ave, Slayton, MN, 56172 (507) 836-6135
Admin Alvin Knutson. *Medical Dir/Dir of Nursing* Larry B Okerlund MD.
Licensure Skilled Care; Intermediate Care.
Beds SNF 32; ICF 32. *Certified* Medicaid.
Ownership Proprietary.
Admissions Requirements Medical examination; Physician's request.
Staff RNs 1 (ft), 3 (pt); LPNs 6 (ft); Nurses aides 16 (ft), 16 (pt); Activities coordinators 1 (ft), 2 (pt).
Facilities Dining room; Activities room; Chapel; Crafts room; Laundry room; Barber/Beauty shop; Whirlpool bath.
Activities Arts and Crafts; Cards; Games; Prayer groups; Movies; Dances/Social or cultural gatherings.
Description Situated in a southwestern farming community, this facility boasts of a pleasant atmosphere with many activity programs daily. A special lounge area has a stained glass window making it also a chapel where devotions are held several times weekly. Many families participate in volunteer work to make this health care facility a happy home for many.

SLEEPY EYE

Divine Providence Home
700 3rd Ave NW, Sleepy Eye, MN, 56085 (507) 794-3011
Admin Sr Rosina LoCoco. *Medical Dir/Dir of Nursing* Dr Michael Ecker.
Licensure Intermediate Care. *Beds* 58. *Certified* Medicaid.
Ownership Nonprofit.
Admissions Requirements Medical examination; Physician's request.
Staff RNs 1 (ft), 1 (pt); LPNs 3 (ft), 2 (pt); Nurses aides 12 (ft), 23 (pt); Activities coordinators 1 (ft), 2 (pt).
Affiliation Roman Catholic
Facilities Dining room; Activities room; Chapel; Crafts room; Laundry room; Barber-/Beauty shop; Library.
Activities Arts and Crafts; Cards; Games; Reading groups; Prayer groups; Movies; Shopping trips; Dances/Social or cultural gatherings.
Description Divine Providence Community Home is beautifully situated near the scenic Sportsman Park and Sleepy Eye Lake. The home offers quality care with a unique home-like atmosphere. Family-style meals, daily church, frequent community outings within the area, and other activities provide a balance of productivity, fun, and relaxation.

Sleepy Eye Care Center
1105 3rd Ave SW, Sleepy Eye, MN, 56085 (507) 794-7995
Admin Del Begalka. *Medical Dir/Dir of Nursing* C M Galvin MD.
Licensure Skilled Care; Intermediate Care. *Beds* 86. *Certified* Medicaid; Medicare.
Ownership Nonprofit.
Admissions Requirements Medical examination.
Staff RNs 4 (ft); LPNs 5 (ft), 6 (pt); Orderlies 2 (pt); Nurses aides 20 (ft), 16 (pt); Physical therapists 1 (pt); Activities coordinators 1 (ft).
Affiliation Volunteers of America
Facilities Dining room; Physical therapy room; Activities room; Chapel; Crafts room; Laundry room; Barber/Beauty shop.
Activities Arts and Crafts; Cards; Games; Reading groups; Prayer groups; Movies; Shopping trips.
Description Facility is the only Medicare certified skilled-nursing facility in 9 county area; VA contract; one-level building.

SOUTH HAVEN

Madden Haven Home*
101 Oak St, South Haven, MN, 55382 (612) 236-7521
Admin Dolores Madden.
Licensure Intermediate Care for Mentally Retarded. *Beds* 45. *Certified* Medicaid.
Ownership Proprietary.

SOUTH SAINT PAUL

Bryant and Summit Avenue Residences
1120 Bryant Ave, South Saint Paul, MN, 55025 (612) 451-1344
Admin Anne Henrickson.

Licensure Supervised Living Facility. *Beds* 30. *Certified* Medicaid.
Ownership Proprietary.
Admissions Requirements Minimum age 18.
Staff RNs 1 (ft).
Facilities Dining room; Activities room; Laundry room; Separate self-contained apartment units.
Activities Arts and Crafts; Cards; Games; Reading groups; Movies; Shopping trips; Dances/Social or cultural gatherings.
Description The goal of our facilities is to support adults who are mentally retarded in their search for meaningful work, personal relationships, and use of the community. We prepare some residents for independent living in their own apartments following our program.

Golden Oaks Nursing Home
1025 9th Ave S, South Saint Paul, MN, 55075 (612) 455-6615
Admin Otto J Olson.
Licensure Skilled Care; Intermediate Care; Boarding Care. *Beds* SNF 96; ICF 2; Boarding Care 8. *Certified* Medicaid.
Ownership Proprietary.
Facilities Dining room; Physical therapy room; Activities room; Chapel; Crafts room; Laundry room; Barber/Beauty shop; Library.
Activities Arts and Crafts; Cards; Games; Reading groups; Prayer groups; Movies; Shopping trips; Dances/Social or cultural gatherings.

Maclare Residence
630 15th Ave N, South Saint Paul, MN, 55075
Admin James Driscoll. *Medical Dir/Dir of Nursing* Angela Pelequin.
Licensure Intermediate Care for Mentally Retarded. *Beds* 6. *Certified* Medicaid.
Ownership Proprietary.
Admissions Requirements Minimum age 18; Medical examination.
Staff RNs 1 (ft); LPNs 1 (pt).
Description Residents must be approved by board before entry. Facility is a regular house in the community; residents are encouraged to organize their own activities to further their independence.

Spruce Avenue Residence*
1249 8th Ave S, South Saint Paul, MN, 55075 (612) 455-0578
Admin James Driscoll.
Licensure Skilled Care; Intermediate Care. *Beds* SNF 6; ICF 6. *Certified* Medicaid.
Ownership Proprietary.

Summit Avenue Residence*
920 Summit Ave, South Saint Paul, MN, 55075 (612) 455-8282
Admin Sarah Cosgrove.
Licensure Skilled Care; Intermediate Care. *Beds* SNF 15; ICF 15. *Certified* Medicaid.
Ownership Proprietary.

SPICER

Alpha Homes Inc
137 W Lake Ave, Spicer, MN, 56288 (612) 796-5792
Admin Barb Ulman.
Licensure Supervised Living Facility. *Beds* 15.

Certified Medicaid.
Ownership Proprietary.
Admissions Requirements Minimum age 18.
Staff RNs 1 (pt); LPNs 1 (ft).
Facilities Dining room; Activities room; Crafts room; Laundry room.
Activities Arts and Crafts; Cards; Games; Shopping trips; Dances/Social or cultural gatherings.

SPRING GROVE

Tweeten Memorial Hospital—Nursing Home
125 5th Ave SE, Spring Grove, MN, 55974
Admin Steven E Moss. *Medical Dir/Dir of Nursing* Joel Mintalar MD.
Licensure Skilled Care; Intermediate Care. *Beds* SNF 32; ICF 47. *Certified* Medicaid.
Ownership Nonprofit.
Admissions Requirements Medical examination; Physician's request.
Staff Physicians 1 (ft); RNs 3 (ft), 5 (pt); LPNs 5 (pt); Nurses aides 3 (ft), 29 (pt); Activities coordinators 1 (ft); Dentists 1 (pt).
Facilities Dining room; Activities room; Chapel; Crafts room; Laundry room; Barber/Beauty shop.
Activities Arts and Crafts; Cards; Games; Reading groups; Prayer groups; Movies; Shopping trips; Dances/Social or cultural gatherings.

SPRING PARK

Twin Birch Health Care Center
4527 Shoreline Dr, Spring Park, MN, 55384 (612) 471-8412
Admin Cory Glad. *Medical Dir/Dir of Nursing* Dr E L Pierce.
Licensure Skilled Care; Intermediate Care. *Beds* SNF 140; ICF 52. *Certified* Medicaid; Medicare.
Ownership Proprietary.
Admissions Requirements Minimum age 16; Medical examination; Physician's request.
Facilities Dining room; Physical therapy room; Activities room; Chapel; Crafts room; Laundry room; Barber/Beauty shop; Library.
Activities Arts and Crafts; Cards; Games; Reading groups; Prayer groups; Movies; Shopping trips; Dances/Social or cultural gatherings.
Description The facility is located on beautiful Lake Minnetonka. We provide pontoon boat rides as an added feature. The facility is constructed of fire resistant materials and automatic alarm and sprinkler systems are installed throughout the facility.

SPRINGFIELD

Saint John Lutheran Home
PO Box 76, Springfield, MN, 56087 (507) 723-6251
Admin Randy Snyder. *Medical Dir/Dir of Nursing* F J Boyle MD.
Licensure Skilled Care; Intermediate Care; Boarding Care. *Beds* SNF 68; ICF 58; Boarding Care 23. *Certified* Medicaid.
Ownership Nonprofit.
Admissions Requirements Medical examination; Physician's request.
Staff RNs 4 (ft), 4 (pt); LPNs 5 (ft), 12 (pt);

Orderlies 1 (ft), 2 (pt); Nurses aides 24 (ft), 47 (pt); Physical therapists 1 (ft); Recreational therapists 5 (ft); Activities coordinators 1 (ft).
Affiliation Lutheran
Facilities Dining room; Physical therapy room; Activities room; Chapel; Crafts room; Laundry room; Barber/Beauty shop.
Activities Arts and Crafts; Cards; Games; Reading groups; Prayer groups; Movies; Shopping trips; Dances/Social or cultural gatherings.
Description Saint John Lutheran Home is a deeply committed, church-related organization for the elderly community members of Sanborn, Comfrey, Sleepy Eye, and Springfield.

ST CLOUD

Opportunity Manor*
961 17th Ave N, St Cloud, MN, 56301 (612) 252-7349
Admin James Steiner.
Licensure Skilled Care; Intermediate Care for Mentally Retarded. *Beds* SNF 15; ICF/MR 15. *Certified* Medicaid.
Ownership Nonprofit.

STAPLES

United District Hospital and Home
401 Prairie Ave N, Staples, MN, 56479
Admin Tim Rice. *Medical Dir/Dir of Nursing* Dennis Amundson.
Licensure Skilled Care; Intermediate Care.
Beds SNF 70; ICF 30. *Certified* Medicaid.
Ownership Nonprofit.
Admissions Requirements Minimum age 16.
Staff Physicians 5 (pt); RNs 2 (ft), 3 (pt); LPNs 3 (ft), 7 (pt); Nurses aides 14 (ft), 37 (pt); Physical therapists 1 (pt); Recreational therapists 1 (ft); Activities coordinators 1 (ft); Dietitians 1 (pt); Social workers 1 (pt).
Facilities Dining room; Physical therapy room; Activities room; Chapel; Crafts room; Barber/Beauty shop.
Activities Arts and Crafts; Cards; Games; Reading groups; Prayer groups; Movies; Shopping trips; Dances/Social or cultural gatherings; Social services 32 hours per week.
Description The nursing home is attached to a 40-bed hospital and has excellent medical staff coverage, as well as outpatient lab and X-ray availability with no need for the residents leaving the building. The hospital home care program is a bridge that frequently makes admission to the nursing home less threatening; adult day care and respite care programs in development stages.

STARBUCK

Minnewaska Lutheran Home
605 Main St, Box 5600, Starbuck, MN, 56381 (612) 239-2217
Admin Bruce Prause.
Licensure Intermediate Care; Boarding Care.
Beds ICF 70; Boarding Care 16. *Certified* Medicaid.
Ownership Nonprofit.
Admissions Requirements Minimum age 16; Medical examination; Physician's request.
Staff RNs 1 (ft), 2 (pt); LPNs 5 (ft); Orderlies 1

(ft); Nurses aides 15 (ft), 15 (pt); Speech therapists 1 (pt); Activities coordinators 2 (ft); Dietitians 1 (pt).
Affiliation Lutheran
Facilities Dining room; Activities room; Chapel; Crafts room; Laundry room; Barber/Beauty shop.
Activities Arts and Crafts; Cards; Games; Reading groups; Movies; Shopping trips; Dances/Social or cultural gatherings.
Description Spacious nursing home located in west central Minnesota is church orientated and community active; offers a full range of physical, religious, social, and cultural services.

Project New Hope—Starbuck*
Box 605, Starbuck, MN, 56381 (612) 762-2349
Admin Glenn Medicraft.
Licensure Intermediate Care for Mentally Retarded. *Beds* 6. *Certified* Medicaid.
Ownership Nonprofit.

STEWARTVILLE

Stewartvilla Nursing Home
120 4th St NE, Stewartville, MN, 55926 (507) 533-4288
Admin Francis Jensen. *Medical Dir/Dir of Nursing* Craig D Thauwald MD.
Licensure Skilled Care; Intermediate Care.
Beds SNF 83; ICF 26. *Certified* Medicaid.
Ownership Public.
Admissions Requirements Medical examination.
Staff RNs 3 (ft), 6 (pt); LPNs 1 (ft), 9 (pt); Orderlies 1 (ft), 1 (pt); Nurses aides 14 (ft), 33 (pt); Physical therapists; Reality therapists 1 (pt); Recreational therapists 1 (ft), 1 (pt); Dietitians 1 (pt).
Facilities Dining room; Physical therapy room; Activities room; Chapel; Crafts room; Laundry room; Barber/Beauty shop; Library.
Activities Arts and Crafts; Cards; Games; Reading groups; Prayer groups; Movies; Shopping trips; Dances/Social or cultural gatherings.
Description Facility is in ideal location within 5 blocks of drug store, grocery store, bank, and several churches.

STILLWATER

Greeley Healthcare Center*
313 S Greeley St, Stillwater, MN, 55082 (612) 439-5775
Admin Joleen A Waalen.
Licensure Skilled Care. *Beds* 83. *Certified* Medicaid.
Ownership Proprietary.

Jamestown
11550 Jasmine Trail N, Stillwater, MN, 55082 (612) 429-5307
Admin Jack Vigen.
Licensure Supervised Living Facility. *Beds* 24.
Ownership Nonprofit.

Linden Healthcare Center
105 W Linden St, Stillwater, MN, 55082 (612) 439-5004
Admin Hilda Gooding. *Medical Dir/Dir of Nursing* Dr Paul Quinn.

Licensure Skilled Care. *Beds* 75. *Certified* Medicaid.
Ownership Proprietary.
Admissions Requirements Medical examination.
Staff RNs 6 (ft), 1 (pt); LPNs 2 (ft); Nurses aides 46 (ft), 1 (pt); Recreational therapists 1 (pt); Occupational therapists 1 (ft); Speech therapists 1 (pt); Activities coordinators 1 (ft).
Facilities Dining room; Physical therapy room; Activities room; Crafts room; Laundry room; Barber/Beauty shop; Library.
Activities Arts and Crafts; Cards; Games; Reading groups; Prayer groups; Movies; Shopping trips; Dances/Social or cultural gatherings.

Nekton on Imperial Court*
8050 Imperial Court, Stillwater, MN, 55802 (612) 429-0079
Admin Steve Kodulboy.
Licensure Intermediate Care for Mentally Retarded. *Beds* 6. *Certified* Medicaid.
Ownership Proprietary.

Stillwater Maple Manor Health Care Center Inc
1119 N Owens St, Stillwater, MN, 55082 (612) 439-7180
Admin Chuck Heidbrink. *Medical Dir/Dir of Nursing* Dr Paul Spilseth.
Licensure Skilled Care; Intermediate Care.
Beds SNF 105; ICF 27. *Certified* Medicaid; Medicare.
Ownership Proprietary.
Staff RNs 17 (ft), 17 (pt); LPNs 10 (ft), 10 (pt); Nurses aides 26 (ft), 60 (pt); Physical therapists 1 (ft); Recreational therapists 1 (ft); Occupational therapists 1 (pt); Speech therapists 1 (pt); Activities coordinators 1 (ft); Dietitians 1 (ft); Dentists 1 (pt); Podiatrists 1 (pt); Music therapists 1 (ft), 1 (pt).
Facilities Dining room; Physical therapy room; Activities room; Chapel; Crafts room; Laundry room; Barber/Beauty shop.
Activities Arts and Crafts; Cards; Games; Reading groups; Prayer groups; Movies; Shopping trips; Dances/Social or cultural gatherings.
Description Manor is proud of its quality services, innovative therapies, and strong sense of community; residents and families are impressed with the attractively redecorated surroundings complete with a relaxing patio and spacious grounds.

Stillwater Residence
220 W Olive St, Stillwater, MN, 55082 (612) 439-1601
Admin Laura L Reynolds.
Licensure Boarding Care. *Beds* 31. *Certified* Medicaid.
Ownership Proprietary.
Staff RNs 1 (pt); LPNs 1 (ft), 1 (pt); Activities coordinators 1 (pt); Dietitians 1 (pt).
Facilities Dining room; Activities room; Crafts room; Laundry room.
Activities Arts and Crafts; Cards; Games; Reading groups; Movies; Shopping trips.

THIEF RIVER FALLS

Crestview Home*
101 S State Ave, Thief River Falls, MN, 56701
(218) 681-3484
Admin Patricia Norberg.
Licensure Intermediate Care. *Beds* 15.
Ownership Proprietary.

Johnsons Riverside Boarding Care Home
Rt 4, Box 21, Thief River Falls, MN, 56701
(218) 681-1278
Admin Paul Johnson.
Licensure Supervised Living Facility. *Beds* 15.
Certified Medicaid.
Ownership Proprietary.
Admissions Requirements Minimum age 18;
Medical examination.
Staff RNs 1 (pt); Nurses aides 2 (ft).
Facilities Dining room; Activities room; Crafts
room; Laundry room.
Activities Arts and Crafts; Cards; Games;
Reading groups; Movies; Shopping trips; Dances/Social or cultural gatherings; Fishing; Snow-
mobiling; Gardening; Pontoon rides.
Description Facility is located along the Red
Lake River in a rural setting with 5 acres of
land to be utilized for raising animals (chick-
ens, horses, dogs, others) along with 2 large gar-
den spots for growing produce.

Oakland Park Nursing Home
123 Baken St, Thief River Falls, MN, 56701
(218) 681-1675
Admin Sherryll Irvine.
Licensure Intermediate Care. *Beds* 75. *Certified* Medicaid.
Ownership Public.

Valley Home*
Hwy 32, S Arnold, Thief River Falls, MN,
56701 (218) 681-3286
Admin Mildred Brekke.
Licensure Boarding Care. *Beds* 136.
Ownership Nonprofit.

TOWER

Hearthside Homes
Pike Bay Dr, Tower, MN, 55790 (218)
753-2700
Admin R L Abrahamson.
Licensure Supervised Living Facility. *Beds* 40.
Certified Medicaid.
Ownership Proprietary.
Admissions Requirements Minimum age 18;
Medical examination.
Staff RNs 1 (ft); LPNs 1 (pt); Nurses aides 4
(ft), 6 (pt); Recreational therapists 2 (ft).
Facilities Dining room; Crafts room.
Activities Arts and Crafts; Cards; Games; Pray-
er groups; Movies; Shopping trips; Dances/So-
cial or cultural gatherings.
Description Residents are programed in areas
of daily living and domestic skills needed to
live independently in the community. Our setting is rural. We are situated on a lake on a
100-acre estate with 4 buildings.

TRACY

Christian Manor Nursing Home
502 5th St E, Tracy, MN, 56175 (507) 629-3331
Admin Homer Dobson. *Medical Dir/Dir of
Nursing* Dr James O'Rourke.
Licensure Skilled Care. *Beds* 67. *Cer-
tified* Medicaid.
Admissions Requirements Medical examina-
tion.
Staff Physicians 2 (pt); RNs 1 (ft), 2 (pt); LPNs
4 (ft), 3 (pt); Orderlies 1 (ft), 1 (pt); Nurses aides
18 (ft), 6 (pt); Recreational therapists 2 (ft);
Occupational therapists 1 (pt); Speech therapists 1 (pt); Activities coordinators 1 (ft); Dietitians 1 (pt); Dentists 1 (pt); Ophthalmologists 1
(pt); Podiatrists 1 (pt); Audiologists 1 (pt).
Affiliation Church of Christ
Facilities Dining room; Physical therapy room;
Activities room; Chapel; Crafts room; Laundry
room.
Activities Arts and Crafts; Cards; Games; Prayer groups; Movies; Dances/Social or cultural
gatherings.

Tracy Nursing Home
487 2nd St, Tracy, MN, 56175 (507) 629-4850
Admin Goldie Wilking.
Licensure Intermediate Care; Boarding Care.
Beds ICF 50; Boarding Care 8. *Certified* Medi-
caid.
Ownership Nonprofit.
Admissions Requirements Minimum age 18;
Medical examination; Physician's request.
Staff Physicians 2 (pt); RNs 1 (ft), 1 (pt); LPNs
2 (ft), 2 (pt); Nurses aides 6 (ft), 18 (pt); Activi-
ties coordinators 1 (ft), 2 (pt).
Facilities Dining room; Activities room; Chap-
el; Crafts room; Laundry room; Barber/Beauty
shop; Library.
Activities Arts and Crafts; Cards; Games;
Reading groups; Prayer groups; Movies; Shopping trips; Dances/Social or cultural gatherings.
Description Facility is located across the street
from city park and is 2 blocks from a shopping
area.

TRIMONT

Trimont Nursing Home
303 Broadway Ave S, Trimont, MN, 56176
(507) 639-2381
Admin Thos Tallant. *Medical Dir/Dir of
Nursing* Dr K L Reddy.
Licensure Skilled Care. *Beds* 41. *Cer-
tified* Medicaid.
Staff RNs 1 (ft), 3 (pt); LPNs 3 (ft), 3 (pt);
Nurses aides 5 (ft), 16 (pt); Recreational thera-
pists 2 (pt); Dietitians 1 (pt).
Facilities Dining room; Laundry room; Barber-
/Beauty shop; Library.
Activities Arts and Crafts; Games; Reading
groups; Movies.

TRUMAN

**Lutheran Retirement Home of Southern
Minnesota**
400 N 4th Ave E, Truman, MN, 56088 (507)
776-2031
Admin Rodney Dahlberg. *Medical Dir/Dir of*

Nursing Dr M J Lester.
Licensure Skilled Care; Intermediate Care.
Beds 113. *Certified* Medicaid.
Ownership Nonprofit.
Admissions Requirements Minimum age 62;
Medical examination; Physician's request.
Staff RNs 2 (ft), 4 (pt); LPNs 4 (ft), 5 (pt);
Orderlies 1 (ft); Nurses aides 21 (ft), 36 (pt);
Activities coordinators 1 (ft); Dietitians 1 (pt);
Rehabilitation aides 2 (ft), 1 (pt).
Affiliation Lutheran
Facilities Dining room; Physical therapy room;
Activities room; Chapel; Crafts room; Laundry
room; Barber/Beauty shop; Library.
Activities Arts and Crafts; Cards; Games;
Reading groups; Prayer groups; Movies; Shop-
ping trips; Dances/Social or cultural gatherings.
Description Apartments are physically attached
to the nursing home on the northeast side and a
clinic (including doctor and dentist) is attached
to the nursing home on the south side. Congregate meal site for the Truman area is provided at the apartment site.

TWIN VALLEY

Lutheran Memorial Nursing Home*
Hwy 32 N, Twin Valley, MN, 56584 (218)
584-5181
Admin Dwight Fuglie.
Licensure Skilled Care; Intermediate Care.
Beds SNF 40; ICF 64. *Certified* Medicaid.
Ownership Nonprofit.
Affiliation Lutheran

Lutheran Memorial Retirement Center*
205 3rd St NW, Twin Valley, MN, 56584 (218)
584-5181
Admin Dwight Fuglie.
Licensure Skilled Care; Intermediate Care.
Beds SNF 44; ICF 44. *Certified* Medicaid.
Ownership Nonprofit.

TWO HARBORS

Sunrise Home
13th Ave & 4th St, Two Harbors, MN, 55616
(218) 834-5574
Admin Joy Winkleblack. *Medical Dir/Dir of
Nursing* Dr Eugene Rondeau.
Licensure Intermediate Care. *Beds* 55. *Certi-
fied* Medicaid.
Ownership Public.
Admissions Requirements Minimum age 16;
Medical examination; Physician's request.
Staff RNs 1 (ft); LPNs 2 (ft), 5 (pt); Recreational therapists 1 (pt); Activities coordinators 1
(ft).
Facilities Dining room; Activities room; Crafts
room; Laundry room; Barber/Beauty shop.
Activities Arts and Crafts; Cards; Games;
Reading groups; Prayer groups; Movies; Shopping trips; Dances/Social or cultural gatherings.
Description Hillside facility with lovely patio
and terrace rose garden, entirely surrounded by
connecting walkways leading to a rustic gazebo
which overlooks Lake Superior. Each resident's
needs are met individually through inter-
departmental coordination; goal of facility is to
provide their medical, emotional, social, and
spiritual needs, emphasizing family support.

TYLER

Al Vadheim Memorial Hospital*
240 Willow St, Tyler, MN, 56178 (507)
247-5521
Admin Robet Patterson.
Licensure Skilled Care; Intermediate Care.
Beds SNF 29; ICF 14. *Certified* Medicaid.
Ownership Nonprofit.

REM-Taylor*
303 Highland Ct, Tyler, MN, 56178 (507)
247-5568
Admin Craig Miller.
Licensure Intermediate Care for Mentally
Retarded. *Beds* 15.
Ownership Proprietary.

ULEN

Viking Manor Nursing Home*
Ulen, MN, 56585 (218) 596-8847
Admin Todd Kjos.
Licensure Intermediate Care. *Beds* 66. *Certified* Medicaid.
Ownership Public.

VICTORIA

Community Living
Box 128, Victoria, MN, 55386 (612) 443-2048
Admin Jerry Gross.
Licensure Supervised Living Facility. *Beds* ICF/MR 66. *Certified* Medicaid.
Ownership Proprietary.
Admissions Requirements Minimum age 18;
Medical examination; Physician's request.
Staff RNs 2 (ft).
Facilities Dining room; Activities room; Laundry room.
Activities Arts and Crafts; Cards; Games;
Reading groups; Movies; Shopping trips; Dances/Social or cultural gatherings.

VILLARD

Jennies Retirement Home*
620 Washington Ave, Villard, MN, 56385 (612)
554-3311
Admin Virginia Grussing.
Licensure Boarding Care. *Beds* 10.
Ownership Proprietary.

VIRGINIA

Arrowhead Nursing Home
1201 8th St S, Virginia, MN, 55792 (218)
741-4590
Admin Philip Schumacher. *Medical Dir/Dir of
Nursing* Dr Mathew Weir.
Licensure Skilled Care; Intermediate Care.
Beds SNF 84; ICF 26. *Certified* Medicaid.
Ownership Proprietary.
Admissions Requirements Physician's request.
Facilities Dining room; Physical therapy room;
Activities room; Crafts room; Laundry room;
Barber/Beauty shop.
Activities Arts and Crafts; Cards; Games;
Reading groups; Prayer groups; Movies; Shopping trips; Dances/Social or cultural gatherings.

Gethsemane Group Home
507 9th Ave S, Virginia, MN, 55792 (218)
741-9437
Admin Sandra Johnson. *Medical Dir/Dir of
Nursing* Valborg Pepelnjak RN.
Licensure Intermediate Care for Mentally
Retarded. *Beds* ICF/MR 12. *Certified* Medicaid.
Ownership Nonprofit.
Admissions Requirements Minimum age 18;
Medical examination.
Staff RNs 1 (pt); Residential counselors 3 (ft),
5 (pt); Others 1 (ft), 1 (pt).
Affiliation Lutheran
Facilities Dining room; Activities room; Crafts
room; Laundry room.
Activities Arts and Crafts; Cards; Games;
Movies; Shopping trips; Dances/Social or cultural gatherings.

Virginia Medical Center and Nursing Home*
901 9th St N, Virginia, MN, 55792 (218)
741-3340
Admin John A Tucker.
Licensure Skilled Care; Intermediate Care.
Beds SNF 34; ICF 88. *Certified* Medicaid;
Medicare.
Ownership Public.

WABASHA

Saint Elizabeth Hospital Nursing Home*
1200 5th Grand Blvd W, Wabasha, MN, 55981
(612) 565-4531
Admin Angelo Vivno.
Licensure Skilled Care. *Beds* 52. *Certified* Medicaid.
Ownership Public.
Affiliation Roman Catholic

717 Rustic Lane
717 Rustic Ln, Wabasha, MN, 55981 (612)
565-4884
Admin Michael Weinandt.
Licensure Supervised Living Facility. *Beds* 8.
Certified Medicaid.
Ownership Nonprofit.
Admissions Requirements Minimum age 18;
Medical examination.
Staff LPNs 1 (ft).
Facilities Dining room; Activities room; Crafts
room; Laundry room.
Activities Arts and Crafts; Cards; Games;
Shopping trips; Dances/Social or cultural gatherings.

Wabasha Nursing Home
626 Shields Ave, Wabasha, MN, 55981 (612)
565-4581
Admin Gary Larson. *Medical Dir/Dir of
Nursing* Max Bachhuber.
Licensure Skilled Care. *Beds* 125. *Certified* Medicaid.
Ownership Public.
Admissions Requirements Medical examination.
Staff RNs 6 (ft), 5 (pt); LPNs 6 (ft), 4 (pt);
Orderlies 3 (ft); Nurses aides 28 (ft), 16 (pt);
Activities coordinators 1 (pt).

WABASSO

Wabasso Health Care Center
Maple & May Sts, Wabasso, MN, 56293 (507)
342-5166
Admin Patrick McNeil. *Medical Dir/Dir of
Nursing* David Dekert.
Licensure Skilled Care; Intermediate Care.
Beds SNF 28; ICF 22. *Certified* Medicaid.
Ownership Proprietary.
Facilities Dining room; Physical therapy room;
Activities room; Laundry room; Barber/Beauty
shop.
Activities Arts and Crafts; Cards; Games;
Reading groups; Movies; Dances/Social or cultural gatherings.

WACONIA

Nightingale Nursing Home
232 S Elm St, Waconia, MN, 55387 (612)
442-2546
Admin Muriel Maass. *Medical Dir/Dir of
Nursing* Dr Russel Heagle.
Licensure Intermediate Care; Boarding Care
Home. *Beds* ICF 37; Boarding Care 6. *Certified* Medicaid.
Ownership Nonprofit.
Admissions Requirements Minimum age 21;
Medical examination; Physician's request.
Staff RNs 1 (ft), 5 (pt); LPNs 1 (pt); Nurses
aides 10 (ft), 15 (pt); Activities coordinators 1
(ft); Dietitians 1 (pt).
Facilities Dining room; Activities room; Laundry room.
Activities Arts and Crafts; Cards; Games; Prayer groups; Movies; Shopping trips.
Description Because we are small, we feel we
can keep close contact with each resident creating a home away from home atmosphere.

Waconia Healthcare Center*
333 W 5th St, Waconia, MN, 55387 (612)
442-5111
Admin Jim DuChene.
Licensure Skilled Care; Intermediate Care.
Beds SNF 70; ICF 30. *Certified* Medicaid;
Medicare.
Ownership Proprietary.

WADENA

Pembina Trail*
Rt 1, Box 127, Wadena, MN, 56482 (218)
631-1853
Admin Karen Crandall.
Licensure Intermediate Care for Mentally
Retarded. *Beds* 8. *Certified* Medicaid.
Ownership Nonprofit.

Shady Lane Nursing Home*
Rt 2, Hwy 110 E, Wadena, MN, 56482 (218)
631-1391
Admin Michael M Givson.
Licensure Intermediate Care. *Beds* 115. *Certified* Medicaid.
Ownership Public.

Tri-County Hospital*
418 Jefferson St N, Wadena, MN, 56482 (218)
631-3510

Admin James G Lawson.
Licensure Intermediate Care. *Beds* 56.
Ownership Nonprofit.

WAITE PARK

REM-Waite Park*
46 9th Ave N, Waite Park, MN, 56387 (612)
251-6142
Admin Craig Miller.
Licensure Intermediate Care for Mentally
Retarded. *Beds* 9. *Certified* Medicaid.
Ownership Proprietary.

Saint Francis Home*
25 2nd St N, Waite Park, MN, $6 56387 (612)
251-7630
Admin Rev Richard Leisen.
Licensure Skilled Care; Intermediate Care for
Mentally Retarded. *Beds* SNF 6; ICF 6. *Certified* Medicaid; Medicare.
Ownership Public.
Affiliation Roman Catholic

Waite Park Nursing Home Inc*
142 NW 1st St, Waite Park, MN, 56387 (612)
252-9595
Admin Myron Nyquist.
Licensure Skilled Care. *Beds* 74. *Certified* Medicaid.
Ownership Proprietary.

WALKER

Johnsons Long Lake Home*
PO Box 687, Walker, MN, 56484 (218)
547-1352
Admin George A Johnson.
Licensure Intermediate Care for Mentally
Retarded. *Beds* 6. *Certified* Medicaid.
Ownership Proprietary.

Woodrest Nursing Home*
Box J, Walker, MN, 56484 (218) 547-1855
Admin Shirley Ziegler.
Licensure Skilled Care; Intermediate Care.
Beds SNF 50; ICF 16. *Certified* Medicaid.
Ownership Proprietary.

WANAMINGO

Riverview Manor*
Riverview Rd, Wanamingo, MN, 55983 (507)
824-2910
Admin Betty Malchow.
Licensure Intermediate Care for Mentally
Retarded. *Beds* 15. *Certified* Medicaid.
Ownership Nonprofit.

WARREN

Good Samaritan Home*
410 S McKinley St, Warren, MN, 56762 (218)
745-5282
Admin Leona M Neegard.
Licensure Intermediate Care. *Beds* 102. *Certified* Medicaid.
Ownership Nonprofit.

WARROAD

Warroad Care Center
Lake St, Warroad, MN, 56763 (218) 386-1234
Admin Scott Batulis. *Medical Dir/Dir of
Nursing* Dr Michael Clark.
Licensure Skilled Care; Intermediate Care.
Beds SNF 30; ICF 19. *Certified* Medicaid.
Ownership Public.
Staff Physicians 2 (ft); RNs 4 (ft); LPNs 5 (ft);
Nurses aides 25 (ft); Recreational therapists 2
(ft); Activities coordinators 1 (ft); Dietitians 1
(ft); Dentists 1 (ft); Audiologists 1 (pt).
Facilities Dining room; Activities room; Chapel; Laundry room; Barber/Beauty shop;
Library.
Activities Arts and Crafts; Cards; Games;
Reading groups; Prayer groups; Movies; Shopping trips; Dances/Social or cultural gatherings.

WASECA

Lakeshore Inn Nursing Home*
108 8th St NW, Waseca, MN, 56093 (507)
835-2800
Admin R P Madel Jr.
Licensure Skilled Care. *Beds* 94. *Certified* Medicaid.
Ownership Proprietary.

Larry James Home
404 2nd St NE, Waseca, MN, 56093 (507)
835-3580
Admin E L Miller. *Medical Dir/Dir of
Nursing* Maryl Scott RN.
Licensure Supervised Living Facility. *Beds* ICF/MR 8. *Certified* Medicaid.
Ownership Proprietary.
Admissions Requirements Minimum age 18;
Medical examination.
Staff RNs 2 (pt); LPNs 1 (pt).
Facilities Dining room; Activities room; Laundry room.
Activities Arts and Crafts; Games; Movies;
Shopping trips; Dances/Social or cultural gatherings.

WATERTOWN

Elim Home
PO Box 638, Watertown, MN, 55388 (612)
955-2691
Admin Gordon Toews. *Medical Dir/Dir of
Nursing* Dr D R Philip.
Licensure Skilled Care; Intermediate Care.
Beds 55. *Certified* Medicaid.
Ownership Nonprofit.
Admissions Requirements Minimum age 16.
Staff Physicians 2 (pt); RNs 1 (ft), 3 (pt); LPNs
3 (ft), 3 (pt); Nurses aides 10 (ft), 25 (pt);
Physical therapists 1 (pt); Activities coordinators 1 (ft); Dietitians 1 (pt); Dentists 1 (pt);
Ophthalmologists 1 (pt); Podiatrists 1 (pt).
Facilities Dining room; Activities room; Laundry room; Barber/Beauty shop.
Activities Arts and Crafts; Cards; Games;
Reading groups; Prayer groups; Movies; Shopping trips.

WATERVILLE

Hope Residences Inc
Paquin and Herbert, Waterville, MN, 56096
(507) 362-8243
Admin Doug Scharfe.
Licensure Supervised Living Facility. *Beds* 14.
Ownership Nonprofit.
Admissions Requirements Minimum age 18.

Waterville Care Center
205 1st St N, Waterville, MN, 56096 (507)
362-4245
Admin Timothy Gauger.
Licensure Skilled Care; Intermediate Care.
Beds SNF 52; ICF 4. *Certified* Medicaid.
Ownership Proprietary.
Admissions Requirements Minimum age 16.
Staff RNs 1 (ft), 7 (pt); LPNs 8 (pt); Nurses
aides 5 (ft), 35 (pt); Physical therapists 1 (pt);
Recreational therapists 2 (pt); Speech therapists
1 (pt); Activities coordinators 2 (pt); Dietitians
1 (ft), 2 (pt).
Facilities Dining room; Physical therapy room;
Activities room; Chapel; Crafts room; Laundry
room; Barber/Beauty shop.
Activities Arts and Crafts; Cards; Games;
Reading groups; Prayer groups; Movies; Shopping trips; Dances/Social or cultural gatherings.
Description Facility is located across from lake
and features pet therapy with live guinea pigs.

WATKINS

Hilltop Nursing Home
PO Box 495, Watkins, MN, 55389 (612)
764-2300
Admin Robert Kleinschmidt. *Medical Dir/Dir
of Nursing* Dr G M Olson.
Licensure Skilled Care; Intermediate Care.
Beds SNF 45; ICF 20. *Certified* Medicaid;
Medi-Cal.
Ownership Public.
Admissions Requirements Medical examination; Physician's request.
Staff RNs 1 (ft), 3 (pt); LPNs 4 (ft), 4 (pt);
Nurses aides 16 (ft), 15 (pt); Physical therapists
1 (pt); Occupational therapists 1 (pt); Activities
coordinators 1 (ft); Dietitians 1 (pt).
Facilities Dining room; Physical therapy room;
Activities room; Crafts room; Laundry room;
Barber/Beauty shop.
Activities Arts and Crafts; Cards; Games;
Reading groups; Prayer groups; Movies; Shopping trips; Dances/Social or cultural gatherings.
Description Currently provides a home delivered meal program to homebound elderly in the
area. VA approved.

WAYZATA

Hammer Residence
1909 E Wayzata Blvd, Wayzata, MN, 55391
(612) 473-1261
Admin Merlyn Larson.
Licensure Supervised Living Facility. *Beds* 68.
Certified Medicaid.
Ownership Nonprofit.

Hillcrest Health Care Center*
15409 Wayzata Blvd, Wayzata, MN, 55391
(612) 473-5466
Admin Ronald D Lauer.
Licensure Skilled Care. *Beds* 155. *Certified* Medicaid; Medicare.
Ownership Proprietary.

Shadyway Group Home
522 Shadyway Rd, Wayzata, MN, 55391 (612)
475-1825
Admin George Johnson.
Licensure Supervised Living Facility. *Beds* ICF/MR 6. *Certified* Medicaid.
Ownership Nonprofit.

Way Twelve Halfway House
645 E Wayzata Blvd, Wayzata, MN, 55391
(612) 473-7371
Licensure Boarding Care. *Beds* 20.
Ownership Nonprofit.
Admissions Requirements Minimum age 16;
Medical examination.
Facilities Laundry room.
Activities Arts and Crafts; Games; Movies;
Shopping trips; Dances/Social or cultural gatherings.
Description Facility offers apartment-style living.

WELLS

Behr Parkview Nursing Home
55 10th St SE, Wells, MN, 56079 (507)
553-3115
Admin R Jesperson. *Medical Dir/Dir of Nursing* Dr Monte Skauffle.
Licensure Skilled Care. *Beds* 61. *Certified* Medicaid.
Ownership Proprietary.
Admissions Requirements Medical examination; Physician's request.
Facilities Dining room; Physical therapy room;
Activities room; Chapel; Crafts room; Laundry room; Barber/Beauty shop.
Activities Arts and Crafts; Cards; Games;
Reading groups; Prayer groups; Movies; Shopping trips; Dances/Social or cultural gatherings.

WEST SAINT PAUL

Dakotas Childrens Home
400 W Marie Ave, West Saint Paul, MN, 55118
(612) 455-1286
Admin Kathleen Pine.
Licensure Supervised Living Facility. *Beds* 48.
Certified Medicaid.
Ownership Nonprofit.
Admissions Requirements Minimum age 3;
Medical examination; Physician's request.
Staff RNs 2 (ft), 1 (pt); LPNs 1 (ft), 1 (pt); Recreational therapists 1 (ft); Occupational therapists 1 (ft); Activities coordinators 2 (ft);
Dietitians 1 (ft).
Facilities Dining room; Activities room; Crafts room; Laundry room.
Activities Arts and Crafts; Games; Reading groups; Movies; Shopping trips; Dances/Social or cultural gatherings; Developmental programming.
Description Facility includes 4 living units of

12 people each, self-contained with living room, dining room, kitchen, bedrooms, and bath. Four beds available for respite/temporary care. Day programs are provided by public school system at the local public schools.

Horizon Apartments*
1094 Waterloo St, West Saint Paul, MN, 55118
(612) 452-4264
Admin James R Driscoll.
Licensure Intermediate Care for Mentally Retarded. *Beds* 15. *Certified* Medicaid.

OCI-Thompson Avenue Group Home*
219 E Thompson Ave, West Saint Paul, MN,
55118 (612) 455-1286
Admin Kathleen Pine.
Licensure Intermediate Care for Mentally Retarded. *Beds* 9. *Certified* Medicaid.
Ownership Nonprofit.

Southview Acres Health Care Center*
2000 Oakdale Ave, West Saint Paul, MN,
55118 (612) 451-1821
Admin Harry J Lemieux.
Licensure Skilled Care; Intermediate Care.
Beds SNF 218; ICF 44. *Certified* Medicaid;
Medicare.
Ownership Proprietary.

WESTBROOK

Westbrook Good Samaritan Center*
Box 218, 149 1st Ave, Westbrook, MN, 56183
(507) 274-6155
Admin Gary Hofer.
Licensure Intermediate Care. *Beds* 49. *Certified* Medicaid.
Ownership Nonprofit.

WHEATON

Traverse County Nursing Home
303 7th St S, Wheaton, MN, 56296 (612)
563-8124
Admin Gael A Coleman. *Medical Dir/Dir of Nursing* James Poole MD.
Licensure Intermediate Care; Boarding Care.
Beds ICF 62; Boarding Care 2. *Certified* Medicaid.
Ownership Public.
Admissions Requirements Medical examination.
Staff RNs 1 (ft), 1 (pt); LPNs 1 (ft), 5 (pt);
Orderlies 1 (ft), 1 (pt); Nurses aides 11 (ft), 21
(pt); Recreational therapists 1 (ft); Activities coordinators 2 (ft), 1 (pt); Dietitians 1 (pt).
Facilities Dining room; Activities room; Chapel; Crafts room; Laundry room; Barber/Beauty shop; Library.
Activities Arts and Crafts; Cards; Games;
Reading groups; Prayer groups; Movies; Shopping trips.
Description Founded in 1959, the Traverse County Nursing Home serves the Wheaton and surrounding area. This 64-bed intermediate and board and care facility is one of the first county-owned homes in the state of Minnesota.

WHITE BEAR LAKE

Northeast Residence 1*
4680 Bald Eagle Ave, White Bear Lake, MN,
55110 (612) 426-1210
Admin Jane Wells.
Licensure Intermediate Care for Mentally Retarded. *Beds* 9. *Certified* Medicaid.
Ownership Nonprofit.

Northeast Residence 2
1995 Oak Knoll, White Bear Lake, MN, 55110
(612) 426-4306
Admin Jane Wells.
Licensure Intermediate Care for Mentally Retarded. *Beds* 6. *Certified* Medicaid.
Ownership Nonprofit.

White Bear Lake Care Center
1891 Florence St, White Bear Lake, MN, 55110
(612) 426-1361
Admin Sergei Shvetzoff. *Medical Dir/Dir of Nursing* T P Henderson MD.
Licensure Skilled Care; Intermediate Care.
Beds SNF 170; ICF 31. *Certified* Medicaid.
Ownership Proprietary.
Admissions Requirements Minimum age 21;
Medical examination; Physician's request.
Staff RNs 6 (ft), 9 (pt); LPNs 18 (ft), 12 (pt);
Orderlies 3 (ft), 4 (pt); Nurses aides 30 (ft), 50
(pt); Physical therapists 1 (ft); Recreational therapists 1 (ft); Dietitians 1 (pt); Physical therapy assistants 1 (ft); Recreational therapy aides 3
(ft), 1 (pt).
Facilities Dining room; Physical therapy room;
Activities room; Crafts room; Laundry room;
Barber/Beauty shop; Meditation room.
Activities Arts and Crafts; Cards; Games;
Reading groups; Prayer groups; Movies; Shopping trips; Dances/Social or cultural gatherings;
Special activities for confused residents; Resident job program.

WILLMAR

Alexander Home*
901 Memorial Pkwy, Willmar, MN, 56201
(612) 235-8315
Admin Beverly Helgeson.
Licensure Intermediate Care for Mentally Retarded. *Beds* 15. *Certified* Medicaid.
Ownership Nonprofit.

Bethesda Heritage Center*
1012 E 3rd St, Willmar, MN, 56201 (612)
235-3924
Admin Douglas Dewane.
Licensure Intermediate Care. *Beds* ICF 130.
Certified Medicaid.
Ownership Nonprofit.

Bethesda Nursing Home—Pleasantview*
901 Willmar Ave SE, Willmar, MN, 56201
(612) 235-9532
Admin Warren Becken.
Licensure Skilled Care. *Beds* 120. *Certified* Medicaid.
Ownership Nonprofit.

Christian Nursing and Living Center
1801 Willmar Ave, Willmar, MN, 56201 (612)
235-0050

Admin D Klanderman. *Medical Dir/Dir of Nursing* Robert P Hodapp MD.
Licensure Skilled Care. *Beds* 86. *Certified* Medicaid.
Ownership Nonprofit.
Admissions Requirements Medical examination; Physician's request.
Staff Physicians 1 (pt); RNs 1 (ft), 4 (pt); LPNs 3 (ft), 13 (pt); Orderlies 2 (pt); Nurses aides 10 (ft), 41 (pt); Physical therapists 1 (pt); Recreational therapists 1 (ft), 2 (pt); Occupational therapists 1 (pt); Speech therapists 1 (pt); Activities coordinators 1 (ft); Dietitians 1 (pt); Dentists 1 (pt); Podiatrists 1 (pt); Audiologists 1 (pt).
Affiliation Christian Reformed
Facilities Dining room; Physical therapy room; Activities room; Crafts room; Laundry room; Barber/Beauty shop; Library.
Activities Arts and Crafts; Cards; Games; Reading groups; Prayer groups; Movies; Shopping trips; Dances/Social or cultural gatherings.

Friendship House*
901 Memorial Pkwy, Willmar, MN, 56201 (612) 235-8444
Admin Beverly Helgeson.
Licensure Intermediate Care for Mentally Retarded. *Beds* 15. *Certified* Medicaid.
Ownership Nonprofit.

Heather Hill*
901 Memorial Pkwy, Willmar, MN, 56201 (612) 235-4373
Admin Beverly Helgeson.
Licensure Intermediate Care for Mentally Retarded. *Beds* 15. *Certified* Medicaid.
Ownership Nonprofit.

Kindlehope
1217 7th St SE, Willmar, MN, 56201 (612) 235-2838
Admin David Meillier. *Medical Dir/Dir of Nursing* Dr Michael T Anderson.
Licensure Supervised Living Facility. *Beds* 64. *Certified* Medicaid.
Ownership Proprietary.
Admissions Requirements Minimum age 16; Medical examination; Physician's request.
Staff RNs 1 (pt); LPNs 2 (ft), 2 (pt); Nurses aides 9 (ft), 21 (pt); Recreational therapists 1 (ft); Dietitians 4 (ft); Social workers 4 (ft), 1 (pt).
Facilities Dining room; Laundry room.
Activities Arts and Crafts; Cards; Games; Movies; Shopping trips; Dances/Social or cultural gatherings; Trips to zoo; Dinner theatre; Camping; Cross-country skiing.

Willmar Health Care Center
500 Russell St, Willmar, MN, 56201 (612) 235-3181
Admin Phyllis Saunders. *Medical Dir/Dir of Nursing* Dr Michael T Anderson.
Licensure Skilled Care; Intermediate Care; Boarding Care. *Beds* SNF 64; ICF 37; Boarding Care 37. *Certified* Medicaid.
Ownership Proprietary.
Staff RNs 2 (ft), 2 (pt); LPNs 5 (ft), 2 (pt); Nurses aides 23 (ft), 16 (pt); Recreational therapists 2 (ft); Activities coordinators 1 (ft).
Facilities Dining room; Physical therapy room; Activities room; Laundry room; Barber/Beauty shop.

Activities Arts and Crafts; Cards; Games; Reading groups; Prayer groups; Movies; Shopping trips; Dances/Social or cultural gatherings.

Willmar State Hospital
PO Box 1128, Willmar, MN, 56201 (612) 235-3322
Admin Lester Johnson. *Medical Dir/Dir of Nursing* Robert Rodhe MD.
Licensure Supervised Living Facility. *Beds* 170. *Certified* Medicaid.
Ownership Public.
Description State facility with several programs among which 50 beds are currently designated for mentally ill geriatric persons.

WINDOM

Home for Creative Living
108 9th St, Windom, MN, 56101 (507) 831-5033
Admin D Bill Olson.
Licensure Supervised Living Facility. *Beds* ICF/MR 45. *Certified* Medicaid.
Ownership Proprietary.
Admissions Requirements Minimum age Birth; Medical examination.
Staff RNs 1 (ft); LPNs 4 (ft); Physical therapists 1 (pt); Occupational therapists 1 (pt); Speech therapists 1 (pt); Dietitians 1 (pt); Corrective therapist 1 (ft).
Facilities Dining room; Physical therapy room; Activities room; Laundry room; Library.
Activities Arts and Crafts; Cards; Games; Reading groups; Movies; Shopping trips.

Sogge Memorial Home*
Fuller Dr, Windom, MN, 56101 (507) 831-1788
Admin Wayne O Brodland.
Licensure Intermediate Care. *Beds* 96. *Certified* Medicaid.
Ownership Nonprofit.

WINNEBAGO

Winnebago Baptist Home
211 6th St NW, Winnebago, MN, 56098 (507) 893-3171
Admin Kenneth E Presley.
Licensure Skilled Care; Intermediate Care; Boarding Care. *Beds* 47. *Certified* Medicaid.
Ownership Nonprofit.
Admissions Requirements Medical examination.
Affiliation Baptist
Facilities Dining room; Activities room; Chapel; Crafts room; Laundry room; Barber/Beauty shop.
Activities Arts and Crafts; Cards; Games; Reading groups; Prayer groups; Movies; Shopping trips; Dances/Social or cultural gatherings.
Description Facility is located on a 4-acre, tree-shaded campus bordering on woods with deer frequently visible on campus.

WINONA

Community Memorial Hospital*
855 Mankato Ave, Winona, MN, 55987 (507) 454-3650
Admin Roger L Metz.

Licensure Skilled Care. *Beds* 145. *Certified* Medicaid; Medicare.
Ownership Nonprofit.

Group Homes of Winona Inc*
377 Main St, Winona, MN, 55987 (507) 452-5909
Admin Sharon Kannenberg.
Licensure Intermediate Care for Mentally Retarded. *Beds* 12. *Certified* Medicaid.
Ownership Nonprofit.

Saint Annes Hospice Inc
1347 W Broadway, Winona, MN, 55987 (507) 454-3621
Admin Sr Dorothy Verkuilen. *Medical Dir/Dir of Nursing* Sidney O Hughes MD.
Licensure Skilled Care; Intermediate Care; Boarding Care. *Beds* SNF 81; ICF 33; Boarding Care 20. *Certified* Medicaid; Medicare.
Ownership Nonprofit.
Admissions Requirements Minimum age 60; Medical examination.
Staff RNs 2 (ft), 8 (pt); LPNs 4 (ft), 19 (pt); Nurses aides 21 (ft), 55 (pt); Physical therapists 1 (ft); Recreational therapists 1 (ft), 4 (pt); Activities coordinators 1 (ft); Dietitians 1 (ft).
Affiliation Roman Catholic
Facilities Dining room; Physical therapy room; Activities room; Chapel; Crafts room; Laundry room; Barber/Beauty shop; Library; Adult day care center.
Activities Arts and Crafts; Cards; Games; Reading groups; Prayer groups; Movies; Shopping trips; Dances/Social or cultural gatherings.

Sauer Memorial Home
1635 Service Dr, Winona, MN, 55987 (507) 454-5540
Admin William H English. *Medical Dir/Dir of Nursing* Dr H J Andersen.
Licensure Skilled Care. *Beds* 114. *Certified* Medicaid; Medicare.
Ownership Nonprofit.
Admissions Requirements Medical examination.
Staff RNs 2 (ft), 2 (pt); LPNs 5 (ft), 5 (pt); Nurses aides 15 (ft), 28 (pt).
Facilities Dining room; Physical therapy room; Activities room; Chapel; Crafts room; Barber/Beauty shop.
Activities Arts and Crafts; Cards; Games; Prayer groups; Movies; Dances/Social or cultural gatherings.

Starzecki Boarding Care Home*
123 E 8th St, Winona, MN, 55987 (507) 452-4798
Admin Margaret Albrecht.
Licensure Supervised Living Facility. *Beds* 11.
Ownership Proprietary.

252 West Wabasha*
252 W Wabasha, Winona, MN, 55987 (507) 454-5377
Admin Sharon Kannenberg.
Licensure Intermediate Care for Mentally Retarded. *Beds* 10. *Certified* Medicaid.
Ownership Nonprofit.

Watkins United Methodist Home*
175 E Wabasha, Winona, MN, 55987 (507)
454-4670
Admin Charles A Barclay.
Licensure Skilled Care; Intermediate Care.
Beds SNF 42; ICF 99. *Certified* Medicaid.
Ownership Nonprofit.

WINSTED

Saint Marys Hospital—Nursing Home
551 4th St N, Winsted, MN, 55395
Admin Jeanne Johnson. *Medical Dir/Dir of
Nursing* Dr Terry Sheldon.
Licensure Skilled Care; Intermediate Care.
Beds 95. *Certified* Medicaid.
Ownership Nonprofit.
Staff RNs 5 (ft), 2 (pt); LPNs 3 (ft), 5 (pt);
Nurses aides 14 (ft), 36 (pt); Physical therapists
1 (ft); Occupational therapists; Speech thera-
pists; Activities coordinators; Dietitians; Den-
tists.
Facilities Dining room; Physical therapy room;
Activities room; Chapel; Crafts room; Laundry
room; Barber/Beauty shop; Library.
Activities Arts and Crafts; Cards; Games;
Reading groups; Prayer groups; Movies; Shopping trips; Dances/Social or cultural gatherings.
Description Attached hospital makes medical
care readily available; clinics for physicians,
dentists, and eye care are a block away. Convenient elderly apartment housing on same
campus.

WINTHROP

Winthrop Care Center
506 High St, Winthrop, MN, 55396 (507)
647-5391
Admin Christine Bonderson. *Medical Dir/Dir
of Nursing* Dean Bergerson MD.
Licensure Skilled Care; Intermediate Care.
Beds 52. *Certified* Medicaid.
Ownership Proprietary.
Admissions Requirements Minimum age 18;
Medical examination; Physician's request.
Staff RNs 1 (ft), 3 (pt); LPNs 4 (pt); Nurses
aides 4 (ft), 26 (pt); Activities coordinators 1
(ft).
Facilities Dining room; Activities room; Laundry room; Barber/Beauty shop.
Activities Arts and Crafts; Cards; Games; Pray-
er groups; Movies; Shopping trips;
Dances/Social or cultural gatherings.
Description Winthrop Care Center offers a
wide range of services in a bright, cheerful,
home-like atmosphere, and has pledged to provide a living situation where each resident's dignity and independence is respected.

WONDOM

Windom CRF
945 Prospect, Wondom, MN, 56101 (507)
831-3803
Admin D Bill Olson.
Licensure Supervised Living Facility. *Beds* 12.
Certified Medicaid.
Ownership Proprietary.
Admissions Requirements Minimum age 18;
Medical examination.

Staff Resident advisors 4 (ft), 5 (pt); Relief staff
3 (pt).
Facilities Activities room; Laundry room.
Description Patients must be ambulatory;
facility has an ordinary house arrangement.

WOODBURY

Jane Dickman House*
1665 Woodbury Dr, Woodbury, MN, 55125
(612) 436-6623
Admin Marsha Neely.
Licensure Intermediate Care for Mentally
Retarded. *Beds* 35. *Certified* Medicaid.
Ownership Nonprofit.

Woodbury Health Care Center
7012 Carver Lake Rd, Woodbury, MN, 55119
(612) 735-6000
Admin Dallas C Reese. *Medical Dir/Dir of
Nursing* Dr Kuhlenkamp.
Licensure Skilled Care; Intermediate Care.
Beds SNF 72; ICF 70. *Certified* Medicaid;
Medicare.
Ownership Proprietary.
Staff Physicians 22 (pt); RNs 5 (ft), 17 (pt);
LPNs 6 (ft), 8 (pt); Orderlies 1 (ft); Nurses aides
25 (ft), 43 (pt); Physical therapists 1 (ft), 1 (pt);
Recreational therapists 2 (ft); Occupational
therapists 1 (ft); Speech therapists 1 (pt); Activi-
ties coordinators 1 (ft); Audiologists 1 (pt);
Music therapists 1 (ft).
Facilities Dining room; Physical therapy room;
Activities room; Chapel; Crafts room; Laundry
room; Barber/Beauty shop; Doctor's examina-
tion office.
Activities Arts and Crafts; Cards; Games;
Reading groups; Prayer groups; Movies; Shopping trips; Dances/Social or cultural gatherings.
Description Facility offers home health care,
hospice care, and respite care.

WOODSTOCK

New Life Treatment Center
PO Box 38, Woodstock, MN, 56186 (507)
777-4321
Admin Wes Van Essen. *Medical Dir/Dir of
Nursing* Donna Hanenburg RN.
Licensure Supervised Living Facility. *Beds* 18.
Staff Physicians 1 (pt); RNs 1 (ft); LPNs 1 (pt);
Nurses aides 1 (ft); Dentists 1 (pt).
Facilities Dining room; Chapel; Laundry
room.
Activities Movies.
Description Facility receives people of all ages,
races, and religious affiliations to 28-day
chemical dependency program and is willing to
help any elderly person who may be chemically
dependent to a "new life" of sobriety.

WORTHINGTON

Fauskee Nursing Home Inc*
965 McMillan St, Worthington, MN, 56187
(507) 376-5312
Admin Ferne E Lundy.
Licensure Skilled Care; Intermediate Care.
Beds SNF 62; ICF 2. *Certified* Medicaid.
Ownership Proprietary.

Lake Haven Nursing Home*
1307 S Shore Dr, Worthington, MN, 56187
(507) 376-3175
Admin Richard Atchison.
Licensure Intermediate Care for Mentally
Retarded. *Beds* 9. *Certified* Medicaid.
Ownership Proprietary.

McMillan Home*
1205 Burlington Ave, Worthington, MN, 56187
(507) 376-9555
Admin Donna Bruns.
Licensure Intermediate Care for Mentally
Retarded. *Beds* 9. *Certified* Medicaid.
Ownership Nonprofit.

Project Independence Ridgewood
Box 23, Worthington, MN, 56187 (507)
376-3057
Admin Irene Holmquist.
Licensure Supervised Living Facility. *Beds* 15.
Certified Medicaid.
Ownership Nonprofit.
Admissions Requirements Minimum age 16;
Medical examination; Physician's request.
Staff RNs 1 (ft); LPNs 2 (ft).
Facilities Dining room; Laundry room;
Library; Living rooms.
Activities Arts and Crafts; Cards; Games;
Movies; Shopping trips; Dances/Social or cul-
tural gatherings; Daytime program outside
facility.
Description Facility staff train and teach
independent living skills.

Southwest Manor
921 7th Ave, Worthington, MN, 56187 (507)
372-7278
Admin Donna Bruns.
Licensure Intermediate Care for Mentally
Retarded. *Beds* 8. *Certified* Medicaid.
Ownership Nonprofit.
Admissions Requirements Minimum age 18;
Medical examination; Physician's request.
Staff RNs 1 (pt); LPNs 1 (pt); Activities coordinators 1 (pt).
Facilities Dining room; Laundry room.
Activities Arts and Crafts; Cards; Games;
Movies; Shopping trips; Dances/Social or cultural gatherings.
Description Southwest Manor is a licensed
intermediate care facility capable of serving a
coed population of 8 residents whose primary
disability is mental retardation in the mild to
moderate range. The home is staffed with a
shift model of supervision and is covered every
hour while the residents are home. The principle of "normalization" is stressed within the
home-like atmosphere emphasized by staff and
program.

Unity House
1224 4th Ave, Worthington, MN, 56187 (507)
372-7671
Admin Sarah Bunker Shippy.
Licensure Supervised Living Facility. *Beds* 9.
Certified Medicaid.
Ownership Nonprofit.
Admissions Requirements Minimum age 12;
Medical examination.
Staff Physicians; Reality therapists 6 (ft);
Activities coordinators.
Facilities Dining room.

Worthington Regional Hospital*
1018 6th Ave, Worthington, MN, 56187 (507)
372-2941
Admin John C Albaugh.
Licensure Skilled Care. *Beds* 95.
Ownership Public.

ZUMBROTA

Zumbrota Nursing Home
433 Mill St, Zumbrota, MN, 55992 (507)
732-5139
Admin Jerry L Hoganson. *Medical Dir/Dir of
Nursing* William Walter MD.
Licensure Skilled Care; Boarding Care.
Beds SNF 65; Boarding Home 8. *Certified* Medicaid.
Ownership Proprietary.
Staff RNs 2 (ft), 3 (pt); LPNs 1 (ft), 5 (pt);
Nurses aides 11 (ft), 26 (pt); Physical therapists
1 (pt); Activities coordinators 1 (ft), 2 (pt); Dietitians 1 (ft).
Facilities Dining room; Activities room; Chapel; Barber/Beauty shop.
Activities Arts and Crafts; Cards; Games;
Reading groups; Prayer groups; Movies; Shopping trips; Dances/Social or cultural gatherings.

MISSISSIPPI

ABERDEEN

Hillcrest Manor Inc*
PO Box 211, Jackson and Chestnut Sts, Aberdeen, MS, 39730 (601) 369-6431
Admin Rita Faye Roberts.
Licensure Skilled Care; Intermediate Care.
Beds 120. *Certified* Medicaid.
Ownership Proprietary.

Monroe County Rest Home
Rt 2, Box 394, Aberdeen, MS, 39730 (601) 369-4485
Admin Barbara Mabry. *Medical Dir/Dir of Nursing* Dr L R Murphree.
Licensure Personal Care. *Beds* 12.
Ownership Public.
Admissions Requirements Medical examination.
Staff Nurses aides 1 (ft).

ACKERMAN

Choctaw County Nursing Home
W Cherry St, Ackerman, MS, 39735 (601) 285-3275
Admin Robert B Hughes. *Medical Dir/Dir of Nursing* Dr Edward Pennington.
Licensure Skilled Care; Intermediate Care.
Beds 32. *Certified* Medicaid.
Ownership Public.
Admissions Requirements Medical examination.
Staff Physicians 4 (ft); RNs 2 (ft); LPNs 4 (ft); Orderlies 1 (ft); Nurses aides 12 (ft); Activities coordinators 1 (ft); Dietitians 1 (ft).
Facilities Dining room; Activities room; Crafts room; Laundry room; Barber/Beauty shop.
Activities Arts and Crafts; Cards; Games; Reading groups; Prayer groups; Shopping trips; Dances/Social or cultural gatherings.

AMORY

Amory Manor Nursing Home*
1215 S Boulevard Dr, Amory, MS, 38821 (601) 256-9344
Admin Kelly Faulkner.
Licensure Intermediate Care. *Beds* 60. *Certified* Medicaid.
Ownership Proprietary.

BALDWYN

Oakview Nursing Home*
423 N 2nd St, Baldwyn, MS, 38824 (601) 365-5276
Admin Lana Maxey.
Licensure Skilled Care. *Beds* 36. *Certified* Medicaid.
Ownership Proprietary.

BATESVILLE

Batesville Manor Nursing Home*
Rt 1, Hospital Rd, Batesville, MS, 38606 (601) 563-5636
Admin James McCauley.
Licensure Intermediate Care. *Beds* 120. *Certified* Medicaid.
Ownership Proprietary.

BAY SAINT LOUIS

Hotel Reed Nursing Center*
400 N Beach Blvd, Bay Saint Louis, MS, 39520 (601) 467-5462
Admin Avonna Z Cain.
Licensure Skilled Care; Intermediate Care.
Beds 88. *Certified* Medicaid.
Ownership Proprietary.

BAY SPRINGS

Jasper County Nursing Home*
PO Box 527, 6th St, Bay Springs, MS, 39422 (601) 764-2101
Admin Noel Hart.
Licensure Skilled Care; Intermediate Care.
Beds SNF 35; ICF 20. *Certified* Medicaid.
Ownership Public.

BELZONI

Humphreys County Nursing Home*
500 CC Rd, Belzoni, MS, 39038 (601) 247-1821
Admin Mary T Gammons.
Licensure Skilled Care; Intermediate Care.
Beds 48. *Certified* Medicaid.
Ownership Proprietary.

BOONEVILLE

Aletha Lodge Nursing Home Inc
200 Long St, PO Box 326, Booneville, MS, 38829 (601) 728-6234
Admin Juanita Evetts. *Medical Dir/Dir of Nursing* Joseph Lewis Hurst MD.
Licensure Skilled Care. *Beds* 64. *Certified* Medicaid.
Ownership Proprietary.
Admissions Requirements Medical examination; Physician's request.
Staff Physicians 1 (ft); RNs 1 (ft), 2 (pt); LPNs 6 (ft), 4 (pt); Nurses aides 18 (ft), 3 (pt); Physical therapists 1 (ft); Speech therapists; Activities coordinators; Dietitians; Dentists.
Facilities Dining room; Activities room; Crafts room; Laundry room; Barber/Beauty shop; Library.
Activities Arts and Crafts; Cards; Games; Reading groups; Prayer groups; Movies; Dances/Social or cultural gatherings.

BRANDON

Crossgate Manor Inc*
PO Box 795, 335 Crossgate Blvd, Brandon, MS, 39042 (601) 825-3192
Admin Shirley Allen.
Licensure Skilled Care; Intermediate Care.
Beds 230. *Certified* Medicaid.
Ownership Proprietary.

BROOKHAVEN

Brook Manor Nursing Center*
Brookman Dr, Brookhaven, MS, 39601 (601) 833-2881
Admin Carolyn Wilson.
Licensure Skilled Care; Intermediate Care.
Beds 58. *Certified* Medicaid.
Ownership Proprietary.

Cartwheel Lodge Nursing Home*
525 Brookman Dr, Brookhaven, MS, 39601 (601) 833-2330
Admin Scholber Roberts.
Licensure Skilled Care; Intermediate Care.
Beds 120. *Certified* Medicaid.
Ownership Proprietary.

Haven Hall Nursing Center*
PO Box 848, 101 Mills St, Brookhaven, MS,
39601 (601) 833-5608
Admin Cindy Freeman.
Licensure Intermediate Care. *Beds* 60. *Certified* Medicaid.
Ownership Proprietary.

Lincoln Residential Center
524 Brookman Dr, Brookhaven, MS, 39601
(601) 835-1884
Admin Deborah Ratcliff. *Medical Dir/Dir of Nursing* Jim Barnett MD.
Licensure Intermediate Care for Mentally Retarded. *Beds* 120. *Certified* Medicaid.
Ownership Proprietary.
Admissions Requirements Minimum age 18; Medical examination.
Staff Physicians 1 (ft); RNs 1 (ft), 1 (pt); LPNs 4 (ft), 5 (pt); Nurses aides 54 (ft), 4 (pt); Physical therapists 1 (pt); Recreational therapists 1 (ft); Occupational therapists 1 (ft); Speech therapists 1 (ft), 1 (pt); Activities coordinators 1 (ft); Dietitians 1 (ft); Dentists 1 (pt); Ophthalmologists 1 (pt); Audiologists 1 (pt).
Facilities Dining room; Physical therapy room; Activities room; Crafts room; Laundry room; Barber/Beauty shop.
Activities Arts and Crafts; Cards; Games; Reading groups; Movies; Shopping trips; Dances/Social or cultural gatherings; Vocational programs.

Silver Cross Home*
303 N Jackson St, Brookhaven, MS, 39601
(601) 833-2361
Admin Gussie Ashley.
Licensure Skilled Care; Intermediate Care.
Beds 60. *Certified* Medicaid.
Ownership Nonprofit.

CALHOUN

Calhoun County Nursing Home
Burke Rd, PO Box 110, Calhoun, MS, 38916
(601) 628-6651
Admin M B Martin. *Medical Dir/Dir of Nursing* Guy Farmer MD.
Licensure Skilled Care; Intermediate Care.
Beds 120. *Certified* Medicaid.
Ownership Public.
Admissions Requirements Medical examination; Physician's request.
Staff RNs 3 (ft); LPNs 10 (ft), 3 (pt); Orderlies 4 (ft), 2 (pt); Nurses aides 32 (ft), 6 (pt); Activities coordinators 1 (ft).
Facilities Dining room; Physical therapy room; Activities room; Laundry room; Barber/Beauty shop.
Activities Arts and Crafts; Cards; Games; Dances/Social or cultural gatherings.
Description Each year the nursing home sponsors a heart fund drive with a Heart Fund Jamboree with TV personalities providing entertainment for residents and guests; a King and Queen of Hearts is chosen through donation to the heart fund; booths for selling arts and crafts; all money raised goes to the heart fund.

CANTON

Canton Nursing Center*
PO Box 269, 1145 Tisdale Ave, Canton, MS,
39046 (601) 859-6712 ,6713
Admin Richard Edwards.
Licensure Intermediate Care for Mentally Retarded. *Beds* 120. *Certified* Medicaid.
Ownership Proprietary.

Madison County Nursing Home*
PO Box 281, 411 S Liberty St, Canton, MS,
39046 (601) 948-6960
Admin Sidney L Whittington.
Licensure Skilled Care. *Beds* 60. *Certified* Medicaid.
Ownership Public.

CARTHAGE

Carthage Health Care Center Inc*
1101 E Franklin St, Carthage, MS, 39051 (601)
267-4551
Admin Robert D Faulkner.
Licensure Skilled Care; Intermediate Care.
Beds 90. *Certified* Medicaid.
Ownership Proprietary.

Leake County Skilled Nursing Facility*
300 Ellis St, Carthage, MS, 39051 (601)
267-4511
Admin Joe H Cooper.
Licensure Skilled Care. *Beds* 37. *Certified* Medicaid.
Ownership Public.

CENTREVILLE

Centreville Health Care Center*
PO Box 69, Lafayette St, Centreville, MS,
39631 (601) 645-5253
Admin Debbie Spence.
Licensure Skilled Care; Intermediate Care.
Beds 96. *Certified* Medicaid.
Ownership Proprietary.

CHARLESTON

Tallahatchie General Hospital—Extended Care Facility*
PO Box F, Charleston, MS, 38921 (601)
647-5535
Admin F W Ergle Jr.
Licensure Skilled Care. *Beds* 27. *Certified* Medicaid.
Ownership Public.

CLARKSDALE

Delta Manor Nursing Center
701 US Hwy 322 W, Clarksdale, MS, 38614
(601) 627-2212
Admin W Edward McLendon. *Medical Dir/Dir of Nursing* Dr P W Hill.
Licensure Intermediate Care for Mentally Retarded. *Beds* ICF/MR 120. *Certified* Medicaid.
Ownership Proprietary.
Admissions Requirements Minimum age 21; Medical examination.

Staff Physicians 1 (pt); RNs 1 (ft); LPNs 8 (ft); Orderlies 40 (ft); Nurses aides 60 (ft); Physical therapists 1 (pt); Recreational therapists 1 (pt); Occupational therapists 1 (pt); Speech therapists 1 (pt); Activities coordinators 1 (ft); Dietitians 1 (ft); Dentists 1 (pt); Ophthalmologists 1 (pt); Podiatrists 1 (pt); Audiologists 1 (pt).
Facilities Dining room; Physical therapy room; Activities room; Crafts room; Laundry room; Barber/Beauty shop.
Activities Arts and Crafts; Cards; Games; Reading groups; Movies; Shopping trips; Dances/Social or cultural gatherings.
Description Delta Manor (ICF/MR) provides developmental programing in a structured environment that enables residents to reach their maximum level of independence so they may be discharged to a less restrictive environment.

Greenbough Nursing Center*
340 DeSoto Ave Extension, Clarksdale, MS,
38614 (601) 627-3486
Admin Shirley J Adcock.
Licensure Skilled Care; Intermediate Care.
Beds 66. *Certified* Medicaid.
Ownership Proprietary.

CLEVELAND

Bolivar County Hospital—Long Term Care Facility
Hwy 8 E, Cleveland, MS, 38732 (601) 846-0061
Admin James L Townsend. *Medical Dir/Dir of Nursing* Dr S D Austin.
Licensure Skilled Care. *Beds* 33. *Certified* Medicaid.
Ownership Public.
Admissions Requirements Medical examination.
Staff RNs 1 (ft); LPNs 5 (ft), 2 (pt); Orderlies 1 (ft); Nurses aides 17 (ft), 3 (pt); Activities coordinators 1 (ft).
Facilities Dining room; Activities room; Barber/Beauty shop.
Activities Arts and Crafts; Games; Prayer groups; Movies; Shopping trips; Dances/Social or cultural gatherings.
Description Ours is a small facility and, although it is hospital based, we have achieved a homey atmosphere by decorating with wallpaper and attractive furniture. Residents are encouraged to decorate their rooms to reflect their individual taste. In addition to social activities, we emphasize reality orientation and success therapy activities for the confused residents.

Care Inn—Cleveland
200 N Pearman Rd, Cleveland, MS, 38732
(601) 843-5347
Admin Sharon W Sauerwein. *Medical Dir/Dir of Nursing* John T Milam MD.
Licensure Skilled Care; Intermediate Care.
Beds 75. *Certified* Medicaid.
Ownership Proprietary.
Staff RNs 2 (ft); LPNs 8 (ft), 4 (pt); Nurses aides 24 (ft), 6 (pt); Activities coordinators 1 (ft); Dietitians 1 (ft).
Facilities Dining room; Activities room; Laundry room; Barber/Beauty shop.
Activities Arts and Crafts; Cards; Games;

Movies; Dances/Social or cultural gatherings.
Description Facility features a large gazebo with ceiling fans, next to rose garden.

Cleveland Health Care Center Inc*
Hwy 8 E, Cleveland, MS, 38732 (601) 843-4014
Admin Jeanette McKinion.
Licensure Skilled Care; Intermediate Care.
Beds 120. *Certified* Medicaid.
Ownership Proprietary.

CLINTON

Care Inn—Clinton*
101 W Northside Dr, Clinton, MS, 39056 (601) 924-7043
Admin Linda Stephens.
Licensure Skilled Care; Intermediate Care.
Beds 135. *Certified* Medicaid.
Ownership Proprietary.

Clinton Country Manor
1251 Pinehaven Rd, Clinton, MS, 39056 (601) 924-0627
Admin Darwin Martin. *Medical Dir/Dir of Nursing* Dr Robert Estess.
Licensure Skilled Care; Intermediate Care.
Beds 120. *Certified* Medicaid.
Ownership Proprietary.
Admissions Requirements Medical examination.
Staff Physicians 1 (ft), 5 (pt); RNs 2 (ft), 3 (pt); LPNs 8 (ft), 2 (pt); Orderlies 1 (ft); Nurses aides 36 (ft), 12 (pt); Physical therapists 1 (pt); Activities coordinators 1 (ft); Dentists 1 (pt); Podiatrists 1 (pt).
Facilities Dining room; Activities room; Crafts room; Laundry room; Barber/Beauty shop.
Activities Arts and Crafts; Cards; Games; Prayer groups; Movies; Shopping trips; Dances/Social or cultural gatherings.
Description Manor is a modern, attractively decorated facility located at the outskirts of Clinton with landscaped grounds and tree shaded areas providing a pleasant atmosphere with opportunities for outdoor activities and relaxation.

COLLINS

Woodland Hills Nursing Home Inc*
PO Box 775, Old Hwy 49 S, Collins, MS, 39428 (601) 765-8262
Admin Judy Thurman.
Licensure Skilled Care; Intermediate Care.
Beds 60. *Certified* Medicaid.
Ownership Proprietary.

COLUMBIA

Cedars Convalescent Center*
511 S Main, Columbia, MS, 39429 (601) 736-4747
Admin Emmett H Mullins.
Licensure Intermediate Care for Mentally Retarded. *Beds* 26. *Certified* Medicaid.
Ownership Proprietary.

Floadrian Manor*
PO Box 70, N Main St, Columbia, MS, 39429 (601) 736-9557

Admin Harold Creecy.
Licensure Skilled Care; Intermediate Care.
Beds 119. *Certified* Medicaid.
Ownership Proprietary.

The Myrtles Health Care Facility*
1018 Alberta Ave, Columbia, MS, 39429 (601) 736-8040
Admin Jeanne H Jones.
Licensure Intermediate Care. *Beds* 66. *Certified* Medicaid.
Ownership Proprietary.

COLUMBUS

Aurora Australis Lodge*
310 N 20th St E, Columbus, MS, 39701 (601) 327-8021
Admin Betty Meadows.
Licensure Skilled Care; Intermediate Care.
Beds 120. *Certified* Medicaid.
Ownership Proprietary.

Magnolia Manor Nursing Home
2002 5th St N, Columbus, MS, 39701 (601) 328-1133
Admin Lowell D Scales.
Licensure Skilled Care; Intermediate Care.
Beds 60. *Certified* Medicaid.
Ownership Proprietary.
Staff RNs 2 (ft); LPNs 10 (ft), 1 (pt); Nurses aides 20 (ft); Activities coordinators 1 (ft); Dietitians 1 (ft).
Facilities Dining room; Physical therapy room; Activities room; Crafts room; Laundry room; Barber/Beauty shop.
Activities Arts and Crafts; Games; Shopping trips.

CORINTH

Alcorn County Care Inn*
PO Box 751, Alcorn Dr, Corinth, MS, 38834 (610) 287-8071
Admin Richard Atkins.
Licensure Skilled Care; Intermediate Care.
Beds 120. *Certified* Medicaid.
Ownership Proprietary.

Care Inn—Corinth*
PO Box 1417, Alcorn Dr, Corinth, MS, 38834 (610) 286-2286
Admin Mary F Mullens.
Licensure Skilled Care; Intermediate Care.
Beds 95. *Certified* Medicaid.
Ownership Proprietary.

Whitfield Nursing Home Inc*
2101 E Proper St, Corinth, MS, 38834 (601) 286-3331
Admin Erit L Burns.
Licensure Intermediate Care. *Beds* 44. *Certified* Medicaid.
Ownership Proprietary.

DEKALB

Kemper County Nursing Home
PO Box 577, DeKalb, MS, 39328 (601) 743-5888
Admin Patty C Nester. *Medical Dir/Dir of*

Nursing Dr Jim Smith.
Licensure Skilled Care; Intermediate Care.
Beds 60. *Certified* Medicaid.
Staff Physicians 3 (pt); RNs 3 (ft); LPNs 6 (ft); Nurses aides 19 (ft); Physical therapists 1 (pt); Activities coordinators 1 (pt); Dietitians 1 (pt); Dentists 1 (pt).
Facilities Dining room; Activities room; Laundry room; Barber/Beauty shop.
Activities Reading groups; Prayer groups; Movies; Dances/Social or cultural gatherings.

DUNCAN

Oak Grove Retirement Home
430 Oak Ave, Duncan, MS, 38740 (601) 395-2577
Admin Charles E Smith. *Medical Dir/Dir of Nursing* R T Hollingsworth MD.
Licensure Skilled Care. *Beds* 59. *Certified* Medicaid.
Ownership Proprietary.
Staff Physicians 1 (pt); RNs 1 (pt); LPNs 2 (ft), 1 (pt); Orderlies 1 (ft), 1 (pt); Nurses aides 9 (ft), 6 (pt); Activities coordinators 1 (ft); Dietitians 1 (pt); Dentists 1 (pt).
Facilities Dining room; Activities room; Laundry room; Barber/Beauty shop; Library.
Activities Arts and Crafts; Cards; Games; Reading groups; Prayer groups; Movies; Dances/Social or cultural gatherings.
Description Residents have their own band named "The Humdingers" which travels to other nursing homes by request.

ELLISVILLE

Ellisville State School-Clover Circle ICF/MR
Hwy 11 S, Ellisville, MS, 39437 (601) 477-9834
Admin Danny Lamier. *Medical Dir/Dir of Nursing* E Mangaoang MD.
Licensure Intermediate Care for Mentally Retarded. *Beds* 132. *Certified* Medicaid.
Ownership Public.
Admissions Requirements Medical examination; Physician's request.
Staff Physicians 1 (ft), 2 (pt); RNs 3 (ft); LPNs 11 (ft); Orderlies 3 (ft); Nurses aides 121 (ft); Physical therapists 1 (pt); Recreational therapists 3 (ft); Occupational therapists 1 (pt); Speech therapists 1 (ft), 1 (pt); Dietitians 1 (pt); Audiologists 1 (pt).
Facilities Dining room; Physical therapy room; Activities room; Chapel; Crafts room; Laundry room; Barber/Beauty shop.
Activities Arts and Crafts; Cards; Games; Reading groups; Prayer groups; Movies; Shopping trips; Dances/Social or cultural gatherings.
Description Clover Circle ICF/MR is a 132-bed facility which consists of 5 cottages, 4 of which have an all male population; the 5th cottage is coed and contains school-aged students under 21 with multihandicaps.

Ellisville State School-Hillside SNF/ICF
Hwy 11 S, Ellisville, MS, 39437 (601) 477-9384
Admin Willie Jefferson. *Medical Dir/Dir of Nursing* Dr Rolando Estrella Vilar.
Licensure Skilled Care; Intermediate Care.
Beds 88. *Certified* Medicaid.
Ownership Public.

Admissions Requirements Minimum age 55; Medical examination; Physician's request.
Staff Physicians 1 (pt); RNs 3 (ft); LPNs 11 (ft); Nurses aides 45 (ft); Physical therapists 1 (pt); Reality therapists 1 (pt); Occupational therapists 1 (pt); Speech therapists 1 (pt); Activities coordinators 1 (ft); Dietitians 1 (pt); Dentists 2 (pt); Audiologists 2 (pt).
Facilities Dining room; Physical therapy room; Activities room; Chapel; Crafts room; Laundry room; Barber/Beauty shop; Library.
Activities Arts and Crafts; Cards; Games; Reading groups; Movies; Shopping trips; Dances/Social or cultural gatherings.
Description Facility provides a special activity each month for an appropriate holiday or a special event such as cookouts, field trips, or hobby sessions. Facility has ceramics room where patients can make different crafts.

Ellisville State School-Lakeview SNF*
Hwy 11 S, Ellisville, MS, 39437 (601) 477-8541
Admin Eliza Shows.
Licensure Skilled Care. *Beds* 155. *Certified* Medicaid.
Ownership Public.

Ellisville State School-Peacan Grove
Hwy 11 S, Ellisville, MS, 39437 (601) 477-8541
Admin Virginia Rendon. *Medical Dir/Dir of Nursing* Evangelina Paulino MD.
Licensure Intermediate Care for Mentally Retarded. *Beds* 217. *Certified* Medicaid.
Ownership Public.
Staff Physicians 1 (pt); RNs 2 (ft); LPNs 13 (ft); Nurses aides 157 (ft); Physical therapists 1 (pt); Recreational therapists 2 (ft); Occupational therapists 1 (pt); Speech therapists 1 (ft), 1 (pt); Activities coordinators 1 (ft); Dietitians 1 (pt); Dentists 3 (pt).
Facilities Dining room; Physical therapy room; Chapel; Laundry room; Barber/Beauty shop; Library.
Activities Arts and Crafts; Cards; Games; Reading groups; Prayer groups; Movies; Shopping trips; Dances/Social or cultural gatherings.
Description Pecan Grove ICF/MR is a 217-bed facility consisting of 7 cottages; residents presently range from 6 to 55 years of age with various mental and physical handicaps. Numerous services are offered in order to train these individuals in areas the habilitation team has determined as necessary.

Jones County Rest Home*
Rt 2, Box 198, Ellisville, MS, 39437 (601) 477-3334
Admin Charles T Smith.
Licensure Skilled Care; Intermediate Care. *Beds* 114. *Certified* Medicaid.
Ownership Public.

EUPORA

Eupora Health Care Center Inc
200 Walnut St, Eupora, MS, 39744 (601) 258-8293
Admin Gerald C Gary. *Medical Dir/Dir of Nursing* Dr Charles A Ozborn.
Licensure Skilled Care; Intermediate Care. *Beds* 90. *Certified* Medicaid.
Ownership Proprietary.

Admissions Requirements Medical examination; Physician's request.
Staff Physicians 1 (pt); RNs 4 (ft), 1 (pt); LPNs 9 (ft), 7 (pt); Orderlies 1 (ft); Nurses aides 28 (ft), 16 (pt); Physical therapists 1 (pt); Recreational therapists 1 (ft); Speech therapists 1 (pt); Activities coordinators 1 (ft); Dietitians 1 (pt).
Facilities Dining room; Physical therapy room; Activities room; Laundry room; Barber/Beauty shop.
Activities Arts and Crafts; Cards; Games; Reading groups; Prayer groups; Movies; Shopping trips; Dances/Social or cultural gatherings.

FLORENCE

Briar Hill Rest Home Inc
Rt 1, Box 157, Florence, MS, 39073 (601) 939-6371
Admin Barbara M Bridges. *Medical Dir/Dir of Nursing* Dr Terry K Brantley.
Licensure Skilled Care; Intermediate Care. *Beds* 55. *Certified* Medicaid.
Ownership Proprietary.
Admissions Requirements Medical examination; Physician's request.
Staff Physicians 2 (pt); RNs 1 (ft), 2 (pt); LPNs 4 (ft), 3 (pt); Orderlies 1 (pt); Nurses aides 18 (ft); Physical therapists 1 (pt); Speech therapists 1 (pt); Activities coordinators 1 (ft); Dietitians 1 (ft), 1 (pt); Dentists 1 (pt).
Facilities Dining room; Laundry room; Barber/Beauty shop.
Activities Arts and Crafts; Cards; Games; Reading groups; Prayer groups; Movies; Shopping trips; Dances/Social or cultural gatherings.

FOREST

Lackey Convalescent Home*
266 1st Ave, Forest, MS, 39074 (601) 469-3951
Admin Paul W Strode Jr.
Licensure Skilled Care. *Beds* 30.
Ownership Public.

FULTON

Daniel Nursing Home
Rt 5, Box 219, Fulton, MS, 38843 (601) 862-2165
Admin James C Holland. *Medical Dir/Dir of Nursing* Grayden Tubb MD.
Licensure Skilled Care; Intermediate Care. *Beds* 120. *Certified* Medicaid.
Ownership Proprietary.
Admissions Requirements Medical examination; Physician's request.
Staff Physicians 1 (pt); RNs 2 (ft), 1 (pt); LPNs 12 (ft), 2 (pt); Orderlies 3 (ft); Nurses aides 38 (ft), 3 (pt); Physical therapists 1 (pt); Activities coordinators 1 (ft); Dietitians 1 (pt); Dentists 1 (pt).
Facilities Dining room; Activities room; Laundry room; Barber/Beauty shop.
Activities Cards; Games; Reading groups; Prayer groups; Movies; Dances/Social or cultural gatherings.

GREENVILLE

Arnold Avenue Nursing Home*
205 E Starling St, Greenville, MS, 38701 (601) 332-0318
Admin D D Felts.
Licensure Skilled Care; Intermediate Care. *Beds* 41. *Certified* Medicaid.
Ownership Proprietary.

Autumn Leaves Nursing Home Inc*
PO Box 4042, 570 N Solomon St, Greenville, MS, 38701 (601) 335-5863
Admin Ernest E McKinney.
Licensure Skilled Care; Intermediate Care. *Beds* 60. *Certified* Medicaid.
Ownership Proprietary.

Greenville Convalescent Home Inc*
1935 N Theobald Extended, Greenville, MS, 38701 (601) 334-4501
Admin Alvin L Freeman.
Licensure Skilled Care; Intermediate Care. *Beds* 120. *Certified* Medicaid.
Ownership Proprietary.

Mississippi Extended Care of Greenville Inc
1221 E Union St, Greenville, MS, 38701 (601) 335-5811
Admin Jimmy W Hayes. *Medical Dir/Dir of Nursing* Dr J Edward Hill.
Licensure Skilled Care; Intermediate Care. *Beds* 116. *Certified* Medicaid.
Ownership Proprietary.
Admissions Requirements Minimum age 18; Medical examination; Physician's request.
Staff Physicians 14 (pt); RNs 2 (ft), 2 (pt); LPNs 10 (ft), 1 (pt); Nurses aides 35 (ft), 10 (pt); Physical therapists 1 (pt); Reality therapists 1 (pt); Speech therapists 1 (pt); Activities coordinators 1 (ft); Dietitians 1 (ft); Dentists 1 (pt).
Facilities Dining room; Physical therapy room; Activities room; Crafts room; Laundry room; Barber/Beauty shop.
Activities Arts and Crafts; Cards; Games; Prayer groups; Movies.

GREENWOOD

Care Inn—Greenwood*
PO Box 1670, Hwy 82 By-Pass, Greenwood, MS, 38930 (601) 453-9173
Admin Mark Waldrop.
Licensure Skilled Care; Intermediate Care. *Beds* 110. *Certified* Medicaid.
Ownership Proprietary.

Golden Age Nursing Home
Hwy 82 E, PO Box 853, Greenwood, MS, 38930 (601) 453-6323
Admin Alvin Loewenberg.
Licensure Skilled Care; Intermediate Care. *Beds* 180. *Certified* Medicaid.
Ownership Nonprofit.

Pemberton Manor Inc
W Claiborne Ext, PO Box 1958, Greenwood, MS, 38930 (601) 453-8140
Admin Carrie L Chastain. *Medical Dir/Dir of Nursing* Dr J Edward Hill.
Licensure Skilled Care; Intermediate Care. *Beds* 120. *Certified* Medicaid.

Ownership Proprietary.
Staff RNs 2 (ft), 3 (pt); LPNs 8 (ft), 9 (pt); Orderlies 2 (ft), 3 (pt); Nurses aides 30 (ft), 11 (pt); Physical therapists 2 (pt); Speech therapists 1 (pt); Activities coordinators 1 (ft); Dietitians 1 (ft).
Facilities Dining room; Physical therapy room; Activities room; Chapel; Crafts room; Laundry room; Barber/Beauty shop.
Activities Arts and Crafts; Cards; Games; Prayer groups; Movies; Shopping trips; Dances/Social or cultural gatherings.

GRENADA

Care Inn—Grenada*
1966 Hill Dr, Grenada, MS, 38901 (601) 226-2442
Admin Joe Bannon.
Licensure Skilled Care; Intermediate Care. *Beds* 137. *Certified* Medicaid.
Ownership Proprietary.

Grandview Health Care Center*
1950 Grandview Dr, Grenada, MS, 38901 (601) 226-9554
Admin Larry Schrader.
Licensure Skilled Care; Intermediate Care. *Beds* 120. *Certified* Medicaid.
Ownership Proprietary.

GULFPORT

Driftwood Nursing Center
4520 15th St, Gulfport, MS, 39501 (601) 868-1314
Admin Jeanette Walker. *Medical Dir/Dir of Nursing* Dr C D Taylor.
Licensure Skilled Care. *Beds* 121. *Certified* Medicaid.
Ownership Proprietary.
Facilities Dining room; Activities room; Crafts room; Laundry room; Barber/Beauty shop; Library.
Activities Arts and Crafts; Cards; Games; Reading groups; Prayer groups; Movies; Shopping trips; Dances/Social or cultural gatherings.

Gulfport Convalescent Center*
1530 Broad St, Gulfport, MS, 39501 (601) 864-6544
Admin Terri Reynolds.
Licensure Skilled Care; Intermediate Care. *Beds* 120. *Certified* Medicaid.
Ownership Proprietary.

Tender Care Home*
01512 Pass Rd, Gulfport, MS, 39501 (601) 896-1302
Admin Aubrey F Dryden.
Licensure Personal Care. *Beds* 8.
Ownership Proprietary.

HATTIESBURG

Conva-Rest of Hattiesburg*
Medical Blvd, Hattiesburg, MS, 39401 (601) 264-3709
Admin Michael E McElroy.

Licensure Skilled Care. *Beds* 192. *Certified* Medicaid.
Ownership Proprietary.

For-Rest Convalescent Home*
907 E Hardy St, Hattiesburg, MS, 39401 (601) 584-7218
Admin Vera Mae Davis.
Licensure Personal Care. *Beds* 7.
Ownership Proprietary.

Green Forest Convalescent Home*
300 Cahal St, Hattiesburg, MS, 39401 (601) 544-5300
Admin Jack Gibson.
Licensure Intermediate Care. *Beds* 100. *Certified* Medicaid.
Ownership Proprietary.

Happy Acres Convalescent Home Inc*
298 Cahal St, Hattiesburg, MS, 39401 (601) 582-9157
Admin Thomas C Knight.
Licensure Skilled Care; Intermediate Care. *Beds* 120. *Certified* Medicaid.
Ownership Proprietary.

Hattiesburg Convalescent Center
514 Bay St, Hattiesburg, MS, 39401 (601) 544-4230
Admin Jewell McMahan. *Medical Dir/Dir of Nursing* Dr Fred Tatum.
Licensure Intermediate Care. *Beds* 164. *Certified* Medicaid; Medicare.
Ownership Proprietary.
Admissions Requirements Medical examination; Physician's request.
Staff Physicians 4 (pt); RNs 6 (pt); LPNs 18 (pt); Orderlies 6 (pt); Recreational therapists 2 (ft); Activities coordinators 1 (pt); Dietitians 1 (pt).
Facilities Dining room; Physical therapy room; Activities room.
Activities Arts and Crafts; Cards; Games; Reading groups; Prayer groups; Movies; Shopping trips; Dances/Social or cultural gatherings; Fishing; Ball games; Music recitals; Dinner outings.
Description Facility is small, new, swank, expensive—$40 to $65 per day. Ready to build "7 Million" project.

HAZLEHURST

Pine Crest Guest Home Inc
133 Pine St, Hazlehurst, MS, 39083 (601) 894-1411
Admin Peggy Gaddy. *Medical Dir/Dir of Nursing* Dr Thomas F McDonnell.
Licensure Skilled Care; Intermediate Care. *Beds* 120. *Certified* Medicaid.
Ownership Proprietary.
Admissions Requirements Medical examination.
Staff Physicians 1 (pt); RNs 2 (ft), 2 (pt); LPNs 10 (ft), 4 (pt); Orderlies 1 (ft), 1 (pt); Nurses aides 39 (ft), 2 (pt); Physical therapists 1 (pt); Activities coordinators 1 (ft); Dietitians 1 (ft).
Facilities Dining room; Activities room; Crafts room; Laundry room; Barber/Beauty shop.

Activities Arts and Crafts; Cards; Games; Reading groups; Prayer groups; Movies; Shopping trips; Dances/Social or cultural gatherings.

HOLLY SPRINGS

Care Inn—Holly Springs*
PO Box 640, 960 E Salem Ave, Holly Springs, MS, 38635 (601) 252-1141
Admin Jerry Beck.
Licensure Skilled Care; Intermediate Care. *Beds* 120. *Certified* Medicaid.
Ownership Proprietary.

HOUSTON

Floy Dyer Manor
Hwy 8 E, Houston, MS, 38851 (601) 456-3701
Admin Ruth Rhodes. *Medical Dir/Dir of Nursing* Dr Edward Gore.
Licensure Skilled Care; Intermediate Care. *Beds* 60. *Certified* Medicaid.
Ownership Proprietary.
Admissions Requirements Medical examination; Physician's request.
Staff RNs 2 (ft), 1 (pt); LPNs 4 (ft), 5 (pt); Orderlies 5 (ft), 1 (pt); Nurses aides 14 (ft), 2 (pt); Activities coordinators 1 (ft); Dietitians 1 (pt).
Facilities Dining room; Activities room; Barber/Beauty shop.
Activities Arts and Crafts; Cards; Games; Movies; Shopping trips; Dances/Social or cultural gatherings.

INDIANOLA

Care Inn—Indianola
401 Hwy 82 W, Indianola, MS, 38751 (601) 887-2682
Admin Eleta Jo Grimmett. *Medical Dir/Dir of Nursing* Dr Joe Hull.
Licensure Skilled Care; Intermediate Care. *Beds* 75. *Certified* Medicaid.
Ownership Proprietary.
Staff RNs 4 (ft); LPNs 10 (ft), 3 (pt); Nurses aides 23 (ft); Activities coordinators 1 (ft); Dietitians 1 (ft).
Facilities Dining room; Activities room; Laundry room; Barber/Beauty shop.
Activities Arts and Crafts; Cards; Games; Reading groups; Prayer groups; Movies; Shopping trips; Dances/Social or cultural gatherings.

IUKA

Pickwick Manor Nursing Home
230 Kaki St, Iuka, MS, 38852 (601) 423-9112
Admin Leonard C Goodin. *Medical Dir/Dir of Nursing* Dr Kelly Segars.
Licensure Skilled Care; Intermediate Care. *Beds* 120. *Certified* Medicaid.
Ownership Proprietary.
Admissions Requirements Medical examination; Physician's request.
Staff Physicians 6 (ft); RNs 2 (ft), 2 (pt); LPNs 13 (ft); Orderlies 1 (pt); Nurses aides 32 (ft), 10 (pt); Physical therapists 1 (pt); Speech therapists 1 (pt); Activities coordinators 1 (ft); Dietitians 1 (pt); Dentists 1 (pt); Ophthalmologists 1 (pt).

Facilities Dining room; Activities room; Chapel; Laundry room; Barber/Beauty shop.
Activities Arts and Crafts; Games; Prayer groups; Movies; Shopping trips; Dances/Social or cultural gatherings.
Description Pickwick Manor delivers the highest quality of health services possible, including community involvement, resocialization programs, preventative rehabilitative services; a health service training program provides a highly skilled and well trained health management and health care delivery staff.

Tishomingo County Rest Home
Rt 3, Box 914, Iuka, MS, 38852 (601) 423-6728
Admin Arwilla Wilson.
Licensure Personal Care. *Beds* 27.
Ownership Public.

JACKSON

Albemarle Health Care Center
3454 Albemarle Rd, Jackson, MS, 39213 (601) 362-5394
Admin Debbie Spence. *Medical Dir/Dir of Nursing* Dr Aaron Shirley and Dr James Anderson.
Licensure Skilled Care; Intermediate Care. *Beds* 119. *Certified* Medicaid; Medicare.
Ownership Proprietary.
Admissions Requirements Physician's request.
Staff RNs 6 (ft); LPNs 14 (ft); Orderlies 3 (ft); Nurses aides 43 (ft); Activities coordinators 1 (ft); Dietitians 1 (ft).
Facilities Dining room; Activities room; Crafts room; Laundry room; Barber/Beauty shop.
Activities Arts and Crafts; Cards; Games; Reading groups; Prayer groups; Movies; Shopping trips; Dances/Social or cultural gatherings.

Alpha and Omega Personal Care Home*
131 S Prentiss St, Jackson, MS, 39203 (601) 354-0783
Admin Myrtle McAllister.
Licensure Personal Care. *Beds* 13.
Ownership Proprietary.

Armstrong's Personal Care Home I*
129 Poindexter St, Jackson, MS, 39203 (601) 355-7029
Admin Minnie Armstrong.
Licensure Personal Care. *Beds* 11.
Ownership Proprietary.

Armstrong's Personal Care Home II*
227 Poindexter St, Jackson, MS, 39203 (601) 355-0364
Admin Minnie Armstrong.
Licensure Personal Care. *Beds* 10.
Ownership Proprietary.

Carter's Guest Home Inc*
941 Cooper Rd, Jackson, MS, 39212 (601) 372-6931
Admin Aline P Carter.
Licensure Skilled Care; Intermediate Care. *Beds* 53. *Certified* Medicaid.
Ownership Proprietary.

Coleman's Personal Care Home*
219 Poindexter St, Jackson, MS, 39203 (601) 355-3390

Admin Theola Coleman.
Licensure Personal Care. *Beds* 9.
Ownership Proprietary.

Community Nursing Home
1129 Langley Ave, Jackson, MS, 39204 (601) 355-0617
Admin Peggy Jones. *Medical Dir/Dir of Nursing* Dr J Daniel Mitchell.
Licensure Intermediate Care. *Beds* 43. *Certified* Medicaid.
Ownership Nonprofit.
Staff Physicians 1 (pt); RNs 1 (ft); LPNs 4 (ft), 3 (pt); Nurses aides 13 (ft), 2 (pt); Recreational therapists 1 (pt); Activities coordinators 1 (ft); Dietitians 1 (ft).
Facilities Dining room; Activities room; Crafts room; Laundry room.
Activities Arts and Crafts; Cards; Games; Prayer groups; Movies; Shopping trips; Dances/Social or cultural gatherings.
Description We are a nonprofit nursing home providing care for the indigent people of Hings County. We offer loving care and attention to our patients. We do not turn anyone away who needs our care, regardless of their ability to pay.

Compere's Nursing Home Inc*
865 North St, Jackson, MS, 39202 (601) 948-6531
Admin Robert F Burkett.
Licensure Skilled Care; Intermediate Care. *Beds* 60. *Certified* Medicaid.
Ownership Proprietary.

Cottage Grove Nursing Home*
3636 Lampton Ave, Jackson, MS, 39213 (601) 366-6461
Admin Juadine Cleveland.
Licensure Intermediate Care. *Beds* 28. *Certified* Medicaid.
Ownership Proprietary.

Crawford Nursing Home Inc
927 Cooper Rd, Jackson, MS, 39212 (601) 372-8662
Medical Dir/Dir of Nursing Robert Lowe MD.
Licensure Intermediate Care. *Beds* 71. *Certified* Medicaid.
Ownership Proprietary.
Admissions Requirements Minimum age 21; Medical examination; Physician's request.
Staff Physicians 2 (pt); RNs 1 (ft), 1 (pt); LPNs 5 (ft), 1 (pt); Orderlies 2 (ft); Nurses aides 30 (ft), 2 (pt); Physical therapists 1 (pt); Reality therapists 1 (pt); Recreational therapists 1 (ft); Occupational therapists 1 (pt); Speech therapists 1 (pt); Activities coordinators 1 (ft); Dietitians 1 (pt); Dentists 1 (pt); Ophthalmologists 1 (pt); Podiatrists 1 (pt); Audiologists 1 (pt).
Affiliation Baptist
Facilities Dining room; Physical therapy room; Activities room; Chapel; Crafts room; Laundry room; Barber/Beauty shop.
Activities Arts and Crafts; Cards; Games; Reading groups; Prayer groups; Movies; Shopping trips; Dances/Social or cultural gatherings; Trips.
Description Our activity program has recently established a new program called "Star Recognition". This program works on the basis of attendance of an activity equals the reward of one star, which is posted on the Star Recogni-

tion Board for everyone to see. If a resident receives 15 stars in one week, he/she will be rewarded by receiving a recognition badge and by being allowed to attend a special party or outside trip. This program gives the residents an incentive to come to activities and it also gives them an opportunity to be proud of themselves for achieving a goal.

Earle Street Personal Care Home*
438 Earle St, Jackson, MS, 39203 (601) 362-4032
Admin Izora Wells.
Licensure Personal Care. *Beds* 11.
Ownership Proprietary.

Henderson's Personal Care
3908 Skyline, Jackson, MS, 39213 (601) 366-1953
Admin Mary Alice Henderson.
Licensure Personal Care. *Beds* 6.
Ownership Proprietary.

Hunt Street Personal Care Home*
933 Hunt St, Jackson, MS, 39203 (601) 352-0046
Admin Mary A Henderson.
Licensure Personal Care. *Beds* 12.
Ownership Proprietary.

Inglewood Manor Nursing Home*
1900 Chadwick Dr, Jackson, MS, 39204 (601) 372-0231
Admin Sylvia Smith.
Licensure Skilled Care; Intermediate Care. *Beds* 103. *Certified* Medicaid.
Ownership Proprietary.

Lakeland Nursing Center
3680 Lakeland Ln, Jackson, MS, 39216 (601) 982-5505
Admin Cynthia Herdry.
Licensure Skilled Care; Intermediate Care. *Beds* 105. *Certified* Medicaid; Medicare.
Ownership Proprietary.

Magnolia Nursing Home*
942 North St, Jackson, MS, 39202 (601) 353-6447
Admin Mildred Spell.
Licensure Intermediate Care. *Beds* 33. *Certified* Medicaid.
Ownership Proprietary.

Manhattan Health Care Center Inc
4540 Manhattan Rd, Jackson, MS, 39206 (601) 982-7421
Admin Gwen Harper. *Medical Dir/Dir of Nursing* Hardy B Woodbridge MD.
Licensure Skilled Care; Intermediate Care. *Beds* 180. *Certified* Medicaid.
Ownership Proprietary.
Admissions Requirements Medical examination.
Staff RNs 5 (ft), 2 (pt); LPNs 22 (ft), 3 (pt); Orderlies 3 (ft); Nurses aides 60 (ft), 5 (pt); Activities coordinators 2 (ft); Dietitians 1 (ft).
Facilities Dining room; Activities room; Laundry room; Barber/Beauty shop.
Activities Arts and Crafts; Games; Reading groups; Prayer groups; Movies; Shopping trips; Dances/Social or cultural gatherings.
Description This is a Beverly Enterprises

Nursing Center giving 24-hour nursing care with social services, activities, therapy, and meals planned by a dietician.

Mississippi Children's Rehabilitation Center
777 Lakeland Dr, Jackson, MS, 39216 (601) 982-2911
Admin David Lightwine. *Medical Dir/Dir of Nursing* Marilyn Graves MD.
Licensure Intermediate Care. *Beds* 60. *Certified* Medicaid.
Ownership Public.
Admissions Requirements Minimum age Birth; Physician's request.
Staff RNs 4 (ft), 1 (pt); LPNs 4 (ft); Nurses aides 16 (ft); Physical therapists 5 (ft); Recreational therapists 2 (ft); Occupational therapists 2 (ft); Speech therapists 1 (ft); Dietitians 1 (pt).
Facilities Dining room; Physical therapy room; Activities room; Crafts room; Laundry room; Library; Outpatient physical therapy room; Education classrooms.
Activities Arts and Crafts; Games; Movies; Field trips.
Description Center provides evaluation and treatment for children and youth with physical and developmental disabilities.

Mississippi Nursing Home
1004 North St, Jackson, MS, 39202 (601) 355-0763
Admin Ellen Ryan.
Licensure Skilled Care; Intermediate Care. *Beds* 60. *Certified* Medicaid.
Ownership Proprietary.

Northside Haven Personal Care Home*
3125 W Northside Dr, Jackson, MS, 39213 (601) 362-1574
Admin J C Marshall.
Licensure Personal Care. *Beds* 12.

Old Ladies Home*
2902 W Capitol St, Jackson, MS, 39209 (601) 355-4581
Admin Grace H Auwater.
Licensure Skilled Care; Personal Care.
Beds SNF 19; Personal Care 21.
Ownership Nonprofit.

Richmond's Boarding Home*
852 Crawford St, Jackson, MS, 39213 (601) 353-7694
Admin R M Richmond Sr.
Licensure Personal Care. *Beds* 14.
Ownership Proprietary.

Spencer's Personal Care Home*
117 Clairborne St, Jackson, MS, 39209 (601) 355-4390
Admin Barbara Spencer.
Licensure Personal Care. *Beds* 9.

Teat Personal Care Home*
3227 Edwards Ave, Jackson, MS, 39213 (601) 982-2872
Admin Ms Eddie L Teat.
Licensure Personal Care. *Beds* 13.
Ownership Proprietary.

Wells Personal Care Home*
2403 Rutledge, Jackson, MS, 39213 (601) 362-4032

Admin Izora Wells.
Licensure Personal Care. *Beds* 5.
Ownership Proprietary.

Westhaven Home
Rt 2, Box 170, Jackson, MS, 29209 (601) 922-2363
Admin John Lea.
Licensure Personal Care. *Beds* 32.
Ownership Proprietary.

Whispering Pines Nursing Home
1480 Raymond Rd, Jackson, MS, 39204 (601) 373-2472
Admin A D Buffington.
Licensure Skilled Care; Intermediate Care. *Beds* 50. *Certified* Medicaid.
Ownership Proprietary.
Admissions Requirements Medical examination.
Staff Physicians 1 (pt); RNs 2 (ft); LPNs 5 (ft), 1 (pt); Nurses aides 17 (ft), 1 (pt); Physical therapists 1 (pt); Reality therapists 1 (pt); Recreational therapists 1 (ft); Speech therapists 1 (pt); Activities coordinators 1 (ft); Dietitians 1 (pt); Dentists 1 (pt); Ophthalmologists 1 (pt); Podiatrists 1 (pt); Audiologists 1 (pt).
Facilities Dining room; Activities room; Barber/Beauty shop.
Activities Arts and Crafts; Games; Reading groups; Prayer groups; Movies.

KOSCIUSKO

Attala County Nursing Center*
Hwy 12 W, Kosciusko, MS, 39090 (601) 289-1200
Admin Myren Hughes.
Licensure Skilled Care; Intermediate Care. *Beds* 119. *Certified* Medicaid.
Ownership Proprietary.

LAUREL

Davison Rest Home Inc*
616 E 19th St, Laurel, MS, 39440 (601) 426-3201
Admin George Harold Huff.
Licensure Skilled Care; Intermediate Care. *Beds* 40. *Certified* Medicaid.
Ownership Proprietary.

Heathside Haven Inc
935 West Dr, Laurel, MS, 39440 (601) 428-0571
Admin J D Mayfield.
Licensure Skilled Care. *Beds* 130. *Certified* Medicaid.
Ownership Proprietary.
Staff RNs 4 (ft); LPNs 14 (ft), 3 (pt); Nurses aides 50 (ft), 15 (pt); Activities coordinators 1 (ft).
Facilities Dining room; Physical therapy room; Activities room; Chapel; Crafts room; Barber/Beauty shop.
Activities Arts and Crafts; Games; Reading groups; Prayer groups; Movies; Shopping trips; Dances/Social or cultural gatherings.

Nucare Convalescent Center
1036 W Dr, Laurel, MS, 39440 (601) 425-3191
Admin Bobby Welborn. *Medical Dir/Dir of*

Nursing James Waites MD.
Licensure Skilled Care. *Beds* 60. *Certified* Medicaid.
Ownership Proprietary.
Admissions Requirements Medical examination; Physician's request.
Staff Physicians 4 (pt); RNs 2 (ft), 2 (pt); LPNs 7 (ft), 2 (pt); Orderlies 1 (ft); Nurses aides 44 (ft), 10 (pt); Physical therapists 1 (pt); Recreational therapists 1 (pt); Occupational therapists 1 (pt); Speech therapists 1 (pt); Activities coordinators 1 (ft); Dietitians 1 (pt); Dentists 1 (pt); Podiatrists 1 (pt); Audiologists 1 (pt).
Facilities Dining room; Activities room; Laundry room; Barber/Beauty shop.
Activities Arts and Crafts; Cards; Games; Prayer groups; Movies; Shopping trips.

LEAKESVILLE

Greene County Hospital—Extended Care Facility*
PO Box 137, Leakesville, MS, 39451 (601) 394-2371
Admin L Earl Debose.
Licensure Skilled Care; Intermediate Care. *Beds* 22. *Certified* Medicaid.
Ownership Public.

Melody Manor Convalescent Center
PO Box 640, Leakesville, MS, 39451 (601) 394-2331
Admin Myrna Green. *Medical Dir/Dir of Nursing* Dr Alvaro Moreno.
Licensure Skilled Care; Intermediate Care. *Beds* 60. *Certified* Medicaid.
Ownership Proprietary.
Admissions Requirements Medical examination; Physician's request.
Staff RNs 1 (ft), 1 (pt); LPNs 7 (ft), 1 (pt); Nurses aides 16 (ft), 3 (pt); Activities coordinators 1 (ft), 1 (pt); Dietitians 1 (pt).
Facilities Dining room; Activities room; Crafts room; Laundry room; Barber/Beauty shop.
Activities Arts and Crafts; Cards; Games; Reading groups; Prayer groups; Movies; Shopping trips.

LONG BEACH

South Mississippi Retardation Center
1170 W Railroad St, Long Beach, MS, 39560 (601) 868-2923
Admin Pamela C Baker.
Licensure Intermediate Care for Mentally Retarded. *Beds* 80. *Certified* Medicaid.
Ownership Public.

LOUISVILLE

Tri-County Nursing Home Inc
PO Box 542, Louisville, MS, 39339 (601) 773-8047 and 773-8048
Admin Erma Stuart. *Medical Dir/Dir of Nursing* Dr Dewitt G Crawford.
Licensure Skilled Care; Intermediate Care. *Beds* 60. *Certified* Medicaid.
Ownership Proprietary.
Admissions Requirements Medical examination; Physician's request.
Staff RNs 3 (ft); LPNs 4 (ft); Orderlies 3 (ft);

Nurses aides 18 (ft); Physical therapists 1 (pt); Speech therapists 1 (pt); Activities coordinators 1 (ft); Dietitians 1 (ft).
Facilities Dining room; Physical therapy room; Activities room; Crafts room; Laundry room; Barber/Beauty shop.
Activities Arts and Crafts; Games; Reading groups; Prayer groups; Movies; Shopping trips; Dances/Social or cultural gatherings.
Description Facility features a rock and roll jamboree for the Heart Fund; warm, inviting, home-like atmosphere; outstanding dietary, physical therapy, and speech pathology departments; and daily activities and entertainment.

Winston County Nursing Home*
PO Box 670, Louisville, MS, 39339 (601) 773-6211
Admin Paul Wood.
Licensure Skilled Care; Intermediate Care.
Beds 42. *Certified* Medicaid; Medicare.
Ownership Public.

LUCEDALE

Glen Oaks Nursing Home*
220 Glenoaks Dr, Lucedale, MS, 39452 (601) 947-2783
Admin John Stinson.
Licensure Skilled Care; Intermediate Care.
Beds 60. *Certified* Medicaid.
Ownership Proprietary.

LUMBERTON

Adventist Health Center
Rt 2, Box 79, Lumberton, MS, 39455 (601) 794-8566
Admin Kenneth A Becker. *Medical Dir/Dir of Nursing* Dr Daniel Stepp.
Licensure Skilled Care; Intermediate Care.
Beds 120. *Certified* Medicaid.
Ownership Nonprofit.
Admissions Requirements Medical examination.
Staff Physicians 4 (pt); RNs 7 (ft), 1 (pt); LPNs 11 (ft), 4 (pt); Orderlies 7 (ft), 2 (pt); Nurses aides 30 (ft), 24 (pt); Reality therapists 1 (ft), 1 (pt); Recreational therapists 2 (ft), 6 (pt); Activities coordinators 1 (ft); Dietitians 9 (ft), 4 (pt); Dentists 1 (pt).
Affiliation Seventh-Day Adventist
Facilities Dining room; Physical therapy room; Activities room; Crafts room; Laundry room; Barber/Beauty shop.
Activities Arts and Crafts; Games; Reading groups; Prayer groups; Movies; Shopping trips.
Description We have a rural setting, 3 miles from the nearest town. We also have a rhythm band in which our patients love to participate. They travel to other homes and perform.

MADISON

Willard F Bond Home*
Rt 1, Box 284, Madison, MS, 39110 (601) 856-8041
Admin Thomas Nichols.
Licensure Intermediate Care. *Beds* 60. *Certified* Medicaid.
Ownership Nonprofit.

MAGEE

Hillcrest Health Center Inc
1401 1st Ave NE, Magee, MS, 39111 (601) 849-5443
Admin Mary Wilson. *Medical Dir/Dir of Nursing* Charles Pruitt Jr MD.
Licensure Skilled Care; Intermediate Care.
Beds 120. *Certified* Medicaid.
Ownership Proprietary.
Staff Physicians 6 (pt); RNs 1 (ft), 1 (pt); Physical therapists 1 (pt); Activities coordinators 1 (ft); Dietitians 1 (pt); Podiatrists 1 (pt).
Facilities Dining room; Activities room; Chapel; Laundry room; Barber/Beauty shop.
Activities Arts and Crafts; Games; Reading groups; Prayer groups.

Millcreek
900 1st Ave NE, Magee, MS, 39111 (601) 849-4221
Admin Lester R Terrell. *Medical Dir/Dir of Nursing* Dr J O Stephens.
Licensure Intermediate Care for Mentally Retarded. *Beds* 125. *Certified* Medicaid.
Ownership Proprietary.
Admissions Requirements Minimum age 5; Medical examination.
Staff RNs 2 (ft); LPNs 4 (ft); Orderlies 65 (ft); Nurses aides 6 (ft); Physical therapists 1 (pt); Recreational therapists 1 (ft); Occupational therapists 1 (pt); Speech therapists 1 (ft); Dietitians 1 (ft); Ophthalmologists 1 (pt); Audiologists 1 (pt).
Facilities Dining room; Physical therapy room; Activities room; Crafts room; Laundry room; Barber/Beauty shop; Library.
Activities Arts and Crafts; Cards; Games; Prayer groups; Movies; Shopping trips; Dances/Social or cultural gatherings.

MARKS

Quitman County Nursing Home
Getwell Dr, PO Box 350, Marks, MS, 38646 (601) 326-8031
Admin Eva Ann Boschert. *Medical Dir/Dir of Nursing* Dr Richard.
Licensure Intermediate Care. *Beds* 60. *Certified* Medicaid.
Ownership Public.
Admissions Requirements Medical examination; Physician's request.
Staff Physicians 1 (pt); RNs 1 (pt); LPNs 5 (ft), 1 (pt); Orderlies 2 (ft); Nurses aides 10 (ft); Activities coordinators 2 (ft); Dietitians 1 (ft).
Facilities Dining room; Physical therapy room; Activities room; Chapel; Crafts room; Laundry room; Barber/Beauty shop; Library.
Activities Arts and Crafts; Cards; Games; Reading groups; Prayer groups; Movies; Shopping trips; Dances/Social or cultural gatherings.

MCCOMB

McComb Extended Care and Nursing Home*
501 S Locust St, McComb, MS, 39648 (601) 684-8111
Admin Elton Beebe.

Licensure Skilled Care; Intermediate Care.
Beds 136. *Certified* Medicaid.
Ownership Proprietary.

Southwest Extended Care Center*
415 Marion Ave, McComb, MS, 39648 (601) 684-8700
Admin Ronald J Smith.
Licensure Skilled Care; Intermediate Care.
Beds 120. *Certified* Medicaid.
Ownership Proprietary.

MEADVILLE

Meadville Nursing Home*
Rt 3, Box 233, Meadville, MS, 39653 (601) 384-5861
Admin Ellen Buckles.
Licensure Skilled Care; Intermediate Care.
Beds 60. *Certified* Medicaid.
Ownership Proprietary.

MENDENHALL

Mendenhall Nursing Home Inc*
PO Box 308, Mangum St, Mendenhall, MS, 39114 (601) 847-1311
Admin Carolyn Davis.
Licensure Skilled Care; Intermediate Care.
Beds 60. *Certified* Medicaid.
Ownership Proprietary.

MERIDIAN

Broadmoor Health Care Center Inc*
4728 Hwy 39 N, Meridian, MS, 39301 (601) 482-8151
Admin Barbara Nester.
Licensure Skilled Care; Intermediate Care.
Beds 120. *Certified* Medicaid.
Ownership Proprietary.

East Mississippi State Nursing Home
PO Box 4128, West Station, Meridian, MS, 39301 (601) 482-6186
Admin Brent Jackson. *Medical Dir/Dir of Nursing* James E Gracey.
Licensure Skilled Care. *Beds* 119. *Certified* Medicaid.
Ownership Public.
Staff Physicians 1 (ft); RNs 4 (ft); LPNs 13 (ft); Nurses aides 57 (ft); Physical therapists 1 (pt); Activities coordinators 1 (ft); Dietitians 1 (pt); Dentists 1 (pt).
Facilities Dining room; Physical therapy room; Activities room; Laundry room; Barber/Beauty shop; Library.
Activities Arts and Crafts; Cards; Games; Prayer groups; Movies; Shopping trips; Dances/Social or cultural gatherings.

Golden Sunset Guest Home
Rt 5, Box 178, Hwy 11 S, Meridian, MS, 39301 (601) 482-3684
Admin Guy J Howard. *Medical Dir/Dir of Nursing* Dr Fred R Hunt.
Licensure Intermediate Care. *Beds* 46. *Certified* Medicaid.
Ownership Proprietary.
Admissions Requirements Medical examination; Physician's request.

Staff Physicians 1 (pt); RNs 1 (pt); LPNs 2 (ft), 3 (pt); Orderlies 1 (ft); Nurses aides 16 (ft); Physical therapists 1 (pt); Reality therapists 1 (pt); Recreational therapists 1 (pt); Occupational therapists 1 (pt); Speech therapists 1 (pt); Activities coordinators 1 (ft); Dietitians 1 (ft); Dentists 1 (pt); Ophthalmologists 1 (pt); Podiatrists 1 (pt); Audiologists 1 (pt).
Facilities Dining room; Activities room; Chapel; Crafts room; Laundry room; Barber/Beauty shop.
Activities Arts and Crafts; Cards; Games; Reading groups; Prayer groups; Movies; Shopping trips; Dances/Social or cultural gatherings.

King's Daughters and Sons Rest Home Inc*
PO Box 3623, Hwy 39 N, Meridian, MS, 39301 (601) 483-5256
Admin Lange F Butler.
Licensure Intermediate Care. *Beds* 120.
Ownership Nonprofit.
Affiliation King's Daughters and Sons

Meridian Convalescent Home*
517 33rd St, Meridian, MS, 39301 (601) 483-3916
Admin Sue Ward.
Licensure Skilled Care; Intermediate Care.
Beds 58. *Certified* Medicaid.
Ownership Proprietary.

Meridian Nursing Center*
3716 Hwy 39 N, Meridian, MS, 39301 (601) 482-7164
Admin Sam R Sturges.
Licensure Skilled Care; Intermediate Care.
Beds 75. *Certified* Medicaid; Medicare.
Ownership Proprietary.

Queen City Nursing Center*
1201 28th Ave, Meridian, MS, 39301 (601) 483-1467
Admin Michael W Howard.
Licensure Skilled Care. *Beds* 60. *Certified* Medicaid.
Ownership Proprietary.

MONTICELLO

Lawrence County Medical Center Inc*
PO Box 398, 700 S Jefferson St, Monticello, MS, 39654 (601) 587-2593
Admin James Todd.
Licensure Skilled Care; Intermediate Care.
Beds 60. *Certified* Medicaid.
Ownership Proprietary.

MORTON

Scott County Nursing Home*
Old Hwy 80 E, Morton, MS, 39117 (601) 732-6361
Admin Gary Pace.
Licensure Skilled Care; Intermediate Care.
Beds 100. *Certified* Medicaid.
Ownership Proprietary.

NATCHEZ

Glenburney Nursing Home*
555 John R Junkin Dr, Natchez, MS, 39120 (601) 442-4395
Admin Sammy Gore.
Licensure Skilled Care; Intermediate Care.
Beds 96. *Certified* Medicaid.
Ownership Proprietary.

Oakwood Lodge of Natchez*
587 John R Junkin Dr, Natchez, MS, 39120 (601) 446-8426
Admin Barbara Evans.
Licensure Skilled Care; Intermediate Care.
Beds 120. *Certified* Medicaid.
Ownership Proprietary.

Trace Haven Nursing Home*
344 Arlington Ave, Natchez, MS, 39120 (601) 442-4393
Admin Kathryn Conn.
Licensure Skilled Care; Intermediate Care.
Beds 58. *Certified* Medicaid.

NEW ALBANY

Roselawn Retirement Home
118 S Glenfield Rd, New Albany, MS, 38652 (601) 534-9506
Admin Walter J Grace. *Medical Dir/Dir of Nursing* Dr Richard Russell.
Licensure Skilled Care; Intermediate Care.
Beds 120. *Certified* Medicaid.
Ownership Proprietary.
Admissions Requirements Minimum age 18; Medical examination; Physician's request.
Staff Physicians 5 (pt); RNs 5 (ft); LPNs 10 (ft); Nurses aides 40 (ft); Physical therapists 1 (pt); Activities coordinators 1 (ft); Dietitians 1 (pt); Dentists 1 (pt); Podiatrists 1 (pt).
Facilities Dining room; Activities room; Crafts room; Laundry room; Barber/Beauty shop.
Activities Arts and Crafts; Games; Reading groups; Prayer groups; Movies; Dances/Social or cultural gatherings.

NEWTON

Conva-Rest of Newton Inc
1009 S Main St, Newton, MS, 39345 (601) 683-6601
Admin Earl Bolton. *Medical Dir/Dir of Nursing* Dr Austin Boggan.
Licensure Skilled Care; Intermediate Care.
Beds 120. *Certified* Medicaid.
Ownership Proprietary.
Admissions Requirements Medical examination.
Staff Physicians 6 (pt); RNs 5 (ft); LPNs 10 (ft), 1 (pt); Orderlies 2 (ft); Nurses aides 35 (ft), 2 (pt); Activities coordinators 1 (ft); Dietitians 1 (pt); Dentists 1 (pt); Social workers 1 (ft).
Facilities Dining room; Activities room; Crafts room; Laundry room; Barber/Beauty shop.
Activities Arts and Crafts; Cards; Games; Prayer groups; Movies; Shopping trips; Dances/Social or cultural gatherings; Fishing trips; Coffee hour; Ladies tea.

OCEAN SPRINGS

Ocean Springs Nursing Center
Vancleave Rd, Ocean Springs, MS, 39564 (601) 875-9363
Admin Jeanette Walker.
Licensure Skilled Care. *Beds* 60. *Certified* Medicaid.
Ownership Proprietary.
Staff Physical therapists 1 (pt); Recreational therapists 1 (ft); Activities coordinators 1 (ft); Dietitians 1 (pt); Dentists 1 (pt); Podiatrists 1 (pt).
Facilities Dining room; Activities room; Chapel; Crafts room; Laundry room; Barber/Beauty shop.
Activities Arts and Crafts; Cards; Games; Reading groups; Prayer groups; Movies; Shopping trips.

TLC Home for the Elderly*
9002 Travis Ave, Ocean Springs, MS, 39564 (601) 875-9525
Admin Marie H McMillian.
Licensure Personal Care. *Beds* 11.

OKOLONA

Shearer-Richardson Memorial Nursing Home
Rockwell Dr, Okolona, MS, 38860 (601) 447-5463
Admin Brenda Wise. *Medical Dir/Dir of Nursing* Dr J H Shoemaker.
Licensure Skilled Care; Intermediate Care.
Beds 43. *Certified* Medicaid.
Ownership Public.
Staff Physicians 2 (pt); RNs 2 (ft); LPNs 4 (ft), 2 (pt); Nurses aides 18 (ft), 4 (pt); Activities coordinators 1 (ft); Dietitians 1 (pt).
Facilities Dining room; Activities room; Crafts room; Laundry room; Barber/Beauty shop.
Activities Arts and Crafts; Cards; Games.

Young at Heart Personal Care Center*
Rt 1, Box 211-3, Okolona, MS, 38860 (601) 447-2388
Admin Ruby Hollimon.
Licensure Personal Care. *Beds* 8.
Ownership Proprietary.

OXFORD

Golden Years Retirement Center*
606 Van Buren Ave, Oxford, MS, 38655 (601) 234-4245
Admin Katie M Overstreet.
Licensure Intermediate Care. *Beds* 37. *Certified* Medicaid.
Ownership Proprietary.

Gracelands Inc
1300 Belk St, Oxford, MS, 38655 (601) 234-7821
Admin James D Braswell. *Medical Dir/Dir of Nursing* J O Gilmore MD.
Licensure Skilled Care; Intermediate Care.
Beds 135. *Certified* Medicaid.
Ownership Proprietary.
Admissions Requirements Minimum age 21; Medical examination; Physician's request.
Staff Physicians 8 (pt); RNs 3 (ft), 1 (pt); LPNs

15 (ft), 2 (pt); Nurses aides 60 (ft), 10 (pt); Physical therapists 1 (pt); Activities coordinators 1 (ft), 1 (pt); Dietitians 2 (ft), 1 (pt); Dentists 1 (pt).
Facilities Dining room; Activities room; Chapel; Crafts room; Laundry room; Barber-/Beauty shop.
Activities Arts and Crafts; Cards; Games; Movies.
Description The building is in the shape of a square which lets the residents walk inside without backtracking; there is a center block with roses for outside activities.

Wood Lane—North Mississippi Retardation Center*
PO Box 967, Hwy 7 By-Pass, Oxford, MS, 38655 (601) 234-1476
Admin William J Lawhorn.
Licensure Intermediate Care for Mentally Retarded. *Beds* 204. *Certified* Medicaid.
Ownership Public.

Woodlea Skilled Nursing Home—North Mississippi Retardation Center*
PO Box 967, Hwy 7 By-Pass, Oxford, MS, 38655 (601) 234-1476
Admin William J Lawhorn.
Licensure Skilled Care. *Beds* 61. *Certified* Medicaid.
Ownership Public.

PASCAGOULA

Gulf Coast Nursing Home of Moss Point Inc*
4501 Jefferson Ave, Pascagoula, MS, 39567 (601) 762-7451
Admin Robert E Sevier.
Licensure Intermediate Care. *Beds* 84. *Certified* Medicaid.
Ownership Proprietary.

Jackson County Personal Care Home*
Rt 2, Box 286, Pascagoula, MS, 39567 (601) 588-6227
Admin Norma Coleman.
Licensure Personal Care. *Beds* 20.
Ownership Public.

Plaza Nursing Center*
4403 Hospital Rd, Pascagoula, MS, 39567 (601) 762-8960
Admin Vic Price.
Licensure Skilled Care; Intermediate Care. *Beds* 120. *Certified* Medicaid.
Ownership Proprietary.

Singing River Hospital System—Extended Care Facility*
2809 Denny Ave, Pascagoula, MS, 39567 (601) 938-5000
Admin Robert L Lingle.
Licensure Skilled Care. *Beds* 10. *Certified* Medicare.
Ownership Public.

PASS CHRISTIAN

Dixie White House Nursing Home Inc*
PO Box 515, Menge Ave, Pass Christian, MS, 39571 (601) 452-4344

Admin Tommie Ann Felts.
Licensure Skilled Care; Intermediate Care.
Beds 57. *Certified* Medicaid.
Ownership Proprietary.

Miramar Lodge Nursing Home
216 W Beach Blvd, Pass Christian, MS, 39571 (601) 452-2416
Admin Billy F Reed. *Medical Dir/Dir of Nursing* C D Taylor Jr.
Licensure Skilled Care; Intermediate Care.
Beds 180. *Certified* Medicaid.
Ownership Proprietary.
Admissions Requirements Medical examination; Physician's request.
Staff Physicians 5 (pt); RNs 3 (ft), 1 (pt); LPNs 18 (ft); Orderlies 3 (ft); Nurses aides 76 (ft); Physical therapists 2 (pt); Reality therapists 1 (ft); Speech therapists 1 (pt); Activities coordinators 3 (ft); Dietitians 1 (ft); Audiologists 1 (pt).

PETAL

Conva-Rest of Petal*
201 10th Ave, Petal, MS, 39465 (601) 544-7441
Admin Johnnie W Walters Jr.
Licensure Skilled Care; Intermediate Care.
Beds 60. *Certified* Medicaid.
Ownership Proprietary.

PHILADELPHIA

Neshoba County Nursing Home*
PO Box 648, Hwy 19 S, Philadelphia, MS, 39350 (601) 656-3554
Admin Robert E Turcotte Jr.
Licensure Skilled Care; Intermediate Care.
Beds SNF 70; ICF 10. *Certified* Medicaid.
Ownership Public.

PICAYUNE

Picayune Convalescent Home*
1620 Read Rd, Picayune, MS, 39466 (601) 798-1811
Admin Edna Gibson.
Licensure Skilled Care; Intermediate Care.
Beds 120. *Certified* Medicaid.
Ownership Proprietary.

PONTOTOC

Graceland's of Pontotoc
278 8th St, Pontotoc, MS, 38863 (601) 489-6411
Admin Jane B Price. *Medical Dir/Dir of Nursing* William B Howard MD.
Licensure Skilled Care; Intermediate Care.
Beds 60. *Certified* Medicaid.
Ownership Proprietary.
Admissions Requirements Medical examination; Physician's request.
Staff RNs 1 (ft), 1 (pt); LPNs 6 (ft), 3 (pt); Nurses aides 18 (ft), 4 (pt); Physical therapists; Recreational therapists 1 (ft); Occupational therapists; Activities coordinators 1 (ft); Dietitians 1 (ft), 1 (pt).
Facilities Dining room; Activities room; Laundry room; Barber/Beauty shop.

Activities Arts and Crafts; Cards; Games; Reading groups; Prayer groups; Movies; Shopping trips; Dances/Social or cultural gatherings.
Description Modern, bright 60-bed facility located on 10 rolling acres.

Pontotoc Community Hospital—Extended Care Facility*
176 S Main St, Pontotoc, MS, 38863 (601) 489-5510
Admin Carl Parrish.
Licensure Skilled Care; Intermediate Care.
Beds 14. *Certified* Medicaid; Medicare.
Ownership Public.

Sunshine Rest Home*
Rt 60, Box 443, Pontotoc, MS, 38863 (601) 489-1189
Admin James Westmoreland.
Licensure Intermediate Care. *Beds* 27. *Certified* Medicaid.
Ownership Public.

POPLARVILLE

Pearl River County Nursing Home
W Moody St, PO Box 392, Poplarville, MS, 39470 (601) 795-4543
Admin Laurel M Jones. *Medical Dir/Dir of Nursing* Joe H Powell MD.
Licensure Skilled Care; Intermediate Care.
Beds 40. *Certified* Medicaid.
Ownership Public.
Staff Physicians 4 (ft); RNs 1 (ft), 2 (pt); LPNs 4 (ft), 1 (pt); Orderlies 4 (ft), 4 (pt); Nurses aides 12 (ft), 10 (pt); Physical therapists 1 (ft), 1 (pt); Occupational therapists 1 (pt); Activities coordinators 1 (ft); Dietitians 1 (pt); Dentists 1 (pt); Ophthalmologists 1 (pt).
Facilities Dining room; Physical therapy room; Activities room; Chapel; Crafts room; Laundry room; Barber/Beauty shop.
Activities Arts and Crafts; Cards; Games; Reading groups; Prayer groups; Movies; Birthday parties.
Description Facility features a Christmas party, Mardi Gras annually, monthly birthday honors, sing-a-long; holiday dinner given by local churches; fish fry outing by riding specially made bus with lift for wheelchairs; weekly church and Sunday school.

PRENTISS

Jefferson Davis County—Extended Care Facility*
PO Drawer P, Berry St, Prentiss, MS, 39474 (601) 792-4276
Admin Dale Saulters.
Licensure Skilled Care; Intermediate Care.
Beds 60. *Certified* Medicaid; Medicare.
Ownership Public.

QUITMAN

Archusa Convalescent Center Inc
Hwy 511 E, Quitman, MS, 39355 (601) 776-2141
Admin Harmon Knight. *Medical Dir/Dir of Nursing* Walter Gunn MD.
Licensure Skilled Care; Intermediate Care.

Beds 120. *Certified* Medicaid.
Ownership Proprietary.
Admissions Requirements Medical examination; Physician's request.
Staff Physicians 5 (pt); RNs 3 (ft); LPNs 7 (ft); Orderlies 2 (ft); Nurses aides 27 (ft); Physical therapists 1 (pt); Reality therapists 1 (pt); Recreational therapists 1 (ft); Occupational therapists 1 (pt); Speech therapists 1 (pt); Activities coordinators 1 (ft); Dietitians 1 (pt); Dentists 1 (pt).
Facilities Dining room; Physical therapy room; Activities room; Crafts room; Laundry room; Barber/Beauty shop.
Activities Arts and Crafts; Cards; Games; Reading groups; Prayer groups; Movies; Shopping trips; Dances/Social or cultural gatherings.
Description Facility is in a beautiful setting overlooking 500-acre water park where residents can fish and picnic.

RALEIGH

Rolling Acres Retirement Center Inc
PO Box 128, Raleigh, MS, 39153 (601) 782-4244
Admin Cleta Mullins. *Medical Dir/Dir of Nursing* Vance Baucum MD.
Licensure Skilled Care; Intermediate Care.
Beds 120. *Certified* Medicaid.
Admissions Requirements Medical examination.
Staff Physicians 4 (pt); RNs 2 (ft); LPNs 10 (ft); Nurses aides 29 (ft), 13 (pt); Physical therapists 1 (pt); Activities coordinators 1 (ft); Dietitians 2 (ft), 1 (pt); Dentists 2 (pt); Podiatrists 1 (pt).
Facilities Dining room; Activities room; Crafts room; Laundry room; Barber/Beauty shop.
Activities Arts and Crafts; Cards; Games; Reading groups; Prayer groups; Movies; Dances/Social or cultural gatherings.

RIPLEY

Rest Haven Nursing Home
103 Cunningham Dr, Ripley, MS, 38663 (601) 837-3062
Admin Mildred Murphree. *Medical Dir/Dir of Nursing* Thomas L Ketchum MD.
Licensure Skilled Care; Intermediate Care.
Beds 60. *Certified* Medicaid.
Ownership Proprietary.
Staff Physicians 7 (ft); RNs 1 (ft), 1 (pt); LPNs 5 (ft), 4 (pt); Orderlies 1 (ft); Nurses aides 14 (ft), 8 (pt); Speech therapists 1 (pt); Activities coordinators 1 (ft); Dietitians 1 (pt); Dentists 1 (pt).
Facilities Dining room; Physical therapy room; Activities room; Chapel; Crafts room; Laundry room; Barber/Beauty shop.
Activities Arts and Crafts; Cards; Games; Reading groups; Prayer groups; Movies; Shopping trips.
Description Motto is "we serve because we care"; specialize in excellent patient care and have special, Christian, dedicated employees.

Ripley Manor Nursing Home*
1010 Cunningham Dr, Ripley, MS, 38663 (601) 837-3011
Admin Bobbye Wells.

Licensure Skilled Care; Intermediate Care.
Beds 120.
Ownership Proprietary.

ROLLING FORK

Care Inn—Rolling Fork*
PO Box 189, 506 W Race St, Rolling Fork, MS, 39159 (601) 873-6218
Admin Kyle Patton.
Licensure Skilled Care; Intermediate Care.
Beds 60. *Certified* Medicaid.
Ownership Proprietary.

RULEVILLE

Ruleville Health Care Center*
800 Stansel Dr, Ruleville, MS, 38771 (601) 756-4361
Licensure Skilled Care; Intermediate Care.
Beds 90. *Certified* Medicaid; Medicare.
Ownership Proprietary.

SANATORIUM

W L Jaquith Home*
PO Box 128, Sanatorium, MS, 39112 (601) 849-3321
Admin Clyde Woodruff.
Licensure Intermediate Care for Mentally Retarded. Beds 84. *Certified* Medicaid.
Ownership Public.

SARDIS

North Panola Regional Hospital—Skilled Nursing Facility*
PO Drawer 160, I-55 at MS 315, Sardis, MS, 38666 (601) 487-2720
Admin Shannon Flynn.
Licensure Skilled Care. Beds 44. *Certified* Medicaid.
Ownership Public.

SENATOBIA

Senatobia Convalescent Center*
402 Getwell Dr, Senatobia, MS, 38668 (601) 562-5664
Admin Denver Northrip.
Licensure Skilled Care; Intermediate Care.
Beds 120. *Certified* Medicaid.
Ownership Proprietary.

SHELBY

Zion Grove Nursing Home*
Church St, Shelby, MS, 38774 (601) 398-5117
Admin Betty Lofton.
Licensure Skilled Care; Intermediate Care.
Beds 120. *Certified* Medicaid.
Ownership Proprietary.

SOUTHAVEN

Southhaven Health Care Center*
1730 Dorchester Dr, Southaven, MS, 38671 (601) 393-0050

Admin James Williams.
Licensure Skilled Care; Intermediate Care.
Beds 120. *Certified* Medicaid.
Ownership Proprietary.

STARKVILLE

Rolling Hills Nursing Center*
PO Drawer 1566, 200 Womack St, Starkville, MS, 39759 (601) 323-9183
Admin Ann Thompson.
Licensure Intermediate Care for Mentally Retarded. Beds 120. *Certified* Medicaid.
Ownership Proprietary.

Starkville Manor Nursing Home*
PO Box 1466, Starkville, MS, 39759 (601) 323-6360
Admin William J Lukacs.
Licensure Skilled Care; Intermediate Care.
Beds 119. *Certified* Medicaid.
Ownership Proprietary.

TUPELO

Cedars Health Center*
2800 W Main St, Tupelo, MS, 38801 (601) 842-8555
Admin Alvin Lowenberg.
Licensure Skilled Care; Intermediate Care.
Beds SNF 60; ICF 60. *Certified* Medicaid.
Ownership Nonprofit.

Lee Manor Nursing Home
1901 Briar Ridge Rd, Tupelo, MS, 38801 (601) 844-0675
Admin Franklin C Lowe. *Medical Dir/Dir of Nursing* Dr James L Brown.
Licensure Intermediate Care. Beds 120. *Certified* Medicaid.
Ownership Proprietary.
Admissions Requirements Medical examination; Physician's request.
Staff Physicians 12 (pt); RNs 1 (ft); LPNs 8 (ft), 1 (pt); Orderlies 3 (ft); Nurses aides 23 (ft); Physical therapists 1 (pt); Speech therapists 1 (pt); Activities coordinators 1 (ft), 1 (pt); Dietitians 1 (pt).
Facilities Dining room; Activities room; Chapel; Crafts room; Laundry room; Barber/Beauty shop; Library; Outside patio.
Activities Arts and Crafts; Cards; Games; Reading groups; Prayer groups; Movies; Shopping trips; Dances/Social or cultural gatherings; Cookouts; Picnics.
Description Facility is located in a rural setting at the edge of town enabling residents to enjoy outdoor activities when weather permits.

Tupelo Manor Nursing Home
646 Eason Blvd, Tupelo, MS, 38801 (601) 842-2461
Admin Mike Bass. *Medical Dir/Dir of Nursing* James Brown MD.
Licensure Skilled Care. Beds 120. *Certified* Medicaid.
Ownership Proprietary.
Admissions Requirements Medical examination; Physician's request.

Activities Arts and Crafts; Cards; Games; Reading groups; Prayer groups; Movies; Shopping trips.

TYLERTOWN

Billdora Rest Home*
314 Enoch St, Tylertown, MS, 39667 (601) 876-2173
Admin Bill Brent.
Licensure Skilled Care. *Beds* 48. *Certified* Medicaid.
Ownership Proprietary.

Tylertown Extended Care Center
200 Medical Circle, Tylertown, MS, 39667 (601) 876-2107
Admin Arline Dillon. *Medical Dir/Dir of Nursing* Dr Ben Crawford.
Licensure Skilled Care; Intermediate Care. *Beds* 60. *Certified* Medicaid; Medicare.
Ownership Proprietary.
Admissions Requirements Medical examination; Physician's request.
Staff Physicians 8 (ft); RNs 2 (ft), 1 (pt); LPNs 6 (ft); Nurses aides 22 (ft); Activities coordinators 1 (ft); Dietitians 1 (ft).
Facilities Dining room; Activities room; Laundry room; Barber/Beauty shop; Day room.
Activities Arts and Crafts; Cards; Games; Reading groups; Prayer groups; Movies; Shopping trips; Dances/Social or cultural gatherings.
Description Facility features fishing trips, barbecues, adopt-a-grandparent, ice cream party, and prayer groups.

UNION

Hilltop Manor Inc*
PO Box 266, County Line St, Union, MS, 39365 (601) 774-8233
Admin Mary D Majure.
Licensure Skilled Care; Intermediate Care. *Beds* 60. *Certified* Medicaid.
Ownership Proprietary.

VICKSBURG

Mercy Extended Care Facility*
100 McAuley Dr, Vicksburg, MS, 39180 (601) 636-2131
Admin Carl E Barry.
Licensure Skilled Care. *Beds* 28.
Ownership Proprietary.

Shady Lawn Nursing Home Inc*
23 Porter's Chapel Rd, Vicksburg, MS, 39180 (601) 636-1448
Admin Jean Corbin.
Licensure Skilled Care; Intermediate Care. *Beds* 61. *Certified* Medicaid.
Ownership Proprietary.

Sydney House
900 Crawford St, PO Box 949, Vicksburg, MS, 39180 (601) 638-1514
Admin Mary Dell Greer. *Medical Dir/Dir of Nursing* Dr M E Hinman.
Licensure Intermediate Care. *Beds* 50.
Ownership Proprietary.
Admissions Requirements Medical examination; Physician's request.
Staff RNs 1 (ft); LPNs 7 (ft), 4 (pt); Nurses aides 20 (ft), 5 (pt); Activities coordinators 1 (pt); Dietitians 1 (pt).
Facilities Dining room; Activities room; Laundry room; Barber/Beauty shop; Library.
Activities Arts and Crafts; Cards; Games; Prayer groups; Movies; Dances/Social or cultural gatherings.
Description Staff caters to senior citizens; apartment residents are offered meals served to their rooms, maid service, laundry service, beauty shop, and activities.

Vicksburg Convalescent Home
1708 Cherry St, Vicksburg, MS, 39180 (601) 638-3632
Admin Lola Snyder. *Medical Dir/Dir of Nursing* M E Hinman.
Licensure Skilled Care; Intermediate Care. *Beds* 100. *Certified* Medicaid.
Ownership Proprietary.
Admissions Requirements Medical examination.
Staff RNs 2 (ft), 2 (pt); LPNs 11 (ft), 2 (pt); Nurses aides 32 (ft), 5 (pt); Activities coordinators 1 (ft); Dietitians 1 (pt).
Facilities Dining room; Laundry room; Patio.
Activities Arts and Crafts; Games; Prayer groups; Movies; Dances/Social or cultural gatherings.

Vicksburg Trace Haven*
40 Porter's Chapel Rd, Vicksburg, MS, 39180 (601) 638-9211
Admin Eva Williams.
Licensure Skilled Care; Intermediate Care. *Beds* 120. *Certified* Medicaid.
Ownership Proprietary.

WATER VALLEY

Yalobusha County Nursing Home
Hwy 7 S, PO Box 728, Water Valley, MS, 38965 (601) 473-1411
Admin Marilyn McCluskey. *Medical Dir/Dir of Nursing* Dr Harold Sexton.
Licensure Skilled Care. *Beds* 40. *Certified* Medicaid.
Ownership Public.
Admissions Requirements Medical examination; Physician's request.
Staff RNs 2 (ft); LPNs 6 (ft); Orderlies 4 (ft); Nurses aides 16 (ft); Activities coordinators 1 (ft); Dietitians 1 (pt).
Facilities Dining room; Activities room; Chapel; Crafts room; Laundry room; Barber/Beauty shop.
Activities Arts and Crafts; Cards; Games; Reading groups; Prayer groups; Movies; Shopping trips; Dances/Social or cultural gatherings.

WAYNESBORO

Restful Acres Nursing Home Inc*
1304 Walnut St, Waynesboro, MS, 39367 (601) 735-9025
Admin Karen S Williams.
Licensure Skilled Care; Intermediate Care. *Beds* 60. *Certified* Medicaid.
Ownership Proprietary.

WEST POINT

Care Inn—West Point
PO Box 817, West Point, MS, 39773 (601) 494-6011
Admin Roger Strickland. *Medical Dir/Dir of Nursing* William Billington DO.
Licensure Skilled Care; Intermediate Care. *Beds* 120. *Certified* Medicaid.
Ownership Proprietary.
Admissions Requirements Minimum age 17; Medical examination; Physician's request.
Staff Physicians 1 (pt); RNs 5 (ft); LPNs 9 (ft), 4 (pt); Orderlies 2 (ft); Nurses aides 40 (ft), 4 (pt); Physical therapists 1 (pt); Activities coordinators 1 (ft); Dietitians 1 (pt); Dentists 1 (pt); Ophthalmologists 1 (pt); Podiatrists 1 (pt).
Facilities Dining room; Activities room; Crafts room; Laundry room; Barber/Beauty shop.
Activities Arts and Crafts; Cards; Games; Reading groups; Prayer groups; Movies; Shopping trips; Dances/Social or cultural gatherings.

Dugan Memorial Home
804 E Main St, West Point, MS, 39773 (601) 494-3640
Admin Gains Hawkins. *Medical Dir/Dir of Nursing* Dr T N Braddock.
Licensure Skilled Care. *Beds* 60.
Ownership Proprietary.
Staff RNs 3 (ft); LPNs 6 (ft), 1 (pt); Nurses aides 19 (ft), 10 (pt); Activities coordinators 1 (ft); Dietitians 1 (ft).
Facilities Dining room; Activities room; Chapel; Laundry room; Barber/Beauty shop; Library.
Activities Games; Reading groups; Prayer groups; Shopping trips; Sightseeing.
Description This is a private-pay-only facility, recently expanded from 54 to 60 beds, concentrating on providing a home-like atmosphere along with quality and personalized care. Located 3 blocks from downtown on a large, wooded acreage which provides seclusion as well as instant access to major shopping centers. Two minutes to fire station; 5 minutes to new hospital being constructed.

WHITFIELD

Azalea Nursing Center
PO Box 127-B, Whitfield, MS, 39193 (601) 939-8640 Ext 463
Admin Roger A McMurtry. *Medical Dir/Dir of Nursing* Margaret Batson MD.
Licensure Intermediate Care for Mentally Retarded. *Beds* 110. *Certified* Medicaid.
Ownership Public.
Admissions Requirements Minimum age 5; Medical examination.
Staff Physicians 1 (pt); RNs 1 (ft), 1 (pt); LPNs 3 (ft), 2 (pt); Nurses aides 18 (ft); Physical therapists 1 (pt); Recreational therapists 1 (pt); Occupational therapists 1 (pt); Speech therapists 1 (pt); Activities coordinators 1 (pt); Dietitians 1 (pt); Dentists 1 (pt); Ophthalmologists 1 (pt); Podiatrists 1 (pt); Audiologists 1 (pt).
Facilities Dining room; Physical therapy room; Activities room; Chapel; Crafts room; Laundry room; Barber/Beauty shop; Library.

Activities Arts and Crafts; Games; Movies; Shopping trips; Dances/Social or cultural gatherings.

Hudspeth Center
PO Box 127-B, Whitfield, MS, 39193
Admin Edwin C LeGrand III. *Medical Dir/Dir of Nursing* Dr Margaret Batson.
Licensure Intermediate Care for Mentally Retarded. *Beds* 210. *Certified* Medicaid.
Ownership Public.
Admissions Requirements Minimum age 5.
Staff Physicians 3 (ft); RNs 12 (ft), 3 (pt); LPNs 18 (ft), 7 (pt); Orderlies 245 (ft); Physical therapists 1 (ft), 1 (pt); Recreational therapists 8 (ft), 3 (pt); Occupational therapists 1 (pt); Speech therapists 4 (ft); Activities coordinators 1 (ft); Dietitians 1 (ft), 1 (pt); Dentists 1 (pt); Ophthalmologists 1 (pt); Podiatrists 1 (pt); Audiologists 1 (pt).
Facilities Dining room; Physical therapy room; Activities room; Chapel; Crafts room; Laundry room; Barber/Beauty shop; Library.
Activities Arts and Crafts; Cards; Games; Reading groups; Prayer groups; Movies; Shopping trips; Dances/Social or cultural gatherings; Vocational training; Special education for residents under 21; Self-help training.
Description Facility additionally has approximately 100 placements for higher functioning mentally retarded citizens who do not necessarily require institutional services; off campus placements are provided as part of a statewide network of group homes, supervised apartments, and more, for persons needing supervision in daily activities but not requiring 24 hour per day training and nursing.

Jaquith Nursing Home—Adams Inn*
PO Box 7, Whitfield, MS, 39193 (601) 939-1221, Exten 364
Admin Robert E Brister.
Licensure Intermediate Care. *Beds* 149. *Certified* Medicaid.
Ownership Public.

Jaquith Nursing Home—Washington Inn*
PO Box 7, Whitfield, MS, 39193 (601) 939-1221, Exten 364
Admin Robert E Brister.
Licensure Skilled Care; Intermediate Care. *Beds* 98. *Certified* Medicaid.
Ownership Public.

Rosewood Skilled Nursing Facility—Hudspeth Center
PO Box 127-B, Whitfield, MS, 39193 (601) 939-8640
Admin Edwin C LeGrand III. *Medical Dir/Dir of Nursing* Margaret Batson MD PhD.
Licensure Skilled Care. *Beds* 55. *Certified* Medicaid.
Ownership Public.
Admissions Requirements Minimum age 5; Medical examination.
Staff Physicians 1 (ft), 1 (pt); RNs 2 (ft), 2 (pt); LPNs 6 (ft), 4 (pt); Nurses aides 36 (ft); Physical therapists 1 (pt); Recreational therapists 1 (ft), 1 (pt); Occupational therapists 1 (pt); Speech therapists 1 (pt); Activities coordinators 1 (ft); Dietitians 1 (pt); Dentists 1 (pt); Ophthalmologists 1 (pt); Podiatrists 1 (pt); Audiologists 1 (pt).

Facilities Dining room; Physical therapy room; Activities room; Chapel; Crafts room; Laundry room; Barber/Beauty shop; Library.
Activities Arts and Crafts; Games; Movies; Education and training activities as appropriate for severe and profound multihandicapped persons.
Description Hudspeth Center is an institution owned and operated by the state of Mississippi to serve 295 severely or profoundly retarded individuals with a catchment area covering the central 22 counties of the state. Institution provides for comprehensive evaluation, habilitation, and care for all residents. One cottage is licensed as a skilled nursing facility with a maximum capacity of 55 beds; all applicable state and federal laws regarding educational services, habilitation training, and individual care are met as appropriate for those receiving services in this facility. Respite (60 days or less) services are provided for persons either not requiring immediate institutional placement or those currently being maintained on the SNF waiting list.

WIGGINS

Azalea Gardens Nursing Center*
530 Hall St, Wiggins, MS, 39577 (601) 928-5281
Admin Bambi Breland.
Licensure Skilled Care; Intermediate Care.
Beds 127. *Certified* Medicaid.
Ownership Proprietary.

WINONA

Winona Manor Nursing Home*
PO Box 311, Hwy 82 W, Winona, MS, 38967 (601) 283-1260
Admin Marvell Morgan.
Licensure Skilled Care; Intermediate Care.
Beds 120. *Certified* Medicaid.
Ownership Proprietary.

YAZOO CITY

Care Inn—Yazoo City*
925 Calhoun Ave, Yazoo City, MS, 39194 (601) 746-6651
Admin Bob Knott.
Licensure Skilled Care; Intermediate Care.
Beds 180. *Certified* Medicaid.
Ownership Proprietary.

Martha Coker Convalescent Home
401 E 9th St, Yazoo City, MS, 39194 (601) 746-4621
Admin Anita S Boyd. *Medical Dir/Dir of Nursing* Dr Charles R Hogue.
Licensure Skilled Care. *Beds* 41.
Ownership Nonprofit.
Admissions Requirements Medical examination.
Staff Physicians 6 (ft); RNs 1 (ft), 1 (pt); LPNs 3 (ft), 2 (pt); Orderlies 1 (ft), 1 (pt); Nurses aides 9 (ft), 3 (pt); Physical therapists 1 (pt); Reality therapists 1 (pt); Recreational therapists 1 (pt); Activities coordinators 1 (pt); Dietitians 1 (ft), 1 (pt); Dentists 1 (pt).
Facilities Dining room; Physical therapy room;

Activities room; Chapel; Crafts room; Laundry room; Barber/Beauty shop.
Activities Arts and Crafts; Cards; Games; Reading groups; Prayer groups; Movies; Shopping trips; Dances/Social or cultural gatherings.
Description Invitational teas are held 3 times in the spring and 3 times in the fall for 60 to 80 people; spacious patio where stage bands perform in suitable weather.

MISSOURI

ADRIAN

Adrian Manor Nursing Home
Box 425, Adrian, MO, 64720 (816) 297-2107
Admin Clarence B Price.
Licensure Intermediate Care. *Beds* 60. *Certified* Medicaid.
Ownership Proprietary.
Staff RNs 1 (ft); LPNs 4 (ft); Orderlies 2 (ft); Nurses aides 18 (ft), 8 (pt); Physical therapists 1 (pt); Recreational therapists 1 (pt); Occupational therapists 1 (pt); Speech therapists 1 (pt); Activities coordinators 1 (ft); Dietitians 1 (pt); Dentists 1 (pt); Audiologists 1 (pt).
Facilities Dining room; Physical therapy room; Activities room; Chapel; Crafts room; Laundry room; Barber/Beauty shop.
Activities Arts and Crafts; Cards; Games; Reading groups; Prayer groups; Movies.
Description Facility is located in a very quiet small town off main streets.

AFFTON

Affton Nursing Home
9009 Gravois, Affton, MO, 63123 (314) 832-4833
Admin Mildred Pulley.
Licensure Intermediate Care. *Beds* 19. *Certified* Medicaid.
Ownership Proprietary.
Staff Physicians 1 (pt); RNs 1 (pt); LPNs 3 (ft); Nurses aides 5 (ft), 5 (pt).
Facilities Dining room; Laundry room; Sun porch.
Description Small facility offers a home-like atmosphere.

ALBANY

Colonial Manor of Albany*
Box 244, Hwy E 136, Albany, MO, 64402 (816) 726-5297
Admin Marvin Dean Teater.
Licensure Intermediate Care. *Beds* 60. *Certified* Medicaid.
Ownership Proprietary.

ANDERSON

Woodlawn Manor Residential Care Facility*
PO Box 81, Anderson, MO, 64831 (417) 845-3326
Admin Suzanne and Paul Peak.
Licensure Residential Care. *Beds* 20.
Ownership Proprietary.

APPLETON CITY

Colonial Manor Nursing Home
600 N Ohio, Box 98, Appleton City, MO, 64724 (816) 476-2128
Admin Paul S Wheeler. *Medical Dir/Dir of Nursing* Glen H Reed MD.
Licensure Intermediate Care. *Beds* 60. *Certified* Medicaid.
Ownership Proprietary.
Staff LPNs 3 (ft); Nurses aides 30 (ft); Activities coordinators 1 (ft).
Facilities Dining room; Physical therapy room; Activities room; Crafts room; Laundry room; Barber/Beauty shop.
Activities Arts and Crafts; Games; Prayer groups; Movies; Shopping trips; Dances/Social or cultural gatherings; Bingo; Dominos; Bowling.
Description A bright and beautiful facility located in a community that heavily supports the facility (i.e., families, visitors and volunteers from all areas of the community). Long-term care given for the full benefit of the residents.

ARNOLD

Hillview Lodge
Rt 2, Hwy 21, PO Box 802A, Arnold, MO, 64010 (314) 296-5141
Admin Marian Kling. *Medical Dir/Dir of Nursing* M Equil Abelardo MD.
Licensure Intermediate Care. *Beds* 155.
Ownership Proprietary.
Admissions Requirements Medical examination; Physician's request.
Staff Physicians 2 (ft); RNs 1 (ft); LPNs 3 (ft), 2 (pt); Nurses aides 51 (ft); Physical therapists 3 (ft), 1 (pt); Recreational therapists 1 (ft), 1 (pt); Occupational therapists 1 (ft), 1 (pt); Speech therapists 1 (pt); Activities coordinators 1 (ft); Dietitians 1 (pt); Dentists 1 (pt); Ophthalmologists 1 (pt); Podiatrists 1 (pt).

Facilities Dining room; Physical therapy room; Crafts room; Laundry room; Barber/Beauty shop.
Activities Arts and Crafts; Cards; Games; Prayer groups; Dances/Social or cultural gatherings.
Description Residents are encouraged to bring some of their own things so they can feel more at home.

ASH GROVE

Ash Grove Nursing Home Inc*
PO Box 247, 400 Meadowview, Ash Grove, MO, 65604 (417) 672-2575
Admin Jimmy L Frieze.
Licensure Intermediate Care. *Beds* 60. *Certified* Medicaid.
Ownership Proprietary.

AURORA

Aurora Nursing Center
1700 S Hudson, Aurora, MO, 65605 (417) 678-2165
Admin Edward James Hitt. *Medical Dir/Dir of Nursing* William P Hamilton MD.
Licensure Skilled Care; Intermediate Care. *Beds* 120. *Certified* Medicaid; Medicare.
Admissions Requirements Minimum age 18.
Staff RNs 3 (ft), 2 (pt); LPNs 3 (ft), 3 (pt); Orderlies 5 (ft), 2 (pt); Nurses aides 38 (ft), 10 (pt); Physical therapists 1 (pt); Reality therapists 1 (pt); Recreational therapists 1 (pt); Occupational therapists 1 (pt); Speech therapists 1 (pt); Activities coordinators 4 (ft); Dietitians 1 (pt); Dentists 1 (pt); Audiologists 1 (pt).
Facilities Dining room; Physical therapy room; Activities room; Chapel; Laundry room; Barber/Beauty shop; Living room.
Activities Arts and Crafts; Cards; Games; Prayer groups; Movies; Shopping trips; Dances/Social or cultural gatherings.
Description Facility was first in Missouri in funds raised by rock-n-roll jamboree.

AVA

Chastain's of Ava Inc*
2001 St Jefferson St, Ava, MO, 65608 (417) 683-4129
Admin Valerie Kempf.

Licensure Intermediate Care. *Beds* 10. *Certified* Medicaid.
Ownership Proprietary.

BALLWIN

Clayton-on-the-Green Nursing Center
477 Clayton Rd, Ballwin, MO, 63011 (314) 394-7515
Admin Catherine Bono. *Medical Dir/Dir of Nursing* Dr Virgil Fish.
Licensure Skilled Care. *Beds* 120.
Ownership Proprietary.
Admissions Requirements Minimum age 21; Medical examination; Physician's request.
Staff RNs 5 (ft), 10 (pt); LPNs 3 (ft), 5 (pt); Nurses aides 50 (ft); Physical therapists 1 (ft); Reality therapists 1 (ft); Recreational therapists 2 (ft); Occupational therapists 1 (pt); Speech therapists 1 (pt); Activities coordinators 1 (ft); Dietitians 1 (pt); Dentists 1 (pt); Ophthalmologists 1 (pt); Podiatrists 1 (pt); Audiologists 1 (pt).
Facilities Dining room; Physical therapy room; Activities room; Crafts room; Laundry room; Barber/Beauty shop; Library.
Activities Arts and Crafts; Cards; Games; Reading groups; Prayer groups; Movies; Shopping trips; Dances/Social or cultural gatherings.

Manchester Nursing Home
PO Box 1407, Ballwin, MO, 63011 (314) 391-0666
Admin Ron Rogers. *Medical Dir/Dir of Nursing* Donald C Walkenhorst DO.
Licensure Intermediate Care. *Beds* 130. *Certified* Medicaid.
Ownership Proprietary.
Admissions Requirements Minimum age 21.
Staff Physicians 1 (pt); RNs 4 (ft); LPNs 3 (ft), 2 (pt).
Facilities Dining room; Physical therapy room; Activities room; Crafts room; Laundry room; Barber/Beauty shop.
Activities Arts and Crafts; Cards; Games; Reading groups; Prayer groups; Movies; Dances/Social or cultural gatherings.

BELL CITY

Shetley Nursing Home*
PO Box 123, N Walnut St, Bell City, MO, 63735 (314) 733-4426
Admin Joyce Gilles.
Licensure Intermediate Care. *Beds* 29.
Ownership Proprietary.

BELLEVIEW

Belleview Valley Nursing Homes Inc
Star Rt, Box 34, Belleview, MO, 63623 (314) 697-5311
Admin Wilma Davis. *Medical Dir/Dir of Nursing* Deborah Payne.
Licensure Intermediate Care. *Beds* 122. *Certified* Medicaid.
Ownership Proprietary.
Admissions Requirements Medical examination.
Staff Physicians 3 (pt); RNs 1 (ft), 1 (pt); LPNs 5 (ft), 1 (pt); Orderlies 2 (ft); Nurses aides 40

(ft), 15 (pt); Physical therapists 1 (pt); Reality therapists 1 (ft); Recreational therapists 1 (ft); Occupational therapists 1 (pt); Speech therapists 1 (pt); Activities coordinators 1 (ft); Dietitians 1 (pt); Dentists 1 (pt); Ophthalmologists 1 (pt).
Facilities Dining room; Physical therapy room; Activities room; Chapel; Crafts room; Laundry room; Barber/Beauty shop.
Activities Arts and Crafts; Cards; Games; Reading groups; Prayer groups; Movies; Shopping trips; Dances/Social or cultural gatherings.
Description Located in the beautiful Belleview Valley nestled among the hills and mountains of Missouri, facility features country living, family-style.

BELLFLOWER

Bellflower Nursing Home*
Box 12, Bellflower, MO, 63333 (314) 929-3617
Admin Nancy Fisher.
Licensure Intermediate Care. *Beds* 27.
Ownership Proprietary.

BELTON

Beautiful Savior Home
Rt 2, Box 306, Belton, MO, 64012 (816) 331-0781
Admin Mary Anderson. *Medical Dir/Dir of Nursing* Ronald La Hue.
Licensure Intermediate Care. *Beds* 60. *Certified* Medicaid.
Ownership Proprietary.
Admissions Requirements Medical examination.
Staff RNs 3 (ft); LPNs 2 (ft), 2 (pt); Nurses aides 31 (ft); Physical therapists 1 (pt); Reality therapists 1 (pt); Occupational therapists 1 (pt); Speech therapists 1 (pt); Activities coordinators 1 (ft); Dietitians 1 (ft); Dentists 1 (pt); Ophthalmologists 1 (pt); Podiatrists 1 (pt); Audiologists 1 (pt).
Affiliation Lutheran
Facilities Dining room; Physical therapy room; Activities room; Chapel; Laundry room; Barber/Beauty shop.
Activities Arts and Crafts; Cards; Games; Reading groups; Prayer groups; Movies; Shopping trips; Dances/Social or cultural gatherings.
Description Home offers a first class facility in a quiet rural setting with close proximity to Kansas City; tastefully decorated rooms all on one level; 24-hour professional nursing care; religious services; occupational, physical, and speech therapy. Facility complies with all state and federal regulations.

BERKELEY

Wood-Acre Inc*
9732 Natural Bridge Rd, Berkeley, MO, 63134 (314) 428-4725
Admin Michael Woodard.
Licensure Intermediate Care. *Beds* 24.
Ownership Proprietary.

BERTRAND

Bertrand Retirement Home Inc*
Rt 1, Bertrand, MO, 63823 (314) 471-6161
Admin Charlotte York.
Licensure Intermediate Care. *Beds* 40. *Certified* Medicaid.
Ownership Proprietary.

BETHANY

Crestview Home Inc
Box 430, Jct Hwy 69 and 13, Bethany, MO, 64424 (816) 425-6337
Admin Dorothy Underwood. *Medical Dir/Dir of Nursing* G F Scamahorn DO.
Licensure Skilled Care; Intermediate Care. *Beds* 120. *Certified* Medicaid.
Ownership Nonprofit.
Staff RNs 3 (ft); LPNs 7 (ft), 1 (pt); Orderlies 3 (ft), 1 (pt); Nurses aides 42 (ft), 7 (pt); Activities coordinators 1 (ft), 1 (pt); Dietitians 13 (ft).
Facilities Dining room; Physical therapy room; Activities room; Chapel; Crafts room; Laundry room; Barber/Beauty shop; Library.
Activities Arts and Crafts; Cards; Games; Reading groups; Prayer groups; Movies; Dances/Social or cultural gatherings.

BIRCH TREE

Birch View Manor Nursing Home
PO Box 180, Birch Tree, MO, 65438 (314) 292-3212
Admin Robert E Jackson. *Medical Dir/Dir of Nursing* K J O'Banion DO.
Licensure Intermediate Care. *Beds* 90. *Certified* Medicaid.
Ownership Proprietary.
Admissions Requirements Minimum age 18.
Staff Physicians 4 (pt); RNs 1 (ft), 1 (pt); LPNs 8 (ft), 2 (pt); Nurses aides 30 (ft), 6 (pt); Physical therapists 1 (pt); Occupational therapists 1 (pt); Speech therapists 1 (pt); Activities coordinators 2 (ft); Dietitians 1 (pt); Dentists 1 (pt).
Facilities Dining room; Activities room; Chapel; Crafts room; Laundry room; Barber/Beauty shop.
Activities Arts and Crafts; Cards; Games; Reading groups; Prayer groups.

BISMARCK

Colonial Retirement Center Inc*
Box 727, 1162 Cedar St, Bismarck, MO, 63624 (314) 734-2846
Admin Bruce Harris.
Licensure Intermediate Care. *Beds* 23.
Ownership Proprietary.

BLOOMFIELD

Bloomfield Convalescent Center*
502 W Missouri St, Bloomfield, MO, 63825 (314) 568-2137
Admin Toni Robinson.
Licensure Skilled Care; Intermediate Care. *Beds* 60. *Certified* Medicaid.
Ownership Proprietary.

BLUE SPRINGS

Blue Springs Care Center*
PO Box 425, 930 Duncan Rd, Blue Springs,
MO, 64015 (816) 229-6677
Admin Barbara Hill.
Licensure Intermediate Care. *Beds* 120. *Certified* Medicaid.
Ownership Proprietary.

Golden Age Project—Boarding Home
630 Lakeview Dr, Blue Springs, MO, 64015
Admin Delores L Wieners.
Licensure Boarding Care. *Beds* 12. *Certified* Medicaid.
Ownership Nonprofit.
Admissions Requirements Minimum age 18;
Medical examination.
Staff RNs 1 (ft); Orderlies 1 (ft); Nurses aides 1
(ft), 1 (pt); Physical therapists 1 (pt); Recreational therapists 1 (pt); Dietitians 1 (pt).
Facilities Dining room; Laundry room.
Activities Arts and Crafts; Cards; Games;
Reading groups; Prayer groups; Movies; Shopping trips; Dances/Social or cultural gatherings;
Bowling; Bible study groups.
Description Facility is a home away from
home, for life between home and a nursing
home; provides day-to-day necessities; features
a large, park-like yard.

BOLIVAR

Bolivar Nursing Home Inc*
1218 W Locust, Bolivar, MO, 65613 (417)
326-7648
Admin Frank Follis.
Licensure Intermediate Care. *Beds* 108. *Certified* Medicaid.
Ownership Nonprofit.

Lindenman Health Care Center Inc*
PO Box 387, 404 E Broadway, Bolivar, MO,
65613 (417) 326-7873
Admin Glen Lindenman.
Licensure Residential Care. *Beds* 20.
Ownership Proprietary.

BONNE TERRE

Bonne Terre Rest Home Inc*
518 Grove St, Bonne Terre, MO, 63628 (314)
358-3400
Admin Thomas W McDowell.
Licensure Intermediate Care. *Beds* 27.
Ownership Proprietary.

BOONVILLE

Ashley Manor Care Center*
Ashley Rd S, Boonville, MO, 65233 (816)
882-6584
Admin Joan McFarren.
Licensure Intermediate Care. *Beds* 52.
Ownership Proprietary.

Colonial Gardens Retirement Center
Hwy 5, Boonville, MO, 65233 (816) 882-7007
Admin Ardell Myer.
Licensure Intermediate Care; Residential Care.
Beds ICF 60; Residential Care 35.

Ownership Proprietary.
Facilities Dining room; Physical therapy room;
Activities room; Crafts room; Laundry room;
Barber/Beauty shop.
Description This unique facility offers physical,
occupational, and speech therapy in an ICF and
also residential care situation.

Cooper County Rest Haven Nursing Home*
PO Box 374, 1121 11th St, Boonville, MO,
65233 (816) 882-7600
Admin Dorothy Young.
Licensure Intermediate Care. *Beds* 57.
Ownership Proprietary.

River Heights Retirement Center Inc*
PO Box 63, Boonville, MO, 65233 (816)
882-2328
Admin Robert Clausen.
Licensure Residential Care. *Beds* 120.
Ownership Proprietary.

BOWLING GREEN

Moore and Pike County Nursing Home*
400 S Saint Charles St, Bowling Green, MO,
63334 (314) 324-5281
Admin Martha E Moore.
Licensure Intermediate Care. *Beds* 68.
Ownership Proprietary.

**Sunset Nursing and Retirement Home of
Bowling Green***
N Main Cross, Bowling Green, MO, 63334
(314) 324-5191
Admin Donald Comer.
Licensure Intermediate Care. *Beds* 51.
Ownership Proprietary.

BRANSON

Rolling Hills Estates
Hwy 248 W, PO Box 1249, Branson, MO,
65616 (417) 334-6431
Admin Everett Franklin Gilles. *Medical Dir/Dir of Nursing* T L Huffman MD.
Licensure Skilled Care; Intermediate Care.
Beds 100. *Certified* Medicaid.
Ownership Proprietary.
Admissions Requirements Minimum age 16.
Staff Physicians 6 (pt); RNs 2 (ft), 2 (pt); LPNs
5 (ft), 2 (pt); Orderlies 2 (ft); Nurses aides 40
(ft), 5 (pt); Physical therapists 1 (pt); Reality
therapists 1 (pt); Occupational therapists 1 (pt);
Speech therapists 1 (pt); Activities coordinators
2 (ft); Dietitians 1 (pt); Dentists 1 (pt); Podiatrists 1 (pt); Audiologists 1 (pt).
Facilities Dining room; Physical therapy room;
Activities room; Crafts room; Laundry room;
Barber/Beauty shop.
Activities Arts and Crafts; Cards; Games;
Reading groups; Prayer groups; Movies; Shopping trips; Dances/Social or cultural gatherings;
Music shows.
Description Facility provides very aggressive
physical therapy program.

BRAYMER

Golden Age Nursing Home District*
Hwy 116, Braymer, MO, 64624 (816) 645-2243
Admin Cara Herring.
Licensure Intermediate Care. *Beds* 110. *Certified* Medicaid.
Ownership Public.

BRIDGETON

De Paul Health Center
12303 DePaul Dr, Bridgeton, MO, 63044 (314)
344-6000
Admin Anthony L Bunker. *Medical Dir/Dir of Nursing* Frank Mohs.
Licensure Skilled Care; Intermediate Care.
Beds 100. *Certified* Medicaid; Medicare.
Ownership Nonprofit.
Admissions Requirements Medical examination; Physician's request.
Affiliation Roman Catholic
Facilities Dining room; Physical therapy room;
Activities room; Chapel; Crafts room; Laundry
room; Barber/Beauty shop; Library.
Activities Arts and Crafts; Cards; Games;
Reading groups; Prayer groups; Shopping trips;
Dances/Social or cultural gatherings.

Mark Twain Manor
11988 Mark Twain Ln, Bridgeton, MO, 63044
(314) 291-8240
Admin Alfred J Jewson. *Medical Dir/Dir of Nursing* Arnold Tepper MD.
Licensure Skilled Care; Intermediate Care.
Beds 120. *Certified* Medicaid.
Ownership Proprietary.
Admissions Requirements Medical examination.
Staff RNs 5 (ft), 2 (pt); LPNs 2 (ft), 2 (pt);
Nurses aides 30 (ft), 15 (pt); Activities coordinators 1 (ft), 2 (pt).
Facilities Dining room; Physical therapy room;
Activities room; Crafts room; Laundry room;
Barber/Beauty shop.
Activities Arts and Crafts; Cards; Games;
Reading groups; Prayer groups; Movies; Shopping trips; Dances/Social or cultural gatherings.

BROOKFIELD

Brookfield Nursing Center
5 Hunt, Brookfield, MO, 64628
Admin Dennis F Sever. *Medical Dir/Dir of Nursing* Robert Smith MD.
Licensure Skilled Care. *Beds* 120. *Certified* Medicaid; Medicare.
Ownership Public.
Admissions Requirements Medical examination; Physician's request.
Staff Physicians 3 (pt); RNs 4 (ft), 1 (pt); LPNs
6 (ft), 2 (pt); Orderlies 2 (ft); Nurses aides 23
(ft), 4 (pt); Physical therapists 1 (pt); Recreational therapists 1 (pt); Occupational therapists
1 (pt); Speech therapists 1 (pt); Activities coordinators 1 (ft); Dietitians 1 (pt); Dentists 1 (pt);
Ophthalmologists 1 (pt); Podiatrists 1 (pt);
Audiologists 1 (pt).
Facilities Dining room; Physical therapy room;
Activities room; Chapel; Crafts room; Laundry
room; Barber/Beauty shop.

Activities Arts and Crafts; Cards; Games; Reading groups; Prayer groups; Movies; Shopping trips; Dances/Social or cultural gatherings. *Description* This new facility offers quality nursing care, total programs for patient rehabilitation, and home health care.

Maranatha Manor
620 West Ave, Brookfield, MO, 64628 (816) 258-7798
Admin Janet Robinson. *Medical Dir/Dir of Nursing* B D Howell MD.
Licensure Intermediate Care; Residential Care. *Beds* ICF 27; Residential Care 20.
Ownership Proprietary.
Staff RNs 1 (ft), 1 (pt); LPNs 1 (ft), 1 (pt); Orderlies 1 (ft); Nurses aides 18 (ft); Physical therapists 1 (pt); Speech therapists 1 (pt); Activities coordinators 1 (pt); Dentists 1 (pt).
Facilities Dining room; Activities room; Laundry room.
Activities Cards; Games; Prayer groups; Movies; Shopping trips.

McLarney Manor
116 E Pratt, Brookfield, MO, 64628 (816) 258-7402
Admin Judith Lewis. *Medical Dir/Dir of Nursing* B D Howell MD.
Licensure Skilled Care. *Beds* 45.
Ownership Proprietary.
Admissions Requirements Minimum age 21; Medical examination.
Staff Physicians 7 (pt); RNs 1 (ft), 1 (pt); LPNs 3 (ft), 3 (pt); Nurses aides 9 (ft), 6 (pt); Physical therapists 1 (pt); Occupational therapists 1 (pt); Speech therapists 1 (pt); Activities coordinators 1 (ft); Dietitians 1 (pt); Dentists 1 (pt).
Facilities Dining room; Physical therapy room; Activities room; Laundry room.
Activities Arts and Crafts; Cards; Games; Prayer groups; Dances/Social or cultural gatherings. *Description* Manor is dedicated to quality care at an affordable price; home-like atmosphere and dedicated staff make residents comfortable while trying to maintain their mental and physical function level.

BRUNSWICK

Grand Chariton Manor Inc*
Rt 2, Box 11, 721 W Filmore, Brunswick, MO, 65236 (816) 548-3182
Admin Sarah F Breshears.
Licensure Intermediate Care. *Beds* 60.
Ownership Proprietary.

BUFFALO

Chastain's of Buffalo Inc*
PO Box 449, Hickory and Cooper Sts, Buffalo, MO, 65622 (417) 345-2228
Admin Barbara Lee Myers.
Licensure Intermediate Care. *Beds* 120. *Certified* Medicaid.
Ownership Proprietary.

BUTLER

Medicalodge of Butler*
Rt 4, Box 130, Butler, MO, 64730 (816) 679-3179
Admin Vicky Petty.
Licensure Intermediate Care. *Beds* 120. *Certified* Medicaid.
Ownership Proprietary.

Pine Tree Nursing Home
Rt 3, Box 208, Butler, MO, 64113 (816) 679-4807
Admin Mildred Reynolds.
Licensure Intermediate Care. *Beds* 59.
Ownership Proprietary.

Willow Lane Nursing Center*
416 S High, Butler, MO, 64730 (816) 679-6157
Admin Robert W Stoffer.
Licensure Intermediate Care. *Beds* 100. *Certified* Medicaid.
Ownership Proprietary.

CABOOL

Kabul Nursing Home*
920 W Main, Cabool, MO, 65689 (417) 962-3713
Admin Robert K Cameron.
Licensure Skilled Care; Intermediate Care. *Beds* 82. *Certified* Medicaid; Medicare.
Ownership Nonprofit.

CALIFORNIA

Convalcare Home
Corner Parkway Dr and Hwy 87 S, California, MO, 65018 (314) 796-3127
Medical Dir/Dir of Nursing Dr Richard Fulks.
Licensure Skilled Care; Intermediate Care. *Beds* 60.
Ownership Proprietary.
Staff RNs 2 (ft); LPNs 2 (ft), 2 (pt); Nurses aides 15 (ft), 4 (pt); Activities coordinators 1 (ft), 1 (pt).
Facilities Dining room; Physical therapy room; Activities room; Crafts room; Laundry room; Barber/Beauty shop; Library.
Activities Arts and Crafts; Cards; Games; Reading groups; Prayer groups; Movies; Shopping trips; Dances/Social or cultural gatherings. *Description* This is a skilled and intermediate care facility with day care and mental health contact.

Tilton Nursing Home Inc
201 N Oak St, PO Box 19, California, MO, 65018 (314) 796-4791
Admin Dennis Tilton. *Medical Dir/Dir of Nursing* Dr Honeywell.
Licensure Intermediate Care. *Beds* 44.
Ownership Proprietary.
Staff Physicians 2 (ft), 1 (pt); RNs 1 (pt); LPNs 1 (ft), 1 (pt); Orderlies 1 (pt); Nurses aides 10 (ft), 6 (pt); Recreational therapists 1 (pt).
Facilities Dining room; Activities room; Laundry room; Barber/Beauty shop.
Activities Arts and Crafts; Reading groups. *Description* Tilton Nursing Home, Inc is located around the center of town. It is located

in a 3-story mansion, which at one time was a private, family-owned home. We have a large yard and porch that everyone enjoys.

CAMDENTON

Mozark Health Resort
Lake Rd 54-85, PO Box 128, Camdenton, MO, 65020 (314) 346-2445
Admin Otis J Eldridge.
Licensure Intermediate Care. *Beds* 32.
Ownership Proprietary.
Admissions Requirements Minimum age 18; Medical examination.
Staff RNs 1 (pt); LPNs 2 (ft); Nurses aides 6 (ft); Activities coordinators 1 (ft).
Facilities Dining room; Activities room; Laundry room.
Activities Arts and Crafts; Cards; Games; Reading groups; Movies; Shopping trips.

Windsor Estates Convalescent Center*
PO Box 812, Hwy 5 N, Camdenton, MO, 65020 (314) 346-5654
Admin John S Freeman.
Licensure Skilled Care; Intermediate Care. *Beds* 60. *Certified* Medicaid; Medicare.
Ownership Proprietary.

CAMERON

Cameron Manor Nursing Home
Rt 1, 801 Euclid St, Box 210 A, Cameron, MO, 64429 (816) 632-7254
Admin Mary E (Betsy) Stevens. *Medical Dir/Dir of Nursing* Robert Compton DO.
Licensure Intermediate Care. *Beds* 60. *Certified* Medicaid.
Ownership Proprietary.
Admissions Requirements Minimum age 17.
Staff Physicians 7 (pt); RNs 1 (ft); LPNs 2 (ft); Nurses aides 21 (ft), 3 (pt); Physical therapists 2 (pt); Occupational therapists 1 (pt); Speech therapists 1 (pt); Activities coordinators 1 (ft).

Indian Hills Health Center Inc*
PO Box 373, Hwy 36 W, Cameron, MO, 64429 (816) 632-2151
Admin Charles W Albin.
Licensure Skilled Care; Intermediate Care. *Beds* 84. *Certified* Medicaid.
Ownership Proprietary.

The Village
320 Little Brick Rd, Cameron, MO, 64429
Admin Ron Wilkinson.
Licensure Residential Care. *Beds* 25.
Ownership Proprietary.
Admissions Requirements Minimum age 21; Medical examination.
Staff Physicians; RNs; Nurses aides.
Facilities Dining room; Activities room; Laundry room.
Activities Cards; Games.
Description Facility offers security and supervision with a home-like atmosphere rather than that of an institution.

CAMPBELL

General Baptist Nursing Home Inc
Hwy 62 W, Rt 2, Box 650, Campbell, MO,
63933 (314) 246-2155
Admin Wanda Britt. *Medical Dir/Dir of
Nursing* Barry B White MD.
Licensure Intermediate Care. *Beds* 90. *Certified* Medicaid.
Ownership Nonprofit.
Admissions Requirements Minimum age 16;
Medical examination; Physician's request.
Staff RNs 1 (ft); LPNs 7 (ft), 1 (pt).
Affiliation Baptist
Facilities Dining room; Physical therapy room;
Activities room; Chapel; Crafts room; Laundry
room; Barber/Beauty shop.
Activities Arts and Crafts; Cards; Games;
Reading groups; Prayer groups; Movies; Shopping trips; Dances/Social or cultural gatherings.

CANTON

Lewis County Nursing Home
Hwy 81 N, Box 269, Canton, MO, 63435 (314)
288-4454
Admin Patricia L Hardin.
Licensure Intermediate Care. *Beds* 90. *Certified* Medicaid.
Ownership Nonprofit.
Admissions Requirements Minimum age 16.
Staff RNs 3 (ft); LPNs 10 (ft); Nurses aides 30
(ft), 8 (pt); Physical therapists 1 (pt); Speech
therapists 1 (pt); Activities coordinators 1 (ft);
Dietitians 1 (ft).
Facilities Dining room; Physical therapy room;
Activities room; Crafts room; Laundry room;
Barber/Beauty shop.
Activities Arts and Crafts; Cards; Games;
Reading groups; Prayer groups; Movies; Shopping trips; Dances/Social or cultural gatherings.
Description Facility is located in a country setting providing physical therapy, social service,
activities, and transportation; have a large sunroom with kitchen and country store used by
the residents.

CAPE GIRARDEAU

Cape Girardeau Care Center
2525 Boutin Dr, Cape Girardeau, MO, 63701
(314) 334-5225
Admin Dianne Carlile. *Medical Dir/Dir of
Nursing* W W Hutton DO.
Licensure Intermediate Care. *Beds* 120. *Certified* Medicaid.
Ownership Nonprofit.
Admissions Requirements Minimum age 19;
Medical examination.
Staff RNs 1 (ft); LPNs 7 (ft); Orderlies 3 (ft);
Nurses aides 37 (ft), 13 (pt); Activities coordinators 3 (ft).
Facilities Dining room; Physical therapy room;
Laundry room; Barber/Beauty shop.
Activities Arts and Crafts; Cards; Games;
Reading groups; Prayer groups; Movies; Shopping trips; Dances/Social or cultural gatherings.

Cape Girardeau Nursing Center*
2852 Independence St, Cape Girardeau, MO,
63701 (314) 335-2086

Admin Gary Crane.
Licensure Skilled Care. *Beds* 120.
Ownership Proprietary.

Chateau Girardeau
3120 Independence, Cape Girardeau, MO,
63701 (314) 335-1281
Admin Carl L Wilkins. *Medical Dir/Dir of
Nursing* E K Burford MD.
Licensure Skilled Care; Life Care Apartments.
Beds SNF 38; Life Care Apartments 151. *Certified* Medicaid; Medicare.
Ownership Nonprofit.
Admissions Requirements Minimum age 18;
Medical examination.
Staff RNs 3 (ft), 1 (pt); LPNs 3 (ft), 1 (pt);
Orderlies 1 (ft); Nurses aides 16 (ft), 6 (pt);
Activities coordinators 1 (ft).
Facilities Dining room; Physical therapy room;
Activities room; Chapel; Crafts room; Laundry
room; Barber/Beauty shop; Library; Billiards
room; Woodshop.
Activities Arts and Crafts; Cards; Prayer
groups; Movies; Shopping trips; Dances/Social
or cultural gatherings; Trips.
Description Health Center offers residents outpatient services, short-term or supportive
nursing care, and permanent care; features private and semi-private rooms, a lounge area, an
activities room, and a dining/multipurpose
room, all decorated in a light and pleasing manner. Through a highly qualified nursing staff on
duty 24 hours a day, medical attention is
always available; speech, physical, and occupational therapy, consulting podiatry, ophthalmology, dentistry, and laboratory services are
also available.

Hill Top Residential Care Facility
430 N Frederick, Cape Girardeau, MO, 63701
(314) 334-2662
Admin Donald McMullin.
Licensure Intermediate Care. *Beds* 30.
Ownership Proprietary.

The Lutheran Home*
2825 Bloomfield Rd, Cape Girardeau, MO,
63701 (314) 335-0158
Admin Janice T Unger.
Licensure Intermediate Care. *Beds* 120. *Certified* Medicaid.
Ownership Nonprofit.
Affiliation Lutheran

Ratliff Nursing Home*
717 N Spriggs, Cape Girardeau, MO, 63701
(314) 335-5810
Admin Emmagene Ratliff.
Licensure Intermediate Care. *Beds* 17.
Ownership Proprietary.

CARROLLTON

Carrollton's Resthaven Inc
307 Grand, Carrollton, MO, 64633 (816)
542-0588
Admin Ruth Ann Hayes.
Licensure Intermediate Care. *Beds* 63.
Ownership Proprietary.

CARTHAGE

Drake Residential Care Facility
406 Howard, Carthage, MO, 64836
Admin Manny Brandt.
Licensure Intermediate Care for Mentally
Retarded. *Beds* 88. *Certified* Medicaid; Medicare.
Ownership Nonprofit.
Staff Orderlies 7 (ft); Nurses aides 11 (ft);
Activities coordinators 1 (ft); Dietitians 1 (ft).
Facilities Dining room; Activities room; Crafts
room; Laundry room; Barber/Beauty shop.
Activities Arts and Crafts; Cards; Games;
Reading groups; Movies; Shopping trips; Dances/Social or cultural gatherings.

Fair Acres
Rt 3, Carthage, MO, 64836 (417) 358-4514
Admin Noel Kenneth Derrick Sr. *Medical Dir/Dir of Nursing* J J Royce MD.
Licensure Intermediate Care. *Beds* 140.
Ownership Nonprofit.
Admissions Requirements Minimum age 18;
Medical examination; Physician's request.
Staff Physicians 1 (pt); RNs 2 (pt); LPNs 8 (ft);
Orderlies 10 (ft); Nurses aides 50 (ft), 3 (pt);
Recreational therapists 3 (pt); Activities coordinators 1 (ft); Dietitians 1 (pt).
Facilities Dining room; Activities room; Chapel; Laundry room; Barber/Beauty shop;
Library.
Activities Arts and Crafts; Cards; Games;
Reading groups; Prayer groups; Movies; Shopping trips; Dances/Social or cultural gatherings.
Description A 140-bed nonprofit organization
dedicated to the care and treatment of the aged,
infirm mentally ill, and mentally retarded individuals who cannot care for themselves.

Maryetta's Rest Home
316 S Fulton, Carthage, MO, 64836 (417)
358-6672
Admin Eldred F Gilbreath.
Licensure Intermediate Care. *Beds* 17.
Ownership Proprietary.

Saint Luke's Nursing Center*
1220 E Fairview, Carthage, MO, 64836 (417)
358-9084
Admin John L Montgomery.
Licensure Skilled Care; Intermediate Care.
Beds 120. *Certified* Medicaid.
Ownership Nonprofit.

CARUTHERSVILLE

Caruthersville Manor*
500 Truman Blvd, Caruthersville, MO, 63830
(314) 333-5150
Admin Paul Stevens.
Licensure Skilled Care; Intermediate Care.
Beds 120. *Certified* Medicaid.
Ownership Proprietary.

CASSVILLE

Cassville Nursing Center
Country Farm Rd, PO Box 117, Cassville, MO,
65625 (417) 847-3386
Admin Mildred Shuster. *Medical Dir/Dir of*

Nursing W G Barns DO and Herman Sardjano MD.
Licensure Intermediate Care. *Beds* 32.
Ownership Proprietary.
Admissions Requirements Minimum age 18;
Medical examination; Physician's request.
Staff Physicians 2 (pt); RNs 1 (pt); LPNs 2 (ft);
Nurses aides 12 (ft); Activities coordinators 1
(ft); Dietitians 1 (pt).
Facilities Dining room; Activities room; Laundry room.
Activities Arts and Crafts; Games; Reading
groups; Movies; Shopping trips; Dances/Social
or cultural gatherings.
Description The home, red brick Colonial-style,
sets on a spacious area of higher elevation surrounded by beautiful trees. We provide excellent care for our residents, good food and with
32-bed capacity it is more like home living.

Sunset Valley Nursing Home*
11th St, Cassville, MO, 65625 (417) 847-4607
Admin Kenneth L Bemis.
Licensure Intermediate Care. *Beds* 25.
Ownership Proprietary.

CENTRALIA

Campbell House*
117 S Hickman, Centralia, MO, 65240 (314)
682-3204
Admin Mildred Campbell.
Licensure Intermediate Care. *Beds* 27.
Ownership Proprietary.

Heritage Hall
750 E Hwy 22, Centralia, MO, 65240 (314)
682-5551
Admin Rita Hampton. *Medical Dir/Dir of
Nursing* Dr William Bradley.
Licensure Intermediate Care. *Beds* 60. *Certified* Medicaid.
Ownership Proprietary.
Admissions Requirements Minimum age 18;
Medical examination; Physician's request.
Staff RNs 1 (pt); LPNs 3 (ft), 1 (pt); Nurses
aides 28 (ft), 6 (pt); Activities coordinators 1
(ft).
Facilities Dining room; Physical therapy room;
Activities room; Chapel; Crafts room; Laundry
room; Barber/Beauty shop.
Activities Arts and Crafts; Cards; Games;
Reading groups; Prayer groups; Movies.

CHARLESTON

Charleston Manor*
1220 E Marshall, Charleston, MO, 63834 (314)
683-3721
Admin Frank Gilles.
Licensure Skilled Care; Intermediate Care.
Beds 120. *Certified* Medicaid; Medicare.
Ownership Proprietary.

Russell Retirement Home
200 E Commercial St, Charleston, MO, 63834
Admin Jane E Jones.
Licensure Residential Care. *Beds* 32.
Ownership Proprietary.
Admissions Requirements Minimum age 18;
Medical examination.

Staff Physicians; LPNs; Orderlies; Nurses
aides.
Facilities Dining room; Activities room; Crafts
room; Laundry room.
Activities Arts and Crafts; Cards; Games;
Reading groups; Prayer groups; Movies; Shopping trips; Dances/Social or cultural gatherings.
Description Residents are free to come and go
as they please; meals are served and laundry
done at no extra charge; residents assisted when
necessary.

CHESTERFIELD

Chesterfield Manor Inc
14001 Olive Street Rd, Chesterfield, MO,
63141 (314) 469-3500
Admin Penny Griffin. *Medical Dir/Dir of
Nursing* Ted Vargas MD.
Licensure Skilled Care; Intermediate Care.
Beds SNF 72; ICF 64. *Certified* Medicaid.
Admissions Requirements Medical examination.
Staff RNs 2 (ft), 2 (pt); LPNs 2 (ft), 4 (pt);
Orderlies 4 (ft), 3 (pt); Nurses aides 10 (ft), 15
(pt); Physical therapists 1 (pt); Speech therapists
1 (pt); Activities coordinators 1 (ft); Dietitians
1 (ft); Dentists 1 (pt); Ophthalmologists 1 (pt);
Podiatrists 1 (pt); Audiologists 1 (pt).
Facilities Dining room; Physical therapy room;
Activities room; Chapel; Crafts room; Laundry
room; Barber/Beauty shop.
Activities Arts and Crafts; Cards; Games; Prayer groups; Movies.

Delmar Gardens of Chesterfield*
14855 N Outer 40 Rd, Chesterfield, MO, 63017
(314) 532-0150
Admin Gabe Grossberg.
Licensure Skilled Care; Intermediate Care.
Beds 180. *Certified* Medicaid.
Ownership Proprietary.

Delmar Gardens West*
13550 S Outer Forty Rd, Chesterfield, MO,
63017 (314) 878-1330
Admin Barbara Grossberg.
Licensure Skilled Care; Intermediate Care.
Beds 330. *Certified* Medicaid; Medicare.
Ownership Proprietary.

Friendship Village of West County
15201 Olive Street Rd, Chesterfield, MO,
63017 (314) 532-1515
Admin Wendell D Wilson. *Medical Dir/Dir of
Nursing* Dr Grant Izmirlian.
Licensure Skilled Care; Intermediate Care.
Beds 60. *Certified* Medicaid; Medicare.
Ownership Nonprofit.
Admissions Requirements Minimum age 62;
Physician's request.
Staff Physicians; RNs; LPNs; Orderlies;
Nurses aides; Physical therapists; Reality therapists; Recreational therapists; Occupational
therapists; Speech therapists; Activities coordinators; Dietitians; Dentists; Ophthalmologists;
Podiatrists; Audiologists.
Facilities Dining room; Physical therapy room;
Activities room; Chapel; Crafts room; Laundry
room; Barber/Beauty shop; Library; Transportation; Assistance in living; Housekeeping; Security.

Activities Arts and Crafts; Cards; Games;
Reading groups; Prayer groups; Movies; Shopping trips; Dances/Social or cultural gatherings.
Description Residents can sign up for a garden
or flower space that gives them a chance to garden during the summer months. Also have
trails through the woods for those who like to
walk.

Jewish Center for Aged
13190 S Outer Forty Rd, Chesterfield, MO,
63017 (314) 434-3330
Admin Miner Brown Fachca.
Licensure Skilled Care; Intermediate Care.
Beds 276. *Certified* Medicaid; Medicare.
Ownership Nonprofit.
Admissions Requirements Medical examination.
Staff Physicians 1 (ft), 3 (pt); RNs 9 (ft), 15
(pt); LPNs 2 (ft); Nurses aides 74 (ft), 17 (pt);
Physical therapists 1 (ft); Recreational therapists
1 (ft); Occupational therapists 1 (ft); Speech
therapists 1 (pt); Dietitians 1 (pt); Dentists 1
(pt); Podiatrists 2 (pt).
Affiliation Jewish
Facilities Dining room; Physical therapy room;
Activities room; Chapel; Barber/Beauty shop;
Library.
Activities Arts and Crafts; Games; Reading
groups; Prayer groups; Movies; Shopping trips;
Dances/Social or cultural gatherings.
Description Facility features extensive medical,
therapy, and social work services; various
outreach programs (e.g. shared living apartments, off-site health clinic, and day services);
unique therapeutic Biblical garden; teaching
center; JCAH approved.

Westchester House
550 White Rd, Chesterfield, MO, 63017 (314)
469-1200
Admin Darlena Voegele. *Medical Dir/Dir of
Nursing* Dr Jamie Aquinaldo.
Licensure Skilled Care. *Beds* 76.
Ownership Proprietary.
Admissions Requirements Minimum age 18.
Staff Physicians 1 (pt); RNs 6 (ft), 4 (pt); LPNs
3 (ft), 3 (pt); Nurses aides 24 (ft), 22 (pt);
Physical therapists 1 (pt); Activities coordinators 1 (ft), 1 (pt).
Facilities Dining room; Physical therapy room;
Activities room; Crafts room; Laundry room;
Barber/Beauty shop; Library.
Activities Arts and Crafts; Cards; Games;
Reading groups; Prayer groups; Movies; Shopping trips; Dances/Social or cultural gatherings.
Description A one-floor facility beautifully decorated featuring outstanding individualized
care, selective menus, a breath-taking view
from each patient's room, noninstitutional
appearance, and limousine service for residents.

CHILICOTHE

Indian Hills Nursing Home Inc
2601 Fair St, Chilicothe, MO, 64601 (816)
646-1230
Admin Marilyn Wever.
Licensure Intermediate Care. *Beds* 60. *Certified* Medicaid.
Ownership Proprietary.
Staff RNs 1 (ft); LPNs 4 (ft), 2 (pt); Nurses

aides 21 (ft), 3 (pt); Physical therapists 1 (pt); Occupational therapists 1 (pt); Speech therapists 1 (pt); Activities coordinators 1 (ft); Dietitians 1 (pt); Audiologists 1 (pt).
Facilities Dining room; Physical therapy room; Activities room; Chapel; Crafts room; Laundry room; Barber/Beauty shop; Library.
Activities Arts and Crafts; Cards; Games; Reading groups; Prayer groups; Movies; Shopping trips; Dances/Social or cultural gatherings.
Description Facility has around-the-clock coverage by licensed personnel in nursing services department; therapy department functions 7 days a week.

CHILLICOTHE

Collins Nursing Care Facility
423 Clay, Chillicothe, MO, 64601 (816) 646-3365
Admin Lillian Deringer.
Licensure Intermediate Care. *Beds* 32.
Ownership Proprietary.

Darrs Home for the Aged
300 J F Kennedy Ave, Chillicothe, MO, 64601 (816) 646-4271
Admin Cathern Darr.
Licensure Intermediate Care. *Beds* 19.
Ownership Proprietary.
Admissions Requirements Minimum age 60; Females only; Medical examination; Physician's request.
Staff RNs 1 (pt); LPNs 1 (ft), 1 (pt); Nurses aides 5 (ft), 2 (pt); Activities coordinators 1 (pt); Dietitians 1 (ft), 1 (pt).
Facilities Dining room; Laundry room.
Activities Prayer groups.

Indian Hills Nursing Home Inc*
2601 Fair St, Chillicothe, MO, 64601 (816) 646-1230
Admin Dorothy R Snyder.
Licensure Intermediate Care. *Beds* 60. *Certified* Medicaid.
Ownership Proprietary.

Livingston Manor Care Center
Hwy 36 E, Chillicothe, MO, 64601 (816) 646-5177
Admin Betty Ernst. *Medical Dir/Dir of Nursing* James Harkness DO.
Licensure Intermediate Care. *Beds* 94.
Ownership Proprietary.
Admissions Requirements Minimum age 16; Medical examination.
Staff RNs 2 (ft); LPNs 3 (ft); Nurses aides 21 (ft), 1 (pt); Physical therapists 1 (pt); Activities coordinators 2 (ft); Dietitians 1 (pt).
Facilities Dining room; Physical therapy room; Activities room; Crafts room; Laundry room; Barber/Beauty shop; Library.
Activities Arts and Crafts; Cards; Games; Reading groups; Prayer groups; Movies; Shopping trips; Dances/Social or cultural gatherings; Transportation to community events.
Description The facility is located in a rural area 2 miles from city limits, surrounded by a green lawn and fields. There are large trees and ample outdoor spaces. The plant is attractively decorated with a spacious and homey atmos-

phere. Nursing care is excellent. Food is wholesome and attractive. Facility offers an extensive activity program.

Long-Blum Retirement Center*
1301 Monroe, Chillicothe, MO, 64601 (816) 646-5180
Admin Barbara S White.
Licensure Residential Care. *Beds* 64.
Ownership Proprietary.

Morningside Center
1700 Morningside Dr, Chillicothe, MO, 64601
Admin Beverly M Keefe.
Licensure Intermediate Care. *Beds* 60. *Certified* Medicaid.
Ownership Nonprofit.
Admissions Requirements Medical examination.
Staff RNs 1 (pt); LPNs 4 (ft), 1 (pt); Nurses aides 25 (ft); Activities coordinators 1 (ft); Dietitians 1 (pt).
Facilities Dining room; Physical therapy room; Activities room; Laundry room; Barber/Beauty shop.
Activities Arts and Crafts; Cards; Games; Reading groups; Prayer groups; Movies; Shopping trips; Dances/Social or cultural gatherings.
Description This beautiful complex is located on 5 rolling acres just east of a shopping center; offers the newest and most modern facilities, designed and built to provide the ultimate in nursing care in a home-like atmosphere.

Susans Nursing Home
505 2nd St, Chillicothe, MO, 64601 (816) 646-3476
Admin Michael Malone.
Licensure Intermediate Care. *Beds* 60.
Ownership Proprietary.
Admissions Requirements Medical examination.
Staff RNs 1 (pt); LPNs 3 (ft); Orderlies 1 (ft); Nurses aides 9 (ft), 11 (pt); Activities coordinators 1 (ft), 1 (pt).
Facilities Dining room; Activities room; Laundry room.
Activities Arts and Crafts; Cards; Games; Reading groups; Prayer groups; Movies; Shopping trips; Dances/Social or cultural gatherings.

CLARENCE

Clarence Nursing Home District
307 East St, PO Box 250, Clarence, MO, 63437 (816) 699-2118
Admin Betty L Barratt. *Medical Dir/Dir of Nursing* Dr D R Hull.
Licensure Intermediate Care. *Beds* 60. *Certified* Medicaid; Medi-Cal.
Ownership Proprietary.
Admissions Requirements Minimum age 16; Medical examination.
Staff Physicians 1 (pt); RNs 1 (pt); LPNs 5 (ft); Nurses aides 21 (ft), 7 (pt); Physical therapists 1 (ft), 1 (pt); Reality therapists 1 (ft); Recreational therapists 1 (ft); Occupational therapists 1 (pt); Speech therapists 1 (pt); Activities coordinators 1 (pt).
Facilities Dining room; Physical therapy room; Activities room; Crafts room; Laundry room; Barber/Beauty shop.

Activities Arts and Crafts; Games; Reading groups; Prayer groups; Shopping trips.
Description Facility is situated in a town of 1000 people with almost all local employees; a very loving, caring staff who have known most of the residents since early childhood; offers a warm feeling of being a large home instead of an institution with all employees having a positive attitude; community is the "watch dog" for the nursing home.

CLINTON

Chastain's of Clinton Inc*
1009 E Ohio St, Clinton, MO, 64735 (816) 885-5571
Admin William Lancaster.
Licensure Intermediate Care. *Beds* 120. *Certified* Medicaid.
Ownership Proprietary.

Golden Valley Nursing Home*
302 E Ohio, Clinton, MO, 64735 (816) 931-4024
Admin Frances Hardy.
Licensure Intermediate Care. *Beds* 29.
Ownership Proprietary.

Truman Health Center
614 S Main, Clinton, MO, 64735 (816) 885-8328
Admin Ernestine Gray.
Licensure Residential Care. *Beds* 25.
Ownership Proprietary.

Westwood Home Inc
Hwy 13 N, Clinton, MO, 64735 (816) 885-8196
Admin Melva Dean Hart. *Medical Dir/Dir of Nursing* R J Powell DO.
Licensure Skilled Care; Intermediate Care.
Beds 100. *Certified* Medicaid; Medicare.
Ownership Proprietary.
Admissions Requirements Minimum age 21; Physician's request.
Staff Physicians 1 (pt); RNs 2 (ft), 1 (pt); LPNs 5 (ft), 3 (pt); Nurses aides 27 (ft), 18 (pt); Physical therapists 2 (ft), 2 (pt); Recreational therapists 1 (pt); Occupational therapists 1 (pt); Speech therapists 1 (pt); Activities coordinators 1 (pt); Dietitians 1 (pt); Dentists 1 (pt); Ophthalmologists 1 (pt).
Facilities Dining room; Physical therapy room; Activities room; Chapel; Crafts room; Laundry room; Barber/Beauty shop.
Activities Arts and Crafts; Cards; Games; Reading groups; Prayer groups; Movies; Dances/Social or cultural gatherings.
Description This friendly facility has outstanding activity and crafts programs.

COLE CAMP

Good Samaritan Nursing Home*
1st and Grother, Cole Camp, MO, 65325 (816) 668-4515
Admin Howard P Ball.
Licensure Intermediate Care. *Beds* 60. *Certified* Medicaid.
Ownership Public.

COLUMBIA

Boone Retirement Center Inc
1623 Anthony St, Columbia, MO, 65201 (314) 449-6105
Admin John Lloyd Jones. *Medical Dir/Dir of Nursing* David Mehr MD.
Licensure Intermediate Care. *Beds* 120. *Certified* Medicaid.
Ownership Nonprofit.
Admissions Requirements Minimum age 21; Medical examination.
Staff Physicians 1 (pt); RNs 2 (ft), 1 (pt); LPNs 13 (ft); Orderlies 18 (ft); Nurses aides 22 (ft), 12 (pt); Physical therapists 3 (ft); Recreational therapists 1 (ft), 1 (pt); Occupational therapists 1 (pt); Speech therapists 1 (pt); Dietitians 1 (ft); Dentists 1 (pt).
Facilities Dining room; Physical therapy room; Activities room; Crafts room; Laundry room; Barber/Beauty shop; Library.
Activities Arts and Crafts; Cards; Games; Prayer groups; Movies; Shopping trips; Dances/Social or cultural gatherings.

Candle Light Lodge Retirement Center*
1406 Business Loop 70 W, Columbia, MO, 65202 (314) 449-5287
Admin Randall P Gross.
Licensure Intermediate Care. *Beds* 45.
Ownership Proprietary.

Columbia House Healthcare
1801 Towne Dr, Columbia, MO, 65201 (314) 474-6111
Admin Jeanne Bouxsein.
Licensure Intermediate Care. *Beds* 141.
Ownership Proprietary.
Staff RNs 3 (ft), 2 (pt); LPNs 6 (ft), 5 (pt); Nurses aides 27 (ft), 21 (pt); Recreational therapists 2 (ft); Activities coordinators 1 (ft); Dietitians 1 (ft).
Facilities Dining room; Physical therapy room; Activities room; Chapel; Crafts room; Laundry room; Barber/Beauty shop.
Activities Arts and Crafts; Cards; Games; Prayer groups; Movies; Shopping trips; Dances/Social or cultural gatherings.

Columbia Manor Care Center
2012 Nifong Blvd, Columbia, MO, 65201 (314) 449-1246
Admin Ruth Ann Libbert. *Medical Dir/Dir of Nursing* B A Moranville MD.
Licensure Intermediate Care. *Beds* 52.
Ownership Proprietary.
Admissions Requirements Minimum age 16.
Staff RNs 1 (pt); LPNs 2 (ft); Orderlies 2 (ft); Nurses aides 8 (ft), 2 (pt); Activities coordinators 1 (ft); Dietitians 1 (ft).
Facilities Dining room; Laundry room; Barber/Beauty shop.
Activities Arts and Crafts; Cards; Games; Prayer groups; Movies; Dances/Social or cultural gatherings.
Description Columbia Manor is a ranch-style facility located in a comfortable country setting on Columbia's southside just minutes from downtown.

Lenoir Memorial Home Inc
3300 New Haven Rd, Columbia, MO, 65201 (314) 443-2478

Admin Alfred J Kalen. *Medical Dir/Dir of Nursing* B A Moranville.
Licensure Skilled Care. *Beds* 60.
Ownership Nonprofit.
Admissions Requirements Minimum age 60; Medical examination; Physician's request.
Staff RNs 3 (ft), 3 (pt); LPNs 2 (ft), 2 (pt); Nurses aides 25 (ft), 2 (pt); Physical therapists 1 (pt); Recreational therapists 1 (ft); Occupational therapists 1 (ft); Speech therapists 1 (pt); Dietitians 1 (pt).
Affiliation Disciples of Christ
Facilities Dining room; Physical therapy room; Activities room; Chapel; Crafts room; Laundry room; Barber/Beauty shop; Library.
Activities Arts and Crafts; Cards; Games; Reading groups; Prayer groups; Movies; Shopping trips; Dances/Social or cultural gatherings.
Description Lenoir is a retirement community situated on the edge of Columbia, Missouri, a major educational, cultural, and medical center in the Midwest. The Lenoir retirement community includes a boarding facility and 120 independent living homes and apartments. Services run the whole gamut from exceptional nursing and therapy care to transportation and maintenance of independent living units and boarding home facility.

Mesa Hills Adult Care
300 Portland, Columbia, MO, 65201 (314) 875-3033
Admin David E Gatewood. *Medical Dir/Dir of Nursing* David Mehue MD.
Licensure Skilled Care. *Beds* 120. *Certified* Medicaid; Medicare.
Ownership Proprietary.
Admissions Requirements Minimum age 18; Medical examination; Physician's request.
Staff Physicians 1 (pt); RNs 2 (ft), 2 (pt); LPNs 6 (ft), 1 (pt); Orderlies 2 (ft); Nurses aides 45 (ft), 4 (pt); Physical therapists 2 (ft); Speech therapists 1 (pt); Activities coordinators 2 (ft); Dietitians 1 (pt); Dentists 1 (pt); Podiatrists 1 (pt).
Facilities Dining room; Physical therapy room; Activities room; Crafts room; Laundry room; Barber/Beauty shop.
Activities Arts and Crafts; Cards; Games; Reading groups; Prayer groups; Movies.

CONCORDIA

Lutheran Good Shepherd Home
3rd and West Sts, Concordia, MO, 64020 (816) 463-2267
Admin Paul R Brackman. *Medical Dir/Dir of Nursing* Dr Robert LaHue.
Licensure Intermediate Care. *Beds* 22.
Ownership Nonprofit.
Staff Physicians 5 (pt); RNs 3 (ft); LPNs 1 (pt); Nurses aides 12 (ft), 5 (pt); Physical therapists 2 (pt); Occupational therapists 1 (pt); Speech therapists 1 (pt); Activities coordinators 1 (ft); Dietitians 1 (ft); Dentists 1 (pt).
Affiliation Lutheran
Facilities Dining room; Physical therapy room; Activities room; Chapel; Crafts room; Barber/Beauty shop.
Activities Arts and Crafts; Cards; Games; Reading groups; Movies.

COOL VALLEY

Bell Crest Inc
1301 S Florissant Rd, Cool Valley, MO, 63121 (314) 521-6060
Admin Gayla Bentley.
Licensure Intermediate Care. *Beds* 76.
Ownership Proprietary.
Admissions Requirements Medical examination.
Staff Physicians 1 (pt); RNs 1 (ft); LPNs 1 (pt); Nurses aides 8 (ft), 4 (pt); Physical therapists 1 (pt); Recreational therapists 1 (ft); Occupational therapists 1 (pt); Speech therapists 1 (pt); Activities coordinators 1 (ft); Dietitians 1 (pt); Dentists 1 (pt); Podiatrists 1 (pt).
Facilities Dining room; Activities room; Crafts room; Laundry room; Barber/Beauty shop.
Activities Arts and Crafts; Cards; Games; Reading groups; Prayer groups; Shopping trips; Dances/Social or cultural gatherings.
Description Very much a family-type atmosphere.

CREVE COEUR

Country Manor of Creve Coeur*
PO Box 12817, 850 Country Manor Ln, Creve Coeur, MO, 63141 (314) 434-5900
Admin Carole L White.
Licensure Intermediate Care. *Beds* 152. *Certified* Medicaid.
Ownership Proprietary.

Evergreen Nursing Home and Rehabilitation Center Inc
12705 Olive Street Rd, Creve Coeur, MO, 63141 (314) 434-8361
Admin Maurice Abrams. *Medical Dir/Dir of Nursing* Thomas Margulies.
Licensure Skilled Care; Intermediate Care. *Beds* 147. *Certified* Medicaid; Medicare.
Ownership Proprietary.
Admissions Requirements Medical examination.
Facilities Dining room; Physical therapy room; Activities room; Chapel; Crafts room; Laundry room; Barber/Beauty shop; Library; Enclosed open air courtyard.
Activities Arts and Crafts; Cards; Games; Reading groups; Prayer groups; Movies.
Description Facility is divided into 3 levels: levels 1 and 2 are for intermediate or custodial care and the 3rd level is for heavy or skilled care.

CUBA

Briarwood Manor Nursing Home
410 N Franklin, Cuba, MO, 65453 (314) 885-2150
Admin Linda B Carwile. *Medical Dir/Dir of Nursing* Dr G Riffel.
Licensure Skilled Care; Intermediate Care. *Beds* 62. *Certified* Medicaid.
Ownership Proprietary.
Admissions Requirements Medical examination.
Staff Physicians 1 (pt); RNs 2 (ft); LPNs 3 (ft), 5 (pt); Nurses aides 38 (ft); Physical therapists 1 (pt); Reality therapists 1 (pt); Recreational ther-

apists 1 (ft); Occupational therapists 1 (pt); Speech therapists 1 (pt); Activities coordinators 1 (ft); Dietitians 1 (pt); Dentists 1 (pt); Ophthalmologists 1 (pt); Podiatrists 1 (pt).
Facilities Dining room; Physical therapy room; Activities room; Chapel; Crafts room; Laundry room; Barber/Beauty shop.
Activities Arts and Crafts; Cards; Games; Reading groups; Prayer groups; Movies; Shopping trips; Dances/Social or cultural gatherings.
Description Briarwood Manor is pleased to announce that it has recently received certification to become a full-service skilled nursing facility. Services provided by staff, or by contract include, but are not limited to: 24-hour professional nursing services, social services, recreational/activity therapy, electrolysis, physical therapy, physician services, restorative nursing, NIG-gastrostomy care, optometry services, occupational therapy, speech therapy, dental services, dermatology services, podiatry services, therapeutic dietary services, beauty/barber services, medical records services, oxygen therapy, and IV therapy.

DES PERES

Chastain's of Des Peres Inc
11692 Manchester Rd, Des Peres, MO, 63131 (314) 966-3350
Admin J Michael Gunn. *Medical Dir/Dir of Nursing* Dr C H Leslie.
Licensure Skilled Care. *Beds* 143. *Certified* Medicaid.
Ownership Proprietary.
Facilities Dining room; Physical therapy room; Activities room; Chapel; Laundry room; Barber/Beauty shop.
Activities Arts and Crafts; Cards; Games; Prayer groups; Movies; Shopping trips; Dances/Social or cultural gatherings.

DESOTO

Burt Manor Nursing Home
Rt 1, Hwy 67, Box 214A, DeSoto, MO, 63020 (314) 586-2291
Admin Mary K Baisch. *Medical Dir/Dir of Nursing* Michael K Blank MD.
Licensure Intermediate Care. *Beds* 61.
Ownership Proprietary.
Admissions Requirements Minimum age 18; Medical examination.
Staff Physicians 1 (pt); RNs 1 (ft); LPNs 4 (ft), 2 (pt); Nurses aides 14 (ft), 9 (pt); Physical therapists 1 (pt); Occupational therapists 1 (pt); Speech therapists 1 (pt); Activities coordinators 1 (pt); Dietitians 1 (pt).
Facilities Dining room; Activities room; Laundry room; Barber/Beauty shop.
Activities Cards; Games; Dances/Social or cultural gatherings.
Description Burt Manor is designed, equipped, and staffed for 61-bed capacity. It is located "in the country" on 13 acres of scenic beauty. A comfortable, friendly home where good patient care combines with modern facilities and a highly skilled staff.

DEXTER

Dexter Convalescent Home*
PO Box 517, Dexter, MO, 63841 (314) 624-7491
Admin Brenda Miller.
Licensure Skilled Care; Intermediate Care. *Beds* 83. *Certified* Medicaid.
Ownership Proprietary.

Sunshine Manor
Star Rt Box 150-B, Dexter, MO, 63841
Admin Patsy Davis.
Licensure Intermediate Care for Mentally Retarded. *Beds* 20. *Certified* Medicaid; Medicare.
Ownership Proprietary.
Admissions Requirements Minimum age 18; Physician's request.
Facilities Dining room; Activities room; Laundry room.
Description Facility has all private rooms.

Vintage Villa*
228 E Market St, Dexter, MO, 63841 (314) 624-8908
Admin Edith Cox.
Licensure Intermediate Care. *Beds* 60. *Certified* Medicaid.
Ownership Proprietary.

DONIPHAN

Doniphan Retirement Home Inc*
PO Box 130, Hwy 142, Doniphan, MO, 63935 (314) 996-2191, 785-0858
Admin Edward Kinworthy.
Licensure Skilled Care; Intermediate Care. *Beds* 90. *Certified* Medicaid.
Ownership Proprietary.

EDINA

Hostel House*
300–302 N Main St, Edina, MO, 63537 (816) 397-3404
Admin Ina Marie Small.
Licensure Residential Care. *Beds* 23.
Ownership Proprietary.

Knox County Nursing Home
Hwy 6 E, Edina, MO, 63537 (816) 397-2282
Admin Gerald Foreman. *Medical Dir/Dir of Nursing* Helen Karhoff LPN.
Licensure Intermediate Care. *Beds* 60. *Certified* Medicaid.
Ownership Proprietary.
Staff Physicians 3 (pt); RNs 1 (pt); LPNs 1 (ft), 2 (pt); Nurses aides 6 (ft), 35 (pt); Physical therapists 1 (pt); Occupational therapists 1 (pt); Speech therapists 1 (pt); Activities coordinators 1 (ft).
Facilities Dining room; Activities room; Chapel; Crafts room; Laundry room; Barber/Beauty shop.
Activities Arts and Crafts; Cards; Games; Reading groups; Prayer groups; Movies.

EL DORADO SPRINGS

Community Nursing Home*
400 E Hospital Rd, El Dorado Springs, MO, 64744 (417) 876-2531
Admin David B Richardson.
Licensure Intermediate Care. *Beds* 120. *Certified* Medicaid.
Ownership Proprietary.

ELDON

Osage Manor Nursing and Care Center
Rt 1, Box 450, Eldon, MO, 65026 (314) 392-3164
Admin Carolyn Nichols. *Medical Dir/Dir of Nursing* Dr Robert Mason.
Licensure Intermediate Care. *Beds* 60. *Certified* Medicaid.
Ownership Proprietary.
Admissions Requirements Minimum age 16; Medical examination; Physician's request.
Staff RNs 1 (ft); LPNs 2 (ft), 1 (pt); Nurses aides 11 (ft), 16 (pt); Activities coordinators 1 (ft).
Facilities Dining room; Physical therapy room; Laundry room; Barber/Beauty shop; Library; Living room; Solarium; Whirlpool bath.
Activities Arts and Crafts; Cards; Games; Reading groups; Prayer groups; Movies; Shopping trips; Dances/Social or cultural gatherings; Book and newspaper reading; Birthday parties monthly; Music programs; Special meals and holiday parties; Exercise group; Coffee group; Resident council; Active community auxilliary; Special pet visitor (dog).
Description Facility has outdoor patio with partial shade for good weather enjoyment.

ELLISVILLE

Westwinds Geriatric Center*
1460 Manchester Rd, Ellisville, MO, 63011 (314) 227-5000
Admin Ronald E Rogers.
Licensure Intermediate Care. *Beds* 120. *Certified* Medicaid.
Ownership Proprietary.

ELSBERRY

Elsberry Missouri Health Care Center
Rt 2, Box 26, Elsberry, MO, 63343 (314) 898-2880
Admin Perry Stonebraker.
Licensure Intermediate Care. *Beds* 60. *Certified* Medicaid.
Ownership Proprietary.
Admissions Requirements Minimum age 18; Medical examination.
Staff RNs 1 (pt); LPNs 3 (ft), 1 (pt); Nurses aides 5 (ft), 4 (pt); Activities coordinators 1 (ft); Dietitians 1 (ft).
Facilities Dining room; Physical therapy room; Activities room; Crafts room; Laundry room; Barber/Beauty shop.
Activities Arts and Crafts; Cards; Games; Prayer groups; Movies; Shopping trips.

Description Facility is located in a rural setting in a modern building with an experienced and friendly staff.

Sunset Nursing and Retirement Home of Elsberry
415 N 5th, Elsberry, MO, 63343 (314) 898-5604
Admin Judith Jordan.
Licensure Intermediate Care. *Beds* 29.
Ownership Proprietary.
Admissions Requirements Minimum age 18.

EUREKA

Marymount Manor
313 Augustine Rd, Eureka, MO, 63025 (314) 587-3234
Admin Charles J Riley. *Medical Dir/Dir of Nursing* Dr Gavini.
Licensure Skilled Care; Intermediate Care.
Beds 120. *Certified* Medicaid; Medicare.
Ownership Nonprofit.
Admissions Requirements Minimum age 21; Medical examination.
Staff Physicians 2 (pt); RNs 3 (ft), 3 (pt); LPNs 8 (ft), 4 (pt); Orderlies 2 (ft), 1 (pt); Nurses aides 48 (ft), 10 (pt); Physical therapists 1 (pt); Reality therapists 1 (pt); Recreational therapists 1 (pt); Occupational therapists 1 (pt); Speech therapists 1 (pt); Activities coordinators 3 (ft), 2 (pt); Dietitians 1 (pt); Dentists 1 (pt); Ophthalmologists 1 (pt); Podiatrists 1 (pt); Audiologists 1 (pt).
Facilities Dining room; Physical therapy room; Activities room; Crafts room; Laundry room; Barber/Beauty shop; Visiting parlors.
Activities Arts and Crafts; Cards; Games; Reading groups; Prayer groups; Movies; Shopping trips; Dances/Social or cultural gatherings.
Description Facility features best of city living in a country setting where you can see for miles the foothills of the Ozark Mountains in the beautiful Meramec River Valley.

Price Memorial*
PO Box 476, Forby Rd, Eureka, MO, 63025 (314) 587-3200
Admin Joseph Spila.
Licensure Skilled Care. *Beds* 120. *Certified* Medicaid.
Ownership Nonprofit.

Saint Joseph's Hill Infirmary Inc*
Saint Joseph's Rd, Eureka, MO, 63025 (314) 587-3661
Admin Br Bernardo Trosa.
Licensure Skilled Care. *Beds* 130.
Ownership Nonprofit.
Affiliation Roman Catholic

EXCELSIOR SPRING

Excelsior Springs Care Center
1410 Hospital Dr, Excelsior Spring, MO, 64024
Admin Thomas Bechtel. *Medical Dir/Dir of Nursing* James Soeldner MD.
Licensure Skilled Care. *Beds* 120. *Certified* Medicaid; Medicare.
Ownership Proprietary.
Staff RNs 2 (ft), 2 (pt); LPNs 7 (ft), 2 (pt);

Orderlies 2 (ft), 1 (pt); Nurses aides 35 (ft), 10 (pt); Activities coordinators 1 (ft), 1 (pt).
Facilities Dining room; Physical therapy room; Activities room; Barber/Beauty shop.
Activities Arts and Crafts; Games; Reading groups; Prayer groups; Shopping trips; Dances/Social or cultural gatherings.

EXCELSIOR SPRINGS

Spa View Nursing Home Inc
120 Bluff St, Excelsior Springs, MO, 64024 (816) 637-3145
Admin Eun Young Hwang. *Medical Dir/Dir of Nursing* Dr Aram Lida.
Licensure Intermediate Care. *Beds* 111.
Ownership Proprietary.
Staff Physicians 3 (pt); RNs 1 (ft), 1 (pt); LPNs 2 (ft), 1 (pt); Nurses aides 17 (ft), 4 (pt); Activities coordinators 1 (ft); Dietitians 1 (pt); Dentists 1 (pt).
Facilities Dining room; Activities room; Chapel; Crafts room; Laundry room; Barber/Beauty shop; Library.
Activities Arts and Crafts; Cards; Games; Reading groups; Prayer groups; Movies; Shopping trips; Dances/Social or cultural gatherings.
Description Facility is located in stone building, 5 floors; at least 2 activities per day; large activity area; private rooms available.

FARMINGTON

Bayless Boarding Home*
Rt 3, Box 228, Farmington, MO, 63640 (314) 756-2856
Admin Emma Lee Bayless.
Licensure Intermediate Care. *Beds* 4.
Ownership Proprietary.

Camelot Nursing Home*
705 Grand Canyon Dr, Farmington, MO, 63640 (314) 756-8911
Admin Carroll Allen.
Licensure Skilled Care; Intermediate Care.
Beds 90. *Certified* Medicaid.
Ownership Proprietary.

Easter's Home of Ruth Inc
401 S Henry, Farmington, MO, 63640 (314) 756-4559
Admin Sandra L Straughan.
Licensure Intermediate Care; ABF. *Beds* ICF 42; ABF 12.
Ownership Proprietary.
Admissions Requirements Minimum age 17.
Staff RNs 1 (pt); LPNs 1 (ft), 2 (pt); Nurses aides 12 (ft), 3 (pt); Physical therapists 2 (pt); Recreational therapists 1 (ft); Speech therapists 2 (pt); Activities coordinators 1 (ft); Dietitians 1 (pt).
Facilities Dining room; Activities room; Chapel; Crafts room; Laundry room; Barber/Beauty shop.
Activities Arts and Crafts; Cards; Games; Reading groups; Prayer groups; Movies; Shopping trips; Dances/Social or cultural gatherings.
Description Facility features family atmosphere, individual personal care, and friendly qualified staff.

Fleur de Lis*
1108 W Liberty, Farmington, MO, 63640 (314) 756-6658
Admin Pearl Underwood.
Licensure Intermediate Care. *Beds* 104. *Certified* Medicaid.
Ownership Proprietary.

Presbyterian Manor at Farmington
500 Cayce, Farmington, MO, 63640 (314) 756-6768
Admin Peter W F Adgie. *Medical Dir/Dir of Nursing* Lana Jinkerson RN.
Licensure Intermediate Care. *Beds* 79.
Ownership Nonprofit.
Admissions Requirements Minimum age 65; Medical examination.
Staff Physicians 1 (pt); RNs 1 (ft), 1 (pt); LPNs 4 (ft), 2 (pt); Nurses aides 37 (ft), 3 (pt); Physical therapists 1 (pt); Occupational therapists 3 (pt); Activities coordinators 2 (ft); Dietitians 1 (pt); Dentists 1 (pt); Podiatrists 1 (pt).
Affiliation Presbyterian

Sunset Nursing and Retirement Home of Farmington*
508 N Washington, Farmington, MO, 63640 (314) 756-5376
Admin Freda Huston.
Licensure Intermediate Care. *Beds* 31.
Ownership Proprietary.

Thomas Dell Nursing Home Inc*
Box 452, Farmington, MO, 63640 (314) 756-6716, 6717
Admin Lester J Straughan and Janet Straughan.
Licensure Intermediate Care. *Beds* 70.
Ownership Proprietary.

FAYETTE

The Greenbriar Home
306 S Main St, Fayette, MO, 65248
Admin Dr Richard L Thurman.
Licensure Residential Care for Mentally Retarded. *Beds* 30.
Ownership Proprietary.
Staff LPNs 1 (pt); Nurses aides 8 (ft); Activities coordinators 1 (pt).
Facilities Dining room; Activities room; Laundry room; Quiet room.
Activities Arts and Crafts; Cards; Games; Reading groups; Prayer groups; Movies; Shopping trips; Dances/Social or cultural gatherings; Musical groups.
Description A quality care home offering a home-like atmosphere, home cooked meals, and a concerned staff.

The Phillips Home*
303 S Main, Fayette, MO, 65248 (816) 248-3333
Admin Lawrence Sapp Jr and Pegi Phillips-Sapp.
Licensure Intermediate Care. *Beds* 30.
Ownership Proprietary.

Rest Haven Nursing Center
400 Mulberry, Fayette, MO, 65248 (816) 248-2277
Admin Chris Losey. *Medical Dir/Dir of

Nursing F Dean MD.
Licensure Intermediate Care. *Beds* 27.
Ownership Proprietary.
Staff Physicians 1 (pt); RNs 1 (pt); LPNs 1 (ft), 1 (pt); Nurses aides 6 (ft), 7 (pt); Physical therapists 1 (pt); Occupational therapists 1 (pt); Speech therapists 1 (pt); Activities coordinators 1 (pt); Dietitians 1 (pt).
Facilities Dining room; Activities room; Laundry room; Barber/Beauty shop.
Activities Arts and Crafts; Cards; Games; Reading groups; Prayer groups.

Vogue Retirement Residence
301 S Main St, Fayette, MO, 65248
Admin Zeda Eaton-Wiehardt and Theda Stidham.
Licensure Adult Boarding Care. *Beds* 11.
Ownership Proprietary.
Admissions Requirements Females only; Medical examination.
Staff Nurses aides 2 (pt).
Facilities Dining room; Crafts room; Barber/Beauty shop.
Activities Arts and Crafts; Cards; Games; Reading groups; Prayer groups; Shopping trips.
Description Facility is newly decorated, close to town, with a big front porch and big yard for the residents' enjoyment; all private rooms, 5 with private bathrooms; a happy home with lots of love.

FENTON

Cori-Manor Nursing Home
560 Corisande Hill Rd, Fenton, MO, 63026
(314) 343-2282
Admin Inez Childress. *Medical Dir/Dir of Nursing* Dr Robert Dorton.
Licensure Skilled Care; Residential Care.
Beds SNF 124; Residential Care 22.
Ownership Proprietary.
Admissions Requirements Medical examination.
Staff Physicians 1 (ft), 3 (pt); RNs 2 (ft), 1 (pt); LPNs 7 (ft); Orderlies 3 (ft); Nurses aides 42 (ft); Recreational therapists 1 (ft); Occupational therapists 1 (ft); Activities coordinators 1 (ft); Dietitians 1 (ft); Dentists 1 (pt); Ophthalmologists 1 (ft); Podiatrists 1 (pt).
Facilities Dining room; Physical therapy room; Activities room; Crafts room; Laundry room; Barber/Beauty shop; Library.
Activities Arts and Crafts; Cards; Games; Reading groups; Prayer groups; Movies; Shopping trips; Dances/Social or cultural gatherings.
Description Staff is very knowledgeable in caring for Alzheimer's patients.

Fieser Nursing Home*
PO Box F, 404 Main, Fenton, MO, 63026 (314) 343-4344
Admin Glen E Fieser.
Licensure Intermediate Care. *Beds* 60.
Ownership Proprietary.

FERGUSON

Christian Old People's Home
800 Chambers Rd, Ferguson, MO, 63135 (314) 522-8100

Admin Richard Klug. *Medical Dir/Dir of Nursing* E Pimentel MD.
Licensure Skilled Care; Intermediate Care.
Beds 120. *Certified* Medicaid.
Admissions Requirements Minimum age 65.
Staff Physicians 4 (pt); RNs 5 (ft), 4 (pt); LPNs 3 (ft), 6 (pt); Nurses aides 39 (ft), 19 (pt); Physical therapists 2 (ft); Activities coordinators 2 (ft); Dietitians 1 (ft); Dentists 1 (pt); Podiatrists 1 (pt).
Facilities Dining room; Physical therapy room; Activities room; Chapel; Crafts room; Laundry room; Barber/Beauty shop; Library.
Activities Arts and Crafts; Cards; Games; Reading groups; Prayer groups; Movies; Shopping trips; Dances/Social or cultural gatherings.

Oak Knoll Health Care
37 N Clark Ave, Ferguson, MO, 63135 (314) 521-7419
Admin Judy Mincher.
Licensure Intermediate Care. *Beds* 60.
Ownership Proprietary.
Facilities Dining room; Physical therapy room; Activities room; Chapel; Crafts room; Laundry room; Barber/Beauty shop; Library.
Activities Arts and Crafts; Cards; Games; Reading groups; Prayer groups; Movies; Shopping trips; Dances/Social or cultural gatherings.

FESTUS

Bolle's Boarding Home Inc
500 Sunshine Dr, Festus, MO, 63028
Admin Louisa E Bolle. *Medical Dir/Dir of Nursing* M Charles MD.
Licensure Intermediate Care. *Beds* 28. *Certified* Medicaid.
Ownership Proprietary.
Admissions Requirements Medical examination.
Staff Physicians 1 (pt); LPNs 2 (ft); Nurses aides 6 (ft), 2 (pt); Physical therapists 1 (ft); Recreational therapists 1 (ft); Activities coordinators 1 (ft); Dietitians 1 (pt); Dentists 1 (pt); Ophthalmologists 1 (pt); Podiatrists 1 (pt); Audiologists 1 (pt).
Facilities Dining room; Physical therapy room; Activities room; Crafts room; Laundry room; Barber/Beauty shop.
Activities Arts and Crafts; Cards; Games; Reading groups; Prayer groups; Movies; Shopping trips; Exercise sessions.
Description Facility is home-like; residents may bring personal belongings; lots of activities outdoors; kind, considerate care at reasonable cost.

Festus Manor*
PO Box 548, Festus, MO, 63028 (314) 937-9066
Admin Gordon Carlson.
Licensure Skilled Care. *Beds* 120. *Certified* Medicaid.
Ownership Proprietary.

Festus Rest Home*
705 Moore St, Festus, MO, 63028 (314) 937-7125
Admin Harry J Reiter.
Licensure Residential Care. *Beds* 21.
Ownership Proprietary.

Mountain View Convalescent Home Inc*
Rt 5, Box 28, Festus, MO, 63028 (314) 296-8666
Admin Margaret Helms.
Licensure Skilled Care. *Beds* 93.
Ownership Proprietary.

Rose Hill Nursing Home Inc*
PO Box 427, Rt 1, Festus, MO, 63028 (314) 937-3150
Admin James DeClue.
Licensure Intermediate Care. *Beds* 81.
Ownership Proprietary.

FLAT RIVER

Desloge Health Care Center*
PO Box AA, 801 Brim St, Flat River, MO, 63601 (314) 431-0223
Admin Nina Blum Holloway.
Licensure Skilled Care; Intermediate Care.
Beds 120. *Certified* Medicaid.
Ownership Proprietary.

Rest Haven
301 Roosevelt, Flat River, MO, 63601
Admin Shirley Bable. *Medical Dir/Dir of Nursing* Sandra Petrie.
Licensure Intermediate Care. *Beds* 14. *Certified* Medicaid; Medicare.
Ownership Proprietary.
Staff Physicians 1 (pt); RNs 1 (pt); LPNs 1 (ft); Nurses aides 5 (ft); Activities coordinators 1 (ft).
Facilities Dining room; Activities room; Crafts room; Laundry room.
Activities Arts and Crafts; Cards; Games; Reading groups; Prayer groups; Shopping trips; Dances/Social or cultural gatherings.
Description Facility offers a small town setting with family atmosphere with emphasis on activities.

FLORISSANT

Americana Healthcare Center*
1200 Graham Rd, Florissant, MO, 63031 (314) 838-6555
Admin Judith Sutton.
Licensure Skilled Care; Intermediate Care.
Beds 98. *Certified* Medicaid; Medicare.
Ownership Proprietary.

Florissant Nursing Center*
Rancho and Patterson, Florissant, MO, 63031 (314) 839-2150
Admin Lawrence Boshert.
Licensure Skilled Care. *Beds* 120. *Certified* Medicaid.
Ownership Proprietary.

Northgate Park Nursing Home
250 S Florissant Rd, Florissant, MO, 63031 (314) 838-2211
Admin Ronald L Sher.
Licensure Skilled Care. *Beds* 170.
Ownership Proprietary.
Staff Physical therapists; Occupational therapists; Speech therapists; Activities coordinators; Dietitians; Dentists; Podiatrists.
Facilities Dining room; Physical therapy room;

Activities room; Crafts room; Laundry room; Barber/Beauty shop.
Activities Arts and Crafts; Cards; Games; Reading groups; Prayer groups; Movies; Shopping trips; Dances/Social or cultural gatherings.
Description Facility also offers residential care (50 beds).

Saint Sophia Geriatric Center*
936 Charbonier Rd, Florissant, MO, 63031 (314) 831-4800
Admin Edward Dering.
Licensure Skilled Care; Intermediate Care.
Beds 240. *Certified* Medicaid; Medicare.
Ownership Proprietary.

FORSYTH

Lakeview Rest Home Inc*
PO Box 276, Forsyth, MO, 65653 (417) 546-3081
Admin Carolyn K Blevins.
Licensure Intermediate Care. *Beds* 67.
Ownership Proprietary.

FREDERICKTOWN

Madison Memorial Hospital
College at Wood Ave, Box 431, Fredericktown, MO, 63645 (314) 783-3341
Admin Bill M Seek. *Medical Dir/Dir of Nursing* Arthur Newcomb MD.
Licensure Intermediate Care. *Beds* 9.
Ownership Public.
Staff Physicians 12 (ft); RNs 2 (ft); LPNs 4 (ft), 2 (pt); Orderlies 3 (ft); Nurses aides 38 (ft); Physical therapists 1 (ft); Speech therapists 1 (pt); Activities coordinators 1 (ft); Dietitians 2 (ft).
Facilities Dining room; Physical therapy room; Activities room; Chapel; Crafts room; Laundry room; Barber/Beauty shop.
Activities Arts and Crafts; Games; Reading groups; Prayer groups; Movies; Dances/Social or cultural gatherings.

Ozark Nursing Home
700 S Main St, Fredericktown, MO, 63645 (314) 783-6833
Admin Florence Wanner.
Licensure Intermediate Care. *Beds* 42.
Ownership Proprietary.
Admissions Requirements Minimum age 40; Medical examination.
Staff Physicians 1 (pt); RNs 1 (pt); LPNs 2 (ft), 1 (pt); Orderlies 1 (ft), 2 (pt); Nurses aides 12 (ft), 5 (pt); Recreational therapists 1 (pt); Dietitians 1 (pt).

FULTON

Fulton Manor Care Center
520 Manor Dr, Fulton, MO, 65251 (314) 642-6834
Admin Charlotte Henderson. *Medical Dir/Dir of Nursing* Dr George Grace.
Licensure Intermediate Care. *Beds* 52.
Ownership Proprietary.
Admissions Requirements Minimum age Birth; Medical examination; Physician's request.
Staff RNs 1 (pt); LPNs 3 (ft), 1 (pt); Nurses

aides 10 (ft), 4 (pt); Activities coordinators 1 (pt).
Facilities Dining room; Activities room; Laundry room.
Activities Arts and Crafts; Cards; Games; Reading groups; Prayer groups; Movies.

Fulton Presbyterian Manor*
802 Court St, Fulton, MO, 65251 (314) 642-6646
Admin Jane E Daniell-Mitchel.
Licensure Intermediate Care; Boarding Care.
Beds ICF 30; Boarding Care 37.
Ownership Nonprofit.
Affiliation Presbyterian

Kingdom Nursing Home Association Inc
Rt 6, 501 Collier Lane, Fulton, MO, 65251-1399 (314) 642-2022
Admin Catherine P Woodson.
Licensure Intermediate Care. *Beds* 44.
Ownership Nonprofit.
Admissions Requirements Medical examination.
Staff RNs 1 (pt); LPNs 1 (ft), 4 (pt); Nurses aides 12 (ft), 15 (pt); Physical therapists 1 (pt); Reality therapists 1 (pt); Recreational therapists 1 (pt); Occupational therapists 1 (pt); Speech therapists 1 (pt); Activities coordinators 1 (pt); Dietitians 1 (pt); Audiologists 1 (pt).
Facilities Dining room; Activities room; Laundry room; Barber/Beauty shop.
Activities Arts and Crafts; Cards; Games; Prayer groups; Movies; Dances/Social or cultural gatherings.
Description Located in a country atmosphere within the city limits, this county home provides a warm, loving, home-like environment at very reasonable rates. Licensed by MO Division of Aging and the MO Dept of Mental Health.

Modern Acre Home
Rt 2, Fulton, MO, 65251 (314) 642-3160
Admin Sodonia Logan.
Licensure Intermediate Care. *Beds* 22.
Ownership Proprietary.

Sodonia's Home
222 E 6th, Fulton, MO, 65251 (314) 642-3160
Admin Warren T Robinson.
Licensure Intermediate Care. *Beds* 22.
Ownership Proprietary.

GALLATIN

Cox Nursing Home
611 W Johnson, Gallatin, MO, 64640 (816) 663-3301
Admin Cynthia Thomas.
Licensure Intermediate Care. *Beds* 18.
Ownership Proprietary.

Daviess County Nursing Home Inc
Hwy 6 W, Gallatin, MO, 64640 (816) 663-2197
Admin Evelyn Morrissey.
Licensure Intermediate Care. *Beds* 97. *Certified* Medicaid.
Ownership Nonprofit.
Staff RNs 1 (ft), 2 (pt); LPNs 5 (ft); Nurses aides 37 (ft), 11 (pt); Physical therapists 1 (pt); Occupational therapists 1 (pt); Speech thera-

pists 1 (pt); Activities coordinators 2 (pt); Dietitians 1 (pt).
Facilities Dining room; Physical therapy room; Activities room; Chapel; Crafts room; Laundry room; Barber/Beauty shop; Library.
Activities Arts and Crafts; Cards; Games; Reading groups; Prayer groups; Movies; Shopping trips; Dances/Social or cultural gatherings.
Description We have bingo, birthday parties (once a month) sponsored by organizations within the county, exercise classes, coffee time, resident council meetings, van rides, golf cart rides, animal fairs (sponsored by local 4-H groups), church services (sponsored by Ministerial Alliance group) and many, many school groups come and put on programs.

GLADSTONE

Kendallwood Trails Nursing Center*
2900 Kendallwood Pkwy, Gladstone, MO, 64119 (816) 453-1222
Admin William D Burford.
Licensure Skilled Care; Intermediate Care.
Beds 280. *Certified* Medicaid; Medicare.
Ownership Proprietary.

GLASGOW

Colonial Manor of Glasgow
100 Audsley Dr, Glasgow, MO, 65254 (816) 338-2297
Admin James C Losey. *Medical Dir/Dir of Nursing* William Marshall MD.
Licensure Intermediate Care. *Beds* 59. *Certified* Medicaid.
Ownership Proprietary.
Staff Physicians 6 (pt); RNs 1 (ft), 1 (pt); LPNs 1 (ft); Orderlies 1 (ft); Nurses aides 18 (ft), 6 (pt); Physical therapists 1 (pt); Recreational therapists 1 (ft); Occupational therapists 1 (pt); Speech therapists 1 (pt); Activities coordinators 1 (ft); Dietitians 1 (pt); Dentists 1 (pt); Ophthalmologists 1 (pt); Podiatrists 1 (pt); Audiologists 1 (pt).
Facilities Dining room; Physical therapy room; Activities room; Chapel; Crafts room; Laundry room; Barber/Beauty shop; Library.
Activities Arts and Crafts; Cards; Games; Reading groups; Prayer groups; Movies; Shopping trips; Dances/Social or cultural gatherings.
Description Facility provides an outstanding care program.

GOWER

Gower Convalescent Center Inc*
Hwy 169 S, Gower, MO, 64454 (816) 424-6483
Admin John Ronald Murawski.
Licensure Intermediate Care. *Beds* 74. *Certified* Medicaid.
Ownership Nonprofit.

GRANDVIEW

Geriatric Center of Grandview
13111 Spring St, Grandview, MO, 64030 (816) 761-4333
Admin Tom Mason. *Medical Dir/Dir of Nursing* Dr Kirk Barnett.

Licensure Intermediate Care. *Beds* 52.
Ownership Proprietary.
Admissions Requirements Medical examination.
Staff Physicians 2 (pt); RNs 1 (pt); LPNs 3 (ft), 1 (pt); Nurses aides 18 (ft), 5 (pt); Physical therapists 3 (pt); Reality therapists 1 (pt); Occupational therapists 1 (pt); Speech therapists 1 (pt); Activities coordinators 2 (pt); Dietitians 1 (pt); Dentists 1 (pt); Podiatrists 1 (pt).
Facilities Dining room; Laundry room.
Activities Arts and Crafts; Cards; Games; Prayer groups.
Description Facility is small with a home-like atmosphere.

Grandview Manor Care Center*
5301 E 125th St, Grandview, MO, 64030 (816) 763-2855
Admin Vada Mae Elder.
Licensure Intermediate Care. *Beds* 102.
Ownership Proprietary.

GRANT CITY

Wilkinson's Health Care Center
Rt 1, Box 88, Grant City, MO, 64456
Admin Susan Holzfaster.
Licensure Residential Care. *Beds* 15.
Ownership Proprietary.
Admissions Requirements Minimum age 21; Medical examination.
Staff Physicians; LPNs; Nurses aides.
Facilities Dining room; Activities room; Laundry room.
Activities Cards; Games.
Description Facility offers security and supervision with a home-like atmosphere rather than that of an institution.

Worth County Convalescent Center
Rt 3, Box 100, Grant City, MO, 64456 (816) 564-3304
Admin Landis L Downing. *Medical Dir/Dir of Nursing* R J Swift DO.
Licensure Intermediate Care. *Beds* 60. *Certified* Medicaid.
Ownership Nonprofit.
Admissions Requirements Medical examination; Physician's request.
Staff RNs 2 (pt); LPNs 5 (pt); Nurses aides 15 (ft), 5 (pt); Physical therapists 1 (pt); Occupational therapists 1 (pt); Speech therapists 1 (pt); Activities coordinators 1 (pt); Dietitians 1 (pt); Audiologists 1 (pt).
Facilities Dining room; Physical therapy room; Activities room; Crafts room; Laundry room; Barber/Beauty shop; TV; Living room.
Activities Arts and Crafts; Games; Reading groups; Prayer groups; Movies; Shopping trips; Dances/Social or cultural gatherings.
Description Facility features 24-hour nursing care at low economic cost.

GREENFIELD

Dade County Nursing Home*
400 S Broad St, Greenfield, MO, 65661 (417) 637-5315
Admin John F Dwyer.

Licensure Intermediate Care. *Beds* 120. *Certified* Medicaid.
Ownership Public.

GREENTOP

Haven of Rest Inc
Main St, Greentop, MO, 63546 (816) 949-2316
Admin Anna J Eastes.
Licensure Intermediate Care. *Beds* 20.
Ownership Proprietary.

HALLSVILLE

Arah's Acres*
Box J, Elizabeth St, Hallsville, MO, 65255 (314) 696-2541
Admin Arah Kathryn Hubbard Grimes.
Licensure Intermediate Care. *Beds* 18.
Ownership Proprietary.

HAMILTON

Hamilton Hill Crest Manor
Irwin and Colby Sts, Hamilton, MO, 64644 (816) 583-2364
Admin Katharine Ensign.
Licensure Intermediate Care. *Beds* 60. *Certified* Medicaid.
Ownership Proprietary.
Staff Physicians 1 (ft); LPNs 4 (pt); Physical therapists 2 (pt); Occupational therapists 2 (pt); Speech therapists 1 (pt); Activities coordinators 1 (ft); Dietitians 1 (pt).
Facilities Dining room; Activities room; Crafts room; Laundry room; Barber/Beauty shop.
Activities Arts and Crafts; Cards; Games; Reading groups; Movies; Shopping trips; Dances/Social or cultural gatherings.

HANNIBAL

Becky Thatcher Nursing Home*
711 Church St, Hannibal, MO, 63401 (314) 221-4288
Admin Bill Callicott.
Licensure Intermediate Care. *Beds* 23.
Ownership Proprietary.

Beth Haven Nursing Home*
2500 Pleasant St, Hannibal, MO, 63401 (314) 221-6000
Admin Steven Ringenberg.
Licensure Skilled Care; Intermediate Care.
Beds 60. *Certified* Medicaid; Medicare.
Ownership Nonprofit.

Hannibal Care Center
Munger Ln, Hannibal, MO, 63401 (314) 221-9122
Admin Lois S Warren. *Medical Dir/Dir of Nursing* J W Walterscheid.
Licensure Skilled Care; Intermediate Care.
Beds 120. *Certified* Medicaid.
Ownership Proprietary.
Admissions Requirements Medical examination.
Facilities Dining room; Physical therapy room; Activities room; Crafts room; Laundry room; Barber/Beauty shop; Library.

Activities Arts and Crafts; Cards; Games; Reading groups; Prayer groups; Movies; Shopping trips; Dances/Social or cultural gatherings.
Description Central nursing care with all resident corridors and activity areas visible. Bright, cheerfully decorated facility with both private and semi-private accommodations. Bath adjoins each room. Individual heating and cooling controls.

Lee Ann's Residential Facility
928 S Arch, Hannibal, MO, 63401
Admin Mildred Riggs.
Licensure Intermediate Care for Mentally Retarded. *Beds* 12. *Certified* Medicaid.
Ownership Proprietary.
Staff Physicians; RNs; LPNs; Nurses aides.
Facilities Dining room; Activities room; Laundry room.
Activities Games; Shopping trips; Dances/Social or cultural gatherings.
Description Facility offers quality care in a home-like atmosphere.

Luther Manor Retirement and Nursing Center
Hwy 61 N, Rt 2, Hannibal, MO, 63401 (314) 221-5533
Admin Martha A Greening.
Licensure Intermediate Care. *Beds* 60. *Certified* Medicaid.
Ownership Nonprofit.
Admissions Requirements Medical examination.
Staff RNs 1 (ft); LPNs 4 (ft), 1 (pt); Nurses aides 23 (ft); Recreational therapists 1 (ft); Dietitians 1 (pt).
Affiliation Lutheran
Facilities Dining room; Physical therapy room; Activities room; Chapel; Crafts room; Laundry room; Barber/Beauty shop; Library.
Activities Arts and Crafts; Cards; Games; Reading groups; Prayer groups; Movies; Shopping trips; Dances/Social or cultural gatherings; Community invited buffets; Daily exercises; Pet therapy.

River View Manor Home*
Box 894, 408 Rock St, Hannibal, MO, 63401 (314) 221-5910
Admin Phyllis Rupp.
Licensure Intermediate Care. *Beds* 39.
Ownership Proprietary.

Shady Lawn Lodge
8 Stillwell Pl, Hannibal, MO, 63401 (314) 221-5133
Admin Mary Comer. *Medical Dir/Dir of Nursing* Dr J H Waltuschild.
Licensure Intermediate Care. *Beds* 36.
Ownership Proprietary.
Staff Physicians 2 (pt); RNs 1 (pt); LPNs 1 (ft), 2 (pt); Nurses aides 9 (ft); Activities coordinators 1 (ft).
Facilities Dining room; Activities room; Crafts room; Laundry room.
Activities Games; Reading groups; Prayer groups; Shopping trips.
Description Staff spends a lot of time giving residents loving attention as well as activities such as church and outside entertainment.

HARRISONVILLE

ABC Health Center
307 E South St, Harrisonville, MO, 64701 (816) 884-3413
Admin Robert Samuelson. *Medical Dir/Dir of Nursing* Ruth Lehr.
Licensure Intermediate Care. *Beds* 60. *Certified* Medicaid.
Ownership Proprietary.
Admissions Requirements Minimum age 18; Medical examination.
Staff Physicians 6 (pt); RNs 1 (ft); LPNs 4 (ft); Nurses aides 18 (ft), 7 (ft); Physical therapists 1 (pt); Reality therapists 1 (pt); Recreational therapists 1 (pt); Occupational therapists 1 (pt); Speech therapists 1 (pt); Activities coordinators 1 (ft); Dietitians 1 (pt); Dentists 1 (pt); Ophthalmologists 1 (pt); Podiatrists 1 (pt); Audiologists 1 (pt).
Facilities Dining room; Physical therapy room; Activities room; Crafts room; Laundry room; Barber/Beauty shop.
Activities Arts and Crafts; Cards; Games; Reading groups; Prayer groups; Movies; Shopping trips; Dances/Social or cultural gatherings.

Camden Health Center
2203 E Mechanic, Harrisonville, MO, 64701 (816) 884-2622
Admin Virginia Samuelson. *Medical Dir/Dir of Nursing* Richard Price.
Licensure Intermediate Care. *Beds* 60. *Certified* Medicaid.
Ownership Proprietary.
Admissions Requirements Minimum age 16; Medical examination.
Staff RNs 1 (ft), 1 (pt); LPNs 3 (ft); Orderlies 1 (pt); Nurses aides 17 (ft); Recreational therapists 1 (ft); Activities coordinators 1 (ft).
Facilities Dining room; Physical therapy room; Activities room; Crafts room; Laundry room; Barber/Beauty shop.
Activities Arts and Crafts; Cards; Games; Prayer groups; Movies; Shopping trips; Dances/Social or cultural gatherings.
Description The staff at Camden is geared to all those entities necessary to provide quality care and love to all residents.

Dunsworth Estates*
104 W Pearl, Harrisonville, MO, 64701 (816) 884-6300
Admin Melvin Dunsworth, Jr.
Licensure Residential Care. *Beds* 51.
Ownership Proprietary.

Pleasant View Rest Home*
PO Box 423, Rt 2, 2001 County Home Rd, Harrisonville, MO, 64701 (816) 884-4731
Admin ALice C Reed.
Licensure Intermediate Care. *Beds* 43.
Ownership Proprietary.

HAYTI

Pemiscot County Memorial Hospital Long Term Care Unit
PO Box 489, Hayti, MO, 63851 (314) 359-1372
Admin Glenn Haynes. *Medical Dir/Dir of Nursing* S Sanan MD.
Licensure Intermediate Care. *Beds* 60. Certified Medicaid.
Ownership Public.
Admissions Requirements Minimum age 16; Medical examination; Physician's request.
Staff Physicians 12 (pt); RNs 1 (ft); LPNs 6 (ft), 1 (pt); Orderlies 4 (ft); Nurses aides 19 (ft), 1 (pt); Recreational therapists 1 (ft); Activities coordinators 1 (ft).
Facilities Dining room; Barber/Beauty shop.
Activities Arts and Crafts; Games; Reading groups; Prayer groups; Movies.
Description Facility is a 60-bed intermediate care, long-term unit built adjacent to Pemiscot County Memorial Hospital and has 24-hour licensed personnel.

HERMANN

Frene Valley Geriatric and Rehabilitation Center
18th/Jefferson St, Rt 1, Box 30C, Hermann, MO, 65041 (314) 486-3193
Admin Robert H Lloyd. *Medical Dir/Dir of Nursing* George Workman MD.
Licensure Intermediate Care. *Beds* 60. *Certified* Medicaid.
Ownership Proprietary.
Admissions Requirements Minimum age 18.
Staff Physicians 6 (pt); RNs 1 (ft); LPNs 1 (ft); Physical therapists 1 (pt); Activities coordinators 1 (ft); Dietitians 1 (pt); Dentists 3 (pt).
Facilities Dining room; Physical therapy room; Activities room; Crafts room; Laundry room; Barber/Beauty shop.
Activities Arts and Crafts; Cards; Games; Prayer groups; Movies; Shopping trips; Dances/Social or cultural gatherings.
Description A family business for over 30 years, this facility is 4 years old, with a good physical therapy program, activities, quilting, crafts, etc. Homemade bread made almost daily.

Frene Valley Health Center
Rt 1, Box 75A, Hermann, MO, 65041 (314) 486-3155
Admin Gary E Lloyd. *Medical Dir/Dir of Nursing* G M Workman MD.
Licensure Intermediate Care. *Beds* 88.
Ownership Proprietary.
Admissions Requirements Minimum age 18; Medical examination.
Staff RNs 1 (ft); LPNs 3 (ft); Nurses aides 16 (ft), 6 (pt); Activities coordinators 1 (ft).
Facilities Dining room; Physical therapy room; Activities room; Crafts room; Laundry room; Barber/Beauty shop.
Activities Arts and Crafts; Games; Prayer groups; Movies; Shopping trips; Dances/Social or cultural gatherings; Exercises; Church services.
Description Facility features a beautiful rural setting, caring concerned staff, and many additional services are provided to the community.

HIGGINSVILLE

Higginsville State School and Hospital*
Box 522, Higginsville, MO, 64037 (816) 584-2142
Admin Ara L Morris.
Licensure Intermediate Care for Mentally Retarded. *Beds* 310.

Meyer Care Center
Truman Rd and 13 Hwy, PO Box 512, Higginsville, MO, 64037 (816) 584-4224
Admin Raymond E Robinson.
Licensure Intermediate Care. *Beds* 60.
Ownership Nonprofit.
Admissions Requirements Minimum age 16; Medical examination.
Staff Physicians 4 (pt); RNs 1 (ft), 2 (pt); LPNs 3 (ft); Nurses aides 22 (ft), 12 (pt); Physical therapists 1 (pt); Occupational therapists 1 (pt); Speech therapists 1 (pt); Activities coordinators 1 (ft), 1 (pt).
Facilities Dining room; Activities room; Chapel; Laundry room; Barber/Beauty shop.
Activities Cards; Games; Reading groups; Movies; Exercise program for all patients.
Description Facility offers excellent care because that personal touch is available; 3 levels of care for patients and 3 flat daily rates, no add-on charges.

Parkview Nursing Home*
PO Box 471, 214 E 13th St, Higginsville, MO, 64037 (816) 584-2543
Admin William W Popp.
Licensure Intermediate Care. *Beds* 18.
Ownership Proprietary.

HILLSBORO

Castle Acres Nursing Home Inc*
PO Box 308, Hillsboro, MO, 63050 (314) 789-2882
Admin Mary E Ouhrabka.
Licensure Intermediate Care. *Beds* 29.
Ownership Proprietary.

Cedar Grove Nursing Home
Box 367, Hillsboro, MO, 63050 (314) 789-2481
Admin Carolyn Dahle. *Medical Dir/Dir of Nursing* Dr Dandamudi.
Licensure Intermediate Care. *Beds* 64.
Ownership Proprietary.
Admissions Requirements Minimum age 18.
Staff Physicians 1 (pt); RNs 1 (pt); LPNs 2 (ft); Orderlies 1 (ft); Nurses aides 13 (ft), 2 (pt); Physical therapists 1 (pt); Speech therapists 1 (pt); Activities coordinators 1 (ft); Dietitians 1 (pt); Dentists 1 (pt); Audiologists 1 (pt).
Facilities Dining room; Activities room; Crafts room; Laundry room.
Activities Arts and Crafts; Cards; Games; Prayer groups; Movies; Shopping trips; Dances/Social or cultural gatherings.

HOLDEN

Virginia Manor Care Center*
2005 S Lexington, Holden, MO, 64040 (816) 732-4138
Admin Virginia Thompson.
Licensure Intermediate Care. *Beds* 52.
Ownership Proprietary.

HOUSTON

Texas County Rest Home Inc*
Rt 1, Houston, MO, 65483 (417) 967-2983
Admin Delores Bowlin.
Licensure Residential Care. *Beds* 30.
Ownership Proprietary.

HUMANSVILLE

Big Springs Nursing Home*
203 E Mill St, Humansville, MO, 65674 (417)
754-2450
Admin Norma Pitts.
Licensure Intermediate Care. *Beds* 38.
Ownership Proprietary.

HUNTSVILLE

Pleasant View Nursing Home*
PO Box 162, Rt JJ, Huntsville, MO, 65259
(816) 277-4455
Admin Leonard Fish.
Licensure Intermediate Care. *Beds* 67.
Ownership Proprietary.

IMPERIAL

Four Oaks Rest Home Inc*
Rt 2, Imperial, MO, 63052 (314) 464-1313
Admin Veronica M Ziegelmeyer.
Licensure Intermediate Care. *Beds* 46.
Ownership Proprietary.

INDEPENDENCE

Cable Rest Home*
1500 N Liberty, Independence, MO, 64050
(816) 252-7435
Admin David K Binger.
Licensure Intermediate Care. *Beds* 37.
Ownership Proprietary.

The Country House
1400 N River, Independence, MO, 64050 (816)
252-2737
Admin Alma Patti Vaughan.
Licensure Intermediate Care. *Beds* 41.
Ownership Proprietary.
Admissions Requirements Minimum age 50;
Females only
Staff Physicians 1 (pt); RNs 1 (pt); Nurses
aides 16 (ft); Physical therapists 1 (pt); Reality
therapists 1 (pt); Occupational therapists 1 (pt);
Speech therapists 1 (pt); Activities coordinators
1 (pt); Dietitians 1 (pt); Dentists 1 (pt);
Ophthalmologists 1 (pt); Podiatrists 1 (pt);
Audiologists 1 (pt).
Facilities Dining room; Activities room; Laun-
dry room.
Activities Arts and Crafts; Cards; Games;
Reading groups; Prayer groups; Movies.
Description Facility is home-like with carpeting
and wallpaper; emphasis on small groups to
eliminate "nursing home" appearance.

Four Pines Retirement Home Inc
3713 Hardy, Independence, MO, 64052 (816)
353-2737
Admin Evelyn Spangler. *Medical Dir/Dir of*

Nursing Ron LaHue DO.
Licensure Intermediate Care. *Beds* 45.
Ownership Proprietary.
Admissions Requirements Medical examina-
tion; Physician's request.
Staff RNs 1 (ft); LPNs 2 (ft), 1 (pt); Nurses
aides 13 (ft), 2 (pt); Activities coordinators 1
(pt); Dietitians 1 (pt).
Facilities Dining room; Physical therapy room;
Activities room; Laundry room.
Activities Games; Reading groups; Prayer
groups; Movies; Shopping trips.
Description Facility offers a very home-like
atmosphere with special care for all residents
with individual attention to diets, etc.

General Baptist Nursing Home*
419 N Hocker, Independence, MO, 64050 (816)
252-4019
Admin Alberta Marshall.
Licensure Intermediate Care. *Beds* 27.
Ownership Nonprofit.
Affiliation Baptist

Independence Health Care Center
17451 E Medical Center Pkwy, Independence,
MO, 64050 (816) 373-7795
Admin Mary Beth Alpers. *Medical Dir/Dir of
Nursing* Keith Broughton DO.
Licensure Skilled Care; Intermediate Care.
Beds 120. *Certified* Medicaid; Medicare.
Ownership Proprietary.
Staff Physicians 1 (pt); RNs 4 (ft), 1 (pt); LPNs
7 (ft), 2 (pt); Orderlies 2 (ft); Nurses aides 40
(ft); Physical therapists 1 (pt); Occupational
therapists 1 (pt); Speech therapists 1 (pt);
Activities coordinators 1 (ft); Dietitians 1 (pt);
Dentists 1 (pt); Podiatrists 1 (pt).
Facilities Dining room; Physical therapy room;
Activities room; Crafts room; Laundry room;
Barber/Beauty shop.
Activities Arts and Crafts; Cards; Games;
Reading groups; Prayer groups; Movies; Shop-
ping trips; Dances/Social or cultural gatherings.

Independence Manor Care Center
1600 S Kingshighway, Independence, MO,
64050 (816) 833-4777
Admin Kim Collins.
Licensure Intermediate Care. *Beds* 102.
Ownership Proprietary.
Admissions Requirements Medical examina-
tion; Physician's request.
Staff Physicians 1 (ft), 9 (pt); RNs 1 (ft), 1 (pt);
LPNs 4 (ft), 3 (pt); Orderlies 1 (pt); Nurses
aides 22 (ft), 14 (pt); Physical therapists 1 (ft);
Reality therapists 1 (ft), 1 (pt); Recreational
therapists 1 (ft), 1 (pt); Occupational therapists
1 (pt); Speech therapists 1 (pt); Activities coor-
dinators 1 (ft), 1 (pt); Dietitians 1 (pt); Dentists
1 (pt); Podiatrists 1 (pt).
Facilities Dining room; Physical therapy room;
Activities room; Crafts room; Laundry room;
Barber/Beauty shop.
Activities Arts and Crafts; Cards; Games;
Reading groups; Prayer groups; Movies; Out-
to-lunch bunch; Classic cooks; Daily exercise.

Independence Sanitarium and Hospital
1509 W Truman Rd, Independence, MO,
64050 (816) 836-8100

Licensure Skilled Care. *Beds* SNF 43. *Certified* Medicare.
Ownership Nonprofit.

Resthaven*
1500 W Truman Rd, Independence, MO,
64050 (816) 254-3500
Admin Homer D Spiers.
Licensure Skilled Care; Intermediate Care.
Beds 259. *Certified* Medicaid.
Ownership Nonprofit.

Windsor Estates of Independence
10300 Truman Rd, Independence, MO, 64052
(816) 836-1250
Admin Denny Barnett. *Medical Dir/Dir of
Nursing* C M Cernech DO.
Licensure Skilled Care; Intermediate Care.
Beds 83. *Certified* Medicaid; Medicare.
Ownership Public.
Admissions Requirements Minimum age 18.
Staff Physicians 1 (ft), 3 (pt); RNs 2 (ft), 1 (pt);
LPNs 6 (ft), 2 (pt); Nurses aides 34 (ft), 6 (pt);
Physical therapists 1 (ft); Occupational thera-
pists 1 (pt); Speech therapists 1 (pt); Activities
coordinators 1 (ft); Dietitians 1 (pt); Dentists 1
(pt); Podiatrists 1 (pt).
Facilities Dining room; Physical therapy room;
Activities room; Crafts room; Laundry room;
Barber/Beauty shop.
Activities Arts and Crafts; Games; Reading
groups; Prayer groups; Movies; Dances/Social
or cultural gatherings.
Description Facility features annual Christmas
cookie bakeoff and a rock and roll jamboree for
the American Heart Association.

IRONTON

The Baptist Home Inc*
PO Box 87, Ironton, MO, 63650 (314)
546-7429
Admin Edward C Goodwin.
Licensure Intermediate Care. *Beds* 140.
Ownership Nonprofit.
Affiliation Baptist

Crawford's Boarding Home
101 S Knob, Ironton, MO, 63650 (314)
546-3080
Admin Violet J Crawford.
Licensure Adult Boarding Facility. *Beds* 8.
Ownership Nonprofit.
Admissions Requirements Males only
Facilities Dining room; Laundry room.
Activities Games; Shopping trips.

Lone Pine Congregate Center
321 S Main St, Ironton, MO, 63650
Admin Sharon Gamble.
Admissions Requirements Minimum age 18.
Staff LPNs 1 (pt); Nurses aides 4 (ft); Activities
coordinators 1 (pt); Dietitians 1 (pt).
Facilities Dining room; Activities room; Crafts
room; Laundry room.
Activities Arts and Crafts; Cards; Games;
Reading groups; Prayer groups; Shopping trips;
Dances/Social or cultural gatherings; Monthly
band.
Description Facility is located in the center of
town with all shopping within walking distance;
stresses independent living.

JACKSON

Deal Nursing Home Inc*
PO Box 371, Jackson, MO, 63755 (314) 243-3121
Admin Billy Joe Thompson.
Licensure Intermediate Care. *Beds* 75.
Ownership Proprietary.

Jackson Manor Nursing Home
710 Broadridge, Jackson, MO, 63755 (314) 243-3101
Admin Eldor J Lorenz.
Licensure Skilled Care. *Beds* 90. *Certified* Medicaid.
Ownership Proprietary.

JEFFERSON CITY

Chastain's of Jefferson City*
1024 Adams St, Jefferson City, MO, 65101 (314) 635-8191
Admin Marie Anders.
Licensure Intermediate Care. *Beds* 120. *Certified* Medicaid.
Ownership Proprietary.

Jefferson City Manor Care Center
1720 Vieth Dr, Jefferson City, MO, 65101 (314) 635-6193
Admin Carol Sims. *Medical Dir/Dir of Nursing* Robert Tanner MD.
Licensure Intermediate Care. *Beds* 102.
Ownership Proprietary.
Admissions Requirements Minimum age 16.
Staff RNs 1 (ft); LPNs 5 (ft); Orderlies; Nurses aides; Physical therapists 1 (ft), 1 (pt); Speech therapists 1 (pt); Activities coordinators 1 (ft); Dietitians 1 (ft).
Facilities Dining room; Activities room; Chapel; Crafts room; Laundry room; Barber/Beauty shop; Library.
Activities Arts and Crafts; Cards; Games; Reading groups; Prayer groups; Movies; Shopping trips; Dances/Social or cultural gatherings.
Description Facility is private by choice, with the motto "Jefferson City Manor, the established and proven nursing home for the best care at the best rates."

Lincoln Manor Nursing Home*
3038 N 10 Mile Dr, Jefferson City, MO, 65102 (314) 893-3404
Admin Diane Strutynski.
Licensure Skilled Care; Intermediate Care. *Beds* 100. *Certified* Medicaid; Medicare.
Ownership Proprietary.

Saint Joseph's Home for the Aged
1306 W Main, Jefferson City, MO, 65101 (314) 635-0166
Admin Sr M Bernardine Moors.
Licensure Intermediate Care. *Beds* 125.
Ownership Nonprofit.

Southgate Nursing Center*
1207 Stadium Rd, Jefferson City, MO, 65101 (314) 635-3131
Admin Tom Hoeferlin.
Licensure Skilled Care. *Beds* 120. *Certified* Medicaid.
Ownership Proprietary.

JENNINGS

Jennings Caring Center
2520 McLaran, Jennings, MO, 63136 (314) 867-5748
Admin Bobby F Reed Jr. *Medical Dir/Dir of Nursing* Arnold S Tepper MD.
Licensure Intermediate Care. *Beds* 41.
Ownership Proprietary.
Staff Physicians 1 (ft); RNs 1 (pt); LPNs 1 (ft), 1 (pt); Nurses aides 8 (ft); Activities coordinators 1 (ft); Dietitians 1 (pt); Podiatrists 1 (pt).
Facilities Dining room; Activities room; Laundry room.
Activities Arts and Crafts; Cards; Games; Reading groups; Prayer groups; Movies; Shopping trips; Dances/Social or cultural gatherings.
Description Facility is located in friendly community in a converted mansion setting featuring home-like atmosphere, spacious rooms, caring staff, and experienced management.

JONESBURG

Country Lane Health Center Inc
Hwy Y, Jonesburg, MO, 63351 (314) 488-5516
Admin Marian Kling. *Medical Dir/Dir of Nursing* Dr Peters.
Licensure Intermediate Care. *Beds* 42.
Admissions Requirements Minimum age 18; Medical examination; Physician's request.
Staff Physicians 1 (pt); RNs 1 (pt); LPNs 1 (ft), 1 (pt); Orderlies 1 (ft); Nurses aides 10 (ft), 1 (pt); Activities coordinators 1 (ft); Dietitians 1 (ft).
Facilities Dining room; Activities room; Laundry room.
Activities Arts and Crafts; Cards; Games; Prayer groups; Movies; Shopping trips.
Description Facility is located in a lovely country setting.

JOPLIN

Chastain's Joplin House Nursing Home
2502 Moffet, Joplin, MO, 64801 (417) 623-3264
Admin Frank Manning. *Medical Dir/Dir of Nursing* W W Hurst MD.
Licensure Skilled Care. *Beds* 120. *Certified* Medicaid.
Ownership Proprietary.
Staff Physicians 1 (ft), 10 (pt); RNs 4 (ft); LPNs 7 (ft); Nurses aides 36 (ft), 1 (pt); Physical therapists 1 (ft); Occupational therapists 1 (ft); Speech therapists 1 (ft); Activities coordinators 2 (ft); Dietitians 1 (ft); Dentists 1 (pt); Ophthalmologists 1 (pt); Podiatrists 1 (pt); Audiologists 1 (pt).
Facilities Dining room; Physical therapy room; Activities room; Laundry room; Barber/Beauty shop.
Activities Arts and Crafts; Cards; Games; Reading groups; Prayer groups; Movies; Shopping trips; Dances/Social or cultural gatherings.

Chastain's Tradition House Nursing Home*
PO Box 2353, 2810 Jackson St, Joplin, MO, 64801 (417) 624-2061
Admin Peggy R Frisinger.

Licensure Intermediate Care. *Beds* 92. *Certified* Medicaid.
Ownership Proprietary.

Empire Nursing Home
2215 Empire Ave, Joplin, MO, 64801 (417)624-8141
Admin Mary F Turner.
Licensure Intermediate Care. *Beds* 15.
Ownership Proprietary.
Admissions Requirements Minimum age 50; Medical examination.
Staff LPNs 1 (ft), 1 (pt); Orderlies 1 (pt); Nurses aides 4 (ft), 2 (pt); Recreational therapists 1 (pt); Occupational therapists 1 (pt).

Hope Manor
1402 Rex, Joplin, MO, 64801 (417) 623-5551
Admin Pat Fenix.
Licensure Intermediate Care. *Beds* 24.
Ownership Proprietary.
Admissions Requirements Minimum age 18; Medical examination.
Staff RNs 1 (pt); LPNs 1 (ft), 1 (pt); Nurses aides 12 (ft).
Facilities Dining room; Activities room; Crafts room; Laundry room; Barber/Beauty shop.
Activities Arts and Crafts; Games; Prayer groups.
Description The size of our home, 24 beds, makes it possible to have a home-like atmosphere with personalized caring.

Joplin Health Care Center*
32nd St, Joplin, MO, 64801 (417) 781-1737
Admin Ed Kenworthy.
Licensure Skilled Care; Intermediate Care. *Beds* 126. *Certified* Medicaid.
Ownership Proprietary.

Meadow View Adult Care
1805 W 32nd St, Joplin, MO, 64801 (417) 782-0114
Admin Jeffrey Carter. *Medical Dir/Dir of Nursing* Stephen Bazzano DO.
Licensure Skilled Care; Intermediate Care. *Beds* 120. *Certified* Medicaid.
Ownership Proprietary.
Admissions Requirements Minimum age 16; Medical examination; Physician's request.
Staff Physicians 1 (pt); RNs 2 (ft), 1 (pt); LPNs 10 (ft), 2 (pt); Orderlies 5 (ft); Nurses aides 38 (ft); Physical therapists 1 (pt); Occupational therapists 1 (pt); Speech therapists 1 (pt); Activities coordinators 2 (ft); Dietitians 1 (pt); Dentists 1 (pt); Ophthalmologists 1 (pt); Podiatrists 1 (pt); Audiologists 1 (pt).
Facilities Dining room; Physical therapy room; Activities room; Laundry room; Barber/Beauty shop; 3 Living rooms.
Activities Arts and Crafts; Cards; Games; Reading groups; Prayer groups; Movies; Shopping trips; Dances/Social or cultural gatherings.
Description VA contract.

KAHOKA

Clark County Nursing Home
Rt 2, Hwy 81 N, Kahoka, MO, 63445 (816) 727-3303
Admin James S Holmes. *Medical Dir/Dir of Nursing* Dr John Beckert DO.

Licensure Intermediate Care. *Beds* 120. *Certified* Medicaid.
Ownership Public.
Admissions Requirements Physician's request.
Staff Physicians 2 (pt); RNs 1 (ft), 1 (pt); LPNs 5 (ft), 4 (pt); Nurses aides 28 (ft), 24 (pt); Physical therapists 2 (ft), 1 (pt); Occupational therapists 1 (pt); Speech therapists 1 (pt); Activities coordinators 1 (ft), 1 (pt); Dietitians 1 (pt); Audiologists 1 (pt).
Facilities Dining room; Physical therapy room; Activities room; Crafts room; Barber/Beauty shop.
Activities Arts and Crafts; Cards; Games; Reading groups; Prayer groups; Movies; Shopping trips; Dances/Social or cultural gatherings.

KANSAS

Meldonia Residential Care Facility*
503–505 Olive St, Kansas, MO, 64124 (816) 483-2911
Admin Nathan Friedman.
Licensure Residential Care. *Beds* 47.
Ownership Proprietary.

KANSAS CITY

Armour Medical Wing*
8100 Wornall Rd, Kansas City, MO, 64114 (816) 363-1510
Admin R Larry Louthain.
Licensure Intermediate Care. *Beds* 22. *Certified* Medicaid.
Ownership Nonprofit.

Beacon Hill Nursing Home
2905 Campbell, Kansas City, MO, 64109 (816) 531-6168
Admin Christena Nicholson. *Medical Dir/Dir of Nursing* Leroy Williams DO.
Licensure Intermediate Care. *Beds* 35.
Ownership Proprietary.
Admissions Requirements Minimum age 25; Medical examination.
Staff Physicians 1 (pt); RNs 1 (pt); LPNs 2 (ft); Orderlies 2 (ft); Nurses aides 18 (ft); Activities coordinators 1 (pt).
Facilities Dining room; Laundry room.
Activities Arts and Crafts; Cards; Games; Prayer groups; Movies; Dances/Social or cultural gatherings.
Description Facility provides quality care for the indigent; home-like atmosphere.

Blue Hills Centre*
12942 Wornall Rd, Kansas City, MO, 64145 (816) 941-0250
Admin Kenneth E Stuart.
Licensure Skilled Care; Intermediate Care.
Beds 140. *Certified* Medicaid.
Ownership Proprietary.

Blue Ridge Nursing Home
7505 E 87th St, Kansas City, MO, 64138 (816) 761-6838
Admin Rodger Richardson.
Licensure Intermediate Care. *Beds* 29.
Ownership Proprietary.

Bra-Ton Nursing Home Inc*
3400 Campbell, Kansas City, MO, 64109 (816) 531-5746
Admin Eleanor R Mochel.
Licensure Intermediate Care. *Beds* 38.
Ownership Proprietary.

Brown Nursing Home
3001 Woodland, Kansas City, MO, 64109 (816) 924-1354
Admin Mary L Younge.
Licensure Intermediate Care. *Beds* 51.
Ownership Proprietary.

Caldwell Manor Nursing Home*
101 E 36th, Kansas City, MO, 64111 (816) 753-6553
Admin Evelyn Caldwell.
Licensure Intermediate Care. *Beds* 49.
Ownership Proprietary.

Cliff Manor Inc*
4700 Cliff View Dr, Kansas City, MO, 64150 (816) 741-5105
Admin Norman Springer.
Licensure Skilled Care. *Beds* 186.
Ownership Proprietary.

Colonial Nursing Home*
100 E 36th, Kansas City, MO, 64111 (816) 561-6373
Admin Cynthia Walters.
Licensure Intermediate Care. *Beds* 51.
Ownership Proprietary.

Compton Home*
PO Box 11008, 5851 N Barnes, Kansas City, MO, 64119 (816) 452-3547
Admin Pearl Myers.
Licensure Residential Care. *Beds* 12.
Ownership Proprietary.

Cresthaven Nursing Home*
3516 Summit, Kansas City, MO, 64111 (816) 931-4024
Admin Charles F Hardy.
Licensure Intermediate Care. *Beds* 42.
Ownership Proprietary.

Garden Grove Nursing Home*
3522 Walnut St, Kansas City, MO, 64111 (816) 561-9344
Admin Jo Ann Gropper.
Licensure Intermediate Care. *Beds* 36.
Ownership Proprietary.

George H Nettleton Home
5125 Swope Pkwy, Kansas City, MO, 64130 (816) 924-5641
Admin James D Wilson. *Medical Dir/Dir of Nursing* Jean Willoughby MD.
Licensure Intermediate Care; Residential Care.
Beds ICF 25; Residential Care 48.
Ownership Nonprofit.
Admissions Requirements Minimum age 70; Females only; Medical examination.
Staff Physicians 1 (pt); RNs 1 (pt); LPNs 2 (ft), 1 (pt); Nurses aides 20 (ft), 10 (pt); Recreational therapists 1 (ft).
Facilities Dining room; Activities room; Chapel; Crafts room; Laundry room; Barber/Beauty shop; Library.
Activities Arts and Crafts; Cards; Games; Reading groups; Prayer groups; Movies; Shopping trips; Dances/Social or cultural gatherings.
Description Facility was declared a Kansas City Historic Landmark November 1983.

Gladstone Nursing Home
435 Gladstone Blvd, Kansas City, MO, 64124 (816) 531-1089
Admin Josephine Whiteley. *Medical Dir/Dir of Nursing* Dr Robert LaHue.
Licensure Intermediate Care. *Beds* 28.
Ownership Proprietary.
Admissions Requirements Females only
Staff Physicians 3 (ft); RNs 1 (pt); LPNs 1 (ft), 2 (pt); Physical therapists 1 (ft); Recreational therapists 1 (pt); Dietitians 1 (pt).
Facilities Activities room; Chapel; Crafts room; Laundry room.
Activities Arts and Crafts; Cards; Games; Prayer groups; Movies.
Description This facility is an old home that has been converted into a nursing home. Therefore it is small, more like a home to our residents. They get alot of personal attention as to their likes, and dislikes, and comfort.

Glennon Place*
128 N Hardesty Ave, Kansas City, MO, 64123 (816) 241-2020
Admin James L Webb.
Licensure Skilled Care; Intermediate Care.
Beds 120. *Certified* Medicaid.
Ownership Proprietary.

Great Oaks Inc
115 E 83rd St, Kansas City, MO, 64114 (816) 363-2900
Admin D Maxine Lord.
Licensure Intermediate Care. *Beds* 12.
Ownership Nonprofit.
Affiliation Christian Science

Grosse Nursing Home Inc*
3918 Charlotte, Kansas City, MO, 64110 (816) 931-0306
Admin J Ruth Richardson.
Licensure Intermediate Care. *Beds* 32.
Ownership Proprietary.

Guardian Angel Nursing Home Inc*
5234 N E Munger Ave, Kansas City, MO, 64119 (816) 452-2654
Admin Thomas Misasi.
Licensure Intermediate Care. *Beds* 19.
Ownership Proprietary.

Harvest Home Estates
2905 Forest Ave, Kansas City, MO, 64109 (816) 531-7356
Admin Hazel Thompson.
Licensure Intermediate Care. *Beds* 55.
Ownership Proprietary.

Haven Manor Nursing Home Inc
3526 Walnut, Kansas City, MO, 64111 (816) 931-9579
Admin William Popp.
Licensure Intermediate Care. *Beds* 28.
Ownership Proprietary.
Admissions Requirements Minimum age 21.
Staff Physicians 1 (pt); RNs 1 (pt); LPNs 2 (ft); Nurses aides 12 (ft), 4 (pt); Recreational therapists 1 (pt); Occupational therapists 1 (pt);

Activities coordinators 1 (pt); Dentists 1 (pt); Podiatrists 1 (pt); Audiologists 1 (pt).
Facilities Dining room; Activities room; Crafts room; Laundry room; Barber/Beauty shop.
Activities Arts and Crafts; Cards; Games; Reading groups; Prayer groups; Movies; Shopping trips.

Holmesdale Convalescent Center*
8039 Holmes, Kansas City, MO, 64131 (816) 363-6222
Admin Lenora Schnabel.
Licensure Skilled Care. *Beds* 100.
Ownership Proprietary.

Hyde Park Nursing Home*
401 E 36th St, Kansas City, MO, 64109 (816) 931-6378
Admin Cheryl Bauer.
Licensure Intermediate Care. *Beds* 45.
Ownership Proprietary.

Indian Creek Nursing Center of Missouri*
12000 Wornall Rd, Kansas City, MO, 64145 (816) 942-1676
Admin James M Sanner.
Licensure Skilled Care. *Beds* 240.
Ownership Proprietary.

Jewish Geriatric and Convalescent Center
7801 Holmes, Kansas City, MO, 64131 (816) 333-7800
Admin Melvyn Weissman. *Medical Dir/Dir of Nursing* Dr Harry Cohen.
Licensure Skilled Care. *Beds* 182. *Certified* Medicaid; Medicare.
Ownership Nonprofit.
Admissions Requirements Minimum age 65; Medical examination; Physician's request.
Affiliation Jewish
Facilities Dining room; Activities room; Crafts room; Laundry room; Library.
Activities Arts and Crafts; Cards; Games; Reading groups; Prayer groups; Movies; Shopping trips; Dances/Social or cultural gatherings; Travel to Las Vegas and Florida.

Kelly Nursing Home
4123 Independence Ave, Kansas City, MO, 64124 (816) 241-3232
Admin Edith M Eckenroed. *Medical Dir/Dir of Nursing* Robert C LaHue DO.
Licensure Intermediate Care; Residential Care. *Beds* 28.
Ownership Proprietary.
Admissions Requirements Minimum age 18.
Staff RNs 1 (pt); LPNs 1 (ft), 1 (pt); Nurses aides 14 (ft); Physical therapists; Reality therapists; Recreational therapists 1 (ft); Occupational therapists; Speech therapists; Activities coordinators 1 (ft); Dietitians 1 (ft), 2 (pt); Dentists 1 (pt); Ophthalmologists 1 (pt); Podiatrists 1 (pt); Audiologists.
Facilities Physical therapy room; Activities room; Crafts room; Laundry room; Barber/Beauty shop; Library.
Activities Arts and Crafts; Cards; Games; Reading groups; Prayer groups; Movies; Shopping trips; Dances/Social or cultural gatherings.
Description Facility is small enough to give each resident special, loving care and individual attention; home-like atmosphere; terrific cooking; state approved menus.

Kinder Care Nursing Home
3240 Norledge, Kansas City, MO, 64123 (816) 231-1161
Admin Elvera Farmer. *Medical Dir/Dir of Nursing* R L Williams DO.
Licensure Intermediate Care. *Beds* 36.
Ownership Proprietary.
Admissions Requirements Minimum age 60.
Staff Physicians 2 (ft), 1 (pt); RNs 1 (ft), 1 (pt); LPNs 1 (ft), 1 (pt); Orderlies 1 (ft); Nurses aides 7 (ft), 4 (pt); Physical therapists 1 (pt); Reality therapists 1 (pt); Recreational therapists 2 (pt); Occupational therapists 1 (pt); Speech therapists 1 (pt); Activities coordinators 1 (pt); Dietitians 1 (pt); Dentists 1 (pt); Ophthalmologists 1 (pt); Podiatrists 1 (pt); Audiologists 1 (pt).
Facilities Laundry room.
Activities Games.

King's Nursing Home*
2836 Benton Blvd, Kansas City, MO, 64128 (816) 924-5662
Admin Opal Lavern King.
Licensure Intermediate Care. *Beds* 34.
Ownership Proprietary.

Little Sisters of the Poor-Saint Alexis Home*
5331 Highland Ave, Kansas City, MO, 64110 (816) 444-9164
Admin Cecilia Honigfort.
Licensure Intermediate Care. *Beds* 140. *Certified* Medicaid.
Ownership Nonprofit.
Affiliation Roman Catholic

Midtown Manor Nursing Home*
2700 Tracy, Kansas City, MO, 64109 (816) 421-1272
Admin Claudia McDaniel.
Licensure Intermediate Care. *Beds* 55.
Ownership Proprietary.

Myers Nursing and Convalescent Center Inc
2315 Walrond, Kansas City, MO, 64127 (816) 231-3180
Admin Agnes Dodd.
Licensure Intermediate Care. *Beds* 84. *Certified* Medicaid.
Ownership Proprietary.

Newberry Nursing Home
3215 Campbell, Kansas City, MO, 64109 (816) 561-5282
Admin Patrick Reznak. *Medical Dir/Dir of Nursing* Dr Robert LaHue.
Licensure Intermediate Care. *Beds* 45.
Ownership Proprietary.
Staff RNs 1 (pt); LPNs 1 (ft), 2 (pt); Orderlies 3 (ft), 1 (pt); Nurses aides 18 (ft), 2 (pt); Physical therapists 1 (pt); Recreational therapists 1 (ft).
Facilities Dining room; Activities room; Laundry room.
Activities Arts and Crafts; Cards; Games; Reading groups; Prayer groups; Movies; Shopping trips; Dances/Social or cultural gatherings.
Description Facility participates in the ombudsman program in Kansas City, Missouri.

Oak Ridge Manor Nursing Home*
512 Woodland, Kansas City, MO, 64106 (816) 474-6869

Admin LoLetta Cordel.
Licensure Intermediate Care. *Beds* 46.
Ownership Proprietary.

Our Lady of Mercy Home
918 E 9th St, Kansas City, MO, 64106 (816) 842-6518
Admin Sr Mary Margaret Sneddon. *Medical Dir/Dir of Nursing* R C Lahue DO.
Licensure Intermediate Care. *Beds* 68. *Certified* Medicaid.
Ownership Nonprofit.
Admissions Requirements Females only; Medical examination; Physician's request.
Staff RNs 3 (ft), 1 (pt); LPNs 3 (ft); Nurses aides 20 (ft); Recreational therapists 1 (ft); Occupational therapists 1 (ft), 3 (pt); Activities coordinators 1 (ft); Dietitians 1 (ft).
Affiliation Roman Catholic
Facilities Dining room; Activities room; Chapel; Crafts room; Laundry room; Barber/Beauty shop; Library.
Activities Arts and Crafts; Cards; Games; Reading groups; Prayer groups; Movies; Shopping trips; Dances/Social or cultural gatherings.
Description Facility is unique in that it offers 3 levels of care under one roof—boarding, residential, and nursing care which affords residents from minimum to maximum care.

Park Lane Manor II*
7001 Cleveland Ave, Kansas City, MO, 64132 (816) 333-0700
Admin Al Wyatt.
Licensure Skilled Care; Intermediate Care. *Beds* 108.
Ownership Proprietary.

Parkview Manor Nursing Home*
300 Benton, Kansas City, MO, 64124 (816) 241-5600
Admin Gary Marvine.
Licensure Intermediate Care. *Beds* 30.
Ownership Proprietary.

Paseo Nursing Home
3433 Paseo, Kansas City, MO, 64109 (816) 921-4938
Admin Charlotte S Hosie. *Medical Dir/Dir of Nursing* Elizabeth Channel.
Licensure Intermediate Care. *Beds* 29.
Ownership Proprietary.
Staff RNs 1 (pt); LPNs 1 (ft); Nurses aides 6 (ft); Physical therapists 1 (pt); Reality therapists 1 (pt); Speech therapists 1 (pt); Activities coordinators 1 (ft); Dentists 1 (pt); Ophthalmologists 1 (pt); Podiatrists 1 (pt).
Facilities Dining room; Activities room; Laundry room.
Activities Arts and Crafts; Cards; Games; Reading groups; Prayer groups; Movies; Shopping trips.

Plaza Nursing Home*
4001 Warwick, Kansas City, MO, 64111 (816) 531-8291
Admin Leona A Villines.
Licensure Intermediate Care. *Beds* 29.
Ownership Proprietary.

Pleasant View Nursing Home*
4400 St John, Kansas City, MO, 64124 (816) 231-1790

Admin Cynthia Marvine.
Licensure Residential Care. *Beds* 16.
Ownership Proprietary.

Red Bridge Health Care Center
11515 Troost, Kansas City, MO, 64131 (816)
942-6700
Admin James G Gatschet. *Medical Dir/Dir of
Nursing* D D Zimmerman MD.
Licensure Skilled Care. *Beds* 120.
Ownership Proprietary.
Admissions Requirements Minimum age 18;
Medical examination.
Staff RNs 4 (ft), 2 (pt); LPNs 3 (ft), 2 (pt);
Orderlies 4 (ft); Nurses aides 23 (ft), 14 (pt);
Activities coordinators 1 (ft), 1 (pt).
Facilities Dining room; Physical therapy room;
Activities room; Chapel; Crafts room; Laundry
room; Barber/Beauty shop; Library.
Activities Arts and Crafts; Games; Reading
groups; Prayer groups; Movies; Shopping trips;
Dances/Social or cultural gatherings.
Description Facility is situated on 20 acres of
wooded land with a warm atmosphere
enhanced by personal touches of residents. An
enclosed patio provides a lovely spot for visiting friends or just enjoying nature and fresh
air.

Roanoke Manor Nursing Home*
3660 Summit, Kansas City, MO, 64111 (816)
753-6566
Admin Miriam J Zwiegel.
Licensure Intermediate Care. *Beds* 43.
Ownership Proprietary.

Rockhill Care Center
904 E 68th St, Kansas City, MO, 64131 (816)
333-5485
Admin Marshall Grant. *Medical Dir/Dir of
Nursing* Harold Keairnes MD.
Licensure Skilled Care; Intermediate Care.
Beds 174. *Certified* Medicaid; Medicare.
Ownership Proprietary.
Admissions Requirements Minimum age 18.
Staff Physicians 1 (ft); RNs 7 (ft); LPNs 21 (ft);
Orderlies 15 (ft); Nurses aides 59 (ft); Physical
therapists 4 (ft); Reality therapists 1 (pt); Recre-
ational therapists 1 (pt); Occupational therapists
1 (pt); Speech therapists 1 (pt); Activities coor-
dinators 3 (ft); Dietitians 1 (pt).
Facilities Dining room; Physical therapy room;
Activities room; Chapel; Crafts room; Laundry
room; Barber/Beauty shop; Library.
Activities Arts and Crafts; Cards; Games; Prayer groups; Movies; Shopping trips; Dances/So-
cial or cultural gatherings.

Rustic Manor Ltd
622 Benton Blvd, Kansas City, MO, 64124
(816) 241-5856
Admin Nancy Cole. *Medical Dir/Dir of
Nursing* Dr Ray Baker and Dr Harvey Mun-
shaw.
Licensure Intermediate Care. *Beds* 55.
Ownership Proprietary.
Staff Physicians 2 (ft); RNs 1 (pt); LPNs 4 (ft);
Orderlies 1 (ft); Nurses aides 4 (ft), 6 (pt);
Physical therapists 1 (pt); Reality therapists 1
(pt); Recreational therapists 1 (pt); Occupa-
tional therapists 1 (ft); Speech therapists 1 (ft);
Activities coordinators 1 (ft); Dietitians 1 (ft), 1
(pt); Dentists 1 (ft); Ophthalmologists 1 (ft);

Podiatrists 2 (ft); Audiologists 2 (ft).
Facilities Dining room; Activities room; Crafts
room; Laundry room.
Activities Arts and Crafts; Cards; Games;
Reading groups; Movies; Shopping trips; Dan-
ces/Social or cultural gatherings.
Description Facility offers home-cooked food
and quality care at affordable prices in a home-
style environment within a rustic setting; transportation is provided for residents' needs.

Senior Estates of Kansas City Inc*
2323 Swope Pkwy, Kansas City, MO, 64130
(816) 924-0211
Admin Eleanor A Dunsworth.
Licensure Skilled Care; Residential Care.
Beds Residential Care 9.
Ownership Proprietary.

Swope Ridge Health Care Center*
5900 Swope Pkwy, Kansas City, MO, 64130
(816) 333-2700
Admin Charles Nigro.
Licensure Skilled Care; Intermediate Care.
Beds 236. *Certified* Medicaid; Medicare.
Ownership Nonprofit.

Troost Avenue Nursing Home*
2839 Troost Ave, Kansas City, MO, 64109
(816) 931-1047
Admin Jerry Shaw and Wendy Morgan.
Licensure Intermediate Care. *Beds* 41.
Ownership Proprietary.

Truman Medical Center—East
7900 Lee's Summit Rd, Kansas City, MO,
64139 (816) 373-4415
Admin Thomas F Edgerton. *Medical Dir/Dir
of Nursing* Jack Mulligan.
Licensure Skilled Care; Intermediate Care.
Beds 24. *Certified* Medicaid; Medicare.
Ownership Nonprofit.
Admissions Requirements Minimum age 55;
Medical examination.
Staff Physicians; RNs; LPNs; Nurses aides;
Physical therapists; Recreational therapists;
Occupational therapists; Speech therapists; Die-
titians; Dentists; Ophthalmologists; Podiatrists;
Audiologists.
Facilities Dining room; Physical therapy room;
Activities room; Chapel; Crafts room; Laundry
room; Barber/Beauty shop; Library.
Activities Arts and Crafts; Cards; Games;
Reading groups; Prayer groups; Movies; Shop-
ping trips; Dances/Social or cultural gatherings.

Vista Del Rio Medical Center*
615 E 6th St, Kansas City, MO, 64106 (816)
234-7800
Admin Willa Hughes.
Licensure Skilled Care. *Beds* 50.
Ownership Nonprofit.

Warwick Manor Nursing Home*
3621 Warwick Blvd, Kansas City, MO, 64111
(816) 756-0460
Admin Jean Ward.
Licensure Intermediate Care. *Beds* 40.
Ownership Proprietary.

Westport Nursing Home*
3940 McGee, Kansas City, MO, 64111 (816)
931-9477

Admin Gloria Tillman.
Licensure Intermediate Care. *Beds* 29.
Ownership Proprietary.

KENNETT

Kennett Health Care Center
PO Box 696, Kennett, MO, 63857
Admin Clay Crossan. *Medical Dir/Dir of
Nursing* Dr Withisak Saanattvakul.
Licensure Skilled Care; Intermediate Care.
Beds 120. *Certified* Medicaid; Medicare.
Ownership Proprietary.
Admissions Requirements Medical examina-
tion; Physician's request.
Staff Physicians 10 (pt); RNs 3 (ft), 4 (pt);
LPNs 12 (ft), 3 (pt); Orderlies 4 (ft); Nurses
aides 40 (ft), 9 (pt); Physical therapists 1 (pt);
Occupational therapists 1 (pt); Speech thera-
pists 1 (pt); Activities coordinators 1 (ft); Dieti-
tians 1 (pt); Dentists 1 (pt).
Facilities Dining room; Physical therapy room;
Activities room; Crafts room; Laundry room;
Barber/Beauty shop.
Activities Arts and Crafts; Cards; Games; Pray-
er groups; Dances/Social or cultural gatherings.
Description VA approved.

KEYTESVILLE

Chariton County Rest Home*
Rt 2, Box 5, Keytesville, MO, 65261 (816)
288-3791
Admin Mildred Coy.
Licensure Residential Care. *Beds* 37.
Ownership Proprietary.

KIMBERLING CITY

Table Rock Health Care Center*
Table Rock Village, Kimberling City, MO,
65686 (417) 739-2481
Admin A L Schluter.
Licensure Skilled Care. *Beds* 60. *Cer-
tified* Medicaid.
Ownership Proprietary.

KING CITY

King City Manor*
300 W Fairview, King City, MO, 64463 (816)
535-4325
Admin Danny L Davis.
Licensure Intermediate Care. *Beds* 60. *Certified* Medicaid.
Ownership Proprietary.

KIRKSVILLE

Adair County Nursing Home*
316 S Osteopathy, Kirksville, MO, 63501 (816)
665-2887
Admin James P Clark.
Licensure Skilled Care; Intermediate Care.
Beds 126. *Certified* Medicaid.
Ownership Nonprofit.

Community Nursing Home*
E Normal, Kirksville, MO, 63501 (816)
665-6135
Admin Wilma Bramhall.
Licensure Residential Care. *Beds* 54.
Ownership Nonprofit.

Kirksville Manor Care Center*
1705 E LaHarpe, Kirksville, MO, 63501 (816)
665-3774
Admin Robert Redman.
Licensure Intermediate Care. *Beds* 132.
Ownership Proprietary.

KIRKWOOD

Blind Girl's Home
221 W Washington Ave, Kirkwood, MO,
63122 (314) 966-6033
Admin Colleen L Hill. *Medical Dir/Dir of
Nursing* Dr Aaron Bernstein.
Licensure Intermediate Care. *Beds* 28.
Ownership Nonprofit.
Admissions Requirements Minimum age 21;
Females only; Medical examination; Physi-
cian's request.
Staff Physicians 1 (ft); RNs 1 (ft), 1 (pt); LPNs
3 (pt); Nurses aides 5 (ft), 12 (pt); Recreational
therapists 1 (pt); Activities coordinators 1 (pt);
Dietitians 1 (ft).
Facilities Dining room; Physical therapy room;
Activities room; Chapel; Laundry room; Bar-
ber/Beauty shop; Auditorium.
Activities Arts and Crafts; Cards; Games;
Reading groups; Shopping trips; Dances/Social
or cultural gatherings; Music programs.
Description A special home that was built to
meet the needs of blind women. It is a home
setting and the ladies are active in helping to
maintain the facility.

Manor Grove
711 S Kirkwood Rd, Kirkwood, MO, 63122
(314) 965-0864
Admin Carolyn Ellerbusch. *Medical Dir/Dir of
Nursing* Dr David Schoenwalder.
Licensure Skilled Care. *Beds* 97.
Ownership Nonprofit.
Staff Physicians 19 (pt); RNs 4 (ft), 8 (pt);
LPNs 1 (ft), 3 (pt); Orderlies 1 (pt); Nurses
aides 20 (ft), 9 (pt); Physical therapists 1 (pt);
Occupational therapists 1 (pt); Speech thera-
pists 1 (pt); Activities coordinators 1 (ft); Dieti-
tians 1 (ft); Dentists 1 (pt); Ophthalmologists 1
(pt); Podiatrists 1 (pt); Audiologists 1 (pt).
Facilities Dining room; Physical therapy room;
Activities room; Chapel; Crafts room; Laundry
room; Barber/Beauty shop; Library.
Activities Arts and Crafts; Cards; Games;
Reading groups; Prayer groups; Movies; Shopping trips; Dances/Social or cultural gatherings.

Saint Agnes Home
10341 Manchester Rd, Kirkwood, MO, 63122
(314) 965-7616
Admin Sr Mary Patrick Gruber.
Licensure Intermediate Care. *Beds* 150.
Ownership Nonprofit.
Admissions Requirements Minimum age 65;
Medical examination; Physician's request.
Staff Physicians 2 (pt); RNs 1 (ft), 1 (pt); LPNs
7 (ft); Orderlies 53 (ft); Physical therapists 2

(pt); Activities coordinators 1 (ft); Dietitians 1
(pt); Podiatrists 1 (pt).
Affiliation Roman Catholic
Facilities Dining room; Physical therapy room;
Activities room; Chapel; Crafts room; Laundry
room; Barber/Beauty shop; Library.
Activities Arts and Crafts; Cards; Games;
Reading groups; Prayer groups; Movies; Shop-
ping trips; Dances/Social or cultural gatherings;
Weekly happy hour; Monthly salad luncheon.

LABELLE

LaBelle Manor Care Center
Hwy 6 W, LaBelle, MO, 63447 (816) 462-3234
Admin Eva Coleman.
Licensure Intermediate Care. *Beds* 92.
Ownership Proprietary.
Staff Physicians 2 (pt); RNs 1 (pt); LPNs 5
(pt); Orderlies 2 (pt); Nurses aides 50 (ft), 24
(pt); Physical therapists 2 (pt); Recreational
therapists 1 (pt); Activities coordinators 1 (ft), 1
(pt); Dietitians 1 (ft); Dentists 1 (pt); Ophthal-
mologists 1 (pt).
Facilities Dining room; Physical therapy room;
Activities room; Chapel; Laundry room; Bar-
ber/Beauty shop.
Activities Arts and Crafts; Cards; Games;
Reading groups; Prayer groups; Movies; Shopping trips; Dances/Social or cultural gatherings.
Description Activities program is well diversified for wide range of interest. Residents have
enjoyed hula dancers.

LAMAR

Chastain's of Lamar Inc*
206 W 1st St, Lamar, MO, 64759 (417)
682-3315
Admin Alvin L Forester.
Licensure Intermediate Care. *Beds* 123. *Certified* Medicaid.
Ownership Proprietary.

Lamar Boarding and Rest Home
505 E 8th St, Lamar, MO, 64759
Admin Tom Dale. *Medical Dir/Dir of Nur-
sing* Catherine Boyer Dale.
Licensure Intermediate Care for Mentally
Retarded. *Beds* 60. *Certified* Medicaid.
Ownership Nonprofit.
Admissions Requirements Medical examina-
tion.
Staff LPNs 1 (ft); Orderlies 1 (ft); Nurses aides
7 (ft); Physical therapists 2 (pt); Recreational
therapists 2 (pt); Activities coordinators 1 (pt).
Facilities Dining room; Physical therapy room;
Activities room; Chapel; Crafts room; Laundry
room; Barber/Beauty shop; Pool room.
Activities Cards; Games; Movies; Dances/So-
cial or cultural gatherings.
Description Facility cares for ambulatory residents who can not or will not care for
themselves.

LANAGAN

Cinnamon Hill Manor Inc*
PO Box 146, Lanagan, MO, 64847 (417)
436-2231

Admin Joetta Jenkins.
Licensure Intermediate Care. *Beds* 43.
Ownership Proprietary.

LAPLATA

LaPlata Nursing Home
Old Stage Coach Rd, LaPlata, MO, 63549 (816)
332-4315
Admin Wanda Smith. *Medical Dir/Dir of
Nursing* O L Woodward DO.
Licensure Intermediate Care. *Beds* 52. *Certi-
fied* Medicaid.
Ownership Nonprofit.
Admissions Requirements Minimum age 21;
Medical examination.
Staff RNs 2 (pt); LPNs 2 (ft); Nurses aides 14
(ft), 14 (pt); Activities coordinators 1 (ft).
Facilities Dining room; Physical therapy room;
Activities room; Laundry room.
Activities Arts and Crafts; Reading groups;
Prayer groups; Movies; Dances/Social or cul-
tural gatherings.

LATHROP

Lathrop Health Facility Inc*
702 Center St, Lathrop, MO, 64465 (816)
528-4257
Admin Evelyn Spiers.
Licensure Intermediate Care. *Beds* 84.
Ownership Nonprofit.

LAURIE

Laurie Nursing Home
State Rd O, Laurie, MO, 65038
Admin Ethel G Jones. *Medical Dir/Dir of
Nursing* Dr H Petry.
Licensure Intermediate Care. *Beds* 60. *Certi-
fied* Medicaid.
Ownership Nonprofit.
Admissions Requirements Minimum age 18;
Medical examination; Physician's request.
Staff Physicians 4 (ft); RNs 2 (ft), 1 (pt); LPNs
1 (ft); Nurses aides 16 (ft), 5 (pt); Physical thera-
pists 1 (ft), 1 (pt); Activities coordinators 1 (ft);
Dentists 2 (ft); Ophthalmologists 2 (ft); Podiatr-
ists 1 (ft); Audiologists 2 (ft); Dietary workers 3
(ft), 4 (pt).
Facilities Dining room; Physical therapy room;
Activities room; Laundry room; Barber/Beauty
shop; Library.
Activities Arts and Crafts; Cards; Games; Prayer groups; Movies; Shopping trips; Dances/So-
cial or cultural gatherings.
Description Facility is situated on beautiful
Lake of the Ozarks; offers complete facilities for
extended care in a friendly atmosphere.

LAWSON

Graceland Manor
Rt 1, Box 460, Lawson, MO, 64062
Admissions Requirements Medical examina-
tion.
Staff Nurses aides 2 (ft).
Facilities Dining room; Activities room; Chap-
el; Laundry room.
Activities Arts and Crafts; Games; Reading

groups; Prayer groups; Shopping trips; Dances-/Social or cultural gatherings.
Description Facility is located in the country, small enough to give individual attention, more like a family than an institution. Residents are encouraged to participate in community activities; although supervised, residents are able to do as they would in their own homes.

Smithview Manor Nursing Home
220 W 8th Terrace, Lawson, MO, 64062 (816) 296-7412
Admin Genevie M Herndon.
Licensure Intermediate Care. *Beds* 60.
Ownership Proprietary.
Staff RNs 1 (pt); LPNs 3 (ft), 1 (pt); Orderlies 1 (ft); Nurses aides 21 (ft), 4 (pt); Physical therapists 1 (pt); Occupational therapists 1 (pt); Speech therapists 1 (pt); Activities coordinators 1 (ft); Dietitians 1 (pt).
Facilities Dining room; Activities room; Laundry room; Barber/Beauty shop; TV room.
Activities Arts and Crafts; Cards; Games; Reading groups; Prayer groups; Movies; Shopping trips; Dances/Social or cultural gatherings; Musical entertainment.
Description Facility is located in a rural area with home-like atmosphere.

LEBANON

Lebanon Care Center*
596 Morton Rd, Lebanon, MO, 65536 (417) 532-9173
Admin John D Foster.
Licensure Skilled Care; Intermediate Care.
Beds 180. *Certified* Medicaid; Medicare.
Ownership Proprietary.

Lebanon Nursing Home*
175 Morton Rd, Lebanon, MO, 65536 (417) 532-5351
Admin Phyllis Appleberry.
Licensure Intermediate Care. *Beds* 29.
Ownership Proprietary.

LEES SUMMIT

Lee's Summit Care Center
615 Oldham Pkwy, Lee's Summit, MO, 64063 (816) 524-3328
Admin Patricia L Stickler. *Medical Dir/Dir of Nursing* Dr Robert LaHue.
Licensure Skilled Care; Intermediate Care.
Beds 120. *Certified* Medicaid.
Ownership Proprietary.
Admissions Requirements Minimum age 16.
Staff Physicians 1 (pt); RNs 3 (ft), 2 (pt); LPNs 7 (ft), 2 (pt); Orderlies 5 (ft); Nurses aides 32 (ft); Physical therapists 1 (pt); Activities coordinators 1 (ft); Dietitians 1 (pt).
Facilities Dining room; Physical therapy room; Activities room; Crafts room; Laundry room; Barber/Beauty shop.
Activities Arts and Crafts; Cards; Games; Reading groups; Prayer groups; Movies; Shopping trips; Dances/Social or cultural gatherings.

Village Care Center
500 N Murray, Lee's Summit, MO, 64063 (816) 524-8400

Admin Sandra Grant. *Medical Dir/Dir of Nursing* John Murphy MD.
Licensure Skilled Care; Intermediate Care.
Beds 300. *Certified* Medicaid; Medicare.
Ownership Nonprofit.
Admissions Requirements Physician's request.
Staff Physicians 2 (ft); RNs 13 (ft), 2 (pt); LPNs 8 (ft), 2 (pt); Nurses aides 120 (ft), 9 (pt); Physical therapists 9 (pt); Occupational therapists 1 (pt); Speech therapists 1 (pt); Activities coordinators 4 (ft), 1 (pt); Dietitians 1 (pt); Dentists 1 (pt); Ophthalmologists 1 (pt); Podiatrists 1 (pt).
Facilities Dining room; Physical therapy room; Activities room; Chapel; Crafts room; Laundry room; Barber/Beauty shop; Library.
Activities Arts and Crafts; Cards; Games; Reading groups; Prayer groups; Movies; Shopping trips; Dances/Social or cultural gatherings.
Description Center is part of the country's largest retirement village, John Knox Village.

LEMAY

Community Care Center of Lemay*
9353 S Broadway, Lemay, MO, 63125 (314) 631-0540
Admin James Giardina.
Licensure Intermediate Care. *Beds* 42.
Ownership Proprietary.

Lemay Nursing Home
1204 Telegraph Rd, Lemay, MO, 63125 (314) 544-2380
Admin Charlotte Sczepanski. *Medical Dir/Dir of Nursing* Juan Castro.
Licensure Intermediate Care. *Beds* 38.
Ownership Proprietary.
Staff Physicians 2 (ft); RNs 1 (pt); LPNs 2 (ft), 1 (pt); Orderlies 1 (ft); Nurses aides 15 (ft); Activities coordinators 1 (ft).
Facilities Dining room; Barber/Beauty shop.
Activities Arts and Crafts; Shopping trips.

LEWISTOWN

Prairie View Rest Home Inc
Rt 2, Lewistown, MO, 63452 (314) 497-2424
Admin Mildred L Huebotter. *Medical Dir/Dir of Nursing* Francis Tarvydas MD.
Licensure Intermediate Care. *Beds* 69.
Ownership Nonprofit.
Admissions Requirements Minimum age 21.
Staff RNs 3 (pt); LPNs 3 (ft), 1 (pt) #13D 1 (ft); Nurses aides 13 (ft), 10 (pt); Occupational therapists 1 (ft), 1 (pt); Speech therapists 1 (pt); Activities coordinators 2 (ft), 1 (pt); Dietitians 1 (ft); Dentists 1 (pt).
Facilities Dining room; Activities room; Laundry room; Barber/Beauty shop.
Activities Arts and Crafts; Cards; Games; Prayer groups; Movies; Shopping trips; Dances/Social or cultural gatherings.
Description Facility offers beautiful country setting with a home-like atmosphere, a full range of activity programs from validation fantasy therapy to intellectual discussion groups, individualized to the residents needs; also offers hospice care both in the patient's home and within the facility.

Stone Haven
401 S Oak, Lewistown, MO, 63452
Admin Jesse Stone and Betty Stone.
Licensure Intermediate Care. *Certified* Medicaid.
Ownership Proprietary.
Admissions Requirements Minimum age 18; Medical examination.
Staff Physicians; RNs; LPNs; Nurses aides; Activities coordinators.
Facilities Dining room; Activities room; Laundry room.
Activities Arts and Crafts; Cards; Games; Prayer groups; Movies; Shopping trips.
Description Facility offers a home-like atmosphere where people are allowed to come and go as they wish; features a park-like lawn that is enjoyed by all residents; large patio for those who wish to sit outside.

LEXINGTON

Lafayette Manor Nursing Home
Hwy 13 S, Lexington, MO, 64067 (816) 259-4697
Admin Harold T Ainsworth Jr. *Medical Dir/Dir of Nursing* Joe W Ward MD.
Licensure Intermediate Care. *Beds* 148. *Certified* Medicaid.
Ownership Proprietary.
Admissions Requirements Minimum age 17; Medical examination.
Staff Physicians 6 (pt); RNs 1 (ft); LPNs 5 (ft); Orderlies 3 (ft); Nurses aides 57 (ft), 4 (pt); Physical therapists 1 (pt); Occupational therapists 1 (pt); Speech therapists 1 (pt); Activities coordinators 2 (ft); Dietitians 1 (pt); Dentists 1 (pt); Audiologists 1 (pt).
Facilities Dining room; Physical therapy room; Activities room; Chapel; Crafts room; Laundry room; Barber/Beauty shop.
Activities Arts and Crafts; Games; Reading groups; Movies; Shopping trips; Dances/Social or cultural gatherings; Resident council.

LIBERTY

Crystal Lane Nursing Center
1200 W College, Liberty, MO, 64068 (816) 781-3020
Admin Michael Velder.
Licensure Intermediate Care. *Beds* 134. *Certified* Medicaid.
Ownership Proprietary.
Admissions Requirements Medical examination; Physician's request.
Staff RNs 2 (ft); LPNs 8 (ft); Nurses aides 30 (ft); Activities coordinators 1 (ft).
Facilities Dining room; Physical therapy room; Activities room; Chapel; Crafts room; Laundry room; Barber/Beauty shop; Library.
Activities Arts and Crafts; Cards; Games; Reading groups; Prayer groups; Movies; Shopping trips; Dances/Social or cultural gatherings.

Odd Fellows Home*
Rt 6, Box 194, Liberty, MO, 64068 (816) 781-4880
Admin Helen Jo White.
Licensure Intermediate Care; Boarding Care.

Beds ICF 20; Boarding Care 45.
Ownership Nonprofit.
Affiliation Independent Order of Odd Fellows

Pleasant Valley Manor Care Center
6814 Sobbie Rd, Liberty, MO, 64068
Medical Dir/Dir of Nursing Dr Nancy Russell.
Staff Physicians 2 (ft); RNs 1 (ft); LPNs 6 (ft),
1 (pt); Nurses aides 22 (ft), 4 (pt); Physical therapists 3 (ft); Reality therapists 1 (ft); Recreational therapists 1 (ft); Occupational therapists 1
(ft); Activities coordinators 1 (ft); Dietitians 1
(ft); Dentists 1 (ft); Podiatrists 1 (ft).
Facilities Dining room; Physical therapy room;
Activities room; Chapel; Laundry room; Bar-
ber/Beauty shop; Library.
Activities Arts and Crafts; Games; Reading
groups; Prayer groups; Movies; Shopping trips;
Dances/Social or cultural gatherings.
Description This one-story brick facility is situated on 1½ wooded acres.

LICKING

**Texas County Missouri Health Care Center
Inc***
600 Hickory, Licking, MO, 65542 (314)
674-2111
Admin Raymond O Wood.
Licensure Intermediate Care. *Beds* 60. *Certi-
fied* Medicaid.
Ownership Nonprofit.

LINCOLN

Lincoln Community Nursing Home
Rt 1, Lincoln, MO, 65338 (816) 547-3322
Admin Ruth Proctor. *Medical Dir/Dir of
Nursing* Arturo Gonzalez DO.
Licensure Intermediate Care. *Beds* 60. *Certi-
fied* Medicaid.
Ownership Nonprofit.
Admissions Requirements Minimum age 16;
Medical examination.
Staff RNs 1 (ft); LPNs 1 (ft), 5 (pt); Nurses
aides 15 (ft), 10 (pt); Activities coordinators 1
(ft); Dietitians 1 (ft).
Facilities Dining room; Physical therapy room;
Activities room; Chapel; Laundry room; Bar-
ber/Beauty shop; Library.
Activities Arts and Crafts; Cards; Games;
Reading groups; Prayer groups; Movies; Dan-
ces/Social or cultural gatherings; Monthly birth-
day parties.

LINN

Linn Manor Nursing Home*
Box 499, Linn, MO, 65051 (314) 897-2247
Admin Dorothy Curry and Weldon Curry.
Licensure Intermediate Care. *Beds* 41.
Ownership Proprietary.

LOCKWOOD

Good Shepherd Nursing Home
200 W 12th, Lockwood, MO, 65682 (417)
232-4571
Admin Doris Lilienkamp. *Medical Dir/Dir of
Nursing* Dr Christiansen.

Licensure Intermediate Care. *Beds* 66. *Certi-
fied* Medicaid.
Ownership Proprietary.
Admissions Requirements Minimum age 14.
Staff RNs 1 (ft); LPNs 3 (ft), 3 (pt); Nurses
aides 18 (ft), 7 (pt); Physical therapists 1 (pt);
Recreational therapists 1 (ft); Occupational
therapists 1 (pt); Activities coordinators 1 (ft);
Dietitians 5 (ft), 2 (pt).
Facilities Dining room; Activities room; Chap-
el; Laundry room; Barber/Beauty shop;
Library.
Activities Games; Prayer groups; Music group;
Popcorn day.
Description Nursing home is in rural setting.
Excellent care given to residents.

LOUISIANA

Louisiana Nursing Home
600 Nebraska, Louisiana, MO, 63353 (314)
754-4556
Admin Rebecca Allen. *Medical Dir/Dir of
Nursing* Phillip Pitney MD.
Licensure Intermediate Care. *Beds* 29.
Ownership Proprietary.
Admissions Requirements Minimum age 21;
Medical examination.
Staff RNs 1 (pt); LPNs 1 (ft), 1 (pt); Nurses
aides 7 (ft), 5 (pt); Recreational therapists 1 (pt);
Activities coordinators 1 (pt).
Facilities Dining room; Activities room; Laun-
dry room.
Activities Arts and Crafts; Cards; Games;
Reading groups; Prayer groups; Shopping trips;
Dances/Social or cultural gatherings.
Description A small ICF facility in a rural area.
Everyone is close to each other here like one big
family.

Maple Grove Lodge Inc*
2407 Kentucky St, Louisiana, MO, 63353 (314)
754-5456
Admin Vera Idabelle Turner.
Licensure Intermediate Care. *Beds* 60.
Ownership Proprietary.

Smith-Barr Manor Nursing Home
2407 W Georgia, Louisiana, MO, 63353 (314)
754-6279
Admin Charles Ulry Jr. *Medical Dir/Dir of
Nursing* John Middleton MD.
Licensure Skilled Care. *Beds* 69. *Cer-
tified* Medicaid.
Admissions Requirements Minimum age 21;
Medical examination; Physician's request.
Staff RNs 1 (ft), 3 (pt); LPNs 9 (ft); Nurses
aides 22 (ft); Physical therapists 1 (ft); Occupa-
tional therapists 1 (pt); Speech therapists 1 (pt);
Activities coordinators 1 (ft); Dietitians 1 (pt).
Facilities Dining room; Physical therapy room;
Activities room; Laundry room; Barber/Beauty
shop; Library.
Activities Arts and Crafts; Games; Reading
groups; Prayer groups; Dances/Social or cul-
tural gatherings.
Description Smith-Barr Manor, specializing in
convalescent and long term care, is located
adjacent to Pike County Memorial Hospital.

LOWRY CITY

Truman Lake Manor Inc
600 E 7th, Box 188, Lowry City, MO, 64763
(417) 644-2248
Admin Robert O Scott. *Medical Dir/Dir of
Nursing* Mark Snell DO.
Licensure Intermediate Care. *Beds* 60. *Certi-
fied* Medicaid.
Ownership Proprietary.
Admissions Requirements Minimum age 18;
Medical examination; Physician's request.
Staff Physicians 3 (pt); RNs 1 (ft), 1 (pt); LPNs
4 (ft), 1 (pt); Nurses aides 18 (ft), 2 (pt);
Physical therapists 1 (pt); Occupational thera-
pists 1 (pt); Speech therapists 1 (pt); Activities
coordinators 1 (ft); Dietitians 1 (pt); Dentists 1
(pt).
Facilities Dining room; Physical therapy room;
Activities room; Chapel; Crafts room; Laundry
room; Barber/Beauty shop; Library.
Activities Arts and Crafts; Cards; Games;
Reading groups; Movies; Shopping trips; Dan-
ces/Social or cultural gatherings.
Description Facility is being renovated and 60
beds added with completion scheduled for late
fall 1984, after which services will include residential care, respite care, intermediate nursing
care, skilled nursing care, Medicare, and adult
day health care.

LUTESVILLE

Bond Nursing Home Inc
3rd and Crown Sts, Lutesville, MO, 63762
(314) 238-2832
Admin Gayle Spooler. *Medical Dir/Dir of
Nursing* John Englehart DO.
Licensure Intermediate Care. *Beds* 34.
Ownership Proprietary.
Admissions Requirements Minimum age 21.
Staff Physicians 1 (ft); RNs 1 (pt); LPNs 1 (ft),
2 (pt); Nurses aides 12 (ft), 3 (pt); Activities
coordinators 1 (ft); Dietitians 1 (pt); Dentists 1
(pt); Ophthalmologists 1 (pt).
Facilities Dining room; Activities room; Chapel; Crafts room; Laundry room.
Activities Arts and Crafts; Cards; Games;
Reading groups; Prayer groups; Movies; Shopping trips; Dances/Social or cultural gatherings.
Description Bond Nursing Home, founded in
1942, is building a new 90-bed nursing home
anticipated to be open by November 1984; new
facilities will offer 24-hour nursing, physical
and occupational therapist, certified aides, full-
time dietician, activity director, beauty and barber shop, and much more.

MACON

Macon County Nursing Home—Loch Haven
Sunset Hills Dr, PO Box 187, Macon, MO,
63552 (816) 385-3113
Admin Richard S Waller. *Medical Dir/Dir of
Nursing* Dr J E Campbell.
Licensure Intermediate Care. *Beds* SNF 60;
ICF 120. *Certified* Medicaid; Medicare.
Ownership Proprietary.
Facilities Dining room; Physical therapy room;
Activities room; Chapel; Crafts room; Laundry
room; Barber/Beauty shop.

Activities Arts and Crafts; Cards; Games; Reading groups; Prayer groups; Movies; Shopping trips; Dances/Social or cultural gatherings.

Macon Health Care Center
PO Box 465, Macon, MO, 63552
Admin Jim Kurtz. *Medical Dir/Dir of Nursing* Joseph Quaranto.
Licensure Skilled Care; Intermediate Care; Intermediate Care for Mentally Retarded.
Beds 120. *Certified* Medicaid; Medicare.
Ownership Proprietary.
Admissions Requirements Medical examination.
Staff Physicians 6 (pt); RNs 2 (ft); LPNs 7 (ft), 2 (pt); Orderlies 3 (ft); Nurses aides 12 (ft), 9 (pt); Physical therapists 1 (ft), 1 (pt); Occupational therapists 1 (pt); Speech therapists 1 (pt); Activities coordinators 1 (ft); Dietitians 1 (pt); Dentists 1 (pt); Ophthalmologists 1 (pt); Podiatrists 1 (pt); Audiologists 1 (pt).
Facilities Dining room; Physical therapy room; Activities room; Chapel; Crafts room; Laundry room; Barber/Beauty shop.
Activities Arts and Crafts; Cards; Games; Reading groups; Prayer groups; Movies; Shopping trips; Dances/Social or cultural gatherings.
Description VA approved.

MADISON

Wildwood Health Center
Rt 2, Madison, MO, 65263 (816) 291-8636
Admin Margery Sue Waller. *Medical Dir/Dir of Nursing* Dr Robert Warbritton.
Licensure Intermediate Care. *Beds* 32.
Ownership Proprietary.
Staff RNs 1 (pt); LPNs 1 (ft), 1 (pt); Nurses aides 8 (ft), 7 (pt); Activities coordinators 1 (ft).
Facilities Dining room; Activities room; Laundry room.
Activities Arts and Crafts; Cards; Games; Reading groups; Prayer groups; Movies; Shopping trips; Dances/Social or cultural gatherings.
Description Small ICF nursing home in the county featuring a real family-life atmosphere with very good nursing care.

MALDEN

Ridgeview Manor Nursing Home
500 Barrett Dr, Malden, MO, 63863 (314) 276-3843
Admin John Hisaw. *Medical Dir/Dir of Nursing* Tom Henderson.
Licensure Intermediate Care. *Beds* 120. *Certified* Medicaid.
Ownership Proprietary.
Admissions Requirements Minimum age 21.
Staff Physicians 5 (ft), 4 (pt); RNs 1 (ft), 2 (pt); LPNs 5 (ft), 3 (pt); Nurses aides 43 (ft), 8 (pt); Physical therapists 2 (ft), 1 (pt); Recreational therapists 2 (ft); Occupational therapists 1 (pt); Speech therapists 1 (pt); Dietitians 1 (pt); Dentists 1 (pt); Ophthalmologists 1 (pt).
Facilities Dining room; Physical therapy room; Activities room; Laundry room; Barber/Beauty shop; Library.
Activities Arts and Crafts; Cards; Games; Reading groups; Prayer groups; Movies; Shopping trips; Dances/Social or cultural gatherings.

MANCHESTER

Clayton House Healthcare
1251 E Clayton Rd, Manchester, MO, 63011 (314) 227-5070
Admin Mark D Lee.
Licensure Skilled Care; Intermediate Care; Residential. *Beds* 282. *Certified* Medicaid; Medicare.
Ownership Proprietary.
Staff RNs; LPNs; Nurses aides; Physical therapists; Reality therapists; Recreational therapists; Occupational therapists; Speech therapists; Activities coordinators; Dietitians; Dentists; Podiatrists.
Facilities Dining room; Physical therapy room; Activities room; Chapel; Crafts room; Laundry room; Barber/Beauty shop; Library.
Activities Arts and Crafts; Cards; Games; Reading groups; Prayer groups; Movies; Shopping trips; Dances/Social or cultural gatherings.

Mari de Villa Retirement Center Inc*
13900 Clayton Rd, Manchester, MO, 63011 (314) 227-5347
Admin Joseph L Linneman.
Licensure Skilled Care. *Beds* 224.
Ownership Proprietary.

MANSFIELD

Mansfield Nursing Home
Rt 1, Mansfield, MO, 65704 (417) 924-8116
Admin Glenda Moore. *Medical Dir/Dir of Nursing* Dr Efraim Reyes.
Licensure Intermediate Care. *Beds* 45. *Certified* Medicaid.
Ownership Proprietary.
Admissions Requirements Minimum age 18; Medical examination.
Staff Physicians 2 (ft); RNs 1 (pt); LPNs 3 (ft); Orderlies 2 (ft); Nurses aides 13 (ft); Physical therapists 1 (pt); Occupational therapists 1 (pt); Speech therapists 1 (pt); Activities coordinators 1 (ft); Dietitians 1 (pt); Dentists 2 (pt); Audiologists 1 (pt).
Facilities Dining room; Physical therapy room; Activities room; Crafts room; Laundry room; Library.
Activities Arts and Crafts; Cards; Games; Reading groups; Prayer groups; Shopping trips; Dances/Social or cultural gatherings.
Description Facility features a country setting with home-like atmosphere.

MARCELINE

Chastain's of Marceline Nursing Home*
108 E Howell St, Marceline, MO, 64658 (816) 376-3579
Admin Shirley White.
Licensure Intermediate Care. *Beds* 81. *Certified* Medicaid.
Ownership Proprietary.

King Rest Home*
215 W Walker St, Marceline, MO, 64658 (816) 376-2165
Admin Thelma Braley.
Licensure Intermediate Care. *Beds* 14.
Ownership Proprietary.

Pioneer Health Center
Rt 1, PO Box 477, Marceline, MO, 64658 (816) 376-2001
Admin Phil McAnulty. *Medical Dir/Dir of Nursing* S P Galvez MD.
Licensure Skilled Care; Intermediate Care.
Beds 84. *Certified* Medicaid; Medicare.
Ownership Proprietary.
Admissions Requirements Minimum age 18; Medical examination; Physician's request.
Staff Physicians 1 (pt); RNs 2 (ft); LPNs 5 (ft), 1 (pt); Orderlies 3 (ft); Nurses aides 26 (ft), 7 (pt); Physical therapists 1 (pt); Occupational therapists 1 (pt); Speech therapists 1 (pt); Activities coordinators 1 (ft), 1 (pt); Dietitians 1 (pt); Dentists 1 (pt); Podiatrists 1 (pt).
Facilities Dining room; Physical therapy room; Activities room; Laundry room; Barber/Beauty shop; Fire protection sprinkler; Individual room controlled heat; Central air conditioning; Cable television.
Activities Arts and Crafts; Cards; Games; Movies; Shopping trips; Dances/Social or cultural gatherings.
Description Facility is a warm and hospitable facility located in beautiful country setting. The building is all one floor, no stairs. Community interest programs, outpatient therapy, part A and B Medicare, VA contract, and home health agency services featured.

Saint Francis Hopital—SNF/ICF Care Facility
225 W Hayden St, Marceline, MO, 64658 (816) 376-3521
Admin Estelle M Vosen. *Medical Dir/Dir of Nursing* David Armin MD.
Licensure Skilled Care; Intermediate Care.
Beds 42.
Ownership Nonprofit.
Admissions Requirements Medical examination.
Staff Physicians 2 (ft), 10 (pt); RNs 4 (ft), 7 (pt); LPNs 12 (ft), 6 (pt); Nurses aides 16 (ft), 3 (pt); Physical therapists 1 (pt); Recreational therapists 1 (ft); Occupational therapists 1 (pt); Speech therapists 1 (pt); Dietitians 1 (ft); Dentists 1 (pt); Ophthalmologists 1 (pt); Podiatrists 1 (pt); Audiologists 1 (pt).
Affiliation Roman Catholic
Facilities Dining room; Physical therapy room; Activities room; Chapel; Crafts room; Barber/Beauty shop.
Activities Arts and Crafts; Cards; Games; Reading groups; Prayer groups; Movies; Shopping trips; Dances/Social or cultural gatherings.
Description Physically attached to a 50-bed acute care hospital and therefore has extensive diagnostic, auxilliary, and physician services available.

MARIONVILLE

Ozarks Methodist Manor
205 S College, Marionville, MO, 65705 (417) 463-2573
Admin William G Sampson.
Licensure Intermediate Care. *Beds* 60.
Ownership Nonprofit.
Admissions Requirements Minimum age 60; Medical examination.
Staff Physicians 1 (pt); RNs 3 (ft); LPNs 5 (ft); Orderlies 2 (ft); Nurses aides 18 (ft), 13 (pt);

Physical therapists 1 (pt); Recreational therapists 1 (ft); Occupational therapists 1 (pt); Activities coordinators 1 (ft); Dietitians 2 (ft); Podiatrists 1 (pt).
Affiliation Methodist
Facilities Dining room; Activities room; Chapel; Crafts room; Laundry room; Barber/Beauty shop; Library.
Activities Arts and Crafts; Games; Prayer groups; Movies; Shopping trips.
Description The Ozarks Methodist Manor provides 3 levels of retirement care—cottages, apartments, and a 60-bed health center. A full range of programs are provided in a lively Ozark setting.

MARSHALL

Mar-Saline Manor Care Center
809 E Gordon St, Marshall, MO, 65340 (816) 886-2247
Admin R Nadine Ozias. *Medical Dir/Dir of Nursing* Jane Coleman LPN.
Licensure Intermediate Care. *Beds* 92.
Ownership Proprietary.
Admissions Requirements Medical examination.
Staff Physicians 1 (ft); RNs 1 (pt); LPNs 6 (ft); Orderlies 30 (ft); Physical therapists 1 (pt); Speech therapists 1 (pt); Activities coordinators 1 (ft); Dietitians 1 (pt); Dentists 1 (pt); Podiatrists 1 (pt).
Facilities Dining room; Activities room; Crafts room; Laundry room; Barber/Beauty shop.
Activities Arts and Crafts; Cards; Games; Reading groups; Prayer groups; Movies; Shopping trips; Dances/Social or cultural gatherings.
Description Resident care is excellent; with pride taken in home and residents.

Marshall State School and Hospital*
PO Box 190, Marshall, MO, 65340 (816) 886-2202
Admin Adriene McKenna.
Licensure Intermediate Care for Mentally Retarded. *Beds* 734.

Saline County Rest Home Inc
Rt 1, Marshall, MO, 65340 (816) 886-9676
Admin D Castle.
Licensure Intermediate Care. *Beds* 82.
Ownership Public.

MARSHFIELD

Webco Manor
1657 W Washington, Marshfield, MO, 65706 (417) 468-5144
Admin Jo Walker. *Medical Dir/Dir of Nursing* Dr T M Macdonnell.
Licensure Skilled Care. *Beds* 100.
Ownership Nonprofit.
Staff Physicians 1 (pt); RNs 4 (ft), 1 (pt); LPNs 3 (ft), 3 (pt); Nurses aides 40 (ft), 10 (pt); Physical therapists 1 (pt); Recreational therapists 1 (pt); Occupational therapists 1 (pt); Speech therapists 1 (pt); Activities coordinators 1 (ft); Dietitians 1 (pt); Podiatrists 1 (pt).
Facilities Dining room; Physical therapy room; Activities room; Chapel; Crafts room; Laundry room; Barber/Beauty shop.

Activities Arts and Crafts; Cards; Games; Reading groups; Prayer groups; Movies.
Description Facility is committed to care.

Webster County Rest Home*
820 S White Oak, Marshfield, MO, 65706 (417) 468-3079
Admin Tressa I George.
Licensure Intermediate Care. *Beds* 28.
Ownership Proprietary.

MARYLAND HEIGHTS

Brook View Nursing Home Inc
2963 Doddridge, Maryland Heights, MO, 63043 (314) 291-4557
Admin Gloria Lierman.
Licensure Skilled Care. *Beds* 116.
Ownership Proprietary.
Facilities Dining room; Activities room; Crafts room; Barber/Beauty shop.
Activities Arts and Crafts; Cards; Games; Reading groups; Prayer groups; Movies; Dances/Social or cultural gatherings.

Fairways Caring Center
3201 Parkwood Ln, Maryland Heights, MO, 63043 (314) 291-1356
Admin Mathias P Dasal. *Medical Dir/Dir of Nursing* Arnold S Tepper MD.
Licensure Skilled Care; Intermediate Care. *Beds* 120. *Certified* Medicaid.
Ownership Proprietary.
Admissions Requirements Medical examination.
Staff Physicians 3 (pt); RNs 3 (ft), 4 (pt); LPNs 5 (ft), 1 (pt); Orderlies 1 (ft), 1 (pt); Nurses aides 36 (ft), 5 (pt); Physical therapists 1 (ft); Reality therapists 1 (pt); Recreational therapists 1 (pt); Occupational therapists 1 (pt); Speech therapists 1 (ft); Activities coordinators 1 (ft); Dietitians 1 (pt); Dentists 1 (pt); Ophthalmologists 1 (pt); Podiatrists 1 (pt); Audiologists.
Facilities Dining room; Physical therapy room; Activities room; Chapel; Crafts room; Laundry room; Barber/Beauty shop; Library.
Activities Arts and Crafts; Games; Reading groups; Prayer groups; Movies; Shopping trips; Dances/Social or cultural gatherings.
Description Modern facility surrounded on all sides by lush rolling acreage; peaceful, secluded from the sounds of traffic yet conveniently located near Highway I-270; superb accommodations similar to those found in deluxe hotels; dramatic 2-level glass enclosed dining room, recreation areas, and therapy rooms; caring staff ensures that medical and therapeutic needs are met, food is well-prepared and attractively served, and a rich variety of social activites are available on ongoing basis.

Villa Capri Manor
2920 Fee Rd, Maryland Heights, MO, 63043 (314) 291-0121
Admin Jane Forness. *Medical Dir/Dir of Nursing* Varkey Philip MD.
Licensure Skilled Care; Intermediate Care. *Beds* 220. *Certified* Medicaid.
Ownership Proprietary.
Admissions Requirements Minimum age 18.
Staff RNs 9 (ft); LPNs 14 (ft), 2 (pt); Nurses aides 135 (ft), 10 (pt); Physical therapists 2 (ft);

Occupational therapists 1 (pt); Speech therapists 1 (pt); Activities coordinators 2 (ft); Dietitians 1 (ft); Dentists 1 (pt); Ophthalmologists 1 (pt); Podiatrists 1 (pt).
Facilities Dining room; Physical therapy room; Laundry room; Barber/Beauty shop.
Activities Arts and Crafts; Games; Prayer groups; Movies; Shopping trips; Dances/Social or cultural gatherings.

MARYVILLE

Maryville Health Care Center
524 N Laura, Maryville, MO, 64468 (816) 582-7447
Admin Keith K Stanton. *Medical Dir/Dir of Nursing* Kenneth R Jefferies MD.
Licensure Skilled Care; Intermediate Care. *Beds* 108. *Certified* Medicaid.
Ownership Proprietary.
Admissions Requirements Minimum age 16; Medical examination; Physician's request.
Staff Physicians 4 (pt); RNs 4 (ft); LPNs 6 (ft), 1 (pt); Nurses aides 35 (ft), 5 (pt); Physical therapists 1 (pt); Recreational therapists 1 (ft); Occupational therapists 1 (pt); Speech therapists 1 (pt); Activities coordinators 1 (ft); Dietitians 1 (pt); Dentists 5 (pt); Audiologists 1 (pt).
Facilities Dining room; Physical therapy room; Activities room; Crafts room; Laundry room; Barber/Beauty shop.
Activities Arts and Crafts; Cards; Games; Reading groups; Prayer groups; Movies; Dances/Social or cultural gatherings.

Nodaway Nursing Home Inc
Hwy 46, Rt 1, Maryville, MO, 64468 (816) 582-5658
Admin Katherine Peniston.
Licensure Intermediate Care. *Beds* 60.
Ownership Proprietary.
Staff RNs 1 (pt); LPNs 2 (ft), 1 (pt); Activities coordinators 1 (ft).
Facilities Dining room; Laundry room.
Activities Arts and Crafts; Cards; Games; Reading groups; Movies.
Description Facility is situated in a rural setting.

Parkdale Manor Care Center
Route V and Munn Ave, Maryville, MO, 64468 (816) 582-8161
Admin Mary Lou Hughes.
Licensure Intermediate Care. *Beds* 92.
Ownership Proprietary.
Admissions Requirements Minimum age 16; Medical examination.
Staff RNs 1 (ft); LPNs 8 (ft); Nurses aides 21 (ft); Physical therapists 1 (pt); Activities coordinators 1 (ft).
Facilities Dining room; Activities room; Laundry room; Barber/Beauty shop; Conference room.
Activities Arts and Crafts; Cards; Games; Reading groups; Prayer groups; Movies; Shopping trips; Dances/Social or cultural gatherings.
Description Facility features picnics and parties for residents and their families; residents may invite card clubs out for lunch and also their family members.

MATTHEWS

Sells Rest Home Inc*
Rt 1, Box 6A, Matthews, MO, 63867 (314)
471-7861
Admin Annie Lee Sells.
Licensure Intermediate Care. *Beds* 94. *Certified* Medicaid.
Ownership Proprietary.

MAYSVILLE

Sunset Home Inc
Hwy 33, Maysville, MO, 64469 (816) 449-2158
Admin Roy Trussell.
Licensure Intermediate Care. *Beds* 119. *Certified* Medicaid.
Ownership Public.
Staff RNs 1 (ft), 1 (pt); LPNs 2 (ft), 1 (pt);
Activities coordinators 1 (ft), 1 (pt).

MEMPHIS

Scotland County Nursing Home District
Sigler St, Box 245, Memphis, MO, 63555 (816)
465-8511
Admin Gerald L Vice.
Licensure Intermediate Care. *Beds* 120. *Certified* Medicaid.
Ownership Public.
Staff Physicians 2 (pt); RNs 1 (ft); LPNs 5 (ft);
Orderlies 1 (pt); Nurses aides 30 (ft); Physical
therapists 1 (pt); Activities coordinators 1 (ft);
Dietitians 1 (pt).

Scottland Company Community Home*
361 Grand Ave, Memphis, MO, 63555 (816)
465-2203
Admin Catherine Aldridge.
Licensure Residential Care. *Beds* 24.
Ownership Proprietary.

MEXICO

Allen Home
219 E Bolivar, Mexico, MO, 65265 (314)
581-1815
Admin Virginia Walker.
Licensure Intermediate Care. *Beds* 31.
Ownership Proprietary.
Admissions Requirements Minimum age 18;
Medical examination.
Staff RNs 1 (pt); LPNs 2 (pt); Nurses aides 18
(ft); Dentists 1 (ft).
Facilities Activities room; Laundry room.
Activities Games; Movies; Shopping trips.

Coldwell Nursing Home
Rt 2, Mexico, MO, 65265 (314) 581-2752
Admin Lenora Coldwell. *Medical Dir/Dir of
Nursing* J E Taft DO.
Licensure Intermediate Care. *Beds* 64.
Ownership Proprietary.
Admissions Requirements Minimum age 21.
Staff RNs 1 (ft); LPNs 2 (ft); Orderlies 1 (ft);
Nurses aides 16 (ft), 4 (pt).
Facilities Dining room; Activities room; Chapel; Crafts room; Laundry room; Barber/Beauty
shop; Library.

Activities Arts and Crafts; Cards; Games;
Reading groups; Prayer groups; Movies; Shopping trips; Dances/Social or cultural gatherings.

King's Daughters Home
620 West Blvd, Mexico, MO, 65265 (314)
581-1577
Admin Joan C Talley.
Licensure Intermediate Care. *Beds* 29.
Ownership Nonprofit.
Admissions Requirements Minimum age 65;
Females only; Medical examination.
Staff RNs 1 (pt); LPNs 1 (ft), 2 (pt); Nurses
aides 8 (ft), 3 (pt); Activities coordinators 1 (pt);
Dietitians 1 (pt).
Affiliation King's Daughters and Sons
Facilities Dining room; Activities room; Chapel; Crafts room; Laundry room; Barber/Beauty
shop; Library.
Activities Arts and Crafts; Games; Prayer
groups; Movies; Shopping trips.
Description Each resident has her own private
room and must be able to take upstairs room
when being admitted and care some for herself;
family-style meals in dining room; hospital area
for those who later become total care.

Pin Oaks Adult Care
Hwy 22 at Curtis Ave, Mexico, MO, 65265
(314) 581-7261
Admin Jay Seigfreid. *Medical Dir/Dir of
Nursing* Steve Taylor MD.
Licensure Skilled Care; Intermediate Care.
Beds 164. *Certified* Medicaid.
Ownership Proprietary.
Admissions Requirements Minimum age 18.
Staff RNs 3 (ft); LPNs 16 (ft); Orderlies 12 (ft);
Nurses aides 51 (ft); Physical therapists 1 (ft);
Recreational therapists 2 (ft); Occupational
therapists 1 (pt); Speech therapists 1 (pt);
Activities coordinators 1 (ft); Dietitians 1 (pt);
Dentists 1 (pt); Ophthalmologists 1 (pt); Podiatrists 1 (pt); Audiologists 1 (pt).
Facilities Dining room; Physical therapy room;
Activities room; Chapel; Crafts room; Laundry
room; Barber/Beauty shop; Library.
Activities Arts and Crafts; Cards; Games;
Reading groups; Prayer groups; Movies; Shopping trips; Dances/Social or cultural gatherings.

MILAN

Leewood Manor Nursing Home Inc
W 3rd, Milan, MO, 63556 (816) 265-4433
Admin Harley E Reece.
Licensure Intermediate Care. *Beds* 81. *Certified* Medicaid.
Ownership Proprietary.
Admissions Requirements Minimum age 17;
Medical examination.
Staff RNs 1 (ft); LPNs 3 (ft); Nurses aides 30
(ft); Physical therapists 1 (pt); Occupational
therapists 1 (pt); Speech therapists 1 (pt);
Activities coordinators 1 (ft); Dietitians 1 (pt).
Facilities Dining room; Laundry room; Barber-
/Beauty shop.
Activities Arts and Crafts; Cards; Games;
Movies; Shopping trips; Dances/Social or cultural gatherings.

Milan Care Center Inc
Rt 3, Box 16, Milan, MO, 63556 (816)
265-3168
Admin Wayne Wheeler.
Licensure Intermediate Care. *Beds* 100.
Ownership Proprietary.
Admissions Requirements Minimum age 16.
Staff Physicians 4 (pt); RNs 2 (ft), 1 (pt); LPNs
6 (ft); Orderlies 2 (ft); Nurses aides 30 (ft), 10
(pt); Physical therapists 1 (pt); Occupational
therapists 1 (pt); Speech therapists 1 (pt);
Activities coordinators 1 (pt); Dietitians 1 (pt);
Dentists 1 (pt).
Facilities Dining room; Physical therapy room;
Activities room; Crafts room; Laundry room;
Barber/Beauty shop.
Activities Arts and Crafts; Cards; Games;
Reading groups; Prayer groups; Movies; Shopping trips; Dances/Social or cultural gatherings.
Description Facility is located in a quiet, tranquil, suburban area in northern Missouri with
a beautiful view of rolling hills, forests, and
lake.

MINERAL POINT

Rainbow Springs Care Center*
Rt 1, Box 666, Mineral Point, MO, 63660 (314)
438-3398
Admin Donald H Bohr.
Licensure Intermediate Care. *Beds* 15.
Ownership Proprietary.

MOBERLY

Maple Lawn Lodge*
415 Woodland Ave, Moberly, MO, 65270 (816)
263-5652
Admin Melba Swope.
Licensure Intermediate Care. *Beds* 49.
Ownership Proprietary.

North Village Manor*
Box 40, 2041 Silva Ln, Moberly, MO, 65270
(816) 263-1894
Admin Carol Wright.
Licensure Intermediate Care. *Beds* 184. *Certified* Medicaid.
Ownership Proprietary.

MOKANE

Riverview Nursing Center
Rt 1, Mokane, MO, 65059 (314) 676-3136
Admin S Jay Hitt. *Medical Dir/Dir of
Nursing* Mel Hector.
Licensure Intermediate Care. *Beds* 60. *Certified* Medicaid.
Ownership Proprietary.
Admissions Requirements Medical examination.
Staff Physicians 1 (pt); RNs 2 (pt); LPNs 2 (ft),
2 (pt); Orderlies 3 (ft); Nurses aides 17 (ft);
Physical therapists 1 (pt); Reality therapists 1
(pt); Recreational therapists 2 (ft); Occupational
therapists 1 (pt); Speech therapists 1 (pt);
Activities coordinators 1 (pt); Dietitians 1 (pt);
Dentists 1 (pt).
Facilities Dining room; Physical therapy room;
Activities room; Laundry room; Barber/Beauty
shop; Lounge.

Activities Arts and Crafts; Cards; Games; Reading groups; Prayer groups; Movies; Shopping trips; Dances/Social or cultural gatherings. *Description* Home-style plan for private pay includes over 50 free benefits; facility features hilltop setting and excellent nursing care.

MONETT

Camden Health Care Center*
410 W Benton St, Monett, MO, 65708 (417) 235-6031
Admin Kerry D Soncrant.
Licensure Intermediate Care. *Beds* 120. *Certified* Medicaid.
Ownership Proprietary.

LaCoba Homes Inc*
Rt 2, Monett, MO, 65708 (417) 235-7895
Admin Bill L Stout.
Licensure Intermediate Care. *Beds* 60.
Ownership Nonprofit.

Rest Haven Nursing Home*
910 4th St, Monett, MO, 65708 (417) 235-7243
Admin Stella Bolles.
Licensure Intermediate Care. *Beds* 26.
Ownership Proprietary.

MONROE CITY

Monroe City Manor Care Center*
Hwy 36 E and Z Rd, Monroe City, MO, 63456 (314) 735-4850
Admin Lillian M Edwards.
Licensure Intermediate Care. *Beds* 52.
Ownership Proprietary.

MONTGOMERY CITY

Montgomery Manor*
230 Pickering St, Box 157, Montgomery City, MO, 63361 (314) 564-7986
Admin Maxine Stone.
Licensure Residential Care. *Beds* 40.
Ownership Proprietary.

Owens Home*
100 S Wentz, Montgomery City, MO, 63361 (314) 564-2207
Admin Sue Owens.
Licensure Residential Care. *Beds* 14.
Ownership Proprietary.

MOSCOW MILLS

Mollie Wells Nursing Home Inc*
PO Box 25, Moscow Mills, MO, 63362 (314) 356-4231
Admin Jewell Wells.
Licensure Intermediate Care. *Beds* 30.
Ownership Proprietary.

MOUND CITY

Tiffany Heights
1531 Nebraska, PO Box 208, Mound City, MO, 64470 (816) 442-3146
Admin P R Northup.

Licensure Intermediate Care. *Beds* 60. *Certified* Medicaid.
Ownership Proprietary.
Staff RNs 3 (pt); LPNs 2 (ft); Orderlies 1 (ft); Nurses aides 15 (ft), 4 (pt); Physical therapists 1 (pt); Occupational therapists 1 (pt); Speech therapists 1 (pt); Activities coordinators 1 (ft); Dietitians 1 (pt).
Facilities Dining room; Physical therapy room; Activities room; Crafts room; Laundry room; Barber/Beauty shop.
Activities Arts and Crafts; Cards; Games; Reading groups; Prayer groups; Movies; Dances/Social or cultural gatherings.

MOUNT VERNON

Lawrence County Nursing Home
Carl Allen Dr, Box 191, Mount Vernon, MO, 65712 (417) 466-2183
Admin Gary M Phillips. *Medical Dir/Dir of Nursing* Sandra Grunnert MD.
Licensure Skilled Care; Intermediate Care.
Beds 120. *Certified* Medicaid.
Ownership Proprietary.
Admissions Requirements Minimum age 17; Medical examination.
Staff Physicians 5 (pt); RNs 3 (ft); LPNs 11 (ft); Orderlies 2 (ft); Nurses aides 44 (ft); Physical therapists 1 (pt); Occupational therapists 1 (pt); Speech therapists 1 (pt); Activities coordinators 1 (ft); Dietitians 1 (pt).
Facilities Dining room; Physical therapy room; Activities room; Chapel; Laundry room; Barber/Beauty shop.
Activities Arts and Crafts; Games; Reading groups; Prayer groups; Movies; Shopping trips; Dances/Social or cultural gatherings.

MOUNTAIN GROVE

Thomas Manor Nursing Center*
13th and Hovis, Mountain Grove, MO, 65711 (417) 926-5128
Admin Jack Ray Thomas.
Licensure Intermediate Care. *Beds* 120. *Certified* Medicaid.
Ownership Proprietary.

NEOSHO

Medicalodge of Neosho*
Rt 6, Box 153, Neosho, MO, 64850 (417) 451-2544
Admin Frank Taylor.
Licensure Intermediate Care. *Beds* 120. *Certified* Medicaid.
Ownership Proprietary.

Neosho Senior Center Inc*
330 S Wood, Neosho, MO, 64850 (417) 451-3600
Admin Barbara Johnson.
Licensure Intermediate Care. *Beds* 94. *Certified* Medicaid.
Ownership Proprietary.

NEVADA

Nevada City Nursing Home
815 S Adams, Nevada, MO, 64772 (417) 667-3355
Admin Shirley Baxter and Albert Ban Jr.
Medical Dir/Dir of Nursing Dr F L Thompson.
Licensure Skilled Care; Intermediate Care.
Beds 80. *Certified* Medicaid; Medicare.
Ownership Public.
Admissions Requirements Medical examination; Physician's request.
Staff Physicians 1 (pt); RNs 1 (ft), 1 (pt); LPNs 7 (ft), 4 (pt); Orderlies 1 (ft); Nurses aides 26 (ft), 8 (pt); Physical therapists 1 (pt); Occupational therapists 1 (pt); Speech therapists 1 (pt); Activities coordinators 1 (ft); Dietitians 1 (pt); Dentists 1 (pt); Ophthalmologists 1 (pt); Podiatrists 1 (pt); Audiologists 1 (pt).
Facilities Dining room; Physical therapy room; Activities room; Chapel; Crafts room; Laundry room; Barber/Beauty shop; Library.
Activities Arts and Crafts; Cards; Games; Reading groups; Prayer groups; Movies; Shopping trips; Dances/Social or cultural gatherings.

Nevada Habilitation Center
Ash and Highland, Nevada, MO, 64772 (417) 667-7833
Admin Charles W Brewer. *Medical Dir/Dir of Nursing* William C Magness MD.
Beds 415.
Ownership Public.
Staff Physicians 4 (ft); RNs 29 (ft); LPNs 40 (ft); Nurses aides 365 (ft); Recreational therapists 1 (ft); Speech therapists 3 (ft); Dietitians 2 (ft); Dentists 1 (ft), 1 (pt); Podiatrists 1 (pt); Audiologists 1 (ft).
Facilities Activities room; Chapel; Barber/Beauty shop; Library.
Activities Arts and Crafts; Movies; Shopping trips; Dances/Social or cultural gatherings.
Description Facility is for mentally retarded/developmentally disabled citizens from a specified catchment area. Admissions are accepted through regional centers for developmental disabled located throughout the state.

Nevada Manor Nursing Home*
1210 W Ashland, Nevada, MO, 64772 (417) 667-5064
Admin Virginia Nash.
Licensure Skilled Care; Intermediate Care.
Beds 100. *Certified* Medicaid.
Ownership Proprietary.

Senior Citizen's Nursing Home*
614 N Washington St, Nevada, MO, 64772 (417) 667-2786
Admin Lola Trego.
Licensure Intermediate Care. *Beds* 17.
Ownership Proprietary.

NEW FLORENCE

New Florence Nursing Home Inc
Rt 1, Box 14, New Florence, MO, 63363 (314) 835-2025
Admin Homer Branham. *Medical Dir/Dir of Nursing* George Workman MD.
Licensure Intermediate Care. *Beds* 60. *Certi-

fied Medicaid.
Ownership Nonprofit.
Admissions Requirements Minimum age 18;
Medical examination.
Staff Physicians 7 (ft); RNs 2 (ft); LPNs 2 (ft),
1 (pt); Nurses aides 22 (ft), 4 (pt); Physical ther-
apists 1 (pt); Reality therapists 1 (pt); Recrea-
tional therapists 1 (pt); Activities coordinators 1
(ft), 1 (pt); Dietitians 1 (ft); Dentists 2 (pt);
Ophthalmologists 1 (pt).
Facilities Dining room; Physical therapy room;
Activities room; Chapel; Crafts room; Laundry
room; Barber/Beauty shop.
Activities Arts and Crafts; Cards; Games;
Reading groups; Prayer groups; Movies; Dan-
ces/Social or cultural gatherings.
Description Facility offers rural setting, beautiful surroundings and landscape, home-like
atmosphere, caring staff.

NEW MADRID

Magnolia Manor
1050 Dawson Rd, New Madrid, MO, 63869
Medical Dir/Dir of Nursing Dr Pattaropong.
Staff RNs 1 (ft), 1 (pt); LPNs 5 (ft), 1 (pt);
Nurses aides 22 (ft); Physical therapists 2 (ft);
Activities coordinators 1 (ft); Dietitians 1 (ft);
Dentists 1 (pt).
Facilities Dining room; Physical therapy room;
Activities room; Laundry room; Barber/Beauty
shop.
Activities Arts and Crafts; Cards; Games;
Reading groups; Prayer groups; Shopping trips;
Dances/Social or cultural gatherings.
Description Modern, well equipped home in a
rural setting; outstanding home-cooked meals
served; loving, caring nursing staff.

NORMANDY

Bell Manor Inc
3715 Saint Ann's Ln, Normandy, MO, 63121
(314) 383-3353
Admin David Joe Bentley.
Licensure Intermediate Care. *Beds* 61.
Ownership Proprietary.
Admissions Requirements Minimum age 18;
Medical examination.
Staff Physicians 1 (pt); RNs 1 (ft), 1 (pt); LPNs
1 (pt); Nurses aides 25 (ft), 5 (pt); Physical ther-
apists 1 (pt); Occupational therapists 1 (pt);
Speech therapists 1 (pt); Activities coordinators
1 (ft); Dietitians 1 (pt); Dentists 1 (pt); Podiatr-
ists 1 (pt).
Facilities Dining room; Activities room; Crafts
room; Laundry room; Barber/Beauty shop.
Activities Arts and Crafts; Cards; Games;
Reading groups; Prayer groups; Movies; Shopping trips; Dances/Social or cultural gatherings.

Castle Park Professional Care Center*
7301 St Charles Rock Rd, Normandy, MO,
63133 (314) 726-5514
Admin Geraldine Potter.
Licensure Skilled Care; Intermediate Care.
Beds 120. *Certified* Medicaid; Medicare.
Ownership Proprietary.

OAK GROVE

Oak Grove Health Care Center
21st and Mitchell, Oak Grove, MO, 64075
(816) 625-4118
Admin Richard Sanders. *Medical Dir/Dir of
Nursing* Dr Robert Lathe and Dr James Soeldner.
Licensure Intermediate Care. *Beds* 82. *Certified* Medicaid.
Ownership Proprietary.
Admissions Requirements Medical
examination.
Staff Physicians 5 (pt); RNs 2 (ft), 2 (pt); LPNs
3 (ft), 3 (pt); Orderlies 1 (ft); Nurses aides 40
(ft); Physical therapists 1 (pt); Recreational therapists 1 (ft); Occupational therapists 1 (pt);
Speech therapists 1 (pt); Activities coordinators
1 (ft); Dietitians 1 (pt); Dentists 1 (pt); Podiatrists 1 (pt); Audiologists 1 (pt).
Facilities Dining room; Physical therapy room;
Activities room; Crafts room; Laundry room;
Barber/Beauty shop.
Activities Arts and Crafts; Cards; Games; Prayer groups; Movies; Dances/Social or cultural
gatherings.

ODESSA

New Haven Nursing Home*
609 Golf St, Odessa, MO, 64076 (816)
633-7539
Admin Daniel Salm.
Licensure Intermediate Care. *Beds* 60. *Certified* Medicaid.
Ownership Proprietary.

OFALLON

Twin Oaks Estate Inc
707 Enge Rd, O'Fallon, MO, 63366
Admin Mary A Huber.
Licensure Residential Care. *Beds* 29.
Ownership Proprietary.
Admissions Requirements Minimum age 16;
Medical examination.
Staff RNs 1 (ft); Nurses aides 2 (ft), 8 (pt); Rec-
reational therapists 1 (pt); Activities coordina-
tors 1 (pt).
Facilities Dining room; Activities room;
Chapel; Laundry room; Barber/Beauty shop.
Activities Arts and Crafts; Cards; Games; Pray-
er groups; Movies; Shopping trips;
Dances/Social or cultural gatherings; Outings
by van.
Description Located on 7 landscaped country
acres, facility is small enough to be geared to
individuality in attention and care; known for
home cooked meals, warm atmosphere, and
planned activities.

OREGON

Oregon Health Care Center
501 S Monroe, Oregon, MO, 64473 (816)
446-3355
Admin John Stein.
Licensure Intermediate Care. *Beds* 60.
Ownership Proprietary.
Staff Physicians 2 (ft); RNs 1 (pt); LPNs 1 (ft),

1 (pt); Orderlies 1 (ft); Nurses aides 31 (ft), 12
(pt); Physical therapists 1 (pt); Occupational
therapists 1 (pt); Speech therapists 1 (pt);
Activities coordinators 2 (ft); Dietitians 1 (pt);
Dentists 1 (pt); Audiologists 1 (pt).
Facilities Dining room; Physical therapy room;
Activities room; Chapel; Crafts room; Laundry
room; Barber/Beauty shop.
Activities Arts and Crafts; Cards; Games; Prayer groups; Movies; Dances/Social or cultural
gatherings.
Description The staff goes to great extremes to
make facility as close to a home as possible.

Pleasant Hill Nursing Home
Rt 1, Oregon, MO, 64473 (816) 446-2281
Admin Dorothy Boehm.
Licensure Intermediate Care. *Beds* 32.
Ownership Proprietary.

OSAGE BEACH

Osage Beach Health Care Center
Lake Rd, Osage Beach, MO, 65065
Admin John R Strawn. *Medical Dir/Dir of
Nursing* Dr Clemmons Haggerty.
Licensure Skilled Care; Intermediate Care;
Intermediate Care for Mentally Retarded.
Beds 120. *Certified* Medicaid; Medicare.
Ownership Proprietary.
Staff Physicians 1 (pt); RNs 4 (ft); LPNs 2 (ft);
Orderlies 1 (ft); Nurses aides 12 (ft); Physical
therapists 1 (pt); Occupational therapists 1 (pt);
Speech therapists 1 (pt); Activities coordinators
1 (ft); Dietitians 1 (pt).
Facilities Dining room; Physical therapy room;
Activities room; Laundry room; Barber/Beauty
shop.
Activities Arts and Crafts; Cards; Games;
Reading groups; Prayer groups; Movies; Shop-
ping trips; Dances/Social or cultural gatherings.
Description VA approved.

Ozark Care Center
Box 278, Osage Beach, MO, 65065
Admin Peggy Culver. *Medical Dir/Dir of
Nursing* T W Garrison MD.
Licensure Skilled Care; Intermediate Care.
Beds 60. *Certified* Medicaid; Medicare.
Ownership Proprietary.
Admissions Requirements Physician's request.
Staff RNs 3 (ft), 1 (pt); LPNs 6 (ft); Nurses
aides 17 (ft), 10 (pt); Physical therapists 1 (pt);
Occupational therapists 1 (pt); Speech thera-
pists 1 (pt); Activities coordinators 1 (ft).
Facilities Dining room; Physical therapy room;
Activities room; Chapel; Crafts room; Laundry
room; Barber/Beauty shop.
Activities Arts and Crafts; Cards; Games;
Reading groups; Prayer groups; Movies; Dan-
ces/Social or cultural gatherings.

OWENSVILLE

Gasconade Manor Nursing and Care Center
PO Box 520, Rt 19 and Springfield Rd, Owens-
ville, MO, 65066 (314) 437-4101
Admin Karen F Yates. *Medical Dir/Dir of
Nursing* Dr Robert LaHue.
Licensure Intermediate Care. *Beds* 60. *Certi-
fied* Medicaid.

Ownership Nonprofit.
Staff RNs 1 (ft); LPNs 2 (ft), 1 (pt); Orderlies 1 (ft); Nurses aides 18 (ft), 7 (pt); Activities coordinators 1 (ft), 1 (pt).
Facilities Dining room; Physical therapy room; Activities room; Laundry room; Barber/Beauty shop.
Activities Arts and Crafts; Games; Prayer groups; Movies; Dances/Social or cultural gatherings.

OZARK

Christian County Nursing Home
PO Box 157, Ozark, MO, 65721 (417) 485-6025
Admin Daniel L Serven.
Licensure Intermediate Care. *Beds* 56.
Ownership Proprietary.

Ozark Nursing and Care Center*
1106 N 3rd Ave, Ozark, MO, 65721 (417) 485-7126
Admin Steven Usery.
Licensure Skilled Care; Intermediate Care.
Beds 120. *Certified* Medicaid; Medicare.
Ownership Proprietary.

PALMYRA

Maple Lawn Nursing Home*
Rt 3, Palmyra, MO, 63461 (314) 769-3216
Admin Linda L Zahn.
Licensure Intermediate Care. *Beds* 73.
Ownership Proprietary.

PARIS

Monroe Manor
200 South St, Paris, MO, 65275 (816) 327-4125
Admin Norma Gritton. *Medical Dir/Dir of Nursing* Dr C R Warbritton.
Licensure Intermediate Care. *Beds* 120.
Ownership Proprietary.
Admissions Requirements Minimum age 18; Medical examination; Physician's request.
Staff RNs 1 (pt); LPNs 7 (ft); Orderlies 2 (ft); Nurses aides 40 (ft); Physical therapists 1 (pt); Reality therapists 1 (pt); Recreational therapists 1 (pt); Occupational therapists 1 (pt); Speech therapists 1 (pt); Activities coordinators 1 (ft); Dietitians 1 (pt).
Facilities Dining room; Physical therapy room; Activities room; Chapel; Crafts room; Laundry room; Barber/Beauty shop; Library.
Activities Arts and Crafts; Cards; Games; Reading groups; Movies; Shopping trips; Dances/Social or cultural gatherings.
Description Manor provides as near a home-like atmosphere as possible to assist residents to live a useful life, adding life to years, not just years to life.

PERRY

Twain Haven Nursing Home
Hwy 154 E, Perry, MO, 63462 (314) 565-2217
Admin Doris G Moore.
Licensure Intermediate Care. *Beds* 50.
Ownership Proprietary.

Admissions Requirements Minimum age 16.
Staff RNs 1 (pt); LPNs 1 (ft), 2 (pt); Nurses aides 12 (ft), 14 (pt); Activities coordinators 1 (pt).
Facilities Dining room; Crafts room.
Activities Games; Prayer groups; Movies; Weekly church services.
Description Nursing home is located in a rural community, owned by the residents of the area, and occupied and staffed by local people. It is not a county-owned or operated facility, however. As a result, we feel we have a lot of community involvement and interest. Staff is a caring one as they have known most of the residents and their families for years. We also have a reputation for giving quality care for a minimal cost.

PERRYVILLE

American Care Center*
430 Northwest St, Perryville, MO, 63775 (314) 547-8383
Admin Norma Jean Steffens.
Licensure Intermediate Care. *Beds* 156. *Certified* Medicaid.
Ownership Nonprofit.

Perry County Nursing Home
Rt 2, 800 S Kingshighway, Perryville, MO, 63775 (314) 547-6546
Admin Frank Bergman. *Medical Dir/Dir of Nursing* L Medrano.
Licensure Intermediate Care. *Beds* 123. *Certified* Medicaid.
Ownership Nonprofit.
Admissions Requirements Minimum age 18.
Staff RNs 2 (pt); LPNs 4 (ft), 1 (pt); Nurses aides 34 (ft), 20 (pt); Activities coordinators 1 (ft); 15 (ft), 19 (pt).
Facilities Dining room; Physical therapy room; Activities room; Chapel; Crafts room; Laundry room; Barber/Beauty shop.
Activities Arts and Crafts; Cards; Games; Reading groups; Prayer groups; Movies; Shopping trips; Dances/Social or cultural gatherings.

PIEDMONT

Clark's Mountain Home*
2100 Barnes, Piedmont, MO, 63957 (314) 223-4297
Admin Wilma Ball.
Licensure Intermediate Care. *Beds* 90. *Certified* Medicaid.
Ownership Proprietary.

PLATTSBURG

Clinton Manor Inc*
Hwy 116, Plattsburg, MO, 64477 (816) 539-2713
Admin Yvonne Breckenridge.
Licensure Intermediate Care. *Beds* 64.
Ownership Proprietary.

Oakridge of Plattsburg
E Clay Ave, PO Box 247, Plattsburg, MO, 64477 (816) 539-2128
Admin Gene Davidson.
Licensure Intermediate Care. *Beds* 60.

Ownership Nonprofit.
Staff Physicians 3 (ft), 1 (pt); RNs 1 (ft), 1 (pt); LPNs 1 (ft), 1 (pt); Nurses aides 19 (ft), 7 (pt); Activities coordinators 1 (ft); Dietitians 1 (pt).
Facilities Dining room; Activities room; Crafts room; Laundry room; Barber/Beauty shop.
Activities Arts and Crafts; Cards; Games; Reading groups; Prayer groups; Movies; Shopping trips; Dances/Social or cultural gatherings.
Description Facility has home-like atmosphere and quality care at reasonable prices.

POPLAR BLUFF

Assembly Nursing Home of Poplar Bluff Inc
203 N "B" St, Poplar Bluff, MO, 63901 (314) 785-6155
Admin Lillian Haley.
Licensure Intermediate Care. *Beds* 48.
Ownership Proprietary.
Admissions Requirements Minimum age 18.
Staff RNs 1 (pt); LPNs 1 (ft), 1 (pt); Orderlies 1 (ft); Nurses aides 13 (ft), 4 (pt); Activities coordinators 1 (ft), 1 (pt).
Facilities Dining room; Activities room; Laundry room; Barber/Beauty shop.
Activities Arts and Crafts; Games; Prayer groups; Movies.
Description Facility is one-floor building with sprinklers throughout. Offers regular activities of many kinds, especially of religious groups. Home-type meals are a specialty.

Bluff Manor Nursing Home
2071 Barron Rd, PO Box 1066, Poplar Bluff, MO, 63901 (314) 686-1147
Admin Samuel D Vancil. *Medical Dir/Dir of Nursing* Barry B White MD.
Licensure Skilled Care; Intermediate Care.
Beds 90. *Certified* Medicaid; Medicare.
Ownership Proprietary.
Admissions Requirements Physician's request.
Staff Physicians 2 (ft); RNs 2 (ft), 1 (pt); LPNs 4 (ft), 4 (pt); Nurses aides 36 (ft), 8 (pt); Physical therapists 1 (pt); Reality therapists 1 (pt); Recreational therapists 1 (pt); Occupational therapists 1 (pt); Speech therapists 1 (pt); Activities coordinators 1 (pt); Dietitians 1 (ft); Dentists 1 (pt); Ophthalmologists 1 (pt); Podiatrists 1 (pt); Audiologists 1 (pt); 10 (ft), 5 (pt).

Cedargate
Hwy PP, PO Box 608, Poplar Bluff, MO, 63901 (314) 785-0188
Admin Ruth Warren. *Medical Dir/Dir of Nursing* Fred Caldwell MD.
Licensure Skilled Care; Intermediate Care.
Beds 108. *Certified* Medicaid.
Ownership Proprietary.
Admissions Requirements Minimum age 16.
Staff Physicians 15 (pt); RNs 2 (ft), 2 (pt); LPNs 12 (ft), 2 (pt); Nurses aides 34 (ft), 4 (pt); Physical therapists 1 (pt); Reality therapists 1 (pt); Recreational therapists 1 (pt); Occupational therapists 1 (pt); Speech therapists 1 (pt); Activities coordinators 1 (ft); Dietitians 1 (pt); Dentists 1 (pt); Ophthalmologists 1 (pt); Podiatrists 1 (pt).
Facilities Dining room; Physical therapy room; Activities room; Crafts room; Laundry room; Barber/Beauty shop.

Activities Arts and Crafts; Cards; Games; Reading groups; Prayer groups; Movies; Shopping trips; Dances/Social or cultural gatherings.

Golden Years Boarding Facility
307 Broadway, Poplar Bluff, MO, 63901
Admin Donald R Johnson. *Medical Dir/Dir of Nursing* Lue Ella Mason.
Licensure Residential Care. *Beds* 17.
Ownership Proprietary.
Admissions Requirements Minimum age 21; Medical examination.
Staff Physicians 1 (pt); RNs 1 (pt).
Facilities Dining room; Activities room; Chapel; Laundry room; Barber/Beauty shop.
Activities Games; Prayer groups; Movies; Shopping trips.
Description Facility has a very large patio in the rear for residents to enjoy; also 2 sun porches to view TV; person must be ambulatory to be admitted.

POTOSI

Moses Austin Group Care Home*
217 E Citadel, Potosi, MO, 63665 (314) 438-3736
Admin Rick J Hurst.
Licensure Intermediate Care for Mentally Retarded. *Beds* 9.
Ownership Public.

PRINCETON

Princeton Care Center Inc
Rt 2, Box 147, Princeton, MO, 64673 (816) 748-3228
Admin Karen Rockhold.
Licensure Intermediate Care. *Beds* 52. *Certified* Medicaid.
Ownership Proprietary.
Staff Physicians; RNs; LPNs; Nurses aides; Physical therapists; Recreational therapists; Occupational therapists; Speech therapists; Activities coordinators; Dietitians; Dentists; Audiologists.
Facilities Dining room; Physical therapy room; Activities room; Laundry room; Barber/Beauty shop; Library.
Activities Arts and Crafts; Cards; Games; Reading groups; Prayer groups; Movies; Shopping trips; Dances/Social or cultural gatherings.
Description Facility is located in a rural area with a beautiful setting; very active therapy department.

PUXICO

Grandview Manor Nursing Home*
PO Box P, Puxico, MO, 63960 (314) 222-3125
Admin Linda K Siler.
Licensure Intermediate Care. *Beds* 60. *Certified* Medicaid.
Ownership Proprietary.

QUEEN CITY

Schuyler County Nursing Home
Hwy 63 N, Queen City, MO, 63561 (816) 766-2291

Admin Robert Seamster. *Medical Dir/Dir of Nursing* Dr E M Roberts.
Licensure Intermediate Care. *Beds* 60. *Certified* Medicaid.
Ownership Proprietary.
Admissions Requirements Minimum age 16.
Staff RNs 1 (ft); LPNs 2 (ft), 1 (pt); Orderlies 2 (ft); Nurses aides 15 (ft), 13 (pt); Physical therapists 1 (pt); Reality therapists 1 (pt); Occupational therapists 1 (pt); Speech therapists 1 (pt); Activities coordinators 1 (ft); Dietitians 1 (pt); Dentists 1 (pt); Podiatrists 1 (pt).
Facilities Dining room; Physical therapy room; Activities room; Crafts room; Laundry room; Barber/Beauty shop.
Activities Arts and Crafts; Games; Reading groups; Prayer groups; Movies; Shopping trips; Dances/Social or cultural gatherings.

RAYMORE

Foxwood Springs Living Center
Box 370, Raymore, MO, 64083 (816) 331-9696
Admin Thomas R Williams. *Medical Dir/Dir of Nursing* Gary Gustafson DO.
Licensure Skilled Care; Intermediate Care. *Beds* 60. *Certified* Medicaid.
Ownership Nonprofit.
Staff RNs 1 (ft), 1 (pt); LPNs 5 (ft), 5 (pt); Nurses aides 16 (ft), 7 (pt); Activities coordinators 1 (ft), 1 (pt); Dietitians 1 (ft).
Affiliation Disciples of Christ
Facilities Dining room; Physical therapy room; Activities room; Crafts room; Laundry room; Barber/Beauty shop; Library.
Activities Arts and Crafts; Cards; Games; Reading groups; Prayer groups; Movies; Shopping trips; Dances/Social or cultural gatherings.
Description Facility offers an educational program organized by residents and staff for all Foxwood residents entitled G.L.O.W.; new heated indoor swimming pool with wheelchair ramp; home health program to aid independent living residents; resident volunteer program that operates a country store, television station, library, etc.

RAYTOWN

Bowen Health Center*
6124 Raytown Rd, Raytown, MO, 64133 (816) 358-8222
Admin Ervin E Smith.
Licensure Intermediate Care. *Beds* 60. *Certified* Medicaid.
Ownership Proprietary.

Heritage Village at Park Place Meadows
11901 Jessica Ln, Raytown, MO, 64138 (816) 358-3535
Admin Nell M Schmidt. *Medical Dir/Dir of Nursing* Thomas Phillips MD.
Licensure Skilled Care. *Beds* 120.
Ownership Proprietary.
Admissions Requirements Minimum age 18; Medical examination.
Staff Physicians 2 (ft); RNs 3 (ft); LPNs 8 (ft); Orderlies 2 (ft); Nurses aides 42 (ft); Physical therapists 2 (pt); Reality therapists 1 (ft); Recreational therapists 1 (ft); Occupational therapists 1 (pt); Speech therapists 1 (pt); Activities coor-

dinators 1 (ft); Dietitians 1 (ft); Dentists 1 (pt); Ophthalmologists 1 (pt); Podiatrists 1 (pt); Audiologists 1 (pt).
Facilities Dining room; Physical therapy room; Activities room; Chapel; Crafts room; Laundry room; Barber/Beauty shop; Library.
Activities Arts and Crafts; Cards; Games; Reading groups; Prayer groups; Movies.

RICHLAND

Tri-County Nursing Home Inc*
PO Box 756, Richland, MO, 65556 (314) 765-3243
Admin Sue Parker.
Licensure Intermediate Care. *Beds* 86.
Ownership Nonprofit.

RICHMOND

Shirkey Leisure Acres
Hwy 13 S, Richmond, MO, 64085 (816) 766-5403
Admin M L Hopkins. *Medical Dir/Dir of Nursing* Dr Robert LaHue.
Licensure Intermediate Care. *Beds* 140.
Ownership Nonprofit.
Staff RNs 1 (ft); LPNs 4 (ft), 1 (pt); Orderlies 3 (ft); Nurses aides 84 (ft); Physical therapists 1 (pt); Recreational therapists 1 (ft); Occupational therapists 1 (pt); Speech therapists 1 (pt); Activities coordinators 1 (ft), 1 (pt); Dietitians 1 (ft); Audiologists 1 (pt).
Facilities Dining room; Physical therapy room; Activities room; Chapel; Crafts room; Laundry room; Barber/Beauty shop; Library.
Activities Arts and Crafts; Games; Reading groups; Prayer groups; Movies; Dances/Social or cultural gatherings.

ROCK HILL

Rock Hill Rest Home*
9803 Manchester, Rock Hill, MO, 63119 (314) 961-8353
Admin Linda Laverne Starnes.
Licensure Intermediate Care. *Beds* 32.
Ownership Proprietary.

ROCK PORT

Pleasant View
Rt 1, Box B, Rock Port, MO, 64482 (816) 744-5490
Admin Charles Loucks.
Licensure Intermediate Care. *Beds* 80. *Certified* Medicaid.
Ownership Proprietary.
Admissions Requirements Minimum age 18.
Facilities Dining room; Physical therapy room; Activities room; Chapel; Crafts room; Laundry room; Barber/Beauty shop; Library.
Activities Arts and Crafts; Cards; Games; Reading groups; Prayer groups; Movies; Shopping trips; Dances/Social or cultural gatherings.

ROLLA

Medigroup Professional Care
1200 McCutchen Rd, Rolla, MO, 65401 (314)
364-2311
Medical Dir/Dir of Nursing Dr John James.
Licensure Skilled Care; Intermediate Care.
Beds 120. *Certified* Medicaid; Medicare.
Ownership Proprietary.
Admissions Requirements Minimum age 16.
Staff RNs 2 (ft), 1 (pt); LPNs 6 (ft); Nurses
aides 40 (ft); Activities coordinators 1 (ft).
Facilities Dining room; Physical therapy room;
Activities room; Chapel; Crafts room; Laundry
room; Barber/Beauty shop; Library.
Activities Arts and Crafts; Cards; Games;
Reading groups; Prayer groups; Movies; Shop-
ping trips; Dances/Social or cultural gatherings.
Description Comprehensive outpatient
rehabilitative facility; family-style dining fea-
tured.

Presbyterian Manor at Rolla*
1200 Homelife Plaza, Rolla, MO, 65401
Admin Pat Look.
Beds 38.
Ownership Nonprofit.
Admissions Requirements Minimum age 65;
Medical examination.
Staff RNs; LPNs; Nurses aides 2 (pt); Activi-
ties coordinators; Dietitians; Podiatrists.
Affiliation Presbyterian

Rolla Manor Care Center*
1800 White Columns Dr, Rolla, MO, 65401
(314) 364-7766
Admin Maria E Carroll.
Licensure Intermediate Care. *Beds* 102.
Ownership Proprietary.

SAINT CHARLES

Charlevoix Professional Nursing Home*
1221 Boonslick Rd, Saint Charles, MO, 63301
(314) 723-1600
Admin William B Mahon.
Licensure Skilled Care; Intermediate Care.
Beds 115. *Certified* Medicaid.
Ownership Proprietary.

Claywest House*
2840 W Clay, Saint Charles, MO, 63301 (314)
925-1500
Admin Harry E Panhorst.
Licensure Skilled Care; Intermediate Care.
Beds 180. *Certified* Medicaid; Medicare.
Ownership Proprietary.

Colonial Rest Home
404 McDonough, Saint Charles, MO, 63301
(314) 724-1147
Admin Lydia Rosenstengel. *Medical Dir/Dir of
Nursing* Dr Poggemeier.
Licensure Intermediate Care. *Beds* 21.
Ownership Proprietary.
Admissions Requirements Medical examina-
tion.
Staff Physicians 1 (ft); RNs 1 (ft); LPNs 1 (ft),
1 (pt); Nurses aides 8 (ft), 2 (pt); Activities coor-
dinators 1 (pt); Dietitians 1 (pt).

Description Facility deals specifically with the
chronic dependent resident; small and able to
create a home-like atmosphere.

Jefferson Street Nursing Home*
1014 Jefferson, Saint Charles, MO, 63301 (314)
724-1565
Admin Leona Winzer.
Licensure Intermediate Care. *Beds* 13.
Ownership Proprietary.

Parkside Meadows Inc
210 W Randolph St, PO Box 430, Saint
Charles, MO, 63301 (314) 724-7800
Admin G Herbert Gessert. *Medical Dir/Dir of
Nursing* Dr Gene Roxas.
Licensure Intermediate Care. *Beds* 60. *Certi-
fied* Medicaid.
Ownership Nonprofit.
Admissions Requirements Minimum age 60;
Medical examination; Physician's request.
Staff RNs 2 (ft), 7 (pt); LPNs 1 (ft), 1 (pt);
Nurses aides 17 (ft), 19 (pt); Activities coordi-
nators 1 (ft); Dietitians 1 (ft).
Affiliation Church of Christ
Facilities Dining room; Physical therapy room;
Crafts room; Laundry room; Barber/Beauty
shop; Library.
Activities Arts and Crafts; Cards; Games;
Reading groups; Movies; Shopping trips; Dan-
ces/Social or cultural gatherings.
Description Parkside philosophy is to serve
persons 60 years of age and older in maintaining their independence; assisting residents
in reaching their optimal physical, emotional,
spiritual and psychological health; and enabling
them to enjoy a full and active life close to family, friends, church, and other community
activities.

Saint Charles Health Care Center*
Sugar Maple Ln, Saint Charles, MO, 63301
(314) 946-8887
Admin Melvin Rector.
Licensure Skilled Care; Intermediate Care.
Beds 120. *Certified* Medicaid; Medicare.
Ownership Proprietary.

Saint Joseph's Home
723 First Capitol Dr, Saint Charles, MO, 63301
(314) 946-4140
Admin Dianne Mossberger. *Medical Dir/Dir
of Nursing* Dr Brian Stuffelbam.
Licensure Intermediate Care. *Beds* 103.
Ownership Nonprofit.
Admissions Requirements Minimum age 65;
Medical examination.
Staff RNs 2 (ft), 1 (pt); LPNs 5 (ft); Nurses
aides 25 (ft), 15 (pt); Physical therapists 1 (pt);
Speech therapists 1 (pt); Activities coordinators
3 (pt); Dietitians 1 (pt); Dentists 1 (pt); Podiatr-
ists 1 (pt).
Facilities Dining room; Physical therapy room;
Activities room; Chapel; Crafts room; Laundry
room; Barber/Beauty shop.
Activities Arts and Crafts; Cards; Games;
Reading groups; Prayer groups; Movies; Shop-
ping trips; Dances/Social or cultural gatherings.

SAINT ELIZABETH

Saint Elizabeth Manor Inc
Rt 1, Box 22, Saint Elizabeth, MO, 65075 (314)
493-2215
Admin Frederick Doerhoff. *Medical Dir/Dir of
Nursing* Carl Bynum DO.
Licensure Intermediate Care. *Beds* 60. *Certi-
fied* Medicaid.
Ownership Proprietary.
Staff Physicians 3 (pt); RNs 1 (pt); LPNs 4 (ft);
Orderlies 1 (ft); Nurses aides 21 (ft), 4 (pt);
Physical therapists 2 (pt); Recreational thera-
pists 1 (ft); Occupational therapists 1 (pt); Spee-
ch therapists 1 (pt); Activities coordinators 1
(ft); Dietitians 2 (pt); Dentists 1 (pt); Podiatrists
1 (pt); Audiologists 1 (pt).
Facilities Dining room; Physical therapy room;
Chapel; Laundry room; Barber/Beauty shop.
Activities Arts and Crafts; Games; Reading
groups; Prayer groups; Movies; Shopping trips.
Description Three-year-old facility with very
reasonable rates located in rural Missouri within 35 miles of 3 area hospitals.

SAINT JAMES

Country Valley Home
Rt 3, Box 356, Saint James, MO, 65559
Admin Mary V Auten.
Licensure Residential Care. *Beds* 23.
Ownership Proprietary.
Admissions Requirements Minimum age 18.
Staff Physicians 1 (pt); RNs 1 (pt); Recrea-
tional therapists 1 (pt); Activities coordinators 1
(pt); Podiatrists 1 (pt).
Facilities Dining room; Laundry room; Barber-
/Beauty shop.
Activities Arts and Crafts; Prayer groups;
Movies; Shopping trips; Dances/Social or cul-
tural gatherings.

Meadow Manor Nursing Home
Sidney St, Box 69, Saint James, MO, 65559
(314) 265-8921
Admin Jo Hancock.
Licensure Skilled Care. *Beds* 90. *Cer-
tified* Medicaid; Medicare.
Ownership Proprietary.
Staff RNs 3 (ft); LPNs 8 (ft); Orderlies 1 (ft);
Nurses aides 60 (ft); Physical therapists 1 (ft);
Reality therapists 1 (ft); Recreational therapists
1 (ft); Occupational therapists 1 (ft); Speech
therapists 1 (ft); Activities coordinators 1 (ft);
Dietitians 1 (ft); Dentists 1 (ft); Podiatrists 1
(ft); Audiologists 1 (ft).
Facilities Dining room; Physical therapy room;
Activities room; Chapel; Crafts room; Laundry
room; Barber/Beauty shop.
Activities Arts and Crafts; Cards; Games;
Reading groups; Prayer groups; Movies; Shop-
ping trips; Dances/Social or cultural gatherings.

Woodland Estates
Rt 1, Box 127, Saint James, MO, 65559
Admin Mel Matlock II. *Medical Dir/Dir of
Nursing* Dr P Pander.
Licensure Residential Care. *Beds* 50.
Certified Medicaid.
Ownership Proprietary.
Admissions Requirements Minimum age 18.
Staff Physicians 1 (pt); RNs 1 (pt); LPNs 1

(pt); Orderlies 1 (ft); Nurses aides 3 (ft), 1 (pt); Activities coordinators 1 (ft); Dentists 1 (pt).
Facilities Dining room; Physical therapy room; Activities room; Crafts room; Laundry room; Barber/Beauty shop; Library.
Activities Arts and Crafts; Cards; Games; Prayer groups; Movies; Shopping trips; Dances/Social or cultural gatherings.
Description Facility is located on 20 acres of wooded land and 10 acres of clearing, quiet with much wildlife and several miles of walking paths for residents.

SAINT JOHNS

Barry Alan Nursing Home
3338 Eminence Ave, Saint Johns, MO, 63114 (314) 427-0988
Admin Deanna Dotson. *Medical Dir/Dir of Nursing* Michael Spezia DO.
Licensure Intermediate Care. *Beds* 34.
Ownership Proprietary.
Admissions Requirements Minimum age 50; Medical examination.
Staff Physicians 1 (pt); RNs 1 (pt); LPNs 1 (ft), 1 (pt); Nurses aides 9 (ft), 3 (pt); Recreational therapists 1 (pt); Activities coordinators 1 (pt); Podiatrists 1 (pt).
Facilities Activities room; Crafts room; Laundry room.
Activities Arts and Crafts; Cards; Games; Reading groups; Movies; Shopping trips; Dances/Social or cultural gatherings.
Description The nursing home is a concrete block, one-floor home situated on a 2 acre lot with trees, a lovely setting for outside activities; home-like atmosphere.

SAINT JOSEPH

Beverly Manor
1317 N 36th, Saint Joseph, MO, 64506 (816) 233-8085
Admin Beverly Jean Cathcart. *Medical Dir/Dir of Nursing* Dr C C DuMont.
Licensure Skilled Care; Intermediate Care. *Beds* 120. *Certified* Medicaid; Medicare.
Ownership Proprietary.
Admissions Requirements Minimum age 18; Medical examination.
Staff Physicians 1 (pt); RNs 1 (ft), 4 (pt); LPNs 5 (ft), 3 (pt); Orderlies 11 (ft); Nurses aides 33 (ft), 2 (pt); Physical therapists 1 (ft), 1 (pt); Occupational therapists 1 (ft), 1 (pt); Speech therapists 1 (pt); Activities coordinators 1 (ft); Dietitians 1 (pt); Dentists 1 (pt); Podiatrists 1 (pt); Audiologists 1 (pt).
Facilities Dining room; Physical therapy room; Activities room; Crafts room; Laundry room; Barber/Beauty shop; Library.
Activities Arts and Crafts; Cards; Games; Reading groups; Prayer groups; Movies; Shopping trips; Dances/Social or cultural gatherings.
Description Beverly Manor specializes in long-term care; provides a mini-community with all of the recreational services as well as stressing life satisfaction through therapies, recreation, spiritual support, and social services. For short-term rehabilitation and respite care, the physical therapy and restorative services are

excellent. Social services constantly monitors residents so they receive the level of care that is needed.

Bliss Manor*
2929 Lafayette, Saint Joseph, MO, 64507 (716) 233-2418
Admin Bernice Vandever.
Licensure Intermediate Care. *Beds* 121.
Ownership Proprietary.

Bright Horizon
701 S 11th, Saint Joseph, MO, 64501 (816) 279-7687
Admin Margaret Pike.
Licensure Residential Care. *Beds* 20.
Ownership Proprietary.
Admissions Requirements Medical examination.
Staff LPNs 1 (pt); Nurses aides 5 (ft), 2 (pt).

Carriage Square Health Care Center
Woodbine and Gene Field Rds, Saint Joseph, MO, 64506 (816) 364-1526
Admin Clara Lash. *Medical Dir/Dir of Nursing* Dr C C DuMont.
Licensure Skilled Care; Intermediate Care.
Beds 120. *Certified* Medicaid.
Ownership Proprietary.
Admissions Requirements Medical examination.
Staff RNs 4 (ft); LPNs 5 (pt); Nurses aides 38 (pt); Physical therapists 1 (pt); Occupational therapists 1 (pt); Speech therapists 1 (pt); Activities coordinators 1 (ft); Dietitians 1 (ft); Dentists 1 (pt); Audiologists 1 (pt).
Facilities Dining room; Physical therapy room; Activities room; Crafts room; Laundry room; Barber/Beauty shop.
Activities Arts and Crafts; Cards; Games; Reading groups; Prayer groups; Movies; Dances/Social or cultural gatherings.

Church Street Manor*
611 N 11th, Saint Joseph, MO, 64501 (816) 232-3740
Admin Veda Sollars.
Licensure Intermediate Care. *Beds* 30.
Ownership Proprietary.

Citadel Health Care Pavilion*
5026 Faraon, Saint Joseph, MO, 64506 (816) 279-1591
Admin Myrtle Wright.
Licensure Intermediate Care. *Beds* 100. *Certified* Medicaid.
Ownership Proprietary.

Lucas Boarding Home
1218-1220 North 3, Saint Joseph, MO, 64501
Admin Mrs John M Lucas.
Licensure Intermediate Care. *Beds* 15.
Ownership Proprietary.
Description Care is provided for residents who need a place to live but are able to care for their own personal needs; all clients from the state hospital; facility serves all meals, provides transportation, washing, and ironing.

Methodist Medical Center—Long Term Care Facility
7th to 9th on Faraon, Saint Joseph, MO, 64501 (816) 271-7111

Admin Jay L Clark. *Medical Dir/Dir of Nursing* Owen W D Craig MD.
Licensure Skilled Care; Intermediate Care.
Beds SNF 20; ICF 139.
Ownership Nonprofit.
Admissions Requirements Medical examination; Physician's request.
Staff RNs 6 (ft), 4 (pt); LPNs 22 (ft), 7 (pt); Nurses aides 46 (ft), 2 (pt); Physical therapists 4 (ft), 2 (pt); Recreational therapists 1 (ft); Occupational therapists 6 (ft); Speech therapists 2 (ft); Dietitians 1 (ft); Dentists 2 (pt); Audiologists 1 (ft).
Affiliation Methodist
Facilities Dining room; Physical therapy room; Activities room; Chapel; Crafts room; Laundry room; Barber/Beauty shop.
Activities Arts and Crafts; Cards; Games; Reading groups; Prayer groups; Movies; Dances/Social or cultural gatherings.

Saint Joseph Convalescent Center
811 N 9th, PO Box 207 Fairleigh Station, Saint Joseph, MO, 64501 (816) 233-5164
Admin Dorothy Blakesley. *Medical Dir/Dir of Nursing* Dr Donald Sklenar.
Licensure Skilled Care. *Beds* 69. *Certified* Medicaid.
Ownership Proprietary.
Admissions Requirements Medical examination.
Staff RNs 1 (ft); LPNs 7 (ft); Nurses aides 27 (ft); Physical therapists 1 (ft), 1 (pt); Occupational therapists 1 (pt); Speech therapists 1 (pt); Activities coordinators 1 (ft).
Facilities Dining room; Activities room; Chapel; Crafts room; Laundry room; Barber/Beauty shop.
Activities Arts and Crafts; Cards; Games; Reading groups; Prayer groups; Dances/Social or cultural gatherings.
Description Programs are provided in a space where there is a lovely view; very well lighted; fish aquarium and a bird. Many musical groups entertain.

Saxton Nursing Home
2421 Francis, Saint Joseph, MO, 64501 (816) 232-9874
Admin Edna Jessica Saxton. *Medical Dir/Dir of Nursing* Dr Sklenar and Dr Christ.
Licensure Intermediate Care. *Beds* 20.
Ownership Proprietary.
Admissions Requirements Minimum age 18; Medical examination; Physician's request.
Staff RNs; LPNs 2 (ft).
Facilities Dining room.
Description New 118-bed facility should open in summer 1984.

Tiffany Square Convalescent Center*
PO Box 1308, 3002 N 18th, Saint Joseph, MO, 64505 (816) 364-4200
Admin S Marian Wilson.
Licensure Intermediate Care. *Beds* 180. *Certified* Medicaid.
Ownership Proprietary.

SAINT LOUIS

Alcazar Home for the Aged Inc*
3127 Locust St, Saint Louis, MO, 63103 (314) 371-5172
Admin Edwin Wayne Cook.
Licensure Residential Care. *Beds* 145.
Ownership Proprietary.

Arena Manor Inc*
3300 Texas Ave, Saint Louis, MO, 63118 (314) 773-3408
Admin Joseph S Arena.
Licensure Intermediate Care. *Beds* 32.
Ownership Proprietary.

Avalon Nursing Home
4359 Taft Ave, Saint Louis, MO, 63149 (314) 752-2022
Admin Gayle Rhee. *Medical Dir/Dir of Nursing* Seoung E Rhee MD.
Licensure Intermediate Care. *Beds* 63.
Ownership Proprietary.
Admissions Requirements Minimum age 16; Medical examination.
Staff Physicians 1 (ft); RNs 1 (ft); LPNs 2 (ft); Nurses aides 22 (ft), 4 (pt); Physical therapists 1 (ft); Reality therapists 1 (ft); Recreational therapists 1 (pt); Occupational therapists 1 (pt); Speech therapists 1 (pt); Activities coordinators 1 (ft); Dietitians 1 (pt); Podiatrists 1 (pt).
Facilities Dining room; Physical therapy room; Activities room; Chapel; Crafts room; Laundry room; Barber/Beauty shop.
Activities Arts and Crafts; Cards; Games; Prayer groups; Movies; Dances/Social or cultural gatherings.
Description Home is a practical nursing home in a beautiful neighborhood with staff physician and director of nursing; administration is on call 24 hours a day; planned meals and snacks; planned activities; member of AHCA and Missouri Health Care Association.

Barry Alan Nursing Home
3326 Eminence Ave, Saint Louis, MO, 63114
Admin Deanna Dotson.
Admissions Requirements Minimum age 55; Medical examination.
Staff Physicians 1 (pt); RNs 1 (pt); LPNs 1 (ft), 1 (pt); Nurses aides 13 (ft), 3 (pt); Activities coordinators 1 (pt); Podiatrists 1 (pt).
Facilities Activities room.
Activities Arts and Crafts; Cards; Games; Reading groups; Movies; Shopping trips.
Description This one-story concrete block facility is completely air conditioned; located on a two-acre wooded lot offering a home-like atmosphere.

Berkeley Manor
PO Box 5606, Saint Louis, MO, 63121 (314) 521-7471
Admin Earl Stamer Jr. *Medical Dir/Dir of Nursing* Dr David Rosenberg.
Licensure Intermediate Care. *Beds* 69.
Ownership Proprietary.
Admissions Requirements Minimum age 18.
Staff Physicians 1 (ft), 5 (pt); RNs 1 (pt); LPNs 1 (ft), 4 (pt); Orderlies 9 (ft), 4 (pt); Nurses aides 12 (ft), 10 (pt); Physical therapists 1 (ft); Reality therapists 1 (ft); Recreational therapists 1 (ft); Occupational therapists 1 (pt); Speech thera-

pists 1 (pt); Activities coordinators 1 (ft), 1 (pt); Dietitians 1 (pt); Dentists 2 (pt); Ophthalmologists 2 (pt); Podiatrists 1 (pt).
Facilities Dining room; Activities room; Crafts room; Laundry room; Barber/Beauty shop; Van.
Activities Arts and Crafts; Cards; Games; Reading groups; Prayer groups; Movies; Shopping trips; Dances/Social or cultural gatherings.
Description Facility offers 24-hour reality orientation and 24-hour medical attention; director services provided for rehabilitation; speech, physical, and occupational therapy provided; dentist, podiatrist, and optician consultancy provided.

Bernard Nursing Home
4385 Maryland Ave, Saint Louis, MO, 63108 (314) 535-9290
Admin Mary E O'Malley RN. *Medical Dir/Dir of Nursing* Mequil Abelardo MD.
Licensure Skilled Care; Intermediate Care.
Beds 120. *Certified* Medicaid; Medicare.
Ownership Proprietary.
Admissions Requirements Minimum age 18; Medical examination; Physician's request.
Staff Physicians 1 (ft), 1 (pt); RNs 1 (ft), 1 (pt); LPNs 8 (ft); Nurses aides 29 (ft); Physical therapists 1 (pt); Occupational therapists 1 (pt); Speech therapists 1 (pt); Activities coordinators 1 (ft); Dietitians 1 (pt); Dentists 1 (pt); Ophthalmologists 1 (pt); Podiatrists 1 (pt).
Facilities Dining room; Physical therapy room; Activities room; Crafts room; Laundry room; Barber/Beauty shop.
Activities Arts and Crafts; Cards; Games; Prayer groups; Movies.

Bernard West Pine Nursing Home
4335 W Pine, Saint Louis, MO, 63108 (314) 371-0200
Admin Patti Crockarell. *Medical Dir/Dir of Nursing* Miguel Abelcuda.
Licensure Skilled Care; Intermediate Care.
Beds 141. *Certified* Medicaid; Medicare.
Ownership Proprietary.
Admissions Requirements Minimum age 18; Medical examination; Physician's request.
Staff Physicians 16 (pt); RNs 2 (ft), 3 (pt); LPNs 7 (ft), 1 (pt); Orderlies 4 (ft); Nurses aides 37 (ft), 7 (pt); Physical therapists 2 (ft), 1 (pt); Occupational therapists 1 (pt); Speech therapists 1 (pt); Activities coordinators 1 (ft); Dietitians 1 (pt); Dentists 1 (pt); Ophthalmologists 1 (pt); Podiatrists 1 (pt); Audiologists 1 (pt).
Facilities Dining room; Physical therapy room; Activities room; Crafts room; Laundry room; Barber/Beauty shop; Enclosed patios.
Activities Arts and Crafts; Games; Reading groups; Prayer groups; Dances/Social or cultural gatherings; Outings to area sights.

Bethesda Skilled Nursing Facility
3655 Vista Ave, Saint Louis, MO, 63110 (314) 772-9200
Admin Connie Siffring. *Medical Dir/Dir of Nursing* B Dandamudi MD.
Licensure Skilled Care. *Beds* 30. *Certified* Medicare.
Ownership Nonprofit.
Admissions Requirements Medical examination; Physician's request.
Staff Physicians 1 (pt); RNs 2 (ft); LPNs 6 (ft);

Orderlies 2 (pt); Nurses aides 10 (ft); Physical therapists 3 (ft); Occupational therapists; Speech therapists; Activities coordinators 1 (pt); Dietitians 1 (ft); Podiatrists 1 (pt); Audiologists 1 (pt).
Facilities Dining room; Physical therapy room; Chapel.
Activities Arts and Crafts; Cards; Games; Reading groups; Prayer groups.

Bethesda-Dilworth Memorial Home
9645 Big Bend Rd, Saint Louis, MO, 63122 (314) 968-5460
Admin Fletcher W Carter. *Medical Dir/Dir of Nursing* Patrick Majors.
Licensure Skilled Care. *Beds* 490. *Certified* Medicaid.
Ownership Nonprofit.
Admissions Requirements Minimum age 55; Medical examination; Physician's request.
Facilities Dining room; Physical therapy room; Activities room; Chapel; Crafts room; Laundry room; Barber/Beauty shop; Library.
Activities Arts and Crafts; Cards; Games; Reading groups; Prayer groups; Movies; Shopping trips; Dances/Social or cultural gatherings.
Description Bethesda provides outstanding health care, therapeutic programs, social activities, beautiful chapel, and attractive accommodations; noted for its graciousness, warmth, beauty, and cozy feeling, enhanced by a wooded setting, handsome landscaping, and intimate patios; day care center assists families with elderly parents living with them.

Birchway Nursing Home
4373 W Pine Blvd, Saint Louis, MO, 63108 (314) 531-2644
Admin Ellen Goodrich. *Medical Dir/Dir of Nursing* Varkey Philip MD.
Licensure Skilled Care; Intermediate Care.
Beds 65.
Ownership Proprietary.
Admissions Requirements Medical examination; Physician's request.
Facilities Dining room; Activities room; Crafts room; Laundry room; Barber/Beauty shop.
Activities Arts and Crafts; Cards; Games; Prayer groups; Shopping trips; Dances/Social or cultural gatherings.

Carrie Elligson Gietner Home Inc*
5000 S Broadway Ave, Saint Louis, MO, 63111 (314) 353-5747
Admin Althea H Wilson.
Licensure Intermediate Care; Residential Care.
Beds ICF 75; Residential Care 111.
Ownership Nonprofit.

Charles the First Medical Center*
5303 Bermuda Rd, Saint Louis, MO, 63121 (314) 385-0910
Admin Charles L Twedell.
Licensure Skilled Care. *Beds* 52.
Ownership Proprietary.

Charless Home
4431 S Broadway, Saint Louis, MO, 63111 (314) 481-4840
Admin W Gene Kury. *Medical Dir/Dir of Nursing* Dr Leonhardt and Dr Brody.
Licensure Intermediate Care. *Beds* 40.
Ownership Nonprofit.

Staff Physicians 2 (pt); RNs 1 (pt); LPNs 6 (pt); Nurses aides 27 (pt); Recreational therapists 1 (pt).
Facilities Dining room; Physical therapy room; Activities room; Chapel; Crafts room; Laundry room; Barber/Beauty shop; Library.
Activities Arts and Crafts; Cards; Games; Reading groups; Prayer groups; Movies; Shopping trips; Dances/Social or cultural gatherings; Day long tours.
Description Beautiful Victorian decor and atmosphere. Home has celebrated 131 years of continuous service to destitute women in this location.

Deaconess Manor*
6220 Oakland Ave, Saint Louis, MO, 63139
(314) 647-7350
Admin Stanley R Ekrem.
Licensure Skilled Care. *Beds* 117. *Certified* Medicaid; Medicare.
Ownership Nonprofit.

Delhaven Manor
5460 Delmar, Saint Louis, MO, 63112 (314) 361-2902
Admin Joseph L Berry. *Medical Dir/Dir of Nursing* Jarkar Philip.
Licensure Skilled Care; Intermediate Care. *Beds* 156. *Certified* Medicaid.
Ownership Proprietary.
Staff RNs 7 (ft); LPNs 13 (ft); Nurses aides 76 (ft); Physical therapists 1 (pt); Occupational therapists 1 (ft); Speech therapists 1 (pt); Activities coordinators 1 (ft); Dietitians 1 (pt); Dentists 1 (pt); Ophthalmologists 1 (pt); Podiatrists 1 (pt); Audiologists 1 (pt).
Facilities Dining room; Physical therapy room; Activities room; Laundry room; Barber/Beauty shop.
Activities Arts and Crafts; Cards; Games; Prayer groups; Movies; Dances/Social or cultural gatherings.

Edgewater Home Inc
5500 S Broadway, Saint Louis, MO, 63111
(314) 832-5800
Admin Bettie J Smith. *Medical Dir/Dir of Nursing* John Daake MD.
Licensure Skilled Care. *Beds* 151.
Ownership Proprietary.
Admissions Requirements Minimum age 21.
Staff RNs 1 (ft), 3 (pt); LPNs 7 (ft); Orderlies 4 (ft); Nurses aides 75; Physical therapists 1 (ft), 1 (pt); Speech therapists 1 (pt); Activities coordinators 1 (ft), 1 (pt); Dietitians 1 (pt).
Facilities Dining room; Activities room; Crafts room; Laundry room; Barber/Beauty shop.
Activities Arts and Crafts; Cards; Games.

Ferrier Harris Home for Aged
3636 Page Ave, Saint Louis, MO, 63106 (314) 531-5549
Admin Bettye Dawson. *Medical Dir/Dir of Nursing* Dr Dunet F Belancourt.
Licensure Intermediate Care. *Beds* 30.
Ownership Nonprofit.
Admissions Requirements Minimum age 45.
Staff Physicians 1 (pt); RNs 1 (pt); LPNs 2 (ft), 1 (pt).
Facilities Dining room; Physical therapy room; Activities room; Chapel; Crafts room; Laundry room; Barber/Beauty shop.

Activities Arts and Crafts; Cards; Games; Reading groups; Prayer groups; Shopping trips; Dances/Social or cultural gatherings.

Fontaine Woods Nursing Home
9500 Bellefontaine Rd, Saint Louis, MO, 63137
(314) 868-1400
Admin Gladys Sullivan. *Medical Dir/Dir of Nursing* Dr David Light.
Licensure Skilled Care. *Beds* 97.
Ownership Proprietary.
Admissions Requirements Minimum age 50.
Staff RNs 2 (ft), 5 (pt); LPNs 2 (ft), 6 (pt); Orderlies 1 (ft); Physical therapists 1 (pt); Activities coordinators 2 (ft); Dietitians 1 (pt).
Facilities Dining room; Physical therapy room; Activities room; Crafts room; Laundry room; Barber/Beauty shop.
Activities Arts and Crafts; Cards; Games; Reading groups; Prayer groups; Movies; Shopping trips; Dances/Social or cultural gatherings.
Description We feel we provide quality nursing care and an outstanding activity program, and especially emphasize that this is a home and our atmosphere reflects this attitude.

Frazier Nursing Home*
4512 W Pine, Saint Louis, MO, 63108 (314) 367-8516
Admin Mabel Frazier.
Licensure Intermediate Care. *Beds* 36.
Ownership Proprietary.

Friendship Village
12503 Village Circle Dr, Saint Louis, MO, 63127 (314) 842-6840
Admin Dave Heeter. *Medical Dir/Dir of Nursing* Grant I Zmirlian MD.
Licensure Skilled Care; Intermediate Care. *Beds* 60. *Certified* Medicaid; Medicare.
Ownership Nonprofit.
Admissions Requirements Minimum age 21; Medical examination; Physician's request.
Staff RNs 2 (ft), 1 (pt); LPNs 4 (ft), 3 (pt); Nurses aides 30 (ft), 2 (pt); Physical therapists 1 (pt); Recreational therapists 1 (ft).
Facilities Dining room; Physical therapy room; Activities room; Crafts room; Laundry room; Barber/Beauty shop; Library.
Activities Arts and Crafts; Cards; Games; Reading groups; Prayer groups.

Fueller Nursing Home
5512 Kerth Rd, Saint Louis, MO, 63128 (314) 487-5929
Admin Doris Fueller.
Licensure Intermediate Care. *Beds* 21.
Ownership Proprietary.

Geriatric Center of Saint Louis Inc*
4560 W Pine Blvd, Saint Louis, MO, 63108
(314) 361-4540
Admin Carolyn Ellerbusch.
Licensure Intermediate Care. *Beds* 260. *Certified* Medicaid.
Ownership Proprietary.

Good Samaritan Home for the Aged
5200 S Boardway, Saint Louis, MO, 63111
(314) 352-2400
Admin Robert A Nolte. *Medical Dir/Dir of Nursing* C E Mueller MD.
Licensure Intermediate Care. *Beds* 86.

Ownership Nonprofit.
Staff Physicians 1 (pt); RNs 3 (ft); LPNs 6 (ft), 1 (pt); Nurses aides 33 (ft), 1 (pt); Physical therapists 1 (pt); Recreational therapists 1 (pt); Activities coordinators 1 (ft); Dietitians 1 (ft); Dentists 1 (pt); Podiatrists 1 (pt); Therapy assistants 1 (ft); Medical technicians 8 (ft), 2 (pt); Pharmacists 1 (pt).
Affiliation Church of Christ
Facilities Dining room; Physical therapy room; Activities room; Chapel; Crafts room; Laundry room; Barber/Beauty shop; Library.
Activities Arts and Crafts; Cards; Games; Reading groups; Prayer groups; Movies; Shopping trips; Dances/Social or cultural gatherings; Outings to municipal opera, ice capades, ballgames, church camp, state park, fishing.
Description Facility is located on a Mississippi River bluff overlooking the river and the Illinois side; a special program held every month related to a holiday or special day.

Grand Manor
3400 S Grand, Saint Louis, MO, 63118 (314) 865-2600
Admin Edwin Heigl. *Medical Dir/Dir of Nursing* David Arunski.
Licensure Intermediate Care; Residential Care. *Beds* ICF 176; Residential Care 32. *Certified* Medicaid.
Ownership Proprietary.
Admissions Requirements Minimum age 21; Medical examination; Physician's request.
Staff Physicians 2 (pt); RNs 4 (ft), 1 (pt); LPNs 3 (ft), 1 (pt); Nurses aides 110 (ft); Physical therapists 1 (pt); Recreational therapists 1 (pt); Speech therapists 1 (pt); Activities coordinators 2 (ft); Dietitians 1 (pt); Dentists 1 (pt); Podiatrists 1 (pt).
Affiliation Roman Catholic
Facilities Dining room; Physical therapy room; Activities room; Chapel; Crafts room; Laundry room; Barber/Beauty shop; Library.
Activities Arts and Crafts; Reading groups; Prayer groups; Movies; Dances/Social or cultural gatherings.
Description The home is licensed ICF and RCF but is staffed as skilled. The Director of Nursing (RN) supervises around-the-clock charge nurses and a staff of RNs, LPNs, and certified nurses aides. The facility is set in a safe, secure, and tranquil environment, close to hospitals, transportation, and shopping.

Gravois Rest Haven Inc*
10954 Kennerly Rd, Saint Louis, MO, 63128
(314) 843-4242
Admin Norma M Conroy.
Licensure Skilled Care. *Beds* 165.
Ownership Proprietary.

Harry S Truman Restorative Center
5700 Arsenal, Saint Louis, MO, 63139 (314) 768-6633
Admin Lily A Landy. *Medical Dir/Dir of Nursing* Dr George Tanaka.
Licensure Skilled Care; Intermediate Care. *Beds* 200. *Certified* Medicaid; Medicare.
Ownership Public.
Staff Physicians 1 (ft), 1 (pt); RNs 15 (ft), 3 (pt); LPNs 36 (ft); Nurses aides 96 (ft); Physical therapists 1 (ft); Recreational therapists 1 (ft); Occupational therapists 1 (ft); Dietitians 1 (ft);

Dentists 1 (pt); Ophthalmologists 1 (pt).
Facilities Dining room; Physical therapy room; Activities room; Chapel; Crafts room; Laundry room; Barber/Beauty shop; Library.
Activities Arts and Crafts; Cards; Games; Reading groups; Prayer groups; Movies; Shopping trips; Dances/Social or cultural gatherings.

Jerri's Benevolent Manor*
730 Hodiamont, Saint Louis, MO, 63112
(314)727-5219
Admin Laverne Haulcy.
Licensure Residential Care. *Beds* 22.
Ownership Proprietary.

K F J Manor Inc 2*
5415 Thelka, Saint Louis, MO, 63136 (314) 385-8180
Admin Willie Jammer.
Licensure Residential Care. *Beds* 25.
Ownership Proprietary.

Little Flower Nursing Home
2500 S 18th, Saint Louis, MO, 63104 (314) 664-2267
Admin Roxie Lavine. *Medical Dir/Dir of Nursing* Leonard Piccione MD.
Licensure Intermediate Care. *Beds* 90.
Ownership Proprietary.
Staff Physicians 1 (ft), 6 (pt); RNs 3 (ft); LPNs 2 (ft), 2 (pt); Nurses aides 21 (ft), 5 (pt); Physical therapists 1 (ft); Reality therapists 1 (pt); Recreational therapists 1 (ft); Occupational therapists 1 (pt); Speech therapists 1 (pt); Activities coordinators 1 (ft); Dietitians 1 (pt); Dentists 1 (pt); Ophthalmologists 1 (pt); Audiologists 1 (pt).
Facilities Dining room; Activities room; Chapel; Crafts room; Laundry room; Barber/Beauty shop.
Activities Arts and Crafts; Cards; Games; Reading groups; Prayer groups; Movies; Shopping trips; Dances/Social or cultural gatherings.

Little Sisters of the Poor
3225 N Florissant Ave, Saint Louis, MO, 63107 (314) 421-6022
Admin Sr Marie Anne.
Licensure Intermediate Care. *Beds* 105. *Certified* Medicaid.
Ownership Nonprofit.
Admissions Requirements Minimum age 60; Medical examination.
Affiliation Roman Catholic
Facilities Dining room; Physical therapy room; Activities room; Chapel; Crafts room; Laundry room; Barber/Beauty shop; Library.
Activities Arts and Crafts; Cards; Games; Reading groups; Prayer groups; Movies; Shopping trips; Dances/Social or cultural gatherings.

Lutheran Altenheim Society of Missouri
1265 McLaran Ave, Saint Louis, MO, 63147 (314) 388-2867
Admin E Willis Piehl.
Licensure Skilled Care; Intermediate Care; Residential Care. *Beds* SNF 60; ICF 68; Residential Care 78. *Certified* Medicaid.
Ownership Nonprofit.
Affiliation Lutheran

Marquette Manor
3419 Gasconade St, Saint Louis, MO, 63118 (314) 351-7512
Admin Mary Schuchardt. *Medical Dir/Dir of Nursing* David Arunski MD.
Licensure Intermediate Care. *Beds* 126. *Certified* Medicaid.
Ownership Nonprofit.
Admissions Requirements Medical examination.
Staff Physicians 2 (ft); RNs 1 (ft); LPNs 6 (ft); Orderlies 12 (ft); Physical therapists 1 (pt); Recreational therapists 2 (ft); Occupational therapists 1 (pt); Speech therapists 1 (pt); Activities coordinators 1 (ft); Dietitians 1 (ft); Dentists 1 (pt); Ophthalmologists 1 (pt); Podiatrists 1 (pt).
Facilities Dining room; Physical therapy room; Activities room; Chapel; Barber/Beauty shop.
Activities Arts and Crafts; Cards; Movies; Shopping trips; Dances/Social or cultural gatherings.

Mary, Queen and Mother Center
7601 Watson Rd, Saint Louis, MO, 63119
Admin Sr Jeanne McGovern. *Medical Dir/Dir of Nursing* Dr Rajendraprasad Dandamudi.
Licensure Skilled Care. *Beds* 220. *Certified* Medicaid; Medicare.
Ownership Nonprofit.
Admissions Requirements Minimum age 60; Medical examination.
Staff Physicians; RNs 15 (ft), 3 (pt); LPNs 15 (ft); Orderlies 3 (ft); Nurses aides 87 (ft), 4 (pt); Physical therapists 1 (pt); Occupational therapists 1 (pt); Speech therapists 1 (pt); Activities coordinators 1 (ft); Dietitians 1 (ft); Dentists 1 (pt); Ophthalmologists 1 (pt); Podiatrists 1 (pt); Audiologists 1 (pt).
Affiliation Roman Catholic
Facilities Dining room; Physical therapy room; Activities room; Chapel; Crafts room; Laundry room; Barber/Beauty shop.
Activities Arts and Crafts; Games; Reading groups; Prayer groups; Movies.

Medicalodge of Halls
2115 Kappel Dr, Saint Louis, MO, 63136 (314) 867-7474
Admin Daryl Hardy. *Medical Dir/Dir of Nursing* Lewis E Littmann MD.
Licensure Skilled Care; Intermediate Care.
Beds SNF 100; ICF 48. *Certified* Medicaid; Medicare.
Ownership Proprietary.
Admissions Requirements Minimum age 16; Medical examination.
Staff Physicians 1 (ft), 4 (pt); RNs 5 (ft); LPNs 8 (ft); Nurses aides 30 (ft), 16 (pt); Physical therapists 1 (pt); Reality therapists 1 (ft); Recreational therapists 2 (ft); Occupational therapists 1 (pt); Speech therapists 1 (pt); Dietitians 1 (pt); Dentists 1 (pt); Ophthalmologists 1 (pt); Podiatrists 1 (pt); Audiologists 1 (pt).
Facilities Dining room; Physical therapy room; Activities room; Crafts room; Laundry room; Barber/Beauty shop.
Activities Arts and Crafts; Cards; Games; Reading groups; Prayer groups; Movies; Shopping trips; Dances/Social or cultural gatherings.

Medigroup Oak Park Nursing Home*
6637 Berthold, Saint Louis, MO, 63139 (314) 781-3444
Admin Marian Kling.
Licensure Skilled Care. *Beds* 120. *Certified* Medicaid.
Ownership Proprietary.

Memorial Home Inc*
2609 S Grand Ave, Saint Louis, MO, 63118 (314) 771-2990
Admin Ann Westhouse.
Licensure Intermediate Care; Residential Care.
Beds 33; Residential Care 51.
Ownership Nonprofit.

Mercy Convalescent Center*
3450 Russell, Saint Louis, MO, 63104 (314) 664-1020
Admin Matthew P Puchta.
Licensure Intermediate Care. *Beds* 254. *Certified* Medicaid.
Ownership Proprietary.

Mother of Good Counsel Home
6825 Natural Bridge Rd, Saint Louis, MO, 63121 (314) 383-4765
Admin Sr M Silvana Budde. *Medical Dir/Dir of Nursing* Dr Harry Stein.
Licensure Skilled Care. *Beds* 110.
Ownership Nonprofit.
Admissions Requirements Females only
Staff RNs 3 (ft), 3 (pt); LPNs 5 (ft), 3 (pt); Nurses aides 38 (ft), 18 (pt); Physical therapists 2 (ft); Recreational therapists 1 (pt); Occupational therapists 1 (pt); Activities coordinators 1 (pt); Dietitians 1 (ft).
Affiliation Roman Catholic
Facilities Dining room; Physical therapy room; Activities room; Chapel; Crafts room; Laundry room; Library.
Activities Arts and Crafts; Cards; Games; Reading groups; Prayer groups; Movies; Dances/Social or cultural gatherings.

Oak Park Professional Care Center
6637 Berthold Ave, Saint Louis, MO, 63139
Admin Mona Hilliard. *Medical Dir/Dir of Nursing* Dr James F Sertl.
Licensure Skilled Care; Intermediate Care.
Beds 120. *Certified* Medicaid.
Ownership Proprietary.
Admissions Requirements Minimum age 16.
Staff Physicians 1 (pt); RNs 2 (ft), 1 (pt); LPNs 10 (ft), 3 (pt); Nurses aides 35 (ft), 6 (pt); Physical therapists 1 (ft), 1 (pt); Reality therapists 2 (ft); Recreational therapists 2 (ft), 2 (pt); Occupational therapists 2 (pt); Speech therapists 1 (pt); Activities coordinators 1 (ft); Dietitians 1 (pt); Dentists 1 (pt); Ophthalmologists 1 (pt); Podiatrists 1 (pt).
Facilities Dining room; Physical therapy room; Activities room; Crafts room; Laundry room; Barber/Beauty shop.
Activities Arts and Crafts; Cards; Games; Prayer groups; Movies; Shopping trips; Dances/Social or cultural gatherings.

Parkside Towers*
4960 Laclede Ave, Saint Louis, MO, 63108 (314) 361-6240
Admin Richard F Pauls.

Licensure Skilled Care; Intermediate Care.
Beds 166. *Certified* Medicaid.
Ownership Proprietary.

Peace Haven Association*
12630 Rott Rd, Saint Louis, MO, 63127 (314) 965-3833
Admin George R Bond.
Licensure Intermediate Care. *Beds* 28.
Ownership Nonprofit.

Ranken Jordan Home for Convalescent Crippled Children*
10621 Ladue Rd, Saint Louis, MO, 63141 (314) 993-1207
Admin Rosa Lee Connor.
Licensure Skilled Care. *Beds* 26.
Ownership Nonprofit.

Robert Koch Hospital
4101 Koch Rd, Saint Louis, MO, 63129 (314) 622-5800
Admin Thomas J Purcell.
Licensure Intermediate Care. *Beds* 428.
Ownership Public.

Rogers Nursing Home Inc*
3326 Eminence Ave, Saint Louis, MO, 63114 (314) 427-0988
Admin Deanna M Dotson.
Licensure Intermediate Care. *Beds* 34. *Certified* Medicaid.
Ownership Proprietary.

Mary Ryder Home for the Aged*
4360 Olive St, Saint Louis, MO, 63108 (314) 531-2981
Admin Ethel Ryder.
Licensure Residential Care. *Beds* 38.
Ownership Nonprofit.

Mary Ryder Homes for the Aged*
4341 Westminister Pl, Saint Louis, MO, 63108 (314) 531-2981
Admin Catherine Jones.
Licensure Residential Care. *Beds* 30.
Ownership Nonprofit.

Saint Anthony's Medical Center—Anthony House*
10016 Kennerly Rd, Saint Louis, MO, 63128 (314) 842-6120
Admin Shirley Herr.
Licensure Skilled Care. *Beds* 240. *Certified* Medicaid; Medicare.
Ownership Nonprofit.

Saint Louis Altenheim*
5408 S Broadway, Saint Louis, MO, 63111 (314) 353-7225
Admin Albert R Emmerth.
Licensure Intermediate Care; Residential Care.
Beds ICF 42; Residential Care 108.
Ownership Nonprofit.

Saint Louis Developmental Disabilities Treatment Center
5400 Arsenal, Saint Louis, MO, 63139 (314) 644-5400
Admin John Twehaus. *Medical Dir/Dir of Nursing* Kyu Her MD.
Licensure Intermediate Care for Mentally Retarded. *Beds* 300.

Staff Physicians 4 (ft), 2 (pt); RNs 31 (ft), 1 (pt); LPNs 5 (ft), 1 (pt); Physical therapists 1 (ft), 1 (pt); Recreational therapists 4 (ft); Occupational therapists 4 (ft), 1 (pt); Speech therapists 4 (ft), 1 (pt); Dietitians 3 (ft); Dentists 1 (ft); Psychologists 7 (ft), 1 (pt).
Facilities Dining room; Physical therapy room; Activities room; Laundry room; Classrooms/modules.
Activities Arts and Crafts; Cards; Games; Movies; Shopping trips; Dances/Social or cultural gatherings; Community trips.
Description Center offers primary programs for over 200 multi-physically handicapped clients; specialized program for dual-diagnosed clients (MR-DD) Facility operates 4 sites: a 46-bed medical unit 4 miles from main facility, a 72-bed unit consisting of 9 cottages and a program center 9 miles from main facility, an 8-bed group home 6 miles from main facility, and 16 living units on main campus. Goal is to decentralize large units in scattered sites within next 3 to 5 years.

Saint Louis Good Shepherd Homes Inc*
9444 Midland Blvd, Saint Louis, MO, 63114 (314) 427-8795
Admin Ed Anthonis Jr.
Licensure Intermediate Care. *Beds* 34.
Ownership Proprietary.

Saint Louis State School and Hospital
10695 Bellefontaine Rd, Saint Louis, MO, 63137 (314) 867-3600
Admin Joseph Kunz.
Licensure Intermediate Care for Mentally Retarded. *Beds* 472.
Ownership Public.

Shamrock Nursing Home
3713 Manola, Box 5747, Saint Louis, MO, 63121 (314) 381-2258
Admin Ermer Latiker. *Medical Dir/Dir of Nursing* Dr Chris Murray.
Licensure Intermediate Care. *Beds* 80.
Ownership Proprietary.
Admissions Requirements Minimum age 18; Medical examination; Physician's request.
Staff Physicians 4 (ft), 3 (pt); RNs 1 (ft); LPNs 1 (ft), 2 (pt); Orderlies 4 (ft); Nurses aides 40 (ft); Physical therapists 1 (pt); Reality therapists 1 (pt); Recreational therapists 1 (pt); Occupational therapists 1 (pt); Speech therapists 1 (pt); Activities coordinators 1 (pt); Dietitians 1 (pt); Dentists 1 (pt); Ophthalmologists 1 (pt); Podiatrists 1 (pt); Audiologists 1 (pt).
Facilities Dining room; Crafts room; Laundry room.
Activities Arts and Crafts; Cards; Games; Shopping trips.

The Shelton Center
4152 W Pine Blvd, Saint Louis, MO, 63108 (314) 533-3030
Admin Richard L Shelton.
Licensure Residential Care.
Ownership Proprietary.
Admissions Requirements Medical examination.
Staff Nurses aides 3 (ft).
Facilities Dining room; Laundry room.
Description Facility offers cheerfully decorated semi-private rooms; residents may bring a

favorite piece of furniture; transportation available for no charge; courteous thoughtful staff to assist with residents' needs.

South Gate Care Center
5934 Telegraph Rd, Saint Louis, MO, 63129 (314) 846-2000
Admin F David Kellogg. *Medical Dir/Dir of Nursing* P Tiongson MD.
Licensure Skilled Care. *Beds* 180.
Ownership Nonprofit.
Staff Physicians 3 (pt); RNs 11 (ft); LPNs 8 (ft); Nurses aides 60 (ft), 30 (pt); Physical therapists 2 (ft), 1 (pt); Occupational therapists 1 (pt); Speech therapists 1 (pt); Activities coordinators 1 (ft), 1 (pt); Dentists 1 (pt); Ophthalmologists 1 (pt); Podiatrists 1 (pt); Audiologists 1 (pt).
Facilities Dining room; Physical therapy room; Activities room; Crafts room; Laundry room; Barber/Beauty shop; Library.
Activities Arts and Crafts; Cards; Games; Prayer groups; Movies; Dances/Social or cultural gatherings.

St Louis Association for Retarded Children Inc*
PO Box 27480, 1240 Dautel, Saint Louis, MO, 63141 (314) 569-2211
Admin Malcolm Harris Jr.
Licensure Intermediate Care for Mentally Retarded. *Beds* 60.
Ownership Public.

Stellar Homes Inc*
4336 Lindell, Saint Louis, MO, 63108 (314) 652-4828
Admin Viola J Huskey.
Licensure Residential Care. *Beds* 24.
Ownership Proprietary.

Tower Village Inc
4518 Blair Ave, Saint Louis, MO, 63107 (314) 534-4000
Admin Charles T Gooden. *Medical Dir/Dir of Nursing* Alphonso Hillard MD.
Licensure Skilled Care; Intermediate Care.
Beds 268. *Certified* Medicaid.
Ownership Nonprofit.
Admissions Requirements Medical examination.
Staff Physicians 3 (pt); RNs 6 (ft); LPNs 30 (ft); Nurses aides 78 (ft); Physical therapists 1 (pt); Recreational therapists 1 (pt); Occupational therapists 1 (pt); Speech therapists 1 (pt); Activities coordinators 2 (ft); Dietitians 1 (ft); Dentists 1 (pt); Ophthalmologists 1 (pt); Podiatrists 1 (pt); Audiologists 1 (pt).
Facilities Dining room; Physical therapy room; Activities room; Chapel; Crafts room; Laundry room; Barber/Beauty shop; Library.
Activities Arts and Crafts; Cards; Games; Reading groups; Prayer groups; Movies; Shopping trips.

Village North Residential Center
11160 Village North Dr, Saint Louis, MO, 63136
Admin Dorothy Espenschied. *Medical Dir/Dir of Nursing* David Smuckler MD.
Licensure Skilled Care. *Beds* 60. *Certified* Medicaid; Medicare.
Ownership Nonprofit.
Admissions Requirements Minimum age 18; Medical examination; Physician's request.

Staff Physicians 1 (pt); RNs 2 (ft), 1 (pt); LPNs 7 (ft), 4 (pt); Orderlies 1 (ft); Nurses aides 10 (ft), 10 (pt); Physical therapists 1 (ft); Reality therapists 1 (pt); Recreational therapists 1 (pt); Occupational therapists 1 (pt); Speech therapists 1 (pt); Activities coordinators 1 (ft); Dietitians 1 (pt); Dentists 1 (pt); Ophthalmologists 1 (pt); Podiatrists 1 (pt).
Facilities Dining room; Physical therapy room; Activities room; Crafts room; Laundry room; Barber/Beauty shop; Library.
Activities Arts and Crafts; Cards; Games; Reading groups; Prayer groups; Movies; Shopping trips; Dances/Social or cultural gatherings; Billiards; Pitch and putt golf.
Description This is a life-care retirement community with services ranging from 213 apartments for independent living to a 60-bed skilled nursing facility. Facility is located on 40 wooded acres with a 5-acre stocked lake.

Walton Home
4527 Forest Park Blvd, Saint Louis, MO, 63108 (314) 361-3424
Admin Lucy H Gordon.
Licensure Intermediate Care. *Beds* 40.
Ownership Proprietary.
Admissions Requirements Medical examination; Physician's request.
Staff RNs 1 (pt); LPNs 2 (ft); Nurses aides 12 (ft); Activities coordinators 1 (pt); Dietitians 1 (pt).
Facilities Dining room; Activities room; Barber/Beauty shop.
Activities Arts and Crafts; Cards; Games; Movies; Shopping trips.

SAINT PETERS

Saint Peters Manor Care Center
150 Spencer Rd, Saint Peters, MO, 63376
Admin Bennie Wiegand. *Medical Dir/Dir of Nursing* Dr Martin Walsch.
Licensure Intermediate Care. *Beds* 102.
Ownership Nonprofit.
Admissions Requirements Medical examination; Physician's request.
Staff RNs 2 (pt); LPNs 6 (ft); Physical therapists 1 (pt); Occupational therapists 1 (pt); Speech therapists 1 (pt); Activities coordinators 1 (ft), 1 (pt); Podiatrists 1 (pt).
Facilities Dining room; Barber/Beauty shop.
Activities Arts and Crafts; Games; Reading groups; Movies; Shopping trips; Dances/Social or cultural gatherings; Adopt-a-grandparent program.

SAINTE GENEVIEVE

Greenfields Nursing Home*
PO Box 346, Little Rock Rd, Sainte Genevieve, MO, 63670 (314) 883-3124
Admin Janet Kemper.
Licensure Intermediate Care. *Beds* 36.
Ownership Proprietary.

Riverview Manor Nursing Home
N 4th at Mathews Dr, PO 151, Sainte Genevieve, MO, 63670 (314) 883-3454
Admin Martin F Radmer.
Licensure Intermediate Care. *Beds* 120.

Certified Medicaid.
Ownership Public.
Admissions Requirements Medical examination; Physician's request.
Staff Physicians 1 (pt); RNs 3 (ft), 1 (pt); LPNs 1 (ft), 1 (pt); Orderlies 1 (ft); Nurses aides 52 (ft), 12 (pt); Activities coordinators 2 (ft).
Facilities Dining room; Activities room; Laundry room; Barber/Beauty shop.
Activities Arts and Crafts; Cards; Games; Reading groups; Prayer groups; Movies; Shopping trips; Dances/Social or cultural gatherings.

SALEM

Elwood Nursing Home
1000 N Jackson, Salem, MO, 65560 (314) 729-3011
Admin Virginia A Elwood.
Licensure Intermediate Care. *Beds* 36.
Ownership Proprietary.

Seville Nursing Home
Hwy 72 W, PO Box 311, Salem, MO, 65560 (314) 729-6141
Admin Mary Wilson. *Medical Dir/Dir of Nursing* James Bass MD.
Licensure Skilled Care; Intermediate Care.
Beds 90. *Certified* Medicaid; Medicare.
Ownership Proprietary.
Admissions Requirements Minimum age 21.
Staff Physicians 1 (pt); RNs 2 (ft), 2 (pt); LPNs 3 (ft), 3 (pt); Nurses aides 20 (ft), 6 (pt); Physical therapists 2 (pt); Recreational therapists 1 (pt); Occupational therapists 1 (pt); Speech therapists 1 (pt); Activities coordinators 1 (ft); Dietitians 1 (pt); Dentists 1 (pt); Podiatrists 1 (pt).
Facilities Dining room; Physical therapy room; Activities room; Crafts room; Laundry room; Barber/Beauty shop; Library.
Activities Arts and Crafts; Cards; Games; Reading groups; Prayer groups; Movies; Shopping trips; Dances/Social or cultural gatherings; Outings.
Description The Seville is a one-story southern-style building located in a quiet country setting 2 miles from the Salem shopping area and only one-quarter mile from Salem Memorial Hospital and dialysis unit.

SALISBURY

Chariton Manor Convalescent Center*
902 New St, Salisbury, MO, 65281 (816) 388-6486
Admin Janet S Schnetzler.
Licensure Intermediate Care; Residential Care.
Beds ICF 60; Residential Care 42. *Certified* Medicaid.
Ownership Proprietary.

SARCOXIE

Royce Manor
16th and Miner, Sarcoxie, MO, 64862 (417) 548-3434
Admin Ann Royce and James J Royce.
Medical Dir/Dir of Nursing J J Royce MD.
Licensure Skilled Care. *Beds* 37.
Admissions Requirements Medical examina-

tion.
Staff Physicians 1 (ft); RNs 2 (ft), 1 (pt); LPNs 3 (ft), 1 (pt); Nurses aides 10 (ft), 4 (pt); Activities coordinators 2 (pt).
Facilities Dining room; Activities room; Chapel; Crafts room; Laundry room; Barber/Beauty shop; Library.
Activities Arts and Crafts; Cards; Games; Prayer groups; Movies; Shopping trips; Dances/Social or cultural gatherings.
Description Family-type atmosphere available with individual skilled care given because of small size; resident does not feel institutionalized.

SAVANNAH

LaVerna Heights
104 E Park Ave, Savannah, MO, 64485 (816) 324-3179
Admin M Magdelene Bergmann.
Licensure Intermediate Care. *Beds* 40.
Ownership Nonprofit.
Admissions Requirements Minimum age 45; Females only; Medical examination.
Staff RNs 1 (pt); LPNs 5 (pt); Nurses aides 6 (ft), 16 (pt); Activities coordinators 1 (pt); Dietitians 1 (pt).
Affiliation Roman Catholic
Facilities Dining room; Chapel; Laundry room; Barber/Beauty shop.
Activities Arts and Crafts; Games; Prayer groups; Movies; Dances/Social or cultural gatherings; Exercises.

LaVerna Village Nursing Home
904 Hall Ave, Savannah, MO, 64485 (816) 324-3185
Admin Leon T Jennings.
Licensure Intermediate Care. *Beds* 120. *Certified* Medicaid.
Ownership Nonprofit.
Staff RNs 1 (ft), 2 (pt); LPNs 9 (ft); Nurses aides 58 (ft), 4 (pt); Activities coordinators 3 (ft).
Affiliation Roman Catholic
Facilities Dining room; Activities room; Chapel; Crafts room; Laundry room; Barber/Beauty shop; Library.
Activities Arts and Crafts; Cards; Games; Reading groups; Prayer groups; Dances/Social or cultural gatherings.

Shady Lawn
PO Box 209, Savannah, MO, 64485 (816) 324-5991
Admin Brenda Elifrits.
Licensure Intermediate Care. *Beds* 76. *Certified* Medicaid.
Ownership Nonprofit.
Admissions Requirements Minimum age 21; Medical examination.
Staff RNs 1 (pt); LPNs 2 (ft), 1 (pt); Orderlies 6 (ft); Nurses aides 20 (ft), 4 (pt); Physical therapists 1 (pt); Occupational therapists 1 (pt); Speech therapists 1 (pt); Activities coordinators 1 (ft); Dietitians 1 (pt).
Facilities Dining room; Physical therapy room; Activities room; Laundry room; Barber/Beauty shop.
Activities Arts and Crafts; Cards; Games; Reading groups; Prayer groups; Movies; Shop-

ping trips; Dances/Social or cultural gatherings.
Description Shady Lawn is very aptly named; residents are proud of their huge old trees and large lawns; greatest attraction is rural setting midst farmlands of Missouri and facility is well known for homey atmosphere and personal, caring staff.

SEDALIA

Brooking Park Geriatric Center Inc
Rt 6, PO Box 1567, Sedalia, MO, 65301 (816) 826-8803
Admin R H "Hank" Monsees. *Medical Dir-/Dir of Nursing* Kenneth Azan MD.
Licensure Skilled Care; Intermediate Care.
Beds 180. *Certified* Medicaid; Medicare.
Ownership Proprietary.
Staff Physicians 1 (pt); RNs 4 (ft), 4 (pt); LPNs 14 (ft), 2 (pt); Orderlies 5 (ft), 1 (pt); Nurses aides 60 (ft), 16 (pt); Physical therapists 1 (pt); Occupational therapists 1 (pt); Speech therapists 1 (pt); Activities coordinators 2 (ft); Dietitians 1 (ft).
Facilities Dining room; Physical therapy room; Activities room; Chapel; Crafts room; Laundry room; Barber/Beauty shop; Library.
Activities Arts and Crafts; Cards; Games; Reading groups; Prayer groups; Movies; Shopping trips; Dances/Social or cultural gatherings.
Description Brooking Park is in a rural setting yet only 2 miles from town; outstanding feature is "continuum of care" that is provided through townhomes that retired individuals purchase complete with warranty deed and title policy and services to one and 2 bedroom garden apartments to a residential care facility to multi-level rehabilitative geriatric center; offers home health services and an in-home attendant program. At Brooking Park, "We help you keep what you've worked a lifetime to save."

Brooking Park Village Residential Care Facility*
300 Brooking Park Ave, Sedalia, MO, 65301 (816) 826-4701
Admin Debbie Hebert.
Licensure Intermediate Care. *Beds* 28.
Ownership Proprietary.

Buena Vista Home for the Aged
Rt 4, Georgetown Rd, Sedalia, MO, 65301 (816) 826-5159
Admin Robert Kessler. *Medical Dir/Dir of Nursing* Dr Donald Allcorn.
Licensure Intermediate Care. *Beds* 48.
Ownership Nonprofit.
Staff Physicians 1 (pt); RNs 1 (pt); LPNs 1 (ft), 1 (pt); Orderlies 1 (ft); Nurses aides 12 (ft); Activities coordinators 1 (ft); Dietitians 1 (pt).
Facilities Dining room; Chapel; Laundry room; Barber/Beauty shop.
Activities Arts and Crafts; Cards; Games; Prayer groups; Movies.
Description Buena Vista (beautiful view) sits on a hill 3 miles north of Sedalia. The home itself is a beautiful 105-year-old, 3-story house. It has been a nursing home for 87 years. Shade trees and a full-screened porch make sitting outside a pleasure.

Burt Manor Nursing Home*
711 N Missouri, Sedalia, MO, 65301 (816) 826-3593
Admin Belva Morney.
Licensure Intermediate Care. *Beds* 33.
Ownership Proprietary.

Fair View Nursing Home*
1714 W 16th St, Sedalia, MO, 65301 (816) 827-1594
Admin Constance Johnson Pope.
Licensure Intermediate Care. *Beds* 58.
Ownership Proprietary.

Gina's Granny Home
1105 E 6th St, Sedalia, MO, 65301
Admin Doris Riley.
Beds 6. *Certified* Medicaid; Medicare.
Ownership Proprietary.
Admissions Requirements Medical examination.
Facilities Dining room.
Activities Prayer groups.
Description Facility is a small boarding home for those who do not wish to live alone; singers, ministers, scouts, and youth come for programs.

Hawthorne House*
1401 W 3rd St, Sedalia, MO, 65301 (816) 826-2080
Admin Brenda Thompson.
Licensure Intermediate Care. *Beds* 31.
Ownership Proprietary.

Rest Haven Convalescent and Retirement Home*
1800 S Ingram, Sedalia, MO, 65301 (816) 827-0845
Admin Lee Stormer and John C Finley.
Licensure Skilled Care; Intermediate Care.
Beds 81. *Certified* Medicaid.
Ownership Proprietary.

SENATH

Senath Nursing Home*
Hwy 25, Box Q, Senath, MO, 63876 (314) 738-2068
Admin George W Krone.
Licensure Skilled Care; Intermediate Care.
Beds 120. *Certified* Medicaid.
Ownership Proprietary.

SHELBINA

Aladdin's of Shelbina*
310 E Walnut, Shelbina, MO, 63468 (314) 588-7749
Admin Mildred Wheeler.
Licensure Residential Care. *Beds* 31.
Ownership Proprietary.

Salt River Nursing Home*
Box 529, Shelbina, MO, 63468 (314) 588-4175
Admin Floyd Sims.
Licensure Skilled Care. *Beds* 120.
Ownership Public.

SIKESTON

Shuffit Nursing Home 1 Inc*
PO Box 827, 509 Ruth St, Sikeston, MO, 63801 (314) 471-2565
Admin Ira B Shuffit.
Licensure Intermediate Care. *Beds* 82. *Certified* Medicaid.
Ownership Proprietary.

Shuffit Nursing Home 3 Inc
Rt 3, PO Box 827, Sikeston, MO, 63801 (314) 471-1174
Admin Randol M York. *Medical Dir/Dir of Nursing* A L Weaver.
Licensure Intermediate Care. *Beds* 100. *Certified* Medicaid.
Ownership Proprietary.
Admissions Requirements Minimum age 21.
Staff Physicians 1 (pt); RNs 1 (ft), 1 (pt); LPNs 8 (ft), 3 (pt); Orderlies and; Nurses aides 37 (ft), 6 (pt); Physical therapists 1 (ft), 1 (pt); Occupational therapists 1 (pt); Speech therapists 1 (pt); Activities coordinators 1 (ft); Dietitians 1 (ft), 1 (pt); Dentists 1 (pt); 16 (ft), 6 (pt).
Facilities Dining room; Physical therapy room; Activities room; Crafts room; Laundry room; Barber/Beauty shop.
Activities Arts and Crafts; Cards; Games; Prayer groups; Movies; Shopping trips; Dances/Social or cultural gatherings.

Sikeston Convalescent Center*
103 Kennedy Dr, Sikeston, MO, 63801 (314) 471-6900
Admin George A Stevens.
Licensure Skilled Care; Intermediate Care.
Beds 120. *Certified* Medicaid.
Ownership Proprietary.

Sikeston Manor Nursing Home
628 N West, Sikeston, MO, 63801 (314) 471-7130
Admin W Charles New. *Medical Dir/Dir of Nursing* Edwin J Masters MD.
Licensure Skilled Care; Intermediate Care.
Beds 120. *Certified* Medicaid.
Ownership Proprietary.
Admissions Requirements Minimum age 21; Medical examination; Physician's request.
Staff Physicians 1 (pt); RNs 2 (ft); LPNs 4 (ft), 2 (pt); Nurses aides 74 (ft), 22 (pt); Physical therapists 1 (pt); Occupational therapists 1 (pt); Speech therapists 1 (pt); Activities coordinators 1 (ft), 1 (pt); Dietitians 1 (pt); Dentists 1 (pt); Audiologists 1 (pt).
Facilities Dining room; Physical therapy room; Activities room; Crafts room; Laundry room; Barber/Beauty shop; Library.
Activities Arts and Crafts; Cards; Games; Reading groups; Prayer groups; Movies; Shopping trips; Dances/Social or cultural gatherings.

SILEX

Rosedale Nursing Home
Rt 1, Box 108, Silex, MO, 63377 (314) 384-5213
Admin Clarence E and Juanita L Beck.
Medical Dir/Dir of Nursing Jose M A Navato MD.
Licensure Intermediate Care. *Beds* 60.

Ownership Proprietary.
Admissions Requirements Minimum age 16; Medical examination; Physician's request.
Staff RNs 1 (ft); LPNs 2 (ft), 1 (pt); Nurses aides 7 (ft), 22 (pt); Activities coordinators 1 (ft).
Facilities Dining room; Physical therapy room; Activities room; Laundry room.
Activities Arts and Crafts; Cards; Games; Reading groups; Prayer groups; Movies; Shopping trips; Dances/Social or cultural gatherings.

SMITHVILLE

Smithville Convalescent Center*
Box F, Smithville, MO, 64089 (816) 532-0888
Admin D Martin Ebert.
Licensure Skilled Care; Intermediate Care. *Beds* 104. *Certified* Medicaid; Medicare.
Ownership Proprietary.

SPRINGFIELD

Cherry Manor Health Care Center*
1330 Cherry St, Springfield, MO, 65802 (417) 862-3753
Admin Marilyn Kupka.
Licensure Intermediate Care. *Beds* 52.
Ownership Proprietary.

Davis Nursing Home
633 Cherry, Springfield, MO, 65806 (417) 869-0612
Admin James E Robertson.
Licensure Intermediate Care. *Beds* 70.
Ownership Proprietary.

Fremont Manor
2915 S Fremont, Springfield, MO, 65804 (417) 883-4022
Admin Betty Luckie. *Medical Dir/Dir of Nursing* Stanley S Peterson MD.
Licensure Skilled Care. *Beds* 180.
Ownership Proprietary.
Staff RNs 5 (ft), 2 (pt); LPNs 15 (ft), 5 (pt); Nurses aides 35 (ft), 15 (pt); Physical therapists 1 (ft); Reality therapists 1 (pt); Recreational therapists 1 (ft), 1 (pt); Occupational therapists 1 (pt); Speech therapists 1 (pt); Activities coordinators 1 (ft), 1 (pt); Dietitians 1 (ft), 1 (pt); Dentists 1 (pt); Podiatrists 1 (pt).
Facilities Dining room; Physical therapy room; Activities room; Chapel; Crafts room; Laundry room; Barber/Beauty shop.
Activities Arts and Crafts; Cards; Games; Reading groups; Prayer groups; Movies; Shopping trips; Dances/Social or cultural gatherings; Service projects.
Description Manor encourages and aids its residents to maintain and maximize levels of independent living including staying active in community affairs; residents hold annual Halloween party—over 700 children attended last year; residents also raise funds for various service organizations such as a rock and roll jamboree for the American Heart Association.

Greene Haven
910 S West Ave, Springfield, MO, 65807 (417) 865-8741
Admin Jane Alexander. *Medical Dir/Dir of*

Nursing Dr Robert LaHue.
Licensure Intermediate Care. *Beds* 120. *Certified* Medicaid.
Ownership Nonprofit.
Admissions Requirements Minimum age 18.
Staff Physicians 1 (pt); RNs 1 (ft); LPNs 6 (ft), 2 (pt); Nurses aides 39 (ft), 5 (pt); Physical therapists 1 (pt); Recreational therapists 1 (ft); Occupational therapists 1 (pt); Speech therapists 1 (pt); Dietitians 1 (pt); Dentists 1 (pt); Podiatrists 1 (pt).
Facilities Dining room; Physical therapy room; Activities room; Crafts room; Laundry room; Barber/Beauty shop.
Activities Arts and Crafts; Cards; Games; Reading groups; Prayer groups; Movies; Shopping trips; Dances/Social or cultural gatherings.

Kimbrough Nursing Home of Springfield Inc
519 Cherry, Springfield, MO, 65806 (417) 862-2109
Admin Jeanne Paris.
Licensure Intermediate Care. *Beds* 66.
Ownership Proprietary.
Staff RNs; LPNs; Orderlies; Nurses aides.

Maranatha Manor
233 E Norton, Springfield, MO, 65803 (417) 833-0016
Admin Charles W Davis. *Medical Dir/Dir of Nursing* K DeWayne Piker MD.
Licensure Skilled Care; Intermediate Care.
Beds 180. *Certified* Medicaid.
Ownership Nonprofit.
Staff Physicians 2 (pt); RNs 2 (ft); LPNs 8 (ft), 3 (pt); Orderlies 7 (ft), 1 (pt); Nurses aides 55 (ft), 7 (pt); Physical therapists 1 (pt); Occupational therapists 1 (pt); Activities coordinators 1 (ft); Dietitians 1 (ft); Dentists 1 (pt).
Affiliation Assembly of God
Facilities Dining room; Physical therapy room; Activities room; Chapel; Crafts room; Laundry room; Barber/Beauty shop; Library.
Activities Arts and Crafts; Games; Prayer groups; Shopping trips; Dances/Social or cultural gatherings.

Mary E Wilson Home for the Aged*
924 N Main, Springfield, MO, 65802 (417) 869-7236
Admin Norma F Akins.
Licensure Residential Care. *Beds* 28.
Ownership Nonprofit.

Medicenter—Springfield*
1911 S National, Springfield, MO, 65804 (417) 883-6521
Admin Charles L Yates.
Licensure Skilled Care; Intermediate Care.
Beds 168. *Certified* Medicaid; Medicare.
Ownership Proprietary.

Mercy Villa
1100 E Montclair, Springfield, MO, 65807 (417) 882-3992
Admin Sue Fergerstrom. *Medical Dir/Dir of Nursing* W Timothy Wilson DO.
Licensure Skilled Care. *Beds* 150.
Ownership Nonprofit.
Admissions Requirements Minimum age 18; Medical examination.
Staff Physicians 1 (pt); RNs 5 (ft); LPNs 6 (ft); Nurses aides 40 (ft), 5 (pt); Physical therapists 1

(pt); Reality therapists 1 (pt); Recreational therapists 1 (pt); Occupational therapists 1 (pt); Speech therapists 1 (pt); Activities coordinators 1 (ft); Dietitians 1 (pt); Dentists 1 (pt).
Affiliation Roman Catholic
Facilities Dining room; Physical therapy room; Activities room; Chapel; Crafts room; Laundry room; Barber/Beauty shop.
Activities Arts and Crafts; Cards; Games; Reading groups; Prayer groups; Movies; Shopping trips; Dances/Social or cultural gatherings.
Description Facility features pet therapy, music therapy, and a "country store" where residents sell crafts they have made.

Mount Vernon Park Care Center*
3403 W Mount Vernon, Springfield, MO, 65802 (417) 866-3533
Admin Bill Foster.
Licensure Skilled Care; Intermediate Care.
Beds 180. *Certified* Medicaid; Medicare.
Ownership Proprietary.

National Care Centers of America Inc*
1610 N Broadway, Springfield, MO, 65803 (417) 866-3533
Admin Kay Schnick.
Licensure Intermediate Care. *Beds* 100. *Certified* Medicaid.
Ownership Proprietary.

Northside Nursing Center
1347 E Valley Water Mill Rd, Springfield, MO, 65803 (417) 833-1220
Admin Cecil Gallop. *Medical Dir/Dir of Nursing* Dennis Morrison.
Licensure Intermediate Care. *Beds* 180. *Certified* Medicaid.
Ownership Proprietary.
Admissions Requirements Minimum age 18; Medical examination.
Staff Physicians 1 (pt); RNs 1 (ft); LPNs 12 (ft); Orderlies 5 (ft); Nurses aides 68 (ft); Physical therapists 1 (pt); Recreational therapists 1 (pt); Occupational therapists 1 (pt); Speech therapists 1 (pt); Activities coordinators 2 (ft); Dietitians 1 (ft), 1 (pt); Medical technicians 6 (ft).
Facilities Dining room; Physical therapy room; Activities room; Crafts room; Laundry room; Barber/Beauty shop.
Activities Arts and Crafts; Cards; Games; Reading groups; Prayer groups; Movies; Shopping trips; Dances/Social or cultural gatherings.
Description Center sets amid 12 acres of beautifully landscaped grounds; clean and modern facility boasts a cheerful, pleasant atmosphere and provides selected spiritual programs, restorative therapy, balanced activity programs, occupational therapy, and social services.

Primrose Place
1115 Primrose St, Springfield, MO, 65807 (417) 883-1546
Admin Sharon Warren. *Medical Dir/Dir of Nursing* Steven Langguith MD.
Licensure Skilled Care. *Beds* 130.
Ownership Nonprofit.
Admissions Requirements Minimum age 18; Medical examination; Physician's request.
Staff Physicians 1 (pt); RNs 4 (ft), 1 (pt); LPNs 16 (ft), 5 (pt); Orderlies 12 (ft); Nurses aides 40 (ft), 5 (pt); Physical therapists 2 (pt); Reality

therapists 1 (pt); Activities coordinators 1 (ft), 2 (pt); Dietitians 1 (ft), 1 (pt).
Facilities Dining room; Physical therapy room; Activities room; Chapel; Crafts room; Laundry room; Barber/Beauty shop; Library; Senior walking course; Miniature golf course.
Activities Arts and Crafts; Games; Reading groups; Movies; Shopping trips; Dances/Social or cultural gatherings; Exercise groups.
Description Primrose Place is a one-story brick structure built like a giant snowflake. The interior is beautifully designed to be functional as well as to provide residents with a home-like atmosphere. Many activities are provided both indoor and out. The area is beautifully landscaped and offers a walking course with exercise stations and a 9-hole miniature golf course.

Springfield Health Care Center*
PO Box 3438 GS, 2800 S Fort St, Springfield, MO, 65807 (417) 882-0035
Admin Don W Long.
Licensure Skilled Care; Intermediate Care. *Beds* 120. *Certified* Medicaid; Medicare.
Ownership Proprietary.

Springfield Rest Home
2323 W Grand, Springfield, MO, 65802 (417) 862-7445
Admin Patricia J Uhlis.
Licensure Intermediate Care. *Beds* 100.
Admissions Requirements Medical examination.
Staff RNs 1 (ft); LPNs 8 (ft); Nurses aides 30 (ft), 2 (pt); Activities coordinators 1 (ft); Dietitians 1 (pt).
Facilities Dining room; Physical therapy room; Activities room; Crafts room; Laundry room; Barber/Beauty shop.
Activities Arts and Crafts; Cards; Games; Reading groups; Prayer groups; Movies.

STANBERRY

Concerned Services Inc*
PO Box 6, RR 2, Stanberry, MO, 64489 (816) 783-2361
Admin Benjamin Rogers.
Licensure Intermediate Care for Mentally Retarded. *Beds* 9.
Ownership Public.

Pine View Manor Inc
Rt 2, Stanberry, MO, 64489 (816) 783-2118
Admin Thomas Hoy. *Medical Dir/Dir of Nursing* A L Carlin MD.
Licensure Intermediate Care. *Beds* 80. *Certified* Medicaid.
Ownership Nonprofit.
Staff LPNs 4 (ft); Nurses aides 23 (ft), 4 (pt); Activities coordinators 1 (ft).
Affiliation Lutheran
Facilities Dining room; Physical therapy room; Activities room; Chapel; Laundry room; Barber/Beauty shop.
Activities Cards; Games; Movies; Bingo.
Description Pine View Manor is an 80-bed ICF, owned by the city and managed by Lutheran Good Samaritan Society.

STEELE

River Oaks*
Box 247, Hwy 164, Steele, MO, 63877 (314) 695-2121, 785-0858
Admin Tom Butler.
Licensure Skilled Care; Intermediate Care. *Beds* 90. *Certified* Medicaid.
Ownership Proprietary.

STEELVILLE

Gibbs Care Center*
Rt 2, Box 140B, Steelville, MO, 65565 (314) 775-5815
Admin Phillip C Marzluf.
Licensure Intermediate Care. *Beds* 60. *Certified* Medicaid.
Ownership Nonprofit.

STELLA

Stella Residential Care Center Inc*
PO Box 87, Ozark St, Stella, MO, 64867 (417) 628-3231
Admin Randy Cooper.
Licensure Residential Care. *Beds* 50.
Ownership Proprietary.

STOCKTON

Stockton Nursing Home Inc
Drawer W, Stockton, MO, 65785 (417) 276-5126
Admin Gilbert W York.
Licensure Intermediate Care. *Beds* 120. *Certified* Medicaid.
Ownership Nonprofit.
Admissions Requirements Minimum age 18.
Staff RNs 1 (ft); LPNs 3 (ft), 2 (pt); Orderlies 2 (ft); Nurses aides 45 (ft), 8 (pt); Activities coordinators 2 (pt).
Facilities Dining room; Activities room; Crafts room; Laundry room; Barber/Beauty shop; Library.
Activities Arts and Crafts; Cards; Games; Reading groups; Movies.

STOVER

Golden Age Nursing Home District 1
3rd and Mimosa Sts, PO Box 307, Stover, MO, 65078 (314) 377-4521
Admin Betty Hollcroft.
Licensure Intermediate Care. *Beds* 60. *Certified* Medicaid.
Ownership Proprietary.
Staff RNs 1 (ft); LPNs 1 (ft); Nurses aides 17 (ft), 15 (pt); Physical therapists; Recreational therapists 1 (pt); Occupational therapists; Speech therapists.
Facilities Dining room; Activities room; Crafts room; Laundry room; Barber/Beauty shop.
Activities Arts and Crafts; Cards; Games; Reading groups; Prayer groups; Movies; Shopping trips; Dances/Social or cultural gatherings.

SULLIVAN

Ridgeway Nursing Home*
431 Russell Rd, Box 267, Sullivan, MO, 63080 (314) 468-4318
Admin Joy J DeLuca.
Licensure Residential Care. *Beds* 18.
Ownership Proprietary.

Sullivan Nursing Center*
Dunsford Dr, Sullivan, MO, 63080 (314) 468-3128
Admin Jo Evelyn Kelley.
Licensure Skilled Care. *Beds* 120. *Certified* Medicaid.
Ownership Proprietary

SWEET SPRINGS

Autumn Lane Nursing Center*
518 E Marshall, Sweet Springs, MO, 65351 (816) 335-6391
Admin John Gilger.
Licensure Intermediate Care. *Beds* 100. *Certified* Medicaid.
Ownership Proprietary.

TARKIO

Bethesda Care Center
N 3rd and Cedar Sts, Tarkio, MO, 64491 (816) 736-4116
Admin Bernard F Correll. *Medical Dir/Dir of Nursing* Dr E F Bare.
Licensure Intermediate Care. *Beds* 95. *Certified* Medicaid.
Ownership Nonprofit.
Staff RNs 1 (ft); LPNs 6 (ft), 1 (pt); Orderlies 2 (ft); Nurses aides 28 (ft); Activities coordinators 1 (ft).
Facilities Dining room; Physical therapy room; Activities room; Chapel; Laundry room; Barber/Beauty shop.
Activities Arts and Crafts; Cards; Games; Reading groups; Prayer groups; Movies; Shopping trips; Dances/Social or cultural gatherings.
Description Facility is located in the northwest corner of Missouri in small community of very nice people in farm setting.

THAYER

Chastain's of Thayer Inc*
PO Box 77, Hwy 142 at 8th St, Thayer, MO, 65791 (417) 264-7256
Admin Phyllis Stayton.
Licensure Intermediate Care. *Beds* 120. *Certified* Medicaid.
Ownership Proprietary.

TIPTON

Tipton Manor
W Morgan St, PO Box 599, Tipton, MO, 65081 (816) 433-5574
Admin John Arth. *Medical Dir/Dir of Nursing* Johannes Schokker MD.
Licensure Intermediate Care. *Beds* 60. *Certified* Medicaid.
Ownership Nonprofit.

Admissions Requirements Minimum age 16; Medical examination; Physician's request.
Staff RNs 1 (ft); LPNs 3 (ft); Orderlies 2 (ft); Nurses aides 22 (ft); Physical therapists 1 (pt); Occupational therapists 1 (pt); Speech therapists 1 (pt); Activities coordinators 1 (ft); Dietitians 1 (pt); Dentists 1 (pt); Audiologists 1 (pt).
Facilities Dining room; Physical therapy room; Activities room; Laundry room; Barber/Beauty shop.
Activities Arts and Crafts; Cards; Games; Reading groups; Prayer groups; Movies; Shopping trips.

TRENTON

Eastview Manor Retirement and Convalescent Home
1622 E 28th St, Trenton, MO, 64683 (816) 359-2251
Admin Mildred Linhart.
Licensure Intermediate Care. *Beds* 60. *Certified* Medicaid.
Ownership Proprietary.
Staff RNs 1 (ft); LPNs 1 (ft), 6 (pt); Nurses aides 15 (ft), 11 (pt); Physical therapists 1 (ft); Activities coordinators 1 (ft).
Facilities Dining room; Physical therapy room; Activities room; Crafts room; Laundry room; Barber/Beauty shop.
Activities Arts and Crafts; Cards; Games; Reading groups; Prayer groups; Movies; Shopping trips.
Description Medical care at Eastview Manor is administered 24 hours a day by registered nurses, licensed practical nurses, and certified nurse aides. Recreational and social programs are individually planned by qualified personnel. Physical therapy, occupational therapy, audiology, and speech pathology available when prescribed by physician.

Sunnyview District Home of Grundy County
1311 E 28th St, Trenton, MO, 64683 (816) 359-5647
Admin Martha L McCreary.
Licensure Intermediate Care. *Beds* 154. *Certified* Medicaid.
Ownership Public.
Admissions Requirements Minimum age 16.
Staff RNs 4 (ft); LPNs 7 (ft), 1 (pt); Nurses aides 49 (ft), 16 (pt); Physical therapists 1 (pt); Occupational therapists 1 (pt); Speech therapists 1 (pt); Activities coordinators 2 (ft); Dietitians 1 (pt); Audiologists 1 (pt).
Facilities Dining room; Physical therapy room; Chapel; Laundry room; Barber/Beauty shop.
Activities Arts and Crafts; Prayer groups; Movies.
Description Sunnyview is a comfortable, busy, happy place for those unable to live at home. Many concerned staff, volunteers, and community people provide for physical, social, and emotional needs of the residents. What we do best is care enough to show it.

TROY

Medicalodges of Troy
PO Box 300, Troy, MO, 63379 (314) 528-8446
Admin William D Sidwell. *Medical Dir/Dir of*

Nursing Dr Donald Mogerman.
Licensure Skilled Care. *Beds* 120. *Certified* Medicaid; Medicare.
Ownership Proprietary.
Staff RNs 3 (ft); LPNs 10 (ft); Nurses aides 60 (ft); Physical therapists 1 (ft), 1 (pt); Occupational therapists 1 (pt); Speech therapists 1 (pt); Activities coordinators 1 (ft); Dietitians 1 (pt).
Facilities Dining room; Physical therapy room; Activities room; Chapel; Crafts room; Laundry room; Barber/Beauty shop.
Activities Arts and Crafts; Cards; Games; Prayer groups; Movies; Shopping trips; Dances/Social or cultural gatherings.

Troy House Inc*
350 Cap-au-Gris, Troy, MO, 63379 (314) 528-4915
Admin Betty O Wermuth.
Licensure Residential Care. *Beds* 15.
Ownership Proprietary.

TUSCUMBIA

Miller County Nursing Home*
Star Rt, Box 20, Tuscumbia, MO, 65082 (314) 369-2282
Admin Beulah Cotten.
Licensure Intermediate Care. *Beds* 60. *Certified* Medicaid.
Ownership Public.

UNION

Sunset Nursing and Retirement Home of Union*
400 W Park, Union, MO, 63084 (314) 583-2252
Admin Ronald F Davis.
Licensure Intermediate Care. *Beds* 165. *Certified* Medicaid.
Ownership Proprietary.

UNIONVILLE

Putnam County Nursing Home
1814 Oak, Unionville, MO, 63565 (816) 947-2492 947-2493
Admin Robert Hodges. *Medical Dir/Dir of Nursing* Steven Casady.
Licensure Intermediate Care. *Beds* 46.
Ownership Nonprofit.
Staff Physicians; RNs; LPNs; Orderlies; Nurses aides; Physical therapists; Reality therapists; Recreational therapists; Occupational therapists; Speech therapists; Activities coordinators; Dietitians; Dentists; Ophthalmologists; Podiatrists; Audiologists.
Facilities Dining room; Physical therapy room; Activities room; Crafts room; Barber/Beauty shop.
Activities Arts and Crafts; Games; Reading groups; Prayer groups; Movies; Shopping trips.

UNIVERSITY CITY

Delmar Gardens East Inc*
894 Leland, University City, MO, 63130 (314) 726-4767
Admin Florine Korlin.

Licensure Skilled Care; Intermediate Care. *Beds* 128. *Certified* Medicaid; Medicare.
Ownership Proprietary.

VALLEY PARK

Cedarcroft Nursing Home
110 Highland Ave, Valley Park, MO, 63088 (314) 225-5144
Admin Marian Kramer. *Medical Dir/Dir of Nursing* Lois Wyatt MD.
Licensure Skilled Care. *Beds* 176. *Certified* Medicaid; Medicare.
Ownership Proprietary.
Admissions Requirements Minimum age 21; Medical examination; Physician's request.
Staff Physicians 1 (pt); RNs 4 (ft), 3 (pt); LPNs 6 (ft), 4 (pt); Orderlies 1 (ft); Nurses aides 53 (ft), 6 (pt); Physical therapists 1 (pt); Occupational therapists 1 (pt); Speech therapists 1 (pt); Activities coordinators 1 (ft), 2 (pt); Dietitians 1 (pt); Dentists 1 (pt); Ophthalmologists 1 (pt); Podiatrists 1 (pt); Audiologists 1 (pt).
Facilities Dining room; Physical therapy room; Activities room; Chapel; Crafts room; Laundry room; Barber/Beauty shop; Library.
Activities Arts and Crafts; Cards; Games; Prayer groups; Movies; Dances/Social or cultural gatherings.
Description Residents enjoy a full program of creative and social activities including handicrafts, painting, bingo, ice cream socials, movies, monthly birthday parties, and spectacular, festive, annual carnival which is complete with live entertainment, clowns, games, and prizes.

Valley Park Nursing Home*
332 Benton Ave, Valley Park, MO, 63088 (314) 225-5105
Admin Barbara Branson Rikard.
Licensure Intermediate Care. *Beds* 76. *Certified* Medicaid.
Ownership Proprietary.

VAN BUREN

Riverways Manor Nursing Home*
PO Box 116, Van Buren, MO, 63965 (314) 323-4282
Admin Helen Jackson.
Licensure Intermediate Care. *Beds* 60. *Certified* Medicaid.
Ownership Proprietary.

VANDALIA

Tri-County Nursing Home
Rt 2, Box 107, Vandalia, MO, 63382 (314) 594-6468
Admin Shirley Whetstine. *Medical Dir/Dir of Nursing* Rex D Carter DO.
Licensure Intermediate Care. *Beds* 60. *Certified* Medicaid.
Ownership Nonprofit.
Admissions Requirements Minimum age 16; Medical examination; Physician's request.
Staff Physicians 5 (pt); RNs 1 (pt); LPNs 6 (ft); Orderlies 2 (pt); Nurses aides 24 (ft), 8 (pt); Physical therapists 5 (ft), 2 (pt); Reality therapists 1 (ft), 1 (pt); Occupational therapists 1 (pt);

Speech therapists 1 (pt); Activities coordinators 1 (ft), 1 (pt); Dietitians 1 (pt); Dentists 1 (pt). *Facilities* Dining room; Physical therapy room; Chapel; Laundry room; Barber/Beauty shop. *Activities* Arts and Crafts; Games; Prayer groups; Movies; Shopping trips; Dances/Social or cultural gatherings; Bus rides; Carry-in smorgasbords (every 3 months with families). *Description* Facility features exercises every morning with some scheduled activity every afternoon; bingo or movies at least one night a week; goal is to have every resident in as homey an atmosphere as possible.

VERSAILLES

Good Shepherd Nursing Home
Fairground Rd, PO Box M, Versailles, MO, 65084 (314) 378-5411
Admin Donna Hurt. *Medical Dir/Dir of Nursing* Ruth Kauffman.
Licensure Skilled Care; Intermediate Care.
Beds 120.
Ownership Proprietary.
Admissions Requirements Minimum age 16.
Staff Physicians 3 (pt); RNs 3 (ft); LPNs 7 (ft); Orderlies 3 (ft); Physical therapists 1 (ft); Recreational therapists 1 (pt); Occupational therapists 1 (pt); Speech therapists 1 (pt); Activities coordinators 1 (ft); Dietitians 1 (pt); Dentists 1 (pt); Ophthalmologists 1 (pt); Podiatrists 1 (pt); Audiologists 1 (pt).
Facilities Dining room; Physical therapy room; Activities room; Chapel; Crafts room; Laundry room; Barber/Beauty shop; Library.
Activities Arts and Crafts; Games; Reading groups; Prayer groups; Movies; Shopping trips; Dances/Social or cultural gatherings.
Description The Good Shepherd Nursing Home has been licensed by the state of Missouri as a skilled nursing home for over 12 years and is certified SN and ICF. One-third of the employees have been employed for over 5 years which puts the home at the top of the list for experienced personnel providing high quality care at a low daily cost.

WARRENSBURG

Messick Nursing Home Inc
122 E Market, Warrensburg, MO, 64093 (816) 747-8101
Admin Valerie Whiteman.
Licensure Intermediate Care. *Beds* 87. *Certified* Medicaid.
Ownership Proprietary.
Staff Physicians 1 (ft); RNs 1 (ft); LPNs 3 (ft), 2 (pt); Nurses aides 30 (ft); Physical therapists 1 (ft); Recreational therapists 1 (ft); Occupational therapists 1 (ft); Speech therapists 1 (ft); Activities coordinators 1 (ft); Dietitians 1 (ft); Dentists 1 (pt); Podiatrists 1 (pt); Audiologists 1 (pt).
Facilities Dining room; Physical therapy room; Activities room; Laundry room; Barber/Beauty shop.
Activities Arts and Crafts; Cards; Games; Prayer groups; Movies; Dances/Social or cultural gatherings.
Description Facility is located in downtown area in the middle of many activities: churches,

senior center, library, shopping, university, public schools, and more; offers an excellent rehabilitation program for hospital recoveries.

Pleasantview Care Center
Rt 2, Hwy 50 E, Warrensburg, MO, 64093 (816) 747-6457
Admin Mary A Bratten. *Medical Dir/Dir of Nursing* Robert LaHue DO.
Licensure Intermediate Care; Residential Care.
Beds ICF 41; Residential Care 9.
Ownership Proprietary.
Admissions Requirements Minimum age 17.
Staff RNs 1 (pt); LPNs 2 (ft); Orderlies 2 (ft), 1 (pt); Nurses aides 13 (ft); Recreational therapists 2 (ft); Activities coordinators 1 (ft).
Facilities Dining room; Activities room; Crafts room; Laundry room.
Activities Arts and Crafts; Cards; Games; Reading groups; Prayer groups; Movies; Shopping trips; Dances/Social or cultural gatherings; Bowling; Ball games; Fishing.
Description Facility is located on a large site outside a small town with acres of green grass to walk in or just look at. Two separate floors with activities on each floor; ages vary from 23 to 97 years.

Ridge Crest Adult Care Center*
706 S Mitchell, Warrensburg, MO, 64093 (816) 429-2177
Admin Ivan R Wilson.
Licensure Skilled Care; Intermediate Care.
Beds 120. *Certified* Medicaid.
Ownership Proprietary.

Warrensburg Manor Care Center
Manor Dr and E Gay St, Warrensburg, MO, 64093 (816) 747-2216
Admin Melba Jones.
Licensure Intermediate Care. *Beds* 52.
Admissions Requirements Minimum age 20; Medical examination.
Staff RNs 1 (pt); LPNs 2 (ft), 3 (pt); Nurses aides 18 (ft), 3 (pt).

WARRENTON

Katie Jane Memorial Home
607 E Main St, Warrenton, MO, 63383 (314) 456-3401
Admin Helen Kinion. *Medical Dir/Dir of Nursing* F O'Conner MD.
Licensure Intermediate Care. *Beds* 75.
Ownership Proprietary.
Admissions Requirements Minimum age 40; Medical examination.
Staff Physicians 2 (ft); RNs 2 (ft); LPNs 2 (ft); Orderlies 1 (ft); Nurses aides 16 (ft), 16 (pt); Physical therapists 1 (ft); Speech therapists 1 (ft); Activities coordinators 1 (ft); Dietitians 2 (ft); Podiatrists 1 (ft).
Facilities Physical therapy room; Crafts room; Laundry room; Barber/Beauty shop.
Activities Games; Reading groups; Prayer groups; Movies.
Description This is an older nursing home in a home-style setting; both residents and families feel more comfortable here than in a skilled nursing home; excellent home-style cooking.

West Boarding Home
707 E Boarding Home, Warrenton, MO, 63383
Admin Donald D West.
Licensure Skilled Care. *Beds* 34.
Ownership Proprietary.
Admissions Requirements Minimum age 16; Medical examination.
Staff Nurses aides 7 (ft), 1 (pt).
Facilities Dining room; Activities room; Chapel; Crafts room; Laundry room.
Activities Cards; Games; Reading groups; Prayer groups.

WARSAW

Oakhaven Manor
810 Kennedy Dr, Warsaw, MO, 65355 (816) 438-5135
Admin Kathy Eichler.
Licensure Intermediate Care. *Beds* 35.
Ownership Proprietary.
Staff Physicians 3 (ft); RNs 1 (ft), 1 (pt); LPNs 1 (pt); Nurses aides 11 (ft); Physical therapists 1 (ft), 1 (pt); Occupational therapists 1 (pt); Activities coordinators 1 (ft); Dietitians 1 (ft); Dentists 1 (pt).

WASHINGTON

Cedarcrest Manor Inc
324 W 5th St, Washington, MO, 63090 (314) 239-7848
Admin Edward R Maschmann. *Medical Dir/Dir of Nursing* B P Eisenmann MD.
Licensure Skilled Care; Intermediate Care.
Beds 187. *Certified* Medicaid.
Ownership Proprietary.
Admissions Requirements Minimum age 16; Medical examination; Physician's request.
Staff Physicians 2 (pt); RNs 6 (ft), 2 (pt); LPNs 9 (ft), 1 (pt); Nurses aides 60 (ft), 15 (pt); Physical therapists 3 (ft); Recreational therapists 2 (ft); Speech therapists 1 (pt); Activities coordinators 2 (ft); Dietitians 1 (pt); Podiatrists 1 (pt).
Facilities Dining room; Physical therapy room; Activities room; Chapel; Crafts room; Laundry room; Barber/Beauty shop.
Activities Arts and Crafts; Cards; Games; Reading groups; Prayer groups; Movies; Shopping trips; Dances/Social or cultural gatherings.
Description Nursing home is located in a busy part of town where the people can enjoy watching traffic, children, and other people. Facility has an outstanding activities and crafts department, many bazaars, and take trips to the zoo and other interesting places.

WAVERLY

Riverview Heights Nursing Home
Box 181, Waverly, MO, 64096 (816) 493-2232
Admin Gordon L Dille. *Medical Dir/Dir of Nursing* Dr Gene McFadden.
Licensure Intermediate Care. *Beds* 60. *Certified* Medicaid.
Ownership Proprietary.
Staff Physicians 1 (pt); RNs 1 (ft); LPNs 5 (ft); Orderlies 1 (ft); Nurses aides 26 (ft); Physical therapists 1 (pt); Reality therapists 1 (pt); Recreational therapists 1 (pt); Occupational therapists 1 (pt); Speech therapists 1 (pt); Activities coor-

dinators 1 (ft); Dietitians 1 (pt); Dentists 1 (pt); Podiatrists 1 (pt); Audiologists 1 (pt).
Facilities Dining room; Physical therapy room; Activities room; Chapel; Crafts room; Laundry room; Barber/Beauty shop.
Activities Arts and Crafts; Cards; Games; Reading groups; Prayer groups; Movies; Dances/Social or cultural gatherings.
Description Facility is located overlooking Missouri River and beautiful Carrolton bottomlands; community involved; supported with many activities and programs.

WAYNESVILLE

Sunset Village of the Ozarks
Rt 2, Box 120, Waynesville, MO, 65583 (314) 336-4322
Admin Dorothy Viau. *Medical Dir/Dir of Nursing* C R Jenkins MD.
Licensure Skilled Care. *Beds* 33. *Certified* Medicaid; Medicare.
Ownership Proprietary.
Admissions Requirements Minimum age 17; Medical examination; Physician's request.
Staff Physicians 1 (ft); RNs 2 (ft), 1 (pt); LPNs 4 (ft), 2 (pt); Nurses aides 14 (ft), 2 (pt); Physical therapists 1 (ft); Occupational therapists 1 (pt); Speech therapists 1 (pt); Activities coordinators 1 (ft); Dietitians 1 (ft); Dentists 1 (pt); Ophthalmologists 1 (pt); Audiologists 1 (pt); Pharmacist 1 (pt).
Facilities Dining room; Physical therapy room; Activities room; Chapel; Crafts room; Laundry room; Barber/Beauty shop; Library; Indoor pool; Workshop.
Activities Arts and Crafts; Cards; Games; Reading groups; Prayer groups; Movies; Shopping trips; Dances/Social or cultural gatherings; Tours.
Description Sunset Village consists of 87 retirement units, 5 garden cottages, 33-bed skilled nursing facility fully Medicare and Medicaid certified, and a Home Health Agency. Full range of supportive services are available to retirement village and full-range rehabilitative therapies for health care center.

Waynesville Nursing Center*
700 Birch Ln, Waynesville, MO, 65583 (314) 774-6456
Admin Jerry Snobl.
Licensure Skilled Care; Intermediate Care. *Beds* 120. *Certified* Medicaid.
Ownership Proprietary.

WEBB CITY

Elmhurst Nursing Home
Rt 1, Box 100-C, Webb City, MO, 64870 (417) 673-4626
Admin Larry G Cole. *Medical Dir/Dir of Nursing* Robert Ferguson MD.
Licensure Skilled Care. *Beds* 144.
Ownership Nonprofit.
Admissions Requirements Minimum age 21; Medical examination.
Staff RNs 2 (ft); LPNs 14 (ft); Orderlies 4 (ft); Nurses aides 48 (ft), 4 (pt); Physical therapists 1 (pt); Speech therapists 1 (pt); Activities coordinators 3 (ft); Dietitians 1 (pt).

Facilities Dining room; Physical therapy room; Activities room; Chapel; Crafts room; Laundry room; Barber/Beauty shop; Patio.
Activities Arts and Crafts; Cards; Games; Reading groups; Prayer groups; Movies; Shopping trips; Dances/Social or cultural gatherings; Adult basic education.
Description Elmhurst is a home that enjoys providing good care to very special people.

WEBSTER GROVE

Lutheran Charities Association Extended Care Facility*
723 S Laclede Station Rd, Webster Grove, MO, 54673 (314) 968-5570
Admin Fred H Aufderheide.
Licensure Skilled Care. *Beds* 144.
Ownership Nonprofit.
Affiliation Lutheran

WELLSTON

Rockwood Manor Nursing Home Inc
6470 Plymouth Ave, Wellston, MO, 63133 (314) 726-0306
Admin Thelma Craig.
Licensure Intermediate Care. *Beds* 36.
Ownership Proprietary.

WELLSVILLE

Gamma Road Lodge
250 Gamma Rd, Wellsville, MO, 63384 (314) 684-2002
Admin Fay Walden. *Medical Dir/Dir of Nursing* Donald Shoup DO.
Licensure Skilled Care. *Beds* 120. *Certified* Medicaid.
Ownership Proprietary.
Admissions Requirements Medical examination; Physician's request.
Staff Physicians 3 (ft); RNs 4 (ft); Nurses aides 2 (ft); Nurses aides 33 (ft), 23 (pt); Physical therapists 1 (ft), 1 (pt); Recreational therapists 1 (ft); Occupational therapists 1 (pt); Speech therapists 1 (pt); Dietitians 1 (ft); Dentists 1 (pt).
Facilities Dining room; Physical therapy room; Activities room; Chapel; Crafts room; Laundry room; Barber/Beauty shop; Library.
Activities Arts and Crafts; Cards; Games; Reading groups; Prayer groups; Movies; Shopping trips; Monthly birthday parties.
Description Facility is located in rural town; weekly activities include social hour of coffee and donuts, Bible study, Sunday church services; a real family setting.

WENTZVILLE

Mar-Le Nursing Home
401 Mar-Le Dr, Wentzville, MO, 63385 (314) 327-5274
Admin Dave Richardson.
Licensure Skilled Care. *Beds* 120.
Ownership Proprietary.

WEST PLAINS

Ozark Nursing Center*
1410 Kentucky St, West Plains, MO, 65775 (417) 256-7975
Admin George Yarbough.
Licensure Skilled Care. *Beds* 120.
Ownership Proprietary.

West Plains Nursing Home
919 Grace Ave, West Plains, MO, 65775
Admin V Walene O'Dell and Paganini Baet.
Licensure Intermediate Care for Mentally Retarded. *Beds* 25. *Certified* Medicaid; Medicare.
Admissions Requirements Minimum age 21; Medical examination; Physician's request.
Staff Physicians 2 (pt); LPNs 1 (pt); Nurses aides 5 (ft); Activities coordinators 1 (pt); Dietitians 1 (pt); Dentists 1 (pt).
Facilities Dining room; Activities room; Laundry room.
Activities Cards; Games; Prayer groups; Shopping trips.

West Vue Home Inc
909 Kentucky St, West Plains, MO, 65775 (417) 256-2152
Licensure Skilled Care; Intermediate Care. *Certified* Medicaid; Medicare.
Ownership Nonprofit.
Admissions Requirements Medical examination.
Staff Physicians 1 (pt); RNs 4 (ft); LPNs 12 (ft); Orderlies 2 (ft); Nurses aides 64 (ft); Physical therapists 1 (pt); Reality therapists 1 (pt); Occupational therapists 1 (pt); Speech therapists 1 (pt); Activities coordinators 2 (ft); Dietitians 1 (pt); Dentists 1 (pt); Ophthalmologists 1 (pt); Podiatrists 1 (pt); Audiologists 1 (pt).
Facilities Dining room; Physical therapy room; Activities room; Crafts room; Laundry room; Barber/Beauty shop.
Activities Arts and Crafts; Games; Reading groups; Prayer groups; Movies; Shopping trips; Dances/Social or cultural gatherings.

WHEELING

Schneiter Boarding Home
Rt 1, 4th St, Wheeling, MO, 64688
Admin Catherine Brown.
Licensure Boarding Care. *Beds* 10.
Ownership Proprietary.
Admissions Requirements Medical examination.
Staff Nurses aides 1 (ft), 2 (pt).
Facilities Laundry room.
Activities Games; Prayer groups; Movies; Shopping trips.

WILLOW SPRINGS

Willow Care Nursing Home
S Hwy 76, PO Box 309, Willow Springs, MO, 65793 (417) 469-3152
Admin Jack Whitaker. *Medical Dir/Dir of Nursing* C F Smith MD.
Licensure Skilled Care; Intermediate Care. *Beds* 120. *Certified* Medicaid.
Ownership Nonprofit.

MONTANA

ANACONDA

Community Nursing Home of Anaconda*
600 Main St, Anaconda, MT, 59711 (406)
563-8417
Admin Warren L Croston.
Licensure Skilled Care; Intermediate Care.
Beds SNF 40; ICF 28. *Certified* Medicaid;
Medicare.

BAKER

Fallon Memorial Nursing Home*
Box 820, 320 Hospital Dr, Baker, MT, 59313
(406) 778-3331
Admin Dan McLeod.
Licensure Skilled Care. *Beds* 32. *Certified* Medicaid; Medicare.

BIG SANDY

Sande Convalescent Home*
PO Box F, Big Sandy, MT, 59520 (406)
378-2402
Admin David Sande.
Licensure Intermediate Care. *Beds* 29. *Certified* Medicaid.

BIG TIMBER

Pioneer Nursing Home
W 7th, Big Timber, MT, 59011 (406) 932-4603
Admin Alyce Alkire. *Medical Dir/Dir of Nursing* Dr Thomas Ivey.
Licensure Skilled Care; Intermediate Care.
Beds SNF 35; ICF 13. *Certified* Medicaid.
Admissions Requirements Medical examination; Physician's request.
Staff RNs 1 (ft), 1 (pt); LPNs 1 (ft), 3 (pt);
Nurses aides 9 (ft), 9 (pt); Activities coordinators 1 (ft).
Facilities Dining room; Activities room; Laundry room; Barber/Beauty shop.
Activities Arts and Crafts; Cards; Games;
Reading groups; Prayer groups; Movies; Shopping trips; Dances/Social or cultural gatherings.

BIGFORK

Bigfork Convalescent Center
Box 338, Bigfork, MT, 59911 (406) 837-5041
and 837-5042

Admin George W Berry. *Medical Dir/Dir of Nursing* Thomas Jenko MD.
Licensure Skilled Care; Intermediate Care.
Beds SNF 40; ICF 43. *Certified* Medicaid;
Medicare.
Admissions Requirements Medical examination; Physician's request.
Staff RNs 3 (ft), 5 (pt); LPNs 3 (ft), 5 (pt);
Orderlies 1 (pt); Nurses aides 16 (ft), 18 (pt);
Activities coordinators 1 (pt).
Facilities Dining room; Physical therapy room;
Activities room; Crafts room; Laundry room;
Barber/Beauty shop.
Activities Arts and Crafts; Cards; Games;
Reading groups; Prayer groups; Movies; Shopping trips; Dances/Social or cultural gatherings.
Description Center is located in the heart of the
Flathead Valley on a hill overlooking Flathead
Lake to the west and the beautiful Swan Mountain Range to the east; van rides through the
area are of particular interest to most residents.

BILLINGS

Glendeen Nursing Home
4001 Rosebud Ln, Billings, MT, 59101 (406)
252-6135
Admin Robert P Gilstrap. *Medical Dir/Dir of Nursing* Dr Ross Lemire.
Licensure Skilled Care; Intermediate Care.
Beds 36. *Certified* Medicaid; Medicare.
Admissions Requirements Medical examination.

Saint John's Lutheran Home
3940 Rimrock Rd, Billings, MT, 59102 (406)
656-2710
Admin Steven F Olson. *Medical Dir/Dir of Nursing* Dr John Schaeffer.
Licensure Skilled Care; Intermediate Care.
Beds SNF 84; ICF 92. *Certified* Medicaid;
Medicare.
Admissions Requirements Medical examination; Physician's request.
Staff Physicians 1 (pt); RNs 7 (ft), 9 (pt); LPNs
11 (ft), 12 (pt); Nurses aides 55 (ft), 1 (pt);
Physical therapists 2 (pt); Dietitians 1 (pt).
Affiliation Lutheran
Facilities Dining room; Physical therapy room;
Activities room; Chapel; Laundry room; Barber/Beauty shop; Library.
Activities Arts and Crafts; Cards; Games;
Reading groups; Prayer groups; Movies; Shop-

ping trips; Dances/Social or cultural gatherings.
Description An adult day care center operates 3
days per week.

Valley Nursing Home*
1807 24th St W, Billings, MT, 59102 (406)
656-5010
Admin Joyce Fisher.
Licensure Skilled Care. *Beds* 100. *Certified* Medicaid; Medicare.

Western Manor Nursing Home
2115 Central Ave, Billings, MT, 59102 (406)
656-6500
Admin Ruth Strickler. *Medical Dir/Dir of Nursing* John Schaeffer MD.
Licensure Skilled Care; Intermediate Care.
Beds 158. *Certified* Medicaid; Medicare.
Admissions Requirements Medical examination.
Staff RNs 6 (ft), 6 (pt); LPNs 7 (ft), 2 (pt);
Orderlies 3 (ft); Nurses aides 35 (ft), 20 (pt);
Physical therapists 1 (pt); Activities coordinators 2 (ft); Dietitians 1 (pt).
Facilities Dining room; Physical therapy room;
Activities room; Crafts room; Laundry room;
Barber/Beauty shop.
Activities Arts and Crafts; Cards; Games;
Reading groups; Prayer groups; Movies; Shopping trips; Dances/Social or cultural gatherings.

Yellowstone County Nursing Home
1415 Yellowstone River Rd, Billings, MT,
59103 (406) 245-6401
Admin Esther Sheets. *Medical Dir/Dir of Nursing* R C Nelson.
Licensure Skilled Care; Intermediate Care.
Beds SNF 15; ICF 43. *Certified* Medicaid.
Ownership Public.
Staff Physicians 1 (pt); RNs 5 (ft), 2 (pt); LPNs
3 (ft); Orderlies 1 (ft); Nurses aides 23 (ft);
Physical therapists 1 (pt); Recreational therapists 1 (pt); Activities coordinators 1 (ft);
Activities coordinators 1 (pt); Dentists 1 (pt).
Facilities Dining room; Physical therapy room;
Chapel; Laundry room; Barber/Beauty shop.
Activities Arts and Crafts; Cards; Games;
Reading groups; Prayer groups; Movies; Shopping trips.
Description Nutrition is a very important part
of total patient care.

BOULDER

Boulder River School and Hospital*
Box 87, Boulder, MT, 59632 (406) 225-3311, Exten 241
Admin Richard Heard.
Licensure Intermediate Care for Mentally Retarded. *Beds* 242. *Certified* Medicaid.

BOZEMAN

Bozeman Convalescent Center*
321 N 5th Ave, Bozeman, MT, 59715 (406) 587-4404
Admin David King.
Licensure Intermediate Care. *Beds* 103. *Certified* Medicaid.

Bozeman Deaconess Hospital—Extended Care Facility
15 W Lamme, Bozeman, MT, 59715 (406) 586-8511
Admin Ed Dahlberg. *Medical Dir/Dir of Nursing* Dr Timothy Adams.
Licensure Skilled Care; Intermediate Care. *Beds* SNF 30; ICF 30. *Certified* Medicare.
Admissions Requirements Minimum age 16; Medical examination; Physician's request.
Staff RNs 2 (ft), 1 (pt); LPNs 5 (ft), 5 (pt); Nurses aides 30 (ft), 16 (pt); Recreational therapists 1 (pt); Activities coordinators 1 (ft).
Facilities Dining room; Physical therapy room; Activities room; Enclosed outside patio with area to garden.
Activities Arts and Crafts; Cards; Games; Reading groups; Prayer groups; Movies; Dances/Social or cultural gatherings; Special painting sessions weekly.

Gallatin County Rest Home
1221 W Durston Rd, Bozeman, MT, 59715 (406) 587-5108
Admin William R Cainan. *Medical Dir/Dir of Nursing* Edward L King MD.
Licensure Skilled Care. *Beds* 56. *Certified* Medicaid; Medicare.
Admissions Requirements Medical examination; Physician's request.
Staff RNs 3 (ft), 5 (pt); LPNs 2 (pt); Orderlies 1 (ft); Nurses aides 9 (ft), 22 (pt); Activities coordinators 2 (pt); Dietitians 1 (pt).
Facilities Dining room; Physical therapy room; Activities room; Laundry room.
Activities Cards; Games; Reading groups; Movies; Shopping trips.
Description A large percentage of patients are confined to wheelchairs; very dedicated compassionate staff.

Hillcrest Health Center*
1201 Highland Blvd, Bozeman, MT, 59715 (406) 587-4411
Admin Harold Goble.
Licensure Personal Care. *Beds* 10.

BROADUS

Powder River Nursing Home
Box 70, Broadus, MT, 59317 (406) 436-2646
Admin Jim Spady. *Medical Dir/Dir of Nursing* Dr David Kidder.

Licensure Skilled Care; Intermediate Care.
Beds SNF 19; ICF 21. *Certified* Medicaid; Medicare.
Admissions Requirements Medical examination; Physician's request.
Staff Physicians 1 (pt); RNs 1 (ft), 4 (pt); LPNs 3 (ft); Nurses aides 9 (ft), 4 (pt); Physical therapists 1 (pt); Activities coordinators 1 (ft); Dietitians 1 (ft); Dentists 1 (ft).
Facilities Dining room; Physical therapy room; Activities room; Crafts room; Laundry room; Barber/Beauty shop.
Activities Arts and Crafts; Cards; Games; Prayer groups; Movies; Shopping trips; Dances/Social or cultural gatherings.
Description This facility offers adult day care and physical therapy services for the surrounding area. Resident activities include scenic tours of the Black Hills, shopping trips to nearby cities, fishing, concerts, and plays. Regular church services are held and community involvement in the nursing home is extensive.

BROWNING

Blackfeet Nursing Home*
Box 728, Browning, MT, 59417 (406) 338-2686
Admin Fae Shelby.
Licensure Skilled Care; Intermediate Care.
Beds SNF 29; ICF 20. *Certified* Medicaid.

BUTTE

Butte Park Royal Convalescent Center Inc
3251 Nettie St, Butte, MT, 59701 (406) 723-3225
Admin Richard O York. *Medical Dir/Dir of Nursing* Dr Gilbert Preston.
Licensure Skilled Care; Intermediate Care.
Beds SNF 50; ICF 150. *Certified* Medicaid; Medicare.
Admissions Requirements Medical examination; Physician's request.
Staff RNs 4 (ft), 2 (pt); LPNs 12 (ft), 7 (pt); Orderlies 4 (ft), 1 (pt); Nurses aides 67 (ft), 8 (pt); Physical therapists 1 (ft), 1 (pt); Recreational therapists 1 (ft); Occupational therapists 1 (pt); Activities coordinators 2 (ft).
Facilities Dining room; Physical therapy room; Activities room; Barber/Beauty shop; Library.
Activities Arts and Crafts; Cards; Games; Prayer groups; Movies; Shopping trips; Dances/Social or cultural gatherings.

Crest Nursing Home Inc*
3131 Amherst Ave, Butte, MT, 59701 (406) 494-7035
Admin Ronald M Ronchetto.
Licensure Skilled Care; Intermediate Care.
Beds SNF 40; ICF 63. *Certified* Medicaid.

CHESTER

Liberty County Nursing Home
Chester, MT, 59522 (406) 759-5181
Admin Richard O Brown. *Medical Dir/Dir of Nursing* Dr Richard S Buker.
Licensure Skilled Care. *Beds* 40. *Certified* Medicaid; Medicare.
Staff Physicians 2 (ft); RNs 1 (ft); LPNs 5 (ft), 3 (pt); Orderlies 1 (ft); Nurses aides 15 (ft), 8

(pt); Physical therapists 1 (pt); Activities coordinators 1 (ft); Dietitians 1 (pt); Dentists 1 (pt).
Facilities Dining room; Physical therapy room; Activities room; Chapel; Crafts room; Laundry room.
Activities Arts and Crafts; Cards; Games; Reading groups; Prayer groups; Movies; Dances/Social or cultural gatherings.
Description Home is connected to an 11-bed progressive hospital; clinic is included in physical plant which allows for availability of physician, dentist, and optometrist services under one roof; physicians visit at least 5 times per week.

CHINOOK

Sweet Memorial Nursing Home
Chinook, MT, 59523 (406) 357-2549
Admin Norma Fraser. *Medical Dir/Dir of Nursing* James Begg MD.
Licensure Skilled Care; Intermediate Care.
Beds SNF 34; ICF 6. *Certified* Medicaid.
Admissions Requirements Physician's request.
Staff RNs 1 (ft), 1 (pt); LPNs 1 (ft), 4 (pt); Nurses aides 11 (ft), 4 (pt); Activities coordinators 2 (pt).
Facilities Dining room; Activities room; Laundry room; Barber/Beauty shop.
Activities Arts and Crafts; Cards; Games; Reading groups; Prayer groups; Movies; Shopping trips; Dances/Social or cultural gatherings; Meals at senior citizen centers.
Description Facility is small community home; very close family feeling because almost all residents come from Chinook and the rest from Blaine County.

CHOTEAU

Teton Nursing Home
24 Main Ave N, Choteau, MT, 59422 (406) 466-2431
Admin Arlene Wolbaum. *Medical Dir/Dir of Nursing* M A Johnson MD.
Licensure Skilled Care; Intermediate Care.
Beds SNF 38; ICF 3. *Certified* Medicaid; Medicare.
Ownership Public.
Admissions Requirements Medical examination; Physician's request.
Staff RNs 1 (ft), 4 (pt); LPNs 3 (pt); Nurses aides 14 (ft), 5 (pt); Activities coordinators 1 (ft), 1 (pt).
Facilities Dining room; Physical therapy room; Activities room; Chapel; Barber/Beauty shop.
Activities Arts and Crafts; Cards; Games; Reading groups; Prayer groups; Movies; Shopping trips; Dances/Social or cultural gatherings.
Description Facility is located on Main Street which makes shopping easy for the residents and easy for visitors to come; excellent activity department with many volunteers; high rating is maintained with Department of Health and Environmental Services.

CIRCLE

McCone County Nursing Home*
Box 198, Circle, MT, 59215 (406) 485-3381
Admin Ronald J Olthoff.

Licensure Skilled Care; Intermediate Care. *Beds* SNF 26; ICF 14. *Certified* Medicaid; Medicare.

CLANCY

Hillbrook Nursing Home
Rt 2, Clancy, MT, 59634 (406) 933-8311
Admin William Chapek. *Medical Dir/Dir of Nursing* Dr William Wise.
Licensure Skilled Care; Intermediate Care.
Beds SNF 24; ICF 43. *Certified* Medicaid; Medicare.
Staff Physicians 1 (pt); RNs 4 (ft), 2 (pt); LPNs 6 (ft); Orderlies 1 (ft), 1 (pt); Nurses aides 36 (ft); Physical therapists 1 (pt); Activities coordinators 1 (ft); Activities coordinators 1 (pt).
Facilities Dining room; Physical therapy room; Activities room; Crafts room; Laundry room; Barber/Beauty shop; Library.
Activities Arts and Crafts; Cards; Games; Reading groups; Prayer groups; Movies; Shopping trips; Dances/Social or cultural gatherings.

COLUMBIA FALLS

Montana Veterans' Home—Nursing Home*
Box 250, Columbia Falls, MT, 59912 (406) 892-3256
Admin Michael Patrick Estenson.
Licensure Skilled Care; Intermediate Care.
Beds SNF 20; ICF 20. *Certified* Medicaid; Medicare.

COLUMBUS

Stillwater Convalescent Center
350 W Pike Ave, Columbus, MT, 59019 (406) 322-5342
Admin Ronald I Borgman. *Medical Dir/Dir of Nursing* Dr Jack Exley.
Licensure Skilled Care; Intermediate Care.
Beds SNF 31; ICF 50. *Certified* Medicaid; Medicare.
Staff Physicians 3 (pt); RNs 3 (ft), 3 (pt); LPNs 5 (ft), 2 (pt); Nurses aides 26 (ft), 6 (pt); Physical therapists 1 (pt); Speech therapists 1 (pt); Activities coordinators 1 (ft); Dietitians 1 (pt).
Facilities Dining room; Physical therapy room; Activities room; Crafts room; Laundry room; Barber/Beauty shop.
Activities Arts and Crafts; Cards; Games; Reading groups; Prayer groups; Movies; Shopping trips; Dances/Social or cultural gatherings.
Description Our facility sits at the base of the Beartooth Mountains beside the Yellowstone River with a beautiful, breathtaking view. Also, unique in our state, a developmentally disabled program for children. We have ages 2-102 years.

CONRAD

Pondera Pioneer Nursing Home*
Conrad, MT, 59425 (406) 278-7581
Admin Esther Johnson.
Licensure Skilled Care; Intermediate Care.
Beds SNF 43; ICF 20. *Certified* Medicaid; Medicare.

CULBERTSON

Roosevelt Memorial Nursing Home*
PO Box 419, Culbertson, MT, 59218 (406) 787-6621
Admin Carolyn M Grazley.
Licensure Skilled Care. *Beds* 40. *Certified* Medicaid; Medicare.

CUT BANK

Memorial Nursing Home*
PO Box 2398, Cut Bank, MT, 59427 (406) 873-2251
Admin Alvin Feldkamp.
Licensure Skilled Care; Intermediate Care.
Beds SNF 23; ICF 16. *Certified* Medicaid; Medicare.

DEER LODGE

Colonial Manor of Deer Lodge*
1100 Texas Ave, Deer Lodge, MT, 59722 (406) 846-1655
Admin Fern Knight.
Licensure Skilled Care; Intermediate Care.
Beds SNF 40; ICF 20. *Certified* Medicaid.

Galen State Hospital*
Rt 1, Galen, Deer Lodge, MT, 59722 (406) 693-2281
Admin Joseph M Balkovatz.
Licensure Intermediate Care. *Beds* 185. *Certified* Medicaid.

DILLON

Parkview Acres Convalescent Center*
200 Oregon St, Dillon, MT, 59725 (406) 683-5105
Admin George Montrose.
Licensure Skilled Care; Intermediate Care; Personal Care. *Beds* SNF 4; ICF 94; Personal Care 10. *Certified* Medicaid.

EKALAKA

Dahl Memorial Nursing Home
PO Box 46, Ekalaka, MT, 59324 (406) 775-8730/8739
Admin Gerald E Hughes.
Licensure Skilled Care. *Beds* 21. *Certified* Medicaid.
Admissions Requirements Medical examination.
Staff RNs 5 (ft); LPNs 8 (ft); Nurses aides 4 (ft); Activities coordinators 1 (ft).
Facilities Dining room; Activities room; Laundry room.
Activities Arts and Crafts; Cards; Games; Reading groups; Prayer groups; Movies.
Description Facility is located in a rural scenic setting in southeastern Montana, quiet and peaceful.

ENNIS

Madison County Nursing Home
Box 335, Ennis, MT, 59729 (406) 682-7171
Admin James R Mantz. *Medical Dir/Dir of Nursing* Dr Gene C Wilkins.
Licensure Skilled Care; Intermediate Care.
Beds SNF 20; ICF 20. *Certified* Medicaid; Medicare.
Admissions Requirements Medical examination; Physician's request.
Staff Physicians 1 (pt); RNs 1 (ft), 2 (pt); LPNs 3 (ft), 2 (pt); Nurses aides 9 (ft), 4 (pt); Activities coordinators 1 (ft); Dietitians 1 (ft); Dentists 1 (pt).
Facilities Dining room; Physical therapy room; Activities room; Crafts room; Laundry room; Barber/Beauty shop; Library.
Activities Arts and Crafts; Cards; Games; Reading groups; Prayer groups; Movies; Dances/Social or cultural gatherings.
Description Active community participation in nursing home projects benefits the residents as well as enhances their comfort.

EUREKA

Mountain View Manor Nursing Home*
PO Box 327, Eureka, MT, 59917 (406) 296-2541
Admin T E Davies.
Licensure Skilled Care; Intermediate Care.
Beds SNF 30; ICF 10. *Certified* Medicaid; Medicare.

FORSYTH

Rosebud Community Nursing Home*
Forsyth, MT, 59327 (406) 356-2161
Admin Webster Russell.
Licensure Skilled Care; Intermediate Care.
Beds SNF 45; ICF 8. *Certified* Medicaid; Medicare.

FORT BENTON

Chouteau County District Nursing Home
1512 Saint Charles St, Fort Benton, MT, 59442 (406) 622-3331
Admin Robert E Smith. *Medical Dir/Dir of Nursing* W F Gertson MD.
Licensure Skilled Care. *Beds* 22. *Certified* Medicaid; Medicare.
Ownership Public.
Staff Physicians 3 (ft); RNs 3 (ft), 6 (pt); LPNs 2 (ft), 1 (pt); Nurses aides 8 (ft), 11 (pt); Physical therapists 1 (pt); Activities coordinators 1 (ft); Dentists 2 (ft).
Facilities Dining room; Physical therapy room; Barber/Beauty shop.
Activities Arts and Crafts; Cards; Games; Movies.

GLASGOW

Frances Mahon Deaconess Hospital— Extended Care Facility
621 2nd St S, Glasgow, MT, 59230 (406) 228-4351
Admin Kyle Hosptad. *Medical Dir/Dir of*

Nursing Louise Johnston.
Licensure Skilled Care. *Beds* 6. *Certified* Medicaid; Medicare.

Valley View Home
1225 Perry Ln, Glasgow, MT, 59230 (406) 228-2461
Admin Patricia M Bondy. *Medical Dir/Dir of Nursing* Dr David Gregory.
Licensure Skilled Care; Intermediate Care.
Beds SNF 40; ICF 52. *Certified* Medicaid; Medicare.
Staff RNs 1 (ft), 3 (pt); LPNs 4 (ft), 3 (pt); Orderlies 1 (pt); Nurses aides 25 (ft), 8 (pt); Physical therapists 1 (pt); Activities coordinators 1 (ft); Dietitians 1 (ft).
Affiliation Lutheran
Facilities Dining room; Activities room; Laundry room; Barber/Beauty shop.
Activities Arts and Crafts; Cards; Games; Reading groups; Prayer groups; Movies; Shopping trips; Dances/Social or cultural gatherings.

GLENDIVE

Eastmont Human Services Center
Box 1383, Glendive, MT, 59330 (406) 365-6001
Admin Gerald F Butcher. *Medical Dir/Dir of Nursing* Sylvia Hammer and Patricia Holm.
Licensure Intermediate Care for Mentally Retarded. *Beds* 55. *Certified* Medicaid.
Staff RNs 2 (ft); LPNs 5 (ft); Recreational therapists 1 (ft).
Facilities Dining room; Activities room; Laundry room.
Activities Arts and Crafts; Games; Prayer groups; Movies; Shopping trips; Dances/Social or cultural gatherings.

Glendive Coummunity Nursing Home
Ames and Prospect, Glendive, MT, 59330 (406) 365-5692
Admin John Nordwick. *Medical Dir/Dir of Nursing* Dr N H Rausch.
Licensure Skilled Care; Intermediate Care.
Beds SNF 30; ICF 45. *Certified* Medicaid; Medicare.
Admissions Requirements Minimum age 18; Medical examination; Physician's request.
Staff Physicians 6 (ft); RNs 3 (ft), 4 (pt); LPNs 3 (ft), 3 (pt); Nurses aides 18 (ft), 18 (pt); Recreational therapists 1 (ft); Activities coordinators 1 (ft); Dietitians 1 (ft).
Facilities Dining room; Physical therapy room; Activities room; Chapel; Crafts room; Laundry room; Barber/Beauty shop.
Activities Arts and Crafts; Cards; Games; Reading groups; Prayer groups; Movies; Shopping trips; Dances/Social or cultural gatherings.
Description Combined hospital-nursing home facility with 75 nursing home beds and 46 hospital beds plus 13 certified swing beds.

GREAT FALLS

Cascade County Convalescent Nursing Home
1130 17th Ave S, Great Falls, MT, 59405 (406) 761-6467
Admin Donald E Pizzini. *Medical Dir/Dir of Nursing* Dr John Hiches.

Licensure Skilled Care; Intermediate Care.
Beds 232. *Certified* Medicaid; Medicare.
Ownership Public.
Admissions Requirements Medical examination; Physician's request.
Staff Physicians 1 (pt); RNs 7 (ft), 13 (pt); LPNs 10 (ft), 7 (pt); Orderlies 5 (ft), 1 (pt); Nurses aides 75 (ft), 10 (pt); Physical therapists 1 (ft); Activities coordinators 1 (ft); Dietitians 1 (pt); Dentists 1 (ft), 1 (pt); Ophthalmologists 1 (pt); Pharmacists 2 (ft).
Facilities Dining room; Physical therapy room; Activities room; Chapel; Crafts room; Laundry room; Barber/Beauty shop; Library.
Activities Arts and Crafts; Cards; Games; Prayer groups; Movies; Shopping trips; Dances/Social or cultural gatherings.
Description Facility features bible study, ceramics, exercise classes, bus rides, conversation groups, ice cream parties, Mass, bingo parties and a monthly birthday party.

Deaconess Skilled Nursing Center
1109 6th Ave N, Great Falls, MT, 59405 (406) 761-1200
Admin Margaret Weedman. *Medical Dir/Dir of Nursing* Dr L L Howard.
Licensure Skilled Care. *Beds* 90. *Certified* Medicaid; Medicare.
Admissions Requirements Medical examination; Physician's request.
Facilities Dining room; Physical therapy room; Activities room; Chapel; Crafts room; Laundry room; Barber/Beauty shop; Library; Outside garden area; Enclosed sun porches; On-site doctor's office.
Activities Arts and Crafts; Cards; Games; Reading groups; Prayer groups; Movies; Shopping trips; Dances/Social or cultural gatherings; Bus; Wheelchair van.
Description Facility currently has on staff a geriatric nurse practitioner and will soon be handling day care patients through the Easter Seal program.

McAuley Nursing Home
1009 3rd Ave N, Great Falls, MT, 59401 (406) 452-6302
Admin George B Eusterman Jr. *Medical Dir/Dir of Nursing* Mary Freeman.
Licensure Skilled Care. *Beds* 42. *Certified* Medicaid; Medicare.

Park Place Health Care Center
15th Ave S and 32nd St, PO Box 5001, Great Falls, MT, 59405 (406) 761-4300
Admin Dale Zulauf. *Medical Dir/Dir of Nursing* Dorothy V Boettcher.
Licensure Skilled Care; Intermediate Care.
Beds SNF 105; ICF 70. *Certified* Medicaid; Medicare.
Facilities Dining room; Physical therapy room; Activities room; Crafts room; Laundry room; Barber/Beauty shop; Library.
Activities Arts and Crafts; Cards; Games; Reading groups; Prayer groups; Movies; Shopping trips; Dances/Social or cultural gatherings.
Description One of the largest, most progressive long-term care facilities in Montana. A "Hillhaven" facility.

HAMILTON

Valley View Estates Nursing Home*
225 N 8th St, Hamilton, MT, 59840 (406) 363-1144
Admin John B Muir.
Licensure Skilled Care; Intermediate Care.
Beds SNF 58; ICF 40. *Certified* Medicaid.

HARDIN

Big Horn County Memorial Nursing Home*
17 N Miles, Hardin, MT, 59034 (406) 665-2310
Admin Michael N Sinclair.
Licensure Skilled Care. *Beds* 34. *Certified* Medicaid; Medicare.

Montain View Rest Haven
520 W 3rd St, Hardin, MT, 59034 (406) 665-2802
Admin Jackie Suko. *Medical Dir/Dir of Nursing* Terry Kuntz.
Licensure Intermediate Care. *Beds* 21. *Certified* Medicaid.

HARLEM

Harlem Rest Home*
Harlem, MT, 59526 (406) 353-2421
Admin A J Fuzesy.
Licensure Intermediate Care. *Beds* 60. *Certified* Medicaid.

HARLOWTON

Wheatland Memorial Nursing Home*
530 3rd St NW, Harlowton, MT, 59036 (406) 632-4351
Admin Robert B Holmes.
Licensure Skilled Care. *Beds* 33. *Certified* Medicaid; Medicare.

HAVRE

Lutheran Home of the Good Shepherd
2229 5th Ave, Havre, MT, 59501 (406) 265-2238
Admin Carol Ann Andrews. *Medical Dir/Dir of Nursing* Dr Tom Booth.
Licensure Skilled Care; Intermediate Care.
Beds SNF 85; ICF 17. *Certified* Medicaid; Medicare.
Admissions Requirements Medical examination; Physician's request.
Staff RNs 6 (ft), 2 (pt); LPNs 4 (ft), 4 (pt); Orderlies 8 (ft), 2 (pt); Nurses aides 33 (ft), 3 (pt); Recreational therapists 3 (ft), 2 (pt); Activities coordinators 1 (ft); Dietitians 1 (ft).
Affiliation Lutheran
Facilities Dining room; Activities room; Chapel; Barber/Beauty shop.
Activities Arts and Crafts; Cards; Games; Reading groups; Prayer groups; Movies; Shopping trips; Dances/Social or cultural gatherings.
Description Final construction completed in 1983, utilizing a diagram of 2 separate crosses connected by a crecent shaped administrative/ancillary wing. Facility provides for 91 private and 5 double resident rooms, allowing individual decorations, and activities 7 days a

week. Our motto: "Do not cast me off in the time of old age; forsake me now when my strength is spent" (Psalm 71:9).

HELENA

Cedar Street Home
721 Cedar St, Helena, MT, 59601 (406) 442-1676
Admin Janet Ford. *Medical Dir/Dir of Nursing* Elizabeth Henry.
Licensure Intermediate Care. *Beds* 7. *Certified* Medicaid.

Cooney Convalescent Home
3404 Cooney Dr, Helena, MT, 59601 (406) 443-1010
Admin Joan Ashley. *Medical Dir/Dir of Nursing* Martin Skinner MD.
Licensure Skilled Care. *Beds* 60. *Certified* Medicaid; Medicare.
Ownership Nonprofit.
Admissions Requirements Minimum age 62; Medical examination; Physician's request.
Staff Physicians 1 (pt); RNs 4 (ft), 3 (pt); LPNs 2 (ft), 2 (pt); Orderlies 1 (ft); Nurses aides 19 (ft), 7 (pt); Physical therapists 1 (pt); Occupational therapists 1 (pt); Speech therapists 1 (pt); Activities coordinators 1 (ft); Dietitians 1 (pt); Dentists 1 (pt).
Facilities Dining room; Physical therapy room; Activities room; Chapel; Crafts room; Laundry room; Barber/Beauty shop.
Activities Arts and Crafts; Cards; Games; Reading groups; Prayer groups; Movies; Shopping trips; Dances/Social or cultural gatherings.
Description A 60-bed replacement facility is currently under contruction; it is located adjacent to St Peter's Community Hospital parking lot; scheduled for completion in late 1984; individual patient independence, rehabilitation, and discharge to community is stressed whenever possible.

Helena Nursing Home Co*
25 S Ewing, Helena, MT, 59601 (406) 443-5880
Admin M H Mahlman.
Licensure Skilled Care; Intermediate Care.
Beds SNF 32; ICF 31. *Certified* Medicaid.

Western Care Nursing Home*
2475 Winne Ave, Helena, MT, 59601 (406) 442-1350
Admin Page Puckett.
Licensure Skilled Care; Intermediate Care.
Beds SNF 12; ICF 96. *Certified* Medicaid; Medicare.

HOT SPRINGS

Hot Springs Convalescent Inc
Drawer U, Hot Springs, MT, 59845 (406) 741-2992
Admin H Kent Ferguson. *Medical Dir/Dir of Nursing* Jacob V Lulack MD.
Licensure Skilled Care; Intermediate Care.
Beds SNF 18; ICF 54. *Certified* Medicaid; Medicare.
Admissions Requirements Medical examination; Physician's request.
Staff RNs 4 (ft), 2 (pt); LPNs 1 (pt); Orderlies 2

(ft), 1 (pt); Nurses aides 9 (ft).
Facilities Dining room; Physical therapy room; Activities room; Laundry room; Barber/Beauty shop.
Activities Arts and Crafts; Cards; Games; Reading groups; Prayer groups; Movies; Shopping trips; Dances/Social or cultural gatherings.
Description Center sits atop a hill just west of the small rural town of Hot Springs and commands a lovely view of the surrounding countryside. It has a more friendly and home-like atmosphere due to its size than do many large institutions.

JORDAN

Garfield County Nursing Home*
Jordan, MT, 59337 (406) 557-2465
Admin Robert O'Connor.
Licensure Skilled Care; Intermediate Care.
Beds SNF 4; ICF 8. *Certified* Medicaid; Medicare.

KALISPELL

Flathead County Nursing Home
1251 Willow Glen Dr, Kalispell, MT, 59901 (406) 257-5575
Admin Marguerite Watne. *Medical Dir/Dir of Nursing* Anna Drew.
Licensure Skilled Care; Intermediate Care.
Beds SNF 49; ICF 17. *Certified* Medicaid; Medicare.
Admissions Requirements Physician's request.
Staff RNs 3 (ft), 3 (pt); LPNs 2 (ft); Nurses aides 18 (ft), 5 (pt); Activities coordinators 1 (ft).
Facilities Dining room; Activities room; Crafts room; Laundry room; Library.
Activities Arts and Crafts; Movies; Shopping trips; Church.

Immanuel Lutheran Home
Crestline Ave, Kalispell, MT, 59901 (406) 755-5034
Admin Lorraine Wagnild. *Medical Dir/Dir of Nursing* Dr Alfred V Swanberg.
Licensure Skilled Care; Intermediate Care.
Beds SNF 54; ICF 90. *Certified* Medicaid.
Admissions Requirements Medical examination; Physician's request.
Staff RNs 7 (ft), 6 (pt); LPNs 9 (ft), 5 (pt); Nurses aides 46 (ft), 22 (pt); Activities coordinators 2 (ft), 1 (pt); Dietitians 1 (ft).
Affiliation Lutheran
Facilities Dining room; Activities room; Chapel; Crafts room; Laundry room; Barber/Beauty shop.
Activities Arts and Crafts; Cards; Games; Reading groups; Prayer groups; Movies; Dances/Social or cultural gatherings; Educational groups with college teachers.

LAUREL

Laurel Nursing Home*
421 Yellowstone Ave, Laurel, MT, 59044 (406) 628-6902
Admin William Siegel.
Licensure Skilled Care. *Beds* 29. *Certified* Medicaid.

LEWISTOWN

Central Montana Nursing Home
408 Wendell, Lewistown, MT, 59457 (406) 538-7711
Admin Gary Fletcher. *Medical Dir/Dir of Nursing* Paul J Gans MD.
Licensure Skilled Care. *Beds* 70. *Certified* Medicaid; Medicare.
Admissions Requirements Minimum age 18; Medical examination; Physician's request.
Staff Physicians 10 (pt); RNs 3 (ft), 5 (pt); LPNs 2 (ft), 4 (pt); Orderlies 2 (pt); Nurses aides 13 (ft), 25 (pt); Physical therapists 1 (pt); Activities coordinators 2 (pt); Dietitians 1 (pt); Dentists 1 (pt); Ophthalmologists 1 (pt).
Facilities Dining room; Physical therapy room; Activities room; Chapel; Crafts room; Laundry room; Barber/Beauty shop; Library.
Activities Arts and Crafts; Cards; Games; Reading groups; Prayer groups; Movies; Shopping trips; Dances/Social or cultural gatherings.

Montana Center for the Aged
Box 820, Lewistown, MT, 59457 (406) 538-7451
Admin Gerald F Butcher.
Licensure Intermediate Care. *Beds* 199. *Certified* Medicaid.
Admissions Requirements Minimum age 55.
Staff RNs 9 (ft); LPNs 5 (ft), 1 (pt); Orderlies 37 (ft), 1 (pt); Physical therapists 1 (pt); Recreational therapists 1 (pt); Dietitians 1 (pt).
Facilities Dining room; Activities room; Laundry room; Barber/Beauty shop.
Activities Arts and Crafts; Cards; Games; Prayer groups; Movies; Shopping trips; Dances/Social or cultural gatherings.
Description Located in the center of Montana in a mountainous area, facility is operated by the state for geriatric-psychiatric residents.

Valle Vista Manor
Summit Ave, Lewistown, MT, 59457 (406) 538-8775
Admin Bill McLain. *Medical Dir/Dir of Nursing* Dr Paul Gans.
Licensure Skilled Care; Intermediate Care.
Beds SNF 29; ICF 66. *Certified* Medicaid; Medicare.
Staff RNs 5 (ft), 4 (pt); LPNs 5 (ft), 3 (pt); Nurses aides 33 (ft), 16 (pt); Activities coordinators 1 (ft), 1 (pt); Dietitians 1 (pt); Dentists 1 (pt).
Facilities Dining room; Activities room; Chapel; Crafts room; Laundry room; Barber/Beauty shop.
Activities Arts and Crafts; Cards; Games; Movies; Shopping trips; Dances/Social or cultural gatherings.
Description Valle Vista is located on the outer edge of Lewistown's residential area with a beautiful view of the surrounding mountains.

LIBBY

Libby Care Center
308 E 3rd, Libby, MT, 59923 (406) 293-6285
Admin Harriet McFadden. *Medical Dir/Dir of Nursing* Roger Brus MD.
Licensure Skilled Care; Intermediate Care.
Beds SNF 40; ICF 23. *Certified* Medicaid;

Medicare.
Admissions Requirements Medical examination; Physician's request.
Staff RNs 3 (pt); LPNs 4 (ft), 2 (pt); Nurses aides 18 (ft), 10 (pt); Physical therapists 1 (pt); Speech therapists 1 (pt); Activities coordinators 1 (ft); Dietitians 1 (ft).
Facilities Dining room; Physical therapy room; Activities room; Crafts room; Laundry room; Barber/Beauty shop.
Activities Arts and Crafts; Cards; Games; Reading groups; Movies; Shopping trips; Dances/Social or cultural gatherings; Church services.

LIVINGSTON

Livingston Convalescent Center
510 S 14th St, Livingston, MT, 59047 (406) 222-0672
Admin Judith A Melin. *Medical Dir/Dir of Nursing* Dr L M Baskett.
Licensure Skilled Care; Intermediate Care.
Beds SNF 9; ICF 116. *Certified* Medicaid; Medicare.
Staff RNs 6 (ft); LPNs 7 (ft); Orderlies 2 (ft); Nurses aides 30 (ft); Physical therapists 1 (ft); Reality therapists 1 (ft); Recreational therapists 1 (ft); Occupational therapists 1 (ft); Speech therapists 1 (ft); Activities coordinators 1 (ft); Dietitians 1 (ft); Dentists 1 (ft).
Facilities Dining room; Activities room; Laundry room; Barber/Beauty shop.
Activities Arts and Crafts; Cards; Games; Reading groups; Prayer groups; Movies; Shopping trips; Dances/Social or cultural gatherings.
Description Facility offers restorative feeding and reality orientation.

MALTA

Phillips County Good Samaritan Retirement Center
Box P, Malta, MT, 59538 (406) 654-1190
Admin Henryka Shelton. *Medical Dir/Dir of Nursing* Michael Emond.
Licensure Skilled Care; Intermediate Care.
Beds SNF 40; ICF 20. *Certified* Medicaid.

MILES CITY

Custer County Rest Home
Box 130, Miles City, MT, 59301 (406) 232-1035
Admin Milton E Benge. *Medical Dir/Dir of Nursing* Patricia Nieffer.
Licensure Skilled Care; Intermediate Care.
Beds SNF 40; ICF 81. *Certified* Medicaid.
Ownership Public.
Staff RNs 5 (ft), 9 (pt); LPNs 2 (ft), 3 (pt); Orderlies 4 (ft); Nurses aides 31 (ft), 19 (pt); Activities coordinators 2 (ft); Dietitians 1 (ft).
Facilities Dining room; Physical therapy room; Activities room; Chapel; Crafts room; Laundry room; Barber/Beauty shop; Library.
Activities Arts and Crafts; Cards; Games; Prayer groups; Movies; Shopping trips.
Description Home has a staff and physical plant providing care for the physical, emotional, social, and religious needs of those people requiring long-term care.

Friendship Villa
1242 S Strevell, Rt 2, Box 3001, Miles City, MT, 59301 (406) 232-2687
Admin Paul J Piper. *Medical Dir/Dir of Nursing* Dr Campodonico.
Licensure Skilled Care; Intermediate Care.
Beds SNF 40; ICF 27. *Certified* Medicaid; Medicare.
Staff RNs 2 (ft), 6 (pt); LPNs 2 (pt); Orderlies 1 (pt); Nurses aides 15 (ft), 7 (pt); Activities coordinators 1 (ft), 1 (pt).
Facilities Dining room; Activities room; Chapel; Laundry room; Barber/Beauty shop.
Activities Arts and Crafts; Cards; Games; Reading groups; Prayer groups; Movies; Shopping trips; Dances/Social or cultural gatherings.
Description Facility provides excellent care for both long-term and rehabilitation patients.

MISSOULA

Community Nursing and Rehabilitation Facility
2823 Fort Missoula Rd, Missoula, MT, 59801 (406) 728-9162
Admin Danna Miller. *Medical Dir/Dir of Nursing* D W Babcock MD.
Licensure Skilled Care; Intermediate Care.
Beds SNF 140; ICF 53. *Certified* Medicaid; Medicare.
Staff RNs 7 (ft), 5 (pt); LPNs 6 (ft), 10 (pt); Nurses aides 38 (ft), 16 (pt); Physical therapists 2 (ft); Recreational therapists 2 (ft); Occupational therapists 2 (ft), 1 (pt); Speech therapists 1 (ft); Activities coordinators 1 (ft); Dietitians 1 (pt).
Facilities Dining room; Physical therapy room; Activities room; Crafts room; Laundry room; Barber/Beauty shop; Library.
Activities Arts and Crafts; Cards; Games; Reading groups; Prayer groups; Movies; Shopping trips; Dances/Social or cultural gatherings.

Hillside Manor
4720 23rd St, Missoula, MT, 59801 (406) 251-5100
Admin Mary Jo Strope. *Medical Dir/Dir of Nursing* D W Babcock.
Licensure Skilled Care; Intermediate Care.
Beds 103. *Certified* Medicaid; Medicare.
Staff RNs 5 (ft), 4 (pt); LPNs 4 (ft), 6 (pt); Orderlies 1 (ft), 4 (pt); Nurses aides 18 (ft), 13 (pt); Activities coordinators 1 (ft); Dietitians 1 (pt).
Facilities Dining room; Physical therapy room; Activities room; Laundry room; Barber/Beauty shop.
Activities Arts and Crafts; Cards; Games; Reading groups; Prayer groups; Movies; Shopping trips; Dances/Social or cultural gatherings.

Royal Manor Inc*
3018 Rattlesnake Dr, Missoula, MT, 59801 (406) 549-0988
Admin Ida Gregory.
Licensure Skilled Care; Personal Care.
Beds SNF 31; Personal Care 20. *Certified* Medicaid; Medicare.

Wayside Nursing Care Facility
2222 Rattlesnake, Missoula, MT, 59802 (406) 549-6158
Admin Jo Waldbillig. *Medical Dir/Dir of*

Nursing Dr D Hubbard.
Licensure Skilled Care; Intermediate Care.
Beds SNF 40; ICF 4. *Certified* Medicaid; Medicare.
Admissions Requirements Physician's request.
Staff Physicians 1 (pt); RNs 2 (pt); LPNs 5 (ft); Orderlies 1 (ft); Nurses aides 13 (ft), 6 (pt); Physical therapists 1 (pt); Activities coordinators 1 (ft); Dietitians 1 (pt); Dentists 1 (pt).
Facilities Dining room; Activities room; Crafts room; Laundry room; Barber/Beauty shop.
Activities Arts and Crafts; Cards; Games; Reading groups; Prayer groups; Movies; Shopping trips; Dances/Social or cultural gatherings.
Description Small facility makes it possible to offer more personal care to each resident; location offers residents a country setting complete with pine trees, wild flowers, chipmunks, squirrels, and an occasional deer or elk passing by on their way to Rattlesnake Creek.

PHILIPSBURG

Granite County Memorial Nursing Home
Box 729, Philipsburg, MT, 59858 (406) 859-3271
Admin Richard T Duke III. *Medical Dir/Dir of Nursing* Steve Egli RN.
Licensure Skilled Care. *Beds* 13. *Certified* Medicaid; Medicare.
Activities Arts and Crafts; Cards; Games; Reading groups; Prayer groups; Movies.

PLAINS

Clark Fort Valley Nursing Home
Kruger Rd, PO Box 768, Plains, MT, 59859 (406) 826-3601
Admin Mike Billing. *Medical Dir/Dir of Nursing* Jacob Lulack MD.
Licensure Skilled Care; Intermediate Care.
Beds 24. *Certified* Medicaid; Medicare.
Staff Physicians 4 (ft); RNs 3 (ft), 4 (pt); LPNs 3 (ft); Nurses aides 7 (ft), 8 (pt); Physical therapists 1 (pt); Activities coordinators 1 (ft); Dietitians 1 (ft); Dentists 1 (pt).
Facilities Dining room; Physical therapy room; Activities room; Crafts room; Laundry room; Barber/Beauty shop.
Activities Arts and Crafts; Games; Reading groups; Prayer groups; Movies; Shopping trips; Dances/Social or cultural gatherings.

PLENTYWOOD

Sheridan Memorial Nursing Home
440 W Laurel Ave, Plentywood, MT, 59254 (406) 765-1423
Admin Mark Rinehardt. *Medical Dir/Dir of Nursing* Dr Kirk Stoner.
Licensure Skilled Care; Intermediate Care.
Beds SNF 34; ICF 31. *Certified* Medicaid; Medicare.
Admissions Requirements Medical examination.
Staff Physicians 2 (ft); RNs 6 (pt); LPNs 2 (ft), 3 (pt); Nurses aides 8 (ft), 28 (pt); Occupational therapists 1 (pt); Activities coordinators 1 (ft); Dietitians 1 (pt); Dentists 1 (pt).
Facilities Dining room; Physical therapy room; Activities room; Crafts room; Laundry room;

Barber/Beauty shop.
Activities Arts and Crafts; Games; Reading groups; Prayer groups; Movies; Dances/Social or cultural gatherings.
Description Facility is rectangular with an entirely enclosed courtyard with wooden deck and cement patio, shrubs and trees, a small plot of wheat, a small vegetable garden; many flowers are enjoyed during the summer.

POLSON

Saint Joseph Convalescent Center*
PO Box 1530, 1st and 14th Ave, Polson, MT, 59860 (406) 883-4378
Admin William McDonald.
Licensure Skilled Care; Intermediate Care.
Beds SNF 40; ICF 72. *Certified* Medicaid; Medicare.

POPLAR

Poplar Community Nursing Home
Poplar, MT, 59255 (406) 768-3452
Admin Jay Portengar. *Medical Dir/Dir of Nursing* Betty Moilanen.
Licensure Skilled Care. *Beds* 22. *Certified* Medicaid; Medicare.
Staff Physicians 4 (ft), 1 (pt); RNs 8 (ft); LPNs 12 (ft); Nurses aides 29 (ft); Activities coordinators 1 (ft).
Facilities Dining room; Activities room; Chapel; Crafts room; Laundry room.
Activities Arts and Crafts; Cards; Games; Reading groups; Prayer groups; Movies.

RED LODGE

Carbon County Health Care Center
1 S Oaks, PO Box 430, Red Lodge, MT, 59068 (406) 446-2525
Admin Mary Williams. *Medical Dir/Dir of Nursing* Dr James Kane.
Licensure Skilled Care; Intermediate Care.
Beds SNF 36; ICF 44. *Certified* Medicaid; Medicare.
Ownership Public.
Admissions Requirements Medical examination; Physician's request.
Staff Physicians 4 (ft); RNs 2 (ft), 1 (pt); LPNs 7 (ft), 1 (pt); Nurses aides 20 (ft), 2 (pt); Physical therapists 1 (ft); Recreational therapists 1 (ft); Activities coordinators 1 (ft); Dietitians 1 (pt).
Facilities Dining room; Physical therapy room; Activities room; Crafts room; Laundry room; Barber/Beauty shop; Library.
Activities Arts and Crafts; Cards; Games; Prayer groups; Movies; Shopping trips.
Description Plans are in the works for a gazebo in the fenced area and a complete redecoration is in progress.

Carbon County Memorial Nursing Home*
PO Box 580, 600 W 21st St, Red Lodge, MT, 59068 (406) 446-2345
Admin Frank J Hilzinger.
Licensure Skilled Care. *Beds* 24. *Certified* Medicaid; Medicare.

RONAN

Happy Acres Rest Home
931 Main St SW, Ronan, MT, 59864 (406) 676-3934
Admin Judith A Frame. *Medical Dir/Dir of Nursing* Dr Jay L Ballhagen.
Licensure Intermediate Care. *Beds* 10. *Certified* Medicaid.
Admissions Requirements Minimum age 18; Females only; Medical examination.
Staff RNs 1 (pt); LPNs 2 (pt); Nurses aides 2 (pt); Reality therapists 1 (pt); Recreational therapists 1 (pt).
Facilities Dining room; Activities room; Laundry room; Library.
Activities Arts and Crafts; Cards; Games; Reading groups; Prayer groups; Shopping trips; Dances/Social or cultural gatherings; Community activities.
Description Family living is provided with habilitation training/activities, individualized to meet the needs of D/D clients. This is located on urban ranch setting one-quarter mile from town.

Saint Luke Community Nursing Home*
901 26th St, Ronan, MT, 59864 (406) 676-3934
Admin James Oliverson.
Licensure Skilled Care; Intermediate Care.
Beds SNF 20; ICF 23. *Certified* Medicaid; Medicare.

West Side Rest Home
829 Main St SW, Box 787, Ronan, MT, 59864 (406) 676-5510
Admin Faye Abrahamson. *Medical Dir/Dir of Nursing* Dr S T McDonald.
Licensure Intermediate Care. *Beds* 23. *Certified* Medicaid.
Admissions Requirements Medical examination.
Staff RNs 1 (ft); LPNs 3 (pt); Nurses aides 6 (pt); Activities coordinators 1 (ft); Dietitians 1 (pt).
Facilities Dining room; Activities room; Crafts room; Laundry room.
Activities Arts and Crafts; Cards; Games; Reading groups; Prayer groups; Movies.
Description A small, fully carpeted facility offering close family-style living.

ROUNDUP

Roundup Memorial Nursing Home*
1202 3rd St W, Roundup, MT, 59072 (406) 323-2302
Admin Fern Mikkelson.
Licensure Skilled Care. *Beds* 16. *Certified* Medicaid; Medicare.

SCOBEY

Daniels Memorial Nursing Home
PO Box 400, Scobey, MT, 59263 (406) 487-2296
Admin David Hubbard. *Medical Dir/Dir of Nursing* Merle Fitz MD.
Licensure Skilled Care; Intermediate Care.
Beds SNF 34; ICF 21. *Certified* Medicaid; Medicare.

Staff Physicians 1 (pt); RNs 3 (pt); LPNs 2 (ft), 2 (pt); Nurses aides 11 (ft), 14 (pt); Activities coordinators 1 (ft); Dietitians 1 (ft); Dentists 1 (pt).
Facilities Dining room; Activities room; Chapel; Crafts room; Laundry room; Barber/Beauty shop; Library.
Activities Arts and Crafts; Cards; Games; Reading groups; Prayer groups; Movies; Shopping trips; Dances/Social or cultural gatherings.

SHELBY

Toole County Nursing Home*
PO Box W, 640 Park Dr, Shelby, MT, 59474 (406) 434-5538
Admin James Holcomb.
Licensure Skilled Care. *Beds* 43. *Certified* Medicaid; Medicare.

SHERIDAN

Madison County Nursing Home
Sheridan, MT, 59749 (406) 842-5600
Admin James Mantz. *Medical Dir/Dir of Nursing* H D Rossiter MD.
Licensure Intermediate Care. *Beds* 39. *Certified* Medicaid.
Admissions Requirements Medical examination.
Staff Physicians 3 (pt); RNs 2 (ft), 2 (pt); LPNs 4 (pt); Nurses aides 11 (ft), 10 (pt); Recreational therapists 1 (pt); Activities coordinators 1 (ft), 1 (pt); Dietitians 1 (pt); Dentists 1 (pt).
Facilities Dining room; Activities room; Crafts room; Laundry room; Barber/Beauty shop.
Activities Arts and Crafts; Cards; Games; Prayer groups; Movies; Shopping trips; Dances/Social or cultural gatherings.

SIDNEY

Richland Homes Inc
Girard Rt, Box 5001, Sidney, MT, 59270 (406) 482-2120
Admin Vern Reed. *Medical Dir/Dir of Nursing* Dr Ashcroft.
Licensure Skilled Care; Intermediate Care.
Beds SNF 10; ICF 75. *Certified* Medicaid.
Admissions Requirements Medical examination; Physician's request.
Staff Physicians 9 (ft); RNs 4 (ft), 3 (pt); LPNs 2 (ft), 2 (pt); Nurses aides 20 (ft), 8 (pt); Activities coordinators 1 (ft); Dietitians 1 (ft); Podiatrists 1 (ft).
Facilities Dining room; Chapel; Laundry room; Barber/Beauty shop.
Activities Arts and Crafts; Cards; Games; Reading groups; Prayer groups; Movies; Shopping trips; Dances/Social or cultural gatherings.
Description Emphasis is placed on caring for the whole person with social, physical, and spiritual needs met. This is accomplished by actively involving residents and their families in the treatment program. Activities department offers a wide range of programs that stress community involvement in day-to-day life of the nursing home.

STEVENSVILLE

North Valley Nursing Home
63 Main, Stevensville, MT, 59870 (406) 777-5411
Admin Nancy Summers. *Medical Dir/Dir of Nursing* W R Spencer MD.
Licensure Skilled Care; Intermediate Care.
Beds SNF 37; ICF 20. *Certified* Medicaid.
Staff Physicians 2 (pt); RNs 1 (ft), 2 (pt); LPNs 4 (ft), 2 (pt); Nurses aides 15 (ft), 7 (pt); Activities coordinators 1 (ft).
Facilities Dining room; Activities room; Crafts room; Laundry room; Barber/Beauty shop.
Activities Arts and Crafts; Cards; Games; Reading groups; Prayer groups; Movies; Shopping trips; Dances/Social or cultural gatherings.

SUPERIOR

Mineral County Nursing Home
Brooklyn and Roosevelt, PO Box 66, Superior, MT, 59872 (406) 822-4841
Admin Robert E Smith. *Medical Dir/Dir of Nursing* James P Hoyne MD.
Licensure Skilled Care. *Beds* 20. *Certified* Medicaid; Medicare.
Admissions Requirements Medical examination; Physician's request.
Staff Physicians 3 (pt); RNs 7 (pt); LPNs 5 (pt); Orderlies 2 (pt); Nurses aides 9 (pt); Physical therapists 1 (pt); Recreational therapists 1 (pt); Activities coordinators 1 (pt); Dietitians 1 (pt); Dentists 1 (pt).
Facilities Dining room; Physical therapy room; Activities room; Crafts room; Laundry room; Barber/Beauty shop.
Activities Arts and Crafts; Cards; Games; Reading groups; Prayer groups; Movies; Shopping trips; Dances/Social or cultural gatherings.
Description Facility is located in the beautiful mountains of western Montana on Interstate 90 just 57 miles from Missoula.

TERRY

Prairie Community Nursing Home
PO Box 156, Terry, MT, 59349 (406) 637-5511
Admin Todd Hansen. *Medical Dir/Dir of Nursing* L T Krogstad MD.
Licensure Skilled Care. *Beds* 14. *Certified* Medicaid; Medicare.
Staff RNs 4 (ft), 4 (pt); Nurses aides 4 (ft), 7 (pt); Physical therapists 1 (pt); Reality therapists 1 (pt); Activities coordinators 1 (pt); Activities coordinators 1 (ft).
Facilities Dining room; Activities room; Chapel.
Activities Arts and Crafts; Games; Reading groups; Prayer groups.

TOWNSEND

Broadwater County Rest Home*
Townsend, MT, 59644 (406) 266-3711
Admin Chester O Solberg.
Licensure Intermediate Care. *Beds* 18. *Certified* Medicaid.

WARM SPRINGS

Warm Springs State Hospital*
Bldg 219, Warm Springs, MT, 59756 (406) 693-2221
Admin Richard Moore.
Licensure Skilled Care; Intermediate Care.
Beds SNF 8; ICF 52. *Certified* Medicaid; Medicare.

WHITE SULPHUR SPRINGS

Mountainview Memorial Nursing Home*
Box Q, White Sulphur Springs, MT, 59645 (406) 547-3321
Admin Joy Short.
Licensure Skilled Care; Intermediate Care.
Beds SNF 16; ICF 15. *Certified* Medicaid; Medicare.

WHITEFISH

Colonial Manor Nursing Home*
PO Box 1359, E 7th St, Whitefish, MT, 59937 (406) 862-3557
Admin Betty Elder.
Licensure Intermediate Care. *Beds* 60. *Certified* Medicaid.

North Valley Hospital and Extended Care Center*
PO Box 68, Hwy 93 S, Whitefish, MT, 59937 (406) 862-2501
Admin Dale Jessup.
Licensure Skilled Care; Intermediate Care.
Beds SNF 50; ICF 6. *Certified* Medicaid; Medicare.

WIBAUX

Wibaux County Nursing Home
601 S Wibaux St, Wibaux, MT, 59353 (406) 795-2429
Admin Verlin D Buechler. *Medical Dir/Dir of Nursing* Dr Nancy Rausch.
Licensure Skilled Care. *Beds* 40. *Certified* Medicaid; Medicare.
Admissions Requirements Medical examination; Physician's request.
Staff RNs 2 (ft), 5 (pt); LPNs 1 (ft); Nurses aides 5 (ft), 14 (pt); Activities coordinators 1 (ft).
Facilities Dining room; Activities room; Chapel; Crafts room; Laundry room; Barber/Beauty shop.
Activities Arts and Crafts; Games; Reading groups; Movies; Shopping trips.

WOLF POINT

Faith Lutheran Home
1000 6th Ave N, Wolf Point, MT, 59201 (406) 653-1400
Admin Monica Matson. *Medical Dir/Dir of Nursing* Susan Barsness.
Licensure Intermediate Care. *Beds* ICF 60; Personal Care 21. *Certified* Medicaid.
Admissions Requirements Medical examination; Physician's request.
Staff RNs 2 (ft); LPNs 6 (ft), 2 (pt); Orderlies 2 (ft); Nurses aides 16 (ft), 2 (pt); Physical therapists 1 (pt); Activities coordinators 1 (ft); Dietitians 1 (pt); 12 (ft), 11 (pt).
Affiliation Lutheran

NEBRASKA

AINSWORTH

Bethesda Care Center of Ainsworth
143 N Fullerton St, Ainsworth, NE, 69210
(402) 387-2500
Admin Donice I Woodworth. *Medical Dir/Dir of Nursing* Dr F Shiffermiler.
Licensure Intermediate Care. *Beds* 47. *Certified* Medicaid.
Ownership Nonprofit.
Admissions Requirements Medical examination; Physician's request.
Staff RNs 1 (ft), 1 (pt); LPNs 1 (ft); Nurses aides 12 (ft), 5 (pt); Recreational therapists 1 (ft); Activities coordinators 1 (ft).
Facilities Dining room; Physical therapy room; Activities room; Crafts room; Laundry room; Barber/Beauty shop.
Activities Arts and Crafts; Cards; Games; Reading groups; Prayer groups; Movies; Shopping trips.
Description This is a small facility in a small community with a great deal of interaction with life-long friends visiting frequently. There is the time to give tender loving care to people who grew up just down the street.

ALBION

Wolf Memorial Good Samaritan Center
1222 S 7th St, Albion, NE, 68620 (402) 395-5050
Admin Marie Alessi.
Licensure Intermediate Care. *Beds* 65. *Certified* Medicaid.
Ownership Nonprofit.
Affiliation Lutheran
Facilities Dining room; Physical therapy room; Activities room; Chapel; Crafts room; Laundry room; Barber/Beauty shop.
Activities Arts and Crafts; Cards; Games; Reading groups; Prayer groups; Movies; Shopping trips; Dances/Social or cultural gatherings.

ALLIANCE

Good Samaritan Village
1016 E 6th St, Alliance, NE, 69301 (308) 762-5675
Admin Clarence A Wegenast. *Medical Dir/Dir of Nursing* Eilean Jensen.
Licensure Intermediate Care. *Beds* 108. *Certified* Medicaid.
Ownership Nonprofit.
Admissions Requirements Medical examination.
Staff RNs 2 (ft), 1 (pt); LPNs 6 (ft), 10 (pt); Nurses aides 5 (ft), 26 (pt); Physical therapists 1 (pt); Activities coordinators 2 (ft), 1 (pt).
Affiliation Lutheran
Facilities Dining room; Physical therapy room; Activities room; Chapel; Crafts room; Laundry room; Barber/Beauty shop; Library.
Activities Arts and Crafts; Cards; Games; Reading groups; Prayer groups; Movies; Dances/Social or cultural gatherings.
Description The Good Samaritan Village offers diversified services to the elderly with 4 levels of care: independent living in garden and high-rise apartments with supportive services such as carryout meals, housekeeping and laundry service, and health coordinator; domiciliary level, room and board; residential level, room and board with some nursing; and complete nursing ICF level of care; a Christian organization where in Christ's love everyone is someone.

Saint Joseph Gerontology Center*
416 W 11th St, Alliance, NE, 69301 (308) 762-2525
Admin Sr Miriam Rubel.
Licensure Skilled Care; Intermediate Care. *Beds* 61. *Certified* Medicaid.
Ownership Nonprofit.
Affiliation Roman Catholic

ALMA

Colonial Villa Good Samaritan Center*
719 N Brown, Alma, NE, 68920 (308) 928-2128
Admin Tom Sutton.
Licensure Intermediate Care. *Beds* 61. *Certified* Medicaid.
Ownership Nonprofit.
Affiliation Lutheran

ARAPAHOE

C A Mues Memorial Good Samaritan Center
601 Main St, Arapahoe, NE, 68922 (308) 962-5230
Admin Patrica A Snyder.
Licensure Intermediate Care. *Beds* 57. *Certified* Medicaid.
Ownership Nonprofit.
Admissions Requirements Medical examination; Physician's request.
Staff RNs 1 (pt); LPNs 4 (ft); Orderlies 1 (ft); Nurses aides 20 (ft), 5 (pt); Physical therapists 1 (ft), 1 (pt); Activities coordinators 1 (ft); Dietitians 1 (pt).
Affiliation Lutheran
Facilities Dining room; Physical therapy room; Activities room; Chapel; Crafts room; Laundry room; Barber/Beauty shop.
Activities Arts and Crafts; Cards; Games; Reading groups; Prayer groups; Movies; Shopping trips; Dances/Social or cultural gatherings.
Description Facility has whirlpool available, a full-time physical rehabilitation aide, and is one block from downtown.

ASHLAND

Bethesda Care Center of Ashland
1700 Furnas St, Ashland, NE, 68003 (402) 944-7031
Admin Shirley L Hemke.
Licensure Intermediate Care. *Beds* 91. *Certified* Medicaid.
Ownership Nonprofit.
Admissions Requirements Medical examination; Physician's request.
Staff RNs 1 (ft); LPNs 4 (ft); Nurses aides 18 (ft), 11 (pt); Physical therapists 1 (ft), 1 (pt); Activities coordinators 1 (ft), 1 (pt); Dietitians 1 (pt); Podiatrists 1 (pt).
Facilities Dining room; Activities room; Chapel; Laundry room; Barber/Beauty shop; Large dayroom.
Activities Arts and Crafts; Games; Prayer groups; Movies; Shopping trips; Dances/Social or cultural gatherings.
Description Facility features cable and color television in lounge with video cassette recorder and movies; 2 large dining rooms and 2 lounges; a large covered patio; a van equipped with wheelchair lift; weekly church services; weekly bible study; a chaplain one full day a week; and a consulting physical therapist weekly.

ATKINSON

Atkinson Good Samaritan Center
PO Box 699, Atkinson, NE, 68713 (402) 925-2875

Admin Phyllis Langan.
Licensure Intermediate Care. *Beds* 62. *Certified* Medicaid.
Ownership Nonprofit.
Admissions Requirements Medical examination.
Staff RNs 1 (ft), 2 (pt); LPNs 1 (ft), 2 (pt); Nurses aides 15 (ft), 10 (pt); Activities coordinators 1 (ft); Dietitians 1 (pt).
Facilities Dining room; Activities room; Chapel; Laundry room.
Activities Arts and Crafts; Cards; Games; Reading groups; Prayer groups; Movies; Shopping trips; Dances/Social or cultural gatherings.

AUBURN

Nemaha County Good Samaritan Center*
Rt 1, Box 4, Auburn, NE, 68305 (402) 274-3109
Admin Daniel H Guenther.
Licensure Intermediate Care. *Beds* 113. *Certified* Medicaid.
Ownership Nonprofit.
Affiliation Lutheran

AURORA

Hamilton Manor*
1515 5th St, Aurora, NE, 68818 (402) 694-2128
Admin Barry D Robertshaw.
Licensure Intermediate Care. *Beds* 109. *Certified* Medicaid.
Ownership Public.

Larson's Pioneer Homes Inc*
610 13th St, Aurora, NE, 68818 (402) 694-6905
Admin Carolyn G Palmer.
Licensure Intermediate Care. *Beds* 45.
Certified Medicaid.
Ownership Proprietary.

AXTELL

Bethpage at Axtell
Axtell, NE, 68924 (308) 743-2401
Admin Randy P May.
Licensure Intermediate Care for Mentally Retarded. *Beds* 187. *Certified* Medicaid.
Ownership Nonprofit.
Staff Physicians; RNs; LPNs; Nurses aides; Physical therapists; Recreational therapists; Occupational therapists; Speech therapists; Activities coordinators; Dietitians; Dentists; Ophthalmologists; Podiatrists; Audiologists.
Affiliation Lutheran
Facilities Dining room; Physical therapy room; Activities room; Chapel; Crafts room; Laundry room; Barber/Beauty shop; Library; Classrooms; Swimming pool.
Activities Arts and Crafts; Cards; Games; Reading groups; Prayer groups; Movies; Shopping trips; Dances/Social or cultural gatherings; Training.
Description Facility provides individuals with mental retardation and developmental disabilities habilitative services and care; accredited through ACMRAH.

BASSETT

Bethesda Care Center of Bassett
Fort St, Bassett, NE, 68714 (402) 684-3388
Admin Elaine Thornton.
Licensure Intermediate Care. *Beds* 30. *Certified* Medicaid.
Ownership Nonprofit.
Admissions Requirements Medical examination.
Staff RNs 2 (ft), 1 (pt); LPNs 1 (ft); Activities coordinators 1 (ft).
Facilities Dining room; Activities room; Laundry room; Barber/Beauty shop.
Activities Arts and Crafts; Cards; Games; Reading groups; Prayer groups; Movies; Shopping trips; Dances/Social or cultural gatherings; Weekly van rides.
Description This is a small facility with a close, family atmosphere.

BAYARD

Chimney Rock Villa*
106 E 13th St, Bayard, NE, 69334 (308) 586-1142
Admin Alexander Beninger.
Licensure Intermediate Care. *Beds* 47. *Certified* Medicaid.
Ownership Public.

BEATRICE

Beatrice Manor Care Center
1800 Irving, Beatrice, NE, 68310 (402) 223-2311
Admin Allen Siebert.
Licensure Intermediate Care. *Beds* 62. *Certified* Medicaid.
Ownership Proprietary.
Admissions Requirements Medical examination; Physician's request.
Staff LPNs 5 (ft); Nurses aides 15 (ft), 10 (pt); Activities coordinators 1 (ft).
Facilities Dining room; Activities room; Laundry room; Barber/Beauty shop.
Activities Arts and Crafts; Cards; Games; Reading groups; Prayer groups; Movies; Shopping trips; Dances/Social or cultural gatherings.
Description Staff uses the team concept and everyone works together to provide the quality of care for which this facility has become known. We feel it is very important to keep the residents involved in the community and the community involved in facility.

Good Samaritan Home and Center*
1306 S 9th St, Beatrice, NE, 68310 (402) 223-3304
Admin William S Kubat Jr.
Licensure Intermediate Care. *Beds* 130. *Certified* Medicaid.
Ownership Nonprofit.
Affiliation Lutheran

Martin Luther Home
804 S 12th St, Beatrice, NE, 68310 (402) 223-4066
Admin Marjorie Sederberg.
Licensure Intermediate Care for Mentally Retarded. *Beds* 146. *Certified* Medicaid.

Ownership Nonprofit.
Admissions Requirements Minimum age 5; Medical examination.
Staff Physicians; RNs 2 (ft); LPNs 4 (ft); Orderlies 43 (ft); Nurses aides 37 (ft); Physical therapists 1 (pt); Recreational therapists 4 (ft); Occupational therapists; Speech therapists 1 (ft); Activities coordinators 1 (ft); Dietitians 1 (ft); Dentists; Ophthalmologists; Podiatrists; Audiologists.
Affiliation Lutheran
Facilities Dining room; Physical therapy room; Activities room; Chapel; Crafts room; Laundry room; Barber/Beauty shop; Library.
Activities Arts and Crafts; Cards; Games; Reading groups; Prayer groups; Movies; Shopping trips; Dances/Social or cultural gatherings.
Description Residential services are structured to provide patterns of experience which approximate social expectations and increase independent living skills. Classrooms, dormitories, and work experiences are used by interdisciplinary teams to meet goals designed to allow students to reach their functional capacity. An indoor pool and gymnasium provide on-campus recreational opportunities.

BEAVER CITY

Beaver City Manor*
905 Floyd St, Beaver City, NE, 68926 (308) 268-5111
Admin Thomas D Hardin.
Licensure Intermediate Care. *Beds* 52. *Certified* Medicaid.
Ownership Public.

BEEMER

Colonial Haven
RR 1, Beemer, NE, 68716 (402) 528-3268
Admin Thomas J Schulte.
Licensure Intermediate Care. *Beds* 55. *Certified* Medicaid.
Ownership Public.
Admissions Requirements Medical examination; Physician's request.
Staff Physicians 10 (pt); RNs 1 (pt); LPNs 1 (ft), 2 (pt); Orderlies 1 (pt); Nurses aides 2 (ft), 27 (pt); Physical therapists 2 (pt); Speech therapists 1 (pt); Activities coordinators 1 (ft), 1 (pt); Dietitians 1 (pt); Dentists 2 (pt); Ophthalmologists 2 (pt); Podiatrists 2 (pt); Audiologists 1 (pt).
Facilities Dining room; Physical therapy room; Activities room; Chapel; Crafts room; Laundry room; Barber/Beauty shop; Library.
Activities Arts and Crafts; Cards; Games; Reading groups; Prayer groups; Movies; Shopping trips; Dances/Social or cultural gatherings; Gardening.
Description Facility features whirlpool baths (2) at no extra charge; each lady gets hair done once a week, no charge.

BELLEVUE

Hillcrest Care Center Inc*
1702 N Hillcrest Dr, Bellevue, NE, 68005 (402) 291-8500
Admin Martha L Tiller.

Licensure Intermediate Care. *Beds* 116. *Certified* Medicaid.
Ownership Proprietary.

BENKELMAN

Sarah Ann Hester Memorial Home
350 East St SW, Benkelman, NE, 69021 (308) 423-2179
Admin Marvin L Zimbelman.
Licensure Intermediate Care. *Beds* 58. *Certified* Medicaid.
Ownership Nonprofit.
Admissions Requirements Medical examination; Physician's request.
Staff RNs 2 (ft); LPNs 3 (ft); Orderlies 1 (ft); Nurses aides 22 (ft); Activities coordinators 1 (ft).
Facilities Dining room; Activities room; Chapel; Crafts room; Laundry room; Barber/Beauty shop.
Activities Arts and Crafts; Cards; Games; Reading groups; Movies.

BERTRAND

Bertrand Nursing Home
100 Minor Ave, Bertrand, NE, 68927 (308) 472-3341
Admin Ray Hanson. *Medical Dir/Dir of Nursing* Sylvia Sattler.
Licensure Intermediate Care. *Beds* 47. *Certified* Medicaid.
Ownership Public.
Admissions Requirements Medical examination; Physician's request.
Facilities Dining room; Activities room; Chapel; Crafts room; Laundry room; Barber/Beauty shop; Library.
Activities Arts and Crafts; Cards; Games; Reading groups; Prayer groups; Movies.
Description We have an art teacher in our activity program. Direct lines to all community churches, so as to have live services; bus trips to museums, lakes, and any other events that are nearby.

BLAIR

Crowell Memorial Home*
245 S 22nd St, Blair, NE, 68008 (402) 426-2177
Admin Morland Adell.
Licensure Intermediate Care. *Beds* 127. *Certified* Medicaid.
Ownership Nonprofit.

Good Shepherd Lutheran Old People's Home
2242 Wright St, Blair, NE, 68008 (402) 426-3307
Admin Harriet Olson.
Licensure Intermediate Care. *Beds* 68. *Certified* Medicaid.
Ownership Nonprofit.
Admissions Requirements Minimum age 64; Physician's request.
Staff RNs 3 (ft), 2 (pt); LPNs 5 (ft); Nurses aides 15 (ft), 13 (pt); Physical therapists 1 (pt); Recreational therapists 1 (pt); Occupational therapists 1 (pt); Speech therapists 1 (pt); Activities coordinators 1 (ft); Dietitians 1 (pt); Dentists 1 (pt).

Affiliation Lutheran
Facilities Dining room; Activities room; Chapel; Crafts room; Laundry room; Barber/Beauty shop; Library.
Activities Arts and Crafts; Cards; Games; Reading groups; Prayer groups; Movies; Shopping trips; Dances/Social or cultural gatherings.

BLOOMFIELD

Bloomfield Good Samaritan Center
PO Box 307, Bloomfield, NE, 68718 (402) 373-4506
Admin Sue Walter.
Licensure Intermediate Care. *Beds* 80. *Certified* Medicaid.
Ownership Nonprofit.
Admissions Requirements Medical examination.
Affiliation Lutheran
Facilities Dining room; Physical therapy room; Activities room; Chapel; Crafts room; Laundry room; Barber/Beauty shop.
Activities Arts and Crafts; Cards; Games; Reading groups; Prayer groups; Movies; Shopping trips; Dances/Social or cultural gatherings; Cable TV.

BLUE HILL

Bethesda Care Center of Blue Hill
Box 156, Blue Hill, NE, 68930 (402) 756-2080
Admin Beatrice Reece. *Medical Dir/Dir of Nursing* Frank Kamm MD.
Licensure Intermediate Care. *Beds* 67. *Certified* Medicaid.
Ownership Nonprofit.
Admissions Requirements Medical examination.
Staff Physicians 1 (pt); RNs 1 (ft); LPNs 1 (ft); Nurses aides 2 (ft), 6 (pt); Recreational therapists 2 (ft); Activities coordinators 1 (ft); Dietitians 1 (ft).
Facilities Dining room; Activities room; Chapel; Crafts room; Laundry room; Barber/Beauty shop.
Activities Arts and Crafts; Cards; Games; Reading groups; Prayer groups; Movies.
Description Monthly, varied, planned activities are part of residence.

BRIDGEPORT

Heritage of Bridgeport
5th and N Sts, Bridgeport, NE, 69336 (308) 262-0725
Admin Kathy Webster. *Medical Dir/Dir of Nursing* Evelyn Rose RN.
Licensure Intermediate Care. *Beds* 61. *Certified* Medicaid.
Ownership Proprietary.
Admissions Requirements Medical examination.
Staff RNs 1 (ft); LPNs 3 (ft), 1 (pt); Nurses aides 11 (ft), 6 (pt); Recreational therapists 1 (ft); Activities coordinators 1 (ft).
Facilities Dining room; Activities room; Chapel; Crafts room; Laundry room; Barber/Beauty shop; Library.
Activities Arts and Crafts; Cards; Games; Reading groups; Prayer groups; Movies; Shop-

ping trips; Dances/Social or cultural gatherings.
Description During each year a rock and roll jamboree is held for the heart fund; activities include art exhibit, ice cream social, family picnic, holiday and birthday parties, dress-up days.

BROKEN BOW

Broken Bow Homes Inc*
E Hwy 2, Broken Bow, NE, 68822 (308) 872-6421
Admin Clarine Dickinson.
Licensure Intermediate Care. *Beds* 90. *Certified* Medicaid.
Ownership Proprietary.

BUTTE

Butte Nursing Home
Box 49, Butte, NE, 68722 (402) 775-2355
Admin Myron Armfield.
Licensure Intermediate Care. *Beds* 62. *Certified* Medicaid.
Ownership Public.
Admissions Requirements Medical examination.
Staff Physicians 2 (pt); RNs 1 (ft), 1 (pt); LPNs 5 (pt); Nurses aides 10 (ft), 15 (pt); Physical therapists 1 (pt); Activities coordinators 1 (ft); Dietitians 1 (ft).

CALLAWAY

Callaway Good Samaritan Home
PO Box 398, Callaway, NE, 68825 (308) 836-2267
Admin Laura Aanenson.
Licensure Intermediate Care. *Beds* 44. *Certified* Medicaid.
Ownership Nonprofit.
Staff RNs 1 (pt); LPNs 2 (ft); Orderlies 2 (pt); Nurses aides 4 (pt); Activities coordinators 1 (ft).
Affiliation Lutheran
Facilities Dining room; Activities room; Chapel; Crafts room; Laundry room; Barber/Beauty shop.
Activities Arts and Crafts; Cards; Games; Reading groups; Prayer groups; Movies; Shopping trips; Dances/Social or cultural gatherings.
Description Home is a Christian organization that believes in serving the spiritual and social needs of residents as well as providing quality nursing care; attractive, well planned building with a new activity room, residents' kitchen, and chapel.

CAMPBELL

Grandview Manor Nursing Home
Broad St and Hwy 4, Campbell, NE, 68932 (402) 756-8701
Admin Shirley L'Heureux.
Licensure Intermediate Care. *Beds* 49. *Certified* Medicaid.
Ownership Nonprofit.
Facilities Dining room; Activities room; Chap-

el; Laundry room; Barber/Beauty shop.
Activities Arts and Crafts; Cards; Games; Reading groups; Prayer groups; Movies.

CENTRAL CITY

Bethesda Care Center of Central City
S 17th Ave, Central City, NE, 68826 (308) 946-3088
Admin Richard C Bauer.
Licensure Intermediate Care. *Beds* 72. *Certified* Medicaid.
Ownership Nonprofit.
Staff RNs 1 (ft), 2 (pt); LPNs 1 (ft), 1 (pt); Nurses aides 25 (ft), 15 (pt); Activities coordinators 1 (ft); Dietitians 4 (ft), 4 (pt).
Facilities Dining room; Activities room; Chapel; Laundry room; Barber/Beauty shop.
Activities Cards; Games; Reading groups; Prayer groups; Movies; Shopping trips; Dances/Social or cultural gatherings.

CHADRON

Crest View Manor
420 Gordon Ave, Chadron, NE, 69337 (308) 432-3355
Admin John Bray. *Medical Dir/Dir of Nursing* R H Rasmussen MD.
Licensure Skilled Care; Intermediate Care. *Beds* 70. *Certified* Medicaid.
Ownership Proprietary.
Staff RNs 2 (ft), 1 (pt); LPNs 6 (ft), 2 (pt); Nurses aides 25 (ft), 5 (pt); Activities coordinators 1 (ft); Dietitians 1 (pt).
Facilities Dining room; Activities room; Chapel; Crafts room; Laundry room; Barber/Beauty shop.
Activities Arts and Crafts; Cards; Games; Reading groups; Prayer groups; Movies; Dances/Social or cultural gatherings.

CHAPPELL

Miller Memorial Nursing Home
589 Vincent Ave, Chappell, NE, 69129 (308) 874-2292
Admin Pat Livergood.
Licensure Intermediate Care. *Beds* 24. *Certified* Medicaid.
Ownership Public.
Admissions Requirements Medical examination; Physician's request.
Staff RNs 1 (pt); LPNs 1 (ft), 3 (pt); Nurses aides 3 (ft), 12 (pt); Physical therapists 1 (pt); Recreational therapists 1 (pt); Occupational therapists 1 (pt); Activities coordinators 2 (pt); Dietitians 1 (pt).
Facilities Dining room; Activities room; Crafts room; Laundry room; Barber/Beauty shop.
Activities Arts and Crafts; Games; Reading groups; Prayer groups; Movies; Dances/Social or cultural gatherings.
Description This attractive facility is located in the western plains of Nebraska with a small, pleasant, caring community and staff who provide an atmosphere of love and security along with a variety of programs for residents. Everybody is somebody here.

CLARKSON

Colonial Manor of Clarkson
W 3rd Sunrise Dr, Clarkson, NE, 68629 (402) 892-3494
Admin William M Harris. *Medical Dir/Dir of Nursing* John O'Neal MD.
Licensure Intermediate Care. *Beds* 60. *Certified* Medicaid.
Ownership Proprietary.
Staff Physicians 1 (pt); RNs 1 (ft), 2 (pt); LPNs 2 (pt); Nurses aides 5 (ft), 15 (pt); Physical therapists 1 (pt); Occupational therapists 1 (pt); Speech therapists 1 (pt); Activities coordinators 1 (ft), 1 (pt); Dietitians 1 (pt); Dentists 1 (pt); Podiatrists 1 (pt); Audiologists 1 (pt).
Languages Czech
Facilities Dining room; Physical therapy room; Activities room; Chapel; Laundry room; Barber/Beauty shop.
Activities Arts and Crafts; Cards; Games; Reading groups; Prayer groups; Movies; Shopping trips; Dances/Social or cultural gatherings.
Description Eighty percent of residents are Czechoslovakian and their favorite foods are served; fifty percent of the staff speak Czech.

COLERIDGE

Parkview Haven*
PO Box 39, 325 N Madison, Coleridge, NE, 68727 (402) 283-4224
Admin Terry Sharron.
Licensure Intermediate Care. *Beds* 67. *Certified* Medicaid.
Ownership Public.

COLUMBUS

Columbus Manor*
3918 27th St, Columbus, NE, 68601 (402) 564-8014
Admin Carl Haase.
Licensure Skilled Care; Intermediate Care. *Beds* 145. *Certified* Medicaid.
Ownership Proprietary.

Val Mory's Haven*
1112 15th St, Columbus, NE, 68601 (402) 564-3197
Admin Gerald Demuth.
Licensure Intermediate Care. *Beds* 46. *Certified* Medicaid.
Ownership Proprietary.

COZAD

Southview Manor Care Center*
318 W 18th St, Cozad, NE, 69130 (308) 784-3715
Admin Rodney A Evanich.
Licensure Intermediate Care. *Beds* 87. *Certified* Medicaid.
Ownership Proprietary.

CRAWFORD

Ponderosa Villa*
1st and Paddock, Crawford, NE, 69339 (308) 655-1224

Admin Dixie G Moody.
Licensure Intermediate Care. *Beds* 55. *Certified* Medicaid.
Ownership Public.

CREIGHTON

Creighton Care Centre*
Main St at Lundberg Dr, Creighton, NE, 68729 (402) 358-3232
Admin Delberta Peterson.
Licensure Intermediate Care. *Beds* 50. *Certified* Medicaid.
Ownership Proprietary.

CRETE

Crete Manor*
1st and Boswell Sts, Crete, NE, 68333 (402) 826-4325
Admin Doris Prahl.
Licensure Intermediate Care. *Beds* 110. *Certified* Medicaid.
Ownership Proprietary.

CURTIS

Sunset Haven Nursing Home
902 Howard St, Curtis, NE, 69025 (308) 367-8388
Admin Elda Roethemeyer.
Licensure Intermediate Care. *Beds* 49. *Certified* Medicaid.
Ownership Nonprofit.
Admissions Requirements Medical examination.
Staff RNs 1 (pt); LPNs 1 (ft), 4 (pt); Nurses aides 6 (ft), 6 (pt); Activities coordinators 1 (ft); Dietitians 1 (pt).
Facilities Dining room; Activities room; Chapel; Laundry room; Barber/Beauty shop.
Activities Arts and Crafts; Cards; Games; Reading groups.

DAVID CITY

Heritage of David City
260 S 10th, PO Box 321, David City, NE, 68632 (402) 367-3144
Admin Mary L High. *Medical Dir/Dir of Nursing* Gerald Luckey MD.
Licensure Skilled Care; Intermediate Care. *Beds* SNF 30; ICF 60. *Certified* Medicaid.
Ownership Proprietary.
Admissions Requirements Medical examination; Physician's request.
Facilities Dining room; Physical therapy room; Activities room; Laundry room; Barber/Beauty shop.
Activities Arts and Crafts; Cards; Games; Reading groups; Prayer groups; Shopping trips; Dances/Social or cultural gatherings.

Saint Joseph's Villa*
927 7th St, David City, NE, 68632 (402) 367-3045
Admin Sr Esther Marie Miller.
Licensure Intermediate Care. *Beds* 65. *Certi-*

fied Medicaid.
Ownership Nonprofit.
Affiliation Roman Catholic

DESHLER

Parkview Haven*
1203 S 4th St, Deshler, NE, 68340 (402)
365-7812
Admin Richard K Kjar.
Licensure Intermediate Care. *Beds* 52. *Certified* Medicaid.
Ownership Public.

DODGE

Parkview Home Inc*
Park Dr, Dodge, NE, 68633 (402) 693-2212
Admin Dwaine E Lauer.
Licensure Intermediate Care. *Beds* 80. *Certified* Medicaid.
Ownership Proprietary.

EDGAR

Bethesda Care Center of Edgar
Box 1183, Edgar, NE, 68935 (402) 224-5015
Admin David Schlegel. *Medical Dir/Dir of Nursing* Frank Kamm MD.
Licensure Intermediate Care. *Beds* 54. *Certified* Medicaid.
Ownership Nonprofit.
Admissions Requirements Medical examination.
Staff RNs 2 (pt); LPNs 2 (ft); Nurses aides 10 (ft), 10 (pt); Activities coordinators 1 (ft), 1 (pt).
Facilities Dining room; Activities room; Chapel; Crafts room; Laundry room; Barber/Beauty shop.
Activities Arts and Crafts; Cards; Games; Reading groups; Prayer groups; Movies; Shopping trips; Dances/Social or cultural gatherings.
Description Facility is in a small town staffed by natives who take a personal interest in each resident, who are friends, not just patients. Families are encouraged to stay actively involved in their loved ones' lives and show care and concern.

ELKHORN

Golden Years Nursing Home
315 Hopper St, Elkhorn, NE, 68022 (402)
289-2572
Admin Julian Walker.
Licensure Intermediate Care. *Beds* 87. *Certified* Medicaid.
Ownership Proprietary.
Staff RNs 4 (ft), 2 (pt); LPNs 9 (ft), 2 (pt); Orderlies 2 (ft); Nurses aides 18 (ft), 8 (pt); Physical therapists 2 (pt); Occupational therapists 2 (pt); Activities coordinators 2 (ft); Dietitians 1 (pt).
Facilities Dining room; Activities room; Chapel; Laundry room; Barber/Beauty shop.

ELWOOD

Elwood Care Center*
613 Smith St, Elwood, NE, 68937 (308)
785-3302
Admin Donna M Misterek.
Licensure Intermediate Care. *Beds* 51. *Certified* Medicaid.
Ownership Public.

EMERSON

Terrace Hill Manor*
Box 310, Emerson, NE, 68733 (402) 695-2616
Admin Jeannia Bottger.
Licensure Intermediate Care. *Beds* 63. *Certified* Medicaid.
Ownership Proprietary.

EXETER

Bethesda Care Center of Exeter
Exeter, NE, 68351 (402) 266-4501
Admin Sonya L Phillis.
Licensure Intermediate Care. *Beds* 67. *Certified* Medicaid.
Ownership Nonprofit.
Admissions Requirements Medical examination.
Staff RNs 1 (pt); LPNs 2 (ft), 2 (pt); Nurses aides 8 (ft), 16 (pt); Physical therapists 1 (pt); Activities coordinators 1 (ft); Dietitians 1 (pt).
Facilities Dining room; Activities room; Chapel; Laundry room; Barber/Beauty shop; Living room setting with 45 inch TV and VCR; Screened in porch and patio; Van used for resident transportation.
Activities Arts and Crafts; Cards; Games; Prayer groups; Movies; Shopping trips; Dances/Social or cultural gatherings; Bowling; Fishing; Resident council.
Description Our Family Support program and Resident Council are an important part of our programs, which are designed to meet physical, emotional, and spiritual needs; enhance the quality of life; and help residents remain active in the community. The facility includes 11 private rooms, 2 apartments, and 25 double rooms.

FAIRBURY

Heritage of Fairbury
909 17th St, Fairbury, NE, 68352 (402)
729-2289
Admin Michael G Steele.
Licensure Intermediate Care. *Beds* 96. *Certified* Medicaid.
Ownership Proprietary.
Admissions Requirements Minimum age 18; Medical examination; Physician's request.
Staff RNs 1 (ft); LPNs 2 (ft), 4 (pt); Nurses aides 15 (ft), 15 (pt); Activities coordinators 1 (ft), 1 (pt); Dietitians 1 (pt).
Facilities Dining room; Physical therapy room; Activities room; Chapel; Crafts room; Laundry room; Barber/Beauty shop.
Activities Arts and Crafts; Cards; Games; Prayer groups; Movies; Shopping trips; Dances/Social or cultural gatherings.

Description Special activities include mother-daughter tea, father-son barbecue, ice cream social, and a family-resident picnic.

FAIRMONT

Fairview Manor*
Fairmont, NE, 68354 (402) 268-2271
Admin Larry L Eichelberger.
Licensure Intermediate Care. *Beds* 50. *Certified* Medicaid.
Ownership Public.

FALLS CITY

Ketter Manor Inc*
1010 E 21st St, Falls City, NE, 68355 (402)
245-3700
Admin Vern B Ketter.
Licensure Intermediate Care. *Beds* 61. *Certified* Medicaid.
Ownership Proprietary.

Midland Villa
Rt 2, Falls City, NE, 68355 (402) 245-4466
Admin Glen J O'Loughlin. *Medical Dir/Dir of Nursing* Dr David E Borg.
Licensure Skilled Care. *Beds* 78. *Certified* Medicaid; Medicare.
Ownership Proprietary.
Admissions Requirements Medical examination.
Staff Physicians 1 (pt); RNs 5 (ft), 4 (pt); LPNs 1 (ft), 3 (pt); Nurses aides 6 (ft), 13 (pt); Physical therapists 1 (pt); Recreational therapists 1 (ft), 1 (pt); Occupational therapists 1 (pt); Speech therapists 1 (pt); Activities coordinators 1 (ft); Dietitians 1 (pt); Dentists 1 (pt).
Facilities Dining room; Physical therapy room; Activities room; Crafts room; Laundry room; Barber/Beauty shop.
Activities Arts and Crafts; Cards; Games; Prayer groups; Movies; Dances/Social or cultural gatherings.
Description Facility offers total care from custodial to skilled; adapted unit-dose medication is given in a newly remodeled setting.

Northview Care Center
28th and Towle, Falls City, NE, 68355 (402)
245-5252
Admin Betty Ann Harmon. *Medical Dir/Dir of Nursing* R L Burghart MD.
Licensure Intermediate Care. *Beds* 100. *Certified* Medicaid.
Ownership Proprietary.
Staff RNs; LPNs; Orderlies; Nurses aides; Physical therapists; Recreational therapists; Occupational therapists; Speech therapists; Activities coordinators; Dietitians; Dentists; Ophthalmologists; Podiatrists; Audiologists.
Facilities Dining room; Physical therapy room; Activities room; Chapel; Crafts room; Laundry room; Barber/Beauty shop.
Activities Arts and Crafts; Cards; Games; Reading groups; Prayer groups; Movies; Shopping trips; Dances/Social or cultural gatherings.
Description Exceptional therapy and activity programs are offered.

FIRTH

Lakeview Rest Home
Firth, NE, 68357 (402) 791-5588
Admin Gary S Nelson. *Medical Dir/Dir of Nursing* Yvonne Wilder LPN.
Licensure Intermediate Care. *Beds* 56. *Certified* Medicaid.
Ownership Nonprofit.
Admissions Requirements Medical examination; Physician's request.
Staff Physicians 1 (pt); RNs 3 (pt); LPNs 1 (ft), 4 (pt); Nurses aides 5 (ft), 13 (pt); Activities coordinators 1 (ft), 1 (pt); Dietitians 1 (pt).
Affiliation Reformed Church
Facilities Dining room; Activities room; Chapel; Laundry room; Barber/Beauty shop.
Activities Cards; Games; Prayer groups; Movies; Shopping trips; Dances/Social or cultural gatherings.

FRANKLIN

Franklin Senior Citizens Home Inc
PO Box 167, Franklin, NE, 68939 (308) 425-6262
Admin James Banark. *Medical Dir/Dir of Nursing* Dian Rogers.
Licensure Intermediate Care. *Beds* 72. *Certified* Medicaid.
Ownership Proprietary.
Staff RNs 1 (ft); LPNs 1 (ft), 2 (pt); Nurses aides 15 (ft), 8 (pt); Activities coordinators 1 (ft); Dietitians 1 (pt).
Facilities Dining room; Activities room; Chapel; Crafts room; Laundry room; Barber/Beauty shop.
Activities Arts and Crafts; Cards; Games; Reading groups; Prayer groups; Movies; Shopping trips; Dances/Social or cultural gatherings.
Description Home has an excellent exercise program, therapeutic diets for any type diet, whirlpool bath, and restorative therapy. Chapel is like a church.

FREMONT

Arbor Manor Inc*
26th and N Nye Ave, Fremont, NE, 68025 (402) 727-1710
Admin Marguerite McCardle.
Licensure Intermediate Care. *Beds* 151. *Certified* Medicaid.
Ownership Proprietary.

Fremont Care Center*
2700 LaVerna St, Fremont, NE, 68025 (402) 727-4900
Admin Jeffrey D Harmon.
Licensure Intermediate Care. *Beds* 60.
Ownership Proprietary.

FRIEND

Friend Manor*
905 2nd St, Friend, NE, 68359 (402) 947-2541
Admin Michael R Bowman.
Licensure Intermediate Care. *Beds* 58. *Certified* Medicaid.
Ownership Public.

FULLERTON

Fullerton Manor
202 N Esther, Fullerton, NE, 68638 (308) 536-2225
Admin Mason Cash Benn.
Licensure Intermediate Care. *Beds* 85. *Certified* Medicaid.
Ownership Proprietary.
Admissions Requirements Minimum age 21; Medical examination; Physician's request.
Staff Physicians 2 (ft); RNs 1 (ft); LPNs 4 (ft), 1 (pt); Nurses aides 18 (ft), 11 (pt); Activities coordinators 1 (ft), 1 (pt); Dietitians 1 (pt); Dentists 1 (ft); Podiatrists 1 (ft).
Facilities Dining room; Physical therapy room; Activities room; Chapel; Crafts room; Laundry room; Barber/Beauty shop.
Activities Arts and Crafts; Cards; Games; Reading groups; Prayer groups; Movies; Shopping trips; Dances/Social or cultural gatherings.
Description Fullerton Manor, in a small town setting, shares its block with the city swimming pool, is just across from the city park, and is only 3 blocks north of the business district.

GENEVA

Fillmore County Long Term Care*
1325 H St, Geneva, NE, 68361 (402) 759-3167
Admin Larry G Warrelman.
Licensure Intermediate Care. *Beds* 20. *Certified* Medicaid.
Ownership Public.

Heritage of Geneva
501 N 13th St, Geneva, NE, 68361 (402) 759-3194
Admin Chester R Frey. *Medical Dir/Dir of Nursing* Katherine Williams.
Licensure Intermediate Care. *Beds* 75. *Certified* Medicaid.
Ownership Proprietary.
Staff RNs 1 (ft), 1 (pt); LPNs 2 (ft), 1 (pt); Nurses aides 12 (ft), 10 (pt); Reality therapists 1 (pt); Recreational therapists 1 (pt); Activities coordinators 1 (ft); Dietitians 1 (pt).
Facilities Dining room; Chapel; Laundry room; Barber/Beauty shop.
Activities Arts and Crafts; Cards; Games; Reading groups; Movies; Shopping trips; Dances/Social or cultural gatherings.
Description Activities include Valentine's Day coronations; picnics for families, residents, and staff; park barbecues; airplane rides; snowmobile rides; van rides; soup suppers; sightseeing tours; and wheelchair square dancing.

GERING

Heritage Health Care Center*
2025 21st St, Gering, NE, 69341 (308) 426-5007
Admin Ardys J Dahl.
Licensure Skilled Care; Intermediate Care. *Beds* 101. *Certified* Medicaid.
Ownership Proprietary.

Northfield Villa Inc*
2550 21st St, Gering, NE, 69341 (308) 436-3101

Admin Floyd Sauer.
Licensure Skilled Care; Intermediate Care.
Beds 28. *Certified* Medicaid; Medicare.
Ownership Nonprofit.

GIBBON

Good Samaritan Center*
7th and Court, Gibbon, NE, 68840 (308) 468-5353
Admin Betty Critel.
Licensure Intermediate Care. *Beds* 45. *Certified* Medicaid.
Ownership Nonprofit.
Affiliation Lutheran

GORDON

Gordon Good Samaritan Center
500 E 10th St, Gordon, NE, 69343 (308) 282-0806
Admin Rollen E Knapp.
Licensure Intermediate Care. *Beds* 61. *Certified* Medicaid.
Ownership Nonprofit.
Affiliation Lutheran

GOTHENBURG

Slack Nursing Home Inc
121 6th St, Gothenburg, NE, 69138 (308) 537-2606
Admin Richard D Slack.
Licensure Intermediate Care. *Beds* 78. *Certified* Medicaid.
Ownership Proprietary.
Admissions Requirements Medical examination.
Staff Physicians 3 (pt); RNs 2 (pt); LPNs 2 (ft); Nurses aides 20 (ft), 18 (pt); Physical therapists 1 (pt); Occupational therapists 1 (pt); Speech therapists 1 (pt); Activities coordinators 1 (ft); Dietitians 1 (pt); Dentists 1 (pt); Ophthalmologists 1 (pt); Podiatrists 1 (pt); Audiologists 1 (pt).
Facilities Dining room; Activities room; Chapel; Crafts room; Laundry room; Barber/Beauty shop.
Activities Arts and Crafts; Cards; Games; Reading groups; Prayer groups; Movies; Shopping trips; Dances/Social or cultural gatherings.

GRAND ISLAND

Heritage of Grand Island—South
1405 W Hwy 34, Grand Island, NE, 68801 (308) 382-6397
Admin Joyce R Anderson. *Medical Dir/Dir of Nursing* Linda Berry RN.
Licensure Intermediate Care. *Beds* 96. *Certified* Medicaid.
Ownership Proprietary.
Staff RNs 2 (ft), 1 (pt); LPNs 4 (ft), 1 (pt); Orderlies 1 (pt); Nurses aides 29 (ft), 3 (pt); Physical therapists 1 (pt); Occupational therapists 1 (pt); Speech therapists 1 (pt); Activities coordinators 1 (ft); Dietitians 1 (pt); Dentists 1 (pt); Podiatrists 1 (pt); Audiologists 1 (pt).
Facilities Dining room; Activities room; Laundry room; Barber/Beauty shop.

Activities Arts and Crafts; Cards; Games; Reading groups; Prayer groups; Movies; Shopping trips; Dances/Social or cultural gatherings. *Description* Facility is located next to a small lake with ducks, in a country atmosphere with a large green lawn. Facility has 4 wings divided by amount of care required; friendly caring staff.

Heritage Village of Grand Island—North
610 N Darr St, Grand Island, NE, 68801 (308) 382-2635
Admin Robert D Steffen.
Licensure Intermediate Care. *Beds* 97. *Certified* Medicaid.
Ownership Proprietary.
Admissions Requirements Medical examination.
Staff RNs 1 (pt); LPNs 8 (ft); Orderlies 2 (ft); Nurses aides 11 (ft), 12 (pt); Physical therapists 1 (pt); Recreational therapists 1 (ft); Occupational therapists 1 (pt); Speech therapists 1 (pt); Activities coordinators 1 (ft); Dietitians 1 (pt); Dentists 1 (pt); Ophthalmologists 1 (pt); Podiatrists 1 (pt); Audiologists 1 (pt).
Facilities Dining room; Laundry room; Barber/Beauty shop.
Activities Arts and Crafts; Cards; Games; Reading groups; Movies; Shopping trips; Dances/Social or cultural gatherings.

Nebraska Veterans Home*
Burkett Station, Grand Island, NE, 68801 (308) 382-9420
Admin Robert W Broadstone.
Licensure Skilled Care; Intermediate Care. *Beds* 414.
Ownership Public.

Wedgewood
800 Stoeger Dr, Grand Island, NE, 68801 (308) 382-5400
Admin Patricia E Wissel.
Licensure Intermediate Care. *Beds* 71.
Ownership Proprietary.
Admissions Requirements Medical examination.
Staff RNs 1 (ft); Physical therapists 1 (pt); Activities coordinators 1 (ft); Dietitians 1 (ft).
Facilities Dining room; Physical therapy room; Activities room; Crafts room; Laundry room; Barber/Beauty shop; Library.
Activities Arts and Crafts; Cards; Games; Reading groups; Prayer groups; Movies; Shopping trips; Dances/Social or cultural gatherings.
Description Wedgewood is a completely private facility, but has the unique quality of being staffed around the clock with professional nurses. It is licensed as an ICF I, but because of the staffing, is able to care for anyone whose case treatment falls within the scope of practice of the licensed practical nurse, according to Nebraska laws. Wedgewood gives very individual, highly personal care and is a very sought-after facility in which to live.

GREELEY

Greeley Care Home*
Greeley, NE, 68842 (308) 428-5145
Admin Mary Haschke.

Licensure Intermediate Care. *Beds* 48. *Certified* Medicaid.
Ownership Public.

GRETNA

Bethesda Care Center of Gretna
700 Hwy 6, Gretna, NE, 68028 (402) 332-3446
Admin Patricia Proctor.
Licensure Intermediate Care. *Beds* 63. *Certified* Medicaid.
Ownership Nonprofit.
Admissions Requirements Medical examination.
Staff RNs; LPNs; Nurses aides; Activities coordinators.
Facilities Dining room; Activities room; Chapel; Laundry room; Barber/Beauty shop.
Activities Arts and Crafts; Cards; Games; Reading groups; Prayer groups; Movies; Shopping trips.
Description Facility has a video cassette recorder with movies circulated by home office for use in each facility.

HARTINGTON

Cedars
Darlene St, Hartington, NE, 68739 (402) 254-3905
Admin Elvera Lewis.
Licensure Intermediate Care. *Beds* 73. *Certified* Medicaid.
Ownership Proprietary.
Admissions Requirements Medical examination.
Staff RNs 1 (ft), 5 (pt); LPNs 2 (ft), 2 (pt); Nurses aides 12 (ft), 6 (pt); Physical therapists 1 (pt); Recreational therapists 1 (ft); Activities coordinators 1 (ft), 1 (pt); Dietitians 1 (pt).
Facilities Dining room; Physical therapy room; Activities room; Chapel; Crafts room; Laundry room; Barber/Beauty shop.
Activities Arts and Crafts; Cards; Games; Reading groups; Prayer groups; Movies; Shopping trips; Dances/Social or cultural gatherings; Outings on bus.
Description Cedars is a ground floor facility with no steps.

HARVARD

Harvard Rest Haven*
400 E 7th St, Harvard, NE, 68944 (402) 772-7591
Admin Ronald E Crosby.
Licensure Intermediate Care. *Beds* 60. *Certified* Medicaid.
Ownership Public.

HASTINGS

Good Samaritan Village—Perkins Pavilion
300 S 1st Ave, Hastings, NE, 68901 (402) 463-3181
Admin G E Doughty. *Medical Dir/Dir of Nursing* Dr Gerald Kuehn.
Licensure Skilled Care; Intermediate Care; Basic Care. *Beds* SNF 59; ICF 89; Basic Care 59. *Certified* Medicaid.

Ownership Nonprofit.
Staff Physicians 1 (pt); RNs 6 (ft), 3 (pt); LPNs 5 (ft), 8 (pt); Orderlies 1 (ft), 5 (pt); Nurses aides 24 (ft), 35 (pt); Physical therapists 1 (pt); Recreational therapists 1 (ft); Occupational therapists 1 (pt); Speech therapists 1 (pt); Dietitians 1 (pt); Dentists 1 (pt); Podiatrists 1 (pt).
Affiliation Lutheran
Facilities Dining room; Physical therapy room; Activities room; Chapel; Crafts room; Laundry room; Barber/Beauty shop; Library.
Activities Arts and Crafts; Cards; Games; Reading groups; Prayer groups; Movies; Shopping trips; Dances/Social or cultural gatherings.
Description Perkins Pavilion is a large nursing center located in the Good Samaritan Village. The Village has 800 apartments with a population of nearly 1400 and has a senior center, bargain center, chapels, childrens day care, snack shop. Perkins Pavilion provides the whole continuum of services—adult day care, residential care, intermediate care and skilled nursing care.

Good Samaritan Village—Villa Grace
931 E "F" St, Hastings, NE, 68901 (402) 463-3181
Admin Gerald Berglin.
Licensure Intermediate Care. *Beds* 156. *Certified* Medicaid.
Ownership Nonprofit.
Admissions Requirements Medical examination; Physician's request.
Staff RNs 4 (ft), 2 (pt); LPNs 1 (ft), 1 (pt); Orderlies 2 (ft), 1 (pt); Nurses aides 42 (ft), 20 (pt); Activities coordinators 1 (ft); Dietitians 1 (pt).
Affiliation Lutheran
Facilities Dining room; Physical therapy room; Activities room; Chapel; Crafts room; Laundry room; Barber/Beauty shop; Library.
Activities Arts and Crafts; Cards; Games; Reading groups; Prayer groups; Movies; Shopping trips; Dances/Social or cultural gatherings.
Description Villa Grace is one of 2 large nursing homes in a 132-acre retirement village. It has a dining room to accommodate all the residents. The facility has a small activity room and a large community room and chapel attached for residents of the nursing home and the village.

Hastings Regional Center
PO Box 579, Hastings, NE, 68901 (402) 463-2471
Admin Charles W Landgraf Jr.
Licensure Intermediate Care; Intermediate Care for Mentally Retarded. *Beds* 20.
Ownership Public.

HAY SPRINGS

Pioneer Manor
E Line Ave, Hay Springs, NE, 69347 (308) 683-4483
Admin Patsy A Bridge.
Licensure Intermediate Care. *Beds* 51. *Certified* Medicaid.
Ownership Public.
Staff Physicians 7 (pt); RNs 1 (ft); LPNs 4 (ft); Orderlies 3 (ft); Nurses aides 12 (ft); Physical therapists 1 (pt); Occupational therapists 1 (pt); Speech therapists 1 (pt); Activities coordinators

1 (ft); Dietitians 1 (pt); Dentists 1 (pt); Ophthalmologists 1 (pt); Podiatrists 1 (pt); Audiologists 1 (pt).
Facilities Dining room; Activities room; Crafts room; Laundry room; Barber/Beauty shop.
Activities Arts and Crafts; Cards; Games; Reading groups; Prayer groups; Movies; Shopping trips; Dances/Social or cultural gatherings.

HEBRON

Blue Valley Lutheran Home
4th and Park Ave, Hebron, NE, 68370 (402) 768-6045
Admin LaVern L Poppe. *Medical Dir/Dir of Nursing* Ruth Kripal RN.
Licensure Intermediate Care. *Beds* 178. *Certified* Medicaid.
Ownership Nonprofit.
Staff Physicians 3 (pt); RNs 1 (ft), 1 (pt); LPNs 11 (ft), 2 (pt); Orderlies 5 (ft), 2 (pt); Nurses aides 57 (ft), 12 (pt); Physical therapists 1 (pt); Reality therapists 1 (pt); Recreational therapists 1 (pt); Occupational therapists 1 (pt); Speech therapists 1 (pt); Activities coordinators 2 (ft); Dietitians 1 (pt); Dentists 1 (pt); Audiologists 1 (pt).
Affiliation Lutheran
Facilities Dining room; Physical therapy room; Activities room; Chapel; Crafts room; Laundry room; Barber/Beauty shop.
Activities Arts and Crafts; Cards; Games; Reading groups; Prayer groups; Movies; Shopping trips.

HOLDREGE

Christian Homes Inc*
Rt 2, Holdrege, NE, 68949 (308) 995-4493
Admin Gordon Jensen.
Licensure Intermediate Care. *Beds* 82. *Certified* Medicaid.
Ownership Nonprofit.

Melvin and Selma Anderson Health Care Unit*
1319 10th Ave, Holdrege, NE, 68949 (308) 995-8631
Admin James S McClure.
Licensure Intermediate Care. *Beds* 59. *Certified* Medicaid.
Ownership Nonprofit.

HOOPER

Hooper Care Center
Box 447, Hooper, NE, 68031 (402) 654-3362
Admin John L Peterson.
Licensure Intermediate Care. *Beds* 64. *Certified* Medicaid.
Ownership Proprietary.
Admissions Requirements Medical examination; Physician's request.
Staff RNs 1 (ft), 2 (pt); LPNs 8 (pt); Nurses aides 3 (ft), 16 (pt); Physical therapists 1 (ft); Recreational therapists 1 (ft); Activities coordinators 1 (ft), 1 (pt); Dietitians 1 (ft); Audiologists 1 (ft).
Facilities Dining room; Physical therapy room; Activities room; Chapel; Laundry room; Barber/Beauty shop; Library.

Activities Arts and Crafts; Cards; Games; Reading groups; Prayer groups; Movies; Shopping trips; Dances/Social or cultural gatherings.
Description Progressive facility is located in a rural hillside setting; has a strong support service staff with 2 people in activities and 2 people in social services.

HUMBOLDT

Colonial Acres*
Humboldt, NE, 68376 (402) 862-3123
Admin Wanda Hancock.
Licensure Intermediate Care. *Beds* 68. *Certified* Medicaid.
Ownership Public.

IMPERIAL

Imperial Manor*
933 Grant, Imperial, NE, 69033 (308) 882-5333
Admin Robert M Allen.
Licensure Intermediate Care. *Beds* 70.
Certified Medicaid.
Ownership Public.

KEARNEY

Mother Hull Home*
125 E 23rd St, Kearney, NE, 68847 (308) 234-2447
Admin Richard Headley.
Licensure Intermediate Care. *Beds* 52. *Certified* Medicaid.
Ownership Nonprofit.

Mount Carmel Home—Keens Memorial
18th St and 5th Ave, Kearney, NE, 68847 (308) 237-2287
Admin Ann Mary Schmidt.
Licensure Intermediate Care. *Beds* 76.
Ownership Nonprofit.
Staff RNs 1 (ft); LPNs 4 (ft), 6 (pt); Nurses aides 21 (ft), 11 (pt); Recreational therapists 1 (ft); Activities coordinators 1 (ft).
Affiliation Roman Catholic
Facilities Dining room; Physical therapy room; Activities room; Chapel; Laundry room; Barber/Beauty shop; Family room.
Activities Arts and Crafts; Cards; Games; Reading groups; Prayer groups; Movies; Dances/Social or cultural gatherings; Rides into the country.

Saint John's Center*
3410 N Central Ave, Kearney, NE, 68847 (308) 234-1888
Admin Harry A Carlsen.
Licensure Intermediate Care. *Beds* 72. *Certified* Medicaid.
Ownership Nonprofit.
Affiliation Lutheran

Saint Luke's Good Samaritan Village*
2300 E 32nd St, Kearney, NE, 68847 (308) 237-3108
Admin Steven R Wolff.
Licensure Intermediate Care. *Beds* 60. *Certified* Medicaid.
Ownership Nonprofit.
Affiliation Lutheran

KENESAW

Haven Home of Kenesaw*
Box 10, Kenesaw, NE, 68956 (402) 752-3212
Admin Robert E Williams.
Licensure Intermediate Care. *Beds* 84. *Certified* Medicaid.
Ownership Proprietary.

KIMBALL

Kimball County Manor
810 E 7th St, Kimball, NE, 69145 (308) 235-4693
Admin Earl L Baker.
Licensure Intermediate Care; Domiciliary Care. *Beds* 70. *Certified* Medicaid.
Ownership Public.
Admissions Requirements Medical examination; Physician's request.
Staff Physicians 3 (pt); RNs 2 (ft), 2 (pt); LPNs 3 (ft), 2 (pt); Orderlies 1 (pt); Nurses aides 10 (ft), 12 (pt); Physical therapists 1 (pt); Occupational therapists 12 (pt); Speech therapists 1 (pt); Activities coordinators 1 (ft), 1 (pt); Dietitians 1 (pt); Dentists 1 (pt).
Facilities Dining room; Activities room; Chapel; Crafts room; Laundry room; Barber/Beauty shop.
Activities Arts and Crafts; Cards; Games; Reading groups; Prayer groups; Movies; Shopping trips.
Description Facility has home-like atmosphere with dedicated staff who care; situated in rural town of 3500 in western Nebraska; community support with many activities brought into the home.

LAUREL

Hillcrest Care Center*
Oak St, Laurel, NE, 68745 (402) 256-3961
Admin Marcia Haisch.
Licensure Intermediate Care. *Beds* 51. *Certified* Medicaid.
Ownership Public.

LEWELLEN

Garden County Lewellen Nursing Home
Box E, Lewellen, NE, 69147 (308) 778-5351
Admin Donna I Fiesterman. *Medical Dir/Dir of Nursing* A B Albee MD.
Licensure Intermediate Care. *Beds* 42. *Certified* Medicaid.
Ownership Public.
Admissions Requirements Medical examination.
Staff Physicians 8 (ft); RNs 1 (ft), 2 (pt); LPNs 6 (ft), 1 (pt); Nurses aides 8 (ft), 34 (pt); Activities coordinators 1 (ft); Dietitians 1 (pt); Social workers 1 (ft).
Facilities Dining room; Activities room; Chapel; Crafts room; Laundry room; Barber/Beauty shop; Library.
Activities Arts and Crafts; Cards; Games; Reading groups; Prayer groups; Movies; Shopping trips; Dances/Social or cultural gatherings.
Description A small home in a small commu-

nity featuring individual care and professional help; a good climate—all seasons; and a variety of diets for residents' likes and dislikes.

LEXINGTON

Westside Home Inc
1505 N Adams St, Lexington, NE, 68850 (308) 324-5531
Admin Susan M Appelt.
Licensure Intermediate Care. *Beds* 124. *Certified* Medicaid.
Ownership Proprietary.
Admissions Requirements Medical examination; Physician's request.
Staff RNs 1 (ft), 3 (pt); LPNs 4 (ft), 2 (pt); Nurses aides 17 (ft), 10 (pt); Activities coordinators 1 (ft); Dietitians 1 (pt).
Facilities Dining room; Activities room; Chapel; Crafts room; Laundry room; Barber-/Beauty shop.
Activities Arts and Crafts; Cards; Games; Reading groups; Prayer groups; Movies; Shopping trips; Dances/Social or cultural gatherings.

LINCOLN

Bethpage at Lincoln*
904 Sumner St, Lincoln, NE, 68502 (402) 475-5895
Admin Charlene K Swanson.
Licensure Intermediate Care for Mentally Retarded. *Beds* 38. *Certified* Medicaid.
Ownership Nonprofit.

Eastmont Tower
6315 O St, Lincoln, NE, 68510 (402) 489-6591
Admin Cecil Wissink. *Medical Dir/Dir of Nursing* J R Thomsen.
Licensure Skilled Care; Intermediate Care. *Beds* 50. *Certified* Medicaid.
Ownership Nonprofit.
Admissions Requirements Minimum age 62.
Staff RNs; LPNs; Nurses aides; Physical therapists; Activities coordinators.
Facilities Dining room; Activities room; Chapel; Laundry room; Barber/Beauty shop; Library.
Activities Arts and Crafts; Cards; Games; Reading groups; Movies; Shopping trips.
Description This is a life-care facility.

Gateway Manor Inc
225 N 56th St, Lincoln, NE, 68504 (402) 464-6371
Admin Mary Lou Philippi. *Medical Dir/Dir of Nursing* Dr George Place.
Licensure Skilled Care. *Beds* SNF 18.
Admissions Requirements Minimum age 62; Medical examination.
Staff RNs 3 (ft), 3 (pt); Nurses aides 7 (ft), 7 (pt); Activities coordinators 1 (pt).
Facilities Dining room; Activities room; Laundry room; Barber/Beauty shop; Library; Penthouse; Auditorium.
Activities Arts and Crafts; Games; Movies; Shopping trips; Religious activities; Current topics—speakers and programs.
Description Gateway Manor is a well-built facility, attractively decorated, well maintained,

with beautiful grounds; the top floor is a penthouse for parties, family gatherings, or walking on open deck.

Holmes Lake Manor
6101 Normal Blvd, Lincoln, NE, 68506 (402) 489-7175
Admin Margaret E Cole.
Licensure Intermediate Care. *Beds* 120. *Certified* Medicaid.
Ownership Proprietary.
Admissions Requirements Minimum age 50; Medical examination.
Staff RNs 4 (ft), 1 (pt); LPNs 6 (ft), 1 (pt); Orderlies 44 (ft), 11 (pt); Nurses aides 44 (ft), 11 (pt); Recreational therapists 1 (ft), 1 (pt); Activities coordinators 1 (ft), 2 (pt).
Facilities Dining room; Physical therapy room; Activities room; Chapel; Crafts room; Laundry room; Barber/Beauty shop.
Activities Arts and Crafts; Cards; Games; Reading groups; Prayer groups; Movies; Shopping trips; Dances/Social or cultural gatherings; Couple club; Social night.
Description Facility is set on 7 acres with city convenience and country lifestyle. The building is star shaped, one story building with automatic sprinkler system and smoke detection. Holmes Lake Manor has a warm, inviting central dining room and bright cheerful resident rooms and lounges.

Homestead Nursing Home
4735 S 54th St, Lincoln, NE, 68516 (402) 488-0877
Admin Mary Morris. *Medical Dir/Dir of Nursing* Marjorie Kwan MD.
Licensure Skilled Care; Intermediate Care. *Beds* 147. *Certified* Medicaid.
Ownership Proprietary.
Admissions Requirements Medical examination.
Staff RNs 4 (ft), 8 (pt); LPNs 6 (ft), 4 (pt); Nurses aides 28 (ft), 26 (pt); Activities coordinators 1 (ft), 1 (pt); Dietitians 1 (pt).
Facilities Dining room; Physical therapy room; Activities room; Chapel; Laundry room; Barber/Beauty shop.
Activities Arts and Crafts; Cards; Games; Reading groups; Prayer groups; Movies; Shopping trips.

Lancaster Manor
1145 South St, Lincoln, NE, 68502 (402) 476-0391
Admin Patricia Snyder.
Licensure Intermediate Care. *Beds* 287. *Certified* Medicaid.
Ownership Public.
Staff RNs 9 (ft); LPNs 13 (ft); Orderlies 5 (ft); Nurses aides 110 (ft); Physical therapists 1 (ft), 1 (pt); Occupational therapists 1 (pt); Speech therapists 1 (pt); Activities coordinators 1 (pt); Dietitians 2 (ft); Dentists 2 (pt); Podiatrists 1 (pt).
Facilities Dining room; Physical therapy room; Activities room; Chapel; Crafts room; Laundry room; Barber/Beauty shop; Library.
Activities Arts and Crafts; Cards; Games; Reading groups; Prayer groups; Movies; Shopping trips; Dances/Social or cultural gatherings.

Lincoln Regional Center—Comprehensive Care Unit
Van Dorn and Folsom Sts, Lincoln, NE, 68501 (402) 471-4444
Admin Klaus Hartmann.
Licensure Intermediate Care for Mentally Retarded. *Beds* 21. *Certified* Medicaid.
Ownership Public.
Admissions Requirements Minimum age 19; Medical examination.
Staff Physicians 1 (pt); RNs 1 (ft); LPNs 3 (ft); Nurses aides 26 (ft); Recreational therapists 14 (ft); Occupational therapists 1 (pt); Speech therapists 1 (pt); Activities coordinators 1 (ft); Dietitians 1 (pt); Dentists 1 (pt); Audiologists 1 (pt).
Facilities Dining room; Activities room; Crafts room; Laundry room; Barber/Beauty shop.
Activities Arts and Crafts; Games; Movies; Shopping trips; Dances/Social or cultural gatherings.

Madonna Professional Care Center*
2200 S 52nd St, Lincoln, NE, 68506 (402) 489-7102
Admin Sr M Phyllis Hunhoff.
Licensure Skilled Care; Intermediate Care. *Beds* 208. *Certified* Medicaid.
Ownership Nonprofit.

Maplewood Care Center
4405 Normal Blvd, Lincoln, NE, 68506 (402) 488-2355
Admin Jill D Molzahn. *Medical Dir/Dir of Nursing* Dr D E Michels.
Licensure Skilled Care; Intermediate Care. *Beds* 68. *Certified* Medicaid.
Ownership Proprietary.
Admissions Requirements Physician's request.
Staff RNs 5 (ft), 2 (pt); LPNs 4 (ft), 1 (pt); Orderlies 3 (ft), 2 (pt); Nurses aides 13 (ft), 12 (pt); Activities coordinators 1 (ft).
Facilities Dining room; Activities room; Crafts room; Laundry room; Barber/Beauty shop.
Activities Arts and Crafts; Cards; Games; Reading groups; Prayer groups; Movies; Shopping trips; Dances/Social or cultural gatherings.
Description Maplewood Care Center is located in the southeast part of residential Lincoln and is surrounded by maple trees and 5 acres of shaded lawn. The center has begun many changes including 24-hour professional nursing, respiratory therapy, intermediate, and skilled care. "We care with the personal touch."

Milder Manor Nursing Home*
1750 S 20th St, Lincoln, NE, 68502 (402) 475-6791
Admin Jerome J Milder.
Licensure Skilled Care. *Beds* 154. *Certified* Medicaid; Medicare.
Ownership Proprietary.

Tabitha Home
4720 Randolph St, Lincoln, NE, 68510 (402) 489-3837
Admin Donna Jean Beccaro. *Medical Dir/Dir of Nursing* Gerald Bunting MD.
Licensure Skilled Care; Intermediate Care. *Beds* 235. *Certified* Medicaid; Medicare.
Ownership Nonprofit.
Admissions Requirements Medical examination; Physician's request.

Staff Physical therapists 2 (pt); Occupational therapists 1 (pt); Speech therapists 1 (pt); Activities coordinators 4 (ft); Dentists 1 (pt); Podiatrists 1 (pt); Audiologists 1 (pt).
Affiliation Lutheran
Facilities Dining room; Physical therapy room; Activities room; Chapel; Crafts room; Laundry room; Barber/Beauty shop; Library.
Activities Arts and Crafts; Cards; Games; Reading groups; Prayer groups; Movies; Shopping trips; Dances/Social or cultural gatherings.

Village Manor Nursing Home*
3220 N 14th St, Lincoln, NE, 68521 (402) 476-3274
Admin Virgil L Carner.
Licensure Intermediate Care. *Beds* 50. *Certified* Medicaid.
Ownership Proprietary.

LOUISVILLE

Louisville Care Center*
6th and Hazel St, Louisville, NE, 68037 (402) 234-2125
Admin Elaine Storovich.
Licensure Intermediate Care. *Beds* 55. *Certified* Medicaid.
Ownership Public.

LOUP CITY

Rose Lane Nursing Home
Box 280, Loup City, NE, 68853 (308) 745-0303
Admin Laura I Whaley. *Medical Dir/Dir of Nursing* K Fowler.
Licensure Intermediate Care. *Beds* 85. *Certified* Medicaid.
Ownership Public.
Staff Physicians 2 (pt); RNs 1 (ft); LPNs 1 (ft); Nurses aides 28 (ft), 7 (pt); Reality therapists 1 (pt); Activities coordinators 1 (ft).
Affiliation Roman Catholic
Facilities Dining room; Physical therapy room; Activities room; Crafts room; Laundry room; Barber/Beauty shop.
Activities Arts and Crafts; Games; Reading groups; Prayer groups; Shopping trips.

LYONS

Logan Valley Manor Inc*
Lyons, NE, 68038 (402) 687-2121
Admin Russell V Peterson.
Licensure Intermediate Care. *Beds* 90. *Certified* Medicaid.
Ownership Proprietary.

MACY

Carl T Curtis Health Education Center
PO Box 250, Macy, NE, 68039 (402) 837-5381
Admin June Cook. *Medical Dir/Dir of Nursing* J E Nicolas MD.
Licensure Intermediate Care. *Beds* 25. *Certified* Medicaid.
Ownership Nonprofit.
Admissions Requirements Medical examination.
Staff Physicians 2 (pt); RNs 7 (ft); LPNs 2 (ft);

Orderlies 3 (ft); Nurses aides 7 (ft); Physical therapists 1 (pt); Recreational therapists 1 (pt); Occupational therapists 1 (pt); Speech therapists 1 (pt); Activities coordinators 1 (ft); Dietitians 1 (pt); Dentists 1 (pt); Podiatrists 1 (pt).
Facilities Dining room; Physical therapy room; Activities room; Laundry room; Barber/Beauty shop.
Activities Arts and Crafts; Cards; Games; Prayer groups; Movies; Shopping trips; Dances/Social or cultural gatherings.
Description Facility is part of a comprehensive health care setting including ambulatory care, home health, dental services, and related services.

MADISON

Countryside Home
N Pearl St, PO Box 505, Madison, NE, 68748 (402) 454-3373
Admin Fern J Saimen.
Licensure Intermediate Care. *Beds* 70. *Certified* Medicaid.
Ownership Public.
Staff Physicians 5 (pt); RNs 2 (ft); LPNs 1 (ft), 6 (pt); Nurses aides 5 (ft), 20 (pt); Activities coordinators 1 (ft); Dietitians 1 (pt); Dentists 1 (pt).
Facilities Dining room; Physical therapy room; Activities room; Chapel; Crafts room; Laundry room; Barber/Beauty shop.
Activities Arts and Crafts; Cards; Games; Prayer groups; Movies; Shopping trips; Dances/Social or cultural gatherings.
Description Nursing home is owned by the city of Madison, a truly viable part of the community; small town setting.

MCCOOK

Hillcrest Nursing Home*
309 W 7th St, McCook, NE, 69001 (308) 345-4600
Admin Dorothy J Schreiber.
Licensure Intermediate Care. *Beds* 96. *Certified* Medicaid.
Ownership Public.

MILFORD

Crestview Care Center*
Rt 1, Box D, Milford, NE, 68405 (402) 761-2261
Admin Jerry Eisenhauer.
Licensure Intermediate Care. *Beds* 66. *Certified* Medicaid.
Ownership Proprietary.

Milford Rest Home Inc*
Rt 2, Milford, NE, 68405 (402) 761-3230
Admin Wanetta Stabenow.
Licensure Intermediate Care. *Beds* 72.
Certified Medicaid.
Ownership Proprietary.

MINDEN

Bethany Home*
515 W 1st St, Minden, NE, 68959 (308) 832-1594
Admin Wesley K Anderson.
Licensure Intermediate Care. *Beds* 61. *Certified* Medicaid.
Ownership Nonprofit.

MITCHELL

Western Nebraska Rest Home*
1508 22nd Ave, Mitchell, NE, 69357 (308) 623-1212
Admin Clara Reisig.
Licensure Intermediate Care. *Beds* 50. *Certified* Medicaid.
Ownership Proprietary.

NEBRASKA CITY

Duff Memorial Nursing Home*
1104 3rd Ave, Nebraska City, NE, 68410 (402) 873-3304
Admin Diane Schneider.
Licensure Intermediate Care. *Beds* 63. *Certified* Medicaid.
Ownership Public.

Nebraska City Manor
1420 N 10th St, Nebraska City, NE, 68410 (402) 873-3304
Admin Edwin M Brass Jr.
Licensure Intermediate Care. *Beds* 120. *Certified* Medicaid.
Ownership Proprietary.
Admissions Requirements Minimum age 18; Medical examination; Physician's request.
Staff RNs 2 (ft), 1 (pt); LPNs 3 (ft); Orderlies 1 (ft); Nurses aides 21 (ft), 12 (pt); Physical therapists; Speech therapists; Activities coordinators 1 (ft), 2 (pt); Dietitians 1 (pt).
Facilities Dining room; Activities room; Chapel; Crafts room; Barber/Beauty shop; Library.
Activities Arts and Crafts; Cards; Games; Reading groups; Prayer groups; Movies; Shopping trips; Dances/Social or cultural gatherings.
Description Facility offers outstanding activities and social service departments, well trained and dedicated nursing staff, and a qualified food service department with capacity to handle therapeutic diets.

Valley View Care Inc
1800 14th St, Nebraska City, NE, 68410 (402) 873-6650
Admin Timothy Juilfs.
Licensure Intermediate Care. *Beds* 73. *Certified* Medicaid.
Ownership Proprietary.
Admissions Requirements Minimum age 16; Medical examination.
Staff RNs 1 (ft), 3 (pt); LPNs 2 (ft), 1 (pt); Orderlies 1 (pt); Nurses aides 17 (ft), 5 (pt); Activities coordinators 1 (ft), 1 (pt); Dentists 11 (ft).
Facilities Dining room; Activities room; Laundry room; Barber/Beauty shop; Bathing area.
Activities Arts and Crafts; Cards; Games; Reading groups; Prayer groups; Movies; Shop-

ping trips; Dances/Social or cultural gatherings.
Description Our most outstanding program is the Magic Me program which involves children from the 6th grade of all of the schools in our town. Our activity program is excellent. In nursing, we strive to be a rehabilitation center, sending approximately 25% of our admissions to their homes. We feel we have the best standard of care in the area.

NELIGH

Heritage Village of Neligh*
Neligh, NE, 68756 (402) 887-4101
Admin Patsy Uttecht.
Licensure Intermediate Care. *Beds* 97. *Certified* Medicaid.
Ownership Proprietary.

NELSON

Evangelical Lutheran Good Samaritan Center*
Nelson, NE, 68961 (402) 225-2411
Admin Betty Deines.
Licensure Intermediate Care. *Beds* 46.
Certified Medicaid.
Ownership Nonprofit.
Affiliation Lutheran

NEWMAN GROVE

Mid-Nebraska Lutheran Homes Inc
Box 459, Newman Grove, NE, 68758 (402) 447-6204
Admin Lee A Jenkins. *Medical Dir/Dir of Nursing* Dr Gary Smith.
Licensure Intermediate Care. *Beds* 55. *Certified* Medicaid.
Ownership Nonprofit.
Admissions Requirements Medical examination.
Staff RNs 1 (pt); LPNs 4 (ft), 1 (pt); Nurses aides 5 (ft), 16 (pt); Physical therapists 1 (pt); Activities coordinators 1 (ft); Dietitians 1 (pt); Social services 1 (ft).
Affiliation Lutheran
Facilities Dining room; Activities room; Chapel; Crafts room; Laundry room; Barber/Beauty shop.
Activities Arts and Crafts; Cards; Games; Reading groups; Prayer groups; Movies; Shopping trips; Dances/Social or cultural gatherings.
Description Facility has semi-private and private rooms, 24-hour nursing care with LPNs or RNs on duty. Active rehabilitation, social services and activity programs.

NORFOLK

Heritage of Bel Air
13th and Bel Air Rd, Norfolk, NE, 68701 (402) 371-4991
Admin Linda S Kellogg.
Licensure Intermediate Care. *Beds* 89. *Certified* Medicaid.
Ownership Proprietary.
Staff Physicians; RNs; LPNs 8 (ft), 2 (pt); Orderlies 1 (ft); Nurses aides 20 (ft), 8 (pt); Physical therapists 1 (ft); Occupational therapists; Speech therapists; Activities coordinators

1 (ft); Dietitians 1 (pt).
Facilities Dining room; Activities room; Crafts room; Laundry room; Barber/Beauty shop.
Activities Arts and Crafts; Cards; Games; Reading groups; Prayer groups; Movies; Shopping trips; Dances/Social or cultural gatherings.

Nebraska Veterans Home
Box 409, Norfolk, NE, 68701 (402) 371-2701
Admin Duane Hodge. *Medical Dir/Dir of Nursing* Dr Harold Dahlheim.
Licensure Intermediate Care. *Beds* 161.
Ownership Public.
Admissions Requirements Medical examination.
Staff Physicians 1 (pt); RNs 7 (ft), 2 (pt); LPNs 7 (ft), 1 (pt); Nurses aides 38 (ft), 7 (pt); Recreational therapists 1 (ft); Occupational therapists 1 (ft); Activities coordinators 1 (ft); Physician assistants 1 (pt).
Facilities Dining room; Activities room; Chapel; Crafts room.
Activities Arts and Crafts; Cards; Games; Reading groups; Prayer groups; Movies; Shopping trips; Dances/Social or cultural gatherings.
Description We have 2 buildings and 1 enclosed picnic shelter. Our facility has an active alcoholics anonymous and volunteer services program.

Saint Joseph's Nursing Home*
401 N 18th St, Norfolk, NE, 68701 (402) 371-9404
Admin Sr M Rita Hess.
Licensure Intermediate Care. *Beds* 70. *Certified* Medicaid.
Ownership Nonprofit.

Valley View Lodge
1900 Vicki Ln, Norfolk, NE, 68701 (402) 371-2303
Admin Sandra Kay Effle.
Licensure Intermediate Care. *Beds* 102. *Certified* Medicaid.
Ownership Proprietary.
Admissions Requirements Medical examination; Physician's request.
Staff RNs 2 (pt); LPNs 5 (ft), 1 (pt); Nurses aides 26 (ft); Activities coordinators 1 (ft).
Facilities Dining room; Physical therapy room; Activities room; Chapel; Crafts room; Laundry room; Barber/Beauty shop.
Activities Arts and Crafts; Cards; Games; Reading groups; Prayer groups; Movies; Shopping trips; Dances/Social or cultural gatherings.

NORTH BEND

Birchwood Manor
1120 Walnut, North Bend, NE, 68649 (402) 652-3242
Admin Harold Ristau.
Licensure Intermediate Care. *Beds* 67. *Certified* Medicaid.
Ownership Proprietary.
Admissions Requirements Medical examination; Physician's request.
Staff Physicians 2 (pt); RNs 1 (pt); LPNs 1 (ft), 5 (pt); Orderlies 4 (ft); Nurses aides 23 (pt); Physical therapists 1 (pt); Recreational therapists 1 (pt); Occupational therapists 1 (pt); Speech therapists 1 (pt); Activities coordinators 1

(ft); Dietitians 1 (pt); Dentists 1 (pt).
Facilities Dining room; Physical therapy room; Activities room; Chapel; Crafts room; Laundry room; Barber/Beauty shop; Library.
Activities Arts and Crafts; Cards; Games; Reading groups; Prayer groups; Movies; Shopping trips.

NORTH PLATTE

Linden Manor Nursing Home*
420 W 4th St, North Platte, NE, 69101 (308) 532-5774
Admin William J Wagner.
Licensure Skilled Care; Intermediate Care. *Beds* 100. *Certified* Medicaid.
Ownership Proprietary.

Valley View Care Centre
3001 W "E" St, North Platte, NE, 69101 (308) 534-2200
Admin Charles Richards. *Medical Dir/Dir of Nursing* Elayne Underwood.
Licensure Intermediate Care. *Beds* 92. *Certified* Medicaid.
Ownership Proprietary.
Admissions Requirements Medical examination.
Staff RNs 1 (ft), 1 (pt); LPNs 4 (ft), 4 (pt); Physical therapists 1 (pt); Occupational therapists 1 (pt); Speech therapists 1 (pt); Dietitians 1 (ft).
Facilities Dining room; Activities room; Laundry room; Barber/Beauty shop.
Activities Arts and Crafts; Cards; Games; Reading groups; Prayer groups; Shopping trips.

OAKLAND

Oakland Heights
207 S Engdahl St, Oakland, NE, 68045 (402) 685-5683
Admin Barbara C Anderson.
Licensure Intermediate Care. *Beds* 57. *Certified* Medicaid.
Ownership Public.
Admissions Requirements Medical examination; Physician's request.
Staff RNs 1 (ft), 4 (pt); LPNs 1 (pt); Orderlies 1 (pt); Nurses aides 8 (ft), 10 (pt); Activities coordinators 1 (ft), 1 (pt); Dietitians 1 (pt).
Facilities Dining room; Activities room; Chapel; Crafts room; Laundry room; Barber/Beauty shop.
Activities Arts and Crafts; Cards; Games; Reading groups; Prayer groups; Movies; Shopping trips; Dances/Social or cultural gatherings.
Description Facility provides meals on wheels and a bus service and is located on a hill overlooking the city giving residents a beautiful view.

OGALLALA

Indian Hills Manor Nursing Home
Rt 2, Box 35A, Ogallala, NE, 69153 (308) 284-4068
Admin Charles Simineo.
Licensure Intermediate Care. *Beds* 82. *Certified* Medicaid.
Ownership Proprietary.

Admissions Requirements Minimum age 21; Medical examination.
Staff RNs 2 (pt); LPNs 4 (ft); Nurses aides 25 (ft); Activities coordinators 1 (ft), 1 (pt).
Facilities Dining room; Activities room; Chapel; Laundry room; Barber/Beauty shop.
Activities Arts and Crafts; Cards; Games; Dances/Social or cultural gatherings.

OMAHA

Doctor Philip Sher Jewish Home*
4801 N 52nd St, Omaha, NE, 68104 (402) 451-7220
Admin Allan Greene.
Licensure Intermediate Care. *Beds* 80. *Certified* Medicaid.
Ownership Nonprofit.
Affiliation Jewish

Florence Height Village Nursing Center Inc
3220 Scott St, Omaha, NE, 68112 (402) 455-6333
Admin Mary Pratkelis. *Medical Dir/Dir of Nursing* Charles M Bressman MD.
Licensure Skilled Care; Intermediate Care. *Beds* 80. *Certified* Medicaid.
Ownership Proprietary.
Admissions Requirements Medical examination; Physician's request.
Staff RNs 3 (ft); LPNs 2 (ft), 2 (pt); Orderlies 1 (ft); Nurses aides 20 (ft), 14 (pt); Physical therapists 1 (pt); Reality therapists 1 (pt); Recreational therapists 1 (pt); Activities coordinators 1 (ft); Dietitians 1 (pt); Dentists 1 (pt).
Facilities Dining room; Physical therapy room; Activities room; Chapel; Crafts room; Laundry room; Barber/Beauty shop; Library.
Activities Arts and Crafts; Cards; Games; Prayer groups; Movies; Shopping trips.
Description Facility is a skilled nursing care facility specifically built and staffed to provide individual nursing care for the retired, aged convalescent, and chronically ill.

Florence Home for the Aged
7915 N 30th St, Omaha, NE, 68112 (402) 457-4111
Admin Richard J Booth.
Licensure Intermediate Care. *Beds* 128. *Certified* Medicaid.
Ownership Nonprofit.
Admissions Requirements Medical examination.
Staff Physicians 1 (pt); RNs 1 (ft), 2 (pt); LPNs 7 (ft), 2 (pt); Nurses aides 43 (ft), 6 (pt); Reality therapists 1 (ft); Recreational therapists 1 (ft); Activities coordinators 2 (ft); Dietitians 1 (pt).
Facilities Dining room; Physical therapy room; Activities room; Chapel; Crafts room; Laundry room; Barber/Beauty shop; Library; Gift shop.
Activities Arts and Crafts; Cards; Games; Reading groups; Prayer groups; Movies; Shopping trips; Dances/Social or cultural gatherings.
Description Outstanding programs within the facility are: an in-house pharmacy staffed by a PhD clinical pharmacist, training provided for Nebraska medical students, Creighton pharmacy and nursing students; a rehabilitation program aimed at each resident attaining their maximum activity potential either at Florence or the community.

Hallmark Care Center*
5505 Grover St, Omaha, NE, 68106 (402) 558-0225
Admin John Miller.
Licensure Intermediate Care. *Beds* 168. *Certified* Medicaid.
Ownership Proprietary.

Haven House
1540 N 72nd St, Omaha, NE, 68114 (402) 393-6500
Admin Robert Freshman.
Licensure Intermediate Care. *Beds* 175. *Certified* Medicaid.
Ownership Proprietary.
Staff Physicians; RNs; LPNs; Orderlies; Nurses aides; Physical therapists; Occupational therapists; Speech therapists; Activities coordinators; Dietitians; Dentists; Podiatrists.
Facilities Dining room; Chapel; Laundry room; Barber/Beauty shop.
Activities Arts and Crafts; Games; Reading groups; Prayer groups; Movies; Shopping trips.

Hillhaven—Omaha
7410 Mercy Rd, Omaha, NE, 68124 (402) 397-1220
Admin Jean E Mazanec. *Medical Dir/Dir of Nursing* Thomas Cotton MD.
Licensure Skilled Care; Intermediate Care. *Beds* 174. *Certified* Medicaid; Medicare.
Ownership Proprietary.
Admissions Requirements Minimum age 18; Medical examination.
Staff Physicians 1 (pt); RNs 5 (ft), 4 (pt); LPNs 8 (ft), 2 (pt); Orderlies 5 (ft), 1 (pt); Nurses aides 36 (ft), 5 (pt); Physical therapists 1 (ft), 1 (pt); Recreational therapists 1 (ft); Occupational therapists 1 (pt); Speech therapists 1 (pt); Dentists 1 (pt); Ophthalmologists 1 (pt); Podiatrists 1 (pt); Audiologists 1 (pt).
Facilities Dining room; Physical therapy room; Activities room; Chapel; Laundry room; Barber/Beauty shop.
Activities Arts and Crafts; Cards; Games; Prayer groups; Movies; Shopping trips; Dances/Social or cultural gatherings.

Lindenwood Nursing Home Inc
910 S 40th St, Omaha, NE, 68105 (402) 342-2015
Admin Charlene Toland. *Medical Dir/Dir of Nursing* Daniel Halm MD.
Licensure Intermediate Care. *Beds* 65. *Certified* Medicaid.
Ownership Proprietary.
Staff RNs 1 (ft), 4 (pt); LPNs 5 (ft), 3 (pt); Nurses aides 18 (ft), 15 (pt); Physical therapists 1 (pt); Recreational therapists 1 (ft); Occupational therapists 1 (pt); Activities coordinators 1 (ft); Dietitians 1 (ft); Podiatrists 1 (pt).
Facilities Dining room; Activities room; Crafts room; Laundry room; Barber/Beauty shop.
Activities Arts and Crafts; Cards; Games; Reading groups; Prayer groups; Movies.

The Lutheran Home*
530 S 26th St, Omaha, NE, 68105 (402) 346-3344
Admin Byron G Will.
Licensure Skilled Care; Intermediate Care.

Beds 177. *Certified* Medicaid.
Ownership Nonprofit.
Affiliation Lutheran

Maple-Crest
2824 N 66th Ave, Omaha, NE, 68104 (402) 551-2110
Admin Richard A Peterson. *Medical Dir/Dir of Nursing* Dr Lyle Nilson.
Licensure Skilled Care; Intermediate Care. *Beds* 184. *Certified* Medicaid.
Ownership Nonprofit.
Admissions Requirements Medical examination.
Staff RNs 9 (ft), 4 (pt); LPNs 6 (ft), 9 (pt); Orderlies 3 (ft); Nurses aides 24 (ft), 25 (pt); Activities coordinators 1 (ft), 2 (pt); Dietitians 1 (pt).
Affiliation Baptist
Facilities Dining room; Physical therapy room; Activities room; Chapel; Crafts room; Laundry room; Barber/Beauty shop; Library.
Activities Arts and Crafts; Cards; Games; Reading groups; Prayer groups; Movies; Shopping trips; Dances/Social or cultural gatherings.
Description Staff tries to provide extra religious services and counseling for families. Facility has a beautiful separate chapel room. Caring is emphasized in staff training programs.

Mercy Care Center*
7500 Mercy Rd, Omaha, NE, 68124 (402) 398-6060
Admin Joyce Gibbs.
Licensure Skilled Care; Intermediate Care. *Beds* 250. *Certified* Medicaid; Medicare.

Millard Good Samaritan Center*
12856 Deauville Dr, Omaha, NE, 68137 (402) 895-2266
Admin Gerald E Doughty.
Licensure Skilled Care; Intermediate Care. *Beds* 113. *Certified* Medicaid.
Ownership Nonprofit.
Affiliation Lutheran

Montclair Nursing Center
2525 S 135th Ave, Omaha, NE, 68144 (402) 333-2304
Admin Eileen J Corns. *Medical Dir/Dir of Nursing* Donald J Darst.
Licensure Skilled Care; Intermediate Care; Hospice. *Beds* 179. *Certified* Medicare.
Ownership Proprietary.
Admissions Requirements Medical examination; Physician's request.
Staff Physicians; RNs; LPNs; Orderlies; Nurses aides; Physical therapists; Reality therapists; Occupational therapists; Speech therapists; Activities coordinators; Dietitians; Dentists; Podiatrists; Audiologists.
Facilities Dining room; Physical therapy room; Activities room; Chapel; Crafts room; Laundry room; Barber/Beauty shop; Library; Family room; Meeting space.
Activities Arts and Crafts; Cards; Games; Reading groups; Prayer groups; Movies; Shopping trips; Dances/Social or cultural gatherings.
Description Facility features a fully-trained, in-house hospice staff. Montclair is a highly motivated restorative/rehabilitative facility; pro-

vides respite care; and is a skilled, intermediate care, and Medicare certified facility with RNs and LPNs staffed 24 hours a day.

Omaha Manor Inc
2406 Fowler Ave, Omaha, NE, 68111 (402) 457-4488
Admin William L Anderson. *Medical Dir/Dir of Nursing* William D Murphy MD.
Licensure Intermediate Care; Intermediate Care for Mentally Retarded. *Beds* 49.
Ownership Proprietary.
Admissions Requirements Minimum age 19; Medical examination.
Staff Physicians; RNs; LPNs; Orderlies; Nurses aides; Physical therapists; Reality therapists; Recreational therapists; Occupational therapists; Speech therapists; Activities coordinators; Dietitians; Dentists; Ophthalmologists; Podiatrists; Audiologists.
Facilities Dining room; Activities room.
Activities Arts and Crafts; Cards; Games; Reading groups; Prayer groups; Movies; Shopping trips; Dances/Social or cultural gatherings.
Description Clients receive medical, religious, and recreational services in community with supervision of staff at all times. Apartment living and pre-vocational training are provided within facility.

Omaha Nursing Home Inc*
4835 S 49th St, Omaha, NE, 68117 (402) 733-7200
Admin Emelie Jonusas.
Licensure Intermediate Care. *Beds* 83. *Certified* Medicaid.
Ownership Proprietary.

Orchard Hill Nursing Home
3853 Decatur St, Omaha, NE, 68111 (402) 556-8878
Admin Joe Hageman.
Licensure Intermediate Care. *Beds* 49. *Certified* Medicaid.
Ownership Proprietary.

Redman Nursing Home
4809 Redman Ave, Omaha, NE, 68104 (402) 455-5025
Admin Brian Farrell.
Licensure Intermediate Care. *Beds* 122. *Certified* Medicaid.
Ownership Proprietary.
Staff RNs 4 (ft), 2 (pt); LPNs 4 (ft), 4 (pt); Orderlies 4 (ft), 1 (pt); Nurses aides 21 (ft), 9 (pt); Activities coordinators 1 (ft), 1 (pt).
Facilities Dining room; Activities room; Crafts room; Laundry room; Barber/Beauty shop.
Activities Arts and Crafts; Cards; Games; Reading groups; Prayer groups; Movies; Shopping trips; Dances/Social or cultural gatherings.

Rose Blumkin Jewish Home
323 S 132nd St, Omaha, NE, 68154
Admin Eugene H Brandt. *Medical Dir/Dir of Nursing* Dr Tom Cotton.
Licensure Skilled Care. *Certified* Medicaid; Medicare.
Ownership Nonprofit.
Admissions Requirements Medical examination.
Staff Physicians 1 (pt); Physical therapists 1 (pt); Recreational therapists 1 (ft).

Affiliation Jewish
Facilities Dining room; Physical therapy room; Activities room; Chapel; Crafts room; Laundry room; Barber/Beauty shop.
Activities Arts and Crafts; Cards; Games; Reading groups; Movies; Shopping trips; Dances/Social or cultural gatherings.

Skyline Manor and Skyline Villa
7300 Graceland Dr, Omaha, NE, 68134 (402) 572-5753
Admin Jacqueline W Fatheree. *Medical Dir/Dir of Nursing* Dr Robert Underriner.
Licensure Intermediate Care. *Beds* 84.
Ownership Proprietary.
Admissions Requirements Minimum age 65; Medical examination.
Staff RNs; LPNs; Orderlies; Nurses aides; Physical therapists; Reality therapists; Recreational therapists; Activities coordinators; Dietitians; Podiatrists.
Affiliation Lutheran
Facilities Dining room; Activities room; Chapel; Crafts room; Laundry room; Barber-/Beauty shop; Library.
Activities Arts and Crafts; Cards; Games; Reading groups; Prayer groups; Movies; Shopping trips; Dances/Social or cultural gatherings; Ceramic shop; Gardens.
Description Skyline Manor and Villa is a retirement facility which strives to meet all the needs of its 500 plus residents. Offers a "home within a home" where residents go on with their private lives, with their own furnishings but with all the services needed to facilitate their getting older. Offers in-apartment nursing services along with 2 nursing homes on premises.

Thomas Fitzgerald Veterans Home
156th and Maple Rd, Omaha, NE, 68164 (402) 554-2180
Admin Gerald N Rhone. *Medical Dir/Dir of Nursing* John G Brazer MD.
Licensure Skilled Care; Intermediate Care. *Beds* 182.
Ownership Public.
Staff Physicians 1 (ft), 1 (pt); RNs 9 (ft); LPNs 14 (ft); Nurses aides 45 (ft); Occupational therapists 1 (ft); Activities coordinators 1 (ft).
Facilities Dining room; Physical therapy room; Activities room; Chapel; Crafts room; Laundry room; Barber/Beauty shop; Library; Kitchenette; Game room; Pavilion; Canteen; Pharmacy; Dental laboratory.
Activities Arts and Crafts; Cards; Games; Reading groups; Prayer groups; Movies; Shopping trips; Dances/Social or cultural gatherings; Bingo; Luncheons; Exercise programs.
Description This facility is located on the western edge of the city of Omaha. The facility is for veterans, their wives or widows. It is a 182-bed skilled facility plus 10 beds for boarding home care.

Ville de Sante Nursing Home
6032 Ville de Sante Dr, Omaha, NE, 68104 (402) 571-6770
Admin Donna Suing. *Medical Dir/Dir of Nursing* Joan Arnold.
Licensure Intermediate Care. *Beds* 128. *Certified* Medicaid.
Ownership Proprietary.
Admissions Requirements Minimum age 50;

Medical examination; Physician's request.
Staff RNs 3 (ft), 2 (pt); LPNs 4 (ft), 2 (pt); Nurses aides 25 (ft), 20 (pt); Activities coordinators 1 (ft), 1 (pt).
Facilities Dining room; Activities room; Chapel; Crafts room; Laundry room; Barber/Beauty shop; Library.
Activities Arts and Crafts; Cards; Games; Reading groups; Prayer groups; Movies; Shopping trips; Dances/Social or cultural gatherings.
Description Our activity program is very active. We stress a home-like atmosphere with quality nursing care given by a dedicated staff.

Williams Care Manor
3525 Evans St, Omaha, NE, 68111 (402) 451-5060
Admin Kinze M Williams. *Medical Dir/Dir of Nursing* Jeanette Moore.
Licensure Intermediate Care. *Beds* 60. *Certified* Medicaid.
Ownership Proprietary.
Admissions Requirements Medical examination; Physician's request.
Staff Physicians; RNs 2 (ft); LPNs 4 (ft), 2 (pt); Orderlies 2 (ft); Nurses aides 20 (ft), 6 (pt); Physical therapists; Recreational therapists; Occupational therapists; Activities coordinators; Dietitians; Podiatrists.
Facilities Dining room; Activities room; Chapel; Crafts room; Laundry room; Barber/Beauty shop.
Activities Arts and Crafts; Cards; Games; Reading groups; Prayer groups; Movies; Shopping trips; Dances/Social or cultural gatherings.

ONEILL

O'Neill Senior Citizen's Home
Box 756, O'Neill, NE, 68763 (402) 336-2384
Admin James R Falk.
Licensure Intermediate Care. *Beds* 72. *Certified* Medicaid.
Ownership Proprietary.
Staff RNs 2 (ft); LPNs 3 (ft); Nurses aides 20 (ft), 5 (pt); Physical therapists 1 (pt); Activities coordinators 1 (ft); Dietitians 1 (ft).
Facilities Dining room; Physical therapy room; Activities room; Chapel; Crafts room; Laundry room; Barber/Beauty shop.
Activities Arts and Crafts; Cards; Games; Reading groups; Prayer groups; Movies; Shopping trips; Dances/Social or cultural gatherings.

OSCEOLA

Osceola Good Samaritan Center
Box 507, Osceola, NE, 68651 (402) 747-2691
Admin James W Barta.
Licensure Intermediate Care. *Beds* 65. *Certified* Medicaid.
Ownership Nonprofit.
Admissions Requirements Medical examination; Physician's request.
Staff Physicians 2 (pt); RNs 2 (pt); LPNs 2 (ft), 6 (pt); Nurses aides 9 (ft), 19 (pt); Physical therapists 1 (pt); Activities coordinators 1 (ft); Dietitians 1 (pt).
Facilities Dining room; Physical therapy room; Activities room; Chapel; Crafts room; Laundry room; Barber/Beauty shop.

Activities Arts and Crafts; Cards; Games; Reading groups; Prayer groups; Movies; Shopping trips; Dances/Social or cultural gatherings; Community activities; Annual special events; Annual bazaar.

OXFORD

Walker Post Manor*
404 W Derby, Oxford, NE, 68967 (308) 824-3293
Admin Dolores J Woodruff.
Licensure Intermediate Care. *Beds* 56. *Certified* Medicaid.
Ownership Proprietary.

PALMER

The Coolidge Center*
Palmer, NE, 68864 (308) 894-2735
Admin Shirley Stratman.
Licensure Intermediate Care. *Beds* 37. *Certified* Medicaid.
Ownership Nonprofit.

PAPILLION

Huntington Park Care Center
1507 Gold Coast Rd, Papillion, NE, 68046 (402) 339-6010
Admin Susan E Anagnostou.
Licensure Intermediate Care. *Beds* 100. *Certified* Medicaid.
Ownership Proprietary.
Admissions Requirements Medical examination.
Staff RNs 3 (ft); LPNs 5 (pt); Nurses aides 11 (ft), 22 (pt); Recreational therapists 1 (pt); Activities coordinators 1 (pt); Dietitians 1 (pt).
Facilities Dining room; Activities room; Crafts room; Laundry room; Barber/Beauty shop; Library.
Activities Arts and Crafts; Cards; Games; Reading groups; Prayer groups; Movies; Shopping trips; Dances/Social or cultural gatherings.
Description Center is located in a suburban and rural setting, close to hospital, 7 miles to Offutt AFB; semi-private and private rooms; van for transportation.

Papillion Manor Inc
610 S Polk St, Papillion, NE, 68046 (402) 339-7700
Admin Virginia Chase.
Licensure Intermediate Care. *Beds* 83. *Certified* Medicaid.
Ownership Proprietary.
Admissions Requirements Medical examination.
Staff RNs 2 (ft), 5 (pt); LPNs 1 (ft), 3 (pt); Orderlies 1 (pt); Nurses aides 10 (ft), 25 (pt); Activities coordinators 1 (ft); Dietitians 1 (pt); Podiatrists 1 (pt).
Facilities Dining room; Physical therapy room; Activities room; Chapel; Barber/Beauty shop.
Activities Arts and Crafts; Cards; Games; Reading groups; Prayer groups; Movies; Shopping trips; Dances/Social or cultural gatherings.

PAWNEE CITY

Pawnee Manor Inc*
438 12th St, Pawnee City, NE, 68420 (402) 852-2975
Admin Jenett Reed.
Licensure Intermediate Care. *Beds* 66. *Certified* Medicaid.
Ownership Proprietary.

PENDER

Pender Care Centre*
200 Valley View Dr, Pender, NE, 68047 (402) 385-3072
Admin Bernice Heath.
Licensure Intermediate Care. *Beds* 66. *Certified* Medicaid.
Ownership Proprietary.

PIERCE

Pierce Manor
515 E Main St, Pierce, NE, 68767 (402) 329-6228
Admin Janet Zierke.
Licensure Intermediate Care. *Beds* 86. *Certified* Medicaid.
Ownership Proprietary.
Staff RNs 1 (pt); LPNs 1 (ft), 2 (pt); Nurses aides 7 (ft), 21 (pt); Physical therapists 1 (pt); Speech therapists 1 (pt); Activities coordinators 1 (ft), 1 (pt); Dietitians 1 (pt).
Facilities Dining room; Activities room; Chapel; Crafts room; Laundry room; Barber/Beauty shop.
Activities Arts and Crafts; Cards; Games; Reading groups; Prayer groups; Movies; Shopping trips; Dances/Social or cultural gatherings.

PLAINVIEW

Plainview Manor*
Plainview, NE, 68769 (402) 582-3849
Admin Berkley E Homstedt.
Licensure Intermediate Care. *Beds* 60. *Certified* Medicaid.
Ownership Proprietary.

PLATTSMOUTH

Plattsmouth Manor*
602 S 18th St, Plattsmouth, NE, 68048 (402) 296-2800
Admin Ivan Craft.
Licensure Intermediate Care. *Beds* 140. *Certified* Medicaid.
Ownership Proprietary.

PONCA

Elms Health Care Center Inc*
Ponca, NE, 68770 (402) 755-2233
Admin Rozanne Elliott.
Licensure Intermediate Care. *Beds* 52.
Certified Medicaid.
Ownership Proprietary.

RANDOLPH

Colonial Manors of Randolph Inc
Box D, Randolph, NE, 68771 (402) 337-0444
Admin Roger E Johnson.
Licensure Intermediate Care. *Beds* 64. *Certified* Medicaid.
Ownership Proprietary.
Staff RNs 1 (pt); LPNs 2 (ft), 1 (pt); Orderlies 1 (ft), 1 (pt); Nurses aides 12 (ft), 1 (pt); Physical therapists 1 (ft), 1 (pt); Occupational therapists 1 (pt); Activities coordinators 1 (ft), 1 (pt); Dietitians 1 (pt); Dentists 1 (pt).
Facilities Dining room; Activities room; Chapel; Laundry room; Barber/Beauty shop.
Activities Arts and Crafts; Cards; Games; Reading groups; Prayer groups; Movies; Shopping trips; Dances/Social or cultural gatherings.
Description Facility features low rates and good care.

RAVENNA

Ravenna Good Samaritan Home*
411 W Genoa, Ravenna, NE, 68869 (308) 452-3230
Admin Eleanor M Carter.
Licensure Intermediate Care. *Beds* 83. *Certified* Medicaid.
Ownership Nonprofit.
Affiliation Lutheran

RED CLOUD

Sprague Nursing Home*
7th and Locust Sts, Red Cloud, NE, 68970 (402) 746-3414
Admin Harry M Sprague.
Licensure Intermediate Care. *Beds* 52. *Certified* Medicaid.
Ownership Proprietary.

SAINT EDWARD

Cloverlodge Care Center*
Box B, Saint Edward, NE, 68660 (402) 678-2294
Admin Denise Nespor.
Licensure Intermediate Care. *Beds* 65. *Certified* Medicaid.
Ownership Proprietary.

SAINT PAUL

Heritage Living Center*
920 Jackson St, Saint Paul, NE, 68873 (308) 754-4837
Admin Doris Raasch.
Licensure Intermediate Care. *Beds* 74. *Certified* Medicaid.
Ownership Proprietary.

SARGENT

Sargent Nursing Home
S Hwy 183, Sargent, NE, 68874 (308) 527-4201
Admin Connie Disbrow.
Licensure Intermediate Care. *Beds* 33. *Certified* Medicaid.

Ownership Proprietary.
Staff RNs 1 (pt); LPNs 1 (ft), 2 (pt); Nurses aides 6 (ft); Activities coordinators 1 (pt).
Facilities Dining room; Activities room; Laundry room; Barber/Beauty shop.
Activities Arts and Crafts; Cards; Games; Reading groups; Prayer groups; Movies; Shopping trips; Dances/Social or cultural gatherings.
Description Clean and attractive facility in small town with country atmosphere; air conditioned; excellent food; local hospital and pharmacy with larger medical centers within 100 miles; local ambulance services; community involvement; personalized care.

SCHUYLER

Schuyler Senior Citizen's Home
2023 Colfax Ave, Schuyler, NE, 68661 (402) 352-3977
Admin Charles R Huyink.
Licensure Intermediate Care. *Beds* 72. *Certified* Medicaid.
Ownership Proprietary.
Staff Physicians 4 (ft); RNs 2 (ft); LPNs 2 (ft); Orderlies 1 (pt); Nurses aides 14 (ft), 9 (pt); Activities coordinators 1 (ft).
Facilities Dining room; Chapel; Laundry room; Barber/Beauty shop.
Activities Arts and Crafts; Cards; Games; Reading groups; Prayer groups; Movies; Shopping trips; Dances/Social or cultural gatherings.

SCOTTSBLUFF

Scottsbluff Villa*
111 W 36th St, Scottsbluff, NE, 69361 (308) 635-2019
Admin Melvin Williams.
Licensure Intermediate Care. *Beds* 134. *Certified* Medicaid.
Ownership Proprietary.

SCRIBNER

Good Samaritan Center
815 Logan St, Scribner, NE, 68057 (402) 664-2527
Admin Ronald A Krause.
Licensure Intermediate Care. *Beds* 81. *Certified* Medicaid.
Ownership Nonprofit.
Admissions Requirements Medical examination; Physician's request.
Staff RNs 1 (ft), 2 (pt); LPNs 5 (pt); Nurses aides 2 (ft), 20 (pt); Physical therapists 1 (ft), 1 (pt); Recreational therapists 2 (pt); Activities coordinators 1 (ft); Dietitians 1 (pt).
Affiliation Lutheran
Facilities Dining room; Physical therapy room; Activities room; Chapel; Crafts room; Laundry room; Barber/Beauty shop; Library.
Activities Arts and Crafts; Cards; Games; Reading groups; Prayer groups; Movies; Shopping trips; Dances/Social or cultural gatherings.

SEWARD

Anna Sundermann Home
446 Pinewood Ave, Seward, NE, 68434 (402) 643-2902
Admin Karen E McConnell.
Licensure Intermediate Care. *Beds* 61. *Certified* Medicaid.
Ownership Nonprofit.
Admissions Requirements Minimum age 55; Medical examination.
Staff RNs 7 (ft), 1 (pt); LPNs 2 (pt); Nurses aides 9 (ft), 17 (pt); Activities coordinators 1 (ft).
Facilities Dining room; Activities room; Chapel; Crafts room; Laundry room; Barber/Beauty shop; Library.
Activities Arts and Crafts; Cards; Games; Reading groups; Prayer groups; Movies; Shopping trips; Dances/Social or cultural gatherings.
Description Excellent physical therapy program for all residents; reality orientation, stimulation, music therapy for disoriented residents.

Bethesda Care Center of Seward*
624 Pinewood Ave, Seward, NE, 68434 (402) 643-4561
Admin Larry Smith.
Licensure Intermediate Care. *Beds* 56. *Certified* Medicaid.
Ownership Nonprofit.

SIDNEY

Lodgepole Plaza Nursing Home
1435 Toledo, Sidney, NE, 69162 (308) 254-4756
Admin Charlotte Fleming.
Licensure Intermediate Care. *Beds* 54. *Certified* Medicaid.
Ownership Proprietary.
Admissions Requirements Medical examination.
Staff RNs 1 (ft), 2 (pt); LPNs 3 (ft), 2 (pt); Nurses aides 11 (ft); Recreational therapists 1 (ft); Activities coordinators 1 (ft); Dietitians 1 (ft).
Facilities Dining room; Physical therapy room; Activities room; Crafts room; Laundry room; Barber/Beauty shop; Library.
Activities Arts and Crafts; Cards; Games; Reading groups; Prayer groups; Movies; Dances/Social or cultural gatherings.
Description Facility offers 24-hour professional, supervised nursing care; cheerful and comfortable home with private and semi-private rooms; sprinkler protected; activities program; physical therapy by physician referral; open visiting hours.

SOUTH SIOUX CITY

Green Acres Nursing Home*
3501 Dakota Ave, South Sioux City, NE, 68776 (402) 494-4273
Admin Jerry Albright.
Licensure Intermediate Care. *Beds* 84. *Certified* Medicaid.
Ownership Proprietary.

Matney's Colonial Manor*
3200 G St, South Sioux City, NE, 68776 (402) 494-3043
Admin Edward H Matney.
Licensure Intermediate Care. *Beds* 66. *Certified* Medicaid.
Ownership Proprietary.

SPALDING

Friendship Villa of Spalding*
Spalding, NE, 68665 (308) 497-2426
Admin Hope Rott.
Licensure Intermediate Care. *Beds* 54. *Certified* Medicaid.
Ownership Proprietary.

STANTON

Stanton Nursing Home
PO Box 397, Stanton, NE, 68779 (402) 439-2201
Admin Ted Boese. *Medical Dir/Dir of Nursing* Dr David.
Licensure Intermediate Care. *Beds* 69. *Certified* Medicaid.
Ownership Public.
Admissions Requirements Medical examination.
Staff Physicians 2 (pt); RNs 2 (pt); LPNs 3 (ft), 2 (pt); Nurses aides 20 (ft), 5 (pt); Physical therapists 1 (pt); Occupational therapists 1 (pt); Speech therapists 1 (pt); Activities coordinators 1 (ft); Dietitians 1 (pt); Dentists 1 (pt).
Facilities Dining room; Physical therapy room; Activities room; Chapel; Laundry room; Barber/Beauty shop.
Activities Arts and Crafts; Cards; Games; Reading groups; Prayer groups; Movies; Shopping trips; Dances/Social or cultural gatherings.

STROMSBURG

Midwest Covenant Home Inc*
615 E 9th St, Stromsburg, NE, 68666 (402) 764-2711
Admin Robert L Greenwall.
Licensure Intermediate Care. *Beds* 88. *Certified* Medicaid.
Ownership Nonprofit.

STUART

Parkside Manor
Stuart, NE, 68780 (402) 924-3263
Admin Evelyn Troshynski.
Licensure Intermediate Care. *Beds* 47. *Certified* Medicaid.
Ownership Public.
Admissions Requirements Medical examination.
Staff RNs 1 (pt); LPNs 2 (ft); Orderlies 1 (ft); Orderlies 15 (ft), 3 (pt); Physical therapists 1 (pt); Recreational therapists; Occupational therapists; Speech therapists; Activities coordinators 1 (ft); Dietitians 1 (pt); Dentists; Ophthalmologists; Podiatrists; Audiologists.
Facilities Dining room; Activities room; Chapel; Crafts room; Laundry room; Barber/Beauty shop.

Activities Arts and Crafts; Cards; Games; Reading groups; Prayer groups; Movies; Shopping trips; Dances/Social or cultural gatherings. *Description* Facility is proud to be able to provide one-to-one nursing services, a benefit of being a smaller nursing home which provides homey atmosphere.

SUPERIOR

Good Samaritan Center*
Hwy 14 N, Superior, NE, 68978 (402) 879-4791
Admin Diane Berens.
Licensure Intermediate Care. *Beds* 84. *Certified* Medicaid.
Ownership Nonprofit.
Affiliation Lutheran

SUTHERLAND

Bethesda Care Center of Sutherland*
333 Maple, Sutherland, NE, 69165 (308) 386-4393
Admin Joan L Anderson.
Licensure Intermediate Care. *Beds* 62. *Certified* Medicaid.
Ownership Nonprofit.

SUTTON

Sutton Community Home*
1106 N Sauders St, Sutton, NE, 68979 (402) 773-5557
Admin Myrna Ulmer.
Licensure Intermediate Care. *Beds* 50. *Certified* Medicaid.
Ownership Proprietary.

SYRACUSE

Good Samaritan Center*
1622 Walnut St, Syracuse, NE, 68446 (402) 269-2251
Admin Mary Kraus.
Licensure Intermediate Care. *Beds* 113. *Certified* Medicaid.
Ownership Nonprofit.
Affiliation Lutheran

TECUMSEH

Maple Grove Home
Rt 2, Tecumseh, NE, 68450 (402) 335-2885
Admin Dennis Mattheis.
Licensure Intermediate Care. *Beds* 30.
Ownership Nonprofit.
Staff RNs 1 (ft), 1 (pt); LPNs 1 (pt); Nurses aides 3 (ft), 8 (pt); Activities coordinators 1 (ft).
Facilities Dining room; Activities room; Chapel; Crafts room; Laundry room; Barber/Beauty shop.
Activities Arts and Crafts; Cards; Games; Reading groups; Prayer groups; Movies.

Tecumseh Care Center*
3rd St, Tecumseh, NE, 68450 (402) 335-3357
Admin Charles Haas and Mary C Haas.

Licensure Intermediate Care. *Beds* 73. *Certified* Medicaid.
Ownership Proprietary.

TEKAMAH

Takamah S-C-H Inc*
823 M St, Tekamah, NE, 68061 (402) 374-1414
Admin Michael Ryan.
Licensure Intermediate Care. *Beds* 65. *Certified* Medicaid.
Ownership Proprietary.

TILDEN

Heritage Villa of Tilden Inc*
Box 400, Tilden, NE, 68781 (402) 368-5388
Admin Gwendolyn Koinzan.
Licensure Intermediate Care. *Beds* 52.
Certified Medicaid.
Ownership Proprietary.

TRENTON

El Dorado Manor
E Junction and Hwys 34 and 25, Trenton, NE, 68044 (308) 334-5241
Admin Virginia L McClure.
Licensure Intermediate Care. *Beds* 52. *Certified* Medicaid.
Ownership Public.
Admissions Requirements Minimum age 35; Medical examination; Physician's request.
Staff RNs 3 (pt); Physical therapists 1 (pt); Activities coordinators 1 (ft); Dietitians 1 (pt).
Facilities Dining room; Physical therapy room; Activities room; Chapel; Crafts room; Laundry room; Barber/Beauty shop; Library.
Activities Arts and Crafts; Cards; Games; Reading groups; Prayer groups; Movies; Shopping trips.
Description Facility is built in the shape of a plus sign, the administration office and living room being in the front along with a multipurpose room. Offers private and semi-private rooms, bordered by a garden and patio area and dining room. Facility takes pride in a very caring atmosphere, with plenty of tender loving care, and excellent food with many home-baked products being served. Features an excellent activity program and much community involvement.

UTICA

Bethesda Care Center
Utica, NE, 68456 (402) 534-2041
Admin Alene E Dittmar. *Medical Dir/Dir of Nursing* Roger Meyer MD.
Licensure Intermediate Care. *Beds* 47. *Certified* Medicaid.
Ownership Nonprofit.
Admissions Requirements Medical examination; Physician's request.
Staff RNs 1 (ft), 2 (pt); LPNs 4 (pt); Nurses aides 10 (ft), 10 (pt); Physical therapists 1 (pt); Recreational therapists 1 (pt); Occupational therapists 1 (pt); Speech therapists 1 (pt); Activities coordinators 1 (ft); Dietitians 1 (pt); Dentists 1 (pt); Audiologists 1 (pt).

Facilities Dining room; Activities room; Chapel; Crafts room; Laundry room; Barber/Beauty shop.
Activities Arts and Crafts; Cards; Games; Reading groups; Prayer groups; Movies; Shopping trips; Dances/Social or cultural gatherings.

VALENTINE

Pine View Good Samaritan Center
W Hwy 83, Valentine, NE, 69201 (402) 376-1260
Admin Marvin Sackschewsky.
Licensure Intermediate Care. *Beds* 66. *Certified* Medicaid.
Ownership Nonprofit.
Admissions Requirements Medical examination; Physician's request.
Staff RNs 2 (ft), 1 (pt).
Affiliation Lutheran
Facilities Dining room; Physical therapy room; Activities room; Chapel; Crafts room; Laundry room; Barber/Beauty shop.
Activities Arts and Crafts; Cards; Games; Prayer groups; Movies; Shopping trips; Dances/Social or cultural gatherings.

VALLEY

Colonial Manor*
PO Box 375, 300 W Meigs, Valley, NE, 68064 (402) 359-2533
Admin Linda Boddy.
Licensure Intermediate Care. *Beds* 60. *Certified* Medicaid.
Ownership Proprietary.

VERDIGRE

Alpine Village of Verdigre
Box 130, Verdigre, NE, 68783 (402) 668-2209
Admin Patricia McElhose. *Medical Dir/Dir of Nursing* James G Carlson MD.
Licensure Intermediate Care. *Beds* 59. *Certified* Medicaid.
Ownership Public.
Admissions Requirements Medical examination.
Staff Physicians; RNs 1 (ft), 1 (pt); LPNs 1 (ft), 2 (pt); Nurses aides 8 (ft), 15 (pt); Activities coordinators 1 (ft); 1 (ft) Social workers; Physical therapy aides 2 (pt).
Facilities Dining room; Physical therapy room; Activities room; Chapel; Crafts room; Laundry room; Barber/Beauty shop; Pool room with TV.
Activities Arts and Crafts; Cards; Games; Reading groups; Prayer groups; Movies; Shopping trips; Dances/Social or cultural gatherings; Numerous clubs; Resident's Council.

WAHOO

Haven House
1145 Laurel St, Wahoo, NE, 68066 (402) 443-3737
Admin Lorraine M Syverson.
Licensure Intermediate Care. *Beds* 75. *Certified* Medicaid.
Ownership Proprietary.

Admissions Requirements Minimum age 16; Medical examination.
Staff RNs 3 (ft), 2 (pt); LPNs 1 (ft), 3 (pt); Nurses aides 21 (ft), 11 (pt); Activities coordinators 1 (ft), 1 (pt).
Facilities Dining room; Laundry room; Barber/Beauty shop.
Activities Arts and Crafts; Cards; Games; Reading groups; Prayer groups; Movies; Shopping trips.

Saunders County Care Center*
844 W 9th St, Wahoo, NE, 68066 (402) 443-4685
Admin Minnie M Olsen.
Licensure Intermediate Care. *Beds* 75. *Certified* Medicaid.
Ownership Public.

WAKEFIELD

Wakefield Health Care Center*
306 Ash St, Wakefield, NE, 68784 (402) 287-2244
Admin W Russell Swigart Jr.
Licensure Intermediate Care. *Beds* 65. *Certified* Medicaid.
Ownership Public.

WAUNETA

Heritage of Wauneta
427 W Legion St, Box 1104, Wauneta, NE, 69045 (308) 394-5738
Admin Elaine E Hink. *Medical Dir/Dir of Nursing* Nona Kerchal.
Licensure Intermediate Care. *Beds* 52. *Certified* Medicaid.
Ownership Nonprofit.
Admissions Requirements Medical examination.
Staff RNs 1 (ft), 1 (pt); LPNs 1 (pt); Orderlies 1 (ft), 1 (pt); Nurses aides 10 (ft), 6 (pt); Activities coordinators 1 (pt).
Facilities Dining room; Activities room; Chapel; Laundry room; Barber/Beauty shop.
Activities Games; Reading groups; Prayer groups; Movies; Shopping trips; Dances/Social or cultural gatherings.
Description Resident orientated programs developed through resident requests and input. We try to involve the community as much as possible and attend community functions.

WAUSA

Valley View Home
Wausa, NE, 68786 (402) 586-2010
Admin Phyllis Hoy.
Licensure Intermediate Care. *Beds* 52. *Certified* Medicaid.
Ownership Proprietary.
Staff RNs 1 (ft), 2 (pt); LPNs 1 (ft); Activities coordinators 1 (ft).
Facilities Dining room; Activities room; Crafts room; Laundry room; Barber/Beauty shop.
Activities Arts and Crafts; Cards; Games; Reading groups; Prayer groups; Movies; Shopping trips; Dances/Social or cultural gatherings.
Description Home is located in a small, very supportive community.

WAYNE

Wayne Care Center*
918 Main St, Wayne, NE, 68787 (402) 375-1922
Admin Alan P Cooper.
Licensure Intermediate Care. *Beds* 94. *Certified* Medicaid.
Ownership Proprietary.

WEST POINT

West Point Nursing Home*
Rt 3, Prospect Rd, West Point, NE, 68788 (402) 372-2441
Admin Betty J Wackel.
Licensure Intermediate Care. *Beds* 72. *Certified* Medicaid.
Ownership Proprietary.

WILBER

Wilber Nursing Home*
610 N Main, Wilber, NE, 68465 (402) 821-2179
Admin Richard Duba.
Licensure Intermediate Care. *Beds* 120. *Certified* Medicaid.
Ownership Public.

WISNER

Wisner Manor
N 9th, Wisner, NE, 68791 (402) 529-3286
Admin Bonnie McGinnis.
Licensure Intermediate Care. *Beds* 65. *Certified* Medicaid.
Ownership Public.
Admissions Requirements Medical examination.
Staff RNs 1 (ft), 2 (pt); LPNs 4 (pt); Nurses aides 5 (ft), 17 (pt); Physical therapists 1 (ft); Reality therapists 1 (pt); Activities coordinators 1 (ft); Dietitians 1 (pt); Dentists 1 (pt).
Facilities Dining room; Physical therapy room; Activities room; Chapel; Crafts room; Laundry room; Barber/Beauty shop; Library.
Activities Arts and Crafts; Cards; Games; Reading groups; Prayer groups; Movies; Shopping trips; Dances/Social or cultural gatherings.

WOOD RIVER

Western Hall County Good Samaritan Center
1401 East St, Box 517, Wood River, NE, 68883-0517 (308) 583-2214
Admin Robert E Sutton.
Licensure Intermediate Care. *Beds* 65. *Certified* Medicaid.
Ownership Nonprofit.
Admissions Requirements Medical examination; Physician's request.
Staff RNs 1 (ft); LPNs 3 (ft), 1 (pt); Nurses aides 13 (ft), 4 (pt); Activities coordinators 2 (pt).
Facilities Dining room; Activities room; Chapel; Crafts room; Laundry room; Barber/Beauty shop; Library.
Activities Arts and Crafts; Cards; Games; Reading groups; Prayer groups; Movies; Shopping trips; Dances/Social or cultural gatherings; Daily services.
Description Facility offers occupational therapy, physical therapy, audio and speech therapy, and dietician. Located in a quiet small town setting just 15 miles from Nebraska's third largest city, Grand Island.

WYMORE

Good Samaritan Center 1
105 E "D" St, Wymore, NE, 68466 (402) 645-3354
Admin Joan Pierce.
Licensure Intermediate Care. *Beds* 59. *Certified* Medicaid.
Ownership Nonprofit.
Staff RNs 1 (ft); LPNs 2 (ft), 4 (pt); Nurses aides 5 (ft), 15 (pt); Activities coordinators 1 (ft).
Affiliation Lutheran
Facilities Dining room; Activities room; Chapel; Crafts room; Laundry room; Barber/Beauty shop; Library.
Activities Arts and Crafts; Cards; Games; Movies; Shopping trips.
Description Facility features excellent care for the aged in clean, well-lighted, attractive surroundings.

YORK

The Hearthstone*
2319 Lincoln Ave, York, NE, 68467 (402) 362-4333
Admin Susan Lynn Leif.
Licensure Intermediate Care. *Beds* 173. *Certified* Medicaid.
Ownership Nonprofit.

NEVADA

BOULDER CITY

Boulder City Care Center*
601 Adams Blvd, Boulder City, NV, 89005
(702) 293-5151
Admin Susan Cabral.
Licensure Skilled Care. *Beds* 84. *Certified* Medicaid; Medicare.

CALIENTE

Grover C Dils Medical Center
Hwy 93 N, Caliente, NV, 89008 (702)
726-3174
Admin Dorine Soper.
Licensure Skilled Care. *Beds* 13. *Certified* Medicaid; Medicare.

CARSON CITY

Carson Convalescent Center*
2898 Hwy 50 E, Carson City, NV, 89701 (702)
882-3301
Admin Jane Hirsch.
Licensure Skilled Care. *Beds* 74. *Certified* Medicaid; Medicare.

Eagle Valley Children's Home
Rt 1, Box 755, Carson City, NV, 89701 (702)
882-1112
Admin Dee Davis. *Medical Dir/Dir of Nursing* Tom Goode.
Licensure Intermediate Care for Mentally Retarded. *Beds* 15. *Certified* Medicaid.
Admissions Requirements Medical examination; Physician's request.
Staff Physicians 1 (pt); RNs 2 (ft), 2 (pt); LPNs 5 (ft); Nurses aides 17 (ft); Physical therapists 1 (ft); Recreational therapists 1 (ft); Occupational therapists 1 (pt); Speech therapists 1 (pt); Dietitians 1 (pt).
Facilities Dining room; Physical therapy room; Activities room; Laundry room.
Activities Movies; Shopping trips.
Description Eagle Valley Children's Home is a 24-hour care facility for mentally retarded children and adults.

Sierra Convalescent Center*
201 Koontz Ln, Carson City, NV, 89701 (702)
883-3622

Admin Irene Kugler.
Licensure Skilled Care. *Beds* 151. *Certified* Medicaid; Medicare.

EAST ELY

White Pine Care Center
1500 Ave G, East Ely, NV, 89315 (702)
289-8801
Admin Russell D Fay.
Licensure Skilled Care. *Beds* 99. *Certified* Medicaid; Medicare.
Staff Physicians 4 (pt); RNs 4 (ft), 1 (pt); LPNs 10 (ft); Orderlies 3 (ft); Nurses aides 32 (ft); Physical therapists 1 (pt); Activities coordinators 1 (ft).
Facilities Dining room; Physical therapy room; Activities room; Laundry room; Barber/Beauty shop.
Activities Arts and Crafts; Cards; Games; Prayer groups; Movies; Birthday parties; Picnics.

ELKO

Ruby Mountains Manor*
701 Walnut St, Elko, NV, 89801 (702)
738-8051
Admin Kenneth W Cook Jr.
Licensure Skilled Care; Intermediate Care.
Beds SNF 50; ICF 23. *Certified* Medicaid; Medicare.

FALLON

Fallon Convalescent Center
365 W "A" St, Fallon, NV, 89406 (702)
423-6551
Admin Thomas R Stutchman. *Medical Dir/Dir of Nursing* Dr Curt Carlson.
Licensure Skilled Care. *Beds* 150. *Certified* Medicaid; Medicare.
Admissions Requirements Medical examination; Physician's request.
Staff Physicians 6 (ft); RNs 12 (ft); LPNs 14 (ft); Orderlies 6 (ft); Nurses aides 48 (ft); Physical therapists 1 (ft); Activities coordinators 2 (ft); Dietitians 1 (ft); Dentists 1 (ft).
Facilities Dining room; Physical therapy room; Activities room; Crafts room; Laundry room; Barber/Beauty shop; Conference room.
Activities Arts and Crafts; Cards; Games; Reading groups; Prayer groups; Movies; Shop-

ping trips; Dances/Social or cultural gatherings.
Description Rural community with stable staff, located 60 miles from Reno, Nevada.

HAWTHORNE

Lefa L Seran Skilled Nursing Facility*
PO Box 1516, 1st and A Sts, Hawthorne, NV, 89415 (702) 945-2461
Admin Richard N Munger.
Licensure Skilled Care. *Beds* 20. *Certified* Medicaid; Medicare.

HENDERSON

Glen Halla Intermediate Care Facility
1745 Athol St, Henderson, NV, 89044 (702)
565-8748
Admin Mary Ann Dolfi.
Licensure Intermediate Care. *Beds* 48. *Certified* Medicaid.
Staff Physicians 4 (ft); RNs 2 (ft), 1 (pt); LPNs 3 (ft), 3 (pt); Orderlies 1 (pt); Nurses aides 8 (ft), 4 (pt); Activities coordinators 1 (ft); Dietitians 1 (ft).
Facilities Dining room; Activities room; Laundry room.
Activities Arts and Crafts; Cards; Games; Reading groups; Prayer groups; Movies; Shopping trips; Dances/Social or cultural gatherings.
Description We are geared towards rehabilitating our residents to independent living. We have a very high success rate. We allow our residents many benefits and an opportunity to do things that are related to their lifestyle prior to admission.

Henderson Convalescent Center*
1180 E Lake Mead Dr, Henderson, NV, 89105
(702) 565-8555
Admin Charles C Perry Jr.
Licensure Skilled Care. *Beds* 120. *Certified* Medicaid; Medicare.

LAS VEGAS

Beverly Manor
660 Desert Ln, Las Vegas, NV, 89106 (702)
382-5580
Admin Joyce L Dahlen. *Medical Dir/Dir of Nursing* Henry Ewy MD.
Licensure Skilled Care. *Beds* 200. *Cer-*

tified Medicaid; Medicare.
Staff RNs 15 (ft), 1 (pt); LPNs 14 (ft); Orderlies 4 (ft); Nurses aides 63 (ft), 1 (pt); Recreational therapists 2 (ft); Activities coordinators 1 (ft); Podiatrists 1 (pt).
Facilities Dining room; Physical therapy room; Activities room; Crafts room; Laundry room; Barber/Beauty shop.
Activities Arts and Crafts; Cards; Games; Reading groups; Prayer groups; Movies; Dances/Social or cultural gatherings.

Charleston Health Care Center
2035 W Charleston Blvd, Las Vegas, NV, 89102 (702) 386-7980
Admin Marian Nielson. *Medical Dir/Dir of Nursing* Thomas Quam MD.
Licensure Skilled Care. *Beds* 100. *Certified* Medicaid; Medicare.
Admissions Requirements Medical examination; Physician's request.
Staff Physical therapists 1 (pt); Reality therapists 1 (ft); Recreational therapists 1 (ft); Occupational therapists 1 (pt); Speech therapists 1 (pt); Activities coordinators 1 (ft); Dietitians 1 (pt); Dentists 1 (pt); Ophthalmologists 1 (pt); Podiatrists 1 (pt); Audiologists 1 (pt).
Facilities Dining room; Physical therapy room; Activities room; Crafts room; Laundry room; Barber/Beauty shop; Central courtyard; Cable TV.
Activities Arts and Crafts; Cards; Games; Reading groups; Prayer groups; Movies; Shopping trips; Dances/Social or cultural gatherings.
Description Facility is newly redecorated with traditional design for home-like surroundings; church services for all denominations; pets in residence.

Desert Developmental Center
1300 S Jones Blvd, Las Vegas, NV, 89158 (702) 870-0220
Admin Henry Meece.
Licensure Intermediate Care for Mentally Retarded. *Beds* 94. *Certified* Medicaid.

El Jen Convalescent Hospital
5538 W Duncan Dr, Las Vegas, NV, 89106 (702) 645-2606
Admin James M Toomey. *Medical Dir/Dir of Nursing* LeRoy Wolever MD.
Licensure Skilled Care. *Beds* 74. *Certified* Medicaid; Medicare.
Staff Physicians 10 (pt); RNs 8 (ft), 1 (pt); LPNs 2 (ft), 1 (pt); Orderlies 2 (ft); Nurses aides 45 (ft); Physical therapists 1 (pt); Reality therapists 1 (pt); Recreational therapists 1 (pt); Occupational therapists 1 (pt); Speech therapists 1 (pt); Activities coordinators 2 (ft); Dietitians 1 (ft), 1 (pt); Dentists 1 (pt); Ophthalmologists 1 (pt); Podiatrists 1 (pt); Audiologists 1 (pt); Social workers 1 (ft).
Facilities Dining room; Physical therapy room; Activities room; Crafts room; Laundry room; Barber/Beauty shop.
Activities Arts and Crafts; Cards; Games; Reading groups; Prayer groups; Movies; Shopping trips; Dances/Social or cultural gatherings.
Description Facility features a diners club, resident council, greetings committee, rhythm band, exercise class, gardening club, reminiscent group, and patient involvement in planning activities.

Gaye Haven Intermediate Care Facility Inc
1813 Betty Ln, Las Vegas, NV, 89115 (702) 452-8399
Admin Sandra V Manetas. *Medical Dir/Dir of Nursing* Amanda Blount DO.
Licensure Intermediate Care. *Beds* 20. *Certified* Medicaid.
Admissions Requirements Minimum age 20; Physician's request.
Staff Physicians 1 (pt); RNs 2 (pt); LPNs 3 (ft), 2 (pt); Nurses aides 3 (ft), 2 (pt); Reality therapists 1 (pt); Recreational therapists 1 (pt); Activities coordinators 1 (ft); Dietitians 1 (ft).
Facilities Dining room; Activities room; Crafts room; Laundry room.
Activities Arts and Crafts; Games; Movies; Shopping trips.
Description Facility is a 20-bed facility featuring intermediate care with planned outings and activities. Meals served according to diets prescribed.

Hillhaven Convalescent Center*
5659 Duncan Dr, Las Vegas, NV, 89130 (702) 645-1900
Admin Judy A Clark.
Licensure Skilled Care. *Beds* 125. *Certified* Medicaid; Medicare.

Las Vegas Convalescent Center*
2832 Maryland Pkwy, Las Vegas, NV, 89109 (702) 735-5848
Admin Myra G Stade.
Licensure Skilled Care. *Beds* 77. *Certified* Medicaid; Medicare.

Torrey Pines Care Center*
1701 S Torrey Pines Dr, Las Vegas, NV, 89102-2999 (702) 871-0005
Admin Sam Sparks.
Licensure Intermediate Care. *Beds* 116. *Certified* Medicaid.

Vegas Valley Convalescent Hospital
2945 Casa Vegas St, Las Vegas, NV, 89109 (702) 735-7179
Admin Charles C Perry Jr. *Medical Dir/Dir of Nursing* Dr Robert Shreck.
Licensure Skilled Care. *Beds* 102. *Certified* Medicaid; Medicare.
Admissions Requirements Medical examination; Physician's request.
Staff RNs 10 (ft), 2 (pt); LPNs 15 (ft), 4 (pt); Orderlies 5 (ft); Nurses aides 50 (ft), 5 (pt); Physical therapists 1 (pt); Occupational therapists 1 (pt); Activities coordinators 2 (pt); Dietitians 2 (pt).
Facilities Dining room; Physical therapy room; Activities room; Crafts room; Laundry room; Barber/Beauty shop.
Activities Arts and Crafts; Cards; Games; Movies; Shopping trips; Dances/Social or cultural gatherings.

LOVELOCK

Pershing General Hospital and Nursing Home
855 6th St, PO Box 661, Lovelock, NV, 89419 (702) 273-2621
Admin Jansen N Blanton. *Medical Dir/Dir of Nursing* J Johnson MD.
Licensure Skilled Care. *Beds* 25. *Cer-*

tified Medicaid; Medicare.
Admissions Requirements Minimum age 50; Physician's request.
Staff Physicians 2 (ft); RNs 10 (ft); LPNs 4 (ft); Orderlies 3 (ft); Nurses aides 12 (ft); Physical therapists 1 (pt); Reality therapists 1 (ft); Recreational therapists 1 (pt); Activities coordinators 1 (ft); Dietitians 1 (pt); Dentists 1 (pt); Podiatrists 1 (pt).

NORTH LAS VEGAS

North Las Vegas Care Center
3215 Cheyenne Ave, North Las Vegas, NV, 89030 (702) 649-7800
Admin Paul M Boyar. *Medical Dir/Dir of Nursing* Dr Henry Ewy.
Licensure Intermediate Care. *Beds* 104. *Certified* Medicaid.
Facilities Dining room; Physical therapy room; Activities room; Crafts room; Laundry room; Barber/Beauty shop.
Activities Arts and Crafts; Cards; Games; Reading groups; Prayer groups; Movies; Shopping trips; Dances/Social or cultural gatherings.

RENO

Physician's Hospital for Extended Care*
2045 Silverada Blvd, Reno, NV, 89512 (702) 359-3161
Admin Kathy L Wagner.
Licensure Skilled Care. *Beds* 100. *Certified* Medicaid; Medicare.

Reno Convalescent Center*
1300 Mill St, Reno, NV, 89502 (702) 786-1933
Admin Norma J Beales.
Licensure Skilled Care. *Beds* 119. *Certified* Medicaid; Medicare.

Riverside Hospital for Skilled Care
2865 Idlewild Dr, Reno, NV, 89509 (702) 329-0691
Admin Patricia Cornelsen. *Medical Dir/Dir of Nursing* Grant Anderson MD.
Licensure Skilled Care. *Beds* 182. *Certified* Medicaid; Medicare.
Admissions Requirements Physician's request.
Staff Physicians 1 (pt); RNs 10 (ft); LPNs 10 (ft); Nurses aides 95 (ft); Physical therapists 1 (ft); Reality therapists 1 (ft); Recreational therapists 1 (ft); Speech therapists 1 (pt); Activities coordinators 1 (ft); Dietitians 1 (pt); Dentists 1 (pt); Podiatrists 1 (pt).
Facilities Dining room; Physical therapy room; Activities room; Crafts room; Laundry room; Barber/Beauty shop; Library.
Activities Arts and Crafts; Cards; Games; Reading groups; Prayer groups; Movies; Shopping trips; Dances/Social or cultural gatherings; All faiths church services; Casino trips; Dinner outings.
Description Facility sits on 4 acres of wooded area with many trees and shrubbery, free of street noises; landscaped interior garden area.

SPARKS

Sierra Developmental Center*
605 S 21st St, Sparks, NV, 89431 (702)
789-0550
Admin David E Luke.
Licensure Intermediate Care for Mentally
Retarded. *Beds* 78. *Certified* Medicaid.

Sierra Health Center*
1835 Oddie Blvd, Sparks, NV, 89431 (702)
359-5420
Admin Tom W Morton.
Licensure Skilled Care; Intermediate Care.
Beds SNF 50; ICF 100. *Certified* Medicaid;
Medicare.

TONOPAH

Nye General Hospital
825 Erie Main, Tonopah, NV, 89049 (702)
482-6233
Admin Ben Aguilera. *Medical Dir/Dir of
Nursing* Ronald Crouch MD.
Licensure Skilled Care. *Beds* 24. *Cer-
tified* Medicaid; Medicare.
Staff Physicians 1 (ft), 1 (pt); RNs 2 (ft); LPNs
4 (ft); Orderlies 1 (ft); Nurses aides 5 (ft);
Activities coordinators 1 (ft); Dietitians 1 (pt).
Facilities Dining room; Activities room; Laun-
dry room; Barber/Beauty shop.
Activities Arts and Crafts; Cards; Games;
Reading groups; Movies; Shopping trips; Dan-
ces/Social or cultural gatherings.
Description Facility is in small town with a
family-type setting.

WINNEMUCCA

Humboldt General Hospital*
118 E Haskell St, Winnemucca, NV, 89445
(702) 623-5222
Admin E J Hanssen.
Licensure Skilled Care. *Beds* 14. *Certified* Medicaid; Medicare.

YERINGTON

Lyon Health Center*
PO Box 940, Suprise at Whitacre, Yerington,
NV, 89447 (702) 463-2301
Admin Paul E LeCave.
Licensure Skilled Care. *Beds* 18. *Cer-
tified* Medicaid; Medicare.

NEW HAMPSHIRE

BEDFORD

Bedford Nursing Home
480 Donald St, Bedford, NH, 03102 (603) 627-4147
Admin Norman L Tiercotti. *Medical Dir/Dir of Nursing* Dr William Heslin.
Licensure Intermediate Care. *Beds* 102. *Certified* Medicaid.
Staff Physicians 1 (pt); RNs 8 (ft), 10 (pt); LPNs 6 (pt); Nurses aides 15 (ft), 34 (pt); Physical therapists 1 (pt); Reality therapists 1 (pt); Recreational therapists 1 (ft); Occupational therapists 1 (pt); Speech therapists 1 (pt); Activities coordinators 1 (ft); Dietitians 1 (pt); Dentists 1 (pt); Ophthalmologists 1 (pt); Podiatrists 1 (pt); Audiologists 1 (pt).
Facilities Dining room; Physical therapy room; Activities room; Crafts room; Laundry room; Barber/Beauty shop; Library.
Activities Arts and Crafts; Cards; Games; Prayer groups; Movies; Shopping trips; Dances/Social or cultural gatherings.
Description Facility has a staff who feels the dignity of human life is their chief concern.

Briston Manor Nursing Home*
Ridgewood Rd, Bedford, NH, 03102 (603) 623-8805
Admin James Glenn.
Licensure Skilled Care; Intermediate Care. *Beds* SNF 9; ICF 141. *Certified* Medicaid; Medicare.

BERLIN

Coos County Nursing Home*
Rt 2, Cates Hill Rd, Berlin, NH, 03570 (603) 752-2343
Admin John Langell.
Licensure Intermediate Care. *Beds* 100. *Certified* Medicaid.

Saint Vincent dePaul Nursing Home*
Providence Ave, Berlin, NH, 03570 (603) 752-1820
Admin Sr Lorraine Boyer.
Licensure Intermediate Care. *Beds* 80. *Certified* Medicaid.

CHESTER

Jodoin Home*
RFD 1, Box 45, Chester, NH, 03036 (603) 483-5508
Admin Anita Jodoin.
Licensure Skilled Care. *Beds* 4.

CLAREMONT

Claremont Nursing Home
Elm and Hanover Sts, Claremont, NH, 03743 (603) 542-2606
Admin Marcia Couitt.
Licensure Intermediate Care. *Beds* 50. *Certified* Medicaid.
Admissions Requirements Medical examination; Physician's request.
Staff Physicians 7 (pt); RNs 3 (ft), 1 (pt); LPNs 3 (ft), 1 (pt); Nurses aides 14 (ft), 16 (pt); Physical therapists 1 (pt); Occupational therapists 1 (pt); Speech therapists 1 (pt); Activities coordinators 1 (ft); Dietitians 1 (pt); Podiatrists 1 (pt).
Facilities Dining room; Activities room; Chapel; Crafts room; Laundry room; Barber/Beauty shop.
Activities Arts and Crafts; Cards; Games; Reading groups; Prayer groups; Movies; Dances/Social or cultural gatherings.
Description Facility is situated in a rural setting with over 2 acres of landscaped grounds for residents to enjoy throughout the summer with games, barbecues, and parades.

Sullivan County Home
RFD 1, Claremont, NH, 03743 (603) 542-9511
Admin Omer Ahern.
Licensure Intermediate Care. *Beds* 194. *Certified* Medicaid.

CONCORD

Havenwood Nursing Home*
33 Christian Ave, Concord, NH, 03301 (603) 224-5364
Admin Albert Dwyer.
Licensure Skilled Care; Intermediate Care. *Beds* SNF 28; ICF 30. *Certified* Medicaid; Medicare.

McKerley Nursing Home*
20 Maitland St, Concord, NH, 03301 (603) 224-6561
Admin James McKerley.
Licensure Skilled Care; Intermediate Care. *Beds* SNF 49; ICF 152. *Certified* Medicaid; Medicare.

New Hampshire Centennial Home*
96 Pleasant St, Concord, NH, 03301 (603) 225-2021
Admin Arthur Bruemmer.
Licensure Skilled Care. *Beds* 46.

New Hampshire Odd Fellows Home*
200 Pleasant St, Concord, NH, 03301 (603) 225-6644
Admin Leslie Sherman.
Licensure Intermediate Care. *Beds* 47.
Affiliation Independent Order of Odd Fellows

DERRY

Birchwood Nursing Home*
20 Chester Rd, Derry, NH, 03038 (603) 432-3801
Admin Dorothy Bimpson.
Licensure Intermediate Care. *Beds* 52. *Certified* Medicaid.

Hoodkroft Convalescent Center*
Peabody Rd, Derry, NH, 03038 (603) 434-1566
Admin Joan McGorry.
Licensure Intermediate Care. *Beds* 100. *Certified* Medicaid; Medicare.

DOVER

Dover House Healthcare*
Plaza Dr, Dover, NH, 03820 (603) 742-2676
Admin Brian Horan.
Licensure Skilled Care; Intermediate Care. *Beds* SNF 11; ICF 91. *Certified* Medicaid; Medicare.

Saint Ann Home
Dover Point Rd, Dover, NH, 03820 (603) 742-2612
Admin Sr M Helen Rosarie.
Licensure Intermediate Care. *Beds* 53. *Certified* Medicaid.

Strafford County Home*
Rt 3, Dover, NH, 03820 (603) 742-1348
Admin Mary Louise Horn.
Licensure Intermediate Care. *Beds* 205. *Certified* Medicaid.

Wentworth Home for the Aged*
795 Central Ave, Dover, NH, 03820 (603) 742-1915
Admin Mary Jane Allen.
Licensure Skilled Care. *Beds* 36.

EPPING

Rockingham County Nursing Home*
PO Box 427, Epping, NH, 03042 (603) 679-5335
Admin William Sturtevant.
Licensure Intermediate Care. *Beds* 290. *Certified* Medicaid.

EPSOM

Epsom Manor*
Rt 1, Epsom Traffic Circle, Epsom, NH, 03234 (603) 736-4772
Admin Susan Lemire.
Licensure Intermediate Care. *Beds* 108. *Certified* Medicaid.

EXETER

Eventide Home*
81 High St, Exeter, NH, 03833 (603) 772-5743
Admin Sandra Cross.
Licensure Intermediate Care. *Beds* 19. *Certified* Medicaid.

Goodwin's of Exeter*
Hampton Rd, Exeter, NH, 03833 (603) 778-0531
Admin William Gilmore.
Licensure Intermediate Care. *Beds* 81. *Certified* Medicaid.

FRANCONIA

North Country Rehabilitation Center
The Willows, Main St, Franconia, NH, 03580 (603) 823-5502
Admin Patricia W Blood.
Licensure Skilled Care; Intermediate Care. *Beds* 62. *Certified* Medicaid; Medicare.

FRANKLIN

Merrill Manor Annex
167 S Main St, Franklin, NH, 03235 (603) 934-5447
Admin Tom Matzke.
Licensure Intermediate Care. *Beds* 24. *Certified* Medicaid.

Mountain Ridge Health Care Center
221 Victory Dr, Franklin, NH, 03235 (603) 934-5447
Admin Edwina Sedgley.
Licensure Intermediate Care. *Beds* 18. *Certified* Medicaid.

Admissions Requirements Medical examination.
Staff Physicians 8 (pt); RNs 3 (ft), 1 (pt); LPNs 2 (ft), 3 (pt); Nurses aides 20 (ft), 12 (pt); Physical therapists; Reality therapists; Recreational therapists 1 (ft); Occupational therapists; Speech therapists; Activities coordinators 1 (ft); Dietitians; Dentists; Ophthalmologists; Podiatrists; Audiologists.
Facilities Dining room; Activities room; Crafts room; Barber/Beauty shop.
Activities Arts and Crafts; Cards; Games; Prayer groups; Movies; Shopping trips; Dances/Social or cultural gatherings.
Description A new facility will open in January, 1985 to be called Mountain Ridge Health Care Center. (Formerly Merrill Manor Nursing Home.)

Peabody Home*
24 Peabody Pl, Franklin, NH, 03235 (603) 934-3718
Admin Arthur Swenson.
Licensure Intermediate Care. *Beds* 29.

FREMONT

Colonial Manor*
PO Box 101, Main St, Fremont, NH, 03044 (603) 895-2911
Admin Russell Philbrick.
Licensure Skilled Care; Intermediate Care. *Beds* 18; ICF 50.

GOFFSTOWN

Bel-Air Nursing Home
19 Center St, Goffstown, NH, 03046 (603) 497-4871
Admin William R Coker.
Licensure Intermediate Care. *Beds* 32. *Certified* Medicaid.
Admissions Requirements Medical examination; Physician's request.
Staff RNs 1 (ft), 1 (pt); LPNs 1 (ft), 5 (pt); Nurses aides 5 (ft), 12 (pt); Recreational therapists 1 (pt); Activities coordinators 1 (pt).
Facilities Dining room; Activities room; Crafts room; Laundry room; Barber/Beauty shop.
Activities Arts and Crafts; Cards; Games; Prayer groups; Movies; Shopping trips; Dances/Social or cultural gatherings.
Description Home offers home-like atmosphere; easy access from Manchester and Boston.

Hillsborough County Nursing Home
Rt 2, Goffstown, NH, 03045 (603) 669-2117
Admin Robert Curran. *Medical Dir/Dir of Nursing* Dr M Dupuis.
Licensure Intermediate Care. *Beds* 300. *Certified* Medicare.
Ownership Public.
Staff RNs 43 (ft); LPNs 9 (ft); Nurses aides 126 (ft); Physical therapists 1 (ft); Recreational therapists 1 (ft); Activities coordinators 1 (ft).
Facilities Dining room; Physical therapy room; Activities room; Chapel; Crafts room; Laundry room; Barber/Beauty shop; Auditorium.
Activities Arts and Crafts; Cards; Games;

Reading groups; Prayer groups; Movies; Shopping trips; Dances/Social or cultural gatherings; Ceramics; Woodworking; Leather; Cooking.

HAMPTON

Seacoast Health Center*
22 Tuck Rd, Hampton, NH, 03842 (603) 926-4551
Admin Daniel Trahan.
Licensure Intermediate Care. *Beds* 83. *Certified* Medicaid.

HANOVER

Hanover Terrace Healthcare
Lyme Rd, Hanover, NH, 03755 (603) 643-2854
Admin Robert Schooler. *Medical Dir/Dir of Nursing* Dr Richard Whiting.
Licensure Skilled Care; Intermediate Care. *Beds* 100. *Certified* Medicaid; Medicare.
Staff Physicians 1 (pt); RNs 7 (ft), 1 (pt); LPNs 6 (ft), 1 (pt); Nurses aides 28 (ft); Physical therapists 1 (pt); Occupational therapists 1 (ft); Speech therapists 1 (pt); Activities coordinators 1 (pt); Dietitians 1 (pt); Dentists 1 (pt); Podiatrists 1 (pt); Audiologists 1 (pt); Social workers 1 (ft); Staff Coordinator 1 (ft).
Facilities Dining room; Physical therapy room; Activities room; Chapel; Crafts room; Laundry room; Barber/Beauty shop; Library.
Activities Arts and Crafts; Cards; Games; Reading groups; Movies; Shopping trips; Dances/Social or cultural gatherings.
Description Only nursing home in Hanover with close proximity to Dartmouth College. Excellent reputation for quality care. New retirement apartment complex of 28 units ready for occupancy in July, 1984.

HILLSBOROUGH

Hillsboro House Nursing Home
School St, Hillsborough, NH, 03244 (603) 464-5561
Admin David Irwin.
Licensure Intermediate Care. *Beds* 30. *Certified* Medicaid.

HUDSON

Fairview Nursing Home*
Rt 2, Lowell Rd, Hudson, NH, 03051 (603) 882-5261
Admin Brian Courville.
Licensure Intermediate Care. *Beds* 49. *Certified* Medicaid.

JAFFREY

Monadnock Christian Nursing Home*
PO Box 346, Jaffrey, NH, 03452 (603) 532-8762
Admin Dorothy Walsh.
Licensure Intermediate Care. *Beds* 51. *Certified* Medicaid.

KEENE

Country Way Retirement and Rehabilitation Center*
677 Court St, Keene, NH, 03431 (603) 357-3800
Admin Donald Duchano.
Licensure Intermediate Care. *Beds* 100. *Certified* Medicaid.

Monadnock Nursing Home
428 Main St, Keene, NH, 03431 (603) 352-0257
Admin Arthur Bottomley. *Medical Dir/Dir of Nursing* Dr Ballou Jr.
Licensure Intermediate Care. *Beds* 35. *Certified* Medicaid.
Staff RNs 2 (ft); LPNs 5 (ft); Nurses aides 9 (ft); Occupational therapists 1 (pt); Activities coordinators 1 (ft); Social workers 1 (ft).
Facilities Dining room; Activities room; Laundry room.
Activities Arts and Crafts; Cards; Games; Reading groups; Prayer groups; Movies; Shopping trips; Dances/Social or cultural gatherings.
Description Home is located in a large remodeled home; strives to aid each resident reach his/her potential for a happy life within a friendly homestyle atmosphere.

180 Court Home*
180 Court St, Keene, NH, 03431 (603) 352-7400
Admin Mary Lund.
Licensure Intermediate Care. *Beds* 15.

151 Court Home*
151 Court St, Keene, NH, 03431 (603) 352-7911
Admin Earl and Mary Lund.
Licensure Skilled Care. *Beds* 10.

Prospect Hill Home*
361 Court St, Keene, NH, 03431 (603) 352-0323
Admin Mary-Lou Hodgdon.
Licensure Skilled Care. *Beds* 20.

39 Summer House*
39 Summer St, Keene, NH, 03431 (603) 352-7117
Admin Earl Lund.
Licensure Intermediate Care. *Beds* 12.

Westwood Healthcare Center
298 Main St, Keene, NH, 03431 (603) 352-7311
Admin Lillian Watkins.
Licensure Skilled Care; Intermediate Care. *Beds* 72. *Certified* Medicaid; Medicare.

Woodward Home*
194–202 Court St, Keene, NH, 03431 (306) 352-3235
Admin Virginia Taylor.
Licensure Skilled Care. *Beds* 24.

KINGWOOD

Heartland of Preston County*
300 Miller Rd, Kingwood, NH, 26537 (304) 329-3195

Admin Eleanor Alvarez.
Licensure Skilled Care; Intermediate Care. *Beds* 111.

LACONIA

Belknap County Nursing Home*
1152 N Main St, Laconia, NH, 03246 (603) 524-4048
Admin Donald D Drouin Sr.
Licensure Intermediate Care. *Beds* 85. *Certified* Medicaid.
Staff Physicians 3 (pt); RNs 9 (ft), 2 (pt); LPNs 4 (ft), 3 (pt); Orderlies 2 (ft); Nurses aides 34 (ft), 4 (pt); Physical therapists 1 (ft), 2 (pt); Recreational therapists 1 (ft), 4 (pt); Occupational therapists 1 (pt); Speech therapists 1 (pt); Activities coordinators 1 (ft); Dietitians 1 (pt); Dentists 1 (pt); Ophthalmologists 1 (pt); Podiatrists 1 (pt).
Facilities Dining room; Physical therapy room; Activities room; Chapel; Laundry room; Barber/Beauty shop.
Activities Arts and Crafts; Cards; Games; Prayer groups; Movies; Shopping trips; Dances/Social or cultural gatherings.
Description Facility offers late breakfast for those residents who desire it, outside shaded patio, and regularly scheduled outside activities.

McKerley Health Care Center*
175 Blueberry Ln, Laconia, NH, 03246 (603) 524-3340
Admin Harold Baldwin.
Licensure Skilled Care; Intermediate Care. *Beds* SNF 26; ICF 82. *Certified* Medicaid; Medicare.

Saint Francis Home
Court St, Laconia, NH, 03246 (603) 524-0466
Admin Mother Dorothy. *Medical Dir/Dir of Nursing* E C Squires MD.
Licensure Intermediate Care. *Beds* 51. *Certified* Medicaid.
Admissions Requirements Minimum age 65; Medical examination.
Staff Physicians; RNs; LPNs; Nurses aides; Physical therapists; Recreational therapists; Occupational therapists; Speech therapists; Activities coordinators; Dietitians; Dentists; Ophthalmologists; Podiatrists; Audiologists.
Affiliation Roman Catholic
Facilities Dining room; Chapel; Laundry room; Barber/Beauty shop.
Activities Arts and Crafts; Cards; Games; Prayer groups; Movies; Shopping trips; Dances/Social or cultural gatherings.
Description The Home overlooks beautiful Lake Winnisquam, and residents watch the sailboats and motorboats in summer and the frozen lake with the many bob houses for ice fishing in winter. Close by are downtown shops and a shopping mall. The beautiful chapel and a resident chaplain are greatly appreciated.

Taylor Home*
435 Union Ave, Laconia, NH, 03246 (603) 524-3409
Admin Howard Chandler.
Licensure Skilled Care. *Beds* 42.

LANCASTER

Country Village Health Care Center
N Main St, Lancaster, NH, 03584 (603) 788-4935
Admin Daniel Estee.
Licensure Intermediate Care. *Beds* 86.
Staff Physicians 8 (pt); RNs 6 (ft), 4 (pt); LPNs 2 (ft), 2 (pt); Nurses aides 15 (ft), 10 (pt); Physical therapists 1 (pt); Recreational therapists 1 (ft); Occupational therapists 1 (pt); Speech therapists 1 (pt); Activities coordinators 1 (ft); Dietitians 1 (pt); Dentists 1 (pt); Podiatrists 1 (pt); Audiologists 1 (pt); Exercise therapists 1 (pt).
Facilities Dining room; Physical therapy room; Activities room; Chapel; Laundry room; Barber/Beauty shop.
Activities Arts and Crafts; Cards; Reading groups; Prayer groups; Movies; Shopping trips; Dances/Social or cultural gatherings.

LITTLETON

Oak Hill Residence*
8 Oak Hill Ave, Littleton, NH, 03561 (603) 444-5590
Admin Bryon and Rita Cascadden.
Licensure Skilled Care. *Beds* 4.

MANCHESTER

Gale Home
133 Ash St, Manchester, NH, 03103 (603) 622-6632
Admin Joan Lemire. *Medical Dir/Dir of Nursing* Dr Gregory White.
Licensure Intermediate Care. *Beds* 24. *Certified* Medicaid.
Admissions Requirements Females only; Medical examination.
Staff Physicians; RNs 2 (ft), 2 (pt); LPNs 2 (ft), 1 (pt); Nurses aides 3 (ft), 5 (pt); Physical therapists; Reality therapists; Recreational therapists 1 (pt); Occupational therapists; Speech therapists; Dietitians 3 (ft); Dentists; Ophthalmologists.
Facilities Dining room; Physical therapy room; Activities room; Crafts room; Laundry room; Barber/Beauty shop.
Activities Arts and Crafts; Cards; Games; Prayer groups; Movies; Shopping trips; Weekly entertainment.
Description Facility offers all private rooms, individually decorated, for permanent or monthly guests.

Hanover Hill Healthcare Center*
700 Hanover St, Manchester, NH, 03104 (603) 627-3826
Admin Theodore Lee.
Licensure Skilled Care; Intermediate Care. *Beds* SNF 6; ICF 115. *Certified* Medicaid; Medicare.

Mammoth Nursing Home*
1 Mammoth Rd, Manchester, NH, 03103 (603) 625-9891
Admin Ralph Allard.
Licensure Intermediate Care. *Beds* 55. *Certified* Medicaid.

Maple Leaf Health Care Center*
198 Pearl St, Manchester, NH, 03104 (603)
669-1660
Admin Rita Miville.
Licensure Skilled Care; Intermediate Care.
Beds SNF 27; ICF 81. *Certified* Medicaid.

Maple Leaf Nursing Home*
593 Maple St, Manchester, NH, 03104 (603)
669-1452
Admin Claire Lemire.
Licensure Intermediate Care. *Beds* 63. *Certified* Medicaid.

Masonic Home*
813 Beech St, Manchester, NH, 03104 (603)
669-7361
Admin Rene Lemire.
Licensure Skilled Care. *Beds* 52.
Affiliation Masons

McKerley Health Care Center—Manchester Inc
191 Hackett Hill Rd, Manchester, NH, 03103
(603) 668-8161
Admin Forrest McKerley.
Licensure Nursing Home. *Beds* 56.
Facilities Dining room; Physical therapy room;
Activities room; Crafts room; Laundry room;
Barber/Beauty shop.
Activities Arts and Crafts; Cards; Games;
Reading groups; Prayer groups; Shopping trips;
Dances/Social or cultural gatherings.
Description Formerly the Demers Nursing
Home, McKerley HCC—Manchester, Inc is a
modern private facility providing the highest
quality nursing care to its residents.

Mount Carmel Home*
235 Myrtle St, Manchester, NH, 03103 (603)
627-3811
Admin Mother Bernadette Therese.
Licensure Intermediate Care. *Beds* 120. *Certified* Medicaid.

Myrtle Convalescent Home*
83 Myrtle St, Manchester, NH, 03103 (603)
623-7110
Admin Grace Trahan.
Licensure Intermediate Care. *Beds* 34. *Certified* Medicaid.

Northwood Nursing Home*
668 Amherst St, Manchester, NH, 03104 (603)
625-6462
Admin Cynthia DuBois.
Licensure Intermediate Care. *Beds* 51. *Certified* Medicaid.

Saint Teresa's Manor
519 Bridge St, Manchester, NH, 03103 (603)
668-2373
Admin Sr Andre Marie Ross. *Medical Dir/Dir
of Nursing* Jonathan Jaffe.
Licensure Intermediate Care. *Beds* 51. *Certified* Medicaid.

Women's Aid Home*
180 Pearl St, Manchester, NH, 03104 (603)
669-6991
Admin Marjorie Huckabee.
Licensure Skilled Care. *Beds* 39.

MEREDITH

Golden View Health Care Center*
Rt 104, Meredith, NH, 03253 (603) 279-8111
Admin Jeanne Murray.
Licensure Intermediate Care. *Beds* 100. *Certified* Medicaid.

MILFORD

McKerley Health Care Center—Milford*
18 Crosby St, Milford, NH, 03055 (603)
673-7061
Admin Mark McKerley.
Licensure Skilled Care; Intermediate Care.
Beds SNF 22; ICF 57. *Certified* Medicaid;
Medicare.

Milford Nursing Home*
41 Elm St, Milford, NH, 03055 (603) 673-2907
Admin Barbara Lemay.
Licensure Intermediate Care. *Beds* 49. *Certified* Medicaid.

MILTON

Kraus House*
41 Old Wakefield Rd, Milton, NH, 03851 (603)
652-9977
Admin Donna Kraus.
Licensure Skilled Care. *Beds* 4.

NASHUA

The Courville at Nashua
22 Hunt St, Nashua, NH, 03060 (603)
889-5450
Admin Richard Courville. *Medical Dir/Dir of
Nursing* Dr John Posner.
Licensure Skilled Care; Intermediate Care.
Beds SNF 50; ICF.
Admissions Requirements Physician's request.
Staff RNs 10 (ft); LPNs 14 (ft); Orderlies 1 (ft);
Nurses aides 26 (ft); Physical therapists 2 (pt);
Recreational therapists 1 (pt); Occupational
therapists 1 (pt); Speech therapists 1 (pt);
Activities coordinators 1 (ft); Dietitians 1 (ft);
Dentists 1 (pt).
Facilities Dining room; Physical therapy room;
Activities room; Chapel; Crafts room; Laundry
room; Barber/Beauty shop; Library.
Activities Arts and Crafts; Cards; Games;
Reading groups; Prayer groups; Movies; Shopping trips; Dances/Social or cultural gatherings;
Current events.

Greenbriar Terrace Healthcare
55 Harris Rd, Nashua, NH, 03060 (603)
888-1573
Admin Wiliam Thoms.
Licensure Skilled Care; Intermediate Care.
Beds 300. *Certified* Medicaid; Medicare.

Mary and John Hunt Home*
10 Allds St, Nashua, NH, 03060 (603)
882-6511
Admin Christine Hallock.
Licensure Skilled Care. *Beds* 63.

Nightingale Home*
381 Main St, Nashua, NH, 03060 (603)
882-1770
Admin Paul Donnelly.
Licensure Skilled Care. *Beds* 8.

Norwell Home*
12 Concord St, Nashua, NH, 03060 (603)
889-9001
Admin Una B Shattuck.
Licensure Intermediate Care. *Beds* 18.

NEWPORT

Woodlawn Nursing Home*
84 Pine St, Newport, NH, 03773 (603)
863-1020
Admin Orey Gadway.
Licensure Intermediate Care. *Beds* 49. *Certified* Medicaid.

OSSIPEE

Carroll County Nursing Home
Ossipee, NH, 03864 (603) 539-7511
Admin Ricahrd J Hamel.
Licensure Intermediate Care. *Beds* 103. *Certified* Medicaid.

PENACOOK

McKerley Harris Hill Nursing Home*
30 Tremont St, Penacook, NH, 03303 (603)
753-6551
Admin Daniel Estee.
Licensure Skilled Care. *Beds* 11.

Merrimack County Nursing Home*
PO Box 9, Penacook, NH, 03303 (603)
224-2284
Admin Howard Teaf.
Licensure Intermediate Care. *Beds* 312. *Certified* Medicaid.

PETERBOROUGH

Pheasant Wood Nursing Home*
Pheasant Rd, Peterborough, NH, 03458 (603)
924-7267
Admin Jamie Pipher.
Licensure Skilled Care; Intermediate Care.
Beds SNF 18; ICF 83. *Certified* Medicaid;
Medicare.

PORTSMOUTH

Clipper Home*
188 Jones Ave, Portsmouth, NH, 03801 (603)
431-2530
Admin Douglas Stockbridge.
Licensure Intermediate Care. *Beds* 78.

Edgewood Manor*
928 South St, Portsmouth, NH, 03801 (603)
436-0099
Admin William Argue.
Licensure Skilled Care; Intermediate Care.
Beds SNF 50; ICF 106. *Certified* Medicaid;
Medicare.

Home for Aged Women
127 Parrott Ave, Portsmouth, NH, 03801
Medical Dir/Dir of Nursing Richard Atten-
borough MD.
Admissions Requirements Minimum age 75;
Females only; Medical examination; Physi-
cian's request.
Staff RNs 2 (ft), 4 (pt); LPNs 4 (pt); Nurses
aides 3 (ft), 3 (pt).
Facilities Dining room; Laundry room; Barber-
/Beauty shop; Library.
Activities Games; Shopping trips.
Description Facility is a retirement home with
a nursing unit; staff encourages independence;
dining room features family-style serving.

Mark Wentworth Home*
346 Pleasant St, Portsmouth, NH, 03801 (603)
436-0169
Admin Donald Reeves.
Licensure Skilled Care. *Beds* 52.

ROCHESTER

Academy Nursing Home*
28 Academy St, Rochester, NH, 03867 (603)
332-3359
Admin Frederick and Eileen Moulton.
Licensure Intermediate Care. *Beds* 31. *Certified* Medicaid.

Gafney Home for the Aged*
90 Wakefield St, Rochester, NH, 03867 (603)
332-2705
Admin Barbara Plante.
Licensure Skilled Care. *Beds* 20.

Rochester Manor*
Whitehall Rd, Rochester, NH, 03867 (603)
332-7711
Admin Mary Flynn.
Licensure Intermediate Care. *Beds* SNF 25;
ICF 83. *Certified* Medicaid.

SALEM

Salemhaven
23 Geremonty Dr, Salem, NH, 03079 (603)
893-5586
Admin Bruce Freeman.
Licensure Intermediate Care. *Beds* 100. *Certified* Medicaid.

WARNER

Austin Home Inc*
Webster Rd, Warner, NH, 03278 (603)
456-3525
Admin C Ivan Health.
Licensure Skilled Care. *Beds* 15.

Pine Rock Farm*
Denny Hill Rd, Box 266, Warner, NH, 03278
(603) 456-3181
Admin Judith Waschsmuth.
Licensure Skilled Care. *Beds* 15.

WEST CHESTERFIELD

Bert-Anne Annex*
PO Box 144, West Chesterfield, NH, 03466
(603) 256-6277
Admin Bertha Bergeron.
Licensure Skilled Care. *Beds* 6.

Bert-Anne Home for the Aged*
PO Box 144, West Chesterfield, NH, 03466
(603) 256-6277
Admin Bertha Bergeron.
Licensure Skilled Care. *Beds* 10.

WEST STEWARTSTOWN

Coos County Nursing Hospital
River Rd, West Stewartstown, NH, 03597 (603)
246-3321
Admin Noella Cote. *Medical Dir/Dir of
Nursing* Dana Merrithew MD.
Licensure Intermediate Care. *Beds* 101. *Certi-
fied* Medicaid.
Staff Physicians 5 (pt); RNs 6 (ft), 2 (pt); LPNs
3 (ft), 2 (pt); Nurses aides 30 (ft), 10 (pt);
Physical therapists 1 (pt); Occupational thera-
pists 1 (pt); Speech therapists 1 (pt); Activities
coordinators 1 (ft), 1 (pt); Dietitians 1 (pt);
Dentists 2 (pt).
Facilities Dining room; Physical therapy room;
Activities room; Chapel; Crafts room; Laundry
room; Barber/Beauty shop; Library.
Activities Arts and Crafts; Cards; Games;
Reading groups; Prayer groups; Movies; Shopping trips; Dances/Social or cultural gatherings.
Description Facility is situated in a beautiful
country setting overlooking Vermont and the
hills of Canada; residents enjoy walking around
the grounds and to the local town for shopping;
excellent community involvement. Individuals
who have a history of destroying property, sui-
cidal attempts, or of harming or disturbing others will not be admitted.

WESTMORELAND

Cedarcrest
Aldrich Rd, Westmoreland, NH, 03467 (603)
399-4446
Admin Sharon Ann Kaiser.
Licensure Nursing Home. *Beds* 23.

Cheshire County Nursing Home
Westmoreland, NH, 03467 (603) 399-4912
Admin Richard A Wilson.
Licensure Intermediate Care. *Beds* 150. *Certi-
fied* Medicaid.

WHITEFIELD

Morrison Nursing Home
2-6 Terrace Ave, Whitefield, NH, 03598 (603)
837-2541
Admin David Monahan. *Medical Dir/Dir of
Nursing* Dr Jorge de Nillafane.
Licensure Intermediate Care. *Beds* 51. *Certified* Medicaid.
Admissions Requirements Physician's request.
Staff Physicians 2 (pt); RNs 2 (ft), 1 (pt); LPNs
3 (ft); Nurses aides 20 (ft), 2 (pt); Physical therapists 1 (pt); Occupational therapists 1 (pt); Spee-

ch therapists 1 (pt); Activities coordinators 1
(ft); Dietitians 1 (pt); Dentists 1 (pt); Podiatrists
1 (pt).
Facilities Dining room; Activities room; Crafts
room; Laundry room; Barber/Beauty shop;
Library.
Activities Arts and Crafts; Cards; Games;
Reading groups; Prayer groups; Movies; Shopping trips; Dances/Social or cultural gatherings.

WOODSVILLE

Grafton County Nursing Home
PO Box 276, Woodsville, NH, 03785 (603)
787-6971
Admin William Siegmund.
Licensure Intermediate Care. *Beds* 139. *Certi-
fied* Medicaid.
Admissions Requirements Medical examina-
tion; Physician's request.
Staff Physicians 2 (pt); RNs 5 (ft), 7 (pt); LPNs
10 (ft), 6 (pt); Nurses aides 56 (ft), 15 (pt);
Physical therapists 1 (pt); Occupational thera-
pists 1 (pt); Speech therapists 1 (pt); Activities
coordinators 1 (ft); Dietitians 1 (pt); Dentists 1
(pt); Ophthalmologists 1 (pt); Podiatrists 1 (pt);
Audiologists 1 (pt); Activity Aides 3 (ft).
Facilities Dining room; Physical therapy room;
Activities room; Chapel; Crafts room; Laundry
room; Barber/Beauty shop; Library.
Activities Arts and Crafts; Cards; Games;
Reading groups; Prayer groups; Movies; Shop-
ping trips; Dances/Social or cultural gatherings.

NEW JERSEY

ALLENDALE

Allendale Nursing Home*
55 Harreton Rd, Allendale, NJ, 07401 (201) 825-0660
Admin Hecter and Ella Giancarlo.
Licensure Skilled Care; Intermediate Care.
Beds SNF 50; ICF 120. *Certified* Medicaid; Medicare.

Wiersma's Nursing Home*
703 Franklin Turnpike, Allendale, NJ, 07401 (201) 327-3150
Admin Alida J Wiersma.
Licensure Long-Term Care. *Beds* 18.

ALLENWOOD

Geraldine L Thompson Medical Home
Allenwood, NJ, 08720 (201) 938-5250
Admin Diana L Massaro. *Medical Dir/Dir of Nursing* Dr James Cashman.
Licensure Long-Term Care. *Beds* 73. *Certified* Medicaid.
Admissions Requirements Minimum age 18.
Staff Physicians 2 (pt); RNs 8 (ft), 2 (pt); LPNs 1 (ft); Orderlies 3 (ft); Nurses aides 24 (ft), 4 (pt); Physical therapists 1 (pt); Recreational therapists 3 (ft); Activities coordinators 1 (ft); Dietitians 1 (pt); Dentists 1 (pt); Podiatrists 1 (pt); Volunteer Coordinator 1 (ft).
Facilities Dining room; Activities room; Chapel; Crafts room; Laundry room; Barber/Beauty shop.
Activities Arts and Crafts; Cards; Games; Reading groups; Prayer groups; Movies; Shopping trips; Dances/Social or cultural gatherings; Video games.
Description Facility is located in a wooded setting; residents enjoy many outdoor activities in the summer months. Volunteer activities are extremely helpful in stimulation for patients.

ANDOVER

Andover Intermediate Care Center
Mulford Creamery, Andover, NJ, 07821 (201) 383-6200
Admin Carla Turco Icolari. *Medical Dir/Dir of Nursing* Dr Pavle Topalovic.
Licensure Intermediate Care. *Beds* 540. *Certified* Medicaid.
Admissions Requirements Physician's request.

Staff Physicians 1 (ft), 22 (pt); RNs 42 (ft), 21 (pt); LPNs 17 (ft), 10 (pt); Orderlies and; Nurses aides 142 (ft), 27 (pt); Physical therapists 1 (ft); Recreational therapists 10 (ft), 3 (pt); Speech therapists 1 (pt); Activities coordinators 1 (ft); Dietitians 2 (ft); Podiatrists 3 (pt); Physical therapy assistants 4 (ft).
Facilities Dining room; Physical therapy room; Activities room; Chapel; Crafts room; Laundry room; Barber/Beauty shop; Swimming pool; Miniature golf course.
Activities Arts and Crafts; Cards; Games; Reading groups; Prayer groups; Movies; Shopping trips; Dances/Social or cultural gatherings; Plays; Validation—fantasy groups; Sensory retraining; Aerobics.
Description Facility is in country-like setting with spacious lawns.

Andover Nursing and Convalescent
Mulford Creamery, Andover, NJ, 07821 (201) 383-6200
Admin Jeryl Turco. *Medical Dir/Dir of Nursing* Pavle Topalovic MD.
Licensure Skilled Care; Intermediate Care.
Beds 159. *Certified* Medicaid; Medicare.
Admissions Requirements Minimum age 20.
Staff Physical therapists 1 (ft); Recreational therapists 4 (ft); Occupational therapists 1 (pt); Speech therapists 1 (pt); Activities coordinators 1 (ft); Dietitians 1 (ft).
Facilities Dining room; Physical therapy room; Activities room; Chapel; Laundry room; Barber/Beauty shop; Library.
Activities Arts and Crafts; Cards; Games; Movies; Shopping trips.
Description Facility is located in beautiful rural area of Sussex County.

ATLANTIC CITY

Beachview Nursing and Convalescent Home
401 Boardwalk, Atlantic City, NJ, 08401 (609) 348-0171
Admin Josephine Boyd. *Medical Dir/Dir of Nursing* Harry P Goodman MD.
Licensure Skilled Care; Intermediate Care.
Beds 104. *Certified* Medicaid.
Admissions Requirements Minimum age 16.
Staff Physicians 5 (pt); RNs 5 (ft), 4 (pt); LPNs 3 (ft), 7 (pt); Orderlies 5 (ft); Nurses aides 29 (ft), 2 (pt); Physical therapists 1 (pt); Recreational therapists 2 (ft), 1 (pt); Occupational therapists 1 (pt); Speech therapists 1 (pt); Activities

coordinators 1 (ft); Dietitians 1 (ft); Dentists 1 (pt); Ophthalmologists 2 (pt); Podiatrists 1 (pt); Audiologists 1 (pt).
Facilities Dining room; Physical therapy room; Activities room; Laundry room; Barber/Beauty shop.
Activities Arts and Crafts; Cards; Games; Reading groups; Prayer groups; Movies; Shopping trips; Dances/Social or cultural gatherings.
Description Facility is located on the Boardwalk in Atlantic City.

Golden Crest Nursing Home*
29-33 N Vermont Ave, Atlantic City, NJ, 08401 (609) 344-8911
Admin Bruce Holden.
Licensure Skilled Care; Intermediate Care.
Beds 208. *Certified* Medicaid.

Presbyterian Home of Atlantic City—Madison House*
123 S Illinois Ave, Atlantic City, NJ, 08401 (609) 344-8191
Admin Edward Conklin.
Licensure Intermediate Care. *Beds* 26. *Certified* Medicaid.
Affiliation Presbyterian

South Carolina Ave Intermediate Care Facility
166 S South Carolina Ave, Atlantic City, NJ, 08401 (609) 344-2181
Admin Lee Jones. *Medical Dir/Dir of Nursing* Harry O Sweeney.
Licensure Skilled Care; Intermediate Care.
Beds 372. *Certified* Medicaid.
Staff RNs 40 (ft); LPNs 40 (ft); Orderlies 12 (ft); Recreational therapists 4 (ft); Activities coordinators 2 (ft); Dietitians 2 (ft).
Facilities Dining room; Physical therapy room; Activities room; Chapel; Laundry room; Barber/Beauty shop.
Activities Arts and Crafts; Games; Reading groups; Prayer groups; Movies; Shopping trips; Dances/Social or cultural gatherings.

Westside Convalescent Center*
2153 Venice Ave, Atlantic City, NJ, 08401 (609) 348-2656
Admin Mary Wilson.
Licensure Skilled Care; Intermediate Care.
Beds 30. *Certified* Medicaid.

ATLANTIC HIGHLANDS

Atlantic Highlands Nursing Home*
8 Middletown Ave, Atlantic Highlands, NJ,
07716 (201) 291-0600
Admin Gezor Kaszierer.
Licensure Skilled Care; Intermediate Care.
Beds 155. *Certified* Medicaid; Medicare.

BAYVILLE

Bay View Convalescent Center Inc
Lakeside Blvd, Bayville, NJ, 08721 (201)
269-0500
Admin Oscar Heller. *Medical Dir/Dir of
Nursing* William Jones DO.
Licensure Skilled Care; Intermediate Care.
Beds SNF 293; ICF 30. *Certified* Medicaid;
Medicare.
Admissions Requirements Physician's request.
Staff Physicians 3 (pt); RNs 19 (ft), 11 (pt);
LPNs 13 (ft), 6 (pt); Orderlies 3 (ft); Nurses
aides 84 (ft), 51 (pt); Physical therapists 1 (ft), 1
(pt); Recreational therapists 7 (ft); Occupational
therapists 1 (pt); Speech therapists 1 (pt);
Activities coordinators 1 (ft); Activities coordi-
nators 1 (ft); Dentists 1 (pt); Ophthalmologists
1 (pt); Podiatrists 1 (pt); Audiologists 1 (pt).
Facilities Dining room; Physical therapy room;
Activities room; Crafts room; Laundry room;
Barber/Beauty shop; Library.
Activities Arts and Crafts; Cards; Games; Prayer groups; Movies; Shopping trips.
Description Center has an excellent physical
therapy and activities group; located in a scenic
rural area with a private lake.

BELLEVILLE

Essex County Geriatrics Center
Belleville and Franklin Avenues, Belleville, NJ,
07109 (201) 751-7200
Admin Reginald R Wells. *Medical Dir/Dir of
Nursing* Ricardo P Alzadon.
Licensure Skilled Care; Intermediate Care.
Beds 332. *Certified* Medicaid.
Ownership Public.
Admissions Requirements Minimum age 18;
Medical examination; Physician's request.
Staff RNs 43 (ft); LPNs 50 (ft); Nurses aides
158 (ft); Physical therapists 1 (ft); Activities
coordinators 1 (ft); Dietitians 2 (ft).
Facilities Dining room; Physical therapy room;
Activities room; Crafts room; Barber/Beauty
shop.
Activities Arts and Crafts; Prayer groups;
Movies; Dances/Social or cultural gatherings.

BERKELEY HEIGHTS

Berkeley Hall Nursing Home
311 Springfield Ave, Berkeley Heights, NJ,
07922 (201) 464-9260
Admin Noel W Swan. *Medical Dir/Dir of
Nursing* Dr J J Aquino.
Licensure Long-Term Care. *Beds* 67.
Admissions Requirements Medical examina-
tion.
Staff Physicians 10 (pt); RNs 6 (ft), 5 (pt);
LPNs 8 (ft), 2 (pt); Nurses aides 11 (ft), 8 (pt);

Physical therapists 1 (pt); Recreational therapists 1 (ft); Occupational therapists 1 (pt); Speech therapists 1 (pt); Activities coordinators 1
(ft); Dietitians 1 (pt); Dentists 1 (pt); Ophthalmologists 1 (pt); Podiatrists 1 (pt); Audiologists
1 (pt).
Facilities Dining room; Physical therapy room;
Activities room; Chapel; Crafts room; Laundry
room; Barber/Beauty shop.
Activities Arts and Crafts; Cards; Games;
Reading groups; Prayer groups; Movies; Shopping trips; Dances/Social or cultural gatherings.
Description This is an intermediate-sized
facility that maintains a large professional staff
of RNs and LPNs in a setting very close to residential.

BERNARDSVILLE

Fellowship Deaconry Inc*
Shannon Lodge, Old Army Rd, Bernardsville,
NJ, 07924 (201) 766-0832
Admin Roy Gaida.
Licensure Long-Term Care; Residential Care.
Beds 74.
Ownership Nonprofit.

BLOOMFIELD

Hazelcrest Nursing Home
60 Hazelwood Rd, Bloomfield, NJ, 07003 (201)
743-2366
Admin Richard Del Vecchio Jr. *Medical Dir-
/Dir of Nursing* R Chhabria MD.
Licensure Long-Term Care. *Beds* 18.
Admissions Requirements Physician's request.
Staff Physicians 2 (pt); RNs 1 (ft), 4 (pt); LPNs
3 (ft), 3 (pt); Nurses aides 4 (ft), 3 (pt); Recreational therapists 1 (pt); Activities coordinators 1
(pt); Dietitians 1 (pt); Dentists 1 (pt); Ophthalmologists 1 (pt); Podiatrists 1 (pt); Audiologists
1 (pt).
Facilities Dining room; Activities room; Laun-
dry room.
Activities Arts and Crafts; Cards; Games;
Reading groups; Prayer groups.
Description Facility offers a noninstitutional,
home-like setting.

Park Manor Nursing Home*
23 Park Pl, Bloomfield, NJ, 07003 (201)
743-7772
Admin Arthur Corneliusen.
Licensure Long-Term Care. *Beds* 61.

Parklane Nursing Home Inc*
15 Church St, Bloomfield, NJ, 07003 (201)
748-4074
Admin Catherine Rittle.
Licensure Intermediate Care. *Beds* 30. *Certified* Medicaid.

BOONTON

New Jersey Firemen's Home
565 Lathrop Ave, Boonton, NJ, 07005 (201)
334-0024
Admin L G Hoth.
Licensure Long-Term Care; Residential Care.
Beds 77.
Admissions Requirements Medical examina-

tion.
Staff Physicians; RNs; LPNs; Orderlies;
Nurses aides; Activities coordinators.
Facilities Dining room; Activities room; Chap-
el; Laundry room; Barber/Beauty shop;
Library.
Activities Arts and Crafts; Cards; Games;
Movies.
Description Residents must have been a
fireman in the State of New Jersey.

Sarah Frances Nursing Home
Powerville Rd, Rt 1, Boonton, NJ, 07005 (201)
334-2454
Admin Timothy Doyle.
Licensure Skilled Care; Intermediate Care;
Residential Care. *Beds* 49; 85.
Admissions Requirements Minimum age 18.
Staff RNs 10 (ft); LPNs 2 (ft); Nurses aides 45
(ft); Physical therapists 1 (pt); Recreational ther-
apists 2 (ft); Occupational therapists 1 (pt);
Speech therapists 1 (pt); Activities coordinators
1 (ft); Dietitians 1 (pt).
Facilities Dining room; Activities room; Chap-
el; Crafts room; Laundry room; Barber/Beauty
shop; Library.
Activities Arts and Crafts; Cards; Games;
Reading groups; Prayer groups; Movies; Shopping trips; Dances/Social or cultural gatherings.
Description Facility is in a lovely country setting of 11 acres, near 2 community hospitals
serving 3 levels of care—skilled, intermediate,
and residential.

Tally Ho Manor*
Rt 1, Powerville Rd, Boonton, NJ, 07005 (201)
334-2454
Admin Timothy Doyle.
Licensure Long-Term Care; Residential Care.
Beds 109.

BOUND BROOK

Somerset Valley Nursing Home*
Donahue Rd, off Rt 22, Bound Brook, NJ,
08005 (201) 469-2000
Admin Robert Armbruster Jr.
Licensure Skilled Care. *Beds* 58. *Cer-
tified* Medicaid; Medicare.

BRIDEWATER

Bridgeway Convalescent Center*
270 Rt 28, Bridewater, NJ, 08807 (201)
722-7022
Admin Esther Gold.
Licensure Intermediate Care. *Beds* 120.

BRIDGETON

Cumberland Manor*
Rt 2, Cumberland Dr, Bridgeton, NJ, 08302
(609) 455-8000
Admin Starret L Hill.
Licensure Skilled Care; Intermediate Care.
Beds 196. *Certified* Medicaid.

Malloy Nursing Centre*
99 Manheim Ave, Bridgeton, NJ, 08302 (609)
455-2100

Admin Gerald Malloy.
Licensure Skilled Care; Intermediate Care.
Beds 185. *Certified* Medicaid; Medicare.

Rainbow Nursing Center
Big Oak Rd, RD 8, Box 318, Bridgeton, NJ,
08302 (609) 451-5000
Admin David J Kinder. *Medical Dir/Dir of
Nursing* Dr Stanley Leshner.
Licensure Long-Term Care. *Beds* 84.
Admissions Requirements Minimum age 21;
Medical examination.
Staff Physicians 3 (ft), 3 (pt); RNs 3 (ft), 7 (pt);
LPNs 5 (ft), 5 (pt); Nurses aides 21 (ft), 16 (pt);
Physical therapists 2 (pt); Reality therapists 1
(pt); Recreational therapists 1 (pt);
Occupational therapists 1 (pt); Speech
therapists 1 (pt); Activities coordinators 1 (ft), 1
(pt); Dietitians 1 (pt); Dentists 1 (pt);
Ophthalmologists 1 (pt); Podiatrists 1 (pt);
Audiologists 1 (pt).
Facilities Dining room; Physical therapy room;
Activities room; Crafts room; Laundry room;
Barber/Beauty shop; Book delivery from
library.
Activities Arts and Crafts; Cards; Games;
Reading groups; Prayer groups; Movies;
Shopping trips; Dances/Social or cultural
gatherings.
Description Center is located in a wooded area
within a country setting. Staff of professionals
provide quality care in a home-like atmosphere.
Emphasis is placed on providing patient
dignity and restorative nursing care.

BRIDGEWATER TOWNSHIP

Greenfield Convalescent Center
875 Rt 202-206 N, Bridgewater Township, NJ,
08876
Admin Linda E Reid. *Medical Dir/Dir of
Nursing* Brewster Miller MD.
Licensure Skilled Care. *Beds* 164.
Certified Medicaid; Medicare.
Ownership Proprietary.
Staff RNs 2 (ft), 9 (pt); LPNs 9 (ft), 6 (pt);
Nurses aides 34 (ft), 34 (pt); Physical therapists;
Recreational therapists 1 (ft), 2 (pt);
Occupational therapists; Speech therapists;
Activities coordinators 1 (ft); Dietitians;
Dentists; Ophthalmologists; Podiatrists.
Facilities Dining room; Physical therapy room;
Activities room; Chapel; Barber/Beauty shop;
Library.
Activities Arts and Crafts; Cards; Games;
Reading groups; Prayer groups; Movies;
Dances/Social or cultural gatherings.
Description Facility offers traditional home-like
setting complete with formal dining room;
activities provided for all levels of care; patio
available for warm weather.

Greenfield Convalescent Center
875 Rt 202-206 N, Bridgewater Township, NJ,
08876 (201) 526-8600
Admin Linda Reid. *Medical Dir/Dir of
Nursing* Dr Brewster Miller.
Licensure Skilled Care; Intermediate Care.
Beds 162. *Certified* Medicaid; Medicare.
Admissions Requirements Minimum age 18.
Facilities Dining room; Physical therapy room;
Activities room; Chapel; Crafts room; Laundry

room; Barber/Beauty shop; Library.
Activities Arts and Crafts; Cards; Games;
Reading groups; Prayer groups; Movies;
Dances/Social or cultural gatherings.
Description Greenfield offers short-term
vacation stays to patients and families which
has proven to be a popular service.

BURLINGTON

Burlington Woods Convalescent Center*
115 Sunset Rd, Burlington, NJ, 08016 (609)
387-3620
Admin Craig R Donoghy.
Licensure Skilled Care; Intermediate Care.
Beds 168. *Certified* Medicaid; Medicare.

Masonic Home of New Jersey
Jacksonville Rd, Burlington, NJ, 08016
Admin Joseph E Becker. *Medical Dir/Dir of
Nursing* Jhin J Cynn MD.
Licensure Skilled Care; Intermediate Care.
Beds 341. *Certified* Medicaid; Medicare.
Ownership Nonprofit.
Staff Physicians 1 (ft), 1 (pt); RNs 15 (ft), 5
(pt); LPNs 9 (ft), 4 (pt); Orderlies 3 (ft); Nurses
aides 85 (ft), 10 (pt); Physical therapists 2 (ft), 2
(pt); Reality therapists 3 (ft); Recreational
therapists 6 (ft); Occupational therapists 3 (ft);
Speech therapists; Activities coordinators 1 (ft);
Dietitians; Dentists 1 (pt); Ophthalmologists 1
(pt); Podiatrists 1 (pt).
Affiliation Masons
Facilities Dining room; Physical therapy room;
Activities room; Chapel; Crafts room; Laundry
room; Barber/Beauty shop; Library.
Activities Arts and Crafts; Cards; Games;
Reading groups; Prayer groups; Movies;
Shopping trips; Dances/Social or cultural
gatherings; Woodworking shop; Cultural
exchange programs; Trips.

CALIFON

Little Brook Nursing and Convalescent Home*
Sliker Rd, PO Box 398, Califon, NJ, 07830
(201) 832-2220
Admin Andrea Berry Shawn.
Licensure Skilled Care; Intermediate Care.
Beds 30. *Certified* Medicaid.

CAPE MAY COURT HOUSE

Cape May Care Center
Shore Rd, Box 538, Cape May Court House,
NJ, 08210 (609) 465-7633
Admin G Nedwed. *Medical Dir/Dir of
Nursing* S Melita MD.
Licensure Skilled Care. *Beds* 116.
Certified Medicaid; Medicare.
Admissions Requirements Minimum age 21.
Facilities Dining room; Physical therapy room;
Activities room; Chapel; Crafts room; Laundry
room; Barber/Beauty shop.
Activities Arts and Crafts; Cards; Games;
Reading groups; Prayer groups; Movies;
Shopping trips; Dances/Social or cultural
gatherings; Casino trips.
Description Facility offers a warm and caring
atmosphere, beautifully decorated with families
and residents in mind. VA approved.

Crest Haven
Cape May Court House, NJ, 08210 (609)
465-7911
Admin Robert Pastoria. *Medical Dir/Dir of
Nursing* Dr C F Carr.
Licensure Skilled Care; Intermediate Care.
Beds 140. *Certified* Medicaid.
Ownership Public.
Staff Physicians 4 (pt); RNs 9 (ft), 1 (pt); LPNs
18 (ft); Orderlies 2 (ft); Nurses aides 82 (ft);
Recreational therapists 3 (ft); Dietitians 1 (pt);
Dentists 1 (pt); Podiatrists 1 (pt).
Facilities Dining room; Activities room;
Laundry room; Barber/Beauty shop.
Activities Arts and Crafts; Cards; Games;
Reading groups; Prayer groups; Movies;
Shopping trips.
Description This is a county-owned institution.

South Cape Nursing Home
Stites Ave, Cape May Court House, NJ, 08210
(609) 465-5335
Admin Larry Powell.
Licensure Skilled Care; Intermediate Care.
Beds 40. *Certified* Medicaid.

CARNEYS POINT

Nicholas Nursing Home
5th and Park Ave, Carney's Point, NJ, 08069
(609) 299-6800
Admin Frank C Morton. *Medical Dir/Dir of
Nursing* A Auerbach DO.
Licensure Long-Term Care. *Beds* 180.
Staff RNs 8 (ft), 13 (pt); LPNs 5 (ft), 5 (pt);
Nurses aides 43 (ft), 38 (pt); Physical therapists
1 (ft); Reality therapists 1 (ft); Activities
coordinators 1 (pt); Activities coordinators 1
(ft); Dietitians 1 (pt); Dentists 2 (pt); Podiatrists
2 (pt).
Facilities Dining room; Physical therapy room;
Activities room; Chapel; Laundry room;
Barber/Beauty shop.
Activities Arts and Crafts; Cards; Games;
Reading groups; Prayer groups; Movies;
Shopping trips.
Description Facility is situated in southern New
Jersey with a beautiful view of the Delaware
River; park for picnics in summer; staff
encourages self-help through restorative
nursing.

CEDAR GROVE

Hartwyck West Nursing Home*
Lindsley Rd and Pompton Ave, Cedar Grove,
NJ, 07009 (201) 256-7220
Admin Emma Pavia.
Licensure Skilled Care; Intermediate Care.
Beds 113. *Certified* Medicaid; Medicare.

Waterview
536 Ridge Rd, Cedar Grove, NJ, 07009 (201)
239-9300
Admin Louise Macchia. *Medical Dir/Dir of
Nursing* Maurice Leon MD.
Licensure Skilled Care; Intermediate Care.
Beds 180. *Certified* Medicaid.
Admissions Requirements Minimum age 16.
Staff Physicians 1 (pt); RNs 5 (ft), 15 (pt);
LPNs 7 (ft), 3 (pt); Nurses aides 41 (ft), 13 (pt);

Recreational therapists 2 (ft); Activities coordinators 1 (ft); Dietitians 1 (pt).
Facilities Dining room; Activities room; Chapel; Crafts room; Barber/Beauty shop; Library; Snack shop.
Activities Arts and Crafts; Cards; Games; Prayer groups; Movies; Shopping trips; Dances/Social or cultural gatherings.

CHATHAM

Garden Terrace Nursing Home*
361 Main St, Chatham, NJ, 07938 (201) 635-0899
Admin Peter R Flemming.
Licensure Long-Term Care. *Beds* 34.

King James Nursing Home
415 Southern Blvd, Chatham, NJ, 07928 (201) 822-1500
Admin Joseph Desher. *Medical Dir/Dir of Nursing* Joseph Fennely MD.
Licensure Skilled Care. *Beds* 104.
Certified Medicaid; Medicare.
Admissions Requirements Minimum age 50; Medical examination; Physician's request.
Staff Physicians 17 (pt); RNs 15 (pt); LPNs 5 (pt); Orderlies 1 (pt); Nurses aides 42 (pt); Physical therapists 1 (ft); Recreational therapists 2 (ft); Occupational therapists 1 (pt); Speech therapists 1 (pt); Activities coordinators 1 (ft); Dietitians 1 (pt); Podiatrists 1 (pt); Audiologists 1 (pt).
Facilities Dining room; Physical therapy room; Activities room; Crafts room; Laundry room; Barber/Beauty shop.
Activities Arts and Crafts; Games; Reading groups; Movies; Shopping trips; Dances/Social or cultural gatherings.
Description Facility has resident/patient council committee, family orientation programs, family support committe, and volunteer committee.

CHERRY HILL

Cadbury Health Care Center*
2150 Rt 38, Cherry Hill, NJ, 08002 (609) 667-4550
Admin John Clancy.
Licensure Intermediate Care. *Beds* 120.

Heritage House of Cherry Hill
100 Arbor Ave, Cherry Hill, NJ, 08034 (609) 795-3131
Admin Joseph Hassman. *Medical Dir/Dir of Nursing* Dr R N Wells.
Licensure Intermediate Care. *Beds* 126.
Certified Medicaid.
Admissions Requirements Physician's request.
Staff Physicians 4 (pt); RNs 9 (ft), 4 (pt); LPNs 5 (ft), 3 (pt); Orderlies 4 (ft); Nurses aides 19 (ft), 11 (pt); Reality therapists 1 (pt); Recreational therapists 2 (ft), 4 (pt); Occupational therapists 1 (pt); Activities coordinators 1 (ft).
Facilities Dining room; Activities room; Crafts room; Laundry room.
Activities Arts and Crafts; Cards; Games; Reading groups; Prayer groups; Movies; Shopping trips; Dances/Social or cultural

gatherings.
Description Free standing ICF has a strong activity program.

Jewish Geriatric Center*
3025 W Chapel Ave, Cherry Hill, NJ, 08034 (609) 667-3100
Admin Isadore Tennenberg.
Licensure Skilled Care; Intermediate Care.
Beds 167. *Certified* Medicaid; Medicare.
Ownership Nonprofit.
Affiliation Jewish

Leader Nursing and Rehabilitation Center*
1412 Marlton Pike, Cherry Hill, NJ, 08034 (609) 428-6100
Admin Joseph B Hoban.
Licensure Skilled Care; Intermediate Care.
Beds 98. *Certified* Medicaid; Medicare.

CHESTER

Glenlora Nursing Home
Rt 24, Chester, NJ, 07930 (201) 879-5055
Admin Ray C Walborn. *Medical Dir/Dir of Nursing* Dr Alan Chanin.
Licensure Long-Term Care. *Beds* 26.
Admissions Requirements Minimum age 16; Medical examination.
Staff RNs 3 (ft), 3 (pt); LPNs 2 (pt); Orderlies 1 (ft), 1 (pt); Nurses aides 6 (ft), 11 (pt); Speech therapists 1 (pt); Activities coordinators 1 (ft); Dietitians 1 (pt); Dentists 1 (pt); Podiatrists 1 (pt).
Facilities Dining room; Activities room; Chapel; Crafts room; Laundry room; Barber/Beauty shop; Library.
Activities Arts and Crafts; Cards; Games; Reading groups; Prayer groups; Movies; Shopping trips; Dances/Social or cultural gatherings.
Description A small nursing home situated in a country environment specializing in individual care and attention with lots of tender loving care; a very family-like homey atmosphere.

CINNAMINSON

Cinnaminson Manor Nursing and Convalescent Center*
1700 Wynwood Dr, Cinnaminson, NJ, 08077 (609) 829-9000
Admin Mildred Waits.
Licensure Skilled Care; Intermediate Care.
Beds 104. *Certified* Medicaid; Medicare.

CLARKSBORO

Shady Lane-Gloucester County Home
County House Rd and Shady Lane, PO Box 275, Clarksboro, NJ, 08020 (609) 423-0020
Admin Jospeh Varelli. *Medical Dir/Dir of Nursing* D B Weems Jr MD.
Licensure Intermediate Care. *Beds* 121.
Certified Medicaid.
Ownership Public.
Admissions Requirements Minimum age 60; Medical examination; Physician's request.
Staff Physicians 1 (pt); RNs 6 (ft), 1 (pt); LPNs 13 (ft), 1 (pt); Nurses aides 60 (ft), 6 (pt); Physical therapists 1 (pt); Recreational

therapists 3 (ft); Speech therapists 1 (pt); Activities coordinators 1 (ft); Dietitians 1 (pt); Dentists 1 (pt); Podiatrists 1 (pt).
Facilities Dining room; Physical therapy room; Activities room; Crafts room; Laundry room; Barber/Beauty shop.
Activities Arts and Crafts; Cards; Games; Reading groups; Movies; Shopping trips; Dances/Social or cultural gatherings.

CLIFFWOOD BEACH

Cliffside Health Care Center
200 Center St, Cliffwood Beach, NJ, 07735 (201) 566-8422
Admin Geraldine S Crockett. *Medical Dir/Dir of Nursing* Dr H O Wiley.
Licensure Intermediate Care. *Beds* 109.
Certified Medicaid.
Admissions Requirements Medical examination.
Staff RNs 3 (ft), 3 (pt); LPNs 6 (ft), 4 (pt); Orderlies 1 (ft); Nurses aides 27 (ft), 20 (pt); Recreational therapists 1 (ft), 2 (pt); Activities coordinators 1 (ft).
Facilities Dining room; Physical therapy room; Activities room; Crafts room; Barber/Beauty shop.
Activities Arts and Crafts; Cards; Games; Reading groups; Prayer groups; Movies; Shopping trips; Dances/Social or cultural gatherings.

CLIFTON

Dolly Mount Nursing Home*
20 Valley Rd, Clifton, NJ, 07013 (201) 278-8781
Admin Sylvia Bolster.
Licensure Skilled Care; Intermediate Care.
Beds 32. *Certified* Medicaid.

COLUMBIA

Clover Rest Home*
Washington and Green Sts, Columbia, NJ, 07836 (201) 496-4307
Admin Lucille Link.
Licensure Intermediate Care; Residential Care.
Beds ICF 30; Residential Care 20.
Certified Medicaid.

CRANBURY

Elms
65 N Main St, Cranbury, NJ, 08512 (609) 395-0725
Admin Anita M Dietrick. *Medical Dir/Dir of Nursing* Syed S Ali MD.
Licensure Long-Term Care. *Beds* 16.
Admissions Requirements Medical examination.
Staff Physicians 2 (pt); RNs 2 (ft), 3 (pt); LPNs 1 (ft), 3 (pt); Nurses aides 3 (ft), 5 (pt); Physical therapists 1 (pt); Reality therapists 1 (pt); Recreational therapists 1 (pt); Occupational therapists 1 (pt); Speech therapists 1 (pt); Activities coordinators 1 (pt); Dietitians 1 (pt); Dentists 1 (pt); Ophthalmologists 1 (pt); Podiatrists 1 (pt); Audiologists 1 (pt).

Facilities Dining room; Activities room; Laundry room.
Activities Arts and Crafts; Cards; Games; Reading groups; Prayer groups; Movies; Shopping trips; Dances/Social or cultural gatherings; Talking books; Exercise groups.
Description Being only a 16-bed nursing home with a home-like setting, facility can offer individualized and personal care; clients come to a home rather than an institution, making the transition to a nursing home a lot easier emotionally.

Sunnyfield Nursing Home Inc*
RFD, Maplewood Ave, Cranbury, NJ, 08521 (609) 395-0641
Admin George Conley.
Licensure Intermediate Care. *Beds* 28.
Certified Medicaid.

CRANFORD

Cranford Hall*
600 Lincoln Park E, Cranford, NJ, 07016 (201) 276-7100
Admin Maryanne Lyons.
Licensure Skilled Care; Intermediate Care.
Beds 112. *Certified* Medicaid; Medicare.

Cranford Health and Extended Care Center*
205 Birchwood Ave, Cranford, NJ, 07016 (201) 272-6660
Admin Edward Grocynski.
Licensure Skilled Care; Intermediate Care.
Beds 128. *Certified* Medicaid; Medicare.

CRESSKILL

Dunroven Nursing Home
221 County Rd, Cresskill, NJ, 07626 (201) 567-9310
Admin Donald C DeVries. *Medical Dir/Dir of Nursing* Harry Roselle MD.
Licensure Skilled Care. *Beds* 100.
Admissions Requirements Minimum age 16; Medical examination; Physician's request.
Staff RNs 14 (ft); LPNs 12 (ft); Nurses aides 88 (ft); Speech therapists 1 (pt); Activities coordinators 1 (ft), 1 (pt); Dietitians 1 (pt).
Facilities Dining room; Physical therapy room; Activities room; Laundry room; Barber/Beauty shop.
Activities Arts and Crafts; Cards; Games; Reading groups; Prayer groups; Movies; Shopping trips; Dances/Social or cultural gatherings.

DEPTFORD

Greenbriar-East Nursing Center
1511 Clements Bridge Rd, Deptford, NJ, 08096 (609) 845-9400
Admin Ruth E Gandek. *Medical Dir/Dir of Nursing* James G Kehler MD.
Licensure Skilled Care; Intermediate Care.
Beds 120. *Certified* Medicaid; Medicare.
Staff Physicians; RNs; LPNs; Orderlies; Nurses aides; Physical therapists; Speech therapists; Activities coordinators; Dietitians; Dentists.
Facilities Dining room; Physical therapy room;

Activities room; Crafts room; Laundry room; Barber/Beauty shop; Library.
Activities Arts and Crafts; Cards; Games; Prayer groups; Movies; Shopping trips; Dances/Social or cultural gatherings.

EAST ORANGE

East Orange Nursing Home*
101 N Grove St, East Orange, NJ, 07017 (201) 672-1700
Admin Joseph Cohen.
Licensure Skilled Care; Intermediate Care.
Beds 195. *Certified* Medicaid; Medicare.

Garden State Health Care Center
140 Park Ave, East Orange, NJ, 07017 (201) 677-1500
Admin Charles Yaker. *Medical Dir/Dir of Nursing* Pasquale Cumpanile.
Licensure Long-Term Care. *Beds* 228.
Staff Physical therapists 1 (pt); Speech therapists 1 (pt); Dentists 1 (pt); Ophthalmologists 1 (pt); Podiatrists 1 (pt); Audiologists 1 (pt); Psychologist 1 (pt).
Facilities Dining room; Physical therapy room; Activities room; Crafts room; Laundry room; Barber/Beauty shop.
Activities Arts and Crafts; Cards; Games; Reading groups; Prayer groups; Movies.

EATONTOWN

Eatontown Convalescent Center*
139 Grant Ave, Eatontown, NJ, 07724 (201) 542-4700
Admin Andrew Shawn.
Licensure Long-Term Care. *Beds* 106.

EDISON

Birchwood Nursing and Convalescent Center
1350 Inman Ave, Edison, NJ, 08817 (201) 754-7100
Admin Gerald Roth. *Medical Dir/Dir of Nursing* Dabney Moon MD.
Licensure Skilled Care; Intermediate Care.
Beds 84. *Certified* Medicaid; Medicare.
Admissions Requirements Minimum age 18.
Staff Physicians; RNs; LPNs; Orderlies; Nurses aides; Physical therapists; Reality therapists; Recreational therapists; Occupational therapists; Speech therapists; Activities coordinators; Dietitians; Dentists; Ophthalmologists; Podiatrists; Audiologists.
Facilities Dining room; Physical therapy room; Activities room; Laundry room; Barber/Beauty shop; Library.
Activities Arts and Crafts; Cards; Games; Reading groups; Movies; Shopping trips.
Description Facility is located in a very pretty suburban setting across from Plainfield Club. Several large local hospitals are located nearby.

Edison Estates Inc
465 Plainfield Ave, Edison, NJ, 08817 (201) 985-1500
Admin Howard A Sukoff. *Medical Dir/Dir of Nursing* Isabel London MD.
Licensure Skilled Care. *Beds* 348.
Certified Medicaid.

Admissions Requirements Minimum age 30; Medical examination; Physician's request.
Staff Physicians 12 (pt); RNs 30 (ft), 3 (pt); LPNs 14 (ft), 7 (pt); Nurses aides 108 (ft), 46 (pt); Physical therapists 5 (pt); Recreational therapists 6 (ft); Occupational therapists 2 (pt); Speech therapists 1 (pt); Activities coordinators 1 (ft); Dietitians 3 (ft); Dentists 1 (pt); Podiatrists 1 (pt); Audiologists 1 (pt).
Facilities Dining room; Physical therapy room; Activities room; Chapel; Crafts room; Laundry room; Barber/Beauty shop; Library.
Activities Arts and Crafts; Cards; Games; Reading groups; Prayer groups; Movies; Shopping trips; Dances/Social or cultural gatherings.
Description There is homogeneous grouping among 8 specific nursing units.

ELIZABETH

Elizabeth Nursing Home*
1048 Grove St, Elizabeth, NJ, 07202 (201) 354-0002
Admin Zev Fishman.
Licensure Skilled Care; Intermediate Care.
Beds 102. *Certified* Medicaid; Medicare.

Plaza Nursing and Convalescent Center
456 Rahway Ave, Elizabeth, NJ, 07202 (201) 354-1300
Admin Menachem Fishman. *Medical Dir/Dir of Nursing* Robert Solomon MD.
Licensure Skilled Care; Intermediate Care.
Beds 128. *Certified* Medicaid; Medicare.
Admissions Requirements Minimum age 60.
Staff Physicians 1 (pt); RNs 3 (ft), 7 (pt); LPNs 4 (ft), 9 (pt); Nurses aides 18 (ft), 14 (pt); Physical therapists 1 (pt); Recreational therapists 1 (pt); Occupational therapists 1 (pt); Speech therapists 1 (pt); Activities coordinators 1 (ft), 3 (pt); Dietitians 1 (pt); Podiatrists 1 (pt).
Facilities Dining room; Physical therapy room; Activities room; Chapel; Crafts room; Laundry room; Barber/Beauty shop; Library.
Activities Arts and Crafts; Cards; Games; Reading groups; Prayer groups; Movies; Shopping trips; Dances/Social or cultural gatherings.
Description Facility features 2 outdoor patios, one at ground level, one on 3rd floor; resident conference room; extensive recreation program including outdoor trips, barbecues, bazaars; overall care delivery is properly expressed by motto, "We care with love and love to care."

EMERSON

Emerson Convalescent Center
100 Kinderkamack Rd, Emerson, NJ, 07630 (201) 265-3700
Admin Nathan Friedman. *Medical Dir/Dir of Nursing* J A Perez MD.
Licensure Skilled Care; Intermediate Care.
Beds 150. *Certified* Medicaid.
Admissions Requirements Minimum age 50; Medical examination.
Staff RNs 12 (ft), 4 (pt); LPNs 8 (ft), 7 (pt); Orderlies 1 (ft); Nurses aides 50 (ft), 7 (pt); Physical therapists 2 (pt); Recreational therapists 1 (ft); Occupational therapists 1 (pt);

Speech therapists 1 (pt); Activities coordinators 1 (ft), 4 (pt); Dietitians 1 (pt); Dentists 1 (pt); Ophthalmologists 1 (pt); Podiatrists 1 (pt).
Facilities Dining room; Physical therapy room; Activities room; Crafts room; Laundry room; Barber/Beauty shop.
Activities Arts and Crafts; Cards; Games; Reading groups; Prayer groups; Movies; Shopping trips; Dances/Social or cultural gatherings; Current events; Bowling; Ceramics.
Description Emerson Convalescent Center is where a community of people with different backgrounds and diverse needs work, play, and live together in a lifestyle of new beginnings.

ENGLEWOOD

Inglemoor Inc
333 Grand Ave, Englewood, NJ, 07631 (201) 568-0900
Admin Doris Neibart. *Medical Dir/Dir of Nursing* Dr Robert Nutt.
Licensure Long-Term Care. *Beds* 62.
Admissions Requirements Medical examination; Physician's request.
Staff RNs 3 (ft), 13 (pt); LPNs 3 (pt); Nurses aides 11 (ft), 15 (pt); Physical therapists 2 (pt); Reality therapists 1 (pt); Recreational therapists 1 (ft); Occupational therapists 1 (pt); Speech therapists 1 (pt); Activities coordinators 1 (ft); Dietitians 1 (ft); Dentists 2 (pt); Ophthalmologists 2 (pt); Podiatrists 2 (pt).
Facilities Dining room; Physical therapy room; Activities room; Crafts room; Laundry room; Barber/Beauty shop.
Activities Arts and Crafts; Cards; Games; Reading groups; Prayer groups; Movies; Dances/Social or cultural gatherings.
Description Facility has an outstanding art exchange program to enhance patients' cultural needs and orient them to time, place, and event. Most unique is the short-term stay, accommodating with full care for as short as one or 2 weeks, a month, or longer.

ENGLEWOOD CLIFFS

Cliff House*
633 Palisade Ave, Englewood Cliffs, NJ, 07632 (201) 567-2626
Admin Richard Heller.
Licensure Skilled Care; Intermediate Care.
Beds 36. *Certified* Medicaid; Medicare.

ENGLISHTOWN

Pinebrook Care Center Inc
Pension Rd, PO Box 448, Englishtown, NJ, 07726 (201) 446-3600
Admin Marvin Beinhorn. *Medical Dir/Dir of Nursing* Dr Rivero.
Licensure Skilled Care; Intermediate Care.
Beds 98. *Certified* Medicaid.
Staff Physicians 3 (pt); RNs 2 (ft), 12 (pt); LPNs 1 (ft), 4 (pt); Orderlies 5 (ft); Nurses aides 24 (ft), 22 (pt); Physical therapists 1 (pt); Recreational therapists 1 (ft), 2 (pt); Speech therapists 1 (pt); Activities coordinators 1 (ft); Dietitians 1 (pt); Dentists 1 (pt); Podiatrists 1 (pt).
Facilities Dining room; Physical therapy room;

Activities room; Chapel; Crafts room; Laundry room; Barber/Beauty shop; Library.
Activities Arts and Crafts; Cards; Games; Reading groups; Prayer groups; Movies; Shopping trips; Dances/Social or cultural gatherings.

FAIR LAWN

Fair Lawn Manor Nursing Home*
12–15 Saddle River Rd, Fair Lawn, NJ, 07410 (201) 797-9522
Admin Eugene Burger.
Licensure Intermediate Care. *Beds* 157.

FAR HILLS

Kate Macy Ladd Convalescent Home
Peapack Rd, Far Hills, NJ, 07931 (201) 234-0860
Admin Barry L Mills.
Licensure Long-Term Care. *Beds* 45.

FLORENCE

Florence Nursing Home*
Front and Iron Sts, Florence, NJ, 08518 (609) 499-3224
Admin Paul Rosenthal.
Licensure Long-Term Care. *Beds* 15.

FLORHAM PARK

Cheshire Home
9 Ridgedale Ave, Florham Park, NJ, 07932
Admin Sharon Logan Gronet. *Medical Dir/Dir of Nursing* Charles I Nadel MD.
Licensure Skilled Care. *Beds* 35.
Certified Medicaid.
Ownership Nonprofit.
Admissions Requirements Minimum age 18; Medical examination.
Staff Physicians 2 (pt); RNs 3 (ft), 2 (pt); LPNs 2 (ft), 1 (pt); Nurses aides 16 (ft), 5 (pt); Recreational therapists 1 (ft); Activities coordinators 1 (ft); Dietitians 1 (ft), 1 (pt).
Facilities Dining room; Activities room; Crafts room; Laundry room; Library.
Activities Arts and Crafts; Games; Movies; Shopping trips; Dances/Social or cultural gatherings.
Description Facility is one of more than 200 Cheshire Homes worldwide, a residential community for physically disabled young adults who cannot live alone and whose alternatives otherwise would be life in nursing homes oriented to care for the elderly or state institutions for the mentally impaired.

FRANKLIN PARK

Franklin Convalescent Center
3371 Rt 27, Franklin Park, NJ, 08823 (201) 821-8000
Admin Eliezer Mendelsohn. *Medical Dir/Dir of Nursing* Dr Lee.
Licensure Skilled Care; Intermediate Care.
Beds 120. *Certified* Medicaid; Medicare.
Staff Physicians; RNs; LPNs; Orderlies;

Nurses aides; Physical therapists; Reality therapists; Recreational therapists; Occupational therapists; Speech therapists; Activities coordinators; Dietitians; Dentists; Ophthalmologists; Podiatrists; Audiologists.
Facilities Dining room; Physical therapy room; Activities room; Chapel; Crafts room; Laundry room; Barber/Beauty shop; Library.
Activities Arts and Crafts; Cards; Games; Reading groups; Prayer groups; Movies; Shopping trips; Dances/Social or cultural gatherings.
Description Facility is modern, bright; fully air-conditioned and has area for 60 more beds under construction.

FREEHOLD

Freehold Convacenter
689 W Main St and Rt 537, Freehold, NJ, 07728 (201) 431-5200
Admin Dean Michals.
Licensure Skilled Care; Intermediate Care.
Beds 120. *Certified* Medicaid; Medicare.

John F Montgomery Medical Home*
Dutch Ln, PO Box 284, Freehold, NJ, 07728 (201) 431-7420
Admin Dora Z Kirby.
Licensure Skilled Care; Intermediate Care.
Beds 119. *Certified* Medicaid; Medicare.

Springview Nursing Home
3419 US Hwy 9, Freehold, NJ, 07728 (201) 780-0660
Admin Benjamin Farber. *Medical Dir/Dir of Nursing* Dr John Gumina.
Licensure Skilled Care; Intermediate Care.
Beds 180. *Certified* Medicaid.

FRENCHTOWN

Valley View Manor Inc
Everittstown Rd, Frenchtown, NJ, 08825 (201) 996-4112
Admin Lester Krosskove.
Licensure Intermediate Care. *Beds* 45.
Facilities Dining room; Activities room; Laundry room; Barber/Beauty shop.
Activities Arts and Crafts; Games; Prayer groups; Dances/Social or cultural gatherings; Church services.
Description The Valley View Manor Nursing Home is a private, intermediate care facility for the aged; licensed by the State of New Jersey to provide nursing care, room and board to persons who cannot care for themselves. To be admitted a person must be ambulatory, either independently or with a cane or walker. Persons confined to a bed or wheelchair cannot be admitted. The facility provides a home-like setting with 24-hour nursing care; all meals and snacks as required; private and semi-private rooms, with intercoms in all rooms; 2 large sitting rooms with color TV; planned recreational activities; and couples are welcome.

GLEN GARDNER

Hunterdon Hills Nursing Home
Hill Rd, Glen Gardner, NJ, 08826 (201)
537-2717
Admin Barry Scheier. *Medical Dir/Dir of
Nursing* John McGowan.
Licensure Skilled Care; Intermediate Care.
Beds 32. *Certified* Medicaid; Medicare.
Staff RNs 4 (ft); LPNs 1 (ft); Nurses aides 10
(ft); Physical therapists 1 (pt); Reality therapists
1 (pt); Recreational therapists 1 (pt); Activities
coordinators 1 (ft); Dietitians 1 (pt).
Facilities Dining room; Activities room;
Laundry room.
Activities Arts and Crafts; Cards; Games;
Reading groups; Prayer groups; Movies;
Shopping trips.

GREENBROOK

Greenbrook Nursing Home*
303 Rock Ave, Greenbrook, NJ, 08812 (201)
968-5500
Admin Herbert Heflich.
Licensure Skilled Care; Intermediate Care.
Beds 180. *Certified* Medicaid; Medicare.

GUTTENBERG

Palisade Nursing Home*
6819 Blvd East, Guttenberg, NJ, 07093 (201)
868-3600
Admin Celeste Post.
Licensure Skilled Care; Intermediate Care.
Beds 106. *Certified* Medicaid.

HACKENSACK

Wellington Hall Nursing Home
301 Union St, Hackensack, NJ, 07601 (201)
487-4900
Admin Ronald Squillace. *Medical Dir/Dir of
Nursing* Irving M Levitas MD.
Licensure Skilled Care; Intermediate Care.
Beds 120. *Certified* Medicaid; Medicare.
Staff RNs 8 (ft); LPNs 5 (ft); Nurses aides 38
(ft); Physical therapists 3 (ft); Reality therapists
1 (ft); Recreational therapists 2 (ft);
Occupational therapists 1 (ft); Speech therapists
1 (ft); Activities coordinators 1 (ft); Dietitians 1
(ft); Dentists; Ophthalmologists; Podiatrists;
Audiologists.
Facilities Dining room; Physical therapy room;
Activities room; Chapel; Crafts room; Laundry
room; Barber/Beauty shop; Library.
Activities Arts and Crafts; Cards; Games;
Prayer groups; Movies; Shopping trips.
Description "Someplace special for special
people."

HADDONFIELD

Presbyterian Home of the Synod
132 Warwick Rd, Haddonfield, NJ, 08033
(609) 429-5500
Admin Patricia White.
Licensure Long-Term Care. *Beds* 65.
Affiliation Presbyterian

HASKELL

Bel Air Manor*
25 5th Ave, Haskell, NJ, 07472 (201) 839-1010
Admin John Fiorillo.
Licensure Skilled Care; Intermediate Care.
Beds 201. *Certified* Medicaid; Medicare.

HAZLET

Arnold Walter Nursing Home*
622 S Laurel Ave, Hazlet, NJ, 07730 (201)
787-6300
Admin Benzion Schachter.
Licensure Skilled Care; Intermediate Care.
Beds 132. *Certified* Medicaid; Medicare.

Brookdale Nursing Center*
3325 Hwy 35, Hazlet, NJ, 07730 (201)
264-5800
Admin Peter Giegerich.
Licensure Skilled Care; Intermediate Care;
Residential Care. *Beds* 184; Residential Care
12. *Certified* Medicaid; Medicare.

HIGHTSTOWN

Applegarth Care Center
Applegarth Rd, Hightstown, NJ, 08520 (609)
448-7036
Admin Jeanette Intravartolo. *Medical Dir/Dir
of Nursing* Dr O Schmensky.
Licensure Long-Term Care. *Beds* 162.
Certified Medicaid.
Staff Physicians 1 (pt); RNs 15 (ft), 10 (pt);
LPNs 10 (ft), 10 (pt); Nurses aides 30 (ft), 20
(pt); Physical therapists 1 (pt); Reality therapists
1 (pt); Recreational therapists 3 (ft);
Occupational therapists 1 (pt); Speech
therapists 1 (pt); Activities coordinators 1 (ft);
Dietitians 1 (ft); Dentists 1 (pt);
Ophthalmologists 1 (pt); Podiatrists 1 (pt);
Audiologists 1 (pt).
Facilities Dining room; Physical therapy room;
Activities room; Chapel; Crafts room; Laundry
room; Barber/Beauty shop; Library.
Activities Arts and Crafts; Cards; Games;
Reading groups; Prayer groups; Movies;
Shopping trips; Dances/Social or cultural
gatherings.

Sunlawn Nursing Home*
576 Main St, Hightstown, NJ, 08520 (609)
448-0528
Admin Joseph Singer.
Licensure Long-Term Care. *Beds* 30.

HOLMDEL

Garden State Manor
16 Van Brackle Rd, Holmdel, NJ, 07733 (201)
264-3548
Admin Helen Dimitrow. *Medical Dir/Dir of
Nursing* Dr Renerito Maquiling.
Licensure Skilled Care; Intermediate Care.
Beds 27. *Certified* Medicaid.
Admissions Requirements Physician's request.
Staff RNs 1 (ft), 4 (pt); LPNs 2 (ft), 3 (pt);
Nurses aides 6 (ft), 6 (pt); Recreational
therapists 1 (pt); Activities coordinators 1 (pt);
Dietitians 1 (pt).

Facilities Dining room; Activities room; Crafts
room.
Activities Arts and Crafts; Cards; Games.
Description Situated in a wooded area off main
road, facility has a home-like quality.

Holmdel Convalescent Center*
Rt 34, Holmdel, NJ, 07733 (201) 946-4200
Admin Valerie Kennedy.
Licensure Skilled Care; Intermediate Care.
Beds 106. *Certified* Medicaid; Medicare.

Holmdel Nursing Home*
Rt 34, Holmdel, NJ, 07733 (201) 946-4200
Admin Valerie Kennedy.
Licensure Skilled Care; Intermediate Care.
Beds 41. *Certified* Medicaid.

HOPE

Forest Manor Health Care Center
PO Box 283, State Park Rd, Hope, NJ, 07844
(201) 459-4128
Admin I Joel Foreman.
Licensure Long-Term Care. *Beds* 42.

JERSEY CITY

**Berthold S Pollak Hospital—Long Term Care
Facility**
100 Clifton Pl, Jersey City, NJ, 07304 (201)
432-1000
Admin A J Robbins. *Medical Dir/Dir of
Nursing* Janet Geraghty-Deutsch MD.
Licensure Skilled Care; Intermediate Care.
Beds 596. *Certified* Medicaid.
Admissions Requirements Minimum age 18;
Physician's request.
Staff Physicians 6 (ft), 20 (pt); Occupational
therapists 1 (pt); Speech therapists 1 (pt);
Dentists 3 (pt); Ophthalmologists 1 (pt);
Podiatrists 1 (pt); Audiologists 1 (pt).
Facilities Dining room; Physical therapy room;
Activities room; Chapel; Crafts room;
Barber/Beauty shop; Library.
Activities Arts and Crafts; Cards; Games;
Reading groups; Prayer groups; Movies;
Shopping trips.

Liberty House Nursing Home
620 Montgomery St, Jersey City, NJ, 07302
(201) 435-0033
Admin Michael Katz. *Medical Dir/Dir of
Nursing* J John DeGoia.
Licensure Skilled Care; Intermediate Care.
Beds 180. *Certified* Medicaid; Medicare.
Staff Physicians; RNs; LPNs; Orderlies;
Nurses aides; Physical therapists; Recreational
therapists; Occupational therapists; Speech
therapists; Activities coordinators; Dietitians;
Dentists; Ophthalmologists; Podiatrists.
Facilities Dining room; Physical therapy room;
Activities room; Crafts room; Laundry room.
Activities Arts and Crafts; Cards; Games;
Reading groups; Prayer groups; Movies;
Dances/Social or cultural gatherings.

KEANSBURG

Beachview Rest Home*
32 Laurel Ave, Keansburg, NJ, 07734 (201)
787-8100
Admin Joseph Cappadona.
Licensure Skilled Care; Intermediate Care.
Beds 119. *Certified* Medicaid; Medicare.

LAKELAND

Camden County Health Services Center*
PO Blackwood, Lakeland, NJ, 08012 (609)
227-3000
Admin Frank Urban.
Licensure Intermediate Care. *Beds* 321.

LAKEWOOD

Hillcrest Manor Inc
485 River Ave, Lakewood, NJ, 08701 (201)
364-7100
Admin David C Smith. *Medical Dir/Dir of
Nursing* Anthony Marasco MD.
Licensure Skilled Care; Intermediate Care;
Residential Care. *Beds* 188.
Certified Medicaid; Medicare.
Admissions Requirements Minimum age 18;
Medical examination.
Staff Physicians 15 (pt); RNs 12 (ft), 3 (pt);
LPNs 8 (ft), 3 (pt); Nurses aides 40 (ft), 10 (pt);
Physical therapists 2 (ft); Recreational therapists
3 (ft), 1 (pt); Occupational therapists 1 (pt);
Speech therapists 2 (pt); Activities coordinators
1 (ft); Dietitians 1 (pt); Dentists 1 (pt);
Ophthalmologists 1 (pt); Podiatrists 1 (pt);
Audiologists 1 (pt).
Facilities Dining room; Physical therapy room;
Activities room; Crafts room; Barber/Beauty
shop.
Activities Arts and Crafts; Cards; Games;
Reading groups; Prayer groups; Movies;
Shopping trips; Dances/Social or cultural
gatherings.
Description A broad continuum of care which,
in addition to above, offers medical day care
services.

Lakewood Pine Aire Nursing Home
901 Monmouth Ave, Lakewood, NJ, 08701
(201) 363-0151
Admin Gary Pizzichillo. *Medical Dir/Dir of
Nursing* Vincent De Muro DO.
Licensure Skilled Care; Intermediate Care.
Beds 61. *Certified* Medicaid.
Staff Physicians 1 (pt); RNs 3 (ft), 1 (pt); LPNs
2 (ft), 2 (pt); Orderlies 2 (ft); Nurses aides 15
(ft), 5 (pt); Reality therapists 2 (ft); Recreational
therapists 1 (ft); Activities coordinators 1 (ft);
Dietitians 1 (ft); Social workers 1 (pt).

Leisure Chateau Care Center*
962 River Ave, Lakewood, NJ, 08701 (201)
370-8600
Admin Leslie McFadden.
Licensure Intermediate Care. *Beds* 120.

Medicenter of Lakewood
685 River Ave, Lakewood, NJ, 08701 (201)
364-8300
Admin Larry Mankoff. *Medical Dir/Dir of

Nursing* Dr James Meehan.
Licensure Skilled Care; Intermediate Care.
Beds 185. *Certified* Medicaid; Medicare.
Admissions Requirements Minimum age 16.
Staff Physicians 12 (ft); RNs 26 (ft); LPNs 30
(ft); Nurses aides 110 (ft); Physical therapists 2
(ft); Recreational therapists 4 (ft); Occupational
therapists 1 (ft); Speech therapists 1 (pt);
Activities coordinators 1 (ft); Dietitians 1 (pt);
Dentists 1 (pt); Ophthalmologists 1 (pt);
Podiatrists 1 (pt); Audiologists 1 (pt).
Facilities Dining room; Physical therapy room;
Activities room; Crafts room; Laundry room;
Barber/Beauty shop.
Activities Arts and Crafts; Cards; Games;
Reading groups; Prayer groups; Movies;
Shopping trips; Dances/Social or cultural
gatherings.

Newman's Lakewood Nursing Home
Monmouth Ave and 7th St, Lakewood, NJ,
08701 (201) 363-2659
Admin Felice Newman. *Medical Dir/Dir of
Nursing* Dr Harish Chander.
Licensure Intermediate Care. *Beds* 44.
Certified Medicaid.
Admissions Requirements Minimum age 35;
Medical examination; Physician's request.
Staff Physicians 4 (pt); RNs 3 (ft); LPNs 3 (pt);
Orderlies 2 (pt); Physical therapists 1 (pt);
Reality therapists 1 (ft); Recreational therapists
1 (ft), 1 (pt); Occupational therapists 1 (pt);
Speech therapists 1 (pt); Activities coordinators
1 (ft); Dietitians 1 (pt); Dentists 1 (pt);
Ophthalmologists 1 (pt); Podiatrists 1 (pt);
Audiologists 1 (pt).
Facilities Dining room; Activities room;
Laundry room.
Activities Arts and Crafts; Cards; Games;
Reading groups; Prayer groups; Movies;
Shopping trips.
Description Facility offers a small, family-like
atmosphere.

Pineland Nursing Home Inc*
Squankum Rd, Lakewood, NJ, 08701 (201)
363-9507
Admin Lucie Zane.
Licensure Skilled Care; Intermediate Care.
Beds 18. *Certified* Medicaid.

Summit Convalescent Home*
285 River Ave, Lakewood, NJ, 08701 (201)
363-0400
Admin Anthony Pagliaro.
Licensure Skilled Care; Intermediate Care.
Beds 180. *Certified* Medicaid; Medicare.

LAWRENCEVILLE

Lawrenceville Nursing Home
112 Franklin Corner Rd, PO Box 6338,
Lawrenceville, NJ, 08648 (609) 896-1494
Admin Frank Puzio. *Medical Dir/Dir of
Nursing* Dr S Goldsmith.
Licensure Skilled Care; Intermediate Care.
Beds 100. *Certified* Medicaid; Medicare.
Staff Physicians 1 (pt); RNs 12 (ft), 4 (pt);
LPNs 4 (ft); Orderlies 2 (ft); Nurses aides 36
(ft), 6 (pt); Physical therapists 1 (pt); Reality
therapists 1 (ft); Recreational therapists 1 (ft);
Occupational therapists 1 (pt); Speech

therapists 1 (pt); Activities coordinators 1 (ft);
Dietitians 1 (pt); Dentists 1 (pt);
Ophthalmologists 1 (pt); Podiatrists 1 (pt);
Audiologists 1 (pt).

LEBANON

Union Forge Nursing Home*
Rd 1, Cratetown Rd, Lebanon, NJ, 08833 (201)
236-2011
Admin Eugene Callahan.
Licensure Residential Care. *Beds* 62.

LINCOLN PARK

Lincoln Park Intermediate Care Center
499 Pinebrook Rd, Lincoln Park, NJ, 07035
(201) 696-3300
Admin Barbara Ackerman. *Medical Dir/Dir of
Nursing* Pavle Topalovic MD.
Licensure Skilled Care; Intermediate Care.
Beds 547. *Certified* Medicaid.
Admissions Requirements Minimum age 21;
Medical examination.
Facilities Dining room; Physical therapy room;
Activities room; Chapel; Crafts room; Laundry
room; Barber/Beauty shop; Library.
Activities Arts and Crafts; Cards; Games;
Reading groups; Prayer groups; Movies;
Shopping trips; Dances/Social or cultural
gatherings.
Description Facility features a pool and a
miniature golf course.

Lincoln Park Nursing and Convalescent Home
521 Pinebrook Rd, Lincoln Park, NJ, 07035
(201) 696-3300
Admin Karen Scienski. *Medical Dir/Dir of
Nursing* Paule Topalovic MD.
Licensure Skilled Care. *Beds* 159.
Certified Medicaid; Medicare.
Admissions Requirements Medical
examination; Physician's request.
Facilities Dining room; Physical therapy room;
Activities room; Chapel; Crafts room; Laundry
room; Barber/Beauty shop; Library.
Activities Arts and Crafts; Games; Reading
groups; Prayer groups; Movies; Shopping trips;
Dances/Social or cultural gatherings.
Description Facility features a picnic involving
staff and residents with entertainment from
9am to 9pm including fireworks.

LINWOOD

Linwood Convalescent Center*
New Rd and Central Ave, Linwood, NJ, 08221
(609) 927-6131
Admin Gary Hand.
Licensure Skilled Care; Intermediate Care.
Beds 154. *Certified* Medicaid; Medicare.

LIVINGSTON

Inglemoor West
311 S Livingston Ave, Livingston, NJ, 07039
(201) 994-0221
Admin Georgia Eitzen. *Medical Dir/Dir of
Nursing* Dr George Kline Jr.
Licensure Skilled Care; Intermediate Care.

Beds 120. *Certified* Medicaid; Medicare.
Admissions Requirements Medical
examination.
Staff RNs 15 (ft), 16 (pt); Nurses aides 40 (ft),
9 (pt); Physical therapists 1 (pt); Occupational
therapists 1 (pt); Speech therapists 1 (pt);
Activities coordinators 2 (ft); Dietitians 1 (ft);
Dentists 1 (pt); Ophthalmologists 1 (pt);
Podiatrists 1 (pt).
Facilities Dining room; Physical therapy room;
Activities room; Crafts room; Laundry room;
Barber/Beauty shop; Library; Diet kitchen.
Activities Arts and Crafts; Cards; Games;
Reading groups; Prayer groups; Movies;
Shopping trips; Dances/Social or cultural
gatherings.
Description Philosophy of the facility: "People
being admitted to nursing homes are not being
'put away', they are moving from one home to
another, where their special needs are taken
care of by a caring staff who enjoy what they are
doing. People go to nursing homes not to die,
but to live and have fun, to interact with and
enjoy people of their own generation in an
atmosphere of comfort and security."

LONG BRANCH

Monmouth Convalescent Center
229 Bath Ave, Long Branch, NJ, 07740 (201)
229-4300
Admin Lori Gabriel. *Medical Dir/Dir of
Nursing* Roger Quinlan.
Licensure Skilled Care. *Beds* 109.
Certified Medicaid.
Staff Physicians 1 (ft), 15 (pt); RNs 7 (ft), 1
(pt); LPNs 6 (ft), 3 (pt); Orderlies 4 (ft); Nurses
aides 30 (ft), 15 (pt); Physical therapists 1 (pt);
Recreational therapists 2 (ft); Occupational
therapists 1 (pt); Speech therapists 1 (pt);
Activities coordinators 1 (ft); Dietitians 1 (pt);
Dentists 1 (pt); Ophthalmologists 1 (pt);
Podiatrists 1 (pt); Audiologists 1 (pt).
Facilities Dining room; Physical therapy room;
Activities room; Crafts room; Laundry room;
Barber/Beauty shop; Library.
Activities Arts and Crafts; Cards; Games;
Reading groups; Prayer groups; Movies;
Shopping trips; Dances/Social or cultural
gatherings; Monthly barbecues May through
September; Vegetable gardening.
Description Facility features outdoor recreation
building surrounded by spacious, landscaped
park; vegetable garden; door ramps for easy
access; patients are not separated from
reception area by any walls or barriers; this is
their home and they move around freely; strong
support given by most families and volunteers;
staff works together well.

Westwood Hall Hebrew Home*
281 Bath Ave, Long Branch, NJ, 07740 (201)
222-5277
Admin Joanne Escovar.
Licensure Skilled Care; Intermediate Care.
Beds 84. *Certified* Medicaid; Medicare.
Ownership Nonprofit.
Affiliation Jewish

Witmer House*
75 Cooper Ave, Long Branch, NJ, 07740 (201)
229-4352

Admin Thomas Armour.
Licensure Intermediate Care; Residential Care.
Beds ICF 80; Residential Care 34.
Certified Medicaid.

MADISON

Pine Acres Nursing Home Inc*
51 Madison Ave, Madison, NJ, 07940 (201)
377-2125
Admin Arnold Perlstein.
Licensure Skilled Care; Intermediate Care.
Beds 102. *Certified* Medicaid; Medicare.

Royal Oaks*
300 Madison Ave, Madison, NJ, 07940 (201)
377-9762
Admin John Flemming.
Licensure Long-Term Care. *Beds* 31.

MANASQUAN

Sunnyside Farms Nursing and Convalescent*
Ramshorn Dr and Lakewood Rd, Manasquan,
NJ, 08736 (201) 528-9311
Admin Joseph Singer.
Licensure Long-Term Care; Residential Care.
Beds 57.

MAPLE SHADE

Maple Hill Convalescent Center*
Rt 38 and Mill Rd, Maple Shade, NJ, 08052
(609) 779-1500
Admin Susan Piscator.
Licensure Skilled Care; Intermediate Care.
Beds 162. *Certified* Medicaid; Medicare.

Pinewood Acres Nursing Home
794 Forklanding Rd, Maple Shade, NJ, 08052
(609) 779-9333
Admin Chaim Teitelbaum. *Medical Dir/Dir of
Nursing* Robert Warden DO.
Licensure Skilled Care; Intermediate Care.
Beds 124. *Certified* Medicaid; Medicare.
Staff Physicians 3 (ft); RNs 8 (ft), 4 (pt); LPNs
4 (ft), 4 (pt); Nurses aides 30 (ft), 13 (pt);
Physical therapists 1 (ft); Recreational therapists
2 (ft); Occupational therapists 1 (pt); Speech
therapists 1 (pt); Activities coordinators 1 (ft);
Dietitians 1 (pt); Dentists 1 (pt); Podiatrists 1
(pt); Audiologists 1 (pt); Food service director 1
(ft).
Facilities Dining room; Physical therapy room;
Activities room; Crafts room; Laundry room;
TV lounges.
Activities Arts and Crafts; Cards; Games;
Reading groups; Prayer groups; Movies;
Dances/Social or cultural gatherings.
Description Pinewood Acres Nursing Center is
located on one floor and has a friendly informal
atmosphere, consequently much time is
devoted to both the families as well as the
residents. Daily activities program is composed
of diversified events designed to meet the
individual needs of all.

MARLTON

Care Inn of Voorhees
Kresson and Evesham Rds, Marlton, NJ,
08053 (609) 424-1222
Admin Ralph K Moore.
Licensure Skilled Care; Intermediate Care.
Beds 89. *Certified* Medicaid; Medicare.

MATAWAN

Emery Manor Nursing Home*
Rt 34, Matawan, NJ, 07747 (201) 566-6400
Admin Richard Emery.
Licensure Skilled Care; Intermediate Care.
Beds 100. *Certified* Medicaid; Medicare.

Mount Pleasant Manor*
38 Freneau Ave, Matawan, NJ, 07747 (201)
566-4633
Admin Frank and Richard LaMura.
Licensure Skilled Care; Intermediate Care.
Beds 27. *Certified* Medicaid.

MEDFORD

Medford Convalescent and Nursing Center
185 Tuckerton Rd, Medford, NJ, 08055 (609)
983-8970
Admin David Graham. *Medical Dir/Dir of
Nursing* Richard Molino MD.
Licensure Skilled Care. *Beds* 180.
Certified Medicaid; Medicare.
Staff Physicians 6 (pt); RNs 8 (ft), 8 (pt); LPNs
6 (ft), 10 (pt); Orderlies 4 (ft); Nurses aides 40
(ft), 43 (pt); Physical therapists 1 (pt); Reality
therapists 1 (pt); Recreational therapists 3 (pt);
Occupational therapists 1 (pt); Speech
therapists 1 (pt); Activities coordinators 2 (ft);
Dietitians 1 (ft); Dentists 1 (pt);
Ophthalmologists 1 (pt); Podiatrists 1 (pt);
Audiologists 1 (pt).
Facilities Dining room; Physical therapy room;
Activities room; Chapel; Laundry room;
Barber/Beauty shop.
Activities Arts and Crafts; Cards; Games;
Reading groups; Prayer groups; Movies;
Dances/Social or cultural gatherings.

Medford Leas
New Freedom Rd, Box 366, Medford, NJ,
08055 (609) 654-3000
Admin Lois Forrest. *Medical Dir/Dir of
Nursing* Benjamin R Paradee MD.
Licensure Skilled Care; Intermediate Care;
Residential Care. *Beds* 239.
Certified Medicaid; Medicare.
Admissions Requirements Minimum age 65;
Medical examination.
Staff Physicians; RNs; LPNs; Orderlies;
Nurses aides; Physical therapists; Recreational
therapists; Occupational therapists; Speech
therapists; Activities coordinators; Dietitians;
Dentists; Ophthalmologists; Podiatrists;
Audiologists.
Affiliation Society of Friends
Facilities Dining room; Physical therapy room;
Activities room; Crafts room; Laundry room;
Barber/Beauty shop; Library; Indoor pool;
Putting green; Walking trails.
Activities Arts and Crafts; Cards; Games;

Reading groups; Prayer groups; Movies; Shopping trips; Dances/Social or cultural gatherings.
Description Medford Leas is a continuing-care retirement community, operated on a nonprofit basis by a corporation composed of members of the Religious Society of Friends (Quakers), located on about 120 acres of wooded and landscaped grounds. Community has 250 one and two bedroom and studio apartments. Two new apartment complexes, of 28 and 21 apartments for more independent living, are under construction.

MENDHAM

Holly Manor Nursing Home
84 Cold Hill Rd, Mendham, NJ, 07945 (201) 543-2500
Admin Kenneth Rothman. *Medical Dir/Dir of Nursing* Dr L Schlessinger.
Licensure Skilled Care; Intermediate Care. *Beds* 114. *Certified* Medicaid; Medicare.
Staff RNs 8 (ft), 7 (pt); LPNs 3 (ft), 2 (pt); Orderlies 2 (ft), 1 (pt); Nurses aides 40 (ft), 30 (pt); Physical therapists 1 (ft); Recreational therapists 2 (ft); Occupational therapists 1 (ft); Speech therapists 1 (ft); Activities coordinators 1 (ft); Dietitians 1 (ft).
Facilities Dining room; Physical therapy room; Activities room; Chapel; Crafts room; Laundry room; Barber/Beauty shop.
Activities Arts and Crafts; Cards; Games; Reading groups; Prayer groups; Movies; Shopping trips; Dances/Social or cultural gatherings.

MERCERVILLE

Mercerville Nursing Center*
2240 White Horse-Mercerville Rd, Mercerville, NJ, 08619 (609) 586-7500
Admin Lois Mulcahy.
Licensure Skilled Care; Intermediate Care. *Beds* 104. *Certified* Medicaid; Medicare.

MERCHANTVILLE

Maple Lane Inc*
30 W Maple Ave, Merchantville, NJ, 08109 (609) 662-4493
Admin F Dumbleton.
Licensure Long-Term Care. *Beds* 22.

MIDDLETOWN

Hilltop Private Nursing Home*
Kings Highway, Middletown, NJ, 07748 (201) 671-0177
Admin Arlene Platzer.
Licensure Skilled Care; Intermediate Care. *Beds* 53. *Certified* Medicaid; Medicare.

New Ivy House
Kings Hwy, Middletown, NJ, 07748 (201) 671-0169
Admin Paul Seidler. *Medical Dir/Dir of Nursing* Dr D Seigel.
Licensure Skilled Care; Intermediate Care. *Beds* 88. *Certified* Medicaid.

Staff RNs 4 (ft), 5 (pt); LPNs 3 (ft), 3 (pt); Orderlies 1 (ft); Nurses aides 27 (ft), 3 (pt); Activities coordinators 1 (ft), 1 (pt).

MONTCLAIR

Cherry Nursing Home*
111 Gates Ave, Montclair, NJ, 07042 (201) 746-6999
Admin Vera Cherry.
Licensure Long-Term Care. *Beds* 58.

Clover Rest Nursing Home*
16 Madison Ave, Montclair, NJ, 07042 (201) 783-4501
Admin David Austin.
Beds 24.

Little Nursing Home*
71 Christopher St, Montclair, NJ, 07042 (201) 744-5518
Admin R Cumiskey.
Licensure Long-Term Care. *Beds* 24.

Madison Nursing Home*
31 Madison Ave, Montclair, NJ, 07042 (201) 783-4502
Admin James Mamary.
Licensure Skilled Care; Intermediate Care. *Beds* 21. *Certified* Medicaid.

Montcalm Manor*
32 Pleasant Ave, Montclair, NJ, 07042 (201) 744-4560
Admin James Mamary.
Licensure Long-Term Care. *Beds* 36.

Montclair Nursing Home*
78 Midland Ave, Montclair, NJ, 07042 (201) 783-4503
Admin David Austin.
Licensure Long-Term Care. *Beds* 24.

St Vincent's Nursing Home*
45 Elm St, Montclair, NJ, 07042 (201) 746-4000
Admin Sr Alicia Mullins.
Licensure Intermediate Care. *Beds* 135.
Affiliation Roman Catholic

Van Dyk's Nursing and Convalescent Home
42 N Mountain Ave, Montclair, NJ, 07042 (201) 783-9400
Admin Robert Brower. *Medical Dir/Dir of Nursing* Dr Bernard Eichler.
Licensure Long-Term Care. *Beds* 62.
Admissions Requirements Medical examination.
Staff RNs 5 (ft), 5 (pt); LPNs 2 (pt); Activities coordinators 1 (ft), 1 (pt); Dietitians 1 (ft).
Facilities Dining room; Physical therapy room; Chapel; Crafts room; Laundry room; Barber/Beauty shop.
Activities Arts and Crafts; Cards; Reading groups; Movies; Bingo; Bowling.
Description Nursery children visit patients one-on-one; RSVP program; bus for handicapped owned by facility.

MOORESTOWN

Greenleaf Extension*
28 E Main St, Moorestown, NJ, 08057 (609) 235-4884
Admin Robert Hawthorne.
Licensure Long-Term Care. *Beds* 33.
Ownership Nonprofit.

Moorestown Nursing Home*
2nd and Pantcoast Sts, Moorestown, NJ, 08057 (609) 235-0110
Admin Marc Gelinas.
Licensure Skilled Care; Intermediate Care. *Beds* 68. *Certified* Medicaid; Medicare.

MORGAN

Oak View Nursing Home Inc*
Ernston Rd and Garden State Pkwy, Morgan, NJ, 08879 (201) 721-8200
Admin Rose Booth.
Licensure Skilled Care; Intermediate Care. *Beds* 197. *Certified* Medicaid; Medicare.

MORGANVILLE

Queen of Carmel*
Reids Hill Rd, Box 203, Morganville, NJ, 07751 (201) 946-4991
Admin Majorie Morey.
Licensure Skilled Care; Intermediate Care. *Beds* 31. *Certified* Medicaid.

MORRIS PLAINS

Morris View
Box 437, Morris Plains, NJ, 07950 (201) 285-6501
Admin John F Merrigan. *Medical Dir/Dir of Nursing* James H Wolf MD.
Licensure Skilled Care; LTC. *Beds* 371. *Certified* Medicaid.
Ownership Public.
Staff Physicians 8 (pt); RNs 42 (ft), 28 (pt); LPNs 6 (ft), 4 (pt); Nurses aides 183 (ft), 11 (pt); Physical therapists 1 (ft); Occupational therapists 1 (pt); Activities coordinators 1 (ft); Dietitians 1 (ft); Dentists 1 (pt); Ophthalmologists 1 (pt); Podiatrists 1 (pt).
Facilities Dining room; Physical therapy room; Activities room; Chapel; Crafts room; Laundry room; Barber/Beauty shop; Library.
Activities Arts and Crafts; Cards; Games; Reading groups; Prayer groups; Movies; Shopping trips; Dances/Social or cultural gatherings.
Description Morris View Nursing Home is a county-operated, skilled nursing facility with 371 Medicaid approved beds (to become 422 beds on or about May 15, 1985).

MORRISTOWN

Morristown Nursing and Rehabilitation Center
66 Morris St, Morristown, NJ, 07960 (201) 539-3000
Admin Patricia George. *Medical Dir/Dir of Nursing* Bernard Grabelle.
Licensure Skilled Care; Intermediate Care.

Beds 70. *Certified* Medicaid; Medicare.
Staff RNs 4 (ft), 6 (pt); LPNs 2 (ft); Nurses
aides 21 (ft), 3 (pt); Physical therapists 1 (pt);
Recreational therapists 1 (ft); Dietitians 1 (pt).
Facilities Dining room; Physical therapy room;
Activities room; Laundry room.
Activities Arts and Crafts; Cards; Games;
Prayer groups; Movies; Shopping trips.

Twin Oaks Nursing Center*
77 Madison Ave, Morristown, NJ, 07960 (201)
540-9800
Admin Jerome Sendar.
Licensure Skilled Care; Intermediate Care.
Beds SNF 138; ICF 166. *Certified* Medicaid;
Medicare.

MOUNT LAUREL

Mount Laurel Convalescent Center
Church Rd, Mount Laurel, NJ, 08057 (609)
235-7100
Admin James R Star.
Licensure Skilled Care; Intermediate Care.
Beds 264. *Certified* Medicaid; Medicare.
Staff 13; Physicians 1 (ft), 1 (pt); RNs 22 (ft), 5
(pt); LPNs 15 (ft), 6 (pt); Orderlies 6 (ft), 3 (pt);
Nurses aides 70 (ft), 19 (pt); Physical therapists
1 (ft); Recreational therapists 1 (ft);
Occupational therapists 1 (ft); Speech therapists
3 (pt); Dietitians 1 (pt); Dentists 1 (pt);
Ophthalmologists 1 (pt).
Facilities Dining room; Physical therapy room;
Activities room; Chapel; Crafts room; Laundry
room; Barber/Beauty shop.
Activities Arts and Crafts; Cards; Games;
Reading groups; Prayer groups; Movies;
Shopping trips; Dances/Social or cultural
gatherings.
Description Facility is primarily one-story, very
modern and bright. Residential rooms are
attached to nursing facilities allowing ease of
transfer.

NAVESINK

King James Nursing Home*
PO Box R, 400 State Hwy 36, Navesink, NJ,
07752 (201) 291-3400
Admin Herman Black.
Licensure Skilled Care; Intermediate Care.
Beds 123. *Certified* Medicaid; Medicare.

NEPTUNE

Conv-A-Center*
101 Walnut St and Hwy 33, Neptune, NJ,
07753 (201) 774-3550
Admin Dean Charles Michals.
Licensure Skilled Care; Intermediate Care.
Beds 100. *Certified* Medicaid; Medicare.

The Grove Health Care Center
919 Green Grove Rd, Neptune, NJ, 07753
(201) 922-3400
Admin Jennifer R Courlas. *Medical Dir/Dir of
Nursing* Marshal Silver.
Licensure Skilled Care; Intermediate Care.
Beds 121. *Certified* Medicaid.
Admissions Requirements Minimum age 16;
Medical examination.

Staff Physicians 1 (pt); RNs 7 (ft); LPNs 4 (ft);
Nurses aides 43 (ft); Physical therapists 1 (pt);
Recreational therapists 2 (pt); Occupational
therapists 1 (pt); Speech therapists 1 (pt);
Activities coordinators 1 (ft); Dietitians 1 (pt);
Dentists 1 (pt); Ophthalmologists 1 (pt);
Podiatrists 1 (pt); Audiologists 1 (pt).
Affiliation Presbyterian
Facilities Dining room; Physical therapy room;
Activities room; Barber/Beauty shop.
Activities Arts and Crafts; Cards; Games;
Prayer groups; Movies; Shopping trips;
Dances/Social or cultural gatherings.
Description The Grove Health Care Center,
designed to provide comfort, safety, and a
home-like atmosphere, features 24-hour
registered nursing service, rehabilitative
therapies, and an extensive activities program
which includes bus trips, evening and weekend
programming and religious services. Owned
and operated by the Presbyterian Homes of
Southern New Jersey, The Grove Health Care
Center offers the elderly and convalescent the
opportunity to continue their lives with
meaning.

The Lodge Intermediate Care Facility
3510 Rt 66, Neptune, NJ, 07753 (201)
922-1900
Admin Jennifer Courlas. *Medical Dir/Dir of
Nursing* Dr Nathan Troum.
Licensure Intermediate Care. *Beds* 167.
Certified Medicaid.
Admissions Requirements Minimum age 16;
Medical examination; Physician's request.
Staff Physicians 1 (pt); RNs 7 (ft); LPNs 5 (ft);
Nurses aides 51 (ft); Recreational therapists 3
(ft); Dietitians 2 (ft).
Affiliation Presbyterian
Facilities Dining room; Physical therapy room
19C; Chapel; Crafts room; Laundry room;
Barber/Beauty shop; Library.
Activities Arts and Crafts; Cards; Games;
Reading groups; Prayer groups; Movies;
Shopping trips; Dances/Social or cultural
gatherings.

NEPTUNE CITY

Medicenter of Neptune City
2050 6th Ave, Neptune City, NJ, 07753 (201)
774-8300
Admin Bruce London.
Licensure Skilled Care; Intermediate Care.
Beds 106. *Certified* Medicaid; Medicare.
Staff RNs 7 (ft), 7 (pt); LPNs 2 (ft), 4 (pt);
Orderlies 1 (ft); Nurses aides 33 (ft), 6 (pt);
Physical therapists 1 (pt); Recreational
therapists 2 (ft); Occupational therapists 1 (pt);
Speech therapists 1 (pt); Activities coordinators
1 (ft); Dietitians 1 (pt).
Facilities Dining room; Physical therapy room;
Activities room; Laundry room; Barber/Beauty
shop; Television rooms.
Activities Arts and Crafts; Cards; Games;
Reading groups; Prayer groups; Movies;
Shopping trips; Dances/Social or cultural
gatherings.
Description Medicenter is situated on a
beautifully landscaped plot, adorned with trees,
flowers, and shrubs. Residents are encouraged
to take advantage of the large patio and yard.

The building is of fire resistant construction
with smoke detectors and heat sensors located
in every patient room. Fire alarm system is
connected electronically to the local police
department.

NESHANIC

Foothill Acres Inc
Amwell Rd, Neshanic, NJ, 08853 (201)
369-8711
Admin J R McGavisk. *Medical Dir/Dir of
Nursing* H K Van Duyne MD.
Licensure Skilled Care. *Beds* 190.
Certified Medicaid.
Staff Physicians 1 (pt); RNs 1 (ft), 8 (pt); LPNs
5 (ft), 4 (pt); Orderlies 4 (ft), 3 (pt); Nurses aides
30 (ft), 31 (pt); Occupational therapists 1 (pt);
Activities coordinators 1 (ft); Dietitians 1 (pt).
Facilities Dining room; Activities room;
Chapel; Laundry room; Barber/Beauty shop.
Activities Arts and Crafts; Cards; Games;
Reading groups; Prayer groups; Movies;
Shopping trips; Dances/Social or cultural
gatherings.
Description Facility is located on 150 acres of
land in a beautiful rural setting with separate
nursing units. We are able to separate our guests
according to physical and mental condition.

NEW BRUNSWICK

Brunswick Park Nursing Home
US 1 and 18, New Brunswick, NJ, 08901 (201)
828-2400
Admin Dennis F Molnar.
Licensure Skilled Care; Intermediate Care.
Beds 112. *Certified* Medicaid; Medicare.
Facilities Dining room; Physical therapy room;
Activities room; Barber/Beauty shop.
Activities Arts and Crafts; Cards; Games;
Reading groups; Prayer groups; Movies;
Shopping trips; Dances/Social or cultural
gatherings.

Frances E Parker Memorial Home*
Easton Ave, New Brunswick, NJ, 08901 (201)
545-3110
Admin Robert Piegari.
Licensure Long-Term Care. *Beds* 51.
Ownership Nonprofit.

Middlesex County Hospital for Chronically Ill
Rt 30, Georges Rd, New Brunswick, NJ, 08902
(201) 246-6155
Admin James Willan.
Licensure Skilled Care; Intermediate Care.
Beds 61. *Certified* Medicaid; Medicare.

NEW LISBON

Buttonwood Hall
Pemberton-Browns Mills Rd, New Lisbon, NJ,
08064 (609) 894-2271
Admin Leo F Bagan. *Medical Dir/Dir of
Nursing* Dr Thomas Mattingal.
Licensure Skilled Care; Intermediate Care.
Beds 135. *Certified* Medicaid.
Admissions Requirements Minimum age 18;
Physician's request.
Staff Physicians; RNs; LPNs; Orderlies;

Physical therapists; Reality therapists; Recreational therapists; Occupational therapists; Speech therapists; Activities coordinators; Dietitians; Dentists; Ophthalmologists; Podiatrists; Audiologists.
Facilities Dining room; Physical therapy room; Activities room; Chapel; Crafts room; Laundry room; Barber/Beauty shop; Library.
Activities Arts and Crafts; Cards; Games; Reading groups; Prayer groups; Movies; Shopping trips; Dances/Social or cultural gatherings.

NEW MILFORD

Woodcrest Center*
800 River Rd, New Milford, NJ, 07646 (201) 967-1700
Admin Romelyn Frieman.
Licensure Skilled Care; Intermediate Care.
Beds 236. *Certified* Medicaid; Medicare.

NEW PROVIDENCE

Glenside Nursing Center
144 Gales Dr, New Providence, NJ, 07974 (201) 464-8600
Admin Marion Penner. *Medical Dir/Dir of Nursing* Dr E B Cuce.
Licensure Skilled Care; Intermediate Care.
Beds 96. *Certified* Medicaid; Medicare.
Staff RNs 7 (ft), 15 (pt); LPNs 2 (pt); Orderlies 1 (ft); Nurses aides 34 (ft), 11 (pt); Physical therapists 1 (ft); Recreational therapists 1 (ft), 1 (pt); Occupational therapists 1 (ft); Speech therapists 1 (ft); Activities coordinators 1 (pt); Dietitians 1 (pt); Dentists 1 (pt); Ophthalmologists 1 (pt); Podiatrists 1 (pt); Audiologists 1 (pt).
Facilities Dining room; Physical therapy room; Activities room; Crafts room; Laundry room; Barber/Beauty shop.
Activities Arts and Crafts; Cards; Games; Reading groups; Prayer groups; Movies.

NEWARK

Newark Health and Extended Care Facility*
65 Jay St, Newark, NJ, 07103 (201) 483-6800
Admin Samuel Paneth.
Licensure Skilled Care; Intermediate Care.
Beds 420. *Certified* Medicaid; Medicare.

NEWFIELD

Mater Dei Nursing Home
Upper Pittsgrove Twp, Rt 40, Newfield, NJ, 08344 (609) 348-2061
Admin Sr Marie de Chantal. *Medical Dir/Dir of Nursing* Dr John Pastore.
Licensure Skilled Care; Intermediate Care.
Beds 64. *Certified* Medicaid.
Staff Physicians 1 (pt); RNs 1 (ft), 10 (pt); LPNs 2 (ft), 5 (pt); Nurses aides 10 (ft), 25 (pt); Activities coordinators 1 (ft); Dietitians 1 (pt); Dentists 1 (pt); Podiatrists 1 (pt).
Affiliation Roman Catholic
Facilities Dining room; Physical therapy room; Activities room; Chapel; Laundry room;

Barber/Beauty shop.
Activities Arts and Crafts; Cards; Games; Reading groups; Prayer groups; Movies.

NEWTON

Barn Hill Convalescent Center
High St, Newton, NJ, 07860 (201) 383-5600
Admin Richard Roberto.
Licensure Skilled Care; Intermediate Care.
Beds 116. *Certified* Medicaid; Medicare.
Admissions Requirements Minimum age 21; Medical examination; Physician's request.
Staff Physicians 1 (pt); RNs 7 (ft), 2 (pt); LPNs 5 (ft), 2 (pt); Physical therapists 1 (pt); Reality therapists 1 (pt); Recreational therapists 2 (ft), Occupational therapists 1 (pt); Speech therapists 1 (pt); Activities coordinators 1 (ft); Dietitians 2 (pt); Dentists 1 (pt); Podiatrists 1 (pt).
Facilities Dining room; Physical therapy room; Activities room; Chapel; Crafts room; Laundry room; Barber/Beauty shop; Library.
Activities Arts and Crafts; Cards; Games; Reading groups; Prayer groups; Movies; Shopping trips; Dances/Social or cultural gatherings.
Description A one-story structure situated in a North Jersey rural area adjacent to the Newton Memorial Hospital.

Newton Nursing Home
1 Summit Ave, Newton, NJ, 07860 (201) 383-1450
Admin Walter H Miller.
Licensure Long-Term Care. *Beds* 36.
Admissions Requirements Medical examination; Physician's request.
Staff RNs 1 (ft), 2 (pt); LPNs 2 (ft), 2 (pt); Nurses aides 10 (ft), 10 (pt); Activities coordinators 1 (pt); Dietitians 1 (pt).
Facilities Activities room.
Activities Arts and Crafts; Games; Prayer groups.
Description A very small nursing home with everything located on one floor.

Sussex County Homestead
Newton, NJ, 07860 (201) 948-5400
Admin Selma Rooney.
Licensure Skilled Care; Intermediate Care.
Beds 98. *Certified* Medicaid.
Ownership Public.

NORTH BERGEN

Hudson Manor Extended Care*
9020 Wall St, North Bergen, NJ, 07047 (201) 861-4040
Admin Harold Herskowitz.
Licensure Skilled Care; Intermediate Care.
Beds 266. *Certified* Medicaid; Medicare.

NORTHFIELD

Atlantic County Home—Meadowview
201 Shore Rd, Northfield, NJ, 08225 (609) 645-7700
Admin Ramon W Lennie. *Medical Dir/Dir of Nursing* Michael S Slotoroff.
Licensure Skilled Care; Intermediate Care.

Beds 180. *Certified* Medicaid.
Staff Physicians 2 (pt); RNs 15 (ft); LPNs 5 (ft); Nurses aides 39 (ft); Physical therapists 1 (pt); Recreational therapists 1 (ft); Occupational therapists 1 (pt); Speech therapists 1 (pt); Dietitians 1 (ft); Dentists 1 (pt); Ophthalmologists 1 (pt); Podiatrists 2 (pt); Audiologists 1 (pt).
Facilities Dining room; Physical therapy room; Activities room; Chapel; Crafts room; Laundry room; Barber/Beauty shop; Library.
Activities Arts and Crafts; Cards; Games; Reading groups; Prayer groups; Movies; Shopping trips; Dances/Social or cultural gatherings.
Description Facility is located on a beautifully landscaped 5-acre tract of land.

OAKLAND

Bel Air Manor of Oakland
20 Breakneck Rd, Oakland, NJ, 07436 (201) 337-3300
Admin John Fiorilla. *Medical Dir/Dir of Nursing* John DeGhetto DO.
Licensure Skilled Care; Intermediate Care.
Beds 252. *Certified* Medicaid; Medicare.
Admissions Requirements Minimum age 50; Medical examination.
Staff Physicians 1 (ft); RNs 9 (ft), 16 (pt); LPNs 10 (ft), 8 (pt); Orderlies 1 (ft); Nurses aides 63 (ft), 16 (pt); Physical therapists 1 (ft); Recreational therapists 1 (ft); Occupational therapists 1 (ft); Speech therapists 1 (pt); Activities coordinators 3 (ft); Dietitians 1 (ft); Dentists 1 (pt); Ophthalmologists 1 (pt); Podiatrists 1 (pt).
Facilities Dining room; Physical therapy room; Activities room; Crafts room; Laundry room; Barber/Beauty shop.
Activities Arts and Crafts; Games; Prayer groups; Movies; Dances/Social or cultural gatherings; Church activities; Bible studies.
Description Bel Air Manor is nestled on beautifully wooded grounds in the suburbs; private and spacious semi-private rooms in a cheery atmosphere; halls are equipped with side rails for those needing assistance; provides TVs, a well equipped physical therapy department, an excellent recreation program; fine food and excellent nursing care allow patients the fullest possible recovery and enjoyment of life.

OCEAN GROVE

Ocean Grove Nursing Home
63 Clark Ave, Ocean Grove, NJ, 07756 (201) 775-0554
Admin James Handford. *Medical Dir/Dir of Nursing* Y D Kong MD.
Licensure Skilled Care; Intermediate Care.
Beds 68. *Certified* Medicaid.
Staff RNs 3 (ft), 2 (pt); LPNs 2 (ft), 4 (pt); Nurses aides 25 (ft), 8 (pt); Physical therapists 1 (ft), 1 (pt); Activities coordinators 2 (ft); Dietitians 1 (pt); Dentists 1 (pt); Podiatrists 1 (pt).
Facilities Dining room; Activities room; Crafts room; Laundry room; Barber/Beauty shop.
Activities Arts and Crafts; Games; Movies.

OCEAN VIEW

Lutheran Home at Ocean View*
Rt 9, 184 Shore Rd, Ocean View, NJ, 08230
(609) 263-6881
Admin Jeffrey Lissam.
Licensure Intermediate Care; Residential Care.
Beds ICF 63; Residential Care 64.
Certified Medicaid.
Ownership Nonprofit.
Affiliation Lutheran

OLD BRIDGE

Summer Hill Nursing Home*
111 Rt 516, Old Bridge, NJ, 08857 (201)
254-8200
Admin Melvin Feigenbaum.
Licensure Skilled Care; Intermediate Care.
Beds 120. *Certified* Medicaid.

OLD TAPPAN

Ingleside Nursing Home
1016 S Washington Ave, Old Tappan, NJ,
07675 (201) 664-3144
Admin Angela Jaworski.
Licensure Long-Term Care. *Beds* 43.
Staff RNs 6 (ft), 5 (pt); LPNs 2 (ft); Nurses
aides 8 (ft), 13 (pt); Activities coordinators 1
(pt); Dietitians 1 (pt).
Facilities Dining room; Activities room; Crafts
room; Laundry room.
Activities Arts and Crafts; Cards; Games;
Reading groups; Prayer groups; Movies;
Dances/Social or cultural gatherings.

ORANGE

White House Nursing Home
560 Berkeley Ave, Orange, NJ, 07050 (201)
672-6500
Admin Eliezer Grossman. *Medical Dir/Dir of
Nursing* James Paolino.
Licensure Skilled Care; Intermediate Care.
Beds 176. *Certified* Medicaid.
Staff RNs 8 (ft), 4 (pt); LPNs 12 (ft), 4 (pt);
Nurses aides 62 (ft), 6 (pt); Recreational
therapists 3 (ft); Occupational therapists 1 (pt);
Speech therapists 1 (pt); Activities coordinators
1 (ft); Dietitians 1 (pt); Dentists 1 (pt);
Ophthalmologists 1 (pt); Podiatrists 1 (pt);
Audiologists 1 (pt).
Facilities Dining room; Physical therapy room;
Activities room; Crafts room; Barber/Beauty
shop; Library.
Activities Arts and Crafts; Cards; Games;
Reading groups; Prayer groups; Movies;
Shopping trips; Dances/Social or cultural
gatherings.

OXFORD

Warren Haven
RFD, Oxford, NJ, 07863 (201) 453-2131
Admin Jean Sickles. *Medical Dir/Dir of
Nursing* Stanton H Sykes MD.
Licensure Skilled Care; Intermediate Care.
Beds 140. *Certified* Medicaid.
Ownership Public.

Admissions Requirements Minimum age 21;
Medical examination; Physician's request.
Staff Physicians 4 (pt); RNs 11 (ft), 6 (pt);
LPNs 9 (ft), 3 (pt); Orderlies 3 (ft); Nurses aides
48 (ft), 10 (pt); Physical therapists 1 (pt);
Recreational therapists 2 (ft); Occupational
therapists 1 (pt); Speech therapists 1 (pt);
Dietitians 1 (pt); Dentists 1 (pt);
Ophthalmologists 1 (pt); Podiatrists 1 (pt);
Audiologists 1 (pt).
Facilities Dining room; Physical therapy room;
Activities room; Laundry room; Barber/Beauty
shop; Lounges for smokers and non-smokers.
Activities Arts and Crafts; Cards; Games;
Reading groups; Prayer groups; Movies;
Shopping trips; Dances/Social or cultural
gatherings.
Description Warren Haven is an excellent
county nursing home, with a reputation for
providing quality care to our elderly residents.

PARAMUS

Dellridge Nursing Home*
532 Fairview Ave, Paramus, NJ, 07652 (201)
261-1589
Admin Sara Denehy.
Licensure Skilled Care; Intermediate Care.
Beds 96. *Certified* Medicaid; Medicare.

Hartwyck Nursing Home*
593 Paramus Rd, Paramus, NJ, 07652 (201)
444-1341
Admin Frances Brown.
Licensure Skilled Care; Intermediate Care.
Beds 35. *Certified* Medicaid.

PARSIPPANY

Beverwyck Nursing Home Inc*
Beverwyck Rd, Parsippany, NJ, 07054 (201)
887-0156
Admin John E Murphy.
Licensure Long-Term Care. *Beds* 24.

PASSAIC

Chestnut Hill Convalescent Center
360 Chestnut St, Passaic, NJ, 07055 (201)
777-7800
Admin Emil Stefanacci. *Medical Dir/Dir of
Nursing* Dr Richard G Stefanacci.
Licensure Skilled Care; Intermediate Care.
Beds 94. *Certified* Medicaid; Medicare.
Admissions Requirements Minimum age 18;
Medical examination.
Staff Physicians; RNs; LPNs; Orderlies;
Nurses aides; Physical therapists; Recreational
therapists; Speech therapists; Activities
coordinators; Dietitians; Dentists;
Ophthalmologists; Podiatrists.
Facilities Dining room; Physical therapy room;
Activities room; Chapel; Crafts room;
Barber/Beauty shop; Library.
Activities Arts and Crafts; Cards; Games;
Reading groups; Prayer groups; Movies; Bingo.

Jefferson Manor Nursing Center*
85 Columbia Ave, Passaic, NJ, 07055 (201)
773-7070

Admin Patrick Meehan.
Licensure Skilled Care; Intermediate Care.
Beds 88. *Certified* Medicaid.

Madison Manor Nursing Center*
141 Madison St, Passaic, NJ, 07055 (201)
773-0450
Admin Patrick Meehan.
Licensure Skilled Care; Intermediate Care.
Beds 65. *Certified* Medicaid; Medicare.

PATERSON

Preakness Hospital
Paterson, NJ, 07509 (201) 942-6800
Admin Bertha Hudak. *Medical Dir/Dir of
Nursing* Dr Vincent Del Guedice.
Licensure Intermediate Care. *Beds* 432.
Certified Medicaid.
Staff RNs 50 (ft); LPNs 45 (ft); Nurses aides
160 (ft); Physical therapists 2 (ft); Recreational
therapists 10 (ft); Occupational therapists 1 (pt);
Speech therapists 1 (pt); Activities coordinators
1 (ft); Dietitians 4 (ft); Dentists 1 (pt);
Ophthalmologists 1 (pt); Podiatrists 1 (pt);
Audiologists 1 (pt).
Facilities Dining room; Physical therapy room;
Activities room; Chapel; Crafts room; Laundry
room; Barber/Beauty shop; Library.
Activities Arts and Crafts; Cards; Games;
Reading groups; Prayer groups; Movies;
Shopping trips; Dances/Social or cultural
gatherings.
Description The Preakness Hospital, a long-
term facility, has a 25-bed admission unit. All
residents admitted are assessed and evaluated
on this unit to determine maximum potential
and level of wellness. Appropriate
interdisciplinary determination will place the
resident where it is believed best suited to
his/her needs. The facility has a skilled nursing
unit, ICF units and our REACH (residents
engaged in actively caring for him/herself)
units. We believe in maintaining independence
and wellness and encourage each resident to do
the most able for him/herself.

White Birch Nursing Home
59 Birch St, Paterson, NJ, 07502 (201)
942-8899
Admin Ernest Gianetti. *Medical Dir/Dir of
Nursing* P Harami DO.
Licensure Skilled Care; Intermediate Care.
Beds 42. *Certified* Medicaid; Medicare.

PENNSAUKEN

Cooper River Convalescent Center*
5101 N Park Dr, Pennsauken, NJ, 08109 (609)
665-9111
Admin Richard Fusco.
Licensure Skilled Care; Intermediate Care.
Beds 263. *Certified* Medicaid; Medicare.

PERTH AMBOY

Amboy Care Center*
Lindberg Ave, Perth Amboy, NJ, 08861 (201)
826-0500

Admin Frank Gabriel.
Licensure Skilled Care; Intermediate Care.
Beds 179. *Certified* Medicare.

Perth Amboy Nursing Home
303 Elm St, Perth Amboy, NJ, 08861 (201)
442-9540
Admin Berel Tennenbaum. *Medical Dir/Dir of
Nursing* Dr Thadius Balinski.
Licensure Skilled Care; Intermediate Care.
Beds 250. *Certified* Medicaid; Medicare.
Admissions Requirements Minimum age 16;
Medical examination; Physician's request.
Staff Physicians 8 (ft); RNs 54 (ft), 22 (pt);
LPNs 73 (ft), 31 (pt); Nurses aides 180 (ft), 73
(pt); Physical therapists 4 (ft), 2 (pt); Reality
therapists 7 (ft); Recreational therapists 7 (ft);
Occupational therapists 1 (ft); Speech therapists
1 (ft); Activities coordinators 1 (ft); Dietitians 1
(ft); Dentists 1 (ft); Ophthalmologists 1 (ft);
Podiatrists 1 (ft); Audiologists 1 (ft).
Facilities Dining room; Physical therapy room;
Activities room; Chapel; Crafts room; Laundry
room; Barber/Beauty shop; Library.
Activities Arts and Crafts; Cards; Games;
Reading groups; Prayer groups; Movies;
Shopping trips; Dances/Social or cultural
gatherings.
Description Ultra-modern facility incorporates
the highest degree of professional and para-
professional care available. Included in teaching
plan are interns, residents, student RNs and
LPNs, and physical therapists in training.
Services are renown in the area for the high
quality, yet providing a homey and
compassionate atmosphere.

PHILLIPSBURG

Garden Nursing Home
843 Wilbur Ave, Phillipsburg, NJ, 08865 (201)
454-8574
Admin Bernard Guttman. *Medical Dir/Dir of
Nursing* Dr Luke Kung and Dr Edward Spoll.
Licensure Skilled Care; Intermediate Care.
Beds 89. *Certified* Medicaid.
Staff Physicians 2 (pt) #13B 9 (ft), 4 (pt); LPNs
5 (ft), 4 (pt); Nurses aides 28 (ft), 8 (pt);
Physical therapists 1 (pt); Activities
coordinators 2 (ft); Dietitians 1 (pt); Social
worker 1 (ft).

PINE BROOK

Hill Top Care Center*
Hook Mountain Rd, Pine Brook, NJ, 07058
Admin Eric Paneth.
Licensure Skilled Care; Intermediate Care.
Beds 114. *Certified* Medicaid; Medicare.

PISCATAWAY

Francis E Parker*
1421 River Rd, Piscataway, NJ, 08854 (201)
545-3110
Admin Robert Piegari.
Licensure Intermediate Care. *Beds* 60.

PITTSTOWN

Stone Arch Health Care Center
Rt 1, Pittstown, NJ, 08857
Admin Nancy Goczalk. *Medical Dir/Dir of
Nursing* Robert Pierce MD.
Licensure Skilled Care; Intermediate Care.
Beds 120. *Certified* Medicaid; Medicare.
Ownership Proprietary.
Admissions Requirements Minimum age 18.
Facilities Dining room; Physical therapy room;
Activities room; Crafts room; Laundry room;
Barber/Beauty shop.
Activities Arts and Crafts; Cards; Games;
Reading groups; Prayer groups; Movies;
Shopping trips; Dances/Social or cultural
gatherings; Bus rides.

PLAINFIELD

Abbott Manor Inc*
808-14 Central Ave, Plainfield, NJ, 07060 (201)
757-0696
Admin Lionel C Rubin.
Licensure Long-Term Care. *Beds* 35.

Hartwyck at Plainfield*
1340 Park Ave, Plainfield, NJ, 07060 (201)
754-3100
Admin Roy T Miller.
Licensure Skilled Care; Intermediate Care.
Beds 106. *Certified* Medicaid.

PLEASANTVILLE

Our Lady's Residence*
Glendale and Clematis Aves, Pleasantville, NJ,
08232 (609) 646-2450
Admin Sr Mary Aurelia.
Licensure Intermediate Care. *Beds* 208.
Certified Medicaid.
Affiliation Roman Catholic

POINT PLEASANT

Claremont Care Center
1550 Hulse Rd, Point Pleasant, NJ, 08742
(201) 295-9300
Admin LaVerne T Kennedy. *Medical Dir/Dir
of Nursing* Clifford Blasi MD.
Licensure Skilled Care; Intermediate Care.
Beds 100. *Certified* Medicaid; Medicare.
Staff Physicians 1 (ft); RNs 4 (ft), 4 (pt); LPNs
4 (ft), 2 (pt); Nurses aides 41 (ft), 11 (pt);
Activities coordinators 1 (ft); Dietitians 1 (ft).
Facilities Dining room; Physical therapy room;
Activities room; Crafts room; Laundry room;
Barber/Beauty shop.
Activities Arts and Crafts; Cards; Games;
Reading groups; Prayer groups; Movies;
Shopping trips; Dances/Social or cultural
gatherings.
Description Center is located on Intercoastal
Waterway; there is a relaxing view of passing
yachts, refreshing salt water breezes, and patios
exposed to the sun.

POINT PLEASANT BEACH

Point Pleasant Beach Nursing Home*
703 Richmond Ave, Point Pleasant Beach, NJ,
08742 (201) 899-2525
Admin William Graubit.
Licensure Intermediate Care. *Beds* 27.
Certified Medicaid.

PRINCETON

Princeton Nursing Home*
35 Quarry St, Princeton, NJ, 08540 (609)
924-9000
Admin Catherine Reusser.
Licensure Skilled Care; Intermediate Care.
Beds 119. *Certified* Medicaid; Medicare.

RARITAN

Raritan Health and Extended Care Center*
Rt 28, Raritan, NJ, 08869 (201) 526-8950
Admin Michael Greenberg.
Licensure Skilled Care; Intermediate Care.
Beds 128. *Certified* Medicaid; Medicare.

RED BANK

Red Bank Convalescent Center
100 Chapin Ave, Red Bank, NJ, 07701 (201)
741-8811
Admin Ethelyn Leiblich. *Medical Dir/Dir of
Nursing* Victor Siegel MD.
Licensure Skilled Care; Intermediate Care.
Beds 150. *Certified* Medicaid.
Staff Physicians 6 (pt); RNs 10 (ft), 2 (pt);
LPNs 4 (ft), 2 (pt); Orderlies 3 (ft), 1 (pt);
Nurses aides 40 (ft), 5 (pt); Physical therapists 1
(pt); Recreational therapists 1 (pt);
Occupational therapists 1 (pt); Activities
coordinators 1 (ft); Dietitians 1 (pt); Dentists 1
(pt); Ophthalmologists 1 (pt); Podiatrists 1 (pt);
Audiologists 1 (pt).
Facilities Dining room; Physical therapy room;
Activities room; Chapel; Crafts room; Laundry
room; Barber/Beauty shop; Library.
Activities Arts and Crafts; Cards; Games;
Reading groups; Prayer groups; Movies;
Dances/Social or cultural gatherings; Outings;
Adopted grandparent programs.
Description We will be adding another 30 beds
to the facility. We have a patio and barbecue
grill for cookouts and picnics. The Shrewsbury
River winds its way around the building. Every
room has a scenic view.

Red Bank Medicenter*
55 W Front St, Red Bank, NJ, 07701 (201)
842-3800
Admin Donald Bisgrove.
Licensure Skilled Care; Intermediate Care.
Beds 104. *Certified* Medicaid; Medicare.

RIDGEWOOD

Pine Rest Nursing Home*
PO Box 71, E Ridgewood Ave, Ridgewood, NJ,
07450 (201) 652-1950
Admin William Maloney.
Licensure Long-Term Care. *Beds* 50.

Ridgewood Nursing Home
330 Franklin Turnpike, Ridgewood, NJ, 07451
(201) 447-1900
Admin Thomas P Sheehy Jr. *Medical Dir/Dir of Nursing* Bernard Sklar MD.
Licensure Skilled Care; Intermediate Care.
Beds 90. *Certified* Medicaid; Medicare.
Admissions Requirements Minimum age 18;
Physician's request.
Activities Arts and Crafts; Cards; Games;
Reading groups; Prayer groups; Movies;
Shopping trips; Dances/Social or cultural
gatherings.

Van Dyks Nursing and Convalescent
304 S Van Dien Ave, Ridgewood, NJ, 07450
(201) 445-8200
Admin William Van Dyk. *Medical Dir/Dir of Nursing* Dr William Hopewell.
Licensure Long-Term Care. *Beds* 93.
Admissions Requirements Medical
examination.
Staff RNs 10 (ft), 5 (pt); LPNs 2 (ft), 2 (pt);
Nurses aides 40 (ft), 30 (pt); Physical therapists
1 (ft), 1 (pt); Recreational therapists 2 (ft);
Speech therapists 1 (pt); Activities coordinators
1 (pt); Dietitians 1 (ft); Dentists 1 (pt);
Ophthalmologists 1 (pt); Podiatrists 1 (pt).
Facilities Dining room; Physical therapy room;
Activities room; Chapel; Crafts room; Laundry
room; Barber/Beauty shop; Library.
Activities Arts and Crafts; Cards; Games;
Reading groups; Movies; Shopping trips.

SADDLE BROOK

Brook Wood Convalescent Home
30 Legregni St, Saddle Brook, NJ, 07663 (201)
843-8411
Admin Frederick Soilson. *Medical Dir/Dir of Nursing* Thomas Bellavia.
Licensure Skilled Care; Intermediate Care.
Beds 52. *Certified* Medicaid.
Admissions Requirements Minimum age 40.
Staff Physicians 3 (pt); RNs 1 (ft), 5 (pt); LPNs
4 (pt); Nurses aides 12 (ft), 6 (pt); Physical
therapists 1 (pt); Occupational therapists 1 (pt);
Activities coordinators 1 (ft), 2 (pt); Dietitians
1 (pt); Dentists 1 (pt); Ophthalmologists 1 (pt);
Podiatrists 1 (pt); Audiologists 1 (pt).
Facilities Dining room; Activities room;
Chapel; Laundry room; Barber/Beauty shop.
Activities Arts and Crafts; Cards; Games;
Reading groups; Prayer groups; Movies.

Saddle Brook Convalescent Home
15 Caldwell St, Saddle Brook, NJ, 07663 (201)
843-7333
Admin Frederick Soilson. *Medical Dir/Dir of Nursing* Dr Bernard Ross.
Licensure Skilled Care; Intermediate Care.
Beds 52. *Certified* Medicaid.
Staff RNs 2 (ft), 3 (pt); LPNs 5 (pt); Nurses
aides 9 (ft), 8 (pt); Physical therapists 1 (pt);
Recreational therapists 1 (pt); Activities
coordinators 1 (pt); Dietitians 1 (pt); Dentists 2
(pt); Podiatrists 2 (pt).
Facilities Dining room; Activities room;
Laundry room; Barber/Beauty shop.
Activities Arts and Crafts; Cards; Games;
Reading groups; Prayer groups; Movies;
Shopping trips; Dances/Social or cultural
gatherings.

SALEM

Salem County Nursing and Convalescent Home
438 Woodstown Rd, Rt 45, Salem, NJ, 08079
(609) 935-6677
Admin Carl Baker. *Medical Dir/Dir of Nursing* Dr Joseph Lacauara Jr.
Licensure Skilled Care; Intermediate Care.
Beds 110. *Certified* Medicaid; Medicare.
Ownership Public.
Admissions Requirements Minimum age 18;
Medical examination; Physician's request.
Staff Physicians 7 (pt); RNs 7 (ft); LPNs 10
(ft); Orderlies 4 (ft); Nurses aides 60 (ft);
Physical therapists 1 (ft); Recreational therapists
2 (ft); Occupational therapists 1 (pt); Speech
therapists 1 (pt); Dietitians 1 (pt); Dentists 1
(pt); Ophthalmologists 1 (pt); Podiatrists 1 (pt);
Audiologists 1 (pt).
Facilities Dining room; Physical therapy room;
Activities room; Crafts room; Laundry room;
Barber/Beauty shop.
Activities Arts and Crafts; Cards; Games;
Reading groups; Prayer groups; Movies;
Shopping trips; Dances/Social or cultural
gatherings.

SCOTCH PLAINS

Ashbrook Nursing Home Inc*
1610 Raritan Rd, Scotch Plains, NJ, 08098
(201) 889-5500
Admin Dan Moles.
Licensure Skilled Care; Intermediate Care.
Beds 102. *Certified* Medicaid; Medicare.

SEWELL

Pinecrest Nursing and Convalescent Home*
Salina and Glassboro-Woodbury Rd, PO Box
146, Sewell, NJ, 08080 (609) 468-2500
Admin Dolores Stark.
Licensure Long-Term Care. *Beds* 226.

SHREWSBURY

Shrewsbury Manor Nursing Home
515 Shrewsbury Ave, Shrewsbury, NJ, 07704
(201) 741-2059
Admin William Johnson.
Licensure Skilled Care; Intermediate Care.
Beds 35. *Certified* Medicaid.

SOMERS POINT

**Ocean Point Health Care Center—
Presbyterian Homes of Southern New Jersey**
555 Bay Ave, Somers Point, NJ, 08244 (609)
927-9151
Admin Charle A Wilkins. *Medical Dir/Dir of Nursing* Dr Stanley Edden.
Licensure Skilled Care; Intermediate Care.
Beds 145. *Certified* Medicaid; Medicare.
Facilities Dining room; Physical therapy room;
Activities room; Chapel; Crafts room; Laundry
room; Barber/Beauty shop; Library.
Activities Arts and Crafts; Cards; Games;
Reading groups; Prayer groups; Movies;
Shopping trips; Dances/Social or cultural
gatherings.

SOMERSET

Central New Jersey Jewish Home for Aged
380 DeMott Ln, Somerset, NJ, 08873 (201)
873-2000
Admin Elliott Solomon. *Medical Dir/Dir of Nursing* Dr Lawrence.
Licensure Intermediate Care. *Beds* 125.
Certified Medicaid.
Admissions Requirements Medical
examination.
Staff RNs 5 (ft); LPNs 9 (ft); Nurses aides 45
(ft); Physical therapists 1 (ft), 2 (pt);
Recreational therapists 2 (ft); Activities
coordinators 1 (ft); Dietitians 1 (ft); Podiatrists
1 (ft).
Affiliation Jewish

King James of Franklin Township*
1165 Easton Ave, Somerset, NJ, 08873 (201)
246-4100
Admin Egon Scheil.
Licensure Skilled Care; Intermediate Care.
Beds 180. *Certified* Medicaid; Medicare.

STRATFORD

Stratford Nursing and Convalescent Center*
Laurel and Warwick Rd, Stratford, NJ, 08084
(609) 784-2400
Admin Anne McNally.
Licensure Skilled Care; Intermediate Care.
Beds 104. *Certified* Medicaid; Medicare.

SUCCASUNNA

Merry Heart Nursing Home Inc*
200 Rt 10, Succasunna, NJ, 07876 (201)
584-4000
Admin John and Hazel Kadimik.
Licensure Skilled Care; Intermediate Care.
Beds 61. *Certified* Medicaid; Medicare.

TEANECK

Teaneck Nursing Home*
1104 Teaneck Rd, Teaneck, NJ, 07660 (201)
833-2400
Admin John J Post.
Licensure Skilled Care; Intermediate Care.
Beds 107. *Certified* Medicaid; Medicare.

TENAFLY

County Manor Nursing Home
133 County Rd, Tenafly, NJ, 07670 (201)
567-7800
Admin Nat Pearl.
Licensure Skilled Care; Intermediate Care.
Beds 64. *Certified* Medicaid; Medicare.
Staff Physicians; RNs; LPNs; Nurses aides;
Physical therapists; Recreational therapists;
Occupational therapists; Speech therapists;

Activities coordinators; Dietitians; Dentists; Ophthalmologists; Podiatrists; Audiologists.
Facilities Dining room; Physical therapy room; Activities room; Chapel; Crafts room; Laundry room; Barber/Beauty shop; Library.
Activities Arts and Crafts; Cards; Games; Reading groups; Prayer groups; Movies.

TINTON FALLS

Heritage Hall Nursing Home*
524 Wardell Rd, Tinton Falls, NJ, 07753 (201) 922-9330
Admin Elliiott Wiener.
Licensure Skilled Care; Intermediate Care.
Beds 115. *Certified* Medicaid.

TOMS RIVER

Country Manor Nursing Home
16 Whitesville Rd, Toms River, NJ, 08753 (201) 341-1600
Admin Edgar H Coxeter. *Medical Dir/Dir of Nursing* Dr Jacob Goldstein.
Licensure Skilled Care; Intermediate Care.
Beds 218. *Certified* Medicaid; Medicare.
Staff Physicians 20 (pt); RNs 16 (ft), 13 (pt); LPNs 17 (ft), 19 (pt); Orderlies 3 (ft), 1 (pt); Nurses aides 80 (ft), 48 (pt); Physical therapists 1 (ft); Recreational therapists 5 (ft), 4 (pt); Occupational therapists 1 (pt); Speech therapists 1 (pt); Activities coordinators 1 (ft); Dietitians 1 (pt); Dentists 1 (pt); Ophthalmologists 1 (pt); Podiatrists 1 (pt); Audiologists 1 (pt).
Facilities Dining room; Physical therapy room; Activities room; Chapel; Crafts room; Laundry room; Barber/Beauty shop; Library.
Activities Arts and Crafts; Cards; Games; Reading groups; Prayer groups; Movies; Shopping trips; Dances/Social or cultural gatherings; Wheelchair square dancing; Pet therapy.
Description Facility features a sparkling, clean, modern environment with an outstanding program of activities. Innovative multidisciplinary coma treatment program for head-injured patients is offered with all therapies and extensive social service.

Toms River Convalescent Center
Hospital Dr, Toms River, NJ, 08753 (201) 244-3100
Admin Jasper B Phelps. *Medical Dir/Dir of Nursing* Jeffrey Brustein MD.
Licensure Skilled Care; Intermediate Care.
Beds 100. *Certified* Medicaid; Medicare.
Description This is the only center in New Jersey to have a "special care program" for young residents; approximately 75% of residents are 16 years through 50 years old.

TOTOWA

Valley Rest Nursing Home
56 Bogert St, Totowa, NJ, 07512 (201) 942-2534
Admin Marion Henze. *Medical Dir/Dir of Nursing* Dr Jan Barnes.
Licensure Skilled Care; Intermediate Care.
Beds 32. *Certified* Medicaid.
Admissions Requirements Minimum age 50.

Staff Physicians 1 (ft); RNs 5 (ft); LPNs 1 (ft), 4 (pt); Nurses aides 18 (ft), 10 (pt); Physical therapists 1 (pt); Reality therapists 1 (pt); Recreational therapists 1 (pt); Occupational therapists 1 (pt); Speech therapists 1 (pt); Activities coordinators 1 (ft); Dietitians 1 (pt); Dentists 1 (pt); Ophthalmologists 1 (pt); Podiatrists 1 (pt); Audiologists 1 (pt).
Facilities Activities room; Crafts room; Laundry room.
Activities Arts and Crafts; Cards; Games; Reading groups; Prayer groups; Movies; Shopping trips; Dances/Social or cultural gatherings.

TRENTON

Bellevue Care Center
439 Bellevue Ave, Trenton, NJ, 08618 (609) 396-2646
Admin Mary Ann McCarty. *Medical Dir/Dir of Nursing* Dr Richard Gordon.
Licensure Skilled Care; Intermediate Care.
Beds 100. *Certified* Medicaid; Medicare.
Staff Physicians 4 (pt); RNs 4 (ft), 4 (pt); LPNs 4 (ft), 6 (pt); Nurses aides 50 (ft), 20 (pt); Physical therapists 1 (pt); Occupational therapists 1 (pt); Speech therapists 1 (pt); Activities coordinators 1 (ft); Dietitians 1 (pt); Dentists 1 (pt); Ophthalmologists 1 (pt); Podiatrists 1 (pt); Audiologists 1 (pt).
Facilities Dining room; Physical therapy room; Activities room; Crafts room; Laundry room; Barber/Beauty shop.
Activities Arts and Crafts; Cards; Games; Reading groups; Prayer groups; Movies; Dances/Social or cultural gatherings.

Ewing Parkway Nursing Home*
1201 Parkway Ave, Trenton, NJ, 08628 (609) 882-6900
Admin Paul Galas.
Licensure Skilled Care; Intermediate Care.
Beds 102. *Certified* Medicaid; Medicare.

Mercer Care Center
1501 State Hwy 33, Trenton, NJ, 08690 (609) 586-1114
Admin Dan Geller. *Medical Dir/Dir of Nursing* Dr Albert Valenzuela.
Licensure Skilled Care; Intermediate Care.
Beds 120. *Certified* Medicaid; Medicare.
Staff RNs 6 (ft), 3 (pt); LPNs 10 (ft), 2 (pt); Nurses aides 44 (ft), 7 (pt); Recreational therapists 2 (ft), 1 (pt).
Facilities Dining room; Physical therapy room; Activities room; Crafts room; Laundry room; Barber/Beauty shop; Library.
Activities Arts and Crafts; Cards; Games; Reading groups; Prayer groups; Movies; Shopping trips; Dances/Social or cultural gatherings.

Mercer County Geriatric Center—F W Donnelly Long-Term Care Facility
2238 Hamilton Ave, Trenton, NJ, 08619 (609) 989-6930
Admin Steven R Mellion. *Medical Dir/Dir of Nursing* A Strauss MD.
Licensure Skilled Care; Intermediate Care.
Beds 214. *Certified* Medicaid.
Staff Physicians 2 (ft), 1 (pt); RNs 15 (ft), 10

(pt); LPNs 30 (ft), 15 (pt); Nurses aides 75 (ft), 10 (pt); Physical therapists 1 (pt); Recreational therapists 6 (ft); Occupational therapists 1 (pt); Speech therapists 1 (pt); Activities coordinators 1 (ft); Dietitians 1 (ft); Dentists 1 (pt); Ophthalmologists 1 (pt); Podiatrists 1 (pt); Audiologists 1 (pt).
Description Applicants must be elderly residents of Mercer County, New Jersey who are Medicaid eligible. No private pay clients accepted.

TROY HILLS

Troy Hills House*
200 Reynolds Ave, Troy Hills, NJ, 07050 (201) 887-8080
Admin Kenneth Pierson.
Licensure Skilled Care. *Beds* 128.
Certified Medicaid; Medicare.

UNION

Cornell Hall Convalescent Center
234 Chestnut St, Union, NJ, 07083 (201) 687-7800
Admin Elizabeth Baitaille. *Medical Dir/Dir of Nursing* Joseph E McDonald MD.
Licensure Skilled Care; Residential Health Care. *Beds* SNF 100; Residential Health Care 20. *Certified* Medicaid; Medicare.
Admissions Requirements Physician's request.
Staff Physicians 1 (pt); RNs 4 (ft), 6 (pt); LPNs 6 (ft), 4 (pt); Nurses aides 33 (ft); Physical therapists 1 (pt); Recreational therapists 1 (ft), 1 (pt); Occupational therapists 1 (pt); Speech therapists 1 (pt); Activities coordinators 1 (ft), 1 (pt); Dietitians 1 (pt).
Facilities Dining room; Physical therapy room; Activities room; Chapel; Crafts room; Laundry room; Barber/Beauty shop; Library; Treatment room/dental/x-ray; Conference room; 2 day rooms; Greenhouse; Clubhouse; 2 patios.
Activities Arts and Crafts; Cards; Games; Reading groups; Prayer groups; Movies; Shopping trips; Dances/Social or cultural gatherings; Religious activities; Special events; Van rides; Leisure counseling; Individual therapy; Bedside activities.
Description Cornell Hall provides total capability in convalescent and long-term care; 24-hour nursing care; patient has choice of own or house physician; private or semi-private rooms with residential health care available. Facility located in suburban Union very near Garden State Parkway and its connections to New York and Pennsylvania; near bus line for buses to and from New York as well as connections to all parts of New Jersey.

VINELAND

Bishop McCarthy Residence*
1045 E Chestnut Ave, Vineland, NJ, 08360 (609) 692-2850
Admin Sr Mary Elvira.
Licensure Skilled Care; Intermediate Care.
Beds 147. *Certified* Medicaid; Medicare.
Ownership Nonprofit.
Affiliation Roman Catholic

VOORHEES

Lakewood of Voorhees*
Laurel Oak Rd, Voorhees, NJ, 08043 (609) 435-5996
Admin Shirley Wagner.
Licensure Intermediate Care. *Beds* 240.

WALL TOWNSHIP

Tower Lodge Nursing Home*
1506 Gully Rd, Wall Township, NJ, 07719 (201) 681-1400
Admin William Seaman.
Licensure Skilled Care; Intermediate Care.
Beds 60. *Certified* Medicaid; Medicare.

WAYNE

Alps Manor Nursing Home
1120 Alps Rd, Wayne, NJ, 07470 (201) 694-2100
Admin Robert Guggenheim. *Medical Dir/Dir of Nursing* Paule Topalovic.
Licensure Skilled Care; Intermediate Care.
Beds 197. *Certified* Medicaid.
Staff RNs 9 (ft), 4 (pt); LPNs 2 (ft), 1 (pt); Orderlies 8 (ft); Nurses aides 38 (ft), 2 (pt); Recreational therapists 2 (ft), 1 (pt); Activities coordinators 1 (ft); Dietitians 1 (pt).
Facilities Dining room; Physical therapy room; Activities room; Laundry room; Barber/Beauty shop.
Activities Arts and Crafts; Cards; Games; Reading groups; Prayer groups; Movies; Shopping trips; Dances/Social or cultural gatherings; Picnics.

Brookside Manor Inc*
499 Newark-Pompton Turnpike, Wayne, NJ, 07470 (201) 694-9783
Admin Ruth O'Keefe.
Licensure Intermediate Care. *Beds* 55.
Certified Medicaid.

Countryside Nursing and Convalescent Center
310 Newark-Pompton Turnpike, Wayne, NJ, 07470 (201) 694-6110
Admin Lee Pohley.
Licensure Skilled Care; Intermediate Care.
Beds 25. *Certified* Medicaid; Medicare.

Lakeview Convalescent Center
130 Terhune Dr, Wayne, NJ, 07470 (201) 839-4500
Admin Richard Grosso Jr. *Medical Dir/Dir of Nursing* Dr Schlossberg.
Licensure Skilled Care; Intermediate Care.
Beds 120. *Certified* Medicaid; Medicare.
Admissions Requirements Minimum age 16.
Staff Physicians 1 (ft), 13 (pt); RNs 8 (ft), 4 (pt); LPNs 4 (ft), 4 (pt); Nurses aides 32 (ft), 15 (pt); Physical therapists 1 (ft); Reality therapists 1 (ft); Recreational therapists 1 (ft); Occupational therapists 1 (pt); Speech therapists 1 (pt); Activities coordinators 1 (ft); Dietitians 1 (pt); Dentists 1 (pt); Ophthalmologists 1 (pt); Podiatrists 1 (pt); Audiologists 1 (pt); Social workers 1 (pt).
Facilities Dining room; Physical therapy room; Activities room; Crafts room; Laundry room; Barber/Beauty shop.
Activities Arts and Crafts; Cards; Games; Reading groups; Prayer groups; Movies; Shopping trips; Dances/Social or cultural gatherings.
Description Lakeview is a warm facility in an attractive setting. Culinary excellence of dietary staff is only surpassed by their ability to accommodate any diet. Programs for cognitive rehabilitation and respirator care have been very successful. Award winning activities staff is sure to make anyone's stay pleasant.

Llanfair House*
1140 Black Oak Ridge Rd, Wayne, NJ, 07470 (201) 835-7443
Admin Adrienne Mayernik.
Licensure Skilled Care; Intermediate Care.
Beds 180. *Certified* Medicaid; Medicare.

North Jersey Nursing and Convalescent Center
296 Hamburg Turnpike, Wayne, NJ, 07470 (201) 956-8007
Admin Isadore Zuckerman. *Medical Dir/Dir of Nursing* Robert Brabston MD.
Licensure Skilled Care; Intermediate Care.
Beds 120. *Certified* Medicaid; Medicare.
Admissions Requirements Medical examination.
Staff RNs 7 (ft); LPNs 5 (pt); Nurses aides 24 (ft), 14 (pt); Physical therapists 1 (ft); Recreational therapists 1 (ft), 2 (pt); Occupational therapists 1 (pt); Speech therapists 1 (pt); Activities coordinators 1 (ft); Dietitians 1 (ft).
Facilities Dining room; Physical therapy room; Activities room; Crafts room; Laundry room; Barber/Beauty shop.
Activities Arts and Crafts; Cards; Games; Reading groups; Prayer groups; Movies; Shopping trips; Dances/Social or cultural gatherings.

Oak Ridge Manor Nursing Center
261 Terhune Dr, Wayne, NJ, 07470 (201) 835-3871
Admin Denise B Dunlap. *Medical Dir/Dir of Nursing* Dr Seymour Schlossberg.
Licensure Skilled Care. *Beds* 64.
Certified Medicaid.
Staff RNs 5 (ft), 4 (pt); LPNs 1 (ft), 2 (pt); Nurses aides 16 (ft), 20 (pt); Activities coordinators 1 (ft), 1 (pt).
Facilities Dining room.
Activities Arts and Crafts; Cards; Games; Reading groups; Prayer groups; Movies; Shopping trips; Shopping trips; Community events; Facility picnics; Special events quarterly.

Wayne Haven Nursing Home*
493 Black Oak Ridge Rd, Wayne, NJ, 07472 (201) 694-1842
Admin James Codiroli.
Licensure Long-Term Care; Residential Care.
Beds 82.

Willowbrook Inc*
897 Black Oak Ridge Rd, Wayne, NJ, 07470 (201) 835-9730
Admin Purita Such.
Licensure Long-Term Care. *Beds* 49.

WEST MILFORD

Milford Manor Nursing Home
69 Maple Rd, West Milford, NJ, 07480 (201) 697-5666
Admin Purita Such. *Medical Dir/Dir of Nursing* Dr Buu.
Licensure New Concepts in Health Care.
Beds 100.
Admissions Requirements Medical examination; Physician's request.
Staff Physicians; RNs; LPNs; Nurses aides; Physical therapists; Reality therapists; Recreational therapists; Occupational therapists; Activities coordinators; Dietitians; Dentists; Ophthalmologists; Podiatrists; Audiologists.

WEST ORANGE

Daughters of Israel Pleasant Valley Home
1155 Pleasant Valley Way, West Orange, NJ, 07052 (201) 731-5100
Admin Lawrence Gelfand. *Medical Dir/Dir of Nursing* Raymond Cogan MD.
Licensure Skilled Care; Intermediate Care.
Certified Medicaid; Medicare.
Ownership Nonprofit.
Admissions Requirements Minimum age 65.
Staff Physicians 1 (ft), 5 (pt); RNs 22 (ft), 16 (pt); LPNs 29 (ft), 5 (pt); Orderlies 9 (ft); Nurses aides 71 (ft), 10 (pt); Physical therapists 2 (pt); Recreational therapists 6 (ft); Occupational therapists 1 (ft); Activities coordinators 1 (ft); Dietitians 1 (ft); Dentists 1 (pt); Podiatrists 1 (pt); Male aides 9 (ft).
Affiliation Jewish
Facilities Dining room; Physical therapy room; Activities room; Chapel; Barber/Beauty shop; Library.
Activities Arts and Crafts; Cards; Games; Reading groups; Prayer groups; Movies; Shopping trips; Dances/Social or cultural gatherings.
Description The Center has a day care program for the frail elderly who can be maintained in present living quarters. Kosher food is served in all programs. Center has a diagnostic and referral service for families seeking advice and treatment.

Northfield Manor
777 Northfield Ave, West Orange, NJ, 07042 (201) 731-4500
Admin Michael Konig. *Medical Dir/Dir of Nursing* Dr Joseph Aaron.
Licensure Skilled Care; Intermediate Care.
Beds 131. *Certified* Medicaid; Medicare.
Staff RNs 5 (ft), 3 (pt); Orderlies 9 (ft), 7 (pt); Nurses aides 28 (ft), 26 (pt); Physical therapists 2 (ft); Reality therapists 2 (ft); Recreational therapists 2 (ft); Occupational therapists 1 (pt); Speech therapists 1 (pt); Activities coordinators 2 (ft); Dietitians 1 (ft); Dentists 1 (pt); Ophthalmologists 1 (pt); Podiatrists 1 (pt); Audiologists 1 (ft).
Facilities Dining room; Physical therapy room; Activities room; Crafts room; Laundry room; Barber/Beauty shop; Library.
Activities Arts and Crafts; Cards; Games; Reading groups; Prayer groups; Movies; Shopping trips; Dances/Social or cultural

gatherings.

Description Northfield Manor is a one-story, 131-bed all level of care facility dedicated to the health and well-being of guests. Provide a variety of daily indoor and outdoor activities; meals are prepared in modern kitchen under strict supervision of a registered dietician.

Theresa Grotta Center*
20 Summit St, West Orange, NJ, 07052 (201) 736-2000
Admin Monroe M Kramer.
Licensure Skilled Care; Intermediate Care.
Beds 142. *Certified* Medicaid; Medicare.
Ownership Nonprofit.

WESTFIELD

Westfield Convalescent Center
1515 Lamberts Mill Rd, Westfield, NJ, 07090 (201) 233-9700
Admin Stuart Zeckendorf. *Medical Dir/Dir of Nursing* Dr Howard Lehr.
Licensure Skilled Care; Intermediate Care.
Beds 158. *Certified* Medicaid; Medicare.
Staff RNs 7 (ft), 5 (pt); LPNs 8 (ft), 5 (pt); Orderlies 1 (ft), 1 (pt); Physical therapists 3 (pt); Recreational therapists 4 (ft), 2 (pt); Occupational therapists 1 (ft); Speech therapists 1 (pt); Activities coordinators 1 (ft); Dietitians 1 (pt); Dentists 1 (pt).
Facilities Dining room; Physical therapy room; Activities room; Crafts room; Laundry room; Barber/Beauty shop.
Activities Arts and Crafts; Cards; Games; Reading groups; Prayer groups; Movies; Shopping trips; Dances/Social or cultural gatherings; Bowling; Aerobics; Pet therapy.

WESTWOOD

Valley Nursing Home
300 Old Hook Rd, Westwood, NJ, 07675 (201) 664-8888
Admin Dorothy Franklin. *Medical Dir/Dir of Nursing* H R Hoff MD.
Licensure Long-Term Care. *Beds* 120.
Ownership Proprietary.
Admissions Requirements Minimum age 17; Medical examination; Physician's request.
Staff RNs; LPNs; Nurses aides; Physical therapists; Occupational therapists; Speech therapists; Activities coordinators; Dietitians; Dentists; Ophthalmologists; Podiatrists; Audiologists.
Facilities Dining room; Physical therapy room; Activities room; Chapel; Crafts room; Laundry room; Barber/Beauty shop; Library.
Activities Arts and Crafts; Cards; Games; Reading groups; Prayer groups; Movies; Shopping trips; Dances/Social or cultural gatherings.
Description Facility has been providing quality skilled nursing care since 1961; staff is caring, loving, progressive, and innovative.

WHIPPANY

Crestwood Nursing Home Inc*
101 Whippany Rd, Whippany, NJ, 07981 (201) 887-0311
Admin William Felts.
Licensure Long-Term Care. *Beds* 75.

WOODBURY

Greenbriar Nursing and Convalescent Center*
190 N Evergreen Ave, Woodbury, NJ, 08096 (609) 848-7400
Admin Paul Zirbser.
Licensure Skilled Care; Intermediate Care.
Beds 220. *Certified* Medicaid; Medicare.

WOODCLIFF LAKE

Woodcliff Lake Manor
555 Chestnut Ridge Rd, Woodcliff Lake, NJ, 07675 (201) 391-0900
Admin Emily Howell. *Medical Dir/Dir of Nursing* Arnold Byer MD.
Licensure Skilled Care; Intermediate Care.
Beds 104. *Certified* Medicare.
Admissions Requirements Minimum age 21.
Staff RNs; LPNs; Orderlies; Nurses aides; Physical therapists; Occupational therapists; Speech therapists; Activities coordinators; Dietitians; Dentists; Podiatrists; Audiologists.
Facilities Dining room; Physical therapy room; Activities room; Chapel; Crafts room; Laundry room; Barber/Beauty shop; Library.
Activities Arts and Crafts; Cards; Games; Prayer groups; Movies; Dances/Social or cultural gatherings.
Description This facility has a social day care center open from 9am to 5pm daily.

WOODSTOWN

Friends Home at Woodstown*
Friends Dr, PO Box 249, Woodstown, NJ, 08098 (609) 769-1500
Admin Robert C Smith.
Licensure Skilled Care; Intermediate Care; Residential Care. *Beds* 60; Residential Care 60.
Certified Medicaid; Medicare.
Ownership Nonprofit.
Affiliation Society of Friends

WYCKOFF

Christian Health Care Center
301 Sicomac Ave, Wyckoff, NJ, 07481 (201) 848-0300
Admin Robert Dahl. *Medical Dir/Dir of Nursing* Dr K Lubansky.
Licensure Skilled Care. *Beds* 120.
Certified Medicaid.
Admissions Requirements Minimum age 18.
Staff Physicians 5 (pt); RNs 5 (ft), 15 (pt); LPNs 3 (ft), 1 (pt); Nurses aides 42 (ft), 30 (pt); Physical therapists 1 (pt); Recreational therapists 1 (ft); Activities coordinators 1 (ft); Dietitians 1 (ft); Dentists 1 (pt); Ophthalmologists 1 (pt); Podiatrists 1 (pt); Audiologists 1 (pt); Social workers 2 (pt).
Affiliation Christian Reformed

Facilities Dining room (with chapel); Physical therapy room; Activities room; Crafts room; Laundry room; Barber/Beauty shop.
Activities Arts and Crafts; Games; Reading groups; Prayer groups; Movies; Shopping trips; Dances/Social or cultural gatherings; Ceramics; Painting class.
Description Facility is located in suburban New Jersey just 17 miles from the George Washington Bridge; committed to providing quality medical and nursing care within a distinctly Christian environment.

NEW MEXICO

ALAMOGORDO

Betty Dare Good Samaritan Center
3101 N Florida, Box 538, Alamogordo, NM, 88310 (505) 434-0033
Admin Betty Sadler.
Licensure Intermediate Care. *Beds* 90. *Certified* Medicaid.
Admissions Requirements Medical examination; Physician's request.
Staff LPNs 11 (ft); Orderlies 2 (ft); Nurses aides 28 (ft); Activities coordinators 1 (ft); Dietitians 1 (ft).
Affiliation Lutheran
Facilities Dining room; Activities room; Chapel; Laundry room; Barber/Beauty shop.
Activities Arts and Crafts; Cards; Games; Reading groups; Prayer groups; Movies; Shopping trips; Dances/Social or cultural gatherings.

ALBUQUERQUE

AARC Group Home 2
5605 Gibson SE, Albuquerque, NM, 87108 (505) 256-1640
Admin Ralph Herrera. *Medical Dir/Dir of Nursing* Vodra Cox.
Licensure Intermediate Care for Mentally Retarded. *Beds* 10. *Certified* Medicaid.

AARC Group Home 3
5609 Gibson SE, Albuquerque, NM, 87108 (505) 256-0846
Admin Ralph Herrera. *Medical Dir/Dir of Nursing* Vodra Cox.
Licensure Intermediate Care for Mentally Retarded. *Beds* 8. *Certified* Medicaid.

Anne Pickard Convalescent Hospital*
5900 Forest Hills Dr NE, Albuquerque, NM, 87109 (505) 822-6000
Admin Gary Weygant.
Beds 90. *Certified* Medicaid.

Casa Angelica
5629 Isleta Blvd SW, Albuquerque, NM, 87105 (505) 877-5763
Admin Stella Negri. *Medical Dir/Dir of Nursing* William K Woodard.
Licensure Nursing Home For Severely Retarded Children. *Beds* 25.
Admissions Requirements Minimum age 6 Months; Medical examination; Physician's request.

Staff Physicians 1 (pt); RNs 3 (ft); LPNs 1 (ft), 1 (pt); Nurses aides 4 (ft), 14 (pt); Physical therapists 1 (pt); Occupational therapists 1 (pt); Speech therapists 1 (pt); Dietitians 1 (pt); Dentists 1 (pt).
Facilities Dining room; Physical therapy room; Activities room; Chapel; Laundry room.
Description This is a home for severely retarded children. We limit our number to 25 in order to be able to offer individual attention in a family-type atmosphere.

El Centro Villa Nursing Center
236 High St NE, Albuquerque, NM, 87102 (505) 243-3561
Admin Laura P Hercey. *Medical Dir/Dir of Nursing* Don Hedges.
Licensure Intermediate Care. *Beds* 105. *Certified* Medicaid.
Admissions Requirements Medical examination; Physician's request.
Staff RNs 2 (ft); LPNs 7 (ft), 1 (pt); Orderlies 5 (ft); Nurses aides 25 (ft); Reality therapists 2 (ft); Recreational therapists 3 (ft); Activities coordinators 1 (ft); Dietitians 1 (pt).
Facilities Dining room; Physical therapy room; Activities room; Chapel; Crafts room; Laundry room; Barber/Beauty shop; Library.
Description Centrally located, easily accesible to public transportation and downtown area of city with individualized services dependent upon needs/desires of residents. Programs directed at restoration and/or maintenance of physical, emotional, and social aspects of individuals.

Four Seasons Nursing Center—Camino Vista*
7900 Constitution NE, Albuquerque, NM, 87110 (505) 296-5567
Admin Alan England.
Licensure Intermediate Care. *Beds* 108. *Certified* Medicaid.
Ownership Proprietary.

Four Seasons Nursing Center—Northeast Heights
2216 Lester Dr NE, Albuquerque, NM, 87112 (505) 296-4808
Admin Dianne Moody. *Medical Dir/Dir of Nursing* Dr Ed Sager.
Licensure Intermediate Care. *Beds* 148. *Certified* Medicaid.
Staff Physicians 1 (pt); RNs 9 (ft), 3 (pt); LPNs 4 (ft), 4 (pt); Orderlies 6 (ft), 2 (pt); Nurses aides

46 (ft); Physical therapists 1 (pt); Recreational therapists 1 (pt); Activities coordinators 1 (ft); Dietitians 1 (ft); Dentists 1 (pt).
Facilities Dining room; Physical therapy room; Activities room; Crafts room; Laundry room; Barber/Beauty shop; Conference room.
Activities Arts and Crafts; Cards; Games; Reading groups; Movies; Shopping trips; Dances/Social or cultural gatherings; Community programs; Outings.
Description Facility is very home-like with lots of love and caring, very clean, good food, very good nursing care, most residents geriatric age with average age 82.

Four Seasons Nursing Center—Ridgecrest
2441 Ridgecrest Dr SE, Albuquerque, NM, 87108 (505) 265-8051
Admin Joyce E Stalgren. *Medical Dir/Dir of Nursing* Marvin D Call MD.
Licensure Skilled Care; Intermediate Care. *Beds* SNF 38; ICF 48. *Certified* Medicaid; Medicare.
Admissions Requirements Medical examination; Physician's request.
Staff Physicians 1 (ft); RNs 3 (ft), 2 (pt); LPNs 11 (ft); Orderlies 5 (ft); Nurses aides 23 (ft), 2 (pt); Physical therapists 1 (ft), 2 (pt); Reality therapists 1 (pt); Recreational therapists 1 (ft); Occupational therapists 1 (ft), 1 (pt); Speech therapists 1 (ft), 1 (pt); Activities coordinators 1 (ft); Dietitians 1 (ft), 1 (pt); Dentists 1 (ft); Ophthalmologists 1 (pt); Podiatrists 1 (ft); Audiologists 1 (pt).
Facilities Dining room; Activities room; Laundry room; Barber/Beauty shop.
Activities Arts and Crafts; Cards; Games; Reading groups; Prayer groups; Movies; Shopping trips; Dances/Social or cultural gatherings; Adapted athletics; City-wide outings; Out for meals; Companions 'N Caring volunteer program.

La Vida Llena Health Care
10501 Lagrima de Oro NE, Albuquerque, NM, 87111
Admin George West. *Medical Dir/Dir of Nursing* Marvin Call MD.
Licensure Skilled Care; Intermediate Care. *Beds* 60. *Certified* Medicaid; Medicare.
Ownership Nonprofit.
Admissions Requirements Physician's request.
Staff Physicians 1 (pt); RNs 4 (ft), 4 (pt); LPNs 5 (ft), 6 (pt); Nurses aides 6 (ft), 8 (pt); Occupa-

tional therapists 1 (pt); Speech therapists 1 (pt); Activities coordinators 1 (ft); Dietitians 1 (pt); Dentists 1 (pt); Podiatrists 1 (pt).
Facilities Dining room; Physical therapy room; Activities room; Crafts room; Laundry room; Barber/Beauty shop; Library; General store; Ice cream shop.
Activities Arts and Crafts; Cards; Games; Reading groups; Movies; Shopping trips; Dances/Social or cultural gatherings.
Description This is a life-care facility; 60-bed nursing facility is also open to community. Center is located at the base of Sandia Mountain with spectacular view of the city and mountain.

Ladera Health Care Centerᴬ
5901 Ourray Rd NW, Albuquerque, NM, 87120 (505) 836-0023
Admin Kate Bradshaw.
Beds 96. *Certified* Medicaid.

Las Palomas Health Care Center*
PO Box 14517, 8100 Palomas Ave, Albuquerque, NM, 87191 (505) 821-4200
Admin Peggy Folk Jones.
Beds 96. *Certified* Medicaid.

Manzano del Sol Good Samaritan Village
5201 Roma Ave NE, Albuquerque, NM, 87108
Admin Marilyn Goodsell. *Medical Dir/Dir of Nursing* Dr Bill Daugherty.
Licensure Intermediate Care. *Beds* 120. *Certified* Medicaid.
Ownership Nonprofit.
Admissions Requirements Medical examination.
Staff Physicians; RNs 5 (ft), 9 (pt); LPNs 3 (ft), 5 (pt); Nurses aides 24 (ft), 9 (pt); Physical therapists; Occupational therapists; Speech therapists; Activities coordinators 2 (ft); Dietitians 1 (ft); Dentists; Ophthalmologists; Podiatrists; Audiologists.
Facilities Dining room; Physical therapy room; Activities room; Chapel; Crafts room; Laundry room; Barber/Beauty shop; Library.
Activities Arts and Crafts; Cards; Games; Reading groups; Prayer groups; Movies; Shopping trips; Dances/Social or cultural gatherings.
Description Facility offers an active hospice program in health care center.

Saint Francis Gardens
904 Las Lomas Rd, NE, Albuquerque, NM, 87102 (505) 842-1410
Admin Marcia Wegmann. *Medical Dir/Dir of Nursing* Dr Paul Greenbaum.
Licensure Intermediate Care. *Beds* 135. *Certified* Medicaid.
Admissions Requirements Medical examination; Physician's request.
Staff RNs 3 (ft); LPNs 8 (ft), 7 (pt); Nurses aides 47 (ft), 12 (pt); Physical therapists 1 (pt); Recreational therapists 1 (ft); Occupational therapists 1 (pt); Speech therapists 1 (pt); Activities coordinators 1 (ft); Dietitians 1 (ft); Dentists 1 (pt); Podiatrists 1 (pt).
Affiliation Roman Catholic
Facilities Dining room; Activities room; Chapel; Crafts room; Laundry room; Barber/Beauty shop; Library.
Activities Arts and Crafts; Cards; Games; Reading groups; Prayer groups; Movies; Shop-

ping trips; Dances/Social or cultural gatherings; Fun and fitness to your health; Conversational Spanish; Pet therapy.
Description Residents eating in the dining room have choice of 4-5 salads from salad bar wheeled to their table. They also have 2 entree choices. Recreational therapy department provides ambulation and range of motion at no extra cost. On-site child care center provides interaction between the elderly and the young.

Western Eldercare Nursing Center*
1509 University Blvd NE, Albuquerque, NM, 87102 (505) 243-2257
Admin Floyd Gardner.
Licensure Intermediate Care. *Beds* 96. *Certified* Medicaid.
Ownership Proprietary.

ARTESIA

Artesia Good Samaritan Center
PO Box 620, 1402 Gilchrist, Artesia, NM, 88210 (505) 746-9865
Admin Dennis Beeman. *Medical Dir/Dir of Nursing* Shirley Sperling.
Licensure Intermediate Care. *Beds* 65. *Certified* Medicaid.
Admissions Requirements Medical examination; Physician's request.
Staff RNs 2 (ft); LPNs 4 (ft), 8 (pt); Orderlies 1 (pt); Nurses aides 5 (ft), 18 (pt); Reality therapists 1 (pt); Recreational therapists 1 (ft); Activities coordinators 1 (ft); Dietitians 1 (pt).
Facilities Dining room; Physical therapy room; Activities room; Chapel; Crafts room; Laundry room; Barber/Beauty shop.
Activities Arts and Crafts; Cards; Games; Reading groups; Prayer groups; Movies; Shopping trips.

AZTEC

Four Corners Good Samaritan
500 Care Ln, Aztec, NM, 87401 (505) 334-9445
Admin Katheryn S Pipho.
Licensure Intermediate Care. *Beds* 80. *Certified* Medicaid.
Staff RNs 4 (ft); LPNs 4 (ft), 3 (pt); Orderlies 1 (ft); Nurses aides 23 (ft), 13 (pt); Physical therapists 1 (ft); Occupational therapists 1 (ft); Activities coordinators 1 (ft); Dietitians 1 (pt).
Affiliation Lutheran
Facilities Dining room; Physical therapy room; Activities room; Chapel; Crafts room; Laundry room; Barber/Beauty shop.
Activities Arts and Crafts; Cards; Games; Reading groups; Prayer groups; Movies; Shopping trips; Dances/Social or cultural gatherings.

CARLSBAD

Lakeview Christian Home—Northgate Unit
1905 W Pierce, Carlsbad, NM, 88220 (505) 885-3161
Admin John Paul Athanasiou. *Medical Dir/Dir of Nursing* Virgil O McCollum.
Licensure Intermediate Care. *Beds* 95. *Certified* Medicaid.
Admissions Requirements Medical examination; Physician's request.

Staff RNs 7 (ft), 1 (pt); LPNs 6 (ft); Orderlies 3 (ft); Nurses aides 46 (ft); Activities coordinators 1 (ft); Dietitians 1 (pt).
Facilities Dining room; Chapel; Crafts room; Barber/Beauty shop.
Activities Arts and Crafts; Games; Reading groups; Prayer groups; Movies; Shopping trips; Dances/Social or cultural gatherings.

Lakeview Christian Home of the Southwest
1300 N Canal St, Carlsbad, NM, 88220 (505) 887-0551
Admin Ray Bailey. *Medical Dir/Dir of Nursing* Virgil McCollum.
Licensure Intermediate Care. *Beds* 118. *Certified* Medicaid.
Admissions Requirements Medical examination; Physician's request.
Staff RNs 3 (ft), 2 (pt); LPNs 11 (ft); Orderlies 1 (ft); Nurses aides 48 (ft); Activities coordinators 1 (ft); Dietitians 1 (pt).
Facilities Dining room; Activities room; Chapel; Crafts room; Laundry room; Barber/Beauty shop; Library.
Activities Arts and Crafts; Cards; Games; Reading groups; Prayer groups; Movies; Shopping trips; Dances/Social or cultural gatherings.

Laundsun Homes Inc
1900 Westridge Rd, Carlsbad, NM, 88220 (505) 887-2894
Admin Jay P Irby. *Medical Dir/Dir of Nursing* Dr T E Hauser.
Licensure Nursing Home. *Beds* 24.
Admissions Requirements Medical examination; Physician's request.
Staff Physicians 1 (pt); RNs 2 (ft), 2 (pt); LPNs 5 (ft), 2 (pt); Nurses aides 17 (ft), 12 (pt); Physical therapists 1 (pt); Reality therapists 1 (pt); Recreational therapists 1 (pt); Activities coordinators 1 (ft); Dietitians 1 (pt); Dentists 1 (pt); Ophthalmologists 1 (pt); Podiatrists 1 (pt); Audiologists 1 (pt).
Affiliation Methodist
Facilities Dining room; Physical therapy room; Activities room; Crafts room; Barber/Beauty shop; Library.
Activities Arts and Crafts; Cards; Games; Reading groups; Prayer groups; Movies; Shopping trips; Dances/Social or cultural gatherings.
Description Landsun Homes is an interactive, comprehensive retirement community, capable of responding to the changing needs of its older adult residents through an assured continuum of care and support as long as they live.

CLAYTON

Town Hall Estates*
419 Harding St, Clayton, NM, 83415 (505) 374-2353
Admin James E Johnson.
Licensure Intermediate Care. *Beds* 59. *Certified* Medicaid.
Ownership Nonprofit.

CLOVIS

Chapparal Nursing Center
1400 W 21st St, Clovis, NM, 88101 (505) 763-6695

Admin John F Pilger. *Medical Dir/Dir of Nursing* Susie Small.
Licensure Intermediate Care. *Beds* 60. *Certified* Medicaid.
Staff LPNs 6 (ft), 1 (pt); Nurses aides 24 (ft); Activities coordinators 1 (ft).
Facilities Dining room; Activities room; Laundry room; Barber/Beauty shop.
Activities Arts and Crafts; Cards; Games; Prayer groups; Shopping trips; Dances/Social or cultural gatherings.

Golden Age Nursing Center
1201 Norris St, Clovis, NM, 88101 (505) 762-3754
Admin Juandell Dougherty. *Medical Dir/Dir of Nursing* Mariellen Bonem.
Licensure Intermediate Care. *Beds* 60. *Certified* Medicaid.
Admissions Requirements Medical examination; Physician's request.
Facilities Dining room; Laundry room; Barber/Beauty shop.
Activities Arts and Crafts; Cards; Games; Prayer groups; Movies; Shopping trips; Dances/Social or cultural gatherings.

Retirement Ranch of Clovis
2210 Mabry Dr, PO Box 1809, Clovis, NM, 88101 (505) 762-4495
Admin William M Kesler. *Medical Dir/Dir of Nursing* Virginia Dickson.
Licensure Intermediate Care. *Beds* 100. *Certified* Medicaid.
Staff RNs 1 (ft), 2 (pt); LPNs 8 (ft), 1 (pt); Orderlies 2 (ft); Nurses aides 33 (ft), 2 (pt); Recreational therapists 2 (ft).
Affiliation Presbyterian
Facilities Dining room; Activities room; Laundry room; Barber/Beauty shop; Library.
Activities Arts and Crafts; Cards; Games; Reading groups; Prayer groups; Shopping trips.
Description Three levels of care offered within the health care unit—self-care, general nursing, and care of the confused.

DEMING

Mimbres Memorial Hospital—Intermediate Care Facility
900 W Ash St, Deming, NM, 88030 (505) 546-2761
Admin Roy Rumbaugh. *Medical Dir/Dir of Nursing* S A Goodman MD.
Licensure Intermediate Care. *Beds* 34. *Certified* Medicaid.
Staff RNs 3 (ft); LPNs 6 (ft); Orderlies 4 (ft); Nurses aides 20 (ft); Physical therapists 1 (pt); Occupational therapists 1 (pt); Speech therapists 1 (pt); Activities coordinators 1 (pt); Dietitians 1 (pt); Dentists 1 (pt); Dentists 1 (pt); Podiatrists 1 (pt).
Facilities Dining room; Activities room; Crafts room; Laundry room; Barber/Beauty shop.
Activities Arts and Crafts; Cards; Games; Reading groups; Prayer groups; Dances/Social or cultural gatherings.

FARMINGTON

San Juan Manor*
806 W Maple, Farmington, NM, 87401 (505) 325-2910
Admin Kay Rogers.
Licensure Intermediate Care. *Beds* 62. *Certified* Medicaid.
Ownership Proprietary.

FORT BAYARD

Fort Bayard Medical Center—Nursing Home Unit
PO Box 219, Fort Bayard, NM, 88036 (505) 537-3302
Admin Art Salas. *Medical Dir/Dir of Nursing* Larry Merrett MD.
Licensure Skilled Care; Intermediate Care. *Beds* 300. *Certified* Medicaid; Medicare.
Admissions Requirements Medical examination; Physician's request.
Staff Physicians 3 (ft); RNs 11 (ft); LPNs 18 (ft); Nurses aides 109 (ft); Physical therapists 1 (ft); Recreational therapists 1 (ft); Activities coordinators 1 (ft); Dietitians 1 (ft); Dentists 1 (pt).
Facilities Dining room; Physical therapy room; Activities room; Crafts room; Barber/Beauty shop; Library.
Activities Arts and Crafts; Cards; Games; Reading groups; Prayer groups; Movies; Shopping trips.
Description Unit provides ancillary services including laboratory, X-ray, physical therapy, social services, pharmacy, activities, hairdressing, and 3 full-time physicians providing 24-hour, on-call coverage.

FORT STANTON

Fort Stanton Hospital and Training School
PO Box 8, Fort Stanton, NM, 88323 (505) 354-2211
Admin Mark Delgado. *Medical Dir/Dir of Nursing* Boyd D Hume Jr MD.
Licensure Intermediate Care for Mentally Retarded. *Beds* 148. *Certified* Medicaid; Medicare.
Staff Physicians 1 (ft), 1 (pt); RNs 5 (ft); LPNs 7 (ft); Nurses aides 68 (ft); Physical therapists 1 (pt); Recreational therapists 3 (ft); Occupational therapists 1 (pt); Speech therapists 1 (ft), 1 (pt); Dietitians 1 (ft); Dentists 1 (pt).
Facilities Dining room; Physical therapy room; Activities room; Chapel; Crafts room; Laundry room; Barber/Beauty shop; Library; Gymnasium; Swimming pool.
Activities Arts and Crafts; Cards; Games; Reading groups; Prayer groups; Movies; Shopping trips; Dances/Social or cultural gatherings; Swimming; Volleyball; Basketball; Physical education.
Description Facility offers ICF/MR residential and outpatient services; multiphase program including academic, prevocational, medical, vocational, and residential services; physical, occupational, and speech therapy, placement, follow-up, case management evaluation, and diagnostic services; physical education, recreation, special olympic affiliation and co-

sponsorship of Southern New Mexico Winter Games, Rainbow Sports Camp, and New Mexico Interagency Games.

FORT SUMNER

Pecos Valley Nursing Home
509 N 10th St, PO Box L, Fort Sumner, NM, 88119 (505) 355-2439
Admin Flora Russell. *Medical Dir/Dir of Nursing* E D Fikany MD.
Licensure Intermediate Care. *Beds* 44. *Certified* Medicaid.
Admissions Requirements Medical examination; Physician's request.
Staff RNs 1 (ft); LPNs 2 (ft), 3 (pt); Orderlies 1 (ft); Nurses aides 15 (ft), 2 (pt); Activities coordinators 1 (ft); Dietitians 1 (pt).
Facilities Dining room; Laundry room; Barber/Beauty shop.
Activities Arts and Crafts; Cards; Games; Reading groups; Prayer groups; Shopping trips; Dances/Social or cultural gatherings; Monthly birthday parties.
Description We are involved in starting residents council, kitchen band, musical melody bells, golf in season on patio, picnics, resident of month has dinner party with a family member, bingo, and publish monthly newsletter.

GALLUP

Gallup Care Center*
3720 Churchrock Dr, Gallup, NM, 87301 (505) 722-2261
Admin Vickie Carathers.
Licensure Intermediate Care. *Beds* 96. *Certified* Medicaid.
Ownership Proprietary.

McKinley Manor*
224 Nizhoni Blvd, Gallup, NM, 87301 (505) 863-9551
Admin Marian L Macrorie.
Licensure Intermediate Care. *Beds* 66. *Certified* Medicaid.
Ownership Proprietary.

GRANTS

Grants Good Samaritan Center*
840 Lobo Canyon Rd, Grants, NM, 87020 (505) 287-8868
Admin Adolph Zoudlik.
Licensure Intermediate Care. *Beds* 80. *Certified* Medicaid.
Ownership Nonprofit.
Affiliation Lutheran

HOBBS

La Siesta Retirement Center
301 Bensing Rd, Hobbs, NM, 88240 (505) 397-1113
Admin Ronnie E Lee.
Licensure Intermediate Care. *Beds* 55. *Certified* Medicaid.
Staff RNs 1 (ft); LPNs 5 (ft); Nurses aides 18 (ft); Physical therapists 1 (pt); Activities coordinators 1 (pt); Dietitians 1 (pt).

Lea County Good Samaritan Village
1701 N Turner, PO Box 2568, Hobbs, NM,
88240 (505) 393-3156
Admin Ken Keller. *Medical Dir/Dir of
Nursing* Rita Wade.
Licensure Intermediate Care. *Beds* 99. *Certified* Medicaid.
Ownership Public.
Admissions Requirements Minimum age 18;
Medical examination; Physician's request.
Staff RNs 1 (ft), 1 (pt); LPNs 8 (ft), 2 (pt);
Nurses aides 18 (ft), 5 (pt); Physical therapists 1
(pt); Recreational therapists 2 (ft); Activities
coordinators 2 (ft); Dietitians 1 (ft).
Facilities Dining room; Physical therapy room;
Activities room; Chapel; Crafts room; Laundry
room; Barber/Beauty shop; Library.
Activities Arts and Crafts; Cards; Games;
Reading groups; Prayer groups; Movies; Shopping trips; Dances/Social or cultural gatherings.
Description We are offering 3 levels of adult
living—ICF nursing care, apartment living
(supervised), and adult day care.

LAS CRUCES

Las Cruces Manor
2905 E Missouri St, Las Cruces, NM, 88001
(505) 522-0404
Admin Jack G Hamlett. *Medical Dir/Dir of
Nursing* Adex Cantu MD.
Licensure Intermediate Care. *Beds* 62. *Certified* Medicaid.
Staff LPNs 5 (ft); Orderlies 3 (ft); Nurses aides
8 (ft); Activities coordinators 1 (ft).
Facilities Dining room; Physical therapy room;
Activities room; Crafts room; Laundry room;
Barber/Beauty shop; Library.
Activities Arts and Crafts; Cards; Games;
Reading groups; Prayer groups; Movies; Shopping trips; Dances/Social or cultural gatherings.
Description A friendly LTC residence with personal concern, a "home away from home."
Facility complies with all state/federal standards. Our philosophy is excellent patient care
and high standards, policies, and procedures.

**Mountain Shadows—Intermediate Care
Facility***
1005 Hill Rd, Las Cruces, NM, 88001 (505)
523-4573
Admin Henry Wesley Handy.
Licensure Intermediate Care. *Beds* 77. *Certified* Medicaid.
Ownership Proprietary.

University Terrace Good Samaritan Village
3025 Terrace Dr, Las Cruces, NM, 88001 (505)
522-1362
Admin L Joe Pomplun.
Licensure Intermediate Care. *Beds* 60. *Certified* Medicaid.
Admissions Requirements Medical examination.
Staff RNs 4 (ft), 1 (pt); LPNs 4 (ft), 1 (pt);
Orderlies 2 (ft), 1 (pt); Nurses aides 23 (ft), 3
(pt); Activities coordinators 1 (ft); Dietitians 1
(ft); Social workers 1 (ft).
Affiliation Lutheran
Facilities Dining room; Chapel; Crafts room;
Laundry room; Barber/Beauty shop; Library;
Swimming pool and jacuzzi.

Activities Arts and Crafts; Cards; Games;
Reading groups; Prayer groups; Movies; Shopping trips; Dances/Social or cultural gatherings;
Sing-a-longs; Birthday parties.
Description Construction has begun on an
additional 166 apartments; when completed,
this will bring the total to 266 retirement apartments.

LAS VEGAS

**New Mexico State Hospital Long Term Care
Division**
PO Box 1388, Las Vegas, NM, 87701 (505)
425-6711 ext 5204
Admin Reynaldo Crespin. *Medical Dir/Dir of
Nursing* Raymond Mathewson MD.
Licensure Skilled Care; Intermediate Care;
Acute Care. *Beds* 239. *Certified* Medicaid;
Medicare.
Admissions Requirements Minimum age 16;
Medical examination; Physician's request.
Staff Physicians 3 (ft); RNs 16 (ft); LPNs 21
(ft); Nurses aides 119 (ft); Physical therapists 1
(ft); Recreational therapists 1 (ft); Occupational
therapists 1 (ft); Speech therapists 2 (ft); Activities coordinators 6 (ft); Dietitians 2 (ft); Dentists 1 (ft); Podiatrists 1 (pt).
Facilities Dining room; Physical therapy room;
Activities room; Crafts room; Barber/Beauty
shop.
Activities Arts and Crafts; Cards; Games;
Reading groups; Prayer groups; Movies; Shopping trips; Dances/Social or cultural gatherings.
Description This facility is unique in that it
provides 3 different levels of care within one
facility: ICF, SNF, and general.

Southwest Senior Care Inc*
2301 Collins Dr, Las Vegas, NM, 87701 (505)
425-9362
Admin Joe C Maestas.
Licensure Intermediate Care. *Beds* 102. *Certified* Medicaid.
Ownership Proprietary.

LORDSBURG

Sunshine Haven
W Railway Ave, PO Box 340, Lordsburg, NM,
88045 (505) 542-3539
Admin Rose Allen. *Medical Dir/Dir of
Nursing* Lalitha Fernicola MD.
Licensure Intermediate Care. *Beds* 82. *Certified* Medicaid.
Admissions Requirements Medical examination.
Staff Physicians 1 (ft); RNs 1 (ft), 4 (pt); LPNs
5 (ft); Orderlies 5 (ft); Nurses aides 23 (ft), 1
(pt); Physical therapists 1 (ft); Recreational therapists 1 (ft), 1 (pt); Activities coordinators 1 (ft);
Dietitians 1 (ft); Podiatrists 1 (pt).
Facilities Dining room; Physical therapy room;
Activities room; Crafts room; Laundry room;
Barber/Beauty shop.
Activities Arts and Crafts; Cards; Games;
Reading groups; Prayer groups; Movies; Dances/Social or cultural gatherings.
Description During summer months residents
really enjoy enclosed patio; activity department

holds barbecues and ice cream socials; also
activity department plants a garden with help
of some residents.

LOS LUNAS

Los Lunas Hospital and Training School
PO Box 1269, Los Lunas, NM, 87031 (505)
865-9611
Admin Joseph F Mateju. *Medical Dir/Dir of
Nursing* Jeffrey Seltz MD.
Licensure Intermediate Care for Mentally
Retarded. *Beds* 404. *Certified* Medicaid.
Staff Physicians 4 (ft); RNs 20 (ft); LPNs 20
(ft); Physical therapists 2 (ft); Recreational therapists 11 (ft); Occupational therapists 2 (ft);
Speech therapists 1 (ft); Dietitians 3 (ft); Dentists 1 (ft); Audiologists 1 (ft).
Facilities Dining room; Physical therapy room;
Activities room; Crafts room; Laundry room;
Barber/Beauty shop; Library.
Activities Arts and Crafts; Games; Prayer
groups; Movies; Shopping trips; Dances/Social
or cultural gatherings.
Description Residential treatment facility operated by state of New Mexico, near Albuquerque.

LOVINGTON

Lovington Good Samaritan Center*
PO Box 1058, 1600 West Ave I, Lovington,
NM, 88260 (505) 396-5212
Admin Mary Ellen Stroope. *Medical Dir/Dir of
Nursing* Peggy Clayton.
Licensure Intermediate Care. *Beds* 62. *Certified* Medicaid.
Ownership Nonprofit.
Affiliation Lutheran

NEW LAGUNA

**Laguna Rainbow Nursing and Elderly Care
Center**
PO Box 236, New Laguna, NM, 87038
Admin Larry Curley. *Medical Dir/Dir of
Nursing* Michael Heisler MD.
Licensure Skilled Care. *Beds* 25. *Certified* Medicaid.
Ownership Nonprofit.
Admissions Requirements Minimum age 60;
Medical examination; Physician's request.
Staff Physicians 2 (pt); RNs 1 (ft); LPNs 3 (ft),
1 (pt); Orderlies 2 (ft); Nurses aides 5 (ft), 4 (pt);
Physical therapists 1 (pt); Activities coordinators 1 (ft); Dietitians 1 (pt); Podiatrists 1 (pt);
Audiologists 1 (pt).
Facilities Dining room; Activities room; Chapel; Crafts room; Laundry room.
Activities Arts and Crafts; Prayer groups;
Movies; Shopping trips; Dances/Social or cultural gatherings.
Description This is the only Indian owned,
Indian operated facility in the state of New
Mexico, located on an Indian reservation;
accommodates all ranges of needs, beginning
with occasional interaction to ICF; provides
social activities, congregate housing and
feeding, and meals on wheels.

PORTALES

Roosevelt General Hospital—Intermediate Care Facility
PO Drawer 60, 1700 S Ave O, Portales, NM, 88130 (505) 356-4411
Admin Ronald McArthur. *Medical Dir/Dir of Nursing* Robnert Timmons MD.
Licensure Intermediate Care. *Beds* 49. *Certified* Medicaid.
Admissions Requirements Medical examination; Physician's request.
Staff RNs 1 (ft); LPNs 3 (ft), 3 (pt); Orderlies 3 (ft), 3 (pt); Nurses aides 8 (ft), 8 (pt); Physical therapists 1 (pt); Activities coordinators 1 (ft).
Facilities Dining room; Physical therapy room; Activities room; Barber/Beauty shop.
Activities Arts and Crafts; Games; Reading groups; Prayer groups; Movies; Dances/Social or cultural gatherings.

RATON

State of New Mexico Miner's Hospital—Intermediate Care Facility, Sheltered and Boarding Care Facility
PO Box 1067, Raton, NM, 87740 (505) 445-2741
Admin J Michael Frost. *Medical Dir/Dir of Nursing* O Tiku MD.
Licensure Intermediate Care. *Beds* 47. *Certified* Medicaid.
Ownership Proprietary.
Admissions Requirements Medical examination; Physician's request.
Staff Physicians 5 (ft); RNs 2 (ft); LPNs 4 (ft), 1 (pt); Orderlies 2 (ft); Nurses aides 11 (ft); Reality therapists 1 (ft); Recreational therapists 1 (ft); Activities coordinators 1 (ft); Dietitians 1 (ft).
Facilities Dining room; Physical therapy room; Activities room; Laundry room; Library.
Activities Arts and Crafts; Cards; Games; Reading groups; Prayer groups; Movies; Shopping trips; Dances/Social or cultural gatherings; Monthly birthday party for residents.
Description State of New Mexico Miners Hospital affords multi-unit care of 4 levels nursing home—17 ICF, 20 sheltered, 10 boarding, and 10 general hospital.

RIO RANCHO

Rio Rancho Health Care Center
4210 Sabana Grande NE, Rio Rancho, NM, 87124
Admin Jim Johnson. *Medical Dir/Dir of Nursing* James Goodwin MD.
Licensure Skilled Care; Intermediate Care. *Beds* SNF 24; ICF 96. *Certified* Medicaid; Medicare.
Ownership Proprietary.
Admissions Requirements Medical examination; Physician's request.
Staff RNs; LPNs; Orderlies; Nurses aides; Physical therapists 1 (pt); Occupational therapists 1 (pt); Speech therapists 1 (pt); Activities coordinators 1 (ft); Dietitians 1 (pt); Dentists 1 (pt); Ophthalmologists 1 (pt); Podiatrists 1 (pt); Audiologists 1 (pt).
Facilities Dining room; Physical therapy room;

Activities room; Crafts room; Laundry room; Barber/Beauty shop.
Activities Arts and Crafts; Cards; Games; Reading groups; Prayer groups; Movies; Shopping trips; Dances/Social or cultural gatherings.
Description Opened in 1982, this facililty is an exquisite example of southwestern decor at its finest; situated on the west mesa of Albuquerque overlooking the majestic Sandia Mountains. VA approved.

ROSWELL

Casa Marie Health Care Centre
1601 S Main, Roswell, NM, 88201 (505) 622-6008
Admin George Macko. *Medical Dir/Dir of Nursing* Peter B Moorhead MD.
Licensure Intermediate Care. *Beds* 120. *Certified* Medicaid.
Staff RNs 3 (ft), 2 (pt); LPNs 11 (ft), 5 (pt); Orderlies 3 (ft); Nurses aides 49 (ft), 3 (pt); Recreational therapists 2 (ft); Speech therapists 1 (ft); Dietitians 1 (ft); Dentists 1 (ft); Podiatrists 1 (ft); Audiologists 1 (ft).
Facilities Dining room; Activities room; Chapel; Crafts room; Laundry room; Barber/Beauty shop.
Activities Arts and Crafts; Cards; Games; Reading groups; Prayer groups; Movies; Dances/Social or cultural gatherings.

Sunset Village Nursing Home
1515 S Sunset Blvd, Roswell, NM, 88201 (505) 623-7097
Admin Lloyd Pharis. *Medical Dir/Dir of Nursing* Gayla Jeter.
Licensure Intermediate Care. *Beds* 78. *Certified* Medicaid.
Staff RNs 2 (ft); LPNs 6 (pt); Nurses aides 35 (ft); Activities coordinators 1 (ft).
Facilities Dining room; Activities room; Laundry room; Barber/Beauty shop.
Activities Arts and Crafts; Games; Reading groups; Prayer groups.

RUIDOSO

Ruidoso Care Center*
PO Box 2214, 5th and D Sts, Ruidoso, NM, 88345 (505) 257-9071
Licensure Intermediate Care. *Beds* 82. *Certified* Medicaid.
Ownership Proprietary.

SANTA FE

El Castillo Retirement Residence*
250 E Alameda, Santa Fe, NM, 87501 (505) 988-2877
Admin R J Wicks.
Licensure Nursing Home. *Beds* 15.
Ownership Proprietary.

Four Seasons Nursing Center—Santa Fe*
555 Saint Michael's Dr, Santa Fe, NM, 87501 (505) 982-2574
Admin Janice Reynolds.
Licensure Skilled Care; Intermediate Care. *Beds* SNF 30; ICF 90. *Certified* Medicaid; Medicare.

Granada de Santa Fe
313 Camino Alire, Santa Fe, NM, 87501 (505) 983-7373
Admin Del Lewis. *Medical Dir/Dir of Nursing* Dr Matthew Kelly.
Licensure Intermediate Care. *Beds* 45. *Certified* Medicaid.
Admissions Requirements Medical examination; Physician's request.
Staff Physicians 1 (pt); Speech therapists 1 (pt); Activities coordinators 1 (ft); Dietitians 1 (pt).
Facilities Dining room.
Activities Arts and Crafts; Games; Prayer groups; Movies; Shopping trips.
Description Facility provides day care by the hour, day, week, and month, and also provides respite care.

SOCORRO

Socorro Good Samaritan Village
Hwy 60 W, PO Box 1279, Socorro, NM, 87801 (505) 835-2724
Admin Tim Faszer. *Medical Dir/Dir of Nursing* Joan Anderson.
Licensure Intermediate Care. *Beds* 62. *Certified* Medicaid.
Admissions Requirements Medical examination.
Staff RNs 2 (ft), 2 (pt); LPNs 2 (ft), 2 (pt); Nurses aides 20 (ft), 10 (pt); Activities coordinators 1 (pt).
Affiliation Lutheran
Facilities Dining room; Activities room; Chapel; Crafts room; Barber/Beauty shop; Library.
Activities Arts and Crafts; Cards; Games; Reading groups; Prayer groups; Movies; Shopping trips; Dances/Social or cultural gatherings.

SPRINGER

Colfax General Hospital—Intermediate Care Facility*
PO Box 458, 615 Prospect Ave, Springer, NM, 87747 (505) 483-2443
Admin John Saint.
Licensure Intermediate Care. *Beds* 18. *Certified* Medicaid.

TRUTH OR CONSEQUENCES

Sierra Health Care Center
1400 Silver St, Truth or Consequences, NM, 87901 (505) 894-7855
Admin Richard J Henry Jr. *Medical Dir/Dir of Nursing* Ruben Marchisano MD.
Licensure Intermediate Care. *Beds* 110. *Certified* Medicare.
Ownership Nonprofit.
Admissions Requirements Physician's request.
Staff Physicians 1 (ft), 4 (pt); RNs 2 (ft); LPNs 7 (ft); Orderlies 1 (ft); Nurses aides 23 (ft), 3 (pt); Activities coordinators 1 (ft); Dietitians 1 (ft).
Facilities Dining room; Physical therapy room; Activities room; Chapel; Crafts room; Laundry room; Barber/Beauty shop; Library.
Activities Arts and Crafts; Cards; Games; Reading groups; Prayer groups; Movies; Shopping trips; Dances/Social or cultural gatherings.

Description This new facility, open one year, sits high atop a hill overlooking the local town and with a beautiful view of the local dam. VA approved.

TUCUMCARI

Van Ark Nursing Home
1005 S Monroe, Tucumcari, NM, 88401 (505) 461-2570
Admin Sarah Haley. *Medical Dir/Dir of Nursing* Jean Anderson.
Licensure Intermediate Care. *Beds* 54. *Certified* Medicaid.
Admissions Requirements Medical examination; Physician's request.
Staff RNs 2 (ft), 1 (pt); LPNs 3 (ft); Nurses aides 13 (ft), 4 (pt); Activities coordinators 1 (ft); Dietitians 1 (ft).
Facilities Dining room; Activities room; Laundry room; Barber/Beauty shop.
Activities Arts and Crafts; Cards; Games; Reading groups; Prayer groups; Movies; Shopping trips; Dances/Social or cultural gatherings.

NEW YORK

ALBANY

Albany County Nursing Home
Albany-Shaker Rd, Albany, NY, 12211 (518) 869-2231
Admin Robert J Lynch. *Medical Dir/Dir of Nursing* George Cuttita MD.
Licensure Skilled Care. *Beds* 420. *Certified* Medicaid; Medicare.
Ownership Public.
Staff Physicians 2 (ft), 6 (pt); RNs 55 (ft); LPNs 84 (ft); Orderlies 194 (ft); Physical therapists 5 (ft); Occupational therapists 3 (ft); Speech therapists 1 (ft); Activities coordinators 8 (ft); Dietitians 2 (ft); Dentists 1 (pt); Ophthalmologists 2 (pt); Podiatrists 1 (pt); Audiologists 1 (ft).
Facilities Dining room; Physical therapy room; Activities room; Crafts room; Laundry room; Barber/Beauty shop.
Activities Arts and Crafts; Cards; Games; Reading groups; Prayer groups; Movies; Shopping trips; Dances/Social or cultural gatherings.

Ann Lee Home and Infirmary*
Albany Shaker Rd, Albany, NY, 12211 (518) 869-5331
Licensure Intermediate Care. *Beds* 175.
Ownership Public.

Childs Nursing Home Company Inc
25 Hackett Blvd, Albany, NY, 12208 (518) 462-4211
Admin Teresa Gustas. *Medical Dir/Dir of Nursing* Dr Pankin, Dr Balsam, and Dr Erwer.
Licensure Skilled Care. *Beds* 120. *Certified* Medicaid; Medicare.
Ownership Nonprofit.
Staff RNs; LPNs; Nurses aides; Physical therapists; Occupational therapists; Speech therapists; Activities coordinators; Dietitians; Dentists.
Facilities Dining room; Physical therapy room; Activities room; Crafts room; Laundry room; Barber/Beauty shop.
Activities Arts and Crafts; Cards; Games; Reading groups; Prayer groups; Movies; Shopping trips; Dances/Social or cultural gatherings.
Description Facility offers staff training which addresses the needs of the elderly and includes sensitive staff to address psycho-social needs and the environmental impact on the residents.

Daughters of Sarah Nursing Home Company Inc*
Washington Ave and Rapp Rd, Albany, NY, 12203 (518) 456-7831
Admin Stanley Poskancer.
Licensure Skilled Care. *Beds* 200. *Certified* Medicare.
Ownership Nonprofit.
Affiliation Jewish

Eden Park Nursing Home
22 Holland Ave, Albany, NY, 12209 (518) 436-8441
Admin Wesley Hale. *Medical Dir/Dir of Nursing* David I Schwartz MD.
Licensure Skilled Care; Intermediate Care. *Beds* 210. *Certified* Medicaid; Medicare.
Ownership Proprietary.
Staff Physicians 11 (pt); RNs 26 (ft), 12 (pt); LPNs 19 (ft), 8 (pt); Orderlies 6 (ft); Nurses aides 95 (ft); Physical therapists 1 (ft); Reality therapists 1 (ft); Occupational therapists 1 (ft); Speech therapists 1 (pt); Activities coordinators 1 (ft); Dietitians 1 (ft); Dentists 1 (pt); Ophthalmologists 1 (pt); Podiatrists 1 (pt); Audiologists 1 (pt).
Facilities Dining room; Physical therapy room; Activities room; Crafts room; Laundry room; Barber/Beauty shop.
Activities Arts and Crafts; Cards; Games; Reading groups; Prayer groups; Movies; Shopping trips; Dances/Social or cultural gatherings.

Saint Margarets House and Hospital for Babies*
27 Hackett Blvd, Albany, NY, 12208 (518) 465-2461
Admin Clinton Lewis.
Licensure Skilled Care. *Beds* 58. *Certified* Medicaid.
Ownership Nonprofit.

Teresian House Nursing Home Co Inc
Washington Ave Ext, Albany, NY, 12203 (518) 456-2000
Licensure Skilled Care; Intermediate Care. *Beds* 300. *Certified* Medicaid; Medicare.
Ownership Nonprofit.
Affiliation Roman Catholic

University Heights Nursing Home*
325 Northern Blvd, Albany, NY, 12204 (518) 449-1100
Admin Thomas Nicolla.

Licensure Skilled Care. *Beds* 200. *Certified* Medicaid; Medicare.
Ownership Proprietary.

Villa Mary Immaculate*
321 S Manning Blvd, Albany, NY, 12208 (518) 482-3363
Admin M DeMontfort Charland.
Licensure Skilled Care; Intermediate Care. *Beds* 90. *Certified* Medicaid; Medicare.
Ownership Nonprofit.
Affiliation Roman Catholic

Westmere Convalescent Home
5 GippRd, Albany, NY, 12203 (518) 456-8355
Admin Michael Levine.
Licensure Intermediate Care. *Beds* 28.
Ownership Proprietary.

ALBION

Arnold Gregory Memorial Hospital—Skilled Nursing Facility
243 S Main St, Albion, NY, 14411 (716) 589-4422
Admin Jay Scott Parisella.
Licensure Skilled Care. *Beds* 30. *Certified* Medicaid; Medicare.
Ownership Nonprofit.

Orleans County Home and Infirmary
Rt 31, Albion, NY, 14411 (716) 589-5673
Admin Stephen Heard. *Medical Dir/Dir of Nursing* Dr A Nassar.
Licensure Skilled Care; Intermediate Care; Health Related Care. *Beds* 132. *Certified* Medicaid; Medicare.
Ownership Public.
Staff Physicians 3 (pt); RNs 8 (ft), 2 (pt); LPNs 11 (ft), 10 (pt); Nurses aides 30 (ft), 36 (pt); Physical therapists 1 (pt); Speech therapists 1 (pt); Activities coordinators 1 (ft); Dietitians 1 (ft); Dentists 1 (pt); Audiologists 1 (pt).
Facilities Dining room; Physical therapy room; Activities room; Crafts room; Laundry room; Barber/Beauty shop.
Activities Arts and Crafts; Cards; Games; Reading groups; Prayer groups; Movies; Shopping trips; Dances/Social or cultural gatherings.

ALDENC

Erie County Home and Infirmary
11580 Walden Ave, Alden, NY, 14004 (716) 937-9131
Admin Chester F Celio.
Licensure Skilled Care; Intermediate Care.
Beds 638. *Certified* Medicaid; Medicare.
Ownership Public.

ALEXANDRIA BAY

Edward John Noble Hospital of Alexandria Bay
19 Fuller St, Alexandria Bay, NY, 13607 (315) 482-2511
Admin Joseph Kehoe.
Licensure Skilled Care. *Beds* 12. *Certified* Medicaid; Medicare.
Ownership Nonprofit.
Staff Physicians 1 (pt); RNs 1 (ft), 1 (pt); LPNs 1 (ft), 1 (pt); Orderlies 1 (pt); Nurses aides 3 (ft), 2 (pt); Physical therapists 1 (pt); Occupational therapists; Speech therapists; Activities coordinators; Dietitians; Dentists; Podiatrists.
Facilities Dining room; Physical therapy room; Activities room; Barber/Beauty shop.
Activities Cards; Games; Reading groups; Movies; Dances/Social or cultural gatherings.
Description Facility features boat tour of the Thousand Islands and shore dinners on the St Lawrence River.

ALLEGANY

Allegany Nursing Home
5th and Maple Ave, Allegany, NY, 14706 (716) 373-2238
Admin Gerald Nye.
Licensure Skilled Care. *Beds* 37. *Certified* Medicaid; Medicare.
Ownership Proprietary.
Admissions Requirements Medical examination.
Staff Physicians 1 (pt); RNs 2 (ft), 1 (pt); LPNs 3 (ft), 4 (pt); Nurses aides 17 (ft), 6 (pt); Physical therapists 1 (pt); Activities coordinators 1 (ft); Dietitians 1 (pt); Dentists 1 (pt); Podiatrists 1 (pt).
Facilities Dining room; Physical therapy room; Activities room; Chapel; Crafts room; Laundry room; Barber/Beauty shop; Library.
Activities Arts and Crafts; Cards; Games; Reading groups; Prayer groups; Movies; Shopping trips; Dances/Social or cultural gatherings.

AMHERST

Amherst Nursing and Convalescent Home
4459 Bailey Ave, Amherst, NY, 14226 (716) 835-2543
Admin Margaret Mary Wagner. *Medical Dir/Dir of Nursing* Howard Lehman MD.
Licensure Skilled Care. *Beds* 83. *Certified* Medicaid; Medicare.
Ownership Proprietary.
Admissions Requirements Minimum age 16; Medical examination; Physician's request.
Staff Physicians 4 (pt); RNs 9 (ft), 12 (pt); LPNs 20 (ft), 8 (pt); Nurses aides 30 (ft), 20

(pt); Physical therapists 1 (pt); Reality therapists 1 (pt); Recreational therapists 1 (ft), 1 (pt); Occupational therapists 3 (pt); Speech therapists 1 (pt); Activities coordinators 1 (ft); Dietitians 1 (pt); Dentists 1 (pt); Ophthalmologists 1 (pt); Podiatrists 1 (pt); Audiologists 1 (pt).
Facilities Dining room; Physical therapy room; Activities room; Crafts room; Laundry room; Barber/Beauty shop; Library.
Activities Arts and Crafts; Cards; Games; Reading groups; Prayer groups; Movies; Shopping trips; Dances/Social or cultural gatherings.
Description Activities department has developed a self-esteem program for alert patients.

AMITYVILLE

Broadlawn Manor Nursing Home*
399 County Line Rd, Amityville, NY, 11701 (516) 264-0222
Admin Chester J Omiecinski.
Licensure Skilled Care; Intermediate Care.
Beds 80. *Certified* Medicaid; Medicare.
Ownership Proprietary.

Brunswick Hospital Center Inc
366 Broadway, Amityville, NY, 11701 (516) 789-7000
Admin John T Digilio Jr. *Medical Dir/Dir of Nursing* Louis Ingrisano MD.
Licensure Skilled Care. *Beds* 94. *Certified* Medicaid; Medicare.
Ownership Proprietary.
Admissions Requirements Minimum age 21; Medical examination; Physician's request.
Staff Physicians; RNs; LPNs; Orderlies; Nurses aides; Physical therapists; Reality therapists; Recreational therapists; Occupational therapists; Speech therapists; Activities coordinators; Dietitians; Dentists; Ophthalmologists; Podiatrists; Audiologists.
Facilities Dining room; Physical therapy room; Activities room; Crafts room.
Activities Arts and Crafts; Cards; Games; Reading groups; Movies; Shopping trips; Dances/Social or cultural gatherings.
Description Facility is hospital-based with extensive therapy programs.

AMSTERDAM

Amsterdam Memorial Hospital—Skilled Nursing Facility*
Upper Market St, Amsterdam, NY, 12010 (518) 842-3100
Admin Francis Cuda.
Licensure Skilled Care. *Beds* 61. *Certified* Medicaid; Medicare.
Ownership Nonprofit.

Montgomery County Infirmary
Sandy Dr, Amsterdam, NY, 12010 (518) 843-3503
Admin Ann Marie Rockwell. *Medical Dir/Dir of Nursing* Alton J Spencer MD.
Licensure Skilled Care. *Beds* 120. *Certified* Medicaid; Medicare.
Ownership Public.
Staff Physicians 1 (ft); RNs 10 (ft), 1 (pt); LPNs 23 (ft), 2 (pt); Orderlies 4 (ft); Nurses aides 50 (ft), 7 (pt); Activities coordinators 1

(ft); Dietitians 2 (ft); Dentists 1 (pt).
Facilities Dining room; Physical therapy room; Activities room; Crafts room; Laundry room; Barber/Beauty shop.
Activities Arts and Crafts; Cards; Games; Reading groups; Prayer groups; Movies; Shopping trips; Dances/Social or cultural gatherings.

Mount Loretto Nursing Home
Rt 3, Amsterdam, NY, 12010 (518) 842-6790
Admin Mary Gertrude. *Medical Dir/Dir of Nursing* Dr A Z Rehman.
Licensure Skilled Care. *Beds* 82. *Certified* Medicaid; Medicare.
Ownership Nonprofit.
Admissions Requirements Minimum age 16.
Staff Physicians 1 (pt); RNs 11 (ft); LPNs 12 (ft); Orderlies 6 (ft); Nurses aides 36 (ft); Physical therapists 3 (ft); Recreational therapists 2 (ft); Dietitians 1 (ft).
Affiliation Roman Catholic
Facilities Dining room; Physical therapy room; Activities room; Chapel; Laundry room; Barber/Beauty shop.
Activities Arts and Crafts; Cards; Games; Reading groups; Prayer groups; Movies; Shopping trips.

ARGYLE

Pleasant Valley Infirmary
Rt 40, Argyle, NY, 12809 (518) 638-8274
Admin Frank Fisk. *Medical Dir/Dir of Nursing* Michael Lynch MD.
Licensure Skilled Care; Intermediate Care.
Beds 120. *Certified* Medicaid; Medicare.
Ownership Public.
Admissions Requirements Minimum age 18; Medical examination; Physician's request.
Staff Physicians 2 (pt); RNs 9 (ft), 10 (pt); LPNs 8 (ft), 3 (pt); Nurses aides 46 (ft), 14 (pt); Physical therapists 1 (pt); Recreational therapists 1 (pt); Occupational therapists 1 (pt); Speech therapists 1 (pt); Dietitians 1 (pt); Dentists 1 (pt).
Facilities Dining room; Physical therapy room; Activities room; Crafts room; Laundry room; Barber/Beauty shop.
Activities Arts and Crafts; Cards; Games; Reading groups; Prayer groups; Movies; Shopping trips; Dances/Social or cultural gatherings; Boat trips.
Description Pleasant Valley Infirmary is a county facility located in a rural area in one of the most beautiful parts of the country.

ARVERNE

Lawrence Nursing Home Inc*
350 Beach 54th St, Arverne, NY, 11692 (212) 945-0400
Admin Benjamin Levine.
Licensure Skilled Care. *Beds* 200. *Certified* Medicaid; Medicare.
Ownership Proprietary.

Resort Health Related Facility*
64–11 Beach Channel Dr, Arverne, NY, 11692 (212) 945-0700
Licensure Skilled Care. *Beds* 280.
Ownership Proprietary.

Resort Nursing Home*
430 Beach 68th St, Arverne, NY, 11692 (212)
474-5200
Admin Michael Tennebaum.
Licensure Skilled Care. *Beds* 280. *Certified* Medicaid; Medicare.
Ownership Proprietary.

ASTORIA

Lyden Nursing Home
27-37 27th St, Astoria, NY, 11102 (212)
932-4613
Admin Chaim Sieger. *Medical Dir/Dir of Nursing* Dr Murray Waksman.
Licensure Skilled Care. *Beds* 114. *Certified* Medicaid; Medicare.
Ownership Proprietary.
Staff Physicians 4 (pt); RNs 7 (ft); LPNs 9 (ft), 3 (pt); Nurses aides 24 (ft), 10 (pt); Physical therapists 1 (pt); Recreational therapists 1 (ft); Occupational therapists 1 (pt); Speech therapists 1 (pt); Activities coordinators 1 (ft); Dietitians 1 (ft); Dentists 1 (ft); Ophthalmologists 1 (pt); Podiatrists 1 (pt); Audiologists 1 (pt).
Affiliation Roman Catholic
Facilities Dining room; Physical therapy room; Activities room; Crafts room; Laundry room; Barber/Beauty shop; Library.
Activities Arts and Crafts; Cards; Games; Prayer groups; Movies; Dances/Social or cultural gatherings; Ball game trips.
Description A very home-style facility with a lot of volunteers and family members involved.

AUBURN

Auburn Nursing Home
85 Thornton Ave, Auburn, NY, 13021 (315)
253-7351
Medical Dir/Dir of Nursing Avanelle P Morgan MD.
Licensure Skilled Care. *Beds* 90. *Certified* Medicaid; Medicare.
Ownership Proprietary.
Admissions Requirements Minimum age 16; Medical examination; Physician's request.
Staff RNs 11 (ft), 7 (pt); LPNs 5 (ft), 5 (pt); Nurses aides 42 (ft), 13 (pt); Physical therapists 1 (pt); Reality therapists 1 (pt); Recreational therapists 1 (ft); Occupational therapists 1 (pt); Speech therapists 1 (pt); Activities coordinators 1 (ft); Dietitians 1 (pt).
Facilities Dining room; Physical therapy room; Activities room; Crafts room; Laundry room; Barber/Beauty shop.
Activities Arts and Crafts; Cards; Games; Reading groups; Movies; Shopping trips.
Description Facility features one-story design with center courtyard and fire resistant construction. High percentage of registered, professional nursing staff. Excellent state survey reports, posted publicly. Nonrestrictive visting hours; progressive therapies.

Mercy Health and Rehabilitation Center
100 Thornton Ave, Auburn, NY, 13021 (315)
253-0351
Admin Sr Mary Aquin. *Medical Dir/Dir of Nursing* Thomas E Vanderloo MD.

Licensure Skilled Care; Intermediate Care.
Beds 297. *Certified* Medicaid; Medicare.
Ownership Nonprofit.
Admissions Requirements Minimum age 16; Medical examination; Physician's request.
Staff Physicians 2 (pt); RNs 26 (ft), 11 (pt); LPNs 50 (ft), 14 (pt); Orderlies 2 (ft), 2 (pt); Nurses aides 111 (ft), 28 (pt); Physical therapists 1 (ft), 1 (pt); Occupational therapists 2 (pt); Speech therapists 1 (pt); Activities coordinators 1 (ft); Dietitians 1 (ft).
Affiliation Roman Catholic
Facilities Dining room; Physical therapy room; Activities room; Chapel; Crafts room; Laundry room; Barber/Beauty shop.
Activities Arts and Crafts; Cards; Games; Reading groups; Prayer groups; Movies; Shopping trips; Dances/Social or cultural gatherings.

AVON

Avon Nursing Home*
Clinton St Extension, Avon, NY, 14414 (716)
226-2225
Admin Carl Baker.
Licensure Skilled Care. *Beds* 40. *Certified* Medicaid; Medicare.
Ownership Proprietary.

BALDDWINSVILLE

Syracuse Home Association*
7740 Meigs Rd, Balddwinsville, NY, 13027
(315) 638-2521
Licensure Intermediate Care. *Beds* 80.
Ownership Nonprofit.

BALLSTON SPA

Saratoga County Infirmary*
Ballston Ave, Ballston Spa, NY, 12020 (518)
885-4315
Admin Loraine Frollo.
Licensure Skilled Care; Intermediate Care.
Beds 160. *Certified* Medicaid; Medicare.
Ownership Public.

BATAVIA

Batavia Nursing Home Inc*
257 State St, Batavia, NY, 14020 (716)
343-1300
Admin David A Novak.
Licensure Skilled Care. *Beds* 62. *Certified* Medicaid; Medicare.
Ownership Proprietary.

Genesee County Nursing Home
278 Bank St, Batavia, NY, 14020 (716)
344-0584
Admin Gary H Breuilly. *Medical Dir/Dir of Nursing* Sydney L McLouth MD.
Licensure Skilled Care; Intermediate Care.
Beds 240. *Certified* Medicaid; Medicare.
Ownership Nonprofit.
Admissions Requirements Minimum age 16.

Saint Luke Manor of Batavia
17 Wiard St, Batavia, NY, 14020 (716)
343-4288

Admin E Greenman. *Medical Dir/Dir of Nursing* Dr Myron E Williams Jr.
Licensure Skilled Care. *Beds* 20. *Certified* Medicaid; Medicare.
Ownership Nonprofit.
Facilities Dining room; Activities room; Chapel.
Activities Arts and Crafts; Cards; Games.

BATH

Steuben County Infirmary*
Bath-Hammondsport Rd, Bath, NY, 14810
(607) 776-7651
Admin Robert R Lezer.
Licensure Skilled Care. *Beds* 105. *Certified* Medicaid; Medicare.
Ownership Public.

BAY SHORE

Sunrise Manor Nursing Home
1325 Brentwood Rd, Bay Shore, NY, 11706
(516) 665-4960
Admin Desmond McMenus. *Medical Dir/Dir of Nursing* Dr George Raniolo.
Licensure Skilled Care. *Beds* 84. *Certified* Medicaid; Medicare.
Ownership Proprietary.
Admissions Requirements Minimum age 16.
Staff RNs 8 (ft), 10 (pt); LPNs 4 (ft), 2 (pt); Orderlies 1 (ft), 2 (pt); Nurses aides 22 (ft), 20 (pt); Physical therapists 1 (pt); Recreational therapists 1 (ft), 3 (pt).

BAYSIDE

Ozanam Hall of Queens Nursing Home Inc
42-41 201 St, Bayside, NY, 11361 (212)
423-2000
Admin Mother M Joseph Augustine. *Medical Dir/Dir of Nursing* Richard L Bodkin Md.
Licensure Skilled Care. *Beds* 332. *Certified* Medicaid; Medicare.
Ownership Nonprofit.
Admissions Requirements Minimum age 65; Medical examination.
Facilities Dining room; Physical therapy room; Activities room; Chapel; Crafts room; Laundry room; Barber/Beauty shop; Library.

Saint Marys Hospital for Children Inc*
29–01 216 St, Bayside, NY, 11360 (212)
224-0400
Licensure Intermediate Care. *Beds* 85.
Ownership Nonprofit.

BEACON

Fishkill Health Related Center Inc*
Dogwood Ln, Beacon, NY, 12508 (914)
831-8704
Licensure Intermediate Care. *Beds* 160.
Ownership Proprietary.

BINGHAMTON

Elizabeth Church Manor
863 Front St, Binghamton, NY, 13905 (607) 722-3463
Admin Ruth Davis. *Medical Dir/Dir of Nursing* Dr Oscar Astur.
Licensure Skilled Care; Intermediate Care. *Beds* 105. *Certified* Medicaid; Medicare.
Ownership Nonprofit.
Admissions Requirements Physician's request.
Staff Physicians 1 (pt); RNs 7 (ft), 8 (pt); LPNs 4 (ft), 3 (pt); Nurses aides 18 (ft), 21 (pt); Physical therapists 1 (pt); Activities coordinators 1 (ft); Dietitians 1 (pt).
Affiliation Methodist
Facilities Dining room; Physical therapy room; Activities room; Chapel; Crafts room; Laundry room; Barber/Beauty shop; Library.
Activities Arts and Crafts; Cards; Games; Reading groups; Prayer groups; Movies; Shopping trips; Dances/Social or cultural gatherings.

Good Shepherd-Fairview Home Inc
80 Fairview Ave, Binghamton, NY, 13904 (607) 724-2477
Admin Eleanor Little. *Medical Dir/Dir of Nursing* Michael J Wasco MD.
Licensure Skilled Care; Intermediate Care; Domiciliary Care. *Beds* SNF 34; ICF 40; Domiciliary Care 82. *Certified* Medicaid; Medicare.
Ownership Nonprofit.
Admissions Requirements Minimum age 65; Medical examination.
Staff Physicians 1 (pt); RNs 9 (pt); LPNs 4 (pt); Orderlies 2 (pt); Nurses aides 27 (pt); Activities coordinators 1 (ft); Dietitians 1 (pt).
Affiliation Episcopal
Facilities Dining room; Activities room; Crafts room; Laundry room; Barber/Beauty shop; Library.
Activities Arts and Crafts; Cards; Games; Reading groups; Prayer groups; Shopping trips; Dances/Social or cultural gatherings.
Description By providing 4 levels of care, home is able to offer services to residents who are relatively independent to those who need full care—the security of knowing they will be housed and receive services as they are needed.

River Mede Manor*
159-163 Front St, Binghamton, NY, 13902 (607) 722-7225
Admin Elizabeth Slutzker.
Licensure Skilled Care; Intermediate Care. *Beds* 258. *Certified* Medicaid; Medicare.
Ownership Proprietary.

BOONVILLE

Sunset Nursing Home
Academy St, Boonville, NY, 13309 (315) 942-4301
Admin Jerome Britton. *Medical Dir/Dir of Nursing* Robert Smith MD.
Licensure Skilled Care. *Beds* 79. *Certified* Medicaid; Medicare.
Ownership Proprietary.
Admissions Requirements Minimum age 16; Physician's request.
Staff Physicians 2 (pt); RNs 6 (ft), 4 (pt); LPNs 4 (ft), 7 (pt); Nurses aides 16 (ft), 26 (pt);

Physical therapists 1 (ft), 1 (pt); Reality therapists 1 (pt); Recreational therapists 1 (pt); Activities coordinators 1 (ft), 1 (pt); Dietitians 1 (ft), 1 (pt).
Facilities Dining room; Physical therapy room; Activities room; Crafts room; Laundry room; Barber/Beauty shop; Library.
Activities Arts and Crafts; Cards; Games; Reading groups; Prayer groups; Movies; Shopping trips; Dances/Social or cultural gatherings.
Description Located in a residential area of the rural community of Boonville, NY, Sunset Nursing Home provides 24-hour care and rehabilitation services; goal is to promote the functional abilities of chronically ill, or disabled persons in all facets: physically, emotionally, mentally, and socially.

BRENTWOOD

Ross Nursing Home Inc*
839 Suffolk Ave, Brentwood, NY, 11717 (516) 273-4000
Admin Victor P Russo.
Licensure Skilled Care. *Beds* 135. *Certified* Medicaid; Medicare.
Ownership Proprietary.

BRIARCLIFF MANOR

Brandywine Nursing Home Inc
620 Sleepy Hollow Rd, Briarcliff Manor, NY, 10510 (914) 941-5100
Admin M Roth. *Medical Dir/Dir of Nursing* Sidney Harvey MD and George Vogel MD.
Licensure Skilled Care. *Beds* 120. *Certified* Medicaid; Medicare.
Ownership Proprietary.
Admissions Requirements Minimum age 16.
Staff RNs 12 (ft), 5 (pt); LPNs 11 (ft), 4 (pt); Orderlies 5 (ft), 2 (pt); Nurses aides 50 (ft), 13 (pt); Physical therapists 2 (pt); Occupational therapists 1 (pt); Speech therapists 1 (pt); Activities coordinators 1 (ft); Dietitians 1 (pt).
Facilities Dining room; Physical therapy room; Activities room; Crafts room; Laundry room; Barber/Beauty shop; Library.
Activities Arts and Crafts; Cards; Games; Reading groups; Prayer groups; Movies; Shopping trips; Dances/Social or cultural gatherings.
Description Facility is a 120-bed skilled nursing facility on 27 acres. Thirty-five of the patients are young adults with quadreplegia, paraplegia, MS and ALS.

BROCKPORT

Cupola Nursing Home*
122 West Ave, Brockport, NY, 14420 (716) 637-4129
Admin Elizabeth Beihirch.
Licensure Skilled Care. *Beds* 87. *Certified* Medicaid; Medicare.
Ownership Proprietary.

BRONX

Astor Gardens Nursing Home
2316 Bruner Ave, Bronx, NY, 10469 (212) 882-6400
Medical Dir/Dir of Nursing Dr David Rim.
Licensure Skilled Care. *Beds* 175. *Certified* Medicaid; Medicare.
Ownership Proprietary.
Admissions Requirements Medical examination.
Staff Physicians 5 (pt); RNs 4 (ft); LPNs 6 (ft), 10 (pt); Orderlies 4 (ft); Nurses aides 40 (ft), 10 (pt); Physical therapists 1 (pt); Occupational therapists 1 (pt); Speech therapists 1 (pt); Activities coordinators 1 (pt); Dietitians 1 (ft).
Facilities Dining room; Physical therapy room; Activities room; Crafts room; Laundry room; Barber/Beauty shop.
Activities Arts and Crafts; Cards; Games; Reading groups; Prayer groups; Movies; Shopping trips; Dances/Social or cultural gatherings.
Description Facility is located in quiet residential neighborhood with outside garden areas for sitting, a TV in every room, and private bath in every room.

Bainbridge Nursing Home
3518 Bainbridge Ave, Bronx, NY, 10467 (212) 655-1991
Admin Isaac Goldbrenner. *Medical Dir/Dir of Nursing* Dr Jay Hershkowitz.
Licensure Skilled Care. *Beds* 200. *Certified* Medicaid; Medicare.
Ownership Proprietary.
Staff Physicians 7 (ft); RNs 7 (ft); LPNs 11 (ft); Orderlies 7 (ft); Nurses aides 53 (ft); Physical therapists 1 (pt); Recreational therapists 3 (ft); Occupational therapists 1 (pt); Speech therapists 1 (pt); Activities coordinators 1 (ft); Dietitians 2 (ft); Dentists 1 (ft); Ophthalmologists 1 (pt); Podiatrists 1 (pt); Audiologists 1 (pt).

Beth Abraham Hospital*
612 Allerton Ave, Bronx, NY, 10467 (212) 920-6001
Admin Carl Eisdorfer.
Licensure Skilled Care. *Beds* 504. *Certified* Medicaid; Medicare.
Ownership Nonprofit.
Affiliation Jewish

Bruckner Nursing Home*
1010 Underhill Ave, Bronx, NY, 10472 (212) 863-6700
Admin Abraham Grossman.
Licensure Skilled Care. *Beds* 200. *Certified* Medicaid; Medicare.
Ownership Proprietary.

Concourse Nursing Home*
1072 Grand Concourse, Bronx, NY, 10456 (212) 681-4000
Admin Helen Neiman.
Licensure Skilled Care. *Beds* 240. *Certified* Medicaid; Medicare.
Ownership Proprietary.

Daughters of Jacob Nursing Home Company Inc
1160 Teller Ave, Bronx, NY, 10456 (212) 293-1500
Admin Steven J Bernstein. *Medical Dir/Dir of*

Nursing Dr Philip Paris.
Licensure Skilled Care; Intermediate Care.
Beds SNF 347; ICF 168. *Certified* Medicaid.
Ownership Nonprofit.
Admissions Requirements Minimum age 65;
Medical examination.
Staff Physicians 7 (ft); RNs 54 (ft); LPNs 23
(ft); Orderlies 16 (ft); Nurses aides 171 (ft);
Physical therapists 2 (ft), 2 (pt); Recreational
therapists 7 (ft); Occupational therapists 2 (ft), 2
(pt); Speech therapists 2 (pt); Activities coordi-
nators 2 (ft); Dietitians 4 (ft); Dentists 1 (pt);
Ophthalmologists 2 (pt); Podiatrists 2 (pt);
Audiologists 1 (pt).
Affiliation Jewish
Facilities Dining room; Physical therapy room;
Activities room; Chapel; Crafts room; Laundry
room; Barber/Beauty shop; Library.
Activities Arts and Crafts; Cards; Games;
Reading groups; Prayer groups; Movies; Shop-
ping trips; Dances/Social or cultural gatherings.
Description Facility features an in-home televi-
sion network and friendly visitor program for
shut-ins.

East Haven*
2323-27 Eastchester Rd, Bronx, NY, 10467
(212) 920-1504
Licensure Intermediate Care. *Beds* 200.
Ownership Proprietary.

Eastchester Park Nursing Home*
2700 Eastchester Rd, Bronx, NY, 10469 (212)
231-5550
Admin May Preira.
Licensure Skilled Care. *Beds* 200. *Certified* Medicaid; Medicare.
Ownership Proprietary.

Fieldston Lodge Nursing Home
666 Kappock St, Bronx, NY, 10463 (212)
549-1203
Admin Michael Birnbaum. *Medical Dir/Dir of
Nursing* Dr Tartaglia.
Licensure Skilled Care. *Beds* 200. *Cer-
tified* Medicaid; Medicare.
Ownership Proprietary.
Staff Physicians 1 (pt); RNs 12 (ft); LPNs 10
(ft); Orderlies 2 (ft); Nurses aides 48 (ft);
Physical therapists 1 (ft); Recreational therapists
2 (ft); Occupational therapists 1 (ft); Speech
therapists 1 (pt); Activities coordinators 1 (ft);
Dietitians 1 (ft).
Facilities Dining room; Physical therapy room;
Activities room; Chapel; Crafts room; Laundry
room; Barber/Beauty shop.
Activities Arts and Crafts; Cards; Games;
Reading groups; Prayer groups; Movies; Dan-
ces/Social or cultural gatherings.
Description Facility features trips to various
places.

Frances Schervier Home and Hospital
2975 Independence Ave, Bronx, NY, 10463
(212) 548-1700
Admin Rita K Kerr. *Medical Dir/Dir of
Nursing* Oscar A Palatucci ME.
Licensure Intermediate Care. *Beds* 284. *Certi-
fied* Medicaid.
Ownership Nonprofit.
Admissions Requirements Minimum age 65;
Medical examination.
Staff Physicians 10 (ft), 3 (pt); RNs 30 (ft), 3

(pt); LPNs 34 (ft), 6 (pt); Nurses aides 116 (ft),
21 (pt); Physical therapists 1 (ft); Recreational
therapists 3 (ft); Occupational therapists 2 (ft), 1
(pt); Speech therapists 2 (pt); Activities coordinators 2 (ft), 1 (pt); Dietitians 4 (ft); Dentists 3
(pt); Ophthalmologists 2 (pt); Podiatrists 1 (pt);
Audiologists 1 (pt).
Affiliation Roman Catholic
Facilities Dining room; Physical therapy room;
Activities room; Chapel; Crafts room; Laundry
room; Barber/Beauty shop; Library; Recreation
hall.
Activities Arts and Crafts; Cards; Games;
Reading groups; Prayer groups; Movies; Shopping trips; Dances/Social or cultural gatherings.
Description Extensive renovations are
underway which will provide higher quality
care in a more attractive environment. Additionally, construction of a new building will
provide 155 apartments for the independent
elderly. Also provide home health care and a
meals-on-wheels program which prepares over
500 hot meals daily.

Grand Manor Health Related Facility*
700 White Plains Rd, Bronx, NY, 10473 (212)
931-5033
Licensure Intermediate Care. *Beds* 240.
Ownership Proprietary.

Hebrew Home for the Aged at Fairfield
3220 Henry Hudson Pkwy, Bronx, NY, 10463
(212) 549-9400
Admin Meyer Greisman. *Medical Dir/Dir of
Nursing* Theodore L Tetenbaum MD.
Licensure Skilled Care. *Beds* 167. *Cer-
tified* Medicaid; Medicare.
Ownership Nonprofit.
Staff Physicians 3 (pt); RNs 20 (ft), 6 (pt);
LPNs 3 (ft); Orderlies 2 (ft); Nurses aides 55
(ft); Physical therapists 2 (ft), 1 (pt); Recrea-
tional therapists 3 (ft); Occupational therapists 1
(ft), 1 (pt); Speech therapists 1 (pt); Activities
coordinators 1 (ft); Dietitians 1 (ft); Dentists 1
(pt); Ophthalmologists 1 (pt); Podiatrists 1 (pt);
Audiologists 1 (pt).
Affiliation Jewish
Facilities Dining room; Physical therapy room;
Activities room; Crafts room; Barber/Beauty
shop; Library; Occupational therapy room;
Outdoor roof garden.
Activities Arts and Crafts; Cards; Games;
Reading groups; Prayer groups; Movies; Shop-
ping trips; Dances/Social or cultural gatherings;
Trips to restaurants and cultural events.

Hebrew Home for the Aged at Riverdale
5901 Palisade Ave, Bronx, NY, 10471 (212)
549-8700
Admin Jacob Reingold. *Medical Dir/Dir of
Nursing* Dr Lawrence Lerman.
Licensure Skilled Care; Intermediate Care.
Beds SNF 486; ICF 298. *Certified* Medicaid;
Medicare.
Ownership Nonprofit.
Admissions Requirements Medical examina-
tion; Physician's request.
Staff Physicians 8 (ft), 2 (pt); RNs 60 (ft), 10
(pt); LPNs 36 (ft), 8 (pt); Orderlies 7 (ft); Nurses
aides 217 (ft); Physical therapists 2 (ft), 2 (pt);
Occupational therapists 2 (ft), 1 (pt); Speech
therapists 1 (ft); Activities coordinators 7 (ft),
14 (pt); Dietitians 5 (ft); Dentists 3 (pt);

Ophthalmologists 4 (pt); Podiatrists 4 (pt);
Audiologists 1 (ft).
Affiliation Jewish
Facilities Dining room; Physical therapy room;
Activities room; Chapel; Crafts room; Laundry
room; Barber/Beauty shop; Library.
Activities Arts and Crafts; Cards; Games;
Reading groups; Prayer groups; Movies; Shop-
ping trips; Dances/Social or cultural gatherings.
Description The Hebrew Home for the Aged at
Riverdale is situated on 18 ¾ acres overlooking
the Hudson River in the Riverdale section of
New York City.

Hebrew Hospital for the Chronic Sick*
2200 Givan Ave, Bronx, NY, 10475 (212)
379-5020
Admin Richard Shedlovsky.
Licensure Skilled Care; Intermediate Care.
Beds 400. *Certified* Medicaid; Medicare.
Ownership Nonprofit.
Affiliation Jewish

House of the Holy Comforter*
2751 Grand Concourse, Bronx, NY, 10468
(212) 867-8100
Admin Luba Mebert.
Licensure Skilled Care. *Beds* 151. *Certified* Medicaid; Medicare.
Ownership Nonprofit.

Jeanne Jugan Residence
3200 Baychester Ave, Bronx, NY, 10475
Medical Dir/Dir of Nursing Dr Giordano.
Admissions Requirements Minimum age 60;
Medical examination.
Staff RNs 6 (ft), 10 (pt); LPNs 8 (ft), 6 (pt);
Nurses aides 28 (ft), 37 (pt); Occupational ther-
apists 1 (pt); Speech therapists 1 (pt); Activities
coordinators 1 (ft); Dietitians 1 (ft), 1 (pt).
Affiliation Roman Catholic
Facilities Dining room; Physical therapy room;
Activities room; Chapel; Crafts room; Laundry
room; Barber/Beauty shop; Library; Occupa-
tional therapy.
Activities Arts and Crafts; Cards; Games;
Reading groups; Prayer groups; Movies; Shop-
ping trips; Dances/Social or cultural gatherings.

Kings Harbor Care Center*
2000 E Gunhill Rd, Bronx, NY, 10469 (212)
320-0400
Licensure Intermediate Care. *Beds* 360.
Ownership Proprietary.

Kings Terrace Nursing Home
2678 Kingsbridge Terrace, Bronx, NY, 10463
(212) 796-5800
Admin Lowell S Feldman. *Medical Dir/Dir of
Nursing* Dr Solomon Abbey.
Licensure Skilled Care; Intermediate Care.
Beds 40. *Certified* Medicaid; Medicare.
Admissions Requirements Minimum age 21;
Medical examination; Physician's request.
Staff Physicians 1 (ft), 10 (pt); RNs 8 (ft), 3
(pt); LPNs 23 (ft), 23 (pt); Orderlies 3 (ft), 3
(pt); Nurses aides 36 (ft), 18 (pt); Physical therapists 2 (pt); Recreational therapists 1 (ft); Occupational therapists 1 (ft), 1 (pt); Speech
therapists 1 (pt); Activities coordinators 3 (ft), 2
(pt); Dietitians 1 (pt); Dentists 1 (pt); Ophthalmologists 1 (pt); Podiatrists 1 (pt); Audiologists
2 (pt).

Facilities Dining room; Physical therapy room; Activities room; Chapel; Crafts room; Laundry room; Barber/Beauty shop; Library.
Activities Arts and Crafts; Cards; Games; Reading groups; Prayer groups; Movies; Shopping trips; Dances/Social or cultural gatherings; Drama therapy; Adult education; Sing-a-long; Live entertainment.
Description Facility is highly integrated both in staffing and in residents. There is a strong emphasis on activities and rehabilitation. The facility is highly decorated as a result of special expertise of the staff. The external appearance is well cared for by staff and residents including the flower garden and manicured lawn.

Kingsbridge Heights Nursing Home*
3400 Cannon Pl, Bronx, NY, 10463 (212) 796-8100
Admin Rose Boritzer.
Licensure Skilled Care; Intermediate Care.
Beds 200. *Certified* Medicaid; Medicare.
Ownership Proprietary.

Laconia Nursing Home*
1050 E 230th St, Bronx, NY, 10466 (212) 654-5875
Admin Lawrence J Moshowitz.
Licensure Skilled Care. *Beds* 240. *Certified* Medicaid; Medicare.
Ownership Proprietary.

Methodist Church Home for the Aged
4499 Manhattan College Pkwy, Bronx, NY, 10471 (212) 548-5100
Admin Margaret V Fishburne. *Medical Dir/Dir of Nursing* Dr Norman Spitzer.
Licensure Skilled Care; Intermediate Care; Health Related Care. *Beds* SNF 80; HRF 33.
Certified Medicaid; Medicare.
Ownership Nonprofit.
Admissions Requirements Minimum age 62; Medical examination; Physician's request.
Staff Physicians 2 (pt); RNs 9 (ft), 7 (pt); LPNs 5 (ft), 6 (pt); Nurses aides 31 (ft), 8 (pt); Physical therapists 1 (pt); Occupational therapists 1 (pt); Activities coordinators 2 (ft); Dietitians 1 (pt); Dentists 1 (pt); Podiatrists 1 (pt).
Affiliation Methodist
Facilities Dining room; Physical therapy room; Activities room; Chapel; Crafts room; Barber/Beauty shop; Library; Lounge/day rooms.
Activities Arts and Crafts; Cards; Games; Reading groups; Prayer groups; Movies; Shopping trips; Dances/Social or cultural gatherings.
Description Facility features outdoor barbecues, and private rooms with toilet facilities. Located in a residential area; car available to take residents to appointments.

Morningside House Nursing Home Company*
1000 Pelham Pkwy S, Bronx, NY, 10461 (212) 863-5800
Admin Cynthia Wallace.
Licensure Skilled Care; Intermediate Care.
Beds 196. *Certified* Medicaid; Medicare.
Ownership Nonprofit.

Morris Park Nursing Home*
1235 Pelham Pkwy N, Bronx, NY, 10469 (212) 231-4300

Licensure Skilled Care. *Beds* 191. *Certified* Medicaid; Medicare.
Ownership Proprietary.

Mosholu Parkway Nursing Home*
3356 Perry Ave, Bronx, NY, 10467 (212) 655-3568
Admin Issac Shapiro.
Licensure Skilled Care. *Beds* 125. *Certified* Medicaid; Medicare.
Ownership Proprietary.

Palisade Nursing Home Company Inc*
5901 Palisade Ave, Bronx, NY, 10471 (212) 549-8700
Licensure Intermediate Care. *Beds* 266.
Ownership Nonprofit.

Pelham Parkway Nursing Home*
2401 Laconia Ave, Bronx, NY, 10469 (212) 798-8600
Admin Lucy Saskin.
Licensure Skilled Care. *Beds* 200. *Certified* Medicaid; Medicare.
Ownership Proprietary.

Providence Rest Home*
3304 Waterbury Ave, Bronx, NY, 10465 (212) 931-3000
Admin S Joanne.
Licensure Skilled Care; Intermediate Care.
Beds 149. *Certified* Medicaid; Medicare.
Ownership Nonprofit.

Riverdale Nursing Home*
641 W 230th St, Bronx, NY, 10463 (212) 796-4800
Admin Sonia Gutcheon.
Licensure Skilled Care. *Beds* 146. *Certified* Medicaid; Medicare.
Ownership Proprietary.

Rofay Nursing Home*
946 E 211th St, Bronx, NY, 10469 (212) 882-1800
Admin Isaac Levy.
Licensure Skilled Care. *Beds* 120. *Certified* Medicaid; Medicare.
Ownership Proprietary.

Sacred Heart Home*
3200 Baychester Ave, Bronx, NY, 10475 (212) 671-2120
Licensure Intermediate Care. *Beds* 44.
Ownership Nonprofit.
Affiliation Roman Catholic

Saint Patricks Home for the Aged and Infirm*
66 Van Cortlandt Park S, Bronx, NY, 10463 (212) 548-0200
Admin Mary Aloysius.
Licensure Skilled Care; Intermediate Care.
Beds 162. *Certified* Medicaid; Medicare.
Ownership Nonprofit.
Affiliation Roman Catholic

Split Rock Nursing Home*
3525 Baychester Ave, Bronx, NY, 10466 (212) 798-8900
Admin Abe Zelmanowicz.
Licensure Skilled Care. *Beds* 240. *Certified* Medicaid; Medicare.
Ownership Proprietary.

United Odd Fellow and Rebekah Home
1072 Havemeyer Ave, Bronx, NY, 10462 (212) 863-6200
Admin Alexander D Sajdak. *Medical Dir/Dir of Nursing* Jack Wagner MD.
Licensure Skilled Care; Intermediate Care.
Beds 213. *Certified* Medicaid; Medicare.
Ownership Nonprofit.
Admissions Requirements Medical examination.
Staff Physicians 1 (ft), 2 (pt); RNs 12 (ft), 3 (pt); LPNs 16 (ft), 3 (pt); Orderlies 4 (ft), 2 (pt); Nurses aides 46 (ft), 10 (pt); Physical therapists 1 (pt); Recreational therapists 1 (ft), 3 (pt); Occupational therapists 1 (pt); Speech therapists 1 (pt); Activities coordinators 1 (pt); Dietitians 1 (ft); Dentists 1 (pt); Ophthalmologists 1 (pt); Podiatrists 1 (pt); Audiologists 1 (pt).
Affiliation Independent Order of Odd Fellows
Facilities Dining room; Physical therapy room; Activities room; Chapel; Crafts room; Barber/Beauty shop.
Activities Arts and Crafts; Cards; Games; Reading groups; Prayer groups; Movies; Shopping trips; Dances/Social or cultural gatherings.

University Nursing Home*
2505 Grand Ave, Bronx, NY, 10468 (212) 295-1400
Admin Eva Spiegel.
Licensure Skilled Care. *Beds* 46. *Certified* Medicaid; Medicare.
Ownership Proprietary.

W K Nursing Home Corporation*
2545 University Ave, Bronx, NY, 10468 (212) 579-0500
Licensure Intermediate Care. *Beds* 540.
Ownership Nonprofit.

Wayne Health Related Facility
3530 Wayne Ave, Bronx, NY, 10467 (212) 655-1700
Admin Joseph Brachfeld. *Medical Dir/Dir of Nursing* Dr J Hershkowitz.
Licensure Skilled Care; Intermediate Care.
Beds 80. *Certified* Medicaid; Medicare.
Ownership Proprietary.
Admissions Requirements Medical examination; Physician's request.
Staff Physicians 5 (pt); RNs 10 (ft), 5 (pt); LPNs 10 (ft), 5 (pt); Nurses aides 30 (ft), 10 (pt); Physical therapists 1 (pt); Reality therapists 1 (pt); Recreational therapists 3 (ft); Occupational therapists 1 (pt); Speech therapists 1 (pt); Activities coordinators 2 (ft), 1 (pt); Dietitians 2 (ft); Dentists 1 (pt); Ophthalmologists 1 (pt); Podiatrists 1 (pt); Audiologists 1 (pt).
Facilities Dining room; Physical therapy room; Activities room; Chapel; Crafts room; Laundry room; Barber/Beauty shop; Library.
Activities Arts and Crafts; Cards; Games; Reading groups; Prayer groups; Movies; Shopping trips; Dances/Social or cultural gatherings.

White Plains Nursing Home*
3845 Carpenter Ave, Bronx, NY, 10467 (212) 882-4464
Admin Barbara Seidner.
Licensure Skilled Care. *Beds* 240. *Certified* Medicaid; Medicare.
Ownership Proprietary.

Williamsbridge Manor Nursing Home
1540 Tomlinson Ave, Bronx, NY, 10461 (212) 892-6600
Admin David Paley. *Medical Dir/Dir of Nursing* Dr Robert Feldman.
Licensure Skilled Care. *Beds* 77. *Certified* Medicaid; Medicare.
Ownership Proprietary.
Admissions Requirements Medical examination; Physician's request.
Staff Physicians; RNs; LPNs; Nurses aides; Physical therapists; Recreational therapists; Occupational therapists; Speech therapists; Dietitians; Dentists; Ophthalmologists; Podiatrists; Audiologists.
Facilities Dining room; Physical therapy room; Activities room; Laundry room.
Activities Arts and Crafts; Cards; Games; Reading groups; Prayer groups; Movies.

Workmens Circle Home and Infirmary
3159 Grace Ave, Bronx, NY, 10469 (212) 379-8100
Admin David Londin. *Medical Dir/Dir of Nursing* Dr Edward Isenberg.
Licensure Skilled Care; Intermediate Care. *Beds* 289. *Certified* Medicaid; Medicare.
Ownership Nonprofit.
Staff Physicians 7 (ft), 21 (pt); RNs 36 (ft), 5 (pt); LPNs 38 (ft), 10 (pt); Orderlies 20 (ft), 5 (pt); Nurses aides 170 (ft), 45 (pt); Physical therapists 2 (ft); Recreational therapists 4 (ft), 10 (pt); Occupational therapists 1 (ft), 1 (pt); Speech therapists 1 (pt); Activities coordinators 1 (ft); Dietitians 3 (ft); Dentists 1 (pt); Ophthalmologists 2 (pt); Podiatrists 2 (pt); Audiologists 1 (pt).
Affiliation Jewish
Facilities Dining room; Physical therapy room; Activities room; Chapel; Crafts room; Laundry room; Barber/Beauty shop; Library; Clinics; Pharmacy.
Activities Arts and Crafts; Cards; Games; Reading groups; Prayer groups; Movies; Shopping trips; Dances/Social or cultural gatherings; Plays.
Description The Workmens Circle Home for the Aged is a fraternal organization with kosher-style food and highlights many Jewish cultural events and holidays.

BROOKLYN

Aishel Avraham Residential Health Facility Inc*
40 Heyward St, Brooklyn, NY, 11211 (212) 858-6200
Admin David Steinberg.
Licensure Skilled Care; Intermediate Care. *Beds* 160. *Certified* Medicaid; Medicare.
Ownership Nonprofit.
Affiliation Jewish

Augustana Home for the Aged Inc
1680 60th St, Brooklyn, NY, 11204 (212) 232-2114
Admin Charles Miller. *Medical Dir/Dir of Nursing* Dr Frank Gulin.
Licensure Skilled Care; Intermediate Care. *Beds* SNF 55; ICF 35. *Certified* Medicaid; Medicare.
Ownership Nonprofit.

Admissions Requirements Medical examination.
Staff Physicians 3 (pt); RNs 12 (ft); LPNs 4 (ft); Nurses aides 35 (ft); Physical therapists 1 (pt); Occupational therapists 1 (pt); Speech therapists 1 (pt); Activities coordinators 1 (ft); Dietitians 1 (ft); Dentists 1 (pt); Ophthalmologists 1 (pt); Podiatrists 1 (pt); Audiologists 1 (pt).
Affiliation Lutheran
Facilities Dining room; Physical therapy room; Activities room; Chapel; Laundry room; Barber/Beauty shop; Outdoor porch.
Activities Arts and Crafts; Cards; Games; Prayer groups; Movies; Shopping trips.
Description Facility has been caring for the elderly of Brooklyn for over 75 years, with special attention to the persons individual and spiritual needs as well as physical problems.

Baptist Medical Center of New York-Nursing Home Divison*
2749 Linden Blvd, Brooklyn, NY, 11208 (212) 277-5100
Licensure Skilled Care. *Beds* 140.
Ownership Nonprofit.
Affiliation Baptist

Brookdale Hospital Center Nursing Home Company Inc*
555 Rockway Pkwy, Brooklyn, NY, 11212 (212) 240-5000
Licensure Intermediate Care. *Beds* 220.
Ownership Nonprofit.

Brooklyn United Methodist Church Home
1485 Dumont Ave, Brooklyn, NY, 11208 (212) 827-4500
Admin H Rober Phillips. *Medical Dir/Dir of Nursing* Dr Babu Jasty.
Licensure Skilled Care. *Beds* SNF 120. *Certified* Medicaid; Medicare.
Ownership Nonprofit.
Admissions Requirements Minimum age 21; Medical examination.
Staff Physicians 4 (pt); RNs 8 (ft), 14 (pt); LPNs 5 (ft), 3 (pt); Orderlies 6 (ft), 2 (pt); Nurses aides 45 (ft), 10 (pt); Physical therapists 1 (pt); Reality therapists 1 (pt); Recreational therapists 1 (pt); Occupational therapists 1 (pt); Speech therapists 1 (pt); Activities coordinators 1 (ft); Dietitians 1 (pt); Dentists 1 (pt); Ophthalmologists 1 (pt); Podiatrists 1 (pt); Audiologists 1 (pt).
Affiliation Methodist
Facilities Dining room; Physical therapy room; Activities room; Chapel; Crafts room; Laundry room; Barber/Beauty shop; Library; Day rooms.
Activities Arts and Crafts; Cards; Games; Reading groups; Prayer groups; Movies; Shopping trips; Dances/Social or cultural gatherings; Pet therapy with adopted cat for patients.

Cabs Nursing Home Company Inc
270 Nostrand Ave, Brooklyn, NY, 11205 (212) 638-0500
Admin David Wieder. *Medical Dir/Dir of Nursing* Dr Francisco Trilla.
Licensure Skilled Care; Intermediate Care. *Beds* 157. *Certified* Medicaid; Medicare.
Ownership Nonprofit.
Admissions Requirements Minimum age 18.
Staff RNs 8 (ft), 3 (pt); LPNs 11 (ft), 4 (pt);

Orderlies 5 (ft), 3 (pt); Nurses aides 35 (ft), 25 (pt); Physical therapists 2 (pt); Recreational therapists 2 (ft); Occupational therapists 1 (pt); Speech therapists 1 (pt); Activities coordinators 1 (ft); Dietitians 1 (ft); Dentists 1 (pt); Ophthalmologists 1 (pt); Podiatrists 1 (pt); Audiologists 1 (pt).
Facilities Dining room; Physical therapy room; Activities room; Crafts room; Laundry room; Barber/Beauty shop.
Activities Arts and Crafts; Cards; Games; Reading groups; Prayer groups; Movies; Shopping trips; Dances/Social or cultural gatherings.

Carlton Nursing Home*
405 Carlton Ave, Brooklyn, NY, 11238 (212) 789-6262
Licensure Skilled Care. *Beds* 148. *Certified* Medicaid; Medicare.
Ownership Proprietary.

Caton Park Nursing Home*
1312 Caton Ave, Brooklyn, NY, 11226 (212) 693-7000
Admin J Weiss.
Licensure Skilled Care. *Beds* 119. *Certified* Medicaid; Medicare.
Ownership Proprietary.

Cobble Hill Nursing Home Inc
380 Henry St, Brooklyn, NY, 11201 (212) 855-6789
Medical Dir/Dir of Nursing Henry Freedman MD.
Licensure Skilled Care. *Beds* 520. *Certified* Medicaid; Medicare.
Ownership Nonprofit.
Staff Physicians 1 (ft), 9 (pt); RNs 27 (ft); LPNs 40 (ft); Orderlies 24 (ft), 9 (pt); Nurses aides 143 (ft); Physical therapists 6 (ft), 1 (pt); Recreational therapists 10 (ft), 2 (pt); Occupational therapists 4 (ft); Speech therapists 1 (ft); Dietitians 4 (ft); Dentists 4 (pt); Ophthalmologists 2 (ft); Podiatrists 4 (ft); Audiologists 1 (ft).
Facilities Dining room; Physical therapy room; Activities room; Laundry room; Barber/Beauty shop; Library; General store; Day rooms; Occupational therapy room; Speech/Hearing Room; Dental clinic.
Activities Arts and Crafts; Games; Prayer groups; Movies; Shopping trips; Dances/Social or cultural gatherings; Octoberfest; Birthday parties; Christmas party; Yearly "Love is..." party; Horse racing; Lectures; Cooking club; Black history club.
Description Home has instituted a dental department which has been very successful. Other successful programs are speech, physical, occupational, and recreation departments. Offers a wide range of recreational activities throughout the facility—now has a men's and women's club—everyone is welcome to join in any activity. Also has a general store where residents and family can purchase small items.

Concord Nursing Home Inc*
300 Madison St, Brooklyn, NY, 11216 (212) 783-3030
Admin James McPherson.
Licensure Skilled Care; Intermediate Care. *Beds* 82. *Certified* Medicaid; Medicare.
Ownership Nonprofit.

Crown Nursing Home
3457 Nostrand Ave, Brooklyn, NY, 11229
(212) 769-6900
Admin Ann Stillman.
Licensure Skilled Care. *Beds* 189. *Certified* Medicaid; Medicare.
Ownership Proprietary.

Dover Nursing Home*
1919 Cortelyou Rd, Brooklyn, NY, 11226 (212) 856-4646
Admin Morey Adler.
Licensure Skilled Care. *Beds* 41. *Certified* Medicaid; Medicare.
Ownership Proprietary.

Flatbush Manor Care Center
2107 Ditmas Ave, Brooklyn, NY, 11226
Medical Dir/Dir of Nursing Dr Maurice Dunst.
Staff Physicians 5 (pt); RNs 14 (ft); LPNs 12 (ft); Orderlies 4 (ft); Nurses aides 28 (ft); Physical therapists 2 (pt); Recreational therapists 5 (pt); Occupational therapists 1 (pt); Speech therapists 1 (pt); Activities coordinators 1 (ft); Dietitians 2 (ft); Dentists 1 (pt); Ophthalmologists 1 (pt); Podiatrists 1 (pt); Audiologists 1 (pt); Psychiatrists 1 (pt); Urologists 1 (pt); Neurologists 1 (pt).
Facilities Dining room; Physical therapy room; Activities room; Chapel; Crafts room; Laundry room.
Activities Arts and Crafts; Cards; Games; Prayer groups; Movies.

Greenpark Care Center*
140 Saint Edwards St, Brooklyn, NY, 11201
(212) 858-6400
Admin Simon Pelman.
Licensure Skilled Care; Intermediate Care.
Beds 120. *Certified* Medicaid; Medicare.
Ownership Proprietary.

Haym Salomon Home for the Aged*
2300 Cropsey Ave, Brooklyn, NY, 11214 (212) 373-1700
Licensure Skilled Care; Intermediate Care.
Beds 110. *Certified* Medicaid; Medicare.
Ownership Nonprofit.
Affiliation Jewish

Holy Family Home for the Aged*
1740 84th St, Brooklyn, NY, 11214 (212) 232-3666
Licensure Skilled Care; Intermediate Care.
Beds 84. *Certified* Medicaid; Medicare.
Ownership Nonprofit.
Affiliation Roman Catholic

JHMCB Center for Nursing and Rehabilitation
520 Prospect Pl, Brooklyn, NY, 11238 (212) 636-1000
Admin Herbert Friedman. *Medical Dir/Dir of Nursing* Ben Ross MD.
Licensure Skilled Care. *Beds* 320. *Certified* Medicaid; Medicare.
Ownership Nonprofit.
Staff Physicians 4 (pt); RNs 50 (pt); LPNs 26 (pt); Nurses aides 158 (pt); Physical therapists 4 (pt); Recreational therapists 5 (pt); Occupational therapists 4 (pt); Speech therapists 1 (ft); Activities coordinators 1 (pt); Dietitians 2 (pt); Dentists 1 (pt); Ophthalmologists 1 (pt); Podiatrists 2 (pt); Audiologists 1 (pt).

Affiliation Jewish
Facilities Dining room; Physical therapy room; Activities room; Chapel; Crafts room; Barber-/Beauty shop; Library.
Activities Arts and Crafts; Cards; Games; Reading groups; Prayer groups; Movies; Shopping trips; Dances/Social or cultural gatherings.
Description Emphasis on rehabilitation services and the acutely ill aged.

Lemberg Home and Geriatric Institute Inc
8629 Bay Pkwy, Brooklyn, NY, 11214 (212) 266-0900
Admin Rose Clee. *Medical Dir/Dir of Nursing* Anthony Loucella MD.
Licensure Skilled Care; Health Related Care.
Beds 20. *Certified* Medicaid; Medicare.
Ownership Nonprofit.
Admissions Requirements Minimum age 65; Medical examination.
Staff Physicians; RNs 3 (ft), 2 (pt); LPNs 2 (ft), 2 (pt); Orderlies 2 (ft); Physical therapists 1 (pt); Recreational therapists 2 (pt); Occupational therapists 1 (pt); Speech therapists 1 (pt); Activities coordinators 1 (pt); Dietitians 1 (pt); Dentists 1 (pt); Ophthalmologists 1 (pt); Podiatrists 1 (pt); Audiologists 1 (pt).
Facilities Dining room; Physical therapy room; Activities room; Chapel; Laundry room; Library.
Activities Arts and Crafts; Cards; Games; Reading groups; Prayer groups; Dances/Social or cultural gatherings; Birthday parties; Holiday parties.
Description Facility is small geriatric institute with personal touch; lovely outside porch with white wicker furniture on SNF floor; lovely day room in HRF section; residents' puppet exhibition shown in museums and other homes.

Madonna Residence*
1 Prospect Park W, Brooklyn, NY, 11215 (212) 857-1200
Admin Regina Carmel.
Licensure Skilled Care; Intermediate Care.
Beds 203. *Certified* Medicaid; Medicare.
Ownership Nonprofit.
Affiliation Roman Catholic

Marcus Garvey Nursing Home Company Inc
810-20 Saint Marks Ave, Brooklyn, NY, 11213 (212) 467-7300
Admin Richard A Harrow. *Medical Dir/Dir of Nursing* Arthur T Risbrook MD.
Licensure Skilled Care; Intermediate Care.
Beds SNF 240; ICF 55. *Certified* Medicaid; Medicare.
Ownership Nonprofit.
Admissions Requirements Minimum age 40; Medical examination.
Staff RNs 13 (ft); LPNs 23 (ft), 7 (pt); Orderlies 10 (ft), 2 (pt); Nurses aides 84 (ft), 27 (pt); Physical therapists 1 (ft); Occupational therapists 1 (ft); Speech therapists 1 (pt); Activities coordinators 1 (ft); Dietitians 4 (ft); Dentists 1 (pt); Podiatrists 1 (pt).
Facilities Dining room; Physical therapy room; Activities room; Laundry room; Barber/Beauty shop.
Activities Arts and Crafts; Cards; Games; Reading groups; Prayer groups; Movies; Shopping trips; Dances/Social or cultural gatherings.
Description Community sponsored facility

with an international/diverse ethnic patient population; community religious/fraternal involvement; award winning architectural design building; personal staff involvement through multi-disciplinary team approach in patient care, food service, and psycho-social activities.

Menorah Home and Hospital for the Aged and Infirm*
871 Bushwick Ave, Brooklyn, NY, 11221 (212) 443-3000
Admin Shirley Windheim.
Licensure Skilled Care; Intermediate Care.
Beds 293. *Certified* Medicaid; Medicare.
Ownership Nonprofit.
Affiliation Jewish

Menorah Nursing Home Inc*
1516 Oriental Blvd, Brooklyn, NY, 11235 (212) 646-4441
Licensure Intermediate Care. *Beds* 120.
Ownership Nonprofit.
Affiliation Jewish

Metropolitan Jewish Geriatric Center
Boardwalk and W 29th St, Brooklyn, NY, 11224 (212) 266-5700
Admin Eli S Feldman. *Medical Dir/Dir of Nursing* Dr Harvey Shapiro.
Licensure Skilled Care; Intermediate Care.
Beds 170. *Certified* Medicaid; Medicare.
Ownership Nonprofit.
Admissions Requirements Medical examination.
Staff Physicians 8 (ft); RNs 25 (ft); LPNs 75 (ft); Orderlies 200 (ft); Physical therapists 4 (ft); Recreational therapists 8 (ft); Occupational therapists 4 (ft); Speech therapists 1 (ft); Activities coordinators 1 (ft); Dietitians 4 (ft); Dentists 1 (ft); Ophthalmologists 1 (ft); Podiatrists 1 (ft); Audiologists 1 (ft).
Affiliation Jewish
Facilities Dining room; Physical therapy room; Activities room; Chapel; Crafts room; Barber-/Beauty shop; Library; Activity space.
Activities Arts and Crafts; Cards; Games; Reading groups; Prayer groups; Movies; Shopping trips; Dances/Social or cultural gatherings.
Description Facility provides long-term home health care, a certified home health agency, the Brooklyn hospice, emergency alarm response system, home electronic monitoring service, respite services, Bay Hospital, adult day care, and Alzheimer's day care. Also located at 4915 10th Ave, Brooklyn, NY 11219.

MJG Nursing Home Company Inc*
4915 10th Ave, Brooklyn, NY, 11219 (212) 853-2800
Licensure Intermediate Care. *Beds* 529.
Ownership Nonprofit.

New York Congregational Home for the Aged
123 Linden Blvd, Brooklyn, NY, 11226 (212) 284-8259
Admin David F Fielding. *Medical Dir/Dir of Nursing* Dr Glenn Morris.
Licensure Skilled Care; Intermediate Care.
Beds SNF 39; ICF 29. *Certified* Medicaid; Medicare.
Ownership Nonprofit.
Affiliation Congregational

Facilities Dining room; Physical therapy room; Activities room; Crafts room; Laundry room; Barber/Beauty shop; Library; Solarium garden. *Activities* Arts and Crafts; Cards; Games; Prayer groups; Movies; Dances/Social or cultural gatherings.

Norwegian Christian Home for the Aged*
1250-70 67th St, Brooklyn, NY, 11219 (212) 232-2322
Licensure Skilled Care; Intermediate Care. *Beds* 41. *Certified* Medicaid; Medicare. *Ownership* Nonprofit.

Oxford Nursing Home*
144 S Oxford St, Brooklyn, NY, 11217 (212) 638-0360
Admin Max Goldberg.
Licensure Skilled Care. *Beds* 235. *Certified* Medicaid; Medicare.
Ownership Proprietary.

Palm Gardens Nursing Home*
615 Ave C, Brooklyn, NY, 11218 (212) 633-3300
Admin Israel Lefkowitz.
Licensure Skilled Care. *Beds* 240. *Certified* Medicaid; Medicare.
Ownership Proprietary.

Palm Tree Nursing Home
5606 15th Ave, Brooklyn, NY, 11219 (212) 851-1000
Admin Esther Lefkowitz. *Medical Dir/Dir of Nursing* George Thagroo.
Licensure Skilled Care. *Beds* 79. *Certified* Medicaid; Medicare.
Ownership Proprietary.
Staff Physicians 2 (pt); RNs 4 (ft); LPNs 7 (ft); Orderlies 2 (ft); Nurses aides 11 (ft); Physical therapists 1 (pt); Recreational therapists 1 (ft); Occupational therapists 1 (pt); Speech therapists 1 (pt); Dietitians 1 (ft); Dentists 1 (pt); Ophthalmologists 1 (pt); Podiatrists 1 (pt); Audiologists 1 (pt).
Facilities Dining room; Physical therapy room; Activities room.
Activities Arts and Crafts; Cards; Games; Reading groups; Prayer groups; Movies.

Parkshore Park Nursing Home*
1555 Rockaway Pkwy, Brooklyn, NY, 11236 (212) 498-6400
Licensure Intermediate Care. *Beds* 270. *Ownership* Proprietary.

Prospect Park Nursing Home
1455 Coney Island Ave, Brooklyn, NY, 11236 (212) 272-1050
Admin Sidney Kurzman. *Medical Dir/Dir of Nursing* Dr Jacob Dimant.
Licensure Skilled Care. *Beds* 215. *Certified* Medicaid; Medicare.
Ownership Nonprofit.
Admissions Requirements Minimum age 50.
Staff Physicians 2 (pt); RNs 7 (ft), 5 (pt); LPNs 21 (ft), 4 (pt); Orderlies 9 (ft), 6 (pt); Nurses aides 18 (ft), 12 (pt); Physical therapists 1 (ft), 1 (pt); Occupational therapists 1 (pt); Speech therapists 1 (pt); Activities coordinators 1 (ft); Dentists 1 (pt); Ophthalmologists 1 (pt); Audiologists 2 (pt).
Facilities Dining room; Physical therapy room;

Activities room; Crafts room; Laundry room.
Activities Arts and Crafts; Cards; Games; Reading groups; Prayer groups; Movies; Shopping trips; Dances/Social or cultural gatherings.

River Manor*
630 E 104th St, Brooklyn, NY, 11236 (212) 272-1050
Licensure Intermediate Care. *Beds* 380. *Ownership* Proprietary.

Rutland Nursing Home Co Inc
585 Schenectady Ave, Brooklyn, NY, 11203 (718) 604-5000
Admin Harris Brodsky. *Medical Dir/Dir of Nursing* Morris Mienfeld MD.
Licensure Skilled Care. *Beds* 538. *Certified* Medicaid; Medicare.
Ownership Nonprofit.
Staff Physicians; RNs; LPNs; Orderlies; Nurses aides; Physical therapists; Reality therapists; Recreational therapists; Occupational therapists; Speech therapists; Activities coordinators; Dietitians; Dentists; Ophthalmologists; Podiatrists; Audiologists.
Affiliation Jewish
Facilities Dining room; Physical therapy room; Activities room; Chapel; Crafts room; Laundry room; Barber/Beauty shop; Library.
Activities Arts and Crafts; Cards; Games; Reading groups; Prayer groups; Movies; Shopping trips; Dances/Social or cultural gatherings.
Description Rutland Nursing Home provides extensive medical rehabilitation and skilled nursing services and is a functional and integral part of the Jewish Medical Center which consists of 343 hospital beds, 538 skilled nursing care beds, outpatient department, emergency room, and home care department.

Saint Johns Episcopal Homes for the Aged and the Blind
452 Herkimer St, Brooklyn, NY, 11213 (212) 467-7000
Admin Vincent DiRubbio. *Medical Dir/Dir of Nursing* Dr Rasikal Amin.
Licensure Skilled Care; Intermediate Care. *Beds* SNF 43; ICF 44. *Certified* Medicaid; Medicare.
Ownership Nonprofit.
Admissions Requirements Minimum age 62 (blind), 65 (aged).
Staff Physicians 8 (pt); RNs 9 (ft), 3 (pt); LPNs 3 (ft); Orderlies 1 (ft); Nurses aides 18 (ft), 4 (pt); Physical therapists 1 (pt); Recreational therapists 1 (ft), 1 (pt); Occupational therapists 1 (pt); Speech therapists 1 (pt); Activities coordinators 1 (ft); Dietitians 1 (ft); Dentists 1 (pt); Ophthalmologists 1 (pt); Podiatrists 1 (pt); Audiologists 1 (pt).
Affiliation Episcopal
Facilities Dining room; Physical therapy room; Activities room; Chapel; Laundry room; Barber/Beauty shop.
Activities Arts and Crafts; Cards; Games; Reading groups; Prayer groups; Movies; Shopping trips; Dances/Social or cultural gatherings.

Sea-Crest Health Care Center*
3035 W 24th St, Brooklyn, NY, 11224 (212) 372-4500
Admin A L Urbach.

Licensure Skilled Care; Intermediate Care. *Beds* 231. *Certified* Medicaid; Medicare. *Ownership* Proprietary.

Sephardic Home for the Aged Inc*
2266 Cropsey Ave, Brooklyn, NY, 11214 (212) 266-6100
Admin Herbert Freeman.
Licensure Intermediate Care. *Beds* 150. *Certified* Medicaid.
Ownership Nonprofit.

Sheepshead Nursing Home*
2840 Knapp St, Brooklyn, NY, 11235 (212) 646-5700
Admin Theresa Holzer.
Licensure Skilled Care. *Beds* 200. *Certified* Medicaid; Medicare.
Ownership Proprietary.

Shore View Nursing Home*
2865 Brighton 3rd St, Brooklyn, NY, 11235 (212) 891-4400
Admin Barbara Withen.
Licensure Skilled Care. *Beds* 320. *Certified* Medicaid; Medicare.
Ownership Proprietary.

Wartburg Nursing Home Inc
2598 Fulton St, Brooklyn, NY, 11207 (212) 498-2340
Admin Ronald B Stuckey. *Medical Dir/Dir of Nursing* S Y Gowd.
Licensure Skilled Care. *Beds* 102. *Certified* Medicaid; Medicare.
Ownership Nonprofit.
Admissions Requirements Minimum age 18.
Staff Physicians 1 (ft), 4 (pt); RNs 11 (ft); LPNs 20 (ft); Orderlies 5 (ft); Nurses aides 55 (ft); Physical therapists 1 (ft); Recreational therapists 2 (ft), 1 (pt); Occupational therapists 1 (ft); Speech therapists 1 (pt); Activities coordinators 1 (ft); Dietitians 2 (ft); Dentists 1 (pt); Ophthalmologists 1 (pt); Podiatrists 1 (pt).
Affiliation Lutheran
Facilities Dining room; Physical therapy room; Activities room; Chapel; Crafts room; Barber-/Beauty shop; Library.
Activities Arts and Crafts; Cards; Games; Prayer groups; Movies; Shopping trips; Dances/Social or cultural gatherings.
Description Wartburg Nursing Home, Inc is a 109-year-old home with nursing services. The programmatic and health care components are designed to respect the knowledge and abilities of our residents. Some of the programs that foster this ideal are adult education, resident theater group, resident advisory groups, and special olympics. Located on the Brooklyn-Queens border, its beautiful courtyard and chapel makes for an oasis in the city.

Willoughby Nursing Home*
949 Willoughby Ave, Brooklyn, NY, 11221 (212) 443-1600
Admin Jerome Mann.
Licensure Skilled Care. *Beds* 161. *Certified* Medicaid; Medicare.
Ownership Proprietary.

BUFFALO

Downtown Nursing Home Inc
200 7th St, Buffalo, NY, 14201 (716) 847-2500
Admin Betty D'Arcy. *Medical Dir/Dir of Nursing* Dr Cheng Shung Fu.
Licensure Skilled Care. *Beds* 80. *Certified* Medicaid; Medicare.
Ownership Nonprofit.
Admissions Requirements Minimum age 16.
Staff RNs 6 (ft), 3 (pt); LPNs 8 (ft), 4 (pt); Orderlies 1 (ft); Nurses aides 18 (ft), 10 (pt); Physical therapists 2 (pt); Occupational therapists 1 (ft); Speech therapists 1 (pt); Activities coordinators 1 (ft); Dentists 1 (pt); Podiatrists 1 (pt).
Facilities Dining room; Physical therapy room; Activities room; Crafts room; Laundry room; Barber/Beauty shop; Library.
Activities Arts and Crafts; Cards; Games; Reading groups; Prayer groups; Movies; Shopping trips; Dances/Social or cultural gatherings.

Georgian Court Nursing Home of Buffalo Inc*
1040 Delaware Ave, Buffalo, NY, 14209 (716) 886-7740
Admin J Hall.
Licensure Skilled Care. *Beds* 134. *Certified* Medicaid; Medicare.
Ownership Proprietary.

Hamlin Terrace Health Care Center
1014 Delaware Ave, Buffalo, NY, 14209
Admin James E Connelly. *Medical Dir/Dir of Nursing* Dr Edwin Lenahan.
Licensure Skilled Care; Intermediate Care. *Certified* Medicaid; Medicare.
Ownership Proprietary.
Admissions Requirements Minimum age 16; Medical examination; Physician's request.
Staff Physicians 25 (ft); RNs 12 (ft); LPNs 22 (ft); Nurses aides 69 (ft); Physical therapists 1 (ft); Recreational therapists 3 (ft); Occupational therapists 1 (pt); Speech therapists 1 (pt); Activities coordinators 1 (ft); Dietitians 1 (pt); Dentists 1 (pt); Ophthalmologists 1 (pt); Podiatrists 1 (pt); Audiologists 1 (pt).
Facilities Dining room; Physical therapy room; Activities room; Chapel; Crafts room; Laundry room; Barber/Beauty shop; Library.
Activities Arts and Crafts; Cards; Games; Reading groups; Prayer groups; Movies; Shopping trips; Dances/Social or cultural gatherings.
Description Facility goal is to maintain and enhance each resident's personality and individuality while meeting his/her physical, psychological, social, and emotional needs; offers both skilled nursing and health related care with professional staff present 24 hours per day. Located near downtown Buffalo, facility is tastefully decorated to provide both classic and traditional charm; private and semi-private rooms available; each floor has smoking and nonsmoking lounges conveniently located for socialization and family visits; the distinctive and progressive professional care provided makes this facility one of the finest nursing homes in the county.

Manhattan Manor Nursing Home*
300 Manhattan Ave, Buffalo, NY, 14214 (716) 838-5460
Admin William Zacher.

Licensure Skilled Care; Intermediate Care. *Beds* 44. *Certified* Medicaid; Medicare.
Ownership Proprietary.

Mercy Hospital—Skilled Nursing Facility*
565 Abbott Rd, Buffalo, NY, 14220 (716) 826-7000
Admin Joel Schimscheiner.
Licensure Skilled Care. *Beds* 60. *Certified* Medicaid; Medicare.
Ownership Nonprofit.

Millard Fillmore Skilled Nursing Facility*
3 Gates Circle, Buffalo, NY, 14209 (716) 887-4837
Licensure Skilled Care. *Beds* 41
Ownership Nonprofit.

Nazareth Nursing Home and Health Related Facility
291 W North St, Buffalo, NY, 14201 (716) 881-2323
Admin Austin J Barrett. *Medical Dir/Dir of Nursing* Donald M Wilson MD.
Licensure Skilled Care; Intermediate Care. *Beds* SNF 95; ICF 30. *Certified* Medicaid; Medicare.
Ownership Nonprofit.
Admissions Requirements Minimum age 16; Females only; Medical examination; Physician's request.
Staff Physicians 1 (pt); RNs 5 (ft), 6 (pt); LPNs 12 (ft), 7 (pt); Nurses aides 40 (ft), 9 (pt); Physical therapists 2 (pt); Occupational therapists 1 (pt); Speech therapists 1 (pt); Activities coordinators 1 (ft); Dietitians 1 (pt); Dentists 1 (pt); Ophthalmologists 1 (pt); Podiatrists 1 (pt); Audiologists 1 (pt).
Affiliation Roman Catholic
Facilities Dining room; Physical therapy room; Activities room; Chapel; Crafts room; Laundry room; Barber/Beauty shop; Library.
Activities Arts and Crafts; Cards; Games; Reading groups; Prayer groups; Movies; Shopping trips; Dances/Social or cultural gatherings.
Description Nazareth Home is a private not-for-profit facility founded by the Franciscan Sisters of the Immaculate Conception. The most outstanding feature of the home is its philosophy of care which gives primary concern to the dignity, rights and self-respect of each individual. The home is dedicated to providing comprehensive and coordinated services to women with varying illnesses and debilities, placing emphasis on assisting and encouraging the individual to do as much for herself in an attempt to maintain as much independence in functioning as possible.

Niagara Lutheran Home Inc
64 Hager St, Buffalo, NY, 14208 (716) 886-4377
Admin Donald L Broecker. *Medical Dir/Dir of Nursing* Sylvia Regalla Spavento MD.
Licensure Skilled Care. *Beds* 169. *Certified* Medicaid; Medicare.
Ownership Nonprofit.
Admissions Requirements Minimum age 21; Medical examination; Physician's request.
Staff Physicians 1 (pt); RNs 17 (ft), 5 (pt); LPNs 10 (ft), 4 (pt); Orderlies 11 (ft), 5 (pt); Nurses aides 48 (ft), 31 (pt); Physical therapists 2 (pt); Occupational therapists 1 (ft); Speech

therapists 1 (pt); Activities coordinators 1 (ft); Dietitians 1 (ft); Dentists 1 (pt); Ophthalmologists 1 (pt); Podiatrists 2 (pt); Audiologists 1 (pt).
Affiliation Lutheran
Facilities Dining room; Physical therapy room; Activities room; Chapel; Crafts room; Laundry room; Barber/Beauty shop; Library; X-ray room; Occupational therapy room; Speech pathology room; Sitting rooms; Treatment room; Podiatry room.
Activities Arts and Crafts; Cards; Games; Reading groups; Movies; Shopping trips; Dances/Social or cultural gatherings; Church services and Catholic Mass; Picnics; Weekly Sing-a-longs; Luncheons; Discussion groups; Trips to area parks and the Buffalo Zoo; Holiday and birthday celebrations.
Description Niagara Lutheran Home, providing quality skilled nursing care for 169 people, of all faiths, is situated in a residential setting—with all areas of the building accessible to wheelchairs. It is conveniently located near major thoroughfares and public transportation routes and is in close proximity to many of the more prominent Buffalo area hospitals.

Rhode Island Street Nursing Home Company Inc
24 Rhode Island St, Buffalo, NY, 14213
Admin Edward C Weeks. *Medical Dir/Dir of Nursing* Ida Levine MD.
Licensure Skilled Care; Intermediate Care. *Beds* 128. *Certified* Medicaid; Medicare.
Ownership Nonprofit.
Admissions Requirements Minimum age 16; Medical examination; Physician's request.
Staff RNs 7 (ft), 6 (pt); LPNs 14 (ft), 5 (pt); Orderlies 5 (ft), 1 (pt); Nurses aides 37 (ft), 25 (pt); Occupational therapists 2 (ft), 1 (pt); Speech therapists 2 (ft); Activities coordinators 1 (ft).
Facilities Dining room; Physical therapy room; Activities room; Chapel; Crafts room; Laundry room; Barber/Beauty shop; Library.
Activities Arts and Crafts; Cards; Games; Reading groups; Prayer groups; Movies; Shopping trips; Dances/Social or cultural gatherings; Camping.
Description This health care campus is comprised of 5 levels of care primarily serving the geriatric population; levels include skilled nursing, health related residential care, respite, medical day treatment, and long-term home health care; with expansion of services, a continuum of care to residents can be provided within facility campus.

Rosa Coplon Jewish Home and Infirmary*
10 Symphony Circle, Buffalo, NY, 14201 (716) 885-3311
Admin Leon R Cantor.
Licensure Skilled Care; Intermediate Care. *Beds* 111. *Certified* Medicaid; Medicare.
Ownership Nonprofit.
Affiliation Jewish

Saint Lukes Presbyterian Nursing Center*
1175 Delaware Ave, Buffalo, NY, 14209 (716) 885-6733
Admin James Walsh.
Licensure Intermediate Care. *Beds* 80. *Certi-*

fied Medicaid.
Ownership Nonprofit.
Affiliation Presbyterian

Sisters of Charity Hospital—Skilled Nursing Facility*
2157 Main St, Buffalo, NY, 14214 (716) 862-2000
Admin Mary Charles.
Licensure Skilled Care. *Beds* 80. *Certified* Medicaid; Medicare.
Ownership Nonprofit.

CAMBRIDGE

Mary McClellan Skilled Nursing Facility*
Cambridge, NY, 12816 (518) 677-2611
Admin Doris Warrick.
Licensure Skilled Care. *Beds* 39. *Certified* Medicaid; Medicare.
Ownership Nonprofit.

CAMPBELL HALL

Doanes Nursing Home*
Rd 2, Box 291, Campbell Hall, NY, 10916 (914) 294-8154
Licensure Intermediate Care. *Beds* 80.
Ownership Proprietary.

CANANDAIGUA

Elm Manor Nursing Home*
210 N Main St, Canandaigua, NY, 14424 (716) 394-3883
Admin Thomas Madigan.
Licensure Skilled Care. *Beds* 46. *Certified* Medicaid; Medicare.
Ownership Proprietary.

Ontario County Health Facility
Rt 2, Canandaigua, NY, 14424 (716) 394-2100
Admin Gerald B Cole. *Medical Dir/Dir of Nursing* Charles Bathrick MD.
Licensure Skilled Care; Health Related Care.
Beds SNF 48; HRC 50. *Certified* Medicaid; Medicare.
Ownership Public.
Admissions Requirements Minimum age 18; Medical examination; Physician's request.
Staff Physicians 1 (pt); RNs 6 (ft), 3 (pt); LPNs 10 (ft), 1 (pt); Nurses aides 30 (ft), 5 (pt); Physical therapists 1 (pt); Recreational therapists 1 (ft); Speech therapists 1 (pt); Activities coordinators 1 (ft), 1 (pt); Dietitians 1 (ft); Dentists 1 (pt); Podiatrists 1 (pt); Audiologists 1 (pt).
Facilities Dining room; Physical therapy room; Activities room; Crafts room; Laundry room; Barber/Beauty shop; Library.
Activities Arts and Crafts; Cards; Games; Reading groups; Prayer groups; Movies; Shopping trips; Dances/Social or cultural gatherings.
Description Opened 1976, this facility features admission and preference to Ontario County residents.

Thompson Nursing Home Inc*
350 Parrish St, Canandaigua, NY, 14424 (716) 394-1100
Admin Patrick Burns.

Licensure Skilled Care; Intermediate Care.
Beds 68. *Certified* Medicaid; Medicare.
Ownership Nonprofit.

CANTON

United Helpers Canton Nursing Home Inc*
W Main St, Canton, NY, 13617 (315) 386-4541
Admin Wheeler D Maynard Jr.
Licensure Skilled Care; Intermediate Care.
Beds 80. *Certified* Medicaid; Medicare.
Ownership Nonprofit.

CARTHAGE

Carthage Area Hospital*
W Street Rd, Carthage, NY, 13619 (315) 493-1000
Licensure Skilled Care; Intermediate Care.
Beds 30.
Ownership Nonprofit.

Greenbriar Nursing Home*
W Street Rd, Carthage, NY, 13619 (315) 493-3220
Admin James Sligar.
Licensure Skilled Care. *Beds* 40. *Certified* Medicaid; Medicare.
Ownership Proprietary.

CASTLETON-ON-HUDSON

Resurrection Rest Home*
Castleton-on-Hudson, NY, 12033 (518) 732-7617
Admin S Therese.
Licensure Skilled Care; Intermediate Care.
Beds 36. *Certified* Medicaid; Medicare.
Ownership Nonprofit.

CATSKILL

Eden Park Health Services Inc*
154 Jefferson Heights, Catskill, NY, 12414 (518) 943-5151
Admin Leitha B Boice.
Licensure Skilled Care; Intermediate Care.
Beds 88. *Certified* Medicaid; Medicare.
Ownership Proprietary.

Memorial Hospital and Nursing Home of Greene County
161 Jefferson Heights, Catskill, NY, 12414 (518) 943-9380
Admin Andrew J Hewat. *Medical Dir/Dir of Nursing* Paul Snapper MD.
Licensure Skilled Care; Intermediate Care.
Beds 120. *Certified* Medicaid; Medicare.
Ownership Public.
Staff Physicians 11 (pt); RNs 11 (ft), 4 (pt); LPNs 11 (ft), 8 (pt); Nurses aides 51 (ft), 15 (pt); Physical therapists 1 (ft); Reality therapists 1 (ft); Recreational therapists 2 (ft); Occupational therapists 1 (ft), 1 (pt); Speech therapists 1 (pt); Activities coordinators 1 (ft); Dietitians 1 (ft); Dentists 1 (pt); Podiatrists 1 (pt).
Facilities Dining room; Physical therapy room; Activities room; Laundry room; Barber/Beauty shop.

Activities Arts and Crafts; Cards; Games; Reading groups; Prayer groups; Movies; Shopping trips; Dances/Social or cultural gatherings.

CENTER MORICHES

Cedar Lodge Nursing Home*
6 Frowein Rd, Center Moriches, NY, 11934 (516) 878-4400
Admin Muriel Corcoran.
Licensure Skilled Care. *Beds* 100. *Certified* Medicaid; Medicare.
Ownership Proprietary.

CHEEKTOWAGA

Garden Gate Manor
2365 Union Rd, Cheektowaga, NY, 14227 (716) 668-8100
Admin John W Barrett. *Medical Dir/Dir of Nursing* Dr Charles Tanner.
Licensure Skilled Care; Intermediate Care.
Beds SNF 120; ICF 40. *Certified* Medicaid; Medicare.
Ownership Proprietary.
Admissions Requirements Medical examination; Physician's request.
Staff Physicians 2 (pt); RNs 6 (ft), 7 (pt); LPNs 15 (ft), 9 (pt); Orderlies 1 (ft), 2 (pt); Nurses aides 55 (ft), 14 (pt); Physical therapists 1 (pt); Occupational therapists 1 (ft); Speech therapists 1 (pt); Activities coordinators 2 (ft), 1 (pt); Dietitians 1 (pt); Dentists 1 (pt); Podiatrists 1 (pt); Audiologists 1 (pt).
Facilities Dining room; Physical therapy room; Activities room; Crafts room; Laundry room; Barber/Beauty shop; Indoor solarium.
Activities Arts and Crafts; Cards; Games; Reading groups; Prayer groups; Movies; Shopping trips; Dances/Social or cultural gatherings.
Description Garden Gate Manor is a modern, health care residence where the elderly receive the type of personal attention that creates a happy, healthy environment, as well as the best professional care available. The concept of care at Garden Gate considers the total well-being of the resident, providing a home-like atmosphere with supervised attention and opportunities for socializing and individual activities.

Manor Oak Skilled Nursing Facilities Inc*
3600 Harlem Rd, Cheektowaga, NY, 14215 (716) 837-3880
Admin Randy Muenzner.
Licensure Skilled Care. *Beds* 158. *Certified* Medicaid; Medicare.
Ownership Proprietary.

CHENANGO BRIDGE

Chenango Bridge Nursing Home
Hospital Hill Rd, Box 37, Chenango Bridge, NY, 13745 (607) 648-8521
Admin Allen W Carkey. *Medical Dir/Dir of Nursing* F Keith Kennedy MD.
Licensure Skilled Care. *Beds* 90. *Certified* Medicaid; Medicare.
Ownership Public.
Admissions Requirements Minimum age 16; Physician's request.
Staff Physicians 1 (pt); RNs 11 (ft), 1 (pt);

LPNs 14 (ft), 3 (pt); Orderlies 2 (ft); Nurses aides 37 (ft), 22 (pt); Physical therapists 1 (pt); Occupational therapists 1 (pt); Activities coordinators 1 (ft); Dietitians 1 (pt); Dentists 1 (pt).
Facilities Dining room; Physical therapy room; Activities room; Chapel; Crafts room; Laundry room; Barber/Beauty shop.
Activities Arts and Crafts; Cards; Games; Reading groups; Prayer groups; Movies; Shopping trips; Dances/Social or cultural gatherings.
Description Facility residents are involved with an intergenerational program one morning each week with pre-schoolers; residents and children look forward to the activity.

CHITTENANGO

Stonehedge-Chittenango Nursing Home
331 Russell St, Chittenango, NY, 13037 (315) 687-7255
Admin Gloria Coughlin. *Medical Dir/Dir of Nursing* Juaquin Solar MD.
Licensure Skilled Care. *Beds* 40. *Certified* Medicaid; Medicare.
Ownership Proprietary.
Admissions Requirements Medical examination; Physician's request.
Staff Physicians 1 (pt); RNs 3 (ft), 3 (pt); LPNs 4 (ft), 4 (pt); Nurses aides 19 (ft), 15 (pt); Physical therapists 1 (pt); Activities coordinators 1 (ft); Dietitians 1 (pt); Dentists 1 (pt).
Facilities Dining room; Physical therapy room; Activities room; Laundry room; Barber/Beauty shop.
Activities Arts and Crafts; Cards; Games; Reading groups; Prayer groups; Movies; Shopping trips; Dances/Social or cultural gatherings.

CLARENCE

Brothers of Mercy Nursing Home Co Inc*
10570 Bergtold Rd, Clarence, NY, 14031 (716) 759-6985
Admin Bruce S Bonsel.
Licensure Skilled Care. *Beds* 200. *Certified* Medicaid; Medicare.
Ownership Nonprofit.
Affiliation Roman Catholic

CLIFTON SPRINGS

Clifton Springs Hospital and Clinic Extended Care*
2 Coulter Rd, Clifton Springs, NY, 14432 (315) 462-9561
Admin Gary Bagley.
Licensure Skilled Care. *Beds* 40. *Certified* Medicaid; Medicare.
Ownership Nonprofit.

CLINTON

Martin Luther Nursing Home Inc
110 Utica Rd, Clinton, NY, 13323 (315) 853-5515
Admin Rev Hans J R Irmer. *Medical Dir/Dir of Nursing* Dr Gerald C Gant.
Licensure Skilled Care; Intermediate Care.
Beds SNF 80; ICF 80. *Certified* Medicaid.
Ownership Nonprofit.

Admissions Requirements Minimum age 17.
Staff Physicians 2 (pt); RNs 4 (ft), 13 (pt); LPNs 9 (ft), 8 (pt); Orderlies 5 (ft), 4 (pt); Nurses aides 48 (ft), 24 (pt); Activities coordinators 3 (ft); Dietitians 2 (pt).
Affiliation Lutheran
Facilities Dining room; Physical therapy room; Activities room; Chapel; Crafts room; Laundry room; Barber/Beauty shop; Library.
Activities Arts and Crafts; Cards; Games; Reading groups; Prayer groups; Movies; Shopping trips; Dances/Social or cultural gatherings.
Description The Martin Luther Nursing Home is part of the Lutheran Homes of Central New York, Inc, which also sponsors the Lutheran Home of Central New York and The Clinton Manor Apartments. The Lutheran Home of Central New York is an adult domiciliary care facility which can accommodate 68 residents. The Clinton Manor Apartments is a 100-unit low-income apartment complex for the elderly and handicapped under HUD Section 8/208.

COBLESKILL

Eden Park Nursing Home
Parkway Dr, Cobleskill, NY, 12043 (518) 234-3557
Admin A Edel Groski. *Medical Dir/Dir of Nursing* Dr Roy G S Dougall.
Licensure Skilled Care; Intermediate Care.
Beds 90. *Certified* Medicaid; Medicare.
Ownership Proprietary.
Admissions Requirements Minimum age 18; Medical examination; Physician's request.
Facilities Dining room; Physical therapy room; Activities room; Crafts room; Barber/Beauty shop; Occupational therapy room.
Activities Arts and Crafts; Cards; Games; Reading groups; Prayer groups; Movies; Shopping trips; Dances/Social or cultural gatherings.

COHOES

Mary and Alice Ford Nursing Home Company Inc
W Columbia St, Cohoes, NY, 12047
Admin Geraldine Laparl. *Medical Dir/Dir of Nursing* James H Mitchell MD.
Licensure Skilled Care. *Beds* 80. *Certified* Medicaid; Medicare.
Ownership Nonprofit.
Admissions Requirements Minimum age 18.
Staff Physicians 1 (pt); RNs 9 (ft), 3 (pt); LPNs 5 (ft), 7 (pt); Orderlies 3 (ft), 4 (pt); Nurses aides 20 (ft), 22 (pt); Physical therapists 3 (ft); Recreational therapists 1 (ft); Occupational therapists 1 (pt); Speech therapists 1 (pt); Activities coordinators 1 (ft); Dietitians 1 (ft); Dentists 1 (pt); Podiatrists 1 (pt).
Facilities Dining room; Activities room; Crafts room; Laundry room; Barber/Beauty shop.
Activities Arts and Crafts; Cards; Games; Reading groups; Prayer groups; Movies; Shopping trips; Dances/Social or cultural gatherings.
Description Skilled nursing facility connected to an acute care hospital providing available service on contractual basis for all types of health care problems.

COLLEGE POINT

Woodcrest Nursing Home
110-09 26th Ave, College Point, NY, 11354 (212) 762-6100
Admin V Lewin. *Medical Dir/Dir of Nursing* Dr Fred Flatav.
Licensure Skilled Care. *Beds* 200. *Certified* Medicaid; Medicare.
Ownership Proprietary.
Admissions Requirements Minimum age 21; Medical examination.
Staff RNs 7 (ft), 6 (pt); LPNs 11 (ft), 8 (pt); Orderlies 8 (ft), 1 (pt); Nurses aides 41 (ft), 26 (pt); Physical therapists 2 (ft), 1 (pt); Recreational therapists 1 (ft), 1 (pt); Occupational therapists 2 (pt); Speech therapists 1 (pt); Activities coordinators 1 (ft); Dietitians 2 (ft); Dentists 1 (pt); Ophthalmologists 1 (pt); Podiatrists 2 (pt).
Facilities Dining room; Physical therapy room; Activities room; Crafts room; Laundry room; Barber/Beauty shop; Library.
Activities Arts and Crafts; Cards; Games; Prayer groups; Movies; Dances/Social or cultural gatherings.
Description Once a month special dinners are ordered from a local German restaurant. Barbecues are held weekly during the summer. Resident council meetings, monthly. We also formed a new-comers group to help ease the adjustment of nursing home environment.

COOPERSTOWN

The Meadows*
Rt 3, Cooperstown, NY, 13326
Licensure Skilled Care; Intermediate Care.
Beds 136. *Certified* Medicaid; Medicare.
Ownership Public.

CORNING

Corning Hospital—Founders Pavilion
205 E 1st St, Corning, NY, 14830 (607) 937-7322
Admin Linda Patrick. *Medical Dir/Dir of Nursing* John G Allen MD.
Licensure Skilled Care. *Beds* 120. *Certified* Medicaid; Medicare.
Ownership Nonprofit.
Staff RNs 13 (ft), 2 (pt); LPNs 16 (ft), 3 (pt); Orderlies 4 (ft); Nurses aides 48 (ft), 8 (pt); Activities coordinators 1 (ft); Dietitians 1 (ft).
Facilities Dining room; Physical therapy room; Activities room; Crafts room; Laundry room; Barber/Beauty shop; Library.
Activities Arts and Crafts; Cards; Games; Reading groups; Prayer groups; Movies; Shopping trips; Dances/Social or cultural gatherings; Entertainment.

CORTLAND

Cortland Nursing Home
193 Clinton Ave, Cortland, NY, 13045 (607) 756-9921
Admin Michael Sweeney.
Licensure Skilled Care. *Beds* 80. *Certified* Medicaid; Medicare.
Ownership Proprietary.

Admissions Requirements Minimum age 16; Medical examination.
Staff RNs 7 (ft), 3 (pt); LPNs 10 (ft), 2 (pt); Orderlies 3 (ft), 1 (pt); Nurses aides 40 (ft), 20 (pt); Physical therapists 1 (pt); Occupational therapists 1 (pt); Speech therapists 1 (pt); Activities coordinators 1 (ft), 1 (pt); Dietitians 1 (pt); Dentists 1 (pt); Ophthalmologists 1 (pt); Podiatrists 1 (pt); Audiologists 1 (pt).
Facilities Dining room; Physical therapy room; Activities room; Crafts room; Laundry room; Barber/Beauty shop; Library.
Activities Arts and Crafts; Cards; Games; Reading groups; Prayer groups; Movies; Shopping trips; Dances/Social or cultural gatherings.

Highgate Manor of Cortland
28 Kellogg Rd, Cortland, NY, 13045 (607) 753-9631
Admin Mitchell S Marsh. *Medical Dir/Dir of Nursing* John E Eckel MD.
Licensure Skilled Care; HRF Care. *Beds* 200. *Certified* Medicaid; Medicare.
Ownership Proprietary.
Admissions Requirements Minimum age 16.
Staff Physicians 13 (pt); RNs 13 (ft), 6 (pt); LPNs 15 (ft), 7 (pt); Orderlies 6 (ft), 3 (pt); Nurses aides 50 (ft), 25 (pt); Physical therapists 1 (pt); Occupational therapists 1 (pt); Speech therapists 1 (pt); Activities coordinators 1 (ft); Dietitians 1 (pt); Dentists 1 (pt); Ophthalmologists 1 (pt); Podiatrists 1 (pt); Audiologists 1 (pt).
Facilities Dining room; Physical therapy room; Activities room; Chapel; Crafts room; Laundry room; Barber/Beauty shop; Library.
Activities Arts and Crafts; Cards; Games; Reading groups; Prayer groups; Movies; Shopping trips; Dances/Social or cultural gatherings.
Description Facility had no deficiencies on annual state surveys. Facility offers clean, attractive, home-like environment; adult oriented activities programing to maximize independence and self-esteem; flexible meal hours, selective menus, waitress service, fine china and fresh flowers in dining service; RN skilled nursing care 24 hours a day, 7 days a week; private and semi-private rooms. JCAH accredited.

CROTON-ON-HUDSON

Sky View Haven Nursing Home
Albany Post Rd, Croton-on-Hudson, NY, 10520 (914) 271-5151
Admin Kurt Oppemheim. *Medical Dir/Dir of Nursing* Leonard Kaufman MD.
Licensure Skilled Care; Intermediate Care. *Beds* SNF 130; HRF 30. *Certified* Medicaid; Medicare.
Ownership Proprietary.
Admissions Requirements Minimum age 16; Medical examination.
Staff RNs 9 (ft), 2 (pt); LPNs 17 (ft), 4 (pt); Orderlies 2 (ft); Nurses aides 65 (ft); Physical therapists 2 (pt); Activities coordinators 1 (ft); Dietitians 1 (ft); Activity workers 2 (ft), 2 (pt).
Facilities Dining room; Physical therapy room; Activities room; Laundry room; Barber/Beauty shop; Sitting rooms.
Activities Arts and Crafts; Cards; Games; Reading groups; Prayer groups; Movies; Shop-

ping trips; Dances/Social or cultural gatherings; House newspaper.
Description Various types of therapists, dentists, podiatrists, ophthalmologists, and audiologists are available if needed. Facility is in a beautiful setting overlooking the Hudson River.

CUBA

Cuba Memorial Hospital Inc—Skilled Nursing Facility
140 W Main St, Cuba, NY, 14727 (716) 968-2000
Admin Margaret McIntire. *Medical Dir/Dir of Nursing* Stephen A Spink MD.
Licensure Skilled Care. *Beds* 30. *Certified* Medicaid; Medicare.
Ownership Nonprofit.
Admissions Requirements Minimum age 17; Medical examination; Physician's request.
Staff RNs 1 (ft), 1 (pt); LPNs 3 (ft), 3 (pt); Nurses aides 12 (ft), 7 (pt); Physical therapists 1 (ft); Activities coordinators 1 (pt); Dietitians 1 (ft).
Facilities Dining room; Physical therapy room; Activities room; Chapel; Laundry room; Barber/Beauty shop.
Activities Arts and Crafts; Games; Reading groups; Prayer groups; Movies; Shopping trips; Dances/Social or cultural gatherings.
Description This hospital-based facility, in Cuba NY, is located in a scenic valley overlooked by the foothills of the Allegany Mountains and easily accessible by the Southern Tier Expressway.

DELHI

Delaware County Home and Infirmary
Rt 1, Box 417, Delhi, NY, 13753 (607) 746-2331
Admin Matthew Luger. *Medical Dir/Dir of Nursing* Fredrick Heinegg MD.
Licensure Skilled Care; Intermediate Care. *Beds* 199. *Certified* Medicaid; Medicare.
Ownership Public.
Admissions Requirements Minimum age 16; Medical examination.
Staff Physicians 3 (pt); RNs 18 (ft), 9 (pt); LPNs 35 (ft), 10 (pt); Nurses aides 70 (ft), 40 (pt); Physical therapists 1 (ft); Occupational therapists 1 (ft); Speech therapists 1 (pt); Activities coordinators 1 (ft); Dietitians 1 (pt); Dentists 1 (pt).
Facilities Dining room; Physical therapy room; Activities room; Crafts room; Laundry room; Barber/Beauty shop.
Activities Arts and Crafts; Cards; Games; Reading groups; Prayer groups; Movies; Shopping trips; Dances/Social or cultural gatherings.

DELMAR

Good Samaritan Nursing Home Inc*
125 Rockefeller Rd, Delmar, NY, 12054 (518) 439-8116
Licensure Intermediate Care. *Beds* 100.
Ownership Nonprofit.

DOBBS FERRY

Saint Cabrini Nursing Home Inc
115 Broadway, Dobbs Ferry, NY, 10522 (914) 693-6800
Admin William T Smith. *Medical Dir/Dir of Nursing* Frank Quattromani MD.
Licensure Skilled Care. *Beds* 200. *Certified* Medicaid; Medicare.
Ownership Nonprofit.
Admissions Requirements Minimum age 65; Medical examination; Physician's request.
Staff Physicians 6 (pt); RNs 29 (ft), 14 (pt); LPNs 7 (ft), 15 (pt); Nurses aides 63 (ft); Physical therapists 1 (ft), 1 (pt); Recreational therapists 2 (ft), 2 (pt); Occupational therapists 1 (ft), 2 (pt); Speech therapists 1 (pt); Activities coordinators 1 (ft).
Affiliation Roman Catholic
Facilities Dining room; Physical therapy room; Activities room; Chapel; Crafts room; Laundry room; Barber/Beauty shop; Library.
Activities Arts and Crafts; Cards; Games; Prayer groups; Movies; Dances/Social or cultural gatherings; Barbecues; Picnics.
Description The facility is located in Dobbs Ferry, on spacious grounds overlooking the Hudson River. Terrace is the setting for residents' weekly barbecue during the summer months and the residents enjoy the use of the grounds with family members using outdoor picnic furniture donated by the auxiliary of the nursing home. There are also 2 annual picnics, with live entertainment on the Fourth of July and Labor Day. The residents have a flower garden and herb garden on the terrace which is cared for by the residents during the spring and summer.

DUNKIRK

Chautauqua County Home and Infirmary
Temple Rd, Dunkirk, NY, 14048 (716) 366-6400
Admin Charles Ferraro. *Medical Dir/Dir of Nursing* Dr Y Y Ting.
Licensure Skilled Care; Intermediate Care. *Beds* 197. *Certified* Medicaid; Medicare.
Ownership Public.
Admissions Requirements Medical examination; Physician's request.
Staff Physicians 1 (ft); RNs 6 (ft); LPNs 35 (ft); Nurses aides 65 (ft); Physical therapists 1 (pt); Occupational therapists 1 (ft); Speech therapists 1 (pt); Activities coordinators 1 (ft); Dietitians 1 (ft); Dentists 1 (pt); Podiatrists 1 (pt); Audiologists 1 (pt).
Facilities Dining room; Physical therapy room; Activities room; Chapel; Crafts room; Laundry room; Barber/Beauty shop; Library.
Activities Arts and Crafts; Cards; Games; Prayer groups.
Description Admission priority given to local residents.

Margaret-Anthony Nursing Home*
447-449 Lake Shore Dr W, Dunkirk, NY, 14048 (716) 366-6710
Admin Margaret Taravella.
Licensure Skilled Care. *Beds* 40. *Certified* Medicaid; Medicare.
Ownership Proprietary.

EAST AURORA

Aurora Park Health Care Center Inc
292 Main St, East Aurora, NY, 14052 (716)
652-1560
Admin Neil Chur.
Licensure Skilled Care; Intermediate Care.
Beds 320. *Certified* Medicaid; Medicare.
Ownership Proprietary.

EAST ISLIP

Little Flower Nursing Home*
340 E Montauk Hwy, East Islip, NY, 11730
(516) 581-6400
Admin Theresa M Santmann.
Licensure Skilled Care; Intermediate Care.
Beds 80. *Certified* Medicaid; Medicare.
Ownership Proprietary.

EAST SYRACUSE

Sunnyside Nursing Home
7000 Collamer Rd, East Syracuse, NY, 13057
(315) 656-7218
Admin Burnell Carney. *Medical Dir/Dir of
Nursing* Dr John Hemmerlein.
Licensure Skilled Care. *Beds* 80. *Certified* Medicaid; Medicare.
Ownership Proprietary.
Admissions Requirements Minimum age 16;
Physician's request.
Staff Physicians 1 (pt); RNs 7 (ft), 6 (pt); LPNs
7 (ft), 8 (pt); Orderlies 1 (ft), 2 (pt); Nurses aides
22 (ft), 22 (pt); Physical therapists 1 (pt);
Reality therapists 1 (ft); Recreational therapists
1 (ft); Occupational therapists 1 (pt); Speech
therapists 1 (pt); Activities coordinators 1 (ft);
Dietitians 1 (ft); Dentists 1 (pt); Podiatrists 1
(pt).
Facilities Dining room; Physical therapy room;
Activities room; Crafts room; Laundry room;
Barber/Beauty shop.
Activities Arts and Crafts; Cards; Games;
Reading groups; Prayer groups; Movies; Shopping trips; Dances/Social or cultural gatherings.
Description Facility is located in a beautiful
country setting; there is a gazebo in back of
building.

EATON

Gerrit Smith Memorial Infirmary*
River Rd, Eaton, NY, 13334 (315) 684-3951
Admin Dennis Smith.
Licensure Skilled Care. *Beds* 95. *Certified* Medicaid; Medicare.
Ownership Public.

EDEN

Saint George Nursing Home*
2806 George St, Eden, NY, 14057 (716)
992-3987
Admin Anthony St George Jr.
Licensure Skilled Care. *Beds* 40. *Certified* Medicaid; Medicare.
Ownership Proprietary.

EDGEMERE

Rockaway Care Center*
353 Beach 48th St, Edgemere, NY, 11691 (212)
471-5000
Admin Mark Stenzler.
Licensure Skilled Care; Intermediate Care.
Beds 80. *Certified* Medicaid; Medicare.
Ownership Proprietary.

ELIZABETHTOWN

Horace Nye Home*
Park St, Elizabethtown, NY, 12932 (518)
873-6301
Admin Chester W Arthur.
Licensure Skilled Care; Intermediate Care.
Beds 60. *Certified* Medicaid; Medicare.
Ownership Public.

ELMHURST

City Hospital at Elmhurst Public Home*
79–01 Broadway, Elmhurst, NY, 11373 (212)
830-1515
Licensure Intermediate Care. *Beds* 36.
Ownership Public.

ELMIRA

**Arnot-Ogden Memorial Hospital—Skilled
Nursing Unit**
Roe Ave, Elmira, NY, 14901 (607) 737-4100
Admin Dallas K Larson. *Medical Dir/Dir of
Nursing* Charles Kinley MD.
Licensure Skilled Care. *Beds* 40. *Certified* Medicaid; Medicare.
Ownership Nonprofit.
Admissions Requirements Minimum age 18;
Medical examination; Physician's request.
Staff Physicians 1 (pt); RNs 5 (ft), 5 (pt);
Orderlies 1 (pt); Nurses aides 22 (ft); Physical
therapists 1 (pt); Occupational therapists 1 (pt);
Speech therapists 1 (pt); Activities coordinators
1 (ft), 1 (pt); Dietitians 1 (pt); Dentists 1 (pt);
Ophthalmologists 1 (pt); Podiatrists 1 (pt);
Audiologists 1 (pt).
Facilities Dining room; Activities room; Crafts
room; Laundry room; Barber/Beauty shop;
Library.
Activities Arts and Crafts; Cards; Games;
Reading groups; Prayer groups; Movies; Shopping trips; Dances/Social or cultural gatherings.
Description This is a 40-bed facility, private
and 2-bed semi-private rooms, located in a
beautiful and quiet setting.

**Chemung County Health Center—Nursing
Facility***
Heritage Park, Elmira, NY, 14901 (607)
737-2068
Admin Warren L Tessier.
Licensure Skilled Care. *Beds* 200. *Certified* Medicaid; Medicare.
Ownership Public.

**Saint Josephs Hospital—Skilled Nursing
Facility**
555 E Market St, Elmira, NY, 14902 (607)
733-6541
Admin Marie Michael Miller. *Medical Dir/Dir*

of Nursing Dr A D Smith.
Licensure Skilled Care. *Beds* 31. *Certified* Medicaid; Medicare.
Ownership Nonprofit.
Admissions Requirements Minimum age 16;
Physician's request.
Activities Arts and Crafts; Cards; Games;
Reading groups; Prayer groups; Movies; Shopping trips.

ENDICOTT

**Endicott Nursing Home and Health Related
Facility***
Nantucket Dr, Endicott, NY, 13760 (607)
754-2705
Admin Charles Yannett.
Licensure Skilled Care; Intermediate Care.
Beds 80. *Certified* Medicaid; Medicare.
Ownership Proprietary.

FAIRPORT

Crest Manor Nursing Home*
6745 Pittsford-Palmyra Rd, Fairport, NY,
14450 (716) 223-3633
Admin Helen Caar.
Licensure Skilled Care. *Beds* 80. *Certified* Medicaid; Medicare.
Ownership Proprietary.

Fairport Baptist Home
4646 9 Mile Point Rd, Fairport, NY, 14450
(716) 377-0350
Admin Alvin C Foster.
Licensure Skilled Care; Intermediate Care.
Beds 196. *Certified* Medicaid; Medicare.
Ownership Nonprofit.
Affiliation Baptist
Facilities Dining room; Physical therapy room;
Activities room; Chapel; Crafts room; Laundry
room; Barber/Beauty shop; Library.

FAR ROCKAWAY

Bezalel Nursing Home Company
29-38 Far Rockaway Blvd, Far Rockaway, NY,
11691
Admin Solomon B Reifman. *Medical Dir/Dir
of Nursing* Dr Tizes.
Licensure Skilled Care; Intermediate Care.
Beds 120. *Certified* Medicaid; Medicare.
Ownership Nonprofit.
Admissions Requirements Minimum age 21.
Staff Physicians 3 (pt); Physical therapists 2
(pt); Occupational therapists 2 (pt); Speech therapists 1 (pt); Activities coordinators 1 (ft), 2
(pt); Dietitians 1 (ft); Dentists 1 (pt); Ophthalmologists 1 (pt); Audiologists 2 (pt).
Affiliation Jewish
Facilities Dining room; Physical therapy room;
Activities room; Chapel; Crafts room; Barber-
/Beauty shop; Library.
Activities Arts and Crafts; Cards; Games;
Reading groups; Prayer groups; Movies; Shopping trips; Dances/Social or cultural gatherings.

Brookhaven Beach Health Related Facility*
250 Beach 17th St, Far Rockaway, NY, 11691
(212) 471-7500
Admin Herbert Rothman.

Licensure Skilled Care; Intermediate Care. *Beds* 58. *Certified* Medicaid; Medicare. *Ownership* Proprietary.

Far Rockaway Nursing Home*
13-11 Virginia St, Far Rockaway, NY, 11691 (212) 327-2909
Admin Aaron Feuereisen.
Licensure Skilled Care. *Beds* 100. *Certified* Medicaid; Medicare.
Ownership Proprietary.

Haven Manor*
1441 Greenport Rd, Far Rockaway, NY, 11691 (212) 471-1500
Licensure Intermediate Care for Mentally Retarded. *Beds* 240.
Ownership Proprietary.

Oceanview Nursing Home
315 Beach 9th St, Far Rockaway, NY, 11691 (212) 471-6000
Admin Alex Weiss. *Medical Dir/Dir of Nursing* Dr John Timothy.
Licensure Skilled Care. *Beds* 102. *Certified* Medicaid; Medicare.
Ownership Proprietary.
Admissions Requirements Minimum age 26; Medical examination; Physician's request.
Staff RNs 6 (ft); LPNs 30 (ft); Orderlies 5 (ft); Nurses aides 30 (ft); Physical therapists 1 (pt); Recreational therapists 1 (pt); Occupational therapists 1 (pt); Speech therapists 1 (pt); Activities coordinators 1 (ft); Dietitians 1 (pt).
Facilities Dining room; Physical therapy room; Activities room; Chapel; Crafts room; Laundry room; Barber/Beauty shop; Library.
Activities Arts and Crafts; Cards; Games; Reading groups; Prayer groups; Movies; Dances/Social or cultural gatherings.

Peninsula General Nursing Home*
50-15 Beach Channel Dr, Far Rockaway, NY, 11691 (212) 945-7100
Admin Bernard Satin.
Licensure Skilled Care. *Beds* 200. *Certified* Medicaid; Medicare.
Ownership Nonprofit.

Queens-Nassau Nursing Home*
520 Beach 19th St, Far Rockaway, NY, 11691 (212) 471-7202
Admin M Krakowski.
Licensure Skilled Care. *Beds* 200. *Certified* Medicaid; Medicare.
Ownership Proprietary.

Seagirt Health Related Facility*
1410 S Seagirt Blvd, Far Rockaway, NY, 11691 (212) 471-7000
Licensure Intermediate Care. *Beds* 210.
Ownership Proprietary.

Surfside Nursing Home*
22-41 New Haven Ave, Far Rockaway, NY, 11691 (212) 471-3400
Admin Raphael Yenowitz.
Licensure Skilled Care. *Beds* 175. *Certified* Medicaid; Medicare.
Ownership Proprietary.

FARMINGDALE

Daleview Nursing Home
574 Fulton St, Farmingdale, NY, 11735 (516) 694-6242
Admin Paul J Dioguardi. *Medical Dir/Dir of Nursing* Armondo Des Champs MD.
Licensure Skilled Care. *Beds* 86. *Certified* Medicaid; Medicare.
Ownership Proprietary.
Staff Physicians 38 (pt); RNs 21 (ft); LPNs 19 (ft); Orderlies 3 (ft); Nurses aides 33 (ft); Physical therapists 2 (ft); Recreational therapists 3 (ft); Occupational therapists 1 (pt); Speech therapists 1 (pt); Activities coordinators 1 (ft); Dietitians 1 (pt); Dentists 3 (pt); Ophthalmologists 1 (pt); Podiatrists 3 (pt); Audiologists 1 (pt).
Facilities Dining room; Physical therapy room; Activities room; Chapel; Crafts room; Laundry room; Barber/Beauty shop.
Activities Arts and Crafts; Cards; Games; Reading groups; Prayer groups; Movies; Shopping trips; Dances/Social or cultural gatherings.
Description Clean, caring, involved, community-oriented facility with large volunteer program and much recreation.

FLUSHING

Cliffside Nursing Home
119-19 Graham Ct, Flushing, NY, 11354 (212) 886-0700
Admin Jack Deutsch. *Medical Dir/Dir of Nursing* G Kreitman MD.
Licensure Skilled Care. *Beds* 220. *Certified* Medicaid; Medicare.
Ownership Proprietary.
Staff Physicians 1 (pt); RNs 8 (ft), 4 (pt); LPNs 20 (ft), 10 (pt); Nurses aides 60 (ft), 30 (pt); Physical therapists 1 (ft); Reality therapists 1 (ft); Recreational therapists 2 (ft), 1 (pt); Occupational therapists 1 (pt); Speech therapists 1 (pt); Activities coordinators 1 (ft); Dietitians 2 (ft); Dentists 1 (pt).
Facilities Dining room; Physical therapy room; Activities room; Crafts room; Barber/Beauty shop; Library.
Activities Arts and Crafts; Cards; Games; Reading groups; Prayer groups; Movies; Dances/Social or cultural gatherings.
Description Modern LTC facility offering full range of skilled nursing and rehabilitative services; convenient location for public and private transportation from the 5 boroughs of New York City, Nassau, Suffolk, and Westchester counties.

College Nursing Home*
119-15 27th Ave, Flushing, NY, 11354 (212) 461-5000
Admin Ivan Howard.
Licensure Skilled Care. *Beds* 200. *Certified* Medicaid; Medicare.
Ownership Proprietary.

Flushing Manor Care Center*
139-62 35th Ave, Flushing, NY, 11354 (212) 961-5300
Admin Herbert Eisen.

Licensure Skilled Care; Intermediate Care. *Beds* 178. *Certified* Medicaid; Medicare. *Ownership* Proprietary.

Flushing Manor Nursing Home*
35-15 Parsons Blvd, Flushing, NY, 11354 (212) 961-3500
Admin Esther Benenson.
Licensure Skilled Care. *Beds* 227. *Certified* Medicaid; Medicare.
Ownership Proprietary.

Franklin Nursing Home
142-27 Franklin Ave, Flushing, NY, 11355 (212) 463-8200
Admin Sylvia Stern. *Medical Dir/Dir of Nursing* Dr George Martin.
Licensure Skilled Care. *Beds* 320. *Certified* Medicaid; Medicare.
Ownership Proprietary.
Admissions Requirements Medical examination.
Staff RNs 15 (ft), 5 (pt); LPNs 23 (ft), 20 (pt); Orderlies 2 (ft), 1 (pt); Nurses aides 77 (ft), 42 (pt); Physical therapists 2 (ft), 2 (pt); Occupational therapists 1 (pt); Speech therapists 1 (pt); Activities coordinators 1 (ft); Dietitians 3 (ft); Dentists 1 (pt); Podiatrists 3 (pt).
Affiliation Jewish
Facilities Dining room; Physical therapy room; Activities room; Crafts room; Barber/Beauty shop.
Activities Arts and Crafts; Games; Reading groups; Prayer groups; Movies; Dances/Social or cultural gatherings.
Description A 320-bed facility offering a wide range of medical, nursing, therapeutic, and supportive service in a spacious and warm environment. Kosher facility.

Long Island Nursing Home
144-61 38th Ave, Flushing, NY, 11354 (212) 939-7500
Admin Phyllis Schindler. *Medical Dir/Dir of Nursing* Dr Michael Shechtman.
Licensure Skilled Care. *Beds* 200. *Certified* Medicaid; Medicare.
Ownership Proprietary.
Admissions Requirements Minimum age 16.
Staff RNs 8 (ft), 4 (pt); LPNs 16 (ft), 9 (pt); Orderlies 7 (ft), 2 (pt); Nurses aides 56 (ft), 10 (pt); Physical therapists 2 (pt); Recreational therapists 1 (ft), 1 (pt); Occupational therapists 2 (pt); Speech therapists 1 (pt); Activities coordinators 1 (ft); Dietitians 1 (ft), 1 (pt); Podiatrists 3 (pt).
Facilities Dining room; Physical therapy room; Activities room; Chapel; Crafts room; Laundry room; Library (mobile).
Activities Arts and Crafts; Cards; Games; Reading groups; Prayer groups; Movies; Shopping trips; Dances/Social or cultural gatherings.
Description Resident Council member of Coalition of Resident Councils; Family Council active in educational programs; drama improvisation workshops; glee club; pet program (resident cat); affiliation with a nursing aide school in that student aides do their clinical training here.

Meadow Park Nursing Home
78-10 164th St, Flushing, NY, 11366 (212) 591-8300

Admin Abraham Schlafrig. *Medical Dir/Dir of Nursing* Dr Harry Miller.
Licensure Skilled Care. *Beds* 143. *Certified* Medicaid; Medicare.
Ownership Proprietary.
Admissions Requirements Minimum age 21.
Staff RNs 6 (ft); LPNs 9 (ft); Orderlies 2 (ft), 1 (pt); Nurses aides 8 (ft), 5 (pt); Recreational therapists 2 (ft); Speech therapists 1 (ft); Dietitians 1 (ft).
Facilities Dining room; Physical therapy room.
Activities Arts and Crafts; Games; Reading groups; Prayer groups.

Rego Park Nursing Home*
111-26 Corona Ave, Flushing, NY, 11368 (212) 592-6400
Admin Israel Fogel.
Licensure Skilled Care. *Beds* 200. *Certified* Medicaid; Medicare.
Ownership Proprietary.

FOREST HILLS

Fairview Nursing Home*
69-70 Grand Central Pkwy, Forest Hills, NY, 11375 (212) 263-4600
Admin Maurice Radzik.
Licensure Skilled Care. *Beds* 200. *Certified* Medicaid; Medicare.
Ownership Proprietary.

Forest Hills Nursing Home*
71-44 Yellowstone Blvd, Forest Hills, NY, 11375 (212) 544-4300
Admin Cathrine Powers.
Licensure Skilled Care. *Beds* 100. *Certified* Medicaid; Medicare.
Ownership Proprietary.

Forest View Nursing Home
108-18 Queens Blvd, Forest Hills, NY, 11375 (212) 793-3200
Admin Joseph L Bloch. *Medical Dir/Dir of Nursing* Irwin Greenbaum MD.
Licensure Skilled Care. *Beds* 159. *Certified* Medicaid; Medicare.
Ownership Proprietary.
Admissions Requirements Medical examination; Physician's request.
Staff Physicians 4 (pt); RNs 4 (ft), 3 (pt); LPNs 18 (ft), 12 (pt); Nurses aides 43 (ft), 28 (pt); Physical therapists 1 (ft), 1 (pt); Recreational therapists 1 (ft), 3 (pt); Occupational therapists 1 (pt); Speech therapists 1 (pt); Activities coordinators 1 (ft); Dietitians 1 (ft).
Facilities Dining room; Physical therapy room; Activities room; Laundry room; Barber/Beauty shop; Library.
Activities Arts and Crafts; Cards; Games; Reading groups; Movies; Dances/Social or cultural gatherings; Barbecues; Trips to museums & race track.

FORT EDWARD

Fort Hudson Nursing Home Inc
Upper Broadway, Fort Edward, NY, 12828 (518) 747-2811
Admin Rita LaClair. *Medical Dir/Dir of Nursing* Philip J Gara Jr MD.

Licensure Skilled Care; Intermediate Care.
Beds 80. *Certified* Medicaid; Medicare.
Ownership Nonprofit.
Admissions Requirements Minimum age 16; Medical examination; Physician's request.
Staff Physicians 1 (pt); RNs 9 (ft), 6 (pt); LPNs 15 (ft), 10 (pt); Orderlies 2 (ft), 3 (pt); Nurses aides 34 (ft), 23 (pt); Physical therapists 2 (pt); Speech therapists 1 (pt); Activities coordinators 1 (ft); Dietitians 1 (pt); Dentists 1 (pt).
Facilities Dining room; Physical therapy room; Activities room; Chapel; Crafts room; Laundry room; Barber/Beauty shop; Library.
Activities Arts and Crafts; Cards; Games; Reading groups; Prayer groups; Movies; Shopping trips; Dances/Social or cultural gatherings.

FRANKLIN SQUARE

Franklin Park Nursing Home
135 Franklin Ave, Franklin Square, NY, 11010 (516) 488-1600
Admin William G Cowen. *Medical Dir/Dir of Nursing* Dr Harold Langs.
Licensure Skilled Care. *Beds* 150. *Certified* Medicaid; Medicare.
Ownership Proprietary.
Admissions Requirements Minimum age 18; Medical examination.

FREEPORT

South Shore Nursing Home Inc*
275 W Merrick Rd, Freeport, NY, 11520 (516) 623-4000
Admin Marilynne Geraghty.
Licensure Skilled Care. *Beds* 100. *Certified* Medicaid; Medicare.
Ownership Proprietary.

FULTON

Andrew Michaud Nursing Home*
450 S 4th St, Fulton, NY, 13069 (315) 592-9521
Admin Fred Blackwood.
Licensure Skilled Care. *Beds* 89. *Certified* Medicaid; Medicare.
Ownership Public.

GASPORT

United Church Colony Homes Inc*
4540 Lincoln Dr, Gasport, NY, 14067 (716) 772-2631
Admin James Surridge.
Licensure Skilled Care. *Beds* 83. *Certified* Medicaid; Medicare.
Ownership Nonprofit.

GENESEO

Livingston County Skilled Nursing Facility
4223 Lakeville Rd, Geneseo, NY, 14454 (716) 243-3340
Admin William Loeber.
Licensure Skilled Care. *Beds* 126. *Certified* Medicaid; Medicare.
Ownership Public.
Admissions Requirements Minimum age 18;

Medical examination; Physician's request.
Staff Physicians 2 (pt); RNs 15 (ft), 2 (pt); LPNs 14 (ft), 1 (pt); Nurses aides 51 (ft), 9 (pt); Physical therapists 1 (ft); Speech therapists 1 (pt); Activities coordinators 1 (ft); Dietitians 1 (pt); Dentists 1 (pt).
Facilities Dining room; Physical therapy room; Activities room; Chapel; Laundry room; Barber/Beauty shop.
Activities Arts and Crafts; Cards; Games; Reading groups; Prayer groups; Movies; Shopping trips; Dances/Social or cultural gatherings.

GENEVA

Geneva General Hospital Nursing Home Co Inc*
196-198 North St, Geneva, NY, 14456 (315) 789-4222
Admin James Dooley.
Licensure Skilled Care; Intermediate Care.
Beds 67. *Certified* Medicaid; Medicare.
Ownership Nonprofit.

GERRY

Gerry Nursing Home Co Inc
Gerry, NY, 14760 (716) 985-4612
Admin Wesley D Pearson.
Licensure Skilled Care; Intermediate Care.
Beds 120. *Certified* Medicaid; Medicare.
Ownership Nonprofit.
Admissions Requirements Minimum age 16.
Affiliation Methodist
Facilities Dining room; Physical therapy room; Activities room; Chapel; Crafts room; Laundry room; Barber/Beauty shop.
Activities Arts and Crafts; Games; Reading groups; Prayer groups; Movies; Shopping trips; Dances/Social or cultural gatherings.

GETZVILLE

Niagara Frontier Nursing Home Co Inc*
100 Stahl Rd, Getzville, NY, 14068 (716) 688-8822
Admin Arthur Shade.
Licensure Skilled Care. *Beds* 120. *Certified* Medicaid; Medicare.
Ownership Nonprofit.

Niagra Frontier Methodist Home Inc*
2235 Millersport Hwy, Getzville, NY, 14068 (716) 688-8822
Licensure Intermediate Care. *Beds* 157.
Ownership Nonprofit.
Affiliation Methodist

GLEN COVE

Forest Manor Health Related Facility*
6 Medical Plaza, Glen Cove, NY, 11542 (516) 671-9010
Licensure Intermediate Care. *Beds* 148.
Ownership Proprietary.

Glengariff Corp
Dosoris Ln, Glen Cove, NY, 11542 (516) 676-1100
Admin Kenneth Winston. *Medical Dir/Dir of*

Nursing Ferdinand Kann MD.
Licensure Skilled Care; Intermediate Care.
Beds SNF 121; ICF 41. *Certified* Medicaid;
Medicare.
Ownership Proprietary.
Admissions Requirements Minimum age 18;
Medical examination.
Staff Physicians 20 (ft); RNs 7 (ft); LPNs 12
(ft); Orderlies 2 (ft); Nurses aides 45 (ft);
Physical therapists 1 (ft); Recreational therapists
2 (ft); Occupational therapists 1 (pt); Speech
therapists 1 (pt); Activities coordinators 1 (ft);
Dietitians 1 (pt); Dentists 1 (pt); Ophthalmolo-
gists 1 (pt); Podiatrists 2 (pt); Audiologists 1
(pt).
Facilities Dining room; Physical therapy room;
Activities room; Crafts room; Laundry room;
Barber/Beauty shop; Library.
Activities Arts and Crafts; Cards; Games;
Reading groups; Prayer groups; Movies; Shop-
ping trips; Dances/Social or cultural gatherings.
Description Over the past 9 years Glengariff
has been accorded accreditation by the Joint
Commission on Accreditation of Hospitals and
has enjoyed recognition by the New York State
Department of Health as having an out-
standing skilled nursing and health related
facility.

Montclair Nursing Home
2 Medical Plaza, Glen Cove, NY, 11542 (516)
671-0858
Admin Joseph Kane. *Medical Dir/Dir of
Nursing* Gabriella Wasserman.
Licensure Skilled Care. *Beds* 102. *Cer-
tified* Medicaid; Medicare.
Ownership Proprietary.
Staff RNs 8 (ft), 4 (pt); LPNs 5 (ft), 4 (pt);
Orderlies 1 (ft); Nurses aides 30 (ft), 11 (pt).
Facilities Dining room; Activities room; Bar-
ber/Beauty shop.
Activities Arts and Crafts; Cards; Games;
Reading groups; Prayer groups; Movies; Shop-
ping trips; Dances/Social or cultural gatherings.

GLEN OAKS

New Glen Oaks Nursing Home*
260-01 79th Ave, Glen Oaks, NY, 11004 (212)
343-0770
Admin Caroline Snigur.
Licensure Skilled Care. *Beds* 60. *Certified* Medicaid; Medicare.
Ownership Proprietary.

GLENS FALLS

**Eden Park Nursing Home and Health Related
Facility**
170 Warren St, Glens Falls, NY, 12801 (518)
793-5163
Admin Lloyd Cote. *Medical Dir/Dir of
Nursing* Dr Allen Kauffman MD.
Licensure Skilled Care; Intermediate Care. *Cer-
tified* Medicaid; Medicare.
Ownership Proprietary.
Admissions Requirements Minimum age 16;
Medical examination; Physician's request.
Staff RNs 10 (ft), 10 (pt); LPNs 8 (ft), 2 (pt);
Nurses aides 35 (ft), 26 (pt); Physical therapists
1 (pt); Recreational therapists 1 (ft); Occupa-

tional therapists 1 (ft), 1 (pt); Speech therapists
1 (pt); Activities coordinators 1 (ft); Dietitians
1 (pt); Dentists 1 (pt).
Facilities Dining room; Physical therapy room;
Activities room; Crafts room; Barber/Beauty
shop; Library; Wheelchair garden.
Activities Arts and Crafts; Games; Reading
groups; Prayer groups; Movies; Shopping trips;
Dances/Social or cultural gatherings; Music,
video, drama programs.
Description Eden Park is located in a lovely
historical district across from the famous Hyde
Art Collection. The well-kept lawns grace the
corner first settled by the original settler of
Glens Falls, Abraham Wing. The facility's
diversified activity department has been
honored by both state and local authorities for
its creative programming.

Hallmark Nursing Centre
152 Sherman Ave, Glens Falls, NY, 12801
(518) 793-2575
Admin M R Kubricky.
Licensure Skilled Care. *Beds* 80. *Certified* Medicaid; Medicare.
Ownership Proprietary.

Westmount Health Facility
Rt 2, Glens Falls, NY, 12801 (518) 761-6540
Admin James Shoemaker. *Medical Dir/Dir of
Nursing* Dr John E Cunnigham Jr.
Licensure Skilled Care. *Beds* 80. *Cer-
tified* Medicaid; Medicare.
Ownership Public.
Admissions Requirements Minimum age 16;
Medical examination; Physician's request.
Staff Physicians 3 (pt); RNs 9 (ft); LPNs 9 (ft);
Nurses aides 39 (ft); Physical therapists 1 (ft), 1
(pt); Recreational therapists 2 (ft); Occupational
therapists; Speech therapists; Activities coordi-
nators 1 (pt); Dietitians 1 (pt); Dentists 1 (pt);
Audiologists.
Facilities Dining room; Physical therapy room;
Activities room; Crafts room; Laundry room;
Barber/Beauty shop.
Activities Arts and Crafts; Cards; Reading
groups; Prayer groups; Movies; Shopping trips;
Dances/Social or cultural gatherings.

GLOVERSVILLE

Fulton County Infirmary
Ext Phelps St Rd, Gloversville, NY, 12078
(518) 725-8631
Admin Ronald Morris. *Medical Dir/Dir of
Nursing* Robert L Kemp MD.
Licensure Skilled Care; Health Related Care.
Beds 176. *Certified* Medicaid; Medicare.
Ownership Public.
Staff Physicians 5 (pt); RNs 9 (ft), 1 (pt); LPNs
16 (ft); Nurses aides 46 (ft), 54 (pt); Physical
therapists 1 (pt); Occupational therapists 1 (pt);
Activities coordinators 1 (ft); Dietitians 1 (pt);
Dentists 1 (pt); Podiatrists 1 (pt).
Facilities Dining room; Physical therapy room;
Activities room; Laundry room; Barber/Beauty
shop.
Activities Arts and Crafts; Cards; Games;
Reading groups; Prayer groups; Movies; Shop-
ping trips; Dances/Social or cultural gatherings.

**Gloversville Extended Care and Nursing Home
Co Inc***
99 E State St, Gloversville, NY, 12078 (518)
725-8621
Admin Danlal Governanti.
Licensure Skilled Care; Intermediate Care.
Beds 84. *Certified* Medicaid; Medicare.
Ownership Nonprofit.

GOSHEN

Orange County Home and Infirmary*
PO Box 59, Goshen, NY, 10924 (914)
294-7971
Admin John Watson.
Licensure Skilled Care; Intermediate Care.
Beds 340. *Certified* Medicaid; Medicare.
Ownership Public.

GOUVERNEUR

Kinney Nursing Home
57 W Barney St, Gouverneur, NY, 13642 (315)
287-1400
Admin Michael Delarm.
Licensure Skilled Care. *Beds* 40. *Cer-
tified* Medicaid; Medicare.
Ownership Nonprofit.
Facilities Dining room; Physical therapy room;
Activities room; Crafts room; Laundry room;
Barber/Beauty shop.
Activities Arts and Crafts; Cards; Games;
Reading groups; Prayer groups; Movies; Shop-
ping trips; Dances/Social or cultural gatherings.

GOWANDA

Gowanda Nursing Home
100 Miller St, Gowanda, NY, 14070
Admin Patricia E Brunsing. *Medical Dir/Dir of
Nursing* C Frederick Kurtz MD.
Licensure Skilled Care; Intermediate Care.
Beds SNF 80; ICF 40. *Certified* Medicaid;
Medicare.
Ownership Proprietary.
Admissions Requirements Minimum age 16;
Medical examination; Physician's request.
Staff Physical therapists 1 (pt); Activities coor-
dinators 2 (ft).
Facilities Dining room; Physical therapy room;
Activities room; Crafts room; Laundry room;
Barber/Beauty shop.
Activities Arts and Crafts; Cards; Games;
Reading groups; Prayer groups; Movies; Shop-
ping trips; Dances/Social or cultural gatherings.

GRAND ISLAND

Grand Island Manor Nursing Home
2850 Grand Island Blvd, Grand Island, NY,
14072 (716) 773-5900
Admin Sam W Ware Jr. *Medical Dir/Dir of
Nursing* Ida Levine MD.
Licensure Skilled Care. *Beds* 80. *Cer-
tified* Medicaid; Medicare.
Ownership Proprietary.
Admissions Requirements Minimum age 16.
Staff Physicians 1 (pt); RNs 5 (ft), 5 (pt); LPNs
10 (ft), 4 (pt); Nurses aides 16 (ft), 24 (pt);
Physical therapists 1 (pt); Recreational thera-

pists 1 (ft), 1 (pt); Occupational therapists 1 (pt); Speech therapists 1 (pt); Dietitians 1 (pt); Dentists 1 (pt); Ophthalmologists 1 (pt); Podiatrists 1 (pt); Audiologists 1 (pt).
Facilities Dining room; Physical therapy room; Activities room; Crafts room; Laundry room; Barber/Beauty shop.
Activities Arts and Crafts; Cards; Games; Reading groups; Prayer groups; Movies; Shopping trips; Dances/Social or cultural gatherings.
Description Facility features a family-like setting with skilled tender loving care.

GRANVILLE

Indian River Nursing Home and Health Related Facility Inc
17 Madison St, Granville, NY, 12832 (518) 642-2710
Admin Daniel L Morris. *Medical Dir/Dir of Nursing* Dr John Glennon.
Licensure Skilled Care; Intermediate Care. *Beds* SNF 40; HRF 40. *Certified* Medicaid; Medicare.
Ownership Proprietary.
Admissions Requirements Medical examination.
Staff Physicians 2 (pt); RNs 3 (ft), 2 (pt); LPNs 3 (ft), 4 (pt); Nurses aides 23 (ft), 8 (pt); Physical therapists 1 (ft), 1 (pt); Recreational therapists 1 (ft); Speech therapists 1 (pt); Activities coordinators 1 (ft); Dietitians 1 (ft); Dentists 1 (pt); Podiatrists 1 (pt).
Facilities Dining room; Physical therapy room; Activities room; Laundry room; Barber/Beauty shop; Library.
Activities Arts and Crafts; Games; Reading groups; Movies; Shopping trips; Dances/Social or cultural gatherings.
Description Patients and residents are taken to local state parks for picnics on several outings, and on a boat cruise of Lake George twice each year.

GREAT NECK

Grace Plaza of Great Neck
15 Saint Pauls Pl, Great Neck, NY, 11021 (516) 466-3001
Admin Celia Strow. *Medical Dir/Dir of Nursing* Dr Lester Corn.
Licensure Skilled Care; Intermediate Care. *Beds* SNF 165; ICF 49. *Certified* Medicaid; Medicare.
Ownership Proprietary.
Admissions Requirements Minimum age 16; Medical examination; Physician's request.
Staff RNs 8 (ft), 7 (pt); LPNs 17 (ft), 12 (pt); Nurses aides 50 (ft), 37 (pt); Physical therapists 1 (pt); Recreational therapists 1 (ft); Occupational therapists 1 (pt); Speech therapists 1 (pt); Activities coordinators 3 (ft), 2 (pt); Dietitians 1 (ft); Dentists 1 (pt); Podiatrists 2 (pt); Audiologists 1 (pt).
Facilities Dining room; Physical therapy room; Activities room; Crafts room; Laundry room; Barber/Beauty shop.
Activities Arts and Crafts; Cards; Games; Reading groups; Prayer groups; Movies; Shopping trips; Dances/Social or cultural gatherings.
Description Facility offers counseling for fam-

ilies of new admissions; internship programs in social work, recreation, administration; clinical team approach in patient assessment.

Wedgewood Nursing Home*
199 Community Dr, Great Neck, NY, 11021 (516) 365-9229
Admin Fred White.
Licensure Skilled Care. *Beds* 200. *Certified* Medicaid; Medicare.
Ownership Proprietary.

GREENHURST

Fenton Park Health Related Facility
Rt 430, Greenhurst, NY, 14742
Admin Warren E Elston. *Medical Dir/Dir of Nursing* Dr Charles Sinatra.
Licensure Intermediate Care. *Certified* Medicaid; Medicare.
Ownership Proprietary.
Staff RNs; LPNs; Orderlies; Nurses aides; Physical therapists; Recreational therapists; Occupational therapists; Speech therapists; Activities coordinators; Dietitians; Dentists; Podiatrists; Audiologists.
Facilities Dining room; Physical therapy room; Activities room; Chapel; Crafts room; Laundry room; Barber/Beauty shop; Library.
Activities Arts and Crafts; Cards; Games; Reading groups; Prayer groups; Movies; Shopping trips; Dances/Social or cultural gatherings.

GREENPORT

San Simeon by the Sound —Skilled Nursing Facility*
North Rd, Greenport, NY, 11944 (516) 477-2110
Admin Arthur Loeffler.
Licensure Skilled Care. *Beds* 70. *Certified* Medicaid; Medicare.
Ownership Nonprofit.

GROTON

Groton Community Health Care Center Residential Care Facility
120 Sykes St, Groton, NY, 13073
Admin James X Kennedy. *Medical Dir/Dir of Nursing* Edwin Mathias MD.
Licensure Skilled Care; Intermediate Care. *Beds* 80. *Certified* Medicaid; Medicare.
Ownership Nonprofit.
Staff Physicians 2 (pt); RNs 4 (ft), 4 (pt); LPNs 2 (ft), 3 (pt); Orderlies 2 (pt); Nurses aides 4 (ft), 7 (pt); Physical therapists 1 (ft); Occupational therapists 1 (pt); Speech therapists 1 (pt); Activities coordinators 1 (ft); Dietitians 1 (ft); Dentists 2 (pt); Ophthalmologists 1 (pt); Podiatrists 1 (pt); Audiologists 1 (pt).
Facilities Dining room; Physical therapy room; Activities room; Laundry room; Barber/Beauty shop.
Activities Arts and Crafts; Games; Prayer groups; Movies; Dances/Social or cultural gatherings.
Description Facility has total community support; located between a senior citizens housing

complex and day care center, and attached to ambulatory health care center; unique for a rural town.

GUILDERLAND CENTER

Guilderland Center Nursing Home Inc*
127 Main St, Guilderland Center, NY, 12085 (518) 861-5141
Admin James Reed and Hazel Reed.
Licensure Skilled Care. *Beds* 127. *Certified* Medicaid; Medicare.
Ownership Proprietary.

HAMBURG

Autumn View Manor
S 4650 Southwestern Blvd, Hamburg, NY, 14075
Admin Susan Miller. *Medical Dir/Dir of Nursing* Douglas Moffat.
Licensure Skilled Care. *Beds* 160. *Certified* Medicaid; Medicare.
Ownership Proprietary.
Admissions Requirements Minimum age 18; Physician's request.
Staff RNs; LPNs; Nurses aides; Physical therapists; Occupational therapists; Speech therapists; Activities coordinators; Dietitians; Dentists; Ophthalmologists; Podiatrists; Audiologists; Social workers.
Facilities Dining room; Physical therapy room; Activities room; Crafts room; Laundry room; Barber/Beauty shop.
Activities Arts and Crafts; Cards; Games; Reading groups; Prayer groups; Movies; Shopping trips; Dances/Social or cultural gatherings; Religious services for all faiths.
Description Facility focal point is the beautiful indoor solarium where residents enjoy therapeutic effects of sunshine and growing plants; constructed on one floor for ease of access, building surrounds 2 grassy outdoor courtyards designed for residents and visitors to enjoy in good weather.

HAMILTON

Community Memorial Hospital Inc—Nursing Home Unit*
150 Broad St, Hamilton, NY, 13346 (315) 824-1100
Admin David Felton.
Licensure Skilled Care. *Beds* 40. *Certified* Medicaid; Medicare.
Ownership Nonprofit.

HARRIS

Community General Hospital of Sullivan County*
Bushville Rd, Harris, NY, 12742 (914) 794-3300
Licensure Intermediate Care. *Beds* 40.
Ownership Nonprofit.

HASTINGS-ON-HUDSON

John E Andrus Memorial*
185 Old Broadway, Hastings-on-Hudson, NY, 10706 (914) 478-3700
Admin E E McAlister.
Licensure Intermediate Care. *Beds* 52.
Ownership Nonprofit.

HAVERSTRAW

Riverside Nursing Home*
87 S Rt 9W, Haverstraw, NY, 10927 (914) 429-5381
Admin Sarah Muschel.
Licensure Skilled Care. *Beds* 100. *Certified* Medicaid; Medicare.
Ownership Proprietary.

HAWTHORNE

Ruth Taylor Geriatric Rehabilitation Institute
25 Bradhurst Ave, Hawthorne, NY, 10532 (914) 347-7762
Admin James Davis. *Medical Dir/Dir of Nursing* Steven R Gambert MD.
Licensure Skilled Care; Intermediate Care. *Beds* 415. *Certified* Medicaid; Medicare.
Ownership Public.
Staff Physicians 2 (ft), 5 (pt); RNs 36 (ft); LPNs 48 (ft), 1 (pt); Nurses aides 155 (ft); Physical therapists 1 (ft); Recreational therapists 8 (ft), 1 (pt); Occupational therapists 1 (ft); Speech therapists 1 (pt); Activities coordinators 1 (ft); Dietitians 4 (ft); Dentists 1 (pt); Podiatrists 1 (pt).
Facilities Dining room; Physical therapy room; Activities room; Chapel; Crafts room; Laundry room; Barber/Beauty shop; Library; Speech therapy; Occupational therapy room; Patient lounge; Patient private rooms; John E Kule Park; Coffee shop; Patient property rooms; Sewing room; Clothing shop.
Activities Arts and Crafts; Cards; Games; Reading groups; Prayer groups; Movies; Shopping trips; Dances/Social or cultural gatherings; Newcomers club; Sunshine club; Resident incentive work programs; Tasting time; RSVP; Resident newspaper; Garden club.
Description All programs are designed to assist in providing the most comprehensive and contemporary approach to patient care in a long-term facility.

HEMPSTEAD

Hempstead Park Nursing Home*
800 Front St, Hempstead, NY, 11550 (516) 560-1200
Admin Joseph J Hines.
Licensure Skilled Care. *Beds* 240. *Certified* Medicaid; Medicare.
Ownership Proprietary.

Mayfair Nursing Home*
100 Baldwin Rd, Hempstead, NY, 11550 (516) 538-7171
Admin Burt Culter.
Licensure Skilled Care. *Beds* 200. *Certified* Medicaid; Medicare.
Ownership Proprietary.

HERKIMER

Folts Home
104 N Washington St, Herkimer, NY, 13350 (315) 866-6964
Admin Virginia Sheehan. *Medical Dir/Dir of Nursing* Stephen P Martell MD.
Licensure Skilled Care; Health Related Care. *Beds* SNF 60; HRC 19. *Certified* Medicaid; Medicare.
Ownership Nonprofit.
Admissions Requirements Minimum age 16; Medical examination.
Staff Physicians 1 (pt); RNs 7 (ft), 4 (pt); LPNs 6 (ft), 6 (pt); Orderlies 1 (ft); Nurses aides 15 (ft), 10 (pt); Physical therapists; Occupational therapists; Activities coordinators; Dietitians; Dentists; Podiatrists.
Affiliation Methodist
Facilities Dining room; Physical therapy room; Activities room; Chapel; Crafts room; Laundry room; Barber/Beauty shop.
Activities Arts and Crafts; Cards; Games; Reading groups; Prayer groups; Movies; Shopping trips; Dances/Social or cultural gatherings.
Description Retirement center with independent living units, HRF and SNF; lovely grounds, well known for rose gardens; enjoys an excellent reputation for good care; now in process of expanding to 79 SNF bed and 45 HRF.

HIGHLAND

Hudson Valley Nursing Center*
Vineyard Ave, Highland, NY, 12528 (914) 691-7201
Admin Alan Porter.
Licensure Skilled Care. *Beds* 120. *Certified* Medicaid; Medicare.
Ownership Proprietary.

HOLLIS

Hollis Park Gardens Nursing Home*
191-06 Hillside Ave, Hollis, NY, 11423 (212) 479-1010
Admin Eli Lewis.
Licensure Skilled Care. *Beds* 80. *Certified* Medicaid; Medicare.
Ownership Proprietary.

Holliswood Care Center Inc*
195-44 Woodhull Ave, Hollis, NY, 11423 (212) 740-3500
Admin Hal Schifter.
Licensure Skilled Care; Intermediate Care. *Beds* 58. *Certified* Medicaid; Medicare.
Ownership Proprietary.

HOLMES

Kent Nursing Home
Ludingtonville Rd, Holmes, NY, 12531 (914) 878-3241
Admin Mary Eble. *Medical Dir/Dir of Nursing* Dr Garrett Vink.
Licensure Skilled Care. *Beds* 160. *Certified* Medicaid; Medicare.
Ownership Proprietary.
Admissions Requirements Minimum age 16.

Staff Physicians 12 (pt); RNs 11 (ft), 11 (pt); LPNs 5 (ft), 11 (pt); Orderlies 2 (pt); Nurses aides 50 (ft), 42 (pt); Physical therapists 1 (pt); Occupational therapists 1 (pt); Speech therapists 1 (pt); Activities coordinators 1 (ft); Dietitians 1 (ft); Dentists 1 (pt); Ophthalmologists 1 (pt); Podiatrists 1 (pt); Audiologists 1 (pt); Social workers 1 (ft).
Facilities Dining room; Physical therapy room; Activities room; Crafts room; Laundry room; Barber/Beauty shop; Occupational therapy room.
Activities Arts and Crafts; Games; Prayer groups; Movies; Dances/Social or cultural gatherings.
Description Home is located in a rural setting surrounded by hills and trees with a view of its own large fishing pond.

HOOSICK FALLS

Hoosick Falls Health Center
Danforth St, PO Box 100, Hoosick Falls, NY, 12090 (518) 686-4371
Licensure Skilled Care. *Beds* 41. *Certified* Medicaid; Medicare.
Ownership Nonprofit.

HORNELL

Hornell Nursing Home*
434 Monroe Ave, Hornell, NY, 14843 (607) 324-7740
Admin James Bicker.
Licensure Skilled Care; Intermediate Care. *Beds* 60. *Certified* Medicaid; Medicare.
Ownership Proprietary.

HORSEHEADS

Bethany Nursing Home and Health Related Facility Inc*
751 Watkins Rd, Horseheads, NY, 14845 (607) 739-8711
Licensure Intermediate Care. *Beds* 40.
Ownership Nonprofit.

Elcor Nursing Home
110 Colonial Dr, Horseheads, NY, 14845 (607) 739-3654
Admin Lester Poes. *Medical Dir/Dir of Nursing* Dr John Roemmelt.
Licensure Skilled Care. *Beds* 105. *Certified* Medicaid; Medicare.
Ownership Proprietary.
Staff RNs 3 (ft), 9 (pt); LPNs 10 (ft), 5 (pt); Nurses aides 46 (ft), 21 (pt); Activities coordinators 1 (ft); Dietitians 1 (ft).
Facilities Dining room; Physical therapy room; Activities room; Crafts room; Laundry room; Barber/Beauty shop; Dental room.
Activities Arts and Crafts; Cards; Games; Reading groups; Prayer groups; Movies; Shopping trips; Dances/Social or cultural gatherings.
Description Elcor Nursing Home is a modern, fire-resistant brick building, especially designed to provide comfort for each patient. Pleasantly situated in a suburban setting, it is licensed as a skilled nursing facility by the New York State

Department of Health. Private, semi-private, and 3- and 4-bed rooms are available upon admission.

Elcor's Mariott Manor
108 Colonial Dr, Horseheads, NY, 14845
Admin Lester Poes and Richard Poes. *Medical Dir/Dir of Nursing* Dr John Roemmelt.
Licensure Skilled Care; Intermediate Care.
Beds SNF 105; ICF 125. *Certified* Medicaid; Medicare.
Ownership Proprietary.
Admissions Requirements Medical examination.
Staff RNs 6 (ft), 11 (pt); LPNs 16 (ft), 11 (pt); Nurses aides 68 (ft), 33 (pt); Recreational therapists 1 (ft); Activities coordinators 4 (ft); Dietitians 1 (ft).
Facilities Dining room; Physical therapy room; Activities room; Crafts room; Laundry room; Barber/Beauty shop; Library service.
Activities Arts and Crafts; Cards; Games; Reading groups; Prayer groups; Movies; Shopping trips; Dances/Social or cultural gatherings.
Description Facility features adult day care.

HOUGHTON

Houghton Nursing Care Center Inc
Rt 1, Box G-12, Houghton, NY, 14744
Admin Harold McIntire. *Medical Dir/Dir of Nursing* Dr Storer Emmett.
Licensure Skilled Care; Intermediate Care.
Beds SNF 40; ICF 40. *Certified* Medicaid; Medicare.
Ownership Proprietary.
Admissions Requirements Minimum age 16; Medical examination; Physician's request.
Staff Physicians 3 (pt); RNs 2 (ft), 7 (pt); LPNs 5 (ft), 2 (pt); Orderlies 1 (ft); Nurses aides 31 (ft), 15 (pt); Activities coordinators 1 (ft); Dietitians 1 (pt); Dentists 1 (pt); Podiatrists 1 (pt).
Facilities Dining room; Physical therapy room; Activities room; Laundry room; Barber/Beauty shop.
Activities Arts and Crafts; Cards; Games; Reading groups; Prayer groups; Movies; Shopping trips.

HUDSON

Eden Park Nursing Home
30 Prospect Ave, Hudson, NY, 12534 (518) 828-9439
Admin Michael A Palmieri. *Medical Dir/Dir of Nursing* Dr Rosewall Shaw.
Licensure Skilled Care. *Beds* 78. *Certified* Medicaid; Medicare.
Ownership Proprietary.
Admissions Requirements Minimum age 16; Medical examination; Physician's request.
Staff Physicians 1 (ft); Physical therapists 1 (ft); Occupational therapists 1 (pt); Speech therapists 1 (pt); Activities coordinators 1 (ft), 1 (pt); Dietitians 1 (pt); Dentists 1 (pt); Ophthalmologists 1 (pt); Podiatrists 1 (pt); Audiologists 1 (pt).
Facilities Dining room; Physical therapy room; Activities room; Crafts room; Laundry room; Barber/Beauty shop.
Activities Arts and Crafts; Cards; Games;

Reading groups; Prayer groups; Movies; Shopping trips; Dances/Social or cultural gatherings.
Description Eden Park is dedicated to the person-centered concept of patient care. We provide a full complement of rehabilitative services designed to improve the patients quality of life and increase or maintain their level of functioning and striving for independence.

Firemans Home of the State of New York*
Harry-Howard Ave, Hudson, NY, 12534 (518) 828-7695
Licensure Intermediate Care. *Beds* 90.
Ownership Nonprofit.

HUNTINGTON

Carillon House Nursing Home*
830 Park Ave, Huntington, NY, 11743 (516) 271-5800
Admin Joseph Alfano.
Licensure Skilled Care; Intermediate Care.
Beds 142. *Certified* Medicaid; Medicare.
Ownership Proprietary.

Hilaire Farm Nursing Home*
Hilaire Dr, Huntington, NY, 11743 (516) 427-0254
Admin Michael M Gottsegen.
Licensure Skilled Care. *Beds* 76. *Certified* Medicaid; Medicare.
Ownership Proprietary.

HUNTINGTON STATION

Birchwood Nursing Home*
78 Birchwood Dr, Huntington Station, NY, 11746 (516) 423-3673
Admin Timothy Steffens.
Licensure Skilled Care; Intermediate Care.
Beds 120. *Certified* Medicaid; Medicare.
Ownership Proprietary.

HYDE PARK

Victory Lake Nursing Center
101 N Quaker Ln, Hyde Park, NY, 12538 (914) 229-9177
Admin George H Pelote.
Licensure Skilled Care. *Beds* 120. *Certified* Medicaid; Medicare.
Ownership Nonprofit.
Admissions Requirements Minimum age 16; Medical examination; Physician's request.
Staff Physicians 1 (ft), 8 (pt); RNs 16 (ft), 6 (pt); LPNs 12 (ft), 8 (pt); Orderlies 2 (ft); Nurses aides 46 (ft), 12 (pt); Physical therapists 1 (pt); Reality therapists 2 (ft); Recreational therapists 2 (ft); Occupational therapists 1 (pt); Speech therapists 1 (pt); Activities coordinators 1 (ft); Dietitians 2 (ft); Dentists 1 (pt); Ophthalmologists 1 (pt); Podiatrists 1 (pt); Audiologists 1 (pt).
Facilities Dining room; Physical therapy room; Activities room; Chapel; Crafts room; Laundry room; Barber/Beauty shop; Library.
Activities Arts and Crafts; Cards; Games; Reading groups; Prayer groups; Movies; Shopping trips; Dances/Social or cultural gatherings.

ILION

Mohawk Valley Nursing Home
295 W Main St, Ilion, NY, 13357 (315) 895-7474
Admin Marjorie Dolch. *Medical Dir/Dir of Nursing* Richard Brown DO.
Licensure Skilled Care. *Beds* 120. *Certified* Medicaid; Medicare.
Ownership Nonprofit.
Admissions Requirements Minimum age 16; Medical examination; Physician's request.
Staff RNs 7 (ft), 9 (pt); LPNs 13 (ft), 13 (pt); Nurses aides 49 (ft), 50 (pt); Physical therapists 1 (ft), 1 (pt); Occupational therapists 1 (ft); Activities coordinators 1 (ft); Dentists 1 (pt).
Facilities Dining room; Activities room; Chapel; Crafts room; Barber/Beauty shop.
Activities Arts and Crafts; Cards; Games; Reading groups; Prayer groups; Movies; Dances/Social or cultural gatherings.

IRVING

Lake Shore Hospital and Nursing Home
845 Rts 5 and 20, Irving, NY, 14081
Admin Sarah Holcomb. *Medical Dir/Dir of Nursing* Russell J Joy DO.
Licensure Skilled Care; Intermediate Care.
Beds SNF 40; ICF 80. *Certified* Medicaid; Medicare.
Ownership Nonprofit.
Admissions Requirements Minimum age 16; Physician's request.
Staff Physicians 1 (pt); RNs 5 (ft), 4 (pt); LPNs 12 (ft), 8 (pt); Nurses aides 23 (ft), 16 (pt); Physical therapists 1 (ft); Recreational therapists 1 (ft), 2 (pt); Occupational therapists 1 (pt); Activities coordinators 2 (ft); Dietitians 1 (pt).
Facilities Dining room; Physical therapy room; Activities room; Crafts room; Laundry room; Barber/Beauty shop.
Activities Arts and Crafts; Cards; Games; Reading groups; Prayer groups; Movies; Shopping trips; Dances/Social or cultural gatherings.
Description This is a semi-rural multilevel facility with a 49-bed acute care hospital attached to a nursing home to offer continuity of care for all ages.

Lake Shore Nursing Home Inc
Rts 5 and 20, Irving, NY, 14081 (716) 934-4606
Admin James Foster. *Medical Dir/Dir of Nursing* R J Joy.
Licensure Skilled Care. *Beds* 40. *Certified* Medicaid; Medicare.
Ownership Nonprofit.
Admissions Requirements Physician's request.
Staff Physicians 1 (pt); RNs 4 (ft), 3 (pt); LPNs 4 (ft); Nurses aides 10 (ft); Occupational therapists; Speech therapists; Activities coordinators; Dietitians; Dentists; Podiatrists.
Facilities Dining room; Physical therapy room; Activities room; Laundry room; Barber/Beauty shop.
Activities Arts and Crafts; Cards; Games; Reading groups; Prayer groups; Movies; Shopping trips; Dances/Social or cultural gatherings.

ISLAND PARK

Bayview Nursing Home*
1 Long Beach Rd, Island Park, NY, 11558
(516) 432-0300
Admin Richard Lap.
Licensure Skilled Care. *Beds* 185. *Certified* Medicaid; Medicare.
Ownership Proprietary.

ITHACA

Lakeside Nursing Home Inc
1229 Trumansburg Rd, Ithaca, NY, 14850
(607) 273-8072
Admin Jeffery Earle. *Medical Dir/Dir of Nursing* Dr Jerry Hersh.
Licensure Skilled Care; Intermediate Care.
Beds 260. *Certified* Medicaid; Medicare.
Ownership Proprietary.
Staff Physicians 1 (pt); RNs 20 (ft), 10 (pt); LPNs 10 (ft), 5 (pt); Nurses aides 100 (ft), 20 (pt); Physical therapists 2 (ft); Recreational therapists 3 (ft); Occupational therapists 1 (pt); Speech therapists 1 (pt); Activities coordinators 1 (ft); Dietitians 2 (ft); Dentists 1 (pt); Ophthalmologists 1 (pt); Podiatrists 1 (pt); Audiologists 1 (pt).
Facilities Dining room; Physical therapy room; Activities room; Chapel; Crafts room; Laundry room; Barber/Beauty shop; Library.
Activities Arts and Crafts; Cards; Games; Reading groups; Prayer groups; Movies; Shopping trips; Dances/Social or cultural gatherings.
Description Facility offers excellent rehabilitation program; overlooks beautiful Cayuga Lake.

Oak Hill Manor Nursing Home
602 Hudson St, Ithaca, NY, 14850 (607) 272-8282
Admin Eugene Battaglini. *Medical Dir/Dir of Nursing* Thomas Mosher MD.
Licensure Skilled Care. *Beds* 60. *Certified* Medicaid; Medicare.
Ownership Proprietary.
Admissions Requirements Minimum age 16.
Staff RNs 6 (ft), 4 (pt); LPNs 3 (ft), 4 (pt); Nurses aides 25 (ft), 7 (pt); Physical therapists 1 (pt); Recreational therapists 1 (ft), 1 (pt); Speech therapists 1 (pt); Dietitians 1 (pt).
Facilities Dining room; Physical therapy room; Activities room; Laundry room; Barber/Beauty shop.
Activities Arts and Crafts; Cards; Games; Reading groups; Prayer groups; Movies; Shopping trips; Dances/Social or cultural gatherings.

Reconstruction Home Inc*
318 S Albany St, Ithaca, NY, 14850 (607) 273-4166
Admin Jerome Lutherhouse.
Licensure Skilled Care. *Beds* 72. *Certified* Medicaid; Medicare.
Ownership Nonprofit.

JAMAICA

Chapin Home for the Aging*
165-01 Chapin Pkwy, Jamaica, NY, 11432
(212) 739-2523
Admin Kathrine Francis.

Licensure Intermediate Care. *Beds* 48. *Certified* Medicaid.
Ownership Nonprofit.

Jamaica Hospital Nursing Home Company Inc*
90-28 Van Wyck Expwy, Jamaica, NY, 11418
(212) 291-5300
Admin Gordon B Alexander Jr.
Licensure Skilled Care. *Beds* 200. *Certified* Medicaid; Medicare.
Ownership Nonprofit.

Margaret Tietz Center for Nursing Care Inc
164-11 Chapin Pkwy, Jamaica, NY, 11432
(212) 523-6400
Admin Kenneth Brown. *Medical Dir/Dir of Nursing* Dr Elaine Fox.
Licensure Skilled Care; Health Related Care.
Beds 120. *Certified* Medicaid; Medicare.
Ownership Nonprofit.
Admissions Requirements Minimum age 18; Medical examination; Physician's request.
Staff Physicians 5 (pt); RNs 21 (ft), 28 (pt); LPNs 4 (ft); Orderlies 6 (ft), 4 (pt); Nurses aides 48 (ft), 28 (pt); Physical therapists 1 (pt); Recreational therapists 2 (ft), 2 (pt); Occupational therapists 1 (ft), 1 (pt); Speech therapists 1 (pt); Activities coordinators 1 (ft); Dietitians 1 (ft); Dentists 2 (pt); Ophthalmologists 2 (pt); Podiatrists 2 (pt); Audiologists 1 (pt).
Facilities Dining room; Physical therapy room; Activities room; Crafts room; Laundry room; Barber/Beauty shop; Library; Garden; Terraces on each floor.
Activities Arts and Crafts; Cards; Games; Reading groups; Prayer groups; Movies; Shopping trips; Dances/Social or cultural gatherings.
Description Center is situated in a 6-story building with all offices and therapy rooms on 1st floor; 2nd, 3rd, and 4th floors for SNF; 5th and 6th floors are HRF. Each floor has a terrace and 1st floor has a beautiful outdoor garden; offers extensive recreation therapy, social service, and pastoral counseling departments to provide well rounded services in addition to the basic patient care services.

Woodhull Care Center*
91-31 175th St, Jamaica, NY, 11432 (212) 523-1100
Admin Chiam Kaminetsky.
Licensure Skilled Care; Intermediate Care.
Beds 120. *Certified* Medicaid; Medicare.
Ownership Proprietary.

JAMAICA ESTATES

Hillside Manor Health Related Facility*
182-15 Hillside Ave, Jamaica Estates, NY, 11432 (212) 523-3300
Admin Bengt Barbaccia.
Licensure Skilled Care; Intermediate Care.
Beds 205. *Certified* Medicaid; Medicare.
Ownership Proprietary.

JAMESTOWN

Fenton Park Nursing Home*
150 Prather Ave, Jamestown, NY, 14701 (716) 488-1921

Admin M Coxson.
Licensure Skilled Care. *Beds* 200. *Certified* Medicaid; Medicare.
Ownership Proprietary.

Lutheran Retirement Home
715 Falconer St, Jamestown, NY, 14701 (716) 665-4905
Admin Floyd Addison. *Medical Dir/Dir of Nursing* John D Voltmann MD.
Licensure Skilled Care; Intermediate Care.
Beds 124. *Certified* Medicaid; Medicare.
Ownership Nonprofit.
Staff RNs 12 (ft); LPNs 16 (ft); Orderlies 5 (ft); Nurses aides 65 (ft); Physical therapists 1 (pt); Recreational therapists 4 (ft), 1 (pt); Occupational therapists 1 (pt); Speech therapists 1 (pt); Activities coordinators 1 (ft); Dietitians 3 (ft), 1 (pt); Dentists 1 (pt); Podiatrists 1 (pt).
Affiliation Lutheran
Facilities Dining room; Physical therapy room; Activities room; Chapel; Laundry room; Barber/Beauty shop.
Activities Arts and Crafts; Cards; Games; Reading groups; Prayer groups; Movies; Shopping trips; Dances/Social or cultural gatherings.
Description Facility is a multilevel care campus, primarily focusing on retirement living and geriatric patients.

Manor Oak Skilled Nursing Facilities Inc
423 Baker St, Jamestown, NY, 14701 (716) 484-9181
Admin Alina T Wiecha MD.
Licensure Skilled Care. *Beds* 104. *Certified* Medicaid; Medicare.
Ownership Proprietary.
Admissions Requirements Minimum age 16.
Staff RNs 4 (ft), 5 (pt); LPNs 5 (ft), 7 (pt); Nurses aides 42 (pt); Physical therapists 1 (ft); Speech therapists 1 (pt); Activities coordinators 1 (ft), 1 (pt); Dietitians 1 (pt); Dentists; Podiatrists; Audiologists.

Presbyterian Homes of Western New York Inc*
715 Falconer St, Jamestown, NY, 14701 (716) 665-5214
Admin Ruthie L Hunt.
Licensure Skilled Care. *Beds* 86. *Certified* Medicaid; Medicare.
Ownership Nonprofit.
Affiliation Presbyterian

Presbyterian Homes of Western New York Inc*
715 Falconer St, Jamestown, NY, 14701 (716) 665-5214
Licensure Intermediate Care. *Beds* 86.
Ownership Proprietary.
Affiliation Presbyterian

JOHNSON CITY

Susquehanna Nursing Home*
282 Riverside Dr, Johnson City, NY, 13790
(607) 729-9206
Admin Paul Sadlon.
Licensure Skilled Care; Intermediate Care.
Beds 100. *Certified* Medicaid; Medicare.
Ownership Proprietary.

United Health Services, Wilson Extended Care Facility
33-57 Harrison St, Johnson City, NY, 13790
(607) 773-6289
Admin Alan Kopman. *Medical Dir/Dir of Nursing* Louis R Borelli MD.
Licensure Skilled Care. *Beds* 100. *Certified* Medicaid; Medicare.
Ownership Nonprofit.
Admissions Requirements Minimum age 16; Medical examination; Physician's request.
Staff RNs 15 (ft), 8 (pt); LPNs 13 (ft), 7 (pt); Nurses aides 24 (ft), 14 (pt); Physical therapists 3 (ft), 3 (pt); Occupational therapists 2 (ft); Speech therapists 1 (ft); Activities coordinators 2 (ft); Dietitians 1 (pt); Dentists 1 (pt); Audiologists 1 (ft).
Facilities Dining room; Physical therapy room; Laundry room; Barber/Beauty shop.
Activities Arts and Crafts; Games; Reading groups; Prayer groups; Movies; Shopping trips; Dances/Social or cultural gatherings.

JOHNSTOWN

Wells Nursing Home Inc*
201 W Madison Ave, Johnstown, NY, 12095
(518) 762-4546
Admin Joyce Brower.
Licensure Skilled Care; Intermediate Care.
Beds 42. *Certified* Medicaid; Medicare.
Ownership Nonprofit.

KENMORE

Abbey Nursing Home
2865 Elmwood Ave, Kenmore, NY, 14217
(716) 876-5900
Admin Frances Larson. *Medical Dir/Dir of Nursing* Dr C T Yu.
Licensure Skilled Care. *Beds* 79. *Certified* Medicaid; Medicare.
Ownership Proprietary.
Admissions Requirements Minimum age 60; Medical examination.
Staff Physicians 5 (pt); RNs 4 (ft), 8 (pt); LPNs 5 (ft), 4 (pt); Orderlies 5 (ft), 2 (pt); Nurses aides 21 (ft), 20 (pt); Physical therapists 1 (pt); Recreational therapists 1 (ft); Occupational therapists 1 (pt); Speech therapists 1 (pt); Activities coordinators 1 (ft); Dietitians 1 (ft); Dentists 1 (pt); Podiatrists 1 (pt); Audiologists 1 (pt).
Facilities Dining room; Physical therapy room; Activities room; Laundry room.
Activities Arts and Crafts; Cards; Games; Reading groups; Prayer groups; Movies; Dances/Social or cultural gatherings; Picnics.
Description Facility features a very effective music therapy program.

Kenmore Mercy Hospital—Skilled Nursing Unit
2950 Elmwood Ave, Kenmore, NY, 14217
(716) 879-6100
Admin Francis J Redding. *Medical Dir/Dir of Nursing* Dr Joseph Tutton.
Licensure Skilled Care. *Beds* 80. *Certified* Medicaid; Medicare.
Ownership Nonprofit.
Admissions Requirements Medical examination.

Staff Physicians 1 (ft); RNs 8 (ft), 7 (pt); LPNs 10 (ft), 9 (pt); Orderlies 19 (ft), 29 (pt); Physical therapists 4 (pt); Occupational therapists 1 (pt); Speech therapists 1 (pt); Activities coordinators 1 (ft); Dietitians 1 (pt); Dentists 1 (pt); Podiatrists 1 (pt); Audiologists 1 (pt).
Affiliation Roman Catholic
Facilities Dining room; Physical therapy room; Activities room; Chapel; Barber/Beauty shop.
Activities Arts and Crafts; Games; Prayer groups; Movies; Dances/Social or cultural gatherings; Baking; Sing-a-longs; Exercise class; Music therapy; Field trips.

Schofield Residence*
3333 Elmwood, Kenmore, NY, 14217 (716) 874-1566
Admin Edward Gray.
Licensure Skilled Care; Intermediate Care.
Beds 80. *Certified* Medicaid; Medicare.
Ownership Nonprofit.

KINGS PARK

Saint Johnland Nursing Home Inc*
Sunken Meadow Rd, Kings Park, NY, 11754
(516) 269-5800
Admin Joan Wood.
Licensure Skilled Care. *Beds* 160. *Certified* Medicaid; Medicare.
Ownership Nonprofit.

KINGSTON

Albany Avenue Nursing Home Inc
166 Albany Ave, Kingston, NY, 12401 (914) 338-1780
Admin Charlotte Shuler. *Medical Dir/Dir of Nursing* Johannes Weltin MD.
Licensure Skilled Care. *Beds* 22.
Ownership Proprietary.
Admissions Requirements Minimum age 21.
Staff RNs 6 (ft), 12 (pt); LPNs 1 (ft), 2 (pt); Nurses aides 6 (ft), 4 (pt); Physical therapists 1 (pt); Recreational therapists 1 (pt); Activities coordinators 1 (pt); Dietitians 1 (pt); Dentists 1 (pt).
Facilities Activities room; Laundry room.
Activities Arts and Crafts; Cards; Games; Reading groups; Prayer groups; Movies.
Description This is a strictly private facility that does not participate in the Medicaid or Medicare programs.

Hutton Nursing Home
346-364 Washington Ave, Kingston, NY, 12401
(914) 331-6327
Admin Nancy A Maxwell. *Medical Dir/Dir of Nursing* Chester Robbins.
Licensure Skilled Care. *Beds* 80. *Certified* Medicaid; Medicare.
Ownership Proprietary.
Admissions Requirements Minimum age 19.
Staff RNs 5 (ft), 6 (pt); LPNs 6 (ft), 5 (pt); Orderlies 3 (ft), 2 (pt); Nurses aides 33 (ft), 11 (pt); Physical therapists 2 (ft); Activities coordinators 2 (ft).
Facilities Dining room; Physical therapy room; Activities room; Laundry room; Barber/Beauty shop.

Activities Arts and Crafts; Cards; Games; Prayer groups; Movies; Shopping trips; Dances/Social or cultural gatherings.

Ulster County Infirmary/Health Related Facility
Golden Hill Dr, Kingston, NY, 12401 (914) 339-4540
Admin Elnora McSpirit. *Medical Dir/Dir of Nursing* Dr Arthur Carr.
Licensure Skilled Care; Intermediate Care.
Beds 280. *Certified* Medicaid; Medicare.
Ownership Public.
Staff Physicians 7 (pt); RNs 28 (ft); LPNs 24 (ft); Nurses aides 106 (ft); Physical therapists 1 (pt); Occupational therapists 1 (pt); Activities coordinators 2 (ft); Dietitians 1 (ft); Dentists 1 (pt).
Facilities Dining room; Physical therapy room; Activities room; Chapel; Crafts room; Laundry room; Barber/Beauty shop; Library.
Activities Arts and Crafts; Cards; Games; Reading groups; Prayer groups; Movies; Shopping trips; Dances/Social or cultural gatherings.
Description Skilled nursing facility has 200 beds and health related facility has 80 beds; rehabilitative or restorative services provided; podiatry, speech, audiology, and other consultative health services available by physicians' request.

LAKE PLACID

Placid Memorial Hospital Inc
Church St, Lake Placid, NY, 12946 (518) 523-3311
Admin Matthew Fulton. *Medical Dir/Dir of Nursing* Dr William Ellis.
Licensure Skilled Care. *Beds* 15. *Certified* Medicaid; Medicare.
Ownership Nonprofit.
Admissions Requirements Physician's request.
Staff Physicians 4 (ft); Physical therapists 1 (pt); Speech therapists 1 (pt); Activities coordinators 1 (pt); Dietitians 1 (pt); Dentists 1 (pt); Ophthalmologists 1 (pt); Podiatrists 1 (pt); Audiologists 1 (pt).
Facilities Dining room; Physical therapy room; Laundry room; Barber/Beauty shop.
Activities Arts and Crafts; Cards; Games; Reading groups; Movies; Shopping trips.

Uihlein Mercy Center Inc
Old Military Rd, Lake Placid, NY, 12946 (518) 523-2464
Admin S Camillus. *Medical Dir/Dir of Nursing* George Hart MD.
Licensure Skilled Care; Intermediate Care.
Beds 96. *Certified* Medicaid; Medicare.
Ownership Nonprofit.
Admissions Requirements Minimum age 16; Medical examination; Physician's request.
Staff Physicians; RNs; LPNs; Orderlies; Nurses aides; Physical therapists; Recreational therapists; Speech therapists; Activities coordinators; Dietitians; Dentists; Ophthalmologists; Podiatrists; Audiologists.
Affiliation Roman Catholic
Facilities Dining room; Physical therapy room; Activities room; Chapel; Crafts room; Laundry room; Barber/Beauty shop; Library.
Activities Arts and Crafts; Cards; Games;

Reading groups; Prayer groups; Movies.
Description Uihlein Mercy Center, a white brick building of unusual design, is located in the Olympic Village of Lake Placid, nestled amid the magnificent Adirondack Mountains with all private rooms, which surround living room lounges in intimate, octagon-shaped clusters of 14 rooms each.

LANCASTER

Furgala Nursing Home
1818 Como Park Blvd, Lancaster, NY, 14086 (716) 683-6165
Admin Chester J Furgala. *Medical Dir/Dir of Nursing* Dr Albert Addesa.
Licensure Skilled Care. *Beds* 89. *Certified* Medicaid; Medicare.
Ownership Proprietary.
Admissions Requirements Minimum age 18; Physician's request.
Staff RNs 14 (ft); LPNs 4 (ft); Nurses aides 76 (ft); Physical therapists 1 (pt); Reality therapists 1 (pt); Recreational therapists 1 (ft); Occupational therapists 1 (ft); Speech therapists 1 (pt); Activities coordinators 1 (ft); Dietitians 1 (pt); Dentists 1 (pt); Ophthalmologists 1 (pt); Podiatrists 1 (pt); Audiologists 1 (pt).
Facilities Dining room; Physical therapy room; Activities room; Chapel; Crafts room; Laundry room; Barber/Beauty shop; Library.
Activities Arts and Crafts; Cards; Games; Reading groups; Prayer groups; Movies; Shopping trips; Dances/Social or cultural gatherings.
Description For three years in a row we have had a 100% Survey report. Facility features a one-floor plan with 2 beautiful courtyards. Clean, odor-free skilled facility operated by proprietor-husband LPN and administrator-wife RNBS-DON.

LATHAM

Our Lady of Hope Residence-Little Sisters of the Poor*
1 Jeanne Jugan Ln, Latham, NY, 12110 (518) 785-4551
Admin M Mary Vincent.
Licensure Skilled Care; Intermediate Care. *Beds* 80. *Certified* Medicaid; Medicare.
Ownership Nonprofit.
Affiliation Roman Catholic

LEROY

Leroy Village Green Nursing Home and Health Related Facility Inc
10 Munson St, Leroy, NY, 14482 (716) 768-2561
Admin Robert Harrington. *Medical Dir/Dir of Nursing* Myron E Williams Jr MD.
Licensure Skilled Care; Intermediate Care. *Beds* SNF 80; ICF 60. *Certified* Medicaid; Medicare.
Ownership Proprietary.
Admissions Requirements Minimum age 16.
Staff Physicians 1 (pt); RNs 12 (ft); LPNs 13 (ft); Nurses aides 46 (ft); Physical therapists 1 (pt); Occupational therapists 1 (pt); Speech therapists 1 (pt); Activities coordinators 1 (ft); Dietitians 1 (pt); Dentists 1 (pt); Podiatrists 1 (pt).

Facilities Dining room; Physical therapy room; Activities room; Laundry room; Barber/Beauty shop.
Activities Arts and Crafts; Cards; Games; Reading groups; Prayer groups; Movies; Dances/Social or cultural gatherings.

LEWISTON

Fairchild Manor Nursing Home
765 Fairchild Pl, Lewiston, NY, 14092 (716) 754-4322
Admin Henry M Sloma. *Medical Dir/Dir of Nursing* Anthony B Schiam MD.
Licensure Skilled Care. *Beds* 100. *Certified* Medicaid; Medicare.
Ownership Proprietary.
Staff Physicians 17 (pt); RNs 6 (ft), 5 (pt); LPNs 12 (ft), 13 (pt); Nurses aides 31 (ft), 22 (pt); Physical therapists 1 (pt); Speech therapists 1 (pt); Activities coordinators 1 (ft); Dietitians 1 (ft), 1 (pt); Dentists 1 (pt); Ophthalmologists 1 (pt); Podiatrists 1 (pt); Audiologists 1 (pt).
Facilities Dining room; Physical therapy room; Activities room; Crafts room; Barber/Beauty shop; Library.
Activities Arts and Crafts; Cards; Games; Reading groups; Prayer groups; Movies; Shopping trips; Dances/Social or cultural gatherings.

LIBERTY

Sullivan County Public Home and Infirmary*
Box 231, Liberty, NY, 12754 (914) 292-8640
Admin George Dudley.
Licensure Skilled Care; Intermediate Care. *Beds* 46. *Certified* Medicaid; Medicare.
Ownership Public.

Walnut Mountain Care Center
Lake St, Liberty, NY, 12754 (914) 292-4200
Admin John J Rada. *Medical Dir/Dir of Nursing* Walter Dobushak MD.
Licensure Skilled Care; Intermediate Care. *Beds* SNF 104; ICF 74. *Certified* Medicaid; Medicare.
Ownership Proprietary.
Admissions Requirements Minimum age 16; Medical examination; Physician's request.
Staff RNs; LPNs; Orderlies; Nurses aides; Physical therapists; Occupational therapists; Speech therapists; Activities coordinators; Dietitians; Dentists; Ophthalmologists; Podiatrists; Audiologists.
Facilities Dining room; Physical therapy room; Activities room; Chapel; Crafts room; Barber/Beauty shop.
Activities Arts and Crafts; Cards; Games; Reading groups; Movies.
Description Center tries to provide the best nursing care and related care to its geriatric patients and residents.

LITTLE FALLS

Little Falls Hospital
140 Burwell St, Little Falls, NY, 13365 (315) 823-1000
Admin Nicholas Prisco. *Medical Dir/Dir of Nursing* Oscar Muller MD.
Licensure Skilled Care. *Beds* 34. *Cer-

tified Medicaid; Medicare.
Ownership Nonprofit.
Admissions Requirements Physician's request.
Staff Physicians 20 (ft); RNs 3 (ft), 3 (pt); LPNs 5 (ft), 2 (pt); Nurses aides 12 (ft), 9 (pt); Physical therapists 3 (pt); Occupational therapists 1 (pt); Speech therapists 1 (pt); Activities coordinators 1 (pt); Dietitians 1 (pt); Dentists 6 (ft); Podiatrists 2 (ft).
Facilities Dining room; Physical therapy room; Activities room; Chapel; Crafts room; Laundry room; Barber/Beauty shop; Library.
Activities Arts and Crafts; Cards; Games; Reading groups; Prayer groups; Movies.
Description This 34-bed home is an integral part of 150-bed acute care hospital facility.

Van Allen Nursing Home
755 E Monroe St, Little Falls, NY, 13365 (315) 823-0973
Admin William Van Allen. *Medical Dir/Dir of Nursing* Dr Oscar Stivala.
Licensure Skilled Care. *Beds* 42. *Certified* Medicaid; Medicare.
Ownership Proprietary.
Admissions Requirements Physician's request.
Staff Physicians 7 (pt); RNs 6 (ft), 6 (pt); LPNs 5 (ft), 6 (pt); Activities coordinators 1 (ft).
Facilities Dining room; Physical therapy room; Activities room; Chapel; Laundry room; Barber/Beauty shop.
Activities Arts and Crafts; Cards; Games; Reading groups; Prayer groups; Movies; Shopping trips; Dances/Social or cultural gatherings.

LITTLE NECK

Little Neck Nursing Home*
260-19 Nassau Blvd, Little Neck, NY, 11362 (212) 423-6400
Admin Raymond Esikoff.
Licensure Skilled Care. *Beds* 120. *Certified* Medicaid; Medicare.
Ownership Proprietary.

LIVINGSTON

Adventist Health and Retirement Center
PO Box 95, Livingston, NY, 12541 (518) 851-3041
Admin Dale Lind. *Medical Dir/Dir of Nursing* Dr Joseph Fusco.
Licensure Skilled Care; Intermediate Care; Domiciliary Care. *Beds* 120; Domiciliary Care 51. *Certified* Medicaid; Medicare.
Ownership Nonprofit.
Staff RNs 21 (ft); LPNs 13 (ft); Orderlies 1 (ft); Nurses aides 80 (ft); Physical therapists 1 (ft); Recreational therapists 1 (ft); Occupational therapists 1 (pt); Speech therapists 1 (pt); Activities coordinators 1 (ft); Dietitians 1 (pt); Dentists 1 (pt); Podiatrists 1 (pt); Audiologists 1 (pt); Physical therapy aides 2 (ft), 1 (pt); Others 2 (pt).
Affiliation Seventh-Day Adventist
Facilities Dining room; Physical therapy room; Activities room; Chapel; Crafts room; Laundry room; Barber/Beauty shop.
Activities Arts and Crafts; Cards; Games;

Reading groups; Prayer groups; Movies; Shopping trips; Dances/Social or cultural gatherings; Day care center 2 days per week.

LIVONIA

Conesus Lake Nursing Home*
Rt 15, Livonia, NY, 14487 (716) 346-3001
Admin Gail West.
Licensure Skilled Care. *Beds* 48. *Certified* Medicaid; Medicare.
Ownership Proprietary.

LOCKPORT

Briody Nursing Home*
909 Lincoln Ave, Lockport, NY, 14094 (716) 434-6361
Admin Joan Briody.
Licensure Skilled Care. *Beds* 82. *Certified* Medicaid; Medicare.
Ownership Proprietary.

Mount View Health Facility*
5465 Upper Mountain Rd, Lockport, NY, 14094 (716) 439-6003
Admin Richard Majlea.
Licensure Skilled Care. *Beds* 172. *Certified* Medicaid; Medicare.
Ownership Public.

Odd Fellow and Rebekah Nursing Home Inc*
104 Old Niagara Rd, Lockport, NY, 14094 (716) 434-6324
Admin Bonnie Cunningham.
Licensure Skilled Care; Intermediate Care. *Beds* 40. *Certified* Medicaid; Medicare.
Ownership Nonprofit.
Affiliation Independent Order of Odd Fellows

Saint Clare Manor
543 Locust, Lockport, NY, 14094 (716) 434-4718
Admin Sr Mary Frances. *Medical Dir/Dir of Nursing* William C Stein MD.
Licensure Skilled Care. *Beds* 28. *Certified* Medicaid; Medicare.
Ownership Nonprofit.
Admissions Requirements Medical examination; Physician's request.
Staff Physicians 3 (pt); RNs 1 (ft), 4 (pt); LPNs 2 (ft), 5 (pt); Nurses aides 8 (ft), 9 (pt); Physical therapists 1 (pt); Activities coordinators 1 (pt); Dietitians 1 (ft).
Affiliation Roman Catholic
Facilities Dining room; Physical therapy room; Activities room; Chapel; Laundry room; Barber/Beauty shop.
Activities Arts and Crafts; Cards; Games; Reading groups; Prayer groups; Movies.

LONG BEACH

Long Beach Grandell Co*
645 W Broadway, Long Beach, NY, 11561 (516) 889-1100
Admin Vernon Rossner.
Licensure Skilled Care; Intermediate Care. *Beds* 54. *Certified* Medicaid; Medicare.
Ownership Proprietary.

Long Beach Memorial Nursing Home Inc*
375 E Bay Dr, Long Beach, NY, 11561 (516) 432-8000
Admin Steven J Frome.
Licensure Skilled Care; Intermediate Care. *Beds* 150. *Certified* Medicaid; Medicare.
Ownership Nonprofit.

Long Island Tides Nursing Home*
640 W Broadway, Long Beach, NY, 11561 (516) 431-4400
Admin Kenneth Kelmenson.
Licensure Skilled Care. *Beds* 182. *Certified* Medicaid; Medicare.
Ownership Proprietary.

LOWVILLE

Lewis County General Hospital—Nursing Home Unit
7785 N State St, Lowville, NY, 13367 (315) 376-6521
Admin Allan Raymond. *Medical Dir/Dir of Nursing* Dr Elwin Stillman.
Licensure Skilled Care; Health Related Care. *Beds* SNF 80; HRC 40. *Certified* Medicaid; Medicare.
Ownership Public.
Admissions Requirements Minimum age 16.
Staff Physicians 4 (ft); RNs 6 (ft), 3 (pt); LPNs 19 (ft), 6 (pt); Orderlies 2 (ft), 1 (pt); Nurses aides 32 (ft), 14 (pt); Physical therapists 1 (ft); Occupational therapists 1 (ft); Activities coordinators 1 (ft); Dietitians 1 (ft); Podiatrists 1 (pt).
Facilities Dining room; Physical therapy room; Activities room; Chapel; Crafts room; Laundry room; Barber/Beauty shop; Library.
Activities Arts and Crafts; Cards; Games; Reading groups; Prayer groups; Movies; Dances/Social or cultural gatherings.
Description This facility is the only SNF/HRF in Lewis County and is attached to the 76-bed general hospital where residents may obtain any needed medical attention without actually leaving the building.

LYNBROOK

East Rockaway Nursing Home
243 Atlantic Ave, Lynbrook, NY, 11563 (516) 599-2744
Admin Robert Keon. *Medical Dir/Dir of Nursing* Dr Herbet Mayer.
Licensure Skilled Care. *Beds* 100. *Certified* Medicaid; Medicare.
Ownership Proprietary.
Admissions Requirements Minimum age 16; Medical examination; Physician's request.
Staff Physicians 30 (pt); RNs 7 (ft), 15 (pt); LPNs 8 (ft), 15 (pt); Orderlies 1 (ft), 2 (pt); Nurses aides 28 (ft), 52 (pt); Physical therapists 1 (pt); Occupational therapists 1 (pt); Speech therapists 1 (pt); Activities coordinators 1 (ft), 3 (pt); Dietitians 1 (pt); Dentists 1 (pt); Ophthalmologists 1 (pt); Podiatrists 3 (pt); Audiologists 1 (pt).
Facilities Dining room; Physical therapy room; Activities room; Crafts room; Barber/Beauty shop; Library.
Activities Arts and Crafts; Cards; Games; Reading groups; Prayer groups; Movies; Shopping trips.
Description The facility is a 2-story red brick structure located in a residential area on a one acre plot that provides adequate parking and a large outdoor patio where barbecues are held during the summer.

LYONS

Wayne County Nursing Home and Health Related Facility
7376 Rt 31, Lyons, NY, 14489 (315) 946-4817
Admin Jeff Glatz. *Medical Dir/Dir of Nursing* Dr David Blaszak.
Licensure Skilled Care; Intermediate Care. *Beds* 139. *Certified* Medicaid; Medicare.
Ownership Public.
Admissions Requirements Minimum age 16.
Staff Physicians 1 (pt); RNs 9 (ft), 3 (pt); LPNs 12 (ft), 5 (pt); Nurses aides 53 (ft), 9 (pt); Physical therapists 1 (pt); Occupational therapists 1 (pt); Speech therapists 1 (pt); Activities coordinators 1 (ft); Dietitians 1 (ft); Dentists 1 (pt); Podiatrists 1 (pt); Audiologists 1 (pt).
Facilities Dining room; Physical therapy room; Activities room; Chapel; Crafts room; Laundry room; Barber/Beauty shop; Library.
Activities Arts and Crafts; Cards; Games; Reading groups; Prayer groups; Movies; Shopping trips; Dances/Social or cultural gatherings.

MACHIAS

Cattaraugus County Home and Infirmary*
Rt 16, Machias, NY, 14101 (716) 353-8516
Admin Margaret Mary Wagner.
Licensure Skilled Care; Intermediate Care. *Beds* 79. *Certified* Medicaid; Medicare.
Ownership Public.

MALONE

Alice Hyde Nursing Home*
115 Park St, Malone, NY, 12953 (518) 483-3000
Admin Paul LaVine.
Licensure Skilled Care. *Beds* 75.
Ownership Nonprofit.

Franklin County Nursing Home
Rt 30, Finney Blvd, Malone, NY, 12953 (518) 483-3300
Admin William O'Reilly. *Medical Dir/Dir of Nursing* Alfred A Hartmann Sr MD.
Licensure Skilled Care. *Beds* 80.
Ownership Public.
Admissions Requirements Minimum age 16; Physician's request.
Facilities Dining room; Physical therapy room; Activities room; Crafts room; Laundry room; Barber/Beauty shop.
Activities Arts and Crafts; Cards; Games; Reading groups; Prayer groups; Movies; Shopping trips; Dances/Social or cultural gatherings.

MAMARONECK

Sarah R Neuman Nursing Home
845 Palmer Ave, Mamaroneck, NY, 10543 (914) 698-6005

Admin Marsha Squires. *Medical Dir/Dir of Nursing* Dr Miele.
Licensure Skilled Care; Intermediate Care.
Beds 180. *Certified* Medicaid; Medicare.
Ownership Proprietary.
Staff Physicians 4 (pt); RNs 10 (ft), 6 (pt); LPNs 11 (ft), 3 (pt); Orderlies 5 (ft), 1 (pt); Nurses aides 66 (ft), 14 (pt); Physical therapists 1 (ft); Occupational therapists 1 (pt); Speech therapists 1 (pt); Activities coordinators 1 (ft), 2 (pt); Dietitians 2 (ft); Dentists 1 (pt); Podiatrists 1 (pt).
Facilities Dining room; Physical therapy room; Activities room; Crafts room; Laundry room; Barber/Beauty shop.
Activities Arts and Crafts; Cards; Games; Reading groups; Prayer groups; Movies; Shopping trips; Dances/Social or cultural gatherings.
Description Facility offers activities 7 days a week, staff physicians, comfortable, home-like atmosphere, and a beauty parlor on premises.

MARGARETVILLE

Margaretville Memorial Hospital Nursing Home*
Rt 28, Margaretville, NY, 12455 (914) 586-2631
Admin Joseph Kehoe.
Licensure Skilled Care; Intermediate Care.
Beds 31. *Certified* Medicaid; Medicare.
Ownership Nonprofit.

MASPETH

Midway Nursing Home*
69-95 Queens Midtown Expwy, Maspeth, NY, 11378 (212) 429-2200
Admin Sam Gottlieb.
Licensure Skilled Care. *Beds* 200. *Certified* Medicaid; Medicare.
Ownership Proprietary.

MASSAPEQUA

Park View Nursing Home Inc*
5353 Merrick Rd, Massapequa, NY, 11758 (516) 798-1800
Admin Owen Kaye.
Licensure Skilled Care. *Beds* 164. *Certified* Medicaid; Medicare.
Ownership Proprietary.

MASSENA

Highland Nursing Home Inc
Highland Rd, Massena, NY, 13662 (315) 769-9956
Admin Edward J Kaneb. *Medical Dir/Dir of Nursing* Dr Joseph Chibnik.
Licensure Skilled Care. *Beds* 140. *Certified* Medicaid; Medicare.
Ownership Proprietary.
Admissions Requirements Physician's request.
Staff Physicians 17 (pt); RNs 6 (ft), 6 (pt); LPNs 16 (ft), 4 (pt); Nurses aides 44 (ft), 21 (pt); Physical therapists 1 (pt); Occupational therapists 1 (pt); Speech therapists 1 (pt); Activities coordinators 1 (ft); Dietitians 1 (pt); Dentists 1 (pt).

Facilities Dining room; Physical therapy room; Activities room; Chapel; Crafts room; Laundry room; Barber/Beauty shop.
Activities Arts and Crafts; Cards; Games; Reading groups; Prayer groups; Movies; Shopping trips; Dances/Social or cultural gatherings.

Saint Regis Nursing Home
Saint Regis Blvd, Massena, NY, 13662 (315) 769-2494
Admin John Bogosian. *Medical Dir/Dir of Nursing* Henry Dobies MD.
Licensure Skilled Care; Intermediate Care.
Beds SNF 44; ICF 108. *Certified* Medicaid; Medicare.
Ownership Proprietary.
Admissions Requirements Physician's request.
Staff RNs 10 (ft); LPNs 12 (ft); Nurses aides 49 (ft), 2 (pt); Physical therapists 1 (pt); Recreational therapists 1 (pt); Occupational therapists 1 (pt); Speech therapists 1 (pt); Activities coordinators 2 (ft); Dietitians 1 (ft).
Facilities Dining room; Physical therapy room; Activities room; Crafts room; Laundry room; Barber/Beauty shop.
Activities Arts and Crafts; Cards; Games; Reading groups; Prayer groups; Movies; Shopping trips; Dances/Social or cultural gatherings.

MEDINA

Medina Memorial Hospital—Skilled Nursing Facility*
500 Ohio St, Medina, NY, 14103 (716) 798-2000
Admin James Morey.
Licensure Skilled Care. *Beds* 30. *Certified* Medicaid; Medicare.
Ownership Nonprofit.

Orchard Manor Nursing Home
600 Bates Rd, Medina, NY, 14103 (716) 798-4100
Admin Barbara B Waters. *Medical Dir/Dir of Nursing* Harvey J Blanchet MD.
Licensure Skilled Care; Intermediate Care.
Beds 64. *Certified* Medicaid; Medicare.
Ownership Proprietary.
Staff RNs 3 (ft), 8 (pt); LPNs 8 (ft), 9 (pt); Nurses aides 19 (ft), 44 (pt); Physical therapists 1 (pt); Occupational therapists 1 (pt); Activities coordinators 2 (ft); Dietitians 1 (ft).
Facilities Dining room; Physical therapy room; Activities room; Chapel; Crafts room; Laundry room; Barber/Beauty shop; Library.
Activities Arts and Crafts; Cards; Games; Reading groups; Prayer groups; Movies; Shopping trips; Dances/Social or cultural gatherings.
Description Facility features centrally located lounges which have been provided and equipped with TV; rooms available to the patients, residents, and their families for private conferences; religious services conducted weekly by members of the local Ministerial Association; landscaped courtyard provides residents and patients with a garden-type atmosphere for supervised outdoor recreation.

MIDDLE ISLAND

Crest Hall Health Related Facility
Oakcrest Ave, Middle Island, NY, 11953
Admin Dwight T Worthy. *Medical Dir/Dir of Nursing* Fred Sherman MD.
Licensure Intermediate Care. *Beds* 120. *Certified* Medicaid.
Ownership Proprietary.
Admissions Requirements Minimum age 18; Physician's request.
Staff RNs 1 (ft); LPNs 12 (ft); Orderlies 1 (ft); Nurses aides 12 (ft); Physical therapists 1 (ft); Reality therapists 1 (pt); Recreational therapists 1 (ft); Activities coordinators 1 (ft).
Facilities Dining room; Physical therapy room; Activities room; Crafts room; Laundry room; Barber/Beauty shop.
Activities Arts and Crafts; Cards; Games; Reading groups; Prayer groups; Movies; Shopping trips; Dances/Social or cultural gatherings.
Description Located in semi-rural area near a small lake, facility emphasizes individual independence and maintenance of self-respect.

Oak Hollow Nursing Center*
Church Ln and Oak Crest Ave, Middle Island, NY, 11953 (516) 924-8820
Admin Morris Goldsmith.
Licensure Skilled Care. *Beds* 164. *Certified* Medicaid; Medicare.
Ownership Proprietary.

MIDDLE VILLAGE

Dry Harbor Nursing Home
61-35 Dry Harbor Rd, Middle Village, NY, 11379 (212) 446-3600
Admin Robert Friedman. *Medical Dir/Dir of Nursing* Dr Crusco.
Licensure Skilled Care; Intermediate Care.
Beds 360. *Certified* Medicaid; Medicare.
Ownership Proprietary.
Admissions Requirements Medical examination.
Staff Physicians 1 (ft), 5 (pt); RNs 8 (ft); LPNs 25 (ft); Nurses aides 76 (ft); Physical therapists 3 (ft); Recreational therapists 1 (ft); Occupational therapists 1 (pt); Speech therapists 1 (pt); Activities coordinators 6 (ft); Dietitians 1 (ft); Dentists 1 (pt); Podiatrists 1 (pt); Audiologists 1 (pt).
Facilities Dining room; Physical therapy room; Activities room; Crafts room; Laundry room; Barber/Beauty shop; Library.
Activities Arts and Crafts; Cards; Games; Reading groups; Prayer groups; Movies; Shopping trips; Dances/Social or cultural gatherings.
Description Facility features an outstanding physical therapy department.

MIDDLETON

Saint Teresas Nursing Home Inc
120 Highland Ave, Middleton, NY, 10940 (914) 342-1033
Admin Mary Grace. *Medical Dir/Dir of Nursing* Samuel Mills MD.
Licensure Skilled Care. *Beds* 92. *Certified* Medicaid; Medicare.
Ownership Nonprofit.

Admissions Requirements Medical examination.
Staff Physicians 2 (pt); RNs 18 (ft), 3 (pt); LPNs 3 (ft); Orderlies 1 (ft); Nurses aides 58 (ft), 9 (pt); Physical therapists 1 (pt); Occupational therapists 1 (pt); Speech therapists 1 (pt); Activities coordinators 1 (ft); Dietitians 1 (pt); Dentists 1 (pt); Podiatrists 1 (pt); Audiologists 1 (pt).
Affiliation Roman Catholic

MIDDLETOWN

Middletown Park Manor*
105 Dunning Rd, Middletown, NY, 10940 (914) 343-0801
Licensure Intermediate Care. *Beds* 40.
Ownership Proprietary.

MILLBROOK

Dutchess County Health Care Facility
Oak Summit Rd, Millbrook, NY, 12545 (914) 677-9781
Licensure Skilled Care. *Beds* 62. *Certified* Medicaid; Medicare.
Ownership Public.
Admissions Requirements Minimum age 16; Medical examination; Physician's request.
Facilities Dining room; Physical therapy room; Activities room; Crafts room; Laundry room; Barber/Beauty shop; Library.
Activities Arts and Crafts; Cards; Games; Reading groups; Prayer groups; Movies; Shopping trips; Dances/Social or cultural gatherings.
Description Dutchess County Health Care Facility is a nonprofit county-based facility located on Oak Summit road in Millbrook, NY. The facility is Medicare and Medicaid certified for 62 skilled nursing beds and is fully staffed to provide and meet all requirements of the NY State Health Department for good patient care.

MINOA

Hallmark Nursing Centre
217 E Ave, Minoa, NY, 13116 (315) 656-7277
Admin Raymond Klocek. *Medical Dir/Dir of Nursing* David Saunders MD.
Licensure Skilled Care. *Beds* 82. *Certified* Medicaid; Medicare.
Ownership Proprietary.
Staff Physicians 5 (pt); RNs 7 (ft), 3 (pt); LPNs 10 (ft), 4 (pt); Orderlies 1 (ft), 2 (pt); Nurses aides 30 (ft), 19 (pt); Physical therapists 1 (pt); Recreational therapists 1 (ft); Occupational therapists 1 (pt); Speech therapists 1 (pt); Activities coordinators 1 (ft); Dietitians 1 (pt); Dentists 1 (pt); Ophthalmologists 1 (pt); Podiatrists 1 (pt); Audiologists 1 (pt).
Facilities Dining room; Physical therapy room; Activities room; Chapel; Crafts room; Laundry room; Barber/Beauty shop; Library.
Activities Arts and Crafts; Cards; Games; Reading groups; Prayer groups; Movies; Shopping trips; Dances/Social or cultural gatherings.
Description Centre offers full range of services, including social services, leisure time activities, dietary consultation, discharge planning, physical therapy, occupational therapy, speech

pathology, audiology, podiatry, ophthalmology, optometry, dental, psychiatry, pharmacy, laboratory, X-ray, religious services, and many other services necessary to maintain a clean, healthy, safe environment.

MOHEGAN LAKE

Marrs Nursing Home*
3550 Lexington Ave, Mohegan Lake, NY, 10547 (914) 528-2000
Admin Kathrine Americo.
Licensure Skilled Care. *Beds* 120. *Certified* Medicaid; Medicare.
Ownership Proprietary.

MONTGOMERY

Montgomery Nursing Home
Albany Post Rd, PO Box 158, Montgomery, NY, 12549 (914) 457-3155
Admin Matthew Marciano. *Medical Dir/Dir of Nursing* Dr Sung J Sohn.
Licensure Skilled Care. *Beds* 100. *Certified* Medicaid; Medicare.
Ownership Proprietary.
Admissions Requirements Medical examination.
Staff RNs 3 (ft), 8 (pt); LPNs 5 (ft), 10 (pt); Orderlies 1 (ft); Nurses aides 33 (ft), 17 (pt); Physical therapists 1 (pt); Recreational therapists 1 (pt); Occupational therapists 1 (pt); Speech therapists 1 (pt); Activities coordinators 1 (ft); Dietitians 1 (ft); Dentists 1 (pt); Ophthalmologists 1 (pt); Podiatrists 1 (pt); Audiologists 1 (pt).
Facilities Dining room; Physical therapy room; Activities room; Chapel; Crafts room; Laundry room; Barber/Beauty shop.
Activities Arts and Crafts; Cards; Games; Reading groups; Prayer groups; Movies; Shopping trips; Dances/Social or cultural gatherings.
Description Facility offers excellence in nursing care, dignified and gracious living, catering to the individual with discriminating taste.

MONTOUR FALLS

Schuyler Hospital Inc—Long Term Care Unit
Montour Townsend Rd, Montour Falls, NY, 14865 (607) 535-7121
Admin Frank Alo. *Medical Dir/Dir of Nursing* James J Norton MD.
Licensure Skilled Care. *Beds* 40. *Certified* Medicaid; Medicare.
Ownership Nonprofit.
Staff Physicians 8 (pt); RNs 4 (ft); LPNs 2 (ft); Nurses aides 21 (ft); Physical therapists 2 (pt); Recreational therapists 1 (ft); Occupational therapists 1 (pt); Speech therapists 1 (pt); Activities coordinators 1 (ft); Dietitians 1 (pt); Dentists 1 (pt); Ophthalmologists 1 (pt); Podiatrists 1 (pt); Audiologists 1 (pt).
Facilities Dining room; Physical therapy room; Activities room; Barber/Beauty shop.
Activities Arts and Crafts; Cards; Games; Reading groups; Prayer groups; Movies; Shopping trips; Dances/Social or cultural gatherings.

MORAVIA

Howd Nursing Home
7 Keeler Ave, Moravia, NY, 13118 (315) 497-0440
Admin Alberta Howd. *Medical Dir/Dir of Nursing* Philip R Robinson MD.
Licensure Skilled Care. *Beds* 40. *Certified* Medicaid; Medicare.
Ownership Proprietary.
Admissions Requirements Minimum age 16; Medical examination; Physician's request.
Staff Physicians 2 (pt); RNs 3 (ft), 1 (pt); LPNs 5 (ft); Orderlies 1 (ft); Nurses aides 19 (ft); Physical therapists 1 (pt); Recreational therapists 1 (pt); Occupational therapists 1 (pt); Speech therapists 1 (pt); Activities coordinators 1 (pt); Dietitians 1 (pt); Dentists 1 (pt).
Facilities Dining room; Physical therapy room; Activities room; Laundry room; Barber/Beauty shop.
Activities Arts and Crafts; Cards; Games; Reading groups; Prayer groups; Movies; Shopping trips.
Description Facility has been in business 38 years, noted for giving quality personal nursing care and meeting dietary needs by a caring staff; located in rural village setting.

MOUNT KISCO

Northern Westchester Hospital Center— Skilled Nursing Unit*
E Main St, Mount Kisco, NY, 10549 (914) 666-1303
Admin John R Shannon.
Licensure Skilled Care. *Beds* 40. *Certified* Medicaid; Medicare.
Ownership Nonprofit.

Swiss Home Health Related Facility*
53 Mountain Ave, Mount Kisco, NY, 10549 (914) 666-4657
Licensure Intermediate Care. *Beds* 28.
Ownership Nonprofit.

MOUNT MORRIS

Livingston County Health Related Facility*
Murray Hill Campus, Mount Morris, NY, 14510 (716) 658-2881
Licensure Skilled Care. *Beds* 42.
Ownership Public.

MOUNT VERNON

Shalom Nursing Home*
10 Claremont Ave, Mount Vernon, NY, 10550 (914) 699-1600
Admin Howard Wolf.
Licensure Skilled Care. *Beds* 240. *Certified* Medicaid; Medicare.
Ownership Nonprofit.

Wartburg Nursing Home
Bradley Ave, Mount Vernon, NY, 10552 (914) 699-0800
Admin Donald A Kraft. *Medical Dir/Dir of Nursing* Dr Debabrata Dutta.
Licensure Skilled Care; Intermediate Care. *Beds* 80. *Certified* Medicaid; Medicare.

Ownership Nonprofit.
Admissions Requirements Minimum age 65.
Affiliation Lutheran

NANUET

Elmwood Manor Nursing Home Inc*
199 N Middletown Rd, Nanuet, NY, 10954
(914) 623-3904
Admin Daniel Harfenist.
Licensure Skilled Care. *Beds* 228. *Certified* Medicaid; Medicare.
Ownership Proprietary.

NEPONSIT

Neponsit Home for the Aged*
149–25 Rockway Beach Blvd, Neponsit, NY, 11694 (212) 474-1900
Licensure Intermediate Care. *Beds* 231.
Ownership Public.

NEW BERLIN

Chase Memorial Nursing Home Co Inc*
1 Terrace Heights, New Berlin, NY, 13411
(607) 847-6117
Admin Merritt C Meyers.
Licensure Skilled Care; Intermediate Care.
Beds 41. *Certified* Medicaid; Medicare.
Ownership Nonprofit.

NEW CITY

Friedwald House
475 Hempstead Rd, New City, NY, 10956
Admin Stephen J Epstein. *Medical Dir/Dir of Nursing* Vincent Garofalo MD.
Licensure Intermediate Care. *Beds* 180. *Certified* Medicaid.
Ownership Proprietary.
Admissions Requirements Minimum age 16;
Medical examination; Physician's request.
Staff Physicians 16 (ft); RNs 10 (ft), 3 (pt);
LPNs 6 (ft), 2 (pt); Nurses aides 10 (ft), 5 (pt);
Physical therapists 1 (pt); Recreational therapists 2 (ft); Occupational therapists 1 (pt); Speech therapists 1 (pt); Activities coordinators 1 (ft); Dietitians 1 (ft); Dentists 1 (pt); Ophthalmologists 1 (pt); Podiatrists 1 (pt); Audiologists 1 (pt).
Facilities Dining room; Physical therapy room;
Activities room; Chapel; Crafts room; Laundry room; Barber/Beauty shop; Library.
Activities Arts and Crafts; Cards; Games;
Reading groups; Prayer groups; Movies; Shopping trips; Dances/Social or cultural gatherings.
Description Facility is located in a wooded area in suburban New York City and is kosher while admitting men and women of all faiths.

NEW HARTFORD

Charles T Sitrin Home Inc*
Rt 1, Box 318, Tilden Ave, New Hartford, NY, 13413 (315) 797-3114
Admin Philip Egeth.

Licensure Skilled Care; Intermediate Care.
Beds 71. *Certified* Medicaid; Medicare.
Ownership Nonprofit.

Presbyterian Home for Central New York Inc
PO Box 1144, New Hartford, NY, 13413 (315) 797-7500
Admin Raymond L Garrett. *Medical Dir/Dir of Nursing* William F Krause MD.
Licensure Skilled Care; Intermediate Care.
Beds SNF 162; ICF 80. *Certified* Medicaid; Medicare.
Ownership Nonprofit.
Admissions Requirements Minimum age 16.
Affiliation Presbyterian
Facilities Dining room; Physical therapy room;
Activities room; Chapel; Crafts room; Laundry room; Barber/Beauty shop; Library.
Activities Arts and Crafts; Cards; Games;
Reading groups; Prayer groups; Movies; Shopping trips; Dances/Social or cultural gatherings.

NEW HYDE PARK

JIGC Nursing Home Co Inc*
271-11 76th Ave, New Hyde Park, NY, 11042
(212) 343-2100
Licensure Skilled Care. *Beds* 527. *Certified* Medicaid; Medicare.
Ownership Nonprofit.

NEW PALTZ

New Paltz Nursing Home*
1 Jansen Rd, New Paltz, NY, 12561 (914) 255-0830
Admin Norton Blue.
Licensure Skilled Care. *Beds* 79. *Certified* Medicaid; Medicare.
Ownership Proprietary.

NEW ROCHELLE

Bayberry Nursing Home*
40 Keogh Ln, New Rochelle, NY, 10805 (914) 636-3947
Admin M Fitzpatrick.
Licensure Skilled Care. *Beds* 60. *Certified* Medicaid; Medicare.
Ownership Proprietary.

German Masonic Home Corp*
676 Pelham Rd, New Rochelle, NY, 10805
(914) 632-9600
Admin Pearl Sherman.
Licensure Skilled Care. *Beds* 120. *Certified* Medicaid; Medicare.
Ownership Nonprofit.
Affiliation Masons

Howe Avenue Nursing Home Inc
16 Guion Pl, New Rochelle, NY, 10802 (914) 632-5000
Admin Carol Zeidler. *Medical Dir/Dir of Nursing* Richard P Barone MD.
Licensure Skilled Care. *Beds* 150. *Certified* Medicaid; Medicare.
Ownership Nonprofit.
Admissions Requirements Minimum age 16.
Staff Physicians 1 (pt); RNs 21 (ft); LPNs 15 (ft); Orderlies 3 (ft); Nurses aides 60 (ft);

Physical therapists; Recreational therapists 4 (ft); Occupational therapists; Speech therapists; Activities coordinators; Dietitians; Audiologists.
Facilities Dining room; Physical therapy room;
Activities room; Chapel; Crafts room; Laundry room; Barber/Beauty shop.
Activities Arts and Crafts; Cards; Games;
Reading groups; Prayer groups; Movies; Dances/Social or cultural gatherings; Ceramics.
Description Facility is structurally connected to New Rochelle Hospital and part of medical center.

New Rochelle Nursing Home
31 Lockwood Ave, New Rochelle, NY, 10801
(914) 576-0600
Admin Gilbert Preira. *Medical Dir/Dir of Nursing* Dr Charles Forman.
Licensure Skilled Care. *Beds* 160. *Certified* Medicaid; Medicare.
Ownership Proprietary.
Admissions Requirements Minimum age 16;
Medical examination.
Staff Physicians 3 (pt); RNs 9 (ft); LPNs 14 (ft); Orderlies 3 (ft); Nurses aides 40 (ft);
Physical therapists 1 (pt); Recreational therapists 1 (ft), 1 (pt); Occupational therapists 1 (pt);
Speech therapists 1 (pt); Activities coordinators 1 (ft); Dietitians 1 (ft), 1 (pt); Dentists 1 (pt);
Ophthalmologists 1 (pt); Podiatrists 1 (pt);
Audiologists 1 (pt).
Facilities Dining room; Physical therapy room;
Activities room; Crafts room; Laundry room;
Barber/Beauty shop.
Activities Arts and Crafts; Cards; Games;
Reading groups; Prayer groups; Movies; Shopping trips; Dances/Social or cultural gatherings.

United Home for Aged Hebrews*
60 Willow Dr, New Rochelle, NY, 10805 (914) 632-2804
Admin Ted Preiss.
Licensure Skilled Care; Intermediate Care.
Beds 46. *Certified* Medicaid; Medicare.
Ownership Nonprofit.
Affiliation Jewish

United Nursing Home for the Aged Inc*
60 Willow Dr, New Rochelle, NY, 10805 (914) 632-2804
Admin Ted Preiss.
Licensure Skilled Care. *Beds* 120. *Certified* Medicaid; Medicare.
Ownership Nonprofit.

Woodland Nursing Home Corp
490 Pelham Rd, New Rochelle, NY, 10805
(914) 636-2800
Admin Elliot Baruch. *Medical Dir/Dir of Nursing* Alan Jaffe.
Licensure Skilled Care. *Beds* 182. *Certified* Medicaid; Medicare.
Ownership Proprietary.
Staff Physicians 1 (pt); RNs 8 (ft), 3 (pt); LPNs 21 (ft), 8 (pt); Orderlies 3 (ft); Nurses aides 72 (ft), 5 (pt); Physical therapists 1 (pt); Occupational therapists 1 (pt); Speech therapists 1 (pt);
Activities coordinators 1 (ft); Dietitians 3 (ft).
Facilities Dining room; Physical therapy room;
Activities room; Crafts room; Laundry room;
Barber/Beauty shop.
Activities Arts and Crafts; Cards; Games;

Reading groups; Prayer groups; Movies; Shopping trips.
Description Woodland Nursing Home is a 182-bed skilled nursing facility, a long term-care facility offering outstanding care. It is based on keeping residents as productive as possible. The staff offers individual treatment as required and enables each resident to have as much independence and interaction as possible.

NEW YORK

American Nursing Home
62 Ave B, New York, NY, 10009 (212) 677-4161
Admin Moses Unger. *Medical Dir/Dir of Nursing* Joseph J Kelter.
Licensure Skilled Care. *Beds* 240. *Certified* Medicaid; Medicare.
Ownership Proprietary.

Amsterdam House Nursing Home*
1060 Amsterdam Ave, New York, NY, 10025 (212) 678-2600
Admin Robert C Bryan.
Licensure Skilled Care; Intermediate Care.
Beds 54. *Certified* Medicaid; Medicare.
Ownership Nonprofit.

Bialystoker Home for the Aged
228 E Broadway, New York, NY, 10002 (212) 475-7755
Medical Dir/Dir of Nursing Dr Albert Khaski.
Licensure Skilled Care; Intermediate Care.
Beds 95. *Certified* Medicaid; Medicare.
Ownership Nonprofit.
Admissions Requirements Minimum age 65; Medical examination.
Affiliation Jewish
Facilities Dining room; Physical therapy room; Activities room; Chapel; Crafts room; Laundry room; Barber/Beauty shop; Library.
Activities Arts and Crafts; Prayer groups; Movies.
Description Facility is noted for quality care, observation of dietary laws, inviting outside garden used for summer cook-outs, and varied recreation programs highlighting Jewish culture.

Bird S Coler Memorial Hospital—Skilled Nursing Facility*
Roosevelt Island, New York, NY, 10044 (212) 688-9400
Admin Loriane Tregde.
Licensure Skilled Care. *Beds* 976. *Certified* Medicaid; Medicare.
Ownership Public.

Dewitt Nursing Home*
211 E 79th St, New York, NY, 10021 (212) 879-1600
Admin Marilyn Lichtman.
Licensure Skilled Care. *Beds* 499. *Certified* Medicaid; Medicare.
Ownership Proprietary.

Florence Nightingale Nursing Home*
175 E 96th St, New York, NY, 10028 (212) 860-6600
Admin Sidney Rosenblatt.

Licensure Skilled Care. *Beds* 968. *Certified* Medicaid; Medicare.
Ownership Proprietary.

Fort Tryon Nursing Home
801 W 190th St, New York, NY, 10040 (212) 923-2530
Admin Israel Sherman. *Medical Dir/Dir of Nursing* Dr Ben W Aberman.
Licensure Skilled Care. *Beds* 205. *Certified* Medicaid; Medicare.
Ownership Proprietary.
Staff RNs 15 (ft), 8 (pt); LPNs 6 (ft), 16 (pt); Orderlies 4 (ft), 4 (pt); Nurses aides 52 (ft), 27 (pt); Physical therapists 3 (pt); Occupational therapists 1 (pt); Speech therapists 1 (pt); Activities coordinators 1 (ft); Dietitians 1 (ft); Dentists 1 (pt); Ophthalmologists 1 (pt); Podiatrists 1 (pt); Audiologists 1 (pt).
Affiliation Jewish
Facilities Dining room; Physical therapy room; Activities room; Chapel; Crafts room; Barber/Beauty shop.
Activities Arts and Crafts; Cards; Games; Movies; Dances/Social or cultural gatherings; Birthday parties; Masquerades.
Description Facility is located in the heart of the city, easily accessible by subway or bus, with a large terrace with a panoramic view; offers strictly kosher food and daily services in the synagogue on premises, with other denominational religious services available as well. Specially trained nursing and medical personnel are available to cater to the long-term care patient; many therapeutic groups are offered to patients and family by social service department.

Goldwater Memorial Hospital—Extended Care Facility
Roosevelt Island, New York, NY, 10044 (212) 750-6800
Admin Bernard Hirsch. *Medical Dir/Dir of Nursing* Mathew H M Lee MD.
Licensure Skilled Care. *Beds* 412. *Certified* Medicaid; Medicare.
Ownership Public.
Staff Physicians 6 (ft); RNs 40 (ft); LPNs 74 (ft); Nurses aides 157 (ft); Physical therapists 11 (ft); Recreational therapists 19 (ft); Occupational therapists 6 (ft); Speech therapists 7 (ft); Dietitians 4 (ft); Dentists 1 (ft), 3 (pt); Ophthalmologists 2 (pt); Podiatrists 2 (pt); Audiologists 3 (ft).
Facilities Dining room; Physical therapy room; Activities room; Chapel; Crafts room; Laundry room; Barber/Beauty shop; Library.
Activities Arts and Crafts; Cards; Games; Reading groups; Prayer groups; Movies; Shopping trips; Dances/Social or cultural gatherings.
Description Facility features geriatric groups and therapy program for reality orientation.

Greater Harlem Nursing Home
30 W 138th St, New York, NY, 10037 (212) 690-7400
Admin Preston Lewis. *Medical Dir/Dir of Nursing* Arthur T Risbrook MD.
Licensure Skilled Care. *Beds* 200. *Certified* Medicaid; Medicare.
Ownership Nonprofit.
Admissions Requirements Minimum age 17; Medical examination.

Staff Physicians 4 (pt); RNs 17 (ft); LPNs 17 (ft); Nurses aides 80 (ft); Physical therapists 2 (ft); Recreational therapists 1 (ft), 2 (pt); Occupational therapists 2 (ft); Speech therapists 1 (pt); Activities coordinators 1 (ft); Dietitians 1 (ft), 1 (pt); Dentists 1 (pt); Ophthalmologists 1 (pt); Audiologists 1 (pt).
Facilities Dining room; Physical therapy room; Activities room; Crafts room; Laundry room; Barber/Beauty shop.
Activities Arts and Crafts; Cards; Games; Reading groups; Prayer groups; Dances/Social or cultural gatherings.
Description Greater Harlem Nursing Home is a truly urban facility. It is set essentially in the middle of the community it serves and attracts predominately those residents as patients. It is in fact a community nursing home.

Home of the Sages of Isreal Inc
25 Willett St, New York, NY, 10002 (212) 673-8500
Admin Hersh Fluss. *Medical Dir/Dir of Nursing* Dr Albert Khaski.
Licensure Skilled Care. *Beds* 58. *Certified* Medicaid; Medicare.
Ownership Proprietary.
Admissions Requirements Minimum age 55; Medical examination.
Staff Physicians; RNs; LPNs; Orderlies; Nurses aides; Physical therapists; Reality therapists; Recreational therapists; Occupational therapists; Speech therapists; Dietitians; Dentists; Ophthalmologists; Podiatrists; Audiologists.
Affiliation Jewish
Facilities Dining room; Physical therapy room; Activities room; Chapel; Laundry room; Library.
Activities Arts and Crafts; Cards; Games; Reading groups; Prayer groups; Movies; Bible study group.

Isabella Home Nursing Home Company Inc*
515 Audubon Ave, New York, NY, 10040 (212) 781-9800
Admin Thomas F Coughlin.
Licensure Intermediate Care. *Beds* 315. *Certified* Medicaid.
Ownership Nonprofit.

Jewish Home and Hospital for the Aged*
120 W 106th St, New York, NY, 10025 (212) 870-5000
Admin Wiliam J Cowley.
Licensure Skilled Care. *Beds* 476. *Certified* Medicaid; Medicare.
Ownership Nonprofit.
Affiliation Jewish

Joy Goldstein Kateri Residence
150 Riverside Dr, New York, NY, 10024
Admin James D Cameron. *Medical Dir/Dir of Nursing* Alfred Shaw MD.
Licensure Skilled Care. *Beds* 520. *Certified* Medicaid; Medicare.
Ownership Nonprofit.
Admissions Requirements Minimum age 65; Medical examination; Physician's request.
Staff Physicians 9 (pt); RNs 41 (ft); LPNs 85 (ft); Nurses aides 247 (ft); Physical therapists 2 (ft); Recreational therapists 6 (ft); Occupational therapists 2 (ft); Speech therapists 1 (ft); Activi-

ties coordinators 1 (ft); Dietitians 70 (ft); Dentists 2 (pt); Ophthalmologists 1 (pt); Podiatrists 2 (pt); Audiologists 1 (pt); Social workers 5 (ft), 2 (pt).
Facilities Dining room; Physical therapy room; Activities room; Chapel; Crafts room; Laundry room; Barber/Beauty shop; Library.
Activities Arts and Crafts; Cards; Games; Reading groups; Prayer groups; Movies; Shopping trips; Dances/Social or cultural gatherings.
Description This is a nonsectarian facility in the heart of New York City near Riverside Park; features group programs for residents and relatives sponsored by social services; volunteer association of friends and relatives.

Mary Manning Walsh Nursing Home Company Inc*
1339 York Ave, New York, NY, 10021 (212) 628-2800
Admin M Robert Romano.
Licensure Skilled Care; Intermediate Care.
Beds 304. *Certified* Medicaid; Medicare.
Ownership Nonprofit.

New Gouverneur Hospital—Skilled Nursing Facility*
227 Madison St, New York, NY, 10002 (212) 374-4000
Admin Alan H Rosenblut.
Licensure Skilled Care. *Beds* 196. *Certified* Medicaid; Medicare.
Ownership Public.

Saint Roses Home*
71 Jackson St, New York, NY, 10002 (212) 677-8132
Licensure Intermediate Care. *Beds* 60.
Ownership Nonprofit.

Village Nursing Home Inc*
607 Hudson St, New York, NY, 10014 (212) 255-3003
Admin John J Issowits.
Licensure Skilled Care. *Beds* 201. *Certified* Medicaid; Medicare.
Ownership Nonprofit.

NEWARK

Newark Manor Nursing Home*
222 W Pearl St, Newark, NY, 14513 (315) 331-4690
Admin Janis Sharrow.
Licensure Skilled Care. *Beds* 60. *Certified* Medicaid; Medicare.
Ownership Proprietary.

Newark-Wayne Community Hospital—Skilled Nursing Facility
Driving Park Ave, Newark, NY, 14513 (315) 332-2022
Admin Sophie Ziegler. *Medical Dir/Dir of Nursing* Gerald Duffner MD.
Licensure Skilled Care. *Beds* 44. *Certified* Medicaid; Medicare.
Ownership Nonprofit.
Admissions Requirements Minimum age 16; Physician's request.
Facilities Dining room; Physical therapy room; Activities room; Laundry room; Barber/Beauty shop.

Activities Arts and Crafts; Cards; Games; Reading groups; Movies; Shopping trips; Dances/Social or cultural gatherings; Church services; Family dinners.

NEWBURGH

Sylcox Nursing Home and Health Related Facility*
56 Meadow Hill Rd, Newburgh, NY, 12550 (914) 564-1700
Admin Edward Sylcox Sr.
Licensure Skilled Care; Intermediate Care.
Beds 100. *Certified* Medicaid; Medicare.
Ownership Proprietary.

NEWFANE

Newfane Health Facility
2709 Transit Rd, Newfane, NY, 14108 (716) 778-7111
Admin Sandra Wieland. *Medical Dir/Dir of Nursing* Dr Walter Altbach.
Licensure Skilled Care; Intermediate Care.
Beds 124. *Certified* Medicaid; Medicare.
Ownership Proprietary.
Admissions Requirements Medical examination; Physician's request.
Staff Physicians 1 (pt); RNs 11 (ft), 2 (pt); LPNs 10 (ft), 13 (pt); Orderlies 5 (ft), 6 (pt); Nurses aides 38 (ft), 44 (pt); Physical therapists 1 (pt); Occupational therapists 1 (pt); Speech therapists 1 (pt); Activities coordinators 1 (ft); Dietitians 4 (ft); Dentists 1 (pt); Podiatrists 1 (pt).
Facilities Dining room; Physical therapy room; Activities room; Laundry room; Barber/Beauty shop.
Activities Arts and Crafts; Cards; Games; Reading groups; Prayer groups; Movies; Shopping trips; Dances/Social or cultural gatherings.
Description Facility features a one-floor design and 24-hour nursing service with restorative services.

NIAGARA FALLS

Deveaux Manor Nursing Home*
2600 Main St, Niagara Falls, NY, 14305 (716) 285-9155
Admin Michael Agmello.
Licensure Skilled Care. *Beds* 129. *Certified* Medicaid; Medicare.
Ownership Proprietary.

Niagara Falls Memorial Nursing Home Co Inc*
621 10th St, Niagara Falls, NY, 14302 (716) 278-4578
Admin David Byers.
Licensure Skilled Care. *Beds* 120. *Certified* Medicaid; Medicare.
Ownership Nonprofit.

Niagara Geriatric Center
822 Cedar Ave, Niagara Falls, NY, 14301
Admin James G Marrione.
Licensure Intermediate Care. *Beds* 160. *Certified* Medicaid.
Ownership Proprietary.
Admissions Requirements Minimum age 16;

Medical examination; Physician's request.
Staff RNs 2 (ft); LPNs 11 (ft), 2 (pt); Nurses aides 18 (ft), 4 (pt); Activities coordinators 1 (ft); Dietitians 1 (pt).
Facilities Dining room; Activities room; Laundry room; Barber/Beauty shop; Library.
Activities Arts and Crafts; Cards; Games; Reading groups; Prayer groups; Movies; Shopping trips; Dances/Social or cultural gatherings.

Saint Mary's Manor
515 6th St, Niagara Falls, NY, 14301 (716) 285-3236
Admin Sr M Joseph Clare. *Medical Dir/Dir of Nursing* Melvin B Dyster MD.
Licensure Skilled Care. *Beds* 119. *Certified* Medicaid; Medicare.
Ownership Nonprofit.
Admissions Requirements Minimum age 17; Medical examination; Physician's request.
Staff RNs 10 (ft), 6 (pt); LPNs 13 (ft), 4 (pt); Orderlies 5 (ft), 3 (pt); Nurses aides 49 (ft), 16 (pt); Physical therapists 2 (pt); Occupational therapists 1 (pt); Speech therapists 1 (pt); Activities coordinators 2 (ft); Dietitians 1 (ft); Dentists 1 (pt).
Facilities Dining room; Physical therapy room; Activities room; Chapel; Crafts room; Laundry room; Barber/Beauty shop.
Activities Arts and Crafts; Cards; Games; Reading groups; Prayer groups; Movies; Shopping trips; Dances/Social or cultural gatherings.

NORTH BELLMORE

Belair Nursing Home*
2478 Jerusalem Ave, North Bellmore, NY, 11710 (516) 826-1160
Admin Mildred Greenberg.
Licensure Skilled Care. *Beds* 102. *Certified* Medicaid; Medicare.
Ownership Proprietary.

NORTH CREEK

Adirondack Tri-County Nursing Home Inc
PO Box 500, North Creek, NY, 12853 (518) 251-2447
Admin Mark Jantzi. *Medical Dir/Dir of Nursing* John Rugge MD.
Licensure Skilled Care. *Beds* 60. *Certified* Medicaid; Medicare.
Ownership Nonprofit.
Admissions Requirements Minimum age 21.
Staff Physicians 4 (pt); RNs 5 (ft), 3 (pt); LPNs 4 (ft), 4 (pt); Nurses aides 24 (ft), 12 (pt); Physical therapists 2 (pt); Speech therapists 1 (pt); Activities coordinators 1 (ft); Dietitians 1 (pt); Dentists 1 (pt); Podiatrists 1 (pt).
Facilities Dining room; Physical therapy room; Activities room; Laundry room; Barber/Beauty shop.
Activities Arts and Crafts; Reading groups; Movies; Shopping trips; Dances/Social or cultural gatherings.
Description Facility features outpatient physical therapy.

NORTH TONOWANDA

Degraff Memorial Hospital—Skilled Nursing Facility
445 Tremont St, North Tonowanda, NY, 14120 (716) 694-4500
Admin Mark E Celmer. *Medical Dir/Dir of Nursing* Dr H Chang.
Licensure Skilled Care. *Beds* 44. *Certified* Medicaid; Medicare.
Ownership Nonprofit.
Admissions Requirements Minimum age 16; Medical examination; Physician's request.
Staff RNs 5 (ft), 5 (pt); LPNs 7 (ft), 7 (pt); Orderlies 2 (ft), 1 (pt); Nurses aides 8 (ft), 7 (pt); Physical therapists 1 (pt); Occupational therapists 1 (pt); Speech therapists 1 (pt); Activities coordinators 1 (pt); Dietitians 1 (ft); Dentists 1 (pt); Podiatrists 1 (pt).
Facilities Dining room; Physical therapy room; Activities room; Barber/Beauty shop; Library.
Activities Arts and Crafts; Cards; Games; Movies.
Description The DeGraff Memorial Hospital Skilled Nursing Facility is a single-story building attached to the acute care hospital. It has 44 beds, 18 2-bed, semi-private rooms and 8 private rooms. Television and telephone service is provided in the rooms. It has a carpeted lobby and dining room with a fenced courtyard with accessibility for wheelchairs. Religious services are held on the premises. The facility is affiliated with various schools of higher education and provides a clinical setting for their students.

NORWICH

Chenango Memorial Hospital Inc—Skilled Nursing Facility*
179 N Broad St, Norwich, NY, 13815 (607) 335-4111
Admin John Kelly.
Licensure Skilled Care. *Beds* 54. *Certified* Medicaid; Medicare.
Ownership Nonprofit.

Valley View Manor Nursing Home
Park St, Norwich, NY, 13815 (607) 334-9931
Admin Leon A Bormann. *Medical Dir/Dir of Nursing* Dr Robert Frank.
Licensure Skilled Care. *Beds* 82. *Certified* Medicaid; Medicare.
Ownership Proprietary.
Staff RNs 7 (ft), 3 (pt); LPNs 6 (ft), 3 (pt); Nurses aides 35 (ft), 16 (pt); Activities coordinators 1 (ft).
Facilities Dining room; Physical therapy room; Laundry room; Barber/Beauty shop.
Activities Arts and Crafts; Cards; Games; Reading groups; Prayer groups; Movies; Shopping trips.
Description Facility is a one-story brick faced building in the city of Norwich on the banks of the Chenango River featuring high quality care and a pet therapy program weekly.

OCEANSIDE

Nassau Nursing Home
2914 Lincoln Ave, Oceanside, NY, 11572 (516) 536-2300
Admin Alex Sreter. *Medical Dir/Dir of Nursing* Frances Kapp MD.
Licensure Skilled Care. *Beds* 100. *Certified* Medicaid; Medicare.
Ownership Proprietary.
Admissions Requirements Minimum age 21; Physician's request.
Facilities Dining room; Physical therapy room; Activities room; Chapel; Crafts room; Laundry room; Barber/Beauty shop.
Activities Arts and Crafts; Cards; Games; Reading groups; Prayer groups; Movies; Shopping trips; Dances/Social or cultural gatherings.

OGDENSBURG

A Barton Hepburn Hospital Skilled Nursing Facility
214 King St, Ogdensburg, NY, 13669 (315) 393-3600
Admin John W Symons. *Medical Dir/Dir of Nursing* Mark Chalom MD.
Licensure Skilled Care. *Beds* 29. *Certified* Medicaid; Medicare.
Ownership Nonprofit.
Admissions Requirements Physician's request.
Staff RNs 98 (ft), 27 (pt); LPNs 16 (ft), 5 (pt); Nurses aides 70 (ft), 25 (pt); Physical therapists 1 (ft); Recreational therapists 1 (ft); Activities coordinators 1 (ft); Dietitians 1 (ft); Dentists 1 (ft); Ophthalmologists 1 (ft).
Affiliation Roman Catholic
Facilities Dining room; Physical therapy room; Activities room; Chapel; Crafts room; Barber/Beauty shop.
Activities Arts and Crafts; Cards; Games; Reading groups; Prayer groups; Movies.
Description Monthly birthday parties held; all holiday events celebrated; crafts are taught with assistance of activities director, staff, and a sizeable number of volunteers from the community.

Saint Josephs Home
420 Lafayette St, Ogdensburg, NY, 13669 (315) 393-3780
Admin Kathleen Sholette. *Medical Dir/Dir of Nursing* Warren Heller MD.
Licensure Skilled Care. *Beds* 82. *Certified* Medicaid; Medicare.
Ownership Nonprofit.
Admissions Requirements Minimum age 16.
Staff RNs 7 (ft), 5 (pt); LPNs 6 (ft), 4 (pt); Nurses aides 30 (ft), 17 (pt); Activities coordinators 2 (ft); Dietitians 1 (pt).
Affiliation Roman Catholic
Facilities Dining room; Physical therapy room; Activities room; Chapel; Laundry room; Barber/Beauty shop.
Activities Games; Prayer groups; Movies; Shopping trips; Dances/Social or cultural gatherings.

United Helpers, Cedars Nursing Home
Rt 4, Box 89, Ogdensburg, NY, 13669 (315) 393-4810
Admin Cynthia L Barlow. *Medical Dir/Dir of*

Nursing Mark Chalom MD.
Licensure Skilled Care. *Beds* 82. *Certified* Medicaid; Medicare.
Ownership Nonprofit.
Admissions Requirements Minimum age 16; Medical examination; Physician's request.
Staff Physicians 1 (pt); RNs 8 (ft), 5 (pt); LPNs 6 (ft), 3 (pt); Orderlies 2 (ft), 3 (pt); Nurses aides 22 (ft), 15 (pt); Physical therapists 1 (pt); Occupational therapists 1 (pt); Activities coordinators 1 (ft); Dietitians 1 (pt).
Facilities Dining room; Physical therapy room; Laundry room; Barber/Beauty shop.
Activities Arts and Crafts; Cards; Games; Prayer groups; Movies; Shopping trips; Dances/Social or cultural gatherings.

United Helpers Nursing Home Inc*
Riverside Dr, Ogdensburg, NY, 13669 (315) 393-0730
Admin Robert Russell.
Licensure Skilled Care; Intermediate Care. *Beds* 40. *Certified* Medicaid; Medicare.
Ownership Nonprofit.

OLEAN

Cattaraugus County Public Nursing Home
2245 W State St, Olean, NY, 14760 (716) 373-1910
Admin Margaret Stuerzebecher. *Medical Dir/Dir of Nursing* Duncan C Wormer MD.
Licensure Skilled Care. *Beds* 120. *Certified* Medicaid; Medicare.
Ownership Public.
Admissions Requirements Minimum age 16; Medical examination; Physician's request.
Staff Physicians 45 (pt); RNs 7 (ft), 7 (pt); LPNs 18 (ft), 10 (pt); Orderlies 2 (ft), 3 (pt); Nurses aides 43 (ft), 15 (pt); Physical therapists 1 (ft); Occupational therapists 1 (pt); Speech therapists 1 (pt); Activities coordinators 1 (ft); Dietitians 1 (pt); Dentists 1 (pt); Podiatrists 2 (pt); Audiologists 1 (pt).
Facilities Dining room; Physical therapy room; Activities room; Chapel; Crafts room; Laundry room; Barber/Beauty shop; Library; Atrium; Patient lounges.
Activities Arts and Crafts; Cards; Games; Reading groups; Prayer groups; Movies; Shopping trips; Dances/Social or cultural gatherings; Cooking; Trading post; Gardening; Makeup; Bowling; Resident council.
Description Home is an excellent rehabilitative facility.

Saint Josephs Manor
W State St, Olean, NY, 14760 (716) 372-7810
Admin Sr Dolores Eileen Thorndike. *Medical Dir/Dir of Nursing* Dr Ben M L Hwang.
Licensure Skilled Care. *Beds* 22. *Certified* Medicaid; Medicare.
Ownership Nonprofit.
Admissions Requirements Minimum age 21.
Staff RNs 2 (ft), 3 (pt); LPNs 2 (ft), 6 (pt); Nurses aides 7 (ft), 9 (pt); Activities coordinators 1 (pt).
Facilities Dining room; Physical therapy room; Activities room; Chapel; Crafts room; Laundry room; Barber/Beauty shop.
Activities Arts and Crafts; Cards; Games; Movies.

ONEIDA

Oneida City Hospital—Extended Care Facility*
221 Broad St, Oneida, NY, 13421 (315) 363-6000
Admin Robert Walker.
Licensure Skilled Care. *Beds* 77. *Certified* Medicaid; Medicare.
Ownership Public.

ONEONTA

Aurelia Osborn Fox Memorial Hospital Nursing Home
1 Norton Ave, Oneonta, NY, 13820 (607) 432-2000
Admin Deborah K Rose. *Medical Dir/Dir of Nursing* Cornelius F Ryan.
Licensure Intermediate Care. *Beds* 130. *Certified* Medicaid.
Ownership Nonprofit.
Admissions Requirements Minimum age 17; Physician's request.
Staff Physicians 1 (pt); RNs 7 (ft), 6 (pt); LPNs 8 (ft), 16 (pt); Orderlies 40 (ft), 28 (pt); Physical therapists 1 (pt); Occupational therapists 1 (pt); Speech therapists 1 (pt); Activities coordinators 1 (ft); Dietitians 1 (ft); Dentists 1 (pt).
Facilities Dining room; Physical therapy room; Activities room; Crafts room; Laundry room; Barber/Beauty shop; Library.
Activities Arts and Crafts; Cards; Games; Reading groups; Prayer groups; Movies; Shopping trips; Dances/Social or cultural gatherings; Outings.

Oneonta-Richmond Inc
330 Chestnut St, Oneonta, NY, 13820
Medical Dir/Dir of Nursing Reade Sisson MD.
Licensure Skilled Care. *Beds* 80. *Certified* Medicaid; Medicare.
Ownership Proprietary.
Admissions Requirements Minimum age 18; Physician's request.
Staff Physicians 1 (pt); RNs 6 (ft), 4 (pt); LPNs 8 (ft), 6 (pt); Orderlies 4 (ft); Nurses aides 25 (ft), 32 (pt); Physical therapists 1 (pt); Speech therapists 1 (pt); Activities coordinators 1 (ft), 1 (pt); Dietitians 1 (pt); Dentists 1 (pt); Podiatrists 1 (pt).
Facilities Dining room; Physical therapy room; Activities room; Crafts room; Barber/Beauty shop.
Activities Arts and Crafts; Cards; Games; Reading groups; Prayer groups; Movies; Shopping trips.
Description Facility strongly emphasizes the residents home concept. We are first, innkeepers who provide health care however needed. Residents are encouraged to bring and have their own personal possessions as space allows. Resident human rights are highly valued and respected.

ORCHARD PARK

Orchard Health Care Center Inc*
6060 Armor Rd, Orchard Park, NY, 14127 (716) 662-4433
Admin Marie Beal.
Licensure Skilled Care; Intermediate Care.
Beds 86. *Certified* Medicaid; Medicare.
Ownership Proprietary.

ORISKANY

Eastern Star Home and Infirmary
Utica St, Oriskany, NY, 13424 (315) 736-9311
Admin Unamae Ferguson.
Licensure Skilled Care; Health Related Care.
Beds 82. *Certified* Medicaid; Medicare.
Ownership Proprietary.
Affiliation Order of Eastern Star

OSSINING

Asthmatic Childrens Foundation of New York Inc
Spring Valley Rd, Ossining, NY, 10562 (914) 762-2110
Admin Roger Tartaglia Sr. *Medical Dir/Dir of Nursing* Dr Armond V Mascia.
Licensure Skilled Care. *Beds* 36. *Certified* Medicaid.
Ownership Nonprofit.
Admissions Requirements Minimum age 5.
Staff Physicians 4 (pt); RNs 1 (ft), 10 (pt); Nurses aides 1 (pt); Activities coordinators 1 (pt); Dietitians 1 (pt); Dentists 1 (pt).
Facilities Dining room; Activities room; Crafts room; Laundry room; Library.
Activities Arts and Crafts; Games; Reading groups; Prayer groups; Movies; Shopping trips; Dances/Social or cultural gatherings.
Description A skilled nursing facility strictly for the treatment of severely-ill asthmatic children between the ages of 5 and 15 years of age; with a country setting and exceptional recreation/activity programs.

Bethel Nursing Home Company Inc
19 Narragansett Ave, Ossining, NY, 10562 (914) 941-7300
Admin Alfred Heim.
Licensure Skilled Care; Intermediate Care.
Beds 78. *Certified* Medicaid; Medicare.
Ownership Nonprofit.
Staff Physicians; RNs; LPNs; Nurses aides; Physical therapists; Recreational therapists; Occupational therapists; Speech therapists; Activities coordinators; Dentists; Ophthalmologists; Podiatrists; Audiologists.
Affiliation Methodist
Facilities Dining room; Physical therapy room; Activities room; Chapel; Crafts room; Laundry room; Barber/Beauty shop; Library; Swimming pool at retirement facility.
Activities Arts and Crafts; Cards; Games; Reading groups; Prayer groups; Movies; Shopping trips; Dances/Social or cultural gatherings.
Description This is a triplex consisting of skilled nursing, health related, and retirement residence (hotel).

Briar Crest Nursing Home
31 Overton Rd, Ossining, NY, 10562 (914) 941-4047
Admin Peter T Gendron. *Medical Dir/Dir of Nursing* Dr M Giatzis.

Licensure Skilled Care. *Beds* 86. *Certified* Medicaid; Medicare.
Ownership Proprietary.
Admissions Requirements Minimum age 18; Medical examination; Physician's request.
Staff Physicians 1 (pt); RNs 10 (ft), 6 (pt); LPNs 3 (ft), 4 (pt); Nurses aides 34 (ft), 10 (pt); Recreational therapists 2 (ft); Occupational therapists 1 (pt); Activities coordinators 1 (pt); Dietitians 1 (pt).
Facilities Dining room; Physical therapy room; Activities room; Barber/Beauty shop.
Activities Arts and Crafts; Cards; Games; Reading groups; Prayer groups; Movies.
Description This is a beautiful home-like facility in the rolling hills of Ossining located on a hill directly above the Ossining High School; offers skilled nursing care by an actively interested staff.

Cedar Manor Nursing Home*
Cedar Ln, Ossining, NY, 10562 (914) 762-1600
Admin Robert Myshrall.
Licensure Skilled Care. *Beds* 153. *Certified* Medicaid; Medicare.
Ownership Proprietary.

Victoria Home for Retired Men and Women*
N Malcolm St, Ossining, NY, 10562 (914) 941-2450
Licensure Intermediate Care. *Beds* 49.
Ownership Nonprofit.

OSWEGO

Harr-Wood Nursing Home*
17 Sunrise Dr, Oswego, NY, 13126 (315) 342-4790
Admin Lloyd Harrington.
Licensure Skilled Care. *Beds* 120. *Certified* Medicaid; Medicare.
Ownership Proprietary.

Hillcrest Nursing Home*
132 Ellen St, Oswego, NY, 13126 (315) 342-2440
Admin Elwin Evans.
Licensure Skilled Care. *Beds* 80. *Certified* Medicaid; Medicare.
Ownership Proprietary.

Oswego Hospital Extended Care Facility*
110 W 6th St, Oswego, NY, 13126 (315) 5511
Licensure Intermediate Care. *Beds* 38.
Ownership Nonprofit.

Pontiac Nursing Home*
E River Rd, Oswego, NY, 13126 (315) 343-1800
Admin John Vivenzio.
Licensure Skilled Care. *Beds* 80. *Certified* Medicaid; Medicare.
Ownership Proprietary.

Saint Luke Nursing Home Company Inc*
Last River Rd, Rd 4, Oswego, NY, 13126 (315) 342-3166
Licensure Intermediate Care. *Beds* 120.
Ownership Nonprofit.

OWEGO

Riverview Manor Nursing Home
510 5th Ave, Owego, NY, 13827 (607) 687-2594
Admin Larry Ramsay. *Medical Dir/Dir of Nursing* W Kokorudz MD.
Licensure Skilled Care. *Beds* 77. *Certified* Medicaid; Medicare.
Ownership Proprietary.
Admissions Requirements Minimum age 16; Medical examination; Physician's request.
Staff Physicians 6 (pt); RNs 7 (ft), 6 (pt); LPNs 4 (ft), 2 (pt); Nurses aides 30 (ft), 20 (pt); Physical therapists 2 (pt); Recreational therapists 1 (ft), 1 (pt); Occupational therapists 1 (pt); Speech therapists 1 (pt); Dietitians 1 (pt); Dentists 1 (pt); Ophthalmologists 1 (pt); Podiatrists 1 (pt); Audiologists 1 (pt).
Facilities Dining room; Physical therapy room; Activities room; Crafts room; Laundry room; Barber/Beauty shop; Library.
Activities Arts and Crafts; Cards; Games; Reading groups; Prayer groups; Movies; Shopping trips; Dances/Social or cultural gatherings.

OXFORD

New York State Veterans Home
Rt 220, E River Rd, Oxford, NY, 13830 (607) 843-2781
Admin Mary Brown. *Medical Dir/Dir of Nursing* Dr Hugh Black.
Licensure Skilled Care; Health Related Care.
Beds SNF 124; Health Related Care 118. *Certified* Medicaid.
Ownership Public.
Admissions Requirements Medical examination; Physician's request.
Staff Physicians 1 (ft), 2 (pt); RNs 20 (ft); LPNs 39 (ft); Nurses aides 74 (ft); Physical therapists 1 (ft); Recreational therapists 4 (ft); Occupational therapists 1 (ft); Speech therapists 1 (pt); Dietitians 1 (ft).
Facilities Dining room; Physical therapy room; Activities room; Chapel; Crafts room; Barber/Beauty shop; Library.
Activities Arts and Crafts; Cards; Games; Reading groups; Prayer groups; Movies; Shopping trips; Dances/Social or cultural gatherings; Pet therapy program twice monthly.
Description Must be a veteran or a spouse, or dependent of a veteran to be admitted. Facility is involved in a geriatric research program with 6 research projects in process at the present time, and at least 5 more to be awarded in 1984.

PAINTED POST

Three Rivers Health Care Center Inc*
Creekside Dr, Painted Post, NY, 14870 (716) 652-1560
Licensure Intermediate Care. *Beds* 80.
Ownership Proprietary.

PALATINE BRIDGE

Palatine Nursing Home
Upper Lafayette St, Palatine Bridge, NY, 13428 (518) 673-5212

Admin Laverne A Bouton III. *Medical Dir/Dir of Nursing* Dr Benjamin Button.
Licensure Skilled Care. *Beds* 50.
Ownership Nonprofit.
Staff Physicians 1 (pt); RNs 4 (ft), 2 (pt); LPNs 5 (ft), 1 (pt); Nurses aides 18 (ft), 9 (pt); Physical therapists 1 (pt); Reality therapists 2 (ft); Recreational therapists 1 (ft); Occupational therapists 1 (pt); Speech therapists 1 (pt); Activities coordinators 1 (ft); Dietitians 1 (pt); Dentists 1 (pt); Podiatrists 1 (pt); Audiologists 1 (pt).
Facilities Dining room; Physical therapy room; Activities room; Chapel; Laundry room; Barber/Beauty shop.
Activities Arts and Crafts; Cards; Games; Reading groups; Prayer groups; Movies; Shopping trips.
Description Facility is located in a country setting.

PATCHOGUE

Patchogue Nursing Center
25 Schoenfeld Blvd, Patchogue, NY, 11772 (516) 289-7700
Admin Paul C Maggio. *Medical Dir/Dir of Nursing* Jack R Muth MD.
Licensure Skilled Care. *Beds* 120. *Certified* Medicaid; Medicare.
Ownership Proprietary.
Staff Physicians 1 (ft); RNs 13 (ft); LPNs 18 (ft); Orderlies 6 (ft); Nurses aides 72 (ft); Physical therapists 1 (ft); Reality therapists 1 (ft); Recreational therapists 1 (ft); Occupational therapists 1 (ft); Speech therapists 1 (pt); Activities coordinators 1 (ft); Dietitians 1 (pt); Dentists 1 (pt); Ophthalmologists 1 (pt); Podiatrists 1 (pt); Audiologists 1 (pt).
Facilities Dining room; Physical therapy room; Activities room; Chapel; Crafts room; Laundry room; Barber/Beauty shop; Library; Dental treatment room.
Activities Arts and Crafts; Cards; Games; Reading groups; Prayer groups; Movies; Shopping trips; Dances/Social or cultural gatherings; Picnics; Fishing trips.
Description Facility features fully air conditioned, fire-proofed building overlooking Swan Lake. Outdoor patios, shuffleboard courts, terrace dining are featured. Owner-operated by registered nurse. All restorative and rehabilitation services are available.

PAWLING

Lovely Hill Nursing Home*
Rt 22 and Reservoir Rd, Pawling, NY, 12564 (914) 855-5700
Admin Everett Alexander.
Licensure Skilled Care; Intermediate Care.
Beds 80. *Certified* Medicaid; Medicare.
Ownership Proprietary.

PEEKSKILL

Cortlandt Nursing Care Center Inc*
110 Oregon Rd, Peekskill, NY, 10566 (914) 739-9150
Admin Joel Garson.

Licensure Skilled Care; Intermediate Care.
Beds 40. *Certified* Medicaid; Medicare.
Ownership Proprietary.

Westledge Nursing Home
2100 E Main St, Peekskill, NY, 10566 (914) 737-8400
Admin Grace H Kinsey. *Medical Dir/Dir of Nursing* Stuart L Pines MD.
Licensure Skilled Care. *Beds* 100. *Certified* Medicaid; Medicare.
Ownership Proprietary.
Admissions Requirements Minimum age 16; Medical examination; Physician's request.
Staff Physicians 1 (pt); RNs 8 (ft), 7 (pt); LPNs 6 (ft), 4 (pt); Nurses aides 30 (ft), 20 (pt); Physical therapists 1 (pt); Recreational therapists 1 (ft), 2 (pt); Occupational therapists 1 (pt); Speech therapists 1 (pt); Activities coordinators 1 (ft); Dietitians 1 (ft), 1 (pt); Dentists 2 (pt); Ophthalmologists 1 (pt); Podiatrists 2 (pt); Audiologists 1 (pt).
Facilities Dining room; Physical therapy room; Activities room; Crafts room; Laundry room; Barber/Beauty shop; Library; Day rooms.
Activities Arts and Crafts; Games; Prayer groups; Movies; Dances/Social or cultural gatherings; Residents council.
Description Facility is centrally located on 5 acres opposite shopping center; fireproof 3-story building with 2 elevators. Particularly well-staffed for rehabilitative programs.

PENFIELD

Penfield Nursing Home
1700 Penfield Rd, Penfield, NY, 14526 (716) 586-7433
Admin Donald R Brown. *Medical Dir/Dir of Nursing* Kenneth S Thomson MD.
Licensure Skilled Care. *Beds* 48. *Certified* Medicaid; Medicare.
Ownership Proprietary.
Admissions Requirements Minimum age 16.
Staff RNs 2 (ft), 6 (pt); LPNs 2 (ft), 5 (pt); Nurses aides 12 (ft), 14 (pt); Recreational therapists 1 (ft), 2 (pt); Activities coordinators 1 (pt); Dietitians 1 (pt).
Facilities Dining room; Physical therapy room; Activities room; Barber/Beauty shop; Living room/TV lounge; Patio; Porches.
Activities Arts and Crafts; Cards; Games; Prayer groups; Movies; Dances/Social or cultural gatherings; Field trips; Performances.
Description A specially designed one-story building, nestled in a quiet, scenic area with a home-like atmosphere; comfortable furnishings and cheerful decor are reassuring to patients and visitors. Modern facilities enable the best in total care. Excellent kitchen, activities, professional staff, and convenience make Penfield the reassuring choice.

PENN YAN

Penn Yan Manor Nursing Home Inc*
655 N Liberty St, Penn Yan, NY, 14527 (315) 536-2311
Admin Noreen B Curtis.

Licensure Skilled Care. *Beds* 46. *Certified* Medicaid; Medicare. *Ownership* Nonprofit.

Soldiers and Sailors Memorial Hospital—Extended Care Unit*
418 N Main St, Penn Yan, NY, 14527 (315) 536-4431
Admin James Krembs.
Licensure Skilled Care. *Beds* 24. *Certified* Medicaid; Medicare.
Ownership Nonprofit.

PHILMONT

Pine Haven Home
Rt 217, Philmont, NY, 12565 (518) 672-4021
Admin Alice Blaauw. *Medical Dir/Dir of Nursing* Andrew McBride MD.
Licensure Skilled Care; Intermediate Care.
Beds SNF 40; ICF 40. *Certified* Medicaid; Medicare.
Ownership Public.
Admissions Requirements Minimum age 18.
Staff Physicians 3 (pt); RNs 7 (ft), 3 (pt); LPNs 5 (ft), 6 (pt); Orderlies 1 (ft); Nurses aides 3 (ft), 8 (pt); Physical therapists 1 (pt); Occupational therapists 1 (pt); Speech therapists 1 (pt); Activities coordinators 1 (ft); Dietitians 1 (pt).
Facilities Dining room; Physical therapy room; Activities room; Chapel; Laundry room; Barber/Beauty shop.
Activities Arts and Crafts; Cards; Games; Reading groups; Prayer groups; Movies; Shopping trips.
Description Residence restricted to those living in Columbia County.

PLAINVIEW

Central Island Nursing Home Inc
825 Old County Rd, Plainview, NY, 11803 (516) 433-0600
Admin Ronni Rosenberg. *Medical Dir/Dir of Nursing* Donald Orofino MD.
Licensure Skilled Care. *Beds* 202. *Certified* Medicaid; Medicare.
Ownership Proprietary.
Facilities Dining room; Physical therapy room; Activities room; Chapel; Crafts room; Laundry room; Barber/Beauty shop; Library; Patio.
Activities Arts and Crafts; Cards; Games; Reading groups; Prayer groups; Movies; Clubs; Council.

PLATTSBURGH

Champlain Valley Physicians Hospital Medical Center—Skilled Nursing Facility*
100 Beekman St, Plattsburgh, NY, 12901 (518) 561-2000
Admin Marilyn O'Connor.
Licensure Skilled Care; Intermediate Care.
Beds 54. *Certified* Medicaid; Medicare.
Ownership Nonprofit.

Clinton County Nursing Home*
3 Flynn Ave, Plattsburgh, NY, 12901 (518) 563-0950
Admin Barbara Tosh.

Licensure Skilled Care; Intermediate Care.
Beds 40. *Certified* Medicaid; Medicare.
Ownership Public.

Meadowbrook Nursing Home*
80 N Prospect Ave, Plattsburgh, NY, 12901 (518) 563-5440
Admin Hobbie Hyatt.
Licensure Skilled Care; Intermediate Care.
Beds 80. *Certified* Medicaid; Medicare.
Ownership Proprietary.

Sacred Heart Home Inc
8 Nickle St, Plattsburgh, NY, 12901 (518) 563-3261
Admin Sr Angela Theresa Chabot. *Medical Dir/Dir of Nursing* John P Dickard MD.
Licensure Skilled Care. *Beds* 89. *Certified* Medicaid; Medicare.
Ownership Nonprofit.
Admissions Requirements Minimum age 65.
Staff RNs 10 (ft), 2 (pt); LPNs 4 (ft), 4 (pt); Nurses aides 48 (ft), 7 (pt); Physical therapists 2 (ft), 1 (pt); Activities coordinators 2 (ft); Dietitians 2 (ft).
Affiliation Roman Catholic
Facilities Dining room; Physical therapy room; Activities room; Chapel; Crafts room; Laundry room; Barber/Beauty shop.
Activities Arts and Crafts; Cards; Games; Reading groups; Prayer groups; Movies; Shopping trips.

POMANA

Rockland County Infirmary*
Sanatorium Rd, Pomana, NY, 10970 (914) 354-0200
Admin George T Giacobbe.
Licensure Skilled Care. *Beds* 300. *Certified* Medicaid; Medicare.
Ownership Public.

PORT CHESTER

King Street Home Inc
787 King St, Port Chester, NY, 10573 (914) 937-5800
Admin Yale Wilner.
Licensure Skilled Care; Intermediate Care.
Beds SNF 80; ICF 40. *Certified* Medicaid; Medicare.
Ownership Proprietary.

Port Chester Nursing Home
1000 High St, Port Chester, NY, 10573 (914) 937-1200
Medical Dir/Dir of Nursing Joseph Silberstein MD.
Licensure Skilled Care. *Beds* 160. *Certified* Medicaid; Medicare.
Ownership Nonprofit.
Staff Physicians 1 (pt); RNs 8 (ft); LPNs 11 (ft); Orderlies 8 (ft); Nurses aides 41 (ft); Physical therapists 1 (pt); Occupational therapists 1 (pt); Speech therapists 1 (pt); Activities coordinators 3 (ft).
Affiliation Jewish
Facilities Dining room; Physical therapy room; Activities room; Laundry room; Barber/Beauty shop; Library.

Activities Arts and Crafts; Cards; Games; Reading groups; Prayer groups; Movies; Shopping trips.
Description Facility features excellent patient care provided in a warm, loving atmosphere.

PORT JEFFERSON

Port Jefferson Nursing Home and Health Related Facility
Dark Hollow Rd, Port Jefferson, NY, 11777 (516) 473-5400
Admin Gail M Miranda. *Medical Dir/Dir of Nursing* Jerome Feldstein MD.
Licensure Skilled Care; Intermediate Care.
Beds 60. *Certified* Medicaid; Medicare.
Ownership Proprietary.
Staff RNs 5 (ft), 5 (pt); LPNs 7 (ft), 7 (pt); Orderlies 1 (ft), 1 (pt); Nurses aides 27 (ft), 18 (pt); Physical therapists 1 (pt); Occupational therapists 1 (pt); Speech therapists 1 (pt); Activities coordinators 1 (ft), 3 (pt); Dietitians 1 (ft); Dentists 1 (pt); Podiatrists 1 (pt).
Facilities Dining room; Physical therapy room; Activities room; Laundry room; Barber/Beauty shop.
Activities Arts and Crafts; Cards; Games; Reading groups; Prayer groups; Movies; Shopping trips; Dances/Social or cultural gatherings.
Description Facility has an excellent staff, dedicated and lively, giving the personal touch to patients/residents. Activity department is proud of its painting program, community trips, and functions dedicated in recognition of all the holidays. Facility, situated in a wooded setting, maintains a good relationship within the community and is proud of its fine standards.

Sunrest Health Facilities Inc*
70 N Country Rd, Port Jefferson, NY, 11777 (516) 928-2000
Admin Paul Dioguardi.
Licensure Skilled Care. *Beds* 138. *Certified* Medicaid; Medicare.
Ownership Proprietary.

PORT JEFFERSON STATION

Woodhaven Nursing Home*
1360 Rt 112, Port Jefferson Station, NY, 11776 (516) 473-7100
Admin Eurydice Loucopoulos.
Licensure Skilled Care. *Beds* 143. *Certified* Medicaid; Medicare.
Ownership Proprietary.

PORT WASHINGTON

Sands Point Nursing Home
1440 Port Washington Blvd, Port Washington, NY, 11050 (516) 767-2320
Admin Herman Landau. *Medical Dir/Dir of Nursing* Sixto Siasoco MD.
Licensure Skilled Care. *Beds* 130. *Certified* Medicaid; Medicare.
Ownership Proprietary.
Staff RNs 5 (ft), 9 (pt); LPNs 13 (ft), 5 (pt); Orderlies 8 (ft), 3 (pt); Nurses aides 41 (ft), 13 (pt); Activities coordinators 1 (ft); Dietitians 1 (pt).

Facilities Dining room; Physical therapy room; Activities room; Laundry room; Barber/Beauty shop; Library.
Activities Arts and Crafts; Games; Movies; Shopping trips; Dances/Social or cultural gatherings; Nursery group visits; Bible study.

POTSDAM

Potsdam Nursing Home*
Cottage Grove, Potsdam, NY, 13676 (315) 265-6330
Admin Norma Secours.
Licensure Skilled Care. *Beds* 80. *Certified* Medicaid; Medicare.
Ownership Proprietary.

POUGHKEEPSIE

Eden Park Nursing Home*
100 Franklin St, Poughkeepsie, NY, 12601 (914) 454-4100
Licensure Skilled Care; Intermediate Care.
Beds 120. *Certified* Medicaid; Medicare.
Ownership Proprietary.

PURDYS

Waterview Hills Nursing Center Inc
Box 257, Old Rt 22, Purdys, NY, 10578 (914) 277-3691
Admin Joseph Cornetta. *Medical Dir/Dir of Nursing* Joseph Nyitray.
Licensure Skilled Care. *Beds* 126. *Certified* Medicaid; Medicare.
Ownership Proprietary.
Admissions Requirements Minimum age 21; Medical examination.
Staff RNs; LPNs; Orderlies; Nurses aides; Activities coordinators.
Facilities Dining room; Physical therapy room; Activities room; Crafts room; Laundry room; Barber/Beauty shop; Library.
Activities Arts and Crafts; Cards; Games; Reading groups; Prayer groups; Movies.

PURDYS STATION

Salem Hills Health Related Facility*
Rt 22, Box 66, Purdys Station, NY, 10578 (914) 277-3626
Licensure Skilled Care; Intermediate Care.
Beds 126.
Ownership Proprietary.

QUEENS VILLAGE

Queen of Peace Residence*
110-30 221st St, Queens Village, NY, 11429 (212) 464-1800
Admin Christine de la Trinite.
Licensure Skilled Care; Intermediate Care.
Beds 70. *Certified* Medicaid; Medicare.
Ownership Nonprofit.

Windsor Park Nursing Home*
212-40 Hillside Ave, Queens Village, NY, 11427 (212) 468-0800
Admin Elizabeth Rothchild.

Licensure Skilled Care. *Beds* 70. *Certified* Medicaid; Medicare.
Ownership Proprietary.

REGO PARK

Van Doren Nursing Home*
59-20 Van Doren St, Rego Park, NY, 11368 (212) 592-9200
Admin A Sreter.
Licensure Skilled Care. *Beds* 200. *Certified* Medicaid; Medicare.
Ownership Proprietary.

RENSSELAER

Rosewood Gardens Health Related Facility*
Rts 4 and 40, Rd 2, Rensselaer, NY, 12144 (518) 286-1621
Licensure Intermediate Care. *Beds* 80.
Ownership Proprietary.

RHINEBECK

Baptist Home of Brooklyn New York
Rt 308, Box 129, Rhinebeck, NY, 12572 (914) 876-2071
Admin Adele Jansson. *Medical Dir/Dir of Nursing* Irma Waldo MD.
Licensure Skilled Care; Health Related Care.
Beds SNF 80; HRC 40. *Certified* Medicaid.
Ownership Nonprofit.
Admissions Requirements Medical examination; Physician's request.
Staff Physicians 3 (pt); RNs 5 (ft), 8 (pt); LPNs 5 (ft), 10 (pt); Nurses aides 35 (ft), 27 (pt); Occupational therapists 1 (pt); Speech therapists 1 (pt); Activities coordinators 1 (ft); Dietitians 1 (pt); Dentists 1 (pt); Ophthalmologists 1 (pt); Podiatrists 1 (pt); Audiologists 1 (pt).
Affiliation Baptist
Facilities Dining room; Physical therapy room; Activities room; Chapel; Crafts room; Laundry room; Barber/Beauty shop; Library; Solarium; Coffee shop.
Activities Arts and Crafts; Cards; Games; Reading groups; Prayer groups; Movies; Shopping trips; Dances/Social or cultural gatherings.
Description Home has served the elderly for over 100 years; annual picnic/barbecue; annual crafts sale.

Ferncliff Nursing Home Co Inc
River Rd, PO Box 386, Rhinebeck, NY, 12572 (914) 876-2011
Admin Mother M Teresa Stephen. *Medical Dir/Dir of Nursing* George Verrilli MD.
Licensure Skilled Care; Health Related Care.
Beds SNF 240; HRC 80. *Certified* Medicaid; Medicare.
Ownership Nonprofit.
Admissions Requirements Medical examination.
Staff Physicians 8 (pt); RNs 14 (ft), 12 (pt); LPNs 18 (ft), 20 (pt); Nurses aides 104 (ft), 49 (pt); Physical therapists 1 (ft); Occupational therapists 1 (pt); Speech therapists 1 (pt); Activities coordinators 1 (ft); Dietitians 1 (ft); Dentists 4 (pt); Ophthalmologists 1 (pt); Podiatrists 1 (pt); Audiologists 1 (pt).
Affiliation Roman Catholic

Facilities Dining room; Physical therapy room; Activities room; Chapel; Crafts room; Laundry room; Barber/Beauty shop; Library; Lounge; Gift shop.
Activities Arts and Crafts; Cards; Games; Reading groups; Movies; Shopping trips; Dances/Social or cultural gatherings; Grooming; Cooking.
Description Ferncliff has 240-skilled nursing and 80-health related beds and is nestled at the outskirts of the Village of Rhinebeck. The facility is administered by the Carmelite Sisters who have a tradition of caring for the elderly with dignity, embracing each with a spirit of loving concern and compassion.

Northern Dutchess Hospital
Springbrook Ave, Rhinebeck, NY, 12572 (914) 876-3001
Admin Michael C Mazzarella. *Medical Dir/Dir of Nursing* Dr William Thompson.
Licensure Skilled Care. *Beds* 50. *Certified* Medicaid; Medicare.
Ownership Nonprofit.
Staff RNs 5 (ft); LPNs 4 (ft), 1 (pt); Nurses aides 23 (ft), 1 (pt); Physical therapists 1 (pt); Recreational therapists 2 (ft), 1 (pt); Occupational therapists 1 (pt); Speech therapists 1 (pt); Dietitians 1 (pt); Dentists 1 (pt); Ophthalmologists 1 (pt); Podiatrists 1 (pt); Audiologists 1 (pt).
Facilities Dining room; Physical therapy room; Activities room; Chapel; Crafts room; Barber/Beauty shop.
Activities Arts and Crafts; Cards; Games; Reading groups; Prayer groups; Movies; Shopping trips; Dances/Social or cultural gatherings.

RIVERDALE

Parkview Nursing Home
6585 Broadway, Riverdale, NY, 10471 (212) 298-7501
Admin Barbara Edwards. *Medical Dir/Dir of Nursing* Stanley Pionin MD.
Licensure Skilled Care. *Beds* 200. *Certified* Medicaid; Medicare.
Ownership Proprietary.
Staff Physicians 6 (pt); RNs 8 (ft), 6 (pt); LPNs 20 (ft), 28 (pt); Orderlies 3 (ft), 1 (pt); Nurses aides 57 (ft), 65 (pt); Physical therapists 2 (pt); Occupational therapists 2 (pt); Speech therapists 1 (pt); Activities coordinators 1 (ft), 2 (pt); Dietitians 1 (ft); Podiatrists 2 (pt).
Facilities Dining room; Physical therapy room; Activities room; Crafts room; Barber/Beauty shop.
Activities Arts and Crafts; Cards; Games; Reading groups; Movies; Shopping trips; Dances/Social or cultural gatherings; Music appreciation.
Description Facility is located close to Yonkers, Bronxville area overlooking Van Cortland Park.

RIVERHEAD

Riverhead Nursing Home*
1146 Woodcrest Ave, Riverhead, NY, 11901 (516) 727-7744
Admin Ira Hunter.

Licensure Skilled Care; Intermediate Care.
Beds 121. *Certified* Medicaid; Medicare.
Ownership Proprietary.

ROCHESTER

Aberdeen Nursing Home*
1290 Lake Ave, Rochester, NY, 14613 (716)
254-1593
Admin Michael Alaimo.
Licensure Skilled Care. *Beds* 98. *Certified* Medicaid; Medicare.
Ownership Proprietary.

Alaimo Nursing Home*
1140 Norton St, Rochester, NY, 14621 (716)
467-2100
Admin Kenneth Alaimo.
Licensure Skilled Care. *Beds* 42. *Certified* Medicaid; Medicare.
Ownership Proprietary.

Baird Nursing Home
2150 Saint Paul Blvd, Rochester, NY, 14621
(716) 342-5540
Admin Richard Bonneville. *Medical Dir/Dir of Nursing* Dr John Burkhardt.
Licensure Skilled Care. *Beds* 28.
Ownership Proprietary.
Admissions Requirements Minimum age 16;
Physician's request.
Staff Physicians; RNs; LPNs; Orderlies;
Nurses aides; Physical therapists; Speech therapists; Activities coordinators; Dietitians; Dentists; Ophthalmologists; Podiatrists;
Audiologists.
Facilities Dining room; Physical therapy room;
Activities room; Crafts room; Laundry room;
Barber/Beauty shop.
Activities Arts and Crafts; Cards; Games;
Reading groups; Prayer groups; Movies; Shopping trips; Dances/Social or cultural gatherings.
Description Bordering the town of Irondequoit,
opposite Seneca Park, home-like surroundings
are enhanced by a lovely residential setting.
Nursing care center has the routine of a small
professional convalescent hospital, yet maintains a home-like atmosphere in modern and
colonial surroundings. Latest addition has been
constructed of all steel and concrete plus the
latest in sprinkler systems making it one of the
finest fireproof buildings in the area. New
kitchen is the latest in design and equipment
and pride is taken in serving excellent food, all
prepared by a staff who delight in home-style
cooking. In addition, food service prepares special diets depending on the needs of the patient.
Light snacks are available at anytime. Food is
served in combination dining and lounge area
or in the patient's room depending upon their
choice.

Beechwood Sanitarium
900 Culver Rd, Rochester, NY, 14609 (716)
288-3335
Admin Herbert Chambery. *Medical Dir/Dir of Nursing* Louis Siegel.
Licensure Skilled Care. *Beds* 80. *Certified* Medicaid; Medicare.
Ownership Proprietary.
Admissions Requirements Medical examination; Physician's request.

Staff Physicians 1 (pt); RNs 5 (ft), 4 (pt); LPNs
12 (ft), 3 (pt); Nurses aides 31 (ft), 14 (pt);
Physical therapists 1 (pt); Occupational therapists 1 (pt); Speech therapists 1 (pt); Activities
coordinators 1 (ft); Dietitians 1 (pt); Dentists 1
(pt); Podiatrists 1 (pt); Audiologists 1 (pt).
Facilities Dining room; Physical therapy room;
Activities room; Crafts room; Laundry room;
Barber/Beauty shop; Library.
Activities Arts and Crafts; Cards; Games;
Reading groups; Shopping trips; Dances/Social
or cultural gatherings.

Blossom Nursing Home
989 Blossom Rd, Rochester, NY, 14610 (716)
482-3500
Admin Barbara Kitanik. *Medical Dir/Dir of Nursing* Ernest T Anderson MD.
Licensure Skilled Care. *Beds* 80. *Certified* Medicaid; Medicare.
Ownership Proprietary.
Admissions Requirements Physician's request.
Staff Physicians 1 (pt); RNs 9 (ft), 6 (pt); LPNs
7 (ft), 1 (pt); Nurses aides 34 (ft), 7 (pt);
Physical therapists 1 (pt); Recreational therapists 1 (ft); Occupational therapists 1 (pt); Speech therapists 1 (pt); Activities coordinators 1
(ft); Dietitians 1 (ft).
Facilities Dining room; Physical therapy room;
Activities room; Crafts room; Laundry room;
Barber/Beauty shop.
Activities Arts and Crafts; Cards; Games;
Reading groups; Movies.
Description Facility is on a bus line and features an active rehabilitation program with
physical, occupational and speech therapy.

Brightonian Nursing Home
1919 Elmwood Ave, Rochester, NY, 14620
(716) 271-8700
Admin Stephen Sclamo. *Medical Dir/Dir of Nursing* Ernest T Anderson MD.
Licensure Skilled Care. *Beds* 54. *Certified* Medicaid; Medicare.
Ownership Proprietary.
Admissions Requirements Minimum age 16;
Medical examination; Physician's request.
Staff Physicians 1 (pt); RNs 6 (ft), 15 (pt);
LPNs 4 (ft), 2 (pt); Nurses aides 25 (ft), 4 (pt);
Physical therapists 1 (pt); Recreational therapists 1 (ft); Occupational therapists 1 (pt); Speech therapists 1 (pt); Dietitians 1 (pt); Dentists 1
(pt); Podiatrists 1 (pt); Audiologists 1 (pt).
Facilities Dining room; Physical therapy room;
Activities room; Chapel; Crafts room; Laundry
room; Barber/Beauty shop.
Activities Arts and Crafts; Games; Reading
groups; Prayer groups; Shopping trips; Dances-
/Social or cultural gatherings.

**Church Home of the Protestant Episcopal
Church***
505 Mount Hope Ave, Rochester, NY, 14620
(716) 546-8400
Admin Rachwood Jenkins.
Licensure Skilled Care; Intermediate Care.
Beds 80. *Certified* Medicaid; Medicare.
Ownership Nonprofit.

Flower City Nursing Home*
1556 Mount Hope Ave, Rochester, NY, 14620
(716) 473-2444
Admin Kathryn S Brady.

Licensure Skilled Care. *Beds* 120. *Certified* Medicaid; Medicare.
Ownership Proprietary.

Genesee Hospital—Extended Care Facility
224 Alexander St, Rochester, NY, 14607 (716)
263-6000
Admin John D Hellems. *Medical Dir/Dir of Nursing* Bernard B Brody MD.
Licensure Skilled Care. *Beds* 40. *Certified* Medicaid.
Ownership Nonprofit.
Staff Physicians 30 (ft); RNs 6 (ft); LPNs 4 (ft);
Orderlies 18 (ft), 5 (pt); Physical therapists 1
(ft); Speech therapists 1 (ft); Activities coordinators 1 (pt); Dietitians 1 (ft); Audiologists 1
(ft).
Facilities Dining room; Activities room; Chapel; Crafts room; Laundry room; Library.
Activities Arts and Crafts; Cards; Games;
Reading groups; Prayer groups; Movies.
Description This 40-bed extended care facility
conducts a balanced activities program with the
following components: spiritual or religious,
physical, intellectual, communal (group activities), and emotional (fulfilling emotional
needs).

Goodman Gardens Nursing Home Co Inc
8 N Goodman St, Rochester, NY, 14607 (716)
473-1970
Admin John R Zemans. *Medical Dir/Dir of Nursing* James M Stormont MD.
Licensure Skilled Care; Intermediate Care.
Beds SNF 83; ICF 71. *Certified* Medicaid;
Medicare.
Ownership Nonprofit.
Admissions Requirements Minimum age 65;
Medical examination; Physician's request.
Staff Physicians 2 (pt); RNs 7 (ft); LPNs 15
(ft); Nurses aides 40 (ft); Physical therapists 1
(pt); Recreational therapists 1 (ft); Occupational
therapists 1 (pt); Speech therapists 1 (pt);
Activities coordinators 3 (ft); Dietitians 1 (ft);
Dentists 1 (pt); Ophthalmologists 1 (pt); Podiatrists 1 (pt); Audiologists 1 (pt).
Facilities Dining room; Physical therapy room;
Activities room; Crafts room; Barber/Beauty
shop.
Activities Arts and Crafts; Cards; Games;
Reading groups; Prayer groups; Movies; Shopping trips; Dances/Social or cultural gatherings.
Description Goodman Gardens Nursing Home
is designed to meet the changing and highly
individualized needs of its residents. Three of
Rochester's major cultural centers are within
easy walking distance. Residents are free to
come and go, and may take advantage of
varied recreation, therapeutic, and activities
programs.

Hamilton Manor Nursing Home*
1172 Long Pond Rd, Rochester, NY, 14626
(716) 225-0450
Admin Daniel Richardson.
Licensure Skilled Care. *Beds* 40. *Certified* Medicaid; Medicare.
Ownership Proprietary.

Hurlbut Nursing Home
1177 E Henrietta Rd, Rochester, NY, 14623
(716) 424-4770
Admin Vincent F Distefano. *Medical Dir/Dir*

of Nursing Kenneth Nudo MD.
Licensure Skilled Care. *Beds* 160. *Certified* Medicaid; Medicare.
Ownership Proprietary.
Staff Physicians; RNs; LPNs.
Facilities Dining room; Physical therapy room; Activities room; Chapel; Crafts room; Laundry room; Barber/Beauty shop; Library.
Activities Arts and Crafts; Cards; Games; Reading groups; Prayer groups.
Description The Hurlbut Nursing Home is well equipped with the latest and most modern conveniences to meet the total nursing care needs of geriatric and convalescent patients. Provides a cheerful, friendly, home-like atmosphere to encourage and promote physical and social enrichment of the individual.

Jewish Home and Infirmary of Rochester New York Inc
1180 Saint Paul St, Rochester, NY, 14621 (716) 232-9478
Admin W Greenberg. *Medical Dir/Dir of Nursing* Bernard Sussman.
Licensure Skilled Care; Intermediate Care.
Beds 242. *Certified* Medicaid; Medicare.
Ownership Nonprofit.
Admissions Requirements Minimum age 60.
Staff Physicians 5 (pt); RNs 15 (ft); LPNs 25 (ft), 18 (pt); Nurses aides 60 (ft), 40 (pt); Physical therapists 2 (ft); Recreational therapists 4 (ft); Occupational therapists 1 (ft), 1 (pt); Dietitians 3 (ft); Dentists 1 (pt); Ophthalmologists 1 (pt); Podiatrists 1 (pt); Audiologists 1 (pt).
Affiliation Jewish
Facilities Dining room; Physical therapy room; Activities room; Chapel; Crafts room; Laundry room; Barber/Beauty shop; Library.
Activities Arts and Crafts; Games; Reading groups; Prayer groups; Movies; Shopping trips; Dances/Social or cultural gatherings.
Description A 3-day program—Communicare, 8 hours per day, Monday, Wednesday, and Friday—provides care to registrants similar to SNF.

Lakeshore Nursing Home*
425 Beach Ave, Rochester, NY, 14612 (716) 663-0930
Admin Claude Flack.
Licensure Skilled Care. *Beds* 229. *Certified* Medicaid; Medicare.
Ownership Proprietary.

Latta Road Nursing Home*
2100 Latta Rd, Rochester, NY, 14612 (716) 225-0920
Admin Eleanor Richardson.
Licensure Skilled Care. *Beds* 40. *Certified* Medicaid; Medicare.
Ownership Proprietary.

Monroe Community Hospital—Extended Care Facility
435 E Henrietta Rd, Rochester, NY, 24603 (716) 473-4080
Admin Raymond Diehl. *Medical Dir/Dir of Nursing* Robert Campbell MD.
Licensure Skilled Care; Intermediate Care.
Beds 354. *Certified* Medicaid; Medicare.
Ownership Public.
Staff Physicians 19 (ft), 75 (pt); RNs 83 (ft), 22 (pt); LPNs 135 (ft), 16 (pt); Nurses aides 131

(ft), 17 (pt); Physical therapists 11 (ft); Recreational therapists 9 (ft); Occupational therapists 5 (ft); Speech therapists 1 (ft); Activities coordinators 1 (ft); Dietitians 4 (ft); Dentists 1 (ft); Ophthalmologists 1 (ft); Podiatrists 3 (pt); Audiologists 1 (pt).
Facilities Dining room; Physical therapy room; Activities room; Chapel; Crafts room; Laundry room; Barber/Beauty shop; Library.
Activities Arts and Crafts; Cards; Games; Reading groups; Prayer groups; Movies; Shopping trips; Dances/Social or cultural gatherings.
Description Hospital is a 634-bed multi-level facility specializing in the care and treatment of the aged and chronically ill; owned by the County of Monroe, it is affiliated with the University of Rochester as a teaching facility.

Nortonian Nursing Home*
1335 Portland Ave, Rochester, NY, 14621 (716) 544-4000
Admin John Hansen.
Licensure Skilled Care. *Beds* 120. *Certified* Medicaid; Medicare.
Ownership Proprietary.

Park Ridge Nursing Home
1555 Longpond Rd, Rochester, NY, 14626 (716) 225-7150
Admin Michael Bierley. *Medical Dir/Dir of Nursing* Nathaniel Hurst MD.
Licensure Skilled Care. *Beds* 120. *Certified* Medicaid; Medicare.
Ownership Nonprofit.
Admissions Requirements Minimum age 16.
Staff RNs 8 (ft), 7 (pt); LPNs 5 (ft), 16 (pt); Nurses aides 30 (ft), 45 (pt); Physical therapists 2 (ft); Recreational therapists 1 (ft); Occupational therapists 1 (pt); Activities coordinators 2 (pt); Dietitians 1 (ft).
Facilities Dining room; Physical therapy room; Activities room; Crafts room; Laundry room; Barber/Beauty shop.
Activities Arts and Crafts; Cards; Games; Reading groups; Prayer groups; Movies; Shopping trips; Dances/Social or cultural gatherings; Gift cart.
Description Park Ridge has a patient bus with a wheelchair lift that is used for social activities, participation in community activities, and cultural events; 40 single rooms and 40 double rooms, each with its own bathroom.

Pinnacle Nursing Home
1175 Monroe Ave, Rochester, NY, 14620 (716) 442-0450
Admin G Bagley. *Medical Dir/Dir of Nursing* Joel Shamaskin MD.
Licensure Skilled Care. *Beds* 161. *Certified* Medicaid; Medicare.
Ownership Proprietary.
Admissions Requirements Minimum age 16; Medical examination.
Staff RNs 9 (ft), 5 (pt); LPNs 17 (ft), 3 (pt); Orderlies 6 (ft); Nurses aides 63 (ft), 6 (pt); Activities coordinators 3 (ft); Dietitians 2 (ft).
Facilities Dining room; Physical therapy room; Activities room; Crafts room; Laundry room; Barber/Beauty shop; Library.
Activities Arts and Crafts; Cards; Games; Reading groups; Prayer groups; Movies; Shopping trips; Dances/Social or cultural gatherings; Garden club, Veterans club, Cooking class.

Description Pinnacle Nursing Home is located within the Rochester, NY city limits on a bus line which is convenient for staff and visiting relatives who may be unable to drive or are themselves elderly and frail. The home has a park directly across the street and is on a naturally wooded hillside which is set back from the main street.

Rochester Friendly Home*
3156 East Ave, Rochester, NY, 14618 (716) 381-1600
Admin Ernest Mount.
Licensure Skilled Care; Intermediate Care.
Beds SNF 80; ICF 124. *Certified* Medicaid; Medicare.
Ownership Nonprofit.

Rochester United Methodist Home
8 N Goodman St, Rochester, NY, 14607
Medical Dir/Dir of Nursing James M Storment MD.
Ownership Nonprofit.
Admissions Requirements Minimum age 16; Medical examination; Physician's request.
Staff RNs 7 (ft), 6 (pt); LPNs 15 (ft), 5 (pt); Nurses aides 38 (ft), 12 (pt); Physical therapists 1 (ft); Recreational therapists 2 (ft), 1 (pt); Occupational therapists 1 (pt); Speech therapists 1 (pt); Activities coordinators 1 (ft); Dietitians 3 (ft); Podiatrists 1 (pt).
Affiliation Methodist
Facilities Dining room; Physical therapy room; Activities room; Chapel; Crafts room; Laundry room; Barber/Beauty shop; Library.
Activities Arts and Crafts; Cards; Games; Reading groups; Prayer groups; Movies; Shopping trips; Dances/Social or cultural gatherings; Exercise sessions; Humanities; Remotivation; Trips; Sing-a-longs.
Description Home is designed to meet the changing and highly individualized needs of its residents. Three local cultural centers are within easy walking distance; residents are free to come and go, and may take advantage of varied recreational, therapeutic, and activities programs.

Saint Ann's Home for the Aged
1500 Portland Ave, Rochester, NY, 14621 (716) 342-1700
Admin Marie Michelle.
Licensure Skilled Care; Intermediate Care.
Beds 354. *Certified* Medicaid; Medicare.
Ownership Nonprofit.
Affiliation Roman Catholic

Saint John's Nursing Home Inc
150 Highland Ave, Rochester, NY, 14620 (716) 271-5413
Admin Vincent Parks. *Medical Dir/Dir of Nursing* R Paul Miller MD.
Licensure Skilled Care. *Beds* 230. *Certified* Medicaid; Medicare.
Ownership Nonprofit.
Admissions Requirements Medical examination.
Staff Physicians 3 (ft), 2 (pt); RNs 23 (ft), 14 (pt); LPNs 29 (ft), 16 (pt); Nurses aides 109 (ft), 24 (pt); Physical therapists 4 (ft); Recreational therapists 4 (ft); Occupational therapists 4 (ft); Occupational therapists 1 (pt); Speech therapists 2 (ft), 1 (pt); Activities coordinators 1 (ft);

Dietitians 1 (pt); Dentists 1 (pt); Ophthalmologists 1 (pt); Podiatrists 1 (pt); Audiologists 1 (pt).
Facilities Dining room; Physical therapy room; Activities room; Chapel; Crafts room; Laundry room; Barber/Beauty shop; Library.
Activities Arts and Crafts; Cards; Games; Reading groups; Prayer groups; Movies; Shopping trips; Dances/Social or cultural gatherings; Performing arts troup for residents; Sunshine olympics ; Recreational outings.
Description St John's Home is a multi-level health care facility which offers a variety of community based programs including: respite care, home healthcare team for the chronically or terminally ill, day break—a medical model adult day care program, rehabilitation, terminal care, and mental health.

Strong Memorial Hospital*
601 Elmwood Ave, Rochester, NY, 14642
(716) 275-2644
Licensure Skilled Care. *Beds* 40.
Ownership Nonprofit.

Westgate Nursing Home*
525 Beahan Rd, Rochester, NY, 14624 (716) 247-7880
Admin David Giunta.
Licensure Skilled Care. *Beds* 124. *Certified* Medicaid; Medicare.
Ownership Proprietary.

Woodside Manor Nursing Home Inc*
2425 Clinton Ave S, Rochester, NY, 14618
(716) 275-0370
Admin Margaret Gallagher.
Licensure Skilled Care. *Beds* 44. *Certified* Medicaid; Medicare.
Ownership Proprietary.

ROCKAWAY PARK

Park Nursing Home*
128 Beach 115th St, Rockaway Park, NY, 11694 (212) 474-6400
Admin Ralph Newman.
Licensure Skilled Care. *Beds* 196. *Certified* Medicaid; Medicare.
Ownership Proprietary.

Promenade Nursing Home
140 Bech 114th St, Rockaway Park, NY, 11694
(212) 945-4600
Admin Moses Vogel. *Medical Dir/Dir of Nursing* Reuben Tizes MD.
Licensure Skilled Care. *Beds* 240. *Certified* Medicaid; Medicare.
Ownership Proprietary.
Admissions Requirements Physician's request.
Staff RNs 5 (ft), 10 (pt); LPNs 17 (ft), 20 (pt); Orderlies 8 (ft), 1 (pt); Nurses aides 57 (ft), 40 (pt); Physical therapists 1 (pt); Occupational therapists 1 (pt); Speech therapists 1 (pt); Activities coordinators 1 (ft); Dietitians 1 (ft); Dentists 1 (pt); Ophthalmologists 1 (pt); Podiatrists 2 (pt); Audiologists 1 (pt).
Facilities Dining room; Physical therapy room; Activities room; Chapel; Crafts room; Laundry room; Barber/Beauty shop; Library.
Activities Arts and Crafts; Cards; Games; Reading groups; Prayer groups; Movies; Shop-

ping trips; Dances/Social or cultural gatherings.
Description Facility is located by the Atlantic Ocean.

ROCKVILLE CENTRE

Rockville Nursing Center Inc
41 Maine Ave, Rockville Centre, NY, 11570
(516) 536-7730
Admin Siegmundo Hirsch. *Medical Dir/Dir of Nursing* Edgar Mendizabal MD.
Licensure Skilled Care. *Beds* 152. *Certified* Medicaid; Medicare.
Ownership Proprietary.
Admissions Requirements Minimum age 16; Physician's request.
Staff Physicians 1 (pt); RNs 11 (ft), 6 (pt); LPNs 15 (ft), 4 (pt); Orderlies 3 (ft); Nurses aides 45 (ft), 13 (pt); Physical therapists 1 (pt); Speech therapists 1 (pt); Activities coordinators 3 (ft); Dietitians 1 (pt).
Facilities Dining room; Physical therapy room; Activities room; Crafts room; Laundry room; Barber/Beauty shop.
Activities Arts and Crafts; Cards; Games; Reading groups; Movies; Dances/Social or cultural gatherings.

Rockville Residence Manor*
50 Maine Ave, Rockville Centre, NY, 11570
(516) 536-8000
Licensure Intermediate Care. *Beds* 66.
Ownership Proprietary.

ROME

Betsy Ross Health Related Facility*
Elsie St-Cedarbrook Ln, Rome, NY, 13440
(315) 339-2220
Licensure Intermediate Care. *Beds* 120.
Ownership Proprietary.

Health Related Facility and Nursing Home Company of Rome Inc*
800 W Chestnut St, Rome, NY, 13440 (315) 339-3210
Licensure Skilled Care; Intermediate Care.
Beds 100.
Ownership Nonprofit.

Rome-Murphy Memorial Hospital—Skilled Nursing Facility Nursing Facility
1500 N James St, Rome, NY, 13440 (315) 338-1400
Admin Melvin J Hitt. *Medical Dir/Dir of Nursing* Neville Harper.
Licensure Skilled Care. *Beds* 40. *Certified* Medicaid; Medicare.
Ownership Public.
Admissions Requirements Minimum age 16.
Staff RNs 3 (ft), 1 (pt); LPNs 4 (ft), 1 (pt); Orderlies 2 (ft), 1 (pt); Nurses aides 16 (ft), 10 (pt); Activities coordinators 1 (pt); Dietitians 1 (pt).
Facilities Activities room.
Activities Arts and Crafts; Cards; Games; Reading groups; Prayer groups; Movies; Shopping trips; Dances/Social or cultural gatherings.

Rome-Parkway Inc
950 Floyd Ave, Rome, NY, 13440 (315) 336-5400
Admin Janette Kinna. *Medical Dir/Dir of Nursing* Dr Peter Haritatos.
Licensure Skilled Care. *Beds* 80. *Certified* Medicaid; Medicare.
Ownership Proprietary.
Admissions Requirements Minimum age 21; Medical examination; Physician's request.
Staff Physicians 1 (pt); RNs 5 (ft), 4 (pt); LPNs 6 (ft), 6 (pt); Orderlies 2 (ft); Nurses aides 25 (ft), 17 (pt); Physical therapists 2 (ft), 1 (pt); Recreational therapists 1 (ft); Occupational therapists 1 (ft), 1 (pt); Speech therapists 2 (pt); Dietitians 1 (ft), 1 (pt); Dentists 1 (pt).
Facilities Dining room; Physical therapy room; Activities room; Laundry room; Barber/Beauty shop.
Activities Arts and Crafts; Cards; Games; Reading groups; Prayer groups; Movies; Shopping trips; Dances/Social or cultural gatherings.
Description Facility is situated on a beautiful 22 acre setting bordered by the historic Mohawk River; provides a full range of patient services including occupational, physical, and rehabilitative therapies, and an active volunteer program.

Stonehedge Nursing Home
801 N James St, Rome, NY, 13440 (315) 337-0550
Admin Brian Jordan. *Medical Dir/Dir of Nursing* Dr James J DiCastro.
Licensure Skilled Care. *Beds* 160. *Certified* Medicaid; Medicare.
Ownership Proprietary.
Admissions Requirements Minimum age 16.
Staff RNs 9 (ft), 4 (pt); LPNs 18 (ft), 10 (pt); Orderlies 2 (ft); Nurses aides 70 (ft), 35 (pt); Physical therapists 1 (pt); Reality therapists 1 (ft); Recreational therapists 1 (ft); Occupational therapists 1 (pt); Speech therapists 1 (pt); Activities coordinators 1 (ft); Dietitians 2 (ft), 6 (pt); Dentists 1 (pt).
Facilities Dining room; Physical therapy room; Activities room; Chapel; Crafts room; Laundry room; Barber/Beauty shop.
Activities Arts and Crafts; Cards; Games; Reading groups; Prayer groups; Movies; Shopping trips; Dances/Social or cultural gatherings.
Description Facility is on one level with 4 40-bed wings and stresses quality care with a quality staff.

ROSCOE

Roscoe Community Nursing Home Co Inc
Rockland Rd, Roscoe, NY, 12776 (607) 498-4121
Medical Dir/Dir of Nursing Lewis G Denman MD.
Licensure Skilled Care. *Beds* 85. *Certified* Medicaid; Medicare.
Ownership Nonprofit.
Admissions Requirements Minimum age 16; Medical examination; Physician's request.
Staff Physicians 1 (pt); RNs 6 (ft), 3 (pt); LPNs 8 (ft), 4 (pt); Orderlies 2 (ft); Nurses aides 29 (ft), 22 (pt); Physical therapists 1 (pt); Occupational therapists 1 (pt); Activities coordinators 1 (ft); Dietitians 1 (pt).

Facilities Dining room; Physical therapy room; Activities room; Crafts room; Laundry room; Barber/Beauty shop; Coffee shop.
Activities Arts and Crafts; Cards; Games; Reading groups; Prayer groups; Movies; Shopping trips; Dances/Social or cultural gatherings.

ROSLYN HEIGHTS

Sunharbor Manor
255 Warner Ave, Roslyn Heights, NY, 11577
(516) 621-5400
Admin Clifford R Osinoff. *Medical Dir/Dir of Nursing* Dr H Levy.
Licensure Skilled Care; Health Related Care.
Beds SNF 160; HRF 106. *Certified* Medicaid.
Ownership Proprietary.
Facilities Dining room; Physical therapy room; Activities room; Crafts room; Laundry room; Barber/Beauty shop; Library.
Activities Arts and Crafts; Cards; Games; Reading groups; Prayer groups; Movies; Shopping trips; Dances/Social or cultural gatherings.

ROUSES POINT

Cedar Hedge Nursing Home*
250 Lake St, Rouses Point, NY, 12979 (518) 297-5190
Admin William Pollock.
Licensure Intermediate Care. *Beds* 30.
Ownership Proprietary.

SAINT JAMES

Saint James Nursing Home*
275 Noriches Rd, Saint James, NY, 11780
(516) 862-8000
Admin Gerald Clifford.
Licensure Skilled Care; Intermediate Care.
Beds 230. *Certified* Medicaid; Medicare.
Ownership Proprietary.

SALAMANCA

Salamanca Nursing Home Inc
451 Broad St, Salamanca, NY, 14779 (716) 945-1800
Admin Anthony J Brunsing. *Medical Dir/Dir of Nursing* Dr Ben Hwang.
Licensure Skilled Care; Intermediate Care.
Beds 80. *Certified* Medicaid; Medicare.
Ownership Proprietary.
Admissions Requirements Minimum age 16; Medical examination; Physician's request.
Staff Physicians 13 (pt); RNs 6 (ft), 4 (pt); LPNs 5 (ft), 12 (pt); Orderlies 5 (pt); Nurses aides 32 (ft), 17 (pt); Physical therapists 1 (pt); Recreational therapists 2 (ft); Occupational therapists 1 (pt); Speech therapists 1 (pt); Activities coordinators 1 (ft); Dietitians 1 (ft); Dentists 1 (pt); Podiatrists 1 (pt); Audiologists 1 (pt).
Facilities Dining room; Physical therapy room; Activities room; Laundry room; Barber/Beauty shop; Library.
Activities Arts and Crafts; Cards; Games; Reading groups; Prayer groups; Movies; Shopping trips; Dances/Social or cultural gatherings.
Description Beautiful rural setting in the south-ern tier near Allegheny State Park featuring skilled nursing services, active activity program, supervised health related care, and an organized medical staff. Quality care provided.

SARATOGA SPRINGS

Saratoga Hospital Nursing Home
211 Church St, Saratoga Springs, NY, 12866
(518) 584-6000
Admin Wilfred Addison. *Medical Dir/Dir of Nursing* Dr Warren Letts.
Licensure Skilled Care. *Beds* 76. *Certified* Medicaid; Medicare.
Ownership Nonprofit.
Staff RNs; LPNs; Nurses aides; Physical therapists; Speech therapists; Activities coordinators; Dietitians; Dentists; Podiatrists; Audiologists.
Facilities Dining room; Physical therapy room; Activities room; Barber/Beauty shop.
Activities Arts and Crafts; Games; Reading groups; Prayer groups; Movies; Shopping trips; Dances/Social or cultural gatherings.
Description Facility features pet therapy program and resident advisory council.

Wesley Health Care Center Inc
Lawrence St, Saratoga Springs, NY, 12866
(518) 587-3600
Admin Ralph Barron. *Medical Dir/Dir of Nursing* William F Meinhardt MD.
Licensure Skilled Care; Intermediate Care.
Beds SNF 88; ICF 76. *Certified* Medicaid; Medicare.
Ownership Nonprofit.
Admissions Requirements Minimum age 16; Medical examination; Physician's request.
Staff RNs 8 (ft), 6 (pt); LPNs 15 (ft), 24 (pt); Nurses aides 38 (ft), 63 (pt); Activities coordinators 1 (ft); Dietitians 1 (ft).
Affiliation Methodist
Facilities Dining room; Physical therapy room; Activities room; Chapel; Crafts room; Laundry room; Barber/Beauty shop; Library.
Activities Arts and Crafts; Cards; Games; Reading groups; Prayer groups; Movies; Shopping trips; Dances/Social or cultural gatherings.

SAYVILLE

Good Samaritan Nursing Home*
101 Elm St, Sayville, NY, 11782 (516) 567-6600
Admin Kenneth B Knutsen.
Licensure Skilled Care. *Beds* 100. *Certified* Medicaid; Medicare.
Ownership Nonprofit.

SCARSDALE

Sprain Brook Manor Nursing Home*
77 Jackson Ave, Scarsdale, NY, 10583 (914) 472-3200
Admin Henry Book.
Licensure Skilled Care. *Beds* 121. *Certified* Medicaid; Medicare.
Ownership Proprietary.

SCHENECTADY

Hallmark Nursing Centre Inc
526 Altamont Ave, Schenectady, NY, 12303
(518) 346-6121
Admin Kathryn Lee.
Licensure Skilled Care. *Beds* 224. *Certified* Medicaid; Medicare.
Ownership Proprietary.

Kingsway Arms Nursing Center Inc*
Kings Rd, Schenectady, NY, 12304 (518) 393-4117
Admin Robert DeAngelin.
Licensure Skilled Care; Intermediate Care.
Beds 131. *Certified* Medicaid; Medicare.
Ownership Proprietary.

Silver Haven Nursing Home
1940 Hamburg St, Schenectady, NY, 12304
(518) 370-5051
Admin Grace W Rooney. *Medical Dir/Dir of Nursing* M Bonoquist MD and A J Arony MD.
Licensure Skilled Care. *Beds* 86. *Certified* Medicaid; Medicare.
Ownership Proprietary.
Staff Physicians 2 (pt); RNs 6 (ft), 13 (pt); LPNs 4 (ft), 15 (pt); Orderlies 1 (ft); Nurses aides 23 (ft), 50 (pt); Recreational therapists 2 (ft), 1 (pt); Physical therapy assistants.
Facilities Dining room; Physical therapy room; Activities room; Chapel; Crafts room.
Activities Movies; Shopping trips; Dances/Social or cultural gatherings.
Description Reputation in the community is for very acute care nursing, well delivered; smallest facility in the area.

SCOTIA

Baptist Retirement Center Corp
297 N Ballston Ave, Scotia, NY, 12302 (518) 370-4700
Admin Timothy W Bartos. *Medical Dir/Dir of Nursing* Robert H Wiese MD.
Licensure Skilled Care; Intermediate Care.
Beds 180. *Certified* Medicaid; Medicare.
Ownership Nonprofit.
Admissions Requirements Medical examination.
Staff RNs 8 (ft), 9 (pt); LPNs 17 (ft), 11 (pt); Nurses aides 48 (ft), 29 (pt); Physical therapists 1 (ft), 1 (pt); Occupational therapists 1 (ft), 1 (pt); Speech therapists 1 (pt); Activities coordinators 2 (ft), 1 (pt); Dietitians 1 (ft), 1 (pt); Dentists 1 (pt); Ophthalmologists 1 (pt); Podiatrists 1 (pt); Audiologists 1 (pt).
Affiliation Baptist
Facilities Dining room; Physical therapy room; Activities room; Chapel; Crafts room; Laundry room; Barber/Beauty shop; Occupational therapy room.
Activities Arts and Crafts; Cards; Games; Reading groups; Prayer groups; Movies; Shopping trips; Dances/Social or cultural gatherings.
Description Respite program is available which provides a temporary, short-term break from the daily responsibilities of at-home care of a frail, elderly loved one. Baptist Retirement Center has reserved a private HRF bed that is designated for respite care.

Glendale Home
Hetcheltown Rd, Scotia, NY, 12302 (518) 384-3601
Admin John McGrath. *Medical Dir/Dir of Nursing* Jesse T Henderson Jr MD.
Licensure Skilled Care; Intermediate Care.
Beds 378. *Certified* Medicaid; Medicare.
Ownership Public.
Staff Physicians 5 (pt); RNs 35 (ft), 19 (pt); LPNs 41 (ft), 8 (pt); Nurses aides 194 (ft), 12 (pt); Physical therapists 1 (ft); Recreational therapists 6 (ft), 1 (pt); Occupational therapists 1 (pt); Activities coordinators 1 (ft); Dietitians 1 (ft); Dentists 1 (pt); Podiatrists 1 (pt).
Facilities Dining room; Physical therapy room; Activities room; Chapel; Crafts room; Laundry room; Barber/Beauty shop; Library.
Activities Arts and Crafts; Cards; Games; Reading groups; Prayer groups; Movies; Shopping trips; Dances/Social or cultural gatherings; Picnics.

SIDNEY

Hospital—Skilled Nursing Facility
Pearl St, Sidney, NY, 13838 (607) 563-3512
Admin Betty Ebert. *Medical Dir/Dir of Nursing* Dr R Hust.
Licensure Skilled Care. *Beds* 30. *Certified* Medicaid; Medicare.
Ownership Public.
Admissions Requirements Minimum age 16; Physician's request.
Staff Physicians 5 (pt); RNs 1 (ft), 1 (pt); LPNs 5 (ft), 2 (pt); Nurses aides 8 (ft), 8 (pt); Physical therapists 1 (ft); Speech therapists 1 (pt); Activities coordinators 1 (pt); Dietitians 1 (pt); Dentists 1 (pt); Podiatrists 1 (pt).
Facilities Dining room; Physical therapy room; Activities room; Chapel; Crafts room; Barber/Beauty shop; Patio.
Activities Arts and Crafts; Cards; Games; Reading groups; Prayer groups; Movies; Dances/Social or cultural gatherings.
Description Facility is carpeted; has good community support.

SMITHTOWN

Lutheran Center for the Aging
Rt 25A, Smithtown, NY, 11787 (516) 724-2200
Admin Ann Ciri. *Medical Dir/Dir of Nursing* Dr Lawrence Werner.
Licensure Skilled Care; Intermediate Care.
Beds 341. *Certified* Medicaid; Medicare.
Ownership Proprietary.
Admissions Requirements Minimum age 62; Medical examination; Physician's request.
Staff Physical therapists 2 (ft); Occupational therapists 1 (pt); Dentists 1 (pt); Podiatrists 1 (pt); Audiologists 1 (pt).
Affiliation Lutheran
Facilities Dining room; Physical therapy room; Activities room; Crafts room; Laundry room; Barber/Beauty shop; Library.
Activities Arts and Crafts; Cards; Games; Reading groups; Prayer groups; Movies; Shopping trips; Dances/Social or cultural gatherings.
Description Progressive facility on 20 acres

offers recognized drama program, long-term home health care program, and outpatient medical and social day care programs.

SODUS

Blossom View Nursing Home
6884 Maple Ave, Sodus, NY, 14551 (315) 483-9118
Admin Donna M Brown. *Medical Dir/Dir of Nursing* John L Ghertner MD.
Licensure Skilled Care. *Beds* 60. *Certified* Medicaid; Medicare.
Ownership Proprietary.
Facilities Dining room; Physical therapy room; Activities room; Barber/Beauty shop.
Activities Arts and Crafts; Games; Reading groups; Prayer groups; Shopping trips; Dances/Social or cultural gatherings.

SOMERS

Somers Manor Nursing Home Inc*
Rt 100, Somers, NY, 10589 (914) 232-5101
Admin Dorothy Gregoire.
Licensure Skilled Care; Intermediate Care.
Beds 123. *Certified* Medicaid; Medicare.
Ownership Proprietary.

SOUTHAMPTON

Southampton Nursing Home
330 Meeting House Ln, Southampton, NY, 11968 (516) 283-2134
Admin Maureen O Mahoney. *Medical Dir/Dir of Nursing* Carver Livingston MD.
Licensure Skilled Care. *Beds* 62. *Certified* Medicaid; Medicare.
Ownership Nonprofit.
Admissions Requirements Minimum age 16.
Staff Physical therapists 1 (pt); Activities coordinators 1 (ft); Dietitians 1 (pt).
Facilities Dining room; Physical therapy room; Activities room; Crafts room; Barber/Beauty shop; Library.
Activities Arts and Crafts; Cards; Games; Reading groups; Prayer groups; Movies; Dances/Social or cultural gatherings.

SPENCERPORT

Wedgewood Nursing Home
5 Church St, Spencerport, NY, 14559 (716) 352-4810
Admin Christine Sinclair. *Medical Dir/Dir of Nursing* Dr P Rapoza.
Licensure Skilled Care. *Beds* 29. *Certified* Medicaid; Medicare.
Ownership Proprietary.
Staff Physicians; RNs; LPNs; Orderlies; Nurses aides; Physical therapists; Occupational therapists; Speech therapists; Activities coordinators; Dietitians; Dentists; Podiatrists; Audiologists.
Facilities Dining room; Activities room; Crafts room; Laundry room; Barber/Beauty shop.
Activities Arts and Crafts; Cards; Games; Prayer groups; Dances/Social or cultural gatherings.

SPRING VALLEY

Hillcrest Nursing Home*
661 N Main St, Spring Valley, NY, 10977 (914) 356-0567
Admin Harry Satin.
Licensure Skilled Care. *Beds* 200. *Certified* Medicaid; Medicare.
Ownership Proprietary.

SPRINGVILLE

Fiddlers Green Manor Nursing Home*
168 W Main St, Springville, NY, 14141 (716) 592-4781
Admin John Barrett.
Licensure Skilled Care. *Beds* 82. *Certified* Medicaid; Medicare.
Ownership Proprietary.

Jennie B Richmond Chaffee Nursing Home Company Inc*
222 E Main St, Springville, NY, 14141 (716) 592-2871
Admin Roger Ford.
Licensure Skilled Care; Intermediate Care.
Beds 40. *Certified* Medicaid; Medicare.
Ownership Nonprofit.

STAATSBURG

Hyde Park Nursing Home
Rt 9 and Anderson School Rd, Staatsburg, NY, 12580 (914) 889-4500
Admin Abraham J Pion. *Medical Dir/Dir of Nursing* Donald Krawitt MD.
Licensure Skilled Care. *Beds* 120. *Certified* Medicaid; Medicare.
Ownership Proprietary.
Facilities Dining room; Physical therapy room; Activities room; Crafts room; Laundry room; Barber/Beauty shop; Library.
Activities Arts and Crafts; Cards; Games; Reading groups; Prayer groups; Movies; Shopping trips; Dances/Social or cultural gatherings.

STAMFORD

Community Hospital—Skilled Nursing Facility*
Harper St, Stamford, NY, 12167 (607) 652-7521
Admin Clayton Bean.
Licensure Skilled Care; Intermediate Care.
Beds 40. *Certified* Medicaid; Medicare.
Ownership Nonprofit.

STATEN ISLAND

Carmel Richmond Nursing Home Inc*
88 Old Town Rd, Staten Island, NY, 10304 (212) 979-5000
Licensure Skilled Care; Intermediate Care.
Beds 270. *Certified* Medicaid; Medicare.
Ownership Nonprofit.

Clove Lakes Nursing Home
25 Fanning St, Staten Island, NY, 10314 (212) 761-2100
Admin N Demisay. *Medical Dir/Dir of*

Nursing Florence Kavaler MD.
Licensure Skilled Care; Intermediate Care.
Beds 286. *Certified* Medicaid; Medicare.
Ownership Proprietary.
Admissions Requirements Medical examination; Physician's request.
Staff RNs 23 (ft), 14 (pt); LPNs 46 (ft), 23 (pt); Orderlies 22 (ft), 13 (pt); Nurses aides 138 (ft), 39 (pt); Physical therapists 2 (ft); Recreational therapists 7 (ft), 2 (pt); Occupational therapists 2 (ft); Speech therapists 1 (pt); Activities coordinators 1 (ft); Dietitians 6 (ft), 1 (pt).
Facilities Dining room; Physical therapy room; Activities room; Chapel; Crafts room; Laundry room; Barber/Beauty shop; Library.
Activities Arts and Crafts; Cards; Games; Prayer groups; Movies; Shopping trips; Dances/Social or cultural gatherings; Horticultural program.

Eger Nursing Home Inc
140 Meisner Ave, Staten Island, NY, 10306
(212) 979-1800
Admin Paul K Jensen. *Medical Dir/Dir of Nursing* Frank Tellefsen MD.
Licensure Skilled Care; Intermediate Care.
Beds 336. *Certified* Medicaid.
Ownership Nonprofit.
Admissions Requirements Minimum age 16; Medical examination; Physician's request.
Staff Physicians 11 (pt); RNs 31 (ft), 40 (pt); LPNs 12 (ft), 19 (pt); Nurses aides 131 (ft), 95 (pt); Physical therapists 3 (ft); Occupational therapists 2 (ft); Speech therapists 1 (pt); Activities coordinators 1 (ft); Dietitians 4 (ft); Dentists 1 (pt); Ophthalmologists 2 (pt); Podiatrists 1 (pt); Audiologists 1 (pt).
Affiliation Lutheran
Facilities Dining room; Physical therapy room; Activities room; Chapel; Crafts room; Laundry room; Barber/Beauty shop; Library; Speech pathology room; Occupational therapy room; Pharmacy.
Activities Arts and Crafts; Cards; Games; Reading groups; Prayer groups; Movies; Shopping trips; Dances/Social or cultural gatherings.
Description A progressive, rehabilitation oriented skilled nursing facility located in the greenbelt of Staten Island; modern high-rise structure is surrounded by spacious grounds, rolling hills, and a beautiful ocean view.

Golden Gate Health Care Center
191 Bradley Ave, Staten Island, NY, 10314
(212) 698-8800
Admin Alan Chopp. *Medical Dir/Dir of Nursing* Dr Rauven Averick.
Licensure Skilled Care; Intermediate Care.
Beds SNF 118; ICF 120. *Certified* Medicaid; Medicare.
Ownership Proprietary.
Admissions Requirements Minimum age 21; Physician's request.
Staff RNs 14 (ft), 14 (pt); LPNs 10 (ft), 9 (pt); Orderlies 18 (ft), 1 (pt); Nurses aides 46 (ft), 5 (pt); Physical therapists 1 (ft), 1 (pt); Recreational therapists 4 (ft), 1 (pt); Occupational therapists 1 (ft); Speech therapists 1 (pt); Activities coordinators 1 (ft); Dietitians 2 (ft).
Facilities Dining room; Physical therapy room; Activities room; Chapel; Crafts room; Laundry room; Barber/Beauty shop; Library.
Activities Arts and Crafts; Cards; Games;

Reading groups; Prayer groups; Movies; Shopping trips; Dances/Social or cultural gatherings.
Description Programs are specifically geared towards instilling a sense of dignity, self-worth, and self determination. Programs include resident operated grievance committee, resident/dietary food service committee, residents as SERVE volunteers, sensory stimulation groups, and drama club. An interdisciplinary approach used for those having Huntington's-Chorea, multiple sclerosis, ALS, hemodialysis, terminal cancer.

Lily Pond Nursing Home*
150 Lily Pond Ave, Staten Island, NY, 10305
(212) 981-5300
Admin Miriam Rosenberg.
Licensure Skilled Care. *Beds* 35. *Certified* Medicaid; Medicare.
Ownership Proprietary.

New Brighton Manor Care Center*
200 Lafayette Ave, Staten Island, NY, 10301
(212) 448-9000
Admin Joshuah Levy.
Licensure Skilled Care; Intermediate Care.
Beds 80. *Certified* Medicaid; Medicare.
Ownership Proprietary.

New Vanderbilt Nursing Home
135 Vanderbilt Ave, Staten Island, NY, 10304
(212) 447-0701
Admin Henry Schon. *Medical Dir/Dir of Nursing* Dr Howard Guterman.
Licensure Skilled Care. *Beds* 320. *Certified* Medicaid; Medicare.
Ownership Proprietary.
Admissions Requirements Minimum age 35; Medical examination.
Staff Physicians 5 (pt); RNs 25 (ft), 10 (pt); LPNs 20 (ft), 8 (pt); Orderlies 10 (ft), 3 (pt); Nurses aides 80 (ft), 20 (pt); Physical therapists 1 (ft), 2 (pt); Recreational therapists 4 (ft), 3 (pt); Occupational therapists 1 (pt); Speech therapists 1 (pt); Activities coordinators 1 (ft); Dietitians 3 (ft), 1 (pt); Dentists 1 (pt); Ophthalmologists 1 (pt); Podiatrists 2 (pt); Audiologists 1 (pt).
Facilities Dining room; Physical therapy room; Activities room; Chapel; Crafts room; Laundry room; Barber/Beauty shop; Library.
Activities Arts and Crafts; Cards; Games; Reading groups; Prayer groups; Movies; Shopping trips; Dances/Social or cultural gatherings.
Description A comfortable, attractive lounge reflects the pleasant, cheerful atmosphere which prevails throughout the home. Centrally located nursing stations on each floor offer around the clock nursing and medical services. Modern, fully equipped physical and occupational therapy room provides doctor-prescribed rehabilitation treatment for each patient under the supervision of a skilled, licensed, physical therapist. The dining room plays an important role in patient socialization. The Recreation Department provides many outside trips.

Beth Rifka Nursing Home*
1000 Targee St, Staten Island, NY, 10304 (212)
720-7800
Licensure Intermediate Care. *Beds* 200.
Ownership Nonprofit.

Sea View Hospital and Home*
460 Brielle Ave, Staten Island, NY, 10314 (212)
390-8181
Admin Michael Cantatore.
Licensure Skilled Care. *Beds* 304. *Certified* Medicaid; Medicare.
Ownership Public.

Silver Lake Nursing Home*
275 Castleton Ave, Staten Island, NY, 10301
(212) 447-7800
Admin Otto Weingarten.
Licensure Skilled Care. *Beds* 278. *Certified* Medicaid; Medicare.
Ownership Proprietary.

Verrazano Nursing Home
100 Castleton Ave, Staten Island, NY, 10301
(212) 273-1300
Admin Israel Weingarten. *Medical Dir/Dir of Nursing* F Tellefsen MD.
Licensure Skilled Care. *Beds* 120. *Certified* Medicaid; Medicare.
Ownership Proprietary.
Admissions Requirements Medical examination; Physician's request.
Staff Physicians 3 (pt); RNs 5 (ft), 2 (pt); LPNs 12 (ft), 5 (pt); Orderlies 45 (ft), 21 (pt); Physical therapists 1 (pt); Occupational therapists 1 (pt); Speech therapists 1 (pt); Activities coordinators 1 (ft); Dietitians 1 (ft), 2 (pt); Dentists 1 (pt); Ophthalmologists 1 (pt); Podiatrists 1 (pt); Audiologists 1 (pt).
Facilities Dining room; Physical therapy room; Activities room; Crafts room; Laundry room; Barber/Beauty shop.
Activities Arts and Crafts; Cards; Games; Reading groups; Prayer groups; Movies; Dances/Social or cultural gatherings.

SUFFERN

Ramapo Manor Nursing Center*
Cragmere Rd, Suffern, NY, 10901 (914)
357-1230
Admin Lawrence A Kluger.
Licensure Skilled Care; Intermediate Care.
Beds 122. *Certified* Medicaid; Medicare.
Ownership Proprietary.

SYRACUSE

Castle Rest Nursing Home*
116 E Castle St, Syracuse, NY, 13205 (315)
475-1641
Admin Thomas Fahey.
Licensure Skilled Care. *Beds* 140. *Certified* Medicaid; Medicare.
Ownership Proprietary.

Hill Haven Nursing Home
4001 E Genesee St, Syracuse, NY, 13214 (315)
446-8310
Admin Gladys Stanton.
Licensure Skilled Care. *Beds* 121. *Certified* Medicaid; Medicare.
Ownership Proprietary.

James Square Nursing Home
918 James St, Syracuse, NY, 13203 (315)
474-1561

Admin Edward Leffler. *Medical Dir/Dir of Nursing* George Tilley MD.
Licensure Skilled Care; Health Related Care.
Beds SNF 415; HRC 40. *Certified* Medicaid; Medicare.
Ownership Proprietary.
Staff Physicians 7 (ft); RNs 33 (ft), 14 (pt); LPNs 53 (ft), 20 (pt); Orderlies 4 (ft), 1 (pt); Nurses aides 181 (ft), 55 (pt); Physical therapists 2 (ft); Recreational therapists 7 (ft); Occupational therapists 2 (ft); Speech therapists 1 (ft); Activities coordinators 1 (ft); Dietitians 3 (ft).
Facilities Dining room; Physical therapy room; Activities room; Crafts room; Laundry room; Barber/Beauty shop.
Activities Arts and Crafts; Cards; Games; Reading groups; Prayer groups; Movies; Shopping trips; Dances/Social or cultural gatherings.
Description The goal of James Square is to assist residents in the performance of any activity which will maintain or improve their health, dignity, and well-being. Each resident receives personalized care 24 hours a day by skilled nursing staff plus the personal concern and attention of an outstanding and dedicated staff.

Jewish Home of Central New York
4101 E Genesee St, Syracuse, NY, 13214 (315) 446-9111
Admin Harvey N Finkelstein. *Medical Dir/Dir of Nursing* Dr Albert Tripodi.
Licensure Skilled Care. *Beds* 145. *Certified* Medicaid; Medicare.
Ownership Nonprofit.
Admissions Requirements Minimum age 62; Medical examination; Physician's request.
Staff Physicians 2 (pt); RNs 16 (ft), 5 (pt); LPNs 26 (ft), 3 (pt); Orderlies 4 (ft); Nurses aides 59 (ft), 6 (pt); Physical therapists 2 (pt); Occupational therapists 1 (pt); Speech therapists 1 (pt); Activities coordinators 1 (ft); Dietitians 1 (pt); Dentists 1 (pt); Podiatrists 1 (pt); Audiologists 91 (ft), 16 (pt).
Affiliation Jewish
Facilities Dining room; Physical therapy room; Activities room; Chapel; Crafts room; Laundry room; Barber/Beauty shop; Library.
Activities Arts and Crafts; Cards; Games; Reading groups; Prayer groups; Movies; Shopping trips; Dances/Social or cultural gatherings.

Loretto Geriatric Center*
700 E Brighton Ave, Syracuse, NY, 13205 (315) 469-5561
Admin Norman E Harper.
Licensure Skilled Care; Intermediate Care.
Beds 180. *Certified* Medicaid; Medicare.
Ownership Nonprofit.

Plaza Nursing Home Company Inc
614 S Crouse Ave, Syracuse, NY, 13210 (315) 474-4431
Admin Edward Leone. *Medical Dir/Dir of Nursing* Leo Jivoff MD.
Licensure Skilled Care. *Beds* 242. *Certified* Medicaid; Medicare.
Ownership Nonprofit.
Admissions Requirements Minimum age 16; Physician's request.
Staff Physicians 4 (pt); RNs 42 (ft), 8 (pt); LPNs 26 (pt), 3 (pt); Nurses aides 94 (ft), 28

(pt); Physical therapists 4 (ft); Recreational therapists 5 (ft); Occupational therapists 4 (ft); Speech therapists 1 (pt); Activities coordinators 1 (ft); Dietitians 1 (ft); Dentists 1 (pt); Audiologists 1 (pt).
Facilities Dining room; Physical therapy room; Activities room; Crafts room; Laundry room; Barber/Beauty shop.
Activities Arts and Crafts; Cards; Games; Reading groups; Prayer groups; Movies; Shopping trips; Dances/Social or cultural gatherings; Cooking groups.

Saint Camillus Nursing Home Company Inc
813 Fay Rd, Syracuse, NY, 13219 (315) 488-2951
Admin Robert Mack. *Medical Dir/Dir of Nursing* Dr John O'Brien.
Licensure Skilled Care; Health Related Care.
Beds 250. *Certified* Medicaid; Medicare.
Ownership Nonprofit.
Admissions Requirements Physician's request.
Staff Physicians 1 (ft), 9 (pt); RNs 18 (ft), 5 (pt); LPNs 17 (ft), 10 (pt); Nurses aides 45 (ft), 20 (pt); Physical therapists 8 (ft); Recreational therapists 6 (ft); Occupational therapists 3 (ft); Speech therapists 6 (ft), 1 (pt); Activities coordinators 1 (ft); Dietitians 3 (ft); Dentists 5 (pt); Podiatrists 2 (pt); Audiologists 1 (ft).
Affiliation Roman Catholic
Facilities Dining room; Physical therapy room; Activities room; Chapel; Crafts room; Laundry room; Barber/Beauty shop; Library.
Activities Arts and Crafts; Cards; Games; Reading groups; Prayer groups; Movies; Shopping trips; Dances/Social or cultural gatherings.
Description A comprehensive rehabilitation facility with more programs and services than any other long-term facility in upstate New York.

Van Duyn Home and Hospital
W Seneca Turnpike, Syracuse, NY, 13215 (315) 469-5511
Admin J Roland Craner. *Medical Dir/Dir of Nursing* Arthur H Dube.
Licensure Skilled Care; Intermediate Care.
Beds SNF 518; ICF 108. *Certified* Medicaid; Medicare.
Ownership Public.
Staff Physicians 1 (ft), 18 (pt); RNs 90 (ft); LPNs 120 (ft); Nurses aides 200 (ft), 40 (pt); Physical therapists 3 (ft); Recreational therapists 7 (ft); Occupational therapists 3 (ft); Activities coordinators 1 (ft); Dietitians 2 (ft); Dentists 2 (pt); Ophthalmologists 1 (pt); Podiatrists 2 (pt); Audiologists 1 (pt).
Facilities Dining room; Physical therapy room; Activities room; Chapel; Crafts room; Laundry room; Barber/Beauty shop; Library; Radiology lab; Occupational therapy room.
Activities Arts and Crafts; Cards; Games; Reading groups; Prayer groups; Movies; Shopping trips; Dances/Social or cultural gatherings; Beach parties; Picnics; Gardening; Aerobics; Wheelchair volley ball.
Description Van Duyn is a 5-year-old modern facility that admits babies and young children with New York State approval.

TARRYTOWN

Tarrytown Hall Nursing Home*
Wood Ct, Tarrytown, NY, 10591 (914) 631-2600
Admin Leslie Kaye.
Licensure Skilled Care; Intermediate Care.
Beds 80. *Certified* Medicaid; Medicare.
Ownership Proprietary.

TICONDEROGA

Moses-Ludington Nursing Home Company Inc
Wicker St, Ticonderoga, NY, 12883 (518) 585-6771
Admin Margaret Haroff. *Medical Dir/Dir of Nursing* Michael Beehner MD.
Licensure Skilled Care; Intermediate Care.
Beds 40. *Certified* Medicaid; Medicare.
Ownership Nonprofit.
Staff Physicians 1 (ft); RNs 5 (ft), 1 (pt); LPNs 4 (ft); Orderlies 1 (ft); Nurses aides 14 (ft), 10 (pt); Physical therapists 1 (pt); Recreational therapists 2 (ft); Activities coordinators 1 (ft); Dietitians 1 (pt); Dentists 1 (pt).
Facilities Dining room; Physical therapy room; Activities room; Barber/Beauty shop.
Activities Arts and Crafts; Cards; Games; Reading groups; Prayer groups; Movies; Shopping trips; Dances/Social or cultural gatherings; Cooking club.
Description Home is located in the beautiful Adirondack Mountains where Lake George meets Lake Champlain.

TONAWANDA

Sheridan Manor Nursing Home Inc*
2799 Sheridan Dr, Tonawanda, NY, 14150 (716) 837-4466
Admin Geraldine Sufrane.
Licensure Skilled Care. *Beds* 100. *Certified* Medicaid; Medicare.
Ownership Proprietary.

TROY

Eddy Memorial Foundation*
Burdett Ave, Troy, NY, 12180 (518) 271-3306
Licensure Intermediate Care. *Beds* 19.
Ownership Nonprofit.

Eden Park Health Services Inc*
2417 15th St, Troy, NY, 12180 (518) 436-4731
Admin Eugene Evans.
Licensure Skilled Care. *Beds* 130. *Certified* Medicaid; Medicare.
Ownership Proprietary.

Hallmark Nursing Centre
49 Marvin Ave, Troy, NY, 12180 (518) 273-6646
Admin Lisa Kaley.
Licensure Skilled Care. *Beds* 80. *Certified* Medicaid; Medicare.
Ownership Proprietary.

Highgate Manor of Rensselaer
100 New Turnpike Rd, Troy, NY, 12182 (518) 235-1410
Admin Gregory J Zucco. *Medical Dir/Dir of*

Nursing Michael Salzman MD.
Licensure Skilled Care; Intermediate Care.
Beds 80. *Certified* Medicaid; Medicare.
Ownership Proprietary.
Staff Physicians 1 (pt); RNs 10 (ft), 12 (pt);
LPNs 9 (ft), 12 (pt); Orderlies 2 (pt); Nurses
aides 27 (ft), 29 (pt); Recreational therapists 3
(ft); Occupational therapists 4 (ft); Speech thera-
pists 3 (ft); Activities coordinators 3 (ft), 2 (pt);
Dietitians 1 (pt); Dentists; Podiatrists; Audiolo-
gists.
Facilities Dining room; Physical therapy room;
Activities room; Crafts room; Laundry room;
Barber/Beauty shop.
Activities Arts and Crafts; Cards; Games;
Reading groups; Prayer groups; Movies; Shop-
ping trips; Dances/Social or cultural gatherings.
Description Facility features an elegant dining
program.

Leisure Arms Health Related Facility*
2406 15th St, Troy, NY, 12180 (518) 436-4731
Licensure Intermediate Care. *Beds* 88.
Ownership Proprietary.

Van Rensselaer Manor*
133 Bloomingrove Dr, Troy, NY, 12181 (518)
283-2000
Admin Bob Beaudion.
Licensure Skilled Care; Intermediate Care.
Beds 194. *Certified* Medicaid; Medicare.
Ownership Public.

TUPPER LAKE

Mercy Healthcare Center
114 Wawbeek Ave, Tupper Lake, NY, 12986
(518) 359-3355
Admin Mary Paschal. *Medical Dir/Dir of
Nursing* W W Frederick MD.
Licensure Skilled Care; Intermediate Care.
Beds 54. *Certified* Medicaid; Medicare.
Ownership Nonprofit.
Staff RNs 5 (ft), 5 (pt); LPNs 6 (ft), 2 (pt);
Nurses aides 24 (ft), 6 (pt); Physical therapists 1
(pt); Occupational therapists 1 (pt); Activities
coordinators 1 (ft); Dietitians 1 (pt); Dentists 1
(pt); Podiatrists 1 (pt).
Affiliation Roman Catholic
Facilities Dining room; Physical therapy room;
Activities room; Chapel; Laundry room; Bar-
ber/Beauty shop.
Activities Arts and Crafts; Games; Reading
groups; Prayer groups; Movies; Shopping trips;
Dances/Social or cultural gatherings.

UNIONDALE

Holly Patterson Home
875 Jerusalem Ave, Uniondale, NY, 11553
(516) 663-5700
Admin William J St George. *Medical Dir/Dir
of Nursing* Harold Fonrose MD.
Licensure Skilled Care. *Beds* 889. *Certified* Medicaid; Medicare.
Ownership Public.
Admissions Requirements Minimum age 16;
Medical examination; Physician's request.
Staff Physicians 3 (ft), 14 (pt); RNs 99 (ft), 34
(pt); LPNs 92 (ft), 43 (pt); Nurses aides 366 (ft),
149 (pt); Physical therapists 1 (ft); Recreational

therapists 17 (ft); Occupational therapists 1 (ft);
Speech therapists 1 (ft); Activities coordinators
1 (ft); Dietitians 5 (ft), 1 (pt); Dentists 2 (pt);
Ophthalmologists 2 (pt); Audiologists 1 (pt).
Facilities Dining room; Physical therapy room;
Activities room; Chapel; Crafts room; Laundry
room; Barber/Beauty shop; Library.
Activities Arts and Crafts; Cards; Games;
Reading groups; Prayer groups; Movies; Shop-
ping trips; Dances/Social or cultural gatherings;
Clubs; Gardening; Workshop; Crafts; Musical
concerts; Exercise program; Cooking programs;
Community group.
Description Facility is a 889-bed skilled nursing
facility that offers all levels of clinical and
rehabilitative care.

UTICA

Broadacres
Walker Rd, Utica, NY, 13502 (315) 798-9200
Admin Richard DuRose. *Medical Dir/Dir of
Nursing* Dr Jeanne F Arnold.
Licensure Skilled Care. *Beds* 168. *Cer-
tified* Medicaid; Medicare.
Ownership Public.
Staff Physicians 17 (pt); RNs 16 (ft), 7 (pt);
LPNs 34 (ft), 7 (pt); Nurses aides 91 (ft), 36
(pt); Physical therapists 1 (pt) Occupational
therapists 1 (pt); Speech therapists 1 (pt);
Activities coordinators 1 (ft); Dietitians 1 (pt);
Dentists 1 (pt); Podiatrists 1 (pt).
Facilities Dining room; Physical therapy room;
Activities room; Crafts room; Laundry room;
Barber/Beauty shop; Library.
Activities Arts and Crafts; Cards; Games;
Reading groups; Prayer groups; Movies; Shop-
ping trips; Dances/Social or cultural gatherings.

Eden Park Nursing Home
1800 Butterfield Ave, Utica, NY, 13501 (315)
797-3570
Admin Clara Mae Durant. *Medical Dir/Dir of
Nursing* Esther Johnston MD.
Licensure Skilled Care; Intermediate Care.
Beds 80. *Certified* Medicaid; Medicare.
Ownership Proprietary.
Admissions Requirements Minimum age 16;
Medical examination; Physician's request.
Staff Physicians 17 (pt); RNs 9 (ft), 4 (pt);
LPNs 13 (ft), 6 (pt); Nurses aides 44 (ft), 15
(pt); Physical therapists 1 (ft); Occupational
therapists 1 (pt); Speech therapists 1 (pt);
Activities coordinators 1 (ft); Dietitians 1 (pt);
Dentists 1 (pt); Podiatrists 1 (pt).
Facilities Dining room; Physical therapy room;
Activities room; Crafts room; Laundry room;
Barber/Beauty shop.
Activities Arts and Crafts; Cards; Games;
Reading groups; Prayer groups; Movies; Shopping trips; Dances/Social or cultural gatherings.
Description Rehabilitation services offered by
the home include occupational, physical, and
speech therapy. These therapies are initiated by
referral of physicians. The social service department initiates contact with the patient/resident
and their families at the time of application.
The activity department provides patients/resi-
dents the opportunity to select leisure time programs to suit individual interests. The
department provides birthday parties, gardening, and planned social functions such as

bingo, cocktail/social hours, and small group
activities for visually handicapped and others
with special needs. Religious and spiritual
needs are met through weekly services.

Faxton-Sunset-Saint Lukes Nursing Home Inc
1657 Sunset Ave, Utica, NY, 13502 (315)
797-7392
Admin Ronald T Cerow. *Medical Dir/Dir of
Nursing* Dr Albert Redmond.
Licensure Skilled Care; Health Related Care.
Beds SNF 59; Health Related Care 140. *Certi-
fied* Medicaid; Medicare.
Ownership Nonprofit.
Admissions Requirements Minimum age 16;
Medical examination; Physician's request.
Staff RNs 8 (ft), 7 (pt); LPNs 15 (ft), 13 (pt);
Nurses aides 42 (ft), 36 (pt); Activities coordi-
nators 1 (ft).
Facilities Dining room; Physical therapy room;
Activities room; Crafts room; Laundry room;
Barber/Beauty shop; Library; Resident lounges.
Activities Arts and Crafts; Cards; Games;
Reading groups; Prayer groups; Movies; Shop-
ping trips; Dances/Social or cultural gatherings.
Description A residential environment with
many private rooms providing personal care,
rehabilitative services, and social programs
designed for the needs of today's elderly. Centrally located on bus lines and adjacent to
medical services, stores, and restaurants.

Genesee Nursing Home
1634 Genesee St, Utica, NY, 13502 (315)
724-2151
Admin Stephen A Ross. *Medical Dir/Dir of
Nursing* Harry Levy.
Licensure Skilled Care. *Beds* 100. *Certified* Medicaid; Medicare.
Ownership Proprietary.
Admissions Requirements Minimum age 18;
Medical examination.
Staff Physicians 2 (ft), 6 (pt); RNs 28 (ft), 4
(pt); LPNs 12 (ft), 6 (pt); Orderlies 7 (ft); Nurses
aides 40 (ft), 8 (pt); Physical therapists 1 (ft), 1
(pt); Reality therapists 1 (pt); Recreational therapists 1 (ft), 1 (pt); Occupational therapists 1
(ft), 1 (pt); Activities coordinators 1 (ft); Dietitians 2 (ft), 1 (pt); Dentists 1 (pt); Podiatrists 1
(pt); Social workers 1 (ft); Others 5 (ft), 1 (pt).
Facilities Dining room; Physical therapy room;
Activities room; Crafts room; Barber/Beauty
shop.
Activities Arts and Crafts; Cards; Games;
Reading groups; Prayer groups; Movies; Shopping trips; Dances/Social or cultural gatherings.

Masonic Home and Health Facility
2150 Bleecker St, Utica, NY, 13504 (315)
798-4833
Admin Richard M Dowe. *Medical Dir/Dir of
Nursing* John Dadow MD.
Licensure Skilled Care; Intermediate Care.
Beds 388. *Certified* Medicaid; Medicare.
Ownership Nonprofit.
Staff Physicians 2 (ft); RNs 20 (ft), 7 (pt);
LPNs 27 (ft), 28 (pt); Orderlies 25 (ft); Nurses
aides 114 (ft), 74 (pt); Physical therapists 3 (ft);
Occupational therapists 2 (ft); Speech therapists
1 (ft); Activities coordinators 6 (ft), 2 (pt); Die-
titians 3 (ft); Dentists 1 (ft); Ophthalmologists 1
(ft); Podiatrists 1 (ft); Audiologists 1 (ft); 271
(ft), 24 (pt).

Affiliation Masons
Facilities Dining room; Physical therapy room; Activities room; Chapel; Crafts room; Laundry room; Barber/Beauty shop; Library.
Activities Arts and Crafts; Cards; Games; Reading groups; Prayer groups; Movies; Shopping trips; Dances/Social or cultural gatherings.

Saint Joseph Nursing Home Co of Utica Inc
2535 Genesee St, Utica, NY, 13501 (315) 797-1230
Admin Sr Shawn Flynn. *Medical Dir/Dir of Nursing* Walter J Karwowski MD.
Licensure Skilled Care. *Beds* 120. *Certified* Medicaid; Medicare.
Ownership Nonprofit.
Staff RNs 6 (ft), 8 (pt); LPNs 10 (ft), 6 (pt); Nurses aides 51 (ft), 36 (pt); Physical therapists 1 (pt); Occupational therapists 1 (pt); Dietitians 1 (pt).
Facilities Dining room; Physical therapy room; Activities room; Chapel; Laundry room; Barber/Beauty shop; Occupational therapy room; Library cart.
Activities Arts and Crafts; Cards; Games; Reading groups; Prayer groups; Movies; Shopping trips; Dances/Social or cultural gatherings; Pen Pal Club with 7th and 8th graders; Prenursery school activity weekly; Fund raising.

Saint Lukes Memorial Hospital Center—Allen Calder Skilled Nursing Facility
Box 479, Utica, NY, 13503 (315) 798-6000
Admin Michael Taurisano. *Medical Dir/Dir of Nursing* Irving Cramer MD.
Licensure Skilled Care. *Beds* 76. *Certified* Medicaid; Medicare.
Ownership Nonprofit.
Admissions Requirements Medical examination; Physician's request.
Staff RNs 12 (ft); LPNs 13 (ft), 9 (pt); Orderlies 4 (ft), 2 (pt); Nurses aides 21 (ft), 37 (pt); Physical therapists 5 (ft); Recreational therapists 1 (ft), 1 (pt); Occupational therapists 2 (ft); Speech therapists 1 (pt); Dietitians 1 (ft); Dentists 1 (ft); Audiologists 1 (pt).
Facilities Dining room; Physical therapy room; Activities room; Chapel; Crafts room.
Activities Arts and Crafts; Cards; Games; Prayer groups; Movies; Shopping trips; Dances/Social or cultural gatherings.

VALATIE

Barnwell Nursing Home and Health Facilities Inc
Church St, Valatie, NY, 12184 (518) 758-6222
Admin Penn J Steuerwald. *Medical Dir/Dir of Nursing* Dr Carl Whitbeck.
Licensure Skilled Care; Intermediate Care.
Beds 152. *Certified* Medicaid; Medicare.
Ownership Proprietary.
Admissions Requirements Physician's request.
Staff RNs; LPNs; Nurses aides; Physical therapists; Recreational therapists; Occupational therapists; Speech therapists; Activities coordinators; Dietitians; Dentists.
Facilities Dining room; Physical therapy room; Activities room; Chapel; Crafts room; Laundry room; Barber/Beauty shop; Library.
Activities Arts and Crafts; Cards; Games; Reading groups; Prayer groups; Shopping trips;

Dances/Social or cultural gatherings.
Description Beautiful, modern facility with warm, caring, loving staff.

VALLEY COTTAGE

Nyack Manor Nursing Home
Christian Herald Rd, Valley Cottage, NY, 10989 (914) 268-6861
Admin Herbert A Rothman. *Medical Dir/Dir of Nursing* Norman Rubinstein MD.
Licensure Skilled Care. *Beds* 160. *Certified* Medicaid; Medicare.
Ownership Proprietary.

Tolstoy Foundation Nursing Home Company Inc
Lake Rd, Valley Cottage, NY, 10989 (914) 268-6813
Admin Vladimir Grigoriev.
Licensure Skilled Care. *Beds* 96. *Certified* Medicaid; Medicare.
Ownership Nonprofit.
Admissions Requirements Minimum age 65; Medical examination.
Staff Physicians 1 (pt); RNs 12 (ft); LPNs 4 (ft); Orderlies 6 (ft); Nurses aides 40 (ft); Physical therapists 1 (pt); Reality therapists 1 (pt); Occupational therapists 1 (pt); Speech therapists 1 (pt); Activities coordinators 1 (ft); Dietitians 1 (pt); Dentists 1 (pt); Ophthalmologists 2 (pt); Podiatrists 2 (pt); Audiologists 1 (pt).
Facilities Dining room; Physical therapy room; Activities room; Chapel; Laundry room; Barber/Beauty shop; Library.
Activities Arts and Crafts; Cards; Games; Reading groups; Prayer groups; Movies; Shopping trips.
Description Facility is in a suburban/rural setting 20 miles from New York City with 5 acres of lawns with shade trees and flower beds; serves entire state admitting mainly persons of Slavic origin, providing multilingual staff.

VESTAL

Vestal-Johnson Inc*
860 Old Vestal Rd, Vestal, NY, 13850 (607) 754-4105
Admin Denise Adams.
Licensure Skilled Care. *Beds* 80. *Certified* Medicaid; Medicare.
Ownership Proprietary.

Willow Point Nursing Home and Health Related Facility
3700 Old Vestal Rd, Vestal, NY, 13850 (607) 729-1543
Admin Walter Stroly. *Medical Dir/Dir of Nursing* F Keith Kennedy MD.
Licensure Skilled Care; Health Related Care.
Beds SNF 162; HRC 180. *Certified* Medicaid; Medicare.
Ownership Public.
Admissions Requirements Minimum age 16.
Staff Physicians 1 (pt); RNs 29 (ft), 1 (pt); LPNs 24 (ft), 1 (pt); Nurses aides 127 (ft), 1 (pt); Physical therapists 1 (pt); Recreational therapists 5 (ft) Occupational therapists 1 (pt); Speech therapists 1 (pt); Activities coordinators 1 (ft); Dietitians 1 (ft); Dentists 1 (pt); Ophthal-

mologists 1 (pt); Podiatrists 1 (pt); Audiologists 1 (pt).
Facilities Dining room; Physical therapy room; Activities room; Chapel; Crafts room; Laundry room; Barber/Beauty shop.
Activities Arts and Crafts; Cards; Games; Reading groups; Prayer groups; Movies; Shopping trips; Dances/Social or cultural gatherings.
Description Home is one of a very few chosen to affiliate with SUNY Binghamton on a Robert Wood Johnson Foundation grant for a teaching nursing home.

WAPPINGERS FALLS

Central Dutchess Nursing Home Inc*
37 Mesier Ave, Wappingers Falls, NY, 12590 (914) 297-3793
Admin Marie Mahr.
Licensure Skilled Care. *Beds* 62. *Certified* Medicaid; Medicare.
Ownership Proprietary.

WARSAW

East Side Nursing Home
62 Prospect St, Warsaw, NY, 14569 (716) 786-8151
Admin Sophia Hayes. *Medical Dir/Dir of Nursing* Dr G Stanley Baker.
Licensure Skilled Care. *Beds* 80. *Certified* Medicaid; Medicare.
Ownership Proprietary.
Staff Physicians 8 (pt); RNs 5 (ft), 5 (pt); LPNs 5 (ft), 7 (pt); Orderlies 1 (ft), 4 (pt); Nurses aides 28 (ft), 16 (pt); Physical therapists 1 (pt); Speech therapists 1 (pt); Activities coordinators 1 (ft); Dietitians 1 (pt); Dentists 1 (pt); Podiatrists 1 (pt).
Facilities Dining room; Physical therapy room; Laundry room; Barber/Beauty shop.
Activities Arts and Crafts; Games; Prayer groups; Movies; Dances/Social or cultural gatherings.
Description East Side Nursing Home is a 3-story facility which accomodates 80 patients. It is a modern facility convenient to downtown Warsaw and is located in a wooded area. We strive to maintain a home-like atmosphere to enable the patient's stay to be pleasant and comfortable.

Manor Oak Skilled Nursing Facilities Inc
283 N Main St, Warsaw, NY, 14569 (716) 786-2211
Admin Peter Young. *Medical Dir/Dir of Nursing* Frederich Downs MD.
Licensure Skilled Care. *Beds* 100. *Certified* Medicaid; Medicare.
Ownership Proprietary.
Admissions Requirements Minimum age 16; Medical examination; Physician's request.
Staff RNs 5 (ft), 5 (pt); LPNs 8 (ft), 7 (pt); Orderlies 6 (ft); Nurses aides 31 (ft), 40 (pt); Physical therapists 1 (ft); Speech therapists 1 (pt); Activities coordinators 1 (ft); Dietitians 1 (ft); Dentists 1 (pt); Ophthalmologists 1 (pt); Podiatrists 1 (pt); Audiologists 1 (pt).
Facilities Dining room; Physical therapy room; Activities room; Crafts room; Laundry room; Barber/Beauty shop.

Activities Arts and Crafts; Cards; Games; Reading groups; Prayer groups; Movies; Shopping trips; Dances/Social or cultural gatherings; Adopt-a-grandparent; Fitness classes; Special dinners; Trips to parks, zoo, racetrack, and restaurants.
Description Facility features an excellent activities program, rehabilitation oriented nursing care, 3 consecutive "no-deficiency" surveys by NY Health Department; progressive and expanding physical therapy program.

Wyoming County Community Hospital—Skilled Nursing Facility*
400 N Main st, Warsaw, NY, 14569 (716) 786-2233
Admin Ralph Waite.
Licensure Skilled Care. *Beds* 72. *Certified* Medicaid; Medicare.
Ownership Public.

WATERLOO

Seneca Nursing Home*
200 Douglas Dr, Waterloo, NY, 13165 (315) 539-9202
Admin James West.
Licensure Skilled Care; Intermediate Care. *Beds* 80. *Certified* Medicaid; Medicare.
Ownership Proprietary.

Waterloo Memorial Hospital Inc-Taylor/Brown Memorial Hospital*
E Main St, Waterloo, NY, 13165 (315) 539-9204
Licensure Intermediate Care. *Beds* 33.
Ownership Nonprofit.

WATERTOWN

Madonna Home of Mercy Hospital—Watertown
218 Stone St, Watertown, NY, 13601 (315) 782-7400
Admin Sr Mary Pierre Seguin. *Medical Dir/Dir of Nursing* Warren Daub MD.
Licensure Skilled Care; Intermediate Care. *Beds* 140. *Certified* Medicaid; Medicare.
Ownership Nonprofit.
Admissions Requirements Minimum age 16; Medical examination; Physician's request.
Staff Physicians 1 (pt); RNs 19 (ft); LPNs 27 (ft), 1 (pt); Orderlies 4 (ft); Nurses aides 68 (ft); Physical therapists 1 (pt); Reality therapists 1 (pt); Recreational therapists 3 (ft); Occupational therapists 1 (pt); Speech therapists 1 (pt); Activities coordinators 1 (ft); Dietitians 2 (ft); Dentists 1 (pt); Audiologists 1 (pt).
Affiliation Roman Catholic
Facilities Dining room; Physical therapy room; Activities room; Chapel; Crafts room; Laundry room; Barber/Beauty shop; Library; Handicap van.
Activities Arts and Crafts; Cards; Games; Reading groups; Prayer groups; Movies; Shopping trips; Dances/Social or cultural gatherings.
Description A day treatment program accommodates 20-30 inpatients daily; utilizes basic principles of reality therapy; encourages socialization within the group and plans special activities.

Samaritan-Keep Nursing Home Inc
133 Pratt St, Watertown, NY, 13601 (315) 785-4400
Admin John Turner. *Medical Dir/Dir of Nursing* Paul M Read MD.
Licensure Skilled Care; Intermediate Care. *Beds* 196. *Certified* Medicaid; Medicare.
Ownership Nonprofit.
Staff Physicians 1 (ft); RNs 14 (ft), 6 (pt); LPNs 27 (ft), 13 (pt); Nurses aides 81 (ft), 33 (pt); Physical therapists 1 (pt); Occupational therapists 1 (ft); Speech therapists 1 (pt); Activities coordinators 1 (ft); Dietitians 1 (ft); Dentists 1 (pt); Podiatrists 1 (pt); Audiologists 1 (pt).
Facilities Dining room; Physical therapy room; Activities room; Crafts room; Laundry room; Barber/Beauty shop; Library.
Activities Arts and Crafts; Cards; Games; Reading groups; Prayer groups; Movies; Shopping trips; Dances/Social or cultural gatherings.
Description Facility is adjacent to and affiliated with a 258-bed general hospital and with 2 housing facilities for the elderly and handicapped. Operates a comprehensive and therapeutic day care program for handicapped or elderly.

WATERVILLE

Harding Nursing Home
220 Tower St, Waterville, NY, 13480 (315) 841-4156
Admin Robert Harding. *Medical Dir/Dir of Nursing* Robert Dolorme MD.
Licensure Skilled Care; Intermediate Care. *Beds* SNF 62; ICF 30. *Certified* Medicaid; Medicare.
Ownership Proprietary.
Admissions Requirements Medical examination.
Facilities Dining room; Physical therapy room; Activities room; Crafts room; Barber/Beauty shop.
Activities Arts and Crafts; Cards; Games; Reading groups; Prayer groups; Movies; Shopping trips; Dances/Social or cultural gatherings.

WAVERLY

Tioga General Hospital*
32 Ithica St, Waverly, NY, 14892 (607) 565-2861
Licensure Intermediate Care. *Beds* 51.
Ownership Nonprofit.

Tioga Nursing Home Inc*
37 N Chemung St, Waverly, NY, 14892 (607) 565-2861
Admin Fred Kauffman.
Licensure Skilled Care. *Beds* 80. *Certified* Medicaid; Medicare.
Ownership Nonprofit.

WEBSTER

Hill Haven Nursing Home
1550 Empire Blvd, Webster, NY, 14580 (716) 671-4300
Admin Robert Goldstein. *Medical Dir/Dir of Nursing* Zsolt de Papp.

Licensure Skilled Care; Intermediate Care. *Beds* SNF 187; ICF 168. *Certified* Medicaid; Medicare.
Ownership Proprietary.
Staff RNs 21 (ft), 21 (pt); LPNs 21 (ft), 14 (pt); Nurses aides 65 (ft), 67 (pt); Physical therapists 1 (ft); Occupational therapists 1 (pt); Activities coordinators 2 (ft).
Facilities Dining room; Physical therapy room; Activities room; Crafts room; Laundry room; Barber/Beauty shop; Library.
Activities Arts and Crafts; Cards; Games; Prayer groups; Movies; Shopping trips; Dances/Social or cultural gatherings.
Description Hill Haven tries to give as much service as possible with dietary, physical therapy, occupational therapy, social services, maintenance, dental, and podiatry within the facility. Located in a wooded area in a secured, safe, protected atmosphere.

Maplewood Nursing Home
100 Daniel Dr, Webster, NY, 14580 (716) 872-1800
Admin James Chambery. *Medical Dir/Dir of Nursing* Dr Robert Wells.
Licensure Skilled Care. *Beds* 72. *Certified* Medicaid; Medicare.
Ownership Proprietary.
Admissions Requirements Medical examination; Physician's request.
Staff RNs 4 (ft), 12 (pt); LPNs 4 (ft), 6 (pt); Physical therapists 1 (pt); Reality therapists 1 (pt); Recreational therapists 1 (pt); Occupational therapists 1 (pt); Speech therapists 1 (pt); Activities coordinators 1 (ft); Dietitians 1 (pt); Dentists 1 (pt); Podiatrists 1 (pt).
Facilities Dining room; Physical therapy room; Activities room; Barber/Beauty shop.
Activities Arts and Crafts; Cards; Games; Prayer groups; Shopping trips; Dances/Social or cultural gatherings.

WELLSVILLE

Wellsville Highland Inc
160 Seneca St, Wellsville, NY, 14895 (716) 593-3750
Admin Beverly Rahr. *Medical Dir/Dir of Nursing* Dr Ogden.
Licensure Skilled Care. *Beds* 80. *Certified* Medicaid; Medicare.
Ownership Proprietary.
Admissions Requirements Minimum age 21.
Staff RNs 5 (ft), 2 (pt); LPNs 6 (ft), 3 (pt); Orderlies 1 (pt); Nurses aides 20 (ft), 22 (pt); Physical therapists 1 (pt); Speech therapists 1 (pt); Activities coordinators 1 (ft), 1 (pt); Dietitians 1 (pt); Dentists 1 (pt).
Facilities Dining room; Physical therapy room; Activities room; Crafts room; Laundry room; Barber/Beauty shop.
Activities Arts and Crafts; Cards; Games; Reading groups; Prayer groups; Movies; Shopping trips.

WEST BABYLON

Berkshire Nursing Center Inc*
10 Berkshire Rd, West Babylon, NY, 11704 (516) 587-0600

Admin Stuart Goldberg.
Licensure Skilled Care. *Beds* 175. *Certified* Medicaid; Medicare.
Ownership Proprietary.

WEST ISLIP

Consolation Nursing Home Inc
111 Beach Dr, West Islip, NY, 11795 (516) 587-1600
Admin Audrey Hansen. *Medical Dir/Dir of Nursing* Dr Martin D Podgainy.
Licensure Skilled Care; Intermediate Care.
Beds 250. *Certified* Medicaid; Medicare.
Ownership Nonprofit.
Admissions Requirements Medical examination; Physician's request.
Staff RNs 11 (ft), 9 (pt); LPNs 19 (ft), 8 (pt); Nurses aides 57 (ft), 26 (pt); Physical therapists 1 (ft), 1 (pt); Recreational therapists 3 (ft), 2 (pt); Activities coordinators 1 (ft); Dietitians 1 (ft).
Affiliation Roman Catholic
Facilities Dining room; Physical therapy room; Activities room; Chapel; Crafts room; Laundry room; Barber/Beauty shop; Library.
Activities Arts and Crafts; Games; Reading groups; Movies; Shopping trips; Dances/Social or cultural gatherings.
Description Discussions, games, and competitions are held in conjunction with other nursing homes; from May through October programs are held in outdoor pavilion; at other times the auditorium is used.

WEST SENECA

Seneca Manor
2987 Seneca St, West Seneca, NY, 14224 (716) 828-0500
Admin Eugene L Urban. *Medical Dir/Dir of Nursing* Dr Herle.
Licensure Skilled Care; Intermediate Care.
Beds 80. *Certified* Medicaid; Medicare.
Ownership Proprietary.
Admissions Requirements Medical examination; Physician's request.
Staff RNs 6 (ft), 4 (pt); LPNs 14 (ft), 8 (pt); Orderlies 2 (ft), 1 (pt); Nurses aides 25 (ft), 12 (pt); Physical therapists 1 (pt); Occupational therapists 1 (ft); Speech therapists 1 (pt); Activities coordinators 1 (ft); Dietitians 1 (pt).
Facilities Dining room; Physical therapy room; Activities room; Barber/Beauty shop.
Activities Arts and Crafts; Cards; Games; Reading groups; Prayer groups; Movies; Shopping trips; Dances/Social or cultural gatherings.

Seneca Manor
2987 Seneca St, West Seneca, NY, 14224
Admin Eugene L Urban. *Medical Dir/Dir of Nursing* Dr Herle.
Licensure Skilled Care; Intermediate Care.
Beds SNF 80; ICF 80. *Certified* Medicaid; Medicare.
Ownership Proprietary.
Admissions Requirements Minimum age 16.
Staff Physicians; RNs; LPNs; Orderlies; Nurses aides; Physical therapists; Reality therapists; Recreational therapists; Occupational therapists; Speech therapists; Activities coordinators; Dietitians; Dentists; Ophthalmologists;

Podiatrists.
Facilities Dining room; Physical therapy room; Activities room; Crafts room; Laundry room; Barber/Beauty shop; Library.
Activities Arts and Crafts; Cards; Games; Reading groups; Prayer groups; Movies; Shopping trips; Dances/Social or cultural gatherings.

WHEATFIELD

North Gate Manor
7264 Nash Rd, Wheatfield, NY, 14120
Admin Dennis M Piatz. *Medical Dir/Dir of Nursing* Richard Carlson MD.
Licensure Skilled Care; Intermediate Care.
Beds 160. *Certified* Medicaid; Medicare.
Ownership Proprietary.
Admissions Requirements Minimum age 16.
Staff RNs 9 (ft), 5 (pt); LPNs 12 (ft), 14 (pt); Orderlies 9 (ft), 1 (pt); Nurses aides 36 (ft), 44 (pt); Physical therapists 1 (pt); Recreational therapists 1 (ft).
Facilities Dining room; Physical therapy room; Activities room; Crafts room; Laundry room; Barber/Beauty shop.
Activities Arts and Crafts; Cards; Games; Reading groups; Prayer groups; Movies; Shopping trips; Dances/Social or cultural gatherings; Annual boat ride.
Description VA approved.

WHITE PLAINS

The Nathan Miller Center for Nursing Care Inc
37 DeKalb Ave, White Plains, NY, 10605 (914) 946-1440
Admin Dulcy B Miller. *Medical Dir/Dir of Nursing* Michael B Miller MD.
Licensure Skilled Care. *Beds* 65. *Certified* Medicaid; Medicare.
Ownership Nonprofit.
Admissions Requirements Minimum age 18; Medical examination; Physician's request.
Staff Physicians 1 (pt); RNs 5 (ft), 4 (pt); LPNs 8 (ft), 3 (pt); Orderlies 2 (ft); Nurses aides 31 (ft), 5 (pt); Physical therapists 1 (pt); Recreational therapists 1 (pt); Occupational therapists 1 (pt); Speech therapists 1 (pt); Activities coordinators 1 (ft); Dietitians 1 (pt); Dentists 1 (pt); Podiatrists 1 (pt).
Facilities Dining room; Physical therapy room; Activities room; Laundry room; Barber/Beauty shop.
Activities Arts and Crafts; Cards; Games; Reading groups; Prayer groups; Movies; Dances/Social or cultural gatherings.
Description The Nathan Miller Center for Nursing Care, Inc is a modern 65-bed skilled nursing facility providing inpatient long-term care to the chronically ill elderly with severe physical and/or psychiatric disabilities. Its main goal is to help its patients function at their highest level physically, socially, and emotionally in a supportive therapeutic environment. The Nathan Miller Center has pioneered in medical, social, and rehabilitative care of the chronically ill aged and has supported research that will bring about improved care for this growing segment of our population.

Tibbits Health Care Facility
12 Tibbits Ave, White Plains, NY, 10606 (914) 428-0910
Admin James Marmon.
Licensure Skilled Care; Health Related Care.
Beds SNF 102; HRF 128. *Certified* Medicaid; Medicare.
Ownership Proprietary.
Staff RNs 10 (ft), 4 (pt); LPNs 13 (ft), 5 (pt); Orderlies 1 (ft); Nurses aides 40 (ft), 26 (pt); Activities coordinators 4 (ft); Dietitians 1 (ft).
Facilities Dining room; Physical therapy room; Activities room; Chapel; Barber/Beauty shop.
Activities Arts and Crafts; Cards; Games; Prayer groups; Movies; Shopping trips; Dances/Social or cultural gatherings.

White Plains Center for Nursing Care
220 W Post Rd, White Plains, NY, 10606 (914) 946-8005
Admin Dulcy B Miller. *Medical Dir/Dir of Nursing* Michael B Miller MD.
Licensure Skilled Care. *Beds* 88. *Certified* Medicaid; Medicare.
Ownership Proprietary.
Admissions Requirements Minimum age 18; Medical examination; Physician's request.
Staff Physicians 1 (pt); RNs 6 (ft), 4 (pt); LPNs 9 (ft), 1 (pt); Orderlies 1 (ft); Nurses aides 44 (ft), 4 (pt); Physical therapists 1 (pt); Recreational therapists 1 (ft); Occupational therapists 1 (pt); Speech therapists 1 (pt); Activities coordinators 1 (ft); Dietitians 1 (pt); Dentists 1 (pt); Podiatrists 1 (pt); Audiologists 1 (pt).
Facilities Dining room; Activities room; Laundry room; Barber/Beauty shop.
Activities Arts and Crafts; Cards; Games; Reading groups; Prayer groups; Movies; Dances/Social or cultural gatherings.
Description White Plains Center for Nursing Care is a modern, 88-bed skilled nursing facility providing inpatient, long-term care to the chronically ill elderly with severe physical and/or psychiatric disabilities. Its main goal is to help its patients function at their highest level physically, socially, and emotionally in a supportive therapeutic environment. White Plains Center for Nursing Care has pioneered in medical, social, and rehabilitative care of the chronically ill aged and has supported research that will bring about improved care for this growing segment of our population.

WHITESTONE

Bridge View Nursing Home
143-10 20th Ave, Whitestone, NY, 11357 (212) 961-1212
Admin Henry Jacoby. *Medical Dir/Dir of Nursing* Alexander Sebo MD.
Licensure Skilled Care. *Beds* 200. *Certified* Medicaid; Medicare.
Ownership Proprietary.
Admissions Requirements Medical examination; Physician's request.
Staff Physicians 3 (pt); RNs 4 (ft); LPNs 15 (ft); Orderlies 6 (ft); Nurses aides 34 (ft); Physical therapists 1 (ft); Recreational therapists 3 (ft); Occupational therapists 1 (pt); Speech therapists 1 (pt); Dietitians 1 (ft); Dentists 1 (pt); Ophthalmologists 1 (pt); Podiatrists 1 (pt); Audiologists 1 (pt).

Clearview Nursing Home*
157-15 19th Ave, Whitestone, NY, 11357 (212) 746-0400
Admin Raymond Small.
Licensure Skilled Care. *Beds* 179. *Certified* Medicaid; Medicare.
Ownership Proprietary.

WILLIAMSVILLE

Amherst Presbyterian Nursing Center*
200 Bassett Rd, Williamsville, NY, 14221 (716) 884-4252
Licensure Intermediate Care. *Beds* 120.
Ownership Nonprofit.
Affiliation Presbyterian

Heathwood Health Care Center Inc
815 Hopkins Rd, Williamsville, NY, 14221 (716) 688-0111
Admin Robert M Chur. *Medical Dir/Dir of Nursing* Dr Ida Levine.
Licensure Skilled Care; Health Related Care. *Beds* SNF 120; HRC 40. *Certified* Medicaid; Medicare.
Ownership Proprietary.
Admissions Requirements Minimum age 16; Medical examination; Physician's request.
Staff Physicians 5 (pt); RNs 10 (ft), 9 (pt); LPNs 13 (ft), 13 (pt); Nurses aides 38 (ft), 37 (pt); Physical therapists 2 (pt); Recreational therapists 1 (ft); Occupational therapists 1 (pt); Speech therapists 2 (pt); Activities coordinators 2 (ft), 1 (pt); Dietitians 1 (pt); Dentists 1 (pt); Podiatrists 1 (pt).
Facilities Dining room; Physical therapy room; Activities room; Chapel; Crafts room; Laundry room; Barber/Beauty shop.
Activities Arts and Crafts; Cards; Games; Reading groups; Prayer groups; Movies; Shopping trips; Dances/Social or cultural gatherings.
Description Besides serving 120 SNF and 40 HRF residents, the staff of Heathwood provides medical services for up to 15 participants a day in the Medical Day Care Program (offered 3 hours per day during weekdays) for persons from Amherst and nearby communities. A rehabilitative approach—physical, social, emotional, and spiritual—is emphasized in the health care planning and treatment programs. The exterior is accented by a large front porch, and a home-like interior has been created with colonial colors and decor.

Saint Francis Home of Williamsville*
147 Reist St, Williamsville, NY, 14221 (716) 633-5400
Admin Daniel Kenny.
Licensure Skilled Care; Intermediate Care. *Beds* 50. *Certified* Medicaid; Medicare.
Ownership Nonprofit.

Williamsville Suburban Nursing Home*
193 S Union Rd, Williamsville, NY, 14221 (716) 632-6152
Licensure Intermediate Care. *Beds* 80.
Ownership Proprietary.

Williamsville View Manor*
165 S Union Rd, Williamsville, NY, 14213 (716) 633-9610
Licensure Intermediate Care. *Beds* 140.
Ownership Nonprofit.

WOODBURY

United Presbyterian Home at Syosset Inc
378 Syosset-Woodbury Rd, Woodbury, NY, 11797 (516) 921-3900
Admin Alfred S Heim. *Medical Dir/Dir of Nursing* Dr Trousdell.
Licensure Skilled Care; Intermediate Care. *Beds* 306. *Certified* Medicaid; Medicare.
Ownership Nonprofit.
Admissions Requirements Minimum age 16; Medical examination.
Staff Physicians 2 (ft); RNs 44 (ft), 13 (pt); LPNs 36 (ft), 18 (pt); Orderlies 5 (ft), 1 (pt); Nurses aides 155 (ft), 56 (pt); Physical therapists 2 (ft); Activities coordinators 12 (ft), 7 (pt); Dietitians 3 (ft), 2 (pt).
Affiliation Presbyterian
Facilities Dining room; Physical therapy room; Activities room; Chapel; Crafts room; Laundry room; Barber/Beauty shop; Library; Game room; Music room.
Activities Arts and Crafts; Cards; Games; Reading groups; Movies; Shopping trips; Dances/Social or cultural gatherings; May festival; Candlelight dinner; Variety shows; Barbeques.

Woodbury Health Related Facility*
8565 Jericho Tpke, Woodbury, NY, 11797 (516) 367-3400
Licensure Intermediate Care. *Beds* 200.
Ownership Proprietary.

Woodbury Nursing Home*
8533 Jericho Turnpike, Woodbury, NY, 11797 (516) 692-4100
Admin Maxwell White.
Licensure Skilled Care. *Beds* 123. *Certified* Medicaid; Medicare.
Ownership Proprietary.

WOODMERE

Woodmere Health Related Facility
130 Irving Pl, Woodmere, NY, 11598 (516) 374-9300
Admin Miriam Feldman. *Medical Dir/Dir of Nursing* Dr Harold Langs.
Licensure Skilled Care. *Beds* 186. *Certified* Medicaid; Medicare.
Ownership Proprietary.
Admissions Requirements Minimum age 18.
Staff Physicians; RNs; LPNs; Orderlies; Nurses aides; Physical therapists; Reality therapists; Recreational therapists; Occupational therapists; Speech therapists; Activities coordinators; Dietitians; Dentists; Ophthalmologists; Podiatrists; Audiologists; Nursing care coord.
Facilities Dining room; Physical therapy room; Activities room; Crafts room; Laundry room; Barber/Beauty shop; Library.
Activities Arts and Crafts; Cards; Games; Reading groups; Prayer groups; Movies; Shopping trips; Dances/Social or cultural gatherings; Various outdoor trips; Picnics.

Description Facility caters to cerebral palsy patients, veterans, and geriatrics, giving an age spread of 21 to 104. Programs are geared accordingly to the various age groups.

YAPHANK

Suffolk Infirmary*
Yaphank Ave, Yaphank, NY, 11980 (516) 924-4300
Admin Jerome Duel.
Licensure Skilled Care. *Beds* 215. *Certified* Medicaid; Medicare.
Ownership Public.

YONKERS

Hudson View Nursing Home Inc*
65 Ashburton Ave, Yonkers, NY, 10701 (914) 963-4000
Admin Scott Sandford.
Licensure Skilled Care. *Beds* 300. *Certified* Medicaid; Medicare.
Ownership Proprietary.

Jewish Guild for the Blind/Home for the Aged Blind
75 Stratton St, Yonkers, NY, 10701 (212) 365-3700 and (914) 963-4661
Licensure Skilled Care; Health Related Care. *Beds* SNF 47; HRF 125. *Certified* Medicaid; Medicare.
Ownership Nonprofit.
Admissions Requirements Medical examination.
Affiliation Jewish
Facilities Dining room; Physical therapy room; Activities room; Crafts room; Barber/Beauty shop.

New Sans Souci Nursing Home
115 Park Ave, Yonkers, NY, 10703 (914) 423-9800
Admin Marylin Mittman. *Medical Dir/Dir of Nursing* Stanley Pianin.
Licensure Skilled Care. *Beds* 120. *Certified* Medicaid; Medicare.
Ownership Proprietary.
Staff RNs 6 (ft), 10 (pt); LPNs 13 (ft), 6 (pt); Orderlies 2 (ft), 2 (pt); Nurses aides 34 (ft), 15 (pt); Physical therapists 1 (ft); Recreational therapists 1 (ft); Occupational therapists 2 (pt); Speech therapists 1 (pt); Activities coordinators 1 (ft), 2 (pt); Dietitians 1 (ft), 1 (pt).
Facilities Dining room; Physical therapy room; Activities room; Chapel; Crafts room; Barber-/Beauty shop.
Activities Arts and Crafts; Cards; Games; Prayer groups; Movies; Dances/Social or cultural gatherings; Boat trips; Barbecues.

Saint Josephs Hospital Nursing Home
127 S Broadway, Yonkers, NY, 10701 (914) 965-6400
Admin Wesley G Hyde. *Medical Dir/Dir of Nursing* Dr Thomas Kalohthaler.
Licensure Skilled Care; Intermediate Care. *Beds* SNF 160; ICF 40. *Certified* Medicaid; Medicare.
Ownership Nonprofit.
Admissions Requirements Minimum age 16;

Medical examination; Physician's request.
Affiliation Roman Catholic
Facilities Dining room; Physical therapy room;
Activities room; Chapel; Barber/Beauty shop.
Activities Arts and Crafts; Cards; Games;
Reading groups; Prayer groups; Movies; Dances/Social or cultural gatherings.
Description Facility also offers adult day care
and long-term home health care programs.

NORTH CAROLINA

AHOSKIE

Guardian Care of Ahoskie*
Stoke St Extension, Ahoskie, NC, 27910 (919)
332-2126
Admin Yvonne F Jernigan.
Licensure Intermediate Care. *Beds* 131. *Certified* Medicaid.

ALBEMARLE

North Carolina Lutheran Homes Inc
Rt 1 Box 204, Albemarle, NC, 28001 (704)
982-8191
Admin D Russell Myers Jr. *Medical Dir/Dir of Nursing* Thomas F Kelley MD.
Licensure Skilled Care; Intermediate Care;
Home for the Aged. *Beds* SNF 50; ICF 4;
Home for the Aged 21. *Certified* Medicaid;
Medicare.
Admissions Requirements Minimum age 60;
Medical examination; Physician's request.
Staff Physicians 13 (pt); RNs 6 (ft), 1 (pt);
LPNs 7 (ft), 4 (pt); Orderlies 5 (ft), 2 (pt);
Nurses aides 18 (ft), 3 (pt); Activities coordinators 1 (ft); Dietitians 1 (pt); Dentists 1 (pt).
Affiliation Lutheran
Facilities Dining room; Physical therapy room;
Chapel; Crafts room; Laundry room; Barber-
/Beauty shop; Library.
Activities Arts and Crafts; Games; Movies;
Shopping trips; Dances/Social or cultural gatherings.

Piedmont Nursing Center*
PO Box 1250, Albemarle, NC, 28001 (704)
983-1195
Admin Melton W Mullinix.
Licensure Skilled Care; Intermediate Care.
Beds SNF 60; ICF 60. *Certified* Medicaid;
Medicare.

ASHEBORO

Brian Center—Asheboro
230 E Presnell St, PO Drawer 1928, Asheboro,
NC, 27203 (919) 629-1447
Admin Leonard P Smith. *Medical Dir/Dir of Nursing* Ken Gobel MD.
Licensure Skilled Care; Intermediate Care.
Beds SNF 90; ICF 124. *Certified* Medicaid;
Medicare.
Admissions Requirements Minimum age 18.

Staff Physicians 22 (pt); RNs 10 (ft), 4 (pt);
LPNs 20 (ft), 10 (pt); Orderlies 4 (ft), 1 (pt);
Nurses aides 65 (ft), 15 (pt); Physical therapists
2 (pt); Speech therapists 1 (pt); Activities coordinators 3 (ft); Dietitians 1 (pt); Dentists 1 (pt);
Ophthalmologists 3 (pt); Podiatrists 1 (pt);
Audiologists 1 (pt).
Facilities Dining room; Physical therapy room;
Activities room; Crafts room; Laundry room;
Barber/Beauty shop; Library.
Activities Arts and Crafts; Cards; Games; Prayer groups; Movies; Shopping trips; Dances/Social or cultural gatherings.
Description Facility features 24-hour RN
supervision, outstanding nursing rehabilitation
program; Alzheimer's support group, stroke
club, resident council, unique, quality assurance
programs in all departments; family support
programs; special programs to prevent decubitus ulcers directed by dermatologist; in-house
dentistry; medical exam and treatment areas.

Clapp's Convalescent Nursing Home Inc*
Rt 1, Box 395, Coleridge Rd, Asheboro, NC,
27203 (919) 625-2074
Admin George Donald Clapp.
Licensure Skilled Care. *Beds* 26. *Certified* Medicaid; Medicare.

ASHEVILLE

Aston Park Health Care Center Inc
380 Brevard Rd, Asheville, NC, 28806 (704)
253-4437
Admin Martha M Smart. *Medical Dir/Dir of Nursing* Dr Claude Steen.
Licensure Skilled Care; Intermediate Care.
Beds SNF 54; ICF 66. *Certified* Medicaid;
Medicare.
Admissions Requirements Medical examination; Physician's request.
Staff RNs 8 (ft); LPNs 15 (ft); Orderlies 8 (ft);
Nurses aides 46 (ft); Physical therapists 1 (pt);
Speech therapists 1 (pt); Activities coordinators
1 (ft); Dietitians 1 (ft); Dentists 1 (pt); Podiatrists 1 (pt).
Facilities Dining room; Physical therapy room;
Activities room; Crafts room; Barber/Beauty
shop.
Activities Arts and Crafts; Cards; Games;
Reading groups; Prayer groups; Movies; Shopping trips; Dances/Social or cultural gatherings.

Biltmore Manor*
PO Box 15073, 14 All Souls Crescent, Asheville, NC, 28803 (704) 274-2336
Admin Robert C Brady.
Licensure Skilled Care; Intermediate Care;
Home for the Aged. *Beds* SNF 53; ICF 26;
Home for the Aged 21. *Certified* Medicaid;
Medicare.

Brentwood Hills Nursing Center*
PO Box 8365, 500 Beaverdam, Asheville, NC,
28814 (704) 254-8833
Admin Jacqueline R Rio.
Licensure Skilled Care. *Beds* 77. *Certified* Medicaid; Medicare.

Brian Center of Nursing Care—Asheville
67 Mountainbrook Rd, Asheville, NC, 28805
(704) 258-8787
Admin Virginia Friedman. *Medical Dir/Dir of Nursing* Dr Olson.
Licensure Skilled Care; Intermediate Care;
Home for the Aged. *Beds* SNF 40; ICF 20;
Home for the Aged 12.
Staff Physicians 12 (ft); RNs 10 (ft), 2 (pt);
LPNs 4 (ft), 2 (pt); Orderlies 3 (ft); Nurses aides
28 (ft); Physical therapists 1 (ft); Occupational
therapists 1 (pt); Speech therapists 1 (pt);
Activities coordinators 1 (ft); Dietitians 1 (ft);
Dentists 1 (pt); Ophthalmologists 1 (pt); Podiatrists 1 (pt); Audiologists 1 (pt).
Facilities Dining room; Activities room; Laundry room; Barber/Beauty shop; Library.
Activities Arts and Crafts; Games; Prayer
groups; Shopping trips; Dances/Social or cultural gatherings.
Description We are situated on top of a
mountain with a magnificent view.

Brooks-Howell Home
29 Spears Ave, Asheville, NC, 28801 (704)
253-6712
Admin Vivian McGraw.
Licensure Skilled Care; Intermediate Care.
Beds SNF 40; ICF 18.
Affiliation Methodist
Facilities Dining room; Physical therapy room;
Activities room; Chapel; Crafts room; Laundry
room; Barber/Beauty shop; Library.
Activities Arts and Crafts; Cards; Games;
Reading groups; Prayer groups; Movies; Shopping trips; Dances/Social or cultural gatherings.

Deerfield Episcopal Retirement Community Inc
1617 Hendersonville Rd, Asheville, NC, 28803
(704) 274-1531
Admin John D Olofson. *Medical Dir/Dir of Nursing* Dr Woodard F Farmer.
Licensure Skilled Care. *Beds* 31.
Admissions Requirements Minimum age 62; Medical examination.
Staff RNs 5 (ft), 6 (pt); LPNs 1 (ft), 1 (pt); Nurses aides 12 (ft), 8 (pt); Activities coordinators 1 (ft).
Affiliation Episcopal
Facilities Dining room; Activities room; Chapel; Crafts room; Laundry room; Barber/Beauty shop; Library.
Activities Arts and Crafts; Cards; Games; Reading groups; Prayer groups; Movies; Shopping trips; Dances/Social or cultural gatherings.
Description Facility has an expansion program in progress that plans to add up to 18 houses and 12 apartments. The skilled care unit will increase to 35 beds, and intermediate-type care will add 14 beds. Beautiful setting in western North Carolina mountains with easy access to city and cultural events. Maximum population to be 150.

Hillhaven Rehabilitation and Convalescent Center*
91 Victoria Rd, Asheville, NC, 28801 (704) 253-0076
Admin Turner T Prickett III.
Licensure Skilled Care; Intermediate Care. *Beds* SNF 60; ICF 60. *Certified* Medicaid; Medicare.

Hillside Nursing Home Inc
PO Box 1530, Asheville, NC, 28802 (704) 254-2151
Admin Harry W Tolley. *Medical Dir/Dir of Nursing* Dr Everett Smith MD.
Licensure Intermediate Care; Home for the Aged. *Beds* ICF 18; Home for the Aged 25. *Certified* Medicaid.
Admissions Requirements Medical examination; Physician's request.
Staff Physicians 5 (ft); RNs 2 (ft); LPNs 3 (ft); Orderlies 2 (ft); Nurses aides 10 (ft), 8 (pt); Physical therapists 3 (pt); Activities coordinators 1 (ft); Dietitians 1 (ft); Dentists 2 (pt); Podiatrists 1 (pt).
Facilities Dining room; Activities room; Laundry room.
Activities Arts and Crafts; Cards; Games; Reading groups; Shopping trips; Dances/Social or cultural gatherings.
Description Facility features an outstanding activity department including a garden club.

Victoria Health Care Center
104 Victoria Rd, Asheville, NC, 28801 (704) 253-4418
Admin Deura G Koontz. *Medical Dir/Dir of Nursing* John Kelly MD.
Licensure Skilled Care; Intermediate Care. *Beds* SNF 60; ICF 60. *Certified* Medicaid; Medicare.
Admissions Requirements Medical examination; Physician's request.
Staff RNs 5 (ft); LPNs 12 (ft); Orderlies 2 (ft); Physical therapists 3 (ft); Recreational therapists 1 (ft); Speech therapists 1 (pt); Activities coordinators 1 (ft); Dietitians 1 (ft); Dentists 1 (pt).

Facilities Dining room; Physical therapy room; Activities room; Laundry room; Barber/Beauty shop.
Activities Arts and Crafts; Cards; Games; Reading groups; Movies; Dances/Social or cultural gatherings.

BANNER ELK

Regency Health Care Center
Norwood Hollow Rd, Banner Elk, NC, 28605 (704) 898-5136
Admin Susan S Willey. *Medical Dir/Dir of Nursing* Dr Carl Nordstrom.
Licensure Skilled Care; Intermediate Care. *Beds* SNF 46; ICF 74. *Certified* Medicaid; Medicare.
Admissions Requirements Medical examination.
Staff Physicians 1 (pt); RNs 5 (ft), 7 (pt); LPNs 8 (ft), 5 (pt); Orderlies 2 (ft), 1 (pt); Nurses aides 41 (ft), 11 (pt); Physical therapists 1 (pt); Speech therapists 1 (pt); Activities coordinators 1 (ft); Dietitians 1 (pt); Dentists 1 (pt); Ophthalmologists 1 (pt); Podiatrists 1 (pt).
Facilities Dining room; Physical therapy room; Activities room; Crafts room; Laundry room; Barber/Beauty shop.
Activities Arts and Crafts; Games; Reading groups; Prayer groups; Movies; Shopping trips; Dances/Social or cultural gatherings; Pet therapy; Outings.
Description VA approved.

BISCOE

Montgomery Nursing Home
Lambert Rd, Box 708, Biscoe, NC, 27209 (919) 428-2117
Admin Jean Allen. *Medical Dir/Dir of Nursing* Dr C N Eckerson.
Licensure Skilled Care. *Beds* 57. *Certified* Medicaid; Medicare.
Admissions Requirements Medical examination.
Staff RNs 2 (ft), 1 (pt); LPNs 6 (ft), 1 (pt); Orderlies 1 (ft); Nurses aides 14 (ft), 4 (pt); Activities coordinators 1 (ft); Dietitians 1 (ft).
Facilities Dining room; Activities room; Chapel; Crafts room; Barber/Beauty shop.
Activities Arts and Crafts; Games; Prayer groups; Movies; Dances/Social or cultural gatherings.
Description Home is located in a quiet setting beside a beautiful lake.

BLACK MOUNTAIN

Black Mountain Facility
Old Hwy 70, Black Mountain, NC, 28711
Medical Dir/Dir of Nursing Don L Pagett.
Licensure Intermediate Care for Mentally Retarded. *Beds* 120. *Certified* Medicaid.
Ownership Public.
Admissions Requirements Medical examination.
Staff Physicians 2 (ft); RNs 10 (ft); LPNs 4 (ft); Nurses aides 70 (ft); Physical therapists 1 (ft); Recreational therapists 3 (ft); Occupational therapists 1 (pt); Speech therapists 2 (ft); Dietitians 1 (ft).

Facilities Dining room; Physical therapy room; Chapel; Barber/Beauty shop; Library.
Activities Recreational program for the mentally retarded.

Highland Farms Health Care Center*
Tabernacle Rd, Black Mountain, NC, 28711 (704) 669-6473
Admin Sheila Morse.
Licensure Skilled Care. *Beds* 60. *Certified* Medicaid; Medicare.

BLOWING ROCK

Blowing Rock Hospital*
PO Box 148, Chestnut St, Blowing Rock, NC, 28605 (704) 295-3136
Admin James P White.
Licensure Skilled Care; Intermediate Care. *Beds* 72. *Certified* Medicaid; Medicare.

BOONE

Watauga Nursing Care Center
535-A Elizabeth Dr, PO Box 2150, Boone, NC, 28607 (704) 264-6720
Admin Jane Pendergrass. *Medical Dir/Dir of Nursing* Mark R Harter MD.
Licensure Skilled Care; Intermediate Care. *Beds* SNF 50; ICF 54. *Certified* Medicaid; Medicare.
Admissions Requirements Minimum age 16; Physician's request.
Staff Physicians 1 (pt); RNs 7 (ft); LPNs 3 (ft), 1 (pt); Orderlies 5 (ft), 1 (pt); Nurses aides 33 (ft), 8 (pt); Physical therapists 1 (ft); Recreational therapists 1 (pt); Speech therapists; Activities coordinators 1 (ft); Dietitians; Dentists; Podiatrists; Physical therapist assistants 1 (ft).
Facilities Dining room; Physical therapy room; Activities room; Laundry room; Barber/Beauty shop; Covered patio area.
Activities Arts and Crafts; Cards; Games; Reading groups; Prayer groups; Movies; Shopping trips; Dances/Social or cultural gatherings.
Description Facility offers 24-hour registered nurse coverage, physical therapy, and speech therapy; cooperates with several departments of Appalachian State University, internship for their students in sociology, psychology, recreation, home economics (marriage, family and gerontology); clinical site for Watauga County High School's health occupations classes. VA approved. JCAH accredited.

BOSTIC

Haven in the Hills
Rt 2, Bostic, NC, 28018 (704) 245-2998
Admin Olive J Hunt.
Licensure Intermediate Care; Home for the Aged. *Beds* ICF 22; Home for the Aged 28.
Admissions Requirements Medical examination; Physician's request.
Staff Physicians 2 (pt); RNs 1 (pt); LPNs 1 (ft); Orderlies 1 (ft); Nurses aides 10 (ft), 6 (pt); Activities coordinators 1 (pt); Dietitians 1 (pt).
Facilities Dining room; Activities room; Chapel; Laundry room; Barber/Beauty shop; Library.

Activities Games; Prayer groups; Movies; Dances/Social or cultural gatherings.
Description A 40' by 60' enclosed tropical garden including exotic animals and plants, and surrounding large porches are used almost the year around for social and recreational activities, and family gatherings such as picnics, birthdays, and family reunions.

BREVARD

Brian Center of Nursing Care—Brevard*
PO Box 1096, 531 Country Club Rd, Brevard, NC, 28712 (704) 884-2031
Admin Patricia F Woody.
Licensure Skilled Care; Intermediate Care; Home for the Aged. *Beds* SNF 54; ICF 53; Home for the Aged 34. *Certified* Medicaid; Medicare.

BRYSON CITY

Mountain View Manor Nursing Center*
PO Drawer Y, Buckner Branch Rd, Bryson City, NC, 28713 (704) 488-2101
Admin Christine Woolfenden.
Licensure Skilled Care; Intermediate Care. *Beds* SNF 41; ICF 79. *Certified* Medicaid; Medicare.

BURGAW

Guardian Care of Burgaw Inc
Hwy 117-A S, PO Box 874, Burgaw, NC, 28425 (919) 259-2149
Admin Joseph Cicatko Jr.
Licensure Intermediate Care. *Beds* 72. *Certified* Medicaid.
Admissions Requirements Medical examination.
Staff Physicians 4 (pt); RNs 1 (ft), 2 (pt); LPNs 6 (ft), 4 (pt); Orderlies 3 (ft); Nurses aides 16 (ft), 7 (pt); Activities coordinators 1 (ft); Dietitians 1 (ft); Dentists 2 (pt); Podiatrists 2 (pt).
Facilities Dining room; Activities room; Laundry room; Barber/Beauty shop.
Activities Arts and Crafts; Cards; Games; Prayer groups; Movies; Shopping trips.

BURLINGTON

Central Piedmont Nursing Center
323 Baldwin Rd, PO Box 3427, Burlington, NC, 27215 (919) 229-5571
Admin Jeanne K Hutcheson. *Medical Dir/Dir of Nursing* James Hawkins Jr.
Licensure Intermediate Care. *Beds* 100. *Certified* Medicaid.
Admissions Requirements Minimum age 18; Medical examination; Physician's request.
Staff RNs 2 (ft), 1 (pt); LPNs 5 (ft), 3 (pt); Orderlies 5 (ft), 2 (pt); Nurses aides 35 (ft), 20 (pt); Physical therapists 1 (pt); Activities coordinators 1 (ft), 4 (pt); Dietitians 1 (pt); Dentists 1 (pt).
Facilities Dining room; Physical therapy room; Activities room; Crafts room; Laundry room; Barber/Beauty shop.
Activities Arts and Crafts; Cards; Games; Reading groups; Prayer groups; Movies; Shop-

ping trips; Dances/Social or cultural gatherings.
Description The Alzheimer's Support Group of Alamance County meets at our facility as does the Alamance Geneological Society. We raised $2500 for the Heart Association and Alzheimer's research in 1984.

Memorial Hospital of Alamace Company Inc—Skilled Nursing Division
730 Hermitage Rd, Burlington, NC, 27215
Admin Robert E Byrd. *Medical Dir/Dir of Nursing* Robert A Watson MD.
Licensure Skilled Care.
Admissions Requirements Medical examination; Physician's request.
Staff RNs 8 (ft), 3 (pt); LPNs 2 (ft), 2 (pt); Orderlies 4 (ft), 2 (pt); Nurses aides 26 (ft), 8 (pt); Physical therapists 1 (ft); Speech therapists 1 (pt); Activities coordinators 2 (ft), 1 (pt); Dietitians 1 (ft).
Facilities Dining room; Physical therapy room; Activities room; Crafts room; Barber/Beauty shop.
Activities Arts and Crafts; Cards; Games; Reading groups; Prayer groups.
Description Facility is hospital based, located in a pleasant setting with wheelchair garden and active volunteer program.

Twin Lakes Care Center
100 Wade Coble Dr, Burlington, NC, 27215
Admin Clyde J Christmas. *Medical Dir/Dir of Nursing* Dr John B Walker III.
Licensure Skilled Care; Intermediate Care. *Beds* SNF 36; ICF 37. *Certified* Medicaid; Medicare.
Ownership Nonprofit.
Admissions Requirements Physician's request.
Staff RNs 4 (ft), 2 (pt); LPNs 6 (ft), 4 (pt); Orderlies 1 (ft); Nurses aides 15 (ft), 10 (pt); Physical therapists 1 (pt); Reality therapists 1 (pt); Recreational therapists 1 (ft); Speech therapists 1 (pt); Activities coordinators 1 (ft); Dietitians 1 (ft); Dentists 1 (pt).
Affiliation Lutheran
Facilities Dining room; Physical therapy room; Activities room; Chapel; Crafts room; Laundry room; Barber/Beauty shop; Library.
Activities Arts and Crafts; Cards; Games; Reading groups; Prayer groups; Movies; Shopping trips.
Description This is a new continuing care community; expansion of retirement housing is anticipated.

BUTNER

John Umstead Hospital*
12th St, Butner, NC, 27509 (919) 575-7211
Admin T J Peters.
Licensure Intermediate Care. *Beds* 32. *Certified* Medicaid.

Murdoch Center*
C St, Butner, NC, 27509 (919) 575-7734
Admin J Michael Hennike.
Licensure Intermediate Care for Mentally Retarded. *Beds* 394. *Certified* Medicaid.

CANDLER

Pisgah Manor Inc
Holcombe Cove Rd, PO Box 1000, Candler, NC, 28715 (704) 667-9851
Admin Morris Arnold. *Medical Dir/Dir of Nursing* Dr Everett Smith.
Licensure Intermediate Care. *Beds* 118. *Certified* Medicaid.
Admissions Requirements Minimum age 18; Medical examination; Physician's request.
Staff Physicians 1 (pt); RNs 1 (ft), 1 (pt); LPNs 9 (ft), 7 (pt); Orderlies 3 (ft), 5 (pt); Nurses aides 12 (ft), 53 (pt); Activities coordinators 1 (ft), 4 (pt); Dietitians 1 (pt).
Affiliation Seventh-Day Adventist
Facilities Dining room; Activities room; Crafts room; Laundry room; Barber/Beauty shop; Library; TV room.
Activities Arts and Crafts; Cards; Games; Reading groups; Prayer groups; Movies; Shopping trips; Dances/Social or cultural gatherings.

CANTON

Canton Nursing Home Inc
27 N Main St, PO Box 949, Canton, NC, 28716 (704) 648-3551
Admin Billy R Talbert. *Medical Dir/Dir of Nursing* F C Morrison MD.
Licensure Skilled Care; Intermediate Care. *Beds* SNF 60; ICF 54. *Certified* Medicaid; Medicare.
Admissions Requirements Medical examination.
Staff Physicians 8 (pt); RNs 3 (ft), 5 (pt); LPNs 15 (ft), 8 (pt); Nurses aides 28 (ft), 12 (pt); Physical therapists 1 (ft); Speech therapists 1 (pt); Activities coordinators 1 (ft), 2 (pt); Dietitians 1 (pt); Dentists 1 (pt).
Facilities Dining room; Physical therapy room; Activities room; Crafts room; Laundry room; Barber/Beauty shop.
Activities Arts and Crafts; Cards; Games; Reading groups; Prayer groups; Movies; Shopping trips; Dances/Social or cultural gatherings.
Description Facility has 3 patient floors each with a dining room; organized nursing rehabilitation program including restorative feeding groups, exercise classes, and grooming classes.

CHAPEL HILL

Carol Woods Health Center
Weaver Dairy Rd, Box 2121, Chapel Hill, NC, 27514 (919) 968-4511
Admin John A Ditty. *Medical Dir/Dir of Nursing* Robert J Sullivan.
Licensure Skilled Care; Home for the Aged. *Beds* SNF 30; Home for the Aged 30.
Ownership Nonprofit.
Admissions Requirements Minimum age 65; Medical examination; Physician's request.
Staff Physicians 1 (pt); RNs 6 (ft), 10 (pt); LPNs 6 (ft), 10 (pt); Nurses aides 15 (ft), 10 (pt); Physical therapists 1 (pt); Recreational therapists 1 (ft); Occupational therapists 1 (pt); Speech therapists 1 (pt); Dietitians 1 (pt); Dentists 1 (pt); Ophthalmologists 1 (pt); Podiatrists 1 (pt).
Facilities Dining room; Physical therapy room;

Activities room; Crafts room; Laundry room; Barber/Beauty shop; Library.
Activities Arts and Crafts; Cards; Games; Reading groups; Prayer groups; Movies; Shopping trips; Dances/Social or cultural gatherings.
Description Beautiful life care community on 100 acres, 4 miles north of Chapel Hill, an attractive university town; owned and operated by a nonprofit community organization with a local board of directors.

Hillhaven Convalescent Center of Chapel Hill
1602 E Franklin St, Chapel Hill, NC, 27514
Admin Vicki B Jones. *Medical Dir/Dir of Nursing* Dr Glen Pickard.
Licensure Skilled Care; Intermediate Care. *Beds* 120. *Certified* Medicaid; Medicare. *Ownership* Proprietary.
Admissions Requirements Medical examination.
Staff RNs 5 (ft), 2 (pt); LPNs 8 (ft), 5 (pt); Nurses aides 33 (ft), 6 (pt); Physical therapists 2 (ft); Recreational therapists 1 (ft); Occupational therapists 1 (pt); Speech therapists 1 (pt); Activities coordinators 1 (pt); Dietitians 1 (ft).
Facilities Dining room; Physical therapy room; Activities room; Laundry room; Barber/Beauty shop.
Activities Arts and Crafts; Cards; Games; Reading groups; Prayer groups; Movies; Shopping trips; Dances/Social or cultural gatherings.
Description This 1½ year old facility offers outpatient physical therapy, speech therapy, and occupational therapy, as well as an adult day care program 5 days a week from 8 am to 5 pm.

Lakeview Manor*
PO Box 2726, 1716 Legion Rd, Chapel Hill, NC, 27514 (919) 929-7146
Admin William L Littlejohn.
Licensure Skilled Care. *Beds* 58. *Certified* Medicaid.

CHARLOTTE

Beverly Manor of Charlotte*
PO Box 220625, 2616 E 5th St, Charlotte, NC, 28222 (704) 333-5665
Admin Ted Jones.
Licensure Skilled Care; Intermediate Care. *Beds* SNF 88; ICF 32. *Certified* Medicaid; Medicare.

Hawthorne Nursing Center
33 Hawthorne Ln, Charlotte, NC, 28204 (704) 372-1270
Admin Raymond P Masneri. *Medical Dir/Dir of Nursing* Otho B Ross Jr MD.
Licensure Skilled Care; Intermediate Care. *Beds* SNF 126; ICF 16. *Certified* Medicaid; Medicare.
Admissions Requirements Physician's request.
Staff RNs 11 (ft), 3 (pt); LPNs 9 (ft), 1 (pt); Orderlies 5 (ft), 2 (pt); Nurses aides 40 (ft), 10 (pt); Physical therapists 1 (ft); Activities coordinators 2 (ft); Dietitians 1 (pt).
Facilities Dining room; Physical therapy room; Activities room; Chapel; Laundry room; Barber/Beauty shop.
Activities Arts and Crafts; Cards; Games; Reading groups; Prayer groups; Movies; Shop-

ping trips; Dances/Social or cultural gatherings.
Description Facility located adjacent to 3 major hospitals.

Hillcrest Manor Nursing Home
2435 Sharon Rd, Charlotte, NC, 28211 (704) 366-1511
Admin W B O'Neal. *Medical Dir/Dir of Nursing* Dr Charles L Stuckey.
Licensure Intermediate Care. *Beds* 24.
Admissions Requirements Medical examination.
Staff RNs 1 (ft), 2 (pt); LPNs 6 (ft); Orderlies 2 (ft); Nurses aides 6 (ft); Activities coordinators 1 (pt); Dietitians 1 (pt).

Hospitality Care Center of Charlotte*
4801 Randolph Rd, Charlotte, NC, 28105 (704) 364-8363
Admin Gregg Plaster.
Licensure Skilled Care; Intermediate Care. *Beds* SNF 62; ICF 38. *Certified* Medicaid; Medicare.

Mecklenburg Autistic Group Home*
3201 Park Rd, Charlotte, NC, 28209 (704) 527-5366
Admin James R Fuller.
Licensure Intermediate Care for Mentally Retarded. *Beds* 5. *Certified* Medicaid.

Presbyterian Home at Charlotte Inc
5100 Sharon Rd, Charlotte, NC, 28210 (704) 553-1670
Admin Ernest B Honter Jr. *Medical Dir/Dir of Nursing* Dr Horace H Hodges.
Licensure Skilled Care; Home for the Aged. *Beds* SNF 63; Home for the Aged 15.
Admissions Requirements Minimum age 65; Medical examination.
Staff RNs 8 (ft), 10 (pt); LPNs 8 (ft), 7 (pt); Nurses aides 32 (ft), 10 (pt); Activities coordinators 1 (ft); Dietitians 1 (ft).
Affiliation Presbyterian
Facilities Dining room; Physical therapy room; Activities room; Chapel; Crafts room; Laundry room; Barber/Beauty shop; Library; Pool table area; Sewing room; Art room.
Activities Arts and Crafts; Cards; Games; Reading groups; Prayer groups; Movies; Shopping trips; Dances/Social or cultural gatherings; Bible study.
Description Our main building has 2 6-story wings connected by a 4-story structure which houses the skilled nursing facility, dining room with the kitchen, maintenance, beauty shop, etc. on the ground floor. We are in a wooded setting of 22 ½ acres. The cottages and duplexes surround the main building.

Providence Convalescent Residence Inc
300 Providence Rd, Charlotte, NC, 28207 (704) 334-1671
Admin William S Bradley Jr. *Medical Dir/Dir of Nursing* Dr Henry Stuckey.
Licensure Skilled Care; Home for the Aged. *Beds* SNF 125; Home for the Aged 25. *Certified* Medicaid; Medicare.
Admissions Requirements Minimum age 55; Medical examination; Physician's request.
Staff Physicians 26 (pt); RNs 9 (ft), 2 (pt); LPNs 10 (ft), 2 (pt); Orderlies 4 (ft), 4 (pt); Nurses aides 46 (ft), 16 (pt); Physical therapists

2 (pt); Speech therapists 1 (pt); Activities coordinators 1 (ft); Dietitians 1 (pt); Dentists 1 (pt); Podiatrists 1 (pt).
Facilities Dining room; Physical therapy room; Activities room; Chapel; Crafts room; Laundry room; Barber/Beauty shop.
Activities Arts and Crafts; Games; Reading groups; Movies; Shopping trips; Dances/Social or cultural gatherings.

Randolph Manor
2623 Cranbrook Ln, Charlotte, NC, 28207 (704) 332-1161
Admin Carolyn H Sherrill. *Medical Dir/Dir of Nursing* Russell Long MD.
Licensure Skilled Care; Intermediate Care; Retirement and Rest Home. *Beds* SNF 56; ICF 52; Retirement Home 30; Rest Home 25. *Certified* Medicaid; Medicare.
Admissions Requirements Minimum age 18; Medical examination; Physician's request.
Staff RNs 8 (ft), 2 (pt); LPNs 10 (ft), 4 (pt); Orderlies 4 (ft), 2 (pt); Nurses aides 42 (ft), 10 (pt); Physical therapists 1 (ft); Activities coordinators 1 (ft).
Facilities Dining room; Physical therapy room; Activities room; Crafts room; Laundry room; Barber/Beauty shop.
Activities Arts and Crafts; Cards; Games; Reading groups; Prayer groups; Movies; Shopping trips; Dances/Social or cultural gatherings.

Sharon Village Inc*
PO Box 221030, 4009 Craig Ave, Charlotte, NC, 28222 (704) 365-2620
Admin David D Little.
Licensure Intermediate Care. *Beds* 60.

Wesleyan Nursing Home Inc
2623 Cranbrook Ln, Charlotte, NC, 28207 (704) 332-1161
Admin Carolyn SHerrill. *Medical Dir/Dir of Nursing* Russell Long MD.
Licensure Skilled Care; Intermediate Care; Home for the Aged; Retirement. *Beds* SNF 56; ICF 52; Home for the Aged 25; Retirement 30. *Certified* Medicaid; Medicare.
Admissions Requirements Minimum age 18; Medical examination; Physician's request.
Staff RNs 7 (ft), 2 (pt); LPNs 8 (ft), 3 (pt); Orderlies 1 (ft); Nurses aides 40 (ft), 13 (pt); Physical therapists; Occupational therapists; Speech therapists; Activities coordinators 2 (ft), 1 (pt); Dietitians; Dentists; Podiatrists.
Facilities Dining room; Physical therapy room; Activities room; Crafts room; Laundry room; Barber/Beauty shop.
Activities Arts and Crafts; Cards; Games; Reading groups; Prayer groups; Movies; Shopping trips; Dances/Social or cultural gatherings.

Wessel's Nursing Home Inc
515 Templeton Ave, Charlotte, NC, 28203 (704) 333-9045
Admin Sonja Kaminin. *Medical Dir/Dir of Nursing* Otho B Ross Jr MD.
Licensure Skilled Care. *Beds* 26. *Certified* Medicaid; Medicare.
Staff Physicians 2 (pt); RNs 1 (ft), 2 (pt); LPNs 2 (ft), 2 (pt); Nurses aides 7 (ft), 4 (pt); Physical therapists 1 (pt); Speech therapists 1 (pt); Activities coordinators 1 (ft); Dietitians 1 (pt); Dentists 1 (pt); Ophthalmologists 1 (pt); Podia-

trists 1 (pt).
Facilities Activities room; Laundry room.
Activities Arts and Crafts; Cards; Games;
Reading groups; Prayer groups; Movies.
Description Facility features a family atmosphere with all patients and their families knowing each other.

CHERRYVILLE

Carolina Care Center*
PO Box 575, Hwy 274 N, Cherryville, NC,
28021 (704) 435-4161
Admin Judy B Beam.
Licensure Intermediate Care; Home for the
Aged. *Beds* ICF 60; Home for the Aged 59.
Certified Medicaid.

Meadowbrook Manor of Cherryville
700 Self St, Cherryville, NC, 28021 (704)
435-6029
Admin Edwin L Ware. *Medical Dir/Dir of
Nursing* Dr M E Agner.
Licensure Intermediate Care; Home for the
Aged. *Beds* ICF 29; Home for the Aged 82.
Certified Medicaid.
Admissions Requirements Medical examination; Physician's request.
Staff Physicians 1 (pt); LPNs 7 (ft), 1 (pt);
Orderlies 1 (ft); Nurses aides 22 (ft); Activities
coordinators 1 (pt); Dietitians 1 (pt).
Facilities Dining room; Chapel; Crafts room;
Laundry room; Barber/Beauty shop.
Activities Arts and Crafts; Prayer groups;
Movies; Shopping trips; Dances/Social or cultural gatherings.

CLEMMONS

The Bluementhal Jewish Home for the Aged*
PO Box 38, 7870 Fair Oaks Dr, Clemmons,
NC, 27012-0038 (919) 766-6401
Admin Al A Mendlovitz.
Licensure Skilled Care; Intermediate Care.
Beds SNF 86; ICF 48. *Certified* Medicaid;
Medicare.
Affiliation Jewish

Meadowbrook Manor
Hwy 158, PO Box 248, Clemmons, NC, 27012
(919) 766-9158
Admin Mindy B Engstrom. *Medical Dir/Dir of
Nursing* Dr Jerome Davis.
Licensure Skilled Care; Intermediate Care.
Beds SNF 60; ICF 60. *Certified* Medicaid;
Medicare.
Admissions Requirements Medical examination; Physician's request.
Staff Physicians; RNs; LPNs; Orderlies;
Nurses aides; Physical therapists; Recreational
therapists; Occupational therapists; Speech therapists; Activities coordinators; Dietitians;
Ophthalmologists; Podiatrists; Audiologists.
Facilities Dining room; Physical therapy room;
Activities room; Chapel; Crafts room; Barber-
/Beauty shop; Library.
Activities Arts and Crafts; Cards; Games;
Reading groups; Prayer groups; Movies; Shopping trips; Dances/Social or cultural gatherings.

CLINTON

Mary-Gran Nursing Center*
PO Box 379, 120 Southwood Dr, Clinton, NC,
28328 (919) 592-7981
Admin George E Wilson.
Licensure Skilled Care; Intermediate Care;
Home for the Aged. *Beds* SNF 90; ICF 30;
Home for the Aged 5. *Certified* Medicaid;
Medicare.

CLYDE

Britthaven of Clyde
Morgan St, PO Box 504, Clyde, NC,
28721-0504 (704) 627-2789
Admin Olivia J Jackson. *Medical Dir/Dir of
Nursing* Dr E B Goodwin Jr.
Licensure Intermediate Care. *Beds* 50. *Certified* Medicaid.
Admissions Requirements Medical examination.
Staff LPNs 5 (ft); Orderlies 1 (ft); Nurses aides
17 (ft); Activities coordinators 1 (ft).
Facilities Dining room; Activities room; Laundry room; Barber/Beauty shop.
Activities Arts and Crafts; Games; Reading
groups; Prayer groups; Movies; Dances/Social
or cultural gatherings.
Description This area is considered as "Little
Clyde," "The Bible Belt," "We Care," and "We
are 'A Family."

CONCORD

Cabarrus Nursing Center Inc
515 Concord Lake Rd, PO Box 3297, Concord,
NC, 28025 (704) 786-9151
Admin Brenda F Safrit. *Medical Dir/Dir of
Nursing* Dr Robert E Hammonds.
Licensure Skilled Care; Intermediate Care.
Beds SNF 88; ICF 32. *Certified* Medicaid;
Medicare.
Admissions Requirements Medical examination; Physician's request.
Staff RNs 5 (ft), 4 (pt); LPNs 7 (ft), 2 (pt);
Nurses aides 31 (ft), 21 (pt); Physical therapists
1 (ft); Activities coordinators 1 (ft); Dietitians 1
(ft); Dentists 1 (ft); Podiatrists 1 (ft).
Facilities Dining room; Physical therapy room;
Activities room; Chapel; Crafts room; Laundry
room; Barber/Beauty shop; Reading Room;
TV Room.
Activities Arts and Crafts; Cards; Games;
Reading groups; Prayer groups; Movies; Shopping trips; Dances/Social or cultural gatherings.
Description Facility features an exceptional volunteer program.

Concord Nursing Center
430 Brookwood Ave NE, PO Box 3297,
Concord, NC, 280025 (704) 4120
Admin Nancy F Taylor. *Medical Dir/Dir of
Nursing* Robert E Hammonds MD.
Licensure Skilled Care; Intermediate Care.
Beds SNF 60; ICF 60. *Certified* Medicaid;
Medicare.
Admissions Requirements Medical examination; Physician's request.
Staff Physicians 4 (pt); RNs 7 (ft); LPNs 9 (ft),
2 (pt); Nurses aides 40 (ft), 6 (pt); Physical ther-

apists 1 (ft); Reality therapists 1 (ft); Recreational therapists 1 (ft); Activities coordinators 1
(ft); Dietitians 1 (ft); Dentists 1 (pt); Podiatrists
1 (pt).
Facilities Dining room; Physical therapy room;
Activities room; Chapel; Crafts room; Laundry
room; Barber/Beauty shop; Library.
Activities Arts and Crafts; Cards; Games;
Reading groups; Prayer groups; Movies; Shopping trips; Dances/Social or cultural gatherings;
Video recorder and video movies; Rowan Technical College classes.
Description Facility is located inside the city
limits of Concord, NC, but offers a rural setting. The facility has a shopping mall within 2
miles. It also offers a clean, warm, and friendly
atmosphere.

Five Oaks Nursing Center
413 Winecoff School Rd, PO Box 384, Concord, NC, 28026-0384 (704) 788-2131
Admin Steve Falkenbury. *Medical Dir/Dir of
Nursing* Dr Vincent Keipper.
Licensure Skilled Care; Intermediate Care;
Home for the Aged. *Beds* SNF 63; ICF 60;
Home for the Aged 12. *Certified* Medicaid;
Medicare.
Admissions Requirements Medical examination.
Staff Physicians 2 (pt); RNs 8 (ft), 4 (pt); LPNs
5 (ft), 1 (pt); Nurses aides 37 (ft), 16 (pt);
Physical therapists 1 (pt); Activities coordinators 2 (ft); Dietitians 1 (pt); Dentists 1 (pt);
Podiatrists 1 (pt).
Facilities Dining room; Physical therapy room;
Activities room; Laundry room; Barber/Beauty
shop.
Activities Arts and Crafts; Cards; Games;
Reading groups; Prayer groups; Movies; Shopping trips; Dances/Social or cultural gatherings.
Description Five Oaks is a 135-bed facility that
has lots of love and compassion for the residents. Excellent care is given by nusing staff,
and excellent food is provided by dietary
department. Support of families is excellent.
Facility has a very good inservice director to
provide continuing education to employees.

Odell Nursing Center*
Rt 2, PO Box 502B, Concord, NC, 28025 (704)
782-9770
Admin Sherry S Johnson.
Licensure Intermediate Care. *Beds* 25. *Certified* Medicaid.

Piedmont Residential Developmental Center*
PO Box 909, Concord, NC, 28025 (704)
788-2304
Admin Paul Caldwell.
Licensure Intermediate Care for Mentally
Retarded. *Beds* 10. *Certified* Medicaid.

DANBURY

**Stokes-Reynolds Memorial Hospital—Skilled
Nursing Facility**
PO Box 38, Danbury, NC, 27016
Admin Sandra D Priddy. *Medical Dir/Dir of
Nursing* Dr Renato Zarate.
Licensure Skilled Care. *Beds* 40. *Certified* Medicaid; Medicare.
Ownership Nonprofit.

Staff Physicians 5 (ft); RNs 1 (ft); LPNs 8 (ft); Orderlies 2 (ft); Nurses aides 22 (ft); Physical therapists 1 (ft); Activities coordinators 1 (ft); Dietitians 1 (ft); Dentists 1 (ft).

DENTON

Mountain Vista/ElderLodge—Denton*
PO Box 458, Jackson Hill Rd, Denton, NC, 27239 (704) 869-2181
Admin Gary L Hedges.
Licensure Skilled Care; Intermediate Care; Home for the Aged. *Beds* SNF 24; ICF 36; Home for the Aged 60. *Certified* Medicaid; Medicare.

DREXEL

Autumn Care of Drexel*
PO Box 1278, Oakland Ave, Drexel, NC, 28619 (704) 433-6180
Admin Douglas C Suddreth.
Licensure Skilled Care; Intermediate Care; Home for the Aged. *Beds* SNF 50; ICF 50; Home for the Aged 20. *Certified* Medicaid; Medicare.

DUNN

Charles Parrish Memorial Nursing Center
201 N Ellis Ave, PO Box 1707, Dunn, NC, 28334 (919) 892-4021
Admin Joy Strickland. *Medical Dir/Dir of Nursing* L R Doffermyre MD.
Licensure Skilled Care; Intermediate Care. *Beds* SNF 63; ICF 39. *Certified* Medicaid; Medicare.
Admissions Requirements Medical examination.
Staff RNs 6 (ft); LPNs 9 (ft), 2 (pt); Orderlies 4 (ft), 2 (pt); Nurses aides 36 (ft), 5 (pt); Physical therapists 1 (ft).
Facilities Dining room; Laundry room.
Activities Arts and Crafts; Cards; Games; Reading groups; Prayer groups; Movies; Dances/Social or cultural gatherings; Exercise classes.

DURHAM

Durham Care Center
3100 Erwin Rd, Durham, NC, 27705 (919) 383-1546
Admin Craig E Miller. *Medical Dir/Dir of Nursing* Marcono Hines MD.
Licensure Skilled Care; Intermediate Care. *Beds* SNF 109; ICF 50. *Certified* Medicaid; Medicare.
Staff RNs 6 (ft), 4 (pt); LPNs 14 (ft), 11 (pt); Nurses aides 42 (ft), 23 (pt); Physical therapists 4 (ft); Speech therapists 1 (pt); Activities coordinators 2 (ft); Dietitians 1 (pt); Dentists 1 (pt); Ophthalmologists 1 (pt); Podiatrists 1 (pt); Audiologists 1 (pt).
Facilities Dining room; Physical therapy room; Activities room; Crafts room; Laundry room; Barber/Beauty shop.
Activities Arts and Crafts; Cards; Games; Reading groups; Prayer groups; Movies; Shopping trips; Dances/Social or cultural gatherings.

Hillcrest Convalescent Center Inc
1417 W Pettigrew St, PO Box 2816, Durham, NC, 27705 (919) 286-7705
Admin J R Garrett Jr. *Medical Dir/Dir of Nursing* Lewis M McKee MD.
Licensure Skilled Care. *Beds* 120. *Certified* Medicaid; Medicare.
Admissions Requirements Medical examination; Physician's request.
Staff RNs 5 (ft), 2 (pt); LPNs 10 (ft), 5 (pt); Orderlies 3 (ft), 2 (pt); Nurses aides 37 (ft), 10 (pt); Physical therapists 1 (ft), 1 (pt); Reality therapists 1 (pt); Recreational therapists 2 (ft); Occupational therapists 1 (pt); Speech therapists 1 (pt); Activities coordinators 1 (ft); Dietitians 1 (ft), 1 (pt); Dentists 1 (pt); Ophthalmologists 1 (pt); Podiatrists 1 (pt); Audiologists 1 (pt).
Facilities Dining room; Physical therapy room; Activities room; Chapel; Crafts room; Laundry room; Barber/Beauty shop; Library.
Activities Arts and Crafts; Cards; Games; Reading groups; Prayer groups; Movies; Shopping trips; Dances/Social or cultural gatherings; Current events; Music appreciation.
Description Center offers community college classes, horticulture classes, and creative arts; annual fashion show with community invited.

Hillhaven LaSalle Nursing Center
411 S LaSalle St, Durham, NC, 27705 (919) 383-5521
Admin Susan Mathews. *Medical Dir/Dir of Nursing* Byron Cole MD.
Licensure Skilled Care; Intermediate Care. *Beds* SNF 46; ICF 80. *Certified* Medicaid; Medicare.
Admissions Requirements Medical examination; Physician's request.
Staff RNs 3 (ft); LPNs 10 (ft); Orderlies 3 (ft); Nurses aides 20 (ft); Physical therapists 1 (ft); Recreational therapists 2 (ft); Occupational therapists 1 (pt); Speech therapists 1 (pt); Dietitians 1 (ft), 1 (pt).
Facilities Dining room; Physical therapy room; Activities room; Chapel; Barber/Beauty shop; TV Room.
Activities Arts and Crafts; Games; Reading groups; Prayer groups; Movies; Shopping trips; Dances/Social or cultural gatherings.
Description Facility located within city of Durham; recently completed renovation of interior.

Hillhaven Orange Nursing Center
Rt 1, Box 155, Mt Sinai Rd, Durham, NC, 27705 (919) 489-2361
Admin Evern G Thompson. *Medical Dir/Dir of Nursing* Dr Byron Cole.
Licensure Skilled Care; Intermediate Care. *Beds* SNF 42; ICF 74. *Certified* Medicaid; Medicare.
Admissions Requirements Medical examination.
Staff Physicians 1 (ft); RNs 5 (ft); LPNs 12 (ft), 4 (pt); Nurses aides 40 (ft), 15 (pt); Physical therapists 1 (pt); Reality therapists 1 (pt); Recreational therapists 1 (ft), 1 (pt); Speech therapists 1 (pt); Activities coordinators 1 (ft); Dietitians 1 (ft); Dentists; Ophthalmologists; Podiatrists; Audiologists.
Facilities Dining room; Physical therapy room; Activities room; Barber/Beauty shop.
Activities Arts and Crafts; Cards; Games;

Reading groups; Prayer groups; Movies; Shopping trips; Dances/Social or cultural gatherings.
Description Hillhaven Orange is located in a beautiful country setting, only minutes away from the excellent medical facilities of both Durham and Chapel Hill. Comfortable private and semi-private rooms with bathroom facilities are available. Dietary staff is recognized for its home-style delicious meals. Involvement in the community is encouraged through participation in a healthy mixture of outings and activities.

Hillhaven Rehabilitation and Convalescent Center*
1515 W Pettigrew St, Durham, NC, 27705 (919) 929-6063
Admin William Littlejohn.
Licensure Skilled Care. *Beds* 107. *Certified* Medicaid; Medicare.

Hillhaven Rose Manor Convalescent Center
4230 N Roxboro Rd, Durham, NC, 27704 (919) 477-9805
Admin Kevin McMahon. *Medical Dir/Dir of Nursing* Gregg Warshaw.
Licensure Skilled Care; Intermediate Care. *Beds* SNF 57; ICF 70. *Certified* Medicaid; Medicare.
Staff RNs 4 (ft), 1 (pt); LPNs 12 (ft), 4 (pt).
Facilities Dining room; Physical therapy room; Activities room; Chapel; Crafts room; Barber-/Beauty shop; Park.
Activities Arts and Crafts; Games; Reading groups; Prayer groups; Movies; Dances/Social or cultural gatherings.

Methodist Retirement Homes Inc
2616 Erwin Rd, Durham, NC, 27705 (919) 383-2567
Admin W Donald Penley. *Medical Dir/Dir of Nursing* Dr Donald Neish.
Licensure Skilled Care; Intermediate Care; Home for the Aged. *Beds* SNF 46; ICF 77; Home for the Aged 40. *Certified* Medicaid; Medicare.
Admissions Requirements Medical examination.
Staff Physicians 1 (pt); RNs 10 (ft), 3 (pt); LPNs 21 (ft), 7 (pt); Orderlies 12 (ft), 4 (pt); Nurses aides 51 (ft), 13 (pt); Physical therapists 2 (pt); Recreational therapists 4 (ft); Speech therapists 1 (pt); Activities coordinators 1 (ft), 1 (pt); Dietitians 1 (ft); Dentists 1 (pt).
Affiliation Methodist
Facilities Dining room; Physical therapy room; Activities room; Chapel; Crafts room; Laundry room; Barber/Beauty shop; Library; Store operated by patients.
Activities Arts and Crafts; Cards; Games; Reading groups; Prayer groups; Movies; Shopping trips; Dances/Social or cultural gatherings; Music and singing; Talent shows; Horticulture; Science; Community service projects; Exercise groups; Cooking.
Description Facility features an excellent volunteer service group who work with patients on individual and group basis; each patient is evaluated and involved according to needs for participation and involvement; quality care given at all times; pet therapy has been very good for patients.

EDENTON

Chowan Hospital*
Virginia Rd, Edenton, NC, 27932 (919)
482-8451
Admin Marvin A Bryan.
Licensure Skilled Care. *Beds* 56. *Certified* Medicaid; Medicare.

ElderLodge—Edenton
Paradise Rd, PO Box 566, Edenton, NC, 27932
(919) 482-7481
Admin Charles Andrews.
Licensure Skilled Care; Intermediate Care;
Rest Home. *Beds* SNF 24; ICF 106; Rest
Home 30. *Certified* Medicaid; Medicare.
Admissions Requirements Minimum age 18;
Medical examination; Physician's request.
Staff Physicians 2 (pt); RNs 3 (ft), 3 (pt); LPNs
9 (ft), 9 (pt); Orderlies 4 (ft); Nurses aides 32
(ft), 4 (pt); Physical therapists 2 (pt); Recreational therapists 1 (ft), 1 (pt); Activities coordinators 1 (ft), 1 (pt); Dietitians 1 (pt); Dentists 1
(pt); Ophthalmologists 1 (pt).
Facilities Dining room; Physical therapy room;
Activities room; Crafts room; Laundry room;
Barber/Beauty shop; Library.
Activities Arts and Crafts; Cards; Games;
Reading groups; Prayer groups; Movies; Shopping trips; Dances/Social or cultural gatherings;
Summer fishing trips; Picnics.

ELIZABETH CITY

Guardian Care of Elizabeth City*
901 S Halstead Blvd, Elizabeth City, NC,
27909 (919) 338-0137
Admin Mitzi L Kilker.
Licensure Skilled Care; Intermediate Care.
Beds SNF 31; ICF 89. *Certified* Medicaid;
Medicare.

W R Winslow Memorial Home Inc*
1700 W Ehringhaus St, Elizabeth City, NC,
27909 (919) 338-3975
Admin David L Fardulis.
Licensure Skilled Care; Intermediate Care.
Beds SNF 34; ICF 87. *Certified* Medicaid;
Medicare.

ELIZABETHTOWN

Elizabethtown Nursing Center
Mercer Rd, PO Box 1447, Elizabethtown, NC,
28337 (919) 862-8181
Admin Elizabeth Boyer. *Medical Dir/Dir of
Nursing* Don Creed MD.
Licensure Skilled Care; Intermediate Care.
Beds SNF 28; ICF 56. *Certified* Medicaid;
Medicare.
Staff RNs 2 (ft), 1 (pt); LPNs 7 (ft), 3 (pt);
Orderlies 1 (ft), 1 (pt); Nurses aides 27 (ft), 8
(pt); Occupational therapists 1 (ft); Activities
coordinators 1 (ft); Dietitians 1 (ft).
Facilities Dining room; Physical therapy room;
Activities room; Laundry room; Barber/Beauty
shop.
Activities Arts and Crafts; Cards; Games;
Reading groups; Prayer groups; Movies; Shopping trips; Dances/Social or cultural gatherings;
Luncheon parties; Birthday and holiday parties.

Description Home-like facility provides the
best quality of care to meet patients needs on
an individual basis; activities carried out in
daily routine; assists each resident in social,
diversional, recreational, and spiritual activities
to promote intellectual growth.

ELKIN

Guardian Care of Elkin
560 Johnson Ridge Rd, Elkin, NC, 28621 (919)
835-7802
Admin Glenn T Pierce.
Licensure Skilled Care; Intermediate Care.
Beds SNF 50; ICF 50. *Certified* Medicaid;
Medicare.

Hugh Chatham Memorial Hospital*
230 Hawthorne Rd, Elkin, NC, 28621 (919)
835-3722
Admin M C Holthouser.
Licensure Skilled Care. *Beds* 64. *Certified* Medicaid; Medicare.

ENFIELD

Convalescent Care of Enfield
208 Cary St, PO Box 456, Enfield, NC, 27823
(919) 445-2111
Admin William R Turner. *Medical Dir/Dir of
Nursing* Dr Alton Anderson.
Licensure Skilled Care. *Beds* 63. *Certified* Medicaid; Medicare.
Admissions Requirements Medical examination; Physician's request.
Staff Physicians 3 (pt); RNs 6 (ft), 1 (pt); LPNs
5 (ft); Orderlies 3 (ft), 2 (pt); Nurses aides 21
(ft), 3 (pt); Physical therapists 1 (pt); Reality
therapists 1 (ft); Recreational therapists 1 (ft);
Occupational therapists 1 (pt); Speech therapists 1 (pt); Activities coordinators 1 (ft); Dietitians 1 (ft), 1 (pt); Dentists 1 (pt);
Ophthalmologists 1 (pt); Podiatrists 1 (pt);
Audiologists 1 (pt).
Facilities Dining room; Physical therapy room;
Activities room; Laundry room; Barber/Beauty
shop.
Activities Arts and Crafts; Cards; Games;
Reading groups; Prayer groups; Movies; Shopping trips.

FALCON

Golden Years Nursing Home*
Hwy 82, PO Box 40, West St, Falcon, NC,
28342 (919) 892-6048
Admin David F Arnn.
Licensure Intermediate Care; Home for the
Aged. *Beds* 58; Home for the Aged 5.
Certified Medicaid.

FARMVILLE

Guardian Care of Farmville*
Rt 1, Box 96, Farmville, NC, 27828 (919)
753-5547
Admin Alawoise S Flanagan.
Licensure Intermediate Care. *Beds* 56. *Certified* Medicaid.

FAYETTEVILLE

Bethesda Health Care Facility*
Rt 1, Box 118-A, Fayetteville, NC, 28301 (919)
323-3223
Admin Thomas L Suggs.
Licensure Skilled Care; Intermediate Care.
Beds SNF 16; ICF 44. *Certified* Medicaid;
Medicare.

Gladhaven Inc*
PO Box 1803, 707 Murchison Rd, Fayetteville,
NC, 28302 (919) 483-3400
Admin Mary W Bissette.
Licensure Skilled Care; Intermediate Care;
Home for the Aged. *Beds* SNF 40; ICF 58;
Home for the Aged 30. *Certified* Medicaid;
Medicare.

Highland House of Fayetteville
1700 Pamalee Dr, PO Box 35887, Fayetteville,
NC, 28303 (919) 488-2295
Admin Allyson M Wherren.
Licensure Intermediate Care; Home for the
Aged. *Beds* ICF 62; Home for the Aged 37.
Certified Medicaid.
Admissions Requirements Minimum age 18;
Medical examination.
Staff RNs 1 (ft); LPNs 7 (ft); Nurses aides 28
(ft); Physical therapists 2 (ft); Speech therapists
1 (pt); Activities coordinators 2 (ft), 1 (pt); Dentists 1 (pt); Podiatrists 1 (pt).
Facilities Dining room; Activities room; Chapel; Crafts room; Laundry room; Barber/Beauty
shop.
Activities Arts and Crafts; Cards; Games;
Reading groups; Prayer groups; Movies; Shopping trips; Dances/Social or cultural gatherings.

Rest Haven Nursing Home
1769 Dunn Rd, Fayetteville, NC, 28301 (919)
483-5027
Admin Charlotte C Fitch.
Licensure Intermediate Care. *Beds* 46. *Certified* Medicaid.
Admissions Requirements Medical examination; Physician's request.
Staff RNs 1 (ft); LPNs 4 (ft), 3 (pt); Orderlies 1
(ft); Nurses aides 12 (ft), 4 (pt); Recreational
therapists 1 (ft); Activities coordinators 1 (ft);
Dietitians 1 (ft).
Facilities Dining room; Activities room; Laundry room.
Activities Arts and Crafts; Games.

Whispering Pines Nursing Home
523 Country Club Dr, Fayetteville, NC, 28301
(910) 488-0711
Admin Jeanne A Novello.
Licensure Intermediate Care; Rest Home.
Beds 58; Rest Home 2. *Certified* Medicaid.
Admissions Requirements Medical examination; Physician's request.
Staff Physicians 9 (pt); RNs 1 (ft), 1 (pt); LPNs
3 (ft), 4 (pt); Orderlies 1 (ft); Nurses aides 17
(ft), 6 (pt); Physical therapists 1 (pt); Recreational therapists 1 (ft); Dietitians 1 (pt).
Facilities Activities room; Barber/Beauty shop;
Library.
Activities Arts and Crafts; Cards; Games;
Reading groups; Prayer groups; Movies; Shopping trips; Dances/Social or cultural gatherings.
Description The first facility to be opened

under licensure requirements in North Carolina, this home has continually offered care since the early 1950s.

FUQUAYVARINA

Kinton Nursing Home*
PO Box 528, 415 Sunset Dr, Fuquay-Varina, NC, 27526 (919) 552-5609
Admin Ruth C Kinton.
Licensure Intermediate Care; Home for the Aged. *Beds* ICF 49; Home for the Aged 31. *Certified* Medicaid.

GASTONIA

Brian Center—Gastonia
969 Cox Rd, Gastonia, NC, 28054 (704) 866-8596
Admin Doris J Powell. *Medical Dir/Dir of Nursing* Dr James S Forrester.
Licensure Skilled Care; Intermediate Care. *Beds* SNF 90; ICF 30. *Certified* Medicaid; Medicare.
Staff RNs 8 (ft), 1 (pt); LPNs 9 (ft), 7 (pt); Nurses aides 41 (ft), 10 (pt); Physical therapists 1 (pt); Activities coordinators 1 (ft); Dietitians 2 (ft).
Facilities Dining room; Physical therapy room; Activities room; Laundry room; Barber/Beauty shop.
Activities Arts and Crafts; Games; Reading groups; Prayer groups; Movies; Dances/Social or cultural gatherings.
Description JCAH accreditation-2 year status; member of NCHCFA and AHCFA, ongoing Quality Assurance programs. Large volunteer program.

Covenant Village
1351 Robinwood Rd, Gastonia, NC, 28052
Admin W David Piner. *Medical Dir/Dir of Nursing* Dr Thomason.
Licensure Skilled Care; Intermediate Care. *Beds* 40.
Ownership Nonprofit.
Admissions Requirements Minimum age 65; Medical examination; Physician's request.
Staff RNs 7 (ft); LPNs 3 (ft); Nurses aides 20 (ft); Physical therapists; Activities coordinators 1 (ft); Dietitians 1 (ft).
Affiliation Presbyterian
Facilities Dining room; Activities room; Chapel; Crafts room; Laundry room; Barber/Beauty shop; Library.
Activities Arts and Crafts; Cards; Games; Reading groups; Prayer groups; Movies; Shopping trips; Dances/Social or cultural gatherings.
Description Health awareness day is held monthly for the residents who live independently. Dietary caters resident parties, affairs, etc. All residents have immediate access to nursing care and all guaranteed a bed in the health care unit.

Guardian Care of Gastonia*
416 N Highland St, Gastonia, NC, 28052 (704) 864-0371
Admin G W Moore.

Licensure Skilled Care; Intermediate Care. *Beds* SNF 61; ICF 58. *Certified* Medicaid; Medicare.

Meadowbrook Manor of Gastonia*
PO Box 1375, 960 X-Ray Dr, Gastonia, NC, 28053 (704) 861-9081
Admin Sharon Stiles.
Licensure Skilled Care; Intermediate Care. *Beds* SNF 60; ICF 60. *Certified* Medicaid; Medicare.

GOLDSBORO

Caswell Annex*
Hwy 581, Goldsboro, NC, 27530 (919) 731-3470
Admin Richard Zaharia.
Licensure Intermediate Care for Mentally Retarded. *Beds* 100. *Certified* Medicaid.

Cherry Hospital*
Caller Box 8000, Hwy 581, Goldsboro, NC, 27530 (919) 731-3202
Admin J Field Montgomery, Jr.
Licensure Intermediate Care. *Beds* 66. *Certified* Medicaid.

Guardian Care of Goldsboro*
501 Forest Hill Dr, Goldsboro, NC, 27530 (919) 735-4427
Admin Juanita M Mansour.
Licensure Skilled Care. *Beds* 49.

Howell's Child Care Center—Walnut Creek*
Rt 9, Box 246, Goldsboro, NC, 27530 (919) 778-3524
Admin Valentine H Gray.
Licensure Intermediate Care. *Beds* 37. *Certified* Medicaid.

Oak Manor Inc
2401 Wayne Memorial Dr, Goldsboro, NC, 27530 (919) 736-2121
Admin Deborah Katkaveck. *Medical Dir/Dir of Nursing* Dr Yeddu Raju.
Licensure Skilled Care; Intermediate Care. *Beds* SNF 111; ICF 53. *Certified* Medicaid; Medicare.
Admissions Requirements Minimum age 18; Medical examination; Physician's request.
Staff RNs 5 (ft), 7 (pt); LPNs 12 (ft), 21 (pt); Orderlies 4 (ft), 2 (pt); Nurses aides 35 (ft), 26 (pt); Activities coordinators 2 (pt).
Facilities Dining room; Physical therapy room; Activities room; Laundry room; Barber/Beauty shop.
Activities Arts and Crafts; Cards; Games; Reading groups; Prayer groups; Movies; Shopping trips; Dances/Social or cultural gatherings.
Description Oak Manor, Inc has the distinct advantage of a peaceful, rural location within minutes of our local hospital and medical community. Our staff continually strives to make our facility as home-like as possible, and continues to maintain an excellent reputation of providing quality professional nursing care.

GOLDSBURG

O'Berry Center*
PO Box 247, Goldsburg, NC, 27530 (919) 731-3545
Admin Jerry H Lyall.
Licensure Skilled Care; Intermediate Care for Mentally Retarded. *Beds* SNF 34; ICF/MR 560. *Certified* Medicaid.

GRAHAM

Care Inns Inc
779 Woody Dr, PO Box 1000, Graham, NC, 27253 (919) 228-8394
Admin Paul C Miller. *Medical Dir/Dir of Nursing* Dr Clinton Crissman.
Licensure Intermediate Care. *Beds* 120. *Certified* Medicaid.
Admissions Requirements Medical examination; Physician's request.
Facilities Dining room; Physical therapy room; Activities room; Crafts room; Laundry room; Barber/Beauty shop.
Activities Arts and Crafts; Cards; Games; Reading groups; Prayer groups; Movies; Shopping trips.

GREENSBORO

Anthony's Care Center
512 Pisgah Church Rd, Greensboro, NC, 27405 (919) 288-5416
Admin Mary H Carroll.
Licensure Intermediate Care. *Beds* 29. *Certified* Medicaid.
Admissions Requirements Medical examination; Physician's request.
Staff RNs 1 (ft), 1 (pt); LPNs 1 (ft), 2 (pt); Orderlies 1 (pt); Nurses aides 3 (ft), 5 (pt); Activities coordinators 1 (ft).
Facilities Dining room; Laundry room; Living room.
Activities Arts and Crafts; Games; Prayer groups; Movies; Shopping trips; Dances/Social or cultural gatherings.

The Evergreens Inc*
PO Box 6706, 4007 Wendover Ave, Greensboro, NC, 27405 (919) 292-8620
Admin Aleita T Hodgin.
Licensure Skilled Care; Intermediate Care; Home for the Aged. *Beds* SNF 94; ICF 172; Home for the Aged 94. *Certified* Medicaid; Medicare.

Friends Home
925 New Garden Rd, Greensboro, NC, 27410 (919) 292-8187
Admin Wilson M Sheldon Jr. *Medical Dir/Dir of Nursing* Dr Robert Thacker.
Licensure Skilled Care; Intermediate Care. *Beds* SNF 26; ICF 24; HFA 60. *Certified* Medicaid; Medicare.
Admissions Requirements Minimum age 60; Medical examination.
Staff RNs 7 (ft), 3 (pt); LPNs 4 (ft), 2 (pt); Nurses aides 29 (ft), 10 (pt); Activities coordinators 2 (ft); Dietitians 1 (ft).
Affiliation Society of Friends
Facilities Dining room; Physical therapy room;

Activities room; Chapel; Crafts room; Laundry room; Barber/Beauty shop; Library; Living rooms.
Activities Arts and Crafts; Cards; Games; Reading groups; Prayer groups; Movies; Shopping trips; Dances/Social or cultural gatherings; Interest groups.
Description Friends Home is a retirement community founded by the North Carolina Yearly Meeting of Friends (Quakers), located in the Guilford College section of Greensboro. Within Friends Home 4 distinct levels of care are available ranging from independent living to skilled nursing care; a waiting period of 10 to 12 years may be expected.

Greenhaven Nursing Center Inc*
801 Greenhaven Dr, Greensboro, NC, 27406-7199 (919) 292-8371
Admin David Huff.
Licensure Skilled Care; Intermediate Care.
Beds SNF 60; ICF 60. *Certified* Medicaid; Medicare.

Greensboro Health Care Center
1201 Carolina St, Greensboro, NC, 27401 (919) 275-0751
Admin Joanne W Moffitt. *Medical Dir/Dir of Nursing* Dr William McKeown.
Licensure Skilled Care; Intermediate Care.
Beds SNF 35; ICF 70. *Certified* Medicaid; Medicare.
Facilities Dining room; Physical therapy room; Activities room; Crafts room; Laundry room; Barber/Beauty shop.
Activities Arts and Crafts; Games; Movies; Shopping trips.
Description Center is located 2 blocks from a medical center, and nearby physician's offices; resident drama club; speech therapy available.

Masonic and Eastern Star Home of North Carolina Inc
700 S Holden Rd, Greensboro, NC, 27420 (919) 299-0031
Admin Tommy L Jones. *Medical Dir/Dir of Nursing* Ella M Payne RN.
Licensure Skilled Care; Intermediate Care.
Beds SNF 32; ICF 56.
Admissions Requirements Minimum age 60; Medical examination.
Staff Physicians 1 (pt); RNs 10 (ft), 3 (pt); LPNs 4 (ft), 1 (pt); Nurses aides 28 (ft), 13 (pt); Physical therapists 2 (pt); Activities coordinators 1 (ft), 2 (pt); Dentists 1 (pt).
Affiliation Masons
Facilities Dining room; Physical therapy room; Activities room; Chapel; Crafts room; Laundry room; Barber/Beauty shop; Library.
Activities Arts and Crafts; Games; Prayer groups; Movies; Shopping trips; Dances/Social or cultural gatherings.

Saint James Nursing Center*
603 S Benbow Rd, Greensboro, NC, 27420 (919) 275-9941
Admin Ann Griffin.
Licensure Skilled Care. *Beds* 100. *Certified* Medicaid; Medicare.

Starmount Villa Nursing Center
109 S Holden Rd, Greensboro, NC, 27407 (919) 292-5390

Admin Bill R Bolton. *Medical Dir/Dir of Nursing* William D McKeown.
Licensure Skilled Care; Intermediate Care.
Beds SNF 64; ICF 62. *Certified* Medicaid; Medicare.
Staff RNs 4 (ft), 1 (pt); LPNs 15 (ft), 4 (pt); Orderlies 7 (ft), 2 (pt); Nurses aides 30 (ft), 6 (pt); Physical therapists 1 (pt); Reality therapists 1 (pt); Speech therapists 1 (pt); Activities coordinators 2 (ft); Dietitians 1 (ft), 1 (pt).
Facilities Dining room; Physical therapy room; Activities room; Chapel; Crafts room; Laundry room; Barber/Beauty shop; Library.
Activities Arts and Crafts; Cards; Games; Reading groups; Prayer groups; Movies; Shopping trips; Dances/Social or cultural gatherings.
Description Starmount Villa is located in the historical Starmount Forest area of Greensboro. We offer a warm, cheerful atmosphere in a relaxing residential setting.

GREENVILLE

Greenville Villa*
PO Box 5046, Greenville, NC, 27834 (919) 758-4121
Admin Robert D Fabian.
Licensure Skilled Care; Intermediate Care.
Beds SNF 40; ICF 112. *Certified* Medicaid; Medicare.

University Nursing Center
Rt 1, Box 21, Greenville, NC, 27834 (919) 758-7100
Admin Kyle Dilday. *Medical Dir/Dir of Nursing* Joseph Ward MD.
Licensure Skilled Care; Intermediate Care.
Beds SNF 51; ICF 69. *Certified* Medicaid; Medicare.
Admissions Requirements Medical examination.
Staff Physicians 21 (pt); RNs 6 (ft), 2 (pt); LPNs 7 (ft), 4 (pt); Orderlies 7 (ft), 1 (pt); Nurses aides 28 (ft), 19 (pt); Physical therapists 2 (pt); Speech therapists 1 (pt); Activities coordinators 1 (ft), 1 (pt); Dietitians 1 (ft); Social workers 1 (ft).

HENDERSON

Guardian Care of Henderson*
519 Roanoke Ave, Henderson, NC, 27536 (919) 438-6141
Admin Helen O Brame.
Licensure Intermediate Care. *Beds* 80. *Certified* Medicaid.

Pine Haven Convalescent Center*
PO Box 1098, 1245 Park Ave, Henderson, NC, 27536 (919) 492-1088
Admin Dianne Walker.
Licensure Intermediate Care; Home for the Aged. *Beds* ICF 52; Home for the Aged 23. *Certified* Medicaid.

HENDERSONVILLE

Carolina Village Inc*
600 Carolina Village Rd, Hendersonville, NC, 28739 (704) 692-6275

Admin Doley S Bell Jr.
Licensure Skilled Care. *Beds* 58. *Certified* Medicaid; Medicare.

Lakewood Manor Nursing Center*
1510 Hebron St, Hendersonville, NC, 28739 (704) 693-8461
Admin Jane Kinard.
Licensure Skilled Care; Intermediate Care.
Beds SNF 30; ICF 120. *Certified* Medicaid; Medicare.

Margaret R Pardee Memorial*
715 Flemming St, Hendersonville, NC, 28739 (704) 693-6522
Admin Harold P Coston.
Licensure Skilled Care. *Beds* 40. *Certified* Medicaid; Medicare.

HICKORY

Brian Center of Nursing Care—Catawba*
Rt 3, Box 518, Hickory, NC, 28601 (704) 322-3343
Admin Max Hodges.
Licensure Skilled Care; Intermediate Care.
Beds SNF 30; ICF 80. *Certified* Medicaid; Medicare.

Brian Center of Nursing Care—Hickory
220 13th Ave Pl NW, Hickory, NC, 28601 (704) 328-5646
Admin Cynthia A Beaver. *Medical Dir/Dir of Nursing* Dr John Earl.
Licensure Skilled Care; Intermediate Care.
Beds SNF 63; ICF 41. *Certified* Medicaid; Medicare.
Admissions Requirements Minimum age 18; Medical examination.
Facilities Dining room; Physical therapy room; Activities room; Crafts room; Laundry room; Barber/Beauty shop.
Activities Arts and Crafts; Cards; Games; Reading groups; Prayer groups; Movies; Shopping trips; Dances/Social or cultural gatherings.

North Carolina Lutheran Home—Hickory Unit
1265 21st St NE, Hickory, NC, 28601 (704) 328-2006
Admin Mark C Johnson.
Licensure Skilled Care; Intermediate Care; Home for the Aged. *Beds* SNF 48; ICF 16; Home for the Aged 16. *Certified* Medicaid; Medicare.
Staff RNs 8 (ft), 2 (pt); LPNs 8 (ft); Orderlies 4 (ft); Nurses aides 17 (ft), 8 (pt); Activities coordinators 1 (ft).
Affiliation Lutheran
Facilities Dining room; Activities room; Chapel; Crafts room; Laundry room; Barber/Beauty shop; Library; Day room.
Activities Arts and Crafts; Cards; Games; Reading groups; Prayer groups; Movies; Shopping trips; Dances/Social or cultural gatherings.
Description The Lutheran Home was opened December 1, 1920 in the former Stapenbeck mansion on Utica Road in Clinton. The home was a pioneer in health care for the aging and infirm. Today, our mission is to provide levels of care for the aging and the handicapped, allowing each individual to excercise those God-given rights which provide a sense of dig-

nity and self-worth. Worship, Bible study, and counseling is offered by our resident chaplain and area clergy.

Pellcare
1125 10th St Blvd NW, Hickory, NC, 28601
(704) 322-6995
Admin Robert N Schappell. *Medical Dir/Dir of Nursing* John K Earl MD.
Licensure Skilled Care; Intermediate Care.
Beds SNF 60; ICF 60. *Certified* Medicaid; Medicare.
Admissions Requirements Minimum age 18; Medical examination; Physician's request.
Staff Physicians 1 (ft); RNs 2 (ft), 3 (pt); LPNs 8 (ft), 5 (pt); Orderlies 2 (ft); Nurses aides 33 (ft), 17 (pt); Activities coordinators 1 (ft); Dietitians 1 (pt); Dentists 1 (pt); Podiatrists 1 (pt).
Facilities Dining room; Physical therapy room; Activities room; Crafts room; Laundry room; Barber/Beauty shop; Library.
Activities Arts and Crafts; Games; Prayer groups; Movies; Shopping trips.

HIGH POINT

Evergreens II Inc
206 Greensboro Rd, High Point, NC, 27260
(919) 886-4121
Admin Aleita T Hodgin. *Medical Dir/Dir of Nursing* Dr Angus Sargeant.
Licensure Skilled Care; Intermediate Care; Home for the Aged. *Beds* SNF 27; ICF; Home for the Aged 27. *Certified* Medicaid; Medicare.
Admissions Requirements Minimum age 21; Medical examination; Physician's request.
Staff RNs 5 (ft), 1 (pt); LPNs 7 (ft), 6 (pt); Nurses aides 36 (ft), 7 (pt); Physical therapists; Reality therapists; Speech therapists; Activities coordinators; Dentists.
Facilities Dining room; Physical therapy room; Activities room; Crafts room; Laundry room; Barber/Beauty shop.
Activities Arts and Crafts; Cards; Games; Reading groups; Prayer groups; Movies; Shopping trips; Dances/Social or cultural gatherings.
Description Modern, bright facility within the city but with an almost rural setting of both open land and woods. Programs are designed for urban residents but the needs of residents with rural backgrounds are considered, such as pet therapy and visits by farm animals for a petting farm.

Lamb's Nursing Home
3830 N Main St, High Point, NC, 27260 (919) 869-3752
Admin Clifton H Lamb. *Medical Dir/Dir of Nursing* Bansi P Shah.
Licensure Skilled Care; Intermediate Care.
Beds SNF 28; ICF 72. *Certified* Medicaid; Medicare.
Admissions Requirements Medical examination.
Staff Physicians 2 (pt); RNs 5 (ft), 2 (pt); LPNs 4 (ft), 1 (pt); Orderlies 1 (ft); Nurses aides 28 (ft), 19 (pt); Physical therapists 1 (pt); Reality therapists 1 (pt); Recreational therapists 1 (pt); Occupational therapists 1 (pt); Speech therapists; Activities coordinators 1 (pt); Dietitians 1 (ft).
Facilities Dining room; Activities room; Chap-

el; Crafts room; Laundry room; Barber/Beauty shop; Library.
Activities Arts and Crafts; Games; Prayer groups; Movies.

Maryfield Nursing Home
1315 Greensboro Rd, High Point, NC, 27260
(919) 454-5313
Admin Mary Coughlan. *Medical Dir/Dir of Nursing* Dr W H Flythe.
Licensure Skilled Care; Intermediate Care.
Beds SNF 107; ICF 8. *Certified* Medicaid; Medicare.
Admissions Requirements Medical examination; Physician's request.
Staff Physicians 2 (pt); RNs 6 (ft), 12 (pt); LPNs 4 (ft); Orderlies 1 (ft); Nurses aides 50 (ft); Physical therapists 1 (pt); Recreational therapists 2 (ft); Speech therapists 1 (pt); Dietitians 1 (ft), 1 (pt); Dentists 1 (pt); Podiatrists 1 (pt).
Affiliation Roman Catholic
Facilities Dining room; Physical therapy room; Activities room; Chapel; Crafts room; Laundry room; Barber/Beauty shop; Library.
Activities Arts and Crafts; Games; Reading groups; Prayer groups; Movies; Shopping trips.
Description Facility features extensive landscaped grounds, with a mini-bus available to patients for drives, shopping, etc. Mass daily in nursing home chapel; non-Catholic services weekly.

Medical Park Nursing Center
707 N Elm St, High Point, NC, 27262 (919) 885-0141
Admin Richard Bennett. *Medical Dir/Dir of Nursing* Sam T Bickley MD.
Licensure Skilled Care; Intermediate Care.
Beds SNF 93; ICF 106. *Certified* Medicaid; Medicare.
Admissions Requirements Medical examination; Physician's request.
Staff Physicians 4 (pt); RNs 20 (ft); LPNs 30 (ft); Orderlies 8 (ft); Nurses aides 60 (ft); Physical therapists 2 (ft); Reality therapists 2 (ft); Recreational therapists 3 (ft); Speech therapists 1 (ft); Activities coordinators 1 (ft); Dietitians 1 (ft); Dentists 1 (ft); Podiatrists 1 (pt).
Facilities Dining room; Physical therapy room; Activities room; Crafts room; Laundry room; Barber/Beauty shop.
Activities Arts and Crafts; Cards; Games; Reading groups; Prayer groups; Movies; Shopping trips; Dances/Social or cultural gatherings.

Presbyterian Home Inc
201 Greensboro Rd, PO Box 2007, High Point, NC, 27261 (919) 883-9111
Admin Betty Hayes.
Licensure Skilled Care; Intermediate Care; Home for the Aged. *Beds* SNF 68; ICF 10; Home for the Aged 75. *Certified* Medicaid; Medicare.
Admissions Requirements Minimum age 62; Medical examination.
Staff Physicians 1 (pt); RNs 12 (ft), 12 (pt); LPNs 2 (ft), 4 (pt); Orderlies 3 (ft), 2 (pt); Nurses aides 33 (ft), 24 (pt); Activities coordinators 3 (ft), 1 (pt); Dietitians 1 (ft).
Affiliation Presbyterian
Facilities Dining room; Physical therapy room; Activities room; Chapel; Crafts room; Laundry room; Barber/Beauty shop; Library.

Activities Arts and Crafts; Games; Reading groups; Movies; Shopping trips; Dances/Social or cultural gatherings.
Description Facility is a life care community providing 4 levels of care.

Wesleyan Arms Inc
1901 N Centennial St, High Point, NC, 27260
(919) 886-5051
Admin James L Denny. *Medical Dir/Dir of Nursing* A A Reeder MD.
Licensure Skilled Care; Intermediate Care; Home for the Aged. *Beds* SNF 50; ICF; Home for the Aged 100. *Certified* Medicaid; Medicare.
Admissions Requirements Medical examination.
Staff Physicians 12 (pt); RNs 9 (ft), 3 (pt); LPNs 9 (ft), 4 (pt); Nurses aides 50 (ft), 21 (pt); Physical therapists 1 (ft); Activities coordinators 3 (ft); Dietitians 2 (ft).
Affiliation First Wesleyan Church
Facilities Dining room; Physical ther   room; Activities room; Crafts room; Laundry   n; Barber/Beauty shop.
Activities Arts and Crafts; Games; Prayer groups; Movies; Shopping trips.

HUNTERSVILLE

Huntersville Hospital—Skilled Nursing and Intermediate Care Facility
Rt 1, Box 390, Huntersville, NC, 28078
Admin Thomas E Smith. *Medical Dir/Dir of Nursing* William T Williams Jr.
Licensure Skilled Care; Intermediate Care.
Beds 274. *Certified* Medicaid; Medicare.
Ownership Nonprofit.
Admissions Requirements Medical examination; Physician's request.
Staff Physicians 8 (ft); RNs 25 (ft), 25 (pt); LPNs 22 (ft), 4 (pt); Orderlies 2 (ft), 3 (pt); Nurses aides 115 (ft), 42 (pt); Physical therapists 1 (ft); Recreational therapists 3 (ft); Speech therapists 1 (pt); Activities coordinators 1 (ft); Dietitians 1 (ft); Dentists 1 (pt); Ophthalmologists 1 (pt); Podiatrists 1 (pt).
Facilities Dining room; Physical therapy room; Activities room; Chapel; Crafts room; Laundry room; Barber/Beauty shop; Library.
Activities Arts and Crafts; Cards; Games; Reading groups; Prayer groups; Movies; Shopping trips; Dances/Social or cultural gatherings.
Description Facility offers a clinical laboratory, pharmacy, radiology department, emergency room, several outpatient clinics, as well as a medical social work department, all available for 87 acute bed hospital and long-term care residents.

JACKSONVILLE

Britthaven of Jacksonville
225 White St, Jacksonville, NC, 28540 (919) 353-7222
Medical Dir/Dir of Nursing Dr Wesley Murfin.
Admissions Requirements Minimum age 18; Medical examination; Physician's request.
Staff RNs 9 (ft), 4 (pt); LPNs 25 (ft), 6 (pt); Orderlies 4 (ft); Nurses aides 75 (ft), 40 (pt); Activities coordinators 2 (ft); Dietitians 1 (ft);

Dentists 1 (pt); Ophthalmologists 1 (pt); Podiatrists 1 (pt).
Facilities Dining room; Activities room; Chapel; Crafts room; Laundry room; Barber/Beauty shop; Library.
Activities Arts and Crafts; Cards; Games; Prayer groups; Movies; Shopping trips; Dances/Social or cultural gatherings.
Description Britthaven is situated in a beautiful pine tree setting just behind Onslow Memorial Hospital. The nursing home is about 2 minutes away from the Onslow mall and other smaller shopping centers.

ElderLodge—Jacksonville
1839 Onslow Dr, PO Box 5021, Jacksonville, NC, 28540 (919) 455-3610
Admin Kate Conway Acevedo. *Medical Dir-/Dir of Nursing* Dr C T Streeter.
Licensure Skilled Care. *Beds* 80. *Certified* Medicaid; Medicare.
Admissions Requirements Minimum age 18; Medical examination.
Staff Physicians 4 (pt); RNs 3 (ft), 4 (pt); LPNs 8 (ft), 1 (pt); Nurses aides 33 (ft), 1 (pt); Physical therapists 1 (pt); Activities coordinators 1 (ft); Dietitians 1 (ft); Dentists 2 (pt); Ophthalmologists 1 (pt); Podiatrists 1 (pt).
Facilities Dining room; Activities room; Laundry room; Barber/Beauty shop.
Activities Arts and Crafts; Games; Prayer groups; Movies; Shopping trips; Dinner out.
Description Facility is located in a residential area; decor attempts to convey a home-like atmosphere; activities include performances by Marine Corps Band, monthly staff and residents picnic during spring and summer, and active arts and crafts program.

KENANSVILLE

Guardian Care of Kenansville*
PO Box 478, Beasley St, Kenansville, NC, 28349 (919) 296-1561
Admin Charles Sharpe Jr.
Licensure Skilled Care; Intermediate Care.
Beds SNF 28; ICF 64. *Certified* Medicaid; Medicare.

KERNERSVILLE

Oakwood Knoll Nurisng Home
2680 Hwy 66 S, Kernersville, NC, 27284 (919) 869-4114
Admin Ruth Carter.
Licensure Intermediate Care. *Beds* 32. *Certified* Medicaid.
Staff RNs 1 (pt); LPNs 3 (ft); Nurses aides 6 (ft), 7 (pt); Activities coordinators 1 (ft); Dietitians 1 (pt).
Facilities Dining room; Activities room; Crafts room; Laundry room; Barber/Beauty shop.
Activities Arts and Crafts.

Willowbrook Care Center
730 Piney Grove Rd, Kernersville, NC, 27284 (919) 996-4038
Admin Rodney Worley. *Medical Dir/Dir of Nursing* Dr Wesley Phillips.
Licensure Intermediate Care. *Beds* 60. *Certified* Medicaid.

Admissions Requirements Minimum age 18; Medical examination.
Staff RNs 2 (ft); LPNs 6 (ft); Nurses aides 25 (ft), 10 (pt); Recreational therapists 1 (pt); Activities coordinators 1 (ft).
Facilities Dining room; Activities room; Laundry room; Barber/Beauty shop.
Activities Arts and Crafts; Cards; Games; Reading groups; Prayer groups; Movies; Shopping trips; Dances/Social or cultural gatherings.
Description Facility is very active in restorative nursing services, bowel and bladder retraining program, restorative feeding program, sensory retraining, reality orientation, good grooming program, restorative nursing (which includes range of joint motion, ambulation, position, etc.). Active residents council.

KINGS MOUNTAIN

Kings Mountain Convalescent Center
716 Sipes St, PO Box 588, Kings Mountain, NC, 28086 (704) 739-8132
Admin Karen V Greene. *Medical Dir/Dir of Nursing* Dr Bruce Wallace.
Licensure Skilled Care; Intermediate Care.
Beds SNF 62; ICF 62. *Certified* Medicaid; Medicare.
Admissions Requirements Physician's request.
Staff RNs 5 (ft), 2 (pt); LPNs 11 (ft), 1 (pt); Orderlies 9 (ft), 1 (pt); Nurses aides 28 (ft), 13 (pt); Physical therapists 1 (ft), 1 (pt); Speech therapists 1 (pt); Activities coordinators 2 (ft); Dietitians 1 (pt); Dentists 1 (pt); Podiatrists 1 (pt).
Facilities Dining room; Physical therapy room; Activities room; Crafts room; Laundry room; Barber/Beauty shop.
Activities Arts and Crafts; Cards; Games; Reading groups; Prayer groups; Movies; Shopping trips; Dances/Social or cultural gatherings.

KINSTON

Caswell Center*
2415 W Vernon Ave, Kinston, NC, 28501 (919) 522-1261
Admin Richard Zaharia.
Licensure Intermediate Care for Mentally Retarded. *Beds* 752. *Certified* Medicaid.

Guardian Care of Kinston Inc
Cunningham Rd, PO Box 1438, Kinston, NC, 28501 (919) 527-5146
Admin Shirley R Fields.
Licensure Intermediate Care. *Beds* 114. *Certified* Medicaid.
Admissions Requirements Minimum age 18; Medical examination; Physician's request.
Staff RNs 3 (ft), 1 (pt); LPNs 7 (ft), 4 (pt); Orderlies 2 (ft); Nurses aides 32 (ft), 9 (pt); Activities coordinators 1 (ft).
Facilities Dining room; Activities room; Crafts room; Laundry room; Barber/Beauty shop; Library.
Activities Arts and Crafts; Games; Reading groups; Movies; Shopping trips; Dances/Social or cultural gatherings.
Description Facility has resident pet program, allowing the adoption of 2 young dogs as pets to live at the facility; although pets are housed out-

doors, they are allowed in the facility daily to visit with residents. A tremendous amount of love and affection is exchanged between pets, residents, and staff in this program.

Oak Manor of Kinston*
317 Rhodes Ave, Kinston, NC, 28501 (919) 523-0083
Admin Deborah A Katkaveck.
Licensure Skilled Care; Intermediate Care.
Beds SNF 83; ICF 99. *Certified* Medicaid; Medicare.

LAGRANGE

Howell's Group Home/Bear Creek
Rt 4, Box 300, LaGrange, NC, 28551 (919) 566-3110
Admin Patricia Faulk RN. *Medical Dir/Dir of Nursing* Dr James Morris.
Licensure Intermediate Care for Mentally Retarded.
Ownership Nonprofit.
Admissions Requirements Minimum age Birth; Medical examination.
Staff RNs 9 (ft), 1 (pt); LPNs 8 (ft), 1 (pt); Nurses aides 100 (ft); Physical therapists 1 (ft); Recreational therapists 1 (ft); Occupational therapists 2 (ft); Speech therapists 1 (ft); Activities coordinators 1 (ft); Dietitians 2 (ft); Dentists 1 (ft); Ophthalmologists 1 (ft); Audiologists 1 (ft).
Facilities Dining room; Physical therapy room; Activities room; Chapel; Crafts room; Laundry room; Barber/Beauty shop.
Activities Arts and Crafts; Games; Reading groups; Movies; Shopping trips; Dances/Social or cultural gatherings; Boy and Girl Scouts; Field trips to beach.
Description Private, nonprofit, ICF/M for severely and profoundly retarded young people.

LAKE WACCAMAW

Lake Waccamaw Convalescent Center
Cameron St, PO Box 196, Lake Waccamaw, NC, 28450 (919) 646-3144
Admin Margaret E Marley. *Medical Dir/Dir of Nursing* John Munroe MD.
Licensure Skilled Care; Intermediate Care; Home for the Aged. *Beds* SNF 21; ICF 56; Home for the Aged 5. *Certified* Medicaid; Medicare.
Admissions Requirements Medical examination; Physician's request.
Staff RNs 5 (ft), 3 (pt); LPNs 4 (ft), 1 (pt); Orderlies 3 (ft), 2 (pt); Nurses aides 20 (ft), 16 (pt); Physical therapists 1 (ft), 1 (pt); Activities coordinators 1 (ft); Dietitians 1 (ft); Dentists 1 (pt); Podiatrists 1 (pt).
Facilities Dining room; Physical therapy room; Activities room; Chapel; Crafts room; Laundry room; Barber/Beauty shop.
Activities Arts and Crafts; Games; Reading groups; Prayer groups; Movies; Shopping trips; Dances/Social or cultural gatherings.

LAURINBURG

Century Care of Laurinburg Inc*
Rt 3, Box 95, Laurinburg, NC, 28352 (919)
276-8400
Admin O Wade Avant Jr.
Licensure Intermediate Care. *Beds* 43. *Certified* Medicaid.

Edwin Morgan Center*
Peden St, Laurinburg, NC, 28352 (919)
276-0016
Admin Robert R Martin.
Licensure Skilled Care. *Beds* 40. *Certified* Medicaid; Medicare.

LENOIR

Brian Center—Lenoir*
322 Nu-Way Circle, Lenoir, NC, 28645 (704)
758-7326
Admin Maxwell D Hodges.
Licensure Skilled Care; Intermediate Care.
Beds SNF 68; ICF 52. *Certified* Medicaid;
Medicare.

LEXINGTON

Brian Center of Nursing Care—Lexington
Rt 17, Box 58A, Lexington, NC, 27292 (704)
249-7521
Admin Marilyn S Pye. *Medical Dir/Dir of
Nursing* Michael Garrison MD.
Licensure Skilled Care; Intermediate Care.
Beds SNF 20; ICF 36. *Certified* Medicaid;
Medicare.
Admissions Requirements Medical examination.
Staff Physicians 4 (pt); RNs 1 (ft), 6 (pt); LPNs
6 (ft), 2 (pt); Nurses aides 21 (ft), 6 (pt);
Physical therapists 1 (pt); Recreational therapists 1 (pt); Speech therapists 1 (pt); Activities
coordinators 1 (ft); Dietitians 1 (ft); Dentists 1
(pt); Ophthalmologists 1 (pt); Podiatrists 1 (pt);
Audiologists 1 (pt).
Facilities Dining room; Activities room; Chapel; Crafts room; Laundry room; Barber/Beauty
shop; Library.
Activities Arts and Crafts; Games; Reading
groups; Prayer groups; Movies; Shopping trips;
Dances/Social or cultural gatherings.
Description Beautiful, old facility in a rural setting atop a hill; because of smallness, there is a
family atmosphere; patient/family/staff
cookouts held May through September.

Buena Vista Nursing Center Inc
PO Box 419, Lexington, NC, 27292 (704)
246-6644
Admin Thurman L Fritts.
Licensure Intermediate Care; Home for the
Aged. *Beds* ICF 36; Home for the Aged 6. *Certified* Medicaid.
Staff RNs 2 (ft), 3 (pt); LPNs 3 (ft), 3 (pt);
Orderlies 2 (pt); Nurses aides 14 (ft), 5 (pt);
Activities coordinators 1 (ft); Dentists 1 (pt);
Podiatrists 1 (pt).
Facilities Dining room; Activities room; Chapel; Crafts room; Laundry room; Barber/Beauty

shop.
Activities Arts and Crafts; Games; Reading
groups; Prayer groups; Movies; Shopping trips.

Centerclair Inc
Rt 2, Box 23, Lexington, NC, 27292 (704)
249-7057
Admin Geneva F Williams. *Medical Dir/Dir
of Nursing* Gerald P Briggs MD.
Licensure Intermediate Care. *Beds* 60. *Certified* Medicaid.
Admissions Requirements Medical examination.
Staff RNs 2 (ft), 1 (pt); LPNs 2 (ft); Orderlies 1
(ft); Nurses aides 11 (ft), 9 (pt); Activities coordinators 1 (ft); Dietitians 1 (pt).
Facilities Dining room; Activities room;
Laundry room; Barber/Beauty shop.
Activities Arts and Crafts; Games; Prayer
groups; Movies; Dining out; Fair.
Description Facility is located in a beautiful,
rural setting with very congenial neighbors. The
size of the facility allows it to be somewhat
informal, and project a home-type environment.

Golden Age Inc*
Rt 15, Box 216, Cowplace Rd, Lexington, NC,
27292 (704) 956-6219
Admin Samuel E McBride.
Licensure Skilled Care; Home for the Aged.
Beds SNF 50; Home for the Aged 14.
Certified Medicaid; Medicare.

LILLINGTON

Adams and Kinton Nursing Home Inc*
PO Box 787, Hwy 421E, Lillington, NC, 27546
(919) 893-5141
Admin John H Kinton Jr.
Licensure Skilled Care; Intermediate Care.
Beds SNF 40; ICF 89. *Certified* Medicaid;
Medicare.

LINCOLNTON

Lincoln Nursing Center*
PO Box 898, 1419 Gaston St Extension, Lincolnton, NC, 28092 (704) 732-1138
Admin Valarie Keck.
Licensure Skilled Care; Intermediate Care;
Home for the Aged. *Beds* SNF 60; ICF 30;
Home for the Aged 30. *Certified* Medicaid;
Medicare.

LOUISBURG

Louisburg Nursing Center
Smoke Tree Way, PO Box 759, Louisburg, NC,
27549 (919) 496-2188
Admin Anne T Hutchinson. *Medical Dir/Dir
of Nursing* B L Patterson MD.
Licensure Intermediate Care. *Beds* 92. *Certified* Medicaid.
Admissions Requirements Medical examination; Physician's request.
Staff RNs 1 (ft), 2 (pt); LPNs 8 (ft), 6 (pt);
Orderlies 5 (ft), 2 (pt); Nurses aides 32 (ft), 8
(pt); Activities coordinators 1 (ft); Dietitians 1
(pt).
Facilities Dining room; Physical therapy room;

Activities room; Crafts room; Laundry room;
Barber/Beauty shop.
Activities Arts and Crafts; Cards; Games;
Reading groups; Prayer groups; Movies; Shopping trips.

LOWELL

Autumnfield Inc
398 Wilkinson Blvd, PO Box 597, Lowell, NC,
28098 (704) 824-4316
Admin Thelma C James. *Medical Dir/Dir of
Nursing* Dr W H Hammond Jr.
Licensure Skilled Care. *Beds* 50. *Certified* Medicaid; Medicare.
Admissions Requirements Minimum age 18.
Staff RNs 3 (ft), 1 (pt); LPNs 3 (ft), 2 (pt);
Nurses aides 15 (ft), 3 (pt); Physical therapists;
Speech therapists; Activities coordinators 1 (ft);
Dietitians 1 (ft); Dentists; Ophthalmologists;
Podiatrists.
Facilities Dining room; Activities room; Barber/Beauty shop.
Activities Arts and Crafts; Cards; Games;
Reading groups; Prayer groups; Movies; Shopping trips; Dances/Social or cultural gatherings.
Description Facility is located on an acre where
residents can go outside when weather permits;
more home atmosphere than medical; good
family and community participation.

LUMBERTON

Kingsdale Manor*
PO Box 1675, 1555 Willis Ave, Lumberton,
NC, 28358 (919) 739-6048
Admin Donald B Joseph.
Licensure Skilled Care; Intermediate Care.
Beds SNF 21; ICF 104. *Certified* Medicaid.

Methodist Retirement Home—Wesley Pines
100 Wesley Pine Rd, Lumberton, NC, 28358
(919) 738-9691
Admin Paul G Bunn. *Medical Dir/Dir of
Nursing* Dr Ben Hardin.
Licensure Skilled Care; Intermediate Care;
Home for the Aged. *Beds* SNF 24; ICF 12;
Home for the Aged 20. *Certified* Medicaid;
Medicare.
Admissions Requirements Minimum age 65;
Medical examination.
Staff Physicians 1 (pt); RNs 3 (ft), 4 (pt); LPNs
3 (ft), 2 (pt); Orderlies 4 (ft); Nurses aides 11
(ft), 5 (pt); Physical therapists 1 (ft), 2 (pt);
Reality therapists 1 (pt); Activities coordinators
1 (ft); Dietitians 1 (pt); Podiatrists 1 (pt).
Affiliation Methodist
Facilities Dining room; Physical therapy room;
Activities room; Chapel; Crafts room; Laundry
room; Barber/Beauty shop; Library; Family
rooms.
Activities Arts and Crafts; Cards; Games;
Reading groups; Prayer groups; Shopping trips;
Dances/Social or cultural gatherings.
Description Wesley Pines is located in the thermal zone of coastal North Carolina that provides warmth, floral beauty, and a Carribean
Island-type appearance; residents come from
northern and southern states; security along
with varied activities make Wesley Pines attractive to many people.

North Carolina Cancer Institute*
PO Box 1445, Hwy 711, Lumberton, NC,
28358 (919) 739-2821
Admin Kenneth Jackson.
Licensure Skilled Care. *Beds* 52. *Certified* Medicaid; Medicare.

Southeastern General Hospital Inc*
300 W 27th St, Lumberton, NC, 28358 (919)
738-6441
Admin Donald C Hiscott.
Licensure Skilled Care; Intermediate Care.
Beds SNF 40; ICF 40. *Certified* Medicaid;
Medicare.

MADISON

Rockingham Nursing Center*
Rt 2, Box 381, Madison, NC, 27025 (919)
548-9658
Admin Susan Mathews.
Licensure Skilled Care; Intermediate Care.
Beds SNF 22; ICF 78. *Certified* Medicaid;
Medicare.

MARION

Autumn Care of Marion
610 Airport Rd, PO 339, Marion, NC, 28752
(704) 652-6701
Admin Thomas G Koontz. *Medical Dir/Dir of Nursing* Dr Michael McCall.
Licensure Skilled Care; Intermediate Care.
Beds SNF 50; ICF 30. *Certified* Medicaid;
Medicare.
Admissions Requirements Minimum age 21;
Medical examination.
Staff Physicians 8 (pt); RNs 7 (ft), 5 (pt); LPNs
6 (ft), 3 (pt); Orderlies 2 (ft); Nurses aides 35
(ft), 15 (pt); Physical therapists 2 (pt); Speech
therapists 1 (pt); Activities coordinators 1 (ft);
Dietitians 1 (pt); Dentists 1 (pt); Ophthalmologists 1 (pt); Podiatrists 1 (pt).
Facilities Dining room; Physical therapy room;
Activities room; Crafts room; Laundry room;
Barber/Beauty shop.
Activities Arts and Crafts; Cards; Games;
Reading groups; Prayer groups; Movies; Shopping trips; Dances/Social or cultural gatherings.
Description Facility is set in the Blue Ridge
Mountains with outstanding views views and
recieved Outstanding Community Involvement Award (NC HCFA 1983).

MARS HILL

Madison Manor Nursing Center
50 Maror Rd, Mars Hill, NC, 28754 (704)
689-5200
Admin Wayne Adams. *Medical Dir/Dir of Nursing* Dr Otis Duck.
Licensure Skilled Care; Intermediate Care.
Beds SNF 51; ICF 49. *Certified* Medicaid;
Medicare.
Admissions Requirements Minimum age 18.
Staff Physicians 5 (pt); RNs 4 (ft), 3 (pt); LPNs
8 (ft), 4 (pt); Nurses aides 29 (ft), 7 (pt);
Physical therapists 2 (pt); Activities coordinators 1 (ft), 1 (pt); Dietitians 1 (ft); Dentists 1
(pt).
Facilities Dining room; Physical therapy room;

Activities room; Crafts room; Laundry room;
Barber/Beauty shop.
Activities Arts and Crafts; Cards; Games;
Reading groups; Prayer groups; Movies; Shopping trips; Dances/Social or cultural gatherings.
Description Madison Manor Nursing Center is
located north of Asheville, NC, in the foothills
of the beautiful Appalachian Mountains. The
setting is reflective of the local mountain heritage in every way, from the vegetable garden, to
the mountain crafts store, to the pet rabbits in
the enclosed courtyard. Plenty of indoor
greenery and open skylights enhance the spacious corridors and rooms. Community volunteer services enrich the lives of residents as well
as support from Mars Hill College, only 2 miles
from the facility.

MOCKSVILLE

Autumn Care of Mocksville
1007 Howard St, PO Box 423, Mocksville, NC,
27028 (704) 634-3535
Admin Nettie Groce. *Medical Dir/Dir of Nursing* Dr George Kimberly.
Licensure Skilled Care; Intermediate Care;
Home for the Aged. *Beds* SNF 35; ICF 42;
Home for the Aged 8. *Certified* Medicaid.
Admissions Requirements Minimum age 18.
Staff RNs 4 (ft), 1 (pt); LPNs 9 (ft); Nurses
aides 29 (ft), 17 (pt); Physical therapists 1 (pt);
Activities coordinators 1 (ft); Dietitians 1 (pt).
Facilities Dining room; Physical therapy room;
Activities room; Crafts room; Laundry room;
Barber/Beauty shop.
Activities Games; Movies.
Description Instructor comes twice a week
from Mitchel Community College to teach
painting, sewing, music, and reading.

MONROE

Guardian Care of Monroe Inc
1212 Sunset Dr, PO Box 1189, Monroe, NC,
28110 (704) 283-8548
Admin Mary M Carter.
Licensure Intermediate Care. *Beds* 114.
Staff RNs 3 (ft); LPNs 10 (ft), 3 (pt); Nurses
aides 35 (ft); Activities coordinators 1 (ft); Dietitians 1 (ft).
Facilities Dining room; Activities room; Crafts
room; Laundry room; Barber/Beauty shop.
Activities Arts and Crafts; Cards; Games;
Reading groups; Prayer groups; Movies; Shopping trips; Dances/Social or cultural gatherings.

Union Memorial Hospital*
Huey St, Box 130, Monroe, NC, 28110 (704)
283-2111
Admin Larry Bishop.
Licensure Skilled Care; Intermediate Care.
Beds 66. *Certified* Medicaid; Medicare.

MOORESVILLE

Brian Center—Mooresville
752 E Center St, Mooresville, NC, 28115 (704)
663-3448
Admin Patsy B Sherrill. *Medical Dir/Dir of Nursing* Dr William S Reen.
Licensure Skilled Care; Intermediate Care.

Beds SNF 55; ICF 45. *Certified* Medicaid;
Medicare.
Admissions Requirements Medical examination; Physician's request.
Staff RNs 7 (ft), 5 (pt); LPNs 5 (ft), 3 (pt);
Nurses aides 26 (ft), 19 (pt); Physical therapists
1 (ft), 2 (pt); Activities coordinators 1 (ft); Dietitians 1 (ft).
Facilities Dining room; Physical therapy room;
Activities room; Crafts room; Laundry room;
Barber/Beauty shop.
Activities Arts and Crafts; Cards; Games;
Reading groups; Prayer groups; Movies; Shopping trips; Dances/Social or cultural gatherings.
Description Facility is JCAH accredited and
features 24-hour RN coverage, physical therapy
and rehabilitative nursing, and full-time
activity and social worker dedicated to high-quality care.

MOREHEAD CITY

Harborview Nursing Home Inc*
812 Shepard St, Morehead City, NC, 28557
(919) 726-6855
Admin Doris B Jernigan.
Licensure Intermediate Care; Home for the
Aged. *Beds* ICF 62; Home for the Aged 6. *Certified* Medicaid.

Morehead Nursing Center
Penny Ln, Morehead City, NC, 28557 (919)
726-0031
Admin James R Saylor. *Medical Dir/Dir of Nursing* Dr Donald Reece.
Licensure Skilled Care; Intermediate Care.
Beds SNF 31; ICF 61. *Certified* Medicaid;
Medicare.
Admissions Requirements Medical examination; Physician's request.
Staff RNs 4 (ft); LPNs 5 (ft), 5 (pt); Nurses
aides 30 (ft), 10 (pt); Physical therapists; Speech
therapists; Activities coordinators 1 (ft); Dietitians 1 (ft).
Facilities Dining room; Physical therapy room;
Activities room; Crafts room; Laundry room;
Barber/Beauty shop.
Activities Arts and Crafts; Cards; Games;
Reading groups; Prayer groups; Movies; Shopping trips; Dances/Social or cultural gatherings.

MORGANTON

Britthaven of Morganton*
107 Magnolia Dr, Morganton, NC, 28655 (704)
437-8760
Admin Nancy N Hipps.
Licensure Skilled Care; Intermediate Care.
Beds SNF 31; ICF 60. *Certified* Medicaid;
Medicare.

Broughton Hospital*
1000 Sterling St, Morganton, NC, 28655 (704)
433-2525
Admin W W Lowrance.
Licensure Skilled Care; Intermediate Care for
Mentally Retarded. *Beds* SNF 30; ICF/MR 78.
Certified Medicaid.

Foothills ICF/MR Group Home*
309 E View St, Morganton, NC, 28655 (704) 433-6488
Admin Janie Cloer.
Licensure Intermediate Care; Intermediate Care for Mentally Retarded. *Beds* 5. *Certified* Medicaid.

Foothills Nursing Center
109 Foothills Dr, Morganton, NC, 28655 (704) 433-7160
Admin Kenneth J Andrews. *Medical Dir/Dir of Nursing* Dr Luther Clontz.
Licensure Skilled Care; Intermediate Care. *Beds* SNF 70; ICF 50. *Certified* Medicaid; Medicare.
Staff Physicians 1 (pt); RNs 6 (ft), 1 (pt); LPNs 10 (ft), 1 (pt); Nurses aides 50 (ft), 15 (pt); Physical therapists 2 (ft); Recreational therapists 2 (ft); Speech therapists 1 (pt); Activities coordinators 1 (ft); Dietitians 1 (ft); Dentists 1 (pt).
Facilities Dining room; Physical therapy room; Activities room; Crafts room; Laundry room; Barber/Beauty shop.
Activities Arts and Crafts; Cards; Games; Reading groups; Prayer groups; Movies; Shopping trips; Dances/Social or cultural gatherings.

Western Carolina Center*
200 Enola Rd, Morganton, NC, 28655 (704) 433-2711
Admin J Iverson Riddle.
Licensure Intermediate Care; Intermediate Care for Mentally Retarded. *Beds* 498. *Certified* Medicaid.

MOUNT AIRY

Surry Community Nursing Center
542 Allred Mill Rd, Mount Airy, NC, 27030 (919) 789-5076
Admin Sondra C Ware. *Medical Dir/Dir of Nursing* Dr J Gillum.
Licensure Skilled Care; Intermediate Care. *Beds* SNF 60; ICF 60. *Certified* Medicaid; Medicare.
Admissions Requirements Medical examination; Physician's request.
Staff RNs 9 (ft), 1 (pt); LPNs 9 (ft), 4 (pt); Nurses aides 39 (ft), 6 (pt); Activities coordinators 1 (ft).
Facilities Dining room; Physical therapy room; Activities room; Crafts room; Laundry room; Barber/Beauty shop; Library; Speech therapy room.
Activities Arts and Crafts; Cards; Games; Reading groups; Prayer groups; Movies; Shopping trips; Dances/Social or cultural gatherings; Adopt-a-grandparent program; Intergenerational sharing.
Description A modern, one-story facility located near the Blue Ridge Mountains offering a variety of individual and group activities, total nursing care, and a rehabilitation program. Dedicated to the quality of life for the residents.

MOUNT OLIVE

Medical Park Nursing Home
228 Smith Chapel Rd, Mount Olive, NC, 28365 (919) 658-9522

Admin Elizabeth H Grady. *Medical Dir/Dir of Nursing* Dr Hervy B Kornegay.
Licensure Skilled Care; Intermediate Care; Home for the Aged. *Beds* SNF 75; ICF 75. *Certified* Medicaid; Medicare.
Admissions Requirements Minimum age 18; Medical examination; Physician's request.
Staff Physicians 5 (pt); RNs 4 (ft), 2 (pt); LPNs 10 (ft), 4 (pt); Orderlies 4 (ft), 2 (pt); Nurses aides 59 (ft), 16 (pt); Physical therapists 1 (ft); Recreational therapists 1 (pt); Speech therapists 1 (pt); Activities coordinators 1 (ft); Dietitians 1 (ft); Dentists 1 (pt).
Facilities Dining room; Physical therapy room; Activities room; Chapel; Crafts room; Laundry room; Barber/Beauty shop.
Activities Arts and Crafts; Games; Reading groups; Prayer groups; Movies; Shopping trips.
Description We have ceramic classes, bingo, and resident's council. In the same complex, we have 5 physician's offices, dentist's office, pharmacy, and our attorney's office.

MURPHY

Murphy Medical Center*
Rt 1, Box 540, Murphy, NC, 28906 (704) 837-8161
Admin Thomas J Taaffe.
Licensure Skilled Care; Intermediate Care. *Beds* SNF 28; ICF 96. *Certified* Medicaid; Medicare.

NAGS HEAD

Elderlodge Outer Banks*
Rt 1, Box 228-N, Nags Head, NC, 27959 (919) 441-3116
Admin Betty Andrews.
Licensure Skilled Care; Intermediate Care. *Beds* SNF 32; ICF 64. *Certified* Medicaid; Medicare.

NEBO

McDowell Nursing Center
Rt 1, Box 850, Nebo, NC, 28761 (704) 652-3032
Admin Robert E Taylor.
Licensure Skilled Care; Intermediate Care. *Beds* 100. *Certified* Medicaid; Medicare.
Staff Physicians 2 (pt); RNs 5 (ft), 1 (pt); LPNs 9 (ft), 1 (pt); Nurses aides 43 (ft); Physical therapists 1 (pt); Activities coordinators 2 (ft); Dietitians 1 (pt); Dentists 1 (pt); Podiatrists 1 (pt).
Facilities Dining room; Activities room; Crafts room; Laundry room; Barber/Beauty shop.
Activities Arts and Crafts; Cards; Games; Reading groups; Prayer groups; Movies; Shopping trips; Dances/Social or cultural gatherings.

NEW BERN

Britthaven of New Bern*
2600 Old Cherry Point Rd, New Bern, NC, 28560 (919) 637-4730
Admin Hobson S Lewis.
Licensure Skilled Care. *Beds* 33. *Certified* Medicaid; Medicare.

Guardian Care of New Bern*
PO Box 2037, 836 Hospital Dr, New Bern, NC, 28560 (919) 638-6001
Admin Iris Willis.
Licensure Intermediate Care. *Beds* 116. *Certified* Medicaid.

Howell's Child Care Center (Riverbend)
Box 239, New Bern, NC, 28560
Admin Joseph A Howell. *Medical Dir/Dir of Nursing* Dr Ron May.
Licensure Intermediate Care for Mentally Retarded. *Beds* 125. *Certified* Medicaid.
Ownership Nonprofit.
Admissions Requirements Minimum age Birth; Medical examination.
Staff Physicians 4 (pt); RNs 6 (ft), 2 (pt); LPNs 14 (ft), 1 (pt); Nurses aides 130 (ft); Physical therapists 1 (ft); Recreational therapists 1 (ft); Occupational therapists 1 (ft); Speech therapists 1 (ft); Activities coordinators 1 (ft); Teachers 10 (ft); Teachers aides 45 (ft).
Facilities Dining room; Physical therapy room; Activities room; Chapel; Crafts room; Laundry room; Barber/Beauty shop; Classrooms; Gymnasium; Swimming pool; Water therapy room.
Activities Arts and Crafts; Games; Movies; Shopping trips; Dances/Social or cultural gatherings.
Description Facility is a community-based ICF/MR for children and young adults offering educational services as well as health care.

NEWTON

The United Church Retirement Home
100 Leonard Ave, Hwy 16 S, Newton, NC, 28658 (704) 464-8260
Admin Donald P Flick. *Medical Dir/Dir of Nursing* Dr William Long.
Licensure Skilled Care; Intermediate Care; Home for the Aged. *Beds* SNF 31; ICF 67; Home for the Aged 20. *Certified* Medicaid; Medicare.
Ownership Nonprofit.
Admissions Requirements Minimum age 62; Medical examination; Physician's request.
Staff RNs 6 (ft), 1 (pt); LPNs 6 (ft), 3 (pt); Orderlies 1 (ft); Nurses aides 32 (ft), 13 (pt); Physical therapists 1 (pt); Activities coordinators 3 (ft); Dietitians 1 (pt).
Affiliation Church of Christ
Facilities Dining room; Physical therapy room; Activities room; Chapel; Crafts room; Laundry room; Barber/Beauty shop; Library.
Activities Arts and Crafts; Cards; Games; Movies; Shopping trips; Dances/Social or cultural gatherings.
Description The Nursing Unit is an integral component of a total life-care community. There is a variety of independent living opportunities available located on an 87-acre tract of land. This nonprofit center strives to respond in creative new ways to the growing concerns of the elderly.

OXFORD

Granville Care Nursing Inc*
PO Box 986, Prospect Ave, Oxford, NC, 27565 (919) 693-1531

Admin Louise B Parham.
Licensure Skilled Care; Intermediate Care.
Beds SNF 60; ICF 60. *Certified* Medicaid;
Medicare.

Granville County Group Home*
Rt 3, Box 193, Oxford, NC, 27565 (919)
693-4610
Admin Ruth E Gierisch.
Licensure Intermediate Care for Mentally
Retarded. *Beds* 5. *Certified* Medicaid.

PINEHURST

Manor Care of Pinehurst
PO Box 1667, Pinehurst, NC, 28374 (919)
295-1781
Admin Carol Lemonds. *Medical Dir/Dir of
Nursing* Dr Joseph Hiatt Jr.
Licensure Skilled Care; Intermediate Care.
Beds SNF 59; ICF 61. *Certified* Medicaid;
Medicare.
Admissions Requirements Medical examina-
tion; Physician's request.
Staff RNs 3 (ft), 6 (pt); LPNs 8 (ft), 3 (pt);
Orderlies 3 (pt); Nurses aides 33 (ft), 3 (pt);
Physical therapists 1 (ft); Speech therapists;
Activities coordinators 1 (ft), 2 (pt); Dietitians;
Dentists; Podiatrists.
Facilities Dining room; Physical therapy room;
Activities room; Laundry room; Barber/Beauty
shop.
Activities Arts and Crafts; Cards; Games;
Reading groups; Prayer groups; Movies; Shop-
ping trips; Dances/Social or cultural gatherings.

Pinehurst Nursing Center
Hwy 5, PO Box 1179, Pinehurst, NC, 28374
(919) 295-6158
Admin James A Hayes. *Medical Dir/Dir of
Nursing* Dr F Owens.
Licensure Intermediate Care; Home for the
Aged. *Beds* ICF 64; Home for the Aged 17.
Certified Medicaid.
Staff RNs 1 (ft); LPNs 5 (ft), 6 (pt); Nurses
aides 25 (ft), 4 (pt); Activities coordinators 1
(ft).
Facilities Dining room; Activities room; Chap-
el; Laundry room; Barber/Beauty shop;
Library.
Activities Arts and Crafts; Cards; Games;
Movies.

PLEASANT GARDEN

Clapp's Nursing Center
4558 Pleasant Garden Rd, PO Box 247,
Pleasant Garden, NC, 27313 (919) 674-2252
Admin Riley W Clapp. *Medical Dir/Dir of
Nursing* Dr W O Elkins.
Licensure Skilled Care; Home for the Aged.
Beds SNF 28; Home for the Aged 5. *Cer-
tified* Medicaid; Medicare.
Admissions Requirements Minimum age 18;
Medical examination; Physician's request.
Staff RNs 2 (ft), 1 (pt); LPNs 4 (ft), 2 (pt);
Orderlies 1 (ft); Nurses aides 10 (ft), 6 (pt);
Physical therapists 1 (pt); Recreational thera-
pists 1 (pt); Speech therapists 1 (pt); Activities
coordinators 1 (pt); Dietitians 1 (pt); Dentists 1
(pt).

RALEIGH

Brian Center of Nursing Care*
3000 Holston Ln, Raleigh, NC, 27610 (919)
828-3904
Admin John A Gryglewicz.
Licensure Skilled Care; Intermediate Care.
Beds SNF 60; ICF 65. *Certified* Medicaid;
Medicare.

Glenwood Hills Intermediate Care Facility*
3910 Blue Ridge Rd, Raleigh, NC, 27612 (919)
787-4747
Admin Rachel Brantley.
Licensure Intermediate Care. *Beds* 30. *Certified* Medicaid.

Hillhaven Convalescent Center
616 Wade Ave, Raleigh, NC, 27605 (919)
828-6251
Admin Mary Ellen Getty.
Licensure Skilled Care; Intermediate Care.
Beds SNF 116; ICF 58. *Certified* Medicaid;
Medicare.
Facilities Dining room; Physical therapy room;
Activities room; Crafts room; Laundry room;
Barber/Beauty shop.
Activities Arts and Crafts; Cards; Games;
Reading groups; Prayer groups; Movies; Shop-
ping trips; Dances/Social or cultural gatherings.

Hillhaven Sunnybrook Convalescent Center*
25 Sunnybrook Rd, Raleigh, NC, 27610 (919)
828-0747
Admin James Strickland.
Licensure Skilled Care; Intermediate Care.
Beds SNF 51; ICF 75. *Certified* Medicaid;
Medicare.

Knollwood Manor Intermediate Care Facility*
4809 North Blvd, Raleigh, NC, 27604 (919)
876-4613
Admin Rachel A Brantley.
Licensure Intermediate Care. *Beds* 108. *Certified* Medicaid.

Mayview Convalescent Center
513 E Whitaker Mill Rd, Raleigh, NC, 27608
(919) 828-2348
Admin Travis H Tomlinson. *Medical Dir/Dir
of Nursing* Dr James S Parsons.
Licensure Skilled Care. *Beds* 139. *Cer-
tified* Medicaid; Medicare.
Admissions Requirements Physician's request.
Facilities Dining room; Physical therapy room;
Activities room; Crafts room; Laundry room;
Barber/Beauty shop.
Activities Arts and Crafts; Cards; Games;
Reading groups; Prayer groups; Movies; Dan-
ces/Social or cultural gatherings.
Description Facility has offered comprehensive
services for 26 years; design emphasizes interi-
or and exterior spaces.

REIDSVILLE

Maplewood Nursing Center*
543 Maple Ave, Reidsville, NC, 27320 (919)
342-1382
Admin J D Lawson.

Licensure Skilled Care; Intermediate Care.
Beds SNF 14; ICF 96. *Certified* Medicaid;
Medicare.

RICH SQUARE

Roanoke Valley Nursing Home Inc*
Box 408, N Main St, Rich Square, NC, 27869
(919) 539-4161
Admin James T Johnson.
Licensure Intermediate Care. *Beds* 69. *Certi-
fied* Medicaid.

ROANOKE RAPIDS

Guardian Care of Roanoke Rapids*
305 14th St, Roanoke Rapids, NC, 27870 (919)
537-6181
Admin Elizabeth P Watkins.
Licensure Intermediate Care. *Beds* 110. *Certified* Medicaid.

ROCKINGHAM

Care Inn—Rockingham
804 Long Dr, PO Box 1237, Rockingham, NC,
28379 (919) 997-4493
Admin Michael W Whitecomb.
Licensure Intermediate Care. *Beds* 120. *Certi-
fied* Medicaid.
Admissions Requirements Medical examina-
tion.
Staff RNs 3 (ft), 1 (pt); LPNs 7 (ft), 1 (pt);
Nurses aides 39 (ft), 2 (pt); Physical therapists 1
(pt).
Facilities Dining room; Physical therapy room;
Activities room; Laundry room; Barber/Beauty
shop.
Activities Arts and Crafts; Cards; Games;
Reading groups; Prayer groups; Movies; Shopping trips; Dances/Social or cultural gatherings;
Bazaars, Heart fund and drive.
Description Facility has a decoration policy
which makes initial visitation a very happy
experience. The overall feeling of well-being is
very evident in all of the residents. This feeling
radiates from residents to their families, visitors
and the rest of the community.

ROCKY MOUNT

Guardian Care of Rocky Mount*
160 Winstead Ave, Rocky Mount, NC, 27801
(919) 443-7666
Admin Edward W Fields.
Licensure Intermediate Care. *Beds* 118. *Certified* Medicaid.

Westgate Nursing Center*
Box 153, Raleigh Rd Extension, Rocky Mount,
NC, 27801 (919) 442-4156
Admin Carrol S Roberson.
Licensure Skilled Care; Intermediate Care.
Beds SNF 36; ICF 50. *Certified* Medicaid;
Medicare.

ROXBORO

Person County Memorial Hospital*
615 Ridge Rd, Roxboro, NC, 27573 (919)
599-2121
Admin Grant Boone.
Licensure Skilled Care. *Beds* 23. *Certified* Medicaid; Medicare.

Roxboro Nursing Center
901 Ridge Rd, PO Box 3070, Roxboro, NC,
27573 (919) 599-0106
Admin Kenneth Stone. *Medical Dir/Dir of Nursing* Dr Thomas Long.
Licensure Intermediate Care. *Beds* 92. *Certified* Medicaid.
Admissions Requirements Medical examination; Physician's request.
Staff Physicians 8 (pt); RNs 1 (pt); LPNs 8 (ft), 3 (pt); Orderlies 1 (ft); Nurses aides 24 (ft), 8 (pt); Activities coordinators 1 (ft), 1 (pt); Dietitians 1 (pt).
Facilities Dining room; Physical therapy room; Activities room; Crafts room; Laundry room; Barber/Beauty shop; Library.
Activities Arts and Crafts; Cards; Games; Reading groups; Prayer groups; Movies; Dances/Social or cultural gatherings.
Description Facility received awards from Arthritis Foundation, local ARC, and Heart Association for contribution made in rock and roll jamborees.

RUTHERFORDTON

Rutherford County Convalescent Center
Rt 2, Box 39-A, Rutherfordton, NC, 28139
(704) 286-9001
Admin Shirley C Frye. *Medical Dir/Dir of Nursing* Dr L P Mitchell.
Licensure Skilled Care. *Beds* 50. *Certified* Medicaid; Medicare.
Staff Physicians 1 (pt); RNs 6 (ft), 2 (pt); LPNs 2 (ft), 1 (pt); Orderlies 1 (pt); Nurses aides 11 (ft), 7 (pt); Physical therapists 1 (pt); Speech therapists 1 (pt); Activities coordinators 1 (ft); Dietitians 1 (ft); Dentists 1 (pt).
Facilities Dining room; Activities room; Laundry room; Barber/Beauty shop.
Activities Arts and Crafts; Cards; Games; Reading groups; Prayer groups; Movies; Shopping trips; Dances/Social or cultural gatherings.

Rutherford Nursing Center Inc*
Box 188, Clubhouse Rd, Rutherfordton, NC,
28139 (704) 287-2169
Admin Anthony Way.
Licensure Skilled Care; Intermediate Care. *Beds* SNF 100; ICF 50. *Certified* Medicaid; Medicare.

SALISBURY

Jo Lene's Nursing Home*
PO Box 2167, 615 W Innes St, Salisbury, NC,
28144 (704) 633-2781
Admin Cherathee Y Hager.
Licensure Skilled Care; Home for the Aged. *Beds* SNF 41; Home for the Aged 25. *Certified* Medicaid; Medicare.

North Carolina Lutheran Home—Salisbury
820 Klumac Rd, Salisbury, NC, 28144 (704)
637-3784
Admin Isaac F Kuhn.
Licensure Skilled Care; Intermediate Care; Home for the Aged. *Beds* SNF 60; ICF 25; Home for the Aged 25. *Certified* Medicaid; Medicare.
Affiliation Lutheran
Facilities Dining room; Physical therapy room; Activities room; Chapel; Crafts room; Laundry room; Barber/Beauty shop; Library; Sun rooms; Visitor rooms.
Activities Arts and Crafts; Cards; Games; Reading groups; Prayer groups; Movies; Shopping trips; Dances/Social or cultural gatherings; Church services; Bible study.
Description Members of the North Carolina Synod of the LCA are served first; others only when possible; space very limited.

Rowan Manor Inc*
PO Box 2105, 635 Statesville Blvd, Salisbury,
NC, 28144 (704) 633-7390
Admin Patricia W Walton.
Licensure Skilled Care; Intermediate Care. *Beds* SNF 116; ICF 69. *Certified* Medicaid; Medicare.

SALUDA

Saluda Nursing and Convalescent Center*
PO Box 488, Esseola Circle, Saluda, NC, 28773
(704) 749-2261
Admin Mary F Adkins.
Licensure Intermediate Care. *Beds* 59. *Certified* Medicaid.

SANFORD

Convalescent Care of Lee County Inc*
PO Box 1346, 714 Western Dr, Sanford, NC,
27330 (919) 776-0601
Admin Kathleen C Foye.
Licensure Skilled Care; Intermediate Care. *Beds* SNF 26; ICF 77. *Certified* Medicaid; Medicare.

Convalescent Center of Sanford Inc
Rt 5, Box 202, Sanford, NC, 27339 (919)
775-7207
Admin Frances H Hall. *Medical Dir/Dir of Nursing* John F Blue MD.
Licensure Skilled Care; Intermediate Care. *Beds* SNF 55; ICF 46. *Certified* Medicaid; Medicare.
Admissions Requirements Minimum age 18; Medical examination.
Staff Physicians 7 (pt); RNs 3 (ft), 2 (pt); LPNs 8 (ft), 5 (pt); Orderlies 1 (ft); Nurses aides 42 (ft), 8 (pt); Physical therapists 1 (pt); Activities coordinators 1 (ft); Dietitians 1 (pt).
Facilities Dining room; Laundry room; Barber/Beauty shop.
Activities Games; Reading groups; Prayer groups; Movies; Shopping trips; Dances/Social or cultural gatherings.
Description Facility is situated on a wooded hillside in a rural, country setting; activities include picnics, watermelon feasts, making ice cream, and annual Christmas covered dish dinner with families.

SCOTLAND NECK

Guardian Care of Scotland Neck*
1400 Junior High School Rd, Scotland Neck,
NC, 27874 (919) 826-5146
Admin Ethel McLean.
Licensure Intermediate Care. *Beds* 62. *Certified* Medicaid.

SEA LEVEL

The Sailors' Snug Harbor*
Rt 70, PO Box 245, Sea Level, NC, 28577 (919)
225-4411
Admin Leo Kraszeski.
Licensure Skilled Care; Intermediate Care; Home for the Aged. *Beds* SNF 22; ICF 20; Home for the Aged 80.

Sea Level Hospital*
Hwy 70E, Sea Level, NC, 28577 (919)
225-4611
Admin Hardy Ledbetter.
Licensure Skilled Care; Intermediate Care. *Beds* 40. *Certified* Medicaid; Medicare.

SHELBY

Meadowbrook Manor of Shelby*
1101 N Morgan St, Shelby, NC, 28150 (704)
482-5396
Admin Judy W Beam.
Licensure Skilled Care; Intermediate Care. *Beds* SNF 35; ICF 65. *Certified* Medicaid; Medicare.

Shelby Convalescent Center
401 N Morgan St, PO Box 790, Shelby, NC,
28150 (704) 482-7326
Admin Gwen Butler. *Medical Dir/Dir of Nursing* Dr Richard Maybin.
Licensure Skilled Care; Intermediate Care. *Beds* SNF 60; ICF 100. *Certified* Medicaid; Medicare.
Admissions Requirements Medical examination; Physician's request.
Staff RNs 5 (ft), 1 (pt); LPNs 14 (ft), 5 (pt); Orderlies 6 (ft), 3 (pt); Nurses aides 52 (ft), 18 (pt); Physical therapists 1 (ft); Activities coordinators 1 (ft); Dietitians 1 (pt).
Facilities Dining room; Physical therapy room; Activities room; Crafts room; Laundry room; Barber/Beauty shop; Resident lounge.
Activities Arts and Crafts; Games; Reading groups; Prayer groups; Movies; Shopping trips; Dances/Social or cultural gatherings; Birthday parties; Exercise class.

SILER CITY

Brian Center of Siler City*
900 W Dolphin St, Siler City, NC, 27344 (919)
663-3431
Admin Jack L Russell.

Licensure Skilled Care; Intermediate Care. *Beds* SNF 68; ICF 52. *Certified* Medicaid; Medicare.

SMITHFIELD

Johnston County Memorial Nursing Center Inc
902 Berkshire Rd, PO Box 1940, Smithfield, NC, 27511 (919) 934-3171
Admin David F Arnn. *Medical Dir/Dir of Nursing* Robert W Wyman MD.
Licensure Skilled Care; Intermediate Care. *Beds* SNF 84; ICF 36. *Certified* Medicaid; Medicare.
Admissions Requirements Medical examination.
Staff Physicians 7 (pt); RNs 5 (ft), 2 (pt); LPNs 13 (ft), 3 (pt); Orderlies 5 (ft), 1 (pt); Nurses aides 45 (ft), 1 (pt); Physical therapists 1 (pt); Activities coordinators 1 (ft); Dietitians 1 (pt); Dentists 1 (pt).
Facilities Dining room; Physical therapy room; Activities room; Crafts room; Laundry room; Barber/Beauty shop.
Activities Arts and Crafts; Games; Reading groups; Prayer groups; Movies; Dances/Social or cultural gatherings.

SNOW HILL

Oak Manor of Snow Hill*
1304 SE 2nd St, Snow Hill, NC, 28580 (919) 747-2868
Admin Myrtle R Tucker.
Licensure Intermediate Care. *Beds* ICF 75. *Certified* Medicaid.

SOUTHERN PINES

Penick Episcopal Home for the Aging
E Rhode Island Ext, PO Box 2001, Southern Pines, NC, 28387 (919) 692-7151
Admin Philip S Brown. *Medical Dir/Dir of Nursing* Joseph Hiatt Jr.
Licensure Skilled Care. *Beds* 33. *Certified* Medicaid; Medicare.
Admissions Requirements Minimum age 60; Medical examination.
Staff RNs 3 (ft), 3 (pt); LPNs 3 (ft), 3 (pt); Nurses aides 16 (ft), 3 (pt); Activities coordinators 1 (ft); Dietitians 1 (pt).
Affiliation Episcopal
Facilities Dining room; Activities room; Chapel; Crafts room; Laundry room; Barber/Beauty shop; Library.
Activities Arts and Crafts; Cards; Games; Reading groups; Movies; Shopping trips; Dances/Social or cultural gatherings.

Saint Joseph of the Pines Hospital*
590 Central Dr, Southern Pines, NC, 28387 (919) 692-2212
Admin George Kecatos.
Licensure Skilled Care. *Beds* 84. *Certified* Medicaid; Medicare.

SOUTHPORT

Ocean Trail Convalescent Center
430 Fodale Ave, Southport, NC, 28461 (919) 457-9581
Admin Edith C Moss. *Medical Dir/Dir of Nursing* Dr Gene A Wallin.
Licensure Intermediate Care; Home for the Aged. *Beds* ICF 64; Home for the Aged 42. *Certified* Medicaid.
Admissions Requirements Medical examination.
Staff Physicians 7 (ft); RNs 2 (ft), 1 (pt); LPNs 9 (ft); Nurses aides 35 (ft); Physical therapists 1 (pt); Reality therapists 1 (ft); Recreational therapists 1 (ft); Speech therapists 1 (pt); Activities coordinators 1 (ft); Dietitians 1 (ft); Dentists 2 (pt).
Facilities Dining room; Activities room; Laundry room; Barber/Beauty shop; Library.
Activities Arts and Crafts; Cards; Games; Reading groups; Prayer groups; Movies; Shopping trips; Dances/Social or cultural gatherings; Exercise classes.
Description Facility is located in the very quaint old town of Southport on the Cape Fear River 24 miles south of Wilmington.

STATESVILLE

Brian Center of Nursing Care—Statesville*
PO Box 1109, 520 Valley St, Statesville, NC, 28677 (704) 873-0517
Admin Edward V Kassab.
Licensure Skilled Care; Intermediate Care. *Beds* SNF 60; ICF 60. *Certified* Medicaid; Medicare.

Hill Haven Nursing and Rest Home Inc*
Rt 10, Box 401, Statesville, NC, 28677 (704) 872-7601
Admin Dorothy S Edwards.
Licensure Skilled Care; Home for the Aged. *Beds* SNF 30; Home for the Aged 77.

STOKESDALE

Country Side Manor
7700 US 158, Stokesdale, NC, 27357 (919) 643-6301
Admin Jeane M Bare. *Medical Dir/Dir of Nursing* Dr John Trotter.
Licensure Intermediate Care. *Beds* 60. *Certified* Medicaid.
Admissions Requirements Medical examination; Physician's request.
Staff Physicians 2 (pt); RNs 4 (ft); LPNs 2 (ft); Orderlies 1 (ft); Physical therapists 1 (pt); Reality therapists 1 (pt); Recreational therapists 1 (ft); Activities coordinators 1 (ft); Dietitians 1 (pt); Dentists 1 (pt); Podiatrists 1 (pt); Audiologists 1 (pt).
Facilities Dining room; Activities room; Crafts room; Laundry room; Barber/Beauty shop; Library.
Activities Arts and Crafts; Cards; Games; Reading groups; Prayer groups; Movies; Shopping trips; Dances/Social or cultural gatherings.
Description Facility is in a rural area and provides professional nursing care in a home-like

environment; staff wears street clothes to make it more home-like. It is an attractive, modern facility with antiques and country setting.

SYLVA

Skyland Care Center Inc
21 Skyland Dr, Sylva, NC, 28779 (704) 586-8935
Admin Mildred M Sloan. *Medical Dir/Dir of Nursing* E H Henning MD.
Licensure Intermediate Care. *Beds* 94. *Certified* Medicaid.
Admissions Requirements Minimum age 18.
Staff RNs 1 (ft); LPNs 9 (ft); Orderlies 1 (ft); Nurses aides 22 (ft); Recreational therapists 1 (ft); Activities coordinators 1 (ft); Dietitians 1 (pt); Dentists 1 (pt).
Facilities Dining room; Activities room; Laundry room; Barber/Beauty shop.
Activities Arts and Crafts; Games; Reading groups; Prayer groups; Movies; Shopping trips.
Description Center offers beautiful view of mountains and a home-like atmosphere to all residents.

TARBORO

Beverly Health Care Center
1000 Western Blvd, Box 7008, Tarboro, NC, 27886 (919) 823-0401
Admin Effie Webb. *Medical Dir/Dir of Nursing* Dr L M Cutchin.
Licensure Skilled Care; Intermediate Care. *Beds* SNF 48; ICF 111. *Certified* Medicaid; Medicare.
Admissions Requirements Medical examination.
Staff Physicians 10 (ft); RNs 6 (ft), 1 (pt); LPNs 11 (ft), 5 (pt); Nurses aides 56 (ft), 15 (pt); Physical therapists 1 (pt); Speech therapists 1 (pt); Activities coordinators 2 (ft); Dietitians 1 (ft); Dentists 1 (pt); Ophthalmologists 1 (pt); Podiatrists 1 (pt).
Facilities Dining room; Physical therapy room; Activities room; Chapel; Crafts room; Laundry room; Barber/Beauty shop.
Activities Arts and Crafts; Cards; Games; Reading groups; Prayer groups; Movies; Shopping trips; Dances/Social or cultural gatherings; Adult basic education class.

Westgate of Tarboro
PO Box 7035, Tarboro, NC, 27886 (919) 823-2041
Admin H S Lewis.
Licensure Intermediate Care. *Beds* 58. *Certified* Medicaid.
Staff RNs 3 (ft); LPNs 4 (ft); Orderlies 3 (ft); Nurses aides 30 (ft); Physical therapists 1 (pt); Reality therapists 1 (pt); Recreational therapists 1 (pt); Occupational therapists 1 (pt); Speech therapists 1 (pt); Activities coordinators 1 (ft); Dietitians 1 (ft); Dentists 1 (pt); Podiatrists 1 (pt).
Facilities Dining room; Activities room; Crafts room; Laundry room; Barber/Beauty shop.
Activities Arts and Crafts; Cards; Games; Reading groups; Prayer groups; Movies; Shopping trips; Dances/Social or cultural gatherings.

THOMASVILLE

Davidson Nursing Center*
706 Pineywood Rd, Thomasville, NC, 27360
(919) 475-9116
Admin Ruth Quate.
Licensure Skilled Care; Intermediate Care.
Beds SNF 60; ICF 52. *Certified* Medicaid;
Medicare.

Liberty House Nursing Home*
PO Box 1168, 1028 Blair St, Thomasville, NC,
27360 (919) 476-7771
Admin Opal C Suggs.
Licensure Skilled Care; Intermediate Care.
Beds SNF 30; ICF 90. *Certified* Medicaid;
Medicare.

TRYON

White Oak Terrace
200 Oak St, PO Box 1535, Tryon, NC, 28782
(704) 859-9161
Admin Doris G Cole.
Licensure Skilled Care. *Beds* 60. *Certified* Medicaid; Medicare.
Facilities Dining room; Physical therapy room;
Activities room; Crafts room; Laundry room;
Barber/Beauty shop.
Activities Arts and Crafts; Cards; Games;
Reading groups; Prayer groups; Movies; Shopping trips; Dances/Social or cultural gatherings.

WADESBORO

Anson County Hospital*
500 Morven Rd, Wadesboro, NC, 28170 (704)
694-5131
Admin Thomas W Northrop.
Licensure Skilled Care. *Beds* 44. *Certified* Medicaid; Medicare.

Wadesboro Nursing Home
2000 Country Club Rd, Wadesboro, NC, 28170
(704) 694-4106
Admin Hilda W Lee.
Licensure Intermediate Care; Home for the
Aged. *Beds* ICF 66; Home for the Aged 53.
Certified Medicaid; Medicare.
Admissions Requirements Medical examination; Physician's request.
Staff RNs 2 (pt); LPNs 10 (ft), 4 (pt); Orderlies
5 (ft), 1 (pt); Nurses aides 10 (ft), 2 (pt); Activities coordinators 1 (ft); Dietitians 1 (ft).
Facilities Dining room; Activities room; Laundry room; Barber/Beauty shop.
Activities Arts and Crafts; Prayer groups;
Shopping trips; Dances/Social or cultural gatherings.

WALNUT COVE

Guardian Care of Walnut Cove
508 Windmill St, PO Box 158, Walnut Cove,
NC, 27052 (919) 591-4353
Admin Joan H Smith. *Medical Dir/Dir of
Nursing* H W Hollingsworth MD.
Licensure Skilled Care. *Beds* 60. *Certified* Medicaid; Medicare.
Admissions Requirements Medical examination.

Staff Physicians 3 (pt); RNs 4 (ft), 7 (pt); LPNs
3 (ft), 3 (pt); Nurses aides 20 (ft), 9 (pt);
Physical therapists 1 (ft), 1 (pt); Occupational
therapists 1 (pt); Speech therapists 1 (pt);
Activities coordinators 1 (ft); Dietitians 1 (ft), 1
(pt); Dentists 1 (pt); Podiatrists 1 (pt).
Facilities Dining room; Physical therapy room;
Activities room; Chapel; Laundry room; Barber/Beauty shop.
Activities Arts and Crafts; Cards; Games;
Reading groups; Prayer groups; Movies; Shopping trips; Dances/Social or cultural gatherings;
Therapeutic activities relating to exercise/strengthening.
Description Facility is located in quiet rural
area conducive to recovery. We believe in
promoting services related to improving the
quality of life and in the effective utilization of
professional and nonprofessional personnel.
Restorative programs are individualized to
maintain a high standard of care with an awareness of cost efficiency to the patient.

WASHINGTON

Britthaven of Washington
120 Washington St, Washington, NC, 27889
(919) 946-7141
Admin Mary Lee Jackson. *Medical Dir/Dir of
Nursing* Dr Frank Sheldon.
Licensure Skilled Care; Intermediate Care.
Beds 60. *Certified* Medicaid; Medicare.
Admissions Requirements Medical examination.
Staff Physicians 15 (pt); RNs 4 (ft), 3 (pt);
LPNs 9 (ft), 4 (pt); Orderlies 4 (ft), 2 (pt);
Nurses aides 40 (ft), 8 (pt); Physical therapists 1
(pt); Speech therapists 1 (pt); Activities coordinators 1 (ft); Dietitians 1 (pt); Dentists 1 (pt);
Podiatrists 1 (pt).
Facilities Dining room; Activities room; Crafts
room; Laundry room; Barber/Beauty shop.
Activities Arts and Crafts; Cards; Games;
Reading groups; Prayer groups; Movies; Shopping trips; Dances/Social or cultural gatherings.

Pamlico Nursing Center Inc
Old Bath Hwy, PO Box 2027, Washington, NC,
27889 (919) 946-9570
Admin James T Logan. *Medical Dir/Dir of
Nursing* Dr Ray G Silverthorne.
Licensure Skilled Care; Intermediate Care.
Beds SNF 96; ICF 24. *Certified* Medicaid;
Medicare.
Ownership Proprietary.
Staff Physicians 2 (pt); RNs 14 (ft), 4 (pt);
LPNs 10 (ft), 5 (pt); Orderlies 10 (ft), 4 (pt);
Nurses aides 80 (ft), 12 (pt); Physical therapists
1 (pt); Recreational therapists 1 (ft); Speech
therapists 1 (pt); Activities coordinators 2 (pt);
Dietitians 1 (ft), 1 (pt); Dentists 1 (pt); Audiologists 1 (pt).
Facilities Dining room; Physical therapy room;
Activities room; Crafts room; Laundry room;
Barber/Beauty shop.
Activities Arts and Crafts; Cards; Games;
Reading groups; Prayer groups; Movies; Dances/Social or cultural gatherings.
Description New spacious modern construction
with carpet and wallpaper; 2 large day rooms.

WAYNESVILLE

Hemlock Nursing Home
Rt 1, Box 642, Waynesville, NC, 28789 (704)
456-7381
Admin Josephine H Smathers. *Medical Dir-
/Dir of Nursing* Dr James B Milling.
Licensure Skilled Care. *Beds* 56. *Certified* Medicaid; Medicare.
Admissions Requirements Medical
examination; Physician's request.
Staff Physicians 5 (pt); RNs 4 (ft); LPNs 5 (ft),
3 (pt); Orderlies 5 (ft); Nurses aides 15 (ft), 3
(pt); Physical therapists 1 (pt); Recreational
therapists 1 (ft); Speech therapists 1 (pt); Activities coordinators 1 (ft); Dietitians 1 (ft), 1 (pt);
Dentists 1 (pt); Audiologists 1 (pt).
Facilities Dining room; Activities room; Crafts
room; Laundry room; Barber/Beauty shop.
Activities Arts and Crafts; Games; Reading
groups; Prayer groups; Movies; Dances/Social
or cultural gatherings.

WHITEVILLE

Century Care Center Inc
316 W Burkhead St, PO Box 1217, Whiteville,
NC, 28472 (919) 642-7139
Admin O Wade Avant Jr. *Medical Dir/Dir of
Nursing* Dr F M Carroll.
Licensure Skilled Care; Intermediate Care.
Beds SNF 32; ICF 74. *Certified* Medicaid;
Medicare.
Admissions Requirements Minimum age 18.
Staff Physicians 1 (pt); RNs 10 (ft), 2 (pt);
LPNs 5 (ft), 1 (pt); Orderlies 2 (ft); Nurses aides
32 (ft); Physical therapists 1 (pt); Speech therapists 1 (pt); Activities coordinators 1 (pt); Dietitians 1 (pt); Dentists 1 (pt); Podiatrists 1 (pt).

WILKESBORO

Britthaven of Wilkesboro Inc
1016 Fletcher St, Rt 3, Wilkesboro, NC, 28697
(919) 667-9261
Admin Glenn W Potter.
Licensure Skilled Care; Intermediate Care.
Beds SNF 68; ICF 58. *Certified* Medicaid;
Medicare.
Admissions Requirements Medical examination.
Staff Physicians 5 (ft); RNs 4 (ft), 2 (pt); LPNs
9 (ft), 10 (pt); Orderlies 6 (ft), 2 (pt); Nurses
aides 39 (ft), 30 (pt); Physical therapists 1 (ft);
Speech therapists 1 (ft); Activities coordinators
2 (ft); Dietitians 1 (ft); Dentists 1 (pt); Podiatrists 1 (pt).
Facilities Dining room; Physical therapy room;
Activities room; Laundry room; Barber/Beauty
shop; Library.
Activities Arts and Crafts; Games; Prayer
groups; Movies; Shopping trips; Dances/Social
or cultural gatherings.
Description Facility features Jail-a-thon activity
for Muscular Distrophy as a fund raiser; child
volunteer program.

Vespers Nursing Home
1000 College St, Wilkesboro, NC, 28697 (919)
838-4141
Admin William E Nye. *Medical Dir/Dir of*

Nursing Larry R Kilby MD.
Licensure Skilled Care; Intermediate Care.
Beds SNF 58; ICF 62. *Certified* Medicaid;
Medicare.
Admissions Requirements Minimum age 65;
Medical examination; Physician's request.
Staff Physicians 3 (pt); RNs 8 (ft), 2 (pt); LPNs
8 (ft), 3 (pt); Nurses aides 33 (ft), 9 (pt);
Physical therapists 1 (pt); Speech therapists 1
(pt); Activities coordinators 1 (ft); Dietitians 1
(ft); Dentists 1 (pt); Ophthalmologists 1 (pt);
Podiatrists 1 (pt); 48 (ft), 8 (pt).
Facilities Dining room; Physical therapy room;
Activities room; Chapel; Crafts room; Laundry
room; Barber/Beauty shop.
Activities Arts and Crafts; Cards; Games; Pray-
er groups; Movies.

WILLIAMSTON

Albemarle Villa*
PO Box 1068, 111 Gatlin St, Williamston, NC,
27892 (919) 792-1616
Admin Al Woodring.
Licensure Skilled Care; Intermediate Care.
Beds SNF 36; ICF 88. *Certified* Medicaid;
Medicare.

WILMINGTON

Bowden Nursing Home*
221 Summer Rest Rd, Wilmington, NC, 28403
(919) 256-3733
Admin James E Bowden.
Licensure Intermediate Care. *Beds* 80. *Certified* Medicaid.
Admissions Requirements Medical examination; Physician's request.
Staff RNs 6 (ft), 3 (pt); LPNs 2 (ft), 1 (pt);
Nurses aides 32 (ft); Dietitians 1 (ft).
Facilities Dining room; Activities room; Chapel; Crafts room; Laundry room; Barber/Beauty
shop.
Activities Arts and Crafts; Games; Prayer
groups; Dances/Social or cultural gatherings.
Description We provide a home-like atmosphere in a quiet setting on the inland waterway
adjacent to Wrightsville Beach. We are fully
licensed by the state and members of the American Health Care Association and the North
Carolina Health Care Facilities Association.

Cornelia Nixon Davis Nursing Home Inc*
Rt 1, Box 644, Wilmington, NC, 28405 (919)
686-7195
Admin John Paluck Jr.
Licensure Skilled Care; Intermediate Care.
Beds SNF 155; ICF 44. *Certified* Medicaid;
Medicare.

Grotgen Nursing Home Inc
5429 Oleander Dr, PO Box 4699, Wilmington,
NC, 28403 (919) 791-3451
Admin Faye K Bell. *Medical Dir/Dir of
Nursing* Dr James Pence Jr.
Licensure Skilled Care. *Beds* 50. *Cer-
tified* Medicaid; Medicare.
Admissions Requirements Minimum age 18;
Medical examination; Physician's request.
Staff RNs 2 (ft), 4 (pt); LPNs 5 (ft), 4 (pt);
Nurses aides 25 (ft), 5 (pt); Recreational thera-

pists 1 (ft); Activities coordinators 1 (ft); Dieti-
tians 1 (pt); Podiatrists 1 (pt).
Facilities Dining room; Activities room;
Laundry room; Barber/Beauty shop.
Activities Arts and Crafts; Cards; Games;
Reading groups; Prayer groups; Movies; Dan-
ces/Social or cultural gatherings.

Hillhaven Convalescent Center
2006 S 16th St, Wilmington, NC, 28401 (919)
763-6271
Admin Faye M Kennedy. *Medical Dir/Dir of
Nursing* H L Armistead Jr MD.
Licensure Skilled Care; Intermediate Care.
Beds SNF 56; ICF 44. *Certified* Medicaid;
Medicare.
Admissions Requirements Medical examina-
tion; Physician's request.
Staff RNs 6 (ft), 3 (pt); LPNs 4 (ft), 3 (pt);
Nurses aides 26 (ft), 6 (pt); Physical therapists 2
(ft); Recreational therapists 1 (ft), 1 (pt); Dieti-
tians 1 (ft).
Facilities Dining room; Physical therapy room;
Activities room; Crafts room; Laundry room;
Barber/Beauty shop.
Activities Arts and Crafts; Cards; Games;
Reading groups; Prayer groups; Movies; Shop-
ping trips; Dances/Social or cultural gatherings.
Description Facility is one-half mile from hospital; large physical therapy department; many
restorative and rehabilitative programs so that
a large number of patients return home or to a
lower level of care. JCAH accredited.

WILSON

North Carolina Special Care Center
Ward Blvd, Wilson, NC, 27893 (919) 237-1121
Admin Joseph G Doby. *Medical Dir/Dir of
Nursing* Thomas R Maloney MD.
Licensure Skilled Care; Intermediate Care.
Beds SNF 109; ICF 99. *Certified* Medicaid;
Medicare.
Staff Physicians 2 (ft); RNs 23 (ft); LPNs 20
(ft); Nurses aides 129 (ft); Physical therapists 1
(pt); Recreational therapists 1 (ft); Activities
coordinators 1 (ft); Dietitians 2 (ft); Dentists 1
(pt); Podiatrists 1 (pt).
Facilities Dining room; Physical therapy room;
Activities room; Chapel; Crafts room; Barber-
/Beauty shop; Library.
Activities Arts and Crafts; Games; Reading
groups; Movies; Shopping trips; Dances/Social
or cultural gatherings.

Westwood Manor Nursing Home*
1804 Forest Hills Rd, Wilson, NC, 27893 (919)
237-8161
Admin Dan R Cotton.
Licensure Skilled Care; Intermediate Care.
Beds SNF 60; ICF 50. *Certified* Medicaid;
Medicare.

Wilson Convalescent Center
403 Crestview Ave, Wilson, NC, 27893 (919)
237-0724
Admin Stephen Harrison. *Medical Dir/Dir of
Nursing* Dr Lawrence Krabill.
Licensure Skilled Care. *Beds* 46.
Admissions Requirements Medical examina-
tion; Physician's request.
Staff Physicians 19 (pt); RNs 2 (ft); LPNs 4

(ft), 2 (pt); Nurses aides 18 (ft), 2 (pt); Physical
therapists 1 (pt); Speech therapists 1 (pt);
Activities coordinators 1 (ft); Dietitians 1 (pt);
Podiatrists 1 (pt).

WINSTON-SALEM

**Baptist Retirement Home of North Carolina
Inc**
2900 Reynolds Park Rd, Winston-Salem, NC,
27107 (919) 788-2441
Admin Jackson S Hoyle. *Medical Dir/Dir of
Nursing* Dr Hugh Napper.
Licensure Skilled Care; Intermediate Care;
Home for the Aged. *Beds* SNF 27; ICF 48;
Home for the Aged 180. *Certified* Medicaid;
Medicare.
Admissions Requirements Minimum age 65.
Staff Physicians 1 (pt); RNs 4 (ft), 1 (pt); LPNs
10 (ft), 5 (pt); Orderlies 3 (ft); Nurses aides 28
(ft), 7 (pt); Physical therapists 1 (pt); Recrea-
tional therapists 2 (ft), 1 (pt); Activities coordi-
nators 1 (ft); Dietitians 1 (ft); Dentists 1 (pt);
Podiatrists 1 (pt).
Affiliation Baptist
Facilities Dining room; Activities room; Chap-
el; Crafts room; Laundry room; Barber/Beauty
shop; Library.
Activities Arts and Crafts; Cards; Games;
Reading groups; Prayer groups; Movies; Shopping trips; Dances/Social or cultural gatherings.
Description We have 5 retirement homes,
independent living in duplex apartments, and
ICF/SNF nursing care.

Knollwood Hall
5755 Shattalon Dr, PO Box 11907, Winston-
Salem, NC, 27116 (919) 767-2750
Admin June L Sides.
Licensure Skilled Care; Intermediate Care.
Beds SNF 100; ICF 100. *Certified* Medicaid;
Medicare.
Facilities Dining room; Physical therapy room;
Activities room; Crafts room; Barber/Beauty
shop.
Activities Arts and Crafts; Cards; Games;
Reading groups; Prayer groups; Movies; Shop-
ping trips; Dances/Social or cultural gatherings.

Moravian Home Inc
5401 Indiana Ave, Winston-Salem, NC, 27106
(919) 767-8130
Admin Harvey Johnson. *Medical Dir/Dir of
Nursing* Clementine Shaw.
Licensure Skilled Care; Intermediate Care;
Home for the Aged. *Beds* SNF 20; ICF 40; 106.
Admissions Requirements Minimum age 65.
Affiliation Moravian
Facilities Dining room; Activities room; Chap-
el; Crafts room; Laundry room; Barber/Beauty
shop; Library.

Pellcare Corporation
Rt 3, Box 315, Winston-Salem, NC, 27105
(919) 595-2166
Admin Norma M Guthrie. *Medical Dir/Dir of
Nursing* Dr Sam Imamura.
Licensure Skilled Care; Intermediate Care.
Beds SNF 60; ICF 158. *Certified* Medicaid;
Medicare.
Admissions Requirements Minimum age 18;
Medical examination.

Staff Physicians 1 (ft); RNs 7 (ft), 3 (pt); LPNs 14 (ft), 6 (pt); Orderlies 4 (ft); Nurses aides 75 (ft), 2 (pt); Physical therapists 1 (ft); Recreational therapists 1 (ft); Speech therapists 1 (ft); Activities coordinators 3 (ft); Dietitians 2 (ft); Podiatrists 1 (pt).
Facilities Dining room; Physical therapy room; Activities room; Chapel; Crafts room; Laundry room; Barber/Beauty shop; Library.
Activities Arts and Crafts; Cards; Games; Reading groups; Prayer groups; Movies; Shopping trips; Dances/Social or cultural gatherings.
Description Pellcare's volunteer program numbers in excess of 75 people, some helping on a continuing basis for 10 or more years. A quarterly newspaper highlights the programing for the public. A country setting amidst farm pastureland provides a pleasant atmosphere.

Silas Creek Manor*
3350 Silas Creek Pkwy, Winston-Salem, NC, 27103 (919) 765-0550
Admin Ronald N Riddle.
Licensure Skilled Care; Intermediate Care.
Beds SNF 69; ICF 30. *Certified* Medicaid; Medicare.

Triad Rehabilitation Center Inc
5581 University Pkwy, Winston-Salem, NC, 27105 (919) 767-2815
Admin Marilyn S Pye. *Medical Dir/Dir of Nursing* Dr Byron McLees.
Licensure Skilled Care. *Beds* 40. *Certified* Medicaid; Medicare.
Admissions Requirements Medical examination.
Staff Physicians 4 (pt); RNs 3 (ft); LPNs 4 (ft), 2 (pt); Orderlies 1 (ft); Nurses aides 11 (ft), 11 (pt); Physical therapists 1 (pt); Speech therapists 1 (pt); Activities coordinators 1 (ft); Dietitians 1 (ft); Dentists 1 (pt); Ophthalmologists 1 (pt); Podiatrists 1 (pt); Audiologists 1 (pt).
Facilities Dining room; Activities room; Crafts room; Laundry room; Barber/Beauty shop.
Activities Games; Reading groups; Prayer groups; Movies; Shopping trips; Dances/Social or cultural gatherings; Patient, families, staff picnics; Cookouts.
Description Even though an old, small facility, staff are very dedicated people. Many employees have worked here 10 years or more; one LPN has been employed over 25 years. The staff are "family" to those patients who have none.

Winston-Salem Convalescent Center
1900 W 1st St, Winston-Salem, NC, 27104 (919) 724-2821
Admin Philip E Denton. *Medical Dir/Dir of Nursing* Lloyd J Story MD.
Licensure Skilled Care; Intermediate Care.
Beds SNF 114; ICF 116. *Certified* Medicaid; Medicare.
Admissions Requirements Minimum age 18; Medical examination; Physician's request.
Staff Physicians; RNs; LPNs; Orderlies; Nurses aides; Physical therapists; Reality therapists; Recreational therapists; Occupational therapists; Speech therapists; Activities coordinators; Dietitians; Dentists; Ophthalmologists; Podiatrists; Audiologists.
Facilities Dining room; Physical therapy room; Activities room; Crafts room; Laundry room; Barber/Beauty shop; Day rooms.
Activities Arts and Crafts; Cards; Games; Reading groups; Prayer groups; Movies; Shopping trips; Dances/Social or cultural gatherings.
Description Rehabilitative nursing supervised by licensed nurses including reality orientation, activities of daily living, restorative feeding, bowel and bladder retraining, ambulation, and joint therapy for motion. VA approved.

YADKINVILLE

Yadkin Nursing Care Center
PO Box 879, Yadkinville, NC, 27055 (919) 679-8863
Admin Nolan G Brown. *Medical Dir/Dir of Nursing* Sam J Crawley MD.
Licensure Skilled Care; Intermediate Care.
Beds SNF 30; ICF 54. *Certified* Medicaid; Medicare.
Admissions Requirements Medical examination; Physician's request.
Staff Physicians 5 (pt); RNs 3 (ft); LPNs 9 (ft); Nurses aides 22 (ft); Physical therapists 1 (pt); Reality therapists 1 (pt); Recreational therapists 2 (ft), 1 (pt); Occupational therapists 1 (pt); Activities coordinators 2 (ft), 1 (pt); Dietitians 1 (ft), 1 (pt); Dentists 1 (pt); Ophthalmologists 1 (pt); Podiatrists 1 (pt).
Facilities Dining room; Physical therapy room; Activities room; Chapel; Crafts room; Laundry room; Barber/Beauty shop; Library.
Activities Arts and Crafts; Cards; Games; Reading groups; Prayer groups; Movies; Shopping trips; Dances/Social or cultural gatherings.

ZEBULON

Guardian Care of Zebulon*
PO Box 1157, 509 Gannon Ave, Zebulon, NC, 27597 (919) 269-9621
Admin Connie M Bass.
Licensure Skilled Care. *Beds* 60. *Certified* Medicaid; Medicare.

NORTH DAKOTA

ANETA

Aneta Good Samaritan Center
Box 287, Aneta, ND, 58212 (701) 326-4234
Admin Marv Shannon. *Medical Dir/Dir of Nursing* Dr Robert DeLano.
Licensure Intermediate Care. *Beds* 51. *Certified* Medicaid.
Admissions Requirements Medical examination.
Staff RNs; LPNs; Orderlies; Nurses aides; Activities coordinators; Total 38.
Facilities Dining room; Activities room; Crafts room; Laundry room; Barber/Beauty shop.
Activities Arts and Crafts; Cards; Games; Reading groups; Prayer groups; Movies; Shopping trips; Dances/Social or cultural gatherings.

ARTHUR

Arthur Good Samaritan Center
Box 16, Arthur, ND, 58006 (701) 967-8316
Admin Henry Reith. *Medical Dir/Dir of Nursing* Laurel Maker.
Licensure Intermediate Care. *Beds* 96. *Certified* Medicaid.
Admissions Requirements Medical examination; Physician's request.
Staff RNs 1 (ft), 5 (pt); LPNs 2 (pt); Nurses aides 20 (ft), 5 (pt); Activities coordinators 2 (ft), 2 (pt).
Affiliation Lutheran
Facilities Dining room; Activities room; Chapel; Crafts room; Laundry room; Barber/Beauty shop; Library.
Activities Arts and Crafts; Cards; Games; Reading groups; Prayer groups; Movies; Shopping trips; Dances/Social or cultural gatherings.

ASHLEY

McIntosh County Hospital—Intermediate Care Facility
612 Center Ave, Ashley, ND, 58413 (701) 288-3433
Admin Leo Geiger. *Medical Dir/Dir of Nursing* U Tilsa.
Licensure Intermediate Care. *Beds* 30. *Certified* Medicaid; Medicare.
Admissions Requirements Medical examination; Physician's request.
Staff Physicians 3 (ft); RNs 14 (ft); LPNs 8 (ft); Nurses aides 10 (ft); Physical therapists 2 (ft); Recreational therapists 1 (ft); Occupational therapists 1 (ft); Activities coordinators 1 (ft); Dietitians 1 (pt); Dentists 1 (pt).
Facilities Dining room; Physical therapy room; Activities room; Chapel; Crafts room; Laundry room; Barber/Beauty shop; Library.
Activities Arts and Crafts; Cards; Games; Reading groups; Prayer groups; Movies; Shopping trips.

BEULAH

Beulah Community Nursing Home*
Box 127B, 106 4th St NE, Beulah, ND, 58523 (701) 873-4322
Admin David Almen.
Licensure Skilled Care; Intermediate Care. *Beds* SNF 50; ICF 20. *Certified* Medicaid; Medicare.

BISMARCK

Baptist Home
1100 E Blvd, Bismarck, ND, 58501 (701) 223-3040
Admin Alvin Haas. *Medical Dir/Dir of Nursing* Shelly Barth.
Licensure Skilled Care; Intermediate Care. *Beds* 64. *Certified* Medicaid; Medicare.
Affiliation Baptist
Facilities Dining room; Physical therapy room; Activities room; Chapel; Crafts room; Laundry room; Barber/Beauty shop.
Activities Arts and Crafts; Prayer groups; Shopping trips.

Missouri Slope Lutheran Home Inc*
2425 Hillview Ave, Bismarck, ND, 58501 (701) 223-9407
Admin Robert Thompson.
Licensure Skilled Care; Intermediate Care. *Beds* 221. *Certified* Medicaid; Medicare.
Affiliation Lutheran

Saint Vincent's Nursing Home
1021 26th St N, Bismarck, ND, 58501 (701) 223-6888
Admin Keith Gendreau. *Medical Dir/Dir of Nursing* Dr Rudolfo Carriedo.
Licensure Skilled Care; Intermediate Care. *Beds* 94. *Certified* Medicaid; Medicare.
Admissions Requirements Medical examination; Physician's request.
Staff Physicians 8 (pt); RNs 10 (ft), 6 (pt); LPNs 10 (ft), 6 (pt); Orderlies 8 (ft), 3 (pt); Nurses aides 70 (ft), 16 (pt); Physical therapists 1 (pt); Recreational therapists 4 (ft), 1 (pt); Occupational therapists 1 (pt); Speech therapists 1 (pt); Activities coordinators 1 (ft); Dietitians 1 (pt); Dentists 1 (pt); Ophthalmologists 1 (pt); Podiatrists 1 (pt); Audiologists 1 (pt).
Affiliation Roman Catholic
Facilities Dining room; Physical therapy room; Activities room; Chapel; Crafts room; Laundry room; Barber/Beauty shop; Library.
Activities Arts and Crafts; Cards; Games; Reading groups; Prayer groups; Movies; Shopping trips; Dances/Social or cultural gatherings; Olympics.
Description Facility is all on one floor located on 13½ acres in a beautiful setting overlooking the city of Bismarck, combined with a community center; independent living with skilled and intermediate levels of care.

BOTTINEAU

Bottineau Good Samaritan Center*
725 E 10th, Bottineau, ND, 58318 (701) 228-3601
Admin Richard Hunt.
Licensure Intermediate Care. *Beds* 81. *Certified* Medicaid.

Saint Andrew's Nursing Home*
316 Ohmer, Bottineau, ND, 58318 (701) 228-2255
Admin Keith Korman.
Licensure Skilled Care. *Beds* 26. *Certified* Medicaid; Medicare.

BOWMAN

Sunset Home Inc
802 NW Dover, Bowman, ND, 58623 (701) 523-3214
Admin Tony Hanson. *Medical Dir/Dir of Nursing* Robert Thom MD.
Licensure Skilled Care; Intermediate Care. *Beds* 63. *Certified* Medicaid; Medicare.
Staff RNs 2 (ft), 8 (pt); LPNs 1 (ft), 4 (pt); Nurses aides 5 (ft), 25 (pt); Recreational therapists 1 (ft), 2 (pt).
Affiliation Lutheran
Facilities Dining room; Physical therapy room; Activities room; Chapel; Crafts room; Laundry

room; Barber/Beauty shop; Day care.
Activities Arts and Crafts; Cards; Games;
Reading groups; Prayer groups; Movies; Shopping trips.
Description Day care program has been a total
community success.

CANDO

Rest Haven Manor Nursing Center
Box 579, 6th Ave and 11th St, Cando, ND,
58324 (701) 968-3351
Admin William Amundson. *Medical Dir/Dir
of Nursing* G H Hitts MD and P W Marsh
MD.
Licensure Skilled Care; Intermediate Care.
Beds 74. *Certified* Medicaid; Medicare.
Admissions Requirements Medical examination.
Staff RNs 2 (ft), 6 (pt); LPNs 2 (pt); Nurses
aides 23 (ft), 10 (pt); Recreational therapists 1
(ft), 1 (pt); Activities coordinators 1 (ft).
Facilities Dining room; Physical therapy room;
Activities room; Chapel; Crafts room; Laundry
room; Barber/Beauty shop.
Activities Arts and Crafts; Cards; Games; Reading
groups; Prayer groups; Movies; Shopping trips;
Dances/Social or cultural gatherings.
Description Facility employs over 60 full- and
part-time staff with a consultant pharmacist,
dietician, physical therapist, and certified occupational assistant.

CARRINGTON

Carrington Hospital—Skilled Nursing Facility*
423 8th Ave N, Carrington, ND, 58421 (701)
652-3141
Admin Sr Dorothy Lorenz.
Licensure Skilled Care. *Beds* 38. *Certified* Medicaid; Medicare.

Golden Acres Manor*
One E Main St, Carrington, ND, 58421 (701)
652-3117
Admin Allan Metzger.
Licensure Skilled Care. *Beds* 60. *Certified* Medicaid; Medicare.

CAVALIER

Pembina County Memorial Nursing Home
Hwy 5, Cavalier, ND, 58220 (701) 265-8453
Admin Ruth Hollis. *Medical Dir/Dir of
Nursing* E J Larson MD.
Licensure Skilled Care. *Certified* Medicaid;
Medicare.
Admissions Requirements Medical examination; Physician's request.
Staff RNs 2 (ft), 2 (pt); LPNs 4 (ft), 4 (pt);
Nurses aides 22 (ft), 16 (pt); Physical therapists
1 (pt); Activities coordinators 1 (ft), 1 (pt); Dietitians 1 (pt).
Affiliation Lutheran
Facilities Dining room; Physical therapy room;
Activities room; Crafts room; Barber/Beauty
shop.
Activities Arts and Crafts; Cards; Games;
Reading groups; Prayer groups; Movies; Shopping trips.

COOPERSTOWN

Griggs County Nursing Home*
Box 728, Cooperstown, ND, 58425 (701)
797-2221
Admin Rick Spilovoy.
Licensure Skilled Care. *Beds* 50. *Certified* Medicaid; Medicare.

CROSBY

Crosby Good Samaritan Center*
Box 187, 705 SE 4th, Crosby, ND, 58730 (701)
965-6086
Admin Marlyn E Tande.
Licensure Intermediate Care. *Beds* 81. *Certified* Medicaid.

DEVILS LAKE

Devils Lake Good Samaritan Center
302 7th Ave, Devils Lake, ND, 58301 (701)
662-7525
Admin Sandra K Bentley. *Medical Dir/Dir of
Nursing* Donna Rook.
Licensure Intermediate Care. *Beds* 80. *Certified* Medicaid.
Admissions Requirements Medical examination.
Staff RNs 1 (ft); LPNs 6 (ft), 8 (pt); Nurses
aides 12 (ft), 14 (pt); Recreational therapists 2
(ft); Activities coordinators 1 (ft); Dietitians 1
(pt).
Facilities Dining room; Activities room; Chapel; Crafts room; Laundry room; Barber/Beauty
shop.
Activities Arts and Crafts; Cards; Games;
Reading groups; Movies; Shopping trips; Dances/Social or cultural gatherings.
Description A resident dog is enjoyed by all the
patients. An art therapist comes in weekly to
work with the residents.

Lake Region Lutheran Home*
E 14th Ave, Devils Lake, ND, 58301 (701)
662-4905
Admin Al Holte.
Licensure Skilled Care. *Beds* 104. *Certified* Medicaid; Medicare.
Affiliation Lutheran

DICKINSON

Dickinson Nursing Center
851 4th Ave E, Dickinson, ND, 58601 (701)
225-5138
Admin Lee Stickland. *Medical Dir/Dir of
Nursing* Dr Ralph Dukart.
Licensure Skilled Care; Intermediate Care.
Beds SNF 110; ICF 75. *Certified* Medicaid;
Medicare.
Admissions Requirements Medical examination; Physician's request.
Staff RNs 5 (ft), 6 (pt); LPNs 5 (ft), 6 (pt);
Orderlies 1 (ft); Nurses aides 47 (ft), 33 (pt);
Activities coordinators 1 (ft); Dietitians 1 (ft).
Facilities Dining room; Physical therapy room;
Activities room; Chapel; Crafts room; Laundry
room; Barber/Beauty shop.
Activities Arts and Crafts; Cards; Games;
Reading groups; Prayer groups; Movies; Shopping trips; Dances/Social or cultural gatherings.
Description Dickinson Nursing Center staffs
each unit with 24-hour professional nursing
coverage. A very active activity department
provides meaningful and enjoyable leisure
opportunities. Staff is prepared to assist residents to maximize all their potential.

Dickinson Saint Luke's Home
242 10th St W, Dickinson, ND, 58601 (701)
225-6026
Admin Lyle D Brudvig. *Medical Dir/Dir of
Nursing* Dr Arne Graff.
Licensure Skilled Care. *Beds* 83. *Certified* Medicaid; Medicare.
Staff RNs 5 (ft), 5 (pt); LPNs 2 (ft), 4 (pt);
Orderlies 1 (pt); Nurses aides 24 (ft), 25 (pt);
Physical therapists 3 (ft); Reality therapists 1
(pt); Recreational therapists 2 (ft), 3 (pt); Activities coordinators 1 (ft); Dietitians 8 (ft), 6 (pt).
Affiliation Lutheran
Facilities Dining room; Physical therapy room;
Activities room; Chapel; Crafts room; Laundry
room; Barber/Beauty shop; Library.
Activities Arts and Crafts; Cards; Games;
Reading groups; Prayer groups; Movies; Shopping trips.

DUNSEITH

Dunseith Community Nursing Home
Box 220, Peace Garden Ave, Dunseith, ND,
58329 (701) 244-5495
Admin Dennis Espe. *Medical Dir/Dir of
Nursing* Dr Dave Crozier.
Licensure Skilled Care; Intermediate Care.
Beds 40. *Certified* Medicaid; Medicare.
Admissions Requirements Medical examination.
Staff Physicians 2 (pt); RNs 2 (ft), 1 (pt); LPNs
3 (ft), 2 (pt); Orderlies 4 (ft), 2 (pt); Nurses aides
9 (ft), 2 (pt); Physical therapists 1 (pt); Activities coordinators 1 (ft), 1 (pt); Dietitians 1 (pt).
Facilities Dining room; Physical therapy room;
Activities room; Crafts room; Laundry room;
Barber/Beauty shop.
Activities Arts and Crafts; Cards; Games;
Reading groups; Prayer groups; Movies; Shopping trips; Dances/Social or cultural gatherings.

ELGIN

Jacobson Memorial Hospital Care Center*
Box 367, 601 East St N, Elgin, ND, 58533 (701)
584-2792
Admin Shelia Kvilvang.
Licensure Skilled Care. *Beds* 25. *Certified* Medicaid; Medicare.

ELLENDALE

Ellendale Nursing Center*
Hwy 281 N, Ellendale, ND, 58436 (701)
349-3312
Admin Adele Spicer.
Licensure Skilled Care. *Beds* 84. *Certified* Medicaid; Medicare.

ENDERLIN

Enderlin Hillcrest Manor
Hillcrest Dr, Enderlin, ND, 58027 (701)
437-5541
Admin Verlin D Buechler.
Licensure Intermediate Care. *Beds* 62. *Certified* Medicaid.
Admissions Requirements Medical examination; Physician's request.
Staff LPNs 1 (ft), 5 (pt); Nurses aides 3 (ft), 17 (pt); Activities coordinators 1 (ft).
Affiliation Lutheran
Facilities Dining room; Activities room; Crafts room; Laundry room; Barber/Beauty shop.
Activities Arts and Crafts; Cards; Games; Reading groups; Prayer groups; Movies; Shopping trips; Dances/Social or cultural gatherings.
Description Manor is now in the process of celebrating 20 years of service, to be held in conjunction with National Nursing Home Week.

FARGO

Americana Healthcare Center*
1315 S University Dr, Fargo, ND, 58103 (701)
237-3030
Admin Gwen L Solien.
Licensure Skilled Care. *Beds* 104. *Certified* Medicaid; Medicare.

Bethany Homes
201 S University Dr, Fargo, ND, 58103 (701)
237-0720
Admin Mavis Whiting. *Medical Dir/Dir of Nursing* Dr G J Kavanaugh.
Licensure Skilled Care; Intermediate Care; Retirement. *Beds* SNF 96; ICF 96; Retirement 151. *Certified* Medicaid; Medicare.
Staff RNs 7 (ft), 8 (pt); LPNs 8 (ft), 8 (pt); Nurses aides 38 (ft), 62 (pt); Physical therapists 1 (pt); Reality therapists 2 (ft); Occupational therapists 1 (pt); Activities coordinators 1 (ft); Dietitians 1 (ft).
Affiliation Lutheran
Facilities Dining room; Physical therapy room; Activities room; Chapel; Crafts room; Laundry room; Barber/Beauty shop; Library; Coffee shop.
Activities Arts and Crafts; Cards; Games; Reading groups; Prayer groups; Movies; Shopping trips; Dances/Social or cultural gatherings.

Elim Home*
3534 S University Dr, Fargo, ND, 58103 (701)
237-4392
Admin Frank A Duncan.
Licensure Skilled Care. *Beds* 125. *Certified* Medicaid; Medicare.

Fargo Nursing Home
1351 Broadway, Fargo, ND, 58421 (701)
235-7597
Admin Richard L Wickie. *Medical Dir/Dir of Nursing* Donald Oliver MD.
Licensure Skilled Care; Intermediate Care. *Beds* 102. *Certified* Medicaid; Medicare.
Ownership Nonprofit.
Admissions Requirements Medical examination; Physician's request.
Staff RNs 5 (ft), 6 (pt); LPNs 4 (ft), 2 (pt);

Orderlies 2 (pt); Nurses aides 34 (ft), 26 (pt); Physical therapists 1 (pt); Recreational therapists 2 (ft); Occupational therapists 1 (pt); Speech therapists 1 (pt); Activities coordinators 1 (ft); Dietitians 1 (ft); Dentists; Ophthalmologists; Podiatrists; Audiologists.
Facilities Dining room; Physical therapy room; Activities room; Chapel; Crafts room; Laundry room; Library.
Activities Arts and Crafts; Cards; Games; Reading groups; Prayer groups; Movies; Shopping trips; Dances/Social or cultural gatherings.
Description The total care concept, in conjunction with patient care plans which are tailored to each patient's specific needs, assures the care and personal attention one expects. Professional concept of recovery and rehabilitative care is coupled with the desire to provide a comfortable, pleasant atmosphere for all the residents and patients.

Villa Maria Healthcare Ltd
3102 S University Dr, Fargo, ND, 58421 (701)
293-7750
Admin Helen C Crary. *Medical Dir/Dir of Nursing* Manette Durand.
Licensure Skilled Care; Intermediate Care.
Beds 132. *Certified* Medicaid; Medicare.

FORMAN

Sargent Manor Inc
Box 196, 575 5th St, Forman, ND, 58032 (701)
724-6211
Admin Dede Diegel. *Medical Dir/Dir of Nursing* Dr Matt Kidd.
Licensure Intermediate Care. *Beds* 62. *Certified* Medicaid.
Staff RNs 1 (ft); LPNs 6 (pt); Nurses aides 7 (ft), 10 (pt); Physical therapists 1 (pt); Occupational therapists 1 (pt); Activities coordinators 1 (ft); Dietitians 1 (pt); Dentists 1 (pt); Audiologists 1 (pt).
Facilities Dining room; Physical therapy room; Activities room; Chapel; Crafts room; Laundry room; Barber/Beauty shop; Library.
Activities Arts and Crafts; Cards; Games; Reading groups; Prayer groups; Movies; Shopping trips; Dances/Social or cultural gatherings.

GARRISON

Garrison Memorial Hospital—Intermediate Care Facility
Box 39, Garrison, ND, 58540 (701) 463-2275
Admin Sr Madonna Wagendorf. *Medical Dir-/Dir of Nursing* John T Boyle MD.
Licensure Intermediate Care. *Beds* 24. *Certified* Medicaid.
Admissions Requirements Medical examination.
Staff Physicians 1 (pt); RNs 3 (pt); LPNs 1 (ft), 6 (pt); Orderlies 1 (pt); Nurses aides 3 (ft), 6 (pt); Physical therapists 1 (pt); Activities coordinators 1 (ft); Dietitians 1 (pt); Dentists 1 (pt).
Affiliation Roman Catholic
Facilities Dining room; Physical therapy room; Activities room; Chapel; Crafts room; Laundry room; Barber/Beauty shop.
Activities Arts and Crafts; Cards; Games; Prayer groups; Movies; Shopping trips; Dances/So-

cial or cultural gatherings.
Description Facility is located on the third floor of Garrison Memorial Hospital.

Garrison Nursing Home Inc*
Eastern Acres, Garrison, ND, 58540 (701)
463-2226
Admin David F Giessinger.
Licensure Skilled Care. *Beds* 71. *Certified* Medicaid; Medicare.

GLEN ULLIN

Marian Manor Nursing Home*
Box 528, 604 Ash Ave E, Glen Ullin, ND,
58631 (701) 348-3107
Admin Rodney Auer.
Licensure Skilled Care. *Beds* 80. *Certified* Medicaid; Medicare.

GRAFTON

Lutheran Sunset Home*
333 Eastern Ave, Grafton, ND, 58237 (701)
352-1901
Admin Rodney Alme.
Licensure Skilled Care. *Beds* 119. *Certified* Medicaid; Medicare.
Affiliation Lutheran

GRAND FORKS

Valley Memorial Home—Almonte
1023 Almonte Ave, Grand Forks, ND, 58201
(701) 772-4815
Admin Paul Opgrande. *Medical Dir/Dir of Nursing* Dr Sandmeyer.
Licensure Intermediate Care. *Beds* 100. *Certified* Medicaid.
Admissions Requirements Minimum age 65; Medical examination.
Staff Physicians 1 (pt); RNs 2 (ft), 11 (pt); LPNs 5 (pt); Orderlies 1 (ft), 5 (pt); Nurses aides 16 (ft), 49 (pt); Physical therapists 5 (pt); Activities coordinators 3 (ft), 3 (pt); Dietitians 1 (ft).
Affiliation Lutheran
Facilities Dining room; Physical therapy room; Activities room; Chapel; Crafts room; Laundry room; Barber/Beauty shop.
Activities Arts and Crafts; Cards; Games; Reading groups; Movies; Shopping trips; Dances/Social or cultural gatherings.

Valley Memorial Home—Medical Park
2900 14th Ave S, Grand Forks, ND, 58201
(701) 780-5500
Admin Karen Johnson. *Medical Dir/Dir of Nursing* Dr Sandmeyer.
Licensure Skilled Care; Intermediate Care.
Beds 160. *Certified* Medicaid; Medicare.
Admissions Requirements Medical examination.
Staff Physicians 1 (pt); RNs 7 (ft), 7 (pt); LPNs 9 (ft), 19 (pt); Orderlies 2 (ft), 7 (pt); Nurses aides 51 (ft), 74 (pt); Physical therapists 1 (ft), 7 (pt); Activities coordinators 4 (ft), 2 (pt); Dietitians 1 (ft), 1 (pt).
Affiliation Lutheran
Facilities Dining room; Physical therapy room; Activities room; Chapel; Crafts room; Laundry

room; Barber/Beauty shop.
Activities Arts and Crafts; Cards; Games; Reading groups; Movies; Shopping trips; Dances/Social or cultural gatherings.

HANKINSON

Saint Gerard's Nursing Home*
Box 279, 613 1st Ave SW, Hankinson, ND, 58041 (701) 242-7891
Admin Gene Hoefs.
Licensure Skilled Care. *Beds* 23. *Certified* Medicaid; Medicare.

HARVEY

Saint Aloisius Skilled Nursing Home
325 E Brewster, Harvey, ND, 58341 (701) 324-4651
Admin Ronald J Volk. *Medical Dir/Dir of Nursing* Dr Charles Nyhys.
Licensure Skilled Care. *Beds* 116. *Certified* Medicaid; Medicare.
Admissions Requirements Medical examination; Physician's request.
Staff Physicians 4 (pt); RNs 2 (ft), 2 (pt); LPNs 8 (ft), 3 (pt); Nurses aides 45 (ft), 20 (pt); Physical therapists 1 (pt); Recreational therapists 2 (ft), 2 (pt); Speech therapists 1 (pt); Activities coordinators 1 (ft); Dietitians 1 (pt); Dentists 2 (pt).
Affiliation Roman Catholic
Facilities Dining room; Activities room; Chapel; Crafts room; Laundry room; Barber/Beauty shop.
Activities Arts and Crafts; Cards; Games; Reading groups; Prayer groups; Movies; Shopping trips; Dances/Social or cultural gatherings.

HATTON

Tri-County Retirement and Nursing Home
930 Dakota Ave, Hatton, ND, 58240 (701) 543-3102
Admin Mark Duncan. *Medical Dir/Dir of Nursing* Dr D J Hlavinka.
Licensure Skilled Care; Intermediate Care. *Beds* 60. *Certified* Medicaid; Medicare.
Staff Physicians 3 (pt); RNs 1 (ft), 5 (pt); LPNs 2 (pt); Nurses aides 7 (ft), 15 (pt); Physical therapists 1 (pt); Activities coordinators 1 (pt); Dietitians 1 (pt).
Affiliation Lutheran
Facilities Dining room; Activities room; Chapel; Crafts room; Laundry room; Barber-/Beauty shop.
Activities Arts and Crafts; Cards; Games; Reading groups; Prayer groups; Movies.

HETTINGER

Lantis of North Dakota Inc
RR 2, Box 126, Hettinger, ND, 58639 (701) 567-2401
Admin Dan Apple.
Licensure Skilled Care; Intermediate Care. *Beds* 88. *Certified* Medicaid; Medicare.
Staff RNs 2 (ft), 2 (pt); LPNs 4 (ft), 2 (pt); Nurses aides 16 (ft), 6 (pt); Physical therapists 1 (pt); Activities coordinators 1 (ft); Dietitians 1

(pt); Dentists 1 (pt).
Facilities Dining room; Physical therapy room; Activities room; Laundry room; Barber/Beauty shop.
Activities Arts and Crafts; Cards; Games; Reading groups; Movies; Dances/Social or cultural gatherings.

HILLSBORO

Community Hospital—Nursing Home Association
Hillsboro, ND, 58045 (701) 436-5755
Admin Bruce Bowersox. *Medical Dir/Dir of Nursing* Dr Breen.
Licensure Skilled Care; Intermediate Care. *Beds* 50. *Certified* Medicaid; Medicare.
Facilities Dining room; Activities room; Chapel; Crafts room; Laundry room; Barber/Beauty shop.
Activities Arts and Crafts; Cards; Games; Reading groups; Prayer groups; Movies; Shopping trips.
Description Facility is closely associated with community that is very supportive.

JAMESTOWN

Central Dakota Nursing Home*
18th St and 5th Ave NE, Jamestown, ND, 58401 (701) 252-5660
Admin Bruce A Johnson.
Licensure Skilled Care. *Beds* 100. *Certified* Medicaid; Medicare.

Hi-Acres Manor Nursing Center
1300 2nd Place St NE, Jamestown, ND, 58401 (701) 252-5881
Admin Gary M Riffe. *Medical Dir/Dir of Nursing* Glenn Kerr MD.
Licensure Skilled Care; Intermediate Care. *Beds* SNF 116; ICF 26. *Certified* Medicaid; Medicare.
Admissions Requirements Medical examination.
Staff RNs 4 (ft), 3 (pt); LPNs 14 (ft), 5 (pt); Orderlies 1 (pt); Nurses aides 45 (ft), 27 (pt); Recreational therapists 1 (ft); Activities coordinators 1 (ft), 3 (pt).
Facilities Dining room; Physical therapy room; Activities room; Chapel; Crafts room; Laundry room; Barber/Beauty shop.
Activities Arts and Crafts; Games; Reading groups; Prayer groups; Movies; Shopping trips; Dances/Social or cultural gatherings.
Description Facility's goal is to meet each residents total needs. In a home-like environment, the care team concept helps residents reach their highest possible level.

KENMARE

Kenmare Community Hospital*
317 1st Ave NW, Kenmare, ND, 58746 (605) 385-4296
Admin Mary Ann Clark.
Beds 12.

LAKOTA

Gronna Good Samaritan Center*
116 E "C" Ave, Lakota, ND, 58344 (701) 247-2902
Admin Edna V Myers.
Licensure Intermediate Care. *Beds* 58. *Certified* Medicaid.

LAMOURE

Colonial Manor of LaMoure*
Box 627, LaMoure, ND, 58458 (701) 883-5363
Admin Bradley Molgard.
Licensure Intermediate Care. *Beds* 60. *Certified* Medicaid.

LANGDON

Maple Manor Nursing Home
Hwy 5 W, Box 549, Langdon, ND, 58249 (701) 256-2987
Admin Charles Shortridge. *Medical Dir/Dir of Nursing* Dr N J Kaluzniak.
Licensure Skilled Care. *Beds* 63.
Staff Physicians 2 (pt); RNs 3 (ft), 1 (pt); LPNs 3 (ft), 1 (pt); Nurses aides 30 (ft); Physical therapists 1 (pt); Activities coordinators 1 (ft); Dietitians 1 (pt).
Facilities Dining room; Activities room; Laundry room; Barber/Beauty shop.
Activities Arts and Crafts; Games; Reading groups; Movies; Shopping trips; Dances/Social or cultural gatherings.
Description Facility specializes in celebrating special heritage days with costumes, food, and decorations pertaining to the nationality being honored; also special entertainment is featured for those days.

LARIMORE

Larimore Good Samaritan Center
501 E Front, Larimore, ND, 58251 (701) 343-6244
Admin Robert P Nixon. *Medical Dir/Dir of Nursing* Dr Jon Rice.
Licensure Intermediate Care. *Beds* 68. *Certified* Medicaid.
Admissions Requirements Medical examination.
Staff RNs 1 (ft), 2 (pt); LPNs 2 (ft), 2 (pt); Nurses aides 5 (ft), 13 (pt); Physical therapists 1 (pt); Activities coordinators 1 (ft); Dietitians 1 (ft).
Affiliation Lutheran
Facilities Dining room; Physical therapy room; Activities room; Crafts room; Laundry room; Barber/Beauty shop.
Activities Arts and Crafts; Cards; Games; Prayer groups; Movies; Shopping trips; Dances/Social or cultural gatherings.
Description Facility provides meals-on-wheels information and refund service, telephone reassurance, local answering service for police, fire, and ambulance; daily devotional services including weekends; day care program available.

LISBON

Community Memorial Nursing Home
905 Main, Box 353, Lisbon, ND, 58054 (701) 683-5241
Admin Stanley E Clouse. *Medical Dir/Dir of Nursing* Dr Matthew Kidd.
Licensure Skilled Care; Intermediate Care.
Beds 45. *Certified* Medicaid; Medicare.
Admissions Requirements Medical examination; Physician's request.
Staff Physicians 5 (pt); RNs 1 (ft), 4 (pt); LPNs 3 (ft), 8 (pt); Orderlies 9 (ft), 15 (pt); Physical therapists 1 (pt); Speech therapists 1 (pt); Activities coordinators 1 (ft); Dietitians 1 (ft); Dentists 3 (pt); Audiologists 1 (pt).
Facilities Dining room; Physical therapy room; Activities room; Chapel; Crafts room; Laundry room; Barber/Beauty shop; Library.
Activities Arts and Crafts; Cards; Games; Reading groups; Prayer groups; Shopping trips; Dances/Social or cultural gatherings.
Description We are co-located with Community Memorial Hospital.

Parkside Lutheran Home*
Box 153, Prospect St, Lisbon, ND, 58054 (701) 683-4391
Admin Arlys Carter.
Licensure Intermediate Care. *Beds* 40. *Certified* Medicaid.
Affiliation Lutheran

MANDAN

Dacotah-Alpha
1007 18th St NW, Mandan, ND, 58554
Admin Dorothy Fisher. *Medical Dir/Dir of Nursing* Paul Knudson MD.
Licensure Intermediate Care. *Beds* 9. *Certified* Medicaid.
Ownership Nonprofit.
Admissions Requirements Minimum age 18; Physician's request.
Staff Physicians 1 (pt); RNs 1 (ft); LPNs 3 (ft); Physical therapists 1 (pt); Occupational therapists 1 (ft); Speech therapists 1 (pt); Activities coordinators 1 (ft); Dietitians 1 (pt); Personal care attendants 7 (ft); Social workers 1 (ft).
Facilities Dining room; Physical therapy room; Activities room; Crafts room; Laundry room.
Description This is a training/treatment facility for severely physically disabled adults who have potential and motivation for more independent lifestyles; a transitional living facility where the average stay is 6 to 24 months. Treatment goal is to maximize residents ability in all areas of functioning so they can live independently in the community with whatever assistance and services they need and that can be provided through community based services.

Mandan Villa
201 14th St NW, Mandan, ND, 58554 (701) 663-4267
Admin David Torkildson. *Medical Dir/Dir of Nursing* Arthur Van Vranken MD.
Licensure Skilled Care; Intermediate Care.
Beds SNF 92; ICF 28. *Certified* Medicaid; Medicare.
Facilities Dining room; Physical therapy room;

Activities room; Crafts room; Laundry room; Barber/Beauty shop.
Activities Arts and Crafts; Cards; Games; Reading groups; Prayer groups; Movies; Shopping trips; Dances/Social or cultural gatherings.

MAYVILLE

Luther Memorial Home*
750 Main St E, Mayville, ND, 58257 (701) 786-3401
Admin Adrian Knudsvig.
Licensure Skilled Care; Intermediate Care.
Beds SNF 69; ICF 30. *Certified* Medicaid; Medicare.
Affiliation Lutheran

MCVILLE

McVille Friendship Manor Nursing Home*
Box K, McVille, ND, 58254 (701) 322-4413
Admin David Iverson.
Licensure Skilled Care. *Beds* 52. *Certified* Medicaid; Medicare.

MINOT

Americana Healthcare Center of Minot
600 S Main, Minot, ND, 58701 (701) 852-1255
Admin Judy L Smith.
Licensure Skilled Care; Intermediate Care.
Beds 106. *Certified* Medicaid; Medicare.
Admissions Requirements Medical examination.
Staff RNs 5 (ft), 5 (pt); LPNs 3 (ft), 3 (pt); Nurses aides 30 (ft), 22 (pt); Physical therapists 1 (ft); Activities coordinators 1 (ft), 2 (pt).
Facilities Dining room; Physical therapy room; Activities room; Crafts room; Laundry room; Barber/Beauty shop; Library.
Activities Arts and Crafts; Cards; Games; Reading groups; Prayer groups; Movies; Shopping trips; Dances/Social or cultural gatherings.

Trinity Medical Center—Nursing Unit*
305 8th Ave NE, Minot, ND, 58701 (701) 857-5000
Admin Howard J Semingson.
Licensure Skilled Care; Intermediate Care.
Beds SNF 208; ICF 121. *Certified* Medicaid; Medicare.

MOHALL

North Central Good Samaritan Center*
602 E Main St, Mohall, ND, 58761 (701) 756-6831
Admin Paul Schroeder.
Licensure Intermediate Care. *Beds* 59. *Certified* Medicaid.

MOTT

Mott Good Samaritan Nursing Center
401 Millionaire Ave, Mott, ND, 586846 (701) 824-3222
Admin Mildred Waddell. *Medical Dir/Dir of Nursing* Jody Bolte Jahner.
Licensure Intermediate Care. *Beds* 60. *Certi-

fied* Medicaid.
Admissions Requirements Medical examination.
Affiliation Lutheran
Facilities Dining room; Activities room; Crafts room; Laundry room; Barber/Beauty shop; Library.
Activities Arts and Crafts; Cards; Games; Reading groups; Prayer groups; Movies; Shopping trips; Dances/Social or cultural gatherings.

NAPOLEON

Logan County Home for the Aged
311 E 4th, Napoleon, ND, 58561 (701) 754-2602
Admin Don Kleppe.
Licensure Intermediate Care. *Beds* 44. *Certified* Medicaid.
Staff RNs 3 (pt); LPNs 2 (pt); Nurses aides 5 (ft), 7 (pt); Activities coordinators 1 (ft); Dietitians 1 (pt).
Facilities Dining room; Activities room; Chapel; Crafts room; Laundry room; Barber/Beauty shop.
Activities Arts and Crafts; Cards; Games; Reading groups; Prayer groups; Movies; Shopping trips; Dances/Social or cultural gatherings.

NEW ROCKFORD

Lutheran Home of the Good Shepard Inc
1226 1st Ave N, New Rockford, ND, 58536 (701) 947-2944
Admin James I Opdahl. *Medical Dir/Dir of Nursing* Dr E J Schwinghamer.
Licensure Skilled Care; Intermediate Care.
Beds SNF 58; ICF 28. *Certified* Medicaid; Medicare.
Admissions Requirements Medical examination.
Affiliation Lutheran
Facilities Dining room; Activities room; Crafts room; Laundry room; Barber/Beauty shop.
Activities Arts and Crafts; Cards; Games; Reading groups; Prayer groups; Movies; Shopping trips; Dances/Social or cultural gatherings.

NEW SALEM

Elm Crest Manor
100 Elm Ave, Box 396, New Salem, ND, 58563 (701) 843-7526
Admin Gary Kreidt. *Medical Dir/Dir of Nursing* Steve Miller.
Licensure Intermediate Care. *Beds* 60. *Certified* Medicaid.
Ownership Nonprofit.
Admissions Requirements Medical examination; Physician's request.
Staff Physicians 1 (pt); RNs 1 (ft), 3 (pt); LPNs 1 (ft), 2 (pt); Nurses aides 6 (ft), 10 (pt); Physical therapists 1 (pt); Activities coordinators 1 (ft), 2 (pt); Dietitians 1 (pt).
Affiliation Church of Christ
Facilities Dining room; Physical therapy room; Activities room; Chapel; Crafts room; Laundry room; Barber/Beauty shop.
Activities Arts and Crafts; Cards; Games; Reading groups; Prayer groups; Movies; Shopping trips; Dances/Social or cultural gatherings.

Description Elm Crest Manor is a 60-bed, non-profit corporation governed by a board of directors. Facility's first concern is to recognize the needs of the individual and to respect their rights and privileges. Main goal is to maintain the individuality of each resident and rehabilitate them to their highest level of care.

NEW TOWN

New Town Health Development Corp
Box 399, New Town, ND, 58763 (701) 627-4711
Admin Mary Feig. *Medical Dir/Dir of Nursing* Herbert J Wilson MD.
Licensure Skilled Care; Intermediate Care. *Beds* 67. *Certified* Medicaid; Medicare.
Admissions Requirements Medical examination; Physician's request.
Staff RNs 1 (ft), 4 (pt); LPNs 1 (ft), 3 (pt); Orderlies 1 (pt); Nurses aides 29 (pt); Physical therapists 1 (ft); Activities coordinators 1 (ft); Dietitians 1 (ft).
Facilities Dining room; Physical therapy room; Activities room; Chapel; Crafts room; Laundry room; Barber/Beauty shop; Library.
Activities Arts and Crafts; Cards; Games; Reading groups; Prayer groups; Movies; Shopping trips.

NORTHWOOD

Northwood Deaconess Nursing Home*
Box 190, 4 Park St, Northwood, ND, 58267 (701) 587-6060
Admin Larry Feickert.
Licensure Skilled Care; Intermediate Care. *Beds* SNF 66; ICF 24. *Certified* Medicaid; Medicare.

OAKES

Oakes Manor Good Samaritan Center
213 N 9th, Oakes, ND, 58474 (701) 742-3274
Admin Gladys Masse. *Medical Dir/Dir of Nursing* Marilyn Folkestad.
Licensure Intermediate Care. *Beds* 142. *Certified* Medicaid.

OSNABROCK

Osnabrock Good Samaritan Center*
PO Box 4, Osnabrock, ND, 58269 (701) 496-3132
Admin August Pepple.
Licensure Intermediate Care. *Beds* 41. *Certified* Medicaid.

PARK RIVER

Park River Good Samaritan Center
Box 659, 301 S County Rd 12-B, Park River, ND, 58270 (701) 284-7115
Admin Jerome Swanson. *Medical Dir/Dir of Nursing* Dr I Afonya.
Licensure Skilled Care; Intermediate Care. *Beds* 79. *Certified* Medicaid; Medicare.
Admissions Requirements Medical examination.

Staff RNs 1 (ft), 7 (pt); LPNs 3 (pt); Nurses aides 26 (pt); Physical therapists 2 (pt); Activities coordinators 1 (ft); Dietitians 1 (ft).
Facilities Dining room; Physical therapy room; Activities room; Chapel; Crafts room; Laundry room; Barber/Beauty shop; Library.
Activities Arts and Crafts; Cards; Games; Reading groups; Prayer groups; Movies; Shopping trips; Dances/Social or cultural gatherings.

PARSHALL

Rock View Good Samaritan Center*
Parshall, ND, 58770 (701) 862-3611
Admin Mary Taylor.
Licensure Intermediate Care. *Beds* 60. *Certified* Medicaid.

ROLLA

Rolla Community Hospital—Nursing Facility
213 3rd St NE, Rolla, ND, 58367 (701) 477-3161
Admin Keith Korman. *Medical Dir/Dir of Nursing* Arnold Overland.
Licensure Skilled Care; Intermediate Care. *Beds* SNF 26; ICF 22. *Certified* Medicaid; Medicare.
Ownership Public.
Staff RNs 2 (ft), 1 (pt); LPNs 4 (ft), 3 (pt); Nurses aides 15 (ft), 7 (pt); Physical therapists 1 (ft); Occupational therapists 1 (ft); Activities coordinators 1 (ft), 1 (pt).
Facilities Dining room; Physical therapy room; Activities room; Chapel; Crafts room; Laundry room; Barber/Beauty shop; Library.
Activities Arts and Crafts; Cards; Games; Reading groups; Prayer groups; Movies; Shopping trips; Dances/Social or cultural gatherings.

RUGBY

Good Samaritan Long Term Care Facility
Rugby, ND, 58368 (701) 776-5203
Admin Alex Schweizter. *Medical Dir/Dir of Nursing* Dr Lee Potter.
Licensure Skilled Care; Intermediate Care. *Beds* SNF 74; ICF 30. *Certified* Medicaid; Medicare.
Affiliation Lutheran
Facilities Dining room; Activities room; Chapel; Crafts room; Laundry room; Barber/Beauty shop; Library; Family room.
Activities Arts and Crafts; Cards; Games; Reading groups; Prayer groups; Movies; Shopping trips; Dances/Social or cultural gatherings.
Description Multilevel health-care organization in a community of 3300, featuring a home health service, senior bus, meals on wheels, congregate meals and lifeline.

Harold S Haaland Home
1025 3rd Ave S, Rugby, ND, 58363 (701) 776-5203
Admin Ronald Waltz. *Medical Dir/Dir of Nursing* Leila Sanderson.
Licensure Intermediate Care. *Beds* 78. *Certified* Medicaid.

STANLEY

Mountrail Bethel Home*
Box 700, Stanley, ND, 58784 (701) 628-2442
Admin John Henkel.
Licensure Skilled Care; Intermediate Care. *Beds* SNF 41; ICF 16. *Certified* Medicaid; Medicare.

STEELE

Golden Manor Inc*
215 4th St NW, Steele, ND, 58482 (701) 475-2251
Admin Leonard Kary.
Licensure Intermediate Care. *Beds* 42. *Certified* Medicaid.

STRASBURG

Strasburg Nursing Home*
Strasburg, ND, 58573 (701) 336-2651
Admin Andrew J Reis.
Licensure Skilled Care. *Beds* 80. *Certified* Medicaid; Medicare.

TIOGA

Tioga Community Nursing Home
810 N Welo St, Box 597, Tioga, ND, 58852 (701) 664-3313
Admin Lowell Herfindahl. *Medical Dir/Dir of Nursing* Dr S K Patel.
Licensure Skilled Care; Intermediate Care. *Beds* 30. *Certified* Medicaid; Medicare.
Admissions Requirements Medical examination; Physician's request.
Staff Physicians 2 (pt); RNs 3 (pt); LPNs 3 (ft), 10 (pt); Nurses aides 5 (ft), 11 (pt); Physical therapists 1 (pt); Activities coordinators 2 (pt); Dietitians 1 (pt); Dentists 1 (pt).
Facilities Dining room; Activities room; Barber/Beauty shop.
Activities Arts and Crafts; Cards; Games; Prayer groups; Movies; Shopping trips; Dances/Social or cultural gatherings.
Description Facility is located adjacent to Tioga Community Hospital.

UNDERWOOD

Prairieview Homes Inc
83 Lincoln Ave, Box 10, Underwood, ND, 58576 (701) 442-3222
Admin Randal Albrecht. *Medical Dir/Dir of Nursing* Dr John T Boyle.
Licensure Skilled Care; Intermediate Care. *Beds* 64. *Certified* Medicaid; Medicare.
Admissions Requirements Medical examination.
Staff Physicians 2 (pt); RNs 2 (ft), 8 (pt); LPNs 3 (pt); Orderlies 4 (pt); Nurses aides 9 (ft), 19 (pt); Physical therapists 1 (pt); Recreational therapists 1 (pt); Speech therapists 1 (pt); Activities coordinators 1 (ft); Dietitians 1 (pt); Dentists 1 (pt); Ophthalmologists 1 (pt); Podiatrists 1 (pt).
Facilities Dining room; Physical therapy room; Activities room; Chapel; Laundry room; Barber/Beauty shop.

Activities Arts and Crafts; Cards; Games; Reading groups; Prayer groups; Movies; Dances/Social or cultural gatherings.

VALLEY CITY

Sheyenne Care Center
1030 2nd Ave NW, Valley City, ND, 58072 (701) 845-2320
Admin James C Tourville. *Medical Dir/Dir of Nursing* Dr R E Wiisanen.
Licensure Skilled Care; Intermediate Care.
Beds SNF 78; ICF 80. *Certified* Medicaid; Medicare.
Admissions Requirements Medical examination; Physician's request.
Facilities Dining room; Physical therapy room; Activities room; Chapel; Crafts room; Laundry room; Barber/Beauty shop.
Activities Arts and Crafts; Cards; Games; Prayer groups; Movies; Shopping trips; Dances/Social or cultural gatherings.
Description Rehabilitation program is tops and unusual for our area. We provide 5 day per week service and will be expanding occupational and physical therapy service to 6 days per week coverage.

VELVA

Souris Valley Care Center*
Hwy 41 S, Velva, ND, 58790 (701) 338-2072
Admin Nancy Demmel.
Licensure Intermediate Care. *Beds* 22.

WAHPETON

Wahpeton Nursing Center*
1307 N 7th St, Wahpeton, ND, 58075 (701) 642-6667
Admin Kathy Hoeft.
Licensure Skilled Care; Intermediate Care.
Beds 110. *Certified* Medicaid; Medicare.

WALHALLA

Pembilier Nursing Center
Box 467, 5th and Delano, Walhalla, ND, 58282 (701) 549-3831
Admin Brett R Ulrich. *Medical Dir/Dir of Nursing* Dr John Wahl.
Licensure Skilled Care; Intermediate Care.
Beds 60. *Certified* Medicaid; Medicare.
Staff Physicians 3 (pt); RNs 4 (ft); LPNs 3 (ft), 3 (pt); Orderlies 1 (pt); Nurses aides 20 (ft), 14 (pt); Physical therapists 1 (ft), 1 (pt); Activities coordinators 1 (ft), 2 (pt); Dietitians 1 (pt).
Facilities Dining room; Physical therapy room; Activities room; Chapel; Crafts room; Laundry room; Barber/Beauty shop.
Activities Arts and Crafts; Cards; Games; Reading groups; Prayer groups; Movies; Shopping trips; Dances/Social or cultural gatherings.

WATFORD CITY

Good Shepherd Home
Box 564, Hwy 23 E, Watford City, ND, 58854 (701) 842-2331

Admin Duane Jerde. *Medical Dir/Dir of Nursing* G D Ebel MD.
Licensure Skilled Care; Intermediate Care.
Beds 47. *Certified* Medicaid; Medicare.
Affiliation Lutheran

WESTHOPE

Westhope Home
Box 366, Westhope, ND, 58793 (701) 245-6477
Admin Albert W Rasmus. *Medical Dir/Dir of Nursing* Dr Kenneth Kohle.
Licensure Skilled Care; Intermediate Care.
Beds 59. *Certified* Medicaid; Medicare.
Admissions Requirements Minimum age 16; Medical examination; Physician's request.
Staff Physicians 5 (pt); RNs 6 (ft); LPNs 2 (ft); Nurses aides 20 (ft), 20 (pt); Physical therapists 1 (pt); Recreational therapists 3 (pt); Activities coordinators 1 (ft); Dietitians 1 (pt); Dentists 1 (pt).
Affiliation Roman Catholic
Facilities Dining room; Physical therapy room; Activities room; Chapel; Crafts room; Laundry room; Barber/Beauty shop.
Activities Arts and Crafts; Cards; Games; Reading groups; Prayer groups; Movies; Shopping trips; Dances/Social or cultural gatherings.
Description Facility has a varied activities program to reach every patient, whether bedridden, senile or physically handicapped.

WILLISTON

Bethel Lutheran Home*
Box 1828, 1515 2nd Ave W, Williston, ND, 58801 (701) 572-6766
Admin Wayne L Hansen.
Licensure Skilled Care; Intermediate Care.
Beds SNF 118; ICF 55. *Certified* Medicaid; Medicare.

WISHEK

Wishek Home for the Aged
Corner 4th St and 4th Ave S, Box 187, Wishek, ND, 58495 (701) 452-2333
Admin Orville R Zimmerman. *Medical Dir/Dir of Nursing* Dr Kosiak.
Licensure Skilled Care; Intermediate Care.
Beds 95. *Certified* Medicaid; Medicare.
Admissions Requirements Medical examination; Physician's request.
Staff Physicians 2 (pt); RNs 3 (ft); LPNs 4 (ft); Nurses aides 21 (ft), 11 (pt); Physical therapists 2 (pt); Activities coordinators 1 (ft); Dietitians 1 (ft).
Affiliation Church of Christ
Facilities Dining room; Physical therapy room; Activities room; Chapel; Crafts room; Laundry room; Barber/Beauty shop.
Activities Arts and Crafts; Games; Prayer groups; Movies; Shopping trips.

OHIO

ADENA

McGraw Nursing Home Inc*
Rt 2, 73841 Pleasant Grove, Adena, OH, 43901
(614) 546-3013
Beds 43.
Ownership Proprietary.

Reynolds Nursing Home Inc*
Rt 1, Adena, OH, 43901 (614) 546-3620
Licensure Intermediate Care. *Beds* 50. *Certified* Medicaid.
Ownership Proprietary.

AKRON

Dee-Maret Nursing Home*
1140 S Hawkins Ave, Akron, OH, 44320 (216)
836-2310
Licensure Nursing Home. *Beds* 13.
Ownership Proprietary.

Ellet Manor*
2755 Ellet Ave, Akron, OH, 44312 (216)
733-3623
Licensure Nursing Home. *Beds* 16.
Ownership Proprietary.

Healthaven Nursing Home
615 Latham Ln, Akron, OH, 44319 (216)
644-3914
Medical Dir/Dir of Nursing Dr John M Kim.
Licensure Intermediate Care. *Beds* 56. *Certified* Medicaid.
Ownership Nonprofit.
Admissions Requirements Minimum age 60;
Medical examination.
Staff Physicians 1 (ft); RNs 1 (ft), 1 (pt); LPNs
4 (ft), 4 (pt); Nurses aides 16 (ft), 9 (pt); Activities coordinators 1 (pt); Dietitians 1 (pt).
Affiliation Methodist
Facilities Dining room; Activities room; Crafts
room; Laundry room; Library.
Activities Arts and Crafts; Cards; Games; Prayer groups; Movies; Shopping trips.
Description Located on a spacious, 17-acre
lakeside estate setting.

Hillhaven Convalescent Center
145 Olive St, Akron, OH, 44310
Medical Dir/Dir of Nursing Walter R Hoffman
DO.
Licensure Skilled Care; Intermediate Care.
Beds SNF 30; ICF 174. *Certified* Medicaid;

Medicare.
Ownership Proprietary.
Admissions Requirements Medical examination; Physician's request.
Staff Physicians 32 (pt); RNs 4 (ft), 6 (pt);
LPNs 6 (ft), 19 (pt); Orderlies 2 (ft); Nurses
aides 32 (ft), 29 (pt); Physical therapists 1 (ft);
Speech therapists 1 (pt); Activities coordinators
2 (ft); Dietitians 1 (ft); Dentists 1 (pt); Ophthalmologists 1 (pt); Podiatrists 1 (pt).
Facilities Dining room; Physical therapy room;
Activities room; Chapel; Crafts room; Laundry
room; Barber/Beauty shop.
Activities Arts and Crafts; Cards; Games;
Reading groups; Prayer groups; Movies; Shopping trips.

Little Forest Medical Center*
797 E Market St, Akron, OH, 44305 (216)
434-4514
Licensure Skilled Care; Intermediate Care.
Beds 256. *Certified* Medicaid; Medicare.
Ownership Proprietary.

Lorantffy Care Center Inc*
2631 Copley Rd, Akron, OH, 44321 (216)
666-1313
Licensure Skilled Care; Intermediate Care;
Rest Home. *Beds* 74; Rest Home 27. *Certified* Medicaid; Medicare.
Ownership Nonprofit.

Manor Care of Akron Inc*
1211 W Market St, Akron, OH, 44313 (216)
867-8530
Licensure Skilled Care. *Beds* 108.
Ownership Proprietary.

**Middlebury Manor Nursing and Convalescent
Home***
974 E Market St, Akron, OH, 44305 (216)
762-9066
Licensure Skilled Care; Intermediate Care.
Beds 141. *Certified* Medicaid; Medicare.
Ownership Proprietary.

Pearlview Extended Care and Nursing Home*
3558 Ridgewood Rd, Akron, OH, 44313 (216)
666-3776
Licensure Skilled Care; Intermediate Care.
Beds 130. *Certified* Medicaid; Medicare.
Ownership Proprietary.

Rockynol Retirement Community*
1150 W Market St, Akron, OH, 44313 (216)
867-2150
Licensure Skilled Care; Intermediate Care;
Rest Home. *Beds* 72; Rest Home 34. *Certified* Medicaid; Medicare.
Ownership Nonprofit.

Saint Edward Home*
3131 Smith Rd, Akron, OH, 44313 (216)
666-1183
Licensure Intermediate Care. *Beds* 100. *Certified* Medicaid.
Ownership Nonprofit.

Summer Home for the Aged
209 Merriman Rd, Akron, OH, 44303 (216)
762-9341
Licensure Nursing Home. *Beds* 98.
Ownership Nonprofit.
Admissions Requirements Minimum age 65;
Medical examination.
Staff RNs 1 (ft), 2 (pt); LPNs 6 (ft), 6 (pt);
Nurses aides 12 (ft), 6 (pt); Recreational therapists 1 (ft); Activities coordinators 1 (ft); Podiatrists 1 (pt).
Facilities Dining room; Physical therapy room;
Activities room; Chapel; Crafts room; Laundry
room; Barber/Beauty shop; Library.
Activities Arts and Crafts; Cards; Games;
Reading groups; Prayer groups; Movies; Shopping trips; Dances/Social or cultural gatherings.
Description This home has 70-room residential
living wing and a 28-bed nursing unit. Residents enter to live in residential wing; when
need arises they are transferred to the nursing
unit. No one is placed in this home; they themselves must choose to come here. We have 2
plans: life care and pay as you go.

Valley View Nursing Home*
721 Hickory St, Akron, OH, 44303 (216)
762-6486
Licensure Skilled Care; Intermediate Care.
Beds 224. *Certified* Medicaid; Medicare.
Ownership Proprietary.

ALBANY

Angel of Mercy
Washington St, Albany, OH, 45710 (614)
698-2101

Licensure Intermediate Care. *Beds* 40. *Certified* Medicaid.
Ownership Proprietary.

Russell Nursing Home
101 Washington St, Box 37, Albany, OH, 45701 (614) 698-3631
Admin Helen Kaylor.
Licensure Intermediate Care. *Beds* 25. *Certified* Medicaid.
Ownership Proprietary.
Admissions Requirements Minimum age 21; Medical examination.
Staff Physicians 1 (pt); RNs 1 (pt); LPNs 2 (ft), 2 (pt); Nurses aides 6 (ft), 3 (pt); Physical therapists 1 (pt); Reality therapists 1 (pt); Recreational therapists 1 (pt); Activities coordinators 1 (pt); Dietitians 1 (pt); Podiatrists 1 (pt).
Facilities Dining room; Activities room; Crafts room; Laundry room; Barber/Beauty shop; Library.
Activities Arts and Crafts; Cards; Games; Reading groups; Prayer groups; Movies; Shopping trips; Dances/Social or cultural gatherings.
Description It is the policy of Russells Nursing Home to see that all residents have the best possible nursing services, care, and attention we can give them.

ALLIANCE

Alliance Nursing Home Inc*
11677 N Rockhill Rd, Alliance, OH, 44601 (216) 821-0071
Licensure Intermediate Care. *Beds* 75. *Certified* Medicaid.
Ownership Proprietary.

Bel-Air Convalescent Center
2350 S Cherry Ave, Alliance, OH, 44601
Licensure Nursing Home. *Beds* 54.
Ownership Proprietary.
Staff Physicians; RNs 1 (pt); LPNs 4 (ft), 3 (pt); Nurses aides 8 (ft), 6 (pt); Physical therapists; Recreational therapists 1 (ft), 1 (pt); Activities coordinators 1 (ft), 1 (pt); Dietitians 1 (pt); Dentists; Ophthalmologists; Podiatrists.
Facilities Dining room; Activities room.
Activities Arts and Crafts; Cards; Games; Reading groups; Prayer groups; Movies; Shopping trips; Dances/Social or cultural gatherings.

Blossom Nursing Center*
11750 Klinger Ave, Alliance, OH, 44601 (216) 823-8263
Licensure Skilled Care; Intermediate Care. *Beds* 100. *Certified* Medicaid; Medicare.
Ownership Proprietary.

Canterbury Villa of Alliance*
9193 Freshley Rd, Alliance, OH, 44601
Beds 100.
Ownership Proprietary.

Health Center*
145 E College St, Alliance, OH, 44601 (216) 823-2333
Licensure Intermediate Care. *Beds* 78. *Certified* Medicaid.
Ownership Nonprofit.

Ro-Ker Nursing Home
9315 Freshley Ave, Alliance, OH, 44601 (216) 823-1097
Licensure Intermediate Care. *Beds* 78. *Certified* Medicaid.
Ownership Proprietary.
Admissions Requirements Medical examination.
Staff RNs 2 (ft), 1 (pt); LPNs 7 (ft), 3 (pt); Nurses aides 12 (ft), 8 (pt); Activities coordinators 1 (ft), 1 (pt); Dietitians 1 (pt); Podiatrists 1 (pt); Audiologists 1 (pt).
Facilities Dining room; Laundry room; Barber/Beauty shop; Lobbies.
Activities Arts and Crafts; Cards; Games; Reading groups; Movies; Shopping trips; Dances/Social or cultural gatherings.
Description Ro-Ker Nursing Home is located in the country. We have a very large porch which the residents enjoy. Some of the residents have a garden. We are known as a homey type facility. We have an activity van and 2 excellent activity employees. The residents are taken on outings.

Rose Lawn Geriatric Center*
11999 Klinger Ave NE, Alliance, OH, 44601 (216) 823-0618
Licensure Nursing Home. *Beds* 15.
Ownership Proprietary.

Sun Valley Nursing Home*
1850 Electric Blvd, Alliance, OH, 44601 (216) 823-4287
Licensure Intermediate Care. *Beds* 37. *Certified* Medicaid.
Ownership Proprietary.

ALVORDTON

Davis Manor Nursing Home*
Box 182, Alvordton, OH, 43501 (419) 924-2898
Licensure Intermediate Care. *Beds* 23. *Certified* Medicaid.
Ownership Proprietary.

AMELIA

Sunrise Manor and Convalescent Center Inc
State Rt 132, Box 3434, Amelia, OH, 45102 (513) 797-5144
Medical Dir/Dir of Nursing John Wheby MD.
Licensure Intermediate Care. *Beds* 52. *Certified* Medicaid.
Ownership Proprietary.
Admissions Requirements Medical examination; Physician's request.
Staff RNs 2 (ft); LPNs 6 (ft); Nurses aides 18 (ft); Physical therapists 1 (pt); Recreational therapists 1 (ft); Speech therapists 1 (ft); Activities coordinators 1 (ft); Dietitians 1 (pt).
Facilities Dining room; Physical therapy room; Activities room; Laundry room.
Activities Arts and Crafts; Cards; Games; Reading groups; Shopping trips; Dances/Social or cultural gatherings.
Description A one-story building located on a wooded lot in a suburban area near the town of Amelia.

AMHERST

Amherst Manor*
175 N Lake Dr, Amherst, OH, 44001 (216) 988-4415
Licensure Intermediate Care. *Beds* 102. *Certified* Medicaid.
Ownership Proprietary.

ANDOVER

Miller Memorial Nursing Center
486 S Main St, Andover, OH, 44003 (216) 293-5416
Admin Carol J Duva. *Medical Dir/Dir of Nursing* Dr Randall Tharp.
Licensure Skilled Care; Intermediate Care. *Beds* 100. *Certified* Medicaid; Medicare.
Ownership Proprietary.
Admissions Requirements Medical examination; Physician's request.
Staff Physicians 4 (pt); RNs 4 (ft), 7 (pt); LPNs 5 (ft), 3 (pt); Orderlies 1 (pt); Nurses aides 28 (ft), 18 (pt); Activities coordinators 2 (ft).
Facilities Dining room; Physical therapy room; Activities room; Crafts room; Laundry room; Barber/Beauty shop; Library.
Activities Arts and Crafts; Cards; Games; Reading groups; Prayer groups; Movies; Shopping trips; Dances/Social or cultural gatherings.
Description Facility is located in a beautiful country setting with a pleasant home-like atmosphere; a wide variety of activities to interest nearly everyone offered; 24-hour skilled nursing care; social services.

APPLE CREEK

Apple Creek Developmental Center*
County Rd 44, Apple Creek, OH, 44606 (216) 698-2411
Licensure Intermediate Care for Mentally Retarded. *Beds* 316. *Certified* Medicaid.
Ownership Public.

ARCHBOLD

Fairlawn Haven
E Lutz Rd, Archbold, OH, 43502 (419) 445-3075
Medical Dir/Dir of Nursing Robert A Ebersole.
Licensure Intermediate Care. *Beds* 100. *Certified* Medicaid.
Ownership Nonprofit.
Admissions Requirements Minimum age 50; Medical examination.
Staff RNs 2 (ft), 10 (pt); LPNs 4 (ft), 5 (pt); Orderlies 2 (ft); Nurses aides 24 (ft), 34 (pt); Physical therapists 1 (pt); Activities coordinators 1 (ft), 2 (pt); Dietitians 1 (pt); Dentists 1 (pt); Podiatrists 1 (pt).
Affiliation Mennonite
Facilities Dining room; Physical therapy room; Activities room; Crafts room; Laundry room; Barber/Beauty shop; Library.
Activities Arts and Crafts; Cards; Games; Reading groups; Prayer groups; Movies; Shopping trips; Dances/Social or cultural gatherings.

ARLINGTON

Arlington Good Samaritan Center*
PO Box 200, State Rt 103, Arlington, OH,
45814 (419) 365-5115
Licensure Intermediate Care. *Beds* 50. *Certified* Medicaid.
Ownership Nonprofit.

ASHLAND

Brethren Care Inc
2000 Center St, Ashland, OH, 44805 (289-1585
Medical Dir/Dir of Nursing Dr Charles Slagle.
Licensure Intermediate Care. *Beds* 91. *Certified* Medicaid.
Ownership Nonprofit.
Admissions Requirements Medical
examination; Physician's request.
Staff RNs 3 (ft), 10 (pt); LPNs 2 (ft), 7 (pt);
Orderlies 3 (pt); Nurses aides 28 (ft), 40 (pt);
Activities coordinators 1 (ft), 1 (pt); Social
workers 1 (ft); Physical therapy assistants 1 (pt).
Affiliation Church of the Brethren
Facilities Dining room; Activities room; Laundry room; Barber/Beauty shop; Conference
room.
Activities Arts and Crafts; Cards; Games;
Reading groups; Prayer groups; Movies; Shopping trips; Dances/Social or cultural gatherings.
Description Facility is currently making provision for an adult day care unit.

Good Shepherd Home for the Aged*
622 S Center St, Ashland, OH, 44805 (419)
289-3523
Licensure Skilled Care; Intermediate Care.
Beds 130. *Certified* Medicaid; Medicare.
Ownership Nonprofit.

Griffeth Nursing Home
1251 Wooster Rd, Ashland, OH, 44805 (419)
322-9595
Licensure Intermediate Care. *Beds* 50. *Certified* Medicaid.
Ownership Proprietary.
Admissions Requirements Medical examination; Physician's request.
Staff RNs 1 (pt); LPNs 3 (ft), 4 (pt); Nurses
aides 10 (ft), 4 (pt); Recreational therapists 2
(ft), 1 (pt); Activities coordinators 1 (ft); Dietitians 1 (pt).
Facilities Dining room; Activities room; Crafts
room; Laundry room.
Activities Arts and Crafts; Cards; Games;
Reading groups; Prayer groups; Movies; Shopping trips; Dances/Social or cultural gatherings.
Description Our home presents a home-like
atmosphere; 4 to 5 activities a day are encouraged.

ASHTABULA

Ashtabula Medicare Nursing Center*
2217 West Ave, Ashtabula, OH, 44004 (216)
964-8446
Licensure Skilled Care; Intermediate Care.
Beds 200. *Certified* Medicaid; Medicare.
Ownership Proprietary.

Smith Home for Aged Women
4533 Park Ave, Ashtabula, OH, 44004 (216)
992-9441
Admin Leonard Kroner. *Medical Dir/Dir of
Nursing* Dr Hassain.
Licensure Home for the Aged. *Beds* 30.
Ownership Nonprofit.
Admissions Requirements Minimum age 65;
Females only; Medical examination.
Staff Physicians 1 (pt); RNs 3 (pt); LPNs 3
(pt); Nurses aides 9 (pt).
Facilities Dining room; Activities room; Chapel; Crafts room; Laundry room; Barber/Beauty
shop; Library.
Activities Cards; Games; Prayer groups; Shopping trips.
Description Facility offers private rooms which
are furnished by residents; within walking distance to churches, library, and shopping areas.

ATHENS

Echoing Meadows Residential Center
319 W Union St, Athens, OH, 45701 (614)
594-3541
Licensure Intermediate Care for Mentally
Retarded; Nursing Home. *Beds* 36.
Ownership Nonprofit.
Admissions Requirements Minimum age 18.
Staff Physicians 1 (pt); RNs 1 (ft), 1 (pt); LPNs
3 (ft), 2 (pt); Orderlies 4 (ft), 2 (pt); Nurses aides
10 (ft); Physical therapists 1 (pt); Occupational
therapists 1 (pt); Speech therapists 1 (pt);
Activities coordinators 1 (ft); Dietitians 1 (pt);
Dentists 2 (pt); Ophthalmologists 1 (pt); Podiatrists 1 (pt).
Facilities Dining room; Physical therapy room;
Crafts room; Laundry room.
Activities Arts and Crafts; Cards; Games;
Reading groups; Prayer groups; Movies; Shopping trips; Dances/Social or cultural gatherings.

Kimes Convalescent Center*
Albany Rd, Athens, OH, 45701 (614) 593-3391
Beds 61.
Ownership Proprietary.

AURORA

Anna Maria of Aurora
889 Aurora Rd, Aurora, OH, 44202 (216)
562-6171
Medical Dir/Dir of Nursing Willard E Stoner.
Licensure Skilled Care. *Beds* 118. *Certified* Medicare.
Ownership Proprietary.
Facilities Dining room; Physical therapy room;
Activities room; Chapel; Crafts room; Laundry
room; Barber/Beauty shop; Library.
Activities Arts and Crafts; Cards; Games;
Reading groups; Prayer groups; Movies; Shopping trips; Dances/Social or cultural gatherings.
Description For those requiring minimal
nursing care, Anna Maria includes a unique
concept, a program which helps the individual
resident remain independent and self sufficient,
yet offers help when needed. Lovely, spacious,
private rooms on our wooded property are perfect for those who prefer to remain on their
own. But they and their families can remain
secure with the knowledge that 24-hour emer-

gency care is available, along with daily supervision of medication by a staff nurse, well-balanced meals, planned activities, special
diets, and assistance in bathing. Our full professional staff, including nurses, registered dietician, and others are there when needed.
Assisted living, the perfect solution for the person who needs an occasional hand.

AUSTINTOWN

Austin Woods Nursing Center Inc
4780 Kirk Rd, Austintown, OH, 44515 (216)
792-7681
Admin Norman Reuven. *Medical Dir/Dir of
Nursing* Dr Wilkens.
Licensure Skilled Care; Intermediate Care.
Beds 230. *Certified* Medicaid; Medicare.
Ownership Proprietary.
Admissions Requirements Minimum age 18.
Staff Physicians; RNs; LPNs; Orderlies;
Nurses aides; Physical therapists; Recreational
therapists; Speech therapists; Activities coordinators; Dietitians; Dentists; Podiatrists.
Facilities Dining room; Physical therapy room;
Activities room; Chapel; Crafts room; Laundry
room; Barber/Beauty shop; Library; Auditorium.
Activities Arts and Crafts; Cards; Games;
Reading groups; Prayer groups; Movies; Shopping trips; Dances/Social or cultural gatherings.
Description Austin Woods Nursing Center sits
on 17 gorgeous acres in a picturesque country
setting yet within close proximity to all hospitals and other conveniences. Facility offers residents patios, recreation fields, and 5 large
lounges with fireplaces. The atmosphere is one
of community with the help of a chapel, a huge
auditorium, and a snack bar operated by residents.

AVON

Avon Oaks Nursing Home
37800 French Creek Rd, Avon, OH, 44011
(216) 934-5204
Admin Joan R Zemanek.
Licensure Intermediate Care. *Beds* 96.
Ownership Proprietary.
Admissions Requirements Medical examination.
Staff Physicians 3 (pt); RNs 1 (ft), 3 (pt); LPNs
7 (ft), 3 (pt); Orderlies 1 (ft); Nurses aides 26
(ft); Reality therapists 1 (pt); Activities coordinators 1 (ft); Dietitians 1 (pt); Podiatrists 1 (pt).
Facilities Dining room; Physical therapy room;
Activities room; Crafts room; Barber/Beauty
shop.
Activities Arts and Crafts; Cards; Games; Prayer groups; Movies; Shopping trips; Dances/Social or cultural gatherings.
Description Facility is located in the country on
10 acres of beautiful land and specializes in
meeting residents needs as individuals through
comprehensive care planning.

Good Samaritan Nursing Home
32900 Detroit Rd, Avon, OH, 44011 (216)
937-6201
Admin Gail Zabell. *Medical Dir/Dir of
Nursing* A J O'Brien MD.

Licensure Skilled Care; Intermediate Care.
Beds SNF 86; ICF 160. *Certified* Medicaid;
Medicare.
Ownership Proprietary.
Admissions Requirements Medical examination.
Staff Physicians 7 (pt); RNs 11 (ft); LPNs 36
(ft), 1 (pt); Nurses aides 95 (ft), 6 (pt); Physical
therapists 2 (ft), 1 (pt); Reality therapists 6 (ft);
Recreational therapists 1 (ft); Occupational
therapists 1 (ft), 1 (pt); Speech therapists 1 (pt);
Activities coordinators 1 (ft); Dietitians 1 (ft);
Dentists 1 (pt); Podiatrists 1 (pt); Audiologists 1
(pt).
Facilities Dining room; Physical therapy room;
Activities room; Chapel; Crafts room; Laundry
room; Barber/Beauty shop; Library.
Activities Arts and Crafts; Cards; Games;
Reading groups; Prayer groups; Movies; Shopping trips; Dances/Social or cultural gatherings;
Camping trips; Gardening.
Description Good Samaritan has the atmosphere of a fine residence in the country and all
the attributes of the most modern hospital. Our
professional staff provides the best possible
skilled nursing care, emphasizing physical,
occupational, speech, recreational, and outpatient therapy. We offer vacation stays, and a
day-care program for Alzheimer's patients.

BAINBRIDGE

Maple View Manor*
Box 613, 430 S Maple St, Bainbridge, OH,
45612 (614) 634-3301
Licensure Intermediate Care. *Beds* 20. *Certified* Medicaid.
Ownership Proprietary.

BALTIMORE

Gaulden Manor Nursing Center*
225 Hansberger St, Baltimore, OH, 43105
Licensure Intermediate Care. *Beds* 45. *Certified* Medicaid.
Ownership Proprietary.

BARBERTON

Manor Care Nursing Center
85 3rd St SE, Barberton, OH, 44203 (216)
753-5005
Medical Dir/Dir of Nursing Dr Robert Littlejohn.
Licensure Skilled Care; Intermediate Care.
Beds SNF 31; ICF 89. *Certified* Medicaid;
Medicare.
Ownership Proprietary.
Admissions Requirements Minimum age 18.
Staff Physicians 2 (pt); RNs 4 (ft), 4 (pt); LPNs
10 (ft), 10 (pt); Orderlies 1 (ft), 3 (pt); Nurses
aides 26 (ft), 22 (pt); Physical therapists 1 (ft), 1
(pt); Speech therapists 1 (pt); Activities coordinators 2 (ft).
Facilities Dining room; Physical therapy room;
Activities room; Crafts room; Laundry room;
Barber/Beauty shop.
Activities Arts and Crafts; Cards; Games;
Reading groups; Prayer groups; Movies; Shopping trips; Dances/Social or cultural gatherings.

Pleasant View Health Care Center
401 Snyder Ave, Barberton, OH, 44203 (216)
745-6028
Medical Dir/Dir of Nursing Phillip N Gilcrest
MD.
Licensure Skilled Care; Intermediate Care.
Beds 48. *Certified* Medicaid; Medicare.
Ownership Proprietary.
Admissions Requirements Medical examination.
Staff Physicians 1 (pt); RNs 1 (ft), 3 (pt); LPNs
3 (ft), 4 (pt); Nurses aides 12 (ft), 6 (pt);
Physical therapists 1 (pt); Speech therapists 1
(pt); Activities coordinators 1 (pt); Dietitians 1
(pt); Dentists 1 (pt); Ophthalmologists 1 (pt);
Podiatrists 1 (pt); Audiologists 1 (pt).
Facilities Dining room; Physical therapy room;
Laundry room.
Activities Arts and Crafts; Games; Prayer
groups; Movies; Dances/Social or cultural gatherings.
Description Spacious grounds give quiet atmosphere with 48-bed capacity on 1 floor, with
pleasant home-like setting.

Toth's Rest Home*
42 1st St SE, Barberton, OH, 44203 (216)
745-5786
Licensure Rest Home. *Beds* 9.
Ownership Proprietary.

BARNESVILLE

Barnesville Health Care Center*
400 Carrie Ave, Barnesville, OH, 43713 (614)
425-3648
Licensure Intermediate Care. *Beds* 100. *Certified* Medicaid.
Ownership Proprietary.

Walton Home for the Aged
Rt 3, Barnesville, OH, 43713 (614) 425-1014
Medical Dir/Dir of Nursing William H
Hodson.
Licensure Rest Home. *Beds* 25.
Ownership Public.
Admissions Requirements Medical examination.
Staff Nurses aides; Activities coordinators;
Dietitians.
Affiliation Society of Friends
Facilities Dining room; Activities room; Crafts
room; Laundry room; Barber/Beauty shop.
Activities Cards; Games; Reading groups; Prayer groups; Movies; Shopping trips.

BATAVIA

Batavia Nursing and Convalescent Inn
4000 Golden Age Dr, Batavia, OH, 45103
(513) 732-6500
Medical Dir/Dir of Nursing Dr Jonathan
Head.
Licensure Skilled Care; Intermediate Care.
Beds 216. *Certified* Medicaid; Medicare.
Ownership Proprietary.
Admissions Requirements Medical examination.
Facilities Dining room; Physical therapy room;
Activities room; Crafts room; Laundry room;
Barber/Beauty shop; Library.

Activities Arts and Crafts; Cards; Games;
Reading groups; Movies; Shopping trips; Dances/Social or cultural gatherings.

Batavia Nursing Home Inc*
Box 93, S 4th St, Batavia, OH, 45103 (513)
732-1535
Licensure Intermediate Care. *Beds* 34. *Certified* Medicaid.
Ownership Proprietary.

BAY VILLAGE

Bradley Road Nursing Home
605 Bradley Rd, Bay Village, OH, 44140 (216)
871-3474
Medical Dir/Dir of Nursing James Rush MD.
Licensure Skilled Care. *Beds* 100. *Certified* Medicare.
Ownership Proprietary.
Staff Physicians 18 (pt); RNs 2 (ft), 2 (pt);
LPNs 6 (ft), 4 (pt); Nurses aides 31 (ft), 6 (pt);
Physical therapists 1 (pt); Recreational therapists 1 (ft); Occupational therapists 1 (pt); Speech therapists 1 (pt); Activities coordinators 1
(pt); Dietitians 1 (pt); Dentists 1 (pt); Ophthalmologists 1 (pt); Podiatrists 1 (pt); Audiologists
1 (pt).
Facilities Dining room; Physical therapy room;
Activities room; Crafts room; Laundry room;
Barber/Beauty shop.
Activities Arts and Crafts; Cards; Games;
Reading groups; Prayer groups; Movies; Shopping trips; Dances/Social or cultural gatherings.
Description Facility offers privacy in the
nursing home setting, 90 private rooms, the
most in one facility on the west side of Cleveland.

BEACHWOOD

Beach Haven Health Care Center
23900 Chagrin Blvd, Beachwood, OH, 44122
(216) 464-1000
Medical Dir/Dir of Nursing Dusan Naunovich
MD.
Licensure Skilled Care; Intermediate Care.
Beds 110. *Certified* Medicaid; Medicare.
Ownership Proprietary.
Admissions Requirements Minimum age 16;
Medical examination.
Staff RNs 5 (ft), 7 (pt); LPNs 10 (ft), 6 (pt);
Nurses aides 53 (ft), 16 (pt); Physical therapists
1 (ft), 1 (pt); Occupational therapists 1 (pt);
Activities coordinators 3 (ft).
Facilities Dining room; Physical therapy room;
Activities room; Crafts room; Laundry room;
Barber/Beauty shop; Library.
Activities Arts and Crafts; Cards; Games;
Reading groups; Prayer groups; Movies; Shopping trips; Dances/Social or cultural gatherings.

Menorah Park—Jewish Home for the Aged
27100 Cedar Rd, Beachwood, OH, 44122 (216)
831-6500
Licensure Skilled Care; Intermediate Care.
Beds 311. *Certified* Medicaid; Medicare.
Ownership Nonprofit.
Admissions Requirements Medical examination.
Staff Physicians 1 (ft), 23 (pt); RNs 14 (ft), 13

(pt); LPNs 22 (ft), 8 (pt); Orderlies 10 (ft), 2 (pt); Nurses aides 113 (ft), 5 (pt); Physical therapists 2 (ft), 2 (pt); Recreational therapists 5 (ft), 3 (pt); Occupational therapists 1 (pt); Activities coordinators 1 (ft); Dietitians 1 (pt); Dentists 1 (pt); Ophthalmologists 1 (pt); Podiatrists 1 (pt); Audiologists 1 (pt).
Affiliation Jewish
Facilities Dining room; Physical therapy room; Activities room; Chapel; Crafts room; Laundry room; Barber/Beauty shop; Library; Sheltered workshop; Day care center; Volunteer office; In-service training.
Activities Arts and Crafts; Cards; Games; Reading groups; Prayer groups; Movies; Shopping trips; Dances/Social or cultural gatherings; Pet therapy; Horticulture therapy; Music and art therapy.
Description Menorah Park is a skilled nursing facility. Its mission is to provide nursing home placement and to help maintain the frail elderly in the community through a range of supportive services. These include a geriatric retirement center, a respite care center and 3-day care programs for frail elderly, physically handicapped and those with Alzheimer's disease. An applied research department will be initiated soon.

BEAVER

Pineview Manor Inc*
4136 German Rd, Beaver, OH, 45613 (614)
Licensure Skilled Care. *Beds* 50. *Certified* Medicaid.
Ownership Proprietary.

BELLBROOK

Carriage-by-the-Lake Nursing Home*
1957 Lakeman Dr, Bellbrook, OH, 45305
Licensure Skilled Care. *Beds* 50. *Certified* Medicaid.
Ownership Proprietary.

BELLEFONTAINE

Bellefontaine Health Care Center*
521 E Columbus Ave, Bellefontaine, OH, 43311 (513) 599-5123
Licensure Skilled Care; Intermediate Care. *Beds* 50. *Certified* Medicaid; Medicare.
Ownership Proprietary.

Logan County Home
County Rd 91, Bellefontaine, OH, 43311 (513) 592-2901
Admin Richard Davis. *Medical Dir/Dir of Nursing* Dr A Roldan.
Licensure Intermediate Care. *Beds* 95. *Certified* Medicaid.
Ownership Public.
Admissions Requirements Medical examination.
Staff Physicians 2 (pt); RNs 4 (ft); LPNs 5 (ft), 2 (pt); Nurses aides 27 (ft), 8 (pt); Activities coordinators 1 (ft); Dietitians 1 (ft).
Facilities Dining room; Crafts room; Barber/Beauty shop.
Activities Arts and Crafts; Reading groups; Prayer groups; Movies.

Description Facility is located 4 miles out of town in a peaceful rural setting next to a large pond.

BELLEVUE

Bellevue Nursing Home
504 W Main St, Bellevue, OH, 44811 (419) 483-6225
Licensure Nursing Home. *Beds* 24.
Ownership Proprietary.

BELLVILLE

Overlook Nursing Home*
Rt 2, Algire Rd, Bellville, OH, 44813 (419) 886-3922
Licensure Intermediate Care. *Beds* 27. *Certified* Medicaid.
Ownership Proprietary.

BELMONT

Bell Nursing Home Inc*
42350 National Rd, Belmont, OH, 43718 (614) 782-1561
Licensure Skilled Care; Intermediate Care. *Beds* 50. *Certified* Medicaid; Medicare.
Ownership Proprietary.

BEREA

Berea North Quality Care Nursing Center*
49 Sheldon Rd, Berea, OH, 44017 (216) 234-0454
Licensure Nursing Home. *Beds* 50.
Ownership Proprietary.

Berea Quality Care Nursing Center
77 W Bagley Rd, Berea, OH, 44017 (216) 234-2294
Medical Dir/Dir of Nursing William Bond MD.
Licensure Nursing Home. *Beds* 50.
Ownership Proprietary.
Staff Physicians 1 (ft), 3 (pt); RNs 1 (ft), 4 (pt); LPNs 1 (ft), 4 (pt); Nurses aides 12 (ft), 14 (pt); Physical therapists 1 (pt); Activities coordinators 1 (ft); Dietitians 1 (pt).
Facilities Dining room; Laundry room; Living room.
Activities Arts and Crafts; Cards; Games; Prayer groups.
Description Home is a 3-story brick building with colonial charm; Adopt-a-grandparent program provided in conjunction with the local schools to enrich both the lives of the residents and the neighborhood children.

BETHEL

Morris Nursing Home*
322 S Charity St, Bethel, OH, 45106 (513) 734-7401
Licensure Intermediate Care. *Beds* 18. *Certified* Medicaid.
Ownership Proprietary.

BETHESDA

Star Nursing Home*
40060 National Rd, Bethesda, OH, 43719 (614) 782-1944
Licensure Intermediate Care. *Beds* 50. *Certified* Medicaid.
Ownership Proprietary.

BEVERLY

Fairview Manor Nursing Home Inc
501 Pinecrest Dr, Box 458, Beverly, OH, 45715 (614) 984-4262
Admin Pansy Pickenpaugh. *Medical Dir/Dir of Nursing* Victor Whitacre MD.
Licensure Skilled Care; Intermediate Care. *Beds* 76. *Certified* Medicaid; Medicare.
Ownership Proprietary.
Admissions Requirements Minimum age 18.
Staff Physicians 3 (pt); RNs 4 (ft), 3 (pt); LPNs 6 (ft), 3 (pt); Nurses aides 22 (ft), 7 (pt); Physical therapists 1 (pt); Activities coordinators 1 (ft); Dietitians 1 (ft); Rehabilitation aides 1 (ft).
Facilities Dining room; Activities room; Crafts room; Laundry room; Barber/Beauty shop; Library; TV lounges.
Activities Arts and Crafts; Cards; Games; Reading groups; Prayer groups; Movies; Shopping trips; Dances/Social or cultural gatherings.
Description Facility offers 24-hour nursing care, home cooked meals, all in a home-like setting where patients are treated like family. VA approved.

BIDWELL

Buckeye Community Services—Bidwell Home*
Box 398, Rt 1, Bidwell, OH, 45614
Licensure Intermediate Care for Mentally Retarded. *Beds* 5. *Certified* Medicaid.
Ownership Nonprofit.

Scenic Hills Nursing Center*
RR 2, Bidwell, OH, 45614
Licensure Skilled Care; Intermediate Care. *Beds* SNF 100; ICF 100. *Certified* Medicaid; Medicare.
Ownership Proprietary.

BLANCHESTER

Blanchester Care Center*
839 E Cherry St, Blanchester, OH, 45107
Licensure Skilled Care; Intermediate Care. *Beds* SNF 50; ICF 50. *Certified* Medicaid; Medicare.
Ownership Proprietary.

Continental Manor of Blanchester*
820 E Center St, Blanchester, OH, 45107
Licensure Skilled Care; Intermediate Care. *Beds* SNF 74; ICF 74. *Certified* Medicaid; Medicare.
Ownership Proprietary.

BLOOMVILLE

Bloomville Nursing Care Center
22 Clinton St, Bloomville, OH, 44818 (419)
983-2021
Medical Dir/Dir of Nursing Dr Olgierd Garlo.
Licensure Intermediate Care. *Beds* 30. *Certified* Medicaid.
Ownership Proprietary.
Staff Physicians 1 (ft); RNs 2 (ft), 2 (pt); LPNs
1 (ft), 2 (pt); Nurses aides 6 (ft), 8 (pt); Activities coordinators 1 (ft); Dietitians 1 (pt).
Facilities Dining room; Activities room; Chapel; Crafts room; Laundry room; Barber/Beauty
shop.
Activities Arts and Crafts; Cards; Games;
Reading groups; Prayer groups; Movies; Shopping trips; Dances/Social or cultural gatherings.

BLUE ASH

Blue Ash Nursing and Convalescent Home Inc*
4900 Cooper Rd, Blue Ash, OH, 45242 (513)
793-3362
Licensure Skilled Care; Intermediate Care.
Beds 114. *Certified* Medicaid; Medicare.
Ownership Proprietary.

BLUFFTON

Mennonite Memorial Home
410 W Elm St, Bluffton, OH, 45817 (419)
358-1015
Admin Paul I Dyck. *Medical Dir/Dir of
Nursing* Dr O Lugibihl.
Licensure Intermediate Care. *Beds* 75. *Certified* Medicaid.
Ownership Nonprofit.
Admissions Requirements Minimum age 62;
Medical examination.
Staff RNs 6 (ft), 3 (pt); LPNs 4 (ft), 4 (pt);
Nurses aides 22 (ft), 29 (pt); Occupational therapists 2 (ft); Activities coordinators 1 (ft); Social
workers 1 (ft).
Affiliation Mennonite
Facilities Dining room; Activities room; Chapel; Crafts room; Laundry room; Barber/Beauty
shop; Library.
Activities Arts and Crafts; Cards; Games; Prayer groups; Movies; Shopping trips; Dances/Social or cultural gatherings.
Description Home specializes in nursing care.
A special unit to care for Alzheimer's victims is
scheduled for completion in October 1984; cottages and residential units being built as
demand dictates.

Richland Manor Nursing Home*
7400 Swaney Rd, Bluffton, OH, 45817 (419)
643-3161, 4511
Licensure Skilled Care; Intermediate Care.
Beds 100. *Certified* Medicaid; Medicare.
Ownership Proprietary.

BOARDMAN

Ron Joy Nursing Home*
830 Boardman Canfield Rd, Boardman, OH,
44512 (216) 758-8106
Licensure Nursing Home. *Beds* 64.
Ownership Proprietary.

**Westwood Skilled Nursing and Rehabilitation
Center**
7148 West Blvd, Boardman, OH, 44512 (216)
726-9061
Medical Dir/Dir of Nursing Anthony Pannozzo MD.
Licensure Skilled Care; Intermediate Care.
Beds 100. *Certified* Medicaid; Medicare.
Ownership Proprietary.
Staff Physicians 2 (pt); RNs 7 (ft); LPNs 10
(ft), 6 (pt); Nurses aides 30 (ft), 12 (pt); Physical
therapists 1 (ft); Occupational therapists 1 (pt);
Speech therapists 1 (pt); Activities coordinators
2 (ft); Dietitians 1 (ft); Dentists 1 (pt); Podiatrists 2 (pt).
Facilities Dining room; Physical therapy room;
Activities room; Crafts room; Laundry room;
Barber/Beauty shop.
Activities Arts and Crafts; Cards; Games;
Reading groups; Prayer groups; Movies; Shopping trips; Dances/Social or cultural gatherings.

BOWERSTON

Bowerston Health Care Center*
9076 Cumberland Rd, Bowerston, OH, 44695
(614) 269-8393
Licensure Intermediate Care. *Beds* 25. *Certified* Medicaid.
Ownership Nonprofit.

Sunnyslope Nursing Home
Bowerston, OH, 44695 (614) 269-8001
Admin Evelyn Boon.
Licensure Nursing Home. *Beds* 48.
Ownership Proprietary.
Staff LPNs 4 (ft), 4 (pt); Nurses aides 15 (ft), 15
(pt); Activities coordinators 1 (ft); Dietitians 1
(ft).
Facilities Dining room; Activities room; Chapel; Crafts room; Laundry room; Barber/Beauty
shop; Library.
Activities Arts and Crafts; Cards; Games;
Reading groups; Prayer groups; Movies; Shopping trips; Dances/Social or cultural gatherings.
Description Facility is located on 5 ½ acres of
landscaped lawn and features shopping trips,
open visiting hours, and special diets.

BOWLING GREEN

Bowling Green Manor
1021 Poe Rd, Bowling Green, OH, 43402 (419)
352-4694
Medical Dir/Dir of Nursing Thomas W
Watson MD.
Licensure Skilled Care; Intermediate Care.
Beds 100. *Certified* Medicaid; Medicare.
Ownership Proprietary.
Admissions Requirements Medical examination.
Staff RNs 6 (ft); LPNs 6 (ft); Nurses aides 36
(ft); Physical therapists 1 (pt); Reality therapists
1 (ft); Recreational therapists 1 (ft); Activities
coordinators 1 (ft); Dietitians 1 (pt).
Facilities Dining room; Physical therapy room;
Activities room; Chapel; Crafts room; Laundry
room; Barber/Beauty shop.
Activities Arts and Crafts; Cards; Games;
Reading groups; Prayer groups; Movies; Shopping trips; Dances/Social or cultural gatherings.

Community Nursing Home*
850 W Poe Rd, Bowling Green, OH, 43402
(419) 352-7558
Licensure Skilled Care; Intermediate Care.
Beds 100. *Certified* Medicaid; Medicare.
Ownership Proprietary.

Maria Nursing Home Inc
308 W Wooster St, Bowling Green, OH, 43402
Licensure Intermediate Care. *Beds* 24. *Certified* Medicaid.
Ownership Proprietary.

Wood County Home
11080 E Gypsy Lane Rd, Bowling Green, OH,
43402 (419) 353 8411
Admin Ken Potter. *Medical Dir/Dir of
Nursing* Dr Roger A Peatee.
Licensure Skilled Care; Intermediate Care.
Beds 127. *Certified* Medicaid; Medicare.
Ownership Nonprofit.
Admissions Requirements Medical examination.
Staff RNs 5 (ft), 5 (pt); LPNs 7 (ft), 6 (pt);
Orderlies 2 (ft); Nurses aides 32 (ft), 16 (pt);
Physical therapists 1 (pt); Activities coordinators 1 (ft), 1 (pt); Dietitians 1 (ft); Recreational
therapy aides 1 (pt).
Facilities Dining room; Physical therapy room;
Activities room; Chapel; Crafts room; Laundry
room; Barber/Beauty shop; Library.
Activities Arts and Crafts; Cards; Games;
Reading groups; Prayer groups; Movies; Shopping trips; Dances/Social or cultural gatherings.

Wooster Nursing Home
416 W Wooster St, PO Box 1102, Bowling
Green, OH, 43402 (419) 352-6414
Medical Dir/Dir of Nursing Dr Gonzales.
Licensure Intermediate Care. *Beds* 21. *Certified* Medicaid.
Ownership Proprietary.
Staff RNs 1 (pt); LPNs 2 (ft), 3 (pt); Orderlies 1
(ft); Nurses aides 5 (ft), 1 (pt); Activities coordinators 1 (ft).
Facilities Dining room.
Activities Arts and Crafts; Cards; Games; Prayer groups; Shopping trips; Dances/Social or
cultural gatherings.

BRADFORD

Bradford Living Care Center Inc*
325 S Miami, Bradford, OH, 45308 (513)
448-2259
Licensure Intermediate Care. *Beds* 17. *Certified* Medicaid.
Ownership Proprietary.

BRATENAHL

Bolton Convalescent Home
13802 Lake Shore Blvd, Bratenahl, OH, 44110
(216) 457-3334
Medical Dir/Dir of Nursing Dr Javier Clemente.
Licensure Intermediate Care. *Beds* 16. *Certified* Medicaid.
Ownership Proprietary.
Admissions Requirements Minimum age 21;
Medical examination.

Staff Physicians 1 (pt); RNs 1 (pt); LPNs 2 (ft); Nurses aides 13 (ft), 3 (pt); Reality therapists 1 (pt); Recreational therapists 1 (pt); Occupational therapists 1 (pt); Activities coordinators 1 (pt); Dietitians 1 (pt); Dentists 1 (pt); Podiatrists 1 (pt).
Facilities Dining room; Activities room; Crafts room; Laundry room.
Activities Arts and Crafts; Cards; Games; Reading groups; Prayer groups; Shopping trips; Dances/Social or cultural gatherings.

BREWSTER

Brewster Convalescent Center
264 Mohican St, Brewster, OH, 44613 (216) 832-2171
Medical Dir/Dir of Nursing Philip R Nicol MD.
Licensure Intermediate Care. *Beds* 51. *Certified* Medicaid.
Ownership Proprietary.
Staff Physicians; RNs 1 (ft), 1 (pt); LPNs 4 (ft), 2 (pt); Nurses aides 9 (ft), 7 (pt); Physical therapists; Activities coordinators 1 (ft); Dietitians 1 (ft); Dentists; Podiatrists.
Facilities Dining room; Chapel; Laundry room; Barber/Beauty shop; Library.
Activities Arts and Crafts; Cards; Games; Reading groups; Prayer groups; Movies; Shopping trips.
Description Facility offers complete independent living program with in-house services provided: meals, housekeeping, laundry, nurse attendant visits.

BROADVIEW HEIGHTS

Broadview Center*
9543 Broadview Rd, Broadview Heights, OH, 44147 (216) 526-5000
Licensure Intermediate Care for Mentally Retarded. *Beds* 262. *Certified* Medicaid.
Ownership Public.

Ohio Residential Services*
9571 Broadview Rd, Broadview Heights, OH, 44147
Licensure Skilled Care. *Beds* 8. *Certified* Medicaid.
Ownership Nonprofit.

BROOK PARK

The Lamp*
6034 Engle Rd, Brook Park, OH, 44142 (216) 433-4446
Licensure Nursing Home. *Beds* 34.
Ownership Proprietary.

BROOKVILLE

Brookhaven Nursing Care Center
770 N Albert Rd, Brookville, OH, 45309 (513) 833-2133
Admin Ruby J Ferrier. *Medical Dir/Dir of Nursing* Vinton Young MD.
Licensure Skilled Care; Intermediate Care. *Beds* 100. *Certified* Medicaid; Medicare.
Ownership Proprietary.

Admissions Requirements Medical examination.
Staff Physicians 8 (pt); RNs 4 (ft), 4 (pt); LPNs 4 (ft), 3 (pt); Orderlies 2 (ft), 1 (pt); Nurses aides 27 (ft), 19 (pt); Physical therapists 2 (pt); Occupational therapists 1 (pt); Speech therapists 1 (pt); Activities coordinators 1 (ft), 1 (pt); Dietitians 1 (pt); Dentists 1 (pt); Ophthalmologists 1 (pt); Podiatrists 1 (pt); Audiologists 1 (pt).
Facilities Dining room; Physical therapy room; Activities room; Chapel; Crafts room; Laundry room; Barber/Beauty shop; Library.
Activities Arts and Crafts; Cards; Games; Reading groups; Prayer groups; Movies; Shopping trips; Dances/Social or cultural gatherings.

BRUNSWICK

Pearlview Nursing Home
4426 Homestead Dr, PO Box 0070, Brunswick, OH, 44212 (216) 225-9121
Medical Dir/Dir of Nursing Dr Gaitanaros.
Licensure Skilled Care; Intermediate Care. *Beds* 118. *Certified* Medicaid; Medicare.
Ownership Proprietary.
Admissions Requirements Minimum age 22.
Staff Physicians 4 (pt); Physical therapists 1 (pt); Speech therapists 1 (pt); Activities coordinators 1 (ft); Dietitians 1 (pt); Dentists 1 (pt); Podiatrists 1 (pt); Audiologists 1 (pt).
Facilities Dining room; Physical therapy room; Activities room; Chapel; Crafts room; Laundry room; Barber/Beauty shop.
Activities Arts and Crafts; Cards; Games; Movies; Dances/Social or cultural gatherings; Patio and bake sales.

Willowood Nursing Home Inc
1186 Hadcock Rd, PO Box 146, Brunswick, OH, 44212 (216) 225-3156
Medical Dir/Dir of Nursing Dr B H Ferrer.
Licensure Intermediate Care for Mentally Retarded. *Beds* 196. *Certified* Medicaid.
Ownership Proprietary.
Admissions Requirements Medical examination.
Staff Physicians 2 (pt); RNs 3 (ft), 5 (pt); LPNs 9 (ft), 26 (pt); Nurses aides 43 (ft), 88 (pt); Physical therapists 1 (ft), 1 (pt); Recreational therapists 2 (ft), 2 (pt); Occupational therapists 1 (ft), 1 (pt); Speech therapists 1 (pt); Activities coordinators 1 (ft); Dietitians 1 (pt); Dentists 1 (pt); Ophthalmologists 1 (pt); Podiatrists 1 (pt); Audiologists 1 (pt).
Facilities Dining room; Physical therapy room; Activities room; Chapel; Crafts room; Laundry room.
Activities Arts and Crafts; Cards; Games; Reading groups; Movies; Shopping trips; Dances/Social or cultural gatherings.
Description Facility is located on 14 acres of land only 20 minutes from Cleveland and Akron; features pre-vocational workshop for the retarded.

BRYAN

Bryan Nursing Care Center
1104 Wesley Avenue, PO Box 647, Bryan, OH, 43506 (419) 636-5071
Medical Dir/Dir of Nursing R K Meyer.

Licensure Skilled Care; Intermediate Care. *Beds* 189. *Certified* Medicaid.
Ownership Proprietary.
Staff Physicians; RNs 5 (ft), 7 (pt); LPNs 8 (ft), 8 (pt); Orderlies 3 (ft); Nurses aides 49 (ft), 24 (pt); Physical therapists; Speech therapists; Activities coordinators.
Facilities Dining room; Physical therapy room; Activities room; Crafts room; Laundry room; Barber/Beauty shop; Library; Isolation room.
Activities Arts and Crafts; Cards; Games; Reading groups; Prayer groups; Movies; Shopping trips; Dances/Social or cultural gatherings.
Description Facility features private and semi-private rooms with adjoining bathrooms, color televisions, 2 outside patios and a large enclosed courtyard.

Williams County Hillside Nursing Home*
Rt 3, Box 234, Bryan, OH, 43506 (419) 636-4508
Licensure Intermediate Care. *Beds* 71. *Certified* Medicaid.
Ownership Public.

BUCYRUS

Belle Hoffman Michael Home*
518 E Rensselaer St, Bucyrus, OH, 44820 (419) 562-0168
Licensure Rest Home. *Beds* 14.
Ownership Nonprofit.

Heartland of Bucyrus
1170 W Mansfield St, Bucyrus, OH, 44820
Medical Dir/Dir of Nursing Dr Mir M Ali.
Licensure Intermediate Care. *Beds* 100. *Certified* Medicaid.
Ownership Nonprofit.
Admissions Requirements Medical examination; Physician's request.
Staff RNs 4 (ft), 2 (pt); LPNs 5 (ft), 6 (pt); Orderlies 3 (pt); Nurses aides 26 (ft), 10 (pt); Physical therapists; Speech therapists; Activities coordinators 1 (ft), 1 (pt); Dietitians 1 (ft); Dentists; Podiatrists.
Facilities Dining room; Physical therapy room; Activities room; Crafts room; Laundry room; Barber/Beauty shop.
Activities Arts and Crafts; Cards; Games; Prayer groups; Movies; Dances/Social or cultural gatherings.
Description Once a month ambulatory residents go out to a local restaurant, while nonambulatory residents have a carried in meal in the activity room with a touch of atmosphere.

Maplecrest Home*
717 Rogers St, Bucyrus, OH, 44820 (419) 562-4988
Licensure Rest Home. *Beds* 25.
Ownership Nonprofit.

Westfall Nursing Home*
320 E Warren St, Bucyrus, OH, 44820 (419) 562-6986
Licensure Nursing Home. *Beds* 17.
Ownership Proprietary.

CADIZ

Carriage Inn of Cadiz Inc*
259 Jamison Ave, Cadiz, OH, 43907 (614) 942-3079
Licensure Skilled Care; Intermediate Care. *Beds* 140. *Certified* Medicaid; Medicare. *Ownership* Proprietary.

CALDWELL

Summit Acres Nursing Home*
Rt 1, Box 140, Caldwell, OH, 43724 (614) 732-2364
Licensure Intermediate Care. *Beds* 100. *Certified* Medicaid.
Ownership Proprietary.

Summit Acres Nursing Home Inc—Home B*
Rt 1, Box 140, Caldwell, OH, 43724 (614) 732-2364
Licensure Intermediate Care. *Beds* 50. *Certified* Medicaid.
Ownership Proprietary.

CAMBRIDGE

Cambridge Developmental Center
County Rd 35, Cambridge, OH, 43725 (614) 439-1371
Medical Dir/Dir of Nursing Clarence R Apel MD.
Licensure Intermediate Care for Mentally Retarded. *Beds* 159.
Ownership Public.
Admissions Requirements Minimum age 18.
Facilities Dining room; Physical therapy room; Activities room; Chapel; Crafts room; Laundry room; Barber/Beauty shop; Library.
Activities Arts and Crafts; Cards; Games; Reading groups; Prayer groups; Movies; Shopping trips; Dances/Social or cultural gatherings.
Description Facility provides behavior modification training to 159 mentally retarded people functioning in the ranges of mental retardation of profound, severe, and moderate who exhibit severe maladoptive behaviors such as agression, and self-injurious behavior. The facility does not provide nursing care for complex medical needs, only routine nursing care.

Cambridge Health Care Center
1471 Wills Creek Valley Dr, Cambridge, OH, 43725 (614) 439-4437
Medical Dir/Dir of Nursing Dr Joseph Boyle.
Licensure Intermediate Care. *Beds* 150. *Certified* Medicaid.
Ownership Proprietary.
Staff RNs 6 (ft), 4 (pt); LPNs 8 (ft), 6 (pt); Nurses aides 40 (ft), 22 (pt); Activities coordinators 3 (ft); Dietitians 1 (pt).
Facilities Dining room; Physical therapy room; Activities room; Chapel; Crafts room; Laundry room; Barber/Beauty shop; Library.
Activities Arts and Crafts; Cards; Games; Reading groups; Prayer groups; Movies; Shopping trips; Dances/Social or cultural gatherings.
Description Facility features an outstanding activities department. Also, rehabilitation department excels in ability to rehabilitate and return residents to their homes.

Red Carpet Health Care Center*
8420 Claysville Rd, Cambridge, OH, 43725 (614) 439-4401
Licensure Intermediate Care; Rest Home. *Beds* ICF 78; Rest Home 84. *Certified* Medicaid.
Ownership Proprietary.

CANAL FULTON

Chapel Home Home
12200 Strausser Rd, Canal Fulton, OH, 44614 (216) 854-4177
Medical Dir/Dir of Nursing Dr Jeffery Duffey.
Licensure Skilled Care; Intermediate Care; Rest Home. *Beds* 152. *Certified* Medicaid; Medicare.
Ownership Nonprofit.
Admissions Requirements Minimum age 65; Medical examination.
Affiliation Church of Christ
Facilities Dining room; Physical therapy room; Activities room; Chapel; Crafts room; Laundry room; Barber/Beauty shop; Library.
Activities Arts and Crafts; Cards; Games; Reading groups; Prayer groups; Movies; Shopping trips; Dances/Social or cultural gatherings.

Echoing Ridge Residential Center*
643 Beverly Ave, Canal Fulton, OH, 44614
Licensure Intermediate Care for Mentally Retarded. *Beds* 50. *Certified* Medicaid.

Gaslite Villa Convalescent Center
7055 High Mill Ave NW, Canal Fulton, OH, 44614 (216) 854-4545
Medical Dir/Dir of Nursing Philip R Nicol MD.
Licensure Intermediate Care. *Beds* 98. *Certified* Medicaid.
Ownership Proprietary.
Admissions Requirements Minimum age 55; Medical examination.
Staff Physicians 1 (ft); RNs 1 (ft), 4 (pt); LPNs 4 (ft), 5 (pt); Nurses aides 27 (ft), 8 (pt); Activities coordinators 1 (ft).
Facilities Dining room; Activities room; Chapel; Crafts room; Laundry room; Barber/Beauty shop.
Activities Arts and Crafts; Cards; Games; Prayer groups; Movies; Shopping trips; Dances/Social or cultural gatherings.
Description Loving care and concern is given by all staff members in each department. Some type of activity program is provided each day. Social services department provides biweekly family group for family members of residing patients. Religious duties are performed by area priests and ministers. Our country setting provides a lovely atmosphere year around.

CANAL WINCHESTER

Winchester Place
36 Lehman Dr, Canal Winchester, OH, 43110 (614) 837-9666
Licensure Intermediate Care. *Beds* 201. *Certified* Medicaid.
Ownership Proprietary.
Staff Physicians 1 (pt); RNs 3 (ft), 1 (pt); LPNs 5 (ft), 2 (pt); Orderlies 2 (ft); Nurses aides 20

(ft), 6 (pt); Physical therapists 1 (pt); Occupational therapists 1 (pt); Activities coordinators 1 (ft); Dietitians 1 (ft); Dentists 1 (pt); Podiatrists 1 (pt).
Facilities Dining room; Physical therapy room; Activities room; Laundry room; Barber/Beauty shop; Library; Multi purpose room.
Activities Arts and Crafts; Cards; Games; Reading groups; Prayer groups; Movies; Shopping trips; Dances/Social or cultural gatherings.
Description Facility is located in south-east Franklin County, 20 minutes from downtown Columbus and 15 minutes from Lancaster, Ohio; short drive from Pickaway, Farfield, and Licking counties in Ohio; quiet village setting.

CANTON

Baker-Sumser Retirement Village
836 34th St, Canton, OH, 44709 (216) 492-7131
Medical Dir/Dir of Nursing Dr Aziz Alasyali.
Licensure Health Care Center; Rest Home. *Beds* 172. *Certified* Medicaid.
Ownership Proprietary.
Admissions Requirements Minimum age 55; Medical examination; Physician's request.
Staff RNs 2 (ft), 8 (pt); LPNs 3 (ft), 3 (pt); Nurses aides 18 (ft), 29 (pt); Activities coordinators 1 (ft); Dietitians 1 (ft).
Facilities Dining room; Physical therapy room; Activities room; Chapel; Crafts room; Laundry room; Barber/Beauty shop; Library; Community rooms.
Activities Arts and Crafts; Cards; Games; Prayer groups; Movies; Shopping trips; Dances/Social or cultural gatherings.
Description Facility is located in a middle-class economic neighborhood, adjacent to a shopping center and public transportation and within short distances to professional offices, social centers, and public entertainment facilities. All levels of care offer a full activity and social program.

Bethany Nursing Home
626 34th St, NW, Canton, OH, 44709 (216) 492-7171
Admin John F Baum. *Medical Dir/Dir of Nursing* Mildred Downerd RN.
Licensure Nursing Home. *Beds* 32.
Ownership Proprietary.
Staff Physicians 2 (pt); RNs 6 (pt); LPNs 2 (pt); Nurses aides 8 (ft), 10 (pt); Recreational therapists 1 (ft); Activities coordinators 1 (ft); Dietitians 1 (pt).
Facilities Dining room; Activities room; Crafts room; Laundry room; Barber/Beauty shop; Library.
Activities Arts and Crafts; Games; Reading groups; Prayer groups; Shopping trips; Musical programs; Sing-a-longs; Social activities; Teas and dinners.
Description Constant personal attention given to residents health, thoughts, fears, and anxieties. Love and professional service given. Fellowship is cemented with occasional social gatherings and open prayer groups.

Canton Christian Home
2550 Cleveland Ave N, Canton, OH, 44709 (216) 456-0004

Admin Paul E Wiener. *Medical Dir/Dir of Nursing* Dr A J Gilbert.
Licensure Intermediate Care; Rest Home.
Beds ICF 53; Rest Home 22; Independent Living Units 115.
Ownership Nonprofit.
Admissions Requirements Minimum age 62; Medical examination.
Staff Physicians 1 (pt); RNs 1 (ft), 6 (pt); LPNs 6 (pt); Nurses aides 7 (ft), 24 (pt); Physical therapists 1 (pt); Activities coordinators 1 (ft), 1 (pt); Dietitians 1 (ft); Dentists 2 (pt); Podiatrists 1 (pt).
Affiliation Church of Christ
Facilities Dining room; Physical therapy room; Activities room; Chapel; Crafts room; Laundry room; Barber/Beauty shop; Library.
Activities Arts and Crafts; Cards; Games; Reading groups; Prayer groups; Movies; Shopping trips; Dances/Social or cultural gatherings.
Description Four-story building on 5 acres of beautifully landscaped property on main city thoroughfare, adjacent to church and within walking distance of shopping center; features transportation to city and malls, outdoor patio, recreational activities, lounges and kitchenettes on each floor, and registered nurses on duty 24 hours a day.

Canton Convalescence Center
1528 Market Ave NW, Canton, OH, 44730
Medical Dir/Dir of Nursing Dr Sandra Beichler.
Licensure Intermediate Care. *Beds* 70. *Certified* Medicaid.
Ownership Proprietary.
Admissions Requirements Minimum age 40; Medical examination.
Staff Physicians 1 (pt); RNs 3 (ft); LPNs 7 (ft), 2 (pt); Nurses aides 20 (ft), 9 (pt); Reality therapists 1 (ft), 1 (pt); Recreational therapists 1 (ft), 1 (pt); Activities coordinators 1 (ft); Dietitians 1 (ft).
Facilities Dining room; Activities room; Laundry room.
Activities Arts and Crafts; Cards; Games; Reading groups; Prayer groups; Movies; Shopping trips; Dances/Social or cultural gatherings.
Description Facility is centrally located in city limits and accessible to shopping centers, doctors offices, and 3 hospitals.

Canton Health Care Center*
1223 N Market St, Canton, OH, 44730 (216) 454-2152
Licensure Intermediate Care. *Beds* 96. *Certified* Medicaid.
Ownership Proprietary.

Convalescent Care*
315 McKinley Ave NW, Canton, OH, 44702 (216) 453-4010
Licensure Intermediate Care. *Beds* 90. *Certified* Medicaid.
Ownership Proprietary.

Corvnor Health Care
1435 N Market Ave, Canton, OH, 44714
Medical Dir/Dir of Nursing Sandra Brickler.
Licensure Intermediate Care. *Beds* 5. *Certified* Medicaid.
Ownership Proprietary.
Admissions Requirements Minimum age 18;

Medical examination; Physician's request.
Staff LPNs 4 (ft); Orderlies 1 (ft); Physical therapists; Reality therapists 1 (ft); Recreational therapists 1 (ft); Occupational therapists; Activities coordinators 1 (ft).
Facilities Dining room; Activities room; Crafts room; Laundry room; Library.
Activities Arts and Crafts; Cards; Games; Movies; Dances/Social or cultural gatherings.
Description Facility in close (approximately one-quarter mile) to art institute, civic center, and downtown shopping area.

House of Loreto*
2812 Harvard Ave NW, Canton, OH, 44709 (216) 453-8137
Licensure Nursing Home. *Beds* 98.
Ownership Nonprofit.

Jean Carol's Nursing Home
1432 E Tuscarawas St, Canton, OH, 44707 (216) 453-2196
Admin Judith Bendick. *Medical Dir/Dir of Nursing* Dr Stuart Goldstein.
Licensure Intermediate Care. *Beds* 50. *Certified* Medicaid.
Ownership Proprietary.
Admissions Requirements Minimum age 18; Medical examination.
Staff Physicians; RNs 1 (ft), 1 (pt); LPNs 3 (ft); Orderlies 1 (ft); Nurses aides 16 (ft), 2 (pt); Occupational therapists; Speech therapists; Activities coordinators 1 (ft); Dietitians; Dentists; Ophthalmologists; Podiatrists; Audiologists.
Facilities Dining room; Activities room; Crafts room; Laundry room; Barber/Beauty shop.
Activities Arts and Crafts; Games; Reading groups; Prayer groups; Shopping trips; Dances/Social or cultural gatherings; In-house fashion shows; Talking books; Exercise to music program; Coffee/social hour.
Description Goal of home is one of personalized attention and above average personal care with emphasis on "home with a heart."

Lyon Nursing Home*
1612 Harrisburg Rd NE, Canton, OH, 44705 (216) 453-6686
Licensure Intermediate Care. *Beds* 50. *Certified* Medicaid.
Ownership Proprietary.

Manor Care-Belden Village*
5005 Higbee Ave NW, Canton, OH, 44718 (216) 492-7835
Licensure Skilled Care; Intermediate Care.
Beds SNF 91; ICF 56. *Certified* Medicaid; Medicare.
Ownership Proprietary.

Smith Nursing Home Inc
2330 Penn Pl NE, Canton, OH, 44704 (216) 456-9070
Admin Olar M Smith.
Licensure Intermediate Care. *Beds* 50. *Certified* Medicaid.
Ownership Proprietary.
Admissions Requirements Medical examination.
Staff Physicians 1 (pt); RNs 1 (ft), 1 (pt); LPNs 4 (ft); Orderlies 1 (ft); Nurses aides 12 (ft), 1 (pt); Physical therapists 1 (pt); Activities coor-

dinators 1 (ft); Dietitians 1 (pt); Dentists 1 (pt); Ophthalmologists 1 (pt); Podiatrists 1 (pt); Audiologists 1 (pt).
Facilities Dining room; Activities room; Chapel; Laundry room.
Activities Arts and Crafts; Cards; Games; Reading groups; Prayer groups; Movies; Shopping trips; Dances/Social or cultural gatherings.
Description Residents Board works with the activities coordinator to plan activities and social gatherings.

Twin-M Nursing Home
1722 Homedale Ave NW, Canton, OH, 44708 9216) 454-6508
Licensure Nursing Home. *Beds* 23.
Ownership Proprietary.
Admissions Requirements Medical examination; Physician's request.
Staff RNs 2 (ft), 7 (pt); LPNs 2 (pt); Nurses aides 3 (ft), 25 (pt); Dietitians 1 (pt).
Facilities Dining room; Activities room; Laundry room.
Activities Prayer groups.
Description Facility features a rural setting in Plain Township with personal physician and pharmacy; monthly programs for families including Christmas, Easter, Mother's Day, Thanksgiving, and picnics with special meals and desserts.

Westbrook Park Nursing Home*
2714 13th St NW, Canton, OH, 44708 (216) 456-2842
Licensure Skilled Care; Intermediate Care; Intermediate Care for Mentally Retarded.
Beds SNF 28; ICF 84; ICF/MR 15. *Certified* Medicaid; Medicare.
Ownership Proprietary.

White Oak Convalescent Home*
3516 White Oak Dr SW, Canton, OH, 44710 (216) 452-3035
Licensure Intermediate Care. *Beds* 40. *Certified* Medicaid.
Ownership Proprietary.

CAREY

Carey Nursing Home
127 Brayton St, Carey, OH, 43316 (419) 396-7488
Medical Dir/Dir of Nursing Dr William Kose.
Licensure Intermediate Care. *Beds* 16. *Certified* Medicaid.
Ownership Proprietary.
Staff RNs 1 (pt); LPNs 2 (ft); Nurses aides 2 (ft), 5 (pt); Physical therapists; Activities coordinators 1 (ft); Dietitians; Dentists; Podiatrists.
Facilities Dining room; Laundry room.
Activities Arts and Crafts; Cards; Games; Movies; Shopping trips.
Description Home has residents 35-60 years of age and can care for difficult residents who need extra attention. Small facility has a home-like atmosphere.

CARROLLTON

Carroll Health Care Center Inc*
648 Long St, Carrollton, OH, 44615
Licensure Skilled Care; Intermediate Care.
Beds 50; 100. *Certified* Medicaid; Medicare.
Ownership Proprietary.

Carroll Nursing Home
347 Steubenville Rd SE, Carrollton, OH, 44615
(216) 627-4233
Medical Dir/Dir of Nursing T J Atchison MD.
Licensure Intermediate Care. *Beds* 18. *Certified* Medicaid.
Ownership Proprietary.
Admissions Requirements Minimum age 18.
Staff Physicians 1 (pt); RNs 1 (ft), 2 (pt); LPNs 2 (ft), 1 (pt); Nurses aides 8 (ft), 8 (pt); Physical therapists 1 (pt); Reality therapists 1 (ft); Recreational therapists 1 (ft); Occupational therapists 1 (pt); Speech therapists 1 (pt); Activities coordinators 1 (ft); Dietitians 1 (ft); Dentists 1 (pt); Podiatrists 1 (pt); Audiologists 1 (pt).
Facilities Dining room; Activities room; Crafts room; Laundry room.
Activities Arts and Crafts; Cards; Games; Reading groups; Prayer groups; Movies; Shopping trips; Dances/Social or cultural gatherings.
Description Carroll Nursing Home is the only nursing facility licensed and certified to provide care for the mentally ill patient in the 10 county catchment area served by Cambridge State Hospital.

CARY

Indian Trail Nursing Home
821 E Findlay St, Cary, OH, 43316 (419) 396-6344
Medical Dir/Dir of Nursing William Kose.
Licensure Intermediate Care. *Beds* 50. *Certified* Medicaid.
Ownership Proprietary.
Staff Physicians 1 (pt); RNs 1 (ft); LPNs 5 (ft); Orderlies 2 (ft); Nurses aides 30 (ft); Activities coordinators 1 (ft); Dietitians 1 (pt); Dentists 1 (pt); Podiatrists 1 (pt).
Facilities Dining room; Activities room; Crafts room; Laundry room; Barber/Beauty shop.
Activities Arts and Crafts; Cards; Games; Reading groups; Prayer groups; Movies; Shopping trips; Dances/Social or cultural gatherings; Cooking; Make-up days.

CELINA

Celina Manor
1001 Myers Rd, Celina, OH, 45822 (419) 586-6645
Licensure Skilled Care; Intermediate Care.
Beds 101. *Certified* Medicaid; Medicare.
Ownership Proprietary.
Admissions Requirements Medical examination; Physician's request.
Facilities Dining room; Physical therapy room; Activities room; Chapel; Crafts room; Laundry room; Barber/Beauty shop; Library; Patios.
Activities Arts and Crafts; Cards; Games; Reading groups; Prayer groups; Movies; Shopping trips; Dances/Social or cultural gatherings; Field trips.

Description Beautiful facility situated in a neighborhood setting. Features 5 outside patios for use by residents and a fountain area in the center of the facility. Each room is individually decorated; 2-bed rooms share a bathroom.

Hometown Nursing Homes, Inc
401 E Meyers, Celina, OH, 45822 (419) 586-3016
Medical Dir/Dir of Nursing George McIlroy MD.
Licensure Skilled Care. *Beds* 50. *Certified* Medicaid.
Ownership Proprietary.
Admissions Requirements Medical examination; Physician's request
Staff RNs 4 (ft), 2 (pt); LPNs 3 (ft), 4 (pt); Orderlies 1 (ft); Nurses aides 10 (ft), 28 (pt); Physical therapists 1 (pt); Occupational therapists 1 (pt); Speech therapists 1 (pt); Activities coordinators 1 (ft); Dietitians 1 (pt); Dentists 1 (pt); Ophthalmologists 1 (pt); Podiatrists 1 (pt).
Facilities Dining room; Activities room; Laundry room; Barber/Beauty shop.
Activities Arts and Crafts; Cards; Games; Reading groups; Prayer groups; Movies; Shopping trips; Dances/Social or cultural gatherings.

CENTERBURG

Harrod Nursing Home
26 N Hartford Ave, Centerburg, OH, 43011 (614) 625-5049
Licensure Nursing Home. *Beds* 28.
Ownership Proprietary.

Morning View Care Center 1*
4531 Columbus Rd, Centerburg, OH, 43011 (614) 625-5401
Licensure Intermediate Care. *Beds* 34. *Certified* Medicaid.
Ownership Proprietary.

Salyer Nursing Home Inc
218 Clayton St, Centerburg, OH, 43011 (614) 625-5774
Medical Dir/Dir of Nursing Hernando Posado MD.
Licensure Skilled Care; Intermediate Care.
Beds 83. *Certified* Medicaid; Medicare.
Ownership Proprietary.
Staff Physicians 1 (pt); RNs 2 (ft), 3 (pt); LPNs 14 (ft), 5 (pt); Orderlies 4 (ft); Nurses aides 30 (ft); Physical therapists 1 (pt); Occupational therapists 1 (pt); Speech therapists 1 (pt); Activities coordinators 1 (ft); Dietitians 1 (pt); Dentists 1 (pt); Podiatrists 1 (pt).
Facilities Dining room; Laundry room; Barber/Beauty shop.
Activities Arts and Crafts; Cards; Games; Reading groups; Prayer groups; Movies; Shopping trips; Dances/Social or cultural gatherings.
Description Facility is located in the center of Ohio and specializes in excellent care of respiratory patients (ventilator care). Facility caters to people of any age and all the young patients are a blessing to staff and other patients; in 1983 youngest resident was one-year-old and the oldest was 99.

Sunrise Convalescent Center Inc*
80 Miller Ave, Centerburg, OH, 43011 (614) 625-6873
Licensure Intermediate Care. *Beds* 50. *Certified* Medicaid.
Ownership Proprietary.

CHAGRIN FALLS

Hamlet Manor
150 Cleveland St, Chagrin Falls, OH, 44022 (216) 247-4200
Medical Dir/Dir of Nursing Helena Hoelscher.
Licensure Nursing Home. *Beds* 98.
Ownership Proprietary
Admissions Requirements Medical examination.
Staff RNs 5 (ft), 12 (pt); LPNs 6 (ft), 1 (pt); Orderlies 2 (ft), 1 (pt); Nurses aides 28 (ft), 15 (pt); Physical therapists; Speech therapists 1 (pt); Activities coordinators 2 (ft), 1 (pt); Dietitians 1 (ft); Podiatrists 2 (ft); Audiologists 1 (ft).
Facilities Dining room; Physical therapy room; Activities room; Crafts room; Laundry room; Barber/Beauty shop; Library.
Activities Arts and Crafts; Cards; Games; Reading groups; Prayer groups; Movies; Shopping trips; Dances/Social or cultural gatherings.

CHARDON

Heather Hill Inc
12340 Bass Lake Rd, Chardon, OH, 44024 (216) 285-9151
Medical Dir/Dir of Nursing Michael H Hackett MD.
Licensure Skilled Care; Intermediate Care.
Beds 99. *Certified* Medicaid; Medicare.
Ownership Nonprofit.
Admissions Requirements Minimum age 18; Medical examination.
Facilities Dining room; Physical therapy room; Activities room; Chapel; Crafts room; Laundry room; Barber/Beauty shop.
Activities Arts and Crafts; Cards; Games; Reading groups; Prayer groups; Movies; Shopping trips; Dances/Social or cultural gatherings.

CHESTERLAND

Maple Nursing Home
13417 Rockhaven Rd, Chesterland, OH, 44026 (216) 286-6180
Medical Dir/Dir of Nursing Dr William Larrick.
Licensure Intermediate Care. *Beds* 21. *Certified* Medicaid.
Ownership Proprietary.
Staff RNs 1 (pt); LPNs 3 (ft), 4 (pt); Orderlies 1 (pt); Nurses aides 3 (ft), 2 (pt); Activities coordinators 1 (pt); Dietitians 1 (pt); Podiatrists 1 (pt).
Facilities Dining room.
Activities Arts and Crafts; Cards; Prayer groups.

Metzenbaum Residence*
8132 Cedar Rd, Chesterland, OH, 44026 (216) 729-9409

Licensure Intermediate Care for Mentally Retarded. *Beds* 36.
Ownership Public.

CHESTERVILLE

Morrow Manor Inc*
PO Box 44, State Rt 95 and 314, Chesterville, OH, 43317 (419) 768-2401
Licensure Intermediate Care. *Beds* 50. *Certified* Medicaid.
Ownership Proprietary.

CHEVIOT

Hillebrand Nursing Center
4307 Bridgetown Rd, Cheviot, OH, 45211 (513) 574-4550
Medical Dir/Dir of Nursing Dr Gene Simon.
Licensure Skilled Care; Intermediate Care.
Beds SNF 52; ICF 58. *Certified* Medicaid; Medicare.
Ownership Proprietary.
Staff Physicians; RNs 6 (ft), 12 (pt); LPNs 2 (ft), 10 (pt); Nurses aides 25 (ft), 28 (pt); Physical therapists 2 (ft); Recreational therapists 2 (ft), 1 (pt); Speech therapists 1 (ft); Activities coordinators 2 (ft); Dietitians 1 (pt); Podiatrists 1 (pt).
Facilities Dining room; Physical therapy room; Activities room; Chapel; Barber/Beauty shop; Library.
Activities Arts and Crafts; Cards; Games; Reading groups; Prayer groups; Movies; Dances/Social or cultural gatherings.

CHILLICOTHE

Deiber Nursing Home Inc*
182 N Bridge St, Chillicothe, OH, 45601 (614) 773-2104
Licensure Intermediate Care. *Beds* 33. *Certified* Medicaid.
Ownership Proprietary.

Heartland of Chillicothe*
1058 Columbus St, Chillicothe, OH, 45601
Licensure Intermediate Care. *Beds* 101. *Certified* Medicaid.
Ownership Nonprofit.

Marietta Place
10 Marietta Pike, Chillicothe, OH, 45601 (614) 772-5900
Licensure Intermediate Care. *Beds* 100. *Certified* Medicaid.
Ownership Proprietary.
Admissions Requirements Medical examination; Physician's request.
Staff RNs 12 (ft); LPNs 4 (ft); Orderlies 2 (ft); Nurses aides 30 (ft), 2 (pt); Physical therapists 1 (pt); Speech therapists 1 (pt); Activities coordinators 1 (ft), 1 (pt); Dietitians 1 (pt); Dentists; Ophthalmologists; Podiatrists.
Facilities Dining room; Activities room; Laundry room; Barber/Beauty shop; Library.
Activities Arts and Crafts; Cards; Games; Reading groups; Prayer groups; Movies; Shopping trips; Dances/Social or cultural gatherings.
Description Facility features registered nurses on duty 24 hours a day, doctors on call at all

times, registered dietician, and daily activities. Friends and families are invited to dine with residents and attend parties.

Westmoreland Place Nursing Home*
230 Cherry St, Chillicothe, OH, 45601 (614) 773-6470
Licensure Skilled Care; Intermediate Care. *Beds* 150. *Certified* Medicaid; Medicare.
Ownership Proprietary.

CINCINNATI

Able Manor Nursing Home*
2927 Douglas Terrace, Cincinnati, OH, 45212 (513) 531-6676
Licensure Intermediate Care. *Beds* 33. *Certified* Medicaid.
Ownership Proprietary.

Alaska Nursing Home*
3584 Alaska Ave, Cincinnati, OH, 45229 (513) 281-7782
Licensure Intermediate Care. *Beds* 43. *Certified* Medicaid.
Ownership Proprietary.

Ambassador North*
5501 Verulam St, Cincinnati, OH, 45213 (513) 531-3654
Licensure Skilled Care; Intermediate Care. *Beds* 50. *Certified* Medicaid; Medicare.
Ownership Proprietary.

Ambassador South*
3030 Carpathia, Cincinnati, OH, 45213 (513) 631-1310
Licensure Skilled Care; Intermediate Care. *Beds* 50. *Certified* Medicaid; Medicare.
Ownership Proprietary.

Amity Convalescent Home*
1804 Kinney Ave, Cincinnati, OH, 45207 (513) 961-9838
Licensure Skilled Care; Intermediate Care. *Beds* 50. *Certified* Medicaid; Medicare.
Ownership Proprietary.

Arcadia Manor*
5500 Verulam Ave, Cincinnati, OH, 45213 (513) 631-0003
Licensure Skilled Care; Intermediate Care. *Beds* 121. *Certified* Medicaid; Medicare.
Ownership Proprietary.

Archbishop Leibold Home*
476 Riddle Rd, Cincinnati, OH, 45220 (513) 281-8001
Licensure Intermediate Care; Rest Home. *Beds* ICF 75; Rest Home 50. *Certified* Medicaid.
Ownership Nonprofit.
Affiliation Roman Catholic

Beechknoll Convalescenter Center
6550 Hamilton Ave, Cincinnati, OH, 45224 (513) 522-5516
Medical Dir/Dir of Nursing Dr Richard Longshore.
Licensure Skilled Care; Intermediate Care; Rest Home. *Beds* SNF 50; ICF 50; Rest Home 104. *Certified* Medicaid; Medicare.

Ownership Proprietary.
Admissions Requirements Minimum age 16; Medical examination.
Staff Physicians 1 (pt); RNs 4 (ft), 8 (pt); LPNs 8 (ft), 16 (pt); Nurses aides 25 (ft), 25 (pt); Physical therapists 1 (ft); Occupational therapists 1 (pt); Speech therapists 1 (pt); Activities coordinators 4 (ft); Dietitians 1 (pt); Dentists 1 (pt); Ophthalmologists 1 (pt); Podiatrists 1 (pt); Audiologists 1 (pt).
Facilities Dining room; Physical therapy room; Activities room; Crafts room; Laundry room; Barber/Beauty shop; Library.
Activities Arts and Crafts; Cards; Games; Reading groups; Prayer groups; Movies; Shopping trips; Dances/Social or cultural gatherings.
Description Facility features 13 wooded acres, park-like setting with park on grounds, transportation van, close to shopping and entertainment; short-term hospitality stay also available in rest home and independent living sections.

Beechwood Home for Incurables Inc
2140 Pogue Ave, Cincinnati, OH, 45208 (513) 321-9294
Licensure Skilled Care; Intermediate Care. *Beds* 70. *Certified* Medicaid; Medicare.
Ownership Nonprofit.

Bethesda Scarlet Oaks Retirement Community
440 Lafayette Ave, Cincinnati, OH, 45220 (513) 861-0400
Medical Dir/Dir of Nursing John Specekelli MD.
Licensure Nursing Home. *Beds* 68.
Ownership Nonprofit.
Admissions Requirements Medical examination.
Staff Physicians 2 (pt); RNs 12 (ft); LPNs 8 (ft); Nurses aides 19 (ft); Physical therapists 1 (ft); Reality therapists 1 (ft); Recreational therapists 1 (ft); Occupational therapists 1 (ft); Speech therapists 1 (pt); Activities coordinators 1 (ft); Dietitians 1 (ft); Dentists 1 (pt); Ophthalmologists 1 (pt); Podiatrists 1 (pt); Audiologists 1 (pt).
Facilities Dining room; Physical therapy room; Activities room; Chapel; Crafts room; Laundry room; Barber/Beauty shop; Library.
Activities Arts and Crafts; Cards; Games; Reading groups; Prayer groups; Movies; Shopping trips; Dances/Social or cultural gatherings.
Description Facility is located in the beautiful gaslight district of Cheftain, surrounded by 48 acres of trees in the middle of Cincinnati; independence, assistance in daily living, and restorative health care with programs tailored to meet the individual's needs.

Briarwood Terrace Nursing Home
3103 Fairfield Ave, Cincinnati, OH, 45207
Licensure Nursing Home. *Beds* 25.
Ownership Proprietary.

Brynes Convalescent Center Inc*
2203 Fulton Ave, Cincinnati, OH, 45206 (513) 751-1752
Licensure Intermediate Care. *Beds* 64. *Certified* Medicaid.
Ownership Proprietary.

Camargo Manor Nursing Home*
7625 Camargo Rd, Cincinnati, OH, 45243
(513) 561-6210
Licensure Nursing Home. *Beds* 50.
Ownership Proprietary.

Christian Care of Cincinnati Inc
1067 Compton Rd, Cincinnati, OH, 45231
(513) 522-5533
Medical Dir/Dir of Nursing Dr Longshore.
Licensure Intermediate Care. *Beds* 33. *Certified* Medicaid.
Ownership Proprietary.
Admissions Requirements Minimum age 21;
Medical examination; Physician's request.
Staff Physicians 1 (pt); RNs 1 (pt); LPNs 2 (ft),
3 (pt); Nurses aides 7 (ft), 4 (pt); Activities coordinators 1 (ft); Dietitians 1 (ft); Dentists;
Ophthalmologists; Podiatrists.

Clifton Care Center Inc*
625 Probasco Ave, Cincinnati, OH, 45220
(513) 281-2464
Licensure Skilled Care; Intermediate Care.
Beds 142. *Certified* Medicaid; Medicare.
Ownership Proprietary.

Clovernook Inc*
7025 Clovernook Ave, Cincinnati, OH, 45220
Licensure Skilled Care; Intermediate Care.
Beds SNF 29; ICF 104. *Certified* Medicare.
Ownership Proprietary.

Crest View Nursing Home*
2420 Harrison Ave, Cincinnati, OH, 45211
(513) 481-1100
Licensure Skilled Care; Intermediate Care.
Beds 131. *Certified* Medicaid; Medicare.
Ownership Proprietary.

Daly Park Geriatric Center
6300 Daly Rd, Cincinnati, OH, 45224 (513)
542-6800
Medical Dir/Dir of Nursing Dr Charles Armstrong.
Licensure Skilled Care; Intermediate Care.
Beds 100. *Certified* Medicaid; Medicare.
Ownership Proprietary.
Admissions Requirements Minimum age 21;
Medical examination.
Staff Physicians 1 (pt); RNs 7 (ft); LPNs 7 (ft);
Orderlies 3 (ft); Nurses aides 34 (ft); Physical
therapists 1 (pt); Recreational therapists 2 (ft);
Occupational therapists 1 (pt); Speech therapists 1 (pt); Activities coordinators 1 (ft); Dietitians 1 (pt); Dentists 1 (pt); Ophthalmologists 1
(pt); Podiatrists 1 (pt); Audiologists 1 (pt).
Facilities Dining room; Physical therapy room;
Activities room; Chapel; Crafts room; Barber-
/Beauty shop; Library.
Activities Arts and Crafts; Cards; Games;
Reading groups; Prayer groups; Movies; Shopping trips; Dances/Social or cultural gatherings.
Description Facility features good activity and
rehabilitation programs; many patients discharged back into the community.

Deer Park Nursing Home*
6922 Ohio Ave, Cincinnati, OH, 45236 (513)
793-2090
Licensure Skilled Care; Intermediate Care.
Beds 136. *Certified* Medicaid; Medicare.
Ownership Proprietary.

Drake Memorial Hospital
151 W Galbraith Rd, Cincinnati, OH, 45216
(513) 761-3440
Medical Dir/Dir of Nursing Morris L Stein
MD.
Licensure Skilled Care; Intermediate Care.
Beds 244. *Certified* Medicaid; Medicare.
Ownership Public.
Admissions Requirements Medical examination.
Staff Physicians 9 (ft), 3 (pt); RNs 115 (ft), 1
(pt); LPNs 80 (ft), 1 (pt); Nurses aides 196 (ft),
1 (pt); Physical therapists 6 (ft); Recreational
therapists 8 (ft); Occupational therapists 6 (ft);
Speech therapists 3 (ft); Dietitians 3 (ft); Dentists 3 (pt); Ophthalmologists 1 (pt); Podiatrists
2 (pt); Audiologists 1 (pt).
Facilities Dining room; Physical therapy room;
Activities room; Chapel; Crafts room; Laundry
room; Barber/Beauty shop; Library.
Activities Arts and Crafts; Cards; Games;
Reading groups; Prayer groups; Movies; Shopping trips; Dances/Social or cultural gatherings;
Outings.
Description Facility provides excellent rehabilitation services and a high level of skilled
nursing care; patients are served who need
treatment for long periods of time; average
length of stay is 8 months.

Eleanora-Connor Convalescent Home
214 Ludlow Ave, Cincinnati, OH, 45220
Licensure Nursing Home. *Beds* 20.
Ownership Proprietary.

Elite Rest and Nursing Home*
965 Burton Ave, Cincinnati, OH, 45229 (513)
221-3900
Licensure Intermediate Care. *Beds* 50. *Certified* Medicaid.
Ownership Proprietary.

Empress Convalescent Home—1
2321 Upland Pl, PO Box 6276, Cincinnati,
OH, 45206-0276 (513) 281-7700
Admin Hugo G Eichelberg. *Medical Dir/Dir of
Nursing* Dr Fausto Vasquez.
Licensure Intermediate Care. *Beds* 45. *Certified* Medicaid.
Ownership Proprietary.
Staff Physicians 4 (pt); RNs 1 (ft); LPNs 2 (ft),
2 (pt); Nurses aides 8 (ft), 4 (pt); Physical therapists 1 (pt); Activities coordinators 1 (ft); Dietitians 1 (pt); Dentists 1 (pt); Ophthalmologists 1
(pt); Podiatrists 1 (pt); Audiologists 1 (pt).
Facilities Dining room; Activities room; Chapel; Crafts room; Laundry room; Library.
Activities Arts and Crafts; Cards; Games;
Reading groups; Prayer groups; Movies; Shopping trips; Dances/Social or cultural gatherings;
Picnics; Outings.

Empress Convalescent Home—2
2327 Upland Pl, PO Box 6276, Cincinnati,
OH, 45206-0276 (513) 281-7700
Admin Hugo G Eichelberg. *Medical Dir/Dir of
Nursing* Dr Fausto Vasquez.
Licensure Intermediate Care. *Beds* 25. *Certified* Medicaid.
Ownership Proprietary.
Staff Physicians 4 (pt); RNs 1 (ft); LPNs 4 (ft),
2 (pt); Nurses aides 8 (ft), 3 (pt); Activities coordinators 1 (ft); Dietitians 1 (pt); Dentists 1 (pt);

Ophthalmologists 1 (pt); Podiatrists 1 (pt);
Audiologists 1 (pt).
Facilities Dining room; Activities room; Chapel; Crafts room; Laundry room; Library.
Activities Arts and Crafts; Cards; Games;
Reading groups; Prayer groups; Movies; Shopping trips; Dances/Social or cultural gatherings;
Picnics; Outings.

Forestview Nursing Home*
610 Forest Ave, Cincinnati, OH, 45229
Licensure Intermediate Care. *Beds* 28. *Certified* Medicaid.
Ownership Proprietary.

Franciscan Terrace
100 Compton Rd, Cincinnati, OH, 45215 (513)
761-9036
Medical Dir/Dir of Nursing Richard Klopp
MD.
Licensure Intermediate Care; Home for the
Aged. *Beds* 160.
Ownership Nonprofit.
Admissions Requirements Minimum age 55;
Medical examination.
Staff Physicians 2 (pt); RNs 5 (ft), 10 (pt);
LPNs 7 (ft), 5 (pt); Orderlies 1 (ft); Nurses aides
29 (ft), 12 (pt); Physical therapists 3 (ft); Activities coordinators 1 (ft), 1 (pt); Dietitians 1 (ft);
Dentists 1 (pt); Podiatrists 2 (pt).
Affiliation Roman Catholic
Facilities Dining room; Physical therapy room;
Activities room; Chapel; Crafts room; Laundry
room; Barber/Beauty shop; Library; Indoor
swimming pool.
Activities Arts and Crafts; Cards; Games;
Reading groups; Prayer groups; Movies; Shopping trips; Dances/Social or cultural gatherings.
Description Our Adapted Aquatic Program is
primarily designed to embrace every part of the
body. Our regular exercise in the therapeutic
range strengthens and tones muscles, improves
range of motion of all joints, enhances flexibility and creates a feeling of well being. The
object of our aquatic program is to use a medically approved program to allow you to determine how fit you want to be and to show you
how to obtain this degree of fitness.

Gardenview Nursing Home*
3544 Washington Ave, Cincinnati, OH, 45229
(513) 751-2241
Licensure Skilled Care; Intermediate Care.
Beds 45. *Certified* Medicaid; Medicare.
Ownership Proprietary.

**George A Martin Gerontology Center, Division
of the Sightless Society of Ohio Inc**
3603 Washington Ave, Cincinnati, OH, 45229
(513) 961-0144
Medical Dir/Dir of Nursing John Falk MD.
Licensure Intermediate Care. *Beds* 25. *Certified* Medicaid.
Ownership Nonprofit.
Admissions Requirements Minimum age 21;
Medical examination; Physician's request.
Staff Physicians; RNs; LPNs; Orderlies;
Nurses aides; Physical therapists; Reality therapists; Recreational therapists; Occupational
therapists; Speech therapists; Activities coordinators; Dietitians; Dentists; Ophthalmologists.
Facilities Dining room; Activities room; Laundry room.

Activities Arts and Crafts; Cards; Games; Reading groups; Prayer groups; Movies; Shopping trips; Dances/Social or cultural gatherings.

Glen Manor
6969 Glenmeadow Ln, Cincinnati, OH, 45237 (513) 351-7072
Medical Dir/Dir of Nursing Stanley Waxman MD.
Licensure Skilled Care; Intermediate Care.
Beds 118. *Certified* Medicaid; Medicare.
Ownership Nonprofit.
Admissions Requirements Minimum age 65; Medical examination.
Staff Physicians; R.Ns 4 (ft), 1 (pt); LPNs 15 (ft), 1 (pt); Nurses aides 48 (ft), 1 (pt); Physical therapists 1 (pt); Recreational therapists 2 (ft), 1 (pt); Occupational therapists 1 (pt); Activities coordinators 1 (ft); Dietitians 1 (pt); Dentists; Ophthalmologists; Podiatrists; Audiologists.
Affiliation Jewish
Facilities Dining room; Physical therapy room; Activities room; Chapel; Crafts room; Laundry room; Barber/Beauty shop; Library.
Activities Arts and Crafts; Cards; Games; Reading groups; Movies; Shopping trips; Dances/Social or cultural gatherings.
Description Manor has 108 single-bed rooms and 5 2-bed rooms emphasizing individual dignity.

Glen Park
548 Glenwood Ave, Cincinnati, OH, 45229 (513) 961-8881
Admin S P Heil. *Medical Dir/Dir of Nursing* Dr Mediodia.
Licensure Intermediate Care. *Beds* 155. *Certified* Medicaid.
Ownership Proprietary.
Staff Physicians 4 (pt); RNs 7 (ft); LPNs 17 (ft); Orderlies 5 (ft); Nurses aides 60 (ft); Physical therapists 2 (pt); Recreational therapists 4 (ft), 1 (pt); Occupational therapists 2 (ft); Speech therapists 1 (pt); Activities coordinators 2 (ft); Dietitians 1 (ft); Dentists 1 (pt); Ophthalmologists 1 (pt); Podiatrists 1 (pt); Audiologists 1 (pt).
Facilities Dining room; Physical therapy room; Activities room; Crafts room; Barber/Beauty shop.
Activities Arts and Crafts; Cards; Games; Reading groups; Prayer groups; Movies; Shopping trips; Dances/Social or cultural gatherings.

Gold Crest Nursing Home
3663 Reading Rd, Cincinnati, OH, 45229 (513) 861-1036
Medical Dir/Dir of Nursing Dr Morris Plotnick.
Licensure Intermediate Care. *Beds* 50. *Certified* Medicaid.
Ownership Proprietary.
Staff RNs 1 (ft); LPNs 3 (ft), 3 (pt); Nurses aides 18 (ft), 5 (pt); Physical therapists 1 (pt); Recreational therapists 1 (ft); Activities coordinators 1 (ft); Dietitians 1 (pt); Podiatrists 1 (pt).
Facilities Dining room; Activities room; Crafts room; Laundry room.
Activities Arts and Crafts; Cards; Games; Reading groups; Prayer groups; Movies.

Golden Age Retirement Home
3635 Reading Rd, Cincinnati, OH, 45229 (513) 281-1922
Admin Mary K Irwin. *Medical Dir/Dir of Nursing* Dr Morris Plotnick.
Licensure Skilled Care; Intermediate Care.
Beds 50. *Certified* Medicaid; Medicare.
Ownership Proprietary.
Staff RNs; LPNs; Nurses aides; Physical therapists; Reality therapists; Recreational therapists; Activities coordinators; Dietitians.
Facilities Dining room; Physical therapy room; Laundry room.
Activities Arts and Crafts; Cards; Games; Reading groups; Prayer groups; Movies; Shopping trips; Dances/Social or cultural gatherings.

Grace Manor Nursing Home
2409 Grandview Ave, Cincinnati, OH, 45206
Admin Hugo G Eichelberg. *Medical Dir/Dir of Nursing* Dr Morris Plotnick.
Licensure Intermediate Care. *Beds* 30. *Certified* Medicaid.
Ownership Proprietary.
Staff Physicians 2 (pt); RNs 1 (ft); LPNs 4 (ft); Nurses aides 9 (ft); Physical therapists 1 (pt); Reality therapists 1 (pt); Recreational therapists 1 (pt); Activities coordinators 1 (ft); Dietitians 1 (pt); Dentists 1 (pt); Ophthalmologists 1 (pt); Podiatrists 1 (pt); Audiologists 1 (pt).
Facilities Dining room; Activities room; Laundry room.
Activities Arts and Crafts; Cards; Games; Reading groups; Prayer groups; Movies; Shopping trips; Dances/Social or cultural gatherings.
Description Facility is small but very patient oriented; food is excellent, as are the nursing, activities, and social services.

Hamilton County Eastern Star Home Inc*
1630 W North Bend Rd, Cincinnati, OH, 45224 (513) 542-6464
Licensure Nursing Home; Rest Home.
Beds Nursing Home 36; Rest Home 34.
Ownership Nonprofit.
Affiliation Order of Eastern Star

Harrison House Inc
2171 Harrison Ave, Cincinnati, OH, 45211 (513) 662-5800
Medical Dir/Dir of Nursing Margaret Schneider MD.
Licensure Skilled Care; Intermediate Care.
Beds 101. *Certified* Medicaid; Medicare.
Ownership Proprietary.
Admissions Requirements Minimum age 18; Medical examination.
Staff Physicians 26 (pt); RNs 2 (ft), 6 (pt); LPNs 5 (ft), 5 (pt); Nurses aides 22 (ft), 23 (pt); Physical therapists 1 (pt); Recreational therapists 1 (ft); Occupational therapists 1 (pt); Speech therapists 1 (pt); Activities coordinators 1 (ft); Dietitians 1 (pt); Ophthalmologists 1 (pt); Podiatrists 1 (pt); Audiologists 1 (pt).
Facilities Dining room; Physical therapy room; Activities room; Chapel; Barber/Beauty shop; Library.
Activities Arts and Crafts; Cards; Games; Reading groups; Prayer groups; Movies; Shopping trips; Dances/Social or cultural gatherings.
Description We believe we have a very caring facility with a homey atmosphere. Our activity

program is geared to all levels of residents, and we also have a van for outings. The staff go out of their way to keep our residents happy.

Hillside Manor Health Care Facility Inc
3539 Eden Ave, Cincinnati, OH, 45229 (216) 861-1482
Admin Karen L Williams. *Medical Dir/Dir of Nursing* James J Alikonis MD.
Licensure Intermediate Care. *Beds* 67. *Certified* Medicaid.
Ownership Proprietary.
Admissions Requirements Minimum age 18; Medical examination.
Staff RNs 1 (ft); LPNs 6 (ft), 6 (pt); Orderlies 3 (ft), 4 (pt); Nurses aides 11 (ft), 7 (pt); Speech therapists; Activities coordinators 1 (ft); Dietitians 1 (pt); Dentists; Ophthalmologists; Podiatrists; Audiologists.
Facilities Dining room; Activities room; Laundry room; Library.
Activities Arts and Crafts; Cards; Games; Prayer groups; Movies; Shopping trips; Dances/Social or cultural gatherings; Discussion groups; Exercise classes.
Description We offer a family atmosphere and excellent nursing care and service. We have varied activities and meet the social needs of our patients via our competent social worker and his department. We serve tasty food and have a very good physical therapy department with qualified personnel. We offer extensive experience in long-term care and specialize in short-term care for those patients who need it.

Hilltop Nursing Home
2856 Lafeuille Ave, Cincinnati, OH, 45211
Admin Frances R Glaser. *Medical Dir/Dir of Nursing* Manuel Mediodia MD.
Licensure Skilled Care; Intermediate Care.
Beds 24. *Certified* Medicaid; Medicare.
Ownership Proprietary.
Admissions Requirements Minimum age 40.
Facilities Dining room; Physical therapy room; Activities room; Crafts room; Laundry room; Barber/Beauty shop; Library.
Activities Arts and Crafts; Cards; Games; Reading groups; Prayer groups; Movies; Shopping trips; Dances/Social or cultural gatherings.
Description Hilltop Nursing and Retirement Home is located on 9 beautifully landscaped acres with full-time registered nurses, full-time dietitian, lovely lounges and dining rooms with sky-lights and sparkling fountain.

Hillview Nursing Home
2025 Wyoming Ave, Cincinnati, OH, 45214 (513) 251-2557
Licensure Skilled Care; Intermediate Care.
Beds SNF 50; ICF 50. *Certified* Medicaid; Medicare.
Ownership Proprietary.
Admissions Requirements Medical examination; Physician's request.
Staff Physicians 2 (pt); RNs 4 (ft), 1 (pt); LPNs 6 (ft); Orderlies 2 (ft), 6 (pt); Nurses aides 26 (ft); Physical therapists 1 (ft), 1 (pt); Reality therapists 1 (ft); Recreational therapists 1 (ft), 1 (pt); Activities coordinators; Dietitians.
Facilities Dining room; Physical therapy room; Activities room; Crafts room; Laundry room; Barber/Beauty shop; Library.
Activities Arts and Crafts; Cards; Games;

Reading groups; Prayer groups; Movies; Shopping trips; Dances/Social or cultural gatherings; Picnics.
Description Modern facility offering physical, occupational, speech, and rehabilitation therapy by registered and licensed therapists; daily activities for residents; 2 lounges, one with tropical fish; outside organizations offer entertainment.

Hyde Park Villa Inc
4015 Red Villa Ct, Cincinnati, OH, 45209 (513) 272-0600
Medical Dir/Dir of Nursing August Lambers MD.
Licensure Skilled Care; Intermediate Care.
Beds 150. *Certified* Medicaid; Medicare.
Ownership Proprietary.
Admissions Requirements Minimum age 18.
Staff RNs 4 (ft), 11 (pt); LPNs 10 (ft), 6 (pt); Nurses aides 34 (ft), 20 (pt); Physical therapists 1 (pt); Occupational therapists 1 (pt); Speech therapists 1 (pt); Activities coordinators 2 (ft); Dietitians 1 (ft); Dentists 1 (pt); Ophthalmologists 1 (pt); Podiatrists 1 (pt); Audiologists 1 (pt).
Facilities Dining room; Physical therapy room; Activities room; Chapel; Barber/Beauty shop; Gift shop; Lounges.
Activities Arts and Crafts; Cards; Games; Reading groups; Prayer groups; Movies; Shopping trips; Dances/Social or cultural gatherings; Cooking and Baking; Field trips; Exercise groups.
Description Facility encircles a picturesque and scenic courtyard with a multilevel fountain, gardens, trees, and umbrella tables; providing a peaceful and serene setting for activities, socializing and enjoying nature.

Judson Village and Baptist Home*
2373 Harrison Ave, Cincinnati, OH, 45211 (513) 662-5880
Licensure Intermediate Care; Rest Home.
Beds ICF 50; Rest Home 50. *Certified* Medicaid.
Ownership Nonprofit.
Affiliation Baptist

Kenwood Terrace Inc*
8440 Montgomery Rd, Cincinnati, OH, 45236 (513) 793-2255
Licensure Skilled Care; Intermediate Care.
Beds 108. *Certified* Medicaid; Medicare.
Ownership Proprietary.

Lebraun Convalescent Home
2125 Alpine Pl, Cincinnati, OH, 45206 (513) 281-1890
Medical Dir/Dir of Nursing Albert I Aronoff MD.
Licensure Intermediate Care. *Beds* 34. *Certified* Medicaid.
Ownership Proprietary.
Staff RNs 1 (ft); LPNs 4 (ft), 1 (pt); Nurses aides 8 (ft), 1 (pt); Physical therapists 1 (pt); Activities coordinators 1 (pt); Dietitians 1 (pt).
Facilities Dining room; Activities room; Laundry room.
Activities Arts and Crafts; Cards; Games; Reading groups; Prayer groups; Shopping trips; Dances/Social or cultural gatherings.

Lincoln Avenue and Crawford's Home for the Aged*
1346 Lincoln Ave, Cincinnati, OH, 45206 (513) 861-2044 and 559-1494
Licensure Skilled Care; Intermediate Care.
Beds 100. *Certified* Medicaid; Medicare.
Ownership Nonprofit.

Llanfair Terrace*
1701 Llanfair Ave, Cincinnati, OH, 45224 (513) 681-4230
Licensure Skilled Care; Intermediate Care; Rest Home. *Beds* 75; Rest Home 25. *Certified* Medicaid; Medicare.
Ownership Nonprofit.

Longview Unit 22 Group Home*
6600 Paddock Rd, Cincinnati, OH, 45216
Licensure Intermediate Care for Mentally Retarded. *Beds* 12. *Certified* Medicaid.
Ownership Public.

Madison Nursing Home*
6845 Indian Hill Rd, Cincinnati, OH, 45227 (613) 271-0429
Licensure Intermediate Care. *Beds* 27. *Certified* Medicaid.
Ownership Proprietary.

Manor Care Nursing Home*
2250 Banning Rd, Cincinnati, OH, 45239 (513) 591-0400
Licensure Skilled Care; Intermediate Care.
Beds 151. *Certified* Medicaid; Medicare.
Ownership Proprietary.

Manor Care-Woodside Nursing Facility
5970 Kenwood Rd, Cincinnati, OH, 45243 (513) 561-4111
Medical Dir/Dir of Nursing Jack Rhodes MD.
Licensure Skilled Care. *Beds* SNF 156. *Certified* Medicare.
Ownership Proprietary.
Staff Physicians 1 (pt); RNs 11 (ft), 5 (pt); LPNs 14 (ft), 4 (pt); Nurses aides 54 (ft), 27 (pt); Physical therapists 1 (ft); Occupational therapists 1 (pt); Speech therapists 1 (pt); Activities coordinators 2 (ft); Dietitians 1 (ft); Dentists 1 (pt); Ophthalmologists 1 (pt); Podiatrists 1 (pt); Audiologists 1 (pt).
Facilities Dining room; Physical therapy room; Activities room; Laundry room; Barber/Beauty shop.
Activities Arts and Crafts; Cards; Games; Reading groups; Prayer groups; Movies; Shopping trips; Dances/Social or cultural gatherings.
Description Center is a 24-hour health care facility in gracious, home-like surroundings; building is climate-controlled and completely fire resistant. Services are backed by the most comprehensive quality assurance program in long-term care; Manor Care maintains a hotline for solving any problems which may arise.

Maple Knoll Village*
11100 Springfield Pike, Cincinnati, OH, 45246 (513) 785-2400
Licensure Skilled Care; Intermediate Care.
Beds 174. *Certified* Medicaid; Medicare.
Ownership Nonprofit.

Marjorie P Lee Home for the Aged*
3550 Shaw Ave, Cincinnati, OH, 45208 (513) 871-2090
Licensure Intermediate Care; Rest Home.
Beds ICF 72; Rest Home 25. *Certified* Medicaid.
Ownership Nonprofit.

Meadowbrook Care Center
8211 Weller Rd, Cincinnati, OH, 45242 (513) 489-2444
Medical Dir/Dir of Nursing Dr Allen Straus.
Licensure Skilled Care. *Certified* Medicaid; Medicare.
Ownership Proprietary.
Admissions Requirements Minimum age 65, Medical examination.
Staff Physicians 1 (pt); RNs 9 (ft), 5 (pt); LPNs 7 (ft), 5 (pt); Nurses aides 55 (ft), 24 (pt); Physical therapists 1 (pt); Speech therapists 1 (pt); Activities coordinators 2 (ft); Dietitians 1 (pt); Dentists 1 (pt); Ophthalmologists 1 (pt); Podiatrists 1 (pt); Audiologists 1 (pt); Social workers 1 (pt).
Facilities Dining room; Physical therapy room; Activities room; Chapel; Crafts room; Laundry room; Barber/Beauty shop; Library; Montisorri school.
Activities Arts and Crafts; Cards; Games; Reading groups; Prayer groups; Movies; Shopping trips; Dances/Social or cultural gatherings.
Description This is a relatively new facility stressing good nursing care and good food; won first prize for beauty in the greater Cincinnati area.

Montgomery Care Center Inc
7777 Cooper Rd, Cincinnati, OH, 45242 (513) 793-5092
Admin Rod McKinly. *Medical Dir/Dir of Nursing* Dr James Grubber.
Licensure Skilled Care; Intermediate Care.
Beds 102. *Certified* Medicaid; Medicare.
Ownership Proprietary.
Staff RNs 11 (ft); LPNs 3 (ft); Orderlies 5 (ft); Nurses aides 95 (ft); Physical therapists 1 (pt); Reality therapists 1 (pt); Recreational therapists 1 (pt); Occupational therapists 1 (pt); Speech therapists 1 (pt); Activities coordinators 1 (ft); Dietitians 1 (ft); Dentists 1 (pt); Ophthalmologists 1 (pt); Podiatrists 1 (pt); Audiologists 1 (pt).
Facilities Dining room; Physical therapy room; Activities room; Chapel; Crafts room; Laundry room; Barber/Beauty shop; Library.
Activities Arts and Crafts; Cards; Games; Reading groups; Prayer groups; Movies; Shopping trips; Dances/Social or cultural gatherings; Eating out; Ethic and special theme dinner.

Mount Healthy Christian Home
8097 Hamilton Ave, Cincinnati, OH, 45231 (513) 931-5000
Medical Dir/Dir of Nursing Dr Leonard Singerman.
Licensure Intermediate Care; Home for the Aged. *Beds* ICF 64; Home for the Aged 32.
Certified Medicaid.
Ownership Nonprofit.
Admissions Requirements Minimum age 62; Medical examination.
Staff Physicians 2 (pt); RNs 3 (ft), 5 (pt); LPNs 9 (ft), 3 (pt); Nurses aides 34 (ft), 4 (pt);

Physical therapists 1 (pt); Recreational therapists 1 (pt); Activities coordinators 1 (ft); Dietitians 1 (pt); Dentists 1 (pt); Podiatrists 1 (pt).
Affiliation Church of Christ
Facilities Dining room; Physical therapy room; Activities room; Chapel; Crafts room; Laundry room; Barber/Beauty shop; Library.
Activities Arts and Crafts; Games; Reading groups; Prayer groups; Movies; Shopping trips; Dances/Social or cultural gatherings.
Description Facility is located in nicely landscaped area within walking distance of a shopping center and fast food shops, on city bus line, with a home-like Christian atmosphere.

Mount Washington Care Center
6900 Beechmont Ave, Cincinnati, OH, 45230
(513) 231-4561
Medical Dir/Dir of Nursing Patricia E Cook MD.
Licensure Skilled Care; Intermediate Care.
Beds 136. *Certified* Medicaid; Medicare.
Ownership Proprietary.
Staff Physicians 28 (pt); RNs 5 (ft), 6 (pt); LPNs 6 (ft), 6 (pt); Orderlies 2 (ft), 1 (pt); Nurses aides 29 (ft), 25 (pt); Physical therapists 1 (ft); Recreational therapists 1 (ft); Occupational therapists 1 (pt); Speech therapists 1 (pt); Activities coordinators 2 (ft); Dietitians 1 (ft), 1 (pt); Dentists 1 (pt); Ophthalmologists 1 (pt); Podiatrists 1 (pt); Audiologists 1 (pt).
Facilities Dining room; Physical therapy room; Activities room; Chapel; Crafts room; Laundry room; Barber/Beauty shop; Library.
Activities Arts and Crafts; Cards; Games; Reading groups; Prayer groups; Movies; Shopping trips; Dances/Social or cultural gatherings; Outpatient physical therapy.
Description Facility is dedicated to the concept of helping people reach and maintain their optimal level of independence; during 1983, 48.5% of all admissions were discharged home. VA approved.

Oak Pavilion Nursing Center
510 Oak St, Cincinnati, OH, 45219 (513) 751-0880
Admin G Edward Ball II. *Medical Dir/Dir of Nursing* Dr Rothfeld.
Licensure Skilled Care; Intermediate Care.
Beds SNF 50; ICF 100. *Certified* Medicaid; Medicare.
Ownership Proprietary.
Staff Physicians; RNs; LPNs; Orderlies; Nurses aides; Physical therapists; Speech therapists; Activities coordinators; Dietitians; Dentists.
Facilities Dining room; Physical therapy room; Activities room; Laundry room; Barber/Beauty shop; Library.
Activities Cards; Games; Reading groups; Movies; Shopping trips; Dances/Social or cultural gatherings.
Description We are located in the exclusively hospital district of Cincinnati. There are approximately 7 hospitals or medical centers within a 3 mile radius of our facility making us very accessible.

Oak Tree Convalescent Center Inc
3545 Eden Ave, Cincinnati, OH, 45229 (216) 861-1483
Admin Karen L Williams. *Medical Dir/Dir of Nursing* James J Alikonis MD.
Licensure Intermediate Care. *Beds* 50. *Certified* Medicaid.
Ownership Proprietary.
Admissions Requirements Minimum age 18; Medical examination.
Staff RNs 1 (ft); LPNs 3 (ft), 3 (pt); Orderlies 3 (ft), 4 (pt); Nurses aides 6 (ft), 3 (pt); Speech therapists; Activities coordinators 1 (ft); Dietitians 1 (pt); Dentists; Ophthalmologists; Podiatrists; Audiologists.
Facilities Dining room; Activities room; Laundry room; Library.
Activities Arts and Crafts; Cards; Games; Prayer groups; Movies; Shopping trips; Dances/Social or cultural gatherings; Discussion groups; Exercise classes.
Description We offer a family atmosphere and excellent nursing care and service. We have varied activities and meet the social needs of our patients via our competent social worker and his department. We serve tasty food and have a good physical therapy department with qualified personnel. We offer extensive experience in long-term care and specialize in short-term care for those patients who need it.

Oakview Nursing Home*
618 Forest Ave, Cincinnati, OH, 45229 (513) 751-2062
Licensure Intermediate Care. *Beds* 27. *Certified* Medicaid.
Ownership Proprietary.

Orthodox Jewish Home for the Aged
1171 Towne St, Cincinnati, OH, 45216 (513) 242-1360
Medical Dir/Dir of Nursing Jan Singerman MD.
Licensure Skilled Care; Intermediate Care.
Beds 172. *Certified* Medicaid; Medicare.
Ownership Nonprofit.
Admissions Requirements Minimum age 65; Medical examination.
Staff RNs; LPNs; Orderlies; Nurses aides; Physical therapists; Reality therapists; Recreational therapists; Activities coordinators; Podiatrists.
Affiliation Jewish
Facilities Dining room; Physical therapy room; Activities room; Chapel; Crafts room; Laundry room; Barber/Beauty shop; Library.
Activities Arts and Crafts; Cards; Games; Reading groups; Prayer groups; Movies; Shopping trips; Dances/Social or cultural gatherings.
Description The Orthodox Jewish Home is a 172-bed Medicare/Medicaid approved, progressive nursing home facility for the Jewish elderly. Leisure time activities, entertainment, expert medical and nursing care, social work, rehabilitative services, adult day care, and respite care are offered in a home-like environment.

Price Hill Nursing Home
584 Elberon Ave, Cincinnati, OH, 45205 (513) 251-0367
Medical Dir/Dir of Nursing Morris Plotnick MD.
Licensure Skilled Care; Intermediate Care.
Beds 48. *Certified* Medicaid; Medicare.
Ownership Proprietary.
Admissions Requirements Minimum age 18; Medical examination.
Staff Physicians 6 (pt); RNs 5 (ft); LPNs 1 (ft), 3 (pt); Nurses aides 11 (ft), 3 (pt); Physical therapists 1 (pt); Occupational therapists; Speech therapists; Activities coordinators; Dietitians; Dentists; Ophthalmologists; Podiatrists; Audiologists.
Facilities Dining room; Activities room; Laundry room; Barber/Beauty shop.
Activities Cards; Games; Reading groups; Prayer groups; Movies; Dances/Social or cultural gatherings.

Queen City Nursing Home*
400 Forest Ave, Cincinnati, OH, 45229 (513) 961-6452
Licensure Intermediate Care. *Beds* 37. *Certified* Medicaid.
Ownership Proprietary.

Red Haven Nursing Home Inc*
751 Greenwood Ave, Cincinnati, OH, 45229 (513) 751-1157
Licensure Skilled Care; Intermediate Care.
Beds 31. *Certified* Medicaid; Medicare.
Ownership Proprietary.

Restview Nursing Home*
3550 Washington Ave, Cincinnati, OH, 45229 (513) 751-1308
Licensure Intermediate Care. *Beds* 44. *Certified* Medicaid.
Ownership Proprietary.

Riverview Home*
5999 Bender Rd, Cincinnati, OH, 45233 (513) 922-1440
Licensure Skilled Care; Intermediate Care; Rest Home. *Beds* 146. *Certified* Medicaid; Medicare.
Ownership Nonprofit.

St Joseph Infant Home*
10722 Wyscarver Rd, Cincinnati, OH, 45241
Licensure Intermediate Care for Mentally Retarded. *Beds* 32. *Certified* Medicaid.
Ownership Nonprofit.

Saint Lawrence Nursing Home
1003 Seton Ave, Cincinnati, OH, 45205 (513) 921-8363
Licensure Intermediate Care. *Beds* 20. *Certified* Medicaid.
Ownership Proprietary.

Saint Margaret Hall*
1960 Madison Rd, Cincinnati, OH, 45206 (513) 751-5880
Licensure Nursing Home; Rest Home.
Beds Nursing Home 99; Rest Home 52.
Ownership Nonprofit.

Saint Theresa Home
6760 Belkenton Ave, Cincinnati, OH, 45236 (513) 891-1090
Licensure Nursing Home; Rest Home.
Beds Nursing Home 37; Rest Home 65.
Ownership Nonprofit.
Staff Physicians 2 (pt); RNs 1 (ft); LPNs 6 (pt); Nurses aides 38 (ft); Dietitians 1 (pt).
Activities Arts and Crafts; Cards; Games; Reading groups; Prayer groups; Movies; Shopping trips; Dances/Social or cultural gatherings.

Salem Park Nursing Home
6128 Salem Rd, Cincinnati, OH, 45230 (513) 231-8292
Medical Dir/Dir of Nursing John Cardosi MD.
Licensure Skilled Care; Intermediate Care.
Beds 107. *Certified* Medicaid; Medicare.
Ownership Proprietary.
Staff Physicians 14 (pt); RNs 7 (ft), 2 (pt); LPNs 4 (ft), 3 (pt); Nurses aides 35 (ft), 6 (pt); Physical therapists 1 (ft), 1 (pt); Recreational therapists 1 (ft); Activities coordinators 1 (ft); Dietitians 1 (ft); Dentists 1 (pt); Ophthalmologists 1 (pt); Podiatrists 1 (pt); Audiologists 1 (pt).
Facilities Dining room; Physical therapy room; Activities room; Crafts room; Laundry room; Barber/Beauty shop.
Activities Arts and Crafts; Cards; Games; Reading groups; Prayer groups; Movies; Shopping trips; Dances/Social or cultural gatherings.
Description Facility provides daily physical therapy; activity program is very good; residents enjoy bingo, many religious programs, bowling, and movies; reality orientation program for all residents; a friendly happy facility.

Summit Nursing and Convalescent Home Inc
2586 Lafeuille Ave, Cincinnati, OH, 45211 (513) 662-2444
Medical Dir/Dir of Nursing Manuel Mediodia MD.
Licensure Skilled Care; Intermediate Care.
Beds 91. *Certified* Medicaid; Medicare.
Ownership Proprietary.
Admissions Requirements Minimum age 40.
Facilities Dining room; Physical therapy room; Activities room; Crafts room; Laundry room; Barber/Beauty shop.
Activities Arts and Crafts; Cards; Games; Reading groups; Prayer groups; Movies; Shopping trips; Dances/Social or cultural gatherings.
Description Summit Nursing and Convalescent Home is located on beautifully landscaped grounds with outside patio. Patient's rooms are spacious and dining rooms and lounges are tastefully decorated.

Three Rivers Convalescent Center*
7800 Jandaracres Dr, Cincinnati, OH, 45211 (513) 941-0787
Licensure Skilled Care; Intermediate Care.
Beds 160. *Certified* Medicaid; Medicare.
Ownership Proprietary.

Twin Towers, The United Methodist Home on College Hill
5343-5353 Hamilton Ave, Cincinnati, OH, 45224 (513) 681-2440
Medical Dir/Dir of Nursing Kenneth A Frederick MD.
Licensure Nursing Home. *Beds* 136.
Ownership Nonprofit.
Admissions Requirements Minimum age 65; Medical examination.
Staff Physicians 2 (pt); RNs 10 (ft), 4 (pt); LPNs 13 (ft), 6 (pt); Orderlies 4 (ft), 1 (pt); Nurses aides 29 (ft), 20 (pt); Physical therapists 1 (pt); Occupational therapists 1 (pt); Speech therapists; Activities coordinators 1 (ft); Dietitians 1 (ft); Dentists; Podiatrists; Audiologists.
Affiliation Methodist
Facilities Dining room; Physical therapy room; Activities room; Chapel; Crafts room; Laundry room; Barber/Beauty shop; Library; Post Office.
Activities Arts and Crafts; Cards; Games; Reading groups; Prayer groups; Movies; Shopping trips; Dances/Social or cultural gatherings; Voting polls.
Description Multilevel care includes independent, assisted living, and intermediate licensed health care; associated with Department of Family Medicine, University of Cincinnati College of Medicine for comprehensive medical coverage.

The Washington*
3615 Washington Ave, Cincinnati, OH, 45229 (513) 751-5223
Licensure Skilled Care; Intermediate Care.
Beds 55. *Certified* Medicaid; Medicare.
Ownership Proprietary.

Wesley Hall Inc
315 Lilienthal St, Cincinnati, OH, 45204 (513) 471-8667
Medical Dir/Dir of Nursing Dr George Shields.
Licensure Intermediate Care. *Beds* 128. *Certified* Medicaid.
Ownership Nonprofit.
Staff Physicians 1 (pt); RNs 5 (ft); LPNs 15 (ft); Orderlies 1 (ft); Nurses aides 56 (ft); Physical therapists 2 (ft); Occupational therapists 1 (pt); Activities coordinators 3 (ft); Dietitians 19 (ft); Podiatrists 1 (pt).
Affiliation Methodist
Facilities Dining room; Physical therapy room; Activities room; Chapel; Crafts room; Laundry room; Barber/Beauty shop.
Activities Arts and Crafts; Cards; Games; Prayer groups; Dances/Social or cultural gatherings.
Description The building we are in is 2 years old. We house 128 residents and offer a large variety of services and activities. We accept only those elderly who are approved for Medicaid.

West Hills Nursing Home Inc*
2841 Harrison Ave, Cincinnati, OH, 45211 (513) 481-4555
Licensure Skilled Care; Intermediate Care.
Beds 46. *Certified* Medicaid; Medicare.
Ownership Nonprofit.

West Park Villa Health Care Center*
One Hegry Court, Cincinnati, OH, 45238
Licensure Skilled Care; Intermediate Care.
Beds 100. *Certified* Medicaid; Medicare.
Ownership Proprietary.

West Side Health Care Center*
1857 Grand Ave, Cincinnati, OH, 45214 (513) 921-4281
Licensure Skilled Care; Intermediate Care.
Beds 69. *Certified* Medicaid; Medicare.
Ownership Proprietary.

Windsor Park Nursing Home Inc*
2245 Park Ave, Cincinnati, OH, 45206 (513) 861-1300
Licensure Skilled Care; Intermediate Care.
Beds 49. *Certified* Medicaid; Medicare.
Ownership Proprietary.

Zion Nursing Home Inc*
3610 Washington Ave, Cincinnati, OH, 45229 (513) 221-2775
Licensure Intermediate Care. *Beds* 50. *Certified* Medicaid.
Ownership Nonprofit.

CIRCLEVILLE

Brown Memorial Home Inc
158 E Mound St, Circleville, OH, 43113 (614) 474-6065
Licensure Intermediate Care. *Beds* 32. *Certified* Medicaid.
Ownership Nonprofit.
Admissions Requirements Medical examination.
Staff RNs 1 (ft), 2 (pt); LPNs 5 (ft), 3 (pt); Nurses aides 18 (ft), 8 (pt); Activities coordinators 1 (ft).
Facilities Dining room; Activities room; Laundry room.
Activities Arts and Crafts; Cards; Games; Reading groups; Prayer groups; Movies; Shopping trips; Dances/Social or cultural gatherings.
Description Facility reflects best of past, present, and future, in its structure; excellent caring staff with a 1:8 ratio; home-style cooking.

Circleville Health Care Center*
1155 Atwater Ave, Circleville, OH, 43113 (614) 477-1695
Licensure Skilled Care; Intermediate Care.
Beds 100. *Certified* Medicaid; Medicare.
Ownership Proprietary.

Circleville Manor
370 Tarlton Rd, Circleville, OH, 43113 (614) 474-3121
Medical Dir/Dir of Nursing R L Sliwinski DO.
Licensure Skilled Care; Intermediate Care.
Beds 101. *Certified* Medicaid; Medicare.
Ownership Proprietary.
Admissions Requirements Medical examination; Physician's request.
Staff Physicians 1 (pt); RNs 3 (ft), 2 (pt); LPNs 9 (ft), 5 (pt); Orderlies 1 (ft); Nurses aides 29 (ft), 2 (pt); Physical therapists 1 (ft); Occupational therapists 1 (pt); Speech therapists 1 (pt); Activities coordinators 1 (ft); Dietitians 1 (pt); Dentists 1 (pt); Ophthalmologists 1 (pt); Podiatrists 1 (pt); Audiologists 1 (pt).
Facilities Dining room; Physical therapy room; Activities room; Crafts room; Laundry room; Barber/Beauty shop; Library.
Activities Arts and Crafts; Cards; Games; Reading groups; Prayer groups; Movies; Shopping trips; Dances/Social or cultural gatherings.
Description Facility has open visiting hours.

Pickaway Manor Inc
391 Clark Dr, Circleville, OH, 43113
Licensure Skilled Care; Intermediate Care.
Beds 100. *Certified* Medicaid; Medicare.
Ownership Proprietary.
Admissions Requirements Physician's request.
Staff RNs 7 (ft); LPNs 7 (ft); Orderlies 2 (ft); Nurses aides 24 (ft); Physical therapists 1 (ft); Reality therapists 1 (ft); Recreational therapists 1 (ft); Occupational therapists 1 (ft); Speech therapists 1 (ft); Activities coordinators 1 (ft); Dietitians 1 (ft); Podiatrists 1 (ft).

Facilities Dining room; Physical therapy room; Activities room; Chapel; Crafts room; Laundry room; Barber/Beauty shop; Library.
Activities Arts and Crafts; Cards; Games; Reading groups; Prayer groups; Movies; Shopping trips; Dances/Social or cultural gatherings.
Description Facility has just added 25 new beds in new addition along with beautiful lounge, living room, and activities room.

CLARKSBURG

Walnut Manor Care Center*
PO Box 158, 11017 Main St, Clarksburg, OH, 43115 (614) 893-4201
Licensure Intermediate Care. *Beds* 22. *Certified* Medicaid.
Ownership Proprietary.

CLEVELAND

Abbey Nursing Home
8205 Euclid Ave, Cleveland, OH, 44103 (216) 421-8580
Medical Dir/Dir of Nursing Bryan Grotte MD.
Licensure Nursing Home. *Beds* 299.
Ownership Proprietary.
Admissions Requirements Minimum age 20; Medical examination; Physician's request.
Staff Physicians 4 (pt); RNs 5 (ft), 2 (pt); LPNs 20 (ft); Nurses aides 100 (ft); Physical therapists 1 (ft); Recreational therapists 7 (ft); Occupational therapists 1 (ft); Activities coordinators 1 (ft); Dietitians 1 (pt).
Facilities Dining room; Physical therapy room; Activities room; Crafts room; Laundry room; Barber/Beauty shop; Library.
Activities Arts and Crafts; Cards; Games; Reading groups; Prayer groups; Movies; Shopping trips.
Description Although an old building in the inner city, the dedicated employees give excellent care to the mostly happy patients.

Algart Health Care Inc*
8902 Detroit Ave, Cleveland, OH, 44102 (216) 631-1550
Licensure Intermediate Care. *Beds* 50. *Certified* Medicaid.
Ownership Proprietary.

Amasa Stone House*
975 East Blvd, Cleveland, OH, 44108 (216) 451-1884
Licensure Intermediate Care. *Beds* 50. *Certified* Medicaid.
Ownership Nonprofit.

Americana Healthcare Center at Lake Shore*
16101 Lake Shore Blvd, Cleveland, OH, 44110 (216) 486-2300
Licensure Skilled Care; Intermediate Care.
Beds 202. *Certified* Medicaid; Medicare.
Ownership Proprietary.

Aristocrat West*
4387 W 150th St, Cleveland, OH, 44135 (216) 252-7730
Licensure Skilled Care; Intermediate Care; Intermediate Care for Mentally Retarded.

Beds SNF 84; ICF 59. *Certified* Medicaid; Medicare.
Ownership Proprietary.

Baldwin Manor Nursing Home Inc
2437 Baldwin Rd, Cleveland, OH, 44104 (216) 229-4800
Medical Dir/Dir of Nursing Jon M Rainey MD.
Licensure Intermediate Care. *Beds* 50. *Certified* Medicaid.
Ownership Proprietary.
Admissions Requirements Medical examination.
Staff Physicians 1 (pt); RNs 2 (ft), 1 (pt); LPNs 6 (ft); Nurses aides 16 (ft), 3 (pt); Physical therapists 1 (pt); Reality therapists 1 (pt); Recreational therapists 1 (pt); Occupational therapists 1 (pt); Activities coordinators 1 (ft); Dietitians 1 (pt).
Facilities Dining room; Physical therapy room; Activities room; Chapel; Crafts room; Laundry room; Barber/Beauty shop; Library.
Activities Arts and Crafts; Cards; Games; Reading groups; Prayer groups; Movies; Shopping trips; Dances/Social or cultural gatherings.

Carnegie Care Center*
8800 Carnegie Ave, Cleveland, OH, 44106
Licensure Intermediate Care. *Beds* 211. *Certified* Medicaid.
Ownership Proprietary.

Cleveland Golden Age Nursing Home*
928 E 152nd St, Cleveland, OH, 44110 (216) 761-3000
Licensure Intermediate Care. *Beds* 100. *Certified* Medicaid.
Ownership Proprietary.

Concord Manor Nursing Home
1877 E 82nd St, Cleveland, OH, 44103 (216) 795-6110
Medical Dir/Dir of Nursing Dr Navnvich.
Licensure Intermediate Care. *Beds* 34. *Certified* Medicaid.
Ownership Proprietary.
Admissions Requirements Medical examination; Physician's request.
Staff Physicians 1 (pt); RNs 1 (pt); LPNs 2 (ft), 2 (pt); Orderlies 1 (ft); Nurses aides 11 (ft); Activities coordinators 1 (pt); Dietitians 1 (pt); Dentists 1 (pt); Ophthalmologists 1 (pt); Podiatrists 1 (pt).
Facilities Dining room; Activities room; Laundry room.
Activities Arts and Crafts; Cards; Games; Prayer groups; Movies; Shopping trips.

Crestmont Nursing Home Inc*
12709 Bellaire Rd, Cleveland, OH, 44135 (216) 941-4545
Licensure Intermediate Care. *Beds* 28. *Certified* Medicaid.
Ownership Proprietary.

Cuyahoga County Nursing Home*
3305 Franklin Blvd, Cleveland, OH, 44113 (216) 961-4344
Licensure Intermediate Care. *Beds* 177. *Certified* Medicaid.
Ownership Public.

Dunbar Nursing Home*
2415 E 55th St, Cleveland, OH, 44104 (216) 391-7100
Licensure Skilled Care; Intermediate Care.
Beds 155. *Certified* Medicaid; Medicare.
Ownership Proprietary.

Eliza Bryant Center*
1380 Addison Rd, Cleveland, OH, 44103 (216) 361-6141
Licensure Intermediate Care. *Beds* 47. *Certified* Medicaid.
Ownership Nonprofit.

Eliza Jennings Home
10603 Detroit Ave, Cleveland, OH, 44102 (216) 226-0282
Licensure Rest Home. *Beds* 58.
Ownership Nonprofit.

Euclid Manor Nursing Home
17322 Euclid Ave, Cleveland, OH, 44112 (216) 486-2280
Medical Dir/Dir of Nursing Nachman Kacen MD.
Licensure Skilled Care; Intermediate Care.
Beds 174. *Certified* Medicaid; Medicare.
Ownership Proprietary.
Staff Physicians; RNs; LPNs; Orderlies; Nurses aides; Physical therapists; Occupational therapists; Activities coordinators; Dietitians; Dentists; Podiatrists.
Facilities Dining room; Physical therapy room; Activities room; Crafts room; Laundry room; Barber/Beauty shop; Library.
Activities Arts and Crafts; Cards; Games; Reading groups; Prayer groups; Movies; Shopping trips.
Description Euclid Manor is a progressive long-term care facility setting the trend as a home for those in need of skilled nursing care along with a therapeutic rehabilitation program and an excellent program of supportive services individually designed to meet each resident's needs.

Forest Hills Nursing Home Inc*
736 Lakeview Rd, Cleveland, OH, 44108 (216) 268-3800
Licensure Skilled Care; Intermediate Care.
Beds 252. *Certified* Medicaid; Medicare.
Ownership Proprietary.

Franklin Plaza
3600 Franklin Blvd, Cleveland, OH, 44113 (216) 651-1600
Medical Dir/Dir of Nursing Dr Thomas Burney.
Licensure Skilled Care; Intermediate Care.
Beds 218. *Certified* Medicaid; Medicare.
Ownership Proprietary.
Admissions Requirements Medical examination.
Staff Physicians 35 (pt); RNs 12 (ft); LPNs 33 (ft); Orderlies 8 (ft); Nurses aides 70 (ft); Physical therapists 1 (ft); Reality therapists 1 (ft); Occupational therapists 2 (ft); Speech therapists 1 (pt); Activities coordinators 2 (ft); Dietitians 1 (pt); Dentists 1 (pt); Ophthalmologists 1 (pt); Podiatrists 1 (pt); Audiologists 1 (pt).
Facilities Dining room; Physical therapy room; Activities room; Laundry room; Barber/Beauty shop.

Activities Arts and Crafts; Cards; Games; Reading groups; Movies; Dances/Social or cultural gatherings.

Geri-Care Inc
2438 Mapleside Rd, Cleveland, OH, 44104 (216) 229-9600
Medical Dir/Dir of Nursing Robert Kurzbauer MD.
Licensure Intermediate Care. *Beds* 36. *Certified* Medicaid.
Ownership Proprietary.
Admissions Requirements Medical examination.
Staff RNs 1 (pt); LPNs 5 (ft); Orderlies 1 (ft); Nurses aides 10 (ft); Physical therapists 1 (pt); Occupational therapists 1 (pt); Activities coordinators 1 (ft); Dietitians 1 (pt).
Facilities Dining room; Activities room; Crafts room; Laundry room.
Activities Arts and Crafts; Cards; Games; Reading groups; Prayer groups; Movies; Shopping trips; Dances/Social or cultural gatherings.

Inner City Nursing Home Inc*
9014 Cedar Ave, Cleveland, OH, 44106 (216) 795-1363
Licensure Intermediate Care. *Beds* 51. *Certified* Medicaid.
Ownership Proprietary.

Jones Nursing Home
8017 Jones Rd, Cleveland, OH, 44105 (216) 641-3712
Medical Dir/Dir of Nursing I Weber MD.
Licensure Skilled Care; Intermediate Care. *Beds* 42. *Certified* Medicaid; Medicare.
Ownership Proprietary.
Admissions Requirements Medical examination.
Staff RNs 2 (ft), 1 (pt); LPNs 2 (ft), 2 (pt); Nurses aides 11 (ft), 2 (pt); Physical therapists 1 (pt); Activities coordinators 1 (ft), 1 (pt).
Facilities Dining room; Physical therapy room; Activities room; Chapel; Crafts room; Library.
Activities Arts and Crafts; Cards; Games; Reading groups; Prayer groups; Movies; Dances/Social or cultural gatherings; Entertainment/shows.
Description Quaint neighborhood facility serving Cuyahoga County's southeast suburbs and the Slavic Village area of Cleveland.

Judson Park*
1801 Chestnut Hills Dr, Cleveland, OH, 44106 (216) 721-1234
Licensure Intermediate Care; Rest Home. *Beds* ICF 80; Rest Home 12. *Certified* Medicaid.
Ownership Nonprofit.

Laub Pavillion of Cleveland Ohio
10603 Detroit Ave, Cleveland, OH, 44102 (216) 226-0282
Licensure Skilled Care; Intermediate Care. *Beds* 131. *Certified* Medicaid; Medicare.
Ownership Nonprofit.

Little Sisters of the Poor
4291 Richmond Rd, Cleveland, OH, 44122 (216) 464-1222
Admin Sr Regis. *Medical Dir/Dir of Nursing* Dr Yalcin Dinceman.

Licensure Intermediate Care; Rest Home; Independent Living. *Beds* ICF 99; Rest Home 31; Independent Living 21. *Certified* Medicaid.
Ownership Nonprofit.
Admissions Requirements Medical examination.
Staff RNs 5 (ft), 11 (pt); LPNs 7 (ft), 6 (pt); Nurses aides 36 (ft), 11 (pt); Physical therapists 1 (pt); Activities coordinators 1 (ft); Dietitians 1 (pt).
Affiliation Roman Catholic
Facilities Dining room; Physical therapy room; Activities room; Chapel; Crafts room; Laundry room; Barber/Beauty shop; Library.
Activities Arts and Crafts; Cards; Games; Reading groups; Prayer groups; Movies; Shopping trips; Dances/Social or cultural gatherings; Social service counseling.

Madonna Hall
1906 E 82nd St, Cleveland, OH, 44103 (216) 421-5660
Admin Howard B Bram. *Medical Dir/Dir of Nursing* Pamala Murphy MD.
Licensure Intermediate Care. *Beds* 99. *Certified* Medicaid.
Ownership Nonprofit.
Admissions Requirements Minimum age 60; Medical examination.
Staff RNs 1 (ft), 1 (pt); LPNs 6 (ft), 4 (pt); Orderlies 2 (ft); Nurses aides 23 (ft); Activities coordinators 2 (ft).
Affiliation Roman Catholic
Facilities Dining room; Physical therapy room; Activities room; Chapel; Crafts room; Laundry room.
Activities Arts and Crafts; Cards; Games; Movies; Shopping trips; Dances/Social or cultural gatherings.

Manor Care Nursing Center—Rocky River
4102 Rocky River Dr, Cleveland, OH, 44135 (216) 251-3300
Admin Thomas A Armagno. *Medical Dir/Dir of Nursing* Javier Clemente MD.
Licensure Skilled Care; Intermediate Care. *Beds* 210. *Certified* Medicaid; Medicare.
Ownership Proprietary.
Admissions Requirements Medical examination.
Staff Physicians 2 (pt); RNs 8 (ft), 9 (pt); LPNs 13 (ft), 11 (pt); Orderlies 3 (ft), 2 (pt); Nurses aides 50 (ft), 32 (pt); Physical therapists 1 (ft), 3 (pt); Reality therapists 1 (ft); Recreational therapists 1 (ft); Occupational therapists 2 (ft), 1 (pt); Speech therapists 1 (ft); Activities coordinators 1 (ft); Dietitians 1 (pt); Dentists 1 (pt); Ophthalmologists 1 (pt); Podiatrists 1 (pt); Audiologists 1 (pt).
Facilities Dining room; Physical therapy room; Activities room; Chapel; Crafts room; Laundry room; Barber/Beauty shop; Library; Patio.
Activities Arts and Crafts; Cards; Games; Reading groups; Prayer groups; Movies; Shopping trips; Dances/Social or cultural gatherings; Field trips.
Description Facility has an excellent rehabilitation therapy program with a full-time licensed physical therapist and 2 full-time licensed occupational therapists on staff.

Marietta Manor
694 E 109th St, Cleveland, OH, 44108 (216) 851-7100
Medical Dir/Dir of Nursing Dr Naunovich.
Licensure Nursing Home. *Beds* 15.
Ownership Proprietary.
Admissions Requirements Females only
Staff Physicians 1 (ft); RNs 1 (ft); LPNs 4 (ft), 2 (pt); Orderlies 1 (ft); Nurses aides 8 (ft), 2 (pt); Activities coordinators 1 (ft); Dietitians 1 (ft); Dentists 1 (ft); Podiatrists 1 (ft).
Affiliation Presbyterian
Facilities Dining room; Activities room; Laundry room.
Activities Arts and Crafts; Games; Prayer groups; Shopping trips.
Description Patients and activities coordinator have established a residents' council and a newsletter with the patients being in charge of both.

Mary Louise Nursing Home*
670 Lakeview Rd, Cleveland, OH, 44108
Licensure Intermediate Care. *Beds* 11. *Certified* Medicaid.
Ownership Proprietary.

Medicare Nursing Homes Inc*
18220 Euclid Ave, Cleveland, OH, 44112 (216) 486-6300
Licensure Skilled Care; Intermediate Care. *Beds* 50. *Certified* Medicaid; Medicare.
Ownership Proprietary.

Mount Pleasant Nursing Home
10406 Kinsman Rd, Cleveland, OH, 44104 (216) 271-0073
Medical Dir/Dir of Nursing Dr Naunovich.
Licensure Intermediate Care. *Beds* 33. *Certified* Medicaid.
Ownership Proprietary.
Staff Physicians 1 (ft); RNs 1 (ft); LPNs 5 (ft), 4 (pt); Orderlies 1 (ft); Nurses aides 10 (ft), 5 (pt); Activities coordinators 1 (ft); Dietitians 1 (ft); Dentists 1 (ft); Podiatrists 1 (ft).
Affiliation Presbyterian
Facilities Dining room; Activities room; Laundry room.
Activities Arts and Crafts; Cards; Games; Prayer groups; Shopping trips.
Description Facility encourages residents' participation, which includes resident council and newspaper.

Northeast Ohio Development Center
4445 Turney Rd, Cleveland, OH, 44105 (216) 441-6200
Licensure Intermediate Care for Mentally Retarded. *Beds* 142.
Ownership Public.

Overlook House
2187 Overlook Rd, Cleveland, OH, 44106 (216) 795-3550
Licensure Nursing Home. *Beds* 33.
Ownership Nonprofit.
Affiliation Christian Science
Facilities Dining room; Activities room; Chapel; Laundry room; Barber/Beauty shop; Library.
Activities Reading groups; Prayer groups; Movies; Dances/Social or cultural gatherings.

Parent's Volunteer Association*
17608 Euclid Ave, Cleveland, OH, 44112 (216)
481-1907
Licensure Intermediate Care for Mentally
Retarded. *Beds* 72.
Ownership Nonprofit.

Prospect Manor*
3912 Prospect Ave, Cleveland, OH, 44115
(216) 361-6655
Licensure Intermediate Care. *Beds* 50. *Certi-fied* Medicaid.
Ownership Proprietary.

Rae-Ann Nursing Center*
18223 Rockland Ave, Cleveland, OH, 44135
(216) 267-5445
Licensure Intermediate Care. *Beds* 28. *Certi-fied* Medicaid.
Ownership Proprietary.

**Rose Park Convalescent and Rehabilitation
Center***
18810 Harvard Ave, Cleveland, OH, 44122
(216) 752-3600
Licensure Skilled Care; Intermediate Care.
Beds 84. *Certified* Medicaid; Medicare.
Ownership Proprietary.

Saint Augustine Manor*
7818 Detroit Ave, Cleveland, OH, 44102 (216)
651-3680
Licensure Skilled Care; Intermediate Care.
Beds 194. *Certified* Medicaid; Medicare.
Ownership Nonprofit.

Singleton Health Care Center*
1867 E 82nd St, Cleveland, OH, 44103 (216)
231-8467
Licensure Intermediate Care. *Beds* 50. *Certi-fied* Medicaid.
Ownership Proprietary.

Slovene Home for the Aged*
18621 Neff Rd, Cleveland, OH, 44119 (216)
486-0268
Licensure Skilled Care; Intermediate Care.
Beds 150. *Certified* Medicaid; Medicare.
Ownership Nonprofit.

Sunset Nursing Home*
1802 Crawford Rd, Cleveland, OH, 44106
(216) 795-5710
Licensure Intermediate Care. *Beds* 15. *Certi-fied* Medicaid.
Ownership Proprietary.

**United Cerebral Palsy Association Home of
Cuyahoga County***
2803 E Boulevard, Cleveland, OH, 44106
Licensure Intermediate Care for Mentally
Retarded. *Beds* 10. *Certified* Medicaid.
Ownership Nonprofit.

Valley Springs Health Center*
18120 Puritas Rd, Cleveland, OH, 44135 (216)
252-5500
Licensure Skilled Care. *Beds* 171. *Cer-tified* Medicare.
Ownership Proprietary.

Villa Care Center
4835 Broadview Rd, Cleveland, OH, 44109
(216) 749-4939
Admin Warren Wolfson. *Medical Dir/Dir of
Nursing* M T Sheth MD.
Licensure Intermediate Care. *Beds* 50. *Certi-fied* Medicaid.
Ownership Proprietary.
Admissions Requirements Minimum age 30;
Medical examination.
Staff Physicians 2 (pt); RNs 3 (ft), 1 (pt); LPNs
1 (ft), 2 (pt); Nurses aides 25 (ft); Physical thera-pists 1 (pt); Reality therapists 1 (pt); Activities
coordinators 2 (ft); Dietitians 1 (pt); Dentists 1
(pt); Podiatrists 1 (pt).
Facilities Dining room; Activities room; Crafts
room; Laundry room; Barber/Beauty shop.
Activities Arts and Crafts; Cards; Games;
Reading groups; Prayer groups; Movies; Shop-ping trips; Dances/Social or cultural gatherings.
Description Award winning nursing home pro-vides superior nursing services and a caring
social milieu. Restorative nursing and stimu-lating activities programs are designed to
maximize the quality of life for residents.

Villa Sancta Anna Home for the Aged
25000 Chagrin Blvd, Cleveland, OH, 44122
(216) 464-9250
Admin Sr Mary Elizabeth Ann Rechka.
Medical Dir/Dir of Nursing Dr Sylvia Mar-shall.
Licensure Intermediate Care. *Beds* 50. *Certi-fied* Medicaid.
Ownership Nonprofit.
Admissions Requirements Minimum age 65;
Medical examination.
Staff Physicians 1 (pt); RNs 3 (pt); LPNs 6 (ft);
Nurses aides 14 (ft), 8 (pt); Physical therapists 1
(pt); Activities coordinators 1 (pt); Dietitians 1
(pt); Dentists 1 (pt); Podiatrists 2 (pt).
Affiliation Roman Catholic
Facilities Dining room; Physical therapy room;
Activities room; Chapel; Crafts room; Laundry
room; Laundry room; Library; Examination
room; Sewing room; Solariums.
Activities Arts and Crafts; Cards; Prayer
groups; Movies; Shopping trips; Dances/Social
or cultural gatherings; Bible study.
Description Chapel with daily liturgy and daily
devotions; resident Catholic chaplain; craft
room with daily activities; grounds for resi-dents to tour and enjoy; enclosed patio for diso-riented residents; semi-private rooms with
shared bath; TV with 72" screen in recreation
room.

CLEVELAND HEIGHTS

Margaret Wagner House
2373 Euclid Hgts Blvd, Cleveland Heights, OH,
44104 (216) 795-5450
Medical Dir/Dir of Nursing George Gelehrter
MD.
Licensure Skilled Care; Intermediate Care.
Beds 175. *Certified* Medicaid; Medicare.
Ownership Nonprofit.
Admissions Requirements Minimum age 60;
Medical examination; Physician's request.
Staff Physicians; RNs; LPNs; Nurses aides;
Physical therapists; Reality therapists; Recrea-tional therapists; Occupational therapists;

Activities coordinators; Dietitians.
Facilities Dining room; Physical therapy room;
Activities room; Chapel; Crafts room; Laundry
room; Barber/Beauty shop; Dentist and podia-trist offices.
Activities Arts and Crafts; Cards; Games;
Reading groups; Prayer groups; Movies; Shop-ping trips; Dances/Social or cultural gatherings.
Description Home is a short-term and long-term facility maintaining a home-like atmos-phere.

Montefiore Home*
3151 Mayfield Rd, Cleveland Heights, OH,
44118 (216) 371-5500
Licensure Skilled Care; Intermediate Care.
Beds 174. *Certified* Medicaid; Medicare.
Ownership Nonprofit.

Rose Nursing Home
2435 W Saint James Pkwy, Cleveland Heights,
OH, 44118 (216) 229-2984
Licensure Nursing Home. *Beds* 22.
Ownership Proprietary.
Admissions Requirements Medical examina-tion.
Staff Physicians 1 (pt); LPNs 3 (ft), 3 (pt);
Nurses aides 5 (ft); Dietitians 1 (pt); Dentists 1
(pt); Podiatrists 1 (pt).
Facilities Laundry room.
Description Home is small; patients receive
good care, home-made meals, and lots of tend-er love.

Whitecliff Manor Nursing Home*
12504 Cedar Rd, Cleveland Heights, OH,
44106 (216) 371-3600
Licensure Skilled Care; Intermediate Care.
Beds 116. *Certified* Medicaid; Medicare.
Ownership Proprietary.

CLEVES

Miami Haven*
5485 State Rt 128, Cleves, OH, 45002 (513)
353-1334
Licensure Intermediate Care. *Beds* 29. *Certi-fied* Medicaid.
Ownership Proprietary.

CLINTON

Rafferty's Nursing Home*
7055 S Cleveland-Massillon Rd, Clinton, OH,
44216 (216) 882-6349
Licensure Intermediate Care. *Beds* 30. *Certi-fied* Medicaid.
Ownership Proprietary.

CLOVERDALE

Paradise Oaks Quality Care Nursing Center*
PO Box 98, Main St, Cloverdale, OH, 45827
(419) 488-3911
Licensure Skilled Care; Intermediate Care.
Beds 100. *Certified* Medicaid; Medicare.
Ownership Proprietary.

CLYDE

Buckeye Nursing Home*
234 W Buckeye St, Clyde, OH, 43410 (419)
547-0711
Licensure Intermediate Care. *Beds* 25. *Certified* Medicaid.
Ownership Proprietary.

Eshelman Nursing Home Inc*
700 Helen St, Clyde, OH, 43410 (419)
547-9595
Licensure Intermediate Care. *Beds* 100. *Certified* Medicaid.
Ownership Proprietary.

Hospitality Nursing Home*
167 E Forest St, Clyde, OH, 43410 (419)
547-0764
Licensure Intermediate Care. *Beds* 21. *Certified* Medicaid.
Ownership Proprietary.

COLDWATER

Briarwood Manor*
W Main St, Coldwater, OH, 45828 (419)
678-2311
Licensure Skilled Care; Intermediate Care.
Beds 100. *Certified* Medicaid; Medicare.
Ownership Proprietary.

COLUMBIA STATION

The Villa Camillus*
10515 E River Rd, Columbia Station, OH,
44028
Licensure Skilled Care. *Beds* 50. *Certified* Medicaid.
Ownership Proprietary.

COLUMBUS

Alum Crest
1599 Alum Creek Dr, Columbus, OH, 43207
(614) 445-8261
Medical Dir/Dir of Nursing Dr Harry Topolosky.
Licensure Skilled Care; Intermediate Care.
Beds 275. *Certified* Medicaid; Medicare.
Ownership Public.
Staff Physicians 1 (ft), 4 (pt); RNs 10 (ft), 5
(pt); LPNs 28 (ft), 6 (pt); Orderlies 22 (ft), 5
(pt); Nurses aides 103 (ft), 24 (pt); Physical
therapists 1 (ft), 1 (pt); Recreational therapists 1
(ft); Occupational therapists 1 (ft); Activities
coordinators 1 (ft); Dietitians 1 (ft), 1 (pt); Dentists 1 (pt); Podiatrists 1 (pt).
Facilities Dining room; Physical therapy room;
Activities room; Chapel; Crafts room; Laundry
room; Barber/Beauty shop; Library.
Activities Arts and Crafts; Cards; Games;
Reading groups; Prayer groups; Movies; Shopping trips; Dances/Social or cultural gatherings;
Occupational therapy.
Description Alum Crest has been actively
serving the public from the same location for
over 100 years; recent construction and programs make it the largest nursing home in the
central Ohio area.

Arlington Court Nursing Home*
1605 NW Professional Plaza, Columbus, OH,
43220 (614) 451-5677
Licensure Nursing Home. *Beds* 120.
Ownership Proprietary.

Avis House MR Unit*
624 S Ohio Ave, Columbus, OH, 43205
Licensure Intermediate Care for Mentally
Retarded. *Beds* 15. *Certified* Medicaid.
Ownership Nonprofit.

Bescare Nursing Home
1288 Bryden Rd, Columbus, OH, 43205 (614)
258-6371
Medical Dir/Dir of Nursing Max Kanter MD.
Licensure Intermediate Care. *Beds* 17. *Certified* Medicaid.
Ownership Proprietary.
Staff RNs; LPNs 1 (ft), 3 (pt); Nurses aides 6
(ft), 2 (pt); Recreational therapists 1 (pt); Activities coordinators 1 (ft); Dietitians 1 (pt).
Facilities Dining room; Activities room; Laundry room.
Activities Arts and Crafts; Cards; Games;
Movies; Shopping trips; Dances/Social or cultural gatherings.
Description Facility features a small, home-like
atmosphere (only 17 beds).

Bon-Ing Inc
173 Woodland Ave, Columbus, OH, 43203
(614) 475-2222
Licensure Intermediate Care. *Beds* 26. *Certified* Medicaid.
Ownership Proprietary.

Bryden Manor*
1138 Bryden Rd, Columbus, OH, 43205 (614)
252-4727
Licensure Intermediate Care. *Beds* 34. *Certified* Medicaid.
Ownership Proprietary.

Christian Home for the Aged*
PO Box 03605, 1454 Eastwood Ave, Columbus, OH, 43203 (614) 258-2769
Licensure Intermediate Care. *Beds* 14.
Certified Medicaid.
Ownership Proprietary.

Clearview Convalescent Center*
2120 E 5th Ave, Columbus, OH, 43219 (614)
258-8437
Licensure Skilled Care; Intermediate Care.
Beds 93. *Certified* Medicaid; Medicare.
Ownership Proprietary.

Columbus Developmental Center*
1601 W Broad St, Columbus, OH, 43223 (614)
272-0509
Licensure Intermediate Care for Mentally
Retarded. *Beds* 509. *Certified* Medicaid.
Ownership Public.

Columbus Home for the Aged
1776 E Broad St, Columbus, OH, 43203
Licensure Home for the Aged. *Beds* 64.
Ownership Nonprofit.

Columbus Nursing Homes Inc*
1169 Bryden Rd, Columbus, OH, 43205 (614)
258-6623

Licensure Skilled Care; Intermediate Care.
Beds 147. *Certified* Medicaid; Medicare.
Ownership Proprietary.

Derrer Road ICF/MR*
340 Derrer Rd, Columbus, OH, 43223
Licensure Intermediate Care for Mentally
Retarded. *Beds* 8. *Certified* Medicaid.
Ownership Nonprofit.

East Broad Manor
1243 Broad St, Columbus, OH, 43205 (614)
252-3836
Medical Dir/Dir of Nursing William Conway
MD.
Licensure Intermediate Care. *Beds* 29. *Certified* Medicaid.
Ownership Proprietary.
Admissions Requirements Minimum age 18;
Females only; Medical examination.
Staff Physicians 1 (pt); RNs 1 (ft); LPNs 3 (ft),
5 (pt); Nurses aides 7 (ft), 3 (pt); Physical therapists 1 (pt); Speech therapists 1 (pt); Activities
coordinators 1 (ft); Dietitians 1 (pt); Dentists 1
(pt); Ophthalmologists 1 (pt); Podiatrists 1 (pt);
Audiologists 1 (pt).
Facilities Dining room; Activities room.
Activities Arts and Crafts; Cards; Games; Prayer groups; Movies; Shopping trips; Dances/Social or cultural gatherings; Camping trips.
Description Facility features small home-like
atmosphere; individualized patient care; excellent activities program; special care given to
meals, all prepared at the facility.

Eastland Care Center*
2425 Kimberly Pkwy E, Columbus, OH, 43227
Licensure Skilled Care; Intermediate Care.
Beds SNF 26; ICF 100. *Certified* Medicaid;
Medicare.
Ownership Nonprofit.

First Community Village
1800 Riverside Dr, Columbus, OH, 43212
(614) 486-9511
Medical Dir/Dir of Nursing Steven Lichtblau
MD.
Licensure Skilled Care; Intermediate Care.
Beds 154. *Certified* Medicaid; Medicare.
Ownership Nonprofit.
Admissions Requirements Minimum age 60;
Medical examination; Physician's request.
Staff Physicians 3 (pt); RNs 12 (ft), 17 (pt);
LPNs 7 (ft), 8 (pt); Nurses aides 50 (ft), 33 (pt);
Physical therapists 3 (ft); Recreational therapists
1 (ft); Occupational therapists 1 (pt); Speech
therapists 1 (pt); Activities coordinators 1 (ft);
Dietitians 1 (ft); Podiatrists 1 (pt); Audiologists
1 (pt).
Affiliation First Community Church
Facilities Dining room; Physical therapy room;
Activities room; Crafts room; Laundry room;
Barber/Beauty shop.
Activities Arts and Crafts; Cards; Games;
Reading groups; Prayer groups; Movies; Shopping trips; Dances/Social or cultural gatherings.
Description Facility provides high-quality
nursing care including a special "protected
unit" to serve individuals who are confused,
tend to wander, and others with Alzheimer's
disease.

Friendship Village Health Center
5800 Forest Hills Blvd, Columbus, OH, 43229
(614) 890-8282
Medical Dir/Dir of Nursing John B Krupko
MD.
Licensure Skilled Care; Intermediate Care.
Beds 90. *Certified* Medicaid; Medicare.
Ownership Nonprofit.
Admissions Requirements Minimum age 64;
Medical examination.
Staff Physicians; RNs 5 (ft), 8 (pt); LPNs 6 (ft),
3 (pt); Orderlies 1 (pt); Nurses aides 35 (ft), 12
(pt); Physical therapists 1 (pt); Occupational
therapists; Speech therapists; Activities coordi-
nators 1 (ft), 2 (pt); Dietitians; Dentists;
Ophthalmologists; Podiatrists.
Facilities Dining room; Physical therapy room;
Activities room; Chapel; Crafts room; Laundry
room; Barber/Beauty shop; Library; Bank;
Store; Exercise room; Game room.
Activities Arts and Crafts; Cards; Games; Prayer groups; Movies; Shopping trips; Dances/So-
cial or cultural gatherings.
Description This center offers carefree living
with none of the tedious chores of home ownership; friendships and activities in warm,
comfortable surroundings and the opportunity
for financial and physical security designed for
a retirement lifestyle. Time to enjoy some of the
best years of life in a community of peers who
seek the same quality of life.

Genesis*
4133 Karl Rd, Columbus, OH, 43224
Licensure Intermediate Care for Mentally
Retarded. *Beds* 24. *Certified* Medicaid.
Ownership Nonprofit.

Glenmont
72 Woodland Ave, Columbus, OH, 43203
(614) 253-8561
Licensure Nursing Home. *Beds* 27.
Ownership Nonprofit.
Affiliation Christian Science
Facilities Dining room; Activities room; Chap-
el; Crafts room; Laundry room; Barber/Beauty
shop; Library.
Activities Arts and Crafts; Reading groups;
Prayer groups; Movies; Shopping trips; Dances-
/Social or cultural gatherings.
Description For over 50 years Glenmont has
provided nursing services to those relying on
spiritual healing as taught in science and health
with the key to the scriptures.

Heartland Thurber Village*
920 Thurber Dr W, Columbus, OH, 43215
(614) 464-2273
Licensure Skilled Care; Intermediate Care.
Beds 148. *Certified* Medicaid; Medicare.
Ownership Proprietary.

Heinzerling Developmental Center
1755 Heinzerling Drive, Columbus, OH, 43223
(614) 272-2000
Licensure Intermediate Care for Mentally
Retarded. *Beds* 104.
Ownership Nonprofit; Proprietary.
Admissions Requirements Minimum age 21.
Description The Heinzerling residents are
severely or profoundly mentally retarded,
nonambulatory, and medically involved. They
all require constant care. The Heinzerling staff

is a highly trained, dedicated group of caring
professionals who bring a large measure of love
and personal involvement to their tasks.

**Heritage House-Columbus Jewish Home for
the Aged***
1151 College Ave, Columbus, OH, 43209 (614)
237-7417
Licensure Skilled Care; Intermediate Care.
Beds 146. *Certified* Medicaid; Medicare.
Ownership Nonprofit.
Affiliation Jewish

Isabelle Ridgway Nursing Center*
1520 Hawthorne Ave, Columbus, OH, 43203
(614) 252-4931
Licensure Skilled Care; Intermediate Care.
Beds 100. *Certified* Medicaid; Medicare.
Ownership Nonprofit.

Lutheran Senior City
935 N Cassady Ave, Columbus, OH, 43219
(614) 252-4987
Licensure Skilled Care; Intermediate Care;
Rest Home. *Beds* ICF 135; Rest Home 25.
Certified Medicaid; Medicare.
Ownership Nonprofit.
Affiliation Lutheran

**Margaret Clark Oakfield Convalescent
Center—Columbus***
500 N Nelson Rd, Columbus, OH, 43219 (614)
252-5244
Licensure Intermediate Care. *Beds* 150. *Certified* Medicaid.
Ownership Proprietary.

Mayfair Nursing Care Center
3000 Bethel Rd, Columbus, OH, 43220 (614)
889-6920
Admin Sharon L Reynolds. *Medical Dir/Dir of
Nursing* Charles Twul MD.
Licensure Skilled Care; Intermediate Care.
Beds 100. *Certified* Medicaid; Medicare.
Ownership Proprietary.
Admissions Requirements Minimum age 18;
Medical examination; Physician's request.
Staff Physicians 1 (pt); RNs 6 (ft), 13 (pt);
LPNs 4 (ft); Nurses aides 26 (ft), 12 (pt);
Physical therapists 1 (pt); Reality therapists 1
(ft); Recreational therapists 1 (ft); Occupational
therapists 1 (pt); Speech therapists 1 (pt); Dieti-
tians 1 (pt); Dentists 1 (pt); Ophthalmologists 1
(pt); Podiatrists 1 (pt); Audiologists 1 (pt).
Facilities Dining room; Physical therapy room;
Activities room; Crafts room; Laundry room;
Barber/Beauty shop; Library.
Activities Arts and Crafts; Cards; Games;
Reading groups; Prayer groups; Movies; Shopping trips; Dances/Social or cultural gatherings.
Description This is a life assurance community
providing retirement living, nursing care, and
home care; 31% of the clients are discharged
back into the community.

Minerva Park Place
5460 Cleveland Ave, Columbus, OH, 43229
(614) 882-2490
Admin Suzanne M Lehman. *Medical Dir/Dir
of Nursing* Dr H T Villavecer.
Licensure Intermediate Care. *Beds* 101. *Certified* Medicaid.
Ownership Proprietary.

Admissions Requirements Medical examina-
tion; Physician's request.
Staff Physicians 12 (pt); RNs 4 (ft), 2 (pt);
LPNs 6 (ft), 2 (pt); Nurses aides 27 (ft), 10 (pt);
Activities coordinators 1 (ft), 2 (pt); Dietitians
1 (pt); Dentists; Ophthalmologists; Podiatrists;
Audiologists.
Facilities Dining room; Activities room; Crafts
room; Laundry room; Barber/Beauty shop.
Activities Arts and Crafts; Cards; Games; Pray-
er groups; Movies; Shopping trips; Dances/So-
cial or cultural gatherings.

Mohun Hall Infirmary
Saint Mary of the Springs, Columbus, OH,
43219
Licensure Nursing Home. *Beds* 48.
Ownership Nonprofit.

Monterey Yorkshire Nursing Inn*
1425 Yorkland Rd, Columbus, OH, 43227
(614) 861-6666
Licensure Skilled Care; Intermediate Care.
Beds 200. *Certified* Medicaid; Medicare.
Ownership Proprietary.

Northland Terrace
5700 Karl Rd, Columbus, OH, 43226 (614)
846-5420
Medical Dir/Dir of Nursing Stephen D Shell
MD.
Licensure Skilled Care; Intermediate Care.
Beds 260. *Certified* Medicaid; Medicare.
Ownership Proprietary.
Admissions Requirements Minimum age 16;
Medical examination.
Staff Physicians 1 (pt); RNs 12 (ft), 9 (pt);
LPNs 21 (ft), 4 (pt); Nurses aides 108 (ft), 36
(pt); Physical therapists 1 (ft); Recreational ther-
apists 4 (ft), 2 (pt); Occupational therapists 1
(ft); Speech therapists 1 (pt); Activities coordi-
nators 1 (pt); Dietitians 1 (ft).
Facilities Dining room; Physical therapy room;
Activities room; Crafts room; Laundry room;
Barber/Beauty shop; Library.
Activities Arts and Crafts; Cards; Games;
Reading groups; Prayer groups; Movies; Shopping trips; Dances/Social or cultural gatherings;
Volunteer services.
Description Facility is JCAH accredited and
has a resident volunteer program; an adopt-
a-grandparent program; ceramics, arts, crafts,
and choir; affiliated with OSU and CTI
teaching programs; and community outreach
programs.

Parkwood Nursing Home
32 Parkwood Ave, Columbus, OH, 43203 (614)
258-3088
Medical Dir/Dir of Nursing William F Conway
MD.
Licensure Intermediate Care. *Beds* 25. *Certi-
fied* Medicaid.
Ownership Proprietary.
Admissions Requirements Minimum age 18;
Females only
Staff Physicians 1 (pt); RNs 1 (ft); LPNs 2 (ft),
3 (pt); Nurses aides 7 (ft), 4 (pt); Activities coor-
dinators 1 (ft); Dietitians 1 (ft); Dentists 1 (pt);
Ophthalmologists 1 (pt); Podiatrists 1 (pt);
Audiologists 1 (pt).
Facilities Dining room; Activities room; Laun-
dry room.

Activities Arts and Crafts; Cards; Games; Reading groups; Prayer groups; Movies; Shopping trips; Dances/Social or cultural gatherings.

Patterson Nursing Home*
71 Woodland Ave, Columbus, OH, 43203 (614) 258-7424
Licensure Intermediate Care. *Beds* 43. *Certified* Medicaid.
Ownership Proprietary.

Pauline Home for the Aged*
1303 E Main St, Columbus, OH, 43205 (614) 258-4822
Licensure Nursing Home. *Beds* 5.
Ownership Nonprofit.

Residential Options Inc Group Home*
3273 Shasta Dr, Columbus, OH, 43229
Licensure Intermediate Care for Mentally Retarded. *Beds* 11. *Certified* Medicaid.

Resthaven*
813 Bryden Rd, Columbus, OH, 43205 (614) 252-4893 and 252-2535
Licensure Skilled Care; Intermediate Care.
Beds 133. *Certified* Medicaid; Medicare.
Ownership Proprietary.

Riverside Hospital
3535 Olentangy River Rd, Columbus, OH, 43214 (614) 261-5000
Medical Dir/Dir of Nursing Dr John Burkhart.
Licensure Skilled Care. *Beds* 48. *Certified* Medicare.
Ownership Nonprofit.
Admissions Requirements Minimum age 16; Physician's request.
Staff RNs 6 (ft), 7 (pt); LPNs 5 (ft); Nurses aides 10 (ft), 2 (pt).
Affiliation Methodist
Facilities Dining room; Physical therapy room; Activities room; Chapel; Crafts room; Barber-/Beauty shop; Library.
Activities Arts and Crafts; Cards; Games; Movies; Holiday parties.
Description Primary emphasis of facility is physical therapy; location in the hospital allows use of all their facilities. Each holiday families attend luncheon or dinner.

Saint Luke Convalescent Center
44 S Souder Ave, Columbus, OH, 43222 (614) 228-5900
Admin G M Boyd. *Medical Dir/Dir of Nursing* Richard Butler MD.
Licensure Skilled Care. *Beds* 92. *Certified* Medicaid; Medicare.
Ownership Proprietary.
Facilities Dining room; Physical therapy room; Activities room; Chapel; Crafts room; Laundry room; Barber/Beauty shop; Library; Lab and x-ray suite.
Activities Arts and Crafts; Cards; Games; Reading groups; Prayer groups; Movies; Shopping trips; Dances/Social or cultural gatherings.

Saint Raphaels Home for the Aged
1550 Roxbury Rd, Columbus, OH, 43212 (614) 486-0436
Medical Dir/Dir of Nursing Haushong Ma'ani MD.
Licensure Skilled Care; Intermediate Care.

Beds 78. *Certified* Medicaid; Medicare.
Ownership Nonprofit.
Admissions Requirements Medical examination.
Staff RNs 6 (ft), 6 (pt); LPNs 3 (ft), 2 (pt); Nurses aides 21 (ft), 15 (pt); Physical therapists 1 (pt); Occupational therapists 1 (pt); Speech therapists 1 (pt); Activities coordinators 1 (ft), 1 (pt); Dietitians 1 (pt); Dentists 1 (pt); Ophthalmologists 1 (pt); Podiatrists 1 (pt).
Affiliation Roman Catholic
Facilities Dining room; Physical therapy room; Activities room; Chapel; Crafts room; Laundry room; Barber/Beauty shop; Library.
Activities Arts and Crafts; Cards; Games; Reading groups; Prayer groups; Movies; Shopping trips; Dances/Social or cultural gatherings.

Saint Rita's Home for the Aged Inc
880 Greenlawn Ave, Columbus, OH, 43223 (614) 443-9433
Medical Dir/Dir of Nursing Ali Mokhtari MD.
Licensure Skilled Care; Intermediate Care.
Beds 100. *Certified* Medicaid; Medicare.
Ownership Nonprofit.
Admissions Requirements Minimum age 65.
Staff Physicians 1 (ft), 3 (pt); RNs 4 (ft), 3 (pt); LPNs 5 (ft), 3 (pt); Nurses aides 45 (ft), 2 (pt); Physical therapists 1 (ft), 1 (pt); Activities coordinators 2 (ft); Dietitians 1 (ft); Dentists 1 (pt); Podiatrists 1 (pt).
Facilities Dining room; Physical therapy room; Activities room; Chapel; Crafts room; Laundry room; Barber/Beauty shop; Library.
Activities Arts and Crafts; Cards; Games; Reading groups; Prayer groups; Movies; Shopping trips; Dances/Social or cultural gatherings.

Wecare Health Facility*
740 Canonby Pl, Columbus, OH, 43223 (614) 224-5738
Licensure Intermediate Care. *Beds* 101. *Certified* Medicaid.
Ownership Proprietary.

Wesley Glen Inc
5155 N High St, Columbus, OH, 43214 (614) 888-7492
Medical Dir/Dir of Nursing Ronald C Van Buren MD.
Licensure Skilled Care; Intermediate Care.
Beds 83. *Certified* Medicaid; Medicare.
Ownership Nonprofit.
Admissions Requirements Minimum age 65; Medical examination; Physician's request.
Staff Physicians 1 (pt); RNs 2 (ft), 8 (pt); LPNs 1 (ft), 2 (pt); Nurses aides 37 (ft), 10 (pt); Physical therapists 1 (pt); Speech therapists 1 (pt); Activities coordinators 2 (ft); Dietitians 1 (ft); Dentists 1 (pt); Podiatrists 1 (pt).
Affiliation Methodist
Facilities Dining room; Physical therapy room; Activities room; Chapel; Crafts room; Laundry room; Barber/Beauty shop; Library.
Activities Arts and Crafts; Cards; Games; Reading groups; Prayer groups; Movies; Shopping trips; Dances/Social or cultural gatherings.
Description Wesley Glen is located in a beautiful park-like setting adjacent to a fine shopping center and not far from Ohio State University.

Westminster Terrace
717 Neil Ave, Columbus, OH, 43215 (614) 228-8888
Medical Dir/Dir of Nursing Dr Roy L Donnerberg.
Licensure Skilled Care; Intermediate Care.
Beds 96. *Certified* Medicaid; Medicare.
Ownership Nonprofit.
Admissions Requirements Minimum age 55; Medical examination.
Staff Physicians 1 (pt); RNs 4 (ft), 2 (pt); LPNs 7 (ft), 6 (pt); Nurses aides 35 (ft), 8 (pt); Physical therapists 1 (pt); Recreational therapists 2 (ft); Occupational therapists 1 (pt); Activities coordinators 1 (ft); Dietitians 2 (pt); Podiatrists 1 (pt).
Affiliation Presbyterian
Facilities Dining room; Physical therapy room; Activities room; Chapel; Crafts room; Laundry room; Barber/Beauty shop; Library.
Activities Arts and Crafts; Cards; Games; Reading groups; Prayer groups; Movies; Shopping trips; Dances/Social or cultural gatherings.
Description Westminster Terrace is part of Westminster-Thurber Community, a unit of Ohio Presbyterian Homes. A full range of care and services including independent apartment living to assisted care to intermediate and skilled nursing care are provided within 2 high-rise buildings.

Whetstone Convalescent Center
3700 Olentangy River Rd, Columbus, OH, 43214 (614) 457-1100
Licensure Skilled Care; Intermediate Care.
Beds 200. *Certified* Medicaid; Medicare.
Ownership Proprietary.
Affiliation Episcopal

Woodland Manor
81 Woodland Ave, Columbus, OH, 43203 (614) 258-8688
Medical Dir/Dir of Nursing William F Conway MD.
Licensure Intermediate Care. *Beds* 29. *Certified* Medicaid.
Ownership Proprietary.
Admissions Requirements Minimum age 18.
Staff Physicians 1 (pt); RNs 1 (ft); LPNs 3 (ft), 5 (pt); Orderlies 3 (ft); Nurses aides 3 (ft), 3 (pt); Physical therapists 1 (pt); Speech therapists 1 (pt); Activities coordinators 1 (ft); Dietitians 1 (pt); Dentists 1 (pt); Ophthalmologists 1 (pt); Podiatrists 1 (pt).
Facilities Dining room; Activities room; Laundry room.
Activities Arts and Crafts; Cards; Games; Prayer groups; Movies; Shopping trips; Dances/Social or cultural gatherings.

CONNEAUT

Ashtabula County Residential Services—Maples 2*
27 Parrish Rd, Conneaut, OH, 44030
Licensure Intermediate Care for Mentally Retarded. *Beds* 8. *Certified* Medicaid.
Ownership Nonprofit.

Inn-Conneaut Health Center
22 Parrish Rd, Conneaut, OH, 44030 (216) 593-6266

Admin Richard D Van Allen. *Medical Dir/Dir of Nursing* William Anderson Jr MD.
Licensure Skilled Care; Intermediate Care.
Beds 100. *Certified* Medicaid; Medicare.
Ownership Proprietary.
Admissions Requirements Minimum age 21; Medical examination.
Staff Physicians 8 (pt); RNs 6 (ft), 4 (pt); LPNs 5 (ft), 3 (pt); Nurses aides 27 (ft), 5 (pt); Physical therapists 1 (pt); Reality therapists 1 (pt); Recreational therapists 1 (ft); Occupational therapists 1 (pt); Speech therapists 1 (pt); Activities coordinators 1 (ft); Dietitians 1 (pt); Dentists 1 (pt); Podiatrists 2 (pt).
Facilities Dining room; Physical therapy room; Activities room; Crafts room; Laundry room; Barber/Beauty shop; Library.
Activities Arts and Crafts; Cards; Games; Reading groups; Prayer groups; Movies; Shopping trips; Dances/Social or cultural gatherings.
Description The Inn-Conneaut Health Center is a therapeutic community where all staff members are involved in providing the best possible atmosphere of acceptance, therapeutic support, and caring; utilizes many emotional as well as physical needs of the patient.

CONVOY

Convoy Care Center*
127 Mentzer Dr, Convoy, OH, 45832
Licensure Intermediate Care. *Beds* 50. *Certified* Medicaid.

COOLVILLE

Arcadia Nursing Center*
PO Box A, E Main St, Coolville, OH, 45723
(614) 667-3196
Licensure Skilled Care; Intermediate Care.
Beds 75. *Certified* Medicaid; Medicare.
Ownership Proprietary.

CORTLAND

Cortland Quality Care Nursing Center
369 N High St, Cortland, OH, 44410 (216) 638-4015
Medical Dir/Dir of Nursing Dr Anthony M Dominic.
Licensure Nursing Home. *Beds* 50.
Ownership Nonprofit.
Admissions Requirements Medical examination.
Staff Physicians 5 (pt); RNs 1 (ft), 1 (pt); LPNs 4 (ft), 1 (pt); Nurses aides 11 (ft), 6 (pt); Physical therapists 1 (pt); Activities coordinators 1 (ft); Dietitians 1 (pt); Dentists 1 (pt); Podiatrists 1 (pt).
Facilities Dining room; Activities room; Crafts room; Laundry room; Barber/Beauty shop; Library.
Activities Arts and Crafts; Cards; Games; Prayer groups; Movies; Shopping trips; Dances/Social or cultural gatherings.
Description Facility provides an adult day care program which helps meet the needs of the community; the older person can come on a daily basis or overnight accommodations can be arranged; certain medical information is required for admission to this program.

Faber Nursing Home*
4250 Sodom-Hutchings Rd NE, Cortland, OH, 44410 (216) 637-7906
Licensure Intermediate Care. *Beds* 38. *Certified* Medicaid.
Ownership Proprietary.

COSHOCTON

Coshocton County Home
Rt 4, Box 53, Coshocton, OH, 43812 (614) 622-2074
Medical Dir/Dir of Nursing G W Stelzner MD.
Licensure Intermediate Care. *Beds* 74. *Certified* Medicaid.
Ownership Public.
Admissions Requirements Minimum age 18; Medical examination.
Staff RNs 2 (ft), 1 (pt); LPNs 8 (ft), 2 (pt); Orderlies 2 (ft), 1 (pt); Nurses aides 15 (ft), 3 (pt); Activities coordinators 2 (ft).
Facilities Dining room; Physical therapy room; Activities room; Chapel; Crafts room; Laundry room; Barber/Beauty shop; TV lounges.
Activities Arts and Crafts; Cards; Games; Reading groups; Prayer groups; Movies; Shopping trips; Dances/Social or cultural gatherings.
Description Home is located in a country setting at the edge of Coshocton; light and airy atmosphere offering many versatile activities such as daily exercise classes, crafts, discussion groups and outings; for some, remotivation and independent habilitation programs are ongoing.

Coshocton County Memorial Hospital*
1460 Orange St, Coshocton, OH, 43812 (614) 622-6411
Licensure Skilled Care; Intermediate Care.
Beds 61. *Certified* Medicaid; Medicare.
Ownership Public.

Coshocton Health Care Center
100 S Whitewoman St, Coshocton, OH, 43812
Admin Ira C Gross.
Licensure Intermediate Care. *Beds* 101. *Certified* Medicaid.
Ownership Proprietary.
Admissions Requirements Minimum age 18; Medical examination; Physician's request.
Staff RNs 5 (ft), 6 (pt); LPNs 3 (ft), 3 (pt); Nurses aides 20 (ft), 18 (pt); Activities coordinators 2 (ft), 1 (pt); Dietitians 1 (pt); Dentists 1 (pt).
Facilities Dining room; Physical therapy room; Activities room; Chapel; Crafts room; Laundry room; Barber/Beauty shop.
Activities Arts and Crafts; Cards; Games; Reading groups; Prayer groups; Movies; Shopping trips; Dances/Social or cultural gatherings.
Description Facility features a very strong nursing and rehabilitation program; active, progressive, and creative activities department; and in a modern facility in historic Roscoe Village in central Ohio (Coshocton County).

Jacob's Dwelling*
25645 T.R. 36, Coshocton, OH, 43812 (614) 824-3635
Licensure Intermediate Care. *Beds* 24. *Certified* Medicaid.
Ownership Nonprofit.

COVINGTON

Covington Community Care Center*
75 Mote Dr, Covington, OH, 45318 (513) 473-2075
Licensure Skilled Care; Intermediate Care.
Beds 101. *Certified* Medicaid; Medicare.
Ownership Proprietary.

Sunny Acres*
8615 W US Rt 36, Covington, OH, 45318 (513) 473-3017
Licensure Intermediate Care. *Beds* 16. *Certified* Medicaid.
Ownership Proprietary.

CRESTLINE

Crestline Nursing Home*
327 W Main St, Crestline, OH, 44827 (419) 683-3255
Licensure Nursing Home. *Beds* 30.
Ownership Proprietary.

CRIDERSVILLE

Cridersville Nursing Home*
603 E Main St, Cridersville, OH, 45806 (419) 645-4468
Licensure Intermediate Care. *Beds* 50. *Certified* Medicaid.
Ownership Proprietary.

CROOKSVILLE

Ketcham's Nursing Home*
Rt 2, 14063 State Rt 37 E, Crooksville, OH, 43731 (614) 342-2877
Licensure Intermediate Care. *Beds* 30. *Certified* Medicaid.
Ownership Proprietary.

CUYAHOGA FALLS

Bethel Rest Home
2107 4th St, Cuyahoga Falls, OH, 44221 (216) 928-5757
Licensure Rest Home. *Beds* 18.
Ownership Proprietary.

Cuyahoga Falls Country Place
2728 Bailey Rd, Cuyahoga Falls, OH, 44221 (216) 929-4231
Medical Dir/Dir of Nursing Walter R Hoffman DO.
Licensure Skilled Care. *Beds* 107. *Certified* Medicare.
Ownership Proprietary.
Admissions Requirements Minimum age 21; Medical examination; Physician's request.
Staff Physicians 3 (pt); RNs 2 (ft), 10 (pt); LPNs 9 (ft), 3 (pt); Orderlies 1 (ft); Nurses aides 29 (ft), 10 (pt); Physical therapists 1 (ft), 1 (pt); Recreational therapists 1 (ft); Speech therapists 1 (pt); Activities coordinators 1 (ft); Dietitians 1 (ft), 1 (pt); Dentists 1 (pt); Ophthalmologists 1 (pt); Podiatrists 1 (pt).
Facilities Dining room; Physical therapy room; Activities room; Crafts room; Laundry room; Barber/Beauty shop; Library.

Activities Arts and Crafts; Cards; Games; Reading groups; Prayer groups; Movies; Shopping trips; Dances/Social or cultural gatherings.
Description Facility has a home-like atmosphere in a country club setting, featuring day care. Accepts private pay and Medicare patients only; 24-hour open visitation; 4 separate units with total capacity of 107.

Twin Pines Retreat*
456 Seasons Rd, Cuyahoga Falls, OH, 44224 (216) 688-5553
Licensure Intermediate Care. *Beds* 50. *Certified* Medicaid.
Ownership Proprietary.

DALTON

Shady Lawn Home Inc
Rt 1, Dalton, OH, 44618 (216) 828-2278
Medical Dir/Dir of Nursing Dr Robert Cananne.
Licensure Intermediate Care. *Beds* 151. *Certified* Medicaid; Medicare.
Ownership Proprietary.
Admissions Requirements Medical examination.
Staff Physicians; RNs; LPNs; Nurses aides; Physical therapists; Reality therapists; Recreational therapists; Speech therapists; Activities coordinators; Dietitians; Dentists; Podiatrists.
Facilities Dining room; Physical therapy room; Activities room; Crafts room; Laundry room; Barber/Beauty shop.
Activities Arts and Crafts; Cards; Games; Reading groups; Prayer groups; Movies; Dances/Social or cultural gatherings.

DANVILLE

Morning View Center of Danville*
25326 Snively Rd, Danville, OH, 43014
Licensure Intermediate Care. *Beds* 42. *Certified* Medicaid.
Ownership Proprietary.

DAYTON

Alta Nursing Home Inc*
20 Livingston Ave, Dayton, OH, 45403 (513) 253-4673
Licensure Intermediate Care. *Beds* 72. *Certified* Medicaid.
Ownership Proprietary.

Bethany Lutheran Village*
6451 Far Hills Ave, Dayton, OH, 45459 (513) 433-2110
Licensure Skilled Care; Intermediate Care.
Beds 233. *Certified* Medicaid; Medicare.
Ownership Nonprofit.
Affiliation Lutheran

Covenant House—Jewish Home for Aged
4911 Covenant House Dr, Dayton, OH, 45426 (513) 837-7323
Licensure Skilled Care; Intermediate Care.
Beds 46. *Certified* Medicaid; Medicare.
Ownership Nonprofit.
Affiliation Jewish
Facilities Dining room; Physical therapy room;

Activities room; Chapel; Crafts room; Barber/Beauty shop.
Activities Arts and Crafts; Cards; Games; Reading groups; Prayer groups; Movies; Shopping trips; Dances/Social or cultural gatherings.

Crawford Convalescent Center
806 W 5th St, Dayton, OH, 45407 (513) 223-3581
Medical Dir/Dir of Nursing Edward Kinkopf OD.
Licensure Skilled Care; Intermediate Care.
Beds 58. *Certified* Medicaid; Medicare.
Ownership Proprietary.
Admissions Requirements Minimum age 18.
Staff Physicians 2 (pt); RNs 4 (ft); LPNs 6 (ft); Nurses aides 19 (ft); Physical therapists 1 (ft), 1 (pt); Reality therapists 1 (ft); Recreational therapists 1 (pt); Occupational therapists 1 (pt); Speech therapists 1 (pt); Activities coordinators 1 (ft); Dietitians 1 (pt); Dentists 1 (pt); Ophthalmologists 1 (pt); Podiatrists 1 (pt); Audiologists 1 (pt).
Facilities Dining room; Physical therapy room; Activities room; Crafts room; Laundry room; Barber/Beauty shop.
Activities Arts and Crafts; Cards; Games; Reading groups; Prayer groups; Shopping trips; Dances/Social or cultural gatherings.

Crestview Nursing Home II*
4381 Tonawanda Trail, Dayton, OH, 45430 (513) 426-5033
Licensure Skilled Care; Intermediate Care.
Beds 102. *Certified* Medicaid; Medicare.
Ownership Proprietary.

Echoing Valley Residential Home*
7040 Union School House Rd, Dayton, OH, 45424
Licensure Intermediate Care for Mentally Retarded. *Beds* 36. *Certified* Medicaid.
Ownership Nonprofit.

Echoing Woods Residential Home*
5455 Salem Bend Dr, Dayton, OH, 45426
Licensure Intermediate Care for Mentally Retarded. *Beds* 36. *Certified* Medicaid.
Ownership Nonprofit.

Franklin Nursing Home of Dayton*
652 Superior Ave, Dayton, OH, 45407 (513) 228-7216
Licensure Intermediate Care. *Beds* 38. *Certified* Medicaid.
Ownership Proprietary.

Friendship Village*
5790 Denlinger Rd, Dayton, OH, 45426 (513) 837-5581
Licensure Skilled Care; Intermediate Care.
Beds 57. *Certified* Medicaid; Medicare.
Ownership Nonprofit.

Glenn Haven Nursing Home
5205 N Main St, Dayton, OH, 45415 (513) 275-0791
Medical Dir/Dir of Nursing Dr Kasimir Oganowski.
Licensure Intermediate Care. *Beds* 34. *Certified* Medicaid.
Ownership Proprietary.
Staff Physicians 1 (pt); RNs 1 (pt); LPNs 3 (ft),

3 (pt); Nurses aides 10 (ft), 1 (pt); Physical therapists 1 (pt); Activities coordinators 1 (pt); Dentists 1 (pt); Podiatrists 1 (pt).
Facilities Dining room; Activities room; Barber/Beauty shop.
Activities Arts and Crafts; Cards; Games; Reading groups; Prayer groups; Shopping trips; Dances/Social or cultural gatherings.

Grandview Manor Nursing Home Inc*
405 Grafton Ave, Dayton, OH, 45406 (513) 276-4040
Licensure Intermediate Care. *Beds* 29. *Certified* Medicaid.
Ownership Proprietary.

Grandview Quality Care Center
923 Grand Ave, Dayton, OH, 45407 (513) 278-6597
Medical Dir/Dir of Nursing Dr O'Samkari.
Licensure Intermediate Care. *Beds* 24. *Certified* Medicaid.
Ownership Proprietary.
Admissions Requirements Females only; Medical examination.
Staff Physicians 2 (pt); RNs 1 (ft), 2 (pt); LPNs 3 (ft); Orderlies 1 (ft); Nurses aides 8 (ft), 2 (pt); Physical therapists 1 (pt); Reality therapists 1 (pt); Recreational therapists 1 (pt); Activities coordinators 1 (ft); Dietitians 1 (pt); Dentists 1 (pt); Ophthalmologists 1 (pt); Podiatrists 1 (pt); Audiologists 1 (pt).
Facilities Dining room; Activities room; Laundry room.
Activities Arts and Crafts; Cards; Games; Reading groups; Prayer groups; Movies; Shopping trips; Dances/Social or cultural gatherings.

Heartland—Beavercreek*
1974 N Fairfield Rd, Dayton, OH, 45432 (513) 429-1106
Licensure Skilled Care; Intermediate Care.
Beds 100. *Certified* Medicaid; Medicare.
Ownership Proprietary.

Hester Memorial Nursing Home
322 Park Dr, Dayton, OH, 45410 (513) 223-5453
Admin Jim McPherson. *Medical Dir/Dir of Nursing* Dr James B Nogle.
Licensure Intermediate Care. *Beds* 45. *Certified* Medicaid.
Ownership Nonprofit.
Admissions Requirements Medical examination.
Affiliation Church of God
Facilities Dining room; Activities room; Laundry room.
Activities Arts and Crafts; Cards; Games; Reading groups; Prayer groups; Movies; Shopping trips; Dances/Social or cultural gatherings.
Description Hester Memorial Nursing Home has been serving the Miami Valley for many years. As of January, 1978, the East Fourth Street Church of God has operated the facility bringing a unique blend of Christian care along with the finest professional care available. We think that fact sets us apart from the rest. These days, Christ-centered care for the aged is a rare thing indeed.

Hickory Creek Nursing Home Inc*
4231 Pinnacle Rd, Dayton, OH, 45418 (513) 268-3488
Licensure Skilled Care; Intermediate Care.
Beds 150. *Certified* Medicaid; Medicare.
Ownership Proprietary.

Hill Top House Nursing Home Inc*
437 Blackwood Ave, Dayton, OH, 45403 (513) 253-8944
Licensure Skilled Care. *Beds* 63. *Certified* Medicare.
Ownership Proprietary.

Jones Nursing and Convalescent Home*
1033 Grand Ave, Dayton, OH, 45407 (513) 277-1281
Licensure Intermediate Care. *Beds* 22. *Certified* Medicaid.
Ownership Proprietary.

Josephine Nursing Home*
519 McLain St, Dayton, OH, 45403 (513) 222-0823
Licensure Intermediate Care. *Beds* 24. *Certified* Medicaid.
Ownership Proprietary.

King Tree Center
1390 King Tree Dr, Dayton, OH, 45405 (513) 278-0723
Medical Dir/Dir of Nursing Dr R Chunduri.
Licensure Skilled Care; Intermediate Care.
Beds 50. *Certified* Medicaid; Medicare.
Ownership Proprietary.
Admissions Requirements Minimum age 16.
Staff Physicians 25 (pt); RNs 14 (ft); LPNs 21 (ft); Nurses aides 82 (ft); Physical therapists 2 (ft); Reality therapists 1 (ft); Recreational therapists 1 (ft); Occupational therapists 1 (pt); Speech therapists 1 (pt); Activities coordinators 1 (ft); Dietitians 1 (pt); Dentists 1 (pt).
Facilities Dining room; Physical therapy room; Activities room; Chapel; Crafts room; Laundry room; Barber/Beauty shop; Library.
Activities Arts and Crafts; Cards; Games; Reading groups; Prayer groups; Movies; Shopping trips; Dances/Social or cultural gatherings.

Linden Health Care Center
42 Linden Ave, Dayton, OH, 45403 (513) 252-4711
Licensure Intermediate Care. *Beds* 25. *Certified* Medicaid.
Ownership Proprietary.
Admissions Requirements Medical examination.
Staff Physicians 1 (pt); RNs 1 (pt); LPNs 2 (ft), 3 (pt); Nurses aides 7 (ft), 3 (pt); Activities coordinators 1 (ft); Dietitians 1 (pt); Dentists 1 (pt); Ophthalmologists 1 (pt); Podiatrists 1 (pt).
Facilities Dining room; Laundry room.
Activities Arts and Crafts; Cards; Games; Prayer groups; Movies; Shopping trips.

Maria Joseph Center
4830 Salem Ave, Dayton, OH, 45416 (513) 278-2692
Admin Warren J Harris. *Medical Dir/Dir of Nursing* Robert J Deger MD.
Licensure Skilled Care; Intermediate Care; Rest Home. *Beds* SNF 106; ICF 190; Rest Home 45. *Certified* Medicaid; Medicare.

Ownership Nonprofit.
Admissions Requirements Medical examination.
Staff Physicians 1 (ft), 4 (pt); RNs 10 (ft), 12 (pt); LPNs 19 (ft), 6 (pt); Orderlies 3 (ft); Nurses aides 76 (ft), 52 (pt); Physical therapists 1 (ft), 1 (pt); Occupational therapists 1 (ft); Speech therapists 1 (pt); Activities coordinators 5 (ft), 1 (pt); Dietitians 1 (ft); Dentists; Ophthalmologists; Podiatrists.
Affiliation Roman Catholic
Facilities Dining room; Physical therapy room; Activities room; Chapel; Crafts room; Laundry room; Barber/Beauty shop; Library.
Activities Arts and Crafts; Cards; Games; Reading groups; Prayer groups; Shopping trips; Shopping trips; Dances/Social or cultural gatherings.
Description Facility offers Lifeline (community emergency call system); home health care program; geriatric rehabilitation unit; geriatric environmental stimulation program (for the confused older adult); and early childhood center.

Mary Scott Nursing Center
3109 Campus Dr, Dayton, OH, 45406 (513) 278-0761
Medical Dir/Dir of Nursing Dr Robert McConnell.
Licensure Skilled Care; Intermediate Care.
Beds 130. *Certified* Medicaid; Medicare.
Ownership Nonprofit.
Admissions Requirements Medical examination.
Staff Physicians 1 (pt); RNs 4 (ft), 1 (pt); LPNs 12 (ft), 1 (pt); Nurses aides 40 (ft), 6 (pt); Activities coordinators 1 (ft); Dietitians 1 (ft).
Facilities Dining room; Physical therapy room; Activities room; Crafts room; Laundry room; Barber/Beauty shop; Library.
Activities Arts and Crafts; Cards; Games; Reading groups; Prayer groups; Movies; Shopping trips; Dances/Social or cultural gatherings.
Description Mary Scott Nursing Center is a 130-bed nursing facility for both skilled and intermediate levels of care. It is located in a lovely residential area and features a spacious dining room, bright activities areas, and an enclosed patio. Of importance is quality care in an atmosphere of warmth, compassion, and dignity.

McGills Nursing Home—South*
15 Arnold Pl, Dayton, OH, 45407 (513) 274-2447
Licensure Intermediate Care. *Beds* 30. *Certified* Medicaid.
Ownership Proprietary.

Oxford Manor Nursing Home
601 Oxford Ave, Dayton, OH, 45407 (513) 275-3288
Medical Dir/Dir of Nursing Dr James Nagle.
Licensure Intermediate Care. *Beds* 24. *Certified* Medicaid.
Ownership Proprietary.
Admissions Requirements Medical examination.
Staff RNs 1 (pt); LPNs 3 (ft), 2 (pt); Nurses aides 9 (ft); Activities coordinators 1 (ft); Dietitians 1 (pt); Podiatrists 1 (pt).

Parkview Manor Nursing Home*
250 Park Dr, Dayton, OH, 45410 (513) 224-7906
Licensure Intermediate Care; Rest Home.
Beds ICF 51; Rest Home 14. *Certified* Medicaid.
Ownership Proprietary.

Rest Haven*
34 Arnold Pl, Dayton, OH, 45407 (513) 275-6033
Licensure Intermediate Care. *Beds* 19. *Certified* Medicaid.
Ownership Proprietary.

Schulze Nursing Home*
409 Forest Ave, Dayton, OH, 45405 (513) 228-7143
Licensure Intermediate Care. *Beds* 35. *Certified* Medicaid.
Ownership Proprietary.

The Siena Home*
235 W Orchard Springs Dr, Dayton, OH, 45415 (513) 278-8211
Licensure Intermediate Care. *Beds* 99. *Certified* Medicaid.
Ownership Nonprofit.

Stilhaven Nursing Home*
201 Central Ave, Dayton, OH, 45406
Licensure Intermediate Care. *Beds* 50. *Certified* Medicaid.
Ownership Proprietary.

Stillwater Children's Center
8100 N Main St, Dayton, OH, 45415 (513) 890-0646
Admin Walter Messer. *Medical Dir/Dir of Nursing* Ceferino Cata MD.
Licensure Intermediate Care for Mentally Retarded. *Beds* 58.
Ownership Public.
Admissions Requirements Minimum age 0-18; Medical examination.
Staff Physicians 1 (pt); RNs 3 (ft), 2 (pt); LPNs 3 (ft), 3 (pt); Nurses aides 14 (ft), 3 (pt); Physical therapists 2 (pt); Recreational therapists 1 (ft); Occupational therapists 2 (pt); Activities coordinators 1 (ft); Dietitians 1 (pt).
Facilities Dining room; Physical therapy room; Activities room; Laundry room.
Activities Arts and Crafts; Reading groups; Movies; Dances/Social or cultural gatherings.
Description Facility provides a very structured concurrent medical/programing model of care to severely profound mentally retarded who also have multiple or severe physical disabilities.

Stillwater Health Center
8100 N Main St, Dayton, OH, 45415 (513) 890-0646
Medical Dir/Dir of Nursing Ceferino Cata MD.
Licensure Intermediate Care for Mentally Retarded. *Beds* ICF/MR 175. *Certified* Medicaid; Medicare.
Ownership Public.
Admissions Requirements Medical examination; Physician's request.
Staff Physicians 2 (pt); RNs 14 (ft), 10 (pt); LPNs 21 (ft), 1 (pt); Nurses aides 84 (ft), 26

(pt); Physical therapists 1 (pt); Recreational therapists 1 (ft); Occupational therapists 1 (pt); Speech therapists 1 (pt); Activities coordinators 1 (ft); Dietitians 1 (ft); Dentists 1 (pt); Ophthalmologists 1 (pt); Podiatrists 1 (pt); Audiologists 1 (pt).
Facilities Dining room; Physical therapy room; Activities room; Chapel; Crafts room; Library.
Activities Arts and Crafts; Cards; Games; Reading groups; Prayer groups; Movies; Shopping trips; Dances/Social or cultural gatherings; News/Views current events; Pet therapy.

Trinity Home*
3218 Indian Ripple Rd, Dayton, OH, 45440 (513) 426-8481
Licensure Skilled Care; Intermediate Care; Rest Home. *Beds* 108. *Certified* Medicaid; Medicare.
Ownership Nonprofit.

Valerie Nursing Home*
3650 Klepinger Rd, Dayton, OH, 45416 (513) 278-0663
Licensure Skilled Care; Intermediate Care.
Beds 201. *Certified* Medicaid; Medicare.
Ownership Proprietary.

Washington Manor*
7300 McEwen Rd, Dayton, OH, 45459 (513) 433-3431
Licensure Skilled Care; Intermediate Care.
Beds 178. *Certified* Medicaid; Medicare.
Ownership Proprietary.

Widows Home of Dayton*
50 S Findlay St, Dayton, OH, 45403 (513) 252-1661, 7280
Licensure Home for the Aged. *Beds* 44.
Ownership Nonprofit.

Yale Manor Inc*
35 Yale Ave, Dayton, OH, 45406 (513) 276-5237
Licensure Intermediate Care. *Beds* 42. *Certified* Medicaid.
Ownership Proprietary.

DEER PARK

East Galbraith Health Care Center Inc*
3889 E Galbraith Rd, Deer Park, OH, 45236 (513) 984-5220
Licensure Intermediate Care. *Beds* 145. *Certified* Medicaid.
Ownership Proprietary.

East Galbraith Nursing Home
3875 E Galbraith Rd, Deer Park, OH, 45236 (513) 793-5220 and 791-9669
Medical Dir/Dir of Nursing Dr Stacey Greenert.
Licensure Skilled Care; Intermediate Care.
Beds 91. *Certified* Medicaid.
Ownership Proprietary.
Staff Physicians 1 (pt); RNs 3 (ft), 4 (pt); LPNs 3 (ft), 5 (pt); Nurses aides 20 (ft), 4 (pt); Physical therapists 1 (pt); Recreational therapists 1 (pt); Occupational therapists 1 (pt); Speech therapists 1 (pt); Activities coordinators 2 (ft); Dietitians 1 (ft); Dentists 1 (pt); Ophthalmologists 1 (pt); Podiatrists 1 (pt); Audiologists

1 (pt).
Facilities Dining room; Physical therapy room; Barber/Beauty shop.
Activities Arts and Crafts; Cards; Games; Reading groups; Prayer groups; Movies; Dances/Social or cultural gatherings.
Description Our facility has 236 activities per month.

DEFIANCE

Defiance Health Care Center
1701 S Jefferson Ave, Defiance, OH, 43512 (419) 782-7879
Medical Dir/Dir of Nursing Dr William Busteed.
Licensure Skilled Care; Intermediate Care.
Beds 51. *Certified* Medicaid; Medicare.
Ownership Proprietary.
Staff Physicians 1 (pt); RNs 1 (ft), 2 (pt); LPNs 2 (ft), 3 (pt); Nurses aides 9 (ft), 17 (pt); Physical therapists 1 (pt); Activities coordinators 1 (ft); Dietitians 1 (pt); Dentists 1 (pt); Podiatrists 1 (pt).
Facilities Dining room; Activities room; Laundry room; Barber/Beauty shop.
Activities Arts and Crafts; Cards; Games; Reading groups; Prayer groups; Movies; Shopping trips.

Glenwood Care Center
301 Glenwood Dr, Defiance, OH, 43512 (419) 782-9761
Medical Dir/Dir of Nursing Dr George Boomer.
Licensure Intermediate Care. *Beds* 50. *Certified* Medicaid.
Ownership Proprietary.
Admissions Requirements Medical examination.
Staff Physicians 5 (pt); RNs 1 (pt); LPNs 3 (ft), 4 (pt); Orderlies 1 (ft), 2 (pt); Nurses aides 2 (ft), 13 (pt); Activities coordinators 1 (ft); Dietitians 1 (pt); Podiatrists 1 (pt).
Facilities Dining room; Activities room; Crafts room; Laundry room; Barber/Beauty shop.
Activities Arts and Crafts; Games; Movies; Shopping trips.
Description Glenwood Care Center has a home-like atmosphere. We are located in a residential area and many times are mistaken for a home instead of a nursing home. We have recently started to redecorate our facility and have made many improvements.

Leisure Oaks Convalescent Center
214 Harding St, Defiance, OH, 43512 (419) 784-1014
Medical Dir/Dir of Nursing John Forester Jr MD.
Licensure Skilled Care; Intermediate Care.
Beds 93. *Certified* Medicaid; Medicare.
Ownership Nonprofit.
Admissions Requirements Medical examination; Physician's request.
Staff RNs 3 (ft), 8 (pt); LPNs 2 (ft), 8 (pt); Nurses aides 20 (ft), 20 (pt); Physical therapists 1 (pt); Speech therapists 1 (pt); Activities coordinators 1 (ft); Dietitians 1 (pt); Dentists 1 (pt); Podiatrists 1 (pt); Audiologists 1 (pt).
Affiliation Volunteers of America
Facilities Dining room; Physical therapy room;

Activities room; Chapel; Crafts room; Laundry room; Barber/Beauty shop; Library.
Activities Arts and Crafts; Cards; Games; Reading groups; Prayer groups; Movies; Shopping trips; Dances/Social or cultural gatherings; Pet therapy.

Twin Rivers Nursing Care Center
395 Harding St, Defiance, OH, 43512 (419) 784-1450
Medical Dir/Dir of Nursing Dr John Fauster.
Licensure Skilled Care; Intermediate Care.
Beds 100. *Certified* Medicaid; Medicare.
Ownership Proprietary.
Admissions Requirements Medical examination.
Staff Physicians 1 (pt); RNs 2 (ft), 3 (pt); LPNs 2 (ft), 11 (pt); Orderlies 1 (ft), 1 (pt); Nurses aides 15 (ft), 29 (pt); Physical therapists 1 (pt); Speech therapists 1 (pt); Activities coordinators 1 (ft), 1 (pt); Dietitians 1 (ft); Dentists 1 (pt); Podiatrists 1 (pt).
Facilities Dining room; Physical therapy room; Activities room; Laundry room; Barber/Beauty shop; Library.
Activities Arts and Crafts; Cards; Games; Reading groups; Movies; Shopping trips; Dances/Social or cultural gatherings.
Description Newest facility in town; van for outside recreation trips.

DELAWARE

Crestmont Nursing Center*
478 S Sandusky St, Delaware, OH, 43015 (614) 369-8741
Licensure Intermediate Care. *Beds* 50. *Certified* Medicaid.
Ownership Proprietary.

Delaware Park Care Center*
2270 Warrensburg Rd, Delaware, OH, 43015 (614) 369-9614
Licensure Skilled Care; Intermediate Care.
Beds 108. *Certified* Medicaid; Medicare.
Ownership Proprietary.

Hel-Ene Nursing Home*
36 Griswold St, Delaware, OH, 43015 (614) 362-6031
Licensure Intermediate Care. *Beds* 34. *Certified* Medicaid.
Ownership Proprietary.

Sarah Moore Home Inc
47 E William St, Delaware, OH, 43015 (614) 362-9641
Licensure Intermediate Care. *Beds* 31. *Certified* Medicaid.
Ownership Nonprofit.

Sunny Vee Nursing Home Inc*
54 W Lincoln Ave, Delaware, OH, 43015 (614) 363-1587
Licensure Skilled Care; Intermediate Care.
Beds 56. *Certified* Medicaid; Medicare.
Ownership Proprietary.

DELPHOS

Delphos Memorial Home
Corner of Rt 30N and 309, Box 388, Delphos,
OH, 45833 (419) 695-2871 and 692-4242
Admin Virginia Christen. *Medical Dir/Dir of
Nursing* W W Wolery MD.
Licensure Intermediate Care. *Beds* 100. *Certified* Medicaid.
Ownership Nonprofit.
Admissions Requirements Minimum age 18;
Medical examination.
Staff RNs 4 (ft), 5 (pt); LPNs 2 (ft), 6 (pt);
Nurses aides 27 (ft), 19 (pt); Activities coordinators 1 (ft), 2 (pt); Dietitians 1 (ft), 2 (pt).
Facilities Dining room; Physical therapy room;
Activities room; Laundry room; Barber/Beauty
shop.
Activities Arts and Crafts; Cards; Games;
Reading groups; Prayer groups; Movies.

Sarah Jane E Chambers Geriatric Center
328 W 2nd St, Delphos, OH, 45833 (419)
695-1921
Medical Dir/Dir of Nursing W W Wolery MD.
Licensure Intermediate Care. *Beds* 50. *Certified* Medicaid.
Ownership Nonprofit.
Admissions Requirements Minimum age 18;
Medical examination.
Staff RNs 1 (ft), 10 (pt); LPNs 1 (pt); Nurses
aides 6 (ft), 19 (pt); Activities coordinators 1
(ft), 1 (pt); Dietitians 1 (ft), 1 (pt).
Facilities Dining room; Physical therapy room;
Activities room; Laundry room; Barber/Beauty
shop.
Activities Arts and Crafts; Cards; Games;
Reading groups; Prayer groups; Movies.

DENNISON

Charity Nursing Facility*
509 Grant St, Dennison, OH, 44621 (614)
922-2036
Licensure Intermediate Care. *Beds* 18. *Certified* Medicaid.
Ownership Proprietary.

DESHLER

Oak Grove Nursing Home Inc*
620 E Water St, Deshler, OH, 43516 (419)
278-2840
Licensure Intermediate Care. *Beds* 66. *Certified* Medicaid.
Ownership Proprietary.

DOVER

Country Club Center
860 Iron Ave, Dover, OH, 44622 (216)
343-5568
Medical Dir/Dir of Nursing Phillip Doughten.
Licensure Skilled Care; Intermediate Care.
Beds 54. *Certified* Medicaid; Medicare.
Ownership Proprietary.
Admissions Requirements Minimum age 18;
Medical examination; Physician's request.
Staff Physicians 1 (pt); RNs 2 (ft), 4 (pt); LPNs
9 (pt); Nurses aides 11 (ft), 13 (pt); Physical
therapists 1 (pt); Speech therapists 1 (pt);

Activities coordinators 1 (ft); Dietitians 1 (pt);
Dentists 1 (pt); Podiatrists 1 (pt); Audiologists 1
(pt).
Facilities Dining room; Physical therapy room;
Activities room; Crafts room; Laundry room;
Barber/Beauty shop.
Activities Arts and Crafts; Games; Reading
groups; Movies; Dances/Social or cultural gatherings; Bingo; "Out-to-lunch" group.
Description Facility is located close to the community hospital, a professional building, golf
club, and a shopping center.

Dover Nursing Center*
1525 Crater Ave, Dover, OH, 44622 (216)
364-4436
Licensure Skilled Care; Intermediate Care.
Beds 50. *Certified* Medicaid.
Ownership Proprietary.

Hennis Care Center*
1720 Cross St, Dover, OH, 44622 (216)
364-8849
Licensure Intermediate Care. *Beds* 52. *Certified* Medicaid.
Ownership Proprietary.

New Dawn Health Care Center
865 E Iron Ave, Dover, OH, 44622 (216)
343-5521
Medical Dir/Dir of Nursing H H Shah.
Licensure Skilled Care; Intermediate Care.
Beds 100. *Certified* Medicaid.
Ownership Proprietary.
Admissions Requirements Medical examination.
Staff Physicians 1 (pt); RNs 3 (ft), 4 (pt); LPNs
1 (ft), 6 (pt); Orderlies 1 (ft); Nurses aides 15
(ft), 29 (pt); Activities coordinators 1 (ft).
Facilities Dining room; Physical therapy room;
Activities room; Chapel; Crafts room; Laundry
room; Barber/Beauty shop; Multipurpose
room.
Activities Arts and Crafts; Cards; Games;
Reading groups; Prayer groups; Movies; Dances/Social or cultural gatherings.
Description Situated next to Union Hospital,
and numerous shopping and recreation centers
New Dawn was developed with a Christian
atmosphere in mind, and designed for safe,
hygenic, sheltered living. New Dawn Health
Care Center represents a new concept in geriatric living.

DOYLESTOWN

Sara Lee Nursing Home
Rt 1, 140 Wall Rd, Doylestown, OH, 44230
(216) 334-4184
Medical Dir/Dir of Nursing P L Gilcrest MD.
Licensure Intermediate Care. *Beds* 48. *Certified* Medicaid.
Ownership Proprietary.
Admissions Requirements Minimum age 18.
Staff Physicians 1 (pt); RNs 1 (ft), 1 (pt); LPNs
3 (ft), 3 (pt); Nurses aides 14 (ft), 6 (pt);
Physical therapists 1 (pt); Speech therapists 1
(pt); Activities coordinators 1 (ft); Dentists 1
(p'); Ophthalmologists 1 (pt); Podiatrists 1 (pt);
Audiologists 1 (pt).
Facilities Dining room; Physical therapy room;
Activities room; Chapel; Laundry room; Bar-

ber/Beauty shop.
Activities Arts and Crafts; Cards; Games;
Reading groups; Prayer groups; Movies; Shopping trips; Dances/Social or cultural gatherings.
Description Facility is located in a country setting.

DUBLIN

Friendship Village of Dublin Health Center*
6000 Riverside Dr, Dublin, OH, 43017
Licensure Skilled Care; Intermediate Care.
Beds SNF 60; ICF 60. *Certified* Medicaid;
Medicare.
Ownership Nonprofit.

EAST CLEVELAND

A M McGregor Home
14900 Terrace Rd, East Cleveland, OH, 44112
(216) 851-8200
Admin Carol A Marks. *Medical Dir/Dir of
Nursing* Barry Siegel MD and Ralph Wieland
MD.
Licensure Rest Home. *Beds* 116.
Ownership Nonprofit.
Admissions Requirements Minimum age 60;
Medical examination; Physician's request.
Staff Physicians 2 (pt); RNs 5 (ft); LPNs 5 (ft);
Nurses aides 5 (ft), 5 (pt); Physical therapists 2
(pt); Reality therapists 1 (pt); Recreational therapists 2 (ft); Speech therapists 1 (pt); Activities
coordinators 1 (ft); Dietitians 1 (pt); Dentists 2
(pt); Ophthalmologists 1 (pt); Podiatrists 1 (pt);
Audiologists 1 (pt).
Facilities Dining room; Physical therapy room;
Activities room; Chapel; Crafts room; Laundry
room; Barber/Beauty shop; Library.
Activities Arts and Crafts; Cards; Games;
Reading groups; Prayer groups; Movies; Shopping trips; Dances/Social or cultural gatherings;
Escorted musicals; Dinners; Plays; Concerts.
Description McGregor Home provides life care
and security, including medical, nursing, and
hospital care.

Ambassador Nursing Center
1835 Belmore Ave, East Cleveland, OH, 44112
(216) 268-3600
Medical Dir/Dir of Nursing Dr Charles Barnes.
Licensure Skilled Care; Intermediate Care.
Beds 159. *Certified* Medicaid; Medicare.
Ownership Proprietary.
Admissions Requirements Minimum age 30.
Staff Physicians; RNs; LPNs; Orderlies;
Nurses aides; Physical therapists; Recreational
therapists; Occupational therapists; Speech therapists; Activities coordinators; Dietitians; Dentists; Ophthalmologists; Podiatrists.
Facilities Dining room; Physical therapy room;
Activities room; Chapel; Crafts room; Laundry
room; Barber/Beauty shop; Library.
Activities Arts and Crafts; Cards; Games;
Reading groups; Prayer groups; Movies; Shopping trips; Dances/Social or cultural gatherings.

Eastern Star Home of Cuyahoga County*
2114 Noble Rd, East Cleveland, OH, 44112
Licensure Intermediate Care. *Beds* 81. *Certi-*

fied Medicaid.
Ownership Nonprofit.
Affiliation Order of Eastern Star

EAST LIVERPOOL

Convalescent Center 2*
701 Armstrong Ln, East Liverpool, OH, 43920
(216) 385-5212
Licensure Intermediate Care. *Beds* 50. *Certified* Medicaid.
Ownership Proprietary.

East Liverpool Convalescent Center*
709 Armstrong Ln, East Liverpool, OH, 43920
(216) 385-3600
Licensure Intermediate Care. *Beds* 60. *Certified* Medicaid.
Ownership Proprietary.

East Liverpool Extended Center
430 W 5th St, East Liverpool, OH, 43920 (216)
385-9500
Medical Dir/Dir of Nursing Dr Edith Gilmore.
Licensure Skilled Care; Intermediate Care.
Beds SNF 30; ICF 20. *Certified* Medicare.
Ownership Proprietary.
Staff Physicians 1 (pt); RNs 4 (ft), 3 (pt); LPNs
4 (ft); Nurses aides 14 (ft), 2 (pt); Physical therapists 1 (pt); Occupational therapists 1 (pt); Speech therapists 1 (pt); Activities coordinators 1
(ft); Dietitians 1 (pt); Dentists 1 (pt).
Facilities Dining room; Physical therapy room;
Activities room; Crafts room; Laundry room;
Barber/Beauty shop.
Activities Arts and Crafts; Games; Movies.

Nentwick Convalescent Home Inc
500 Seltridge St, East Liverpool, OH, 43920
(216) 385-5001
Medical Dir/Dir of Nursing Dr William Sarger.
Licensure Intermediate Care. *Beds* 100. *Certified* Medicaid.
Ownership Proprietary.
Admissions Requirements Medical examination.
Staff Physicians 1 (pt); RNs 6 (ft); LPNs 4 (ft);
Orderlies 2 (ft), 1 (pt); Nurses aides 35 (ft), 4
(pt); Physical therapists 1 (pt); Occupational
therapists 1 (pt); Speech therapists 1 (pt);
Activities coordinators 3 (ft); Dietitians 1 (pt);
Dentists 1 (pt); Podiatrists 1 (pt); Audiologists 1
(pt).
Facilities Dining room; Physical therapy room;
Activities room; Chapel; Crafts room; Laundry
room; Barber/Beauty shop; Library; Courtyard;
Whirlpool baths.
Activities Arts and Crafts; Cards; Games;
Reading groups; Prayer groups; Movies; Shopping trips; Dances/Social or cultural gatherings;
Ceramics; Newspaper; Leathercraft; Exercise
groups; Resident council; Resident dietary support group.
Description Facility has an active family support group and is deeply involved with a
resident oral history group.

Ross Nursing Home
941-949 Ambrose Ave, East Liverpool, OH,
43920 (216) 385-6623
Medical Dir/Dir of Nursing Dr William Horger.

fied Medicaid.
Ownership Nonprofit.
Admissions Requirements Medical
examination; Physician's request.
Staff Physicians 1 (ft), 3 (pt); RNs 1 (ft), 1 (pt);
LPNs 7 (ft); Nurses aides 20 (ft), 6 (pt); Recreational therapists 1 (ft); Activities coordinators 1
(ft); Dietitians 2 (pt).
Facilities Dining room; Activities room; Laundry room.
Activities Arts and Crafts; Games; Prayer
groups; Shopping trips.

EAST ORWELL

Village Square Nursing Center*
7787 Staley Rd, East Orwell, OH, 44034
Licensure Intermediate Care. *Beds* 38. *Certified* Medicaid.
Ownership Proprietary.

EATON

Governor Harris Homestead*
PO Box 147, 310 N Cherry St, Eaton, OH,
45320 (513) 456-5120
Licensure Intermediate Care. *Beds* 27. *Certified* Medicaid.
Ownership Proprietary.

Heartland of Eaton
515 S Maple St, Eaton, OH, 45320 (513)
456-5537
Admin Adelaide Neil Helmke. *Medical Dir/Dir of Nursing* Richard Siehl DO.
Licensure Skilled Care. *Beds* 100. *Certified* Medicaid; Medicare.
Ownership Proprietary.
Admissions Requirements Minimum age 35;
Medical examination; Physician's request.
Staff Physicians 1 (pt); RNs 3 (ft), 3 (pt); LPNs
3 (ft), 8 (pt); Nurses aides 29 (ft), 11 (pt);
Physical therapists 1 (pt); Occupational therapists 1 (pt); Speech therapists 1 (pt); Activities
coordinators 1 (ft); Dietitians 1 (ft).
Facilities Dining room; Physical therapy room;
Activities room; Barber/Beauty shop.
Activities Arts and Crafts; Cards; Games;
Reading groups; Shopping trips; Dances/Social
or cultural gatherings; Fair; Pork festival;
Picnics; Rock 'n roll jamboree; Flower
arranging; Bible study; Worship services.
Description Heartland of Eaton is dedicated to
providing the very best service, care, and facilities. Home is equipped with smoke detectors,
magnetic door closures, automatic sprinkler
systems, fire alarms, and handrails ensuring a
safe environment. It is a warm and friendly
place where residents receive the professional
health care and personal attention that will
allow the fullest possible recovery and enjoyment of life.

Morris Oak Lawn Nursing Home
120 N Cherry St, Eaton, OH, 45320 (513)
456-7167
Licensure Intermediate Care. *Beds* 34. *Certified* Medicaid.
Ownership Proprietary.
Staff RNs 1 (pt); LPNs 3 (ft), 3 (pt); Nurses

aides 6 (ft), 4 (pt); Activities coordinators 1 (pt).
Facilities Dining room; Activities room; Crafts
room; Laundry room.
Activities Arts and Crafts; Cards; Games;
Reading groups; Prayer groups; Movies; Shopping trips; Dances/Social or cultural gatherings.

The Rust Home*
119 W Somers St, Eaton, OH, 45320 (513)
456-3640
Licensure Nursing Home. *Beds* 23.
Ownership Proprietary.

EDGERTON

Park View Nursing Home
US Rt 6 W, Edgerton, OH, 43517 (419)
298-2512
Medical Dir/Dir of Nursing Dr R Meyer.
Licensure Intermediate Care. *Beds* 100. *Certified* Medicaid.
Ownership Proprietary.
Admissions Requirements Medical examination.
Staff RNs 3 (ft), 1 (pt); LPNs 3 (ft), 6 (pt);
Nurses aides 24 (ft), 2 (pt); Physical therapists 1
(pt); Activities coordinators 2 (ft); Dietitians 1
(pt); Podiatrists 1 (pt).
Facilities Dining room; Physical therapy room;
Activities room; Laundry room; Barber/Beauty
shop.
Activities Arts and Crafts; Cards; Games;
Reading groups; Prayer groups; Movies; Shopping trips; Dances/Social or cultural gatherings.
Description Park View is located in rural
northwest Ohio and as such has a pleasant,
peaceful, country setting. Facility takes pride in
its home-like, family atmosphere. Active activities program includes a number of progressive,
innovative events designed for both the alert
and ambulatory and the bedridden residents.

ELYRIA

Crestmont Nursing Home Inc—East*
1251 East Ave, Elyria, OH, 44035 (216)
322-0726
Licensure Intermediate Care; Intermediate
Care for Mentally Retarded. *Beds* ICF 30;
ICF/MR 20. *Certified* Medicaid.
Ownership Proprietary.

Crestmont Nursing Home Inc—West*
221 West Ave, Elyria, OH, 44035 (216)
322-2525
Licensure Intermediate Care. *Beds* 50. *Certified* Medicaid.
Ownership Nonprofit.

The Elyria United Methodist Home
807 West Ave, Elyria, OH, 44035 (216)
323-3395
Admin C Rue McIntyre. *Medical Dir/Dir of
Nursing* Roger L Baldoza MD.
Licensure Skilled Care; Intermediate Care.
Beds 209. *Certified* Medicaid; Medicare.
Ownership Nonprofit.
Admissions Requirements Minimum age 65;
Medical examination.
Staff Physicians 6 (pt); RNs 7 (ft), 7 (pt); LPNs
27 (ft), 19 (pt); Nurses aides 80 (ft), 14 (pt);

Physical therapists 1 (pt); Occupational therapists 1 (pt); Speech therapists 1 (pt); Activities coordinators 1 (ft); Dietitians 1 (pt); Dentists 1 (pt); Ophthalmologists 1 (pt); Podiatrists 1 (pt).
Affiliation Methodist
Facilities Dining room; Physical therapy room; Activities room; Chapel; Crafts room; Laundry room; Barber/Beauty shop; Library; Kitchen-/lounge; Store.
Activities Arts and Crafts; Cards; Games; Reading groups; Prayer groups; Movies; Shopping trips; Dances/Social or cultural gatherings; Exercises; Painting class; Support groups; Cooking and baking; Mens club.
Description A master plan has been approved by Board of Trustees that will include 160-bed nursing unit for more efficient operation, central services care, 50 independent living units, and renovating building to accommodate 66 personal care units for residential living.

J Ferry Nursing Home*
1015 Middle Ave, Elyria, OH, 44035 (216) 323-2892
Licensure Intermediate Care. *Beds* 26. *Certified* Medicaid.
Ownership Proprietary.

ENGLEWOOD

Englewood Manor Nursing Home
20 Union Blvd, Englewood, OH, 45322 (513) 836-5143
Admin James A Launcello Sr.
Licensure Skilled Care; Intermediate Care.
Beds 80. *Certified* Medicaid; Medicare.
Ownership Proprietary.
Admissions Requirements Medical examination.
Facilities Dining room; Physical therapy room; Activities room; Crafts room; Laundry room; Barber/Beauty shop.
Activities Arts and Crafts; Cards; Games; Reading groups; Movies; Dances/Social or cultural gatherings.

Grace Brethren Village
1010 Taywood Rd, Englewood, OH, 45322 (513) 836-4011
Licensure Intermediate Care. *Beds* 50. *Certified* Medicaid.
Ownership Nonprofit.
Admissions Requirements Minimum age 60; Medical examination.
Staff RNs 1 (ft), 2 (pt); LPNs 3 (ft), 3 (pt); Nurses aides 8 (ft), 5 (pt); Recreational therapists 1 (ft); Activities coordinators 1 (ft); Dietitians 1 (pt).
Affiliation Church of the Brethren
Facilities Dining room; Activities room; Chapel; Crafts room; Laundry room; Barber-/Beauty shop; Library.
Activities Arts and Crafts; Cards; Games; Reading groups; Prayer groups; Movies; Shopping trips; Dances/Social or cultural gatherings.

EUCLID

Cuy-La Home*
1691 Hillandale Dr, Euclid, OH, 44132 (216) 731-2690

Licensure Intermediate Care. *Beds* 30. *Certified* Medicaid.
Ownership Proprietary.

Euclid General Hospital
E 185th St and Lake Erie, Euclid, OH, 44119 (216) 531-9000
Medical Dir/Dir of Nursing John G Nemunaitis MD.
Licensure Skilled Care. *Beds* 24.
Admissions Requirements Minimum age 14; Physician's request.
Staff Physicians 2 (pt); RNs 4 (ft), 6 (pt); LPNs 5 (ft), 5 (pt); Orderlies 1 (ft); Nurses aides 5 (ft); Physical therapists 2 (ft), 1 (pt); Recreational therapists 1 (ft), 1 (pt); Occupational therapists 2 (ft); Speech therapists 2 (ft); Dietitians 1 (ft).
Facilities Dining room; Physical therapy room; Activities room; Chapel; Crafts room; Laundry room; Barber/Beauty shop.
Activities Arts and Crafts; Cards; Games; Movies; Dances/Social or cultural gatherings.
Description Weekly education program are conducted for the patients and families to enable the patient to return to their own home.

Mount Saint Joseph*
21800 Chardon Rd, Euclid, OH, 44117
Licensure Skilled Care; Intermediate Care.
Beds 100. *Certified* Medicaid; Medicare.
Ownership Nonprofit.

Park Rehabilitation Center*
20611 Euclid Ave, Euclid, OH, 44117 (216) 486-9300
Licensure Skilled Care; Intermediate Care.
Beds 237. *Certified* Medicaid; Medicare.
Ownership Proprietary.

Rose-Mary, The Grasselli Rehabilitation and Education Center*
19350 Euclid Ave, Euclid, OH, 44117
Licensure Intermediate Care for Mentally Retarded. *Beds* 40. *Certified* Medicaid.
Ownership Nonprofit.

FAIRBORN

Christel Manor Nursing Home*
789 Stoneybrook Trail, Fairborn, OH, 45324 (513) 878-0262
Licensure Intermediate Care. *Beds* 100. *Certified* Medicaid.
Ownership Proprietary.

Heritage Inn Nursing Home*
201 W Dayton Dr, Fairborn, OH, 45324 (513) 878-6153
Licensure Intermediate Care. *Beds* 34. *Certified* Medicaid.
Ownership Proprietary.

FAIRFIELD

Community Multicare Center
908 Symmes Rd, Fairfield, OH, 45014 (513) 868-6500
Medical Dir/Dir of Nursing Kurt Landé MD.
Licensure Skilled Care; Intermediate Care.
Beds 101. *Certified* Medicaid; Medicare.
Ownership Proprietary.

Staff Physicians 1 (pt); Physical therapists 1 (ft), 1 (pt); Occupational therapists 2 (pt); Speech therapists 1 (pt); Activities coordinators 1 (ft); Dietitians 1 (ft).
Facilities Dining room; Physical therapy room; Activities room; Laundry room; Barber/Beauty shop.
Activities Arts and Crafts; Cards; Games; Reading groups; Prayer groups; Movies; Shopping trips; Dances/Social or cultural gatherings.
Description A facility where a holistic approach is taken to the patient and rehabilitation is a process in which the entire health care team participates. The rehabilitation department consists of a physical therapist, occupational therapist, speech pathologist, and social worker for both inpatient and outpatient care. JCAH accredited.

Crestwood Care Center*
PO Box 169, 6200 Pleasant Ave, Fairfield, OH, 45014 (513) 829-5349
Licensure Skilled Care; Intermediate Care.
Beds 60. *Certified* Medicaid; Medicare.
Ownership Proprietary.

Tri-County Extended Care Center*
5200 Camelot Dr, Fairfield, OH, 45014 (513) 874-3390
Licensure Skilled Care; Intermediate Care.
Beds 254. *Certified* Medicaid; Medicare.
Ownership Proprietary.

FAIRLAWN

Fairlawn Chateau
200 Wyant Rd, Fairlawn, OH, 44313 (216) 836-7953
Medical Dir/Dir of Nursing Robert Norman MD.
Licensure Intermediate Care. *Beds* 200. *Certified* Medicaid.
Ownership Proprietary.
Admissions Requirements Medical examination.
Staff Physicians 20 (ft); RNs 5 (ft), 3 (pt); LPNs 18 (ft), 5 (pt); Orderlies 10 (ft); Nurses aides 34 (ft), 10 (pt); Activities coordinators 1 (ft), 1 (pt); Dietitians 1 (ft); Social workers 1 (ft).
Facilities Dining room; Physical therapy room; Activities room; Chapel; Crafts room; Laundry room; Barber/Beauty shop.
Activities Arts and Crafts; Cards; Games; Reading groups; Prayer groups; Movies; Shopping trips; Dances/Social or cultural gatherings.
Description Thorough staff orientation program emphasizes patients' emotional needs as well as physical. Activities offered include biweekly picnics in summer, monthly "residents meal of the month" selected from residents' requests, regular lunch outings, van trips, bowling, and fishing.

FELICITY

Longworth Manor
Main and Union Sts, Felicity, OH, 45120 (513) 579-9644
Admin Patricia Driggs.
Licensure Intermediate Care for Mentally

Retarded. *Beds* 30. *Certified* Medicaid. *Ownership* Nonprofit.
Admissions Requirements Minimum age 21.
Staff Physicians 3 (pt); RNs 2 (pt); LPNs 3 (ft), 1 (pt); Nurses aides 6 (ft), 3 (pt); Occupational therapists 1 (pt); Speech therapists 1 (pt); Activities coordinators 1 (ft); Dietitians 1 (pt); Dentists 1 (pt); Ophthalmologists 1 (pt); Podiatrists 1 (pt); Audiologists 1 (pt).
Facilities Dining room; Activities room; Laundry room.
Activities Arts and Crafts; Games; Prayer groups; Shopping trips.
Description Facility for mild to moderate mentally retarded adults. Emphasis is on habilitation and normalization in activities of daily living.

FINDLAY

Fox Run Manor*
2101 Greendale Blvd, Findlay, OH, 45840 (419) 424-0832
Licensure Skilled Care; Intermediate Care.
Beds 100. *Certified* Medicaid; Medicare.
Ownership Proprietary.

Heritage Manor
2820 Greenacre Dr, Findlay, OH, 45840 (419) 424-0402
Medical Dir/Dir of Nursing Chester Samuelson MD.
Licensure Skilled Care. *Beds* 150. *Certified* Medicare.
Ownership Proprietary.
Staff RNs 4 (ft), 1 (pt); LPNs 8 (ft), 1 (pt); Nurses aides 29 (ft), 1 (pt); Physical therapists 1 (pt); Reality therapists 1 (pt); Recreational therapists 1 (pt); Activities coordinators 1 (ft); Dietitians 1 (pt).
Facilities Dining room; Physical therapy room; Activities room; Chapel; Crafts room; Laundry room; Barber/Beauty shop.
Activities Arts and Crafts; Cards; Games; Reading groups; Prayer groups; Movies; Shopping trips; Dances/Social or cultural gatherings.
Description Approximately 50% of admissions return home after a short period (1-3 months) of intensive therapy.

Judson Palmer Home
PO Box 119, Findlay, OH, 45840 (419) 422-9599
Admin Lester B Moss. *Medical Dir/Dir of Nursing* Dr T Shoupe.
Licensure Rest Home. *Beds* 18.
Ownership Nonprofit.
Admissions Requirements Minimum age 55; Medical examination.
Staff Physicians 1 (pt); RNs 1 (ft); Nurses aides 4 (ft), 7 (pt); Dietitians 2 (pt).
Facilities Dining room; Laundry room; Barber/Beauty shop.
Activities Cards; Prayer groups.

Manley's Manor Nursing Home Inc*
1918 N Main St, Findlay, OH, 45840
Licensure Nursing Home. *Beds* 50.
Ownership Proprietary.

Marlesta 1
401 Infirmary Rd, Findlay, OH, 45840 (419) 423-9183
Medical Dir/Dir of Nursing Dr C L Samuelson.
Licensure Intermediate Care. *Beds* 40. *Certified* Medicaid.
Ownership Proprietary.
Admissions Requirements Medical examination.
Staff Physicians 1 (pt); RNs 2 (pt); LPNs 4 (ft); Nurses aides 9 (ft), 4 (pt); Activities coordinators 1 (ft); Dietitians 1 (pt).
Facilities Dining room; Activities room; Crafts room.
Activities Arts and Crafts; Cards; Games; Reading groups; Movies.
Description Facility provides quality nursing care at minimal expense to the resident and family; located in beautiful country setting giving personal care with a personal family touch where the resident comes first; especially proud of home-cooked meals.

Marlesta 2
401 Infirmary Rd, Findlay, OH, 45840 (419) 422-3978
Medical Dir/Dir of Nursing C L Samuelson MD.
Licensure Intermediate Care. *Beds* 60. *Certified* Medicaid.
Ownership Proprietary.
Admissions Requirements Medical examination; Physician's request.
Staff Physicians 1 (pt); RNs 1 (pt); LPNs 4 (ft), 3 (pt); Nurses aides 14 (ft), 3 (pt); Activities coordinators 1 (ft).
Facilities Dining room; Activities room; Laundry room; Barber/Beauty shop; Examination room.
Activities Arts and Crafts; Cards; Games; Reading groups; Movies.
Description Facility enjoys a country setting with informal or family atmosphere where residents are treated as individuals; outstanding home cooked meals served.

Winebrenner Extended Care Facility
425 Frazer St, Findlay, OH, 45840 (419) 424-9591
Medical Dir/Dir of Nursing C L Samuelson MD.
Licensure Intermediate Care. *Beds* 150. *Certified* Medicaid.
Ownership Nonprofit.
Admissions Requirements Medical examination.
Staff Physicians 1 (pt); RNs 4 (ft), 6 (pt); LPNs 9 (ft), 6 (pt); Physical therapists 1 (pt); Activities coordinators 2 (ft); Dietitians 1 (ft).
Affiliation Church of God
Facilities Dining room; Chapel; Laundry room; Barber/Beauty shop; Solarium; Gift shop.
Activities Arts and Crafts; Games; Reading groups; Prayer groups; Movies; Shopping trips.
Description Winebrenner Village provides a complete range of total care for the resident including cottages, assisted living, and extended care. The village is dedicated to elderly people of the church and community affording them gracious living, modern day care, security, and Christian fellowship in their advancing years.

Winebrenner Haven
425 Frazer St, Findlay, OH, 45840 (419) 422-2773
Medical Dir/Dir of Nursing C L Samuelson MD.
Licensure Intermediate Care. *Beds* 24. *Certified* Medicaid.
Ownership Nonprofit.
Admissions Requirements Medical examination.
Staff Physicians 1 (pt); LPNs 3 (ft), 2 (pt); Nurses aides 2 (pt); Activities coordinators 1 (ft).
Affiliation Church of God
Facilities Dining room; Activities room; Chapel; Laundry room; Barber/Beauty shop; Library.
Activities Arts and Crafts; Cards; Games; Reading groups; Prayer groups; Movies; Shopping trips.
Description Winebrenner Village provides a complete range of total care for the resident including cottages, assisted living, and extended care. The village is dedicated to elderly people of the church and community affording them gracious living, modern day care, security, and Christian fellowship in their advancing years.

FLAT ROCK

Flat Rock Children's Center*
Country Rd 29, Flat Rock, OH, 44828
Licensure Skilled Care; Intermediate Care for Mentally Retarded. *Beds* 29. *Certified* Medicaid.
Ownership Nonprofit.

FLUSHING

Hillview Nursing Home
E High St, Box 33, Flushing, OH, 43977 (614) 968-3113
Medical Dir/Dir of Nursing Dr Modi.
Licensure Intermediate Care. *Beds* 23. *Certified* Medicaid.
Ownership Proprietary.
Admissions Requirements Medical examination.
Staff Physicians 1 (ft); RNs 1 (ft); LPNs 2 (ft), 3 (pt); Nurses aides 4 (ft), 4 (pt); Dietitians 1 (pt).
Facilities Dining room; Laundry room.
Activities Arts and Crafts; Cards; Games; Prayer groups.

FOSTORIA

Edgewood Manor of Fostoria Inc
25 Christopoher Dr, Fostoria, OH, 44830 (419) 435-8112
Admin Marilyn J Smith. *Medical Dir/Dir of Nursing* L W Watson MD.
Licensure Skilled Care; Intermediate Care.
Beds 60. *Certified* Medicaid; Medicare.
Ownership Proprietary.
Admissions Requirements Medical examination; Physician's request.
Staff RNs 1 (ft), 2 (pt); LPNs 8 (ft), 2 (pt); Orderlies 1 (ft), 2 (pt); Nurses aides 11 (ft), 16 (pt); Physical therapists 1 (pt); Activities coordinators 1 (ft).

Facilities Dining room; Activities room; Laundry room; Barber/Beauty shop; Lounge.
Activities Cards; Games; Prayer groups; Movies; Community entertainment.
Description Facility is located at edge of city in well-kept residential area with plenty of lawn and trees; known primarily for excellent nursing care; good reputation with physicians; key personnel have long tenures; family involvement encouraged.

Good Shepherd Home
725 Columbus Ave, PO Box G, Fostoria, OH, 44830 (419) 435-1801
Licensure Intermediate Care. *Beds* 100. *Certified* Medicaid.
Ownership Nonprofit.
Admissions Requirements Medical examination.
Staff RNs 3 (ft), 2 (pt); LPNs 10 (ft), 3 (pt); Orderlies 3 (ft), 3 (pt); Nurses aides 38 (ft), 17 (pt); Physical therapists 1 (pt); Recreational therapists 2 (ft); Speech therapists 1 (pt); Activities coordinators 1 (ft).
Affiliation Church of the Brethren

FOWLER

Meadow Brook Manor Nursing Home*
Angling Rd No 1, Fowler, OH, 44418 (216) 772-5253
Licensure Intermediate Care. *Beds* 52. *Certified* Medicaid.
Ownership Proprietary.

FRANKFORT

Valley View Manor
3363 Ragged Ridge Rd, Frankfort, OH, 45628 (614) 998-2948
Medical Dir/Dir of Nursing Dr Patrick J McKibben.
Licensure Intermediate Care. *Beds* 44. *Certified* Medicaid.
Ownership Proprietary.
Admissions Requirements Medical examination.
Staff Physicians 2 (ft); RNs 1 (ft); LPNs 3 (ft), 2 (pt); Nurses aides 2 (ft), 7 (pt); Activities coordinators 2 (ft); Dietitians 1 (pt).
Facilities Dining room; Activities room; Crafts room; Laundry room; Barber/Beauty shop; Library.
Activities Arts and Crafts; Cards; Games; Movies; Shopping trips.

FRANKLIN

Carlisle Manor
730 Hillcrest Ave, Franklin, OH, 45005 (513) 746-2662
Admin Terri L Dickey. *Medical Dir/Dir of Nursing* Harvey Kiley DO.
Licensure Intermediate Care. *Beds* 44. *Certified* Medicaid.
Ownership Proprietary.
Staff Physicians 1 (ft); RNs 3 (ft); LPNs 5 (ft); Nurses aides 9 (ft), 2 (pt); Physical therapists 1 (pt); Occupational therapists 1 (pt); Activities coordinators 1 (ft); Dietitians 1 (pt); Dentists 1 (pt); Ophthalmologists 1 (pt); Podiatrists 1 (pt);

Audiologists 1 (pt).
Facilities Dining room; Activities room; Laundry room.
Activities Arts and Crafts; Cards; Games; Reading groups; Prayer groups; Movies; Shopping trips; Dances/Social or cultural gatherings.

Franklin Nursing Home of Franklin
422 Mission Lane, Franklin, OH, 45005 (513) 746-3943
Medical Dir/Dir of Nursing Scott Swope DO.
Licensure Skilled Care; Intermediate Care. *Beds* 99. *Certified* Medicaid; Medicare.
Ownership Proprietary.
Admissions Requirements Minimum age 18; Medical examination.
Staff Physicians 2 (pt); RNs 3 (ft), 3 (pt); LPNs 9 (ft), 3 (pt); Orderlies 3 (ft); Nurses aides 35 (ft), 1 (pt); Physical therapists 1 (pt); Occupational therapists 1 (pt); Speech therapists 1 (pt); Activities coordinators 2 (ft); Dietitians 1 (pt); Dentists 1 (pt); Ophthalmologists 1 (pt); Podiatrists 1 (pt); Audiologists 1 (pt).
Facilities Dining room; Physical therapy room; Activities room; Laundry room; Barber/Beauty shop; Patient lounges; Formal living room.
Activities Arts and Crafts; Cards; Games; Reading groups; Prayer groups; Movies; Shopping trips; Dances/Social or cultural gatherings.

Zartman Nursing Home*
120 S Main St, Franklin, OH, 45005 (513) 746-9588
Licensure Nursing Home. *Beds* 10.
Ownership Nonprofit.

FRANKLIN FURNACE

Fountainhead Nursing Home*
PO Box 36, Old Rt 52, Franklin Furnace, OH, 45629 (614) 574-6200
Licensure Intermediate Care. *Beds* 30. *Certified* Medicaid.
Ownership Proprietary.

FREDERICKTOWN

Hillcrest Nursing Home Inc*
Rt 3, Painter Rd, Fredericktown, OH, 43019
Licensure Intermediate Care. *Beds* 44. *Certified* Medicaid.
Ownership Proprietary.

Salem Home*
26 Salem Ave, Fredericktown, OH, 43019
Licensure Nursing Home. *Beds* 25.
Ownership Proprietary.

FREEMONT

Bethesda Care Center*
600 N Broad St, Freemont, OH, 43420 (419) 334-9521
Licensure Skilled Care; Intermediate Care. *Beds* 19. *Certified* Medicaid; Medicare.
Ownership Nonprofit.

FREMONT

Countryside Continuing Care Center
1865 Countryside Dr, Fremont, OH, 43420 (419) 334-2602
Admin Bryon Eshelman. *Medical Dir/Dir of Nursing* Michael J Hazlett MD.
Licensure Skilled Care; Intermediate Care. *Beds* 119. *Certified* Medicaid; Medicare.
Ownership Public.
Admissions Requirements Medical examination.
Staff Physicians 1 (ft); RNs 4 (ft); LPNs 10 (ft), 6 (pt); Nurses aides 49 (ft), 17 (pt); Physical therapists 1 (pt); Reality therapists 1 (pt); Occupational therapists 1 (pt); Speech therapists 1 (pt); Activities coordinators 1 (ft); Dietitians 1 (ft); Dentists 1 (pt); Podiatrists 2 (pt).
Facilities Dining room; Physical therapy room; Activities room; Chapel; Crafts room; Laundry room; Barber/Beauty shop.
Activities Arts and Crafts; Cards; Games; Prayer groups; Movies; Shopping trips; Dances/Social or cultural gatherings.
Description Center has adopted the philosophy that each resident is a unique individual; as a human being, each person is entitled to dignity, respect, consideration, growth, and the opportunity to lead as full and satisfying a life as possible.

Fremont Quality Care Nursing Center
825 June St, Fremont, OH, 43420 (419) 332-0357
Medical Dir/Dir of Nursing Dr John Gray.
Licensure Intermediate Care. *Beds* 100. *Certified* Medicaid.
Ownership Proprietary.
Admissions Requirements Medical examination.
Staff Physicians 1 (pt); RNs 1 (ft), 3 (pt); LPNs 6 (ft), 5 (pt); Orderlies 1 (ft); Nurses aides 24 (ft), 17 (pt); Activities coordinators 1 (ft); Dietitians 1 (pt); Social workers 1 (ft).
Facilities Dining room; Activities room; Laundry room; Barber/Beauty shop.
Activities Arts and Crafts; Cards; Games; Prayer groups; Movies; Shopping trips.
Description Center is a beautiful, modern facility located in a quiet, residential area.

Parkview Care Center
1406 Oak Harbor Rd, Fremont, OH, 43420 (419) 332-2589
Medical Dir/Dir of Nursing Dr Lowery.
Licensure Intermediate Care. *Beds* 50. *Certified* Medicaid.
Ownership Proprietary.
Admissions Requirements Medical examination.
Staff Physicians 1 (pt); RNs 1 (ft); LPNs 5 (ft), 1 (pt); Nurses aides 22 (ft); Physical therapists 1 (pt); Recreational therapists 1 (ft); Occupational therapists 1 (pt); Speech therapists 1 (pt); Activities coordinators 1 (ft); Dietitians 1 (pt); Dentists 1 (pt); Ophthalmologists 1 (pt); Podiatrists 1 (pt); Audiologists 1 (pt).

FULTON

Morning View Care Center 2*
PO Box 38, Fulton, OH, 43321 (419) 864-6941
Licensure Intermediate Care. *Beds* 50. *Certified* Medicaid.
Ownership Proprietary.

Morning View Care Center 2 Annex*
PO Box 38, Fulton, OH, 43321 (419) 864-6941
Licensure Intermediate Care. *Beds* 15.
Certified Medicaid.
Ownership Proprietary.

GAHANNA

Bon-Ing Care Center*
121 James Rd, Gahanna, OH, 43230
Licensure Intermediate Care. *Beds* 100. *Certified* Medicaid.
Ownership Proprietary.

GALION

Galion Nursing Home*
347 W Atwood St, Galion, OH, 44833 (419) 468-1893
Licensure Intermediate Care. *Beds* 50. *Certified* Medicaid.
Ownership Proprietary.

Rosewood Manor
935 Rosewood Dr, Galion, OH, 44833 (419) 468-7544
Admin Betty Wagner.
Licensure Skilled Care; Intermediate Care.
Beds 90. *Certified* Medicaid; Medicare.
Ownership Proprietary.
Staff Physicians 2 (pt); RNs 1 (ft), 3 (pt); LPNs 9 (ft), 3 (pt); Nurses aides 12 (ft), 15 (pt); Physical therapists 1 (pt); Speech therapists 1 (pt); Activities coordinators 1 (ft); Dietitians 1 (ft); Dentists 1 (pt); Podiatrists 1 (pt).
Facilities Dining room; Laundry room; Barber-/Beauty shop.
Activities Arts and Crafts; Cards; Games; Prayer groups; Movies; Shopping trips.

Village Care Center
925 Wagner Ave, Galion, OH, 44833 (419) 468-1090
Admin Helen J Lundon. *Medical Dir/Dir of Nursing* Dr William Mantley and Dr Warren Sawyer.
Licensure Skilled Care; Intermediate Care.
Beds 58. *Certified* Medicaid; Medicare.
Ownership Nonprofit.
Admissions Requirements Medical examination.
Staff Physicians 2 (pt); RNs 8 (ft), 4 (pt); LPNs 3 (ft), 9 (pt); Nurses aides 11 (ft), 22 (pt); Physical therapists 1 (pt); Reality therapists 1 (pt); Recreational therapists 1 (pt); Occupational therapists 1 (pt); Speech therapists 1 (pt); Activities coordinators 1 (ft), 1 (pt); Dietitians 1 (ft), 1 (pt); Dentists 1 (pt); Ophthalmologists 1 (pt); Podiatrists 1 (pt); Audiologists 1 (pt).
Facilities Dining room; Physical therapy room; Activities room; Crafts room; Laundry room; Barber/Beauty shop; Library; Greenhouse.
Activities Arts and Crafts; Cards; Games;

Reading groups; Prayer groups; Movies; Shopping trips; Dances/Social or cultural gatherings.
Description Facility is located on 5 acres, one floor, all rooms ground level, individual heating and air conditioniong, personalized staffing, 24-hour professional care, Medicare and Medicaid certified. No discrimination.

GALLIPOLIS

Alternative Residence Two Inc—Middleton Estates*
Rt 1, Gallipolis, OH, 45631
Licensure Intermediate Care for Mentally Retarded. *Beds* 32. *Certified* Medicaid.
Ownership Nonprofit.

Buckeye Community Services—Transitional Facility*
PO Box 906, Gallipolis, OH, 45631
Licensure Intermediate Care for Mentally Retarded. *Beds* 8. *Certified* Medicaid.
Ownership Nonprofit.

Gallipolis State Institute*
2500 Ohio Ave, Gallipolis, OH, 45631 (614) 446-1642
Licensure Intermediate Care for Mentally Retarded. *Beds* 320.
Ownership Public.

Pinecrest Care Center
555 Jackson Pike, Gallipolis, OH, 45631 (614) 446-7112
Medical Dir/Dir of Nursing Dr Balusamy Subbiah.
Licensure Skilled Care; Intermediate Care.
Beds 116. *Certified* Medicaid; Medicare.
Ownership Proprietary.
Admissions Requirements Physician's request.
Facilities Dining room; Physical therapy room; Activities room; Laundry room; Barber/Beauty shop.
Activities Arts and Crafts; Games; Reading groups; Prayer groups; Movies; Shopping trips.

GARFIELD HEIGHTS

Jennings Hall Inc
10204 Granger Rd, Garfield Heights, OH, 44125 (216) 581-2900
Medical Dir/Dir of Nursing Dr Sylvia Marshall.
Licensure Intermediate Care. *Beds* 100. *Certified* Medicaid.
Ownership Nonprofit.
Admissions Requirements Minimum age 65; Medical examination.
Staff Physicians; RNs; LPNs; Nurses aides; Physical therapists; Recreational therapists; Activities coordinators; Dietitians; Dentists; Ophthalmologists; Podiatrists.
Affiliation Roman Catholic
Facilities Dining room; Physical therapy room; Activities room; Chapel; Crafts room; Laundry room; Barber/Beauty shop; Library.
Activities Arts and Crafts; Cards; Games; Reading groups; Prayer groups; Movies; Shopping trips; Dances/Social or cultural gatherings.
Description Jennings Hall, Inc offers companionship, comfort and fine professional care. Set

in a peaceful suburban setting, each resident can find dignity, security, spiritual enrichment and years of deepening fulfillment.

GENEVA

Broadway Nursing Home*
162 S Broadway, Geneva, OH, 44041 (216) 466-4843
Licensure Intermediate Care. *Beds* 85. *Certified* Medicaid.
Ownership Proprietary.

Catherine Ellen Convalescent Home
750 Eastlawn Ave, Geneva, OH, 44041 (216) 466-3942
Medical Dir/Dir of Nursing Miroslav Kavur DO.
Licensure Intermediate Care. *Beds* 16. *Certified* Medicaid.
Ownership Proprietary.
Admissions Requirements Minimum age 25; Medical examination; Physician's request.
Staff RNs 1 (pt); LPNs 4 (ft), 1 (pt); Nurses aides 8 (ft); Activities coordinators 1 (ft).
Facilities Dining room; Laundry room.
Activities Arts and Crafts; Cards; Games; Prayer groups; Shopping trips.
Description Small home-like facility offers individualized care; picnics at beach in summer; bowling team.

Con Lea Nursing Home*
388 S Broadway, Geneva, OH, 44041 (216) 466-3512
Licensure Intermediate Care. *Beds* 42. *Certified* Medicaid.
Ownership Proprietary.

Esther Marie Nursing Center*
60 West St, Geneva, OH, 44041 (216) 466-1181
Licensure Intermediate Care. *Beds* 53. *Certified* Medicaid.
Ownership Proprietary.

Geneva Medicare Nursing Center
840 Sherman St, Geneva, OH, 44041 (216) 466-4881
Admin David W Martin. *Medical Dir/Dir of Nursing* Cheng-Nan Huang MD.
Licensure Skilled Care; Intermediate Care.
Beds 106. *Certified* Medicaid; Medicare.
Ownership Proprietary.
Admissions Requirements Minimum age 16; Medical examination; Physician's request.
Staff Physicians 8 (pt); RNs 6 (ft); LPNs 9 (ft); Orderlies 1 (pt); Nurses aides 33 (ft); Physical therapists 1 (pt); Speech therapists 1 (pt); Activities coordinators 2 (ft); Dietitians 1 (pt); Dentists 1 (pt); Podiatrists 1 (pt); Audiologists 1 (pt).
Facilities Dining room; Physical therapy room; Activities room; Crafts room; Laundry room; Barber/Beauty shop.
Activities Arts and Crafts; Cards; Games, Reading groups; Prayer groups; Movies; Shopping trips; Dances/Social or cultural gatherings.
Description Facility is an attractive, odor-free, one-story building with free cable TV available, spacious dining and living rooms, 45 inch wide-screen TV, and enclosed courtyard in a

rural location. Staffed by a capable, professional staff. Winner of OHCA Buckeye Award for quality care.

Homestead Nursing Home*
599 W Main St, Geneva, OH, 44041 (216) 466-1079
Licensure Intermediate Care for Mentally Retarded. *Beds* 50. *Certified* Medicaid.
Ownership Proprietary.

Lakeland Nursing Home
PO Box 271, Geneva, OH, 44041 (216) 466-1678
Medical Dir/Dir of Nursing John Popovick MD.
Licensure Intermediate Care for Mentally Retarded. *Beds* 25.
Ownership Proprietary.
Admissions Requirements Minimum age 18; Medical examination.
Staff Physicians 1 (pt); RNs 1 (ft); LPNs 3 (ft); Nurses aides 9 (ft), 3 (pt); Occupational therapists 1 (pt); Activities coordinators 1 (ft); Dietitians 1 (pt).
Facilities Dining room; Activities room; Crafts room; Laundry room.
Activities Arts and Crafts; Cards; Games; Prayer groups; Movies; Shopping trips; Dances/Social or cultural gatherings.
Description Programs are developed to enhance the growth of residents in the social, physical, and mental areas of their day-to-day living. This long-term care facility is their permanent home.

Manor Home*
PO Box 640, 246 N Broadway, Geneva, OH, 44041 (216) 466-1808
Licensure Intermediate Care for Mentally Retarded. *Beds* 50. *Certified* Medicaid.
Ownership Proprietary.

Rae-Ann Geneva*
PO Box 653, 839 W Main St, Geneva, OH, 44041 (216) 466-5733
Licensure Intermediate Care. *Beds* 77. *Certified* Medicaid.
Ownership Proprietary.

GEORGETOWN

Georgetown Nursing Home Inc
312 W State St, Georgetown, OH, 45121 (513) 378-6616
Admin Dr McGann.
Licensure Intermediate Care. *Beds* 33. *Certified* Medicaid.
Ownership Proprietary.
Staff Physicians 1 (pt); RNs 3 (ft), 6 (pt); Nurses aides 14 (ft), 2 (pt); Activities coordinators 1 (ft); Dietitians 1 (pt).
Facilities Dining room; Activities room; Laundry room; Barber/Beauty shop.
Activities Arts and Crafts; Cards; Games; Reading groups; Prayer groups; Movies; Shopping trips; Dances/Social or cultural gatherings.
Description Georgetown Nursing Home, Inc is a 33-bed facility with a home-like atmosphere where we care for the people we care for. Recent remodeling projects have produced a new kitchen where meals are prepared from RD

supervised diets and a new nursing station for more efficient management and the best patient care available.

Meadow Wood Nursing Home Inc
Stephens Ave, Georgetown, OH, 45121 (513) 378-3727
Admin Jack Crout. *Medical Dir/Dir of Nursing* Leslie Hampton MD.
Licensure Skilled Care; Intermediate Care. *Beds* 49. *Certified* Medicaid; Medicare.
Ownership Proprietary.
Admissions Requirements Medical examination.
Staff Physicians 6 (pt); RNs 2 (ft), 2 (pt); LPNs 4 (ft), 3 (pt); Orderlies 3 (ft), 4 (pt); Nurses aides 11 (ft), 18 (pt); Physical therapists 1 (pt); Speech therapists 1 (pt); Activities coordinators 1 (pt); Dietitians 1 (pt); Dentists 1 (pt); Podiatrists 1 (pt); Audiologists 1 (pt).
Facilities Dining room; Physical therapy room; Activities room.
Activities Arts and Crafts; Cards; Games; Movies; Dances/Social or cultural gatherings.
Description Facility has rural setting with homey atmosphere.

GLENDALE

Saint Mary's Memorial Home*
469 Albion Ave, Glendale, OH, 45246 (513) 771-2170
Licensure Nursing Home. *Beds* 21.
Ownership Nonprofit.

GRAND RAPIDS

Rapids Nursing Home
24305 3rd St, Grand Rapids, OH, 43522 (419) 832-5195
Licensure Intermediate Care. *Beds* 25. *Certified* Medicaid.
Ownership Proprietary.
Admissions Requirements Medical examination.
Staff RNs 1 (ft), 1 (pt); LPNs 2 (ft), 2 (pt); Nurses aides 8 (ft), 2 (pt); Activities coordinators 1 (ft); Dietitians 1 (pt).
Facilities Dining room; Crafts room; Laundry room; Barber/Beauty shop.
Activities Arts and Crafts; Cards; Games; Prayer groups; Movies; Shopping trips; Dances/Social or cultural gatherings.
Description Facility is located in a historical tourist area geared toward a family/hospitable style of living.

GREEN SPRINGS

Elmwood
430 Broadway St, Green Springs, OH, 44836 (419) 639-2581
Admin Kathy Luhring. *Medical Dir/Dir of Nursing* Roberto Pagarigan MD.
Licensure Intermediate Care. *Beds* 31. *Certified* Medicaid.
Ownership Proprietary.
Admissions Requirements Medical examination.
Staff Physicians 1 (pt); RNs 1 (ft), 1 (pt); LPNs 3 (ft); Nurses aides 10 (ft), 10 (pt); Physical

therapists; Reality therapists; Recreational therapists; Occupational therapists; Speech therapists; Activities coordinators 1 (ft); Dentists; Ophthalmologists; Podiatrists; Audiologists.
Facilities Dining room; Activities room; Laundry room; Barber/Beauty shop; Living room.
Activities Arts and Crafts; Cards; Games; Reading groups; Prayer groups; Movies; Shopping trips; Dances/Social or cultural gatherings; Happy hour; Diners' club; Camping trips; Devotions; Sunday drives; Ice cream socials.
Description Elmwood is a very family oriented facility offering homemade delicious meals. Residents are taken out of the facility as much as possible. Residents are given a lot of personal attention and love.

Saint Francis Rehabilitation Hospital and Nursing Home
401 N Boadway St, Green Springs, OH, 44836 (419) 639-2626
Medical Dir/Dir of Nursing William R Bauer MD.
Licensure Skilled Care; Intermediate Care. *Beds* SNF 40; ICF 146. *Certified* Medicaid; Medicare.
Ownership Nonprofit.
Admissions Requirements Minimum age 13; Physician's request.
Staff Physicians 1 (ft), 22 (pt); RNs 15 (ft), 7 (pt); LPNs 20 (ft), 21 (pt); Orderlies 4 (ft), 3 (pt); Nurses aides 68 (ft), 56 (pt); Physical therapists 10 (ft), 1 (pt); Reality therapists 2 (ft); Recreational therapists 4 (ft), 2 (pt); Occupational therapists 10 (ft); Speech therapists 4 (ft); Activities coordinators 1 (ft); Dietitians 2 (ft); Dentists 1 (pt); Ophthalmologists 1 (pt); Podiatrists 1 (pt); Audiologists 1 (pt).
Affiliation Roman Catholic
Facilities Dining room; Physical therapy room; Activities room; Chapel; Crafts room; Laundry room; Barber/Beauty shop.
Activities Arts and Crafts; Cards; Games; Reading groups; Prayer groups; Movies; Shopping trips; Dances/Social or cultural gatherings; Camping.
Description An integrated approach enabling patients/residents from all age and disability ranges to work toward independence together.

GREENFIELD

Buckingham Nursing Home*
238 S Washington St, Greenfield, OH, 45123 (513) 981-3349
Licensure Intermediate Care. *Beds* 22. *Certified* Medicaid.
Ownership Proprietary.

Greenfield Manor*
850 Nellie St, Greenfield, OH, 45123 (513) 981-2165
Licensure Skilled Care; Intermediate Care. *Beds* 63. *Certified* Medicaid; Medicare.
Ownership Proprietary.

GREENVILLE

Brethren's Home
750 Chestnut St, Greenville, OH, 45331 (513) 548-4117

Admin Robert D Cain Jr.
Licensure Skilled Care; Intermediate Care; Independent. *Beds* SNF 160; ICF 93; Independent 250. *Certified* Medicaid; Medicare.
Ownership Nonprofit.
Admissions Requirements Medical examination.
Affiliation Church of the Brethren
Facilities Dining room; Physical therapy room; Activities room; Chapel; Crafts room; Laundry room; Barber/Beauty shop; Library.
Activities Arts and Crafts; Cards; Games; Reading groups; Prayer groups; Shopping trips; Dances/Social or cultural gatherings.
Description Facility is a Christian retirement community with health services. Attractive, modern, facility located in west central Ohio; sponsored by the Southeren Ohio District Church of the Brethren.

Gade Nursing Home Inc*
405 Chestnut St, Greenville, OH, 45331 (513) 548-1993
Licensure Skilled Care; Intermediate Care. *Beds* 51. *Certified* Medicaid; Medicare.
Ownership Proprietary.

Gade Nursing Home Inc*
208 Sweitzer St, Greenville, OH, 45331 (513) 548-1913
Licensure Intermediate Care. *Beds* 19. *Certified* Medicaid.
Ownership Proprietary.

Heartland of Greenville*
130 Marion Dr, Greenville, OH, 45331 (513) 548-3141, 3142
Licensure Skilled Care; Intermediate Care. *Beds* 70. *Certified* Medicaid; Medicare.
Ownership Proprietary.

Rest Haven Nursing Home Inc
1096 N Ohio St, Greenville, OH, 45331 (513) 548-1138 and 548-4405
Admin Elma L Moss. *Medical Dir/Dir of Nursing* Dr Alvin Heise.
Licensure Skilled Care; Intermediate Care. *Beds* 68. *Certified* Medicaid; Medicare.
Ownership Proprietary.
Admissions Requirements Minimum age 20; Medical examination.
Staff RNs 2 (ft), 3 (pt); LPNs 5 (ft), 3 (pt); Nurses aides 20 (ft), 17 (pt); Physical therapists; Recreational therapists 1 (pt); Speech therapists; Activities coordinators 1 (pt); Dietitians 1 (ft); Dentists; Podiatrists.
Facilities Dining room; Physical therapy room; Chapel; Laundry room; Barber/Beauty shop.
Activities Arts and Crafts; Cards; Games; Prayer groups; Movies; Trips to fairs, parades, and more.
Description This home provides skilled nursing care but still maintains a warm homey atmosphere; very active activities department which keeps residents occupied.

GROVE CITY

Monterey Nursing Inn*
3929 Hoover Rd, Grove City, OH, 43123 (614) 875-7700

Licensure Skilled Care; Intermediate Care. *Beds* 200. *Certified* Medicaid; Medicare.
Ownership Proprietary.

HAMDEN

Huston Nursing Home Inc*
Rt 1, Hamden, OH, 45634 (614) 384-3485
Licensure Skilled Care; Intermediate Care. *Beds* 77. *Certified* Medicaid; Medicare.
Ownership Proprietary.

HAMILTON

Butler County Home*
1800 Princeton Rd, Hamilton, OH, 45011 (513) 837-5721
Licensure Intermediate Care. *Beds* 101. *Certified* Medicaid.
Ownership Public.

Centerhaven Nursing Home*
422 N 2nd St, Hamilton, OH, 45011 (513) 893-1661
Licensure Intermediate Care. *Beds* 29. *Certified* Medicaid.
Ownership Proprietary.

Fairfield Nursing Home*
4070 Hamilton-Mason Rd, Hamilton, OH, 45011 (513) 868-8861
Licensure Intermediate Care. *Beds* 82. *Certified* Medicaid.
Ownership Proprietary.

Glenward Health Care Center
3472 Hamilton-Mason Rd, Hamilton, OH, 45011
Admin Glyndon Powell. *Medical Dir/Dir of Nursing* Edward Drohan MD.
Licensure Skilled Care; Intermediate Care. *Beds* 117. *Certified* Medicaid; Medicare.
Ownership Proprietary.
Admissions Requirements Minimum age 18.
Staff Physicians 6 (pt); RNs 12 (ft), 1 (pt); LPNs 12 (ft), 1 (pt); Nurses aides 47 (ft), 3 (pt); Physical therapists 2 (ft); Reality therapists 2 (ft); Recreational therapists 1 (ft), 1 (pt); Occupational therapists 1 (pt); Speech therapists 1 (pt); Activities coordinators 1 (ft), 1 (pt); Dietitians 1 (pt); Dentists 1 (pt); Ophthalmologists 1 (pt); Podiatrists 1 (pt); Audiologists 1 (pt).
Facilities Dining room; Physical therapy room; Activities room; Crafts room; Laundry room; Barber/Beauty shop.
Activities Arts and Crafts; Cards; Games; Reading groups; Prayer groups; Movies; Shopping trips; Dances/Social or cultural gatherings.
Description Volunteer groups from the community provide some activities and religious programs.

Golden Years Healthcare
2436 Old Oxford Rd, Hamilton, OH, 45013 (513) 893-0471
Medical Dir/Dir of Nursing Harry Davin MD.
Licensure Intermediate Care. *Beds* 50. *Certified* Medicaid.
Ownership Proprietary.
Staff RNs 2 (pt); LPNs 3 (ft), 3 (pt); Nurses aides 9 (ft), 5 (pt); Activities coordinators 1 (ft);

Dietitians 1 (pt).
Facilities Dining room; Laundry room; Barber/Beauty shop.
Activities Arts and Crafts; Cards; Games; Dances/Social or cultural gatherings.
Description Facility features 10 acres of beautiful country grounds and a one-acre lake with family-style living, home-style meals, and 24-hour professional nursing.

Greenwood Quality Care Center
925 Greenwood Ave, Hamilton, OH, 45011 (513) 867-8334
Admin M O'Reilly. *Medical Dir/Dir of Nursing* Dr E Ringel.
Licensure Intermediate Care. *Beds* 27. *Certified* Medicaid.
Ownership Proprietary.
Admissions Requirements Medical examination.
Staff Physicians; LPNs; Orderlies; Nurses aides; Physical therapists; Recreational therapists; Occupational therapists; Speech therapists; Activities coordinators; Dietitians; Dentists; Podiatrists.
Facilities Dining room; Activities room; Laundry room.
Activities Arts and Crafts; Cards; Games; Shopping trips.
Description Facility provides personalized care in a home-like atmosphere and specializes in those individuals with mental, emotional, and behavioral problems; one of 6 homes under Buckeye Quality Care Centers, Inc.

Helton's Nursing Home*
819 Buckeye St, Hamilton, OH, 45011 (513) 868-8842
Licensure Intermediate Care. *Beds* 26. *Certified* Medicaid.
Ownership Proprietary.

Hillandale Nursing Home*
4195 Hamilton-Mason Rd, Hamilton, OH, 45011 (513) 868-2266
Licensure Nursing Home. *Beds* 53.
Ownership Proprietary.

Mary Black Schroder Home for Aging Inc
1302 Millville Ave, Hamilton, OH, 45013 (513) 867-1300
Medical Dir/Dir of Nursing Kurt Landé MD.
Licensure Skilled Care; Rest Home. *Beds* 23. *Certified* Medicare.
Ownership Proprietary.
Admissions Requirements Medical examination.
Staff Physicians 1 (pt); RNs 3 (ft), 2 (pt); LPNs 2 (ft), 3 (pt); Orderlies 1 (ft); Nurses aides 7 (ft), 9 (pt); Physical therapists 1 (pt); Recreational therapists 3 (pt); Speech therapists 1 (pt); Activities coordinators 1 (pt); Dietitians 1 (ft), 1 (pt); Dentists 1 (pt); Audiologists 1 (pt).
Affiliation Roman Catholic
Facilities Dining room; Physical therapy room; Activities room; Chapel; Crafts room; Laundry room; Barber/Beauty shop; Library; Outdoor shelter.
Activities Arts and Crafts; Cards; Games; Reading groups; Prayer groups; Movies; Shopping trips; Dances/Social or cultural gatherings; Shuffleboard.
Description Schroder Manor offers a real home

for active retirement in a spiritual setting; open to active seniors regardless of sex, race, religion, or national origin. Facility now offers 3 levels of care and will soon open the new independent living units presently under construction. Facility located on bus line, close to shopping centers, and situated on a beautifully landscaped area with 2 lakes; real country atmosphere with city conveniences.

Powell's Convalescent Home*
PO Box 845, 2923 Hamilton-Mason Rd, Hamilton, OH, 45011 (513) 863-0360
Licensure Skilled Care; Intermediate Care. *Beds* 99. *Certified* Medicaid; Medicare. *Ownership* Proprietary.

Sunny Breeze Healthcare
350 Hancock Ave, Hamilton, OH, 45011 (513) 863-4218
Medical Dir/Dir of Nursing Harry Davin MD. *Licensure* Nursing Home. *Beds* 81. *Ownership* Proprietary.
Admissions Requirements Medical examination; Physician's request.
Staff Physicians 4 (pt); RNs 2 (ft), 2 (pt); LPNs 8 (ft), 4 (pt); Nurses aides 22 (ft), 14 (pt); Physical therapists 1 (pt); Recreational therapists 1 (pt); Occupational therapists 1 (pt); Speech therapists 1 (pt); Activities coordinators 1 (ft); Dietitians 1 (pt); Dentists 1 (pt); Podiatrists 1 (pt); Audiologists 1 (pt).
Facilities Dining room; Activities room; Laundry room; Barber/Beauty shop.
Activities Arts and Crafts; Cards; Games; Reading groups; Movies; Shopping trips; Dances/Social or cultural gatherings.
Description Facility features a beautiful estate setting with 10 acres and many 100-year-old trees; dedicated loving staff and home-cooked meals in a friendly environment.

Westhaven Quality Care Center
215 N "C" St, Hamilton, OH, 45013 (513) 863-5511
Admin M O'Reilly. *Medical Dir/Dir of Nursing* Dr E Ringel.
Licensure Intermediate Care. *Beds* 23. *Certified* Medicaid.
Ownership Proprietary.
Admissions Requirements Females only; Medical examination.
Staff Physicians; LPNs; Nurses aides; Recreational therapists; Occupational therapists; Speech therapists; Activities coordinators; Dietitians; Dentists; Podiatrists.
Facilities Dining room; Activities room; Laundry room.
Activities Cards; Games; Shopping trips.
Description Facility provides personalized care in a home-like atmosphere and specializes in those individuals with mental, emotional, and behavioral problems; this is one of 6 homes under Buckeye Quality Care Centers, Inc.

Westover Retirement Community
855 Stahlheber Rd, Hamilton, OH, 45013 (513) 895-9539
Medical Dir/Dir of Nursing Dr Arnold Gross. *Licensure* Nursing; Residential; Home for the Aged. *Beds* 116. *Ownership* Nonprofit.
Admissions Requirements Minimum age 55;

Medical examination.
Staff Physicians 1 (pt); RNs 2 (ft); LPNs 3 (ft), 3 (pt); Nurses aides 20 (ft), 6 (pt); Physical therapists 1 (pt); Activities coordinators 1 (ft); Dietitians 1 (pt).
Facilities Dining room; Activities room; Chapel; Crafts room; Laundry room; Barber/Beauty shop; Library.
Activities Arts and Crafts; Cards; Reading groups; Prayer groups; Movies; Shopping trips; Dances/Social or cultural gatherings.
Description A private pay nonprofit retirement community; all rooms (nursing, assisted living, apartments, and independent housing) are private.

HARTVILLE

Hartville Manor Nursing Home*
1420 Smith-Kramer Rd, Hartville, OH, 44632 (216) 877-2666
Licensure Intermediate Care. *Beds* 66. *Ownership* Proprietary.

Hartville Meadows*
844 W Orange, Hartville, OH, 44632
Licensure Intermediate Care for Mentally Retarded. *Beds* 32. *Certified* Medicaid. *Ownership* Nonprofit.

HAYESVILLE

Collins Nursing Home Inc
82 S Mechanic St, Hayesville, OH, 44838 (419) 368-7163
Licensure Intermediate Care. *Beds* 22. *Certified* Medicaid.
Ownership Proprietary.
Admissions Requirements Medical examination; Physician's request.
Staff RNs 1 (pt); LPNs 3 (ft), 1 (pt); Nurses aides 9 (ft), 2 (pt); Activities coordinators 1 (ft); Dietitians 1 (pt).
Facilities Dining room; Activities room; Crafts room; Laundry room.
Activities Arts and Crafts; Cards; Games; Reading groups; Prayer groups; Shopping trips.
Description Facility is located in a very small village, in a 2-story mansion-type home which is very clean with good food and snacks; home-like atmosphere; special nursing care for each resident.

HICKSVILLE

Fountain Manor
401 Fountain St, Hicksville, OH, 43526 (419) 542-8535
Licensure Intermediate Care. *Beds* 64. *Certified* Medicaid.
Ownership Proprietary.
Admissions Requirements Minimum age 18; Medical examination; Physician's request.
Staff Physicians 5 (pt); RNs 4 (pt); LPNs 9 (pt); Nurses aides 22 (pt); Physical therapists 1 (pt); Activities coordinators 1 (ft); Dietitians 1 (pt).
Facilities Dining room; Physical therapy room; Activities room; Laundry room; Barber/Beauty shop.

Activities Arts and Crafts; Cards; Games; Reading groups; Dances/Social or cultural gatherings.

HILLIARD

Scioto-Crest Convalescent Center
5471 Scioto Darby Rd, Hilliard, OH, 43026 (614) 876-4322
Admin Betty Ball. *Medical Dir/Dir of Nursing* George Hoeflinger MD.
Licensure Skilled Care; Intermediate Care. *Beds* 122. *Certified* Medicaid; Medicare. *Ownership* Proprietary.
Staff RNs 2 (ft), 11 (pt); LPNs 4 (ft), 4 (pt); Nurses aides 35 (ft), 13 (pt); Physical therapists 1 (pt); Activities coordinators 2 (ft); Dietitians 1 (pt).
Facilities Dining room; Activities room; Crafts room; Laundry room; Barber/Beauty shop.
Activities Arts and Crafts; Cards; Games; Prayer groups; Movies; Shopping trips; Dances/Social or cultural gatherings.
Description Facility is community oriented and features a very dedicated activities program.

HILLSBORO

Oakland Nursing Center
175 Chillicothe Ave, Hillsboro, OH, 45133 (513) 393-1925
Admin George Oney.
Licensure Intermediate Care. *Beds* 101. *Certified* Medicaid.
Ownership Proprietary.
Admissions Requirements Medical examination; Physician's request.
Staff RNs 3 (ft), 1 (pt); LPNs 5 (ft), 7 (pt); Nurses aides 27 (ft), 13 (pt); Activities coordinators 3 (ft), 2 (pt); Dietitians 1 (pt).
Facilities Dining room; Physical therapy room; Activities room; Laundry room; Barber/Beauty shop.
Activities Arts and Crafts; Cards; Games; Reading groups; Prayer groups; Movies; Shopping trips; Dances/Social or cultural gatherings.

Whitehouse Health Care Center*
410 E Main St, Hillsboro, OH, 45133 (513) 393-1012
Licensure Intermediate Care. *Beds* 46. *Certified* Medicaid.
Ownership Proprietary.

HOLGATE

Holgate Quality Care Nursing Center
400 Joe E Brown Ave, Holgate, OH, 43527 (419) 264-2921
Medical Dir/Dir of Nursing Dr John Fouster. *Licensure* Intermediate Care. *Beds* 51. *Certified* Medicaid.
Ownership Proprietary.
Admissions Requirements Medical examination; Physician's request.
Staff RNs 1 (ft), 3 (pt); LPNs 1 (ft), 4 (pt); Orderlies 3 (ft), 20 (pt); Activities coordinators 1 (ft); 1 (ft).
Facilities Dining room; Activities room; Chapel; Crafts room; Laundry room; Barber/Beauty shop.

Activities Arts and Crafts; Cards; Games; Reading groups; Prayer groups; Movies; Shopping trips; Dances/Social or cultural gatherings; Pet therapy.
Description Summer picnics held in yard for residents and their families and friends; facility located in the quiet countryside.

HUBER HEIGHTS

Montgomery Developmental Center*
7679 Timbercrest Dr, Huber Heights, OH, 45424
Licensure Intermediate Care for Mentally Retarded. *Beds* 104. *Certified* Medicaid.
Ownership Public.

HUDSON

Hudson Elms Inc*
597 E Streetsboro Rd, Hudson, OH, 44236 (216) 650-0436
Licensure Intermediate Care. *Beds* 50. *Certified* Medicaid.
Ownership Proprietary.

HUNTSBURG

Blossom Hill Nursing Home*
12496 Princeton Rd, Huntsburg, OH, 44046 (216) 635-5567
Licensure Intermediate Care. *Beds* 30. *Certified* Medicaid.
Ownership Proprietary.

HURON

Erie County Care Facility
3916 E Perkins Ave, Huron, OH, 44839 (419)
Admin James C Speer. *Medical Dir/Dir of Nursing* Dean J Reichenbach MD and Paul G Steinbicker MD.
Licensure Intermediate Care. *Beds* 160. *Certified* Medicaid.
Ownership Public.
Admissions Requirements Medical examination.
Staff Physicians 2 (pt); RNs 4 (ft), 3 (pt); LPNs 17 (ft), 7 (pt); Nurses aides 53 (ft), 3 (pt); Recreational therapists 1 (ft); Activities coordinators 1 (ft); Dietitians 1 (ft), 1 (pt); Dentists 1 (pt); Podiatrists 1 (pt).
Facilities Dining room; Activities room; Chapel; Crafts room; Laundry room; Barber/Beauty shop.
Activities Arts and Crafts; Cards; Games; Prayer groups; Movies; Shopping trips; Dances/Social or cultural gatherings.
Description The following are some of the outstanding programs offered: adult day care program, happy harvesters garden club, dancersize for handicapped, pet therapy, resident's council, individual recreational therapy, and hydro-therapy pool. Every summer all able residents taken on a 2-day overnight camping trip and also schedule 2 hay rides in the fall.

IRONTON

Dalton Health Center*
5th and Clinton Sts, Ironton, OH, 45638 (614) 532-6188
Licensure Intermediate Care. *Beds* 91. *Certified* Medicaid.
Ownership Proprietary.

Jo-Lin Health Center Inc*
1050 Clinton St, Ironton, OH, 45638 (614) 532-6096
Licensure Intermediate Care. *Beds* 112. *Certified* Medicaid.
Ownership Nonprofit.

Sunset Nursing Home Inc
813 1/2 Marion Pike, Ironton, OH, 45638 (614) 532-0449
Medical Dir/Dir of Nursing Dr A B Payne.
Licensure Intermediate Care. *Beds* 50. *Certified* Medicaid.
Ownership Proprietary.
Facilities Dining room; Physical therapy room; Activities room; Chapel; Crafts room; Laundry room; Barber/Beauty shop; Library.
Activities Arts and Crafts; Cards; Games; Reading groups; Prayer groups; Movies; Shopping trips; Dances/Social or cultural gatherings.

JACKSON

Buckeye Community Services—South Street Home*
6 South St, Jackson, OH, 45640
Licensure Intermediate Care. *Beds* 8. *Certified* Medicaid.
Ownership Nonprofit.

Heartland of Jackson
8668 SR 93, Jackson, OH, 45640 (614) 286-5026
Medical Dir/Dir of Nursing Dr Louis J Jindra.
Licensure Skilled Care; Intermediate Care.
Beds 100. *Certified* Medicaid; Medicare.
Ownership Proprietary.
Admissions Requirements Minimum age 18; Medical examination.
Staff Physicians 3 (pt); RNs 5 (ft); LPNs 7 (ft), 3 (pt); Orderlies 1 (ft); Nurses aides 29 (ft), 10 (pt); Physical therapists 1 (pt); Occupational therapists 1 (pt); Speech therapists 1 (pt); Activities coordinators 1 (ft); Dietitians 1 (pt); Dentists 1 (pt); Podiatrists 1 (pt); Audiologists 1 (pt).
Facilities Dining room; Physical therapy room; Activities room; Laundry room; Barber/Beauty shop.
Activities Arts and Crafts; Cards; Games; Reading groups; Prayer groups; Movies; Shopping trips; Dances/Social or cultural gatherings.
Description Heartland of Jackson offers the highest quality of care including complete ancillary therapy services. The facility is located in a rural setting with access to nearby towns.

JAMESTOWN

Heathergreen II Inc*
4960 US Rt 35 E, Jamestown, OH, 45335 (513) 675-3311

Licensure Skilled Care; Intermediate Care.
Beds 100. *Certified* Medicaid; Medicare.
Ownership Proprietary.

JOHNSTOWN

Northview Nursing Home
267 N Main, Johnstown, OH, 43031 (614) 967-7896
Medical Dir/Dir of Nursing Robert Young MD.
Licensure Intermediate Care. *Beds* 36. *Certified* Medicaid.
Ownership Proprietary.
Staff Physicians 2 (pt); RNs 1 (ft), 2 (pt); LPNs 1 (ft), 3 (pt); Nurses aides 8 (ft), 5 (pt); Activities coordinators 1 (ft); Dietitians 1 (pt); Dentists 1 (pt); Ophthalmologists 1 (pt); Podiatrists 1 (pt).
Facilities Dining room; Activities room; Chapel; Crafts room; Laundry room; Barber/Beauty shop.
Activities Arts and Crafts; Cards; Games; Reading groups; Prayer groups; Movies; Dances/Social or cultural gatherings.
Description Northview offers intermediate care in a clean home-like atmosphere with full fire protection, where families and friends are always welcome. Staff is dedicated, compassionate, and professional; planned activity program and church services are offered. Northview is noted for "good home cooking."

KENSINGTON

East Carroll Nursing Home
7233 Apollo Rd NE, Kensington, OH, 44427 (216) 223-1536
Medical Dir/Dir of Nursing Dr Thomas Atchison.
Licensure Intermediate Care for Mentally Retarded. *Beds* 24. *Certified* Medicaid.
Ownership Nonprofit.
Staff RNs 1 (ft); LPNs 2 (ft); Nurses aides 6 (ft); Activities coordinators 1 (ft).
Facilities Dining room; Crafts room; Laundry room.
Activities Arts and Crafts; Games; Reading groups; Shopping trips; Dances/Social or cultural gatherings.
Description The facility has a rural setting and a staff that cares about the residents.

KENT

Kent Quality Care Nursing Center*
1290 Fairchild Rd, Kent, OH, 44240
Beds 100.

KENTON

Green Acres Nursing Home Inc*
117 Cemetery Rd, Kenton, OH, 43326 (419) 674-4197
Licensure Skilled Care; Intermediate Care.
Beds 101. *Certified* Medicaid; Medicare.
Ownership Proprietary.

Hardin County Home*
Rt 2, Kenton, OH, 43326 (419) 673-5251
Licensure Intermediate Care. *Beds* 51. *Certified* Medicaid.
Ownership Public.

Lovin' Care Center*
911 W Pattison Ave, Kenton, OH, 43326
Licensure Intermediate Care. *Beds* 50. *Certified* Medicaid.
Ownership Proprietary.

San Antonio Professional Care Facility
320 N Wayne St, Kenton, OH, 43326 (419) 673-1295
Medical Dir/Dir of Nursing Dr Sanders.
Licensure Intermediate Care. *Beds* 82. *Certified* Medicaid.
Ownership Proprietary.
Admissions Requirements Minimum age 18; Medical examination; Physician's request.
Staff Physicians 10 (pt); RNs 4 (ft), 1 (pt); LPNs 7 (ft), 3 (pt); Nurses aides 17 (ft), 12 (pt); Physical therapists 1 (pt); Reality therapists 1 (pt); Recreational therapists 1 (pt); Speech therapists 1 (pt); Activities coordinators 1 (ft), 1 (pt); Dietitians 1 (pt); Dentists 1 (pt); Ophthalmologists 1 (pt); Podiatrists 1 (pt).
Facilities Dining room; Physical therapy room; Activities room; Chapel; Crafts room; Laundry room; Barber/Beauty shop; Library.
Activities Arts and Crafts; Cards; Games; Reading groups; Prayer groups; Movies; Shopping trips; Dances/Social or cultural gatherings.

KETTERING

Heartland of Kettering*
3313 Wilmington Pike, Kettering, OH, 45429 (513) 298-8084
Licensure Intermediate Care. *Beds* 100. *Certified* Medicaid.
Ownership Proprietary.

Kettering Convalescent Center
1150 W Dorothy Ln, Kettering, OH, 45409 (513) 293-1152
Medical Dir/Dir of Nursing C Y Rhee MD.
Licensure Skilled Care; Intermediate Care.
Beds SNF 57; ICF 168. *Certified* Medicaid; Medicare.
Ownership Nonprofit.
Admissions Requirements Medical examination; Physician's request.
Staff RNs 10 (ft), 13 (pt); LPNs 3 (ft), 12 (pt); Nurses aides 50 (ft), 47 (pt); Physical therapists 2 (ft); Recreational therapists 3 (pt); Activities coordinators 1 (ft).
Affiliation Volunteers of America
Facilities Dining room; Physical therapy room; Activities room; Chapel; Laundry room; Barber/Beauty shop.
Activities Arts and Crafts; Cards; Games; Reading groups; Prayer groups; Movies; Shopping trips; Dances/Social or cultural gatherings.

KIMBOLTON

Bell Nursing Home*
PO Box 51, Main St, Kimbolton, OH, 43749 (614) 432-7717

Licensure Intermediate Care. *Beds* 50. *Certified* Medicaid.
Ownership Proprietary.

KINGSTON

Gospel Light Nursing Home
3rd St, Kingston, OH, 45644 (614) 642-2503
Admin Helen M Davis. *Medical Dir/Dir of Nursing* Dr Nissimor.
Licensure Intermediate Care. *Beds* 50. *Certified* Medicaid.
Ownership Proprietary.
Admissions Requirements Medical examination.
Staff Physicians 1 (ft), 1 (pt); RNs 1 (ft); LPNs 4 (ft); Orderlies 2 (ft); Nurses aides 25 (ft); Recreational therapists 1 (ft); Activities coordinators 1 (ft); Dietitians 1 (pt); Podiatrists 1 (ft).
Facilities Dining room; Activities room; Laundry room; Barber/Beauty shop.
Activities Arts and Crafts; Cards; Games; Reading groups; Prayer groups; Movies; Shopping trips; Dances/Social or cultural gatherings.

KINGSVILLE

Ashtabula County Home*
Dibble Rd, Kingsville, OH, 44048 (216) 224-2161
Licensure Intermediate Care. *Beds* 295. *Certified* Medicaid.
Ownership Public.

KINSMAN

Boyd's—Kinsman Home
Rt 5, PO Box 315, Kinsman, OH, 44428 (216) 876-5581
Admin Paula L Ruley.
Licensure Intermediate Care for Mentally Retarded. *Beds* 47. *Certified* Medicaid.
Ownership Proprietary.
Admissions Requirements Minimum age 18.
Staff RNs 1 (ft), 1 (pt); LPNs 1 (pt); Nurses aides 3 (ft), 7 (pt); Occupational therapists; Speech therapists; Activities coordinators 1 (ft).
Facilities Dining room; Activities room; Crafts room; Laundry room.
Activities Arts and Crafts; Cards; Games; Movies; Shopping trips; Dances/Social or cultural gatherings; Church; Bowling.
Description The facility is the resident's home where they will live out their lives. Everything in and about the home is family-oriented. Dining room, living, bedroom areas are as in anyone's personal home—no institutional feeling here at all. The founders are lovingly called mom and pop.

Windsor House Nursing Home 4
Rt 1, Kinsman, OH, 44428 (216)
Licensure Nursing Home. *Beds* 32.
Ownership Nonprofit.

KIRKERSVILLE

Pine Kirk Nursing Home Inc
205 E Main St, Kirkersville, OH, 43033 (614) 927-3209
Medical Dir/Dir of Nursing Dr J I Fast DO.
Licensure Intermediate Care. *Beds* 39. *Certified* Medicaid.
Ownership Proprietary.
Staff Physicians 2 (pt); RNs 3 (ft); LPNs 2 (ft), 4 (pt); Nurses aides 7 (ft), 4 (pt); Activities coordinators 1 (ft).
Facilities Dining room; Activities room; Laundry room.
Activities Arts and Crafts; Cards; Games; Reading groups; Prayer groups; Movies; Shopping trips; Dances/Social or cultural gatherings.

KIRTLAND

Western Reserve Convalescent Homes Inc
9769 Chillicothe Rd, Kirtland, OH, 44094 (216) 946-7858
Admin William E Rabe. *Medical Dir/Dir of Nursing* Donald Patchin MD.
Licensure Nursing Home. *Beds* 150.
Ownership Proprietary.
Admissions Requirements Minimum age 18; Medical examination; Physician's request.
Staff Physicians 5 (pt); RNs 5 (ft), 2 (pt); LPNs 5 (ft), 5 (pt); Nurses aides 40 (ft); Physical therapists 2 (ft); Occupational therapists 1 (pt); Speech therapists 1 (ft); Activities coordinators 1 (ft), 1 (pt); Dietitians 1 (ft); Dentists 1 (pt); Ophthalmologists 1 (pt); Podiatrists 1 (pt); Audiologists 1 (pt).
Facilities Dining room; Physical therapy room; Activities room; Chapel; Crafts room; Laundry room; Barber/Beauty shop; Library.
Activities Arts and Crafts; Cards; Games; Reading groups; Prayer groups; Movies; Shopping trips; Dances/Social or cultural gatherings.
Description Facility features day-care program for the mentally impaired, vacation (respite care), and is located in a quaint rural area setting.

Western Reserve Extended Care Inc*
9685 Chillicothe Rd, Kirtland, OH, 44094 (216) 951-7272
Medical Dir/Dir of Nursing Paul W Hanahan MD.
Licensure Skilled Care. *Beds* 52. *Certified* Medicare.
Ownership Proprietary.
Admissions Requirements Minimum age 18; Medical examination; Physician's request.
Staff Physicians 5 (pt); RNs 8 (ft); LPNs 6 (ft); Orderlies 2 (ft); Nurses aides 38 (ft); Physical therapists 2 (ft), 3 (pt); Activities coordinators 1 (ft); Dietitians 1 (ft); Dentists 1 (pt); Ophthalmologists 1 (pt); Podiatrists 1 (pt); Audiologists 1 (ft).
Facilities Dining room; Physical therapy room; Activities room; Crafts room; Laundry room; Barber/Beauty shop; Library.
Activities Arts and Crafts; Cards; Games; Reading groups; Prayer groups; Movies; Shopping trips; Dances/Social or cultural gatherings.

LAKE MILTON

Edgewater Quality Care Nursing Center*
1930 Craig Dr, Lake Milton, OH, 44429 (216) 654-3700
Licensure Intermediate Care. *Beds* 75. *Certified* Medicaid.
Ownership Proprietary.

Milton Manor Nursing Home*
Box 98, 1574 Jersey St, Lake Milton, OH, 44429 (216) 654-5555
Licensure Intermediate Care. *Beds* 45. *Certified* Medicaid.
Ownership Proprietary.

LAKEVIEW

Indian Lake Manor
Rt 2, Lakeview, OH, 43331 (513) 843-4929
Medical Dir/Dir of Nursing Dr Karen Flanagan.
Licensure Skilled Care; Intermediate Care. *Beds* 100. *Certified* Medicaid; Medicare.
Ownership Proprietary.
Admissions Requirements Medical examination; Physician's request.
Staff Physicians 1 (pt); RNs 4 (ft), 1 (pt); LPNs 6 (ft), 1 (pt); Nurses aides 33 (ft), 2 (pt); Physical therapists 1 (pt); Activities coordinators 1 (ft); Dietitians 1 (pt); Dentists 1 (pt); Podiatrists 1 (pt); Audiologists 1 (pt).
Facilities Dining room; Physical therapy room; Activities room; Crafts room; Laundry room; Barber/Beauty shop; Country store; Ice cream parlor.
Activities Arts and Crafts; Cards; Games; Prayer groups; Movies; Shopping trips; Dances/Social or cultural gatherings.

LAKEWOOD

Aristocrat Lakewood*
13900 Detroit Ave, Lakewood, OH, 44107 (216) 228-7650
Licensure Skilled Care; Intermediate Care. *Beds* 132. *Certified* Medicaid; Medicare.
Ownership Proprietary.

Crestmont Nursing Home North Inc*
13330 Detroit Ave, Lakewood, OH, 44107 (216) 228-9550
Licensure Intermediate Care; Rest Home.
Beds ICF 73; Rest Home 19. *Certified* Medicaid.
Ownership Proprietary.

Wright Nursing Center*
13315 Detroit Ave, Lakewood, OH, 44107 (216) 226-3858
Licensure Intermediate Care. *Beds* 50. *Certified* Medicaid.
Ownership Proprietary.

LANCASTER

Crestview Manor Nursing Home I
925 Becks Knob Rd, Lancaster, OH, 43130 (614) 654-2634
Admin Helen Sheridan. *Medical Dir/Dir of Nursing* Dr Richard E Hartle MD.

Licensure Skilled Care; Intermediate Care. *Beds* 101. *Certified* Medicaid; Medicare.
Ownership Proprietary.
Admissions Requirements Minimum age 18; Medical examination.
Staff Physicians 3 (pt); RNs 6 (ft), 2 (pt); LPNs 8 (ft), 2 (pt); Orderlies 6 (ft), 2 (pt); Nurses aides 58 (ft), 4 (pt); Physical therapists 1 (pt); Recreational therapists 1 (pt); Activities coordinators 1 (pt); Dietitians 1 (pt); Dentists 1 (pt); Podiatrists 1 (pt).
Facilities Dining room; Physical therapy room; Activities room; Crafts room; Laundry room; Barber/Beauty shop.
Activities Arts and Crafts; Cards; Games; Reading groups; Prayer groups; Movies.
Description Facility has all semi-private rooms with bath, phone, and TV jacks.

Crestview Manor Nursing Home II
957 Becks Knob Rd, Rt 3, Lancaster, OH, 43130 (614) 654-2634
Admin Winfield S Eckert and Helen Sheridan.
Medical Dir/Dir of Nursing Richard E Hartle MD.
Licensure Skilled Care; Intermediate Care. *Beds* 101. *Certified* Medicaid; Medicare.
Ownership Proprietary.
Admissions Requirements Minimum age 18; Medical examination.
Staff Physicians 3 (pt); RNs 5 (ft), 2 (pt); LPNs 7 (ft), 2 (pt); Orderlies 8 (ft), 2 (pt); Nurses aides 56 (ft), 2 (pt); Physical therapists 1 (pt); Recreational therapists 1 (pt); Activities coordinators 1 (pt); Dietitians 1 (pt); Dentists 1 (pt); Podiatrists 1 (pt).
Facilities Dining room; Physical therapy room; Activities room; Crafts room; Laundry room; Barber/Beauty shop.
Activities Arts and Crafts; Cards; Games; Reading groups; Prayer groups; Movies.
Description Facility has all semi-private rooms with bath, phone, and TV jacks.

Crites Nursing Home 2
1318 E Main St, Lancaster, OH, 43130 (614) 653-3431
Medical Dir/Dir of Nursing Dr John R Barsking.
Licensure Intermediate Care. *Beds* 60. *Certified* Medicaid.
Ownership Proprietary.
Staff Physicians 1 (pt); RNs 1 (ft), 1 (pt); LPNs 6 (ft); Nurses aides 24 (ft); Physical therapists 1 (pt); Recreational therapists 1 (pt); Occupational therapists 1 (pt); Speech therapists 1 (pt); Activities coordinators 1 (ft); Dietitians 1 (pt); Dentists 1 (pt); Ophthalmologists 1 (pt); Podiatrists 1 (pt); Audiologists 1 (pt).

Homestead III*
1900 E Main St, Lancaster, OH, 43130 (614) 653-8630
Licensure Skilled Care; Intermediate Care. *Beds* 102. *Certified* Medicaid; Medicare.
Ownership Proprietary.

Johnston Nursing Home
1246 E Main St, Lancaster, OH, 43130 (614) 653-1410
Medical Dir/Dir of Nursing Dr John R Bowling.
Licensure Intermediate Care. *Beds* 30. *Certi-*

fied Medicaid.
Ownership Proprietary.
Staff Physicians 1 (pt); RNs 2 (ft); LPNs 10 (ft); Orderlies 1 (ft); Nurses aides 40 (ft); Physical therapists 1 (pt); Recreational therapists 2 (ft); Occupational therapists 1 (pt); Speech therapists 1 (pt); Activities coordinators 1 (ft); Dietitians 1 (pt); Dentists 1 (pt); Ophthalmologists 1 (pt); Podiatrists 1 (pt); Audiologists 1 (pt).

Lancaster Health Care Center
Dolson Ct NW, Lancaster, OH, 43130 (614) 654-0641
Medical Dir/Dir of Nursing Dr John Bowling.
Licensure Skilled Care; Intermediate Care.
Beds 100. *Certified* Medicaid; Medicare.
Ownership Proprietary.
Staff Physicians 1 (pt); RNs 5 (ft), 3 (pt); LPNs 5 (ft), 2 (pt); Nurses aides 29 (ft), 18 (pt); Physical therapists 2 (pt); Occupational therapists 1 (pt); Speech therapists 1 (pt); Activities coordinators 1 (ft); Dietitians 1 (pt); Podiatrists 1 (pt).
Facilities Dining room; Physical therapy room; Activities room; Crafts room; Laundry room; Barber/Beauty shop.
Activities Arts and Crafts; Cards; Games; Reading groups; Prayer groups; Movies; Shopping trips; Dances/Social or cultural gatherings.

Valley View Nursing Home
5185 Lithopolis Rd, Lancaster, OH, 43130 (614) 687-0566
Medical Dir/Dir of Nursing Dr Ralph R Romaker.
Licensure Intermediate Care. *Beds* 25. *Certified* Medicaid.
Ownership Proprietary.
Admissions Requirements Medical examination.
Staff Physicians 1 (pt); RNs 2 (ft), 2 (pt); LPNs 2 (pt); Nurses aides 5 (ft), 3 (pt); Physical therapists 1 (pt); Activities coordinators 1 (pt); Dietitians 1 (pt).
Facilities Dining room; Activities room; Laundry room.
Activities Arts and Crafts; Cards; Games; Reading groups; Prayer groups; Movies; Shopping trips; Dances/Social or cultural gatherings.
Description We are a small nursing home specializing in individualized home-type care in a home-type country setting.

LANSING

Heartland-Lansing*
300 Commercial Dr, Lansing, OH, 43934
Licensure Skilled Care; Intermediate Care.
Beds SNF 100; ICF 100. *Certified* Medicaid; Medicare.
Ownership Proprietary.

LAURELVILLE

Hoover Nursing Home Inc
16128 Pike St, Box 128, Laurelville, OH, 43135 (614) 332-3221
Admin Joyce Hoover.
Licensure Intermediate Care. *Beds* 18. *Certified* Medicaid.

Ownership Proprietary.
Staff Physicians 2 (pt); RNs 2 (pt); LPNs 2 (ft), 1 (pt); Nurses aides 7 (ft), 3 (pt); Activities coordinators 1 (pt); Dietitians 1 (pt).
Facilities Dining room; Laundry room.
Activities Arts and Crafts; Cards; Games; Reading groups; Prayer groups.
Description Facility is small with a home-like atmosphere and a great staff who insist on giving residents tender loving care.

LEBANON

Lebanon Health Care Center*
115 Oregonia Rd, Lebanon, OH, 45036 (513) 932-1121
Licensure Skilled Care; Intermediate Care.
Beds 57. *Certified* Medicaid; Medicare.
Ownership Proprietary.

Lebanon Nursing Home
220 S Mechanic St, Lebanon, OH, 45036 (513) 932-4861
Medical Dir/Dir of Nursing Ralph Young DO.
Licensure Intermediate Care. *Beds* 36. *Certified* Medicaid.
Ownership Proprietary.
Staff Physicians 1 (ft); RNs 1 (ft); LPNs 4 (ft), 5 (pt); Nurses aides 12 (ft), 5 (pt); Physical therapists 1 (ft); Recreational therapists 1 (ft); Activities coordinators 1 (ft); Dietitians 1 (ft).
Facilities Dining room; Activities room; Laundry room.
Activities Arts and Crafts; Games; Reading groups; Prayer groups; Movies; Shopping trips; Dances/Social or cultural gatherings.

Otterbein Home
585 N State Rt 741, Lebanon, OH, 45036 (513) 932-2020
Medical Dir/Dir of Nursing James Barry.
Licensure Skilled Care; Intermediate Care.
Beds SNF 132; ICF 224. *Certified* Medicaid; Medicare.
Ownership Nonprofit.
Admissions Requirements Minimum age 62; Medical examination.
Staff Physicians 1 (ft), 1 (pt); RNs 19 (ft), 13 (pt); LPNs 23 (ft), 4 (pt); Nurses aides 92 (ft), 9 (pt); Physical therapists 1 (ft); Recreational therapists 1 (ft); Occupational therapists 1 (ft); Speech therapists 1 (pt); Activities coordinators 3 (ft), 2 (pt); Dietitians 1 (pt); Dentists 1 (pt); Ophthalmologists 1 (pt); Podiatrists 1 (pt); Audiologists 1 (pt).
Affiliation Methodist
Facilities Dining room; Physical therapy room; Activities room; Chapel; Crafts room; Laundry room; Barber/Beauty shop; Library.
Activities Arts and Crafts; Cards; Games; Reading groups; Prayer groups; Movies; Shopping trips; Dances/Social or cultural gatherings.

LEXINGTON

Griffeth Nursing Home
Rt 7, Vanderbilt Rd, PO Box 3167, Lexington, OH, 44404 (419) 756-3623
Licensure Intermediate Care. *Beds* 50. *Certified* Medicaid.
Ownership Proprietary.

Admissions Requirements Medical examination; Physician's request.
Staff RNs 1 (pt); LPNs 3 (ft), 4 (pt); Nurses aides 10 (ft), 4 (pt); Recreational therapists 2 (ft), 1 (pt); Activities coordinators 1 (ft); Dietitians 1 (pt).
Facilities Dining room; Activities room; Crafts room; Laundry room.
Activities Arts and Crafts; Cards; Games; Reading groups; Prayer groups; Movies; Shopping trips; Dances/Social or cultural gatherings.
Description Home-like facility that encourages participation in daily activities.

LIMA

Allen County Inn
3125 Ada Rd, Lima, OH, 45801
Medical Dir/Dir of Nursing Dr William Noble.
Licensure Intermediate Care. *Beds* 134. *Certified* Medicaid.
Ownership Public.
Admissions Requirements Medical examination; Physician's request.
Staff Physicians; RNs; LPNs; Orderlies; Nurses aides; Activities coordinators; Podiatrists.
Facilities Dining room; Activities room; Chapel; Crafts room; Laundry room; Barber/Beauty shop; Library.
Activities Arts and Crafts; Cards; Games; Reading groups; Prayer groups; Movies; Shopping trips; Dances/Social or cultural gatherings.
Description Facility is located in a beautiful scenic country setting.

Columbia Nursing Home
651 Columbia Dr, Lima, OH, 45805 (419) 227-2441
Medical Dir/Dir of Nursing Dr James Bowlus.
Licensure Skilled Care; Intermediate Care.
Beds 50. *Certified* Medicaid; Medicare.
Ownership Nonprofit.
Admissions Requirements Medical examination; Physician's request.
Staff Physicians 1 (pt); RNs 3 (ft), 2 (pt); LPNs 1 (ft), 2 (pt); Nurses aides 10 (ft), 8 (pt); Physical therapists 1 (pt); Recreational therapists 1 (pt); Occupational therapists 1 (pt); Speech therapists 1 (pt); Activities coordinators 1 (ft); Dietitians 1 (pt).
Facilities Dining room.
Activities Arts and Crafts; Cards; Games; Reading groups; Prayer groups; Movies; Dances/Social or cultural gatherings.
Description Facility offers small home atmosphere with many daily activities, excellent nursing care, and carefully planned meals; facility is designed, constructed, and maintained to ensure the safety and well being of its residents; 24-hour training for nursing personnel.

Lima Convalescent Home*
1650 W Allentown Rd, Lima, OH, 45805 (419) 224-9741
Beds 100.
Ownership Nonprofit.

Lima Manor*
750 Brower Rd, Lima, OH, 45801 (419) 227-2611

Licensure Skilled Care; Intermediate Care.
Beds 100. *Certified* Medicaid; Medicare.
Ownership Proprietary.

Lost Creek Care Center*
804 S Mumaugh, Lima, OH, 45802
Licensure Intermediate Care. *Beds* 75. *Certified* Medicaid.
Ownership Nonprofit.

Oaks Convalescent Center*
599 S Shawnee St, Lima, OH, 45804 (419) 227-2154
Licensure Skilled Care; Intermediate Care.
Beds 100. *Certified* Medicaid; Medicare.
Ownership Proprietary.

Shawnee Manor*
2535 Fort Amanda Rd, Lima, OH, 45804 (419) 999-2055
Licensure Skilled Care; Intermediate Care.
Beds 100. *Certified* Medicaid; Medicare.
Ownership Proprietary.

Springview Manor
883 W Spring St, Lima, OH, 45805 (419) 227-3661
Licensure Intermediate Care. *Beds* 43. *Certified* Medicaid.
Ownership Proprietary.
Staff Physicians 1 (ft), 1 (pt); RNs 3 (ft), 1 (pt); LPNs 3 (ft); Orderlies 1 (ft); Nurses aides 15 (ft), 2 (pt); Physical therapists 1 (ft); Recreational therapists 1 (ft); Occupational therapists 1 (ft); Speech therapists 1 (ft); Activities coordinators 1 (ft); Dietitians 1 (ft); Podiatrists 1 (ft).
Facilities Dining room; Physical therapy room; Activities room; Crafts room; Laundry room; Barber/Beauty shop; Library.
Activities Arts and Crafts; Cards; Games; Reading groups; Prayer groups; Movies; Shopping trips; Dances/Social or cultural gatherings.

LINCOLN HEIGHTS

Brown's Nursing Home*
PO Box 15488, 1153 Lindy St, Lincoln Heights, OH, 45215 (513) 733-4240
Licensure Intermediate Care. *Beds* 70. *Certified* Medicaid.
Ownership Proprietary.

Martin's Nursing Home
723 Adams St, Lincoln Heights, OH, 45215
Licensure Intermediate Care. *Beds* 35. *Certified* Medicaid.
Ownership Proprietary.

Turner Nursing Home*
1333 Jackson St, Lincoln Heights, OH, 45215 (513) 554-4060
Licensure Intermediate Care. *Beds* 17. *Certified* Medicaid.
Ownership Proprietary.

LISBON

Opportunity Homes Inc*
7891 State Rt 45, Lisbon, OH, 44432
Licensure Intermediate Care. *Beds* 50.
Certified Medicaid.
Ownership Proprietary.

Pleasant View Nursing Home
7451 Pleasant View Dr, Lisbon, OH, 44432
(216) 424-3721
Admin Iva G Myers. *Medical Dir/Dir of
Nursing* Dr Larry Smith.
Licensure Intermediate Care. *Beds* 50. *Certified* Medicaid.
Ownership Nonprofit.
Staff Physicians 1 (pt); RNs 1 (pt); LPNs 3 (ft),
3 (pt); Nurses aides 12 (ft), 7 (pt); Activities
coordinators 1 (ft).
Facilities Dining room; Activities room; Crafts
room; Laundry room; Barber/Beauty shop.
Activities Arts and Crafts; Cards; Games;
Reading groups; Prayer groups; Movies; Shopping trips; Dances/Social or cultural gatherings.
Description Facility features a "home away
from home" atmosphere.

Windsor Manor
8473 County Home Rd, Lisbon, OH, 44432
(216) 424-7203
Medical Dir/Dir of Nursing Dr William Stevenson.
Licensure Skilled Care; Intermediate Care.
Beds 50. *Certified* Medicaid; Medicare.
Ownership Proprietary.
Admissions Requirements Medical examination.
Staff Physicians 1 (pt); RNs 1 (ft), 3 (pt); LPNs
4 (ft), 10 (pt); Orderlies 3 (pt); Nurses aides 20
(ft), 6 (pt); Physical therapists 1 (pt); Occupational therapists 1 (pt); Speech therapists 1 (pt);
Activities coordinators 1 (pt); Dietitians 1 (pt);
Dentists 1 (pt); Podiatrists 1 (pt); Audiologists 1
(pt).
Facilities Dining room; Activities room; Crafts
room; Laundry room; Barber/Beauty shop;
Library.
Activities Arts and Crafts; Games; Prayer
groups; Movies; Shopping trips; Dances/Social
or cultural gatherings.
Description Facility is located in a beautiful
country setting surrounded by county farm land
with county dog pound on the premises.

LOGAN

Arcadia Acres*
20017 State Rt 93 S, Logan, OH, 43138 (614)
385-2461
Licensure Intermediate Care. *Beds* 50. *Certified* Medicaid.
Ownership Proprietary.

**Buckeye Community Services—Culver Street
Home***
30 N Culver St, Logan, OH, 43138
Licensure Skilled Care. *Beds* 8. *Certified* Medicaid.
Ownership Nonprofit.

**Buckeye Community Services—Hunter Street
Home***
412 W Hunter St, Logan, OH, 43138
Licensure Intermediate Care for Mentally
Retarded. *Beds* 5. *Certified* Medicaid.
Ownership Nonprofit.

**Buckeye Community Services—Walnut Street
Home***
823 Walnut-Dowler Rd, Logan, OH, 43138
Licensure Intermediate Care for Mentally
Retarded. *Beds* 10. *Certified* Medicaid.
Ownership Nonprofit.

Hocking Valley Community Hospital*
PO Box 550, Logan, OH, 43138 (614) 385-5631
Licensure Skilled Care; Intermediate Care.
Beds SNF 30; ICF 30. *Certified* Medicaid;
Medicare.
Ownership Public.

Logan Health Care Center*
300 Arlington Ave, Logan, OH, 43138 (614)
385-2155
Licensure Skilled Care; Intermediate Care.
Beds 155. *Certified* Medicaid; Medicare.
Ownership Proprietary.

LONDON

Madison Elms
218 Elm St, London, OH, 43140 (614)
852-3100
Admin Mary Louise Worthington. *Medical
Dir/Dir of Nursing* William T Bacon MD.
Licensure Skilled Care; Intermediate Care.
Beds 100. *Certified* Medicaid; Medicare.
Ownership Proprietary.
Staff RNs 5 (ft), 4 (pt); LPNs 3 (ft); Nurses
aides 39 (ft); Physical therapists 1 (ft); Speech
therapists; Activities coordinators 1 (ft); Dietitians 1 (pt); Dentists; Ophthalmologists; Podiatrists.
Facilities Dining room; Physical therapy room;
Chapel; Laundry room; Barber/Beauty shop.
Activities Arts and Crafts; Cards; Games;
Reading groups; Prayer groups; Movies; Shopping trips; Dances/Social or cultural gatherings.
Description Facility features special shopping
days where items are brought to Madison Elms
for residents to do shopping.

LORAIN

Anchor Lodge Nursing Home
3756 W Erie Ave, Lorain, OH, 44053 (216)
244-2019
Admin Marenia G Davis. *Medical Dir/Dir of
Nursing* Dr I A Eren.
Licensure Intermediate Care. *Beds* 60. *Certified* Medicaid.
Ownership Proprietary.
Staff Physicians 20 (pt); RNs 4 (ft); LPNs 8
(ft); Nurses aides 26 (ft), 8 (pt); Physical therapists 1 (pt); Activities coordinators 1 (ft); Dietitians 1 (pt); Dentists 1 (pt); Ophthalmologists 1
(pt); Podiatrists 1 (pt); Audiologists 1 (pt).
Facilities Dining room; Physical therapy room;
Activities room; Crafts room; Laundry room;
Barber/Beauty shop; Library.
Activities Arts and Crafts; Cards; Games;

Reading groups; Prayer groups; Movies; Shopping trips; Dances/Social or cultural gatherings.
Description Facility is located on the shores of
beautiful Lake Erie with spacious grounds and
resident rooms and areas. Also, flower and vegetable gardens; and van for shopping and fun
trips available. Entire facility is designer coordinated.

Autumn Aegis Nursing Home*
3905 Oberlin Ave, Lorain, OH, 44053 (216)
292-6768
Licensure Intermediate Care. *Beds* 100. *Certified* Medicaid.
Ownership Proprietary.

Lorain Manor Nursing Home*
1882 E 32nd St, Lorain, OH, 44055
Licensure Intermediate Care. *Beds* 76. *Certified* Medicaid.
Ownership Proprietary.

Meister Road Homes*
4609 Meister Rd, Lorain, OH, 44052
Licensure Intermediate Care for Mentally
Retarded. *Beds* 16. *Certified* Medicaid.
Ownership Public.

Oak Hills Nursing Home*
3650 Beavercrest Dr, Lorain, OH, 44053 (216)
282-9171
Licensure Skilled Care; Intermediate Care.
Beds 100. *Certified* Medicaid; Medicare.
Ownership Proprietary.

Ohio Extended Care Center*
3364 Kolbe Rd, Lorain, OH, 44053 (216)
282-2244
Licensure Intermediate Care. *Beds* 203. *Certified* Medicaid.
Ownership Proprietary.

LOUDONVILLE

Colonial Manor Health Care Center Inc*
747 S Mount Vernon Ave, Loudonville, OH,
44842 (419) 994-4191
Licensure Intermediate Care. *Beds* 80. *Certified* Medicaid.
Ownership Proprietary.

Colonial Manor Health Care Center Inc II*
Rt 1, Box 4-A, Loudonville, OH, 44842 (419)
994-3148
Licensure Intermediate Care. *Beds* 36. *Certified* Medicaid.
Ownership Proprietary.

Loudonville Nursing Home
205 N Water, Loudonville, OH, 44842 (419)
994-4250
Licensure Intermediate Care. *Beds* 25. *Certified* Medicaid.
Ownership Proprietary.
Staff RNs 1 (pt); LPNs 2 (ft), 1 (pt); Nurses
aides 7 (ft), 2 (pt); Activities coordinators 1 (pt);
Dietitians 1 (pt).
Facilities Dining room; Activities room; Crafts
room; Laundry room; Barber/Beauty shop.
Activities Arts and Crafts; Cards; Games;
Reading groups; Prayer groups; Movies; Shopping trips; Dances/Social or cultural gatherings.

Description Facility is a turn of the century brick home converted to a nursing home in 1963, located one block from downtown; very home-like atmosphere.

LOUISVILLE

Joseph T Nist Geriatric Nursing Home
7770 Columbus Rd NE, Louisville, OH, 44641 (216) 875-1456
Licensure Intermediate Care. *Beds* 248. *Certified* Medicaid.
Ownership Public.
Admissions Requirements Minimum age 16; Medical examination; Physician's request.
Staff Physicians 3 (ft); Physical therapists 1 (ft).
Facilities Dining room; Physical therapy room; Activities room; Crafts room; Laundry room; Barber/Beauty shop; Dental office.
Activities Arts and Crafts; Cards; Games; Prayer groups; Movies; Shopping trips; Dances/Social or cultural gatherings.
Description Facility includes 50-person classroom and a 300-person auditorium.

Mapleview Care Center Inc*
4466 Lynnhaven Ave NE, Louisville, OH, 44641 (216) 875-5060
Licensure Intermediate Care. *Beds* 50. *Certified* Medicaid.
Ownership Proprietary.

The Marcelle Home*
7121 W Saint Francis St, Louisville, OH, 44641 (216) 875-4224
Licensure Intermediate Care. *Beds* 50. *Certified* Medicaid.
Ownership Proprietary.

Miller Care Center Inc*
11701 Louisville St NE, Louisville, OH, 44641 (216) 875-8444
Licensure Intermediate Care. *Beds* 50. *Certified* Medicaid.
Ownership Proprietary.

Molly Stark Hospital
7900 Columbus Rd, Louisville, OH, 44701 (216) 875-5531
Medical Dir/Dir of Nursing Juan M Gonzalez MD.
Licensure Skilled Care; Intermediate Care.
Beds 65. *Certified* Medicaid; Medicare.
Ownership Public.
Admissions Requirements Physician's request.
Staff Physicians 3 (ft), 1 (pt); RNs 16 (ft), 9 (pt); LPNs 27 (ft), 18 (pt); Nurses aides 44 (ft), 27 (pt); Physical therapists 1 (ft); Occupational therapists 1 (ft), 2 (pt); Speech therapists 1 (pt); Activities coordinators 1 (ft); Dietitians 1 (ft); Dentists 1 (pt); Podiatrists 3 (pt).
Facilities Dining room; Physical therapy room; Activities room; Chapel; Crafts room; Laundry room; Barber/Beauty shop.
Activities Arts and Crafts; Cards; Games; Reading groups; Prayer groups; Movies; Shopping trips; Dances/Social or cultural gatherings.

Saint Joseph Hospice Home for the Aged
2308 Reno Dr, Louisville, OH, 44641 (216) 875-5562
Admin Sr Monica Bellinger. *Medical Dir/Dir of Nursing* V J Blumentals MD.
Licensure Intermediate Care. *Beds* 100. *Certified* Medicaid.
Ownership Nonprofit.
Admissions Requirements Minimum age 60; Medical examination; Physician's request.
Staff Physicians 4 (ft), 10 (pt); RNs 6 (ft), 10 (pt); LPNs 3 (ft), 3 (pt); Nurses aides 15 (ft), 29 (pt); Activities coordinators 1 (ft), 1 (pt); Dietitians 1 (pt); Podiatrists 1 (pt).
Affiliation Roman Catholic
Facilities Dining room; Physical therapy room; Activities room; Chapel; Crafts room; Laundry room; Barber/Beauty shop; Library.
Activities Arts and Crafts; Cards; Games; Reading groups; Prayer groups; Movies; Shopping trips; Dances/Social or cultural gatherings.
Description Facility is new with all residents' rooms on ground level with easy access to porch, patio, and 16 acres of grounds; main lounge is spacious with high ceiling creating an attractive atmosphere. Restorative nursing department ensures each resident of reaching and maintaining optimum level of mobility; resident council provides input from residents on all matters concerning them; pastoral team provides personal time for each resident who, created in the likeness of God, deserves respect and dignity; interfaith services offered as well as Catholic.

LOVELAND

Colonial Acres Nursing Home
11887 Lebanon Rd, Loveland, OH, 45140
Licensure Nursing Home. *Beds* 10.
Ownership Proprietary.

Loveland Health Care Center
State Rt 48, 501 N 2nd St, Loveland, OH, 45140 (513) 683-0010
Admin Donald J Benson. *Medical Dir/Dir of Nursing* William Blake Selnick DO.
Licensure Skilled Care; Intermediate Care.
Beds 100. *Certified* Medicaid; Medicare.
Ownership Proprietary.
Admissions Requirements Minimum age 18; Medical examination; Physician's request.
Staff RNs 5 (ft), 9 (pt); LPNs 4 (ft), 5 (pt); Nurses aides 27 (ft), 17 (pt); Physical therapists 1 (pt); Activities coordinators 1 (ft).
Facilities Dining room; Physical therapy room; Activities room; Laundry room; Barber/Beauty shop.
Activities Arts and Crafts; Cards; Games; Reading groups; Prayer groups; Movies; Shopping trips; Dances/Social or cultural gatherings.

LUCASVILLE

Taylor's Health Care Inc—Riverview*
PO Box 785, Rt 5, Lucasville, OH, 45648 (614) 259-5536
Licensure Mental Nursing Home. *Beds* 100.
Ownership Proprietary.

MADEIRA

Madeira Nursing Inc
6940 Stiegler Ln, Madeira, OH, 45243 (513) 561-6400

Admin Lisa G Falk. *Medical Dir/Dir of Nursing* Jerome N Janson MD.
Licensure Skilled Care; Intermediate Care.
Beds 98. *Certified* Medicaid; Medicare.
Ownership Proprietary.
Admissions Requirements Minimum age 18; Medical examination.
Staff RNs 5 (ft), 2 (pt); LPNs 5 (ft), 1 (pt); Nurses aides 30 (ft), 2 (pt); Physical therapists 1 (pt); Speech therapists 1 (pt); Activities coordinators 1 (ft); Dietitians 1 (pt); Dentists 1 (pt); Ophthalmologists 1 (pt); Podiatrists 1 (pt); Audiologists 1 (pt).
Facilities Dining room; Activities room; Barber/Beauty shop.
Activities Arts and Crafts; Cards; Games; Reading groups; Prayer groups; Movies; Dances/Social or cultural gatherings.
Description Patients accepted who are characterized as "difficult" and those who wander away from traditional nursing home settings; residents can be allowed to be up and about without the worry of their wandering off.

MADISON

Broadfield Manor Nursing and Convalescent Home
7927 Middle Ridge, Madison, OH, 44057 (216) 466-3702
Admin Torild Barbins. *Medical Dir/Dir of Nursing* Janis Zemzars MD.
Licensure Skilled Care; Intermediate Care; Intermediate Care for Mentally Retarded.
Beds ICF 133. *Certified* Medicaid; Medicare.
Ownership Proprietary.
Admissions Requirements Medical examination.
Staff Physicians 4 (pt); Physical therapists 1 (pt); Occupational therapists 1 (pt); Speech therapists 1 (pt); Activities coordinators 2 (ft); Dietitians 1 (pt); Dentists 1 (pt); Podiatrists 1 (pt).
Facilities Dining room; Physical therapy room; Activities room; Crafts room; Laundry room; Barber/Beauty shop.
Activities Arts and Crafts; Cards; Games; Reading groups; Prayer groups; Movies; Shopping trips; Dances/Social or cultural gatherings; Organ music at mealtime 3 times a week.
Description Facility is located on 25 acres of beautiful scenic grounds. The Home was founded in 1957 by the late Reverend George Barbins. The original building was an elegant historic mansion which has been adapted into a modern nursing home facility.

Gables Nursing Home*
PO Box 272, 731 Lake St, Madison, OH, 44057 (216) 428-1519
Licensure Intermediate Care for Mentally Retarded. *Beds* 20.
Ownership Proprietary.

Madison Village Nursing Home*
148 E Main St, Madison, OH, 44057 (216) 428-4322
Licensure Intermediate Care. *Beds* 12. *Certified* Medicaid.
Ownership Proprietary.

Shady Acres Nursing Home
7600 S Ridge Rd, Madison, OH, 44057 (216)
428-1492, 428-1116 and 951-9299
Medical Dir/Dir of Nursing Dr Moschkovich.
Licensure Skilled Care; Intermediate Care.
Beds 130. *Certified* Medicaid; Medicare.
Ownership Proprietary.
Admissions Requirements Medical examination.
Staff Physicians 3 (ft); RNs 6 (ft), 4 (pt); LPNs
15 (ft), 2 (pt); Orderlies 2 (ft); Nurses aides 52
(ft), 4 (pt); Physical therapists 1 (ft); Speech
therapists 1 (pt); Activities coordinators 1 (ft);
Dietitians 1 (pt); Dentists 2 (pt); Podiatrists 1
(pt).
Facilities Dining room; Physical therapy room;
Activities room; Chapel; Crafts room; Laundry
room; Barber/Beauty shop.
Activities Arts and Crafts; Cards; Games;
Reading groups; Prayer groups; Movies; Shopping trips; Dances/Social or cultural gatherings;
Community service projects and fund raisers
for Heart and Arthritis Associations.
Description Shady Acres has participated in the
American Health Care Association Rock and
Roll Jamboree for the past 5 years. We are an
Ohio Health Care Association Community Ser-
vice Award winning and Buckeye Award winning facility. We are situated in the country,
with a beautiful courtyard and greenhouse, yet
close to city conveniences.

Stewart Lodge*
7774 Warner Rd, Madison, OH, 44057 (216)
428-7121
Licensure Intermediate Care for Mentally
Retarded. *Beds* 50. *Certified* Medicaid.
Ownership Proprietary.

MALTA

Parmiter Nursing Home*
300 N Main St, Malta, OH, 43758 (614)
962-4861
Licensure Intermediate Care. *Beds* 30. *Certified* Medicaid.
Ownership Proprietary.

MANSFIELD

Chenita Nursing Home 1*
245 W 4th St, Mansfield, OH, 44902 (419)
524-4149
Licensure Intermediate Care. *Beds* 13. *Certified* Medicaid.
Ownership Proprietary.

Chenita Nursing Home 2
111 S Diamond St, Mansfield, OH, 44903 (419)
524-4149
Medical Dir/Dir of Nursing Dr Gordon
Morkel.
Licensure Intermediate Care. *Beds* 50. *Certi-
fied* Medicaid.
Ownership Proprietary.
Admissions Requirements Minimum age 16;
Medical examination.
Staff Physicians 1 (pt); RNs 2 (ft); LPNs 4 (ft);
Orderlies 1 (ft); Nurses aides 14 (ft); Physical
therapists 1 (pt); Reality therapists 1 (pt); Recre-
ational therapists 1 (ft); Occupational therapists

1 (pt); Speech therapists 1 (pt); Activities coor-
dinators 1 (ft); Dietitians 1 (pt); Dentists 1 (pt);
Ophthalmologists 1 (pt); Podiatrists 1 (pt);
Audiologists 1 (pt).
Facilities Dining room; Physical therapy room;
Activities room; Crafts room; Laundry room;
Library.
Activities Arts and Crafts; Cards; Games;
Reading groups; Prayer groups; Movies; Shop-
ping trips; Dances/Social or cultural gatherings.

Crestwood Care Center—Mansfield*
Rock Rd, Mansfield, OH, 44903 (419)
529-9855
Licensure Nursing Home. *Beds* 25.
Ownership Proprietary.

Geriatric Center-Mansfield Memorial Homes
50 Blymyer Ave, PO Box 966, Mansfield, OH,
44901 (419) 524-4178
Medical Dir/Dir of Nursing Charles G Young
MD.
Licensure Skilled Care; Intermediate Care.
Beds 99. *Certified* Medicaid; Medicare.
Ownership Nonprofit.
Admissions Requirements Minimum age;
Medical examination; Physician's request.
Staff RNs 7 (ft), 8 (pt); LPNs 5 (ft), 7 (pt);
Nurses aides 25 (ft), 15 (pt); Physical therapists
1 (ft); Reality therapists 1 (ft); Recreational ther-
apists 1 (ft); Occupational therapists 1 (ft), 1
(pt); Speech therapists 1 (pt); Activities coordi-
nators 1 (ft); Dietitians 1 (pt).
Facilities Dining room; Physical therapy room;
Activities room; Chapel; Crafts room; Laundry
room; Barber/Beauty shop; Library.
Activities Arts and Crafts; Cards; Games;
Reading groups; Prayer groups; Movies; Shopping trips; Dances/Social or cultural gatherings;
Occupational therapy; Speech therapy.
Description The Geriatric Center specializes in
rehabilitation of the elderly. It is the hub for 18
different programs for older Americans.

The Glendale Home*
624 Glendale Blvd, Mansfield, OH, 44907
Licensure Intermediate Care for Mentally
Retarded. *Beds* 12. *Certified* Medicaid.
Ownership Public.

The Raintree*
721 Scholl Rd, Mansfield, OH, 44907
Licensure Intermediate Care for Mentally
Retarded. *Beds* 48. *Certified* Medicaid.
Ownership Public.

Rosemont Nursing Home*
1159 Wyandotte Ave, Mansfield, OH, 44906
(419) 747-2666
Licensure Intermediate Care. *Beds* 24. *Certified* Medicaid.
Ownership Proprietary.

Sturges Convalescent Home*
81 Sturges Ave, Mansfield, OH, 44902 (419)
522-3651
Licensure Intermediate Care. *Beds* 29. *Certified* Medicaid.
Ownership Proprietary.

Twin Oaks
73 Madison, Mansfield, OH, 44905 (419)
526-0124

Medical Dir/Dir of Nursing Dr Charles Brown.
Licensure Intermediate Care for Mentally
Retarded. *Beds* 32.
Ownership Proprietary.
Admissions Requirements Minimum age 16;
Medical examination.
Staff Physicians; RNs 1 (ft), 1 (pt); LPNs 5 (ft);
Orderlies 1 (pt); Nurses aides 10 (ft); Physical
therapists 1 (pt); Reality therapists 1 (pt); Recre-
ational therapists 1 (pt); Occupational therapists
1 (pt); Speech therapists 1 (pt); Activities coor-
dinators 1 (pt); Dietitians 1 (pt); Dentists 1 (pt);
Ophthalmologists 1 (pt); Podiatrists 1 (pt);
Audiologists 1 (pt).
Facilities Dining room; Physical therapy room;
Activities room; Crafts room; Laundry room;
Library.
Activities Arts and Crafts; Cards; Games;
Reading groups; Prayer groups; Movies; Shopping trips; Dances/Social or cultural gatherings.
Description Fire resistant facility is situated on
8 acres of land with private recreational areas;
private and semi-private rooms only, (with pri-
vate or semi-private baths); no discrimination.

Winchester Terrace Inc
70 Winchester Rd, Mansfield, OH, 44907 (419)
524-2356
Licensure Nursing Home. *Beds* 63.
Ownership Proprietary.
Admissions Requirements Medical examination.
Staff RNs 5 (ft), 3 (pt); LPNs 4 (ft); Nurses
aides 20 (ft); Activities coordinators 1 (ft); Dietitians 1 (pt).
Facilities Dining room; Activities room; Crafts
room; Laundry room; Barber/Beauty shop;
Library.
Activities Arts and Crafts; Cards; Games;
Reading groups; Prayer groups; Movies; Shopping trips; Dances/Social or cultural gatherings.
Description Winchester Terrace is a modern
one-story home designed for the convalescence
of the chronically ill. The beautiful porch across
the front of the building provides fresh air and a
scenic view. Superb food is served in the spacious colonial dining room. Residents enjoy
many different crafts, activities, and outings.
Facility is devoted to providing a home-like
atmosphere for all residents.

Woodlawn Nursing Home*
535 Lexington Ave, Mansfield, OH, 44907
(419) 756-7111
Licensure Skilled Care; Intermediate Care;
Rest Home. *Beds* 150; Rest Home 9. *Certified* Medicaid; Medicare.
Ownership Proprietary.

MANTUA

Hattie Larlham Foundation
9772 Diagonal Rd, Mantua, OH, 44255 (216)
274-2272
Medical Dir/Dir of Nursing Mary Marsick
MD.
Licensure Intermediate Care for Mentally
Retarded. *Beds* 130.
Ownership Nonprofit.
Admissions Requirements Medical examina-
tion.
Staff Physicians 1 (ft); RNs 9 (ft); LPNs 17 (ft);

Nurses aides 94 (ft); Physical therapists 3 (ft); Recreational therapists 1 (ft); Occupational therapists 4 (ft); Speech therapists 1 (ft); Dietitians 1 (ft); Dentists 1 (pt); Audiologists 1 (pt).
Facilities Physical therapy room; Activities room; Chapel; Laundry room.

Mantua Manor Inc
11056 State Rt 44, Mantua, OH, 44255
Licensure Skilled Care; Intermediate Care.
Beds 35. *Certified* Medicaid; Medicare.
Ownership Proprietary.

MAPLE HEIGHTS

Pedone Nursing Center
19900 Clare Ave, Maple Heights, OH, 44137
(216) 662-3343
Licensure Skilled Care; Intermediate Care.
Beds 100. *Certified* Medicaid; Medicare.
Ownership Proprietary.
Admissions Requirements Medical examination.
Facilities Dining room; Physical therapy room; Activities room; Chapel; Crafts room; Laundry room; Barber/Beauty shop; Library.
Activities Arts and Crafts; Cards; Games; Reading groups; Prayer groups; Movies; Shopping trips.
Description By having 3 different levels of care, facility caters to every need.

MARIETTA

Christian Anchorage Retirement Home Inc*
355 Putnam Ave, Marietta, OH, 45715
Licensure Intermediate Care. *Beds* 48. *Certified* Medicaid.

Heartland of Marietta*
Rt 60, Devola, Marietta, OH, 45750 (614) 373-8920
Licensure Intermediate Care. *Beds* 101. *Certified* Medicaid.
Ownership Proprietary.

Jackson-Brawne Enterprises Inc
117 Barlett St, Marietta, OH, 45750 (614) 373-1867
Medical Dir/Dir of Nursing Kenneth E Bennett MD.
Licensure Intermediate Care. *Beds* 120. *Certified* Medicaid.
Ownership Proprietary.
Admissions Requirements Medical examination; Physician's request.
Staff Physicians 1 (pt); RNs 3 (ft), 5 (pt); LPNs 7 (ft), 1 (pt); Orderlies 1 (ft); Nurses aides 30 (ft), 5 (pt); Activities coordinators 2 (ft); Dietitians 1 (pt).
Facilities Dining room; Activities room; Chapel; Crafts room; Laundry room; Barber/Beauty shop.
Activities Arts and Crafts; Cards; Games; Reading groups; Prayer groups; Movies; Shopping trips; Dances/Social or cultural gatherings.
Description A modern one-story structure with private and semi-private rooms, all with private baths. Committed to providing a therapeutic atmosphere in which physical, spiritual, psychological, and social needs are met.

The Marie Antoinette
355 Putnam Ave, Marietta, OH, 45750 (614) 373-3597
Medical Dir/Dir of Nursing C Dehmlow MD.
Licensure Intermediate Care. *Beds* 100. *Certified* Medicaid.
Ownership Proprietary.
Staff Physicians 1 (pt); RNs 6 (ft); LPNs 14 (ft); Nurses aides 46 (ft); Physical therapists 1 (ft), 1 (pt); Occupational therapists 1 (ft); Activities coordinators 1 (ft); Dietitians 1 (ft); Dentists 1 (pt); Podiatrists 1 (pt).
Facilities Dining room; Physical therapy room; Activities room; Crafts room; Laundry room; Barber/Beauty shop; Library.
Activities Arts and Crafts; Cards; Games; Prayer groups; Movies; Shopping trips; Dances/Social or cultural gatherings.

Washington County Woman's Home*
812 3rd St, Marietta, OH, 45750
Licensure Rest Home. *Beds* 22.
Ownership Nonprofit.
Admissions Requirements Females only

MARION

Community Nursing Center
175 Community Dr, Marion, OH, 43302 (614) 387-7537
Licensure Skilled Care; Intermediate Care.
Beds 109. *Certified* Medicaid; Medicare.
Ownership Proprietary.
Admissions Requirements Minimum age 18.
Facilities Dining room; Physical therapy room; Activities room; Crafts room; Laundry room; Barber/Beauty shop; Library.
Activities Arts and Crafts; Cards; Games; Reading groups; Movies; Shopping trips; Dances/Social or cultural gatherings.

Hillside Nursing Home*
333 N Prospect St, Marion, OH, 43302 (614) 382-5042
Licensure Intermediate Care. *Beds* 24. *Certified* Medicaid.
Ownership Proprietary.

Maplewood Nursing Center Inc
409 Bellefontaine Ave, Marion, OH, 43302 (614) 383-2126
Medical Dir/Dir of Nursing Dr Warren Sawyer.
Licensure Skilled Care; Intermediate Care.
Beds 50. *Certified* Medicaid; Medicare.
Ownership Proprietary.
Admissions Requirements Minimum age 21.
Staff Physicians 1 (pt); RNs 4 (ft); LPNs 4 (ft); Nurses aides 25 (ft); Physical therapists 1 (ft); Occupational therapists 1 (pt); Speech therapists 1 (pt); Activities coordinators 1 (ft); Dietitians 1 (pt); Dentists 1 (pt); Ophthalmologists 1 (pt); Podiatrists 1 (pt); Audiologists 1 (pt).
Facilities Dining room; Physical therapy room; Activities room; Chapel; Laundry room; Barber/Beauty shop.
Activities Arts and Crafts; Cards; Prayer groups; Movies.

Marion County Home*
1422 Mt Vernon Ave, Marion, OH, 43302
Licensure Intermediate Care. *Beds* 140. *Certified* Medicaid.
Ownership Public.

Marion Manor Nursing Home Inc
195 Executive Dr, Marion, OH, 43302 (614) 387-9545
Licensure Skilled Care; Intermediate Care.
Beds 100. *Certified* Medicaid; Medicare.
Ownership Proprietary.

Morning View Care Center of Marion*
W Marion-Cardington Rd, Marion, OH, 43302
Licensure Intermediate Care. *Beds* 30. *Certified* Medicaid.
Ownership Proprietary.

MARTINS FERRY

Martins Ferry Hospital—Nursing Home*
90 N 4th St, Martins Ferry, OH, 43935
Licensure Skilled Care; Intermediate Care.
Beds SNF 75, ICF 75. *Certified* Medicaid; Medicare.
Ownership Proprietary.

Valley View Nursing Home
56143 Colerain Pike, Martins Ferry, OH, 43935 (614) 633-9637
Medical Dir/Dir of Nursing Dr Modi.
Licensure Intermediate Care. *Beds* 25. *Certified* Medicaid.
Admissions Requirements Minimum age 18; Medical examination; Physician's request.
Staff Physicians 1 (ft); RNs 1 (ft); LPNs 5 (ft), 1 (pt); Orderlies 1 (pt); Nurses aides 8 (ft); Physical therapists 1 (ft).
Facilities Dining room; Activities room; Crafts room; Laundry room; Barber/Beauty shop.
Activities Arts and Crafts; Cards; Games; Reading groups; Prayer groups; Movies; Shopping trips; Dances/Social or cultural gatherings.
Description Facility features inservice programs for staff and residents ongoing all year; located entirely on one floor with sprinklers and smoke detector throughout; rooms range from private to 3-beds to a room. Facility takes both private and Medicaid in a home-like setting with plenty of outdoor space, porches, ramps, lawn area—in business for over 25 years.

MARYSVILLE

Heartland of Marysville*
755 Plum St, Marysville, OH, 43040
Licensure Skilled Care; Intermediate Care.
Beds SNF 100; ICF 100. *Certified* Medicaid; Medicare.

Milcrest Nursing Center
730 Milcrest Dr, Marysville, OH, 43040 (513) 642-1026
Medical Dir/Dir of Nursing Dr Malcolm MacIvor.
Licensure Skilled Care; Intermediate Care.
Beds 50. *Certified* Medicaid.
Ownership Proprietary.
Admissions Requirements Minimum age 40.
Staff RNs 2 (ft), 2 (pt); LPNs 3 (ft), 2 (pt);

Nurses aides 11 (ft), 10 (pt); Physical therapists 1 (pt); Activities coordinators 1 (ft); Dietitians 1 (pt).
Facilities Dining room; Physical therapy room; Activities room; Laundry room; Barber/Beauty shop.
Activities Arts and Crafts; Cards; Games; Prayer groups; Movies; Current events; Adopt-a-grandparent program; Children's hour; Pet visiting.
Description Small facility maintains home-like atmosphere featuring carpeted dining room and corridors. Center's philosophy and trademark is a "caring community".

Union Manor*
18000 State Rt 4, Marysville, OH, 43040 (513) 642-3893
Licensure Intermediate Care. *Beds* 112. *Certified* Medicaid.
Ownership Public.

MASON

Brookside Extended Care Center*
780 Snider Rd, Mason, OH, 45040
Licensure Intermediate Care for Mentally Retarded. *Beds* 104. *Certified* Medicaid.

Mason Health Care Center*
5640 Cox-Smith Rd, Mason, OH, 45040 (513) 398-2981
Licensure Intermediate Care. *Beds* 50. *Certified* Medicaid.
Ownership Proprietary.

MASSILLON

Eventide Nursing Home*
200 Stewart Ave NW, Massillon, OH, 44646 (216) 477-4686
Licensure Nursing Home. *Beds* 14.
Ownership Proprietary.

Hanover House Inc
435 Avis Ave, Massillon, OH, 44646 (216) 837-1741
Medical Dir/Dir of Nursing M Kamel MD.
Licensure Skilled Care; Intermediate Care.
Beds 200. *Certified* Medicaid; Medicare.
Ownership Proprietary.
Admissions Requirements Minimum age 16; Medical examination.
Staff RNs 10 (ft), 5 (pt); LPNs 5 (ft), 11 (pt); Orderlies 3 (pt); Nurses aides 52 (ft), 7 (pt); Physical therapists 1 (ft); Recreational therapists 2 (ft); Occupational therapists 1 (pt); Speech therapists 1 (pt); Activities coordinators 1 (ft); Dietitians 1 (pt); Dentists 1 (pt); Ophthalmologists 1 (pt); Podiatrists 1 (pt); Audiologists 1 (pt).
Facilities Dining room; Physical therapy room; Activities room; Chapel; Crafts room; Barber/Beauty shop.
Activities Arts and Crafts; Cards; Games; Reading groups; Prayer groups; Movies; Shopping trips.

Hospitality House
205 Rohr Ave, Massillon, OH, 44646 (216) 837-2100

Medical Dir/Dir of Nursing Dr Wayne Lutzke.
Licensure Intermediate Care. *Beds* 28. *Certified* Medicaid.
Ownership Proprietary.
Admissions Requirements Minimum age 60; Medical examination.
Staff RNs 1 (pt); LPNs 3 (ft), 4 (pt); Nurses aides 5 (ft), 10 (pt); Activities coordinators 1 (pt).
Facilities Dining room; Activities room; Crafts room; Laundry room; Barber/Beauty shop.
Activities Arts and Crafts; Cards; Games; Movies; Shopping trips.
Description Facility features professional, individualized nursing care; originally designed and constructed to be nursing home in 1972.

Park View Manor Inc
54 Pine St NE, Massillon, OH, 44646 (216) 833-8352
Medical Dir/Dir of Nursing Dr H J Gashash.
Licensure Intermediate Care. *Beds* 23. *Certified* Medicaid.
Ownership Proprietary.
Admissions Requirements Females only
Staff Physicians 1 (pt); LPNs 2 (ft), 2 (pt); Nurses aides 6 (ft), 3 (pt); Activities coordinators 1 (pt); Dietitians 1 (pt); Dentists 1 (pt); Ophthalmologists 1 (pt); Podiatrists 1 (pt).
Facilities Dining room; Activities room; Crafts room.
Activities Arts and Crafts; Cards; Games; Reading groups; Prayer groups; Movies; Shopping trips; Dances/Social or cultural gatherings.

PATH Unit*
3000 S Erie St, Massillon, OH, 44648
Licensure Intermediate Care for Mentally Retarded. *Beds* 8. *Certified* Medicaid.
Ownership Public.

Rose Lane Health Center*
5425 High Mill Ave NW, Massillon, OH, 44646 (216) 833-3174
Licensure Skilled Care; Intermediate Care.
Beds 178. *Certified* Medicaid; Medicare.
Ownership Proprietary.

Shalem Rest Nursing Home
906 16th St SE, Massillon, OH, 44646 (216) 832-0403
Medical Dir/Dir of Nursing A Alasyali MD.
Licensure Intermediate Care. *Beds* 19. *Certified* Medicaid.
Ownership Proprietary.
Admissions Requirements Minimum age; Medical examination.
Staff Physicians; RNs; LPNs; Nurses aides; Physical therapists; Reality therapists; Recreational therapists; Occupational therapists; Speech therapists; Activities coordinators; Dietitians; Dentists; Ophthalmologists; Podiatrists; Audiologists.
Facilities Dining room; Activities room; Crafts room; Laundry room.
Activities Arts and Crafts; Cards; Games; Reading groups; Prayer groups; Movies; Dances/Social or cultural gatherings.
Description Facility is close to shopping areas, bus stop, and historical sites.

Walnut Hills Pavillion
1236 Huron Rd, Massillon, OH, 44646 (216) 832-8252
Medical Dir/Dir of Nursing Dr Joseph Urabel DO.
Licensure Intermediate Care. *Beds* 23. *Certified* Medicaid.
Ownership Proprietary.
Admissions Requirements Minimum age 12; Medical examination; Physician's request.
Staff RNs 1 (pt); LPNs 3 (ft), 3 (pt); Orderlies 1 (ft); Nurses aides 8 (ft); Physical therapists 1 (pt); Activities coordinators 1 (ft); Dietitians 1 (pt); Dentists 1 (pt); Ophthalmologists 1 (pt); Podiatrists 1 (pt).
Facilities Dining room; Activities room; Laundry room.
Activities Arts and Crafts; Cards; Games; Reading groups; Prayer groups; Shopping trips.
Description Walnut is a small home with home cooking, large yard, garden, and outside activities.

MASURY

O'Brien Memorial Nursing Home*
563 Brookfield Ave, SE, Masury, OH, 44438
Licensure Skilled Care; Intermediate Care.
Beds 100. *Certified* Medicaid; Medicare.

Orange Village Care Center Inc*
8055 Addison Rd SE, Masury, OH, 44438
Licensure Intermediate Care; Intermediate Care for Mentally Retarded. *Beds* ICF 76; ICF/MR 40. *Certified* Medicaid; Medicare.

MAUMEE

Elizabeth Scott Memorial Care Center*
2720 Albon Rd, Maumee, OH, 43537 (419) 865-7321
Licensure Intermediate Care. *Beds* 50. *Certified* Medicaid.
Ownership Proprietary.

Lucas Company Children Services-Extended Care Unit*
2500 River Rd, Maumee, OH, 43537
Licensure Intermediate Care for Mentally Retarded. *Beds* 32. *Certified* Medicaid.
Ownership Public.

MAYFIELD HEIGHTS

Manor Care Nursing Center
6757 Mayfield Rd, Mayfield Heights, OH, 44124 (216) 473-0090
Medical Dir/Dir of Nursing T Isakov MD.
Licensure Skilled Care; Intermediate Care.
Beds 150. *Certified* Medicare.
Ownership Proprietary.
Admissions Requirements Minimum age 14.
Staff Physicians 1 (ft), 40 (pt); RNs 11 (ft), 9 (pt); LPNs 7 (ft), 9 (pt); Orderlies 2 (pt); Nurses aides 30 (ft), 17 (pt); Physical therapists 3 (ft); Recreational therapists 2 (ft); Occupational therapists 2 (ft); Speech therapists 1 (ft); Dietitians 1 (ft); Dentists 1 (pt); Ophthalmologists 1 (pt); Podiatrists 1 (pt); Audiologists 1 (pt).
Facilities Dining room; Physical therapy room; Activities room; Barber/Beauty shop; Library;

Lounges; Occupational therapy room.
Activities Arts and Crafts; Cards; Games; Reading groups; Prayer groups; Movies; Shopping trips; Dances/Social or cultural gatherings; Educational programs for elderly.
Description Center decor is in soft shades of peach. Facility is known for rehabilitation programs and excellent nursing staff; offers extra care and ambiance that discriminating residents demand.

MCARTHUR

Twin Maples Nursing Home
Rt 1, McArthur, OH, 45651 (614) 596-5955
Medical Dir/Dir of Nursing Dr Susan Crapes.
Licensure Intermediate Care. *Beds* 42. *Certified* Medicaid.
Ownership Proprietary.
Admissions Requirements Medical examination; Physician's request.
Staff RNs 3 (pt); LPNs 4 (ft), 3 (pt); Nurses aides 11 (ft), 4 (pt); Physical therapists 1 (pt); Activities coordinators 1 (ft), 1 (pt); Dietitians 1 (pt); Dentists 1 (pt); Podiatrists 1 (pt).
Facilities Dining room; Activities room; Laundry room.
Activities Cards; Games; Reading groups; Shopping trips.
Description Facility features beautiful, spacious yard, big porch with swings, some animals, aquarium, player piano, and a very friendly atmosphere. TVs are also available.

MCCLURE

Floro's Nursing Home
Rt 1, McClure, OH, 43534 (419) 748-8196
Licensure Intermediate Care. *Beds* 29. *Certified* Medicaid.
Ownership Proprietary.

MCCONNELSVILLE

Mark Rest Center
N Kennebec Ave, McConnelsville, OH, 43756 (614) 962-3761
Admin David D Bankes. *Medical Dir/Dir of Nursing* Milton Levitin MD.
Licensure Skilled Care; Intermediate Care.
Beds 141. *Certified* Medicaid; Medicare.
Ownership Proprietary.
Staff RNs 3 (ft), 6 (pt); LPNs 11 (ft), 11 (pt); Nurses aides 21 (ft), 37 (pt); Activities coordinators 1 (ft); Dietitians 1 (pt).
Facilities Dining room; Physical therapy room; Activities room; Crafts room; Laundry room; Barber/Beauty shop; Library.
Activities Arts and Crafts; Games; Reading groups; Prayer groups; Movies.
Description Center is located in the uplands of the Muskingum Valley. Rooms are tastefully decorated and furnished, available as private, or semi-private accomodations. Renovation of the present building and addition of a new living facility should be completed in early 1985.

Morgan County Care Center*
856 S Riverside Dr NE, McConnelsville, OH, 43756 (614) 962-6141

Licensure Intermediate Care. *Beds* 50. *Certified* Medicaid.
Ownership Proprietary.

MCDERMOTT

Rendezvous Medi-Home*
Rt 2, Box 135, McDermott, OH, 45652 (614) 858-4546
Licensure Intermediate Care. *Beds* 46. *Certified* Medicaid.
Ownership Proprietary.

Rest Haven Nursing Home*
Baker St, McDermott, OH, 45652 (614) 259-2838
Licensure Intermediate Care. *Beds* 23. *Certified* Medicaid.
Ownership Proprietary.

MEDINA

Care House
809 E Washington St, Medina, OH, 44256 (216) 725-4123
Licensure Rest Home. *Beds* 50.
Ownership Proprietary.
Admissions Requirements Medical examination.
Facilities Dining room; Activities room; Crafts room; Barber/Beauty shop; Library.
Activities Arts and Crafts; Cards; Games; Reading groups; Prayer groups; Movies; Shopping trips.

Crestview Nursing Home
806 E Washington St, Medina, OH, 44256 (216) 725-4123
Admin Gary L DeHass.
Licensure Nursing Home; Rest Home.
Beds Nursing Home 49; Rest Home 81.
Ownership Proprietary.
Admissions Requirements Medical examination.
Facilities Dining room; Physical therapy room; Activities room; Barber/Beauty shop.
Activities Arts and Crafts; Cards; Games; Reading groups; Prayer groups; Movies.

Eckfield Rest Home*
1530 Remsen Rd, Medina, OH, 44256 (216) 239-1717
Licensure Rest Home. *Beds* 22.
Ownership Proprietary.

Ohio Pythian Sisters Home of Medina*
550 Miner Dr, Medina, OH, 44256
Licensure Intermediate Care. *Beds* 50. *Certified* Medicaid.
Ownership Nonprofit.

Paradise Village*
PO Box 481, 4281 Paradise Rd, Medina, OH, 44256 (216) 722-2100
Licensure Intermediate Care for Mentally Retarded. *Beds* 24.
Ownership Nonprofit.

Shangri-La Rest Home Inc*
2400 Columbia Rd, Medina, OH, 44256 (216) 483-3131

Licensure Skilled Care; Intermediate Care; Rest Home. *Beds* 109; Rest Home 38. *Certified* Medicaid; Medicare.
Ownership Proprietary.

Sophia Huntington Parker Home
635 Huntington St, Medina, OH, 44256 (216) 722-4672
Medical Dir/Dir of Nursing Dr Irene Leszkiewicz.
Licensure Nursing Home. *Beds* 34.
Ownership Nonprofit.
Admissions Requirements Minimum age 62; Females only; Medical examination.
Staff LPNs 3 (ft), 4 (pt); Nurses aides 7 (ft), 12 (pt); Activities coordinators 1 (ft); Dietitians 1 (pt); Podiatrists 1 (pt).
Affiliation Knights of Pythias
Facilities Dining room; Activities room; Chapel; Laundry room; Barber/Beauty shop.
Activities Arts and Crafts; Cards; Games; Reading groups; Prayer groups; Movies; Shopping trips; Dances/Social or cultural gatherings.
Description We are a nonprofit home and our philosophy is to provide high quality care. This means we continually strive to meet the emotional, social and spiritual needs of our residents while at the same time providing good nursing care. Our residents, staff, administration, and Board of Trustees truly embody the meaning of family in our home. All of us enjoy the family atmosphere at the Sophia Huntington Parker Home. The home has 21 private rooms for ambulatory residents. There are 2 wards with 6 beds in each and one private room for non-ambulatory residents.

MEDWAY

Utopia Estates Rest Home Inc*
10917 Gerlaugh Rd, Medway, OH, 45341 (513) 849-1353
Licensure Rest Home. *Beds* 37.
Ownership Proprietary.

MENTOR

Greenlawn Health Care Center
9901 Johnnycake Ridge Rd, Box 119, Mentor, OH, 44060 (216) 357-7900
Medical Dir/Dir of Nursing Franklin D Krause MD.
Licensure Intermediate Care. *Beds* 71. *Certified* Medicaid.
Ownership Proprietary.
Admissions Requirements Medical examination.
Staff Physicians 1 (pt); RNs 4 (ft), 2 (pt); LPNs 3 (ft), 5 (pt); Orderlies 1 (ft); Nurses aides 30 (ft), 2 (pt); Activities coordinators 3 (ft), 2 (pt); Dietitians 1 (pt); Dentists 1 (pt); Ophthalmologists 1 (pt); Podiatrists 1 (pt).
Facilities Dining room; Activities room; Laundry room; Barber/Beauty shop.
Activities Arts and Crafts; Cards; Games; Reading groups; Prayer groups; Movies.
Description Facility offers adult-day care services.

Lake County Adult Resident Center*
8211 Deepwood Blvd, Mentor, OH, 44060
Licensure Intermediate Care for Mentally
Retarded. *Beds* 64.
Ownership Public.

Lake County Child Development Center*
8121 Deepwood Blvd, Mentor, OH, 44060
Licensure Intermediate Care for Mentally
Retarded. *Beds* 26.
Ownership Public.

Mentor Way Villa Nursing Home*
Mentor Ave and 8903 Schaefer St, Mentor,
OH, 44060 (216) 255-9309
Licensure Intermediate Care. *Beds* 79. *Certified* Medicaid.
Ownership Proprietary.

MIAMISBURG

Friendly Nursing Home Inc*
542 E Linden Ave, Miamisburg, OH, 45342
(513) 866-4051
Licensure Intermediate Care. *Beds* 36. *Certified* Medicaid.
Ownership Proprietary.

Miami Christel Manor Inc*
1120 S Dunaway St, Miamisburg, OH, 45342
(513) 866-9089
Licensure Intermediate Care. *Beds* 101. *Certified* Medicaid.
Ownership Proprietary.

MIDDLEFIELD

Briar Hill Nursing Home*
PO Box 277, Middlefield, OH, 44062 (216)
632-5241
Licensure Intermediate Care. *Beds* 39. *Certified* Medicaid.
Ownership Proprietary.

MIDDLETOWN

Barbara Park Convalescent Center
751 Kensington St, Middletown, OH, 45042
(513) 424-3511
Licensure Skilled Care; Intermediate Care.
Beds 208. *Certified* Medicaid; Medicare.
Ownership Proprietary.
Staff Physicians; RNs; LPNs; Orderlies;
Nurses aides; Physical therapists; Reality therapists; Recreational therapists.
Facilities Dining room; Physical therapy room;
Activities room; Chapel; Crafts room; Laundry
room; Barber/Beauty shop.

Colonial Manor Inc
508 S Main St, Middletown, OH, 45042 (513)
423-3882
Medical Dir/Dir of Nursing Dr Jeff Zollett.
Licensure Nursing Home. *Beds* 29.
Ownership Nonprofit.
Admissions Requirements Medical examination; Physician's request.
Staff Physicians 2 (ft); RNs 1 (ft); LPNs 6 (ft),
3 (pt); Nurses aides 12 (ft), 6 (pt); Physical therapists 1 (pt); Dietitians 1 (pt); Dentists 1 (pt);
Ophthalmologists 1 (pt); Podiatrists 1 (pt).

Facilities Dining room; Laundry room.
Activities Cards; Games; Reading groups.
Description Facility is a private ICF with an
excellent reputation for outstanding nursing
and personal care within a home-like environment.

Garden Manor Extended Care Center Inc
6898 Hamilton-Middletown Rd, Middletown,
OH, 45042 (513) 424-5321
Medical Dir/Dir of Nursing Jeffery Zollett
MD.
Licensure Skilled Care; Intermediate Care.
Beds 202. *Certified* Medicaid; Medicare.
Ownership Nonprofit.

Middletown Quality Care Center*
3100 S Main St, Middletown, OH, 45042 (513)
423-9621
Licensure Intermediate Care. *Beds* 24. *Certified* Medicaid.
Ownership Proprietary.

MILAN

Canterbury Villa of Milan
185 S Main St, PO Box 479, Milan, OH,
44846-0479 (419) 499-2576
Medical Dir/Dir of Nursing R L Blackann DO.
Licensure Intermediate Care. *Beds* 96. *Certified* Medicaid.
Ownership Proprietary.
Admissions Requirements Medical examination; Physician's request.
Staff RNs 1 (ft), 2 (pt); LPNs 8 (ft), 5 (pt);
Nurses aides 25 (ft), 13 (pt); Activities coordinators 1 (ft); Dietitians 1 (pt); Social workers.
Facilities Dining room; Barber/Beauty shop.
Activities Arts and Crafts; Games; Prayer
groups; Movies; Shopping trips.
Description Resident service van available;
volunteers with activity program; all inclusive
rates for services.

MILFORD

Clermont Nursing and Convalescent Center*
934 Star Rt 28, Milford, OH, 45150 (513)
831-1770
Licensure Skilled Care; Intermediate Care.
Beds 206. *Certified* Medicaid; Medicare.
Ownership Proprietary.

Sem Haven Health Care Center*
225 Cleveland Ave, Milford, OH, 45150 (513)
248-1270
Licensure Intermediate Care. *Beds* 100. *Certified* Medicaid.
Ownership Proprietary.

MILLERSBURG

Fairview Castle Nursing Home*
W Jackson St, Millersburg, OH, 44654
Licensure Intermediate Care. *Beds* 34. *Certified* Medicaid.
Ownership Proprietary.

Overlook Castle Nursing Home*
Hebron St, Millersburg, OH, 44654
Licensure Intermediate Care. *Beds* 35.
Certified Medicaid.
Ownership Proprietary.

Scenic View Nursing Home*
Twp Rd 190, Millersburg, OH, 44654
Licensure Intermediate Care. *Beds* 164. *Certified* Medicaid.
Ownership Proprietary.

Sunset View*
Rt 5, Millersburg, OH, 44654
Licensure Intermediate Care. *Beds* 75.
Certified Medicaid.
Ownership Proprietary.

Terrace View Castle Nursing Home*
Hebron St, Millersburg, OH, 44654
Licensure Intermediate Care. *Beds* 120. *Certified* Medicaid.
Ownership Proprietary.

Valley View Castle Nursing Home*
Rt 1, Millersburg, OH, 44654
Licensure Intermediate Care. *Beds* 42.
Certified Medicaid.
Ownership Proprietary.

MINERAL RIDGE

Glenn View Manor
3379 Main St, Mineral Ridge, OH, 44440 (216)
652-9901
Medical Dir/Dir of Nursing E G Caskey.
Licensure Intermediate Care. *Beds* 216. *Certified* Medicaid.
Ownership Proprietary.
Admissions Requirements Minimum age 50;
Medical examination; Physician's request.
Staff Physicians 2 (pt); RNs 12 (ft); LPNs 21
(ft); Nurses aides 73 (ft); Activities coordinators
3 (ft); Dietitians 1 (ft); Podiatrists 1 (pt).
Facilities Dining room; Physical therapy room;
Activities room; Chapel; Crafts room; Laundry
room; Barber/Beauty shop; Library; Pool; Sun
room; Gift shop.
Activities Arts and Crafts; Cards; Games;
Reading groups; Prayer groups; Movies; Shopping trips; Dances/Social or cultural gatherings;
Fireworks.
Description Facility is in country setting,
heavily landscaped, with putting green, picnic
area, and a snack grill.

Youngstown Developmental Center*
4891 E County Line Rd, Mineral Ridge, OH,
44440
Licensure Intermediate Care for Mentally
Retarded. *Beds* 117. *Certified* Medicaid;
Medicare.
Ownership Public.

MINERVA

Minerva Convalescent Center Inc
1035 E Lincoln Way, Minerva, OH, 44657
(216) 868-4147
Medical Dir/Dir of Nursing Dr Samuel Weir.
Licensure Intermediate Care. *Beds* 57. *Certi-*

fied Medicaid.
Ownership Proprietary.
Staff Physicians 1 (pt); RNs 4 (ft), 3 (pt); LPNs 2 (ft), 3 (pt); Nurses aides 20 (ft), 30 (pt); Recreational therapists 2 (ft); Activities coordinators 2 (ft); Dietitians 1 (pt); Podiatrists 1 (pt).
Facilities Dining room; Laundry room; Barber-/Beauty shop.
Activities Arts and Crafts; Cards; Games; Shopping trips; Dances/Social or cultural gatherings.
Description A psychologist is on staff to work with residents who need counseling. Music and exercise therapy provided daily. Remotivation and reality orientation in groups and one-on-one is also available.

Minerva Nursing Home*
301 W Lincoln Way, Minerva, OH, 44657
Beds 15.

MINSTER

Heritage Manor Nursing Center
24 N Hamilton St, Minster, OH, 45865 (419) 628-2396
Admin Donald J Crock. *Medical Dir/Dir of Nursing* Joseph Steurnagel MC.
Licensure Skilled Care. *Beds* 100. *Certified* Medicaid; Medicare.
Ownership Proprietary.
Admissions Requirements Medical examination; Physician's request.
Staff RNs 7 (ft), 7 (pt); LPNs 8 (ft), 1 (pt); Nurses aides 31 (ft), 31 (pt); Physical therapists 2 (pt); Occupational therapists 1 (pt); Speech therapists 1 (pt); Activities coordinators 2 (ft); Dietitians 1 (pt).
Facilities Dining room; Physical therapy room; Activities room; Chapel; Laundry room; Barber/Beauty shop.
Activities Arts and Crafts; Cards; Games; Prayer groups; Movies; Shopping trips; Dances/Social or cultural gatherings; Remotivation.
Description Center is equipped with the latest and most modern medical equipment within a clean, one-story, easy access building; staff is genuinely interested in the well being and happiness of each resident, and is ready to give the extra care and attention for which the center is noted.

MONCLOVA

Monclova Care Center*
9831 Garden Rd, Monclova, OH, 43542 (419) 865-6421
Licensure Intermediate Care. *Beds* 100. *Certified* Medicaid.
Ownership Proprietary.

Villa Homes West Inc
10005 Garden Rd, Monclova, OH, 43542 (419) 865-1248
Licensure Intermediate Care. *Beds* ICF 100. Certified Medicaid.
Ownership Proprietary.
Staff Physicians 5 (pt); RNs 5 (ft); LPNs 9 (ft); Orderlies 2 (ft); Nurses aides 24 (ft); Physical therapists 1 (pt); Recreational therapists 2 (ft);

Activities coordinators 1 (ft); Dietitians 1 (pt).
Facilities Dining room; Physical therapy room; Activities room; Crafts room; Laundry room; Barber/Beauty shop; Library.
Activities Arts and Crafts; Cards; Games; Reading groups; Prayer groups; Movies; Shopping trips; Dances/Social or cultural gatherings.

MONROE

Mount Pleasant Retirement Village
225 Britton Rd, Monroe, OH, 45050 (513) 539-7391
Medical Dir/Dir of Nursing Dr Gordon Smith.
Licensure Skilled Care; Intermediate Care.
Beds 110. *Certified* Medicaid; Medicare.
Ownership Nonprofit.
Admissions Requirements Minimum age 60; Medical examination.
Affiliation Presbyterian
Facilities Dining room; Physical therapy room; Activities room; Chapel; Crafts room; Laundry room; Barber/Beauty shop; Library.
Activities Arts and Crafts; Cards; Games; Reading groups; Prayer groups; Movies; Shopping trips.

MONTPELIER

Evergreen Manor Nursing Home Inc
924 Robinair Way, Montpelier, OH, 43543 (419) 485-3416
Medical Dir/Dir of Nursing Dr C A Bell and Dr R O Kanney.
Licensure Skilled Care; Intermediate Care.
Beds 50. *Certified* Medicaid; Medicare.
Ownership Proprietary.
Staff Physicians 4 (pt); RNs 1 (ft), 1 (pt); LPNs 3 (ft), 1 (pt); Orderlies 1 (ft), 1 (pt); Nurses aides 13 (ft), 7 (pt); Physical therapists 1 (pt); Recreational therapists 1 (ft); Activities coordinators 1 (ft); Dietitians 1 (pt); Dentists 1 (pt); Ophthalmologists 1 (pt); Podiatrists 1 (pt).
Facilities Dining room; Activities room; Chapel; Crafts room; Laundry room; Barber/Beauty shop.
Activities Arts and Crafts; Cards; Games; Reading groups; Prayer groups; Movies; Shopping trips.
Description Evergreen Manor welcomes visitors anytime and is conveniently located near Ohio Turnpike Exit 2, across the street from the Montpelier City Park.

MORROW

Pine Crest Nursing Home
463 E Pike St, Morrow, OH, 45152 (513) 899-2801
Medical Dir/Dir of Nursing Carl Durning MD.
Licensure Intermediate Care. *Beds* 42. *Certified* Medicaid.
Ownership Proprietary.
Admissions Requirements Medical examination.
Staff RNs 1 (pt); LPNs 5 (ft), 3 (pt); Nurses aides 11 (ft), 7 (pt); Activities coordinators 1 (ft), 1 (pt); Dietitians 1 (pt).
Facilities Dining room; Activities room; Crafts room; Laundry room; Barber/Beauty shop.
Activities Arts and Crafts; Games; Prayer

groups.
Description Home is in rural setting with approximately 2 acres of beautifully landscaped grounds with pine trees; outdoor recreation is available; walking is encouraged on grounds; large screened-in sun porch for relaxation.

MOUNT GILEAD

Morrow County Extended Care Facility
651 W Marion Rd, Mount Gilead, OH, 43338
Medical Dir/Dir of Nursing John T Sweeney MD.
Licensure Skilled Care. *Beds* 10. *Certified* Medicare.
Ownership Public.
Admissions Requirements Medical examination; Physician's request.
Staff Physicians; RNs; LPNs; Orderlies; Nurses aides; Physical therapists; Speech therapists; Activities coordinators; Dietitians.
Facilities Dining room; Physical therapy room; Activities room; Chapel; Crafts room; Barber-/Beauty shop; Library.
Description Facility is attached to an acute care hospital. The admitting physician is responsible for giving total care to patients. Facility has consulting dentist.

Woodside Village Care Center Ltd*
W Marion Rd, Mount Gilead, OH, 43338 (419) 947-2015
Licensure Intermediate Care. *Beds* 100. *Certified* Medicaid.
Ownership Proprietary.

MOUNT ORAB

Mount Orab Nursing Care Center
Farley Lane, Mount Orab, OH, 45154 (513) 444-3511
Licensure Intermediate Care. *Beds* 25. *Certified* Medicaid.
Ownership Nonprofit.
Staff RNs 1 (pt); LPNs 4 (ft), 1 (pt); Nurses aides 8 (ft), 2 (pt); Activities coordinators 1 (ft).
Facilities Dining room; Activities room; Laundry room.
Activities Arts and Crafts; Cards; Games; Reading groups; Prayer groups; Shopping trips.
Description Control living and dining area surrounded by 8 rooms of various sizes and kitchen and laundry room at rear—gives a homey friendly atmosphere.

MOUNT SAINT JOSEPH

Mother Margaret Hall
Delhi Pike, Mount Saint Joseph, OH, 45051 (513) 244-4692
Admin Sr Agnes Celestia. *Medical Dir/Dir of Nursing* Ronald Gall MD.
Licensure Skilled Care; Intermediate Care.
Beds 132. *Certified* Medicaid; Medicare.
Ownership Nonprofit.
Admissions Requirements Medical examination; Physician's request.
Staff Physicians 2 (pt); Physical therapists 2 (pt); Recreational therapists 1 (ft); Occupational therapists 1 (pt); Speech therapists 1 (pt); Activities coordinators 1 (ft); Dietitians 1 (ft), 1

(pt); Dentists 1 (pt); Podiatrists 1 (pt).
Affiliation Roman Catholic
Facilities Dining room; Physical therapy room;
Activities room; Chapel; Crafts room; Laundry
room; Barber/Beauty shop; Library; Speech
therapists room.
Activities Arts and Crafts; Cards; Games;
Reading groups; Prayer groups; Movies; Shop-
ping trips; Dances/Social or cultural gatherings.
Description Nursing home primarily serves the
members of Sisters of Charity of Cincinnati,
OH. When there is room, accept mothers, fath-
ers, sisters, and brothers who apply and need
the care given in a nursing home.

MOUNT VERNON

Country Club Center II
1350 Yauger Rd, Mount Vernon, OH, 43050
(614) 397-2350
Medical Dir/Dir of Nursing Dr James Kennedy.
Licensure Skilled Care; Intermediate Care.
Beds 54. *Certified* Medicaid; Medicare.
Ownership Proprietary.
Admissions Requirements Medical examination; Physician's request.
Staff Physicians 1 (pt); RNs 3 (ft); LPNs 5 (ft),
3 (pt); Orderlies 3 (ft); Physical therapists 1 (pt);
Reality therapists 1 (pt); Recreational therapists
1 (pt); Occupational therapists 1 (pt); Speech
therapists 1 (pt); Activities coordinators 1 (ft);
Dietitians 1 (pt); Dentists 1 (pt); Ophthalmolo-
gists 1 (pt); Podiatrists 1 (pt); Audiologists 1
(pt).
Facilities Dining room; Physical therapy room;
Activities room; Chapel; Crafts room; Laundry
room; Barber/Beauty shop; Library.
Activities Arts and Crafts; Cards; Games;
Reading groups; Prayer groups; Movies; Shopping trips; Dances/Social or cultural gatherings;
Choral group travels to other facilities; Out to
lunch bunch.

Country Court*
1076 Coshocton Ave, Mount Vernon, OH,
43050 (614) 397-4125
Licensure Skilled Care; Intermediate Care.
Beds 122. *Certified* Medicaid; Medicare.
Ownership Proprietary.

Hannah Browning Home
7 E Sugar St, Mount Vernon, OH, 43050 (614)
392-7111
Licensure Rest Home. *Beds* 9.
Ownership Nonprofit.
Admissions Requirements Minimum age 70;
Medical examination.
Staff Nurses aides 4 (ft), 6 (pt).
Facilities Dining room; Laundry room.
Activities Shopping trips.
Description Facility is a small residential home
for ambulatory residents only; not government
supported. At the present time, we have only 5
residents and do not anticipate taking in more
in the future.

Mount Vernon Developmental Center
PO Box 762, Mount Vernon, OH, 43050
Medical Dir/Dir of Nursing Raymond L Sheets
MD.
Licensure Intermediate Care for Mentally

Retarded. *Beds* 392. *Certified* Medicaid.
Ownership Public.
Admissions Requirements Minimum age 6.
Staff Physicians 3 (ft); RNs 23 (ft); LPNs 33
(ft), 3 (pt); Nurses aides 168 (ft); Physical thera-
pists 2 (ft); Recreational therapists 1 (ft); Occu-
pational therapists 2 (ft); Speech therapists 3
(ft); Activities coordinators 18 (ft); Dietitians 1
(ft); Dentists 2 (pt); Podiatrists 1 (pt); Audiologists 1 (pt).
Facilities Dining room; Physical therapy room;
Activities room; Crafts room; Laundry room;
Barber/Beauty shop; Library.
Activities Arts and Crafts; Cards; Games;
Reading groups; Prayer groups; Movies; Shopping trips; Dances/Social or cultural gatherings.
Description Facility has 15 resident living units
and a population of approximately 400 residents and 630 employees; most of the older
buildings have been renovated and 5 new resident living units, a storage/maintenance
building, and a physical habilitation and education building has been added.

Mount Vernon Nursing Home*
PO Box 790, 414 Wooster Rd, Mount Vernon,
OH, 43050 (614) 397-9626
Licensure Intermediate Care. *Beds* 44. *Certi-
fied* Medicaid.
Ownership Proprietary.

Northside Manor Inc
13 Avalon Rd, Mount Vernon, OH, 43050
(614) 397-3200
Licensure Skilled Care; Intermediate Care.
Beds 109. *Certified* Medicaid; Medicare.
Ownership Proprietary.
Admissions Requirements Minimum age 30;
Medical examination.
Staff RNs 8 (ft); LPNs 4 (ft), 3 (pt); Nurses
aides 29 (ft), 11 (pt); Physical therapists 1 (pt);
Recreational therapists 1 (ft); Occupational
therapists 1 (pt); Speech therapists 1 (pt);
Activities coordinators 1 (ft); Dietitians 1 (ft);
Dentists 2 (pt); Ophthalmologists 1 (pt); Podia-
trists 1 (pt); Audiologists 1 (pt).

Ohio Eastern Star Home*
1451 E Gambier Rd, Mount Vernon, OH,
43050 (614) 397-1706
Licensure Nursing Home. *Beds* 86.
Ownership Nonprofit.
Affiliation Order of Eastern Star

Rose Garden Nursing Home
303 N Main St, Mount Vernon, OH, 43050
(614) 393-2046
Admin Eleanor Burke.
Licensure Intermediate Care. *Beds* 30. *Certified* Medicaid.
Ownership Proprietary.
Admissions Requirements Medical examination; Physician's request.
Staff RNs 1 (pt); LPNs 2 (ft), 2 (pt); Nurses
aides 7 (ft), 3 (pt); Activities coordinators 1 (pt).
Facilities Dining room; Laundry room.
Activities Arts and Crafts; Cards; Games; Prayer groups; Movies; Shopping trips;
Dances/Social or cultural gatherings; Exercise
daily.
Description Staff prides itself in giving excellent
individual attention; activities director works
with residents as a group and as individuals.

NAPOLEON

Filling Memorial Home of Mercy*
Rt 5, Napoleon, OH, 43545 (419) 592-6451
Licensure Intermediate Care for Mentally
Retarded. *Beds* 53. *Certified* Medicaid.
Ownership Nonprofit.

Northcrest Nursing Home*
Rt 6, Northcrest Dr, Napoleon, OH, 43545
(419) 599-4070
Licensure Skilled Care; Intermediate Care.
Beds 100. *Certified* Medicaid; Medicare.
Ownership Proprietary.

NAVARRE

Country Lawn Nursing Home*
Rt 3, 10608 Navarre Rd S, Navarre, OH,
44662 (216) 767-3455
Licensure Intermediate Care. *Beds* 126. *Certi-
fied* Medicaid.
Ownership Proprietary.

Lodge Nursing Home*
23 Ohio St, Navarre, OH, 44662 (216)
879-5930
Licensure Intermediate Care. *Beds* 30. *Certified* Medicaid.
Ownership Proprietary.

Navarre Community Health Center*
517 Park St W, Navarre, OH, 44662 (216)
879-2765
Licensure Skilled Care; Intermediate Care.
Beds 78. *Certified* Medicaid; Medicare.
Ownership Proprietary.

NEW BREMEN

Lone Pine Nursing Home Inc
403 N Main St, New Bremen, OH, 45869 (419)
629-2793
Medical Dir/Dir of Nursing Dr Harbard.
Licensure Intermediate Care. *Beds* 19. *Certified* Medicaid.
Ownership Proprietary.
Admissions Requirements Medical examination.
Staff RNs 1 (ft); LPNs 2 (ft), 1 (pt); Nurses
aides 10 (ft), 2 (pt); Recreational therapists 1
(pt); Activities coordinators 1 (ft); Dentists 1
(pt); Ophthalmologists 1 (pt); Podiatrists 1 (pt).
Facilities Dining room; Activities room; Laundry room.
Activities Arts and Crafts; Cards; Games;
Reading groups; Prayer groups; Movies; Shopping trips; Dances/Social or cultural gatherings.
Description We are located in a semi-rural area.
Our activity program is extremely community
oriented and involved with the residents. Since
we are a smaller home, our staff-ratio is approximately 1:1.

NEW CARLISLE

Belle Manor Nursing Home
107-111 N Pike St, New Carlisle, OH, 45344
(513) 845-3561
Medical Dir/Dir of Nursing Thomas Honing-
ford DO.

Licensure Skilled Care; Intermediate Care.
Beds 123. Certified Medicaid; Medicare.
Ownership Nonprofit.
Admissions Requirements Medical examination.
Staff Physicians 1 (pt); RNs 6 (ft), 2 (pt); LPNs 4 (ft), 3 (pt); Nurses aides 40 (ft), 12 (pt); Physical therapists 2 (ft); Reality therapists 1 (pt); Recreational therapists 1 (ft); Occupational therapists 1 (pt); Speech therapists 1 (pt); Activities coordinators 1 (ft); Dietitians 1 (pt); Dentists 1 (pt); Ophthalmologists 1 (pt); Podiatrists 1 (pt); Audiologists 1 (pt).
Facilities Dining room; Physical therapy room; Activities room; Chapel; Crafts room; Laundry room; Barber/Beauty shop; Library.
Activities Arts and Crafts; Cards; Games; Reading groups; Prayer groups; Movies; Shopping trips; Dances/Social or cultural gatherings.

Ohio Missionary Home*
1885 N Dayton-Lakeview Rd, New Carlisle, OH, 45344 (513) 845-8219
Licensure Intermediate Care. Beds 50. Certified Medicaid.
Ownership Nonprofit.

NEW CONCORD

New Concord Nursing Center
75 Fox Creek Rd, Rt 3, New Concord, OH, 43762 (614) 826-7649
Medical Dir/Dir of Nursing Carl Spragg MD.
Licensure Intermediate Care. Beds 50. Certified Medicaid.
Ownership Proprietary.
Admissions Requirements Medical examination.
Staff Physicians 1 (pt); RNs 2 (pt); LPNs 2 (ft), 3 (pt); Nurses aides 10 (ft), 5 (pt); Activities coordinators 1 (ft); Dietitians 1 (ft).
Facilities Dining room; Physical therapy room; Activities room; Laundry room; Barber/Beauty shop; Solarium.
Activities Arts and Crafts; Cards; Games; Reading groups; Prayer groups; Movies; Shopping trips; Coffee hour; Current events.
Description In the fall, residents participate in apple butter making outside. Residents and their families participate in holiday celebrations, holiday programs for children, and a petting zoo with Future Farmers of America.

NEW LEBANON

Royal Villa Care Center Inc
101 Mills Pl, New Lebanon, OH, 45345 (513) 687-1311
Medical Dir/Dir of Nursing Michael O Phillips MD.
Licensure Skilled Care; Intermediate Care.
Beds 101. Certified Medicaid; Medicare.
Ownership Proprietary.
Admissions Requirements Medical examination.
Staff Physicians 2 (pt); RNs 3 (ft); LPNs 7 (ft), 3 (pt); Nurses aides 28 (ft), 20 (pt); Physical therapists 1 (pt); Recreational therapists 1 (ft), 2 (pt); Occupational therapists 1 (pt); Speech therapists 1 (pt); Activities coordinators 1 (ft); Dietitians 1 (pt); Dentists 1 (pt); Ophthalmologists

1 (pt); Podiatrists 1 (pt); Audiologists 1 (pt).
Facilities Dining room; Physical therapy room; Activities room; Chapel; Crafts room; Laundry room; Barber/Beauty shop; Library.
Activities Arts and Crafts; Cards; Games; Reading groups; Prayer groups; Movies; Shopping trips; Dances/Social or cultural gatherings.
Description Facility is "serving God's special people" in a small town atmosphere yet only 10 minutes from downtown Dayton and 25 minutes from Richmond, Indiana.

NEW LEXINGTON

New Lexington Health Care Center*
920 S Main St, New Lexington, OH, 43764
Licensure Skilled Care; Intermediate Care.
Beds 100. Certified Medicaid; Medicare.

NEW PARIS

Heartland of Cedar Springs
7739 Rt 40, New Paris, OH, 45347 (513) 437-2311
Medical Dir/Dir of Nursing Dr S Ahn.
Licensure Intermediate Care for Mentally Retarded. Beds 66. Certified Medicaid.
Ownership Nonprofit.
Admissions Requirements Minimum age 45; Medical examination.
Staff Physicians 1 (pt); RNs 5 (ft), 3 (pt); LPNs 3 (ft), 4 (pt); Orderlies 5 (ft), 1 (pt); Nurses aides 21 (ft), 2 (pt); Physical therapists 2 (pt); Recreational therapists 1 (ft); Occupational therapists 1 (pt); Speech therapists 1 (pt); Activities coordinators 1 (ft); Dietitians 1 (pt); Dentists 1 (pt); Ophthalmologists 1 (pt); Podiatrists 1 (pt); Podiatrists 1 (pt); Audiologists 1 (pt); QMRPs 2 (pt).
Facilities Dining room; Physical therapy room; Activities room; Laundry room; Barber/Beauty shop.
Activities Arts and Crafts; Cards; Games; Reading groups; Prayer groups; Movies; Shopping trips; Dances/Social or cultural gatherings; Boy/Girl Scouts; Swimming; Bowling.
Description Habilitation programs for residents include: training in major areas of self-help, communication, cognitive development, fine-/gross motor and social/leisure skills. Based upon each residents individual needs, each program is developed/supervised by a team of professionals including psychologists; speech, occupational, and physical therapists, and qualified mental retardation professionals.

NEW PHILADELPHIA

South Broadway Nursing Home Inc*
245–251 S Broadway, New Philadelphia, OH, 44663 (216) 339-4544
Licensure Intermediate Care. Beds 49. Certified Medicaid.
Ownership Proprietary.

Valley Manor Nursing Home*
Rt 5, Box 5440, New Philadelphia, OH, 44663 (216) 339-3595
Licensure Skilled Care; Intermediate Care.
Beds 219. Certified Medicaid; Medicare.
Ownership Proprietary.

NEW PHILIDELPHIA

Kaderly Home*
1416 Kaderly, NW, New Philidelphia, OH, 44663
Licensure Intermediate Care for Mentally Retarded. Beds 12. Certified Medicaid.

NEW RICHMOND

Dobbins Nursing Home Inc
400 Main St, New Richmond, OH, 45157 (513) 553-4139
Admin Patricia Meeker. Medical Dir/Dir of Nursing John Wehby MD.
Licensure Intermediate Care. Beds 22. Certified Medicaid.
Ownership Nonprofit.
Admissions Requirements Females only
Staff RNs 1 (pt); LPNs 3 (ft), 2 (pt); Nurses aides 12 (ft); Physical therapists 1 (pt); Recreational therapists 1 (pt); Activities coordinators 1 (ft); Dietitians 1 (pt); Dentists 1 (pt); Podiatrists 1 (pt).
Facilities Dining room; Activities room; Crafts room; Laundry room; Barber/Beauty shop.
Activities Arts and Crafts; Cards; Games; Reading groups; Prayer groups; Movies; Shopping trips; Dances/Social or cultural gatherings; Fund raisers.
Description Most outstanding program is annual "rock and roll jamboree" fund raiser for the heart fund and arthritis. The facility houses 22 ladies in a very home-like atmosphere. The home is an older building and has been an intermediate nursing home since 1945.

NEWARK

Arlington Nursing Home Inc
98 S 30th St, Newark, OH, 43055 (614) 344-0303
Admin Roy Hodges. Medical Dir/Dir of Nursing Dr T T Mills.
Licensure Skilled Care; Intermediate Care.
Beds 200. Certified Medicaid; Medicare.
Ownership Proprietary.
Staff Physicians; RNs; LPNs; Orderlies; Nurses aides; Physical therapists; Reality therapists; Recreational therapists; Occupational therapists; Speech therapists; Activities coordinators; Dietitians; Dentists; Ophthalmologists; Podiatrists; Audiologists.
Facilities Dining room; Physical therapy room; Activities room; Crafts room; Laundry room; Barber/Beauty shop; Library; Hydrotherapy room; Occupational therapy room.
Activities Arts and Crafts; Cards; Games; Reading groups; Prayer groups; Movies; Shopping trips; Dances/Social or cultural gatherings.

Athena Nursing Center
17 Forry St, Newark, OH, 43055 (614) 349-8175
Medical Dir/Dir of Nursing Dr Donald Adams.
Licensure Intermediate Care. Beds 48. Certified Medicaid.
Ownership Proprietary.
Staff Physicians 1 (pt); RNs 1 (pt); LPNs 4 (ft), 3 (pt); Nurses aides 7 (ft), 6 (pt); Activities coor-

dinators 1 (ft); Dietitians 2 (ft), 2 (pt); Dentists 1 (pt); Ophthalmologists 1 (pt); Podiatrists 2 (pt).
Facilities Dining room; Laundry room.
Activities Cards; Games; Reading groups; Prayer groups; Movies; Shopping trips; Dances/Social or cultural gatherings.
Description Center has a fun bus in which patients take trips to the Columbus Zoo, Lancaster Fair, fishing, doctors appointments, shopping, and just rides to various places of interest. No extra charges for these trips.

Heath Nursing and Convalescent Center*
717 S 30th St, Newark, OH, 43055 (614) 522-1171
Licensure Skilled Care; Intermediate Care.
Beds 216. *Certified* Medicaid; Medicare.
Ownership Nonprofit.

Hopewell Skilled Villa
McMillen Dr, Newark, OH, 43055 (614) 344-0357
Licensure Skilled Care; Intermediate Care.
Beds 100. *Certified* Medicaid; Medicare.
Ownership Proprietary.

LPN Geriatric Nursing Center
1450 W Main St, Newark, OH, 43055 (614) 344-9465
Medical Dir/Dir of Nursing Charles F Sinsabaugh MD.
Licensure Skilled Care; Intermediate Care.
Beds 101. *Certified* Medicaid; Medicare.
Ownership Proprietary.
Admissions Requirements Medical examination.
Facilities Dining room; Physical therapy room; Activities room; Chapel; Crafts room; Laundry room; Barber/Beauty shop; Library.
Activities Arts and Crafts; Cards; Games; Reading groups; Prayer groups; Movies; Shopping trips; Dances/Social or cultural gatherings; Bingo; Dancercise; Pet therapy; Grandparent program; Political participation; Volunteer for community non-profit agencies; Fishing trips.
Description Facility features skilled nursing care with a beautiful home-like atmosphere featuring an Alzheimer's program.

LPN Health Care Facility
151 Price Rd, Newark, OH, 43055 (614) 366-2321
Medical Dir/Dir of Nursing Charles F Sinsabaugh MD.
Licensure Skilled Care; Intermediate Care.
Beds 101. *Certified* Medicaid; Medicare.
Ownership Proprietary.
Admissions Requirements Physician's request.
Staff RNs 8 (ft), 2 (pt); LPNs 9 (ft), 3 (pt); Nurses aides 26 (ft), 8 (pt); Physical therapists 2 (ft); Speech therapists 1 (pt); Activities coordinators 1 (ft); Dietitians 1 (pt).
Facilities Dining room; Physical therapy room; Activities room; Chapel; Laundry room; Barber/Beauty shop.
Activities Arts and Crafts; Cards; Games; Prayer groups; Movies; Shopping trips; Dances/Social or cultural gatherings.
Description The LPN social service program director has developed special programing for

the dementia patients. It is found that there are still many awarenesses in these people that can be reached.

Newark Healthcare Centre
75-85 McMillen Dr, Newark, OH, 43055 (614) 344-0357
Admin Bill Jackson.
Licensure Skilled Care; Intermediate Care.
Beds 300. *Certified* Medicaid; Medicare.
Ownership Proprietary.
Description Facility offers day care for adults, home health agency, independent living apartments, and Alzheimer's unit. VA approved. JCAH accredited.

NEWBURY

Holly Hills Farms
10190 Fairmount Rd, Newbury, OH, 44065 (216) 564-2209
Medical Dir/Dir of Nursing Dr Jay Polinar and Dr Barry Polinar.
Licensure Intermediate Care. *Beds* 33. *Certified* Medicaid.
Ownership Proprietary.
Admissions Requirements Medical examination; Physician's request.
Staff Physicians; RNs 3 (ft), 2 (pt); LPNs 2 (ft), 4 (pt); Nurses aides 15 (ft), 20 (pt); Physical therapists; Speech therapists; Activities coordinators 1 (ft); Dietitians 1 (pt); Dentists; Podiatrists; 1 (pt).
Facilities Dining room; Activities room; Crafts room; Laundry room; TV lounges.
Activities Arts and Crafts; Cards; Games; Reading groups; Prayer groups; Movies; Formal tea party monthly; Birthday party monthly.
Description All rooms have been carefully decorated to present a homey atmosphere to residents. The facility is on one floor which makes it easier and safer for the residents and staff.

NEWCOMERSTOWN

Riverside Manor Nursing and Rehabilitation Center
1100 E State Rd, Newcomerstown, OH, 43832 (614) 498-5165
Medical Dir/Dir of Nursing Dr Terry Overholsen.
Licensure Skilled Care; Intermediate Care.
Beds 100. *Certified* Medicaid; Medicare.
Ownership Proprietary.
Admissions Requirements Medical examination.
Staff RNs; LPNs; Orderlies; Nurses aides; Physical therapists; Reality therapists; Recreational therapists; Speech therapists; Activities coordinators; Dietitians; Dentists; Ophthalmologists; Podiatrists; Audiologists.
Facilities Dining room; Physical therapy room; Activities room; Chapel; Crafts room; Laundry room; Barber/Beauty shop; Library.
Activities Arts and Crafts; Cards; Games; Reading groups; Prayer groups; Movies; Shopping trips; Dances/Social or cultural gatherings.
Description Offers specialized services not found in most facilities. Philosophy is built entirely around the concept of rehabilitation;

equipped to handle patients labeled as super skilled as well as providing home health care services.

NEWTON FALLS

Colvin Nursing Home
150 Charles Court, Newton Falls, OH, 44444 (216) 872-1987
Medical Dir/Dir of Nursing Ellis List Jr MD.
Licensure Nursing Home. *Beds* 25.
Ownership Proprietary.
Admissions Requirements Females only; Medical examination.
Staff RNs 1 (pt); LPNs 4 (ft); Nurses aides 6 (ft), 5 (pt).
Facilities Laundry room.
Activities Arts and Crafts; Cards; Games; Prayer groups.
Description Parties are held for all holidays and a monthly birthday party; churches and local organizations are supportive with visitations, programs, and gifts; activity program is handled by volunteers.

NILES

Shepherd of the Valley Nursing Home*
1500 McKinley Ave, Niles, OH, 44446 (216) 544-0771
Licensure Skilled Care; Intermediate Care.
Beds 120. *Certified* Medicaid; Medicare.
Ownership Nonprofit.

NORTH BALTIMORE

Blakely Care Center*
600 Sterling Dr, North Baltimore, OH, 45872 (419) 257-2421
Licensure Skilled Care; Intermediate Care.
Beds 53. *Certified* Medicaid; Medicare.
Ownership Proprietary.

NORTH CANTON

Saint Lukes Lutheran Home for the Aging*
220 Applegrove St NE, North Canton, OH, 44720 (216) 499-8341
Licensure Skilled Care; Intermediate Care; Rest Home. *Beds* 122; Rest Home 27. *Certified* Medicaid; Medicare.
Ownership Nonprofit.
Affiliation Lutheran

Windsor Medical Center Inc*
1454 Easton St NW, North Canton, OH, 44720 (216) 499-8300
Licensure Nursing Home. *Beds* 41.
Ownership Proprietary.

NORTH LIMA

Diamondhead Extended Care Center 1*
9174 Market St, North Lima, OH, 44452 (216) 758-5743
Licensure Skilled Care; Intermediate Care.
Beds 130. *Certified* Medicaid; Medicare.
Ownership Proprietary.

Diamondhead Nursing Home 2
9184 Market St, North Lima, OH, 44452 (216) 758-5743
Medical Dir/Dir of Nursing Anthony Dominic DO.
Licensure Intermediate Care. *Beds* 106. *Certified* Medicaid.
Ownership Proprietary.
Admissions Requirements Medical examination.
Staff RNs 5 (ft), 3 (pt); LPNs 8 (ft), 6 (pt); Orderlies 5 (ft), 1 (pt); Nurses aides 37 (ft), 13 (pt); Physical therapists 1 (pt); Recreational therapists 1 (ft); Speech therapists 1 (pt); Activities coordinators 1 (ft); Dietitians 1 (ft); Dentists 1 (pt); Ophthalmologists 1 (pt); Podiatrists 1 (pt); Audiologists 1 (pt).
Facilities Dining room; Physical therapy room; Activities room; Crafts room; Laundry room; Barber/Beauty shop.
Activities Arts and Crafts; Games; Prayer groups; Movies; Shopping trips; Dances/Social or cultural gatherings; Bingo; Sing-a-longs; Exercise.
Description Our building is new, modern, and fully equipped with fire safety equipment. We have all semi-private rooms that are tastefully decorated in different color schemes.

Rolling Acres Care Center
9625 Market Street Ext, North Lima, OH, 44452 (216) 549-3939
Medical Dir/Dir of Nursing Dr Joseph Mersol.
Licensure Intermediate Care. *Beds* 92. *Certified* Medicaid.
Ownership Proprietary.
Admissions Requirements Minimum age 18; Medical examination; Physician's request.
Staff Physicians 1 (ft), 4 (pt); RNs 3 (ft), 3 (pt); LPNs 8 (ft), 3 (pt); Nurses aides 22 (ft), 5 (pt); Speech therapists 1 (ft); Activities coordinators 1 (ft); Dietitians 1 (ft); Dentists 1 (ft); Ophthalmologists 1 (ft); Podiatrists 1 (ft).
Facilities Dining room; Activities room; Crafts room; Laundry room; Barber/Beauty shop.
Activities Arts and Crafts; Cards; Games; Reading groups; Prayer groups; Movies; Shopping trips; Dances/Social or cultural gatherings; Pet therapy; Exercises; Ethnic days.
Description The facility sits far back off the road, in a very country-like setting. Some nurses aides attend a 90-hour training program. Pet therapy is in use once a month, where the kennel brings various sizes and types of dogs and cats to do tricks, and for the residents to play with.

NORTH OBERLIN

Will-O-Lee Nursing Home
Rt 58 N, Box 149, North Oberlin, OH, 44074 (216) 775-3639
Medical Dir/Dir of Nursing George Hoover DO.
Licensure Intermediate Care. *Beds* 45. *Certified* Medicaid.
Ownership Proprietary.
Admissions Requirements Medical examination.
Staff Physicians 2 (pt); RNs 2 (ft), 1 (pt); LPNs 9 (ft); Nurses aides 14 (ft); Activities coordinators 1 (ft); Dietitians 1 (pt); Dentists 1 (pt);

Podiatrists 1 (pt).
Facilities Dining room; Activities room; Chapel; Crafts room; Laundry room.
Activities Arts and Crafts; Cards; Games; Reading groups; Prayer groups; Movies; Shopping trips; Dances/Social or cultural gatherings.
Description Facility tries to make the setting home-like rather than institutional.

NORTH OLMSTED

Manor Care of North Olmsted Inc*
23225 Lorain Rd, North Olmsted, OH, 44070 (216) 779-6900
Medical Dir/Dir of Nursing Klaus Neumann MD.
Licensure Skilled Care; Intermediate Care. *Beds* 198. *Certified* Medicaid; Medicare.
Ownership Proprietary.
Admissions Requirements Medical examination.
Staff Physicians 5 (pt); RNs 13 (ft), 7 (pt); LPNs 8 (ft), 5 (pt); Orderlies 1 (ft); Nurses aides 41 (ft), 34 (pt); Physical therapists 1 (ft); Recreational therapists 1 (pt); Speech therapists 1 (pt); Activities coordinators 2 (ft), 1 (pt); Dietitians 1 (ft), 1 (pt); Dentists 1 (pt); Podiatrists 1 (pt).
Facilities Dining room; Physical therapy room; Activities room; Crafts room; Laundry room; Barber/Beauty shop.
Activities Arts and Crafts; Cards; Games; Reading groups; Prayer groups; Movies; Shopping trips.

Margies Nursing Home
27048 Lorain Rd, North Olmsted, OH, 44070 (216) 777-4811
Medical Dir/Dir of Nursing Dr Louis La Riccia.
Licensure Intermediate Care. *Beds* 35. *Certified* Medicaid.
Ownership Proprietary.
Admissions Requirements Medical examination; Physician's request.
Staff Physicians 1 (ft); RNs 1 (pt); LPNs 3 (ft), 2 (pt); Nurses aides 9 (ft); Recreational therapists 1 (pt); Activities coordinators 1 (ft); Dietitians 1 (pt); Dentists 1 (pt); Ophthalmologists 1 (pt); Podiatrists 1 (pt).

Olmsted Manor Nursing Home
27500 Mill Rd, North Olmsted, OH, 44070 (216) 777-8444
Medical Dir/Dir of Nursing Dr W Wozniak.
Licensure Skilled Care; Intermediate Care.
Beds 99. *Certified* Medicaid; Medicare.
Ownership Proprietary.
Admissions Requirements Minimum age 40; Medical examination.
Staff Physicians 1 (pt); RNs 2 (ft), 7 (pt); LPNs 5 (ft), 2 (pt); Nurses aides 19 (ft), 8 (pt); Physical therapists 1 (pt); Activities coordinators 1 (ft), 1 (pt); Dietitians 1 (pt); Dentists 1 (pt); Podiatrists 1 (pt).
Facilities Dining room; Physical therapy room; Activities room; Laundry room; Barber/Beauty shop.
Activities Arts and Crafts; Cards; Games; Reading groups; Prayer groups; Movies; Shopping trips; Dances/Social or cultural gatherings.

NORTH RANDALL

Suburban Pavillion Inc
20265 Emery Rd, North Randall, OH, 44128 (216) 475-8880
Medical Dir/Dir of Nursing Alan Kravitz MD.
Licensure Skilled Care; Intermediate Care. *Beds* 98. *Certified* Medicaid; Medicare.
Ownership Proprietary.
Admissions Requirements Medical examination; Physician's request.
Staff RNs 7 (ft), 2 (pt); LPNs 10 (ft), 2 (pt); Nurses aides 35 (ft), 5 (pt); Physical therapists 1 (ft); Recreational therapists 1 (ft); Occupational therapists 1 (pt); Speech therapists 1 (pt); Activities coordinators 1 (ft); Dietitians 1 (pt); Dentists 1 (pt); Podiatrists 1 (pt); Audiologists 1 (pt).
Facilities Dining room; Physical therapy room; Activities room; Crafts room; Barber/Beauty shop.
Activities Arts and Crafts; Cards; Games; Reading groups; Prayer groups; Movies; Dances/Social or cultural gatherings.
Description Facility's spacious entry, lobby, lounge and dining rooms, and attractive artwares present therapeutic milieu for residents; rehabilitation program returns many clients to the community.

NORTH RIDGEVILLE

Holly Terrace Nursing Home
32415 Center Ridge Rd, North Ridgeville, OH, 44039 (216) 327-8382
Admin Ruth M Jackson. *Medical Dir/Dir of Nursing* Firas Atassi MD.
Licensure Intermediate Care. *Beds* 18. *Certified* Medicaid.
Ownership Proprietary.
Admissions Requirements Medical examination.
Staff Physicians 3 (pt); RNs 2 (ft), 1 (pt); LPNs 2 (ft), 1 (pt); Nurses aides 5 (ft), 5 (pt); Activities coordinators 1 (ft); Dietitians 1 (pt); Dentists 1 (pt); Podiatrists 1 (pt).
Facilities Dining room; Activities room; Laundry room.
Activities Arts and Crafts; Cards; Games; Reading groups; Prayer groups.

NORTH ROYALTON

Mount Royal Villa*
13900 Bennett Rd, North Royalton, OH, 44133 (216) 237-7966
Licensure Nursing Home; Rest Home.
Beds Nursing Home 43; Rest Home 63.
Ownership Proprietary.

Patrician Nursing Center Inc
9001 W 130th St, North Royalton, OH, 44133 (216) 237-3104
Licensure Skilled Care; Intermediate Care.
Beds 206. *Certified* Medicaid; Medicare.
Ownership Proprietary.
Staff Physicians 1 (pt); RNs 10 (ft), 11 (pt); LPNs 10 (ft), 11 (pt); Orderlies 7 (ft); Nurses aides 56 (ft), 32 (pt); Physical therapists 1 (ft); Reality therapists 1 (ft); Recreational therapists 1 (ft); Occupational therapists 1 (pt); Speech

therapists 1 (pt); Activities coordinators 1 (ft); Dietitians 1 (pt); Dentists 1 (pt); Ophthalmologists 1 (pt); Podiatrists 1 (pt); Audiologists 1 (pt).
Facilities Dining room; Physical therapy room; Activities room; Chapel; Crafts room; Barber-/Beauty shop; Library.
Activities Arts and Crafts; Cards; Games; Reading groups; Prayer groups; Movies; Dances/Social or cultural gatherings.

NORTHFIELD

Western Reserve Psychiatric Center*
PO Box 305, 1756 Sagamore Rd, Northfield, OH, 44067
Licensure Intermediate Care for Mentally Retarded. *Beds* 60. *Certified* Medicaid.

NORTON

Ideal Nursing Home Inc*
5671 Wooster Rd W, Norton, OH, 44203 (216) 825-2525
Licensure Intermediate Care. *Beds* 20. *Certified* Medicaid.
Ownership Proprietary.

NORWALK

Gaymont Nursing Center
66 Norwood Ave, Norwalk, OH, 44857 (419) 668-8258
Medical Dir/Dir of Nursing Warren Sawyer MD.
Licensure Skilled Care; Intermediate Care. *Beds* 100. *Certified* Medicaid; Medicare.
Ownership Proprietary.
Admissions Requirements Medical examination; Physician's request.
Staff Physicians 21 (pt); RNs 4 (ft); LPNs 16 (pt); Nurses aides 42 (pt); Physical therapists 1 (pt); Reality therapists 1 (pt); Recreational therapists 1 (pt); Occupational therapists 1 (pt); Speech therapists 1 (pt); Activities coordinators 2 (ft); Dietitians 1 (ft), 1 (pt); Dentists 1 (pt); Podiatrists 1 (pt); Audiologists 1 (pt).
Facilities Dining room; Physical therapy room; Activities room; Chapel; Crafts room; Laundry room; Barber/Beauty shop.
Activities Arts and Crafts; Games; Reading groups; Prayer groups; Movies; Shopping trips; Dances/Social or cultural gatherings.
Description The facility is in the city limits with a rural setting featuring a large lawn with shade trees and an enclosed courtyard. It is one mile from hospital, and one mile from center of town. Highly qualified, personalized care is offered.

Norwalk Memorial Home*
269 W Main St, Norwalk, OH, 44857 (419) 668-5162
Licensure Intermediate Care. *Beds* 35. *Certified* Medicaid.
Ownership Nonprofit.

Twilight Gardens Home Inc
196 W Main St, Norwalk, OH, 44587 (419) 668-2086
Medical Dir/Dir of Nursing Ronald D Win-

land.
Licensure Skilled Care; Intermediate Care.
Beds 100. *Certified* Medicaid; Medicare.
Ownership Proprietary.
Admissions Requirements Medical examination.
Staff RNs 2 (ft), 1 (pt); LPNs 9 (ft), 12 (pt); Nurses aides 36 (ft), 11 (pt); Physical therapists; Recreational therapists; Occupational therapists; Speech therapists; Activities coordinators 1 (ft); Dietitians; Dentists; Podiatrists.
Facilities Dining room; Activities room; Crafts room; Laundry room; Barber/Beauty shop; Library; Sunroom; Meditation room; TV room.
Activities Arts and Crafts; Cards; Games; Reading groups; Prayer groups; Movies; Shopping trips; Dances/Social or cultural gatherings.

NORWOOD

Victory Park Nursing Home*
1578 Sheman Ave, Norwood, OH, 45212 (513) 351-0153
Licensure Skilled Care; Intermediate Care.
Beds 92. *Certified* Medicaid; Medicare.
Ownership Proprietary.

OAK HARBOR

Ottawa County Riverview Nursing Home
Box 188, Oak Harbor, OH, 43449 (419) 898-1214
Medical Dir/Dir of Nursing R W Minick MD.
Licensure Skilled Care; Intermediate Care.
Beds 110. *Certified* Medicaid; Medicare.
Ownership Public.
Admissions Requirements Medical examination; Physician's request.
Staff Physicians 1 (pt); RNs 5 (ft), 4 (pt); LPNs 5 (ft), 3 (pt); Nurses aides 31 (ft), 16 (pt); Physical therapists 1 (pt); Activities coordinators 1 (ft); Dietitians 1 (pt).
Facilities Dining room; Physical therapy room; Activities room; Crafts room; Laundry room; Barber/Beauty shop.
Activities Arts and Crafts; Cards; Games; Reading groups; Prayer groups; Movies; Shopping trips; Dances/Social or cultural gatherings.

OAK HILL

Davis Home for the Aged
315 Washington St, Oak Hill, OH, 45656 (614) 682-7585
Licensure Rest Home. *Beds* 32.
Ownership Nonprofit.
Admissions Requirements Minimum age 60; Females only; Medical examination.
Staff LPNs 1 (ft).
Facilities Dining room; Activities room; Laundry room; Barber/Beauty shop.
Activities Arts and Crafts; Prayer groups.
Description This facility is not a nursing home. We have supportive care for the female elderly. Capacity for 32 individual rooms for residents. Hoping to incorporate more activities in the near future. A very lovely home.

OAKWOOD VILLAGE

Oak Park*
24613 Broadway, Oakwood Village, OH, 44146 (216) 439-1448
Licensure Skilled Care; Intermediate Care.
Beds 125. *Certified* Medicaid; Medicare.
Ownership Proprietary.

OBERLIN

Carter's Nursing Home
284 E Lorain St, Oberlin, OH, 44074 (216) 774-7202
Licensure Intermediate Care. *Beds* 50. *Certified* Medicaid.
Ownership Proprietary.
Staff Physicians 6 (ft); RNs 1 (ft); LPNs 86 (ft), 2 (pt); Orderlies 2 (ft); Nurses aides 10 (ft), 4 (pt); Activities coordinators 2 (ft); Dietitians 2 (pt); Podiatrists 1 (pt).
Facilities Dining room; Activities room; Crafts room; Laundry room.
Activities Arts and Crafts; Cards; Games; Reading groups; Prayer groups; Movies; Shopping trips; Dances/Social or cultural gatherings.
Description Home offers excellent holistic care to the aged; staff is genuinely interested in the residents' well-being.

Tressie's Nursing Home*
277 N Professor St, Oberlin, OH, 44074 (216) 774-1255
Licensure Intermediate Care. *Beds* 19. *Certified* Medicaid.
Ownership Proprietary.

Welcome Nursing Home Inc
54 E Hamilton St, Oberlin, OH, 44074 (216) 775-1491
Medical Dir/Dir of Nursing Dr Hofman.
Licensure Skilled Care; Intermediate Care.
Beds 53. *Certified* Medicaid; Medicare.
Ownership Proprietary.
Admissions Requirements Minimum age 14; Medical examination; Physician's request.
Staff RNs 2 (ft), 3 (pt); LPNs 5 (ft), 3 (pt); Nurses aides 11 (ft), 10 (pt); Physical therapists 1 (pt); Activities coordinators 1 (ft); Dietitians 1 (ft).
Facilities Dining room; Activities room; Barber/Beauty shop; Library.
Activities Arts and Crafts; Cards; Games; Reading groups; Prayer groups; Movies; Shopping trips; Dances/Social or cultural gatherings.

Will-O-Lee Nursing Home 2
345 N Professor St, Oberlin, OH, 44074 (216) 775-3639
Medical Dir/Dir of Nursing George Hoover.
Licensure Intermediate Care for Mentally Retarded. *Beds* 25. *Certified* Medicaid.
Ownership Proprietary.
Admissions Requirements Medical examination.
Staff Physicians 2 (pt); RNs 1 (ft), 1 (pt); LPNs 10 (ft); Nurses aides 9 (ft); Recreational therapists 1 (ft); Activities coordinators 1 (ft); Dietitians 1 (ft); Dentists 1 (pt); Podiatrists 1 (pt).
Facilities Dining room; Activities room; Crafts room; Laundry room.
Activities Arts and Crafts; Cards; Games;

Reading groups; Prayer groups; Movies; Shopping trips; Dances/Social or cultural gatherings.
Description Our home strives for a family atmosphere. We strive to make our residents feel that they are important and are loved. Tender loving care is our specialty.

OREGON

Americare Nursing Center Inc*
904 Isaac Street Dr, Oregon, OH, 43616 (419) 691-2483
Licensure Skilled Care; Intermediate Care.
Beds 100. *Certified* Medicaid; Medicare.
Ownership Proprietary.

Eastview Nursing Home
1065 Isaac Street Dr, Oregon, OH, 43616 (419) 698-1606
Medical Dir/Dir of Nursing Dr Peter Flockenhaus.
Licensure Skilled Care; Intermediate Care.
Beds 79. *Certified* Medicaid; Medicare.
Ownership Proprietary.
Admissions Requirements Minimum age 16.
Staff Physicians 34 (pt); RNs 3 (ft); LPNs 9 (ft); Orderlies 3 (ft); Nurses aides 21 (ft), 8 (pt); Physical therapists 2 (pt); Reality therapists 1 (ft); Recreational therapists 1 (ft); Occupational therapists 2 (pt); Speech therapists 2 (pt); Activities coordinators 1 (ft), 1 (pt); Dietitians 1 (pt); Dentists 1 (pt); Podiatrists 1 (pt); Audiologists 1 (pt).
Languages Spanish
Facilities Dining room; Activities room; Crafts room; Laundry room; Barber/Beauty shop.
Activities Arts and Crafts; Cards; Games; Reading groups; Prayer groups; Movies; Shopping trips; Dances/Social or cultural gatherings; Social service.
Description As a full functioning therapeutic community, Eastview Nursing Home is able offer language facilities to the deaf and in Spanish in addition to English. A single-story facility with multiground level egresses located on a rural street one-eighth of a mile from an acute care hospital.

Family Tree Care Center*
3952 Navarre Ave, Oregon, OH, 43616 (419) 698-4521
Licensure Skilled Care; Intermediate Care.
Beds SNF 43; ICF 58. *Certified* Medicaid; Medicare.
Ownership Proprietary.

Home for Aged—Little Sisters of the Poor*
4900 Navarre Ave, Oregon, OH, 43616 (419)
Licensure Intermediate Care; Rest Home.
Beds 90; Rest Home 42. *Certified* Medicaid.
Ownership Nonprofit.
Affiliation Roman Catholic

ORIENT

Orient Developmental Center*
State Rt 762, Orient, OH, 43146
Licensure Intermediate Care for Mentally Retarded. *Beds* 528.
Ownership Public.

ORRVILLE

Brenn-Field Nursing Center
1980 Lynn Dr, Orrville, OH, 44667 (216) 683-4075
Licensure Intermediate Care. *Beds* 100. *Certified* Medicaid.
Ownership Proprietary.

OTTAWA

Calvary Manor Nursing Home
Glandorf Rd, Rt 4, Ottawa, OH, 45875
Admin Larry Schroeder. *Medical Dir/Dir of Nursing* Dr Biery J Ogle.
Licensure Intermediate Care. *Beds* 51. *Certified* Medicaid.
Ownership Nonprofit.
Admissions Requirements Medical examination.
Staff RNs 3 (ft), 2 (pt); LPNs 2 (pt); Nurses aides 8 (ft), 13 (pt).
Facilities Dining room; Physical therapy room; Activities room; Chapel; Laundry room; Barber/Beauty shop.
Activities Arts and Crafts; Cards; Games; Prayer groups; Movies; Shopping trips.
Description Facility is only 5 years old and is located in an nice, quiet area.

Putnam Acres Care Center
10170 Rd 5-H, Ottawa, OH, 45825 (419) 523-4092
Admin Joanne Cox. *Medical Dir/Dir of Nursing* Dr James Overmier.
Licensure Intermediate Care. *Beds* 88. *Certified* Medicaid.
Ownership Public.
Admissions Requirements Minimum age 16; Medical examination; Physician's request.
Staff Physicians 1 (pt); RNs 4 (ft), 5 (pt); LPNs 2 (ft), 1 (pt); Nurses aides 19 (ft), 14 (pt); Physical therapists; Activities coordinators 1 (ft); Dietitians 1 (pt); Dentists; Ophthalmologists; Podiatrists; Audiologists.
Facilities Dining room; Physical therapy room; Activities room; Chapel; Crafts room; Laundry room; Barber/Beauty shop; Library.
Activities Arts and Crafts; Cards; Games; Reading groups; Prayer groups; Movies; Shopping trips; Dances/Social or cultural gatherings.
Description Putnam Acres is situated in a beautiful country setting 4 miles east of Ottawa. It is a one-story modern, air conditioned facility and offers many special activities, including machinery for fine woodworking. Safety area outside has approximately 2 acres with a beautiful, large shelter house for summer family activities.

Total Care of Ottawa
1925 E 4th St, Ottawa, OH, 45875 (419) 523-4370
Medical Dir/Dir of Nursing Dr James Overmier.
Licensure Intermediate Care. *Beds* 50. *Certified* Medicaid.
Ownership Proprietary.
Admissions Requirements Minimum age 18; Medical examination.
Staff RNs 3 (ft); LPNs 1 (ft), 4 (pt); Nurses aides 8 (ft), 14 (pt); Physical therapists 1 (pt);

Reality therapists 1 (pt); Recreational therapists 1 (pt); Occupational therapists 1 (pt); Speech therapists 1 (pt); Activities coordinators 1 (ft), 1 (pt); Dietitians 1 (pt); Dentists 1 (pt); Ophthalmologists 1 (pt); Podiatrists 1 (pt); Audiologists 1 (pt).
Facilities Dining room; Activities room; Chapel; Crafts room; Laundry room; Barber/Beauty shop; Library.
Activities Arts and Crafts; Cards; Games; Reading groups; Prayer groups; Movies; Shopping trips; Dances/Social or cultural gatherings.

OXFORD

Oxford View Nursing Center
6099 Fairfield Rd, Oxford, OH, 45056 (513) 523-6353 and 523-9462
Medical Dir/Dir of Nursing Dr Robert Prots.
Licensure Skilled Care; Intermediate Care.
Beds 54. *Certified* Medicaid; Medicare.
Ownership Proprietary.
Admissions Requirements Medical examination; Physician's request.
Staff Physicians 8 (pt); RNs 5 (pt); LPNs 6 (ft), 7 (pt); Nurses aides 20 (ft), 17 (pt); Physical therapists 2 (pt); Speech therapists 1 (pt); Activities coordinators 1 (ft); Dietitians 1 (pt); Dentists 1 (pt); Ophthalmologists 1 (pt); Podiatrists 1 (pt); Audiologists 1 (pt).
Facilities Dining room; Physical therapy room; Activities room; Laundry room; Barber/Beauty shop; Library.
Activities Arts and Crafts; Games; Reading groups; Prayer groups; Movies; Shopping trips; Dances/Social or cultural gatherings.
Description Facility provides day care and has a home care program; also has staff who have special training in the home care for the Alzheimer's patient; facility is at present adding more beds and an occupational therapy unit.

Woodland Manor Nursing Home*
4166 Somerville Rd, Oxford, OH, 45064 (513) 523-4449 and 523-7486
Licensure Intermediate Care. *Beds* 50. *Certified* Medicaid.
Ownership Nonprofit.

PAINESVILLE

Cerri's Painesville Nursing Home*
252 W Jackson St, Painesville, OH, 44077 (216) 354-5300
Licensure Intermediate Care. *Beds* 18. *Certified* Medicaid.
Ownership Proprietary.

Homestead Nursing Home 1*
164 Liberty St, Painesville, OH, 44077 (216) 357-6181
Licensure Intermediate Care. *Beds* 53. *Certified* Medicaid.
Ownership Proprietary.

Homestead Nursing Home 2*
60 Wood St, Painesville, OH, 44077 (216) 352-0788
Licensure Skilled Care; Intermediate Care.
Beds 52. *Certified* Medicaid; Medicare.
Ownership Proprietary.

Ivy House
308 S State St, Painesville, OH, 44077 (216)
354-2131
Admin Marie Swaim. *Medical Dir/Dir of
Nursing* Dr F Veroni.
Licensure Intermediate Care. *Beds* 50. *Certified* Medicaid.
Ownership Proprietary.
Admissions Requirements Minimum age 60;
Medical examination.
Staff Physicians 1 (pt); RNs 1 (ft); LPNs 4 (ft);
Recreational therapists 1 (ft), 1 (pt); Activities
coordinators 1 (ft), 1 (pt); Dietitians 1 (pt).
Facilities Dining room; Activities room; Chapel; Crafts room; Laundry room; Barber/Beauty
shop; Library.
Activities Arts and Crafts; Cards; Games;
Reading groups; Prayer groups; Movies; Shopping trips; Dances/Social or cultural gatherings.
Description Facility features home-like atmosphere overlooking the scenic Grand River
Valley. Assisted living and intermediate care is
available with 24-hour nursing; assisted living
is for those who want independence but need
supervision; intermediate care is for those who
require nursing care; both are available on a
short- or long-term basis.

PANDORA

Hilty Memorial Home
Rt 12, Pandora, OH, 45877 (419) 384-3218
Medical Dir/Dir of Nursing Dr Oliver Lugibihl.
Licensure Intermediate Care. *Beds* 61. *Certified* Medicaid.
Ownership Nonprofit.
Admissions Requirements Medical
examination.
Staff RNs; LPNs; Nurses aides.
Facilities Dining room; Physical therapy room;
Activities room; Chapel; Laundry room; Barber/Beauty shop.
Activities Arts and Crafts; Cards; Reading
groups; Movies; Bible study; Sunshine rhythm
band; Current events discussion.

PARMA

Broadview Nursing Home*
5520 Broadview Rd, Parma, OH, 44134 (216)
749-4010
Licensure Skilled Care; Intermediate Care.
Beds 198. *Certified* Medicaid; Medicare.
Ownership Proprietary.

Holy Family Home
6707 State Rd, Parma, OH, 44134 (216)
885-3100
Licensure Nursing Home. *Beds* 50.
Ownership Nonprofit.
Staff Physicians 1 (pt); RNs 2 (ft), 2 (pt); LPNs
7 (ft); Orderlies 6 (ft), 6 (pt); Dietitians 1 (pt);
Dentists 2 (pt); Podiatrists 1 (pt).
Affiliation Roman Catholic
Facilities Chapel; Crafts room; Laundry room;
Barber/Beauty shop.
Activities Arts and Crafts; Movies.
Description Home is free for terminally ill cancer victims unable to pay for care elsewhere.
The weakened condition of residents preclude

few activities presented. Ideal is to make their
final days as cheerful and comfortable as possible. Any age, sex, race, creed, religious belief,
or national origin accepted.

Mount Alverna Home
6765 State Rd, Parma, OH, 44134 (216)
843-7800
Medical Dir/Dir of Nursing Dr Wiliam Dowdell.
Licensure Intermediate Care. *Beds* 200. *Certified* Medicaid.
Ownership Nonprofit.
Staff Physicians 3 (pt); RNs 9 (ft), 7 (pt); LPNs
9 (ft), 6 (pt); Orderlies 4 (ft), 1 (pt); Nurses aides
45 (ft), 18 (pt); Physical therapists 2 (pt); Recreational therapists 1 (pt); Speech therapists 1 (pt);
Activities coordinators 2 (ft); Dietitians 2 (ft);
Dentists 1 (pt); Ophthalmologists 1 (pt); Podiatrists 1 (pt); Audiologists 1 (pt).
Affiliation Roman Catholic
Facilities Dining room; Physical therapy room;
Activities room; Chapel; Crafts room; Laundry
room; Barber/Beauty shop; Library.
Activities Arts and Crafts; Cards; Games;
Reading groups; Prayer groups; Movies; Dances/Social or cultural gatherings.
Description Mount Alverna Home Inc, a residential and long-term health care facility for the
elderly is situated in Parma, Ohio and features
caring dedicated 24-hour nursing supervision;
nurse to resident ratio of 25 to 1; registered dietician; planned social and physical activities;
private, or semi-private air-conditioned rooms;
daily religious services; available social service
department; dental care, podiatry, speech, and
physical therapy services available; lovely
solariums and patio on grounds.

Nelson Broadview Nursing Home
5520 Broadview Rd, Parma, OH, 44134 (216)
749-4010
Licensure Intermediate Care. *Beds* 27. *Certified* Medicaid.
Ownership Proprietary.

Parma Nursing Home Inc*
5553 Broadview Rd, Parma, OH, 44134 (216)
741-7195
Licensure Intermediate Care. *Beds* 30. *Certified* Medicaid.
Ownership Proprietary.

Pleasantview Nursing Home
7377 Ridge Rd, Parma, OH, 44129 (216)
845-0200
Medical Dir/Dir of Nursing Dr T Burney.
Licensure Skilled Care; Intermediate Care.
Beds 187. *Certified* Medicaid; Medicare.
Ownership Proprietary.
Admissions Requirements Medical examination.
Staff RNs 7 (ft), 5 (pt); LPNs 11 (ft), 12 (pt);
Orderlies 7 (ft), 2 (pt); Nurses aides 43 (ft), 35
(pt); Physical therapists 1 (ft), 1 (pt); Recreational therapists 1 (ft); Speech therapists 1 (pt);
Activities coordinators 1 (pt); Dietitians 1 (pt);
Dentists 1 (pt); Ophthalmologists 1 (pt); Podiatrists 2 (pt).
Facilities Dining room; Physical therapy room;
Activities room; Chapel; Crafts room; Laundry
room; Barber/Beauty shop; Library.
Activities Arts and Crafts; Games; Reading

groups; Prayer groups; Movies; Dances/Social
or cultural gatherings.
Description There are 5 physicians on staff and
residents are given the option of retaining their
own physician. The building has 3 floors with 5
nursing stations; private, semi-private, and
4-bed wards are available.

PARMA HEIGHTS

Aristocrat South
6455 Pearl Rd, Parma Heights, OH, 44130
(216) 888-5900
Licensure Skilled Care; Intermediate Care;
Intermediate Care for Mentally Retarded.
Beds ICF 160; ICF/MR 39. *Certified* Medicaid; Medicare.
Ownership Proprietary.
Admissions Requirements Medical examination.
Facilities Dining room; Physical therapy room;
Activities room; Crafts room; Laundry room;
Barber/Beauty shop; Library.
Activities Arts and Crafts; Cards; Games;
Reading groups; Prayer groups; Movies; Shopping trips; Dances/Social or cultural gatherings.

PAULDING

Totalcare Nursing Home of Paulding*
Rt 2, Box 1241, Paulding, OH, 45879 (419)
399-4940
Licensure Intermediate Care. *Beds* 50. *Certified* Medicaid.
Ownership Proprietary.

PAYNE

Dallas Lamb Foundation Home*
PO Box 56, 650 N Main, Payne, OH, 45880
(419) 263-2334
Licensure Intermediate Care. *Beds* 50. *Certified* Medicaid.
Ownership Nonprofit.

PEEBLES

Hillcrest Nursing Home
Rt 2, Box 188, Peebles, OH, 45660 (513)
386-2522
Medical Dir/Dir of Nursing Dr K Lim.
Licensure Intermediate Care. *Beds* 50. *Certified* Medicaid.
Ownership Proprietary.
Staff RNs 2 (ft); LPNs 6 (ft); Nurses aides 15
(ft); Physical therapists 1 (pt); Activities coordinators 1 (ft); Dietitians 1 (pt).
Facilities Dining room; Activities room; Crafts
room; Laundry room; Barber/Beauty shop;
Library.
Activities Arts and Crafts; Cards; Games;
Reading groups; Prayer groups; Movies; Shopping trips.
Description Facility is also licensed as a mental
health nursing home.

PEMBERVILLE

Portage Valley Inc*
20311 Pemberville, Pemberville, OH, 43450
Licensure Intermediate Care. *Beds* 100. *Certified* Medicaid.
Ownership Nonprofit.

PENINSULA

Wayside Farm Inc*
4557 Quick Rd, Peninsula, OH, 44264 (216)
Licensure Intermediate Care. *Beds* 95. *Certified* Medicaid.
Ownership Proprietary.

PERRY

Perry Ridge Nursing Home Inc*
5051 S Ridge Rd, Perry, OH, 44081 (216)
259-4300
Licensure Intermediate Care. *Beds* 39. *Certified* Medicaid.
Ownership Proprietary.

PERRYSBURG

Heartland of Perrysburg
10540 Fremont Pike, Perrysburg, OH, 43551
(419) 874-3578
Admin Loma Overmyer. *Medical Dir/Dir of Nursing* S R Torres.
Licensure Skilled Care; Intermediate Care.
Beds 131. *Certified* Medicare.
Ownership Proprietary.
Admissions Requirements Minimum age 16;
Medical examination; Physician's request.
Staff RNs 5 (ft), 7 (pt); LPNs 9 (ft), 4 (pt);
Nurses aides 31 (ft), 23 (pt); Physical therapists;
Occupational therapists; Speech therapists;
Activities coordinators 2 (ft); Dietitians 1 (ft);
Dentists; Ophthalmologists; Podiatrists.
Facilities Dining room; Physical therapy room;
Activities room; Laundry room; Barber/Beauty shop.
Activities Arts and Crafts; Cards; Games;
Reading groups; Prayer groups; Movies; Dances/Social or cultural gatherings.

PICKERINGTON

Echo Manor Extended Care Center*
10270 Blacklick Eastern Rd NW, Pickerington,
OH, 43147
Licensure Skilled Care; Intermediate Care.
Beds 100. *Certified* Medicaid; Medicare.
Ownership Nonprofit.

PIKETON

Casey Nursing Home
Rt 3, Piketon, OH, 45661 (614) 289-437
Admin Erma Jewett. *Medical Dir/Dir of Nursing* K A Wilkinson MD.
Licensure Intermediate Care. *Beds* 38. *Certified* Medicaid.
Ownership Proprietary.
Admissions Requirements Medical examination; Physician's request.

Staff RNs 1 (pt); LPNs 4 (ft), 1 (pt); Nurses aides 9 (ft); Recreational therapists 1 (ft); Activities coordinators 1 (ft).
Facilities Dining room; Activities room; Crafts room; Laundry room.
Activities Arts and Crafts; Games; Reading groups; Prayer groups; Movies; Shopping trips; Dances/Social or cultural gatherings.
Description Facility features summer activities including weekly trips to the lake and picnicing and weekly cookouts; 2 vans for transportation to outings; a pool table in the activities room is enjoyed.

Gayhart's Nursing Home*
2582 Wakefield Mound Rd, Piketon, OH,
45661 (614) 289-4024
Licensure Intermediate Care. *Beds* 32. *Certified* Medicaid.
Ownership Proprietary.

Mullins Nursing Home*
2266 Wakefield Mound Rd, Piketon, OH,
45661 (614) 289-4360
Licensure Intermediate Care. *Beds* 32. *Certified* Medicaid.
Ownership Proprietary.

Pike Manor Nursing Home*
PO Box 308, 214 E Main St, Piketon, OH,
45661 (614) 289-2129
Licensure Intermediate Care. *Beds* 25. *Certified* Medicaid.
Ownership Nonprofit.

Pleasant Hill Convalescent Center*
Box 334, Piketon, OH, 45661 (614) 289-2394
Licensure Skilled Care; Intermediate Care.
Beds 101. *Certified* Medicaid; Medicare.
Ownership Proprietary.

Spears and Spears Nursing Home*
300 Overlook Dr, Piketon, OH, 45661 (614)
289-4074
Licensure Intermediate Care. *Beds* 25. *Certified* Medicaid.
Ownership Proprietary.

PIQUA

Hilltop Haven Nursing Home Inc
306 Stauton St, Piqua, OH, 45356 (513)
773-0861
Licensure Intermediate Care. *Beds* 23. *Certified* Medicaid.
Ownership Proprietary.

Piqua Health Care Center*
650 N Downing St, Piqua, OH, 45356
Licensure Intermediate Care. *Beds* 50. *Certified* Medicaid.
Ownership Proprietary.

Piqua Manor
W High St, Piqua, OH, 45356 (513) 773-0040
Medical Dir/Dir of Nursing Jack P Steinhilben MD.
Licensure Skilled Care; Intermediate Care.
Beds 100. *Certified* Medicaid; Medicare.
Ownership Proprietary.
Admissions Requirements Medical examination; Physician's request.

Staff RNs 2 (ft), 5 (pt); LPNs 7 (ft), 5 (pt);
Orderlies 3 (ft), 6 (pt); Nurses aides 13 (ft), 20
(pt); Physical therapists 1 (ft); Activities coordinators 2 (ft).
Facilities Dining room; Physical therapy room;
Activities room; Crafts room; Laundry room;
Barber/Beauty shop.
Activities Arts and Crafts; Cards; Games;
Reading groups; Prayer groups; Movies; Shopping trips; Dances/Social or cultural gatherings.
Description Health Care Facilities Inc homes are designed by award-winning architects for the enjoyment, comfort, convenience, and safety of the geriatric resident. Life again becomes a meaningful experience in HCF establishments.
Lounges, outdoor patios, activity centers, ice cream parlour, beauty and barber shop, book shop, TV rooms, and cheerful group dining facilities are available during daytime and evening hours. Special resident services including physical and speech therapy as well as social services encourage constant resident progress, increasing mobility, alertness, and physical well-being. HCF has become a recognized exponent of excellence in resident care delivery among geriatric and convalescent centers.

POMEROY

Pomeroy Health Care Center
36759 Rocksprings Rd, Pomeroy, OH, 45769
(614) 992-6606
Licensure Skilled Care; Intermediate Care.
Beds 100. *Certified* Medicaid; Medicare.
Ownership Proprietary.

PORT CLINTON

Edgewood Manor Nursing Center
1330 S Fulton, Port Clinton, OH, 43452 (419)
734-5506
Medical Dir/Dir of Nursing R W Minick MD.
Licensure Skilled Care; Intermediate Care.
Beds 100. *Certified* Medicaid; Medicare.
Ownership Proprietary.
Admissions Requirements Medical examination.
Staff Physicians 7 (pt); RNs 6 (ft); LPNs 3 (ft),
6 (pt); Nurses aides 44 (ft); Physical therapists;
Recreational therapists; Occupational therapists; Speech therapists; Activities coordinators
1 (ft); Dietitians 1 (pt); Dentists; Podiatrists 1
(pt); Audiologists.
Facilities Dining room; Physical therapy room;
Activities room; Chapel; Laundry room; Barber/Beauty shop; Library; Living room.
Activities Arts and Crafts; Cards; Games; Prayer groups; Movies; Shopping trips;
Dances/Social or cultural gatherings; Exercises.
Description Facility features home-like atmosphere and excellent care with a holistic approach.

PORTAGE

Nichols Home*
355 W Main St, Portage, OH, 43451
Licensure Intermediate Care for Mentally Retarded. *Beds* 8. *Certified* Medicaid.
Ownership Nonprofit.

Restle Home*
353 W Main St, Portage, OH, 43451
Licensure Intermediate Care for Mentally
Retarded. *Beds* 8. *Certified* Medicaid.
Ownership Nonprofit.

Werner Home*
351 W Main St, Portage, OH, 43451
Licensure Intermediate Care for Mentally
Retarded. *Beds* 10. *Certified* Medicaid.
Ownership Nonprofit.

PORTSMOUTH

Elmwood Village*
2001 Scioto Trail, Portsmouth, OH, 45662
(614) 354-8631
Licensure Intermediate Care. *Beds* 110. *Certified* Medicaid.
Ownership Proprietary.

Flannery Nursing Home Inc
605 Front St, Portsmouth, OH, 45662 (614)
353-5535
Admin Geraldine Jenkins.
Licensure Intermediate Care. *Beds* 29. *Certified* Medicaid.
Ownership Proprietary.
Admissions Requirements Minimum age 21;
Medical examination; Physician's request.
Staff Physicians 3 (pt); RNs 1 (pt); LPNs 4 (ft),
1 (pt); Nurses aides 7 (ft), 1 (pt); Activities coor-
dinators 1 (ft); Dietitians 1 (pt); Dentists 1 (pt);
Ophthalmologists 1 (pt); Podiatrists 1 (pt);
Audiologists 1 (pt).
Facilities Dining room; Laundry room.
Activities Arts and Crafts; Cards; Games;
Reading groups; Prayer groups; Movies; Shop-
ping trips; Dances/Social or cultural gatherings.
Description Facility offers a home lifestyle.

Golden Years Convalescent Center
2125 Royce St, PO Box 1148, Portsmouth,
OH, 45662 (614) 354-6635
Medical Dir/Dir of Nursing Dr Charles Chanz.
Licensure Skilled Care; Intermediate Care.
Beds 100. *Certified* Medicaid; Medicare.
Ownership Proprietary.
Admissions Requirements Medical examina-
tion.
Staff Physicians 8 (pt); RNs 4 (ft), 3 (pt); LPNs
12 (ft); Orderlies 3 (ft); Nurses aides 36 (ft);
Physical therapists 1 (pt); Reality therapists 2
(pt); Recreational therapists 2 (ft); Speech thera-
pists 1 (pt); Activities coordinators 1 (ft); Dieti-
tians 1 (ft); Dentists 1 (pt); Ophthalmologists 1
(pt); Podiatrists 1 (pt); Audiologists 1 (pt).
Facilities Dining room; Physical therapy room;
Activities room; Chapel; Crafts room; Laundry
room; Barber/Beauty shop.
Activities Arts and Crafts; Cards; Games;
Reading groups; Prayer groups; Movies; Shopping trips; Dances/Social or cultural gatherings.

Heartland of Portsmouth*
Box 10, Rt 6, Feurt Hill Rd, Portsmouth, OH,
45662
Licensure Skilled Care; Intermediate Care.
Beds 100. *Certified* Medicaid; Medicare.

Hill View Health Care Facility
1610 28th St, Portsmouth, OH, 45662 (614)
353-2746
Medical Dir/Dir of Nursing Thomas K Swope
DO.
Licensure Skilled Care; Intermediate Care.
Beds 55. *Certified* Medicaid; Medicare.
Ownership Nonprofit.
Admissions Requirements Medical examina-
tion.
Staff Physicians 1 (ft); RNs 3 (ft), 2 (pt); LPNs
6 (ft), 5 (pt); Nurses aides 20 (ft), 5 (pt);
Physical therapists 1 (pt); Reality therapists 1
(ft); Recreational therapists 1 (ft); Activities
coordinators 1 (ft); Dietitians 1 (ft); Dentists 1
(pt); Podiatrists 1 (pt); Audiologists 1 (pt).
Affiliation Methodist
Facilities Dining room; Physical therapy room;
Activities room; Crafts room; Laundry room;
Barber/Beauty shop; Library.
Activities Arts and Crafts; Cards; Games;
Reading groups; Prayer groups; Movies; Shopping trips; Dances/Social or cultural gatherings.
Description United Methodist affiliated health
care facility is part of a life care retirement community located on 20 acres of rolling hills in
southern Ohio; excellent health care services
provided.

Hilltop Nursing Home*
1319 Spring St, Portsmouth, OH, 45662 (614)
354-6619
Licensure Intermediate Care. *Beds* 25. *Certified* Medicaid.
Ownership Proprietary.

Villa Nursing Home
1112 2nd St, Portsmouth, OH, 45662 (614)
353-6098
Licensure Intermediate Care. *Beds* 22. *Certified* Medicaid.
Ownership Nonprofit.

RAVENNA

Jane Francis Nursing Home*
245 New Milford Rd, Ravenna, OH, 44266
(216) 296-6415
Licensure Skilled Care; Intermediate Care.
Beds 99. *Certified* Medicaid; Medicare.
Ownership Proprietary.

Longmeadow Care Center*
565 Bryn Mawr, Ravenna, OH, 44266 (216)
297-5781
Licensure Skilled Care; Intermediate Care.
Beds 100. *Certified* Medicaid; Medicare.
Ownership Proprietary.

Portage County Nursing Home
7988 Infirmary Rd, Ravenna, OH, 44266 (216)
296-9977
Medical Dir/Dir of Nursing Albert Tsai MD.
Licensure Intermediate Care. *Beds* 99. *Certified* Medicaid.
Ownership Public.
Admissions Requirements Medical examina-
tion.
Staff Physicians 1 (pt); RNs 4 (ft); LPNs 5 (ft),
5 (pt); Nurses aides 21 (ft), 14 (pt); Physical
therapists 1 (pt); Activities coordinators 1 (ft);
Dietitians 1 (pt); Dentists 1 (pt); Ophthalmolo-

gists 1 (pt); Podiatrists 1 (pt).
Facilities Dining room; Physical therapy room;
Activities room; Chapel; Crafts room; Barber-
/Beauty shop.
Activities Arts and Crafts; Cards; Games;
Reading groups; Prayer groups; Movies; Shop-
ping trips; Dances/Social or cultural gatherings.
Description Facility has a rural setting with a
friendly, family atmosphere.

READING

Aaron Convalescent Home*
21 W Columbia, Reading, OH, 45215 (513)
554-1141
Licensure Intermediate Care. *Beds* 142. *Certified* Medicaid.
Ownership Proprietary.

RICHFIELD

Pine Valley Nursing Center
4360 Brecksville Rd, Richfield, OH, 44286
(216) 659-6166
Admin Dr Sheth.
Licensure Skilled Care; Intermediate Care.
Beds 95. *Certified* Medicaid; Medicare.
Ownership Proprietary.
Admissions Requirements Minimum age 14;
Medical examination.
Staff Physicians 4 (pt); RNs 4 (ft), 3 (pt); LPNs
10 (ft), 1 (pt); Orderlies 2 (ft), 2 (pt); Nurses
aides 30 (ft), 17 (pt); Physical therapists 1 (pt);
Activities coordinators 1 (ft); Dietitians 1 (pt).
Facilities Dining room; Activities room; Laun-
dry room; Barber/Beauty shop.
Activities Arts and Crafts; Cards; Games; Pray-
er groups; Movies; Shopping trips;
Dances/Social or cultural gatherings.
Description Pine Valley is a unique facility set
in the pine-wooded hills of Richfield Village. A
center courtyard makes enjoying the outdoors
possible all year round. Our staff has a genuine
love and caring for the elderly and is always
eager to help.

RIPLEY

Ohio Valley Manor Convalescent Center
5280 Rts 62 and 68, Ripley, OH, 45167 (513)
392-4318
Medical Dir/Dir of Nursing Gene Conway
MD.
Licensure Skilled Care; Intermediate Care.
Beds 100. *Certified* Medicaid; Medicare.
Ownership Proprietary.
Staff Physicians 4 (pt); RNs 6 (ft), 4 (pt); LPNs
5 (ft), 6 (pt); Nurses aides 19 (ft), 33 (pt);
Physical therapists 1 (pt); Occupational thera-
pists 1 (pt); Speech therapists 1 (pt); Activities
coordinators 1 (ft); Dietitians 1 (ft), 1 (pt); Den-
tists 1 (pt).
Facilities Dining room; Physical therapy room;
Activities room; Laundry room; Barber/Beauty
shop.
Activities Arts and Crafts; Cards; Games;
Reading groups; Prayer groups; Movies; Shop-
ping trips; Dances/Social or cultural gatherings.
Description Facility features 2 annual perfor-
mances by the Cincinnati Symphony
Orchestra. Joint commission accredited.

RITTMAN

Apostolic Christian Home Inc*
10680 Steiner Rd, Rittman, OH, 44270 (216) 927-1010
Licensure Intermediate Care. *Beds* 51. *Certified* Medicaid.
Ownership Nonprofit.
Affiliation Apostolic Christian

Rittman Health Care Center*
275 E Sunset Dr, Rittman, OH, 44270
Licensure Skilled Care; Intermediate Care.
Beds 100. *Certified* Medicaid; Medicare.

ROCK CREEK

Char-Lotte Nursing Home Inc
Rt 45, Box 177, Rock Creek, OH, 44084 (216) 563-5547
Licensure Skilled Care; Intermediate Care.
Beds 119. *Certified* Medicaid; Medicare.
Ownership Proprietary.

ROCKFORD

Colonial Nursing Home*
611 S Main St, Rockford, OH, 45882 (419) 363-2193
Licensure Intermediate Care. *Beds* 34. *Certified* Medicaid.
Ownership Proprietary.

Shane Hill Nursing Home
Rt 3, State Rt 118, Rockford, OH, 45882 (419) 363-2620
Admin John L Smith.
Licensure Intermediate Care. *Beds* 100. *Certified* Medicaid.
Ownership Proprietary.
Admissions Requirements Medical examination; Physician's request.
Staff Physicians 2 (pt); RNs 6 (ft), 2 (pt); LPNs 8 (ft), 4 (pt); Nurses aides 35 (ft), 5 (pt); Physical therapists 1 (pt); Recreational therapists 2 (ft), 1 (pt); Speech therapists 1 (pt); Activities coordinators 1 (ft); Dietitians 1 (pt); Dentists 1 (pt); Ophthalmologists 1 (pt); Podiatrists 1 (pt).
Facilities Dining room; Physical therapy room; Activities room; Chapel; Crafts room; Laundry room; Barber/Beauty shop; Library.
Activities Arts and Crafts; Cards; Games; Reading groups; Prayer groups; Movies; Dances/Social or cultural gatherings.
Description Shane Hill is family-owned and has a countryside setting; quiet home-like atmosphere.

ROCKY RIVER

Welsh Home for the Aged*
22199 Center Ridge Rd, Rocky River, OH, 44116 (216) 331-0420
Licensure Intermediate Care. *Beds* 34. *Certified* Medicaid.
Ownership Nonprofit.

SABINA

Autumn Years Nursing Center*
580 E Washington Ave, Sabina, OH, 45169 (513) 584-4440
Licensure Skilled Care; Intermediate Care.
Beds 51. *Certified* Medicaid; Medicare.
Ownership Proprietary.

Eden Manor Nursing Home*
273 S Howard St, Sabina, OH, 45169 (513) 584-4313
Licensure Intermediate Care. *Beds* 30. *Certified* Medicaid.
Ownership Proprietary.

SAINT CLAIRSVILLE

Belmont County Oakview Nursing Home*
Rt 1, Saint Clairsville, OH, 43950 (614) 695-4925
Licensure Intermediate Care. *Beds* 71. *Certified* Medicaid.
Ownership Public.

Belmont Habilitation Center*
68401 Hammond Rd, Saint Clairsville, OH, 43950
Licensure Intermediate Care for Mentally Retarded. *Beds* 85. *Certified* Medicaid.
Ownership Proprietary.

Woodland Acres Nursing Home Inc*
Rt 4, Cresent Rd, Saint Clairsville, OH, 43950 (614) 695-0800
Licensure Nursing Home. *Beds* 16.
Ownership Proprietary.

SAINT MARYS

Valley Nursing Home*
1140 Knoxville Ave, Saint Marys, OH, 45885 (419) 394-3308
Licensure Skilled Care; Intermediate Care.
Beds 100. *Certified* Medicaid; Medicare.
Ownership Proprietary.

SALEM

Hutton Nursing Center*
2511 Bentley Dr, Salem, OH, 44460 (216) 337-9503
Licensure Intermediate Care. *Beds* 100. *Certified* Medicaid.
Ownership Proprietary.

Hutton Nursing Center II Inc*
250 Continental Drive, Salem, OH, 44460
Beds 100.

Mary Fletcher Health Care Center 1*
767 Benton Rd, Salem, OH, 44460 (216) 332-0391
Licensure Intermediate Care. *Beds* 24. *Certified* Medicaid.
Ownership Proprietary.

Salem Convalescent Center
1985 E Pershing St, Salem, OH, 44460 (216) 332-1588
Medical Dir/Dir of Nursing Dr W F Stevenson.
Licensure Intermediate Care; Rest Home.
Beds ICF 30; Rest Home 44. *Certified* Medicaid.
Ownership Nonprofit.
Staff RNs 3 (ft); LPNs 6 (ft), 6 (pt); Nurses aides 27 (ft), 5 (pt); Physical therapists; Activities coordinators 1 (ft), 1 (pt); Dietitians 3 (ft), 3 (pt); Dentists; Ophthalmologists; Podiatrists; Audiologists; Social workers 1 (ft).
Facilities Dining room; Activities room; Chapel; Crafts room; Laundry room; Barber/Beauty shop.
Activities Arts and Crafts; Cards; Games; Prayer groups; Shopping trips; Dances/Social or cultural gatherings.
Description Facility has activities and social services 7 days a week.

Valley Road Nursing Home*
451 Valley Rd, Salem, OH, 44460
Licensure Intermediate Care. *Beds* 44. *Certified* Medicaid.
Ownership Proprietary.

SANDUSKY

Classic Care South*
3423 S Columbus Ave, Sandusky, OH, 44870 (419) 625-6534
Licensure Intermediate Care. *Beds* 34. *Certified* Medicaid.
Ownership Proprietary.

Classic Center
620 W Strub Rd, Sandusky, OH, 44870 (419) 626-5373
Medical Dir/Dir of Nursing D B Cuthbertson MD.
Licensure Intermediate Care. *Beds* 51.
Ownership Proprietary.
Admissions Requirements Medical examination; Physician's request.
Staff Physicians 1 (ft), 4 (pt); RNs 2 (ft), 1 (pt); LPNs 3 (ft), 3 (pt); Nurses aides 10 (ft), 7 (pt); Physical therapists 1 (pt); Reality therapists 1 (pt); Recreational therapists 1 (ft); Occupational therapists 1 (pt); Speech therapists 1 (pt); Activities coordinators 1 (ft); Dietitians 1 (pt); Dentists 1 (pt); Ophthalmologists 1 (pt); Podiatrists 2 (pt); Audiologists 1 (pt).
Facilities Dining room; Activities room; Chapel; Laundry room; Barber/Beauty shop; Library.
Activities Arts and Crafts; Cards; Games; Reading groups; Prayer groups; Movies; Shopping trips; Dances/Social or cultural gatherings; Outings.
Description Facility is set in a home-like atmosphere; staff members include certified geriatric assistants who are specifically trained for long-term care patients; features private and semi-private rooms with 8-foot sliding glass doors leading to a covered patio.

Hospitality Care Center 1*
531 Wayne St, Sandusky, OH, 44870 (419) 625-4449
Licensure Nursing Home. *Beds* 23.
Ownership Proprietary.

Hospitality Care Center 2*
403 E Adams St, Sandusky, OH, 44870 (419)
626-5444
Licensure Intermediate Care. *Beds* 26. *Certified* Medicaid.
Ownership Proprietary.

Lutheran Memorial Home
795 Bardshar Rd, Sandusky, OH, 44870 (419)
625-4046
Admin Frances Landis. *Medical Dir/Dir of Nursing* Dean J Reichenbach MD and Paul G Steinbicker MD.
Licensure Nursing Home. *Beds* 50.
Ownership Nonprofit.
Admissions Requirements Medical examination.
Staff Physicians 2 (pt); RNs 1 (ft); LPNs 3 (ft), 5 (pt); Nurses aides 13 (ft), 12 (pt); Physical therapists 1 (pt); Speech therapists 1 (pt); Activities coordinators 1 (ft); Dietitians 1 (pt); Podiatrists 1 (pt).
Affiliation Lutheran
Facilities Dining room; Physical therapy room; Activities room; Chapel; Laundry room; Barber/Beauty shop.
Activities Arts and Crafts; Cards; Games; Reading groups; Prayer groups; Movies; Shopping trips; Dances/Social or cultural gatherings; Group entertainment.

Saint Ann Skilled Nursing Center
1912 Hayes Ave, Sandusky, OH, 44870 (419)
625-8450
Admin Sr Jeanne Stack. *Medical Dir/Dir of Nursing* Sidhaiyan Aiyappasamy MD.
Licensure Skilled Care. *Beds* 46. *Certified* Medicaid; Medicare.
Ownership Nonprofit.
Admissions Requirements Medical examination; Physician's request.
Staff Physicians 1 (pt); RNs 4 (ft), 5 (pt); LPNs 9 (ft), 5 (pt); Orderlies 1 (ft); Nurses aides 6 (ft), 6 (pt); Physical therapists 4 (ft); Occupational therapists 3 (ft); Speech therapists 1 (pt); Activities coordinators 1 (ft); Dietitians 2 (ft); Dentists 1 (pt); Ophthalmologists 2 (pt); Podiatrists 1 (pt); Audiologists 1 (pt).
Affiliation Roman Catholic
Facilities Dining room; Physical therapy room; Activities room; Chapel; Crafts room; Laundry room; Barber/Beauty shop.
Activities Arts and Crafts; Cards; Games; Reading groups; Prayer groups; Movies; Shopping trips; Dances/Social or cultural gatherings; Baking and cooking; Reality orientation; Remotivation groups; Individual activities; Physical activities.
Description Saint Ann's is a 46-bed unit located within Providence Hospital (total 261 beds), thus patients have immediate access to emergency and technical facilities that include a new 8-bed ICU, 6-bed CCU, 8-bed Step Down Unit, and the area's only inpatient/outpatient cardiac rehabilitation program. The campus also houses Providence Hospital's School of Nursing and School of Radiologic Technology.

Sandusky Nursing Home Inc
232 Jackson St, Sandusky, OH, 44870 (419)
626-6688
Medical Dir/Dir of Nursing W P Skirball MD.

Licensure Intermediate Care; Intermediate Care for Mentally Retarded. *Beds* ICF 65; ICF/MR 64. *Certified* Medicaid.
Ownership Proprietary.
Staff Physicians 3 (pt); RNs 1 (ft), 2 (pt); LPNs 9 (ft), 3 (pt); Nurses aides 30 (ft); Physical therapists 1 (pt); Recreational therapists 1 (ft); Occupational therapists 1 (pt); Speech therapists 1 (pt); Activities coordinators 1 (pt); Dietitians 1 (pt); Dentists 1 (pt); Ophthalmologists 1 (pt); Podiatrists 1 (pt); Audiologists 1 (pt).
Facilities Dining room; Physical therapy room; Activities room; Crafts room; Laundry room; Barber/Beauty shop; Library.
Activities Arts and Crafts; Cards; Games; Prayer groups; Movies; Shopping trips; Dances/Social or cultural gatherings.

True Light Nursing Home
507 Wayne St, Sandusky, OH, 44870
Admin William J Hunt. *Medical Dir/Dir of Nursing* Sidhaiyan Aiyappasamy MD.
Licensure Intermediate Care. *Beds* 50. *Certified* Medicaid.
Ownership Proprietary.
Admissions Requirements Medical examination.
Staff Physicians 1 (pt); RNs 1 (pt); LPNs 6 (ft), 2 (pt); Orderlies 2 (ft); Nurses aides 12 (ft), 6 (pt); Physical therapists 1 (pt); Occupational therapists 1 (pt); Speech therapists 1 (pt); Activities coordinators 1 (ft); Dietitians 1 (pt); Dentists 1 (pt); Ophthalmologists 1 (pt); Podiatrists 1 (pt); Audiologists 1 (pt).
Facilities Dining room; Activities room; Crafts room; Laundry room.
Activities Arts and Crafts; Cards; Games; Reading groups; Prayer groups; Movies; Shopping trips; Dances/Social or cultural gatherings.
Description As a small nursing home, we can offer more individual care not only to the resident, but also the families; attempt to give the resident more of a home environment for the individual attention.

Vacationland Rest Home*
6412 Milan Rd, Sandusky, OH, 44870 (419)
626-6828
Licensure Nursing Home. *Beds* 19.
Ownership Proprietary.

SEBRING

Crandall Medical Center
800 S 15th St, Sebring, OH, 44672 (216)
938-9831
Medical Dir/Dir of Nursing George H Davies MD.
Licensure Skilled Care; Intermediate Care; Rest Home. *Beds* SNF 144; ICF 144; Rest Home 48. *Certified* Medicaid; Medicare.
Ownership Nonprofit.
Admissions Requirements Medical examination.
Staff Physicians 8 (pt); RNs 5 (ft), 3 (pt); LPNs 12 (ft), 7 (pt); Orderlies 4 (ft); Nurses aides 23 (ft), 16 (pt); Physical therapists 2 (pt); Occupational therapists 1 (ft); Speech therapists 1 (pt); Activities coordinators 2 (ft); Dietitians 1 (pt); Dentists 1 (pt); Podiatrists 2 (pt); Audiologists 1 (pt).
Affiliation Methodist

Facilities Dining room; Physical therapy room; Activities room; Chapel; Crafts room; Laundry room; Barber/Beauty shop; Library.
Activities Arts and Crafts; Cards; Games; Reading groups; Prayer groups; Movies; Shopping trips; Dances/Social or cultural gatherings; Discussion groups; Sing-a-longs; Ceramics.
Description Facility offers high quality at all points; emphasis on self-determination and decision making by residents. JCAH accredited.

SEVILLE

Canterbury Villa of Seville*
76 High St, Seville, OH, 44256
Licensure Skilled Care; Intermediate Care.
Beds 100. *Certified* Medicaid; Medicare.
Ownership Proprietary.

SHADYSIDE

Shadyside Care Center
State Rt 7, Shadyside, OH, 43947 (614)
767-8381
Licensure Intermediate Care. *Beds* 100. *Certified* Medicaid.
Ownership Proprietary.
Admissions Requirements Medical examination.
Staff Physicians; RNs; LPNs; Orderlies; Nurses aides; Physical therapists; Reality therapists; Recreational therapists; Occupational therapists; Activities coordinators; Dietitians; Podiatrists.
Facilities Dining room; Physical therapy room; Activities room; Chapel; Crafts room; Laundry room; Barber/Beauty shop; Library.
Activities Arts and Crafts; Cards; Reading groups; Prayer groups; Movies; Shopping trips; Dances/Social or cultural gatherings; Pig roasts; 5K distance race.
Description Facility is nestled in the hills of southeastern Ohio along the Ohio River in a rich coal mining area. The philosophy behind the Shadyside Care Center is one of social committment to the Ohio Valleys infirm elderly population, "someone to share—someone to care."

SHELBY

Crestwood Care Center*
225 W Main St, Shelby, OH, 44875 (419)
526-3509
Licensure Skilled Care; Intermediate Care.
Beds 127. *Certified* Medicaid; Medicare.
Ownership Proprietary.

Heritage Care Center*
100 Roger Ln, Shelby, OH, 44875 (419)
347-1313
Licensure Skilled Care; Intermediate Care.
Beds 50. *Certified* Medicaid; Medicare.
Ownership Proprietary.

SIDNEY

Dorothy Love Retirement Community
3003 W Cisco Rd, Sidney, OH, 45365 (513)
498-2391

Admin Paul T Schultz.
Licensure Skilled Care; Intermediate Care.
Beds 96. *Certified* Medicaid; Medicare.
Ownership Nonprofit.
Admissions Requirements Minimum age 55;
Medical examination.
Staff RNs 7 (ft), 4 (pt); LPNs 3 (ft), 6 (pt);
Nurses aides 32 (ft), 15 (pt); Activities coordi-
nators 1 (ft).
Affiliation Presbyterian
Facilities Dining room; Physical therapy room;
Activities room; Chapel; Crafts room; Laundry
room; Barber/Beauty shop; Library; Green-
house.
Activities Arts and Crafts; Cards; Games;
Reading groups; Prayer groups; Movies; Shop-
ping trips; Dances/Social or cultural gatherings;
Volunteer program; Shuffleboard; Current
events; Horseshoes.
Description Facility is located in a rural setting;
full service retirement community including
resident gardening, fishing, bicycling, physical
fitness program and scheduled transportation.

Fairhaven Shelby County Home
Fair Rd, Sidney, OH, 45365 (513) 492-6900
Admin Bill Stine. *Medical Dir/Dir of Nur-
sing* George Schroer MD.
Licensure Intermediate Care; Custodial Care.
Beds ICF 125; Custodial Care 20. *Cer-
tified* Medicaid.
Ownership Public.
Admissions Requirements Minimum age 18;
Medical examination.
Staff Physicians 1 (ft); RNs 5 (ft), 10 (pt);
LPNs 8 (ft), 5 (pt); Orderlies 1 (ft); Nurses aides
40 (ft), 9 (pt); Recreational therapists 2 (ft);
Activities coordinators 2 (ft); Dietitians 1 (pt);
Podiatrists 1 (pt).
Facilities Dining room; Activities room; Chap-
el; Crafts room; Laundry room; Barber/Beauty
shop; Library; TV lounges.
Activities Arts and Crafts; Cards; Games;
Reading groups; Prayer groups; Movies; Shop-
ping trips; Dances/Social or cultural gatherings;
Community functions; Band concert, Picnics.
Description Fair Haven is located in a rural setting and has a farm which raises garden pro-
duce, cattle, pigs, and chickens for use in the
facility.

Franklin Nursing Center of Sidney*
510 Buckeye St, Sidney, OH, 45365 (513)
492-3171
Licensure Skilled Care; Intermediate Care.
Beds 51. *Certified* Medicaid; Medicare.
Ownership Proprietary.

Sunny Acres Care Center*
705 Fulton St, Sidney, OH, 45365 (513)
492-9591
Licensure Skilled Care; Intermediate Care.
Beds 60. *Certified* Medicaid; Medicare.
Ownership Proprietary.

SOUTH POINT

Pulley Care Center*
Rt 4, Box 349A, South Point, OH, 45680 (614)
894-3476

Licensure Skilled Care; Intermediate Care.
Beds 100. *Certified* Medicaid; Medicare.
Ownership Nonprofit.

Pulley Nursing Home*
Rt 2, Box 44, South Point, OH, 45680 (614)
894-3442
Licensure Intermediate Care. *Beds* 35. *Certi-
fied* Medicaid.
Ownership Proprietary.

SOUTH VIENNA

Sharonview Nursing Home
Box 447, South Vienna, OH, 45369 (513)
568-4342
Medical Dir/Dir of Nursing William A Gar-
ringer MD.
Licensure Intermediate Care. *Beds* 50. *Certified* Medicaid.
Ownership Nonprofit.
Admissions Requirements Minimum age 21;
Medical examination.
Staff Physicians 2 (pt); RNs 4 (ft), 5 (pt); LPNs
2 (ft), 2 (pt); Nurses aides 12 (ft), 6 (pt);
Physical therapists 1 (pt); Recreational therapists 1 (pt); Occupational therapists 1 (pt); Speech therapists 1 (pt); Activities coordinators 1
(ft); Dietitians 1 (pt); Dentists 1 (pt); Ophthalmologists 1 (pt); Podiatrists 1 (pt); Audiologists
1 (pt).
Facilities Dining room; Activities room; Crafts
room; Barber/Beauty shop.
Activities Arts and Crafts; Cards; Games;
Reading groups; Prayer groups; Movies; Shopping trips; Dances/Social or cultural gatherings.
Description Sharonview Nursing Home is
located 7 miles east of Springfield in the country; provides a specialized habilitation training
program for mentally retarded adults with multiple physical handicaps; programs are varied
and are directed to the individual's need.

SPENCERVILLE

Rose Lawn Manor Home*
420 E 4th St, Spencerville, OH, 45887 (419)
647-6022
Licensure Intermediate Care. *Beds* 100. *Certified* Medicaid.
Ownership Proprietary.

SPRINGFIELD

Applin Nursing Home
237 W Pleasant St, Springfield, OH, 45506
Licensure Intermediate Care. *Beds* 22. *Certified* Medicaid.
Ownership Nonprofit.

Clark Memorial Home*
106 Kewbury Rd, Springfield, OH, 45504 (513)
399-4262
Licensure Rest Home. *Beds* 20.
Ownership Nonprofit.

Compton's Nursing Home*
1103 S Fountain Ave, Springfield, OH, 45506
(513) 323-1511

Licensure Intermediate Care. *Beds* 20. *Certified* Medicaid.
Ownership Proprietary.

The Good Shepherd Village*
422 N Burnett Rd, Springfield, OH, 45503
(513) 322-1911
Licensure Nursing Home. *Beds* 61.
Ownership Proprietary.

Heartland of Springfield*
2615 Derr Rd, Springfield, OH, 45506 (513)
390-0095
Licensure Skilled Care; Intermediate Care.
Beds 98. *Certified* Medicaid; Medicare.
Ownership Proprietary.

Hope House Manor Inc
2317 E Home Rd, Springfield, OH, 45503 (513)
399-9217
Licensure Skilled Care; Intermediate Care.
Beds 100. *Certified* Medicaid; Medicare.
Ownership Proprietary.
Facilities Dining room; Physical therapy room;
Activities room; Chapel; Crafts room; Laundry
room; Barber/Beauty shop; Library.
Activities Arts and Crafts; Cards; Games;
Reading groups; Prayer groups; Movies; Shop-
ping trips; Dances/Social or cultural gatherings.

K W Hess Ohio Pythian Home*
901 W High St, Springfield, OH, 45506 (513)
322-3271
Licensure Intermediate Care. *Beds* 98. *Certified* Medicaid.
Ownership Nonprofit.
Affiliation Knights of Pythias

Max-Ull 1*
735 W North St, Springfield, OH, 45504 (513)
323-0321
Licensure Intermediate Care. *Beds* 15. *Certified* Medicaid.
Ownership Proprietary.

New Dawn Convalescent Center
1301 S Limestone St, Springfield, OH, 45505
(513) 324-5709 and 324-5700
Medical Dir/Dir of Nursing Dr Kneisley.
Licensure Intermediate Care. *Beds* 21. *Certi-
fied* Medicaid.
Ownership Nonprofit.
Admissions Requirements Females only
Staff RNs 1 (pt); LPNs 4 (ft); Nurses aides 10
(ft); Activities coordinators 1 (ft).
Affiliation Swedenborgian

New Horizon Nursing Home*
1157 Driscoll Ave, Springfield, OH, 45506
(513) 324-1831
Licensure Intermediate Care. *Beds* 24. *Certified* Medicaid.
Ownership Proprietary.

Odd Fellows Home of Ohio
404 E McCreight Ave, Springfield, OH, 45501
(513) 399-8311
Medical Dir/Dir of Nursing Barry Paxton MD.
Licensure Intermediate Care. *Beds* 100. *Certified* Medicaid.
Ownership Proprietary.
Admissions Requirements Medical examination.

Staff Physicians 1 (pt); RNs 4 (ft); LPNs 10 (ft); Nurses aides 80 (ft); Recreational therapists 5 (ft); Activities coordinators 1 (ft); Dietitians 1 (ft); Podiatrists 1 (pt).
Affiliation Independent Order of Odd Fellows
Facilities Dining room; Physical therapy room; Activities room; Chapel; Crafts room; Laundry room; Barber/Beauty shop; Library.
Activities Arts and Crafts; Cards; Games; Reading groups; Prayer groups; Movies; Shopping trips; Dances/Social or cultural gatherings.
Description Facility has a wheelchair and bus to transport residents to many outside functions such as shopping, fishing, picnics, movies, and plays.

Ohio Masonic Home
2655 W National Rd, PO Box 120, Springfield, OH, 45501 (513) 325-1531
Medical Dir/Dir of Nursing William C Fippin MD.
Licensure Long Term Care; Residential Care.
Beds Long Term Care 378; Residential Care 96.
Ownership Proprietary.
Admissions Requirements Medical examination.
Staff Physicians 1 (ft); RNs 22 (ft), 11 (pt); LPNs 10 (ft), 2 (pt); Nurses aides 149 (ft), 28 (pt); Physical therapists 1 (ft); Activities coordinators 1 (ft); Dietitians 1 (ft); Dentists 1 (pt); Podiatrists 1 (pt).
Affiliation Masons
Facilities Dining room; Physical therapy room; Activities room; Chapel; Crafts room; Laundry room; Barber/Beauty shop; Library.
Activities Arts and Crafts; Cards; Games; Reading groups; Movies; Shopping trips; Dances/Social or cultural gatherings.

Pillars Nursing Home
336 W Columbia St, PO Box 88, Springfield, OH, 15504 (513) 323-9104
Medical Dir/Dir of Nursing Nicholas B Pavlatos MD.
Licensure Intermediate Care. *Beds* 46. *Certified* Medicaid.
Ownership Proprietary.
Staff Physicians 1 (pt); RNs 1 (ft), 2 (pt); LPNs 3 (ft), 4 (pt); Orderlies 3 (ft); Nurses aides 8 (ft), 2 (pt); Physical therapists; Speech therapists; Activities coordinators 1 (ft).
Facilities Dining room; Activities room; Laundry room; Barber/Beauty shop.
Activities Arts and Crafts; Cards; Games; Reading groups; Prayer groups; Movies; Shopping trips; Dances/Social or cultural gatherings.
Description Pillars Nursing Home is located in the center of Springfield making activities in the downtown area easily accessible to all residents.

Ridgewood Nursing Home*
1600 Saint Paris Pike, Springfield, OH, 45504 (513) 399-8131
Licensure Skilled Care; Intermediate Care.
Beds 50. *Certified* Medicaid; Medicare.
Ownership Proprietary.

Saint John's Center
100 W McCreight Ave, Springfield, OH, 45504 (513) 399-9910
Medical Dir/Dir of Nursing Sally Abbott MD.
Licensure Skilled Care; Intermediate Care.

Beds 150. *Certified* Medicaid; Medicare.
Ownership Nonprofit.
Facilities Dining room; Physical therapy room; Activities room; Chapel; Crafts room; Laundry room; Barber/Beauty shop.
Activities Arts and Crafts; Cards; Games; Reading groups; Prayer groups; Movies; Shopping trips; Dances/Social or cultural gatherings.
Description St John's Center is intensely medically oriented and has many residents who have care needs normally found in hospitals. There are 8 full-time equivalents in the respiratory therapy area providing 24-hour coverage in that speciality.

Seminole Villa Care Center
1365 Seminole Ave, Springfield, OH, 45506 (515) 323-1471
Admin A Kent Adams. *Medical Dir/Dir of Nursing* Dr Barry Paxton.
Licensure Intermediate Care for Mentally Retarded. *Beds* 34. *Certified* Medicaid.
Ownership Proprietary.
Admissions Requirements Minimum age 40; Medical examination.
Staff Physicians 1 (pt); RNs 2 (ft); LPNs 2 (ft), 2 (pt); Nurses aides 10 (ft), 6 (pt); Physical therapists 1 (pt); Occupational therapists 1 (pt); Speech therapists 1 (pt); Activities coordinators 1 (ft); Dietitians 1 (pt); Dentists 1 (pt); Ophthalmologists 1 (pt); Podiatrists 1 (pt); Audiologists 1 (pt).
Facilities Dining room; Activities room; Laundry room; Barber/Beauty shop.
Activities Arts and Crafts; Cards; Games; Movies; Shopping trips; Dances/Social or cultural gatherings.
Description Center is for clients who need a balance of nursing care and developmental programing; activities are community oriented.

Springview Center*
3130 E Main St, Springfield, OH, 45505 (513) 325-9263
Licensure Intermediate Care for Mentally Retarded. *Beds* 90.
Ownership Public.

Sunnyland Villa
1365 1/2 Seminole Ave, Springfield, OH, 45506 (513) 322-3436
Medical Dir/Dir of Nursing Dr Venema.
Licensure Skilled Care; Intermediate Care.
Beds 100. *Certified* Medicaid; Medicare.
Ownership Proprietary.
Admissions Requirements Medical examination; Physician's request.
Staff Physicians 1 (ft); LPNs 16 (ft); Orderlies 7 (ft); Nurses aides 39 (ft); Physical therapists 1 (pt); Reality therapists 1 (pt); Recreational therapists 1 (pt); Occupational therapists 1 (pt); Speech therapists 1 (pt); Activities coordinators 1 (ft); Dietitians 1 (pt); Dentists 1 (pt); Ophthalmologists 1 (pt); Podiatrists 1 (pt); Audiologists 1 (pt).
Facilities Dining room; Physical therapy room; Activities room; Laundry room; Barber/Beauty shop.
Activities Arts and Crafts; Cards; Games; Reading groups; Prayer groups; Movies; Shopping trips; Dances/Social or cultural gatherings; Trips to zoos, fairs, museums.
Description Sunnyland Villa is a 5-year-old

modern facility situated on one-floor located just outside the city of Springfield on 17 acres with a park-like setting. Each room has maximum exposure to sunlight and is tastefully decorated. We also have an active auxillary and social program.

STEUBENVILLE

Labelle View Nursing Center
1336 Maryland Ave, Steubenville, OH, 43952 (614) 282-4581
Medical Dir/Dir of Nursing Ah O Pack MD.
Licensure Intermediate Care. *Beds* 101. *Certified* Medicaid.
Ownership Proprietary.
Admissions Requirements Medical examination.
Staff RNs 1 (ft), 4 (pt); LPNs 11 (ft), 1 (pt); Nurses aides 24 (ft), 7 (pt); Reality therapists 1 (ft); Activities coordinators 1 (ft); Dietitians 1 (pt); Ophthalmologists 1 (pt); Podiatrists 1 (pt); Audiologists 1 (pt).
Facilities Dining room; Activities room; Laundry room; Barber/Beauty shop.
Activities Arts and Crafts; Cards; Games; Reading groups; Prayer groups; Dances/Social or cultural gatherings.
Description Facility has a home-like atmosphere.

Lancia Convalescent Center
717 N 6th St, Steubenville, OH, 43952 (614) 282-3605
Medical Dir/Dir of Nursing John P Smarella MD.
Licensure Skilled Care; Intermediate Care.
Beds 50. *Certified* Medicaid.
Ownership Proprietary.
Admissions Requirements Medical examination.
Staff Physicians 1 (pt); RNs 1 (ft); LPNs 5 (pt); Nurses aides 12 (ft), 6 (pt); Physical therapists 1 (pt); Speech therapists 1 (pt); Activities coordinators 1 (ft); Dietitians 1 (pt); Dentists 1 (pt); Podiatrists 1 (pt).
Facilities Dining room; Physical therapy room; Laundry room; Barber/Beauty shop.
Activities Arts and Crafts; Cards; Games; Prayer groups; Shopping trips.

Lancia Villa Royale Nursing Home*
1852 Sinclair Ave, Steubenville, OH, 43952 (614) 264-7101
Licensure Skilled Care; Intermediate Care.
Beds 100. *Certified* Medicaid; Medicare.
Ownership Proprietary.

Martha Manor Home for Aged Women
408 N 5th St, Steubenville, OH, 43952 (614) 282-5623
Admin Pat Dines.
Licensure Rest Home. *Beds* 24.
Ownership Nonprofit.
Admissions Requirements Females only; Medical examination.
Staff RNs 1 (ft); LPNs 1 (ft), 1 (pt); Nurses aides 2 (ft), 4 (pt).
Facilities Dining room; Laundry room; Barber/Beauty shop.
Description Facility has vespers service once a

month; many civic groups come in for programs. Ladies are not confined—they come and go as they like.

Riverview Nursing Home
925 N 4th St, Steubenville, OH, 43952 (614) 282-4158
Admin Joseph C Pino. *Medical Dir/Dir of Nursing* Laura K Mesaros MD.
Licensure Intermediate Care. *Beds* 44. *Certified* Medicaid.
Ownership Proprietary.
Admissions Requirements Medical examination.
Staff Physicians 1 (pt); RNs 1 (ft), 7 (pt); LPNs 1 (pt); Orderlies 1 (ft); Nurses aides 13 (ft); Physical therapists 1 (pt); Recreational therapists 1 (pt).
Facilities Dining room; Activities room; Television lounge.
Activities Arts and Crafts; Cards; Games; Movies; Shopping trips.
Description The facility is located across the street from the Ohio River which gives it a very restful atmosphere. The atmosphere within the home is an informal and friendly one where, because of its size, staff and residents become involved with each other.

Royal Pavilion Extended Care Facility
3102 Saint Charles Dr, Steubenville, OH, 43952 (614) 264-7161
Admin Robert J Sherrin. *Medical Dir/Dir of Nursing* Anthony V Scurti MD.
Licensure Skilled Care; Intermediate Care. *Beds* SNF 95; ICF 25. *Certified* Medicaid; Medicare.
Ownership Proprietary.
Admissions Requirements Physician's request.
Staff Physicians 1 (pt); RNs 5 (ft), 4 (pt); LPNs 1 (ft), 9 (pt); Nurses aides 12 (ft), 18 (pt); Physical therapists 1 (ft); Recreational therapists 1 (pt); Occupational therapists; Speech therapists; Activities coordinators 1 (pt); Dietitians; Dentists; Podiatrists; Audiologists.
Facilities Dining room; Physical therapy room; Activities room; Chapel; Crafts room; Laundry room; Barber/Beauty shop.
Activities Arts and Crafts; Cards; Games; Prayer groups; Movies; Shopping trips; Dances/Social or cultural gatherings.
Description Facility has an excellent physical therapy department and a visiting nurse association.

Shaffer Plaza*
256 John Scott Hwy, Steubenville, OH, 43952
Licensure Intermediate Care for Mentally Retarded. *Beds* 33. *Certified* Medicaid.
Ownership Public.

STRONGSVILLE

Stoney Hill Health Center
15653 Pearl Rd, Strongsville, OH, 44136 (216) 273-2022
Licensure Skilled Care; Intermediate Care. *Beds* 100. *Certified* Medicaid; Medicare.
Ownership Proprietary.

STRUTHERS

Maplecrest Nursing Home for the Aged
400 Sexton St, Struthers, OH, 44471 (216) 755-1466
Medical Dir/Dir of Nursing Dr Jeffery Resch.
Licensure Nursing Home. *Beds* 48.
Ownership Proprietary.
Admissions Requirements Medical examination.
Staff Physicians 1 (pt); RNs 2 (ft), 1 (pt); LPNs 2 (ft), 1 (pt); Nurses aides 13 (ft), 2 (pt); Physical therapists 1 (pt); Occupational therapists 1 (pt); Speech therapists 1 (pt); Dietitians 1 (pt); Podiatrists 1 (pt).
Facilities Dining room; Physical therapy room; Activities room; Laundry room; Barber/Beauty shop.
Activities Games; Prayer groups; Dances/Social or cultural gatherings.
Description This small facility specializes in personal concern for each patient and their families; staff shows caring; good home cooked meals are served in a clean, pleasant, relaxed atmosphere. Outdoor setting is particularly beautiful.

SUNBURY

Morning View Care Center 3*
14961 N Old CCC Hwy, Sunbury, OH, 43074 (614) 965-3984
Licensure Intermediate Care. *Beds* 50. *Certified* Medicaid.
Ownership Proprietary.

Sunbury Nursing Home*
144 N Columbus St, Sunbury, OH, 43074 (614) 965-4915
Licensure Intermediate Care. *Beds* 30. *Certified* Medicaid.
Ownership Proprietary.

SWANTON

Maple Tree Inn Inc
Box 46, Swanton, OH, 43558 (419) 825-1111
Medical Dir/Dir of Nursing Dr Fred Hill and Dr George Darah.
Licensure Intermediate Care. *Beds* 47. *Certified* Medicaid.
Ownership Proprietary.
Admissions Requirements Medical examination.
Staff RNs 1 (ft), 4 (pt); LPNs 1 (ft), 4 (pt); Nurses aides 6 (ft), 10 (pt); Physical therapists; Occupational therapists; Speech therapists; Activities coordinators 1 (ft); Dietitians 1 (pt); Dentists; Ophthalmologists; Podiatrists; Audiologists.
Facilities Dining room; Activities room; Crafts room; Laundry room.
Activities Arts and Crafts; Cards; Games; Prayer groups; Movies; Dances/Social or cultural gatherings.
Description Staff is well educated and trained in the area of Alzheimer's disease, and were featured with facility and residents on local TV. Facility has enclosed courtyard.

Mielke's Nursing Home
108 E Airport Hwy, Swanton, OH, 43558 (419) 826-4891
Admin Helen Brown. *Medical Dir/Dir of Nursing* Clara Mausser LPN.
Licensure Intermediate Care. *Beds* 12. *Certified* Medicaid.
Ownership Proprietary.
Staff Physicians 2 (pt); RNs 1 (pt); LPNs 1 (ft), 2 (pt); Nurses aides 4 (ft), 6 (pt); Physical therapists 1 (pt); Recreational therapists 1 (pt); Activities coordinators 1 (pt); Dietitians 1 (pt); Podiatrists 1 (pt).
Facilities Dining room; Activities room; Laundry room.
Activities Arts and Crafts; Cards; Games; Reading groups; Prayer groups; Shopping trips; Barber and beauty services available; Various religious services Sunday afternoon and Wednesday evening.
Description Motto of home is "Cast me not off in the time of old age; forsake me not when my strength faileth."

SYLVANIA

Briarfield Incorporated
5757 Whiteford Rd, Sylvania, OH, 43560 (419) 882-1875
Medical Dir/Dir of Nursing Dr A Quinto.
Licensure Intermediate Care. *Beds* 100. *Certified* Medicaid.
Ownership Proprietary.
Admissions Requirements Medical examination.
Staff RNs 3 (ft); LPNs 8 (ft); Nurses aides 25 (ft), 8 (pt); Activities coordinators 2 (ft); Dietitians 1 (pt); Social workers 1 (ft).
Activities Arts and Crafts; Cards; Games; Movies; Dances/Social or cultural gatherings.
Description Briarfield residents volunteer at a facility for severely retarded children on a one-to-one basis.

Lake Park Nursing Care Center
5100 Harroun Rd, Sylvania, OH, 43560
Licensure Skilled Care. *Beds* 171. *Certified* Medicaid.
Ownership Nonprofit.
Admissions Requirements Medical examination; Physician's request.
Staff RNs 15 (ft), 10 (pt); LPNs 18 (ft), 5 (pt); Orderlies 6 (ft); Nurses aides 36 (ft), 52 (pt); Physical therapists 3 (ft), 2 (pt); Recreational therapists 2 (ft); Occupational therapists 4 (ft); Speech therapists 3 (ft); Dietitians 1 (ft), 1 (pt).
Affiliation Methodist
Facilities Dining room; Physical therapy room; Activities room; Chapel; Crafts room; Barber/Beauty shop; Library.
Activities Arts and Crafts; Cards; Games; Reading groups; Prayer groups; Movies; Shopping trips; Dances/Social or cultural gatherings.
Description Facility provides rehabilitation services twice daily with multidisciplinary care team planning; average length of stay is 32.8 days.

TALLMADGE

Colonial Garden Inc*
563 Colony Park, Tallmadge, OH, 44278
Licensure Intermediate Care. *Beds* 180. *Certified* Medicaid.

Cooper Nursing Home Inc
340 Southwest Ave, Tallmadge, OH, 44278
(216) 633-4723
Admin Robert L Zucker. *Medical Dir/Dir of Nursing* Dr Stuart Goldstein.
Licensure Intermediate Care. *Beds* 31. *Certified* Medicaid.
Ownership Proprietary.
Admissions Requirements Minimum age 21; Females only; Medical examination; Physician's request.
Staff Physicians 1 (pt); RNs 1 (pt); LPNs 5 (ft), 1 (pt); Nurses aides 11 (ft), 4 (pt); Reality therapists 1 (pt); Activities coordinators 1 (ft); Dietitians 1 (pt); Dentists 1 (pt); Ophthalmologists 1 (pt); Podiatrists 1 (pt).
Facilities Dining room; Activities room; Laundry room; Kitchen; Lounge areas.
Activities Arts and Crafts; Games; Prayer groups; Dances/Social or cultural gatherings.
Description Facility is within city in suburban setting with acres of lawn and wooded areas; patients generaly have mental handicaps; approximately 8 or 9 are bedfast while others have limited mobility; all require assistance in daily living.

THE PLAINS

Buckeye Community Services-Childrens Transitional Facility*
33 Hartman Rd, The Plains, OH, 45780
Licensure Intermediate Care for Mentally Retarded. *Beds* 10. *Certified* Medicaid.
Ownership Nonprofit.

Hickory Creek of Athens*
51 E 4th St, The Plains, OH, 45780
Licensure Skilled Care; Intermediate Care.
Beds SNF 100; ICF 100. *Certified* Medicaid; Medicare.
Ownership Proprietary.

THORNVILLE

Heatland-Fairfield
7820 Pleasantville Rd, Thornville, OH, 43076
(614) 536-7381
Admin Carl M L Holbrook. *Medical Dir/Dir of Nursing* Dr Robert Sprouse.
Licensure Skilled Care; Intermediate Care.
Beds SNF 150; ICF 150. *Certified* Medicaid; Medicare.
Ownership Proprietary.
Admissions Requirements Medical examination; Physician's request.
Staff Physicians 2 (pt); RNs 10 (ft); LPNs 25 (ft), 2 (pt); Orderlies 10 (ft), 2 (pt); Nurses aides 90 (ft), 20 (pt); Physical therapists 2 (pt); Recreational therapists 2 (ft); Occupational therapists 1 (pt); Speech therapists 1 (pt); Activities coordinators 1 (ft); Dietitians 1 (pt); Dentists 2 (pt); Ophthalmologists 1 (pt); Podiatrists 1 (pt); Audiologists 1 (pt).

Facilities Dining room; Physical therapy room; Activities room; Crafts room; Laundry room; Barber/Beauty shop.
Activities Arts and Crafts; Cards; Games; Reading groups; Prayer groups; Movies; Shopping trips; Dances/Social or cultural gatherings.
Description Newly remodled facility located in lovely country atmosphere provides the best in care at any skill level. Accept quadrapaleglics, hyperalimentation, venilators, etc. Extra special services available for priviate pay residents. Private rooms are available.

TIFFIN

Alta Mira Nursing Home*
55 Seneca St, Tiffin, OH, 44883 (419) 447-7373
Licensure Intermediate Care. *Beds* 40. *Certified* Medicaid.
Ownership Proprietary.

Autumnwood Care Center*
670 E State Rt 18, Tiffin, OH, 44883 (419) 447-7151
Licensure Skilled Care; Intermediate Care.
Beds 100. *Certified* Medicaid; Medicare.
Ownership Nonprofit.

Riverfront Manor Inc
Rt 2, New Haven Rd, Tiffin, OH, 44883 (419) 447-4662
Medical Dir/Dir of Nursing Dr Daniels.
Licensure Intermediate Care. *Beds* 44. *Certified* Medicaid.
Ownership Proprietary.
Staff Physicians 1 (ft); RNs 1 (ft), 1 (pt); LPNs 3 (ft), 1 (pt); Orderlies 1 (ft); Nurses aides 12 (ft), 5 (pt); Activities coordinators 1 (ft); Dietitians 1 (pt).
Facilities Dining room; Activities room; Chapel; Crafts room; Laundry room; Barber/Beauty shop.
Activities Arts and Crafts; Cards; Games; Reading groups; Prayer groups; Movies; Shopping trips; Dances/Social or cultural gatherings.

Saint Francis Home for the Aged
182 Saint Francis Ave, Tiffin, OH, 44883 (419) 447-2723
Licensure Intermediate Care; Rest Home.
Beds ICF 56; Rest Home 60. *Certified* Medicaid.
Ownership Nonprofit.
Admissions Requirements Minimum age 70; Medical examination.
Staff RNs 3 (ft); LPNs 4 (ft), 3 (pt); Nurses aides 12 (ft), 15 (pt); Reality therapists 1 (pt); Recreational therapists 1 (ft); Activities coordinators 1 (ft); Dietitians 1 (pt).
Affiliation Roman Catholic
Facilities Dining room; Physical therapy room; Activities room; Chapel; Crafts room; Laundry room; Barber/Beauty shop; Library.
Activities Arts and Crafts; Cards; Games; Prayer groups; Movies; Shopping trips; Dances/Social or cultural gatherings.

South Washington Street Nursing Home*
248 S Washington St, Tiffin, OH, 44883 (419) 447-0773

Licensure Intermediate Care. *Beds* 25. *Certified* Medicaid.
Ownership Proprietary.

Tiffin Developmental Center
600 N River Rd, Tiffin, OH, 44883 (419) 447-1450
Licensure Intermediate Care for Mentally Retarded. *Beds* 220.
Ownership Public.

Virginia Lee Care Center
235 N Sandusky St, Tiffin, OH, 44883 (419) 447-8106
Licensure Intermediate Care. *Beds* 20. *Certified* Medicaid.
Ownership Proprietary.
Admissions Requirements Medical examination.
Staff RNs 1 (pt); LPNs 2 (ft), 1 (pt); Nurses aides 6 (ft); Recreational therapists 1 (ft); Activities coordinators 1 (ft); Dietitians 1 (pt).
Facilities Dining room; Activities room; Crafts room; Laundry room.
Activities Arts and Crafts; Cards; Games; Reading groups; Prayer groups; Shopping trips.
Description Facility offers 24-hour nursing care for men and women in a home-like atmosphere.

TIPP CITY

Feghtly Lutheran Home
300 W Main St, Tipp City, OH, 45371
Licensure Rest Home. *Beds* 15.
Ownership Nonprofit.

TOLEDO

Ashland Avenue Nursing Home
2283 Ashland Ave, Toledo, OH, 43620 (419) 241-6457
Licensure Intermediate Care. *Beds* 50. *Certified* Medicaid.
Ownership Proprietary.
Admissions Requirements Minimum age 18; Medical examination; Physician's request.
Staff RNs 1 (pt); LPNs 3 (ft), 5 (pt); Nurses aides 9 (ft), 11 (pt); Activities coordinators 1 (ft); Dietitians 1 (ft); Audiologists 1 (ft).
Facilities Dining room; Activities room; Chapel; Crafts room; Laundry room; Barber/Beauty shop; Library.
Activities Arts and Crafts; Cards; Games; Reading groups; Prayer groups; Movies; Shopping trips; Dances/Social or cultural gatherings.
Description Facility has home-like atmosphere.

Brookhaven Convalescent Center
2051 Collingwood Blvd, Toledo, OH, 43620 (419) 243-5191
Medical Dir/Dir of Nursing Dr Antonio Paat.
Licensure Skilled Care; Intermediate Care.
Beds 174. *Certified* Medicaid; Medicare.
Ownership Proprietary.
Admissions Requirements Medical examination.
Staff RNs 6 (ft), 6 (pt); LPNs 9 (ft), 16 (pt); Nurses aides 38 (ft), 26 (pt); Activities coordinators 1 (ft).
Facilities Dining room; Physical therapy room;

Activities room; Chapel; Laundry room; Barber/Beauty shop; Patio.
Activities Arts and Crafts; Cards; Games; Prayer groups; Movies; Shopping trips; Dances/Social or cultural gatherings.
Description Brookhaven Convalescent Center prides itself in it's excellent rehabilitative program. Physical therapy, occupational therapy, and speech therapy is available. Brookhaven also has a strong involvement in the community and encourages families to become involved at the facility.

Byrnebrook Nursing Home
1011 N Byrne Rd, Toledo, OH, 43607 (419) 531-5321
Medical Dir/Dir of Nursing Frederick Hiss MD.
Licensure Skilled Care; Intermediate Care.
Beds 67. *Certified* Medicaid; Medicare.
Ownership Proprietary.
Admissions Requirements Medical examination.
Staff RNs 5 (ft), 3 (pt); LPNs 3 (ft); Nurses aides 16 (ft), 5 (pt); Physical therapists; Occupational therapists; Speech therapists; Activities coordinators 1 (ft); Dietitians; Podiatrists.
Facilities Dining room; Physical therapy room; Activities room; Chapel; Crafts room; Laundry room; Barber/Beauty shop; Library.
Activities Arts and Crafts; Games; Reading groups; Prayer groups; Movies; Dances/Social or cultural gatherings.

Cherry Hill Nursing Home*
2900 Cherry St, Toledo, OH, 43608 (419) 242-7458
Licensure Skilled Care; Intermediate Care.
Beds 100. *Certified* Medicaid; Medicare.
Ownership Proprietary.

Collingwood Park Nursing Home*
PO Box 6006, 1835 Collingwood Blvd, Toledo, OH, 43614 (419) 255-0333
Licensure Intermediate Care. *Beds* 34. *Certified* Medicaid.
Ownership Proprietary.

Colonial Nursing Home*
3121 Glanzman Rd, Toledo, OH, 43614 (419) 385-6616
Licensure Skilled Care; Intermediate Care.
Beds 94. *Certified* Medicaid; Medicare.
Ownership Proprietary.

Darlington House—The Toledo Jewish Home for the Aged
2735 Darlington Rd, Toledo, OH, 43606 (419) 531-4465
Medical Dir/Dir of Nursing Eli C Abramson MD.
Licensure Skilled Care; Intermediate Care.
Beds 116. *Certified* Medicaid; Medicare.
Ownership Nonprofit.
Staff Physicians 3 (pt); RNs 11 (ft); LPNs 14 (ft); Orderlies 8 (ft); Nurses aides 45 (ft); Physical therapists 2 (pt); Activities coordinators 2 (ft); Dietitians 1 (pt); Dentists 1 (pt); Podiatrists 1 (pt).
Affiliation Jewish
Facilities Dining room; Physical therapy room; Activities room; Chapel; Crafts room; Laundry room; Barber/Beauty shop; Library; Little

theater; Handicap garden.
Activities Arts and Crafts; Cards; Games; Reading groups; Movies; Shopping trips; Dances/Social or cultural gatherings.
Description Member facility of North American Association of Jewish Homes and Housing for the Elderly; American Association of Homes for the Aging; affiliated with Medical College of Ohio, University of Michigan, University of Toledo, and Bowling Green State University; plus 5 schools of nursing in a variety of training programs.

Edgewood Nursing Home
4848 Dorr St, Toledo, OH, 43615 (419) 531-2037
Licensure Nursing Home. *Beds* 48.
Ownership Proprietary.
Staff LPNs 3 (ft); Nurses aides 10 (ft).
Facilities Dining room; Laundry room; Barber/Beauty shop.
Activities Cards; Games; Dances/Social or cultural gatherings.

The Extended Care Center of Toledo*
2005 Ashland Ave, Toledo, OH, 43620 (419) 255-5050
Licensure Skilled Care; Intermediate Care.
Beds 212. *Certified* Medicaid; Medicare.
Ownership Proprietary.

Fairview Manor Nursing Center*
4420 South St, Toledo, OH, 43615 (419) 531-5201
Licensure Skilled Care; Intermediate Care.
Beds 137. *Certified* Medicaid; Medicare.
Ownership Proprietary.

Golden Haven Nursing Home
2901 Tremainsville Rd, Toledo, OH, 43613 (419) 472-2183
Medical Dir/Dir of Nursing Dr Margaret Miller.
Licensure Skilled Care. *Beds* 94. *Certified* Medicaid.
Ownership Proprietary.
Admissions Requirements Minimum age 18; Medical examination.
Staff RNs 1 (ft), 1 (pt); LPNs 10 (ft); Nurses aides 25 (ft), 1 (pt); Activities coordinators 1 (ft); Dietitians 1 (pt).
Facilities Dining room; Activities room; Barber/Beauty shop.
Activities Arts and Crafts; Cards; Games; Prayer groups; Movies.

Holly Glen Care Center Inc*
4293 Monroe St, Toledo, OH, 43606 (419) 474-6021
Licensure Nursing Home. *Beds* 100.
Ownership Proprietary.

Hospitality Care Center Inc—Toledo*
3225 Glanzman Rd, Toledo, OH, 43614 (419) 382-5694
Licensure Intermediate Care. *Beds* 26. *Certified* Medicaid.
Ownership Proprietary.

Imperial Manor*
4816 Dorr St, Toledo, OH, 43615 (419) 536-7656

Licensure Intermediate Care. *Beds* 29. *Certified* Medicaid.
Ownership Proprietary.

Josina Lott Foundation Residential Center*
120 S Holland-Sylvania Rd, Toledo, OH, 43615 (419) 866-9013
Licensure Intermediate Care for Mentally Retarded. *Beds* 32.
Ownership Nonprofit.

Lutheran Old Folks Home
2411 Seaman St, Toledo, OH, 43605 (419) 693-0681
Medical Dir/Dir of Nursing William Winslow MD.
Licensure Skilled Care; Intermediate Care; Rest Home. *Beds* SNF 110; ICF; Rest Home 8.
Certified Medicaid; Medicare.
Ownership Nonprofit.
Admissions Requirements Minimum age 65.
Affiliation Lutheran
Facilities Dining room; Physical therapy room; Activities room; Chapel; Crafts room; Laundry room; Barber/Beauty shop; Library; Resident bakery.
Activities Arts and Crafts; Cards; Games; Reading groups; Prayer groups; Movies; Shopping trips; Dances/Social or cultural gatherings; Discussion groups; Couples club; Association for residents' children.

Maples Nursing Home
2256 Collingwood Blvd, Toledo, OH, 43620
Licensure Intermediate Care. *Beds* 23. *Certified* Medicaid.
Ownership Proprietary.

Marigarde-Sylvania Nursing Home*
4111 Holland-Sylvania Rd, Toledo, OH, 43623 (419) 882-2087
Licensure Intermediate Care. *Beds* 99. *Certified* Medicaid.
Ownership Proprietary.

Marks Nursing Home*
PO Box 6006, 2109 Collingwood Blvd, Toledo, OH, 43614 (419) 246-6082
Licensure Intermediate Care. *Beds* 31. *Certified* Medicaid.
Ownership Proprietary.

Northwest Ohio Development Center*
1101 S Detroit Ave, Toledo, OH, 43612 (419) 385-0231
Licensure Intermediate Care for Mentally Retarded. *Beds* 170.
Ownership Public.

Point North Nursing Home*
2803 117th St, Toledo, OH, 43611 (419) 726-9820
Licensure Intermediate Care. *Beds* 19. *Certified* Medicaid.
Ownership Proprietary.

Resthaven Manor Nursing Home Inc
424 Winthrop St, Toledo, OH, 43620 (419) 241-3328
Licensure Intermediate Care. *Beds* 50. *Certified* Medicaid.
Ownership Proprietary.
Staff Physicians 1 (pt); RNs 3 (ft), 3 (pt); LPNs

5 (ft); Nurses aides 20 (ft); Reality therapists 1 (ft); Recreational therapists 1 (ft); Occupational therapists 1 (pt); Activities coordinators 1 (ft); Dietitians 1 (pt); Dentists 1 (pt); Podiatrists 1 (pt).
Facilities Dining room; Activities room.
Activities Arts and Crafts; Cards; Games; Reading groups; Shopping trips.
Description The building is an old mansion-type that gives the facility a homey atmosphere.

Riverside Convalescent Home
1819 Summit St, Toledo, OH, 43611 (419) 729-2881
Medical Dir/Dir of Nursing R O Naturdad MD.
Licensure Intermediate Care. *Beds* 10. *Certified* Medicaid.
Ownership Proprietary.
Admissions Requirements Medical examination.
Staff Physicians 1 (pt); RNs 3 (ft); Nurses aides 1 (ft); Occupational therapists 1 (pt); Activities coordinators 1 (pt); Podiatrists 1 (pt).
Facilities Dining room; Activities room.
Activities Arts and Crafts; Cards; Games; Movies; Shopping trips; Dances/Social or cultural gatherings.

Robinwood Rest Home
2024 Robinwood Ave, Toledo, OH, 43620 (419) 242-3702
Medical Dir/Dir of Nursing Isador Binzer MD.
Licensure Intermediate Care. *Beds* 20. *Certified* Medicaid.
Ownership Proprietary.
Staff Physicians 1 (ft), 4 (pt); RNs 1 (pt); LPNs 2 (ft), 1 (pt); Nurses aides 7 (ft), 2 (pt); Dietitians 1 (ft); Podiatrists 1 (pt).
Facilities Dining room; Laundry room.
Activities Arts and Crafts; Cards; Games.

Saint Ann's Nursing Home*
2262 Collingwood Blvd, Toledo, OH, 43620 (419) 241-2094
Licensure Intermediate Care. *Beds* 38. *Certified* Medicaid.
Ownership Proprietary.

Saint Theresa's Nursing Home*
PO Box 6006, 132 Prescott St, Toledo, OH, 43614 (419) 246-2751
Licensure Intermediate Care. *Beds* 25. *Certified* Medicaid.
Ownership Proprietary.

Sunset House*
4020 Indian Rd, Toledo, OH, 43606 (419) 536-4645
Licensure Home for the Aged. *Beds* 80.
Ownership Nonprofit.

Toledo Mental Health Center*
930 S Detroit Ave, Toledo, OH, 43699
Licensure Intermediate Care for Mentally Retarded. *Beds* 24. *Certified* Medicaid.
Ownership Public.

Villa North Nursing Home*
4645 Lewis Ave, Toledo, OH, 43612
Licensure Skilled Care; Intermediate Care.
Beds 250. *Certified* Medicaid; Medicare.
Ownership Proprietary.

Villa North Nursing Home*
4645 Lewis Ave, Toledo, OH, 43612 (419) 478-5131
Licensure Skilled Care; Intermediate Care.
Beds 250. *Certified* Medicaid; Medicare.
Ownership Proprietary.

Wunderley Nursing Home*
2205 Parkwood Ave, Toledo, OH, 43620 (419) 244-8205
Licensure Intermediate Care. *Beds* 29. *Certified* Medicaid.
Ownership Proprietary.

TROY

Highland View Nursing Home*
500 Crescent Dr, Troy, OH, 45373 (513) 335-7161
Licensure Nursing Home. *Beds* 61. *Certified* Medicaid.
Ownership Proprietary.

Johnston Nursing Home*
845 N Harrison St, Troy, OH, 45373 (513) 335-2125
Licensure Intermediate Care. *Beds* 18. *Certified* Medicaid.
Ownership Proprietary.

Miami Health Care Center
3232 N Dixie Hwy, Troy, OH, 45373 (513) 339-5946
Medical Dir/Dir of Nursing Robert J Price MD.
Licensure Intermediate Care. *Beds* 150. *Certified* Medicaid.
Ownership Nonprofit.
Staff Physicians 1 (pt); RNs 8 (ft), 6 (pt); LPNs 12 (ft), 6 (pt); Orderlies 3 (ft), 3 (pt); Nurses aides 40 (ft), 12 (pt); Physical therapists; Recreational therapists 4 (ft); Speech therapists; Activities coordinators 1 (ft); Dietitians 1 (pt); Dentists; Ophthalmologists; Podiatrists; Audiologists.
Facilities Dining room; Physical therapy room; Activities room; Chapel; Crafts room; Laundry room; Barber/Beauty shop; Library.
Activities Arts and Crafts; Cards; Games; Reading groups; Prayer groups; Movies; Shopping trips; Dances/Social or cultural gatherings; Dinners; Theater; Special outings.
Description Spacious and luxurious facility is situated on a 10-acre rural site, 1 mile off I-75, featuring large lounges and activity areas, patios and gardens; semi-private rooms are 400 square feet and patients have their own windows.

Villa Convalescent Center Inc*
512 Crescent Dr, Troy, OH, 45373 (513) 335-7161
Licensure Skilled Care; Intermediate Care.
Beds 95. *Certified* Medicaid; Medicare.
Ownership Proprietary.

UHRICHSVILLE

Dove Nursing Facility*
Rt 1, Newport County Rd 28, Uhrichsville, OH, 44683 (614) 922-2629

Licensure Intermediate Care. *Beds* 32. *Certified* Medicaid.
Ownership Proprietary.

Rohrig's Nursing Home 1*
449-451 E 4th St, Uhrichsville, OH, 44683 (614) 922-2610
Licensure Intermediate Care. *Beds* 14. *Certified* Medicaid.
Ownership Proprietary.

Twin City Health Care Center Inc*
200 Spanson Dr, Uhrichsville, OH, 44683
Licensure Skilled Care; Intermediate Care.
Beds SNF 32; ICF 67. *Certified* Medicaid; Medicare.

UNION CITY

Crotinger Nursing Home
907 Central Ave, Union City, OH, 47390 (513) 968-5284 and 968-3571
Admin Ruth E Jenks. *Medical Dir/Dir of Nursing* Dr C R Chambers.
Licensure Intermediate Care. *Beds* 50. *Certified* Medicaid.
Ownership Proprietary.
Staff RNs 2 (ft), 1 (pt); LPNs 2 (ft), 1 (pt); Orderlies 1 (ft), 1 (pt); Nurses aides 29 (ft), 3 (pt); Dietitians 1 (ft).
Facilities Dining room; Laundry room.
Activities Arts and Crafts; Cards; Games; Reading groups; Prayer groups.

Gade ICF/MR
400 Gade Ave, Union City, OH, 47390
Licensure Intermediate Care for Mentally Retarded. *Beds* 51. *Certified* Medicaid; Medicare.
Ownership Proprietary.

UPPER SANDUSKY

Cozy Rest
342 S 8th St, Upper Sandusky, OH, 43351 (419) 294-3482
Medical Dir/Dir of Nursing N J Zohourg MD.
Licensure Intermediate Care. *Beds* 22. *Certified* Medicaid.
Ownership Proprietary.
Admissions Requirements Medical examination.
Staff RNs 1 (ft); LPNs 1 (ft), 2 (pt); Nurses aides 5 (ft), 1 (pt); Activities coordinators 1 (pt).
Facilities Dining room; Activities room; Laundry room.
Activities Arts and Crafts; Cards; Games; Prayer groups; Movies; Shopping trips; Dances/Social or cultural gatherings.
Description Facility features home-like atmosphere as opposed to institutional.

Fairhaven Home
850 S Marseilles Ave, Upper Sandusky, OH, 43351 (419) 294-1995
Medical Dir/Dir of Nursing Dr N J Zohoury.
Licensure Skilled Care; Rest Home. *Beds* SNF 84; Rest Home 100. *Certified* Medicaid.
Ownership Nonprofit.
Admissions Requirements Minimum age 65.
Staff RNs 7 (ft), 6 (pt); LPNs 2 (ft), 5 (pt);

Nurses aides 31 (ft), 29 (pt); Activities coordinators 2 (ft).
Affiliation Church of Christ
Facilities Dining room; Physical therapy room; Activities room; Chapel; Crafts room; Laundry room; Barber/Beauty shop; Library.
Activities Arts and Crafts; Cards; Games; Shopping trips.
Description A multimillion dollar renovation/expansion program will be completed by mid-1985 after which there will be 150 nursing beds, all levels, and 30 independent living apartments available. Facility highlights are a sloped, glazed glass activity area, country store, and in-house physical therapy/wellness area.

Wyandot County Home*
Rt 2, 7830 N State Hwy 199, Upper Sandusky, OH, 43351 (419) 294-1714
Licensure Intermediate Care. *Beds* 100. *Certified* Medicaid.
Ownership Nonprofit.

Wyandot Manor Inc
800 Mission Dr, Upper Sandusky, OH, 43351 (419) 294-3803
Medical Dir/Dir of Nursing Dr William Kose.
Licensure Skilled Care; Intermediate Care.
Beds 100. *Certified* Medicaid.
Ownership Nonprofit.
Admissions Requirements Medical examination; Physician's request.
Staff Physicians 6 (pt); RNs 6 (ft); LPNs 12 (ft); Orderlies 6 (ft); Nurses aides 28 (ft), 28 (pt); Physical therapists 2 (pt); Reality therapists 6 (pt); Activities coordinators 1 (ft), 1 (pt); Dietitians 1 (ft); Dentists 1 (pt); Ophthalmologists 1 (pt); Podiatrists 1 (pt); Audiologists 1 (pt).
Facilities Dining room; Physical therapy room; Activities room; Chapel; Crafts room; Laundry room; Barber/Beauty shop; Library.
Activities Arts and Crafts; Cards; Games; Reading groups; Prayer groups; Movies; Shopping trips; Dances/Social or cultural gatherings; Bingo; Church groups; Welcome new residents; Birthdays.
Description A 100-bed skilled facility in a small, rural, middle-class farming district. Most of the residents are from Wyandot County and many residents are related to each other and staff. Warm, loving, family-like environment provided for residents.

URBANA

Champaign County Home
Box 149, Urbana, OH, 43078 (513) 653-7229
Medical Dir/Dir of Nursing Jae J Koh MD.
Licensure Intermediate Care. *Beds* 152. *Certified* Medicaid.
Ownership Public.
Admissions Requirements Medical examination; Physician's request.
Staff RNs 10 (ft); LPNs 12 (ft), 3 (pt); Nurses aides 45 (ft), 45 (pt); Physical therapists 1 (pt); Recreational therapists 1 (ft); Occupational therapists 1 (ft), 1 (pt); Speech therapists 1 (pt); Activities coordinators 2 (ft), 1 (pt); Dietitians 1 (pt); Dentists 1 (pt); Podiatrists 1 (pt); Audiologists 1 (pt).
Facilities Dining room; Physical therapy room; Activities room; Crafts room; Laundry room;

Barber/Beauty shop.
Activities Arts and Crafts; Cards; Games; Reading groups; Prayer groups; Movies; Shopping trips; Dances/Social or cultural gatherings; Cooking time.

Champaign County Residential Services Inc*
400 N Oakland, Urbana, OH, 43078
Licensure Intermediate Care for Mentally Retarded. *Beds* 10. *Certified* Medicaid.
Ownership Nonprofit.

Heartland of Urbana
741 E Water St, Urbana, OH, 43078 (513) 652-1381
Medical Dir/Dir of Nursing Dr Barry Paxton.
Licensure Skilled Care; Intermediate Care.
Beds 100. *Certified* Medicaid; Medicare.
Ownership Nonprofit.
Admissions Requirements Minimum age 14; Medical examination; Physician's request.
Staff RNs 6 (ft), 2 (pt); LPNs 2 (ft), 4 (pt); Nurses aides 14 (ft), 14 (pt); Physical therapists 1 (ft), 1 (pt); Occupational therapists; Speech therapists; Activities coordinators; Dietitians; Podiatrists.
Facilities Dining room; Physical therapy room; Activities room; Crafts room; Laundry room; Barber/Beauty shop; Library.
Activities Arts and Crafts; Cards; Games; Reading groups; Prayer groups; Movies; Shopping trips; Dances/Social or cultural gatherings.

UTICA

Williams Nursing Home
233 N Main St, PO Box 618, Utica, OH, 43080 (614) 892-3414
Licensure Intermediate Care. *Beds* 35. *Certified* Medicaid.
Ownership Proprietary.
Admissions Requirements Medical examination.
Staff Physicians 1 (pt); RNs 1 (ft), 1 (pt); LPNs 1 (ft), 4 (pt); Nurses aides 5 (ft), 6 (pt); Activities coordinators 1 (pt); Dietitians 1 (pt).
Facilities Activities room; Laundry room.
Activities Arts and Crafts; Games; Reading groups; Prayer groups; Church.
Description Specialty of facility is tender loving care.

VAN WERT

Hillcrest Nursing Home*
308 S Washington St, Van Wert, OH, 45891 (419) 238-0975
Licensure Intermediate Care. *Beds* 25. *Certified* Medicaid.
Ownership Proprietary.

Van Wert Manor
160 Fox Rd, Van Wert, OH, 45891 (419) 238-6655
Medical Dir/Dir of Nursing R W Ayres MD.
Licensure Skilled Care; Intermediate Care.
Beds 100. *Certified* Medicaid; Medicare.
Ownership Proprietary.
Admissions Requirements Medical examination; Physician's request.
Staff Physicians 1 (pt); RNs 5 (ft), 1 (pt); LPNs

7 (ft), 3 (pt); Orderlies 1 (pt); Nurses aides 30 (ft), 10 (pt); Physical therapists 1 (pt); Speech therapists 1 (pt); Activities coordinators 1 (pt); Dietitians 1 (pt); Dentists 1 (pt); Ophthalmologists 1 (pt); Podiatrists 1 (pt); Audiologists 1 (pt).
Facilities Dining room; Physical therapy room; Activities room; Chapel; Crafts room; Laundry room; Barber/Beauty shop; Library.
Activities Arts and Crafts; Cards; Games; Reading groups; Prayer groups; Movies; Shopping trips; Dances/Social or cultural gatherings; Discussion groups.
Description Facility offers wellness program for residents and is located very close to the county hospital and medical arts building.

Vancrest*
Rt 4, Van Wert, OH, 45891 (419) 238-4646
Licensure Skilled Care; Intermediate Care.
Beds 50. *Certified* Medicaid; Medicare.
Ownership Proprietary.

VANDALIA

Franklin Nursing Center of Vandalia*
1208 Cassell Rd, Vandalia, OH, 45377 (513) 898-4202
Licensure Skilled Care; Intermediate Care.
Beds 161. *Certified* Medicaid; Medicare.
Ownership Proprietary.

VERMILLION

Riverview Nursing Home
5472 Liberty St, Vermillion, OH, 44089 (216) 967-6614
Admin C York.
Licensure Intermediate Care. *Beds* 19. *Certified* Medicaid.
Ownership Proprietary.
Admissions Requirements Medical examination; Physician's request.
Staff RNs 1 (pt); LPNs 2 (ft), 4 (pt); Nurses aides 9 (ft), 2 (pt); Reality therapists 1 (pt); Activities coordinators 1 (ft); Dietitians 1 (ft); Podiatrists 1 (ft).
Facilities Dining room; Activities room; Crafts room; Laundry room; Barber/Beauty shop.
Activities Arts and Crafts; Cards; Games; Reading groups; Prayer groups; Movies; Shopping trips.
Description Facility sits on the bank of the Vermillion River in the center of town; small size helps to contribute to "at home" atmosphere.

WADSWORTH

Magnolia Care Center
720 Johnson Rd, Wadsworth, OH, 44281 (216) 335-1158
Medical Dir/Dir of Nursing William Knapic MD.
Licensure Skilled Care; Intermediate Care.
Beds 15. *Certified* Medicaid; Medicare.
Ownership Proprietary.
Admissions Requirements Minimum age 14.
Facilities Dining room; Physical therapy room; Activities room; Crafts room; Laundry room; Barber/Beauty shop; Library.

Activities Arts and Crafts; Cards; Games; Reading groups; Prayer groups; Movies; Shopping trips; Dances/Social or cultural gatherings.

Wadsworth Health Care Center Inc*
147 Garfield St, Wadsworth, OH, 44281 (216) 335-2555
Licensure Skilled Care; Intermediate Care.
Beds 112. *Certified* Medicaid; Medicare.
Ownership Proprietary.

WALNUT CREEK

Walnut Hills Nursing Home*
PO Box 127, Walnut Creek, OH, 44687 (216) 852-2457
Licensure Intermediate Care; Rest Home.
Beds ICF 102; Rest Home 50. *Certified* Medicaid.
Ownership Proprietary.

WAPAKONETA

Auglaize Acres
Rt 4, Wapakoneta, OH, 45895 (419) 738-3816
Admin Jeri Engel. *Medical Dir/Dir of Nursing* Robert J Herman MD.
Licensure Intermediate Care; Male Residential Care. *Beds* ICF 142; Male Residential Care 18. *Certified* Medicaid.
Ownership Public.
Admissions Requirements Minimum age 18; Medical examination.
Staff Physicians 1 (pt); RNs 2 (ft), 10 (pt); LPNs 9 (ft), 3 (pt); Orderlies 1 (ft), 1 (pt); Nurses aides 35 (ft), 1 (pt); Activities coordinators 2 (ft).
Facilities Dining room; Activities room; Chapel; Crafts room; Laundry room; Barber/Beauty shop.
Activities Arts and Crafts; Cards; Games; Reading groups; Prayer groups; Movies; Shopping trips; Dances/Social or cultural gatherings.
Description Many social and religious programs are open to public; families are incorporated into activity plans; community very responsive to residents' needs and contribute money and time to ensure residents have the best quality of care possible in a county facility.

Wapakoneta Manor
Rt 501, Wapakoneta, OH, 45895 (419) 738-3711
Medical Dir/Dir of Nursing R J Herman MD.
Licensure Skilled Care; Intermediate Care.
Beds 100. *Certified* Medicaid; Medicare.
Ownership Proprietary.
Staff RNs 2 (ft), 3 (pt); LPNs 6 (ft), 6 (pt); Nurses aides 29 (ft), 17 (pt); Physical therapists 1 (pt); Activities coordinators 1 (ft); Ophthalmologists 1 (pt); Podiatrists 1 (pt).
Facilities Dining room; Physical therapy room; Activities room; Laundry room; Barber/Beauty shop; Library.
Activities Arts and Crafts; Games; Reading groups; Prayer groups; Movies; Dances/Social or cultural gatherings.
Description Facility is set back from the road which gives residents a quiet atmosphere. Tasty

foods and new upbeat activities are just 2 daily highlights for residents, who are treated with care and concern.

WARREN

Albert's Nursing and Residential Facility
2120 Van Wye St SE, Warren, OH, 44484 (216) 369-2137
Medical Dir/Dir of Nursing Dr Frank Guarnieri.
Licensure Intermediate Care for Mentally Retarded. *Beds* 32. *Certified* Medicaid.
Ownership Proprietary.
Staff Physicians 1 (pt); RNs 1 (pt); LPNs 4 (ft), 1 (pt); Nurses aides 32 (ft), 8 (pt); Physical therapists 1 (pt); Occupational therapists 1 (pt); Speech therapists 1 (pt); Activities coordinators 1 (ft); Dietitians 1 (pt); Dentists 1 (pt); Ophthalmologists 1 (pt); Podiatrists 1 (pt); Audiologists 1 (pt).
Activities Arts and Crafts; Cards; Games; Reading groups; Prayer groups; Movies; Shopping trips; Dances/Social or cultural gatherings.

Albert's Nursing Home
2035 Van Wye SE, Warren, OH, 44484 (216) 369-2934
Medical Dir/Dir of Nursing Frank Guarnieri MD.
Licensure Intermediate Care; Intermediate Care for Mentally Retarded. *Beds* ICF 32; ICF/MR 18. *Certified* Medicaid.
Ownership Proprietary.
Admissions Requirements Medical examination; Physician's request.
Staff Physicians 3 (pt); RNs 1 (ft), 3 (pt); LPNs 4 (ft), 4 (pt); Orderlies 2 (ft), 1 (pt); Nurses aides 19 (ft), 3 (pt); Physical therapists 1 (pt); Occupational therapists 1 (pt); Speech therapists 1 (pt); Activities coordinators 2 (ft); Dietitians 1 (pt); Dentists 1 (pt); Podiatrists 1 (pt); Audiologists 1 (pt).
Facilities Dining room; Physical therapy room; Activities room; Chapel; Crafts room; Laundry room; Barber/Beauty shop.
Activities Arts and Crafts; Cards; Games; Reading groups; Prayer groups; Movies; Shopping trips; Dances/Social or cultural gatherings.
Description Residents attend different social events as a group; annual Christmas program with 5 to 10 churches, schools, and other organizatons participating and city and state officials attending; swim program for mentally retarded.

Community Skilled Nursing Centre of Warren*
1320 Mahoning Ave NW, Warren, OH, 44483 (216) 373-1160
Licensure Skilled Care; Intermediate Care.
Beds 160. *Certified* Medicaid; Medicare.
Ownership Proprietary.

Gillette Nursing Home
3214 Elm St, Warren, OH, 44483 (216) 372-4513
Medical Dir/Dir of Nursing Dr List.
Licensure Intermediate Care. *Beds* 35. *Certified* Medicaid.
Ownership Nonprofit.
Admissions Requirements Medical examination; Physician's request.

Staff Physicians 1 (pt); RNs 1 (pt); LPNs 5 (ft); Nurses aides 9 (ft); Activities coordinators 1 (pt); Dietitians 1 (pt); Podiatrists 1 (pt).

Gillette's Country Place
2473 North Rd NE, Warren, OH, 44483 (216) 372-2251
Medical Dir/Dir of Nursing Ellis List Jr MD.
Licensure Skilled Care; Intermediate Care.
Beds 222. *Certified* Medicaid; Medicare.
Ownership Proprietary.
Admissions Requirements Minimum age 18.
Staff RNs 4 (ft), 14 (pt); LPNs 15 (ft), 8 (pt); Orderlies 6 (ft); Nurses aides 54 (ft), 12 (pt); Physical therapists 1 (pt); Speech therapists 1 (pt); Activities coordinators 2 (ft); Dietitians 1 (pt).
Facilities Dining room; Physical therapy room; Activities room; Crafts room; Laundry room; Barber/Beauty shop.
Activities Arts and Crafts; Cards; Games; Reading groups; Prayer groups; Movies; Shopping trips; Dances/Social or cultural gatherings.

Imperial Skilled Care Center*
4121 Tod Ave NW, Warren, OH, 44485 9216) 898-4033
Licensure Skilled Care; Intermediate Care.
Beds 121. *Certified* Medicaid; Medicare.
Ownership Proprietary.

Parkview Nursing Center*
1926 Ridge Ave SE, Warren, OH, 44484 (216) 369-2000
Licensure Intermediate Care. *Beds* 100. *Certified* Medicaid.
Ownership Proprietary.

Washington Square Inc
202 Washington St NW, Warren, OH, 44483 (216) 399-8997
Medical Dir/Dir of Nursing Ellis List Jr MD.
Licensure Intermediate Care. *Beds* 100. *Certified* Medicaid.
Ownership Proprietary.
Staff Physicians 2 (pt); RNs 4 (ft), 3 (pt); LPNs 6 (ft), 5 (pt); Orderlies 1 (ft), 1 (pt); Nurses aides 18 (ft), 11 (pt); Activities coordinators 1 (ft), 1 (pt); Dentists 1 (pt); Ophthalmologists 1 (pt); Podiatrists 1 (pt).
Facilities Dining room; Activities room; Chapel; Crafts room; Laundry room; Barber/Beauty shop.
Activities Arts and Crafts; Cards; Games; Reading groups; Prayer groups; Movies; Shopping trips; Dances/Social or cultural gatherings.
Description Facility has landscaped grounds with spacious patio, air conditioning, spacious rooms, and reasonable rates; offers qualified personnel, professional supervision, assistance with personal needs; excellent meals plus snacks and refreshments, meals in rooms available; doctor and dentist offices and hospitals only minutes away; devotional programs, individual and group recreational activities; housekeeping and laundry, lounges for TV and activities; public transportation available.

WARRENSVILLE

Cuyahoga County Hospital—Sunny Acres Skilled Nursing Facility
4310 Richmond Rd, Warrensville, OH, 44122
(216) 464-9500
Admin W J Wilson. *Medical Dir/Dir of Nursing* William G Ansley MD.
Licensure Skilled Care; Intermediate Care.
Beds 320. *Certified* Medicaid; Medicare.
Ownership Public.
Admissions Requirements Minimum age 15.
Staff Physicians 9 (ft); RNs 75 (ft), 20 (pt); LPNs 19 (ft), 3 (pt); Nurses aides 158 (ft); Physical therapists 4 (ft), 1 (pt); Occupational therapists 1 (ft); Occupational therapists 3 (ft); Activities coordinators 1 (ft); Dietitians 2 (ft); Dentists 1 (pt).
Facilities Dining room; Physical therapy room; Activities room; Chapel; Crafts room; Laundry room; Barber/Beauty shop; Library.
Activities Arts and Crafts; Cards; Games; Reading groups; Prayer groups; Movies; Shopping trips; Special entertainments.
Description Sunny Acres is accredited by the Joint Commission on Accreditation of Long-Term Care Facilities. Patients are housed on 4 floors of a modern 5-story, air conditioned building with licensed medical and nursing staff on hand 24 hours daily. Almost all patients have multiple diagnoses.

WARRENSVILLE HEIGHTS

Warrensville Center*
4325 Green Rd, Warrensville Heights, OH, 44128
Licensure Intermediate Care for Mentally Retarded. *Beds* 261. *Certified* Medicaid.
Ownership Public.

WARSAW

Echoing Hills Residential Center
Rt 2, Warsaw, OH, 43844 (614) 327-2311
Medical Dir/Dir of Nursing Jerold Meyer MD.
Licensure Intermediate Care for Developmentally Disabled. *Beds* 36.
Ownership Proprietary.
Admissions Requirements Minimum age 18; Medical examination.
Staff Physicians 1 (pt); RNs 3 (ft); LPNs 2 (ft), 2 (pt); Orderlies 2 (ft); Nurses aides 22 (ft), 1 (pt); Physical therapists 1 (pt); Occupational therapists 1 (pt); Speech therapists 1 (pt); Activities coordinators 1 (ft); Dietitians 1 (pt); Dentists 1 (pt); Ophthalmologists 1 (pt); Podiatrists 1 (pt); Audiologists 1 (pt).
Facilities Dining room; Physical therapy room; Activities room; Laundry room; Library.
Activities Arts and Crafts; Prayer groups; Movies; Shopping trips; Dances/Social or cultural gatherings; Camping; Travel.
Description Echoing Hills Residential Center is an outgrowth of Camp Echoing Hills, a year round camping facility for the developmentally disabled. This is primarily a Christian facility. We operate a workshop and a gift shop in which the residents work. Echoing Hills Village, Inc operates 5 such homes in the state of Ohio—Echoing Hills, Echoing Ridge, Echoing Woods, Echoing Valley, and Echoing Meadows. We also run travel programs through our camp facility taking the handicapped to many vacation spots and places of national interest.

WASHINGTON COURT HOUSE

Court House Manor
250 Glen Ave, Washington Court House, OH, 43160 (614) 335-9290
Admin William J Bias. *Medical Dir/Dir of Nursing* Joseph Herbert.
Licensure Skilled Care; Intermediate Care.
Beds 100. *Certified* Medicaid; Medicare.
Ownership Proprietary.
Staff RNs 3 (ft), 1 (pt); LPNs 10 (ft), 2 (pt); Nurses aides 27 (ft), 17 (pt); Physical therapists 1 (pt); Recreational therapists 2 (ft); Speech therapists 1 (pt); Activities coordinators 1 (ft); Dietitians 1 (pt); Dentists 1 (pt); Ophthalmologists 1 (pt); Podiatrists 1 (pt); Audiologists 1 (pt).
Facilities Dining room; Physical therapy room; Activities room; Chapel; Crafts room; Laundry room; Barber/Beauty shop; Library.
Activities Arts and Crafts; Cards; Games; Reading groups; Prayer groups; Movies; Shopping trips; Dances/Social or cultural gatherings.
Description Recipient of Ohio Health Care Association's Buckeye Award for excellent patient care.

Deanview Nursing Home Inc
719 Rawling St, Washington Court House, OH, 43160 (614) 335-1380
Medical Dir/Dir of Nursing Dr Hugh Payton.
Licensure Intermediate Care. *Beds* 50. *Certified* Medicaid.
Ownership Proprietary.
Staff Physicians 5 (pt); RNs 1 (ft), 1 (pt); LPNs 4 (ft); Nurses aides 10 (ft), 6 (pt); Activities coordinators 1 (ft); Dietitians 1 (pt); Podiatrists 1 (pt).
Facilities Dining room; Activities room; Laundry room.
Activities Arts and Crafts; Cards; Games; Reading groups; Prayer groups; Shopping trips.
Description Facility features a small, home-like atmosphere and personal care.

Green Acres Nursing Home
6674 Stafford Rd, Washington Court House, OH, 43160 (614) 335-2511
Licensure Intermediate Care. *Beds* 25. *Certified* Medicaid.
Ownership Proprietary.
Admissions Requirements Medical examination; Physician's request.
Staff Physicians 1 (ft); RNs 1 (pt); LPNs 3 (ft); Nurses aides 7 (ft); Physical therapists 1 (ft); Activities coordinators 1 (ft); Dietitians 1 (ft); Dentists 1 (pt).
Facilities Dining room; Laundry room.
Activities Arts and Crafts; Cards; Games; Prayer groups; Shopping trips.
Description Facility is in a rural area with lots of nature for the residents to enjoy; cookouts held; garden patch for those who want to plant flowers.

Margaret Clark Oakfield Convalescent Center*
726 Rawling St, Washington Court House, OH, 43160 (614) 335-7143
Licensure Skilled Care; Intermediate Care.
Beds 144. *Certified* Medicaid; Medicare.
Ownership Proprietary.

Quiet Acres Nursing Home Inc*
1771 Palmer Rd NW, Washington Court House, OH, 43160 (614) 335-6391
Licensure Intermediate Care. *Beds* 50. *Certified* Medicaid.
Ownership Proprietary.

WATERVILLE

Hillcrest Care Center*
564 S River Rd, Waterville, OH, 43566 (419) 878-3901 and 878-0108
Licensure Intermediate Care. *Beds* 100. *Certified* Medicaid.
Ownership Proprietary.

WAUSEON

Detwiler Manor—Fulton County Home
604 S Shoop Ave, Wauseon, OH, 43567 (419) 337-3186
Medical Dir/Dir of Nursing Ben H Reed MD.
Licensure Intermediate Care. *Beds* 71. *Certified* Medicaid.
Ownership Public.
Admissions Requirements Medical examination; Physician's request.
Staff RNs 2 (ft); LPNs 6 (ft), 7 (pt); Orderlies 2 (ft); Nurses aides 21 (ft), 5 (pt); Activities coordinators 1 (ft); Dietitians 1 (pt).
Facilities Dining room; Activities room; Chapel; Crafts room; Laundry room; Barber/Beauty shop.
Activities Arts and Crafts; Cards; Games; Prayer groups; Movies; Shopping trips; Group singing; Piano and organ music entertainment.

Northwest Care Center*
303 W Leggett St, Wauseon, OH, 43567 (419) 337-3050
Licensure Skilled Care; Intermediate Care.
Beds 51. *Certified* Medicaid; Medicare.
Ownership Proprietary.

WAVERLY

Buckeye Community Services—Grandview Avenue Homes*
207 Grandview Ave, Waverly, OH, 45690
Licensure Intermediate Care for Mentally Retarded. *Beds* 8. *Certified* Medicaid.
Ownership Nonprofit.

WAYNESVILLE

Heffner's Ivy Cottage Nursing Home
5596 Elbon Rd, Waynesville, OH, 45068 (513) 932-3950
Admin Phyllis D Arnold.
Licensure Intermediate Care. *Beds* 25. *Certified* Medicaid.
Ownership Proprietary.
Admissions Requirements Minimum age 18;

Medical examination.
Staff RNs 1 (pt); LPNs 2 (ft), 1 (pt); Orderlies 1 (pt); Nurses aides 5 (ft), 1 (pt); Activities coordinators 1 (pt).
Facilities Dining room; Activities room.
Activities Arts and Crafts; Games; Movies; Shopping trips; Dances/Social or cultural gatherings.
Description Facility is a small, country home in the Ceaser Creek Lake area. Residents enjoy country atmosphere and grounds with walks, picnics, and drives; bird watching has become a hobby for some and the changing seasons always give something new to see.

Quaker Heights Nursing Home
514 W High St, Waynesville, OH, 45068 (513) 897-6050
Medical Dir/Dir of Nursing John Murphy III.
Licensure Skilled Care; Intermediate Care.
Beds 98. *Certified* Medicaid; Medicare.
Ownership Nonprofit.
Admissions Requirements Medical examination.
Staff Physicians 6 (pt); RNs 7 (ft); LPNs 9 (ft); Orderlies 3 (ft); Nurses aides 37 (ft); Physical therapists 1 (pt); Activities coordinators 2 (ft); Dietitians 1 (ft); Dentists 1 (ft).
Affiliation Society of Friends
Facilities Dining room; Physical therapy room; Activities room; Crafts room; Laundry room; Barber/Beauty shop.
Activities Arts and Crafts; Cards; Games; Reading groups; Prayer groups; Movies; Dances/Social or cultural gatherings.
Description Located in a rural setting—small village of 2500, known as the town of antiques, 27 shops of beautiful antiques located in the village.

WELLINGTON

Elms Convalescent Home and Rehabilitation Center
136 S Main St, Wellington, OH, 44090 (216) 647-2414
Medical Dir/Dir of Nursing G T Derikito MD.
Licensure Intermediate Care. *Beds* 74. *Certified* Medicaid.
Ownership Proprietary.
Admissions Requirements Minimum age 21; Medical examination.
Staff Physicians 1 (pt); RNs 2 (ft), 2 (pt); LPNs 4 (ft), 7 (pt); Nurses aides 14 (ft), 16 (pt); Activities coordinators 1 (pt); Dietitians 1 (pt).
Facilities Dining room; Activities room; Laundry room; Barber/Beauty shop; Day room.
Activities Arts and Crafts; Cards; Games; Reading groups; Prayer groups; Movies; Shopping trips; Dances/Social or cultural gatherings; Monthly birthday parties; Sing-a-longs.
Description Facility is conveniently located in downtown yet with a suburban atmosphere and has a patio for sunning and an enclosed area for strolling.

Webers Nursing Home*
214 Herrick Ave E, Wellington, OH, 44090 (216) 647-2088
Licensure Intermediate Care. *Beds* 69. *Certified* Medicaid.
Ownership Proprietary.

Wellington Manor Nursing Home
116 Prospect St, PO Box 393, Wellington, OH, 44090 (216) 647-3910
Medical Dir/Dir of Nursing Dr G T Derikito.
Licensure Intermediate Care. *Beds* 17. *Certified* Medicaid.
Ownership Proprietary.
Admissions Requirements Medical examination.
Staff Physicians 1 (ft); RNs 2 (ft); LPNs 2 (ft); Nurses aides 12 (ft); Activities coordinators 1 (ft); Dietitians 1 (pt); Dentists 1 (pt); Podiatrists 1 (pt).
Facilities Dining room; Laundry room.
Activities Arts and Crafts; Cards; Games; Reading groups; Prayer groups; Movies; Shopping trips; Dances/Social or cultural gatherings.
Description Facility offers a home-like atmosphere and close personal contact with all residents.

WELLSTON

Jenkins Memorial Nursing Home
142 Jenkins Memorial Rd, Wellston, OH, 45692 (614) 384-2119
Licensure Skilled Care; Intermediate Care.
Beds 40. *Certified* Medicaid; Medicare.
Ownership Nonprofit.

Maple Heights Nursing Home
406 E "A" St, Wellston, OH, 45692 (614) 384-2245
Admin Mary A Ingalls.
Licensure Intermediate Care. *Beds* 16. *Certified* Medicaid.
Ownership Proprietary.
Admissions Requirements Females only; Medical examination.
Staff Physicians; RNs; LPNs; Nurses aides; Physical therapists; Activities coordinators; Dietitians.
Facilities Dining room; Activities room.
Activities Arts and Crafts; Cards; Games; Reading groups; Prayer groups; Movies.
Description Facility features a home-like setting in the one-time mansion home of Wellston's founder Harvey Wells with home-cooked meals and personal nursing care. Flower beds and other outdoor gardening activities are available to those who are interested. Spacious veranda porches overlook the small community of Wellston.

Wellston Nursing Home
405 N Park Ave, Wellston, OH, 45692 (614) 384-2880
Medical Dir/Dir of Nursing Dr A R Hambrick.
Licensure Intermediate Care. *Beds* 50. *Certified* Medicaid.
Ownership Proprietary.
Admissions Requirements Medical examination.
Staff Physicians 1 (pt); RNs 1 (pt); LPNs 6 (ft); Nurses aides 12 (ft), 1 (pt); Recreational therapists 1 (ft); Activities coordinators 1 (ft); Dentists 1 (pt); Podiatrists 1 (pt); Audiologists 1 (pt).
Facilities Dining room; Activities room; Crafts room; Laundry room; Barber/Beauty shop.
Activities Arts and Crafts; Cards; Games; Reading groups; Prayer groups; Movies; Shop-

ping trips; Dances/Social or cultural gatherings.
Description Home is located close to town and beside the city park with picnic areas, fishing, and ball courts.

WELLSVILLE

Mary Fletcher Health Care Center 2*
1037 Main St, Wellsville, OH, 43968 (216) 532-2085
Licensure Intermediate Care. *Beds* 21. *Certified* Medicaid.
Ownership Proprietary.

WEST CARROLLTON

Elm Creek Nursing Center*
115 Elmwood Cir, West Carrollton, OH, 45449
Licensure Skilled Care; Intermediate Care.
Beds 100. *Certified* Medicaid; Medicare.

WEST CHESTER

Bonnie's Nursing Home*
9018 Cincinnati-Columbus Rd, West Chester, OH, 45069 (513) 772-6363
Licensure Nursing Home. *Beds* 40.
Ownership Proprietary.

Willows Nursing Home*
9117 Cincinnati-Columbus Rd, West Chester, OH, 45069 (513) 777-6164
Licensure Skilled Care; Intermediate Care.
Beds 105. *Certified* Medicaid; Medicare.
Ownership Proprietary.

WEST JEFFERSON

Hampton Court*
375 W Main St, West Jefferson, OH, 43162
Licensure Skilled Care; Intermediate Care.
Beds 50. *Certified* Medicaid; Medicare.
Ownership Proprietary.

WEST LAFAYETTE

Edgerton Manor—ICF/MR
22059 Orchard St, Box 28, West Lafayette, OH, 43845 (614) 545-6366
Admin Renee¢1 Guilliams. *Medical Dir/Dir of Nursing* W R Agricola MD.
Licensure Intermediate Care for Mentally Retarded. *Beds* 15.
Ownership Nonprofit.
Admissions Requirements Minimum age 4; Medical examination.
Staff Physicians 1 (pt); RNs 1 (ft); LPNs 4 (ft), 1 (pt); Nurses aides 9 (ft), 3 (pt); Physical therapists 1 (pt); Recreational therapists 1 (ft); Occupational therapists 1 (pt); Speech therapists 1 (pt); Activities coordinators 1 (ft); Dietitians 2 (ft); Dentists 1 (pt); Ophthalmologists 1 (pt); Podiatrists 1 (pt); Audiologists 1 (pt).
Facilities Dining room; Activities room; Crafts room; Laundry room; Library.
Activities Arts and Crafts; Cards; Games; Reading groups; Movies; Shopping trips; Dances/Social or cultural gatherings.
Description Manor offers habilitation training

in conjunction with 24-hour medical services to the mentally retarded and developmentally disabled individual. An interdisciplinary team approach is utilized in planning for and delivering care to the residents.

Guilliams Family Home
220 S Kirk, Box 28, West Lafayette, OH, 43845
(614) 545-6337
Admin Renee¢1 Guilliams. *Medical Dir/Dir of Nursing* W R Agricola MD.
Licensure Intermediate Care for Mentally Retarded. *Beds* 5.
Ownership Proprietary.
Admissions Requirements Minimum age 16; Females only; Medical examination.
Staff Physicians 1 (pt); RNs 1 (pt); LPNs 1 (ft); Nurses aides 3 (ft), 1 (pt); Physical therapists 1 (pt); Recreational therapists 1 (pt); Occupational therapists 1 (pt); Speech therapists 1 (pt); Activities coordinators 1 (pt); Dentists 1 (pt); Ophthalmologists 1 (pt); Podiatrists 1 (pt); Audiologists 1 (pt).
Facilities Dining room; Activities room; Crafts room; Laundry room.
Activities Arts and Crafts; Cards; Games; Reading groups; Movies; Shopping trips; Dances/Social or cultural gatherings.
Description Home offers habilitation training and residential care to adult female MR/DD residents in a community integrated setting. An interdisciplinary team approach is utilized in planning for and delivering care to the resident.

Rose Lawn ICF/MR
21990 Orchard St, Box 28, West Lafayette, OH, 43845 (614) 545-6366
Admin Renee¢1 Guilliams. *Medical Dir/Dir of Nursing* W R Agricola MD.
Licensure Intermediate Care for Mentally Retarded. *Beds* 30. *Certified* Medicaid.
Ownership Proprietary.
Admissions Requirements Minimum age 4; Medical examination.
Staff Physicians 1 (pt); RNs 1 (ft), 1 (pt); LPNs 5 (ft), 1 (pt); Nurses aides 13 (ft), 4 (pt); Physical therapists 1 (pt); Reality therapists 1 (pt); Occupational therapists 1 (pt); Speech therapists 1 (pt); Activities coordinators 1 (ft); Dietitians 4 (ft), 1 (pt); Dentists 1 (pt); Ophthalmologists 1 (pt); Podiatrists 1 (pt); Audiologists 1 (pt); Mental health technician; Behavior modification specialist; Social worker; Special education teacher; Qualified mental retardation professional.
Facilities Dining room; Activities room; Crafts room; Laundry room; Library; Program areas.
Activities Arts and Crafts; Cards; Games; Reading groups; Movies; Shopping trips; Dances/Social or cultural gatherings.
Description Facility offers habilitation training in conjunction with 24-hour medical services to the MR/DD individual. An interdisciplinary team approach is utilized in planning for and delivering care to the resident.

West Lafayette Care Center
620 E Main St, West Lafayette, OH, 43845
(614) 545-6345
Licensure Intermediate Care. *Beds* 96. *Certified* Medicaid.
Ownership Proprietary.
Facilities Dining room; Physical therapy room;

Activities room; Laundry room; Barber/Beauty shop.
Activities Arts and Crafts; Cards; Games; Reading groups; Prayer groups; Movies; Shopping trips.

WEST LIBERTY

Green Hills Center
6557 US Rt 68 S, West Liberty, OH, 43357
(513) 465-5065
Admin Kathy Sommers. *Medical Dir/Dir of Nursing* James Steiner MD.
Licensure Skilled Care; Intermediate Care.
Beds 105. *Certified* Medicaid; Medicare.
Ownership Nonprofit.
Admissions Requirements Medical examination; Physician's request.
Staff RNs 9 (ft), 11 (pt); Orderlies 1 (ft); Nurses aides 27 (ft), 21 (pt); Physical therapists 1 (pt); Occupational therapists 1 (pt); Speech therapists 1 (pt); Activities coordinators 2 (ft), 1 (pt); Dietitians 1 (pt); Dentists 1 (pt); Podiatrists 1 (pt); Audiologists 1 (pt).
Facilities Dining room; Physical therapy room; Activities room; Chapel; Crafts room; Laundry room; Barber/Beauty shop; Library.
Activities Arts and Crafts; Cards; Games; Reading groups; Prayer groups; Movies; Shopping trips; Dances/Social or cultural gatherings.
Description Center has a rural setting with enclosed courtyard, child care center and Alzheimer's unit.

WEST UNION

Adams County Manor Nursing Home
10856 State Rt 41, West Union, OH, 45693
(513) 544-2205
Admin Glenda Walton and Rosalie Hughes.
Medical Dir/Dir of Nursing Gary Greenlee MD.
Licensure Intermediate Care. *Beds* 40. *Certified* Medicaid.
Ownership Public.
Staff RNs 2 (pt); LPNs 4 (ft), 2 (pt); Nurses aides 11 (ft), 5 (pt); Recreational therapists 2 (pt); Activities coordinators 1 (ft); Dietitians 3 (pt).
Facilities Dining room; Activities room; Crafts room; Laundry room.
Activities Arts and Crafts; Cards; Games; Reading groups; Prayer groups; Shopping trips; Dances/Social or cultural gatherings.
Description Moderate size facility with a home-like atmosphere is located on 5 beautiful acres; private and ward rooms available; 24-hour licensed nursing care; activity program; approved diets; social services on premises; total lab, X-ray, and therapies program under agreement with Adams County Hospital; dentist, podiatrist, and eye care available; admissions without regard to race, creed, national origin, or financial status.

Eagle Creek Nursing Center*
141 Spruce Lane, West Union, OH, 45693
Licensure Intermediate Care. *Beds* 40. *Certified* Medicaid.

Revmont Nursing Home*
7980 State Rt 125, West Union, OH, 45693
(513) 544-2923
Licensure Intermediate Care. *Beds* 16. *Certified* Medicaid.
Ownership Proprietary.

WESTERVILLE

Columbus Colony for the Elderly Care Inc
1150 Colony Dr, Westerville, OH, 43081 (614) 891-5055
Admin Willliam L Stewart. *Medical Dir/Dir of Nursing* H T Villavacer MD.
Licensure Skilled Care; Intermediate Care.
Beds 100. *Certified* Medicaid; Medicare.
Ownership Nonprofit.
Staff Physicians 1 (pt); RNs 5 (ft), 3 (pt); LPNs 5 (ft), 5 (pt); Nurses aides 23 (ft), 23 (pt); Recreational therapists 1 (ft), 1 (pt); Activities coordinators 1 (ft).
Facilities Dining room; Physical therapy room; Activities room; Crafts room; Laundry room; Barber/Beauty shop.
Activities Arts and Crafts; Cards; Games; Reading groups; Prayer groups; Movies; Shopping trips; Dances/Social or cultural gatherings; Outings; Special meals.
Description Columbus Colony Elderly Care and Columbus Colony Housing are primarily for the deaf and handicapped. Both facilities opened in August 1979.

Elmhurst Convalescent Center
140 N State St, Westerville, OH, 43081 (614) 882-4055
Medical Dir/Dir of Nursing H T Villavacer.
Licensure Intermediate Care. *Beds* 70. *Certified* Medicaid.
Ownership Proprietary.
Admissions Requirements Medical examination.
Staff Physicians 1 (ft), 1 (pt); RNs 3 (ft), 5 (pt); LPNs 1 (ft), 1 (pt); Orderlies 3 (ft); Nurses aides 18 (ft), 2 (pt); Recreational therapists 2 (pt); Occupational therapists; Speech therapists; Activities coordinators 1 (ft); Dietitians 1 (ft); Dentists; Ophthalmologists; Podiatrists; Audiologists.
Facilities Dining room; Activities room; Crafts room; Laundry room; Barber/Beauty shop.
Activities Arts and Crafts; Cards; Games; Reading groups; Prayer groups; Movies; Shopping trips; Dances/Social or cultural gatherings.
Description Center works with St Anthony's Hospital to provide a habilitation plan for 20 residents (approximately); treatment team provides occupational, speech, music, and art therapies.

Mann Nursing Home*
25 W Home St, Westerville, OH, 43081 (614) 882-2565
Licensure Intermediate Care. *Beds* 129. *Certified* Medicaid.
Ownership Proprietary.

The Village at Westerville Nursing Center*
1060 Eastwind Rd, Westerville, OH, 43081
Beds 100.

Westerville Convalescent and Nursing Center*
140 County Line Rd, Westerville, OH, 43081
(614) 882-1511
Licensure Skilled Care; Intermediate Care.
Beds 180. *Certified* Medicaid; Medicare.
Ownership Proprietary.

WESTLAKE

Country Estate*
31156 Detroit Rd, Westlake, OH, 44145 (216)
871-2261
Licensure Intermediate Care. *Beds* 44. *Certified* Medicaid.
Ownership Proprietary.

Dover Nursing Home*
28305 Detroit Rd, Westlake, OH, 44145 (216)
871-0500
Licensure Skilled Care; Intermediate Care.
Beds 100. *Certified* Medicaid; Medicare.
Ownership Proprietary.

Lutheran Home for the Aged*
2116 Dover Center Rd, Westlake, OH, 44145
(216) 871-0090
Licensure Skilled Care; Intermediate Care.
Beds 222. *Certified* Medicaid; Medicare.
Ownership Nonprofit.
Affiliation Lutheran

Oakridge Home
26520 Center Ridge Rd, Westlake, OH, 44145
(216) 871-3030
Medical Dir/Dir of Nursing James L Rush
MD.
Licensure Skilled Care; Intermediate Care.
Beds 117. *Certified* Medicaid; Medicare.
Ownership Proprietary.
Admissions Requirements Medical examination.
Staff RNs 4 (ft), 6 (pt); LPNs 6 (ft), 5 (pt);
Nurses aides 33 (ft), 23 (pt); Physical therapists
1 (ft); Speech therapists 1 (pt); Activities coordinators 1 (ft); Dietitians 1 (pt).
Facilities Dining room; Physical therapy room;
Activities room; Crafts room; Laundry room;
Barber/Beauty shop.
Activities Arts and Crafts; Cards; Games;
Reading groups; Prayer groups; Movies; Shopping trips; Dances/Social or cultural gatherings;
Religious services; Resident suggested activities.
Description Facility located on 12 acres in a
wooded area, very peaceful and pretty; sidewalks around the facility and areas available for
patients to be outside with their families.

Rae-Ann Suburban*
29505 Detroit Rd, Westlake, OH, 44145 (216)
871-5181
Licensure Intermediate Care. *Beds* 50. *Certified* Medicaid.
Ownership Proprietary.

Westbay Manor
27601 Westchester Pkwy, Westlake, OH, 44145
(216) 871-5900
Medical Dir/Dir of Nursing Bradley Hull MD.
Licensure Skilled Care; Intermediate Care.
Beds 144. *Certified* Medicaid; Medicare.
Ownership Proprietary.

Admissions Requirements Minimum age 14;
Medical examination.
Staff Physical therapists 1 (ft), 1 (pt); Occupational therapists 1 (pt); Speech therapists 1 (pt);
Activities coordinators 1 (ft); Dietitians 1 (ft);
Dentists 1 (pt); Ophthalmologists 1 (pt); Podiatrists 1 (pt); Audiologists 1 (pt).
Facilities Dining room; Physical therapy room;
Activities room; Crafts room; Laundry room;
Barber/Beauty shop; Library.
Activities Arts and Crafts; Games; Reading
groups; Prayer groups; Movies; Dances/Social
or cultural gatherings.
Description Westbay is located in a lovely residential section of Westlake, a western suburb of
Cleveland. A 106-bed addition which will
include a 10-bed acute care unit is scheduled for
completion in the fall of this year. We are also
adding a 50-unit assisted living complex during
this construction phase.

WHEELERSBURG

Best Care Nursing Home
2159 Dogwood Ridge, Wheelersburg, OH,
45694 (614) 574-2558
Medical Dir/Dir of Nursing W L Herrmann
MD.
Licensure Skilled Care; Intermediate Care.
Beds 151. *Certified* Medicaid; Medicare.
Ownership Proprietary.
Admissions Requirements Medical examination; Physician's request.
Staff Physicians; RNs; LPNs; Nurses aides;
Physical therapists; Reality therapists; Recreational therapists; Occupational therapists; Speech therapists; Activities coordinators 2 (ft), 2
(pt); Dietitians; Dentists; Ophthalmologists;
Podiatrists; Audiologists.
Facilities Dining room; Physical therapy room;
Activities room; Chapel; Crafts room; Laundry
room; Barber/Beauty shop; Library.
Activities Arts and Crafts; Cards; Games;
Reading groups; Prayer groups; Movies; Shopping trips; Dances/Social or cultural gatherings.

Greenbriar Convalescent Center*
PO Box 21, 1242 Crescent Dr, Wheelersburg,
OH, 45694 (614) 574-8441
Licensure Skilled Care; Intermediate Care.
Beds 151. *Certified* Medicaid; Medicare.
Ownership Proprietary.

WHITEHOUSE

Whitehouse Country Manor
11239 Waterville St, Whitehouse, OH, 43571
(419) 877-5338
Medical Dir/Dir of Nursing Dr James Mann.
Licensure Intermediate Care. *Beds* 100. *Certified* Medicaid.
Ownership Proprietary.
Admissions Requirements Medical examination.
Staff Physicians 14 (pt); RNs 1 (ft), 2 (pt);
LPNs 5 (ft), 6 (pt); Orderlies 4 (ft); Nurses aides
37 (ft); Activities coordinators 1 (ft); Dietitians
2 (pt).

WICKLIFFE

Wickliffe Country Place
1919 Bishop Rd, Wickliffe, OH, 44092 (216)
944-9400
Admin Bartlett T Bell. *Medical Dir/Dir of
Nursing* Leo Romisher DO.
Licensure Skilled Care; Intermediate Care.
Beds 189. *Certified* Medicare.
Ownership Proprietary.
Admissions Requirements Minimum age 15;
Medical examination; Physician's request.
Staff Physicians 5 (pt); RNs 5 (ft), 6 (pt);
Orderlies 3 (ft); Physical therapists 1 (ft);
Reality therapists 1 (pt); Recreational therapists
2 (ft); Occupational therapists 1 (pt); Speech
therapists 1 (pt); Activities coordinators 1 (ft);
Dietitians 1 (ft); Dentists 1 (pt); Ophthalmologists 1 (pt); Podiatrists 1 (pt); Audiologists 1
(pt).
Facilities Dining room; Physical therapy room;
Activities room; Crafts room; Laundry room;
Barber/Beauty shop; Library.
Activities Arts and Crafts; Cards; Games;
Reading groups; Prayer groups; Movies; Shopping trips; Dances/Social or cultural gatherings.
Description Wickliffe County Place is a scenic
facility projecting a country club setting with
oak beam cathedral ceilings. Meals are served
restaurant-style featuring gourmet menus.

WILLARD

Hillside Acres*
370 E Howard St, Willard, OH, 44890 (419)
935-0148
Licensure Skilled Care; Intermediate Care.
Beds 125. *Certified* Medicaid; Medicare.
Ownership Proprietary.

Willard Quality Care Nursing Center*
725 Wessor Ave, Willard, OH, 44890 (419)
935-6511
Licensure Intermediate Care. *Beds* 51. *Certified* Medicaid.
Ownership Proprietary.

WILLIAMSBURG

Locust Ridge Nursing Home Inc
12745 Elm Corner Rd, Williamsburg, OH,
45176 (513) 444-3162
Medical Dir/Dir of Nursing John H Wehby.
Licensure Skilled Care; Intermediate Care.
Beds 101. *Certified* Medicaid; Medicare.
Ownership Nonprofit.
Staff Physicians 4 (pt); RNs 6 (ft), 1 (pt); LPNs
5 (ft), 3 (pt); Nurses aides 45 (ft); Physical therapists 1 (pt); Activities coordinators 2 (ft); Dietitians 1 (pt).
Facilities Dining room; Physical therapy room;
Activities room; Laundry room; Barber/Beauty
shop.
Activities Arts and Crafts; Games; Reading
groups; Prayer groups; Movies; Shopping trips;
Dances/Social or cultural gatherings.

WILLISTON

Luther Home of Mercy
5810 N Main St, Williston, OH, 43468 (419)
836-7741
Medical Dir/Dir of Nursing Albert Perras MD.
Licensure Intermediate Care for Mentally
Retarded. *Beds* 129.
Ownership Nonprofit.
Staff Physicians 1 (pt); RNs 5 (ft), 7 (pt); LPNs
11 (ft), 6 (pt); Orderlies 4 (ft); Nurses aides 50
(ft), 21 (pt); Physical therapists 1 (pt); Recrea-
tional therapists 1 (ft); Occupational therapists 1
(ft); Speech therapists 1 (ft); Activities coordi-
nators 1 (ft); Dietitians 1 (ft); Dentists 1 (pt).
Affiliation Lutheran
Facilities Dining room; Physical therapy room;
Activities room; Chapel; Crafts room; Laundry
room; Barber/Beauty shop; Library.
Activities Arts and Crafts; Cards; Games;
Reading groups; Prayer groups; Movies; Shopping trips; Dances/Social or cultural gatherings.

WILLOUGBY

Fairmount Health Center*
36855 Ridge Rd, Willougby, OH, 44094
Licensure Skilled Care; Intermediate Care.
Beds SNF 50; ICF 100. *Certified* Medicaid;
Medicare.
Ownership Nonprofit.

WILLOUGHBY

Manor Care of Willoughby Inc*
37603 Euclid Ave, Willoughby, OH, 44094
(216) 951-5551
Licensure Skilled Care; Intermediate Care.
Beds 157. *Certified* Medicaid; Medicare.
Ownership Proprietary.

WILMINGTON

Carriage Inn Nursing Home*
201 E Locust St, Wilmington, OH, 45177
Licensure Intermediate Care. *Beds* 18. *Certified* Medicaid.
Ownership Proprietary.

Wilmington Extended Care Facility*
75 Hale St, Wilmington, OH, 45177 (513)
382-1621
Licensure Skilled Care; Intermediate Care.
Beds 104. *Certified* Medicaid; Medicare.
Ownership Proprietary.

WINDSOR

Town Hall Estates Nursing Home
Rts 322 and 534, Windsor, OH, 44099
Medical Dir/Dir of Nursing E DePasquale DO.
Licensure Intermediate Care. *Beds* 99. *Certi-
fied* Medicaid.
Ownership Nonprofit.
Admissions Requirements Minimum age 55;
Medical examination; Physician's request.
Staff Physicians 2 (pt); RNs 2 (ft), 1 (pt); LPNs
7 (ft), 4 (pt); Nurses aides 24 (ft), 4 (pt); Activi-
ties coordinators 1 (ft); Dietitians 1 (pt); Den-
tists 1 (pt); Ophthalmologists 1 (pt); Podiatrists

1 (pt).
Facilities Dining room; Laundry room; Barber-
/Beauty shop.
Activities Arts and Crafts; Cards; Games;
Reading groups; Prayer groups; Movies; Shopping trips.
Description Facility is located in a peaceful
rural area about 40 miles east of Cleveland;
small town atmosphere; residents are encouraged to bring something personal, such as pictures or a favorite chair, so that it seems more
like home to them.

WINTERSVILLE

Forester Nursing Home Inc
524 Canton Rd, Wintersville, OH, 43952 (614)
264-7788
Admin Ruth Eddy. *Medical Dir/Dir of
Nursing* Carolyn Kennedy.
Licensure Nursing Home. *Beds* 50.
Ownership Proprietary.
Admissions Requirements Minimum age 30;
Medical examination; Physician's request.
Staff RNs 3 (ft), 1 (pt); LPNs 1 (ft), 3 (pt);
Orderlies 1 (ft); Nurses aides 18 (ft), 5 (pt);
Physical therapists 1 (pt); Speech therapists 1
(pt); Dentists 1 (pt); Ophthalmologists 1 (pt);
Podiatrists 2 (pt).
Facilities Dining room; Activities room; Chap-
el; Crafts room; Laundry room; Barber/Beauty
shop.
Activities Arts and Crafts; Cards; Games; Pray-
er groups; Movies; Shopping trips; Vegetable
garden.
Description This is the oldest nursing home in
Jefferson County; family operated and has a
waiting list for admission.

WOODSFIELD

Monroe County Home
Rt 4, Woodsfield, OH, 43793 (614) 472-0144
Admin Elizabeth Schupp.
Licensure Intermediate Care. *Beds* 49. *Certi-
fied* Medicaid.
Ownership Nonprofit.
Staff Physicians 1 (pt); RNs 1 (ft); LPNs 4 (ft),
4 (pt); Nurses aides 11 (ft), 9 (pt); Reality thera-
pists 1 (ft); Activities coordinators 1 (ft); Dieti-
tians 1 (pt).
Facilities Dining room; Activities room;
Chapel; Laundry room; Barber/Beauty shop.
Activities Arts and Crafts; Games; Reading
groups; Prayer groups; Movies; Shopping trips;
Dances/Social or cultural gatherings.

Woodsfield Health Care Center
Airport Rd, Woodsfield, OH, 43793 (614)
472-1678
Medical Dir/Dir of Nursing Dr Jack Matheny.
Licensure Skilled Care; Intermediate Care.
Beds 100. *Certified* Medicaid; Medicare.
Ownership Proprietary.
Admissions Requirements Medical examina-
tion; Physician's request.
Staff Physicians 1 (ft), 1 (pt); RNs 4 (ft); LPNs
7 (ft), 3 (pt); Orderlies 3 (ft), 1 (pt); Nurses aides
25 (ft), 5 (pt); Physical therapists 1 (pt); Recrea-
tional therapists 1 (ft); Speech therapists 1 (pt);
Activities coordinators 1 (ft); Dietitians 1 (pt);

Podiatrists 1 (pt).
Facilities Dining room; Physical therapy room;
Activities room; Laundry room; Barber/Beauty
shop; Library.
Activities Arts and Crafts; Cards; Games;
Reading groups; Prayer groups; Movies; Shop-
ping trips; Dances/Social or cultural gatherings.
Description Facility emphasizes rehabilitative
nursing and has a very active activity program.

WOODSTOCK

Fountain Park Nursing Home Inc*
1649 Park Rd, Woodstock, OH, 43084 (513)
826-3351
Licensure Skilled Care; Intermediate Care.
Beds 51. *Certified* Medicaid; Medicare.
Ownership Proprietary.

WOOSTER

Glendora Meadows Inc
1552 N Honeytown Rd, Wooster, OH, 44691
(216) 264-0912
Licensure Intermediate Care. *Beds* 36. *Certi-
fied* Medicaid.
Ownership Proprietary.
Admissions Requirements Medical examina-
tion.
Staff RNs 1 (pt); LPNs 3 (ft), 3 (pt); Nurses
aides 12 (ft), 3 (pt); Activities coordinators 1
(ft); Dietitians 1 (ft).
Facilities Dining room; Laundry room; Barber-
/Beauty shop.
Activities Arts and Crafts; Cards; Games;
Reading groups; Prayer groups; Movies; Dan-
ces/Social or cultural gatherings.
Description Facility is located 5 miles from
Wooster in a country setting.

Gruter Foundation Inc
3071 N Elyria Rd, Wooster, OH, 44691 (216)
264-2446
Admin Ben Parker. *Medical Dir/Dir of
Nursing* Edward A Gatz MD.
Licensure Intermediate Care for Mentally
Retarded. *Beds* 190.
Ownership Proprietary.
Admissions Requirements Medical examina-
tion.
Staff Physicians 1 (pt); RNs 4 (ft), 8 (pt); LPNs
19 (ft); Nurses aides 72 (ft); Physical therapists
1 (pt); Recreational therapists 8 (ft); Occupa-
tional therapists 1 (ft), 1 (pt); Speech therapists
2 (pt); Activities coordinators 2 (ft).
Facilities Dining room; Physical therapy room;
Activities room; Chapel; Crafts room; Laundry
room; Barber/Beauty shop; Library.
Activities Arts and Crafts; Cards; Games;
Reading groups; Prayer groups; Movies; Shopping trips; Dances/Social or cultural gatherings;
Special Olympics; Field trips; Clubs—Scouting,
4-H; Sports.
Description Gruter Foundation is a residential
facility for the mentally retarded and developmentally disabled consisting of a complex of
buildings on approximately 30 acres. This
makes it possible to offer a great deal of outdoor
activity and clean fresh air. We accept those
with all levels of retardation including those
with physical handicaps and medical problems.

We take pride in the level of care provided to our residents and have a full-time equivalency approaching one staff person per resident.

Horn Nursing Home Inc
230 N Market St, Wooster, OH, 44691 (216) 262-2951
Licensure Intermediate Care. *Beds* 78. *Certified* Medicaid.
Ownership Proprietary.
Admissions Requirements Medical examination; Physician's request.
Staff RNs; LPNs; Nurses aides; Physical therapists; Activities coordinators; Dietitians.
Facilities Dining room; Physical therapy room; Activities room; Chapel; Crafts room; Laundry room; Barber/Beauty shop.
Activities Arts and Crafts; Cards; Games; Reading groups; Prayer groups; Movies; Shopping trips; Dances/Social or cultural gatherings; Spell down; Book reviews.
Description Facility is located in downtown Wooster near public transportation. Intermediate care facility with a concerned, caring staff; building for the future with independent and congregate living units.

Smithville-Western Care Center*
4110 Smithville-Western Rd, Wooster, OH, 44691 (216) 345-6050
Licensure Skilled Care; Intermediate Care.
Beds 127. *Certified* Medicaid; Medicare.
Ownership Proprietary.

West View Manor
1715 Mechanicsburg Rd, Wooster, OH, 44691 (216) 264-8640
Licensure Intermediate Care; Rest Home.
Beds ICF 86; Rest Home 56.
Ownership Nonprofit.
Admissions Requirements Minimum age 62; Medical examination.
Affiliation Church of the Brethren
Facilities Dining room; Physical therapy room; Activities room; Chapel; Crafts room; Laundry room; Barber/Beauty shop.
Activities Arts and Crafts; Cards; Games; Reading groups; Shopping trips; Bible study.
Description Thoughtful care is given in a pleasant home offering 3 levels of care: independent apartments, assisted living, and nursing care.

WORTHINGTON

Norworth Convalescent Center*
6830 High St, Worthington, OH, 43085 (614) 888-4553
Licensure Skilled Care; Intermediate Care.
Beds 152. *Certified* Medicaid; Medicare.
Ownership Proprietary.

Willow Brook Christian Home Inc
55 Lazelle Rd, Worthington, OH, 43085 (614) 885-3300
Licensure Intermediate Care. *Beds* 50. *Certified* Medicaid.
Ownership Nonprofit.
Admissions Requirements Medical examination.
Staff RNs 5 (ft), 1 (pt); LPNs 3 (pt); Nurses aides 14 (ft), 8 (pt); Physical therapists 1 (pt);

Activities coordinators 1 (ft); Dietitians 1 (pt).
Affiliation Church of Christ
Facilities Dining room; Physical therapy room; Activities room; Chapel; Crafts room; Laundry room; Barber/Beauty shop.
Activities Arts and Crafts; Cards; Games; Reading groups; Prayer groups; Movies; Shopping trips; Dances/Social or cultural gatherings.

Worthington Nursing and Convalescent Center*
1030 N High St, Worthington, OH, 43085 (614) 885-0408
Licensure Skilled Care; Intermediate Care.
Beds 100. *Certified* Medicaid; Medicare.
Ownership Proprietary.

XENIA

Greenwood Manor
711 Dayton Xenia Rd, Xenia, OH, 45385 (513) 376-5045
Admin M Caroline Frost. *Medical Dir/Dir of Nursing* Dr R D Hendrickson.
Licensure Skilled Care; Intermediate Care.
Beds 100. *Certified* Medicaid; Medicare.
Ownership Public.
Admissions Requirements Medical examination.
Staff Physicians; RNs 7 (ft), 4 (pt); LPNs 11 (ft), 4 (pt); Nurses aides 46 (ft), 13 (pt); Physical therapists; Occupational therapists; Speech therapists; Activities coordinators 1 (ft); Dietitians; Dentists; Podiatrists.
Facilities Dining room; Physical therapy room; Activities room; Chapel; Crafts room; Laundry room; Barber/Beauty shop.
Activities Arts and Crafts; Cards; Games; Reading groups; Movies; Shopping trips; Dances/Social or cultural gatherings.
Description Focus of facility is the welfare of residents, their individuality being respected and supported as appropriate resources are utilized to maximize their functioning within the constraints of their conditions. Care and restorative services are provided to enable residents to maximize functioning within the setting of the home or upon return to the community.

Heathergreene I*
126 Wilson Dr, Xenia, OH, 45385 (513) 376-2121
Licensure Skilled Care; Intermediate Care.
Beds 100. *Certified* Medicaid; Medicare.
Ownership Proprietary.

Hospitality Home East*
1301 Monroe Dr, Xenia, OH, 45385 (513) 372-4495
Licensure Skilled Care; Intermediate Care.
Beds 100. *Certified* Medicaid; Medicare.
Ownership Proprietary.

Hospitality Home West*
1384 Monroe Dr, Xenia, OH, 45385 (513) 372-8081
Licensure Skilled Care; Intermediate Care.
Beds 90. *Certified* Medicaid; Medicare.
Ownership Proprietary.

YELLOW SPRINGS

Friends Care Center of Yellow Springs*
150 E Herman St, Yellow Springs, OH, 45387
Licensure Skilled Care; Intermediate Care.
Beds SNF 50; ICF 50. *Certified* Medicaid; Medicare.
Ownership Nonprofit.

YORKVILLE

Ford Hull Mar
212 4th St, Yorkville, OH, 43971 (614) 859-6496
Medical Dir/Dir of Nursing Dr Myia.
Licensure Intermediate Care. *Beds* 21. *Certified* Medicaid.
Ownership Proprietary.
Staff Physicians 1 (ft); RNs 1 (ft); LPNs 3 (ft); Orderlies 2 (ft); Nurses aides 5 (ft); Physical therapists; Reality therapists; Recreational therapists; Speech therapists; Activities coordinators 1 (ft); Dietitians 1 (ft); Dentists; Podiatrists 1 (pt).
Facilities Dining room; Activities room; Chapel; Crafts room; Laundry room; Library.
Activities Arts and Crafts; Cards; Games; Reading groups; Prayer groups; Movies; Shopping trips; Dances/Social or cultural gatherings; Bake sales; Carnival.
Description Christmas parties and summer outings are the main social events with the families and friends of residents attending. Birthdays are also celebrated and an annual resident king and queen are elected.

YOUNGSTOWN

Ashley Place Health Care Inc*
PO Box 4240, 491 Ashley Cir, Youngstown, OH, 44515
Licensure Skilled Care; Intermediate Care.
Beds SNF 29; ICF 100. *Certified* Medicaid; Medicare.
Ownership Proprietary.

Assumption Nursing Home*
550 W Chalmers Ave, Youngstown, OH, 44511 (216) 743-1186
Licensure Intermediate Care. *Beds* 126. *Certified* Medicaid.
Ownership Nonprofit.

Camelot Arms Care Center*
2958 Canfield Rd, Youngstown, OH, 44511
Licensure Skilled Care; Intermediate Care.
Beds 100. *Certified* Medicaid; Medicare.

Colonial Manor Nursing Home
196 Colonial Dr, Youngstown, OH, 44505 (216) 759-3790
Admin James R Asbury. *Medical Dir/Dir of Nursing* Ellis List MD.
Licensure Skilled Care; Intermediate Care.
Beds SNF 30; ICF 100. *Certified* Medicaid; Medicare.
Ownership Proprietary.
Admissions Requirements Medical examination; Physician's request.
Staff Physicians 2 (pt); RNs 3 (ft), 6 (pt); LPNs 4 (ft), 5 (pt); Orderlies 1 (pt); Nurses aides 20

(ft), 5 (pt); Physical therapists 1 (ft); Reality therapists 1 (ft); Recreational therapists 1 (ft); Speech therapists 1 (pt); Activities coordinators 1 (ft); Dietitians 1 (pt); Ophthalmologists 1 (pt); Podiatrists 1 (pt); Audiologists 1 (pt).
Facilities Dining room; Physical therapy room; Activities room; Chapel; Crafts room; Laundry room; Barber/Beauty shop.
Activities Arts and Crafts; Cards; Games; Reading groups; Prayer groups; Movies; Shopping trips; Dances/Social or cultural gatherings; Exercise program.
Description Facility features spacious one floor plan on large landscaped grounds located within easy access to Ohio State Routes 76, 11, 80, and the Ohio Turnpike; a suburban setting within 5 miles of 3 major acute care hospitals.

Danridge Nursing Home
1825 Oak Hill Ave, Youngstown, OH, 44507 (216) 746-5157
Medical Dir/Dir of Nursing Dr William Johnson.
Licensure Intermediate Care. *Beds* 32. *Certified* Medicaid.
Ownership Proprietary.
Admissions Requirements Medical examination.
Staff RNs 1 (ft), 1 (pt); LPNs 4 (ft), 2 (pt); Nurses aides 16 (ft), 2 (pt); Speech therapists 1 (pt); Dietitians 1 (ft); Dietitians 1 (ft), 1 (pt); Dentists 1 (pt); Podiatrists 1 (ft).
Facilities Dining room; Activities room; Laundry room; Library.
Activities Arts and Crafts; Cards; Games; Prayer groups; Movies; Dances/Social or cultural gatherings.

Gateways to Better Living 1
1406 5th Ave, Youngstown, OH, 44504 (216) 792-2854
Licensure Intermediate Care for Mentally Retarded. *Beds* 10.
Ownership Nonprofit.
Admissions Requirements Minimum age 14.
Staff Physicians 1 (pt); RNs 1 (pt); LPNs 1 (pt); Recreational therapists 1 (pt); Speech therapists 1 (pt); Activities coordinators 1 (pt); Dietitians 1 (pt); Audiologists 1 (pt).
Facilities Dining room.
Activities Arts and Crafts; Cards; Games; Reading groups; Movies; Shopping trips; Dances/Social or cultural gatherings.
Description Facility is a group home providing rehabilitation service to residents who actively participate in community programing.

Gateways to Better Living 2
359 Redondo Rd, Youngstown, OH, 44504 (216) 792-2854
Licensure Intermediate Care for Mentally Retarded. *Beds* 11.
Ownership Nonprofit.
Admissions Requirements Minimum age 14.
Staff Physicians 1 (pt); RNs 1 (pt); LPNs 1 (pt); Recreational therapists 1 (pt); Speech therapists 1 (pt); Activities coordinators 1 (pt); Dietitians 1 (pt); Audiologists 1 (pt).
Facilities Dining room.
Activities Arts and Crafts; Cards; Games; Reading groups; Movies; Shopping trips; Dances/Social or cultural gatherings.

Description Facility is a group home providing rehabilitation services to residents who actively participate in community programing.

Gateways to Better Living 3
1934 Volney Rd, Youngstown, OH, 44511 (216) 792-2854
Licensure Intermediate Care for Mentally Retarded. *Beds* 12.
Ownership Nonprofit.
Admissions Requirements Minimum age 14.
Staff Physicians 1 (pt); RNs 1 (pt); LPNs 1 (pt); Recreational therapists 1 (pt); Speech therapists 1 (pt); Activities coordinators 1 (pt); Dietitians 1 (pt); Audiologists 1 (pt).
Facilities Dining room; Library.
Activities Arts and Crafts; Cards; Games; Reading groups; Movies; Shopping trips; Dances/Social or cultural gatherings.
Description Facility is a group home providing rehabilitation services to residents who actively participate in community programing.

Gateways to Better Living 4
7246 Ronjoy Pl, Youngstown, OH, 44512 (216) 792-2854
Licensure Intermediate Care for Mentally Retarded. *Beds* 10.
Ownership Proprietary.
Admissions Requirements Minimum age 14.
Staff Physicians 1 (pt); RNs 1 (pt); LPNs 1 (pt); Recreational therapists 1 (pt); Occupational therapists 1 (pt); Speech therapists 1 (pt); Activities coordinators 1 (pt); Dietitians 1 (pt); Audiologists 1 (pt).
Facilities Dining room.
Activities Arts and Crafts; Cards; Games; Reading groups; Movies; Shopping trips; Dances/Social or cultural gatherings.
Description Facility is a group home providing rehabilitation services to residents who actively participate in community programing.

Gateways to Better Living Inc—No 9*
660 Early Rd, Youngstown, OH, 44505
Licensure Intermediate Care for Mentally Retarded. *Beds* 11. *Certified* Medicaid.
Ownership Public.

Heritage Manor—Jewish Home for Aged
517 Gypsy Lane, Box 449, Youngstown, OH, 44501 (216) 746-1076
Medical Dir/Dir of Nursing William D Loeser.
Licensure Skilled Care; Intermediate Care.
Beds 72. *Certified* Medicaid; Medicare.
Ownership Nonprofit.
Staff Physicians 2 (pt); RNs 6 (ft), 6 (pt); LPNs 6 (ft); Orderlies 1 (ft); Nurses aides 19 (ft); Physical therapists 1 (pt); Reality therapists 1 (pt); Recreational therapists 1 (pt); Activities coordinators 1 (ft); Dentists 1 (pt); Podiatrists 1 (pt).
Affiliation Jewish
Facilities Dining room; Physical therapy room; Activities room; Chapel; Crafts room; Laundry room; Barber/Beauty shop.
Activities Arts and Crafts; Cards; Games; Reading groups; Movies; Shopping trips; Dances/Social or cultural gatherings.

Little Forest Medical Center*
5665 South Ave, Youngstown, OH, 44512 (216) 782-1173

Licensure Skilled Care; Intermediate Care.
Beds 221. *Certified* Medicaid; Medicare.
Ownership Proprietary.

Manor House
259 Park Ave, Youngstown, OH, 44504 (216) 746-0043
Medical Dir/Dir of Nursing Dr Joseph Fogarty.
Licensure Intermediate Care. *Beds* 21. *Certified* Medicaid.
Ownership Proprietary.
Staff Physicians 1 (pt); RNs 1 (pt); LPNs 3 (ft), 3 (pt); Nurses aides 5 (ft); Activities coordinators 1 (pt).
Facilities Dining room; Activities room; Laundry room.
Activities Arts and Crafts; Cards; Games; Prayer groups; Shopping trips.

Millcreek Manor*
PO Box 3085, 721 Cohasset Dr, Youngstown, OH, 44511 (216) 747-6277
Licensure Intermediate Care. *Beds* 20. *Certified* Medicaid.
Ownership Proprietary.

North Manor Center*
115 Illinois Ave, Youngstown, OH, 44505
Licensure Intermediate Care. *Beds* 100. *Certified* Medicaid.
Ownership Proprietary.

North Side Nursing Home*
PO Box 2287, 480 Lora Ave, Youngstown, OH, 44504 (216) 743-5235
Licensure Intermediate Care. *Beds* 31. *Certified* Medicaid.
Ownership Proprietary.

Omni Manor*
3245 Vestal Rd, Youngstown, OH, 44509 (216) 793-5648
Licensure Skilled Care; Intermediate Care.
Beds 100. *Certified* Medicaid; Medicare.
Ownership Proprietary.

Paisley House for Aged Women
1408 Mahoning Ave, Youngstown, OH, 44509 (216) 799-9431
Licensure Rest Home. *Beds* 20.
Ownership Proprietary.
Admissions Requirements Females only

Park Vista Unit—Ohio Presbyterian Home
1216 Fifth Ave, Youngstown, OH, 44504 (216) 746-2944
Admin James E Latham. *Medical Dir/Dir of Nursing* James L Smeltzer MD.
Licensure Skilled Care; Intermediate Care; Rest Home. *Beds* SNF 49; ICF 98; Rest Home 81. *Certified* Medicaid; Medicare.
Ownership Nonprofit.
Admissions Requirements Minimum age 65; Medical examination.
Staff Physicians 2 (pt); RNs 12 (ft), 6 (pt); LPNs 5 (ft), 7 (pt); Orderlies 1 (ft), 3 (pt); Nurses aides 37 (ft), 7 (pt); Physical therapists 1 (pt); Speech therapists 1 (pt); Activities coordinators 1 (ft); Dietitians 1 (pt); Dentists 1 (pt); Podiatrists 1 (pt).
Affiliation Presbyterian
Facilities Dining room; Physical therapy room; Activities room; Chapel; Crafts room; Laundry

room; Barber/Beauty shop; Library.
Activities Arts and Crafts; Cards; Games; Reading groups; Prayer groups; Movies; Shopping trips; Dances/Social or cultural gatherings; Trips to local entertainment; Sightseeing.
Description This is a retirement community on Youngstown's north side across from Wick Park; 4 levels of care (including totally independent and congregate living).

Ridgewood Nursing Center Inc
1012 Glenwood Ave, Youngstown, OH, 44502
Licensure Intermediate Care. *Beds* 38. *Certified* Medicaid.
Ownership Proprietary.

Seven Gables*
Box 2249, 264 Broadway Ave, Youngstown, OH, 44504
Licensure Intermediate Care. *Beds* 28. *Certified* Medicaid.
Ownership Proprietary.

Sleigh Bell Residence*
461 S Canfield-Niles Rd, Youngstown, OH, 44515
Licensure Intermediate Care. *Beds* 98. *Certified* Medicaid.
Ownership Proprietary.

Windsor House
1735 Belmont Ave, Youngstown, OH, 44504 (216) 743-1393
Medical Dir/Dir of Nursing Dr Joseph Masternick.
Licensure Skilled Care; Intermediate Care. *Beds* 100. *Certified* Medicaid; Medicare.
Ownership Proprietary.
Staff RNs 6 (ft), 2 (pt); LPNs 20 (ft), 4 (pt); Orderlies 6 (ft); Nurses aides 38 (ft); Physical therapists 1 (ft); Activities coordinators 2 (ft); Dietitians 6 (ft), 10 (pt).
Facilities Dining room; Physical therapy room; Activities room; Crafts room; Laundry room; Barber/Beauty shop; Living room; TV lounges.
Activities Arts and Crafts; Cards; Games; Reading groups; Prayer groups; Movies; Shopping trips; Dances/Social or cultural gatherings.

ZANESVILLE

Cedar Hill Care Center*
1136 Adair Ave, Zanesville, OH, 43701
Beds 104.

Drake Nursing Home*
750 Findley Ave, Zanesville, OH, 43701 (614) 452-3449
Licensure Intermediate Care. *Beds* 30. *Certified* Medicaid.
Ownership Proprietary.

Good Samaritan Medical Center
800 Forest, Zanesville, OH, 43701 (614) 454-5000
Medical Dir/Dir of Nursing James Caton DO.
Licensure Skilled Care. *Beds* 18. *Certified* Medicare.
Ownership Nonprofit.
Admissions Requirements Medical examination; Physician's request.
Staff RNs 4 (ft), 5 (pt); LPNs 6 (ft); Nurses aides 4 (ft), 3 (pt); Physical therapists 1 (pt); Recreational therapists 1 (pt); Occupational therapists 1 (pt); Speech therapists 1 (pt); Activities coordinators 1 (pt); Dietitians 1 (pt); Audiologists 1 (pt).
Affiliation Roman Catholic
Facilities Dining room; Physical therapy room; Activities room; Chapel; Crafts room.
Activities Arts and Crafts; Cards; Games; Prayer groups; Dances/Social or cultural gatherings; Orientation group.
Description Good Samaritan's SNF is an 18-bed hospital based unit. Excellent rehabilitation center has exceptional equipment and facilities available. Doctors are available on a 24-hour basis, and other medical personnel are also easily contacted.

Helen Purcell Home
1854 Norwood Blvd, Zanesville, OH, 43701 (614) 453-1745
Licensure Home for the Aged. *Beds* 74.
Ownership Nonprofit.
Admissions Requirements Medical examination.
Staff Physicians 1 (pt); RNs 1 (ft), 1 (pt); LPNs 3 (ft), 4 (pt); Nurses aides 7 (ft), 5 (pt); Dietitians 1 (pt).
Facilities Dining room; Laundry room; Barber/Beauty shop; Library.
Activities Arts and Crafts; Cards; Prayer groups; Shopping trips; Dances/Social or cultural gatherings.
Description Facility is located on 5 acres of wooded land in a quiet but easily accessible part of Zanesville convenient to hospitals, stores, and personal service centers.

Ohio District Council Nursing
3125 E Pike, Zanesville, OH, 43701 (614) 452-4351
Medical Dir/Dir of Nursing Dr Eugene Capocasale.
Licensure Skilled Care; Intermediate Care. *Beds* 100. *Certified* Medicaid; Medicare.
Ownership Proprietary.
Admissions Requirements Medical examination; Physician's request.
Staff Physicians 1 (ft); RNs 3 (ft), 2 (pt); LPNs 13 (ft); Physical therapists 1 (pt); Reality therapists 2 (ft); Recreational therapists 2 (ft); Occupational therapists; Speech therapists; Activities coordinators 2 (ft); Dietitians; Dentists; Ophthalmologists; Podiatrists; Audiologists.
Facilities Dining room; Physical therapy room; Activities room; Chapel; Crafts room; Laundry room; Barber/Beauty shop; Library.
Activities Arts and Crafts; Cards; Games; Prayer groups; Movies; Shopping trips; Dances/Social or cultural gatherings.
Description Facility is in beautiful rural setting 2 miles from town; activities for residents include county fair, church, other activities in town; first home in area to admit small children.

Sunny View
2991 Maple Ave, Zanesville, OH, 43701 (614) 453-4404
Admin L H Boor. *Medical Dir/Dir of Nursing* Joe Booth MD.
Licensure Nursing Home. *Beds* 100.
Ownership Proprietary.

Admissions Requirements Medical examination.
Staff Physicians 1 (pt); RNs 2 (ft), 3 (pt); LPNs 6 (ft), 2 (pt); Nurses aides 19 (ft), 7 (pt).
Facilities Dining room; Activities room; Laundry room; Barber/Beauty shop; Library.
Activities Arts and Crafts; Cards; Games; Prayer groups; Movies; Shopping trips.

Willow Haven Nursing Home
1122 Taylor St, Zanesville, OH, 43701 (614) 454-9747
Medical Dir/Dir of Nursing Dr David Klein.
Licensure Intermediate Care. *Beds* 100. *Certified* Medicaid.
Ownership Proprietary.
Admissions Requirements Minimum age 18; Medical examination.
Staff RNs 3 (ft), 3 (pt); LPNs 6 (ft), 1 (pt); Orderlies 1 (ft); Nurses aides 38 (ft), 15 (pt); Physical therapists 1 (pt); Reality therapists 2 (ft); Recreational therapists 2 (ft); Dietitians 1 (ft).
Facilities Dining room; Physical therapy room; Activities room; Crafts room; Laundry room; Barber/Beauty shop; Library.
Activities Arts and Crafts; Cards; Games; Reading groups; Prayer groups; Dances/Social or cultural gatherings.

Winter House
1856 Adams Ln, Zanesville, OH, 43701 (614) 454-9769
Medical Dir/Dir of Nursing Thomas P Forrestal MD.
Licensure Skilled Care; Intermediate Care. *Beds* 101. *Certified* Medicaid; Medicare.
Ownership Proprietary.
Staff Physicians 1 (pt); RNs 4 (ft), 3 (pt); LPNs 6 (ft), 1 (pt); Orderlies 4 (ft); Nurses aides 41 (ft), 8 (pt); Activities coordinators 3 (ft); Dietitians 11 (ft).
Facilities Dining room; Activities room; Crafts room; Laundry room; Barber/Beauty shop.
Activities Arts and Crafts; Cards; Games; Reading groups; Prayer groups; Movies; Shopping trips; Dances/Social or cultural gatherings.
Description All meals are served in the dining room unless medical necessity indicates otherwise, it is the single most beneficial activity that has been found for the residents because it encourages conversation, social activity, and physical activity.

OKLAHOMA

ADA

Ada Retirement and Care Center*
PO Box 1185, 931 N Country Club Rd, Ada, OK, 74820 (405) 332-3631
Admin Gussie J Corvin.
Licensure Intermediate Care. *Beds* 85. *Certified* Medicaid.

Ballard Nursing Center*
210 W 5th, Ada, OK, 74820 (405) 436-1414
Admin Gary Reed.
Licensure Intermediate Care. *Beds* 73. *Certified* Medicaid.

Jan Frances Care Center
815 N Country Club Rd, Ada, OK, 74820 (405) 332-5328
Admin Alandra Needham.
Licensure Intermediate Care. *Beds* 120. *Certified* Medicaid.
Staff Physicians 4 (pt); RNs 1 (pt); LPNs 5 (ft); Nurses aides 50 (ft); Physical therapists 1 (pt); Activities coordinators 1 (ft); Dietitians 1 (pt).
Facilities Crafts room; Laundry room.
Activities Arts and Crafts; Cards; Games; Reading groups; Prayer groups; Movies; Shopping trips; Dances/Social or cultural gatherings.

McCall's Chapel School Inc
Rt 4, Ada, OK, 74820 (405) 436-0373
Admin Josie Cole. *Medical Dir/Dir of Nursing* George K Stephens MD.
Licensure Intermediate Care. *Beds* 98. *Certified* Medicaid.
Facilities Dining room; Activities room; Crafts room; Laundry room; Barber/Beauty shop.
Activities Arts and Crafts; Games; Reading groups; Prayer groups; Movies; Shopping trips; Dances/Social or cultural gatherings.
Description Fully accredited as a school in the state of Oklahoma.

ALLEN

Woodland Hills Nursing Center*
200 N Easton, Allen, OK, 74825 (405) 857-2472
Admin Buford K Canaday.
Licensure Intermediate Care. *Beds* 49. *Certified* Medicaid.

ALTUS

Altus Home Nursing Home
1059 E Pecan, Altus, OK, 73521 (405) 482-8342
Admin LaVerne Jackson.
Licensure Intermediate Care. *Beds* 90. *Certified* Medicaid.
Admissions Requirements Medical examination.
Staff RNs 1 (ft); LPNs 3 (ft); Nurses aides 23 (ft), 2 (pt); Activities coordinators 1 (ft); Dietitians 1 (pt).
Facilities Dining room; Activities room; Crafts room; Barber/Beauty shop.
Activities Arts and Crafts; Games; Reading groups; Prayer groups; Dances/Social or cultural gatherings.

English Village Manor Inc*
1515 Canterbury, Altus, OK, 73521 (405) 477-1133
Admin LaVerne Jackson.
Licensure Intermediate Care. *Beds* 128. *Certified* Medicaid.

Park Lane Manor*
702 N Park Lane, Altus, OK, 73521 (405) 482-8800
Admin Billy R Jones.
Licensure Intermediate Care. *Beds* 55. *Certified* Medicaid.

ALVA

Beadles Rest Home
916 Noble, Alva, OK, 73717 (405) 327-1274
Admin Ruth Heitt.
Licensure Intermediate Care. *Beds* 64. *Certified* Medicaid.
Admissions Requirements Medical examination; Physician's request.
Staff RNs 2 (ft); LPNs 2 (ft), 1 (pt); Orderlies 2 (ft); Nurses aides 16 (ft); Activities coordinators 1 (ft); Dietitians 1 (pt).
Facilities Dining room; Activities room; Library.
Activities Arts and Crafts; Cards; Games; Reading groups; Prayer groups; Movies; Shopping trips; Special days each month.
Description Sitting and dining rooms are decorated each month to go along with that months special events.

Share Medical Center
730 Share Dr, Alva, OK, 73717 (405) 327-2800
Admin Mary Ruth Hiett. *Medical Dir/Dir of Nursing* Dr John Simon.
Licensure Intermediate Care. *Beds* 80. *Certified* Medicaid.
Staff RNs 1 (pt); LPNs 3 (ft), 1 (pt); Nurses aides 16 (ft), 16 (pt); Physical therapists 1 (pt); Activities coordinators 1 (pt); Dietitians 1 (pt).
Facilities Dining room; Physical therapy room; Activities room; Chapel; Barber/Beauty shop; Library.
Activities Arts and Crafts; Cards; Games.

ANADARKO

Friendship Manor*
201 W Kansas, Anadarko, OK, 73005 (405) 247-6611
Admin Charlotte Gibbs.
Licensure Intermediate Care. *Beds* 224. *Certified* Medicaid.

Silver Crest Manor Inc*
300 W Washington, Anadarko, OK, 73005 (405) 247-3347
Admin Wanda Silvers.
Licensure Intermediate Care. *Beds* 92. *Certified* Medicaid.

ANTLERS

Antlers Nursing Home*
507 E Main, Antlers, OK, 74523 (405) 298-3294
Admin Kathy Hannan Young.
Licensure Intermediate Care. *Beds* 133. *Certified* Medicaid.

ARDMORE

Ardmore Memorial Convalescent Home*
1037 15th NW, Ardmore, OK, 73401 (405) 223-8304
Admin Eugene Lutts.
Licensure Intermediate Care. *Beds* 56. *Certified* Medicaid.

Edgewood Lodge Home*
111 13th NW, Ardmore, OK, 73401 (405) 223-4803

Admin Bob R Wood.
Licensure Intermediate Care. *Beds* 76. *Certified* Medicaid.

Elmbrook Home*
1811 9th NW, Ardmore, OK, 73401 (405) 223-3303
Admin Bob Walker.
Licensure Intermediate Care. *Beds* 100. *Certified* Medicaid.

Lakeland Manor Inc*
604 Lake Murray Dr, Ardmore, OK, 73401 (405) 223-4501
Admin Michael Stringer.
Licensure Intermediate Care. *Beds* 32. *Certified* Medicaid.

Lu-Ken Manor*
832 Isabel SW, Ardmore, OK, 73401 (405) 223-5901
Admin James A Kenaga.
Licensure Intermediate Care. *Beds* 104. *Certified* Medicaid.

Woodview Home
1630 3rd NE, Ardmore, OK, 73401 (405) 226-5454
Admin Kenneth Walker.
Licensure Intermediate Care. *Beds* 43. *Certified* Medicaid.
Staff RNs 1 (ft), 1 (pt); LPNs 1 (ft); Nurses aides 13 (ft); Physical therapists 1 (pt); Activities coordinators 1 (ft); Dietitians 1 (pt).
Facilities Dining room; Physical therapy room; Activities room; Crafts room; Laundry room; Barber/Beauty shop.
Activities Arts and Crafts; Cards; Games; Reading groups; Movies; Shopping trips; Dances/Social or cultural gatherings.
Description Facility offers complete physical therapy; complete respiratory therapy; and special diets.

ARKOMA

Medi-Home of Arkoma Inc
Sicard and Arkansas, Arkoma, OK, 74901 (918) 875-3107
Admin Millie B Wentz.
Licensure Intermediate Care. *Beds* 56. *Certified* Medicaid.
Admissions Requirements Medical examination; Physician's request.
Staff RNs 1 (ft); LPNs 4 (pt); Nurses aides 15 (ft), 4 (pt); Activities coordinators 1 (ft); Dietitians 1 (pt).
Facilities Dining room; Activities room.
Activities Arts and Crafts; Cards; Games; Reading groups; Prayer groups.
Description Facility is a small, country-type nursing home near a city that furnishes hospital and medical facilities equivalent to the best.

ATOKA

Atoka Care Center
323 W 6th, Atoka, OK, 74525 (405) 889-3373
Admin Beatrice Maxey. *Medical Dir/Dir of Nursing* Edna Sheffield.
Licensure Intermediate Care. *Beds* 96. *Certi-

fied* Medicaid.
Admissions Requirements Medical examination; Physician's request.

Atoka Colonial Manor Inc*
100 Virginia St, Atoka, OK, 74525 (405) 889-7341, 7342
Admin Louise Moore.
Licensure Intermediate Care. *Beds* 80. *Certified* Medicaid.

Plantation Manor Inc
505 E "B" St, Atoka, OK, 74525 (405) 889-2517
Admin Mona A Simpson.
Licensure Intermediate Care. *Beds* 85. *Certified* Medicaid.
Admissions Requirements Minimum age 19; Medical examination; Physician's request.
Staff RNs 1 (pt); LPNs 2 (ft); Nurses aides 23 (ft); Activities coordinators 1 (ft); Dietitians 1 (pt).
Facilities Dining room; Physical therapy room; Activities room; Crafts room; Laundry room.
Activities Arts and Crafts; Cards; Games; Reading groups; Shopping trips; Dances/Social or cultural gatherings.

BARNSDALL

Barnsdall Nursing Home*
4th and Chestnut, Barnsdall, OK, 74002 (918) 847-2826
Admin Janet Mayo Hardin.
Licensure Intermediate Care. *Beds* 40. *Certified* Medicaid.

BARTLESVILLE

Heritage House Nursing Home
417 N Santa Fe, Bartlesville, OK, 74003 (918) 336-1821
Admin M Colleen Jones.
Licensure Intermediate Care. *Beds* 67. *Certified* Medicaid.
Staff RNs 1 (pt); LPNs 6 (ft); Nurses aides 28 (ft); Physical therapists 1 (pt); Activities coordinators 1 (ft); Dietitians 1 (pt).
Facilities Dining room; Physical therapy room; Activities room; Crafts room; Laundry room; Barber/Beauty shop; Library.
Activities Arts and Crafts; Cards; Games; Reading groups; Prayer groups; Movies; Shopping trips; Dances/Social or cultural gatherings.
Description Facility features large rooms with baths, fenced yard, daily activities.

Heritage Manor Nursing and Convalescent Center*
215 SE Howard, Bartlesville, OK, 74003 (918) 333-9545
Admin Paul A Roll.
Licensure Intermediate Care. *Beds* 126. *Certified* Medicaid.

BEAVER

Beaver County Nursing Home*
200 E 8th, Beaver, OK, 73932 (405) 625-4571
Admin LaVern Melton.
Licensure Intermediate Care. *Beds* 62. *Certified* Medicaid.

BEGGS

Beggs Nursing Home*
7th and Cherokee, Beggs, OK, 74421 (918) 267-3362
Admin Judy McKee.
Licensure Intermediate Care. *Beds* 50. *Certified* Medicaid.

BETHANY

Bethany Village Health Care Center
6900 NW 39th Expwy, Bethany, OK, 73008 (405) 495-6110
Admin Larry L Cain. *Medical Dir/Dir of Nursing* John Pittman MD.
Licensure Intermediate Care. *Beds* 159. *Certified* Medicaid.
Admissions Requirements Medical examination.
Staff Physicians 2 (ft); RNs 3 (ft); LPNs 9 (ft); Orderlies 4 (ft); Nurses aides 38 (ft), 4 (pt); Physical therapists 1 (pt); Recreational therapists 2 (ft); Occupational therapists 1 (ft); Dietitians 1 (ft); Dentists 1 (pt); Podiatrists 1 (pt).
Facilities Dining room; Physical therapy room; Activities room; Chapel; Crafts room; Laundry room; Barber/Beauty shop; Library.
Activities Arts and Crafts; Cards; Games; Prayer groups; Movies; Shopping trips; Dances/Social or cultural gatherings.
Description Center is a modern progressive facility that offers comprehensive health care services and has received national attention for its unique and innovative activities program.

Children's Convalescent Center*
6800 NW 39th Expwy, Bethany, OK, 73008 (405) 789-6711
Admin Shirley Walker.
Licensure Intermediate Care. *Beds* 82. *Certified* Medicaid.

Evening Star Nursing Home*
6912 NW 23rd, Bethany, OK, 73008 (405) 789-8491
Admin Shirley Walker.
Licensure Intermediate Care. *Beds* 55. *Certified* Medicaid.

Golden Acres Health Care Center*
7000 NW 32nd St, Bethany, OK, 73008 (405) 789-7242
Admin Barbara Breedlove.
Licensure Intermediate Care. *Beds* 161. *Certified* Medicaid.

Western Oaks Health Care Center*
2200 N Flamingo, Bethany, OK, 73008 (405) 787-2844
Admin Dennis Farmer.
Licensure Intermediate Care. *Beds* 235. *Certified* Medicaid.

BILLINGS

Billings Fairchild Center*
Hwy 15, Billings, OK, 74630 (405) 725-3533
Admin Albert Hardin.
Licensure Intermediate Care. *Beds* 154. *Certified* Medicaid.

BIXBY

Bixby Manor Nursing Home
15600 S Memorial Dr, Bixby, OK, 74008 (918) 366-3400
Admin Wayne Wood.
Licensure Intermediate Care. *Beds* 102. *Certified* Medicaid.
Admissions Requirements Minimum age 18; Medical examination.
Staff Physicians 5 (pt); RNs 1 (ft); LPNs 5 (ft); Orderlies 1 (ft); Nurses aides 37 (ft); Physical therapists 1 (pt); Recreational therapists 1 (pt); Occupational therapists 1 (pt); Speech therapists 1 (pt); Activities coordinators 1 (ft); Dietitians 1 (pt); Dentists 1 (pt); Ophthalmologists 1 (pt); Podiatrists 1 (pt).
Facilities Dining room; Physical therapy room; Activities room; Crafts room; Laundry room; Barber/Beauty shop.
Activities Arts and Crafts; Cards; Games; Reading groups; Prayer groups; Shopping trips; Dances/Social or cultural gatherings.

BLACKWELL

Blackwell Nursing Home Inc*
1200 W Coolidge, Blackwell, OK, 74631 (405) 363-1624
Admin John Johnson.
Licensure Intermediate Care. *Beds* 71. *Certified* Medicaid.

Hillcrest Manor*
1110 S 6th, Blackwell, OK, 74631 (405) 363-3244
Admin Adrian Taylor.
Licensure Intermediate Care. *Beds* 110. *Certified* Medicaid.

BLANCHARD

Senior Village Nursing Home*
1100 N Madison, Blanchard, OK, 73010 (405) 485-3314
Admin Linda S Simmons.
Licensure Intermediate Care. *Beds* 50. *Certified* Medicaid.

BOISE CITY

Cimarron Nursing Home
100 S Ellis, Boise City, OK, 73933 (405) 544-2501
Admin Barbara J Wardlaw.
Licensure Intermediate Care. *Beds* 44. *Certified* Medicaid.
Staff RNs 1 (pt); LPNs 2 (ft); Nurses aides 10 (ft), 10 (pt); Activities coordinators 1 (ft); Dietitians 1 (pt).

Facilities Dining room; Barber/Beauty shop.
Activities Arts and Crafts; Movies; Shopping trips.

BOLEY

Boley Intermediate Care Facility*
Hwy 62, Boley, OK, 74829 (918) 667-3311
Admin John B Bruner.
Licensure Intermediate Care. *Beds* 25. *Certified* Medicaid.

BRISTOW

Rainbow Nursing Home*
111 E Washington, Bristow, OK, 74010 (918) 367-2656
Admin Joe H Hamra.
Licensure Intermediate Care. *Beds* 74. *Certified* Medicaid.

BROKEN ARROW

Broken Arrow Nursing Home Inc*
425 N Date, Broken Arrow, OK, 74012 (918) 251-5343
Admin Tommy Cooper.
Licensure Intermediate Care. *Beds* 81. *Certified* Medicaid.

Franciscan Villa
17110 E 51st St S, Broken Arrow, OK, 74012 (918) 258-7596
Admin Sr Roseann Koskie. *Medical Dir/Dir of Nursing* Dr L A Poplin.
Licensure Intermediate Care. *Beds* 60. *Certified* Medicaid.
Admissions Requirements Minimum age 65; Medical examination.
Staff RNs 3 (ft); LPNs 3 (ft), 1 (pt); Nurses aides 25 (ft), 3 (pt); Activities coordinators 2 (ft).
Affiliation Roman Catholic
Facilities Dining room; Physical therapy room; Activities room; Chapel; Crafts room; Laundry room; Barber/Beauty shop; Library; Solarium; Patio.
Activities Arts and Crafts; Cards; Games; Reading groups; Prayer groups; Movies; Shopping trips; Dances/Social or cultural gatherings.
Description Franciscan Villa is situated in Broken Arrow, just minutes from Tulsa; located on the same acreage as the sisters convent. Facility has an excellent reputation in the nursing home field, providing the best of care for residents.

Gatesway Foundations Inc
1217 E College, Broken Arrow, OK, 74012 (918) 251-2676
Admin Helen V Gates. *Medical Dir/Dir of Nursing* Dorothy Terebesy RN.
Licensure Intermediate Care. *Beds* 62. *Certified* Medicaid.
Admissions Requirements Medical examination.
Staff RNs 1 (ft); LPNs 1 (ft), 1 (pt); Orderlies 2 (pt); Nurses aides 13 (ft); Activities coordinators 1 (ft).
Facilities Dining room; Physical therapy room; Activities room; Crafts room; Laundry room;

Indoor gym; Solar roof pool.
Activities Arts and Crafts; Cards; Games; Reading groups; Prayer groups; Movies; Shopping trips; Dances/Social or cultural gatherings.
Description Sheltered workshop where two-thirds of residents work; cottage program with goal of training residents to live on their own. Large involvement with community.

Helen Raney Nursing Home Inc*
700 S Ash, Broken Arrow, OK, 74012 (918) 251-5384
Admin Reba Raney.
Licensure Intermediate Care. *Beds* 52. *Certified* Medicaid.

Senior Citizens Nursing Home*
1300 E College, Broken Arrow, OK, 74012 (918) 251-1571
Admin Leonard Brill.
Licensure Intermediate Care. *Beds* 89. *Certified* Medicaid.

Tidings of Peace
1709 S Main, Broken Arrow, OK, 74012 (918) 251-7744
Admin LaDonna Ross. *Medical Dir/Dir of Nursing* Fred Ferguson DO.
Licensure Intermediate Care. *Beds* 80. *Certified* Medicaid.
Admissions Requirements Medical examination; Physician's request.
Staff RNs 1 (pt); LPNs 5 (ft); Orderlies 2 (ft); Nurses aides 25 (ft); Activities coordinators 1 (ft); Dietitians 1 (pt).
Facilities Dining room; Activities room; Crafts room; Laundry room; Barber/Beauty shop.
Activities Arts and Crafts; Cards; Games; Reading groups; Prayer groups; Movies; Shopping trips; Dances/Social or cultural gatherings.

BROKEN BOW

Broken Bow Nursing Home*
805 N Bock St, Broken Bow, OK, 74728 (405) 584-6433
Admin Lois Hutchison.
Licensure Intermediate Care. *Beds* 95. *Certified* Medicaid.

McCurtain Manor Nursing Center*
Box 880, 1201 Dierks, Broken Bow, OK, 74728 (405) 584-9158
Admin John V Rich Jr.
Licensure Intermediate Care. *Beds* 38. *Certified* Medicaid.

BUFFALO

Western Nursing Home
Walnut Dr, Buffalo, OK, 73834 (405) 735-2415
Admin Arlan Engeseth.
Licensure Intermediate Care. *Beds* 74. *Certified* Medicaid.
Facilities Dining room; Activities room; Crafts room; Laundry room; Barber/Beauty shop.
Activities Arts and Crafts; Games; Reading groups; Prayer groups; Movies; Shopping trips; Dances/Social or cultural gatherings.

CADDO

Caddo Nursing Home
203 S McPherren, Caddo, OK, 74729 (405) 367-2264
Admin Hatsene Milligan.
Licensure Intermediate Care. *Beds* 34. *Certified* Medicaid.
Staff RNs 1 (pt); LPNs 2 (ft); Nurses aides 6 (ft), 10 (pt); Activities coordinators 1 (ft); Dietitians 1 (pt).
Facilities Dining room; Activities room; Crafts room; Laundry room; Barber/Beauty shop.
Activities Arts and Crafts; Games; Reading groups; Prayer groups; Movies; Shopping trips; Dances/Social or cultural gatherings.
Description Small town facility features a spacious yard. Tries to be next best to being at home.

CALERA

Calera Manor Nursing Home
Access and Blue Ave, Calera, OK, 74730 (405) 434-5727
Admin Gerald Buchanan. *Medical Dir/Dir of Nursing* Rao Sureddi MD.
Licensure Intermediate Care. *Beds* 50. *Certified* Medicaid.
Admissions Requirements Medical examination.
Staff RNs 1 (pt); LPNs 2 (ft), 1 (pt); Nurses aides 10 (ft); Activities coordinators 1 (ft); Dietitians 1 (pt).
Facilities Dining room; Physical therapy room; Activities room; Laundry room.
Activities Arts and Crafts; Cards; Games; Prayer groups; Dances/Social or cultural gatherings.

CARMEN

Carmen Home
N Grand St, Box 158, Carmen, OK, 73726 (405) 987-2577
Admin J M Lemmon. *Medical Dir/Dir of Nursing* Betty Oakley.
Licensure Intermediate Care. *Beds* 65. *Certified* Medicaid.
Admissions Requirements Medical examination; Physician's request.
Staff RNs 1 (ft); LPNs 3 (ft), 1 (pt); Orderlies 1 (pt); Nurses aides 11 (ft), 10 (pt); Physical therapists 1 (pt); Recreational therapists 1 (pt); Activities coordinators 1 (ft); Dietitians 1 (pt); Dentists 1 (pt).
Affiliation Pentecostal Holiness
Facilities Dining room; Activities room; Chapel; Crafts room; Laundry room; Barber/Beauty shop.
Activities Arts and Crafts; Cards; Games; Prayer groups; Dances/Social or cultural gatherings.

CARNEGIE

Carnegie Nursing Home*
225 N Broadway, Carnegie, OK, 73015 (405) 654-1439
Admin Lloyd Hilburn.
Licensure Intermediate Care. *Beds* 100. *Certified* Medicaid.

CHANDLER

Chandler Hillcrest Manor Inc*
401 W 1st, Chandler, OK, 74834 (405) 258-1131
Admin Judith Austin Cox.
Licensure Intermediate Care. *Beds* 52. *Certified* Medicaid.

Pioneer Estate
2nd and Steele, Chandler, OK, 74834 (405) 258-1375
Admin Peggy Inskeep. *Medical Dir/Dir of Nursing* Doris McCorkle.
Licensure Intermediate Care. *Beds* 49. *Certified* Medicaid.
Admissions Requirements Medical examination.
Staff RNs 1 (pt); LPNs 3 (ft); Nurses aides 12 (ft), 4 (pt); Physical therapists 1 (pt); Activities coordinators 1 (ft); Dietitians 1 (pt).
Facilities Dining room; Activities room; Chapel; Crafts room; Laundry room; Barber/Beauty shop.
Activities Arts and Crafts; Cards; Games; Reading groups; Prayer groups; Movies; Shopping trips.

CHECOTAH

Cedars Manor Inc
1001 W Gentry, Checotah, OK, 74426 (918) 473-2247
Admin Betty Kelsoe. *Medical Dir/Dir of Nursing* Dr John F Rice.
Licensure Intermediate Care. *Beds* 76. *Certified* Medicaid.
Admissions Requirements Medical examination.
Staff RNs 1 (pt); LPNs 3 (ft), 2 (pt); Nurses aides 20 (ft), 7 (pt); Activities coordinators 1 (ft), 1 (pt); Dietitians 1 (pt).
Facilities Dining room; Physical therapy room; Laundry room; Barber/Beauty shop.
Activities Arts and Crafts; Cards; Games; Reading groups; Prayer groups; Movies; Shopping trips; Dances/Social or cultural gatherings.

Checotah Manor Inc
112 SE 1st and Audd, Checotah, OK, 74426 (918) 473-2251
Admin Deborah Kelsoe. *Medical Dir/Dir of Nursing* Dian Leeper LPN.
Licensure Intermediate Care. *Beds* 82. *Certified* Medicaid.
Staff Physicians 3 (pt); RNs 1 (pt); LPNs 3 (ft), 2 (pt); Nurses aides 20 (ft); Activities coordinators 1 (ft); Dietitians 1 (pt); Dentists 1 (pt).
Facilities Dining room; Laundry room.
Activities Arts and Crafts; Cards; Games; Prayer groups; Movies; Shopping trips; Dances/Social or cultural gatherings.

Odd Fellows Rest Home*
211 North Ave, Checotah, OK, 74426 (918) 473-5814
Admin Willie M Harris.
Licensure Intermediate Care. *Beds* 28. *Certified* Medicaid.
Affiliation Independent Order of Odd Fellows

CHELSEA

Colonial Manor of Chelsea
4th and Hickory, Chelsea, OK, 74016 (918) 789-3215
Admin Henry R Malone. *Medical Dir/Dir of Nursing* Larry Lane DO.
Licensure Intermediate Care. *Beds* 60. *Certified* Medicaid.
Staff Physicians 1 (ft), 1 (pt); RNs 1 (ft); LPNs 1 (ft), 1 (pt); Orderlies 1 (ft); Nurses aides 20 (ft), 5 (pt); Physical therapists 1 (pt); Activities coordinators 1 (ft); Dietitians 1 (pt).
Facilities Dining room; Physical therapy room; Activities room; Crafts room; Laundry room; Barber/Beauty shop.
Activities Arts and Crafts; Cards; Games; Prayer groups; Shopping trips; Dances/Social or cultural gatherings.
Description Facility has a very outstanding patient therapy program.

CHEROKEE

Cherokee Memorial Manor Inc
10th St and Memorial Dr, Cherokee, OK, 73728 (405) 596-2141
Admin Oliver Harris. *Medical Dir/Dir of Nursing* Dr Dean Vaughan.
Licensure Intermediate Care. *Beds* 54. *Certified* Medicaid.
Admissions Requirements Medical examination.
Staff Physicians 5 (pt); RNs 1 (ft), 1 (pt); LPNs 1 (ft), 1 (pt); Nurses aides 15 (ft); Physical therapists 1 (ft), 1 (pt); Reality therapists 1 (ft); Activities coordinators 1 (ft); Dietitians 1 (ft), 1 (pt); Dentists 1 (pt); Ophthalmologists 1 (pt).
Facilities Dining room; Physical therapy room; Activities room; Crafts room; Laundry room; Barber/Beauty shop; Library.
Activities Arts and Crafts; Cards; Games; Reading groups; Prayer groups; Movies; Shopping trips; Dances/Social or cultural gatherings.
Description Residents are encouraged to bring some of their own furniture for their room to feel at home. Facility provides recreation; resident and family social gatherings, barbecues, picnics, ice-cream socials, and parties, remotivation and spelling bees, poetry circles and charades, quizzes weekly, monthly cooking.

CHEYENNE

Cheyenne Convalescent Home
301 S 4th, Cheyenne, OK, 73628 (405) 497-3328
Admin Terry Joe Bauermeister. *Medical Dir/Dir of Nursing* F K Buster MD.
Licensure Intermediate Care. *Beds* 36. *Certified* Medicaid.
Admissions Requirements Medical examination; Physician's request.
Staff RNs 1 (pt); LPNs 1 (ft), 2 (pt); Nurses aides 8 (ft), 6 (pt); Activities coordinators 1 (ft), 1 (pt); Dietitians 1 (pt).
Facilities Dining room; Activities room; Crafts room; Laundry room.
Activities Arts and Crafts; Cards; Games; Reading groups; Prayer groups; Movies.

CHICKASHA

Chickasha Nursing Center Inc*
2700 S 9th, Chickasha, OK, 73018 (405)
224-3593
Admin Linda Martin.
Licensure Intermediate Care. *Beds* 60. *Certified* Medicaid.

Eventide Care Center*
2300 Iowa Ave, Chickasha, OK, 73018 (405)
224-6456
Admin Patsy I Banks.
Licensure Intermediate Care. *Beds* 100. *Certified* Medicaid.

Shanoan Springs Residence Inc
12th and Montana, Chickasha, OK, 73018
(405) 224-1397
Admin Paula McCathern.
Licensure Intermediate Care. *Beds* 82. *Certified* Medicaid.
Staff RNs 1 (ft); LPNs 2 (ft); Nurses aides 28
(ft); Recreational therapists 1 (ft); Occupational
therapists 1 (ft); Dietitians 1 (ft).

Sunnytide Nursing Home*
2027 Idaho Ave, Chickasha, OK, 73018 (405)
224-1513
Admin Patsy I Banks.
Licensure Intermediate Care. *Beds* 58. *Certified* Medicaid.

CHOUTEAU

Meadowbrook Nursing Home*
113 E Jones Ave, Chouteau, OK, 74337 (918)
476-8918
Admin Tad Sampsel.
Licensure Intermediate Care. *Beds* 55. *Certified* Medicaid.

CLAREMORE

Claremore Nursing Home Inc
1500 N Sioux, Claremore, OK, 74017 (918)
341-4857
Admin Sam Lessley.
Licensure Intermediate Care. *Beds* 72. *Certified* Medicaid.
Staff RNs 1 (ft), 1 (pt); LPNs 2 (ft), 1 (pt);
Nurses aides 23 (ft); Activities coordinators 2
(pt); Dietitians 1 (pt); 8 (ft), 6 (pt).
Facilities Dining room; Activities room; Crafts
room; Laundry room; Barber/Beauty shop.
Activities Arts and Crafts; Cards; Games;
Shopping trips; Dances/Social or cultural gatherings.

Wood Manor Inc
630 N Dorothy, Claremore, OK, 74017 (918)
341-4365
Admin Wayne Wood.
Licensure Intermediate Care. *Beds* 101. *Certified* Medicaid.
Admissions Requirements Medical examination; Physician's request.
Staff RNs 1 (ft); LPNs 4 (ft); Orderlies 2 (ft);
Nurses aides 37 (ft); Physical therapists 1 (pt);
Speech therapists 1 (pt); Dietitians 1 (pt).
Facilities Dining room; Crafts room; Laundry

room; Barber/Beauty shop.
Activities Arts and Crafts; Cards; Games;
Reading groups; Prayer groups; Shopping trips;
Dances/Social or cultural gatherings.

CLEVELAND

Cleveland Nursing Home Inc*
519 W Pawnee, Cleveland, OK, 74020 (918)
358-3135
Admin Carrie Myers.
Licensure Intermediate Care. *Beds* 50. *Certified* Medicaid.

CLINTON

Highland Park Manor*
2400 Modelle, Clinton, OK, 73601 (405)
323-1110
Admin Rebecca White.
Licensure Intermediate Care. *Beds* 100. *Certified* Medicaid.

Methodist Home of Clinton Inc
2316 Modelle, Clinton, OK, 73601 (405)
323-0912
Admin Michael R Sewell. *Medical Dir/Dir of
Nursing* Dr Curtis Cunningham.
Licensure Intermediate Care. *Beds* 61. *Certified* Medicaid.
Admissions Requirements Medical examination; Physician's request.
Staff RNs 1 (ft); LPNs 3 (ft); Nurses aides 26
(ft), 5 (pt); Physical therapists 1 (ft); Recreational therapists 1 (ft); Activities coordinators 1
(ft); Dietitians 1 (pt).
Affiliation Methodist
Facilities Dining room; Physical therapy room;
Activities room; Chapel; Crafts room; Laundry
room; Barber/Beauty shop.
Activities Arts and Crafts; Cards; Games;
Reading groups; Movies; Shopping trips.
Description Facility provides meals-on-wheels
to surrounding area.

COALGATE

Hurley Manor*
Ohio and Covington, Coalgate, OK, 74538
(405) 927-2000
Admin Buford Canaday.
Licensure Intermediate Care. *Beds* 75. *Certified* Medicaid.

COLLINSVILLE

Collinsville Manor*
2300 Broadway, Collinsville, OK, 74021 (918)
371-2545
Admin Jacquelyn Hudson.
Licensure Intermediate Care. *Beds* 100. *Certified* Medicaid.

COMANCHE

B and B Nursing Home*
701 S 9th, Comanche, OK, 73529 (405)
439-5569

Admin Betty Cloghorn.
Licensure Intermediate Care. *Beds* 90. *Certified* Medicaid.

Meridian Nursing Home
Rt 2, Comanche, OK, 73529 (405) 439-2398
Admin Coweta Bishop.
Licensure Intermediate Care. *Beds* 46. *Certified* Medicaid.
Admissions Requirements Medical
examination; Physician's request.
Staff Physicians 1 (pt); RNs 1 (ft); LPNs 6 (ft);
Orderlies 1 (ft), 1 (pt); Nurses aides 11 (ft);
Physical therapists 1 (ft); Recreational therapists
1 (ft); Activities coordinators 1 (ft); Dietitians 4
(ft); Social workers 1 (ft).
Facilities Dining room; Physical therapy room;
Activities room; Crafts room; Laundry room;
Barber/Beauty shop; Library.
Activities Cards; Games; Reading groups; Prayer groups; Shopping trips; Community plays;
Seasonal parties.
Description Small community and small
nursing home—everyone knows everyone; like
one large happy family.

COMMERCE

**Eastwood Manor Nursing and Rehabilitation
Center***
Hwy 66 and 6th St, Commerce, OK, 74339
(918) 675-4455
Admin Margaret Eastwood.
Licensure Intermediate Care. *Beds* 53. *Certified* Medicaid.

CORDELL

Cordell Christian Home*
1400 N College St, Cordell, OK, 73632 (405)
832-3371
Admin Lowell Donley.
Licensure Intermediate Care. *Beds* 110. *Certified* Medicaid.

CORN

Menonite Bretheren Home for the Aged*
207 S Dewey, Corn, OK, 73024 (405) 343-2295
Admin Loren Penner.
Licensure Intermediate Care. *Beds* 61. *Certified* Medicaid.
Affiliation Mennonite

COWETA

Coweta Manor*
Coweta, OK, 74429 (918) 251-6075
Admin Stella Maria Walker.
Licensure Intermediate Care. *Beds* 100.
Certified Medicaid.

CRESCENT

Crescent Care Center*
E Sanderson, Crescent, OK, 73028 (405)
969-2680

Admin Elsie Hall.
Licensure Intermediate Care. *Beds* 47. *Certified* Medicaid.

CUSHING

Colonial Plaza Nursing Home Inc*
1405 E Moses, Cushing, OK, 74023 (918) 255-2220
Admin Genevieve Gary.
Licensure Intermediate Care. *Beds* 67. *Certified* Medicaid.

Rest Haven Nursing Home*
310 N Central, Cushing, OK, 74023 (918) 225-1477
Admin Russell E Meyers Jr.
Licensure Intermediate Care. *Beds* 55. *Certified* Medicaid.

CYRIL

Cyril Nursing Home*
4th and Colorado Sts, Cyril, OK, 73029 (405) 464-2242
Admin Leonard R Stewart.
Licensure Intermediate Care. *Beds* 80. *Certified* Medicaid.

DAVIS

Burford Manor*
505 S 7th, Davis, OK, 73030 (405) 369-2653
Admin Bill M Burford.
Licensure Intermediate Care. *Beds* 51. *Certified* Medicaid.

DEL CITY

Evergreen Nursing Home
400 S Scott, Del City, OK, 73115 (405) 677-3349
Admin Ross Campbell. *Medical Dir/Dir of Nursing* Tracy Skolnick DO.
Licensure Intermediate Care. *Beds* 61. *Certified* Medicaid.
Admissions Requirements Medical examination; Physician's request.
Staff Physicians 1 (pt); RNs 1 (pt); LPNs 3 (ft); Orderlies 1 (ft); Nurses aides 13 (ft); Physical therapists 1 (pt); Recreational therapists 1 (ft); Occupational therapists 1 (ft); Activities coordinators 1 (ft); Dietitians 1 (pt); Dentists 1 (pt); Ophthalmologists 1 (pt); Podiatrists 1 (pt); Audiologists 1 (pt).
Facilities Dining room; Physical therapy room; Activities room; Chapel; Crafts room; Laundry room; Barber/Beauty shop; Library.
Activities Arts and Crafts; Cards; Games; Reading groups; Prayer groups; Movies; Shopping trips; Dances/Social or cultural gatherings.

DEWEY

Forrest Manor Nursing Home
1410 N Choctaw, Dewey, OK, 74029 (918) 534-3355
Admin J D Fitzgerald.
Licensure Intermediate Care. *Beds* 116. *Certi-

fied* Medicaid.
Staff RNs; LPNs; Orderlies; Nurses aides; Physical therapists; Activities coordinators; Dietitians; Dentists.
Facilities Dining room; Physical therapy room; Activities room; Crafts room; Laundry room; Barber/Beauty shop.
Activities Arts and Crafts; Cards; Games; Shopping trips; Dances/Social or cultural gatherings.

Medicalodge of Dewey*
PO Box 520, Dewey, OK, 74029 (918) 534-2848
Admin Leila Arlene Dick.
Licensure Intermediate Care. *Beds* 62. *Certified* Medicaid.

DRUMRIGHT

Drumright Nursing Home*
Pine and Bristow, Drumright, OK, 74030 (918) 352-3249
Admin Marie Cooper.
Licensure Intermediate Care. *Beds* 118. *Certified* Medicaid.

DUNCAN

Duncan Care Center*
700 Palm, Duncan, OK, 73533 (405) 255-9000
Admin Phyllis Hill.
Licensure Intermediate Care. *Beds* 180. *Certified* Medicaid.

Kanukuk Nursing Home*
N Hwy 81, Duncan, OK, 73533 (405) 255-4600
Admin Jack Gregston.
Licensure Intermediate Care. *Beds* 94. *Certified* Medicaid.

Kenya Village Nursing Home
1205 S 4th St, Duncan, OK, 73533 (405) 252-3955
Admin Worth McGee.
Licensure Intermediate Care. *Beds* 31. *Certified* Medicaid.
Admissions Requirements Minimum age 18; Medical examination.
Staff RNs 1 (pt); LPNs 2 (ft); Orderlies 1 (pt); Nurses aides 6 (ft), 3 (pt); Physical therapists 1 (pt); Recreational therapists 1 (ft); Activities coordinators 1 (ft); Dietitians 1 (pt).
Facilities Dining room; Physical therapy room; Laundry room; Barber/Beauty shop.
Activities Arts and Crafts; Cards; Games; Reading groups; Prayer groups; Shopping trips.

Lahey's Nursing Home
1004 N 5th St, Duncan, OK, 73533 (405) 255-6378
Admin Donald J Legner. *Medical Dir/Dir of Nursing* David Fisher MD.
Licensure Intermediate Care. *Beds* 47. *Certified* Medicaid.
Admissions Requirements Medical examination.
Staff RNs 1 (ft); LPNs 3 (ft); Nurses aides 15 (ft), 4 (pt); Physical therapists 1 (pt); Activities coordinators 1 (ft), 1 (pt); Dietitians 1 (pt); Dentists 1 (pt).

Facilities Dining room; Physical therapy room; Activities room; Crafts room; Laundry room; Barber/Beauty shop.
Activities Arts and Crafts; Cards; Games; Reading groups; Prayer groups; Movies; Shopping trips; Dances/Social or cultural gatherings.
Description Facility has been family owned and operated since 1961.

DURANT

Bryan County Manor*
1401 N Washington, Durant, OK, 74701 (405) 924-1263
Admin Kurt Stumpff.
Licensure Intermediate Care. *Beds* 65. *Certified* Medicaid.

Four Seasons Nursing Center*
1212 4-Seasons Dr, Durant, OK, 74701 (405) 924-5300
Admin Lloyd Allen Wheeler.
Licensure Intermediate Care. *Beds* 110. *Certified* Medicaid.

King's Daughters and Sons Nursing Home
1223 Baltimore, Durant, OK, 74701 (405) 924-0496
Admin Bonnie A Bates.
Licensure Intermediate Care. *Beds* 65. *Certified* Medicaid.
Staff RNs; LPNs; Nurses aides.
Affiliation King's Daughters and Sons
Facilities Dining room; Physical therapy room; Activities room; Chapel; Crafts room; Laundry room; Barber/Beauty shop.
Activities Arts and Crafts; Cards; Games; Prayer groups.

Oak Ridge Manor
1100 Oak Ridge, Durant, OK, 74701 (405) 924-3244
Admin Erik Stumpff. *Medical Dir/Dir of Nursing* Patricia Henderson RN.
Licensure Intermediate Care. *Beds* 84. *Certified* Medicaid.
Admissions Requirements Minimum age 18; Medical examination; Physician's request.
Staff RNs 1 (ft); LPNs 2 (ft); Orderlies 1 (ft), 1 (pt); Nurses aides 24 (ft); Reality therapists 1 (pt); Recreational therapists 1 (pt); Activities coordinators 1 (ft); Dietitians 2 (pt).
Facilities Dining room; Physical therapy room; Activities room; Chapel; Crafts room; Laundry room; Barber/Beauty shop; Library.
Activities Arts and Crafts; Cards; Games; Reading groups; Prayer groups; Movies; Shopping trips; Dances/Social or cultural gatherings.
Description Oak Ridge Manor is located in a quiet residential area, shaded by huge oak trees. It is only 2 blocks from hospital and 3 from doctor's clinic.

EDMOND

Edmond Nursing Center*
39 SE 33rd, Edmond, OK, 73034 (405) 341-5555
Admin Sharon Holland.
Licensure Intermediate Care. *Beds* 109. *Certified* Medicaid.

Oklahoma Christian Home Inc*
906 N Blvd, Edmond, OK, 73034 (405)
341-0810
Admin Charles D Hattendorf.
Licensure Intermediate Care. *Beds* 122. *Certi-fied* Medicaid.

Timberlane Manor Nursing Home
Box 2017, Edmond, OK, 73083 (405) 341-1433
Admin Shanna Shade.
Licensure Intermediate Care. *Beds* 58. *Certi-fied* Medicaid.
Staff RNs 1 (ft); LPNs 2 (ft), 1 (pt); Activities coordinators 1 (ft); Dietitians 1 (pt).
Facilities Dining room; Activities room; Laundry room; Barber/Beauty shop.
Activities Arts and Crafts; Cards; Games; Prayer groups; Movies; Dances/Social or cultural gatherings.

EL RENO

El Reno Nursing Center
1901 Parkview Dr, PO Box 1399, El Reno, OK, 73036 (405) 262-2833
Admin Linda Jones.
Licensure Intermediate Care. *Beds* 121. *Certi-fied* Medicaid.
Admissions Requirements Medical examination; Physician's request.
Staff RNs 3 (ft); LPNs 3 (ft); Nurses aides 23 (ft), 2 (pt); Activities coordinators 1 (ft); Dietitians 1 (ft).
Facilities Dining room; Activities room; Crafts room; Laundry room; Barber/Beauty shop; Library.
Activities Arts and Crafts; Cards; Games; Reading groups; Prayer groups; Movies; Shopping trips; Dances/Social or cultural gatherings.

Sunset Estates of El Reno Inc*
2100 Townsend Dr, El Reno, OK, 73036 (405) 262-3323
Admin Johnie L Harris.
Licensure Intermediate Care. *Beds* 66. *Certi-fied* Medicaid.

ELK CITY

Hodges Nursing Home Inc
301 N Garrett, Elk City, OK, 73644 (405) 225-2811
Admin Mary E Porter. *Medical Dir/Dir of Nursing* R R Heine MD.
Licensure Intermediate Care. *Beds* 112. *Certi-fied* Medicaid.
Admissions Requirements Medical examination; Physician's request.
Staff RNs 3 (ft); LPNs 4 (ft); Orderlies 4 (ft); Nurses aides 60 (ft); Physical therapists 1 (pt); Reality therapists 1 (ft); Activities coordinators 2 (ft); Dietitians 1 (pt); Dentists 1 (pt); Ophthalmologists 1 (pt).
Facilities Dining room; Physical therapy room; Activities room; Chapel; Crafts room; Laundry room; Barber/Beauty shop; Library.
Activities Arts and Crafts; Cards; Games; Reading groups; Prayer groups; Movies; Shopping trips; Dances/Social or cultural gatherings; Cooking class.
Description We tailor our programs to fit the

individual. Our facilities are geared to be as much like home as possible. Facility features a lake with wildlife on the grounds.

ENID

Enid Living Center
1409 N 17th St, Enid, OK, 73701 (405) 234-1411
Admin Betty J Harris. *Medical Dir/Dir of Nursing* Dr Stafford.
Licensure Intermediate Care. *Beds* 50.
Facilities Dining room; Physical therapy room; Activities room; Chapel; Crafts room; Laundry room; Barber/Beauty shop; Library.
Activities Arts and Crafts; Cards; Games; Reading groups; Prayer groups; Movies; Shopping trips; Dances/Social or cultural gatherings.
Description All efforts are made to make the residents feel at home.

Greenbrier Nursing Home*
1121 E Owen Garriott, Enid, OK, 73701 (405) 233-0121
Admin Dortha Schmitz.
Licensure Intermediate Care. *Beds* 52. *Certi-fied* Medicaid.

Highland Park Manor*
1410 W Willow Rd, Enid, OK, 73701 (405) 234-2526
Admin Darlene Braley.
Licensure Intermediate Care. *Beds* 110. *Certi-fied* Medicaid.

Kenwood Manor
502 W Pine, Enid, OK, 73701 (405) 233-2722
Admin Betty J Harris. *Medical Dir/Dir of Nursing* Dr Stafford.
Licensure Intermediate Care. *Beds* 45. *Certi-fied* Medicaid.
Admissions Requirements Medical examination.
Facilities Dining room; Physical therapy room; Activities room; Crafts room; Laundry room; Barber/Beauty shop.
Activities Arts and Crafts; Cards; Games; Reading groups; Prayer groups; Movies; Shopping trips; Dances/Social or cultural gatherings.
Description Birthday parties and social events planned with the families invited; all effort is made for residents to feel at home.

Methodist Home of Enid Inc*
PO Box 10489, 301 S Oakwood Rd, Enid, OK, 73702 (405) 237-6164
Admin Betty Kellet.
Licensure Intermediate Care. *Beds* 81. *Certi-fied* Medicaid.
Affiliation Methodist

Pekrul Manor*
313 E Oxford, Enid, OK, 73701 (405) 237-3871
Admin Virgil Pekrul.
Licensure Intermediate Care. *Beds* 50. *Certi-fied* Medicaid.

Sunny Side Center
1824 S Van Buren, Enid, OK, 73701 (405) 233-6422
Admin Anita Hartling. *Medical Dir/Dir of Nursing* Jaspal Chawla MD.

Licensure Intermediate Care. *Beds* 112. *Certi-fied* Medicaid.
Staff LPNs 4 (ft), 1 (pt); Orderlies 2 (ft); Nurses aides 38 (ft); Physical therapists 1 (ft); Activities coordinators 1 (ft); Dietitians 1 (pt).
Facilities Dining room; Physical therapy room; Activities room; Crafts room; Laundry room; Barber/Beauty shop.
Activities Arts and Crafts; Cards; Games; Reading groups; Prayer groups; Movies; Shopping trips; Dances/Social or cultural gatherings; Special Olympics.

Sunset Estates of Enid Inc*
410 N 30th St, Enid, OK, 73701 (405) 237-1973
Admin Joe Bussey.
Licensure Intermediate Care. *Beds* 102. *Certi-fied* Medicaid.

ERICK

Erick Nursing Home*
112 S Magnolia, Erick, OK, 73645 (405) 526-3088
Admin Joe Bauermeister.
Licensure Intermediate Care. *Beds* 31. *Certi-fied* Medicaid.

EUFAULA

Eufaula Manor Inc
107 McKinley, Eufaula, OK, 74432 (918) 689-3211
Admin Bonnie Brockman.
Licensure Intermediate Care. *Beds* 80. *Certi-fied* Medicaid.
Facilities Dining room; Activities room; Laundry room; Barber/Beauty shop.
Activities Arts and Crafts; Cards; Games; Reading groups; Prayer groups; Movies; Shopping trips; Dances/Social or cultural gatherings.

Friendly Manor Nursing Home
6th and Woodland, Eufaula, OK, 74432 (918) 689-2508
Admin Jim Nixon. *Medical Dir/Dir of Nursing* J Howard Bakers Jr MD.
Licensure Intermediate Care. *Beds* 70. *Certi-fied* Medicaid.
Admissions Requirements Medical examination; Physician's request.
Staff Physicians 5 (pt); RNs 1 (ft); LPNs 4 (ft), 1 (pt); Nurses aides 19 (ft), 2 (pt); Recreational therapists 1 (ft); Activities coordinators 1 (pt); Dietitians 1 (pt); Dentists 3 (pt).
Facilities Dining room; Physical therapy room; Activities room; Chapel; Crafts room; Laundry room; Barber/Beauty shop.
Activities Arts and Crafts; Cards; Games; Reading groups; Prayer groups; Movies; Shopping trips; Dances/Social or cultural gatherings.
Description Home is located in quiet residential area within blocks of beautiful Lake Eufaula.

FAIRFAX

Fairfax Nursing Home*
401 S 8th, Fairfax, OK, 74637 (918) 642-3234
Admin Clayton Farmer.
Licensure Intermediate Care. *Beds* 50. *Certified* Medicaid.

FAIRLAND

Fairland Nursing Home
12 E Conner, Fairland, OK, 74343 (918) 676-3685
Admin Jane A Wooley.
Licensure Intermediate Care. *Beds* 29. *Certified* Medicaid.
Admissions Requirements Medical examination; Physician's request.
Staff RNs; LPNs; Nurses aides; Physical therapists; Activities coordinators.
Facilities Dining room; Activities room; Laundry room; Barber/Beauty shop.
Activities Arts and Crafts; Games; Reading groups; Prayer groups; Movies; Shopping trips.

FAIRVIEW

Fairview Fellowship Home*
710 N 10th, Fairview, OK, 73737 (405) 227-3784
Admin Dwight D Martin.
Licensure Intermediate Care. *Beds* 100. *Certified* Medicaid.

FORT GIBSON

Fort Gibson Nursing Home*
205 E Popular, Fort Gibson, OK, 74434 (918) 478-2456
Admin Michael Scott.
Licensure Intermediate Care. *Beds* 48. *Certified* Medicaid.

FREDERICK

Pioneer Manor*
313 E Lucille, Frederick, OK, 73542 (405) 335-5591
Admin Mary Deane.
Licensure Intermediate Care. *Beds* 110. *Certified* Medicaid.

GARBER

Garber Nursing Home*
E Garber Rd, Garber, OK, 73738 (405) 863-2297
Admin Frank T Hagerman.
Licensure Intermediate Care. *Beds* 57. *Certified* Medicaid.

GEARY

Geary Community Nursing Home Inc
PO Box 47, Geary, OK, 73040 (405) 884-5440
Admin William Perry. *Medical Dir/Dir of Nursing* Dr R A Conley.
Licensure Intermediate Care. *Beds* 47. *Certi-*

fied Medicaid.
Ownership Nonprofit.
Admissions Requirements Medical examination.
Staff Physicians 4 (pt); RNs 1 (pt); LPNs 3 (ft); Nurses aides 20 (ft); Activities coordinators 1 (ft); Dietitians 1 (pt); Dentists 1 (pt).
Facilities Dining room; Laundry room; Barber/Beauty shop.
Activities Arts and Crafts; Cards; Games; Prayer groups; Shopping trips; Dances/Social or cultural gatherings.
Description This is a community-owned, nonprofit facility located in a small town. Our nurses and aides have known most of our residents and their families all of their lives. This gives us a unique home-like atmosphere.

GRANDFIELD

Colonial Village*
900 Westfield St, Grandfield, OK, 73546 (405) 479-5244
Admin Frances Faye Sanders.
Licensure Intermediate Care. *Beds* 40. *Certified* Medicaid.

GROVE

Betty Ann Nursing Home
1202 S Main, Grove, OK, 74344 (918) 786-2275
Admin Bob Maynard.
Licensure Intermediate Care. *Beds* 60. *Certified* Medicaid.
Staff RNs 1 (pt); LPNs 3 (ft); Nurses aides 20 (ft); Activities coordinators 1 (ft); Dietitians 1 (pt).
Facilities Dining room; Physical therapy room; Activities room; Chapel; Crafts room; Laundry room; Barber/Beauty shop; Library.
Activities Arts and Crafts; Cards; Games; Reading groups; Prayer groups; Movies; Shopping trips; Dances/Social or cultural gatherings.
Description Bus trips taken each season: spring trip to state park for picnics and fishing; fall trip is a foliage tour through Ozarks; winter trip down Xmas Tree Lane to see special lights; summer trip to a circus. Facility located 50 yards from Grove General Hospital.

Grand Lake Manor
110 W 11th St, Grove, OK, 74344 (918) 786-2276
Admin Gary Dominguez. *Medical Dir/Dir of Nursing* Alice Wolf LPN.
Licensure Intermediate Care. *Beds* 100. *Certified* Medicaid.
Admissions Requirements Medical examination.
Staff RNs 1 (pt); LPNs 5 (ft), 1 (pt); Nurses aides 18 (ft), 3 (pt); Physical therapists 1 (pt); Activities coordinators 1 (ft); Dietitians 1 (pt).
Facilities Dining room; Physical therapy room; Laundry room; Barber/Beauty shop.
Activities Arts and Crafts; Games; Movies; Shopping trips; Dances/Social or cultural gatherings.

GUTHRIE

Cole's Rest Haven Nursing Home*
1310 E Oklahoma, Guthrie, OK, 73044 (405) 282-1686
Admin John Chambers.
Licensure Intermediate Care. *Beds* 50. *Certified* Medicaid.

Golden Age Nursing Home of Guthrie Inc
419 E Okalhoma, Guthrie, OK, 73044 (405) 282-0144
Admin Gerald Duehning.
Licensure Intermediate Care. *Beds* 72. *Certified* Medicaid.
Staff RNs 1 (ft), 2 (pt); LPNs 3 (ft), 2 (pt); Nurses aides 35 (ft), 5 (pt); Dietitians 1 (pt).
Facilities Dining room; Physical therapy room; Barber/Beauty shop.
Activities Arts and Crafts; Games; Shopping trips.

Guthrie Nursing Center*
405 N 20th, Guthrie, OK, 73044 (405) 282-1515
Admin Debra Ratliff.
Licensure Intermediate Care. *Beds* 100. *Certified* Medicaid.

Senior Citizens Nursing Home*
1924 E Perkins, Guthrie, OK, 73044 (405) 282-3630
Admin Charles M Holthaus.
Licensure Intermediate Care. *Beds* 81. *Certified* Medicaid.

Westview Nursing Center*
1900 W Harrison, Guthrie, OK, 73044 (405) 282-0205
Admin Charles M Holthaus.
Licensure Intermediate Care. *Beds* 51. *Certified* Medicaid.

GUYMON

Dunaway Manor Nursing Home of Guymon Inc
1401 N Lelia, Box 831, Guymon, OK, 73942 (405) 338-3186
Admin Malinda Adams.
Licensure Intermediate Care. *Beds* 72. *Certified* Medicaid.
Admissions Requirements Medical examination.
Staff RNs 1 (ft); LPNs 2 (ft); Nurses aides 30 (ft); Activities coordinators 1 (ft), 1 (pt).
Affiliation Methodist
Facilities Dining room; Activities room; Chapel; Laundry room; Library.
Activities Arts and Crafts; Cards; Games; Reading groups; Prayer groups; Movies; Shopping trips; Dances/Social or cultural gatherings.

HARTSHORNE

Twin City Nursing Home*
310 S 11th, Hartshorne, OK, 74547 (918) 297-2414
Admin Frances Mordecai.
Licensure Intermediate Care. *Beds* 55. *Certified* Medicaid.

HASKELL

Haskell Nursing Center Inc*
Hwy 64 and Ash, Haskell, OK, 74436 (918)
482-3310
Admin Judy McKee.
Licensure Intermediate Care. *Beds* 58. *Certified* Medicaid.

HEALDTON

Healdton Nursing Home*
406 E Main, Healdton, OK, 73438 (405)
229-0737
Admin Patricia Garrison.
Licensure Intermediate Care. *Beds* 51. *Certified* Medicaid.

HEAVENER

Heavener Nursing Home Inc
204 W 1st, Heavener, OK, 74937 (918)
653-2464
Admin Archie Farmer. *Medical Dir/Dir of Nursing* Don Stumiller DO.
Licensure Intermediate Care. *Beds* 41. *Certified* Medicaid.
Admissions Requirements Medical examination; Physician's request.
Staff RNs 1 (pt); LPNs 3 (ft), 1 (pt); Nurses aides 16 (ft), 3 (pt); Activities coordinators 1 (ft); Dietitians 1 (pt).
Facilities Dining room; Activities room; Laundry room.
Activities Arts and Crafts; Games; Reading groups; Movies; Shopping trips; Exercise classes.
Description Facility participates in Oklahoma nursing home queen pageant held yearly; residents are involved in a rock-a-thon also held yearly with donations given to the heart fund.

Vista Nursing Home*
114 W 2nd, Heavener, OK, 74937 (918)
653-2472
Admin Ola Bruesch.
Licensure Intermediate Care. *Beds* 51. *Certified* Medicaid.

HELENA

Ro-Mel Guest Manor Inc
200 W 3rd, Helena, OK, 73741 (405) 852-3286
Admin Jerry Vilhauer. *Medical Dir/Dir of Nursing* Dr Gaylon Crawford.
Licensure Intermediate Care. *Beds* 50. *Certified* Medicaid.
Admissions Requirements Medical examination; Physician's request.
Staff Physicians 1 (pt); RNs 1 (pt); LPNs 1 (ft); Nurses aides 12 (ft), 3 (pt); Physical therapists 2 (pt); Reality therapists 1 (pt); Recreational therapists 1 (pt); Activities coordinators 1 (ft), 1 (pt); Dietitians 1 (ft); Dentists 1 (pt).
Facilities Dining room; Physical therapy room; Activities room; Crafts room; Laundry room; Barber/Beauty shop.
Activities Arts and Crafts; Cards; Games; Reading groups; Prayer groups; Movies; Shopping trips; Church services.

HENNESSEY

Hennessey Care Center*
705 E 3rd, Hennessey, OK, 73742 (405)
853-6027
Admin Maxine Day.
Licensure Intermediate Care. *Beds* 50. *Certified* Medicaid.

HENRYETTA

Bono Nursing Home
212 N Antes, Henryetta, OK, 74437 (918)
652-8797
Admin Toni Johnson. *Medical Dir/Dir of Nursing* Kathy Cox.
Licensure Intermediate Care. *Beds* 53. *Certified* Medicaid.
Staff RNs 1 (ft); LPNs 2 (pt); Nurses aides 14 (ft), 11 (pt); Recreational therapists 1 (ft); Activities coordinators 1 (ft); Dietitians 1 (pt).
Facilities Dining room; Activities room; Crafts room; Laundry room; Barber/Beauty shop.
Activities Arts and Crafts; Cards; Games; Reading groups; Prayer groups; Movies; Shopping trips; Dances/Social or cultural gatherings.

Fountain View Manor*
Box 520, Barclay and Lake Rds, Henryetta, OK, 74437 (918) 652-7021
Admin Opal Molet.
Licensure Intermediate Care. *Beds* 140. *Certified* Medicaid.

Lake Drive Nursing Home Inc*
600 Lake Rd, Henryetta, OK, 74437 (918)
652-8101
Admin Judith Cochran.
Licensure Intermediate Care. *Beds* 60. *Certified* Medicaid.

HINTON

Red Rock Manor Nursing Home Inc
501 W Main, Hinton, OK, 73047 (405)
542-6677
Admin Anita Reimers.
Licensure Intermediate Care. *Beds* 40. *Certified* Medicaid.
Admissions Requirements Medical examination; Physician's request.
Staff Physicians 1 (ft); RNs 1 (pt); LPNs 1 (ft), 2 (pt); Nurses aides 16 (ft); Physical therapists 1 (pt); Reality therapists 1 (pt); Recreational therapists 1 (ft); Activities coordinators 1 (ft); Dietitians 1 (pt); Dentists 1 (pt); Podiatrists 1 (pt).
Facilities Dining room; Activities room; Laundry room; Barber/Beauty shop.
Activities Arts and Crafts; Cards; Games; Reading groups; Prayer groups; Shopping trips.
Description Facility is small and in a beautiful setting. Small community is very supportive of facility; residents participate in community activities.

HOBART

B and K Nursing Center*
100 S Main St, Hobart, OK, 73651 (405)
726-3394

Admin Robert Lyde.
Licensure Intermediate Care. *Beds* 50. *Certified* Medicaid.

Good Samaritan Center*
PO Box 680, 709 N Lowe, Hobart, OK, 73651
(405) 726-3381
Admin Paul Hierstein.
Licensure Intermediate Care. *Beds* 60. *Certified* Medicaid.

Good Samaritan Convalescent Home*
PO Box 680, 330 N Randlett, Hobart, OK,
73651 (405) 726-5597
Admin Paul Hierstein.
Licensure Intermediate Care. *Beds* 28. *Certified* Medicaid.

HOLDENVILLE

Boyce Manor Inc
1600 E Hwy St, Holdenville, OK, 74848 (405)
379-3560
Admin Jerry L Boyce. *Medical Dir/Dir of Nursing* T E Trow MD.
Licensure Intermediate Care. *Beds* 125. *Certified* Medicaid.
Admissions Requirements Minimum age 17; Medical examination; Physician's request.
Staff Physicians 1 (pt); RNs 1 (ft); LPNs 11 (ft); Orderlies 3 (ft); Nurses aides 35 (ft); Physical therapists 1 (ft); Reality therapists 1 (ft); Recreational therapists 1 (ft); Speech therapists 1 (pt); Activities coordinators 1 (pt); Dietitians 1 (pt); Dentists 1 (pt).

Holdenville Nursing Home
515 S Chestnut, Holdenville, OK, 74848 (405)
379-2126
Admin Gerrol Adkins. *Medical Dir/Dir of Nursing* Ruth White.
Licensure Intermediate Care. *Beds* 51. *Certified* Medicaid.
Admissions Requirements Minimum age 18; Medical examination.
Staff Physicians; RNs; LPNs; Nurses aides; Physical therapists; Activities coordinators; Dietitians.
Facilities Dining room; Crafts room; Laundry room; Barber/Beauty shop.
Activities Arts and Crafts; Games; Prayer groups; Shopping trips; Dances/Social or cultural gatherings.
Description Facility is family owned and operated.

HOLLIS

Colonial Manor I*
400 E Sycamore, Hollis, OK, 73550 (405)
688-2223
Admin Robert P Metcalf.
Licensure Intermediate Care. *Beds* 69. *Certified* Medicaid.

Colonial Manor II*
120 W Versa, Hollis, OK, 73550 (405)
688-2828
Admin Robert P Metcalf.
Licensure Intermediate Care. *Beds* 92. *Certified* Medicaid.

HOMINY

Hominy Nursing Home
700 N Katy, Box 577, Hominy, OK, 74035
(918) 885-4746
Admin Zoe Kinney. *Medical Dir/Dir of
Nursing* Carol Passmore LPN.
Licensure Intermediate Care. *Beds* 63. *Certified* Medicaid.
Admissions Requirements Medical examination; Physician's request.
Staff LPNs 2 (ft), 1 (pt); Orderlies 1 (ft); Nurses
aides 15 (ft); Activities coordinators 1 (pt); Dietitians 1 (pt).
Facilities Dining room; Activities room;
Chapel; Crafts room; Laundry room; Barber-/Beauty shop.
Activities Arts and Crafts; Cards; Games;
Prayer groups; Shopping trips; Dances/Social
or cultural gatherings.
Description Facility is located 7 blocks from
downtown in a quiet secluded area surrounded
by the city park and a beautifully landscaped
lawn. The home is well lighted and brightly
decorated in rich autumn colors. Tours are welcome.

HUGO

Hugo Golden Age Home*
1200 W Finley, Hugo, OK, 74743 (405)
326-9628
Admin Sam L Garner.
Licensure Intermediate Care. *Beds* 100. *Certified* Medicaid.

Hugo Manor Nursing Home
601 N Broadway, Hugo, OK, 74743 (405)
326-6278
Admin W M McEwing.
Licensure Intermediate Care. *Beds* 80. *Certified* Medicaid.
Admissions Requirements Medical examination.
Staff Physicians 1 (pt); RNs 1 (pt); LPNs 2 (ft);
Activities coordinators 1 (ft); Dietitians 1 (pt);
Dentists 1 (pt).
Facilities Dining room; Physical therapy room;
Activities room; Crafts room; Laundry room;
Barber/Beauty shop.
Activities Arts and Crafts; Cards; Games;
Reading groups; Prayer groups; Movies; Shopping trips; Dances/Social or cultural gatherings.

Rose Haven Health Care Center
605 S "A", Hugo, OK, 74743 (405) 326-3677
Admin Florence Harrison. *Medical Dir/Dir of
Nursing* Dr James Grimand.
Licensure Intermediate Care. *Beds* 30. *Certified* Medicaid.
Admissions Requirements Medical examination; Physician's request.
Staff RNs 1 (ft), 1 (pt); LPNs 1 (ft); Orderlies 1
(ft); Nurses aides 6 (ft); Reality therapists 1 (pt);
Recreational therapists 1 (pt); Activities coordinators 1 (ft); Dietitians 1 (pt); Dentists 1 (pt).
Facilities Dining room; Physical therapy room;
Laundry room; Barber/Beauty shop.
Activities Arts and Crafts; Cards; Games;
Reading groups; Prayer groups; Movies; Shopping trips; Dances/Social or cultural gatherings.

Description Small, family-like facility gives
personal service to residents; believes in faith,
hope, love and reality.

HYDRO

Hydro Manor Inc
800 Arapaho, Hydro, OK, 73048 (405)
663-2455
Admin Jerry Unruh. *Medical Dir/Dir of
Nursing* Dr Ralph Buller.
Licensure Intermediate Care. *Beds* 42. *Certified* Medicaid.
Staff RNs 1 (ft), 1 (pt); LPNs 1 (ft); Nurses
aides 12 (ft), 4 (pt); Activities coordinators 1
(ft).
Affiliation Mennonite

IDABEL

Hill Nursing Home*
808 NW 1st, Idabel, OK, 74745 (405) 286-5398
Admin Gladys Hill.
Licensure Intermediate Care. *Beds* 51. *Certified* Medicaid.

Memorial Heights Nursing Center*
1305 SE Adams, Idabel, OK, 74745 (405)
286-3366
Admin John V Rich Jr.
Licensure Intermediate Care. *Beds* 110. *Certified* Medicaid.

Oak Grove Manor Inc
PO Box 299, Idabel, OK, 74745 (405) 286-2537
Admin James Brown.
Licensure Intermediate Care. *Beds* 81. *Certified* Medicaid.
Staff RNs 2 (ft); LPNs 3 (ft); Nurses aides 30
(ft); Physical therapists 1 (pt); Occupational
therapists 1 (pt); Speech therapists 1 (pt);
Activities coordinators 1 (ft); Dietitians 1 (ft);
Dentists 1 (pt); Ophthalmologists 1 (pt); Podiatrists 1 (pt); Audiologists 1 (pt).
Facilities Dining room; Laundry room; Barber-/Beauty shop; Lounges.
Activities Arts and Crafts; Cards; Games;
Reading groups; Prayer groups; Movies; Shopping trips; Dances/Social or cultural gatherings.
Description A country setting amidst tall oaks
on the outskirts of town; a happy atmosphere
with scores of family members going and
coming throughout the day. Quality nursing
care with love and concern given.

JAY

Guinn Nursing Home 1*
N Main, Jay, OK, 74346 (918) 253-4500
Admin Danny Guinn.
Licensure Intermediate Care. *Beds* 48. *Certified* Medicaid.

Guinn Nursing Home 2*
E Monroe, Jay, OK, 74346 (918) 253-4226
Admin Charles Guinn.
Licensure Intermediate Care. *Beds* 50. *Certified* Medicaid.

JENKS

Ambassador Manor South*
711 N 5th, Jenks, OK, 74037 (918) 299-8500
Admin JoAnne Posey.
Beds 80.

Riverside Nursing Home Inc
601 N 5th, Jenks, OK, 74037 (918) 299-9444
Admin JoAnne Latimer.
Licensure Intermediate Care. *Beds* 102.
Certified Medicaid.
Admissions Requirements Medical examination; Physician's request.
Staff RNs 1 (ft), 1 (pt); LPNs 4 (ft); Nurses
aides 36 (ft); Physical therapists 1 (pt); Recreational therapists 1 (ft); Occupational therapists 1
(pt); Speech therapists 1 (pt); Dietitians 1 (pt).
Facilities Dining room; Physical therapy room;
Activities room; Crafts room; Laundry room;
Barber/Beauty shop.
Activities Arts and Crafts; Cards; Games;
Reading groups; Prayer groups; Movies; Shopping trips; Dances/Social or cultural gatherings.
Description Riverside Nursing Center is
designed to give bedfast, chairfast patients adequate care.

JONES

Oak Hills Nursing Home*
1100 W Georgia, Jones, OK, 73049 (405)
399-2294
Admin Phyllis Murry.
Licensure Intermediate Care. *Beds* 106. *Certified* Medicaid.

KINGFISHER

Care Manor Nursing Center*
200 Will Rogers Dr, Kingfisher, OK, 73750
(405) 375-3106
Admin Delores Armstrong.
Licensure Intermediate Care. *Beds* 48. *Certified* Medicaid.

Care Villa Nursing Center*
1415 S Main, Kingfisher, OK, 73750 (405)
375-3157
Admin Wanda D Willms.
Licensure Intermediate Care. *Beds* 55. *Certified* Medicaid.

KINGSTON

Texoma Health Care Center Inc*
Hwy 32 W, Box 156, Kingston, OK, 73439
(405) 564-2351
Admin Juanima Davis.
Licensure Intermediate Care. *Beds* 60. *Certified* Medicaid.

KONAWA

New Horizons Nursing Home
500 E Main, Konawa, OK, 74849 (405)
925-3645
Admin F C Williamson. *Medical Dir/Dir of
Nursing* Martin Stokes MD.
Licensure Intermediate Care. *Beds* 208. *Certi-*

fied Medicaid.
Admissions Requirements Minimum age 18; Medical examination.
Staff Physicians 1 (pt); RNs 1 (ft); LPNs 7 (ft), 2 (pt); Orderlies 14 (ft); Nurses aides 59 (ft); Reality therapists 1 (ft); Recreational therapists 1 (ft); Activities coordinators 5 (ft); Dietitians 1 (pt); Dentists 1 (pt); Ophthalmologists 1 (pt); Podiatrists 1 (pt).
Facilities Dining room; Physical therapy room; Activities room; Chapel; Crafts room; Laundry room; Barber/Beauty shop; Library.
Activities Arts and Crafts; Cards; Games; Reading groups; Prayer groups; Movies; Shopping trips; Dances/Social or cultural gatherings.
Description Home has one section for geriatrics and a completely separate section for the mentally retarded; very excellent activity program for the mentally retarded.

LAWTON

Arlington Manor*
1202 Arlington, Lawton, OK, 73501 (405) 353-3373
Admin Don W Greb.
Licensure Intermediate Care. *Beds* 54. *Certified* Medicaid.

Cedar Crest Manor*
1700 Fort Sill Blvd, Lawton, OK, 73501 (405) 355-1616
Admin Don W Greb.
Licensure Intermediate Care. *Beds* 92. *Certified* Medicaid.

Cotton's Nursing Home*
7403 W Gore, Lawton, OK, 73505 (405) 536-7401
Admin Larry Cotton.
Licensure Intermediate Care. *Beds* 100. *Certified* Medicaid.

Joseph's Nursing Home
5396 NW Cache Rd, Lawton, OK, 73505 (405) 353-3653
Admin Joseph Amyx. *Medical Dir/Dir of Nursing* Thomas Leckman.
Licensure Intermediate Care. *Beds* 130. *Certified* Medicaid.
Admissions Requirements Minimum age 21; Medical examination; Physician's request.
Staff RNs 1 (pt); LPNs 6 (ft), 2 (pt); Nurses aides 48 (ft); Physical therapists 1 (ft), 1 (pt); Reality therapists 1 (pt); Speech therapists 1 (pt); Activities coordinators 1 (ft); Dietitians 1 (pt).
Activities Arts and Crafts; Cards; Games; Reading groups; Prayer groups; Movies; Shopping trips; Dances/Social or cultural gatherings; Grandfriends program; Visiting pets program; Residents advisory council.
Description Facility is a modern (1983) facility, fireproof construction, fire sprinkler system, 130 intermediate care facility beds (90 geriatric, 40-bed closed psychiatric intensive care unit); all public areas monitored by closed circuit TV. Opening in December 1984, adult geriatric day care center, 30 skilled nursing beds, 50 additional intermediate care facility beds.

Lawton Heights Nursing Center
1301 Andrews, Lawton, OK, 73501 (405) 355-5720
Admin David H Dennis. *Medical Dir/Dir of Nursing* Grace Morrow LPN.
Licensure Intermediate Care. *Beds* 96. *Certified* Medicaid.
Staff RNs 1 (pt); LPNs 9 (ft); Nurses aides 22 (ft); Physical therapists 1 (pt); Speech therapists 1 (pt); Activities coordinators 1 (ft); Dietitians 1 (pt).
Facilities Dining room; Activities room; Crafts room; Laundry room; Barber/Beauty shop.
Activities Arts and Crafts; Cards; Games; Movies; Shopping trips; Dances/Social or cultural gatherings.

McMahon Tomlinson Nursing Center*
3126 Arlington, Lawton, OK, 73505 (405) 357-3240
Admin Floyd Sanders.
Licensure Intermediate Care. *Beds* 118. *Certified* Medicaid.

LEXINGTON

Lexington Nursing Home
632 SE 3rd, Lexington, OK, 73051 (405) 527-6531
Admin Bonnie R Hackney.
Licensure Intermediate Care. *Beds* 60. *Certified* Medicaid.
Admissions Requirements Medical examination.
Staff RNs; LPNs; Nurses aides; Physical therapists; Reality therapists; Recreational therapists; Activities coordinators; Dietitians.
Facilities Dining room; Activities room; Crafts room; Laundry room; Barber/Beauty shop.
Activities Arts and Crafts; Cards; Games; Reading groups; Prayer groups; Movies; Shopping trips; Dances/Social or cultural gatherings.

Sunset Manor of Lexington Inc*
2nd and Broadway, Lexington, OK, 73051 (405) 527-6519
Admin Tony Baird.
Licensure Intermediate Care. *Beds* 101. *Certified* Medicaid.

LINDSAY

Lindsay Care Center
Rt 1, Box 3, Lindsay, OK, 73052 (405) 756-4334
Admin H Joan Wood.
Licensure Intermediate Care. *Beds* 106. *Certified* Medicaid.
Staff LPNs 4 (ft); Nurses aides 28 (ft); Activities coordinators 1 (ft).
Facilities Dining room; Physical therapy room; Activities room; Crafts room; Barber/Beauty shop; Library.
Activities Arts and Crafts; Cards; Games; Shopping trips; Dances/Social or cultural gatherings.
Description Facility has a large whirlpool bath with Sackary chair and lift.

LOCUST GROVE

Parkhill East Nursing Home*
Park and Radcliffe, Locust Grove, OK, 74352 (918) 479-8411
Admin Burl H Trickett.
Licensure Intermediate Care. *Beds* 50. *Certified* Medicaid.

Parkhill South Nursing Home*
Wyandotte and Ross, Locust Grove, OK, 74352 (918) 479-5784
Admin Burl H Trickett.
Licensure Intermediate Care. *Beds* 54. *Certified* Medicaid.

MADILL

Brookside Manor Nursing Home*
Hwy 99 S, Madill, OK, 73446 (405) 795-2100
Admin Phillip W Stumpff.
Licensure Intermediate Care. *Beds* 120. *Certified* Medicaid.

MANGUM

Mangum Nursing Center
320 Carey, Mangum, OK, 73554 (405) 782-3346
Admin John H Fish. *Medical Dir/Dir of Nursing* R Kay Staton LPN.
Licensure Intermediate Care. *Beds* 112. *Certified* Medicaid.
Admissions Requirements Minimum age 18; Physician's request.
Staff RNs 1 (ft); LPNs 4 (pt); Orderlies 1 (pt); Nurses aides 49 (pt); Physical therapists 1 (ft); Speech therapists 1 (ft).
Facilities Dining room; Physical therapy room; Activities room; Laundry room.
Activities Arts and Crafts; Cards; Games; Reading groups; Prayer groups; Movies; Shopping trips; Dances/Social or cultural gatherings.

MARIETTA

Marietta Nursing Home Ltd*
500 Medical Circle Dr, Marietta, OK, 73448 (405) 276-3318
Admin Jerry Cole.
Beds 62.

MARLOW

Gregston Nursing Home
711 S Broadway, Marlow, OK, 73055 (405) 658-2319
Admin JoJean Gregston. *Medical Dir/Dir of Nursing* Charlotte Loughridge.
Licensure Intermediate Care. *Beds* 86. *Certified* Medicaid.
Staff Physicians 1 (ft); RNs 1 (pt); LPNs 3 (ft), 1 (pt); Nurses aides 16 (ft); Physical therapists 1 (pt); Recreational therapists 1 (ft); Activities coordinators 1 (ft); Dietitians 1 (ft), 1 (pt); Dentists 2 (pt).
Facilities Dining room; Physical therapy room; Activities room; Chapel; Crafts room; Laundry room; Barber/Beauty shop; Library.
Activities Arts and Crafts; Cards; Games;

Reading groups; Prayer groups; Shopping trips; Singing groups; Band groups; Bingo; Quilting. *Description* We have a new patio with new picnic tables and a rock garden. One of our new tables has umbrella with matching chairs. We have our own vegetable garden.

Marlow Manor Inc
702 S 9th, PO Box 148, Marlow, OK, 73055 (405) 658-5468
Admin Barbara Besherse. *Medical Dir/Dir of Nursing* Dr W K Walker.
Licensure Intermediate Care. *Beds* 69. *Certified* Medicaid.
Admissions Requirements Medical examination.
Staff RNs 1 (pt); LPNs 2 (ft), 5 (pt); Orderlies 1 (pt); Nurses aides 45 (ft); Physical therapists 1 (pt); Recreational therapists 1 (ft); Activities coordinators 1 (ft); Dietitians 1 (pt); Dentists 1 (pt).
Facilities Dining room; Activities room; Crafts room; Laundry room; Barber/Beauty shop.
Activities Arts and Crafts; Cards; Games; Reading groups; Prayer groups.

MAUD

Maud Nursing Home*
409 W King, Maud, OK, 74854 (405) 374-2263
Admin Jerry Nelson.
Licensure Intermediate Care. *Beds* 32. *Certified* Medicaid.

MAYSVILLE

McCaskill Nursing Home Inc*
903 Parkview Dr, Maysville, OK, 73057 (405) 867-4412
Admin B H McCaskill.
Licensure Intermediate Care. *Beds* 58. *Certified* Medicaid.

MCALESTER

Blevins Retirement and Care Center
1220 E Electric, McAlester, OK, 74501 (918) 423-9095
Admin Charles H Blevins. *Medical Dir/Dir of Nursing* Donna Guthrie.
Licensure Intermediate Care. *Beds* 55. *Certified* Medicaid.
Admissions Requirements Medical examination.
Staff RNs 1 (ft); LPNs 3 (ft); Orderlies 2 (ft); Nurses aides 15 (ft); Dietitians 1 (ft).
Facilities Dining room; Activities room; Chapel; Crafts room; Laundry room; Barber/Beauty shop.
Activities Arts and Crafts; Cards; Games; Prayer groups; Movies; Shopping trips; Dances/Social or cultural gatherings.

Colonial Lodge Nursing Home*
614 W Harrison, McAlester, OK, 74501 (918) 423-6011
Admin Lee Stephens.
Licensure Intermediate Care. *Beds* 80. *Certified* Medicaid.

Colonial Park Nursing Home
1600 N "D" St, McAlester, OK, 74501 (918) 423-0330
Admin Carol Bullett. *Medical Dir/Dir of Nursing* William Gupton MD.
Licensure Intermediate Care. *Beds* 55. *Certified* Medicaid.
Admissions Requirements Medical examination; Physician's request.
Staff RNs 1 (pt); LPNs 2 (ft), 4 (pt); Orderlies 1 (ft); Nurses aides 14 (ft), 4 (pt); Activities coordinators 1 (ft); Dietitians 1 (pt); Dentists 1 (pt).
Facilities Dining room; Activities room; Crafts room; Laundry room; Barber/Beauty shop.
Activities Arts and Crafts; Cards; Games; Reading groups; Prayer groups; Movies; Shopping trips; Dances/Social or cultural gatherings.
Description Home features family/resident pitch-in dinner for holidays; 2 picnics at Arrowhead Lodge; full activity during nursing home week; special olympics for nursing home residents.

Mitchell Manor Nursing Home*
Hickory and Electric, McAlester, OK, 74501 (918) 423-4661
Admin Oleta Mitchell.
Licensure Intermediate Care. *Beds* 50. *Certified* Medicaid.

Plantation Plaza
411 N West St, McAlester, OK, 74501 (918) 423-2920
Admin Ed R Turley. *Medical Dir/Dir of Nursing* Francis Lonergan MD.
Licensure Intermediate Care. *Beds* 56. *Certified* Medicaid.
Staff RNs 1 (ft); LPNs 3 (ft), 4 (pt); Nurses aides 7 (ft), 4 (pt); Activities coordinators 1 (ft); Dietitians 1 (pt).
Facilities Dining room; Activities room; Crafts room; Laundry room; Barber/Beauty shop.
Activities Arts and Crafts; Games; Shopping trips; Dances/Social or cultural gatherings.
Description Facility has recently undergone remodeling for a more home-like atmosphere with updated lobby, day room, and dining room; licensed nurses 24 hours a day. VA approved.

Regency House Convalescent Center
615 E Morris, McAlester, OK, 74501 (918) 426-0850
Admin Margaret Cravins.
Licensure Intermediate Care. *Beds* 63. *Certified* Medicaid.
Admissions Requirements Minimum age 25; Physician's request.
Staff RNs 2 (ft); LPNs 2 (ft); Orderlies 3 (ft); Nurses aides 14 (ft), 6 (pt); Physical therapists 1 (ft); Activities coordinators 1 (ft); Dietitians 1 (ft); Dentists 1 (ft); Podiatrists 1 (pt); Audiologists 1 (pt).
Facilities Dining room; Physical therapy room; Activities room; Crafts room; Laundry room; Barber/Beauty shop.
Activities Arts and Crafts; Cards; Games; Reading groups; Prayer groups; Movies; Shopping trips; Dances/Social or cultural gatherings.
Description One of the outstanding programs of this nursing facility is the annual Nursing Home Olympics of McAlester, Oklahoma. The 6 area homes, with the assistance of the VFW

Post 1098 and auxillary, hold an all day activity featuring a contestant from each facility for each event participating in dominoes, checkers, horseshoes, ball toss and a King and Queen contest, with a cake walk, bingo and a dance, following the events. Each winner receives a trophy, and the facility receiving the highest score of the day receives a grand champion trophy. The merchants, club members, church groups and civic organizations of McAlester all help with this project.

MEDFORD

Medford Nursing Home
616 S Front St, Medford, OK, 73759 (405) 395-2105
Licensure Intermediate Care. *Beds* 69. *Certified* Medicaid.

MIAMI

Care Nursing Home*
130 W Steve Owens, Miami, OK, 74354 (918) 542-9324
Admin Delores Nelson.
Licensure Intermediate Care. *Beds* 58. *Certified* Medicaid.

Heritage House
1410 E Steve Owens, Miami, OK, 74354 (918) 542-8407
Admin Ronald Marquette.
Licensure Intermediate Care. *Beds* 100. *Certified* Medicaid.
Staff RNs 1 (pt); LPNs 5 (ft); Orderlies 2 (ft); Nurses aides 20 (ft); Physical therapists 1 (pt); Speech therapists 1 (pt); Activities coordinators 1 (ft); Dietitians 1 (pt).
Facilities Dining room; Activities room; Laundry room; Barber/Beauty shop.
Activities Arts and Crafts; Games; Prayer groups; Shopping trips; Dances/Social or cultural gatherings; Daily exercise class.
Description Facility features full-time restorative nursing aide under direction of registered physical therapist. Daily exercise class, chaplain services available on request, school for handicapped nearby with bus service to and from nursing home.

Miami Nursing Center*
1100 E St NE, Miami, OK, 74354 (918) 542-3335
Admin Louis D Eastwood.
Licensure Intermediate Care. *Beds* 82. *Certified* Medicaid.

MIDWEST CITY

Colonial Manor Nursing Home
8016 SE 15th, Midwest City, OK, 73110 (405) 737-5685
Admin Troy Matchen.
Licensure Intermediate Care. *Beds* 50. *Certified* Medicaid.
Admissions Requirements Medical examination; Physician's request.
Staff RNs 1 (pt); LPNs 1 (ft), 2 (pt); Nurses aides 20 (ft); Recreational therapists 1 (pt); Activities coordinators 1 (ft); Dietitians 1 (ft).

Facilities Dining room; Activities room.
Activities Arts and Crafts; Cards; Games; Reading groups; Prayer groups; Movies; Shopping trips; Dances/Social or cultural gatherings.
Description We have an "employee of the month" and a "resident of the month." Everyone looks forward to this.

Four Seasons Nursing Center of Midwest City*
2900 Parklawn Dr, Midwest City, OK, 73110
(405) 373-6601
Admin Linda Coventon.
Licensure Intermediate Care. *Beds* 112. *Certified* Medicaid.

Mid-Del Manor Nursing Home*
1401 Crosby Blvd, Midwest City, OK, 73110
(405) 733-1794
Admin Edward Price.
Licensure Intermediate Care. *Beds* 170. *Certified* Medicaid.

MOORE

Hillcrest Nursing Center
2120 N Broadway, Moore, OK, 73160 (405) 794-4429
Admin Sheila Dattolie. *Medical Dir/Dir of Nursing* Perry Taaca MD.
Licensure Intermediate Care. *Beds* 154. *Certified* Medicaid.
Admissions Requirements Medical examination; Physician's request.
Staff RNs 1 (ft); LPNs 5 (ft); Orderlies 2 (ft); Nurses aides 48 (ft); Physical therapists 1 (pt); Activities coordinators 1 (ft); Dietitians 1 (ft).
Facilities Dining room; Activities room; Crafts room; Laundry room; Barber/Beauty shop; Library.
Activities Arts and Crafts; Cards; Games; Reading groups; Prayer groups; Movies; Shopping trips; Dances/Social or cultural gatherings.

MOORELAND

Mooreland Golden Age Nursing Home
402 SE 6th, Mooreland, OK, 73852 (405) 994-5570
Admin Virginia Shaw. *Medical Dir/Dir of Nursing* Lois Roedell LPN.
Licensure Intermediate Care. *Beds* 52. *Certified* Medicaid.
Ownership Public.
Staff RNs 1 (ft); LPNs 3 (ft).
Facilities Dining room; Laundry room; Barber/Beauty shop.
Activities Arts and Crafts; Cards; Games; Prayer groups; Movies; Shopping trips; Dances/Social or cultural gatherings.

MOUNTAIN VIEW

Mountain View Nursing Home
320 N 7th, Mountain View, OK, 73062 (405) 347-2120
Admin Peggy Hines. *Medical Dir/Dir of Nursing* J B Tolbert MD.
Licensure Intermediate Care. *Beds* 32. *Certified* Medicaid.
Admissions Requirements Medical examination; Physician's request.

Staff RNs 1 (pt); LPNs 3 (ft), 2 (pt); Orderlies 1 (ft); Nurses aides 14 (ft), 3 (pt); Activities coordinators 1 (ft); Dietitians 1 (pt).
Facilities Dining room; Activities room; Crafts room; Laundry room.
Activities Arts and Crafts; Cards; Games; Reading groups; Prayer groups; Movies; Shopping trips; Dances/Social or cultural gatherings.
Description Facility offers 24-hour nursing service; qualified health care supervisor; concerned physicians; all types of activities to meet individual needs; consultation arrangement outside facility for services not provided.

MULDROW

Muldrow Nursing Home*
308 S Main, Muldrow, OK, 74948 (918) 427-3441
Admin Judith Henry.
Licensure Intermediate Care. *Beds* 33. *Certified* Medicaid.

MUSKOGEE

Broadway Manor*
1622 E Broadway, Muskogee, OK, 74401 (918) 683-2851
Admin Samuel D Scott.
Licensure Intermediate Care. *Beds* 95. *Certified* Medicaid.

Heritage Nursing Home Inc*
3317 Denver, Muskogee, OK, 74401 (918) 683-3227
Admin Brenda Haxton.
Licensure Intermediate Care. *Beds* 114. *Certified* Medicaid.

Honor Heights Nursing Center*
4717 W Okmulgee, Muskogee, OK, 74401 (918) 683-2914
Admin Dennis Cheek.
Licensure Intermediate Care. *Beds* 105. *Certified* Medicaid.

McIntosh Nursing Home
2100 Fondulac, Muskogee, OK, 74401 (918) 682-4831
Admin Johnnie C McIntosh. *Medical Dir/Dir of Nursing* Robert Smith MD.
Licensure Intermediate Care. *Beds* 64. *Certified* Medicaid.
Staff Physicians 2 (ft); RNs 2 (ft); LPNs 3 (ft); Orderlies 2 (ft); Nurses aides 11 (ft); Activities coordinators 1 (ft); Dietitians 1 (pt); Dentists 1 (pt); Podiatrists 1 (pt).
Facilities Dining room; Activities room; Laundry room; Barber/Beauty shop.
Activities Arts and Crafts; Cards; Games; Reading groups; Prayer groups; Movies; Dances/Social or cultural gatherings.
Description Home has been family owned and operated since 1956.

Muskogee Convalescent Center
602 N "M", Muskogee, OK, 74401 '918) 682-9232
Admin Fern Knight.
Licensure Intermediate Care. *Beds* 58. *Certified* Medicaid.

Staff Physicians 1 (pt); RNs 1 (pt); LPNs 2 (ft); Orderlies 2 (ft); Nurses aides 20 (ft); Activities coordinators 1 (pt); Dietitians 1 (pt); Dentists 1 (pt).
Facilities Dining room; Laundry room; Barber/Beauty shop.
Activities Arts and Crafts; Cards; Games; Reading groups; Prayer groups; Shopping trips; Dances/Social or cultural gatherings.

Pleasant Valley Health Care Center
1120 Illinois, Muskogee, OK, 74401 (918) 682-5391
Admin Louis Nevitt. *Medical Dir/Dir of Nursing* Velma Trussell RN.
Licensure Intermediate Care. *Beds* 68. *Certified* Medicaid.
Staff RNs 1 (ft), 1 (pt); LPNs 3 (ft), 2 (pt); Nurses aides 18 (ft); Reality therapists 1 (ft); Recreational therapists 10 (pt); Activities coordinators 1 (ft); Dietitians 1 (ft); Dentists 1 (ft); Podiatrists 1 (ft).
Facilities Dining room; Activities room; Chapel; Laundry room; Barber/Beauty shop.
Activities Arts and Crafts; Cards; Games; Reading groups; Prayer groups; Movies; Shopping trips; Dances/Social or cultural gatherings.

Tower Hill Nursing Home*
PO Box 1310, 424 Tower Hill Dr, Muskogee, OK, 74401 (918) 683-2983
Admin Samuel D Scott.
Licensure Intermediate Care. *Beds* 48. *Certified* Medicaid.

York Manor Nursing Home
500 S York, Muskogee, OK, 74401 (918) 682-6724
Admin Elaine Peters.
Licensure Intermediate Care. *Beds* 60. *Certified* Medicaid.
Admissions Requirements Medical examination.
Staff Physicians 1 (pt); RNs 1 (ft); LPNs 2 (ft); Nurses aides 15 (ft), 4 (pt); Dietitians 1 (pt).

NEWKIRK

Newkirk Nursing Center
Box 427, Newkirk, OK, 74647 (405) 362-3277
Admin W F Eichor. *Medical Dir/Dir of Nursing* Dr Palmer.
Licensure Intermediate Care. *Beds* 43. *Certified* Medicaid.
Staff Physicians; RNs; LPNs; Nurses aides 20 (ft); Physical therapists; Recreational therapists; Activities coordinators; Dietitians.
Facilities Dining room; Activities room; Chapel; Crafts room; Laundry room; Barber/Beauty shop.
Activities Arts and Crafts; Cards; Games; Reading groups; Prayer groups; Movies; Shopping trips; Dances/Social or cultural gatherings.

NORMAN

Four Seasons Nursing Center of Norman*
1210 W Robinson, Norman, OK, 73069 (405) 321-8824

Admin Lola Burnett.
Licensure Intermediate Care. *Beds* 118. *Certified* Medicaid.

Holiday Heights Nursing Home*
301 E Dale, Norman, OK, 73069 (405)
321-7932
Admin Bob Simmons.
Licensure Intermediate Care. *Beds* 51. *Certified* Medicaid.

Morningside Nursing Home*
512 N Interstate Rd, Norman, OK, 73069 (405)
321-7483
Admin Kay Simmons.
Licensure Intermediate Care. *Beds* 52. *Certified* Medicaid.

Rosewood Manor Ltd*
501 E Robinson, Norman, OK, 73071 (405)
321-6666
Admin Ben Primrose.
Licensure Intermediate Care. *Beds* 200. *Certified* Medicaid.

NOWATA

Hays House Nursing Home
300 S Mississippi, Nowata, OK, 74048 (918)
273-2002
Admin Ramona B Wilson.
Licensure Intermediate Care. *Beds* 112. *Certified* Medicaid.
Admissions Requirements Medical examination.
Staff RNs 1 (ft); LPNs 2 (ft), 1 (pt); Orderlies 2 (ft); Nurses aides 28 (ft), 4 (pt); Recreational therapists 6 (ft); Activities coordinators 1 (ft); Dietitians 1 (ft), 1 (pt).
Facilities Dining room; Activities room; Crafts room; Laundry room; Barber/Beauty shop.
Activities Arts and Crafts; Cards; Games; Reading groups; Prayer groups; Movies; Shopping trips; Dances/Social or cultural gatherings.
Description Home is intended for mentally retarded adults.

Nowata Nursing Home*
516 S Joe, Nowata, OK, 74048 (918) 273-2236
Admin Patricia Lee Harris.
Licensure Intermediate Care. *Beds* 43. *Certified* Medicaid.

Osage Nursing Home*
725 W Osage, Nowata, OK, 74048 (918)
273-2012
Admin James L Cooper.
Licensure Intermediate Care. *Beds* 50. *Certified* Medicaid.

OKARCHE

Center of Family Love*
PO Box 245, 6th and Texas, Okarche, OK, 73762 (405) 263-4658
Admin Thomas D Scott.
Beds 48.

OKEENE

Buchanan Nursing Home of Okeene Inc*
119 N 6th, Okeene, OK, 73763 (405) 822-4441
Admin Mildred Buchanan.
Licensure Intermediate Care. *Beds* 119. *Certified* Medicaid.

OKEMAH

Okemah Pioneer Nursing Home Inc*
202 N Division, Okemah, OK, 74859 (918)
623-1126
Admin James Robert Smart.
Licensure Intermediate Care. *Beds* 72. *Certified* Medicaid.

OKLAHOMA CITY

Bellevue Nursing Center
6500 N Portland, Oklahoma City, OK, 73116 (405) 843-5796
Admin Norman L Thompson. *Medical Dir/Dir of Nursing* Hugh A Stout MD.
Licensure Skilled Care. *Beds* 160.
Staff Physicians 1 (pt); RNs 4 (ft); LPNs 5 (ft), 1 (pt); Physical therapists 2 (ft); Occupational therapists 1 (ft), 1 (pt); Speech therapists 1 (pt); Activities coordinators 1 (ft); Dietitians 1 (pt); Dentists 1 (pt).
Facilities Dining room; Physical therapy room; Activities room; Chapel; Crafts room; Laundry room; Barber/Beauty shop.
Activities Arts and Crafts; Cards; Games; Reading groups; Prayer groups; Movies; Dances/Social or cultural gatherings.
Description Facility offers complete physical, occupational, speech and hydro therapy by a full-time, licensed staff. Opened a new 5,000 square foot therapy department and 60 additional nursing home beds in August, 1984.

Central Oklahoma Christian Home
6312 N Portland, Oklahoma City, OK, 73112 (405) 946-6932
Admin Royce W Dunn.
Licensure Intermediate Care. *Beds* 148. *Certified* Medicaid.
Admissions Requirements Medical examination.
Staff RNs 1 (ft); LPNs 6 (ft), 1 (pt); Orderlies 4 (ft); Nurses aides 28 (ft); Occupational therapists 1 (ft); Activities coordinators 1 (ft); Dietitians 1 (pt).
Affiliation Church of Christ
Facilities Dining room; Activities room; Crafts room; Laundry room; Barber/Beauty shop; Living and lounge areas.
Activities Arts and Crafts; Games; Prayer groups; Movies; Shopping trips; Religious services.

Fairview Manor Nursing Center*
3233 NW 10th, Oklahoma City, OK, 73107 (405) 943-8366
Admin Anna Warner.
Licensure Intermediate Care. *Beds* 142. *Certified* Medicaid.

Four Seasons Nursing Care of Northwest Oklahoma City
5301 N Brookline, Oklahoma City, OK, 73112 (405) 946-3351
Admin June Garver. *Medical Dir/Dir of Nursing* Jan Probst RN.
Licensure Skilled Care; Intermediate Care.
Beds SNF 72; ICF 64. *Certified* Medicaid; Medicare.
Admissions Requirements Medical examination.
Facilities Dining room; Physical therapy room; Activities room; Laundry room; Barber/Beauty shop.
Activities Arts and Crafts; Cards; Games; Reading groups; Prayer groups; Movies; Shopping trips; Dances/Social or cultural gatherings.
Description A progressive, well-established geriatric facility dedicated to meeting the physical, social, psychological, and spiritual aspects of all residents; offers levels of care from a retirement area through intermediate and skilled care.

Four Seasons Nursing Center of Southwest Oklahoma City*
5600 S Walker, Oklahoma City, OK, 73109 (405) 632-7771
Admin Jackie Bosler.
Licensure Intermediate Care. *Beds* 120. *Certified* Medicaid.

Four Seasons Nursing Center of Warr Acres*
6501 N MacArthur, Oklahoma City, OK, 73132 (405) 721-5444
Admin Linda Swain.
Licensure Intermediate Care. *Beds* 103. *Certified* Medicaid.

Four Seasons Nursing Center of Windsor Hills*
2416 N Ann Arbor, Oklahoma City, OK, 73127 (405) 942-8566
Admin Glenda Kauba.
Licensure Skilled Care. *Beds* 112. *Certified* Medicaid.

Ghana Village Home Inc*
3000 NE 17th, Oklahoma City, OK, 73121 (405) 427-0300
Admin Rose Greer.
Licensure Intermediate Care. *Beds* 44. *Certified* Medicaid.

Hefner Village Nursing Center
5701 W Britton Rd, Oklahoma City, OK, 73132 (405) 722-1010
Admin Chiquita Henderson.
Licensure Intermediate Care. *Beds* 173. *Certified* Medicaid.
Admissions Requirements Medical examination; Physician's request.
Staff RNs 2 (ft), 1 (pt); LPNs 7 (ft), 1 (pt); Nurses aides 40 (ft); Physical therapists 1 (ft); Activities coordinators 3 (ft); Dietitians 1 (ft).
Facilities Dining room; Physical therapy room; Activities room; Crafts room; Laundry room; Barber/Beauty shop.
Activities Arts and Crafts; Cards; Games; Reading groups; Prayer groups; Movies; Shopping trips; Dances/Social or cultural gatherings.
Description Facility features open door policy for communications with staff and family;

24-hour licensed nursing coverage; activities department works closely with each resident toward orientation and motivation; VA contract. Staff takes time to care and share; active volunteer program.

Lackey Manor*
9700 Mashburn Blvd, Oklahoma City, OK, 73132 (405) 721-2466
Admin Don Donalson.
Licensure Intermediate Care. *Beds* 114. *Certified* Medicaid.

Morning Star Nursing Home
3804 N Barr, Oklahoma City, OK, 73122 (405) 787-0522
Admin Judy Smith.
Licensure Intermediate Care. *Beds* 55. *Certified* Medicaid.
Admissions Requirements Minimum age 18; Medical examination; Physician's request.
Staff Physicians 11 (pt); RNs 1 (pt); LPNs 6 (ft), 1 (pt); Orderlies 4 (ft); Nurses aides 11 (ft); Activities coordinators 1 (ft); Dietitians 1 (pt).
Facilities Dining room; Activities room; Laundry room; Barber/Beauty shop.
Activities Arts and Crafts; Cards; Games; Reading groups; Prayer groups; Movies; Shopping trips; Dances/Social or cultural gatherings.
Description Facility is small and quiet with a family atmosphere.

Northeast Nursing Center*
1215 NE 34th, Oklahoma City, OK, 73111 (405) 424-4000
Admin Patricia Ann Hurt.
Licensure Intermediate Care. *Beds* 72. *Certified* Medicaid.

Northwest Nursing Center
2801 NW 61st, Oklahoma City, OK, 73112 (405) 842-6601
Admin T G Barker. *Medical Dir/Dir of Nursing* Hugh A Stout MD.
Licensure Intermediate Care. *Beds* 100. *Certified* Medicaid.
Admissions Requirements Medical examination; Physician's request.
Staff RNs 3 (ft); LPNs 4 (ft), 1 (pt); Physical therapists 1 (ft); Activities coordinators 1 (ft).
Facilities Dining room; Physical therapy room; Activities room; Laundry room; Barber/Beauty shop.
Activities Arts and Crafts; Cards; Games; Reading groups; Prayer groups; Movies; Shopping trips; Dances/Social or cultural gatherings.

Oklahoma County Home*
7401 NE 23rd, Oklahoma City, OK, 73141 (405) 427-2426
Admin Mary Thomas.
Licensure Intermediate Care. *Beds* 84. *Certified* Medicaid.

Park Manor Nursing Home
1214 N Broadway Dr, Oklahoma City, OK, 73103 (405) 235-7488
Admin Kaylene Bass. *Medical Dir/Dir of Nursing* Perry Taaca MD.
Licensure Intermediate Care. *Beds* 120. *Certified* Medicaid.
Admissions Requirements Minimum age 18; Medical examination; Physician's request.

Staff RNs 1 (pt); LPNs 4 (ft), 3 (pt); Orderlies 3 (ft), 1 (pt); Nurses aides 22 (ft); Physical therapists 1 (pt); Occupational therapists 1 (pt); Speech therapists 1 (pt); Activities coordinators 1 (ft); Dietitians 1 (pt); Dentists 1 (pt); Ophthalmologists 1 (pt); Podiatrists 1 (pt); Audiologists 1 (pt).
Facilities Dining room; Physical therapy room; Activities room; Chapel; Crafts room; Laundry room; Barber/Beauty shop; 2 Indoor patios.
Activities Arts and Crafts; Cards; Games; Reading groups; Prayer groups; Movies; Shopping trips; Dances/Social or cultural gatherings.
Description All residents receive lots of understanding, tender loving care, and all types of physical care.

Portland Health Care Facility
3718 N Portland, Oklahoma City, OK, 73112 (405) 942-1014
Admin Stephen Terrell. *Medical Dir/Dir of Nursing* Mayuri Shah MD.
Licensure Intermediate Care. *Beds* 24. *Certified* Medicaid.
Staff RNs 1 (ft), 1 (pt); LPNs 1 (pt); Nurses aides 16 (ft); Reality therapists 1 (ft); Recreational therapists 1 (ft); Activities coordinators 1 (ft); Dietitians 1 (ft).
Facilities Dining room; Activities room; Crafts room; Laundry room; Barber/Beauty shop.
Activities Arts and Crafts; Cards; Games; Reading groups; Prayer groups; Movies; Shopping trips; Dances/Social or cultural gatherings.
Description Facility is a small ICF unit with a family base orientation which deals with family therapy and patient therapy; majority of rooms are private.

Saint Ann's Home*
3825 NW 19th, Oklahoma City, OK, 73107 (405) 942-8607
Admin Robert T Martin II.
Licensure Intermediate Care. *Beds* 82. *Certified* Medicaid.

Saint's Nursing Home*
1913 NE 50th, Oklahoma City, OK, 73111 (405) 427-5414
Admin Wanda Boyd Rucker.
Licensure Intermediate Care. *Beds* 107. *Certified* Medicaid.

Shady View Nursing Home*
1163 E Madison, Oklahoma City, OK, 73111 (405) 424-1486
Admin Riley Brown.
Licensure Intermediate Care. *Beds* 70. *Certified* Medicaid.

South Park Health Care Center*
5725 S Ross, Oklahoma City, OK, 73119 (405) 685-4791
Admin Troy Matchen.
Beds 113.

Southern Oaks Manor Nursing Home*
301 SW 74th, Oklahoma City, OK, 73139 (405) 634-0573
Admin Chiquita Henderson.
Licensure Intermediate Care. *Beds* 105. *Certified* Medicaid.

Southwestern Convalescent Manor
5512 S Western, Oklahoma City, OK, 73109 (405) 632-2318
Admin Thomas D Scott. *Medical Dir/Dir of Nursing* Roger Lienke MD.
Licensure Intermediate Care. *Beds* 59. *Certified* Medicaid.
Admissions Requirements Minimum age 21.
Staff RNs 1 (pt); LPNs 4 (ft); Nurses aides 16 (ft); Activities coordinators 1 (ft).
Facilities Dining room; Activities room; Laundry room; Barber/Beauty shop.
Activities Arts and Crafts; Games; Prayer groups; Movies; Shopping trips.

Suburban Square Nursing Center
225 SW 35th, Oklahoma City, OK, 73109 (405) 634-3323
Admin Arthur A Durkee.
Licensure Intermediate Care. *Beds* 30. *Certified* Medicaid.
Staff Physicians 3 (pt); RNs 2 (pt); LPNs 1 (ft), 3 (pt); Nurses aides 9 (ft), 3 (pt); Activities coordinators 2 (pt); Dietitians 1 (pt); Dentists 1 (pt); Podiatrists 1 (pt).
Facilities Dining room; Laundry room.
Activities Arts and Crafts; Games; Prayer groups; Shopping trips; Dances/Social or cultural gatherings.

Terrace Gardens*
1921 NE 21st St, Oklahoma City, OK, 73111 (405) 424-1449
Admin JoAnn Scruggs.
Licensure Intermediate Care. *Beds* 105. *Certified* Medicaid.

United Cerebral Palsy Intermediate Care Facility*
2901 SE 22nd, Oklahoma City, OK, 73129 (405) 677-0502
Admin Guy Anderson.
Licensure Intermediate Care. *Beds* 93. *Certified* Medicaid.

Walnut Creek Nursing Home*
2400 SW 55th, Oklahoma City, OK, 73109 (405) 681-5381
Admin Delories Gilliland.
Licensure Intermediate Care. *Beds* 100. *Certified* Medicaid.

Watkins Stephens Skyview Nursing Home*
2200 Coltrane Rd, Oklahoma City, OK, 73121 (405) 427-1322
Admin Betty R Lynch.
Licensure Intermediate Care. *Beds* 60. *Certified* Medicaid.

Wilshire Nursing Home
505 E Wilshire, Oklahoma City, OK, 73105 (405) 478-0531
Admin Anna Warner.
Licensure Intermediate Care. *Beds* 52. *Certified* Medicaid.
Staff LPNs 2 (ft), 1 (pt); Nurses aides 14 (ft), 4 (pt); Activities coordinators 1 (ft); Dietitians 1 (ft).

Woodside Nursing Center*
3601 N Eastern, Oklahoma City, OK, 73111 (405) 427-6533

Admin Rosalie Richardson.
Licensure Intermediate Care. *Beds* 137. *Certified* Medicaid.

OKMULGEE

Highland Park Manor*
1300 E Walnut, Okmulgee, OK, 74447 (918) 756-5611
Admin Donna Wells.
Licensure Intermediate Care. *Beds* 100. *Certified* Medicaid.

Leisure Manor Nursing Home*
1535 E 6th, Okmulgee, OK, 74447 (918) 756-3355
Admin Bob Barnard.
Licensure Intermediate Care. *Beds* 63. *Certified* Medicaid.

Okmulgee Terrace Nursing Home Inc*
1st and Miami, Okmulgee, OK, 74447 (918) 756-3556
Admin Judith Cochran.
Licensure Intermediate Care. *Beds* 63. *Certified* Medicaid.

Rebold Manor*
1701 E 6th, Okmulgee, OK, 74447 (918) 756-1967
Admin Bob Barnard.
Licensure Intermediate Care. *Beds* 114. *Certified* Medicaid.

PAULS VALLEY

Colonial Nursing Home*
105 Washington, Pauls Valley, OK, 73075 (405) 238-5528
Admin Eulean Reed.
Licensure Intermediate Care. *Beds* 104. *Certified* Medicaid.

Pauls Valley Health Care Facility
1413 S Chickasaw, Pauls Valley, OK, 73075 (405) 238-6411
Admin Gussie J Corvin.
Licensure Intermediate Care. *Beds* 51. *Certified* Medicaid.

PAWHUSKA

Pawhuska Nursing Home
Box 959, Pawhuska, OK, 74056 (918) 287-3940
Admin Jerry L Cline.
Licensure Intermediate Care. *Beds* 80. *Certified* Medicaid.
Staff RNs 1 (pt); LPNs 2 (ft), 1 (pt); Dietitians 1 (pt).
Facilities Dining room; Crafts room; Laundry room; Barber/Beauty shop.
Activities Arts and Crafts; Cards; Games; Prayer groups; Shopping trips.
Description Facility features group exercising each Thursday led by ladies club from Pawhuska.

PAWNEE

Pawnee Care Center
800 9th St, Pawnee, OK, 74058 (918) 762-2515
Admin Mary Hurt.
Licensure Intermediate Care. *Beds* 52. *Certified* Medicaid.
Staff RNs 1 (ft); LPNs 1 (ft); Orderlies 1 (ft); Nurses aides 18 (ft), 4 (pt); Activities coordinators 1 (ft); Dietitians 1 (ft).
Facilities Dining room; Physical therapy room; Activities room; Crafts room; Laundry room; Barber/Beauty shop.
Activities Arts and Crafts; Games; Reading groups; Shopping trips; Dances/Social or cultural gatherings.

PERRY

Perry Green Valley Nursing Center*
1103 Birch St, Perry, OK, 73077 (405) 336-2285
Admin Anita Schwandt.
Licensure Intermediate Care. *Beds* 82. *Certified* Medicaid.

Perry Nursing Home*
410 15th St, Perry, OK, 73077 (405) 336-4461
Admin Anita Schwandt.
Licensure Intermediate Care. *Beds* 51. *Certified* Medicaid.

PICHER

Rest Haven Nursing Home*
2nd and Francis, Picher, OK, 74360 (918) 673-1660
Admin James A Patrick.
Licensure Intermediate Care. *Beds* 26. *Certified* Medicaid.

PONCA CITY

Highland Nursing Center*
1401 W Highland, Ponca City, OK, 74601 (405) 765-4454
Admin Joe M Nimmo.
Licensure Intermediate Care. *Beds* 97. *Certified* Medicaid.

Ponca City Nursing Home*
1400 N Waverly, Ponca City, OK, 74601 (405) 762-6668
Admin Wesley E Nimmo.
Licensure Intermediate Care. *Beds* 143. *Certified* Medicaid.

Shawn Manor Nursing Home*
2024 Turner Rd, Ponca City, OK, 74601 (405) 765-3364
Admin Janet Fronko.
Licensure Intermediate Care. *Beds* 56. *Certified* Medicaid.

POTEAU

LeFlore Nursing Home*
410 Carter St, Poteau, OK, 74953 (918) 647-4194

Admin Archie Farmer.
Licensure Intermediate Care. *Beds* 63. *Certified* Medicaid.

Poteau Nursing Home*
1212 Reynolds, Poteau, OK, 74953 (918) 647-4247
Admin Arthur Wayne Hoffman.
Licensure Intermediate Care. *Beds* 81. *Certified* Medicaid.

PRAGUE

Parkland Manor*
1400 D Ave, Prague, OK, 74864 (405) 567-2201
Admin Dorothea Thomas.
Licensure Intermediate Care. *Beds* 58. *Certified* Medicaid.

PRYOR

Colonial Terrace Care Center Inc*
1320 NE 1st Pl, Pryor, OK, 74361 (918) 825-5311
Admin Dorothy Hagerman.
Licensure Intermediate Care. *Beds* 51. *Certified* Medicaid.

Grand Valley Care Center Inc
201 N Kentucky, Pryor, OK, 74361 (918) 825-2558
Admin Frank Hagerman.
Licensure Intermediate Care. *Beds* 65. *Certified* Medicaid.

Shady Rest Care Center Inc*
210 S Adair, Pryor, OK, 74361 (918) 825-4455
Admin Dorothy Hagerman.
Licensure Intermediate Care. *Beds* 65. *Certified* Medicaid.

PURCELL

Broadlawn Manor
915-1017 N 7th, Purcell, OK, 73080 (405) 527-2122
Admin Louise Deane. *Medical Dir/Dir of Nursing* Dr John Rollins.
Licensure Intermediate Care. *Beds* 69. *Certified* Medicaid.
Admissions Requirements Minimum age 29; Medical examination.
Staff Physicians; RNs; LPNs; Nurses aides; Reality therapists; Recreational therapists; Activities coordinators; Dietitians; Dentists.
Facilities Dining room; Activities room; Crafts room; Laundry room; Barber/Beauty shop; Library.
Activities Arts and Crafts; Cards; Games; Reading groups; Prayer groups; Movies; Shopping trips; Dances/Social or cultural gatherings; Easter egg hunt.

Purchell Nursing Home
639 Van Buren, Purcell, OK, 73080 (405) 527-3129
Admin Kenneth Greiner.
Licensure Intermediate Care. *Beds* 105. *Certified* Medicaid.
Staff Physicians 1 (ft); RNs 1 (pt); LPNs 4 (ft);

Orderlies 1 (ft); Nurses aides 30 (ft), 5 (pt); Recreational therapists 1 (ft); Occupational therapists 1 (pt); Activities coordinators 1 (ft); Dietitians 6 (ft).
Facilities Dining room; Physical therapy room; Activities room; Crafts room; Laundry room; Barber/Beauty shop.
Activities Arts and Crafts; Cards; Games; Reading groups; Prayer groups; Movies; Shopping trips; Dances/Social or cultural gatherings.

QUAPAW

Quapaw Nursing Home*
407 Whitebird, Quapaw, OK, 74363 (918) 674-2464
Admin Tom Housh.
Licensure Intermediate Care. *Beds* 66. *Certified* Medicaid.

QUINTON

Quinton Nursing Home Inc
1209 W Main, Quinton, OK, 74561 (918) 469-2655
Admin Mike A Hawkins.
Licensure Intermediate Care. *Beds* 63. *Certified* Medicaid.
Staff Physicians 1 (ft), 1 (pt); RNs 1 (pt); LPNs 5 (ft); Nurses aides 16 (ft); Activities coordinators 1 (ft); Dietitians 1 (pt); Dentists 2 (pt); Podiatrists 1 (pt).
Facilities Dining room; Activities room; Crafts room; Laundry room; Barber/Beauty shop.
Activities Arts and Crafts; Cards; Games; Reading groups; Shopping trips; Dances/Social or cultural gatherings.

RINGLING

Ringling Nursing Home*
2nd and H Sts, Ringling, OK, 73456 (405) 662-2262
Admin Bobbie Woodall.
Licensure Intermediate Care. *Beds* 50. *Certified* Medicaid.

ROLAND

Sequoyah East Nursing Center*
East of Roland, Roland, OK, 74954 (918) 427-7401
Admin Bob G Mitchell.
Licensure Intermediate Care. *Beds* 60. *Certified* Medicaid.

RYAN

Ryan Nursing Home Inc*
702 Lee Ave, Ryan, OK, 73565 (405) 757-2517
Admin Jimmy L Thorn.
Licensure Intermediate Care. *Beds* 69. *Certified* Medicaid.

SALINA

Parkhill North Nursing Home*
Hwys 20 and 82, Salina, OK, 74365 (918) 434-5600
Admin Caroline Trickett.
Licensure Intermediate Care. *Beds* 53. *Certified* Medicaid.

SALLISAW

Sequoyah Manor*
615 E Redwood, Sallisaw, OK, 74955 (918) 775-4881
Admin Laveta Kyle.
Licensure Intermediate Care. *Beds* 154. *Certified* Medicaid.

SAND SPRINGS

Oak Dale Manor*
1025 N Adams, Sand Springs, OK, 74063 (918) 245-5908
Admin T A Connery.
Licensure Intermediate Care. *Beds* 207. *Certified* Medicaid.

SAPULPA

Northside Manor Nursing Home
102 E Line, PO Box 1110, Sapulpa, OK, 74066 (918) 224-0833
Admin Nellie Wallace. *Medical Dir/Dir of Nursing* Louis Martin MD.
Licensure Intermediate Care. *Beds* 33. *Certified* Medicaid.
Admissions Requirements Medical examination; Physician's request.
Staff Physicians 1 (ft); RNs 1 (ft); LPNs 2 (ft); Orderlies 1 (ft); Nurses aides 10 (ft); Physical therapists 1 (ft); Recreational therapists 1 (ft); Activities coordinators 1 (ft); Dietitians 1 (ft); Dentists 1 (ft).
Facilities Dining room; Activities room; Crafts room; Laundry room; Barber/Beauty shop.
Activities Arts and Crafts; Cards; Games; Reading groups; Prayer groups; Movies; Shopping trips; Dances/Social or cultural gatherings.

Pleasant Manor Nursing Home Inc*
310 W Taft, Sapulpa, OK, 74066 (918) 224-6012
Admin Evla May Williams.
Licensure Intermediate Care. *Beds* 142. *Certified* Medicaid.

Ranch Terrace Nursing Home Inc*
1310 E Cleveland, Sapulpa, OK, 74066 (918) 224-2578
Admin Kay Isbell.
Licensure Intermediate Care. *Beds* 85. *Certified* Medicaid.

Sapulpa Nursing Center Inc
1701 S Main, PO Box 1108, Sapulpa, OK, 74066 (918) 224-5790
Admin Coy V Cardin.
Licensure Intermediate Care. *Beds* 57. *Certified* Medicaid.
Staff Physicians 2 (pt); RNs 1 (pt); LPNs 2 (ft); Nurses aides 28 (ft); Physical therapists 1 (pt);

Activities coordinators 1 (ft); Dietitians 1 (pt); Dentists 1 (pt).
Facilities Dining room; Physical therapy room; Activities room; Crafts room; Laundry room; Barber/Beauty shop.
Activities Arts and Crafts; Cards; Games; Prayer groups; Shopping trips.
Description Facility is small with a home-like atmosphere. The many long-time employees and quality nursing services create a clean, professional, and comfortable place for residents to live.

SAYRE

Hensley Nursing Home*
Rt 4, Box 136, Sayre, OK, 73662 (405) 928-2494
Admin Elmer Barr.
Licensure Intermediate Care. *Beds* 67. *Certified* Medicaid.

Town Hall Estates Nursing Center*
501 E Grand, Sayre, OK, 73662 (405) 928-3374
Admin Lawrence Thomas.
Licensure Intermediate Care. *Beds* 101. *Certified* Medicaid.

SEILING

Seiling Nursing Center*
Hwy 60 N, Seiling, OK, 73663 (405) 922-4433
Admin Jeneva Helterbrake.
Licensure Intermediate Care. *Beds* 31. *Certified* Medicaid.

SEMINOLE

Seminole Pioneer Nursing Home Inc
1705 State St, Seminole, OK, 74868 (405) 382-1270
Admin Marchetta Black. *Medical Dir/Dir of Nursing* Auttis Johnson.
Licensure Intermediate Care. *Beds* 146. *Certified* Medicaid.

SENTINEL

Sentinel Nursing Home
221 S 7th, Sentinel, OK, 73664 (405) 393-4385
Admin Albert Gray.
Licensure Intermediate Care. *Beds* 25. *Certified* Medicaid.

SHATTUCK

Convalescent Center of Shuttuck
201 N Alfalfa, Box 189, Shattuck, OK, 73858 (405) 938-2501
Admin Karen Bittman.
Licensure Intermediate Care. *Beds* 60. *Certified* Medicaid.
Admissions Requirements Minimum age 18; Medical examination.
Staff RNs 1 (pt); LPNs 2 (ft), 1 (pt); Nurses aides 13 (ft), 2 (pt); Physical therapists 1 (pt); Recreational therapists 1 (pt); Activities coordinators 1 (pt); Dietitians 1 (pt).
Facilities Dining room; Activities room; Crafts

room; Laundry room; Barber/Beauty shop.
Activities Arts and Crafts; Cards; Games; Prayer groups; Movies; Shopping trips; Dances/Social or cultural gatherings.

SHAWNEE

Golden Rule Home Inc
W Hardesty Rd, Shawnee, OK, 74801 (405) 273-7106
Admin Charles R Smith.
Licensure Intermediate Care. *Beds* 34. *Certified* Medicaid.

Independence Manor*
909 E Independence, Shawnee, OK, 74801 (405) 273-7156
Admin Jimmy E Rose.
Licensure Intermediate Care. *Beds* 100. *Certified* Medicaid.

Parkview Nursing Home Inc*
1100 E Edwards, Shawnee, OK, 74801 (405) 273-4835
Admin Jearl Smart.
Licensure Intermediate Care. *Beds* 78. *Certified* Medicaid.

Shawnee Care Center*
1202 W Gilmore, Shawnee, OK, 74801 (405) 273-8043
Admin Dennis P Wodowski.
Licensure Intermediate Care. *Beds* 114. *Certified* Medicaid.

Shawnee Colonial Estates Inc
535 W Federal, Shawnee, OK, 74801 (405) 273-1826
Admin Sue Kanady.
Licensure Intermediate Care. *Beds* 106. *Certified* Medicaid.

Shawnee Sunset Estates*
1402 E Independence, Shawnee, OK, 74801 (405) 275-1574
Admin William R Stewart II.
Licensure Intermediate Care. *Beds* 72. *Certified* Medicaid.

SKIATOOK

Skiatook Nursing Home*
318 S Cherry, Skiatook, OK, 74070 (918) 396-2149
Admin Evelyn Reed.
Licensure Intermediate Care. *Beds* 70. *Certified* Medicaid.

SNYDER

Ayers Nursing Home*
801 B St, Snyder, OK, 73566 (405) 569-2258
Admin Jerry W Ayers.
Licensure Intermediate Care. *Beds* 87. *Certified* Medicaid.

SPIRO

Spiro Nursing Home*
401 S Main, Spiro, OK, 74959 (918) 962-2308
Admin Gary McClure.
Licensure Intermediate Care. *Beds* 95. *Certified* Medicaid.

STIGLER

Stigler Nursing Home*
114 NE 3rd and B St, Stigler, OK, 74462 (918) 967-2389
Admin G C Cody Jr.
Licensure Intermediate Care. *Beds* 74. *Certified* Medicaid.

STILLWATER

Hearthstone Nursing Home Inc*
PO Box 2437, 3014 S Main, Stillwater, OK, 74076 (405) 372-9526
Admin Gary Smart.
Licensure Intermediate Care. *Beds* 84. *Certified* Medicaid.

Stillwater Nursing Home Inc
1215 W 10th, Stillwater, OK, 74074 (405) 372-1000
Admin Jeannie Fitzgerald.
Licensure Intermediate Care. *Beds* 104. *Certified* Medicaid.
Staff RNs 1 (ft), 1 (pt); LPNs 3 (ft); Orderlies 27 (ft), 6 (pt); Physical therapists 1 (pt); Activities coordinators 1 (ft); Dietitians 1 (pt); Dentists 1 (pt).

Stillwater Rosewood Nursing Home Inc
1601 S Main, PO Box 2437, Stillwater, OK, 74076 (405) 377-4000
Admin Gary Smart. *Medical Dir/Dir of Nursing* Dr Sid Williams.
Licensure Intermediate Care. *Beds* 104. *Certified* Medicaid.
Staff Physicians 3 (pt); RNs 2 (pt); LPNs 3 (ft), 3 (pt); Activities coordinators 2 (ft); Dietitians 1 (pt).
Facilities Dining room; Physical therapy room; Activities room; Crafts room; Laundry room; Barber/Beauty shop.
Activities Arts and Crafts; Cards; Games; Prayer groups; Movies; Shopping trips; Dances/Social or cultural gatherings; Remotivation.

Westhaven Nursing Home Inc*
1215 S Western, Stillwater, OK, 74074 (405) 743-1140
Admin LaDonna Ross.
Licensure Intermediate Care. *Beds* 112. *Certified* Medicaid.

STILWELL

Stilwell Nursing Home*
422 W Locust, Stilwell, OK, 74960 (918) 696-7715
Admin Fredna Latta.
Licensure Intermediate Care. *Beds* 104. *Certified* Medicaid.

STONEWALL

Stonegate Nursing Center
6th and Collins, Stonewall, OK, 74868 (405) 265-4247
Admin Betty Hilton. *Medical Dir/Dir of Nursing* Kim Tallman LPN.
Licensure Intermediate Care. *Beds* 53. *Certified* Medicaid.
Admissions Requirements Minimum age 18; Physician's request.
Staff Physicians 1 (pt); RNs 1 (pt); LPNs 4 (ft); Nurses aides 20 (ft); Recreational therapists 1 (ft); Activities coordinators 1 (pt); Dietitians 1 (pt).
Facilities Dining room; Activities room; Crafts room; Laundry room; Barber/Beauty shop.
Activities Arts and Crafts; Cards; Games; Reading groups; Prayer groups; Movies; Shopping trips; Dances/Social or cultural gatherings.
Description This is a small nursing home with family atmosphere; contracts with Valley View Hospital for physical therapy; also with dentist for care of residents.

STRATFORD

Oklahoma Care Center
Cottonwood and Smith, PO Box 636, Stratford, OK, 74871 (405) 759-2268
Admin Dolores Tucker.
Licensure Intermediate Care. *Beds* 106. *Certified* Medicaid.
Staff RNs 1 (pt); LPNs 3 (ft); Orderlies 1 (ft); Nurses aides 30 (ft); Physical therapists 1 (pt); Reality therapists 1 (ft); Recreational therapists 1 (ft); Activities coordinators 1 (ft); Dietitians 1 (pt).
Facilities Dining room; Physical therapy room; Activities room; Crafts room; Laundry room; Barber/Beauty shop.
Activities Arts and Crafts; Cards; Games; Reading groups; Prayer groups; Movies; Shopping trips; Dances/Social or cultural gatherings.
Description Staff is a caring group of people from a small town, who believe in giving good food and happy feelings about the home to residents.

STROUD

Care Manor Nursing Center*
721 W Olive, Stroud, OK, 74079 (918) 968-2075
Admin Susan Williams.
Licensure Intermediate Care. *Beds* 58. *Certified* Medicaid.

Stroud Health Care Center*
416 N 7th Ave, Stroud, OK, 74079 (918) 968-2507
Admin Roberta Snow.
Licensure Intermediate Care. *Beds* 40. *Certified* Medicaid.

SULPHUR

Artesian Home*
1415 W 15th, Sulphur, OK, 73086 (405) 622-2030

Admin Robert H Walker.
Licensure Intermediate Care. *Beds* 62. *Certified* Medicaid.

Callaway Nursing Home*
1300 W Lindsay, Sulphur, OK, 73086 (405) 622-2416
Admin Billy G Lance.
Licensure Intermediate Care. *Beds* 86. *Certified* Medicaid.

TAHLEQUAH

Davis Nursing Home*
1201 N Vinita Ave, Tahlequah, OK, 74464 (918) 456-6181
Admin Billie Davis.
Licensure Intermediate Care. *Beds* 139. *Certified* Medicaid.

Go Ye Village Medical Center
1201 W 4th St, Tahlequah, OK, 74464 (918) 456-4542
Admin James Richardson. *Medical Dir/Dir of Nursing* John F Porter DO.
Licensure Intermediate Care. *Beds* 32.
Staff Physicians 1 (ft); RNs 2 (ft); LPNs 5 (ft), 2 (pt); Orderlies 2 (ft); Nurses aides 15 (ft), 5 (pt); Physical therapists 1 (pt); Reality therapists 1 (pt); Occupational therapists 1 (pt); Activities coordinators 1 (ft); Dietitians 1 (ft).
Facilities Dining room; Physical therapy room; Activities room; Chapel; Crafts room; Laundry room; Barber/Beauty shop; Library; Store.
Activities Arts and Crafts; Games; Reading groups; Prayer groups; Movies; Shopping trips; Dances/Social or cultural gatherings.
Description Facility is life care in that the resident purchases life-use of apartment, or nursing unit. Residents are encouraged to pre-plan their care.

Tahlequah Nursing Home*
614 E Cherry, Tahlequah, OK, 74464 (918) 456-2573
Admin Billie Davis.
Licensure Intermediate Care. *Beds* 125. *Certified* Medicaid.

Ward Nursing Home*
124 E Chickasaw, Tahlequah, OK, 74464 (918) 456-3456
Admin Dennis Cheek.
Licensure Intermediate Care. *Beds* 45. *Certified* Medicaid.

TALIHINA

Talihina Manor Nursing Home*
1st and Thomas, Talihina, OK, 74571 (918) 567-2279
Admin Gilbert F Green.
Licensure Intermediate Care. *Beds* 69. *Certified* Medicaid.

TECUMSEH

Sunset Estates Inc
201 W Walnut, Tecumseh, OK, 74873 (405) 598-2167
Admin Ken Prator. *Medical Dir/Dir of*

Nursing Robert Zumwalt MD.
Licensure Intermediate Care. *Beds* 100. *Certified* Medicaid.
Admissions Requirements Minimum age 18; Physician's request.
Staff RNs 1 (ft); LPNs 6 (ft), 2 (pt); Orderlies 4 (ft); Nurses aides 39 (ft); Physical therapists 1 (pt); Activities coordinators 1 (ft); Dietitians 1 (pt).
Facilities Dining room; Physical therapy room; Activities room; Crafts room; Laundry room; Barber/Beauty shop.
Activities Arts and Crafts; Cards; Games; Prayer groups; Movies; Shopping trips; Dances/Social or cultural gatherings.
Description Home town owner takes pride in the town and nursing home. Employees are from town and have same outlook.

TEMPLE

Temple Manor Inc*
100 W Green, Temple, OK, 73568 (405) 342-6411
Admin Virginia Faye Stringer.
Licensure Intermediate Care. *Beds* 48. *Certified* Medicaid.

THOMAS

Thomas Nursing Center
601 E Frisco, PO Box 38, Thomas, OK, 73669 (405) 661-2171
Admin Jerry D Jones.
Licensure Intermediate Care. *Beds* 60. *Certified* Medicaid.
Staff RNs 1 (ft); LPNs 2 (ft); Nurses aides 15 (ft), 7 (pt); Activities coordinators 1 (ft), 1 (pt); Dietitians 1 (pt).
Facilities Dining room; Activities room; Chapel; Crafts room; Laundry room; Barber/Beauty shop.
Activities Arts and Crafts; Cards; Games; Movies; Shopping trips; Dances/Social or cultural gatherings.
Description Thomas Nursing Center is situated within the medical complex of a modern rural hospital and clinic and is connected to the hospital. An active volunteer program and an involved community make Thomas Nursing Center a center of activity as well as a professional care center.

TISHOMINGO

Hillcrest Nursing Home*
1200 E Main, Tishomingo, OK, 73460 (405) 371-2636
Admin Frank Harris.
Licensure Intermediate Care. *Beds* 50. *Certified* Medicaid.

Lawn View Nursing Home*
607 S Byrd, Tishomingo, OK, 73460 (405) 371-2317
Admin Melodye Tittle.
Licensure Intermediate Care. *Beds* 35. *Certified* Medicaid.

TONKAWA

C and R Nursing Center*
1301 N 5th St, Tonkawa, OK, 74653 (405) 628-2529
Admin Jessie Phillips.
Licensure Intermediate Care. *Beds* 49. *Certified* Medicaid.

TULSA

Ambassador Manor
1340 E 61st St, Tulsa, OK, 74136 (918) 743-8978
Admin Sharon Covey.
Licensure Intermediate Care. *Beds* 122.
Admissions Requirements Medical examination.
Staff RNs 1 (ft), 1 (pt); LPNs 6 (ft); Orderlies 3 (ft); Nurses aides 35 (ft); Physical therapists 1 (pt); Activities coordinators 1 (ft); Dietitians 1 (ft).
Facilities Dining room; Activities room; Crafts room; Laundry room; Barber/Beauty shop.
Activities Arts and Crafts; Cards; Games; Reading groups; Prayer groups; Movies; Dances/Social or cultural gatherings.

Black's Nursing Home
3601 N Columbia, Tulsa, OK, 74110 (918) 425-1668
Admin Mary Henderson.
Licensure Intermediate Care. *Beds* 54. *Certified* Medicaid.
Admissions Requirements Minimum age 18; Medical examination; Physician's request.
Staff Physicians 1 (pt); LPNs 3 (ft); Nurses aides 14 (ft), 2 (pt); Dietitians 1 (pt).
Facilities Dining room; Laundry room; Barber/Beauty shop.
Activities Arts and Crafts; Cards; Games; Reading groups; Prayer groups; Movies; Shopping trips; Dances/Social or cultural gatherings.
Description Friendly and family-type facility where the resident comes first.

Chamor Nursing Center*
2550 E 36th N, Tulsa, OK, 74110 (918) 425-7548
Admin T Oscar Chappelle.
Licensure Intermediate Care. *Beds* 100. *Certified* Medicaid.

Colonial Manor Nursing Home*
1815 E Skelly Dr, Tulsa, OK, 74105 (918) 743-7838
Admin Robert H Gary.
Licensure Intermediate Care. *Beds* 120. *Certified* Medicaid.

Convalescent Center Inc*
3333 E 28th, Tulsa, OK, 74114 (918) 747-8008
Admin Robert H Gray.
Licensure Intermediate Care. *Beds* 56. *Certified* Medicaid.

Four Seasons Nursing Center of Tulsa
2425 S Memorial Dr, Tulsa, OK, 74129 (918) 628-0932
Admin Lewisa Gouker. *Medical Dir/Dir of Nursing* Dr Robert Gray.
Licensure Intermediate Care. *Beds* 118. *Certi-*

fied Medicaid.
Admissions Requirements Medical examination; Physician's request.
Staff RNs 1 (ft); Nurses aides 42 (ft).
Facilities Dining room; Physical therapy room; Activities room; Laundry room; Barber/Beauty shop.
Activities Arts and Crafts; Cards; Games; Movies; Shopping trips; Dances/Social or cultural gatherings.

Georgian Court Nursing Home of Tulsa
2552 E 21st, Tulsa, OK, 74114 (918) 742-7319
Admin Dan E Johnson. *Medical Dir/Dir of Nursing* Dr G Bryant Boyd.
Licensure Skilled Care. *Beds* 48.
Admissions Requirements Physician's request.
Staff Physicians 1 (pt); RNs 1 (ft), 1 (pt); LPNs 5 (ft), 4 (pt); Orderlies 1 (pt); Nurses aides 12 (ft), 7 (pt); Physical therapists 1 (pt); Activities coordinators 1 (ft); Dietitians 1 (pt); Dentists 1 (pt); Podiatrists 1 (pt).
Facilities Dining room; Laundry room; Barber-/Beauty shop.
Activities Arts and Crafts; Cards; Games; Reading groups; Movies; Shopping trips; Dances/Social or cultural gatherings.

Homestead Nursing Home*
1021 Charles Page Blvd, Tulsa, OK, 74127 (918) 587-4189
Admin Wilma Corely.
Licensure Intermediate Care. *Beds* 53. *Certified* Medicaid.

Leisure Village Nursing Center*
2154 S 85th E Ave, Tulsa, OK, 74129 (918) 622-4747
Admin Joe H Hamra.
Licensure Intermediate Care. *Beds* 117. *Certified* Medicaid.

Oklahoma Methodist Home for the Aged
4134 E 31st, Tulsa, OK, 74135 (918) 743-2565
Admin Douglas Fleming.
Licensure Intermediate Care. *Beds* 100. *Certified* Medicaid.
Affiliation Methodist

Park Terrace Convalescent Center
5115 E 51st, Tulsa, OK, 74135 (918) 627-5961
Admin J Janice Meredith.
Licensure Intermediate Care. *Beds* 126.
Admissions Requirements Medical examination.
Staff RNs; LPNs; Nurses aides; Recreational therapists; Activities coordinators.
Facilities Dining room; Activities room; Crafts room; Laundry room; Barber/Beauty shop.
Activities Arts and Crafts; Cards; Games; Reading groups; Movies; Shopping trips.

Regency Park Manor Health Care Center*
3910 Park Rd, Tulsa, OK, 74115 (918) 425-1354
Admin Colette Capper.
Licensure Intermediate Care. *Beds* 105. *Certified* Medicaid.

Rest Haven Nursing Home
1944 N Iroquois, Tulsa, OK, 74106 (918) 583-1509
Admin T Oscar Chappelle. *Medical Dir/Dir of Nursing* Dr Angelo Dagessandro.
Licensure Intermediate Care. *Beds* 100. *Certified* Medicaid.
Admissions Requirements Minimum age 21; Medical examination; Physician's request.
Staff Physicians 3 (pt); RNs 2 (pt); LPNs 3 (ft); Orderlies 4 (ft); Nurses aides 23 (ft); Physical therapists 1 (pt); Reality therapists 1 (ft); Recreational therapists 1 (pt); Activities coordinators 1 (ft); Dietitians 1 (pt).
Facilities Dining room; Physical therapy room; Activities room; Chapel; Laundry room; Barber/Beauty shop.
Activities Arts and Crafts; Games; Reading groups; Prayer groups; Movies; Shopping trips; Dances/Social or cultural gatherings.
Description This 100-bed facility plans shopping trips, picnics, and 4th of July celebrations for all residents; open house is held during National Nursing Home Week.

Saint Simeon's Episcopal Home Inc*
3701 N Cincinnati, Tulsa, OK, 74106 (918) 425-3583
Admin Jerry D Pinson.
Licensure Intermediate Care. *Beds* 25. *Certified* Medicaid.
Affiliation Episcopal

Sherwood Manor Nursing Home*
2415 W Skelly Dr, Tulsa, OK, 74107 (918) 446-4284
Admin Opal Carter.
Licensure Intermediate Care. *Beds* 102. *Certified* Medicaid.

Skyline Terrace Nursing Center
6202 E 61st, Tulsa, OK, 74136 (918) 494-8830
Admin Joyce Lyons, Carl Lyons, and Cindy Lyons. *Medical Dir/Dir of Nursing* Arthur Hale MD.
Licensure Skilled Care. *Beds* 209. *Certified* Medicare.
Admissions Requirements Medical examination; Physician's request.
Facilities Dining room; Physical therapy room; Activities room; Chapel; Crafts room; Laundry room; Barber/Beauty shop; Library.
Activities Arts and Crafts; Cards; Games; Reading groups; Prayer groups; Movies; Shopping trips; Dances/Social or cultural gatherings.

Southern Hills Nursing Center*
5170 S Vandalia, Tulsa, OK, 74135 (918) 496-3963
Admin Julia Galvin.
Licensure Intermediate Care. *Beds* 118. *Certified* Medicaid.

Tulsa Christian Home Inc
6201 E 36th St, Tulsa, OK, 74135 (918) 622-3430
Admin Jewell Dessinger. *Medical Dir/Dir of Nursing* Dr Boyd and Dr Betty Smith.
Licensure Intermediate Care. *Beds* 100. *Certified* Medicaid.
Admissions Requirements Medical examination; Physician's request.
Staff RNs 1 (ft), 1 (pt); LPNs 4 (ft), 2 (pt); Orderlies 1 (ft); Nurses aides 32 (ft), 3 (pt); Physical therapists 1 (pt); Activities coordinators 2 (ft); Dietitians 1 (pt); Dentists 1 (pt); Podiatrists 1 (pt).

Affiliation Church of Christ
Facilities Dining room; Physical therapy room; Activities room; Crafts room; Laundry room; Barber/Beauty shop; Library.
Activities Arts and Crafts; Games; Reading groups; Movies; Shopping trips.
Description Not an institution, but a home away from home, for all ages, races, and religions, where all residents are free to come and go as their physical conditions allow.

Tulsa Nursing Center*
10912 E 14th St, Tulsa, OK, 74128 (918) 438-2440
Admin Wilma Corley.
Licensure Intermediate Care. *Beds* 150. *Certified* Medicaid.

University Village Inc
8555 S Lewis, Tulsa, OK, 74137 (918) 299-2661
Admin Don Steele. *Medical Dir/Dir of Nursing* Dr Edward Slothour.
Licensure Skilled Care. *Beds* 70.
Admissions Requirements Medical examination.
Staff Physicians 1 (ft); RNs 5 (ft), 1 (pt); LPNs 3 (ft), 2 (pt); Orderlies 4 (ft); Nurses aides 24 (ft), 6 (pt); Physical therapists 1 (ft); Activities coordinators 1 (ft); Dietitians 1 (ft).
Affiliation Oral Roberts Ministries
Facilities Dining room; Physical therapy room; Activities room; Chapel; Crafts room; Laundry room; Barber/Beauty shop; Library.
Activities Arts and Crafts; Cards; Games; Reading groups; Prayer groups; Movies; Shopping trips; Dances/Social or cultural gatherings.
Description Facility is affiliated with Oral Roberts University with classes and many combined activities with students open to residents; next door to City of Faith Medical and Research Center.

Woodland Park Home*
5707 S Memorial Dr, Tulsa, OK, 74145 (918) 252-2521
Admin Genevieve Gary.
Licensure Intermediate Care. *Beds* 101. *Certified* Medicaid.

TUTTLE

Care Manor Nursing Center of Tuttle*
108 S 12th, Tuttle, OK, 73089 (405) 381-3363
Admin Thelma Green.
Licensure Intermediate Care. *Beds* 52. *Certified* Medicaid.

VALLIANT

Valliant Nursing Center Inc*
300 N Dalton, Valliant, OK, 74764 (405) 933-7803
Admin Judy Ney.
Licensure Intermediate Care. *Beds* 65. *Certified* Medicaid.

VIAN

Vian Nursing Home*
Thornton St, Vian, OK, 74962 (918) 773-5258
Admin Billy E Fullbright.
Licensure Intermediate Care. *Beds* 112.
Certified Medicaid.

VICI

Town of Vici Nursing Home*
619 Speck, Vici, OK, 73859 (405) 995-4216
Admin Ileta Allen.
Licensure Intermediate Care. *Beds* 61. *Certified* Medicaid.

VINITA

Autumn Nursing Centers Inc 1
240 N Scraper, Vinita, OK, 74301 (918)
256-7861
Admin Kunigunda M Lodes. *Medical Dir/Dir of Nursing* Clara Jo Moyers LPD.
Licensure Intermediate Care. *Beds* 62. *Certified* Medicaid.
Admissions Requirements Medical examination.
Staff RNs 1 (pt); LPNs 1 (ft), 3 (pt); Orderlies 1 (pt); Nurses aides 13 (ft), 7 (pt); Recreational therapists 1 (ft); Dietitians 1 (pt).
Facilities Dining room; Activities room; Laundry room; Barber/Beauty shop.
Activities Arts and Crafts; Cards; Games; Reading groups; Prayer groups; Movies; Shopping trips; Dances/Social or cultural gatherings.
Description Center has a good nursing program with people who give good care under the direction of LPN who has hospital experience. Excellent activities program with several groups of church affiliation having services; good prepared meals and good communication between departments.

Autumn Nursing Centers Inc 2*
1200 W Canadian, Vinita, OK, 74301 (918)
256-6366
Admin Edwina Hoskin.
Licensure Intermediate Care. *Beds* 121. *Certified* Medicaid.

Home of Hope Inc
Hope Blvd and N Adair, Vinita, OK, 74301
(918) 256-2372
Admin Charlotte McComb.
Licensure Intermediate Care for Mentally Retarded. *Beds* 94. *Certified* Medicaid.

WAGONER

Ross Nursing Home 1 Inc*
205 N Lincoln, Wagoner, OK, 74467 (918)
485-2203
Admin Dwana Barnes.
Licensure Intermediate Care. *Beds* 73. *Certified* Medicaid.

Ross Nursing Home 2 Inc*
109 S Harrill, Wagoner, OK, 74467 (918)
485-3972

Admin Dwana Barnes.
Licensure Intermediate Care. *Beds* 54. *Certified* Medicaid.

WAKITA

Community Health Center
Cherokee St, Wakita, OK, 73771 (405)
594-2292
Admin James Schuelke. *Medical Dir/Dir of Nursing* D L Graves MD.
Licensure Intermediate Care. *Beds* 47. *Certified* Medicaid.
Staff Physicians 1 (ft), 1 (pt); RNs 5 (ft), 4 (pt); LPNs 2 (ft); Nurses aides 27 (ft); Physical therapists 1 (pt); Activities coordinators 1 (ft); Dietitians 1 (ft); Dentists 1 (ft).
Facilities Dining room; Physical therapy room; Activities room; Chapel; Crafts room; Laundry room; Barber/Beauty shop; Library.
Activities Arts and Crafts; Cards; Games; Reading groups; Prayer groups; Movies; Shopping trips; Dances/Social or cultural gatherings.
Description Center contains in one building a nursing home, hospital, laboratory and X-ray, physician clinic, dental clinic, pharmacy, ambulance, and retirement apartments; 24-hour care by registered nurses.

WALTERS

Parkview Manor*
600 E California, Walters, OK, 73752 (405)
875-3376
Admin Eva Miller.
Licensure Intermediate Care. *Beds* 54. *Certified* Medicaid.

WARNER

Countryside Estates Inc
Box 629, Warner, OK, 74469 (918) 463-5143
Admin Margie Burris.
Licensure Intermediate Care. *Beds* 90. *Certified* Medicaid.
Staff Physicians 1 (pt); RNs 1 (pt); LPNs 5 (ft); Nurses aides 27 (ft); Physical therapists 1 (pt); Activities coordinators 1 (ft); Dietitians 1 (pt).
Facilities Dining room; Laundry room; Barber/Beauty shop; TV area.
Activities Arts and Crafts; Cards; Games; Prayer groups; Shopping trips; Dances/Social or cultural gatherings.

WATONGA

Hillcrest of Watonga Inc
816 N Hook, Watonga, OK, 73772 (405)
623-7249
Admin Walter C Deane. *Medical Dir/Dir of Nursing* Regina Stinson RN.
Licensure Intermediate Care. *Beds* 70. *Certified* Medicaid.
Staff Physicians 4 (pt); RNs 1 (ft); LPNs 3 (pt); Nurses aides 19 (ft), 3 (pt); Activities coordinators 1 (ft); Dietitians 1 (pt).
Facilities Dining room; Activities room; Crafts room; Laundry room; Barber/Beauty shop.
Activities Arts and Crafts; Cards; Games; Reading groups; Prayer groups; Movies; Shop-

ping trips; Dances/Social or cultural gatherings.
Description Facility features outstanding programs including annual Easter egg hunt for community and annual fireworks display. Exercise classes 6 days a week and Bible study 5 days a week. There are plans to add 20 more beds in the near future.

WAURIKA

Wood Nursing and Convalescent Center*
1100 N Ash, Waurika, OK, 73573 (405)
228-2249
Admin Virgil L Wood Jr.
Licensure Intermediate Care. *Beds* 83. *Certified* Medicaid.

WAYNOKA

Waynoka Nursing Center*
Rt 1, Waynoka, OK, 73860 (405) 824-5661
Admin Jeneva Helterbrake.
Licensure Intermediate Care. *Beds* 40. *Certified* Medicaid.

WEATHERFORD

Little Bird Nursing Home Inc*
801 N Washington, Weatherford, OK, 73096
(405) 772-3993
Admin Lola Little Bird.
Licensure Intermediate Care. *Beds* 81. *Certified* Medicaid.

Weatherford Nursing Center*
1001 N 7th, Weatherford, OK, 73096 (405)
772-3368
Admin Daisey Meier.
Licensure Intermediate Care. *Beds* 52. *Certified* Medicaid.

WELEETKA

Adkins Nursing Home*
300 W 9th, Weleetka, OK, 74880 (405)
786-2244
Admin Gerrol Adkins.
Licensure Intermediate Care. *Beds* 60. *Certified* Medicaid.

Adkins-Weleetka Nursing Home*
122 E 10th, Weleetka, OK, 74880 (405)
786-2401
Admin Gerrol Akins.
Licensure Intermediate Care. *Beds* 45. *Certified* Medicaid.

WESTVILLE

Westville Nursing Home*
308 Williams St, Westville, OK, 74965 (918)
723-5476
Admin Sadie Blackwood.
Licensure Intermediate Care. *Beds* 79. *Certified* Medicaid.

WETUMKA

Pioneer Nursing Home of Hughes Inc
620 S Alabama, Wetumka, OK, 74883 (405)
452-3296
Admin Helen Robinson-Knight. *Medical Dir-
/Dir of Nursing* Jane Gustin LPN.
Licensure Intermediate Care. *Beds* 50.
Certified Medicaid.
Staff Physicians; RNs; LPNs; Orderlies;
Nurses aides; Physical therapists; Activities
coordinators; Dietitians; Dentists; Ophthal-
mologists.
Facilities Dining room; Activities room; Crafts
room; Laundry room; Barber/Beauty shop.
Activities Arts and Crafts; Games; Reading
groups; Prayer groups; Shopping trips; Dances-
/Social or cultural gatherings.
Description Facility is locally owned and run.

Wetumka Nursing Home Inc
700 N Main, Wetumka, OK, 74883 (405)
452-5126
Admin Loretta Goodin. *Medical Dir/Dir of
Nursing* Dr Wade Warren.
Licensure Intermediate Care. *Beds* 50. *Certi-
fied* Medicaid.
Staff Physicians 1 (ft); RNs 1 (ft); LPNs 2 (ft);
Orderlies 1 (ft); Nurses aides 15 (ft); Reality
therapists 1 (ft); Recreational therapists 1 (ft);
Occupational therapists 1 (ft); Activities coordi-
nators 1 (ft); Dietitians 1 (ft); Dentists 1 (ft).
Facilities Dining room; Physical therapy room;
Activities room; Chapel; Crafts room; Laundry
room; Barber/Beauty shop; Library.
Activities Arts and Crafts; Cards; Games;
Reading groups; Prayer groups; Shopping trips;
Dances/Social or cultural gatherings.
Description The chapel is off to itself and the
family can use it privately for visiting; also
prayer room.

WEWOKA

Elmwood Manor Inc*
300 S Seminole, Wewoka, OK, 74884 (405)
257-2576
Admin John Grimes.
Licensure Intermediate Care. *Beds* 47. *Certified* Medicaid.

Oakridge Home Inc
7th and Compton, Wewoka, OK, 74884 (405)
257-5800
Admin Max Filson.
Licensure Intermediate Care. *Beds* 160. *Certified* Medicaid.
Staff Physicians 1 (pt); RNs 1 (ft); LPNs 6 (ft);
Orderlies 4 (ft); Nurses aides 30 (ft); Recreational therapists 1 (ft); Activities coordinators 4
(ft); Dietitians 1 (ft).

Wewoka Nursing Home Inc*
200 E 4th, Wewoka, OK, 74884 (405) 257-3393
Admin James Robert Smart.
Licensure Intermediate Care. *Beds* 57. *Certified* Medicaid.

WILBURTON

Community Nursing Home
200 NE 1st, Box 607, Wilburton, OK, 74578
(918) 465-2221
Admin Philip M Green. *Medical Dir/Dir of
Nursing* Deborah Morgan LPN.
Licensure Intermediate Care. *Beds* 29. *Certi-
fied* Medicaid.
Admissions Requirements Medical examina-
tion.
Staff Physicians 1 (pt); RNs 1 (pt); LPNs 2 (ft);
Nurses aides 11 (ft); Reality therapists 1 (ft);
Recreational therapists 1 (ft); Activities coordinators 1 (ft); Dietitians 1 (pt); Dentists 1 (pt);
Ophthalmologists 1 (pt); Podiatrists 1 (pt).
Facilities Dining room; Activities room; Chapel; Crafts room; Laundry room; Barber/Beauty
shop; Library.
Activities Arts and Crafts; Cards; Games; Prayer groups; Movies; Shopping trips; Dances/So-
cial or cultural gatherings.
Description Facility is located one block from
downtown area, making it convenient for shopping trips, doctor visits; walking distance to
most stores.

Latimer Nursing Home*
Hwy 2 N, Wilburton, OK, 74578 (918)
465-2255
Admin Frances Mordecai.
Licensure Intermediate Care. *Beds* 39. *Certi-
fied* Medicaid.

Ranchwood Lodge Home
900 W Ranchwood Dr, Wilburton, OK, 74578
(918) 465-2314
Admin Rosie Foster. *Medical Dir/Dir of
Nursing* Liz Hawthorne.
Licensure Intermediate Care. *Beds* 55. *Certified* Medicaid.
Admissions Requirements Medical examination; Physician's request.
Staff Physicians; RNs; LPNs; Orderlies;
Nurses aides; Physical therapists; Reality therapists; Recreational therapists; Occupational
therapists; Activities coordinators; Dietitians;
Dentists; Podiatrists; Audiologists.
Facilities Dining room; Activities room; Chapel; Crafts room; Laundry room; Barber/Beauty
shop.
Activities Arts and Crafts; Cards; Games; Prayer groups; Movies; Shopping trips; Dances/So-
cial or cultural gatherings.
Description This is a home away from home
giving clean nursing care with physicians'
supervision, activities provided, and craft work
encouraged.

WILSON

Wilson Nursing Center
406 E Main, Wilson, OK, 73463 (405)
668-2337
Admin Helen Knight. *Medical Dir/Dir of
Nursing* Virginia McLane.
Licensure Intermediate Care. *Beds* 60. *Certi-
fied* Medicaid.
Admissions Requirements Medical examination; Physician's request.
Staff LPNs 2 (ft); Nurses aides 10 (ft), 3 (pt);
Dietitians 1 (pt).
Facilities Dining room; Activities room; Crafts
room; Laundry room; Barber/Beauty shop.
Activities Arts and Crafts; Games; Reading
groups; Prayer groups; Movies; Shopping trips;
Dances/Social or cultural gatherings; Exercise
group.
Description Located on Main Street one block
east of local shopping, Wilson Nursing Center
offers 24-hour nursing care and semi-private
rooms. Church service and visitation provided
by all churches in area. Shaded and fenced back
yard with lawn furniture, picnic tables, and barbecue grill for family entertainment and facility
activities.

WOODWARD

**Colonial Manor Nursing Home of Woodward
Inc***
2608 Reardon Rd, Woodward, OK, 73801
(405) 254-3456
Admin Kenneth Morrison.
Licensure Intermediate Care. *Beds* 50. *Certified* Medicaid.

Woodward Nursing Center*
429 Downs Ave, Woodward, OK, 73801 (405)
256-6448
Admin Nina Clabaugh.
Licensure Intermediate Care. *Beds* 80. *Certified* Medicaid.

WYNNEWOOD

Wynnewood Nursing Center*
810 E California, Wynnewood, OK, 73098
(405) 665-2330
Admin Jo Ann Clayton.
Licensure Intermediate Care. *Beds* 79. *Certified* Medicaid.

YALE

Yale Nursing Home
E Chicago and H St, Yale, OK, 74085 (918)
387-2412
Admin Susan G Williams.
Licensure Intermediate Care. *Beds* 50. *Certi-
fied* Medicaid.
Staff RNs 1 (pt); LPNs 2 (ft); Orderlies 1 (ft);
Nurses aides 26 (ft); Physical therapists 1 (pt);
Activities coordinators 1 (ft); Dietitians 1 (pt);
Dentists 1 (pt).
Facilities Dining room; Physical therapy room;
Activities room; Chapel; Crafts room; Laundry
room; Barber/Beauty shop.
Activities Arts and Crafts; Cards; Games; Pray-
er groups; Shopping trips; Dances/Social or cul-
tural gatherings.
Description Facility offers a family atmosphere
with 24-hour nursing care.

YUKON

Cottonwood Manor Nursing Home*
300 Walnut, Yukon, OK, 73099 (405) 354-2563
Admin Liz Cummings.
Licensure Intermediate Care. *Beds* 122. *Certified* Medicaid.

Yukon Convalescent Center
1110 Cornwell, Yukon, OK, 73099 (405)
354-5373
Admin Judy Greenameyer. *Medical Dir/Dir of Nursing* Dianne Lee.
Licensure Intermediate Care. *Beds* 69. *Certified* Medicaid.
Admissions Requirements Medical examination.
Staff Physicians 1 (ft); RNs 1 (pt); LPNs 6 (ft); Orderlies 1 (pt); Nurses aides 17 (ft), 1 (pt); Physical therapists 1 (pt); Occupational therapists 1 (pt); Activities coordinators 2 (ft); Dietitians 1 (pt); Podiatrists 1 (pt).
Facilities Dining room; Activities room; Crafts room; Laundry room; Barber/Beauty shop.
Activities Arts and Crafts; Cards; Games; Reading groups; Prayer groups; Movies; Shopping trips; Dances/Social or cultural gatherings.
Description Facility features 24-hour licensed nursing; therapeutic diets; open house once a month; and spacious grounds/patio.

OREGON

ALBANY

Linn Care Center
1023 W 6th Ave, Albany, OR, 97321 (503) 926-8664
Admin Don Petersen. *Medical Dir/Dir of Nursing* Benjamin Bonnlander.
Licensure Skilled Care. *Beds* 106. *Certified* Medicaid; Medicare.
Staff RNs 5 (ft), 2 (pt); LPNs 3 (ft), 3 (pt); Orderlies 3 (ft), 5 (pt); Nurses aides 13 (ft), 12 (pt); Physical therapists 1 (pt); Recreational therapists 2 (pt); Occupational therapists 1 (pt); Speech therapists 1 (pt); Activities coordinators 1 (ft); Podiatrists 1 (pt); Audiologists 1 (pt).

Mennonite Home
5353 SE Columbus, Albany, OR, 97321 (503) 928-7232
Admin Luke Birky. *Medical Dir/Dir of Nursing* Donald Kerr MD.
Licensure Intermediate Care. *Beds* 80. *Certified* Medicaid.
Admissions Requirements Minimum age 65; Medical examination; Physician's request.
Staff RNs 5 (ft), 7 (pt); LPNs 2 (ft), 2 (pt); Nurses aides 36 (ft), 22 (pt); Physical therapists 1 (ft); Activities coordinators 1 (ft); Dietitians 1 (pt).
Affiliation Mennonite
Facilities Dining room; Activities room; Crafts room; Laundry room; Barber/Beauty shop; Library.
Activities Arts and Crafts; Games; Reading groups; Prayer groups; Movies; Shopping trips; Dances/Social or cultural gatherings.
Description Facility features continuing care, independent living, personal care, intermediate care, nursing and full pastoral care departments.

Sunset Care Center
805 E 19th, Albany, OR, 97321 (503) 926-4741
Admin Betty Lusetti. *Medical Dir/Dir of Nursing* Dr Bonnlanden.
Licensure Intermediate Care. *Beds* 92. *Certified* Medicaid.
Staff RNs 8 (ft), 5 (pt); LPNs 6 (ft), 5 (pt); Orderlies 4 (ft), 1 (pt); Nurses aides 40 (ft), 15 (pt); Physical therapists 1 (pt); Recreational therapists 1 (pt); Occupational therapists; Activities coordinators 1 (ft); Dietitians 1 (ft); Dentists; Ophthalmologists; Podiatrists; Audiologists.

Facilities Dining room; Activities room; Crafts room; Laundry room; Barber/Beauty shop.
Activities Arts and Crafts; Cards; Games; Reading groups; Prayer groups; Movies; Shopping trips; Dances/Social or cultural gatherings.
Description Facility features a large backyard with a sidewalk, with planter box, for wheelchair patients; family council meetings with emphasis on Alzheimer's disease; also geriatric patients with behavior problems and wandering patients are protected.

ASHLAND

Linda Vista Care Center*
135 Maple St, Ashland, OR, 97520 (503) 482-2341
Admin Charles (Doug) Fogg.
Licensure Intermediate Care. *Beds* 36. *Certified* Medicaid.

ASTORIA

Clatsop Care and Rehabilitation District
646 16th St, Astoria, OR, 97103 (503) 325-0313
Admin Arne Eilertsen. *Medical Dir/Dir of Nursing* Paul Voeller MD.
Licensure Skilled Care; Intermediate Care.
Beds 30. *Certified* Medicaid; Medicare.
Admissions Requirements Medical examination; Physician's request.
Staff RNs 1 (ft), 5 (pt); LPNs 2 (ft), 3 (pt); Orderlies 1 (ft); Nurses aides 18 (ft), 7 (pt); Physical therapists 1 (pt); Activities coordinators 1 (ft), 1 (pt); Dietitians 1 (pt).
Facilities Dining room; Physical therapy room; Chapel; Laundry room; Barber/Beauty shop.

Crestview Care Center*
263 W Exchange, Astoria, OR, 97103 (503) 325-1753
Admin Don Johnston.
Licensure Intermediate Care. *Beds* 82. *Certified* Medicaid.

BAKER

Cedar Manor
4000 Cedar St, Baker, OR, 97814 (503) 523-6333
Admin Chuck Williams.
Licensure Intermediate Care. *Beds* 55. *Certi-*

fied Medicaid.
Admissions Requirements Physician's request.
Staff RNs 1 (ft), 1 (pt); LPNs 4 (ft), 1 (pt); Orderlies 1 (ft); Nurses aides 25 (ft), 5 (pt); Activities coordinators 1 (ft); Dietitians 1 (pt).
Facilities Dining room; Activities room; Laundry room; Barber/Beauty shop; Library.
Activities Arts and Crafts; Cards; Games; Reading groups; Movies; Shopping trips; Dances/Social or cultural gatherings.
Description Facility is in rural setting in eastern Oregon with lovely grounds, dedicated concerned staff, and exceptional activity programs keeping residents involved in community.

Saint Elizabeth Nursing Home*
2365 4th St, Baker, OR, 97814 (503) 523-4452, 4453
Admin Sr Philomena Joseph Ludwig.
Licensure Intermediate Care. *Beds* 96. *Certified* Medicaid.

BANDON

Ocean View Care Center
2790 Beach Loop, Bandon, OR, 97411 (503) 347-2228
Admin Donald L Veverher.
Licensure Intermediate Care. *Beds* 37. *Certified* Medicaid.
Admissions Requirements Medical examination; Physician's request.
Staff RNs 2 (ft), 1 (pt); Orderlies 2 (ft); Nurses aides 19 (ft); Physical therapists; Occupational therapists; Speech therapists; Activities coordinators 1 (ft); Dietitians; Dentists; Ophthalmologists.
Facilities Dining room; Activities room; Crafts room; Laundry room.
Activities Arts and Crafts; Cards; Games; Reading groups; Prayer groups; Movies; Shopping trips; Dances/Social or cultural gatherings.
Description Facility is located on the Oregon coast with an unobstructed view of the ocean, beach, and rock formations off the shore.

BEAVERTON

Bel Air Care Center*
11850 SW Allen Blvd, Beaverton, OR, 97005 (503) 646-7164

Admin Robert Berger.
Licensure Intermediate Care. *Beds* 104. *Certified* Medicaid.

Maryville Nursing Home
14645 SW Farmington Rd, Beaverton, OR, 97005 (503) 643-8626
Admin Sr M Theresa Margaret. *Medical Dir/Dir of Nursing* Donald R Alson MD.
Licensure Intermediate Care. *Beds* 132. *Certified* Medicaid.
Staff RNs 10 (ft); LPNs 3 (ft); Orderlies 3 (ft); Nurses aides 36 (ft); Physical therapists 2 (pt); Recreational therapists 2 (ft); Activities coordinators 1 (ft); Dietitians 1 (pt); Dentists 1 (pt); Ophthalmologists 1 (pt); Podiatrists 1 (pt).
Affiliation Roman Catholic
Facilities Dining room; Physical therapy room; Activities room; Chapel; Crafts room; Laundry room; Barber/Beauty shop; Library; Lounge.
Activities Arts and Crafts; Cards; Games; Prayer groups; Movies; Dances/Social or cultural gatherings; Sing-a-longs.

BEND

Bachelor Butte Nursing Center
119 SE Wilson, Bend, OR, 97701 (503) 382-7161
Admin Robert A Phillips. *Medical Dir/Dir of Nursing* P W Ford MD.
Licensure Intermediate Care. *Beds* 87. *Certified* Medicaid.
Staff RNs 2 (ft), 1 (pt); LPNs 4 (ft), 2 (pt); Nurses aides 30 (ft), 5 (pt); Activities coordinators 1 (ft), 2 (pt); Dietitians 1 (pt).
Facilities Dining room; Activities room; Crafts room; Laundry room; Barber/Beauty shop.
Activities Arts and Crafts; Cards; Games; Reading groups; Prayer groups; Movies; Shopping trips; Dances/Social or cultural gatherings.
Description BBNC is situated on the east side of the beautiful Cascade Range of central Oregon. It is located within minutes of breathtaking scenic and outdoor recreational splendor.

Central Oregon Health Care Center*
1876 NE Hwy 20, Bend, OR, 97701 (503) 382-5531
Admin Craig Riley.
Licensure Skilled Care; Intermediate Care. *Beds* 100. *Certified* Medicaid; Medicare.

Harmony House Nursing Home*
95 E Xerxes St, Bend, OR, 97701 (503) 382-0479
Admin Phyllis Field.
Licensure Intermediate Care. *Beds* 18. *Certified* Medicaid.

BERLIN

Fox View Acres*
284 Mound St, Berlin, OR, 54923 (414) 499-4892
Admin Glenn T Beaudry.
Licensure Intermediate Care. *Beds* 10. *Certified* Medicaid.
Ownership Nonprofit.

BROOKINGS

Curry Good Samaritan Center*
PO Box 1217, Park Ave, Brookings, OR, 97415 (503) 469-3111
Admin Rosemary Rosengren.
Licensure Intermediate Care. *Beds* 71. *Certified* Medicaid.

BURNS

Burns Nursing Home*
348 W Adams, Burns, OR, 97720 (503) 573-6888
Admin Karen Dinsmore.
Licensure Intermediate Care. *Beds* 40. *Certified* Medicaid.

CANBY

Canby Care Center
390 NW 2nd Ave, Canby, OR, 97013 (503) 266-5541
Admin Miriam Larson.
Licensure Intermediate Care. *Beds* 48. *Certified* Medicaid.
Staff RNs 2 (ft), 2 (pt); LPNs 1 (ft), 3 (pt); Nurses aides 20 (ft), 5 (pt); Activities coordinators 1 (ft).
Facilities Dining room; Crafts room; Laundry room.
Activities Arts and Crafts; Games; Reading groups; Prayer groups; Movies.
Description Convenient location in downtown Canby; drug store, doctors, dentists, shopping, and park are within 2 blocks.

Elmhurst Nursing Home
1105 S Elm St, Canby, OR, 97013 (503) 266-1131
Admin Dale Stephens.
Licensure Intermediate Care. *Beds* 43. *Certified* Medicaid.
Admissions Requirements Minimum age 20; Physician's request.
Staff RNs 2 (ft); LPNs 1 (ft); Nurses aides 15 (ft), 6 (pt); Physical therapists 1 (pt); Reality therapists 1 (pt); Recreational therapists 1 (ft); Occupational therapists 1 (ft); Speech therapists 1 (ft); Activities coordinators 1 (ft); Dietitians 1 (pt).
Facilities Dining room; Activities room; Crafts room; Laundry room.
Activities Arts and Crafts; Cards; Games; Reading groups; Prayer groups; Movies; Shopping trips.

CENTRAL POINT

Central Point Care Center
155 S 1st St, Central Point, OR, 97502 (503) 664-3355
Admin Verna Pool. *Medical Dir/Dir of Nursing* Mike Robinson DO.
Licensure Intermediate Care. *Beds* 33. *Certified* Medicaid.
Admissions Requirements Physician's request.
Staff RNs 1 (ft); LPNs 2 (ft); Nurses aides 15 (ft); Recreational therapists 1 (ft); Activities coordinators 1 (ft).
Facilities Dining room; Activities room; Laun-

dry room; Barber/Beauty shop.
Activities Arts and Crafts; Cards; Games; Movies; Shopping trips; Dances/Social or cultural gatherings.
Description We take pride in our clean atmosphere, family-like setting, and loving attitude.

COLTON

Lutheran Pioneer Home*
29872 S Hult Rd, Colton, OR, 97017 (503) 824-3311
Admin Beverly Rice.
Licensure Intermediate Care. *Beds* 28. *Certified* Medicaid.
Affiliation Lutheran

CONDON

Condon Nursing Home*
311 W Gilliam, Condon, OR, 97823 (503) 384-2323
Admin Elvira McQuain.
Licensure Intermediate Care. *Beds* 31. *Certified* Medicaid.

COOS BAY

Coos Bay Care Center
2625 Coos Bay Blvd, Coos Bay, OR, 97420 (503) 267-2161
Admin Julie Tullock.
Licensure Intermediate Care; Residential Care. *Beds* ICF 83; Residential Care 9. *Certified* Medicaid.
Admissions Requirements Physician's request.
Facilities Dining room; Physical therapy room; Activities room; Crafts room; Laundry room; Barber/Beauty shop; Library.
Activities Arts and Crafts; Cards; Games; Reading groups; Prayer groups; Movies; Shopping trips; Dances/Social or cultural gatherings.

Life Care Center of Coos Bay
2890 Ocean Blvd, Coos Bay, OR, 97420 (503) 267-5811
Admin Ronald Green. *Medical Dir/Dir of Nursing* Ennis Keiser MD.
Licensure Skilled Care; Intermediate Care. *Beds* SNF 30; ICF 84. *Certified* Medicaid.
Admissions Requirements Minimum age 9; Physician's request.
Staff RNs 5 (ft), 2 (pt); LPNs 2 (ft), 1 (pt); Nurses aides 50 (ft), 10 (pt); Physical therapists 1 (ft); Reality therapists 1 (ft); Activities coordinators 1 (ft); Dietitians 1 (ft).
Facilities Dining room; Physical therapy room; Activities room; Chapel; Crafts room; Laundry room; Barber/Beauty shop; Library.
Activities Arts and Crafts; Cards; Games; Reading groups; Prayer groups; Movies; Dances/Social or cultural gatherings.
Description We are set in a coastal fishing town. We have a wide variety of patient classifications within our facility, we accept Medicare/VA/Medicaid and private. We are also licensed for residential care as well as intermediate and skilled care.

COQUILLE

Coquille Care Center
Fairview Rt, Box 5610, Coquille, OR, 97423
(503) 396-2302
Admin Clay Green. *Medical Dir/Dir of
Nursing* F Keith Mantee MD.
Licensure Intermediate Care. *Beds* 37. *Certified* Medicaid.
Admissions Requirements Minimum age 59;
Medical examination; Physician's request.
Staff RNs 1 (ft), 3 (pt); LPNs 1 (pt); Nurses
aides 10 (ft), 7 (pt); Activities coordinators 1
(ft).
Facilities Dining room; Activities room; Crafts
room; Laundry room.
Activities Arts and Crafts; Games; Prayer
groups; Movies.
Description Facility has homey country atmosphere; specializes in "caring."

CORNELIUS

**Good Shepherd Lutheran Home for Mentally
Retarded**
Rt 4, Box 96, Cornelius, OR, 97113 (503)
648-8976
Admin Gary Mrosko. *Medical Dir/Dir of
Nursing* Otto Loehden MD.
Licensure Intermediate Care for Mentally
Retarded. *Beds* 87. *Certified* Medicaid.
Admissions Requirements Medical examination.
Staff RNs 3 (ft), 1 (pt); LPNs 4 (ft), 2 (pt);
Orderlies 50 (ft), 4 (pt); Physical therapists 1
(pt); Recreational therapists 1 (ft), 1 (pt); Occupational therapists 1 (ft); Speech therapists 1
(ft); Dietitians 1 (pt).
Affiliation Lutheran
Facilities Dining room; Activities room; Chapel; Crafts room; Laundry room; Library.
Activities Arts and Crafts; Cards; Games;
Reading groups; Prayer groups; Movies; Shopping trips; Dances/Social or cultural gatherings.

CORVALLIS

Corvallis Care Center
980 NW Spruce St, Corvallis, OR, 97330 (503)
757-0151
Admin Velda Fancher. *Medical Dir/Dir of
Nursing* James W Gulick MD.
Licensure Intermediate Care. *Beds* 84. *Certified* Medicaid; Medicare.
Staff RNs 8 (ft); LPNs 3 (ft); Orderlies 1 (ft), 1
(pt); Nurses aides 30 (ft), 4 (pt); Physical therapists 1 (pt); Occupational therapists 1 (pt); Speech therapists 1 (pt); Activities coordinators 1
(ft); Dietitians 1 (pt); Podiatrists 1 (pt);
Audiologists 1 (pt).
Facilities Dining room; Activities room; Laundry room; Barber/Beauty shop.
Activities Arts and Crafts; Cards; Reading
groups; Prayer groups; Movies; Shopping trips;
Dances/Social or cultural gatherings; Music
and crafts.
Description Our community college sends
instructors to our facility to conduct classes for
our residents, one class is ceramics on Monday

mornings, the other is music therapy on Tuesdays and Fridays. We pay tuition for the residents who attend.

Corvallis Manor
160 NE Conifer Ave, Corvallis, OR, 97330
(503) 757-1651
Admin Merlin Hart. *Medical Dir/Dir of
Nursing* Dr Norman Castillo.
Licensure Skilled Care; Intermediate Care.
Beds SNF 30; ICF 104. *Certified* Medicaid;
Medicare.
Admissions Requirements Physician's request.
Staff Physicians 1 (pt); RNs 6 (ft), 5 (pt); LPNs
2 (ft), 1 (pt); Orderlies 4 (ft), 4 (pt); Nurses aides
30 (ft), 20 (pt); Physical therapists 1 (pt); Occupational therapists 1 (ft), 1 (pt); Speech therapists 1 (pt); Activities coordinators 1 (ft), 1 (pt);
Dietitians 1 (pt).
Facilities Dining room; Physical therapy room;
Activities room; Laundry room; Barber/Beauty
shop; Library.
Activities Arts and Crafts; Cards; Games;
Reading groups; Prayer groups; Movies; Shopping trips; Dances/Social or cultural gatherings.
Description We employ a geriatric nurse practitioner full-time, and a house physician visits
4-5 days a week. These staff people enable us to
handle more complex medical problems than
the average nursing home. Also over 50% of the
patients admitted have a discharge back home.

Heart of the Valley
2700 NW Harrison, Corvallis, OR, 97330 (503)
757-1763
Admin Richard Prout. *Medical Dir/Dir of
Nursing* Dr James Gallant.
Licensure Skilled Care. *Beds* 59. *Certified* Medicaid; Medicare.
Staff RNs 6 (ft), 4 (pt); LPNs 4 (ft), 1 (pt);
Nurses aides 20 (ft), 10 (pt); Physical therapists
1 (pt); Recreational therapists 1 (pt); Occupational therapists; Speech therapists; Activities
coordinators 2 (ft), 1 (pt); Dietitians 1 (ft).
Facilities Dining room; Physical therapy room;
Activities room; Chapel; Crafts room; Laundry
room; Barber/Beauty shop; Library.
Activities Arts and Crafts; Cards; Games;
Reading groups; Prayer groups; Movies; Shopping trips; Dances/Social or cultural gatherings.
Description Facililty is an 80,000 sq ft structure, formally the Good Samaritan Hospital,
80% private, 100 adult residential care private
rooms, maintain a 95% occupany level. Facility
is located in the center of the community next
to Oregan State University.

COTTAGE GROVE

**Cottage Grove Hospital—North Wing Skilled
Nursing Facility**
1340 Birch Ave, Cottage Grove, OR, 97424
Admin John L Hoopes. *Medical Dir/Dir of
Nursing* Huntington Kooiker MD.
Licensure Skilled Care. *Beds* 30. *Certified* Medicaid.
Ownership Nonprofit.
Admissions Requirements Medical examination; Physician's request.
Staff Physicians 19 (ft); RNs 2 (ft); LPNs 2 (ft),
2 (pt); Nurses aides 2 (ft), 12 (pt); Physical therapists 1 (ft), 1 (pt); Activities coordinators 1

(pt); Dietitians 1 (ft); Dentists 8 (ft); Ophthalmologists 1 (ft); Podiatrists 1 (ft).
Facilities Dining room; Physical therapy room;
Activities room; Crafts room; Laundry room;
Barber/Beauty shop.
Activities Arts and Crafts; Cards; Games;
Reading groups; Prayer groups; Movies; Shopping trips; Dances/Social or cultural gatherings.
Description Facility provides long-term care as
part of a comprehensive program which
includes access to acute, rehabilitative and
home health care, only one of 2 nursing homes
in Lane County accredited by the JCAH.

Edgewood Nursing Center
515 Grant St, Cottage Grove, OR, 97424 (503)
942-5528
Admin Charles D Fogg.
Licensure Skilled Care; Intermediate Care.
Beds SNF 12; ICF 68. *Certified* Medicaid;
Medicare.
Facilities Dining room; Physical therapy room;
Activities room; Chapel; Crafts room; Laundry
room; Barber/Beauty shop; Library.
Activities Arts and Crafts; Cards; Games;
Reading groups; Prayer groups; Movies; Shopping trips; Dances/Social or cultural gatherings.

CRESWELL

Creswell Care Center
525 S 2nd, Creswell, OR, 97426 (503) 895-3333
Admin Connie Johnson.
Licensure Intermediate Care. *Beds* 80. *Certified* Medicaid.
Ownership Proprietary.
Admissions Requirements Medical
examination; Physician's request.
Facilities Dining room; Physical therapy room;
Activities room; Crafts room; Laundry room;
Barber/Beauty shop; Library.
Activities Arts and Crafts; Cards; Games;
Reading groups; Prayer groups; Movies; Shopping trips; Dances/Social or cultural gatherings.
Description Caring and cheerful atmosphere
with a homey touch. Conveniently located to
the center of town, yet retains a rural setting
overlooking the valley and tree covered hills—
on clear days enjoys a lovely view of the snow
covered Three Sisters in the Cascade Range.

DALLAS

Birch Street Manor*
862 SW Birch St, Dallas, OR, 97338 (503)
623-8131
Admin Patricia Jandera.
Licensure Intermediate Care. *Beds* 39. *Certified* Medicaid.

Dallas Nursing Home
348 W Ellendale, Dallas, OR, 97338 (503)
623-3291
Admin Allan Tschiegg. *Medical Dir/Dir of
Nursing* Dr Tom Flaming.
Licensure Intermediate Care. *Beds* 117. *Certified* Medicaid.
Staff RNs 6 (ft); LPNs 4 (ft), 1 (pt); Nurses
aides 50 (ft), 6 (pt); Activities coordinators 1
(ft); Dietitians 1 (pt).
Affiliation Mennonite

Facilities Dining room; Activities room; Chapel; Crafts room; Laundry room; Barber/Beauty shop.
Activities Arts and Crafts; Cards; Games; Reading groups; Prayer groups; Movies; Shopping trips.

ENTERPRISE

Wallowa County Memorial Hospital*
401 E 1st St, Enterprise, OR, 97828 (503) 426-3111
Admin Jim Gwilliam.
Licensure Intermediate Care. *Beds* 32. *Certified* Medicaid.

EUGENE

Cascade Manor*
65 W 30th Ave, Eugene, OR, 97405 (503) 344-4851
Admin Doris Keown.
Licensure Intermediate Care. *Beds* 21.

Emerald Nursing Center
2360 Chambers St, Eugene, OR, 97405 (503) 687-1310
Admin David Chinchurreta. *Medical Dir/Dir of Nursing* T A McKenzie MD.
Licensure Skilled Care; Intermediate Care.
Beds SNF 32; ICF 106. *Certified* Medicaid; Medicare.
Admissions Requirements Physician's request.
Staff Physicians 1 (pt); RNs 10 (ft); LPNs 20 (ft); Orderlies 10 (ft), 5 (pt); Nurses aides 30 (ft), 20 (pt); Physical therapists 1 (pt); Recreational therapists 2 (ft); Occupational therapists 1 (pt); Speech therapists 1 (pt); Activities coordinators 1 (ft); Dietitians 1 (pt); Dentists 1 (pt).
Facilities Dining room; Physical therapy room; Activities room; Crafts room; Laundry room; Barber/Beauty shop; Library.
Activities Arts and Crafts; Cards; Games; Reading groups; Prayer groups; Movies; Shopping trips; Shopping trips; Dances/Social or cultural gatherings.

Emerald Nursing Center
2369 Chambers St, Eugene, OR, 97405
Admin G David Chinchurreta. *Medical Dir-/Dir of Nursing* T A McKenzie MD.
Licensure Skilled Care; Intermediate Care.
Beds 138. *Certified* Medicaid; Medicare.
Ownership Proprietary.
Staff Physicians 1 (pt); RNs 10 (ft); LPNs 15 (ft); Orderlies 10 (ft); Nurses aides 50 (ft); Physical therapists 1 (ft); Recreational therapists 2 (ft); Occupational therapists 1 (pt); Speech therapists 1 (pt); Activities coordinators 1 (ft); Dietitians 1 (ft); Dentists 1 (pt).
Facilities Dining room; Physical therapy room; Activities room; Crafts room; Laundry room; Barber/Beauty shop; Library.
Activities Arts and Crafts; Cards; Games; Reading groups; Prayer groups; Movies; Shopping trips; Dances/Social or cultural gatherings.

Eugene Care Center Inc
1201 McLean Blvd, Eugene, OR, 97405 (503) 683-2155
Admin Sandi Johnson.

Licensure Skilled Care; Intermediate Care.
Beds 83. *Certified* Medicaid.
Admissions Requirements Medical examination.
Staff Physicians 2 (pt); RNs 8 (ft), 3 (pt); LPNs 1 (ft), 1 (pt); Physical therapists 1 (pt).
Facilities Dining room; Physical therapy room; Activities room; Chapel; Crafts room; Laundry room; Barber/Beauty shop.
Activities Arts and Crafts; Games; Reading groups; Prayer groups; Movies; Shopping trips; Dances/Social or cultural gatherings.
Description Eugene Care Center, located in the foothills of southeast Eugene, offers care for rehabilitative and long-term illness. Our private and semi-private rooms have individual furniture, private closets, and adjoining bathroom facilities. We encourage our residents to decorate their own rooms with personal possessions, thus creating a more home-like atmosphere.

Eugene Good Samaritan Center*
3500 Hilyard St, Eugene, OR, 97405 (503) 687-9211
Admin Gunter Brunk.
Licensure Skilled Care; Intermediate Care.
Beds SNF 36; ICF 114. *Certified* Medicaid; Medicare.

Garber's University Nursing Center
1166 E 28th, PO Box 505, Eugene, OR, 97405 (503) 345-0534
Admin Aaron Garber. *Medical Dir/Dir of Nursing* Donald England MD.
Licensure Skilled Care; Intermediate Care.
Beds SNF 14; ICF 124. *Certified* Medicaid; Medicare.
Admissions Requirements Medical examination; Physician's request.
Staff Physicians 1 (pt); RNs 6 (ft), 1 (pt); LPNs 1 (ft), 1 (pt); Nurses aides 31 (ft), 2 (pt); Physical therapists 1 (pt); Occupational therapists 1 (pt); Speech therapists 1 (pt); Activities coordinators 1 (ft); Dietitians 1 (pt); Podiatrists 1 (pt).
Facilities Dining room; Activities room; Laundry room; Barber/Beauty shop.
Activities Arts and Crafts; Cards; Games; Reading groups; Prayer groups; Movies; Shopping trips; Dances/Social or cultural gatherings.
Description We provide a quality skilled and intermediate nursing program supplemented by enrichment for spiritual and social programs, implemented by an organized special service department; location is in nice residential area, hospitals, churches, shopping areas, and restuarants within 15 block range.

Green Valley Care Center Inc
1735 Adkins St, Eugene, OR, 97401 (503) 683-5032
Admin Carl Helms. *Medical Dir/Dir of Nursing* Jeffery Beckwith MD.
Licensure Skilled Care; Intermediate Care.
Beds 104. *Certified* Medicaid; Medicare.
Admissions Requirements Physician's request.
Staff Physicians; RNs 5 (ft), 1 (pt); LPNs 3 (ft), 1 (pt); Orderlies 4 (ft); Nurses aides 58 (ft); Physical therapists 1 (ft); Recreational therapists 1 (ft); Occupational therapists 1 (ft); Speech therapists 1 (pt); Activities coordinators 1 (ft); Dentists 1 (pt).
Facilities Dining room; Physical therapy room;

Activities room; Crafts room; Barber/Beauty shop; Library.
Activities Arts and Crafts; Cards; Games; Reading groups; Movies; Dances/Social or cultural gatherings.

Ivorena Care Center*
687 Cheshire Ave, Eugene, OR, 97402 (503) 484-2117
Admin J Brandt Spence.
Licensure Intermediate Care. *Beds* 102. *Certified* Medicaid.

Pleasant Valley Nursing Home Inc
395 W 29th Ave, Eugene, OR, 97405 (503) 687-2240
Admin Millicent Redford.
Licensure Intermediate Care. *Beds* 60. *Certified* Medicaid.
Staff RNs 5 (ft); LPNs 1 (ft); Orderlies 3 (ft); Nurses aides 20 (ft), 2 (pt); Activities coordinators 1 (ft); Dietitians 1 (pt).
Facilities Dining room; Activities room; Crafts room; Laundry room; Barber/Beauty shop.
Activities Arts and Crafts; Cards; Games; Reading groups; Prayer groups; Shopping trips; Dances/Social or cultural gatherings.
Description We specialize in caring for emotionally disturbed, mentally handicapped people as well as geriatric.

Twilight Acres Nursing Home
85434 Dilley Ln, Eugene, OR, 97405 (503) 746-7611
Admin Hazel Stebbeds.
Licensure Intermediate Care. *Beds* 60. *Certified* Medicaid.
Admissions Requirements Medical examination; Physician's request.
Staff RNs 2 (ft), 2 (pt); LPNs 2 (ft), 2 (pt); Orderlies 2 (ft); Nurses aides 18 (ft), 6 (pt); Activities coordinators 1 (ft); Dietitians 1 (pt).
Facilities Dining room; Activities room; Barber/Beauty shop.
Activities Arts and Crafts; Cards; Games; Reading groups; Movies; Shopping trips; Outings; Barbecues.
Description Facility is located on 4 acres in a country setting 10 minutes from city with beautiful flower gardens, lawns, and 2 patios, creating a home-like atmosphere.

Valley West Retirement Center
2300 Warren Ave, Eugene, OR, 97405 (503) 686-2828
Admin Jane F Boren. *Medical Dir/Dir of Nursing* Dwayne Rice MD.
Licensure Skilled Care; Intermediate Care.
Beds 120. *Certified* Medicare.
Admissions Requirements Medical examination; Physician's request.
Staff Physicians 4 (pt); RNs 18 (ft); LPNs 2 (ft); Nurses aides 50 (ft); Physical therapists 1 (ft); Recreational therapists 1 (ft), 2 (pt); Occupational therapists 1 (pt); Speech therapists 1 (pt); Activities coordinators 3 (ft), 1 (pt); Dietitians 1 (pt); Dentists 1 (pt); Podiatrists 1 (pt).
Facilities Dining room; Physical therapy room; Activities room; Crafts room; Laundry room; Barber/Beauty shop; Library.
Activities Arts and Crafts; Cards; Games; Reading groups; Prayer groups; Movies; Shopping trips; Dances/Social or cultural gatherings.

Description Facility is decorated with antiques, fully carpeted and includes a putting green. Staffing levels exceed Oregon requirements. Licensed for day care. Facility has 33% more square footage per licensed bed than any other facility in Oregon. JCAH accredited.

FLORENCE

Siuslaw Care Center
1951 21st St, Florence, OR, 97439 (503) 997-8222
Admin Karen Fields.
Licensure Skilled Care; Intermediate Care; Intermediate Care for Mentally Retarded. *Beds* SNF 8; ICF 51; ICF/MR 32. *Certified* Medicaid; Medicare.

FOREST GROVE

Camelot Care Center*
3900 Pacific Ave, Forest Grove, OR, 97116 (503) 357-5612
Admin Merlin Hathaway.
Licensure Intermediate Care. *Beds* 114. *Certified* Medicaid.

Forest View Care Center*
3300 19th Ave, Forest Grove, OR, 97116 (503) 357-7119
Admin Harley Clendenon.
Licensure Intermediate Care. *Beds* 114. *Certified* Medicaid.

Lou Del Health Care
2122 Oak St, Forest Grove, OR, 97116 (503) 357-9780
Admin Arliss Roman. *Medical Dir/Dir of Nursing* Dr Robert Martens.
Licensure Intermediate Care. *Beds* 40. *Certified* Medicaid.
Admissions Requirements Minimum age 18; Medical examination; Physician's request.
Staff RNs 1 (ft); LPNs 5 (pt); Nurses aides 14 (ft), 5 (pt); Activities coordinators 1 (ft); 1 (ft).
Facilities Dining room; Laundry room.
Activities Arts and Crafts; Games; Reading groups; Prayer groups; Movies; Shopping trips; Dances/Social or cultural gatherings.

Masonic and Eastern Star Home*
3505 Pacific Ave, Forest Grove, OR, 97116 (503) 359-4465
Admin Bob Surina.
Licensure Intermediate Care. *Beds* 49.
Affiliation Masons

GASTON

Laurelwood Manor Nursing Home*
Rt 2, Box 145, Gaston, OR, 97119-9511 (503) 985-7484
Admin Ruth J Moreno.
Licensure Intermediate Care. *Beds* 20. *Certified* Medicaid.

GLADSTONE

Clackamas Terrace Convalescent Center*
340 1st St, Gladstone, OR, 97027 (503) 656-1646
Admin Maureen Kehoe.
Licensure Intermediate Care. *Beds* 126. *Certified* Medicaid.

Franklin Care Center
220 E Hereford, Gladstone, OR, 97027 (503) 656-0393
Admin Richard A Dillon. *Medical Dir/Dir of Nursing* Dr David Leaf.
Licensure Intermediate Care. *Beds* 91. *Certified* Medicaid.
Staff RNs 2 (ft), 2 (pt); LPNs 3 (ft); Orderlies 3 (ft), 1 (pt); Nurses aides 30 (ft), 10 (pt); Activities coordinators 2 (ft).
Facilities Dining room; Physical therapy room; Activities room; Crafts room; Laundry room; Barber/Beauty shop.
Activities Arts and Crafts; Cards; Games; Reading groups; Prayer groups; Shopping trips; Dances/Social or cultural gatherings.

Gladstone Convalescent Care Facility
1315 Webster Rd, Gladstone, OR, 97027 (503) 656-1644
Admin Mini Jorgenson. *Medical Dir/Dir of Nursing* Roy Payne MD.
Licensure Intermediate Care. *Beds* 130. *Certified* Medicaid.
Admissions Requirements Medical examination; Physician's request.
Staff RNs 3 (ft), 2 (pt); LPNs 3 (ft), 2 (pt); Nurses aides 40 (ft), 7 (pt); Physical therapists 1 (pt); Activities coordinators 1 (ft), 1 (pt); Dietitians 1 (pt).
Facilities Dining room; Physical therapy room; Activities room; Crafts room; Laundry room; Barber/Beauty shop.
Activities Arts and Crafts; Cards; Games; Prayer groups; Shopping trips; Dances/Social or cultural gatherings.
Description Facility is a 130-bed intermediate care facility providing quality professional care in a homey atmosphere, focusing on the physical, mental and spiritual well-being of our patients.

GRANTS PASS

Highland House Nursing Home
2201 NW Highland, Grants Pass, OR, 97526 (503) 474-1901
Admin Phil Stephens. *Medical Dir/Dir of Nursing* Dr Daniel Moline.
Licensure Skilled Care; Intermediate Care. *Beds* 134. *Certified* Medicaid.
Admissions Requirements Medical examination; Physician's request.
Staff RNs 12 (ft), 9 (pt); LPNs 9 (ft), 9 (pt); Nurses aides 40 (ft), 28 (pt); Physical therapists 1 (ft); Reality therapists 1 (ft); Recreational therapists 2 (ft); Occupational therapists 1 (pt); Speech therapists 1 (pt); Activities coordinators 1 (ft); Dietitians 1 (pt); Dentists 1 (pt); Ophthalmologists 1 (pt); Podiatrists 1 (pt); Audiologists 1 (pt).
Facilities Dining room; Physical therapy room; Activities room; Chapel; Crafts room; Laundry room; Barber/Beauty shop.
Activities Arts and Crafts; Cards; Games; Reading groups; Prayer groups; Movies; Shopping trips; Dances/Social or cultural gatherings.
Description This is southern Oregon's newest skilled nursing facility.

Laurel Hill Nursing Center
859 NE 6th, Grants Pass, OR, 97526 (503) 476-7274
Admin Orville Lang.
Licensure Intermediate Care. *Beds* 40. *Certified* Medicaid.
Admissions Requirements Physician's request.
Staff RNs 1 (ft); LPNs 1 (ft), 3 (pt); Nurses aides 12 (ft), 10 (pt); Physical therapists 1 (pt); Speech therapists 1 (pt); Activities coordinators 1 (pt); Dietitians 1 (pt); Dentists 1 (pt).
Facilities Dining room; Activities room; Chapel; Laundry room; Library.
Activities Arts and Crafts; Cards; Games; Reading groups; Prayer groups; Movies.

Mariola Nursing Home*
1450 NE Fairview Ave, Grants Pass, OR, 97526 (503) 479-2606
Admin Kenneth Selvey.
Licensure Skilled Care; Intermediate Care. *Beds* 102. *Certified* Medicaid; Medicare.

Royale Gardens Health Care Facility
2075 NW Highland, Grants Pass, OR, 97526 (503) 476-8891
Admin Robert Puntney. *Medical Dir/Dir of Nursing* Thomas M Tusk MD.
Licensure Skilled Care; Intermediate Care. *Beds* 194. *Certified* Medicaid.
Admissions Requirements Minimum age 18.
Staff Physicians 1 (pt); RNs 8 (ft), 1 (pt); LPNs 7 (ft), 2 (pt); Orderlies 56 (ft), 23 (pt); Nurses aides 56 (ft), 23 (pt); Physical therapists 1 (pt); Reality therapists 1 (ft), 1 (pt); Recreational therapists 1 (pt); Speech therapists 1 (pt); Activities coordinators 1 (pt); Dietitians 1 (ft); Dentists 1 (pt); Podiatrists 1 (pt).
Activities Arts and Crafts; Cards; Games; Reading groups; Movies; Shopping trips; Dances/Social or cultural gatherings.
Description Royal Gardens is a completely modern health care facility where residents enjoy a warm friendly atmosphere while receiving the finest in personalized nursing care. Located in the heart of beautiful southern Oregon, our facility provides a continuum of health care services for individuals requiring residential, intermediate, or skilled nursing care. These services are carried out under the guidance of a medical director and with the supervision of skilled, professional nurses. We strive to help each resident achieve his or her highest potential and to maintain a sense of dignity and individuality.

GRESHAM

Colbert Nursing Home Inc*
PO Box 352, 2022 NW Division St, Gresham, OR, 97030 (503) 666-5541
Admin Kathleen Schwerzler.
Licensure Intermediate Care. *Beds* 71. *Certified* Medicaid.

Fairlawn Care Center
3457 NE Division, Gresham, OR, 97030 (503)
667-1965
Admin John E Palmer. *Medical Dir/Dir of
Nursing* Dr MacKay.
Licensure Skilled Care. *Beds* 123. *Certified* Medicaid; Medicare.
Admissions Requirements Minimum age 60;
Medical examination; Physician's request.
Staff RNs 4 (ft), 17 (pt); LPNs 3 (ft), 6 (pt);
Nurses aides 46 (ft), 25 (pt); Recreational therapists 2 (ft); Activities coordinators 1 (ft); Dietitians 1 (ft).
Affiliation Lutheran
Facilities Dining room; Physical therapy room;
Activities room; Chapel; Laundry room; Barber/Beauty shop; Library.
Activities Arts and Crafts; Cards; Games;
Prayer groups; Movies; Shopping trips; Current
events; Bus trips; Music appreciation; Gardening; Church services; Grandparent program.
Description Center is full of activity featuring a
complete range of creative programs designed
to assist each resident spiritually, socially,
physically, and psychologically.

Neighbors of Woodcraft Home*
1250 SE Roberts, Gresham, OR, 97030 (503)
667-5430
Admin Jessie Johnson, Jr.
Licensure Intermediate Care. *Beds* 4.

Rest Harbor Nursing Home
5905 E Powell Blvd, PO Box 525, Gresham,
OR, 97030 (503) 665-1151
Admin Greg Dempsey. *Medical Dir/Dir of
Nursing* Elton Teabitt MD.
Licensure Skilled Care. *Beds* 128. *Certified* Medicaid; Medicare.
Admissions Requirements Medical examination; Physician's request.
Staff Physicians 1 (pt); RNs 8 (ft), 5 (pt); LPNs
5 (ft), 7 (pt); Nurses aides 40 (ft), 20 (pt);
Physical therapists 1 (ft); Reality therapists 1
(pt); Recreational therapists 1 (ft); Occupational
therapists 1 (ft); Activities coordinators 1 (ft);
Dietitians 1 (pt).
Affiliation Seventh-Day Adventist
Facilities Dining room; Physical therapy room;
Activities room; Laundry room; Barber/Beauty
shop.
Activities Arts and Crafts; Cards; Games;
Reading groups; Prayer groups; Movies; Shopping trips; Dances/Social or cultural gatherings.

Village Convalescent Center
3955 SE 182nd Ave, Gresham, OR, 97030
(503) 665-0183
Admin John L Mack. *Medical Dir/Dir of
Nursing* Dr Donald K Bohlman.
Licensure Skilled Care; Intermediate Care.
Beds 88. *Certified* Medicaid; Medicare.
Staff Physicians; RNs; LPNs; Orderlies;
Nurses aides; Physical therapists; Reality therapists; Recreational therapists; Occupational
therapists; Speech therapists; Activities coordinators; Dietitians; Dentists; Ophthalmologists;
Podiatrists; Audiologists.
Facilities Dining room; Physical therapy room;
Activities room; Crafts room; Laundry room;
Barber/Beauty shop; Library.
Activities Arts and Crafts; Cards; Games;
Reading groups; Prayer groups; Movies.

Description Facility is located next to 2 retirement centers in a very serene setting just outside the Portland city limits; has a reputation of
providing quality care; outstanding physical
therapy department with a full-time therapist
on duty.

Willow Tree Care Center*
311 NE Division, Gresham, OR, 97030 (503)
667-8050
Admin Gayle Palmer.
Licensure Intermediate Care. *Beds* 40. *Certified* Medicaid.

HEPPNER

Pioneer Memorial Hospital
564 Pioneer Dr, Heppner, OR, 97836
Admin Albert J Ochsner III. *Medical Dir/Dir
of Nursing* Wallace Wolff MD and Clare Kosnek DO.
Licensure Intermediate Care. *Beds* 28. *Certified* Medicaid.
Ownership Public.
Admissions Requirements Medical
examination.
Staff Physicians 3 (ft); RNs 1 (ft), 10 (pt);
LPNs 3 (ft), 3 (pt); Nurses aides 14 (ft), 7 (pt);
Activities coordinators 1 (ft); Dietitians 1 (ft).
Facilities Dining room; Laundry room; Solarium; Patio.
Activities Arts and Crafts; Games; Prayer
groups; Movies; Dances/Social or cultural gatherings.
Description Facility sits high on a hill overlooking the city with one 4-bed and the rest
2-bed wards; patio with a picnic table out under
the trees which residents are encouraged to use
when the weather is good.

HERMISTON

Hermiston Good Samaritan Center
970 Juniper Ave, Hermiston, OR, 97838 (503)
567-8337
Admin Richard Alexander. *Medical Dir/Dir of
Nursing* Wendell Ford.
Licensure Intermediate Care. *Beds* 95. *Certified* Medicaid.
Admissions Requirements Medical examination; Physician's request.
Staff Physicians 1 (pt); RNs 2 (ft); LPNs 5 (ft),
4 (pt); Orderlies 2 (ft); Nurses aides 18 (ft), 14
(pt); Physical therapists 1 (pt); Activities coordinators 1 (ft), 1 (pt); Dietitians 1 (pt); Dentists
1 (pt); Podiatrists 1 (pt).
Facilities Dining room; Physical therapy room;
Activities room; Chapel; Crafts room; Laundry
room; Barber/Beauty shop; Library.
Activities Arts and Crafts; Cards; Games;
Reading groups; Prayer groups; Movies; Shopping trips; Dances/Social or cultural gatherings.
Description Facility features meal of the
month, representing a different country each
month; enclosed patio with fountain and walks.

HILLSBORO

Gardenview Care Center*
33465 SW Tualatin Valley Hwy, Hillsboro, OR,
97123 (503) 648-7181

Admin Donald T Mikkelson.
Licensure Intermediate Care. *Beds* 30. *Certified* Medicaid.

Hillaire Manor Inc*
1778 NE Cornell Rd, Hillsboro, OR, 97123
(503) 648-6621
Admin William Danner.
Licensure Intermediate Care. *Beds* 51. *Certified* Medicaid.

Oak Villa Health Care*
650 Oak St E, Hillsboro, OR, 97123 (503)
648-8588
Admin Joyce Gallovich.
Licensure Intermediate Care. *Beds* 104. *Certified* Medicaid.

HOOD RIVER

Hood River Care Center
729 Henderson Rd, Hood River, OR, 97031
(503) 386-2688
Admin Anita Hays. *Medical Dir/Dir of
Nursing* Gary Regalbuto M.D..
Licensure Intermediate Care. *Beds* 131. *Certified* Medicaid; Medicare.
Staff Physicians 1 (pt); RNs 6 (ft), 2 (pt); LPNs
3 (ft); Orderlies 5 (ft), 1 (pt); Nurses aides 32
(ft), 18 (pt); Physical therapists 1 (pt); Occupational therapists 1 (pt); Speech therapists 1 (pt);
Activities coordinators 1 (ft); Dietitians 1 (pt);
Dentists 1 (pt); Audiologists 1 (pt).
Facilities Dining room; Physical therapy room;
Activities room; Crafts room; Laundry room;
Barber/Beauty shop; Library.
Activities Arts and Crafts; Cards; Games;
Reading groups; Prayer groups; Movies; Shopping trips; Dances/Social or cultural gatherings.

INDEPENDENCE

Cedarwood Care Center*
1525 Monmouth Ave, Independence, OR,
97351 (503) 838-0001
Admin Betty Martin.
Licensure Intermediate Care; Intermediate
Care for Mentally Retarded. *Beds* ICF 48;
ICF/MR 32. *Certified* Medicaid.

JUNCTION CITY

Grandview Manor Care Center
530 Birch St, Junction City, OR, 97448 (503)
998-2395
Admin Judy Wittekind.
Licensure Intermediate Care. *Beds* 72. *Certified* Medicaid.

KLAMATH FALLS

Highland Care
2555 Main St, Klamath Falls, OR, 97601 (503)
882-6341
Admin Hal Elliott. *Medical Dir/Dir of
Nursing* Dr Raymond Tice.
Licensure Intermediate Care; Residential Care.
Beds ICF 92; Residential Care 15. *Certified* Medicaid.
Admissions Requirements Minimum age 18;

Medical examination; Physician's request.
Staff Physicians 1 (pt); RNs 4 (ft); LPNs 3 (ft), 2 (pt); Nurses aides 24 (ft), 12 (pt); Physical therapists 1 (pt); Activities coordinators 1 (ft); Dietitians 1 (pt); Dentists 1 (pt).
Facilities Dining room; Physical therapy room; Activities room; Crafts room; Laundry room; Barber/Beauty shop; Sun room; TV room; Smoking area.
Activities Arts and Crafts; Cards; Games; Movies; Shopping trips; Dances/Social or cultural gatherings; Religious services; Singing.
Description This facility is located in a mountainous region. The most outstanding quality we have is a clean-smelling and clean-looking facility with a happy, loving atmosphere. Because we are not too big, our patients are all treated "special" and they are.

Klamath County Nursing Home and Convalescent Center
1401 Campus Dr, Klamath Falls, OR, 97601 (503) 882-6691
Admin Linda Kruse. *Medical Dir/Dir of Nursing* Dr. Howard.
Licensure Skilled Care; Intermediate Care. *Beds* 129. *Certified* Medicaid; Medicare.
Admissions Requirements Physician's request.
Staff Physical therapists 1 (ft); Recreational therapists 1 (ft); Occupational therapists 1 (ft); Speech therapists 1 (ft).
Facilities Dining room; Physical therapy room; Activities room; Chapel; Crafts room; Laundry room; Barber/Beauty shop; Library.
Activities Arts and Crafts; Games; Reading groups; Prayer groups; Movies; Dances/Social or cultural gatherings.

Mountain View Care Center*
711 Washburn Way, Klamath Falls, OR, 97601 (503) 882-4471
Admin Beverly Wilmoth.
Licensure Intermediate Care. *Beds* 114. *Certified* Medicaid.

LAGRANDE

LaGrande Nursing Center*
95 Aries Way, LaGrande, OR, 97850 (503) 963-8678
Admin Dave Slaght.
Licensure Intermediate Care. *Beds* 80. *Certified* Medicaid.

Valley View Manor
Rt 1, Box 1855, LaGrande, OR, 97850 (503) 963-4184
Admin Dennis Clayville.
Licensure Intermediate Care. *Beds* 82. *Certified* Medicaid.
Staff RNs 3 (ft), 1 (pt); LPNs 4 (ft); Nurses aides 26 (ft), 7 (pt); Activities coordinators 1 (ft), 1 (pt); Dietitians 1 (pt).
Facilities Dining room; Laundry room; Barber/Beauty shop.
Activities Arts and Crafts.

LAKE OSWEGO

Mountain Park Convalescent Care Facility
4 Greenridge Ct, Lake Oswego, OR, 97034 (503) 636-9614
Admin Jeanette Kenney. *Medical Dir/Dir of Nursing* Gary Geddes MD.
Licensure Intermediate Care. *Beds* 182. *Certified* Medicaid.
Admissions Requirements Medical examination; Physician's request.
Facilities Dining room; Physical therapy room; Activities room; Crafts room; Laundry room; Barber/Beauty shop; Library.
Activities Arts and Crafts; Cards; Games; Reading groups; Prayer groups; Movies; Shopping trips; Dances/Social or cultural gatherings.
Description Facility has lovely rural setting with wind-sheltered courtyard; emphasis is on rehabilitation through in-facility physical therapy program.

LAKEVIEW

Lake District Hospital*
700 S J St, Lakeview, OR, 97630 (503) 947-2114, 2115
Admin Frank Occhuito.
Licensure Skilled Care. *Beds* 47. *Certified* Medicare.

LEBANON

Villa Cascade Nursing Home*
350 S 8th, Lebanon, OR, 97355 (503) 259-1221
Admin Jerry Yost.
Licensure Intermediate Care. *Beds* 107. *Certified* Medicaid.

LINCOLN CITY

Evergreen Care Center
3011 NE Park Dr, Lincoln City, OR, 97367 (503) 994-8111
Admin Lavonne Davis. *Medical Dir/Dir of Nursing* E Oksenholt DO.
Licensure Intermediate Care. *Beds* 80. *Certified* Medicaid.
Admissions Requirements Minimum age 16; Medical examination.
Staff Physicians 15 (ft); RNs 3 (ft), 1 (pt); LPNs 4 (ft); Orderlies 3 (ft); Nurses aides 20 (ft), 2 (pt); Physical therapists 1 (ft); Activities coordinators 1 (ft); Dietitians 1 (pt).
Facilities Dining room; Activities room; Crafts room; Laundry room; Barber/Beauty shop; Library.
Activities Arts and Crafts; Cards; Games; Reading groups; Prayer groups; Movies; Shopping trips; Dances/Social or cultural gatherings.
Description Facility is a one-story building in natural wooded area next to hospital.

MADRAS

Mountain View Hospital*
1270 A St, Madras, OR, 97741 (503) 475-3882
Admin Ken Jones.
Licensure Intermediate Care. *Beds* 68. *Certified* Medicaid.

MARYLHURST

Kerr Center for Handicapped Children
PO Box 115, Marylhurst, OR, 97036 (503) 656-5636
Admin Michael Maley.
Licensure Intermediate Care for Mentally Retarded. *Beds* 30. *Certified* Medicaid.

MCMINNVILLE

Careousel Care Center
1309 E 27th St, McMinnville, OR, 97128 (503) 472-4678
Admin Stan Smith.
Licensure Skilled Care; Intermediate Care. *Beds* SNF 11; ICF 96. *Certified* Medicaid.

Oakwood Glen Care Center
421 S Evans St, McMinnville, OR, 97128 (503) 472-3141
Admin Andrew J Stynes. *Medical Dir/Dir of Nursing* Mark Olson MD.
Licensure Intermediate Care. *Beds* 109. *Certified* Medicaid.
Admissions Requirements Minimum age 18; Medical examination; Physician's request.
Staff RNs 3 (ft), 3 (pt); LPNs 5 (ft), 2 (pt); Orderlies 2 (ft); Nurses aides 30 (ft), 5 (pt); Activities coordinators 3 (ft), 1 (pt).
Facilities Dining room; Physical therapy room; Activities room; Crafts room; Laundry room; Barber/Beauty shop.
Activities Arts and Crafts; Cards; Games; Reading groups; Prayer groups; Movies; Shopping trips; Dances/Social or cultural gatherings.
Description Facility features an in-house restorative therapy program including whirlpool baths and is located in quiet (cul-de-sac) residential setting surrounded by trees, 2 blocks to Community Hospital and close in to City Center.

MEDFORD

Hearthstone Manor
2901 E Barnett Rd, Medford, OR, 97501 (503) 779-4221
Admin Helen Tweedy. *Medical Dir/Dir of Nursing* W G Bishop MD.
Licensure Skilled Care; Intermediate Care. *Beds* 161. *Certified* Medicaid; Medicare.
Staff RNs 8 (ft); LPNs 6 (ft), 2 (pt); Orderlies 6 (ft); Nurses aides 50 (ft), 20 (pt); Physical therapists 1 (ft); Recreational therapists 2 (ft); Activities coordinators 2 (ft); Dietitians 1 (ft).
Facilities Dining room; Physical therapy room; Activities room; Crafts room; Laundry room; Barber/Beauty shop; Library.
Activities Arts and Crafts; Cards; Games; Reading groups; Prayer groups; Movies; Shopping trips; Dances/Social or cultural gatherings.
Description Outstanding rehabilitation and restorative care programs with emphasis on achieving and/or maintaining the highest degree of independence that is possible in activities of daily living. High quality of life at whatever level of functioning is our goal for each resident.

Rogue Valley Care Center
3693 S Pacific Hwy, Medford, OR, 97501 (503) 535-4636
Admin Jackie Connell. *Medical Dir/Dir of Nursing* Dr John Shonerd.
Licensure Intermediate Care. *Beds* 33. *Certified* Medicaid.
Staff RNs 1 (ft), 1 (pt); LPNs 1 (ft), 1 (pt); Orderlies 1 (ft); Nurses aides 9 (ft), 2 (pt); Activities coordinators 1 (ft); Dietitians 1 (pt); Dentists 1 (pt).
Activities Arts and Crafts; Games; Reading groups; Prayer groups; Movies; Shopping trips.

Rogue Valley Manor
1200 Mira Mar Ave, Medford, OR, 97501 (503) 773-7411
Admin Thomas Becker.
Licensure Intermediate Care. *Beds* 40. *Certified* Medicaid.

The Three Fountains*
835 Crater Lake Ave, Medford, OR, 97501 (503) 773-7717
Admin Shirley Inge.
Licensure Skilled Care. *Beds* 156. *Certified* Medicaid; Medicare.

Villa Royal Health Care Center*
625 Stevens St, Medford, OR, 97501 (503) 779-3551
Admin William Daniel Gregory.
Licensure Skilled Care; Intermediate Care. *Beds* 130. *Certified* Medicaid; Medicare.

MERLIN

Merlin Health Retreat
PO Box 340, 816 Sanitarium Rd, Merlin, OR, 97532 (503) 476-5300
Admin Charles Werner.
Licensure Intermediate Care. *Beds* 40. *Certified* Medicaid.
Facilities Dining room; Activities room; Chapel.
Activities Games; Prayer groups; Movies; Dances/Social or cultural gatherings.

MILTON-FREEWATER

Elzora Manor
120 Elzora St, PO Box 498, Milton-Freewater, OR, 97862 (503) 938-3318
Admin Uva Berry.
Licensure Skilled Care; Intermediate Care. *Beds* 130. *Certified* Medicaid; Medicare.
Admissions Requirements Physician's request.
Staff Physicians 1 (pt); RNs 9 (ft), 2 (pt); LPNs 8 (ft), 3 (pt); Orderlies 2 (ft), 2 (pt); Nurses aides 28 (ft), 15 (pt); Physical therapists 1 (pt); Reality therapists 1 (pt); Recreational therapists 1 (pt); Occupational therapists 1 (pt); Speech therapists 1 (pt); Activities coordinators 1 (ft); Dietitians 1 (pt); Dentists 1 (pt); Ophthalmologists 1 (pt); Audiologists 1 (pt).
Facilities Dining room; Physical therapy room; Activities room; Crafts room; Laundry room; Barber/Beauty shop; Library.
Activities Arts and Crafts; Cards; Games; Reading groups; Prayer groups; Movies; Shopping trips; Dances/Social or cultural gatherings.
Description Facility has country-like setting with fenced backyard.

MILWAUKIE

Milwaukie Convalescent Center*
12045 SE Stanley Ave, Milwaukie, OR, 97222 (503) 659-2323
Admin Nash Barinaga.
Licensure Intermediate Care. *Beds* 68. *Certified* Medicaid.

Rose Villa Inc*
13505 SE River Rd, Milwaukie, OR, 97222 (503) 654-3171
Admin James Sturgis.
Licensure Skilled Care. *Beds* 55.

Willamette Methodist Convalescent Center
13021 SE River Rd, Milwaukie, OR, 97222 (503) 652-6200
Admin Ruth Slick. *Medical Dir/Dir of Nursing* Dr Roy Payne.
Licensure Skilled Care; Intermediate Care. *Beds* SNF 54; ICF 66. *Certified* Medicaid; Medicare.
Admissions Requirements Minimum age 21; Medical examination; Physician's request.
Staff RNs 9 (ft), 10 (pt); LPNs 2 (ft); Orderlies 4 (ft); Nurses aides 47 (ft), 15 (pt); Physical therapists 4 (pt); Occupational therapists 1 (pt); Speech therapists 1 (pt); Activities coordinators 1 (ft); Dietitians 1 (pt); Dentists 1 (pt); Podiatrists 1 (pt).
Affiliation Methodist
Facilities Dining room; Physical therapy room; Activities room; Chapel; Crafts room; Laundry room; Barber/Beauty shop; Library.
Activities Arts and Crafts; Cards; Games; Reading groups; Prayer groups; Movies; Shopping trips; Dances/Social or cultural gatherings.
Description Retirement and continuing care complex is located on a 22-acre site bordering the Willamette River. New building to be completed in January 1985 will have indoor swimming pool and therapy spa.

MOLALLA

Molalla Manor
301 Riding Ave, Molalla, OR, 97038 (503) 829-5591
Admin Kathryn Gustaveson. *Medical Dir/Dir of Nursing* Dr A B Willeford.
Licensure Skilled Care; Intermediate Care; Home for the Aged. *Beds* 92. *Certified* Medicaid; Medicare.
Admissions Requirements Minimum age 65; Medical examination; Physician's request.
Staff RNs 8 (ft), 2 (pt); LPNs 2 (ft), 2 (pt); Nurses aides 30 (ft), 10 (pt); Physical therapists 3 (pt); Reality therapists 1 (pt); Recreational therapists 1 (ft); Occupational therapists 1 (pt); Speech therapists 1 (pt); Activities coordinators 1 (ft); Dietitians 1 (pt); Dentists 1 (pt); Podiatrists 1 (pt).
Facilities Dining room; Physical therapy room; Activities room; Crafts room; Laundry room; Barber/Beauty shop.

Activities Arts and Crafts; Cards; Games; Reading groups; Prayer groups; Movies; Shopping trips; Dances/Social or cultural gatherings.

MOUNT ANGEL

Benedictine Nursing Center
540 S Main St, Mount Angel, OR, 97362 (503) 845-6841
Admin Lucia Gamroth. *Medical Dir/Dir of Nursing* Virgil Peters MD.
Licensure Skilled Care. *Beds* SNF 127. *Certified* Medicaid; Medicare.
Admissions Requirements Minimum age 16; Medical examination; Physician's request.
Staff RNs 12 (ft), 20 (pt); LPNs 2 (ft), 8 (pt); Physical therapists 4 (ft), 3 (pt); Occupational therapists 2 (ft); Speech therapists 3 (pt); Activities coordinators 1 (ft); Dietitians 1 (ft); 1 (ft), 1 (pt).
Affiliation Roman Catholic
Facilities Dining room; Physical therapy room; Activities room; Chapel; Barber/Beauty shop.
Activities Cards; Games; Reading groups; Prayer groups; Movies; Shopping trips; Dances/Social or cultural gatherings.

MYRTLE POINT

Myrtle Point Nursing Home Inc
637 Ash St, Myrtle Point, OR, 97458 (503) 572-2066
Admin Jan Shorb.
Licensure Intermediate Care. *Beds* 32. *Certified* Medicaid.
Admissions Requirements Medical examination; Physician's request.
Staff Physicians 2 (pt); RNs 1 (ft), 2 (pt); LPNs 1 (ft); Orderlies 2 (ft); Physical therapists 1 (pt); Activities coordinators 1 (ft); Dietitians 1 (ft).
Facilities Dining room; Activities room; Laundry room.
Activities Arts and Crafts; Games; Reading groups; Prayer groups; Shopping trips; Exercise groups; Lunch outings; Fairs; Community programs.
Description Small facility in downtown is well intergrated with the local people and activities; emphasis is on providing a home-like atmosphere with individual attention to clients.

NEWBERG

Chehalem Care Center*
1900 E Fulton St, Newberg, OR, 97132 (503) 538-2108
Admin Shirley Weissenbuehler.
Licensure Intermediate Care. *Beds* 86. *Certified* Medicaid.

Newberg Care Home
1500 E 1st St, Newberg, OR, 97132 (503) 538-9436
Admin John P Jones. *Medical Dir/Dir of Nursing* John Cummings.
Licensure Intermediate Care. *Beds* 67. *Certified* Medicaid.
Admissions Requirements Minimum age Geriatrics only; Medical examination; Physician's request.
Staff Physicians 1 (pt); RNs 4 (ft); LPNs 3 (ft);

Orderlies 1 (ft); Nurses aides 35 (ft), 5 (pt); Physical therapists 1 (pt); Activities coordinators 1 (ft), 1 (pt); Dietitians 1 (pt).
Facilities Dining room; Physical therapy room; Activities room; Chapel; Crafts room; Laundry room; Barber/Beauty shop.
Activities Arts and Crafts; Cards; Games; Reading groups; Prayer groups; Movies; Shopping trips; Dances/Social or cultural gatherings.
Description Facility features a home-like atmosphere, caring staff, community involvement.

NEWBURG

Friendsview Manor Infirmary*
1301 E Fulton St, Newburg, OR, 97132 (503) 538-3144
Admin Dean R Campbell.
Licensure Skilled Care. *Beds* 31.

NEWPORT

Yaquina Care Center Inc*
835 SW 11th, Newport, OR, 97365 (503) 265-5356
Admin Julie Carlson.
Licensure Intermediate Care. *Beds* 80. *Certified* Medicaid.

NORTH BEND

Saint Catherine's Residence and Nursing Center
3959 Sheridan Ave, North Bend, OR, 97459 (503) 756-4151
Admin Sr Mary Laetice Williams. *Medical Dir/Dir of Nursing* Charles Lindsay MD.
Licensure Skilled Care; Intermediate Care; Residential Care. *Beds* SNF 19; ICF 142; Residential Care 5.
Ownership Nonprofit.
Admissions Requirements Medical examination; Physician's request.
Staff Physicians 1 (pt); RNs 11 (ft), 1 (pt); LPNs 5 (ft), 1 (pt); Orderlies 1 (ft); Nurses aides 91 (ft), 5 (pt); Physical therapists 2 (ft); Recreational therapists 1 (ft); Activities coordinators 1 (ft); Dietitians 1 (ft).
Affiliation Roman Catholic
Facilities Dining room; Physical therapy room; Activities room; Chapel; Crafts room; Laundry room; Barber/Beauty shop; Library.
Activities Arts and Crafts; Cards; Games; Reading groups; Prayer groups; Movies; Shopping trips; Dances/Social or cultural gatherings.
Description St Catherine's is a nonprofit, multilevel health care facility providing professional, personalized nursing care for skilled, intermediate, and residential care patients, as well as outpatient grooming services. Services include a 72-room retirement living apartment complex now in its marketing and pre-construction phase.

NYSSA

Malheur Memorial Hospital
1109 Park Ave, Nyssa, OR, 97913
Admin Richard W Jones. *Medical Dir/Dir of*
Nursing David W Sarazin MD.
Admissions Requirements Physician's request.
Staff Physicians 5 (ft); RNs 1 (ft), 3 (pt); LPNs 6 (ft); Nurses aides 18 (ft); Physical therapists 1 (pt); Recreational therapists 1 (pt); Activities coordinators 1 (ft); Dietitians 1 (ft); Dentists 1 (pt); Ophthalmologists 1 (pt); Podiatrists 1 (pt).
Facilities Dining room; Physical therapy room; Activities room; Crafts room; Laundry room; Barber/Beauty shop; Library Special dining room for residents needing assistance.
Activities Arts and Crafts; Cards; Games; Reading groups; Prayer groups; Movies; Shopping trips; Dances/Social or cultural gatherings.
Description Our nursing home has a partially covered patio with a fish pond and fountain. We have a van equipped with wheelchair lift for rides in the country, parades, shopping, etc. The nursing home is attached to a general hospital for acute care services.

Malheur Memorial Hospital*
1109 Park Ave, Nyssa, OR, 97913 (503) 372-2211
Admin Ted Holly.
Licensure Skilled Care. *Beds* 46. *Certified* Medicare.

ONTARIO

Presbyterian Nursing Home Inc
1085 N Oregon, Ontario, OR, 97914 (503) 889-9133
Admin Elizabeth Nelson. *Medical Dir/Dir of Nursing* Joseph Burdic MD.
Licensure Skilled Care; Intermediate Care; Residential Care. *Beds* SNF 18; ICF 96; Residential Care 10. *Certified* Medicaid; Medicare.
Admissions Requirements Minimum age 16; Medical examination; Physician's request.
Staff Physicians 1 (pt); RNs 4 (ft), 2 (pt); LPNs 10 (ft); Orderlies 5 (ft); Nurses aides 65 (ft), 10 (pt); Physical therapists 1 (ft); Activities coordinators 3 (ft).
Affiliation Presbyterian
Facilities Dining room; Physical therapy room; Activities room; Chapel; Crafts room; Laundry room; Barber/Beauty shop; Library; Classroom.
Activities Arts and Crafts; Cards; Games; Reading groups; Prayer groups; Movies; Guest entertainments; Barbecues; Picnics.
Description Our facility is built surrounding a lovely large and landscaped courtyard with outdoor furniture and equipment for preparing and serving meals.

OREGON CITY

Golden Age Care Center
1506 Division St, Oregon City, OR, 97045 (503) 656-1973
Admin Eleanor Johnson. *Medical Dir/Dir of Nursing* Joseph Intile.
Licensure Intermediate Care. *Beds* 48. *Certified* Medicaid.
Admissions Requirements Minimum age 18.
Staff RNs 2 (ft), 2 (pt); LPNs 1 (ft); Orderlies 1 (ft), 1 (pt); Nurses aides 25 (ft), 5 (pt); Activities coordinators 1 (ft).
Facilities Dining room; Activities room.
Activities Arts and Crafts; Cards; Games; Prayer groups; Movies.

Mountain View Convalescent Care Facility*
1400 Division, Oregon City, OR, 97045 (503) 656-0367
Admin Diane Maxwell.
Licensure Skilled Care; Intermediate Care.
Beds 120. *Certified* Medicaid; Medicare.

Oregon City Nursing Home
148 Hood St, Oregon City, OR, 97045 (503) 656-4035
Admin Sharon Miller Hart. *Medical Dir/Dir of Nursing* Dr Julian Markin.
Licensure Intermediate Care. *Beds* 45. *Certified* Medicaid.
Admissions Requirements Physician's request.
Staff RNs 1 (ft); LPNs 6 (ft); Orderlies 2 (ft); Nurses aides 22 (ft); Activities coordinators 1 (ft); Dietitians 1 (pt); Dentists 1 (pt); Podiatrists 1 (pt).
Facilities Dining room; Activities room; Crafts room; Laundry room; Barber/Beauty shop.
Activities Arts and Crafts; Games; Prayer groups; Movies; Shopping trips.
Description Facility specializes in Alzheimer's.

Sierra Vista Care Center
1680 Molalla Ave, PO Box 644, Oregon City, OR, 97045 (503) 655-2588
Admin Carol Prael.
Licensure Intermediate Care. *Beds* 102. *Certified* Medicaid.
Admissions Requirements Medical examination; Physician's request.
Staff Physicians 5 (pt); RNs 3 (ft); LPNs 6 (ft); Orderlies 35 (ft), 10 (pt); Nurses aides 35 (ft), 10 (pt); Physical therapists 1 (pt); Recreational therapists 1 (pt); Speech therapists 1 (pt); Activities coordinators 1 (ft); Dietitians 1 (ft).
Facilities Dining room; Activities room; Crafts room; Laundry room; Barber/Beauty shop.
Activities Arts and Crafts; Movies; Shopping trips.

PENDLETON

Amber Valley Care Center*
707 SW 37th St, Pendleton, OR, 97801 (503) 276-3374
Admin Nancy Nielsen.
Licensure Intermediate Care. *Beds* 99. *Certified* Medicaid; Medicare.

Delamarter Care Center*
PO Box 35, Rt 1, Mission Rd, Pendleton, OR, 97801 (503) 276-7157
Admin Elizabeth Delamarter.
Licensure Intermediate Care. *Beds* 83. *Certified* Medicaid.

Eastern Oregon Hospital and Training Center*
PO Box A, Pendleton, OR, 97801 (503) 276-1711
Admin Al Baxter.
Licensure Intermediate Care; Intermediate Care for Mentally Retarded. *Beds* 370. *Certified* Medicaid.

PORTLAND

Baptist Manor
900 NE 81st, Portland, OR, 97213 (503) 255-0860
Admin Lawrence Bienert.
Licensure Intermediate Care. *Beds* 94. *Certified* Medicaid.
Admissions Requirements Medical examination.
Staff RNs 4 (ft), 3 (pt); LPNs 6 (ft), 4 (pt); Nurses aides 46 (ft); Activities coordinators 1 (ft).
Affiliation Baptist
Facilities Dining room; Activities room; Chapel; Laundry room; Barber/Beauty shop; Library.
Activities Arts and Crafts; Games; Reading groups; Prayer groups; Movies; Dances/Social or cultural gatherings.

Belmont Care Center Inc*
4914 SE Belmont, Portland, OR, 97215 (503) 235-3179
Admin Robert Allen.
Licensure Intermediate Care. *Beds* 59. *Certified* Medicaid.

Care Center East*
11325 NE Weidler, Portland, OR, 97220 (503) 253-1181
Admin David G Johnson.
Licensure Intermediate Care. *Beds* 93. *Certified* Medicaid.

Care Vista
9911 SE Mount Scott Blvd, Portland, OR, 97266 (503) 777-5642
Admin Barbara J Foster.
Licensure Intermediate Care. *Beds* 137. *Certified* Medicaid.
Staff Physicians 4 (pt); RNs 10 (ft), 1 (pt); LPNs 4 (ft); Orderlies 2 (ft); Nurses aides 28 (ft); Physical therapists 1 (pt); Recreational therapists 2 (ft); Occupational therapists 1 (pt); Activities coordinators 1 (ft); Activities coordinators 1 (ft); Dietitians 1 (pt); Dentists 1 (pt).
Facilities Dining room; Physical therapy room; Activities room; Crafts room; Laundry room; Barber/Beauty shop; Library.
Activities Arts and Crafts; Cards; Games; Reading groups; Prayer groups; Movies; Shopping trips; Dances/Social or cultural gatherings.

Care West Plaza Inc*
2250 NW Kearney St, Portland, OR, 97210 (503) 224-3910
Admin Ellen Engelent.
Licensure Skilled Care; Intermediate Care. *Beds* SNF 24; ICF 88. *Certified* Medicaid; Medicare.

Centennial Health Care Center*
725 SE 202nd Ave, Portland, OR, 97233 (503) 665-3118
Admin Daniel Lopez.
Licensure Intermediate Care. *Beds* 106. *Certified* Medicaid.

Columbia Manor Convalescent Center
6010 SW Shattuck Rd, Portland, OR, 97221 (503) 246-8811
Admin Karleen Vinyard. *Medical Dir/Dir of*

Nursing William Spisak MD.
Licensure Intermediate Care. *Beds* 102. *Certified* Medicaid.
Admissions Requirements Medical examination; Physician's request.
Staff RNs 2 (ft); LPNs 6 (ft); Orderlies 34 (ft), 4 (pt); Reality therapists 1 (ft); Recreational therapists 1 (ft); Activities coordinators 1 (ft).
Facilities Dining room; Activities room; Crafts room; Laundry room; Barber/Beauty shop; Library.
Activities Arts and Crafts; Cards; Games; Reading groups; Prayer groups; Movies; Shopping trips; Dances/Social or cultural gatherings.
Description Facility features restorative nursing program and discharge planning.

Crestview Convalescent*
6530 SW 30th Ave, Portland, OR, 97201 (503) 244-7533
Admin Jean Glanz.
Licensure Skilled Care. *Beds* 99. *Certified* Medicare.

Del's Care Center Inc
319 NE Russett, Portland, OR, 97211 (503) 289-5571
Admin Caroline Schie. *Medical Dir/Dir of Nursing* Dr. Gordon Myers.
Licensure Intermediate Care. *Beds* ICF 70; 20 RCF. *Certified* Medicaid.

Friendship Health Center
3320 SE Holgate, Portland, OR, 97202 (503) 231-1411
Admin Tom DeJardin. *Medical Dir/Dir of Nursing* H Lenox H Dick MD.
Licensure Skilled Care; Intermediate Care. *Beds* SNF 40; ICF 60. *Certified* Medicaid; Medicare.
Admissions Requirements Minimum age 18; Medical examination.
Staff Physicians 5 (pt); RNs 12 (ft), 5 (pt); LPNs 5 (ft), 4 (pt); Orderlies 1 (ft), 2 (pt); Nurses aides 47 (ft), 13 (pt); Physical therapists 1 (ft); Recreational therapists 2 (ft); Occupational therapists 1 (pt); Speech therapists 1 (pt); Dietitians 1 (ft); Dentists 1 (pt); Podiatrists 1 (pt); Audiologists 1 (pt).
Facilities Dining room; Physical therapy room; Activities room; Chapel; Crafts room; Laundry room; Barber/Beauty shop; Library.
Activities Arts and Crafts; Cards; Games; Reading groups; Prayer groups; Movies; Shopping trips; Dances/Social or cultural gatherings.
Description Aggressive rehabilitation department is responsible for high discharge rate of patients returning home and to other lesser level of care facilities. Also offer rehabilitative and nursing services on out patient basis.

Gateway Care Center
39 NE 102nd Ave, Portland, OR, 97220 (503) 252-2461
Admin Daniel Halverson. *Medical Dir/Dir of Nursing* Gayla L Brown.
Licensure Intermediate Care. *Beds* 42. *Certified* Medicaid.
Admissions Requirements Medical examination; Physician's request.
Staff Physicians 1 (ft); RNs 1 (ft), 1 (pt); LPNs 4 (ft), 2 (pt); Orderlies 2 (ft); Nurses aides 12 (ft); Physical therapists 1 (ft); Activities coordi-

nators 1 (ft); Dietitians 1 (ft); Dentists 1 (ft); Podiatrists 1 (ft).
Facilities Dining room; Physical therapy room; Activities room; Laundry room; Barber/Beauty shop.
Activities Arts and Crafts; Games; Exercise class; Discussion of current events.
Description We have a lovely enclosed courtyard. We are located less than 5 minutes from a large shopping center. Our facility has both nursing and retirement care which has proven most advantageous.

Glenaire Care Center
12441 SE Stark St, Portland, OR, 97233 (503) 255-7040
Admin Ray Finch. *Medical Dir/Dir of Nursing* Estill Deitz.
Licensure Intermediate Care. *Beds* 95. *Certified* Medicaid.
Admissions Requirements Medical examination; Physician's request.
Staff RNs 4 (ft), 1 (pt); LPNs 4 (ft), 1 (pt); Nurses aides 34 (ft), 2 (pt); Activities coordinators 1 (ft).
Facilities Dining room; Activities room; Laundry room.
Activities Arts and Crafts; Games; Prayer groups; Movies.
Description Facility features a lovely, landscaped setting on a 3-acre knoll away from traffic but convenient to transportation.

Glisan Care Center Inc*
9750 NE Glisan St, Portland, OR, 97220 (503) 256-3920
Admin Dale Hammersly.
Licensure Skilled Care; Intermediate Care. *Beds* 97. *Certified* Medicaid; Medicare.

Graystone Manor Convalescent Center*
12640 SE Bush, Portland, OR, 97236 (503) 761-6621
Admin David Heeb.
Licensure Intermediate Care. *Beds* 36. *Certified* Medicaid.

Har-Lyn Care Center
10948 SE Boise St, Portland, OR, 97266 (503) 760-1727
Admin Linda M Glidden. *Medical Dir/Dir of Nursing* Dr Ruth Wilcox.
Licensure Intermediate Care. *Beds* 80. *Certified* Medicaid.
Staff Physicians 1 (ft); RNs 3 (ft); LPNs 2 (ft); Orderlies 3 (ft); Nurses aides 63 (ft), 12 (pt); Reality therapists 1 (ft); Recreational therapists 1 (ft); Activities coordinators 2 (ft); Dietitians 1 (ft); Dentists 1 (ft); Podiatrists 1 (ft).
Facilities Dining room; Activities room; Crafts room; Laundry room; Barber/Beauty shop; Library.
Activities Arts and Crafts; Cards; Games; Reading groups; Prayer groups; Movies; Shopping trips; Dances/Social or cultural gatherings.
Description Facility specializes in the care of Alzheimer's disease patients, working with various associations and groups; a fenced facility for the security of the wandering residents. Facility has a park-like setting creating a peaceful atmosphere.

Hillhaven Nursing Home
745 NE 122nd Ave, Portland, OR, 97230 (503)
252-0241
Admin George V Novak Jr.
Licensure Skilled Care. *Beds* 83. *Certified* Medicare.
Admissions Requirements Medical examination; Physician's request.
Facilities Dining room; Activities room; Crafts room; Laundry room; Barber/Beauty shop.
Activities Arts and Crafts; Games; Reading groups; Prayer groups; Movies; Dances/Social or cultural gatherings.

Hillside Convalescent Inc*
800 NW 25th Ave, Portland, OR, 97210 (503)
224-0535
Admin Jo Ann Bavier.
Licensure Skilled Care. *Beds* 25.

Holiday Park Plaza*
1300 NE 16th Ave, Portland, OR, 97232 (503)
288-6671
Admin Ernest Vetter.
Licensure Intermediate Care. *Beds* 33.

House of Care Inc*
PO Box 66156, 6003 SE 136th, Portland, OR,
97266 (503) 761-1155
Admin Michael Duffy.
Licensure Intermediate Care. *Beds* 63. *Certified* Medicaid.

Jallo's Nursing Home
5737 NE 37th Ave, Portland, OR, 97211 (503)
288-5967
Admin Caroline Schie.
Licensure Intermediate Care. *Beds* 63. *Certified* Medicaid.
Facilities Dining room; Activities room; Laundry room; Barber/Beauty shop.
Activities Arts and Crafts; Cards; Games; Reading groups; Prayer groups; Movies; Shopping trips; Dances/Social or cultural gatherings.

Laurelhurst Care Center
2827 SE Salmon St, Portland, OR, 97214 (503)
232-8504
Admin Cheryl Lien. *Medical Dir/Dir of Nursing* Dr Andris Antoniskis.
Licensure Intermediate Care. *Beds* 85. *Certified* Medicaid.
Admissions Requirements Physician's request.
Staff Physicians 2 (pt); RNs 3 (ft), 2 (pt); LPNs 4 (ft), 1 (pt); Nurses aides 21 (ft), 1 (pt); Physical therapists 1 (ft); Speech therapists 1 (ft); Activities coordinators 1 (ft); Dietitians 1 (ft); Dentists 1 (pt); Podiatrists 1 (pt).
Facilities Dining room; Physical therapy room; Activities room; Laundry room; Barber/Beauty shop; Solarium.
Activities Arts and Crafts; Cards; Games; Reading groups; Prayer groups; Movies; Dances/Social or cultural gatherings.

Lawrence Convalescent Center
812 SE 48th, Portland, OR, 97215 (503)
236-2624
Admin Alex Fehrer. *Medical Dir/Dir of Nursing* Martha Gail DO.
Licensure Intermediate Care. *Beds* 40. *Certified* Medicaid.
Admissions Requirements Medical examina-

tion; Physician's request.
Staff RNs 1 (ft); LPNs 2 (ft), 1 (pt); Orderlies 2 (ft); Nurses aides 22 (ft); Reality therapists 1 (ft); Recreational therapists 1 (ft); Occupational therapists 1 (pt); Speech therapists 1 (pt); Activities coordinators 1 (ft); Dietitians 1 (pt); Dentists 1 (pt); Podiatrists 1 (pt).
Facilities Dining room; Laundry room; Barber/Beauty shop.
Activities Arts and Crafts; Games; Prayer groups; Movies.

Midway Care Center Inc*
5601 SE 122nd, Portland, OR, 97236 (503)
761-3181
Admin Antonette Petrecca.
Licensure Intermediate Care. *Beds* 43. *Certified* Medicaid.

Mount Saint Joseph Extended Care Center
3060 SE Stark St, Portland, OR, 97214 (503)
232-6193
Admin Mary Alban. *Medical Dir/Dir of Nursing* Donald McGreevey.
Licensure Skilled Care. *Beds* 190. *Certified* Medicaid; Medicare.
Admissions Requirements Medical examination.
Staff RNs 15 (ft), 2 (pt); LPNs 15 (ft), 4 (pt); Nurses aides 107 (ft), 3 (pt); Occupational therapists 8 (ft); Activities coordinators 1 (ft); Dietitians 1 (pt).
Affiliation Roman Catholic
Facilities Dining room; Physical therapy room; Activities room; Chapel; Crafts room; Laundry room; Barber/Beauty shop.
Activities Arts and Crafts; Cards; Games; Prayer groups; Movies; Shopping trips.
Description Facility features a fully equipped dental department, a dental assistant, and a dentist on call.

Mount Tabor Care Center
7100 SE Division, Portland, OR, 97206 (503)
775-8601
Admin Ken Chamberlin. *Medical Dir/Dir of Nursing* Richard Orth DO.
Licensure Intermediate Care. *Beds* 120. *Certified* Medicaid.
Admissions Requirements Medical examination; Physician's request.
Staff Physicians 1 (ft); RNs 4 (ft), 1 (pt); LPNs 8 (ft); Orderlies 3 (ft); Nurses aides 33 (ft), 1 (pt); Physical therapists 1 (pt); Occupational therapists 1 (pt); Activities coordinators 1 (ft); Dietitians 1 (pt); Podiatrists 1 (pt); Social workers 1 (ft); Physical therapy aides 1 (ft); Medical aides 1 (ft).
Facilities Dining room; Physical therapy room; Laundry room.
Activities Arts and Crafts; Cards; Games; Reading groups; Prayer groups; Dances/Social or cultural gatherings.
Description Facility features easy access by bus for families/visitors, large beautiful enclosed courtyard, plenty of available parking, locked doors for protection, and an emphasis on rehabilitative nursing care.

Park Forest Care Center*
8643 NE Beech St, Portland, OR, 97220 (503)
256-2151

Admin David Park.
Licensure Intermediate Care. *Beds* 68. *Certified* Medicaid.

Park Royal Convalescent Center*
2430 NW Marshall, Portland, OR, 97210 (503)
227-3791
Admin Earl W Green Jr.
Licensure Skilled Care. *Beds* 110. *Certified* Medicaid.

Park View Nursing Home*
2425 SW 6th, Portland, OR, 97201 (503)
228-6684
Admin Jeanne Dawson.
Licensure Intermediate Care. *Beds* 102.

Parkrose Nursing Home
10336 NE Wygant, Portland, OR, 97220 (503)
255-7677
Admin Roger Stewart. *Medical Dir/Dir of Nursing* Sharon Faulk.
Licensure Intermediate Care. *Beds* 56. *Certified* Medicaid.
Admissions Requirements Minimum age 14; Medical examination; Physician's request.
Staff RNs 3 (ft); LPNs 2 (ft); Orderlies 3 (ft); Nurses aides 14 (ft), 5 (pt); Activities coordinators 1 (ft).
Facilities Dining room.
Activities Arts and Crafts; Cards; Games; Reading groups; Prayer groups; Movies; Dances/Social or cultural gatherings; Individualized activities.

Porthaven Nursing Home
5330 NE Prescott, Portland, OR, 97218 (503)
288-6585
Admin Jacquelyn H Janes. *Medical Dir/Dir of Nursing* Dr Weber.
Licensure Skilled Care. *Beds* 99. *Certified* Medicare.
Staff Physicians 1 (pt); RNs 13 (ft); LPNs 1 (pt); Nurses aides 38 (ft), 2 (pt); Physical therapists 1 (pt); Reality therapists 1 (pt); Recreational therapists 1 (pt); Speech therapists 1 (pt); Activities coordinators 1 (ft); Dietitians 1 (pt); Dentists 1 (pt); Ophthalmologists 1 (pt); Podiatrists 1 (pt); Audiologists 1 (pt).
Facilities Dining room; Physical therapy room; Activities room; Crafts room; Laundry room; Barber/Beauty shop.
Activities Arts and Crafts; Cards; Games; Reading groups; Prayer groups; Movies; Shopping trips; Dances/Social or cultural gatherings.

Portland Adventist Convalescent Center*
6045 SE Belmont, Portland, OR, 97215 (503)
231-7166
Admin Don Buel.
Licensure Skilled Care; Intermediate Care. *Beds* 160. *Certified* Medicaid; Medicare.

Powellhurst Nursing Home
13033 SE Holgate Blvd, Portland, OR, 97236
(503) 761-1533
Admin Margaret K Covert. *Medical Dir/Dir of Nursing* Martha Gail DO.
Licensure Intermediate Care. *Beds* 77. *Certified* Medicaid.
Facilities Dining room; Physical therapy room; Activities room; Crafts room; Laundry room; Barber/Beauty shop.

Activities Arts and Crafts; Cards; Games; Reading groups; Prayer groups; Movies; Shopping trips; Dances/Social or cultural gatherings. *Description* Facility offers strong physical therapy, restorative nursing program; rehabilitation oriented; quality care in small, community promoted setting.

Providence Children's Nursing Center
830 NE 47th Ave, Portland, OR, 97213 (503) 234-9991
Admin Sr Katherine Smith. *Medical Dir/Dir of Nursing* Margaret M Wayson MD.
Licensure Skilled Care. *Beds* 54. *Certified* Medicaid.
Admissions Requirements Medical examination; Physician's request.
Staff Physicians 1 (pt); RNs 6 (ft), 6 (pt); LPNs 3 (ft); Nurses aides 40 (ft), 28 (pt); Physical therapists 1 (pt); Speech therapists 1 (ft); Activities coordinators 1 (ft); Dietitians 1 (ft), 2 (pt).
Affiliation Roman Catholic
Facilities Physical therapy room; Activities room; Chapel; Laundry room.
Activities Games; Reading groups; Shopping trips; Dances/Social or cultural gatherings; Outings; Swimming.
Description Ours is the only pediatric skilled nursing facility in the Northwest. We provide long-term and respite care to infants and young children from Oregon, Washington, Idaho, and Montana. We provide transdisciplinary habilitative services in conjunction with the local school district, in order to encourage the child's development to his/her fullest potential.

Raleigh Care Center
6630 SW Beaverton-Hillsdale Hwy, Portland, OR, 97225 (503) 292-4488
Admin Allen Cortez. *Medical Dir/Dir of Nursing* Juliana Markin MD.
Licensure Intermediate Care. *Beds* 90. *Certified* Medicaid.
Staff Physicians 1 (pt); RNs 4 (ft), 1 (pt); LPNs 3 (ft), 3 (pt); Orderlies 1 (ft), 1 (pt); Nurses aides 20 (ft), 25 (pt); Physical therapists 1 (pt); Speech therapists 1 (pt); Activities coordinators 1 (ft); Dietitians 1 (pt); Dentists 1 (pt); Podiatrists 1 (pt).
Facilities Dining room; Physical therapy room; Activities room; Laundry room; Barber/Beauty shop.
Activities Arts and Crafts; Cards; Games; Reading groups; Prayer groups; Movies; Shopping trips; Dances/Social or cultural gatherings.

Reedwood Extended Care Center Corp
3540 SE Francis St, Portland, OR, 97002 (503) 232-5240
Admin Glenn Nelson.
Licensure Skilled Care. *Beds* 60. *Certified* Medicare.
Admissions Requirements Minimum age 21.
Staff Physicians 1 (pt); RNs 5 (ft), 3 (pt); LPNs 1 (ft), 1 (pt); Orderlies 2 (ft); Nurses aides 25 (ft), 2 (pt); Physical therapists 1 (pt); Recreational therapists 1 (ft); Occupational therapists 1 (pt); Speech therapists 1 (pt); Dietitians 1 (pt).
Facilities Dining room; Activities room; Chapel; Laundry room.
Activities Arts and Crafts; Cards; Games;

Reading groups; Prayer groups; Movies.
Description Facility specializes in individual care.

Robison Jewish Home*
6125 SW Boundary Rd, Portland, OR, 97221 (503) 246-7706
Admin Carl Rogat.
Licensure Skilled Care. *Beds* 69. *Certified* Medicaid; Medicare.
Affiliation Jewish

Rose City Nursing Home
34 NE 20th Ave, Portland, OR, 97232 (503) 231-0276
Admin David Graber. *Medical Dir/Dir of Nursing* Dr Gerald Durris.
Licensure Intermediate Care. *Beds* 30. *Certified* Medicaid.
Staff Physicians; RNs 1 (ft), 4 (pt); LPNs 2 (ft), 2 (pt); Orderlies 2 (ft); Nurses aides 15 (ft); Activities coordinators 1 (ft).
Facilities Dining room; Activities room; Laundry room; Barber/Beauty shop.
Activities Arts and Crafts; Cards; Games; Reading groups; Prayer groups; Movies; Shopping trips; Dances/Social or cultural gatherings.

Sunny Vista Care Center
10435 SE Cora St, Portland, OR, 97266
Admin Doris Fogg.
Licensure Intermediate Care. *Beds* 53.
Ownership Proprietary.
Staff RNs 1 (ft), 1 (pt); LPNs 3 (ft); Orderlies 1 (ft); Nurses aides 15 (ft); Activities coordinators 1 (ft), 1 (pt); Dietitians 1 (pt); Dentists 1 (pt).
Facilities Dining room; Physical therapy room; Activities room; Crafts room; Laundry room; Barber/Beauty shop.
Activities Arts and Crafts; Cards; Games; Prayer groups; Shopping trips.
Description Facility has entirely fenced area; provides 24 hour nursing supervision and care for Alzheimer's patients.

Terwilliger Plaza Inc*
2545 SW Terwilliger Blvd, Portland, OR, 97201 503) 226-4911
Admin Gerald Ruby.
Licensure Intermediate Care. *Beds* 9.

Victoria Nursing Home*
3339 SE Division St, Portland, OR, 97202 (503) 235-4135
Admin Esther Pearson.
Licensure Intermediate Care. *Beds* 44. *Certified* Medicaid.

West Hills Convalescent Center
5701 SW Multnomah Blvd, Portland, OR, 97219 (503) 244-1107
Admin Margaret M Danner. *Medical Dir/Dir of Nursing* Hester Fieldhouse MD.
Licensure Skilled Care; Intermediate Care.
Beds 116. *Certified* Medicaid; Medicare.
Admissions Requirements Physician's request.
Staff RNs 10 (ft); LPNs 6 (ft); Orderlies 5 (ft); Nurses aides 35 (ft); Physical therapists 2 (ft); Recreational therapists 1 (pt); Speech therapists 1 (pt); Activities coordinators 1 (ft); Dietitians 1 (pt).
Facilities Dining room; Physical therapy room; Activities room; Crafts room; Laundry room;

Barber/Beauty shop; Library.
Activities Arts and Crafts; Cards; Games; Reading groups; Prayer groups; Movies; Shopping trips; Dances/Social or cultural gatherings.
Description Facility is located in a country setting.

Willamette Nursing Home Inc*
3125 N Willamette Blvd, Portland, OR, 97217 (503) 285-8334
Admin Miriam M Drake.
Licensure Intermediate Care. *Beds* 43. *Certified* Medicaid.

PRAIRIE CITY

Blue Mountain Nursing Home
112 E 5th St, Prairie City, OR, 97869 (503) 820-3541
Admin Phyllis McCarthy.
Licensure Intermediate Care. *Beds* 52. *Certified* Medicaid.
Admissions Requirements Minimum age 16; Medical examination; Physician's request.
Staff RNs 2 (ft), 1 (pt); LPNs 1 (ft), 1 (pt); Nurses aides 18 (ft), 2 (pt); Occupational therapists 1 (pt); Activities coordinators 1 (ft), 1 (pt).
Facilities Dining room; Physical therapy room; Activities room; Laundry room; Barber/Beauty shop.
Activities Cards; Games; Reading groups; Prayer groups; Movies; Shopping trips; Dances/Social or cultural gatherings.
Description Blue Mountain Nursing Home features only 2 beds per room, all on ground floor, has a mini-bus with lift, has Senior citizen dinner twice weekly, and is located in middle of small town.

PRINEVILLE

Crook County Nursing Home
1201 N Elm, Prineville, OR, 97754 (503) 447-6254
Admin George Pifer. *Medical Dir/Dir of Nursing* B Baker RN.
Licensure Intermediate Care; Residential Care.
Beds 42.
Ownership Nonprofit.
Admissions Requirements Medical examination; Physician's request.
Staff RNs 1 (ft); LPNs 3 (ft), 5 (pt); Orderlies 1 (pt); Nurses aides 9 (ft), 5 (pt); Recreational therapists 1 (pt); Activities coordinators 1 (ft), 1 (pt); Dietitians 1 (ft).
Facilities Dining room; Activities room; Chapel; Crafts room; Laundry room; Barber/Beauty shop; Library; Sun room.
Activities Arts and Crafts; Cards; Games; Reading groups; Prayer groups; Movies; Shopping trips; Dances/Social or cultural gatherings; Outdoor activity.
Description Facility is located adjacent to Pioneer Memorial Hospital with both buildings attached. Emergency and skilled care available 24-hours a day. Located atop hill overlooking city of Prineville with view of surrounding mountain ranges, facility features excellent activities and social services program with individual programs planned for the needs of each client and family.

Ochoco Nursing Home*
950 N Elm St, Prineville, OR, 97754 (503) 447-7667
Admin Gary Arnett.
Licensure Intermediate Care. *Beds* 63. *Certified* Medicaid.

REDMOND

Redmond Health Care Center*
3025 SW Reservoir Dr, Redmond, OR, 97756 (503) 548-5066
Admin Tim Eide.
Licensure Intermediate Care. *Beds* 67. *Certified* Medicaid.

REEDSPORT

Lower Umpqua Hospital*
PO Box 6, Reedsport, OR, 97567 (503) 271-2171
Admin Richard Bell.
Licensure Intermediate Care. *Beds* 20. *Certified* Medicaid.

ROSEBURG

Douglas County Nursing Home
778 W Harvard Ave, Roseburg, OR, 97470 (503) 672-8266
Admin Harvey Young. *Medical Dir/Dir of Nursing* Louis Michalek MD.
Licensure Skilled Care; Intermediate Care. *Beds* 116. *Certified* Medicaid; Medicare.
Admissions Requirements Minimum age 12.
Staff RNs 19 (ft); LPNs 6 (ft); Nurses aides 34 (ft), 8 (pt); Physical therapists 1 (pt); Activities coordinators 1 (ft); Dietitians 1 (pt).
Facilities Dining room; Physical therapy room; Activities room; Chapel; Laundry room; Barber/Beauty shop; TV.
Activities Arts and Crafts; Cards; Games; Reading groups; Prayer groups; Movies.

Grandview Care Home Inc*
1199 NW Grandview Dr, Roseburg, OR, 97490 (503) 672-1638
Admin Richard L Trotter.
Licensure Intermediate Care. *Beds* 83. *Certified* Medicaid.

Rose Haven
740 NW Hill Pl, Roseburg, OR, 97470 (503) 672-1631
Admin Duane Miner. *Medical Dir/Dir of Nursing* Dr Timothy Powell.
Licensure Intermediate Care. *Beds* 199. *Certified* Medicaid.
Admissions Requirements Medical examination; Physician's request.
Staff RNs 6 (ft), 3 (pt); Orderlies 2 (pt); Nurses aides 40 (ft), 40 (pt); Physical therapists 1 (ft); Recreational therapists 4 (ft); Activities coordinators 1 (ft); Dietitians 1 (ft).
Facilities Dining room; Physical therapy room; Activities room; Chapel; Crafts room; Laundry room; Barber/Beauty shop.
Activities Arts and Crafts; Cards; Games; Reading groups; Prayer groups; Movies; Shopping trips; Dances/Social or cultural gatherings.
Description Facility features day care, respite care, and yearly family forums.

SAINT HELENS

Meadow Park Care Center
75 Shore Dr, Saint Helen's, OR, 97051 (503) 397-2713
Admin Bunia Hampson.
Licensure Intermediate Care. *Beds* 92. *Certified* Medicaid.
Admissions Requirements Medical examination; Physician's request.
Staff RNs 1 (ft), 4 (pt); LPNs 4 (ft), 2 (pt); Orderlies 2 (ft); Nurses aides 30 (ft), 14 (pt); Activities coordinators 1 (ft).
Facilities Dining room; Physical therapy room; Activities room; Crafts room; Laundry room; Barber/Beauty shop; TV room.
Activities Arts and Crafts; Cards; Games; Prayer groups; Movies; Dances/Social or cultural gatherings; Birthday parties; Anniversary parties; Open house.
Description Meadow Park Care Center is located in a small country town and supported by a community of very caring people. Our staff of nurses and certified nursing aides work hard to create a home-like atmosphere for our residents. All our acitvities are centered around our residents. We care.

SALEM

Capitol View Health Care Center*
875 Oak St, Salem, OR, 97301 (503) 581-1457
Admin Mark Robinson.
Licensure Skilled Care; Intermediate Care. *Beds* 69. *Certified* Medicaid; Medicare.

Colonial Arms Nursing Home*
1687 Summer St NE, Salem, OR, 97303 (503) 585-4602
Admin Mabel Baughman.
Licensure Intermediate Care. *Beds* 46. *Certified* Medicaid.

Elderest Nursing Home*
2630 Church St, Salem, OR, 97303 (503) 585-6712
Admin Gerald Guentner.
Licensure Intermediate Care. *Beds* 65. *Certified* Medicaid.

Fairview Training Center*
2250 Strong Rd SE, Salem, OR, 97310 (503) 378-2268
Admin Martha Warkentin.
Licensure Intermediate Care for Mentally Retarded. *Beds* 1475. *Certified* Medicaid.

Medical Center Nursing Home
2360 Grear St NE, Salem, OR, 97301 (503) 363-8554
Admin I Maurenn Debacon. *Medical Dir/Dir of Nursing* Dr Richard E Kiem.
Licensure Intermediate Care. *Beds* 32. *Certified* Medicaid.
Admissions Requirements Physician's request.
Staff RNs 2 (ft); LPNs 2 (pt); Orderlies 1 (ft), 1 (pt); Nurses aides 14 (ft), 1 (pt); Activities coordinators 1 (pt).
Facilities Dining room; Activities room; Laundry room.
Activities Arts and Crafts; Cards; Games; Reading groups; Prayer groups; Movies; Shopping trips; Dances/Social or cultural gatherings.
Description Small facility is more reassuring for many people—they feel closer to staff and feel we understand their condition better.

Oak Crest Care Center
2933 Center St NE, Salem, OR, 97301 (503) 585-5850
Admin Ron Colburn. *Medical Dir/Dir of Nursing* Dr Casterline.
Licensure Intermediate Care. *Beds* 110. *Certified* Medicaid.
Staff Physicians; RNs; LPNs; Orderlies; Nurses aides; Physical therapists; Recreational therapists; Activities coordinators; Dietitians; Dentists.
Facilities Dining room; Activities room; Crafts room; Laundry room; Barber/Beauty shop.
Activities Arts and Crafts; Cards; Games; Reading groups; Prayer groups; Movies; Shopping trips; Dances/Social or cultural gatherings.
Description Facility features excellent direct nursing care.

Plantation Care Center Inc*
820 Cottage St NE, Salem, OR, 97301 (503) 399-1135
Admin Claudia Jones.
Licensure Intermediate Care. *Beds* 100. *Certified* Medicaid.

Shangri-La
2887 74th SE, Salem, OR, 97301 (503) 581-1732
Admin Nancy Glass.
Licensure Intermediate Care for Mentally Retarded. *Beds* 70. *Certified* Medicaid.
Admissions Requirements Minimum age 6; Medical examination; Physician's request.
Staff Physicians 1 (pt); RNs 2 (ft), 1 (pt); Orderlies 31 (ft), 15 (pt); Physical therapists 1 (pt); Recreational therapists 5 (ft); Occupational therapists 1 (pt); Speech therapists 1 (pt); Activities coordinators 1 (ft); Dietitians 1 (pt).
Facilities Dining room; Activities room; Laundry room.
Activities Arts and Crafts; Cards; Games; Movies; Shopping trips; Dances/Social or cultural gatherings.
Description Shangri-La ICF/MR is located east of Salem, Oregon in a rural area providing a clear view of the Oregon Cascades. The ICF/MR program has a unique recreation program which ensures exposure to the community and its services. Training is directed toward eventual movement into a community group home.

Sherwood Park Nursing Home
4062 Arleta Ave NE, Salem, OR, 97303 (503) 390-2271
Admin Scott R Turner.
Licensure Intermediate Care. *Beds* 44. *Certified* Medicaid.

South Salem Care Center
4620 Kurth St S, Salem, OR, 97302 (503) 581-8666

Admin Loretta A Androes. *Medical Dir/Dir of Nursing* Chris Edwardson.
Licensure Intermediate Care. *Beds* 72. *Certified* Medicaid.
Ownership Proprietary.
Admissions Requirements Medical examination.
Staff Physicians 1 (pt); RNs 2 (ft); LPNs 5 (ft); Orderlies 5 (ft); Nurses aides 30 (ft), 4 (pt); Physical therapists 1 (pt); Reality therapists 1 (pt); Recreational therapists 1 (ft); Occupational therapists 1 (pt); Speech therapists 1 (pt); Activities coordinators 1 (pt); Dietitians 1 (pt); Dentists 1 (pt); Ophthalmologists 1 (pt); Podiatrists 1 (pt); Audiologists 1 (pt).
Facilities Dining room; Activities room; Laundry room; Barber/Beauty shop.
Activities Arts and Crafts; Cards; Games; Reading groups; Prayer groups; Movies; Shopping trips; Dances/Social or cultural gatherings.
Description Facility offers rehabilitation services provided at no extra charge to residents, park-like backyard with fencing, and 3 delicious meals a day. An atmosphere of peace and love for all who enter our home.

Sunnyside Care Center
4515 Sunnyside Rd SE, Salem, OR, 97302 (503) 370-8284
Admin Dixie Irwin. *Medical Dir/Dir of Nursing* Paul Young MD.
Licensure Intermediate Care. *Beds* 124. *Certified* Medicaid.
Admissions Requirements Minimum age 21; Physician's request.
Staff Physicians; RNs 2 (ft), 3 (pt); LPNs 1 (ft), 6 (pt); Orderlies 2 (ft); Nurses aides 40 (ft), 10 (pt); Recreational therapists 1 (ft); Activities coordinators 1 (ft); Dietitians 1 (pt).
Facilities Dining room; Physical therapy room; Activities room; Crafts room; Barber/Beauty shop.
Activities Arts and Crafts; Cards; Games; Reading groups; Prayer groups; Movies; Shopping trips; Dances/Social or cultural gatherings.
Description This is the newest facility in town, with 32 retirement apartments adjacent as well as a 50-bed residential care facility, all on the same property but nicely separated.

Willamette Lutheran Homes Inc*
PO Box 169, 7693 Wheatland Rd NE, Salem, OR, 97308 (503) 393-1491
Admin David Barnet.
Licensure Intermediate Care. *Beds* 18.
Affiliation Lutheran

SANDY

Orchard Crest Care Center
19130 SE Barnstedt, Sandy, OR, 97055 (503) 668-6336
Admin Arlene Anibal. *Medical Dir/Dir of Nursing* Dr Fred Bradshaw.
Licensure Intermediate Care. *Beds* 28. *Certified* Medicaid.
Staff Physicians 2 (ft); RNs 1 (ft), 1 (pt); Nurses aides 8 (ft), 7 (pt); Physical therapists; Reality therapists 1 (ft); Recreational therapists 1 (ft); Speech therapists; Activities coordinators 1 (ft); Podiatrists 1 (pt).
Facilities Dining room; Physical therapy room;

Activities room; Chapel; Crafts room; Laundry room; Library.
Activities Arts and Crafts; Cards; Games; Reading groups; Prayer groups; Movies; Shopping trips; Dances/Social or cultural gatherings.
Description Small facility has cozy, rural setting allowing all residents to get much individual attention; very organized social and recreational activities; residents go out to entertain at other facilities; resident garden club; volunteer groups.

Saint Jude's Home Inc*
39641 Scenic St, Sandy, OR, 97055 (503) 668-4108
Admin Marilee Swarthout.
Licensure Intermediate Care. *Beds* 63. *Certified* Medicaid.

SCAPPOOSE

Victorian Manor
33910 Columbia Blvd, Box 1068, Scappoose, OR, 97056 (503) 543-7131
Admin Howard Lavin.
Licensure Intermediate Care. *Beds* 41. *Certified* Medicaid.
Admissions Requirements Minimum age 18; Medical examination; Physician's request.
Staff RNs 1 (ft); LPNs 3 (pt); Orderlies 1 (ft), 1 (pt); Nurses aides 5 (ft), 15 (pt); Activities coordinators 1 (ft), 1 (pt).
Facilities Dining room; Activities room; Barber/Beauty shop.
Activities Arts and Crafts; Games; Reading groups; Prayer groups; Movies; Dances/Social or cultural gatherings.

SEASIDE

Ocean Park Nursing Home
1420 E 10th, PO Box 836, Seaside, OR, 97138 (503) 738-6142
Admin Kathy Park.
Licensure Intermediate Care. *Beds* 22. *Certified* Medicaid.
Admissions Requirements Physician's request.
Staff RNs 1 (ft), 1 (pt); LPNs 1 (ft), 3 (pt); Nurses aides 9 (ft), 9 (pt); Activities coordinators 1 (ft).
Facilities Dining room; Activities room; Laundry room.
Activities Arts and Crafts; Cards; Games; Reading groups; Prayer groups; Movies; Shopping trips; Dances/Social or cultural gatherings.
Description Quiet, peaceful surrounding on one acre of land, 3 blocks from the Pacific Ocean, 2 blocks from fir-studded mountains.

Seaside Care Center*
822 Necanicum Dr, Seaside, OR, 97138 (503) 738-8383
Admin Nellie O'Malley.
Licensure Intermediate Care. *Beds* 100. *Certified* Medicaid.

SHERIDAN

Sheridan Care Center*
411 SE Sheridan Rd, Sheridan, OR, 97378 (503) 843-2204

Admin Linda Hill.
Licensure Intermediate Care. *Beds* 54. *Certified* Medicaid.

SILVERTON

Silver Gardens Care Home Inc
115 S James Ave, Silverton, OR, 97381 (503) 873-5362
Admin Michael McCoy. *Medical Dir/Dir of Nursing* Dr McNeilly.
Licensure Intermediate Care. *Beds* 52. *Certified* Medicaid.
Facilities Dining room; Activities room.
Activities Arts and Crafts; Games; Dances/Social or cultural gatherings.

Silverton Nursing Home
1164 S Water St, Silverton, OR, 97381 (503) 873-5391
Admin Dorothy Yost. *Medical Dir/Dir of Nursing* Michael Grady MD.
Licensure Intermediate Care. *Beds* 64. *Certified* Medicaid.
Staff RNs 2 (ft); LPNs 3 (ft), 2 (pt); Nurses aides 18 (ft), 4 (pt); Activities coordinators 1 (ft); Dietitians 1 (ft), 1 (pt).
Facilities Dining room; Physical therapy room; Activities room; Crafts room; Laundry room; Barber/Beauty shop; 2 Solariums.
Activities Arts and Crafts; Cards; Games; Reading groups; Prayer groups; Movies; Shopping trips; Dances/Social or cultural gatherings.
Description Facility has a volunteer coordinator and an actively growing volunteer staff; located at the foot of the Silver Hills on the banks of Silver Creek which is in full view of the residents as they dine.

SPRINGFIELD

McKenzie Manor Nursing Home
1333 N 1st St, Springfield, OR, 97477 (503) 746-6581
Admin Florence Miller. *Medical Dir/Dir of Nursing* Wallace Baldwin MD.
Licensure Skilled Care. *Beds* 153. *Certified* Medicaid; Medicare.
Admissions Requirements Minimum age 18; Medical examination; Physician's request.
Staff Physicians 1 (pt); RNs 7 (ft), 8 (pt); LPNs 5 (ft), 4 (pt); Orderlies 3 (ft), 2 (pt); Nurses aides 52 (ft), 30 (pt); Physical therapists 1 (pt); Occupational therapists 1 (pt); Speech therapists 1 (pt); Activities coordinators 1 (ft); Dietitians 1 (ft); Dentists 1 (pt); Podiatrists 1 (pt); Audiologists 1 (pt).
Facilities Dining room; Physical therapy room; Activities room; Crafts room; Laundry room; Barber/Beauty shop; Library.
Activities Arts and Crafts; Cards; Games; Reading groups; Prayer groups; Movies; Shopping trips; Dances/Social or cultural gatherings.
Description Our staff is dedicated and committed to a philosophy of the finest personalized care for each resident and the needs of the family. It is our hope to assist in making the transition from home or the hospital to our facility as pleasant as possible.

SUBLIMITY

Marian Nursing Home
360 Church St, Sublimity, OR, 97385 Stayton
(503) 769-3499, Salem (503) 581-2006
Admin Maurice Reece.
Licensure Intermediate Care. *Beds* ICF 154;
Home for the Aged 21, Retirement Apartments
23. *Certified* Medicaid; Medicare.
Admissions Requirements Minimum age 43;
Medical examination; Physician's request.
Staff Physicians 2 (pt); RNs 8 (ft); LPNs 7 (ft);
Physical therapists 2 (pt); Occupational thera-
pists 1 (pt); Speech therapists 1 (pt); Activities
coordinators 2 (ft); Dietitians 1 (ft), 1 (pt); Den-
tists 1 (pt); Ophthalmologists 1 (pt); Audiolo-
gists 1 (pt).
Facilities Dining room; Activities room;
Chapel; Crafts room; Laundry room; Barber-
/Beauty shop.
Activities Arts and Crafts; Cards; Games;
Reading groups; Prayer groups; Movies; Shop-
ping trips; Dances/Social or cultural gatherings;
Short trips to mountains, coast park.
Description Facility is located in 28-acre rural
setting.

SWEET HOME

Oakhurst Nursing Home
950 Nandina St, Sweet Home, OR, 97386 (503)
367-2191
Admin Derek R Salway. *Medical Dir/Dir of
Nursing* Alice Hyland.
Licensure Intermediate Care. *Beds* 40. *Certi-
fied* Medicaid.
Staff Physicians 5 (pt); RNs 1 (ft), 1 (pt); LPNs
1 (ft); Nurses aides 15 (ft), 15 (pt); Physical
therapists 1 (pt); Activities coordinators 1 (ft);
Dietitians 1 (pt).
Facilities Dining room; Activities room; Laundry room; Multi-purpose room.
Activities Arts and Crafts; Cards; Games;
Reading groups; Prayer groups; Movies; Shop-
ping trips; Dances/Social or cultural gatherings.
Description Small home, located in a beautiful
lakeside town, is able to give individual attention.

THE DALLES

Columbia Basin Nursing Home
1015 Webber Rd, The Dalles, OR, 97058 (503)
296-2156
Admin Joyce Williams. *Medical Dir/Dir of
Nursing* Thomas Hodge MD.
Licensure Skilled Care; Intermediate Care.
Beds SNF 30; ICF 89. *Certified* Medicaid;
Medicare.
Admissions Requirements Medical examina-
tion; Physician's request.
Staff RNs 8 (ft); LPNs 7 (ft); Orderlies 4 (ft);
Nurses aides 35 (ft); Physical therapists 1 (ft);
Speech therapists 1 (pt); Activities coordinators
1 (ft); Dietitians 1 (ft); Dentists 1 (pt); Ophthal-
mologists 1 (pt); Podiatrists 1 (pt); Audiologists
1 (pt).
Facilities Dining room; Physical therapy room;
Activities room; Crafts room; Laundry room;
Barber/Beauty shop; Store.
Activities Arts and Crafts; Games; Reading

groups; Prayer groups; Movies; Shopping trips;
Dances/Social or cultural gatherings; Bus trips;
Gourmet cooking class.
Description Our facility is owned and operated
by Wasco County, with preference for admission
given to Wasco County residents. We pride ourselves on providing a quality of life for our residents that is second to none and use a team
effort to achieve it. Our comprehensive activities' department has received recognition for
the cooking class held twice weekly and led by
one of our many volunteers. The residents help
prepare many tasty foods and sample the
results.

Valle Vista Care Center
1023 W 25th Ave, PO Box 6, The Dalles, OR,
97058 (503) 298-5158
Admin Vera McDowell.
Licensure Intermediate Care. *Beds* 80. *Certi-
fied* Medicaid.
Admissions Requirements Medical examina-
tion; Physician's request.
Facilities Dining room; Physical therapy room;
Activities room; Crafts room; Laundry room;
Barber/Beauty shop.
Activities Arts and Crafts; Cards; Games;
Reading groups; Prayer groups; Movies; Shopping trips; Dances/Social or cultural gatherings;
Community activities.
Description Facility is situated on a hill over-
looking a creek, surrounded by a cherry
orchard; beautiful view is seen from the sliding
glass doors in each patient's room. Employees
are all dedicated to the belief that residents
have much to offer the younger residents of the
town.

TIGARD

King City Convalescent Center
16485 SW Pacific Hwy, Tigard, OR, 97223
(503) 620-5141
Admin Jack Wall. *Medical Dir/Dir of Nursing* Dr Charles O Mansfield.
Licensure Skilled Care. *Beds* 148. *Certified* Medicaid; Medicare.
Admissions Requirements Medical
examination.
Staff Physicians 1 (pt); LPNs 16 (ft); LPNs 6
(ft); Orderlies 3 (ft); Nurses aides 31 (ft);
Physical therapists 2 (ft); Occupational therapists 1 (ft); Speech therapists 1 (pt); Activities
coordinators 2 (ft); Dietitians 1 (ft); Podiatrists
1 (pt).
Facilities Dining room; Physical therapy room;
Activities room; Crafts room; Barber/Beauty
shop; Library.
Activities Arts and Crafts; Cards; Games;
Reading groups; Prayer groups; Movies; Shopping trips; Dances/Social or cultural gatherings.
Description We are a Medicare certified SNF
with a strong emphasis on rehabilitation.

Tigard Care Center*
14145 SW 105th St, Tigard, OR, 97223 (503)
639-1144
Admin Dennis Wade.
Licensure Intermediate Care. *Beds* 112. *Certified* Medicaid.

TILLAMOOK

Tillamook Care Center
2500 Nielson Rd, Tillamook, OR, 97141 (503)
842-6664
Admin Robert S Hutchinson. *Medical Dir/Dir
of Nursing* Calvin Hill MD.
Licensure Skilled Care; Intermediate Care;
Residential Care. *Beds* SNF 9; ICF 84; Residential Care 8. *Certified* Medicaid; Medicare.
Staff RNs 3 (ft), 3 (pt); LPNs 2 (ft), 3 (pt);
Nurses aides 27 (ft), 2 (pt); Physical therapists 1
(pt); Reality therapists 1 (ft); Recreational therapists 1 (ft); Occupational therapists 1 (pt); Speech therapists 1 (pt); Activities coordinators 1
(ft); Dietitians 1 (pt); Dentists 1 (pt); Podiatrists
1 (pt); Audiologists 1 (pt).
Facilities Dining room; Physical therapy room;
Activities room; Crafts room; Laundry room;
Barber/Beauty shop.
Activities Arts and Crafts; Cards; Games;
Reading groups; Prayer groups; Movies; Shopping trips; Dances/Social or cultural gatherings.
Description Facility offers intergenerational
sharing, Adopt-a-grandparent program, and pet
therapy.

TOLEDO

New Lincoln Hospital*
PO Box 490, Toledo, OR, 97391 (503) 336-2237
Admin David Bloomer, Jr.
Licensure Skilled Care. *Beds* 18. *Cer-
tified* Medicare.

TROUTDALE

Edgefield Manor Nursing Home
2126 SW Halsey St, Troutdale, OR, 97060 (503)
665-0161
Admin Laverne E Jones.
Licensure Intermediate Care. *Beds* 91. *Certified* Medicaid.

Woodvillage Nursing Manor Inc*
2060 NE 238th Dr, Troutdale, OR, 97060 (503)
666-3864
Admin Marsha Johnson.
Licensure Intermediate Care. *Beds* 46. *Certified* Medicaid.

VALE

Pioneer Nursing Home
1060 D St W, Vale, OR, 97918 (503) 473-3131
Admin Gaynelle Edmondson. *Medical Dir/Dir
of Nursing* D W Sarazin MD.
Licensure Intermediate Care; Residential Care.
Beds ICF 51; Residential Care 9. *Cer-
tified* Medicaid.
Admissions Requirements Medical examina-
tion; Physician's request.
Staff RNs 1 (ft), 1 (pt); LPNs 4 (ft), 3 (pt);
Orderlies 1 (ft), 1 (pt); Nurses aides 17 (ft), 1
(pt); Activities coordinators 1 (ft).
Facilities Dining room; Physical therapy room;
Activities room; Crafts room; Laundry room;
Barber/Beauty shop.
Activities Arts and Crafts; Cards; Games;
Reading groups; Prayer groups; Movies; Shop-
ping trips; Dances/Social or cultural gatherings.

WEST LINN

West Linn Care Center Inc
2330 DeBok Rd, West Linn, OR, 97068 (503)
655-6331
Admin Carol M Graeber.
Licensure Intermediate Care. *Beds* 61. *Certified* Medicaid.
Languages Spanish, Vietnamese, Sign
Description Special features and services
include a specialization in psychiatric needs,
offering special care for special needs. Facility
includes security fencing allowing residents to
roam free or to garden. Interpreters available in
Spanish, Vietnamese, and Sign.

WHEELER

Harvey E Rinehart Memorial Hospital
PO Box 16, Wheeler, OR, 97147 (503)
368-5119
Medical Dir/Dir of Nursing Dr Oscar Marin.
Licensure Skilled Care; Intermediate Care.
Beds 50. *Certified* Medicaid; Medicare.
Ownership Public.
Admissions Requirements Medical examination; Physician's request.
Staff Physicians 4 (ft); RNs 2 (ft), 4 (pt); LPNs
1 (ft); Orderlies 2 (ft), 1 (pt); Nurses aides 21
(ft); Physical therapists 1 (ft); Recreational therapists 1 (ft); Occupational therapists 1 (pt);
Speech therapists 1 (pt); Activities coordinators
1 (pt); Dietitians 1 (pt); Dentists 1 (pt);
Audiologists 1 (pt).
Facilities Dining room; Physical therapy room;
Activities room; Chapel; Crafts room; Laundry
room; Barber/Beauty shop; Library; Family
room; Lounges.
Activities Arts and Crafts; Games; Prayer
groups; Dances/Social or cultural gatherings;
Exercise programs; Community education; Bus
sight-seeing weekly; Pets.
Description Facility is located on Oregon coast
overlooking Nehalem Bay with 4 porches, pet
yard, all private rooms, 50 hydromassage tubs.
respite, hospice, skilled and intermediate care,
wanderers/Alzeheimer's Wing (minimum
chemical or physical restraints).

WOODBURN

French Prairie Care Center
601 Evergreen Rd, Woodburn, OR, 97071 (503)
982-9946
Admin Nancy Buntin. *Medical Dir/Dir of
Nursing* Gordon D. Haynie MD.
Licensure Skilled Care; Intermediate Care.
Beds SNF 11; ICF 69. *Certified* Medicaid;
Medicare.
Staff Physicians 1 (pt); RNs 4 (ft), 2 (pt); LPNs
3 (ft), 2 (pt); Orderlies 2 (ft); Nurses aides 23
(ft), 1 (pt); Physical therapists 1 (pt); Speech
therapists 1 (pt); Activities coordinators 1 (ft);
Dietitians 1 (pt).
Facilities Dining room; Physical therapy room;
Activities room; Crafts room; Laundry room;
Barber/Beauty shop.
Activities Arts and Crafts; Cards; Games;
Reading groups; Prayer groups; Movies; Shopping trips; Dances/Social or cultural gatherings.

Woodburn Convalescent Center
540 Settlemier St, Woodburn, OR, 97071 (503)
981-9566
Admin Dixie Irwin.
Licensure Intermediate Care. *Beds* 60. *Certified* Medicaid.
Admissions Requirements Minimum age 18;
Physician's request.
Staff RNs 1 (ft), 1 (pt); LPNs 3 (ft), 2 (pt);
Activities coordinators 1 (ft); Dietitians 1 (pt).
Facilities Dining room; Laundry room.
Activities Arts and Crafts; Cards; Games;
Reading groups; Prayer groups; Movies; Shopping trips; Dances/Social or cultural gatherings.
Description Facility has long-term staff and
beautiful spacious grounds.

PENNSYLVANIA

ABBOTTSTOWN

Childrens Developmental Center Inc*
PO Box 236, Abbottstown, PA, 17301 (717)
624-2455
Licensure Intermediate Care for Mentally
Retarded. *Beds* 64. *Certified* Medicaid.
Ownership Proprietary.

AKRON

Maple Farm Nursing Center*
Box F, Akron, PA, 17501 (717) 859-1191
Licensure Skilled Care. *Beds* 123. *Certified* Medicaid; Medicare.
Ownership Proprietary.

ALIQUIPPA

Golfview Manor Nursing Home
616 Golf Course Rd, Aliquippa, PA, 15001
(412) 375-0345
Medical Dir/Dir of Nursing Dr Glenn Roberts.
Licensure Skilled Care. *Beds* 59. *Certified* Medicaid; Medicare.
Ownership Proprietary.
Admissions Requirements Medical examination.
Staff Physicians 1 (pt); RNs 1 (ft), 10 (pt);
LPNs 2 (pt); Orderlies 1 (ft); Nurses aides 15
(ft), 12 (pt); Physical therapists 1 (pt); Recreational therapists 2 (ft); Speech therapists 1 (pt);
Activities coordinators 1 (pt); Dietitians 1 (pt);
Dentists 1 (pt); Podiatrists 2 (pt).
Facilities Dining room; Activities room; Crafts
room; Laundry room; Barber/Beauty shop.
Activities Arts and Crafts; Cards; Games;
Reading groups; Prayer groups; Movies; Dances/Social or cultural gatherings.
Description Facility features a garden area for
residents to care for.

ALLENTOWN

Cedarbrook
350 S Cedarbrook Rd, Allentown, PA, 18104
(215) 395-3727
Medical Dir/Dir of Nursing Frank T Anderko
MD.
Licensure Skilled Care; Intermediate Care.
Beds SNF 516; ICF 108. *Certified* Medicaid;
Medicare.

Ownership Nonprofit.
Admissions Requirements Medical examination; Physician's request.
Staff Physicians 3 (ft), 2 (pt); RNs 41 (ft), 32
(pt); LPNs 41 (ft), 14 (pt); Orderlies 268 (ft), 15
(pt); Physical therapists 2 (ft); Occupational
therapists 2 (ft); Speech therapists 1 (ft); Activities coordinators 1 (ft); Dietitians 1 (ft); Dentists 1 (pt); Ophthalmologists 1 (pt); Podiatrists
2 (pt).
Facilities Dining room; Physical therapy room;
Activities room; Chapel; Crafts room; Laundry
room; Barber/Beauty shop; Library.
Activities Arts and Crafts; Cards; Games;
Reading groups; Prayer groups; Movies; Shopping trips; Dances/Social or cultural gatherings.
Description Facility believes that comprehensive care is concerned with the skillful
treatment of the geriatric and disabled person,
the prevention of disease, and the conservation
of health. Also, that effectual total care
embodies recognition of the dignity of worth of
each individual, and the ability to perceive and
meet his/her physical needs in a wholesome
and friendly environment.

**The Good Shepherd Home Long-Term Care
Facility Inc**
Sixth and Saint John Sts, Allentown, PA, 18103
(215) 776-3111
Medical Dir/Dir of Nursing E Joel Carpenter
IV.
Licensure Skilled Care; Intermediate Care.
Beds 135. *Certified* Medicaid; Medicare.
Ownership Nonprofit.
Admissions Requirements Minimum age 12;
Medical examination.
Staff Physicians 2 (pt); RNs 15 (ft), 9 (pt);
LPNs 9 (ft), 1 (pt); Nurses aides 52 (ft), 16 (pt);
Physical therapists 1 (ft), 1 (pt); Recreational
therapists 1 (ft); Occupational therapists 1 (ft);
Speech therapists 1 (pt); Activities coordinators
1 (ft); Dietitians 1 (ft); Dentists 1 (pt); Podiatrists 1 (pt).
Affiliation Lutheran
Facilities Dining room; Physical therapy room;
Activities room; Chapel; Crafts room; Laundry
room; Barber/Beauty shop; Academic educational center; Vocational evaluation center.
Activities Arts and Crafts; Cards; Games;
Reading groups; Prayer groups; Movies; Shopping trips; Dances/Social or cultural gatherings.
Description Good Shepherd Home has just celebrated its 75th anniversary in the care of the

handicapped, specializing in care and services
to young physically disabled adults. Offers a
comprehensive rehabilitation program
including community independent living
training. Although younger residents attend
public school, Good Shepherd Home now
offers an academic education program for adult
residents.

Liberty Nursing Center*
N 17th and Allen Sts, Allentown, PA, 18104
(215) 432-4351
Licensure Skilled Care. *Beds* 150. *Certified* Medicaid; Medicare.
Ownership Proprietary.

Parkway Rest Home Inc
3600 Hamilton St, Allentown, PA, 18104 (215)
395-4011
Admin Donald Lanquell. *Medical Dir/Dir of
Nursing* Dr E Baum.
Licensure Skilled Care. *Beds* 28. *Certified* Medicaid.
Ownership Proprietary.
Admissions Requirements Minimum age 35;
Medical examination.
Staff Physicians 4 (pt); RNs 4 (ft); LPNs 4 (ft);
Nurses aides 6 (pt); Physical therapists 1 (pt);
Recreational therapists 1 (pt); Occupational
therapists 1 (pt); Activities coordinators 1 (ft);
Dietitians 1 (pt); Dentists 1 (pt); Podiatrists 1
(pt).
Facilities Dining room; Activities room; Laundry room.
Activities Arts and Crafts; Cards; Games;
Reading groups; Prayer groups; Movies; Dances/Social or cultural gatherings.
Description Small, noninstitutional-type
facility tries to be as home-like as possible.

Phoebe-Devitt Home
1925 Turner St, Allentown, PA, 18104 (215)
435-9037
Medical Dir/Dir of Nursing Dr Warren H
Endres.
Licensure Skilled Care; Intermediate Care.
Beds SNF 184; ICF 144. *Certified* Medicaid;
Medicare.
Admissions Requirements Minimum age 62;
Medical examination.
Staff Physicians 1 (ft), 3 (pt); RNs 25 (ft), 31
(pt); LPNs 16 (ft), 3 (pt); Nurses aides 104 (ft),
68 (pt); Physical therapists 1 (ft), 2 (pt); Reality
therapists 2 (ft); Recreational therapists 2 (ft);

Occupational therapists 2 (ft); Activities coordinators 1 (ft); Dietitians 2 (ft); Dentists 1 (pt); Podiatrists 1 (pt).
Affiliation Church of Christ
Facilities Dining room; Physical therapy room; Activities room; Chapel; Crafts room; Laundry room; Barber/Beauty shop; Library.
Activities Arts and Crafts; Cards; Games; Reading groups; Prayer groups; Movies; Shopping trips; Dances/Social or cultural gatherings.
Description Phoebe-Devitt Home is a not-for-profit home related to the United Church of Christ. It is located in a residential area of Allentown. It endeavors to provide quality care in both intermediate and skilled nursing care levels. Forty beds are available for residential care. The Home also manages 2 apartment facilities. One is a HUD project for middle-income elderly and the other is a continuing care project.

Westminster Village
803 N Wahneta St, Allentown, PA, 18103 (215) 434-6245
Medical Dir/Dir of Nursing Dr Bruce Eisenhardt.
Licensure Skilled Care; Intermediate Care.
Beds 151. *Certified* Medicaid; Medicare.
Ownership Nonprofit.
Staff RNs 12 (ft), 5 (pt); LPNs 1 (ft), 2 (pt); Nurses aides 30 (ft), 25 (pt); Physical therapists 1 (ft), 3 (pt); Recreational therapists 1 (ft); Occupational therapists 1 (ft).
Affiliation Presbyterian
Facilities Dining room; Physical therapy room; Activities room; Crafts room; Laundry room; Barber/Beauty shop; Library; Gift shop; Occupational therapy kitchen; Dental office; Exercise room.
Activities Arts and Crafts; Cards; Games; Reading groups; Prayer groups; Movies; Shopping trips; Dances/Social or cultural gatherings; Cooking group; Lunch trips.
Description Excellent program on continuing care campus with an active auxiliary of over 800 members, an active volunteer group and a dedicated staff with a high regard for continuing education in a long-term care environment. Conveniently located in an urban location with shopping, churches, and public transportation immediately available.

White Haven Center Annex—Allentown*
1700 Hanover Ave, Allentown, PA, 18103 (215) 821-6201
Licensure Intermediate Care for Mentally Retarded. *Beds* 43. *Certified* Medicaid.
Ownership Nonprofit.

ALLISON PARK

Regency Hall Nursing Home Inc
9399 Babcock Blvd, Allison Park, PA, 15101 (412) 366-8540
Medical Dir/Dir of Nursing Robert Carroll MD.
Licensure Skilled Care. *Beds* 130. *Certified* Medicaid.
Ownership Nonprofit.
Admissions Requirements Medical examination; Physician's request.
Staff Physicians 10 (pt); RNs 3 (ft), 17 (pt);

LPNs 4 (ft), 6 (pt); Orderlies 3 (ft); Nurses aides 41 (ft), 27 (pt); Physical therapists 1 (pt); Reality therapists 1 (ft); Recreational therapists 1 (ft); Speech therapists 1 (pt); Activities coordinators 1 (pt); Dietitians 1 (pt); Dentists 1 (pt); Ophthalmologists 1 (pt); Podiatrists 1 (pt); Audiologists 1 (pt).
Affiliation Roman Catholic
Facilities Dining room; Activities room; Chapel; Barber/Beauty shop.
Activities Arts and Crafts; Cards; Games; Reading groups; Prayer groups; Movies.
Description Facility offers day care for the homebound frail elderly 3 days a week, caregivers must provide transportation. Two snacks, one hot meal given; participants involved in activities provided.

ALTOONA

Altoona Center
1515 Fourth St, Altoona, PA, 16601 (814) 946-1664
Medical Dir/Dir of Nursing M Feizal Zavahir.
Licensure Intermediate Care for Mentally Retarded. *Beds* 138. *Certified* Medicaid; Medicare.
Ownership Nonprofit.
Staff Physicians 1 (ft); RNs 16 (ft), 2 (pt); LPNs 6 (ft); Nurses aides 70 (ft); Physical therapists 1 (ft); Recreational therapists 25 (ft); Occupational therapists 1 (pt); Speech therapists 1 (ft); Activities coordinators 1 (ft); Dietitians 1 (ft); Dentists 1 (pt); Podiatrists 1 (pt); Audiologists 1 (pt).
Facilities Dining room; Physical therapy room; Activities room; Crafts room.
Activities Arts and Crafts; Games; Prayer groups; Movies; Shopping trips; Dances/Social or cultural gatherings.
Description Altoona Center is a public residential facility located in the city of Altoona in south central Pennsylvania. It is operated by the Department of Public Welfare as one of the major mental retardation centers within the Commonwealth service delivery system. The center's mission is to serve mentally retarded-/physically handicapped persons from the central region. The facility provides for a full range of services to persons in residence—assessment, diagnostic, habilitative.

Hillview Nursing and Convalescent Home*
700 S Cayuga Ave, Altoona, PA, 16602 (814) 946-0471
Licensure Skilled Care; Intermediate Care.
Beds SNF 64; ICF 64. *Certified* Medicaid; Medicare.
Ownership Proprietary.

Mid State ICFMR Broad*
2605 Broad Ave, Altoona, PA, 16601 (717) 946-4618
Licensure Residential MR Care. *Beds* 8. *Certified* Medicaid.
Ownership Proprietary.

Mid State ICFMR Inc*
1908 8th Ave, Altoona, PA, 16602 (814) 946-4623

Licensure Residential MR Care. *Beds* 8. *Certified* Medicaid.
Ownership Proprietary.

Mid State ICFMR Inc*
2210 16th St, Altoona, PA, 16601 (814) 946-4637
Licensure Residential MR Care. *Beds* 8. *Certified* Medicaid.
Ownership Proprietary.

Valley View Home*
301 Pleasant Valley Blvd, Altoona, PA, 16602 (814) 944-0845
Licensure Skilled Care; Intermediate Care.
Beds SNF 78; ICF 166. *Certified* Medicaid; Medicare.
Ownership Nonprofit.

AMBLER

Ambler Rest Center
Bethlehem and Butler Pikes, Ambler, PA, 19002 (215) 646-7050
Medical Dir/Dir of Nursing Samuel D Kim MD.
Licensure Skilled Care. *Beds* 100. *Certified* Medicaid; Medicare.
Ownership Proprietary.
Staff RNs 8 (ft), 5 (pt); LPNs 2 (ft), 6 (pt); Orderlies 3 (ft); Nurses aides 24 (ft), 16 (pt); Physical therapists 2 (pt); Recreational therapists 3 (pt); Occupational therapists 1 (pt); Speech therapists 1 (pt); Activities coordinators 1 (ft); Dietitians 1 (pt); Social workers 1 (ft), 1 (pt).
Facilities Dining room; Physical therapy room; Activities room; Laundry room; Barber/Beauty shop.
Activities Arts and Crafts; Cards; Games; Reading groups; Movies; Shopping trips; Dances/Social or cultural gatherings.
Description Facility offers an experience in living featuring personal, sensitive care in a cheerful atmosphere; lovely tree shaded patios overlooking duck populated stream; children included in regular activities; pets in residence; respite care; gracious dining in garden room with fresh flowers, china, and courteous service.

Anna Christie Nursing Home
Butler Pike and Welsch Rd, Ambler, PA, 19002 (215) 646-1742
Medical Dir/Dir of Nursing Dr L B Shaffer.
Licensure Skilled Care. *Beds* 39.
Ownership Proprietary.
Admissions Requirements Medical examination; Physician's request.
Staff Physicians 3 (ft), 1 (pt); RNs 3 (ft); LPNs 2 (ft), 2 (pt); Nurses aides 4 (ft), 6 (pt); Physical therapists 1 (pt); Reality therapists 1 (pt); Recreational therapists 1 (pt); Occupational therapists; Speech therapists; Activities coordinators; Dietitians; Dentists; Ophthalmologists; Podiatrists; Audiologists.
Facilities Dining room; Physical therapy room; Activities room; Chapel; Crafts room; Laundry room; Library.
Description Facility provides skilled nursing care, church on Sundays, TV; outside visitors include relatives, friends, church organizations, clubs.

Artman Lutheran Home
250 Behtlehem Pike, Ambler, PA, 19002 (215) 643-6333
Admin Luanne B Sejhe. *Medical Dir/Dir of Nursing* Dr Henry Borska.
Licensure Skilled Care. *Beds* 30. *Certified* Medicaid.
Ownership Nonprofit.
Admissions Requirements Minimum age 65.
Staff Physicians 1 (pt); RNs 3 (ft), 7 (pt); LPNs 3 (pt); Nurses aides 8 (ft), 5 (pt); Recreational therapists 1 (ft), 1 (pt); Dietitians 1 (pt); Dentists 1 (pt); Ophthalmologists 1 (pt); Podiatrists 1 (pt).
Affiliation Lutheran
Facilities Dining room; Activities room; Chapel; Crafts room; Laundry room; Barber/Beauty shop; Library.
Activities Arts and Crafts; Cards; Games; Reading groups; Prayer groups; Movies; Shopping trips; Dances/Social or cultural gatherings.
Description Facility has lovely Victorian ambiance on 13 acres in Montgomery County; excellent holistic program.

ANNVILLE

Lebanon Valley Home*
550 E Main St, Annville, PA, 17003 (717) 867-4467
Licensure Skilled Care. *Beds* 53. *Certified* Medicaid; Medicare.
Ownership Nonprofit.

United Christian Church Home
Drawer E, Annville, PA, 17003-0404 (717) 867-4636
Admin Roy J Kreider.
Licensure Skilled Care. *Beds* 33. *Certified* Medicaid.
Ownership Nonprofit.
Admissions Requirements Minimum age 65; Medical examination.
Staff Physicians; RNs; LPNs; Orderlies; Nurses aides; Physical therapists; Reality therapists; Recreational therapists; Occupational therapists; Speech therapists; Activities coordinators; Dietitians; Dentists; Ophthalmologists; Podiatrists; Audiologists.
Facilities Dining room; Physical therapy room; Activities room; Chapel; Crafts room; Laundry room; Barber/Beauty shop.
Activities Arts and Crafts; Cards; Games; Reading groups; Prayer groups; Movies; Shopping trips.
Description We have a country setting and residents can have flower and vegetable gardens and help prepare fruits and vegetables for preserving.

APOLLO

West Haven Nursing Home Inc*
Goodview Dr, Apollo, PA, 15613 (412) 727-3451
Licensure Skilled Care; Intermediate Care.
Beds SNF 51; ICF 47. *Certified* Medicaid; Medicare.
Ownership Proprietary.

ASHLAND

Ashland State General Hospital*
Rt 61, RFD 1, Fountain Springs, Ashland, PA, 17921 (717) 875-2000
Licensure Skilled Care. *Beds* 18. *Certified* Medicaid; Medicare.
Ownership Nonprofit.

ATHENS

Heritage Nursing Home Inc*
200 S Main St, Athens, PA, 18810 (717) 885-5805
Licensure Skilled Care; Intermediate Care.
Beds SNF 65; ICF 56. *Certified* Medicaid; Medicare.
Ownership Proprietary.

BADEN

Naugle Manor Inc
1061 Phillips St, Baden, PA, 15005 (412) 869-2730
Medical Dir/Dir of Nursing C Nadiga MD.
Licensure Intermediate Care. *Beds* 19.
Ownership Proprietary.
Admissions Requirements Minimum age 18; Medical examination.
Staff Physicians 1 (pt); RNs 1 (ft); LPNs 1 (ft), 4 (pt); Orderlies 1 (ft); Nurses aides 2 (ft), 4 (pt); Activities coordinators 1 (pt); Dietitians 1 (ft), 1 (pt).
Facilities Dining room; Activities room.
Activities Arts and Crafts; Cards; Games; Prayer groups.
Description Facility was established in 1952 and features a heated swimming pool.

BALA CYNWYD

Mary J Drexel Home
238 Belmont Ave, Bala Cynwyd, PA, 19004 (215) 664-5967
Medical Dir/Dir of Nursing William Miller MD.
Licensure Skilled Care. *Beds* 27. *Certified* Medicaid.
Ownership Nonprofit.
Admissions Requirements Minimum age 65; Medical examination.
Staff Physicians 1 (pt); RNs 2 (ft); LPNs 6 (ft); Nurses aides 18 (ft); Physical therapists 1 (pt); Recreational therapists 1 (ft); Occupational therapists 1 (pt); Speech therapists 1 (pt); Activities coordinators 1 (ft); Dietitians 1 (ft); Dentists 1 (pt); Podiatrists 3 (pt); Audiologists 1 (pt).
Affiliation Lutheran
Facilities Dining room; Physical therapy room; Activities room; Chapel; Crafts room; Laundry room; Barber/Beauty shop; Library.
Activities Arts and Crafts; Cards; Games; Reading groups; Movies; Shopping trips.
Description Facility features a warm, cozy, home-like atmosphere with wooded and landscaped grounds; safety and security are a specialty.

BANGOR

Slate Belt Medical Center Inc
701 Slate Belt Blvd, Bangor, PA, 18013 (215) 588-6161
Medical Dir/Dir of Nursing John G Oliver MD.
Licensure Skilled Care; Intermediate Care.
Beds SNF 90; ICF 30.
Ownership Nonprofit.
Admissions Requirements Medical examination; Physician's request.
Staff Physicians 3 (ft), 25 (pt); Physical therapists 2 (ft); Recreational therapists 1 (ft); Occupational therapists 1 (ft), 1 (pt); Speech therapists 1 (ft); Activities coordinators 1 (ft), Dietitians 1 (pt); Dentists 1 (pt); Ophthalmologists 1 (pt); Podiatrists 2 (pt); Audiologists 1 (pt).
Facilities Dining room; Physical therapy room; Activities room; Chapel; Crafts room; Laundry room; Barber/Beauty shop.
Activities Arts and Crafts; Cards; Games; Reading groups; Prayer groups; Movies; Shopping trips; Dances/Social or cultural gatherings.
Description Skilled nursing facility with primary care center attached; family practice physicians; lab; X-ray; surgery center; rehabilitation team with physiatrist; orthopedic clinics on premises; surgicenter.

BEAR CREEK

Bear Creek Health Care Center
7001 Bear Creek Blvd, PO Box 58, Bear Creek, PA, 18602-0058 (717) 472-3785
Medical Dir/Dir of Nursing Dr Richard Howell.
Licensure Intermediate Care. *Beds* 32. *Certified* Medicaid.
Ownership Proprietary.
Admissions Requirements Medical examination; Physician's request.
Staff Physicians 1 (pt); RNs 1 (ft); LPNs 2 (ft), 4 (pt); Orderlies 2 (ft); Nurses aides 6 (ft), 6 (pt); Physical therapists 1 (pt); Speech therapists 1 (pt); Activities coordinators 1 (ft).
Facilities Dining room; Activities room; Crafts room; Laundry room; Barber/Beauty shop.
Activities Arts and Crafts; Cards; Games; Reading groups; Prayer groups; Movies; Shopping trips; Dances/Social or cultural gatherings.
Description Facility features individual attention and a home-like atmosphere.

BEAVER

Beaver Valley Geriatrics Center
Dutch Ridge Rd, Beaver, PA, 15009 (412) 775-7100
Admin Fred Clerici. *Medical Dir/Dir of Nursing* Nicholas Vasilopolous MD.
Licensure Skilled Care; Intermediate Care.
Beds SNF 337; ICF 339. *Certified* Medicaid; Medicare.
Ownership Nonprofit.
Admissions Requirements Medical examination.
Staff Physicians 3 (ft), 2 (pt); RNs 68 (ft), 32 (pt); LPNs 32 (ft), 10 (pt); Orderlies 2 (ft), 2 (pt); Nurses aides 235 (ft), 42 (pt); Physical

therapists 1 (ft); Reality therapists 2 (pt); Recreational therapists 1 (pt); Activities coordinators 1 (ft); Dietitians 1 (ft); Dentists 2 (pt); Podiatrists 1 (pt).
Facilities Dining room; Physical therapy room; Activities room; Crafts room; Laundry room; Barber/Beauty shop; Library; Auditorium; Pharmacy; Clinic; X-ray room.
Activities Arts and Crafts; Cards; Games; Reading groups; Prayer groups; Movies; Shopping trips; Dances/Social or cultural gatherings.

BEAVER FALLS

Beaver Valley Nursing Center
RD 1, Georgetown Rd, Beaver Falls, PA, 15070 (412) 846-8200
Medical Dir/Dir of Nursing Dr Nelson Kennedy.
Licensure Skilled Care. *Beds* SNF 60; ICF 60.
Certified Medicaid; Medicare.
Ownership Proprietary.
Admissions Requirements Medical examination.
Staff Physicians 4 (pt); RNs 2 (ft), 7 (pt); LPNs 7 (ft), 4 (pt); Orderlies 2 (ft); Nurses aides 37 (ft), 12 (pt); Physical therapists 1 (ft); Speech therapists 1 (ft); Activities coordinators 2 (ft); Dietitians 1 (ft); Dentists 2 (pt); Podiatrists 1 (pt).
Facilities Dining room; Physical therapy room; Activities room; Chapel; Crafts room; Laundry room; Barber/Beauty shop; Library.
Activities Arts and Crafts; Cards; Games; Reading groups; Prayer groups; Movies; Shopping trips; Dances/Social or cultural gatherings.
Description Facility has been renovated at a cost of $180,000. Paint, wallpaper, equipment, and furniture have been added. Also, 24-hour cardiac monitoring and restaurant dining have been added.

Blair Nursing Home Inc
Rt 2, Box 196, Beaver Falls, PA, 15010 (412) 843-2209
Medical Dir/Dir of Nursing Dr E Damazo.
Licensure Skilled Care. *Beds* 28.
Ownership Proprietary.
Staff Physicians 2 (pt); RNs 4 (ft), 2 (pt); LPNs 4 (pt); Nurses aides 10 (ft), 5 (pt); Physical therapists 1 (pt); Activities coordinators 1 (ft), 1 (pt); Dietitians 1 (pt); Dentists 1 (pt); Podiatrists 1 (pt).
Facilities Activities room.
Activities Arts and Crafts; Cards; Games; Reading groups; Prayer groups; Movies.
Description Facility features one of Pennsylvania's most outstanding volunteer programs.

BEDFORD

Donahoe Manor*
Rt 5, Box 55, Bedford, PA, 15522 (814) 623-9075
Licensure Skilled Care; Intermediate Care.
Beds SNF 48; ICF 24. *Certified* Medicaid; Medicare.
Ownership Proprietary.

BELLEFONTE

Centre Crest Nursing Home
502 E Howard St, Bellefonte, PA, 16823 (814) 355-6777
Medical Dir/Dir of Nursing Dr Ralph E Pilgram.
Licensure Skilled Care; Intermediate Care.
Beds SNF 68; ICF 157. *Certified* Medicaid; Medicare.
Ownership Public.
Admissions Requirements Medical examination; Physician's request.
Staff Physicians 1 (ft); RNs 3 (ft), 11 (pt); LPNs 40 (ft), 10 (pt); Orderlies 4 (pt); Nurses aides 40 (ft), 8 (pt); Physical therapists 1 (ft); Reality therapists 1 (ft); Recreational therapists 3 (ft); Occupational therapists 1 (pt); Speech therapists 1 (pt); Activities coordinators 1 (ft); Dietitians 1 (ft); Dentists 1 (pt); Ophthalmologists 1 (pt); Podiatrists 1 (pt); Audiologists 1 (pt).
Facilities Dining room; Physical therapy room; Activities room; Chapel; Crafts room; Laundry room; Barber/Beauty shop; Library.
Activities Arts and Crafts; Cards; Games; Reading groups; Prayer groups; Movies; Shopping trips; Dances/Social or cultural gatherings; Boating; Fishing; Theatre.
Description Facility provides an excellent adult day care program. The interaction of those individuals with the Home's patients has enhanced the internal program. Facility offers monthly pet therapy program through a local group called PACT.

BERLIN

Maple Mountain Manor
Hay St, Berlin, PA, 15530 (814) 267-4212
Medical Dir/Dir of Nursing Paul L Klose MD.
Licensure Intermediate Care. *Beds* 162. *Certified* Medicaid.
Ownership Nonprofit.
Staff Physicians 1 (ft); RNs 5 (ft), 3 (pt); LPNs 14 (ft), 14 (pt); Nurses aides 46 (ft), 17 (pt); Occupational therapists 1 (pt); Activities coordinators 1 (ft); Dietitians 1 (pt).
Facilities Dining room; Physical therapy room; Activities room; Chapel; Crafts room; Laundry room; Barber/Beauty shop; Library.
Activities Arts and Crafts; Cards; Prayer groups; Movies; Shopping trips.
Description An attractive home for the aged located in Berlin, Pennsylvania, in the heart of the Laurel Highlands.

BERWICK

Berwick Retirement Village Nursing Home
801 E 16th St, Berwick, PA, 18603 (717) 759-2040
Medical Dir/Dir of Nursing Frank Gegwich MD.
Licensure Skilled Care; Intermediate Care.
Beds SNF 60; ICF 60. *Certified* Medicaid; Medicare.
Ownership Nonprofit.
Admissions Requirements Minimum age; Medical examination; Physician's request.
Staff RNs 7 (ft), 5 (pt); LPNs 8 (ft); Orderlies 3 (ft), 1 (pt); Nurses aides 25 (ft), 27 (pt); Recreational therapists 1 (ft).
Facilities Dining room; Physical therapy room; Activities room; Crafts room; Laundry room; Barber/Beauty shop; Library.
Activities Arts and Crafts; Cards; Games; Reading groups; Prayer groups; Movies; Shopping trips; Dances/Social or cultural gatherings.
Description Facility is physically connected to Berwick Hospital which offers MD on premises 24-hours-a-day, lab, X-ray, etc. Special functions: resident council, rock and roll jamboree benefiting American Heart Association, senior recreational festival, groups visiting from preschool to senior high school, grandparent program, wheelchair square dancing. VA approved.

BETHEL PARK

Meadow Crest Inc
1200 Braun Rd, Bethel Park, PA, 15102 (412) 854-5500
Medical Dir/Dir of Nursing Walter Hoover MD.
Licensure Skilled Care. *Beds* 50.
Ownership Proprietary.
Staff RNs 4 (ft), 4 (pt); LPNs 1 (ft), 4 (pt); Nurses aides 13 (ft), 8 (pt); Physical therapists 1 (pt); Activities coordinators 1 (ft).
Activities Arts and Crafts; Cards; Games; Reading groups; Prayer groups; Movies; Dances/Social or cultural gatherings.

BETHLEHEM

Blough Nursing Home Inc
316 E Market St, Bethlehem, PA, 18042 (215) 868-4982
Medical Dir/Dir of Nursing Jack Cole MD.
Licensure Skilled Care. *Beds* 41. *Certified* Medicare.
Ownership Proprietary.
Staff RNs 2 (ft); LPNs 2 (ft), 3 (pt); Nurses aides 11 (ft), 5 (pt); Activities coordinators 1 (ft).
Facilities Dining room; Physical therapy room; Activities room; Laundry room; Barber/Beauty shop.
Activities Arts and Crafts; Games; Reading groups; Prayer groups; Movies; Shopping trips; Dances/Social or cultural gatherings.
Description Facility offers very personal care and a home environment for residents; believes in meeting the total needs of patients.

Cedarbrook Fountain Hill Annex*
724 Delaware Ave, Bethlehem, PA, 18015 (215) 691-6700
Licensure Skilled Care. *Beds* 197. *Certified* Medicaid; Medicare.
Ownership Nonprofit.

Holy Family Manor
1200 Spring St, Bethlehem, PA, 18018 (215) 865-5595
Licensure Skilled Care; Intermediate Care.
Beds SNF 158; ICF 40. *Certified* Medicaid; Medicare.
Ownership Nonprofit.
Affiliation Roman Catholic

Leader Nursing and Rehabilitation Center*
Westgate and Catasauqua Dr, Bethlehem, PA,
18017 (215) 865-6077
Licensure Skilled Care; Intermediate Care.
Beds SNF 199; ICF 14. *Certified* Medicaid;
Medicare.
Ownership Proprietary.

Murlenberg Medical Center
Schoenersville Rd, Bethlehem, PA, 18017 (215)
861-2203
Licensure Skilled Care. *Beds* 22. *Certified* Medicaid; Medicare.
Ownership Nonprofit.

BLOOMSBURG

Bloomsburg Health Care Center*
211 E 1st St, Bloomsburg, PA, 17815 (717)
784-5930
Licensure Skilled Care. *Beds* 85. *Certified* Medicaid.
Ownership Proprietary.

BLUE BALL

Wetzler Convalescent Home Inc*
Box 115, Blue Ball, PA, 17506 (717) 354-7601
Licensure Skilled Care. *Beds* 17. *Certified* Medicaid.
Ownership Proprietary.

BOOTHWYN

Longwood Villa Geriatric Nursing Center*
1194 Naamans Creek Rd, Boothwyn, PA,
19061 (215) 459-9150
Licensure Skilled Care. *Beds* 53. *Certified* Medicaid.
Ownership Proprietary.

BRACKENRIDGE

Georgian Manor*
1050 Broadview Blvd, Brackenridge, PA, 15014
(412) 224-9200
Licensure Skilled Care. *Beds* 97. *Certified* Medicaid; Medicare.
Ownership Proprietary.

BRADFORD

Bradford Nursing Pavilion*
200 Pleasant St, Bradford, PA, 16701 (814)
362-4533
Licensure Skilled Care. *Beds* 95. *Certified* Medicaid; Medicare.
Ownership Nonprofit.

Dresser Memorial Presbyterian Home*
149 Jackson Ave, Bradford, PA, 16701 (814)
362-5585
Licensure Intermediate Care. *Beds* 32. *Certified* Medicaid.
Ownership Nonprofit.
Affiliation Presbyterian

Hannum Memorial Rest Home Inc
139 Minard Run Rd, Bradford, PA, 16701
(814) 368-5648
Admin Deborah M Sprague.
Licensure Intermediate Care. *Beds* 34. *Certified* Medicaid.
Ownership Nonprofit.
Staff Physicians 1 (pt); RNs 2 (ft), 2 (pt); LPNs
1 (ft), 2 (pt); Nurses aides 8 (ft), 4 (pt); Physical
therapists 1 (pt); Speech therapists 1 (pt);
Activities coordinators 1 (ft); Dietitians 1 (pt);
Podiatrists 1 (pt); Audiologists 1 (pt).
Affiliation Baptist
Facilities Dining room; Activities room; Laundry room; Barber/Beauty shop.
Activities Arts and Crafts; Cards; Games;
Reading groups; Movies; Shopping trips; Dances/Social or cultural gatherings.

Ramsbottom Center Inc*
800 E Main St, Bradford, PA, 16701 (814)
362-7401
Licensure Intermediate Care for Mentally
Retarded. *Beds* 24. *Certified* Medicaid.
Ownership Nonprofit.

BRIDGEVILLE

Mayview State Hospital*
Bridgeville, PA, 15017 (412) 221-7500
Licensure Intermediate Care for Mentally
Retarded. *Beds* 120. *Certified* Medicaid.
Ownership Public.

**Mayview State Hospital—Long Term Care
Unit**
Bridgeville, PA, 15017 (412) 343-2700
Admin Joan Malarbey. *Medical Dir/Dir of
Nursing* Charles L Squires MD.
Licensure Intermediate Care. *Beds* 184. *Certified* Medicaid.
Ownership Public.
Staff Physicians 2 (ft); RNs 17 (ft), 1 (pt);
LPNs 9 (ft); Nurses aides 70 (ft).
Facilities Dining room; Activities room; Chapel; Crafts room; Laundry room; Barber/Beauty
shop; Conference room.
Activities Arts and Crafts; Cards; Games;
Reading groups; Prayer groups; Movies; Shopping trips; Dances/Social or cultural gatherings;
Bowling.

BRISTOL

Medicenter of America—Bristol*
King St and Fayette Dr, Bristol, PA, 19007
(215) 785-3201
Licensure Skilled Care. *Beds* 174. *Certified* Medicaid; Medicare.
Ownership Proprietary.

BROMALL

Broomall Nursing Home
43 Church Ln, Bromall, PA, 19008 (215)
356-3003
Medical Dir/Dir of Nursing David S Ceshel
DO.
Licensure Skilled Care. *Beds* 126. *Certified* Medicaid; Medicare.
Ownership Proprietary.

Admissions Requirements Minimum age 60.
Staff RNs 5 (ft), 9 (pt); LPNs 6 (ft); Nurses
aides 38 (ft), 10 (pt); Physical therapists 2 (ft);
Reality therapists 1 (pt); Recreational therapists
2 (ft); Occupational therapists 2 (ft); Speech
therapists 1 (pt); Activities coordinators 1 (pt);
Dietitians 1 (ft); Podiatrists 1 (pt).
Facilities Dining room; Physical therapy room;
Activities room; Crafts room; Laundry room;
Barber/Beauty shop; Occupational therapy; TV
rooms; Solarium; Garden.
Activities Arts and Crafts; Cards; Games;
Reading groups; Prayer groups; Movies; Shopping trips; Dances/Social or cultural gatherings;
Bazars; Nutrition class; Hoagie parties; Special
masses.
Description Facility includes a south wing for
patients who require 24-hour nursing care and a
north wing for healthier patients.

BROOKVILLE

Jefferson Manor*
Rt 5, Brookville, PA, 15825 (814) 849-2386
Licensure Skilled Care; Intermediate Care.
Beds SNF 112; ICF 112. *Certified* Medicaid.
Ownership Nonprofit.

Pennsylvania Memorial Home*
51 Euclid Ave, Brookville, PA, 15825 (814)
849-2368
Licensure Skilled Care; Intermediate Care.
Beds SNF 51; ICF 49. *Certified* Medicaid;
Medicare.
Ownership Nonprofit.

BROOMALL

Broomall Nursing Home
43 Church Ln, Broomall, PA, 19008
Admin Rosemary Kuhlman. *Medical Dir/Dir
of Nursing* Dr David Ashel.
Licensure Skilled Care; Intermediate Care.
Beds 126. *Certified* Medicaid; Medicare.
Ownership Proprietary.
Admissions Requirements Minimum age 75.
Staff RNs; LPNs; Orderlies; Nurses aides;
Physical therapists; Recreational therapists;
Occupational therapists; Speech therapists;
Activities coordinators; Dietitians; Audiologists.
Facilities Dining room; Physical therapy room;
Activities room; Crafts room; Laundry room;
Barber/Beauty shop.
Activities Arts and Crafts; Cards; Games;
Reading groups; Prayer groups; Movies; Shopping trips; Dances/Social or cultural gatherings.
Description Facility offers full range of rehabilitation services, recreational activities, and
nutritional services to aid the skilled and intermediate level patients reach and maintain full
potential.

Broomall Presbyterian Home*
Marple Rd, Broomall, PA, 19008 (215)
356-0100
Licensure Skilled Care. *Beds* 147. *Certified* Medicaid; Medicare.
Ownership Nonprofit.
Affiliation Presbyterian

Rest Haven Convalescent Home*
Malin Rd, Broomall, PA, 19008 (215) 356-0800
Licensure Skilled Care. *Beds* 250. *Certified* Medicaid; Medicare.
Ownership Proprietary.

BROWNSVILLE

Brownsville Golden Age*
501 Church St, Brownsville, PA, 15417 (412) 785-3900
Licensure Skilled Care. *Beds* 68. *Certified* Medicaid; Medicare.
Ownership Proprietary.

BRYN MAWR

Bryn Mawr Terrace Convalescent
Haverford and Rugby Rds, Bryn Mawr, PA, 19010 (215) 525-8300
Licensure Skilled Care. *Beds* 160. *Certified* Medicare.
Ownership Proprietary.

Chateau Convalescent Center*
956 Railroad Ave amd Polo Rd, Bryn Mawr, PA, 19010 (215) 525-8412
Licensure Skilled Care. *Beds* 152. *Certified* Medicaid; Medicare.
Ownership Proprietary.

BUCKINGHAM

Buckingham Valley Nursing Home*
PO Box 447, Buckingham, PA, 18912 (215) 598-7781
Licensure Skilled Care. *Beds* 100. *Certified* Medicaid; Medicare.
Ownership Proprietary.

BUTLER

Sunny View Home*
Freeport Rd, Butler, PA, 16001 (412) 282-1800
Licensure Skilled Care; Intermediate Care.
Beds SNF 120; ICF 120. *Certified* Medicaid; Medicare.
Ownership Nonprofit.

CABOT

Lutheran Welfare Concordia Home*
Rt 1, Cabot, PA, 16023 (412) 352-1571
Licensure Skilled Care; Intermediate Care.
Beds SNF 59; ICF 67. *Certified* Medicaid.
Ownership Nonprofit.
Affiliation Lutheran

CAMBRIDGE SPRINGS

Presbyterian Home—Cambridge Springs*
229 N Main St, Cambridge Springs, PA, 16403 (814) 398-2813
Licensure Intermediate Care. *Beds* 10. *Certified* Medicaid.
Ownership Nonprofit.
Affiliation Presbyterian

Springs Manor
110 Canfield St, Cambridge Springs, PA, 16403 (814) 398-4626
Medical Dir/Dir of Nursing Dr Edward Owens.
Licensure Skilled Care. *Beds* 86. *Certified* Medicaid; Medicare.
Ownership Proprietary.
Admissions Requirements Medical examination; Physician's request.
Staff Physicians 1 (ft); RNs 1 (ft); LPNs 1 (ft); Nurses aides 1 (ft), 1 (pt); Physical therapists 1 (ft); Occupational therapists 1 (pt); Speech therapists 1 (pt); Activities coordinators 1 (ft); Dietitians 1 (ft); Dentists 1 (pt); Ophthalmologists 1 (pt); Podiatrists 1 (pt); Audiologists 1 (pt).
Facilities Dining room; Physical therapy room; Activities room; Chapel; Crafts room; Laundry room; Barber/Beauty shop.
Activities Arts and Crafts; Cards; Games; Reading groups; Prayer groups; Movies; Bowling league.
Description Springs Manor is located in a quiet neighborhood in a small rural town with a population of approximately 2100, 25 miles south of Erie with acccss to 3 major hospitals there. Young people from nearby Edinboro University of Pennsylvania and Allegheny College contribute much to an ever-growing activities program.

CAMP HILL

Blue Ridge Haven Convalescent Center West*
770 Poplar Church Rd, Camp Hill, PA, 17011 (717) 763-7070
Licensure Skilled Care; Intermediate Care.
Beds SNF 120; ICF 214. *Certified* Medicaid; Medicare.
Ownership Proprietary.

Camp Hill Nursing and Convalescent Center Inc*
46 Erford Rd, Camp Hill, PA, 17011 (717) 238-0411
Licensure Skilled Care; Intermediate Care.
Beds SNF 60; ICF 58. *Certified* Medicaid; Medicare.
Ownership Proprietary.

Leader Nursing and Rehabilitation Center
1700 Market St, Camp Hill, PA, 17011 (717) 737-4650
Admin Elizabeth O Middleworth. *Medical Dir/Dir of Nursing* Earl Moyer MD.
Licensure Skilled Care. *Beds* 60. *Certified* Medicaid; Medicare.
Ownership Proprietary.
Admissions Requirements Medical examination.
Staff RNs 4 (ft), 6 (pt); LPNs 3 (ft), 3 (pt); Nurses aides 17 (ft), 15 (pt); Physical therapists 2 (pt); Occupational therapists 1 (pt); Speech therapists 1 (pt); Activities coordinators 2 (pt); Dietitians 1 (pt); Dentists 1 (pt); Podiatrists 1 (pt); Audiologists 1 (pt).
Facilities Dining room; Physical therapy room; Activities room; Chapel; Crafts room; Laundry room; Barber/Beauty shop; Library; Lounge.
Activities Arts and Crafts; Cards; Games; Reading groups; Prayer groups; Movies; Shopping trips.

Description The staff's priority is to rehabilitate the residents so that they can go home and function as they did prior to their illness.

CAMPBELLTOWN

Twin Oaks Nursing Home*
90 W Main St, Campbelltown, PA, 17010 (717) 838-2231
Licensure Skilled Care. *Beds* 42. *Certified* Medicaid.
Ownership Proprietary.

CANNONSBURG

South Hills Convalescent Center
201 Village Dr, Cannonsburg, PA, 15317 (412) 341-9191
Medical Dir/Dir of Nursing Robert G Lesnock MD.
Licensure Skilled Care. *Beds* 104. *Certified* Medicaid; Medicare.
Ownership Proprietary.
Admissions Requirements Minimum age 18; Medical examination.
Staff Physicians 1 (ft); RNs 7 (ft), 5 (pt); LPNs 6 (ft), 13 (pt); Nurses aides 32 (ft), 21 (pt); Physical therapists 1 (pt); Speech therapists 1 (pt); Activities coordinators 1 (ft); Dietitians 1 (pt).
Facilities Dining room; Physical therapy room; Activities room; Chapel; Crafts room; Laundry room; Barber/Beauty shop; Library.
Activities Arts and Crafts; Cards; Games; Reading groups; Prayer groups; Movies; Shopping trips; Dances/Social or cultural gatherings.
Description Center provides high quality skilled nursing care to the elderly community of the tri-county area; located in a lovely rural setting minutes from downtown.

CANONSBURG

Western Center*
333 Curry Hill Rd, Canonsburg, PA, 15317 (412) 745-0700
Licensure Intermediate Care for Mentally Retarded. *Beds* 474. *Certified* Medicaid.
Ownership Nonprofit.

CARBONDALE

Carbondale Nursing Home Inc
57 N Main St, Carbondale, PA, 18407 (717) 282-1020
Medical Dir/Dir of Nursing Dr John W Keyes.
Licensure Skilled Care. *Beds* 105. *Certified* Medicaid; Medicare.
Ownership Proprietary.
Staff Physicians 1 (ft), 6 (pt); RNs 10 (ft); LPNs 15 (ft); Orderlies 6 (ft); Nurses aides 15 (ft); Physical therapists 2 (pt); Recreational therapists 1 (ft); Occupational therapists 2 (pt); Speech therapists 2 (pt); Activities coordinators 1 (ft); Dietitians 1 (pt); Dentists 1 (pt); Podiatrists 1 (pt).

CARLISLE

Alliance Home of Carlisle
770 S Hanover St, Carlisle, PA, 17013 (717)
249-1363
Licensure Skilled Care. *Beds* 30. *Certified* Medicaid.
Ownership Nonprofit.

Church of God Home
801 Harrisburg Pike, Carlisle, PA, 17013 (717)
249-5322
Medical Dir/Dir of Nursing Dr Kenneth Guistwite.
Licensure Skilled Care. *Beds* 79. *Certified* Medicaid.
Ownership Nonprofit.
Admissions Requirements Medical examination.
Staff Physicians 1 (pt); RNs 10 (ft); LPNs 6 (ft); Nurses aides 39 (ft), 8 (pt); Reality therapists 1 (ft); Occupational therapists 1 (ft); Activities coordinators 2 (ft); Dietitians 1 (ft).
Affiliation Church of God

Cumberland County Home*
Box 50, Rt 10, Carlisle, PA, 17013 (717)
243-2031
Licensure Skilled Care; Intermediate Care.
Beds SNF 195; ICF 192. *Certified* Medicaid.
Ownership Nonprofit.

Forest Park Nursing Home
700 Walnut Bottom Rd, Carlisle, PA, 17013
(717) 243-1032
Medical Dir/Dir of Nursing Dr Harold Krelzing.
Licensure Skilled Care; Intermediate Care.
Beds SNF 66; ICF 34. *Certified* Medicaid; Medicare.
Ownership Proprietary.
Staff RNs 5 (ft), 6 (pt); LPNs 3 (ft), 2 (pt); Nurses aides 34 (ft), 11 (pt); Physical therapists 1 (ft); Speech therapists 1 (pt); Activities coordinators 1 (ft).
Affiliation Presbyterian
Facilities Dining room; Physical therapy room; Activities room; Laundry room; Barber/Beauty shop.
Activities Arts and Crafts; Games; Reading groups; Prayer groups; Movies.

Sarah A Todd Memorial Home Inc
50 Mooreland Ave, Carlisle, PA, 17013 (717)
249-1614
Admin Dorothy E Kline. *Medical Dir/Dir of Nursing* Dr K Guistwite.
Licensure Skilled Care; Intermediate Care; Licensed Personal Care Boarding Home.
Beds SNF 11; ICF 17; Personal Care Boarding Home 42; Independant Living Cottages 25.
Certified Medicaid.
Ownership Nonprofit.
Admissions Requirements Medical examination; Physician's request.
Facilities Dining room; Physical therapy room; Activities room; Laundry room; Barber/Beauty shop.
Activities Arts and Crafts; Cards; Games; Reading groups; Prayer groups; Movies; Dances/Social or cultural gatherings.

Thornwald Home*
422 Walnut Bottom Rd, Carlisle, PA, 17013
(717) 249-4118
Licensure Skilled Care. *Beds* 79. *Certified* Medicaid.
Ownership Nonprofit.

CARNEGIE

Step by Step Inc*
112 7th Ave, Carnegie, PA, 15106 (412)
279-8943
Licensure Intermediate Care for Mentally Retarded. *Beds* 8. *Certified* Medicaid.
Ownership Nonprofit.

CHAMBERSBURG

Franklin County Nursing Home*
201 Franklin Farm Ln, Chambersburg, PA,
17201 (717) 264-2715
Licensure Skilled Care; Intermediate Care.
Beds SNF 17; ICF 191. *Certified* Medicaid.
Ownership Nonprofit.

John H Shook Home
55 S 2nd St, PO Box 226, Chambersburg, PA,
17201 (717) 264-6815
Licensure Intermediate Care. *Beds* 64. *Certified* Medicaid.
Ownership Nonprofit.
Admissions Requirements Minimum age 65; Medical examination.
Staff RNs 2 (ft); LPNs 7 (ft), 6 (pt); Nurses aides 10 (ft), 7 (pt); Activities coordinators 2 (ft), 2 (pt); Dietitians 1 (pt).
Facilities Dining room; Activities room; Chapel; Crafts room; Laundry room; Barber/Beauty shop.
Activities Arts and Crafts; Games; Reading groups; Movies; Shopping trips; Church and Sunday school classes.
Description The Shook Home is an intermediate care nursing facility offering long-term health care to those requiring assistance and supervision in their daily living. Professional nursing services are provided on a 24-hour basis with registered nurses and/or licensed practical nurses on duty at all times.

Leader Nursing and Rehabilitation Center—Chambersburg*
1070 Stouffer Ave, Chambersburg, PA, 17201
(717) 263-9463
Licensure Skilled Care; Intermediate Care.
Beds SNF 120; ICF 60. *Certified* Medicaid; Medicare.
Ownership Proprietary.

Menno Haven Inc
2075 Scotland Ave, Chambersburg, PA, 17201
(717) 263-8545
Medical Dir/Dir of Nursing George Rahauser MD.
Licensure Skilled Care. *Beds* 129. *Certified* Medicaid; Medicare.
Ownership Nonprofit.
Staff Physicians 4 (pt); RNs 11 (ft); LPNs 12 (ft); Orderlies 9 (ft); Nurses aides 39 (ft); Physical therapists 2 (pt); Reality therapists 1 (pt); Recreational therapists 1 (pt); Occupational therapists 1 (pt); Speech therapists 1 (pt); Activities coordinators 1 (ft); Dietitians 1 (ft); Podiatrists 1 (pt).
Facilities Dining room; Physical therapy room; Activities room; Chapel; Crafts room; Laundry room; Barber/Beauty shop; Library.
Activities Arts and Crafts; Cards; Games; Reading groups; Prayer groups; Movies; Shopping trips.

CHATHAM

Chatham Acres*
Box 1, London Grove Rd, Chatham, PA, 19318
(215) 869-2456
Licensure Skilled Care. *Beds* 127. *Certified* Medicaid.
Ownership Proprietary.

CHESTER

The Belvedere
2507 Chestnut St, Chester, PA, 19013 (215)
872-5373
Medical Dir/Dir of Nursing Barry Holms DO.
Licensure Skilled Care. *Beds* 120.
Ownership Proprietary.
Staff Physicians; RNs; LPNs; Orderlies; Nurses aides; Physical therapists; Occupational therapists; Speech therapists; Activities coordinators; Dietitians; Dentists; Ophthalmologists; Podiatrists; Audiologists.
Facilities Dining room; Physical therapy room; Activities room; Laundry room; Barber/Beauty shop; Lounges.
Activities Arts and Crafts; Cards; Games; Reading groups; Prayer groups; Movies; Shopping trips; Dances/Social or cultural gatherings.
Description New construction, just completed, has more than tripled space and updated all service facilities. The heart remains a beautiful, pre-Civil War mansion. Emphasis is on the psycho-social aspects of care along with nursing and medical.

Chester Care Center
15th and Shaw Terrace, Chester, PA, 19013
(215) 876-7241
Medical Dir/Dir of Nursing Dr Leonard Haltrecht.
Licensure Skilled Care; Intermediate Care; Personal Care. *Beds* 190. *Certified* Medicaid; Medicare.
Ownership Proprietary.
Admissions Requirements Minimum age 16.
Staff RNs 15 (pt); LPNs 3 (pt); Orderlies 5 (pt); Nurses aides 63 (pt); Physical therapists 2 (pt); Recreational therapists 3 (pt); Occupational therapists 1 (pt); Speech therapists 1 (pt); Activities coordinators 1 (pt); Dietitians 1 (ft); Audiologists 1 (pt).
Facilities Dining room; Physical therapy room; Activities room; Laundry room; Barber/Beauty shop.
Activities Arts and Crafts; Games; Reading groups; Prayer groups; Movies; Shopping trips.

Chester Care Center
210 W 14th St, Chester, PA, 19013
Admin Aubrey C Smith. *Medical Dir/Dir of Nursing* Dr Leonard Haltrecht.

Licensure Intermediate Care. *Beds* 97. *Certified* Medicaid.
Ownership Proprietary.
Admissions Requirements Medical examination.
Staff Physicians 8 (pt); RNs 1 (pt); LPNs 9 (ft), 12 (pt); Orderlies 3 (ft), 1 (pt); Nurses aides 27 (ft), 20 (pt); Physical therapists 1 (pt); Reality therapists 1 (pt); Recreational therapists 1 (pt); Occupational therapists 1 (pt); Speech therapists 1 (pt); Activities coordinators 1 (ft); Dietitians 1 (pt); Podiatrists 1 (pt).
Facilities Dining room; Physical therapy room; Activities room; Crafts room; Laundry room; Barber/Beauty shop; Library.
Activities Arts and Crafts; Cards; Games; Reading groups; Prayer groups; Movies; Shopping trips; Dances/Social or cultural gatherings.

CHESTNUT HILL

Fairview Nursing Home of Papermill
850 Paper Mill Rd, Chestnut Hill, PA, 19118 (215) 247-0595
Admin June Hudak. *Medical Dir/Dir of Nursing* Louis A Pegel MD.
Licensure Skilled Care. *Beds* 144. *Certified* Medicaid; Medicare.
Ownership Proprietary.
Staff Physicians 15 (pt); Physical therapists 1 (ft), 1 (pt); Recreational therapists 2 (ft), 1 (pt); Occupational therapists 1 (pt); Speech therapists 1 (pt); Activities coordinators 1 (ft); Dietitians 1 (pt); Dentists 1 (pt); Ophthalmologists 1 (pt); Podiatrists 3 (pt).
Facilities Dining room; Physical therapy room; Activities room; Crafts room; Laundry room; Barber/Beauty shop.
Activities Arts and Crafts; Cards; Games; Reading groups; Prayer groups; Movies; Shopping trips; Dances/Social or cultural gatherings.

Harston Hall Nursing Home Inc*
350 Haws Ln, Chestnut Hill, PA, 19118 (215) 233-0700
Licensure Skilled Care. *Beds* 72. *Certified* Medicaid.
Ownership Proprietary.

CHESWICK

Valley View Nursing Home
RD 2, Box 234, Cheswick, PA, 15024 (412) 767-4998
Medical Dir/Dir of Nursing Dr Nick Bourdakos.
Licensure Skilled Care. *Beds* 128. *Certified* Medicaid.
Ownership Proprietary.
Facilities Dining room; Physical therapy room; Crafts room; Laundry room; Barber/Beauty shop.
Activities Arts and Crafts; Cards; Games; Reading groups; Prayer groups; Movies; Dances/Social or cultural gatherings; Adopt-a-grandparent program; Music therapy; Pet therapy; Plant therapy.
Description Valley View is located in a rural wooded area, 7 miles outside of Pittsburgh. It is close to all major roads including the Pennsylvania Turnpike and Route 28 Expressway.

CHICORA

Chicora Medical Center Inc
Rt 2, Chicora, PA, 16025 (412) 445-2000
Admin Yvonne De Bacco. *Medical Dir/Dir of Nursing* E P Molchany MD.
Licensure Skilled Care. *Beds* 60. *Certified* Medicaid; Medicare.
Ownership Proprietary.
Admissions Requirements Minimum age 16.
Staff RNs 4 (ft), 1 (pt); LPNs 4 (ft); Nurses aides 22 (ft), 4 (pt); Physical therapists 1 (ft); Recreational therapists 1 (ft); Speech therapists 1 (ft); Activities coordinators 1 (ft); Dietitians 1 (ft); Dentists 1 (pt); Ophthalmologists 1 (pt); Podiatrists 1 (pt); Audiologists 1 (ft).
Facilities Dining room; Physical therapy room; Activities room; Laundry room; Barber/Beauty shop; Library.
Activities Arts and Crafts; Cards; Games; Movies; Shopping trips.

CHRISTIANA

Harrison House
41 Newport Pike, Christiana, PA, 17509 (219) 593-6901
Medical Dir/Dir of Nursing Paul W Herr DO.
Licensure Skilled Care. *Beds* 139. *Certified* Medicaid; Medicare.
Ownership Proprietary.
Admissions Requirements Minimum age 16.
Staff RNs 3 (ft), 10 (pt); LPNs 5 (ft), 10 (pt); Nurses aides 24 (ft), 58 (pt); Activities coordinators 2 (ft); Dietitians 1 (ft); Physical therapists; Occupational therapists; Speech therapists.
Facilities Dining room; Physical therapy room; Activities room; Chapel; Crafts room; Laundry room; Barber/Beauty shop; Greenhouse.
Activities Arts and Crafts; Cards; Games; Reading groups; Prayer groups; Movies; Shopping trips; Dances/Social or cultural gatherings; Church; Sunday school.
Description Facility is located in a lovely small town/rural setting in southeastern Lancaster County.

CLAIRTON

Beatrice Lawson Nursing Home Inc*
540 Coal Valley Rd, Clairton, PA, 15025 (412) 466-8448
Licensure Skilled Care. *Beds* 55.
Ownership Proprietary.

CLARION

Clarion Medical Services*
999 Heidrick St, Clarion, PA, 16214 (814) 226-6380
Licensure Skilled Care. *Beds* 73. *Certified* Medicaid; Medicare.
Ownership Proprietary.

CLARKS SUMMIT

Clarks Summit State Hospital—Long Term Care Facility*
Clarks Summit, PA, 18411 (717) 586-2011
Licensure Skilled Care. *Beds* 179. *Certified* Medicaid.
Ownership Nonprofit.

White Haven Annex at Clark Summit*
Clark Summit State Hospital, Clarks Summit, PA, 18411 (717) 586-2011
Licensure Intermediate Care. *Beds* 52. *Certified* Medicaid.
Ownership Nonprofit.

CLEARFIELD

Clear Haven Nursing Center*
700 Leonard St, Clearfield, PA, 16830 (814) 765-7546
Licensure Skilled Care; Intermediate Care. *Beds* SNF 82; ICF 160. *Certified* Medicaid; Medicare.
Ownership Proprietary.

COALDALE

Coaldale State General Hospital*
7th St, Coaldale, PA, 18218 (717) 645-2131
Licensure Skilled Care. *Beds* 48. *Certified* Medicaid; Medicare.
Ownership Nonprofit.

COATESVILLE

Embreeville State Hospital*
Rt 162, Coatesville, PA, 19320 (215) 486-0800
Licensure Intermediate Care for Mentally Retarded. *Beds* 313. *Certified* Medicaid.
Ownership Public.

COLUMBIA

Heatherbank
745 Chiques Hill Rd, Columbia, PA, 17512 (717) 684-7555
Medical Dir/Dir of Nursing Ray Wilson MD.
Licensure Skilled Care; Intermediate Care. *Beds* SNF 139; ICF 41. *Certified* Medicaid; Medicare.
Ownership Proprietary.
Facilities Dining room; Physical therapy room; Activities room; Crafts room; Laundry room; Barber/Beauty shop; Library; Solarium; TV lounges; Smoking area.
Description Facility has a comprehensive patient care management system to develop an individualized plan of care to meet patients' needs and periodic evaluation of care outcome. It is developed and implemented by the interdisciplinary health care team using a client-centered approach, measureable goals and intergrated services.

Saint Anne's Home
RD 2, Columbia, PA, 17512 (717) 285-5443
Admin Sr M Carmela Ginto.
Licensure Skilled Care; Intermediate Care. *Beds* SNF 44; ICF 77. *Certified* Medicaid;

Medicare.
Ownership Nonprofit.
Admissions Requirements Medical examination.
Staff RNs 3 (ft), 5 (pt); LPNs 14 (ft), 11 (pt); Nurses aides 26 (ft), 19 (pt); Physical therapists 1 (pt); Reality therapists 1 (pt); Occupational therapists 1 (ft); Activities coordinators 1 (ft); Dietitians 1 (pt).
Affiliation Roman Catholic
Facilities Dining room; Physical therapy room; Activities room; Chapel; Crafts room; Laundry room; Barber/Beauty shop; Library; Gift shop.
Activities Arts and Crafts; Cards; Games; Reading groups; Prayer groups; Movies; Musical entertainments; Dinner trips.
Description The purpose of St Anne's Home is to provide its guest with a care which reflects the loving concern of Christ for His own. Together the entire staff forms the serving body, which through its united efforts, tells the guests of our concern for all aspects of their being: spiritual, psychological, emotional, social, and physical.

CONCORDVILLE

Concord Villa Convalescent
US Rt 1, Scott Rd, Concordville, PA, 19331 (215) 459-2900
Medical Dir/Dir of Nursing LaFenus Hutchins MD.
Licensure Skilled Care. *Beds* 101. *Certified* Medicare.
Ownership Proprietary.
Admissions Requirements Minimum age 18.
Staff Physicians 4 (pt); RNs 9 (ft), 4 (pt); LPNs 3 (ft); Recreational therapists 1 (ft), 1 (pt); Occupational therapists 1 (pt); Speech therapists 1 (pt); Dietitians 1 (pt); Dentists 1 (pt); Podiatrists 1 (pt).
Facilities Dining room; Physical therapy room; Activities room; Crafts room; Laundry room; Barber/Beauty shop.
Activities Arts and Crafts; Cards; Games; Movies.

CONNEAUTVILLE

Rolling Fields Nursing Home Inc*
Rt 2, Conneautville, PA, 16406 (814) 587-2012
Licensure Skilled Care. *Beds* 121. *Certified* Medicaid.
Ownership Proprietary.

COOPERSBURG

American Medical Nursing Centers—Valley Manor*
PO Box 163, Coopersburg, PA, 18036 (215) 282-1919
Licensure Skilled Care; Intermediate Care.
Beds SNF 120; ICF 59. *Certified* Medicaid; Medicare.
Ownership Nonprofit.

CORAOPOLIS

Allegheny Valley School for Exceptional Children*
1992 Ewing Mill Rd, Coraopolis, PA, 15108 (412) 262-3500
Licensure Intermediate Care for Mentally Retarded. *Beds* 160. *Certified* Medicaid.
Ownership Nonprofit.

Allegheny Valley School Group Home*
1992 Ewing Mill Rd, Coraopolis, PA, 15108 (412) 262-3500
Licensure Intermediate Care for Mentally Retarded. *Beds* 9. *Certified* Medicaid.
Ownership Nonprofit.

CORNWALL

Cornwall Manor of the United Methodist Church
Pleasant View Health Center, Cornwall, PA, 17016 (717) 273-2647
Medical Dir/Dir of Nursing Dr Robert Nielsen.
Licensure Skilled Care. *Beds* 75. *Certified* Medicaid; Medicare.
Ownership Nonprofit.
Admissions Requirements Medical examination; Physician's request.
Staff Physicians 3 (pt); RNs 4 (ft), 5 (pt); LPNs 20 (ft), 9 (pt); Orderlies 1 (pt); Nurses aides 30 (ft), 13 (pt); Physical therapists 1 (pt); Activities coordinators 2 (ft); Dietitians 1 (ft).
Affiliation Methodist
Facilities Dining room; Physical therapy room; Activities room; Chapel; Laundry room; Barber/Beauty shop; Library.
Activities Arts and Crafts; Cards; Games; Reading groups; Prayer groups; Movies; Shopping trips; Dances/Social or cultural gatherings.
Description Facility provides short-term rehabilitation and respite care as well as long-term care; also has a retirement community with cottages, apartments, and suites available for those capable of independent living.

CORNWELL HEIGHTS

Muffett Nursing Home
958 Flushing Rd, Cornwell Heights, PA, 19020 (215) 639-3568
Licensure Skilled Care. *Beds* 23.
Ownership Proprietary.

CORRY

Corry Manor Nursing Home
640 Worth St, Corry, PA, 16407 (814) 664-9606
Medical Dir/Dir of Nursing Dr John E Brown.
Licensure Skilled Care. *Beds* 121. *Certified* Medicaid.
Ownership Proprietary.
Admissions Requirements Medical examination.
Staff RNs; LPNs; Orderlies; Nurses aides; Physical therapists 1 (pt); Speech therapists 1 (pt); Activities coordinators 1 (ft), 1 (pt).
Facilities Dining room; Physical therapy room; Activities room; Crafts room; Laundry room; Barber/Beauty shop; Library; Patios; Lounges; Soda shop.
Activities Arts and Crafts; Cards; Games; Reading groups; Prayer groups; Movies; Dances/Social or cultural gatherings; Bowling; Bingo; Nail clinic.
Description Building is surrounded by woodland. Activity program is varied. Trained staff supplies much love.

COUDERSPORT

Charles Cole Memorial Hospital-ECF*
Rd 3, Coudersport, PA, 16915 (814) 274-9300
Licensure Skilled Care; Intermediate Care.
Beds SNF 32; ICF 50. *Certified* Medicaid; Medicare.
Ownership Nonprofit.

CRESSON

Cresson Center
Rt 22, Cresson, PA, 16630 (814) 886-8111
Licensure Intermediate Care for Mentally Retarded. *Beds* 232. *Certified* Medicaid.
Ownership Nonprofit.

DALLAS

Carpenter Nursing Home
Rt 4, Box 357, Dallas, PA, 18612 (717) 639-1885
Medical Dir/Dir of Nursing Dr Gary Smith.
Licensure Skilled Care. *Beds* 30. *Certified* Medicaid.
Ownership Proprietary.
Admissions Requirements Minimum age 56.
Staff Physicians 4 (pt); RNs 2 (ft); LPNs 4 (pt); Physical therapists 1 (pt); Reality therapists 1 (ft); Recreational therapists 1 (pt); Occupational therapists 1 (pt); Speech therapists 1 (pt); Activities coordinators 1 (ft); Dietitians 1 (pt); Dentists 1 (pt); Ophthalmologists 1 (pt); Podiatrists 1 (pt); Audiologists 1 (pt).
Facilities Dining room; Physical therapy room; Activities room; Crafts room; Laundry room.
Activities Arts and Crafts; Cards; Games; Reading groups; Prayer groups; Movies; Shopping trips; Dances/Social or cultural gatherings.
Description Facility located ¼ mile from Harvey's Lake; beautiful scenic setting; excellent boating and fishing.

Maple Hill Nursing Home*
Rt 2, Dallas, PA, 18612 (717) 675-1787
Licensure Skilled Care. *Beds* 24. *Certified* Medicaid.
Ownership Proprietary.

DALLASTOWN

Leader Nursing and Rehabilitation Center*
100 W Queen St, Dallastown, PA, 17313 (717) 246-1671
Licensure Skilled Care; Intermediate Care.
Beds SNF 120; ICF 60. *Certified* Medicaid; Medicare.
Ownership Proprietary.

Seitz Nursing Home
623 E Main St, Dallastown, PA, 17313 (717) 244-2295
Admin Sylvia Snyder. *Medical Dir/Dir of Nursing* Dr Edward F Holland.
Licensure Skilled Care. *Beds* 24.
Ownership Proprietary.
Admissions Requirements Minimum age 16; Medical examination.
Staff RNs 2 (ft), 2 (pt); LPNs 3 (pt); Recreational therapists 1 (pt); Activities coordinators 1 (pt); Dietitians 1 (pt).
Facilities Dining room; Activities room; Chapel; Crafts room.
Activities Arts and Crafts; Cards; Games; Prayer groups.
Description Small facility with private rooms featuring personal care.

DANVILLE

Danville Hospital—Long Term Care Unit*
Danville, PA, 17821 (717) 275-7011
Licensure Skilled Care; Intermediate Care.
Beds SNF 91; ICF 210. *Certified* Medicaid.
Ownership Nonprofit.

Gold Star Nursing Home
School House Rd, Danville, PA, 17821 (717) 275-4946
Licensure Intermediate Care. *Beds* 100. *Certified* Medicaid.
Ownership Proprietary.
Admissions Requirements Medical examination.
Staff Physicians 11 (pt); RNs 4 (ft), 2 (pt); LPNs 6 (ft), 1 (pt); Orderlies 3 (ft); Nurses aides 25 (ft), 1 (pt); Physical therapists 1 (pt); Speech therapists 1 (pt); Activities coordinators 1 (ft); Dietitians 1 (pt); Dentists 1 (pt); Podiatrists 1 (pt); Audiologists 1 (pt).
Facilities Dining room; Physical therapy room; Activities room; Crafts room; Laundry room; Barber/Beauty shop.
Activities Arts and Crafts; Cards; Games; Reading groups; Prayer groups; Movies; Dances/Social or cultural gatherings.

Grand View Health Home
Woodbine Lane, Danville, PA, 17821 (717) 275-5240
Medical Dir/Dir of Nursing Dr Norman Ekberg.
Licensure Skilled Care; Intermediate Care.
Beds SNF 50; ICF 100. *Certified* Medicaid.
Ownership Proprietary.
Admissions Requirements Medical examination.
Staff RNs 5 (ft), 6 (pt); LPNs 6 (ft), 4 (pt); Orderlies 3 (ft); Nurses aides 45 (ft), 4 (pt); Physical therapists 2 (ft); Recreational therapists 2 (ft); Speech therapists 1 (pt); Activities coordinators 2 (ft); Dietitians 1 (pt); Dentists 1 (pt); Podiatrists 1 (pt); Audiologists 1 (pt).
Facilities Dining room; Physical therapy room; Activities room; Chapel; Crafts room; Laundry room; Barber/Beauty shop; Library.
Activities Arts and Crafts; Cards; Games; Reading groups; Prayer groups; Movies; Shopping trips; Dances/Social or cultural gatherings.

Maria Joseph Manor
Rt 11, Bloomsburg Hwy, Danville, PA, 17821 (717) 275-4221
Admin Sr M Jeanetto. *Medical Dir/Dir of Nursing* James A Collins MD.
Licensure Skilled Care. *Beds* 30. *Certified* Medicaid.
Ownership Nonprofit.
Admissions Requirements Minimum age 65; Medical examination.
Staff Physicians 2 (pt); RNs 4 (ft), 2 (pt); LPNs 3 (ft), 3 (pt); Nurses aides 16 (ft), 14 (ft); Physical therapists 1 (pt); Activities coordinators 1 (ft); Dietitians 1 (ft).
Affiliation Roman Catholic
Facilities Dining room; Physical therapy room; Activities room; Chapel; Crafts room; Laundry room; Barber/Beauty shop; Lounges; auditorium.
Activities Arts and Crafts; Cards; Games; Reading groups; Prayer groups; Movies; Shopping trips; Cocktail hour; Ice cream social; Various parties.

DARBY

Little Flower Manor
1201 Springfield Rd, PO Box 190, Darby, PA, 19023 (215) 534-4040
Admin Sr M Nicolette. *Medical Dir/Dir of Nursing* Morris F Guirguis MD.
Licensure Skilled Care. *Beds* 122. *Certified* Medicaid.
Ownership Nonprofit.
Admissions Requirements Medical examination; Physician's request.
Staff Physicians 6 (pt); RNs 7 (ft), 18 (pt); LPNs 3 (ft), 4 (pt); Nurses aides 23 (ft), 49 (pt); Physical therapists 3 (pt); Reality therapists 2 (pt); Recreational therapists 2 (ft); Occupational therapists 1 (ft); Speech therapists 1 (pt); Activities coordinators 1 (ft); Dietitians 1 (ft); Dentists 1 (pt); Ophthalmologists 1 (pt); Podiatrists 1 (pt); Audiologists 1 (pt).
Affiliation Roman Catholic
Description This year, outstanding programs are our art exhibit and talent show. Patients are pleased and happy to participate. Art works are displayed and a write-up in county newspaper brings delight and a sense of worth to residents.

Saint Francis Country Home
14th and Lansdown Ave, Darby, PA, 19023 (215) 461-6510
Medical Dir/Dir of Nursing Edumund Del Guercio MD.
Licensure Skilled Care. *Beds* 318. *Certified* Medicaid; Medicare.
Ownership Nonprofit.
Admissions Requirements Medical examination.
Staff RNs 10 (ft), 10 (pt); LPNs 15 (ft), 15 (pt); Orderlies 5 (ft), 5 (pt); Nurses aides 88 (ft), 88 (pt); Physical therapists 1 (pt); Occupational therapists 1 (pt); Speech therapists 1 (pt); Activities coordinators 1 (ft); Dietitians 1 (ft).
Affiliation Roman Catholic
Facilities Dining room; Physical therapy room; Activities room; Chapel; Crafts room; Barber/Beauty shop.
Activities Arts and Crafts; Cards; Games; Reading groups; Prayer groups; Movies; Shop-
ping trips; Dances/Social or cultural gatherings.
Description Facility is designed to care for the physically handicapped adult. Philosophy is to maintain the integrity and dignity of the human person; people come here to live their lives to the fullest and all residents are expected to function at their highest level. This care is provided through a program of health care concerned with prevention, treatment, and rehabilitation. The needs of the poor and dying receive special attention.

DEVON

Devon Manor Retirement Center
235 Lancaster Ave, Devon, PA, 19333 (215) 688-8080
Medical Dir/Dir of Nursing Dr William Lander.
Licensure Skilled Care. *Beds* 80. *Certified* Medicare.
Ownership Proprietary.
Admissions Requirements Medical examination.
Staff Physicians 4 (pt); RNs 15 (ft), 12 (pt); LPNs 2 (ft); Nurses aides 27 (ft), 16 (pt); Physical therapists 1 (pt); Reality therapists 1 (ft); Recreational therapists 1 (ft); Occupational therapists 2 (ft); Speech therapists 1 (pt); Activities coordinators 2 (ft); Dietitians 1 (ft), 1 (pt); Dentists 1 (pt); Podiatrists 1 (pt); Audiologists 1 (pt).
Facilities Dining room; Physical therapy room; Activities room; Chapel; Crafts room; Laundry room; Barber/Beauty shop; Library; Health club; Cocktail lounge.
Activities Arts and Crafts; Cards; Games; Reading groups; Movies; Shopping trips; Dances/Social or cultural gatherings; Lectures; Shows; Classical music groups.
Description Devon Manor Retirement Center offers a unique alternative in lifecare. Residents are not charged an entrance fee; only a security deposit equal to one months rent. Monthly rent includes meals, maid service, linen service, maintenance, security, and activities; short-term leases are available.

Eliza Cathcart Home*
445 Valley Forge Rd, Devon, PA, 19333 (215) 688-0833
Licensure Skilled Care. *Beds* 47. *Certified* Medicaid; Medicare.
Ownership Nonprofit.

DOYLESTOWN

Briarleaf Nursing and Convalescent Center*
252 Belmont and Spruce Sts, Doylestown, PA, 18901 (215) 348-2983
Licensure Skilled Care. *Beds* 148. *Certified* Medicaid; Medicare.
Ownership Proprietary.

Bucks County Association of Retarded Citizens*
252 Belmont Dr, Doylestown, PA, 18901 (215) 348-3524
Licensure Intermediate Care for Mentally Retarded. *Beds* 8. *Certified* Medicaid.
Ownership Nonprofit.

Doylestown Manor
Maple Ave and East St, Doylestown, PA, 18901
(215) 345-1452
Admin Harry K Hobbs.
Licensure Skilled Care; Intermediate Care.
Beds 120. *Certified* Medicaid; Medicare.
Ownership Proprietary.
Staff RNs 8 (ft), 3 (pt); LPNs 5 (ft), 2 (pt);
Nurses aides 30 (ft), 10 (pt); Physical therapists
1 (ft), 1 (pt); Reality therapists 2 (ft); Activities
coordinators 1 (ft).
Facilities Dining room; Physical therapy room;
Activities room; Crafts room; Laundry room;
Barber/Beauty shop.
Activities Arts and Crafts; Cards; Games;
Reading groups; Prayer groups; Movies; Shop-
ping trips; Dances/Social or cultural gatherings.
Description We have a meals-on-wheels pro-
gram to serve the community and an activities
of daily living program to facilitate greater independence on the part of the resident.

Greenleaf Nursing and Convalescent Center*
400 S Main St, Doylestown, PA, 18901 (215)
348-2980
Licensure Skilled Care. *Beds* 108. *Certified* Medicaid; Medicare.
Ownership Proprietary.

Heritage Towers
200 Veterans Lane, Doylestown, PA, 18901
Admin Harold J Schieck. *Medical Dir/Dir of
Nursing* Charles W Burmeister MD.
Licensure Skilled Care. *Beds* 60. *Cer-
tified* Medicare.
Ownership Nonprofit.
Admissions Requirements Medical
examination; Physician's request.
Staff RNs 4 (ft), 4 (pt); LPNs 1 (ft), 2 (pt);
Orderlies 1 (ft); Nurses aides 9 (ft), 10 (pt);
Physical therapists 1 (pt); Reality therapists 1
(pt); Recreational therapists 1 (pt); Occupa-
tional therapists 1 (pt); Speech therapists 1 (pt);
Activities coordinators 1 (ft); Dietitians 1 (ft);
Dentists 1 (pt); Ophthalmologists 1 (pt); Podia-
trists 1 (pt); Audiologists 1 (pt).
Facilities Dining room; Physical therapy room;
Activities room; Chapel; Crafts room; Laundry
room; Barber/Beauty shop; Library; Auditorium.
Activities Arts and Crafts; Prayer groups;
Movies; Shopping trips; Dances/Social or cultural gatherings.
Description Facility is located in one of the
most historic sections of the nation and is a
modern, 3-year-old facility providing dignity
and independence for persons 65 and older.
Nursing facility is staffed for nursing care for
persons of any age.

Medical Center for Aging—Doylestown
777 Ferry Rd, Doylestown, PA, 18901 (215)
345-9000 or 348-7770
Medical Dir/Dir of Nursing Dr Gary Sussman.
Licensure Skilled Care; Intermediate Care;
Self-Care. *Beds* SNF 166; ICF 34; Self-Care 36.
Certified Medicare.
Ownership Proprietary.
Staff Physicians 8 (pt); RNs 10 (ft), 9 (pt);
LPNs 10 (ft), 6 (pt); Orderlies 51 (ft), 28 (pt);
Physical therapists 1 (ft); Recreational therapists
4 (ft), 2 (pt); Occupational therapists 1 (ft);
Speech therapists 1 (pt); Activities coordinators

1 (ft); Dietitians 2 (ft); Ophthalmologists 1 (pt);
Podiatrists 1 (pt); Audiologists 1 (pt).
Facilities Dining room; Physical therapy room;
Activities room; Crafts room; Laundry room;
Barber/Beauty shop; Library.
Activities Arts and Crafts; Cards; Games;
Reading groups; Prayer groups; Movies; Shop-
ping trips; Dances/Social or cultural gatherings.
Description Facility has taken the forefront in a
new and progressive approach to sophisticated
care for the older adult. Concern is first and
foremost for guests and residents; for their dig-
nity, comfort, convenience, and rapid return to
their own homes and to normal daily activities.

Neshaminy Manor
Rt 611 and Almhouse Rd, Doylestown, PA,
18901 (215) 343-2800
Admin Harriet Armstrong-Hinkle. *Medical
Dir/Dir of Nursing* Dr Richard Vanderbeek.
Licensure Skilled Care; Intermediate Care.
Beds SNF 150; ICF 210. *Certified* Medicaid;
Medicare.
Ownership Public.
Staff Physicians 1 (ft), 2 (pt); RNs 38 (ft), 4
(pt); LPNs 22 (ft); Orderlies 15 (ft), 4 (pt);
Nurses aides 90 (ft), 15 (pt); Physical therapists
1 (ft); Activities coordinators 1 (ft); Dietitians 1
(ft).
Facilities Dining room; Physical therapy room;
Activities room; Chapel; Crafts room; Laundry
room; Barber/Beauty shop; Library.
Activities Arts and Crafts; Cards; Games; Prayer groups; Movies; Dances/Social or cultural
gatherings.
Description Facility meets the individual needs
of the residents for total patient care; all programs are "umbrella-ed" to reach the optimum
level of care be it physical or emotional.

DRESHER

**American Medical Nursing Center Inc-Dresher
Hill***
Susquehanna and Camp Hill Rds, Dresher, PA,
19025 (215) 641-1710
Licensure Skilled Care. *Beds* 120. *Cer-
tified* Medicaid; Medicare.
Ownership Proprietary.

DRUMS

Butler Valley Manor*
Rt 1, Box 206, Drums, PA, 18222 (717)
788-4175
Licensure Skilled Care. *Beds* 37. *Cer-
tified* Medicaid; Medicare.
Ownership Proprietary.

Sparr Convalescent Home*
Rt 2, Drums, PA, 18222 (717) 788-4178
Licensure Skilled Care. *Beds* 27. *Cer-
tified* Medicaid.
Ownership Proprietary.

DUBOIS

Christ the King Manor
1100 W Long Ave, Dubois, PA, 15801 (814)
371-3180
Medical Dir/Dir of Nursing Dr Stanley Lang.

Licensure Skilled Care; Intermediate Care.
Beds 160. *Certified* Medicaid; Medicare.
Ownership Nonprofit.
Admissions Requirements Medical examina-
tion.
Staff Physicians 3 (pt); RNs 11 (ft), 2 (pt);
LPNs 20 (ft), 2 (pt); Orderlies 1 (ft); Nurses
aides 60 (ft), 16 (pt); Physical therapists 3 (pt);
Recreational therapists 1 (ft); Occupational
therapists 1 (pt); Speech therapists 1 (pt);
Activities coordinators 1 (ft); Dietitians 1 (ft);
Dentists 1 (pt); Ophthalmologists 1 (pt); Podia-
trists 1 (pt); Audiologists 1 (pt).
Affiliation Roman Catholic
Facilities Dining room; Physical therapy room;
Activities room; Chapel; Crafts room; Laundry
room; Barber/Beauty shop.
Activities Arts and Crafts; Cards; Games;
Reading groups; Prayer groups; Movies; Shop-
ping trips; Dances/Social or cultural gatherings.
Description Modern new geriatric center offers
full activity and physical therapy programs.

Dubois Nursing Home
200 S 8th St, Dubois, PA, 15801 (814)
375-9100
Medical Dir/Dir of Nursing Dr Jauahar Suvar-
naker.
Licensure Skilled Care; Intermediate Care.
Beds SNF 60; ICF 120. *Certified* Medicaid;
Medicare.
Ownership Nonprofit.
Admissions Requirements Minimum age 16.
Staff Physicians 3 (pt); RNs 5 (ft), 3 (pt); LPNs
16 (ft), 5 (pt); Nurses aides 80 (ft), 20 (pt);
Physical therapists 1 (pt); Recreational thera-
pists 3 (ft); Activities coordinators 3 (ft); Dieti-
tians 1 (ft); Dentists 1 (pt); Podiatrists 1 (pt);
Audiologists 1 (pt).
Facilities Dining room; Physical therapy room;
Activities room; Crafts room; Laundry room;
Barber/Beauty shop.
Activities Arts and Crafts; Cards; Games;
Reading groups; Prayer groups; Movies; Shop-
ping trips; Dances/Social or cultural gatherings.
Description Home is the regional training cen-
ter for Unicare health facilities.

DUNCANNON

Kinkora Pythian Home
Rt 3, Duncannon, PA, 17020 (717) 834-4887
Licensure Intermediate Care. *Beds* 27.
Certified Medicaid.
Ownership Nonprofit.
Admissions Requirements Medical examina-
tion.
Staff RNs 1 (ft), 4 (pt); LPNs 2 (pt); Nurses
aides 8 (pt); Physical therapists; Activities coor-
dinators 1 (ft); Activities coordinators.
Affiliation Knights of Pythias
Facilities Dining room; Activities room;
Laundry room; Living room.
Activities Arts and Crafts; Cards; Games;
Reading groups; Prayer groups; Movies; Shop-
ping trips; Dances/Social or cultural gatherings.
Description Facility is not institutionally ori-
ented. Offers home-like living, cooking, love
and caring like one big family.

DUNMORE

Laurel Hill Inc*
Smith and Mill Sts, Dunmore, PA, 18512 (717) 342-7624
Licensure Skilled Care. *Beds* 127. *Certified* Medicaid.
Ownership Proprietary.

EAST LANSDOWNE

Lansdowne Rest Home
246 Melrose Ave, East Lansdowne, PA, 19050 (215) 623-2233
Licensure Intermediate Care. *Beds* 26.
Ownership Proprietary.
Staff RNs 4 (pt); LPNs 2 (ft); Nurses aides 4 (ft), 6 (pt); Activities coordinators 1 (pt); Dietitians 1 (pt).
Facilities Dining room; Activities room; Laundry room.
Activities Arts and Crafts; Cards; Games; Reading groups; Dances/Social or cultural gatherings.

EAST NORRISTOWN

Leader Nursing Rehabilitation Center—#1
Johnson Hwy and Old Arch Rd, East Norristown, PA, 19401 (215) 275-6401
Medical Dir/Dir of Nursing Joseph Maerz MD.
Licensure Skilled Care. *Beds* 120. *Certified* Medicaid; Medicare.
Ownership Proprietary.
Facilities Dining room; Physical therapy room; Activities room; Chapel; Crafts room; Laundry room; Barber/Beauty shop; Library; Head trauma and spinal cord rehabilitation program.
Activities Arts and Crafts; Cards; Games; Reading groups; Prayer groups; Movies; Shopping trips; Dances/Social or cultural gatherings.

EAST STROUDSBURG

Stroud Manor Inc*
229 E Brown St, East Stroudsburg, PA, 18301 (717) 421-6200
Licensure Skilled Care. *Beds* 129. *Certified* Medicaid; Medicare.
Ownership Proprietary.

EASTON

Blough Nursing Home Inc*
316 E Market St, Easton, PA, 18042 (215) 868-4982
Licensure Skilled Care. *Beds* 41. *Certified* Medicaid.
Ownership Proprietary.

The Easton Home for Aged Women
1022 Northampton St, Easton, PA, 18042 (215) 258-7773
Admin Janice A Hoffman.
Licensure Skilled Care. *Beds* 26.
Ownership Nonprofit.
Admissions Requirements Minimum age 65; Females only; Medical examination.
Staff Physicians 1 (pt); RNs 3 (ft), 7 (pt); LPNs

1 (ft); Nurses aides 5 (ft), 4 (pt); Physical therapists 1 (pt); Reality therapists 1 (pt); Recreational therapists 1 (pt); Occupational therapists 1 (pt); Speech therapists 1 (pt); Activities coordinators 1 (ft); Dietitians 1 (pt); Dentists 1 (pt); Ophthalmologists 1 (pt); Podiatrists 1 (pt); Audiologists 1 (pt).
Facilities Dining room; Activities room; Chapel; Crafts room; Laundry room; Barber/Beauty shop; Library.
Activities Arts and Crafts; Cards; Games; Reading groups; Prayer groups; Movies; Shopping trips; Dances/Social or cultural gatherings.

Eastwood Convalescent Home Inc
2125 Fairview Ave, Easton, PA, 18042 (215) 258-2801
Licensure Skilled Care. *Beds* 105. *Certified* Medicare.
Ownership Proprietary.
Staff RNs 7 (ft), 9 (pt); LPNs 6 (ft), 4 (pt); Nurses aides 41 (ft), 18 (pt); Physical therapists; Reality therapists; Recreational therapists; Occupational therapists; Speech therapists; Activities coordinators; Dietitians; Dentists; Ophthalmologists; Podiatrists; Audiologists.
Facilities Dining room; Physical therapy room; Activities room; Crafts room; Laundry room; Barber/Beauty shop; Lift-equipped bus.
Activities Arts and Crafts; Cards; Games; Reading groups; Prayer groups; Movies; Shopping trips; Dances/Social or cultural gatherings; Bus trips.

Leader Nursing and Rehabilitation Center*
2600 Northampton St, Easton, PA, 18042 (215) 250-0150
Licensure Skilled Care. *Beds* 120. *Certified* Medicaid; Medicare.
Ownership Proprietary.

Northampton Convalescent Center
S 5th and Washington Sts, Easton, PA, 18042 (215) 258-2988
Licensure Skilled Care; Intermediate Care.
Beds SNF 21; ICF 160. *Certified* Medicaid; Medicare.
Ownership Proprietary.

Praxis
5th and Washington St, Easton, PA, 18042 (215) 253-3573
Licensure Intermediate Care for Mentally Retarded. *Beds* 60. *Certified* Medicaid.
Ownership Proprietary.

EBENSBURG

Cambria County Home and Hospital*
Box 360, Ebensburg, PA, 15931 (814) 472-8100
Licensure Skilled Care; Intermediate Care.
Beds SNF 250; ICF 455. *Certified* Medicaid; Medicare.
Ownership Nonprofit.

Ebensburg Center
Rt 22, Ebensburg, PA, 15931 (814) 472-7350
Admin Peter H O'Meara. *Medical Dir/Dir of Nursing* Gerard T Humma MD.
Licensure Intermediate Care for Mentally Retarded. *Beds* 648. *Certified* Medicaid.
Ownership Nonprofit.

Staff Physicians 2 (ft), 2 (pt); RNs 39 (ft), 6 (pt); Nurses aides 404 (ft), 3 (pt); Physical therapists 1 (pt); Recreational therapists 8 (ft); Occupational therapists 1 (pt); Speech therapists 8 (ft); Activities coordinators 1 (ft); Dietitians 3 (ft); Dentists 1 (ft), 4 (pt); Ophthalmologists 1 (pt); Podiatrists 1 (ft); Audiologists 1 (ft).
Facilities Dining room; Physical therapy room; Activities room; Chapel; Crafts room; Laundry room; Barber/Beauty shop; Vocational training room; Visually handicapped and communications training units; Behavior therapy unit.
Activities Arts and Crafts; Games; Movies; Shopping trips; Dances/Social or cultural gatherings.

EFFORT

Brookmont Health Care Center Inc*
PO Box 50, Brookmont Dr, Effort, PA, 18330 (215) 681-4070
Licensure Skilled Care. *Beds* 84. *Certified* Medicaid; Medicare.
Ownership Proprietary.

ELIZABETHTOWN

Leader Nursing and Rehabilitation Center
320 S Market St, Elizabethtown, PA, 17022 (717) 367-1377
Licensure Skilled Care. *Beds* 61. *Certified* Medicaid; Medicare.
Ownership Proprietary.
Admissions Requirements Medical examination; Physician's request.
Facilities Dining room; Physical therapy room; Activities room; Chapel; Crafts room; Laundry room; Barber/Beauty shop.
Activities Arts and Crafts; Cards; Games; Reading groups; Prayer groups; Movies; Dances/Social or cultural gatherings.

Masonic Home Inc*
Masonic Dr, Elizabethtown, PA, 17022 (717) 367-1121
Licensure Skilled Care; Intermediate Care.
Beds SNF 348; ICF 134. *Certified* Medicaid; Medicare.
Ownership Nonprofit.
Affiliation Masons

ELIZABETHVILLE

The Kepler Home Inc
44 S Market St, Elizabethville, PA, 17023 (717) 362-8370
Licensure Intermediate Care. *Beds* 36. *Certified* Medicaid.
Ownership Proprietary.
Staff RNs 1 (ft), 4 (pt); LPNs 2 (ft), 2 (pt); Nurses aides 18 (ft); Activities coordinators 1 (ft); Dietitians 1 (pt).
Facilities Dining room; Activities room; Crafts room; Barber/Beauty shop.
Activities Arts and Crafts; Cards; Games; Reading groups; Prayer groups; Movies; Shopping trips; Dances/Social or cultural gatherings; Picnics; Sight-seeing trips.

ELKINS PARK

American Medical Nursing Centers—Township Manor*
265 Township Line Rd, Elkins Park, PA, 19117 (215) 379-2700
Licensure Skilled Care; Intermediate Care.
Beds SNF 102; ICF 48. *Certified* Medicaid; Medicare.
Ownership Proprietary.

ELLWOOD CITY

Mary Evans Extended Care Facility
724 Pershing St, Ellwood City, PA, 16117 (412) 752-0081
Licensure Skilled Care. *Beds* 19. *Certified* Medicaid; Medicare.
Ownership Nonprofit.

ELMHURST

St Mary's Villa
St Mary's Villa Rd, Elmhurst, PA, 18416 (717) 842-7621
Medical Dir/Dir of Nursing Joseph Demko MD.
Licensure Skilled Care. *Beds* 121. *Certified* Medicaid; Medicare.
Ownership Nonprofit.
Admissions Requirements Minimum age 65; Medical examination; Physician's request.
Staff RNs 6 (ft), 11 (pt); LPNs 2 (ft), 9 (pt); Nurses aides 24 (ft), 40 (pt); Physical therapists 2 (pt); Recreational therapists 1 (ft); Activities coordinators 1 (ft); Dietitians 1 (pt); Podiatrists 2 (pt).
Affiliation Roman Catholic
Facilities Dining room; Physical therapy room; Activities room; Chapel; Crafts room; Laundry room; Barber/Beauty shop; Library; Lounges; Patio; Pavillion; Porches; Coffee/snack shop; Gift shop.
Activities Arts and Crafts; Cards; Games; Reading groups; Prayer groups; Movies; Shopping trips; Dances/Social or cultural gatherings.
Description Facility has a beautiful outdoor patio and a new pavilion for various spring and summer outdoor activities and cultural gatherings.

EMPORIUM

Guy and Mary Felt Manor Inc
110 E 4th St, Emporium, PA, 15834 (814) 486-3736
Admin Nancy Umbenhauer. *Medical Dir/Dir of Nursing* Dr J M Blackburn.
Licensure Skilled Care. *Beds* 40. *Certified* Medicaid; Medicare.
Ownership Proprietary.
Admissions Requirements Minimum age 18; Medical examination; Physician's request.
Staff RNs 3 (ft), 2 (pt); LPNs 1 (ft); Nurses aides 11 (ft), 8 (pt); Activities coordinators 1 (ft); Dietitians 1 (pt).
Facilities Dining room; Physical therapy room; Activities room; Laundry room; Barber/Beauty

shop.
Activities Arts and Crafts; Cards; Games; Reading groups; Prayer groups; Movies.

EPHRATA

Ephrata Nursing Home Inc
25 W Locust St, Ephrata, PA, 17522 (717) 733-2189
Admin C M Wagner. *Medical Dir/Dir of Nursing* Dr William Noller.
Licensure Skilled Care; Residential Care.
Beds SNF 24; Residential Care 6. *Certified* Medicaid; Medicare.
Ownership Proprietary.
Admissions Requirements Minimum age 45; Medical examination.
Staff Physicians 4 (pt); RNs 1 (ft), 2 (pt); LPNs 2 (ft), 2 (pt); Nurses aides 5 (ft), 6 (pt); Physical therapists 1 (pt); Reality therapists 1 (pt); Recreational therapists 1 (ft); Occupational therapists 1 (pt); Speech therapists 1 (pt); Activities coordinators 1 (ft); Dietitians 1 (pt); Dentists 1 (pt); Ophthalmologists 1 (pt); Podiatrists 1 (pt).
Facilities Dining room; Physical therapy room; Activities room; Laundry room.
Activities Arts and Crafts; Cards; Games; Reading groups; Prayer groups.

Fairmont Rest Home*
Rt 4, Ephrata, PA, 17522 (717) 354-4111
Licensure Skilled Care. *Beds* 112. *Certified* Medicaid.
Ownership Nonprofit.

ERIE

Alpine Manor Nursing Home Inc—Erie*
4114 Schaper Ave, Erie, PA, 16509 (814) 868-0831
Licensure Skilled Care. *Beds* 121. *Certified* Medicaid; Medicare.
Ownership Proprietary.

Ball Pavilion Inc*
5416 E Lake Rd, Erie, PA, 16511 (814) 899-3102
Licensure Skilled Care; Intermediate Care.
Beds SNF 31; ICF 53. *Certified* Medicaid; Medicare.
Ownership Nonprofit.

Battersby Convalescent Home*
2686 Peach St, Erie, PA, 16508 (814) 453-6641
Licensure Skilled Care. *Beds* 115. *Certified* Medicaid; Medicare.
Ownership Proprietary.

Dr Gertrude A Barber Center Inc
126 East Ave, Erie, PA, 16507 (814) 453-7661
Admin Gertrude A Barber. *Medical Dir/Dir of Nursing* Dr Joseph DeFranco.
Licensure Intermediate Care for Mentally Retarded. *Beds* 8. *Certified* Medicaid.
Ownership Nonprofit.
Admissions Requirements Minimum age 18; Males only; Medical examination.
Staff Physicians 1 (pt); RNs 1 (pt); LPNs 1 (pt); Orderlies 4 (ft), 4 (pt); Physical therapists 1 (pt); Recreational therapists 1 (pt); Speech therapists 1 (pt); Psychologists 1 (pt); Social work-

ers 1 (pt).
Facilities Dining room; Physical therapy room; Activities room; Chapel; Crafts room; Laundry room; Library; Gymnasium; Vocational rehabilitation area.
Activities Arts and Crafts; Cards; Games; Reading groups; Movies; Shopping trips; Dances/Social or cultural gatherings.
Description All programing is individualized and based upon the specific needs of each resident as determined by an interdisciplinary team of professionals and provides for 24-hour a day continuity of care.

Erie County Geriatric Annex*
4728 Lake Pleasant Rd, Erie, PA, 16522 (814) 864-3001
Licensure Skilled Care. *Beds* 80. *Certified* Medicaid; Medicare.
Ownership Nonprofit.

Lake Erie Institute of Rehabilitation
137 W 2nd St, Erie, PA, 16507 (814) 453-5602
Medical Dir/Dir of Nursing Charles C Mehegan MD.
Licensure Skilled Care; Acute Rehabilitation.
Beds SNF 61; Acute Rehabilitation 61. *Certified* Medicaid; Medicare.
Ownership Proprietary.
Staff Physicians 3 (ft), 2 (pt); RNs 25 (ft), 6 (pt); LPNs 7 (ft), 1 (pt); Orderlies 1 (ft); Nurses aides 48 (ft), 19 (pt); Physical therapists 6 (ft); Recreational therapists 5 (ft); Occupational therapists 8 (ft); Speech therapists 8 (ft); Dietitians 1 (pt); Dentists 1 (pt); Ophthalmologists 1 (pt); Podiatrists 1 (pt).
Facilities Dining room; Physical therapy room; Activities room; Crafts room; Laundry room; Barber/Beauty shop; Library; EEG and evoked potential lab; Research department; Occupational therapy rooms; Recreation therapy rooms; Speech therapy rooms.
Activities Arts and Crafts; Cards; Games; Movies; Shopping trips; Dances/Social or cultural gatherings; Stimulation groups.
Description Facility specializing in rehabilitation and treatment of the head injured patient, provides a complement of full-time services including physical therapy, speech therapy, occupational therapy, recreation therapy, psychological services, and social services. Each discipline pursues a rehabilitation program dealing with the physical, cognitive, and emotional deficits of the patient. The team approach facilitates the hope that the patient can return to society as a functioning family member, citizen, and economic contributor.

Lutheran Home for the Aged
149 W 22nd St, Erie, PA, 16502 (814) 452-3271
Admin Joseph S Bienick. *Medical Dir/Dir of Nursing* Robert B Allison DO.
Licensure Skilled Care; Intermediate Care.
Beds SNF 57; ICF 57. *Certified* Medicaid; Medicare.
Ownership Nonprofit.
Admissions Requirements Minimum age 65; Medical examination.
Staff Physicians 1 (pt); RNs 3 (ft), 10 (pt); LPNs 3 (pt); Orderlies 1 (pt); Nurses aides 20 (ft), 8 (pt); Physical therapists 1 (pt); Recreational therapists 1 (pt); Occupational therapists 1 (pt); Speech therapists 1 (pt); Activities coor-

dinators 1 (ft); Dietitians 1 (ft); Dentists 1 (pt); Ophthalmologists 1 (pt); Podiatrists 1 (pt); Audiologists 1 (pt).
Affiliation Lutheran
Facilities Dining room; Physical therapy room; Activities room; Chapel; Crafts room; Laundry room; Barber/Beauty shop.
Activities Arts and Crafts; Cards; Games; Reading groups; Prayer groups; Movies; Shopping trips; Dances/Social or cultural gatherings.

Manor Home for the Aged*
3401 Poplar St, Erie, PA, 16508 (814) 866-7449
Licensure Intermediate Care. *Beds* 33. *Certified* Medicaid.
Ownership Proprietary.

The New Pennsylvania Soldiers' and Sailors' Home
PO Box 6239, Erie, PA, 16512
Admin Stanley E Snyder. *Medical Dir/Dir of Nursing* Dr William A Rowane.
Licensure Skilled Care; Intermediate Care. *Beds* 175.
Ownership Public.
Admissions Requirements Minimum age 50; Medical examination.
Staff Physicians 1 (ft); RNs 21 (ft), 2 (pt); LPNs 7 (ft); Orderlies 6 (ft); Nurses aides 24 (ft); Physical therapists 1 (ft); Speech therapists; Activities coordinators 1 (ft); Dietitians 1 (ft); Dentists; Ophthalmologists; Podiatrists; Audiologists.
Facilities Dining room; Physical therapy room; Activities room; Chapel; Crafts room; Laundry room; Barber/Beauty shop; Library; Exercise room; Snack bar.
Activities Arts and Crafts; Cards; Games; Movies; Shopping trips; Dances/Social or cultural gatherings.
Description Facility offers fishing and camping trips overnight, weekend, and whole week even for nursing care unit patients. VA approved.

Presbyterian Lodge*
2628 Elmwood Ave, Erie, PA, 16508 (814) 864-4802
Licensure Skilled Care; Intermediate Care. *Beds* SNF 40; ICF 15. *Certified* Medicaid; Medicare.
Ownership Nonprofit.
Affiliation Presbyterian

Rondale Nursing and Convalescent Home
1267 S Hill Rd, Erie, PA, 16509 (814) 864-4081
Admin Mary Ann Balsign. *Medical Dir/Dir of Nursing* Dr Ronald W Pearson.
Licensure Skilled Care; Intermediate Care. *Beds* SNF 50; ICF 30. *Certified* Medicaid; Medicare.
Ownership Proprietary.
Admissions Requirements Minimum age 16; Medical examination; Physician's request.
Staff RNs 4 (ft), 4 (pt); LPNs 4 (ft), 4 (pt); Orderlies 1 (ft), 1 (pt); Nurses aides 21 (ft), 10 (pt); Physical therapists 1 (pt); Recreational therapists 1 (ft); Activities coordinators 1 (ft).
Facilities Dining room; Physical therapy room; Activities room; Chapel; Crafts room; Barber/Beauty shop.
Activities Arts and Crafts; Cards; Games; Movies; Dances/Social or cultural gatherings.
Description Rondale is located in a picturesque

country setting with an outdoor pond adjacent to the Millcreek Mall and all urban conveniences. Newly redecorated, the facility generates a warm home-like atmosphere.

Saint Marys Home of Erie*
607 E 26th St, Erie, PA, 16504 (814) 459-0621
Licensure Skilled Care. *Beds* 196. *Certified* Medicaid; Medicare.
Ownership Nonprofit.

Sarah A Reed Retirement Center*
2224 Sassafras St, Erie, PA, 16502 (814) 453-6797
Licensure Skilled Care; Intermediate Care. *Beds* SNF 43; ICF 36. *Certified* Medicaid; Medicare.
Ownership Nonprofit.

Twinbrook Nursing and Convalescent Home*
3805 Field St, Erie, PA, 16511 (814) 899-0671
Licensure Skilled Care. *Beds* 133. *Certified* Medicaid; Medicare.
Ownership Proprietary.

Western Reserve Convalescent Home of Erie*
1521 W 54th St, Erie, PA, 16509 (814) 864-0671
Licensure Skilled Care. *Beds* 133. *Certified* Medicaid; Medicare.
Ownership Proprietary.

EVERETT

Pennknoll Village Nursing Home*
Everett, PA, 15537 (814) 765-7545
Licensure Skilled Care; Intermediate Care. *Beds* SNF 29; ICF 104. *Certified* Medicaid; Medicare.
Ownership Nonprofit.

FAYETTE CITY

Waddington Convalescent Home*
Rt 1, Fayette City, PA, 15438 (412) 326-4077
Licensure Skilled Care. *Beds* 40.
Ownership Proprietary.

FAYETTEVILLE

Guilford Convalesarium*
3301 Lincoln Way East, Fayetteville, PA, 17222 (717) 352-2101
Licensure Skilled Care. *Beds* 64. *Certified* Medicaid; Medicare.
Ownership Proprietary.

Piney Mountain Home*
Rt 2, Fayetteville, PA, 17222 (717) 352-2721
Licensure Skilled Care. *Beds* 92. *Certified* Medicaid.
Ownership Nonprofit.

FEASTERVILLE

Ridge Crest Convalescent Home*
1730 Buck Rd N, Feasterville, PA, 19047 (215) 355-3131

Licensure Skilled Care. *Beds* 118. *Certified* Medicaid; Medicare.
Ownership Proprietary.

FLOURTOWN

Kenneson Convalescent Home*
31 W Mill Rd, Flourtown, PA, 19031 (215) 836-4286
Licensure Skilled Care. *Beds* 28. *Certified* Medicaid.
Ownership Proprietary.

Saint Josephs Villa
Stenton and Wissahickon Aves, Flourtown, PA, 19031 (215) 836-4179
Admin Sr Celestine. *Medical Dir/Dir of Nursing* Jude Damian MD.
Licensure Skilled Care. *Beds* 295. *Certified* Medicaid.
Ownership Nonprofit.
Staff Physicians 3 (pt); RNs 10 (ft), 10 (pt); LPNs 6 (ft), 1 (pt); Nurses aides 28 (ft), 2 (pt); Physical therapists 2 (ft); Reality therapists 1 (ft); Activities coordinators 2 (ft); Dietitians 1 (ft); Dentists 1 (pt); Ophthalmologists 1 (pt); Podiatrists 1 (pt).
Affiliation Roman Catholic
Facilities Dining room; Physical therapy room; Activities room; Chapel; Crafts room; Laundry room; Barber/Beauty shop.
Activities Arts and Crafts; Cards; Games; Reading groups; Prayer groups; Shopping trips.
Description St Josephs Villa, a 295-bed facility, contains offices for doctors, examining room, dental and podiatry offices, an X-ray department, state licensed laboratory, and electrocardiogram. An adult day care program with provision for medical, social, and spiritual services is licensed by Pennsylvania.

FORKSVILLE

Dar Way Nursing Home Inc
Rt 1, Forksville, PA, 18616 (717) 924-3411
Admin Dora McCarty. *Medical Dir/Dir of Nursing* Michael Gross MD.
Licensure Intermediate Care. *Beds* 70. *Certified* Medicaid.
Ownership Proprietary.
Admissions Requirements Medical examination; Physician's request.
Staff Physicians 2 (ft); RNs 3 (ft), 3 (pt); LPNs 2 (ft), 1 (pt); Nurses aides 25 (ft), 7 (pt); Activities coordinators 1 (ft); Dietitians 1 (pt).
Facilities Dining room; Activities room; Chapel; Crafts room; Laundry room; Barber/Beauty shop.
Activities Arts and Crafts; Cards; Games; Movies.
Description Facility features an attractive, rural setting.

FORT WASHINGTON

Fort Washington Estates*
Fort Washington Ave and Susquehanna Rd, Fort Washington, PA, 19034 (215) 542-8111
Licensure Skilled Care. *Beds* 62.
Ownership Nonprofit.

FRACKVILLE

Broad Mountain Nursing Center*
500 Laurel St, Frackville, PA, 17901 (717)
874-0696
Licensure Skilled Care. *Beds* 129. *Certified* Medicaid; Medicare.
Ownership Proprietary.

FRANKLIN

Granview Health Care Inc—Franklin*
1 Dale Ave, Franklin, PA, 16323 (814)
437-6802
Licensure Skilled Care; Intermediate Care.
Beds SNF 76; ICF 29. *Certified* Medicaid;
Medicare.
Ownership Proprietary.

Venango Manor
Rt 3, Box 29, Sugarcreek Rd, Franklin, PA,
16323 (814) 437-6522
Medical Dir/Dir of Nursing Dr Manson Brown
and Dr Kamal Aoun.
Licensure Skilled Care; Intermediate Care.
Beds SNF 90; ICF 88. *Certified* Medicaid.
Ownership Nonprofit.
Admissions Requirements Medical examination.
Staff Physicians; RNs; LPNs; Orderlies;
Nurses aides; Physical therapists; Activities
coordinators; Dietitians; Dentists; Podiatrists.
Facilities Dining room; Physical therapy room;
Activities room; Crafts room; Laundry room;
Barber/Beauty shop; Library.
Activities Arts and Crafts; Cards; Games; Prayer groups; Movies.
Description Facility is located in a beautiful
country setting with 3-story, 110-year-old
building, extensively remodeled in the late sixties to provide nursing care. We provide both
skilled and intermediate nursing care with
rehabilitation as a primary concern.

FREDERICK

Frederick Mennonite Home*
Rt 73, Frederick, PA, 19435 (215) 754-7878
Licensure Skilled Care. *Beds* 50. *Certified* Medicaid.
Ownership Nonprofit.
Affiliation Mennonite

GERMANTOWN

Unitarian Universalist Home
224 W Tulpenhocken St, Germantown, PA,
19144
Medical Dir/Dir of Nursing Norman Stahlheber MD.
Licensure Skilled Care. *Beds* 39. *Certified* Medicaid.
Ownership Nonprofit.
Admissions Requirements Minimum age 60;
Medical examination.
Staff RNs 5 (ft), 2 (pt); LPNs 3 (ft), 1 (pt);
Nurses aides 12 (ft), 10 (pt); Activities coordinators 1 (pt); Dietitians 1 (ft).
Affiliation Unitarian Universalist
Facilities Dining room; Activities room; Laundry room; Barber/Beauty shop; Library; All

purpose rooms.
Activities Arts and Crafts; Cards; Games;
Reading groups; Prayer groups; Movies; Shopping trips; Dances/Social or cultural gatherings;
Music.
Description Volunteers from 15 area Unitarian
Universalist churches add warmth and vitality
to our program each day.

GETTYSBURG

Gettysburg Lutheran Retirement Village
1075 Old Harrisburg Rd, Gettysburg, PA,
17325 (717) 334-6204
Admin Herbert S Hinman. *Medical Dir/Dir of Nursing* Charles R Williams MD.
Licensure Skilled Care; Intermediate Care.
Beds SNF 69; ICF 23. *Certified* Medicaid.
Admissions Requirements Medical examination; Physician's request.
Staff RNs 4 (ft), 6 (pt); LPNs 9 (ft), 6 (pt);
Nurses aides 21 (ft), 15 (pt); Activities coordinators 1 (ft).
Affiliation Lutheran
Facilities Dining room; Physical therapy room;
Activities room; Laundry room; Barber/Beauty
shop; Library.
Activities Arts and Crafts; Cards; Games;
Reading groups; Movies; Shopping trips; Dances/Social or cultural gatherings; Bible study.
Description Located in historic Gettysburg, the
Gettysburg Lutheran Retirement Village offers
a continuum of care for senior citizens. Cottages are available for purchase or rental and
nursing care provided as needed.

Green Acres-Adams County Home
595 Biglerville Rd, Gettysburg, PA, 17325 (717)
334-6249
Admin Carol A Knisely. *Medical Dir/Dir of Nursing* Robert S Lefever MD.
Licensure Skilled Care; Intermediate Care.
Beds SNF 12; ICF 144. *Certified* Medicaid;
Medicare.
Ownership Proprietary.
Admissions Requirements Medical examination.
Staff Physicians 2 (pt); RNs 6 (ft), 3 (pt); LPNs
15 (ft), 5 (pt); Nurses aides 38 (ft), 17 (pt);
Physical therapists 1 (pt); Activities coordinators 1 (ft); Dietitians 1 (ft); Podiatrists 1 (pt).
Facilities Dining room; Physical therapy room;
Activities room; Chapel; Crafts room; Laundry
room; Barber/Beauty shop.
Activities Arts and Crafts; Cards; Games;
Reading groups; Prayer groups; Movies; Shopping trips; Dances/Social or cultural gatherings.

Michael Manor Inc*
741 Chambersburg Rd, Gettysburg, PA, 17325
(717) 334-6764
Licensure Skilled Care; Intermediate Care.
Beds SNF 78; ICF 28. *Certified* Medicaid;
Medicare.
Ownership Proprietary.

GIBSONIA

Saint Barnabas Inc
5827 Meridian Rd, Gibsonia, PA, 15044 (412)
443-1552

Admin William V Day. *Medical Dir/Dir of Nursing* Dr F Scott Lydick.
Licensure Skilled Care. *Beds* 107. *Certified* Medicaid; Medicare.
Ownership Nonprofit.
Admissions Requirements Medical examination; Physician's request.
Facilities Dining room; Physical therapy room;
Activities room; Chapel; Crafts room; Laundry
room; Barber/Beauty shop; Library.
Activities Arts and Crafts; Cards; Games;
Reading groups; Prayer groups; Movies; Shopping trips; Dances/Social or cultural gatherings.

GIRARD

Erie County Geriatric Center*
Rt 2, Girard, PA, 16417 (814) 474-5521
Licensure Skilled Care; Intermediate Care.
Beds SNF 398; ICF 41. *Certified* Medicaid;
Medicare.
Ownership Nonprofit.

GLENFIELD

Dixmont State Hospital—Long Term Care Unit
Glenfield, PA, 15115 (412) 761-1780
Admin Thomas J Fahey. *Medical Dir/Dir of Nursing* T E Thompson MD.
Licensure Intermediate Care. *Beds* 36. *Certified* Medicaid.
Ownership Nonprofit.
Admissions Requirements Minimum age 55.
Staff Physicians 2 (ft); RNs 6 (ft); LPNs 7 (ft);
Nurses aides 13 (ft); Physical therapists 1 (pt);
Reality therapists 1 (pt); Recreational therapists
1 (pt); Occupational therapists 1 (pt); Speech
therapists 1 (pt); Activities coordinators 1 (ft);
Dietitians 1 (ft); Dentists 2 (pt); Ophthalmologists 1 (pt); Podiatrists 1 (pt); Audiologists 1
(pt).
Facilities Dining room; Physical therapy room;
Activities room; Chapel; Crafts room; Laundry
room; Barber/Beauty shop; Library.
Activities Arts and Crafts; Cards; Games;
Reading groups; Prayer groups; Movies; Shopping trips; Dances/Social or cultural gatherings.
Description Facility has an outstanding program therapy agenda in order to rehabilitate
former mental patients to a less restrictive environment.

GLENSIDE

Edgehill Nursing Home
146 Edgehill Rd, Glenside, PA, 19038 (215)
886-1043
Admin Margret W Creighton. *Medical Dir/Dir of Nursing* Howard Fein DO.
Licensure Skilled Care. *Beds* 60.
Ownership Proprietary.
Admissions Requirements Minimum age 50;
Medical examination.
Staff Physicians 4 (pt); RNs 3 (ft), 3 (pt); LPNs
5 (ft), 5 (pt); Nurses aides 16 (ft), 16 (pt);
Physical therapists 1 (pt); Reality therapists 1
(pt); Recreational therapists 1 (ft); Occupational
therapists 1 (pt); Speech therapists 1 (pt);
Activities coordinators 1 (ft); Dietitians 1 (pt);
Dentists 1 (pt); Ophthalmologists 2 (pt); Podiatrists 4 (pt); Audiologists 1 (pt).

Facilities Dining room; Physical therapy room; Activities room; Crafts room; Laundry room; Barber/Beauty shop.
Activities Arts and Crafts; Cards; Games; Reading groups; Prayer groups; Movies; Shopping trips.
Description Together with Temple University, a council has been set up involving patients, patients' families, community members, and professionals.

GRANVILLE

Malta Home for the Aging
PO Box E, Granville, PA, 17029 (717) 248-3988
Medical Dir/Dir of Nursing Stephen J Marthouse MD.
Licensure Skilled Care. *Beds* 62. *Certified* Medicaid; Medicare.
Ownership Nonprofit.
Admissions Requirements Medical examination.
Staff RNs 2 (ft), 1 (pt); LPNs 3 (ft), 3 (pt); Nurses aides 13 (ft), 4 (pt); Activities coordinators 1 (ft).
Affiliation Knights of Malta
Facilities Dining room; Physical therapy room; Activities room; Crafts room; Laundry room; Barber/Beauty shop; Library.
Activities Arts and Crafts; Cards; Games; Prayer groups; Dances/Social or cultural gatherings; Spring and fall bus trips.
Description Facility is equipped with 24-beds for skilled nursing patients and 38-beds for ambulatory patients. Located in quiet, picturesque, rural central Pennsylvania; ten minutes away from Lewistown, the Mifflin county seat, which contains: Greyhound terminal, Conrail Railroad Station, taxi service, a community hospital, public library, churches of all prominent faiths, senior citizens center, movie theater, and shopping centers.

GREENSBURG

Greensburg Home
6 Garden Center Dr, Greensburg, PA, 15601 (412) 832-8400
Admin John A Mobley.
Licensure Intermediate Care. *Beds* 64. *Certified* Medicaid.
Ownership Nonprofit.
Admissions Requirements Minimum age 62; Medical examination.
Staff RNs 4 (ft), 3 (pt); LPNs 3 (ft), 4 (pt); Nurses aides 18 (ft), 7 (pt); Physical therapists 1 (pt); Recreational therapists 1 (pt), 2 (pt); Dietitians 1 (pt); Dentists 1 (pt); Podiatrists 1 (pt).
Facilities Dining room; Physical therapy room; Activities room; Chapel; Crafts room; Laundry room; Barber/Beauty shop; Library.
Activities Arts and Crafts; Cards; Games; Reading groups; Prayer groups; Movies; Shopping trips; Dances/Social or cultural gatherings.

Mountain View Center Inc
Rt 7, Box 249, Greensburg, PA, 15601 (412) 537-7360
Medical Dir/Dir of Nursing Jake Fong MD.
Licensure Skilled Care. *Beds* 137. *Certified* Medicaid; Medicare.

Ownership Proprietary.
Admissions Requirements Minimum age 16; Medical examination.
Staff Physicians 2 (pt); RNs 8 (ft), 10 (pt); LPNs 2 (ft), 3 (pt); Orderlies 3 (ft), 2 (pt); Nurses aides 41 (ft), 24 (pt); Physical therapists 1 (ft); Recreational therapists 2 (ft); Speech therapists 1 (pt); Activities coordinators 1 (ft); Dietitians 1 (pt); Dentists 1 (pt); Ophthalmologists 1 (pt); Podiatrists 1 (pt).
Facilities Dining room; Physical therapy room; Activities room; Crafts room; Laundry room; Barber/Beauty shop.
Activities Arts and Crafts; Cards; Games; Reading groups; Prayer groups; Movies; Dances/Social or cultural gatherings.

Oak Hill Home of Rest and Care*
Rt 7, Box 77A, Luxor Rd, Greensburg, PA, 15601 (412) 837-7100
Licensure Skilled Care. *Beds* 48.
Ownership Proprietary.

Saint Anne Home for the Elderly
615 Angela Dr, Greensburg, PA, 15601 (412) 837-6070
Medical Dir/Dir of Nursing Theodore A Schultz MD.
Licensure Skilled Care; Intermediate Care. *Beds* SNF 39; ICF 86. *Certified* Medicaid; Medicare.
Ownership Nonprofit.
Admissions Requirements Minimum age 65; Medical examination.
Staff Physicians 2 (pt); RNs 3 (ft), 6 (pt); LPNs 11 (ft), 11 (pt); Nurses aides 35 (ft), 29 (pt); Physical therapists 1 (ft); Reality therapists 1 (pt); Recreational therapists 2 (ft); Occupational therapists 1 (pt); Speech therapists 2 (pt); Activities coordinators 1 (ft); Dentists 1 (pt); Ophthalmologists 1 (pt); Podiatrists 1 (pt).
Affiliation Roman Catholic
Facilities Dining room; Physical therapy room; Activities room; Chapel; Crafts room; Laundry room; Barber/Beauty shop; Library.
Activities Arts and Crafts; Cards; Games; Prayer groups; Dances/Social or cultural gatherings.
Description The home is set on a hill overlooking a part of the town and rests on 11 acres of ground with plenty of trees and well-kept gardens; ample space for walking, being wheeled in wheel chair, enjoying the outdoors.

Westmoreland Manor*
Box 10, Greensburg, PA, 15601 (412) 834-0200
Licensure Skilled Care. *Beds* 540. *Certified* Medicaid; Medicare.
Ownership Nonprofit.

GREENVILLE

Gilmores White Cliff Nursing Home*
110 Fredonia Rd, Greenville, PA, 16125 (412) 588-8090
Licensure Skilled Care. *Beds* 127. *Certified* Medicaid; Medicare.
Ownership Proprietary.

Saint Paul Homes
339 E Jamestown Rd, Greenville, PA, 16125 (412) 588-4070
Medical Dir/Dir of Nursing David M Simpson

MD.
Licensure Skilled Care; Intermediate Care. *Beds* SNF 48; ICF 178. *Certified* Medicaid; Medicare.
Ownership Nonprofit.
Admissions Requirements Minimum age 62; Medical examination.
Staff RNs 10 (ft), 6 (pt); LPNs 18 (ft), 8 (pt); Physical therapists 1 (ft); Reality therapists 1 (ft); Recreational therapists 2 (ft); Occupational therapists 2 (ft); Speech therapists 1 (pt); Dietitians 1 (ft); Dentists 1 (pt).
Affiliation Church of Christ
Facilities Dining room; Physical therapy room; Activities room; Chapel; Crafts room; Laundry room; Barber/Beauty shop; Library.
Activities Arts and Crafts; Shopping trips.
Description Gardening areas available for independent living. Small town, yet rural setting within 80 miles of 3 large metropolitan areas. Brick duplex houses with garage, all appliances, and very reasonable monthly fee after construction cost of home.

GROVE CITY

Grove Manor
435 N Broad St, Grove City, PA, 16127 (412) 452-7800
Admin Mary C Gray.
Licensure Skilled Care. *Beds* 52. *Certified* Medicaid; Medicare.
Ownership Nonprofit.
Admissions Requirements Medical examination.
Staff RNs 2 (ft), 4 (pt); LPNs 2 (ft), 1 (pt); Nurses aides 17 (ft), 8 (pt); Physical therapists 1 (ft); Speech therapists 1 (pt); Dietitians 1 (pt).
Affiliation Church of God
Facilities Dining room; Physical therapy room; Chapel; Crafts room; Laundry room; Barber/Beauty shop.
Activities Arts and Crafts; Games; Reading groups; Prayer groups; Movies.
Description Bright, cheerful, home-like atmosphere for the elderly. Providing comfort and concern by dedicated people.

Orchard Manor Inc
Rt 3, Grove City, PA, 16127 (412) 458-7760
Medical Dir/Dir of Nursing William C Menzies MD.
Licensure Skilled Care. *Beds* 120. *Certified* Medicaid.
Ownership Nonprofit.
Staff Physicians 2 (pt); RNs 8 (ft), 2 (pt); LPNs 5 (ft), 1 (pt); Orderlies 2 (pt); Nurses aides 40 (ft), 3 (pt); Physical therapists 1 (pt); Activities coordinators 1 (ft); Dietitians 1 (pt); Podiatrists 1 (pt); Physical therapy aides 1 (ft).
Affiliation Independent Order of Odd Fellows
Facilities Dining room; Physical therapy room; Activities room; Chapel; Crafts room; Laundry room; Barber/Beauty shop; Library; Podiatrist room.
Activities Arts and Crafts; Cards; Games; Reading groups; Prayer groups; Movies; Shopping trips; Dances/Social or cultural gatherings; Trips in van.
Description Focus is on a real home-type atmosphere, persons are permitted to bring their own furniture (excluding bed) and to dec-

orate their rooms according to their preferred colors; has very spacious grounds far from the road and surrounded by acres of farm land yet adjacent to Grove City College grounds. Open visiting, no limit other than 9:00 p.m. closing; very few restrictions.

GWYNEDD

Foulkeways at Gwynedd Inc
Meeting House Rd, Gwynedd, PA, 19436 (215) 643-2200
Medical Dir/Dir of Nursing James C Alden.
Licensure Skilled Care; Personal Care.
Beds SNF 62; Personal Care 32. *Certified* Medicare.
Ownership Nonprofit.
Admissions Requirements Minimum age 65; Medical examination.
Affiliation Society of Friends
Facilities Dining room; Physical therapy room; Activities room; Crafts room; Laundry room; Barber/Beauty shop; Library.
Activities Arts and Crafts; Games; Reading groups; Movies; Shopping trips; Dances/Social or cultural gatherings.

HAMBURG

Hamburg Center
Old Rt 22, Hamburg, PA, 19526 (215) 562-6000
Licensure Intermediate Care for Mentally Retarded. *Beds* 450. *Certified* Medicaid.
Ownership Nonprofit.

Laurel Nursing and Retirement Center
Rt 3, Box 670, Hamburg, PA, 19526 (215) 562-2284
Medical Dir/Dir of Nursing Dr Baney, Dr Lyons, and Dr Blauser.
Licensure Skilled Care; Intermediate Care.
Beds SNF 60; ICF 60.
Ownership Proprietary.
Admissions Requirements Minimum age; Medical examination.
Staff RNs 4 (ft), 10 (pt); LPNs 6 (ft), 10 (pt); Nurses aides 25 (ft), 34 (pt); Recreational therapists 1 (ft), 4 (pt); Activities coordinators 1 (ft); Dietitians 1 (ft); Audiologists 2 (ft).
Facilities Dining room; Physical therapy room; Activities room; Crafts room; Barber/Beauty shop; Library.
Activities Arts and Crafts; Cards; Games; Prayer groups; Movies; Shopping trips; Dances/Social or cultural gatherings; Cooking; Choir.
Description Facility is located in a rural neighborhood approximately 2 miles from Hamburg. The staff of Laurel Nursing Center is dedicated to providing the nursing care and residential care necessary for the individual's comfort, happiness, and dignity. Spiritual care is provided as well as medical and physical care.

HANOVER

Hanover Hall*
267 Frederick St, Hanover, PA, 17331 (717) 637-8937
Licensure Skilled Care; Intermediate Care.

Beds SNF 123; ICF 33. *Certified* Medicaid; Medicare.
Ownership Proprietary.

Hillview House—Hanover General Hospital*
Highland Ave and Charles St, Hanover, PA, 17331 (717) 637-3711
Licensure Skilled Care. *Beds* 41. *Certified* Medicaid; Medicare.
Ownership Nonprofit.

Homewood Retirement Center
11 York St, Hanover, PA, 17331 (717) 637-4160
Medical Dir/Dir of Nursing Ralph E Bittinger MD.
Licensure Skilled Care. *Beds* 39. *Certified* Medicaid.
Ownership Nonprofit.
Admissions Requirements Minimum age 60; Medical examination.
Staff Physicians 1 (pt); RNs 2 (ft), 2 (pt); LPNs 3 (ft), 1 (pt); Nurses aides 11 (ft), 12 (pt); Physical therapists 1 (pt); Reality therapists 1 (pt); Activities coordinators 2 (ft); Dietitians 1 (pt); Dentists 1 (pt); Ophthalmologists 1 (pt); Podiatrists 1 (pt); Audiologists 1 (pt).
Affiliation Church of Christ
Facilities Dining room; Physical therapy room; Activities room; Chapel; Crafts room; Laundry room; Barber/Beauty shop; Library.
Activities Arts and Crafts; Cards; Games; Reading groups; Prayer groups; Movies; Shopping trips; Dances/Social or cultural gatherings.
Description Center offers skilled, intermediate, sheltered, residential care; operates meals on wheels; reality orientation, remotivation, and discusion groups for residents.

HARLEYSVILLE

Peter Becker Community
Marple Ave and Yoder Rd, Harleysville, PA, 19438 (215) 256-9501
Medical Dir/Dir of Nursing Ray P Landes MD.
Licensure Skilled Care. *Beds* 155. *Certified* Medicaid; Medicare.
Ownership Nonprofit.
Admissions Requirements Medical examination.
Staff RNs; LPNs; Nurses aides; Physical therapists; Occupational therapists; Activities coordinators; Dietitians; Dentists; Ophthalmologists; Podiatrists.
Affiliation Church of the Brethren
Facilities Dining room; Physical therapy room; Activities room; Chapel; Crafts room; Laundry room; Barber/Beauty shop; Library; Pharmacy.
Activities Arts and Crafts; Cards; Games; Reading groups; Prayer groups; Movies; Shopping trips; Dances/Social or cultural gatherings.
Description Facility is located in a rural-/suburban setting with wooded grove; pavilion; atrium/greenhouse; shuffleboard; chaplain; concerts; etc.

HARMONY

Evergreen Convalescent Home*
Box 189, Harmony, PA, 16037 (412) 452-6970
Licensure Skilled Care. *Beds* 51. *Certified* Medicaid; Medicare.
Ownership Proprietary.

HARRISBURG

Aspin Center
1205 S 28th St, Harrisburg, PA, 17111 (717) 558-1155
Medical Dir/Dir of Nursing Dr Angana Popat.
Licensure Intermediate Care for Mentally Retarded. *Beds* 22. *Certified* Medicaid.
Ownership Nonprofit.
Staff Physicians 1 (pt); RNs 3 (ft), 2 (pt); LPNs 2 (ft), 4 (pt); Physical therapists 1 (pt); Occupational therapists 1 (pt); Speech therapists 1 (pt); Dentists 1 (pt); Ophthalmologists 1 (pt); Audiologists 1 (pt).
Facilities Dining room; Physical therapy room; Activities room; Crafts room; Laundry room.
Activities Arts and Crafts; Games; Reading groups; Movies; Shopping trips; Dances/Social or cultural gatherings.
Description Facility serves the severe and profound mentally retarded; aim is to provide an environment that maximizes the opportunities for individual growth and development in order that each individual can reach his/her fullest potential.

Blue Ridge Haven Convalescent Center Inc
3625 N Progress Ave, Harrisburg, PA, 17110 (717) 652-2345
Medical Dir/Dir of Nursing Maurice Lewis MD.
Licensure Skilled Care; Intermediate Care.
Beds 67. *Certified* Medicaid; Medicare.
Ownership Proprietary.
Admissions Requirements Minimum age 18; Medical examination; Physician's request.
Staff RNs 3 (ft), 4 (pt); LPNs 1 (ft), 2 (pt); Nurses aides 15 (ft), 15 (pt); Physical therapists; Speech therapists; Activities coordinators 1 (pt); Dietitians; Dentists; Podiatrists; Audiologists.
Facilities Dining room; Physical therapy room; Activities room; Barber/Beauty shop.
Activities Arts and Crafts; Cards; Games; Reading groups; Prayer groups; Movies; Shopping trips; Dances/Social or cultural gatherings.
Description Facility is located in a quiet and picturesque setting outside of the city of Harrisburg. Excellent nursing care, a variety of recreational therapy, as well as an adopt-a-grandparent program enhances the quality of life of the residents.

Dauphin Manor*
1205 S 28th St, Harrisburg, PA, 17111 (717) 564-4580
Licensure Skilled Care; Intermediate Care.
Beds SNF 28; ICF 447. *Certified* Medicaid; Medicare.
Ownership Proprietary.

Homeland
1901 N 5th St, Harrisburg, PA, 17102 (717) 232-0883

Medical Dir/Dir of Nursing Donald B Freeman MD.
Licensure Skilled Care. *Beds* 33. *Certified* Medicaid; Medicare.
Ownership Nonprofit.
Admissions Requirements Minimum age 65; Medical examination.
Staff RNs 4 (ft), 2 (pt); LPNs 5 (ft), 1 (pt); Orderlies 1 (pt); Nurses aides 14 (ft), 5 (pt); Recreational therapists 1 (ft); Activities coordinators 1 (ft).
Facilities Dining room; Activities room; Chapel; Crafts room; Laundry room; Barber/Beauty shop; Library.
Activities Arts and Crafts; Cards; Games; Reading groups; Prayer groups; Movies; Shopping trips; Dances/Social or cultural gatherings.
Description Nestled among the trees of Fifth and Muench Streets in Harrisburg, Homeland provides for its residents the comfort and freedom of an independent life-style with social services, housekeeping, nursing care, and therapeutic diets as needed. There also is a skilled and intermediate care unit for those requiring 24-hour nursing care.

Jewish Home of Greater Harrisburg
4000 Linglestown Rd, Harrisburg, PA, 17112 (717) 657-0700
Medical Dir/Dir of Nursing Dr Maurice Lewis.
Licensure Skilled Care. *Beds* 120. *Certified* Medicaid; Medicare.
Ownership Nonprofit.
Admissions Requirements Minimum age 18.
Staff RNs 6 (ft), 4 (pt); LPNs 3 (pt); Nurses aides 19 (ft), 17 (pt); Recreational therapists 2 (pt); Activities coordinators 1 (pt).
Affiliation Jewish
Facilities Dining room; Physical therapy room; Activities room; Chapel; Crafts room; Laundry room; Barber/Beauty shop.
Activities Arts and Crafts; Cards; Games; Reading groups; Prayer groups; Movies; Shopping trips; Dances/Social or cultural gatherings.
Description Activity department believes in exercising body as well as mind, therefore, we have aerobics and exercise 4 mornings a week, timely topics, news on slides, and discussion groups weekly.

Leader Nursing Rehabilitation Center*
800 King Russ Rd, Harrisburg, PA, 17109 (717) 657-1520
Licensure Skilled Care; Intermediate Care.
Beds SNF 100; ICF 80. *Certified* Medicaid; Medicare.
Ownership Proprietary.

Polyclinic Medical Center Ltc Unit*
2601 N 3rd St, Bldg 56, Harrisburg, PA, 17105 (717) 782-4124
Licensure Skilled Care. *Beds* 80.
Ownership Proprietary.

Villa Teresa Nursing Home*
1051 Avilla Rd, Harrisburg, PA, 17109 (717) 652-5900
Licensure Skilled Care; Intermediate Care.
Beds SNF 135; ICF 45. *Certified* Medicaid; Medicare.
Ownership Nonprofit.

HARRISVILLE

Bonnetti Health Care Center Inc*
Main St, Harrisville, PA, 16038 (412) 735-2655
Licensure Skilled Care. *Beds* 103. *Certified* Medicaid; Medicare.
Ownership Proprietary.

HASTINGS

Haida Manor
3rd Extension, Hastings, PA, 16646
Admin William J Meenan. *Medical Dir/Dir of Nursing* Dr Joseph Sabo.
Licensure Skilled Care; Intermediate Care.
Beds 90. *Certified* Medicaid; Medicare.
Ownership Proprietary.
Admissions Requirements Medical examination; Physician's request.
Staff Physicians 5 (pt); RNs 5 (ft), 4 (pt); LPNs 5 (ft), 5 (pt); Orderlies 1 (ft); Nurses aides 22 (ft), 5 (pt); Physical therapists 1 (pt); Recreational therapists 1 (ft); Occupational therapists 1 (pt); Speech therapists 1 (pt); Activities coordinators 1 (ft); Dietitians 1 (ft); Dentists 1 (pt); Ophthalmologists 1 (pt); Podiatrists 1 (pt); Audiologists 1 (pt).
Facilities Dining room; Physical therapy room; Activities room; Laundry room; Barber/Beauty shop.
Activities Arts and Crafts; Cards; Games; Reading groups; Prayer groups; Movies; Shopping trips; Dances/Social or cultural gatherings.
Description Manor is a new, modern, skilled and long-term care facility located in a rural, western Pennsylvania setting.

HATBORO

Luther Woods Convalescent Center*
313 County Line Rd, Hatboro, PA, 19040 (215) 055-5005
Licensure Skilled Care. *Beds* 120. *Certified* Medicaid; Medicare.
Ownership Proprietary.
Affiliation Lutheran

Orange Home Inc
Byberry and Betz Rd, Hatboro, PA, 19040 (215) 675-0103
Medical Dir/Dir of Nursing Dr Maurice Gross and Dr Harvey Nassau.
Licensure Intermediate Care. *Beds* 14. *Certified* Medicaid.
Ownership Nonprofit.
Admissions Requirements Minimum age 65; Medical examination.
Staff RNs 1 (ft), 3 (pt); LPNs 1 (ft), 2 (pt); Nurses aides 2 (ft), 7 (pt); Activities coordinators 1 (pt); Dietitians 1 (pt).
Facilities Dining room; Activities room; Chapel; Crafts room; Laundry room; Barber/Beauty shop.
Activities Arts and Crafts; Prayer groups; Movies; Shopping trips; Dances/Social or cultural gatherings.

White Billet Nursing Home
412 S York Rd, Hatboro, PA, 19040 (215) 675-2828
Medical Dir/Dir of Nursing Dr R Bruce Lutz.

Licensure Skilled Care. *Beds* 33.
Ownership Proprietary.
Admissions Requirements Medical examination.
Staff RNs 1 (ft), 9 (pt); LPNs 5 (pt); Nurses aides 5 (ft), 14 (pt); Physical therapists 2 (ft); Recreational therapists 1 (ft); Activities coordinators 1 (ft); Dietitians 1 (ft); Dentists 1 (ft); Podiatrists 1 (ft).
Facilities Dining room; Activities room; Chapel; Crafts room; Barber/Beauty shop.
Activities Arts and Crafts; Reading groups; Prayer groups; Movies; Dances/Social or cultural gatherings.
Description Since its establishment in 1960, the White Billet Nursing Home has developed a reputation for maintaining the highest standards of skilled nursing care to the aged and the infirmed.

HAVERTOWN

Haverford Nursing and Rehabilitation Center*
2050 Old West Chester Pike, Havertown, PA, 19083 (215) 449-8600
Licensure Skilled Care. *Beds* 100. *Certified* Medicare.
Ownership Proprietary.

HAZELTON

Lutheran Home—Hazelton*
143 W Broad St, Hazelton, PA, 18201 (717) 455-7578
Licensure Skilled Care. *Beds* 61. *Certified* Medicaid; Medicare.
Ownership Nonprofit.
Affiliation Lutheran

Saint Luke Manor*
1711 E Broad St, Hazelton, PA, 18201 (717) 455-8571
Licensure Skilled Care. *Beds* 104. *Certified* Medicaid.
Ownership Nonprofit.

HELLERTOWN

Mary Ellen Convalescent Home Inc
204 Leithsville Rd, Hellertown, PA, 18055 (215) 838-7901
Licensure Intermediate Care. *Beds* 52. *Certified* Medicare.
Ownership Proprietary.
Admissions Requirements Medical examination.
Staff RNs 3 (ft), 3 (pt); LPNs 3 (ft), 3 (pt); Nurses aides 30 (ft); Physical therapists 1 (pt); Reality therapists 1 (pt); Recreational therapists 1 (pt); Occupational therapists 1 (pt); Speech therapists 1 (pt); Activities coordinators 1 (pt); Dietitians 1 (pt); Dentists 1 (pt); Ophthalmologists 1 (pt); Podiatrists 1 (pt); Audiologists 1 (pt).
Facilities Dining room; Activities room; Library.
Activities Arts and Crafts; Cards; Games; Reading groups; Prayer groups; Shopping trips; Dances/Social or cultural gatherings.

Description Facility is located in a country setting, one story with grounds for walking; not an institution but a home for residents.

HERMITAGE

Hospital Care Center of Hermitage
3726 E State St, Hermitage, PA, 16146 (412) 342-5279
Medical Dir/Dir of Nursing M Jane Morris DO.
Licensure Intermediate Care. *Beds* 28. *Certified* Medicaid; Medicare.
Ownership Proprietary.
Admissions Requirements Medical examination.
Staff RNs 1 (ft), 6 (pt); LPNs 1 (ft); Nurses aides 7 (ft), 2 (pt); Activities coordinators 1 (ft).
Facilities Dining room; Activities room; Laundry room.
Activities Arts and Crafts; Cards; Games; Reading groups; Prayer groups; Movies; Shopping trips.

John XXIII Home For Senior Citizens
2250 Shenango Valley Fwy, Hermitage, PA, 16148 (412) 981-3200
Medical Dir/Dir of Nursing Dr Amanto D'Amore.
Licensure Skilled Care; Intermediate Care. *Beds* SNF 37; ICF 32. *Certified* Medicaid.
Ownership Nonprofit.
Admissions Requirements Minimum age 65; Medical examination.
Staff RNs 3 (ft), 5 (pt); LPNs 6 (ft), 8 (pt); Nurses aides 14 (ft), 27 (pt); Activities coordinators 1 (ft), 2 (pt); Social workers 1 (ft).
Affiliation Roman Catholic
Facilities Dining room; Physical therapy room; Activities room; Chapel; Laundry room; Barber/Beauty shop.
Activities Arts and Crafts; Cards; Games; Reading groups; Prayer groups; Movies; Shopping trips.

Nugent Convalescent Home Inc
500 Clarksville Rd, Hermitage, PA, 16148 (412) 342-7344
Admin Lillian E Nugent. *Medical Dir/Dir of Nursing* Dr T Armour, Dr W McDowell, and Dr J Bolotin.
Licensure Skilled Care. *Beds* 101. *Certified* Medicaid; Medicare.
Ownership Proprietary.
Admissions Requirements Minimum age 18; Medical examination.
Staff Physicians 2 (pt); RNs 4 (ft), 7 (pt); LPNs 4 (ft), 4 (pt); Orderlies 2 (ft); Nurses aides 22 (ft), 11 (pt); Physical therapists 1 (pt); Speech therapists 1 (pt); Dietitians 1 (pt); Dentists 1 (pt); Podiatrists 1 (pt).
Facilities Dining room; Physical therapy room; Activities room; Crafts room; Laundry room; Barber/Beauty shop.
Activities Arts and Crafts; Cards; Games; Reading groups; Prayer groups; Movies; Dances/Social or cultural gatherings.
Description Centrally located near shopping, churches, and main highways, our programs include an annual picnic, annual Christmas party, bridal show, and monthly birthday parties. Various activities take place weekly.

HERSHEY

Alpine Nursing and Convalescent Center*
PO Box 377, Ruhe Haus Ln, Hershey, PA, 17033 (717) 533-3351
Licensure Skilled Care; Intermediate Care. *Beds* SNF 147; ICF 60. *Certified* Medicaid; Medicare.
Ownership Proprietary.

HILLSDALE

Mountain View Nursing Home
Rt 286, Box 2, Hillsdale, PA, 15746 (814) 743-6613 or (412) 254-2244
Medical Dir/Dir of Nursing Dr Chester Kauffmann.
Licensure Skilled Care. *Beds* 89. *Certified* Medicaid; Medicare.
Ownership Proprietary.
Admissions Requirements Minimum age 21; Medical examination; Physician's request.
Staff RNs 5 (ft), 5 (pt); LPNs 4 (ft), 8 (pt); Nurses aides 18 (ft), 11 (pt); Activities coordinators 1 (ft), 1 (pt).
Facilities Dining room; Physical therapy room; Activities room; Chapel; Crafts room; Laundry room; Barber/Beauty shop; Library; Enclosed garden/courtyard.
Activities Arts and Crafts; Cards; Games; Reading groups; Prayer groups; Movies; Shopping trips; Dances/Social or cultural gatherings; Special holiday events and outings.
Description A chapel exists for both community and in-house religious services. Free meals and special social hours with entertainment are available for residents and guests. Visiting hours are open and overnight accomodations are arranged for families with very ill loved ones.

HOLLAND

Gloria Dei Village Health Care Center*
280 Middle Holland Rd, Holland, PA, 18966 (215) 322-6100
Licensure Skilled Care. *Beds* 80. *Certified* Medicaid; Medicare.
Ownership Nonprofit.

Saint Joseph's Home for the Aged
1182 Holland Rd, Holland, PA, 18966 (215) 357-5511
Medical Dir/Dir of Nursing Dr Thomas Kardish.
Licensure Skilled Care. *Beds* 38. *Certified* Medicaid.
Ownership Nonprofit.
Admissions Requirements Minimum age 65; Medical examination.
Staff Physicians; RNs; LPNs; Nurses aides; Physical therapists; Recreational therapists; Occupational therapists; Speech therapists; Activities coordinators; Dietitians; Dentists; Ophthalmologists; Podiatrists; Audiologists.
Affiliation Roman Catholic
Facilities Dining room; Physical therapy room; Activities room; Chapel; Crafts room; Laundry room; Barber/Beauty shop; Library.

Activities Arts and Crafts; Cards; Games; Reading groups; Prayer groups; Movies; Dances/Social or cultural gatherings.

HOLLIDAYSBURG

Allegheny Lutheran Home
916 Hickory St, Hollidaysburg, PA, 16648 (814) 695-5563
Admin Lois J Gutshall. *Medical Dir/Dir of Nursing* J DeKoning.
Licensure Skilled Care; Intermediate Care. *Beds* SNF 32; ICF 57. *Certified* Medicaid; Medicare.
Ownership Nonprofit.
Admissions Requirements Minimum age 65; Medical examination.
Staff Physicians 2 (pt); RNs 3 (ft), 6 (pt); LPNs 8 (ft), 8 (pt); Nurses aides 22 (ft), 10 (pt); Physical therapists 3 (ft); Recreational therapists 3 (ft), 1 (pt); Speech therapists 1 (pt); Activities coordinators 1 (ft); Dietitians 1 (ft); Podiatrists 1 (pt).
Affiliation Lutheran
Facilities Dining room; Physical therapy room; Activities room; Crafts room; Barber/Beauty shop.
Activities Arts and Crafts; Cards; Games; Prayer groups; Movies; Shopping trips; Dances/Social or cultural gatherings.

Garvey Manor
Logan Blvd, Hollidaysburg, PA, 16648 (814) 695-5571
Medical Dir/Dir of Nursing Dr John Sheedy.
Licensure Skilled Care; Intermediate Care. *Beds* SNF 29; ICF 127. *Certified* Medicaid; Medicare.
Ownership Nonprofit.
Admissions Requirements Minimum age 65; Medical examination; Physician's request.
Staff RNs 6 (ft), 3 (pt); LPNs 13 (ft), 9 (pt); Nurses aides 56 (ft); Physical therapists 1 (pt); Reality therapists 1 (pt); Recreational therapists 1 (ft); Occupational therapists 1 (pt); Activities coordinators; Dietitians; Podiatrists.
Affiliation Roman Catholic
Facilities Dining room; Physical therapy room; Activities room; Chapel; Crafts room; Laundry room; Barber/Beauty shop; Library.
Activities Arts and Crafts; Cards; Games; Reading groups; Prayer groups; Movies; Shopping trips; Dances/Social or cultural gatherings.
Description Facility features a day care center for children 4 days per week providing intergenerational grouping.

Hollidaysburg Veteran Home*
PO Box 391, Hollidaysburg, PA, 16648 (814) 696-5555
Licensure Skilled Care. *Beds* 202.
Ownership Nonprofit.

United Presbyterian Home of Hollidaysburg
220 Newry St, Hollidaysburg, PA, 16648 (814) 695-5095
Medical Dir/Dir of Nursing K L Beers MD.
Licensure Skilled Care. *Beds* 67. *Certified* Medicaid.
Ownership Nonprofit.
Staff Physicians 1 (pt); RNs 5 (ft), 5 (pt); LPNs 5 (ft), 6 (pt); Nurses aides 29 (ft), 8 (pt);

Physical therapists 1 (pt); Occupational therapists 1 (pt); Activities coordinators 1 (ft).
Affiliation Presbyterian
Facilities Dining room; Physical therapy room; Chapel; Laundry room; Barber/Beauty shop.
Activities Arts and Crafts; Games; Reading groups; Prayer groups; Shopping trips; Local groups provide entertainment.
Description Facility strives to maintain a home-like atmosphere for all residents. Goal is to provide understanding and quality care for the aging and convalescing. Each resident is encouraged to become an important part of a very special family.

HOMESTEAD

Willis Nursing Center
1800 West St, Homestead, PA, 15120 (412) 462-2000
Medical Dir/Dir of Nursing Shin H Choi MD.
Licensure Skilled Care. *Beds* 74. *Certified* Medicaid; Medicare.
Ownership Nonprofit.
Admissions Requirements Medical examination.
Staff RNs 4 (ft), 8 (pt); LPNs 8 (ft), 4 (pt); Nurses aides 16 (ft), 17 (pt); Physical therapists 2 (ft); Recreational therapists 1 (pt); Occupational therapists 1 (pt); Speech therapists 1 (ft); Dietitians 1 (ft); Dentists 1 (pt); Ophthalmologists 1 (pt); Podiatrists 1 (pt); Audiologists 1 (pt).
Facilities Physical therapy room; Activities room; Chapel; Laundry room.
Activities Arts and Crafts; Prayer groups; Weekly church services.
Description Facility is hospital-based.

HONESDALE

Ellen Memorial Health Care Center
PO Box 625, Rt 1, Honesdale, PA, 18431 (717) 253-5690
Medical Dir/Dir of Nursing Young Woo Lee MD.
Licensure Skilled Care. *Beds* SNF 122. *Certified* Medicaid; Medicare.
Ownership Proprietary.
Admissions Requirements Physician's request.
Staff Physicians 1 (pt); RNs 5 (ft), 4 (pt); Occupational therapists 3 (pt); Speech therapists 1 (pt); Activities coordinators 2 (ft); Dietitians 1 (pt).
Facilities Dining room; Physical therapy room; Activities room; Chapel; Crafts room; Laundry room; Barber/Beauty shop.
Activities Arts and Crafts; Cards; Games; Reading groups; Prayer groups; Movies; Dances/Social or cultural gatherings.

Peck Convalescent Home
814 Court St, Honesdale, PA, 18431 (717) 253-0390
Admin Norma Nonvenmacher.
Licensure Intermediate Care. *Beds* 27. *Certified* Medicaid.
Ownership Proprietary.
Admissions Requirements Medical examination; Physician's request.
Staff RNs 3 (pt); LPNs 3 (ft); Nurses aides 6

(ft); Occupational therapists 1 (pt); Activities coordinators 1 (ft); Dietitians 1 (pt).
Facilities Dining room; Activities room; Laundry room.
Activities Arts and Crafts; Cards; Games; Reading groups; Prayer groups; Movies; Shopping trips; Dances/Social or cultural gatherings.
Description Facility has a small, home-like atmosphere.

Wayne County Memorial Hospital*
Park and West Sts, Honesdale, PA, 18431 (717) 253-1300
Licensure Skilled Care. *Beds* 28. *Certified* Medicaid; Medicare.
Ownership Nonprofit.

HONEYBROOK

Hickory House Nursing Home Inc
Rt 3, Box 84, Honeybrook, PA, 19344 (215) 942-2377
Licensure Skilled Care; Intermediate Care.
Beds SNF 70; ICF 30. *Certified* Medicaid; Medicare.
Ownership Proprietary.

Tel Hai Retirement Community
Rt 2, Honeybrook, PA, 19344 (215) 273-3149
Medical Dir/Dir of Nursing Dr Richard Smith.
Licensure Skilled Care. *Beds* 120. *Certified* Medicare.
Ownership Nonprofit.
Admissions Requirements Medical examination.
Staff RNs 5 (ft), 5 (pt); LPNs 9 (ft), 4 (pt); Nurses aides 42 (ft), 21 (pt); Physical therapists 4 (pt); Reality therapists 1 (pt); Recreational therapists 1 (pt); Occupational therapists 1 (pt); Speech therapists 1 (pt); Activities coordinators 3 (ft); Dietitians 1 (pt); Dentists 1 (pt); Ophthalmologists 1 (pt); Podiatrists 1 (pt); Audiologists 1 (pt).
Affiliation Mennonite
Facilities Dining room; Physical therapy room; Activities room; Chapel; Crafts room; Laundry room; Barber/Beauty shop; Library.
Activities Arts and Crafts; Cards; Games; Reading groups; Prayer groups; Movies; Shopping trips; Dances/Social or cultural gatherings; Pleasure trips; Parade participation.
Description Facility is located in a rural area.

HUNTINGDON

Huntingdon County Nursing Home
Warm Springs Ave, Huntingdon, PA, 16652 (814) 643-4210
Admin Pat K Magdaj. *Medical Dir/Dir of Nursing* Dr Thomas Meloy.
Licensure Skilled Care; Intermediate Care.
Beds SNF 25; ICF 68. *Certified* Medicaid; Medicare.
Ownership Public.
Admissions Requirements Medical examination; Physician's request.
Staff Physicians 1 (ft); RNs 3 (ft), 3 (pt); LPNs 4 (ft), 8 (pt); Orderlies 3 (ft), 4 (pt); Nurses aides 11 (ft), 35 (pt); Recreational therapists 1 (ft); Activities coordinators 1 (pt); Dietitians 1 (ft).
Facilities Dining room; Physical therapy room;

Activities room; Crafts room; Barber/Beauty shop.
Activities Arts and Crafts; Cards; Games; Reading groups; Prayer groups; Movies; Pet therapy; Gourmet club; Intergenerational programs.

IMMACULATA

Camilla Hall
Immaculata, PA, 19345 (215) 644-1152
Licensure Skilled Care. *Beds* 150.
Ownership Nonprofit.

INDIANA

Cameron Manor Inc*
1515 Wayne Ave, Indiana, PA, 15701 (412) 349-5300
Licensure Skilled Care; Intermediate Care.
Beds SNF 63; ICF 58. *Certified* Medicaid; Medicare.
Ownership Proprietary.

Indian Haven
1671 Saltsburg Ave, Indiana, PA, 15701 (412) 465-2294 or (412) 463-9333
Admin Ruth McCurdy. *Medical Dir/Dir of Nursing* Dr William C Vernocy.
Licensure Skilled Care; Intermediate Care.
Beds 125. *Certified* Medicaid; Medicare.
Ownership Public.
Admissions Requirements Medical examination.
Staff Physicians 1 (pt); RNs 10 (ft), 1 (pt); LPNs 15 (ft); Nurses aides 54 (ft); Speech therapists; Activities coordinators 2 (ft); Dietitians 1 (ft).
Facilities Dining room; Physical therapy room; Activities room; Barber/Beauty shop.
Activities Arts and Crafts; Cards; Games; Reading groups; Prayer groups; Movies; Dances/Social or cultural gatherings.

Indiana Presbyterian Homes*
1155 Indian Springs Rd, Indiana, PA, 15701 (412) 349-4870
Licensure Skilled Care; Intermediate Care.
Beds SNF 60; ICF 60. *Certified* Medicaid.
Ownership Nonprofit.
Affiliation Presbyterian

Scenery Hill Manor Inc*
Rt 5, Lions Health Camp Rd, Indiana, PA, 15701 (412) 463-7600
Licensure Skilled Care. *Beds* 58. *Certified* Medicaid; Medicare.
Ownership Proprietary.

JEANNETTE

Harmony Golden Years Home Inc
206 N 1st St, Jeannette, PA, 15644 (412) 527-1358
Licensure Intermediate Care. *Beds* 26. *Certified* Medicaid.
Ownership Proprietary.

JERSEY SHORE

Leader Nursing Rehabilitation Center*
Thompson and Kerr Sts, Jersey Shore, PA,
17740 (717) 398-4747
Licensure Skilled Care; Intermediate Care.
Beds SNF 50; ICF 70. *Certified* Medicaid;
Medicare.
Ownership Proprietary.

JOHNSTOWN

Allegheny Lutheran Home*
807 Goucher St, Johnstown, PA, 15905 (814)
255-4103
Licensure Skilled Care; Intermediate Care.
Beds SNF 40; ICF 29. *Certified* Medicaid;
Medicare.
Ownership Nonprofit.
Affiliation Lutheran

Arbutus Park Manor Inc*
207 Ottawa St, Johnstown, PA, 15904 (814)
266-3559
Licensure Intermediate Care. *Beds* 102. *Certified* Medicaid.
Ownership Nonprofit.

Cambria County Nursing Care Center
1017 Franklin St, Johnstown, PA, 15905 (814)
539-8561
Medical Dir/Dir of Nursing Geroge W Katter
MD.
Licensure Skilled Care. *Beds* 75. *Certified* Medicaid; Medicare.
Ownership Public.
Admissions Requirements Medical examination.
Staff Physicians 1 (ft); RNs 10 (ft), 2 (pt);
LPNs 9 (ft), 2 (pt); Nurses aides 27 (ft);
Physical therapists 1 (ft); Reality therapists 1
(pt); Recreational therapists 1 (ft); Occupational
therapists 1 (ft); Speech therapists 1 (pt); Activities coordinators 1 (ft); Podiatrists 1 (pt).
Facilities Dining room; Physical therapy room;
Activities room; Laundry room.
Activities Arts and Crafts; Cards; Games;
Reading groups; Prayer groups; Movies.
Description Facility is unique in that it is
owned by the county, but managed under contract by Mercy Hospital; being adjacent to a
hospital allows for a high level of skilled care.

Hiram G Andrews Center*
727 Goucher St, Johnstown, PA, 15905 (814)
225-5881
Licensure Intermediate Care. *Beds* 61. *Certified* Medicare.
Ownership Nonprofit.

Presbyterian Home—Johnstown
787 Goucher St, Johnstown, PA, 15905 (814)
255-5539
Admin Leah H Williams. *Medical Dir/Dir of
Nursing* Dr Harry Bremer.
Licensure Intermediate Care. *Beds* 23. *Certified* Medicaid.
Ownership Nonprofit.
Admissions Requirements Minimum age 62;
Medical examination.
Staff RNs 1 (ft); LPNs 7 (ft); Nurses aides 13
(ft); Activities coordinators 1 (ft); Dietitians 1

(pt).
Affiliation Presbyterian
Facilities Dining room; Activities room; Chapel; Laundry room; Barber/Beauty shop;
Library.
Activities Games; Reading groups; Prayer
groups; Movies; Shopping trips.
Description Quality care in a Christian setting.

KANE

Lutheran Home—Kane
S Clay St Ext, Kane, PA, 16735 (814) 837-6706
Admin Betty J Bush. *Medical Dir/Dir of
Nursing* C R Bentz MD.
Licensure Skilled Care. *Beds* 90. *Certified* Medicaid.
Ownership Nonprofit.
Admissions Requirements Minimum age 65;
Medical examination.
Staff RNs 3 (ft), 4 (pt); LPNs 3 (ft), 2 (pt);
Nurses aides 21 (ft), 20 (pt); Physical therapists
1 (ft), 1 (pt); Activities coordinators 1 (ft), 1
(pt).
Affiliation Lutheran
Facilities Dining room; Physical therapy room;
Activities room; Chapel; Crafts room; Laundry
room; Barber/Beauty shop; Library.
Activities Arts and Crafts; Cards; Games; Prayer groups; Movies; Dances/Social or cultural
gatherings; Music 'n motion (exercise therapy).
Description Provides skilled nursing (restorative and rehabilitative) care; continuous life
care programs in independent private cottages;
respite care (short-term stay).

KENNETT SQUARE

Crosslands Inc
PO Box 100, Rt 926, Kennett Square, PA,
19348 (215) 399-0704
Licensure Skilled Care. *Beds* 40. *Certified* Medicare.
Ownership Proprietary.

Kendal at Longwood*
Box 100, Kennett Square, PA, 19348 (215)
388-7001
Licensure Skilled Care; Intermediate Care.
Beds SNF 58; ICF 32. *Certified* Medicare.
Ownership Nonprofit.

Linden Hall
147 W State St, Kennett Square, PA, 19348
(215) 444-2577
Medical Dir/Dir of Nursing Clifton M Durning
MD.
Licensure Skilled Care. *Beds* 16.
Ownership Nonprofit.
Admissions Requirements Medical examination.
Staff RNs 6 (pt); LPNs 3 (pt); Nurses aides 8
(ft); Activities coordinators 2 (pt).
Affiliation Society of Friends
Facilities Dining room; Physical therapy room;
Activities room.
Activities Arts and Crafts; Games; Reading
groups; Movies; Dances/Social or cultural gatherings.

KINGSTON

**Leader Nursing and Rehabilitation Center—
East***
200 2nd Ave, Kingston, PA, 18704 (717)
299-9315
Licensure Skilled Care; Intermediate Care.
Beds SNF 160; ICF 20. *Certified* Medicaid;
Medicare.
Ownership Proprietary.

Leader Nursing Rehabilitation Center—West
Wyoming and Dorrance Sts, Kingston, PA,
18704 (717) 288-5496
Medical Dir/Dir of Nursing Dr Richard
Crompton.
Licensure Skilled Care. *Beds* 152. *Certified* Medicaid; Medicare.
Ownership Proprietary.
Staff RNs 8 (ft), 2 (pt); LPNs 5 (ft), 7 (pt);
Nurses aides 44 (ft), 11 (pt); Physical therapists
1 (ft); Recreational therapists 3 (pt); Occupational therapists 1 (pt); Speech therapists 1 (pt);
Activities coordinators 1 (ft).
Facilities Dining room; Physical therapy room;
Activities room; Chapel; Crafts room; Laundry
room; Barber/Beauty shop; Library.
Activities Arts and Crafts; Cards; Games;
Reading groups; Prayer groups; Movies; Shopping trips; Dances/Social or cultural gatherings.
Description The Leader Nursing and Rehabilitation Center-West is located in a prime
location, accessible by the major artery of the
valley, Wyoming Avenue. Besides having inhouse physical therapy, an out-patient physical
therapy program has been developed.

KITTANNING

Armstrong County Health Center*
Kittanning, PA, 16201 (412) 548-2222
Admin James R Bender. *Medical Dir/Dir of
Nursing* Dr Cyrus Slease.
Licensure Skilled Care. *Beds* 126. *Certified* Medicaid.
Ownership Nonprofit.
Admissions Requirements Medical examination; Physician's request.
Staff Physicians 1 (ft), 1 (pt); RNs 11 (ft), 3
(pt); LPNs 16 (ft), 4 (pt); Orderlies 5 (ft); Nurses
aides 57 (ft), 8 (pt); Physical therapists 1 (ft);
Speech therapists 1 (pt); Activities coordinators
1 (ft); Dietitians 1 (pt); Dentists 1 (pt); Ophthalmologists 1 (pt); Podiatrists 1 (pt).
Facilities Dining room; Physical therapy room;
Activities room; Crafts room; Laundry room;
Barber/Beauty shop.
Activities Arts and Crafts; Cards; Games;
Reading groups; Prayer groups; Movies; Shopping trips; Dances/Social or cultural gatherings.
Description Located within the boundaries of a
small county seat, this facility is a 4-story, renovated hospital with only a small yard. Because
independent movement of residents is
restricted, activities are brought to the unit
whenever possible. Socialization is encouraged
through a foster grandparent program, rides,
field trips, pet therapy, and a variety of group
programs.

Wesley Manor Health Care Center Inc
Rt 1, Box 27C, Rt 422, Kittanning, PA, 16201
(412) 545-2273
Admin Carol A Rohrabaugh. *Medical Dir/Dir of Nursing* Jeffrey Minteer MD.
Licensure Skilled Care; Intermediate Care.
Beds SNF 60; ICF 60. *Certified* Medicaid; Medicare.
Ownership Proprietary.
Admissions Requirements Medical examination.
Staff Physicians 2 (pt); RNs 5 (ft), 7 (pt); LPNs 5 (ft), 11 (pt); Orderlies 2 (pt); Nurses aides 28 (ft), 20 (pt); Physical therapists; Speech therapists; Activities coordinators 1 (ft); Dietitians 1 (pt); Dentists; Podiatrists.
Facilities Dining room; Physical therapy room; Activities room; Crafts room; Laundry room; Barber/Beauty shop.
Activities Arts and Crafts; Cards; Games; Prayer groups; Movies; Dances/Social or cultural gatherings.
Description Facility provides 24-hour professional care in warm, pleasant surroundings; offers semi-private and private rooms with private bathrooms, nurse call system, individual heat and air conditioning, comfortable chairs, and a view of the surrounding countryside; residents are encouraged to bring personal items to individualize their rooms.

LAFAYETTE HILLS

Masonic Home of Pennsylvania*
801 Ridge Pike, Lafayette Hills, PA, 19444
(215) 825-6100
Licensure Skilled Care; Intermediate Care.
Beds SNF 37; ICF 38. *Certified* Medicaid; Medicare.
Ownership Nonprofit.
Affiliation Masons

LAKE ARIEL

Julia Ribaudo Home*
297-298 Center Dr, Lake Ariel, PA, 18436
(717) 937-4381
Licensure Skilled Care. *Beds* 100. *Certified* Medicaid; Medicare.
Ownership Proprietary.

LANCASTER

Calvary Fellowship Home Inc*
502 Elizabeth Dr, Lancaster, PA, 17601 (717) 393-0711
Licensure Skilled Care. *Beds* 45. *Certified* Medicaid; Medicare.
Ownership Nonprofit.

Community Services Inc
PO Box 4631, Lancaster, PA, 17604
Admin Maria N Chee.
Licensure Intermediate Care for Mentally Retarded. *Beds* 32. *Certified* Medicaid.
Ownership Proprietary.

Conestoga View*
900 E King St, Lancaster, PA, 17602 (717) 299-7854
Licensure Skilled Care; Intermediate Care.
Beds SNF 132; ICF 320. *Certified* Medicaid.
Ownership Nonprofit.

Duke Convalescent Residence*
425 N Duke St, Lancaster, PA, 17602 (717) 397-4281
Licensure Skilled Care; Intermediate Care.
Beds SNF 74; ICF 65. *Certified* Medicaid; Medicare.
Ownership Proprietary.

Hamilton Arms of Pennsylvania*
336 S West End Ave, Lancaster, PA, 17603 (717) 393-0419
Licensure Skilled Care. *Beds* 56. *Certified* Medicaid; Medicare.
Ownership Proprietary.

Henry G Long Asylum
200 N West End Ave, Lancaster, PA, 17603 (717) 397-3926
Medical Dir/Dir of Nursing Peter J Altiman MD.
Licensure Skilled Care. *Beds* 16.
Ownership Nonprofit.
Admissions Requirements Minimum age 45; Medical examination.
Staff Physicians 4 (ft); RNs 3 (ft), 10 (pt); LPNs 1 (ft), 1 (pt); Nurses aides 5 (ft), 2 (pt); Physical therapists 1 (pt); Reality therapists 1 (pt); Recreational therapists 1 (pt); Occupational therapists 1 (pt); Activities coordinators 1 (pt); Dietitians 1 (pt); Dentists 1 (pt); Ophthalmologists 1 (pt); Podiatrists 1 (pt).
Facilities Dining room; Physical therapy room; Activities room; Chapel; Crafts room; Laundry room; Barber/Beauty shop; Library.
Activities Cards; Games; Shopping trips.

Lancashire Hall Inc*
2829 Lititz Pike, Lancaster, PA, 17601 (717) 569-3211
Licensure Skilled Care; Intermediate Care.
Beds SNF 96; ICF 96. *Certified* Medicaid; Medicare.
Ownership Proprietary.

Mennonite Home
1520 Old Harrisburg Pike, Lancaster, PA, 17601 (717) 393-1301
Admin Paul G Leaman. *Medical Dir/Dir of Nursing* Dr Harry H Hoffman.
Licensure Skilled Care; Intermediate Care.
Beds SNF 51; ICF 60. *Certified* Medicaid.
Ownership Nonprofit.
Admissions Requirements Minimum age 65; Medical examination.
Staff Physicians 3 (pt); RNs 5 (ft), 5 (pt); LPNs 12 (ft), 15 (pt); Orderlies 1 (ft); Nurses aides 20 (ft), 26 (pt); Physical therapists 1 (pt); Recreational therapists 1 (ft); Activities coordinators 1 (ft); Dietitians 1 (ft); Podiatrists 1 (pt).
Affiliation Mennonite
Facilities Dining room; Physical therapy room; Activities room; Chapel; Crafts room; Laundry room; Barber/Beauty shop; Library.
Activities Arts and Crafts; Cards; Games; Reading groups; Prayer groups; Shopping trips.
Description Facility is adjacent to metropolitan area with East's largest shopping mall across the street; render 100 meals-on-wheels 5 days a

week; planning on enlarging for personal care and independent living; volunteer and auxiliary programs.

Village Vista Skilled Nursing Facility
1941 Benmar Dr, Lancaster, PA, 17603 (717) 397-5583
Medical Dir/Dir of Nursing J D Kemrer MD.
Licensure Skilled Care. *Beds* 31. *Certified* Medicaid.
Ownership Proprietary.
Staff RNs 1 (ft), 3 (pt); LPNs 4 (ft), 1 (pt); Nurses aides 6 (ft), 9 (pt); Physical therapists; Activities coordinators 1 (pt); Dietitians.
Facilities Dining room; Activities room; Laundry room.
Activities Arts and Crafts; Games; Reading groups; Prayer groups.
Description Facility is located in a quiet residential setting with beautiful grounds surrounding nursing home. Small, intimate, homey setting with excellent reputation for quality care. Staff is willingly adaptable to needs and concerns of residents and their families.

Whitehall Nursing and Convalescent Center*
100 Abbeyville Rd, Lancaster, PA, 17603 (717) 397-4261
Licensure Skilled Care; Intermediate Care.
Beds SNF 145; ICF 30. *Certified* Medicaid; Medicare.
Ownership Proprietary.

LANDISVILLE

Community Services Inc-Main*
180 Main St, Landisville, PA, 17538 (717) 898-6323
Licensure Intermediate Care for Mentally Retarded. *Beds* 6. *Certified* Medicaid.
Ownership Proprietary.

Community Services Inc-Stanley*
180 Stanley Rd, Landisville, PA, 17538 (717) 569-5970
Licensure Intermediate Care for Mentally Retarded. *Beds* 4. *Certified* Medicaid.
Ownership Nonprofit.

LANGHORNE

American Medical Nursing Centers— Langhorne*
350 Manor Ave, Langhorne, PA, 19047 (215) 757-7667
Licensure Skilled Care. *Beds* 120. *Certified* Medicare.
Ownership Proprietary.

Crestview North Nursing and Rehabilitation Center
262 Toll Gate Rd, Langhorne, PA, 19047 (215) 968-4650
Medical Dir/Dir of Nursing Robert Kane DO.
Licensure Skilled Care. *Beds* 131. *Certified* Medicaid; Medicare.
Ownership Proprietary.
Admissions Requirements Medical examination.
Staff Physicians 8 (ft); RNs 5 (ft), 6 (pt); LPNs 9 (ft), 7 (pt); Orderlies 2 (ft), 1 (pt); Nurses aides

37 (ft), 15 (pt); Physical therapists 1 (ft); Occupational therapists 1 (pt); Speech therapists 1 (ft); Activities coordinators 2 (ft), 1 (pt); Dietitians 1 (ft); Dentists 1 (ft); Ophthalmologists 1 (ft); Podiatrists 1 (ft).
Facilities Physical therapy room; Laundry room; Barber/Beauty shop; Library; Lounges.
Activities Arts and Crafts; Cards; Games; Reading groups; Prayer groups; Movies; Shopping trips; Dances/Social or cultural gatherings.
Description Crestview North is a progressive skilled nursing facility located in a beautiful country setting that overlooks Core Creek Park. Provides sub-acute and skilled nursing care for patients coming from a hospital or home setting.

Maple Manor Nursing Home*
309 N Pine St, Langhorne, PA, 19047 (215) 757-3739
Licensure Skilled Care. *Beds* 82. *Certified* Medicaid; Medicare.
Ownership Proprietary.

LANSDALE

Elm Terrace Gardens*
660 N Broad St, Lansdale, PA, 19446 (215) 362-6087
Licensure Skilled Care. *Beds* 45. *Certified* Medicaid; Medicare.
Ownership Nonprofit.

Gwynedd Square for Nursing Convalescent Care
773 Sumneytown Pike, Lansdale, PA, 19446 (215) 699-7571
Licensure Skilled Care; Intermediate Care.
Beds SNF 111; ICF 70. *Certified* Medicaid; Medicare.
Ownership Proprietary.
Facilities Dining room; Physical therapy room; Activities room; Chapel; Laundry room; Barber/Beauty shop.
Activities Arts and Crafts; Cards; Games; Reading groups; Prayer groups; Movies; Shopping trips; Shopping trips; Dances/Social or cultural gatherings.

North Pennsylvania Convalescent Residence Inc*
25 W 5th St, Lansdale, PA, 19446 (215) 855-9765
Licensure Skilled Care. *Beds* 128. *Certified* Medicaid; Medicare.
Ownership Proprietary.

Saint Marys Manor
Lansdale Ave, Lansdale, PA, 19446 (215) 368-0900
Admin George C Stauffer. *Medical Dir/Dir of Nursing* Leonardo V Arano MD.
Licensure Skilled Care; Intermediate Care.
Beds SNF 30; ICF 40. *Certified* Medicaid.
Ownership Nonprofit.
Admissions Requirements Minimum age 60; Medical examination.
Staff Physicians 1 (pt); RNs 3 (ft), 13 (pt); LPNs 1 (ft), 7 (pt); Nurses aides 13 (ft), 17 (pt); Physical therapists 1 (pt); Occupational therapists 1 (pt); Activities coordinators 1 (ft), 1 (pt); Dietitians 1 (ft); Podiatrists 1 (pt).

Affiliation Roman Catholic
Facilities Dining room; Physical therapy room; Activities room; Chapel; Crafts room; Laundry room; Barber/Beauty shop; Library; Auditorium; Canteen; Gift shop.
Activities Arts and Crafts; Cards; Games; Reading groups; Prayer groups; Movies; Dances/Social or cultural gatherings; Entertainment provided by clubs.
Description Saint Mary's Manor is a one-story building with spacious, attractive grounds surrounding the entire facility. Saint Mary's Chapel is one of beauty and distinction. Facility offers a variety of activities to help keep the elderly active and content.

Villa of Divine Providence*
1001 Valley Forge Rd, Lansdale, PA, 19446 (215) 855-9700
Licensure Skilled Care. *Beds* 82.
Ownership Nonprofit.

LATROBE

Latrobe Area Hospital—Extended Care Facility
W 2nd Ave, Latrobe, PA, 15650 (412) 537-1176
Medical Dir/Dir of Nursing J R Mazero.
Licensure Skilled Care. *Beds* 18. *Certified* Medicaid; Medicare.
Ownership Nonprofit.
Admissions Requirements Medical examination; Physician's request.
Staff RNs 7 (ft), 2 (pt); LPNs 3 (ft), 5 (pt); Nurses aides 4 (ft), 3 (pt); Physical therapists 5 (ft); Reality therapists 1 (ft); Recreational therapists 1 (ft); Occupational therapists 2 (ft); Speech therapists 1 (ft); Activities coordinators 1 (ft); Dietitians 3 (ft); Audiologists 1 (ft).
Facilities Dining room; Physical therapy room; Activities room; Chapel; Crafts room; Laundry room.
Activities Arts and Crafts; Cards; Games; Reading groups; Birthday and special holiday celebrations.
Description Emphasis is on restorative and rehabilitation services to stabilize a medical/surgical problem and continue physical, occupational, or speech therapies begun in the hospital to prepare the patients for discharge to their home, personal care home, long-term care, or rehabilitative facility.

LAURELTON

Laurelton Center*
Laurelton, PA, 17835 (717) 922-3311
Licensure Intermediate Care for Mentally Retarded. *Beds* 413. *Certified* Medicaid.
Ownership Nonprofit.

LEBANON

Cedar Haven-Lebanon County Home*
500 S 5th Ave, Lebanon, PA, 17042 (717) 274-0421
Licensure Skilled Care; Intermediate Care.
Beds SNF 108; ICF 252. *Certified* Medicaid; Medicare.
Ownership Nonprofit.

Leader Nursing and Rehabilitation Center
900 Tuck St, Lebanon, PA, 17042 (717) 273-8595
Medical Dir/Dir of Nursing Dr Dale Brown-Bieber.
Licensure Skilled Care. *Beds* 120. *Certified* Medicaid; Medicare.
Ownership Proprietary.
Admissions Requirements Medical examination.
Staff RNs 4 (ft), 3 (pt); LPNs 6 (ft), 9 (pt); Nurses aides 23 (ft), 43 (pt); Physical therapists 1 (ft); Activities coordinators 1 (ft), 2 (pt); Cota 1 (pt).
Facilities Dining room; Physical therapy room; Activities room; Chapel; Crafts room; Laundry room; Barber/Beauty shop.
Activities Arts and Crafts; Cards; Games; Reading groups; Prayer groups; Movies; Shopping trips; Dances/Social or cultural gatherings.

Lebanon County Life Support
25 Metro Dr, Lebanon, PA, 17042 (717) 274-0493
Medical Dir/Dir of Nursing Bruce Yeamans MD and Drew Coutney MD.
Licensure Intermediate Care for Mentally Retarded. *Beds* 25. *Certified* Medicaid.
Ownership Nonprofit.
Admissions Requirements Medical examination; Physician's request.
Staff RNs 2 (ft); LPNs 8 (ft); Orderlies 1 (ft); Nurses aides 18 (ft), 3 (pt); Recreational therapists 1 (ft); Occupational therapists 1 (ft).
Facilities Activities room.
Activities Arts and Crafts; Games; Movies; Shopping trips.

Oakview
1407 Oak St, Lebanon, PA, 17042 (717) 273-5541
Admin Nancy S Mickel. *Medical Dir/Dir of Nursing* Dr Glenn Hirsch.
Licensure Skilled Care. *Beds* 28. *Certified* Medicaid.
Ownership Nonprofit.
Admissions Requirements Medical examination; Physician's request.
Staff RNs 1 (ft), 2 (pt); LPNs 1 (ft), 4 (pt); Nurses aides 8 (ft), 4 (pt); Recreational therapists 1 (ft); Occupational therapists 1 (pt).
Facilities Dining room; Activities room; Chapel; Crafts room; Laundry room; Barber/Beauty shop; Library.
Activities Arts and Crafts; Cards; Games; Reading groups; Prayer groups; Movies; Shopping trips; Dances/Social or cultural gatherings; Pet therapy; Kitchen band; Morning exercises.
Description Oakview Nursing Home is a facility large enough to operate successfully, yet small enough to offer its residents a home-like atmosphere. Under the capable direction of a board of directors, an administrator and a staff of 40 people, Oakview offers a well-rounded program striving to satisfy the spiritual, physical, and psycho-social needs of each resident. Provides 24-hour nursing service and 3 attending physicians provide 24-hour on call service and one weekly in-house visit. An excellent dietary service according to physicians orders; business, laundry, housekeeping, maintenance, and recreational services are provided.

Spang Crest Home*
1000 Quentin Rd, Lebanon, PA, 17042 (717)
272-4115
Licensure Skilled Care; Intermediate Care.
Beds SNF 35; ICF 70. *Certified* Medicaid;
Medicare.
Ownership Nonprofit.

LEHIGHTON

**Gnaden Huetten Nursing and Convalescent
Home***
11th and Hamilton Sts, Lehighton, PA, 18235
(215) 377-1300
Licensure Skilled Care. *Beds* 82. *Certified* Medicaid; Medicare.
Ownership Nonprofit.

**Mahoning Valley Nursing and Rehabilitation
Center**
Rt 1, Box 46, Lehighton, PA, 18235-9640 (717)
386-5522
Medical Dir/Dir of Nursing Dr Robert Frantz.
Licensure Skilled Care; Intermediate Care.
Beds SNF 59; ICF 61. *Certified* Medicaid;
Medicare.
Ownership Nonprofit.
Staff Physicians 3 (pt); RNs 4 (ft), 2 (pt); LPNs
9 (ft); Orderlies 5 (ft); Nurses aides 28 (ft);
Physical therapists 1 (pt); Occupational therapists 1 (pt); Speech therapists 1 (pt); Activities
coordinators 1 (ft); Dietitians 1 (pt); Dentists 1
(pt); Ophthalmologists 1 (pt); Podiatrists 1 (pt);
Audiologists 1 (pt).
Facilities Dining room; Physical therapy room;
Activities room; Crafts room; Barber/Beauty
shop.
Activities Arts and Crafts; Cards; Games;
Reading groups; Movies; Shopping trips.
Description The type of care needed depends
upon the condition of the guest which is determined by a physician. A dedicated, knowledgeable health care team is the hallmark of
Mahoning Valley's excellent reputation in the
community.

LEOLA

Community Services Inc*
312 Pleasant Valley Dr, Leola, PA, 17540 (717)
656-8005
Licensure Intermediate Care for Mentally
Retarded. *Beds* 5. *Certified* Medicaid.
Ownership Proprietary.

LEVITTOWN

**American Medical Nursing Centers—
Statesman***
2629 Trenton Rd, Levittown, PA, 19056 (215)
943-7777
Licensure Skilled Care; Intermediate Care.
Beds SNF 70; ICF 32. *Certified* Medicaid;
Medicare.
Ownership Proprietary.

LEWISBURG

Buffalo Valley Lutheran Village*
Old Fairground Rd, Lewisburg, PA, 17837
(717) 524-2221
Licensure Skilled Care; Intermediate Care.
Beds SNF 20; ICF 88. *Certified* Medicaid;
Medicare.
Ownership Nonprofit.
Affiliation Lutheran

Lewisburg United Methodist Home
Lewisburg, PA, 17837 (717) 524-2271
Medical Dir/Dir of Nursing Dr Donald
Steckel.
Licensure Skilled Care; Intermediate Care.
Beds SNF 90; ICF 136. *Certified* Medicaid;
Medicare.
Ownership Nonprofit.
Admissions Requirements Minimum age 65;
Medical examination.
Staff RNs 7 (ft), 4 (pt); LPNs 22 (ft), 8 (pt);
Orderlies 1 (ft); Nurses aides 86 (ft), 26 (pt);
Activities coordinators 1 (ft).
Affiliation Methodist
Facilities Dining room; Physical therapy room;
Activities room; Chapel; Crafts room; Laundry
room; Barber/Beauty shop; Library.
Activities Arts and Crafts; Cards; Games;
Reading groups; Prayer groups; Movies; Shopping trips; Dances/Social or cultural gatherings;
Regular church services.
Description Facility features a meals-on-wheels
program served from Home for Lewisburg
area. An area university uses home for clinical
training with success; pet dog on premises; local
public school students interact periodically with
residents; Victorian Mansion Museum listed on
the National and Pennsylvania Historical Register.

LEWISTOWN

Ohesson Manor*
350 Green Ave Extension, Lewistown, PA,
17044 (717) 242-1417
Licensure Skilled Care; Intermediate Care.
Beds SNF 35; ICF 99. *Certified* Medicaid;
Medicare.
Ownership Nonprofit.

William Penn Nursing Center Inc*
163 Summit Dr, Lewistown, PA, 17044 (717)
248-3941
Licensure Skilled Care; Intermediate Care.
Beds SNF 61; ICF 60. *Certified* Medicaid;
Medicare.
Ownership Proprietary.

LIGONIER

Bethlen Hungarian Home*
PO Box 657, Ligonier, PA, 15658 (412)
238-6711
Licensure Skilled Care; Intermediate Care.
Beds SNF 45; ICF 58. *Certified* Medicaid;
Medicare.
Ownership Nonprofit.

Pine Hurst Nursing and Convalescent Home
Rt 4, Ligonier, PA, 15658 (412) 593-7720
Licensure Skilled Care. *Beds* 23.
Ownership Proprietary.

LIMA

Fair Acres Geriatric Center*
Rt 352, Middletown Rd, Lima, PA, 19037
(215) 891-7411
Licensure Skilled Care; Intermediate Care.
Beds SNF 706; ICF 211. *Certified* Medicaid;
Medicare.
Ownership Nonprofit.

Lima Estates*
411 N Middletown Rd, Lima, PA, 19037 (215)
565-7020
Licensure Skilled Care. *Beds* 60.
Ownership Nonprofit.

LIMEPORT

Mount Trexler Skilled Nursing Unit
Limeport, PA, 18049 (215) 965-9937
Licensure Skilled Care. *Beds* 65. *Certified* Medicaid; Medicare.
Ownership Nonprofit.

LITITZ

Audubon Villa*
125 S Broad St, Lititz, PA, 17543 (717)
626-0211
Licensure Skilled Care. *Beds* 32.
Ownership Proprietary.

Friendship Community*
Rt 3, Box 254, Lititz, PA, 17543 (717) 656-2466
Licensure Intermediate Care for Mentally
Retarded. *Beds* 14. *Certified* Medicaid.
Ownership Nonprofit.

Landis Home*
Rt 3, Lititz, PA, 17543 (717) 569-3271
Licensure Skilled Care; Intermediate Care.
Beds SNF 47; ICF 62. *Certified* Medicaid.
Ownership Nonprofit.

Luther Acres*
600 E Main St, Lititz, PA, 17543 (717)
626-1171
Licensure Skilled Care; Intermediate Care.
Beds SNF 41; ICF 57. *Certified* Medicaid;
Medicare.
Ownership Nonprofit.
Affiliation Lutheran

Moravian Manor*
300 W Lemon St, Lititz, PA, 17543 (717)
626-0214
Licensure Skilled Care; Intermediate Care.
Beds SNF 55; ICF 55. *Certified* Medicaid;
Medicare.
Ownership Nonprofit.
Affiliation Moravian

United Zion Home Inc*
Rt 2, Lititz, PA, 17543 (717) 626-2071
Licensure Skilled Care. *Beds* 46. *Certified* Medicaid.
Ownership Nonprofit.

LIVERPOOL

Good Samaritan Home
Front St, Liverpool, PA, 17045 (717) 444-3713
Admin Esther J Mohler. *Medical Dir/Dir of Nursing* Dr James Minahan.
Licensure Intermediate Care. *Beds* 25. *Certified* Medicaid.
Ownership Proprietary.
Admissions Requirements Minimum age 16; Medical examination.
Staff RNs 1 (ft), 2 (pt); LPNs 4 (pt); Nurses aides 8 (pt); Recreational therapists 1 (pt); Activities coordinators 1 (pt).
Facilities Dining room.
Activities Arts and Crafts; Cards; Games; Reading groups; Prayer groups; Movies; Shopping trips; Dances/Social or cultural gatherings.

Nipple Convalescent Home
100 S Front St, Liverpool, PA, 17045 (717) 444-3413
Medical Dir/Dir of Nursing William L Youngling MD.
Licensure Skilled Care. *Beds* 37. *Certified* Medicaid.
Ownership Proprietary.
Admissions Requirements Minimum age 17; Medical examination; Physician's request.
Staff Physicians 1 (pt); RNs 2 (ft), 1 (pt); LPNs 4 (ft); Nurses aides 20 (ft); Physical therapists; Occupational therapists; Speech therapists; Activities coordinators; Dietitians; Dentists.
Facilities Dining room; Physical therapy room; Activities room; Crafts room; Laundry room; Barber/Beauty shop; Library.
Activities Arts and Crafts; Cards; Games; Reading groups; Movies.

LOCK HAVEN

Lock Haven Hospital—Extended Care Facility*
Fourth and Nelson Sts, Lock Haven, PA, 17745 (717) 748-7721
Licensure Skilled Care; Intermediate Care. *Beds* SNF 60; ICF 60. *Certified* Medicaid; Medicare.
Ownership Nonprofit.

Susque View Home Inc
Cree Dr, Lock Haven, PA, 17745 (717) 748-9377
Medical Dir/Dir of Nursing Gerald Del Gorippo MD.
Licensure Skilled Care; Intermediate Care. *Beds* SNF 40; ICF 120. *Certified* Medicaid; Medicare.
Ownership Nonprofit.
Staff Physicians 2 (pt); RNs 3 (ft), 5 (pt); LPNs 4 (ft), 12 (pt); Orderlies 1 (ft), 1 (pt); Nurses aides 24 (ft), 22 (pt); Activities coordinators 2 (ft); Podiatrists 1 (pt).
Facilities Dining room; Physical therapy room; Activities room; Chapel; Crafts room; Laundry

room; Barber/Beauty shop.
Activities Arts and Crafts; Games; Movies; Shopping trips.
Description The facility is closely associated with a community hospital and is located in north central Pennsylvania. The building contains some hospital-based services and a large indoor garden.

LOWER BURRELL

Belair Nursing Home*
Chester Dr and Little Rd, Lower Burrell, PA, 15068 (412) 339-1071
Licensure Skilled Care; Intermediate Care. *Beds* SNF 89; ICF 18. *Certified* Medicare.
Ownership Proprietary.

MANHEIM

Mount Hope Dunkard Brethren Church Home
Mount Hope Rd, Box 312 RD 3, Manheim, PA, 17545 (717) 665-6365
Medical Dir/Dir of Nursing Dr William Stout.
Licensure Skilled Care. *Beds* 65. *Certified* Medicaid.
Ownership Nonprofit.
Admissions Requirements Minimum age 65; Medical examination.
Staff Physicians 7 (pt); RNs 3 (ft), 3 (pt); LPNs 4 (ft), 4 (pt); Orderlies 2 (pt).
Affiliation Church of the Brethren
Facilities Dining room; Activities room; Chapel; Crafts room; Laundry room.
Activities Arts and Crafts; Games; Reading groups; Prayer groups; Shopping trips.
Description A rural nursing facility, very common, not concerned about extravagance, but only concerned about good daily nursing care and providing a comfortable setting, good food, and a pleasant, Christian environment.

Pleasant View Rest Home Inc
Box 487, Manheim, PA, 17545 (717) 665-2445
Medical Dir/Dir of Nursing Dr Terrence Jones.
Licensure Skilled Care. *Beds* 130. *Certified* Medicaid.
Ownership Nonprofit.
Admissions Requirements Medical examination.
Staff Physicians; RNs; LPNs; Nurses aides; Physical therapists; Reality therapists; Recreational therapists; Activities coordinators; Dietitians; Dentists; Ophthalmologists; Podiatrists.
Facilities Dining room; Physical therapy room; Activities room; Chapel; Crafts room; Laundry room; Barber/Beauty shop.
Activities Arts and Crafts; Games; Reading groups; Prayer groups; Movies; Shopping trips.
Description Pleasant View is located in a pleasant, picturesque, rural setting in Penn Township, Lancaster County; licensed as a skilled nursing facility, intermediate beds are allocated. Pleasant View Manor, a residential facility, consists of 11 apartments.

MARKLESBURG

Fazio Nursing Home
Rt 40, Marklesburg, PA, 15459 (412) 329-5545
Admin Anthony Fazio. *Medical Dir/Dir of Nursing* E M Price MD.
Licensure Skilled Care; Intermediate Care. *Beds* 74. *Certified* Medicaid; Medicare.
Ownership Proprietary.
Admissions Requirements Minimum age 15; Medical examination.
Staff Physicians 1 (pt); RNs 6 (ft); LPNs 3 (ft); Orderlies 1 (ft); Nurses aides 36 (ft); Physical therapists 1 (pt); Recreational therapists 1 (pt); Occupational therapists 1 (pt); Speech therapists 1 (ft); Activities coordinators 1 (ft); Dietitians 1 (pt); Dentists 1 (pt); Podiatrists 1 (pt); Audiologists 1 (pt).
Facilities Dining room; Physical therapy room; Activities room; Barber/Beauty shop.
Activities Arts and Crafts; Cards; Games; Reading groups; Prayer groups; Movies; Dances/Social or cultural gatherings.
Description We provide full range of services at very reasonable cost. Nursing home sits on 37 acres of ground to give a very safe, private environment.

Spear Convalescent Home*
PO Box 37, Marklesburg, PA, 15459 (412) 329-4830
Licensure Skilled Care. *Beds* 79. *Certified* Medicaid.
Ownership Nonprofit.

MARS

Saint Johns Lutheran Home
Box 429, Mars, PA, 16046 (412) 625-1571
Medical Dir/Dir of Nursing William Schwerin MD.
Licensure Skilled Care; Intermediate Care. *Beds* SNF 150; ICF 103. *Certified* Medicaid; Medicare.
Ownership Nonprofit.
Admissions Requirements Minimum age 60; Medical examination.
Staff Physicians 2 (pt); RNs 8 (ft), 18 (pt); LPNs 16 (ft), 18 (pt); Orderlies 1 (ft); Nurses aides 100 (ft), 35 (pt); Physical therapists 2 (pt); Reality therapists 2 (pt); Recreational therapists 1 (ft), 2 (pt); Speech therapists 1 (pt); Activities coordinators 1 (ft); Dietitians 1 (ft), 1 (pt); Dentists 1 (pt); Podiatrists 1 (pt).
Affiliation Lutheran
Facilities Dining room; Physical therapy room; Activities room; Chapel; Crafts room; Laundry room; Barber/Beauty shop; Library.
Activities Arts and Crafts; Cards; Games; Reading groups; Prayer groups; Movies; Shopping trips; Dances/Social or cultural gatherings.
Description Founded in 1893, St John's is located on 20 acres in a residential community, nonprofit, affiliated with American Lutheran Church, open to all denominations. Provides all levels of geriatric care: post-hospital, sub-acute, short-term convalescence/rehabilitation, and other short-term therapeutic services (e.g. physical/speech therapy); intermediate/skilled nursing care; residential care; and independent apartment living.

Sherwood Oaks and Cranberry Lake Health Center
100 Norman Dr, Mars, PA, 16046
Admin Jace Gerie. *Medical Dir/Dir of Nursing* Dr J Robert Love.
Licensure Skilled Care; Residential Care.
Beds SNF 59; Residential Care 37. *Certified* Medicaid; Medicare.
Ownership Nonprofit.
Admissions Requirements Medical examination.
Staff Physicians 2 (pt); RNs 5 (ft), 4 (pt); LPNs 3 (ft), 3 (pt); Nurses aides 14 (ft), 8 (pt); Recreational therapists 1 (ft); Occupational therapists 1 (pt); Speech therapists 1 (pt); Dietitians 1 (pt); Dentists 1 (pt); Ophthalmologists; Podiatrists 1 (pt); Occupational therapy aides 1 (pt); Physical therapy aides 1 (pt).
Facilities Dining room; Physical therapy room; Activities room; Chapel; Crafts room; Laundry room; Barber/Beauty shop; Library; Indoor heated pool and Jaccuzzi; Greenhouse; Bank; Convenience store; Woodworking shop; Lapidary shop.
Activities Arts and Crafts; Cards; Games; Reading groups; Prayer groups; Movies; Shopping trips; Dances/Social or cultural gatherings; Bible study.
Description Located on 81 acres in Cranberry Township 23 miles north of Pittsburgh, facility offers those of retirement age an opportunity to ensure their independent lifestyle with the protection of health care at no additional charge.

MARTINSBURG

Homewood Retirement Center
430 S Market St, Martinsburg, PA, 16662 (814) 793-3728
Medical Dir/Dir of Nursing Richard H Bulger MD.
Beds 67. *Certified* Medicaid.
Ownership Nonprofit.
Admissions Requirements Minimum age 65; Medical examination.
Staff RNs 3 (ft), 4 (pt); LPNs 4 (ft), 3 (pt); Nurses aides 12 (ft), 15 (pt); Activities coordinators 1 (ft).
Affiliation Church of Christ
Facilities Dining room; Physical therapy room; Activities room; Crafts room; Laundry room; Barber/Beauty shop.
Activities Arts and Crafts; Cards; Games; Reading groups; Prayer groups; Movies; Shopping trips; Dances/Social or cultural gatherings.
Description A gracious retirement center located on a scenic 34 acre site in Morrison's Cove. In the shadow of the majestic Blue Mountains of south central Pennsylvania, residents enjoy a warm home-like atmosphere and the finest care available through the efforts of a thoughtful and dedicated staff.

Morrison Cove Home
429 S Market, Martinsburg, PA, 16662 (814) 793-2104
Licensure Skilled Care; Intermediate Care.
Beds SNF 47; ICF 57. *Certified* Medicaid; Medicare.
Admissions Requirements Medical examination.

Staff RNs; LPNs; Orderlies; Nurses aides; Occupational therapists.
Affiliation Church of the Brethren
Facilities Dining room; Physical therapy room; Activities room; Chapel; Crafts room; Laundry room; Barber/Beauty shop; Library.
Activities Arts and Crafts; Games; Reading groups; Prayer groups; Shopping trips.

MC KEES ROCKS

Robinson Development Center
Clever Rd, Mc Kees Rocks, PA, 15136 (412) 787-2350
Medical Dir/Dir of Nursing Timothy Ivey MD.
Licensure Intermediate Care for Mentally Retarded. *Beds* 133. *Certified* Medicaid.
Ownership Nonprofit.

MCCONNELLSBURG

Fulton County Medical Center
216 S 1st St, PO Box 68, McConnellsburg, PA, 17233 (717) 485-3155
Medical Dir/Dir of Nursing Dr Witt.
Licensure Skilled Care; Intermediate Care.
Beds SNF 41; ICF 15. *Certified* Medicaid; Medicare.
Ownership Nonprofit.
Staff Physicians 1 (ft), 5 (pt); RNs 2 (pt); LPNs 5 (ft), 5 (pt); Nurses aides 12 (ft), 16 (pt); Physical therapists 2 (pt); Speech therapists 1 (pt); Activities coordinators 1 (ft); Dietitians 1 (pt); Dentists 1 (pt); Ophthalmologists 1 (pt); Podiatrists 1 (pt); Audiologists 1 (pt).
Facilities Dining room; Physical therapy room; Activities room; Chapel; Laundry room; Barber/Beauty shop.
Activities Arts and Crafts; Cards; Games; Reading groups; Prayer groups; Shopping trips; Dances/Social or cultural gatherings.
Description Nestled in the beautiful mountains of south central Pennsylvania, facility offers a unique dimension in health care—long term and hospital care in the same facility; provides the necessary step between hospital and home; offers a new accommodating lifestyle to those with disabilities and chronic illnesses; helps individuals reach their maximum level of functioning.

MCMURRAY

McMurray Hills Manor Inc
249 W McMurray Rd, McMurray, PA, 15317 (412) 561-4406
Medical Dir/Dir of Nursing Dr Jon Adler.
Licensure Skilled Care; Intermediate Care.
Beds SNF 74; ICF 25. *Certified* Medicare.
Ownership Proprietary.
Admissions Requirements Minimum age 40; Medical examination.
Staff Physicians 2 (pt); RNs 22 (ft); LPNs 1 (ft), 1 (pt); Physical therapists 1 (ft); Speech therapists 1 (pt); Activities coordinators 1 (ft); Dietitians 1 (ft); Dentists 1 (pt); Podiatrists 1 (pt); Audiologists 1 (pt).
Facilities Dining room; Physical therapy room; Activities room; Chapel; Laundry room; Barber/Beauty shop; Library.

Activities Arts and Crafts; Cards; Games; Reading groups; Prayer groups; Movies; Shopping trips; Dances/Social or cultural gatherings.
Description Facility is located in country setting, features home cooked meals, and is located near 2 shopping malls; bus stop by facility.

MEADOWBROOK

Saint Josephs Manor*
1616 Huntingdon Pike, Meadowbrook, PA, 19046 (215) 947-4445
Licensure Skilled Care. *Beds* 197. *Certified* Medicaid; Medicare.
Ownership Nonprofit.

MEADVILLE

Mead Nursing Home*
N Park Ave Extension, Meadville, PA, 16335 (814) 337-4229
Licensure Skilled Care. *Beds* 150. *Certified* Medicaid.
Ownership Proprietary.

Meadville Hillside Home*
535 Williamson Rd, Meadville, PA, 16335 (814) 724-3117
Licensure Intermediate Care. *Beds* 17. *Certified* Medicaid.
Ownership Nonprofit.

United Methodist Home and Hopsital
31 N Park Ave, Meadville, PA, 16335 (814) 724-8000
Medical Dir/Dir of Nursing Dr Spiro E Moutsas.
Licensure Skilled Care; Intermediate Care.
Beds SNF 140; ICF 70. *Certified* Medicaid; Medicare.
Ownership Nonprofit.
Admissions Requirements Medical examination; Physician's request.
Staff RNs 10 (ft), 7 (pt); LPNs 13 (ft), 9 (pt); Nurses aides 43 (ft), 65 (pt); Occupational therapists 1 (ft); Activities coordinators 1 (ft), 4 (pt); Dietitians 1 (ft).
Affiliation Methodist
Facilities Dining room; Physical therapy room; Activities room; Chapel; Crafts room; Laundry room; Barber/Beauty shop; Library; Members' lounge; Picnic shelter.
Activities Arts and Crafts; Cards; Games; Reading groups; Prayer groups; Movies; Shopping trips; Dances/Social or cultural gatherings.

MECHANICSBURG

Bethany Village Retirement Center
325 Wesley Dr, Mechanicsburg, PA, 17055 (717) 766-0279
Admin Carol H Flusher. *Medical Dir/Dir of Nursing* Dr Kenneth Smeltier.
Licensure Skilled Care; Intermediate Care; Personal Care. *Beds* 69. *Certified* Medicaid; Medicare.
Ownership Nonprofit.
Admissions Requirements Minimum age 62; Medical examination.
Staff Physicians 2 (pt); RNs 5 (ft), 12 (pt);

LPNs 2 (ft), 8 (pt); Orderlies 1 (ft), 4 (pt); Nurses aides 5 (ft), 28 (pt); Physical therapists 1 (pt); Recreational therapists 1 (ft); Occupational therapists 1 (pt); Speech therapists 1 (pt); Activities coordinators 1 (ft); Dietitians 1 (ft); Dentists 1 (pt); Ophthalmologists 1 (pt); Podiatrists 2 (pt); Audiologists 1 (pt).
Affiliation Methodist
Facilities Dining room; Physical therapy room; Activities room; Chapel; Crafts room; Laundry room; Barber/Beauty shop; Library.
Activities Arts and Crafts; Games; Prayer groups; Movies; Shopping trips; Dances/Social or cultural gatherings.
Description Center has 5 levels of care—cottage, residential, personal, intermediate, and skilled; motto is "An adventure in creative living." Alexander Wholistic Clinic recently opened using the holistic approach to health; many programs offered residents including Venture which is an educational program covering topics such as nature, finance, religion, and history.

Messiah Village
100 Mt Allen Rd, Mechanicsburg, PA, 17055 (717) 697-4666
Medical Dir/Dir of Nursing Paul A Kase MD.
Licensure Skilled Care. *Beds* 90. *Certified* Medicaid; Medicare.
Ownership Nonprofit.
Admissions Requirements Minimum age 65; Medical examination.
Staff Physicians 1 (pt); RNs 7 (ft), 15 (pt); LPNs 1 (ft), 1 (pt); Orderlies 1 (ft), 1 (pt); Nurses aides 23 (ft), 24 (pt); Physical therapists 1 (ft); Recreational therapists 2 (ft), 1 (pt); Speech therapists 1 (pt); Activities coordinators 1 (ft); Dietitians 2 (ft); Podiatrists 2 (pt); Audiologists 1 (pt).
Affiliation Church of the Brethren
Facilities Dining room; Physical therapy room; Activities room; Chapel; Crafts room; Laundry room; Barber/Beauty shop; Library.
Activities Arts and Crafts; Games; Prayer groups; Movies; Shopping trips; Dances/Social or cultural gatherings.
Description Facility includes a day care center whose children participate in senior activities, promoting intergenerational relationships.

Seidle Memorial Hospital—Extended Care Unit*
Simpson and Filbert Sts, Mechanicsburg, PA, 17055 (717) 766-7691
Licensure Skilled Care. *Beds* 37. *Certified* Medicaid; Medicare.
Ownership Nonprofit.

MEDIA

Bishop Nursing Home Inc
318 S Orange St, Media, PA, 19063 (215) 565-4836
Medical Dir/Dir of Nursing Peter Binnion MD.
Licensure Skilled Care. *Beds* 164. *Certified* Medicaid.
Ownership Proprietary.
Staff Physicians 1 (pt); RNs 4 (ft), 8 (pt); LPNs 5 (ft), 8 (pt); Orderlies 4 (ft); Nurses aides 56 (ft), 8 (pt); Physical therapists 1 (pt); Occupa-

tional therapists 1 (pt); Activities coordinators 1 (ft); Dietitians 1 (pt).
Facilities Dining room; Physical therapy room; Activities room; Chapel; Crafts room; Laundry room; Barber/Beauty shop; Library.
Activities Arts and Crafts; Cards; Games; Reading groups; Prayer groups; Movies; Shopping trips; Dances/Social or cultural gatherings; Van trips; Bus trips; Special Parties; Weekly barbeque; Communioty speakers.

Care Center at Martins Run*
11 Martins Run, Marple Township, Media, PA, 19063 (215) 353-7660
Licensure Skilled Care. *Beds* 60. *Certified* Medicaid; Medicare.
Ownership Nonprofit.

Manchester House Nursing Home*
411 Manchester Ave, Media, PA, 19063 (215) 565-1800
Licensure Skilled Care. *Beds* 297. *Certified* Medicaid.
Ownership Proprietary.

Workmens Circle Home
3rd and Jackson Sts, Media, PA, 19063 (215) 566-2357
Medical Dir/Dir of Nursing Dr Reitsma.
Licensure Intermediate Care; Residential Care.
Beds ICF 32; Residential Care 53. *Certified* Medicaid.
Ownership Nonprofit.
Staff Physicians 1 (pt); RNs 3 (ft).

MERCER

Countryside Convalescent Home
Rt 7, Mercer, PA, 16137 (412) 662-5860
Admin Gerald Furma. *Medical Dir/Dir of Nursing* V A Ciambotti DO.
Licensure Skilled Care. *Beds* 48. *Certified* Medicaid.
Ownership Proprietary.
Admissions Requirements Medical examination; Physician's request.
Staff RNs 4 (ft); LPNs 5 (ft); Nurses aides 22 (ft); Physical therapists 1 (ft); Recreational therapists 2 (ft); Activities coordinators 1 (ft); Dietitians 1 (ft); Dentists 1 (pt); Podiatrists 1 (pt).
Facilities Dining room; Physical therapy room; Activities room; Chapel; Crafts room; Laundry room; Barber/Beauty shop.
Activities Arts and Crafts; Cards; Games; Reading groups; Prayer groups; Movies; Dances/Social or cultural gatherings.

Mercer County Home and Hospital*
Rt 2, Box 2060, Mercer, PA, 16137 (412) 662-5400
Licensure Skilled Care; Intermediate Care.
Beds SNF 171; ICF 42. *Certified* Medicaid; Medicare.
Ownership Nonprofit.

MIDDLETOWN

Frey Village
1020 N Union St, Middletown, PA, 17057 (717) 944-0451

Medical Dir/Dir of Nursing Robert P Dutlinger MD.
Licensure Skilled Care; Intermediate Care.
Beds SNF 43; ICF 93. *Certified* Medicaid; Medicare.
Ownership Nonprofit.
Admissions Requirements Minimum age 62; Medical examination.
Staff Physicians 1 (pt); RNs 8 (ft), 9 (pt); LPNs 7 (ft), 6 (pt); Nurses aides 26 (ft), 34 (pt); Physical therapists 1 (ft); Speech therapists 1 (pt); Activities coordinators 1 (ft); Dietitians 2 (ft), 1 (pt); Dentists 1 (pt); Podiatrists 2 (pt); Audiologists 1 (pt).
Affiliation Lutheran
Facilities Dining room; Physical therapy room; Activities room; Chapel; Crafts room; Laundry room; Barber/Beauty shop; Library; Guest house.
Activities Arts and Crafts; Cards; Games; Reading groups; Prayer groups; Movies; Shopping trips; Dances/Social or cultural gatherings.
Description Frey Village is a nonprofit retirement and caring facility of Tressler-Lutheran Service Associates. It is designed to serve retired senior adults with a wide variety of activities and accomodations. Some of those available to all residents are: chapel/auditorium, craftroom, convenience market/gift shop, personal laundry facilities, lounges; cultural, entertainment, and religious programs, scheduled transportation. Every effort is made to create and sustain a well-rounded community environment.

Odd Fellows Home of Pennsylvania Inc
999 W Harrisburg Pike, Middletown, PA, 17057 (717) 944-3351
Licensure Skilled Care; Intermediate Care; Residential Care. *Beds* SNF 51; ICF 51; Residential Care 71. *Certified* Medicaid; Medicare.
Ownership Nonprofit.
Affiliation Independent Order of Odd Fellows
Facilities Dining room; Physical therapy room; Activities room; Chapel; Crafts room; Laundry room; Barber/Beauty shop; Library.
Activities Arts and Crafts; Cards; Games; Reading groups; Prayer groups; Movies; Shopping trips; Dances/Social or cultural gatherings.

MIFFLIN

Locust Grove Retirement Village
Star Rt, Mifflin, PA, 17058 (717) 436-8921
Medical Dir/Dir of Nursing L G Guiser MD.
Licensure Skilled Care; Intermediate Care.
Beds SNF 12; ICF 61. *Certified* Medicaid; Medicare.
Ownership Nonprofit.
Admissions Requirements Medical examination.
Staff Physicians; RNs; LPNs; Nurses aides; Physical therapists; Speech therapists; Activities coordinators; Dietitians; Dentists; Ophthalmologists; Podiatrists; Audiologists.
Facilities Dining room; Physical therapy room; Activities room; Chapel; Crafts room; Laundry room; Barber/Beauty shop; Library.
Activities Arts and Crafts; Games; Prayer groups; Movies; Shopping trips.

MIFFLINTOWN

Brookline Manor Convalescent Home*
Rt 1, Box 63, Mifflintown, PA, 17059 (717)
436-2178
Licensure Skilled Care; Intermediate Care.
Beds SNF 55; ICF 28. *Certified* Medicaid;
Medicare.
Ownership Proprietary.

MILFORD

Hillcrest Home Inc*
404 E Harford St, Milford, PA, 18337 (717)
296-6812
Licensure Skilled Care. *Beds* 68. *Certified* Medicaid; Medicare.
Ownership Proprietary.

Milford Valley Convalescent Home Inc*
Rt 6 and 209, Milford, PA, 18337 (717)
296-6311
Licensure Skilled Care. *Beds* 80. *Certified* Medicaid; Medicare.
Ownership Proprietary.

MILLERSBURG

Susquehanna Lutheran Village
990 Medical Rd, Millersburg, PA, 17061 (717)
692-4751
Medical Dir/Dir of Nursing James Bower MD.
Licensure Skilled Care; Intermediate Care.
Beds SNF 45; ICF 47. *Certified* Medicaid;
Medicare.
Ownership Nonprofit.
Admissions Requirements Minimum age 65;
Medical examination; Physician's request.
Affiliation Lutheran
Facilities Dining room; Physical therapy room;
Activities room; Chapel; Crafts room; Laundry
room; Barber/Beauty shop; Library.
Activities Arts and Crafts; Cards; Games;
Reading groups; Prayer groups; Movies; Shopping trips; Dances/Social or cultural gatherings.
Description Facility offers Operation Lovebug
and a geriatric assistant training program.

MILLFORD

Hillcrest Home Inc*
404 E Harford St, Millford, PA, 18337 (717)
296-6812
Licensure Skilled Care. *Beds* 50. *Certified* Medicaid; Medicare.
Ownership Proprietary.

MILLMONT

Friendly Nursing Home
Rt 1, Millmont, PA, 17845 (717) 922-3177
Medical Dir/Dir of Nursing Dr Charles Fasano.
Licensure Skilled Care. *Beds* 60. *Certified* Medicaid; Medicare.
Ownership Proprietary.
Admissions Requirements Medical
examination.
Staff RNs 1 (ft), 1 (pt); LPNs 4 (ft), 3 (pt);
Nurses aides 9 (ft), 13 (pt); Physical therapists 1
(pt); Recreational therapists 1 (ft); Dietitians 1

(pt).
Facilities Dining room; Activities room; Chapel; Crafts room; Laundry room.
Activities Arts and Crafts; Games; Reading
groups; Prayer groups; Movies; Shopping trips.
Description Social communication is encouraged among patients through group activities
and recreation. Shopping trips, movies, picnics,
parties (birthdays, Valentine, Christmas, etc.)
are planned. Celebrate National Nursing Home
Week with a balloon lift, pet show and
employees dress up differently each day to represent the customs of different nationalities.

MILLVILLE

Boone Nursing Home
Rt 1, Eyers Grove, Millville, PA, 17846 (717)
458-6751
Medical Dir/Dir of Nursing Dr Winski.
Licensure Skilled Care. *Beds* 60. *Certified* Medicaid.
Ownership Proprietary.
Admissions Requirements Minimum age 18;
Medical examination; Physician's request.
Staff Physicians 1 (pt); RNs 3 (ft), 2 (pt); LPNs
2 (ft), 2 (pt); Nurses aides 18 (ft), 8 (pt);
Physical therapists 1 (pt); Occupational therapists 1 (pt); Speech therapists 1 (pt); Activities
coordinators 1 (ft); Dietitians 1 (pt); Dentists 1
(pt); Podiatrists 1 (pt); Audiologists 1 (pt).

MILTON

Gold Star Nursing Home
560 E Broadway, Milton, PA, 17847 (717)
742-7651
Admin Maheon L Fritz. *Medical Dir/Dir of
Nursing* Barclay M Wilson DO.
Licensure Intermediate Care. *Beds* 39. *Certified* Medicaid.
Ownership Proprietary.
Admissions Requirements Medical examination.
Staff RNs 1 (ft); LPNs 6 (ft), 1 (pt); Nurses
aides 11 (ft), 5 (pt); Physical therapists 1 (pt);
Activities coordinators 1 (ft).
Facilities Dining room; Physical therapy room;
Activities room; Crafts room; Laundry room;
Barber/Beauty shop.
Activities Arts and Crafts; Cards; Games;
Reading groups; Movies.

Kramm Healthcare Center Inc
743 Mahoning St, Milton, PA, 17847 (717)
742-2681
Admin Randall D Kramm. *Medical Dir/Dir of
Nursing* Dr Robert Yannaccone.
Licensure Skilled Care; Intermediate Care.
Beds SNF 61; ICF 59. *Certified* Medicaid;
Medicare.
Ownership Proprietary.
Admissions Requirements Medical examination.
Staff Physicians 10 (pt); RNs 3 (ft), 4 (pt);
LPNs 3 (ft), 4 (pt); Nurses aides 20 (ft), 20 (pt);
Physical therapists 1 (pt); Recreational therapists 1 (ft); Activities coordinators 1 (ft); Dietitians 1 (pt); Dentists 1 (pt); Podiatrists 1 (pt).
Facilities Dining room; Physical therapy room;
Activities room; Crafts room; Laundry room;

Barber/Beauty shop.
Activities Arts and Crafts; Cards; Games;
Reading groups; Prayer groups; Movies; Shopping trips; Dances/Social or cultural gatherings.
Description New facility opened in 1984 provides care, comfort, and companionship in a
home-like atmosphere.

MONONGAHELIA

Haven Crest Inc*
1277 Country Club Rd, Monongahelia, PA,
15063 (412) 258-3000
Licensure Skilled Care. *Beds* 48. *Certified* Medicaid.
Ownership Proprietary.

MONT CLARE

Janney House
Rt 29, River Crest Center, Mont Clare, PA,
19453 (215) 935-1581
Licensure Intermediate Care for Mentally
Retarded. *Beds* 6. *Certified* Medicaid.
Ownership Nonprofit.

River Crest Center—Mont Clare*
Mont Clare, PA, 19453 (215) 935-1581
Licensure Intermediate Care for Mentally
Retarded. *Beds* 76. *Certified* Medicaid.
Ownership Nonprofit.

Ye Olde House
Rt 29, River Crest Center, Mont Clare, PA,
19453 (215) 935-1581
Licensure Intermediate Care for Mentally
Retarded. *Beds* 8. *Certified* Medicaid.
Ownership Nonprofit.

MONTOURSVILLE

Lysock View*
Rt 2, Montoursville, PA, 17754 (717) 433-3161
Licensure Skilled Care; Intermediate Care.
Beds SNF 58; ICF 156. *Certified* Medicaid;
Medicare.
Ownership Nonprofit.

Sycamore Manor Nursing Home
Rt 3, Montoursville, PA, 17754 (717) 326-2037
Admin Edward Parks. *Medical Dir/Dir of
Nursing* Dr Nancy Story.
Licensure Skilled Care. *Beds* 123. *Certified* Medicaid; Medicare.
Ownership Nonprofit.
Staff RNs 4 (ft), 7 (pt); LPNs 10 (ft), 3 (pt);
Orderlies 2 (ft); Nurses aides 36 (ft), 13 (pt);
Physical therapists 1 (ft); Occupational therapists 1 (ft), 1 (pt); Dietitians 1 (pt).
Affiliation Presbyterian
Facilities Dining room; Physical therapy room;
Activities room; Chapel; Crafts room; Laundry
room; Barber/Beauty shop; Library.
Activities Arts and Crafts; Prayer groups;
Movies.

MONTROSE

Asa Park Manor
Park St, Montrose, PA, 18801 (717) 278-3836
Medical Dir/Dir of Nursing Paul B Kerr MD.
Licensure Skilled Care. *Beds* 63. *Certified* Medicaid; Medicare.
Ownership Proprietary.
Admissions Requirements Medical examination; Physician's request.
Staff Physicians 3 (pt); RNs 4 (ft), 11 (pt); LPNs 4 (pt); Orderlies 1 (ft); Nurses aides 19 (ft), 23 (pt); Recreational therapists 1 (pt); Speech therapists; Activities coordinators 1 (ft); Dietitians 1 (pt); Dentists; Podiatrists.
Facilities Dining room; Physical therapy room; Activities room; Chapel; Crafts room; Laundry room; Barber/Beauty shop.
Activities Arts and Crafts; Cards; Games; Reading groups; Movies; Dances/Social or cultural gatherings.
Description Facility is in a quiet area overlooking hills and valley on the edge of a small town.

MOUNTAINTOP

Davis Nursing Home Inc
Rt 309, Mountaintop, PA, 18707 (717) 474-6378
Medical Dir/Dir of Nursing Dr Basil Rudusky.
Licensure Skilled Care. *Beds* 79. *Certified* Medicaid; Medicare.
Ownership Proprietary.
Staff Physicians; RNs 11 (ft); LPNs 8 (ft); Nurses aides 40 (ft), 15 (pt); Physical therapists; Reality therapists 1 (ft), 1 (pt); Recreational therapists 1 (ft); Occupational therapists 1 (pt); Speech therapists 1 (pt); Activities coordinators 1 (ft), 1 (pt); Dietitians 1 (pt); Dentists 1 (pt); Ophthalmologists 1 (pt); Podiatrists 1 (ft); Audiologists 1 (pt).
Facilities Dining room; Physical therapy room; Activities room; Crafts room; Laundry room; Barber/Beauty shop.
Activities Arts and Crafts; Cards; Games; Prayer groups; Shopping trips; Dances/Social or cultural gatherings.

Smith Nursing and Convalescent Home of Mountaintop*
453 Main Rd, Mountaintop, PA, 18707 (717) 868-3664
Licensure Skilled Care. *Beds* 16. *Certified* Medicaid.
Ownership Proprietary.

MUNCY

Muncy Valley Hospital—Skilled Nursing Facility
215 E Water St, Muncy, PA, 17756 (717) 546-8282
Admin Sybil R Harriman. *Medical Dir/Dir of Nursing* Howard Weaner Jr MD.
Licensure Skilled Care. *Beds* 59. *Certified* Medicaid; Medicare.
Ownership Nonprofit.
Admissions Requirements Medical examination; Physician's request.
Staff RNs 3 (ft); LPNs 4 (ft), 6 (pt); Nurses aides 15 (ft), 6 (pt); Speech therapists; Activities coordinators; Dietitians; Dentists; Ophthalmologists; Podiatrists.
Facilities Dining room; Physical therapy room; Activities room; Crafts room; Laundry room; Barber/Beauty shop.
Activities Arts and Crafts; Cards; Games; Reading groups; Prayer groups; Movies; Shopping trips; Dances/Social or cultural gatherings.

MUNHALL

Elder Crest Nursing Home
2600 W Run Rd, Munhall, PA, 15120 (412) 462-8002
Admin Clara Radesausz. *Medical Dir/Dir of Nursing* John C Wain MD.
Licensure Skilled Care. *Beds* 48. *Certified* Medicare.
Ownership Proprietary.
Admissions Requirements Minimum age 17.
Staff Physicians 1 (pt); RNs 2 (ft), 6 (pt); Nurses aides 12 (ft), 13 (pt); Physical therapists 1 (pt); Activities coordinators 1 (ft); Dietitians 1 (pt); Dentists 1 (pt); Ophthalmologists 1 (pt); Podiatrists 1 (pt).
Facilities Dining room; Physical therapy room; Activities room; Crafts room; Laundry room; Barber/Beauty shop.
Activities Arts and Crafts; Cards; Games; Reading groups; Dances/Social or cultural gatherings.

MURRAYSVILLE

Murray Manor Convalescent Center
3300 Logan Ferry Rd, Murraysville, PA, 15668 (412) 325-1500
Medical Dir/Dir of Nursing Dr Frederick Bode.
Licensure Skilled Care; Intermediate Care.
Beds SNF 102; ICF 20. *Certified* Medicaid; Medicare.
Ownership Proprietary.
Staff Physicians 8 (ft); RNs 10 (ft), 11 (pt); LPNs 6 (ft), 1 (pt); Nurses aides 28 (ft), 24 (pt); Physical therapists 1 (ft); Recreational therapists 1 (ft); Occupational therapists 1 (ft); Speech therapists 1 (ft); Activities coordinators 1 (ft); Dietitians 1 (ft); Podiatrists 1 (pt); Audiologists 1 (pt).
Facilities Dining room; Physical therapy room; Activities room; Crafts room; Laundry room; Barber/Beauty shop; Library.
Activities Arts and Crafts; Cards; Games; Reading groups; Prayer groups; Movies; Shopping trips; Dances/Social or cultural gatherings; Stroke group; Adopted grandparent program.
Description Murray Manor provides a total health care program tailored to the individual needs of residents with a special emphasis on enhancing quality of life.

MYERSTOWN

Evangelical Congregational Church Retirement Village
S Railroad St, Myerstown, PA, 17067 (717) 866-6541
Admin Franklin H Schock. *Medical Dir/Dir of Nursing* Dr Jose Sayson.
Licensure Skilled Care; Intermediate Care.
Beds SNF 101; ICF 51. *Certified* Medicaid; Medicare.
Ownership Nonprofit.
Admissions Requirements Medical examination.
Staff RNs 12 (ft); LPNs 15 (ft), 6 (pt); Nurses aides 40 (ft), 40 (pt); Physical therapists 1 (pt); Reality therapists 1 (pt); Recreational therapists 3 (ft); Speech therapists 1 (pt); Activities coordinators 1 (ft); Dietitians 1 (pt); Dentists 1 (ft); Ophthalmologists 1 (pt); Podiatrists 1 (pt); Audiologists 1 (pt).
Affiliation Congregational
Facilities Dining room; Physical therapy room; Activities room; Chapel; Crafts room; Laundry room; Barber/Beauty shop; Library.
Activities Arts and Crafts; Cards; Games; Reading groups; Prayer groups; Movies; Shopping trips; Dances/Social or cultural gatherings.
Description Facility is located on a 7 acre, former college campus site; small community is tranquil yet stimulating.

NANTICOKE

Saint Stanislaus Medical Care Center*
Newport St, Nanticoke, PA, 18634 (717) 735-7300
Licensure Skilled Care. *Beds* 100. *Certified* Medicaid; Medicare.
Ownership Nonprofit.

NARVON

Zerbe Sisters Nursing Center Inc
Rt 1, Hammertown Rd, Box 209, Narvon, PA, 17555 (215) 445-4551
Medical Dir/Dir of Nursing James B Albrecht MD.
Licensure Skilled Care. *Beds* 79. *Certified* Medicaid; Medicare.
Ownership Proprietary.
Admissions Requirements Medical examination.
Staff Physicians 4 (pt); RNs 7 (ft), 2 (pt); LPNs 3 (ft), 4 (pt); Nurses aides 27 (ft), 17 (pt); Physical therapists 1 (pt); Occupational therapists 1 (pt); Speech therapists 1 (pt); Activities coordinators 1 (ft); Dietitians 1 (pt); Podiatrists 1 (pt).
Facilities Dining room; Physical therapy room; Activities room; Crafts room; Laundry room; Barber/Beauty shop; Recreation room.
Activities Arts and Crafts; Cards; Games; Reading groups; Prayer groups; Movies; Dances/Social or cultural gatherings; Recreational day trips.
Description Our facility is located 2 ½ miles north of Churchtown, Pennsylvania, in a beautiful country setting surrounded by woods.

NAZARETH

Bible Fellowship Church Home*
7 S New St, Nazareth, PA, 18064 (215) 759-5121
Licensure Intermediate Care. *Beds* 28. *Certified* Medicaid.
Ownership Nonprofit.

Northhampton County Home—Gracedale
Gracedale Avenue, Nazareth, PA, 18064 (215) 759-3200
Medical Dir/Dir of Nursing Wesley R Stancombe MD.
Licensure Skilled Care; Intermediate Care.
Beds SNF 496; ICF 295. *Certified* Medicaid; Medicare.
Ownership Nonprofit.
Admissions Requirements Minimum age 18; Medical examination.
Staff Physicians 2 (ft), 1 (pt); RNs 43 (ft), 26 (pt); LPNs 69 (ft), 39 (pt); Orderlies 34 (ft), 27 (pt); Nurses aides 135 (ft), 133 (pt); Physical therapists 1 (ft); Occupational therapists 1 (ft); Speech therapists 1 (ft); Activities coordinators 1 (ft); Dietitians 1 (ft).
Facilities Dining room; Physical therapy room; Activities room; Chapel; Crafts room; Laundry room; Barber/Beauty shop.
Activities Arts and Crafts; Cards; Games; Reading groups; Prayer groups; Movies; Shopping trips.

NEFFSVILLE

Brethern Village*
3001 Litiz Pike, Neffsville, PA, 17601 (717) 569-2657
Licensure Skilled Care; Intermediate Care.
Beds SNF 67; ICF 81. *Certified* Medicaid; Medicare.
Ownership Nonprofit.

NEW BLOOMFIELD

Perry Village Nursing Home
Rt 2, Box 68, New Bloomfield, PA, 17068 (717) 582-4346
Medical Dir/Dir of Nursing Dr H Robert Gasull.
Licensure Skilled Care; Intermediate Care.
Beds SNF 39; ICF 84. *Certified* Medicaid; Medicare.
Ownership Nonprofit.
Staff Physicians 3 (pt); RNs 3 (ft), 10 (pt); LPNs 4 (ft), 10 (pt); Nurses aides 22 (ft), 35 (pt); Physical therapists 1 (pt); Speech therapists 1 (pt); Activities coordinators 2 (pt); Dietitians 1 (pt); Dentists 1 (pt); Ophthalmologists 1 (pt); Podiatrists 1 (pt).
Affiliation Lutheran
Facilities Dining room; Physical therapy room; Activities room; Chapel; Crafts room; Laundry room; Barber/Beauty shop.
Activities Arts and Crafts; Cards; Games; Reading groups; Prayer groups; Movies; Shopping trips; Dances/Social or cultural gatherings; Bus tours.

NEW BRIGHTON

McGuire Memorial Home for Retired Children*
2119 Mercer Rd, New Brighton, PA, 15066 (412) 843-3400
Licensure Intermediate Care for Mentally Retarded. *Beds* 99. *Certified* Medicaid.
Ownership Nonprofit.

NEW CASTLE

Almira Home*
1001 E Washington St, New Castle, PA, 16101 (412) 652-4131
Licensure Intermediate Care. *Beds* 17.
Ownership Nonprofit.

Golden Hill Nursing Home Inc*
520 Friendship St, New Castle, PA, 16101 (412) 654-7791
Licensure Skilled Care. *Beds* 204. *Certified* Medicaid; Medicare.
Ownership Proprietary.

Haven Convalescent Home Inc*
725 Paul St, New Castle, PA, 16101 (412) 654-8833
Licensure Intermediate Care. *Beds* 91. *Certified* Medicaid.
Ownership Proprietary.

Highland Hall Care Center
233 Pittsburgh Rd, New Castle, PA, 16101 (412) 658-4781
Medical Dir/Dir of Nursing Dr Raymond Seniow.
Licensure Skilled Care; Intermediate Care.
Beds SNF 49; ICF 34. *Certified* Medicaid; Medicare.
Ownership Proprietary.
Admissions Requirements Medical examination.
Staff RNs 4 (ft), 1 (pt); LPNs 4 (ft), 5 (pt); Nurses aides 19 (ft), 5 (pt); Reality therapists; Activities coordinators.
Facilities Dining room; Activities room; Crafts room; Laundry room; Barber/Beauty shop.
Activities Arts and Crafts; Cards; Games; Reading groups; Movies; Shopping trips; Dances/Social or cultural gatherings.
Description Facility provides a home-like atmosphere in which each patient is treated as an individual.

Hillview Manor
2801 Ellwood Rd, New Castle, PA, 16101 (412) 658-1521
Medical Dir/Dir of Nursing Mohammad I Ali MD.
Licensure Skilled Care; Intermediate Care.
Beds SNF 54; ICF 82. *Certified* Medicaid.
Ownership Nonprofit.
Admissions Requirements Medical examination.
Staff Physicians 1 (pt); RNs 6 (ft); LPNs 13 (ft), 2 (pt); Orderlies 3 (ft), 3 (pt); Nurses aides 42 (ft), 5 (pt); Reality therapists 1 (pt); Activities coordinators 1 (ft), 1 (pt); Dietitians 1 (pt); Podiatrists 1 (pt).
Facilities Dining room; Activities room; Chapel; Crafts room; Laundry room; Barber/Beauty shop; Library.
Activities Arts and Crafts; Cards; Games; Reading groups; Prayer groups; Movies; Shopping trips; Dances/Social or cultural gatherings; Adopt-a-grandparent program.

Indian Creek Nursing Center*
222 W Edison Ave, New Castle, PA, 16101 (412) 652-6340
Licensure Skilled Care; Intermediate Care.

Beds SNF 61; ICF 59. *Certified* Medicaid; Medicare.
Ownership Proprietary.

Jack Rees Nursing and Rehabilitation Center
715 Harbor St, New Castle, PA, 16101 (412) 652-3863
Medical Dir/Dir of Nursing Dr Ross Houston.
Licensure Skilled Care; Intermediate Care.
Beds SNF 51; ICF 33. *Certified* Medicaid; Medicare.
Ownership Proprietary.
Admissions Requirements Minimum age 18.
Staff Physicians 2 (pt); RNs 3 (ft), 3 (pt); LPNs 3 (ft), 4 (pt); Physical therapists 2 (pt); Recreational therapists 1 (pt); Speech therapists 1 (pt); Activities coordinators 1 (ft); Dietitians 1 (ft); Podiatrists 1 (pt).
Facilities Dining room; Physical therapy room; Activities room; Crafts room; Laundry room; Barber/Beauty shop; Library.
Activities Arts and Crafts; Cards; Games; Reading groups; Prayer groups; Movies; Shopping trips; Dances/Social or cultural gatherings.
Description Facility encompasses full range of rehabilitation services. Professional staff is trained to handle any type of patient to include those requiring IV therapy, physical therapy, occupational therapy, speech therapy, swallowing therapy, etc.

NEW OXFORD

The Brethren Home
2990 Carlisle Pike, PO Box 128, New Oxford, PA, 17350 (717) 624-2161
Medical Dir/Dir of Nursing David E Zickafoose MD.
Licensure Skilled Care; Intermediate Care.
Beds SNF 80; ICF 91. *Certified* Medicaid; Medicare.
Ownership Nonprofit.
Admissions Requirements Medical examination.
Staff RNs 8 (ft), 9 (pt); LPNs 18 (ft), 31 (pt); Orderlies 1 (ft), 1 (pt); Nurses aides 37 (ft), 73 (pt); Recreational therapists 7 (ft); Activities coordinators 5 (ft), 1 (pt); Dietitians 1 (ft).
Affiliation Church of the Brethren
Facilities Dining room; Physical therapy room; Activities room; Chapel; Crafts room; Laundry room; Barber/Beauty shop; Library.
Activities Arts and Crafts; Cards; Games; Reading groups; Prayer groups; Movies; Shopping trips; Dances/Social or cultural gatherings.
Description The Brethren Home, a church related nursing home/retirement community, has grown from the 1970's of 120 nursing care beds to 410 residents offering 5 levels of care-/living arrangements. A current strategic planning program professionally developed will provide guidance for future growth. "The Resident is the Reason" is a phrase taken seriously in daily operations reflected in wide community acceptance for providing quality care. Services individualized and programing include full-time chaplaincy and program activities and extensive volunteer program activities supplements the staff.

NEW WILIMINGTON

Overlook Medical Clinic Inc*
408 New Castle St, New Wilimington, PA
16142 (412) 946-6113
Licensure Skilled Care. *Beds* 105. *Certified* Medicaid; Medicare.
Ownership Proprietary.

NEW WILMINGTON

Shenango United Presbyterian Home
238 S Market St, New Wilmington, PA, 16142
(412) 946-6142
Admin Ross Byers.
Licensure Intermediate Care. *Beds* 21.
Ownership Nonprofit.
Admissions Requirements Minimum age 65;
Medical examination.
Staff RNs; LPNs; Nurses aides; Reality therapists; Recreational therapists; Activities coordinators; Dietitians.
Affiliation Presbyterian
Facilities Dining room; Activities room;
Chapel; Crafts room; Laundry room; Barber-/Beauty shop; Library; Lounges.
Activities Arts and Crafts; Games; Reading groups; Prayer groups; Movies; Dances/Social or cultural gatherings; Entertainment by college and community groups.
Description Shenango Home is a nonprofit retirement facility which exists for older church members who want an atmosphere of Christian companionship and security with gracious living. Located in the heart of a delightful small town, it is near churches, stores, and the Westminster College campus.

NEWFOUNDLAND

Holiday Hill Nursing Home*
Rt 7, Newfoundland, PA, 18445 (717)
676-3237
Licensure Intermediate Care. *Beds* 25. *Certified* Medicaid.
Ownership Proprietary.

NEWTOWN

Chandler Hall Nursing Home*
Barkley St and Buck Rd, Newtown, PA, 18940
(215) 988-4786
Licensure Skilled Care. *Beds* 55. *Certified* Medicaid; Medicare.
Ownership Nonprofit.

Pennswood Village
Rt 413, Newtown, PA, 18940 (215) 968-9110
Medical Dir/Dir of Nursing James C Alden
MD.
Licensure Skilled Care. *Beds* 45. *Certified* Medicare.
Ownership Nonprofit.
Admissions Requirements Minimum age 65;
Medical examination.
Staff Physicians 2 (pt); RNs 5 (ft), 7 (pt); LPNs
4 (ft), 3 (pt); Orderlies 1 (ft); Nurses aides 26
(ft), 10 (pt); Physical therapists 1 (pt); Occupational therapists 1 (pt); Speech therapists 1 (pt);
Activities coordinators 2 (ft); Dietitians 1 (ft);

Dentists 1 (pt); Ophthalmologists 1 (pt); Podiatrists 1 (pt); Audiologists 1 (pt).
Affiliation Society of Friends

Pickering Manor
Lincoln Ave, Newtown, PA, 18940 (215)
968-3878
Medical Dir/Dir of Nursing Blaine R Garner
MD.
Licensure Skilled Care. *Beds* 47. *Certified* Medicaid; Medicare.
Ownership Nonprofit.
Admissions Requirements Minimum age 18.
Facilities Dining room; Physical therapy room;
Activities room; Laundry room; Barber/Beauty
shop; Library.
Activities Arts and Crafts; Cards; Games;
Reading groups; Prayer groups; Movies; Shopping trips; Dances/Social or cultural gatherings.

NEWTOWN SQUARE

Dowden Nursing Home
3503 Rhoads Ave, Newtown Square, PA, 19073
(215) 356-7423
Admin Anna E Helfrich. *Medical Dir/Dir of
Nursing* Robert McAndrew DO.
Licensure Skilled Care. *Beds* 51.
Ownership Proprietary.
Staff RNs 4 (ft); LPNs 4 (ft), 2 (pt); Nurses
aides 19 (ft), 3 (pt); Physical therapists 1 (pt);
Reality therapists 1 (pt); Recreational therapists
2 (pt); Activities coordinators 1 (ft); Dietitians
1 (pt); Art therapists 1 (pt).
Facilities Dining room; Activities room; Laundry room; Barber/Beauty shop.
Activities Arts and Crafts; Cards; Games;
Reading groups; Movies; Shopping trips; Dances/Social or cultural gatherings.

Dunwoody Home Medical Center*
3500 West Chester Pike, Newtown Square, PA,
19073 (215) 359-4400
Licensure Skilled Care. *Beds* 71. *Certified* Medicare.
Ownership Nonprofit.

NEWVILLE

Swaim Health Center
Green Ridge Village, Big Spring Rd, Newville,
PA, 17241 (717) 776-5112
Medical Dir/Dir of Nursing Dr J A Townsend.
Licensure Skilled Care. *Beds* 49. *Certified* Medicaid; Medicare.
Ownership Nonprofit.
Admissions Requirements Medical examination; Physician's request.
Staff RNs 2 (ft); LPNs 2 (ft), 3 (pt); Orderlies 1
(pt); Nurses aides 13 (ft), 21 (pt); Physical therapists; Speech therapists; Activities coordinators
1 (ft), 3 (pt); Dietitians 1 (ft).
Affiliation Presbyterian
Facilities Dining room; Physical therapy room;
Activities room; Crafts room; Laundry room;
Barber/Beauty shop; Library.
Activities Arts and Crafts; Cards; Games;
Reading groups; Prayer groups; Movies; Shopping trips; Dances/Social or cultural gatherings;
Pet therapy.
Description Facility is a multi-level continuing

care retirement community in a rural setting.
Independent living cottages and apartments,
residential care units, skilled and intermediate
nursing care, and retreat facilities are all
available.

NORRISTOWN

Fair Villa Nursing Home
1240 W Main St, Norristown, PA, 19401 (215)
275-6799
Medical Dir/Dir of Nursing Dr Yu Jen Tsai.
Licensure Skilled Care. *Beds* 57. *Certified* Medicaid.
Ownership Proprietary.
Admissions Requirements Medical examination; Physician's request.
Staff Physicians 10 (pt); RNs 1 (ft), 1 (pt);
LPNs 3 (ft), 1 (pt); Nurses aides 31 (ft), 14 (pt);
Physical therapists 1 (pt); Speech therapists 1
(pt); Activities coordinators 1 (ft); Dietitians 1
(pt); Dentists 1 (pt); Podiatrists 1 (pt); Audiologists 1 (pt).
Facilities Dining room; Activities room; Crafts
room; Laundry room; Library.
Activities Arts and Crafts; Cards; Games;
Reading groups; Prayer groups; Movies; Shopping trips; Dances/Social or cultural gatherings.

Leader Health Care Center
2004 Old Arch Rd, Norristown, PA, 19401
(215) 277-0380
Medical Dir/Dir of Nursing John McLoone
MD.
Licensure Skilled Care. *Beds* 120. *Certified* Medicaid; Medicare.
Ownership Proprietary.
Admissions Requirements Medical examination.
Staff RNs 14 (ft); LPNs 11 (ft); Nurses aides 45
(ft); Physical therapists 1 (ft); Reality therapists
1 (ft); Recreational therapists 1 (ft); Occupational therapists 1 (pt); Speech therapists 1 (pt);
Activities coordinators 1 (ft); Dietitians 1 (ft);
Audiologists 1 (pt).

Plymouth House Health Care Center
900 E Germantown Pike, Norristown, PA,
19401 (215) 279-7300
Medical Dir/Dir of Nursing James Bard MD.
Licensure Skilled Care; Intermediate Care.
Beds SNF 88; ICF 62. *Certified* Medicaid;
Medicare.
Ownership Proprietary.
Admissions Requirements Minimum age 18;
Medical examination; Physician's request.
Staff Physicians 50 (pt); RNs 12 (ft), 8 (pt);
LPNs 3 (ft), 3 (pt); Orderlies 3 (pt); Nurses
aides 50 (ft), 20 (pt); Physical therapists 1 (pt);
Recreational therapists 1 (ft); Occupational
therapists 1 (pt); Speech therapists 1 (pt);
Activities coordinators 1 (ft); Dietitians 1 (pt);
Dentists 1 (pt); Ophthalmologists 1 (pt); Podiatrists 1 (pt); Audiologists 1 (pt).
Facilities Dining room; Physical therapy room;
Activities room; Crafts room; Laundry room;
Barber/Beauty shop.
Activities Arts and Crafts; Cards; Games;
Reading groups; Prayer groups; Movies; Shopping trips; Dances/Social or cultural gatherings.

Regina Community Nursing Center*
550 E Fornance St, Norristown, PA, 19401
(215) 272-5600
Licensure Skilled Care. *Beds* 121. *Certified* Medicaid; Medicare.
Ownership Nonprofit.

NORTH HUNTINGDON

Briarcliff Pavilion Special Care
249 Maus Dr, North Huntingdon, PA, 15642
(412) 863-4374
Admin Janet Maxwell.
Licensure Skilled Care. *Beds* 110. *Certified* Medicaid; Medicare.
Ownership Proprietary.
Staff Physicians 5 (pt); RNs 6 (ft), 10 (pt);
LPNs 7 (ft), 4 (pt); Orderlies 2 (ft); Nurses aides 31 (ft), 12 (pt); Physical therapists 1 (ft); Reality therapists 1 (pt); Recreational therapists 2 (ft); Occupational therapists 1 (pt); Speech therapists 1 (pt); Dietitians 1 (pt); Dentists 1 (pt); Podiatrists 1 (pt); Audiologists 1 (pt).
Facilities Dining room; Physical therapy room; Activities room; Laundry room; Barber/Beauty shop.
Activities Arts and Crafts; Cards; Games; Reading groups; Prayer groups; Movies; Shopping trips; Dances/Social or cultural gatherings; Nationality day monthly.
Description Facility is dedicated to rehabilitation and attempts to bring the patient to their highest level of wellness. Encourages active participation of the patient and family in the plan of care.

NORTH WALES

Angeline Nursing Home Inc*
Rt 309 and N Wales Rd, North Wales, PA, 19545 (215) 855-8670
Licensure Skilled Care. *Beds* 32. *Certified* Medicaid.
Ownership Proprietary.

NORTHUMBERLAND

Nottingham Village*
Strawbridge Rd, Northumberland, PA, 17857
(717) 473-8366
Licensure Skilled Care. *Beds* 121. *Certified* Medicaid; Medicare.
Ownership Proprietary.

Pleasant View Convalescent Home*
Rt 1, Northumberland, PA, 17857 (717) 473-9433
Licensure Skilled Care. *Beds* 26. *Certified* Medicaid.
Ownership Proprietary.

OAKMONT

Oakmont Nursing Center*
26 Ann St, Oakmont, PA, 15139 (412) 828-7300
Licensure Skilled Care. *Beds* 81. *Certified* Medicaid; Medicare.
Ownership Proprietary.

Oakmont Presbyterian Home*
1215 Hulton Rd, Oakmont, PA, 15139 (412) 828-5600
Licensure Skilled Care. *Beds* 134. *Certified* Medicaid; Medicare.
Ownership Nonprofit.
Affiliation Presbyterian

OIL CITY

Grandview Health Care Inc—Oil City
1293 Grandview Rd, Oil City, PA, 16301 (814) 676-8208
Medical Dir/Dir of Nursing Dr Gold.
Licensure Skilled Care; Intermediate Care.
Beds SNF 25; ICF 124. *Certified* Medicaid; Medicare.
Ownership Proprietary.
Admissions Requirements Minimum age 16; Medical examination.
Staff Physicians 1 (pt); RNs 3 (ft), 1 (pt); LPNs 1 (ft), 3 (pt); Nurses aides 13 (ft), 5 (pt); Speech therapists 1 (pt); Activities coordinators 1 (ft), 1 (pt); Dietitians 1 (ft).
Facilities Dining room; Physical therapy room; Activities room; Crafts room; Laundry room; Barber/Beauty shop.
Activities Arts and Crafts; Cards; Games; Reading groups; Movies; Shopping trips; Dances/Social or cultural gatherings.
Description Excellent physical care provided by an experienced staff. Rural, peaceful, hilltop setting with farm surroundings. Reflects the experience of our residents and provides a window on seasonal changes.

Oil City Presbyterian Home
10 Vo Tech Dr, Oil City, PA, 16301
Admin Yvonne D Atkinson. *Medical Dir/Dir of Nursing* Dr Jane Marshall.
Licensure Skilled Care; Intermediate Care.
Beds 121. *Certified* Medicaid; Medicare.
Ownership Nonprofit.
Admissions Requirements Minimum age 16; Medical examination.
Staff Physicians 1 (pt); RNs 19 (ft), 1 (pt);
LPNs 9 (ft), 1 (pt); Orderlies 1 (ft); Nurses aides 43 (ft); Physical therapists 1 (pt); Recreational therapists 1 (ft); Speech therapists 1 (pt); Activities coordinators 1 (ft); Dietitians 1 (pt); Dentists; Ophthalmologists; Podiatrists; Audiologists.
Affiliation Presbyterian
Facilities Dining room; Physical therapy room; Activities room; Crafts room; Laundry room; Barber/Beauty shop; Library.
Activities Arts and Crafts; Cards; Games; Reading groups; Prayer groups; Movies; Shopping trips; Dances/Social or cultural gatherings.
Description New facility built in 1981; staff takes time to care.

OLYPHANT

Lackawanna County Home
Rt 1, Olyphant, PA, 18447 (717) 489-8611
Medical Dir/Dir of Nursing Dr Clause.
Licensure Skilled Care; Intermediate Care.
Beds SNF 150; ICF 50. *Certified* Medicaid; Medicare.
Ownership Public.

Staff Physicians 4 (pt); RNs 9 (ft); LPNs 12 (ft); Orderlies 6 (ft); Nurses aides 74 (ft); Physical therapists 1 (ft); Reality therapists; Recreational therapists 1 (ft); Occupational therapists; Speech therapists; Activities coordinators; Dietitians; Dentists; Ophthalmologists; Podiatrists; Audiologists.
Facilities Dining room; Physical therapy room; Activities room; Crafts room; Laundry room; Barber/Beauty shop; Library.
Activities Arts and Crafts; Cards; Games; Reading groups; Prayer groups; Movies; Shopping trips; Dances/Social or cultural gatherings.

ORANGEVILLE

Char Mund Nursing Home
Rt 2, Orangeville, PA, 17859 (717) 683-5333
Licensure Skilled Care. *Beds* 36. *Certified* Medicaid; Medicare.
Ownership Proprietary.

Klingerman Nursing Center
Rt 2, Orangeville, PA, 17859 (717) 683-5036
Medical Dir/Dir of Nursing Dr L A Winski.
Licensure Intermediate Care. *Beds* 118.
Certified Medicaid.
Ownership Proprietary.
Staff Physicians 2 (ft), 5 (pt); RNs 4 (ft), 6 (pt);
LPNs 4 (ft), 1 (pt); Orderlies 1 (ft), 1 (pt);
Nurses aides 28 (ft), 13 (pt); Physical therapists 1 (pt); Reality therapists 1 (ft), 1 (pt); Recreational therapists 1 (ft), 1 (pt); Activities coordinators 1 (ft), 1 (pt); Dietitians 1 (pt); Dentists 1 (pt); Podiatrists 2 (pt).
Facilities Dining room; Activities room; Chapel; Crafts room; Laundry room; Barber/Beauty shop.
Activities Arts and Crafts; Cards; Games; Reading groups; Prayer groups; Movies; Shopping trips; Dances/Social or cultural gatherings.
Description Nursing home living designed to eliminate the institutional atmosphere; 118-bed facility with pleasant small town atmosphere providing tender loving care away from home.

OXFORD

Oxford Manor Presbyterian Home
7 Locust St, Oxford, PA, 19363 (215) 932-2900
Admin Geoffrey L Henry. *Medical Dir/Dir of Nursing* Dr Faye R Doyle.
Licensure Skilled Care; Intermediate Care.
Beds SNF 51; ICF 49. *Certified* Medicaid; Medicare.
Ownership Nonprofit.
Staff Physicians 10 (pt); RNs 10 (ft); LPNs 4 (ft); Nurses aides 37 (ft); Physical therapists 1 (ft); Speech therapists 1 (pt); Activities coordinators 1 (ft); Dietitians 1 (pt); Dentists 2 (pt); Podiatrists 1 (pt).
Affiliation Presbyterian
Facilities Dining room; Physical therapy room; Activities room; Laundry room; Barber/Beauty shop; Library.
Activities Arts and Crafts; Cards; Games; Reading groups; Prayer groups; Movies; Shopping trips.
Description Two 7-year-old 2-story facility separated by a core area. Houses a licensed child care center.

PALMYRA

Lebanon Valley Brethren Home
1200 Grubb St, Palmyra, PA, 17078 (717)
838-5406
Licensure Skilled Care; Intermediate Care.
Beds SNF 60; ICF 40. *Certified* Medicaid;
Medicare.
Ownership Nonprofit.

Palmyra Nursing Home
341-45 N Railroad St, Palmyra, PA, 17078
(717) 838-3011
Medical Dir/Dir of Nursing Harold H Engle
MD.
Licensure Skilled Care. *Beds* 39. *Certified* Medicaid; Medicare.
Ownership Proprietary.
Staff Physicians 1 (pt); RNs 2 (ft), 2 (pt); LPNs
1 (ft), 2 (pt); Nurses aides 7 (ft), 9 (pt); Physical
therapists 1 (ft), 1 (pt); Recreational therapists 1
(ft); Speech therapists 1 (pt); Activities coordinators 1 (ft); Dietitians 1 (pt); Dentists 1 (pt);
Ophthalmologists 1 (pt); Podiatrists 1 (pt);
Audiologists 1 (pt).
Facilities Dining room; Physical therapy room;
Activities room; Laundry room; Barber/Beauty
shop.
Activities Arts and Crafts; Cards; Games;
Reading groups; Prayer groups; Movies; Shopping trips; Dances/Social or cultural gatherings.

PAOLI

Main Line Nursing and Rehabilitation Center*
PO Box E, 283 E Lancaster Ave, Paoli, PA,
19301 (215) 296-4170
Licensure Skilled Care. *Beds* 180. *Certified* Medicare.
Ownership Proprietary.

PHILADELPHIA

American Medical Nursing Centers—Cedars*
125 W School House Ln, Philadelphia, PA,
19144 (215) 233-4111
Licensure Skilled Care. *Beds* 180. *Certified* Medicaid; Medicare.
Ownership Proprietary.

Arden Hall Inc*
7141 McCallum St, Philadelphia, PA, 19119
(215) 247-0444
Licensure Skilled Care. *Beds* 35.
Ownership Proprietary.

Ashton Hall Nursing and Convalescent Home*
2109 Red Lion Rd, Philadelphia, PA, 19114
(215) 673-7000
Licensure Skilled Care. *Beds* 148. *Certified* Medicaid; Medicare.
Ownership Proprietary.

Baptist Home
8301 Roosevelt Blvd, Philadelphia, PA, 19152
(215) 624-7575
Medical Dir/Dir of Nursing Dr Vernando Jaurique.
Licensure Skilled Care; Intermediate Care.
Beds SNF 72; ICF 37. *Certified* Medicaid;
Medicare.

Ownership Nonprofit.
Admissions Requirements Minimum age 65;
Medical examination.
Staff Physicians 2 (pt); RNs 13 (ft), 8 (pt);
LPNs 6 (ft), 6 (pt); Nurses aides 75 (ft);
Physical therapists 1 (ft); Recreational therapists
2 (ft); Occupational therapists 1 (pt); Speech
therapists 1 (pt); Activities coordinators 1 (ft);
Dietitians 1 (ft); Dentists 1 (pt); Ophthalmologists 1 (pt); Podiatrists 1 (pt).
Affiliation Baptist
Facilities Dining room; Physical therapy room;
Activities room; Chapel; Crafts room; Laundry
room; Barber/Beauty shop; Library; Gift shop.
Activities Arts and Crafts; Games; Prayer
groups; Shopping trips; Dances/Social or cultural gatherings; Bingo; Basketball (with nurf
ball); Gardening.
Description The Baptist Home of Philadelphia
is a modern retirement community located in
northeast Philadelphia. The Home offers residential accomodations for single persons and
couples. A modern infirmary, professionally
staffed, is also available. The Home accepts
direct admission to the residential and infirmary facilities. The Baptist Home is open to all
interested individuals, 65 or over, regardless of
race, color, or creed.

Bergers Greenhill Nursing Home*
Knorr St and Tabor Ave, Philadelphia, PA,
19111 (215) 742-0500
Licensure Skilled Care. *Beds* 47. *Certified* Medicaid.
Ownership Proprietary.

Boulevard Nursing
7950 Roosevelt Blvd, Philadelphia, PA, 19152
(215) 332-3700
Admin S Malamut.
Licensure Skilled Care. *Beds* 135. *Certified* Medicaid; Medicare.
Ownership Proprietary.
Facilities Dining room; Physical therapy room;
Activities room; Crafts room; Barber/Beauty
shop.
Activities Arts and Crafts; Cards; Games;
Reading groups; Prayer groups; Movies; Shopping trips; Dances/Social or cultural gatherings.
Description Facility is located in a semi-
suburban setting.

Care Pavillion of Walnut Park
6212 Walnut St, Philadelphia, PA, 19139 (215)
476-6264
Medical Dir/Dir of Nursing Dr R Weisberg.
Licensure Skilled Care; Intermediate Care.
Beds SNF 258; ICF 120. *Certified* Medicaid;
Medicare.
Ownership Proprietary.
Staff Physicians 6 (pt); RNs 20 (ft), 6 (pt);
LPNs 30 (ft), 10 (pt); Nurses aides 180 (ft), 20
(pt); Physical therapists 1 (ft), 1 (pt); Recreational therapists 4 (ft), 1 (pt); Occupational therapists 1 (ft); Speech therapists 1 (ft); Activities
coordinators 1 (ft); Dietitians 1 (ft).
Facilities Dining room; Physical therapy room;
Activities room; Laundry room; Barber/Beauty
shop.
Activities Arts and Crafts; Cards; Games;
Reading groups; Prayer groups; Movies; Shopping trips; Dances/Social or cultural gatherings.
Description Facility is a 378-bed skilled and

intermediate care facility located on a city
block square in west Philadelphia. We specialize in sub-acute care and are accepting limited
referrals for respirator care.

Cathedral Village
600 E Cathedral Rd, Philadelphia, PA, 19128
(215) 487-1300
Licensure Skilled Care. *Beds* 148.
Ownership Nonprofit.
Facilities Dining room; Physical therapy room;
Activities room; Crafts room; Laundry room;
Barber/Beauty shop; Library.
Activities Arts and Crafts; Cards; Games;
Reading groups; Prayer groups; Movies; Shopping trips; Dances/Social or cultural gatherings.

Central Park Lodge - Rest Haven (Chestnut Hill)
8833 Stenton Ave, Philadelphia, PA, 19118
(215) 247-8800
Medical Dir/Dir of Nursing Dr Maurice Tepper.
Licensure Skilled Care. *Beds* 195. *Certified* Medicaid; Medicare.
Ownership Proprietary.
Admissions Requirements Minimum age 21;
Medical examination.
Staff Physicians 1 (pt); RNs 6 (ft), 16 (pt);
LPNs 11 (ft), 6 (pt); Orderlies 16 (ft), 2 (pt);
Nurses aides 64 (ft), 7 (pt); Physical therapists 3
(pt); Recreational therapists 2 (ft); Occupational
therapists 1 (pt); Activities coordinators 1 (ft);
Dietitians 1 (ft).
Facilities Dining room; Physical therapy room;
Activities room; Crafts room; Laundry room;
Barber/Beauty shop.
Activities Arts and Crafts; Cards; Games;
Reading groups; Movies; Shopping trips; Dances/Social or cultural gatherings.
Description Facility is staffed and equipped to
handle any nonacute medical problem. Located
in beautiful Philadelphia suburbs.

Chapel Manor Nursing and Convalescent Home*
1104 Welsh Rd, Philadelphia, PA, 19115 (215)
676-9191
Licensure Skilled Care. *Beds* 144. *Certified* Medicaid; Medicare.
Ownership Proprietary.

Cheltenham-York Road Nursing Rehabilitation Center*
7107 Old York Rd, Philadelphia, PA, 19126
(215) 424-4090
Licensure Skilled Care. *Beds* 125. *Certified* Medicaid.
Ownership Proprietary.

Chetleham Nursing and Rehabilitation Center*
600 W Cheltenham Ave, Philadelphia, PA,
19126 (215) 924-0405
Licensure Skilled Care. *Beds* 255. *Certified* Medicaid; Medicare.
Ownership Proprietary.

Christ Church Hospital Episcopal*
49th and Monument Ave, Philadelphia, PA,
19121 (215) 877-1565
Licensure Skilled Care; Intermediate Care.

Beds SNF 20; ICF 19. *Certified* Medicaid.
Ownership Nonprofit.
Affiliation Episcopal

Cobbs Creek Nursing Inc*
6900 Cobbs Creek Pkwy, Philadelphia, PA,
19142 (215) 729-1414
Licensure Skilled Care. *Beds* 219. *Certified* Medicaid; Medicare.
Ownership Proprietary.

Crown Nursing Home*
1425 Snyder Ave, Philadelphia, PA, 19145
(215) 467-8282
Licensure Skilled Care. *Beds* 185. *Certified* Medicaid.
Ownership Proprietary.

Downtown Jewish Home for the Aged*
4001 Ford Rd, Philadelphia, PA, 19131 (215)
877-5400
Licensure Skilled Care; Intermediate Care.
Beds SNF 30; ICF 85. *Certified* Medicaid;
Medicare.
Ownership Nonprofit.
Affiliation Jewish

Drueding Infirmary*
Lawrence and Master Sts, Philadelphia, PA,
19122 (215) 769-1830
Licensure Intermediate Care. *Beds* 46. *Certified* Medicaid.
Ownership Nonprofit.

Elmira Jeffries Memorial Home*
1500–1514 N Fifteenth St, Philadelphia, PA,
19121 (215) 785-3201
Licensure Skilled Care. *Beds* 180. *Certified* Medicaid; Medicare.
Ownership Nonprofit.

Evangelical Manor
8401 Roosevelt Blvd, Philadelphia, PA, 19152
(215) 624-5800
Medical Dir/Dir of Nursing Dr John C Crawford.
Licensure Skilled Care; Intermediate Care;
Retirement Apartments. *Beds* SNF 60; ICF 60
Retirement Apartments 220. *Certified* Medicaid; Medicare.
Ownership Nonprofit.
Admissions Requirements Minimum age 65;
Medical examination.
Staff Physicians 1 (ft); RNs; LPNs; Orderlies;
Nurses aides; Physical therapists 1 (ft); Recreational therapists 2 (ft); Occupational therapists 1
(pt); Speech therapists 1 (pt); Activities coordinators 1 (ft); Dietitians 1 (ft); Dentists 1 (pt);
Ophthalmologists 1 (pt); Podiatrists 1 (pt);
Audiologists 1 (pt).
Affiliation Methodist
Facilities Dining room; Physical therapy room;
Activities room; Chapel; Crafts room; Laundry
room; Barber/Beauty shop; Library.
Activities Arts and Crafts; Cards; Games;
Reading groups; Prayer groups; Movies; Shopping trips; Dances/Social or cultural gatherings;
Art show; Senior olympics; Theme dinners;
Drug holiday program.

Fairview Nursing Home—Bethlehem Pike*
184 Bethlehem Pike, Philadelphia, PA, 19118
(215) 247-5311

Licensure Skilled Care. *Beds* 153. *Certified* Medicaid.
Ownership Proprietary.

Friends Hall at Fox Chase*
Hartel and Hasbrook Aves, Philadelphia, PA,
19111 (215) 728-1500
Licensure Skilled Care. *Beds* 74. *Certified* Medicare.
Ownership Nonprofit.

George L Harrison Memorial*
Front St and Lehigh Ave, Philadelphia, PA,
19125 (215) 427-7000
Licensure Skilled Care. *Beds* 35. *Certified* Medicaid; Medicare.
Ownership Nonprofit.

Grand Oak Nursing Home*
6200 Ardleigh St, Philadelphia, PA, 19138
(215) 844-4200
Licensure Skilled Care. *Beds* 114. *Certified* Medicaid; Medicare.
Ownership Proprietary.

Greystone on the Greene Inc*
6400 Greene St, Philadelphia, PA, 19119 (215)
844-6401
Licensure Skilled Care. *Beds* 180. *Certified* Medicaid; Medicare.
Ownership Proprietary.

Holy Family Home*
5300 Chester Ave, Philadelphia, PA, 19143
(215) 729-5153
Licensure Skilled Care; Intermediate Care.
Beds SNF 55; ICF 75. *Certified* Medicaid.
Ownership Nonprofit.
Affiliation Roman Catholic

Home for the Jewish Aged*
5301 Old York Rd, Philadelphia, PA, 19141
(215) 455-6100
Licensure Skilled Care; Intermediate Care.
Beds SNF 443; ICF 25. *Certified* Medicaid.
Ownership Nonprofit.
Affiliation Jewish

Immaculate Mary Home*
Holmes Circle and Welsh Rd, Philadelphia, PA,
19136 (215) 335-3100
Licensure Skilled Care; Intermediate Care.
Beds SNF 196; ICF 100. *Certified* Medicaid;
Medicare.
Ownership Nonprofit.
Affiliation Roman Catholic

Inglis House
2600 Belmont Ave, Philadelphia, PA, 19131
(215) 878-5600
Medical Dir/Dir of Nursing Dr Francis Harrison.
Licensure Skilled Care. *Beds* 297. *Certified* Medicaid; Medicare.
Ownership Nonprofit.
Admissions Requirements Minimum age 17;
Medical examination.
Staff Physicians 4 (ft); RNs 20 (ft), 4 (pt);
LPNs 40 (ft), 2 (pt); Nurses aides 156 (ft);
Physical therapists 2 (ft); Reality therapists 2
(ft); Recreational therapists 4 (ft); Occupational
therapists 3 (ft); Speech therapists 1 (pt); Activities coordinators 1 (ft); Dietitians 1 (pt); Den-

tists 1 (pt); Ophthalmologists 1 (pt); Podiatrists
1 (pt).
Facilities Physical therapy room; Activities
room; Chapel; Crafts room; Laundry room;
Barber/Beauty shop; Library; Classroom.
Activities Arts and Crafts; Cards; Games;
Reading groups; Prayer groups; Movies; Shopping trips; Dances/Social or cultural gatherings;
Field trips.
Description Inglis House is a long-term care
facility for physically disabled persons. Patients
encouraged to function at their optimum capacity and to participate in a wheelchair community; now reinstituting a day-care (out-patient)
program.

Ivy Ridge Nursing Home Inc
5627 Ridge Ave, Philadelphia, PA, 19128 (215)
483-7522
Admin Annette Fabriean. *Medical Dir/Dir of
Nursing* Mark Warren Cohen DO.
Licensure Intermediate Care. *Beds* 47. *Certified* Medicaid.
Ownership Proprietary.
Staff RNs 1 (ft); LPNs 3 (ft); Nurses aides 8
(ft); Activities coordinators 1 (ft), 1 (pt).
Facilities Dining room; Activities room; Laundry room.
Activities Arts and Crafts; Cards; Games;
Reading groups; Prayer groups; Movies; Dances/Social or cultural gatherings; Bazaars.

Landers Nursing Home*
342 Green Ln, Philadelphia, PA, 19128 (215)
483-5974
Licensure Skilled Care. *Beds* 53. *Certified* Medicaid.
Ownership Proprietary.

Lutheran Home at Germantown
6950 Germantown Ave, Philadelphia, PA,
19119 (215) 848-3306
Medical Dir/Dir of Nursing Bruce Silver MD.
Licensure Skilled Care; Intermediate Care.
Beds SNF 105; ICF 64. *Certified* Medicaid;
Medicare.
Ownership Nonprofit.
Admissions Requirements Minimum age 65;
Medical examination; Physician's request.
Staff Physicians 3 (pt); RNs 10 (ft), 7 (pt);
LPNs 10 (ft), 5 (pt); Orderlies 2 (ft); Nurses
aides 58 (ft), 12 (pt); Physical therapists 1 (ft);
Recreational therapists 3 (ft); Dietitians 1 (pt);
Dentists 2 (pt); Ophthalmologists 1 (pt); Podiatrists 2 (pt).
Affiliation Lutheran
Facilities Dining room; Physical therapy room;
Activities room; Chapel; Crafts room; Laundry
room; Barber/Beauty shop; Library.
Activities Arts and Crafts; Games; Reading
groups; Prayer groups; Movies; Shopping trips;
Dances/Social or cultural gatherings; Food fun;
Ceramics; Manicure magic; African violet club;
Bedside sensory stimulation; Senior olympics.
Description The Lutheran Home at Germantown has the entire spectrum of geriatric care:
skilled nursing, intermediate nursing, residential care, independent living apartments, and an
adult day care center.

Marwood Rest Home Inc
1020 Oak Lane Ave, Philadelphia, PA, 19126
(215) 224-9898

Admin R Lyle Carpenter. *Medical Dir/Dir of Nursing* Leonard Cinberg MD.
Licensure Skilled Care. *Beds* 82. *Certified* Medicaid; Medicare.
Ownership Proprietary.
Admissions Requirements Minimum age 65; Medical examination.
Staff Physicians 3 (pt); RNs 3 (ft), 4 (pt); LPNs 6 (ft), 5 (pt); Orderlies 2 (ft); Physical therapists 1 (pt); Recreational therapists 1 (pt); Speech therapists 1 (pt); Activities coordinators 1 (ft); Dietitians 1 (ft).
Facilities Dining room; Physical therapy room; Activities room; Crafts room; Laundry room; Barber/Beauty shop.
Activities Arts and Crafts; Cards; Games; Reading groups; Prayer groups; Movies; Shopping trips; Dances/Social or cultural gatherings.
Description Marwood Rest Home is a 4-year-old facility located in the residential Oak Lane section. Marwood has available to residents a program offered by the Thomas Jefferson University for confused or depressed residents.

Mayo Nursing and Convalescent Home
650 Edison Ave, Philadelphia, PA, 19116 (213) 673-5700
Admin Helen Cordelli. *Medical Dir/Dir of Nursing* R J Kane DO.
Licensure Skilled Care. *Beds* 175. *Certified* Medicaid; Medicare.
Ownership Proprietary.
Admissions Requirements Medical examination.
Staff RNs 20 (ft); LPNs 22 (ft); Nurses aides 70 (ft), 30 (pt); Physical therapists 1 (ft); Occupational therapists 1 (pt); Speech therapists 1 (pt); Activities coordinators 1 (ft), 3 (pt); Dietitians 1 (ft); Dentists 1 (pt); Ophthalmologists 1 (pt); Podiatrists 1 (pt); Audiologists 1 (pt).
Facilities Dining room; Physical therapy room; Activities room; Crafts room; Barber/Beauty shop.
Activities Arts and Crafts; Cards; Games; Reading groups; Prayer groups; Movies; Shopping trips.
Description Mayo is proud of its fine teamwork producing highest quality nursing and rehabilitiation in a warm, caring atmosphere.

Mercy Douglass Human Service Center
4508-39 Chestnut St, Philadelphia, PA, 19139 (215) 382-9495
Admin Jessie D James. *Medical Dir/Dir of Nursing* Nathaniel H Copeland MD.
Licensure Skilled Care. *Beds* 180. *Certified* Medicaid; Medicare.
Ownership Nonprofit.
Admissions Requirements Minimum age 60; Medical examination; Physician's request.
Staff Physicians 5 (pt); RNs 6 (ft), 3 (pt); LPNs 10 (ft), 3 (pt); Orderlies 5 (ft), 2 (pt); Nurses aides 50 (ft), 15 (pt); Physical therapists 1 (pt); Recreational therapists 3 (ft); Speech therapists 1 (pt); Activities coordinators 1 (pt); Dietitians 1 (ft), 1 (pt); Dentists 2 (pt); Ophthalmologists 1 (pt); Podiatrists 1 (pt); Audiologists 1 (pt).
Facilities Dining room; Physical therapy room; Activities room; Chapel; Crafts room; Laundry room; Barber/Beauty shop; Library.
Activities Arts and Crafts; Cards; Games;

Reading groups; Prayer groups; Movies.
Description Center is a modern health care facility.

Northwood Nursing and Convalescent Center*
4621 Castor Ave, Philadelphia, PA, 19124 (215) 744-6464
Licensure Skilled Care. *Beds* 66. *Certified* Medicaid.
Ownership Proprietary.

Park Pleasant Inc*
Drawer D University City, 4712-16 Chester Ave, Philadelphia, PA, 19143 (215) 727-4450
Licensure Skilled Care. *Beds* 121. *Certified* Medicaid
Ownership Proprietary.

Penny Pack Manor Nursing Home*
8015 Lawndale St, Philadelphia, PA, 19111 (215) 725-2525
Licensure Skilled Care. *Beds* 56. *Certified* Medicare.
Ownership Proprietary.

Perkins Convalescent Home*
2107 W Tioga St, Philadelphia, PA, 19140 (215) 226-0407
Licensure Skilled Care. *Beds* 27. *Certified* Medicaid.
Ownership Proprietary.

Philadelphia Nursing Home
7979 State Rd, Philadelphia, PA, 19136 (215) 335-8715
Medical Dir/Dir of Nursing Richard Gibbon MD.
Licensure Intermediate Care. *Beds* 129. *Certified* Medicaid.
Ownership Public.
Admissions Requirements Medical examination; Physician's request.
Staff Physicians 1 (ft), 1 (pt); RNs 8 (ft), 4 (pt); Recreational therapists 1 (ft); Dietitians 1 (pt); Dentists 1 (pt); Ophthalmologists 1 (pt); Podiatrists 1 (pt); Audiologists 1 (pt).
Facilities Dining room; Physical therapy room; Chapel; Crafts room; Laundry room; Barber-/Beauty shop.
Activities Arts and Crafts; Cards; Games; Reading groups; Prayer groups; Movies; Shopping trips; Dances/Social or cultural gatherings.

Philadelphia Nursing Home*
Girard and Corinthian Aves, Philadelphia, PA, 19130 (215) 978-2100
Licensure Skilled Care; Intermediate Care. *Beds* SNF 426; ICF 74. *Certified* Medicaid; Medicare.
Ownership Nonprofit.

Philadelphia Protestant Home for the Aging
700 E Gilham St, Philadelphia, PA, 19111 (215) 745-1986
Medical Dir/Dir of Nursing Dr Paul Moyer.
Licensure Skilled Care; Intermediate Care. *Beds* SNF 53; ICF 69. *Certified* Medicaid; Medicare.
Ownership Nonprofit.
Admissions Requirements Minimum age 65; Medical examination; Physician's request.
Staff Physicians 1 (ft), 4 (pt); RNs 4 (ft), 8 (pt); LPNs 4 (ft), 4 (pt); Orderlies 1 (ft), 1 (pt);

Nurses aides 26 (ft), 15 (pt); Physical therapists 1 (ft); Reality therapists 1 (ft); Recreational therapists 1 (pt); Occupational therapists 1 (pt); Speech therapists 1 (pt); Activities coordinators 1 (ft); Dietitians 1 (ft); Dentists 1 (pt); Ophthalmologists 1 (pt); Podiatrists 1 (pt); Audiologists 1 (pt).
Facilities Dining room; Physical therapy room; Activities room; Chapel; Crafts room; Laundry room; Barber/Beauty shop; Library.
Activities Arts and Crafts; Cards; Games; Reading groups; Prayer groups; Movies; Shopping trips; Dances/Social or cultural gatherings; Special holidays, Family reunions.
Description Facility is entering into an expansion program of 200 apartments for independent living to be completed in 2 phases—January 1, 1985 and January 1, 1986, with added medical suites and swimming pool, expansion of administrative offices, and computerization of administration and medical procedures.

Pinehill Rehabilitation Center*
9990 Verree Rd, Philadelphia, PA, 19115 (215) 677-9500
Licensure Intermediate Care for Mentally Retarded. *Beds* 161. *Certified* Medicaid.
Ownership Proprietary.

Presbyterian Home for the Aged*
4700 City Line Ave, Philadelphia, PA, 19131 (215) 877-8929
Licensure Skilled Care. *Beds* 30.
Ownership Nonprofit.
Affiliation Presbyterian

Presyterian Home at 58th St
58th and Greenway Ave, Philadelphia, PA, 19143 (215) 724-2218
Admin Henrietta D Roberts. *Medical Dir/Dir of Nursing* Donald J Corey MD.
Licensure Skilled Care. *Beds* 50.
Ownership Nonprofit.
Admissions Requirements Medical examination.
Staff Physicians; RNs; LPNs; Nurses aides; Physical therapists; Occupational therapists; Speech therapists; Activities coordinators; Dietitians; Dentists; Ophthalmologists; Podiatrists.
Affiliation Presbyterian
Facilities Dining room; Physical therapy room; Activities room; Chapel; Laundry room; Barber/Beauty shop; Library.
Activities Arts and Crafts; Games; Reading groups; Prayer groups; Movies; Shopping trips; Dances/Social or cultural gatherings.
Description Facility emphasizes preventive health and wellness by utilization of consultant services.

Ralston House
3615 Chestnut St, Philadelphia, PA, 19104 (215) 386-2984
Medical Dir/Dir of Nursing Dr Herb Cohen.
Licensure Skilled Care; Intermediate Care. *Beds* SNF 120; ICF 12. *Certified* Medicaid.
Ownership Nonprofit.
Staff Physicians 1 (pt); RNs 7 (ft); LPNs 5 (ft), 6 (pt); Orderlies 3 (ft), 1 (pt); Nurses aides 50 (ft), 9 (pt); Physical therapists 1 (ft); Recreational therapists 2 (ft); Occupational therapists 1 (ft); Activities coordinators 1 (ft); Dietitians 1

(ft).

Facilities Dining room; Physical therapy room; Activities room; Chapel; Crafts room; Laundry room; Barber/Beauty shop; Library.
Activities Arts and Crafts; Games; Reading groups; Prayer groups; Movies; Shopping trips; Dances/Social or cultural gatherings.
Description Original facility started in 1817 in the heart of Philadelphia; part of University of Pennsylvania setting; experienced in greater health care delivery systems.

Regina Community Nursing Center at Vine Street
230 N 65th and Vine Sts, Philadelphia, PA, 19139 (215) 472-0541
Medical Dir/Dir of Nursing Martin J Kearney MD.
Licensure Skilled Care. *Beds* 44. *Certified* Medicaid.
Ownership Nonprofit.
Admissions Requirements Medical examination.
Staff Physicians; RNs; LPNs; Nurses aides; Reality therapists; Recreational therapists; Occupational therapists; Speech therapists; Activities coordinators; Dietitians; Dentists; Ophthalmologists; Podiatrists; Audiologists.
Facilities Dining room; Physical therapy room; Activities room.
Activities Cards; Games; Prayer groups; Movies.
Description Center is small and very home-like offering all private and semi-private rooms; Medicaid and private pay.

Rest Haven—Whitemarsh*
9209 Ridge Pike, Philadelphia, PA, 19128 (215) 825-4050
Licensure Skilled Care. *Beds* 227. *Certified* Medicaid; Medicare.
Ownership Proprietary.

Rittenhouse Care Center*
1526 Lombrd St, Philadelphia, PA, 19146 (215) 546-5960
Licensure Skilled Care. *Beds* 198. *Certified* Medicaid; Medicare.
Ownership Proprietary.

Sacred Heart Free Home*
1315 W Hunting Park Ave, Philadelphia, PA, 19140 (215) 329-8800
Licensure Skilled Care. *Beds* 60.
Ownership Nonprofit.

Sacred Heart Manor
6445 Germantown Ave, Philadelphia, PA, 19119 (215) 438-5368
Medical Dir/Dir of Nursing Wilfreta Baugh MD.
Licensure Skilled Care; Intermediate Care; Residential. *Beds* SNF 71; ICF 9; Residential 62. *Certified* Medicaid.
Ownership Nonprofit.
Admissions Requirements Minimum age 65; Medical examination.
Staff Physicians; RNs; LPNs; Nurses aides; Physical therapists; Recreational therapists; Speech therapists; Activities coordinators; Dietitians; Dentists; Ophthalmologists; Podiatrists.
Affiliation Roman Catholic
Facilities Dining room; Physical therapy room;

Activities room; Chapel; Crafts room; Laundry room; Barber/Beauty shop; Library.
Activities Arts and Crafts; Cards; Games; Reading groups; Prayer groups; Movies; Shopping trips; Dances/Social or cultural gatherings.
Description The generations are bridged between area youths and senior citizens by fostering friendships between students from the local "Project Learn" and a local vocational high school and the residents. Facility's unique pet therapy program helps foster well-being through the therapeutic emotional effects of the human/companion animal bond.

Saint Ignatius Nursing Home*
4401 Haverford Ave, Philadelphia, PA, 19104 (215) 349-8800
Licensure Skilled Care. *Beds* 176. *Certified* Medicaid.
Ownership Nonprofit.

Saint John Neumann Nursing Home
10400 Roosevelt Blvd, Philadelphia, PA, 19116 (215) 698-5600
Medical Dir/Dir of Nursing Robert E Chmielewski MD.
Licensure Skilled Care. *Beds* 218. *Certified* Medicaid; Medicare.
Ownership Nonprofit.
Admissions Requirements Minimum age 16; Medical examination.
Staff Physicians 5 (pt); RNs 4 (ft), 7 (pt); LPNs 12 (ft), 12 (pt); Orderlies 1 (pt); Nurses aides 83 (ft), 65 (pt); Physical therapists 1 (pt); Recreational therapists 1 (ft); Speech therapists 1 (pt); Activities coordinators 1 (pt); Dietitians 1 (ft); Dentists 1 (pt); Ophthalmologists 1 (pt); Podiatrists 2 (pt).
Affiliation Roman Catholic
Facilities Dining room; Physical therapy room; Activities room; Chapel; Crafts room; Laundry room; Barber/Beauty shop; Library; Gift shop.
Activities Arts and Crafts; Cards; Games; Prayer groups; Movies; Shopping trips; Dances/Social or cultural gatherings.
Description Saint John Neumann provides comprehensive convalescent and rehabilitative care in pleasant and peaceful surroundings. It is handsomely furnished in a cheerful, modern decor; patient rooms provide comfort, convenience and privacy to all regardless of race, color, or creed. The road to recovery at Saint John Neumann is paved with programs of recuperative therapy. Patients benefit from the most advanced equipment and techniques under the direction of a licensed physical therapist. Saint John Neumann is dedicated to meeting the spiritual and physical needs of patients.

Saunders House
100 Lancaster Ave, Philadelphia, PA, 19151 (215) 896-7955
Medical Dir/Dir of Nursing Bruce G Silver MD.
Licensure Skilled Care; Intermediate Care. *Beds* SNF 135; ICF 45. *Certified* Medicaid; Medicare.
Ownership Nonprofit.
Admissions Requirements Minimum age 62; Medical examination.
Staff Physicians 3 (pt); RNs 29 (ft); LPNs 5 (ft); Orderlies 14 (ft); Nurses aides 85 (ft); Physical therapists 1 (pt); Reality therapists 5

(pt); Occupational therapists 1 (pt); Speech therapists 1 (pt); Activities coordinators 3 (pt); Dietitians 1 (pt); Dentists 1 (pt); Ophthalmologists 1 (pt); Podiatrists 1 (pt).
Facilities Dining room; Physical therapy room; Activities room; Chapel; Crafts room; Laundry room; Barber/Beauty shop; Library; Outdoor patio.
Activities Arts and Crafts; Games; Reading groups; Prayer groups; Movies; Shopping trips; Dances/Social or cultural gatherings.

Simpson House of the United Methodist Church*
Belmont and Monument Aves, Philadelphia, PA, 19131 (215) 878-3600
Licensure Skilled Care; Intermediate Care. *Beds* SNF 76; ICF 54. *Certified* Medicaid; Medicare.
Ownership Nonprofit.
Affiliation Methodist

Stenton Hall Nursing and Convalescent Center
7310 Stenton Ave, Philadelphia, PA, 19150 (215) 242-2727
Licensure Skilled Care; Intermediate Care. *Beds* 95. *Certified* Medicaid; Medicare.
Ownership Proprietary.
Staff Physicians 1 (pt); RNs 5 (ft), 1 (pt); LPNs 4 (ft), 2 (pt); Nurses aides 30 (ft); Physical therapists 1 (pt); Recreational therapists 1 (ft); Occupational therapists 1 (pt); Speech therapists 1 (pt); Activities coordinators 1 (ft); Dietitians 1 (pt); Dentists 1 (pt); Podiatrists 1 (pt).
Affiliation Jewish
Facilities Dining room; Physical therapy room; Activities room.
Activities Arts and Crafts; Cards; Games; Reading groups; Prayer groups; Movies.
Description Facility is kosher, under strict orthodox rabbinical supervision, and features adopt-a-grandparent program and quality assurance program that enhances the quality of life.

Stephen Smith Home for the Aged*
4400 W Girard Ave, Philadelphia, PA, 19104 (215) 581-4700
Licensure Skilled Care. *Beds* 180. *Certified* Medicaid.
Ownership Nonprofit.

Thoroughgood Nursing Home*
400 S 40th St, Philadelphia, PA, 19104 (215) 222-1875
Licensure Skilled Care. *Beds* 86. *Certified* Medicaid.
Ownership Proprietary.

Tucker House
1001 11 Wallace St, Philadelphia, PA, 19123 (215) 235-1600
Medical Dir/Dir of Nursing Nathaniel Copeland MD.
Licensure Skilled Care; Intermediate Care. *Beds* SNF 60; ICF 120. *Certified* Medicaid; Medicare.
Ownership Nonprofit.
Staff Physicians 5 (pt); RNs 6 (ft), 3 (pt); LPNs 10 (ft), 4 (pt); Nurses aides 100 (ft), 30 (pt); Physical therapists 1 (pt); Recreational therapists 3 (ft); Speech therapists 1 (pt); Dietitians 1 (pt); Dentists 1 (pt); Ophthalmologists 1 (pt);

Podiatrists 2 (pt).
Facilities Dining room; Physical therapy room; Activities room; Chapel; Laundry room; Barber/Beauty shop.
Activities Arts and Crafts; Cards; Games; Reading groups; Prayer groups; Movies; Shopping trips.

Uptown Home for the Aged
7800 Bustleton Ave, Philadelphia, PA, 19152
(215) 722-2300
Admin Samuel T Lewis. *Medical Dir/Dir of Nursing* Sidney Brenner MD.
Licensure Skilled Care; Intermediate Care.
Beds SNF 84; ICF 156. *Certified* Medicaid; Medicare.
Ownership Nonprofit.
Admissions Requirements Minimum age 65; Medical examination.
Staff Physicians 2 (pt); RNs 7 (ft), 6 (pt); LPNs 11 (ft), 17 (pt); Orderlies 5 (ft), 3 (pt); Nurses aides 51 (ft), 26 (pt); Physical therapists 1 (pt); Recreational therapists 1 (ft); Occupational therapists 1 (pt); Speech therapists 1 (pt); Activities coordinators 1 (ft); Dietitians 1 (pt); Dentists 1 (pt); Ophthalmologists 1 (pt); Podiatrists 1 (pt); Audiologists 1 (pt); Ward clerks 3 (ft).
Facilities Dining room; Physical therapy room; Activities room; Chapel; Crafts room; Laundry room; Barber/Beauty shop; Library.
Activities Arts and Crafts; Cards; Games; Reading groups; Prayer groups; Movies; Shopping trips; Dances/Social or cultural gatherings.
Description Facility is known for its bright, cheery appearance with partially covered patio; roof garden is impressive with multi-colored umbrellas and tables. Most unique program held is mini-college graduation in which 6 residents in caps and gowns received diplomas. The activity showing the greatest amount of varied talent is the art class with its permanent clothes line exhibit with changing paintings.

William J Perry Convalescent Home*
4042-44 Spruce St, Philadelphia, PA, 19104
(215) 382-9180
Licensure Intermediate Care. *Beds* 48. *Certified* Medicaid.
Ownership Proprietary.

Pauls Run*
9896 Bustleton Ave, Phdelphia, PA, 19115
(215) 934-3000
Licensure Skilled Care. *Beds* 120. *Certified* Medicare.
Ownership Nonprofit.

Willowcrest Bamberger*
York and Tabor Rds, Philadelphia, PA, 19141
(215) 457-6300
Licensure Skilled Care. *Beds* 102. *Certified* Medicaid; Medicare.
Ownership Nonprofit.

PHILIPSBURG

United Presbyterian Home of Philipsburg*
Presqueisle and 2nd Sts, Philipsburg, PA, 16866
(814) 342-0340
Licensure Skilled Care. *Beds* 38. *Certified* Medicaid; Medicare.
Ownership Nonprofit.
Affiliation Presbyterian

PHOENIXVILLE

Phoenixville Convalescent Manor Inc*
833 S Main St, Phoenixville, PA, 19460 (215) 933-5867
Licensure Skilled Care. *Beds* 135. *Certified* Medicaid; Medicare.
Ownership Proprietary.

PITTMAN

Friendly Nursing Home
Rt 1, Pittman, PA, 17964 (717) 644-0489
Medical Dir/Dir of Nursing William LeMasters DO.
Licensure Skilled Care. *Beds* 48. *Certified* Medicaid.
Ownership Nonprofit.
Admissions Requirements Medical examination.
Staff RNs 1 (ft), 5 (pt); LPNs 2 (ft); Nurses aides 15 (ft), 19 (pt); Activities coordinators 1 (ft), 1 (pt).
Facilities Dining room; Activities room; Crafts room; Laundry room.
Activities Arts and Crafts; Cards; Games; Reading groups; Prayer groups; Movies; Shopping trips; Dances/Social or cultural gatherings.
Description Facility is located in a rural area with quiet surroundings.

PITTSBURGH

Angelus Convalescent Center Inc*
200 Amber St, Pittsburgh, PA, 15206 (412) 362-6300
Licensure Skilled Care. *Beds* 84. *Certified* Medicaid; Medicare.
Ownership Proprietary.

Baptist Homes Nursing Center
489 Castle Shannon Blvd, Pittsburgh, PA, 15234 (412) 563-6550
Medical Dir/Dir of Nursing Dr Joyce Sandberg.
Licensure Skilled Care; Intermediate Care.
Beds SNF 78; ICF 48. *Certified* Medicaid; Medicare.
Ownership Nonprofit.
Admissions Requirements Medical examination; Physician's request.
Staff RNs 9 (ft), 11 (pt); LPNs 8 (ft), 3 (pt); Nurses aides 36 (ft), 20 (pt); Recreational therapists 1 (ft); Activities coordinators 1 (ft).
Affiliation Baptist
Facilities Dining room; Physical therapy room;
Activities room; Chapel; Crafts room; Laundry room; Barber/Beauty shop; Lounges; Solarium.
Activities Arts and Crafts; Cards; Games; Reading groups; Prayer groups; Movies; Shopping trips; Dances/Social or cultural gatherings; Sewing; Cooking; Exercise classes.
Description The Baptist Homes Nursing Center has a 75-year commitment to high quality resident care, emphasizing the potential and individuality of each resident. We are located 6 miles from downtown Pittsburgh, and are close to neighborhood shopping areas and mass transit lines.

C Howard Marcy State Hospital
Leech Farm Rd, Pittsburgh, PA, 15206 (412) 665-2010
Licensure Intermediate Care for Mentally Retarded. *Beds* 128. *Certified* Medicaid.
Ownership Nonprofit.

Collins Nursing Home Inc
5511 Baum Blvd, Pittsburgh, PA, 15232 (412) 661-1740
Medical Dir/Dir of Nursing Dr Maranatti.
Licensure Skilled Care; Intermediate Care.
Beds SNF 31; ICF 41. *Certified* Medicaid; Medicare.
Ownership Proprietary.
Admissions Requirements Minimum age 65; Medical examination; Physician's request.
Staff Physicians 1 (pt); RNs 4 (ft), 3 (pt); LPNs 6 (ft), 3 (pt); Physical therapists 1 (ft); Recreational therapists 1 (ft); Speech therapists 1 (pt); Activities coordinators 1 (ft); Dietitians 1 (ft); Dentists 1 (pt); Ophthalmologists 1 (pt); Podiatrists 1 (pt).
Facilities Dining room; Physical therapy room; Activities room; Laundry room; Barber/Beauty shop.
Activities Arts and Crafts; Cards; Games; Reading groups.

Episcopal Church Home
4001 Penn Ave, Pittsburgh, PA, 15224 (412) 682-0153
Medical Dir/Dir of Nursing Dr John Morphy.
Licensure Skilled Care. *Beds* 24. *Certified* Medicaid; Medicare.
Ownership Nonprofit.
Admissions Requirements Medical examination.
Staff Physicians 1 (pt); RNs 5 (ft), 3 (pt); LPNs 8 (ft), 18 (pt); Recreational therapists 1 (ft); Dietitians 1 (ft).
Affiliation Episcopal
Facilities Dining room; Activities room; Chapel; Laundry room; Library.
Activities Arts and Crafts; Cards; Games; Reading groups; Prayer groups; Movies; Shopping trips; Dances/Social or cultural gatherings.
Description This is a small well-staffed facility giving high levels of personal attention. Best recent initiative is a pet therapy program.

Forbes Center for Gerontology
Frankstown Ave at Washington Blvd, Pittsburgh, PA, 15206 (412) 665-3165
Medical Dir/Dir of Nursing Dr J F O'Keefe and Dr J R Friday.
Licensure Skilled Care. *Beds* 132. *Certified* Medicaid; Medicare.
Ownership Proprietary.

Admissions Requirements Minimum age 16; Medical examination; Physician's request.
Staff Physicians 2 (ft); RNs 8 (ft), 4 (pt); LPNs 12 (ft); Nurses aides 30 (ft); Physical therapists 1 (ft); Reality therapists 1 (ft); Recreational therapists 2 (ft); Occupational therapists 1 (pt); Speech therapists 1 (pt); Activities coordinators 1 (ft); Dietitians 1 (ft).
Facilities Dining room; Physical therapy room; Activities room; Chapel; Laundry room; Barber/Beauty shop; Library; Music therapy room.
Activities Arts and Crafts; Games; Prayer groups; Movies; Shopping trips; Dances/Social or cultural gatherings.
Description A progressive post-hospital nursing facility which features the necessary treatment services and sponsors approved educational programs.

Highland Park Center*
745 N Highland Ave, Pittsburgh, PA, 15206
(412) 661-4632
Licensure Intermediate Care for Mentally Retarded. *Beds* 132. *Certified* Medicaid.
Ownership Nonprofit.

Holmes House
5500 Butler St, Pittsburgh, PA, 15201 (412) 781-3526
Licensure Skilled Care. *Beds* 60. *Certified* Medicaid.
Ownership Nonprofit.

Home for Aged Protestant Women
900 Rebecca Ave, Pittsburgh, PA, 15221 (412) 731-2338
Medical Dir/Dir of Nursing Noel Gillette MD.
Licensure Intermediate Care. *Beds* 37.
Ownership Nonprofit.
Admissions Requirements Minimum age 65; Females only; Medical examination, Physician's request.
Staff Physicians 1 (pt); RNs 1 (ft), 4 (pt); LPNs 3 (ft), 2 (pt); Nurses aides 8 (ft), 5 (pt); Physical therapists 1 (pt); Speech therapists 1 (pt); Activities coordinators 1 (ft).
Facilities Dining room; Physical therapy room; Activities room; Chapel; Crafts room; Laundry room; Barber/Beauty shop; Library.
Activities Arts and Crafts; Cards; Games; Reading groups; Prayer groups; Movies; Dances/Social or cultural gatherings.
Description Facility offers well-rounded activities program including exercise class every morning, many outings, bingo each month, and a fall bazaar.

Ivy Nursing Home Inc
5609 5th Ave, Pittsburgh, PA, 15213 (412) 362-3500
Licensure Skilled Care. *Beds* 150. *Certified* Medicaid; Medicare.
Ownership Proprietary.

Jefferson Hills Manor Inc
PO Box 10805, Pittsburgh, PA, 15236 (412) 653-1128
Licensure Skilled Care. *Beds* 57.
Ownership Proprietary.

Jewish Home and Hospital for the Aged*
4724 Browns Hill Rd, Pittsburgh, PA, 15217
(412) 521-5900

Licensure Skilled Care; Intermediate Care.
Beds SNF 324; ICF 133. *Certified* Medicaid; Medicare.
Ownership Nonprofit.
Affiliation Jewish

John J Kane Allegheny County Home*
Vanadium Rd, Pittsburgh, PA, 15243 (412) 928-1400
Licensure Skilled Care; Intermediate Care.
Beds SNF 1087; ICF 378. *Certified* Medicaid; Medicare.
Ownership Nonprofit.

Ladies GAR Home
2622 Woodstock Ave, Pittsburgh, PA, 15218
(412) 271-1316
Medical Dir/Dir of Nursing Dr Mangan.
Licensure Intermediate Care. *Beds* ICF 65.
Certified Medicaid.
Ownership Nonprofit.
Admissions Requirements Females only; Medical examination.
Staff Physicians 2 (ft); RNs 1 (ft), 4 (pt); LPNs 2 (ft), 2 (pt); Nurses aides 15 (ft); Physical therapists 1 (pt); Reality therapists 1 (ft); Occupational therapists 1 (ft); Activities coordinators 1 (ft); Dietitians 1 (ft); Dentists 1 (ft).
Facilities Dining room; Activities room; Chapel; Crafts room; Laundry room; Barber/Beauty shop; Library.
Activities Arts and Crafts; Cards; Games; Reading groups; Prayer groups; Movies; Shopping trips; Dances/Social or cultural gatherings.

Lemington Home for the Aged
7081 Lemington Ave, Pittsburgh, PA, 15206
(412) 441-1815
Admin Juanita King. *Medical Dir/Dir of Nursing* Dr Labib Rizk.
Licensure Skilled Care. *Beds* 34. *Certified* Medicaid; Medicare.
Ownership Nonprofit.
Admissions Requirements Minimum age 60; Medical examination.
Staff Physicians 4 (pt); RNs 6 (ft); LPNs 5 (ft); Orderlies 3 (ft); Nurses aides 35 (ft), 10 (pt); Physical therapists 1 (ft), 2 (pt); Occupational therapists 1 (pt); Speech therapists 1 (pt); Activities coordinators 1 (ft); Dietitians 1 (pt); Dentists 1 (pt); Ophthalmologists 1 (pt); Podiatrists 1 (pt); Audiologists 1 (pt).
Facilities Dining room; Physical therapy room; Activities room; Chapel; Crafts room; Laundry room; Barber/Beauty shop.
Activities Arts and Crafts; Cards; Games; Reading groups; Prayer groups; Movies; Shopping trips; Dances/Social or cultural gatherings.
Description Agency sponsors a multi-purpose center for the aged handicapped; sponsors 2 congregate sites; funding for these centers comes through the area agency on aging.

Little Sisters of the Poor Home for the Aged
1028 Benton Ave, Pittsburgh, PA, 15212 (412) 761-5373
Admin Sr Madeline.
Licensure Skilled Care; Intermediate Care; Residential Care. *Beds* SNF 40; ICF 70; Residential Care 30. *Certified* Medicaid.
Ownership Nonprofit.
Admissions Requirements Minimum age 58; Medical examination.

Staff RNs 3 (ft), 6 (pt); LPNs 6 (ft), 7 (pt); Nurses aides 24 (ft), 20 (pt); Physical therapists 1 (pt); Activities coordinators 1 (ft); Dietitians 1 (pt).
Affiliation Roman Catholic
Facilities Dining room; Physical therapy room; Activities room; Chapel; Crafts room; Laundry room; Barber/Beauty shop; Library.
Activities Arts and Crafts; Cards; Games; Prayer groups; Movies; Shopping trips; Dances/Social or cultural gatherings.

Marian Manor*
2695 Winchester Dr, Pittsburgh, PA, 15220
(412) 563-6866
Licensure Skilled Care; Intermediate Care.
Beds SNF 72; ICF 50. *Certified* Medicaid.
Ownership Nonprofit.

McDonough Home
1540 Evergreen Ave, Pittsburgh, PA, 15209
(412) 821-3088
Licensure Intermediate Care. *Beds* 25.
Ownership Proprietary.

Mount Lebanon Manor Convalescent Center
350 Gilkeson Rd, Pittsburgh, PA, 15228 (412) 563-4994
Medical Dir/Dir of Nursing Ralph Schmeltz MD.
Licensure Skilled Care; Intermediate Care.
Beds SNF 60; ICF 61. *Certified* Medicaid.
Ownership Proprietary.
Staff Physicians 11 (pt); RNs 6 (ft), 6 (pt); LPNs 6 (ft), 6 (pt); Nurses aides 20 (ft), 20 (pt); Physical therapists 1 (ft); Recreational therapists 1 (ft), 1 (pt); Occupational therapists 1 (pt); Speech therapists 1 (pt); Dietitians 1 (ft); Dentists 1 (pt); Ophthalmologists 1 (pt); Podiatrists 1 (pt); Audiologists 1 (pt).
Facilities Dining room; Physical therapy room; Activities room; Crafts room; Laundry room; Barber/Beauty shop.
Activities Arts and Crafts; Cards; Games; Reading groups; Prayer groups; Movies; Shopping trips; Dances/Social or cultural gatherings.
Description Facility specializes in rehabilitation; has a small adult day care program; plans in the near future to provide a specialized Alzheimer's unit as part of a study being done by corporation.

Negley House Inc
550 S Negley Ave, Pittsburgh, PA, 15232 (412) 665-2400
Medical Dir/Dir of Nursing Richard Rosenthal MD.
Licensure Skilled Care; Intermediate Care.
Beds SNF 168; ICF 56. *Certified* Medicaid; Medicare.
Ownership Proprietary.
Admissions Requirements Medical examination.
Staff RNs 16 (ft), 13 (pt); LPNs 10 (ft), 46 (pt); Nurses aides 47 (ft), 46 (pt); Physical therapists 3 (ft), 1 (pt); Recreational therapists 3 (ft); Occupational therapists 1 (ft); Speech therapists 1 (pt); Dietitians 2 (pt); Dentists 1 (pt); Ophthalmologists 1 (pt); Podiatrists 1 (pt); Audiologists 1 (pt).
Facilities Dining room; Physical therapy room; Activities room; Chapel; Crafts room; Laundry room; Barber/Beauty shop; Library.

Activities Arts and Crafts; Cards; Games; Reading groups; Prayer groups; Movies; Shopping trips; Dances/Social or cultural gatherings. *Description* Facility features woodcraft classes, physical and occupational therapy, hyper-alimentation, and selective menus. Our buildings are newly renovated and are very close to public transportation and shopping facilities.

Reformed Presbyterian Home for the Aged*
2344 Perrysville Ave, Pittsburgh, PA, 15214 (412) 321-4139
Licensure Skilled Care. *Beds* 58. *Certified* Medicaid; Medicare.
Ownership Nonprofit.
Affiliation Presbyterian

Saint Joseph Home for the Aged*
5324 Penn Ave, Pittsburgh, PA, 15224 (412) 665-5100
Licensure Skilled Care. *Beds* 155. *Certified* Medicaid; Medicare.
Ownership Nonprofit.

Sky Vue Terrace
2170 Rhine St, Pittsburgh, PA, 15212 (412) 323-0420
Medical Dir/Dir of Nursing Dr Harry Heck.
Licensure Skilled Care. *Beds* 100. *Certified* Medicaid.
Ownership Proprietary.
Admissions Requirements Minimum age 18.
Staff RNs 6 (ft), 4 (pt); LPNs 5 (ft), 4 (pt); Nurses aides 37 (ft); Physical therapists 1 (pt); Activities coordinators 1 (ft); Dietitians 1 (pt).
Facilities Dining room; Physical therapy room; Activities room; Chapel.
Activities Arts and Crafts; Cards; Games; Movies; Shopping trips; Dances/Social or cultural gatherings.
Description Facility provides tender loving care to all.

United Methodist Home
700 Bower Hill Rd, Mount Lebanon, Pittsburgh, PA, 15243 (412) 341-1030
Medical Dir/Dir of Nursing Lawrence Wilson MD.
Licensure Skilled Care; Intermediate Care.
Beds SNF 90; ICF 33. *Certified* Medicaid; Medicare.
Ownership Nonprofit.
Admissions Requirements Minimum age 65; Medical examination.
Staff Physicians 1 (pt); RNs 9 (ft), 10 (pt); LPNs 6 (ft), 11 (pt); Orderlies 1 (ft); Nurses aides 30 (ft), 25 (pt); Physical therapists 1 (pt); Recreational therapists 2 (pt); Speech therapists 1 (pt); Activities coordinators 1 (ft); Dietitians 1 (ft); Dentists 1 (pt); Podiatrists 1 (pt).
Affiliation Methodist
Facilities Dining room; Physical therapy room; Chapel; Crafts room; Laundry room; Barber-/Beauty shop; Library.
Activities Arts and Crafts; Cards; Games; Reading groups; Prayer groups; Movies; Shopping trips; Dances/Social or cultural gatherings; Trips to local points of interest.
Description Planning is underway to become a complete retirement community by 1987.

United Presbyterian Home for Aged People*
306 Pennsylvania Ave at Trenton Ave, Pittsburgh, PA, 15221 (412) 242-3606
Licensure Skilled Care; Intermediate Care.
Beds SNF 14; ICF 15.
Ownership Nonprofit.
Affiliation Presbyterian

Villa Demarillac Nursing Home Inc*
5300 Stanton Ave, Pittsburgh, PA, 15206 (412) 361-2833
Licensure Skilled Care. *Beds* 50. *Certified* Medicaid.
Ownership Nonprofit.

Vincentian Home for the Chronically Ill*
Perrymont Rd, Pittsburgh, PA, 15237 (412) 931-4222
Licensure Skilled Care. *Beds* 219. *Certified* Medicaid; Medicare.
Ownership Nonprofit.

Western Pennsylvania Eastern Star Home*
226 Bellevue Rd, Pittsburgh, PA, 15229 (412) 931-2256
Licensure Skilled Care. *Beds* 40.
Ownership Nonprofit.
Affiliation Order of Eastern Star

Western Restoration Center*
2851 Bedford Ave, Pittsburgh, PA, 15219 (412) 683-5000
Licensure Skilled Care; Intermediate Care.
Beds SNF 66; ICF 35. *Certified* Medicaid.
Ownership Nonprofit.

Wightman Health Center
2025 Wightman St, Pittsburgh, PA, 15217 (412) 421-8443
Medical Dir/Dir of Nursing Martin H Nalrath III MD.
Licensure Skilled Care; Intermediate Care.
Beds SNF 134; ICF 47. *Certified* Medicaid; Medicare.
Ownership Proprietary.
Admissions Requirements Minimum age 16; Medical examination.
Staff Physicians 6 (pt); RNs 7 (ft), 8 (pt); LPNs 15 (ft), 2 (pt); Orderlies 3 (ft); Nurses aides 58 (ft), 2 (pt); Physical therapists 1 (ft); Recreational therapists 1 (ft); Occupational therapists 1 (ft), 1 (pt); Speech therapists 1 (pt); Activities coordinators 3 (ft); Dietitians 1 (pt).
Facilities Dining room; Physical therapy room; Activities room; Crafts room; Laundry room; Barber/Beauty shop; Library; Dental office; Occupational therapy room.
Activities Arts and Crafts; Cards; Games; Prayer groups; Movies; Shopping trips; Dances/Social or cultural gatherings.
Description Our coma management program is designed for patients functioning at low cognitive levels, due to head injuries, anoxia, or metabolic coma. Quality nursing care, along with sensory stimulation intervention, occupational, physical, and speech therapies aid the development of the patients' maximum functional level. The program provides the ultimate capability of respiratory support for ventilator dependent patients.

PITTSTON

Wesley Village
Laflin Rd, Pittston, PA, 18640 (717) 655-2891
Admin H R Bean. *Medical Dir/Dir of Nursing* Joseph Lombardo MD.
Licensure Skilled Care; Personal Care. *Beds* ICF 59; Personal Care 20. *Certified* Medicaid; Medicare.
Ownership Nonprofit.
Admissions Requirements Medical examination.
Staff RNs 11 (ft), 14 (pt); LPNs 4 (ft), 8 (pt); Nurses aides 41 (ft), 55 (pt); Physical therapists 2 (ft); Activities coordinators 3 (ft); Dentists; Ophthalmologists.
Facilities Dining room; Physical therapy room; Activities room; Chapel; Crafts room; Laundry room; Barber/Beauty shop; Library.
Activities Arts and Crafts; Cards; Games; Reading groups; Prayer groups; Movies.

PLYMOUTH MEETING

Clara Burke Nursing Home*
251 Stenton Ave, Plymouth Meeting, PA, 19462 (215) 828-2272
Licensure Skilled Care. *Beds* 71.
Ownership Proprietary.

POTTSTOWN

Coventry Manor Nursing Home Inc*
PO Star Rt, Pottstown, PA, 19464 (215) 469-6228
Licensure Skilled Care. *Beds* 41. *Certified* Medicaid; Medicare.
Ownership Proprietary.

Leader Nursing and Rehabilitation Center—Pottstown*
724 N Charlotte St, Pottstown, PA, 19464 (215) 323-1837
Licensure Skilled Care. *Beds* 159. *Certified* Medicaid; Medicare.
Ownership Proprietary.

Manatawny Manor
Rt 724, Old Schuylkill Rd, Pottstown, PA, 19466 (215) 327-0840
Medical Dir/Dir of Nursing John A Lupas MD.
Licensure Skilled Care; Residential Care.
Beds 120; Residential Care 120. *Certified* Medicaid; Medicare.
Ownership Proprietary.
Admissions Requirements Medical examination.
Staff RNs 8 (ft), 16 (pt); LPNs 6 (ft), 8 (pt); Nurses aides 38 (ft), 13 (pt); Physical therapists 1 (ft), 3 (pt); Recreational therapists 2 (ft); Speech therapists 2 (pt); Activities coordinators 1 (ft); Dietitians 1 (pt); Podiatrists 2 (pt).
Facilities Dining room; Physical therapy room; Activities room; Chapel; Crafts room; Laundry room; Barber/Beauty shop; Library; Gift shop.
Activities Arts and Crafts; Cards; Games; Reading groups; Prayer groups; Movies; Shopping trips; Dances/Social or cultural gatherings; Exercise class; Parkinson's class.

POTTSVILLE

Leader Nursing Rehabilitation Center*
Polaski and Leader Dr, Pottsville, PA, 17091
(717) 622-9582
Licensure Skilled Care. *Beds* 152. *Certified* Medicaid; Medicare.
Ownership Proprietary.

York Terrace Nursing and Convalescent Center*
24th and W Market Sts, Pottsville, PA, 17901
(717) 622-3982
Licensure Skilled Care. *Beds* 80. *Certified* Medicaid; Medicare.
Ownership Proprietary.

PROSPECT PARK

Prospect Park Nursing Home*
815 Chester Pike, Prospect Park, PA, 19076
(215) 586-6262
Licensure Skilled Care. *Beds* 90. *Certified* Medicaid; Medicare.
Ownership Proprietary.

PUNXSUTAWNEY

Blose McGregor Health Care Center Inc
407 1/2 W Mahoning St, Punxsutawney, PA, 15767 (814) 938-6020
Medical Dir/Dir of Nursing Ming Shang Tsai MD.
Licensure Skilled Care. *Beds* 86. *Certified* Medicaid.
Ownership Proprietary.
Admissions Requirements Minimum age 21; Medical examination; Physician's request.
Staff RNs 3 (ft), 4 (pt); LPNs 5 (ft), 5 (pt); Nurses aides 22 (ft), 6 (pt); Activities coordinators 2 (pt).
Facilities Dining room; Physical therapy room; Activities room; Crafts room; Laundry room; Barber/Beauty shop; Library.
Activities Arts and Crafts; Games; Movies.

QUAKERTOWN

Belle Haven Nursing Home Inc
1320 Mill Rd, Quakertown, PA, 18951 (215) 536-7666
Medical Dir/Dir of Nursing Walter Tice MD.
Licensure Skilled Care; Intermediate Care.
Beds SNF 30; ICF 23. *Certified* Medicaid; Medicare.
Ownership Proprietary.
Admissions Requirements Minimum age 18; Medical examination.
Staff Physicians 11 (pt); RNs 2 (ft), 1 (pt); LPNs 6 (ft), 2 (pt); Nurses aides 30 (ft), 8 (pt); Physical therapists 1 (pt); Reality therapists 1 (ft); Recreational therapists 1 (ft); Occupational therapists 1 (pt); Speech therapists 1 (pt); Activities coordinators 1 (ft); Dentists 1 (pt); Ophthalmologists 2 (pt); Podiatrists 3 (pt); Audiologists 1 (pt).
Facilities Dining room; Physical therapy room; Activities room; Crafts room; Laundry room; Barber/Beauty shop; Library.
Activities Arts and Crafts; Cards; Games; Reading groups; Prayer groups; Movies; Shopping trips; Dances/Social or cultural gatherings; Cooking classes, Church every Sunday; Pet therapy.
Description Facility features fenced in yard; large parking lot; outdoor activities, weather permitting; picnics; parties; dog and birds on premises.

Quakertwon Manor Convalescent and Rehabilitation Center*
1020 S Main St, Quakertown, PA, 18951 (215) 536-9300
Licensure Skilled Care. *Beds* 126. *Certified* Medicaid; Medicare.
Ownership Proprietary.

Upper Bucks Nursing and Convalescent Center*
Rt 5, Box 56, Quakertown, PA, 18951 (215) 536-2400
Licensure Skilled Care. *Beds* 55. *Certified* Medicaid; Medicare.
Ownership Nonprofit.

Yingst Nursing Home Inc*
219 E Broad St, Quakertown, PA, 18951 (215) 536-4240
Licensure Skilled Care. *Beds* 41. *Certified* Medicaid.
Ownership Proprietary.

QUARRYVILLE

Quarryville Presbyterian Home
RD 20, Box 20, Quarryville, PA, 17566 (717) 786-7321
Medical Dir/Dir of Nursing Dr Charles Bair.
Licensure Skilled Care. *Beds* 160. *Certified* Medicaid; Medicare.
Ownership Nonprofit.
Admissions Requirements Minimum age 65; Medical examination.
Staff RNs 6 (ft), 9 (pt); LPNs 10 (ft), 15 (pt); Orderlies 3 (ft); Nurses aides 28 (ft), 25 (pt); Activities coordinators 2 (ft), 1 (pt).
Affiliation Presbyterian
Facilities Dining room; Physical therapy room; Activities room; Chapel; Crafts room; Laundry room; Barber/Beauty shop; Library.
Activities Arts and Crafts; Games; Reading groups; Prayer groups; Movies; Shopping trips.

QUINCY

Donely House ICFMR*
PO Box 217, Quincy, PA, 17247 (717) 749-3151
Licensure Intermediate Care for Mentally Retarded. *Beds* 8. *Certified* Medicaid.
Ownership Nonprofit.

Quincy United Methodist Home
Box 217, Quincy, PA, 17247 (717) 749-3151
Medical Dir/Dir of Nursing Dr David Hess.
Licensure Skilled Care; Intermediate Care.
Beds SNF 144; ICF 51. *Certified* Medicaid; Medicare.
Ownership Nonprofit.
Admissions Requirements Medical examination.

Staff RNs 12 (ft), 13 (pt); LPNs 12 (ft), 13 (pt); Activities coordinators 1 (ft); Dietitians 1 (ft).
Affiliation Methodist
Facilities Dining room; Physical therapy room; Activities room; Chapel; Crafts room; Laundry room; Barber/Beauty shop; Library.
Activities Arts and Crafts; Cards; Games; Prayer groups; Movies; Shopping trips; Dances/Social or cultural gatherings; Weekly worship services.
Description Quincy has provided benevolent care for the old and the young since 1903; currently combines a long-term care facility with a retirement village. Facility provides laundry service and sponsors a day care center for staff and families in surrounding community; JCAH certified.

READING

Berks County Home
PO Box 1495, Reading, PA, 19603 (215) 376-4847
Medical Dir/Dir of Nursing Lynwood V Keller MD.
Licensure Skilled Care; Intermediate Care.
Beds SNF 125; ICF 670. *Certified* Medicaid; Medicare.
Ownership Nonprofit.
Admissions Requirements Minimum age 55; Medical examination.
Staff Physicians 14 (pt); RNs 32 (ft), 6 (pt); LPNs 73 (ft), 6 (pt); Nurses aides 309 (ft), 90 (pt); Physical therapists 1 (ft), 1 (pt); Recreational therapists 2 (ft); Occupational therapists 1 (pt); Speech therapists 1 (ft); Activities coordinators 1 (ft); Dietitians 2 (ft), 1 (pt); Dentists 1 (pt); Ophthalmologists 1 (pt); Podiatrists 1 (pt); Audiologists 1 (pt).
Facilities Dining room; Physical therapy room; Activities room; Chapel; Crafts room; Laundry room; Barber/Beauty shop; Library.
Activities Arts and Crafts; Cards; Games; Reading groups; Prayer groups; Movies; Shopping trips; Dances/Social or cultural gatherings.
Description Berks Heim is composed of 2 distinct buildings. Each building is equipped to provide complete services for both skilled and intermediate care. Clinics on the premises are available for services such as dermatology, urology, psychiatry, ophthalmology, surgery, orthopedics, gynecology, podiatry, and dentistry.

Leader Nursing and Rehabilitation Center—Laureldale*
2125 Elizabeth Ave, Reading, PA, 19605 (215) 921-9292
Licensure Skilled Care; Intermediate Care.
Beds SNF 108; ICF 12. *Certified* Medicaid; Medicare.
Ownership Proprietary.

Mineral Spring Manor
1501 Mineral Spring Rd, Reading, PA, 19602 (215) 375-9698
Medical Dir/Dir of Nursing Irving H Jones MD.
Licensure Skilled Care. *Beds* 45.
Ownership Nonprofit.
Staff Physicians 1 (ft); RNs 3 (ft); LPNs 2 (ft); Nurses aides 12 (ft).

Facilities Dining room; Laundry room; Barber-/Beauty shop.
Activities Cards; Games; Prayer groups; Shopping trips.

Wyomissing Lodge
1000 E Wyomissing Blvd, Reading, PA, 19611 (215) 376-3991
Medical Dir/Dir of Nursing Robert Demby MD.
Licensure Skilled Care. *Beds* 107. *Certified* Medicare.
Ownership Proprietary.
Staff Physicians 20 (pt); RNs 5 (ft), 12 (pt); LPNs 4 (ft), 3 (pt); Nurses aides 27 (ft), 10 (pt); Physical therapists 1 (pt); Recreational therapists 1 (pt); Occupational therapists 1 (pt); Speech therapists 1 (pt); Activities coordinators 1 (pt); Dietitians 1 (pt); Podiatrists 1 (pt).
Facilities Dining room; Physical therapy room; Activities room; Crafts room; Barber/Beauty shop; Library.
Activities Arts and Crafts; Cards; Games; Prayer groups; Movies; Shopping trips; Wine and cheese gatherings.

RENOVO

Bucktail Medical Center
Pine St, Renovo, PA, 17764 (717) 923-1000
Admin Donna C Paloskey. *Medical Dir/Dir of Nursing* Rizalito Advinceila MD.
Licensure Skilled Care. *Beds* 33. *Certified* Medicaid; Medicare.
Ownership Nonprofit.
Staff Physicians 2 (ft); RNs 5 (ft), 4 (pt); LPNs 5 (ft), 3 (pt); Nurses aides 10 (ft), 12 (pt); Physical therapists 1 (ft); Recreational therapists 1 (ft); Occupational therapists 1 (pt); Speech therapists 1 (pt); Activities coordinators 1 (ft); Dietitians 1 (ft); Dentists 1 (pt); Podiatrists 1 (pt).
Facilities Dining room; Physical therapy room; Activities room; Chapel; Crafts room; Laundry room; Barber/Beauty shop; Library.
Activities Arts and Crafts; Cards; Games; Reading groups; Prayer groups; Movies; Shopping trips; Dances/Social or cultural gatherings.

RHEEMS

Lehmans Guest and Nursing Home
Broad St, Rheems, PA, 17570 (717) 367-1831
Admin Nancy M Thompson.
Licensure Skilled Care. *Beds* 18.
Ownership Proprietary.
Staff Physicians 1 (pt); RNs 2 (ft), 3 (pt); LPNs 2 (ft), 2 (pt); Nurses aides 4 (ft), 6 (pt); Recreational therapists 1 (pt); Activities coordinators 1 (ft); Dietitians 1 (pt).
Facilities Dining room; Activities room; Laundry room; Barber/Beauty shop.
Activities Arts and Crafts; Cards; Games; Reading groups; Prayer groups; Shopping trips.
Description Facility features home-like atmosphere and family-style home cooked meals.

RICHBORO

Richboro Care Center*
Twining Ford Rd, Richboro, PA, 18954 (215) 357-2032
Licensure Skilled Care. *Beds* 65. *Certified* Medicaid; Medicare.
Ownership Proprietary.

RICHFIELD

Zendt Nursing Home*
Main St, Richfield, PA, 17086 (717) 694-3434
Licensure Intermediate Care. *Beds* 46. *Certified* Medicaid.
Ownership Proprietary.

RICHLANDTOWN

Zohlman Nursing Home
108 S Main St, Richlandtown, PA, 18955 (215) 536-2252
Medical Dir/Dir of Nursing Dr Alfred Vasta.
Licensure Skilled Care. *Beds* 169. *Certified* Medicaid; Medicare.
Ownership Proprietary.
Admissions Requirements Minimum age 16; Medical examination.
Staff Physicians 14 (ft); RNs 7 (ft), 15 (pt); LPNs 4 (ft), 3 (pt); Orderlies 3 (pt); Nurses aides 50 (ft), 17 (pt); Physical therapists 1 (ft), 1 (pt); Recreational therapists 1 (ft), 2 (pt); Occupational therapists 1 (pt); Speech therapists 1 (pt); Activities coordinators 1 (ft); Dietitians 1 (pt); Dentists 1 (pt); Ophthalmologists 1 (pt); Podiatrists 1 (pt); Audiologists 1 (pt).
Facilities Dining room; Physical therapy room; Activities room; Crafts room; Laundry room; Barber/Beauty shop.
Activities Arts and Crafts; Cards; Games; Reading groups; Prayer groups; Movies; Shopping trips; Dances/Social or cultural gatherings.

RIDLEY PARK

Conner Williams Nursing Home*
105 Morton Ave, Ridley Park, PA, 19078 (215) 521-1331
Licensure Skilled Care. *Beds* 52. *Certified* Medicaid.
Ownership Proprietary.

Ross Manor Nursing Home*
316 E Hinckley Ave, Ridley Park, PA, 19078 (215) 521-0193
Licensure Skilled Care. *Beds* 25. *Certified* Medicaid.
Ownership Proprietary.

ROSEMONT

Rosemont Manor
35 Rosemont Ave, Rosemont, PA, 19010 (215) 525-1500
Admin Susan L Ulmer. *Medical Dir/Dir of Nursing* Dr Ian C Deener.
Licensure Skilled Care. *Beds* 76. *Certified* Medicaid; Medicare.
Ownership Proprietary.
Admissions Requirements Minimum age 16.

Staff RNs; LPNs; Nurses aides; Physical therapists; Recreational therapists; Occupational therapists; Speech therapists; Activities coordinators; Dietitians; Dentists; Podiatrists; Audiologists; Social Workers.
Facilities Dining room; Physical therapy room; Activities room; Crafts room; Laundry room; Barber/Beauty shop.
Activities Arts and Crafts; Cards; Games; Reading groups; Prayer groups; Movies; Dances/Social or cultural gatherings; Adopt-a-grandparent.
Description Manor has full range of activities; special programs developed by Beverly Enterprises; VA approved.

ROSLYN

Roslyn Convalescent Home
2630 Woodland Ave, Roslyn, PA, 19001 (215) 884-8238
Licensure Skilled Care. *Beds* 85. *Certified* Medicaid; Medicare.
Ownership Proprietary.
Admissions Requirements Minimum age 16; Medical examination.
Facilities Dining room; Physical therapy room; Activities room; Crafts room; Laundry room; Barber/Beauty shop.
Activities Arts and Crafts; Cards; Games; Reading groups; Prayer groups; Movies; Shopping trips; Dances/Social or cultural gatherings.

ROYERSFORD

Montgomery Country Geriatric and Rehabilitation Center
1600 Black Rock Rd, Royersford, PA, 19468 (215) 948-8800
Licensure Skilled Care; Intermediate Care.
Beds SNF 350; ICF 241. *Certified* Medicaid; Medicare.
Ownership Nonprofit.

RYDAL

Rydal Park of Philadelphia Presbyterian Home on the Fairway
Rydal, PA, 19046 (215) 885-6800
Medical Dir/Dir of Nursing Charles Ewing MD.
Licensure Skilled Care. *Beds* 120. *Certified* Medicaid; Medicare.
Ownership Nonprofit.
Admissions Requirements Minimum age 65.
Affiliation Presbyterian
Facilities Dining room; Physical therapy room; Activities room; Chapel; Crafts room; Laundry room; Barber/Beauty shop; Library.
Activities Arts and Crafts; Cards; Games; Reading groups; Prayer groups; Movies; Shopping trips; Dances/Social or cultural gatherings.

SAEGERTOWN

Crawford County Home*
Rt 1, Saegertown, PA, 16433 (814) 763-2445
Licensure Skilled Care; Intermediate Care.
Beds SNF 41; ICF 138. *Certified* Medicaid.
Ownership Nonprofit.

SAINT MARYS

Andrew Kaul Memorial Hospital—Extended Care Facility
Johnsonburg Rd, Saint Marys, PA, 15857 (814) 781-7500
Medical Dir/Dir of Nursing Bernard L Cappalo MD.
Licensure Skilled Care. *Beds* 138. *Certified* Medicaid; Medicare.
Ownership Nonprofit.
Staff Physicians 1 (pt); RNs 5 (ft), 6 (pt); LPNs 9 (ft), 7 (pt); Nurses aides 32 (ft), 26 (pt); Physical therapists 2 (ft); Recreational therapists 1 (ft), 1 (pt); Activities coordinators 1 (ft); Dietitians 1 (ft).
Facilities Dining room; Physical therapy room; Activities room; Chapel; Crafts room; Laundry room; Barber/Beauty shop; Library.
Activities Arts and Crafts; Cards; Games; Prayer groups; Dances/Social or cultural gatherings.
Description Facility is a hospital-based nursing home located approximately 500 feet from acute care providing opportunity for all services which are provided by acute care if necessary.

Elk Haven Nursing Home*
Box 271, Johnsonburg Rd, Saint Marys, PA, 15857 (814) 834-2618
Licensure Skilled Care; Intermediate Care. *Beds* SNF 60; ICF 60. *Certified* Medicaid; Medicare.
Ownership Nonprofit.

SARVER

Fair Winds Inc*
126 Iron Bridge Rd, Sarver, PA, 16055 (412) 353-1531
Licensure Skilled Care. *Beds* 66. *Certified* Medicaid; Medicare.
Ownership Proprietary.

SAXONBURG

Sunny Crest Convalescent Home*
Saxonburg Blvd, Box 157, Saxonburg, PA, 16056 (412) 352-1666
Medical Dir/Dir of Nursing William Knab DO.
Licensure Skilled Care. *Beds* 56. *Certified* Medicaid; Medicare.
Ownership Proprietary.
Staff RNs 6 (ft), 2 (pt); LPNs 2 (ft); Nurses aides 17 (ft), 8 (pt).
Facilities Dining room; Physical therapy room; Laundry room; Barber/Beauty shop; Library.
Activities Arts and Crafts; Movies.
Description We are a skilled care facility offering an activities program, speech and physical therapy, and are certified for Medicare and Medicaid. Located in a lovely rural setting with quality care and outstanding employees.

SAYRE

Sayre House Inc*
N Elmer Ave, Sayre, PA, 18840 (717) 883-1401
Licensure Skilled Care. *Beds* 50. *Certified* Medicaid; Medicare.

Ownership Proprietary.

SCHUYLKILL HAVEN

Green View Nursing and Convalescent Center*
Rt 1, Schuylkill Haven, PA, 17972 (717) 866-2661
Licensure Skilled Care. *Beds* 30. *Certified* Medicaid.
Ownership Proprietary.

Rest Haven Schuylkill County Home
Rt 1, Schuylkill Haven, PA, 17972 (717) 385-0331
Medical Dir/Dir of Nursing Dr Joseph Weber.
Licensure Skilled Care; Intermediate Care.
Beds SNF 302; ICF 134. *Certified* Medicaid; Medicare.
Ownership Nonprofit.
Admissions Requirements Minimum age 18; Medical examination.
Staff Physicians 5 (ft); RNs 15 (ft), 6 (pt); LPNs 32 (ft), 2 (pt); Orderlies 22 (ft); Nurses aides 143 (ft), 3 (pt); Physical therapists 1 (pt); Occupational therapists 1 (ft); Speech therapists 1 (pt); Activities coordinators 1 (ft); Dentists 2 (pt); Podiatrists 1 (pt).
Facilities Dining room; Physical therapy room; Activities room; Chapel; Crafts room; Laundry room; Barber/Beauty shop; Library.
Activities Arts and Crafts; Cards; Games; Reading groups; Prayer groups; Movies; Shopping trips; Dances/Social or cultural gatherings; Trips to historical sites; Fishing trips.

SCOTTDALE

Wolfe Nursing Home Inc*
521 Overholt St, Scottdale, PA, 15683 (412) 887-7680
Licensure Skilled Care. *Beds* 20.
Ownership Proprietary.

SCRANTON

Adams Manor*
824 Adams Ave, Scranton, PA, 18510 (717) 346-5704
Licensure Skilled Care. *Beds* 139. *Certified* Medicaid; Medicare.
Ownership Proprietary.

Allied Services
475 Morgan Hwy, Scranton, PA, 18508 (717) 347-1373
Medical Dir/Dir of Nursing Daniel Parsick MD.
Licensure Intermediate Care for Mentally Retarded. *Beds* 89. *Certified* Medicaid.
Ownership Nonprofit.
Admissions Requirements Minimum age 18; Medical examination.
Staff Physicians 1 (pt); RNs 7 (ft), 12 (pt); Orderlies 64 (ft); Recreational therapists 3 (ft); Dietitians 1 (ft).
Facilities Dining room; Physical therapy room; Laundry room; Barber/Beauty shop.
Activities Arts and Crafts; Games; Prayer groups; Movies; Shopping trips; Dances/Social or cultural gatherings.

Description Allied Services offers comprehensive programs and treatment for the handicapped. Aside from residential facilities, provides a full range of supportive staff, and a wide range of day programing activities geared to all functioning levels and ages.

Allied Services—Long Term Care Facility
303 Smallcombe Dr, PO Box 1103, Scranton, PA, 18501 (717) 348-1424
Medical Dir/Dir of Nursing Dr Joseph Geombetti.
Licensure Skilled Care. *Beds* 180. *Certified* Medicaid; Medicare.
Ownership Nonprofit.
Facilities Dining room; Physical therapy room; Activities room; Chapel; Crafts room; Laundry room; Barber/Beauty shop.
Activities Arts and Crafts; Cards; Games; Prayer groups; Movies; Shopping trips; Dances/Social or cultural gatherings.

Allied Services—Lynett Village*
475 Morgan Hwy, Scranton, PA, 18508 (717) 348-1300
Licensure Intermediate Care for Mentally Retarded. *Beds* 42. *Certified* Medicaid.
Ownership Nonprofit.

Ellen Memorial Convalescent Home*
1554 Sanderson Ave, Scranton, PA, 18509 (717) 344-6946
Licensure Skilled Care. *Beds* 34. *Certified* Medicaid.
Ownership Proprietary.

Green Ridge Nursing Home
1530 Sanderson Ave, Scranton, PA, 18509 (717) 344-6121
Admin Madelyn R Legge. *Medical Dir/Dir of Nursing* Michael J Turock MD.
Licensure Skilled Care. *Beds* 65. *Certified* Medicaid; Medicare.
Ownership Proprietary.
Facilities Dining room; Activities room; Laundry room; Barber/Beauty shop; Library.
Activities Arts and Crafts; Games; Reading groups; Prayer groups; Movies.

Holiday Manor*
Franklin Ave and Mulberry Sts, Scranton, PA, 18503 (717) 347-3303
Licensure Intermediate Care. *Beds* 154. *Certified* Medicaid.
Ownership Proprietary.

Holy Family Residence
2500 Adams Ave, Scranton, PA, 18509 (717) 343-4065
Medical Dir/Dir of Nursing Dr Thomas Clause.
Licensure Skilled Care; Intermediate Care.
Beds SNF 41; ICF 41. *Certified* Medicaid.
Ownership Nonprofit.
Admissions Requirements Minimum age 60; Medical examination.
Affiliation Roman Catholic
Facilities Dining room; Physical therapy room; Activities room; Chapel; Crafts room; Laundry room; Barber/Beauty shop; Library.
Activities Arts and Crafts; Games; Reading groups; Prayer groups; Movies; Shopping trips; Dances/Social or cultural gatherings.

Hoyt Cresthome Inc
712 Harrison Ave, Scranton, PA, 18510 (717) 346-2045
Admin Paul Magida. *Medical Dir/Dir of Nursing* Lee Besen MD.
Licensure Skilled Care. *Beds* 40. *Certified* Medicaid.
Ownership Proprietary.
Admissions Requirements Minimum age 16; Medical examination; Physician's request.
Staff Physicians 1 (pt); RNs 3 (ft), 1 (pt); LPNs 3 (ft); Nurses aides 18 (ft); Activities coordinators 1 (ft); Dietitians 1 (pt); Dentists 1 (pt); Podiatrists 1 (pt).
Facilities Dining room; Activities room; Laundry room; Barber/Beauty shop.
Activities Arts and Crafts; Cards; Games; Reading groups; Prayer groups; Movies; Shopping trips; Dances/Social or cultural gatherings.
Description As a small facility with ample grounds, an informal atmosphere is provided, as well as picnics and other outdoor functions as the weather permits.

Jewish Home of Eastern Pennsylvania*
1101 Vine St, Scranton, PA, 18510 (717) 344-6177
Licensure Skilled Care. *Beds* 175. *Certified* Medicaid; Medicare.
Ownership Nonprofit.
Affiliation Jewish

Moses Taylor Hospital—Skilled Nursing Facility*
700 Quincy Ave, Scranton, PA, 18510 (717) 346-3801
Licensure Skilled Care. *Beds* 32. *Certified* Medicaid; Medicare.
Ownership Nonprofit.

Mountain Rest Nursing Home Inc*
Linwood Ave, Scranton, PA, 18505 (717) 346-7381
Licensure Skilled Care. *Beds* 60. *Certified* Medicaid.
Ownership Proprietary.

Saint Josephs Center*
2010 Adams Ave, Scranton, PA, 18509 (717) 342-8379
Licensure Intermediate Care for Mentally Retarded. *Beds* 85. *Certified* Medicaid.
Ownership Nonprofit.

SECANE

Haskins Nursing Home
1009 Rhoads Ave, Secane, PA, 19018 (215) 623-3624
Medical Dir/Dir of Nursing James W Dunn MD.
Licensure Skilled Care. *Beds* 22. *Certified* Medicaid.
Staff Physicians; RNs; Nurses aides; Physical therapists; Recreational therapists; Occupational therapists; Speech therapists; Activities coordinators; Dietitians; Podiatrists.
Facilities Dining room; Laundry room.
Activities Arts and Crafts; Cards; Reading groups; Prayer groups; Movies; Shopping trips.

SELINSGROVE

The Doctors' Convalescent Center Inc
800 Broad St, Selinsgrove, PA, 17870-1299 (717) 374-8181
Admin Rae A Adams. *Medical Dir/Dir of Nursing* Robert A Grubb MD.
Licensure Skilled Care; Intermediate Care.
Beds SNF 79; ICF 118. *Certified* Medicaid; Medicare.
Ownership Proprietary.
Staff Physicians 1 (ft), 1 (pt); RNs 4 (ft), 12 (pt); LPNs 10 (ft), 13 (pt); Nurses aides 48 (ft), 34 (pt); Physical therapists 3 (pt); Recreational therapists 1 (ft), 1 (pt); Speech therapists 1 (pt); Dietitians 1 (ft); Podiatrists 1 (pt).
Facilities Dining room; Physical therapy room; Activities room; Chapel; Crafts room; Laundry room; Barber/Beauty shop; Library.
Activities Arts and Crafts; Cards; Games; Reading groups; Prayer groups; Movies; Shopping trips; Dances/Social or cultural gatherings.
Description Facility is celebrating 20 years of service to the community providing professional and loving care to elderly citizens; younger patients who require much rehabilitative services are now being served.

Rathfons Convalescent Home
308 S Market St, Selinsgrove, PA, 17870 (717) 374-5331
Admin Jean A Rathfon. *Medical Dir/Dir of Nursing* Dr Robert Heinback.
Licensure Intermediate Care. *Beds* 44. *Certified* Medicaid.
Ownership Proprietary.
Admissions Requirements Medical examination.
Staff Physicians 1 (pt); RNs 2 (ft), 1 (pt); LPNs 1 (ft), 3 (pt); Nurses aides 14 (ft); Physical therapists 1 (pt); Activities coordinators 1 (pt); Dietitians 1 (pt).
Facilities Dining room; Activities room.
Activities Arts and Crafts; Cards; Games; Reading groups; Prayer groups; Shopping trips.
Description Facility has been in business 37 years.

Selinsgrove Center*
Box 500, Kreamer Rd, Selinsgrove, PA, 17870 (717) 374-2911
Licensure Intermediate Care for Mentally Retarded. *Beds* 1068. *Certified* Medicaid.
Ownership Nonprofit.

SELLERSVILLE

Community Foundation for Human Development
22 Almont Rd, Sellersville, PA, 18960 (215) 257-1155
Medical Dir/Dir of Nursing Dr Joseph Gerone.
Licensure Intermediate Care for Mentally Retarded. *Beds* 37. *Certified* Medicaid.
Ownership Nonprofit.
Admissions Requirements Minimum age Birth.
Staff Physicians 6 (pt); RNs 5 (ft); LPNs 2 (ft), 22 (pt); Nurses aides 25 (ft), 25 (pt); Physical therapists 1 (pt); Occupational therapists 1 (pt); Speech therapists 1 (pt); Dietitians 1 (pt); Den-

tists 1 (pt); Ophthalmologists 1 (pt).
Facilities Dining room.
Activities Shopping trips.

Grandview Hospital*
700 Lawn Ave, Sellersville, PA, 18960 (215) 257-3611
Licensure Skilled Care. *Beds* 20. *Certified* Medicaid; Medicare.
Ownership Nonprofit.

Rockhill Mennonite Home
Rt 152, Box 21, Sellersville, PA, 18960 (215) 257-2751
Admin Randy L Shelly. *Medical Dir/Dir of Nursing* Dr Winfield Hedrick.
Licensure Skilled Care; Intermediate Care.
Beds SNF 60; ICF 36. *Certified* Medicaid; Medicare.
Ownership Nonprofit.
Admissions Requirements Minimum age F 62 M 65; Medical examination.
Affiliation Mennonite
Facilities Dining room; Physical therapy room; Activities room; Chapel; Crafts room; Laundry room; Barber/Beauty shop; Library.
Activities Arts and Crafts; Cards; Games; Reading groups; Prayer groups; Movies; Shopping trips; Dances/Social or cultural gatherings.
Description Facility offers independent residential living and adult day care program.

SEWICKLY

Long Term Care at Dixmont Hospital*
Sewickly, PA, 15143 (412) 761-1780
Licensure Intermediate Care. *Beds* 36. *Certified* Medicaid.
Ownership Nonprofit.

Verland Foundation Inc*
Iris Rd, RD 2, Sewickly, PA, 15143 (412) 741-2375
Licensure Intermediate Care for Mentally Retarded. *Beds* 50. *Certified* Medicaid.
Ownership Proprietary.

SHAMOKIN

Northumberland County Home—Shamokin
Rt 1, Box 228, Shamokin, PA, 17872 (717) 644-0801
Medical Dir/Dir of Nursing Dr James Gehris.
Licensure Skilled Care; Intermediate Care.
Beds SNF 207; ICF 153. *Certified* Medicaid; Medicare.
Ownership Nonprofit.
Admissions Requirements Medical examination.
Staff Physicians 4 (ft); RNs 15 (ft), 11 (pt); LPNs 28 (ft), 5 (pt); Orderlies 18 (ft), 2 (pt); Nurses aides 100 (ft), 13 (pt); Physical therapists 1 (pt); Speech therapists 1 (pt); Activities coordinators 1 (ft); Dietitians 1 (ft); Podiatrists 1 (pt).
Facilities Dining room; Physical therapy room; Activities room; Chapel; Crafts room; Laundry room; Barber/Beauty shop.
Activities Arts and Crafts; Cards; Games; Prayer groups; Movies; Shopping trips; Dances/Social or cultural gatherings.

Description The Manor is truly a visionary dream; a sprawling ranch-type complex, overlooking a breathtaking survey of a continuously extending valley of mountain ranges observable from every guest room. The primary objective is to maintain the highest quality resident care; admission available to all. Manor constantly strives to provide a natural environment where personal dignity and individual satisfaction is maintained.

SHARON

Clepper Convalescent Home*
959 E State St, Sharon, PA, 16146 (412) 981-2750
Licensure Skilled Care. *Beds* 61. *Certified* Medicaid; Medicare.
Ownership Proprietary.

SHARON HILL

Kearney Home
753 Woodland Terrace, Sharon Hill, PA, 19079 (215) 586-1662
Licensure Intermediate Care. *Beds* 17. *Certified* Medicaid; Medicare.
Ownership Proprietary.

SHILLINGTON

Hassler Home*
500 E Philadelphia Ave, Shillington, PA, 19607 (215) 777-7841
Licensure Skilled Care. *Beds* 136. *Certified* Medicaid; Medicare.
Ownership Proprietary.

SHINGLEHOUSE

Hewitt Manor Inc*
59 Honeoye St, Shinglehouse, PA, 16748 (814) 697-6340
Licensure Skilled Care. *Beds* 28. *Certified* Medicaid; Medicare.
Ownership Proprietary.

SHREWSBURY

Shrewsbury Lutheran Retirement Village*
Luther Rd, Shrewsbury, PA, 17361 (717) 235-6895
Licensure Skilled Care; Intermediate Care. *Beds* SNF 33; ICF 67. *Certified* Medicaid; Medicare.
Ownership Nonprofit.
Affiliation Lutheran

SINKING SPRING

Leader Nursing Rehabilitation Center
3000 Windmill Rd, Sinking Spring, PA, 19608
Admin Madelon Joyce Book. *Medical Dir/Dir of Nursing* Joseph Pew MD.
Licensure Skilled Care; Intermediate Care. *Beds* 180. *Certified* Medicaid; Medicare.
Ownership Proprietary.
Staff RNs 7 (ft), 8 (pt); LPNs 10 (ft), 8 (pt);

Nurses aides 30 (ft), 50 (pt); Physical therapists 2 (ft); Occupational therapists 1 (ft); Activities coordinators 1 (ft).
Facilities Dining room; Physical therapy room; Activities room; Chapel; Crafts room; Laundry room; Barber/Beauty shop; Library.
Activities Arts and Crafts; Cards; Games; Reading groups; Prayer groups; Movies; Shopping trips; Dances/Social or cultural gatherings.
Description This beautifully decorated one-floor facility with attractive enclosed courtyards features an outstanding physical therapy department with 75% of rehabilitation candidates returning home; hospice and respite care provided.

SLIGO

Clarview Rest Home*
Rt 1, Sligo, PA, 16255 (814) 745-2031
Licensure Skilled Care; Intermediate Care. *Beds* SNF 60; ICF 60. *Certified* Medicaid; Medicare.
Ownership Nonprofit.

SMETHPORT

C K Stones Manor Inc*
15 W Willow St, Smethport, PA, 16749 (814) 887-5716
Licensure Intermediate Care. *Beds* 34. *Certified* Medicaid.
Ownership Proprietary.

Sena Kean Manor
Marvin St, Smethport, PA, 16749 (814) 887-5601
Licensure Skilled Care; Intermediate Care. *Beds* SNF 27; ICF 131. *Certified* Medicaid; Medicare.
Ownership Nonprofit.
Admissions Requirements Minimum age 18; Medical examination; Physician's request.
Staff Physicians 4 (pt); RNs 5 (ft), 4 (pt); LPNs 10 (ft), 5 (pt); Nurses aides 56 (ft), 11 (pt); Physical therapists 2 (pt); Recreational therapists 2 (ft); Speech therapists 1 (pt); Activities coordinators 1 (ft); Dietitians 1 (ft); Podiatrists 1 (pt).
Facilities Dining room; Physical therapy room; Activities room; Crafts room; Laundry room; Barber/Beauty shop; Library.
Activities Arts and Crafts; Cards; Games; Reading groups; Prayer groups; Movies; Shopping trips; Dances/Social or cultural gatherings.

SOMERSET

Seimon Lakeview Manor Estate
Rt 7, Box 195A, Somerset, PA, 15501 (814) 443-2811
Medical Dir/Dir of Nursing Dr Wayne McKee.
Licensure Skilled Care; Intermediate Care. *Beds* SNF 30; ICF 90. *Certified* Medicaid; Medicare.
Ownership Proprietary.
Admissions Requirements Minimum age 18.
Facilities Dining room; Physical therapy room; Activities room; Crafts room; Laundry room; Barber/Beauty shop.

Activities Arts and Crafts; Cards; Games; Reading groups; Prayer groups; Movies; Shopping trips; Dances/Social or cultural gatherings; Fishing.
Description Facility is situated on a 34-acre wooded site overlooking Somerset Lake.

Somerset Community Hospital—Skilled Nursing Unit
225 S Center St, Somerset, PA, 15530 (814) 443-2626
Medical Dir/Dir of Nursing Dr Arthur Orlidge.
Licensure Skilled Care. *Beds* 18. *Certified* Medicaid; Medicare.
Ownership Nonprofit.
Staff Physicians; RNs; LPNs; Nurses aides; Physical therapists; Recreational therapists; Speech therapists; Activities coordinators; Dietitians; Dentists; Ophthalmologists; Podiatrists; Audiologists.
Facilities Activities room.
Activities Cards; Games; Prayer groups; Cooking club.
Description Facility is located on the third south wing of acute care hospital; has easy transfer to acute care should patient need inpatient hospitalization or outpatient surgery.

Somerset State Hospital—Mentally Retarded Unit*
PO Box 631, Somerset, PA, 15501 (814) 445-6501
Licensure Intermediate Care for Mentally Retarded. *Beds* 127. *Certified* Medicaid.
Ownership Nonprofit.

SOUDERTON

Eastern Mennonite Home
207 W Summit St, Souderton, PA, 18964 (215) 723-9881
Medical Dir/Dir of Nursing Dr John D Nuschke.
Licensure Skilled Care. *Beds* 59. *Certified* Medicaid.
Ownership Nonprofit.
Admissions Requirements Medical examination.
Affiliation Mennonite
Facilities Dining room; Chapel; Laundry room; Barber/Beauty shop; Library; multi-purpose activites room.
Activities Arts and Crafts; Games; Reading groups; Movies; Shopping trips; Bible Study; Choir and Sing-a-long; Birthday parties; Physical fitness; Spelling bee.

SOUTH MOUNTAIN

South Mountain Restoration Center
South Mountain, PA, 17261 (717) 749-3121
Medical Dir/Dir of Nursing Emmett P Davis MD.
Licensure Skilled Care; Intermediate Care. *Beds* SNF 106; ICF 922. *Certified* Medicaid; Medicare.
Ownership Nonprofit; Public.
Admissions Requirements Minimum age 40; Medical examination; Physician's request.
Staff Physicians 6 (ft), 1 (pt); RNs 40 (ft); LPNs 91 (ft); Nurses aides 250 (ft); Physical

therapists 1 (ft); Occupational therapists 1 (ft); Speech therapists 2 (ft); Activities coordinators 4 (ft); Dietitians 4 (ft); Dentists 1 (ft); Podiatrists 2 (pt).
Facilities Dining room; Physical therapy room; Activities room; Chapel; Crafts room; Laundry room; Barber/Beauty shop; Library.
Activities Arts and Crafts; Cards; Games; Reading groups; Prayer groups; Movies; Shopping trips; Dances/Social or cultural gatherings.

SOUTH WILLIAMSPORT

Freezers Home for the Aged*
6 E Central Ave, South Williamsport, PA, 17701 (717) 323-5954
Licensure Intermediate Care. *Beds* 20. *Certified* Medicaid.
Ownership Proprietary.

SOUTHAMPTON

Southhampton Estates
238 Street Rd, Southampton, PA, 18969 (215) 364-2551
Medical Dir/Dir of Nursing Arthur Lintgen.
Licensure Skilled Care. *Beds* 60. *Certified* Medicare.
Ownership Nonprofit.

SPRING CITY

Pennhurst Modular Home Community*
Spring City, PA, 19475 (215) 948-3500
Licensure Intermediate Care for Mentally Retarded. *Beds* 150. *Certified* Medicaid.
Ownership Nonprofit.

SPRINGFIELD

C R Center
Sproul Rd, Springfield, PA, 19064 (215) 543-3380
Medical Dir/Dir of Nursing Dr Rocco Sciubba.
Licensure Intermediate Care for Mentally Retarded. *Beds* 93. *Certified* Medicaid.
Ownership Nonprofit.
Admissions Requirements Minimum age 21; Males only; Medical examination.
Staff Physicians 1 (ft); RNs 1 (ft), 1 (pt); LPNs 1 (ft); Occupational therapists 1 (ft); Speech therapists 2 (ft); Activities coordinators 1 (ft); Dietitians 1 (ft); 45 (ft).
Affiliation Roman Catholic
Facilities Dining room; Activities room; Chapel; Crafts room; Laundry room; Barber/Beauty shop; Library.
Activities Arts and Crafts; Cards; Games; Reading groups; Prayer groups; Movies; Shopping trips; Dances/Social or cultural gatherings.
Description Facility has a work activity center with support programs such as vocational training, occupational therapy, adult education, psychological and speech services, recreational and daily living training.

Harlee Manor
463 W Sproul Rd, Springfield, PA, 19064 (215) 544-2200
Licensure Skilled Care. *Beds* 173. *Cer-

tified* Medicare.
Ownership Proprietary.

SPRINGHOUSE

Silverstream Nursing Home
Pennllyn Pike, Springhouse, PA, 19477 (215) 646-1500
Admin Florence Werlinsky. *Medical Dir/Dir of Nursing* Dr Robert Leopold.
Licensure Skilled Care. *Beds* 89. *Certified* Medicaid; Medicare.
Ownership Proprietary.
Admissions Requirements Medical examination.
Staff RNs 5 (ft), 3 (pt); LPNs 3 (ft), 3 (pt); Orderlies 3 (pt); Nurses aides 23 (ft), 12 (pt); Physical therapists 2 (pt); Reality therapists 1 (pt); Recreational therapists 1 (ft), 1 (pt); Occupational therapists 1 (pt); Speech therapists 1 (pt); Dietitians 1 (pt); Dentists 1 (pt); Ophthalmologists 1 (pt); Podiatrists 2 (pt); Audiologists 1 (pt).
Facilities Dining room; Physical therapy room; Activities room; Crafts room; Laundry room; Barber/Beauty shop.
Activities Arts and Crafts; Cards; Games; Reading groups; Prayer groups; Movies; Dances/Social or cultural gatherings.
Description Facility in a country setting offers excellent recreational programs geared to all levels of comprehension.

Spring House Estates Nursing Facility
Norristown Rd and McKean St, Springhouse, PA, 19477 (215) 628-3545
Medical Dir/Dir of Nursing Arthur Lintgen MD.
Licensure Skilled Care. *Beds* 60.
Ownership Nonprofit.
Admissions Requirements Minimum age 17; Physician's request.
Staff RNs 3 (ft), 4 (pt); LPNs 2 (ft), 3 (pt); Orderlies 1 (ft), 1 (pt); Nurses aides 14 (ft), 27 (pt); Physical therapists 1 (ft); Speech therapists 1 (pt); Activities coordinators 1 (ft); Dietitians 1 (ft).
Facilities Dining room; Physical therapy room; Activities room; Laundry room; Barber/Beauty shop.
Activities Arts and Crafts; Cards; Games; Prayer groups; Movies; Shopping trips; Dances/Social or cultural gatherings.

STATE COLLEGE

State College Manor Ltd*
450 Waupelani Dr, State College, PA, 16801 (814) 238-5065
Licensure Skilled Care; Intermediate Care.
Beds SNF 137; ICF 36. *Certified* Medicaid; Medicare.
Ownership Proprietary.

STEVENS

Denver Nursing Home*
Rt 1, Stevens, PA, 17578 (215) 267-2213
Licensure Skilled Care. *Beds* 73. *Certified* Medicaid; Medicare.

Ownership Proprietary.

STILLWATER

Bonham Nursing Center
Register Rd 1, Stillwater, PA, 17878 (717) 864-3174
Medical Dir/Dir of Nursing Dr Robert Campbell.
Licensure Skilled Care; Intermediate Care.
Beds 58. *Certified* Medicaid.
Ownership Proprietary.
Staff Physicians 4 (ft); RNs 2 (ft), 4 (pt); LPNs 4 (pt); Orderlies 1 (ft); Nurses aides 15 (ft), 16 (pt); Physical therapists 1 (pt); Activities coordinators 1 (ft), 1 (pt); Dietitians 1 (pt); Dentists 1 (pt); Podiatrists 1 (pt).
Facilities Dining room; Activities room; Laundry room; Barber/Beauty shop; Recreational park; Bus.
Activities Arts and Crafts; Games; Prayer groups; Movies; Shopping trips; Dances/Social or cultural gatherings; Fairs; Circus; Bible Study.
Description Center is situated in a rural village with a bus for outside events; a trout stream runs through property along with a recreational park.

STROUDSBURG

Laurel Manor
1170 W Main St, Stroudsburg, PA, 18360 (717) 421-1240
Medical Dir/Dir of Nursing James G Kitchen II MD.
Licensure Intermediate Care. *Beds* 54. *Certified* Medicaid.
Ownership Nonprofit.
Admissions Requirements Medical examination.
Staff Physicians 1 (pt); RNs 10 (ft); LPNs 5 (ft); Nurses aides 13 (ft); Reality therapists 1 (pt); Activities coordinators 1 (ft); Dietitians 1 (pt).
Facilities Dining room; Activities room; Crafts room.
Activities Arts and Crafts; Cards; Games; Reading groups; Prayer groups; Movies; Dances/Social or cultural gatherings.

Pleasant Valley Manor
Rt 2, Stroudsburg, PA, 18360 (717) 992-4172
Medical Dir/Dir of Nursing John Lim MD.
Licensure Skilled Care; Intermediate Care.
Beds SNF 28; ICF 146. *Certified* Medicaid; Medicare.
Ownership Nonprofit.
Admissions Requirements Medical examination.
Staff Physicians 1 (ft); RNs 5 (ft), 3 (pt); LPNs 6 (ft), 6 (pt); Orderlies 2 (ft), 1 (pt); Nurses aides 42 (ft); Reality therapists 1 (ft); Recreational therapists 3 (pt); Occupational therapists 1 (pt); Activities coordinators 1 (ft); Dietitians 1 (ft); Podiatrists 1 (pt).
Facilities Dining room; Physical therapy room; Activities room; Chapel; Crafts room; Laundry room; Barber/Beauty shop.
Activities Arts and Crafts; Games; Prayer groups; Movies; Shopping trips; Dances/Social

or cultural gatherings.
Description Facility is set in rural part of the county with an excellent activity program and quality nursing care. Priorities given to low-income county residents.

SUNBURY

Leader Nursing and Rehabilitation Center
Circle Dr, 800 Court St, Sunbury, PA, 17801
Admin Sandra Deppen. *Medical Dir/Dir of Nursing* Dr Mohammed Munir.
Licensure Skilled Care; Intermediate Care.
Beds 120. *Certified* Medicaid; Medicare.
Ownership Proprietary.
Staff RNs 5 (ft), 3 (pt); LPNs 7 (ft), 8 (pt); Nurses aides 25 (ft), 66 (pt); Physical therapists 1 (ft); Recreational therapists 1 (ft), 1 (pt); Occupational therapists 1 (ft); Speech therapists 1 (pt); Dietitians 1 (pt).
Facilities Dining room; Physical therapy room; Activities room; Chapel; Crafts room; Laundry room; Barber/Beauty shop; Library.
Activities Arts and Crafts; Cards; Games; Reading groups; Prayer groups; Movies; Shopping trips; Dances/Social or cultural gatherings.
Description This is a modern progressive nursing center with a strong emphasis on rehabilitation; friendly, courteous staff that functions as a team in pleasant surroundings.

Mansion Nursing and Convalescent Home Inc*
1040-1052 Market St, Sunbury, PA, 17801
(717) 286-6922
Licensure Skilled Care. *Beds* 71. *Certified* Medicaid; Medicare.
Ownership Proprietary.

Sunbury Community Hospital—Skilled Nursing Unit*
305 N 11th St, Sunbury, PA, 17801 (717) 286-5811
Licensure Skilled Care. *Beds* 29. *Certified* Medicaid; Medicare.
Ownership Nonprofit.

SUSQUEHANNA

Barnes-Kasson County Hospital
400 Turnpike St, Susquehanna, PA, 18847
(717) 853-3135
Medical Dir/Dir of Nursing Dr Robert M Shelly.
Licensure Skilled Care. *Beds* 49. *Certified* Medicaid; Medicare.
Ownership Nonprofit.
Admissions Requirements Physician's request.
Staff Physicians 1 (pt); RNs 2 (ft), 1 (pt); LPNs 5 (ft), 1 (pt); Nurses aides 14 (ft), 8 (pt); Physical therapists 1 (ft); Reality therapists 1 (ft); Activities coordinators 1 (pt); Dietitians 1 (ft); Dentists 2 (ft), 1 (pt); Podiatrists 1 (pt).
Facilities Dining room; Physical therapy room; Activities room; Crafts room; Laundry room; Barber/Beauty shop; Library.
Activities Arts and Crafts; Cards; Games; Reading groups; Prayer groups; Movies; Shopping trips.
Description Facility is located in the Susquehanna County Hills; attached to Barnes-Kesson County Hospital and has quick access

to Acute Care and other supportive services.

TELFORD

Lutheran Home—Telford*
235 N Washington Ave, Telford, PA, 18969
(215) 723-9819
Licensure Skilled Care. *Beds* 55. *Certified* Medicaid.
Ownership Nonprofit.
Affiliation Lutheran

THOMPSONTOWN

Meda Nipple Convalescent Home
Rt 1, Box 109, Thompsontown, PA, 17094
(717) 463-2632
Licensure Skilled Care. *Beds* 23. *Certified* Medicaid; Medicare.
Ownership Proprietary.
Staff RNs 2 (ft), 1 (pt); LPNs 1 (ft), 1 (pt); Nurses aides 2 (ft), 5 (pt); Physical therapists 1 (pt); Recreational therapists 1 (pt); Occupational therapists 1 (pt); Speech therapists 1 (pt); Activities coordinators 1 (ft); Dietitians 1 (pt); Dentists 1 (pt); Podiatrists 1 (pt); Audiologists 1 (pt).

TITUSVILLE

Presbyterian Home—Titusville
701 N Perry St, Titusville, PA, 16354 (814) 827-1221
Licensure Intermediate Care. *Beds* 3. *Certified* Medicaid.
Ownership Nonprofit.

Titusville Medical Services
81 Dillon Dr, Titusville, PA, 16354 (814) 827-2727
Medical Dir/Dir of Nursing Barbara Barnes.
Licensure Skilled Care; Intermediate Care.
Beds SNF 35; ICF 30. *Certified* Medicaid; Medicare.
Ownership Proprietary.
Staff RNs 5 (ft), 2 (pt); LPNs 3 (ft), 4 (pt); Nurses aides 12 (ft), 13 (pt); Speech therapists 1 (pt); Activities coordinators 1 (ft); Dietitians 1 (ft).
Facilities Dining room; Physical therapy room; Activities room; Crafts room; Laundry room.
Activities Arts and Crafts; Cards; Games; Reading groups; Prayer groups; Movies; Dances/Social or cultural gatherings.

TOPTON

Lutheran Home at Topton
Topton, PA, 19562 (215) 682-2145
Medical Dir/Dir of Nursing Dr Raymond Hauser MD.
Licensure Skilled Care. *Beds* 120. *Certified* Medicaid; Medicare.
Ownership Nonprofit.
Admissions Requirements Minimum age 65.
Staff Physicians 2 (ft); RNs 16 (ft), 11 (pt); LPNs 16 (ft); Orderlies 1 (ft); Nurses aides 42 (ft), 92 (pt); Physical therapists 2 (ft); Recreational therapists 1 (ft); Occupational therapists 4 (ft); Activities coordinators 2 (ft); Dietitians 1

(pt).
Affiliation Lutheran
Facilities Dining room; Physical therapy room; Activities room; Chapel; Crafts room; Laundry room; Barber/Beauty shop; Library.
Activities Arts and Crafts; Cards; Games; Reading groups; Prayer groups; Movies; Shopping trips; Dances/Social or cultural gatherings.
Description First class quality care facility; rural setting overlooking East Penn Valley; 40 acres of land; continuing care; long-term care; low, moderate, and upper income units for residential, retirement living.

TORRANCE

Torrance State Hospital—IMR Unit*
PO Box 103, Torrance, PA, 15779 (412) 459-8000
Licensure Intermediate Care for Mentally Retarded. *Beds* 94. *Certified* Medicaid.
Ownership Nonprofit.

Torrance State Hospital—Long Term Care Facility*
PO Box 103, Torrance, PA, 15779 (412) 459-8000
Licensure Skilled Care; Intermediate Care.
Beds SNF 141; ICF 137. *Certified* Medicaid.
Ownership Nonprofit.

TOWANDA

Memorial Hospital Inc and Skilled Nursing Unit
RD 1, Towanda, PA, 18848 (717) 265-2191
Medical Dir/Dir of Nursing Raymond A Perry MD.
Licensure Skilled Care. *Beds* 44. *Certified* Medicaid; Medicare.
Ownership Nonprofit.
Admissions Requirements Physician's request.
Staff Physicians 11 (pt); RNs 2 (ft); LPNs 5 (ft), 2 (pt); Orderlies 1 (ft); Nurses aides 12 (ft), 7 (pt); Physical therapists 1 (ft); Activities coordinators 1 (ft).
Facilities Dining room; Physical therapy room; Activities room; Crafts room; Laundry room; Barber/Beauty shop.
Activities Arts and Crafts; Cards; Games; Reading groups; Prayer groups; Dances/Social or cultural gatherings.

TREMONT

Tremont Nursing Center*
44 Donaldson Rd, Tremont, PA, 17981 (717) 695-3141
Licensure Skilled Care; Intermediate Care.
Beds SNF 60; ICF 60. *Certified* Medicaid; Medicare.
Ownership Proprietary.

TREXLERTOWN

Mosser Nursing Home Inc*
Old Rt 222, Trexlertown, PA, 18087 (215) 395-5661
Licensure Skilled Care. *Beds* 54. *Certified* Medicaid; Medicare.

Ownership Proprietary.

TROY

Bradford County Manor*
Rt 3, Box 161, Troy, PA, 16947 (717) 297-2882
Licensure Skilled Care; Intermediate Care.
Beds SNF 135; ICF 91. *Certified* Medicaid.
Ownership Nonprofit.

Martha Lloyd School—Camelot ICF/MR
W Main St, Troy, PA, 16947 (717) 297-2185
Admin LuAnn Simcoe.
Licensure Intermediate Care for Mentally
Retarded. *Beds* 18.
Ownership Nonprofit.
Admissions Requirements Females only;
Medical examination.
Staff RNs 1 (pt); LPNs 3 (ft), 1 (pt); Nurses
aides 9 (ft), 3 (pt); Activities coordinators 1 (ft).
Facilities Dining room; Activities room; Crafts
room; Laundry room; Barber/Beauty shop;
Library; Gym; Work shop; School store; Home
economics room.
Activities Arts and Crafts; Cards; Games; Pray-
er groups; Movies; Shopping trips; Dances/So-
cial or cultural gatherings; Ceramics; Music.
Description The Camelot ICF/MR Unit,
located on the campus of the Martha Lloyd
School in northeastern Pennsylvania, offers an
active treatment program for mentally retarded
adults, aimed at community placement. A full
range of therapeutic, recreational, and vocational services is offered.

TUNKHANNOCK

Carpenter Care Center Inc
Rt 3, Virginia Ave, Tunkhannock, PA, 18657
Admin Virginia Carpenter. *Medical Dir/Dir of
Nursing* Dr Arthur Sherwood.
Admissions Requirements Minimum age 18;
Medical examination.
Staff Physicians 7 (pt); Orderlies 4 (ft);
Physical therapists 1 (ft); Reality therapists 1
(ft); Recreational therapists 3 (ft), 1 (pt); Occu-
pational therapists 2 (ft), 1 (pt); Speech thera-
pists 1 (pt); Activities coordinators 1 (pt);
Dietitians 1 (ft); Dentists 1 (pt); Ophthalmolo-
gists 1 (pt); Podiatrists 1 (pt); Audiologists 1
(pt).
Facilities Dining room; Physical therapy room;
Activities room; Chapel; Crafts room; Laundry
room; Barber/Beauty shop; Library.
Activities Arts and Crafts; Cards; Games;
Reading groups; Prayer groups; Movies; Shopping trips; Dances/Social or cultural gatherings.
Description Facility features birthday parties
and wine and cheese parties monthly, outdoor
barbecues during summer months, and an
adopt-a-grandparent program.

TYRONE

Epworth Manor
951 Washington Ave, Tyrone, PA, 16686 (814)
684-0320
Admin Paul D Schroeder. *Medical Dir/Dir of
Nursing* Carlos A Wiegering MD.
Licensure Skilled Care; Intermediate Care.
Beds SNF 68; ICF 34. *Certified* Medicaid;
Medicare.
Ownership Nonprofit.
Admissions Requirements Minimum age 62;
Medical examination.
Staff Physicians 1 (pt); RNs 1 (ft); LPNs 3 (ft);
Nurses aides 13 (ft); Physical therapists 1 (pt);
Speech therapists 1 (pt); Activities coordinators
1 (ft); Dietitians 1 (ft); Dentists 1 (pt); Ophthal-
mologists 1 (pt); Podiatrists 1 (pt).
Affiliation Methodist
Facilities Dining room; Physical therapy room;
Activities room; Chapel; Crafts room; Laundry
room; Barber/Beauty shop.
Activities Arts and Crafts; Cards; Games;
Reading groups; Prayer groups; Movies; Shop-
ping trips; Dances/Social or cultural gatherings.
Description Epworth Manor is located in the
Borough of Tyrone which is nestled in the
foothills of the Allegheny Mountains of central
Pennsylvania, along the Little Juniata River. It
is a comprehensive health care facility licensed
by the Pennsylvania Department of Health. All
aspects of medical services, professional
nursing supervision, complete fire safety, balanced nutrition, and adequate staffing by qualified personnel exceed state regulations.

UNIONTOWN

Lafayette Manor*
Rt 4, Box 682, New Salem Rd, Uniontown, PA,
15401 (412) 437-9804
Licensure Skilled Care. *Beds* 98. *Cer-
tified* Medicaid.
Ownership Nonprofit.

Laurel Rest Home*
75 Hickle St, Uniontown, PA, 15401 (412)
437-9871
Licensure Skilled Care. *Beds* 50. *Certified* Medicare.
Ownership Proprietary.

Mount Macrina Manor Nursing Home
Box 548, Uniontown, PA, 15401 (412)
437-1303
Licensure Skilled Care. *Beds* 54. *Cer-
tified* Medicaid.
Ownership Nonprofit.
Admissions Requirements Medical
examination; Physician's request.
Staff Physicians 2 (pt); RNs 3 (ft); LPNs 11
(ft); Nurses aides 25 (ft), 3 (pt); Physical thera-
pists 1 (pt); Speech therapists 1 (pt); Activities
coordinators 2 (ft); Dietitians 1 (ft).
Affiliation Roman Catholic
Facilities Dining room; Physical therapy room;
Activities room; Chapel; Laundry room; Bar-
ber/Beauty shop.
Activities Arts and Crafts; Cards; Games;
Reading groups; Prayer groups; Movies.

VALENCIA

Grahams Nursing Home Inc
Rt 1, Sandy Hill Rd, Valencia, PA, 16059 (412)
898-1894
Admin Herbert S White. *Medical Dir/Dir of
Nursing* Donald L Kelley MD.
Licensure Intermediate Care. *Beds* 24. *Certi-*
fied Medicaid.
Ownership Proprietary.
Staff Physicians 1 (pt); RNs 4 (ft), 1 (pt); LPNs
2 (ft), 2 (pt); Nurses aides 22 (ft); Physical thera-
pists 1 (pt); Reality therapists 1 (pt); Recrea-
tional therapists 1 (pt); Activities coordinators 1
(ft); Dietitians 1 (pt).
Facilities Dining room; Physical therapy room;
Activities room; Crafts room; Laundry room.
Activities Arts and Crafts; Cards; Games;
Reading groups; Prayer groups; Movies; Shopping trips; Dances/Social or cultural gatherings.
Description Facility features a beautiful country
setting, 25 miles north of Pittsburgh.

VALENCIA BOROUGH

Saint Johns Convalescent Unit
Rt 4, Box 357, Valencia Borough, PA, 16059
(412) 625-1561
Medical Dir/Dir of Nursing Dr Allen P Snyder.
Licensure Skilled Care. *Beds* 69. *Cer-
tified* Medicaid; Medicare.
Ownership Nonprofit.
Admissions Requirements Medical examina-
tion.
Staff RNs 4 (ft), 6 (pt); LPNs 1 (ft), 5 (pt);
Nurses aides 18 (ft), 10 (pt); Physical therapists
2 (pt); Reality therapists 1 (ft).
Facilities Dining room; Physical therapy room;
Laundry room; Barber/Beauty shop.
Activities Arts and Crafts; Cards; Games;
Reading groups; Prayer groups; Movies; Shop-
ping trips; Dances/Social or cultural gatherings.
Description Facility features lawn picnics, Mar-
di Gras celebration, ice cream festival, movies,
watermelon festival, Octoberfest, and shopping
trips to malls.

WALLINGFORD

The Wallingford*
115 S Providence Rd, Wallingford, PA, 19086
(215) 565-3232
Licensure Skilled Care. *Beds* 207. *Certified* Medicaid; Medicare.
Ownership Proprietary.

WARMINSTER

Centennial Spring Health Care Center*
333 Newtown Rd, Warminster, PA, 18974
(215) 672-9082
Licensure Skilled Care. *Beds* 180. *Certified* Medicaid; Medicare.
Ownership Proprietary.

Christ Home Retirement Center
1220 W Street Rd, Warminster, PA, 18974
(215) 675-1540
Medical Dir/Dir of Nursing Dr Alan Miller.
Licensure Skilled Care. *Beds* 18. *Cer-
tified* Medicaid; Medicare.
Ownership Nonprofit.
Admissions Requirements Minimum age 65;
Medical examination.
Staff Physicians 2 (pt); RNs 3 (ft), 5 (pt); LPNs
1 (ft), 3 (pt); Nurses aides 8 (ft), 15 (pt);
Physical therapists 1 (pt); Speech therapists 1
(pt); Activities coordinators 1 (pt); Dietitians 1

(pt); Dentists 1 (pt); Ophthalmologists 1 (pt); Podiatrists 1 (pt).
Facilities Dining room; Activities room; Chapel; Crafts room; Barber/Beauty shop.
Activities Arts and Crafts; Games; Movies; Dances/Social or cultural gatherings.
Description Christ Home Retirement Center is located on the outskirts of the Philadelphia metropolitan area in a semi-rural setting; has a caring Christian atmosphere.

Eastern Pennsylvania Eastern Star Home*
850 Norristown Rd, Warminster, PA, 18974 (215) 672-2500
Licensure Skilled Care. *Beds* 26.
Ownership Nonprofit.
Affiliation Order of Eastern Star

WARREN

Warren Medical Services
205 Water St, Warren, PA, 16365 (814) 726-0820)
Admin Joseph P Darrington. *Medical Dir/Dir of Nursing* Dr Robert Donaldson.
Licensure Skilled Care. *Beds* 111. *Certified* Medicaid; Medicare.
Ownership Proprietary.
Admissions Requirements Medical examination; Physician's request.
Staff Physicians 1 (pt); RNs 3 (ft), 6 (pt); LPNs 6 (ft), 5 (pt); Orderlies 3 (ft), 2 (pt); Nurses aides 26 (ft), 18 (pt); Physical therapists 1 (pt); Reality therapists 1 (ft); Recreational therapists 1 (ft); Occupational therapists 1 (pt); Speech therapists 1 (pt); Dietitians 1 (pt); Dentists 1 (pt); Ophthalmologists 1 (pt); Podiatrists 1 (pt); Audiologists 1 (pt).
Facilities Dining room; Physical therapy room; Activities room; Laundry room; Barber/Beauty shop.
Activities Arts and Crafts; Cards; Games; Reading groups; Movies; Shopping trips; Dances/Social or cultural gatherings; Music therapy.

Warren Nursing Home Inc
121 Central Ave, Warren, PA, 16365 (814) 726-1420
Admin D C Deal. *Medical Dir/Dir of Nursing* Ronald Simonsen MD.
Licensure Skilled Care. *Beds* 48. *Certified* Medicaid.
Ownership Proprietary.
Staff Physicians 1 (pt); RNs 4 (ft), 2 (pt); LPNs 1 (ft), 1 (pt); Nurses aides 14 (ft), 12 (pt); Physical therapists 1 (pt); Reality therapists 1 (pt); Recreational therapists 1 (pt); Activities coordinators 1 (ft); Dietitians 1 (pt); Podiatrists 1 (pt).
Facilities Dining room; Physical therapy room; Activities room; Crafts room; Laundry room; Barber/Beauty shop.
Activities Arts and Crafts; Cards; Games; Reading groups; Prayer groups; Movies; Shopping trips; Dances/Social or cultural gatherings.

Warren State Hospital—Long Term Care Facility
Warren, PA, 16365 (814) 723-5500
Admin Gezelle G Buner. *Medical Dir/Dir of Nursing* A C Myers DO.
Licensure Skilled Care. *Beds* 75; ICF 93. *Certi-*

fied Medicaid; Medicare.
Ownership Public.
Admissions Requirements Medical examination; Physician's request.
Staff Physicians 1 (ft), 2 (pt); RNs 30 (ft), 3 (pt); LPNs 9 (ft); Nurses aides 49 (ft); Physical therapists 1 (ft); Reality therapists 1 (ft); Recreational therapists 2 (ft); Occupational therapists 1 (ft); Speech therapists 1 (ft); Activities coordinators 1 (ft); Dietitians 3 (ft); Dentists 1 (ft); Podiatrists 3 (pt).
Facilities Dining room; Physical therapy room; Activities room; Chapel; Crafts room; Laundry room; Barber/Beauty shop; Library; Greenhouse.
Activities Arts and Crafts; Cards; Games; Reading groups; Prayer groups; Movies; Shopping trips; Dances/Social or cultural gatherings.

WARRINGTON

Fox Nursing Home Inc
2644 Bristol Rd, Warrington, PA, 18976 (215) 343-2700
Admin Rudolph A Lucente. *Medical Dir/Dir of Nursing* Dr Dennis Tafflin.
Licensure Skilled Care. *Beds* 35. *Certified* Medicare.
Ownership Proprietary.
Admissions Requirements Minimum age 25; Medical examination.
Staff RNs 7 (ft); LPNs 5 (ft); Nurses aides 30 (ft), 15 (pt); Physical therapists 1 (pt); Reality therapists 1 (pt); Recreational therapists 1 (ft); Occupational therapists 1 (pt); Speech therapists 1 (pt); Activities coordinators 1 (ft); Dietitians 1 (pt); Podiatrists 1 (pt).
Facilities Dining room; Physical therapy room; Activities room; Crafts room; Laundry room.
Activities Arts and Crafts; Cards; Games; Reading groups; Prayer groups; Movies; Dances/Social or cultural gatherings.

WASHINGTON

Kade Nursing Home
1198 W Wylie Ave Ext, Washington, PA, 15301 (412) 222-2148
Admin Janice Marianna. *Medical Dir/Dir of Nursing* Dr John McCarrell.
Licensure Skilled Care. *Beds* 57. *Certified* Medicaid.
Ownership Proprietary.
Staff RNs; LPNs; Nurses aides; Physical therapists; Speech therapists; Activities coordinators; Dietitians.
Facilities Dining room; Physical therapy room; Activities room; Laundry room; Barber/Beauty shop.
Activities Arts and Crafts; Cards; Games; Prayer groups; Shopping trips.

Washington County Health Center
Rt 1, Box 94, Washington, PA, 15301 (412) 228-5010
Admin Barry W Parks. *Medical Dir/Dir of Nursing* Frederick Large MD.
Licensure Skilled Care; Intermediate Care.
Beds SNF 100; ICF 150. *Certified* Medicaid.
Ownership Nonprofit.
Admissions Requirements Minimum age 18;

Medical examination.
Staff Physicians 2 (pt); RNs 15 (ft), 6 (pt); LPNs 13 (ft), 7 (pt); Nurses aides 81 (ft), 1 (pt); Physical therapists 1 (pt); Speech therapists 1 (pt); Activities coordinators 1 (ft); Dietitians 1 (pt); Dentists 1 (pt); Podiatrists 1 (pt).
Facilities Dining room; Physical therapy room; Activities room; Chapel; Crafts room; Laundry room; Barber/Beauty shop; Library.
Activities Arts and Crafts; Games; Reading groups; Prayer groups; Movies; Shopping trips; Dances/Social or cultural gatherings.

Washington Hospital—Extended Care Facility*
Manor Dr, Washington, PA, 15301 (412) 225-8580
Licensure Skilled Care. *Beds* 92. *Certified* Medicaid; Medicare.
Ownership Nonprofit.

Washington Presbyterian Home
825 S Main St, Box 677, Washington, PA, 15301 (412) 222-4300
Admin Evelyn M Vandever. *Medical Dir/Dir of Nursing* J Evangelista MD.
Licensure Skilled Care; Residential Care.
Beds SNF 28; Residential Care 56. *Certified* Medicaid; Medicare.
Ownership Nonprofit.
Admissions Requirements Minimum age 62; Medical examination.
Staff Physicians 1 (pt); RNs 2 (ft), 6 (pt); LPNs 1 (pt); Nurses aides 12 (ft), 2 (pt); Physical therapists 1 (pt); Recreational therapists 1 (ft); Occupational therapists 1 (pt); Speech therapists 1 (pt); Activities coordinators 1 (pt); Dietitians 1 (pt); Dentists 1 (pt); Ophthalmologists 1 (pt); Podiatrists 1 (pt); Audiologists 1 (pt).
Affiliation Presbyterian
Facilities Dining room; Activities room; Crafts room; Laundry room; Library.
Activities Arts and Crafts; Cards; Games; Reading groups; Prayer groups; Movies; Shopping trips.
Description The Washington Presbyterian Home provides residential long-term health care facilities and personal services to older persons desiring and seeking a group living environment.

WATSONTOWN

Kramm Nursing Home Inc
245-47 E 8th St, Watsontown, PA, 17777 (717) 538-1160
Admin Randall D Kramm. *Medical Dir/Dir of Nursing* Dr Robert Yannaccone.
Licensure Skilled Care. *Beds* 74. *Certified* Medicaid.
Ownership Proprietary.
Admissions Requirements Medical examination.
Staff Physicians 9 (pt); RNs 2 (ft), 2 (pt); LPNs 2 (ft), 3 (pt); Nurses aides 20 (ft), 14 (pt); Physical therapists 1 (pt); Activities coordinators 1 (ft); Dietitians 1 (pt); Dentists 1 (pt); Ophthalmologists 1 (pt); Podiatrists 1 (pt).
Facilities Dining room; Physical therapy room; Activities room; Crafts room; Laundry room; Barber/Beauty shop; Library.
Activities Arts and Crafts; Cards; Games; Reading groups; Prayer groups; Movies; Shop-

ping trips; Dances/Social or cultural gatherings.
Description Staff can learn to know every patient well; all residents treated as family.

WAYNE

Wayne Nursing and Rehabilitation Center
30 West Ave, Wayne, PA, 19087 (215) 688-3635
Medical Dir/Dir of Nursing Ian Ballard MD.
Licensure Skilled Care; Intermediate Care.
Beds 108. *Certified* Medicaid; Medicare.
Ownership Proprietary.
Staff Physicians 3 (pt); RNs 9 (ft), 8 (pt); LPNs 4 (ft), 2 (pt); Orderlies 3 (ft); Nurses aides 25 (ft), 20 (pt); Physical therapists 1 (ft); Recreational therapists 1 (ft); Occupational therapists 1 (pt); Speech therapists 1 (pt); Activities coordinators 1 (ft); Dietitians 1 (pt); Dentists 1 (pt); Ophthalmologists 1 (pt); Podiatrists 1 (pt); Audiologists 1 (pt).
Facilities Dining room; Physical therapy room; Activities room; Laundry room; Barber/Beauty shop; Library.
Activities Arts and Crafts; Cards; Games; Reading groups; Prayer groups; Movies; Shopping trips; Wine and cheese parties; Theme lunches; Weekend and evening activities.
Description This nursing and rehabilitation center is located in Wayne, a small quaint suburb of Philadelphia; provides a homey and warm atmosphere and a full range of services for residents. In addition to excellent nursing care, there is a full time in-house licensed physical therapist; occupational and speech therapy and audiological services are provided as needed. VA approved.

WAYNESBURG

Curry Memorial Home
Rt 2, Waynesburg, PA, 15370 (412) 627-3153
Medical Dir/Dir of Nursing Dr Prayun Chayapruks.
Licensure Skilled Care; Intermediate Care.
Beds SNF 61; ICF 50. *Certified* Medicaid.
Ownership Public.
Staff Physicians 1 (ft); RNs 5 (ft), 4 (pt); LPNs 20 (ft), 7 (pt); Nurses aides 39 (ft), 15 (pt); Physical therapists 1 (pt); Speech therapists 1 (pt); Activities coordinators 1 (ft), 2 (pt); Dietitians 1 (ft); Podiatrists 1 (pt).
Facilities Dining room; Physical therapy room; Activities room; Chapel; Crafts room; Barber/Beauty shop.
Activities Arts and Crafts; Reading groups; Movies; Shopping trips; Dances/Social or cultural gatherings.
Description Facility is located in southwestern Pennsylvania, in beautiful Greene County on old route 21.

WEATHERLY

Weatherwood—Carbon County Home
Evergreen Ave, Rt 2, Weatherly, PA, 18255 (717) 427-8683
Medical Dir/Dir of Nursing Dr Larry Antolick.
Licensure Skilled Care; Intermediate Care.
Beds SNF 150; ICF 50. *Certified* Medicaid; Medicare.
Ownership Nonprofit.

Admissions Requirements Minimum age 17; Medical examination; Physician's request.
Staff Physicians 2 (ft); Reality therapists 1 (ft); Recreational therapists 1 (ft); Occupational therapists 1 (pt); Speech therapists 1 (pt); Activities coordinators 1 (ft); Dietitians 1 (ft); Dentists 1 (pt); Ophthalmologists 1 (pt); Podiatrists 1 (pt); Audiologists 1 (pt).
Facilities Dining room; Physical therapy room; Activities room; Chapel; Crafts room; Laundry room; Barber/Beauty shop; Library.
Activities Arts and Crafts; Cards; Games; Reading groups; Movies; Shopping trips; Dances/Social or cultural gatherings.
Description Fishing trips outside of facility for 35-55 residents at a time; annual carnival; wet bar for males and social activities with beer, near beer, wine and cheese parties.

WELLSBORO

Broad Acres Nursing Home Association*
Rt 3, Wellsboro, PA, 16901 (717) 724-3913
Licensure Skilled Care; Intermediate Care.
Beds SNF 60; ICF 60. *Certified* Medicaid; Medicare.
Ownership Nonprofit.

Carleton Nursing Home*
10 West Ave, Wellsboro, PA, 16901 (717) 724-2631
Licensure Skilled Care. *Beds* 26. *Certified* Medicaid.
Ownership Proprietary.

Green Home
37 Central Ave, PO Box 836, Wellsboro, PA, 16901 (717) 724-3131
Admin G E Danning. *Medical Dir/Dir of Nursing* Anne K Butler MD.
Licensure Skilled Care. *Beds* 122. *Certified* Medicaid; Medicare.
Ownership Nonprofit.
Admissions Requirements Medical examination; Physician's request.
Staff RNs 7 (ft), 6 (pt); LPNs 7 (ft), 3 (pt); Orderlies 2 (ft), 1 (pt); Nurses aides 36 (ft), 27 (pt); Physical therapists 1 (pt); Activities coordinators 1 (ft), 1 (pt); Dietitians 1 (ft).
Facilities Dining room; Physical therapy room; Activities room; Crafts room; Laundry room; Barber/Beauty shop.
Activities Arts and Crafts; Cards; Games; Prayer groups; Movies; Shopping trips; Dances/Social or cultural gatherings.
Description The Green Home is a beautiful 2-story, brick building located on a quiet tree-lined avenue in Wellsboro. At night the old fashioned gas lights lining the boulevard cast a warm glow across the quiet neighborhood, while the morning sun brings the cheerful singing of birds. This is a lovely home for lovely people.

WERNERSVILLE

Hamburg Center Annex
Wernersville, PA, 19565 (215) 678-3411
Licensure Intermediate Care for Mentally Retarded. *Beds* 48. *Certified* Medicaid.
Ownership Nonprofit.

Wernersville State Hospital—Long Term Care Facility
Wernersville, PA, 19565 (215) 3346
Admin John D Sholly. *Medical Dir/Dir of Nursing* Phyllis A Murr MD.
Licensure Skilled Care. *Beds* 86. *Certified* Medicaid.
Ownership Public.
Admissions Requirements Minimum age 22; Medical examination; Physician's request.
Staff Physicians 1 (ft); RNs 11 (ft), 2 (pt); LPNs 24 (ft), 2 (pt); Nurses aides 15 (ft), 4 (pt); Physical therapists 1 (pt); Recreational therapists 2 (ft); Occupational therapists 1 (pt); Speech therapists 1 (pt); Activities coordinators 1 (ft); Dentists 1 (pt); Podiatrists 1 (pt).
Facilities Dining room; Physical therapy room; Activities room; Chapel; Laundry room; Barber/Beauty shop; Library.
Activities Arts and Crafts; Cards; Games; Movies; Shopping trips; Dances/Social or cultural gatherings.
Description State-owned facility with admissions restricted to those eligible individuals from the state mental health system.

WEST CHESTER

Brandywine Hall Inc
800 W Miner St, PO Box 524, West Chester, PA, 19381-0524 (215) 696-3120
Medical Dir/Dir of Nursing Philip Kistler MD.
Licensure Intermediate Care. *Beds* 80. *Certified* Medicaid.
Ownership Proprietary.
Admissions Requirements Medical examination; Physician's request.
Staff Reality therapists 1 (ft); Recreational therapists 1 (ft); Activities coordinators 1 (ft).
Facilities Dining room; Activities room; Crafts room; Laundry room; Barber/Beauty shop; Library.
Activities Arts and Crafts; Cards; Games; Prayer groups; Movies; Shopping trips; Dances/Social or cultural gatherings.
Description Facility offers total dedication to geriatric care in a country setting.

County of Chester—Pocopson Home
1695 Lenape Rd, West Chester, PA, 19382 (215) 793-1212
Admin Thomas C Burd. *Medical Dir/Dir of Nursing* Philip E Kistler MD.
Licensure Skilled Care; Intermediate Care.
Beds SNF 46; ICF 315. *Certified* Medicaid; Medicare.
Ownership Nonprofit.
Admissions Requirements Medical examination.
Staff Physicians 4 (ft), 2 (pt); RNs 13 (ft), 11 (pt); LPNs 29 (ft), 15 (pt); Nurses aides 149 (ft), 4 (pt); Physical therapists 2 (pt); Occupational therapists 1 (pt); Speech therapists 1 (pt); Activities coordinators 1 (ft); Dietitians 1 (ft); Dentists 1 (pt); Ophthalmologists 1 (pt); Podiatrists 1 (pt); Audiologists 1 (pt).
Facilities Dining room; Physical therapy room; Activities room; Chapel; Crafts room; Laundry room; Barber/Beauty shop; Library.
Activities Arts and Crafts; Games; Reading groups; Prayer groups; Movies; Shopping trips; Dances/Social or cultural gatherings.

Description Pocopson Home is a skilled/intermediate 361-bed nursing facility set in the rolling hills of Chester County.

Friends Hall at West Chester*
424 N Matlack St, West Chester, PA, 19380
(215) 696-5211
Licensure Skilled Care. *Beds* 80.
Ownership Nonprofit.

West Chester Arms of Pennsylvania Inc
1130 West Chester Pike, West Chester, PA,
19380 (215) 692-3636
Medical Dir/Dir of Nursing Dr Ben Reniello.
Licensure Skilled Care; Intermediate Care.
Beds SNF 90; ICF 150. *Certified* Medicaid;
Medicare.
Ownership Proprietary.
Staff Physical therapists 1 (ft); Recreational
therapists 3 (ft); Occupational therapists; Speech therapists; Activities coordinators; Dietitians; Dentists; Podiatrists.
Facilities Physical therapy room; Activities
room; Crafts room; Laundry room; Barber-/Beauty shop.
Activities Arts and Crafts; Cards; Games;
Reading groups; Prayer groups; Movies; Shopping trips; Dances/Social or cultural gatherings.
Description The rehabilitation department is
excellent with full-time physical, occupational,
and speech therapists; full range of activities
offered with 3 full-time employees and several
volunteer groups working with the residents.

WEST READING

Leader Nursing and Rehabilitation Center
425 Buttonwood St, West Reading, PA, 19611
(215) 373-5166
Licensure Skilled Care; Intermediate Care.
Beds SNF 120; ICF 60. *Certified* Medicaid;
Medicare.
Ownership Proprietary.
Admissions Requirements Medical examination; Physician's request.
Staff RNs 8 (ft), 8 (pt); LPNs 14 (ft), 6 (pt);
Nurses aides 54 (ft), 36 (pt); Physical therapists
1 (ft); Reality therapists 1 (ft); Recreational therapists 1 (ft), 2 (pt); Activities coordinators 1 (ft);
Dietitians 1 (ft).
Facilities Dining room; Physical therapy room;
Activities room; Chapel; Laundry room; Barber/Beauty shop; Library.
Activities Arts and Crafts; Cards; Reading
groups; Prayer groups; Shopping trips; Dances-/Social or cultural gatherings.
Description Facility features an agressive
rehabilitation program discharging approximately 20% of the residents back into the community. Educational outreach program in the
community. Career advancement opportunities.

Reading Nursing Center
4th and Spruce Sts, West Reading, PA, 19602
(215) 374-5175
Admin Diane G Fonzone. *Medical Dir/Dir of
Nursing* Dr Henry Bialas.
Licensure Skilled Care; Intermediate Care.
Beds SNF 50; ICF 150. *Certified* Medicaid;
Medicare.
Ownership Proprietary.

Staff RNs 6 (ft), 4 (pt); LPNs 11 (ft), 12 (pt);
Orderlies 2 (ft); Nurses aides 41 (ft), 43 (pt);
Physical therapists 1 (ft); Occupational therapists 1 (pt); Speech therapists 1 (pt); Activities
coordinators 4 (ft); Dietitians 1 (ft); Podiatrists
1 (pt); Audiologists 1 (pt).
Facilities Dining room; Physical therapy room;
Activities room; Crafts room; Laundry room;
Barber/Beauty shop.
Activities Arts and Crafts; Cards; Games;
Reading groups; Prayer groups; Movies; Shopping trips; Dances/Social or cultural gatherings.
Description Facility features restaurant-style
food service.

WEST SUNBURY

Allegheny Valley School—Butler Campus*
Rt 1, West Sunbury, PA, 16061 (412) 637-2981
Licensure Intermediate Care for Mentally
Retarded. *Beds* 15. *Certified* Medicaid.
Ownership Nonprofit.

WEXFORD

Pineview Manor*
PO Box 191, Swinderman Rd, Wexford, PA,
15090 (412) 935-3781
Licensure Skilled Care. *Beds* 32. *Certified* Medicaid.
Ownership Proprietary.

Wexford House*
9800 Old Perry Hwy, Wexford, PA, 15090
(412) 366-7900
Licensure Skilled Care. *Beds* 224. *Certified* Medicaid; Medicare.
Ownership Proprietary.

WHITE HAVEN

White Haven Center*
Oley Valley Rd, White Haven, PA, 18661 (717)
443-9564
Licensure Intermediate Care for Mentally
Retarded. *Beds* 567. *Certified* Medicaid.
Ownership Nonprofit.

WILKES-BARRE

Hampton House*
Sans Souci Pkwy, Wilkes-Barre, PA, 18702
(717) 825-8725
Licensure Skilled Care. *Beds* 104. *Certified* Medicaid; Medicare.
Ownership Proprietary.

Heritage House
80 E Northampton St, Wilkes-Barre, PA, 18701
(717) 826-1031
Admin Margaret R Spencer. *Medical Dir/Dir
of Nursing* Clinton J Lehman MD.
Licensure Skilled Care; Intermediate Care.
Beds SNF 50. *Certified* Medicaid; Medicare.
Ownership Nonprofit.
Admissions Requirements Minimum age 62;
Medical examination; Physician's request.
Staff Physicians 1 (pt); RNs 2 (ft), 4 (pt); LPNs
3 (ft), 3 (pt); Nurses aides 11 (ft), 12 (pt);
Physical therapists 1 (pt); Occupational thera-

pists 1 (pt); Speech therapists 1 (pt); Activities
coordinators 1 (ft); Dietitians 1 (ft); Dentists 1
(pt); Ophthalmologists 1 (pt); Podiatrists 1 (pt);
Audiologists 1 (pt).
Facilities Dining room; Physical therapy room;
Activities room; Crafts room; Laundry room;
Barber/Beauty shop; Library; Outdoor patio.
Activities Arts and Crafts; Cards; Games; Prayer groups; Movies; Shopping trips; Dances/Social or cultural gatherings.
Description Sponsored as a nonprofit facility,
Heritage House now provides gracious living
and compassionate nursing care for retired men
and women. Here, in completely modern facilities, an atmosphere of quiet dignity, comfort
and security is maintained. Situated in downtown Wilkes-Barre, Heritage House is close to
all of the amenities of the community—houses
of worship, shops and stores, restaurants, theatres, libraries, and services. Local bus transportation and intercity bus terminals are nearby.
Facilities for crafts and hobbies, a library and a
music area are linked to active recreational,
entertainment, and cultural programs. Beautifully landscaped grounds and a large patio and
outdoor recreation area help to encourage open
air activity. Space is set aside for gardening by
residents.

Little Flower Manor
200 S Meade St, Wilkes-Barre, PA, 18702 (717)
823-6131
Medical Dir/Dir of Nursing John Valenti MD.
Licensure Skilled Care. *Beds* 127. *Certified* Medicaid; Medicare.
Ownership Nonprofit.
Staff Physicians 3 (ft); RNs 6 (ft), 4 (pt); LPNs
13 (ft), 6 (pt); Nurses aides 36 (ft), 30 (pt); Recreational therapists 1 (ft); Dietitians 1 (ft); Dentists 1 (pt); Ophthalmologists 1 (pt); Podiatrists
1 (pt).
Affiliation Roman Catholic
Facilities Dining room; Physical therapy room;
Activities room; Chapel; Crafts room; Laundry
room; Barber/Beauty shop.
Activities Arts and Crafts; Cards; Games; Prayer groups; Movies; Shopping trips; Dances/Social or cultural gatherings.

Step by Step Inc
293 Franklin St, Wilkes-Barre, PA, 18702
Admin George A Seman.
Licensure Intermediate Care for Mentally
Retarded. *Beds* 16. *Certified* Medicaid.
Ownership Nonprofit.
Admissions Requirements Medical examination; Physician's request.
Staff Physicians 1 (pt); RNs 1 (pt); LPNs 1
(pt); Physical therapists 1 (pt); Occupational
therapists 1 (pt); Speech therapists 1 (pt);
Activities coordinators 1 (pt); Dietitians 1 (pt);
Dentists 1 (pt); Ophthalmologists 1 (pt); Podiatrists 1 (pt); Audiologists 1 (pt).
Facilities Dining room; Activities room; Laundry room.
Activities Arts and Crafts; Cards; Games;
Movies; Shopping trips; Dances/Social or cultural gatherings.
Description Facility operates 2 8-bed
community ICF/MRs, an adult (Wilkes-Barre)
and a children's (Kingston) program; each is
geared as a transitional placement prior to a less

restrictive option (e g, CLA). Neither facility is equipped to accommodate nonambulatory residents.

Summit Health Care Center*
50 N Pennsylvania Ave, Wilkes-Barre, PA, 18701 (714) 474-5661
Licensure Skilled Care. *Beds* 120. *Certified* Medicaid; Medicare.
Ownership Proprietary.

Valley Crest Nursing Home
Rt 115, Plains Twp, Wilkes-Barre, PA, 18711 (717) 826-1011
Admin Robert A Reed. *Medical Dir/Dir of Nursing* David W Greenwald MD.
Licensure Skilled Care. *Beds* 386. *Certified* Medicaid; Medicare.
Ownership Nonprofit.
Admissions Requirements Minimum age 18.
Staff Physicians 7 (ft); RNs 30 (ft), 2 (pt); LPNs 45 (ft); Nurses aides 177 (ft); Physical therapists 1 (pt); Occupational therapists 1 (pt); Speech therapists 1 (pt); Activities coordinators 1 (ft); Dietitians 2 (ft); Dentists 1 (pt); Ophthalmologists 1 (pt); Podiatrists 1 (pt); Audiologists 1 (pt).
Facilities Dining room; Physical therapy room; Activities room; Chapel; Crafts room; Laundry room; Barber/Beauty shop; Library.
Activities Arts and Crafts; Cards; Games; Reading groups; Prayer groups; Movies; Shopping trips; Dances/Social or cultural gatherings.

WILLIAMSPORT

Divine Providence—Extended Care Facility
1100 Gramrion Blvd, Williamsport, PA, 17701 (717) 326-8181
Licensure Skilled Care. *Beds* 34. *Certified* Medicaid; Medicare.
Ownership Nonprofit.

Hope Enterprizes Inc*
136 Catawissa Ave, Williamsport, PA, 17701 (717) 332-3206
Licensure Intermediate Care for Mentally Retarded. *Beds* 7. *Certified* Medicaid.
Ownership Nonprofit.

Leader Nursing and Rehabilitation Center—North*
300 Leader Dr, Williamsport, PA, 17701 (717) 323-8627
Licensure Skilled Care; Intermediate Care. *Beds* SNF 90; ICF 60. *Certified* Medicaid; Medicare.
Ownership Proprietary.

Leader Nursing Rehabilitation Center—South
101 Leader Dr, Williamsport, PA, 17701 (717) 323-3758
Admin Dorothy J Dangle. *Medical Dir/Dir of Nursing* Dr Tobias.
Licensure Skilled Care. *Beds* 120. *Certified* Medicaid; Medicare.
Ownership Proprietary.
Staff Physicians 1 (ft); RNs 4 (ft), 6 (pt); LPNs 7 (ft), 5 (pt); Orderlies 1 (ft); Nurses aides 29 (ft), 21 (pt); Physical therapists 1 (ft); Reality therapists 1 (pt); Recreational therapists 1 (pt); Occupational therapists 1 (pt); Speech thera-

pists 1 (pt); Activities coordinators 1 (ft); Dietitians 1 (pt); Dentists 1 (pt); Ophthalmologists 1 (pt); Podiatrists 1 (pt); Audiologists 1 (pt).
Facilities Dining room; Physical therapy room; Activities room; Chapel; Crafts room; Laundry room; Barber/Beauty shop; Library.
Activities Arts and Crafts; Cards; Games; Reading groups; Prayer groups; Movies; Shopping trips; Dances/Social or cultural gatherings.
Description Facility with quiet and restful atmosphere is located on a hill overlooking the Williamsport area, surrounded by beautiful grounds; many excellent programs for patients and staff.

Williamsport Home*
1900 Ravine Rd, Williamsport, PA, 17701 (717) 323-8781
Licensure Skilled Care; Intermediate Care. *Beds* SNF 8; ICF 141. *Certified* Medicaid.
Ownership Nonprofit.

WILLOW GROVE

The Homestead*
1113 N Easton Rd, Willow Grove, PA, 19090 (215) 659-3060
Licensure Skilled Care. *Beds* 175. *Certified* Medicaid; Medicare.
Ownership Proprietary.

WINDBER

Church of the Brethren Home*
1005 Hoffman Ave, Windber, PA, 15963 (814) 467-5505
Licensure Skilled Care; Intermediate Care. *Beds* SNF 76; ICF 71. *Certified* Medicaid; Medicare.
Ownership Nonprofit.

WORTHINGTON

Sugar Creek Rest Inc
Rt 2, Worthington, PA, 16262 (412) 445-7146
Medical Dir/Dir of Nursing D W Minteer.
Licensure Skilled Care; Intermediate Care. *Beds* SNF 60; ICF 43. *Certified* Medicaid; Medicare.
Ownership Proprietary.
Admissions Requirements Medical examination.
Staff Physicians 2 (pt); RNs 5 (ft), 4 (pt); LPNs 3 (ft), 8 (pt); Nurses aides 22 (ft), 19 (pt); Physical therapists 2 (ft); Reality therapists 1 (ft); Recreational therapists 2 (ft); Speech therapists 1 (pt); Activities coordinators 1 (ft); Dietitians 1 (ft); Podiatrists 1 (pt); Audiologists 1 (pt).
Facilities Dining room; Physical therapy room; Activities room; Crafts room; Laundry room; Barber/Beauty shop; Library.
Activities Arts and Crafts; Cards; Games; Reading groups; Prayer groups; Movies; Dances/Social or cultural gatherings.
Description Facility has a quiet rural setting located on 150 acre farm with fields, lake and trees plus much wildlife. Physical therapy program is very active and progressive.

WYNCOTE

Crestview Convalescent Home*
Church Rd, Wyncote, PA, 19095 (215) 884-7983
Licensure Skilled Care. *Beds* 70. *Certified* Medicaid; Medicare.
Ownership Proprietary.

Hopkins House Nursing & Rehabilitation Center*
8100 Washington Ln, Wyncote, PA, 19095 (215) 576-8000
Medical Dir/Dir of Nursing Dr Leonard Winegrad.
Licensure Skilled Care. *Beds* 99. *Certified* Medicaid; Medicare.
Ownership Proprietary.
Staff RNs 7 (ft), 9 (pt); LPNs 10 (ft), 7 (pt); Orderlies 2 (ft); Nurses aides 27 (ft), 24 (pt); Activities coordinators 2 (ft); Dietitians 1 (ft).
Facilities Dining room; Physical therapy room; Activities room; Laundry room; Barber/Beauty shop.
Activities Arts and Crafts; Cards; Games; Reading groups; Movies; Shopping trips; Dances/Social or cultural gatherings; Religious services.
Description Hopkins House provides skilled nursing care for all age groups and has speech, physical, and occupational therapy daily. We have a very full activity calendar including all types of events. Located in the suburbs of Philadelphia.

The Oaks*
Church and Greenwood Aves, Wyncote, PA, 19095 (215) 884-3639
Licensure Skilled Care. *Beds* 55. *Certified* Medicaid; Medicare.
Ownership Proprietary.

Wyncote Church Home
Fernbrook and Maple Aves, Wyncote, PA, 19095 (215) 885-2620
Medical Dir/Dir of Nursing Earl S Krick MD.
Licensure Skilled Care; Intermediate Care. *Beds* SNF 32; ICF 31. *Certified* Medicaid; Medicare.
Ownership Proprietary.
Admissions Requirements Minimum age 65; Medical examination.
Staff Physicians 1 (pt); RNs 2 (ft), 15 (pt); LPNs 1 (pt); Nurses aides 17 (ft), 11 (pt); Physical therapists 1 (pt); Recreational therapists 2 (pt); Occupational therapists 1 (pt); Speech therapists 1 (pt); Dietitians 1 (ft); Dentists 1 (pt); Ophthalmologists 1 (pt); Podiatrists 1 (pt); Audiologists 1 (pt).
Affiliation Church of Christ
Facilities Dining room; Activities room; Chapel; Crafts room; Laundry room; Barber/Beauty shop; Library.
Activities Arts and Crafts; Cards; Games; Reading groups; Prayer groups; Movies; Shopping trips; Dances/Social or cultural gatherings; Remotivation; Choir groups.
Description Home is located in a lovely residential suburb of Philadelphia offering sheltered care for the aging with a health care center able to accommodate skilled and intermediate care needs.

WYNDMOOR

All Saints Rehabilitation Hospital/Springfield Retirement Residence
8601 Stenton Ave, Wyndmoor, PA, 19118 (215) 233-9000
Medical Dir/Dir of Nursing D Michael Geller MD.
Licensure Skilled Care. *Beds* 31. *Certified* Medicaid; Medicare.
Ownership Nonprofit.
Admissions Requirements Physician's request.
Staff Physicians 4 (ft); RNs 18 (ft), 19 (pt); LPNs 2 (ft), 4 (pt); Nurses aides 29 (ft), 19 (pt); Physical therapists 6 (ft); Recreational therapists 3 (ft), 1 (pt); Occupational therapists 6 (ft); Speech therapists 1 (pt); Activities coordinators 1 (ft); Dietitians 1 (ft); Dentists 1 (pt); Podiatrists 1 (pt); Audiologists 1 (pt).
Affiliation Episcopal
Facilities Dining room; Physical therapy room; Activities room; Chapel; Crafts room; Laundry room; Barber/Beauty shop; Library; Various sitting areas.
Activities Arts and Crafts; Cards; Games; Reading groups; Prayer groups; Movies; Shopping trips; Dances/Social or cultural gatherings.
Description Facility is located on 11 ½ acres; operated by Episcopal Community Services.

Green Acres Home for Convalescents Inc*
1401 Ivy Hill Rd, Wyndmoor, PA, 19150 (215) 233-5605
Licensure Skilled Care. *Beds* 120. *Certified* Medicaid; Medicare.
Ownership Proprietary.

YEADON

Leader Nursing Rehabilitation Center
Lansdowne and Lincoln Aves, Yeadon, PA, 19050 (215) 626-7700
Medical Dir/Dir of Nursing Dr Jame Kelly.
Licensure Skilled Care. *Beds* 166. *Certified* Medicaid; Medicare.
Ownership Proprietary.
Admissions Requirements Minimum age 16; Medical examination.
Staff Physicians 1 (pt); RNs 7 (ft), 4 (pt); LPNs 8 (ft), 10 (pt); Orderlies 2 (pt); Nurses aides 45 (ft), 24 (pt); Physical therapists 1 (ft); Reality therapists 1 (pt); Recreational therapists 1 (ft); Occupational therapists 1 (ft); Speech therapists 1 (ft); Activities coordinators 1 (pt); Dietitians 1 (ft); Dentists 1 (ft); Ophthalmologists 1 (ft); Podiatrists 1 (ft); Audiologists 1 (ft).
Facilities Dining room; Physical therapy room; Activities room; Chapel; Crafts room; Laundry room; Barber/Beauty shop.
Activities Arts and Crafts; Cards; Games; Reading groups; Prayer groups; Movies; Shopping trips; Dances/Social or cultural gatherings.
Description Facility is able to provide a well planned rehabilitative program for both long- and short-term stays. Professional staff is capable of providing not only quality nursing services, but sees to the spiritual and social needs of all residents.

YORK

Barley Convalescent Home—North*
1775 Barley Rd, York, PA, 17404 (717) 767-6530
Licensure Skilled Care. *Beds* 121. *Certified* Medicaid; Medicare.
Ownership Proprietary.

Barley Convalescent Home—South*
200 Pauline Dr, York, PA, 17402 (717) 741-1037
Licensure Skilled Care. *Beds* 102. *Certified* Medicaid; Medicare.
Ownership Proprietary.

Colonial Manor Nursing Home*
970 Colonial Ave, York, PA, 17403 (717) 845-2661
Licensure Skilled Care; Intermediate Care.
Beds SNF 123; ICF 96. *Certified* Medicaid; Medicare.
Ownership Proprietary.

Manor Care of Barley Kingston Court
2400 Kingston Court, York, PA, 17402 (717) 755-5911
Medical Dir/Dir of Nursing August A Gabriele MD.
Licensure Skilled Care. *Beds* 121. *Certified* Medicaid; Medicare.
Ownership Proprietary.
Admissions Requirements Minimum age 16; Medical examination.
Staff RNs; LPNs; Nurses aides; Physical therapists; Recreational therapists 1 (ft); Occupational therapists; Speech therapists; Activities coordinators 1 (ft); Audiologists.
Facilities Dining room; Physical therapy room; Activities room; Crafts room; Laundry room; Barber/Beauty shop; 4 large lounges/TV rooms.
Activities Arts and Crafts; Cards; Games; Reading groups; Prayer groups; Movies; Shopping trips; Dances/Social or cultural gatherings; Residents council; Current events; Discussion group; Spelling bees; Pokeno.
Description Facility is very convenient to major highways, located in a wooded setting, exquisitely decorated with Ethan Allen furniture and art prints throughout. No deposit or advance payment required on admission. No ancillary charges beyond daily rate of $50.00 except physician and pharmacy billing.

Margaret E Moul Home
2050 Barley Rd, York, PA, 17404
Admin Dennis V Reese. *Medical Dir/Dir of Nursing* James Harberger MD.
Licensure Skilled Care. *Beds* 52. *Certified* Medicaid; Medicare.
Ownership Nonprofit.
Admissions Requirements Minimum age 18; Medical examination; Physician's request.
Staff RNs 3 (ft), 3 (pt); LPNs 3 (ft), 4 (pt); Nurses aides 16 (ft), 13 (pt); Physical therapists 1 (ft), 1 (pt); Recreational therapists 2 (ft); Speech therapists 1 (pt); Activities coordinators 1 (ft); Dietitians 1 (pt).
Facilities Dining room; Physical therapy room; Activities room; Chapel; Crafts room; Laundry room.
Activities Arts and Crafts; Cards; Games;

Reading groups; Prayer groups; Movies; Shopping trips; Dances/Social or cultural gatherings.
Description Home specializes in caring for severely physically handicapped between the ages of 18 and 55. Most of the residents are mentally alert and oriented; the majority are afflicted with cerebral palsy.

Misericordia Convalescent Home
998 S Russell St, York, PA, 17402 (717) 755-1965
Admin Sr Rosella Marie. *Medical Dir/Dir of Nursing* Edward T Lis MD.
Licensure Skilled Care. *Beds* 55. *Certified* Medicaid.
Ownership Nonprofit.
Staff RNs 3 (ft), 2 (pt); LPNs 3 (ft), 3 (pt); Nurses aides 15 (ft), 18 (pt); Physical therapists 2 (pt); Reality therapists 1 (ft); Recreational therapists 1 (ft), 1 (pt); Occupational therapists 1 (pt); Activities coordinators 1 (ft), 1 (pt); Dietitians 1 (pt); Dentists 1 (pt); Ophthalmologists 1 (pt); Podiatrists 1 (pt).
Affiliation Roman Catholic
Facilities Dining room; Activities room; Chapel; Crafts room; Laundry room; Barber/Beauty shop.
Activities Arts and Crafts; Games; Movies.
Description We try to do a good job for the elderly under our care.

Rest Haven York
1050 S George St, York, PA, 17403 (717) 843-9866
Admin Margaret B Miller. *Medical Dir/Dir of Nursing* Dr Andrew Hickey.
Licensure Skilled Care. *Beds* 167. *Certified* Medicaid; Medicare.
Ownership Proprietary.
Staff Physicians 1 (pt); RNs 8 (ft), 7 (pt); LPNs 19 (ft), 7 (pt); Nurses aides 34 (ft), 34 (pt); Physical therapists 1 (pt); Recreational therapists 1 (ft), 2 (pt); Occupational therapists 1 (ft), 1 (pt); Speech therapists 1 (pt); Activities coordinators 1 (ft); Dietitians 1 (ft); Dentists 1 (pt); Ophthalmologists 1 (pt); Podiatrists 1 (pt); Audiologists 1 (pt).
Facilities Dining room; Physical therapy room; Activities room; Chapel; Crafts room; Laundry room; Barber/Beauty shop.
Activities Arts and Crafts; Cards; Games; Reading groups; Prayer groups; Movies; Shopping trips; Dances/Social or cultural gatherings.
Description Facility has a psychologist on staff at no extra charge to guests; bus trips planned monthly.

York County Hospital and Home
118 Pleasant Acres Rd, York, PA, 17402 (717) 755-9601
Admin Eileen Jenkins. *Medical Dir/Dir of Nursing* Dr Kenneth Yinger.
Licensure Skilled Care; Intermediate Care.
Beds SNF 114; ICF 485. *Certified* Medicaid; Medicare.
Ownership Nonprofit.
Admissions Requirements Minimum age 18.
Staff Physicians 3 (ft), 1 (pt); RNs 20 (ft), 10 (pt); LPNs 45 (ft), 13 (pt); Nurses aides 120 (ft), 119 (pt); Physical therapists 5 (ft); Reality therapists 3 (ft); Recreational therapists 6 (ft); Speech therapists 1 (pt); Activities coordinators 1 (ft); Dietitians 1 (pt); Dentists 1 (pt); Ophthalmolo-

gists 1 (pt); Podiatrists 3 (pt); Audiologists 1 (pt).
Facilities Dining room; Physical therapy room; Activities room; Chapel; Crafts room; Laundry room; Barber/Beauty shop; Library.
Activities Arts and Crafts; Cards; Games; Reading groups; Prayer groups; Movies; Shopping trips; Dances/Social or cultural gatherings; Boating; Bowling; Voting.

York Lutheran Home
750 Kelly Dr, York, PA, 17404 (717) 848-2585
Admin Jeanne M Wildasin.
Licensure Skilled Care; Intermediate Care.
Beds SNF 33; ICF 103. *Certified* Medicaid; Medicare.
Ownership Nonprofit.
Affiliation Lutheran

Yorkview Convalescent and Nursing Home*
2091 Herman Ct, York, PA, 17402 (717) 755-6454
Licensure Skilled Care. *Beds* 19. *Certified* Medicaid; Medicare.
Ownership Proprietary.

YOUNGSTOWN

Edgewood Nursing Center Inc
PO Box 277, E Main St, Youngstown, PA, 15650 (412) 537-4441
Admin Rita M Immel.
Licensure Skilled Care. *Beds* 107. *Certified* Medicaid.
Ownership Proprietary.
Admissions Requirements Minimum age 16; Medical examination.
Staff RNs 4 (ft), 8 (pt); LPNs 6 (ft), 3 (pt); Nurses aides 31 (ft), 7 (pt); Physical therapists 1 (pt); Reality therapists 1 (ft); Recreational therapists 1 (ft); Speech therapists 1 (pt); Activities coordinators 2 (ft).
Facilities Dining room; Activities room; Crafts room; Laundry room; Barber/Beauty shop; Library; Lounges.
Activities Arts and Crafts; Cards; Games; Reading groups; Prayer groups; Movies; Dances/Social or cultural gatherings; Bingo.
Description Facility features a bazaar of craft items twice annually, a formal dinner for alert patients, a carnival annually, summer picnic, Valentine party with a king and queen of the year, church groups, Easter parade, Christmas tea and parties, adopted grandparents, aunts, or uncles, volunteer groups, and many musical groups.

YOUNGSVILLE

Rouse Warren County Home
Rt 1, PO Box 207, Youngsville, PA, 16371 (814) 563-7565
Medical Dir/Dir of Nursing Stanley J Swab MD.
Licensure Skilled Care; Intermediate Care.
Beds SNF 144; ICF 35. *Certified* Medicaid.
Ownership Nonprofit.
Admissions Requirements Physician's request.
Staff Physicians 1 (ft), 1 (pt); RNs 8 (ft); LPNs 20 (ft); Orderlies 4 (ft); Nurses aides 67 (ft); Reality therapists 1 (ft); Recreational therapists

1 (ft); Occupational therapists 1 (ft); Speech therapists 1 (pt); Activities coordinators 1 (ft); Dietitians 1 (pt); Podiatrists 1 (pt); Audiologists 1 (pt).
Facilities Dining room; Physical therapy room; Activities room; Chapel; Crafts room; Laundry room; Barber/Beauty shop.
Activities Arts and Crafts; Cards; Games; Reading groups; Prayer groups; Movies; Shopping trips; Dances/Social or cultural gatherings.

ZELLENOPLE

Passavant Health Center
401 S Main St, Zellenople, PA, 16063 (412) 452-5400
Admin Elwood J Culp. *Medical Dir/Dir of Nursing* Dr William Schwerin.
Licensure Skilled Care; Intermediate Care.
Beds SNF 160; ICF 52. *Certified* Medicaid; Medicare.
Ownership Nonprofit.
Admissions Requirements Minimum age 65; Medical examination.
Staff Physicians 2 (ft); RNs 12 (ft), 15 (pt); LPNs 3 (ft); Nurses aides 72 (ft), 15 (pt); Physical therapists 1 (ft); Reality therapists 1 (ft); Recreational therapists 2 (ft), 5 (pt); Activities coordinators 1 (ft); Dentists 1 (pt); Podiatrists 1 (pt).
Affiliation Lutheran
Facilities Dining room; Physical therapy room; Activities room; Chapel; Crafts room; Laundry room; Barber/Beauty shop; Library.
Activities Arts and Crafts; Cards; Games; Reading groups; Prayer groups; Movies; Shopping trips; Dances/Social or cultural gatherings.
Description Passavant offers 5 levels of retirement living: (1) totally independent living in 106 cottages and 132 apartments; (2) independent living with assisted care; (3) independent living with personal care (assistance with prescribed medications, personal hygiene, tasks of daily living); (4) intermediate nursing; and (5) skilled nursing.

RHODE ISLAND

BRISTOL

Metacom Manor Health Center*
1 Dawn Hill, Bristol, RI, 02809 (401) 253-2300
Admin Ursula M Beauregard.
Licensure Skilled Care; Intermediate Care.
Beds 121. *Certified* Medicaid; Medicare.

Silver Creek Manor
7 Creek Ln, Bristol, RI, 02809 (401) 253-3000
Admin Gerald P Romano. *Medical Dir/Dir of Nursing* Peter J Sansone MD.
Licensure Skilled Care; Intermediate Care.
Beds 126. *Certified* Medicaid; Medicare.
Staff Physicians 4 (pt); RNs 2 (ft), 9 (pt); LPNs 3 (ft); Nurses aides 18 (ft), 40 (pt); Physical therapists; Activities coordinators 1 (ft); Podiatrists.
Facilities Dining room; Physical therapy room; Activities room; Crafts room; Laundry room; Barber/Beauty shop.
Activities Arts and Crafts; Cards; Games; Reading groups; Prayer groups; Movies; Shopping trips; Dances/Social or cultural gatherings.
Description Manor is a skilled nursing and convalescent facility located in a lovely community; offers full rehabilitative services, complete activities program, and excellent nursing care in a homey, comfortable setting; caring and dedicated staff assist each resident to reach his/her full potential.

BURRILLVILLE

Nicole Manor
130 Sayles Ave, Burrillville, RI, 02859 (401) 568-6978
Admin Joan Sabella.
Licensure Intermediate Care. *Beds* 14. *Certified* Medicaid.
Staff Physicians 3 (pt); RNs 1 (pt); LPNs 1 (ft), 1 (pt); Nurses aides 2 (ft), 3 (pt); Recreational therapists 1 (ft); Activities coordinators 1 (ft); Dentists 2 (pt); Ophthalmologists 2 (pt); Podiatrists 1 (pt).
Facilities Dining room; Activities room; Crafts room; Laundry room; Barber/Beauty shop; Library.
Activities Arts and Crafts; Cards; Games; Reading groups; Prayer groups; Movies; Shopping trips; Dances/Social or cultural gatherings.
Description Facility is home-like in a country setting located in Victorian-type home with a wrap-around porch.

Overlook Nursing Home*
14 Rock Ave, Burrillville, RI, 02859 (401) 568-2549
Admin Harold Kenoian.
Licensure Skilled Care; Intermediate Care.
Beds 100. *Certified* Medicaid; Medicare.

Rest Well Rest Home Inc*
132 Sayles Ave, Burrillville, RI, 02859 (401) 568-3000
Admin Anthony Annarino.
Licensure Intermediate Care. *Beds* 19. *Certified* Medicaid.

CENTRAL FALLS

Cartie's Health Center
21 Lincoln Ave, Central Falls, RI, 02863 (401) 727-0900
Admin John Prew. *Medical Dir/Dir of Nursing* Eugene Gaudet MD.
Licensure Skilled Care; Intermediate Care.
Beds 210. *Certified* Medicaid; Medicare.
Admissions Requirements Minimum age 14; Medical examination; Physician's request.
Staff Physicians 35 (pt); RNs 5 (ft), 8 (pt); LPNs 14 (ft), 11 (pt); Orderlies 5 (ft); Nurses aides 77 (ft), 23 (pt); Physical therapists 1 (ft), 1 (pt); Occupational therapists 1 (pt); Speech therapists 1 (pt); Activities coordinators 3 (ft); Dietitians 1 (pt); Dentists 1 (pt); Ophthalmologists 1 (pt); Podiatrists 1 (pt); Audiologists 1 (ft); Bed makers 2 (ft), 3 (pt).
Facilities Dining room; Physical therapy room; Activities room; Crafts room; Laundry room; Barber/Beauty shop.
Activities Arts and Crafts; Cards; Games; Reading groups; Prayer groups; Movies; Dances/Social or cultural gatherings.
Description Center is proud of its restorative nursing program; this consists of "wheelchair aerobics," providing range of motion exercises to music and also individualized attention and exercise for those who do not qualify for full-time physical therapy.

Frigon Nursing Home Inc*
60 Eben Brown Ln, Central Falls, RI, 02863 (401) 726-0371
Admin James H Frigon.
Licensure Intermediate Care. *Beds* 27. *Certified* Medicaid.

The Mansion*
104 Clay St, Central Falls, RI, 02863 (401) 722-0830
Admin Andrew Chopoorian.
Licensure Intermediate Care. *Beds* 62. *Certified* Medicaid.

Paquette Home Inc*
649 Broad St, Central Falls, RI, 02863 (401) 725-7045
Admin Ronald Paquette.
Licensure Intermediate Care. *Beds* 30. *Certified* Medicaid.

Rose Cottage Health Care Center*
151 Hunt St, Central Falls, RI, 02863 (401) 722-4610
Admin Leonard Lamphear.
Licensure Skilled Care; Intermediate Care.
Beds 104. *Certified* Medicaid; Medicare.

COVENTRY

Alpine Rest Home Inc
Weaver Hill Rd, Coventry, RI, 02816 (401) 397-5001
Admin Elizabeth A Gauvin.
Licensure Intermediate Care. *Beds* 28. *Certified* Medicaid.
Admissions Requirements Minimum age 50; Medical examination.
Staff RNs 1 (pt); LPNs 1 (ft), 1 (pt); Nurses aides 6 (ft); Recreational therapists 1 (ft); Dietitians 1 (pt); Podiatrists 1 (pt).
Facilities Dining room; Activities room; Crafts room; Laundry room; Barber/Beauty shop.
Activities Arts and Crafts; Cards; Games; Reading groups; Prayer groups; Movies; Shopping trips; Dances/Social or cultural gatherings.
Description Facility is a one-story structure set in a rural wooded area.

Coventry Health Center*
10 Woodland Dr, Coventry, RI, 02816 (401) 826-0136
Admin Richard Lasko.
Licensure Skilled Care; Intermediate Care.
Beds SNF 50; ICF 250. *Certified* Medicaid; Medicare.

Laurel Foster Home Inc
51 Laurel Ave, Coventry, RI, 02893 (401) 821-0136
Admin Thomas Whipple. *Medical Dir/Dir of*

Nursing Dr Anthony Kazlauskas.
Licensure Intermediate Care. *Beds* 57. *Certified* Medicaid.
Admissions Requirements Females only; Medical examination; Physician's request.
Staff RNs 1 (pt); LPNs 1 (ft), 1 (pt); Orderlies 1 (ft); Nurses aides 8 (ft), 10 (pt); Activities coordinators 1 (ft); Dietitians 1 (pt).
Facilities Dining room; Activities room; Chapel; Crafts room; Barber/Beauty shop; Library.
Activities Arts and Crafts; Cards; Games; Reading groups; Prayer groups; Movies; Shopping trips; Dances/Social or cultural gatherings; Resident council; Gardening club; Bowling trips weekly.
Description Home provides services exclusively for women, with 57 beds, including a newly constructed wing which is both comfortable and attractive; specializes in providing a home-like feeling, excellent food service, all at reasonable rates.

Riverview Nursing Home Inc
546 Main St, Coventry, RI, 02816 (401) 821-6837
Admin Mark Wozniak. *Medical Dir/Dir of Nursing* Dr C Lanphear.
Licensure Intermediate Care. *Beds* 65. *Certified* Medicaid.
Admissions Requirements Females only
Staff Physicians 5 (pt); RNs 2 (ft), 1 (pt); LPNs 4 (ft), 3 (pt); Nurses aides 12 (ft), 14 (pt); Activities coordinators 1 (ft); Dietitians 1 (pt); Dentists 1 (pt); Ophthalmologists 1 (pt); Podiatrists 1 (pt).
Facilities Dining room; Activities room; Crafts room; Barber/Beauty shop.
Activities Arts and Crafts; Games; Prayer groups; Movies; Outings; Gardening; Sing-a-longs; Parties.
Description A private nursing home with porches, patio, and grounds, in a post-Civil War mansion; located in a small village in a mixed residential and commercial neighborhood. Facility has a warm, home-like, friendly environment and has an excellent activity/recreation program; visiting hours 11:30 am–8:00 pm daily.

Woodpecker Hill Foster Home
Plainfield Pike, Coventry, RI, 02827 (401) 397-7504
Admin Thomas Haynes. *Medical Dir/Dir of Nursing* Dr Robert Spencer.
Licensure Intermediate Care. *Beds* 31. *Certified* Medicaid.
Admissions Requirements Medical examination.
Staff RNs; LPNs; Orderlies; Nurses aides; Activities coordinators; Dietitians; Dentists; Ophthalmologists; Podiatrists; Audiologists.
Facilities Dining room; Activities room; Laundry room.
Activities Arts and Crafts; Cards; Games; Movies; Shopping trips; Dances/Social or cultural gatherings.

CRANSTON

Cedar Crest Nursing Centre Inc*
125 Scituate Ave, Cranston, RI, 02920 (401) 944-8500

Admin Mary DeConti.
Licensure Skilled Care; Intermediate Care. *Beds* 135. *Certified* Medicaid; Medicare.

Cra-Mar Nursing Home Inc*
575 7-Mile Rd, Cranston, RI, 02831 (401) 828-5010
Admin Thomas J Grzych.
Licensure Skilled Care; Intermediate Care. *Beds* 40. *Certified* Medicaid; Medicare.

Scandinavian Home for the Aged*
1811 Broad St, Cranston, RI, 02905 (401) 461-1433
Admin John C Woulfe.
Licensure Skilled Care; Intermediate Care. *Beds* 70. *Certified* Medicaid; Medicare.

CUMBERLAND

Diamond Hill Nursing Center Inc
3579 Diamond Hill Rd, Cumberland, RI, 02864 (401) 333-5050
Admin Jeanne Abbruzzese.
Licensure Intermediate Care. *Beds* 48. *Certified* Medicaid.
Staff Physicians 2 (ft); RNs 2 (ft), 3 (pt); LPNs 4 (ft), 4 (pt); Nurses aides 10 (ft), 12 (pt); Occupational therapists 1 (ft); Activities coordinators 1 (ft).
Facilities Dining room; Activities room; Crafts room; Barber/Beauty shop.
Activities Arts and Crafts; Cards; Games; Reading groups; Prayer groups; Movies; Shopping trips; Dances/Social or cultural gatherings.
Description The above programs are all offered but on a small scale and depend on the patients.

Grandview Nursing Home Inc*
Chambers and John Sts, Cumberland, RI, 02864 (401) 724-7500
Admin Frances McDermott.
Licensure Skilled Care; Intermediate Care. *Beds* 72. *Certified* Medicaid; Medicare.

Mount Saint Rita Health Centre*
Sumner Brown Rd, Cumberland, RI, 02864 (401) 333-6352
Admin Sr Jane Coleman.
Licensure Skilled Care; Intermediate Care. *Beds* 65.

EAST GREENWICH

Greenwich Bay Manor
945 Main St, East Greenwich, RI, 02818 (401) 885-3334
Admin R L Tetreault.
Licensure Intermediate Care. *Beds* 45. *Certified* Medicaid.

EAST PROVIDENCE

East Side Manor*
2424 Pawtucket Ave, East Providence, RI, 02914 (401) 438-6925
Admin George Von Housen.
Licensure Intermediate Care. *Beds* 12. *Certified* Medicaid.

Evergreen House Health Center*
1 Evergreen Dr, East Providence, RI, 02914 (401) 438-3250
Admin Richard A Lewis.
Licensure Skilled Care; Intermediate Care. *Beds* 156. *Certified* Medicaid; Medicare.

Harris Nursing Home Inc
833 Broadway, East Providence, RI, 02914 (401) 434-7404
Admin Charles Harris. *Medical Dir/Dir of Nursing* Peter J Sansone MD.
Licensure Intermediate Care. *Beds* 29. *Certified* Medicaid.
Admissions Requirements Medical examination, Physician's request.
Staff Physicians 1 (pt); RNs 2 (ft), 3 (pt); LPNs 2 (ft), 3 (pt); Orderlies 1 (ft), 1 (pt); Nurses aides 10 (ft), 5 (pt); Physical therapists 1 (pt); Occupational therapists 1 (pt); Speech therapists 1 (pt); Activities coordinators 1 (ft); Dietitians 1 (pt); Dentists 1 (pt); Ophthalmologists 1 (pt); Podiatrists 1 (pt); Audiologists 1 (pt).
Facilities Dining room; Activities room.
Activities Arts and Crafts; Cards; Games; Reading groups; Prayer groups; Movies; Shopping trips; Dances/Social or cultural gatherings; Day trips.
Description Facility offers quality care in a family atmosphere that has served the elderly communities of Rhode Island and nearby Massachusetts for over 25 years.

Hattie Ide Chaffee Home
200 Wampanoag Trail, East Providence, RI, 02914 (401) 434-1520
Admin Adeline Frederick. *Medical Dir/Dir of Nursing* Fred Vohr MD.
Licensure Skilled Care. *Beds* 58. *Certified* Medicaid; Medicare.
Admissions Requirements Minimum age 16; Medical examination.
Staff Physicians 7 (pt); RNs 12 (ft), 4 (pt); Nurses aides 27 (ft), 16 (pt); Recreational therapists 2 (ft); Speech therapists 1 (pt).
Facilities Dining room; Physical therapy room; Activities room; Chapel; Crafts room; Laundry room; Barber/Beauty shop.
Activities Arts and Crafts; Cards; Games; Prayer groups; Movies.
Description Home is near residential areas with good facilities. Home gives preference to cancer patients.

Health Havens Inc
100 Wampanoag Trail, East Providence, RI, 02915 (401) 438-4275
Admin Barbara M Lagerquist. *Medical Dir/Dir of Nursing* A Lloyd Lagerquist MD.
Licensure Skilled Care; Intermediate Care. *Beds* 58. *Certified* Medicaid; Medicare.
Admissions Requirements Minimum age 25.
Staff RNs 3 (ft), 4 (pt); LPNs 1 (ft), 4 (pt); Nurses aides 18 (ft), 12 (pt); Physical therapists 1 (pt); Speech therapists 1 (pt); Dietitians 1 (pt).
Facilities Dining room; Activities room.
Activities Arts and Crafts; Cards; Games; Movies.
Description Health Haven strives to provide the ultimate in nursing services.

Hillcrest Nursing Home Inc
198 Waterman Ave, East Providence, RI,
02914 (401) 434-5960
Admin Paul Marra.
Licensure Intermediate Care. *Beds* 76. *Certi-
fied* Medicaid.
Staff Physicians 4 (pt); RNs 3 (ft); LPNs 1 (ft);
Orderlies 1 (ft) #13E 18 (ft); Activities coordi-
nators 1 (ft); Dietitians 1 (pt); Podiatrists 1 (pt).
Facilities Dining room; Activities room; Laun-
dry room; Library.
Activities Arts and Crafts; Cards; Games;
Reading groups; Movies; Shopping trips; Dan-
ces/Social or cultural gatherings.

The Nicholas Marra Nursing Home*
135 Tripps Ln, East Providence, RI, 02915
(401) 438-2250
Admin Nicholas Marra.
Licensure Skilled Care; Intermediate Care.
Beds 180. *Certified* Medicaid; Medicare.

Riverside Nursing Home
336 Willett Ave, East Providence, RI, 02915
(401) 433-0844
Admin Barbara Monteleone. *Medical Dir/Dir
of Nursing* Dr Howard Perrone.
Licensure Intermediate Care. *Beds* 27. *Certified* Medicaid.
Staff Physicians 7 (pt); RNs 1 (ft), 4 (pt); LPNs
1 (ft), 3 (pt); Nurses aides 3 (ft), 12 (pt); Activities coordinators 1 (ft); Dietitians 1 (pt); Dentists 1 (pt); Ophthalmologists 1 (pt); Podiatrists
1 (pt); Audiologists 1 (pt).
Facilities Dining room; Activities room; Laundry room.
Activities Arts and Crafts; Cards; Games;
Reading groups; Prayer groups; Movies; Shopping trips.
Description Facility has a friendly home-type
atmosphere. The activities program is outstanding featuring plays involving the residents,
bazaars, outings to restaurants, and an excellent
Nursing Home Week program, which includes
a 1920s day and an international day.

United Methodist Health Care Center
30 Alexander Ave, East Providence, RI, 02914
(401) 438-7210
Admin Carl Helgerson. *Medical Dir/Dir of
Nursing* Dr John Demicco.
Licensure Intermediate Care. *Beds* 83. *Certified* Medicaid.
Admissions Requirements Medical examina-
tion; Physician's request.
Staff Physicians 1 (pt); RNs 4 (ft), 2 (pt); LPNs
2 (ft), 1 (pt); Orderlies 1 (ft); Nurses aides 14
(ft), 4 (pt); Reality therapists 1 (pt); Recreational
therapists 1 (ft), 1 (pt); Activities coordinators 1
(ft); Dietitians 1 (pt).
Affiliation Methodist
Facilities Dining room; Physical therapy room;
Activities room; Chapel; Crafts room; Laundry
room; Barber/Beauty shop; Library.
Activities Arts and Crafts; Cards; Games;
Reading groups; Prayer groups; Movies; Shopping trips; Dances/Social or cultural gatherings.
Description Close proximity (3 blocks to ½
mile) to emergency health service, fire department, 2 shopping malls, 4 banks, and many restaurants.

Waterview Villa
1275 S Broadway, East Providence, RI, 02914
(401) 438-7020
Admin Linda Monteleone. *Medical Dir/Dir of
Nursing* Rocco Marzilli.
Licensure Skilled Care; Intermediate Care.
Beds 132. *Certified* Medicaid; Medicare.
Admissions Requirements Medical examina-
tion.
Staff RNs 6 (ft), 4 (pt); LPNs 8 (ft), 3 (pt);
Orderlies 2 (ft), 2 (pt); Nurses aides 20 (ft), 50
(pt); Physical therapists 1 (pt); Speech therapists
1 (pt); Activities coordinators 1 (ft), 1 (pt).
Facilities Dining room; Physical therapy room;
Activities room; Chapel; Crafts room; Laundry
room; Barber/Beauty shop; Library.
Activities Arts and Crafts; Cards; Games;
Reading groups; Prayer groups; Movies; Shopping trips; Dances/Social or cultural gatherings.
Description Offers free weekly full bar with hot
hors d'oeuvres. Once a month transforms main
dining facilities to a restaurant-type atmosphere
with waitresses and hostess, an open cash bar,
and gourmet meals from baked stuffed lobsters
to boneless breast of chicken. Residents invite
their family members as guests to these
eventful evenings.

EXETER

Shady Acres Inc*
Gardiner Rd, Exeter, RI, 02892 (401) 295-8520
Admin Charles W Miga.
Licensure Intermediate Care. *Beds* 60. *Certi-
fied* Medicaid.

FOSTER

Nancy Ann Convalescent Home
E Killingly Rd, Box 180, Foster, RI, 02825
(401) 647-2170
Admin Esther O'Dette.
Licensure Intermediate Care. *Beds* 18. *Certi-
fied* Medicaid.
Admissions Requirements Minimum age 50;
Medical examination; Physician's request.
Staff RNs 1 (pt); LPNs 3 (ft); Orderlies 1 (pt);
Nurses aides 2 (ft), 4 (pt); Recreational therapists 1 (pt); Activities coordinators 1 (pt); Podiatrists 1 (pt).
Facilities Dining room; Laundry room;
Barber/Beauty shop; All purpose room.
Activities Arts and Crafts; Cards; Games; Prayer groups; Movies; Dances/Social or cultural
gatherings.
Description Home in wooded country setting
with 12 private and 3 double rooms offers family atmosphere; smoking only in special all purpose room; alcoholic beverages on special
occasions with doctor's permission; van for
transportation.

HARRISVILLE

Lakeview Health Center
Steere Farm Rd, Harrisville, RI, 02859 (401)
568-6242
Admin Michael Monteleone. *Medical Dir/Dir
of Nursing* Clayton Lanphear DO.
Licensure Skilled Care; Intermediate Care.
Beds 195. *Certified* Medicaid; Medicare.

Staff RNs 8 (ft), 10 (pt); LPNs 3 (ft), 16 (pt);
Nurses aides 31 (ft), 81 (pt); Activities coordi-
nators 1 (ft).
Facilities Dining room; Physical therapy room;
Activities room; Chapel; Crafts room; Barber-
/Beauty shop.
Activities Arts and Crafts; Cards; Games; Pray-
er groups; Movies; Cooking classes.
Description A modern facility located in a
country setting providing a full range of nursing
and rehabilitative services.

JOHNSTON

Briarcliffe Healthcare Facility
Old Pocasset Rd, PO Box 7236, Johnston, RI,
02919 (401) 944-2450
Admin Alphonse R Cardi.
Licensure Skilled Care; Intermediate Care.
Beds 120. *Certified* Medicaid; Medicare.
Admissions Requirements Medical examina-
tion; Physician's request.
Staff RNs 3 (ft), 5 (pt); LPNs 6 (ft), 4 (pt);
Nurses aides 28 (ft), 26 (pt); Activities coordi-
nators 1 (ft), 3 (pt).
Facilities Dining room; Physical therapy room;
Activities room; Chapel; Crafts room; Laundry
room; Barber/Beauty shop; Library.
Activities Arts and Crafts; Cards; Games;
Reading groups; Prayer groups; Movies; Dan-
ces/Social or cultural gatherings.

Cherry Hill Manor
2 Cherry Hill Rd, Johnston, RI, 02919 (401)
231-3102
Admin Elena Pisaturo. *Medical Dir/Dir of
Nursing* Michael Baccari MD.
Licensure Skilled Care; Intermediate Care.
Beds 168. *Certified* Medicaid; Medicare.
Staff Physicians; RNs; LPNs; Orderlies;
Nurses aides; Physical therapists; Recreational
therapists; Occupational therapists; Speech ther-
apists; Activities coordinators; Dietitians; Den-
tists; Ophthalmologists; Podiatrists;
Audiologists.
Facilities Dining room; Physical therapy room;
Activities room; Chapel; Crafts room; Laundry
room; Barber/Beauty shop; Library.
Activities Arts and Crafts; Cards; Games;
Reading groups; Prayer groups; Movies; Shop-
ping trips; Dances/Social or cultural gatherings;
Painting; Baking; Picnics.
Description Facility offers comprehensive specialized rehabilitative services, long-term or
short-term.

Marie Josephine Rest Home*
203 Greenville Ave, Johnston, RI, 02919 (401)
231-1950
Admin Kim A Dehn.
Licensure Intermediate Care. *Beds* 16. *Certified* Medicaid.

Morgan Health Center*
80 Morgan Ave, Johnston, RI, 02919 (401)
944-7800
Admin Eugene Abbruzzese.
Licensure Skilled Care; Intermediate Care.
Beds 120. *Certified* Medicaid; Medicare.

LINCOLN

Holiday Retirement Home Inc
30 Sayles Hill Rd, Lincoln, RI, 02838 (401)
765-1440
Admin Marcia Stevens. *Medical Dir/Dir of
Nursing* Dr William Reeves.
Licensure Skilled Care; Intermediate Care.
Beds 129. *Certified* Medicaid; Medicare.
Staff RNs 6 (ft), 7 (pt); LPNs 3 (ft), 3 (pt);
Nurses aides 37 (ft), 14 (pt); Activities coordi-
nators 1 (ft).
Facilities Dining room; Activities room; Laundry room; Barber/Beauty shop.
Activities Arts and Crafts; Cards; Games;
Reading groups; Prayer groups; Movies; Shopping trips; Dances/Social or cultural gatherings;
Trips other than shopping.
Description Holiday Retirement Home is a
proprietary home in rural residential neighborhood, with pathed grounds and patios. Constructed in 1973, single-level design features 4
sunny lounges, private dining room for family
gatherings, and other rooms which do allow a
personal touch. Live entertainment, religious
services, and recreation, varying from bowling
to blackjack, highlight activity choices. Staff
councils meet regularly for residents and families.

MIDDLETOWN

The John Clarke Retirement Center*
600 Valley Rd, Middletown, RI, 02840 (401)
846-0743
Admin Harry Randall.
Licensure Skilled Care; Intermediate Care.
Beds 50. *Certified* Medicaid; Medicare.

Forest Farm Health Care Centre Inc*
201 Forest Ave, Middletown, RI, 02840 (401)
847-2786
Admin Karl Lyon.
Licensure Skilled Care; Intermediate Care.
Beds 60. *Certified* Medicaid; Medicare.

Grand Islander Health Care Center*
333 Green End Ave, Middletown, RI, 02840
(401) 849-7100
Admin Jeffrey S Waddell.
Licensure Skilled Care; Intermediate Care.
Beds 148. *Certified* Medicaid; Medicare.

NEWPORT

Bayview Convalescent Home Inc*
PO Box 3750, Broadway Sta, Newport, RI,
02840 (401) 847-6300
Admin Brenda C Nagle.
Licensure Intermediate Care. *Beds* 51. *Certi-
fied* Medicaid.

Bellevue-Newport Health Center*
Bellevue Ave, Newport, RI, 02840 (401)
849-6600
Admin Madeline Ernest.
Licensure Skilled Care; Intermediate Care.
Beds 116. *Certified* Medicaid; Medicare.

Catherine Manor
44 Catherine St, Newport, RI, 02840 (401)
847-7455
Admin Edwina Sebest.
Licensure Intermediate Care. *Beds* 19.
Admissions Requirements Medical examina-
tion.
Staff RNs 1 (pt); LPNs 2 (ft), 1 (pt); Nurses
aides 3 (ft), 6 (pt); Activities coordinators 1 (ft);
Dietitians 1 (ft); Podiatrists 1 (pt).
Facilities Dining room; Activities room; Laundry room; Barber/Beauty shop; Library.
Activities Cards; Games; Prayer groups; Dance
exercise classes; Weekly rap group.
Description Facility is an 1863 Victorian home
located in a residential setting within walking
distance of beautiful downtown Newport. Level
II in care and caters to the individual who
desires a home-like atmosphere and the ability
to maintain independence in the community.
Home is small enough for the residents to be in
a family-like setting and to have their individual needs met.

Saint Clare's Home
309 Spring St, Newport, RI, 02840 (401)
849-3204
Admin Mary Ann Altrui.
Licensure Intermediate Care. *Beds* 44. *Certi-
fied* Medicaid.
Admissions Requirements Medical examina-
tion.
Staff RNs 2 (ft), 1 (pt); LPNs 1 (ft), 1 (pt);
Nurses aides 13 (ft), 1 (pt); Activities coordina-
tors 1 (ft); Dietitians 1 (ft).
Affiliation Roman Catholic
Facilities Dining room; Activities room;
Chapel; Crafts room; Laundry room; Barber-
/Beauty shop; Library.
Activities Arts and Crafts; Cards; Games;
Reading groups; Prayer groups; Movies; Shop-
ping trips; Dances/Social or cultural gatherings;
Gardening.
Description St Clare Home, adjacent chapel,
gardens and grounds provide a retirement
atmosphere in the heart of this resort area with
many organized activities. St Clare Home is
licensed to accept residents able to care for
themselves and as their health declines.

Village House*
70 Harrison Ave, Newport, RI, 02840 (401)
849-5222
Admin Sally J Ryan.
Licensure Skilled Care; Intermediate Care.
Beds 50. *Certified* Medicaid; Medicare.

NORTH KINGSTOWN

Lafayette Nursing Home Inc*
691 10-Rod Rd, North Kingstown, RI, 02852
(401) 295-8816
Admin Domenic Mandolfi.
Licensure Skilled Care; Intermediate Care.
Beds 52. *Certified* Medicaid; Medicare.

Roberts Health Centre Inc
990 10-Rod Rd, North Kingstown, RI, 02852
(401) 884-6661
Admin Richard A. Catallozzi. *Medical Dir/Dir
of Nursing* Dr Capalbo.
Licensure Intermediate Care. *Beds* 61. *Certi-

fied Medicaid.
Staff Physicians 1 (pt); RNs 2 (ft), 6 (pt); LPNs
3 (ft), 2 (pt); Nurses aides 15 (ft), 8 (pt);
Physical therapists 1 (pt); Reality therapists 1
(pt); Recreational therapists 1 (ft); Occupational
therapists 1 (pt); Speech therapists 1 (pt);
Activities coordinators 1 (ft); Dietitians 1 (pt);
Dentists 1 (pt); Ophthalmologists 1 (pt); Podiatrists 1 (pt); Audiologists 1 (pt).
Facilities Dining room; Physical therapy room;
Activities room; Chapel; Crafts room; Laundry
room; Barber/Beauty shop; Library.
Activities Arts and Crafts; Cards; Games;
Reading groups; Prayer groups; Movies; Shopping trips.
Description Facility offers a family-like atmosphere mixed with the highest quality medical
care. Roberts' residents enjoy a completely contained, peaceful estate-like living on a
beautifully landscaped 3½ acres; visitors welcome.

Scalabrini Villa*
860 N Quidnesset Rd, North Kingstown, RI,
02852 (401) 884-1802
Admin Oscar Kenneth Swanson.
Licensure Skilled Care; Intermediate Care.
Beds 70. *Certified* Medicaid; Medicare.

South County Nursing Centre
Rt 4 and Oak Hill Rd, North Kingstown, RI,
02852 (401) 294-4545
Admin Domenic Mandolfi. *Medical Dir/Dir of
Nursing* Charles Sawson MD.
Licensure Skilled Care; Intermediate Care.
Beds 120. *Certified* Medicaid; Medicare.
Staff RNs 7 (ft), 12 (pt); LPNs 3 (ft), 3 (pt);
Orderlies 1 (ft), 1 (pt); Nurses aides 80 (ft), 80
(pt); Activities coordinators 2 (ft); Dietitians 1
(ft).
Facilities Dining room; Physical therapy room;
Activities room; Chapel; Crafts room; Laundry
room; Barber/Beauty shop.
Activities Arts and Crafts; Cards; Games;
Reading groups; Prayer groups; Movies; Shop-
ping trips; Dances/Social or cultural gatherings.

NORTH PROVIDENCE

Golden Crest Nursing Center Inc*
100 Smithfield Rd, North Providence, RI,
02904 (410) 353-1710, 1711
Admin Susan Catalozzi.
Licensure Skilled Care; Intermediate Care.
Beds 145. *Certified* Medicaid; Medicare.

Hopkins Health Center
610 Smithfield Rd, North Providence, RI,
02904 (401) 353-6300
Admin Ronald Robidoux. *Medical Dir/Dir of
Nursing* Dr Robert Brochu.
Licensure Skilled Care; Intermediate Care.
Beds 200. *Certified* Medicaid; Medicare.
Admissions Requirements Medical examina-
tion.
Staff Physicians 1 (ft); RNs 8 (ft), 5 (pt); LPNs
6 (ft), 8 (pt); Nurses aides 55 (ft), 33 (pt);
Physical therapists 1 (ft); Reality therapists 1
(ft); Recreational therapists 2 (ft), 1 (pt); Occu-
pational therapists 1 (pt); Speech therapists 1
(pt); Dietitians 1 (ft); Social workers 2 (ft).
Facilities Dining room; Physical therapy room;

Activities room; Chapel; Crafts room; Barber-/Beauty shop; Library.
Activities Arts and Crafts; Cards; Games; Reading groups; Prayer groups; Movies; Shopping trips; Dances/Social or cultural gatherings.
Description Hopkins provides rehabilitation care and also accepts enteral food pump patients; resident council, outside functions, reality orientation, international coffee hour, cooking classes, current events, bookmobile, musical band, and a grandparent program. Hopkins, for those who want care, from those who do care.

NORTH SMITHFIELD

Hospice Saint Antoine
Mendon Rd, North Smithfield, RI, 02895 (401) 767-3500
Admin Sr Aldea Beauregard.
Licensure Intermediate Care. *Beds* 243. *Certified* Medicaid.
Admissions Requirements Minimum age 18; Medical examination.
Staff Physicians 8 (pt); RNs 3 (ft); LPNs 11 (ft), 4 (pt); Orderlies 5 (ft), 4 (pt); Nurses aides 68 (ft), 33 (pt); Activities coordinators 1 (ft); Dietitians 1 (pt); Podiatrists 1 (pt).
Affiliation Roman Catholic
Facilities Dining room; Activities room; Chapel; Crafts room; Laundry room; Barber/Beauty shop; Library.
Activities Arts and Crafts; Cards; Games; Reading groups; Prayer groups; Movies; Shopping trips; Dances/Social or cultural gatherings.
Description Facility is a nonprofit, Catholic-sponsored home with beautiful grounds and porches, located in country setting at top of a hill. Facilities for residents include: activities room, dining room, chapel, solarium on each floor, smoking in designated areas. Activities include: reality orientation, arts and crafts, knitting, crocheting, reading, bingo, line dancing, band and choral outings, and cookouts in season; Catholic mass daily; volunteers active in the home. Menu cycle repeated monthly.

Woodland Convalescent Center Inc*
70 Woodland St, North Smithfield, RI, 02895 (401) 765-0499
Admin Mary Ann Abbruzzi.
Licensure Intermediate Care. *Beds* 40. *Certified* Medicaid.

PASCOAG

Jolly Rest Home Inc
RFD 1, Box A33, S Main St, Pascoag, RI, 02859 (401) 568-3091
Admin T Lloyd Ryan. *Medical Dir/Dir of Nursing* Dr Louis Moran.
Licensure Intermediate Care. *Beds* 36. *Certified* Medicaid.
Staff Physicians 1 (ft), 5 (pt); RNs 1 (ft); LPNs 2 (pt); Nurses aides 1 (ft), 11 (pt); Physical therapists 1 (pt); Reality therapists 1 (pt); Recreational therapists 1 (pt); Occupational therapists 1 (pt); Speech therapists 1 (pt); Activities coordinators 1 (ft); Dietitians 1 (ft), 3 (pt); Dentists 1 (pt); Ophthalmologists 3 (pt); Podiatrists 1 (pt); Audiologists 1 (pt).

Facilities Dining room; Activities room; Crafts room; Laundry room; Library.
Activities Arts and Crafts; Cards; Games; Prayer groups; Movies; Shopping trips; Dances/Social or cultural gatherings.
Description Home has started a day care center for the elderly.

PAWTUCKET

Boulevard Rest Home
123 Armistice Blvd, Pawtucket, RI, 02860 (401) 724-8170
Admin Oma Hawkins. *Medical Dir/Dir of Nursing* Regenal Boucher MD.
Licensure Intermediate Care. *Beds* 14. *Certified* Medicaid.
Admissions Requirements Medical examination.
Staff Physicians 3 (ft); RNs 1 (ft); LPNs 2 (ft); Orderlies 1 (pt); Nurses aides 4 (ft); Recreational therapists 1 (pt); Occupational therapists 1 (pt); Activities coordinators 1 (pt).
Affiliation Roman Catholic

Elsie May's Rest Home Inc*
105 Beechwood Ave, Pawtucket, RI, 02860 (401) 722-2630
Admin Stella Mandolfi.
Licensure Intermediate Care. *Beds* 14. *Certified* Medicaid.

Jeanne Jugan Residence*
964 Main St, Pawtucket, RI, 02860 (401) 723-4314
Admin Regina Jones.
Licensure Skilled Care; Intermediate Care. *Beds* 120. *Certified* Medicaid; Medicare.

Mary V Gillis Home
240 Broadway, Pawtucket, RI, 02860 (401) 723-5565
Admin Mary V Jorge.
Licensure Skilled Care. *Beds* 11.

Maynard Rest Home
56 Maynard St, Pawtucket, RI, 02860 (401) 725-0517
Admin Linda Bertrand.
Licensure Intermediate Care. *Beds* 18. *Certified* Medicaid.
Staff Physicians 1 (ft); RNs 1 (pt); LPNs 2 (ft); Nurses aides 3 (ft), 4 (pt); Activities coordinators 1 (ft); Dentists 1 (pt); Podiatrists 1 (pt).
Facilities Dining room; Activities room; Crafts room; Laundry room.
Activities Arts and Crafts; Cards; Games; Reading groups; Prayer groups; Movies; Shopping trips; Dances/Social or cultural gatherings.

Neighborhood Convalescent Home Inc
362 Daggett Ave, Pawtucket, RI, 02861 (401) 724-2111
Admin Raymond Dumas. *Medical Dir/Dir of Nursing* Dr R Boucher MD.
Licensure Intermediate Care. *Beds* 17. *Certified* Medicaid.
Admissions Requirements Medical examination.
Staff RNs 1 (ft), 1 (pt); LPNs 2 (ft), 4 (pt); Nurses aides 3 (ft), 4 (pt); Activities coordinators 1 (ft).

Facilities Dining room; Activities room; Laundry room.
Activities Arts and Crafts; Cards; Games; Prayer groups; Movies; Shopping trips; Dances/Social or cultural gatherings.
Description A small facility with a home environment.

Oak Hill Nursing Home Inc*
544 Pleasant St, Pawtucket, RI, 02864 (401) 725-8888
Admin John Almeida.
Licensure Skilled Care; Intermediate Care. *Beds* 104. *Certified* Medicaid; Medicare.

Pawtucket Institute for Health Services
70 Gill Ave, Pawtucket, RI, 02861 (401) 722-7900
Admin George Dassenko. *Medical Dir/Dir of Nursing* B N Paul MD.
Licensure Skilled Care; Intermediate Care. *Beds* 160. *Certified* Medicaid; Medicare.
Admissions Requirements Minimum age 14; Medical examination.
Staff Physicians 1 (pt); RNs 8 (ft), 4 (pt); LPNs 9 (ft), 2 (pt); Orderlies 4 (ft), 3 (pt); Nurses aides 60 (ft), 18 (pt); Recreational therapists 1 (ft), 1 (pt); Speech therapists 1 (pt); Activities coordinators 1 (ft); Dietitians 1 (pt); Dentists 1 (pt); Podiatrists 1 (pt); Audiologists 1 (pt).
Affiliation Advent Christian Church
Facilities Dining room; Physical therapy room; Activities room; Chapel; Barber/Beauty shop.
Activities Arts and Crafts; Cards; Games; Prayer groups; Movies; Shopping trips; Dances/Social or cultural gatherings.
Description Facility's emphasis is on quality nursing care and service.

PROVIDENCE

Ann's Rest Home*
599 Broad St, Providence, RI, 02907 (401) 421-7576
Admin Diane Arzoumanian.
Licensure Intermediate Care. *Beds* 14. *Certified* Medicaid.

Bannister Nursing Care Center*
135 Dodge St, Providence, RI, 02907 (401) 274-3220
Admin Richard E Miller.
Licensure Skilled Care; Intermediate Care. *Beds* 164. *Certified* Medicaid; Medicare.

Bay Tower Nursing Center
101 Plain St, Providence, RI, 02903
Admin Genevieve A Francis. *Medical Dir/Dir of Nursing* John Demicco MD.
Licensure Skilled Care; Intermediate Care. *Beds* 160. *Certified* Medicaid; Medicare.
Ownership Proprietary.
Admissions Requirements Physician's request.
Staff Physicians 6 (pt); RNs 8 (ft), 3 (pt); LPNs 8 (ft), 3 (pt); Nurses aides 1 (pt); Physical therapists 1 (pt); Occupational therapists 1 (pt); Speech therapists 1 (pt); Activities coordinators 2 (ft), 1 (pt); Dietitians 1 (pt); Dentists 1 (pt); Ophthalmologists 1 (pt); Podiatrists 1 (pt).
Facilities Dining room; Physical therapy room; Activities room; Chapel; Laundry room; Barber/Beauty shop.

Description Staff has program for teaching residents to learn to feed themselves to become more self-sufficient; rehabilitation department provides therapy on a regular basis.

Bethany Home of Rhode Island*
111 S Angell St, Providence, RI, 02906 (401) 831-2870
Admin Margaret Shippee.
Licensure Intermediate Care. *Beds* 30. *Certified* Medicaid.

Charlesgate Nursing Center*
100 Randall St, Providence, RI, 02904 (401) 861-5858
Admin Robert S Gerskoff.
Licensure Skilled Care; Intermediate Care. *Beds* 200. *Certified* Medicaid; Medicare.

Elmwood Health Center Inc*
225 Elmwood Ave, Providence, RI, 02907 (401) 272-0600
Admin Norma Trenholm.
Licensure Skilled Care; Intermediate Care. *Beds* 76. *Certified* Medicaid; Medicare.

Hallworth House
66 Benefit St, Providence, RI, 02904 (401) 274-4505
Admin Donald C Baker. *Medical Dir/Dir of Nursing* Paul J Conley MD.
Licensure Skilled Care. *Beds* 51. *Certified* Medicaid; Medicare.
Admissions Requirements Medical examination; Physician's request.
Staff RNs 16 (ft); LPNs 1 (ft); Nurses aides 22 (ft); Physical therapists 1 (pt); Recreational therapists 1 (pt); Dietitians 1 (pt).
Facilities Dining room; Physical therapy room; Activities room; Chapel; Crafts room; Barber-/Beauty shop; Library.
Activities Arts and Crafts; Cards; Games; Reading groups; Prayer groups; Movies.

Jewish Home for the Aged
99 Hillside Ave, Providence, RI, 02906 (401) 351-4750
Admin William A Edelstein. *Medical Dir/Dir of Nursing* Henry Izeman MD.
Licensure Skilled Care; Intermediate Care. *Beds* 254. *Certified* Medicaid; Medicare.
Admissions Requirements Minimum age 62.
Staff Physicians 1 (pt); RNs 13 (ft), 8 (pt); LPNs 20 (ft), 10 (pt); Orderlies 11 (ft), 2 (pt); Nurses aides 84 (ft), 25 (pt); Physical therapists 1 (pt); Occupational therapists 1 (pt); Speech therapists 1 (pt); Activities coordinators 1 (ft); Dietitians 1 (ft); Dentists 1 (pt); Ophthalmologists 1 (pt); Podiatrists 1 (pt); Audiologists 1 (pt).
Affiliation Jewish
Facilities Chapel; Crafts room; Laundry room; Barber/Beauty shop; Library.
Activities Arts and Crafts; Cards; Games; Movies; Shopping trips; Dances/Social or cultural gatherings.
Description Facility is affiliated with Brown University and has medical students do a rotation at the home. A teaching nursing home and has a variety of graduate and undergraduate students in the allied health services do clerk-

ships at the home. Admitants must be Rhode Island residents or have children who are Rhode Island residents.

Lynn-Ann Convalescent Home
292 Elmwood Ave, Providence, RI, 02907 (401) 421-1020
Admin Linda Monteleone. *Medical Dir/Dir of Nursing* Alton Curran.
Licensure Intermediate Care. *Beds* 21. *Certified* Medicaid.
Admissions Requirements Medical examination.
Staff Physicians 1 (pt); RNs 1 (pt); LPNs 1 (ft), 1 (pt); Nurses aides 2 (ft), 3 (pt); Recreational therapists 1 (pt); Podiatrists 1 (pt); Cook & Dietary Aides 1 (ft), 2 (pt).
Facilities Dining room; Activities room; Crafts room; Laundry room.
Activities Arts and Crafts; Cards; Games; Reading groups; Prayer groups; Movies.

Parkview Nursing Home
31 Parade St, Providence, RI, 02909 (401) 351-2600
Admin Lloyd H Turoff. *Medical Dir/Dir of Nursing* Dr Kwang Ahn.
Licensure Skilled Care; Intermediate Care. *Beds* 67. *Certified* Medicaid; Medicare.
Staff Physicians 8 (pt); RNs 3 (ft), 5 (pt); LPNs 6 (ft), 4 (pt); Orderlies 4 (ft), 3 (pt); Nurses aides 30 (ft), 8 (pt); Physical therapists 1 (ft), 1 (pt); Reality therapists 1 (pt); Occupational therapists 1 (pt); Speech therapists 1 (pt); Activities coordinators 2 (ft); Dietitians 1 (pt); Dentists 1 (pt); Ophthalmologists 1 (pt); Podiatrists 2 (pt); Audiologists 1 (pt); Psychological nurses 1 (pt); Resperation therapist 1 (pt).
Facilities Dining room; Physical therapy room; Activities room; Laundry room; Barber/Beauty shop; Library.
Activities Arts and Crafts; Cards; Games; Reading groups; Prayer groups; Movies; Shopping trips; Dances/Social or cultural gatherings.

Saint Elizabeth Home
109 Melrose St, Providence, RI, 02907 (401) 941-0200
Admin George E Schwarz. *Medical Dir/Dir of Nursing* Daniel Moore MD.
Licensure Skilled Care; Intermediate Care. *Beds* 108. *Certified* Medicaid; Medicare.
Admissions Requirements Females only; Medical examination.
Staff Physicians 15 (pt); RNs 6 (ft), 8 (pt); LPNs 4 (ft); Nurses aides 46 (ft), 10 (pt); Physical therapists 2 (ft); Recreational therapists 1 (pt); Occupational therapists 1 (ft); Dietitians 1 (ft); Dentists 1 (ft); Ophthalmologists 1 (ft); Podiatrists 1 (ft); Nurse Practitioners 1 (pt).
Facilities Dining room; Physical therapy room; Activities room; Chapel; Crafts room; Barber-/Beauty shop; Library.
Activities Arts and Crafts; Cards; Games; Reading groups; Movies; Dances/Social or cultural gatherings.

Steere House*
807 Broad St, Providence, RI, 02907 (401) 461-3340
Admin Harmon P B Jordan Jr.
Licensure Intermediate Care. *Beds* 90. *Certified* Medicaid.

Summit Medical Center Inc*
1085 N Main St, Providence, RI, 02904 (401) 272-9600
Admin Thelma Kerzner.
Licensure Skilled Care; Intermediate Care. *Beds* 138. *Certified* Medicaid; Medicare.

Tockwotton Home
180 George M Cohan Memorial Blvd, Providence, RI, 02906 (401) 272-5280 and 751-1550
Admin Joseph T Runner. *Medical Dir/Dir of Nursing* John Gilman MD.
Licensure Intermediate Care. *Beds* 48. *Certified* Medicaid.
Ownership Nonprofit.
Admissions Requirements Minimum age 65; Females only; Medical examination.
Staff Physicians$2 (pt); RNs 5 (ft), 3 (pt); Nurses aides 8 (ft), 6 (pt); Physical therapists 1 (pt); Occupational therapists 1 (pt); Activities coordinators 1 (pt); Dietitians 1 (pt); Dentists 1 (pt); Podiatrists 2 (pt).
Facilities Dining room; Activities room; Crafts room; Laundry room; Barber/Beauty shop; Library.
Activities Arts and Crafts; Movies; Shopping trips; Dances/Social or cultural gatherings.
Description Home overlooks Providence harbor; provides lifetime care for residents.

Wayland Health Center*
140 Pitman St, Providence, RI, 02906 (401) 274-4200
Admin Frank Pezzelli.
Licensure Skilled Care; Intermediate Care. *Beds* 146. *Certified* Medicaid; Medicare.

SCITUATE

Oak Crest Manor Inc*
334 Chopmist Hill Rd, Scituate, RI, 02857 (401) 647-3890
Admin Muriel Beauregard.
Licensure Intermediate Care. *Beds* 50. *Certified* Medicaid.

SMITHFIELD

Elmbrook Home Inc
40 Farnum Pike, Smithfield, RI, 02917 (401) 231-4646
Admin Pasquale Pezzelli. *Medical Dir/Dir of Nursing* Dr C K Lee.
Licensure Intermediate Care. *Beds* 65. *Certified* Medicaid.
Staff RNs 1 (ft), 2 (pt); LPNs 3 (ft), 1 (pt); Nurses aides 11 (ft), 14 (pt); Physical therapists 1 (pt); Activities coordinators 1 (ft); Dietitians 1 (pt); Dentists 1 (pt); Ophthalmologists 1 (pt); Podiatrists 1 (pt).
Facilities Dining room; Activities room; Crafts room.
Activities Arts and Crafts; Cards; Games; Prayer groups; Shopping trips; Dances/Social or cultural gatherings.

Hebert's Nursing Home Inc*
Log Rd, Smithfield, RI, 02917 (401) 231-7016
Admin Paul J Hebert.
Licensure Skilled Care; Intermediate Care. *Beds* 86. *Certified* Medicaid; Medicare.

Heritage Hills Nursing Centre
RFD 3, Douglas Pike, Smithfield, RI, 02917
(401) 231-2700
Admin John W Sormanti. *Medical Dir/Dir of Nursing* Dr Ovid Vezza.
Licensure Skilled Care; Intermediate Care.
Beds 110. *Certified* Medicaid; Medicare.
Staff RNs 5 (ft), 6 (pt); LPNs 4 (ft), 3 (pt); Nurses aides 20 (ft), 24 (pt); Physical therapists 1 (ft); Activities coordinators 2 (pt); Dietitians 1 (ft); Podiatrists 1 (pt).
Facilities Dining room; Physical therapy room; Activities room; Chapel; Crafts room; Laundry room; Barber/Beauty shop; Library.
Activities Arts and Crafts; Games; Prayer groups; Movies; Dances/Social or cultural gatherings; Cooking.
Description Although patients are in need of medical and nursing care with other supportive services, they also need loving personal contacts as well as meaningful social roles. Health is not really an elusive concept, but it does require that we make commitments as human beings to human beings.

Waterman Heights Nursing Home Ltd
Putnam Pike, Smithfield, RI, 02828 (401) 949-1200
Admin Claire Thibeault. *Medical Dir/Dir of Nursing* Robert F Spencer MD.
Licensure Skilled Care; Intermediate Care.
Beds 105. *Certified* Medicaid; Medicare.
Admissions Requirements Minimum age 14; Medical examination.
Facilities Dining room; Physical therapy room; Activities room; Chapel; Barber/Beauty shop.
Activities Arts and Crafts; Cards; Games; Prayer groups; Movies; Dances/Social or cultural gatherings.
Description This is a one-story, brick, Colonial-type nursing home situated on a hill overlooking a lake.

SOUTH KINGSTOWN

Allen's Health Centre Inc*
S County Trail, South Kingstown, RI, 02892
(401) 884-0425
Admin Mary Crossen.
Licensure Skilled Care; Intermediate Care.
Beds 101. *Certified* Medicaid; Medicare.

Scallop Shell Nursing Home Inc*
Kingstown Rd, South Kingstown, RI, 02883
(401) 789-3006
Admin Neil Mahoney.
Licensure Skilled Care; Intermediate Care.
Beds 67. *Certified* Medicaid; Medicare.

WARREN

Grace Barker Nursing Home Inc*
54 Barker Ave, Warren, RI, 02885 (401) 245-9100
Admin Linda Machado.
Licensure Skilled Care; Intermediate Care.
Beds 84. *Certified* Medicaid; Medicare.

Crestwood Nursing and Convalescent Home Inc
568 Child St, Warren, RI, 02885 (401) 245-1574

Admin Donna A St Ours. *Medical Dir/Dir of Nursing* Dr Howard Perrone.
Licensure Skilled Care; Intermediate Care.
Beds 76. *Certified* Medicaid; Medicare.
Admissions Requirements Minimum age 18.
Staff RNs 10 (ft), 5 (pt); LPNs 5 (ft), 5 (pt); Orderlies 2 (ft), 1 (pt); Nurses aides 40 (ft), 20 (pt); Reality therapists 1 (pt); Recreational therapists 1 (ft), 2 (pt); Activities coordinators 1 (ft), 1 (pt).
Facilities Dining room; Activities room; Crafts room.
Activities Arts and Crafts; Cards; Games; Reading groups; Prayer groups; Movies; Shopping trips; Dances/Social or cultural gatherings.
Description Ongoing physical therapy rehabilitation, feeding, and exercise programs; all fully staffed and coordinated by professional consultants.

Desilets Nursing Home Inc*
642 Metacom Ave, Warren, RI, 02885 (401) 245-2860
Admin Richard Desilets.
Licensure Skilled Care; Intermediate Care.
Beds 80. *Certified* Medicaid; Medicare.

WARWICK

Avalon Nursing Home Inc
57 Stokes, Warwick, RI, 02889 (401) 738-1200
Admin Francis Kowalik. *Medical Dir/Dir of Nursing* Stanley Cate MD.
Licensure Skilled Care; Intermediate Care.
Beds 30. *Certified* Medicaid; Medicare.
Staff RNs; LPNs; Nurses aides; Activities coordinators.
Facilities Dining room; Activities room.
Activities Arts and Crafts; Cards; Games; Prayer groups; Movies.

Brentwood Nursing Home Inc*
3986 Post Rd, Warwick, RI, 02886 (401) 884-8020
Admin Richard Miga.
Licensure Skilled Care; Intermediate Care.
Beds 96. *Certified* Medicaid; Medicare.

Burdick Convalescent Home Inc
57 Fair St, Warwick, RI, 02888 (401) 781-6628
Admin Elizabeth Moone. *Medical Dir/Dir of Nursing* Jorge Scott MD.
Licensure Intermediate Care. *Beds* 13. *Certified* Medicaid.
Staff LPNs 2 (ft), 1 (pt); Nurses aides 4 (ft), 4 (pt).
Facilities Dining room; Activities room.
Activities Cards; Games; Prayer groups; Shopping trips.
Description This small rest home accepts ambulatory residents only; semi-private rooms are very home-like; meals are served in dinning room only.

Buttonwoods Crest Home
139 Hemlock Ave, Warwick, RI, 02886 (401) 737-7325
Admin Roger Handy. *Medical Dir/Dir of Nursing* Stanley Cate MD.
Licensure Intermediate Care. *Beds* 31. *Certified* Medicaid.
Staff RNs 1 (ft), 7 (pt); LPNs 2 (pt); Nurses

aides 2 (ft), 10 (pt); Recreational therapists 2 (pt); Activities coordinators 1 (pt); Dietitians 1 (pt); Podiatrists 1 (pt).
Facilities Dining room; Activities room; Crafts room; Laundry room.
Activities Arts and Crafts; Cards; Games; Prayer groups; Shopping trips; Dances/Social or cultural gatherings.
Description Facility located right on Narragansett Bay where scenery, activities, and sea breezes are unlimited.

Greenwood House Nursing Home Inc
1139 Main Ave, Warwick, RI, 02886 (401) 739-6600 and 737-9609
Admin Paul T Buonaiuto.
Licensure Skilled Care; Intermediate Care.
Beds 88. *Certified* Medicaid; Medicare.

Greenwood Oaks Rest Home*
14 Lake St, Warwick, RI, 02886 (401) 739-3297
Admin Dorothy Von Housen.
Licensure Intermediate Care. *Beds* 16. *Certified* Medicaid.

Kent Nursing Home Inc
660 Commonwealth Ave, Warwick, RI, 02886 (401) 739-4241
Admin Joan Williams. *Medical Dir/Dir of Nursing* Dr Hossein Shushtari.
Licensure Skilled Care; Intermediate Care.
Beds 153. *Certified* Medicaid; Medicare.
Facilities Dining room; Physical therapy room; Activities room; Crafts room; Laundry room; Barber/Beauty shop.
Activities Arts and Crafts; Cards; Games; Reading groups; Prayer groups; Movies; Shopping trips; Pets.

Pawtuxet Village Nursing Home Inc*
270 Post Rd, Warwick, RI, 02888 (401) 467-3555
Admin Richard Parkinson.
Licensure Skilled Care; Intermediate Care.
Beds 131. *Certified* Medicaid; Medicare.

Royal Manor Inc
159 Division St, Warwick, RI, 02818 (401) 884-5590
Admin Jeannette E Del Padre.
Licensure Intermediate Care. *Beds* 55.
Admissions Requirements Medical examination; Physician's request.
Staff RNs 5 (ft); Nurses aides 24 (ft); Activities coordinators 1 (ft); Dietitians 1 (pt).
Facilities Dining room; Barber/Beauty shop.
Activities Arts and Crafts; Cards; Prayer groups; Movies; Shopping trips; Dances/Social or cultural gatherings.
Description Facility has lovely home-like atmosphere in a country manor setting.

Sunny View Nursing Home*
83 Corona St, Warwick, RI, 02886 (401) 737-9193
Admin Patricia Miga.
Licensure Skilled Care; Intermediate Care.
Beds 37. *Certified* Medicaid; Medicare.

Warwick Health Centre
109 W Shore Rd, Warwick, RI, 02889 (401) 739-9440
Admin Harry Nahigian.

Licensure Skilled Care; Intermediate Care.
Beds 101. *Certified* Medicaid; Medicare.
Admissions Requirements Medical examination.
Staff RNs 12 (ft), 5 (pt); LPNs 10 (ft), 4 (pt); Nurses aides 48 (ft), 18 (pt); Physical therapists 1 (pt); Speech therapists 1 (pt); Activities coordinators 2 (ft); Dietitians 1 (pt); Dentists 1 (pt); Ophthalmologists 1 (pt); Podiatrists 1 (pt); Audiologists 1 (pt).
Facilities Dining room; Physical therapy room; Activities room; Chapel; Crafts room; Barber-/Beauty shop.
Activities Arts and Crafts; Cards; Games; Prayer groups; Movies; Dances/Social or cultural gatherings.
Description Facility features a lively atmosphere, porches, excellent arts and crafts program, smoking in recreation and public areas only. Residents may have own TV in room. Trips, sing-a-long, bingo, movies, ceramics, and religious services are part of activity program. Our menu is repeated on a 3-week cycle and is changed twice yearly.

Warwick Manor
643 Sandy Ln, Warwick, RI, 02886 (401) 739-0628
Admin Stephen Von Housen.
Licensure Intermediate Care. *Beds* 13. *Certified* Medicaid.

Warwick Rest Home Inc*
348 Warwick Neck Ave, Warwick, RI, 02889 (401) 737-4909
Admin Pasquale P Squillante Jr.
Licensure Intermediate Care. *Beds* 16. *Certified* Medicaid.

West Bay Manor*
2783 W Shore Rd, Warwick, RI, 02886 (401) 739-7300
Admin David R Velander.
Licensure Intermediate Care. *Beds* 45. *Certified* Medicaid.

WEST WARWICK

West View Nursing Home Inc
239 Legris Ave, West Warwick, RI, 02983 (401) 828-9000
Admin Robert Horton. *Medical Dir/Dir of Nursing* Frank Fallon DO.
Licensure Skilled Care; Intermediate Care.
Beds 120. *Certified* Medicaid; Medicare.
Staff Physicians 23 (pt); RNs 6 (ft), 4 (pt); LPNs 6 (ft), 3 (pt); Orderlies 1 (ft); Nurses aides 40 (ft), 25 (pt); Physical therapists 1 (pt); Recreational therapists 2 (ft); Speech therapists 1 (pt); Activities coordinators 1 (ft); Dietitians 1 (pt); Dentists 1 (pt); Ophthalmologists 1 (pt); Podiatrists 2 (pt); Audiologists 1 (pt).
Facilities Dining room; Physical therapy room; Activities room; Chapel; Laundry room; Barber/Beauty shop.
Activities Arts and Crafts; Cards; Games; Reading groups; Prayer groups; Movies; Shopping trips; Dances/Social or cultural gatherings.
Description One of the most important things done for residents is work to create a warm, friendly atmosphere; with caring attitudes, in an atmosphere designed to make residents feel

at home. Staff is dedicated to serve and preserve life through spiritual support, understanding, and empathy.

WESTERLY

Watch Hill Manor Ltd
RR 1, Watch Hill Rd, Box 78, Westerly, RI, 02891 (401) 596-2664
Admin Philip Hovey. *Medical Dir/Dir of Nursing* Bruce M Gillie MD.
Licensure Skilled Care; Intermediate Care.
Beds 59. *Certified* Medicaid; Medicare.
Admissions Requirements Medical examination; Physician's request.
Staff Recreational therapists.
Facilities Dining room; Activities room; Barber/Beauty shop.
Activities Arts and Crafts; Games; Prayer groups; Shopping trips.
Description Facility overlooks a scenic salt water cove in the Watch Hill section of Westerly. It has heat and smoke detectors and sprinklers througout. Dietary needs are met in a spacious dining room using selective menus. Religious services and individualized activities are part of the recreation program.

Westerly Nursing Home Inc*
81 Beach St, Westerly, RI, 02891 (401) 596-4925
Admin Bernadette O Martin.
Licensure Skilled Care; Intermediate Care.
Beds 60. *Certified* Medicaid; Medicare.

WOONSOCKET

Ballou Home for the Aged
Mendon Rd, Woonsocket, RI, 02895 (401) 769-0437
Admin Marion Church.
Licensure Intermediate Care. *Beds* 27. *Certified* Medicaid.
Ownership Nonprofit.
Admissions Requirements Minimum age 65; Medical examination; Physician's request.
Staff RNs 1 (ft); LPNs 2 (ft), 5 (pt); Nurses aides 5 (ft), 8 (pt).
Facilities Dining room; Activities room; Laundry room; Barber/Beauty shop; Library.
Activities Arts and Crafts; Cards; Games; Movies; Shopping trips; Dances/Social or cultural gatherings.
Description Facility offers private rooms for ambulatory ICF II residents who may bring own furniture, telephones, air conditioners, TVs, automobiles if licensed by state. Transportation is provided for appointments.

Evergreens Nursing Home Inc*
116 Greene St, Woonsocket, RI, 02895 (401) 769-8042
Admin Jeannette Kelly.
Licensure Intermediate Care. *Beds* 35. *Certified* Medicaid.

The Friendly Home Inc*
303 Rhodes Ave, Woonsocket, RI, 02895 (401) 769-7220

Admin William A Ryan.
Licensure Skilled Care; Intermediate Care.
Beds 120. *Certified* Medicaid; Medicare.

Woonsocket Health Centre*
262 Poplar St, Woonsocket, RI, 02895 (401) 765-2100
Admin Norma Pezzelli.
Licensure Skilled Care; Intermediate Care.
Beds 275. *Certified* Medicaid; Medicare.

SOUTH CAROLINA

ABBEVILLE

Abbeville Nursing Home Inc*
PO Box 190, Abbeville, SC, 29620 (803)
459-5122
Admin Ethel L Hughes.
Licensure Skilled Care; Intermediate Care.
Beds 50. *Certified* Medicaid; Medicare.

AIKEN

Aiken Nursing Home*
123 DuPont Dr, Aiken, SC, 29801 (803)
648-0434
Admin June R Barrett.
Licensure Skilled Care; Intermediate Care.
Beds 86. *Certified* Medicaid; Medicare.

Hall Health Care Center*
830 Laurens St N, Aiken, SC, 29801
Admin Vicki L Lollis.
Licensure Skilled Care; Intermediate Care.
Beds 44. *Certified* Medicaid; Medicare.

Laurens Street Community Residence
767 Laurens St, Aiken, SC, 29801
Medical Dir/Dir of Nursing Joan Viernes.
Licensure Intermediate Care for Mentally
Retarded.
Admissions Requirements Males only
Staff Physicians 1 (pt); RNs 1 (pt); LPNs 3 (ft);
Nurses aides 3 (ft).
Facilities Dining room; Activities room; Laun-
dry room.
Activities Arts and Crafts; Cards; Games;
Reading groups; Prayer groups; Movies; Shop-
ping trips; Dances/Social or cultural gatherings.
Description Nice country setting.

Richland Street Community Residence
1111 Richland St, Aiken, SC, 29801
Admin John Viernes Jr.
Licensure Intermediate Care for Mentally
Retarded. *Beds* 8. *Certified* Medicare.
Admissions Requirements Minimum age 18;
Females only
Staff Physicians 1 (pt); RNs 1 (pt); LPNs 4 (ft);
Nurses aides 2 (pt); Recreational therapists 1
(pt); Speech therapists 1 (pt); Dietitians 1 (pt);
Dentists 1 (pt).
Facilities Activities room; Laundry room.
Activities Arts and Crafts; Games; Movies;
Dances/Social or cultural gatherings.

Description Facility offers services specifically
to adult females who are developmentally disabled.

ANDERSON

Anderson Health Care Center*
PO Box 989, Anderson, SC, 29622 (803)
226-8356
Admin Betty J Finley.
Licensure Skilled Care; Intermediate Care.
Beds 146. *Certified* Medicaid; Medicare.

Ellenburg Nursing Center Inc*
611 E Hampton, Anderson, SC, 29624 (803)
226-5054
Admin M L Ellenburg.
Licensure Skilled Care; Intermediate Care.
Beds 88. *Certified* Medicaid; Medicare.

Latham Nursing Home
208 James St, Anderson, SC, 29621 (803)
226-3427
Admin Lillian L Latham. *Medical Dir/Dir of
Nursing* Warren W White MD.
Licensure Skilled Care; Intermediate Care.
Beds 44. *Certified* Medicaid; Medicare.
Admissions Requirements Minimum age 14;
Medical examination; Physician's request.
Staff Physicians 21 (pt); RNs 3 (ft), 2 (pt);
LPNs 2 (ft), 1 (pt); Orderlies 1 (ft); Nurses aides
10 (ft), 4 (pt); Occupational therapists 1 (pt);
Speech therapists 1 (pt); Activities coordinators
1 (ft); Dietitians 1 (pt); Dentists 1 (pt); Podiatr-
ists 1 (pt); Social workers 1 (pt).
Facilities Dining room; Physical therapy room;
Activities room; Chapel; Crafts room; Laundry
room; Barber/Beauty shop.
Activities Arts and Crafts; Cards; Games;
Reading groups; Prayer groups; Movies; Dan-
ces/Social or cultural gatherings.
Description Facility is located in a residential
area with several large trees—a home away
from home where residents are very dear to
staff; major project is rock and roll jamboree
which raised $2000 for Heart Association;
annual picnic for residents and families a great
success.

AUGUSTA

Anne Maria Medical Care Nursing Home Inc
Talisman Drive, Augusta, SC, 29841 (803)
278-2170
Admin Marianne Luckey. *Medical Dir/Dir of
Nursing* J W Thurmond III MD.
Licensure Skilled Care; Intermediate Care.
Beds 120. *Certified* Medicaid; Medicare.
Admissions Requirements Medical examina-
tion.
Staff Physicians 1 (ft); RNs 2 (ft), 3 (pt); LPNs
10 (ft), 6 (pt); Nurses aides 43 (ft), 6 (pt);
Physical therapists 1 (pt); Activities coordina-
tors 1 (ft), 2 (pt); Dietitians 1 (pt); Podiatrists 1
(pt).
Facilities Dining room; Physical therapy room;
Activities room; Chapel; Crafts room; Laundry
room; Barber/Beauty shop; Library.
Activities Arts and Crafts; Cards; Games;
Reading groups; Prayer groups; Dances/Social
or cultural gatherings; Garden club.

BAMBERG

Bamberg County Memorial Nursing Center
North and McGee Sts, Bamberg, SC, 29003
(803) 245-4321
Admin Charles V Morgan. *Medical Dir/Dir of
Nursing* Dr M C Watson.
Licensure Skilled Care; Intermediate Care.
Beds 22. *Certified* Medicaid; Medicare.
Admissions Requirements Medical examina-
tion; Physician's request.
Facilities Dining room; Activities room; Laun-
dry room.
Activities Arts and Crafts; Games; Reading
groups; Prayer groups.

BARNWELL

Barnwell County Nursing Home*
PO Box 588, Barnwell, SC, 29812 (803)
259-5547
Admin Paula Eames.
Licensure Skilled Care; Intermediate Care.
Beds 40. *Certified* Medicaid; Medicare.

BEAUFORT

Bay View Nursing Center Inc*
PO Box 1103, S Todd Dr, Beaufort, SC, 29902
(803) 524-8911
Admin Danny Charpentier.
Licensure Skilled Care; Intermediate Care.
Beds 132. *Certified* Medicaid; Medicare.

BENNETTSVILLE

Dundee Nursing Home
401 Bypass, Bennettsville, SC, 29512 (803)
479-6251
Admin Harold D Branton. *Medical Dir/Dir of Nursing* John May MD.
Licensure Skilled Care; Intermediate Care.
Beds SNF 87; ICF 24. *Certified* Medicaid;
Medicare.
Staff RNs 3 (ft), 5 (pt); LPNs 10 (ft), 6 (pt);
Nurses aides 33 (ft), 13 (pt); Physical therapists;
Recreational therapists 1 (ft), 1 (pt); Speech
therapists; Activities coordinators 1 (ft); Dieti-
tians; Dentists.
Facilities Dining room; Physical therapy room;
Activities room; Chapel; Laundry room; Bar-
ber/Beauty shop.
Activities Arts and Crafts; Games; Reading
groups; Prayer groups; Movies; Shopping trips.

BLACKVILLE

**Healing Springs Intermediate Care Facility
Inc***
Rt 1, Box 518, Blackville, SC, 29817 (803)
284-2341
Admin Sara Jane Odom.
Licensure Intermediate Care. *Beds* 26. *Certi-
fied* Medicaid; Medicare.

Wildwood Health Care Center*
PO Box 215, Jones Bridge Rd, Blackville, SC,
29817 (803) 284-2213
Admin Pace B Hungerford.
Licensure Intermediate Care. *Beds* 85. *Certi-
fied* Medicaid; Medicare.

CAMDEN

A Sam Karesh LTC Center
1315 Roberts St, Camden, SC, 29020 (803)
432-4311
Admin L H Young. *Medical Dir/Dir of
Nursing* John Dubose MD.
Licensure Skilled Care; Intermediate Care.
Beds 88. *Certified* Medicare.
Admissions Requirements Medical examina-
tion; Physician's request.
Staff Physicians 1 (pt); RNs 4 (ft), 1 (pt); LPNs
12 (ft), 1 (pt); Orderlies 2 (ft); Nurses aides 25
(ft), 4 (pt); Activities coordinators 1 (ft), 1 (pt).
Facilities Dining room; Physical therapy room;
Activities room; Barber/Beauty shop.
Activities Arts and Crafts; Cards; Games; Pray-
er groups; Shopping trips; Dances/Social or cul-
tural gatherings.

CHARLESTON

Driftwood Health Care Center
341 Calhoun St, Charleston, SC, 29407 (803)
723-9276

Admin Calvin D Lipscomb. *Medical Dir/Dir
of Nursing* Dr Alexander Marshall.
Licensure Skilled Care; Intermediate Care.
Beds 77. *Certified* Medicaid; Medicare.
Admissions Requirements Physician's request.
Staff Physicians 1 (pt); RNs 4 (ft), 1 (pt); LPNs
11 (ft), 4 (pt); Orderlies 1 (ft), 1 (pt); Nurses
aides 27 (ft), 14 (pt); Physical therapists 1 (pt);
Reality therapists 2 (ft); Recreational therapists
2 (ft); Speech therapists 1 (pt); Activities coordi-
nators 2 (ft); Dietitians 1 (ft); Podiatrists 1 (pt).
Facilities Dining room; Activities room; Laun-
dry room; Barber/Beauty shop.
Activities Arts and Crafts; Cards; Games;
Reading groups; Prayer groups; Movies; Shopping trips.

**Driftwood Health Care Center—Long Term
Care Facility**
341 Calhoun St, Charleston, SC, 29407 (803)
723-9276
Admin Calvin D Lipscomb. *Medical Dir/Dir
of Nursing* Dr Alexander Marshall.
Licensure Nursing Care. *Beds* 102. *Cer-
tified* Medicaid; Medicare.
Staff Physicians; RNs; LPNs; Orderlies;
Nurses aides; Physical therapists; Reality thera-
pists; Recreational therapists; Speech therapists;
Activities coordinators; Dietitians; Dentists.
Facilities Dining room; Activities room; Laun-
dry room; Barber/Beauty shop.
Activities Arts and Crafts; Cards; Games;
Reading groups; Prayer groups; Movies; Shop-
ping trips; Dances/Social or cultural gatherings.

Firestone Rd Community Residence—Unit 1*
3641 Firestone Rd N, Charleston, SC, 29405
Admin Wilson V Inabinet Jr.
Licensure Intermediate Care for Mentally
Retarded. *Beds* 14. *Certified* Medicare.

Firestone Rd Community Residence—Unit 2*
3641 Firestone Rd N, Charleston, SC, 29405
Admin Wilson V Inabinet Jr.
Licensure Intermediate Care for Mentally
Retarded. *Beds* 14. *Certified* Medicare.

Manor Care of Charlston Inc*
1137 Sam Rittenburg Blvd, Charleston, SC,
29407
Admin Edwin Keys.
Licensure Skilled Care. *Beds* 132. *Certified* Medicaid.

North Charleston Convalescent Center*
9319 Medical Plaza Dr, Charleston, SC, 29405
(803) 797-8282
Admin Steve Prater.
Licensure Skilled Care; Intermediate Care.
Beds 132. *Certified* Medicaid; Medicare.

Rutledge Avenue Community Residence*
887 Rutledge Ave, Charleston, SC, 29403
Admin Wilson V Inabinet Jr.
Licensure Intermediate Care for Mentally
Retarded. *Beds* 8. *Certified* Medicare.

CHERAW

Cheraw Nursing Home Inc
Hwy 9 W, PO Box 1321, Cheraw, SC, 29520
(803) 537-3621

Admin Ruth S Laney. *Medical Dir/Dir of
Nursing* Winston Y Godwin Sr MD.
Licensure Skilled Care; Intermediate Care.
Beds 100. *Certified* Medicaid; Medicare.
Staff Physicians 1 (ft), 5 (pt); RNs 3 (ft); LPNs
7 (ft), 4 (pt); Orderlies 4 (ft); Nurses aides 33
(ft); Physical therapists 2 (pt); Reality therapists
1 (ft); Activities coordinators 1 (ft), 1 (pt); Die-
titians 1 (ft); Dentists 1 (pt).
Facilities Dining room; Physical therapy room;
Activities room; Laundry room; Barber/Beauty
shop.
Activities Arts and Crafts; Games; Prayer
groups; Dances/Social or cultural gatherings.

CHESTER

Chester County Nursing Center
Great Falls Rd, Chester, SC, 29706 (803)
377-3151
Admin Ron V Hunter. *Medical Dir/Dir of
Nursing* J N Gaston Jr MD.
Licensure Skilled Care; Intermediate Care.
Beds 62. *Certified* Medicaid; Medicare.
Admissions Requirements Medical examina-
tion; Physician's request.
Staff Physicians 19 (ft); RNs 2 (ft); LPNs 10
(ft), 1 (pt); Orderlies 1 (ft), 2 (pt); Nurses aides
21 (ft), 8 (pt); Physical therapists 1 (ft); Occupa-
tional therapists 1 (ft); Speech therapists 1 (pt);
Activities coordinators 1 (ft); Dietitians 1 (ft);
Dentists 5 (ft).
Facilities Dining room; Physical therapy room;
Activities room; Chapel; Crafts room; Laundry
room; Barber/Beauty shop; Library.
Activities Arts and Crafts; Cards; Games; Prayer groups; Movies; Dances/Social or cultural
gatherings.
Description Facility is hospital based.

CLEMSON

Clemson Area Retirement Health Care Center
Clemson Downs, Clemson, SC, 29631 (803)
654-1155
Admin Virginia Phillips. *Medical Dir/Dir of
Nursing* Robert Burley MD.
Licensure Skilled Care. *Beds* 44. *Cer-
tified* Medicare.
Admissions Requirements Medical examina-
tion; Physician's request.
Staff Physicians 11 (pt); RNs 5 (ft), 5 (pt);
LPNs 3 (ft), 2 (pt); Orderlies 2 (ft); Nurses aides
8 (ft), 8 (pt); Physical therapists 1 (ft), 1 (pt);
Reality therapists 1 (pt); Recreational therapists
1 (pt); Activities coordinators 1 (pt); Dietitians
1 (pt); Dentists 1 (pt); Podiatrists 1 (pt).
Facilities Dining room; Physical therapy room;
Activities room; Laundry room; Barber/Beauty
shop; Library; Patio.
Activities Arts and Crafts; Games; Prayer
groups.
Description Facility features adult day care, respite care, and night care which are all provided
to meet the specialized needs of one who wishes
to maintain their own household with temporary skilled or intermediate relief from self-care
at home.

CLINTON

Bailey Nursing Home
Jacobs Hwy, Clinton, SC, 29325 (803)
833-2550
Admin Clem P Ham.
Licensure Skilled Care; Intermediate Care.
Beds 43. *Certified* Medicaid; Medicare.
Admissions Requirements Medical examination; Physician's request.
Staff Physicians 10 (pt); RNs 2 (ft), 1 (pt);
LPNs 7 (ft); Orderlies 3 (ft); Nurses aides 22
(ft), 5 (pt); Physical therapists 1 (pt); Reality
therapists 1 (pt); Recreational therapists 1 (ft);
Activities coordinators 1 (ft); Dietitians 1 (ft);
Dentists 1 (pt).
Facilities Dining room; Activities room; Laundry room; Barber/Beauty shop.
Activities Games; Reading groups; Prayer
groups; Shopping trips.

Whitten Center*
PO Drawer 239, Clinton, SC, 29325
Admin Armicia M Lilley.
Licensure Skilled Care; Intermediate Care.
Beds 50.

COLUMBIA

Amelia Community Residence*
8301 Farrow Rd, Columbia, SC, 29203 (803)
534-1615
Admin John Viernes Jr.
Licensure Intermediate Care for Mentally
Retarded. *Beds* 8. *Certified* Medicare.

Boulevard Community Residence*
8301 Farrow Rd, Columbia, SC, 29203 (803)
534-0682
Admin John Viernes Jr.
Licensure Intermediate Care for Mentally
Retarded. *Beds* 8. *Certified* Medicare.

Brian Center of Nursing Care—Columbia
3514 Sidney Rd, Columbia, SC, 29210 (803)
798-9715
Admin Sarah Kirchman. *Medical Dir/Dir of
Nursing* Dr Shawn Chillag.
Licensure Skilled Care; Intermediate Care.
Beds 60. *Certified* Medicaid; Medicare.
Staff Physicians 1 (pt); RNs 4 (ft), 4 (pt); LPNs
7 (ft), 3 (pt); Orderlies 5 (ft), 2 (pt); Nurses aides
34 (ft), 5 (pt); Physical therapists 1 (pt); Speech
therapists; Activities coordinators 1 (ft), 1 (pt);
Dentists; Ophthalmologists; Podiatrists;
Audiologists.
Facilities Dining room; Physical therapy room;
Activities room; Chapel; Crafts room; Laundry
room; Barber/Beauty shop.
Activities Arts and Crafts; Cards; Games;
Reading groups; Prayer groups; Dances/Social
or cultural gatherings.
Description Modern facility in residential setting, tastefully decorated; very caring staff
members.

C M Tucker Jr Human Resources Center
2200 Harden St, Columbia, SC, 29203 (803)
758-8155
Medical Dir/Dir of Nursing Charles N Still
MD.
Licensure Skilled Care; Intermediate Care.

Beds SNF 100; ICF 458; Dual Certified 50.
Certified Medicaid; Medicare.
Admissions Requirements Minimum age 18;
Medical examination; Physician's request.
Staff Physicians 6 (ft), 6 (pt); RNs 24 (ft), 4
(pt); LPNs 37 (ft), 2 (pt); Nurses aides 213 (ft);
Physical therapists 1 (ft); Recreational therapists
8 (ft); Occupational therapists 1 (pt); Speech
therapists 1 (ft); Activities coordinators 1 (ft);
Dietitians 2 (ft); Dentists 1 (pt); Audiologists 1
(ft); Pharmacists 4 (ft).
Facilities Dining room; Physical therapy room;
Activities room; Crafts room; Laundry room;
Barber/Beauty shop; Library.
Activities Arts and Crafts; Cards; Games;
Reading groups; Movies; Shopping trips; Dances/Social or cultural gatherings.
Description Center is a teaching nursing home
affiliated with the University of South Carolina
School of Medicine, College of Nursing and
College of Social Work. VA approved.

Capitol Convalescent Center
3001 Beechaven Rd, Columbia, SC, 29204
(803) 782-4363
Admin Anne O Winn. *Medical Dir/Dir of
Nursing* Waitus O Tanner.
Licensure Skilled Care; Intermediate Care.
Beds 120. *Certified* Medicaid; Medicare.
Admissions Requirements Medical examination; Physician's request.
Staff Physicians 5 (pt); RNs 5 (ft), 1 (pt); LPNs
9 (ft), 3 (pt); Orderlies 2 (ft), 2 (pt); Nurses aides
40 (ft), 9 (pt); Physical therapists 1 (pt); Recreational therapists 2 (ft); Speech therapists 1 (pt);
Dentists 1 (pt); Podiatrists 1 (pt).
Facilities Dining room; Physical therapy room;
Activities room; Crafts room; Laundry room;
Barber/Beauty shop.
Activities Arts and Crafts; Cards; Games;
Reading groups; Prayer groups; Movies; Shopping trips; Dances/Social or cultural gatherings.
Description Philosophy of the center is to provide a high quality of patient care which
extends beyond the immediate physical needs.
Prevention of disabilities intensified by the
aging process is emphasized and restoration of
the person to a level consistent with his limitations. VA approved.

David E Stewart Home—Babcock Center
5540 Ridgewood Camp Rd, Columbia, SC,
29230 (803) 779-2073
Admin John Bradford. *Medical Dir/Dir of
Nursing* J William Pitts.
Licensure Intermediate Care for Mentally
Retarded. *Beds* 50. *Certified* Medicare.
Ownership Nonprofit.
Admissions Requirements Males only; Medical
examination.
Staff Physicians 1 (pt); RNs 2 (ft); LPNs 2 (ft),
1 (pt); Orderlies 10 (ft); Physical therapists 1
(pt); Recreational therapists 2 (ft); Occupational
therapists 1 (pt); Speech therapists 1 (ft); Activities coordinators 1 (pt); Dietitians 1 (pt); Dentists 1 (pt); Ophthalmologists 1 (pt); Podiatrists
1 (pt); Audiologists 1 (pt).
Facilities Dining room; Activities room; Crafts
room; Laundry room.
Activities Arts and Crafts; Cards; Games;
Reading groups; Prayer groups; Movies; Shopping trips; Dances/Social or cultural gatherings;
Generic services.

Description This is a community-based
ICFMR operated by a private, nonprofit
organization (Babcock Center, Inc). All activities are community oriented using existing
generic (community) services.

First Midlands ICMRF*
8301 Farrow Rd, Columbia, SC, 29203
Admin Curtis Murph.
Licensure Skilled Care; Intermediate Care.
Beds 112.

Forest Hills Nursing Center*
2451 Forest Dr, Columbia, SC, 29204 (803)
254-5960
Admin George H Butler.
Licensure Skilled Care; Intermediate Care.
Beds 146. *Certified* Medicaid; Medicare.

Lexington West Inc
PO Box 3817, Columbia, SC, 29230
Admin Ralph E Courtney.
Licensure Intermediate Care for Mentally
Retarded. *Beds* 8. *Certified* Medicaid.
Ownership Nonprofit.
Admissions Requirements Minimum age;
Females only 18.
Staff RNs 1 (pt); LPNs 1 (ft); Nurses aides 3
(ft), 1 (pt); Occupational therapists 1 (pt); Speech therapists 1 (pt); Dietitians 1 (pt).
Facilities Dining room; Activities room; Laundry room.
Activities Arts and Crafts; Cards; Games;
Prayer groups; Movies; Shopping trips; Dances/Social or cultural gatherings.
Description This group home has been in
operation since 1981. Residents participate in
many community activities and many opportunities are available for participation in social
activities with community members including
other mentally retarded individuals.

Manor Care—Columbia
2601 Forest Dr, Columbia, SC, 29204 (803)
256-4983
Admin Helen Myers. *Medical Dir/Dir of
Nursing* Dr James Vardell.
Licensure Skilled Care. *Beds* 118. *Certified* Medicare.
Admissions Requirements Medical examination; Physician's request.
Staff RNs 7 (ft), 1 (pt); LPNs 11 (ft), 4 (pt);
Orderlies 2 (ft); Nurses aides 37 (ft), 3 (pt);
Physical therapists 1 (ft); Occupational therapists; Speech therapists; Activities coordinators
2 (ft).
Facilities Dining room; Physical therapy room;
Activities room; Laundry room; Barber/Beauty
shop.
Activities Arts and Crafts; Cards; Games;
Reading groups; Prayer groups; Dances/Social
or cultural gatherings.
Description Facility is extremely attractive and
well decorated, appealing to private pay residents.

Mary E White Developmental Center*
8301 S Farrow Rd, Columbia, SC, 29203
Admin Alice R Tollison.
Licensure Skilled Care; Intermediate Care.
Beds 112. *Certified* Medicaid; Medicare.
Ownership Public.

Midlands Center Infant Care Unit*
8301 Farrow Rd, Columbia, SC, 29203 (803)
758-4668
Admin Olieda B Ress.
Licensure Skilled Care; Intermediate Care.
Beds 22. *Certified* Medicaid; Medicare.
Ownership Public.

Pine Lake ICMRF—Babcock Center
140 Flora Dr, Columbia, SC, 29230
Admin Christie Lineback. *Medical Dir/Dir of
Nursing* J William Pitts.
Licensure Intermediate Care for Mentally
Retarded. *Beds* 44. *Certified* Medicare.
Ownership Nonprofit.
Admissions Requirements Medical examina-
tion; Physician's request.
Staff Physicians 1 (pt); RNs 2 (ft), 1 (pt); LPNs
3 (ft); Orderlies 50 (ft); Physical therapists 1
(pt); Recreational therapists 2 (ft); Occupational
therapists 1 (pt); Speech therapists 2 (ft); Activi-
ties coordinators 1 (pt); Dietitians 1 (pt); Den-
tists 1 (pt); Ophthalmologists 1 (pt); Podiatrists
1 (pt); Audiologists 1 (pt).
Facilities Dining room; Physical therapy room;
Activities room; Crafts room; Laundry room;
Barber/Beauty shop; Library.
Activities Arts and Crafts; Cards; Games;
Reading groups; Prayer groups; Movies; Shopping trips; Dances/Social or cultural gatherings.
Description Pine Lake Intermediate Care
Facility is an enity of Babcock Center, Inc, a
private, nonprofit organization. While many
services are offered on site we specialize in
community based (generic) services.

Richland Convalescent Center*
PO Drawer 4600, 4112 Hartford St, Columbia,
SC, 29240 (803) 754-4203
Admin Judith R Clark.
Licensure Intermediate Care. *Beds* 152. *Certi-
fied* Medicaid; Medicare.

Richland Street Community Residence
8301 Farrow Rd, Columbia, SC, 29203
Admin John Viernes Jr.
Licensure Intermediate Care for Mentally
Retarded.
Admissions Requirements Females only
Staff Physicians 1 (pt); RNs 1 (pt); LPNs 3 (ft);
Nurses aides 3 (ft).
Facilities Dining room; Activities room; Laun-
dry room.
Activities Arts and Crafts; Cards; Games; Pray-
er groups; Movies; Shopping trips;
Dances/Social or cultural gatherings.

Second Midlands ICMRF*
8301 Farrow Rd, Columbia, SC, 29203
Admin Dorothea Friday.
Licensure Skilled Care; Intermediate Care.
Beds 226. *Certified* Medicaid; Medicare.

Woodrow Intermediate Care Facility*
University of South Carolina, Green St,
Columbia, SC, 29208
Admin Jean S Sox.
Licensure Skilled Care; Intermediate Care.
Beds 8.

CONWAY

Conway Nursing Center Inc
3300 4th Ave, Conway, SC, 29526 (803)
248-5728
Admin Melanie H Connelly. *Medical Dir/Dir
of Nursing* Dr R L Ramseur.
Licensure Skilled Care; Intermediate Care.
Beds 130. *Certified* Medicaid; Medicare.
Admissions Requirements Minimum age 12;
Medical examination.
Staff RNs 5 (ft); LPNs 14 (ft); Nurses aides 46
(ft); Physical therapists 1 (ft); Recreational ther-
apists 2 (ft); Dietitians 1 (pt); Dentists 1 (pt);
Podiatrists 1 (pt).
Facilities Dining room; Physical therapy room;
Activities room; Crafts room; Laundry room;
Barber/Beauty shop; Library; Greenhouse.
Activities Arts and Crafts; Cards; Games;
Reading groups; Prayer groups; Movies; Shop-
ping trips; Dances/Social or cultural gatherings.
Description Warm and loving atmosphere in a
modern facility featuring a well-trained staff
who take pride in their work.

DARLINGTON

Bethea Baptist Home*
PO Drawer 4000, Florence-Darlington Hwy,
Darlington, SC, 29532 (803) 393-2867
Admin J Thomas Garrett.
Licensure Skilled Care. *Beds* 88.
Ownership Nonprofit.

Darlington Convalescent Center*
PO Box 185, 352 Pearl St, Darlington, SC,
29532
Admin Shirley L Morse.
Licensure Intermediate Care. *Beds* 44. *Certi-
fied* Medicaid; Medicare.

Oakhaven Inc*
PO Box 516, 131 Oak St, Darlington, SC,
29532 (803) 393-5892
Admin Mary Lou Blackmon.
Licensure Skilled Care; Intermediate Care.
Beds 88. *Certified* Medicaid; Medicare.

DILLON

Pines Nursing and Convalescent Home*
203 Lakeside Dr, Dillon, SC, 29536 (803)
774-2741
Admin Rosalee H Lemmond.
Licensure Skilled Care; Intermediate Care.
Beds 84. *Certified* Medicaid; Medicare.

EASLEY

Alta Vista Inc*
Anne Dr, Easley, SC, 29640 (803) 859-9754
Admin Margaret B Lollis.
Licensure Skilled Care; Intermediate Care.
Beds 103. *Certified* Medicaid; Medicare.

Blue Ridge Care Center*
Rt 7, Box 790, Crestview Rd, Easley, SC, 29640
(803) 859-3236
Admin Virginia B Boger.
Licensure Intermediate Care. *Beds* 67. *Certi-

fied Medicaid; Medicare.

EDGEFIELD

Edgefield Health Care Center
1 W A Reel Dr, PO Box 668, Edgefield, SC,
29824 (803) 637-5312
Admin Cynthia R Vann. *Medical Dir/Dir of
Nursing* Dr H R Kylstra.
Licensure Intermediate Care. *Beds* 81. *Certi-
fied* Medicaid; Medicare.
Admissions Requirements Medical examination.
Staff RNs 3 (ft), 2 (pt); LPNs 2 (ft), 6 (pt);
Nurses aides 23 (ft), 10 (pt); Physical therapists
1 (pt); Activities coordinators 1 (ft); Dietitians
6 (ft), 1 (pt).
Facilities Dining room; Physical therapy room;
Laundry room; Barber/Beauty shop; TV and
recreation room.
Activities Arts and Crafts; Games; Prayer
groups; Movies; Dances/Social or cultural gatherings; Cookouts; Pet therapy.
Description A clean facility staffed with courteous personnel; visitors always welcome.

ESTILL

Stiles M Harper Convalescent Center*
PO Box 386, S Liberty Ave, Estill, SC, 29918
Admin J Albert McNab.
Licensure Intermediate Care. *Beds* 44.
Certified Medicaid; Medicare.

FAIRFAX

John Edward Harter Nursing Center
Hwy 278 W, Fairfax, SC, 29827 (803) 632-3334
Admin M K Hiatt. *Medical Dir/Dir of
Nursing* H L Laffitte MD.
Licensure Skilled Care; Intermediate Care.
Beds 44. *Certified* Medicaid; Medicare.
Ownership Public.
Admissions Requirements Medical examina-
tion; Physician's request.
Staff RNs 2 (ft), 2 (pt); LPNs 5 (ft); Orderlies 3
(ft), 1 (pt); Physical therapists 1 (pt); Recrea-
tional therapists 1 (pt); Speech therapists 1 (pt);
Activities coordinators 1 (ft); Dietitians 1 (ft).
Facilities Dining room; Activities room.
Activities Arts and Crafts; Games; Prayer
groups; Movies.
Description County owned and operated, affili-
ated with Allendale County Hospital and
located on the same grounds.

FLORENCE

Clyde Street Home*
PO Box 3209, 509 Clyde St, Florence, SC,
29502
Admin Kenneth Ward.
Licensure Intermediate Care for Mentally
Retarded. *Beds* 20. *Certified* Medicare.

Coit Street Community Residence
654 S Coit St, Florence, SC, 29502
Admin Fred Fuller.
Licensure Intermediate Care for Mentally
Retarded. *Beds* 8. *Certified* Medicare.

Ownership Public.
Admissions Requirements Minimum age 21.
Staff RNs 1 (pt); LPNs 1 (pt).
Activities Arts and Crafts; Games; Movies; Shopping trips; Dances/Social or cultural gatherings.

Commander Nursing Home*
Rt 3, Pamplico Hwy, Florence, SC, 29501 (803) 669-3502
Admin Joe Commander III.
Licensure Skilled Care; Intermediate Care.
Beds 133. *Certified* Medicaid; Medicare.

Faith Health Care Facility Inc*
PO Box 908, 617 W Marion St, Florence, SC, 29503 (803) 662-5148, 669-2534
Admin Rayshaw L Gaddy.
Licensure Skilled Care; Intermediate Care.
Beds 44. *Certified* Medicaid; Medicare.

Florence Convalescent Center
Clarke Rd, Florence, SC, 29501 (803) 669-4374
Admin Genevieve M Lawrence. *Medical Dir/Dir of Nursing* Dr H H Jeter.
Licensure Intermediate Care. *Beds* 88. *Certified* Medicaid; Medicare.
Staff Physicians 5 (pt); RNs 2 (ft); LPNs 6 (ft), 1 (pt); Orderlies 1 (ft); Nurses aides 20 (ft); Activities coordinators 1 (ft); Dietitians 7 (pt); Social workers 1 (ft).
Facilities Dining room; Activities room; Crafts room; Laundry room; Barber/Beauty shop.
Activities Arts and Crafts; Cards; Games; Reading groups; Prayer groups; Movies; Shopping trips; Dances/Social or cultural gatherings; Cookouts.

Folk Convalescent Home*
Rt 9, Box 64, Pamplico Hwy, Florence, SC, 29501 (803) 669-4403
Admin Charles S Commander.
Licensure Intermediate Care. *Beds* 88. *Certified* Medicaid; Medicare.

Heritage Home of Florence Inc*
515 S Warley St, Florence, SC, 29501 (803) 662-4573
Admin Sherwin David Welch.
Licensure Intermediate Care. *Beds* 44. *Certified* Medicaid; Medicare.

Honorage Nursing Center
1207 N Cashua Rd, Florence, SC, 29501 (803) 665-6172
Admin Howard W Clarke. *Medical Dir/Dir of Nursing* Harold H Jeter Jr MD.
Licensure Skilled Care; Intermediate Care.
Beds 88. *Certified* Medicaid; Medicare.
Admissions Requirements Medical examination.
Staff RNs 7 (ft); LPNs 7 (ft); Orderlies 2 (ft); Nurses aides 30 (ft); Activities coordinators 1 (ft).
Facilities Dining room; Activities room; Chapel; Crafts room; Laundry room; Barber/Beauty shop.
Activities Arts and Crafts; Games; Reading groups; Prayer groups; Movies; Dances/Social or cultural gatherings.
Description Honorage Nursing Center is located on 10-acres of property surrounded by quiet farm lands, yet one mile away from the

business and shopping district of Florence. Patients enjoy a home-like atmosphere with all their physical needs being met by a qualified caring staff. Cleanliness, efficiency, and quality are reflected by the facility, grounds, and personnel.

Lake City/Scranton Convalesent Center Inc— Village Green Convalescent Center*
PO Box 9, Florence, SC, 29501
Admin Paul E Clark.
Licensure Skilled Care; Intermediate Care.
Beds 74. *Certified* Medicaid; Medicare.

Mulberry Park*
PO Box 3029, Florence, SC, 29502
Admin Kenneth Ward.
Licensure Skilled Care; Intermediate Care.
Beds 112.

Pamplico Road Residence*
PO Box 3209, 801 Pamplico Hwy, Florence, SC, 29502
Admin Fred Fuller.
Licensure Intermediate Care for Mentally Retarded. *Beds* 8. *Certified* Medicare.

Pecan Lane*
PO Box 3209, Florence, SC, 29502
Admin Kenneth Ward.
Licensure Skilled Care; Intermediate Care.
Beds 160.

FORK

Sunny Acres Nursing Home Inc
Rt 1, Box 115, Fork, SC, 29543 (803) 464-6212
Admin Tony R Cooke. *Medical Dir/Dir of Nursing* Ira Barth MD.
Licensure Skilled Care; Intermediate Care.
Beds SNF 57; ICF 54. *Certified* Medicaid; Medicare.
Staff Physicians 3 (ft); RNs 4 (ft), 3 (pt); LPNs 11 (ft), 3 (pt); Orderlies 3 (ft), 1 (pt); Nurses aides 28 (ft), 4 (pt); Recreational therapists 2 (ft), 2 (pt); Dietitians 9 (ft).
Facilities Dining room; Physical therapy room; Activities room; Chapel; Crafts room; Laundry room; Barber/Beauty shop.
Activities Arts and Crafts; Games; Reading groups; Prayer groups; Movies; Shopping trips; Dances/Social or cultural gatherings.

FOUNTAIN INN

Fountain Inn Convalescent Home*
PO Box 67, 501 Gulliver St, Fountain Inn, SC, 29644 (803) 862-2554
Admin Alan Lee Hughes.
Licensure Intermediate Care. *Beds* 44. *Certified* Medicaid; Medicare.

GAFFNEY

Brookview House Inc
Thompson St, Gaffney, SC, 29340 (803) 489-3101
Admin Charles L Blanton Jr. *Medical Dir/Dir of Nursing* L L DuBose MD.
Licensure Skilled Care; Intermediate Care.

Beds 44. *Certified* Medicaid; Medicare.
Staff RNs 3 (ft), 4 (pt); LPNs 10 (ft), 5 (pt); Orderlies 1 (ft), 3 (pt); Nurses aides 35 (ft), 10 (pt); Activities coordinators 3 (pt); Dietitians 1 (ft).
Facilities Dining room; Activities room; Crafts room; Laundry room; Barber/Beauty shop; Library.
Activities Arts and Crafts; Games; Movies; Dances/Social or cultural gatherings.

Cherokee County Hospital—Long Term Care Unit
1420 N Limestone St, Gaffney, SC, 29340 (803) 487-4271
Admin Nicholas Marzocco. *Medical Dir/Dir of Nursing* W K Brumbach MD.
Licensure Skilled Care; Intermediate Care.
Beds 44. *Certified* Medicaid; Medicare.
Admissions Requirements Medical examination.
Staff Physicians 9 (pt); RNs 3 (pt); LPNs 8 (pt); Orderlies 2 (pt); Nurses aides 9 (pt); Physical therapists 1 (pt); Activities coordinators 1 (ft); Dietitians 1 (ft); Dentists 1 (pt).
Facilities Dining room; Activities room; Crafts room; Barber/Beauty shop.
Activities Arts and Crafts; Games; Reading groups; Prayer groups; Movies; Shopping trips; Dances/Social or cultural gatherings; Exercise; Music groups.
Description A 44-bed facility located centrally to all areas of Cherokee County; adjoins Cherokee Memorial Hospital where acute care can easily be provided. Space is provided for social gatherings and special activities. Residents are free to use all available resources for entertainment.

GEORGETOWN

Winyah Extended Care Center Inc*
PO Box 8158, S Island Rd, Georgetown, SC, 29440 (803) 546-4123
Admin W William Mitchell.
Licensure Skilled Care; Intermediate Care.
Beds 84. *Certified* Medicaid; Medicare.

GREENVILLE

Betheden Nursing Home*
8 N Texas Ave, Greenville, SC, 29611
Admin Larry Dean Lollis.
Licensure Skilled Care; Intermediate Care.
Beds 88. *Certified* Medicaid; Medicare.

Grady H Hipp Nursing Center*
661 Rutherford Rd, Greenville, SC, 29609 (803) 232-2442
Admin Agnes D Roe.
Licensure Skilled Care; Intermediate Care.
Beds 102. *Certified* Medicaid; Medicare.

NHE—Greenville Inc*
411 Ansel St, Greenville, SC, 29601 (803) 232-5368
Admin Jane B Owings.
Licensure Skilled Care; Intermediate Care.
Beds 78. *Certified* Medicaid; Medicare.

Oakmont East Nursing Center*
601 Sulphur Springs Rd, Greenville, SC, 29611
(803) 246-9941
Admin Wiley M Crittenden Jr.
Licensure Skilled Care; Intermediate Care.
Beds 132. *Certified* Medicaid; Medicare.

Oakmont Nursing Home
600 Sulphur Springs Rd, Greenville, SC, 29611
(803) 246-2721
Admin David S Harper. *Medical Dir/Dir of Nursing* W W Goodlett MD.
Licensure Intermediate Care. *Beds* 125. *Certified* Medicaid; Medicare.
Staff Physicians 5 (ft); LPNs 8 (ft); Nurses aides 40 (ft); Dietitians 1 (ft).
Facilities Dining room; Activities room; Chapel; Barber/Beauty shop.
Activities Arts and Crafts; Cards; Games; Prayer groups; Movies; Shopping trips; Dances/Social or cultural gatherings.

Piedmont Nursing Center Inc*
809 Laurens Rd, Greenville, SC, 29607 (803) 232-8196
Admin Otis E Ridgeway Jr.
Licensure Skilled Care; Intermediate Care.
Beds 44. *Certified* Medicaid; Medicare.

Resthaven Geriatric Center
423 Vardry St, Greenville, SC, 29601 (803) 242-4730
Admin Joan T King. *Medical Dir/Dir of Nursing* Norris Boone MD.
Licensure Skilled Care. *Beds* 30.
Admissions Requirements Minimum age 16; Medical examination; Physician's request.
Staff RNs 1 (ft), 1 (pt); LPNs 3 (ft), 2 (pt); Orderlies 1 (ft); Nurses aides 10 (ft), 2 (pt).
Facilities Activities room; Laundry room.
Activities Prayer groups.

Ridge Road Residence*
PO Box 17007, Greenville, SC, 29606 (803) 297-0712
Admin Marian W Blackwell.
Licensure Intermediate Care for Mentally Retarded. *Beds* 16.

GREENWOOD

Greenwood Community Residence*
Rt 1, Box 146, S Main St, Greenwood, SC, 29646 (803) 223-1306
Admin Vicki A Neely.
Licensure Intermediate Care for Mentally Retarded. *Beds* 8. *Certified* Medicare.

Greenwood Nursing Home Inc*
PO Box 3109, 437 E Cambridge Ave, Greenwood, SC, 29646 (803) 223-1950
Admin Effie N Dorn.
Licensure Skilled Care; Intermediate Care.
Beds 89. *Certified* Medicaid; Medicare.

Nursing Center of Greenwood Methodist Home
1110 Marshall Rd, Greenwood, SC, 29646
(803) 229-5566
Admin Ingrid L Speer. *Medical Dir/Dir of Nursing* O L Thomas MD.
Licensure Skilled Care; Intermediate Care.
Beds 102. *Certified* Medicare.

Ownership Nonprofit.
Staff Physicians 2 (pt); RNs 8 (ft), 6 (pt); LPNs 2 (ft); Orderlies 4 (ft), 7 (pt); Nurses aides 32 (ft), 12 (pt); Physical therapists 1 (pt); Speech therapists 1 (pt); Activities coordinators 2 (ft), 1 (pt); Dietitians 1 (ft); Dentists 2 (pt); Podiatrists 1 (pt).
Affiliation Methodist
Facilities Dining room; Physical therapy room; Activities room; Chapel; Crafts room; Laundry room; Barber/Beauty shop.
Activities Arts and Crafts; Cards; Games; Reading groups; Prayer groups; Movies; Shopping trips; Dances/Social or cultural gatherings.
Description Nonprofit nursing home sponsored by the Methodist Church; 102 beds with dual licensure. Many programs and holiday and festive luncheons and activities are featured.

GREER

Greer Health Care Inc
Chandler Rd at Memorial Dr Ext, Greer, SC, 29651 (803) 879-7474
Admin Nekoda L McCauley. *Medical Dir/Dir of Nursing* Lewis M Davis MD.
Licensure Skilled Care; Intermediate Care.
Beds 132. *Certified* Medicaid; Medicare.
Admissions Requirements Medical examination; Physician's request.
Staff Physicians 18 (pt); RNs 8 (ft), 1 (pt); LPNs 14 (ft), 1 (pt); Orderlies 6 (ft); Nurses aides 55 (ft); Physical therapists 2 (ft), 1 (pt); Speech therapists; Dietitians 2 (ft); Dentists; Podiatrists; Audiologists; Physical therapy assistants 2 (ft), 1 (pt).
Facilities Dining room; Physical therapy room; Activities room; Crafts room; Laundry room; Barber/Beauty shop; Library.
Activities Arts and Crafts; Cards; Games; Reading groups; Prayer groups; Movies; Shopping trips; Dances/Social or cultural gatherings; Residents council; Current events groups; Weekly socials; Trips to community events; Annual bazaar; Fashion shows.
Description Quality oriented facility and staff specialize in rehabilitative services for long-term and short-term patients; appealing non-institutional environment in patient rooms and courtyard gardens.

Roger Huntington Nursing Center
313 Memorial Dr, Greer, SC, 29651
Admin Michael W Massey.
Licensure Skilled Care; Intermediate Care.
Beds 80. *Certified* Medicaid; Medicare.
Admissions Requirements Medical examination; Physician's request.
Staff RNs 5 (ft), 3 (pt); LPNs 5 (ft), 3 (pt); Orderlies 3 (ft), 1 (pt); Nurses aides 20 (ft), 8 (pt); Activities coordinators 1 (ft); Dietitians 1 (ft).
Facilities Dining room; Activities room; Laundry room; Barber/Beauty shop.
Activities Arts and Crafts; Games; Prayer groups; Shopping trips.

HARTSVILLE

Morrell Memorial Convalescent Center Inc
PO Box 1318, Hartsville, SC, 29550 (803)

383-5164
Admin Thomas S Stewart. *Medical Dir/Dir of Nursing* Dr Darrel Gant.
Licensure Skilled Care; Intermediate Care.
Beds 132. *Certified* Medicaid; Medicare.
Admissions Requirements Medical examination; Physician's request.
Staff Physicians 4 (pt); RNs 4 (ft); LPNs 16 (ft), 4 (pt); Orderlies 6 (ft); Nurses aides 53 (ft); Physical therapists 1 (ft), 1 (pt); Activities coordinators 2 (ft), 1 (pt); Dietitians 13 (ft).
Facilities Dining room; Physical therapy room; Activities room; Chapel; Crafts room; Laundry room; Barber/Beauty shop.
Activities Arts and Crafts; Cards; Games; Reading groups; Prayer groups.
Description Facility is one-level and is accessible to handicapped. VA approved.

Thad A Saleeby Developmental Center
714 Lewellen Ave, Hartsville, SC, 29550 (803) 332-4104
Admin Imogene S Williams. *Medical Dir/Dir of Nursing* James O Morphis MD and Jesse T Cox Jr MD.
Licensure Skilled Care; Intermediate Care for Mentally Retarded. *Beds* 132. *Certified* Medicaid; Medicare.
Admissions Requirements Minimum age Birth; Medical examination; Physician's request.
Staff Physicians 2 (ft); Physical therapists 1 (pt); Recreational therapists 1 (ft); Occupational therapists 1 (pt); Speech therapists 1 (ft); Dietitians 1 (ft); Dentists 1 (pt); Audiologists 1 (pt).
Facilities Dining room; Physical therapy room; Activities room; Crafts room; Laundry room; Barber/Beauty shop; Library.
Activities Arts and Crafts; Games; Reading groups; Movies; Shopping trips; Dances/Social or cultural gatherings.
Description The center serves the profoundly or severely mentally retarded with multi-handicaps; serves the Pee Dee Region (13 counties) of South Carolina.

HILTON HEAD ISLAND

Hilton Head Center of South Carolina Inc
PO Box 4926, Hilton Head Island, SC, 29938
Admin Stephani G Johnson. *Medical Dir/Dir of Nursing* Dr Paul Long.
Licensure Skilled Care; Intermediate Care.
Beds 44. *Certified* Medicaid; Medicare.
Ownership Public.
Admissions Requirements Medical examination.
Staff Physicians 7 (pt); RNs 3 (ft), 3 (pt); LPNs 3 (ft), 5 (pt); Orderlies 2 (ft); Nurses aides 20 (ft), 5 (pt); Physical therapists 1 (pt); Reality therapists 1 (pt); Recreational therapists 1 (ft); Occupational therapists 1 (pt); Speech therapists 1 (pt); Activities coordinators 1 (ft); Dietitians 1 (ft); Dentists 1 (pt); Podiatrists 1 (pt); Audiologists 1 (pt).
Facilities Dining room; Activities room; Laundry room; Barber/Beauty shop.
Activities Arts and Crafts; Cards; Games; Reading groups; Prayer groups; Shopping trips.
Description Facility offers pet therapy once a week and has started an Alzheimer's support group for families. VA approved.

Seabrook of Hilton Head Inc*
300, Woodhaven Dr, Hilton Head Island, SC, 29938
Admin Robert J Allen.
Licensure Skilled Care. *Beds* 22. *Certified* Medicaid.

HOPKINS

Stanton Pines Convalescent Home Inc*
Rt 2, Box 241, Ridge Rd, Hopkins, SC, 29061 (803) 776-3536
Admin Daisy N Stanton.
Licensure Intermediate Care. *Beds* 26.

INMAN

Camp Care Inc
PO Box 847, Inman, SC, 29349 (803) 472-2028
Admin Carole N Camp. *Medical Dir/Dir of Nursing* Dr Thomas Malone.
Licensure Intermediate Care. *Beds* 88. *Certified* Medicaid; Medicare.
Staff Physicians 1 (pt); RNs 1 (ft); LPNs 8 (ft), 2 (pt); Nurses aides 24 (ft), 3 (pt); Recreational therapists 1 (ft); Activities coordinators 1 (ft); Dietitians 1 (pt); Dentists 1 (pt).
Facilities Dining room; Activities room; Crafts room; Laundry room; Barber/Beauty shop.
Activities Arts and Crafts; Games; Prayer groups; Movies; Shopping trips; Dances/Social or cultural gatherings.

Camphaven Nursing Home*
Rt 4, Box 1, Blackstock Rd, Inman, SC, 29349 (803) 472-9055
Admin W R Camp.
Licensure Skilled Care; Intermediate Care. *Beds* 176. *Certified* Medicaid; Medicare.

Inman Nursing Home
51 N Main St, Inman, SC, 29349 (803) 472-9370
Admin H Wayne Johnson. *Medical Dir/Dir of Nursing* Arnold L Denler MD.
Licensure Skilled Care; Intermediate Care. *Beds* 40. *Certified* Medicaid; Medicare.
Admissions Requirements Medical examination; Physician's request.
Staff Physicians 1 (pt); RNs 1 (ft), 3 (pt); LPNs 3 (ft), 3 (pt); Nurses aides 17 (ft), 4 (pt); Activities coordinators 1 (pt); Dietitians 1 (pt).
Facilities Dining room; Activities room; Laundry room.
Activities Arts and Crafts; Cards; Games; Reading groups; Prayer groups.

IVA

Golden Acres Intermediate Care Facility*
PO Box 505, Hampton St, Iva, SC, 29655 (803) 348-7433
Admin Elizabeth L Tucker.
Licensure Intermediate Care. *Beds* 26. *Certified* Medicaid; Medicare.

JOHNS ISLAND

Hermina Traeye Memorial Nursing Home
Rt 3, Maybank Hwy, Johns Island, SC, 29455

(803) 559-5501
Admin Melvin H Stepp. *Medical Dir/Dir of Nursing* Allen Rashford MD.
Licensure Skilled Care; Intermediate Care. *Beds* 44. *Certified* Medicaid; Medicare.
Admissions Requirements Medical examination.
Staff Physicians 2 (pt); RNs 3 (ft), 1 (pt); LPNs 7 (ft), 8 (pt); Nurses aides 24 (ft), 5 (pt); Physical therapists 1 (pt); Activities coordinators 1 (ft), 1 (pt); Dietitians 1 (pt).
Facilities Dining room; Physical therapy room; Activities room; Crafts room; Laundry room; Barber/Beauty shop.
Activities Arts and Crafts; Games; Reading groups; Prayer groups; Movies; Shopping trips; Dances/Social or cultural gatherings.

KINGSTREE

Kingstree Community Residence*
Frierson Homes, Lexington St, Kingstree, SC, 29556
Admin Fred Fuller.
Licensure Skilled Care; Intermediate Care. *Beds* 15.

Kingstree Nursing Facility Inc*
PO Box 359, 110 Mill St, Kingstree, SC, 29556 (803) 354-6116
Admin Carlyle Cooke.
Licensure Skilled Care; Intermediate Care. *Beds* 44. *Certified* Medicaid; Medicare.

LADSOM

Coastal Center—Live Oak Village*
12 Jamison Rd, Ladsom, SC, 29456 (803) 871-2335
Admin Chanson A Wieters.
Licensure Skilled Care; Intermediate Care. *Beds* 50.

LANCASTER

Lancaster County Care Center
Hwy 9 E, Lancaster, SC, 29720 (803) 285-7907
Admin J B Kinney Jr.
Licensure Intermediate Care. *Beds* 88. *Certified* Medicaid; Medicare.
Ownership Public.
Admissions Requirements Medical examination.
Staff Physicians 3 (ft); RNs 2 (ft); LPNs 7 (ft), 1 (pt); Nurses aides 30 (ft); Reality therapists 1 (ft); Activities coordinators 1 (ft); Dietitians 1 (pt).
Facilities Dining room; Activities room; Chapel; Crafts room; Laundry room; Barber/Beauty shop.
Activities Arts and Crafts; Cards; Games; Reading groups; Prayer groups; Movies; Shopping trips; Dances/Social or cultural gatherings.
Description This 88-bed facility is situated in a quiet setting just outside of the city limits. The activities are geared toward the needs of our residents and range from very simple programs of pet therapy to more involved programs like adult education, sponsored by our local school district. The facility is proud of its very active

family council and feels continued family involvement is essential to the well-being of our residents.

Marion Sims Nursing Center*
800 W Meeting St, Lancaster, SC, 29720 (803) 285-4311
Admin Dace W Jones Jr.
Licensure Skilled Care; Intermediate Care. *Beds* 111. *Certified* Medicaid; Medicare.

LAURENS

Laurens Nursing Home Inc
301 Pinehaven St Ext, Laurens, SC, 29360 (803) 984-6584
Admin Richard L Ellickson. *Medical Dir/Dir of Nursing* Julian Atkinson.
Licensure Skilled Care; Intermediate Care. *Beds* 132. *Certified* Medicaid; Medicare.
Admissions Requirements Medical examination; Physician's request.
Staff Physicians 12 (pt); RNs 3 (ft); LPNs 7 (ft), 9 (pt); Orderlies 8 (ft); Nurses aides 51 (ft); Physical therapists 1 (pt); Reality therapists 2 (pt); Recreational therapists 1 (pt); Speech therapists 1 (pt); Activities coordinators 1 (pt); Dietitians 1 (ft); Dentists 1 (pt); Audiologists 1 (pt).
Facilities Dining room; Physical therapy room; Activities room; Chapel; Crafts room; Laundry room; Barber/Beauty shop.
Activities Arts and Crafts; Cards; Games; Reading groups; Prayer groups; Movies; Shopping trips; Dances/Social or cultural gatherings.
Description VA approved.

LEXINGTON

Rikard Nursing Home—Rikard Convalescent Bldg*
PO 517, Old Cherokee Rd, Lexington, SC, 29072 (803) 359-5181
Admin Melvin Ellis.
Licensure Skilled Care; Intermediate Care. *Beds* 63. *Certified* Medicaid; Medicare.

Rikard Nursing Homes—Keisler and Holstedt Bldgs*
PO Box 517, Lexington, SC, 29072 (803) 359-5181
Admin Joseph D Wright.
Licensure Skilled Care; Intermediate Care. *Beds* 212. *Certified* Medicaid; Medicare.

LORIS

Loris Hospital—Extended Care Facility*
3212 Casey St, Loris, SC, 29569 (803) 357-6106
Admin Frank M Watts.
Licensure Skilled Care; Intermediate Care. *Beds* 40. *Certified* Medicaid; Medicare.

MANNING

Briggs Nursing Home*
Rt 3, Box 265, Manning, SC, 29102
Admin Jerry E Spann.
Licensure Skilled Care; Intermediate Care. *Beds* 38. *Certified* Medicare.

MARIETTA

Stroud Memorial Intermediate Care Facility
Hwy 276, PO Box 216, Marietta, SC, 29661
(803) 836-6381
Admin Earlene G Jones. *Medical Dir/Dir of Nursing* James E Barnett.
Licensure Intermediate Care. *Beds* 42. *Certified* Medicaid.
Admissions Requirements Medical examination.
Staff RNs 2 (ft); LPNs 4 (ft); Nurses aides 10 (ft), 2 (pt); Recreational therapists 1 (ft); Activities coordinators 1 (ft); Dietitians 1 (ft).
Facilities Dining room; Activities room; Chapel; Crafts room; Laundry room; Barber/Beauty shop; Library.
Activities Arts and Crafts; Cards; Games; Reading groups; Prayer groups; Movies; Dances/Social or cultural gatherings.

MARION

Jenkins Nursing Home Inc*
PO Box 917, 401 Murray St, Marion, SC, 29571 (803) 423-6947
Admin Simon M Jenkins.
Licensure Skilled Care; Intermediate Care. *Beds* 22. *Certified* Medicaid; Medicare.

Marion County Convalescent Center*
PO Drawer 1106, Hwy 501, Marion, SC, 29571 (803) 423-2601
Admin Crystal H Isom.
Licensure Skilled Care; Intermediate Care. *Beds* 62. *Certified* Medicaid; Medicare.

MONUCKS CONRNER

Berkeley Convalescent Center*
PO Box 1467, Monucks Conrner, SC, 29461
Admin Carol S Gordon.
Licensure Skilled Care; Intermediate Care. *Beds* 44. *Certified* Medicaid; Medicare.

MOUNT PLEASANT

Charleston Nursing Center Inc
921 Bowman Rd, Mount Pleasant, SC, 29464
(803) 884-8903
Admin James B Connelly. *Medical Dir/Dir of Nursing* George G Durst Sr MD.
Licensure Skilled Care; Intermediate Care. *Beds* 132. *Certified* Medicaid; Medicare.
Admissions Requirements Medical examination; Physician's request.
Staff Physicians 1 (pt); RNs 6 (ft), 5 (pt); LPNs 8 (ft), 5 (pt); Nurses aides 46 (ft); Physical therapists 1 (ft); Recreational therapists 1 (ft); Speech therapists 1 (pt); Activities coordinators 1 (ft); Dietitians 1 (ft); Dentists 1 (pt).
Facilities Dining room; Physical therapy room; Activities room; Crafts room; Laundry room; Barber/Beauty shop.
Activities Arts and Crafts; Games; Reading groups; Prayer groups; Movies; Dances/Social or cultural gatherings.
Description Facility features 24-hour reality orientation.

Sandpiper Convalescent Center*
1049 Anna Knapp Blvd, Mount Pleasant, SC, 29464
Admin Richard Poole.
Licensure Skilled Care. *Beds* 88. *Certified* Medicaid.

MYRTLE BEACH

Myrtle Beach Manor*
PO Box 7337, Hwy 17 N, Myrtle Beach, SC, 29577 (803) 449-5283
Admin Juana C Newber.
Licensure Skilled Care; Intermediate Care. *Beds* 50. *Certified* Medicaid; Medicare.

Sandstrom Home Intermediate Care Facility
6309-11 Hawthorne Ln, Myrtle Beach, SC, 29577 (803) 449-5615
Admin Grace Sandstrom.
Licensure Intermediate Care. *Beds* 30. *Certified* Medicaid.
Admissions Requirements Minimum age 30; Medical examination.
Staff RNs 1 (ft), 1 (pt); LPNs 4 (ft); Orderlies 1 (ft); Nurses aides 14 (ft); Activities coordinators 1 (ft).
Facilities Dining room; Activities room; Laundry room; Barber/Beauty shop.
Activities Arts and Crafts; Cards; Games; Prayer groups; Shopping trips.

NEW ELLENTON

Anna Maria ICF of New Ellenton*
412 Main St, New Ellenton, SC, 29809 (803) 652-2230
Admin D Annette Hobbs.
Licensure Intermediate Care. *Beds* 26. *Certified* Medicaid; Medicare.

NEWBERRY

J F Hawkins Nursing Home
1330 Kinard St, Newberry, SC, 29108 (803) 276-2601
Medical Dir/Dir of Nursing Dr James Underwood.
Licensure Skilled Care; Intermediate Care. *Beds* 78. *Certified* Medicaid; Medicare.
Admissions Requirements Medical examination; Physician's request.
Staff RNs 6 (ft), 1 (pt); LPNs 4 (ft), 2 (pt); Orderlies 3 (ft); Nurses aides 32 (ft), 6 (pt); Activities coordinators 1 (ft), 1 (pt); Dietitians 1 (ft).
Facilities Dining room; Activities room; Chapel; Crafts room; Laundry room; Barber/Beauty shop.
Activities Arts and Crafts; Games; Reading groups; Prayer groups.

Newberry Convalescent Center
Kinard St, Newberry, SC, 29108 (803) 276-6060
Admin Edith C Goforth. *Medical Dir/Dir of Nursing* Dr E E Epting.
Licensure Skilled Care; Intermediate Care. *Beds* 44. *Certified* Medicaid; Medicare.
Admissions Requirements Medical examina-

tion; Physician's request.
Staff RNs 4 (ft), 3 (pt); LPNs 4 (ft), 1 (pt); Nurses aides 26 (ft); Recreational therapists 1 (ft); Activities coordinators 1 (ft); Dietitians; Dentists.
Facilities Dining room; Activities room; Laundry room; Barber/Beauty shop.
Activities Arts and Crafts; Games; Reading groups; Prayer groups; Dances/Social or cultural gatherings.

NORTH CHARLESTON

Baker Hospital Long Term Care Unit*
2750 Speissegger Dr, North Charleston, SC, 29406
Admin Lynn C Orfgen.
Licensure Skilled Care; Intermediate Care. *Beds* 44.

ORANGEBURG

Edisto Convalescent Center
500 Enterprise St SW, Orangeburg, SC, 29115
(803) 534-7771
Admin Ervin A Green. *Medical Dir/Dir of Nursing* Hymie Marcus MD.
Licensure Skilled Care; Intermediate Care. *Beds* SNF 43; ICF 43. *Certified* Medicaid; Medicare.
Admissions Requirements Minimum age 35; Medical examination; Physician's request.
Staff Physicians 4 (pt); RNs 3 (ft), 2 (pt); LPNs 4 (ft), 4 (pt); Orderlies 3 (ft), 1 (pt); Nurses aides 18 (ft), 8 (pt); Physical therapists 1 (pt); Reality therapists 1 (pt); Recreational therapists 1 (pt); Speech therapists 1 (pt); Activities coordinators 1 (ft); Dietitians 1 (pt); Dentists 1 (pt); Podiatrists 1 (pt); Audiologists 1 (pt).
Facilities Dining room; Physical therapy room; Activities room; Chapel; Crafts room; Laundry room; Barber/Beauty shop.
Activities Arts and Crafts; Cards; Games; Reading groups; Movies; Shopping trips.
Description Facility features whirlpool bath.

Jolley Acres Nursing Home Inc*
PO Drawer 1909, 1180 Wolfe Trail SW, Orangeburg, SC, 29115 (803) 534-1001
Admin Deana G Houser.
Licensure Skilled Care; Intermediate Care. *Beds* 43. *Certified* Medicaid; Medicare.

The Methodist Home
PO Drawer 327, Orangeburg, SC, 29115 (803) 534-1212
Admin Ernest M Heape. *Medical Dir/Dir of Nursing* Dr W O Whetsell.
Licensure Skilled Care; Intermediate Care. *Beds* SNF 52; ICF 72. *Certified* Medicaid; Medicare.
Admissions Requirements Minimum age 65; Medical examination.
Staff Physicians 5 (pt); RNs 10 (ft); LPNs 25 (ft); Nurses aides 20 (ft); Physical therapists 1 (pt); Recreational therapists 3 (ft); Activities coordinators 1 (ft); Dietitians 1 (ft).
Affiliation Methodist
Facilities Dining room; Physical therapy room; Activities room; Chapel; Crafts room; Laundry room; Barber/Beauty shop; Library.

Activities Arts and Crafts; Games; Prayer groups; Shopping trips; Dances/Social or cultural gatherings.
Description The Methodist Home is primarily a retirement center. It is located in a quiet, beautiful setting. It is designed as a caring community and provides most services needed from date of entry to departure.

Orangeburg Nursing Home
755 Whitman SE, Orangeburg, SC, 29115 (803) 534-7036
Admin Catherine D Young. *Medical Dir/Dir of Nursing* W O Whetsell MD.
Licensure Skilled Care; Intermediate Care.
Beds 73. *Certified* Medicaid; Medicare.
Admissions Requirements Medical examination; Physician's request.
Staff Physicians 5 (pt); RNs 4 (ft), 5 (pt); LPNs 3 (ft), 4 (pt); Nurses aides 23 (ft), 7 (pt); Physical therapists 1 (pt); Speech therapists 1 (pt); Activities coordinators 1 (ft); Dietitians 1 (pt); Dentists 1 (pt).
Facilities Dining room; Laundry room; Barber-/Beauty shop.
Activities Arts and Crafts; Cards; Games; Reading groups; Prayer groups; Movies; Shopping trips; Dances/Social or cultural gatherings.

PALMETTO

South Carolina Crippled Children's Convalescent Center
2310 W Palmetto St, Palmetto, SC, 29502 (803) 669-0931
Admin Dorothy M Asman.
Licensure Skilled Care; Intermediate Care.
Beds 44.

PICKENS

Laurel Hill Nursing Center Inc
601 E Cedar Rock St, Pickens, SC, 29671 (803) 878-4739
Admin W Bird Lewis. *Medical Dir/Dir of Nursing* David W Mauldin.
Licensure Skilled Care; Intermediate Care.
Beds 80. *Certified* Medicaid; Medicare.
Admissions Requirements Minimum age 60; Medical examination; Physician's request.
Facilities Dining room; Physical therapy room; Activities room; Chapel; Crafts room; Laundry room; Barber/Beauty shop; Library.
Activities Arts and Crafts; Cards; Games; Reading groups; Prayer groups; Movies; Dances/Social or cultural gatherings.
Description Eighty-bed facility with emphasis on individual care and rehabilitation to return the patient home when possible; located atop a hill on the outskirts of Pickens with very pleasant surroundings.

McKinney Intensive Care Facility*
PO Box 895, 113 Rosemond St, Pickens, SC, 29671 (803) 878-2266
Admin Iris L Robinson.
Licensure Intermediate Care. *Beds* 44. *Certified* Medicaid; Medicare.

PORT ROYAL

Port Royal Community Residence*
1508 Old Shell Rd, Port Royal, SC, 29935
Admin Anita White.
Licensure Intermediate Care for Mentally Retarded. *Beds* 16.

RIDGELAND

Ridgecrest Convalescent Center*
PO Box 1570, Grays Rd, Ridgeland, SC, 29936 (803) 726-5581
Admin Faye Cleland.
Licensure Skilled Care; Intermediate Care.
Beds 88. *Certified* Medicaid; Medicare.

RIDGEWAY

Fairfield Homes*
PO Drawer 157, Longtown Rd, Ridgeway, SC, 29130 (803) 337-2257
Admin Annette B Cooper.
Licensure Intermediate Care. *Beds* 112. *Certified* Medicaid; Medicare.

Tanglewood Health Care Center
Third St, Ridgeway, SC, 29130 (803) 337-3211
Admin James R Fulmer. *Medical Dir/Dir of Nursing* J E Campbell MD.
Licensure Intermediate Care. *Beds* 150. *Certified* Medicaid; Medicare.
Admissions Requirements Minimum age 35; Medical examination.
Staff Physicians 1 (pt); RNs 1 (ft), 1 (pt); LPNs 10 (ft), 7 (pt); Orderlies 8 (ft); Nurses aides 37 (ft), 4 (pt); Activities coordinators 2 (ft); Dietitians 1 (pt); Dentists 1 (pt); Ophthalmologists 1 (pt); Podiatrists 1 (pt); Audiologists 1 (pt).
Facilities Dining room; Activities room; Chapel; Crafts room; Laundry room; Barber/Beauty shop; Library.
Activities Arts and Crafts; Cards; Games; Prayer groups; Movies; Shopping trips; Dances/Social or cultural gatherings.
Description Facility is a one-story building with private and semi-private rooms with private baths; located in a country setting with picnic areas; features a transportation department.

ROCK HILL

Anne's Convalescent Home
127 Murrah Dr, Rock Hill, SC, 29730 (803) 328-6518
Admin Doris M Singley.
Licensure Intermediate Care. *Beds* 62. *Certified* Medicaid.
Admissions Requirements Medical examination.
Staff LPNs 6 (ft), 6 (pt); Nurses aides 11 (ft), 8 (pt); Activities coordinators 1 (ft); Dietitians 1 (ft).
Facilities Dining room; Physical therapy room; Laundry room; Barber/Beauty shop.
Activities Arts and Crafts; Cards; Games; Prayer groups; Movies; Shopping trips; Dances/Social or cultural gatherings.

Meadow Haven Nursing Center*
PO Box 4478, 205 S Herlong Ave, Rock Hill, SC, 29730 (803) 366-7133
Admin Thomas Leonard.
Licensure Skilled Care; Intermediate Care.
Beds 44. *Certified* Medicaid; Medicare.

Rock Hill Convalescent Center*
1915 Ebenezer Rd, Rock Hill, SC, 29730 (803) 366-8155
Admin Brenda Parris.
Licensure Skilled Care; Intermediate Care.
Beds 141. *Certified* Medicaid; Medicare.

SAINT GEORGE

St George Health Care Center Inc*
PO Box 187, Saint George, SC, 29477
Admin William M Rogers Sr.
Licensure Skilled Care. *Beds* 88. *Certified* Medicaid.

SALUDA

Saluda Nursing Center
Hwy 121, PO Box 398, Saluda, SC, 29138 (803) 445-2146
Admin Robert F Bowles. *Medical Dir/Dir of Nursing* Robert L Sawyer MD.
Licensure Skilled Care; Intermediate Care.
Beds SNF 88; ICF 44. *Certified* Medicaid; Medicare.
Admissions Requirements Minimum age 14; Medical examination.
Staff Physicians 3 (ft); RNs 5 (ft), 4 (pt); LPNs 14 (ft); Nurses aides 52 (ft), 2 (pt); Activities coordinators 2 (ft), 1 (pt).
Facilities Dining room; Physical therapy room; Activities room; Chapel; Crafts room; Laundry room; Barber/Beauty shop.
Activities Arts and Crafts; Cards; Games; Reading groups; Prayer groups; Movies; Shopping trips; Dances/Social or cultural gatherings.

SCRANTON

ANEA—Golden Years Nursing Center
Hwy S-41, Scranton, SC, 29591 (803) 389-2787
Admin Roy Drake.
Licensure Skilled Care; Intermediate Care.
Beds 74. *Certified* Medicaid; Medicare.

SENECA

Lila Doyle Nursing Care Facility
Westminster Hwy 123, PO Box 858, Seneca, SC, 29678 (803) 882-3351
Admin W H Hudson. *Medical Dir/Dir of Nursing* D A Richardson MD.
Licensure Skilled Care; Intermediate Care.
Beds 79. *Certified* Medicaid; Medicare.
Staff Physicians 20 (pt); RNs 3 (ft), 6 (pt); LPNs 9 (ft), 3 (pt); Orderlies 3 (ft), 1 (pt); Nurses aides 26 (ft), 9 (pt); Physical therapists 2 (pt); Activities coordinators 1 (ft); Dietitians 1 (ft).
Facilities Dining room; Physical therapy room; Activities room; Chapel; Crafts room; Barber-/Beauty shop; Library.

Activities Arts and Crafts; Cards; Games; Reading groups; Prayer groups; Movies; Shopping trips.

Oconee Geriatric Center Inc*
PO Box 189, Hwy 59, Seneca, SC, 29678 (803) 882-1642
Admin Leslie D Parks.
Licensure Skilled Care; Intermediate Care.
Beds 88. *Certified* Medicaid; Medicare.

Seneca Community Residence*
Rt 1, Box 31-A, Hwy 188, Seneca, SC, 29678 (803) 882-2126
Admin Vicki Neely.
Licensure Intermediate Care for Mentally Retarded. *Beds* 16. *Certified* Medicare.

SIMPSONVILLE

J Health Care Center*
PO Box 757, Hwy 14 S, Laurens Rd, Simpsonville, SC, 29681 (803) 963-3666
Admin Mary G Anderson.
Licensure Skilled Care; Intermediate Care.
Beds 88. *Certified* Medicaid; Medicare.

Palmetto Convalescent Center Inc*
721 W Curtis St, Simpsonville, SC, 29681 (803) 967-7191
Admin Joseph D Schofield.
Licensure Intermediate Care. *Beds* 42. *Certified* Medicaid; Medicare.

SIX MILE

Harvey's Love and Care Home*
Rt 1, Box 515, Hwy 183 W, Six Mile, SC, 29682 (803) 868-2307
Admin Helen D Towe.
Licensure Intermediate Care. *Beds* 40. *Certified* Medicaid; Medicare.

SPARTANBURG

Lakeview Nursing Center
Rt 13, Hwy 585, Spartanburg, SC, 29303 (803) 578-2523
Admin Patsy P Jewell. *Medical Dir/Dir of Nursing* Dr Lawrence A Heavrin.
Licensure Skilled Care; Intermediate Care.
Beds 44. *Certified* Medicaid; Medicare.
Admissions Requirements Minimum age 18; Medical examination; Physician's request.
Staff RNs 1 (ft), 3 (pt); LPNs 5 (ft), 3 (pt); Nurses aides 12 (ft), 6 (pt); Activities coordinators 1 (ft); Dietitians 4 (ft), 3 (pt).
Facilities Dining room; Activities room; Crafts room.
Activities Arts and Crafts; Games; Reading groups; Prayer groups; Movies.

Mountainview Nursing Home*
340 Cedar Springs Rd, Spartanburg, SC, 29302 (803) 582-4175
Admin Wilson K Dillard.
Licensure Skilled Care; Intermediate Care.
Beds 88. *Certified* Medicaid; Medicare.

Pinewood Convalescent Center
375 Serpentine Dr, Spartanburg, SC, 29303 (803) 585-0218
Admin Martha G Cathcart. *Medical Dir/Dir of Nursing* Warren C Lovett MD.
Licensure Skilled Care; Intermediate Care.
Beds 95. *Certified* Medicaid; Medicare.
Admissions Requirements Minimum age 12; Physician's request.
Staff Physicians 1 (pt); RNs 6 (ft); LPNs 9 (ft); Orderlies 1 (ft); Nurses aides 33 (ft); Physical therapists 1 (pt); Recreational therapists 1 (ft); Speech therapists 1 (pt); Activities coordinators 1 (ft); Dietitians 1 (ft); Dentists 1 (pt); Podiatrists 1 (pt).
Facilities Dining room; Activities room; Crafts room; Laundry room; Barber/Beauty shop.
Activities Arts and Crafts; Games; Reading groups; Prayer groups; Shopping trips.
Description Facility is less than 200 feet from 650-bed hospital.

Spartanburg Community Residence 1
29 Long Dr, Spartanburg, SC, 29302 (803) 582-8842
Admin R B Williams. *Medical Dir/Dir of Nursing* Dr Ron Tollison.
Licensure Intermediate Care for Mentally Retarded. *Beds* 15. *Certified* Medicare.
Admissions Requirements Medical examination.
Staff Physicians 1 (ft); RNs 1 (ft); LPNs 2 (ft); Recreational therapists 1 (ft); Activities coordinators 1 (ft); Dietitians 1 (ft).
Facilities Dining room; Activities room; Crafts room; Laundry room.
Activities Arts and Crafts; Cards; Games; Reading groups; Movies; Shopping trips; Dances/Social or cultural gatherings.

Spartanburg Commununity Residence 2
29 Long Dr, Spartanburg, SC, 29302 (803) 582-8842
Admin R B Williams. *Medical Dir/Dir of Nursing* Dr Ron Tollison.
Licensure Intermediate Care for Mentally Retarded. *Beds* 15. *Certified* Medicare.
Admissions Requirements Medical examination.
Staff Physicians 1 (ft); RNs 1 (ft); LPNs 2 (ft); Recreational therapists 1 (ft); Activities coordinators 1 (ft); Dietitians 1 (ft).
Facilities Dining room; Activities room; Crafts room; Laundry room.
Activities Arts and Crafts; Cards; Games; Reading groups; Movies; Shopping trips; Dances/Social or cultural gatherings.

Spartanburg Convalescent Center Inc*
PO Box 4246, 295 E Pearl St, Spartanburg, SC, 29303 (803) 585-0241
Admin Oliver K Cecil.
Licensure Skilled Care; Intermediate Care.
Beds 148. *Certified* Medicaid; Medicare.

SUMMERVILLE

Presbyterian Home of South Carolina— Summerville*
Box 140, 9th N, Summerville, SC, 29483 (803) 873-2550
Admin Charles R Tapp.

Licensure Skilled Care; Intermediate Care.
Beds 90.
Ownership Nonprofit.
Affiliation Presbyterian

SUMTER

Community Intermediate Care Facility
703 Broad St, Sumter, SC, 29150 (803) 773-6525
Admin Harold Hallums. *Medical Dir/Dir of Nursing* Dr Brenda Williams.
Licensure Intermediate Care. *Beds* 20. *Certified* Medicaid; Medicare.
Staff LPNs 3 (ft), 1 (pt); Nurses aides 5 (ft), 2 (pt); Activities coordinators 1 (ft), 1 (pt).
Facilities Dining room; Laundry room.
Activities Arts and Crafts; Games; Shopping trips.

Cypress Nursing Facility Inc
Carolina Ave, PO Box 1526, Sumter, SC, 29150 (803) 775-5394
Admin Janice G Jones. *Medical Dir/Dir of Nursing* Dr R Lee Denny.
Licensure Skilled Care. *Beds* 88. *Certified* Medicaid; Medicare.
Admissions Requirements Medical examination; Physician's request.
Staff RNs 4 (ft), 1 (pt); LPNs 6 (ft), 2 (pt); Orderlies 4 (ft), 1 (pt); Nurses aides 28 (ft); Activities coordinators 1 (pt); Dietitians 1 (pt).
Facilities Dining room; Physical therapy room; Activities room; Laundry room; Barber/Beauty shop.
Activities Arts and Crafts; Cards; Games; Reading groups; Prayer groups; Dances/Social or cultural gatherings.
Description Facility features 24-hour skilled care, private and semi-private rooms. Physical, speech, and occupational therapy; approved by Medicare, Medicaid, VA, Champus - BCBS, South Carolina DEHC; Members of American Health Care Association and South Carolina Health Care Association.

Hampton Nursing Center Inc
975 Miller Rd, Sumter, SC, 29150 (803) 795-8376
Admin Wade H Jones Jr. *Medical Dir/Dir of Nursing* Lee Denny MD.
Licensure Skilled Care; Intermediate Care.
Beds 88. *Certified* Medicaid; Medicare.
Admissions Requirements Medical examination.
Staff RNs; LPNs; Orderlies; Nurses aides; Physical therapists; Occupational therapists.
Facilities Dining room; Physical therapy room; Activities room; Laundry room; Barber/Beauty shop.
Activities Arts and Crafts; Cards; Games; Reading groups; Prayer groups.

Hopewell Intermediate Care Center*
Pinewood Rd, PO Box 818, Sumter, SC, 29150 (803) 481-8591
Admin Eleanor B Moses. *Medical Dir/Dir of Nursing* Dr R E McDowell.
Licensure Intermediate Care. *Beds* 96. *Certified* Medicaid; Medicare.
Admissions Requirements Minimum age 14; Medical examination.

Williamsburg Nursing Center*
PO Box 1524, 1018 N Guignard Dr, Sumter, SC, 29150 (803) 773-5567
Admin William P Betchman.
Licensure Skilled Care; Intermediate Care.
Beds 100. *Certified* Medicaid; Medicare.

TRAVELERS REST

Oakmont North Nursing Center*
6 Hart St, Travelers Rest, SC, 29690
Admin Ann A Crittenden.
Licensure Skilled Care; Intermediate Care.
Beds 22. *Certified* Medicaid; Medicare.

UNION

Ellen Sagar Nursing Home
Spartanburg Hwy #176, Union, SC, 29379
(803) 427-9533
Admin Leo Melle Newton. *Medical Dir/Dir of Nursing* Dr Boyd Hames.
Licensure Skilled Care; Intermediate Care.
Beds 64. *Certified* Medicaid; Medicare.
Admissions Requirements Minimum age 15.
Staff RNs 3 (ft), 3 (pt); LPNs 6 (ft); Nurses aides 25 (ft), 3 (pt); Physical therapists 1 (pt); Activities coordinators 1 (ft); Dietitians 1 (ft); Dentists 1 (pt).
Facilities Dining room; Physical therapy room; Activities room; Chapel; Laundry room; Barber/Beauty shop.
Activities Arts and Crafts; Games; Reading groups; Prayer groups; Movies; Dances/Social or cultural gatherings.

Oakmont of Union*
201 Rice St Extension, Union, SC, 29379
Admin Frances A Harvey.
Licensure Skilled Care; Intermediate Care.
Beds 44. *Certified* Medicaid; Medicare.

WALTERBORO

Oakwood Health Care Center Inc*
PO Box 1154, 401 Witsell St, Walterboro, SC, 29488 (803) 549-5546
Admin Mack B Whittle.
Licensure Skilled Care; Intermediate Care.
Beds 40. *Certified* Medicaid; Medicare.

Walterboro Community Residence*
505 Forest Circle, Walterboro, SC, 29488
Admin Wilson V Inabiet, Jr.
Licensure Skilled Care; Intermediate Care.
Beds 8.

WEST COLUMBIA

Manor Care of Lexington Inc*
2416 Sunset Blvd, West Columbia, SC, 29169
(803) 796-8024
Admin Melvin Stepp.
Licensure Skilled Care; Intermediate Care.
Beds 82. *Certified* Medicaid; Medicare.

South Carolina Episcopal Home at Still Hopes
7th St Extension, West Columbia, SC, 29169
Medical Dir/Dir of Nursing Dr James Ebersole.

Admissions Requirements Minimum age 55; Medical examination.
Staff Physicians 1 (pt); RNs 2 (ft), 1 (pt); LPNs 2 (ft), 1 (pt); Nurses aides 6 (ft), 3 (pt); Physical therapists 1 (pt); Activities coordinators 2 (pt); Dietitians 1 (pt).
Affiliation Episcopal
Facilities Dining room; Physical therapy room; Chapel; Laundry room; Barber/Beauty shop; Library.
Activities Arts and Crafts; Cards; Games; Prayer groups; Movies; Shopping trips; Dances/Social or cultural gatherings.
Description Must be a member of the Still Hopes community to be admitted; duplex cottages are a part of the community.

South Carolina Vocational Rehabilitation Comprehensive Center
1400 Boston Ave, West Columbia, SC, 29169
(803) 758-8731
Admin Jack B Herndon. *Medical Dir/Dir of Nursing* J Robert Dunn III MD.
Licensure Intermediate Care. *Beds* 18. *Certified* Medicare.
Staff Physicians 1 (pt); RNs 1 (ft), 2 (pt); LPNs 4 (ft), 1 (pt); Nurses aides 1 (ft), 3 (pt); Physical therapists 1 (ft); Recreational therapists 2 (ft); Occupational therapists 1 (ft); Speech therapists 1 (ft); Dietitians 1 (ft).
Facilities Dining room; Physical therapy room; Activities room; Crafts room; Laundry room; Library.
Activities Arts and Crafts; Cards; Games; Reading groups; Movies; Shopping trips; Dances/Social or cultural gatherings.

WHITE ROCK

Lowman Home—Wynne C Boliek
PO Box 444, White Rock, SC, 29177 (803) 781-3919
Admin J Kenneth Webb. *Medical Dir/Dir of Nursing* Robert K Moxon MD.
Licensure Skilled Care; Intermediate Care.
Beds 85. *Certified* Medicare.
Admissions Requirements Minimum age 18; Medical examination; Physician's request.
Staff Physicians 3 (pt); RNs 8 (ft), 4 (pt); LPNs 4 (ft), 4 (pt); Orderlies 5 (ft), 1 (pt); Nurses aides 86 (ft), 14 (pt); Physical therapists 1 (pt); Recreational therapists 1 (ft); Activities coordinators 1 (ft); Dietitians 1 (ft), 1 (pt); Dentists 1 (pt).
Affiliation Lutheran
Facilities Dining room; Activities room; Chapel; Crafts room; Barber/Beauty shop; Library.
Activities Arts and Crafts; Cards; Games; Reading groups; Prayer groups; Movies; Shopping trips; Dances/Social or cultural gatherings.
Description Facility features a full-time educational and training center for residents and staff for Southern Theological Seminary and University of South Carolina College of Nursing.

WILLISTON

Kirkland Convalescent Home Inc*
PO Box 250, Hwy 78, Williston, SC, 29853
(803) 266-3229
Admin Barbara T Kirkland.
Licensure Intermediate Care. *Beds* 20. *Certi-

fied Medicaid; Medicare.

YORK

Divine Saviour Nursing Home*
PO Box 629, 111 S Congress St, York, SC, 29745 (803) 684-4231
Admin John W Bailey.
Licensure Skilled Care. *Beds* 51. *Certified* Medicaid; Medicare.

SOUTH DAKOTA

ABERDEEN

Aberdeen Nursing Center*
1700 N Hwy 281, Aberdeen, SD, 57401 (605)
225-7315
Admin Craig Prokupek.
Licensure Skilled Care; Intermediate Care.
Beds SNF 46; ICF 126. *Certified* Medicaid.

Americana Healthcare Center*
400 8th Ave NW, Aberdeen, SD, 57401 (605)
225-2550
Admin Dolores Inman.
Licensure Skilled Care. *Beds* 69. *Certified* Medicaid; Medicare.

Bethesda Home of Aberdeen
1224 S High St, Aberdeen, SD, 57401 (605)
225-7580
Admin Bob Vevle. *Medical Dir/Dir of Nursing* Dr William Bormes.
Licensure Skilled Care; Supervised Care.
Beds SNF 85; ICF Supervised Care 1. *Certified* Medicaid.
Affiliation Lutheran
Facilities Dining room; Physical therapy room; Activities room; Chapel; Crafts room; Laundry room; Barber/Beauty shop; Library; Childrens daycare.
Activities Arts and Crafts; Cards; Games; Reading groups; Prayer groups; Movies; Shopping trips; Dances/Social or cultural gatherings.

Mother Joseph Manor
1002 N Jay, Aberdeen, SD, 57401 (605)
229-0550
Admin Gertrude Mangan. *Medical Dir/Dir of Nursing* J P Chang MD.
Licensure Skilled Care; Intermediate Care.
Beds SNF 50; ICF 30. *Certified* Medicaid.
Admissions Requirements Medical examination; Physician's request.
Staff RNs 2 (ft), 3 (pt); LPNs 1 (ft), 4 (pt); Orderlies 2 (pt); Nurses aides 5 (ft), 15 (pt); Activities coordinators 1 (ft); Dietitians 1 (ft).
Affiliation Roman Catholic
Facilities Dining room; Physical therapy room; Activities room; Chapel; Crafts room; Laundry room; Barber/Beauty shop; Library.
Activities Arts and Crafts; Cards; Games; Reading groups; Prayer groups; Movies; Shopping trips; Dances/Social or cultural gatherings.

Description Facility features outreach program, adult day care, blood pressure screening clinics, respite care, and family support council.

ALCESTER

Morningside Manor
Box 188, Alcester, SD, 57001 (605) 934-2011
Admin Dorothy Millage. *Medical Dir/Dir of Nursing* James Daggett MD.
Licensure Skilled Care; Intermediate Care.
Beds SNF 42; ICF 42. *Certified* Medicaid; Medicare.
Staff Physicians; RNs; LPNs; Orderlies; Nurses aides; Physical therapists; Recreational therapists; Occupational therapists; Speech therapists; Activities coordinators; Dietitians; Dentists.
Facilities Dining room; Physical therapy room; Activities room; Crafts room; Laundry room; Barber/Beauty shop; Library.
Activities Arts and Crafts; Cards; Games; Reading groups; Prayer groups; Movies; Shopping trips; Dances/Social or cultural gatherings.
Description Facility features a campus setting covering all facets of health care. Inpatient, outpatient, patient home health care, meals on wheels, apartments-independent living, ambulance are all available.

ARLINGTON

Arlington Care Center
403 N 4th St, Arlington, SD, 57212 (605)
983-5796
Admin Layne Gross.
Licensure Skilled Care. *Beds* 52. *Certified* Medicaid.
Staff RNs 3 (ft), 2 (pt); LPNs 1 (ft), 1 (pt); Orderlies 4 (ft); Nurses aides 8 (ft), 3 (pt); Activities coordinators 2 (ft); Dietitians 1 (pt).
Facilities Dining room; Activities room; Chapel; Crafts room; Laundry room; Barber/Beauty shop.
Activities Arts and Crafts; Cards; Games; Reading groups; Prayer groups; Movies; Shopping trips; Dances/Social or cultural gatherings.
Description Facility is owned by Beverly Enterprises.

ARMOUR

Colonial Manor of Armour
Armour, SD, 57313 (605) 724-2546
Admin Elsie S Jensen. *Medical Dir/Dir of Nursing* Dr Ronald Price.
Licensure Skilled Care. *Beds* 45. *Certified* Medicaid.
Admissions Requirements Medical examination.
Staff RNs 1 (ft), 2 (pt); LPNs 2 (ft), 2 (pt); Nurses aides 5 (ft), 6 (pt); Physical therapists 1 (pt); Occupational therapists 1 (pt); Speech therapists 1 (pt); Activities coordinators 1 (ft), 1 (pt).
Facilities Dining room; Physical therapy room; Activities room; Chapel; Laundry room; Barber/Beauty shop.
Activities Arts and Crafts; Cards; Games; Reading groups; Prayer groups; Movies; Dances/Social or cultural gatherings.

BELLE FOURCHE

Belle Fourche Health Care Center—Long Term Care Unit*
2200 13th Ave, Belle Fourche, SD, 57717 (605)
892-3331
Admin Larry Potter.
Licensure Skilled Care; Intermediate Care.
Beds SNF 50; ICF 50. *Certified* Medicaid.

Julia Olson Rest Home
1112 6th St, Belle Fourche, SD, 57717 (605)
892-4187
Admin Julia Olson.
Licensure Supervised Care. *Beds* 4.

BERESFORD

Bethesda Home for the Aged
Rt 2, Box 3, Beresford, SD, 57004 (605)
957-4122
Admin Paul Collins. *Medical Dir/Dir of Nursing* Dr Nelson.
Licensure Skilled Care. *Beds* 80. *Certified* Medicaid.
Admissions Requirements Medical examination.
Staff Physicians 4 (pt); RNs 3 (ft), 3 (pt); LPNs 3 (pt); Orderlies 1 (pt); Nurses aides 10 (ft), 25 (pt); Physical therapists 1 (pt); Occupational therapists 1 (pt); Speech therapists 1 (pt);

Activities coordinators 1 (ft), 3 (pt); Dietitians 1 (pt); Dentists 1 (pt).
Facilities Dining room; Activities room; Chapel; Crafts room; Laundry room; Barber/Beauty shop.
Activities Arts and Crafts; Cards; Games; Reading groups; Prayer groups; Movies; Shopping trips; Dances/Social or cultural gatherings.
Description Bethesda Home is a skilled nursing facility that is a Christian-oriented home. Our care reflects the Christian ethic. Our home is in a country setting providing excellent service.

BOWDLE

Bowdle Nursing Home—Adventist Health System
Bowdle, SD, 57428 (605) 285-6391
Admin Dave Green.
Licensure Intermediate Care. *Beds* 40. *Certified* Medicaid.
Staff RNs 1 (ft), 1 (pt); LPNs 1 (pt); Nurses aides 10 (ft), 3 (pt); Activities coordinators 1 (ft); Dietitians 1 (ft).
Affiliation Seventh-Day Adventist
Facilities Dining room; Activities room; Laundry room; Barber/Beauty shop.
Activities Arts and Crafts; Cards; Games; Reading groups; Prayer groups; Movies; Shopping trips; Dances/Social or cultural gatherings.

BRIDGEWATER

Diamond Care Center*
PO Box 300, Bridgewater, SD, 57319 (605) 729-2525
Admin Ivo J Weber.
Licensure Intermediate Care. *Beds* 56. *Certified* Medicaid.

BRISTOL

Sun Dial Manor*
PO Box 337, Bristol, SD, 57219 (605) 492-3615
Admin Gary Baule.
Licensure Intermediate Care. *Beds* 37. *Certified* Medicaid.

BRITTON

Marshall Manor*
PO Box 939, Britton, SD, 57430 (605) 448-2251
Admin Robert Marx.
Licensure Intermediate Care. *Beds* 63. *Certified* Medicaid.

BROOKINGS

Brookview Manor
300 22nd Ave, Brookings, SD, 57006 (605) 692-6351
Admin Robert Polk. *Medical Dir/Dir of Nursing* Dr Bruce Lushbough MD.
Licensure Skilled Care. *Beds* 79. *Certified* Medicaid.
Admissions Requirements Physician's request.
Staff RNs 3 (ft), 9 (pt); LPNs 5 (ft), 6 (pt); Orderlies 3 (ft), 1 (pt); Nurses aides 6 (ft), 24

(pt); Reality therapists 1 (ft); Activities coordinators 1 (ft), 1 (pt); Dietitians 1 (pt).
Facilities Dining room; Physical therapy room; Activities room; Chapel; Crafts room; Laundry room; Barber/Beauty shop.
Activities Arts and Crafts; Cards; Games; Reading groups; Prayer groups; Movies; Shopping trips; Dances/Social or cultural gatherings; Camping.
Description Our overnight camping experience has been very successful. Residents, together with volunteers (employees give their time), have gone to a nearby lake (campgrounds with cabins/lodge) for overnight.

United Retirement Center
405 1st Ave, Brookings, SD, 57006 (605) 692-5351
Admin David B Johnson.
Licensure Intermediate Care. *Beds* 60. *Certified* Medicaid.
Admissions Requirements Medical examination; Physician's request.
Staff Physicians 8 (pt); RNs 1 (ft), 3 (pt); LPNs 3 (pt); Nurses aides 5 (ft), 13 (pt); Reality therapists 1 (pt); Activities coordinators 3 (pt); Dietitians 1 (pt); Dentists 1 (pt); Ophthalmologists 1 (pt); Podiatrists 1 (pt).
Facilities Dining room; Physical therapy room; Activities room; Chapel; Laundry room; Barber/Beauty shop.
Activities Arts and Crafts; Cards; Games; Reading groups; Prayer groups; Movies; Shopping trips; Dances/Social or cultural gatherings; Campouts; Outings.
Description Facility is located on the edge of a city park.

BRYANT

Parkview Care Center
Bryant, SD, 57221 (605) 628-2771
Admin Robert Gergen. *Medical Dir/Dir of Nursing* Dr G R Bell.
Licensure Intermediate Care. *Beds* 52. *Certified* Medicaid.
Admissions Requirements Medical examination.
Staff RNs 1 (ft), 3 (pt); LPNs 2 (ft), 2 (pt); Orderlies 1 (ft); Nurses aides 9 (ft), 12 (pt); Physical therapists 1 (pt); Activities coordinators 1 (ft); Dietitians 1 (pt).
Facilities Dining room; Activities room; Chapel; Crafts room; Laundry room; Barber/Beauty shop.
Activities Arts and Crafts; Cards; Games; Reading groups; Prayer groups; Movies; Shopping trips; Dances/Social or cultural gatherings.

CANISTOTA

Good Samaritan Center*
PO Box 6, Canistota, SD, 57012 (605) 296-3442
Admin Norman Bergquist.
Licensure Intermediate Care; Supervised Care. *Beds* ICF 58; Supervised Care 6. *Certified* Medicaid.

CANTON

Good Samaritan Center*
PO Box 198, Canton, SD, 57013 (605) 987-2696
Admin John B Larson.
Licensure Skilled Care; Intermediate Care. *Beds* SNF 68; ICF 10. *Certified* Medicaid.

CENTERVILLE

Good Samaritan Center
500 Vermillion, PO Box 190, Centerville, SD, 57014 (605) 563-2251
Licensure Intermediate Care; Supervised Care. *Beds* ICF 56; Supervised Care 4. *Certified* Medicaid.
Admissions Requirements Medical examination; Physician's request.
Staff RNs 1 (ft).
Facilities Dining room; Physical therapy room; Activities room; Chapel; Crafts room; Laundry room; Barber/Beauty shop; Library.
Activities Arts and Crafts; Cards; Games; Reading groups; Prayer groups; Movies; Shopping trips; Dances/Social or cultural gatherings.

CHAMBERLAIN

Sunset Valley Haven
211 W 16th St, Chamberlain, SD, 57325 (605) 734-6518
Admin Janet Evangelisto. *Medical Dir/Dir of Nursing* Dr John Jones.
Licensure Skilled Care. *Beds* 52. *Certified* Mcdicaid.
Staff RNs 1 (ft), 2 (pt); LPNs 1 (ft), 3 (pt); Nurses aides 6 (ft), 13 (pt); Activities coordinators 1 (ft), 1 (pt); Dietitians 1 (pt).
Facilities Dining room; Activities room; Crafts room; Laundry room; Barber/Beauty shop.
Activities Arts and Crafts; Cards; Games; Reading groups; Prayer groups; Movies; Shopping trips; Dances/Social or cultural gatherings.
Description We also provide meals on wheels to the community and operate a public transportation system for the elderly and handicapped.

CLARK

Clark Nursing Home*
201 NW 8th Ave, Clark, SD, 57225 (605) 532-3641
Admin Joyce Helkenn.
Licensure Skilled Care. *Beds* 45. *Certified* Medicaid.

CLEAR LAKE

Deuel County Samaritan Center
913 4th Ave S, Clear Lake, SD, 57226 (605) 874-2159
Admin Daisy Bergjord. *Medical Dir/Dir of Nursing* Dr H Dean Hughes.
Licensure Skilled Care. *Beds* SNF 44. *Certified* Medicaid.
Affiliation Lutheran
Facilities Dining room; Activities room; Chapel; Crafts room; Laundry room; Barber/Beauty

shop; Library.
Activities Arts and Crafts; Cards; Games; Reading groups; Prayer groups; Movies; Shopping trips.

CORSICA

Pleasant View Nursing Home
Good Samaritan Society, Corsica, SD, 57328 (605) 946-5467
Admin Verle Ralston.
Licensure Intermediate Care. *Beds* 62. *Certified* Medicaid.
Admissions Requirements Medical examination; Physician's request.
Staff RNs 1 (ft), 3 (pt); LPNs 1 (ft), 2 (pt); Nurses aides 21 (pt); Physical therapists 1 (pt); Reality therapists 1 (pt); Speech therapists 1 (pt); Activities coordinators 1 (ft), 1 (pt); Dietitians 1 (pt).
Affiliation Lutheran
Facilities Dining room; Activities room; Chapel; Crafts room; Laundry room; Barber/Beauty shop; Library; Conference room.
Activities Arts and Crafts; Cards; Games; Reading groups; Prayer groups; Movies; Shopping trips; Dances/Social or cultural gatherings; Bible study.
Description Our facility enjoys the services of 16 pastors. All churches come to the facility at least twice a year on Thursday evenings to present musical programs. Each meal is preceded and followed with prayer. A 20 minute daily devotion is also provided.

CUSTER

Colonial Manor of Custer*
1065 Montgomery St, Custer, SD, 57730 (605) 673-2237
Admin Gerald Woodford.
Licensure Skilled Care. *Beds* 80. *Certified* Medicaid.

DE SMET

Good Samaritan Center
411 Calumet Ave, De Smet, SD, 57231 (605) 854-3327
Admin Jerry Keller.
Licensure Intermediate Care; Supervised Care.
Beds ICF 62; Supervised Care 10. *Certified* Medicaid.
Staff RNs 1 (ft), 2 (pt); LPNs 1 (ft), 4 (pt); Nurses aides 10 (ft), 18 (pt); Activities coordinators 1 (ft), 1 (pt).
Facilities Dining room; Activities room; Chapel; Crafts room; Laundry room; Barber/Beauty shop; Library.
Activities Arts and Crafts; Cards; Games; Reading groups; Prayer groups; Movies; Shopping trips; Dances/Social or cultural gatherings.
Description De Smet is located in east central South Dakota at the site of the famous "Little House on the Prairie" books by Laura Ingalls Wilder and from which the famous TV show has been adapted.

DEADWOOD

Friendship Home*
48 Highland, Deadwood, SD, 57732 (605) 578-2482
Admin LaEtta Heltibridle.
Licensure Supervised Care. *Beds* 8.

DELL RAPIDS

Odd Fellows Home
100 W 10th St, Dell Rapids, SD, 57022 (605) 428-3398
Admin Ervin Ommen.
Licensure Intermediate Care. *Beds* 54. *Certified* Medicaid.
Admissions Requirements Medical examination.
Staff Physicians 4 (pt); RNs 2 (ft), 2 (pt); LPNs 4 (ft), 1 (pt); Orderlies 1 (pt); Nurses aides 12 (ft); Activities coordinators 1 (ft); Dietitians 1 (pt); Dentists 1 (pt).
Affiliation Independent Order of Odd Fellows
Facilities Dining room; Activities room; Chapel; Crafts room; Laundry room; Barber/Beauty shop.
Activities Arts and Crafts; Cards; Games; Reading groups; Prayer groups; Movies; Shopping trips; Dances/Social or cultural gatherings.
Description Facility is located on large, spacious grounds with many large trees and wildlife. Plenty of walkways for long leisurely walks.

Terrace Manor*
1400 Thresher Dr, Dell Rapids, SD, 57022 (605) 428-5478
Admin Linda Ljunggren.
Licensure Skilled Care. *Beds* 76. *Certified* Medicaid.

ELK POINT

Prairie Estates
Elk Point, SD, 57025 (605) 356-2622
Admin Larry DeBaha. *Medical Dir/Dir of Nursing* Matt Marvel MD.
Licensure Intermediate Care. *Beds* 50. *Certified* Medicaid.
Admissions Requirements Medical examination; Physician's request.
Staff Physicians 1 (ft); RNs 2 (ft); LPNs 3 (ft); Orderlies 4 (ft); Nurses aides 15 (ft); Activities coordinators 1 (ft); Dietitians 1 (ft); Dentists 1 (ft).
Facilities Dining room; Activities room; Chapel; Crafts room; Laundry room; Barber/Beauty shop.
Activities Arts and Crafts; Cards; Games; Reading groups; Prayer groups; Movies; Shopping trips; Field trips.
Description We offer many field trips. We have formal dining once a month. Residents enjoy the peacefulness of country retirement.

ELKTON

Elkton Rest Home*
PO Box 327, Elkton, SD, 57026 (605) 542-7251
Admin Roween Cameron.

Licensure Supervised Care. *Beds* 10.

ESTELLINE

Estelline Nursing and Care Center
PO Box 190, Estelline, SD, 57234 (605) 873-2278
Admin Evelyn Saathoff. *Medical Dir/Dir of Nursing* K Yemmanur MD.
Licensure Skilled Care; Intermediate Care.
Beds SNF 30; ICF 30. *Certified* Medicaid.
Staff Physicians 2 (pt); RNs 2 (ft), 2 (pt); LPNs 3 (ft), 2 (pt); Nurses aides 15 (ft), 9 (pt); Activities coordinators 1 (pt).
Facilities Dining room; Physical therapy room, Crafts room; Barber/Beauty shop.
Activities Arts and Crafts; Cards; Games; Movies; Sing-a-longs; Ladies groups; Mens groups.

EUREKA

Lutheran Home
Eureka, SD, 57437 (605) 284-2534
Admin V R Just. *Medical Dir/Dir of Nursing* Dr Susan Ostrowski.
Licensure Intermediate Care. *Beds* 62. *Certified* Medicaid.
Admissions Requirements Medical examination; Physician's request.
Staff Physicians 2 (ft); RNs 2 (ft), 1 (pt); LPNs 2 (ft); Nurses aides 16 (ft), 14 (pt); Recreational therapists 1 (ft), 1 (pt); Occupational therapists 1 (ft); Activities coordinators 1 (ft), 1 (pt); Dietitians 1 (ft); Dentists 1 (ft); Ophthalmologists 1 (ft).
Affiliation Lutheran
Facilities Dining room; Activities room; Chapel; Crafts room; Laundry room; Barber/Beauty shop.
Activities Arts and Crafts; Cards; Games; Reading groups; Prayer groups; Movies; Shopping trips; Dances/Social or cultural gatherings; Fishing trips; Farm outings.
Description Residents have a rhythm band which goes to other facilities to perform; Masons take residents to Shrine circus each year.

FAULKTON

John P Shirk Memorial Home
Pearl and 13th Sts, Faulkton, SD, 57438 (605) 598-6214
Admin Pat Van Syoc. *Medical Dir/Dir of Nursing* Dr Kenneth Bartholomew.
Licensure Skilled Care; Intermediate Care.
Beds SNF 27; ICF 27. *Certified* Medicaid.
Admissions Requirements Medical examination.
Staff RNs 1 (ft), 6 (pt); LPNs 3 (ft), 1 (pt); Orderlies 1 (pt); Nurses aides 5 (ft), 23 (pt); Activities coordinators 1 (ft), 1 (pt).
Facilities Dining room; Activities room; Crafts room; Laundry room; Barber/Beauty shop.
Activities Arts and Crafts; Cards; Games; Reading groups; Prayer groups; Movies; Shopping trips; Dances/Social or cultural gatherings.
Description Our facility is in a small town setting providing home-style care and atmosphere. Our community is supportive of our facility

and we encourage community and facility interaction in all phases of living.

FLANDREAU

Riverview Manor*
611 E 2nd Ave, Flandreau, SD, 57028 (605) 997-2481
Admin JoAnn Lind.
Licensure Skilled Care. *Beds* 80. *Certified* Medicaid.

FREEMAN

Freeman Community Nursing Home*
PO Box 370, Freeman, SD, 57029 (605) 925-4231
Admin Larry Ravenburg.
Licensure Skilled Care; Intermediate Care. *Beds* SNF 54; ICF 5. *Certified* Medicaid.

Salem Mennonite Home for the Aged
106 W 7th St, Freeman, SD, 57029 (605) 925-4994
Admin Erwin Schrag.
Licensure Supervised Care. *Beds* 52.
Admissions Requirements Medical examination; Physician's request.
Staff RNs 1 (ft); Nurses aides 2 (ft), 2 (pt); Activities coordinators 1 (pt); Dietitians 1 (ft).
Affiliation Mennonite

GARRETSON

Palisade Manor*
920 4th St, Garretson, SD, 57030 (605) 594-3466
Admin Gloria Schultz.
Licensure Skilled Care; Intermediate Care. *Beds* SNF 16; ICF 62. *Certified* Medicaid.

GETTYSBURG

Oahe Manor
700 E Garfield, Gettysburg, SD, 57442 (605) 765-2461
Admin Timothy J Tracy.
Licensure Intermediate Care. *Beds* 70. *Certified* Medicaid.
Admissions Requirements Medical examination; Physician's request.
Staff RNs 1 (ft); LPNs 4 (ft); Nurses aides 34 (ft); Activities coordinators 1 (ft); Dietitians 1 (ft).
Facilities Dining room; Activities room; Chapel; Crafts room; Laundry room; Barber/Beauty shop.
Activities Arts and Crafts; Cards; Games; Reading groups; Prayer groups; Movies.

GREGORY

Rosebud Nursing Home*
300 Park St, Gregory, SD, 57533 (605) 835-8296
Admin Terry E Davis.
Licensure Skilled Care. *Beds* 58. *Certified* Medicaid; Medicare.

GROTON

Colonial Manor of Groton*
PO Box 418, Groton, SD, 57445 (605) 397-2365
Admin Ken Opp.
Licensure Skilled Care. *Beds* 60. *Certified* Medicaid.

HERREID

Good Samaritan Center
Herreid, SD, 57632 (605) 437-2425
Admin Dolores Riedlinger.
Licensure Supervised Care. *Beds* 27.
Admissions Requirements Medical examination.
Staff RNs 1 (pt); LPNs 1 (pt); Nurses aides 7 (ft).
Affiliation Lutheran
Facilities Dining room; Laundry room.
Activities Games; Shopping trips.

HIGHMORE

Highmore Nursing Home
Highmore, SD, 57345 (605) 852-2255
Admin Robert Bonato. *Medical Dir/Dir of Nursing* Kathy Freier.
Licensure Intermediate Care. *Beds* 48. *Certified* Medicaid.
Admissions Requirements Medical examination; Physician's request.
Staff Physicians 2 (pt); RNs 3 (pt); LPNs 4 (ft); Nurses aides 16 (ft), 3 (pt); Physical therapists 1 (pt); Reality therapists 1 (pt); Recreational therapists 1 (pt); Activities coordinators 1 (pt); Dietitians 1 (pt); Dentists 1 (pt); Podiatrists 1 (pt).
Facilities Dining room; Activities room; Laundry room; Barber/Beauty shop.
Activities Arts and Crafts; Cards; Games; Reading groups; Prayer groups; Movies; Shopping trips; Social hour.
Description Highmore Nursing Home is located in central South Dakota. It's a bright and cheery place with plenty of happy residents. We have weekly parties, free cable TV, and a loving staff.

HOSMER

Senior Citizen's Home
Hosmer, SD, 57448 (605) 283-2203
Admin Carol Ulmer. *Medical Dir/Dir of Nursing* Dr John McFee.
Licensure Intermediate Care. *Beds* 40. *Certified* Medicaid.
Admissions Requirements Medical examination; Physician's request.
Staff RNs 1 (ft), 2 (pt); LPNs 1 (ft); Nurses aides 6 (ft), 7 (pt); Activities coordinators 1 (ft), 1 (pt).
Facilities Dining room; Activities room; Chapel; Crafts room; Laundry room; Barber/Beauty shop.
Activities Arts and Crafts; Games; Reading groups; Prayer groups; Movies; Shopping trips; Dances/Social or cultural gatherings.
Description Facility is an attractive, clean, one-story brick building located in a quiet, rural set-

ting. Community takes pride in offering high quality care and the geniune touch of "home" with a kind, family atmosphere.

HOT SPRINGS

Lutheran Nursing Home*
209 N 16th St, Hot Springs, SD, 57747 (605) 745-3159
Admin James Rotert.
Licensure Intermediate Care. *Beds* 48. *Certified* Medicaid.
Affiliation Lutheran

HOWARD

Good Samaritan Center
Howard, SD, 57349 (605) 772-4481
Admin Leonard A Witt. *Medical Dir/Dir of Nursing* H J Sample MD.
Licensure Skilled Care; Supervised Care. *Beds* SNF 64; Supervised Care 12. *Certified* Medicaid.
Admissions Requirements Physician's request.
Staff Physicians 6 (pt); RNs 2 (ft), 9 (pt); LPNs 2 (pt); Nurses aides 12 (ft), 23 (pt); Activities coordinators 1 (ft), 2 (pt); Dietitians 1 (pt); Dentists 1 (pt).
Affiliation Lutheran
Facilities Dining room; Activities room; Chapel; Crafts room; Laundry room; Barber/Beauty shop.
Activities Cards; Games; Reading groups; Prayer groups; Movies; Shopping trips; Dances/Social or cultural gatherings.
Description Facility offers an annual bazaar, active residents' council; residents host parties for volunteers and other groups, active with 4-H groups, center open to local clubs, "History of Our Lives" drama group, family nights, public barbecues, and 20th anniversary celebration.

HUDSON

Colonial Manor of Hudson
Hwy 46 W, Hudson, SD, 57032 (605) 984-2244
Admin Leonard Dahl. *Medical Dir/Dir of Nursing* Monte Harvey DO.
Licensure Intermediate Care. *Beds* 42. *Certified* Medicaid.
Admissions Requirements Medical examination; Physician's request.
Staff Physicians 1 (pt); RNs 1 (ft), 1 (pt); LPNs 3 (pt); Nurses aides 24 (pt); Activities coordinators 1 (ft); Dietitians 1 (pt).
Facilities Dining room; Activities room; Chapel; Crafts room; Laundry room; Barber/Beauty shop; Library.
Activities Arts and Crafts; Cards; Games; Reading groups; Prayer groups; Movies; Shopping trips.
Description We have an outstanding activity department and volunteer program with excellent community relations. Our nursing department provides excellent care for our residents.

HURON

Huron Nursing Home*
PO Box 1277, Huron, SD, 57350 (605) 352-8471
Admin Sharon Grayson.
Licensure Skilled Care; Intermediate Care.
Beds SNF 125; ICF 38. *Certified* Medicaid; Medicare.

Violet Tschetter Memorial Home
50 7th St SE, Huron, SD, 57350 (605) 352-8533
Medical Dir/Dir of Nursing Dr Paul Hohm.
Licensure Skilled Care. *Beds* 58. *Certified* Medicaid.
Admissions Requirements Medical examination; Physician's request.
Staff RNs 1 (ft), 6 (pt); LPNs 3 (ft), 1 (pt); Nurses aides 15 (ft), 12 (pt); Activities coordinators 1 (ft); Dietitians 1 (pt).
Facilities Dining room; Activities room; Chapel; Crafts room; Laundry room; Barber-/Beauty shop.
Activities Arts and Crafts; Cards; Games; Reading groups; Prayer groups; Movies; Shopping trips; Dances/Social or cultural gatherings.

IPSWICH

Colonial Manor of Ipswich
Ipswich, SD, 57451 (605) 426-662
Admin Diane Horning. *Medical Dir/Dir of Nursing* John L McFee.
Licensure Skilled Care. *Beds* 59. *Certified* Medicaid.
Admissions Requirements Minimum age 16; Medical examination.
Staff RNs 3 (ft), 4 (pt); LPNs 2 (ft), 2 (pt); Nurses aides 11 (ft), 8 (pt); Activities coordinators 1 (ft), 2 (pt).
Facilities Dining room; Activities room; Chapel; Crafts room; Laundry room; Barber/Beauty shop; Library.
Activities Arts and Crafts; Cards; Games; Reading groups; Prayer groups; Movies; Shopping trips; Dances/Social or cultural gatherings.
Description The facility's best asset is a stable, caring staff. The most frequent compliment addresses the pleasant, warm atmosphere.

IRENE

Sunset Manor*
Irene, SD, 57037 (605) 263-3318
Admin Kathleen Stanage.
Licensure Intermediate Care. *Beds* 66. *Certified* Medicaid.

KADOKA

Kadoka Retirement Home
Kadoka, SD, 57543 (605) 837-2270
Admin Wilma Uhlir. *Medical Dir/Dir of Nursing* Dr L P Swisher.
Licensure Intermediate Care. *Beds* 35. *Certified* Medicaid.
Admissions Requirements Medical examination.
Staff Physicians 1 (ft), 1 (pt); RNs 1 (ft); LPNs 1 (ft), 1 (pt); Orderlies 1 (pt); Nurses aides 5 (ft), 5 (pt); Speech therapists 1 (pt); Activities coordinators 1 (ft); Dietitians 1 (pt).
Facilities Dining room; Laundry room; Barber-/Beauty shop.
Activities Arts and Crafts; Cards; Games; Reading groups; Prayer groups; Movies; Shopping trips.

LAKE ANDES

Lake Andes Health Care Center*
PO Box 129, Lake Andes, SD, 57356 (605) 487-7674
Admin Lennis Spicer.
Licensure Intermediate Care. *Beds* 52. *Certified* Medicaid.

LAKE NORDEN

Lake Norden Care Center
Lake Norden, SD, 57248 (605) 783-3654
Admin Joe Ward. *Medical Dir/Dir of Nursing* Dr G R Bartron.
Licensure Skilled Care. *Beds* 63. *Certified* Medicaid.
Staff RNs 2 (ft); LPNs 3 (ft), 2 (pt); Nurses aides 10 (ft), 10 (pt); Physical therapists 1 (pt); Activities coordinators 1 (ft), 1 (pt); Dietitians 1 (pt).
Facilities Dining room; Physical therapy room; Activities room; Chapel; Crafts room; Laundry room; Barber/Beauty shop; Library.
Activities Arts and Crafts; Cards; Games; Reading groups; Prayer groups; Movies; Shopping trips; Dances/Social or cultural gatherings.

LAKE PRESTON

Kingsbury Memorial Manor*
PO Box 308, Lake Preston, SD, 57249 (605) 847-4405
Admin Charles Schulz.
Licensure Skilled Care; Intermediate Care.
Beds SNF 30; ICF 35. *Certified* Medicaid.

LEMMON

Five Counties Nursing Home*
PO Box 449, Lemmon, SD, 57638 (605) 374-3872
Admin Leslie O Urvand.
Licensure Skilled Care. *Beds* 32. *Certified* Medicaid.

LENNOX

Good Samaritan Center*
PO Box 78, Lennox, SD, 57039 (605) 647-2251
Admin Raymond Roti.
Licensure Skilled Care; Intermediate Care.
Beds SNF 60; ICF 9. *Certified* Medicaid.

LETCHER

Storla Sunset Home*
PO Box 46, Letcher, SD, 57359 (605) 248-2244
Admin L Burdell Nelson.
Licensure Intermediate Care. *Beds* 53. *Certified* Medicaid.

MADISON

Bethel Lutheran Home*
1001 S Egan Ave, Madison, SD, 57042 (605) 256-4539
Admin James T Iverson.
Licensure Skilled Care. *Beds* 59. *Certified* Medicaid.
Affiliation Lutheran

North American Baptist Home*
718 NE 8th St, Madison, SD, 57042 (605) 256-6621
Admin Mary DeWaard.
Licensure Skilled Care; Intermediate Care.
Beds SNF 42; ICF 20. *Certified* Medicaid.
Affiliation Baptist

MARION

The Tieszen Memorial Home*
Rt 1, Box 209, Marion, SD, 57043 (605) 648-3384
Admin Paul I Engbrecht.
Licensure Intermediate Care; Supervised Care.
Beds ICF 36; Supervised Care 28. *Certified* Medicaid.

MARTIN

Bennett County Nursing Home
PO Box 70-D, Martin, SD, 57551
Admin Darvin Jemming. *Medical Dir/Dir of Nursing* John Krecht MD.
Licensure Skilled Care. *Beds* 50. *Certified* Medicaid.
Ownership Public.
Staff Physicians 2 (ft); RNs 1 (ft), 2 (pt); LPNs 2 (ft), 6 (pt); Nurses aides 7 (ft), 9 (pt); Occupational therapists 1 (pt); Activities coordinators 1 (ft); Dietitians 1 (pt).

MENNO

Menno-Olivet Care Center
Menno, SD, 57045 (605) 387-5139
Admin Ted Boese. *Medical Dir/Dir of Nursing* Dr Kaufman.
Licensure Intermediate Care. *Beds* 49. *Certified* Medicaid.
Admissions Requirements Minimum age 21; Medical examination; Physician's request.
Staff RNs 1 (pt); LPNs 1 (ft), 2 (pt); Nurses aides 8 (ft), 4 (pt); Reality therapists 1 (ft); Recreational therapists 2 (pt); Activities coordinators 1 (ft); Dietitians 1 (pt).
Facilities Dining room; Physical therapy room; Activities room; Crafts room; Laundry room; Barber/Beauty shop.
Activities Arts and Crafts; Cards; Games; Reading groups; Prayer groups; Movies; Shopping trips.

MILBANK

Saint Williams Home for Aged
901 E Virgil Ave, Milbank, SD, 57252 (605)

432-4538
Admin Sr Bernardine Kauffmann. *Medical Dir/Dir of Nursing* V Janavs MD.
Licensure Intermediate Care; Supervised Care. *Beds* ICF 60; Supervised Care 15. *Certified* Medicaid.
Admissions Requirements Medical examination; Physician's request.
Staff Physicians 3 (pt); RNs 1 (ft); LPNs 4 (ft), 3 (pt); Nurses aides 13 (ft), 15 (pt); Activities coordinators 2 (ft).
Affiliation Roman Catholic
Facilities Dining room; Activities room; Chapel; Crafts room; Laundry room; Barber/Beauty shop.
Activities Arts and Crafts; Cards; Games; Reading groups; Prayer groups; Movies.

Whetstone Valley Nursing Home*
1103 S 2nd St, Milbank, SD, 57252 (605) 432-4556
Admin Terrance J Price.
Licensure Skilled Care. *Beds* 83. *Certified* Medicaid; Medicare.

MILLER

Prairie Good Samaritan Center
421 E 4th St, Miller, SD, 57362 (605) 853-2701
Admin Byron Israel. *Medical Dir/Dir of Nursing* Stephan Schroeder MD.
Licensure Skilled Care; Supervised Care. *Beds* SNF 64; Supervised Care 14. *Certified* Medicaid.
Staff RNs 1 (ft), 4 (pt); LPNs 2 (ft), 3 (pt); Nurses aides 18 (ft), 9 (pt); Activities coordinators 1 (ft), 1 (pt).
Affiliation Lutheran
Facilities Dining room; Activities room; Crafts room; Laundry room.
Activities Arts and Crafts; Cards; Games; Reading groups; Prayer groups; Movies; Shopping trips; Dances/Social or cultural gatherings.

MITCHELL

Brady Memorial Home
500 S Ohlman, Mitchell, SD, 57301 (605) 996-7701
Admin Irene Talbott. *Medical Dir/Dir of Nursing* W A Delaney MD.
Licensure Skilled Care. *Beds* 60. *Certified* Medicaid.
Admissions Requirements Medical examination.
Staff RNs 4 (ft), 2 (pt); LPNs 1 (pt); Nurses aides 7 (ft), 18 (pt); Activities coordinators 1 (ft), 1 (pt).
Affiliation Roman Catholic
Facilities Dining room; Activities room; Chapel; Crafts room; Laundry room; Barber/Beauty shop.
Activities Arts and Crafts; Cards; Games; Reading groups; Movies; Dances/Social or cultural gatherings.
Description Facility offers family support group, respite care, daily mass, weekly Protestant services, and free blood pressure screenings to the public.

Firesteel Heights Nursing Home
1120 E 7th St, Mitchell, SD, 57301 (605) 996-6526
Admin Fred Janklow.
Licensure Skilled Care; Intermediate Care. *Beds* SNF 66; ICF 20. *Certified* Medicaid.
Admissions Requirements Medical examination; Physician's request.
Facilities Dining room; Physical therapy room; Activities room; Crafts room; Laundry room; Barber/Beauty shop.
Activities Arts and Crafts; Cards; Games; Reading groups; Prayer groups; Movies; Shopping trips; Dances/Social or cultural gatherings.

Mitchell Retirement Home
101 S Main St, Mitchell, SD, 57301 (605) 996-6251
Admin Ronald D Gates.
Licensure Intermediate Care. *Beds* 82. *Certified* Medicaid.
Admissions Requirements Medical examination; Physician's request.
Staff RNs 2 (ft), 1 (pt); LPNs 3 (ft), 5 (pt); Orderlies 1 (ft); Nurses aides 14 (ft), 8 (pt); Recreational therapists 1 (ft); Activities coordinators 1 (ft); Dietitians 1 (pt).
Facilities Dining room; Activities room; Chapel; Crafts room.
Activities Arts and Crafts; Cards; Games; Reading groups; Prayer groups; Movies; Shopping trips; Dances/Social or cultural gatherings.
Description Facility offers fine food and excellent nursing care.

Mogck Home for Aged
1520 E 1st Ave, Mitchell, SD, 57301 (605) 996-2221
Admin Dolores Juhnke.
Licensure Supervised Care. *Beds* 11.
Staff LPNs 1 (ft); Nurses aides 3 (ft).
Facilities Dining room; Laundry room.
Activities Games; Movies; Shopping trips.

Mogck's Rest Home*
1510 E 1st Ave, Mitchell, SD, 57301 (605) 996-2221
Admin Dolores Juhnke.
Licensure Supervised Care. *Beds* 11.

Wilge Memorial Home
619 N Kittridge, Mitchell, SD, 57301 (605) 996-4280
Admin David E Miles.
Licensure Intermediate Care. *Beds* 23. *Certified* Medicaid.
Admissions Requirements Medical examination.
Staff RNs 1 (ft); LPNs 1 (ft), 2 (pt); Orderlies 1 (pt); Nurses aides 3 (pt); Dietitians 1 (pt).
Facilities Dining room; Activities room; Crafts room; Laundry room.
Activities Arts and Crafts; Cards; Games; Prayer groups; Movies; Shopping trips.

MOBRIDGE

Mobridge Care Center
1100 4th Ave E, Mobridge, SD, 57601 (605) 845-7201
Admin John Miller. *Medical Dir/Dir of Nursing* Dr Leonard Linde.

Licensure Skilled Care. *Beds* 127. *Certified* Medicaid.
Staff Physicians.
Facilities Dining room; Physical therapy room; Activities room; Chapel; Crafts room; Laundry room; Barber/Beauty shop.
Activities Arts and Crafts; Cards; Games; Reading groups; Prayer groups; Movies; Shopping trips; Dances/Social or cultural gatherings.

NEW UNDERWOOD

Good Samaritan Center
New Underwood, SD, 57761 (605) 754-6489
Admin J Lynn Thomas.
Licensure Intermediate Care. *Beds* 49. *Certified* Medicaid.
Admissions Requirements Medical examination.
Staff RNs 1 (ft); LPNs 2 (ft), 1 (pt); Nurses aides 7 (ft), 2 (pt); Activities coordinators 1 (ft); Dietitians 3 (ft), 4 (pt).
Facilities Dining room; Activities room; Crafts room; Laundry room; Barber/Beauty shop; Library.
Activities Arts and Crafts; Cards; Games; Prayer groups; Movies; Shopping trips; Dances/Social or cultural gatherings.
Description Our facility now has a puppy which has been very well accepted.

NEWELL

Lee's Rest Home
218 S Girard, Newell, SD, 57760 (605) 456-2108
Admin Norman Lee and Joan Lee.
Licensure Supervised Care. *Beds* 5.
Admissions Requirements Minimum age 50; Males only; Medical examination; Physician's request.
Facilities Dining room; Activities room; Crafts room; Laundry room.
Activities Arts and Crafts; Cards; Prayer groups; Shopping trips; Dances/Social or cultural gatherings.
Description Clients are active in the meals-on-wheels program, and gardening. We are looking forward to taking them on vacation to visit relatives.

PARKER

Hilltop Nursing Home
Box 218, Parker, SD, 57053 (605) 297-3488
Admin Maxine Christensen.
Licensure Intermediate Care. *Beds* 40. *Certified* Medicaid.
Admissions Requirements Medical examination; Physician's request.
Staff Physicians 3 (pt); RNs 1 (ft), 1 (pt); LPNs 1 (ft), 2 (pt); Nurses aides 4 (ft), 17 (pt); Recreational therapists 1 (pt); Activities coordinators 1 (ft); Dietitians 1 (pt).
Facilities Dining room; Activities room; Chapel; Crafts room; Laundry room; Barber/Beauty shop; Library.
Activities Arts and Crafts; Cards; Games; Reading groups; Prayer groups; Movies; Shopping trips; Dances/Social or cultural gatherings.
Description Facility provides air conditioned

building, cable TV, home-like atmosphere, 3 visiting doctors every 2 months, whirlpool, Sunday services, active activities program, qualified nursing staff, and nurse coverage 24-hours a day.

PARKSTON

Good Samaritan Center
205 E Ash, Parkston, SD, 57366 (605) 928-3561
Admin William B Bender.
Licensure Supervised Care. *Beds* 26.
Certified Medicaid.
Ownership Nonprofit.
Admissions Requirements Medical examination; Physician's request.
Staff LPNs 1 (pt); Nurses aides 7 (pt); Activities coordinators 1 (pt); Dietitians 1 (pt).
Affiliation Lutheran
Facilities Dining room; Activities room; Chapel; Crafts room.
Activities Arts and Crafts; Games; Movies; Dances/Social or cultural gatherings.
Description Facility is situated on the edge of town nestled amid beautiful farm land.

Good Samaritan Nursing Center
501 W Main, Parkston, SD, 57366 (605) 928-3384
Admin William B Bender.
Licensure Intermediate Care. *Beds* 47. *Certified* Medicaid.
Ownership Nonprofit.
Admissions Requirements Medical examination; Physician's request.
Staff RNs 1 (ft); LPNs 4 (ft); Nurses aides 4 (ft), 19 (pt); Activities coordinators 1 (ft), 1 (pt); Dietitians 1 (ft).
Affiliation Lutheran
Facilities Dining room; Activities room; Chapel; Crafts room; Laundry room.
Activities Arts and Crafts; Cards; Games; Reading groups; Movies; Dances/Social or cultural gatherings.

PHILIP

Philip Nursing Home
603 W Pine, Philip, SD, 57567 (605) 859-2511
Admin David B Creal. *Medical Dir/Dir of Nursing* George Mangulis MD.
Licensure Skilled Care. *Beds* 30. *Certified* Medicaid.
Staff Physicians 1 (ft); RNs 2 (pt); LPNs 4 (ft); Nurses aides 8 (ft), 4 (pt); Activities coordinators 1 (ft).
Facilities Dining room; Activities room; Crafts room; Barber/Beauty shop.
Activities Arts and Crafts; Cards; Games; Reading groups; Prayer groups; Movies.

PIERRE

Maryhouse
PO Box 1023, Pierre, SD, 57501 (605) 224-4434
Admin Keith Wilcox. *Medical Dir/Dir of Nursing* John Davis MD.
Licensure Skilled Care. *Beds* 82. *Certified* Medicaid.

Admissions Requirements Medical examination; Physician's request.
Staff RNs 2 (ft), 2 (pt); LPNs 5 (ft), 5 (pt); Nurses aides 17 (ft), 19 (pt); Recreational therapists 2 (pt); Occupational therapists 1 (pt).
Affiliation Roman Catholic
Facilities Dining room; Activities room; Chapel; Crafts room; Laundry room; Barber-/Beauty shop; Library.
Activities Arts and Crafts; Cards; Games; Reading groups; Prayer groups; Movies; Shopping trips; Dances/Social or cultural gatherings.

Rivercrest Manor
951 E Dakota, Pierre, SD, 57501 (605) 224-8628
Admin Jan Paulson. *Medical Dir/Dir of Nursing* Thomas Huber MD.
Licensure Skilled Care; Intermediate Care.
Beds SNF 64; ICF 8. *Certified* Medicaid.
Admissions Requirements Medical examination; Physician's request.
Staff RNs 4 (ft); LPNs 6 (ft); Orderlies 1 (ft); Nurses aides 9 (ft), 13 (pt); Physical therapists 1 (ft); Activities coordinators 1 (ft); Dietitians 1 (ft).
Facilities Dining room; Activities room; Crafts room; Laundry room; Barber/Beauty shop.
Activities Arts and Crafts; Cards; Games; Reading groups; Prayer groups; Movies; Shopping trips; Dances/Social or cultural gatherings.
Description Facility is located in the state capitol close to hospitals and clinics. Surrounding area is scenic with Missouri River, camping areas and a large lake.

PLATTE

Platte Nursing Home
Platte, SD, 57369 (605) 337-3131
Admin Patricia Biddle. *Medical Dir/Dir of Nursing* Dr L P Mills.
Licensure Skilled Care; Intermediate Care.
Beds 48. *Certified* Medicaid.
Admissions Requirements Physician's request.
Staff Physical therapists 1 (pt); Activities coordinators 1 (ft), 1 (pt); Dietitians 1 (pt).
Facilities Dining room; Activities room; Crafts room; Barber/Beauty shop.
Activities Arts and Crafts; Cards; Games; Reading groups; Prayer groups; Shopping trips.

QUINN

Hilltop Retirement Home*
PO Box 8, Quinn, SD, 57775 (605) 386-2421
Admin Augusta Murphy.
Licensure Supervised Care. *Beds* 8.

RAPID CITY

Black Hills Retirement Center*
1620 N 7th St, Rapid City, SD, 57701 (605) 343-4958
Admin Karen Jensen.
Licensure Intermediate Care. *Beds* 74. *Certified* Medicaid.

Boardman Community Care Home*
302 E Philadelphia, Rapid City, SD, 57701 (605) 342-0885
Admin Dottie Boardman.
Licensure Supervised Care. *Beds* 7.

Clarkson Mountain View Guest Home*
1015 Mountain View Rd, Rapid City, SD, 57701 (605) 343-5882
Admin Corrinne Haedt.
Licensure Skilled Care. *Beds* 52. *Certified* Medicaid.

Hillview Nursing Home
302 Saint Cloud St, Rapid City, SD, 57701 (605) 343-4738
Admin Chet Beebe. *Medical Dir/Dir of Nursing* Dr Finely.
Licensure Skilled Care. *Beds* 70. *Certified* Medicaid.
Admissions Requirements Medical examination.
Staff RNs 2 (ft), 2 (pt); LPNs 2 (ft), 2 (pt); Nurses aides 21 (ft), 6 (pt); Physical therapists 1 (pt); Activities coordinators 2 (ft); Dietitians 1 (ft); Dentists 1 (pt).
Facilities Dining room; Physical therapy room; Activities room; Chapel; Crafts room; Laundry room; Barber/Beauty shop; Library.
Activities Arts and Crafts; Games; Reading groups; Prayer groups; Movies; Shopping trips; Dances/Social or cultural gatherings.

Meadowbrook Manor
2500 Arrowhead Dr, Rapid City, SD, 57701 (605) 348-0285
Admin Luanne Erickson. *Medical Dir/Dir of Nursing* Dr Barreis.
Licensure Skilled Care. *Beds* 76. *Certified* Medicaid.
Admissions Requirements Physician's request.
Staff RNs 3 (ft), 1 (pt); LPNs 2 (ft), 4 (pt); Orderlies 2 (ft), 2 (pt); Nurses aides 14 (ft), 9 (pt); Physical therapists 1 (pt); Occupational therapists 1 (pt); Speech therapists 1 (pt); Activities coordinators 1 (ft), 1 (pt); Dietitians 1 (pt); Dentists 1 (pt).
Facilities Dining room; Activities room; Crafts room; Laundry room; Barber/Beauty shop.
Activities Arts and Crafts; Cards; Games; Reading groups; Prayer groups; Movies; Shopping trips; Dances/Social or cultural gatherings.
Description The newly remodeled Manor overlooks a golf course.

O'Brien's Rest Home
1131 Wood Ave, Rapid City, SD, 57701 (605) 342-4570
Admin Elizabeth O'Brien.
Licensure Supervised Care. *Beds* 6.

Rapid City Care Center*
916 Mountain View Rd, Rapid City, SD, 57701 (605) 343-8500
Admin Ron Ross.
Licensure Intermediate Care. *Beds* 99. *Certified* Medicaid.

Rapid City Nursing Center*
2908 5th St, Rapid City, SD, 57701 (605) 343-8500
Admin Roland Marinkovic.
Licensure Skilled Care. *Beds* 51. *Cer-

tified Medicaid.

REDFIELD

Eastern Star Home of South Dakota*
126 W 12th Ave, Redfield, SD, 57469 (605) 472-2255
Admin Sylvia Mitchell.
Licensure Intermediate Care. *Beds* 30. *Certified* Medicaid.
Affiliation Order of Eastern Star

James Valley Nursing Home*
1015 3rd St E, Redfield, SD, 57469 (605) 472-2288
Admin Joan Williams.
Licensure Skilled Care. *Beds* 87. *Certified* Medicaid.

ROSHOLT

Rosholt Nursing Home
Rosholt, SD, 57260 (605) 537-4272
Admin Viola Pedersen. *Medical Dir/Dir of Nursing* Dr Joseph Kass.
Licensure Intermediate Care. *Beds* 49. *Certified* Medicaid.
Admissions Requirements Medical examination; Physician's request.
Staff Physicians 1 (pt); RNs 1 (ft); LPNs 4 (pt); Nurses aides 6 (ft), 15 (pt); Occupational therapists 1 (pt); Activities coordinators 1 (ft); Dietitians 1 (pt); Pharmacists 1 (pt).
Facilities Dining room; Activities room; Crafts room; Laundry room; Barber/Beauty shop.
Activities Arts and Crafts; Cards; Games; Reading groups; Prayer groups; Movies; Shopping trips; Dances/Social or cultural gatherings.
Description Facility offers a warm, friendly atmosphere with a caring staff.

ROSLYN

Strand-Kjorsvig Community Rest Home
Roslyn, SD, 57261 (605) 486-4523
Admin Alfred Monshaugen.
Licensure Intermediate Care. *Beds* 36. *Certified* Medicaid.
Admissions Requirements Medical examination; Physician's request.
Staff RNs 2 (pt); LPNs 1 (ft), 1 (pt); Nurses aides 8 (ft), 5 (pt); Occupational therapists 1 (pt); Activities coordinators 1 (ft); Dietitians 1 (pt).
Facilities Dining room; Activities room; Chapel; Laundry room; Barber/Beauty shop.
Activities Arts and Crafts; Cards; Games; Reading groups; Prayer groups; Movies.

SALEM

Colonial Manor of Salem*
500 Colonial Dr, Salem, SD, 57058 (605) 425-2203
Admin Steve Sorensen.
Licensure Skilled Care. *Beds* 63. *Certified* Medicaid.

SCOTLAND

Good Samaritan Center
Box 428, Scotland, SD, 57059 (605) 583-2216
Admin Douglas Cruff. *Medical Dir/Dir of Nursing* Dr M Romes and Dr E Muellet.
Licensure Intermediate Care; Supervised Care.
Beds ICF 58; Supervised Care 4. *Certified* Medicaid.
Admissions Requirements Medical examination; Physician's request.
Staff RNs 1 (ft), 1 (pt); LPNs 3 (pt); Nurses aides 19 (pt); Physical therapists 1 (pt); Speech therapists 1 (pt); Activities coordinators 1 (ft), 2 (pt).
Affiliation Lutheran
Facilities Dining room; Physical therapy room; Activities room; Chapel; Crafts room; Laundry room; Barber/Beauty shop; Library; Adult day care room.
Activities Arts and Crafts; Cards; Games; Reading groups; Prayer groups; Movies; Shopping trips; Dances/Social or cultural gatherings; Worship services and devotions.
Description We provide an adult day care program for our community of 1000.

SELBY

Good Samaritan Center
4861 Lincoln Ave, Selby, SD, 57472 (605) 649-7744
Admin Dolores Riedlinger.
Licensure Intermediate Care. *Beds* 64. *Certified* Medicaid.
Admissions Requirements Medical examination.
Staff RNs 1 (ft); LPNs 4 (ft); Nurses aides 9 (ft), 18 (pt); Activities coordinators 1 (ft); Dietitians 1 (pt).
Affiliation Lutheran
Facilities Dining room; Activities room; Chapel; Crafts room; Laundry room; Barber-/Beauty shop.
Activities Arts and Crafts; Cards; Games; Reading groups; Prayer groups; Movies; Shopping trips.

SIOUX FALLS

Bethany Lutheran Home
1901 S Holly, Sioux Falls, SD, 57105 (605) 338-2351
Admin John Roth. *Medical Dir/Dir of Nursing* Tim Hurley.
Licensure Skilled Care. *Beds* 112. *Certified* Medicaid.
Admissions Requirements Medical examination; Physician's request.
Staff RNs 9 (ft), 7 (pt); LPNs 5 (ft), 4 (pt); Nurses aides 31 (ft), 49 (pt); Reality therapists 2 (ft), 1 (pt); Recreational therapists 2 (ft), 2 (pt); Activities coordinators 1 (ft); Dietitians 1 (pt).
Affiliation Lutheran
Facilities Dining room; Physical therapy room; Activities room; Crafts room; Laundry room; Barber/Beauty shop; Hospitality room.
Activities Arts and Crafts; Cards; Games; Reading groups; Prayer groups; Movies; Shopping trips; Exercises.
Description The facility is newly decorated

with a warm dining and living room setting. We have an RN on duty at all times. We are doing IV therapy within the facility. The facility has been reorganized according to resident care requirements.

Dow-Rummel Village
1000 N Lake Ave, Sioux Falls, SD, 57104 (605) 336-1490
Admin Ralph Jensen.
Licensure Skilled Care; Intermediate Care; Self Care. *Beds* SNF 10; ICF 15; Self Care 72. *Certified* Medicaid.
Admissions Requirements Medical examination.
Staff RNs 2 (ft), 4 (pt); LPNs 2 (pt); Nurses aides 4 (ft), 7 (pt).
Affiliation Church of Christ
Facilities Dining room; Activities room; Chapel; Crafts room; Laundry room; Barber/Beauty shop; Library; Private dining room.
Activities Arts and Crafts; Cards; Prayer groups; Movies; Shopping trips.

Good Samaritan Center
401 W 2nd, Sioux Falls, SD, 57104 (605) 336-6252
Admin Norman Stordahl. *Medical Dir/Dir of Nursing* Dr P E Lakstigala.
Licensure Skilled Care. *Beds* 141. *Certified* Medicaid.
Admissions Requirements Minimum age 14; Medical examination.
Staff Physicians 1 (pt); RNs 7 (ft), 4 (pt); LPNs 7 (ft), 2 (pt); Orderlies 3 (ft); Nurses aides 39 (ft), 28 (pt); Physical therapists 2 (pt); Recreational therapists 2 (ft); Occupational therapists 1 (pt); Speech therapists 1 (pt); Activities coordinators 1 (ft), 1 (pt); Dietitians 1 (pt); Dentists 1 (pt); Podiatrists 1 (pt); Audiologists 1 (pt).
Facilities Dining room; Physical therapy room; Activities room; Chapel; Crafts room; Laundry room; Barber/Beauty shop.
Activities Arts and Crafts; Cards; Games; Reading groups; Prayer groups; Movies; Shopping trips; Dances/Social or cultural gatherings; Bible study.
Description Facility features walk alongs which encourage residents to exercise, art classes, and spelling bees; Golden Chords sing for community church events.

Good Samaritan Village*
3901 S Marion Rd, Sioux Falls, SD, 57101 (605) 336-9030
Admin Charles Dingler.
Licensure Skilled Care; Intermediate Care; Supervised Care. *Beds* SNF 28; ICF 87; Supervised Care 56. *Certified* Medicaid.

Luther Manor
2900 S Lake Ave, Sioux Falls, SD, 57105 (605) 336-1997
Admin Orville Berkland.
Licensure Skilled Care. *Beds* 118. *Certified* Medicaid.
Admissions Requirements Medical examination.
Staff Physicians 1 (pt); RNs 6 (ft), 6 (pt); LPNs 6 (ft), 3 (pt); Orderlies 2 (ft); Nurses aides 38 (ft), 26 (pt); Activities coordinators 3 (ft); Dietitians 2 (ft), 1 (pt); Dentists 1 (pt); Podiatrists 1 (pt).

Affiliation Lutheran
Facilities Dining room; Physical therapy room; Activities room; Chapel; Laundry room; Barber/Beauty shop.
Activities Arts and Crafts; Cards; Games; Reading groups; Prayer groups; Movies; Shopping trips; Dances/Social or cultural gatherings.

Mom and Dad's Home and Health Care Center
3600-01 S Norton Ave, Sioux Falls, SD, 57105 (605) 338-9891
Admin Barbara Severson. *Medical Dir/Dir of Nursing* Dr A P Reding.
Licensure Skilled Care; Intermediate Care.
Beds SNF 109; ICF 50. *Certified* Medicaid.
Admissions Requirements Medical examination; Physician's request.
Staff Physicians 1 (ft); RNs 7 (ft); LPNs 11 (ft); Orderlies 5 (ft); Nurses aides 36 (ft), 18 (pt); Physical therapists 3 (ft); Activities coordinators 3 (ft); Dietitians 3 (ft); Dentists 1 (ft).
Facilities Dining room; Physical therapy room; Activities room; Chapel; Laundry room; Barber/Beauty shop.
Activities Cards; Games; Reading groups; Prayer groups; Movies; Shopping trips; Dances/Social or cultural gatherings.
Description Center delivers qualitiy nursing care.

Sioux Falls Care Center*
3900 Cathie Dr, Sioux Falls, SD, 57106 (605) 336-8822
Admin Marcella Hauswald.
Licensure Skilled Care. *Beds* 107. *Certified* Medicaid.

Wee Rest Home
5405 Romar Dr, Sioux Falls, SD, 57107 (605) 332-0280
Admin Dewey Hartsuiker.
Licensure Supervised Care. *Beds* 5.
Admissions Requirements Females only
Facilities Dining room; Laundry room.
Description I have 3 residents and they make their own entertainment—read, write letters, and watch TV.

SISSETON

Tekakwitha Nursing Home
6 E Chestnut, Sisseton, SD, 57262 (605) 698-7693
Admin Louis Sondgeroth. *Medical Dir/Dir of Nursing* David Oey MD.
Licensure Skilled Care; Intermediate Care.
Beds SNF 20; ICF 81. *Certified* Medicaid.
Admissions Requirements Medical examination.
Staff RNs 2 (ft), 1 (pt); LPNs 5 (ft), 3 (pt); Nurses aides 25 (ft), 17 (pt); Activities coordinators 1 (ft), 1 (pt); Dietitians 1 (ft).
Facilities Dining room; Physical therapy room; Activities room; Chapel; Crafts room; Laundry room; Barber/Beauty shop.
Activities Arts and Crafts; Cards; Games; Reading groups; Prayer groups; Movies; Shopping trips; Dances/Social or cultural gatherings.

SPEARFISH

David M Dorsett Home*
1020 10th St, Spearfish, SD, 57783 (605) 642-2716
Admin James L Haeder.
Licensure Skilled Care; Intermediate Care.
Beds SNF 62; ICF 58. *Certified* Medicaid.

The Hyde Home*
Rt 1, Box 171, Spearfish, SD, 57783 (605) 642-5563
Admin Douglas Hyde.
Licensure Supervised Care. *Beds* 9.

Upper Valley Rest Home
262 Upper Valley Rd, Spearfish, SD, 57783 (605) 642-5021
Admin Donovan Sigle.
Licensure Supervised Care. *Beds* 9.
Admissions Requirements Medical examination.
Activities Arts and Crafts; Cards; Shopping trips.
Description We provide care in a home-like family setting.

Walker's Veterans Home
1004 5th St, Spearfish, SD, 57783 (605) 642-3911
Admin Ronald Walker.
Licensure Supervised Care. *Beds* 8.
Admissions Requirements Minimum age 18; Medical examination.
Staff Nurses aides; Recreational therapists; Activities coordinators.
Facilities Dining room; Activities room; Crafts room; Laundry room.
Activities Arts and Crafts; Cards; Shopping trips.
Description Facility is located in a beautiful Black Hills town with beautiful yard and garden within a block of 5 different churches, 3 blocks from downtown and one block from library; family atmosphere.

STURGIS

McKee Rest Home
341 9th St, Sturgis, SD, 57785 (605) 347-3659
Admin Charles E Jones.
Licensure Supervised Care. *Beds* 25.
Admissions Requirements Medical examination; Physician's request.
Staff Orderlies 1 (ft); Nurses aides 4 (ft).
Facilities Dining room; Activities room; Laundry room.
Activities Cards; Games; Shopping trips.
Description Facility is located at the edge of town about 1 mile from shopping center, in a country setting with lots of green grass and places to walk around and enjoy the outdoors in private.

Nelson's Rest Home*
1124 2nd St, Sturgis, SD, 57785 (605) 347-2405
Admin Wayne Nelson and Betty Nelson.
Licensure Supervised Care. *Beds* 9.

Pina Home for the Aged*
1542 Davenport St, Sturgis, SD, 57785 (605) 347-2770
Admin Ingrid Pina.
Licensure Supervised Care. *Beds* 13.

Sturgis Community Nursing Home
2100 Fulton St, Sturgis, SD, 57785 (605) 347-2536
Admin Michael Penticoff. *Medical Dir/Dir of Nursing* LL Massa DO.
Licensure Skilled Care; Intermediate Care.
Beds SNF 39; ICF 45. *Certified* Medicaid; Medicare.
Admissions Requirements Physician's request.
Staff RNs 2 (ft), 3 (pt); LPNs 2 (ft), 7 (pt); Nurses aides 21 (ft), 24 (pt); Physical therapists 1 (pt); Activities coordinators 2 (ft); Dietitians 1 (pt).
Facilities Dining room; Physical therapy room; Activities room; Chapel; Crafts room; Laundry room; Barber/Beauty shop.
Activities Arts and Crafts; Cards; Games; Reading groups; Prayer groups; Movies; Shopping trips; Dances/Social or cultural gatherings.

We Care Home for the Aged*
1733 Davenport St, Sturgis, SD, 57785 (605) 347-2251
Admin Allen Moeller and Sandra Moeller.
Licensure Supervised Care. *Beds* 8.

TRIPP

Good Samaritan Center*
PO Box 370, Tripp, SD, 57376 (605) 935-6101
Admin Daniel J Fosness.
Licensure Intermediate Care; Supervised Care.
Beds ICF 62; Supervised Care 5. *Certified* Medicaid.

TYNDALL

Good Samaritan Center*
PO Box 460, Tyndall, SD, 57066 (605) 589-3350
Admin Reuben Arlt.
Licensure Intermediate Care; Supervised Care.
Beds ICF 60; Supervised Care 11. *Certified* Medicaid.

Saint Michael's Nursing Home*
PO Box 27, Tyndall, SD, 57066 (605) 589-3341
Admin Gale Walker.
Licensure Skilled Care. *Beds* 9. *Certified* Medicaid.

VERMILLION

Southeastern Dakota Nursing Home
102 S Plum St, Vermillion, SD, 57069 (605) 624-4481
Admin Dale Garris.
Licensure Intermediate Care. *Beds* 66. *Certified* Medicaid.
Admissions Requirements Medical examination.
Staff RNs 2 (ft), 2 (pt); LPNs 1 (ft), 5 (pt); Orderlies 4 (pt); Nurses aides 11 (ft), 16 (pt); Activities coordinators 2 (ft), 1 (pt).

Facilities Dining room; Physical therapy room; Chapel; Crafts room; Barber/Beauty shop.
Activities Arts and Crafts; Cards; Games; Reading groups; Prayer groups; Movies.

VIBORG

Pioneer Memorial Nursing Home
Viborg, SD, 57070 (605) 326-5161
Admin Warren Kuhler. *Medical Dir/Dir of Nursing* E G Nelson MD.
Licensure Intermediate Care. *Beds* 52. *Certified* Medicaid.
Staff RNs 2 (ft), 1 (pt); LPNs 2 (pt); Nurses aides 23 (pt); Physical therapists 1 (pt); Activities coordinators 1 (ft); Dietitians 1 (pt).
Facilities Dining room; Physical therapy room; Activities room; Chapel; Laundry room; Barber/Beauty shop.
Activities Arts and Crafts; Cards; Games; Reading groups; Prayer groups; Movies; Shopping trips; Dances/Social or cultural gatherings.
Description The 52-bed intermediate care facility is operated by and physically attached to Pioneer Memorial Hospital. The hospital has a medical office building attached and therefore a health care setting is offered that is attractive to nursing home clientele.

VOLGA

Parkview Home*
PO Box 328, Volga, SD, 57071 (605) 627-9141
Admin Mabel Eggebraaten.
Licensure Supervised Care. *Beds* 25.

WAGNER

Good Samaritan Center
Wagner, SD, 57380 (605) 384-3661
Admin Lawrence Stahlecker.
Licensure Intermediate Care; Supervised Care. *Beds* ICF 63; Supervised Care 14. *Certified* Medicaid.
Staff RNs 3 (ft); LPNs 1 (ft); Nurses aides 23 (ft); Physical therapists 1 (pt); Recreational therapists 1 (ft); Activities coordinators 1 (ft); Dietitians 1 (pt).
Affiliation Lutheran
Description Facility offers child day care.

WAKONDA

Wakonda Heritage Manor
Wakonda, SD, 57073 (605) 267-2081
Admin Carolyn Scribner.
Licensure Intermediate Care; Supervised Care. *Beds* ICF 21; Supervised Care 24. *Certified* Medicaid.
Admissions Requirements Medical examination; Physician's request.
Staff Physicians 7 (pt); RNs 1 (ft), 4 (pt); LPNs 1 (pt); Orderlies 1 (pt); Nurses aides 2 (ft), 12 (pt); Physical therapists 1 (pt); Activities coordinators 1 (ft), 1 (pt); Dietitians 1 (pt); Dentists 1 (pt); Podiatrists 1 (pt).
Facilities Dining room; Physical therapy room; Activities room; Crafts room; Laundry room; Barber/Beauty shop; Library.
Activities Arts and Crafts; Cards; Games;

Reading groups; Prayer groups; Movies; Shopping trips; Dances/Social or cultural gatherings.
Description Facility offers adult day services; church services on Sunday (Protestant), Mass 1st of each month, Rosary weekly, confessions and communion (all denominations) monthly; aerobics; sing-a-longs; picnics; individual birthday cakes; and private family dinners.

WATERTOWN

Brugman Home
1365 2nd St NW, Watertown, SD, 57201 (605) 886-8395
Admin Joyce Brugman.
Licensure Supervised Care. *Beds* 4.
Admissions Requirements Medical examination.
Facilities Dining room.
Activities Arts and Crafts; Games; Movies.
Description The home is a 4-bed ranch-style home with rooms on main floor. Family-style living is encourgaged. The home is located near outskirts of town but convenient to most areas of town.

Hazel's Rest Home
520 2nd Ave SE, Watertown, SD, 57201 (605) 882-1768
Admin Hazel Pekelder.
Licensure Supervised Care. *Beds* 6.
Admissions Requirements Medical examination.
Description Facility features home-like atmosphere.

Jenkin's Methodist Home
12 2nd Ave SE, Watertown, SD, 57201 (605) 886-5777
Admin Allen Swan. *Medical Dir/Dir of Nursing* G R Bartron MD.
Licensure Skilled Care; Intermediate Care. *Beds* SNF 166; ICF 18. *Certified* Medicaid.
Admissions Requirements Medical examination.
Staff RNs 3 (ft), 7 (pt); LPNs 5 (ft), 13 (pt); Orderlies 1 (pt); Nurses aides 49 (ft), 42 (pt); Recreational therapists 3 (ft); Activities coordinators 1 (ft); Dietitians 1 (ft); Dentists 1 (pt).
Affiliation Methodist
Facilities Dining room; Physical therapy room; Activities room; Chapel; Crafts room; Laundry room; Barber/Beauty shop; Library.
Activities Arts and Crafts; Cards; Games; Reading groups; Prayer groups; Movies; Shopping trips; Dances/Social or cultural gatherings.

Memorial Medical Center Nursing Home
420 4th St NE, Watertown, SD, 57201 (605) 886-8431
Admin David M Gustafson. *Medical Dir/Dir of Nursing* G R Bartron MD.
Licensure Skilled Care. *Beds* 51. *Certified* Medicaid.
Admissions Requirements Medical examination.
Staff RNs 2 (ft), 1 (pt); LPNs 4 (ft), 6 (pt); Nurses aides 13 (ft), 8 (pt); Physical therapists 1 (ft); Activities coordinators 1 (ft), 1 (pt); Dietitians 1 (ft).
Facilities Dining room; Physical therapy room; Activities room; Chapel; Crafts room; Laundry

room; Barber/Beauty shop.
Activities Arts and Crafts; Cards; Games; Reading groups; Prayer groups; Movies; Shopping trips; Dances/Social or cultural gatherings.

WAUBAY

Waubay Rest Home
1st Ave W, Waubay, SD, 57273 (605) 947-4361
Admin Mildred Gregerson and Mary Warns.
Licensure Supervised Care. *Beds* 9.
Admissions Requirements Medical examination.
Staff Orderlies 2 (ft); Nurses aides 2 (ft).
Facilities Dining room; Laundry room.
Activities Cards; Prayer groups; Shopping trips; Dances/Social or cultural gatherings.
Description We provide a home-like living facility with dignity for the residents.

WEBSTER

Bethesda Home
West Highway 12, Webster, SD, 57274 (605) 345-3331
Admin Steven J Fritzke. *Medical Dir/Dir of Nursing* Dr Lawrence Nelson.
Licensure Skilled Care. *Beds* 58. *Certified* Medicaid.
Staff RNs 5 (ft), 4 (pt); LPNs 2 (pt); Nurses aides 12 (ft), 12 (pt); Physical therapists 1 (pt); Activities coordinators 1 (ft), 1 (pt).
Affiliation Lutheran
Facilities Dining room; Physical therapy room; Activities room; Chapel; Crafts room; Laundry room; Barber/Beauty shop.
Activities Arts and Crafts; Cards; Games; Reading groups; Prayer groups; Movies.
Description Facility is currently involved with the community on various education programs; topics such as stress, criticism, and death and dying are being discussed.

WESSINGTON SPRINGS

Weskota Manor
Wessington Springs, SD, 57382 (605) 539-1621
Admin Janice Schwartz. *Medical Dir/Dir of Nursing* Dr R E Dean.
Licensure Intermediate Care. *Beds* 41. *Certified* Medicaid.
Staff Physicians 2 (pt); RNs 1 (ft); LPNs 2 (ft); Nurses aides 5 (ft), 10 (pt); Physical therapists 1 (pt); Activities coordinators 1 (ft); Dietitians 1 (pt); Dentists 1 (pt).
Facilities Dining room; Activities room; Chapel; Crafts room; Barber/Beauty shop.
Activities Cards; Games; Reading groups; Prayer groups; Movies; Shopping trips; Dances/Social or cultural gatherings; School programs.

WHITE

White Care Center
PO Box 68, White, SD, 57276 (605) 629-2881
Admin Allen Svennes.
Licensure Intermediate Care; Supervised Care. *Beds* ICF 50; Supervised Care 10. *Certified* Medicaid.

Staff RNs 1 (ft), 3 (pt); LPNs 3 (ft), 1 (pt); Orderlies 1 (ft); Nurses aides 9 (ft), 12 (pt); Activities coordinators 1 (ft); Dietitians 1 (pt).
Facilities Dining room; Activities room; Laundry room; Barber/Beauty shop; Library.
Activities Arts and Crafts; Cards; Games; Reading groups; Prayer groups; Movies; Shopping trips.
Description The White Care Center is located in White, a community of 500 residents. The facility has 2 hospitals within 15 miles; is VA approved; and has a large amount of community involvement with day-to-day operations.

WHITE LAKE

Aurora-Brule Nursing Home*
PO Box 217, White Lake, SD, 57383 (605) 249-2216
Admin Larry Fredericksen.
Licensure Intermediate Care. *Beds* 77. *Certified* Medicaid.

WHITE RIVER

Heritage of White River
Box 310, White River, SD, 57579 (605) 259-3161
Admin Jon Covault.
Licensure Intermediate Care. *Beds* 52. *Certified* Medicaid.
Admissions Requirements Medical examination.
Staff RNs 1 (ft), 1 (pt); LPNs 1 (ft); Orderlies 1 (ft); Nurses aides 15 (ft), 2 (pt); Activities coordinators 1 (ft), 1 (pt).
Facilities Dining room; Physical therapy room; Activities room; Chapel; Crafts room; Laundry room; Barber/Beauty shop.
Activities Arts and Crafts; Cards; Games; Reading groups; Movies; Shopping trips.
Description A new facility (1976) that is carpeted in most rooms. A nursing home that is beautiful, roomy, and has a homey atmosphere.

WHITEWOOD

Sedig Castle-Rock Home
Box 384, Whitewood, SD, 57793 (605) 269-2422
Admin Angela Sedig.
Licensure Supervised Care. *Beds* 8.
Admissions Requirements Minimum age 50; Males only; Medical examination; Physician's request.
Staff RNs 1 (ft); Nurses aides 1 (pt).
Facilities Dining room; Laundry room; Music room.
Activities Shopping trips.
Description Most of the residents are veterans from Ft Meade, SD. They have privileges to attend social and recreational functions at Ft Meade. Enjoyment results from 3 golden retrievers and 2 lovely cats.

WILMOT

Wilmot Community Home
Wilmot, SD, 57279 (605) 938-4418
Admin Phyllis Harms.

Licensure Intermediate Care. *Beds* 46. *Certified* Medicaid.
Admissions Requirements Medical examination; Physician's request.
Staff RNs 1 (ft), 1 (pt); LPNs 1 (pt); Orderlies 4 (ft); Nurses aides 5 (ft), 15 (pt); Activities coordinators 1 (ft).
Facilities Dining room; Activities room; Laundry room; Barber/Beauty shop.
Activities Arts and Crafts; Cards; Games; Reading groups; Movies; Shopping trips; Dances/Social or cultural gatherings.
Description This 46-bed facility is located on the edge of a small town in the heart of the Whetstone Valley. The service area is quite large with residents from 12 different communities.

WINNER

Winner Nursing Home
956 E 7th St, Winner, SD, 57580 (605) 842-3483
Admin John Komraus. *Medical Dir/Dir of Nursing* Dr Tony Berg.
Licensure Skilled Care. *Beds* 81. *Certified* Medicaid.
Staff RNs 2 (ft), 2 (pt); LPNs 3 (ft), 4 (pt); Nurses aides 22 (ft), 11 (pt).
Facilities Dining room; Activities room; Chapel; Crafts room; Laundry room; Barber/Beauty shop.
Activities Arts and Crafts; Cards; Games; Reading groups; Prayer groups; Movies; Shopping trips; Dances/Social or cultural gatherings.

WOONSOCKET

Prairie View Care Center
Woonsocket, SD, 57385 (605) 796-4467
Admin Charlene Nash.
Licensure Intermediate Care. *Beds* 52. *Certified* Medicaid.
Admissions Requirements Medical examination; Physician's request.
Staff RNs 1 (ft), 2 (pt); LPNs 3 (ft); Orderlies 2 (pt); Nurses aides 7 (ft), 6 (pt); Activities coordinators 1 (ft), 1 (pt).
Facilities Dining room; Activities room; Chapel; Laundry room; Barber/Beauty shop.
Activities Arts and Crafts; Cards; Games; Reading groups; Prayer groups; Movies; Shopping trips; Dances/Social or cultural gatherings.
Description Prairie View Care Center is a 52-bed intermediate care facility. Because of our size, we are able to offer personal care in a family-type setting. The activities personnel have programs to meet the needs of all residents, which include weekends and evenings. Prairie View Care Center has a lot of community support and interest. We provide 24-hour professional nursing.

YANKTON

Sister James' Nursing Home
W 4th St, Yankton, SD, 57078 (605) 665-9371
Admin Pamela Rezac. *Medical Dir/Dir of Nursing* Dr T H Sattler.
Licensure Skilled Care. *Beds* 97. *Certified* Medicaid.

Admissions Requirements Medical examination; Physician's request.
Staff RNs 6 (ft); Orderlies 2 (pt); Nurses aides 7 (ft), 10 (pt); Speech therapists; Activities coordinators 1 (ft), 1 (pt); Dietitians 1 (ft).
Facilities Dining room; Activities room; Chapel; Crafts room; Laundry room; Barber/Beauty shop.
Activities Arts and Crafts; Cards; Games; Reading groups; Prayer groups; Shopping trips; Dances/Social or cultural gatherings.
Description Careful preassessment done with families and guardians to ensure proper placement in institution. Philosophy of rehabilitation: help each person achieve and/or maintain their highest level of independence. Kindness, love, and gentle understanding are most essential in the healing process.

Sunshine Nursing Home*
1014 W 8th St, Yankton, SD, 57078 (605) 665-5348
Admin Margaret Jansen.
Licensure Intermediate Care. *Beds* 15. *Certified* Medicaid.

Yankton Care Center
1212 W 8th, Yankton, SD, 57078 (605) 665-9429
Admin Anthony D Cates.
Licensure Intermediate Care. *Beds* 74. *Certified* Medicaid.
Admissions Requirements Medical examination.
Staff RNs 2 (ft), 1 (pt); LPNs 2 (ft), 2 (pt); Nurses aides 14 (ft), 6 (pt); Physical therapists 1 (pt); Speech therapists 1 (pt); Activities coordinators 1 (ft); Dietitians 1 (pt).
Facilities Dining room; Physical therapy room; Activities room; Chapel; Crafts room; Laundry room; Barber/Beauty shop; Library; Solarium.
Activities Arts and Crafts; Cards; Games; Reading groups; Prayer groups; Movies; Shopping trips; Dances/Social or cultural gatherings.
Description A comfortable home-like setting especially designed to meet the physical, mental, recreational, social, and spiritual needs of all the residents. Our goal as an intermediate care facility is to promote independence and quality of life.

TENNESSEE

ADAMSVILLE

Tri-County Convalescent Home Inc
Park Ave, PO Box 325, Adamsville, TN, 38310
(901) 632-3301
Medical Dir/Dir of Nursing Harry L Peeler
MD.
Licensure Skilled Care. *Beds* 124. *Certified* Medicaid; Medicare.
Admissions Requirements Minimum age 16;
Medical examination; Physician's request.
Staff Physicians 7 (pt); RNs 1 (ft), 2 (pt); LPNs
9 (ft), 4 (pt); Nurses aides 34 (ft), 2 (pt);
Physical therapists 1 (pt); Speech therapists 1
(pt); Activities coordinators 1 (ft); Dietitians 1
(pt); Dentists 1 (pt).
Facilities Dining room; Physical therapy room;
Activities room; Crafts room; Laundry room;
Barber/Beauty shop.
Activities Arts and Crafts; Cards; Games;
Movies; Shopping trips; Dances/Social or cultural gatherings; Daily devotions.
Description The nursing home participates
yearly in American Heart Association rock and
roll jamboree, special events all week for
National Nursing Home Week, and a special
event monthly. Enclosed outside square with
patio furniture, apple trees, flower garden, and
walkway is used for cookouts, outside gatherings, and for relaxing in fresh air.

ALAMO

Crockett County Nursing Home Inc
Rt 2, Box 218, Alamo, TN, 38001 (901)
696-4541
Licensure Intermediate Care. *Beds* 121. *Certified* Medicaid.
Admissions Requirements Minimum age 16;
Medical examination; Physician's request.
Staff Physicians 2 (pt); RNs 1 (ft); LPNs 9 (ft);
Nurses aides 40 (ft); Physical therapists 1 (pt);
Recreational therapists 1 (ft); Activities coordinators 1 (ft); Dietitians 1 (pt); Dentists 1 (pt).
Facilities Dining room; Physical therapy room;
Activities room; Crafts room; Laundry room;
Barber/Beauty shop; Library.
Activities Arts and Crafts; Cards; Games;
Reading groups; Prayer groups; Movies; Shopping trips; Dances/Social or cultural gatherings.

ALGOOD

Masters Health Care Center*
278 Dry Valley Rd, Algood, TN, 38501 (615)
537-6524
Licensure Skilled Care; Intermediate Care.
Beds 166. *Certified* Medicaid; Medicare.

ANDERSONVILLE

Wayside Health Care Center*
Rt 2, Box 34-A, Andersonville, TN, 37705
(615) 494-0986
Beds 90.

ARDMORE

Ardmore Nursing Home Inc
Hwy 31, Box 257, Ardmore, TN, 38449 (615)
427-2143
Admin Ted Barnett. *Medical Dir/Dir of
Nursing* A C Foronda.
Licensure Intermediate Care. *Beds* 70. *Certified* Medicaid.
Admissions Requirements Medical examination.
Staff Physicians 3 (pt); RNs 1 (pt); LPNs 2 (ft),
4 (pt); Nurses aides 16 (ft), 2 (pt); Physical therapists; Recreational therapists; Occupational
therapists; Speech therapists; Activities coordinators 1 (ft); Dietitians 1 (ft).
Facilities Dining room; Activities room;
Laundry room; Lobby; 2 Sun rooms.
Activities Arts and Crafts; Cards; Games;
Reading groups; Prayer groups; Dances/Social
or cultural gatherings.
Description The Ardmore Nursing Home is
approximately one mile from town. The home
sits on a hill in a country setting with trees surrounding the home. The patients enjoy activities daily. They enjoy picnics and musical
entertainment outside when weather permits.

ASHLAND CITY

Cheatham County Rest Home
Rt 6, River Rd, Ashland City, TN, 37015 (615)
792-4948
Medical Dir/Dir of Nursing James Baldwin
MD.
Licensure Intermediate Care. *Beds* 100. *Certified* Medicaid.

Admissions Requirements Minimum age 14.
Facilities Dining room; Activities room; Chapel; Crafts room; Laundry room; Barber/Beauty
shop.
Activities Arts and Crafts; Cards; Games; Prayer groups; Shopping trips; Dances/Social or
cultural gatherings.

Montgomery County Nursing Home*
Rt 5, Box 292, Ashland City, TN, 37015 (615)
362-3203
Licensure Intermediate Care. *Beds* 81. *Certified* Medicaid.

ATHENS

Athens Convalescent and Nursing Center*
214 Grove St NW, Athens, TN, 37303 (615)
745-0434
Licensure Skilled Care; Intermediate Care.
Beds 87. *Certified* Medicaid; Medicare.

Life Care Center of Athens*
1234 Frye St, Athens, TN, 37303 (615)
745-8181
Licensure Intermediate Care. *Beds* 124. *Certified* Medicaid.

BLOUNTVILLE

Care Inn Blountville
Dunlap Rd, Blountville, TN, 37617 (615)
323-7112
Medical Dir/Dir of Nursing Dr T H Raberson.
Licensure Intermediate Care. *Beds* 170. *Certified* Medicaid.
Admissions Requirements Minimum age 14;
Medical examination; Physician's request.
Staff Physicians 13 (ft); RNs 1 (ft), 1 (pt);
LPNs 12 (ft), 3 (pt); Orderlies 5 (ft); Nurses
aides 44 (ft), 6 (pt); Physical therapists 1 (pt);
Reality therapists 2 (pt); Speech therapists 1
(pt); Activities coordinators 1 (ft); Dietitians 1
(ft).
Facilities Dining room; Physical therapy room;
Activities room; Laundry room; Barber/Beauty
shop.
Activities Arts and Crafts; Games; Reading
groups; Prayer groups; Movies; Holiday parties;
Western day; Mexican day.
Description We have 3 floors with connecting
elevator, a fenced-in patio, big screen TV, fireplace, a day room on each floor with a color

TV, nice country setting. Complete dietary, laundry and housekeeping services, with 24-hour nursing services.

Sullivan County Home for the Aged
Rt 2, Blountville, TN, 37617 (615) 323-7527
Licensure Home for the Aged. *Beds* 22.

BOLIVAR

Brint Nursing Home*
214 N Water St, Bolivar, TN, 38008 (901) 658-5287
Licensure Intermediate Care. *Beds* 42. *Certified* Medicaid.

Care Inn—Bolivar*
700 Nuckols Rd, Bolivar, TN, 38008 (901) 658-4707
Licensure Intermediate Care. *Beds* 132. *Certified* Medicaid.

BRISTOL

Bristol Nursing Home Inc*
261 North St, Bristol, TN, 37620 (615) 764-6151
Licensure Intermediate Care. *Beds* 240. *Certified* Medicaid.

BROWNSVILLE

Crestview Nursing Home
704 Dupree St, Brownsville, TN, 38012 (901) 772-3356
Licensure Intermediate Care. *Beds* 138. *Certified* Medicaid.

BRUCETON

Life Care Center of Bruceton-Hollow Rock*
105 Rowland Ave, Bruceton, TN, 38317
Licensure Nursing Home. *Beds* 60.

BYRDSTOWN

Pickett County Nursing Home*
PO Box 388, Hillcrest Dr, Byrdstown, TN, 38549
Licensure Nursing Home. *Beds* 48.

CAMDEN

Care Inn—Camden*
Hospital Dr, Camden, TN, 38320 (901) 584-3500
Licensure Intermediate Care. *Beds* 186. *Certified* Medicaid.

CARTHAGE

Smith County Manor*
Hospital Dr, Carthage, TN, 37030 (615) 735-0570
Licensure Intermediate Care. *Beds* 48. *Certified* Medicaid.

CELINA

Clay County Nursing Home
Hwy 53, Celina, TN, 38551 (615) 243-3139
Medical Dir/Dir of Nursing Nora B Tiongson MD.
Licensure Intermediate Care. *Beds* 60. *Certified* Medicaid.
Ownership Public.
Admissions Requirements Medical examination; Physician's request.
Staff Physicians 4 (pt); RNs 1 (pt); LPNs 5 (ft), 4 (pt); Orderlies 6 (ft); Nurses aides 8 (ft), 4 (pt); Physical therapists 1 (pt); Speech therapists 1 (pt); Activities coordinators 1 (pt); Dietitians 5 (ft), 1 (pt); Dentists 1 (pt); Ophthalmologists 1 (pt); Audiologists 1 (pt).
Facilities Dining room; Physical therapy room; Activities room; Crafts room; Laundry room; Barber/Beauty shop; Library.
Activities Arts and Crafts; Cards; Games; Reading groups; Movies; Picnics; Campouts; Parties.
Description Facility is located in small rural town near large Tennessee Valley Authority lake with many outdoor recreation areas designed for handicapped usage.

CENTERVILLE

Centerville Health Care Center
112 Old Dickson Rd, Centerville, TN, 37033 (615) 729-4236
Medical Dir/Dir of Nursing Rebecca McGee MD.
Licensure Intermediate Care. *Beds* 120. *Certified* Medicaid.
Staff Physicians 5 (pt); RNs 2 (ft); LPNs 6 (ft), 1 (pt); Nurses aides 45 (ft); Speech therapists 1 (pt); Activities coordinators 1 (ft); Dietitians 1 (pt); Dentists 1 (pt).
Facilities Dining room; Physical therapy room; Activities room; Chapel; Crafts room; Laundry room; Barber/Beauty shop; Library.
Activities Arts and Crafts; Cards; Games; Reading groups; Prayer groups; Movies; Dances/Social or cultural gatherings.
Description A beautifully located new facility with a lovely building, woodwork, and vinyl wall covering, overlooking the Duck River with fine activities program and rhythm band.

Hickman County Nursing Home
135 E Swan St, Centerville, TN, 37033 (615) 729-3513
Medical Dir/Dir of Nursing B L Holladay MD.
Licensure Intermediate Care. *Beds* 40. *Certified* Medicaid.
Admissions Requirements Medical examination; Physician's request.
Staff Physicians 2 (pt); RNs 2 (ft); LPNs 2 (ft), 4 (pt); Nurses aides 12 (ft), 3 (pt); Physical therapists; Occupational therapists; Speech therapists; Activities coordinators 1 (pt); Dietitians 1 (pt).
Facilities Dining room; Activities room; Barber/Beauty shop.
Activities Arts and Crafts; Cards; Games; Prayer groups; Movies.
Description Our facility is attached to the Hickman County Hospital which provides our residents immediate emergency and acute care

services, if needed. Our hospital and nursing home are accredited by JCAH.

CHATTANOOGA

Asbury Center at Oak Manor*
716 Dodds Ave, Chattanooga, TN, 37404 (615) 622-6424
Licensure Home for the Aged. *Beds* 49.

Caldsted Foundation Inc*
3701 Cherryton Dr, Chattanooga, TN, 37411 (615) 624-9906
Licensure Home for the Aged. *Beds* 52.

Dempsey Nursing Home Inc*
8249 Standifer Gap Rd, Chattanooga, TN, 37421
Licensure Intermediate Care. *Beds* 34.

Friendship Haven
950 Dodson Ave, Chattanooga, TN, 37406 (615) 629-2847
Admin Mabel Abernathy.
Licensure Home for the Aged. *Beds* 25.
Admissions Requirements Minimum age 47; Females only; Medical examination.
Facilities Dining room; Laundry room.
Activities Prayer groups; Shopping trips; Exercise groups.
Description Facility provides a home for females who can no longer live independently in the community; also provides supporting services.

Hamilton County Nursing Home*
2626 Walker Rd, Chattanooga, TN, 37421 (615) 892-9442
Licensure Skilled Care; Intermediate Care; Residential Care. *Beds* 676; Presidential Care 99. *Certified* Medicaid; Medicare.

Heritage Manor Nursing Home Inc*
708 Dwight St, Chattanooga, TN, 37406 (615) 622-4301
Licensure Intermediate Care. *Beds* 78. *Certified* Medicaid.

Life Care Center of East Ridge
1500 Fincher Ave, Chattanooga, TN, 37412 (615) 894-7254
Medical Dir/Dir of Nursing Dr Winters.
Licensure Intermediate Care. *Beds* 120. *Certified* Medicaid.
Admissions Requirements Medical examination; Physician's request.
Staff Physicians 2 (ft); RNs 2 (ft); LPNs 6 (ft), 4 (pt); Orderlies 4 (ft); Nurses aides 20 (ft), 6 (pt); Physical therapists 1 (ft), 1 (pt); Recreational therapists 1 (ft); Activities coordinators 1 (ft); Dietitians 1 (ft); Dentists 1 (ft); Podiatrists 1 (ft).
Facilities Dining room; Physical therapy room; Activities room; Crafts room; Laundry room; Barber/Beauty shop.
Activities Arts and Crafts; Cards; Games; Reading groups; Prayer groups; Movies; Shopping trips; Dances/Social or cultural gatherings.
Description Facility is committed to Christian care.

Mountain View Nursing Home*
PO Box 2318, 5410 Lee Ave, Chattanooga, TN, 37410 (615) 821-4836
Licensure Intermediate Care. *Beds* 28. *Certified* Medicaid.

Mountain View Rest Home*
PO Box 2318, 5412 Lee Ave, Chattanooga, TN, 37410 (615) 821-4836
Licensure Intermediate Care. *Beds* 19. *Certified* Medicaid.

Parkwood Health Care Center
2700 Parkwood Ave, Chattanooga, TN, 37404 (615) 624-1533
Medical Dir/Dir of Nursing Dr Paul Hawkins.
Licensure Skilled Care. *Beds* 212. *Certified* Medicaid; Medicare.
Admissions Requirements Minimum age 14; Medical examination.
Staff Physicians 2 (ft); RNs 7 (ft), 5 (pt); LPNs 14 (ft), 14 (pt); Orderlies 7 (ft), 3 (pt); Nurses aides 54 (ft), 12 (pt); Physical therapists 1 (ft); Recreational therapists 2 (ft); Speech therapists 1 (pt), Activities coordinators 1 (ft); Dietitians 1 (ft); Dentists 1 (pt); Podiatrists 1 (pt); Assistant physical therapists 3 (ft).
Facilities Dining room; Physical therapy room; Activities room; Chapel; Crafts room; Laundry room; Barber/Beauty shop; Library.
Activities Arts and Crafts; Games; Movies; Shopping trips; Dances/Social or cultural gatherings.

Saint Barnabas Nursing Home
Pine and W 6th, Chattanooga, TN, 37402 (615) 267-3764
Licensure Skilled Care; Intermediate Care. *Beds* 87. *Certified* Medicaid; Medicare.
Staff RNs 4 (ft), 3 (pt); LPNs 6 (ft), 3 (pt); Orderlies 3 (ft), 1 (pt); Nurses aides 27 (ft), 16 (pt); Physical therapists 1 (pt); Activities coordinators 1 (ft); Dietitians 1 (ft); Dentists 1 (pt).
Facilities Dining room; Physical therapy room; Chapel; Barber/Beauty shop; Library.
Activities Arts and Crafts; Games; Reading groups; Prayer groups; Movies; Pet program.
Description Facility is located in the heart of downtown Chattanooga.

CHUCKEY

Durham-Hensley Nursing Homes Inc
Rt 3, Chuckey, TN, 36741 (615) 257-6761
Medical Dir/Dir of Nursing Dr Ronald Cole.
Licensure Intermediate Care. *Beds* 100. *Certified* Medicaid.
Staff Physicians 7 (pt); RNs 2 (ft); LPNs 9 (ft); Nurses aides 21 (ft), 6 (pt); Physical therapists 1 (pt); Speech therapists 1 (pt); Activities coordinators 1 (ft); Dietitians 1 (pt).
Facilities Dining room; Physical therapy room; Activities room; Laundry room; Barber/Beauty shop.
Activities Arts and Crafts; Cards; Games; Reading groups; Prayer groups; Movies; Shopping trips; Dances/Social or cultural gatherings.
Description Facility is located in the country 8 miles from the closest town.

CHURCH HILL

Life Care Center of Church Hill
W Main St, Church Hill, TN, 37642 (615) 357-7178
Licensure Intermediate Care. *Beds* 124. *Certified* Medicaid.
Admissions Requirements Minimum age 14; Medical examination; Physician's request.
Facilities Dining room; Physical therapy room; Activities room; Crafts room; Laundry room; Barber/Beauty shop.
Activities Arts and Crafts; Cards; Games; Dances/Social or cultural gatherings.
Description Center has built its reputation for quality patient care through careful attention to details, going beyond what is required; much is expected from the staff who take pride in living up to high standards; visitors welcome; affordable rates.

CLARKSVILLE

Clarksville Manor Nursing Center*
2134 Ashland City Rd, Clarksville, TN, 37040 (615) 552-3002
Licensure Intermediate Care. *Beds* 66. *Certified* Medicaid.

General Care Convalescent Center*
111 Usery Rd, Clarksville, TN, 37040 (615) 647-0269
Licensure Skilled Care; Intermediate Care. *Beds* 120. *Certified* Medicaid; Medicare.

CLEVELAND

Bradley County Nursing Home
2910 Peerless Rd NW, Cleveland, TN, 37311 (615) 472-7116
Admin Ernest M Vincett. *Medical Dir/Dir of Nursing* Dr Stanley Pettit.
Licensure Skilled Care; Intermediate Care. *Beds* SNF 20; ICF 135. *Certified* Medicaid.
Staff RNs 4 (ft), 1 (pt); LPNs 15 (ft), 4 (pt); Orderlies 4 (ft); Nurses aides 30 (ft), 29 (pt); Physical therapists 1 (pt); Activities coordinators 1 (ft); Dentists 1 (pt).
Facilities Dining room; Physical therapy room; Activities room; Crafts room; Laundry room; Barber/Beauty shop.
Activities Arts and Crafts; Cards; Games; Reading groups; Prayer groups; Movies; Shopping trips; Dances/Social or cultural gatherings.

Life Care Center of Cleveland
3530 Keith St NW, Cleveland, TN, 37311 (615) 476-3254
Licensure Intermediate Care. *Beds* 163. *Certified* Medicaid.
Admissions Requirements Minimum age 14; Medical examination; Physician's request.
Staff RNs 2 (ft); LPNs 11 (ft), 2 (pt); Orderlies 5 (ft); Nurses aides 41 (ft), 9 (pt); Physical therapists 1 (pt); Speech therapists 1 (pt); Activities coordinators 1 (ft), 1 (pt); Dietitians 1 (pt).
Facilities Dining room; Physical therapy room; Activities room; Crafts room; Laundry room; Barber/Beauty shop.
Activities Arts and Crafts; Cards; Games; Reading groups; Prayer groups; Movies; Dan-ces/Social or cultural gatherings.
Description Facility has immaculate grounds and a garden courtyard; active pet therapy program. VA approved.

CLINTON

Anderson County Health Care Center*
220 Longmire Rd, Clinton, TN, 37716 (615) 457-6925
Licensure Intermediate Care. *Beds* 120. *Certified* Medicaid.

COLLEGEDALE

Life Care Center of Collegedale
Apison Pike, PO Box 658, Collegedale, TN, 37315 (615) 396-2182
Licensure Intermediate Care. *Beds* 124. *Certified* Medicaid.
Staff RNs 2 (ft), 1 (pt); LPNs 13 (ft), 3 (pt); Orderlies 1 (ft); Nurses aides 33 (ft); Physical therapists 1 (ft); Reality therapists 1 (pt); Recreational therapists 1 (pt); Occupational therapists 1 (pt); Speech therapists 1 (pt); Activities coordinators 1 (ft); Dietitians 1 (ft).
Facilities Dining room; Physical therapy room; Activities room; Chapel; Laundry room; Barber/Beauty shop.
Activities Arts and Crafts; Games; Movies; Shopping trips; Dances/Social or cultural gatherings.

COLLIERVILLE

Care Inn—Collierville*
490 Hwy 57 W, Collierville, TN, 38017 (615) 853-8561
Licensure Skilled Care. *Beds* 114. *Certified* Medicaid; Medicare.

COLUMBIA

Bel-Air Health Care Inc
105 N Campbell Blvd, Columbia, TN, 38401 (615) 389-5035
Medical Dir/Dir of Nursing Dr William A Robinson.
Licensure Intermediate Care. *Beds* 95. *Certified* Medicaid.
Admissions Requirements Medical examination; Physician's request.
Staff RNs 1 (ft); LPNs 5 (ft), 3 (pt); Orderlies 1 (pt); Nurses aides 23 (ft), 8 (pt); Physical therapists 1 (pt); Speech therapists 1 (pt); Activities coordinators 1 (pt); Dietitians 1 (pt); Dentists 1 (pt); Podiatrists 1 (pt).
Facilities Dining room; Activities room; Laundry room; Barber/Beauty shop.
Activities Arts and Crafts; Cards; Games; Reading groups; Prayer groups; Movies; Shopping trips; Dances/Social or cultural gatherings.

Columbia Health Care Center*
101 Walnut Ln, Columbia, TN, 38401 (615) 381-3712
Licensure Skilled Care; Intermediate Care. *Beds* 120. *Certified* Medicaid; Medicare.

Graymere Nursing Center Inc*
1410 Trotwood Ave, Columbia, TN, 38401
(615) 388-6443
Licensure Intermediate Care. *Beds* 171. *Certified* Medicaid.

Hillview Health Care Center Inc
2710 Trotwood Ave, Columbia, TN, 38401
(615) 388-7182
Medical Dir/Dir of Nursing Dr Carl C Gardner.
Licensure Skilled Care; Intermediate Care.
Beds 98. *Certified* Medicaid; Medicare.
Admissions Requirements Minimum age 18;
Physician's request.
Staff Physicians 1 (pt); RNs 6 (ft), 4 (pt); LPNs 5 (ft), 2 (pt); Orderlies 3 (ft); Nurses aides 22 (ft), 5 (pt); Physical therapists 1 (ft); Speech therapists 1 (ft); Activities coordinators 1 (ft); Dietitians 1 (ft); Dentists 1 (pt); Podiatrists 1 (pt); Audiologists 1 (pt).
Facilities Dining room; Physical therapy room; Activities room; Chapel; Crafts room; Laundry room; Barber/Beauty shop; Library.
Activities Arts and Crafts; Cards; Games; Reading groups; Prayer groups; Movies; Shopping trips; Dances/Social or cultural gatherings.
Description Hillview prides itself on giving excellent quality nursing care and rehabilitation services, such as physical therapy, speech therapy, meal training, exercise program, and bowel and bladder training.

COOKEVILLE

Cookeville Health Care Center Inc*
815 Bunker Hill Rd, Cookeville, TN, 38501
(615) 528-5516
Licensure Skilled Care; Intermediate Care.
Beds 96. *Certified* Medicaid; Medicare.

Cookeville Manor Nursing Home*
215 W 6th St, Cookeville, TN, 38501 (615) 528-7466
Licensure Intermediate Care. *Beds* 49. *Certified* Medicaid.

CORDOVA

Care Inn—Germantown*
955 Germantown Rd, Cordova, TN, 38018
(615) 754-1393
Licensure Intermediate Care. *Beds* 264. *Certified* Medicaid.

COVINGTON

Covington Manor Nursing Home*
Box 827, 1992 Hwy 51 S, Covington, TN, 38019 (615) 476-1820
Licensure Intermediate Care. *Beds* 194. *Certified* Medicaid.

CROSSVILLE

Life Care Center of Crossville
407 Wayne Ave, Crossville, TN, 38555 (615) 484-6129
Licensure Intermediate Care. *Beds* 109. *Certified* Medicaid.

Staff Physicians 8 (pt); RNs 1 (ft), 1 (pt); LPNs 8 (ft), 2 (pt); Orderlies 4 (ft), 2 (pt); Nurses aides 32 (ft), 6 (pt); Physical therapists 1 (pt); Activities coordinators 1 (ft); Dietitians 1 (pt); Dentists 1 (pt).
Facilities Dining room; Physical therapy room; Activities room; Crafts room; Laundry room; Barber/Beauty shop; Library.
Activities Arts and Crafts; Cards; Games; Reading groups; Prayer groups; Movies; Shopping trips; Dances/Social or cultural gatherings.

DANDRIDGE

Jefferson County Nursing Home*
Rt 5, Box 369, Dandridge, TN, 37725 (615) 397-3163
Licensure Intermediate Care. *Beds* 83. *Certified* Medicaid.

DAYTON

Laurelbrook Sanitarium
Rt 3, Ogden Rd, Dayton, TN, 37321 (615) 775-3338
Admin Steve Marlow. *Medical Dir/Dir of Nursing* Lester Littell MD.
Licensure Intermediate Care. *Beds* 49. *Certified* Medicaid.
Staff Physicians 1 (pt); RNs 2 (ft); LPNs 3 (ft); Orderlies 3 (ft), 1 (pt); Nurses aides 12 (ft), 1 (pt); Activities coordinators 1 (ft); Dietitians 1 (ft), 1 (pt).
Affiliation Seventh-Day Adventist
Facilities Dining room; Activities room; Chapel.
Activities Arts and Crafts; Games; Prayer groups; Movies; Shopping trips; Dances/Social or cultural gatherings.

Rhea County Nursing Home*
Hwy 27 N, Dayton, TN, 37321 (615) 775-1121
Licensure Intermediate Care. *Beds* 107. *Certified* Medicaid.

DICKSON

Dickson County Nursing Home
901 N Charlotte St, Dickson, TN, 37055 (615) 446-5171
Licensure Intermediate Care. *Beds* 49. *Certified* Medicaid.
Admissions Requirements Medical examination; Physician's request.
Staff LPNs 3 (ft), 3 (pt); Nurses aides 11 (ft), 7 (pt); Physical therapists 1 (pt); Activities coordinators 1 (ft); Dietitians 1 (ft).
Facilities Dining room; Physical therapy room; Activities room; Laundry room; Barber/Beauty shop; Library.
Activities Arts and Crafts; Cards; Games; Reading groups; Prayer groups; Movies; Shopping trips; Dances/Social or cultural gatherings.
Description Forty-nine bed facility, brick building all on one floor located in sight of 3 schools; residents can watch children and buses going to and from school. Old timer day is a yearly thing for all old timers in county. The residents who are able go to the parade or ride in the parade as they wish.

Green Valley Health Care Center Inc*
812 Charlotte St, Dickson, TN, 37055 (615) 446-8046
Licensure Skilled Care; Intermediate Care.
Beds 157. *Certified* Medicaid; Medicare.

DRESDEN

Hillview Nursing Home Inc*
Rt 1, Dresden, TN, 38225 (901) 364-2450
Licensure Intermediate Care. *Beds* 70. *Certified* Medicaid.

Weakley County Nursing Home
Rt 1, County Farm Rd, Dresden, TN, 38225
(901) 364-3158
Licensure Intermediate Care. *Beds* 139. *Certified* Medicaid.
Admissions Requirements Minimum age 14; Medical examination; Physician's request.
Staff RNs 1 (ft); LPNs 14 (ft), 1 (pt); Orderlies 5 (ft); Nurses aides 44 (ft), 9 (pt); Physical therapists 1 (pt); Activities coordinators 1 (ft), 1 (pt); Dietitians 1 (pt).
Facilities Dining room; Activities room; Laundry room; Barber/Beauty shop.
Activities Arts and Crafts; Cards; Games; Movies; Shopping trips; Dances/Social or cultural gatherings.
Description Home is located on 130 acres of country farm land in rural, western Tennessee.

DUNLAP

Sequatchie Health Care Center
Taylor St, PO Box 685, Dunlap, TN, 37327
(615) 949-4651
Medical Dir/Dir of Nursing Charles Graves MD.
Licensure Skilled Care; Intermediate Care.
Beds 60. *Certified* Medicaid; Medicare.
Admissions Requirements Minimum age 18; Medical examination; Physician's request.
Staff Physicians 1 (pt); RNs 1 (ft), 1 (pt); LPNs 5 (ft), 3 (pt); Orderlies 1 (pt); Nurses aides 12 (ft), 12 (pt); Physical therapists 1 (pt); Recreational therapists 1 (pt); Speech therapists 1 (pt); Activities coordinators 1 (pt); Dietitians 1 (pt); Dentists 1 (pt).
Facilities Dining room; Physical therapy room; Activities room; Laundry room; Barber/Beauty shop.
Activities Arts and Crafts; Games; Reading groups; Prayer groups; Movies; Shopping trips; Dances/Social or cultural gatherings.
Description Sequatchie Health Care Center lies within a 120-mile-long valley. This beautiful setting is in a quiet rural area.

DYERSBURG

Nucare Convalescent Center
1636 Woodlawn, Dyersburg, TN, 38024 (901) 285-6400
Medical Dir/Dir of Nursing W I Thornton MD.
Licensure Intermediate Care. *Beds* 50. *Certified* Medicaid.
Admissions Requirements Physician's request.
Staff LPNs 5 (ft), 3 (pt); Nurses aides 12 (ft), 4

(pt); Activities coordinators 1 (ft); Dietitians 5 (ft), 1 (pt).
Facilities Dining room; Activities room; Laundry room; Barber/Beauty shop; Library.
Activities Arts and Crafts; Cards; Games; Prayer groups; Movies.
Description We have a large activity room for crafts, and bingo is held in the dining room which is connected to the crafts room. A physical therapy room is available. Library is sponsored and organized by the Forked Deer Library which comes monthly and reshelves materials.

Parkview Convalescent Unit*
Parr and Tickle Sts, Dyersburg, TN, 38024
(901) 285-2710
Licensure Intermediate Care. *Beds* 113. *Certified* Medicaid.

ELIZABETHTON

Hermitage Nursing Home Inc
1633 Hillview Dr, Elizabethton, TN, 37643
(615) 543-2571
Admin Jeannette F Bradshaw. *Medical Dir/Dir of Nursing* Royce L Holsey Jr.
Licensure Intermediate Care. *Beds* 48. *Certified* Medicaid.
Admissions Requirements Minimum age 14; Medical examination; Physician's request.
Staff Physicians 1 (pt); RNs 1 (ft), 1 (pt); LPNs 3 (ft), 2 (pt); Orderlies 1 (ft); Nurses aides 6 (ft), 6 (pt); Physical therapists 1 (pt); Activities coordinators 1 (ft); Dietitians 1 (pt).
Facilities Dining room; Physical therapy room; Activities room; Laundry room; Barber/Beauty shop; Library.
Activities Arts and Crafts; Cards; Games; Reading groups; Prayer groups; Movies; Shopping trips; Dances/Social or cultural gatherings.

Hillview Nursing Home
1666 Hillview Dr, Elizabethton, TN, 37643
(615) 542-5061
Admin Carol Hutchins.
Licensure Intermediate Care. *Beds* 42. *Certified* Medicaid.
Admissions Requirements Minimum age 14; Physician's request.
Staff Physicians 6 (pt); RNs 2 (ft); LPNs 4 (ft), 1 (pt); Nurses aides 10 (ft), 4 (pt); Activities coordinators 1 (ft); Dietitians 1 (pt).
Facilities Dining room; Laundry room; Outdoor activities shed.
Activities Arts and Crafts; Games; Reading groups; Prayer groups; Shopping trips.
Description Home is dedicated to the care of the aged without regard to race, color, national origin, or handicap.

Ivy Hall Nursing Home
301 Watauga Ave, Elizabethton, TN, 37643
(615) 542-6512
Admin Judy C Taylor. *Medical Dir/Dir of Nursing* Dr E E Perry.
Licensure Intermediate Care. *Beds* 76. *Certified* Medicaid.
Admissions Requirements Medical examination; Physician's request.
Staff Physicians 1 (ft), 5 (pt); RNs 1 (ft); LPNs 6 (ft), 2 (pt); Orderlies 2 (ft), 1 (pt); Nurses aides

28 (ft), 5 (pt); Physical therapists 1 (pt); Speech therapists 1 (pt); Activities coordinators 1 (ft); Dietitians 1 (ft), 1 (pt); Dentists 1 (pt); Ophthalmologists 1 (pt); Podiatrists 1 (pt); Audiologists 1 (pt).
Facilities Dining room; Physical therapy room; Activities room; Crafts room; Laundry room; Barber/Beauty shop; Library.
Activities Arts and Crafts; Cards; Games; Reading groups; Prayer groups; Movies; Shopping trips; Dances/Social or cultural gatherings.
Description Ivy Hall is equipped with 28 private rooms at no extra charge and are available on a first come, first serve basis. Each resident is allowed their own physician or may choose our house physician.

Regency Health Care Center
1641 Hwy 19E, Elizabethton, TN, 37643 (615) 542-4133
Medical Dir/Dir of Nursing R Eugene Galloway MD and Jerry Gastinern MD.
Licensure Intermediate Care. *Beds* 148. *Certified* Medicaid.
Admissions Requirements Minimum age 18; Medical examination; Physician's request.
Staff Physicians 2 (pt); RNs 2 (ft); LPNs 10 (ft), 2 (pt); Orderlies 2 (ft); Nurses aides 40 (ft), 6 (pt); Physical therapists 1 (pt); Activities coordinators 1 (ft); Dietitians 1 (pt).
Facilities Dining room; Physical therapy room; Activities room; Laundry room; Barber/Beauty shop.
Activities Arts and Crafts; Cards; Games; Prayer groups; Movies; Shopping trips; Dances/Social or cultural gatherings.
Description This facility has a beautiful courtyard in the center with shade trees and patios.

Southwood Nursing Home
Pineridge Circle, Elizabethton, TN, 37643 (615) 543-3202
Medical Dir/Dir of Nursing Dr E E Perry.
Licensure Intermediate Care. *Beds* 76. *Certified* Medicaid.
Staff Physicians 1 (pt); RNs 1 (ft); LPNs 7 (ft), 2 (pt); Orderlies 4 (ft); Nurses aides 18 (ft), 2 (pt); Physical therapists 1 (pt); Speech therapists 1 (pt); Activities coordinators 1 (ft); Dietitians 1 (ft); Podiatrists 1 (pt).
Facilities Dining room; Physical therapy room; Activities room; Barber/Beauty shop.
Activities Arts and Crafts; Cards; Games; Movies; Shopping trips.
Description We have an excellent physical therapy program with a registered physical therapist and a physical therapy aide on duty. We are situated in a quiet residential setting with a beautiful view of the mountains. We serve good home-like meals for patients.

ERIN

Royal Care of Erin Inc
Knight Rd, Rt 3, Box 137-B, Erin, TN, 37061
(615) 289-4141
Admin Helen L Stout. *Medical Dir/Dir of Nursing* Daniel Martin MD.
Licensure Intermediate Care. *Beds* 100. *Certified* Medicaid.
Admissions Requirements Minimum age 18;

Medical examination.
Staff Physicians 3 (ft), 1 (pt); RNs 3 (ft); LPNs 4 (ft), 4 (pt); Nurses aides 20 (ft), 12 (pt); Physical therapists 1 (pt); Activities coordinators 1 (ft), 1 (pt); Dietitians 1 (pt).
Facilities Dining room; Physical therapy room; Activities room; Chapel; Crafts room; Laundry room; Barber/Beauty shop; Library.
Activities Arts and Crafts; Games; Reading groups; Prayer groups; Movies; Dances/Social or cultural gatherings.
Description This is a beautiful, modern, and contemporary nursing home with many of the amenities of a luxurious hotel—crystal chandeliers, baby grand piano, beautiful relaxed rural setting; unique in offering 5 meals a day: continental breakfast in patients' rooms, brunch, lunch, dinner, and evening snack; outstanding rehabilitation program; provides best in patient care; nursing staff gives tender loving care and has genuine concern for the patients.

ERWIN

Unicoi County Nursing Home*
Greenway Circle, Erwin, TN, 37650 (615) 743-3141
Licensure Skilled Care; Intermediate Care. *Beds* 46. *Certified* Medicaid; Medicare.

ETOWAH

Etowah Health Care Center
Old Grady Rd, Etowah, TN, 37331 (615) 263-1138
Medical Dir/Dir of Nursing Dr Thomas W Williams.
Licensure Intermediate Care. *Beds* 120. *Certified* Medicaid.
Admissions Requirements Minimum age 18; Medical examination; Physician's request.
Staff Physicians 1 (pt); RNs 1 (ft); LPNs 7 (ft), 3 (pt); Orderlies 4 (ft), 2 (pt); Nurses aides 30 (ft), 8 (pt); Physical therapists 1 (pt); Speech therapists 1 (pt); Activities coordinators 1 (ft), 1 (pt); Dietitians 1 (pt).
Facilities Dining room; Physical therapy room; Activities room; Laundry room; Barber/Beauty shop.
Activities Arts and Crafts; Games; Prayer groups; Movies; Dances/Social or cultural gatherings.
Description Four-year-old facility surrounded by the mountains of the Cherokee National Forest; many activities available to the patients, including ceramics. Nursing care is excellent; food is well prepared and all diets are followed.

McMinn Memorial Nursing Home
Hwy 411 N, PO Box 410, Etowah, TN, 37331
(615) 263-5521
Licensure Intermediate Care. *Beds* 40. *Certified* Medicaid.
Facilities Dining room; Physical therapy room; Activities room; Barber/Beauty shop.

FAYETTEVILLE

Donalson Care Center*
510 W Market St, Fayetteville, TN, 37334 (615)
433-7156
Licensure Intermediate Care. *Beds* 37. *Certified* Medicaid.

Health Inn Inc*
Rt 7, Thornton Pkwy, Fayetteville, TN, 37334
(615) 433-9973
Beds 49.

Lincoln Care Center
501 Morgan Ave, Fayetteville, TN, 37334 (615)
433-61 ,6
Admin Sara Hamlin. *Medical Dir/Dir of Nursing* Anne U Bolner.
Licensure Intermediate Care. *Beds* 127. *Certified* Medicaid.
Staff Physicians 1 (pt); RNs 1 (ft), 1 (pt); LPNs
17 (ft), 6 (pt); Nurses aides 58 (ft), 12 (pt);
Physical therapists 1 (pt); Occupational therapists 1 (pt); Speech therapists 1 (pt); Activities
coordinators 2 (ft), 1 (pt); Dietitians 1 (pt);
Dentists 1 (pt); Ophthalmologists 1 (pt); Podiatrists 1 (pt).
Facilities Dining room; Physical therapy room;
Activities room; Chapel; Crafts room; Laundry
room; Barber/Beauty shop; Library.
Activities Arts and Crafts; Cards; Games;
Reading groups; Prayer groups; Movies; Shopping trips; Dances/Social or cultural gatherings;
Picnics; Coffee breaks; Cookouts; Exercise
classes; Fishing; Quilting; Bingo; Sensory stimulation.
Description We care about our patients.

FRANKLIN

Claiborne and Hughes Convalescent Center Inc*
Strahl and Carter Sts, Franklin, TN, 37064
Licensure Nursing Home. *Beds* 156.

Franklin Health Care Center*
216 Fairground St, Franklin, TN, 37064 (615)
794-9287
Licensure Skilled Care; Intermediate Care.
Beds 76. *Certified* Medicaid; Medicare.

Graystone Home
137 4th Ave S, Franklin, TN, 37064 (615)
794-4877
Medical Dir/Dir of Nursing Rosemary Fouver
RN.
Beds 37.
Admissions Requirements Minimum age 14;
Medical examination.
Staff RNs 2 (pt); LPNs 1 (ft); Nurses aides 11
(ft), 2 (pt); Dietitians 2 (ft), 2 (pt).
Facilities Activities room; Laundry room.
Activities Cards; Games; Group singing.
Description Facility features home-cooked
meals, a homey-type atmosphere, with 24-hour
nursing care.

Harpeth Terrace Convalescent Center Inc
1287 W Main St, Franklin, TN, 37064 (615)
794-8417
Licensure Skilled Care; Intermediate Care.
Beds 89. *Certified* Medicaid.

Facilities Dining room; Physical therapy room;
Activities room; Laundry room; Barber/Beauty
shop.
Activities Arts and Crafts; Cards; Games; Prayer groups; Dances/Social or cultural gatherings.

Lofton Nursing Home Inc*
1501 Columbia Ave, Franklin, TN, 37064 (615)
794-2624
Beds 49.

GAINESBORO

Theo Spivey Nursing Home*
Rt 2, Box 271-A, Gainesboro, TN, 38562 (615)
268-0291
Licensure Intermediate Care. *Beds* 64. *Certified* Medicaid.

GALLATIN

Brandywood Nursing Home*
555 E Bledsoe St, Gallatin, TN, 37066 (615)
452-7132
Licensure Skilled Care; Intermediate Care.
Beds 100. *Certified* Medicaid; Medicare.

Gallatin Nursing Home Inc*
438 N Water Ave, Gallatin, TN, 37066 (615)
452-2322
Licensure Intermediate Care. *Beds* 199. *Certified* Medicaid.

L M Swanson Nursing Home*
647 Pace St, Gallatin, TN, 37066 (615)
452-0611
Licensure Intermediate Care. *Beds* 25. *Certified* Medicaid.

GALLAWAY

Layton Watson Nursing Home
435 Old Brownsville Rd, PO Box 128, Gallaway, TN, 38036 (901) 867-2010
Medical Dir/Dir of Nursing Dr Robert Oliver.
Licensure Intermediate Care. *Beds* 120.
Certified Medicaid.
Admissions Requirements Minimum age 14;
Medical examination; Physician's request.
Staff Physicians 6 (ft), 10 (pt); RNs 1 (pt);
LPNs 14 (ft); Nurses aides 36 (ft); Physical therapists 1 (pt); Occupational therapists 1 (pt);
Activities coordinators 1 (ft); Dietitians 1 (ft).
Facilities Dining room; Physical therapy room;
Activities room; Chapel; Crafts room; Laundry
room; Barber/Beauty shop; Library.
Activities Arts and Crafts; Cards; Games;
Reading groups; Prayer groups; Movies; Shopping trips; Dances/Social or cultural gatherings.

GOODLETTSVILLE

Vanco Manor Nursing Home*
813 S Dickerson Rd, Goodlettsville, TN, 37072
(615) 859-6600
Licensure Intermediate Care. *Beds* 66. *Certified* Medicaid.

GRAY

Anderson Health Care Center*
PO Box 8275, Rt 15, Gray, TN, 37615 (615)
477-7146
Licensure Intermediate Care. *Beds* 86. *Certified* Medicaid.

GRAYSVILLE

Graysville Nursing Home
Star Rt, Graysville, TN, 37338 (615) 775-1262
Licensure Nursing Home. *Beds* 19.
Admissions Requirements Medical examination.
Staff RNs 1 (pt); LPNs 1 (ft), 1 (pt); Nurses
aides 6 (ft), 3 (pt).
Facilities Dining room; Laundry room.
Description Facility features a home-like
atmosphere with reasonable rates.

GREENEVILLE

Life Care Center of Greeneville
725 Crum St, Greeneville, TN, 37743 (615)
639-8131
Licensure Intermediate Care. *Beds* 161. *Certified* Medicaid.
Facilities Dining room; Physical therapy room;
Activities room; Chapel; Crafts room; Laundry
room; Barber/Beauty shop; EKG; X-ray; IPPB.
Activities Arts and Crafts; Games; Reading
groups; Movies; Shopping trips; Dances/Social
or cultural gatherings.

Life Care—West*
210 Holt Court, Greeneville, TN, 37743 (615)
639-0213
Licensure Intermediate Care. *Beds* 124. *Certified* Medicaid.

HARRIMAN

Johnson's Health Care Center Inc*
Box 290, Hannah Rd, Harriman, TN, 37748
(615) 882-9159
Licensure Intermediate Care. *Beds* 160. *Certified* Medicaid.

HARTSVILLE

Beene Health Care Inc*
Rt 3, Box 222, Hartsville, TN, 37074 (615)
374-2167
Licensure Intermediate Care. *Beds* 72. *Certified* Medicaid.

HENDERSON

Chester County Nursing Home
831 E Main St, Henderson, TN, 38340 (901)
989-7598
Licensure Intermediate Care. *Beds* 89. *Certified* Medicaid.
Admissions Requirements Minimum age 18;
Medical examination; Physician's request.
Staff RNs 1 (ft); LPNs 6 (ft), 3 (pt); Orderlies 1
(ft); Nurses aides 13 (ft), 8 (pt); Activities coordinators 1 (ft); Dietitians 1 (ft).

Facilities Dining room; Activities room; Laundry room; Barber/Beauty shop.
Activities Arts and Crafts; Cards; Games; Reading groups; Prayer groups; Movies.
Description Facility offers 24-hour nursing care under the direction of a registered nurse, meals prepared under the supervision of a registered dietician, free cable TV, and laundry service.

HENDERSONVILLE

Hendersonville Nursing Home*
672 W Main St, Hendersonville, TN, 37075 (615) 824-8301
Beds 32.

HERMITAGE

McKendree Village Inc
4347 Lebanon Rd, Hermitage, TN, 37076 (615) 889-6990
Medical Dir/Dir of Nursing Dr Edward King.
Licensure Intermediate Care. *Beds* 199. *Certified* Medicaid.
Admissions Requirements Minimum age 60; Medical examination.
Affiliation Methodist
Facilities Dining room; Physical therapy room; Activities room; Chapel; Crafts room; Laundry room; Barber/Beauty shop; Library.
Activities Arts and Crafts; Cards; Games; Reading groups; Prayer groups; Movies; Shopping trips; Dances/Social or cultural gatherings.
Description Facility is located 11 miles east of Nashville across from "The Hermitage", home of Andrew Jackson; offers 7-levels of service: cottages, apartments, licensed home for the aged, and 4 levels of health care—intermediate to skilled; not-for-profit corporation whose directors are named by the United Methodist Church, Tennessee Annual Conference.

HOHENWALD

Lewis County Manor*
Box 92, Linden Hwy, Hohenwald, TN, 38462 (615) 796-3233
Licensure Intermediate Care. *Beds* 60. *Certified* Medicaid.

HUMBOLDT

Nucare Convalescent Center*
2400 Mitchell St, Humboldt, TN, 38343 (901) 784-5183
Licensure Intermediate Care. *Beds* 142. *Certified* Medicaid.

HUNTINGDON

Care Inn—Huntingdon
635 High St, Huntingdon, TN, 38344 (901) 986-8943
Admin William W Wright.
Licensure Intermediate Care. *Beds* 132. *Certified* Medicaid.
Staff RNs 1 (ft); LPNs 13 (ft); Nurses aides 26 (ft); Physical therapists 1 (pt); Activities coordinators 1 (ft); Dietitians 1 (ft).

Facilities Dining room; Activities room; Crafts room; Laundry room; Barber/Beauty shop.
Activities Arts and Crafts; Cards; Games; Reading groups; Prayer groups; Movies; Shopping trips; Dances/Social or cultural gatherings.

HUNTSVILLE

Stonehenge Health Care Center Inc
Baker St Extension, Huntsville, TN, 37756
Admin William J Stout Jr. *Medical Dir/Dir of Nursing* Dr George Kline.
Licensure Intermediate Care. *Beds* 79. *Certified* Medicaid.
Ownership Proprietary.
Admissions Requirements Minimum age 14; Medical examination; Physician's request.
Staff RNs 1 (pt); LPNs 5 (ft); Orderlies 3 (ft); Nurses aides 11 (ft), 5 (pt); Physical therapists 1 (pt); Activities coordinators 1 (ft); Dietitians 1 (ft); Dentists 1 (pt); Ophthalmologists 1 (pt).
Facilities Dining room; Physical therapy room; Activities room; Laundry room; Barber/Beauty shop; Library.
Activities Arts and Crafts; Cards; Games; Reading groups; Prayer groups; Movies; Shopping trips; Dances/Social or cultural gatherings.
Description Facility is nestled in the Smokey Mountains in a beautiful natural setting; offers 5-meals-a-day program which increases nourishment while decreasing discomfort and use of stomach settling agents. This is a licensed geriatric day care center.

JACKSON

Forest Cove Nursing Center
45 Forest Cove, Jackson, TN, 38301 (901) 424-4200
Licensure Intermediate Care. *Beds* 150. *Certified* Medicaid.
Admissions Requirements Minimum age 18.
Staff RNs 2 (ft); LPNs 12 (ft), 3 (pt); Nurses aides 36 (ft), 13 (pt); Recreational therapists 1 (pt); Activities coordinators 1 (ft).
Facilities Dining room; Activities room; Crafts room; Barber/Beauty shop.
Activities Arts and Crafts; Cards; Games; Prayer groups; Movies.

Laurel Wood Health Care Inc
200 Birch St, Jackson, TN, 38301 (901) 422-5641
Admin Leonard L Usery. *Medical Dir/Dir of Nursing* Robert Tucker.
Licensure Intermediate Care. *Beds* 66. *Certified* Medicaid.
Admissions Requirements Minimum age 14; Medical examination; Physician's request.
Staff Physicians 2 (ft), 8 (pt); RNs 1 (pt); LPNs 4 (ft), 3 (pt); Nurses aides 28 (ft), 10 (pt); Physical therapists 2 (pt); Reality therapists 1 (ft); Recreational therapists 1 (ft); Occupational therapists 1 (pt); Activities coordinators 1 (ft); Dietitians 1 (ft); Dentists 1 (pt); Podiatrists 1 (pt).
Facilities Dining room; Physical therapy room; Activities room; Chapel; Laundry room; Barber/Beauty shop.
Activities Arts and Crafts; Cards; Games; Reading groups; Prayer groups; Movies; Shop-

ping trips.
Description Facility offers excellent patient care in beautiful surroundings.

Maplewood Health Care Center*
100 Cherrywood Pl, Jackson, TN, 38301 (901) 668-1900
Licensure Intermediate Care. *Beds* 133. *Certified* Medicaid.

Mission Convalescent Home
118 Glass St, Jackson, TN, 38301 (901) 424-2951
Licensure Intermediate Care. *Beds* 30. *Certified* Medicaid.
Admissions Requirements Minimum age 16; Medical examination; Physician's request.
Staff Physicians 5 (pt); RNs 1 (pt); LPNs 3 (ft); Nurses aides 9 (ft); Activities coordinators 2 (ft); Dietitians 1 (pt); Dentists 1 (pt).
Facilities Dining room; Activities room; Chapel; Laundry room.
Activities Arts and Crafts; Cards; Games; Prayer groups; Movies; Shopping trips.

Royal Care of Jackson Inc
131 Cloverdale St, Jackson, TN, 38301 (901) 423-8750
Medical Dir/Dir of Nursing Curtis Clark MD.
Licensure Skilled Care; Intermediate Care. *Beds* 107. *Certified* Medicaid; Medicare.
Admissions Requirements Minimum age 14; Medical examination; Physician's request.
Staff Physicians 1 (pt); RNs 1 (ft), 1 (pt); LPNs 7 (ft), 4 (pt); Orderlies 1 (ft); Nurses aides 28 (ft), 11 (pt); Physical therapists 1 (pt); Activities coordinators 1 (ft); Dietitians 1 (pt).
Facilities Dining room; Physical therapy room; Activities room; Crafts room; Laundry room; Barber/Beauty shop.
Activities Arts and Crafts; Cards; Games; Prayer groups; Movies; Shopping trips; Dances/Social or cultural gatherings.

JAMESTOWN

Fentress County Nursing Home*
Hwy 52 W, Jamestown, TN, 38556 (615) 879-9915
Licensure Intermediate Care. *Beds* 38. *Certified* Medicaid.

JEFFERSON CITY

Care Inn—Jefferson City
Hwy 11E, Jefferson City, TN, 37760 (615) 475-9037
Medical Dir/Dir of Nursing Henry J Prezutti MD.
Licensure Intermediate Care. *Beds* 186. *Certified* Medicaid.
Staff Physicians 10 (pt); RNs 2 (ft), 2 (pt); LPNs 9 (ft), 6 (pt); Nurses aides 38 (ft), 22 (pt); Physical therapists 1 (pt); Activities coordinators 2 (ft); Dietitians 1 (ft); Dentists 1 (pt).
Facilities Dining room; Activities room; Laundry room; Barber/Beauty shop; TV lounge.
Activities Arts and Crafts; Cards; Games; Prayer groups; Movies; Shopping trips; Dances/Social or cultural gatherings; Resident council.
Description Facility is a beautiful home located

in east Tennessee near the foothills of the Great Smokies situated on 5 beautifully landscaped acres.

JOHNSON CITY

Appalachian Christian Village
2012 Sherwood Dr, Johnson City, TN, 37601
(615) 928-2870
Licensure Intermediate Care. *Beds* 74. *Certified* Medicaid.

Asbury Center Health and Retirement Home*
Boone and Fairview Sts, Johnson City, TN, 37601 (615) 929-1161
Licensure Intermediate Care. *Beds* 164. *Certified* Medicaid.

Colonial Hill Health Care Center*
Box 3218, 3209 Bristol Hwy, Johnson City, TN, 37601 (615) 282-3311
Licensure Skilled Care; Intermediate Care. *Beds* 177. *Certified* Medicaid; Medicare.

JONESBORO

Four Oaks Health Care Center*
Persimmon Ridge Rd, Jonesboro, TN, 37659
Licensure Nursing Home. *Beds* 66.

Jonesboro Nursing Home Inc
210 Jackson Blvd, Jonesboro, TN, 37659 (615) 753-4281
Licensure Intermediate Care. *Beds* 65. *Certified* Medicaid.
Admissions Requirements Medical examination; Physician's request.
Staff Physicians 1 (pt); RNs 1 (pt); LPNs 4 (ft), 2 (pt); Orderlies 6 (ft); Nurses aides 12 (ft); Activities coordinators 1 (ft); Dietitians 1 (ft).
Facilities Dining room; Activities room; Crafts room; Laundry room; Barber/Beauty shop.
Activities Arts and Crafts; Games; Reading groups; Prayer groups; Dances/Social or cultural gatherings.

KINGSPORT

Kingsport Health Care Center Inc*
3641 Memorial Blvd, Kingsport, TN, 37664
(615) 846-2411
Licensure Intermediate Care. *Beds* 198. *Certified* Medicaid.

KNOXVILLE

Brakebill Nursing Homes Inc
5837 Lyons View Pike, Knoxville, TN, 37919
(615) 584-3902
Licensure Skilled Care; Intermediate Care. *Beds* 212. *Certified* Medicaid; Medicare.
Admissions Requirements Medical examination; Physician's request.
Staff Physicians 20 (pt); RNs 5 (ft), 5 (pt); LPNs 8 (ft), 4 (pt); Orderlies 4 (ft); Nurses aides 50 (ft); Physical therapists 3 (ft); Recreational therapists 3 (ft); Speech therapists 2 (ft); Activities coordinators 3 (ft); Dietitians 1 (ft); Dentists 1 (pt); Podiatrists 1 (pt); Audiologists 1 (ft).
Facilities Dining room; Physical therapy room;

Activities room; Crafts room; Laundry room; Barber/Beauty shop; Library.
Activities Arts and Crafts; Cards; Games; Reading groups; Prayer groups; Movies; Shopping trips; Dances/Social or cultural gatherings.

Hillcrest—Beverly*
Rt 12, Tazewell Pike, Knoxville, TN, 37918
(615) 687-6881
Licensure Skilled Care; Intermediate Care. *Beds* 173. *Certified* Medicaid; Medicare.

Hillcrest—North*
Rt 12, Maloneyville Rd, Knoxville, TN, 37918
Licensure Nursing Home. *Beds* 386.

Hillcrest—South*
1758 Hillwood Ave, Knoxville, TN, 37920
(615) 573-9621
Licensure Intermediate Care. *Beds* 106. *Certified* Medicaid.

Hillcrest—West*
6801 Middlebrook Pike, Knoxville, TN, 37919
(615) 588-7661
Licensure Skilled Care; Intermediate Care. *Beds* 212. *Certified* Medicaid; Medicare.

Kingston Pike Nursing Home
2633 Kingston Pike SW, Knoxville, TN, 37919
(615) 523-0433
Licensure Intermediate Care. *Beds* 50. *Certified* Medicaid.

Knoxville Convalescent and Nursing Home Inc*
809 Emerald Ave, Knoxville, TN, 37917 (615) 524-7366
Licensure Skilled Care; Intermediate Care. *Beds* 152. *Certified* Medicaid; Medicare.

Knoxville Health Care Center Inc*
2120 Highland Ave, Knoxville, TN, 37916
(615) 525-4131
Licensure Skilled Care; Intermediate Care. *Beds* 180. *Certified* Medicaid; Medicare.

Little Creek Sanitarium*
1810 Little Creek Ln, Knoxville, TN, 37922
(615) 690-6727
Beds 38.

Northhaven Health Care Center
3300 Broadway NE, Knoxville, TN, 37917
(615) 698-2052
Medical Dir/Dir of Nursing Dr Mosley.
Licensure Intermediate Care. *Beds* 96. *Certified* Medicaid.
Admissions Requirements Minimum age 14; Medical examination; Physician's request.
Staff RNs 2 (ft), 3 (pt); LPNs 2 (ft), 4 (pt); Nurses aides 24 (ft), 8 (pt); Physical therapists 2 (pt); Activities coordinators 1 (ft); Dietitians 1 (ft); Dentists 1 (pt); Ophthalmologists 1 (pt); Podiatrists 1 (pt); Audiologists 1 (pt).
Facilities Dining room; Physical therapy room; Activities room; Crafts room; Laundry room; Barber/Beauty shop.
Activities Arts and Crafts; Cards; Games; Reading groups; Prayer groups; Movies; Pet therapy.

Serene Manor Medical Center
970 Wray St, Knoxville, TN, 37917 (615) 523-9171
Medical Dir/Dir of Nursing Dr George Schacklett.
Licensure Intermediate Care. *Beds* 73. *Certified* Medicaid.
Admissions Requirements Minimum age 14; Medical examination; Physician's request.
Staff RNs 2 (ft); LPNs 7 (pt); Orderlies 5 (ft); Nurses aides 15 (ft); Recreational therapists 1 (ft); Activities coordinators 1 (ft); Dietitians 1 (ft).
Facilities Dining room; Physical therapy room; Activities room; Chapel; Crafts room; Laundry room; Barber/Beauty shop; Library.
Activities Arts and Crafts; Cards; Games; Reading groups; Prayer groups; Movies; Shopping trips; Dances/Social or cultural gatherings.

Shannondale Health Care Center
801 Vanosdale Rd, Knoxville, TN, 37921 (615) 690-3411
Licensure Skilled Care; Intermediate Care. *Beds* 200. *Certified* Medicaid; Medicare.

Shannondale Retirement Home
801 Vanosdale Rd, Knoxville, TN, 37919 (615) 690-3411
Medical Dir/Dir of Nursing Dr Harry K Ogden.
Licensure Home for the Aged. *Beds* 149.
Admissions Requirements Minimum age 62.
Staff Physicians 1 (pt); RNs 1 (ft), 2 (pt); LPNs 2 (ft), 1 (pt); Activities coordinators 1 (ft); Dietitians 1 (ft); Podiatrists 1 (pt).
Affiliation Presbyterian
Facilities Dining room; Activities room; Chapel; Crafts room; Laundry room; Barber/Beauty shop; Library.
Activities Arts and Crafts; Cards; Games; Prayer groups; Movies; Shopping trips; Dances/Social or cultural gatherings; Theatre; Zoo; Dogwood Arts Festival; Art shows.
Description Located in Knoxville, Tennessee, the gateway to the Smokey Mountains, Shannondale Retirement Home is within a complex which contains Shannondale Health Care Center and the soon to be added condominium retirement village, Buckingham Place. Open spaces, manicured lawn, and service are the themes for the area. Easy access to bus lines and shopping centers.

LAFAYETTE

Janwynella Nursing Home Inc
405 Times Ave, Lafayette, TN, 37083 (615) 666-3170
Medical Dir/Dir of Nursing C C Chitwood Jr MD.
Beds 39.
Admissions Requirements Minimum age 14; Medical examination.
Staff RNs 1 (ft); LPNs 1 (ft); Orderlies 2 (ft); Nurses aides 15 (ft); Activities coordinators 1 (ft); Dietitians 1 (pt).

LAFOLLETTE

LaFollette Community Nursing Home
106 E Ave, LaFollette, TN, 37766 (615) 562-2211
Medical Dir/Dir of Nursing Dr J C Pryse.
Licensure Intermediate Care. *Beds* 98. *Certified* Medicaid.
Admissions Requirements Medical examination; Physician's request.
Staff Physicians 17 (pt); RNs 2 (pt); Physical therapists 1 (pt); Recreational therapists 1 (pt); Speech therapists 1 (ft); Activities coordinators 1 (pt); Dietitians 1 (pt); Dentists 10 (ft).
Facilities Dining room; Physical therapy room; Activities room; Chapel; Crafts room; Laundry room; Barber/Beauty shop.
Activities Arts and Crafts; Cards; Games; Reading groups; Prayer groups; Movies; Dances/Social or cultural gatherings.
Description Facility is located in a small community, surrounded by Appalachian Mountain range.

LAKE CITY

Lake City Health Care Center
Industrial Park Dr, Lake City, TN, 37769 (615) 426-2147
Licensure Intermediate Care. *Beds* 115. *Certified* Medicaid.
Staff RNs 2 (ft); LPNs 7 (ft), 6 (pt); Nurses aides 18 (ft), 15 (pt); Activities coordinators 1 (ft); Dietitians 1 (ft).
Facilities Dining room; Physical therapy room; Activities room; Laundry room; Barber/Beauty shop; Library.
Activities Arts and Crafts; Cards; Games; Reading groups; Prayer groups; Movies; Shopping trips; Dances/Social or cultural gatherings.
Description VA approved.

LAWRENCEBURG

Laurenceburg Health Care Center*
Rt 3, Kennedy St, Lawrenceburg, TN, 38464 (615) 762-9418
Licensure Skilled Care; Intermediate Care. *Beds* 37. *Certified* Medicaid; Medicare.

Lawrence County Lions Nursing Home Inc*
374 Brink St, Lawrenceburg, TN, 38464
Licensure Intermediate Care. *Beds* 88. *Certified* Medicaid.

Royal Care of Lawrenceburg
Buffalo Rd, Rt 1, Lawrenceburg, TN, 38464 (615) 762-7518
Admin Kaun Porter. *Medical Dir/Dir of Nursing* J Carmack Hudgins MD.
Licensure Skilled Care; Intermediate Care. *Beds* SNF 64; ICF 88. *Certified* Medicaid; Medicare.
Admissions Requirements Minimum age 14; Medical examination; Physician's request.
Staff RNs 4 (ft), 1 (pt); LPNs 11 (ft), 5 (pt); Orderlies 1 (pt); Nurses aides 6 (ft), 35 (pt); Physical therapists; Speech therapists; Activities coordinators 1 (ft); Dietitians 1 (ft); Dentists; Social workers 1 (ft); Physical therapy aides 2 (ft).

Facilities Dining room; Physical therapy room; Activities room; Crafts room; Laundry room; Barber/Beauty shop; Library.
Activities Arts and Crafts; Cards; Games; Reading groups; Prayer groups; Movies; Shopping trips; Dances/Social or cultural gatherings; Painting classes; Quilting bees; Special singing; Church services.
Description Facility is located just one mile north of town in a beautiful rural setting, dedicated to creating a dynamic environment in which residents, their families, and friends can experience satisfaction in their lives. VA approved.

LEBANON

Cedars Nursing Home
933 Baddour Parkway, Lebanon, TN, 37087 (615) 444-1836
Medical Dir/Dir of Nursing Morris Ferguson MD.
Licensure Skilled Care. *Beds* 60. *Certified* Medicaid; Medicare.
Staff RNs 4 (ft), 1 (pt); LPNs 5 (ft); Nurses aides 28 (ft); Physical therapists 1 (ft); Activities coordinators 1 (ft).
Facilities Dining room; Physical therapy room; Laundry room; Barber/Beauty shop.
Activities Arts and Crafts; Cards; Games; Reading groups; Movies; Shopping trips; Dances/Social or cultural gatherings.

Margie Anna Nursing Home*
152 S College St, Lebanon, TN, 37087 (615) 444-2882
Licensure Intermediate Care. *Beds* 46. *Certified* Medicaid.

Quality Care Health Center
932 Baddour Pkwy, Lebanon, TN, 37087 (615) 444-1836
Medical Dir/Dir of Nursing Morris Ferguson MD.
Licensure Intermediate Care. *Beds* 160. *Certified* Medicaid.
Staff RNs 1 (pt); LPNs 16 (ft); Nurses aides 60 (ft); Reality therapists 1 (ft); Activities coordinators 1 (ft); Dietitians 1 (ft).
Facilities Dining room; Physical therapy room; Activities room; Crafts room; Laundry room; Barber/Beauty shop.
Activities Arts and Crafts; Cards; Games; Prayer groups; Movies; Shopping trips.

University Medical Pavilion*
1411 Baddour Pkwy, Lebanon, TN, 37087 (615) 449-4976
Beds 24.

LENOIR CITY

Baptist Health Care Center
Route 1, Williams Ferry Rd, Lenoir City, TN, 37771 (615) 986-3583
Admin Dr Peggy Savage. *Medical Dir/Dir of Nursing* W B Harrison MD.
Licensure Skilled Care; Intermediate Care. *Beds* 102. *Certified* Medicaid.
Admissions Requirements Medical examination.

Staff RNs 3 (ft); LPNs 10 (ft); Nurses aides 45 (ft); Physical therapists 1 (pt); Recreational therapists 1 (ft); Speech therapists 1 (pt); Activities coordinators 1 (ft); Dietitians 1 (ft).
Affiliation Baptist
Facilities Dining room; Physical therapy room; Activities room; Crafts room; Barber/Beauty shop.
Activities Arts and Crafts; Cards; Games; Reading groups; Prayer groups; Movies; Shopping trips.

LEWISBURG

Merihil Health Care Center Inc*
1653 Mooresville Hwy, Lewisburg, TN, 37091 (615) 359-4506
Licensure Skilled Care; Intermediate Care. *Beds* 95. *Certified* Medicaid; Medicare.

Oakwood Health Care Center Inc*
244 Oakwood Dr, Lewisburg, TN, 37091 (615) 359-3563
Licensure Skilled Care; Intermediate Care. *Beds* 62. *Certified* Medicaid; Medicare.

LEXINGTON

Lexington Manor Nursing Center*
Hwy 20 E, Lexington, TN, 38351 (901) 968-2004
Licensure Intermediate Care. *Beds* 66. *Certified* Medicaid.

Nucare Convalescent Center*
41 Hospital Dr, Lexington, TN, 38351 (901) 968-6629
Licensure Intermediate Care. *Beds* 55. *Certified* Medicaid.

LIMESTONE

John M Reed Home
Rt 2, Box 301, Limestone, TN, 37681 (615) 257-2951
Medical Dir/Dir of Nursing N F Garland MD.
Licensure Intermediate Care. *Beds* 32. *Certified* Medicaid.
Admissions Requirements Minimum age 60; Medical examination; Physician's request.
Staff Physicians 2 (pt); RNs 1 (ft); LPNs 4 (ft), 2 (pt); Orderlies 1 (ft), 1 (pt); Nurses aides 11 (ft), 3 (pt); Physical therapists 1 (pt); Activities coordinators 1 (ft); Dietitians 1 (pt).
Affiliation Church of the Brethren
Facilities Dining room; Physical therapy room; Activities room; Laundry room; Barber/Beauty shop.
Activities Arts and Crafts; Cards; Reading groups; Prayer groups; Movies.
Description Facility features beautiful rural setting with unexcelled diet and nursing care. No resident care deficiencies in survey. Retirement facilities planned on our 18 acres.

LINDEN

Perry County Nursing Home*
Rt 4, Box 48, Linden, TN, 37096 (615) 589-2134

Licensure Intermediate Care. *Beds* 72. *Certified* Medicaid.

LIVINGSTON

Overton County Nursing Home
Bilbrey St, Livingston, TN, 38570 (615) 823-6403
Admin Sylvia Gibson. *Medical Dir/Dir of Nursing* Dr J Roe.
Licensure Skilled Care. *Beds* 162. *Certified* Medicaid; Medicare.
Admissions Requirements Medical examination; Physician's request.
Staff Physicians 1 (pt); RNs 1 (ft), 1 (pt); LPNs 16 (ft), 5 (pt); Orderlies 8 (ft), 2 (pt); Nurses aides 36 (ft), 20 (pt); Recreational therapists 2 (ft); Activities coordinators 1 (ft); Dietitians 1 (pt).
Facilities Dining room; Physical therapy room; Activities room; Crafts room; Laundry room; Barber/Beauty shop.
Activities Arts and Crafts; Games; Reading groups; Prayer groups; Movies.

LOUDON

Care Inn Loudon
1320 Grove St, Loudon, TN, 37774 (615) 458-5436
Licensure Intermediate Care. *Beds* 186. *Certified* Medicaid.
Admissions Requirements Medical examination.
Staff RNs 3 (ft); LPNs 9 (ft); Orderlies 1 (ft); Nurses aides 23 (ft), 5 (pt); Activities coordinators 2 (ft); Dietitians 1 (ft).
Facilities Dining room; Physical therapy room; Activities room; Crafts room; Laundry room; Barber/Beauty shop.
Activities Arts and Crafts; Cards; Games; Reading groups; Prayer groups; Movies; Shopping trips; Dances/Social or cultural gatherings.

MADISON

Hillhaven Convalescent Center*
431 Larkin Springs Rd, Madison, TN, 37115 (615) 865-8520
Licensure Skilled Care; Intermediate Care. *Beds* 96. *Certified* Medicaid; Medicare.

Imperial Manor Convalescent Center*
300 W Due West Ave, Madison, TN, 37115 (615) 865-5001
Licensure Skilled Care; Intermediate Care. *Beds* 175. *Certified* Medicaid; Medicare.

MADISONVILLE

East Tennessee Health Care Facility*
PO Box 25, Isbill Rd, Madisonville, TN, 37354
Licensure Nursing Home. *Beds* 72.

MANCHESTER

Coffee Nursing Home
1001 McArthur St, Manchester, TN, 37355 (615) 728-3586

Medical Dir/Dir of Nursing June Jordan.
Licensure Intermediate Care. *Beds* 60. *Certified* Medicaid.
Admissions Requirements Minimum age 18; Medical examination; Physician's request.
Staff RNs 1 (ft); LPNs 5 (ft), 2 (pt); Nurses aides 20 (ft), 2 (pt).
Facilities Dining room; Physical therapy room; Activities room; Chapel; Crafts room; Laundry room; Barber/Beauty shop.
Activities Arts and Crafts; Cards; Games; Reading groups; Prayer groups; Movies.

Crestwood Nursing Home
Rt 1, Taylor St, Manchester, TN, 37355 (615) 728-7549
Medical Dir/Dir of Nursing Mary Arwood.
Licensure Intermediate Care. *Beds* 59. *Certified* Medicaid.
Staff RNs 1 (ft); LPNs 10 (ft); Orderlies 3 (ft); Nurses aides 10 (ft); Activities coordinators 1 (ft); Dietitians 1 (ft).
Facilities Dining room; Activities room; Laundry room; Barber/Beauty shop.
Activities Arts and Crafts; Cards; Games; Reading groups; Prayer groups; Shopping trips; Dances/Social or cultural gatherings.
Description Family oriented facility with a home-like atmosphere.

MARTIN

VanAyer Manor Nursing Center*
640 Hannings Ln, Martin, TN, 38237 (901) 587-3193
Licensure Intermediate Care. *Beds* 66. *Certified* Medicaid.

MARYVILLE

Asbury Acres Health Center
Sevierville Rd, Maryville, TN, 37801 (615) 984-1660
Admin Melba B Bruce. *Medical Dir/Dir of Nursing* Dr O L Simpson.
Licensure Skilled Care; Intermediate Care. *Beds* 193. *Certified* Medicaid; Medicare.
Ownership Nonprofit.
Admissions Requirements Minimum age 14; Medical examination; Physician's request.
Staff RNs 8 (ft), 4 (pt); LPNs 9 (ft), 11 (pt); Orderlies 8 (ft), 3 (pt); Nurses aides 47 (ft), 36 (pt); Physical therapists 2 (pt); Recreational therapists 1 (ft); Activities coordinators 1 (ft); Dietitians 2 (ft), 1 (pt).
Affiliation Methodist
Facilities Dining room; Physical therapy room; Activities room; Crafts room; Laundry room; Barber/Beauty shop; Library.
Activities Arts and Crafts; Cards; Games; Reading groups; Prayer groups; Movies; Dances/Social or cultural gatherings.

Asbury Acres Retirement Home
Sevierville Rd, Maryville, TN, 37801 (615) 984-1660
Admin Betty Sturner. *Medical Dir/Dir of Nursing* Dr O L Simpson.
Licensure Intermediate Care. *Beds* 99.
Admissions Requirements Minimum age 65; Medical examination.

Staff RNs; Nurses aides; Physical therapists; Recreational therapists; Activities coordinators; Dietitians.
Affiliation Methodist
Facilities Dining room; Activities room; Chapel; Crafts room; Laundry room; Barber/Beauty shop; Library.
Activities Arts and Crafts; Cards; Games; Reading groups; Prayer groups; Movies; Shopping trips; Dances/Social or cultural gatherings.

Care Inn Maryville*
1602 Montvale Station Rd, Maryville, TN, 37801 (615) 984-7400
Licensure Intermediate Care. *Beds* 186. *Certified* Medicaid.

Colonial Hills Nursing Center
2034 Cochran Rd, Maryville, TN, 37801
Admin Jerry Hill.
Licensure Intermediate Care. *Beds* 133. *Certified* Medicaid.
Ownership Proprietary.
Admissions Requirements Minimum age 21; Medical examination; Physician's request.
Staff RNs 3 (ft), 1 (pt); LPNs 12 (ft), 4 (pt); Orderlies 4 (ft); Nurses aides 50 (ft); Physical therapists 1 (ft); Recreational therapists 1 (ft); Activities coordinators 1 (ft).
Facilities Dining room; Physical therapy room; Activities room; Crafts room; Laundry room; Barber/Beauty shop; Library.
Activities Arts and Crafts; Cards; Games; Prayer groups; Movies.

Montvale Health Center
Montvale Rd, Rt 6, Maryville, TN, 37801 (615) 982-6161
Licensure Intermediate Care. *Beds* 107. *Certified* Medicaid.

MCKENZIE

Oak Manor Nursing Home
Rt 4, McKenzie, TN, 38201 (901) 352-5317
Admin Larry Hardy.
Licensure Intermediate Care. *Beds* 49. *Certified* Medicaid.

MCMINNVILLE

McMinnville Health Care Center*
Rt 8, Box 528, McMinnville, TN, 37110 (615) 473-8431
Licensure Skilled Care; Intermediate Care. *Beds* 82. *Certified* Medicaid; Medicare.

South Oaks Health Care Inc
South Oaks Ln, McMinnville, TN, 37110 (615) 668-2011
Medical Dir/Dir of Nursing Dr T L Pedigo.
Licensure Intermediate Care; Personal Care. *Beds* ICF 120; Personal Care 32. *Certified* Medicaid.
Admissions Requirements Medical examination; Physician's request.
Staff Physicians 1 (pt); RNs 1 (ft); LPNs 7 (ft), 2 (pt); Orderlies 1 (ft); Nurses aides 29 (ft), 15 (pt); Physical therapists 1 (pt); Speech therapists 1 (pt); Activities coordinators 1 (ft); Dietitians 1 (ft); Dentists 1 (pt).

Facilities Dining room; Physical therapy room; Activities room; Chapel; Crafts room; Laundry room; Barber/Beauty shop; Library.
Activities Arts and Crafts; Cards; Games; Reading groups; Prayer groups; Shopping trips; Dances/Social or cultural gatherings.
Description We take pride in the fact that on the average only 3 residents require decubitus care. We support the rock-a-thon.

MEMPHIS

Allenbrooke Nursing Home
3933 Allenbrooke Cove, Memphis, TN, 38118
Licensure Skilled Care; Intermediate Care. *Beds* 180. *Certified* Medicaid.
Ownership Proprietary.

Ave Marie Home
2805 Charles Bryan Rd, Memphis, TN, 38134
(615) 386-3211
Licensure Intermediate Care. *Beds* 73.
Admissions Requirements Minimum age 60; Medical examination.
Facilities Dining room; Activities room; Chapel; Barber/Beauty shop.
Activities Arts and Crafts; Games; Prayer groups; Movies; Shopping trips.

Bright Glade Convalescent Center
5070 Sanderlin Ave, Memphis, TN, 38117
(615) 682-5677
Medical Dir/Dir of Nursing Saul Seigel MD.
Beds 77.
Admissions Requirements Minimum age 16; Physician's request.
Staff Physicians 1 (ft), 1 (pt); RNs 2 (ft); LPNs 5 (ft), 1 (pt); Nurses aides 11 (ft), 5 (pt); Physical therapists 1 (pt); Recreational therapists 1 (pt); Podiatrists 1 (pt).
Facilities Dining room; Activities room; Crafts room; Barber/Beauty shop.
Activities Cards; Games; Prayer groups.

Care Inn—Memphis*
2491 Joy Ln, Memphis, TN, 38114 (615)
743-7700
Licensure Intermediate Care. *Beds* 110. *Certified* Medicaid.

Care Inn—Raleigh*
3909 Covington Pike, Memphis, TN, 38134
(615) 377-1011
Licensure Intermediate Care. *Beds* 246. *Certified* Medicaid.

Collins Chapel Health Care Center
409 N Ayers, Memphis, TN, 38105 (615)
522-9243
Medical Dir/Dir of Nursing Cary Anderson MD.
Licensure Intermediate Care. *Beds* 88. *Certified* Medicaid.
Admissions Requirements Medical examination; Physician's request.
Staff Physicians 1 (ft), 1 (pt); RNs 1 (pt); LPNs 7 (ft); Orderlies 4 (ft); Nurses aides 18 (ft); Physical therapists 1 (pt); Activities coordinators 1 (ft); Dietitians 6 (ft); Dentists 1 (ft).
Affiliation Christian Methodist Episcopal
Facilities Dining room; Physical therapy room; Activities room; Crafts room; Laundry room;

Barber/Beauty shop.
Activities Arts and Crafts; Cards; Games; Reading groups; Prayer groups; Movies; Dances/Social or cultural gatherings.

Durham Memorial Home
6005 Stage Rd, Memphis, TN, 38134 (901)
386-4531
Medical Dir/Dir of Nursing Bertha Free.
Licensure Home for the Aged. *Beds* 80.
Admissions Requirements Minimum age 55; Medical examination.
Staff LPNs 3 (ft); Nurses aides 4 (ft); Activities coordinators 1 (pt); Dietitians 1 (ft).
Facilities Dining room; Activities room; Chapel; Crafts room; Barber/Beauty shop; Library.
Activities Arts and Crafts; Cards; Games; Prayer groups; Movies; Shopping trips; Dances/Social or cultural gatherings.
Description Facility features a "one-to-one" volunteer program, regular shopping trips, van service to the election polls, and lovely grounds and antique-filled sitting rooms.

Evergreen Care Center
1755 Eldridge Ave, Memphis, TN, 38108 (615)
278-3840
Admin Bea Boyd. *Medical Dir/Dir of Nursing* Leslie Shumaker MD.
Licensure Intermediate Care. *Beds* 49. *Certified* Medicaid.
Admissions Requirements Minimum age 21; Medical examination; Physician's request.
Staff RNs 1 (pt); LPNs 6 (ft); Orderlies 2 (ft); Nurses aides 20 (ft), 2 (pt); Physical therapists 1 (ft); Activities coordinators 1 (ft); Dietitians 1 (ft).
Facilities Dining room; Activities room; Laundry room.
Activities Arts and Crafts; Cards; Games; Reading groups; Shopping trips.

Hillhaven Convalescent Center*
6025 Primacy Pkwy, Memphis, TN, 38119
(615) 767-1040
Licensure Intermediate Care. *Beds* 120. *Certified* Medicaid.

James E Kerwin Housing for the Elderly and Elderly Disabled*
1150 Dovercrest Rd, Memphis, TN, 38134
(615) 382-1700
Licensure Intermediate Care. *Beds* 100. *Certified* Medicaid.

Johnson Care Home*
1279 Peabody Ave, Memphis, TN, 38104 (615)
725-7821
Licensure Intermediate Care. *Beds* 24. *Certified* Medicaid.

Johnson Nursing Home
154 Stonewall, Memphis, TN, 38104 (615)
274-6201
Beds 22.
Admissions Requirements Minimum age 75; Medical examination; Physician's request.
Staff RNs 1 (pt); LPNs 4 (ft), 4 (pt); Nurses aides 6 (ft), 6 (pt); Occupational therapists 1 (pt); Speech therapists 1 (pt); Activities coordinators 1 (ft); Dietitians 1 (ft); Dentists 1 (pt); Ophthalmologists 1 (pt); Podiatrists 1 (pt).
Facilities Dining room; Activities room; Chap-

el; Laundry room; Barber/Beauty shop.
Activities Arts and Crafts; Cards; Games; Reading groups; Prayer groups; Movies.

Kings Daughters and Sons Home
1467 E McLemore, Memphis, TN, 38016 (615)
272-7405
Medical Dir/Dir of Nursing Jean McFarland.
Licensure Intermediate Care. *Beds* 107. *Certified* Medicaid.
Admissions Requirements Minimum age 18.
Staff Physicians 1 (pt); RNs 3 (ft); LPNs 11 (ft), 6 (pt); Orderlies 9 (ft), 2 (pt); Nurses aides 40 (ft), 3 (pt); Recreational therapists 1 (ft), 1 (pt); Dietitians 1 (ft); Dentists 2 (pt).
Affiliation King's Daughters and Sons
Facilities Dining room; Physical therapy room; Activities room; Chapel; Crafts room; Laundry room; Barber/Beauty shop; Library.
Activities Arts and Crafts; Cards; Games; Prayer groups; Movies; Shopping trips; Dances/Social or cultural gatherings.

Mary Galloway Home for the Aged
5389 Poplar Ave, Memphis, TN, 38117 (901)
682-6646
Admin Helen N Miller.
Licensure Home for the Aged. *Beds* 46.
Admissions Requirements Minimum age 60; Females only; Medical examination.
Staff Dietitians 1 (ft).
Facilities Dining room; Activities room; Chapel; Crafts room; Laundry room; Barber/Beauty shop.
Activities Arts and Crafts; Prayer groups; Shopping trips.
Description Facility provides a home of dignity and comfort in a modern, functional building surrounding 2 charming courtyards; 52 private rooms each with half bath connecting with one other room, a full bath nearby, an outside entrance, and an individual garden plot; set in a grove of giant oak trees on spacious 4½ acres; 2 bright lounges.

Memphis Health Care Center*
6733 Quince Rd, Memphis, TN, 38119 (615)
755-3860
Licensure Skilled Care; Intermediate Care. *Beds* 180. *Certified* Medicaid; Medicare.

Memphis Sunshine Home for Aged Men
3411 Poplar Ave, Memphis, TN, 38111 (901)
452-6532
Licensure Home for the Aged. *Beds* 36.
Admissions Requirements Males only

Mid-City Care Center
1428 Monroe, Memphis, TN, 38104 (615)
726-5171
Medical Dir/Dir of Nursing George Bassett.
Licensure Intermediate Care. *Beds* 79. *Certified* Medicaid.
Admissions Requirements Medical examination.
Staff Physicians 1 (ft); RNs 1 (ft); LPNs 12 (ft); Orderlies 3 (ft); Nurses aides 25 (ft); Physical therapists 2 (pt); Reality therapists 2 (ft); Recreational therapists 2 (ft); Occupational therapists 1 (pt); Speech therapists 1 (pt); Activities coordinators 2 (ft); Dietitians 1 (pt); Dentists 1 (pt); Ophthalmologists 1 (pt); Podiatrists 1 (pt); Audiologists 1 (pt).

Facilities Dining room; Physical therapy room; Activities room; Chapel; Crafts room; Laundry room; Barber/Beauty shop; Library.
Activities Arts and Crafts; Cards; Games; Reading groups; Prayer groups; Movies; Shopping trips; Dances/Social or cultural gatherings.

Mid-South Christian Nursing Home
2380 James Rd, Memphis, TN, 38127 (901) 358-1707
Admin John Faughts. *Medical Dir/Dir of Nursing* Dr J H Ijams.
Licensure Intermediate Care. *Beds* 152. *Certified* Medicaid.
Admissions Requirements Minimum age 25; Medical examination; Physician's request.
Staff Physicians 1 (pt); RNs 2 (ft); LPNs 12 (ft), 5 (pt); Orderlies 1 (ft); Nurses aides 40 (ft), 12 (pt); Activities coordinators 2 (ft); Dietitians 1 (ft); Podiatrists 1 (ft).
Affiliation Church of Christ
Facilities Dining room; Physical therapy room; Activities room; Chapel; Crafts room; Laundry room; Barber/Beauty shop.
Activities Arts and Crafts; Games; Reading groups; Prayer groups; Movies; Shopping trips.

The Allen Morgan Nursing Center*
177 N Highland, Memphis, TN, 38111 (615) 324-2273
Licensure Skilled Care. *Beds* 60. *Certified* Medicaid; Medicare.

NHE—Memphis*
1414 Court St, Memphis, TN, 38104 (615) 272-2494
Licensure Intermediate Care. *Beds* 96. *Certified* Medicaid.

The Oaks Care Center Inc
642 Semmes St, Memphis, TN, 38111 (615) 454-0048
Admin Buford Street. *Medical Dir/Dir of Nursing* Karen Hensley DO.
Licensure Intermediate Care. *Beds* 56. *Certified* Medicaid.
Admissions Requirements Medical examination; Physician's request.
Staff Physicians 1 (pt); RNs 1 (pt); LPNs 4 (ft), 3 (pt); Orderlies 1 (ft); Nurses aides 15 (ft), 1 (pt); Physical therapists 1 (ft); Reality therapists 1 (ft); Recreational therapists 1 (ft); Activities coordinators 1 (ft); Dietitians 1 (ft); Dentists 1 (pt); Ophthalmologists 1 (pt); Podiatrists 1 (pt); Audiologists 1 (pt).
Facilities Dining room; Physical therapy room; Activities room; Laundry room; Barber/Beauty shop.
Activities Arts and Crafts; Games; Reading groups; Prayer groups; Shopping trips.
Description We have at least one cookout per summer for all residents, their families, and all employees.

Oakville Health Care Center
3391 Old Getwell Rd, Memphis, TN, 38118 (901) 369-9100
Admin James D Brown. *Medical Dir/Dir of Nursing* Eugene Barrette MD.
Licensure Skilled Care; Intermediate Care. *Beds* 312. *Certified* Medicaid; Medicare.
Staff Physicians 1 (ft), 1 (pt); RNs 10 (ft), 1 (pt); LPNs 36 (ft); Orderlies 18 (ft); Nurses aides 67 (ft); Physical therapists 1 (pt); Recreational therapists 2 (ft); Occupational therapists 1 (pt); Speech therapists 1 (pt); Activities coordinators 1 (ft); Dietitians 1 (ft); Dentists 1 (pt); Ophthalmologists 1 (pt); Podiatrists 1 (pt); Audiologists 1 (pt).
Facilities Dining room; Physical therapy room; Activities room; Chapel; Crafts room; Barber/Beauty shop; Library.
Activities Arts and Crafts; Cards; Games; Reading groups; Prayer groups; Movies; Shopping trips; Dances/Social or cultural gatherings.
Description Oakville Health Care Center's function is to operate a licensed nursing facility for the citizens of Shelby County requiring the professional services of health care personnel on an inpatient basis. Oakville is dually certified as a skilled and intermediate care facility, with the ultimate goal of admitting only those patients requiring skilled care services.

Resthaven Nursing Home
300 N Bellevue, Memphis, TN, 38105 (615) 726-9786
Medical Dir/Dir of Nursing Billie Jeanne Johnson.
Beds 64.
Admissions Requirements Minimum age 20; Medical examination; Physician's request.
Staff Physicians; RNs 2 (ft), 2 (pt); LPNs 2 (ft), 2 (pt); Nurses aides 15 (ft), 2 (pt); Physical therapists 1 (pt); Recreational therapists 1 (ft); Occupational therapists 1 (pt); Speech therapists 1 (pt); Activities coordinators 1 (ft); Dietitians 1 (pt).
Facilities Dining room; Activities room; Laundry room; Barber/Beauty shop.
Activities Cards; Games; Reading groups; Prayer groups; Dances/Social or cultural gatherings.

Rosewood Nursing Center*
3030 Walnut Grove Rd, Memphis, TN, 38111 (615) 458-1146
Licensure Skilled Care; Intermediate Care. *Beds* 211. *Certified* Medicaid; Medicare.

Saint Francis Hospital Skilled Nursing Unit*
PO Box 171808, 5959 Park Ave, Memphis, TN, 38119
Licensure Skilled Care. *Beds* 52.

Saint Peter Villa
141 N McLean, Memphis, TN, 38104 (615) 725-0320
Medical Dir/Dir of Nursing Dr Mohamad Akbik.
Licensure Skilled Care; Intermediate Care. *Beds* 180. *Certified* Medicaid; Medicare.
Admissions Requirements Medical examination; Physician's request.
Staff RNs 4 (ft); LPNs 19 (ft), 4 (pt); Orderlies 4 (ft), 3 (pt); Nurses aides 34 (ft), 21 (pt); Physical therapists 1 (ft); Reality therapists 1 (ft); Recreational therapists 1 (ft); Activities coordinators 1 (ft).
Affiliation Roman Catholic
Facilities Dining room; Physical therapy room; Activities room; Chapel; Barber/Beauty shop; Library.
Activities Arts and Crafts; Cards; Games; Reading groups; Prayer groups; Movies; Dances/Social or cultural gatherings.
Description The Villa is part of St Peter Village which also consists of St Peter Home for Children; Memphis Catholic High School, and St Peter Manor housing for the elderly. The Villa is a modern health care facility for the young and old alike. Residents live in an environment which provides a sense of family and community living.

Shelby County Health Care Center
1075 Mullins Station Rd, Memphis, TN, 38134 (615) 386-4361
Admin James D Brown. *Medical Dir/Dir of Nursing* Eugene Barnette MD.
Licensure Intermediate Care. *Beds* 575. *Certified* Medicaid.
Ownership Public.
Admissions Requirements Medical examination; Physician's request.
Staff Physicians 2 (ft); RNs 16 (ft); LPNs 45 (ft); Nurses aides 255 (ft); Recreational therapists 5 (ft); Activities coordinators 1 (ft); Dietitians 2 (ft); Dentists 1 (pt).
Facilities Dining room; Physical therapy room; Activities room; Chapel; Crafts room; Laundry room; Barber/Beauty shop; Library.
Activities Arts and Crafts; Cards; Games; Reading groups; Prayer groups; Movies; Shopping trips; Dances/Social or cultural gatherings.
Description Shelby County Health Care Center is a 575-bed intermediate care facility licensed as a nonprofit agency under the auspices of Shelby County government. A wide range of health care services are provided by trained medical and allied health professionals including physicians, nurse practitioners, nursing staff, pharmacists, social workers, recreational therapists, laboratory and radiology technicians, and support staff.

Wesley Highland Manor
3549 Norriswood, Memphis, TN, 38111 (615) 458-7186
Medical Dir/Dir of Nursing Dr Oakley Jordan.
Licensure Intermediate Care. *Beds* 150. *Certified* Medicaid.
Admissions Requirements Physician's request.
Staff Physicians 1 (pt); RNs 3 (pt); LPNs 18 (pt); Activities coordinators 1 (ft); Dietitians 1 (ft); Dentists 1 (pt); Podiatrists 1 (pt).
Affiliation Methodist
Facilities Dining room; Physical therapy room; Activities room; Chapel; Crafts room; Laundry room; Barber/Beauty shop; Library.
Activities Arts and Crafts; Cards; Games; Reading groups; Prayer groups; Movies; Shopping trips.

Whitehaven Care Center
1076 Chambliss, Memphis, TN, 38116 (615) 396-8470
Medical Dir/Dir of Nursing Dr Charles Parrott.
Licensure Intermediate Care. *Beds* 90. *Certified* Medicaid.
Admissions Requirements Minimum age 19; Medical examination.
Staff RNs 1 (ft); LPNs 12 (ft); Orderlies 1 (ft); Nurses aides 43 (ft); Activities coordinators 1 (ft); Dietitians 1 (pt).
Facilities Dining room; Activities room; Laundry room; Barber/Beauty shop.
Activities Arts and Crafts; Cards; Games; Reading groups; Prayer groups; Movies; Shop-

ping trips.

MILAN

Douglas Nursing Home Inc*
235 W Main St, Milan, TN, 38358 (901)
686-8321
Licensure Intermediate Care. *Beds* 72. *Certified* Medicaid.

Ridgewood Health Care Center
Dogwood Ln, Milan, TN, 38358 (901)
686-8311
Admin Timothy Sullivan. *Medical Dir/Dir of Nursing* Fred Friedman MD.
Licensure Skilled Care; Intermediate Care.
Beds 119. *Certified* Medicaid; Medicare.
Admissions Requirements Minimum age 21;
Medical examination; Physician's request.
Staff RNs 5 (ft), 1 (pt); LPNs 10 (ft), 1 (pt);
Orderlies 1 (ft); Nurses aides 39 (ft), 4 (pt);
Physical therapists 1 (ft); Speech therapists 1
(ft); Activities coordinators 1 (ft); Dietitians 1
(ft).
Facilities Dining room; Physical therapy room;
Activities room; Laundry room; Barber/Beauty
shop; Library.
Activities Arts and Crafts; Cards; Games;
Reading groups; Prayer groups; Movies; Dances/Social or cultural gatherings.

Sante Care Center
Rt 1, Stinson Rd, Milan, TN, 38358 (901)
686-8364
Medical Dir/Dir of Nursing Mildred Braddy.
Licensure Intermediate Care. *Beds* 66. *Certified* Medicaid.
Admissions Requirements Minimum age 14;
Medical examination.
Staff RNs 1 (ft); LPNs 4 (ft), 2 (pt); Orderlies 1
(ft); Nurses aides 16 (ft), 3 (pt); Activities coordinators 1 (ft); Dietitians 6 (ft), 1 (pt).
Facilities Dining room; Activities room; Laundry room; Barber/Beauty shop.
Activities Arts and Crafts; Games; Reading
groups; Prayer groups; Movies; Shopping trips;
Dances/Social or cultural gatherings.

MONTEAGLE

Regency Health Care Center
218 2nd St NE, Box 429, Monteagle, TN,
37356 (615) 924-2041
Licensure Intermediate Care. *Beds* 140. *Certified* Medicaid.
Admissions Requirements Minimum age 14.
Staff Physicians 5 (ft); RNs 4 (ft); LPNs 7 (ft);
Nurses aides 45 (ft); Physical therapists 1 (pt);
Occupational therapists 1 (pt); Speech therapists 1 (pt); Activities coordinators 1 (ft); Dietitians 1 (pt).
Facilities Dining room; Physical therapy room;
Activities room; Crafts room; Laundry room;
Barber/Beauty shop; Library.
Activities Arts and Crafts; Cards; Games;
Reading groups; Prayer groups; Movies; Shopping trips; Dances/Social or cultural gatherings.
Description VA approved.

MONTEREY

Standing Stone Health Care Center
410 W Crawford Ave, Monterey, TN, 38574
(615) 839-2244
Medical Dir/Dir of Nursing Danny Hall MD.
Licensure Intermediate Care. *Beds* 104. *Certified* Medicaid.
Admissions Requirements Minimum age 14;
Medical examination; Physician's request.
Staff RNs 2 (ft); LPNs 5 (ft), 8 (pt); Nurses
aides 21 (ft), 12 (pt); Activities coordinators 1
(ft).
Facilities Dining room; Physical therapy room;
Activities room; Chapel; Crafts room; Laundry
room; Barber/Beauty shop.
Activities Arts and Crafts; Games; Reading
groups; Prayer groups; Shopping trips; Dances/Social or cultural gatherings.

MORRISTOWN

Life Care Center of Morristown
501 W Economy Rd, Morristown, TN, 37814
(615) 581-5435
Licensure Intermediate Care. *Beds* 161. *Certified* Medicaid.
Staff RNs 2 (ft); LPNs 8 (ft), 6 (pt); Nurses
aides 39 (ft), 14 (pt); Reality therapists 1 (pt);
Activities coordinators 2 (ft).
Facilities Dining room; Physical therapy room;
Activities room; Crafts room; Laundry room;
Barber/Beauty shop; Library.
Activities Arts and Crafts; Cards; Games;
Reading groups; Prayer groups; Movies; Shopping trips; Dances/Social or cultural gatherings.
Description The lovely entrance hall, with soothing shades of blues, rust, and beiges welcomes
everyone to Life Care Center of Morristown. A
large, carpeted dining area, with beams, chrystal chandeliers, and tables with silk flower
arrangements, seats nearly 60 residents. Rooms
hold many of the residents' personal pieces of
furniture and a loving atmosphere prevails.

MOUNT PLEASANT

Hidden Acres Manor*
Hidden Acres Dr, Mount Pleasant, TN, 38474
(615) 379-5502
Licensure Intermediate Care. *Beds* 60. *Certified* Medicaid.

MOUNTAIN CITY

Johnson County Health Care
919 Medical Park Dr, Mountain City, TN,
37683 (615) 727-7800
Medical Dir/Dir of Nursing John Whitlock
MD.
Licensure Intermediate Care. *Beds* 86. *Certified* Medicaid.
Admissions Requirements Minimum age 14;
Medical examination.
Staff Physicians 8 (pt); RNs 1 (ft), 1 (pt); LPNs
8 (ft), 2 (pt); Orderlies 9 (ft), 2 (pt); Nurses aides
11 (ft), 1 (pt); Physical therapists 1 (pt); Reality
therapists 1 (pt); Speech therapists 1 (pt);
Activities coordinators 1 (ft); Dietitians 1 (ft);
Ophthalmologists 1 (pt); Podiatrists 1 (pt);
Audiologists 1 (pt); Psychiatrists 1 (pt).
Facilities Dining room; Physical therapy room;
Activities room; Crafts room; Laundry room;
Barber/Beauty shop.
Activities Arts and Crafts; Cards; Games;
Reading groups; Prayer groups; Movies; Shopping trips; Dances/Social or cultural gatherings.
Description Quiet, restful facility nestled in the
mountains of upper eastern Tennessee.

MURFREESBORO

Boulevard Terrace Nursing Home*
915 S Tennessee Blvd, Murfreesboro, TN,
37130 (615) 896-4504
Licensure Intermediate Care. *Beds* 64. *Certified* Medicaid.

Murfreesboro Health Care Center
610 E Bell St, Murfreesboro, TN, 37130 (615)
893-2602
Medical Dir/Dir of Nursing Dr Susan
Andrews.
Licensure Skilled Care. *Beds* 184. *Certified* Medicaid; Medicare.
Admissions Requirements Physician's request.
Staff RNs 10 (ft); LPNs 20 (ft); Nurses aides 40
(ft); Physical therapists 2 (ft); Recreational therapists 2 (ft); Occupational therapists 1 (ft); Speech therapists 2 (ft); Activities coordinators 1
(ft); Dietitians 1 (ft).
Facilities Dining room; Physical therapy room;
Activities room; Crafts room; Laundry room;
Barber/Beauty shop; Library.
Activities Arts and Crafts; Games; Reading
groups; Prayer groups; Movies; Shopping trips;
Dances/Social or cultural gatherings.

Rutherford County Nursing Home*
Rt 1, County Farm Rd, Murfreesboro, TN,
37130 (615) 893-2624
Licensure Intermediate Care. *Beds* 130. *Certified* Medicaid.

Stones River Manor
205 Haynes Dr, Murfreesboro, TN, 37130
(615) 893-5617
Licensure Home for the Aged. *Beds* 59.
Admissions Requirements Minimum age 65;
Medical examination.
Staff LPNs; Nurses aides; Dietitians.
Affiliation Church of Christ
Facilities Dining room; Activities room; Laundry room; Barber/Beauty shop; Library.
Activities Cards; Games; Prayer groups; Shopping trips; Dances/Social or cultural gatherings.
Description We are a retirement center, patient
must be ambulatory to be here (no permanent
wheel chairs allowed and used only in case of
temporary problems.) Walkers and canes are
allowed. Patients must be able to care for themselves and need an aide/or supervisory care
only.

NASHVILLE

Belcourt Terrace Nursing Home*
1710 Belcourt Ave, Nashville, TN, 37312 (615)
383-3570
Licensure Intermediate Care. *Beds* 49. *Certified* Medicaid.

Belmont Health Care Center
1400 18th Ave S, Nashville, TN, 37212 (615) 383-4715
Medical Dir/Dir of Nursing Dr Dee Baker.
Licensure Intermediate Care. *Beds* 210. *Certified* Medicaid; Medicare.
Staff Physicians; RNs; LPNs; Orderlies; Nurses aides; Physical therapists; Reality therapists; Recreational therapists; Occupational therapists; Speech therapists; Activities coordinators; Dietitians; Dentists; Podiatrists; Audiologists.
Facilities Dining room; Physical therapy room; Activities room; Chapel; Crafts room; Laundry room; Barber/Beauty shop; Library.
Activities Arts and Crafts; Cards; Games; Reading groups; Prayer groups; Movies; Shopping trips; Dances/Social or cultural gatherings.
Description Centrally located next to Vanderbilt University and Medical Center with ongoing cooperation programs with their medical and nursing schools; large grounds around a renovated historical, solid masonry building.

Care Group Nursing Home
701 Porter Rd, Nashville, TN, 37206 (615) 226-3264
Medical Dir/Dir of Nursing Charles Wiggins MD.
Licensure Intermediate Care. *Beds* 151. *Certified* Medicaid.
Admissions Requirements Minimum age 14; Medical examination.
Staff Physicians 8 (pt); RNs 2 (ft); LPNs 14 (ft); Orderlies 2 (ft); Nurses aides 70 (ft); Physical therapists 1 (pt); Reality therapists 1 (ft); Recreational therapists 1 (pt); Speech therapists 2 (pt); Activities coordinators 1 (ft); Dietitians 1 (ft); Dentists 1 (pt); Podiatrists 1 (pt).
Facilities Dining room; Activities room; Chapel; Crafts room; Laundry room; Barber/Beauty shop.
Activities Arts and Crafts; Cards; Games; Reading groups; Prayer groups.

Church of Christ Home for Aged*
1900 Eastland Ave, Nashville, TN, 37206 (615) 227-9566
Licensure Home for the Aged. *Beds* 44.
Affiliation Church of Christ

Crestview Nursing Home Inc*
2030 25th Ave N, Nashville, TN, 37208 (615) 256-4697
Licensure Intermediate Care. *Beds* 111. *Certified* Medicaid.

East Villa Nursing Home*
800 Fatherland St, Nashville, TN, 37206 (615) 226-9287
Licensure Intermediate Care. *Beds* 49. *Certified* Medicaid.

Jackson Park Christian Home*
4107 Gallatin Rd, Nashville, TN, 37216 (615) 228-0356
Licensure Home for the Aged. *Beds* 49.

Joseph B Knowles Home for the Aged
625 Benton Ave, Nashville, TN, 37204 (615) 259-6429
Licensure Home for the Aged. *Beds* 70.

Admissions Requirements Minimum age 55; Medical examination.
Staff Orderlies 3 (ft); Nurses aides 12 (ft); Recreational therapists 1 (ft).
Facilities Dining room; Physical therapy room; Activities room; Chapel; Crafts room; Laundry room; Barber/Beauty shop; Library.
Activities Arts and Crafts; Cards; Games; Reading groups; Shopping trips; Dances/Social or cultural gatherings.
Description Along with our residential care program, we have an adult day care for elderly and handicapped adults. It is funded in part by Title XX. Both of our programs have a social service department.

Lakeshore Home for the Aged
832 Wedgewood Ave, PO Box 12295, Nashville, TN, 37212 (615) 383-4079
Medical Dir/Dir of Nursing Dr Richard Garman.
Licensure Home for the Aged. *Beds* 182.
Admissions Requirements Minimum age 65; Medical examination.
Staff Physicians 1 (pt); RNs 2 (ft); LPNs 6 (ft); Nurses aides 19 (ft).
Affiliation Church of Christ
Facilities Dining room; Activities room; Laundry room; Barber/Beauty shop.
Activities Arts and Crafts; Cards; Games; Shopping trips; Dances/Social or cultural gatherings.
Description This is not a nursing home but a retirement home for the aged. Infirmary for those sick and mentally not able to care for themselves. We have a 36 passenger bus to take the group to worship, sightseeing, and short trips.

Nashville Health Care Center
2215 Patterson St, Nashville, TN, 37205 (615) 327-3011
Admin Rosalind James. *Medical Dir/Dir of Nursing* B H Webster MD.
Licensure Skilled Care; Intermediate Care. *Beds* 156. *Certified* Medicaid; Medicare.
Admissions Requirements Medical examination; Physician's request.
Staff Physicians 1 (ft), 10 (pt); RNs 6 (ft); Orderlies 14 (ft); Nurses aides 77 (ft); Physical therapists 2 (ft); Occupational therapists 1 (pt); Speech therapists 1 (pt); Activities coordinators 1 (ft); Dietitians 1 (ft); Dentists 1 (pt); Podiatrists 1 (pt).
Facilities Dining room; Physical therapy room; Activities room; Barber/Beauty shop.
Activities Arts and Crafts; Cards; Games; Prayer groups; Movies; Dances/Social or cultural gatherings.
Description Facility provides excellent nursing care and has an excellent therapy program; located near 3 hospitals.

Nashville Manor Nursing Home
1306 Katie Ave, Nashville, TN, 37207 (615) 228-3494
Admin Mildred Ray. *Medical Dir/Dir of Nursing* Charles Wiggins MD.
Licensure Intermediate Care. *Beds* 79. *Certified* Medicaid.
Admissions Requirements Minimum age 14; Medical examination; Physician's request.
Staff Physicians 1 (pt); RNs 2 (ft); LPNs 3 (ft),

3 (pt); Orderlies 3 (ft), 1 (pt); Nurses aides 22 (ft), 6 (pt); Physical therapists 1 (pt); Activities coordinators 1 (ft); Dietitians 1 (pt); Dentists 1 (pt); Podiatrists 1 (pt).
Facilities Dining room; Activities room; Crafts room; Laundry room; Barber/Beauty shop.
Activities Arts and Crafts; Games; Reading groups; Prayer groups; Movies; Dances/Social or cultural gatherings.

Trevecca Health Care Center
329 Murfreesboro Rd, Nashville, TN, 37210 (615) 244-6900
Admin M L McCaskell. *Medical Dir/Dir of Nursing* Earl E Vastbinder MD
Licensure Skilled Care; Intermediate Care. *Beds* 240. *Certified* Medicaid; Medicare.
Admissions Requirements Minimum age 45; Medical examination.
Staff Physicians 6 (pt); RNs 6 (ft), 4 (pt); LPNs 18 (ft), 6 (pt); Orderlies 4 (ft), 3 (ft); Nurses aides 82 (ft), 14 (pt); Physical therapists 1 (ft), 1 (pt); Occupational therapists 1 (pt); Speech therapists 1 (pt); Activities coordinators 2 (ft); Dietitians 1 (pt); Dentists 1 (pt); Ophthalmologists 1 (pt); Podiatrists 1 (pt); Audiologists 1 (pt).
Facilities Dining room; Activities room; Chapel; Crafts room; Laundry room; Barber/Beauty shop; Library.
Activities Arts and Crafts; Cards; Games; Movies; Shopping trips; Dances/Social or cultural gatherings.
Description Facility is located adjacent to 85-acre college campus with access to fine arts and athletic programs. Classes can be taken for credit or monitored without credit. Tours (short and long) are arranged at discounted rates.

University Health Care Center Inc
2015 Terrace Pl, Nashville, TN, 37203 (615) 327-2144
Medical Dir/Dir of Nursing B H Webster MD.
Licensure Intermediate Care. *Beds* 49. *Certified* Medicaid.
Staff Physicians 1 (pt); RNs 3 (ft); LPNs 4 (ft); Orderlies 1 (pt); Nurses aides 14 (ft), 5 (pt); Physical therapists 1 (pt); Speech therapists 1 (pt); Activities coordinators 1 (pt); Dietitians 1 (ft).
Facilities Dining room; Physical therapy room; Activities room; Laundry room; Barber/Beauty shop.
Activities Games; Movies; Shopping trips.
Description Facility is small and very personalized; excellent patient care.

West End Home for Ladies
2817 West End Home for Ladies, Nashville, TN, 37203 (615) 327-4066
Medical Dir/Dir of Nursing Dr Robert Quinn.
Licensure Home for the Aged. *Beds* 55.
Admissions Requirements Minimum age 65; Medical examination.
Staff RNs 1 (ft); LPNs 2 (ft); Nurses aides 5 (ft), 1 (pt); Dietitians.
Facilities Dining room; Laundry room; Barber/Beauty shop.
Activities Cards; Prayer groups; Shopping trips.

NEWPORT

Cocke County Convalescent Center*
603 College St, Newport, TN, 37821 (615)
623-8631
Licensure Intermediate Care. *Beds* 56. *Certified* Medicaid.

Regency Health Care Center
Hwy 25 and 70 at 411, Newport, TN, 37821
(615) 623-0929
Admin Cathy Lindsey.
Licensure Intermediate Care. *Beds* 100. *Certified* Medicaid.
Admissions Requirements Medical examination; Physician's request.
Staff RNs 1 (ft); LPNs 8 (ft); Orderlies 5 (ft); Nurses aides 23 (ft); Activities coordinators 1 (ft).
Facilities Dining room; Physical therapy room; Activities room; Crafts room; Laundry room; Barber/Beauty shop; Library.
Activities Arts and Crafts; Reading groups; Prayer groups; Movies; Dances/Social or cultural gatherings.
Description Our nursing home is known across the state for its outstanding community support program. We also have an active family resident council and provide in-services for community organizations detailing life in a nursing home.

OAK RIDGE

Oak Ridge Health Care Center
300 Laboratory Rd, Oak Ridge, TN, 37830
(615) 482-7698
Medical Dir/Dir of Nursing Anthony Garton.
Licensure Skilled Care; Intermediate Care. *Beds* 120. *Certified* Medicaid; Medicare.
Staff Physicians 2 (pt); RNs 4 (ft), 5 (pt); LPNs 13 (ft), 8 (pt); Nurses aides 23 (ft), 15 (pt); Physical therapists 1 (ft); Recreational therapists 1 (ft); Speech therapists 1 (pt); Activities coordinators 1 (ft); Dietitians 1 (ft).
Facilities Dining room; Physical therapy room; Activities room; Crafts room; Laundry room; Barber/Beauty shop.
Activities Arts and Crafts; Cards; Games; Reading groups; Prayer groups; Movies; Shopping trips; Dances/Social or cultural gatherings.

ONEIDA

Scott County Nursing Home*
PO Box 308, Alberta Ave, Oneida, TN, 37841
(615) 569-8521
Licensure Intermediate Care. *Beds* 48. *Certified* Medicaid.

PALMYRA

Palmyra Intermediate Care Center
Hwy 149, Palmyra, TN, 37142 (615) 326-5252
Licensure Intermediate Care; Intermediate Care for Mentally Retarded. *Beds* ICF 73; ICF/MR 20. *Certified* Medicaid.
Admissions Requirements Minimum age 21; Medical examination.
Staff Physicians; RNs; LPNs; Orderlies;

Nurses aides; Physical therapists; Reality therapists; Recreational therapists; Speech therapists; Activities coordinators; Dietitians; Dentists; Ophthalmologists; Podiatrists.
Facilities Dining room; Physical therapy room; Activities room; Chapel; Laundry room; Barber/Beauty shop; Library.
Activities Arts and Crafts; Games; Movies; Shopping trips; Dances/Social or cultural gatherings; Current events.
Description Ceramics are very popular and the residents participate in local craft fairs.

PARIS

Henry County Nursing Home*
Hospital Circle, Paris, TN, 38242 (901)
642-5700
Licensure Intermediate Care. *Beds* 114. *Certified* Medicaid.

Paris Manor Nursing Center*
Rt 3, Old Murray Rd, Paris, TN, 38242 (901)
642-2535
Licensure Intermediate Care. *Beds* 72. *Certified* Medicaid.

PARSONS

Decatur County Manor Nursing Center*
1501 Kentucky Ave S, Parsons, TN, 38363
(910) 847-6371
Licensure Intermediate Care. *Beds* 65. *Certified* Medicaid.

PIKEVILLE

Bledsoe County Nursing Home*
Hwy 30 W, Pikeville, TN, 37367 (615)
447-6811
Licensure Intermediate Care. *Beds* 49. *Certified* Medicaid.

PLEASANT HILL

May Cravath Wharton Nursing Home
Lake Dr, PO Box 168, Pleasant Hill, TN, 38578 (615) 277-3511
Medical Dir/Dir of Nursing Dr Fred Munson and Dr John Daugherty.
Licensure Intermediate Care. *Beds* 80. *Certified* Medicaid.
Admissions Requirements Minimum age 65; Medical examination.
Staff Physicians 2 (pt); RNs 1 (ft); LPNs 4 (ft), 2 (pt); Nurses aides 21 (ft), 3 (pt); Activities coordinators 1 (ft); Dietitians 1 (ft).
Affiliation Church of Christ
Facilities Dining room; Activities room; Crafts room; Laundry room; Barber/Beauty shop; Library; Lounges.
Activities Arts and Crafts; Cards; Games; Reading groups; Prayer groups; Movies; Shopping trips; Dances/Social or cultural gatherings; Coffee and conversation.
Description Facility is a homey, pleasant, comfortable nursing home in a rural setting with lots of family-like loving tender care. Located in the center of Uplands Retirement Community with an active volunteer program which

adds to the "family" atmosphere.

PORTLAND

Highland Manor Nursing Home
Rt 4, Box 104, Portland, TN, 37148 (615)
325-9263
Licensure Intermediate Care. *Beds* 110. *Certified* Medicaid.
Admissions Requirements Medical examination; Physician's request.
Staff Physicians 6 (ft); RNs 1 (ft), 1 (pt); LPNs 10 (ft), 5 (pt); Orderlies 2 (ft); Nurses aides 18 (ft), 3 (pt); Physical therapists; Occupational therapists; Speech therapists; Activities coordinators 1 (ft), 1 (pt); Dietitians 1 (pt); Dentists; Ophthalmologists.

PULASKI

Austin Hewitt Home Retirement Center
322 E Washington St, Pulaski, TN, 38478
Licensure Home for the Aged. *Beds* 35.
Admissions Requirements Medical examination.
Staff Physicians 1 (pt); LPNs 1 (pt); Nurses aides 5 (ft), 2 (pt); Physical therapists 1 (pt); Activities coordinators 1 (pt); Dietitians 1 (ft).
Facilities Dining room; Activities room; Laundry room; Library.
Activities Cards; Games; Reading groups; Prayer groups; Movies; Shopping trips; Dances/Social or cultural gatherings.
Description Facility is a renovated Civil War residence with colonial brick design and a historic listing; primarily for residential living and personal care services.

Meadowbrook Nursing Home
Hwy 64 E, Pulaski, TN, 38478 (615) 363-7548
Admin Christine Edwards.
Licensure Intermediate Care. *Beds* 71. *Certified* Medicaid.
Admissions Requirements Minimum age 18; Medical examination.
Staff RNs 1 (ft); LPNs 5 (ft); Nurses aides 17 (ft); Activities coordinators 1 (ft).
Facilities Dining room; Activities room; Laundry room; Barber/Beauty shop.
Activities Arts and Crafts; Cards; Games; Reading groups; Prayer groups; Movies; Shopping trips; Dances/Social or cultural gatherings.
Description Ongoing activities with very capable activity director; very dedicated personnel give total care to residents; also numerous volunteer workers assisting in daily planned activities for all residents.

Pulaski Health Care Center
Rt 4, Pulaski, TN, 38478 (615) 363-3572
Admin Betty T Pope. *Medical Dir/Dir of Nursing* W K Owen MD.
Licensure Skilled Care; Intermediate Care. *Beds* 75. *Certified* Medicaid; Medicare. *Ownership* Proprietary.
Staff RNs 3 (ft), 1 (pt); LPNs 11 (ft); Orderlies 1 (ft); Nurses aides 13 (ft), 13 (pt); Physical therapists 1 (ft); Speech therapists 1 (pt); Activities coordinators 1 (ft); Dietitians 1 (ft); Dentists 1 (pt).
Facilities Dining room; Activities room;

Barber/Beauty shop.
Activities Arts and Crafts; Cards; Games; Reading groups; Prayer groups; Movies.
Description Long-term health care center, emphasis is on individual care and rehabilitation to return the patient home when possible. The center is a subsidiary of National Health Corporation and a member of the National Health Foundation and the National Council of Health Centers. Facility is accredited by the Joint Commission on Accreditation of Hospitals, the highest rating which a health care facility can obtain.

PURYEAR

Puryear Nursing Home*
233 W Chestnut St, Puryear, TN, 38251 (901) 247-3206
Licensure Intermediate Care. *Beds* 25. *Certified* Medicaid.

RED BOILING SPRINGS

Regency Health Care Center*
Hwy 52, Red Boiling Springs, TN, 37150 (615) 699-2238
Licensure Intermediate Care. *Beds* 109. *Certified* Medicaid.

RIDGETOP

Ridgetop Haven Inc*
Box 138, Woodruff, Ridgetop, TN, 37152 (615) 643-4548
Beds 32.

RIPLEY

Care Inn—Ripley*
118 Halliburton St, Ripley, TN, 38063 (901) 635-5180
Licensure Intermediate Care. *Beds* 130. *Certified* Medicaid.

Lauderdale County Nursing Home*
Lackey Ln, Ripley, TN, 38063 (901) 635-1331
Licensure Intermediate Care. *Beds* 71. *Certified* Medicaid.

ROCKWOOD

Rockwood Health Care Center*
PO Box 476, Hwy 70 E, Rockwood, TN, 37854 (615) 354-3366
Licensure Intermediate Care. *Beds* 120. *Certified* Medicaid.

ROGERSVILLE

Regency Health Care Center
Rt 4, Box 1A, Rogersville, TN, 37857 (615) 272-3099
Licensure Intermediate Care. *Beds* 140. *Certified* Medicaid.
Staff RNs 2 (ft); LPNs 10 (ft); Nurses aides 40 (ft), 15 (pt); Physical therapists 1 (pt); Speech therapists 1 (pt); Activities coordinators 1 (ft);

Dietitians 1 (pt).
Facilities Dining room; Physical therapy room; Activities room; Laundry room; Barber/Beauty shop.
Activities Arts and Crafts; Games; Prayer groups; Shopping trips.

RUTLEDGE

Ridgeview Terrace Convalescent and Nursing Center
Rt 2, Coffey Ln, Rutledge, TN, 37861 (615) 828-5295
Medical Dir/Dir of Nursing Dr John Kinser.
Licensure Intermediate Care. *Beds* 132. *Certified* Medicaid.
Staff Physicians 8 (pt); RNs 1 (ft); LPNs 9 (ft); Nurses aides 8 (ft); Physical therapists 1 (pt); Reality therapists 1 (pt); Speech therapists 1 (pt); Activities coordinators 1 (ft); Dietitians 1 (pt).
Facilities Dining room; Physical therapy room; Activities room; Crafts room; Laundry room; Barber/Beauty shop; Library.
Activities Arts and Crafts; Games; Prayer groups; Movies; Shopping trips.

SAVANNAH

Harbert Hills Academy Nursing Home*
Rt 2, Box 212, Lonesome Pine Rd, Savannah, TN, 38372 (901) 925-5495
Licensure Intermediate Care. *Beds* 35. *Certified* Medicaid.

Hardin County Nursing Home
2006 Wayne Rd, Savannah, TN, 38372 (901) 925-4954
Admin Joyce O'Neal.
Licensure Intermediate Care. *Beds* 39. *Certified* Medicaid.
Admissions Requirements Medical examination; Physician's request.
Staff RNs 1 (ft); LPNs 3 (ft), 5 (pt); Orderlies 2 (ft), 3 (pt); Nurses aides 7 (ft), 5 (pt); Activities coordinators 1 (ft).
Facilities Dining room; Activities room; Laundry room; Barber/Beauty shop; Library.
Activities Arts and Crafts; Games; Dances/Social or cultural gatherings.
Description Hospital-based facility with access to all services provided by the hospital.

Hardin Home Nursing Home*
Hwy 64 E, Savannah, TN, 38372 (901) 925-4004
Licensure Intermediate Care. *Beds* 52. *Certified* Medicaid.

SELMER

Maple Hill Nursing Home*
6th St S, Selmer, TN, 38375 (901) 645-7908
Licensure Intermediate Care. *Beds* 31. *Certified* Medicaid.

SEVIERVILLE

Fort Sanders—Sevier Medical Center Nursing Home
Middle Creek Rd, Sevierville, TN, 37862 (615) 453-7111
Medical Dir/Dir of Nursing Charles H Bozeman MD.
Licensure Skilled Care; Intermediate Care.
Beds 54. *Certified* Medicaid; Medicare.
Admissions Requirements Medical examination; Physician's request.
Staff Physicians 1 (pt); RNs 3 (ft), 3 (pt); LPNs 3 (ft), 4 (pt); Nurses aides 19 (ft), 5 (pt); Physical therapists 1 (pt); Occupational therapists 1 (pt); Speech therapists 1 (pt); Activities coordinators 1 (ft); Dietitians 1 (pt); Dentists 1 (pt); Social workers 2 (pt).
Facilities Dining room; Physical therapy room; Activities room; Chapel; Crafts room; Barber/Beauty shop; Library.
Activities Arts and Crafts; Cards; Games; Reading groups; Prayer groups; Movies; Shopping trips; Dances/Social or cultural gatherings.
Description Home is involved in pet therapy program with a "live-in" dog.

Sevier County Health Care Center Inc*
415 Catlett Rd, Sevierville, TN, 37862 (615) 453-4747
Licensure Skilled Care; Intermediate Care.
Beds 120. *Certified* Medicaid; Medicare.

SHELBYVILLE

Bedford County Nursing Home
845 Union St, Shelbyville, TN, 37160 (615) 684-3426
Medical Dir/Dir of Nursing Sara Womack MD.
Licensure Intermediate Care. *Beds* 88. *Certified* Medicaid.
Ownership Public.
Admissions Requirements Medical examination; Physician's request.
Staff RNs 2 (ft); LPNs 8 (ft), 4 (pt); Orderlies 2 (pt); Nurses aides 17 (ft), 19 (pt); Physical therapists 1 (pt); Activities coordinators 1 (pt); Dietitians 1 (pt).
Facilities Dining room; Physical therapy room; Activities room; Chapel; Crafts room; Laundry room; Barber/Beauty shop; Library.
Activities Arts and Crafts; Cards; Games; Reading groups; Prayer groups; Shopping trips; Dances/Social or cultural gatherings.

Glen Oaks Convalescent Center
1101 Glen Oaks Rd, Shelbyville, TN, 37160 (615) 684-8340
Admin P W Jones. *Medical Dir/Dir of Nursing* Dr Samuel Sells.
Licensure Intermediate Care. *Beds* 100. *Certified* Medicaid.
Admissions Requirements Medical examination.
Staff Physicians 1 (ft); RNs 3 (ft), 1 (pt); LPNs 6 (ft), 2 (pt); Nurses aides 28 (ft), 3 (pt); Physical therapists 2 (pt); Activities coordinators 1 (ft); Dietitians 1 (pt); Dentists 1 (pt).
Facilities Dining room; Activities room; Crafts room; Laundry room; Barber/Beauty shop.
Activities Arts and Crafts; Cards; Games;

Reading groups; Prayer groups; Shopping trips; Dances/Social or cultural gatherings.
Description Glen Oaks Convalescent Center features private and semi-private rooms, physical therapy, speech therapy, dietician, consultant, beauty shop, pharmacy, and religious services. Now accepting Medicaid and VA approved residents.

SIGNAL MOUNTAIN

Alexian Village of Tennesse Inc
100 James Blvd, Signal Mountain, TN, 37377
(615) 870-0101 and 870-0100
Medical Dir/Dir of Nursing Arch Y Smith MD.
Licensure Skilled Care; Intermediate Care.
Beds 124. *Certified* Medicaid; Medicare.
Admissions Requirements Medical examination; Physician's request.
Staff Physicians 1 (ft); RNs 1 (ft), 6 (pt); LPNs 12 (ft), 2 (pt); Orderlies 1 (ft); Nurses aides 37 (ft), 2 (pt); Physical therapists 1 (pt); Speech therapists 1 (pt); Activities coordinators 1 (ft); Dietitians 2 (ft), 1 (pt); Dentists 1 (ft).
Affiliation Roman Catholic
Facilities Dining room; Physical therapy room; Activities room; Chapel; Crafts room; Laundry room; Barber/Beauty shop; Library.
Activities Arts and Crafts; Cards; Games; Reading groups; Prayer groups; Movies; Shopping trips; Dances/Social or cultural gatherings.

SMITHVILLE

Sunny Point Health Care Center Inc*
Rt 1, Spring St, Smithville, TN, 37166 (615) 597-4284 or (615) 597-6271
Licensure Skilled Care; Intermediate Care.
Beds 76. *Certified* Medicaid; Medicare.

SMYRNA

Smyrna Nursing Center*
202 Enon Springs Rd, Smyrna, TN, 37167
(615) 459-5621
Licensure Intermediate Care. *Beds* 89. *Certified* Medicaid.

SOMERVILLE

Somerville Health Care Center*
Lakeview Dr, Somerville, TN, 38068 (901) 465-9861
Licensure Skilled Care; Intermediate Care.
Beds 80. *Certified* Medicaid; Medicare.

SOUTH PITTSBURG

Rivermont Convalescent and Nursing Center*
201 E 10th St, South Pittsburg, TN, 37380
(615) 837-7981
Licensure Intermediate Care. *Beds* 124. *Certified* Medicaid.

SPARTA

Sparta Health Care Center Inc*
Box 236, 108 E Gracey St, Sparta, TN, 38583
(615) 836-2211
Licensure Skilled Care; Intermediate Care.
Beds 120. *Certified* Medicaid; Medicare.

SPRINGFIELD

Elm Hurst Nursing Home
705 5th Ave E, Springfield, TN, 37172
Medical Dir/Dir of Nursing J R Quartes.
Licensure Intermediate Care. *Beds* 70. *Certified* Medicaid.
Admissions Requirements Minimum age 14; Medical examination; Physician's request.
Staff RNs 2 (ft); LPNs 4 (ft), 4 (pt); Nurses aides 18 (ft), 5 (pt); Activities coordinators 1 (ft); Dietitians 1 (pt).
Facilities Dining room; Activities room; Chapel; Crafts room; Laundry room; Barber/Beauty shop; Library.
Activities Arts and Crafts; Cards; Games; Dances/Social or cultural gatherings.

Robertson County Health Care Center
Rt 6, Box 236, Springfield, TN, 37172 (615) 384-9565
Medical Dir/Dir of Nursing John Bassel.
Licensure Skilled Care; Intermediate Care.
Beds SNF 60; ICF 60. *Certified* Medicaid; Medicare.
Admissions Requirements Minimum age 14.
Staff RNs 3 (ft), 5 (pt); LPNs 8 (ft), 2 (pt); Orderlies 4 (ft), 2 (pt); Physical therapists 1 (pt); Speech therapists 1 (pt); Activities coordinators 1 (ft), 1 (pt); Dietitians 1 (ft).
Facilities Dining room; Physical therapy room; Activities room; Crafts room; Laundry room; Barber/Beauty shop.
Activities Arts and Crafts; Cards; Games; Reading groups; Prayer groups; Movies; Shopping trips; Dances/Social or cultural gatherings.

Springfield Health Care Center Inc*
608 8th Ave E, Springfield, TN, 37172 (615) 384-4548
Licensure Skilled Care; Intermediate Care.
Beds 102. *Certified* Medicaid; Medicare.

SWEETWATER

Sweetwater Valley Convalescent and Nursing Home Inc*
S Lee Hwy, Sweetwater, TN, 37874 (615) 337-6631
Licensure Intermediate Care. *Beds* 93. *Certified* Medicaid.

Wood Presbyterian Home Inc
310 S High St, Sweetwater, TN, 37874 (615) 337-5326
Admin Corinne Erickson. *Medical Dir/Dir of Nursing* Jean Edmonds RN.
Licensure Intermediate Care. *Beds* 30. *Certified* Medicaid.
Admissions Requirements Medical examination.
Staff RNs 1 (ft); LPNs 3 (ft), 3 (pt); Nurses aides 10 (ft), 3 (pt); Activities coordinators 1 (pt); Dietitians 1 (pt).
Affiliation Presbyterian
Facilities Dining room; Activities room; Laundry room.
Activities Cards; Games; Reading groups; Movies.
Description Small facility with home-like surroundings features individual care.

TAZEWELL

Claiborne County Nursing Home*
1000 Old Knoxville Rd, Tazewell, TN, 37879
(615) 626-4211
Licensure Skilled Care; Intermediate Care.
Beds 50. *Certified* Medicaid; Medicare.

TIPTONVILLE

Reelfoot Manor Nursing Home*
Reelfoot Dr, Tiptonville, TN, 38079 (901) 253-6681
Licensure Intermediate Care. *Beds* 120. *Certified* Medicaid.

TRENTON

Harlan Morris Home
Rt 1, Trenton, TN, 38382 (901) 855-0702
Licensure Home for the Aged. *Beds* 49.
Admissions Requirements Minimum age 50; Medical examination.
Facilities Dining room; Activities room; Barber/Beauty shop; Library.
Activities Arts and Crafts; Games; Reading groups; Prayer groups; Shopping trips; Birthday parties once a month.
Description Home is for the aged or retired; no nurses on duty, just employees.

Memorial Convalescent Center*
Hwy 45 By-Pass, Trenton, TN, 38382 (901) 855-4500
Licensure Intermediate Care. *Beds* 44. *Certified* Medicaid.

TULLAHOMA

Life Care Center of Tullahoma*
1715 N Jackson St, Tullahoma, TN, 37388
(615) 455-8557
Licensure Intermediate Care. *Beds* 169. *Certified* Medicaid.

UNION CITY

Obion County Rest Home
Rt 1, Box 207, Union City, TN, 38261 (901) 885-9065
Admin Bill Jordan. *Medical Dir/Dir of Nursing* Dr Grover Schleifer.
Licensure Intermediate Care. *Beds* 52. *Certified* Medicaid.
Admissions Requirements Medical examination; Physician's request.
Staff Physicians 1 (pt); RNs 1 (ft); LPNs 5 (ft); Orderlies 4 (ft); Nurses aides 9 (ft); Activities coordinators 1 (ft); Dietitians 1 (ft).
Facilities Dining room; Activities room; Laun-

dry room; Barber/Beauty shop.
Activities Arts and Crafts; Games; Reading groups; Prayer groups; Movies; Dances/Social or cultural gatherings.
Description Facility is located in a rural setting with 5 acres of land; newly refurbished building with new patient-room furniture.

Union City Health Care Center*
1105 Sunswept Dr, Union City, TN, 38261 (901) 885-6400
Licensure Skilled Care; Intermediate Care. *Beds* 120. *Certified* Medicaid; Medicare.

Union City Manor Nursing Center*
PO Box 509, 1630 Reelfoot Ave, Union City, TN, 38261
Licensure Nursing Home. *Beds* 74.

WARTBURG

Life Care Center of Morgan County
Potters Falls Rd, Wartburg, TN, 37887 (615) 346-6691
Admin Stephen Brown. *Medical Dir/Dir of Nursing* Dwight Willett MD.
Licensure Intermediate Care. *Beds* 124. *Certified* Medicaid.
Admissions Requirements Minimum age 18; Medical examination; Physician's request.
Staff Physicians 3 (pt); RNs 2 (ft), 2 (pt); LPNs 8 (ft), 4 (pt); Orderlies 2 (ft); Nurses aides 20 (ft), 30 (pt); Physical therapists 1 (pt); Reality therapists 1 (pt); Speech therapists 1 (pt); Activities coordinators 1 (ft); Dietitians 1 (pt); Dentists 1 (pt).
Facilities Dining room; Physical therapy room; Activities room; Crafts room; Laundry room; Barber/Beauty shop.
Activities Arts and Crafts; Cards; Games; Reading groups; Prayer groups; Movies; Shopping trips; Dances/Social or cultural gatherings.

WAVERLY

Humphreys County Nursing Home*
S Church St, Waverly, TN, 37185 (615) 296-2532
Licensure Intermediate Care. *Beds* 66. *Certified* Medicaid.

WAYNESBORO

Nelson's Health Care Center Inc*
Box 715, 500 S High St, Waynesboro, TN, 38485 (615) 722-5832
Licensure Intermediate Care. *Beds* 46. *Certified* Medicaid.

Wayne County Nursing Home*
Box 442, Waynesboro, TN, 38485 (615) 722-3641
Licensure Intermediate Care. *Beds* 72. *Certified* Medicaid.

WINCHESTER

Franklin County Health Care Center*
Rt 3, 41A By Pass, Winchester, TN, 37398
(615) 967-7082
Licensure Intermediate Care. *Beds* 120. *Certified* Medicaid.

Franklin County Nursing Home*
Cowan Rd, Winchester, TN, 37398 (615) 967-4571
Licensure Intermediate Care. *Beds* 35. *Certified* Medicaid.

Lakeside Manor Home for the Aged*
Rt 4, Lynchburg Rd, Winchester, TN, 37398 (615) 967-0865
Licensure Home for the Aged. *Beds* 12.

WOODBURY

Woodbury Nursing Center Inc*
119 W High St, Woodbury, TN, 37190 (615) 563-5930
Licensure Intermediate Care. *Beds* 82. *Certified* Medicaid.

TEXAS

ABILENE

Bur-Mont Nursing Center*
725 Medical Dr, Abilene, TX, 79601 (915)
672-3236
Admin Carolyn Martin.
Licensure Intermediate Care. *Beds* 118. *Certified* Medicaid.
Ownership Proprietary.

Care Inn of Abilene*
4934 S 7th St, Abilene, TX, 79605 (915)
692-2172
Admin Joyce Pylant.
Licensure Intermediate Care. *Beds* 106. *Certified* Medicaid.
Ownership Proprietary.

Happy Haven Nursing Center
1751 N 15th St, Abilene, TX, 79603 (915)
673-8892
Admin Ernest C Valle. *Medical Dir/Dir of Nursing* S Daggubati MD.
Licensure Intermediate Care. *Beds* 235. *Certified* Medicaid.
Staff RNs 3 (ft); LPNs 18 (ft); Orderlies 10 (ft); Nurses aides 70 (ft); Activities coordinators 1 (ft); Dietitians 1 (ft).
Facilities Dining room; Activities room; Crafts room; Laundry room; Barber/Beauty shop.
Activities Arts and Crafts; Cards; Games; Reading groups; Prayer groups; Movies; Shopping trips; Dances/Social or cultural gatherings.
Description Facility maintains 2 full-time licensed activity directors; also 2 full-time positions for doing therapy, i.e. ambulating and ROM; maintains van for transportation.

Sears Memorial Methodist Nursing Center
3202 S Willis St, Abilene, TX, 79605 (915)
692-6145
Admin Chris Spence. *Medical Dir/Dir of Nursing* Dr W Kenneth Day.
Licensure Intermediate Care; Custodial Care.
Beds ICF 60; Custodial Care 55. *Certified* Medicaid.
Admissions Requirements Minimum age 65; Medical examination; Physician's request.
Staff Physicians 1 (pt); RNs 1 (pt); LPNs 8 (ft), 8 (pt); Nurses aides 23 (ft), 10 (pt); Activities coordinators 2 (ft).
Affiliation Methodist
Facilities Dining room; Activities room; Laundry room; Barber/Beauty shop; Library; Parlor.

Activities Arts and Crafts; Games; Prayer groups; Movies; Shopping trips; Dances/Social or cultural gatherings; Birthday parties.
Description Facility features a beautiful physical setting in a modern residential development, near shopping malls, motels, restaurants, and freeway, for convenience of residents and visiting families and friends.

Shady Oaks Lodge 1*
2722 Old Anson Rd, Abilene, TX, 79603 (915)
673-7358
Admin Melba Fisher.
Licensure Intermediate Care. *Beds* 114. *Certified* Medicaid.
Ownership Proprietary.

Shady Oaks Lodge 2
2722 Old Anson Rd, Abilene, TX, 79603 (915)
673-7358
Admin Velda Howard. *Medical Dir/Dir of Nursing* Jack S Haynes MD.
Licensure Skilled Care. *Beds* 100. *Certified* Medicaid.
Admissions Requirements Medical examination; Physician's request.
Staff Physicians 1 (pt); RNs 1 (ft), 3 (pt); LPNs 12 (ft), 2 (pt); Nurses aides 26 (ft); Activities coordinators 1 (ft); Dietitians 1 (pt); Dentists 1 (pt).
Facilities Dining room; Physical therapy room; Activities room; Crafts room; Laundry room; Barber/Beauty shop; Library.
Activities Arts and Crafts; Cards; Games; Reading groups; Prayer groups; Movies; Shopping trips.

West Texas Nursing Center*
2630 Old Anson Rd, Abilene, TX, 79603 (915)
673-5101
Admin Lexie L Hutchison.
Licensure Intermediate Care. *Beds* 114. *Certified* Medicaid.
Ownership Proprietary.

Western Hills Nursing Center*
2102 Amy Lyn Ave, Abilene, TX, 79603 (915)
677-2296
Admin Leslie Kay Lane.
Licensure Intermediate Care. *Beds* 118. *Certified* Medicaid.
Ownership Proprietary.

ALBANY

Bluebonnet Nursing Home*
PO Box 608, Baird Hwy, Albany, TX, 76430
(915) 762-3329
Admin William D Wakefield.
Licensure Intermediate Care. *Beds* 80. *Certified* Medicaid.
Ownership Proprietary.

ALICE

Hospitality House Inc*
PO Box 1458, 219 N King St, Alice, TX, 78332
(512) 664-4366
Admin Phyl E Drake.
Licensure Skilled Care; Intermediate Care; Personal Care. *Beds* 132; Personal Care 15. *Certified* Medicaid; Medicare.
Ownership Proprietary.

Retama Manor Nursing Center*
606 Coyote Trail, Alice, TX, 78332 (512)
664-5479
Admin Mary Lou Van Alstyne.
Licensure Intermediate Care. *Beds* 140. *Certified* Medicaid.
Ownership Proprietary.

ALPINE

Valley Hi Nursing Home
1003 Loop Rd, Alpine, TX, 79830 (915)
837-3307
Admin Dalona L Murphy.
Licensure Intermediate Care. *Beds* 59. *Certified* Medicaid.
Admissions Requirements Minimum age 18; Medical examination.

ALVARADO

Alvarado Nursing Home*
R6t 3, Box 320, 500 Glenwood Dr, Alvarado,
TX, 76009 (817) 783-3304
Admin Genevieve H Tucker.
Licensure Skilled Care. *Beds* 60. *Certified* Medicaid.
Ownership Proprietary.

ALVIN

Alvin Convalescent Center
416 N Shirley, Alvin, TX, 77511 (713)
585-8484
Admin Roberta Miller.
Licensure Intermediate Care. *Beds* 98. *Certified* Medicaid.
Admissions Requirements Medical examination; Physician's request.
Staff RNs 1 (ft); LPNs 7 (ft), 1 (pt); Orderlies 1 (ft); Nurses aides 20 (ft), 2 (pt); Physical therapists 1 (pt); Occupational therapists 1 (pt); Speech therapists 1 (pt); Activities coordinators 1 (ft), 1 (pt); Dietitians 1 (pt).
Facilities Dining room; Crafts room; Laundry room; Barber/Beauty shop.
Activities Arts and Crafts; Cards; Games; Prayer groups; Movies; Shopping trips; Dances/Social or cultural gatherings.

Winchester Lodge*
1112 Smith Dr, Alvin, TX, 77511 (713)
331-6125
Admin Joyce R Flaugher.
Licensure Intermediate Care; Personal Care.
Beds ICF 122; Personal Care 20. *Certified* Medicaid.
Ownership Proprietary.

AMARILLO

Amarillo Nursing Center
4033 W 51st St, Amarillo, TX, 79109 (806)
355-4488
Admin Peggy Richburg. *Medical Dir/Dir of Nursing* Suzane Porter.
Licensure Intermediate Care; Personal Care.
Beds ICF 130; Personal Care 30. *Certified* Medicaid.
Staff RNs 1 (ft); LPNs 5 (ft); Nurses aides 10 (ft); Activities coordinators 1 (ft); Dietitians 1 (ft).
Facilities Dining room; Activities room; Crafts room; Laundry room; Barber/Beauty shop.
Activities Arts and Crafts; Cards; Games; Reading groups; Prayer groups; Movies; Shopping trips; Dances/Social or cultural gatherings.

Bivins Memorial Nursing Home
1001 Wallace Blvd, Amarillo, TX, 79106 (806)
355-7453
Admin Landis Oran Clark. *Medical Dir/Dir of Nursing* Patricia Bloom MD.
Licensure Skilled Care. *Beds* 68. *Certified* Medicaid; Medicare.
Ownership Nonprofit.
Admissions Requirements Minimum age 16.
Staff Physicians 1 (pt); RNs 6 (ft), 1 (pt); LPNs 9 (ft), 3 (pt); Nurses aides 33 (ft), 4 (pt); Physical therapists 1 (ft); Activities coordinators 2 (ft); Dietitians 1 (ft); Dentists 1 (pt); Music therapist 1 (pt); Others 44 (ft), 1 (pt).
Facilities Dining room; Physical therapy room; Activities room; Chapel; Crafts room; Laundry room; Barber/Beauty shop; Library.
Activities Arts and Crafts; Cards; Games; Reading groups; Prayer groups; Movies; Shopping trips; Dances/Social or cultural gatherings.
Description Facility is supported by a foundation trust.

Bryanwood Care Center*
2423 Line Ave, Amarillo, TX, 79106 (806)
376-7241
Admin Margurite Van Zandt.
Licensure Intermediate Care. *Beds* 74. *Certified* Medicaid.
Ownership Proprietary.

Country Club Manor*
9 Medical Dr, Amarillo, TX, 79106 (806)
352-2731
Admin Beverly Clark.
Licensure Intermediate Care. *Beds* 102. *Certified* Medicaid.
Ownership Proprietary.

Elizabeth Jane Bivins Home for the Aged*
PO Box 31450, 3115 Tee Anchor Blvd,
Amarillo, TX, 79104 (806) 373-7671
Admin Maggie Cleo Cox.
Licensure Intermediate Care. *Beds* 36. *Certified* Medicaid.
Ownership Nonprofit.

Georgia Manor Nursing Home
2611 SW 46th St, Amarillo, TX, 79110 (806)
355-6517
Admin Jean B Holt.
Licensure Intermediate Care. *Beds* 56. *Certified* Medicaid.
Staff LPNs 5 (ft), 1 (pt); Nurses aides 8 (ft); Activities coordinators; Dietitians.
Facilities Dining room; Laundry room; Barber/Beauty shop.
Activities Arts and Crafts; Cards; Games; Reading groups; Prayer groups; Movies; Shopping trips.

Golden Age Memorial Home
1601 Kirkland Dr, Amarillo, TX, 79106 (806)
355-8281
Admin Sarah Rice. *Medical Dir/Dir of Nursing* Fay Hinkle.
Licensure Intermediate Care. *Beds* 98. *Certified* Medicaid.
Admissions Requirements Medical examination; Physician's request.
Staff Physicians 1 (pt); RNs 1 (pt); LPNs 5 (ft); Orderlies 1 (ft); Nurses aides 12 (ft); Physical therapists 1 (pt); Activities coordinators 1 (ft); Dietitians 1 (ft).
Facilities Dining room; Activities room; Barber/Beauty shop.
Activities Arts and Crafts; Cards; Games; Reading groups; Prayer groups; Movies; Shopping trips.
Description Facility is situated among apartments to be inconspicuous as a nursing home; pleasant relaxed atmosphere; loving care given to all residents.

Heritage Convalescent Center
1009 Clyde, Amarillo, TX, 79106 (806)
352-5295
Admin Richard K Stebbins. *Medical Dir/Dir of Nursing* Dr Donald Frank.
Licensure Skilled Care; Intermediate Care.
Beds 112. *Certified* Medicaid; Medicare.
Staff Physicians 2 (pt); RNs 3 (ft); LPNs 6 (ft); Orderlies 3 (ft); Nurses aides 18 (ft); Physical therapists 1 (pt); Recreational therapists 1 (ft); Occupational therapists 1 (pt); Speech therapists 1 (pt); Activities coordinators 1 (ft); Dietitians 1 (pt).
Facilities Dining room; Activities room; Crafts room; Laundry room; Barber/Beauty shop.
Activities Arts and Crafts; Cards; Games; Dances/Social or cultural gatherings.
Description Heritage Convalescent Center is a recently remodeled nursing home with a caring staff of professionals.

Medi Park Care Center Inc
1931 Medi Park Dr, Amarillo, TX, 79106 (806)
353-7433
Admin Wayne Gray. *Medical Dir/Dir of Nursing* Harlan Wilson.
Licensure Intermediate Care. *Beds* 124. *Certified* Medicaid.
Staff RNs 1 (ft); LPNs 9 (ft); Orderlies 6 (ft); Nurses aides 25 (ft); Physical therapists 1 (pt); Occupational therapists 1 (pt); Speech therapists 1 (pt); Activities coordinators 1 (ft); Dietitians 1 (ft).
Facilities Dining room; Activities room; Crafts room; Laundry room; Barber/Beauty shop.
Activities Arts and Crafts; Cards; Games; Reading groups; Prayer groups; Movies; Shopping trips; Dances/Social or cultural gatherings.

Olsen Manor Nursing Home*
3350 Olsen Blvd, Amarillo, TX, 79109 (806)
355-9726
Admin Phillip E Kielpinski.
Licensure Intermediate Care; Custodial Care.
Beds ICF 60; Custodial Care 60. *Certified* Medicaid.
Ownership Proprietary.

Vivian's Nursing Home*
508 N Taylor St, Amarillo, TX, 79107 (806)
372-6822
Admin Jack D Rude.
Licensure Intermediate Care. *Beds* 53. *Certified* Medicaid.
Ownership Proprietary.

AMHERST

Amherst Manor Nursing Home
700 Main St, Amherst, TX, 79312 (806)
246-3583
Admin Mamie Dangerfield.
Licensure Intermediate Care. *Beds* 30. *Certified* Medicaid.
Admissions Requirements Medical examination; Physician's request.
Staff Nurses aides 6 (ft), 1 (pt); Activities coordinators 1 (ft); Dietitians 2 (ft), 1 (pt); LVNs 1 (ft), 4 (pt).
Activities Arts and Crafts; Games; Reading groups; Prayer groups; Movies; Shopping trips; Dances/Social or cultural gatherings.

ANAHUAC

Leisure Lodge—Anahuac*
Drawer W, Front St, Anahuac, TX, 77514 (713)
267-3164
Admin Joy Lee Green.
Licensure Intermediate Care. *Beds* 100. *Certified* Medicaid.
Ownership Proprietary.

ANDREWS

Andrews Nursing Center*
620 Hospital Dr, Andrews, TX, 79714 (915)
523-4986
Admin Virginia S Clegg.
Licensure Intermediate Care. *Beds* 98. *Certified* Medicaid.
Ownership Proprietary.

ANGLETON

Angleton-Danbury Convalescent Center*
135½ Hospital Dr, Angleton, TX, 77515 (713)
849-8221
Admin Melba J Benton.
Licensure Intermediate Care. *Beds* 104. *Certified* Medicaid.
Ownership Proprietary.

Golden Villa Nursing Home*
721 W Mulberry St, Angleton, TX, 77515 (713)
849-8281
Admin Joy Teague.
Licensure Intermediate Care. *Beds* 103. *Certified* Medicaid.
Ownership Proprietary.

ANSON

Briarstone Manor*
125 Ave J, Anson, TX, 79501 (915) 823-3471
Admin Carolyn Burns.
Licensure Intermediate Care. *Beds* 70. *Certified* Medicaid.
Ownership Proprietary.

Valley View Care Center
101 Liberty Ln, Anson, TX, 79501 (915)
823-2141
Admin Frances A Ward.
Licensure Intermediate Care. *Beds* 36. *Certified* Medicaid.
Admissions Requirements Medical
examination; Physician's request.
Staff RNs 1 (pt); LPNs 3 (ft), 2 (pt); Orderlies 2
(pt); Nurses aides 9 (ft), 2 (pt); Activities coordinators 1 (ft); Dietitians 1 (pt).
Facilities Dining room; Activities room; Chapel; Crafts room; Laundry room; Barber/Beauty shop.
Activities Arts and Crafts; Cards; Games;
Reading groups; Prayer groups; Shopping trips;
Dances/Social or cultural gatherings.

ARANSAS PASS

Aransas Pass Nursing and Convalescent Center*
1661 W Yoakum St, Aransas Pass, TX, 78336
(512) 758-5712
Admin Henry W Hall.
Licensure Intermediate Care. *Beds* 170. *Certified* Medicaid.
Ownership Proprietary.

ARCHER CITY

Archer Nursing Home
201 E Chestnut, Archer City, TX, 76351 (817)

574-4551
Admin Edith V Lawrence.
Licensure Intermediate Care. *Beds* 46. *Certified* Medicaid.
Admissions Requirements Medical examination.
Staff RNs 1 (pt); LPNs 2 (ft), 1 (pt); Nurses
aides 13 (ft), 2 (pt); Activities coordinators 1
(ft); Dietitians 1 (ft).
Facilities Dining room; Activities room; Laundry room.
Activities Arts and Crafts; Cards; Games;
Reading groups; Prayer groups; Movies; Dances/Social or cultural gatherings; Church;
Singing; Square dancing.
Description Facility is clean and offers good
food; many parties with outsiders volunteering
to help and play music; patients are happy and
content.

ARLINGTON

Arlington Nursing Center*
301 W Randol Mill Rd, Arlington, TX, 76010
(817) 460-2002
Admin Victoria Ray.
Licensure Intermediate Care. *Beds* 120. *Certified* Medicaid.
Ownership Proprietary.

Arlington Villa for Senior Citizens
2601 W Randol Mill Rd, Arlington, TX, 76012
(817) 274-5571
Admin Genevieve Sims.
Licensure Intermediate Care. *Beds* 148. *Certified* Medicaid.
Admissions Requirements Minimum age 62;
Medical examination; Physician's request.
Staff RNs 1 (ft), 1 (pt); LPNs 7 (ft), 1 (pt);
Nurses aides 14 (ft); Activities coordinators 1
(ft); Dietitians 1 (ft).
Facilities Dining room; Activities room; Chapel; Laundry room; Barber/Beauty shop;
Library.
Activities Arts and Crafts; Games; Prayer
groups; Movies; Shopping trips; Dances/Social
or cultural gatherings.
Description Facility offers ICF nursing, room
and board, and apartments, all ground level
accomodations; cafeteria, bus service, full-time
Chaplain.

Dalworth Care Center*
405 Duncan Perry Rd, Arlington, TX, 76010
(817) 649-3366
Admin Ann Collins.
Licensure Intermediate Care. *Beds* 120. *Certified* Medicaid.
Ownership Proprietary.

Eastern Star Home*
1201 E Division, Arlington, TX, 76011 (817)
265-1513
Admin Minnie M Sawyer Foster.
Licensure Intermediate Care. *Beds* 40.
Ownership Nonprofit.
Affiliation Order of Eastern Star

Knights Templar Clinic*
1501 W Division, Arlington, TX, 76012 (817)
275-2893
Admin Dorothy B Health.

Licensure Intermediate Care. *Beds* 60.
Ownership Nonprofit.
Affiliation Masons

Oakhaven Nursing Center
1112 Gibbins Rd, Arlington, TX, 76012 (817)
261-6881
Admin Kathy Blasingame. *Medical Dir/Dir of Nursing* Dr Dorab Patel.
Licensure Skilled Care. *Beds* 175. *Certified* Medicaid.
Staff RNs 6 (ft); Nurses aides 40 (ft), 15 (pt);
Physical therapists 2 (ft); Activities coordinators 1 (ft); Dietitians 1 (ft); Dentists; Podiatrists; LVNs 8 (ft), 4 (pt).
Facilities Dining room; Activities room; Crafts
room; Laundry room; Barber/Beauty shop;
Library.
Activities Arts and Crafts; Cards; Games;
Reading groups; Prayer groups; Movies; Shopping trips; Dances/Social or cultural gatherings.
Description Only skilled nursing facility in
Arlington.

Villa Nursing Center Inc
2645 W Randol Mill Rd, Arlington, TX, 76012
(817) 277-6789
Admin Barbara J Perkins.
Licensure Intermediate Care. *Beds* 120. *Certified* Medicaid.
Admissions Requirements Medical examination.
Staff RNs 2 (ft); LPNs 8 (ft); Orderlies 2 (ft);
Nurses aides 30 (ft); Activities coordinators 1
(ft); Dietitians 1 (ft).
Facilities Dining room; Physical therapy room;
Activities room; Laundry room; Barber/Beauty
shop.
Activities Arts and Crafts; Cards; Games; Prayer groups; Movies; Dances/Social or cultural
gatherings.
Description When it comes to excellent care
and a warm feeling for the patient, people come
to the Villa Nursing Center. Pleasant surroundings with beautiful rooms and recreational areas
topped by staffs of the highest professional
standing.

ASPERMONT

Gibson Nursing Center*
1000 N Broadway, Aspermont, TX, 79502
(817) 989-3526
Admin James W Kendall.
Licensure Intermediate Care. *Beds* 80. *Certified* Medicaid.
Ownership Proprietary.

ATHENS

Athens Development Center
101 Lila Ln, Athens, TX, 75751 (214) 675-2004
Admin Bobby L Yates.
Licensure Intermediate Care for Mentally
Retarded. *Beds* 60.

Athens Nursing Home*
305 S Palestine St, Athens, TX, 75751 (214)
675-2046, 5604
Admin Thelma L Adair.

Licensure Intermediate Care. *Beds* 82. *Certified* Medicaid.
Ownership Proprietary.

Park Highlands*
711 Lucas, Athens, TX, 75751 (214) 675-7156, 8538
Admin Melba L Edwards.
Licensure Intermediate Care. *Beds* 140. *Certified* Medicaid.
Ownership Proprietary.

Valvista Pavillion
500 Valle Vista Dr, Athens, TX, 75751 (214) 675-8591
Admin Marie J Wood. *Medical Dir/Dir of Nursing* Dr A Dyphrone
Licensure Intermediate Care. *Beds* 118. *Certified* Medicaid.
Staff Physicians 1 (pt); RNs 1 (ft), 1 (pt); LPNs 8 (ft); Nurses aides 33 (ft), 2 (pt); Activities coordinators 2 (ft); Dietitians 1 (ft), 1 (pt).
Facilities Dining room; Laundry room; Barber-/Beauty shop.
Activities Arts and Crafts; Games; Prayer groups; Movies; Shopping trips; Dances/Social or cultural gatherings; Exercise class.
Description Facility is a very caring, home atmosphere type nursing home. Residents taken for car rides in the country, on picnics, and cook hamburgers outside. Residents are really spoiled.

ATLANTA

Pine Lodge Nursing Home*
201 E 3rd St, Atlanta, TX, 75551 (214) 796-4461
Admin Theodore T Asimos.
Licensure Intermediate Care. *Beds* 109. *Certified* Medicaid.
Ownership Proprietary.

Rose Haven Retreat Inc
Live Oak and Williams, Atlanta, TX, 75551 (214) 796-4127
Admin Leonard M Jester Jr. *Medical Dir/Dir of Nursing* James Morris MD.
Licensure Skilled Care; Intermediate Care.
Beds SNF 45; ICF 63. *Certified* Medicaid.
Admissions Requirements Medical examination; Physician's request.
Staff Physicians 8 (pt); RNs 2 (ft), 1 (pt); LPNs 6 (ft), 2 (pt); Nurses aides 22 (ft), 6 (pt); Activities coordinators 1 (ft); Dietitians 1 (pt); Dentists 1 (pt); Ophthalmologists 1 (pt).
Facilities Dining room; Physical therapy room; Activities room; Chapel; Crafts room; Laundry room; Barber/Beauty shop.
Activities Arts and Crafts; Cards; Games; Reading groups; Prayer groups; Movies; Shopping trips; Dances/Social or cultural gatherings.
Description VA approved.

AUSTIN

Anderson Lane Nursing Home
901 Lazy Ln, Austin, TX, 78758 (512) 454-5621
Admin Rebecca Boyd-Hubik.
Licensure Intermediate Care. *Beds* 48. *Certi-

fied Medicaid.
Staff LPNs 2 (ft); Nurses aides 10 (ft); Activities coordinators 1 (ft).
Facilities Dining room; Activities room; Crafts room; Laundry room.
Activities Arts and Crafts; Cards; Games; Reading groups; Prayer groups; Movies; Shopping trips; Dances/Social or cultural gatherings; Cooking.

Arnold's Care Center*
3101 Govalle Ave, Austin, TX, 78702 (512) 926-8117
Admin Marjorie D Austin.
Licensure Intermediate Care. *Beds* 83. *Certified* Medicaid.
Ownership Proprietary.

Austin Manor Nursing Home*
5413 Guadalupe St, Austin, TX, 78751 (512) 452-7316
Admin Lillian B Laughlin.
Licensure Intermediate Care. *Beds* 60. *Certified* Medicaid.
Ownership Proprietary.

Austin Nursing Convalescent Center Inc*
110 E Live Oak, Austin, TX, 78704 (512) 444-3511
Admin Mildred L Taylor.
Licensure Intermediate Care. *Beds* 150. *Certified* Medicaid.
Ownership Proprietary.

Austin's Rest Haven Nursing Home
6222 N Lamar, Austin, TX, 78752 (512) 453-6658
Admin Shirley Matthews.
Licensure Intermediate Care. *Beds* 80. *Certified* Medicaid.
Staff LPNs 5 (ft), 3 (pt); Orderlies 1 (ft); Nurses aides 12 (ft), 3 (pt); Activities coordinators 1 (ft); Dietitians 1 (ft).
Facilities Dining room; Activities room; Laundry room; Barber/Beauty shop.
Activities Arts and Crafts; Games; Reading groups; Prayer groups; Movies; Shopping trips; Dances/Social or cultural gatherings.

Barton Heights Nursing Home Inc*
1606 Nash St, Austin, TX, 78704 (512) 444-6708
Admin Mary E Zumwalt.
Licensure Intermediate Care. *Beds* 60. *Certified* Medicaid.
Ownership Proprietary.

Belle Mount Nursing Center*
2915 Webberville Rd, Austin, TX, 78702 (512) 474-5461
Admin Jacqueline S Allen.
Licensure Intermediate Care. *Beds* 120. *Certified* Medicaid.
Ownership Proprietary.

Buckner Baptist Monte Siesta Home*
4700 Dudmar Dr, Austin, TX, 78735 (512) 892-1131
Admin Steven H Lee.
Licensure Intermediate Care. *Beds* 128. *Certified* Medicaid.
Ownership Nonprofit.
Affiliation Baptist

Buckner Villa Siesta Home*
1001 E Braker Ln, Austin, TX, 78753 (512) 836-1515
Admin James H Cantrell.
Licensure Intermediate Care. *Beds* 128. *Certified* Medicaid.
Ownership Nonprofit.
Affiliation Baptist

Cameron Villa Rest Home*
1109 E 52nd St, Austin, TX, 78723 (512) 451-1673
Admin Charles Collins.
Licensure Intermediate Care. *Beds* 41. *Certified* Medicaid.
Ownership Proprietary.

Capitol City Nursing Home
9052 Galewood Dr, Austin, TX, 78758 (512) 836-9172
Admin Rita Balmforth. *Medical Dir/Dir of Nursing* Dr George Robison.
Licensure Skilled Care. *Beds* 120. *Certified* Medicaid.
Admissions Requirements Medical examination.
Staff RNs 1 (ft), 1 (pt); LPNs 10 (ft), 5 (pt); Orderlies 2 (ft); Nurses aides 27 (ft), 2 (pt); Activities coordinators 2 (ft); Dietitians 1 (ft).
Facilities Dining room; Activities room; Laundry room; Barber/Beauty shop; Library.
Activities Arts and Crafts; Cards; Games; Reading groups; Prayer groups; Movies; Shopping trips; Dances/Social or cultural gatherings.
Description Facility features a greatly varied activity program.

Central Texas Nursing Home*
8007 Burnet Rd, Austin, TX, 78758 (512) 453-7389
Admin Mildred O Scheumack.
Licensure Intermediate Care. *Beds* 96. *Certified* Medicaid.
Ownership Proprietary.

Cresthaven Children's Center
4800 S 1st St, Austin, TX, 78745 (512) 444-8551
Admin Jean J Harrison. *Medical Dir/Dir of Nursing* Don Sartok MD.
Licensure Intermediate Care for Mentally Retarded. *Beds* 72. *Certified* Medicaid.
Admissions Requirements Minimum age Birth; Medical examination.
Staff RNs 3 (ft), 1 (pt); LPNs 7 (ft), 4 (pt); Orderlies 7 (ft), 1 (pt); Nurses aides 21 (ft), 9 (pt); Recreational therapists; Occupational therapists; Activities coordinators; Dietitians.
Facilities Dining room; Physical therapy room; Activities room; Laundry room; AISD school rooms.
Activities Games; Movies; Shopping trips; Dances/Social or cultural gatherings.
Description In addition to excellent nursing care, there is a full school program manned by 9 AISD teachers. Center offers recreational and occupational programing; therapy pool used in summer.

Cresthaven Nursing Center*
6400 E Martin Luther King Blvd, Austin, TX, 78724 (512) 926-5976

Admin John White.
Licensure Intermediate Care for Mentally Retarded. *Beds* 96. *Certified* Medicaid.

Cullen Avenue Rest Home
2105 Cullen, Austin, TX, 78757 (512) 454-2731
Admin Bobby Dockal. *Medical Dir/Dir of Nursing* Louise Eeds MD.
Licensure Intermediate Care. *Beds* 60. *Certified* Medicaid.
Staff Physicians 1 (ft), 2 (pt); RNs 1 (pt); LPNs 2 (ft), 4 (pt); Orderlies 5 (ft), 1 (pt); Nurses aides 14 (ft), 3 (pt); Physical therapists 1 (pt); Speech therapists 1 (pt); Activities coordinators 1 (ft); Dietitians 1 (pt); Dentists 1 (pt); Podiatrists 1 (pt).
Facilities Dining room; Activities room; Crafts room; Laundry room; Barber/Beauty shop.
Activities Arts and Crafts; Cards; Games; Reading groups; Prayer groups; Movies; Shopping trips; Dances/Social or cultural gatherings.

Delwood Nursing Center Inc
4407 Red River St, Austin, TX, 78751 (512) 452-2533
Admin Billie G McGee.
Licensure Intermediate Care. *Beds* 40. *Certified* Medicaid.
Staff RNs 1 (ft); LPNs 2 (ft), 3 (pt); Nurses aides 11 (ft), 3 (pt); Activities coordinators 1 (pt).
Facilities Dining room; Activities room.
Activities Arts and Crafts; Games; Prayer groups; Dances/Social or cultural gatherings.
Description Facility is centrally located, convenient to doctors and hospitals, in an old established neighborhood; stresses good, individualized care.

Eastfair Nursing Home
2820 Martin Luther King Blvd, Austin, TX, 78702 (512) 472-5444
Admin Richard H Matthews.
Licensure Intermediate Care. *Beds* 60. *Certified* Medicaid.
Admissions Requirements Physician's request.
Staff LPNs 4 (ft); Orderlies 4 (ft); Nurses aides 10 (ft); Activities coordinators 1 (ft).

Four Seasons Nursing Center
500 E Saint Johns, Austin, TX, 78752 (512) 454-9581
Admin R Ron Semingson. *Medical Dir/Dir of Nursing* Alan Sonstien MD.
Licensure Skilled Care; Intermediate Care. *Beds* 233. *Certified* Medicaid; Medicare.
Admissions Requirements Medical examination; Physician's request.
Staff RNs 9 (ft), 10 (pt); LPNs 4 (ft), 12 (pt); Nurses aides 18 (ft), 32 (pt); Physical therapists 1 (pt); Reality therapists 2 (ft), 1 (pt); Activities coordinators 1 (ft); Dietitians 1 (pt).
Facilities Dining room; Physical therapy room; Activities room; Crafts room; Laundry room; Barber/Beauty shop.
Activities Arts and Crafts; Cards; Games; Reading groups; Prayer groups; Movies; Shopping trips; Dances/Social or cultural gatherings.
Description Center offers very strong restorative program with therapists and restorative aides.

Francis Southwood Nursing Home Inc*
3759 Valley View Rd, Austin, TX, 78704 (512) 443-3436
Admin Irene G Richter.
Licensure Intermediate Care. *Beds* 120. *Certified* Medicaid.
Ownership Proprietary.

Lyndon Baines Johnson Nursing Center*
3509 Rogge Ln, Austin, TX, 78723 (512) 926-2070
Admin Barbara F Hudspeth.
Licensure Intermediate Care. *Beds* 120. *Certified* Medicaid.
Ownership Proprietary.

Maggie Johnson's Nursing Center*
3406 E 17th St, Austin, TX, 78721 (512) 926-4760
Admin Johnny E Slaughter.
Licensure Intermediate Care. *Beds* 48. *Certified* Medicaid.
Ownership Proprietary.

Miller's Rest Home Inc*
4606 Connelly, Austin, TX, 78751 (512) 452-0155
Admin Rosalie M Miller.
Licensure Intermediate Care. *Beds* 38. *Certified* Medicaid.
Ownership Proprietary.

Northwest Mediplex
11612 Angus Rd, Austin, TX, 78759 (512) 345-1805
Admin Irene G Richter. *Medical Dir/Dir of Nursing* Ernest Schmatolla.
Licensure Intermediate Care. *Beds* 388. *Certified* Medicaid.
Facilities Dining room; Physical therapy room; Activities room; Laundry room; Barber/Beauty shop; Library.

Oakcrest Manor*
9507 Hwy 290 E, Austin, TX, 78724 (512) 272-5511
Admin Mary A Neal.
Licensure Intermediate Care. *Beds* 60. *Certified* Medicaid.
Ownership Proprietary.

Retirement and Nursing Center*
6909 Burnet Ln, Austin, TX, 78757 (512) 452-5719
Admin Susan S Williams.
Licensure Intermediate Care. *Beds* 100. *Certified* Medicaid.
Ownership Proprietary.

Southwest Mediplex
1015 William Cannon Dr, Austin, TX, 78745 (512) 443-1640
Admin Lisa Wilson. *Medical Dir/Dir of Nursing* Dr Allen Sonstein.
Licensure Intermediate Care. *Beds* 120. *Certified* Medicaid.
Admissions Requirements Medical examination; Physician's request.
Staff RNs 2 (ft), 3 (pt); LPNs 6 (ft), 1 (pt); Nurses aides 21 (ft), 6 (pt); Activities coordinators 1 (ft); Dietitians 1 (ft).
Facilities Dining room; Laundry room; Barber/Beauty shop.

Activities Arts and Crafts; Cards; Games; Reading groups; Prayer groups; Movies; Shopping trips; Dances/Social or cultural gatherings.
Description Southwest Mediplex is a reputable facility which provides good patient care. The facility is beautiful and has an excellent staff dedicated to meeting the needs of the elderly.

Stonebrook Nursing Home*
2806 Real St, Austin, TX, 78722 (512) 474-1411
Admin Linda Matlock.
Licensure Skilled Care; Intermediate Care. *Beds* 204. *Certified* Medicaid; Medicare.
Ownership Proprietary.

AZLE

Azle Manor Inc
225 Church St, Azle, TX, 76020 (817) 444-2536
Admin McKinley Wayne Pack. *Medical Dir/Dir of Nursing* Jim Savage MD.
Licensure Skilled Care. *Beds* 127. *Certified* Medicaid.
Staff RNs 1 (ft), 2 (pt); Nurses aides 35 (ft), 7 (pt); Activities coordinators 1 (ft); Dietitians 1 (pt); Dentists 2 (pt); Ophthalmologists 1 (pt); Podiatrists 1 (pt); LVNs 12 (ft), 5 (pt).
Facilities Dining room; Activities room; Crafts room; Laundry room; Barber/Beauty shop.
Activities Arts and Crafts; Cards; Games; Reading groups; Prayer groups; Movies; Shopping trips.

BAIRD

Golden Holiday Care Center
240 E 6th St, Baird, TX, 79504 (915) 854-1429
Admin Emma G Underwood.
Licensure Intermediate Care. *Beds* 78. *Certified* Medicaid.
Ownership Proprietary.
Admissions Requirements Medical examination; Physician's request.
Staff LPNs 7 (ft); Dietitians 1 (ft).
Facilities Dining room; Activities room; Crafts room; Laundry room; Barber/Beauty shop.

BALCH SPRINGS

Balch Springs Nursing Home
4200 Shepherd Ln, Balch Springs, TX, 75180 (214) 286-0335
Admin Merril M Grey. *Medical Dir/Dir of Nursing* Paul Schorr.
Licensure Intermediate Care. *Beds* 120. *Certified* Medicaid.
Admissions Requirements Medical examination; Physician's request.
Staff RNs 1 (ft); LPNs 10 (ft); Nurses aides 26 (ft); Activities coordinators 1 (ft); Dietitians 1 (pt).
Facilities Dining room; Activities room; Chapel; Crafts room; Laundry room; Barber/Beauty shop; Library.
Activities Arts and Crafts; Cards; Games; Reading groups; Prayer groups; Movies; Shopping trips; Dances/Social or cultural gatherings.

BALLINGER

Ballinger Manor
Bronte Hwy, Ballinger, TX, 76821 (915)
365-2538
Admin D W Sims. *Medical Dir/Dir of
Nursing* Dr Antoine Albert.
Licensure Intermediate Care. *Beds* 154. *Certified* Medicaid.
Staff Physicians 4 (pt); LPNs 4 (ft), 2 (pt);
Orderlies 1 (ft); Nurses aides 9 (ft), 7 (pt);
Physical therapists 1 (pt); Activities coordinators 1 (ft); Dietitians 2 (ft).
Facilities Dining room; Physical therapy room;
Activities room; Chapel; Crafts room; Laundry
room; Barber/Beauty shop; Library.
Activities Arts and Crafts; Cards; Games;
Reading groups; Prayer groups; Movies; Shopping trips; Dances/Social or cultural gatherings.

Ballinger Nursing Center*
PO Box 622, 1400 Country Club Ave, Ballinger, TX, 76821 (915) 365-2632
Admin Darlene McDaniel.
Licensure Intermediate Care. *Beds* 48.
Certified Medicaid.
Ownership Proprietary.

BANDERA

Purple Hills Nursing Home Inc*
PO Box 836, Montague Dr, Bandera, TX,
78003 (512) 796-3767
Admin Eloise F Nixon.
Licensure Intermediate Care. *Beds* 62. *Certified* Medicaid.
Ownership Proprietary.

BANGS

Bangs Nursing Home*
1400 Fitzgerald St, Bangs, TX, 76823 (915)
752-6321
Admin Glorris A Wolford.
Licensure Intermediate Care. *Beds* 48. *Certified* Medicaid.
Ownership Proprietary.

Twilight Nursing Home Inc*
205 S West St, Bangs, TX, 76823 (915)
752-6322
Admin Wendell H Byler.
Licensure Intermediate Care. *Beds* 41. *Certified* Medicaid.
Ownership Proprietary.

BARTLETT

Will-O-Bell Inc
412 N Dalton, Bartlett, TX, 76511 (817)
527-3371
Admin June D Fugate. *Medical Dir/Dir of
Nursing* Ralph Clearman MD.
Licensure Intermediate Care. *Beds* 60. *Certified* Medicaid.
Staff Physicians 2 (pt); RNs 1 (pt); LPNs 3 (ft),
2 (pt); Nurses aides 45 (ft); Activities coordinators 1 (ft); Dietitians 1 (pt).
Facilities Dining room; Activities room; Laundry room; Barber/Beauty shop.

Activities Arts and Crafts; Cards; Games;
Reading groups; Prayer groups; Movies; Shopping trips.

BASTROP

Bastrop Nursing Center*
PO Box 649, 400 Old Austin Hwy, Bastrop,
TX, 78602 (512) 321-2529
Admin Sherri L Hoskins.
Licensure Intermediate Care. *Beds* 96. *Certified* Medicaid.
Ownership Proprietary.

BAY CITY

Bay Villa Nursing Home*
1800 13th St, Bay City, TX, 77414 (713)
245-6327
Admin Doris Bergerson.
Licensure Skilled Care; Intermediate Care.
Beds 105. *Certified* Medicaid.
Ownership Proprietary.

**Matagorda Home-Matagorda General
Hospital**
1115 Ave G, Bay City, TX, 77414 (713)
245-6383
Admin Emil L Villafranca. *Medical Dir/Dir of
Nursing* H C Matthes MD.
Licensure Skilled Care. *Beds* 28. *Certified* Medicaid.
Admissions Requirements Physician's request.
Staff RNs 2 (ft); LPNs 4 (ft), 1 (pt); Nurses
aides 14 (ft); Activities coordinators 1 (ft); Dietitians 1 (pt).
Facilities Dining room; Activities room; Chapel; Crafts room.

BAYTOWN

Allenbrook Healthcare Center*
4109 Allenbrook Dr, Baytown, TX, 77520
(713) 422-3546
Admin Janet Morris.
Licensure Intermediate Care. *Beds* 120. *Certified* Medicaid.
Ownership Proprietary.

Baytown Nursing Home*
1106 Park St, Baytown, TX, 77520 (713)
427-1644, 1421
Admin Edward R Garrett.
Licensure Intermediate Care. *Beds* 90. *Certified* Medicaid.
Ownership Proprietary.

Green Acres Convalescent Center*
2000 Beaumont, Baytown, TX, 77520 (713)
427-4774
Admin Beverly Miller.
Licensure Intermediate Care. *Beds* 100. *Certified* Medicaid.
Ownership Proprietary.

Saint James House of Baytown
5800 Baker Rd, Baytown, TX, 77520 (713)
424-7214
Admin Elizabeth Alexander. *Medical Dir/Dir
of Nursing* Joy Crow.

Licensure Intermediate Care; Custodial Care.
Beds ICF 38; Custodial Care 48. *Certified* Medicaid.
Staff RNs 1 (ft); LPNs 7 (ft); Nurses aides 15
(ft), 4 (pt); Physical therapists 2 (ft); Activities
coordinators 1 (ft), 1 (pt); Dietitians 1 (ft).
Affiliation Episcopal
Facilities Dining room; Physical therapy room;
Activities room; Chapel; Laundry room; Barber/Beauty shop; Library.
Activities Cards; Games; Reading groups; Prayer groups; Movies; Shopping trips;
Dances/Social or cultural gatherings.

BEAUMONT

A W Schlesinger Geriatric Center
4195 Milam, PO Box 1990, Beaumont, TX,
77707 (409) 842-4550
Admin Emma Jo Smith. *Medical Dir/Dir of
Nursing* Nicolas Rodriguez MD.
Licensure Skilled Care; Intermediate Care.
Beds 412. *Certified* Medicaid; Medicare.
Admissions Requirements Minimum age 16;
Medical examination; Physician's request.
Staff RNs 5 (ft), 3 (pt); LPNs 34 (ft); Physical
therapists 2 (pt); Recreational therapists 2 (ft);
Occupational therapists 1 (pt); Speech therapists 1 (pt); Activities coordinators 1 (ft); Dietitians 1 (ft); Podiatrists 1 (pt).
Facilities Dining room; Physical therapy room;
Activities room; Chapel; Crafts room; Barber-/Beauty shop; Library.
Activities Arts and Crafts; Cards; Games;
Reading groups; Prayer groups; Movies; Shopping trips; Dances/Social or cultural gatherings.
Description Facility located 1/2 mile west of
Interstate 10 on 15 improved wooded acres
within 2 miles of all hospitals in Beaumont.
Large, active group of volunteers provide many
resident services, i.e., door-to-door library service, letter writing, reading, and visiting.

Adaptive Living Center—Southeast Texas
3755 Corley St, Beaumont, TX, 77701 (713)
842-5900
Admin Martha Kirkpatrick.
Licensure Intermediate Care for Mentally
Retarded. *Beds* 130. *Certified* Medicaid.

Centerbury Villa—Beaumont
1175 Denton Dr, Beaumont, TX, 77704 (713)
842-3120
Admin Margie Anders. *Medical Dir/Dir of
Nursing* Dr J S Douglas.
Licensure Intermediate Care. *Beds* 122. *Certified* Medicaid.
Staff Physicians 1 (pt); RNs 1 (ft); LPNs 8 (ft),
1 (pt); Nurses aides 16 (ft), 2 (pt); Activities
coordinators 1 (ft); Dietitians 1 (ft), 1 (pt);
Podiatrists 1 (pt).
Facilities Dining room; Activities room; Crafts
room; Laundry room; Barber/Beauty shop.
Activities Arts and Crafts; Cards; Games;
Reading groups; Prayer groups; Movies; Shopping trips; Dances/Social or cultural gatherings.
Description The facility is located within a one-mile radius of 3 hospitals, physicians offices,
medical centers, shopping centre, theatres, restaurants, dental offices, and ophthamologist

offices. There is only one other facility in this area of Texas that participates in the Supervised Living Program.

College Street Nursing Center*
4150 College Ave, Beaumont, TX, 77707 (713) 842-0333
Admin Kaye Vaden.
Licensure Intermediate Care. *Beds* 80. *Certified* Medicaid.
Ownership Proprietary.

Glad Day Nursing Center
795 Lindberg Dr, Beaumont, TX, 77707 (713) 842-0311
Admin Maggie E Davis.
Licensure Skilled Care; Intermediate Care.
Beds 84. *Certified* Medicaid.
Facilities Dining room; Physical therapy room; Chapel; Crafts room.
Activities Arts and Crafts; Cards; Games; Reading groups; Prayer groups; Movies; Shopping trips; Dances/Social or cultural gatherings.

Green Acres Convalescent Center—Parkdale*
11025 Old Voth Rd, Beaumont, TX, 77708 (713) 892-9722
Admin Ruby L Marrero.
Licensure Intermediate Care. *Beds* 150. *Certified* Medicaid.
Ownership Proprietary.

Hamilton Nursing Home Inc
2660 Brickyard Rd, Beaumont, TX, 77703 (713) 892-1533
Admin Martha Kirkpatrick.
Licensure Intermediate Care. *Beds* 115. *Certified* Medicaid.
Admissions Requirements Physician's request.
Staff LPNs 8 (ft), 1 (pt); Nurses aides 47 (ft), 4 (pt); Activities coordinators 2 (ft).
Facilities Dining room; Activities room; Crafts room; Laundry room; Barber/Beauty shop.
Activities Arts and Crafts; Cards; Games; Prayer groups.
Description Hamilton Nursing Home is the oldest nursing home in Texas.

Sabine Oaks Home*
1945 Pennsylvania Ave, Beaumont, TX, 77701 (713) 833-1989
Admin Olive Jack Shannon.
Licensure Custodial Care. *Beds* 40. *Certified* Medicaid.

BEDFORD

La Dora Lodge Nursing Home
1960 Bedford Rd, Bedford, TX, 76021 (817) 283-4771
Admin Mary T Uebelhart.
Licensure Intermediate Care. *Beds* 66. *Certified* Medicaid.

Stanford Convalescent Center—Bedford*
2716 Tibbets Dr, Bedford, TX, 76021 (817) 283-5511
Admin Sandra Hale.
Licensure Skilled Care; Intermediate Care.
Beds 160. *Certified* Medicaid.
Ownership Proprietary.

BEEVILLE

Hillside Lodge Nursing Home*
600 Hillside Dr, Beeville, TX, 78102 (512) 358-8880
Admin Robert Curtis.
Licensure Intermediate Care. *Beds* 120. *Certified* Medicaid.
Ownership Proprietary.

Meridian Nursing Center-Beeville
Hwy 181, N Rt 1, Box 35-A, Beeville, TX, 78102 (512) 358-5612
Admin William L Phelps Jr. *Medical Dir/Dir of Nursing* Tom Reagan MD.
Licensure Skilled Care; Intermediate Care.
Beds SNF 50; ICF 50. *Certified* Medicaid.
Staff Physicians 1 (pt); RNs 3 (ft), 1 (pt); LPNs 3 (ft), 6 (pt); Nurses aides 26 (ft), 10 (pt); Physical therapists 1 (pt); Reality therapists 1 (pt); Speech therapists 1 (pt); Activities coordinators 1 (ft); Dietitians 1 (pt); Dentists 1 (pt); Podiatrists 1 (pt).

BELLVILLE

Colonial Belle Nursing Home
104 N Baron St, Bellville, TX, 77418 (713) 865-3689
Medical Dir/Dir of Nursing J B Harle MD.
Licensure Skilled Care. *Beds* 73. *Certified* Medicaid.
Admissions Requirements Medical examination; Physician's request.
Staff Physicians 4 (ft); RNs 2 (ft), 1 (pt); LPNs 9 (ft); Orderlies 4 (ft); Physical therapists 1 (pt); Recreational therapists 1 (pt); Activities coordinators 1 (pt); Dietitians 1 (pt); Dentists 1 (pt); Ophthalmologists 1 (pt); Podiatrists 1 (pt).
Facilities Dining room; Physical therapy room; Activities room; Chapel; Laundry room; Barber/Beauty shop; Library.
Activities Arts and Crafts; Cards; Games; Reading groups; Prayer groups; Movies; Shopping trips; Dances/Social or cultural gatherings.
Description A nursing facility which creates the image of a home, not an institution, with space, fresh air, and lovely surroundings.

Sweetbriar Nursing Home*
PO Box 638, Hwy 36 N, Bellville, TX, 77418 (713) 865-3145
Admin Melvin Kiemsteadt.
Licensure Intermediate Care. *Beds* 170. *Certified* Medicaid.
Ownership Proprietary.

BELTON

Crestview Manor Nursing Center
1103 Mary Jane St, Belton, TX, 76513 (817) 939-3662
Admin Bettye H Evans. *Medical Dir/Dir of Nursing* William B Long MD.
Licensure Skilled Care. *Beds* 91. *Certified* Medicaid.
Admissions Requirements Minimum age 18; Medical examination; Physician's request.
Staff Physicians 6 (pt); RNs 2 (ft); LPNs 10 (ft); Nurses aides 40 (ft); Activities coordinators 1 (ft); Ophthalmologists; Podiatrists; Audiolo-

gists.
Facilities Dining room; Activities room; Laundry room; Barber/Beauty shop; Living room.
Activities Arts and Crafts; Cards; Games; Reading groups; Prayer groups; Movies; Shopping trips; Dances/Social or cultural gatherings.
Description Facility has a beautiful corner site easily reached on Highway 190 service road; offers a small community home-like atmosphere; participates in senior olympics annually.

BENBROOK

Benbrook Sweetbriar Nursing Home
1000 McKinley St, Benbrook, TX, 76126 (817) 249-0020
Admin Alma B Schumacher. *Medical Dir/Dir of Nursing* Dr James T Hawa.
Licensure Intermediate Care. *Beds* 133. *Certified* Medicaid.
Staff Physicians 1 (ft); RNs 1 (ft), 1 (pt); LPNs 8 (ft); Orderlies 5 (ft); Nurses aides 21 (ft); Physical therapists 1 (pt); Speech therapists 1 (pt); Activities coordinators 1 (ft); Dietitians 2 (pt); Dentists 1 (pt); Podiatrists 1 (pt).
Facilities Dining room; Physical therapy room; Activities room; Chapel; Crafts room; Laundry room; Barber/Beauty shop; Library.
Activities Arts and Crafts; Cards; Games; Reading groups; Prayer groups; Movies; Shopping trips; Dances/Social or cultural gatherings.
Description Facility features a garden area surrounding a gazebo with a walk way.

BERTRAM

Bertram Nursing Home
Hwy 29, Box 209, Bertram, TX, 78605 (512) 355-2116
Admin Dixie Ann Westen. *Medical Dir/Dir of Nursing* H James Wall MD.
Licensure Intermediate Care. *Beds* 32. *Certified* Medicaid.
Ownership Nonprofit.
Admissions Requirements Medical examination; Physician's request.
Staff Physicians 1 (pt); RNs 1 (pt); LPNs 6 (pt); Nurses aides 11 (ft), 6 (pt); Reality therapists 1 (pt); Recreational therapists 1 (pt); Occupational therapists 1 (pt); Speech therapists 1 (pt); Activities coordinators 1 (ft); Dietitians 1 (pt).
Facilities Dining room; Activities room; Laundry room; Barber/Beauty shop.
Activities Arts and Crafts; Cards; Games; Reading groups; Movies; Shopping trips; Parties; Church; Sing-a-longs; Recreational outings.

BIG SPRING

Mountain View Lodge Inc*
2009 Virginia, Big Spring, TX, 79720 (915) 263-1271
Admin Billy M Hendrix.
Licensure Intermediate Care. *Beds* 92. *Certified* Medicaid.
Ownership Proprietary.

United Health Care Center*
901 Goliad St, Big Spring, TX, 79720 (915) 263-7633
Admin Raymond Junker.
Licensure Intermediate Care. *Beds* 200. *Certified* Medicaid.
Ownership Proprietary.

BLANCO

Blanco Mill Nursing Home*
PO Box 327, 3rd and Elm, Blanco, TX, 78606 (512) 833-4710
Admin Sophie A Johnson.
Licensure Intermediate Care. *Beds* 30. *Certified* Medicaid.
Ownership Proprietary.

Live Oak Medical Center
300 E 7th, Blanco, TX, 78606 (512) 833-4818
Admin Mary F Toms.
Licensure Intermediate Care. *Beds* 64. *Certified* Medicaid.
Admissions Requirements Medical examination; Physician's request.
Staff RNs 1 (pt); LPNs 4 (ft); Orderlies 1 (ft); Nurses aides 15 (ft); Physical therapists 1 (pt); Recreational therapists 1 (ft); Dietitians 1 (pt).
Facilities Dining room; Activities room; Crafts room; Laundry room.
Activities Arts and Crafts; Cards; Games; Reading groups; Prayer groups; Movies; Shopping trips.
Description This is an outstanding rural nursing facility with easy access to major medical centers.

BOERNE

Hill Top Nursing Home*
200 Ryan St, Boerne, TX, 78006 (512) 249-2594
Admin Betty Buel Price.
Licensure Intermediate Care. *Beds* 72. *Certified* Medicaid.

Town and Country Manor Inc
625 N Main, Boerne, TX, 78006 (512) 249-3085
Admin Lois F Wertheim.
Licensure Intermediate Care. *Beds* 131. *Certified* Medicaid.

BOGATA

Red River Haven Nursing Home Inc*
319 Paris Rd, Bogata, TX, 75417 (214) 632-5756
Admin Bobbie Lee Cawley.
Licensure Intermediate Care. *Beds* 154. *Certified* Medicaid.
Ownership Proprietary.

BONHAM

Bonham Nursing Center
709 W 5th St, Bonham, TX, 75418 (214) 583-8551
Admin Juanita Awbrey.
Licensure Intermediate Care. *Beds* 65. Certi-

fied Medicaid.
Admissions Requirements Physician's request.
Staff LPNs 8 (ft); Nurses aides 10 (ft); Activities coordinators 1 (ft); Dietitians 3 (ft), 2 (pt).
Facilities Dining room; Activities room; Crafts room; Laundry room; Barber/Beauty shop.
Activities Arts and Crafts; Cards; Games; Reading groups; Prayer groups; Movies; Shopping trips; Dances/Social or cultural gatherings; Exercise; Field trips.

Fairview Nursing Home*
1500 N Kennedy St, Bonham, TX, 75418 (214) 583-2148
Admin Betty West.
Licensure Intermediate Care. *Beds* 103. *Certified* Medicaid.
Ownership Proprietary.

Seven Oakes Care Center
901 Seven Oaks Rd, Bonham, TX, 75418 (214) 583-2191
Admin Tom M McDonald.
Licensure Intermediate Care. *Beds* 108. *Certified* Medicaid.
Staff Physicians 4 (pt); RNs 1 (ft); LPNs 7 (ft); Nurses aides 28 (ft); Activities coordinators 1 (ft); Dietitians 1 (pt); Dentists 1 (pt).
Facilities Dining room; Activities room; Crafts room; Barber/Beauty shop.
Activities Arts and Crafts; Games; Prayer groups; Shopping trips; Dances/Social or cultural gatherings; Exercises.
Description A complete nursing care facility up to the intermediate III level, a very quiet place to live with good care.

BORGER

Leisure Lodge—Borger
1316 S Florida, Borger, TX, 79007 (806) 273-3785
Admin Mildred L Parnell. *Medical Dir/Dir of Nursing* Dr A L Sherer.
Licensure Intermediate Care. *Beds* 120. *Certified* Medicaid.
Staff Physicians 11 (pt); RNs 1 (pt); Nurses aides 15 (pt); Activities coordinators 1 (ft); Dietitians 1 (pt).
Facilities Dining room; Activities room; Laundry room; Barber/Beauty shop.
Activities Arts and Crafts; Cards; Games; Reading groups; Prayer groups; Movies; Shopping trips; Dances/Social or cultural gatherings.
Description We have an outstanding volunteer program and adopt-a-grandparent program with local youngsters. We presently are in the process of hiring a new activities social director. We have a patio, fence, and have started a new garden area. We have a medical director who works very close with us and takes calls for any resident emergency.

Magic Plains Nursing Home*
PO Box 409, 200 Tyler, Borger, TX, 79007 (806) 273-3725
Admin Terri Lynn Willis.
Licensure Intermediate Care. *Beds* 58. *Certified* Medicaid; Medicare.

BOWIE

Bellmire Home Inc*
PO Box 1227, 1101 Rock St, Bowie, TX, 76230 (817) 872-2283
Admin Mary H Duvall.
Licensure Intermediate Care. *Beds* 201. *Certified* Medicaid.
Ownership Proprietary.

Bowie Convalescing Home*
601 Central Ave, Bowie, TX, 76230 (817) 872-1231
Admin Carol S Brewer.
Licensure Intermediate Care. *Beds* 95. *Certified* Medicaid.
Ownership Proprietary.

BRADY

Leisure Lodge—Brady*
PO Box 551, Menard Hwy, Brady, TX, 76825 (915) 597-2906
Admin Kenny Owings.
Licensure Intermediate Care. *Beds* 110. *Certified* Medicaid.
Ownership Proprietary.

Shuffield Rest Home 1
1605 S Bradley, Brady, TX, 76825 (915) 597-2916
Admin Eugene E Frost.
Licensure Intermediate Care. *Beds* 67. *Certified* Medicaid.
Admissions Requirements Minimum age 18; Medical examination; Physician's request.
Staff RNs 1 (ft); LPNs 3 (ft), 3 (pt); Nurses aides 20 (ft), 4 (pt); Activities coordinators 1 (ft); Dietitians 1 (pt).
Facilities Dining room; Physical therapy room; Activities room; Crafts room; Laundry room; Barber/Beauty shop; Library.
Activities Arts and Crafts; Games; Reading groups; Movies; Shopping trips; Dances/Social or cultural gatherings.
Description Small facility, with a homey atmosphere, food is delicious, nursing care is great, rated superior by Texas Department of Health. Full time social activity director; Medicaid certified.

Shuffield Rest Home 2*
US Hwy 87 S, Brady, TX, 76825 (915) 597-2947
Admin Patsy E Lohn.
Licensure Intermediate Care. *Beds* 60. *Certified* Medicaid.
Ownership Proprietary.

BRECKENRIDGE

Town Hall Estates*
1900 W Elliott, Breckenridge, TX, 76024 (817) 559-3303
Admin Kenneth V Campbell.
Licensure Intermediate Care. *Beds* 72. *Certified* Medicaid.
Ownership Nonprofit.

Villa Haven
300 S Jackson, Breckenridge, TX, 76024 (817)
559-3386
Admin Marjorie A Duncan.
Licensure Intermediate Care. *Beds* 92. *Certified* Medicaid.
Staff RNs 2 (pt); LPNs 6 (ft), 3 (pt); Activities coordinators 1 (ft); Dietitians 1 (pt).
Facilities Dining room; Activities room; Crafts room; Laundry room; Barber/Beauty shop.
Activities Arts and Crafts; Cards; Games; Reading groups; Prayer groups; Movies; Shopping trips; Dances/Social or cultural gatherings.
Description Facility features Century Whirlpool bath.

BREMOND

Bremond Nursing Center
PO Box 520, N Main St, Bremond, TX, 76629
(817) 746-7666
Admin Holis U McGee.
Licensure Intermediate Care. *Beds* 82. *Certified* Medicaid.
Staff Physicians 2 (pt); RNs 1 (pt); LPNs 6 (ft); Nurses aides 30 (ft); Activities coordinators 1 (ft); Dietitians 1 (pt); Dentists 1 (pt).
Facilities Dining room; Physical therapy room; Activities room; Chapel; Crafts room; Laundry room; Barber/Beauty shop; Library.
Activities Arts and Crafts; Games; Reading groups; Prayer groups; Movies; Shopping trips; Dances/Social or cultural gatherings.
Description Facility features TELECARE a cheery telephone call to those who live alone every weekday morning. (Weekend calls can be arranged.) TELECARE can help one continue to live at home.

BRENHAM

Brenham Rest Home Inc
406 Cottonwood St, Brenham, TX, 77833 (409)
836-3434
Admin H S Hughes.
Licensure Intermediate Care. *Beds* 108. *Certified* Medicaid.
Admissions Requirements Medical examination; Physician's request.
Staff RNs 1 (ft), 1 (pt); LPNs 7 (ft); Nurses aides 28 (ft), 12 (pt); Activities coordinators 1 (ft), 1 (pt).
Facilities Dining room; Activities room; Crafts room; Laundry room.
Activities Arts and Crafts; Cards; Games; Reading groups; Prayer groups; Movies; Dances/Social or cultural gatherings.
Description Facility offers outstanding activity program with daily group activities, regularly scheduled special events, activities tailored to the individual, and an arts and crafts program supervised by a professional artist; excellent dietary services with many foods prepared from scratch.

Sweetbriar Nursing Home
401 E Horton St, Brenham, TX, 77833 (713)
836-6611
Admin Betty C Fife. *Medical Dir/Dir of Nursing* W F Hasskarl Jr.
Licensure Skilled Care; Intermediate Care.

Beds 265. *Certified* Medicaid.
Admissions Requirements Minimum age 18.
Staff Physicians 1 (pt); RNs 2 (ft); LPNs 15 (ft), 6 (pt); Orderlies 4 (ft); Nurses aides 76 (ft), 20 (pt); Recreational therapists 2 (ft); Dietitians 1 (pt).
Facilities Dining room; Activities room; Barber/Beauty shop.

BRIDGE CITY

Green Acres Convalescent and Development Center*
PO Box 606, 625 Meadowlawn, Bridge City, TX, 77611 (713) 735-3528
Admin Anne Williams.
Licensure Intermediate Care; Intermediate Care for Mentally Retarded. *Beds* ICF 110; ICF/MR 40. *Certified* Medicaid.

BRIDGEPORT

Golden Years Retreat*
1st at Cates, Bridgeport, TX, 76026 (817)
683-4615
Admin Maxine Smith.
Licensure Intermediate Care. *Beds* 98. *Certified* Medicaid.
Ownership Proprietary.

BRONTE

Bronte Nursing Home
900 State St, Bronte, TX, 76933 (915) 473-3621
Admin Joy F Bagwell. *Medical Dir/Dir of Nursing* Lloyd L Downing MD.
Licensure Intermediate Care. *Beds* 40. *Certified* Medicaid.
Admissions Requirements Minimum age 18; Medical examination; Physician's request.
Staff LPNs 3 (ft), 3 (pt); Nurses aides 14 (ft), 2 (pt); Activities coordinators 1 (ft).
Facilities Dining room; Activities room; Crafts room; Laundry room; Barber/Beauty shop; Library.
Activities Arts and Crafts; Cards; Games; Reading groups; Prayer groups; Shopping trips; Dances/Social or cultural gatherings.

BROOKSHIRE

Brookshire Arms Inc
Hwy 359, Brookshire, TX, 77423 (713)
934-2224
Admin Marvin E Cole. *Medical Dir/Dir of Nursing* Gail Bernhausen MD.
Licensure Intermediate Care. *Beds* 134. *Certified* Medicaid.
Admissions Requirements Medical examination; Physician's request.
Staff RNs 2 (ft); LPNs 9 (ft); Orderlies 6 (ft); Nurses aides 28 (ft), 7 (pt); Activities coordinators 2 (ft); Dietitians 1 (ft); 27 (ft).
Facilities Dining room; Activities room; Chapel; Laundry room.
Activities Arts and Crafts; Cards; Games; Shopping trips.
Description Facility has rural location with spacious grounds.

BROWNFIELD

Brownfield Nursing Home*
510 S 1st St, Brownfield, TX, 79316 (806)
637-4307, 4626
Admin Denton O'Dell Bates.
Licensure Intermediate Care. *Beds* 54. *Certified* Medicaid.
Ownership Proprietary.

South Plains Memorial Home*
1101 E Lake St, Brownfield, TX, 79316 (806)
637-7561
Admin Julia Merrill.
Licensure Intermediate Care. *Beds* 116. *Certified* Medicaid.
Ownership Proprietary.

BROWNSVILLE

Brownsville Good Samaritan Center
510 Parades Line Rd, Brownsville, TX, 78520
(512) 546-5358
Admin Cletus M Solar. *Medical Dir/Dir of Nursing* Marcos Reis.
Licensure Skilled Care; Intermediate Care. *Beds* 112. *Certified* Medicaid.
Admissions Requirements Physician's request.
Staff RNs; LPNs; Orderlies; Nurses aides; Physical therapists; Reality therapists; Recreational therapists; Activities coordinators; Dietitians.
Facilities Dining room; Physical therapy room; Activities room; Crafts room; Laundry room; Barber/Beauty shop; Library.
Activities Arts and Crafts; Cards; Games; Prayer groups; Movies; Shopping trips; Dances/Social or cultural gatherings.
Description Home has gotten superior rating for 4 years in a row; we take care of residents body and soul.

Mother of Perpetual Help Home*
519 E Madison at 6th, Brownsville, TX, 78520
(512) 546-6745
Admin Mary P Collins.
Licensure Intermediate Care. *Beds* 37. *Certified* Medicaid.

Retama Manor Nursing Center*
1415 W Washington, Brownsville, TX, 78520
(512) 546-3711
Admin Dalona Riggs Murphy.
Licensure Intermediate Care; Intermediate Care for Mentally Retarded. *Beds* ICF 91; ICF/MR 74. *Certified* Medicaid.
Ownership Proprietary.

Valley Grande Manor Inc
901 Wild Rose Ln, Brownsville, TX, 78520
(512) 546-4568
Admin Ruben Mohan Raj Moses. *Medical Dir/Dir of Nursing* Gustavo F Stern.
Licensure Skilled Care; Intermediate Care. *Beds* SNF 67; ICF 64. *Certified* Medicaid; Medicare.
Admissions Requirements Minimum age 18; Medical examination; Physician's request.
Staff RNs 2 (ft), 4 (pt); LPNs 8 (ft), 3 (pt); Orderlies 5 (ft), 1 (pt); Nurses aides 35 (ft), 2 (pt); Activities coordinators 1 (ft); Dietitians 1 (ft).

Affiliation Seventh-Day Adventist
Facilities Dining room; Activities room; Crafts
room; Laundry room; Barber/Beauty shop;
Library.
Activities Arts and Crafts; Cards; Games; Prayer groups; Movies; Dances/Social or cultural
gatherings.
Description All residents have group therapy
sessions which are headed by licensed counselors who are volunteering their services.

BROWNWOOD

Brownwood Care Center
101 Miller Dr, Brownwood, TX, 76801 (915)
643-1596
Admin Betty F Turner.
Licensure Intermediate Care. *Beds* 130. *Certified* Medicaid.
Admissions Requirements Minimum age 18;
Medical examination; Physician's request.
Staff RNs 1 (ft); LPNs 15 (ft); Nurses aides 40
(ft), 5 (pt); Physical therapists 5 (pt); Activities
coordinators 1 (ft); Dietitians 1 (ft).
Facilities Dining room; Activities room; Chapel; Crafts room; Laundry room; Barber/Beauty
shop; TV room.
Activities Arts and Crafts; Cards; Games; Prayer groups; Movies; Shopping trips; Dances/Social or cultural gatherings; Bingo; Dominoes;
Happy hour.
Description All aides are trained in the assist-o-kinetic technique being able to transfer
patients with the least amount of handling
(bouncing technique); also use splints to avoid
patients getting into the fetal position. Facility
is located across from county hospital and most
of the doctors' offices.

Cross Country Care Center—Brownwood
1514 Indian Creek Rd, Brownwood, TX, 76801
(915) 646-6529
Admin I Douglas Streckert.
Licensure Intermediate Care. *Beds* 146. *Certified* Medicaid.
Staff RNs 1 (ft); LPNs 10 (ft); Orderlies 5 (ft);
Nurses aides 30 (ft); Activities coordinators 1
(ft).
Facilities Dining room; Activities room; Crafts
room; Laundry room; Barber/Beauty shop.
Activities Cards; Games; Prayer groups;
Movies; Shopping trips; Dances/Social or cultural gatherings.

Golden Age Nursing Home
Star Rt 3, Box 6-A, Brownwood, TX, 76801
(915) 646-5521
Admin Jerry D McGuffey. *Medical Dir/Dir of
Nursing* Dr Fred Spencer.
Licensure Skilled Care. *Beds* 63. *Certified* Medicaid.
Admissions Requirements Minimum age 16;
Medical examination; Physician's request.
Staff Physicians 1 (pt); RNs 1 (ft); LPNs 8 (ft),
4 (pt); Orderlies 1 (ft), 1 (pt); Nurses aides 22
(ft), 4 (pt); Reality therapists 1 (pt); Occupational therapists 1 (pt); Activities coordinators 1
(ft); Dietitians 1 (ft), 1 (pt).
Facilities Dining room; Physical therapy room;
Activities room; Chapel; Crafts room; Barber-/Beauty shop; Library.
Activities Arts and Crafts; Cards; Games;

Reading groups; Prayer groups; Movies; Shopping trips; Dances/Social or cultural gatherings.
Description Facility features 24-hour licensed
nursing; physicians on call; licensed dietician;
special diets; private and semi-private rooms;
smoke and fire detection-sprinkler protection;
electronic bedside voice call system; scheduled
religious services; social activities program; spacious lawn and chapel and activity area.

Plantation Nursing Home
405 W Anderson, Brownwood, TX, 76801
(915) 643-3606
Admin Patrick H McLaughlin III.
Licensure Intermediate Care. *Beds* 46. *Certified* Medicaid.
Staff LPNs 3 (ft); Nurses aides 12 (ft), 3 (pt);
Activities coordinators 1 (ft).
Facilities Dining room; Laundry room.
Activities Arts and Crafts; Cards; Games;
Movies; Dances/Social or cultural gatherings.
Description Facility features big screen television; oil painting classes by a professional;
located in town across from a grocery store and
Montgomery Wards; home-style atmosphere
and cooking.

South Park Development Center
Morris-Sheppard Dr, Brownwood, TX, 76801
(915) 646-9531
Admin Ann Daniel.
Licensure Intermediate Care for Mentally
Retarded. *Beds* 108. *Certified* Medicaid.
Admissions Requirements Minimum age 18.
Staff RNs 1 (ft); LPNs 5 (ft); Orderlies 25 (ft);
Physical therapists 1 (pt); Reality therapists 1
(ft); Recreational therapists 1 (ft); Occupational
therapists 1 (pt); Speech therapists 1 (pt);
Activities coordinators 1 (ft); Dietitians 1 (pt);
Dentists 1 (pt); Ophthalmologists 1 (pt); Podiatrists 1 (pt); Audiologists 1 (pt).
Facilities Dining room; Physical therapy room;
Activities room; Crafts room; Laundry room.
Activities Arts and Crafts; Cards; Games;
Reading groups; Movies; Shopping trips; Dances/Social or cultural gatherings.

BRYAN

Crestview Retirement Community
2501 Villa Maria Rd, Bryan, TX, 77801 (409)
775-4778
Admin Robert J Boening.
Licensure Intermediate Care; Custodial Care.
Beds ICF 21; Custodial Care 36. *Certified* Medicaid.
Admissions Requirements Minimum age 62;
Medical examination; Physician's request.
Staff RNs 1 (ft), 1 (pt); LPNs 5 (ft), 4 (pt);
Nurses aides 6 (ft), 6 (pt); Activities coordinators 1 (ft), 1 (pt); Dietitians 1 (pt).
Affiliation Methodist
Facilities Dining room; Activities room; Chapel; Crafts room; Laundry room; Barber/Beauty
shop; Library.
Activities Arts and Crafts; Games; Reading
groups; Prayer groups; Movies; Shopping trips;
Dances/Social or cultural gatherings.

Leisure Lodge Bryan
2001 E 29th St, Bryan, TX, 77801 (713)
822-7361

Admin Loretta Henk.
Licensure Intermediate Care. *Beds* 150. *Certified* Medicaid.
Facilities Dining room; Physical therapy room;
Laundry room; Barber/Beauty shop.
Activities Arts and Crafts; Cards; Games;
Reading groups; Prayer groups; Shopping trips;
Dances/Social or cultural gatherings.

Sherwood Health Care Inc
1401 Memorial Dr, Bryan, TX, 77801 (409)
823-7521
Admin Edwin P Sulik. *Medical Dir/Dir of
Nursing* Harry Lipscomb MD.
Licensure Skilled Care; Intermediate Care.
Beds 246. *Certified* Medicaid; Medicare.
Staff RNs 5 (pt); LPNs 24 (pt); Nurses aides 78
(pt); Physical therapists 1 (pt); Activities coordinators 1 (pt); Dietitians 1 (ft); Dentists 1 (ft).
Facilities Dining room; Physical therapy room;
Chapel; Barber/Beauty shop.
Activities Arts and Crafts; Games; Prayer
groups; Movies; Shopping trips.
Description Facility features a physical therapy
department.

BUFFALO

Buffalo Nursing Center*
Pearlstone St at Hospital Dr, Buffalo, TX,
75831 (214) 322-4208
Admin Pauline Bulen.
Licensure Intermediate Care. *Beds* 60. *Certified* Medicaid.
Ownership Proprietary.

BUNA

Buna Nursing Home*
PO Drawer H, Hwy 96 N, Buna, TX, 77612
(713) 994-3576
Admin Wayne Daniel Butchee.
Licensure Intermediate Care. *Beds* 62. *Certified* Medicaid.
Ownership Nonprofit.

BURKBURNETT

Evergreen Care Center*
406 E 7th, Burkburnett, TX, 76354 (817)
569-2236
Admin Susie M Brown.
Licensure Intermediate Care. *Beds* 60. *Certified* Medicaid.
Ownership Proprietary.

Hickory Elm Convalescent Center*
800 Red River Expwy, Burkburnett, TX,
76354 (817) 569-1466
Admin Gail Mary Newcombe.
Licensure Intermediate Care. *Beds* 74. *Certified* Medicaid.
Ownership Proprietary.

BURLESON

Burleson Nursing Home*
144 SW Thomas St, Burleson, TX, 76028 (817)
295-2271
Admin Dorothy Hanuschak.

Licensure Skilled Care; Intermediate Care.
Beds 126. *Certified* Medicaid.
Ownership Proprietary.

Silver Haven Care Center*
600 Maple, Burleson, TX, 76028 (817)
295-8118
Admin Richard L Nelson.
Licensure Intermediate Care. *Beds* 120. *Certified* Medicaid.
Ownership Nonprofit.

BURNET

Oaks Nursing Home
507 W Jackson, Burnet, TX, 78611 (512)
756-6044
Admin Judy Edgar Allen. *Medical Dir/Dir of Nursing* Billy B Ozier MD.
Licensure Intermediate Care. *Beds* 92. *Certified* Medicaid.
Ownership Nonprofit.
Staff RNs 1 (ft); LPNs 5 (ft); Nurses aides 32
(ft), 3 (pt); Activities coordinators 1 (ft); Dietitians 1 (pt).
Facilities Dining room; Activities room; Laundry room; Barber/Beauty shop.
Activities Cards; Games; Prayer groups;
Movies; Shopping trips.

CALDWELL

Leisure Lodge—Caldwell
701 N Broadway, Caldwell, TX, 77836 (713)
567-3237
Admin Lavern Balcar.
Licensure Intermediate Care. *Beds* 156. *Certified* Medicaid.
Admissions Requirements Minimum age 16;
Medical examination; Physician's request.
Staff RNs 1 (ft); LPNs 9 (ft); Nurses aides 70
(ft), 6 (pt); Activities coordinators 1 (ft), 1 (pt).
Facilities Dining room; Physical therapy room;
Activities room; Chapel; Crafts room; Laundry
room; Barber/Beauty shop; Library.
Activities Arts and Crafts; Games; Reading
groups; Prayer groups; Shopping trips; Dances-
/Social or cultural gatherings; Family council;
Resident council.
Description Facility has a 4-year superior
rating.

CALVERT

Calvert Nursing Center
701 Browning, Calvert, TX, 77837 (713)
364-2391
Admin Audrey G Williamson.
Licensure Intermediate Care. *Beds* 32. *Certified* Medicaid.
Ownership Proprietary.
Admissions Requirements Minimum age 21.
Staff Physicians 1 (pt); RNs 1 (pt); LPNs 3 (ft),
1 (pt); Nurses aides 9 (ft), 2 (pt); Activities coordinators 1 (ft); Dietitians 1 (pt).
Facilities Dining room; Activities room; Laundry room; Barber/Beauty shop.
Activities Arts and Crafts; Cards; Games;
Reading groups; Prayer groups; Movies; Dances/Social or cultural gatherings.

Description Facility is located in a quiet
country setting among oak trees; family atmosphere; small home with lots of love and it
shows; excellent care given by all departments.

CAMERON

Cameron Nursing Home*
PO Box 831, 700 E 11th St, Cameron, TX,
76520 (817) 697-6564
Admin Donna Sue Stephenson.
Licensure Intermediate Care. *Beds* 43. *Certified* Medicaid.
Ownership Proprietary.

Colonial Nursing Home*
PO Box 831, 1002 E 10th St, Cameron, TX,
76520 (817) 697-6578
Admin Claudia Cox.
Licensure Intermediate Care. *Beds* 84. *Certified* Medicaid.
Ownership Proprietary.

CANADIAN

Edward Abraham Memorial Home
803 Birch, Canadian, TX, 79014 (806)
323-6453
Admin Sue Flanagan Collier.
Licensure Intermediate Care. *Beds* 59. *Certified* Medicaid.
Facilities Dining room; Activities room; Chapel; Laundry room; Barber/Beauty shop.
Activities Arts and Crafts; Cards; Games;
Reading groups; Prayer groups; Movies; Shopping trips; Dances/Social or cultural gatherings.
Description Home is community sponsored.

CANTON

Canton Nursing Center*
1661 S Buffalo St, Canton, TX, 75103 (214)
567-4135
Admin Barbara Jeanine Rutherford.
Licensure Intermediate Care. *Beds* 66. *Certified* Medicaid.
Ownership Proprietary.

Canton Residential Center
1755 Elliott St, Canton, TX, 75103 (214)
567-2901
Admin Debbie Davenport.
Licensure Intermediate Care. *Beds* 42. *Certified* Medicaid.

Heritage Manor*
901 W College St, Canton, TX, 75103 (214)
567-4169
Admin Curtis D Bjornlie.
Licensure Intermediate Care. *Beds* 110. *Certified* Medicaid.
Ownership Proprietary.

CANYON

La Casa Canyon Nursing Home
2623 12th Ave, Canyon, TX, 79015 (806)
655-4352
Admin Mike Mayo.
Licensure Intermediate Care. *Beds* 36. *Certified* Medicaid.

Admissions Requirements Medical
examination.
Staff RNs 1 (pt); LPNs 4 (ft), 1 (pt); Orderlies 1
(ft); Nurses aides 7 (ft), 5 (pt); Activities coordinators 1 (ft); Dietitians 1 (pt).
Facilities Dining room; Activities room; Crafts
room; Barber/Beauty shop.
Activities Arts and Crafts; Cards; Games;
Reading groups; Prayer groups; Shopping trips;
Dances/Social or cultural gatherings.
Description Excellent volunteer programs and
community involvement support this nursing
home.

CARRIZO SPRINGS

Carrizo Springs Nursing Home Inc*
8th and Clark Sts, Carrizo Springs, TX, 78834
(512) 876-5090, 2320
Admin Margaret Terrell.
Licensure Skilled Care; Intermediate Care; Personal Care. *Beds* ICF 100; Personal Care 24.
Certified Medicaid.
Ownership Proprietary.

CARROLLTON

Carrollton Manor*
1618 Kirby, Carrollton, TX, 75006 (214)
245-1573
Admin Sybil Perrin.
Licensure Intermediate Care. *Beds* 120. *Certified* Medicaid.
Ownership Proprietary.

Northwood Manor Nursing Home*
2135 Denton Dr, Carrollton, TX, 75006 (214)
242-0666
Admin Charles William Hames.
Licensure Intermediate Care. *Beds* 150. *Certified* Medicaid.
Ownership Proprietary.

CARTHAGE

Leisure Lodge—Carthage
701 S Market, Carthage, TX, 75633 (214)
693-6671
Admin Tommie Hight.
Licensure Intermediate Care. *Beds* 96. *Certified* Medicaid.
Staff RNs 1 (ft); LPNs 5 (ft), 4 (pt); Nurses
aides 20 (ft), 4 (pt); Activities coordinators 1
(ft).
Facilities Dining room; Activities room; Chapel; Crafts room; Laundry room; Barber/Beauty
shop.
Activities Arts and Crafts; Cards; Games;
Reading groups; Prayer groups; Movies; Shopping trips; Dances/Social or cultural gatherings.

Panola Nursing Home*
501 Cottage Rd, Carthage, TX, 75633 (214)
693-7141
Admin Janet S Chamness.
Licensure Skilled Care; Intermediate Care.
Beds 108. *Certified* Medicaid.
Ownership Nonprofit.

CEDAR HILL

Cedar Hill-Duncanville Nursing Center*
303 S Clark Rd, Cedar Hill, TX, 75104 (214)
291-7176
Admin Eva F Myrick.
Licensure Intermediate Care. *Beds* 120. *Certified* Medicaid.
Ownership Proprietary.

CELINA

Celina Nursing Center Inc
S 2nd St, Celina, TX, 75009 (214) 382-2356
Admin Jeanie Knickerbocker. *Medical Dir/Dir of Nursing* Glen Mitchell MD.
Licensure Intermediate Care. *Beds* 88. *Certified* Medicaid.
Admissions Requirements Medical examination; Physician's request.
Staff RNs 1 (ft); LPNs 5 (ft); Nurses aides 35 (ft); Activities coordinators 1 (ft); Dietitians 1 (ft).
Facilities Dining room; Activities room; Chapel; Crafts room; Barber/Beauty shop; Library.
Activities Arts and Crafts; Cards; Games; Reading groups; Prayer groups; Shopping trips; Dances/Social or cultural gatherings.
Description Facility features a nice, quiet small-town atmosphere, excellent volunteer program, and community involvement.

CENTER

Green Acres Convalescent Center
501 Timpson, Center, TX, 75935 (409)
598-2483
Admin Evelyn R Russell.
Licensure Intermediate Care. *Beds* 102. *Certified* Medicaid.
Admissions Requirements Medical examination; Physician's request.
Staff RNs 1 (ft); LPNs 8 (ft); Orderlies 1 (ft); Nurses aides 27 (ft); Physical therapists 1 (ft); Activities coordinators 1 (ft); Podiatrists 1 (pt).
Facilities Dining room; Activities room; Chapel; Crafts room; Laundry room; Barber/Beauty shop.
Activities Arts and Crafts; Cards; Games; Reading groups; Prayer groups; Movies.

Holiday Nursing Home*
100 Holiday Circle, Center, TX, 75935 (713)
598-3371
Admin Gayla Adams.
Licensure Skilled Care; Intermediate Care.
Beds 137. *Certified* Medicaid.
Ownership Proprietary.

CENTERVILLE

Leisure Lodge—Centerville*
103 Teakwood Center, Centerville, TX, 75833
(214) 536-2596
Admin Beth J Rodell.
Licensure Intermediate Care. *Beds* 102. *Certified* Medicaid.
Ownership Proprietary.

CHILDRESS

Childress Nursing Center
1200 7th St NW, Childress, TX, 79201 (817)
937-8668
Admin Shirley Southard.
Licensure Intermediate Care; Personal Care.
Beds ICF 110; Personal Care 10. *Certified* Medicaid.
Admissions Requirements Medical examination; Physician's request.
Staff LPNs 8 (ft); Orderlies 3 (ft); Nurses aides 12 (ft); Activities coordinators 1 (ft); Dietitians 1 (ft).
Facilities Dining room; Activities room; Laundry room; Barber/Beauty shop.
Activities Arts and Crafts; Cards; Games; Reading groups; Prayer groups; Movies; Shopping trips; Dances/Social or cultural gatherings.
Description Bright, cheery building with a loving, caring staff. We have a down to earth atmosphere. Everyone is happy with a home setting.

Turner Nursing Home
1610 Ave G NW, Childress, TX, 79201 (817)
937-3675
Admin Linda Bohannon.
Licensure Intermediate Care. *Beds* 60. *Certified* Medicaid.
Admissions Requirements Medical examination; Physician's request.
Staff RNs 2 (pt); LPNs 5 (ft); Nurses aides 18 (ft), 2 (pt); Physical therapists 2 (pt); Speech therapists 1 (pt); Activities coordinators 1 (ft); Dietitians 1 (pt); Dentists 1 (pt); Ophthalmologists 1 (pt).
Facilities Dining room; Activities room; Laundry room; Barber/Beauty shop; Library.
Activities Arts and Crafts; Cards; Games; Prayer groups; Movies; Shopping trips; Dances/Social or cultural gatherings.
Description Nursing facility strives for the best in patient care; maintains a clean, home-like atmosphere for residents. Also takes pride in the fact that many residents recover and are now back in their homes.

CHILLICOTHE

Iris Haven Nursing and Convalescent Center*
PO Drawer 667, 209 Ave I, Chillicothe, TX,
79225 (817) 852-5151
Admin Helen W Holt.
Licensure Intermediate Care. *Beds* 46. *Certified* Medicaid.
Ownership Proprietary.

CHRISTOVAL

Christoval Golden Years Nursing Home
116 McKee St, Christoval, TX, 76935 (915)
896-2391
Admin Gilberto Aguirre.
Licensure Intermediate Care; Custodial Care.
Beds ICF 45; Custodial Care 14. *Certified* Medicaid.

Christoval Golden Years Nursing Home Inc
116 McKee St, PO Box 45, Christoval, TX,
76935

Admin June Pettitt. *Medical Dir/Dir of Nursing* Louise Thomerson.
Licensure Intermediate Care. *Certified* Medicaid; Medicare.
Ownership Proprietary.
Staff Physicians 1 (pt); RNs 1 (ft); LPNs 5 (ft); Orderlies 1 (ft); Nurses aides 8 (ft), 6 (pt); Activities coordinators 1 (ft); Dietitians 1 (pt).
Facilities Dining room; Activities room; Laundry room.
Activities Arts and Crafts; Cards; Games; Reading groups.

CISCO

Cisco Nursing Center
1404 Front St, Cisco, TX, 76437 (817)
442-1471
Admin Forrest S Tatum.
Licensure Intermediate Care. *Beds* 106. *Certified* Medicaid.
Admissions Requirements Physician's request.
Staff Activities coordinators 1 (ft).
Facilities Dining room; Physical therapy room; Activities room; Laundry room; Barber/Beauty shop.
Activities Arts and Crafts; Games; Prayer groups; Shopping trips; Dances/Social or cultural gatherings.
Description Arts and crafts program features an activity (a type of crewel work with plastic) that has been very beneficial to the arthritic fingers of some of the patients.

CLARENDON

Medical Center Nursing Home
Hwy 70 N, Clarendon, TX, 79226 (806)
874-3760
Admin Billy R Johnston.
Licensure Intermediate Care. *Beds* 43. *Certified* Medicaid.
Admissions Requirements Medical examination.
Staff Physicians 2 (ft); RNs 2 (ft); LPNs 1 (ft); Orderlies 2 (ft); Nurses aides 40 (ft); Physical therapists 1 (pt); Reality therapists 1 (ft); Recreational therapists 1 (ft); Occupational therapists 1 (pt); Speech therapists 1 (pt); Activities coordinators 1 (ft); Dietitians 3 (ft); Dentists 1 (pt); Ophthalmologists 1 (pt); LVNs 15 (ft).
Facilities Dining room; Physical therapy room; Activities room; Crafts room; Laundry room; Barber/Beauty shop.
Activities Arts and Crafts; Cards; Games; Reading groups; Prayer groups; Movies; Shopping trips.
Description Facility located in a farming-ranching area, rated superior by the Texas Health Department, giving superior care to residents.

CLARKSVILLE

Clarksville Nursing Center
300 E Baker St, Clarksville, TX, 75426 (214)
427-2236
Admin Edna Nelson. *Medical Dir/Dir of Nursing* Dr B C Muthappa.
Licensure Intermediate Care. *Beds* 132. *Certified* Medicaid.

Staff RNs 1 (ft); LPNs 10 (ft), 2 (pt); Nurses aides 35 (ft); Physical therapists 1 (pt); Activities coordinators 1 (ft); Dietitians 1 (pt).
Facilities Dining room; Chapel; Laundry room; Barber/Beauty shop.
Activities Arts and Crafts; Games; Reading groups; Prayer groups; Movies; Shopping trips; Dances/Social or cultural gatherings.

CLAUDE

Palo Duro Convalescent Home Inc
405 S Collins St, Claude, TX, 79019 (806) 226-2201
Admin Sharon K Kelley. *Medical Dir/Dir of Nursing* Herbert T Smith MD.
Licensure Skilled Care. *Beds* 54. *Certified* Medicaid.
Admissions Requirements Minimum age 21.
Staff RNs 2 (ft), 1 (pt); LPNs 7 (ft), 2 (pt); Orderlies 1 (ft); Nurses aides 19 (ft), 2 (pt); Activities coordinators 1 (ft); Dietitians 1 (pt); Dentists 1 (pt).
Facilities Dining room; Activities room; Crafts room; Laundry room; Barber/Beauty shop.
Activities Arts and Crafts; Cards; Games; Reading groups; Prayer groups.
Description Facility has an ongoing pet therapy program through the Loving Paws program, recognized by the Texas Department of Health as an extremely useful tool for reaching withdrawn and confused patients.

CLEBURNE

Colonial Manor Nursing and Convalescent Center*
2035 N Granbury St, Cleburne, TX, 76031 (817) 645-9134, 477-3009
Admin Harold D Werning.
Licensure Skilled Care; Intermediate Care.
Beds 150. *Certified* Medicaid.
Ownership Proprietary.

Golden Age Nursing Home Inc*
1102 Williams Ave, Cleburne, TX, 76031 (817) 645-8049
Admin Wanda Dean.
Licensure Intermediate Care. *Beds* 102. *Certified* Medicaid.
Ownership Proprietary.

Leisure Lodge—Cleburne*
PO Box 138, 1108 W Kilpatrick St, Cleburne, TX, 76031 (817) 645-3931
Admin Donna Poteet.
Licensure Intermediate Care. *Beds* 120. *Certified* Medicaid.
Ownership Proprietary.

CLEVELAND

Galaxy Manor Nursing Home
903 E Houston, Cleveland, TX, 77327 (713) 592-8775
Admin Ann Yeager.
Licensure Intermediate Care. *Beds* 160. *Certified* Medicaid.

CLIFTON

Clifton Lutheran Sunset Home
College Hill, Clifton, TX, 76634 (817) 675-8637
Admin Elmer F Luckenbach. *Medical Dir/Dir of Nursing* Dr D A Gloff.
Licensure Skilled Care; Intermediate Care.
Beds 180. *Certified* Medicaid.
Admissions Requirements Medical examination; Physician's request.
Staff RNs 3 (ft); LPNs 11 (ft); Nurses aides 66 (ft); Physical therapists 1 (pt); Activities coordinators 1 (ft), 2 (pt); Dietitians 1 (pt).
Affiliation Lutheran
Facilities Dining room; Physical therapy room; Activities room; Chapel; Laundry room; Barber/Beauty shop; Library.
Activities Arts and Crafts; Games; Reading groups; Prayer groups; Movies; Shopping trips; Dances/Social or cultural gatherings.

CLUTE

Sunset Nursing Home*
914 N Hwy 288, Clute, TX, 77531 (713) 265-4794
Admin Glenna L Morlan.
Licensure Intermediate Care. *Beds* 120. *Certified* Medicaid.
Ownership Proprietary.

Wood Lake Nursing Home*
603 E Plantation Rd, Clute, TX, 77531 (713) 265-4221
Admin Polly Hedrick.
Licensure Intermediate Care. *Beds* 98. *Certified* Medicaid.
Ownership Proprietary.

CLYDE

Leisure Lodge—Clyde*
Rt 3, Box 148, Old Hwy 80, Clyde, TX, 79510 (915) 893-4288
Admin Glenn R Gray.
Licensure Intermediate Care. *Beds* 48. *Certified* Medicaid.
Ownership Proprietary.

COLEMAN

Coleman Care Center
FM 53, Box 392, Coleman, TX, 76834 (915) 625-4157
Admin Novella I Gilbreath.
Licensure Intermediate Care. *Beds* 74. *Certified* Medicaid.
Admissions Requirements Physician's request.
Staff RNs 1 (pt); LPNs 10 (ft); Nurses aides 26 (ft), 11 (pt); Activities coordinators 1 (ft); Dietitians 1 (pt).
Facilities Dining room; Activities room; Chapel; Crafts room; Laundry room; Barber/Beauty shop.
Activities Arts and Crafts; Games; Prayer groups.
Description Facility features a western band and singing 2 times a week, Wednesday night worship, and morning and afternoon worship

service on Sundays. Forty-two games with high-rise Bingo twice a week, crafts, and travel van for excursions.

Leisure Lodge—Coleman*
PO Box 853, 2713 Commercial Ave, Coleman, TX, 76834 (915) 625-4105
Admin Jimmie Don Simpson.
Licensure Intermediate Care. *Beds* 64. *Certified* Medicaid.
Ownership Proprietary.

COLLEGE STATION

Brazos Valley Geriatric Center
1115 Anderson, College Station, TX, 77840 (713) 693-1515
Admin Freddie M White. *Medical Dir/Dir of Nursing* Sally Perez LVN.
Licensure Intermediate Care. *Beds* 150. *Certified* Medicaid.
Admissions Requirements Medical examination; Physician's request.
Staff LPNs 7 (ft), 3 (pt); Orderlies 1 (ft); Nurses aides 16 (ft), 2 (pt); Activities coordinators 1 (ft); Dietitians 1 (ft).
Facilities Dining room; Physical therapy room; Activities room; Crafts room; Laundry room; Barber/Beauty shop.
Activities Arts and Crafts; Cards; Games; Shopping trips; Dances/Social or cultural gatherings; Birthday parties; Church; Singing.
Description Facility has an outstanding volunteer program with many active and well qualified volunteers; receives support from Texas A&M University professors and student organizations. Residents always have something to do.

COLLINSVILLE

Collinsville Care Home Inc
400 Main St, Collinsville, TX, 76233 (214) 429-6426
Admin Anita Murphree. *Medical Dir/Dir of Nursing* John Galewaler DO.
Licensure Intermediate Care. *Beds* 88. *Certified* Medicaid.
Admissions Requirements Medical examination; Physician's request.
Staff RNs 1 (ft); LPNs 5 (ft); Nurses aides 20 (ft), 6 (pt); Activities coordinators 1 (ft); Dietitians 1 (ft).
Facilities Dining room; Activities room; Chapel; Crafts room; Laundry room; Barber/Beauty shop.
Activities Arts and Crafts; Games; Prayer groups; Movies; Shopping trips; Dances/Social or cultural gatherings; Picnics; Olympics.

COLORADO CITY

Kristi Lee Manor Inc*
1941 Chestnut St, Colorado City, TX, 79512 (915) 728-5247
Admin Chester C Moody.
Licensure Intermediate Care. *Beds* 118. *Certified* Medicaid.
Ownership Proprietary.

Root Valley Fair Lodge
1541 Chestnut, Colorado City, TX, 79512 (915)
728-2634
Admin Marsha Rickard. *Medical Dir/Dir of
Nursing* Dr Thomas Aquillion.
Licensure Intermediate Care. *Beds* 50. *Certified* Medicaid.
Admissions Requirements Medical examination; Physician's request.
Staff Physicians 1 (pt); RNs 1 (pt); LPNs 12
(ft); Nurses aides 17 (ft), 4 (pt); Physical therapists 1 (pt); Activities coordinators 1 (ft);
Dietitians 2 (ft).
Facilities Dining room; Physical therapy room;
Activities room; Laundry room; Barber/Beauty
shop.
Activities Arts and Crafts; Games; Reading
groups; Prayer groups; Movies; Shopping trips;
Dances/Social or cultural gatherings.

COLUMBUS

Columbus Convalescent Center
300 N St, Columbus, TX, 78934 (713)
732-2347
Admin Robert E Gay III. *Medical Dir/Dir of
Nursing* R Cecil Marburger MD.
Licensure Intermediate Care. *Beds* 90. *Certified* Medicaid.
Admissions Requirements Medical examination.
Staff Activities coordinators 1 (ft).
Facilities Dining room; Activities room;
Laundry room; Barber/Beauty shop; Library.
Activities Cards; Games; Reading groups; Prayer groups; Movies; Shopping trips;
Dances/Social or cultural gatherings.
Description Facility is located in a small town;
a rural facility on the Colorado River with
beautiful large oaks and pasture land. Facility is
clean and rated superior.

Sweetbriar Nursing Home
103 Sweetbriar Ln, Columbus, TX, 78934
(713) 732-5716
Admin Joyce Brokmeyer. *Medical Dir/Dir of
Nursing* R Cecil Marburger MD.
Licensure Intermediate Care. *Beds* 150. *Certified* Medicaid.
Admissions Requirements Physician's request.
Staff LPNs 6 (ft); Nurses aides 18 (ft); Activities coordinators
Facilities Dining room; Activities room;
Laundry room; Barber/Beauty shop.
Activities Arts and Crafts; Cards; Games;
Reading groups; Prayer groups; Movies; Shopping trips; Dances/Social or cultural gatherings.
Description Facility has superior rating.

COMANCHE

Western Hills Nursing Home
Rt 5, Box 26, Comanche, TX, 76442 (915)
356-2571
Admin Bobbie Nichols.
Licensure Skilled Care; Intermediate Care.
Beds 166. *Certified* Medicaid.
Staff RNs 1 (ft); Physical therapists 1 (pt).
Facilities Dining room; Physical therapy room;
Activities room; Crafts room; Laundry room;
Barber/Beauty shop.

Activities Arts and Crafts; Cards; Games;
Reading groups; Prayer groups; Shopping trips.

COMMERCE

Care Inn of Commerce*
2901 Sterling Hart Dr, Commerce, TX, 75428
(214) 886-2510
Admin Shelby Weatherbee.
Licensure Intermediate Care. *Beds* 116. *Certified* Medicaid.
Ownership Proprietary.

Heart Manor
2902 Sterling Hart Dr, Commerce, TX, 75428
(214) 886-2839
Admin Barbara S Kersey.
Beds 112.
Ownership Proprietary.
Staff LPNs 3 (ft); Nurses aides 3 (ft), 1 (pt);
Activities coordinators 1 (pt); Dietitians 1 (ft).
Facilities Dining room; Activities room; Chapel; Crafts room; Laundry room; Barber/Beauty
shop.
Activities Arts and Crafts; Cards; Games; Prayer groups; Shopping trips.
Description Facility accepts residents who are
ambulatory and can care for their own basic
needs; wheelchairs and walkers are acceptable if
residents can move themselves.

CONROE

Autumn Hills Convalescent Center—Conroe*
2019 N Frazier, Conroe, TX, 77301 (713)
756-5535
Admin Faye D Thompson.
Licensure Intermediate Care. *Beds* 108. *Certified* Medicaid.
Ownership Proprietary.

Care Inn of Conroe Inc
99 Rigby Owen Rd, Conroe, TX, 77301 (713)
539-1701
Admin Charles T Smith.
Licensure Intermediate Care. *Beds* 150. *Certified* Medicaid.
Admissions Requirements Medical examination.
Staff RNs; LPNs; Orderlies; Nurses aides;
Physical therapists; Speech therapists; Activities
coordinators; Dietitians; Podiatrists.
Facilities Dining room; Activities room; Crafts
room; Laundry room; Barber/Beauty shop;
Library.
Activities Arts and Crafts; Cards; Games; Prayer groups; Movies; Shopping trips; Dances/Social or cultural gatherings.
Description Facility is located directly behind
Doctor's Hospital and is convenient to nearby
shopping centers.

COOPER

Birchwood Manor Nursing Home
Hwy 64 W, Cooper, TX, 75432 (214) 395-2125
Admin Delma Wintermute.
Licensure Intermediate Care. *Beds* 100. *Certified* Medicaid.

Delta Nursing Home
101 SE 8th St, Cooper, TX, 75432 (214)
395-2184
Admin Shelby J Weatherbee.
Licensure Intermediate Care; Personal Care.
Beds ICF 38; Personal Care 24. *Certified* Medicaid.
Admissions Requirements Medical examination; Physician's request.
Staff LPNs 2 (ft), 2 (pt); Nurses aides 9 (ft);
Activities coordinators 1 (ft), 1 (pt).
Facilities Dining room; Laundry room; Barber-
/Beauty shop.
Activities Arts and Crafts; Games; Reading
groups; Prayer groups; Dances/Social or cultural gatherings.
Description In addition to 38-bed ICF section,
there are 24 beds in personal care wing that are
available for ambulatory self-help persons. This
setting is ideal for those who cannot prepare
their meals or do routine housekeeping anymore, but do not require nursing home care.

COPPERAS COVE

Wind Crest Nursing Center Inc
607 W Ave B, Copperas Cove, TX, 76522 (817)
547-1033
Admin Lou Ann Cross. *Medical Dir/Dir of
Nursing* Dr Franklin House.
Licensure Intermediate Care. *Beds* 120. *Certified* Medicaid.
Staff Physicians 1 (pt); RNs 1 (ft); LPNs 9 (ft);
Nurses aides 33 (ft); Physical therapists 1 (pt);
Activities coordinators 1 (ft); Dietitians 1 (pt);
Dentists 1 (pt).
Facilities Dining room; Physical therapy room;
Activities room; Crafts room; Laundry room;
Barber/Beauty shop.
Activities Arts and Crafts; Cards; Games;
Reading groups; Prayer groups; Movies; Shopping trips; Dances/Social or cultural gatherings.

CORPUS CHRISTI

Corpus Christi Nursing Center*
5607 Everhart Rd, Corpus Christi, TX, 78411
(512) 854-4601
Admin Ann Thomas.
Licensure Intermediate Care. *Beds* 204. *Certified* Medicaid.
Ownership Proprietary.

The Hearth*
1125 S 19th St, Corpus Christi, TX, 78405
(512) 884-5522
Admin Betty Fleet Carcamo.
Licensure Skilled Care; Intermediate Care.
Beds 107. *Certified* Medicaid.
Ownership Public.

Hillhaven Convalescent Center
1314 3rd St, Corpus Christi, TX, 78404 (512)
888-5511
Admin Jerry E Bell. *Medical Dir/Dir of
Nursing* Dr B B Grossman.
Licensure Skilled Care; Intermediate Care.
Beds 174. *Certified* Medicaid; Medicare.
Admissions Requirements Physician's request.
Staff Physicians 1 (ft); RNs 4 (ft); LPNs 25 (ft);
Orderlies 2 (ft); Nurses aides 60 (ft); Physical

therapists 1 (ft); Recreational therapists 1 (ft); Occupational therapists 1 (pt); Speech therapists 1 (pt); Activities coordinators 1 (ft); Dietitians 1 (ft).
Facilities Dining room; Physical therapy room; Activities room; Laundry room; Barber/Beauty shop; Library; Country store.
Activities Arts and Crafts; Cards; Games; Prayer groups; Movies; Shopping trips; Dances/Social or cultural gatherings; Happy hours; Religious services; Bowling.
Description Facility is located one block off Ocean Drive with view of Corpus Christi Bay; offers excellent reality orientation, physical therapy for rehabilitation, and extended care programs.

Human Development Center
3031 McArdle Rd, Corpus Christi, TX, 78415 (512) 854-1458
Admin Lillie O Bryant. *Medical Dir/Dir of Nursing* Dr Antonio Hernandez.
Licensure Intermediate Care for Mentally Retarded. *Beds* 100. *Certified* Medicaid.
Admissions Requirements Medical examination.
Staff RNs 2 (ft); LPNs 9 (ft); Orderlies 2 (ft); Nurses aides 39 (ft), 11 (pt); Activities coordinators 1 (ft).
Facilities Dining room; Physical therapy room; Activities room; Crafts room.
Description This facility houses only the severly/profoundly mentally retarded; nonambulatory clients ages 1-16 years.

Lynnhaven Nursing Home Inc*
3030 Fig St, Corpus Christi, TX, 78404 (512) 882-1948
Admin Johnnie D Humiston.
Licensure Intermediate Care. *Beds* 180. *Certified* Medicaid.
Ownership Proprietary.

Retama Manor Nursing Center—North*
2322 Morgan Ave, Corpus Christi, TX, 78405 (512) 882-4242
Admin Lillie O Bryant.
Licensure Skilled Care; Intermediate Care.
Beds 180. *Certified* Medicaid.
Ownership Proprietary.

Retama Manor Nursing Center—West*
4130 Santa Elena, Corpus Christi, TX, 78405 (512) 882-3655
Admin Nancy Reihenau.
Licensure Intermediate Care. *Beds* 106. *Certified* Medicaid.
Ownership Proprietary.

Retirement and Nursing Center*
3050 Sunnybrook, Corpus Christi, TX, 78415 (512) 853-9981
Admin Richard Stebbins.
Licensure Skilled Care; Intermediate Care.
Beds 178. *Certified* Medicaid.
Ownership Proprietary.

South Park Manor*
3115 McArdle, Corpus Christi, TX, 78415 (512) 853-2577
Admin F E Deere.

Licensure Intermediate Care. *Beds* 194. *Certified* Medicaid.
Ownership Proprietary.

Westwood Manor
801 Cantwell, Corpus Christi, TX, 78408 (512) 882-4284
Admin Mary Braly.
Licensure Intermediate Care. *Beds* 60. *Certified* Medicaid.
Admissions Requirements Minimum age 18; Medical examination; Physician's request.
Staff Physicians 1 (ft); RNs 1 (ft); LPNs 5 (ft); Nurses aides 10 (ft), 9 (pt); Physical therapists; Occupational therapists; Speech therapists; Activities coordinators 1 (ft); Dietitians 1 (ft); Podiatrists.
Facilities Dining room; Activities room; Chapel; Crafts room; Laundry room; Barber/Beauty shop.
Activities Arts and Crafts; Cards; Games; Prayer groups; Movies; Shopping trips; Dances/Social or cultural gatherings; Monthly birthday parties; Cooking class.
Description Facility is a one-story cartwheel structure with centralized nurses' station located in the rotunda, each nursing care unit is visable from the nurses' station.

CORSICANA

Corsicana Nursing Home Inc
1500 N 45th, Corsicana, TX, 75110 (214) 872-4606
Admin Bassel E Bolton Jr. *Medical Dir/Dir of Nursing* Dr J H Barnebee.
Licensure Skilled Care; Intermediate Care.
Beds 120. *Certified* Medicaid.
Admissions Requirements Minimum age 18.
Staff Physicians 1 (pt); RNs 1 (ft), 3 (pt); LPNs 7 (ft), 5 (pt); Nurses aides 21 (ft), 8 (pt); Physical therapists 2 (pt); Activities coordinators 1 (ft); Dietitians 1 (ft); Medical aides 5 (ft), 2 (pt).
Facilities Dining room; Activities room; Laundry room; Barber/Beauty shop.
Activities Arts and Crafts; Cards; Games; Prayer groups.

Leisure Lodge—Corsicana*
3301 Park Row, Corsicana, TX, 75110 (214) 872-2455
Admin Alla Mae Capps.
Licensure Intermediate Care. *Beds* 102. *Certified* Medicaid.
Ownership Proprietary.

Mel-Haven Convalescent Home
901 E 16th Ave, Corsicana, TX, 75110 (214) 874-7454
Admin Mildred J Jennings. *Medical Dir/Dir of Nursing* Dr J H Barnebee.
Licensure Skilled Care; Intermediate Care.
Beds 106. *Certified* Medicaid.
Admissions Requirements Minimum age 18; Medical examination; Physician's request.
Staff Physicians 1 (pt); RNs 2 (ft), 1 (pt); LPNs 7 (ft); Nurses aides 23 (ft), 4 (pt); Activities coordinators 1 (ft); Dietitians 1 (pt).
Facilities Dining room; Physical therapy room; Activities room; Crafts room; Laundry room; Barber/Beauty shop.

Activities Arts and Crafts; Cards; Games; Prayer groups; Shopping trips; Dances/Social or cultural gatherings.
Description The facility is light and airy.

Northside Nursing Center
106 W Gorman, Corsicana, TX, 75110 (214) 874-7520
Admin Pauline Bulen.
Licensure Intermediate Care. *Beds* 51. *Certified* Medicaid.
Staff Nurses aides 9 (ft); Physical therapists 2 (pt); Activities coordinators 1 (ft).

Twilight Home
3001 W 4th Ave, Corsicana, TX, 75110 (214) 872-2521
Admin Mary B Beamon. *Medical Dir/Dir of Nursing* L E McGary MD.
Licensure Skilled Care. *Beds* 106. *Certified* Medicaid.
Ownership Nonprofit.
Admissions Requirements Medical examination; Physician's request.
Staff Physicians 1 (pt); RNs 3 (ft), 1 (pt); LPNs 9 (ft), 5 (pt); Nurses aides 33 (ft), 9 (pt); Activities coordinators 2 (ft); Dietitians 1 (pt); Dentists 1 (pt).
Facilities Dining room; Laundry room; Barber/Beauty shop.
Activities Arts and Crafts; Games; Prayer groups; Movies; Shopping trips; Dances/Social or cultural gatherings.
Description Planned, medically-oriented social/recreational programs are carried out to ensure each patient the opportunity to achieve and maintain his/her maximum level of participation; directed toward helping patients live the most satisfying life possible within their physical and mental capacities.

Westside Development Center
421 N 40th St, Corsicana, TX, 75110 (214) 874-6543
Admin Billy Bruce Apperson.
Licensure Intermediate Care for Mentally Retarded. *Beds* 71. *Certified* Medicaid.

CRANE

Golden Manor Nursing Home*
PO Box 1026, 1205 S Sue St, Crane, TX, 79731 (915) 558-3888
Admin Carolyn Belshe.
Licensure Intermediate Care. *Beds* 30. *Certified* Medicaid.
Ownership Proprietary.

CROCKETT

Houston County Nursing Home Inc
210 E Pease St, Crockett, TX, 75835 (409) 544-7884
Admin Loraine E Baker.
Licensure Intermediate Care. *Beds* 60. *Certified* Medicaid.
Staff RNs 1 (pt); LPNs 2 (ft); Nurses aides 10 (ft); Physical therapists 1 (pt); Occupational therapists 1 (pt); Speech therapists 1 (pt); Activities coordinators 1 (ft); Dietitians 1 (pt); Dentists 1 (pt).

Facilities Dining room; Activities room; Chapel; Barber/Beauty shop.
Activities Arts and Crafts; Games; Prayer groups; Shopping trips; Dances/Social or cultural gatherings.
Description Facility features good nursing care, good food, and a home-like environment.

Leisure Lodge—Crockett
Loop 304 E, Crockett, TX, 75835 (713) 544-2051
Admin Andrea K Hill.
Licensure Intermediate Care. *Beds* 120. *Certified* Medicaid.
Staff RNs 1 (ft); LPNs 5 (ft); Nurses aides 14 (ft); Activities coordinators 2 (ft).
Facilities Dining room; Activities room; Laundry room; Barber/Beauty shop.
Activities Arts and Crafts; Games; Prayer groups; Movies; Shopping trips; Dances/Social or cultural gatherings.

Whitehall Nursing Center Inc*
PO Box 998, 1116 E Loop 304, Crockett, TX, 75835 (713) 544-2163
Admin Terri Smith Hutcherson.
Licensure Skilled Care. *Beds* 71. *Certified* Medicaid.
Ownership Proprietary.

CROSBYTON

Crosbyton Care Center*
222 N Farmer St, Crosbyton, TX, 79322 (806) 675-2415
Admin Vickie Dian Griffin.
Licensure Intermediate Care. *Beds* 62. *Certified* Medicaid.
Ownership Proprietary.

CROSS PLAINS

Colonial Oaks Nursing Home*
PO Box 398, 1431 E 14th and Ave A, Cross Plains, TX, 76443 (817) 725-6175
Admin Frances M Wolf.
Licensure Intermediate Care. *Beds* 42. *Certified* Medicaid.
Ownership Proprietary.

CROWELL

Crowell Nursing Center
200 S "B" Ave, Crowell, TX, 79227 (817) 684-1422
Admin Pat Keen.
Licensure Intermediate Care. *Beds* 80. *Certified* Medicaid.
Staff Physicians; RNs; LPNs; Orderlies; Nurses aides; Physical therapists; Reality therapists; Recreational therapists; Occupational therapists; Speech therapists; Activities coordinators; Dietitians.
Facilities Dining room; Physical therapy room; Activities room; Crafts room; Laundry room; Barber/Beauty shop; Library.
Activities Arts and Crafts; Cards; Games; Reading groups; Prayer groups; Shopping trips; Shopping trips; Dances/Social or cultural gatherings.

CUERO

Retama Manor—East
1010 Macarthur, Cuero, TX, 77954 (512) 275-6133
Admin Rebecca M Adams.
Licensure Intermediate Care; Personal Care.
Beds ICF 60; Personal Care 24. *Certified* Medicaid.
Staff LPNs 3 (ft), 1 (pt); Orderlies 3 (ft); Nurses aides 13 (ft); Activities coordinators 1 (ft).
Facilities Dining room; Activities room; Chapel; Laundry room; Barber/Beauty shop.
Activities Arts and Crafts; Games; Reading groups; Prayer groups; Dances/Social or cultural gatherings; Field trips.
Description Facility newly remodeled to create nice home-like living areas; monthly family nights held.

Retama Manor Nursing Center—Cuero*
PO Box 630, Hwy 77-A, Cuero, TX, 77954 (512) 275-3421
Admin Orlo W Lang.
Licensure Intermediate Care. *Beds* 98. *Certified* Medicaid.
Ownership Proprietary.

CUSHING

Cushing Care Center Inc
Hwy 225 N, Cushing, TX, 75760 (409) 326-4529
Admin Yvonne Williamson.
Licensure Intermediate Care. *Beds* 60. *Certified* Medicaid.
Admissions Requirements Medical examination; Physician's request.
Staff LPNs 4 (ft), 2 (pt); Activities coordinators 1 (ft).
Facilities Dining room; Chapel; Crafts room; Laundry room; Barber/Beauty shop.
Activities Arts and Crafts; Games; Prayer groups; Shopping trips; Dances/Social or cultural gatherings.
Description Facility features an excellent volunteer program; nearby park that has been completely designed by volunteers and residents.

DAINGERFIELD

Pinecrest Convalescent Home*
PO Box 464, 507 E Watson Blvd, Daingerfield, TX, 75638 (214) 645-3791
Admin Judy L Dodd.
Licensure Intermediate Care. *Beds* 117. *Certified* Medicaid.
Ownership Proprietary.

DALHART

Coon Memorial Home
210 Texas Blvd, Dalhart, TX, 79022 (806) 249-6474
Admin Jammie Sue Chisum.
Licensure Intermediate Care; Custodial Care.
Beds ICF 30; Custodial Care 58. *Certified* Medicaid.
Admissions Requirements Medical examina-

tion; Physician's request.
Staff RNs 3 (ft); LPNs 4 (ft); Physical therapists 1 (pt); Activities coordinators 1 (ft); Dietitians 1 (ft).
Facilities Dining room; Activities room; Crafts room; Laundry room; Barber/Beauty shop; Library.
Activities Arts and Crafts; Cards; Games; Prayer groups; Movies; Dances/Social or cultural gatherings.

DALLAS

Autumn Leaves*
1010 Emerald Isle Dr, Dallas, TX, 75218 (214) 328-4161
Admin Karen G Sherman.
Licensure Intermediate Care. *Beds* 28. *Certified* Medicaid.
Ownership Proprietary.

Bryan Manor Nursing Home*
3401 Bryan St, Dallas, TX, 75204 (214) 823-9071
Admin Bonnie B Gayton.
Licensure Intermediate Care. *Beds* 80. *Certified* Medicaid.
Ownership Proprietary.

Buckner Baptist Ryburn Nursing Center*
4810 Samuell Blvd, Dallas, TX, 75228 (214) 388-0426
Admin Lenora M Anderson.
Licensure Intermediate Care. *Beds* 120.
Ownership Nonprofit.
Affiliation Baptist

Buckner Baptist Trew Retirement Center*
4800 Samuell Blvd, Dallas, TX, 75228 (214) 388-2171
Admin Robert L Herring Jr.
Licensure Skilled Care; Custodial Care.
Beds SNF 104; Custodial Care 75. *Certified* Medicaid.
Affiliation Baptist

C C Young Memorial Home—Young Health Center*
4829 W Lawther Dr, Dallas, TX, 75214 (214) 827-8080
Admin Julian D Thomas.
Licensure Intermediate Care; Personal Care.
Beds ICF 244; Personal Care 60. *Certified* Medicaid.
Ownership Nonprofit.
Affiliation Methodist

Central Park Manor Inc
3922 Capitol Ave, Dallas, TX, 75204 (214) 823-5641
Admin Sarah Kirkpatrick. *Medical Dir/Dir of Nursing* Dr L S Thompson Jr.
Licensure Intermediate Care. *Beds* 64.
Admissions Requirements Minimum age 16; Medical examination; Physician's request.
Staff Physicians 1 (pt); RNs 1 (ft); LPNs 10 (ft), 2 (pt); Nurses aides 18 (ft), 2 (pt); Physical therapists 1 (pt); Occupational therapists 1 (pt); Speech therapists 1 (pt); Dietitians 1 (pt); Dentists 1 (pt); Podiatrists 1 (pt).
Facilities Dining room; Chapel; Laundry

room.
Activities Games.
Description This is a skilled nursing facility.

Cliff Gardens Nursing Home
801 W 10th, Dallas, TX, 75208 (214) 946-8709
Admin Freda M Phillips.
Licensure Intermediate Care. *Beds* 34. *Certified* Medicaid.
Admissions Requirements Medical examination; Physician's request.
Staff LPNs 3 (ft), 3 (pt); Nurses aides 8 (ft), 2 (pt); Activities coordinators 1 (pt).
Facilities Dining room; Activities room; Chapel; Crafts room.
Activities Arts and Crafts; Cards; Games; Reading groups; Prayer groups; Shopping trips.
Description The small, one-story brick veneer facility promotes a home-like atmosphere.

Cliff Towers Nursing Home
329 E Colorado Blvd, Dallas, TX, 75203 (214) 942-8425
Admin Jack L Anders. *Medical Dir/Dir of Nursing* B Northam DO and T V Nguyen MD.
Licensure Skilled Care; Intermediate Care; Custodial Care. *Beds* 214; Custodial Care 37. *Certified* Medicaid.
Admissions Requirements Medical examination; Physician's request.
Staff LPNs 23 (ft), 4 (pt); Orderlies 4 (ft), 1 (pt); Nurses aides 55 (ft), 16 (pt); Physical therapists 1 (ft); Reality therapists 1 (pt); Recreational therapists 1 (pt); Occupational therapists 1 (pt); Speech therapists 1 (pt); Activities coordinators 2 (ft); Dietitians 1 (ft).
Facilities Dining room; Physical therapy room; Activities room; Chapel; Crafts room; Laundry room; Barber/Beauty shop.
Activities Arts and Crafts; Cards; Games; Reading groups; Prayer groups; Movies; Shopping trips; Dances/Social or cultural gatherings.

The Convalescent Center*
4005 Gaston Ave, Dallas, TX, 75246 (214) 826-3891
Admin Susan M Franklin.
Licensure Intermediate Care; Intermediate Care for Mentally Retarded. *Beds* ICF 100; ICF/MR 144. *Certified* Medicaid.
Ownership Proprietary.

Crestview Retirement Hotel*
7820 Churchill Way, Dallas, TX, 75251 (214) 239-7261
Admin Virginia B Brawley.
Licensure Custodial Care. *Beds* 150.
Ownership Proprietary.

Crystal Hill Nursing Home Inc*
630 Elsbeth Ave, Dallas, TX, 75208 (214) 948-3996
Admin Peggy Grayson.
Licensure Intermediate Care. *Beds* 60.
Ownership Proprietary.

Dallas Home for Jewish Aged*
2525 Centerville Rd, Dallas, TX, 75228 (214) 327-4503
Admin Mary Jo Pompeo.
Licensure Intermediate Care. *Beds* 180. *Certified* Medicaid.
Ownership Nonprofit.
Affiliation Jewish

Devonshire Manor*
8069 Scyene Circle, Dallas, TX, 75227 (214) 388-0609
Admin Doris Dittman.
Licensure Intermediate Care. *Beds* 120. *Certified* Medicaid.
Ownership Proprietary.

Doctor's Nursing Center Foundation Inc
9009 White Rock Trail, Dallas, TX, 75238 (214) 348-8100
Admin Beverly Holt. *Medical Dir/Dir of Nursing* Dr Jose Pilatovsky.
Licensure Intermediate Care; Custodial Care. *Beds* ICF 154; Custodial Care 48. *Certified* Medicaid.
Admissions Requirements Minimum age 16; Medical examination; Physician's request.
Staff Physicians 3 (ft), 1 (pt); RNs 5 (ft), 5 (pt); LPNs 12 (ft), 6 (pt); Orderlies 3 (ft); Nurses aides 49 (ft), 5 (pt); Physical therapists 1 (ft); Recreational therapists 1 (ft); Occupational therapists 1 (pt); Speech therapists 1 (pt); Activities coordinators 1 (ft); Dietitians 1 (ft); Dentists 1 (pt); Podiatrists 1 (pt); Audiologists 1 (pt).
Facilities Dining room; Activities room; Chapel; Crafts room; Laundry room; Barber/Beauty shop; Library.
Activities Arts and Crafts; Cards; Games; Reading groups; Prayer groups; Movies; Shopping trips; Dances/Social or cultural gatherings; Cocktail hours, Residents council.
Description Facility is located on a beautiful, wooded, scenic 24 acres. DNC is a 202-bed private pay facility dedicated to quality care. It prides itself on the same strong management for over 20 years and a broad spectrum of activities with the help of individuals and groups who volunteer over 6,000 hours each year.

Fair Park Health Care Center
2815 Forest Ave, Dallas, TX, 75215 (214) 421-2159
Admin Merril M Grey.
Licensure Intermediate Care. *Beds* 120. *Certified* Medicaid.
Admissions Requirements Minimum age 12; Medical examination; Physician's request.
Staff RNs 1 (ft), 1 (pt); LPNs 8 (ft), 1 (pt); Orderlies 5 (ft); Nurses aides 23 (ft); Physical therapists; Reality therapists; Recreational therapists; Occupational therapists; Activities coordinators 1 (ft); Dietitians 1 (pt); Dentists; Ophthalmologists; Podiatrists; Audiologists.
Facilities Dining room; Activities room; Laundry room; Barber/Beauty shop.
Activities Arts and Crafts; Cards; Games; Reading groups; Prayer groups; Movies; Shopping trips; Dances/Social or cultural gatherings.

Fairmount Company Inc
3500 Fairmount, Dallas, TX, 75219 (214) 528-0577
Admin Patsy A Kirksey.
Licensure Intermediate Care; Custodial Care. *Beds* 30; Custodial Care 64.

Ferguson Nursing Center
7626 Ferguson Rd, Dallas, TX, 75228 (214) 327-9321
Admin Jerry Amsler. *Medical Dir/Dir of Nursing* Vickie Lowry.
Licensure Intermediate Care. *Beds* 92. *Certified* Medicaid.
Admissions Requirements Medical examination; Physician's request.
Staff Physicians 1 (pt); RNs 1 (ft); LPNs 8 (ft), 5 (pt); Orderlies 3 (ft); Nurses aides 14 (ft), 6 (pt); Physical therapists 1 (pt); Activities coordinators 1 (ft); Dietitians 1 (pt).
Facilities Dining room; Activities room; Laundry room; Barber/Beauty shop.
Activities Arts and Crafts; Games; Prayer groups; Movies.
Description Ferguson Nursing Center offers a home-type atmosphere with friendly, helpful staff; ongoing activity programs under a specially trained director; operates on the idea that being active keeps you healthy and happy.

Four Seasons Nursing Center of Dallas*
3326 Burgoyne St, Dallas, TX, 75233 (214) 330-9291
Admin Estelle Bauer.
Licensure Skilled Care; Intermediate Care. *Beds* 210. *Certified* Medicaid.
Ownership Proprietary.

Garrett Park Manor
1407 N Garrett, Dallas, TX, 75206 (214) 824-8030
Admin Nora Hauck. *Medical Dir/Dir of Nursing* .
Licensure Skilled Care; Intermediate Care. *Beds* 77. *Certified* Medicaid.
Admissions Requirements Minimum age 18; Medical examination; Physician's request.
Staff Physicians 3 (pt); RNs 1 (pt); LPNs 8 (pt); Orderlies 1 (pt); Nurses aides 30 (pt); Activities coordinators 1 (ft); Dietitians 1 (pt).
Facilities Dining room; Activities room.
Activities Arts and Crafts; Cards; Games; Reading groups; Prayer groups; Movies; Shopping trips; Dances/Social or cultural gatherings.

Holiday Hills Retirement and Nursing Center Inc*
2428 Bahama, Dallas, TX, 75211 (214) 948-3811
Admin Mae E Maddox.
Licensure Skilled Care; Intermediate Care. *Beds* 135. *Certified* Medicaid.
Ownership Proprietary.

Juliette Fowler Homes Inc
100 S Fulton St, Dallas, TX, 75214 (214) 827-0813
Admin Marcela Luise Wentzel.
Licensure Intermediate Care. *Beds* 131. *Certified* Medicaid.
Admissions Requirements Medical examination.
Affiliation Disciples of Christ
Facilities Dining room; Activities room; Chapel; Crafts room; Laundry room; Barber/Beauty shop; Library.
Activities Arts and Crafts; Cards; Games; Reading groups; Prayer groups; Movies; Shopping trips; Dances/Social or cultural gatherings; Resident council; Resident food consultants

committee.

Description Juliette Fowler Homes provides intermediate 24-hour nursing care. In addition, a high emphasis is placed on individualized nursing care with assigned staff to each resident. The program is enhanced by additional effort to meet the resident's social, emotional, recreational, therapeutic, and spiritual needs.

Kensington Manor*
8039 Scyene Circle, Dallas, TX, 75227 (214) 388-0424
Admin Billie C Hardin.
Licensure Intermediate Care. *Beds* 120. *Certified* Medicaid.
Ownership Proprietary.

Kenwood Nursing Home
2922 Duncanville Rd, Dallas, TX, 75211 (214) 339-8341
Admin Mary G Squiers. *Medical Dir/Dir of Nursing* Carl Willeford.
Licensure Intermediate Care. *Beds* 60. *Certified* Medicaid.
Admissions Requirements Medical examination.
Staff RNs 1 (pt); LPNs 5 (ft), 3 (pt); Orderlies 2 (ft); Nurses aides 10 (ft), 3 (pt); Activities coordinators 1 (ft).
Facilities Dining room; Activities room; Barber/Beauty shop.
Activities Arts and Crafts; Prayer groups; Movies.
Description Facility offers Sunday school, church, one to one visiting, bingo parties, bingo, exercise, DAV manicures, seasonal parties, birthday party of the month gifts, flower gifts for birthday, popcorn, movies, magic shows, field trips, sing-along, Christ for the Nations, and one to one therapy visits.

La Boure Care Center*
1950 Record Crossing, Dallas, TX, 75235 (214) 638-8050
Admin Douglas Daugherty.
Licensure Skilled Care. *Beds* 168. *Certified* Medicaid; Medicare.
Ownership Proprietary.

Meadows
8383 Meadow Rd, Dallas, TX, 75231 (214) 369-7811
Admin Ernest W Angell. *Medical Dir/Dir of Nursing* James Galbraith MD.
Licensure Intermediate Care; Custodial Care. *Beds* ICF 128; Custodial Care 104.
Admissions Requirements Minimum age 18.
Staff Physicians 1 (pt); RNs 3 (ft); LPNs 14 (ft); Orderlies 2 (ft); Nurses aides 50 (ft); Physical therapists 1 (ft); Recreational therapists 2 (ft); Activities coordinators 2 (ft); Dietitians 1 (ft).
Facilities Dining room; Physical therapy room; Activities room; Laundry room; Barber/Beauty shop.
Activities Arts and Crafts; Games; Reading groups; Prayer groups; Movies; Shopping trips.
Description Facility has country club setting with numerous patios, formal dining room, individual heating/air conditioning in each room, and an 18-passenger bus for touring and shopping.

North Dallas Nursing Home Inc*
9009 Forest Ln, Dallas, TX, 75243 (214) 234-0223
Admin Bobbie J LeBlanc.
Licensure Intermediate Care. *Beds* 120. *Certified* Medicaid.
Ownership Proprietary.

Northaven Nursing Center
11301 Dennis Rd, Dallas, TX, 75229 (214) 241-2551
Admin Evelyn R Artall. *Medical Dir/Dir of Nursing* Stan Pull MD and S A Redfern MD.
Licensure Intermediate Care. *Beds* 208. *Certified* Medicaid.
Admissions Requirements Minimum age 21; Medical examination, Physician's request.
Staff Physicians 1 (ft); RNs 3 (ft), 2 (pt); LPNs 14 (ft), 6 (pt); Nurses aides 37 (ft), 10 (pt); Activities coordinators 1 (ft); Dietitians 1 (ft); Dentists 1 (ft); Podiatrists 1 (ft).
Facilities Dining room; Activities room; Crafts room; Barber/Beauty shop; Library.
Activities Arts and Crafts; Cards; Games; Reading groups; Prayer groups; Movies; Shopping trips; Dances/Social or cultural gatherings.
Description Facility features a delightful home-like atmosphere enhanced by an extra large greenhouse entrance area. The greenhouse provides a fully enclosed, heated outdoor setting for all residents to enjoy year round. Also private and semiprivate luxurious suites are available for residents desiring alternate living.

Nottingham Manor
8059 Scyene Circle, Dallas, TX, 75227 (214) 388-0519
Admin Jeanine Rutherford. *Medical Dir/Dir of Nursing* Dr Bill Morgan.
Licensure Intermediate Care. *Beds* 120. *Certified* Medicaid.
Admissions Requirements Physician's request.
Staff Physicians 1 (ft); LPNs 6 (ft), 1 (pt); Nurses aides 28 (ft), 4 (pt); Physical therapists 1 (pt); Recreational therapists 1 (pt); Occupational therapists 1 (pt); Activities coordinators 1 (ft); Podiatrists 1 (pt); Rehab LVNs 1 (ft).
Facilities Dining room; Activities room; Crafts room; Laundry room; Barber/Beauty shop; Rehab Room.
Activities Arts and Crafts; Cards; Games; Reading groups; Prayer groups; Movies; Shopping trips; Dances/Social or cultural gatherings.
Description Facility has a "Deaf Wing" for the blind and deaf; classes held each Monday to teach new staff members the art of sign language; rehabilitation program.

Presbyterian Village Inc
550 Ann Arbor, Dallas, TX, 75216 (214) 376-1701
Admin Charles L McGowan. *Medical Dir/Dir of Nursing* Allen M Fain MD.
Licensure Skilled Care; Intermediate Care; Personal Care. *Beds* SNF 35; ICF 35; Personal Care 49. *Certified* Medicaid; Medicare.
Admissions Requirements Medical examination.
Staff Physicians 3 (pt); RNs 7 (ft); LPNs 17 (ft), 5 (pt); Nurses aides 59 (ft), 2 (pt); Physical therapists 1 (pt); Occupational therapists 1 (pt); Speech therapists 1 (pt); Activities coordinators 1 (ft); Dietitians 2 (pt); Dentists 1 (pt); Ophthal-

mologists 1 (pt); Podiatrists 1 (pt).
Affiliation Presbyterian
Facilities Dining room; Physical therapy room; Activities room; Chapel; Crafts room; Laundry room; Barber/Beauty shop; Library.
Activities Arts and Crafts; Cards; Games; Reading groups; Prayer groups; Shopping trips; Dances/Social or cultural gatherings.

Presbyterian Village North Nursing Health Service
8600 Skyline Dr, Dallas, TX, 75243 (214) 349-3960
Admin Ann Gomez. *Medical Dir/Dir of Nursing* Manning B Shannon MD.
Licensure Skilled Care. *Beds* 124.
Staff Physicians 1 (ft); Occupational therapists 1 (ft); Activities coordinators 1 (ft); Dietitians 1 (ft).
Affiliation Presbyterian
Facilities Dining room; Physical therapy room; Chapel; Crafts room; Barber/Beauty shop; Library.
Activities Arts and Crafts; Cards; Games; Prayer groups; Shopping trips; Dances/Social or cultural gatherings; Variable outside trips.
Description Presbyterian Village North has been open 3 ½ years, offering excellent nursing care and an exceptional living environment; still expanding the nursing unit and the independent living units.

Saint Joseph's Residence
330 W Pembroke St, Dallas, TX, 75208 (214) 948-3597
Admin Adelaide R Bocanegra. *Medical Dir-/Dir of Nursing* Dr Ross M Carmichael.
Licensure Custodial Care. *Beds* 49.
Admissions Requirements Minimum age 70; Medical examination.
Staff LPNs; Nurses aides; Occupational therapists; Activities coordinators; Dietitians.
Affiliation Roman Catholic
Facilities Dining room; Chapel; Laundry room; Barber/Beauty shop; Library.
Activities Cards; Games; Prayer groups; Dances/Social or cultural gatherings; Musicals; Bus trips.

South Dallas Nursing Home
3808 S Central Expwy, Dallas, TX, 75215 (214) 428-2851
Admin Leona Hawkins.
Licensure Intermediate Care. *Beds* 76. *Certified* Medicaid.
Admissions Requirements Physician's request.
Staff RNs; LPNs; Orderlies; Nurses aides; Occupational therapists; Speech therapists; Activities coordinators; Dietitians.
Facilities Dining room; Activities room; Chapel; Crafts room; Laundry room.
Activities Arts and Crafts; Cards; Games; Reading groups; Prayer groups; Movies; Dances/Social or cultural gatherings.

Sunnyvale Manor 1*
3212 E Ledbetter, Dallas, TX, 75203 (214) 371-2359
Admin Karen M Chronister.
Licensure Intermediate Care. *Beds* 62. *Certified* Medicaid.
Ownership Proprietary.

Sunnyvale Manor 2*
5300 Houston School Rd, Dallas, TX, 75241
(214) 372-1496
Admin Steve Vaughn.
Licensure Intermediate Care. *Beds* 200. *Certified* Medicaid.
Ownership Proprietary.

The Traymore*
7602 Culcourt, Dallas, TX, 75209 (214)
358-3131
Admin Betty L Gallaher.
Licensure Skilled Care. *Beds* 150. *Certified* Medicaid.
Ownership Proprietary.

Treemot Health Care Center
5550 Harvest Hill Rd, Dallas, TX, 75230 (214)
661-1862
Admin Stephen Jones.
Licensure Intermediate Care. *Beds* 104.
Admissions Requirements Medical examination; Physician's request.
Staff Physicians 2 (pt); RNs 5 (ft), 2 (pt); LPNs 4 (ft), 1 (pt); Orderlies 5 (ft); Nurses aides 18 (ft), 3 (pt); Physical therapists 1 (ft); Activities coordinators 1 (ft), 1 (pt); Dietitians 1 (pt); Podiatrists 1 (pt).
Facilities Dining room; Physical therapy room; Activities room; Crafts room; Laundry room; Barber/Beauty shop; Library.
Activities Arts and Crafts; Cards; Games; Reading groups; Prayer groups; Movies; Shopping trips; Dances/Social or cultural gatherings.

Walnut Place
5515 Glen Lakes Dr, Dallas, TX, 75231 (214)
361-8923
Admin Richard Pratt.
Licensure Intermediate Care. *Beds* 184.
Admissions Requirements Medical examination.
Facilities Dining room; Physical therapy room; Activities room; Chapel; Crafts room; Laundry room; Barber/Beauty shop; Library.
Activities Arts and Crafts; Cards; Games; Reading groups; Prayer groups; Movies; Shopping trips; Dances/Social or cultural gatherings.

Westminster Manor
7979 Scyene Circle, Dallas, TX, 75227 (214)
388-0549
Admin L Clay Stephenson.
Licensure Custodial Care. *Beds* 96.

DAYTON

Heritage Manor Care Center*
310 E Lawrence, Dayton, TX, 77535 (713)
258-5562
Admin Jack Mallard.
Licensure Skilled Care. *Beds* 60. *Certified* Medicaid.
Ownership Proprietary.

DE LEON

De Leon Nursing Home
205 E Ayers, De Leon, TX, 76444 (817)
893-6676
Admin Billie R Butler.

Licensure Intermediate Care. *Beds* 53. *Certified* Medicaid.
Admissions Requirements Medical examination; Physician's request.
Staff RNs 1 (ft); LPNs 2 (ft); Nurses aides 8 (ft); Activities coordinators 1 (ft); Dietitians 1 (pt).
Facilities Dining room; Activities room; Laundry room; Barber/Beauty shop.
Activities Arts and Crafts; Games; Reading groups; Prayer groups; Shopping trips; Dances/Social or cultural gatherings.

Natatana Care Center*
PO Box 287, Hwy 6 E, De Leon, TX, 76444
(817) 893-2075
Admin Charles L Pollock.
Licensure Intermediate Care. *Beds* 102. *Certified* Medicaid.
Ownership Proprietary.

DECATUR

Decatur Convalescent Center*
PO Box 68, 605 W Mulberry St, Decatur, TX,
76234 (817) 627-5444
Admin Geneva Galloway.
Licensure Intermediate Care. *Beds* 42. *Certified* Medicaid.
Ownership Proprietary.

Golden Years Haven
Hwy 81 S, Rt 2, Box 226, Decatur, TX, 76234
(817) 627-2234
Admin Lezlie McWhorter. *Medical Dir/Dir of Nursing* Verda Slimp.
Licensure Intermediate Care. *Beds* 42. *Certified* Medicaid.
Admissions Requirements Medical examination.
Staff Physicians 5 (ft); RNs 1 (ft); LPNs 3 (ft), 1 (pt); Orderlies 4 (ft); Nurses aides 16 (ft); Activities coordinators 1 (ft); Dietitians 1 (ft); Dentists 1 (ft).
Facilities Dining room; Activities room; Crafts room; Laundry room; Barber/Beauty shop.
Activities Arts and Crafts; Cards; Games; Prayer groups; Movies.
Description Since the facility is very small, everyone is very close and participates together in the activities.

Sunny Hills Nursing Center*
200 E Thompson, Decatur, TX, 76234 (817)
627-2165
Admin Gary M Hendrix.
Licensure Intermediate Care. *Beds* 102. *Certified* Medicaid.
Ownership Proprietary.

DEER PARK

San Jacinto Heritage Manor*
206 W Ave P, Deer Park, TX, 77536 (713)
479-8471
Admin Pat Monroe.
Licensure Intermediate Care. *Beds* 96. *Certified* Medicaid.
Ownership Proprietary.

DEKALB

Sunny Acres of Dekalb Inc
540 S E Front St, Dekalb, TX, 75559 (214)
667-2011
Admin Dora S Perry.
Licensure Intermediate Care. *Beds* 66. *Certified* Medicaid.
Staff RNs 1 (pt); LPNs 5 (ft); Nurses aides 15 (ft), 15 (pt); Activities coordinators 1 (ft).
Facilities Dining room; Activities room; Chapel; Laundry room; Barber/Beauty shop.
Activities Arts and Crafts; Cards; Games; Reading groups; Prayer groups.
Description Facility features home-like atmosphere and quality nursing care.

DEL RIO

Del Rio Nursing Home Inc
301 Moore, Del Rio, TX, 78840 (512) 775-2459
Admin Lois Nell Gardner.
Licensure Intermediate Care. *Beds* 52. *Certified* Medicaid.
Admissions Requirements Minimum age 16; Medical examination; Physician's request.
Staff RNs 1 (pt); LPNs 6 (ft), 4 (pt); Nurses aides 11 (ft), 3 (pt); Activities coordinators 1 (ft); Dietitians 1 (pt).
Facilities Dining room; Activities room; Laundry room; Barber/Beauty shop.
Activities Arts and Crafts; Cards; Games; Reading groups; Prayer groups; Movies; Shopping trips; Dances/Social or cultural gatherings.
Description Retirement home with traditional Spanish atmosphere.

Retama Manor Nursing Center—Del Rio*
100 Herrmann Dr, Del Rio, TX, 78840 (512)
775-7477
Admin Janet Tennis.
Licensure Intermediate Care. *Beds* 88. *Certified* Medicaid.
Ownership Proprietary.

DENISON

Cantex Healthcare Center—Denison*
801 W Washington St, Denison, TX, 75020
(214) 465-9670
Admin Nancy Raulston.
Licensure Intermediate Care. *Beds* 50. *Certified* Medicaid.
Ownership Proprietary.

Care Inn of Denison*
1300 Memorial Dr, Denison, TX, 75020 (214)
465-7442
Admin Adelia Shepherd.
Licensure Intermediate Care. *Beds* 150. *Certified* Medicaid.
Ownership Proprietary.

Denison Manor Inc
601 E Hwy 69, Denison, TX, 75020 (214)
465-2438
Admin Ruth E Brinson. *Medical Dir/Dir of Nursing* M Y Stokes MD.
Licensure Skilled Care; Intermediate Care. *Beds* 71. *Certified* Medicaid.
Admissions Requirements Medical examina-

tion; Physician's request.
Staff RNs 2 (ft), 2 (pt); LPNs 5 (ft), 2 (pt); Orderlies 1 (ft); Nurses aides 14 (ft), 4 (pt); Activities coordinators 1 (ft).
Facilities Dining room; Activities room; Crafts room; Barber/Beauty shop.
Activities Arts and Crafts; Games.

DENTON

The Beaumont Nursing Home*
2224 N Carroll Blvd, Denton, TX, 76201 (817) 387-6656, 382-5713
Admin Pat B Kayser.
Licensure Intermediate Care. *Beds* 55. *Certified* Medicaid
Ownership Proprietary.

Denton Development Center
909 E Loop 288, Denton, TX, 76201 (817) 387-8525
Admin Robert Routh.
Licensure Intermediate Care for Mentally Retarded. *Beds* 138. *Certified* Medicaid.

Denton Good Samaritan Village*
2500 Hinkle Dr, Denton, TX, 76201 (817) 383-2651
Admin Douglas F Wuenschel.
Licensure Skilled Care. *Beds* 92. *Certified* Medicaid.
Ownership Nonprofit.
Affiliation Lutheran

Denton Nursing Center*
2229 Carroll Blvd, Denton, TX, 76201 (817) 387-8508
Admin Arveta M Shields.
Licensure Intermediate Care. *Beds* 148. *Certified* Medicaid.
Ownership Proprietary.

DENVER CITY

Stonebrook Nurse Center
315 Mustang, Denver City, TX, 79323 (806) 592-2127
Admin Virginia Clegg. *Medical Dir/Dir of Nursing* Carol Jones RN.
Licensure Intermediate Care. *Beds* 100. *Certified* Medicaid.

DEPORT

Deport Nursing Home
US Hwy 271, Deport, TX, 75435 (214) 652-4410
Admin Martha Castlebury. *Medical Dir/Dir of Nursing* T H Glover MD.
Licensure Intermediate Care. *Beds* 102. *Certified* Medicaid.
Admissions Requirements Physician's request.
Staff Physicians 1 (pt); RNs 1 (ft); LPNs 5 (ft), 4 (pt); Nurses aides 24 (ft), 6 (pt); Activities coordinators 1 (ft); Dietitians 1 (pt).
Facilities Dining room; Laundry room; Barber/Beauty shop.
Activities Arts and Crafts; Cards; Games; Reading groups; Prayer groups; Shopping trips; Dances/Social or cultural gatherings.

Description Sensory therapy group meets weekly; great improvement has been seen in moderately confused residents.

DESOTO

DeSoto Nursing Home*
1101 N Hampton, DeSoto, TX, 75115 (214) 223-3944
Admin Wilma King.
Licensure Intermediate Care. *Beds* 120. *Certified* Medicaid.

Skyline Nursing Home*
PO Box 489, Parkerville Rd at 135 E, DeSoto, TX, 75115 (214) 223-6311
Admin Mike Henrie.
Licensure Intermediate Care. *Beds* 110. *Certified* Medicaid.
Ownership Proprietary.

DEVINE

Devine Nursing Home Inc*
307 Briscoe Ave, Devine, TX, 78016 (512) 663-2832
Admin Eileen M Lyall.
Licensure Intermediate Care. *Beds* 45. *Certified* Medicaid.
Ownership Proprietary.

Heritage Manor Inc
104 Enterprize, Devine, TX, 78016 (512) 663-4451 and 663-4452
Admin Eileen Lyall.
Licensure Intermediate Care. *Beds* 100. *Certified* Medicaid.
Staff RNs 1 (ft); LPNs 4 (ft), 4 (pt); Activities coordinators 1 (ft); Dietitians 1 (pt).
Facilities Dining room; Physical therapy room; Activities room; Chapel; Crafts room; Laundry room; Barber/Beauty shop; Library.
Activities Arts and Crafts; Cards; Games; Reading groups; Prayer groups; Movies; Shopping trips; Dances/Social or cultural gatherings.

DIBOLL

South Meadows Nursing Home*
900 S Temple Dr, Diboll, TX, 75941 (713) 829-5581
Admin Jo Nell Placker.
Licensure Intermediate Care. *Beds* 54. *Certified* Medicaid.
Ownership Proprietary.

DIMMITT

South Hills Manor*
1619 Butler Blvd, Dimmitt, TX, 79027 (806) 647-3117
Admin Jean B Holt.
Licensure Intermediate Care. *Beds* 118. *Certified* Medicaid.
Ownership Proprietary.

DUBLIN

Dublin Nursing Center*
715 Sheehan St, Dublin, TX, 76446 (817) 445-2257
Admin Dessie Deane Christian.
Licensure Intermediate Care. *Beds* 102. *Certified* Medicaid.
Ownership Proprietary.

Golden Age Manor Nursing Center*
Rt 5 Box 4A, 704 Dobkins St, Dublin, TX, 76446 (817) 445-3370
Admin Bobbie M Nichols.
Licensure Intermediate Care. *Beds* 90. *Certified* Medicaid
Ownership Proprietary.

DUMAS

Dumas Memorial Home
1009 S Maddox Ave, Dumas, TX, 79029 (806) 935-4143
Admin Faye Lockhart.
Licensure Intermediate Care. *Beds* 47. *Certified* Medicaid.
Staff LPNs 4 (ft), 2 (pt); Nurses aides 15 (ft), 3 (pt); Activities coordinators 1 (ft); Dietitians 2 (ft).

DUNCANVILLE

Colonial Acres Care Center*
1023 E Hwy 67, Duncanville, TX, 75137 (214) 298-3326
Admin David L Bartlett.
Licensure Intermediate Care. *Beds* 100. *Certified* Medicaid.
Ownership Proprietary.

Shadyside Nursing Home Inc
330 W Camp Wisdom Rd, Duncanville, TX, 75116 (214) 298-3398
Admin Beverly V Johnson. *Medical Dir/Dir of Nursing* Dr Don E Christiansen.
Licensure Intermediate Care. *Beds* 61. *Certified* Medicaid.
Admissions Requirements Minimum age 50; Physician's request.
Staff Physicians 5 (pt); RNs 1 (ft); LPNs 4 (ft), 1 (pt); Nurses aides 11 (ft), 5 (pt); Physical therapists 2 (pt); Occupational therapists 1 (pt); Speech therapists 1 (pt); Activities coordinators 1 (ft); Dietitians 1 (ft), 1 (pt); Dentists 1 (pt); Podiatrists 1 (pt).
Facilities Dining room; Activities room; Chapel; Laundry room; Barber/Beauty shop.
Activities Arts and Crafts; Cards; Games; Prayer groups.

EAGLE LAKE

Heritage House
200 Heritage Ln, Eagle Lake, TX, 77434 (713) 234-3591
Admin Marian J Werland. *Medical Dir/Dir of Nursing* Raymond R Thomas MD.
Licensure Intermediate Care. *Beds* 102. *Certified* Medicaid.
Facilities Dining room; Activities room; Crafts room; Laundry room; Barber/Beauty shop.

Activities Arts and Crafts; Cards; Games; Reading groups; Prayer groups; Movies; Shopping trips; Dances/Social or cultural gatherings.
Description Our facility is located in a small town and licensed for intermediate care. We encourage all families to actively participate in the daily lives and care of our residents. We strive to maintain an atmosphere that is peaceful and homey, and always filled with smiles. We feel that the key to success is a happy and active resident, so we encourage involvement with relatives, friends, community, staff, volunteers, and other residents.

EAGLE PASS

Retama Manor Nursing Center—Eagle Pass*
PO Box 1530, 2550 Zacatecas, Eagle Pass, TX, 78852 (512) 773-9563
Admin Louise Omenson.
Licensure Intermediate Care. *Beds* 120. *Certified* Medicaid.
Ownership Proprietary.

EASTLAND

Eastland Manor*
1405 W Commerce St, Eastland, TX, 76448 (817) 629-2686
Admin Phillip Dalgleish.
Licensure Intermediate Care. *Beds* 102. *Certified* Medicaid.
Ownership Proprietary.

Northview Development Center
411 W Moss St, Eastland, TX, 76448 (817) 629-2624
Admin Lauretta Davis Lawler.
Licensure Intermediate Care for Mentally Retarded. *Beds* 54. *Certified* Medicaid.
Admissions Requirements Minimum age 18; Medical examination; Physician's request.
Staff Physicians 1 (pt); RNs 1 (ft); LPNs 3 (ft), 3 (pt); Nurses aides 14 (ft), 6 (pt); Physical therapists 1 (pt); Recreational therapists 1 (ft); Occupational therapists 1 (pt); Speech therapists 1 (pt); Dietitians 1 (pt); Dentists 1 (pt); Ophthalmologists 1 (pt); Audiologists 1 (pt).
Facilities Dining room; Activities room; Crafts room; Laundry room; Barber/Beauty shop.
Activities Arts and Crafts; Cards; Games; Reading groups; Movies; Shopping trips; Dances/Social or cultural gatherings; Camping; Swimming; Hiking; Exercise classes; Make-up classes.
Description This is an MR5 level facility. Our people are moderately retarded and capable of learning many things. We have some who work out in the public (mowing lawns, washing dishes, etc).

Valley View Lodge*
PO Box 552, 700 S Ostrom St, Eastland, TX, 76448 (817) 629-1779
Admin Judith M Chaney.
Licensure Intermediate Care. *Beds* 102. *Certified* Medicaid.
Ownership Proprietary.

EDEN

Concho Nursing Center*
Eaker and Burleson Sts, Eden, TX, 76837 (915) 869-5531
Admin Pearl Murrah.
Licensure Intermediate Care. *Beds* 82. *Certified* Medicaid.
Ownership Proprietary.

EDINBURG

Colonial Manor of Edinburg
1401 S 2nd, Edinburg, TX, 78539 (512) 383-4978
Admin Harlin L Sadler. *Medical Dir/Dir of Nursing* Carlos Saca MD.
Licensure Intermediate Care. *Beds* 44. *Certified* Medicaid.
Admissions Requirements Medical examination.
Staff Physicians 1 (pt); RNs 1 (ft); LPNs 4 (ft); Nurses aides 15 (ft); Activities coordinators 1 (ft); Dietitians 1 (pt); Dentists 1 (pt).
Facilities Dining room; Activities room; Crafts room; Laundry room.
Activities Arts and Crafts; Cards; Games; Reading groups; Prayer groups; Movies; Shopping trips; Dances/Social or cultural gatherings.

Retama Manor Nursing Center
1505 S Closner, Edinburg, TX, 78539 (512) 383-5656
Admin Leonides E Molina.
Licensure Intermediate Care. *Beds* 104. *Certified* Medicaid.
Staff LPNs 9 (ft); Orderlies 1 (ft); Nurses aides 26 (ft); Activities coordinators 1 (ft); Dietitians 7 (pt); Social workers 1 (ft).
Facilities Dining room; Activities room; Crafts room; Laundry room; Barber/Beauty shop.
Activities Arts and Crafts; Cards; Games; Reading groups; Prayer groups; Movies; Shopping trips; Dances/Social or cultural gatherings.

EDNA

Care Inn of Edna*
1204 N Wells, Edna, TX, 77957 (512) 782-3581
Admin Daphne Jean Sablatura.
Licensure Intermediate Care. *Beds* 61. *Certified* Medicaid.
Ownership Proprietary.

EL CAMPO

Czech Catholic Home for the Aged*
Rt 3, Box 40, El Campo, TX, 77437 (713) 648-2628
Admin Edith Sohrt Molberg.
Licensure Intermediate Care. *Beds* 59. *Certified* Medicaid.
Ownership Nonprofit.
Affiliation Roman Catholic

Garden Villa Nursing Home*
106 Del Norte Dr, El Campo, TX, 77437 (713) 543-6762
Admin Robert B Reeves.

Licensure Intermediate Care. *Beds* 150. *Certified* Medicaid.
Ownership Proprietary.

EL PASO

Coronado Nursing Center Inc
223 S Resler, El Paso, TX, 79912 (915) 584-9417
Admin William Jabalie.
Licensure Intermediate Care. *Beds* 120. *Certified* Medicaid.
Facilities Dining room; Activities room; Laundry room; Barber/Beauty shop; Library.
Activities Arts and Crafts; Games; Prayer groups; Movies; Dances/Social or cultural gatherings.

El Paso Convalescent Center
11525 Vista Del Sol Dr, El Paso, TX, 79936 (915) 598-1211
Admin Tim W Kelly.
Licensure Intermediate Care. *Beds* 150. *Certified* Medicaid.
Admissions Requirements Minimum age 21; Medical examination; Physician's request.
Staff RNs 1 (ft); LPNs 7 (ft); Nurses aides 35 (ft); Physical therapists 1 (pt); Speech therapists 1 (pt); Activities coordinators 1 (ft), 1 (pt); Dietitians 1 (pt); Dentists 1 (pt); Podiatrists 1 (pt).
Facilities Dining room; Physical therapy room; Activities room; Crafts room; Barber/Beauty shop; Library.
Activities Arts and Crafts; Cards; Games; Prayer groups; Dances/Social or cultural gatherings.
Description Center has a caring, attentive staff who take time to really care for residents, whether it is walking those who need it to hugging those who don't ask for anything.

Four Seasons Nursing Center of El Paso*
1600 Murchison Rd, El Paso, TX, 79902 (915) 544-2002
Admin Betty Turner.
Licensure Skilled Care; Intermediate Care. *Beds* 208. *Certified* Medicaid.
Ownership Proprietary.

Hillhaven Convalescent Center*
2301 N Oregon St, El Paso, TX, 79902 (915) 532-8941
Admin Agnes K Pierce.
Licensure Skilled Care; Intermediate Care. *Beds* 183. *Certified* Medicaid; Medicare.
Ownership Proprietary.

Nazareth Hall*
4614 Trowbridge Dr, El Paso, TX, 79903 (915) 565-4677
Admin Sr Bernice B Juen.
Licensure Intermediate Care. *Beds* 50. *Certified* Medicaid.
Ownership Nonprofit.

Rest Haven Nursing Home*
2729 Porter Ave, El Paso, TX, 79930 (915) 566-2111
Admin Joseph B Johns.
Licensure Intermediate Care. *Beds* 51.
Ownership Proprietary.

RN Nursing Convalescent Home Inc
180 Croom Rd, El Paso, TX, 79915 (915)
772-5480
Admin Joseph Johns. *Medical Dir/Dir of
Nursing* Dr W C Autroy.
Licensure Intermediate Care. *Beds* 48.
Admissions Requirements Medical examination; Physician's request.
Staff Physicians 1 (pt); RNs 1 (pt); LPNs 4 (ft),
2 (pt); Orderlies 1 (ft); Nurses aides 15 (ft);
Physical therapists 1 (pt); Recreational therapists 1 (ft); Activities coordinators 1 (ft); Dietitians 1 (pt).
Facilities Dining room; Activities room; Crafts
room; Laundry room; Barber/Beauty shop.
Activities Arts and Crafts; Cards; Games;
Reading groups; Prayer groups; Movies; Dances/Social or cultural gatherings; Picnics; Barbeques; Gardening.

Sunset Haven Nursing Center Ltd*
9001 N Loop Dr, El Paso, TX, 79907 (915)
859-1650
Admin Pamela Z Elrod.
Licensure Intermediate Care. *Beds* 120. *Certified* Medicaid.
Ownership Proprietary.

Vista Hills Health Care Center*
1599 Lomaland Dr, El Paso, TX, 79935 (915)
593-1131
Admin Miguel M Martinez.
Licensure Skilled Care; Intermediate Care.
Beds 120. *Certified* Medicaid.
Ownership Proprietary.

ELDORADO

Schleicher County Medical Center
305 Murchison St, Eldorado, TX, 76936 (915)
853-2507
Admin Lilliam M Kroeger. *Medical Dir/Dir of
Nursing* Dr H Shih.
Licensure Intermediate Care. *Beds* 38. *Certified* Medicaid.
Admissions Requirements Medical examination.
Staff Physicians; RNs; LPNs 7 (ft); Orderlies 2
(ft); Nurses aides 8 (ft); Activities coordinators
1 (ft); Dietitians 4 (ft).
Facilities Dining room; Activities room; Laundry room; Barber/Beauty shop.
Activities Arts and Crafts; Cards; Games; Prayer groups; Shopping trips; Annual barbeque for
residents' families; Monthly birthday parties.

ELECTRA

Electra Nursing Center
511 S Bailey, Electra, TX, 76360 (817)
495-2184
Admin Oneta Gregg.
Licensure Intermediate Care. *Beds* 69. *Certified* Medicaid.

ELGIN

Elgin Golden Years Retirement Nursing Home
605 N US Hwy 290, Elgin, TX, 78621 (512)
285-3444
Admin Patricia Ann McCullough.

Licensure Intermediate Care. *Beds* 56. *Certified* Medicaid.
Staff RNs 1 (pt); LPNs 4 (ft); Nurses aides 24
(ft), 2 (pt); Activities coordinators 1 (ft), 2 (pt);
Dietitians 1 (pt).
Facilities Dining room; Activities room; Laundry room; Barber/Beauty shop.
Activities Arts and Crafts; Cards; Games; Prayer groups.
Description Golden Years is a small-town
nursing home run and owned by Elgin people.
The community is very supportive and active.

ELKHART

Elkhart Nursing Home Inc^
PO Drawer 7, Jones Rd, Elkhart, TX, 75839
(214) 764-2291
Admin Frank M Bryan.
Licensure Intermediate Care. *Beds* 99. *Certified* Medicaid.
Ownership Proprietary.

ENNIS

Claystone Manor*
PO Box 795, 1107 S Clay, Ennis, TX, 75119
(214) 875-8411
Admin Christine Martin.
Licensure Intermediate Care. *Beds* 120. *Certified* Medicaid.
Ownership Proprietary.

Four Seasons Nursing Center
1200 S Hall St, Ennis, TX, 75119 (214)
875-2673
Admin Mark R Cummings. *Medical Dir/Dir
of Nursing* W D Kinzie MD.
Licensure Skilled Care; Intermediate Care.
Beds 154. *Certified* Medicaid.
Admissions Requirements Minimum age 18.
Staff Physicians 9 (pt); RNs 6 (ft); LPNs 13
(ft), 6 (pt); Orderlies 2 (ft); Nurses aides 39 (ft),
11 (pt); Physical therapists 2 (pt); Recreational
therapists 1 (ft); Occupational therapists 1 (pt);
Speech therapists 1 (pt); Activities coordinators
2 (ft); Dietitians 1 (pt); Dentists 1 (pt); Ophthalmologists 1 (pt); Podiatrists 1 (pt); Audiologists
1 (pt).
Facilities Dining room; Activities room; Chapel; Crafts room; Barber/Beauty shop; Library;
Living and lounge rooms.
Activities Arts and Crafts; Cards; Games;
Reading groups; Prayer groups; Movies; Shopping trips; Dances/Social or cultural gatherings;
Outside trips; Garden club; College classes.
Description Two beautifully decorated buildings on 4 ½ acre campus; 62-bed private
building, with private carpeted rooms, meals
served on china, ICAH approved, superior
rating by Texas Department of Health; 92-bed
ICF/Skilled Medicaid Building.

Odd Fellow and Rebekah Nursing Home*
Rt 1, Oak Grove Rd, Ennis, TX, 75119 (214)
875-8641
Admin David A Dunnahoo.
Licensure Intermediate Care. *Beds* 58. *Certified* Medicaid.
Ownership Nonprofit.
Affiliation Independent Order of Odd Fellows

EULESS

Euless Nursing Center*
901 Clinic Dr, Euless, TX, 76039 (817)
283-5326
Admin Virginia Dare Thomas.
Licensure Intermediate Care. *Beds* 120. *Certified* Medicaid.
Ownership Proprietary.

EVANT

January Care Home
506 Circle Dr, Evant, TX, 76525 (817)
471-5526
Admin Sammie Lemons. *Medical Dir/Dir of
Nursing* Dr C B Wright.
Licensure Intermediate Care. *Beds* 53. *Certified* Medicaid.
Staff Physicians 4 (pt); RNs 1 (pt); LPNs 4 (ft),
1 (pt); Nurses aides 7 (ft), 3 (pt); Activities coordinators 1 (ft); Dietitians 1 (pt); Dentists 1 (pt).
Facilities Dining room; Activities room; Crafts
room; Laundry room; Barber/Beauty shop.
Activities Arts and Crafts; Cards; Games;
Reading groups; Prayer groups; Shopping trips;
Dances/Social or cultural gatherings.

FAIRFIELD

Fairview Manor*
PO Box 166, Ray at Reunion St, Fairfield, TX,
75840 (214) 389-4121
Admin Nellie H Halbert.
Licensure Intermediate Care. *Beds* 90. *Certified* Medicaid.
Ownership Proprietary.

FALFURRIAS

Retama Manor Nursing Center*
1301 S Terrell St, Falfurrias, TX, 78355 (512)
325-3691
Admin Ann P Rotge.
Licensure Intermediate Care. *Beds* 100. *Certified* Medicaid.
Ownership Proprietary.

FARMERS BRANCH

Brookhaven Nursing Center
5 Medical Pkwy, Farmers Branch, TX, 75234
(214) 247-1000
Admin William A Rohloff. *Medical Dir/Dir of
Nursing* Roger Beaudoing MD.
Licensure Skilled Care. *Beds* 102. *Certified* Medicaid; Medicare.
Admissions Requirements Medical examination; Physician's request.
Staff RNs 7 (ft), 5 (pt); LPNs 8 (ft); Orderlies 1
(ft); Nurses aides 30 (ft), 6 (pt); Physical therapists 2 (ft); Occupational therapists 1 (ft), 1 (pt);
Speech therapists 1 (ft); Activities coordinators
2 (ft); Dietitians 1 (ft); Dentists 1 (ft); Ophthalmologists 2 (ft).
Affiliation Lutheran
Facilities Dining room; Physical therapy room;
Activities room; Chapel; Crafts room; Barber/Beauty shop.

Activities Arts and Crafts; Cards; Games; Prayer groups; Movies; Shopping trips; Dances/Social or cultural gatherings.

FARMERSVILLE

Hinton Home Inc
205 Beach St, Farmersville, TX, 75031 (214) 782-6191
Admin Opal Hinton.
Licensure Intermediate Care. *Beds* 74. *Certified* Medicaid.
Staff RNs 1 (pt); Orderlies 4 (pt); Nurses aides 28 (ft), 2 (pt); Activities coordinators 1 (ft); Dietitians 1 (pt).
Facilities Dining room; Activities room; Chapel; Laundry room; Barber/Beauty shop.
Activities Cards; Games; Prayer groups; Movies; Shopping trips.
Description This is a family-operated facility.

FARWELL

Farwell Convalescent Center*
305 5th St, Farwell, TX, 79325 (806) 481-9027
Admin Mary A Resch.
Licensure Intermediate Care. *Beds* 100. *Certified* Medicaid.
Ownership Proprietary.

FERRIS

Brookhaven Nursing Home
201 E 5th St, Ferris, TX, 75125 (214) 544-2418
Admin William E Campbell.
Licensure Intermediate Care. *Beds* 56. *Certified* Medicaid.
Staff LPNs 5 (ft); Nurses aides 18 (ft); Activities coordinators 1 (ft).
Facilities Dining room; Laundry room.
Activities Arts and Crafts; Games; Prayer groups; Dances/Social or cultural gatherings.
Description Brookhaven is located in a small town just south of Dallas, conveniently located just off Intersate 45.

FLATONIA

Oak Manor Nursing Center
624 N Converse St, Flatonia, TX, 78941 (512) 865-3571
Admin Debbie Grosenbacher.
Licensure Intermediate Care. *Beds* 90. *Certified* Medicaid.
Staff Physicians 1 (pt); RNs 1 (pt); LPNs 8 (ft), 2 (pt); Nurses aides 20 (ft), 5 (pt); Physical therapists 1 (pt); Activities coordinators 1 (ft); Dietitians 1 (pt); Dentists 1 (pt); Podiatrists 1 (pt).
Facilities Dining room; Activities room; Crafts room; Laundry room; Barber/Beauty shop; Library.
Activities Arts and Crafts; Cards; Games; Reading groups; Prayer groups; Movies; Shopping trips; Dances/Social or cultural gatherings.
Description Oak Manor Nursing Center is located in a beautiful rural setting in south central Texas. In April, 1984 we qualified for a Superior Rating awarded by the Texas Department of Health. This is the third consecutive year we have received this certificate.

FLORESVILLE

Floresville Nursing Home*
1811 6th St, Floresville, TX, 78114 (512) 393-2561
Admin James R Moses.
Licensure Intermediate Care. *Beds* 84. *Certified* Medicaid.
Ownership Proprietary.

FLOYDADA

Floydada Nursing Home*
Box 609, 925 W Crockett, Floydada, TX, 79235 (806) 983-3704
Admin Steve Westbrook.
Licensure Intermediate Care. *Beds* 52. *Certified* Medicaid.
Ownership Proprietary.

FORT STOCKTON

Comanche View Nursing Home*
PO Box 128, 101 N Rooney, Fort Stockton, TX, 79735 (915) 336-5261
Admin David B Herrell.
Licensure Intermediate Care. *Beds* 68. *Certified* Medicaid.
Ownership Proprietary.

FORT WORTH

Arlington Heights Nursing Center Inc
4825 Wellesley St, Fort Worth, TX, 76107 (817) 732-6608
Admin Lisbeth Miller. *Medical Dir/Dir of Nursing* Randall E Hayes DO.
Licensure Skilled Care; Intermediate Care. *Beds* 180. *Certified* Medicaid.
Admissions Requirements Medical examination; Physician's request.
Staff RNs 3 (ft), 2 (pt); LPNs 22 (ft); Nurses aides 46 (ft); Activities coordinators 1 (ft); Dietitians 1 (ft); Psychotherapist 1 (ft).
Facilities Dining room; Physical therapy room; Activities room; Laundry room; Barber/Beauty shop.
Activities Arts and Crafts; Cards; Games; Reading groups; Prayer groups; Movies; Shopping trips; Dances/Social or cultural gatherings.

Autumn Place*
1617 W Cannon, Fort Worth, TX, 76014 (817) 336-7283
Admin Betty J Ezell.
Licensure Skilled Care; Intermediate Care. *Beds* 104. *Certified* Medicaid.
Ownership Proprietary.

Autumn Years Lodge Inc
424 S Adams, Fort Worth, TX, 76104 (817) 335-5781
Admin Betty L Giaimo. *Medical Dir/Dir of Nursing* George McIlheran Jr MD.
Licensure Skilled Care; Intermediate Care. *Beds* 139. *Certified* Medicaid.
Admissions Requirements Medical examination.
Staff Physicians 1 (pt); RNs 3 (ft), 1 (pt); LPNs 8 (ft), 1 (pt); Nurses aides 40 (ft), 3 (pt); Recreational therapists 1 (pt); Occupational therapists 1 (pt); Speech therapists 1 (pt); Activities coordinators 1 (ft); Dietitians 1 (pt); Dentists 1 (pt).
Facilities Dining room; Physical therapy room; Chapel; Barber/Beauty shop; Library.
Activities Arts and Crafts; Cards; Games; Prayer groups; Movies.
Description Autumn Years Lodge is a nursing facility in the hospital district of Fort Worth, giving highest quality nursing care; activities program is interesting, restorative, and educational.

Brookhaven Nursing and Convalescent Center
4208 E Lancaster, Fort Worth, TX, 76103 (817) 535-0816
Admin Idalene Fuller. *Medical Dir/Dir of Nursing* Randall E Hayes DO.
Licensure Intermediate Care. *Beds* 61. *Certified* Medicaid.
Admissions Requirements Medical examination; Physician's request.
Staff RNs 1 (ft); LPNs 6 (ft); Nurses aides 16 (ft), 4 (pt); Activities coordinators 1 (ft); Dietitians 1 (ft).
Facilities Dining room; Activities room; Chapel; Laundry room; Barber/Beauty shop.
Activities Arts and Crafts; Games; Reading groups; Prayer groups; Movies; Dances/Social or cultural gatherings.

Colonial Manor Nursing Center
400 S Beach, Fort Worth, TX, 76105 (817) 535-2135
Admin Ann Williams. *Medical Dir/Dir of Nursing* Barry Ungerleider DO.
Licensure Skilled Care. *Beds* 181. *Certified* Medicaid.
Admissions Requirements Minimum age 21.
Staff RNs 3 (ft); Nurses aides 18 (ft), 7 (pt); Activities coordinators 2 (ft); Dietitians 1 (ft).
Facilities Dining room; Activities room; Chapel; Crafts room; Barber/Beauty shop.
Activities Arts and Crafts; Cards; Games; Reading groups; Prayer groups; Movies; Shopping trips; Dances/Social or cultural gatherings; Voter registration; Dallas Cowgirl visits; Indoor bowling; Gardening.
Description Central Fort Worth location; full dietary services including kosher meals upon request; locally owned by Trucare, Inc; a quality care community; private and semi-private rooms; professional staff; physicians always available.

Cumberland Rest Inc*
1628 6th Ave, Fort Worth, TX, 76104 (817) 924-1740, 926-0426
Admin Gayle L Shelton.
Licensure Custodial Care. *Beds* Custodial Care 18.
Ownership Proprietary.

Eastwood Village Nursing and Retirement Center*
3825 Village Creek Rd, Fort Worth, TX, 76119 (817) 531-3696
Admin Dovie J Webber.
Licensure Intermediate Care. *Beds* 100. *Certified* Medicaid.
Ownership Proprietary.

Fireside Lodge of Fort Worth*
4800 White Settlement Rd, Fort Worth, TX, 76114 (817) 738-6556
Admin Elsie Lee Gaston.
Licensure Intermediate Care. *Beds* 92. *Certified* Medicaid.
Ownership Proprietary.

Forest Hill Nursing Center Inc
4607 California Pkwy E, Fort Worth, TX, 76119 (817) 535-0851
Admin Lois M Jenkins. *Medical Dir/Dir of Nursing* William A Griffith DO.
Licensure Skilled Care. *Beds* 120. *Certified* Medicaid.
Admissions Requirements Medical examination; Physician's request.
Staff RNs 1 (ft), 2 (pt); LPNs 12 (ft), 3 (pt); Nurses aides 32 (ft), 2 (pt); Reality therapists 1 (ft); Dietitians 1 (pt).
Facilities Dining room; Activities room; Laundry room; Barber/Beauty shop.
Activities Arts and Crafts; Cards; Games; Prayer groups; Shopping trips; Dances/Social or cultural gatherings.
Description Residents/patients have started a Memorial Rose Garden in the center of one of the totally enclosed patios. Families are donating all of the bushes.

Fort Worth Western Hills Nursing Home Inc
8001 Western Hills Blvd, Fort Worth, TX, 76108 (817) 246-4953
Admin Dorothy Sullivan. *Medical Dir/Dir of Nursing* Dr C E Everett.
Licensure Intermediate Care. *Beds* 270. *Certified* Medicaid; Medicare.
Admissions Requirements Minimum age 18; Medical examination; Physician's request.
Staff Physicians 1 (ft); RNs 4 (ft), 1 (pt); LPNs 20 (ft), 1 (pt); Orderlies 1 (pt); Nurses aides 67 (ft), 2 (pt); Physical therapists 1 (ft); Activities coordinators 1 (ft), 1 (pt); Dietitians 1 (ft).
Facilities Dining room; Physical therapy room; Activities room; Chapel; Crafts room; Laundry room; Barber/Beauty shop; TV lounges.
Activities Arts and Crafts; Cards; Games; Reading groups; Prayer groups; Movies; Shopping trips; Dances/Social or cultural gatherings; Exercise class.
Description VA approved.

Four Seasons Nursing Center—North Richland Hills
7625 Glenview, Fort Worth, TX, 76118 (817) 284-1427
Admin Kathleen H Peterson. *Medical Dir/Dir of Nursing* Alexander Graham MD.
Licensure Skilled Care; Intermediate Care. *Beds* 114. *Certified* Medicaid.
Staff Physicians 1 (pt); RNs 7 (ft), 2 (pt); LPNs 5 (ft), 1 (pt); Nurses aides 29 (ft), 2 (pt); Physical therapists 1 (pt); Occupational therapists 1 (pt); Speech therapists 1 (pt); Activities coordinators 1 (ft), 1 (pt); Dietitians 1 (pt); Rheumatologist 1 (pt).
Facilities Dining room; Physical therapy room; Activities room; Crafts room; Laundry room; Barber/Beauty shop; Library.
Activities Arts and Crafts; Cards; Games; Reading groups; Prayer groups; Movies; Dances/Social or cultural gatherings; Adult education; Cooking; Gardening; Pet-a-pet.
Description This center specializes in arthritic and rehabilitative nursing care.

Four Seasons Nursing Center—Northwest
2129 Skyline Dr, Fort Worth, TX, 76114 (817) 626-1956
Admin Kay Severson. *Medical Dir/Dir of Nursing* Barry Ungerleider DO.
Licensure Skilled Care; Intermediate Care. *Beds* 108. *Certified* Medicaid; Medicare.
Admissions Requirements Medical examination; Physician's request.
Staff Physicians 1 (ft); RNs 2 (ft), 3 (pt); LPNs 7 (ft), 3 (pt); Orderlies 1 (pt); Nurses aides 27 (ft), 3 (pt); Activities coordinators 1 (ft).
Facilities Dining room; Physical therapy room; Activities room; Laundry room; Barber/Beauty shop.
Activities Games; Prayer groups; Shopping trips; Dances/Social or cultural gatherings.
Description Facility is JCAH accredited and superior rated.

Francis Convalescent Center
1000 6th Ave, Fort Worth, TX, 76104 (817) 336-2586
Admin Joan Bingman.
Licensure Skilled Care; Intermediate Care. *Beds* 130. *Certified* Medicaid.
Staff Physicians 2 (ft); RNs 2 (ft), 3 (pt); LPNs 9 (ft), 3 (pt); Nurses aides 25 (ft), 4 (pt); Physical therapists 1 (ft); Occupational therapists 1 (pt); Speech therapists 1 (pt); Activities coordinators 2 (ft), 1 (pt); Dietitians 1 (ft), 1 (pt); Dentists 1 (pt); Ophthalmologists 1 (pt); Podiatrists 1 (pt); Medical aides 1 (ft), 1 (pt).
Facilities Dining room; Activities room; Crafts room; Laundry room; Barber/Beauty shop; Sunroom.
Activities Arts and Crafts; Cards; Games; Reading groups; Prayer groups; Movies; Shopping trips; Dances/Social or cultural gatherings.
Description Facility has been recently remodeled and a wing added; rooms are spacious, color coordinated, professionally decorated throughout building; 3 different living/activity areas.

Haltom Convalescent Center
2936 Markum Dr, Fort Worth, TX, 76117 (817) 831-0545
Admin Joan Bellah. *Medical Dir/Dir of Nursing* Charles Riddle MD.
Licensure Intermediate Care. *Beds* 146. *Certified* Medicaid.
Admissions Requirements Minimum age 18; Medical examination; Physician's request.
Staff RNs 1 (ft); LPNs 9 (ft); Orderlies 2 (ft); Nurses aides 44 (ft); Activities coordinators 2 (ft).
Facilities Dining room; Activities room; Crafts room; Barber/Beauty shop.
Activities Arts and Crafts; Cards; Games; Reading groups; Prayer groups; Movies; Shopping trips; Dances/Social or cultural gatherings.

Hearthstone Nursing Home*
701 Saint Louis, Fort Worth, TX, 76104 (817) 335-4151
Admin Elizabeth A Strange.

Licensure Intermediate Care. *Beds* 103. *Certified* Medicaid.
Ownership Proprietary.

Jackson Square Nursing Center
814 Weiler Blvd, Fort Worth, TX, 76112 (817) 451-8111
Admin Mamie Jo Gentry. *Medical Dir/Dir of Nursing* John E Johnson Jr MD.
Licensure Skilled Care. *Beds* 60. *Certified* Medicaid.
Staff RNs 2 (ft), 4 (pt); LPNs 3 (ft), 2 (pt); Nurses aides 10 (ft), 6 (pt); Activities coordinators 1 (ft); Dietitians 1 (ft), 1 (pt); Dentists 1 (pt); Podiatrists 1 (pt).
Facilities Dining room; Activities room; Laundry room; Barber/Beauty shop.
Activities Arts and Crafts; Games; Prayer groups; Movies; Dances/Social or cultural gatherings.
Description Facility offers an ongoing activity program. VA approved.

Jackson Square Nursing Center of Texas Inc*
921 W Cannon, Fort Worth, TX, 76104 (817) 332-9261
Admin Linda M Hazel.
Licensure Intermediate Care. *Beds* 53. *Certified* Medicaid.
Ownership Proprietary.

Jarvis Heights Nursing Center
3601 Hardy St, Fort Worth, TX, 76106 (817) 625-2739
Admin Carol M Egbert. *Medical Dir/Dir of Nursing* Harold C Shilling MD PA.
Licensure Skilled Care. *Beds* 124. *Certified* Medicaid.
Admissions Requirements Medical examination; Physician's request.
Staff Physicians 1 (ft); RNs 3 (ft), 2 (pt); LPNs 10 (ft), 7 (pt); Orderlies 1 (pt); Nurses aides 36 (ft), 5 (pt); Activities coordinators 1 (ft), 1 (pt).
Facilities Dining room; Activities room; Laundry room; Library.
Activities Arts and Crafts; Cards; Games; Reading groups; Movies; Dances/Social or cultural gatherings.

Kent Nursing Homes Inc*
2416 NW 18th St, Fort Worth, TX, 76106 (817) 626-5454
Admin James R McIntosh.
Licensure Skilled Care. *Beds* 120. *Certified* Medicaid.
Ownership Proprietary.

Kent's Nursing Center*
900 W Leuda St, Fort Worth, TX, 76104 (817) 332-7003
Admin Jack M Roe.
Licensure Skilled Care. *Beds* 107. *Certified* Medicaid.
Ownership Proprietary.

Lake Worth Nursing Home
4220 Wells Dr, Fort Worth, TX, 76135 (817) 237-6101
Admin Martha Patrick. *Medical Dir/Dir of Nursing* H B Stilwell DO.
Licensure Skilled Care. *Beds* 70. *Certified* Medicaid.
Admissions Requirements Minimum age 16;

Medical examination; Physician's request.
Staff RNs 2 (ft); LPNs 9 (ft); Orderlies 2 (ft); Nurses aides 30 (ft); Activities coordinators 1 (ft).
Facilities Dining room; Laundry room.
Activities Arts and Crafts; Cards; Games; Reading groups; Prayer groups; Movies; Shopping trips; Dances/Social or cultural gatherings.
Description Lake Worth Nursing Home overlooks Lake Worth which provides a beautiful view and excellent facilities for fishing.

Luxton Nursing Center Inc*
1000 Luxton St, Fort Worth, TX, 76104 (817) 332-4042
Admin Ola Mae Montgomery.
Licensure Intermediate Care. *Beds* 130. *Certified* Medicaid.
Ownership Proprietary.

Meadowbrook Nursing Home*
3301 View St, Fort Worth, TX, 76103 (817) 531-3616
Admin Phyllis M Massey.
Licensure Skilled Care; Intermediate Care. *Beds* 187. *Certified* Medicaid.
Ownership Proprietary.

Richland Hills Nursing Home
3109 Kings Ct, Fort Worth, TX, 76118 (817) 589-2431
Admin Yvonne Jabri. *Medical Dir/Dir of Nursing* John Byarley MD.
Licensure Skilled Care; Intermediate Care. *Beds* 92. *Certified* Medicaid.
Admissions Requirements Minimum age 16; Medical examination; Physician's request.
Staff RNs 1 (ft), 3 (pt); LPNs 6 (ft), 2 (pt); Orderlies 2 (ft); Nurses aides 34 (ft); Activities coordinators 1 (ft); Dietitians 1 (pt).
Facilities Dining room; Activities room; Laundry room; Barber/Beauty shop.
Activities Arts and Crafts; Cards; Games; Prayer groups; Movies; Shopping trips; Dances/Social or cultural gatherings.

Ridgewood Manor
201 Sycamore School Rd, Fort Worth, TX, 76134 (817) 293-7610
Admin Ruth Cahall. *Medical Dir/Dir of Nursing* David Engleking MD.
Licensure Intermediate Care. *Beds* 150. *Certified* Medicaid.
Admissions Requirements Medical examination; Physician's request.
Staff Physicians 1 (pt); RNs 1 (ft), 2 (pt); LPNs 9 (ft), 3 (pt); Nurses aides 31 (ft), 5 (pt); Physical therapists 1 (pt); Recreational therapists 1 (pt); Occupational therapists 1 (pt); Speech therapists 1 (pt); Activities coordinators 1 (ft); Dietitians 1 (pt); Dentists 1 (pt); Ophthalmologists 1 (pt); Podiatrists 1 (pt).
Facilities Dining room; Activities room; Chapel; Crafts room; Laundry room; Barber-/Beauty shop; Library; Living room; Covered patio; Smoking areas.
Activities Arts and Crafts; Cards; Games; Reading groups; Prayer groups; Movies; Shopping trips; Dances/Social or cultural gatherings; Swimming; Baking Clan; Residents council; Meet the New Residents.
Description At Ridgewood Manor great pride is taken in cleanliness inside and outside. Huge

covered patio with carpet is most beautiful with hanging baskets and running roses across courtyard fence. Love is ageless and truly is in abundance at the Ridgewood Manor.

Stanford Convalescent Center—Eighth Ave
1535 Pennsylvania, Fort Worth, TX, 76104 (817) 336-2786
Admin Ollie C Wilson.
Licensure Intermediate Care. *Beds* 89. *Certified* Medicaid.

Stanford Convalescent Center—Hemphill*
1617 Hemphill, Fort Worth, TX, 76104 (817) 926-9201
Admin Sharlene Crisp.
Licensure Skilled Care; Intermediate Care. *Beds* 132. *Certified* Medicaid.
Ownership Proprietary.

Stanford Convalescent Center—Jennings*
929 Hemphill St, Fort Worth, TX, 76104 (817) 336-9191
Admin James Roberts.
Licensure Intermediate Care. *Beds* 120. *Certified* Medicaid.
Ownership Nonprofit.

Stanford Convalescent Center—Pennsylvania*
901 Pennsylvania, Fort Worth, TX, 76104 (817) 335-3030
Admin Kathleen A Gerrity.
Licensure Intermediate Care. *Beds* 125. *Certified* Medicaid.
Ownership Proprietary.

Stonebrook*
Rt 2, Box 935A, 8401 Jacksboro Hwy, Fort Worth, TX, 76135 (817) 237-3335
Admin Thomas R Michael.
Licensure Intermediate Care. *Beds* 104. *Certified* Medicaid.
Ownership Proprietary.

Watson Nursing Home*
5000 E Lancaster, Fort Worth, TX, 76102 (817) 535-3447
Admin Eudora Marie Pack.
Licensure Intermediate Care. *Beds* 69. *Certified* Medicaid.
Ownership Proprietary.

Webber Nursing Center
4900 E Berry St, Fort Worth, TX, 76105 (817) 531-3707
Admin Virginia N Como. *Medical Dir/Dir of Nursing* Dr M J Brooks.
Licensure Intermediate Care. *Beds* 145. *Certified* Medicaid.
Admissions Requirements Medical examination; Physician's request.
Staff Physicians 1 (ft); RNs 1 (ft), 1 (pt); LPNs 6 (ft), 1 (pt); Orderlies 2 (ft); Nurses aides 16 (ft), 8 (pt); Physical therapists 1 (pt); Activities coordinators 2 (ft), 1 (pt); Dietitians 1 (pt); Podiatrists 1 (pt).
Facilities Dining room; Activities room; Laundry room; Barber/Beauty shop.
Activities Arts and Crafts; Cards; Games; Reading groups; Prayer groups; Movies; Shopping trips; Dances/Social or cultural gatherings; Male chorus; Resident of the Month; Newsletter.

Wedgewood Nursing Home*
6621 Old Granbury Rd, Fort Worth, TX, 76133 (817) 292-6330
Admin Henry C Hames.
Licensure Skilled Care. *Beds* 129. *Certified* Medicaid.
Ownership Proprietary.

White Settlement Nursing Center
7820 Skyline Park Dr, Fort Worth, TX, 76108 (817) 246-4671
Admin Betty S Martin. *Medical Dir/Dir of Nursing* Robert Irwin DO.
Licensure Skilled Care. *Beds* 108. *Certified* Medicaid.
Admissions Requirements Minimum age 18; Medical examination; Physician's request.
Staff RNs 4 (ft); LPNs 9 (ft); Nurses aides 26 (ft); Physical therapists; Reality therapists; Recreational therapists; Occupational therapists; Speech therapists; Activities coordinators; Dietitians; Dentists; Podiatrists.
Facilities Dining room; Activities room; Laundry room; Barber/Beauty shop.
Activities Arts and Crafts; Cards; Games; Reading groups; Prayer groups; Movies; Shopping trips; Dances/Social or cultural gatherings.

FRANKSTON

Frankston Nursing Center*
Hwy 155, Frankston, TX, 75763 (214) 876-3208
Admin Martha Bevel.
Licensure Intermediate Care. *Beds* 76. *Certified* Medicaid.
Ownership Proprietary.

FREDERICKSBURG

Brown's Nursing Home Inc
Kerr Rt Box 12, W Live Oak Rd, Fredericksburg, TX, 78624 (512) 997-4391
Admin Bernice Dryden. *Medical Dir/Dir of Nursing* Leona Black LVN.
Licensure Intermediate Care. *Beds* 92. *Certified* Medicaid.
Staff RNs 1 (pt); Orderlies 2 (pt); Nurses aides 24 (pt); Physical therapists 1 (pt); Occupational therapists 1 (pt); Speech therapists 1 (pt); Dietitians 1 (pt).
Facilities Dining room; Activities room; Chapel; Crafts room; Laundry room; Barber/Beauty shop.

Fredericksburg Nursing Home*
1117 S Adams, Fredericksburg, TX, 78624 (512) 997-4364
Admin Lynn J Hecht.
Licensure Intermediate Care. *Beds* 90. *Certified* Medicaid.
Ownership Nonprofit.
Affiliation Seventh-Day Adventist

Knopp Nursing and Retirement Home 2
202 Holmig Ln, Rt 1, Box 311, Fredericksburg, TX, 78624 (512) 997-7924
Admin Jerry Luckenbach. *Medical Dir/Dir of Nursing* Dr Lorence Fellen.
Licensure Intermediate Care. *Beds* 60. *Certified* Medicaid.

Staff LPNs 4 (ft), 1 (pt); Orderlies 1 (ft); Nurses aides 11 (ft), 4 (pt); Activities coordinators 1 (ft).
Facilities Dining room; Activities room; Laundry room; Barber/Beauty shop.
Activities Arts and Crafts; Games; Prayer groups; Movies; Dances/Social or cultural gatherings.

Knopp Nursing Home Inc 1*
Rt 1, Box 311, Fredericksburg, TX, 78624 (512) 997-3704
Admin Irene Luckenbach.
Licensure Skilled Care; Intermediate Care.
Beds 123. *Certified* Medicaid; Medicare.
Ownership Proprietary.

FRIENDSWOOD

Friendswood Arms Convalescent Center*
213 Heritage Dr, Friendswood, TX, 77546 (713) 482-1281
Admin Patricia A Beem.
Licensure Skilled Care; Intermediate Care.
Beds 121. *Certified* Medicaid.
Ownership Proprietary.

FRIONA

Prairie Acres
201 E 15th St, Friona, TX, 79035 (806) 247-3922
Admin Jo Gene Blackwell.
Licensure Intermediate Care. *Beds* 65. *Certified* Medicaid.
Ownership Public.
Admissions Requirements Medical examination; Physician's request.
Staff Physicians 3 (pt); RNs 1 (pt); LPNs 5 (ft), 2 (pt); Nurses aides 18 (ft); Activities coordinators 1 (ft), 2 (pt); Dietitians 1 (pt); Pharmacist 1 (pt); Others 13 (ft), 1 (pt).
Facilities Dining room; Activities room; Crafts room; Laundry room; Barber/Beauty shop; Van.
Activities Arts and Crafts; Cards; Games; Reading groups; Prayer groups; Movies; Shopping trips; Dances/Social or cultural gatherings.
Description Facility is owned by City of Friona and receives community support and involvement; excellent nursing care; rated superior by Texas Department of Health; trip van has hydraulic wheelchair lift and tiedowns and will accommodate stretcher and normal seating.

GAINESVILLE

Frontier Manor*
1907 Refinery Rd, Gainesville, TX, 76240 (817) 665-0386
Admin Leo A Ladouceur.
Licensure Intermediate Care. *Beds* 118. *Certified* Medicaid.
Ownership Proprietary.

Gainesville Convalescent Center*
1900 O'Neal St, Gainesville, TX, 76240 (817) 665-2826
Admin Milie P Belcher.

Licensure Intermediate Care. *Beds* 120. *Certified* Medicaid.
Ownership Proprietary.

Oak Tree Lodge
Hwy 51, Black Hill Dr, Gainesville, TX, 76240 (817) 665-5221
Admin Linda Edgett. *Medical Dir/Dir of Nursing* Dr William Powell.
Licensure Intermediate Care. *Beds* 48. *Certified* Medicaid.
Admissions Requirements Medical examination; Physician's request.
Staff Physicians 1 (ft); RNs 1 (ft); Nurses aides 7 (ft), 2 (pt); Physical therapists 2 (ft); Activities coordinators 1 (ft); Dietitians 1 (ft); Dentists 1 (ft).
Description Facility also offers an adult day care program for approximately 12 hours, not overnight, which includes 2 hot meals.

GALVESTON

Turner Geriatric Center
2228 Seawall Blvd, Galveston, TX, 77550 (713) 763-6437
Admin Arthur C Johnson III. *Medical Dir/Dir of Nursing* Dr Edward Lefeber.
Licensure Intermediate Care. *Beds* 164. *Certified* Medicaid.
Admissions Requirements Minimum age 62; Medical examination; Physician's request.
Staff Physicians 1 (pt); RNs 7 (pt); LPNs 3 (ft), 13 (pt); Nurses aides 5 (ft), 45 (pt); Occupational therapists 1 (ft), 1 (pt); Activities coordinators 1 (ft); Dietitians 2 (ft); Pharmacists 1 (ft); Social workers 1 (ft).
Affiliation Methodist
Facilities Dining room; Physical therapy room; Activities room; Chapel; Crafts room; Laundry room; Barber/Beauty shop; Private showers in each room.
Activities Arts and Crafts; Cards; Games; Reading groups; Prayer groups; Movies; Shopping trips; Dances/Social or cultural gatherings.
Description Turner Geriatric Center offers 5 levels of care from personal care through (and featuring) a "sheltered unit" for the mentally impaired; although typed ICF, Turner exceeds the skilled staffing requirements and Medicaid rules. Outstanding programs include a full-service pharmacy, full-time social worker, and a consulting psychologist.

GANADO

Care Inn of Ganado*
205 W Rogers St, Ganado, TX, 77962 (512) 771-3315
Admin Judy A Liberda.
Licensure Intermediate Care. *Beds* 57. *Certified* Medicaid.
Ownership Proprietary.

GARLAND

Castle Manor*
1922 Castle Dr, Garland, TX, 75040 (214) 494-1471
Admin Margaret Wylie.

Licensure Intermediate Care. *Beds* 100. *Certified* Medicaid.
Ownership Proprietary.

Garland Convalescent Center
321 N Shiloh Rd, Garland, TX, 75042 (214) 276-9571
Admin Henry C Hames. *Medical Dir/Dir of Nursing* James R McLean DO.
Licensure Intermediate Care. *Beds* 120. *Certified* Medicaid.
Admissions Requirements Minimum age 18; Physician's request.
Staff Physicians 1 (pt); RNs 1 (ft); LPNs 8 (ft), 1 (pt); Nurses aides 22 (ft); Physical therapists 1 (pt); Reality therapists 1 (pt); Recreational therapists 1 (pt); Occupational therapists 1 (ft); Speech therapists 1 (ft); Activities coordinators 1 (ft); Dietitians 1 (pt).
Facilities Dining room; Activities room; Crafts room; Laundry room; Barber/Beauty shop.
Activities Arts and Crafts; Cards; Games; Reading groups; Prayer groups; Movies; Shopping trips; Dances/Social or cultural gatherings.

Garland Manors Nursing Home Inc
2101 W Walnut, Garland, TX, 75042 (214) 276-8547
Admin Billy Ray Jacobs.
Licensure Intermediate Care; Custodial Care.
Beds ICF 52; Custodial Care 8. *Certified* Medicaid.

Serenity Haven Nursing Home
106 N Beltline Rd, Garland, TX, 75040 (214) 495-7700
Admin Lois Y Jabri.
Licensure Skilled Care; Intermediate Care.
Beds 120. *Certified* Medicaid.

Silver Leaves Inc
505 W Centerville Rd, Garland, TX, 75041 (214) 278-3566
Admin George E Powell.
Licensure Intermediate Care. *Beds* 250. *Certified* Medicaid.
Ownership Public.
Admissions Requirements Minimum age 18; Medical examination; Physician's request.
Staff LPNs 13 (pt); Nurses aides 39 (pt); Reality therapists 1 (ft); Recreational therapists 1 (ft); Activities coordinators 2 (ft); Dietitians 1 (ft), 1 (pt).
Facilities Dining room; Activities room; Chapel; Crafts room; Laundry room; Barber/Beauty shop; Library.
Activities Arts and Crafts; Cards; Games; Prayer groups; Movies; Shopping trips; Dances/Social or cultural gatherings; Modified sports.
Description Facility offers recreation therapy and social work services utilizing group and individual therapy sessions; organized volunteer program and volunteer council; adopt-a-grandparent program; community involvement; reality orientation and successful experience therapy; active resident council.

GARRISON

Garrison Nursing Home Inc*
PO Box 600, Elm St, Garrison, TX, 75946 (713) 347-2234

Admin Darrell G Yarbrough.
Licensure Intermediate Care. *Beds* 43. *Certified* Medicaid.
Ownership Proprietary.

GATESVILLE

Hillside Manor Nursing Center
101 S 34th St, Gatesville, TX, 76528
Admin Vicki Pressley. *Medical Dir/Dir of Nursing* William F Floyd MD.
Licensure Intermediate Care. *Beds* 110. *Certified* Medicaid.
Ownership Proprietary.
Admissions Requirements Physician's request.
Staff RNs 1 (pt); LPNs 5 (ft), 2 (pt); Nurses aides 16 (ft); Activities coordinators 1 (ft); Dietitians 1 (ft).
Facilities Dining room; Activities room; Laundry room; Barber/Beauty shop.
Activities Arts and Crafts; Games; Prayer groups.
Description Facility is a clean pleasant home small enough to feel like home and large enough to give residents someone to talk with and activities to occupy their time. This home is in a small town where most residents have lived all their lives.

Rotunda Retirement and Convalescent Facility*
2525 Osage Rd, Gatesville, TX, 76528 (817) 865-2231
Admin Walton O Newton.
Licensure Skilled Care; Intermediate Care. *Beds* 210. *Certified* Medicaid.
Ownership Proprietary.

GEORGETOWN

Georgetown Sweetbriar Nursing Home Inc*
N San Gabriel Park Dr, Georgetown, TX, 78626 (512) 255-2746
Admin Linda L Duncan.
Licensure Intermediate Care. *Beds* 120. *Certified* Medicaid.
Ownership Proprietary.

Wesleyan Nursing Home
2001 Scenic Dr, Georgetown, TX, 78626 (512) 863-9511
Admin Charles Bostock. *Medical Dir/Dir of Nursing* Dr Douglas Benold.
Licensure Intermediate Care. *Beds* 98. *Certified* Medicaid.
Admissions Requirements Medical examination; Physician's request.
Staff RNs 2 (ft), 2 (pt); LPNs 11 (ft), 1 (pt); Nurses aides 25 (ft), 9 (pt); Activities coordinators 1 (ft); Dietitians 1 (ft).
Affiliation Methodist
Facilities Dining room; Activities room; Chapel; Laundry room; Barber/Beauty shop; Library.
Activities Arts and Crafts; Cards; Games; Reading groups; Prayer groups; Movies; Shopping trips; Dances/Social or cultural gatherings.
Description Facility has superior rating.

GIDDINGS

Giddings Convalescent Center*
1747 E Hempstead, Giddings, TX, 78942 (713) 542-2150
Admin Ida Nell Baker.
Licensure Intermediate Care. *Beds* 50. *Certified* Medicaid.
Ownership Proprietary.

Hennesey Nursing Home Inc*
PO Box 540, N Williamson St, Giddings, TX, 78942 (713) 542-3611
Admin Pansy H Dismukes.
Licensure Intermediate Care. *Beds* 92. *Certified* Medicaid.
Ownership Proprietary.

GILMER

Gilmer Convalescent Center
703 N Titus St, Gilmer, TX, 75644 (214) 843-5529
Admin JoAnn Hinson. *Medical Dir/Dir of Nursing* Roger Whitman MD.
Licensure Intermediate Care. *Beds* 109. *Certified* Medicaid.
Admissions Requirements Physician's request.
Staff RNs 1 (ft); LPNs 10 (ft), 1 (pt); Nurses aides 38 (ft), 3 (pt); Physical therapists 1 (pt); Speech therapists 1 (pt); Activities coordinators 1 (ft); Dietitians 1 (pt); Dentists 1 (pt).
Affiliation Baptist
Facilities Dining room; Activities room; Laundry room; Barber/Beauty shop.
Activities Arts and Crafts; Games; Reading groups; Prayer groups; Shopping trips; Dances/Social or cultural gatherings.
Description Facility provides quality nursing care, and has an active volunteer group helping with activities; located adjacent to Ford Memorial Hospital.

Leisure Lodge—Gilmer*
1704 Bradford St, Gilmer, TX, 75644 (214) 843-5696
Admin J Louise Knight.
Licensure Intermediate Care. *Beds* 102. *Certified* Medicaid.
Ownership Proprietary.

GLADEWATER

Care Inn of Gladewater
300 N Money St, Gladewater, TX, 75647 (214) 845-2101
Admin Royce Jean Walton.
Licensure Intermediate Care. *Beds* 80. *Certified* Medicaid.
Staff RNs 2 (pt); LPNs 4 (ft), 2 (pt); Nurses aides 16 (ft), 4 (pt); Activities coordinators 1 (ft); Dietitians 1 (ft).
Facilities Dining room; Activities room; Laundry room.
Activities Arts and Crafts; Games; Reading groups; Prayer groups; Shopping trips; Dances/Social or cultural gatherings.
Description Family night is enjoyed by all; facility is located in a small community, which enables residents to share more of a family-type atmosphere.

Oak Manor Nursing Home
Hwy 80 E, Gladewater, TX, 75647 (214) 845-5291
Admin Shirley Mullins. *Medical Dir/Dir of Nursing* Charles McKenzie MD.
Licensure Intermediate Care. *Beds* 120. *Certified* Medicaid.

GLEN ROSE

Glen Rose Nursing Home*
1309 Holden St, Glen Rose, TX, 76043 (817) 897-2215
Admin John Clayton Read.
Licensure Intermediate Care. *Beds* 42. *Certified* Medicaid.
Ownership Nonprofit.

GOLDTHWAITE

Heritage Nursing Home Inc
1207 Reynolds, Goldthwaite, TX, 76844 (915) 648-2258
Admin Beverly K Freeman. *Medical Dir/Dir of Nursing* Dr M A Childress.
Licensure Skilled Care; Intermediate Care. *Beds* 134. *Certified* Medicaid.
Staff RNs 1 (ft), 1 (pt); LPNs 6 (ft), 5 (pt); Orderlies 2 (ft); Nurses aides 22 (ft), 10 (pt); Activities coordinators 1 (ft); Dietitians 1 (pt).
Facilities Dining room; Activities room; Crafts room; Laundry room; Barber/Beauty shop; Library.
Activities Games; Reading groups; Prayer groups; Shopping trips; Dances/Social or cultural gatherings.

Hillview Manor*
PO Box 588, 1110 Rice St, Goldthwaite, TX, 76844 (915) 648-2247
Admin Geraldine Geeslin.
Licensure Intermediate Care. *Beds* 60. *Certified* Medicaid.
Ownership Proprietary.

GOLIAD

Goliad Manor Inc
106 N Welch St, Goliad, TX, 77963 (512) 645-3352
Admin Sherry Newton.
Licensure Intermediate Care. *Beds* 60. *Certified* Medicaid.
Staff LPNs 7 (ft); Nurses aides 25 (ft), 5 (pt); Activities coordinators 1 (pt).
Facilities Dining room; Activities room; Laundry room; Barber/Beauty shop.
Activities Arts and Crafts; Games; Prayer groups; Movies; Shopping trips.

GONZALES

Care Inn of Gonzales*
Rt 4, Box 145, Gonzales, TX, 78629 (512) 672-2867
Admin Audrey A Perkovich.
Licensure Intermediate Care. *Beds* 90. *Certified* Medicaid.
Ownership Proprietary.

Cartwheel Lodge—Gonzales*
PO Box 659, 1800 Cartwheel Dr, Gonzales,
TX, 78629 (512) 672-2887
Admin Kathy E Powell.
Licensure Intermediate Care. *Beds* 98. *Certified* Medicaid.
Ownership Proprietary.

GORMAN

Gorman Care Center*
PO Box 668, 600 W Roosevelt St, Gorman,
TX, 76454 (817) 734-2202
Admin Claude W Swanner.
Licensure Intermediate Care. *Beds* 97. *Certified* Medicaid.
Ownership Proprietary.

GRAHAM

Burgess Manor Nursing Center*
1309 Brazos St, Graham, TX, 76046 (817)
549-3760
Admin Nell E Bullock.
Licensure Intermediate Care. *Beds* 64. *Certified* Medicaid.
Ownership Proprietary.

Cherry Oaks Nursing Center
1201 Cherry St, Graham, TX, 76046 (817)
549-3677
Admin Brenda Freeman. *Medical Dir/Dir of
Nursing* Dr R G McDaniels.
Licensure Intermediate Care. *Beds* 66. *Certified* Medicaid.
Staff LPNs 5 (ft); Orderlies 1 (ft); Nurses aides
11 (ft); Activities coordinators 1 (ft); Dietitians
1 (ft).
Facilities Dining room; Activities room; Chapel; Laundry room; Barber/Beauty shop.
Activities Arts and Crafts; Games; Reading
groups; Prayer groups; Movies; Shopping trips.

Garden Terrace Nursing Center*
1224 Corvadura St, Graham, TX, 76046 (817)
549-4646
Admin Mary L Shabay.
Licensure Intermediate Care. *Beds* 120. *Certified* Medicaid.
Ownership Proprietary.

Leisure Lodge—Graham-West Third
320 W 3rd St, Graham, TX, 76046 (817)
549-1332
Admin Shirley A Moody.
Licensure Intermediate Care. *Beds* 57. *Certified* Medicaid.

GRANBURY

Granbury Care Center
301 Park Dr at Doyle St, Granbury, TX, 76048
(817) 573-3726
Admin Dean E Lindner. *Medical Dir/Dir of
Nursing* Larry G Padget DO.
Licensure Intermediate Care. *Beds* 101. *Certified* Medicaid.
Admissions Requirements Medical examination; Physician's request.
Staff LPNs 6 (ft), 6 (pt); Nurses aides 29 (ft), 7
(pt); Activities coordinators 1 (ft).

Facilities Dining room; Physical therapy room;
Activities room; Chapel; Laundry room; Barber/Beauty shop; Library.
Activities Arts and Crafts; Cards; Games; Prayer groups; Movies; Dances/Social or cultural
gatherings.
Description Granbury Care Center is a 101-bed
facility located on a spacious 20-acre tract situated in the heart of Lake Granbury country,
providing a peaceful setting away from the
hustle and bustle of the big city. Many local civic and church groups help to provide educational and recreational sessions for residents.

Valley View Home*
Drawer M, 600 Reunion St, Granbury, TX,
76048 (817) 573-3773
Admin Carolyn Sue Wilson.
Licensure Intermediate Care. *Beds* 108. *Certified* Medicaid.
Ownership Proprietary.

GRAND PRAIRIE

Great Southwest Convalescent Center
2337 Doreen St, Grand Prairie, TX, 75050
(214) 641-2921
Admin Scott W Donaldson. *Medical Dir/Dir of
Nursing* Ben Capote MD.
Licensure Skilled Care. *Beds* 120. *Certified* Medicaid.
Staff RNs 1 (ft), 1 (pt); LPNs 8 (ft), 3 (pt);
Orderlies 3 (ft); Nurses aides 55 (ft); Activities
coordinators 1 (ft); Dietitians 1 (pt).
Facilities Dining room; Activities room; Crafts
room; Laundry room; Barber/Beauty shop.
Activities Arts and Crafts; Cards; Games;
Reading groups; Prayer groups; Movies.

Metroplex Care Center*
658 SW 3rd St, Grand Prairie, TX, 75051 (214)
264-2464
Admin Elma Gloria Gomez.
Licensure Intermediate Care. *Beds* 150. *Certified* Medicaid.
Ownership Proprietary.

Pleasant Dale Home 1*
305 NW 13th St, Grand Prairie, TX, 75050
(214) 262-1776
Admin Hazel O Walker.
Licensure Intermediate Care. *Beds* 39. *Certified* Medicaid.
Ownership Proprietary.

Pleasant Dale Nursing Home 2
930 NW 19th St, Grand Prairie, TX, 75050
(214) 262-1351
Admin Robert W Donaldson.
Licensure Skilled Care; Intermediate Care.
Beds 96. *Certified* Medicaid.
Facilities Dining room; Activities room; Chapel; Laundry room; Barber/Beauty shop;
Library.
Activities Arts and Crafts; Games; Reading
groups; Prayer groups; Movies; Shopping trips;
Dances/Social or cultural gatherings.

GRAND SALINE

Anderson Memorial Care Homes Inc*
PO Drawer K, Bradburn Rd at High St, Grand
Saline, TX, 75140 (214) 962-4234
Admin Carolyn E La Prade.
Licensure Intermediate Care. *Beds* 76. *Certified* Medicaid.
Ownership Proprietary.

Grand Saline Manor*
441 Spring Creek Rd, Grand Saline, TX, 75140
(214) 962-4226
Admin James Fleet.
Licensure Intermediate Care. *Beds* 76.
Ownership Proprietary.

GRANDVIEW

Grandview Nursing Home*
501 W Criner, Grandview, TX, 76050 (817)
866-3367
Admin Linda Rae Smith.
Licensure Intermediate Care. *Beds* 68. *Certified* Medicaid.
Ownership Nonprofit.

GRANGER

Bluebonnet Nursing Care of Granger
Hwy 95 N, Granger, TX, 76530 (512) 859-2800
Admin Lydia Kurtin.
Licensure Intermediate Care. *Beds* 68. *Certified* Medicaid.
Staff RNs 1 (pt); LPNs 3 (ft), 2 (pt); Nurses
aides 16 (ft), 3 (pt); Activities coordinators 1
(ft).
Facilities Dining room; Chapel; Laundry
room; Barber/Beauty shop.
Activities Arts and Crafts; Games; Prayer
groups; Dances/Social or cultural gatherings.

GRAPELAND

Grapeland Nursing Home
US 287 at Church St, Grapeland, TX, 75844
(409) 687-4655
Admin Carolyn L Garrett.
Licensure Intermediate Care. *Beds* 68. *Certified* Medicaid.
Staff LPNs 6 (ft); Nurses aides 16 (ft); Activities coordinators 1 (ft).
Facilities Dining room; Physical therapy room;
Activities room; Laundry room; Barber/Beauty
shop.
Activities Arts and Crafts; Games; Reading
groups; Prayer groups; Movies; Shopping trips;
Dances/Social or cultural gatherings.

GRAPEVINE

Autumn Haven*
414 N Main St, Grapevine, TX, 76051 (817)
481-1141
Admin Sarah Mitchell.
Licensure Intermediate Care. *Beds* 36. *Certified* Medicaid.
Ownership Proprietary.

Brookhollow Manor Nursing Home Inc
925 Minters Chapel Rd, Grapevine, TX, 76051
(817) 481-1551
Admin Dorothy Johnson. *Medical Dir/Dir of Nursing* E L Lancaster MD.
Licensure Skilled Care; Intermediate Care.
Beds 78. *Certified* Medicaid.
Admissions Requirements Medical examination; Physician's request.
Staff Physicians 1 (pt); RNs 2 (ft), 1 (pt); Orderlies 2 (ft); Nurses aides 20 (ft), 1 (pt); Dentists 1 (pt); Podiatrists 1 (pt); LVNs 7 (ft), 1 (pt).
Facilities Dining room; Activities room; Barber/Beauty shop.
Activities Arts and Crafts; Cards; Games; Shopping trips; Dances/Social or cultural gatherings.

Grapevine Nursing Home*
1500 Autumn Dr, Grapevine, TX, 76051 (817) 488-8585, 481-3622
Admin Terry J Barcelo.
Licensure Intermediate Care. *Beds* 142. *Certified* Medicaid.
Ownership Proprietary.

GREENVILLE

Greencrest Manor Inc
FM 1570, Greenville, TX, 75401 (214) 455-7942
Admin Martha L Ford. *Medical Dir/Dir of Nursing* Henry H Mehmert MD.
Licensure Intermediate Care. *Beds* 112. *Certified* Medicaid.
Admissions Requirements Medical examination; Physician's request.
Staff RNs 2 (ft); LPNs 6 (ft), 1 (pt); Nurses aides 16 (ft); Physical therapists 1 (pt); Speech therapists 1 (pt); Activities coordinators 1 (ft); Dietitians 1 (pt); Dentists 1 (pt); Ophthalmologists 1 (pt); Podiatrists 1 (pt); Audiologists 1 (pt).
Facilities Dining room; Chapel; Laundry room; Barber/Beauty shop.
Activities Arts and Crafts; Cards; Games; Reading groups; Prayer groups; Movies; Shopping trips; Dances/Social or cultural gatherings.

Greenville Nursing Home Inc*
4910 Wellington, Greenville, TX, 75401 (214) 454-3772
Admin Myra L Porter.
Licensure Skilled Care; Intermediate Care.
Beds 120. *Certified* Medicaid.
Ownership Proprietary.

Home for Aged Pythians Inc
6017 Interstate 30, Greenville, TX, 75401 (214) 455-0180
Admin Virginia A Masters. *Medical Dir/Dir of Nursing* Henry E Mehmert MD.
Licensure Intermediate Care. *Beds* 48. *Certified* Medicaid.
Admissions Requirements Medical examination; Physician's request.
Staff Physicians; RNs; LPNs 5 (ft); Nurses aides 9 (ft); Activities coordinators 1 (ft); Dietitians 1 (pt).
Affiliation Knights of Pythias
Facilities Dining room; Activities room;

Laundry room.
Activities Arts and Crafts; Games; Reading groups; Movies; Shopping trips; Dances/Social or cultural gatherings.

Park Haven Nursing Center Inc
3500 Park St, Greenville, TX, 75401 (214) 455-2220
Admin Janet Waldon. *Medical Dir/Dir of Nursing* Dr Henry Mehmert.
Licensure Skilled Care. *Beds* 100. *Certified* Medicaid.
Staff RNs 4 (ft); Nurses aides 28 (ft); Activities coordinators 1 (ft); Dietitians 1 (ft); LVNs 6 (ft), 5 (pt).
Facilities Dining room; Activities room; Chapel; Laundry room; Barber/Beauty shop.
Activities Cards; Reading groups; Movies.

GROESBECK

Groesbeck Park Plaza
6707 Parkside Dr, Groesbeck, TX, 76642 (817) 729-3245
Admin Patricia R Monroe.
Licensure Intermediate Care. *Beds* 90. *Certified* Medicaid.
Admissions Requirements Physician's request.
Staff Physicians 3 (pt); RNs 1 (ft); LPNs 6 (ft), 2 (pt); Nurses aides 20 (ft), 3 (pt); Occupational therapists; Speech therapists; Activities coordinators 1 (ft); Dietitians; Dentists; Podiatrists.
Facilities Dining room; Activities room; Crafts room; Laundry room; Barber/Beauty shop.
Activities Arts and Crafts; Cards; Games; Prayer groups; Shopping trips; Dances/Social or cultural gatherings; Ceramics; Church services.
Description Facility features a hometown atmosphere with a lot of community involvement.

GROVES

Cresthaven Nursing Residence
4400 Gulf Ave, Groves, TX, 77619 (713) 962-5785
Admin Joyce N Lewis. *Medical Dir/Dir of Nursing* Dr H H Randolph Jr.
Licensure Skilled Care; Intermediate Care.
Beds 138. *Certified* Medicaid.
Staff Physicians 1 (pt); RNs 1 (ft), 2 (pt); LPNs 13 (ft); Orderlies 2 (ft); Nurses aides 29 (pt); Activities coordinators 1 (ft), 1 (pt); Dietitians 1 (ft), 1 (pt); Dentists 1 (pt).
Facilities Dining room; Activities room; Chapel; Crafts room; Laundry room; Barber/Beauty shop.
Activities Arts and Crafts; Cards; Games; Reading groups; Prayer groups; Movies; Dances/Social or cultural gatherings.
Description Facility features excellent nursing care; individual therapeutic diets; large trained volunteer program; and activities.

Oak Grove Nursing Home Inc*
6230 Warren St, Groves, TX, 77619 (713) 963-1266
Admin Lois Rushing.
Licensure Intermediate Care. *Beds* 100. *Certified* Medicaid.
Ownership Proprietary.

GROVETON

Groveton Hospital and Nursing Home*
PO Box 890, Hwy 287, Groveton, TX, 75845
(713) 642-1221
Admin LaVerne Alexander.
Licensure Intermediate Care. *Beds* 32. *Certified* Medicaid.
Ownership Public.

GUNTER

Hilltop Haven Home for the Aged
308 E College St, Gunter, TX, 75058 (214) 433-2415
Admin Linda Morrison.
Licensure Intermediate Care; Custodial Care.
Beds ICF 215. *Certified* Medicaid.
Admissions Requirements Minimum age 16; Medical examination; Physician's request.
Staff RNs 4 (ft); LPNs 13 (ft), 6 (pt); Orderlies 1 (ft), 1 (pt); Nurses aides 53 (ft), 7 (pt); Activities coordinators 2 (ft); Dietitians 18 (ft), 5 (pt).
Affiliation Church of Christ
Facilities Dining room; Activities room; Chapel; Crafts room; Laundry room; Barber/Beauty shop; Library.
Activities Arts and Crafts; Cards; Games; Prayer groups; Movies; Shopping trips.
Description Facility has 148 out of 215 beds located in private rooms. There is no extra charge for the private room.

HALE CENTER

Hi-Plains Nursing Home*
202 W 3rd, Hale Center, TX, 79041 (806) 839-2471
Admin Gordon Russell.
Licensure Intermediate Care. *Beds* 44. *Certified* Medicaid.
Ownership Nonprofit.

HALLETTSVILLE

Stevens Convalescent Center Inc
106 Kahn St, PO Box 526, Hallettsville, TX, 77964 (512) 798-3606
Admin Virginia Jagerson.
Licensure Intermediate Care. *Beds* 190. *Certified* Medicaid.
Staff RNs 2 (ft); LPNs 16 (ft), 3 (pt); Orderlies 2 (ft); Nurses aides 56 (ft); Physical therapists 1 (ft); Activities coordinators 3 (ft); Dietitians 12 (ft), 1 (pt).

HALTOM CITY

Crossroads Development Center
5700 Midway, Haltom City, TX, 76117 (817) 834-5576
Admin Charles J McDermott.
Licensure Intermediate Care for Mentally Retarded. *Beds* 124. *Certified* Medicaid.

HAMILTON

Forest Oaks Nursing Home
726 E Coke St, Hamilton, TX, 76531 (817) 386-5319
Admin Forrest S Tatum.
Licensure Intermediate Care. *Beds* 28. *Certified* Medicaid.
Staff RNs 1 (pt); LPNs 3 (ft); Nurses aides 5 (ft), 1 (pt); Activities coordinators 1 (ft); Dietitians 1 (pt).
Facilities Dining room; Activities room.
Activities Arts and Crafts; Cards; Games; Movies; Dances/Social or cultural gatherings.
Description With just 28 beds, facility offers a family-like atmosphere.

Hamilton Nursing Home*
205 W Gentry St, Hamilton, TX, 76531 (817) 386-3011
Admin Georgia M Robinson.
Licensure Intermediate Care. *Beds* 41. *Certified* Medicaid.
Ownership Proprietary.

Hillcrest Nursing Home
400 W Grogan, Hamilton, TX, 76531 (817) 386-3171
Admin Evalyn Young.
Licensure Intermediate Care. *Beds* 78. *Certified* Medicaid.
Staff RNs 2 (ft); LPNs 5 (ft), 2 (pt); Nurses aides 18 (ft), 4 (pt); Activities coordinators 1 (ft); Dietitians 1 (pt).
Facilities Dining room; Barber/Beauty shop.
Activities Games; Movies; Dances/Social or cultural gatherings.

Leisure Lodge—Hamilton*
910 E Pierson, Hamilton, TX, 76531 (817) 386-8113
Admin Dennis P Dorton.
Licensure Intermediate Care. *Beds* 96. *Certified* Medicaid.
Ownership Proprietary.

HAMLIN

Holiday Lodge*
PO Box 381, 425 SW Ave F, Hamlin, TX, 79520 (915) 576-3643
Admin James B Crowley.
Licensure Intermediate Care. *Beds* 60. *Certified* Medicaid.
Ownership Proprietary.

HAMPSTEAD

Hampstead Nursing Home*
1111 San Antonio, Hampstead, TX, 77445 (713) 816-3382, 6220
Admin Joyce Brokmeyer.
Licensure Skilled Care; Intermediate Care. *Beds* 110. *Certified* Medicaid; Medicare.
Ownership Proprietary.

HARLINGEN

Harlingen Good Samaritan Center*
4301 S "F" St, Harlingen, TX, 78550 (512) 423-4959
Admin Reese L Greaves.
Licensure Skilled Care; Intermediate Care.
Beds 112. *Certified* Medicaid.
Ownership Nonprofit.
Affiliation Lutheran

Retama Manor Nursing Center—Harlingen*
2201 Pease St, Harlingen, TX, 78550 (512) 423-2663
Admin Edelmira Resendez.
Licensure Intermediate Care. *Beds* 197. *Certified* Medicaid.
Ownership Proprietary.

TLC Nursing Center
2204 Pease, Harlingen, TX, 78550 (512) 425-2812
Admin Martha Ann Hamby. *Medical Dir/Dir of Nursing* Sam Carter MD.
Licensure Skilled Care; Intermediate Care.
Beds 120. *Certified* Medicaid.
Admissions Requirements Medical examination.
Staff RNs 3 (ft), 4 (pt); LPNs 12 (ft), 3 (pt); Orderlies 4 (ft), 2 (pt); Nurses aides 24 (ft), 4 (pt); Activities coordinators 1 (ft), 1 (pt); Dietitians 1 (ft).
Facilities Dining room; Activities room; Crafts room; Laundry room; Barber/Beauty shop.
Description We have 7-day coverage in our activity department and have an outstanding program.

HASKELL

Haskell Nursing Center*
Rt 1, Box 670, 1504 N 1st St, Haskell, TX, 79521 (817) 864-3556
Admin Lorene A Beason.
Licensure Intermediate Care. *Beds* 68. *Certified* Medicaid.
Ownership Proprietary.

Rice Springs Care Home Inc
1302 N 1st St, Haskell, TX, 79521 (817) 864-2652
Admin Ruth Ann Klose.
Licensure Intermediate Care. *Beds* 82. *Certified* Medicare.
Admissions Requirements Physician's request.
Staff RNs 1 (pt); LPNs 5 (ft), 4 (pt); Nurses aides 25 (ft), 4 (pt); Activities coordinators 1 (ft); Dietitians 1 (pt).
Facilities Dining room; Activities room; Laundry room; Barber/Beauty shop.
Activities Arts and Crafts; Cards; Games; Reading groups; Prayer groups; Movies; Shopping trips; Dances/Social or cultural gatherings.

HAWKINS

Hawkins Care Center
230 S Beulah, Hawkins, TX, 75765 (214) 769-2941
Admin Lavonia J Stone. *Medical Dir/Dir of Nursing* Dr R A Lester III.
Licensure Intermediate Care. *Beds* 46. *Certified* Medicaid.
Staff RNs 1 (pt); LPNs 3 (ft); Nurses aides 8 (ft); Physical therapists 1 (pt); Reality therapists 1 (pt); Recreational therapists 1 (pt); Occupa-

tional therapists 1 (pt); Speech therapists 1 (pt); Activities coordinators 1 (ft); Dietitians 1 (pt); Podiatrists 1 (pt).
Facilities Dining room; Laundry room; Barber/Beauty shop.
Activities Arts and Crafts; Cards; Games; Reading groups; Prayer groups; Movies; Shopping trips; Dances/Social or cultural gatherings.
Description Hawkins Care Center makes every effort to create a home-like atmosphere with attractive surroundings, excellent food, recreational and social programs, and 24-hour nursing care provided by concerned, qualified professionals. We care about those you care about.

HEARNE

Leisure Lodge—Hearne*
1100 Brown St, Hearne, TX, 77859 (713) 279-5361
Admin Velma Windham.
Licensure Intermediate Care. *Beds* 148. *Certified* Medicaid.
Ownership Proprietary.

HENDERSON

Leisure Lodge—Henderson
1010 W Main, Henderson, TX, 75652 (214) 657-6513
Admin Marilyn A Johnson.
Licensure Intermediate Care. *Beds* 179. *Certified* Medicaid.
Staff LPNs 9 (ft), 2 (pt); Nurses aides 44 (ft), 7 (pt).
Facilities Dining room; Laundry room; Barber/Beauty shop.
Activities Arts and Crafts; Games; Reading groups; Prayer groups; Movies; Dances/Social or cultural gatherings.

Southwood Convalescent Center Inc*
PO Box 1066, Hwy 79 at 259, Henderson, TX, 75652 (214) 657-6506
Admin Gloria L George.
Licensure Intermediate Care. *Beds* 90. *Certified* Medicaid.
Ownership Proprietary.

HENRIETTA

Bur-Mont Nursing Center*
Hwy 287 E, Henrietta, TX, 76365 (817) 538-5665
Admin Rebecca Rae Spikes.
Licensure Intermediate Care. *Beds* 90. *Certified* Medicaid.
Ownership Nonprofit.

Henrietta Care Center*
807 W Bois D'Arc, Henrietta, TX, 76365 (817) 538-4303
Admin Robert G Holmes.
Licensure Intermediate Care. *Beds* 60. *Certified* Medicaid.
Ownership Proprietary.

HEREFORD

King's Manor Methodist Home
430 Ranger Dr, Hereford, TX, 79045 (806)
364-0661
Admin Joyce L Lyons.
Licensure Intermediate Care. *Beds* 79. *Certi-fied* Medicaid.
Admissions Requirements Medical examina-tion; Physician's request.
Staff Physicians 5 (ft); RNs 1 (ft), 1 (pt); LPNs
12 (ft); Nurses aides 35 (ft); Activities coordina-tors 2 (ft); Dietitians 1 (pt).
Affiliation Methodist
Facilities Dining room; Chapel; Laundry
room; Barber/Beauty shop; Library.
Activities Arts and Crafts; Cards; Games;
Shopping trips.

HICO

Village Nursing Home
Hemphill and Railroad Sts, Hico, TX, 76457
(817) 796-2111
Admin Velaine Swedelius.
Licensure Intermediate Care. *Beds* 114. *Certi-fied* Medicaid.
Admissions Requirements Physician's request.
Staff LPNs 8 (ft); Nurses aides 32 (ft); Activi-ties coordinators 1 (ft); Dietitians 1 (ft).
Facilities Dining room; Activities room;
Laundry room.
Activities Arts and Crafts; Cards; Games;
Reading groups; Prayer groups; Movies; Shop-ping trips; Dances/Social or cultural gatherings.

HILLSBORO

Canterbury Villa of Hillsboro
Old Brandon Rd, Rt 3, Box 759, Hillsboro,
TX, 76645 (817) 582-8416
Admin Linda Bohannon.
Licensure Intermediate Care. *Beds* 162. *Certi-fied* Medicaid.
Admissions Requirements Medical examina-tion; Physician's request.
Staff RNs 1 (ft); LPNs 10 (ft), 2 (pt); Nurses
aides 50 (ft); Physical therapists; Reality thera-pists 1 (ft); Occupational therapists; Speech
therapists; Activities coordinators 1 (ft); Dieti-tians 1 (ft); Dentists; Podiatrists 1 (pt);
Audiologists.
Facilities Dining room; Activities room; Chap-el; Crafts room; Laundry room; Barber/Beauty
shop; Library.
Activities Arts and Crafts; Cards; Games;
Reading groups; Prayer groups; Movies; Shop-ping trips; Dances/Social or cultural gatherings.
Description Canterbury Villa of Hillsboro is
operated by Texas Health Enterprises, Inc. This
newly renovated nursing facility offers superior
nursing care with therapeutic diets and an
extensive activity/recreation program. VA
approved.

Town Hall Estates*
300 Happy Ln, Hillsboro, TX, 76645 (817)
582-8482
Admin Betsy H Dohse.

Licensure Intermediate Care. *Beds* 118. *Certi-fied* Medicaid.
Ownership Nonprofit.

HITCHCOCK

Hitchcock Nursing Home
6701 FM 2004, Hitchcock, TX, 77563 (713)
986-6516
Admin Ann Wallace.
Licensure Intermediate Care. *Beds* 60. *Certi-fied* Medicaid.
Admissions Requirements Physician's request.
Staff Physicians 1 (pt); RNs 1 (pt); LPNs 4 (ft);
Nurses aides 15 (ft), 5 (pt); Physical therapists 1
(pt); Recreational therapists 1 (pt); Activities
coordinators 1 (ft); Dietitians 1 (pt).
Facilities Dining room; Activities room; Crafts
room; Laundry room; Barber/Beauty shop.
Activities Arts and Crafts; Cards; Games; Pray-er groups; Shopping trips; Dances/Social or cul-tural gatherings.

HOLLAND

K'Way Kare Nursing Home*
PO Box 209, 610 Josephine St, Holland, TX,
76534 (817) 657-2494
Admin Gilbert W Goodnight.
Licensure Intermediate Care. *Beds* 31. *Certi-fied* Medicaid.
Ownership Proprietary.

HONDO

Four Seasons Nursing Home
2001 Ave E, Hondo, TX, 78861 (512) 426-2124
Admin Imogene Bohmfalk. *Medical Dir/Dir of
Nursing* Dr Parker Meyer.
Licensure Intermediate Care. *Beds* 75. *Certi-fied* Medicaid.
Admissions Requirements Minimum age 14;
Medical examination.
Staff Physicians 4 (pt); RNs 2 (pt); LPNs 7 (ft);
Nurses aides 30 (ft), 8 (pt); Physical therapists 1
(pt); Speech therapists 1 (pt); Activities coordi-nators 2 (ft); Dietitians 1 (pt); Dentists 1 (pt);
Podiatrists 1 (pt); Audiologists 1 (pt).
Facilities Dining room; Activities room; Crafts
room; Laundry room; Barber/Beauty shop.
Activities Arts and Crafts; Cards; Games; Pray-er groups; Movies; Shopping trips; Dances/So-cial or cultural gatherings.
Description We have had a waiting list for 6 or
7 years. Very good activity program that is self-sufficient.

Hondo Nursing Center
3002 Ave Q, Hondo, TX, 78861 (512)
426-3057
Admin Lisa Burger. *Medical Dir/Dir of
Nursing* Dr Roberto Fernandez.
Licensure Intermediate Care. *Beds* 118. *Certi-fied* Medicaid.
Staff LPNs 4 (ft); Orderlies 1 (ft); Nurses aides
13 (ft); Activities coordinators 1 (ft); Dietitians
1 (ft); Podiatrists 1 (ft).
Facilities Dining room; Physical therapy room;
Activities room; Laundry room; Barber/Beauty
shop.
Activities Arts and Crafts; Cards; Games;

Reading groups; Prayer groups; Movies; Shop-ping trips; Dances/Social or cultural gatherings.
Description Annual Special Senior Olympics
held here last 3 years.

HONEY GROVE

Grove Manor Nursing Home Inc
Rt 2, Honey Grove, TX, 75446 (214) 378-2293
Admin Alice J Edelhauser. *Medical Dir/Dir of
Nursing* Jeff Duncan MD.
Licensure Intermediate Care. *Beds* 90. *Certi-fied* Medicaid.
Admissions Requirements Medical examina-tion; Physician's request.
Staff RNs 1 (ft); LPNs 5 (ft); Nurses aides 19
(ft); Activities coordinators 1 (ft).
Facilities Dining room; Activities room; Chap-el; Laundry room; Barber/Beauty shop.
Activities Games; Prayer groups; Movies;
Dances/Social or cultural gatherings.
Description Facility features a very good volun-teer program with volunteers in the home daily
to help with a wide variety of activities.

HOUSTON

Autumn Convalescent Center—Janisch*
617 W Janisch St, Houston, TX, 77018 (713)
697-2891
Admin Jim K Triplett.
Licensure Intermediate Care. *Beds* 119. *Certi-fied* Medicaid.
Ownership Proprietary.

**Autumn Hills Convalescent Center—Hermann
Park Manor**
5600 Chenevert, Houston, TX, 77024 (713)
523-6831
Admin Forest B Smith. *Medical Dir/Dir of
Nursing* Margaret Saw MD.
Licensure Skilled Care; Intermediate Care.
Beds 185. *Certified* Medicaid.
Admissions Requirements Minimum age 45.
Staff RNs 2 (ft), 2 (pt); LPNs 17 (ft); Nurses
aides 65 (ft); Physical therapists 1 (ft); Reality
therapists 1 (ft); Recreational therapists 1 (ft);
Activities coordinators 1 (ft); Dietitians 1 (ft);
Dentists 1 (pt); Ophthalmologists 1 (pt); Podia-trists 1 (pt).
Facilities Dining room; Physical therapy room;
Activities room; Crafts room; Laundry room;
Barber/Beauty shop; Library.
Activities Arts and Crafts; Cards; Games;
Reading groups; Prayer groups; Movies; Shop-ping trips; Dances/Social or cultural gatherings.

Bayou Glen Nursing Center*
8820 Town Park Dr, Houston, TX, 77036 (713)
777-7241
Admin Barbara L Martin.
Licensure Skilled Care; Intermediate Care.
Beds 180. *Certified* Medicaid.
Ownership Proprietary.

Bayou Glen-Jones Road Nursing Center*
10851 Crescent Moon Rd, Houston, TX, 77064
(713) 890-0171
Admin Sherry A Reid.
Licensure Intermediate Care. *Beds* 120.
Ownership Nonprofit.

Bayou Glen-Northwest Nursing Center*
9303 W Gulfbank Rd, Houston, TX, 77040
(713) 466-8933
Admin Nancy L Wood.
Licensure Skilled Care; Intermediate Care.
Beds 180. *Certified* Medicaid.
Ownership Proprietary.

Benner Convalescent Center*
3510 Sherman St, Houston, TX, 77003 (713)
224-5344
Admin Martha Reyes.
Licensure Intermediate Care. *Beds* 117. *Certified* Medicaid.
Ownership Proprietary.

Blalock Nursing Home—East*
1405 Holland Ave, Houston, TX, 77029 (713)
455-1744
Admin Golden Wiltz.
Licensure Intermediate Care. *Beds* 160. *Certified* Medicaid.
Ownership Proprietary.

Blalock Nursing Home—North*
5329 N Freeway, Houston, TX, 77022 (713)
695-5821
Admin Claude Anderson.
Licensure Skilled Care; Intermediate Care.
Beds 169. *Certified* Medicaid.
Ownership Proprietary.

Blalock Nursing Home—North Shores
12350 Wood Bayou Dr, Houston, TX, 77013
(713) 453-0446
Admin Elsie Hawkins.
Licensure Intermediate Care. *Beds* 150. *Certified* Medicaid.
Admissions Requirements Minimum age 18;
Medical examination.
Staff RNs 1 (ft); LPNs 6 (ft), 4 (pt); Nurses
aides 22 (ft), 11 (pt); Activities coordinators 1
(ft), 1 (pt).
Facilities Dining room; Activities room; Crafts
room; Laundry room; Barber/Beauty shop;
Library.
Activities Arts and Crafts; Cards; Games; Prayer groups; Movies; Shopping trips; Dances/Social or cultural gatherings.
Description We have a beautifully designed
cartwheel shape, facilitating easier access to all
residents at all times. The dining room is attractively designed and will accommodate 100 or
more. The living room area is attractively
designed and furnished and has a fireplace.

Blalock Nursing Home—Northwest*
1341 Blalock Dr, Houston, TX, 77055 (713)
468-7821
Admin Sandra Klein.
Licensure Intermediate Care. *Beds* 240. *Certified* Medicaid.
Ownership Proprietary.

Blalock Nursing Home—Spring Branch
8955 Long Point Rd, Houston, TX, 77055
(713) 464-7625
Admin Doris Bauer.
Licensure Intermediate Care. *Beds* 106. *Certified* Medicaid.
Admissions Requirements Medical examination.
Staff Physicians; RNs; LPNs; Nurses aides;

Physical therapists; Reality therapists; Recreational therapists; Occupational therapists;
Speech therapists; Activities coordinators; Dietitians; Dentists; Ophthalmologists; Podiatrists.
Facilities Dining room; Activities room; Crafts
room; Laundry room; Barber/Beauty shop;
Library.
Activities Arts and Crafts; Cards; Games;
Reading groups; Movies; Shopping trips; Dances/Social or cultural gatherings.
Description Residents raise money through
special projects for charities, i.e., Leukemia,
Heart Fund, etc.; bowling and take trips to
McDonalds in community; also trips to Ice
Capades, concerts, and circuses.

Blalock Nursing Home Stoneybrook
2808 Stoneybrook, Houston, TX, 77063 (713)
782-4355
Admin Carolyn Larson. *Medical Dir/Dir of
Nursing* Dr William Wylie.
Licensure Intermediate Care. *Beds* 112. *Certified* Medicaid.
Admissions Requirements Minimum age 18;
Medical examination; Physician's request.
Staff RNs 1 (ft); LPNs 7 (ft); Nurses aides 25
(ft); Physical therapists; Activities coordinators
1 (ft); Dietitians; Podiatrists.
Facilities Dining room; Activities room; Laundry room; Barber/Beauty shop; Library.
Activities Arts and Crafts; Games; Prayer
groups; Dances/Social or cultural gatherings.
Description Regency rooms are available.

Buckner Baptist Haven*
12601 Memorial Dr, Houston, TX, 77024 (713)
465-3406
Admin Tom J Drewett.
Licensure Intermediate Care; Custodial Care.
Beds ICF 60; Custodial Care 93. *Certified* Medicaid.
Ownership Nonprofit.
Affiliation Baptist

Center for the Retarded—Cullen
810 Marston, Houston, TX, 77019 (713)
523-6741
Admin Dalona L Riggs.
Licensure Intermediate Care for Mentally
Retarded. *Beds* 86. *Certified* Medicaid.

Clarewood House Infirmary
7400 Clarewood, Houston, TX, 77036 (713)
774-5821
Admin Lynn E Eads.
Licensure Intermediate Care. *Beds* 24.
Ownership Nonprofit.
Admissions Requirements Minimum age 65;
Medical examination.
Staff RNs 3 (ft), 6 (pt); Nurses aides 3 (ft), 5
(pt).
Facilities Dining room; Activities room; Chapel; Crafts room; Laundry room; Barber/Beauty
shop; Library.
Description An 11-story high-rise apartment
located across the street from one of the largest
shopping centers in southwest Houston; also
very near numerous churches, a movie theatre,
and a city library.

Courtyard Convalescent Center
7499 Stanwick Dr, Houston, TX, 77087 (713)
644-8048

Admin Delight L Finnell. *Medical Dir/Dir of
Nursing* J Winston Morrison MD.
Licensure Intermediate Care. *Beds* 120. *Certified* Medicaid.
Admissions Requirements Minimum age 21;
Medical examination; Physician's request.
Staff Physicians 1 (pt); RNs 1 (ft); LPNs 8 (ft),
4 (pt); Orderlies 1 (ft), 1 (pt); Nurses aides 30
(ft), 2 (pt); Physical therapists 1 (pt); Occupational therapists 1 (pt); Speech therapists 1 (pt);
Activities coordinators 1 (ft); Dietitians 1 (pt);
Dentists 1 (pt); Ophthalmologists 1 (pt); Podiatrists 1 (pt); Audiologists 1 (pt).
Facilities Dining room; Activities room; Barber/Beauty shop.
Activities Arts and Crafts; Cards; Games;
Reading groups; Prayer groups; Movies; Shopping trips; Dances/Social or cultural gatherings.

Dever Nursing Home*
3310 W Main St, Houston, TX, 77098 (713)
529-1218
Admin Grace French.
Licensure Intermediate Care. *Beds* 37.
Ownership Proprietary.

The Eliza Johnson Center for Aging Inc*
PO Box 14132, 10010 Cullen Blvd, Houston,
TX, 77021 (713) 734-1673
Admin Eddie W Gibbs.
Licensure Intermediate Care. *Beds* 76. *Certified* Medicaid.
Ownership Nonprofit.

Golden Age Manor—Bellfort
7633 Bellfort Blvd, Houston, TX, 77061 (713)
644-2101
Admin Mary Lee Seeley. *Medical Dir/Dir of
Nursing* L W Johnson MD.
Licensure Skilled Care; Intermediate Care.
Beds 200. *Certified* Medicaid.
Admissions Requirements Medical examination; Physician's request.
Staff RNs 5 (ft), 2 (pt); LPNs 14 (ft), 3 (pt);
Nurses aides 60 (ft); Physical therapists 2 (ft);
Activities coordinators 2 (ft).
Facilities Dining room; Physical therapy room;
Activities room; Barber/Beauty shop; Library.
Activities Arts and Crafts; Cards; Games;
Reading groups; Prayer groups; Movies; Dances/Social or cultural gatherings.
Description Facility offers reality orientation
program.

Golden Age Manor—Holmes*
6150 S Loop E, Houston, TX, 77087 (713)
643-2628
Admin Mildred M Stanley.
Licensure Intermediate Care. *Beds* 120. *Certified* Medicaid.
Ownership Proprietary.

Golden Age Manor—Long Point*
8810 Long Point Rd, Houston, TX, 77055
(713) 468-7833
Admin Marion L Martin.
Licensure Intermediate Care. *Beds* 174. *Certified* Medicaid.
Ownership Proprietary.

Golden Age Manor—North Loop
1737 North Loop W, Houston, TX, 77008
(713) 869-5551

Admin Sue Morgan. *Medical Dir/Dir of Nursing* Dr William Cruce.
Licensure Skilled Care; Intermediate Care.
Beds 200. *Certified* Medicaid; Medicare.
Admissions Requirements Medical examination; Physician's request.
Staff Physicians 1 (pt); RNs 4 (ft), 4 (pt); LPNs 15 (ft); Nurses aides 75 (ft); Physical therapists 1 (pt); Occupational therapists 1 (pt); Speech therapists 1 (pt); Activities coordinators 2 (ft); Dietitians 1 (ft); Dentists 1 (pt); Ophthalmologists 1 (pt); Podiatrists 1 (pt).
Facilities Dining room; Physical therapy room; Activities room; Crafts room; Laundry room; Barber/Beauty shop; Library.
Activities Arts and Crafts; Cards; Games; Reading groups; Prayer groups; Movies; Shopping trips; Dances/Social or cultural gatherings; Exercise classes.

Golden Age Manor—Rookin
6500 Rookin St, Houston, TX, 77074 (713) 774-9736
Admin Paul A Smith. *Medical Dir/Dir of Nursing* Jean M Samaan MD.
Licensure Skilled Care; Intermediate Care.
Beds 284. *Certified* Medicaid.
Admissions Requirements Physician's request.
Staff RNs 5 (ft); LPNs 20 (ft); Orderlies 8 (ft); Nurses aides 110 (ft); Physical therapists 4 (ft); Activities coordinators 2 (ft); Dietitians 1 (ft).
Facilities Dining room; Physical therapy room; Activities room; Barber/Beauty shop; Library.
Activities Arts and Crafts; Cards; Games; Reading groups; Movies; Dances/Social or cultural gatherings.
Description This facility offers semi-private and private rooms with private baths. All rooms are fully furnished, with a choice of decor. Also features several enclosed patio areas, as well as specially designed lounges and dining areas.

Graystone Manor Nursing Home*
2702 Little York Rd, Houston, TX, 77093 (713) 692-2202, 2386
Admin William F Swabado.
Licensure Intermediate Care. *Beds* 90. *Certified* Medicaid.
Ownership Proprietary.

Graystone Manor Nursing Home 2*
1911 Aldine Mail Rt, Houston, TX, 77039 (713) 442-8436
Admin Mary Lou McMillan.
Licensure Intermediate Care. *Beds* 49. *Certified* Medicaid.
Ownership Proprietary.

Hallmark Anderson Health Care
4718 Hallmark Ln, Houston, TX, 77056 (713) 622-6633
Admin Helen S Hampton.
Licensure Intermediate Care; Custodial Care.
Beds ICF 20; Custodial Care 22.
Admissions Requirements Minimum age 65; Medical examination.
Staff Physicians 3 (pt); RNs 4 (ft); LPNs 6 (ft), 1 (pt); Nurses aides 17 (ft), 2 (pt); Activities coordinators 1 (ft); Dietitians 1 (ft); Podiatrists 1 (pt).
Facilities Dining room; Activities room; Laundry room; Barber/Beauty shop; Library.

Activities Cards; Games; Reading groups; Prayer groups; Shopping trips; Dances/Social or cultural gatherings.

Highland Park Care Center
2714 Morrison, Houston, TX, 77009 (713) 869-1491
Admin Charlene Hinton.
Licensure Intermediate Care. *Beds* 67. *Certified* Medicaid.
Admissions Requirements Medical examination; Physician's request.
Staff RNs 1 (pt); LPNs 4 (ft); Nurses aides 16 (ft); Activities coordinators 1 (ft); Podiatrists 1 (pt).
Facilities Dining room; Activities room; Laundry room; Barber/Beauty shop.
Activities Arts and Crafts; Cards; Games; Prayer groups; Movies.
Description A very nice nursing home, located in the Heights area of Houston.

Holly Hall
8304 Knight, Houston, TX, 77054 (713) 747-2810
Admin Wesley F Stevens.
Licensure Skilled Care. *Beds* 70.
Ownership Nonprofit.
Admissions Requirements Minimum age 70; Medical examination.
Staff RNs 1 (ft), 1 (pt); LPNs 6 (ft), 1 (pt); Nurses aides 15 (ft), 1 (pt); Dietitians 1 (ft).
Facilities Dining room; Activities room; Chapel; Crafts room; Laundry room; Barber/Beauty shop; Library.
Activities Arts and Crafts; Cards; Games; Reading groups; Prayer groups; Shopping trips; Dances/Social or cultural gatherings.
Description Directly across the street from the Astrodome, Holly Hall does have a Harris County residency requirement (18 months before making application) then a waiting time of 12 to 15 months.

Isla Carroll Turner Health Care Center
4141 S Braeswood, Houston, TX, 77025 (713) 666-2651
Admin Todd Larson.
Licensure Nursing Care. *Beds* 25.
Admissions Requirements Minimum age 65.
Staff RNs; LPNs; Nurses aides; Activities coordinators; Dietitians.
Facilities Dining room; Activities room; Chapel; Crafts room; Laundry room; Barber/Beauty shop; Library.
Activities Arts and Crafts; Shopping trips; Dances/Social or cultural gatherings.

Jewish Home for the Aged*
6200 N Braeswood, Houston, TX, 77074 (713) 771-4111
Admin Anita Cabelli.
Licensure Skilled Care; Intermediate Care.
Beds 218. *Certified* Medicaid.
Ownership Nonprofit.
Affiliation Jewish

Leisure Arms Nursing Home
4225 Denmark, Houston, TX, 77016 (713) 631-0200
Admin Geraldine L McElroy.
Licensure Intermediate Care. *Beds* 83. *Certified* Medicaid.

Admissions Requirements Minimum age 20; Medical examination; Physician's request.
Staff Physicians 1 (ft); LPNs 4 (ft), 3 (pt); Nurses aides 12 (ft), 6 (pt).
Facilities Dining room; Activities room; Crafts room; Laundry room.
Activities Arts and Crafts; Cards; Games; Prayer groups; Movies; Shopping trips; Dances/Social or cultural gatherings.
Description Residents love the side patio; the whirlpool allows for better nursing care. We all know "history lives here".

Manda Ann Convalescent Home Inc
7441 Coffee, Houston, TX, 77033 (713) 733-9471
Admin Jaromey R Roberts.
Licensure Intermediate Care. *Beds* 100. *Certified* Medicaid.
Activities Arts and Crafts; Cards; Games; Prayer groups; Movies; Shopping trips.

Manor Care—Sharpview
7505 Bellerive, Houston, TX, 77036 (713) 774-9611
Admin Pat Redman. *Medical Dir/Dir of Nursing* Avid Bendahri MD.
Licensure Skilled Care; Intermediate Care.
Beds 160. *Certified* Medicare.
Admissions Requirements Medical examination.
Staff Physicians 2 (ft); RNs 9 (ft), 5 (pt); LPNs 14 (ft), 3 (pt); Orderlies 33 (ft), 12 (pt); Physical therapists 1 (ft); Recreational therapists 1 (ft); Occupational therapists 1 (ft); Activities coordinators 1 (ft); Dietitians 1 (ft).
Facilities Dining room; Physical therapy room; Activities room; Crafts room; Laundry room; Barber/Beauty shop; Day room; Special skills unit for ambulatory confused.
Activities Arts and Crafts; Cards; Games; Reading groups; Prayer groups; Movies; Shopping trips; Dances/Social or cultural gatherings; Happy hour; Tee ball baseball games; Family cook-outs; Bingo; Auctions; Wine & cheese parties; Manicures.
Description Sharpview has 3 beautifully landscaped courtyards to ensure that most residents have a courtyard view. The center courtyard is enclosed and is safe for our residents. They often have cook-outs, special events in courtyard. We have the vacation plan for those short-term stays whether it be 2 days, 1 week, or month.

Mercy Nursing Home Inc*
3901 Los Angeles St, Houston, TX, 77026 (713) 672-7654
Admin Brenda Joyce H Edwards.
Licensure Intermediate Care. *Beds* 65. *Certified* Medicaid.
Ownership Proprietary.

Montrose Care Center*
3508 Milam St, Houston, TX, 77002 (713) 529-3071
Admin Ronald Betterton.
Licensure Intermediate Care. *Beds* 159. *Certified* Medicaid.
Ownership Proprietary.

Northline Manor
7210 Northline Dr, Houston, TX, 77076 (713)
697-4771
Admin W William Jahn.
Licensure Intermediate Care; Personal Care.
Beds ICF 180; Personal Care 24. *Certified* Medicaid.
Admissions Requirements Minimum age 18;
Medical examination.
Staff RNs 1 (ft); LPNs 10 (ft); Orderlies 4 (ft);
Nurses aides 65 (ft); Physical therapists 1 (ft);
Occupational therapists 1 (pt); Speech therapists 1 (pt); Activities coordinators 1 (ft), 1 (pt);
Dietitians 1 (pt).
Facilities Dining room; Physical therapy room;
Activities room; Chapel; Laundry room; Barber/Beauty shop; Library.
Activities Arts and Crafts; Cards; Games;
Reading groups; Prayer groups; Movies; Shopping trips; Dances/Social or cultural gatherings.
Description Nursing home with opportunities
for minimum dependency with care directed to
individual maximum independence.

Pharmcare—Aldine*
PO Box 38392, 10110 Airline Dr, Houston,
TX, 77037 (713) 447-0376
Admin Richard Lewis Simpson.
Licensure Intermediate Care. *Beds* 197. *Certified* Medicaid.
Ownership Proprietary.

Saint Anthony Center
6301 Almeda Rd, Houston, TX, 77021 (713)
748-5021
Admin Sr Mary Alma Murphy. *Medical Dir-/Dir of Nursing* Bernard Flanz MD.
Licensure Skilled Care; Intermediate Care.
Beds 325. *Certified* Medicaid; Medicare.
Admissions Requirements Physician's request.
Staff Physicians 2 (ft); RNs 24 (ft); LPNs 48
(ft); Nurses aides 128 (ft); Physical therapists 7
(ft); Recreational therapists 2 (ft); Occupational
therapists 9 (ft), 2 (pt); Speech therapists 2 (ft);
Activities coordinators 1 (ft); Dietitians 1 (ft);
Dentists 2 (ft); Podiatrists 1 (pt); Audiologists 2
(ft).
Affiliation Roman Catholic
Facilities Dining room; Physical therapy room;
Activities room; Chapel; Crafts room; Laundry
room; Barber/Beauty shop; Library.
Activities Arts and Crafts; Games; Prayer
groups; Movies; Shopping trips.
Description St Anthony Center is a 10-story
center which provides a Christ-like environment in which patients of all ages receive a
wide range of superior rehabilitative, social,
medical, and nursing services. All departments
within the center work together to provide the
total care needed by patients and residents.

St Dominic's Nursing Home*
502 Grand St, Houston, TX, 77021 (713)
41-6601
Admin Nancy A Evans.
Licensure Intermediate Care. *Beds* 120.
Ownership Nonprofit.
Affiliation Roman Catholic

Saint Thomas Convalescent Center*
25 Almeda Rd, Houston, TX, 77004 (713)
2-5107
Admin Marjorie Turner.

Licensure Intermediate Care. *Beds* 125. *Certified* Medicaid.
Ownership Proprietary.

Silver Threads Nursing Center*
3402 Vintage St, Houston, TX, 77026 (713)
675-8105
Admin Helen M Spencer.
Licensure Intermediate Care. *Beds* 82. *Certified* Medicaid.
Ownership Proprietary.

Thomas Care Centers Inc
3827 W Fuqua St, Houston, TX, 77045 (713)
433-7206
Admin James R Hale. *Medical Dir/Dir of
Nursing* Dr William L Mize.
Licensure Intermediate Care; Intermediate
Care for Mentally Retarded. *Beds* 250. *Certified* Medicaid.
Staff Physicians 2 (ft), 4 (pt); RNs 8 (ft), 12
(pt); LPNs 10 (ft), 10 (pt); Nurses aides 25 (ft),
35 (pt); Physical therapists 3 (ft); Recreational
therapists 4 (ft); Occupational therapists 4 (ft);
Speech therapists 2 (ft); Activities coordinators
2 (ft); Dietitians 2 (ft); Dentists 1 (ft); Ophthalmologists 1 (pt); Podiatrists 1 (pt); Audiologists
1 (ft).
Facilities Dining room; Physical therapy room;
Activities room; Crafts room; Laundry room;
Barber/Beauty shop.
Activities Arts and Crafts; Cards; Games;
Reading groups; Prayer groups; Movies; Shopping trips; Dances/Social or cultural gatherings.

Treemont Health Care Center
2501 Westerland Dr, Houston, TX, 77042 (713)
783-4100
Admin Jean C Rogers. *Medical Dir/Dir of
Nursing* William J Wylie.
Licensure Intermediate Care; Custodial Care.
Beds ICF 70; Custodial Care 54.
Admissions Requirements Minimum age 60;
Medical examination; Physician's request.
Staff RNs 2 (ft); LPNs 10 (ft), 1 (pt); Orderlies
1 (ft); Nurses aides 40 (ft), 3 (pt); Recreational
therapists 1 (ft); Dietitians 1 (ft).
Facilities Dining room; Activities room; Crafts
room; Laundry room; Barber/Beauty shop;
Library.
Activities Arts and Crafts; Cards; Games; Prayer groups; Movies; Shopping trips; Dances/Social or cultural gatherings.
Description Treemont offers a cheerful, active,
warm and friendly atmosphere created by
health professionals who care about not only
the physical, but also the emotional and psychological needs of referred patients. Carpeted
floors, colorful draperies with matching bedspreads, and furnishings in a colonial Williamsburg design keep the center from appearing
clinical. Important facets of patient care are
activities to stimulate interest and creativity,
programs to develop and improve physical and
mental capabilities, and social events to look
forward to. Offers 4 distinct services: infirmary
care for acute illnesses not requiring hospitalization, convalescent care for post-hospital
rehabilitative care, minimal care for patients
requiring daily supervision, and nursing care
for patients requiring prolonged and more
intensified nursing skills.

Villa Northwest Convalescent Center
17600 Cali Dr, Houston, TX, 77090 (713)
440-9000
Admin Venita C Johnson. *Medical Dir/Dir of
Nursing* M Javed Aslam MD.
Licensure Skilled Care; Intermediate Care.
Beds 150. *Certified* Medicaid.
Admissions Requirements Minimum age 21;
Medical examination.
Staff RNs 7 (ft); LPNs 13 (ft), 3 (pt); Nurses
aides 38 (ft), 4 (pt); Activities coordinators 1
(ft), 1 (pt); Dietitians 1 (ft).
Facilities Dining room; Activities room; Crafts
room; Laundry room; Barber/Beauty shop.
Activities Arts and Crafts; Cards; Games;
Reading groups; Prayer groups; Movies; Dances/Social or cultural gatherings.
Description Facility is located adjacent to the
Northwest Medical Center Hospital; accepts
VA contract patients as well as private pay.

Watkins Convalescent Home
730 W 23rd St, Houston, TX, 77008 (713)
862-9584
Admin William R Watkins.
Licensure Intermediate Care. *Beds* 116. *Certified* Medicaid.
Admissions Requirements Medical examination; Physician's request.
Staff Physicians ; 1 (pt); RNs 1 (ft), 1 (pt);
LPNs 6 (ft), 2 (pt); Nurses aides 43 (ft); Recreational therapists 1 (ft), 1 (pt); Dietitians 1 (pt).
Facilities Dining room; Activities room;
Barber/Beauty shop.
Activities Arts and Crafts; Cards; Games;
Reading groups; Prayer groups; Movies; Shopping trips; Dances/Social or cultural gatherings.
Description Facility offers transportation, with
nurse assistance, to and from doctors' offices,
clinic, or hospital.

The Westbury Place*
5201 S Willow Dr, Houston, TX, 77035 (713)
721-0297
Admin Fannie Lou Cox.
Licensure Intermediate Care; Custodial Care.
Beds ICF 84; Custodial Care 28. *Certified* Medicaid.
Ownership Proprietary.

Wileyvale Community Nursing Home
7915 Wileyvale Rd, Houston, TX, 77016 (713)
633-2890
Admin Claude Anderson.
Licensure Intermediate Care. *Beds* 130. *Certified* Medicaid.
Staff Physicians 3 (pt); RNs 1 (pt); LPNs 15
(pt); Nurses aides 35 (pt); Activities coordinators 1 (ft), 1 (pt); Dietitians 1 (ft); Dentists 3
(pt); Ophthalmologists 1 (pt); Podiatrists 1 (pt).
Facilities Dining room; Activities room; Laundry room.
Activities Cards; Games; Prayer groups.
Description Friendly, home-like atmosphere
with a caring staff.

Williams Nursing Home Inc*
7514 Kingsley, Houston, TX, 77087 (713)
644-8393
Admin Frances L Easter.
Licensure Intermediate Care. *Beds* 112. *Certified* Medicaid.
Ownership Proprietary.

Winter Haven Nursing Home
6534 Stuebner Airline Dr, Houston, TX, 77091
(713) 692-5137
Admin Norma A Hall.
Licensure Intermediate Care. *Beds* 149. *Certified* Medicaid.
Staff RNs 1 (ft); LPNs 10 (ft), 4 (pt); Nurses aides 42 (ft); Physical therapists 1 (pt); Activities coordinators 2 (ft); Dietitians 1 (ft); Medical aides 4 (pt).
Facilities Dining room; Physical therapy room; Activities room; Crafts room; Laundry room; Barber/Beauty shop; Library; Gift shop.
Activities Arts and Crafts; Cards; Games; Prayer groups; Movies; Shopping trips; Dances/Social or cultural gatherings.
Description Winterhaven is located on 5 beautifully wooded acres including park and picnic facilities; outdoor barbecues, baking; ceramics; trips to rodeos and circuses for residents; new ice cream parlor on grounds for residents' enjoyment; staff stress people caring.

HUBBARD

Oakview Manor Nursing Center*
PO Box 561, 6th and Hickory, Hubbard, TX, 76648 (817) 576-2518
Admin Geraldine D Michalek.
Licensure Intermediate Care. *Beds* 60. *Certified* Medicaid.
Ownership Proprietary.

HUGHES SPRINGS

Hughes Springs Convalescent Center
N Taylor St, Hughes Springs, TX, 75656 (214) 639-2531
Admin Betty M McCarley.
Licensure Intermediate Care. *Beds* 60. *Certified* Medicaid.
Staff RNs 1 (pt); LPNs 4 (ft); Nurses aides 25 (ft); Physical therapists 1 (pt); Occupational therapists 1 (pt); Speech therapists 1 (pt); Activities coordinators 1 (ft).
Facilities Dining room; Activities room; Crafts room; Laundry room; Barber/Beauty shop.
Activities Arts and Crafts; Games; Prayer groups; Movies; Shopping trips; Dances/Social or cultural gatherings.

Theron Grainger Nursing Home Inc
Hwy 161, Hughes Springs, TX, 75656 (214) 639-2561
Admin Angelin Schnabel. *Medical Dir/Dir of Nursing* Dr Don Smith.
Licensure Intermediate Care. *Beds* 69. *Certified* Medicaid.
Staff RNs 1 (ft); LPNs 5 (ft), 1 (pt); Nurses aides 16 (ft), 1 (pt); Activities coordinators 1 (ft).
Facilities Dining room; Activities room; Laundry room; Barber/Beauty shop.
Activities Arts and Crafts; Cards; Games; Reading groups; Movies; Shopping trips; Dances/Social or cultural gatherings.
Description Facility has an excellent activity program to ensure exposure to all residents; located in a rural setting with a view of spacious lawns from all rooms.

HUMBLE

Green Acres Convalescent Center—Humble*
93 Isaacks Rd, Humble, TX, 77338 (713) 446-7159
Admin Deborah Sehlke.
Licensure Intermediate Care. *Beds* 140. *Certified* Medicaid.
Ownership Proprietary.

Humble Skilled Care Facility
18903 Memorial S, Humble, TX, 77338
Medical Dir/Dir of Nursing Dr N N Izzat.
Admissions Requirements Minimum age 6 months; Medical examination; Physician's request.
Staff Physicians 22 (ft), 8 (pt); RNs 11 (ft), 5 (pt); LPNs 26 (ft), 7 (pt); Nurses aides 43 (ft), 15 (pt); Physical therapists 14 (ft), 7 (pt); Recreational therapists 1 (ft); Occupational therapists 9 (ft); Speech therapists 3 (ft); Activities coordinators 1 (ft); Dietitians 1 (ft); Dentists 4 (ft); Ophthalmologists 2 (ft); Podiatrists 2 (ft); Audiologists 1 (ft).
Facilities Dining room; Physical therapy room; Activities room; Chapel; Crafts room; Laundry room; Barber/Beauty shop; Library.
Activities Cards; Games; Reading groups; Prayer groups; Dances/Social or cultural gatherings.
Description Facility offers total program of physical rehabilitation; average length of stay is 37 days; most patients are stroke victims, amputees, have hand or spinal cord injuries.

HUNTSVILLE

Fair Park Nursing Center*
2628 Milam St, Huntsville, TX, 77340 (713) 295-6464
Admin Gwendolyn Ann Yeager.
Licensure Intermediate Care. *Beds* 109. *Certified* Medicaid.
Ownership Proprietary.

Green Acres Convalescent Center
1302 Inverness, Huntsville, TX, 77340 (713) 295-6313
Admin Anna E Carpenter. *Medical Dir/Dir of Nursing* Hugh Poindexter MD.
Licensure Intermediate Care. *Beds* 102. *Certified* Medicaid.
Staff Physicians 1 (pt); RNs 1 (ft); Nurses aides 15 (ft); Reality therapists 1 (pt); Recreational therapists 1 (pt); Activities coordinators 1 (ft); Dietitians 1 (ft); LVNs 8 (ft).
Facilities Dining room; Activities room; Chapel; Crafts room; Laundry room; Barber/Beauty shop.
Activities Arts and Crafts; Cards; Games; Reading groups; Prayer groups; Movies; Shopping trips; Dances/Social or cultural gatherings.
Description Green Acres tries very hard to keep a homey environment for residents. Has had a superior rating with the state of Texas for 3 consecutive years. Facility prides itself on patient care and hard teamwork.

HURST

Autumn Leaf Lodge*
215 E Plaza Blvd, Hurst, TX, 76053 (817) 282-6777
Admin Mary Tharp.
Licensure Skilled Care; Intermediate Care. *Beds* 116. *Certified* Medicaid.
Ownership Proprietary.

Bishop Davies Center Inc*
2712 N Hurstview, Hurst, TX, 76053 (817) 498-2390
Admin Sidney Tucker.
Licensure Skilled Care. *Beds* 100. *Certified* Medicaid.
Ownership Proprietary.

IOWA PARK

Heritage Manor of Iowa Park
1109 N 3rd St, Iowa Park, TX, 76367 (817) 592-4139
Admin Eileen M Addison.
Licensure Intermediate Care. *Beds* 77. *Certified* Medicaid.
Staff Physicians 3 (pt); RNs 1 (pt); LPNs 9 (ft); Nurses aides 34 (ft), 6 (pt); Activities coordinators 1 (ft); Dietitians 1 (ft).
Facilities Dining room; Laundry room; Barber/Beauty shop.
Activities Arts and Crafts; Games; Prayer groups; Movies; Shopping trips; Dances/Social or cultural gatherings.
Description Facility offers a home-like atmosphere, good meals, and lots of tender loving care.

IRVING

Irving Campus of Care
2021 Shoaf Dr, Irving, TX, 75061 (214) 579-1919
Medical Dir/Dir of Nursing James Galbraith MD.
Licensure Skilled Care; Intermediate Care. *Beds* 360. *Certified* Medicaid; Medicare.
Staff Physicians 6 (ft); RNs 5 (ft); LPNs 17 (ft); Orderlies 4 (ft); Nurses aides 42 (ft); Physical therapists 1 (ft); Reality therapists 1 (ft); Recreational therapists 1 (ft); Occupational therapists 1 (ft); Speech therapists 1 (ft); Activities coordinators 2 (ft); Dietitians 1 (pt); Dentists 1 (pt); Ophthalmologists 1 (pt); Podiatrists 1 (pt).
Facilities Dining room; Physical therapy room; Activities room; Chapel; Crafts room; Laundry room; Barber/Beauty shop; Library.
Activities Arts and Crafts; Cards; Games; Prayer groups; Movies; Shopping trips; Dances/Social or cultural gatherings.
Description Extended care facility; private rooms.

Irving Care Center*
619 N Britain Rd, Irving, TX, 75060 (214) 438-4161
Admin Lisa J Dillard.
Licensure Intermediate Care. *Beds* 86. *Certified* Medicaid.
Ownership Proprietary.

Irving Manors Nursing Home Inc
1317 W Airport Fwy, Irving, TX, 75062 (214) 255-4135
Admin Brad L Carpenter.
Licensure Intermediate Care. *Beds* 110. *Certified* Medicaid.

Pioneer Place
225 Sowers Rd, Irving, TX, 75061 (214) 253-4173
Admin Bobbie J LeBlanc. *Medical Dir/Dir of Nursing* James Galbraith MD.
Licensure Intermediate Care. *Beds* 120. *Certified* Medicaid.
Admissions Requirements Medical examination; Physician's request.
Staff RNs 2 (ft), 1 (pt); LPNs 8 (ft), 2 (pt); Orderlies 4 (ft); Nurses aides 24 (ft); Physical therapists 1 (pt); Reality therapists 1 (pt); Occupational therapists 1 (pt); Speech therapists 1 (pt); Activities coordinators 1 (ft); Dietitians 1 (pt); Dentists 1 (pt).
Facilities Dining room; Activities room; Laundry room; Barber/Beauty shop; Library; Large living room; Front and back patios.
Activities Arts and Crafts; Cards; Games; Reading groups; Prayer groups; Shopping trips; Dances/Social or cultural gatherings; Sing-a-longs; Manicures; Adopt-a-grandparent program; Residents council; Reminiscence therapy; Exercise.
Description Facility offers an active program for bedfast residents; papers, radios, and talking books available for those who need them; 2 dogs are enjoyed by residents.

ITALY

Italy Convalescent Center
601 Mosley, Italy, TX, 76651 (214) 483-6369
Admin Billie Farrington. *Medical Dir/Dir of Nursing* Zenaida Robles.
Licensure Intermediate Care. *Beds* 61. *Certified* Medicaid.
Admissions Requirements Medical examination; Physician's request.
Staff Physicians 1 (pt); RNs 1 (pt); LPNs 8 (ft), 3 (pt); Nurses aides 18 (ft), 6 (pt); Physical therapists 1 (pt); Activities coordinators 1 (ft); Dietitians 1 (pt); Dentists 1 (pt); Podiatrists 1 (pt).
Facilities Dining room; Laundry room; Barber/Beauty shop; Library.
Activities Arts and Crafts; Cards; Games; Reading groups; Prayer groups; Movies; Shopping trips; Dances/Social or cultural gatherings.
Description Facility is located in a small farming community with family atmosphere, good food, and caring nurses.

ITASCA

Itasca Nursing Home
9 S Files St, Itasca, TX, 76055 (817) 7-2383
Admin Nelda Prause. *Medical Dir/Dir of Nursing* Dr Charles Allen.
Licensure Intermediate Care. *Beds* 82. *Certified* Medicaid.
Staff RNs 3 (ft); LPNs 5 (ft); Nurses aides 14, 4 (pt); Activities coordinators 1 (ft); Dieti-

tians 2 (pt).
Facilities Dining room; Activities room; Chapel; Crafts room; Laundry room; Barber/Beauty shop.
Activities Arts and Crafts; Cards; Games; Prayer groups; Shopping trips; Dances/Social or cultural gatherings; Shopping trips.
Description Small town setting with home-like atmosphere; very little staff turnover; superior rating.

Sanford Nursing Home
107 Marion St, Itasca, TX, 76055 (817) 687-2358
Admin Alan L Lee.
Licensure Intermediate Care. *Beds* 52. *Certified* Medicaid.

JACKSBORO

Cox Convalescent Center*
527 W Belknap, Jacksboro, TX, 76056 (817) 567-2371
Admin Billie L Pippert.
Licensure Intermediate Care. *Beds* 50. *Certified* Medicaid; Medicare.

Jacksboro Nursing Center*
211 E Jasper, Jacksboro, TX, 76056 (817) 567-2686
Admin Patsy Snow.
Licensure Intermediate Care. *Beds* 108. *Certified* Medicaid.
Ownership Proprietary.

JACKSONVILLE

Gardendale Nursing Home
Hwy 79 E, Jacksonville, TX, 75766 (214) 586-3626
Admin Pattie Gray. *Medical Dir/Dir of Nursing* D B Turner MD.
Licensure Skilled Care; Intermediate Care. *Beds* 120. *Certified* Medicaid.
Admissions Requirements Physician's request.

Sunset Care Center*
407 Bonita St, Jacksonville, TX, 75766 (214) 586-3616
Admin Jean C Allen.
Licensure Intermediate Care. *Beds* 53. *Certified* Medicaid.
Ownership Proprietary.

Twin Oaks Convalescent Center*
PO Box 1271, 1123 N Bolton, Jacksonville, TX, 75766 (214) 586-9031
Admin Jeffie Caldwell.
Licensure Intermediate Care. *Beds* 96. *Certified* Medicaid.
Ownership Proprietary.

JASPER

Jasper Convalescent Center Inc
350 Springhill Rd, Jasper, TX, 75951 (713) 384-5411
Admin Lillie Carrell.
Licensure Intermediate Care. *Beds* 88. *Certified* Medicaid.
Admissions Requirements Medical examina-

tion.
Staff RNs 2 (ft); LPNs 6 (ft), 3 (pt); Nurses aides 25 (ft), 3 (pt); Physical therapists 1 (pt); Occupational therapists 1 (pt); Speech therapists 1 (pt); Activities coordinators 1 (ft); Dietitians 1 (ft); Podiatrists 1 (pt).
Facilities Dining room; Activities room; Laundry room; Barber/Beauty shop.
Activities Arts and Crafts; Cards; Games; Movies; Shopping trips; Dances/Social or cultural gatherings.

Pinewood Manor Nursing Home*
315 W Gibson, Jasper, TX, 75951 (713) 384-5768
Admin Doris Evelyn Chapman.
Licensure Intermediate Care. *Beds* 120. *Certified* Medicaid.
Ownership Proprietary.

JAYTON

Kent County Nursing Home*
Hwy 70 W, Jayton, TX, 79528 (806) 237-3036
Admin O Joyce Reynolds.
Licensure Intermediate Care. *Beds* 33. *Certified* Medicaid.
Ownership Proprietary.

JEFFERSON

Douglas Memorial Nursing Home*
PO Box 527, 100-06 Walnut St, Jefferson, TX, 75657 (214) 665-8541
Admin Willie Mae Douglas.
Licensure Intermediate Care. *Beds* 42. *Certified* Medicaid.
Ownership Proprietary.

Magnolia Manor
510 E Bonham St, Jefferson, TX, 75657 (214) 665-3903
Admin Brenda J Cox. *Medical Dir/Dir of Nursing* Dr W S Terry.
Licensure Intermediate Care. *Beds* 60. *Certified* Medicaid.
Admissions Requirements Medical examination; Physician's request.
Staff RNs 1 (ft); LPNs 4 (ft), 2 (pt); Nurses aides 17 (ft), 2 (pt); Activities coordinators 1 (ft).
Facilities Dining room; Laundry room; Barber/Beauty shop.
Activities Arts and Crafts; Cards; Games; Reading groups; Prayer groups; Shopping trips; Dances/Social or cultural gatherings.
Description Only nursing home in Jefferson with ICF III level of care.

JOHNSON CITY

Lyndon B Johnson Memorial Nursing Home*
Ave C and 10th St, Johnson City, TX, 78636 (512) 868-7115
Admin Lucille M Newman.
Licensure Intermediate Care. *Beds* 24. *Certified* Medicaid.
Ownership Nonprofit.

JOURDANTON

Retama Manor Nursing Center Inc
1504 Oak, Jourdanton, TX, 78026 (512) 769-3531
Admin Zettie B McLerran.
Licensure Skilled Care. *Beds* 48. *Certified* Medicaid.
Admissions Requirements Minimum age 21.
Staff Physicians 1 (pt); RNs 2 (ft); LPNs 4 (ft); Nurses aides 12 (ft), 4 (pt); Physical therapists 1 (pt); Reality therapists 1 (pt); Recreational therapists 1 (pt); Occupational therapists 1 (pt); Speech therapists 1 (pt); Activities coordinators 1 (ft); Dietitians 1 (pt).
Facilities Dining room; Crafts room; Laundry room; Barber/Beauty shop.
Activities Arts and Crafts; Cards; Games; Reading groups; Prayer groups; Movies; Dances/Social or cultural gatherings.
Description Lovely small home with roses all around building.

JUNCTION

Leisure Lodge—Junction
111 Hospital Dr, Junction, TX, 76849 (915) 446-3351
Admin Marion L Seba. *Medical Dir/Dir of Nursing* Ronald A Graham MD.
Licensure Intermediate Care. *Beds* 70. *Certified* Medicaid.
Admissions Requirements Medical examination; Physician's request.
Staff Physicians 1 (pt); RNs 1 (pt); LPNs 3 (ft); Orderlies 3 (ft); Nurses aides 13 (ft), 2 (pt); Activities coordinators 1 (ft); Dietitians 1 (pt).
Facilities Dining room; Activities room; Chapel; Crafts room; Laundry room; Barber/Beauty shop; Library.
Activities Arts and Crafts; Cards; Games; Prayer groups; Movies; Shopping trips; Dances/Social or cultural gatherings.

KARNES CITY

Four Seasons Nursing Center—Karnes City*
209 Country Club Dr, Karnes City, TX, 78118 (512) 780-2426
Admin Helen A Lyons.
Licensure Intermediate Care. *Beds* 60. *Certified* Medicaid.
Ownership Proprietary.

KATY

Katyville Healthcare Center*
5129 E 5th St, Katy, TX, 77450 (713) 371-7087
Admin Virginia E Harrell.
Licensure Intermediate Care. *Beds* 98.
Certified Medicaid.
Ownership Proprietary.

KAUFMAN

Leisure Lodge—Kaufman
3001 S Houston St, Kaufman, TX, 75142 (214) 932-2118
Admin Sue Rice.
Licensure Intermediate Care. *Beds* 118. *Certified* Medicaid.
Staff LPNs 7 (ft), 4 (pt); Orderlies 1 (ft); Nurses aides 21 (ft), 3 (pt); Activities coordinators 1 (ft).
Facilities Dining room; Activities room; Crafts room; Laundry room; Barber/Beauty shop.
Activities Arts and Crafts; Cards; Games; Reading groups; Prayer groups; Movies; Shopping trips; Dances/Social or cultural gatherings.

Rose Haven of Kaufman Inc*
102 E 9th St, Kaufman, TX, 75142 (214) 932-2326
Admin Richard Mullin.
Licensure Intermediate Care. *Beds* 37. *Certified* Medicaid.
Ownership Proprietary.

KEENE

Town Hall Estates
207 Old Betsy Rd, Keene, TX, 76059 (817) 641-9843
Admin Alberta Ann Bunnell.
Licensure Intermediate Care. *Beds* 75. *Certified* Medicaid.
Staff RNs 2 (ft); LPNs 5 (ft); Nurses aides 23 (ft); Activities coordinators 1 (ft); Dietitians 1 (pt).
Facilities Dining room; Laundry room; Barber/Beauty shop.
Activities Arts and Crafts; Games; Reading groups; Prayer groups; Movies.
Description Outstanding factors about the nursing home are the excellent nursing care given and excellent food served.

KELLER

Mimosa Manor Care Center*
PO Box 485, 459 E Price St, Keller, TX, 76248 (817) 431-2518
Admin Robert W Walker.
Licensure Intermediate Care. *Beds* 150. *Certified* Medicaid.
Ownership Proprietary.

KEMP

Kemp Care Center Inc
600 N Adams St, Kemp, TX, 75143 (214) 498-5701
Admin A W Baldwin.
Licensure Intermediate Care. *Beds* 60. *Certified* Medicaid.
Admissions Requirements Medical examination; Physician's request.
Staff Physicians; RNs; LPNs; Nurses aides; Physical therapists; Reality therapists; Recreational therapists; Occupational therapists; Speech therapists; Activities coordinators; Dietitians; Podiatrists.
Facilities Dining room; Physical therapy room; Activities room; Chapel; Crafts room; Laundry room; Barber/Beauty shop; Library.
Activities Cards; Games; Prayer groups; Movies; Shopping trips.

KENEDY

Green's Rest Home
505 W Main St, Kenedy, TX, 78119 (512) 583-3406
Admin Patsy L Marchant.
Licensure Intermediate Care. *Beds* 59. *Certified* Medicaid.
Staff RNs 1 (ft), 1 (pt); LPNs 2 (ft), 2 (pt); Nurses aides 20 (ft); Activities coordinator (ft); Dietitians 1 (ft).
Facilities Dining room; Activities room; Crafts room; Laundry room; Barber/Beauty shop.
Activities Arts and Crafts; Cards; Games; Reading groups; Prayer groups; Dances/Social or cultural gatherings.
Description This is a small nursing home, ily oriented, giving good patient care.

John Paul II Nursing Center*
215 Tilden, Kenedy, TX, 78119 (512) 583-
Admin Pauline Wernli.
Licensure Intermediate Care; Personal Ca Beds ICF 73; Personal Care 21. *Certified* Medicaid.
Ownership Nonprofit.
Affiliation Roman Catholic

Restful Acres Nursing Home Inc*
Box E, Hwy 181 S, Kenedy, TX, 78119 (5 583-3421
Admin Lana K Green.
Licensure Intermediate Care. *Beds* 60. *Certified* Medicaid.
Ownership Proprietary.

KENNEDALE

Kennedale Nursing Home*
PO Box 447, Old Mansfield Rd, Kennedal TX, 76060 (817) 478-5454
Admin Mildred K Garrett.
Licensure Skilled Care. *Beds* 60. *Certified* Medicaid.
Ownership Proprietary.

KERENS

Maywood Manor Inc
4th and Margaret, Kerens, TX, 75144 (21 396-2905
Admin Joan K Kilcrease.
Licensure Intermediate Care. *Beds* 53. *C fied* Medicaid.
Admissions Requirements Physician's req
Staff LPNs 4 (ft), 1 (pt); Nurses aides 13 ((pt); Activities coordinators; Dietitians.
Facilities Dining room; Laundry room; B /Beauty shop.
Activities Arts and Crafts; Games; Movie
Description Facility is a home-owned 53-t intermediate III facility licensed by the St Department of Health and State Departm of Human Services, with Medicaid, priva and VA supported residents.

KERMIT

Kermit Nursing Center*
PO Box 1035, School St, Kermit, TX, 79
(915) 586-6665

Admin Jemmie Nell Cooke.
Licensure Skilled Care. *Beds* 100. *Certified* Medicaid.
Ownership Proprietary.

KERRVILLE

Alpine Terrace
746 Alpine Dr, Kerrville, TX, 78028 (512) 896-2323
Admin Richard L Gehle. *Medical Dir/Dir of Nursing* Gregory G McKenzie MD.
Licensure Intermediate Care; Custodial Care.
Beds ICF 60; Custodial Care 60.
Ownership Proprietary.
Admissions Requirements Medical examination.
Staff Physicians 1 (pt); RNs 1 (ft); LPNs 5 (ft), 2 (pt); Nurses aides 13 (ft), 3 (pt); Activities coordinators 1 (ft); Dietitians 1 (pt).
Facilities Dining room; Activities room; Crafts room; Laundry room; Barber/Beauty shop; Library.
Activities Arts and Crafts; Cards; Games; Reading groups; Prayer groups; Movies; Shopping trips; Dances/Social or cultural gatherings.
Description Located in the picturesque Texas hill country, Kerrville provides one of the most temperate and healthful climates in the United States. Alpine Terrace is on the northern edge of town surrounded by oak-covered hills.

Colonial Nursing Home
1213 Water St, Kerrville, TX, 78028 (512) 896-2411
Admin James Vaughn.
Licensure Intermediate Care. *Beds* 138; Personal Care 45. *Certified* Medicaid.
Admissions Requirements Minimum age 18; Medical examination; Physician's request.
Staff RNs 1 (ft); LPNs 8 (ft); Orderlies 3 (ft); Nurses aides 30 (ft); Activities coordinators 1 (ft); Dietitians 1 (pt).
Facilities Dining room; Activities room; Barber/Beauty shop.
Activities Arts and Crafts; Cards; Games; Prayer groups; Movies; Shopping trips; Dances/Social or cultural gatherings.

Hilltop Village
Hilltop Circle, Kerrville, TX, 78028 (512) 895-3200
Admin Jack Reynolds.
Licensure Intermediate Care; Custodial Care.
Beds ICF 90; Custodial Care 60. *Certified* Medicaid.
Admissions Requirements Medical examination; Physician's request.
Staff RNs 3 (ft), 1 (pt); LPNs 14 (ft), 2 (pt); Orderlies 2 (ft); Nurses aides 39 (ft), 5 (pt); Activities coordinators 2 (ft); Dietitians 1 (ft).
Facilities Dining room; Activities room; Chapel; Crafts room; Laundry room; Barber/Beauty shop; Library.
Activities Arts and Crafts; Cards; Games; Prayer groups; Movies; Shopping trips; Dances/Social or cultural gatherings.

Meadowview Care Center
00 Leslie Dr, Kerrville, TX, 78028 (512) 6-3711
Admin Paul Toops.

Licensure Intermediate Care. *Beds* 96; Personal Care 22. *Certified* Medicaid.
Admissions Requirements Medical examination; Physician's request.
Staff RNs 1 (ft); Activities coordinators 1 (ft).
Facilities Dining room; Activities room; Crafts room; Laundry room; Barber/Beauty shop.
Activities Arts and Crafts; Cards; Games; Reading groups; Prayer groups; Movies; Shopping trips; Exercise groups.

KILGORE

Gregg Home for the Aged Inc
Rt 5, Box 135, Kilgore, TX, 75662 (214) 984-5688, 4391
Admin Barbara A Garner.
Licensure Intermediate Care. *Beds* 62. *Certified* Medicaid.
Ownership Nonprofit.
Admissions Requirements Minimum age 21; Medical examination; Physician's request.
Staff RNs 1 (pt); LPNs 6 (ft); Nurses aides 9 (ft); Physical therapists; Reality therapists; Occupational therapists; Speech therapists; Activities coordinators 1 (ft); Dietitians 1 (ft); Dentists; Ophthalmologists; Podiatrists; Audiologists.
Facilities Dining room; Activities room; Chapel; Crafts room; Laundry room; Barber/Beauty shop; Library.
Activities Arts and Crafts; Cards; Games; Reading groups; Prayer groups; Movies; Shopping trips; Dances/Social or cultural gatherings.
Description Facility is located in rural setting on 43 acres, 4 miles north of Kilgore and 7 miles west of Longview; offers all private rooms with TV and phone available in room, family-style meals, and a miniature golf course.

Kilgore Nursing Center*
2700 Henderson Blvd, Kilgore, TX, 75662 (214) 984-3511
Admin Henry M Bradford.
Licensure Skilled Care. *Beds* 115. *Certified* Medicaid.
Ownership Proprietary.

Stone Road Nursing Center Inc*
PO Box 1317, 3607 Stone Rd, Kilgore, TX, 75662 (214) 984-5036
Admin Ruth J Tucker.
Licensure Intermediate Care. *Beds* 60. *Certified* Medicaid.
Ownership Proprietary.

KILLEEN

Bell Haven Convalescent and Nursing Care
1002 Medical Dr, Killeen, TX, 76541 (817) 634-0374
Admin Darrell K Cross. *Medical Dir/Dir of Nursing* Precha Suvurungsi MD.
Licensure Skilled Care. *Beds* 120. *Certified* Medicaid.
Staff Physicians 3 (pt); RNs 4 (ft); Nurses aides 41 (ft), 2 (pt); Activities coordinators 1 (ft); LVNs 12 (ft), 1 (pt).
Facilities Dining room; Activities room; Crafts room; Laundry room; Barber/Beauty shop.
Activities Arts and Crafts; Cards; Reading

groups; Prayer groups; Movies; Shopping trips; Dances/Social or cultural gatherings; Exercise classes.
Description Facility prides itself on the skilled intensive nursing care given; 3 respirators in-house; other difficult cases handled that are not taken at other centers.

Killeen Nursing Home*
710 W Rancier Ave, Killeen, TX, 76544 (817) 526-3130, 6398
Admin Sandra Springwater.
Licensure Skilled Care. *Beds* 50. *Certified* Medicaid.
Ownership Proprietary.

KINGSLAND

Kingsland Hill Care Center*
Drawer 1079, Hwy 1431, Kingsland, TX, 78639 (915) 388-4538
Admin Katherine E Arnold.
Licensure Intermediate Care. *Beds* 105. *Certified* Medicaid.
Ownership Proprietary.

KINGSVILLE

Retama Manor
316 Military Hwy, Kingsville, TX, 78363 (512) 592-9366
Admin Emma Aguilar.
Licensure Intermediate Care; Custodial Care.
Beds ICF 156; Custodial Care 42. *Certified* Medicaid.
Admissions Requirements Medical examination; Physician's request.
Staff RNs 1 (ft); LPNs 8 (ft), 2 (pt); Activities coordinators 1 (ft).
Facilities Dining room; Activities room; Chapel; Crafts room; Laundry room; Barber/Beauty shop.
Activities Arts and Crafts; Cards; Games; Prayer groups; Movies.
Description Retama Manor-Kingsville is located off Highway 77 marked by a large sign; facilities include a beautifully decorated living room with smoking section, 2 large patios for summertime use, a large dining area, and 2 sitting rooms with a large color TV; the personal care section includes a very nice separate dining and living room area.

KNOX CITY

Brazos Valley Care Home Inc
605 Ave "F" S, Knox City, TX, 79529 (817) 658-3543
Admin Doyle Graham. *Medical Dir/Dir of Nursing* Dr Hooker.
Licensure Intermediate Care. *Beds* 70. *Certified* Medicaid.
Admissions Requirements Minimum age 18; Medical examination.
Staff Physicians 3 (pt); RNs 1 (pt); LPNs 5 (ft), 5 (pt); Nurses aides 16 (ft); Physical therapists 1 (pt); Recreational therapists 1 (pt); Activities coordinators 1 (ft); Dietitians 1 (pt); Dentists 1 (pt).
Facilities Dining room; Activities room; Crafts room; Laundry room; Barber/Beauty shop.

Activities Arts and Crafts; Games; Prayer groups; Movies; Shopping trips; Dances/Social or cultural gatherings.
Description Facility features excellent care, good activity program, and is close to hospital and doctors.

KOUNTZE

Kountze Nursing Center*
PO Box 940, FM Rd 1293, Kountze, TX, 77625 (713) 246-3418
Admin Saundra Rhame.
Licensure Skilled Care. *Beds* 60. *Certified* Medicaid.
Ownership Proprietary.

LA GRANGE

Care Inn of La Grange*
PO Box 398, 457 N Main, La Grange, TX, 78945 (713) 968-5865
Admin Marjorie Heinrich.
Licensure Intermediate Care. *Beds* 98. *Certified* Medicaid.
Ownership Proprietary.

LA PORTE

Happy Harbor Methodist Home*
PO Box 1337, 1106 Bayshore Dr, La Porte, TX, 77571 (713) 471-1210
Admin H Frank Carter.
Licensure Intermediate Care. *Beds* 140. *Certified* Medicaid.
Ownership Nonprofit.
Affiliation Methodist

La Porte Care Center
208 S Utah, La Porte, TX, 77571 (713) 471-1810
Admin Norma J Shamblin.
Licensure Intermediate Care. *Beds* 58. *Certified* Medicaid.
Staff RNs 1 (pt); LPNs 4 (ft); Nurses aides 13 (ft); Activities coordinators 1 (ft); Dietitians 1 (ft); 8 (ft).
Facilities Dining room; Chapel; Laundry room; Barber/Beauty shop.
Activities Arts and Crafts; Cards; Games; Reading groups; Prayer groups; Movies; Shopping trips; Dances/Social or cultural gatherings.

LAKE JACKSON

Lake Jackson Nursing Home
413 Garland Dr, Lake Jackson, TX, 77566 (713) 297-3266
Admin Rebecca Grether. *Medical Dir/Dir of Nursing* A O McCary MD.
Licensure Skilled Care; Intermediate Care. *Beds* 120. *Certified* Medicaid; Medicare.
Admissions Requirements Medical examination; Physician's request.
Staff Physicians 1 (ft), 2 (pt); RNs 4 (ft); LPNs 11 (ft); Orderlies 1 (ft); Nurses aides 45 (ft); Physical therapists 1 (pt); Occupational therapists 1 (pt); Speech therapists 1 (pt); Activities coordinators 1 (ft); Dietitians 1 (pt); Dentists 1 (pt); Podiatrists 1 (pt).

Facilities Dining room; Activities room; Crafts room; Laundry room; Barber/Beauty shop.
Activities Arts and Crafts; Cards; Games; Reading groups; Prayer groups; Movies; Shopping trips; Dances/Social or cultural gatherings.
Description Located in the "City of Enchantment," Lake Jackson Nursing Home specializes in geriatric and long-term care. Licensed nurses, certified aides, and physician care are available on a 24-hour basis. Laboratory, X-ray and EKG services are provided; beauty shop and barber services are also available.

LAKE WORTH

Lake Lodge*
3800 Marina Dr, Lake Worth, TX, 76135 (817) 237-7221
Admin Martha F Patrick.
Licensure Intermediate Care. *Beds* 150. *Certified* Medicaid.
Ownership Proprietary.

LAMESA

Heritage Nursing Manor*
PO Box 1285, 1201 N 15th St, Lamesa, TX, 79331 (806) 872-2141
Admin David O Crowson.
Licensure Intermediate Care. *Beds* 80. *Certified* Medicaid.
Ownership Proprietary.

Lamesa Nursing Center*
1818 N 7th St, Lamesa, TX, 79331 (806) 872-8351
Admin Eugenia F Herrin.
Licensure Intermediate Care. *Beds* 48. *Certified* Medicaid.
Ownership Proprietary.

LAMPASAS

Lampasas Manor*
PO Box 970, 611 N Broad St, Lampasas, TX, 76550 (512) 556-3688
Admin Don Carlos Lacey.
Licensure Skilled Care. *Beds* 68. *Certified* Medicaid.
Ownership Proprietary.

Leisure Lodge—Lampasas*
FM Rd 580 E, Lampasas, TX, 76550 (512) 556-6267
Admin Ima B Kelley.
Licensure Intermediate Care. *Beds* 96. *Certified* Medicaid.
Ownership Proprietary.

LANCASTER

Lancaster Nursing Home Inc
1515 N Elm, Lancaster, TX, 75134 (214) 227-6066
Admin Mina L Ellison. *Medical Dir/Dir of Nursing* Charles Waldrop MD.
Licensure Skilled Care; Intermediate Care. *Beds* 120. *Certified* Medicaid.
Admissions Requirements Medical examina-

tion; Physician's request.
Facilities Dining room; Activities room; Laundry room; Barber/Beauty shop.
Activities Arts and Crafts; Games; Prayer groups; Shopping trips; Dances/Social or cultural gatherings.

Lancaster Residential Center
3901 N Dallas Ave, Lancaster, TX, 75134 (214) 224-3554
Admin James L Roberts Jr.
Licensure Intermediate Care for Mentally Retarded. *Beds* 68. *Certified* Medicaid.

Silent Night Nursing Home*
346 W Redbud, Lancaster, TX, 75146 (214) 227-1205, 1255
Admin Helen G Robinson.
Licensure Intermediate Care. *Beds* 62. *Certified* Medicaid.
Ownership Proprietary.

Texas Healthcare Center*
1241 Westridge, Lancaster, TX, 75146 (214) 227-5110
Admin Joyce Steuer.
Licensure Intermediate Care. *Beds* 120. *Certified* Medicaid.
Ownership Proprietary.

LAREDO

Retama Manor Nursing Center—East
2520 Arkansas, Laredo, TX, 78040 (512) 722-0584
Admin Virginia Rodriguez.
Licensure Skilled Care. *Beds* 100. *Certified* Medicaid.

Retama Manor Nursing Center—South*
1100 Galveston, Laredo, TX, 78040 (512) 723-2068
Admin Virginia Rodriguez.
Licensure Intermediate Care. *Beds* 120. *Certified* Medicaid.
Ownership Proprietary.

Retama Manor Nursing Center—West*
1200 Lane, Laredo, TX, 78040 (512) 722-0031
Admin Betty Funkhouser.
Licensure Intermediate Care; Custodial Care. *Beds* ICF 168; Custodial Care 40. *Certified* Medicaid.
Ownership Proprietary.

LEONARD

Gilbert Nursing Home*
PO Box 358, E Hackberry St, Leonard, TX, 75452 (214) 587-2282
Admin Billy Wayne Gilbert.
Licensure Intermediate Care. *Beds* 80. *Certified* Medicaid.
Ownership Proprietary.

LEVELLAND

Levelland Development Center
1515 5th St, Levelland, TX, 79336 (806) 894-4902

Bethany Terrace Nursing Home, Morton
 Grove, IL
Methodist Home, Chicago, IL
North Rockford Convalescent Home,
 Rockford, IL
Oak Crest, De Kalb, IL
Sunset Home of the United Methodist Church,
 Quincy, IL
Sunset Manor (Division of Woodstock
 Christian Care Inc), Woodstock, IL
United Methodist Village, Lawrenceville, IL
Wesley Village Health Care Center,
 Macomb, IL
Willows Health Center, Rockford, IL

Order of Eastern Star
Eastern Star Home, Macon, IL

Presbyterian
Illinois Presbyterian Home, Springfield, IL
Presbyterian Home, Evanston, IL
Titus Memorial Presbyterian Home,
 Sullivan, IL

Roman Catholic
A Merkle-C Knipprath Nursing Home,
 Clifton, IL
Addolorata Villa, Wheeling, IL
Alvernia Manor, Lemont, IL
Brother James Court, Springfield, IL
Franciscan Nursing Home, Joliet, IL
Good Shepherd Manor, Momence, IL
Holy Family Health Center, Des Plaines, IL
Holy Family Villa, Lemont, IL
Little Sisters of the Poor, Chicago, IL
Misericordia Home, Chicago, IL
Mother Teresa Home, Lemont, IL
Mount Saint Joseph, Lake Forest, IL
Nazarethville, Des Plaines, IL
Our Lady of Angels Retirement, Joliet, IL
Our Lady of Victory Nursing Home,
 Bourbonnais, IL
Rosary Hill Home, Justice, IL
Saint Anthonys Continuing Care Center, Rock
 Island, IL
Saint Benedict Home for Aged, Niles, IL
Saint Joseph Home of Chicago Inc,
 Chicago, IL
Saint Joseph Home of Peoria, Peoria, IL
Saint Joseph Home of Springfield,
 Springfield, IL
Saint Joseph's Home for the Elderly,
 Palatine, IL
Saint Patrick's Residence, Joliet, IL
Villa Saint Cyril, Highland Park, IL

Slovak American Charitable Association
Rolling Hills Manor, Zion, IL

INDIANA

Baptist
Saint Paul Baptist Church Home for the Aged,
 Indianapolis, IN

Church of Christ
Altenheim Community, Indianapolis, IN
Golden Years Homestead, Fort Wayne, IN
Maple Manor Christian Home Inc—Adult
 Division, Sellersburg, IN

Church of the Brethren
Brethren's Home of Indiana Inc, Flora, IN

Grace Village Health Care Facility, Winona
 Lake, IN
Timbercrest—Church of the Brethren Home,
 North Manchester, IN

Church of the Nazarene
Westside Christian Village, Indianapolis, IN

Disciples of Christ
Emily E Flinn Home Inc, Marion, IN
Kennedy Memorial Christian Home Inc,
 Martinsville, IN

First Wesleyan Church
Wesleyan Nursing Home, Marion, IN

Independent Order of Odd Fellows
Odd Fellows Home, Greensburg, IN

Jewish
Hooverwood, Indianapolis, IN

Knights of Pythias
Indiana Pythian Home, Lafayette, IN

Lutheran
Lutheran Community Home Inc, Seymour, IN
Lutheran Home of Northwest Indiana Inc,
 Crown Point, IN
Lutheran Homes Inc, Kendallville, IN
Lutheran Homes Inc, Fort Wayne, IN
Mulberry Lutheran Home, Mulberry, IN
Shakamak Good Samaritan Center,
 Jasonville, IN

Masons
Indiana Masonic Home, Franklin, IN

Mennonite
Greencroft Nursing Center, Goshen, IN

Methodist
Asbury Towers, Greencastle, IN
Franklin United Methodist Home,
 Franklin, IN
Hamilton Grove, New Carlisle, IN
United Methodist Memorial Home,
 Warren, IN
Wesley Manor—Northwest Indiana Methodist
 Home Inc, Frankfort, IN

Missionary Church
Hubbard Hill Estates Inc, Elkhart, IN

Presbyterian
Roe-Seal Memorial Home, Lexington, IN

Roman Catholic
Providence Retirement Home, New
 Albany, IN
Regina Pacis Home, Evansville, IN
Sacred Heart Home, Avilla, IN
Saint Ann's Home, Hammond, IN
Saint Anthony Home Inc, Crown Point, IN
Saint Augustine Home for the Aged,
 Indianapolis, IN
Saint John's Home for the Aged,
 Evansville, IN
Saint Paul Hermitage, Beech Grove, IN

Seventh-Day Adventist
Bethel Sanitarium Inc, Evansville, IN

IOWA

Baptist
Baptist Memorial Home, Harlan, IA
Crest Group Home, Des Moines, IA
Crest Group Home, Ottumwa, IA
Salsbury Baptist Home, Charles City, IA

Church of Christ
Mayflower Home, Grinnell, IA

Disciples of Christ
Ramsey Memorial Home, Des Moines, IA

Evangelical Free Church
Evangelical Free Church Home, Boone, IA

Independent Order of Odd Fellows
Iowa Odd Fellows Home, Mason City, IA

Jewish
Iowa Jewish Home, Des Moines, IA

Lutheran
Bartels Lutheran Home Inc, Waverly, IA
Bethany Lutheran Home Inc, Council
 Bluffs, IA
Cedar Falls Lutheran Home, Cedar Falls, IA
Davenport Lutheran Home, Davenport, IA
Eventide Lutheran Home for the Aged,
 Denison, IA
Faith Lutheran Home Inc, Osage, IA
Good Samaritan Center, Postville, IA
Lakeside Lutheran Home, Emmetsburg, IA
Luther Manor, Dubuque, IA
Luther Park Health Center, Des Moines, IA
Lutheran Home for the Aged, Vinton, IA
Lutheran Home for the Aged, Perry, IA
Lutheran Homes Society, Muscatine, IA
Lutheran Retirement Home, Northwood, IA
Saint Luke Lutheran Home, Spencer, IA
Salem Lutheran Home, Elk Horn, IA
Strawberry Point Lutheran Home, Strawberry
 Point, IA
Valborg Lutheran Home, Des Moines, IA

Masons
Iowa Masonic Nursing Home, Bettendorf, IA
Rowley Memorial Masonic Home, Perry, IA

Mennonite
Parkview Home, Wayland, IA
Pleasant View Home, Kalona, IA

Methodist
Friendship Haven Inc, Fort Dodge, IA
Heritage House, Atlantic, IA
Methodist Manor, Storm Lake, IA
Meth-Wick Manor, Cedar Rapids, IA
Saint Luke's Methodist Hospital, Cedar
 Rapids, IA
Wesley Acres, Des Moines, IA
Western Home, Cedar Falls, IA

Order of Eastern Star
Eastern Star Masonic Home, Boone, IA
M A Barthell Order of Eastern Star Home,
 Decorah, IA

Presbyterian
Ackley United Presbyterian Home, Ackley, IA
United Presbyterian Home, Washington, IA

Roman Catholic
Alverno Health Care Facility, Clinton, IA

Bishop Drumm Care Center, Des Moines, IA
Kahl Home for the Aged and Infirm,
 Davenport, IA
Marian Home, Fort Dodge, IA
Saint Anthony Nursing Home, Carroll, IA
Saint Francis Continuation Center,
 Burlington, IA
Saint Francis Manor Inc, Grinnell, IA

KANSAS

Apostolic Christian
Apostolic Christian Home, Sabetha, KS

Baptist
Sunset Nursing Center, Concordia, KS

Church of Christ
Christ Villa Nursing Center, Wichita, KS
Winfield Rest Haven Inc, Winfield, KS

Church of the Brethren
Cedars—Church of the Bretheren Home,
 McPherson, KS

Lutheran
Bethany Home Association of Lindsborg,
 Lindsborg, KS
Cedar View Good Samaritan Center,
 Wellington, KS
Decatur County Good Samaritan Center,
 Oberlin, KS
Ellsworth Good Samaritan Center—Villa
 Hope, Ellsworth, KS
Good Samaritan Center, Junction City, KS
Good Samaritan Center, Ellis, KS
Good Samaritan Center, Dodge City, KS
Good Samaritan Center, Winfield, KS
Good Samaritan Center, Olathe, KS
Good Samaritan Village, Saint Francis, KS
Hutchinson Good Samaritan Center,
 Hutchinson, KS
Liberal Good Samaritan Center, Liberal, KS
Lutheran Home Inc, Herington, KS
Lyons Good Samaritan Center, Lyons, KS
Manor Nursing Home, Independence, KS
Minneapolis Good Samaritan Center,
 Minneapolis, KS
Shiloh Manor, Canton, KS
Trinity Lutheran Manor, Merriam, KS
Valley Vista Good Samaritan Center,
 Wamego, KS

Masons
Kansas Masonic Home, Wichita, KS

Mennonite
Bethel Home for the Aged, Newton, KS
Bethel Home Inc, Montezuma, KS
Garden Valley Retirement Village, Garden
 City, KS
Lone Tree Lodge, Meade, KS
Memorial Home for the Aged,
 Moundridge, KS
Mennonite Friendship Manor Inc, South
 Hutchison, KS
Moundridge Manor, Moundridge, KS
Parkside Homes Inc, Hillsboro, KS
Schowalter Villa, Hesston, KS

Methodist
Aldersgate Village Health Unit, Topeka, KS
Friendly Acres, Newton, KS

Trinity Manor, Dodge City, KS
United Methodist Home, Topeka, KS
Wesley Towers Inc, Hutchinson, KS

Presbyterian
Arkansas City Presbyterian Manor, Arkansas
 City, KS
Clay Center Presbyterian Manor, Clay
 Center, KS
Kansas City Presbyterian Manor, Kansas
 City, KS
Lawrence Presbyterian Manor, Lawrence, KS
Newton Presbyterian Manor Inc, Newton, KS
Parsons Presbyterian Manor, Parsons, KS
Salina Presbyterian Manor, Salina, KS
Sterling Presbyterian Manor, Sterling, KS
Topeka Presbyterian Manor Inc, Topeka, KS
Wichita Presbyterian Manor Inc, Wichita, KS

Roman Catholic
Catholic Center for the Aging, Wichita, KS
Mount Joseph, Concordia, KS
Saint John Rest Home, Victoria, KS
St John's of Hays, Hays, KS
Saint Joseph Home, Kansas City, KS
Villa Maria, Mulvane, KS

KENTUCKY

Baptist
Baptist Convalescent Center, Newport, KY
Baptist Home East, Louisville, KY

Episcopal
Episcopal Church Home, Louisville, KY
Home of the Innocents, Louisville, KY

King's Daughters and Sons
Kings Daughters and Sons Home,
 Louisville, KY
King's Daughters and Sons Home for the Aged,
 Ashland, KY

Lutheran
Louisville Lutheran Home Inc,
 Jeffersontown, KY

Masons
Masonic Widows and Orphans Home and
 Infirmary, Masonic Home, KY
Old Masons Home of Kentucky,
 Shelbyville, KY

Methodist
Lewis Memorial Methodist Home,
 Franklin, KY

Order of Eastern Star
Eastern Star Home of Kentucky,
 Louisville, KY

Presbyterian
Rose Anna Hughes Presbyterian Home,
 Louisville, KY
Westminster Terrace, Louisville, KY

Roman Catholic
Carmel Manor, Fort Thomas, KY
Loretto Motherhouse Infirmary, Nerinx, KY
Marian Home, Louisville, KY
Nazareth Home, Louisville, KY
Sacred Heart Home, Louisville, KY
Saint Margaret of Cortona Home,
 Lexington, KY

Sansbury Memorial Infirmary, Saint
 Catherine, KY
Taylor Manor Nursing Home, Versailles, KY

Salvation Army
Salvation Army Adult Day Care Center,
 Newport, KY

Seventh-Day Adventist
Friendship Manor Nursing Home, Pewee
 Valley, KY
Memorial Hospital—Skilled Nursing Facility,
 Manchester, KY
Pinecrest Manor, Hopkinsville, KY

LOUISIANA

Baptist
Arcadia Baptist Home, Arcadia, LA
Madison Parish Home for the Aged,
 Tallulah, LA

Church of God
Prayer Tower Rest Home, New Orleans, LA

Jewish
Willow Wood—New Orleans Home for Jewish
 Aged, Algiers, LA

Lutheran
Lutheran Home of New Orleans, New
 Orleans, LA

Presbyterian
Evergreen Manor, Minden, LA
Presbyterian Village of Homer, Homer, LA

Roman Catholic
Bethany MHS Health Care Center,
 Lafayette, LA
Consolata Home, New Iberia, LA
Lafon Home of the Holy Family, New
 Orleans, LA
Martin de Porres Nursing Home, Lake
 Charles, LA
Mary-Joseph Residence for the Elderly, New
 Orleans, LA
Our Lady of Prompt Succor Nursing Home,
 Opelousas, LA
Saint Anthony's Nursing Home, Metairie, LA
Saint Joseph's Home for Infirm and Aged,
 Monroe, LA
Saint Margaret's Daughters' Home, New
 Orleans, LA
Saint Mary's Training School, Alexandria, LA

VFW Womens' Auxiliary
Opelousas Health Care Inc, Opelousas, LA

MAINE

Jewish
Jewish Home for the Aged, Portland, ME

Roman Catholic
d'Youville Pavilion Nursing Home,
 Lewiston, ME
Saint Andre Health Care Facility,
 Biddeford, ME
Saint Casimir Health Care Facility,
 Lewiston, ME
Saint Joseph Nursing Home, Upper
 Frenchville, ME

Seventh-Day Adventist
Ledgeview Memorial Home, West Paris, ME

MARYLAND

Baptist
Arlington Baptist Nursing Center,
  Baltimore, MD
Baptist Home of Maryland, Owings Mills, MD
Maryland Baptist Aged Home, Baltimore, MD

Church of Christ
Homewood Retirement Center—Frederick,
  Frederick, MD

Church of the Brethren
Fahrney-Keedy Memorial Home Inc,
  Boonsboro, MD

Episcopal
Uplands Home for Church Women,
  Baltimore, MD

Jewish
Hebrew Home of Greater Washington,
  Rockville, MD
Hurwitz House, Baltimore, MD
Jewish Convalescent Center—Scotts Level,
  Baltimore, MD
Levindale Hebrew Geriatric Center and
  Hospital, Baltimore, MD
Milford Manor Nursing Home,
  Baltimore, MD
Pikesville Nursing and Convalescent Center,
  Pikesville, MD

Lutheran
Augsburg Lutheran Home of Maryland Inc,
  Pikesville, MD
National Lutheran Home for the Aged,
  Rockville, MD
Ravenwood Lutheran Village Nursing Home,
  Hagerstown, MD

Masons
Maryland Masonic Homes, Cockeysville, MD

Mennonite
Goodwill Mennonite Home Inc,
  Grantsville, MD
Mennonite Old People's Home,
  Maugansville, MD

Methodist
Wesley Home Inc, Baltimore, MD

Presbyterian
Presbyterian Home of Maryland Inc,
  Towson, MD

Roman Catholic
Carroll Manor Nursing Home,
  Hyattsville, MD
Jenkins Memorial Nursing Home,
  Baltimore, MD
Little Sisters of the Poor—Saint Martin's,
  Baltimore, MD
Saint Joseph's Nursing Home,
  Catonsville, MD
Stella Maris/The Cardinal Shehan Center for
  the Aging, Towson, MD

Society of Friends
Broadmead, Cockeysville, MD

Friends Nursing Home Inc, Sandy Spring, MD

MASSACHUSETTS

Afro-American
Hurstdale Rest Home, Springfield, MA

Baptist
Baptist Home of Massachusetts, Newton, MA

Episcopal
Saint Monica's Home, Roxbury, MA

German Ladies Aid Society
Deutsches Altenheim, Boston, MA

Hellenic Women's Benevolent Society
Hellenic Nursing Home for Aged, Canton, MA

Independent Order of Odd Fellows
Odd Fellows Home of Massachusetts,
  Worcester, MA

Jewish
Chelsea Jewish Nursing Home, Chelsea, MA
Fall River Jewish Home for the Aged, Fall
  River, MA
Jewish Home for the Aged, Worcester, MA
Jewish Nursing Home of Western
  Massachusetts, Longmeadow, MA
Jewish Rehabilitation Center for the Aged,
  Swampscott, MA
New Bedford Jewish Convalescent Home, New
  Bedford, MA

King's Daughters and Sons
Kings Daughters and Sons Home for the Aged
  in Norfolk County, Wrentham, MA

Lutheran
Fair Havens Rest Home, Middleboro, MA
Lutheran Home of Brockton, Brockton, MA
Lutheran Home of Worcester Inc,
  Worcester, MA

Masons
Masonic Home, Charlton, MA

Methodist
Rivercrest Long Term Care Facility,
  Concord, MA

Order of Eastern Star
Eastern Star Home, Orange, MA

Roman Catholic
Beaven Kelly Home, Holyoke, MA
Campion Residence and Renewal Center,
  Weston, MA
Catholic Memorial Home, Fall River, MA
D'Youville Manor, Lowell, MA
Madonna Manor, North Attleboro, MA
Marian Manor, Boston, MA
Mary Immaculate Nursing Home,
  Lawrence, MA
Mount Saint Vincent Home, Holyoke, MA
Our Lady's Haven, Fairhaven, MA
Sacred Heart Nursing Home, New
  Bedford, MA
Saint Francis Home, Worcester, MA
Saint Joseph's Manor, Boston, MA
Saint Lukes Home, Springfield, MA
Saint Patricks Manor, Framingham, MA

Tower Hill Rest Home, Fitchburg, MA

Society of Friends
New England Friends Home, Hingham, MA

Unitarian Universalist
Doolittle Universalist Home, Foxboro, MA

MICHIGAN

Church of Christ
Church of Christ Care Center, Mount
  Clemens, MI
The Evangelical Home—Port Huron, Port
  Huron, MI

Congregational
Pilgrim Manor, Grand Rapids, MI

Episcopal
Saint Lukes Episcopal Home, Highland
  Park, MI

Independent Order of Odd Fellows
Odd Fellow and Rebekah Home, Jackson, MI

Jewish
Jewish Home for the Aged 1, Southfield, MI
Jewish Home for the Aged 2, Detroit, MI

Lutheran
Luther Haven, Detroit, MI
Luther Home, Grand Rapids, MI
Luther Manor, Saginaw, MI
Lutheran Home, Frankenmuth, MI
The Lutheran Home, Monroe, MI
Martin Luther—Holt Home, Holt, MI
Martin Luther Memorial Home, South
  Lyon, MI
Martin Luther Saginaw Home, Saginaw, MI
Martin Luther—South Haven, South
  Haven, MI

Masons
Michigan Masonic Home, Alma, MI

Mennonite
Froh Community Home, Sturgis, MI

Methodist
Boulevard Temple Methodist Home,
  Detroit, MI
Chelsea United Methodist, Chelsea, MI

Presbyterian
Porter Hills Presbyterian Village, Grand
  Rapids, MI
Presbyterian Village, Detroit, MI

Roman Catholic
Bishop Noa Home, Escanaba, MI
Grand Blanc Convalescent Center, Grand
  Blanc, MI
Little Sisters of the Poor, Detroit, MI
Lourdes, Pontiac, MI
Our Lady of Mercy Convalescent Home Inc,
  Hubbell, MI
Saint Ann's Home, Grand Rapids, MI
Saint Anthony Nursing Center, Warren, MI
Saint Francis Home, Saginaw, MI
Saint Joseph Nursing Home, Hamtramck, MI
Saint Jude Convalescent Center, Livonia, MI
Saint Lawrence Diamondale Center,
  Dimondale, MI

Saint Martin Deporres Nursing Home,
Detroit, MI
Villa Elizabeth, Grand Rapids, MI

Royal Order of Moose
Whitehall Convalescent Home 2, Novi, MI

MINNESOTA

Baptist
Castle Ridge Care Center, Eden Prairie, MN
Maranatha Conservative Baptist Home Inc,
Brooklyn Center, MN
Thorne Crest Retirement Center, Albert
Lea, MN
Winnebago Baptist Home, Winnebago, MN

Christian Reformed
Christian Nursing and Living Center,
Willmar, MN

Christian Science
Clifton House, Minneapolis, MN

Church of Christ
Christian Manor Nursing Home, Tracy, MN
St Lucas Convalescent and Geriatric Care,
Faribault, MN
Saint Pauls Church Home Inc, Saint Paul, MN
Samaritan Bethany Home, Rochester, MN

Episcopal
Episcopal Church Home of Minnesota, Saint
Paul, MN

Evangelical Covenant Church
Colonial Acres Health Care Center, Golden
Valley, MN
Ebenezer Covenant Home, Buffalo, MN

Evangelical Free Church
Elim Home, Milaca, MN

Independent Order of Odd Fellows
Minnesota Odd Fellows Home,
Northfield, MN

Jewish
Minnesota Jewish Group Home 1, Saint Louis
Park, MN
Minnesota Jewish Group Home II, Saint
Paul, MN
Sholom Home, Saint Paul, MN

Lutheran
Aftenro Home, Duluth, MN
Albert Lea Good Samaritan Center, Albert
Lea, MN
Arlington Good Samaritan Center,
Arlington, MN
Augustana Home, Minneapolis, MN
Bethany Good Samaritan Center,
Brainerd, MN
Bethany Home, Litchfield, MN
Bethesda Lutheran Infirmary, Saint Paul, MN
Brainerd Good Samaritan Center,
Brainerd, MN
Christus Group Home, Grand Rapids, MN
Clinton Good Samaritan Center, Clinton, MN
Crest View Lutheran Home, Columbia
Heights, MN
Ebenezer Hall, Minneapolis, MN
Ebenezer Ridges, Burnsville, MN

Ebenezer Society/Luther Hall,
Minneapolis, MN
Elders Home, New York Mills, MN
Emmanuel Home, Litchfield, MN
Emmanuel Nursing Home, Detroit
Lakes, MN
Eventide Lutheran Home, Moorhead, MN
Gethsemane Group Home, Virginia, MN
Good Samaritan Center, Pelican Rapids, MN
Good Samaritan Center, Clearbrook, MN
Good Samaritan Nursing Center, East Grand
Forks, MN
Good Samaritan Village, Pipestone, MN
Good Samaritan Village, Mountain Lake, MN
Good Shepherd Lutheran Home, Sauk
Rapids, MN
Good Shepherd Lutheran Home,
Rushford, MN
Halstad Lutheran Memorial Home,
Halstad, MN
Kenyon Sunset Home, Kenyon, MN
Lafayette Good Samaritan Center,
Lafayette, MN
Lake Park-Wild Rice Residential Treatment
Center for Children, Fergus Falls, MN
Lakeshore Lutheran Home, Duluth, MN
Loring Nursing Home, Minneapolis, MN
Luther Haven Nursing Home,
Montevideo, MN
Luther Memorial Home, Madelia, MN
The Lutheran Home, Belle Plaine, MN
Lutheran Memorial Nursing Home, Twin
Valley, MN
Lutheran Retirement Home of Southern
Minnesota, Truman, MN
Lutheran Senior Citizen Home, Little
Falls, MN
Lyngblomsten Care Center, Saint Paul, MN
Madison Lutheran Home, Madison, MN
Mankato Lutheran Home For the Aged,
Mankato, MN
Martin Luther Manor, Bloomington, MN
Mary J Brown Good Samaritan Center,
Luverne, MN
Minnewaska Lutheran Home, Starbuck, MN
Northern Pines Good Samaritan,
Blackduck, MN
Northfield Retirement Center, Northfield, MN
Paynesville Good Samaritan Home,
Paynesville, MN
Pelican Valley Health Center, Pelican
Rapids, MN
Pioneer Home, Fergus Falls, MN
Pleasant View Good Samaritan Center, Saint
James, MN
Saint John Lutheran Home, Springfield, MN
Saint Johns Lutheran Home, Albert Lea, MN
Saint Lukes Lutheran Home, Blue Earth, MN
Saint Marks Lutheran Home, Austin, MN
Saint Stephen Group Home,
Bloomington, MN
Seminary Memorial Home, Red Wing, MN
Vasa Lutheran Home for Children, Red
Wing, MN

Masons
Minnesota Masonic Home, Bloomington, MN

Methodist
Lakeview Methodist Health Care Center,
Fairmont, MN
Walker Methodist Health Center Inc,
Minneapolis, MN

Moravian
Lake Auburn Home for Aged, Excelsior, MN

Presbyterian
Minneapolis Outreach Home,
Minneapolis, MN
Presbyterian Homes, Arden Hills, MN

Roman Catholic
Assumption Home, Cold Spring, MN
Divine Providence Home, Sleepy Eye, MN
Little Sisters of the Poor, Saint Paul, MN
Madonna Towers, Rochester, MN
Mother of Mercy Nursing Home, Albany, MN
Mother Teresa Home, Cold Spring, MN
Our Lady of Good Counsel, Saint Paul, MN
Sacred Heart Hospice, Austin, MN
Saint Annes Hospice Inc, Winona, MN
Saint Benedicts Center, Saint Cloud, MN
Saint Elizabeth Hospital Nursing Home,
Wabasha, MN
Saint Francis Home, Waite Park, MN
Saint Lucan Convalescent Center,
Faribault, MN
Saint Marys Villa Nursing Home, Pierz, MN
St Frances Home for the Aged,
Breckenridge, MN

Volunteers of America
Crystal Care Center, Crystal, MN
Sleepy Eye Care Center, Sleepy Eye, MN

MISSISSIPPI

Baptist
Crawford Nursing Home Inc, Jackson, MS

King's Daughters and Sons
King's Daughters and Sons Rest Home Inc,
Meridian, MS

Seventh-Day Adventist
Adventist Health Center, Lumberton, MS

MISSOURI

Assembly of God
Maranatha Manor, Springfield, MO

Baptist
The Baptist Home Inc, Ironton, MO
General Baptist Nursing Home,
Independence, MO
General Baptist Nursing Home Inc,
Campbell, MO

Christian Science
Great Oaks Inc, Kansas City, MO

Church of Christ
Good Samaritan Home for the Aged, Saint
Louis, MO
Parkside Meadows Inc, Saint Charles, MO

Disciples of Christ
Foxwood Springs Living Center,
Raymore, MO
Lenoir Memorial Home Inc, Columbia, MO

Independent Order of Odd Fellows
Odd Fellows Home, Liberty, MO

Jewish
Jewish Center for Aged, Chesterfield, MO
Jewish Geriatric and Convalescent Center,
Kansas City, MO

King's Daughters and Sons
King's Daughters Home, Mexico, MO

Lutheran
Beautiful Savior Home, Belton, MO
Luther Manor Retirement and Nursing Center,
Hannibal, MO
Lutheran Altenheim Society of Missouri, Saint
Louis, MO
Lutheran Charities Association Extended Care
Facility, Webster Grove, MO
Lutheran Good Shepherd Home,
Concordia, MO
The Lutheran Home, Cape Girardeau, MO
Pine View Manor Inc, Stanberry, MO

Methodist
Methodist Medical Center—Long Term Care
Facility, Saint Joseph, MO
Ozarks Methodist Manor, Marionville, MO

Presbyterian
Fulton Presbyterian Manor, Fulton, MO
Presbyterian Manor at Farmington,
Farmington, MO
Presbyterian Manor at Rolla, Rolla, MO

Roman Catholic
De Paul Health Center, Bridgeton, MO
Grand Manor, Saint Louis, MO
LaVerna Heights, Savannah, MO
LaVerna Village Nursing Home,
Savannah, MO
Little Sisters of the Poor, Saint Louis, MO
Little Sisters of the Poor-Saint Alexis Home,
Kansas City, MO
Mary, Queen and Mother Center, Saint
Louis, MO
Mercy Villa, Springfield, MO
Mother of Good Counsel Home, Saint
Louis, MO
Our Lady of Mercy Home, Kansas City, MO
Saint Agnes Home, Kirkwood, MO
Saint Francis Hopital—SNF/ICF Care Facility,
Marceline, MO
Saint Joseph's Hill Infirmary Inc, Eureka, MO

MONTANA

Lutheran
Faith Lutheran Home, Wolf Point, MT
Immanuel Lutheran Home, Kalispell, MT
Lutheran Home of the Good Shepherd,
Havre, MT
Saint John's Lutheran Home, Billings, MT
Valley View Home, Glasgow, MT

NEBRASKA

Baptist
Maple-Crest, Omaha, NE

Jewish
Doctor Philip Sher Jewish Home, Omaha, NE
Rose Blumkin Jewish Home, Omaha, NE

Lutheran
Bethpage at Axtell, Axtell, NE

Bloomfield Good Samaritan Center,
Bloomfield, NE
Blue Valley Lutheran Home, Hebron, NE
C A Mues Memorial Good Samaritan Center,
Arapahoe, NE
Callaway Good Samaritan Home,
Callaway, NE
Colonial Villa Good Samaritan Center,
Alma, NE
Evangelical Lutheran Good Samaritan Center,
Nelson, NE
Good Samaritan Center, Syracuse, NE
Good Samaritan Center, Gibbon, NE
Good Samaritan Center, Scribner, NE
Good Samaritan Center, Superior, NE
Good Samaritan Center 1, Wymore, NE
Good Samaritan Home and Center,
Beatrice, NE
Good Samaritan Village, Alliance, NE
Good Samaritan Village—Perkins Pavilion,
Hastings, NE
Good Samaritan Village—Villa Grace,
Hastings, NE
Good Shepherd Lutheran Old People's Home,
Blair, NE
Gordon Good Samaritan Center, Gordon, NE
The Lutheran Home, Omaha, NE
Martin Luther Home, Beatrice, NE
Mid-Nebraska Lutheran Homes Inc, Newman
Grove, NE
Millard Good Samaritan Center, Omaha, NE
Nemaha County Good Samaritan Center,
Auburn, NE
Pine View Good Samaritan Center,
Valentine, NE
Ravenna Good Samaritan Home,
Ravenna, NE
Saint John's Center, Kearney, NE
Saint Luke's Good Samaritan Village,
Kearney, NE
Skyline Manor and Skyline Villa, Omaha, NE
Tabitha Home, Lincoln, NE
Wolf Memorial Good Samaritan Center,
Albion, NE

Reformed Church
Lakeview Rest Home, Firth, NE

Roman Catholic
Mount Carmel Home—Keens Memorial,
Kearney, NE
Rose Lane Nursing Home, Loup City, NE
Saint Joseph Gerontology Center,
Alliance, NE
Saint Joseph's Villa, David City, NE

NEW HAMPSHIRE

Independent Order of Odd Fellows
New Hampshire Odd Fellows Home,
Concord, NH

Masons
Masonic Home, Manchester, NH

Roman Catholic
Saint Francis Home, Laconia, NH

NEW JERSEY

Christian Reformed
Christian Health Care Center, Wyckoff, NJ

Jewish
Central New Jersey Jewish Home for Aged,
Somerset, NJ
Daughters of Israel Pleasant Valley Home, West
Orange, NJ
Jewish Geriatric Center, Cherry Hill, NJ
Westwood Hall Hebrew Home, Long
Branch, NJ

Lutheran
Lutheran Home at Ocean View, Ocean
View, NJ

Masons
Masonic Home of New Jersey, Burlington, NJ

Presbyterian
The Grove Health Care Center, Neptune, NJ
The Lodge Intermediate Care Facility,
Neptune, NJ
Presbyterian Home of Atlantic City—Madison
House, Atlantic City, NJ
Presbyterian Home of the Synod,
Haddonfield, NJ

Roman Catholic
Bishop McCarthy Residence, Vineland, NJ
Mater Dei Nursing Home, Newfield, NJ
Our Lady's Residence, Pleasantville, NJ
St Vincent's Nursing Home, Montclair, NJ

Society of Friends
Friends Home at Woodstown, Woodstown, NJ
Medford Leas, Medford, NJ

NEW MEXICO

Lutheran
Betty Dare Good Samaritan Center,
Alamogordo, NM
Four Corners Good Samaritan, Aztec, NM
Grants Good Samaritan Center, Grants, NM
Lovington Good Samaritan Center,
Lovington, NM
Socorro Good Samaritan Village,
Socorro, NM
University Terrace Good Samaritan Village,
Las Cruces, NM

Methodist
Laundsun Homes Inc, Carlsbad, NM

Presbyterian
Retirement Ranch of Clovis, Clovis, NM

Roman Catholic
Saint Francis Gardens, Albuquerque, NM

NEW YORK

Baptist
Baptist Home of Brooklyn New York,
Rhinebeck, NY
Baptist Medical Center of New York-Nursing
Home Divison, Brooklyn, NY
Baptist Retirement Center Corp, Scotia, NY
Fairport Baptist Home, Fairport, NY

Congregational
New York Congregational Home for the Aged,
Brooklyn, NY

Episcopal
Good Shepherd-Fairview Home Inc,
Binghamton, NY
Saint Johns Episcopal Homes for the Aged and
the Blind, Brooklyn, NY

Independent Order of Odd Fellows
Odd Fellow and Rebekah Nursing Home Inc,
Lockport, NY
United Odd Fellow and Rebekah Home,
Bronx, NY

Jewish
Aishel Avraham Residential Health Facility
Inc, Brooklyn, NY
Beth Abraham Hospital, Bronx, NY
Bezalel Nursing Home Company, Far
Rockaway, NY
Bialystoker Home for the Aged, New
York, NY
Daughters of Jacob Nursing Home Company
Inc, Bronx, NY
Daughters of Sarah Nursing Home Company
Inc, Albany, NY
Fort Tryon Nursing Home, New York, NY
Franklin Nursing Home, Flushing, NY
Haym Salomon Home for the Aged,
Brooklyn, NY
Hebrew Home for the Aged at Fairfield,
Bronx, NY
Hebrew Home for the Aged at Riverdale,
Bronx, NY
Hebrew Hospital for the Chronic Sick,
Bronx, NY
Home of the Sages of Isreal Inc, New
York, NY
Jewish Guild for the Blind/Home for the Aged
Blind, Yonkers, NY
Jewish Home and Hospital for the Aged, New
York, NY
Jewish Home and Infirmary of Rochester New
York Inc, Rochester, NY
Jewish Home of Central New York,
Syracuse, NY
JHMCB Center for Nursing and
Rehabilitation, Brooklyn, NY
Menorah Home and Hospital for the Aged and
Infirm, Brooklyn, NY
Menorah Nursing Home Inc, Brooklyn, NY
Metropolitan Jewish Geriatric Center,
Brooklyn, NY
Port Chester Nursing Home, Port Chester, NY
Rosa Coplon Jewish Home and Infirmary,
Buffalo, NY
Rutland Nursing Home Co Inc, Brooklyn, NY
United Home for Aged Hebrews, New
Rochelle, NY
Workmens Circle Home and Infirmary,
Bronx, NY

Lutheran
Augustana Home for the Aged Inc,
Brooklyn, NY
Eger Nursing Home Inc, Staten Island, NY
Lutheran Center for the Aging,
Smithtown, NY
Lutheran Retirement Home, Jamestown, NY
Martin Luther Nursing Home Inc,
Clinton, NY
Niagara Lutheran Home Inc, Buffalo, NY
Wartburg Nursing Home, Mount Vernon, NY
Wartburg Nursing Home Inc, Brooklyn, NY

Masons
German Masonic Home Corp, New
Rochelle, NY
Masonic Home and Health Facility, Utica, NY

Methodist
Bethel Nursing Home Company Inc,
Ossining, NY
Brooklyn United Methodist Church Home,
Brooklyn, NY
Elizabeth Church Manor, Binghamton, NY
Folts Home, Herkimer, NY
Gerry Nursing Home Co Inc, Gerry, NY
Methodist Church Home for the Aged,
Bronx, NY
Niagra Frontier Methodist Home Inc,
Getzville, NY
Rochester United Methodist Home,
Rochester, NY
Wesley Health Care Center Inc, Saratoga
Springs, NY

Order of Eastern Star
Eastern Star Home and Infirmary,
Oriskany, NY

Presbyterian
Amherst Presbyterian Nursing Center,
Williamsville, NY
Presbyterian Home for Central New York Inc,
New Hartford, NY
Presbyterian Homes of Western New York Inc,
Jamestown, NY
Presbyterian Homes of Western New York Inc,
Jamestown, NY
Saint Lukes Presbyterian Nursing Center,
Buffalo, NY
United Presbyterian Home at Syosset Inc,
Woodbury, NY

Roman Catholic
A Barton Hepburn Hospital Skilled Nursing
Facility, Ogdensburg, NY
Brothers of Mercy Nursing Home Co Inc,
Clarence, NY
Consolation Nursing Home Inc, West
Islip, NY
Ferncliff Nursing Home Co Inc,
Rhinebeck, NY
Frances Schervier Home and Hospital,
Bronx, NY
Holy Family Home for the Aged,
Brooklyn, NY
Jeanne Jugan Residence, Bronx, NY
Kenmore Mercy Hospital—Skilled Nursing
Unit, Kenmore, NY
Lyden Nursing Home, Astoria, NY
Madonna Home of Mercy Hospital—
Watertown, Watertown, NY
Madonna Residence, Brooklyn, NY
Mercy Health and Rehabilitation Center,
Auburn, NY
Mercy Healthcare Center, Tupper Lake, NY
Mount Loretto Nursing Home,
Amsterdam, NY
Nazareth Nursing Home and Health Related
Facility, Buffalo, NY
Our Lady of Hope Residence-Little Sisters of
the Poor, Latham, NY
Sacred Heart Home, Bronx, NY
Sacred Heart Home Inc, Plattsburgh, NY
Saint Ann's Home for the Aged,
Rochester, NY

Saint Cabrini Nursing Home Inc, Dobbs
Ferry, NY
Saint Camillus Nursing Home Company Inc,
Syracuse, NY
Saint Clare Manor, Lockport, NY
Saint Josephs Home, Ogdensburg, NY
Saint Josephs Hospital Nursing Home,
Yonkers, NY
Saint Patricks Home for the Aged and Infirm,
Bronx, NY
Saint Teresas Nursing Home Inc,
Middleton, NY
Teresian House Nursing Home Co Inc,
Albany, NY
Uihlein Mercy Center Inc, Lake Placid, NY
Villa Mary Immaculate, Albany, NY

Seventh-Day Adventist
Adventist Health and Retirement Center,
Livingston, NY

NORTH CAROLINA

Baptist
Baptist Retirement Home of North Carolina
Inc, Winston-Salem, NC

Church of Christ
The United Church Retirement Home,
Newton, NC

Episcopal
Deerfield Episcopal Retirement Community
Inc, Asheville, NC
Penick Episcopal Home for the Aging,
Southern Pines, NC

First Wesleyan Church
Wesleyan Arms Inc, High Point, NC

Jewish
The Bluementhal Jewish Home for the Aged,
Clemmons, NC

Lutheran
North Carolina Lutheran Home—Hickory
Unit, Hickory, NC
North Carolina Lutheran Home—Salisbury,
Salisbury, NC
North Carolina Lutheran Homes Inc,
Albemarle, NC
Twin Lakes Care Center, Burlington, NC

Masons
Masonic and Eastern Star Home of North
Carolina Inc, Greensboro, NC

Methodist
Brooks-Howell Home, Asheville, NC
Methodist Retirement Home—Wesley Pines,
Lumberton, NC
Methodist Retirement Homes Inc,
Durham, NC

Moravian
Moravian Home Inc, Winston-Salem, NC

Presbyterian
Covenant Village, Gastonia, NC
Presbyterian Home at Charlotte Inc,
Charlotte, NC
Presbyterian Home Inc, High Point, NC

Roman Catholic
Maryfield Nursing Home, High Point, NC

Seventh-Day Adventist
Pisgah Manor Inc, Candler, NC

Society of Friends
Friends Home, Greensboro, NC

NORTH DAKOTA

Baptist
Baptist Home, Bismarck, ND

Church of Christ
Elm Crest Manor, New Salem, ND
Wishek Home for the Aged, Wishek, ND

Lutheran
Arthur Good Samaritan Center, Arthur, ND
Bethany Homes, Fargo, ND
Dickinson Saint Luke's Home, Dickinson, ND
Enderlin Hillcrest Manor, Enderlin, ND
Good Samaritan Long Term Care Facility,
    Rugby, ND
Good Shepherd Home, Watford City, ND
Lake Region Lutheran Home, Devils
    Lake, ND
Larimore Good Samaritan Center,
    Larimore, ND
Luther Memorial Home, Mayville, ND
Lutheran Home of the Good Shepard Inc, New
    Rockford, ND
Lutheran Sunset Home, Grafton, ND
Missouri Slope Lutheran Home Inc,
    Bismarck, ND
Mott Good Samaritan Nursing Center,
    Mott, ND
Parkside Lutheran Home, Lisbon, ND
Pembina County Memorial Nursing Home,
    Cavalier, ND
Sunset Home Inc, Bowman, ND
Tri-County Retirement and Nursing Home,
    Hatton, ND
Valley Memorial Home—Almonte, Grand
    Forks, ND
Valley Memorial Home—Medical Park, Grand
    Forks, ND

Roman Catholic
Garrison Memorial Hospital—Intermediate
    Care Facility, Garrison, ND
Saint Aloisius Skilled Nursing Home,
    Harvey, ND
Saint Vincent's Nursing Home, Bismarck, ND
Westhope Home, Westhope, ND

OHIO

Apostolic Christian
Apostolic Christian Home Inc, Rittman, OH

Baptist
Judson Village and Baptist Home,
    Cincinnati, OH

Christian Science
Glenmont, Columbus, OH
Overlook House, Cleveland, OH

Church of Christ
Canton Christian Home, Canton, OH
Chapel Home Home, Canal Fulton, OH

Fairhaven Home, Upper Sandusky, OH
Mount Healthy Christian Home,
    Cincinnati, OH
Willow Brook Christian Home Inc,
    Worthington, OH

Church of God
Hester Memorial Nursing Home, Dayton, OH
Winebrenner Extended Care Facility,
    Findlay, OH
Winebrenner Haven, Findlay, OH

Church of the Brethren
Brethren Care Inc, Ashland, OH
Brethren's Home, Greenville, OH
Good Shepherd Home, Fostoria, OH
Grace Brethren Village, Englewood, OH
West View Manor, Wooster, OH

Episcopal
Whetstone Convalescent Center,
    Columbus, OH

First Community Church
First Community Village, Columbus, OH

Independent Order of Odd Fellows
Odd Fellows Home of Ohio, Springfield, OH

Jewish
Covenant House—Jewish Home for Aged,
    Dayton, OH
Darlington House—The Toledo Jewish Home
    for the Aged, Toledo, OH
Glen Manor, Cincinnati, OH
Heritage House-Columbus Jewish Home for
    the Aged, Columbus, OH
Heritage Manor—Jewish Home for Aged,
    Youngstown, OH
Menorah Park—Jewish Home for the Aged,
    Beachwood, OH
Orthodox Jewish Home for the Aged,
    Cincinnati, OH

Knights of Pythias
K W Hess Ohio Pythian Home,
    Springfield, OH
Sophia Huntington Parker Home,
    Medina, OH

Lutheran
Bethany Lutheran Village, Dayton, OH
Luther Home of Mercy, Williston, OH
Lutheran Home for the Aged, Westlake, OH
Lutheran Memorial Home, Sandusky, OH
Lutheran Old Folks Home, Toledo, OH
Lutheran Senior City, Columbus, OH
Saint Lukes Lutheran Home for the Aging,
    North Canton, OH

Masons
Ohio Masonic Home, Springfield, OH

Mennonite
Fairlawn Haven, Archbold, OH
Mennonite Memorial Home, Bluffton, OH

Methodist
Crandall Medical Center, Sebring, OH
The Elyria United Methodist Home,
    Elyria, OH
Healthaven Nursing Home, Akron, OH
Hill View Health Care Facility,
    Portsmouth, OH

Lake Park Nursing Care Center, Sylvania, OH
Otterbein Home, Lebanon, OH
Riverside Hospital, Columbus, OH
Twin Towers, The United Methodist Home on
    College Hill, Cincinnati, OH
Wesley Glen Inc, Columbus, OH
Wesley Hall Inc, Cincinnati, OH

Order of Eastern Star
Eastern Star Home of Cuyahoga County, East
    Cleveland, OH
Hamilton County Eastern Star Home Inc,
    Cincinnati, OH
Ohio Eastern Star Home, Mount Vernon, OH

Presbyterian
Dorothy Love Retirement Community,
    Sidney, OH
Marietta Manor, Cleveland, OH
Mount Pleasant Nursing Home,
    Cleveland, OH
Mount Pleasant Retirement Village,
    Monroe, OH
Park Vista Unit—Ohio Presbyterian Home,
    Youngstown, OH
Westminster Terrace, Columbus, OH

Roman Catholic
Archbishop Leibold Home, Cincinnati, OH
Franciscan Terrace, Cincinnati, OH
Good Samaritan Medical Center,
    Zanesville, OH
Holy Family Home, Parma, OH
Home for Aged—Little Sisters of the Poor,
    Oregon, OH
Jennings Hall Inc, Garfield Heights, OH
Little Sisters of the Poor, Cleveland, OH
Madonna Hall, Cleveland, OH
Maria Joseph Center, Dayton, OH
Mary Black Schroder Home for Aging Inc,
    Hamilton, OH
Mother Margaret Hall, Mount Saint
    Joseph, OH
Mount Alverna Home, Parma, OH
Saint Ann Skilled Nursing Center,
    Sandusky, OH
Saint Francis Home for the Aged, Tiffin, OH
Saint Francis Rehabilitation Hospital and
    Nursing Home, Green Springs, OH
Saint Joseph Hospice Home for the Aged,
    Louisville, OH
Saint Raphaels Home for the Aged,
    Columbus, OH
Villa Sancta Anna Home for the Aged,
    Cleveland, OH

Society of Friends
Quaker Heights Nursing Home,
    Waynesville, OH
Walton Home for the Aged, Barnesville, OH

Swedenborgian
New Dawn Convalescent Center,
    Springfield, OH

Volunteers of America
Kettering Convalescent Center, Kettering, OH
Leisure Oaks Convalescent Center,
    Defiance, OH

OKLAHOMA

Church of Christ
Central Oklahoma Christian Home, Oklahoma City, OK
Tulsa Christian Home Inc, Tulsa, OK

Episcopal
Saint Simeon's Episcopal Home Inc, Tulsa, OK

Independent Order of Odd Fellows
Odd Fellows Rest Home, Checotah, OK

King's Daughters and Sons
King's Daughters and Sons Nursing Home, Durant, OK

Mennonite
Hydro Manor Inc, Hydro, OK
Menonite Bretheren Home for the Aged, Corn, OK

Methodist
Dunaway Manor Nursing Home of Guymon Inc, Guymon, OK
Methodist Home of Clinton Inc, Clinton, OK
Methodist Home of Enid Inc, Enid, OK
Oklahoma Methodist Home for the Aged, Tulsa, OK

Oral Roberts Ministries
University Village Inc, Tulsa, OK

Pentecostal Holiness
Carmen Home, Carmen, OK

Roman Catholic
Franciscan Villa, Broken Arrow, OK

OREGON

Baptist
Baptist Manor, Portland, OR

Jewish
Robison Jewish Home, Portland, OR

Lutheran
Fairlawn Care Center, Gresham, OR
Good Shepherd Lutheran Home for Mentally Retarded, Cornelius, OR
Lutheran Pioneer Home, Colton, OR
Willamette Lutheran Homes Inc, Salem, OR

Masons
Masonic and Eastern Star Home, Forest Grove, OR

Mennonite
Dallas Nursing Home, Dallas, OR
Mennonite Home, Albany, OR

Methodist
Willamette Methodist Convalescent Center, Milwaukie, OR

Presbyterian
Presbyterian Nursing Home Inc, Ontario, OR

Roman Catholic
Benedictine Nursing Center, Mount Angel, OR
Maryville Nursing Home, Beaverton, OR

Mount Saint Joseph Extended Care Center, Portland, OR
Providence Children's Nursing Center, Portland, OR
Saint Catherine's Residence and Nursing Center, North Bend, OR

Seventh-Day Adventist
Rest Harbor Nursing Home, Gresham, OR

PENNSYLVANIA

Baptist
Baptist Home, Philadelphia, PA
Baptist Homes Nursing Center, Pittsburgh, PA
Hannum Memorial Rest Home Inc, Bradford, PA

Church of Christ
Homewood Retirement Center, Hanover, PA
Homewood Retirement Center, Martinsburg, PA
Phoebe-Devitt Home, Allentown, PA
Saint Paul Homes, Greenville, PA
Wyncote Church Home, Wyncote, PA

Church of God
Church of God Home, Carlisle, PA
Grove Manor, Grove City, PA

Church of the Brethren
The Brethren Home, New Oxford, PA
Messiah Village, Mechanicsburg, PA
Morrison Cove Home, Martinsburg, PA
Mount Hope Dunkard Brethren Church Home, Manheim, PA
Peter Becker Community, Harleysville, PA

Congregational
Evangelical Congregational Church Retirement Village, Myerstown, PA

Episcopal
All Saints Rehabilitation Hospital/Springfield Retirement Residence, Wyndmoor, PA
Christ Church Hospital Episcopal, Philadelphia, PA
Episcopal Church Home, Pittsburgh, PA

Independent Order of Odd Fellows
Odd Fellows Home of Pennsylvania Inc, Middletown, PA
Orchard Manor Inc, Grove City, PA

Jewish
Downtown Jewish Home for the Aged, Philadelphia, PA
Home for the Jewish Aged, Philadelphia, PA
Jewish Home and Hospital for the Aged, Pittsburgh, PA
Jewish Home of Eastern Pennsylvania, Scranton, PA
Jewish Home of Greater Harrisburg, Harrisburg, PA
Stenton Hall Nursing and Convalescent Center, Philadelphia, PA

Knights of Malta
Malta Home for the Aging, Granville, PA

Knights of Pythias
Kinkora Pythian Home, Duncannon, PA

Lutheran
Allegheny Lutheran Home, Johnstown, PA
Allegheny Lutheran Home, Hollidaysburg, PA
Artman Lutheran Home, Ambler, PA
Buffalo Valley Lutheran Village, Lewisburg, PA
Frey Village, Middletown, PA
Gettysburg Lutheran Retirement Village, Gettysburg, PA
The Good Shepherd Home Long-Term Care Facility Inc, Allentown, PA
Luther Acres, Lititz, PA
Luther Woods Convalescent Center, Hatboro, PA
Lutheran Home at Germantown, Philadelphia, PA
Lutheran Home at Topton, Topton, PA
Lutheran Home for the Aged, Erie, PA
Lutheran Home—Hazelton, Hazelton, PA
Lutheran Home—Kane, Kane, PA
Lutheran Home—Telford, Telford, PA
Lutheran Welfare Concordia Home, Cabot, PA
Mary J Drexel Home, Bala Cynwyd, PA
Passavant Health Center, Zellenople, PA
Perry Village Nursing Home, New Bloomfield, PA
Saint Johns Lutheran Home, Mars, PA
Shrewsbury Lutheran Retirement Village, Shrewsbury, PA
Susquehanna Lutheran Village, Millersburg, PA
York Lutheran Home, York, PA

Masons
Masonic Home Inc, Elizabethtown, PA
Masonic Home of Pennsylvania, Lafayette Hills, PA

Mennonite
Eastern Mennonite Home, Souderton, PA
Frederick Mennonite Home, Frederick, PA
Mennonite Home, Lancaster, PA
Rockhill Mennonite Home, Sellersville, PA
Tel Hai Retirement Community, Honeybrook, PA

Methodist
Bethany Village Retirement Center, Mechanicsburg, PA
Cornwall Manor of the United Methodist Church, Cornwall, PA
Epworth Manor, Tyrone, PA
Evangelical Manor, Philadelphia, PA
Lewisburg United Methodist Home, Lewisburg, PA
Quincy United Methodist Home, Quincy, PA
Simpson House of the United Methodist Church, Philadelphia, PA
United Methodist Home, Pittsburgh, PA
United Methodist Home and Hopsital, Meadville, PA

Moravian
Moravian Manor, Lititz, PA

Order of Eastern Star
Eastern Pennsylvania Eastern Star Home, Warminster, PA
Western Pennsylvania Eastern Star Home, Pittsburgh, PA

Presbyterian
Broomall Presbyterian Home, Broomall, PA
Dresser Memorial Presbyterian Home, Bradford, PA

Forest Park Nursing Home, Carlisle, PA
Indiana Presbyterian Homes, Indiana, PA
Oakmont Presbyterian Home, Oakmont, PA
Oil City Presbyterian Home, Oil City, PA
Oxford Manor Presbyterian Home,
Oxford, PA
Presbyterian Home—Cambridge Springs,
Cambridge Springs, PA
Presbyterian Home for the Aged,
Philadelphia, PA
Presbyterian Home—Johnstown,
Johnstown, PA
Presbyterian Lodge, Erie, PA
Presyterian Home at 58th St, Philadelphia, PA
Quarryville Presbyterian Home,
Quarryville, PA
Reformed Presbyterian Home for the Aged,
Pittsburgh, PA
Rydal Park of Philadelphia Presbyterian Home
on the Fairway, Rydal, PA
Shenango United Presbyterian Home, New
Wilmington, PA
Swaim Health Center, Newville, PA
Sycamore Manor Nursing Home,
Montoursville, PA
United Presbyterian Home for Aged People,
Pittsburgh, PA
United Presbyterian Home of Hollidaysburg,
Hollidaysburg, PA
United Presbyterian Home of Philipsburg,
Philipsburg, PA
Washington Presbyterian Home,
Washington, PA
Westminster Village, Allentown, PA

Roman Catholic
C R Center, Springfield, PA
Christ the King Manor, Dubois, PA
Garvey Manor, Hollidaysburg, PA
Holy Family Home, Philadelphia, PA
Holy Family Manor, Bethlehem, PA
Holy Family Residence, Scranton, PA
Immaculate Mary Home, Philadelphia, PA
John XXIII Home For Senior Citizens,
Hermitage, PA
Little Flower Manor, Darby, PA
Little Flower Manor, Wilkes-Barre, PA
Little Sisters of the Poor Home for the Aged,
Pittsburgh, PA
Maria Joseph Manor, Danville, PA
Misericordia Convalescent Home, York, PA
Mount Macrina Manor Nursing Home,
Uniontown, PA
Regency Hall Nursing Home Inc, Allison
Park, PA
Sacred Heart Manor, Philadelphia, PA
Saint Anne Home for the Elderly,
Greensburg, PA
Saint Anne's Home, Columbia, PA
Saint Francis Country Home, Darby, PA
Saint John Neumann Nursing Home,
Philadelphia, PA
Saint Joseph's Home for the Aged,
Holland, PA
Saint Josephs Villa, Flourtown, PA
Saint Marys Manor, Lansdale, PA
St Mary's Villa, Elmhurst, PA

Society of Friends
Foulkeways at Gwynedd Inc, Gwynedd, PA
Linden Hall, Kennett Square, PA
Pennswood Village, Newtown, PA

Unitarian Universalist
Unitarian Universalist Home,
Germantown, PA

RHODE ISLAND

Advent Christian Church
Pawtucket Institute for Health Services,
Pawtucket, RI

Jewish
Jewish Home for the Aged, Providence, RI

Methodist
United Methodist Health Care Center, East
Providence, RI

Roman Catholic
Boulevard Rest Home, Pawtucket, RI
Hospice Saint Antoine, North Smithfield, RI
Saint Clare's Home, Newport, RI

SOUTH CAROLINA

Episcopal
South Carolina Episcopal Home at Still Hopes,
West Columbia, SC

Lutheran
Lowman Home—Wynne C Boliek, White
Rock, SC

Methodist
The Methodist Home, Orangeburg, SC
Nursing Center of Greenwood Methodist
Home, Greenwood, SC

Presbyterian
Presbyterian Home of South Carolina—
Summerville, Summerville, SC

SOUTH DAKOTA

Baptist
North American Baptist Home, Madison, SD

Church of Christ
Dow-Rummel Village, Sioux Falls, SD

Independent Order of Odd Fellows
Odd Fellows Home, Dell Rapids, SD

Lutheran
Bethany Lutheran Home, Sioux Falls, SD
Bethel Lutheran Home, Madison, SD
Bethesda Home, Webster, SD
Bethesda Home of Aberdeen, Aberdeen, SD
Deuel County Samaritan Center, Clear
Lake, SD
Good Samaritan Center, Wagner, SD
Good Samaritan Center, Howard, SD
Good Samaritan Center, Herreid, SD
Good Samaritan Center, Scotland, SD
Good Samaritan Center, Parkston, SD
Good Samaritan Center, Selby, SD
Good Samaritan Nursing Center,
Parkston, SD
Luther Manor, Sioux Falls, SD
Lutheran Home, Eureka, SD
Lutheran Nursing Home, Hot Springs, SD
Pleasant View Nursing Home, Corsica, SD
Prairie Good Samaritan Center, Miller, SD

Mennonite
Salem Mennonite Home for the Aged,
Freeman, SD

Methodist
Jenkin's Methodist Home, Watertown, SD

Order of Eastern Star
Eastern Star Home of South Dakota,
Redfield, SD

Roman Catholic
Brady Memorial Home, Mitchell, SD
Maryhouse, Pierre, SD
Mother Joseph Manor, Aberdeen, SD
Saint Williams Home for Aged, Milbank, SD

Seventh-Day Adventist
Bowdle Nursing Home—Adventist Health
System, Bowdle, SD

TENNESSEE

Baptist
Baptist Health Care Center, Lenoir City, TN

Christian Methodist Episcopal
Collins Chapel Health Care Center,
Memphis, TN

Church of Christ
Church of Christ Home for Aged,
Nashville, TN
Lakeshore Home for the Aged, Nashville, TN
May Cravath Wharton Nursing Home,
Pleasant Hill, TN
Mid-South Christian Nursing Home,
Memphis, TN
Stones River Manor, Murfreesboro, TN

Church of the Brethren
John M Reed Home, Limestone, TN

King's Daughters and Sons
Kings Daughters and Sons Home,
Memphis, TN

Methodist
Asbury Acres Health Center, Maryville, TN
Asbury Acres Retirement Home,
Maryville, TN
McKendree Village Inc, Hermitage, TN
Wesley Highland Manor, Memphis, TN

Presbyterian
Shannondale Retirement Home,
Knoxville, TN
Wood Presbyterian Home Inc, Sweetwater, TN

Roman Catholic
Alexian Village of Tennesse Inc, Signal
Mountain, TN
Saint Peter Villa, Memphis, TN

Seventh-Day Adventist
Laurelbrook Sanitarium, Dayton, TN

TEXAS

American Religious Town Hall Meeting
Town Hall Estates, Rusk, TX

Baptist
Baptist Memorial Geriatric Center, San
    Angelo, TX
Buckner Baptist Haven, Houston, TX
Buckner Baptist Monte Siesta Home,
    Austin, TX
Buckner Baptist Ryburn Nursing Center,
    Dallas, TX
Buckner Baptist Trew Retirement Center,
    Dallas, TX
Buckner Villa Siesta Home, Austin, TX
Gilmer Convalescent Center, Gilmer, TX

Challenge Ministries
Moody Care Center, Moody, TX

Church of Christ
Eden Home for the Aged Inc, New
    Braunfels, TX
Hilltop Haven Home for the Aged,
    Gunter, TX
Texhoma Christian Care Center, Wichita
    Falls, TX

Disciples of Christ
Juliette Fowler Homes Inc, Dallas, TX

Episcopal
Morningside Manor, San Antonio, TX
Saint James House of Baytown, Baytown, TX

Independent Order of Odd Fellows
Odd Fellow and Rebekah Nursing Home,
    Ennis, TX

Jewish
Dallas Home for Jewish Aged, Dallas, TX
Golden Manor Jewish Home for the Aged, San
    Antonio, TX
Jewish Home for the Aged, Houston, TX

Knights of Pythias
Home for Aged Pythians Inc, Greenville, TX

Lutheran
Brookhaven Nursing Center, Farmers
    Branch, TX
Clifton Lutheran Sunset Home, Clifton, TX
Denton Good Samaritan Village, Denton, TX
Harlingen Good Samaritan Center,
    Harlingen, TX
McAllen Good Samaritan Center,
    McAllen, TX
Trinity Lutheran Home, Shiner, TX
Trinity Lutheran Home, Round Rock, TX

Masons
Knights Templar Clinic, Arlington, TX

Methodist
C C Young Memorial Home—Young Health
    Center, Dallas, TX
Chandler Memorial Nursing Home, San
    Antonio, TX
Crestview Retirement Community, Bryan, TX
Golden Age Home, Lockhart, TX
Happy Harbor Methodist Home, La
    Porte, TX
King's Manor Methodist Home, Hereford, TX
Meridian Geriatric Center, Meridian, TX
Sears Memorial Methodist Nursing Center,
    Abilene, TX
Turner Geriatric Center, Galveston, TX
Wesleyan Nursing Home, Georgetown, TX

Order of Eastern Star
Eastern Star Home, Arlington, TX

Presbyterian
Presbyterian Manor, Wichita Falls, TX
Presbyterian Village Inc, Dallas, TX
Presbyterian Village North Nursing Health
    Service, Dallas, TX
Trinity Towers, Midland, TX

Roman Catholic
Czech Catholic Home for the Aged, El
    Campo, TX
John Paul II Nursing Center, Kenedy, TX
Saint Ann's Nursing Home, Panhandle, TX
Saint Anthony Center, Houston, TX
Saint Benedict Nursing Home, San
    Antonio, TX
St Dominic's Nursing Home, Houston, TX
Saint Francis Nursing Home, San Antonio, TX
Saint Joseph's Residence, Dallas, TX
San Juan Nursing Home Inc, San Juan, TX

Seventh-Day Adventist
Fredericksburg Nursing Home,
    Fredericksburg, TX
Town Hall Estates, Whitney, TX
Valley Grande Manor, Weslaco, TX
Valley Grande Manor Inc, Brownsville, TX

UTAH

Church of Latter-Day Saints (Mormon)
Cedar Manor, Cedar City, UT
Wasatch Villa, Salt Lake City, UT

Roman Catholic
Saint Joseph Villa, Salt Lake City, UT

VERMONT

Independent Order of Odd Fellows
Gill Odd Fellows Home, Ludlow, VT

VIRGINIA

Baptist
Lakewood Manor—Health Care Unit,
    Richmond, VA
Virginia Baptist Home Inc, Culpeper, VA
Virginia Baptist Homes Inc—Health Care
    Unit, Newport News, VA

Church of the Brethren
Bridgewater Home Inc, Bridgewater, VA

Episcopal
Goodwin House—Nursing Care Unit,
    Alexandria, VA
Westminster-Canterbury House—Health Care
    Unit, Richmond, VA

Jewish
Beth Sholom Home of Central Virginia,
    Richmond, VA
Beth Sholom Home of Eastern Virginia,
    Virginia Beach, VA

Lutheran
Virginia Synod Lutheran Home at Roanoke,
    Roanoke, VA

Masons
Masonic Home of Virginia—Health Care Unit,
    Richmond, VA

Mennonite
Mountain View Nursing Home Inc,
    Aroda, VA
Virginia Mennonite Home Inc—Health Care
    Unit, Harrisonburg, VA

Methodist
Asbury Center at Birdmont, Wytheville, VA
Hermitage on the Eastern Shore—Nursing
    Home Unit, Onancock, VA
United Methodist Home in Roanoke—
    Nursing Home Unit, Roanoke, VA
Via Health Care Center for the Hermitage
    Methodist Home, Richmond, VA

Presbyterian
Sunnyside Presbyterian Home—Health Care
    Unit, Harrisonburg, VA
Westminster-Canterbury in Virginia Beach,
    Virginia Beach, VA

Roman Catholic
Little Sisters of the Poor—Saint Joseph Home
    for Aged, Richmond, VA
Saint Mary's Hospital—Long Term Care Unit,
    Norton, VA

WASHINGTON

Church of Christ
Horizon House Inc, Seattle, WA

Independent Order of Odd Fellows
Washington Odd Fellows Home, Walla
    Walla, WA

Knights of Pythias
Oregon-Washington Pythian Home,
    Vancouver, WA

Lutheran
Columbia Lutheran Home, Seattle, WA
Hearthstone, Seattle, WA
Josephine Sunset Home, Stanwood, WA
Martha and Mary Nursing Home,
    Poulsbo, WA
Riverview Lutheran Memorial Medical Center,
    Spokane, WA
Spokane Valley Good Samaritan,
    Greenacres, WA
Tacoma Lutheran Home, Tacoma, WA

Masons
Masonic Home of Washington, Seattle, WA

Methodist
Elmer McDowell Health Care, Stanwood, WA
Wesley Care Center, Des Moines, WA
Wesley Gardens—The Gardens, Des
    Moines, WA

Presbyterian
Kenney Presbyterian Home, Seattle, WA
Park Shore, Seattle, WA

Roman Catholic
Mount Saint Vincent Nursing Center,
    Seattle, WA

WEST VIRGINIA

Lutheran
Barbour County Good Samaritan Center,
    Belington, WV

Methodist
Glenwood Park United Methodist Home,
    Princeton, WV

Presbyterian
Presbyterian Manor, Huntington, WV

WISCONSIN

Baptist
Tudor Oaks Health Center, Hales Corners, WI

Church of Christ
Fairhaven Corporation, Whitewater, WI
New Glarus Home Inc, New Glarus, WI

Congregational
Congregational Home, Brookfield, WI

Episcopal
Saint John's Home of Milwaukee,
    Milwaukee, WI

Independent Order of Odd Fellows
Wisconsin Odd Fellow-Rebekah Nursing
    Home, Green Bay, WI

Jewish
Milwaukee Jewish Convalescent Center,
    Milwaukee, WI
Milwaukee Jewish Home, Milwaukee, WI

Lutheran
American Lutheran Home—Menomonie,
    Menomonie, WI
American Lutheran—Mondovi Unit,
    Mondovi, WI
Beckar/Shoop Center, Racine, WI
Bethany Riverside, La Crosse, WI
Bethel Home, Viroqua, WI
Bethesda Lutheran Home, Watertown, WI
Capeside Cove Good Samaritan Center,
    Siren, WI
Fennimore Good Samaritan Center,
    Fennimore, WI
Fond Du Lac Lutheran Home, Fond Du
    Lac, WI
Lincoln Lutheran of Racine, Racine, WI
Lincoln Village Convalescent Center,
    Racine, WI
Luther Home, Marinette, WI
Luther Manor, Milwaukee, WI
Luther Manor, Wauwatosa, WI
Lutheran Home for the Aging Inc,
    Wauwatosa, WI
M B Syverson Lutheran Home, Eau Claire, WI
Oakwood Lutheran Homes—Hebron Hall,
    Madison, WI
Saint Croix Valley Good Samaritan Center,
    Saint Croix Falls, WI
Saint Michael's Evangelical Lutheran Home,
    Fountain City, WI
Scandia Village Retirement Center, Sister
    Bay, WI
Skaalen Sunset Home, Stoughton, WI
Wisconsin Lutheran Child and Family Service,
    Milwaukee, WI

Woodside Lutheran Home, Green Bay, WI

Masons
Wisconsin Masonic Home—Health Care
    Center, Dousman, WI

Methodist
Christian Community Home of Hudson,
    Hudson, WI
Evergeen Manor, Oshkosh, WI
Methodist Health Center, Madison, WI
Methodist Manor, West Allis, WI
Methodist Manor Health Center, West
    Allis, WI
Morrow Memorial Home for the Aged,
    Sparta, WI
Schmitt Woodland Hills Inc, Richland
    Center, WI
Sheboygan Retirement Home Inc,
    Sheboygan, WI

Roman Catholic
Alexian Village of Milwaukee Inc,
    Milwaukee, WI
Clement Manor Health Care Center,
    Greenfield, WI
Divine Savior Hospital Nursing Home,
    Portage, WI
Franciscan Villa of South Milwaukee, South
    Milwaukee, WI
Holy Family Hospital—Extended Care Facility,
    Manitowoc, WI
Hope Nursing Home, Lomira, WI
Marian Catholic Home, Milwaukee, WI
Maryhill Manor, Niagara, WI
Milwaukee Catholic Home, Milwaukee, WI
Nazareth House, Stoughton, WI
Saint Anne's Home for the Elderly,
    Milwaukee, WI
Saint Ann's Rest Home, Milwaukee, WI
Saint Camillus Health Center, Wauwatosa, WI
Saint Catherine's Infirmary, Racine, WI
Saint Elizabeth Nursing Home, Brookfield, WI
Saint Elizabeth's Nursing Home,
    Janesville, WI
Saint Frances Home, Fond Du Lac, WI
Saint Francis Home Inc, Superior, WI
Saint Joseph's Home for the Aged, West
    Allis, WI
Saint Joseph's Nursing Home, La Crosse, WI
Saint Mary's Home for the Aged,
    Manitowoc, WI
Saint Mary's Nursing Home, Sparta, WI
Villa Loretto Nursing Home, Mount
    Calvary, WI

Seventh-Day Adventist
Bethel Convalescent Center, Arpin, WI
Chippewa Valley Hospital and Nursing Home,
    Durand, WI
Lancaster Nursing Home, Lancaster, WI
Prairie Convalescent Center, Prairie Du
    Chien, WI
River Pines Community Health Center,
    Stevens Point, WI
Villa Pines Nursing Center, Friendship, WI

PUERTO RICO

Church of Christ
Ryder Memorial Skilled Nursing Facility,
    Humacao, PR

ALPHABETICAL LISTING OF FACILITIES

A and E Nursing Home, Salt Lake City, UT
A G Gaston Home for Senior Citizens, Birmingham, AL
A G Rhodes Home Inc, Atlanta, GA
A M McGregor Home, East Cleveland, OH
A Merkle-C Knipprath Nursing Home, Clifton, IL
A Sam Karesh LTC Center, Camden, SC
A W Schlesinger Geriatric Center, Beaumont, TX
AARC Group Home 2, Albuquerque, NM
AARC Group Home 3, Albuquerque, NM
Aaron Convalescent Home, Reading, OH
Aaron Manor Health Care Facility, Chester, CT
Aase Haugen Homes Inc, Decorah, IA
Abbeville Nursing Home Inc, Abbeville, SC
Abbeville Nursing Home Intermediate Care Facility, Abbeville, GA
Abbey Convalescent and Nursing Home, Warren, MI
Abbey Forest Nursing Home, Waltham, MA
Abbey Hill Nursing Home, Saugus, MA
Abbey Manor, Windham, CT
Abbey Nursing Home, Saint Petersburg, FL
Abbey Nursing Home, Kenmore, NY
Abbey Nursing Home, Cleveland, OH
Abbiejean Russell Care Center, Fort Pierce, FL
Abbington House, Roselle, IL
Abbot Group Home, Abbot, ME
Abbott House, Highland Park, IL
Abbott House Nursing Home, Lynn, MA
Abbott Manor Inc, Plainfield, NJ
ABC Health Center, Harrisonville, MO
Aberdeen Nursing Center, Aberdeen, SD
Aberdeen Nursing Home, Rochester, NY
Aberjona Nursing Home Inc, Winchester, MA
Abilene House Inc, Tacoma, WA
Abilene Nursing Center, Abilene, KS
Able Manor Nursing Home, Cincinnati, OH
Acacia Convalescent Center, Phoenix, AZ
Acacias NRTA and AARP Nursing Home, Ojai, CA
Academy Manor of Andover, Andover, MA
Academy Nursing Home, Rochester, NH
Acadia—Saint Landry Guest Home, Church Point, LA
Acadiana Nursing Home, Lafayette, LA
Accomack County Nursing Home, Parksley, VA
Ace Placid Home, Fairland, IN
Achenbach Learning Center, Hardtner, KS
Ackley United Presbyterian Home, Ackley, IA
Acocks Medical Facility, Marquette, MI
Acr Homes on Cummings, Arden Hills, MN

Acushnet Nursing Home, Acushnet, MA
Ada Municipal Hospital, Ada, MN
Ada Retirement and Care Center, Ada, OK
Adair Community Health Center Inc, Adair, IA
Adair County Nursing Home, Kirksville, MO
Adams and Kinton Nursing Home Inc, Lillington, NC
Adams County Care Facility, Corning, IA
Adams County Manor Nursing Home, West Union, OH
Adams County Memorial—Nursing Addition, Friendship, WI
Adams Group Home, Westminster, CO
Adams Group Home, Adams, MN
Adams Health Care Center, Adams, MN
Adams House Healthcare, Torrington, CT
Adams Manor, Scranton, PA
Adams Manor Nursing Home, Commerce City, CO
Adams Nursing Home, Alexander City, AL
Adams Nursing Home, Williamstown, MA
Adams Nursing Home of North Adams, North Adams, MA
Adams Rest Home Inc, Adams, MA
Adaptive Living Center—Southeast Texas, Beaumont, TX
Adaptive Livng Center—Central Texas, Waco, TX
Adare Medical Center, Rockledge, FL
Addolorata Villa, Wheeling, IL
Adel Acres Care Center, Adel, IA
Adelphi Manor, Adelphi, MD
Adirondack Tri-County Nursing Home Inc, North Creek, NY
Adkins Nursing Home, Weleetka, OK
Adkins-Weleetka Nursing Home, Weleetka, OK
Adobe Nursing Home, West Allis, WI
Adrian Manor Nursing Home, Adrian, MO
Adult Care Services, La Junta, CO
Advance Nursing Center, Inkster, MI
Adventist Convalescent Hospital, Glendora, CA
Adventist Health and Retirement Center, Livingston, NY
Adventist Health Center, Lumberton, MS
Affton Nursing Home, Affton, MO
Aftenro Home, Duluth, MN
Afton Care Center Inc, Afton, IA
Agape Halfway House, Austin, MN
Agape House, Ellsworth, ME
Ah Gwah Ching Nursing Home, Ah Gwah Ching, MN
Aicota Nursing Home, Aitkin, MN
Aid Acres, Leitchfield, KY

Aiken Nursing Home, Aiken, SC
Air Force Village Foundation Inc, San Antonio, TX
Aishel Avraham Residential Health Facility Inc, Brooklyn, NY
Aivert Nursing Home, Ceredo, WV
Akin's Convalescent Hospital, Long Beach, CA
Akron City Hospital, Akron, IA
Al Mar Residence, Julesburg, CO
Al Vadheim Memorial Hospital, Tyler, MN
Ala Fern Nursing Home, Russell, KS
Aladdin's of Shelbina, Shelbina, MO
Alaimo Nursing Home, Rochester, NY
Alamitos Belmont Rehabilitation Hospital, Long Beach, CA
Alamitos West Convalescent Hospital, Los Alamitos, CA
Alamo Nursing Home, Kalamazoo, MI
Alaska Nursing Home, Cincinnati, OH
Alba Nursing Home, Lynn, MA
Albany Avenue Nursing Home Inc, Kingston, NY
Albany County Nursing Home, Albany, NY
Albany Nursing Care Inc, Albany, IN
Albany Personal Care Home, Albany, KY
Albemarle Health Care Center, Jackson, MS
Albemarle Villa, Williamston, NC
Albert Lea Boarding Care Home, Albert Lea, MN
Albert Lea Good Samaritan Center, Albert Lea, MN
Albert Lea Health Care Center, Albert Lea, MN
Albert's Nursing and Residential Facility, Warren, OH
Albert's Nursing Home, Warren, OH
Albertville Nursing Home Inc, Albertville, AL
Albia Care Center, Albia, IA
Albia Manor, Albia, IA
Albion Manor, Albion, MI
Alcazar Home for the Aged Inc, Saint Louis, MO
Alcorn County Care Inn, Corinth, MS
Alcott Rehabilitation Hospital, Los Angeles, CA
Alden House, Fort Lauderdale, FL
Alden Manor Nursing Home, Lynn, MA
Alden Terrace Convalescent Hospital, Los Angeles, CA
Aldersgate Village Health Unit, Topeka, KS
Aldersly Inc—Danish Home Senior Citizens, San Rafael, CA
Alderson Convalescent Hospital, Woodland, CA
Alderwood Manor, Spokane, WA

Alderwood Manor Convalescent Hospital, San Gabriel, CA
Alderwood Park Convalescent and Retirment Center, Bellingham, WA
Aldrich Boarding Care Home, Minneapolis, MN
Aletha Lodge Nursing Home Inc, Booneville, MS
Alexander Continuing Care Center, Royal Oak, MI
Alexander Home, Willmar, MN
Alexander Human Development Center, Alexander, AR
Alexandria Convalescent Center, Alexandria, IN
Alexandria Convalescent Hospital, Los Angeles, CA
Alexian Village of Milwaukee Inc, Milwaukee, WI
Alexian Village of Tennesse Inc, Signal Mountain, TN
Algart Health Care Inc, Cleveland, OH
Algoma Memorial Nursing Home—Extended Care Facility, Algoma, WI
Algona Good Samaritan Center, Algona, IA
Alhambra Convalescent Home, Alhambra, CA
Alhambra Convalescent Hospital, Martinez, CA
Alhambra Nursing Home, Saint Petersburg, FL
Alice Byrd Tawes Nursing Home, Crisfield, MD
Alice Haney Annex, Lester Prairie, MN
Alice Haney Home, Lester Prairie, MN
Alice Hyde Nursing Home, Malone, NY
Aliceville Manor Nursing Home, Aliceville, AL
All American Nursing Home, Chicago, IL
All Saints Catholic Nursing Home, Jacksonville, FL
All Saints Convalescent Center, North Hollywood, CA
All Saints Rehabilitation Hospital/Springfield Retirement Residence, Wyndmoor, PA
Allamakee County Care Center, Waukon, IA
Allegan County Medical Care Facility, Allegan, MI
Allegany County Nursing Home, Cumberland, MD
Allegany Nursing Home, Allegany, NY
Allegheny Lutheran Home, Hollidaysburg, PA
Allegheny Lutheran Home, Johnstown, PA
Allegheny Valley School—Butler Campus, West Sunbury, PA
Allegheny Valley School for Exceptional Children, Coraopolis, PA
Allegheny Valley School Group Home, Coraopolis, PA
Allen County Inn, Lima, OH
Allen Hall, Milledgeville, GA
Allen Home, Mexico, MO
Allen Memorial Home, Mobile, AL
Allen Park Convalescent Home, Allen Park, MI
Allenbrook Healthcare Center, Baytown, TX
Allenbrooke Nursing Home, Memphis, TN
Allendale Nursing Home, Allendale, NJ
Allen's Health Centre Inc, South Kingstown, RI
Allen's Rest Home, West Liberty, KY
Allenvale Convalescent Hospital, Glendale, CA
Alliance Home of Carlisle, Carlisle, PA
Alliance Nursing Center, Deland, FL
Alliance Nursing Home Inc, Alliance, OH
Allied Services, Scranton, PA

Allied Services—Long Term Care Facility, Scranton, PA
Allied Services—Lynett Village, Scranton, PA
Allison Manor, Litchfield, IL
Allison Manor Healthcare Center, Litchfield, IL
Allison Manor Nursing Home, Allison, IA
Allison Nursing Care Center, Lakewood, CO
Allison Nursing Home Inc, Poseyville, IN
Allshore House, Chicago, IL
Allston Manor Nursing Home, Boston, MA
Alma Manor Nursing Home, Alma, KS
Alma Nelson Manor, Rockford, IL
Almana Rest Home, Quincy, MA
Almeida Rest Home, Boston, MA
Almira Home, New Castle, PA
Alondra Nursing Home, Gardena, CA
Alpha and Omega Personal Care Home, Jackson, MS
Alpha Annex Nursing Center, Detroit, MI
Alpha Convalescent Hospital, Oakland, CA
The Alpha Home, Indianapolis, IN
Alpha Homes Inc, Spicer, MN
Alpha Manor Nursing Home, Detroit, MI
Alpha Village Long Term Care Facility, Middleborough, MA
Alpha-Wilshire Convalescent Hospital, Los Angeles, CA
Alpine Convalescent Center, Alpine, CA
Alpine Fireside Health Center, Rockford, IL
Alpine Guest Care Center, Ruston, LA
Alpine Manor, Thornton, CO
Alpine Manor Nursing Home Inc—Erie, Erie, PA
Alpine Nursing and Convalescent Center, Hershey, PA
Alpine Nursing Center, Saint Petersburg, FL
Alpine Nursing Home, Chelmsford, MA
Alpine Rest Home Inc, Coventry, RI
Alpine Terrace, Kerrville, TX
Alpine Valley Care Center, Pleasant Grove, UT
Alpine Village of Verdigre, Verdigre, NE
Alpine-Chavis Care Center, Salt Lake City, UT
Alps Manor Nursing Home, Wayne, NJ
Alta Care Center, Salt Lake City, UT
Alta Loma Convalescent Hospital, Alta Loma, CA
Alta Mira Nursing Home, Tiffin, OH
Alta Nursing Home Inc, Dayton, OH
Alta Vista Group Home, Trinidad, CO
Alta Vista Healthcare, Arlington, CA
Alta Vista Inc, Easley, SC
Altamaha Convalescent Center Inc, Jesup, GA
Altenheim Community, Indianapolis, IN
Altenheim German Home, Forest Park, IL
Altenheim Inc, Oakland, CA
Alternative Residence Two Inc—Middleton Estates, Gallipolis, OH
Althea Woodland Nursing Home, Silver Spring, MD
Altnacraig Convalescent Home Inc, Ridgefield, CT
Altoona Center, Altoona, PA
Altoona Manor Care Center, Altoona, IA
Altoona Nursing Home Inc, Altoona, AL
Altus Home Nursing Home, Altus, OK
Alum Crest, Columbus, OH
Alvarado Convalescent and Rehabilitation Hospital, San Diego, CA
Alvarado Nursing Home, Alvarado, TX
Alvernia Manor, Lemont, IL
Alverno Health Care Facility, Clinton, IA
Alvin Convalescent Center, Alvin, TX

Alvista Care Home Inc, Greenville, GA
Amarillo Nursing Center, Amarillo, TX
Amasa Stone House, Cleveland, OH
Ambassador Convalescent Hospital, West Covina, CA
Ambassador Manor, Tulsa, OK
Ambassador Manor South, Jenks, OK
Ambassador North, Cincinnati, OH
Ambassador Nursing Center, Detroit, MI
Ambassador Nursing Center, East Cleveland, OH
Ambassador Nursing Center Inc, Chicago, IL
Ambassador Nursing Home, New Hope, MN
Ambassador South, Cincinnati, OH
Amber House, Lexington Park, MD
Amber Valley Care Center, Pendleton, OR
Amberwood Convalescent Hospital, Los Angeles, CA
Amberwood Health Care Centre, Rockford, IL
Ambler Rest Center, Ambler, PA
Amboy Care Center, Perth Amboy, NJ
Ambrosia Home, Tampa, FL
Amelia Community Residence, Columbia, SC
Amelia Island Care Center, Fernandina Beach, FL
Amelia Manor Nursing Home, Lafayette, LA
Amenity Manor, Topsham, ME
American Beauty Nursing Home, West Frankfort, IL
American Care Center, Perryville, MO
American Convalescent, Longview, WA
American Finnish Nursing Home, Finnish-American Rest Home, Inc, Lake Worth, FL
American Health Care Center—East, Green Bay, WI
American Heritage Care Center, Hammond, WI
American Indian Nursing Home, Laveen, AZ
American Lutheran Home—Menomonie, Menomonie, WI
American Lutheran—Mondovi Unit, Mondovi, WI
American Medical Nursing Center Inc-Dresher Hill, Dresher, PA
American Medical Nursing Center—Montgomery, Montgomery, AL
American Medical Nursing Centers—Cedars, Philadelphia, PA
American Medical Nursing Centers—Langhorne, Langhorne, PA
American Medical Nursing Centers—Statesman, Levittown, PA
American Medical Nursing Centers—Township Manor, Elkins Park, PA
American Medical Nursing Centers—Valley Manor, Coopersburg, PA
American Nursing Center of Naperville, Naperville, IL
American Nursing Home, New York, NY
American Plaza Nursing Center, Evanston, IL
Americana Health Care Center, Naples, FL
Americana Health Care Center, Decatur, GA
Americana Health Care Center, Appleton, WI
Americana Health Care Center of Orlando, Orlando, FL
Americana Health Care Center of Winter Park, Winter Park, FL
Americana Healthcare Center, Jacksonville, FL
Americana Healthcare Center, Marietta, GA
Americana Healthcare Center, Arlington Heights, IL

Americana Healthcare Center, Champaign, IL
Americana Healthcare Center, Danville, IL
Americana Healthcare Center, Decatur, IL
Americana Healthcare Center, Hinsdale, IL
Americana Healthcare Center, Normal, IL
Americana Healthcare Center, Oak Lawn, IL
Americana Healthcare Center, Peoria, IL
Americana Healthcare Center, Rolling Meadows, IL
Americana Healthcare Center, Urbana, IL
Americana Healthcare Center, Westmont, IL
Americana Healthcare Center, Cedar Rapids, IA
Americana Healthcare Center, Davenport, IA
Americana Healthcare Center, Dubuque, IA
Americana Healthcare Center, Mason City, IA
Americana Healthcare Center, Waterloo, IA
Americana Healthcare Center, Kingsford, MI
Americana Healthcare Center, Florissant, MO
Americana Healthcare Center, Fargo, ND
Americana Healthcare Center, Aberdeen, SD
Americana Healthcare Center, Fond Du Lac, WI
Americana Healthcare Center—Anderson, Anderson, IN
Americana Healthcare Center at Lake Shore, Cleveland, OH
Americana Healthcare Center—Elkhart, Elkhart, IN
Americana Healthcare Center—Indianapolis, Indianapolis, IN
Americana Healthcare Center—Indianapolis Midtown, Indianapolis, IN
Americana Healthcare Center—Indianapolis North, Indianapolis, IN
Americana Healthcare Center—Kokomo, Kokomo, IN
Americana Healthcare Center—Lafayette, Lafayette, IN
Americana Healthcare Center of Kankakee, Kankakee, IL
Americana Healthcare Center of Minot, Minot, ND
Americana Healthcare Center—West, Green Bay, WI
Americana Nursing Center, Elgin, IL
Americana-Monticello Convalescent Center, Oak Lawn, IL
Americare Convalescent Center, Detroit, MI
Americare Nursing Center Inc, Oregon, OH
Amery Constant Care Inc, Amery, WI
Ames Way House, Arvada, CO
Amesbury Nursing and Retirement Home, Amesbury, MA
Amherst Home for Aged Women, Amherst, MA
Amherst Manor, Amherst, OH
Amherst Manor Nursing Home, Amherst, TX
Amherst Nursing and Convalescent Home, Amherst, NY
Amherst Nursing Home Inc, Amherst, MA
Amherst Presbyterian Nursing Center, Williamsville, NY
Amie Holt Memorial Nursing Wing, Buffalo, WY
Amistad Nursing Home Inc, Uvalde, TX
Amite Nursing Home Inc, Amite, LA
Amity Convalescent Home, Cincinnati, OH
Amory Manor Nursing Home, Amory, MS
AMS Green Tree Health Care Center, Milwaukee, WI
Amsterdam House Nursing Home, New York, NY

Amsterdam Memorial Hospital—Skilled Nursing Facility, Amsterdam, NY
Amy Johnson Residence, Saint Paul, MN
Anacortes Convalescent Center, Anacortes, WA
Anaheim Terrace Convalescent Hospital, Anaheim, CA
Anamosa Care Center, Anamosa, IA
Anchor Lodge Nursing Home, Lorain, OH
Anchorage Bensenville Home, Bensenville, IL
Anchorage Convalescent Center, Detroit, MI
Anchorage Nursing Home, Shelburne, MA
Andbe Home Inc, Norton, KS
Anderson County Health Care Center, Clinton, TN
Anderson Health Care Center, Anderson, SC
Anderson Health Care Center, Gray, TN
Anderson Healthcare Center, Anderson, IN
Anderson House Inc, Seattle, WA
Anderson Lane Nursing Home, Austin, TX
Anderson Memorial Care Homes Inc, Grand Saline, TX
Andover Intermediate Care Center, Andover, NJ
Andover Nursing and Convalescent, Andover, NJ
Andrew Care Home, Minneapolis, MN
Andrew House Healthcare, New Britain, CT
Andrew Kaul Memorial Hospital—Extended Care Facility, Saint Marys, PA
Andrew Michaud Nursing Home, Fulton, NY
Andrews Nursing Center, Andrews, TX
ANEA—Golden Years Nursing Center, Scranton, SC
Aneta Good Samaritan Center, Aneta, ND
Angel of Mercy, Albany, OH
Angel View Childrens Habilitation Center, Desert Hot Springs, CA
Angelina Nursing Home Inc, Lufkin, TX
Angeline Nursing Home Inc, North Wales, PA
Angels Nursing Center Inc, Los Angeles, CA
Angelus Convalescent Center—East, Inglewood, CA
Angelus Convalescent Center Inc, Pittsburgh, PA
Angelus Convalescent Center—West, Inglewood, CA
Angelus Convalescent Home, Minneapolis, MN
Angleton-Danbury Convalescent Center, Angleton, TX
Angola Nursing Home, Angola, IN
Anlaw Nursing Home, Lawrence, MA
Ann Lee Home and Infirmary, Albany, NY
Ann Pearl Intermediate Care Facility, Kaneohe, HI
Ann Stock Center, Fort Lauderdale, FL
Anna Christie Nursing Home, Ambler, PA
Anna L Lee Nursing Home, Mason, TX
Anna Maria ICF of New Ellenton, New Ellenton, SC
Anna Maria of Aurora, Aurora, OH
Anna Maria Rest Home, Worcester, MA
Anna Sundermann Home, Seward, NE
Annaburg Manor, Manassas, VA
Anna-Henry Nursing Home, Edwardsville, IL
Annandale Care Center, Annandale, MN
Annapolis Convalescent Center, Annapolis, MD
Anne E Anderson Health Center, Miami, FL
Anne Maria Medical Care Nursing Home Inc, Augusta, SC
Anne Pickard Convalescent Hospital, Albuquerque, NM

Annemark Nursing Home Inc, Revere, MA
Anne's Convalescent Home, Rock Hill, SC
Annie Mae Matthews Memorial Nursing Home, Alexandria, LA
Annie Walker Nursing Home, Mount Sterling, KY
Anniston Nursing Home, Anniston, AL
Ann's Rest Home, Boston, MA
Ann's Rest Home, Providence, RI
Ann's Rest Home, Salt Lake City, UT
Ann's Siesta Villa, Springville, UT
Anoka Maple Manor Care Center, Anoka, MN
Anoka State Hospital, Anoka, MN
Ansley Pavilion, Atlanta, GA
Anson County Hospital, Wadesboro, NC
Antelope Valley Convalescent Hospital and Nursing Home, Lancaster, CA
Anthony Hall Nursing Home, Indianapolis, IN
Anthony's Care Center, Greensboro, NC
Antigo Community Care Center, Antigo, WI
Antioch Convalescent Hospital, Antioch, CA
Antlers Nursing Home, Antlers, OK
Anza Convalescent Hospital, El Cajon, CA
Apalachicola Health Care Center, Apalachicola, FL
Apalachicola Valley Nursing Center, Blounstown, FL
Apostolic Christian Home, Roanoke, IL
Apostolic Christian Home, Sabetha, KS
Apostolic Christian Home Inc, Rittman, OH
Apostolic Christian Resthaven, Elgin, IL
Apostolic Christian Restmor I, Morton, IL
Apostolic Morton, Morton, IL
Apostolic of Peoria, Peoria, IL
Appalachian Christian Village, Johnson City, TN
Apple Creek Developmental Center, Apple Creek, OH
Apple Tree Inn, Fayetteville, AR
Apple Tree Lane Convalescent Home, Romulus, MI
Apple Tree Nursing Center, Richardson, TX
Applegarth Care Center, Hightstown, NJ
Applegate East, Galesburg, IL
Applegate Inn Inc, Monmouth, IL
Applegate Manor Inc, Monmouth, IL
Appleton Extended Care Center, Appleton, WI
Appleton Municipal Hospital, Appleton, MN
Applewood Hills Care Centre Inc, Lakewood, CO
Applewood Living Center, Longmont, CO
Applewood Manor Convalescent Center, Bloomingdale, IL
Applewood Manor Inc, McMillan, MI
Applewood Nursing Center, Woodhaven, MI
Applewood Nursing Home, Matteson, IL
Applin Nursing Home, Springfield, OH
Appling County Nursing Home, Baxley, GA
Approved Home Inc, Chicago, IL
Arah's Acres, Hallsville, MO
Aransas Pass Nursing and Convalescent Center, Aransas Pass, TX
Ararat Convalescent Hospital, Eagle Rock, CA
The Arbor, Itasca, IL
Arbor Manor Care Center, Spring Arbor, MI
Arbor Manor Inc, Fremont, NE
Arbor View Healthcare Center Inc, Madison, WI
Arborway Manor Convalescent Home, Boston, MA
Arbourway Rest Home, New Bedford, MA
Arbutus Park Manor Inc, Johnstown, PA

Arcadia Acres, Logan, OH
Arcadia Baptist Home, Arcadia, LA
Arcadia Children's Home, Arcadia, IN
Arcadia Convalescent Hospital Inc, Arcadia, CA
Arcadia Manor, Cincinnati, OH
Arcadia Nursing Center, Coolville, OH
Arcadia Nursing Home, Lowell, MA
Arcadia Retirement Residents, Honolulu, HI
Arch Creek Nursing Home, Miami, FL
Archbishop Leibold Home, Cincinnati, OH
Archer Nursing Home, Archer City, TX
Archibald Memorial Home for Aged Deaf, Brookston, IN
Archusa Convalescent Center Inc, Quitman, MS
Arden Hall Inc, Philadelphia, PA
Arden House, Hamden, CT
Arden Memorial Convalescent Hospital, Sacramento, CA
Arden Nursing Home, Seattle, WA
Ardis Nursing Home, Farwell, MI
Ardleigh Nursing Home Inc, Baltimore, MD
Ardmore Memorial Convalescent Home, Ardmore, OK
Ardmore Nursing Home Inc, Ardmore, TN
Area Nursing Home, Colfax, WI
Arena Manor Inc, Saint Louis, MO
Argyle House, Spring Valley, IL
Aristocrat Lakewood, Lakewood, OH
Aristocrat South, Parma Heights, OH
Aristocrat West, Cleveland, OH
Arizona Convalescent Hospital, Santa Monica, CA
Arizona Eastern Star Home, Phoenix, AZ
Arizona Elks Long Term Care Unit, Tucson, AZ
Arizona William-Wesley, Tucson, AZ
Arkadelphia Human Developmental Center, Arkadelphia, AR
Arkansas City Presbyterian Manor, Arkansas City, KS
Arkansas Easter Seals Research Center, Little Rock, AR
Arkansas Health Care Center Inc, Hot Springs, AR
Arkansas Manor Nursing Home Inc, Denver, CO
Arkansas Nursing Home Inc, Little Rock, AR
Arkhaven at Erie, Erie, KS
Arkhaven at Fort Scott, Fort Scott, KS
Arkhaven at Garnett, Garnett, KS
Arkhaven of Iola, Iola, KS
Arlington Baptist Nursing Center, Baltimore, MD
Arlington Care Center, Arlington, SD
Arlington Convalescent Center, Arlington, WA
Arlington Court Nursing Home, Columbus, OH
Arlington Gardens Convalescent Hospital, Riverside, CA
Arlington Good Samaritan Center, Arlington, MN
Arlington Good Samaritan Center, Arlington, OH
Arlington Health Care Inc, Parkersburg, WV
Arlington Heights Nursing Center Inc, Fort Worth, TX
Arlington Manor, Lawton, OK
Arlington Manor Care Center, Jacksonville, FL
Arlington Nursing Center, Arlington, TX
Arlington Nursing Home Inc, Newark, OH
Arlington Rest Home Inc, Arlington, MA

Arlington Villa for Senior Citizens, Arlington, TX
Armacost Nursing Home, Baltimore, MD
Armenian Nursing Home, Boston, MA
Armour Heights Nursing Home Inc, Fort Smith, AR
Armour Medical Wing, Kansas City, MO
Arms of Mercy Care Center Inc, San Antonio, TX
Armstrong County Health Center, Kittanning, PA
Armstrong Nursing Home, Worcester, MA
Armstrong's Personal Care Home I, Jackson, MS
Armstrong's Personal Care Home II, Jackson, MS
Army Distaff Hall, Washington, DC
Arndt Convalescent Hospital, Campbell, CA
Arnett Pritchett Foundation Home, Lexington, KY
Arnold Avenue Nursing Home, Greenville, MS
Arnold Gregory Memorial Hospital—Skilled Nursing Facility, Albion, NY
Arnold Home, Detroit, MI
Arnold House Nursing Home, Stoneham, MA
Arnold Memorial Hospital, Adrian, MN
Arnold Walter Nursing Home, Hazlet, NJ
Arnold's Care Center, Austin, TX
Arnot-Ogden Memorial Hospital—Skilled Nursing Unit, Elmira, NY
Arolyn Heights Home, Chanute, KS
Aroostook Health Center, Mars Hill, ME
Arrington Nursing Home, Jackson, AL
Arrowhead Home, San Bernardino, CA
Arrowhead Nursing Home, Eveleth, MN
Arrowhead Nursing Home, Virginia, MN
Arrowood Nursing Center, Battle Creek, MI
Arroyo Vista Convalescent Center, San Diego, CA
Arroyo-Creekside Convalescent Hospital, Walnut Creek, CA
Arterburn Convalescent Home, West Haven, CT
Artesia Good Samaritan Center, Artesia, NM
Artesian Home, Sulphur, OK
Arthur B Hodges Center, Charleston, WV
Arthur Good Samaritan Center, Arthur, ND
The Arthur Home, Arthur, IL
Artman Lutheran Home, Ambler, PA
Artrips Personal Care Home, Ashland, KY
Arvada Health Care Center Inc, Arvada, CO
Asa Park Manor, Montrose, PA
Asbury Acres Health Center, Maryville, TN
Asbury Acres Retirement Home, Maryville, TN
Asbury Center at Birdmont, Wytheville, VA
Asbury Center at Oak Manor, Chattanooga, TN
Asbury Center Health and Retirement Home, Johnson City, TN
Asbury Circle Nursing Home Inc, Denver, CO
Asbury Towers, Bradenton, FL
Asbury Towers, Greencastle, IN
Ash Flat Convalescent Home, Ash Flat, AR
Ash Grove Nursing Home Inc, Ash Grove, MO
Ashbrook Nursing Home Inc, Scotch Plains, NJ
Ashburn Conver-Care Inc, Ashburn, GA
Ashburton Nursing Home, Baltimore, MD
Ashby Geriatric Hospital Inc, Berkeley, CA
Ashfield House Rest Home, Ashfield, MA
Ashland Avenue Nursing Home, Toledo, OH

Ashland Convalescent Center Inc, Ashland, VA
Ashland Manor, Sacramento, CA
Ashland Manor Nursing Home, Ashland, MA
Ashland Nursing Home Inc, Ashland, WI
Ashland State General Hospital, Ashland, PA
Ashland Terrace, Lexington, KY
Ashlar of Newtown, Newtown, CT
Ashley Manor, Wilmot, AR
Ashley Manor Care Center, Miami, FL
Ashley Manor Care Center, Boonville, MO
Ashley Place Health Care Inc, Youngstown, OH
Ashmere Manor Nursing Center, Hinsdale, MA
Ashmore Estates, Ashmore, IL
Ashtabula County Home, Kingsville, OH
Ashtabula County Residential Services—Maples 2, Conneaut, OH
Ashtabula Medicare Nursing Center, Ashtabula, OH
Ashton Hall Nursing and Convalescent Home, Philadelphia, PA
Ashton Nursing Home, Ashton, ID
Ashton Woods Convalescent Center, Atlanta, GA
Ashville-Whitney Nursing Home, Ashville, AL
Aspen Care Center, Ogden, UT
Aspen Care Center—East, Westminster, CO
Aspen Care Center—West, Westminster, CO
Aspen Siesta, Denver, CO
Aspin Center, Harrisburg, PA
Assembly Nursing Home of Poplar Bluff Inc, Poplar Bluff, MO
Assisi Residence I, Blue Earth, MN
Assisi Residence II, Blue Earth, MN
Assumption Health Care, Napoleonville, LA
Assumption Home, Cold Spring, MN
Assumption Nursing Home, Youngstown, OH
Asthmatic Childrens Foundation of New York Inc, Ossining, NY
Aston Park Health Care Center Inc, Asheville, NC
Astor Gardens Nursing Home, Bronx, NY
Astoria Care Center Inc, Astoria, IL
Astoria Convalescent Hospital, Sylmar, CA
Atchison County Nursing Home, Atchison, KS
Athena Nursing Center, Newark, OH
Athens Convalescent and Nursing Center, Athens, TN
Athens Convalescent Center Inc, Athens, AL
Athens Development Center, Athens, TX
Athens Group Home, Athens, ME
Athens Health Care Center Inc, Athens, GA
Athens Heritage Home Inc, Athens, GA
Athens Nursing Home, Athens, TX
Atkinson Good Samaritan Center, Atkinson, NE
Atlanta Health Care Center, Austell, GA
Atlantacare Convalescent Center, Decatur, GA
Atlantic Care Center, Atlantic, IA
Atlantic County Home—Meadowview, Northfield, NJ
Atlantic Highlands Nursing Home, Atlantic Highlands, NJ
Atlantic Rest Home, Lynn, MA
Atlantis Convalescent Center, Lantana, FL
Atmore Nursing Care Center, Atmore, AL
Atoka Care Center, Atoka, OK
Atoka Colonial Manor Inc, Atoka, OK
Atrium Village, Hills, IA
Attala County Nursing Center, Kosciusko, MS
Attalla Nursing Home Inc, Attalla, AL
Attic Angel Nursing Home, Madison, WI
Atwater House, Atwater, MN

Auburn Convalescent Hospital, Auburn, CA
Auburn House Nursing Home, Boston, MA
Auburn Nursing Center, Auburn, KY
Auburn Nursing Center, Auburn, WA
Auburn Nursing Home, Auburn, NY
Auburn Nursing Home Inc, Auburn, ME
Auburn Park Club, Chicago, IL
Auburn Ravine Terrace, Auburn, CA
Audubon Health Care Center, New Orleans, LA
Audubon Villa, Lititz, PA
Auglaize Acres, Wapakoneta, OH
Augsburg Lutheran Home of Maryland Inc, Pikesville, MD
Augusta Area Nursing Home, Augusta, WI
Augusta Convalescent Center, Augusta, ME
Augusta Health Care Facility, Augusta, GA
Augusta Mental Health Institute, Augusta, ME
Augustana Center for Developmentally Disabled Children, Chicago, IL
Augustana Home, Minneapolis, MN
Augustana Home for the Aged Inc, Brooklyn, NY
Aurelia Osborn Fox Memorial Hospital Nursing Home, Oneonta, NY
Aurora Australis Lodge, Columbus, MS
Aurora Community Living Facility, Aurora, IL
Aurora House, Saint Paul, MN
Aurora Manor, Aurora, IL
Aurora Nursing Center, Aurora, MO
Aurora Park Health Care Center Inc, East Aurora, NY
Aurora-Brule Nursing Home, White Lake, SD
Aurora-Edmonds Nursing Home, Edmonds, WA
Ausable Valley Home, Fairview, MI
Austin Hewitt Home Retirement Center, Pulaski, TN
Austin Home Inc, Warner, NH
Austin Manor Nursing Home, Austin, TX
Austin Nursing Convalescent Center Inc, Austin, TX
Austin Nursing Home, Seattle, WA
Austin Woods Nursing Center Inc, Austintown, OH
Austin's Rest Haven Nursing Home, Austin, TX
Autumn Aegis Nursing Home, Lorain, OH
Autumn Breeze Nursing Home, Marietta, GA
Autumn Care of Chesapeake, Chesapeake, VA
Autumn Care of Drexel, Drexel, NC
Autumn Care of Great Bridge, Chesapeake, VA
Autumn Care of Marion, Marion, NC
Autumn Care of Mocksville, Mocksville, NC
Autumn Care of Portsmouth, Portsmouth, VA
Autumn Care of Suffolk, Suffolk, VA
Autumn Convalescent Center—Janisch, Houston, TX
Autumn Haven, Grapevine, TX
Autumn Hills, Glendale, CA
Autumn Hills Convalescent Center—Conroe, Conroe, TX
Autumn Hills Convalescent Center—Hermann Park Manor, Houston, TX
Autumn Hills Convalescent Center—Richmond, Richmond, TX
Autumn Hills Convalescent Center—Sugar Land, Sugar Land, TX
Autumn Hills Convalescent Center—Tomball, Tomball, TX
Autumn Hills Nursing Center Inc, Warren, AR
Autumn Lane Nursing Center, Sweet Springs, MO

Autumn Leaf Lodge, Hurst, TX
Autumn Leaves, Dallas, TX
Autumn Leaves Nursing Home, Winnfield, LA
Autumn Leaves Nursing Home Inc, Greenville, MS
Autumn Manor Inc 1, Yates Center, KS
Autumn Manor Inc 2, Yates Center, KS
Autumn Manor of Lawrence, Lawrence, KS
Autumn Nursing Centers Inc 1, Vinita, OK
Autumn Nursing Centers Inc 2, Vinita, OK
Autumn Place, Fort Worth, TX
Autumn View Manor, Hamburg, NY
Autumn Winds Retirement Lodge, Schertz, TX
Autumn Years Convalescent Center Inc, Hilltop, WV
Autumn Years Lodge Inc, Fort Worth, TX
Autumn Years Nursing Center, Sabina, OH
Autumnfield Inc, Lowell, NC
Autumnwood Care Center, Tiffin, OH
Auxilio Mutuo Hospital, Hato Rey, PR
Avalon Manor, Hagerstown, MD
Avalon Manor Infirmary, Waukesha, WI
Avalon Nursing Home, Lynn, MA
Avalon Nursing Home, Saint Louis, MO
Avalon Nursing Home Inc, Warwick, RI
Ave Maria Convalescent Hospital, Monterey, CA
Ave Marie Home, Memphis, TN
Avery Nursing Home, Hartford, CT
Aveyron Homes Inc, Hutchinson, MN
Avis B Adams Christian Convalescent Center, Emporia, VA
Avis House MR Unit, Columbus, OH
Aviva Manor, Lauderdale Lakes, FL
Avon Convalescent Home Inc, Avon, CT
Avon Nursing Home, Dewitt, MI
Avon Nursing Home, Avon, NY
Avon Nursing Home Inc, Avon, IL
Avon Oaks Nursing Home, Avon, OH
Avondale Nursing Center, Rochester, MI
Avonside Nursing Home, Detroit, MI
Avonwood Rest Home Inc, Birmingham, AL
Avoyelles Manor Nursing Home, Plaucheville, LA
Ayer Lar Sanitarium, Gardena, CA
Ayers Nursing Home, Snyder, OK
Azalea Gardens Nursing Center, Wiggins, MS
Azalea Manor, Sealy, TX
Azalea Nursing Center, Whitfield, MS
Azalea Trace, Pensacola, FL
Azalea Villa Nursing Home, New Iberia, LA
Azalealand Nursing Home Inc, Savannah, GA
Azle Manor Inc, Azle, TX
B and B Nursing Home, Comanche, OK
B and K Nursing Center, Hobart, OK
B J Perino Nursing Home Inc, Pekin, IL
Bachelor Butte Nursing Center, Bend, OR
Bacon Nursing Home Inc, Harrisburg, IL
Badillo Convalescent Hospital, Covina, CA
Bagwell Nursing Home Inc, Carrollton, GA
Baha'i Home, Wilmette, IL
Bailey Nursing Home, Clinton, SC
Bailie's Rest Home, Fairhaven, MA
Bainbridge Health Care Inc, Bainbridge, GA
Bainbridge Nursing Home, Bronx, NY
Baird Nursing Home, Rochester, NY
Baker County Nursing Home, MacClenny, FL
Baker Hospital Long Term Care Unit, North Charleston, SC
Baker Katz Nursing Home, Haverhill, MA
Baker Manor, Baker, LA
Baker Manor Rest Home, Lynn, MA

Baker's Rest Haven Inc, Boonville, IN
Bakersfield Convalescent Hospital, Bakersfield, CA
Baker-Sumser Retirement Village, Canton, OH
Balch Springs Nursing Home, Balch Springs, TX
Baldwin City Nursing Facility, Baldwin City, KS
Baldwin Manor Nursing Home Inc, Cleveland, OH
Baldwin Park Convalescent Hospital, Baldwin Park, CA
Baldwin Park Health Care Center, Baldwin Park, CA
Baldwinville Nursing Home, Templeton, MA
Ball Pavilion Inc, Erie, PA
Ballard Convalescent Center, Seattle, WA
Ballard Nursing Center, Ada, OK
Ballard Nursing Center Inc, Des Plaines, IL
Ballinger Manor, Ballinger, TX
Ballinger Nursing Center, Ballinger, TX
Ballou Home for the Aged, Woonsocket, RI
Balmoral Nursing Centre Inc, Chicago, IL
Balmoral Skilled Nursing Home, Trenton, MI
Balowen Convalescent Hospital, Van Nuys, CA
Bamberg County Memorial Nursing Center, Bamberg, SC
Bancroft Convalescent Hospital, San Leandro, CA
Bancroft House Healthcare Nursing Home, Worcester, MA
Bangor City Nursing Facility, Bangor, ME
Bangor Convalescent Center, Bangor, ME
Bangor Mental Health Institute, Bangor, ME
Bangs Nursing Home, Bangs, TX
Banks-Jackson-Commerce Nursing Home, Commerce, GA
Banning Convalescent Hospital, Banning, CA
Bannister Nursing Care Center, Providence, RI
Bannochie Nursing Home, Minneapolis, MN
Bannock County Nursing Home, Pocatello, ID
Baptist Convalescent Center, Newport, KY
Baptist Health Care Center, Lenoir City, TN
Baptist Home, Bismarck, ND
Baptist Home, Philadelphia, PA
Baptist Home East, Louisville, KY
Baptist Home for Senior Citizens, Cook Springs, AL
The Baptist Home Inc, Ironton, MO
Baptist Home of Brooklyn New York, Rhinebeck, NY
Baptist Home of DC, Washington, DC
Baptist Home of Maryland, Owings Mills, MD
Baptist Home of Massachusetts, Newton, MA
Baptist Homes Nursing Center, Pittsburgh, PA
Baptist Manor, Portland, OR
Baptist Medical Center of New York-Nursing Home Divison, Brooklyn, NY
Baptist Memorial Geriatric Center, San Angelo, TX
Baptist Memorial Home, Harlan, IA
Baptist Residence, Minneapolis, MN
Baptist Retirement Center Corp, Scotia, NY
Baptist Retirement Home, Maywood, IL
Baptist Retirement Home of North Carolina Inc, Winston-Salem, NC
Baptist Village Inc, Waycross, GA
Baraga County Memorial Hospital, Lanse, MI
Barbara Park Convalescent Center, Middletown, OH
Barbour County Good Samaritan Center, Belington, WV

Barbourville Nursing Home, Barbourville, KY
Barcley Boarding Home, Seattle, WA
Barcroft Institute, Falls Church, VA
Barfield Health Care Inc, Guntersville, AL
Grace Barker Nursing Home Inc, Warren, RI
Barker Rest Home, Galena, KS
Barley Convalescent Home—North, York, PA
Barley Convalescent Home—South, York, PA
Barn Hill Convalescent Center, Newton, NJ
Barnard Nursing Home Inc, Calais, ME
Barnard Rest Home, Westfield, MA
Barnes-Kasson County Hospital, Susquehanna, PA
Barnesville Care Center, Barnesville, MN
Barnesville Health Care Center, Barnesville, OH
Barnsdall Nursing Home, Barnsdall, OK
Barnwell County Nursing Home, Barnwell, SC
Barnwell Nursing Home and Health Facilities Inc, Valatie, NY
Barr House, Canon, CO
Barren County Health Care Center, Glasgow, KY
Barrett Care Center, Barrett, MN
Barrett Convalescent Home Inc, Commerce, GA
Barrett Convalescent Hospital Inc, Hayward, CA
Barrington Terrace Nursing Home, Orlando, FL
Barron Center, Portland, ME
Barron Memorial Medical Center Nursing Home, Barron, WI
Barron Riverside Manor, Barron, WI
Barry Alan Nursing Home, Saint Johns, MO
Barry Alan Nursing Home, Saint Louis, MO
Barry Care Center of Carlinville, Carlinville, IL
Barry Care Center of Gillespie, Gillespie, IL
Barry Care Center of Litchfield, Litchfield, IL
Barry Care Center of Pana, Pana, IL
Barry Care Center of Staunton, Staunton, IL
Barry Community Care Center, Barry, IL
Barry County Medical Care Facility, Hastings, MI
Bartels Lutheran Home Inc, Waverly, IA
Barth Nursing Home, Anacortes, WA
Bartholomew County Home, Columbus, IN
Bartlett Convalescent Hospital, Hayward, CA
Bartlett Manor Nursing Home, Malden, MA
Bartmann Nursing Home 2, Atlanta, IL
Bartmann Shelter Care Home, Atlanta, IL
Barton Heights Nursing Home Inc, Austin, TX
A Barton Hepburn Hospital Skilled Nursing Facility, Ogdensburg, NY
The Barton House, Indianapolis, IN
Barton Nursing Home, Detroit, MI
Barton W Stone Christian Home, Jacksonville, IL
Bartow Convalescent Center, Bartow, FL
Bashford East Health Care Facility, Louisville, KY
Basile Care Center Inc, Basile, LA
Bassard Rehabilitation Hospital, Hayward, CA
Bastrop Nursing Center, Bastrop, TX
Batavia Nursing and Convalescent Inn, Batavia, OH
Batavia Nursing Home Inc, Batavia, NY
Batavia Nursing Home Inc, Batavia, OH
Batesville Manor Nursing Home, Batesville, MS
Bath Nursing Home, Bath, ME
Baton Rouge Extensive Care Facility, Baton Rouge, LA

Baton Rouge General Hospital Annex, Baton Rouge, LA
Battersby Convalescent Home, Erie, PA
Batterson Nursing Home and Convalescent Center, Santa Cruz, CA
Battle Lake Nursing Home, Battle Lake, MN
Battlefield Park Convalescent Center, Petersburg, VA
Battles Home, Lowell, MA
Bauer-Home Residential Care, Rocky Ford, CO
Baxley Manor Inc—Intermediate Care Facility, Baxley, GA
Baxter Manor Nursing Home, Mountain Home, AR
Bay Convalescent Center, Panama City, FL
Bay Convalescent Hospital, Long Beach, CA
Bay County Medical Care Facility, Essexville, MI
Bay Crest Convalescent Hospital, Torrance, CA
Bay Harbor Rehabilitation Center, Torrance, CA
Bay Manor Nursing Home, Annapolis, MD
Bay Shore Sanitarium, Hermosa Beach, CA
Bay State Rehabilitation Care, Billerica, MA
Bay to Bay Nursing Center, Tampa, FL
Bay Tower Nursing Center, Providence, RI
Bay View Convalescent Center Inc, Bayville, NJ
Bay View Convalescent Hospital, Costa Mesa, CA
Bay View Nursing Center Inc, Beaufort, SC
Bay View Nursing Home, Winthrop, MA
Bay Villa Nursing Home, Bay City, TX
Bay Village of Sarasota, Sarasota, FL
Bay Vista Convalescent Hospital, Santa Monica, CA
Bayard Care Center, Bayard, IA
Bayberry Convalescent Hospital, Concord, CA
Bayberry Nursing Home, New Rochelle, NY
Bayless Boarding Home, Farmington, MO
Bayou Chateau Nursing Center, Simmesport, LA
Bayou Glen Nursing Center, Houston, TX
Bayou Glen-Jones Road Nursing Center, Houston, TX
Bayou Glen-Northwest Nursing Center, Houston, TX
Bayou Manor, Saint Petersburg, FL
Bayou Village Nursing Center, Crowley, LA
Bayou Vista Manor Nursing Home, Bunkie, LA
Bayside Convalescent Hospital, Kentfield, CA
Bayside Nursing Home, Boston, MA
Bayside Terrace, Waukegan, IL
Baytown Nursing Home, Baytown, TX
Baytree Nursing Center, Palm Harbor, FL
Bayview Convalescent Home Inc, Newport, RI
Bayview Convalescent Hospital, Burlingame, CA
Bayview Inn, Olympia, WA
Bayview Manor, Seattle, WA
Bayview Nursing Home, Island Park, NY
Baywood Convalescent Hospital, Pleasant Hill, CA
Baywood Nursing Home, Ludington, MI
Beach Cliff Lodge Nursing Home, Michigan City, IN
Beach Convalescent Hotel, Saint Petersburg, FL
Beach Haven Health Care Center, Beachwood, OH
Beach Nursing Home, Monroe, MI

Beach Wood, Kennebunk, ME
Beachland Intermediate Care Home, Prospect, KY
Beachview Nursing and Convalescent Home, Atlantic City, NJ
Beachview Rest Home, Keansburg, NJ
Beacon Hill Nursing Home, Kansas City, MO
Beacon Light Christian Nursing Home, Marne, MI
Beaconcrest Nursing Home, Lowell, MA
Beacon-Donegan Manor, Fort Myers, FL
Beadles Rest Home, Alva, OK
Beane Nursing Home, Saco, ME
Bear Creek Health Care Center, Bear Creek, PA
Bear Creek House, Rochester, MN
Bear Creek Nursing Center, Morrison, CO
Bear Hill Nursing Center at Wakefield, Stoneham, MA
Bear Lake Memorial Nursing Home, Montpelier, ID
Beatitudes Care Center, Phoenix, AZ
Beatrice Catherine Rest Home, Boston, MA
Beatrice Lawson Nursing Home Inc, Clairton, PA
Beatrice Manor Care Center, Beatrice, NE
Beatrice Marie Nursing Home, Boston, MA
Beaulieu Nursing Home, Newnan, GA
Beaumont Convalescent Hospital, Beaumont, CA
Beaumont Nursing Home, Northbridge, MA
The Beaumont Nursing Home, Denton, TX
Beauregard Nursing Home, DeRidder, LA
Beautiful Savior Home, Belton, MO
Beaven Kelly Home, Holyoke, MA
Beaver City Manor, Beaver City, NE
Beaver County Nursing Home, Beaver, OK
Beaver Dam Care Center, Beaver Dam, WI
Beaver Dam Lakeview Unit, Beaver Dam, WI
Beaver Valley Geriatrics Center, Beaver, PA
Beaver Valley Nursing Center, Beaver Falls, PA
Bechthold Convalescent Hospital, Lodi, CA
Beckar/Shoop Center, Racine, WI
Becky Thatcher Nursing Home, Hannibal, MO
Bedford County Memorial Hospital Long-Term Care Unit, Bedford, VA
Bedford County Nursing Home, Shelbyville, TN
Bedford County Nursing Home, Bedford, VA
Bedford Group Home, Woodinville, WA
Bedford Manor, Bedford, IA
Bedford Manor, Gardner, KS
Bedford Nursing Home, Bedford, IN
Bedford Nursing Home, Bedford, NH
Bedford Villa Nursing Center, Southfield, MI
Beech Grove Healthcare Center, Beech Grove, IN
Beech Manor Rest Home, Springfield, MA
Beechaven Nursing Home, Worcester, MA
Beechknoll Convalescenter Center, Cincinnati, OH
Beechwood Home for Incurables Inc, Cincinnati, OH
Beechwood Manor, New London, CT
Beechwood Nursing Home, Elma, WA
Beechwood Rest Home, Kewaskum, WI
Beechwood Sanitarium, Rochester, NY
Beeler Street East, Aurora, CO
Beemans Sanitarium, Whittier, CA
Beene Health Care Inc, Hartsville, TN
Beggs Nursing Home, Beggs, OK
Behr Parkview Nursing Home, Wells, MN
Bel Air Care Center, Beaverton, OR
Bel Air Convalescent Center Inc, Bel Air, MD

Bel Air Health Care Center Inc, Milwaukee, WI
Bel Air Manor, Haskell, NJ
Bel Air Manor of Oakland, Oakland, NJ
Bel Air Nursing Home, Tacoma, WA
Bel Isle Nursing Home, Phoenix, AZ
Bel Pre Health Care Center, Silver Spring, MD
Bel Vista Convalescent Hospital Inc, Long
    Beach, CA
The Belair Convalesarium, Baltimore, MD
Bel-Air Convalescent Center, Alliance, OH
Bel-Air Health Care Inc, Columbia, TN
Bel-Air Lodge Convalescent Hospital,
    Turlock, CA
Bel-Air Manor, Newington, CT
Bel-Air Nursing Home, Goffstown, NH
Belair Nursing Home, North Bellmore, NY
Belair Nursing Home, Lower Burrell, PA
Bel-Aire Convalescent Residence, Newport, VT
Bel-Arbor Med-Care Nursing Home,
    Macon, GA
Belchertown State School, Belchertown, MA
Belcourt Terrace Nursing Home, Nashville, TN
Belding Christian Home, Belding, MI
Belgrade Nursing Home, Belgrade, MN
Belhaven Inc, Chicago, IL
Belknap County Nursing Home, Laconia, NH
Bell Crest Inc, Cool Valley, MO
Bell Gardens Convalescent Center, Bell
    Gardens, CA
Bell Haven Convalescent and Nursing Care,
    Killeen, TX
Bell Manor Inc, Normandy, MO
Bell Nursing Home, Kimbolton, OH
Bell Nursing Home Inc, Belmont, OH
Bella Vista Convalescent Hospital Inc,
    Ontario, CA
Bella Vita Towers Inc, Denver, CO
Belle Chasse State School, Belle Chasse, LA
Belle Fourche Health Care Center—Long Term
    Care Unit, Belle Fourche, SD
Belle Haven Nursing Home Inc, Quakertown,
    PA
Belle Hoffman Michael Home, Bucyrus, OH
Belle Maison Nursing Home, Hammond, LA
Belle Manor Nursing Home, New Carlisle, OH
Belle Meade Home, Greenville, KY
Belle Mount Nursing Center, Austin, TX
Belleair East Health Center, Clearwater, FL
Bellefontaine Health Care Center,
    Bellefontaine, OH
Bellerose Convalescent Hospital, San Jose, CA
Belleview Valley Nursing Homes Inc,
    Belleview, MO
Belleville Health Care Center, Belleville, KS
Belleville Nursing Center, Belleville, IL
Bellevue Care Center, Trenton, NJ
Bellevue Care Center, Tacoma, WA
Bellevue Nursing Center, Oklahoma City, OK
Bellevue Nursing Home, Bellevue, OH
Bellevue Terrace Nursing Center, Bellevue, WA
Bellevue-Newport Health Center, Newport, RI
Bellflower Convalescent Hospital,
    Bellflower, CA
Bellflower Golden Age Convalescent Home,
    Bellflower, CA
Bellflower Nursing Home, Bellflower, MO
Bellingham Villa Care Center, Bellingham, WA
Bellmead Nursing Home Inc, Waco, TX
Bell-Minor Home Inc, Gainesville, GA
Bellmire Home Inc, Bowie, TX
Bells Lodge, Phoenix, AZ
Belmond Nursing Home, Belmond, IA
Belmont Care Center Inc, Portland, OR

Belmont Convalescent Hospital, Belmont, CA
Belmont County Oakview Nursing Home,
    Saint Clairsville, OH
Belmont Habilitation Center, Saint Clairsville,
    OH
Belmont Health Care Center, Nashville, TN
Belmont Home, Worcester, MA
Belmont Lodge Inc, Pueblo, CO
Belmont Manor Nursing Home, Belmont, MA
Belmont Nursing Home Inc, Chicago, IL
Belmont Terrace Inc, Bremerton, WA
Beloit Convalescent Center, Beloit, WI
Bel-Terrace Nursing Home Inc,
    Indianapolis, IN
Beltrami Nursing Home, Bemidji, MN
The Belvedere, Chester, PA
Bel-Wood Nursing Home, Peoria, IL
Bement Manor, Bement, IL
Ben Franklin Nursing Home Inc, Franklin, MA
Ben Hur Home Inc, Crawfordsville, IN
Benbrook Sweetbriar Nursing Home,
    Benbrook, TX
Bender Terrace Nursing Home, Lubbock, TX
Benedictine Nursing Center, Mount Angel, OR
Beneva Nursing Pavilion, Sarasota, FL
Benjamin Hershey Memorial Convalescent
    Home, Muscatine, IA
Benner Convalescent Center, Houston, TX
Bennett County Nursing Home, Martin, SD
Bennington Convalescent Center, Bennington,
    VT
Bennion Care Center, Salt Lake City, UT
Benson Heights Rehabilitation Center, Kent,
    WA
Benson's Nursing Home, Nashville, AR
Bent County Memorial Hospital and Nursing
    Home, Las Animas, CO
Bent Nursing Home Inc, Reisterstown, MD
Bentley Gardens Nursing Home, West
    Haven, CT
Benton County Care Facility, Vinton, IA
Benton Retirement Inn, Benton, AR
Benton Services Center Nursing Home,
    Benton, AR
Benton's Personal Care Home,
    Russellville, KY
Bentonville Manor Nursing Home,
    Bentonville, AR
Benzie County Medical Care Facility,
    Frankfort, MI
Berea Health Care Center, Berea, KY
Berea Hospital—Skilled Nursing Facility,
    Berea, KY
Berea North Quality Care Nursing Center,
    Berea, OH
Berea Quality Care Nursing Center, Berea, OH
Bergers Greenhill Nursing Home, Philadelphia,
    PA
Berkeley Convalescent Center, Monucks
    Conrner, SC
Berkeley Hall Nursing Home, Berkeley
    Heights, NJ
Berkeley Hills Convalescent Hospital,
    Berkeley, CA
Berkeley Manor, Saint Louis, MO
Berkley Convalescent Hospital, Santa
    Monica, CA
Berkley East Convalescent Hospital, Santa
    Monica, CA
Berkley Manor Care Center, Denver, CO
Berkley Retirement Home, Lawrence, MA
Berks County Home, Reading, PA
Berkshire, A Skilled Nursing Facility, Santa
    Monica, CA

Berkshire Hills Nursing Home—North, Lee,
    MA
Berkshire Nursing Center Inc, West Babylon,
    NY
Berkshire Nursing Home Inc, Pittsfield, MA
Berkshire Place, Pittsfield, MA
Berkshire Residence, Osseo, MN
Berlin Convalescent Center, Barre, VT
Berlin Nursing Home, Berlin, MD
Bernard Nursing Home, Saint Louis, MO
Bernard West Pine Nursing Home, Saint Louis,
    MO
Berne Nursing Home, Berne, IN
Berrien General Hospital, Berrien Center, MI
Berrien Nursing Center Inc, Nashville, GA
Berry Hill Nursing Home Inc, South Boston,
    VA
Bert-Anne Annex, West Chesterfield, NH
Bert-Anne Home for the Aged, West
    Chesterfield, NH
Bertha D Garten Ketcham Meorial Center Inc,
    Odon, IN
Bertha M Young Rest Home, Pittsfield, MA
Berthold S Pollak Hospital—Long Term Care
    Facility, Jersey City, NJ
Bertram Nursing Home, Bertram, TX
Bertran Home for Aged Men, Salem, MA
Bertrand Nursing Home, Bertrand, NE
Bertrand Retirement Home Inc, Bertrand, MO
Berwick Retirement Village Nursing Home,
    Berwick, PA
Bescare Nursing Home, Columbus, OH
Best Care Convalescent Hospital Corp,
    Torrance, CA
Best Care Nursing Home, Marion, KY
Best Care Nursing Home, Wheelersburg, OH
Beth Abraham Hospital, Bronx, NY
Beth Haven Nursing Home, Hannibal, MO
Beth Israel Hospital and Geriatric Center,
    Denver, CO
Beth Sholom Home of Central Virginia,
    Richmond, VA
Beth Sholom Home of Eastern Virginia,
    Virginia Beach, VA
Bethalto Care Center Inc, Bethalto, IL
Bethany Care Center, Lakewood, CO
Bethany Convalescent Hospital, San Jose, CA
Bethany Covenant Home, Minneapolis, MN
Bethany Good Samaritan Center, Brainerd,
    MN
Bethany Home, Chicago, IL
Bethany Home, Dubuque, IA
Bethany Home, Alexandria, MN
Bethany Home, Litchfield, MN
Bethany Home, Minden, NE
Bethany Home, Waupaca, WI
Bethany Home Association of Lindsborg,
    Lindsborg, KS
Bethany Home for Ladies, Vidalia, GA
Bethany Home for Men, Millen, GA
Bethany Home for the Aged, Everett, WA
Bethany Home of Rhode Island, Providence,
    RI
Bethany Home Society San Joaquin County,
    Ripon, CA
Bethany Homes, Fargo, ND
Bethany Inc, Albion, ME
Bethany Lutheran Home, Sioux Falls, SD
Bethany Lutheran Home Inc, Council
    Bluffs, IA
Bethany Lutheran Village, Dayton, OH
Bethany Manor Inc, Story City, IA
Bethany MHS Health Care Center, Lafayette,
    LA

Bethany Nursing Home, Bloomingdale, MI

Bethany Nursing Home, Canton, OH

Bethany Nursing Home and Health Related Facility Inc, Horseheads, NY

Bethany Riverside, La Crosse, WI

Bethany Samaritain Heights, Rochester, MN

Bethany Terrace Nursing Home, Morton Grove, IL

Bethany Village, Indianapolis, IN

Bethany Village Health Care Center, Bethany, OK

Bethany Village Retirement Center, Mechanicsburg, PA

Bethany-Saint Joseph Health Center, La Crosse, WI

Bethea Baptist Home, Darlington, SC

Betheden Nursing Home, Greenville, SC

Bethel Care Center, Saint Paul, MN

Bethel Care Center Inc, Milwaukee, WI

Bethel Convalescent Center, Arpin, WI

Bethel Home, Oshkosh, WI

Bethel Home, Viroqua, WI

Bethel Home for the Aged, Newton, KS

Bethel Home Inc, Montezuma, KS

Bethel Lutheran Home, Williston, ND

Bethel Lutheran Home, Madison, SD

Bethel Lutheran Home Inc, Selma, CA

Bethel Nursing Home Company Inc, Ossining, NY

Bethel Rest Home, Cuyahoga Falls, OH

Bethel Sanitarium Inc, Evansville, IN

Bethesda Care Center, Brighton, CO

Bethesda Care Center, Canon City, CO

Bethesda Care Center, Delta, CO

Bethesda Care Center, Grand Junction, CO

Bethesda Care Center, Clarinda, IA

Bethesda Care Center, Mediapolis, IA

Bethesda Care Center, Muscatine, IA

Bethesda Care Center, Toledo, IA

Bethesda Care Center, Winterset, IA

Bethesda Care Center, Smith Center, KS

Bethesda Care Center, Tarkio, MO

Bethesda Care Center, Utica, NE

Bethesda Care Center, Freemont, OH

Bethesda Care Center, San Antonio, TX

Bethesda Care Center of Ainsworth, Ainsworth, NE

Bethesda Care Center of Ashland, Ashland, NE

Bethesda Care Center of Bassett, Bassett, NE

Bethesda Care Center of Blue Hill, Blue Hill, NE

Bethesda Care Center of Central City, Central City, NE

Bethesda Care Center of Edgar, Edgar, NE

Bethesda Care Center of Exeter, Exeter, NE

Bethesda Care Center of Gretna, Gretna, NE

Bethesda Care Center of Laramie, Laramie, WY

Bethesda Care Center of Paonia, Paonia, CO

Bethesda Care Center of Seward, Seward, NE

Bethesda Care Center of Sutherland, Sutherland, NE

Bethesda Care Center of Worland, Worland, WY

Bethesda Health Care Center Inc, Bethesda, MD

Bethesda Health Care Facility, Fayetteville, NC

Bethesda Heritage Center, Willmar, MN

Bethesda Home, Hayward, CA

Bethesda Home, Webster, SD

Bethesda Home for the Aged, Beresford, SD

Bethesda Home of Aberdeen, Aberdeen, SD

Bethesda Lutheran Home, Watertown, WI

Bethesda Lutheran Infirmary, Saint Paul, MN

Bethesda Manor and Convalescent Center, Los Gatos, CA

Bethesda Manor Nursing Home, Louisville, KY

Bethesda Nursing Center, Chanute, KS

Bethesda Nursing Home—Pleasantview, Willmar, MN

Bethesda Retirement Nursing Center, Chevy Chase, MD

Bethesda Scarlet Oaks Retirement Community, Cincinnati, OH

Bethesda Skilled Nursing Facility, Saint Louis, MO

Bethesda-Dilworth Memorial Home, Saint Louis, MO

Bethesda-Ritter Dierker, Watertown, WI

Bethlen Hungarian Home, Ligonier, PA

Bethpage at Axtell, Axtell, NE

Bethpage at Lincoln, Lincoln, NE

Bethune Plaza Inc, Chicago, IL

Betsy Ross Health Related Facility, Rome, NY

Bettendorf Health Care Center, Bettendorf, IA

Betty Ann Nursing Home, Grove, OK

Betty Dare Good Samaritan Center, Alamogordo, NM

Betz Nursing Home Inc, Auburn, IN

Beulah Community Nursing Home, Beulah, ND

Beulah Home Inc, Oakland, CA

Beulah Land Christian Home, Flanagan, IL

Beverly Farm Foundation, Godfrey, IL

Beverly Health Care Center, Tarboro, NC

Beverly Health Care Center, Glasgow, WV

Beverly Hills Convalescent Center Inc, Chicago, IL

Beverly Hills Recovery Center, Colorado Springs, CO

Beverly Manor, Burbank, CA

Beverly Manor, Boulder, CO

Beverly Manor, Belle Plaine, IA

Beverly Manor, Southgate, MI

Beverly Manor, Saint Joseph, MO

Beverly Manor, Las Vegas, NV

Beverly Manor Convalescent Center, Sun City, AZ

Beverly Manor Convalescent Center, Saint Petersburg, FL

Beverly Manor Convalescent Center, Augusta, GA

Beverly Manor Convalescent Center, Honolulu, HI

Beverly Manor Convalescent Center, Grundy Center, IA

Beverly Manor Convalescent Center, Iowa City, IA

Beverly Manor Convalescent Center, Novi, MI

Beverly Manor Convalescent Center, Plainwell, MI

Beverly Manor Convalescent Center, Rutland, VT

Beverly Manor Convalescent Center—53, Decatur, GA

Beverly Manor Convalescent Hospital, Anaheim, CA

Beverly Manor Convalescent Hospital, Bakersfield, CA

Beverly Manor Convalescent Hospital, Burbank, CA

Beverly Manor Convalescent Hospital, Canoga Park, CA

Beverly Manor Convalescent Hospital, Capistrano Beach, CA

Beverly Manor Convalescent Hospital, Chico, CA

Beverly Manor Convalescent Hospital, Costa Mesa, CA

Beverly Manor Convalescent Hospital, Escondido, CA

Beverly Manor Convalescent Hospital, Fresno, CA

Beverly Manor Convalescent Hospital, Glendale, CA

Beverly Manor Convalescent Hospital, La Mesa, CA

Beverly Manor Convalescent Hospital, Laguna Hills, CA

Beverly Manor Convalescent Hospital, Los Altos, CA

Beverly Manor Convalescent Hospital, Los Gatos, CA

Beverly Manor Convalescent Hospital, Los Gatos, CA

Beverly Manor Convalescent Hospital, Monrovia, CA

Beverly Manor Convalescent Hospital, Monterey, CA

Beverly Manor Convalescent Hospital, Redding, CA

Beverly Manor Convalescent Hospital, Redlands, CA

Beverly Manor Convalescent Hospital, Riverside, CA

Beverly Manor Convalescent Hospital, San Francisco, CA

Beverly Manor Convalescent Hospital, Santa Barbara, CA

Beverly Manor Convalescent Hospital, Santa Monica, CA

Beverly Manor Convalescent Hospital, Seal Beach, CA

Beverly Manor Convalescent Hospital, Van Nuys, CA

Beverly Manor Convalescent Hospital, West Covina, CA

Beverly Manor Convalescent Hospital, Yreka, CA

Beverly Manor Convalescent Hospital—East, Whittier, CA

Beverly Manor Convalescent Hospital—West, Whittier, CA

Beverly Manor Nursing Home, Denver, CO

Beverly Manor of Brighton, Brighton, CO

Beverly Manor of Charlotte, Charlotte, NC

Beverly Manor of Grand Junction, Grand Junction, CO

Beverly Manor of Petaluma, Petaluma, CA

Beverly Manor of Portsmouth, Portsmouth, VA

Beverly Manor of Santa Cruz, Santa Cruz, CA

Beverly Manor Sanitarium, Riverside, CA

Beverly Nursing Home, Chicago, IL

Beverly Nursing Home, Beverly, MA

Beverly Palms Rehabilitation Hospital, Los Angeles, CA

Beverly Terrace Nursing Home, Watertown, WI

Beverly West Convalescent Hospital, Los Angeles, CA

Beverwyck Nursing Home Inc, Parsippany, NJ

Bezalel Nursing Home Company, Far Rockaway, NY

Bialystoker Home for the Aged, New York, NY

Bibb Medical Center Hospital and Nursing Home, Centreville, AL

Bible Fellowship Church Home, Nazareth, PA

Bickford Convalescent Home, Windsor Locks, CT

Bicknell Health Care Center, Bicknell, IN
Bi-County Clinic and Nursing Home Inc, Bloxom, VA
Bide-A-Wee, Estes Park, CO
Big G Rest Home, Ashburnham, MA
Big Horn County Memorial Nursing Home, Hardin, MT
Big Meadows, Savanna, IL
Big Spring Manor, Huntsville, AL
Big Springs Nursing Home, Humansville, MO
Big Town Nursing Home, Mesquite, TX
Bigfork Convalescent Center, Bigfork, MT
Billdora Rest Home, Tylertown, MS
Billings Fairchild Center, Billings, OK
Billings Park Nursing Home, Superior, WI
Biltmore Manor, Asheville, NC
Bingham County Nursing Home, Blackfoot, ID
Birch Hill Care Center, Shawano, WI
Birch Manor, Kalamazoo, MI
Birch Manor Nursing Home, Chicopee, MA
Birch Street Manor, Dallas, OR
Birch View Manor Nursing Home, Birch Tree, MO
Birchway Nursing Home, Saint Louis, MO
Birchwood, Casey, IL
Birchwood Care Home, Minneapolis, MN
Birchwood Health Care Center, Forest Lake, MN
Birchwood Manor, Holland, MI
Birchwood Manor, North Bend, NE
Birchwood Manor Nursing Home, Fitchburg, MA
Birchwood Manor Nursing Home, Cooper, TX
Birchwood Nursing and Convalescent Center, Edison, NJ
Birchwood Nursing Center, Traverse City, MI
Birchwood Nursing Home, Derry, NH
Birchwood Nursing Home, Huntington Station, NY
Birchwood Rest Home Inc, Waterbury, CT
Birchwood Terrace Healthcare, Burlington, VT
Bird Haven Christian Convalescent Hospital, Bellflower, CA
Bird Haven Christian Convalescent Hospital, Norwalk, CA
Bird Haven Christian Convalescent Hospital, Paramount, CA
Bird Island Manor Healthcare Center, Bird Island, MN
Bird S Coler Memorial Hospital—Skilled Nursing Facility, New York, NY
Birk's Mountain Home, Hurricane, UT
Bishop Davies Center Inc, Hurst, TX
Bishop Drumm Care Center, Des Moines, IA
Bishop McCarthy Residence, Vineland, NJ
Bishop Noa Home, Escanaba, MI
Bishop Nursing Home Inc, Media, PA
Bivins Memorial Nursing Home, Amarillo, TX
Bixby Knolls Towers Nursing Home, Long Beach, CA
Bixby Manor Nursing Home, Bixby, OK
Black Earth Manor, Black Earth, WI
Black Hawk County Health Care, Waterloo, IA
Black Hills Retirement Center, Rapid City, SD
Black Mountain Facility, Black Mountain, NC
Blackfeet Nursing Home, Browning, MT
Black's Nursing Home, Tulsa, OK
Blackstone Nursing Home, Blackstone, MA
Blackwell Nursing Home Inc, Blackwell, OK
Blair House, Augusta, GA
Blair House LTCF of Milford, Milford, MA
Blair Nursing Home Inc, Beaver Falls, PA

Blaire House LTCF of New Bedford, New Bedford, MA
Blaire House of Worcester, Worcester, MA
Blakedale Rest Home, Danvers, MA
Blakely Care Center, North Baltimore, OH
Blalock Nursing Home—East, Houston, TX
Blalock Nursing Home—North, Houston, TX
Blalock Nursing Home—North Shores, Houston, TX
Blalock Nursing Home—Northwest, Houston, TX
Blalock Nursing Home—Southeast, Pasadena, TX
Blalock Nursing Home—Spring Branch, Houston, TX
Blalock Nursing Home Stoneybrook, Houston, TX
Blancaflor Nursing Home, Baltimore, MD
Blanchester Care Center, Blanchester, OH
Blanco Mill Nursing Home, Blanco, TX
Bland Residential Care Home, Erie, CO
Bledsoe County Nursing Home, Pikeville, TN
Blenwood Nursing Home, Methuen, MA
Blevins Retirement and Care Center, McAlester, OK
Blind Girl's Home, Kirkwood, MO
Bliss Manor, Saint Joseph, MO
Bloomer Community Memorial Hospital— Skilled Nursing Facility, Bloomer, WI
Bloomfield Convalescent Center, Bloomfield, MO
Bloomfield Good Samaritan Center, Bloomfield, NE
Bloomfield Hills Care Center, Bloomfield Hills, MI
Bloomfield Manor Nursing Home, Bloomfield, IA
Bloomfield Manor Nursing Home, Dodgeville, WI
Bloomfield Nursing Center, Bloomfield, IN
Bloomingdale Pavilion, Bloomingdale, IL
Bloomington Convalescent Center, Bloomington, IN
Bloomington Manor, Bloomington, IL
Bloomington Maple Manor Care Center, Bloomington, MN
Bloomington Nursing and Rehabilitation Center, Bloomington, IL
Bloomington Nursing Home, Bloomington, IN
Bloomington Nursing Home, Bloomington, MN
Bloomington Outreach Home, Bloomington, MN
Bloomsburg Health Care Center, Bloomsburg, PA
Bloomville Nursing Care Center, Bloomville, OH
Blose McGregor Health Care Center Inc, Punxsutawney, PA
Blossom Care Center, Benton Harbor, MI
Blossom Convalescent Hospital, Hayward, CA
Blossom Hill Nursing Home, Huntsburg, OH
Blossom Nursing Center, Alliance, OH
Blossom Nursing Home, Rochester, NY
Blossom View Nursing Home, Sodus, NY
Blough Nursing Home Inc, Bethlehem, PA
Blough Nursing Home Inc, Easton, PA
Blowing Rock Hospital, Blowing Rock, NC
Blue Ash Nursing and Convalescent Home Inc, Blue Ash, OH
Blue Hills Centre, Kansas City, MO
Blue Hills Convalescent Home, Stoughton, MA

Blue Island Nursing Home, Blue Island, IL
Blue Mountain Convalescent Center, College Place, WA
Blue Mountain Nursing Home, Prairie City, OR
Blue Ridge Care Center, Easley, SC
Blue Ridge Haven Convalescent Center Inc, Harrisburg, PA
Blue Ridge Haven Convalescent Center West, Camp Hill, PA
Blue Ridge Highlands Nursing Home, Galax, VA
Blue Ridge Nursing Home, Kansas City, MO
Blue Ridge Nursing Home Inc, Stuart, VA
Blue Springs Care Center, Blue Springs, MO
Blue Spruce Rest Home, Springfield, MA
Blue Valley Lutheran Home, Hebron, NE
Blue Valley Nursing Home, Blue Rapids, KS
Blueberry Hill Healthcare Nursing Home, Beverly, MA
Bluebonnet Nursing Care of Granger, Granger, TX
Bluebonnet Nursing Home, Albany, TX
Bluefield Multi-Care, Bluefield, WV
Bluemound Manor Nursing Home, Milwaukee, WI
Bluff Manor Nursing Home, Poplar Bluff, MO
The Bluffs Care Center, Pensacola, FL
Blu-Fountain Manor, Godfrey, IL
The Bluementhal Jewish Home for the Aged, Clemmons, NC
Blythe Convalescent Hospital, Blythe, CA
Boardman Community Care Home, Rapid City, SD
Boca Raton Convalescent Center, Boca Raton, FL
Boddy Nursing Center, Woodstock, GA
Bohannon Nursing Home Inc, Lebanon, IL
Bohemian Home for the Aged, Chicago, IL
Boise Group Home 1, Boise, ID
Boise Group Home 2, Boise, ID
Boise Group Home 3, Boise, ID
Boise Samaritan Village, Boise, ID
Boley Intermediate Care Facility, Boley, OK
Bolivar County Hospital—Long Term Care Facility, Cleveland, MS
Bolivar Nursing Home Inc, Bolivar, MO
Bolle's Boarding Home Inc, Festus, MO
Bolster Heights Health Care Facility, Auburn, ME
Bolton Convalescent Home, Bratenahl, OH
Bon Air Life Care Center, Augusta, GA
Bon Air Nursing Home, Auburn, ME
Bon Secours Hospital/Villa Maria Nursing Center, North Miami, FL
Bond Nursing Home Inc, Lutesville, MO
Bonell Good Samaritan Center, Greeley, CO
Bonham Nursing Center, Stillwater, PA
Bonham Nursing Center, Bonham, TX
Bonifay Nursing Home, Bonifay, FL
Bon-Ing Care Center, Gahanna, OH
Bon-Ing Inc, Columbus, OH
Bonne Terre Rest Home Inc, Bonne Terre, MO
Bonner Health Center, Bonner Springs, KS
Bonnetti Health Care Center Inc, Harrisville, PA
Bonnie Brae Manor Convalescent Hospital, Los Angeles, CA
Bonnie Brae's, Tucson, AZ
Bonnie's Nursing Home, West Chester, OH
Bono Nursing Home, Henryetta, OK
Bonterra Nursing Center, East Point, GA
Booker Convalescent Annex, Dayton, WA

Booker T Washington Nursing Home, Shreveport, LA
Booker-Watts Nursing Home, Indianapolis, IN
Bookside Manor, Overbrook, KS
Boone County Health Care Center, Danville, WV
Boone Guest Home, Boone, CO
Boone Nursing Home, Millville, PA
Boone Retirement Center Inc, Columbia, MO
Booneville Convalescent Center, Salt Lake City, UT
Booneville Human Development Center, Booneville, AR
Boonville Convalescent Center Inc, Boonville, IN
Borden Nursing Home, Forrest City, AR
Borderview Manor, Van Buren, ME
Boreen Nursing Home, Minneapolis, MN
Bornemann's Nursing Home 2, Green Bay, WI
Bossier Health Care Center, Bossier City, LA
Boston Home Inc, Boston, MA
Bottineau Good Samaritan Center, Bottineau, ND
Boulder City Care Center, Boulder City, NV
Boulder Good Samaritan Health Care Center, Boulder, CO
Boulder Manor, Boulder, CO
Boulder River School and Hospital, Boulder, MT
Boulevard Community Residence, Columbia, SC
Boulevard Manor Care Center, Richland Hills, TX
Boulevard Manor Nursing Center, Boynton Beach, FL
Boulevard Nursing, Philadelphia, PA
Boulevard Rest Home, Pawtucket, RI
Boulevard Temple Methodist Home, Detroit, MI
Boulevard Terrace Nursing Home, Murfreesboro, TN
Boundary County Nursing Home, Bonners Ferry, ID
Bountiful Convalescent Center, Bountiful, UT
Bountiful Nursing Home, Bountiful, UT
Bourbon Heights Nursing Home, Paris, KY
Bourbonnais Terrace, Bourbonnais, IL
Bowden Nursing Home, Wilmington, NC
Bowdle Nursing Home—Adventist Health System, Bowdle, SD
Bowen Health Center, Raytown, MO
Bowerston Health Care Center, Bowerston, OH
Bowie Convalescing Home, Bowie, TX
Bowling Green Health Care Center, Bowling Green, KY
Bowling Green Manor, Bowling Green, OH
Bowman Nursing Home, Midlothian, IL
Bowman-Harrison Convalescent Hospital, San Francisco, CA
Bowmans Nursing Center, Ormond Beach, FL
Box Elder County Nursing Home, Tremonton, UT
Boyce Manor Inc, Holdenville, OK
Boyd's—Kinsman Home, Kinsman, OH
Boyds Nursing Home, Phoenix, AZ
Bozeman Convalescent Center, Bozeman, MT
Bozeman Deaconess Hospital—Extended Care Facility, Bozeman, MT
Bracken Center, Augusta, KY
Bradbury Memorial Nursing Home, Belfast, ME
Bradegan Manor Rest Home, Boston, MA
Bradenton Convalescent Center, Bradenton, FL

Bradenton Manor, Bradenton, FL
Bradford Convalescent Home, Boston, MA
Bradford County Manor, Troy, PA
Bradford Living Care Center Inc, Bradford, OH
Bradford Nursing Pavilion, Bradford, PA
Bradlee Rest Home, Boston, MA
Bradley Convalescent Center, Milwaukee, WI
Bradley County Nursing Home, Cleveland, TN
The Bradley Home Infirmary, Meriden, CT
Bradley Manor Nursing Home, Weymouth, MA
Bradley Nursing Home, Boston, MA
Bradley Road Nursing Home, Bay Village, OH
Bradley Royale Healthcare Centre, Bradley, IL
Bradner Village Residential Care Facility Inc, Marion, IN
Brady Memorial Home, Mitchell, SD
Brae Burn, Bloomfield Hills, MI
Brae Burn Nursing Home, Whitman, MA
Braeburn Nursing Home, Newton, MA
Braemoor East of Marlboro Nursing Home, Marlborough, MA
Braemoor Nursing Home Inc, Brockton, MA
Braemoor of Marlborough Nursing Home, Marlborough, MA
Braewood Convalescent Center, South Pasadena, CA
Bragg Residential Care Home Inc, Denver, CO
Brainerd Good Samaritan Center, Brainerd, MN
Brainerd Group Home II, Baxter, MN
Braintree Manor Nursing and Retirement Center, Braintree, MA
Brakebill Nursing Homes Inc, Knoxville, TN
Branch Villa Convalescent Home, Seattle, WA
Brandel Care Center, Northbrook, IL
Brandel Manor, Turlock, CA
Brandywine Convalescent Home, Wilmington, DE
Brandywine Hall Inc, West Chester, PA
Brandywine Manor, Greenfield, IN
Brandywine Nursing Home Inc, Briarcliff Manor, NY
Brandywood Nursing Home, Gallatin, TN
Branford Hills Health Care Center, Branford, CT
Braswell's Ivy Retreat, Mentone, CA
Braswell's Yucaipa Valley Convalescent Hospital, Yucaipa, CA
Bra-Ton Nursing Home Inc, Kansas City, MO
Braun's Nursing Home Inc, Evansville, IN
Braxton Health Care Center, Sutton, WV
Brazos Valley Care Home Inc, Knox City, TX
Brazos Valley Geriatric Center, College Station, TX
Brazosview Healthcare Center, Richmond, TX
Breakers Convalescent Home, West Haven, CT
Breese Nursing Home, Breese, IL
Breightonwood, Catonsville, MD
Bremerton Convalescent Center, Bremerton, WA
Bremond Nursing Center, Bremond, TX
Brenham Rest Home Inc, Brenham, TX
Brenn-Field Nursing Center, Orrville, OH
Brent-Lox Residential Nursing Center, Chesapeake, VA
Brentwood Care Center, Tacoma, WA
Brentwood Convalescent Hospital, Red Bluff, CA
Brentwood Good Samaritan Center, Lemars, IA
Brentwood Hills Nursing Center, Asheville, NC

Brentwood Manor, Yarmouth, ME
Brentwood Manor Care Center, Lubbock, TX
Brentwood North Nursing and Rehabilitation Center, Deerfield, IL
Brentwood Nursing and Rehabilitation Center, Burbank, IL
Brentwood Nursing Home Inc, Brookline, MA
Brentwood Nursing Home Inc, Warwick, RI
Brentwood Park Nursing Home, Rome, GA
Brentwood Terrace Health Center, Waynesboro, GA
Brethern Village, Neffsville, PA
Brethren Care Inc, Ashland, OH
The Brethren Home, New Oxford, PA
Brethren's Home, Greenville, OH
Brethren's Home of Indiana Inc, Flora, IN
Brevin Nursing Home Inc, Havre de Grace, MD
Brewer Convalescent Center, Brewer, ME
Brewster Convalescent Center, Brewster, OH
Brewster Manor Nursing and Retirement Home, Brewster, MA
Brewster Place—The Congregational Home, Topeka, KS
Brian Center—Asheboro, Asheboro, NC
Brian Center—Gastonia, Gastonia, NC
Brian Center—Lenoir, Lenoir, NC
Brian Center—Mooresville, Mooresville, NC
Brian Center of Nursing Care, Austell, GA
Brian Center of Nursing Care, Raleigh, NC
Brian Center of Nursing Care—Asheville, Asheville, NC
Brian Center of Nursing Care—Brevard, Brevard, NC
Brian Center of Nursing Care—Catawba, Hickory, NC
Brian Center of Nursing Care—Columbia, Columbia, SC
Brian Center of Nursing Care—Hickory, Hickory, NC
Brian Center of Nursing Care—Lexington, Lexington, NC
Brian Center of Nursing Care—Statesville, Statesville, NC
Brian Center of Siler City, Siler City, NC
Briar Crest Nursing Home, Ossining, NY
Briar Glen Healthcare Centre, Rockford, IL
Briar Hill Manor Inc, Garden City, KS
Briar Hill Nursing Center, Auburndale, FL
Briar Hill Nursing Home, Middlefield, OH
Briar Hill Rest Home Inc, Florence, MS
Briarcliff Care Center, Topeka, KS
Briarcliff Haven, Atlanta, GA
Briarcliff Health Care Center, East Saint Louis, IL
Briarcliff Manor, New London, CT
Briarcliff Nursing Home Inc, Alabaster, AL
Briarcliff Pavilion Special Care, North Huntingdon, PA
Briarcliffe Healthcare Facility, Johnston, RI
Briarfield Incorporated, Sylvania, OH
Briarleaf Nursing and Convalescent Center, Doylestown, PA
Briarstone Manor, Anson, TX
Briarwood Healthcare Nursing Home, Needham, MA
Briarwood Manor, Coldwater, OH
Briarwood Manor Nursing Home, Flint, MI
Briarwood Manor Nursing Home, Cuba, MO
Briarwood Nursing and Convalescent Center, Louisville, KY
Briarwood Nursing Center Inc, Tucker, GA
Briarwood Terrace Nursing Home, Cincinnati, OH

Briarwood Way, Lakewood, CO
Bridge View Nursing Home, Whitestone, NY
Bridgeport Healthcare Center, Bridgeport, IL
Bridgeview Convalescent Center,
  Bridgeview, IL
Bridgewater Home Inc, Bridgewater, VA
Bridgewater Nursing Home, Bridgewater, MA
Bridgeway Convalescent Center, Bridewater,
  NJ
Bridgewood Manor Inc, Plainwell, MI
Brier Oak Terrace Convalescent Center, Los
  Angeles, CA
Briggs Nursing Home, Manning, SC
Brigham Manor Convalescent Home,
  Newburyport, MA
Bright Glade Convalescent Center, Memphis,
  TN
Bright Horizon, Saint Joseph, MO
Brighter Day Residence, Mora, MN
Brightmoor Medical Care Home, Griffin, GA
Brighton Hall Nursing Center, New Haven, IN
Brightonian Nursing Home, Rochester, NY
Brightview Manor Convalescent Home,
  Chicago, IL
Brightview Nursing and Retirement Center
  Ltd, Avon, CT
Brint Nursing Home, Bolivar, TN
Briody Nursing Home, Lockport, NY
Bristol Convalescent Home Inc, Bristol, CT
Bristol Health Care Center, Bristol, VA
Bristol Nursing and Convalescent Home, New
  Bedford, MA
Bristol Nursing Home, Attleboro, MA
Bristol Nursing Home Inc, Bristol, TN
Briston Manor Nursing Home, Bedford, NH
British Home, Brookfield, IL
Brittany Convalescent Home, Natick, MA
Brittany Farms Health Center, New
  Britain, CT
Britthaven of Clyde, Clyde, NC
Britthaven of Jacksonville, Jacksonville, NC
Britthaven of Morganton, Morganton, NC
Britthaven of New Bern, New Bern, NC
Britthaven of Washington, Washington, NC
Britthaven of Wilkesboro Inc, Wilkesboro, NC
Broad Acres Nursing Home Association,
  Wellsboro, PA
Broad Mountain Nursing Center, Frackville,
  PA
Broad Ripple Nursing Home, Indianapolis, IN
Broadacres, Utica, NY
Broadfield Manor Nursing and Convalescent
  Home, Madison, OH
Broadlawn Manor, Purcell, OK
Broadlawn Manor Nursing Home, Amityville,
  NY
Broadlawns West, Des Moines, IA
Broadmead, Cockeysville, MD
Broadmoor Health Care Center Inc, Meridian,
  MS
Broadstreet Medical, Detroit, MI
Broadview Center, Broadview Heights, OH
Broadview Nursing Home, Parma, OH
Broadwater County Rest Home, Townsend,
  MT
Broadway Arms Community Living Center,
  Leha, IL
Broadway Care Home, Albert Lea, MN
Broadway Convalescent Home, Methuen, MA
Broadway Convalescent Hospital, San
  Gabriel, CA
Broadway Lodge, San Antonio, TX
Broadway Manor, Muskogee, OK

Broadway Manor Convalescent Hospital,
  Glendale, CA
Broadway Nursing Home, Joliet, IL
Broadway Nursing Home, Geneva, OH
Broderick Convalescent Hospital, San
  Francisco, CA
Broen Memorial Home, Fergus Falls, MN
Broken Arrow Nursing Home Inc, Broken
  Arrow, OK
Broken Bow Homes Inc, Broken Bow, NE
Broken Bow Nursing Home, Broken Bow, OK
Brommer Manor, Santa Cruz, CA
Bronte Nursing Home, Bronte, TX
Brook Haven Rest Home, West Brookfield,
  MA
Brook Manor Nursing Center, Brookhaven,
  MS
Brook View Nursing Home Inc, Maryland
  Heights, MO
Brook Wood Convalescent Home, Saddle
  Brook, NJ
Brookbend Rest Home, Weymouth, MA
Brookcrest Nursing Home, Grandville, MI
Brookdale Hospital Center Nursing Home
  Company Inc, Brooklyn, NY
Brookdale Nursing Center, Hazlet, NJ
Brooke Grove Nursing Home, Olney, MD
Brookfield Manor, Hopkinsville, KY
Brookfield Nursing Center, Brookfield, MO
Brookhaven Beach Health Related Facility, Far
  Rockaway, NY
Brookhaven Care Facility, Kalamazoo, MI
Brookhaven Convalescent Center, Toledo, OH
Brookhaven Group Home, Woodinville, WA
Brookhaven Medical Care Facility, Muskegon,
  MI
Brookhaven Nursing and Convalescent Center,
  Fort Worth, TX
Brookhaven Nursing Care Center, Brookville,
  OH
Brookhaven Nursing Center, Farmers Branch,
  TX
Brookhaven Nursing Home, Brooklyn, IA
Brookhaven Nursing Home, Ferris, TX
Brookhollow Manor Nursing Home Inc,
  Grapevine, TX
Brooking Park Geriatric Center—Charleston,
  Charleston, IL
Brooking Park Geriatric Center Inc, Sedalia,
  MO
Brooking Park Village Residential Care
  Facility, Sedalia, MO
Brookline Manor Convalescent Home,
  Mifflintown, PA
Brooklyn Center Outreach Home, Brooklyn
  Center, MN
Brooklyn Rest Home, Brooklyn, CT
Brooklyn United Methodist Church Home,
  Brooklyn, NY
Brookmont Health Care Center Inc, Effort, PA
Brooks Center Health Care Facility, Marquette,
  MI
Brookshire Arms Inc, Brookshire, TX
Brooks-Howell Home, Asheville, NC
Brookside Care Center, Kenosha, WI
Brookside Care Convalescent Hospital,
  Redlands, CA
Brookside Convalescent Hospital, San
  Mateo, CA
Brookside Extended Care Center, Mason, OH
Brookside Manor Inc, Centralia, IL
Brookside Manor Inc, Wayne, NJ
Brookside Manor Nursing Home, Madill, OK

Brookside Manor Nursing Home, Bountiful,
  UT
Brookside Nursing Home, White River
  Junction, VT
Brooksville Nursing Manor, Brooksville, FL
Brookview Convalescent Home, West
  Hartford, CT
Brookview House Inc, Gaffney, SC
Brookview Manor, Indianapolis, IN
Brookview Manor, Brookings, SD
Brookvue Convalescent Hospital, San
  Pablo, CA
Brookwood Court Nursing Home, Holyoke,
  MA
Brookwood Nursing Home, Stafford, VA
Broomall Nursing Home, Bromall, PA
Broomall Nursing Home, Broomall, PA
Broomall Presbyterian Home, Broomall, PA
Brother James Court, Springfield, IL
Brothers of Mercy Nursing Home Co Inc,
  Clarence, NY
Broughton Hospital, Morganton, NC
Broward Association for Retarded Citizens,
  Davie, FL
Broward Convalescent Home, Fort
  Lauderdale, FL
Brown County Community Care,
  Nashville, IN
Brown County Health Care Center, Green Bay,
  WI
Brown Memorial Convalescent Center,
  Royston, GA
Brown Memorial Home Inc, Circleville, OH
Brown Nursing Home, Alexander City, AL
Brown Nursing Home, Perrinton, MI
Brown Nursing Home, Kansas City, MO
Brownfield Nursing Home, Brownfield, TX
Browning House, Durango, CO
Browning Manor Convalescent Hospital,
  Delano, CA
Browns Nursing Home, Statesboro, GA
Brown's Nursing Home, Lincoln Heights, OH
Brown's Nursing Home Inc, Fredericksburg,
  TX
Brown's Rest Home, Madisonville, KY
Browns Valley Community Nursing Home,
  Browns Valley, MN
Brownsboro Hills Nursing Home,
  Louisville, KY
Brownsville Golden Age, Brownsville, PA
Brownsville Good Samaritan Center,
  Brownsville, TX
Brownwood Care Center, Brownwood, TX
Brownwood Manor, Van Buren, AR
Brownwood Nursing Home, Moultrie, GA
Bruce Manor Nursing Home, Clearwater, FL
Bruckner Nursing Home, Bronx, NY
Brugman Home, Watertown, SD
Brunswick Convalescent Center, Brunswick,
  ME
Brunswick Hospital Center Inc, Amityville,
  NY
Brunswick Manor Inc, Brunswick, ME
Brunswick Park Nursing Home, New
  Brunswick, NJ
Bry Fern Care Center, Berrien Center, MI
Bryan County Manor, Durant, OK
Bryan Manor, Salem, IL
Bryan Manor Nursing Home, Dallas, TX
Bryan Nursing Care Center, Bryan, OH
Bryant and Summit Avenue Residences, South
  Saint Paul, MN
Bryant Nursing Center, Cochran, GA

Bryant-Butler-Kitchen Nursing Home, Kansas City, KS
Bryanwood Care Center, Amarillo, TX
Bryden Manor, Columbus, OH
Brykirk Extended Care Hospital, Alhambra, CA
Bryn Mawr Nursing Home, Minneapolis, MN
Bryn Mawr Terrace Convalescent, Bryn Mawr, PA
Brynes Convalescent Center Inc, Cincinnati, OH
Buchanan Nursing Home, Chisholm, MN
Buchanan Nursing Home Inc, Malden, MA
Buchanan Nursing Home of Okeene Inc, Okeene, OK
Buckeye Community Services—Bidwell Home, Bidwell, OH
Buckeye Community Services—Culver Street Home, Logan, OH
Buckeye Community Services—Grandview Avenue Homes, Waverly, OH
Buckeye Community Services—Hunter Street Home, Logan, OH
Buckeye Community Services—South Street Home, Jackson, OH
Buckeye Community Services—Transitional Facility, Gallipolis, OH
Buckeye Community Services—Walnut Street Home, Logan, OH
Buckeye Community Services-Childrens Transitional Facility, The Plains, OH
Buckeye Nursing Home, Clyde, OH
Buckingham Nursing Home, Greenfield, OH
Buckingham Pavilion, Chicago, IL
Buckingham Valley Nursing Home, Buckingham, PA
Buckingham-Smith Memorial Home, Saint Augustine, FL
Buckley Convalescent Home, Hartford, CT
Buckley Nursing and Retirement Home, Holyoke, MA
Buckner Baptist Haven, Houston, TX
Buckner Baptist Monte Siesta Home, Austin, TX
Buckner Baptist Ryburn Nursing Center, Dallas, TX
Buckner Baptist Trew Retirement Center, Dallas, TX
Buckner Villa Siesta Home, Austin, TX
Bucks County Association of Retarded Citizens, Doylestown, PA
Bucktail Medical Center, Renovo, PA
Buckwell Rest Home, Monson, MA
Budd Terrace Intermediate Care Home, Atlanta, GA
Buena Ventura Convalescent Hospital, Los Angeles, CA
Buena Vista Convalescent Hospital, Anaheim, CA
Buena Vista Home for the Aged, Sedalia, MO
Buena Vista Manor, Duarte, CA
Buena Vista Manor Care Center, Storm Lake, IA
Buena Vista Nursing Center Inc, Lexington, NC
Buena Vista Nursing Home, Colville, WA
Bueno's Group Home, Las Animas, CO
Buffalo Group Home, Buffalo, MN
Buffalo Lake Nursing Home, Buffalo Lake, MN
Buffalo Nursing Center, Buffalo, TX
Buffalo Valley Lutheran Village, Lewisburg, PA
Buford Manor Nursing Home, Buford, GA

Buhler Sunshine Home Inc, Buhler, KS
Bullock County Hospital and Nursing Home, Union Springs, AL
Buna Nursing Home, Buna, TX
Bunce Convalescent Center, Provo, UT
The Bungalow, Salt Lake City, UT
Burbank Convalescent Hospital, Burbank, CA
Burcham Hills Retirement Center, East Lansing, MI
Burdick Convalescent Home Inc, Warwick, RI
Burford Manor, Davis, OK
Burgess Manor Nursing Center, Graham, TX
Burgess Nursing Home, Birmingham, AL
Burgin Manor, Olney, IL
Burgoyne Rest Home, Boston, MA
Burien Terrace Nursing Center, Seattle, WA
Burleson Nursing Home, Burleson, TX
Burley Care Center, Burley, ID
Burlington Care Center, Burlington, IA
Burlington Convalescent Center, Burlington, VT
Burlington Convalescent Hospital, Los Angeles, CA
Burlington Medical Center, Burlington, IA
Burlington Woods Convalescent Center, Burlington, NJ
Bur-Mont Nursing Center, Abilene, TX
Bur-Mont Nursing Center, Henrietta, TX
Bur-Mont Nursing Center, Livingston, TX
Bur-Mont Nursing Center, Silsbee, TX
Bur-Mont Nursing Center, Temple, TX
Burncoat Plains Rest Home, Worcester, MA
Burnett General Hospital, Grantsburg, WI
Burnham Terrace Care Center, Chicago, IL
Burns Manor Nursing Home, Hutchinson, MN
Burns Nursing Home, Burns, OR
Burns Nursing Home Inc, Russellville, AL
Burnside Convalescent Home Inc, East Hartford, CT
Burnside Nursing Home Inc, Marshall, IL
Burr Oak Manor, Austin, MN
Burroughs Home Inc, Bridgeport, CT
Burt Manor Nursing Home, DeSoto, MO
Burt Manor Nursing Home, Sedalia, MO
Burt Sheltered Care Home, Alton, IL
Burton Convalescent Home Corp, Newton, MA
Burton Family Care Home, Denver, CO
Burton Nursing Home, Burlington, WA
Burzenski Nursing Home, Sarasota, FL
Butler County Home, Hamilton, OH
Butler Hotel Rest Home Inc, Butler, IN
Butler Rest Home, Butler, KY
Butler Valley Manor, Drums, PA
Butte Nursing Home, Butte, NE
Butte Park Royal Convalescent Center Inc, Butte, MT
Buttonwood Hall, New Lisbon, NJ
Buttonwoods Crest Home, Warwick, RI
Byrd Haven Nursing Home, Searcy, AR
Byrnebrook Nursing Home, Toledo, OH
Byron Health Center, Fort Wayne, IN
Bywood East, Minneapolis, MN
C A Mues Memorial Good Samaritan Center, Arapahoe, NE
C and R Nursing Center, Tonkawa, OK
C C Young Memorial Home—Young Health Center, Dallas, TX
C Howard Marcy State Hospital, Pittsburgh, PA
C K Stones Manor Inc, Smethport, PA
C M Tucker Jr Human Resources Center, Columbia, SC

C R Center, Springfield, PA
Cabarrus Nursing Center Inc, Concord, NC
Cable Rest Home, Independence, MO
Cabot Manor Nursing Home Inc, Cabot, AR
Cabrillo Extended Care Hospital, San Luis Obispo, CA
Cabs Nursing Home Company Inc, Brooklyn, NY
Cadbury Health Care Center, Cherry Hill, NJ
Caddo Nursing Home, Caddo, OK
Cadillac Nursing Home, Detroit, MI
Caguas Regional Skilled Nursing Facility, Caguas, PR
Cal Haven Convalescent Hospital, Glendale, CA
Caldsted Foundation Inc, Chattanooga, TN
Caldwell Care Center, Caldwell, ID
Caldwell Health Center, Seattle, WA
Caldwell Manor Nursing Home, Kansas City, MO
Calera Manor Nursing Home, Calera, OK
Calhoun Care Center, Hardin, IL
Calhoun County Medical Care Facility, Battle Creek, MI
Calhoun County Nursing Home, Calhoun, MS
Calhoun Nursing Home, Edison, GA
California Christian Home, Rosemead, CA
California Convalescent Center 1, Los Angeles, CA
California Convalescent Center 2, Los Angeles, CA
California Convalescent Hospital, Long Beach, CA
California Convalescent Hospital, San Francisco, CA
California Convalescent Hospital of La Mesa, La Mesa, CA
California Gardens Nursing Center, Chicago, IL
California Home for the Aged Inc, Fresno, CA
California Nursing and Rehabilitation Center of Palm Springs, Palm Springs, CA
California PEO Home, Alhambra, CA
California PEO Home—San Jose Unit, San Jose, CA
The California-Ventura Convalescent Hospital, Ventura, CA
The Californian—Pasadena Convalescent Hospital, Pasadena, CA
Calistoga Convalescent Hospital, Calistoga, CA
Callaway Good Samaritan Home, Callaway, NE
Callaway Nursing Home, Sulphur, OK
Calumet Homestead, New Holstein, WI
Calusa Retirement Center, Fort Meyers, FL
Calvary Fellowship Home Inc, Lancaster, PA
Calvary Manor Nursing Home, Ottawa, OH
Calvert City Convalescent Center, Calvert City, KY
Calvert County Nursing Center Inc, Prince Frederick, MD
Calvert House Corp, Prince Frederick, MD
Calvert Manor Nursing Home Inc, Rising Sun, MD
Calvert Nursing Center, Calvert, TX
Calvin D Johnson Nursing Home, Belleville, IL
Calvin Manor, Des Moines, IA
CAM Center for Human Development, Chicago, IL
Camano Shores Nursing Home, Camano Island, WA

Camano Shores Nursing Home, Stanwood, WA

Camargo Manor Nursing Home, Cincinnati, OH

Camarillo Convalescent Hospital, Camarillo, CA

Cambria County Home and Hospital, Ebensburg, PA

Cambria County Nursing Care Center, Johnstown, PA

Cambridge Care Center, Cambridge, MN

Cambridge Convalescent Center, Tampa, FL

Cambridge Developmental Center, Cambridge, OH

Cambridge Health Care Center, Cambridge, OH

Cambridge Home for Aged People, Cambridge, MA

Cambridge House, Cambridge, MD

Cambridge Manor, Richmond, VA

Cambridge Nursing Center—East, Madison Heights, MI

Cambridge Nursing Center—North, Clawson, MI

Cambridge Nursing Center—South, Birmingham, MI

Cambridge Nursing Center—West, Redford Township, MI

Cambridge Nursing Home, Cambridge, MA

Cambridge State Hospital, Cambridge, MN

Camden Convalescent Hospital, Campbell, CA

Camden County Health Services Center, Lakeland, NJ

Camden Health Care Center, Camden, ME

Camden Health Care Center, Monett, MO

Camden Health Center, Harrisonville, MO

Camden Nursing Facility, Camden, AL

Camden Nursing Home Inc, Camden, ME

Camellia Care Center Inc, Aurora, CO

Camellia Garden Nursing Home, Pineville, LA

Camellia Garden of Life Care, Thomasville, GA

Camelot, New London, CT

Camelot Arms Care Center, Youngstown, OH

Camelot Care Center, Logansport, IN

Camelot Care Center, Forest Grove, OR

Camelot Care Intermediate Care Facility, Gainesville, GA

Camelot Group Home, Seattle, WA

Camelot Hall—Cherrydale, Arlington, VA

Camelot Hall Convalescent Centre, Livonia, MI

Camelot Hall Nursing Home, Chesapeake, VA

Camelot Hall Nursing Home, Danville, VA

Camelot Hall Nursing Home, Harrisonburg, VA

Camelot Hall Nursing Home, Lynchburg, VA

Camelot Hall Nursing Home, Richmond, VA

Camelot Hall Nursing Home, Salem, VA

Camelot Hall Nursing Home, Virginia Beach, VA

Camelot Hall—Vinton, Vinton, VA

Camelot Healthcare Centre, Westmont, IL

Camelot Manor, Peoria, AZ

Camelot Manor, Streator, IL

Camelot Nursing Home, Farmington, MO

Cameo Convalescent Center, Milwaukee, WI

Cameron Manor Inc, Indiana, PA

Cameron Manor Nursing Home, Cameron, MO

Cameron Nursing Home, Cameron, TX

Cameron Villa Rest Home, Austin, TX

Camila Rose Group Home, Coon Rapids, MN

Camilia Rose Convalescent Center, Coon Rapids, MN

Camilla Hall, Immaculata, PA

Camilla Street Intermediate Care Home, Atlanta, GA

Camlu Care Center of Oak Hills, San Antonio, TX

Camlu Care Center of Woodlawn Hills, San Antonio, TX

Camlu Care Center-Louis Pasteur, San Antonio, TX

Camp Care Inc, Inman, SC

Camp Hill Nursing and Convalescent Center Inc, Camp Hill, PA

Campbell House, Centralia, MO

Campbell's Ingersoll Rest Home, Springfield, MA

Campen's Nursing Home Inc, Norfolk, VA

Camphaven Nursing Home, Inman, SC

Campion Residence and Renewal Center, Weston, MA

Canby Care Center, Canby, OR

Canby Community Hospital, Canby, MN

Candle Light Lodge Retirement Center, Columbia, MO

Candlewood Valley Care Center, New Milford, CT

Caney Rest Home, Caney, KS

Cannon Falls Manor Nursing Home, Cannon Falls, MN

Cannon Valley Center, Cannon Falls, MN

Canoga Terrace Convalescent Hospital, Canoga Park, CA

Canon Lodge, Canon City, CO

Canterbury Court Intermediate Care Unit, Atlanta, GA

Canterbury Manor, Waterloo, IL

Canterbury Manor, Rochester, IN

Canterbury Place, Valparaiso, IN

Canterbury Towers, Tampa, FL

Canterbury Villa of Alliance, Alliance, OH

Canterbury Villa of Bloomfield, Bloomfield, CT

Canterbury Villa of Danielson Inc, Danielson, CT

Canterbury Villa of Hillsboro, Hillsboro, TX

Canterbury Villa of Milan, Milan, OH

Canterbury Villa of Navasota, Navasota, TX

Canterbury Villa of Savoy, Savoy, TX

Canterbury Villa of Seville, Seville, OH

Canterbury Villa of Waterford Inc, Waterford, CT

Canterbury Villa of Willimantic, Willimantic, CT

Canterbury Woods, Pacific Grove, CA

Cantex Healthcare Center—Denison, Denison, TX

Canton Christian Home, Canton, OH

Canton Convalescence Center, Canton, OH

Canton Health Care Center, Canton, OH

Canton Intermediate Care Home, Canton, GA

Canton Nursing Center, Canton, MS

Canton Nursing Center, Canton, TX

Canton Nursing Home Inc, Canton, NC

Canton Residential Center, Canton, TX

Canyon Convalescent Hospital, Lakeview Terrace, CA

Canyon Manor, Novato, CA

Cape Cod Nursing and Retirement Home, Wareham, MA

Cape Coral Nursing Pavilion, Cape Coral, FL

Cape End Manor, Provincetown, MA

Cape Girardeau Care Center, Cape Girardeau, MO

Cape Girardeau Nursing Center, Cape Girardeau, MO

Cape May Care Center, Cape May Court House, NJ

Cape Regency Nursing Home, Barnstable, MA

Capeside Cove Good Samaritan Center, Siren, WI

Capital Care Center, Boise, ID

Capital Hall, Frankfort, KY

Capital Health Care Center, Tallahassee, FL

Capital Villa Nursing Center, Springfield, IL

Capitol City Nursing Home, Austin, TX

Capitol Convalescent Center, Columbia, SC

Capitol Health Care Center Inc, Washington, DC

Capitol Manor, Salem, WA

Capitol Nursing Home, Baton Rouge, LA

Capitol Park Care Center, Tumwater, WA

Capitol View Health Care Center, Salem, OR

Capri Nursing Home, Phoenix, AZ

Caravilla, Beloit, WI

Carbon County Health Care Center, Red Lodge, MT

Carbon County Memorial Nursing Home, Red Lodge, MT

Carbon County Nursing Home, Price, UT

Carbon Hill Health Care Inc, Carbon Hill, AL

Carbondale Manor, Carbondale, IL

Carbondale Nursing Home Inc, Carbondale, PA

Carci Hall, Chicago, IL

Cardigan Nursing Home, Scituate, MA

Cardinal Manor, South Bend, IN

Cardinal Nursing Home Inc, South Bend, IN

Cardome, Georgetown, KY

Care Center, Baton Rouge, LA

Care Center at Martins Run, Media, PA

Care Center East, Portland, OR

Care Center—East, Fond Du Lac, WI

Care Center of Iowa Inc, Creston, IA

Care Center—West, Fond Du Lac, WI

Care Group Nursing Home, Nashville, TN

Care House, Medina, OH

Care Inn, Ripley, WV

Care Inn Blountville, Blountville, TN

Care Inn—Bolivar, Bolivar, TN

Care Inn—Camden, Camden, TN

Care Inn—Cleveland, Cleveland, MS

Care Inn—Clinton, Clinton, MS

Care Inn—Collierville, Collierville, TN

Care Inn Convalescent Center, La Salle, IL

Care Inn Convalescent Center, Litchfield, IL

Care Inn—Corinth, Corinth, MS

Care Inn—Germantown, Cordova, TN

Care Inn—Greenwood, Greenwood, MS

Care Inn—Grenada, Grenada, MS

Care Inn—Holly Springs, Holly Springs, MS

Care Inn—Huntingdon, Huntingdon, TN

Care Inn—Indianola, Indianola, MS

Care Inn—Jefferson City, Jefferson City, TN

Care Inn Loudon, Loudon, TN

Care Inn Maryville, Maryville, TN

Care Inn—Memphis, Memphis, TN

Care Inn of Abilene, Abilene, TX

Care Inn of Commerce, Commerce, TX

Care Inn of Conroe Inc, Conroe, TX

Care Inn of Denison, Denison, TX

Care Inn of Edna, Edna, TX

Care Inn of Ganado, Ganado, TX

Care Inn of Gladewater, Gladewater, TX

Care Inn of Gonzales, Gonzales, TX

Care Inn of La Grange, La Grange, TX

Care Inn of Llano, Llano, TX

Care Inn of Mayfield, Mayfield, KY

Care Inn of Plainview, Plainview, TX

Care Inn of San Marcos, San Marcos, TX
Care Inn of Sanger, Sanger, TX
Care Inn of Seguin, Seguin, TX
Care Inn of Shamrock, Shamrock, TX
Care Inn of Voorhees, Marlton, NJ
Care Inn of Waco, Waco, TX
Care Inn—Raleigh, Memphis, TN
Care Inn—Ripley, Ripley, TN
Care Inn—Rockingham, Rockingham, NC
Care Inn—Rolling Fork, Rolling Fork, MS
Care Inn—West Point, West Point, MS
Care Inn—Yazoo City, Yazoo City, MS
Care Inns Inc, Graham, NC
Care Manor Nursing Center, Kingfisher, OK
Care Manor Nursing Center, Stroud, OK
Care Manor Nursing Center of Tuttle, Tuttle,
    OK
Care Manor of Farmington, Farmington, CT
Care Manor—Parkway, Wichita Falls, TX
Care Nursing Home, Miami, OK
Care Nursing Home Inc, Oakdale, LA
Care Pavillion of Walnut Park, Philadelphia,
    PA
Care Villa Nursing Center, Kingfisher, OK
Care Vista, Portland, OR
Care Well Manor Nursing Home, Malden, MA
Care West Plaza Inc, Portland, OR
Careage North Health Care Center,
    Fairbanks, AK
Carehouse Convalescent Hospital, Santa
    Ana, CA
Careousel Care Center, McMinnville, OR
Careview Home Inc, Minneapolis, MN
Carewell Rest Home, New Haven, CT
Carey Nursing Home, Carey, OH
Caribou Memorial Nursing Home, Soda
    Springs, ID
Caribou Nursing Home, Caribou, ME
Carillon House Nursing Home, Huntington,
    NY
Carl T Curtis Health Education Center, Macy,
    NE
Carl Vinson Skilled Nursing Home,
    Milledgeville, GA
Carleton Nursing Home, Wellsboro, PA
Carleton-Willard Retirement and Nursing
    Center, Bedford, MA
Carlin Park Nursing Home Inc, Angola, IN
Carlisle Care Center, Carlisle, IA
Carlisle Manor, Franklin, OH
Carlmont Convalescent Hospital, Belmont, CA
Carlsbad Nursing Home, Dry Ridge, KY
Carlson Convalescent Hospital Inc, El
    Cerrito, CA
Carlton Group Home, Duvall, WA
Carlton House, Chicago, IL
Carlton Nursing Home, Carlton, MN
Carlton Nursing Home, Brooklyn, NY
Carlyle, Beloit, WI
Carlyle Healthcare Center Inc, Carlyle, IL
Carlyle Nursing Home, South Bend, IN
Carmel Care Center, Carmel, IN
Carmel Convalescent Hospital, Carmel, CA
Carmel Home, Owensboro, KY
Carmel Ltd, Boulder, CO
Carmel Manor, Fort Thomas, KY
Carmel Richmond Nursing Home Inc, Staten
    Island, NY
Carmel Valley Manor, Carmel, CA
Carmen Home, Carmen, OK
Carmen Manor, Chicago, IL
Carmen Nursing Home Inc,
    Crawfordsville, IN

Carmichael Convalescent Hospital,
    Carmichael, CA
Carnegie Care Center, Cleveland, OH
Carnegie Gardens Nursing Home,
    Melbourne, FL
Carnegie Nursing Home, Carnegie, OK
Carol Lou Mora Care Center, Bradenton, FL
Carol Woods Health Center, Chapel Hill, NC
Carolina Care Center, Cherryville, NC
Carolina Village Inc, Hendersonville, NC
Caroline K Galland Home, Seattle, WA
Caroline Nursing Home Inc, Denton, MD
Carolton Chronic and Convalescent Hospital
    Inc, Fairfield, CT
Caromin House—Dodge, Duluth, MN
Caromin House—Tioga, Duluth, MN
Carpenter Care Center Inc, Tunkhannock, PA
Carpenter Nursing Home, Dallas, PA
Carriage Hill—Arlington, Arlington, VA
Carriage Hill—Bethesda Inc, Bethesda, MD
Carriage Hill Nursing Center—Silver Spring,
    Silver Spring, MD
Carriage Inn Convalescent Center, Coldwater,
    MI
Carriage Inn Nursing Home, Wilmington, OH
Carriage Inn of Cadiz Inc, Cadiz, OH
Carriage Square Health Care Center, Saint
    Joseph, MO
Carriage Square Nursing Home, San Antonio,
    TX
Carriage-by-the-Lake Nursing Home,
    Bellbrook, OH
Carrie Elligson Gietner Home Inc, Saint Louis,
    MO
Carrier Mills Nursing Home, Carrier Mills, IL
Carrington Hospital—Skilled Nursing Facility,
    Carrington, ND
Carrizo Springs Nursing Home Inc, Carrizo
    Springs, TX
Carroll Convalescent Center, Carrollton, GA
Carroll County Good Samaritan Center,
    Mount Carroll, IL
Carroll County Nursing Home, Ossipee, NH
Carroll Health Care Center Inc, Carrollton, OH
Carroll Health Center, Carroll, IA
Carroll Manor, Carroll, IA
Carroll Manor Nursing Home, Hyattsville, MD
Carroll Nursing Home, Oak Grove, LA
Carroll Nursing Home, Carrollton, OH
Carroll's Convalescent Hospital, El Cajon, CA
Carroll's Intermediate Care, El Cajon, CA
Carroll's Intermediate Care—Anza, El
    Cajon, CA
Carroll's Skilled Nursing Facility—Lexington,
    El Cajon, CA
Carrollton Manor, Carrollton, TX
Carrollton Nursing Home, Carrollton, KY
Carrollton's Resthaven Inc, Carrollton, MO
Carson Convalescent Center, Carson City, NV
Carson Nursing Home, Rigby, ID
Carter Hall Nursing Home, Dryden, VA
Carter Nursing Home, Jonesboro, LA
Carter Nursing Home Corp, Seagoville, TX
Carter's Guest Home Inc, Jackson, MS
Carter's Nursing Home, Oberlin, OH
Carthage Area Hospital, Carthage, NY
Carthage Health Care Center Inc, Carthage, MS
Carthage Nursing Home, Carthage, AR
Cartie's Health Center, Central Falls, RI
Cartmell Home for Aged, Palestine, TX
Cartwheel Lodge—Gonzales, Gonzales, TX
Cartwheel Lodge—Lockhart, Lockhart, TX
Cartwheel Lodge Nursing Home, Brookhaven,
    MS

Cartwheel Lodge of Luling, Luling, TX
Caruthersville Manor, Caruthersville, MO
Casa Angelica, Albuquerque, NM
Casa Bonita Convalescent Hospital, San
    Dimas, CA
Casa Central Center, Chicago, IL
Casa Coloma Health Care Center, Rancho
    Cordova, CA
Casa de Armstad Care Center, San Antonio,
    TX
Casa de Belita Convalescent Center Inc, Long
    Beach, CA
Casa De Modesto, Modesto, CA
Casa De Paz, Sioux City, IA
Casa de San Antonio, San Antonio, TX
Casa De Vida, San Luis Obispo, CA
Casa de Vida, Lake Charles, LA
Casa Delmar, Scottsdale, AZ
Casa Dorinda, Montecito, CA
Casa Grande Intermediate Care Facility,
    Anaheim, CA
Casa Grande Long Term Care Facility,
    Tewksbury, MA
Casa Inc, Scarborough, ME
Casa Loma Convalescent Center, Payette, ID
Casa Maria Convalescent Hospital,
    Fontana, CA
Casa Marie Health Care Centre, Roswell, NM
Casa Olga Intermediate Health Care Facility,
    Palo Alto, CA
Casa Pacifica, Anaheim, CA
Casa Primera, Grand Junction, CO
Casa San Miguel, Concord, CA
Casa Serena, San Jose, CA
Casa Serena de Salinas, Salinas, CA
Casa Verdugo Convalescent Lodge,
    Glendale, CA
Casabello Estate Intermediate Care Facility,
    Salmon, ID
Cascade Care Center, Caldwell, ID
Cascade Care Center, Grand Rapids, MI
Cascade County Convalescent Nursing Home,
    Great Falls, MT
Cascade Manor, Eugene, OR
Cascade Vista Convalescent Center, Redmond,
    WA
Casey Manor Nursing Home, Mount
    Vernon, IL
Casey Nursing Home, Casey, IL
Casey Nursing Home, Piketon, OH
Cashmere Convalescent Center, Cashmere, WA
Cass County Home, Logansport, IN
Cass County Medical Care Facility, Cassopolis,
    MI
Cassia Memorial Hospital—Long Term Care
    Unit, Burley, ID
Cassville Nursing Center, Cassville, MO
Castle Acres Nursing Home Inc, Hillsboro, MO
Castle Gardens Nursing Home,
    Northglenn, CO
Castle Manor, Garland, TX
Castle Nursing Center, Belleville, IL
Castle Nursing Home, Tewksbury, MA
Castle Park Nursing Home, Worcester, MA
Castle Park Professional Care Center,
    Normandy, MO
Castle Rest Nursing Home, Syracuse, NY
Castle Ridge Care Center, Eden Prairie, MN
Castle Shannon Nursing Home, Rockville, IN
Caswell Annex, Goldsboro, NC
Caswell Center, Kinston, NC
Catered Manor, Long Beach, CA
Cathedral Health and Rehabilitation Center,
    Jacksonville, FL

Cathedral Village, Philadelphia, PA
Catherine Ellen Convalescent Home, Geneva, OH
Catherine Manor, Newport, RI
Catherine Rest Home, Worcester, MA
Catherine Windsor Rest Home, Worcester, MA
Catholic Center for the Aging, Wichita, KS
Catholic Memorial Home, Fall River, MA
Caton Park Nursing Home, Brooklyn, NY
Cattaraugus County Home and Infirmary, Machias, NY
Cattaraugus County Public Nursing Home, Olean, NY
Cavallo Convalescent Hospital, Antioch, CA
Cedar Apartments, Montesano, WA
Cedar County Care Facility, Tipton, IA
Cedar Crest, Montgomery, AL
Cedar Crest at Greensburg, Greensburg, KS
Cedar Crest at Haviland, Haviland, KS
Cedar Crest at Pratt, Pratt, KS
Cedar Crest Convalescent Center Inc, Roosevelt, UT
Cedar Crest Health Center, Janesville, WI
Cedar Crest Health Center Inc, Indianapolis, IN
Cedar Crest Inc, Anthony, KS
Cedar Crest Inc of Kingman, Kingman, KS
Cedar Crest Manor, Lawton, OK
Cedar Crest Nursing Centre Inc, Cranston, RI
Cedar Crest Senior Citizens Home, Calvert City, KY
Cedar Falls Health Care Center, Cedar Falls, IA
Cedar Falls Lutheran Home, Cedar Falls, IA
Cedar Glen Nursing Home, Danvers, MA
Cedar Grove Nursing Home, Hillsboro, MO
Cedar Haven-Lebanon County Home, Lebanon, PA
Cedar Hedge Nursing Home, Rouses Point, NY
Cedar Hill Care Center, Zanesville, OH
Cedar Hill Nursing Home, Athens, GA
Cedar Hill-Duncanville Nursing Center, Cedar Hill, TX
Cedar Hills Nursing Center, Jacksonville, FL
Cedar House Inc, Ottawa, KS
Cedar I, Austin, MN
Cedar II, Austin, MN
Cedar III, Austin, MN
Cedar IV, Austin, MN
Cedar Knoll Rest Home, Grass Lake, MI
Cedar Lake Home Campus, West Bend, WI
Cedar Lake Lodge, LaGrange, KY
Cedar Lake Nursing Home, Malakoff, TX
Cedar Lane Rehabilitational Health Care Center, Waterbury, CT
Cedar Lawn Convalescent Center, Abingdon, VA
Cedar Lodge Nursing Home, Center Moriches, NY
Cedar Lodge Nursing Home Inc, Marvell, AR
Cedar Manor, Tipton, IA
Cedar Manor, Baker, OR
Cedar Manor, Cedar City, UT
Cedar Manor Nursing Home, Ossining, NY
Cedar Manor Nursing Home Inc, Windsor, VT
Cedar Pines Nursing Home, Minneapolis, MN
Cedar Rapids Care Center, Cedar Rapids, IA
Cedar Ridge Inc, Skowhegan, ME
Cedar Springs Nursing Center, Cedar Springs, MI
Cedar Street Home, Helena, MT
Cedar Street Home Inc, Fitchburg, MA

Cedar Vale Manor, Cedar Vale, KS
Cedar View Good Samaritan Center, Wellington, KS
Cedarbrook, Allentown, PA
Cedarbrook Fountain Hill Annex, Bethlehem, PA
Cedarbrook Manor Nursing Home, Deerwood, MN
Cedarcrest, Westmoreland, NH
Cedarcrest Manor Inc, Washington, MO
Cedarcroft Nursing Home, Valley Park, MO
Cedardale Health Care Facility, Wray, CO
Cedargate, Poplar Bluff, MO
Cedars, Hartington, NE
Cedars—Church of the Brethren Home, McPherson, KS
Cedars Convalescent Center, Columbia, MS
Cedars Convalescent Hospital, Red Bluff, CA
Cedars Health Center, Lakewood, CO
Cedars Health Center, Tupelo, MS
Cedars Manor Inc, Checotah, OK
Cedars Nursing Home, Lebanon, TN
Cedars Nursing Home, Charlottesville, VA
Cedars of Lebanon Rest Home, Lebanon, KY
Cedartown Intermediate Care Center, Cedartown, GA
Cedarview Nursing Home, Owatonna, MN
Cedarwood Care Center, Independence, OR
Cedarwood Health Care Center Inc, Colorado Springs, CO
Celina Manor, Celina, OH
Celina Nursing Center Inc, Celina, TX
Centennial Health Care Center, Greeley, CO
Centennial Health Care Center, Portland, OR
Centennial Homestead, Washington, KS
Centennial Spring Health Care Center, Warminster, PA
Center for Living, Fort Lauderdale, FL
Center for Personal Development, Ames, IA
Center for the Retarded—Cullen, Houston, TX
Center Green Rest Home, Fairhaven, MA
Center of Family Love, Okarche, OK
Center Skilled Nursing Facility, Sacramento, CA
Centerbury Villa—Beaumont, Beaumont, TX
Centerclair Inc, Lexington, NC
Centerhaven Nursing Home, Hamilton, OH
Centerville Care Center Inc, Centerville, IA
Centerville Health Care Center, Centerville, TN
Centerville Nursing Home, Centerville, MA
Centinela Park Convalescent Hospital, Inglewood, CA
Central Baptist Home for the Aged, Harwood Heights, IL
Central Convalescent, Yakima, WA
Central Dakota Nursing Home, Jamestown, ND
Central Dutchess Nursing Home Inc, Wappingers Falls, NY
Central Gardens, San Francisco, CA
Central Healthcare Center, Indianapolis, IN
Central Island Nursing Home Inc, Plainview, NY
Central Manor Health Care Center Inc, Indianapolis, IN
Central Montana Nursing Home, Lewistown, MT
Central New Jersey Jewish Home for Aged, Somerset, NJ
Central Nursing, Chicago, IL
Central Nursing Home, Le Center, MN
Central Nursing Home, Minneapolis, MN

Central Oklahoma Christian Home, Oklahoma City, OK
Central Oregon Health Care Center, Bend, OR
Central Park Lodge - Rest Haven (Chestnut Hill), Philadelphia, PA
Central Park Manor Inc, Dallas, TX
Central Piedmont Nursing Center, Burlington, NC
Central Plaza Residential Home, Chicago, IL
Central Point Care Center, Central Point, OR
Central State Hospital, Milledgeville, GA
Central Texas Nursing Home, Austin, TX
Central Todd County Care Center, Clarissa, MN
Central Utah Rehabilitation and Convalescent Center, Orem, UT
Central Wisconsin Center, Madison, WI
Centralia Care Center, Centralia, IL
Centralia Convalescent Center, Centralia, WA
Centralia Convalescent Center Inc, Long Beach, CA
Centralia Fireside House, Centralia, IL
Centralia Friendship House Inc, Centralia, IL
Centre Crest Nursing Home, Bellefonte, PA
Centre Manor Nursing Home, Boston, MA
Centreville Health Care Center, Centreville, MS
Centuria Nursing Home, Centuria, WI
Century Care Center Inc, Whiteville, NC
Century Care of Laurinburg Inc, Laurinburg, NC
Century Home Inc, Baltimore, MD
Cerri's Painesville Nursing Home, Painesville, OH
Chabot Convalescent Hospital, Castro Valley, CA
Chaffey Nursing Home Inc, Superior, WI
The Chalet Nursing Home, Yakima, WA
Chamberlain Nursing Home, Brookline, MA
Chambers Nursing Home Inc, Carlisle, AR
Chamor Nursing Center, Tulsa, OK
Champaign Childrens Home, Champaign, IL
Champaign County Home, Urbana, OH
Champaign County Nursing Home, Urbana, IL
Champaign County Residential Services Inc, Urbana, OH
Champion Childrens Home, Duluth, MN
Champlain Valley Physicians Hospital Medical Center—Skilled Nursing Facility, Plattsburgh, NY
Chandler Care Center—Bristol, Santa Ana, CA
Chandler Care Center—El Monte, El Monte, CA
Chandler Care Center—Fairfax, Los Angeles, CA
Chandler Care Center—Romona, El Monte, CA
Chandler Convalescent Hospital, Glendale, CA
Chandler Convalescent Hospital Inc, North Hollywood, CA
Chandler Hall Nursing Home, Newtown, PA
Chandler Hillcrest Manor Inc, Chandler, OK
Chandler Manor Rest Home, Somerville, MA
Chandler Memorial Nursing Home, San Antonio, TX
Changing Seasons Commuity Care Complex, Vidor, TX
Chanhassen Center, Chanhassen, MN
Channing House, Palo Alto, CA
Chaparrel House, Berkeley, CA
Chapel Hill Convalescent Home, Randallstown, MD
Chapel Hill Nursing Home, Holyoke, MA

Chapel Home Home, Canal Fulton, OH
Chapel Manor Nursing and Convalescent Home, Philadelphia, PA
Chapel of Care Nursing Home, Sherman, TX
Chapel View Inc, Hopkins, MN
Chapin Center Skilled Nursing Facility, Springfield, MA
Chapin Home for the Aging, Jamaica, NY
Chaplinwood Nursing Home, Milledgeville, GA
Chapman Convalescent Home, Hazelhurst, GA
Chapman Convalescent Hospital, Riverside, CA
Chapman Harbor Convalescent Hospital, Garden Grove, CA
Chapman Nursing Home Inc, Alexander City, AL
Chapman Valley Manor, Chapman, KS
Chapparal Nursing Center, Clovis, NM
Char Mund Nursing Home, Orangeville, PA
Chariot Nursing and Convalescent Home, Wilmington, DE
Charis House, Brainerd, MN
Chariton County Rest Home, Keytesville, MO
Chariton Group Home, Chariton, IA
Chariton Manor, Chariton, IA
Chariton Manor Convalescent Center, Salisbury, MO
Charity Nursing Facility, Dennison, OH
Charles A Dean Memorial Hospital—Intermediate Care Unit, Greenville, ME
Charles Bronstien Home, Minneapolis, MN
Charles Cole Memorial Hospital-ECF, Coudersport, PA
Charles County Nursing Home, La Plata, MD
Charles Ford Memorial Home, New Harmony, IN
Charles Harwood Memorial Hospital—Skilled Nursing Unit, Christiansted, VI
Charles House Convalescent Home, Boston, MA
Charles P Moorman Home for Women, Louisville, KY
Charles Parrish Memorial Nursing Center, Dunn, NC
Charles T Sitrin Home Inc, New Hartford, NY
Charles the First Medical Center, Saint Louis, MO
Charles V Hogan Regional Center, Danvers, MA
Charlesgate Manor Convalescent Home Inc, Watertown, MA
Charlesgate Nursing Center, Providence, RI
Charless Home, Saint Louis, MO
Charleston Health Care Center, Las Vegas, NV
Charleston Manor, Charleston, IL
Charleston Manor, Charleston, MO
Charleston Nursing Center Inc, Mount Pleasant, SC
Charlevoix Professional Nursing Home, Saint Charles, MO
Char-Lotte Nursing Home Inc, Rock Creek, OH
Charlton Manor Rest Home, Charlton, MA
Charlwell House Nursing Home, Norwood, MA
Charm Acres Health Care Center Inc, Lakewood, CO
Charm Cove Nursing Home Inc, Denver, CO
Charstelle Nursing Home, Worcester, MA
Chase County Nursing Center, Cottonwood Falls, KS

Chase Manor Nursing and Convalescent Center, Logansport, IN
Chase Memorial Nursing Home Co Inc, New Berlin, NY
Chastain's Joplin House Nursing Home, Joplin, MO
Chastain's of Ava Inc, Ava, MO
Chastain's of Buffalo Inc, Buffalo, MO
Chastain's of Clinton Inc, Clinton, MO
Chastain's of Des Peres Inc, Des Peres, MO
Chastains of Highland Inc, Highland, IL
Chastain's of Jefferson City, Jefferson City, MO
Chastain's of Lamar Inc, Lamar, MO
Chastain's of Marceline Nursing Home, Marceline, MO
Chastain's of Mountain Home, Mountain Home, AR
Chastain's of Thayer Inc, Thayer, MO
Chastain's Tradition House Nursing Home, Joplin, MO
Chateau Convalescent Center, Bryn Mawr, PA
Chateau Convalescent Centre, Muncie, IN
Chateau Convalescent Hospital, Stockton, CA
Chateau de Notre Dame, New Orleans, LA
Chateau Gardens, Flint, MI
Chateau Girardeau, Cape Girardeau, MO
Chateau Healthcare Center, Minneapolis, MN
Chateau Home, Northbrook, IL
Chatham Acres, Chatham, PA
Chatham Nursing Home I, Savannah, GA
Chatham Nursing Home II, Savannah, GA
Chatsworth Health and Rehabilitation Center, Chatsworth, CA
Chatsworth Health Care Center, Chatsworth, GA
Chatsworth Park Convalescent Hospital, Chatsworth, CA
Chautauqua Avenue Guest Home 1, Charles City, IA
Chautauqua County Home and Infirmary, Dunkirk, NY
Chautauqua Guest Home 2, Charles City, IA
Chautauqua Guest Home 3, Charles City, IA
Cheatham County Rest Home, Ashland City, TN
Checotah Manor Inc, Checotah, OK
Chehalem Care Center, Newberg, OR
Chelsea Group Home, Duvall, WA
Chelsea Jewish Nursing Home, Chelsea, MA
Chelsea United Methodist, Chelsea, MI
Cheltenham-York Road Nursing Rehabilitation Center, Philadelphia, PA
Chemung County Health Center—Nursing Facility, Elmira, NY
Chenango Bridge Nursing Home, Chenango Bridge, NY
Chenango Memorial Hospital Inc—Skilled Nursing Facility, Norwich, NY
Cheney Care Center, Cheney, WA
Cheney Golden Age Home Inc, Cheney, KS
Chenita Nursing Home 1, Mansfield, OH
Chenita Nursing Home 2, Mansfield, OH
Cheraw Nursing Home Inc, Cheraw, SC
Cherish Nursing Center, Richmond, IN
Cherokee County Hospital—Long Term Care Unit, Gaffney, SC
Cherokee County Nursing Home, Centre, AL
Cherokee Lodge Adult Care, Oskaloosa, KS
Cherokee Memorial Manor Inc, Cherokee, OK
Cherokee Nursing Home, Calhoun, GA
Cherokee Villa, Cherokee, IA
Cherrelyn Manor Nursing Home, Littleton, CO

Cherry Creek Nursing Center Inc, Aurora, CO
Cherry Creek Village, Wichita, KS
Cherry Heights Villa Care, Seattle, WA
Cherry Hill Manor, Johnston, RI
Cherry Hill Nursing Home, Toledo, OH
Cherry Hills Nursing Home, Englewood, CO
Cherry Hospital, Goldsboro, NC
Cherry Manor Health Care Center, Springfield, MO
Cherry Nursing Home, Montclair, NJ
Cherry Oaks Nursing Center, Graham, TX
Cherry Park Health Care Facility, Englewood, CO
Cherry Ridge Nursing Home, Bastrop, LA
Cherry Street Annex, Paris, TX
Cherry Street Manor, Paris, TX
Cherry Village, Great Bend, KS
Cherrylee Lodge Sanitarium, El Monte, CA
Cherryvale Medi-Lodge, Cherryvale, KS
Chesaning Rest Home, Chesaning, MI
Cheshire County Nursing Home, Westmoreland, NH
Cheshire Home, Florham Park, NJ
Cheshire Rehabilitation and Convalescent Center, Cheshire, CT
Chestelm Convalescent Home, Moodus, CT
Chester Care Center, Chester, PA
Chester Care Center, Chester, PA
Chester County Nursing Center, Chester, SC
Chester County Nursing Home, Henderson, TN
Chester House, Eldorado Springs, CO
Chester Manor Rest Home, Cambridge, MA
Chesterfield County Nursing Home, Chesterfield, VA
Chesterfield Manor Inc, Chesterfield, MO
Chesterfields Chronic and Convalescent Hospital, Chester, CT
Chestnut Hill Convalescent Center, Passaic, NJ
Chestnut Knoll, Springfield, MA
Chetleham Nursing and Rehabilitation Center, Philadelphia, PA
Chetopa Nursing Home, Chetopa, KS
Chetwynde Convalescent Home, Newton, MA
Chetwynde Nursing Home, Newton, MA
Cheviot Garden Convalescent Hospital, Los Angeles, CA
Chevy Chase Nursing Center, Chicago, IL
Chevy Chase Retirement and Nursing Center, Silver Spring, MD
Cheyenne Convalescent Home, Cheyenne, OK
Cheyenne Lodge Nursing Home, Jamestown, KS
Cheyenne Manor, Cheyenne, CO
Cheyenne Mountain Nursing Center, Colorado Springs, CO
Cheyenne Village, Manitou Springs, CO
Chez Nous, Saint Paul, MN
Chicago Heights Terrace, Chicago Heights, IL
Chicago Ridge Nursing Center, Chicago Ridge, IL
Chickasha Nursing Center Inc, Chickasha, OK
Chico Convalescent Hospital, Chico, CA
Chicopee Municipal Home, Chicopee, MA
Chicopee Rest Home, Chicopee, MA
Chicora Medical Center Inc, Chicora, PA
Children's Convalescent Center, Bethany, OK
Childrens Convalescent Hospital, San Diego, CA
Childrens Developmental Center Inc, Abbottstown, PA
Children's Haven Inc, Harvey, IL
Childress Nursing Center, Childress, TX

Childs Nursing Home Company Inc, Albany, NY

Chilton Village, Chilton, WI

Chimney Rock Villa, Bayard, NE

Chinle Nursing Home, Chinle, AZ

Chippenham Manor Inc, Richmond, VA

Chippewa County War Memorial, Sault Sainte Marie, MI

Chippewa Health Care Center, Chippewa Falls, WI

Chippewa Manor Nursing Home, Chippewa Falls, WI

Chippewa Valley Hospital and Nursing Home, Durand, WI

Chisholm Memorial Nursing Home, Chisholm, MN

Choctaw County Nursing Home, Ackerman, MS

Chosen Valley Care Center, Chatfield, MN

Chouteau County District Nursing Home, Fort Benton, MT

Chowan Hospital, Edenton, NC

Chowchilla Convalescent Hospital, Chowchilla, CA

Christ Church Hospital Episcopal, Philadelphia, PA

Christ Home Retirement Center, Warminster, PA

Christ Sanctified Holy Church Home for the Aged, Perry, GA

Christ the King, West Chicago, IL

Christ the King Manor, Dubois, PA

Christ Villa Nursing Center, Wichita, KS

Christel Manor Nursing Home, Fairborn, OH

Christensen's Nursing Home, Greenville, MI

Christian Anchorage Retirement Home Inc, Marietta, OH

Christian Buehler Memorial Home, Peoria, IL

Christian Care Center, Mesquite, TX

Christian Care Nursing Home, Phoenix, AZ

Christian Care of Cincinnati Inc, Cincinnati, OH

Christian Church Home of Louisville, Louisville, KY

Christian City Convalescent Center, Atlanta, GA

Christian Community Home of Hudson, Hudson, WI

Christian Convalescent Home, Muskegon, MI

Christian County Nursing Home, Ozark, MO

Christian Health Care Center, Hopkinsville, KY

Christian Health Care Center, Wyckoff, NJ

Christian Health Center, Corbin, KY

Christian Hill Convalescent Home, Lowell, MA

Christian Hill Rest Home, Barre, MA

Christian Home, Waupun, WI

Christian Home for the Aged, Columbus, OH

Christian Homes Inc, Holdrege, NE

The Christian League for the Handicapped, Walworth, WI

Christian Manor Nursing Home, Tracy, MN

Christian Nursing and Living Center, Willmar, MN

Christian Nursing Center, Grand Rapids, MI

Christian Nursing Home, Fayetteville, WV

Christian Nursing Home Inc, Lincoln, IL

Christian Old People's Home, Ferguson, MO

Christian Opportunity Center, Pella, IA

Christian Rest Home, Lynden, WA

Christian Rest Home Association, Grand Rapids, MI

Christian Shelticenter, Quincy, IL

Christian Union Home, Minneapolis, MN

Christian Villa, Crowley, LA

Christiana, Green Bay, WI

Christopher—East, Louisville, KY

Christopher House Nursing Home, Wheat Ridge, CO

Christoval Golden Years Nursing Home, Christoval, TX

Christoval Golden Years Nursing Home Inc, Christoval, TX

Christus Group Home, Grand Rapids, MN

Christus Group Home, Little Falls, MN

Chrystal's Country Home Inc, Parker City, IN

Chula Vista Nursing Home, Mesa, AZ

The Church Home, Chicago, IL

Church Home of the Protestant Episcopal Church, Rochester, NY

Church Lane Convalescent Hospital, San Pablo, CA

Church of Christ Care Center, Mount Clemens, MI

Church of Christ Home for Aged, Nashville, TN

Church of God Home, Carlisle, PA

Church of the Brethren Home, Windber, PA

Church Street Manor, Saint Joseph, MO

Churchman Manor, Indianapolis, IN

Churchman Village, Newark, DE

Churchview Health Center Retirement Home, Haverhill, MA

Cicero Children's Center Inc, Cicero, IN

Cimarron Nursing Home, Boise City, OK

Cinnaminson Manor Nursing and Convalescent Center, Cinnaminson, NJ

Cinnamon Hill Manor Inc, Lanagan, MO

Circle Manor Nursing Home, Kensington, MD

Circle Manor Nursing Home, Boston, MA

Circleville Health Care Center, Circleville, OH

Circleville Manor, Circleville, OH

Cisco Nursing Center, Cisco, TX

Cisne Manor Inc, Cisne, IL

Citadel Health Care, Pueblo, CO

Citadel Health Care Pavilion, Saint Joseph, MO

Citizens Nursing Home of Frederick County, Frederick, MD

Citizens Nursing Home of Harford County, Havre de Grace, MD

Citronelle Convalescent Center, Citronelle, AL

Citrus Care Convalescent Hospital, Fontana, CA

City Care Center, Anna, IL

City Hospital at Elmhurst Public Home, Elmhurst, NY

City View Nursing Home, Madison, WI

City View Nursing Home Inc, Brookline, MA

Civic Center Nursing Home, Birmingham, AL

Civitan House, Denver, CO

Clackamas Terrace Convalescent Center, Gladstone, OR

Cla-Clif Home for the Aged, Brinkley, AR

Claiborne and Hughes Convalescent Center Inc, Franklin, TN

Claiborne County Nursing Home, Tazewell, TN

Clanton Health Care Center Inc, Clanton, AL

Clanton Health Care—South, Clanton, AL

Clapp's Convalescent Nursing Home Inc, Asheboro, NC

Clapp's Nursing Center, Pleasant Garden, NC

Clara Baldwin Stocker Home for Women, West Covina, CA

Clara Barton Terrace, Flint, MI

Clara Burke Nursing Home, Plymouth Meeting, PA

Clara City Community Nursing Home, Clara City, MN

Clara Doerr-Lindley Hall, Minneapolis, MN

Clara Fairbanks and Chauncey Rose Home Inc, Terre Haute, IN

Clara Werner Dormitory, Watertown, WI

Clare Nursing Home, Clare, MI

Claremont Care Center, Point Pleasant, NJ

Claremont Convalescent Hospital, Berkeley, CA

Claremont Convalescent Hospital, Claremont, CA

Claremont Nursing Home, Claremont, NH

Claremore Nursing Home Inc, Claremore, OK

Clarence Nursing Home, Clarence, IA

Clarence Nursing Home District, Clarence, MO

Clarendon Hill Nursing Home, Somerville, MA

Clarewood House Infirmary, Houston, TX

Clarion Care Center, Clarion, IA

Clarion Medical Services, Clarion, PA

Clark County Health Care Center, Owen, WI

Clark County Nursing Home, Kahoka, MO

Clark Fort Valley Nursing Home, Plains, MT

Clark Institute of Restorative Tech, Battle Ground, WA

Clark Manor Convalescent Center, Chicago, IL

Clark Manor Nursing Home, Worcester, MA

Clark Memorial Home, Springfield, OH

Clark Nursing Home, Clark, SD

Clark Nursing Home, Vergennes, VT

Clark Residential Care Facility, Sterling, CO

The John Clarke Retirement Center, Middletown, RI

Clarkfield Care Center, Clarkfield, MN

Clark-Lindsey Village Inc, Urbana, IL

Clark's Creek Health Care Center, Plainfield, IN

Clark's Mountain Home, Piedmont, MO

Clarks Summit State Hospital—Long Term Care Facility, Clarks Summit, PA

Clarkson Mountain View Guest Home, Rapid City, SD

Clarksville Convalescent Home Inc, Clarksville, AR

Clarksville Healthcare Center, Clarksville, IN

Clarksville Manor Nursing Center, Clarksville, TN

Clarksville Nursing Center, Clarksville, TX

Clarview Rest Home, Sligo, PA

Clarytona Manor, Lewistown, IL

Classic Care South, Sandusky, OH

Classic Center, Sandusky, OH

Clatsop Care and Rehabilitation District, Astoria, OR

Claxton Nursing Home, Claxton, GA

Clay Center Presbyterian Manor, Clay Center, KS

Clay County—Fort Gaines Nursing Home, Fort Gaines, GA

Clay County Health Center Inc, Brazil, IN

Clay County Hospital and Nursing Home, Ashland, AL

Clay County Nursing Home, Celina, TN

Clay County Residence, Hawley, MN

Clay County Residence II, Moorhead, MN

Clayberg Fulton County Nursing Center, Cuba, IL

Claystone Manor, Ennis, TX

Clayton House Healthcare, Manchester, MO

Clayton Residential Home, Chicago, IL
Clayton-on-the-Green Nursing Center, Ballwin, MO
Claywest House, Saint Charles, MO
Clear Haven Nursing Center, Clearfield, PA
Clear Lake Care Center, Webster, TX
Clear View Convalescent Center, Gardena, CA
Clear View Nursing Care Center, Thomaston, GA
Clear View Sanitarium, Gardena, CA
Clearbrook House, Arcola, IL
Clearfield Convalescent and Nursing Center, Clearfield, UT
Clearview Convalescent Center, Columbus, OH
Clearview Home, Clearfield, IA
Clearview Home, Mount Ayr, IA
Clearview Manor, Prairie City, IA
Clearview Manor Convalescent and Rehabilitation Center, Tacoma, WA
Clearview Nursing Home, Framingham, MA
Clearview Nursing Home, Whitestone, NY
Clearview Nursing Home, Juneau, WI
Clearview Nursing Home Inc, Hagerstown, MD
Clearview Sanatorium, Delafield, WI
Clearwater Convalescent Center, Clearwater, FL
Cleaver Memorial Convalescent Center, Longview, TX
Cleburne County Hospital and Nursing Home, Heflin, AL
Clement Manor Health Care Center, Greenfield, WI
Clemson Area Retirement Health Care Center, Clemson, SC
Clepper Convalescent Home, Sharon, PA
Clermont Nursing and Convalescent Center, Milford, OH
Cleveland County Nursing Home, Rison, AR
Cleveland Golden Age Nursing Home, Cleveland, OH
Cleveland Health Care Center Inc, Cleveland, MS
Cleveland Nursing Home Inc, Cleveland, OK
Clewiston Health Care Center, Clewiston, FL
Cliff Gables Nursing Home, Fall River, MA
Cliff Gardens Nursing Home, Dallas, TX
Cliff Haven Nursing Home, Fall River, MA
Cliff Health Care Facility Inc, Waterbury, CT
Cliff Heights Nursing Home, Fall River, MA
Cliff House, Duluth, MN
Cliff House, Englewood Cliffs, NJ
Cliff House Nursing Home Inc, Winthrop, MA
Cliff Lawn Nursing Home, Fall River, MA
Cliff Manor, Spokane, WA
Cliff Manor Inc, Kansas City, MO
Cliff Manor Nursing Home, Fall River, MA
Cliff Towers Nursing Home, Dallas, TX
Cliffside Health Care Center, Cliffwood Beach, NJ
Cliffside Nursing Home, Flushing, NY
Clifton Care Center Inc, Cincinnati, OH
Clifton Geriatric Center Long Term Care Facility, Somerset, MA
Clifton House, Park Ridge, IL
Clifton House, Minneapolis, MN
Clifton Lutheran Sunset Home, Clifton, TX
Clifton Springs Hospital and Clinic Extended Care, Clifton Springs, NY
Clifty Falls Convalescent Center, Madison, IN
Clinch Valley Manor Inc, Wise, VA
Clinic Convalescent Center, Madisonville, KY

Clinton Aire Nursing Center, Mount Clemens, MI
Clinton Center, Frankfort, IN
Clinton Convalescent Center, Clinton, MD
Clinton Country Manor, Clinton, MS
Clinton County Nursing Home, Plattsburgh, NY
Clinton Good Samaritan Center, Clinton, MN
Clinton Health Care Center, Clinton, CT
Clinton Home for Aged People, Clinton, MA
Clinton House Inc, Frankfort, IN
Clinton Manor, New Baden, IL
Clinton Manor Inc, Plattsburg, MO
Clinton Manor Nursing Home, Clinton, MA
Clinton Meadow Park Nursing Home, Clinton, WI
Clinton Nursing Home, Clinton, IN
Clinton Retirement Village, Clinton, IA
Clinton Village Convalescent Hospital, Oakland, CA
Clinton-Hickman County Hospital—Intermediate Care Facility, Clinton, KY
Clintonview Care, Mount Clemens, MI
Clio Convalescent Center, Clio, MI
Clipper Home, Portsmouth, NH
Cloisters of La Jolla Convalescent Hospital, La Jolla, CA
Cloisters of Mission Hills Convalescent Hospital, San Diego, CA
Clove Lakes Nursing Home, Staten Island, NY
Clover Healthcare, Auburn, ME
Clover Rest Home, Columbia, NJ
Clover Rest Nursing Home, Montclair, NJ
Cloverlodge Care Center, Saint Edward, NE
Clovernook Inc, Cincinnati, OH
Clovis Convalescent Hospital, Clovis, CA
Clovis Nursing Home, Clovis, CA
Clyatt Memorial Center, Daytona Beach, FL
Clyde Street Home, Florence, SC
Coachella House Inc, Palm Springs, CA
Coaldale State General Hospital, Coaldale, PA
Coastal Care Center, Texas City, TX
Coastal Center—Live Oak Village, Ladsom, SC
Coastal Manor, Yarmouth, ME
Coastview Convalescent Hospital, Long Beach, CA
Cobalt Lodge Convalescent Home, East Hampton, CT
Cobble Hill Nursing Home Inc, Brooklyn, NY
Cobbs Creek Nursing Inc, Philadelphia, PA
Coberly Green Intermediate Care Facility, Oakland, CA
Coburn Charitable Society, Ipswich, MA
Cochituate Nursing Home Inc, Wayland, MA
Cochran Family Care Home, Arvada, CO
Cocke County Convalescent Center, Newport, TN
Cockrum Intermediate Care Facility, Benton, IL
Coeur d'Alene Convalescent Center, Coeur d'Alene, ID
Coffee Nursing Home, Manchester, TN
Coffman Home for the Aging Inc, Hagerstown, MD
Cogburn Health Center Inc, Mobile, AL
Cohasset Knoll Nursing Home, Cohasset, MA
Cohen's Retreat, Savannah, GA
Coit Street Community Residence, Florence, SC
Cojeunaze Nursing Center, Chicago, IL
Cokato Manor, Cokato, MN
Coker Intermediate Care Home, Canton, GA

Cokesbury Village, Hockessin, DE
Colbert Nursing Home Inc, Gresham, OR
Colbert Place, Cedar Rapids, IA
Colby Manor Nursing Home Inc, Everett, WA
Colchester Convalescent Home, Colchester, CT
Coldwater Manor Nursing Home, Stratford, TX
Coldwell Nursing Home, Mexico, MO
Coleman Care Center, Coleman, TX
Coleman's Personal Care Home, Jackson, MS
Cole's Rest Haven Nursing Home, Guthrie, OK
Colfax General Hospital—Intermediate Care Facility, Springer, NM
Coliseum Medical Center, New Orleans, LA
College Hill Skilled Nursing Center, Manhattan, KS
College Nursing Home, Flushing, NY
College Park Care Center, Texas City, TX
College Park Convalescent Home, College Park, GA
College Park Convalescent Hospital, Menlo Park, CA
College Street Nursing Center, Beaumont, TX
College Vista Convalescent Hospital, Los Angeles, CA
Collier Manor, Highland, KS
Collier's Nursing Home, Ellsworth, ME
Collingswood Nursing Center, Rockville, MD
Collingwood Manor, Chula Vista, CA
Collingwood Park Nursing Home, Toledo, OH
Collins Chapel Health Care Center, Memphis, TN
Collins Nursing Care Facility, Chillicothe, MO
Collins Nursing Home Inc, Hayesville, OH
Collins Nursing Home Inc, Pittsburgh, PA
Collins Rest Home Inc, Ashburnham, MA
Collinsville Care Home Inc, Collinsville, TX
Collinsville Manor, Collinsville, OK
Collinsville Nursing Home Inc, Collinsville, AL
Colonial Acres, Rock Falls, IL
Colonial Acres, Chanute, KS
Colonial Acres, Humboldt, NE
Colonial Acres Care Center, Duncanville, TX
Colonial Acres Health Care Center, Golden Valley, MN
Colonial Acres Nursing Home, Lincoln, ME
Colonial Acres Nursing Home, Loveland, OH
Colonial Acres Nursing Home, Round Rock, TX
Colonial Arms Nursing Home, Salem, OR
Colonial Belle Nursing Home, Bellville, TX
Colonial Care Home, Somerset, KY
Colonial Columns Nursing Center Inc, Colorado Springs, CO
Colonial Convalescent Hospital, Bakersfield, CA
Colonial Convalescent Hospital Inc, San Jacinto, CA
Colonial Convalescent Nursing Home, Nixon, TX
Colonial Garden Inc, Tallmadge, OH
Colonial Gardens Nursing Home, Pico Rivera, CA
Colonial Gardens Retirement Center, Boonville, MO
Colonial Hall Nursing Home, Princeton, IL
Colonial Halls Property's Inc, Shelbyville, KY
Colonial Haven, Beemer, NE
Colonial Haven Nursing Home Inc, Granite City, IL

Colonial Heights Convalescent Center, Colonial Heights, VA

Colonial Hill Health Care Center, Johnson City, TN

Colonial Hills Nursing Center, Maryville, TN

Colonial House, Bardstown, KY

Colonial House Manor, Waterville, ME

Colonial House of Colby, Colby, WI

Colonial House of Shepherdsville, Shepherdsville, KY

Colonial Lodge—Independence, Independence, KS

Colonial Lodge Nursing Home, McAlester, OK

Colonial Manor, Anita, IA

Colonial Manor, Baxter, IA

Colonial Manor, Elma, IA

Colonial Manor, LaPorte City, IA

Colonial Manor, Lakefield, MN

Colonial Manor, Valley, NE

Colonial Manor, Fremont, NH

Colonial Manor, Milwaukee, WI

Colonial Manor—Columbus Junction, Columbus Junction, IA

Colonial Manor Convalescent Hospital, West Covina, CA

Colonial Manor Convalescent Hospital— Extended Care Facility, Long Beach, CA

Colonial Manor Guest House, Rayville, LA

Colonial Manor Health Care Center Inc, Loudonville, OH

Colonial Manor Health Care Center Inc II, Loudonville, OH

Colonial Manor I, Hollis, OK

Colonial Manor II, Hollis, OK

Colonial Manor Inc, Danville, IL

Colonial Manor Inc, Middletown, OH

Colonial Manor Nursing and Care Center, Wheatland, IA

Colonial Manor Nursing and Convalescent Center, Cleburne, TX

Colonial Manor Nursing and Convalescent Center, Nephi, UT

Colonial Manor Nursing and Health Care Center, Lansing, KS

Colonial Manor Nursing Center, Fort Worth, TX

Colonial Manor Nursing Center, Madison, WI

Colonial Manor Nursing Home, Bowling Green, KY

Colonial Manor Nursing Home, Appleton City, MO

Colonial Manor Nursing Home, Whitefish, MT

Colonial Manor Nursing Home, Youngstown, OH

Colonial Manor Nursing Home, Midwest City, OK

Colonial Manor Nursing Home, Tulsa, OK

Colonial Manor Nursing Home, York, PA

Colonial Manor Nursing Home, New Braunfels, TX

Colonial Manor Nursing Home of Woodward Inc, Woodward, OK

Colonial Manor of Albany, Albany, MO

Colonial Manor of Armour, Armour, SD

Colonial Manor of Balaton, Balaton, MN

Colonial Manor of Chelsea, Chelsea, OK

Colonial Manor of Clarkson, Clarkson, NE

Colonial Manor of Corning, Corning, IA

Colonial Manor of Custer, Custer, SD

Colonial Manor of Deer Lodge, Deer Lodge, MT

Colonial Manor of Edinburg, Edinburg, TX

Colonial Manor of Glasgow, Glasgow, MO

Colonial Manor of Groton, Groton, SD

Colonial Manor of Hudson, Hudson, SD

Colonial Manor of Ipswich, Ipswich, SD

Colonial Manor of LaMoure, LaMoure, ND

Colonial Manor of McAllen, McAllen, TX

Colonial Manor of Odebolt, Odebolt, IA

Colonial Manor of Salem, Salem, SD

Colonial Manor of Tyler, Tyler, TX

Colonial Manor of Wathena, Wathena, KS

Colonial Manor of Wausau, Wausau, WI

Colonial Manor of Zearing, Zearing, IA

Colonial Manors—Correctionville, Correctionville, IA

Colonial Manors of Amana Inc, Amana, IA

Colonial Manors of Avoca, Avoca, IA

Colonial Manors of Kingsley, Kingsley, IA

Colonial Manors of Randolph Inc, Randolph, NE

Colonial Nursing and Rehabilitation Center, Weymouth, MA

Colonial Nursing Home, Benton, AR

Colonial Nursing Home, Nashville, AR

Colonial Nursing Home, Marksville, LA

Colonial Nursing Home, Kansas City, MO

Colonial Nursing Home, Rockford, OH

Colonial Nursing Home, Toledo, OH

Colonial Nursing Home, Pauls Valley, OK

Colonial Nursing Home, Cameron, TX

Colonial Nursing Home, Kerrville, TX

Colonial Nursing Home Inc, Crown Point, IN

Colonial Nursing Home Inc, Schulenburg, TX

Colonial Oaks Health Care Center, Marion, IN

Colonial Oaks Nursing and Convalescent Home, Metairie, LA

Colonial Oaks Nursing Home, Cross Plains, TX

Colonial of San Angelo, San Angelo, TX

Colonial Palms, Pompano Beach, FL

Colonial Palms East Nursing Home, Pompano Beach, FL

Colonial Park Nursing Home, McAlester, OK

Colonial Park Nursing Home, Marshall, TX

Colonial Pines Health Care Center, Oxford, AL

Colonial Plaza Nursing Home Inc, Cushing, OK

Colonial Rest Home, Decatur, AL

Colonial Rest Home, Owingsville, KY

Colonial Rest Home, Lowell, MA

Colonial Rest Home, Williamsburg, MA

Colonial Rest Home, Bay City, MI

Colonial Rest Home, Saint Charles, MO

Colonial Retirement Center Inc, Bismarck, MO

Colonial Terrace Care Center Inc, Pryor, OK

Colonial Terrace Intermediate Care, Sebree, KY

Colonial Villa Good Samaritan Center, Alma, NE

Colonial Villa Nursing Home, Silver Spring, MD

Colonial Village, Grandfield, OK

Colonial Vista, Wenatchee, WA

The Colonnades, Granite City, IL

Colony House Healthcare Nursing Home, Abington, MA

Colony Oaks Care Center, Appleton, WI

Colorado Lutheran Health Care Center, Arvada, CO

Colorado State Veterans Center, Homelake, CO

Colorado State Veterans Nursing Home, Florence, CO

Colorow Care Center, Olathe, CO

Colton Villa Nursing Center, Hagerstown, MD

Columbia Basin Nursing Home, The Dalles, OR

Columbia City Community Care Center, Columbia City, IN

Columbia City Nursing Home, Columbia City, IN

Columbia Convalescent Center, Granada Hills, CA

Columbia Convalescent Home, Long Beach, CA

Columbia County Home, Wyocena, WI

Columbia Health Care Center, Columbia, TN

Columbia Health Care Facility, Evansville, IN

Columbia Heights Nursing Home, Columbia, LA

Columbia House Healthcare, Columbia, MO

Columbia Lutheran Home, Seattle, WA

Columbia Manor Care Center, Columbia, MO

Columbia Manor Convalescent Center, Portland, OR

Columbia Nursing Home, Andalusia, AL

Columbia Nursing Home, Lima, OH

Columbia State School, Columbia, LA

Columbia View Nursing Home, Cathlamet, WA

Columbine Care Center, Fort Collins, CO

Columbine Manor, Salida, CO

Columbine Manor Inc, Wheatridge, CO

Columbus Care Center, Columbus, WI

Columbus Colony for the Elderly Care Inc, Westerville, OH

Columbus Convalescent Center, Columbus, IN

Columbus Convalescent Center, Columbus, TX

Columbus Developmental Center, Columbus, OH

Columbus Home for the Aged, Columbus, OH

Columbus Intermediate Care Home, Columbus, GA

Columbus Manor, Columbus, NE

Columbus Manor Residential Care Home, Chicago, IL

Columbus Nursing Home, Columbus, IN

Columbus Nursing Home, Boston, MA

Columbus Nursing Homes Inc, Columbus, OH

Colvin Nursing Home, Newton Falls, OH

Colwich Health Center, Colwich, KS

Comanche View Nursing Home, Fort Stockton, TX

Comer Health Care Inc, Comer, GA

Comforcare Center, Austin, MN

Comfort Harbor Home, Milan, IL

Comfort Retirement and Nursing Home Inc, Lafayette, IN

Commander Nursing Home, Florence, SC

Commodore Inn Inc, Chicago, IL

Commonwealth Care Center, Des Moines, IA

Commonwealth Health Care, Martinsville, VA

Commonwealth Healthcare Center, Saint Paul, MN

Community Care Center, Duarte, CA

Community Care Center Inc, Stuart, IA

Community Care Center of Lemay, Lemay, MO

Community Center, De Kalb, IL

Community Comfort Cottage, Rayville, LA

Community Convalescent Center, Riverside, CA

Community Convalescent Center, Gainesville, FL

Community Convalescent Center, Plant City, FL

Community Convalescent Center of Naperville, Naperville, IL

Community Convalescent Center of Sunland Tujunga, Tujunga, CA

Community Convalescent Center of Yucaipa/Calimesa, Yucaipa, CA

Community Convalescent Hospital, Lynwood, CA

Community Convalescent Hospital of Glendora, Glendora, CA

Community Convalescent Hospital of La Mesa, La Mesa, CA

Community Convalescent Hospital of San Gabriel, San Gabriel, CA

Community Foundation for Human Development, Sellersville, PA

Community General Hospital, Fort Fairfield, ME

Community General Hospital of Sullivan County, Harris, NY

Community Health Center, Wakita, OK

Community Hospital, Saint Peter, MN

Community Hospital and Health Center, Sioux Center, IA

Community Hospital—Nursing Home Association, Hillsboro, ND

Community Hospital—Skilled Nursing Facility, Stamford, NY

Community Intermediate Care Facility, Sumter, SC

Community Living, Coon Rapids, MN

Community Living, Victoria, MN

Community Memorial, Cheboygan, MI

Community Memorial Home, Osakis, MN

Community Memorial Hospital, Hartley, IA

Community Memorial Hospital, Postville, IA

Community Memorial Hospital, Winona, MN

Community Memorial Hospital and Homestead, Deer River, MN

Community Memorial Hospital Inc—Nursing Home Unit, Hamilton, NY

Community Memorial Hospital—Long-Term Care Unit, Sheldon, IA

Community Memorial Hospital—Nursing Home, Spooner, WI

Community Memorial Hospital—W S Hundley Annex, South Hill, VA

Community Memorial Nursing Home, Lisbon, ND

Community Mercy Hospital, Onamia, MN

Community Multicare Center, Fairfield, OH

Community Nursing and Rehabilitation Facility, Missoula, MT

Community Nursing Center, Marion, OH

Community Nursing Home, Jackson, MS

Community Nursing Home, El Dorado Springs, MO

Community Nursing Home, Kirksville, MO

Community Nursing Home, Bowling Green, OH

Community Nursing Home, Wilburton, OK

Community Nursing Home, Stephenville, TX

Community Nursing Home Inc, Clarksville, IA

Community Nursing Home of Anaconda, Anaconda, MT

Community Services Inc, Lancaster, PA

Community Services Inc, Leola, PA

Community Services Inc-Main, Landisville, PA

Community Services Inc-Stanley, Landisville, PA

Community Skilled Nursing Centre of Warren, Warren, OH

Compere's Nursing Home Inc, Jackson, MS

Comprehensive Systems Inc, Charles City, IA

Compton Convalescent Hospital, Compton, CA

Compton Home, Kansas City, MO

Compton's Nursing Home, Springfield, OH

Compton's Oak Grove Lodge, Mountain View, AR

Comstock Nursing Home, Milwaukee, WI

Con Lea Nursing Home, Geneva, OH

Concerned Services Inc, Stanberry, MO

Concho Nursing Center, Eden, TX

Concord Extended Care, Oak Lawn, IL

Concord Manor, Garner, IA

Concord Manor Nursing Home, Cleveland, OH

Concord Nursing Center, Concord, NC

Concord Nursing Home Inc, Brooklyn, NY

Concord Villa Convalescent, Concordville, PA

Concordia Care Center, Bella Vista, AR

Concordia Manor, Saint Petersburg, FL

Concordia Parish Rest Home, Ferriday, LA

Concordia Rest Home, Concordia, KS

Concourse Nursing Home, Bronx, NY

Condon Nursing Home, Condon, OR

Conestoga View, Lancaster, PA

Conesus Lake Nursing Home, Livonia, NY

Congregational Home, Brookfield, WI

Congress Care Center, Chicago, IL

Congress Convalescent Hospital, Pasadena, CA

Conner Nursing Home, Glenwood, GA

Conner Williams Nursing Home, Ridley Park, PA

Conser House, Overland Park, KS

Consolata Home, New Iberia, LA

Consolation Nursing Home Inc, West Islip, NY

Constance Bultman Wilson Center, Faribault, MN

Contemporary Care Inc, Bluefield, WV

Continana Convalescent Hospital, National City, CA

Continana Convalescent Hospital, Santa Maria, CA

Continental Care Center Inc, Chicago, IL

Continental Convalescent Center, Indianapolis, IN

Continental Manor, Abbotsford, WI

Continental Manor of Blanchester, Blanchester, OH

Continental Manor of Newman, Newman, IL

Continental Manor of Wisconsin Dells, Wisconsin Dells, WI

Continental Manor—Randolph, Randolph, WI

Continental Manors Inc, Dwight, IL

Conv-A-Center, Neptune, NJ

Convalcare Home, California, MO

Convalescence Pavilion, Jupiter, FL

Convalescent Care, Canton, OH

Convalescent Care Center, Los Angeles, CA

Convalescent Care Center, Saint Petersburg, FL

Convalescent Care of Enfield, Enfield, NC

Convalescent Care of Lee County Inc, Sanford, NC

The Convalescent Center, Dallas, TX

Convalescent Center 2, East Liverpool, OH

Convalescent Center Inc, Conway, AR

Convalescent Center Inc, Tulsa, OK

Convalescent Center Mission Street Inc, San Francisco, CA

Convalescent Center of Honolulu, Honolulu, HI

Convalescent Center of Norwich Inc, Norwich, CT

Convalescent Center of Reseda, Reseda, CA

Convalescent Center of Sanford Inc, Sanford, NC

Convalescent Center of Shuttuck, Shattuck, OK

Convalescent Center of the Palm Beaches, West Palm Beach, FL

Convalescent Home for Children, Des Moines, IA

Convalescent Home of the First Church of Deliverance, Chicago, IL

Convalescent Hospital Casa Descanso, Los Angeles, CA

Convalescent Hospital University Branch, Menlo Park, CA

Conva-Rest of Hattiesburg, Hattiesburg, MS

Conva-Rest of Newton Inc, Newton, MS

Conva-Rest of Petal, Petal, MS

Convention Street Nursing Center, Baton Rouge, LA

Convoy Care Center, Convoy, OH

Conway Human Development Center, Conway, AR

Conway Nursing Center Inc, Conway, SC

Cook Community Hospital, Cook, MN

Cook County Northshore Hospital—Care and Nursing Center, Grand Marais, MN

Cookeville Health Care Center Inc, Cookeville, TN

Cookeville Manor Nursing Home, Cookeville, TN

Cook-Willow Convalescent Hospital Inc, Plymouth, CT

The Coolidge Center, Palmer, NE

Coolidge Street Rest Home, Brookline, MA

Coon Memorial Home, Dalhart, TX

Cooney Convalescent Home, Helena, MT

Cooper Community Care Center, Bluffton, IN

Cooper County Rest Haven Nursing Home, Boonville, MO

Cooper Nursing Home Inc, Tallmadge, OH

Cooper River Convalescent Center, Pennsauken, NJ

Cooper's Rest Haven, Saint George, UT

Coos Bay Care Center, Coos Bay, OR

Coos County Nursing Home, Berlin, NH

Coos County Nursing Hospital, West Stewartstown, NH

Coosa Valley Convalescent Center, Glencoe, AL

Coplin Manor Convalescent Home, Detroit, MI

Copper Queen Community Hospital, Bisbee, AZ

Coquille Care Center, Coquille, OR

Coral Gables Convalescent Home, Miami, FL

Corbin Convalescent Hospital, Reseda, CA

Cordell Christian Home, Cordell, OK

Cordelleras Center, Redwood City, CA

Cordova Community Hospital, Cordova, AK

Cordova Nursing Home Inc, Cordova, AL

Cordova Residential Care, Pueblo, CO

Corey Hill Nursing Home, Boston, MA

Cori-Manor Nursing Home, Fenton, MO

Cornelia Nixon Davis Nursing Home Inc, Wilmington, NC

Cornell Area Care Center, Cornell, WI

Cornell Hall Convalescent Center, Union, NJ

Corner House Nursing Inc, Meriden, CT

Corning Hospital—Founders Pavilion, Corning, NY

Corning Nursing Home, Corning, AR

Cornwall Manor of the United Methodist Church, Cornwall, PA
Corona Gables Retirement Home and Convalescent Hospital, Corona, CA
Coronado Nursing Center, Pampa, TX
Coronado Nursing Center Inc, El Paso, TX
Coronado Sanitarium, Los Angeles, CA
Corpus Christi Nursing Center, Corpus Christi, TX
Corry Manor Nursing Home, Corry, PA
Corsicana Nursing Home Inc, Corsicana, TX
Cortland Acres, Thomas, WV
Cortland Nursing Home, Cortland, NY
Cortland Quality Care Nursing Center, Cortland, OH
Cortlandt Nursing Care Center Inc, Peekskill, NY
Corvallis Care Center, Corvallis, OR
Corvallis Manor, Corvallis, OR
Corvnor Health Care, Canton, OH
Corydon Care Center, Corydon, IA
Corydon Nursing Home, Corydon, IN
Cosada Villa Nursing Home, Mesa, AZ
Cosgrove Convalescent Hospital, Santa Monica, CA
Coshocton County Home, Coshocton, OH
Coshocton County Memorial Hospital, Coshocton, OH
Coshocton Health Care Center, Coshocton, OH
Cosmos Healthcare Center, Cosmos, MN
Costigan Family Care Home, Denver, CO
Cotillion Ridge Nursing Center, Robinson, IL
Cottage Grove Hospital—North Wing Skilled Nursing Facility, Cottage Grove, OR
Cottage Grove Nursing Home, Jackson, MS
Cottage Hill Nursing Home, Pleasant Grove, AL
Cottage Manor Nursing Home, Chelsea, MA
The Cottage Rest Home, New Bedford, MA
Cottage-Belmont Nursing Center, Harper Woods, MI
Cottesmore Nursing Home Inc, Gig Harbor, WA
Cottle County Nursing Home, Paducah, TX
Cotton's Nursing Home, Lawton, OK
Cottonwood Care Center, Wichita Falls, TX
Cottonwood Manor Nursing Home, Yukon, OK
Council Bluffs Care Center, Council Bluffs, IA
Country Care Convalescent Hospital, Atascadero, CA
Country Club Center, Dover, OH
Country Club Center II, Mount Vernon, OH
Country Club Convalescent Hospital Inc, Santa Ana, CA
Country Club Home, Council Grove, KS
Country Club Manor, Amarillo, TX
Country Court, Mount Vernon, OH
Country Estate, Westlake, OH
Country Gardens Nursing Home, Swansea, MA
Country Haven, Paola, KS
Country Haven Nursing Home, Norton, MA
Country Health Inc, Gifford, IL
Country Hills Convalescent Hospital, Sylmar, CA
Country House, Pomona, CA
The Country House, Independence, MO
Country Inn Care Center, Van, TX
Country Lane Health Center Inc, Jonesburg, MO
Country Lawn Nursing Home, Navarre, OH
Country Manor Convalescent Home, Newburyport, MA

Country Manor Convalescent Hospital, San Fernando, CA
Country Manor Nursing Center, Dolton, IL
Country Manor Nursing Home, Commerce City, CO
Country Manor Nursing Home, Coopers Mills, ME
Country Manor Nursing Home, Sartell, MN
Country Manor Nursing Home, Toms River, NJ
Country Manor Nursing Home Inc, Dunkirk, IN
Country Manor of Creve Coeur, Creve Coeur, MO
Country Manor of Todd County, Elkton, KY
Country Meadows, Ogden, UT
Country Meadows Rest Haven, Providence, KY
Country Rest Home, Greenwood, DE
Country Rest Home, Dartmouth, MA
Country Side Estates, Cherokee, IA
Country Side Manor, Stokesdale, NC
Country Valley Home, Saint James, MO
Country View Care Center, Longmont, CO
Country View Care Center, Weld County, CO
Country View Convalescent Hospital, Fresno, CA
Country View Estates, Seneca, KS
Country View Manor, Irvington, IL
Country View Manor Inc, Sibley, IA
Country View Nursing Home, Billerica, MA
Country Villa South Convalescent Center, Los Angeles, CA
Country Villa Westwood Convalescent Center, Los Angeles, CA
Country Villa Wilshire, Los Angeles, CA
Country Village Health Care Center, Lancaster, NH
Country Way Retirement and Rehabilitation Center, Keene, NH
Countryaire Health Care Center, Florence, WI
Countryside Continuing Care Center, Fremont, OH
Countryside Convalescent Home, Mercer, PA
Countryside Estates, Iola, KS
Countryside Estates Inc, Warner, OK
Countryside Health Center, Topeka, KS
Countryside Healthcare Center, Aurora, IL
Countryside Home, Madison, NE
Countryside Home, Jefferson, WI
Countryside Intermediate Care Facility, Woodland, CA
Countryside Manor Inc, Bristol, CT
Countryside Nursing and Convalescent Center, Wayne, NJ
Countryside Nursing Home, South Haven, MI
Countryside Nursing Home Inc, Framingham, MA
Countryside Place, Knox, IN
Countryside Place, LaPorte, IN
Countryside Place of Mishawaka, Mishawaka, IN
Countryside Retirement Home, Sioux City, IA
Countryside Villa, Hutchinson, KS
County Manor Nursing Home, Tenafly, NJ
County of Chester—Pocopson Home, West Chester, PA
Courage Residence, Golden Valley, MN
Court House Manor, Washington Court House, OH
Court Manor Convalescent Home, Ashland, WI
Courtland Gardens, Stamford, CT

Courtland Manor Nursing and Convalescent Home, Dover, DE
Courtney's Rest Home, Indianapolis, IN
Courtyard Convalescent Center, Houston, TX
The Courville at Nashua, Nashua, NH
Cove Manor Convalescent Center Inc, New Haven, CT
Covenant Care Center, Plantation, FL
Covenant Home, Chicago, IL
Covenant Home, New Orleans, LA
Covenant House—Jewish Home for Aged, Dayton, OH
Covenant Village, Gastonia, NC
Coventry Hall Nursing Home, Spencer, MA
Coventry Health Center, Coventry, RI
Coventry Manor Nursing Home Inc, Pottstown, PA
Covina Convalescent Center, Covina, CA
Covington Community Care Center, Covington, OH
Covington Ladies Home Inc, Covington, KY
Covington Manor Inc, Opp, AL
Covington Manor Inc, Covington, IN
Covington Manor Intermediate Care Home, Covington, GA
Covington Manor Nursing Center, Fort Wayne, IN
Covington Manor Nursing Home, Covington, TN
Covington's Convalescent Center, Hopkinsville, KY
Coweta Manor, Coweta, OK
Cowlitz Convalescent Center, Longview, WA
Cox Convalescent Center, Jacksboro, TX
Cox Nursing Home, Gallatin, MO
Cozy Corner Nursing Home Inc, Sunderland, MA
Cozy Inn Nursing Home, Rumford, ME
Cozy Rest, Upper Sandusky, OH
Craft Care Center, Panora, IA
Craighead County Nursing Home, Jonesboro, AR
Craigmont Care Center, Des Moines, IA
Cra-Mar Nursing Home Inc, Cranston, RI
Cranbrook Nursing Home, Detroit, MI
Crandall Medical Center, Sebring, OH
Crandon Health Care Center, Crandon, WI
Crane Retirement Home Inc, Cordele, GA
Cranford Hall, Cranford, NJ
Cranford Health and Extended Care Center, Cranford, NJ
Crawford Convalescent Center, Dayton, OH
Crawford County Convalescent Center Inc, Robinson, IL
Crawford County Home, Saegertown, PA
Crawford House Convalescent Home, Fall River, MA
Crawford Nursing Home Inc, Jackson, MS
Crawford Retreat Inc, Baltimore, MD
Crawford's Boarding Home, Ironton, MO
Crawford's Convalescent Home, Haleiwa, HI
Creal Springs Nursing Home, Creal Springs, IL
Creekside Care Center, Salt Lake City, UT
Creekside Terrace Intermediate Care Facility Inc, Hayward, CA
Creighton Care Centre, Creighton, NE
Crenshaw Nursing Home, Los Angeles, CA
Crescent Bay Convalescent Hospital, Santa Monica, CA
Crescent Care Center, Crescent, OK
Crescent City Convalescent Hospital, Crescent City, CA
Crescent Convalescent Center, Yakima, WA

Crescent Farm Convalescing and Nursing Home, Dover, DE

Crescent Hill Nursing Center, Springfield, MA

Crescent Manor Nursing Home, Greenfield, IN

Crescent Manor Nursing Home, Bennington, VT

Crescent Manor Rest Home, Grafton, MA

Cresco Care Center Inc, Cresco, IA

Cresson Center, Cresson, PA

Crest Group Home, Des Moines, IA

Crest Group Home, Ottumwa, IA

Crest Hall Health Related Facility, Middle Island, NY

Crest Haven, Cape May Court House, NJ

Crest Haven Rest Home, Plainfield, CT

Crest Home of Albert Lea, Albert Lea, MN

Crest Knoll Convalescent Hospital, Long Beach, CA

Crest Manor Nursing Center, Lake Worth, FL

Crest Manor Nursing Home, Fairport, NY

Crest Nursing Home Inc, Butte, MT

Crest View Lutheran Home, Columbia Heights, MN

Crest View Manor, Chadron, NE

Crest View Manor Inc, Houlton, ME

Crest View Nursing Home, Clinton, IL

Crest View Nursing Home, Cincinnati, OH

Cresta Loma Convalescent and Guest Home, Lemon Grove, CA

Crestfield Convalescent Home, Manchester, CT

Cresthaven Children's Center, Austin, TX

Cresthaven Childrens Center, San Antonio, TX

Cresthaven Inc, Santa Cruz, CA

Cresthaven Nursing Center, Austin, TX

Cresthaven Nursing Home, Kansas City, MO

Cresthaven Nursing Residence, Groves, TX

Crestline Nursing Home, Crestline, OH

Crestmont Medical Care Facility, Fenton, MI

Crestmont Nursing Center, Delaware, OH

Crestmont Nursing Home Inc, Cleveland, OH

Crestmont Nursing Home Inc—East, Elyria, OH

Crestmont Nursing Home Inc—West, Elyria, OH

Crestmont Nursing Home North Inc, Lakewood, OH

Creston Manor Nursing Home, Creston, IA

Crestpark of Helena, Helena, AR

Crestpark of Helena—Intermediate, Helena, AR

Crestpark of Marianna, Marianna, AR

Crestpark of Stuttgart Inc, Stuttgart, AR

Crestpark of Wynne—Intermediate, Wynne, AR

Crestpark of Wynne—Skilled, Wynne, AR

Crestpark Retirement Inn, Forrest City, AR

Crestridge Inc, Maquoketa, IA

Crestview Acres Inc, Marion, IA

Crestview Care Center, West Branch, IA

Crestview Care Center, Milford, NE

Crestview Care Center, Astoria, OR

Crestview Care Home, Somerset, KY

Crestview Convalescent, Portland, OR

Crestview Convalescent and Nursing Home, Moses Lake, WA

Crestview Convalescent Home, Vincennes, IN

Crestview Convalescent Home, Wyncote, PA

Crestview Convalescent Hospital, Petaluma, CA

Crestview Convalescent Hospital, Rialto, CA

Crestview Convalescent Lodge, Phoenix, AZ

Crestview Health Care Facility Inc, Indianapolis, IN

Crestview Home, Thief River Falls, MN

Crestview Home Inc, Bethany, MO

Crestview Lodge, Arma, KS

Crestview Manor, Haleyville, AL

Crestview Manor, Webster City, IA

Crestview Manor, Seneca, KS

Crestview Manor, Evansville, MN

Crestview Manor Nursing Center, Belton, TX

Crestview Manor Nursing Home, Lynn, MA

Crestview Manor Nursing Home I, Lancaster, OH

Crestview Manor Nursing Home II, Lancaster, OH

Crestview Manor Retirement and Convalescent Center, Waco, TX

Crestview North Nursing and Rehabilitation Center, Langhorne, PA

Crestview Nursing and Convalescent Manor, Crestview, FL

Crestview Nursing Home, Atlanta, GA

Crestview Nursing Home, Ottawa, KS

Crestview Nursing Home, Shelbyville, KY

Crestview Nursing Home, Quincy, MA

Crestview Nursing Home, Medina, OH

Crestview Nursing Home, Brownsville, TN

Crestview Nursing Home II, Dayton, OH

Crestview Nursing Home Inc, Nashville, TN

Crestview Personal Care Home, Richmond, KY

Crestview Retirement Community, Bryan, TX

Crestview Retirement Hotel, Dallas, TX

Crestwood Care Center, Fairfield, OH

Crestwood Care Center, Shelby, OH

Crestwood Care Center, Ogden, UT

Crestwood Care Center—Mansfield, Mansfield, OH

Crestwood Convalescent Center, Port Angeles, WA

Crestwood Convalescent Home, Fall River, MA

Crestwood Convalescent Hospital, Chico, CA

Crestwood Convalescent Hospital, Redding, CA

Crestwood Convalescent Hospital, Stockton, CA

Crestwood Heights Nursing Center, Midlothian, IL

Crestwood Manor, Bakersfield, CA

Crestwood Manor, Eureka, CA

Crestwood Manor, Modesto, CA

Crestwood Manor, Sacramento, CA

Crestwood Manor, San Jose, CA

Crestwood Manor, Stockton, CA

Crestwood Manor, Vallejo, CA

Crestwood Manor—Carmichael, Carmichael, CA

Crestwood Nursing and Convalescent Home Inc, Warren, RI

Crestwood Nursing Home, Valdosta, GA

Crestwood Nursing Home, Manchester, TN

Crestwood Nursing Home Inc, Whippany, NJ

Crestwood Rehabilitation and Convalescent Hospital, Fremont, CA

Crestwood Terrace, Midlothian, IL

Creswell Care Center, Creswell, OR

Creswell Care Center, Creswell, WA

Creswell Convalescent Center, Rome, GA

Crete Manor, Crete, NE

Cridersville Nursing Home, Cridersville, OH

Crisp County Medical Nursing Center, Cordele, GA

Crista Senior Community, Seattle, WA

Crites Nursing Home 2, Lancaster, OH

Crocker Family Care Home, Commerce City, CO

Crockett County Care Center, Ozona, TX

Crockett County Nursing Home Inc, Alamo, TN

Crofton Convalescent Center, Crofton, MD

Croixdale Residence, Bayport, MN

Cromwell Crest Convalescent Home Inc, Cromwell, CT

Crook County Nursing Home, Prineville, OR

Crookston Group Home, Crookston, MN

Crookston Group Home 2, Crookston, MN

Crosby Good Samaritan Center, Crosby, ND

Crosbyton Care Center, Crosbyton, TX

Cross Country Care Center—Brownwood, Brownwood, TX

Cross Roads Intermediate Care Facility, Cleveland, GA

Crossgate Manor Inc, Brandon, MS

Crosslands Inc, Kennett Square, PA

Crossroads Development Center, Haltom City, TX

Crossville Nursing Home Inc, Crossville, AL

Crotinger Nursing Home, Union City, OH

Crowell Memorial Home, Blair, NE

Crowell Nursing Center, Crowell, TX

Crowley County Nursing Center, Ordway, CO

Crowley Town and Country Nursing Center Inc, Crowley, LA

Crown Manor Nursing Home, Zion, IL

Crown Nursing Home, Saint Petersburg Beach, FL

Crown Nursing Home, Brooklyn, NY

Crown Nursing Home, Philadelphia, PA

Crownsville Hospital Center-Phillips Building, Crownsville, MD

Crow's Haven Nursing Home, Fort Wayne, IN

Crystal Care Center, Crystal, MN

Crystal Hill Nursing Home Inc, Dallas, TX

Crystal Lake Health Care Center, Robbinsdale, MN

Crystal Lane Nursing Center, Liberty, MO

Crystal Manor, Crystal Falls, MI

Crystal Pines, Crystal Lake, IL

Crystal River Geriatric Center, Crystal River, FL

Cuba Memorial Hospital Inc—Skilled Nursing Facility, Cuba, NY

Cullen Avenue Rest Home, Austin, TX

Cullman Health Care Center North, Cullman, AL

Culver West Convalescent Hospital, Los Angeles, CA

Cumberland County Home, Carlisle, PA

Cumberland Manor, Bridgeton, NJ

Cumberland Manor Rest Home, Parker's Lake, KY

Cumberland Memorial Hospital—Extended Care Unit, Cumberland, WI

Cumberland Nursing Center, Greenup, IL

Cumberland Rest Inc, Fort Worth, TX

Cumberland Valley Manor, Burkesville, KY

Cumberland Villa Nursing Center, Cumberland, MD

Cumming Convalescent Home, Cumming, GA

Cupola Nursing Home, Brockport, NY

Cuppett and Weeks Nursing Home Inc, Oakland, MD

Currey Nursing Home Inc, Mount Pleasant, TX

Curry Good Samaritan Center, Brookings, OR
Curry Memorial Home, Waynesburg, PA
The Curtis Home Infimary, Meriden, CT
Curtis Manor Retirement Home, Dalton, MA
Cushing Care Center Inc, Cushing, TX
Cushing Manor Rest Home, Boston, MA
Custer County Rest Home, Miles City, MT
Custodial Care Home, Tyler, TX
Cuyahoga County Hospital—Sunny Acres
    Skilled Nursing Facility, Warrensville, OH
Cuyahoga County Nursing Home, Cleveland,
    OH
Cuyahoga Falls Country Place, Cuyahoga Falls,
    OH
Cuy-La Home, Euclid, OH
Cypress Acres, Paradise, CA
Cypress Acres Convalescent Hospital,
    Paradise, CA
Cypress Convalescent Center, Burbank, CA
Cypress Convalescent Hospital, Pleasant
    Hill, CA
Cypress Gardens Convalescent Hospital,
    Riverside, CA
Cypress Manor, Hancock, MI
Cypress Nursing Facility Inc, Sumter, SC
Cyril Nursing Home, Cyril, OK
Czech Catholic Home for the Aged, El Campo,
    TX
Dacotah-Alpha, Mandan, ND
Dade City Geriatric Center, Dade City, FL
Dade County Nursing Home, Greenfield, MO
Dadeville Convalescent Home, Dadeville, AL
D'Adrian Convalescent Center, Godfrey, IL
Daggett-Crandall-Newcomb Home, Norton,
    MA
Dahl Memorial Nursing Home, Ekalaka, MT
Dailey's Convalescent Home Inc,
    Indianapolis, IN
Dakotas Childrens Home, West Saint Paul,
    MN
Daleview Nursing Home, Farmingdale, NY
Dallas County Nursing Home Inc,
    Fordyce, AR
Dallas Home for Jewish Aged, Dallas, TX
Dallas Lamb Foundation Home, Payne, OH
Dallas Nursing Home, Dallas, OR
Dallas Nursing Home Inc, Dallas, WI
Dalton Health Center, Ironton, OH
Dalton Nursing Home Inc, Dalton, MA
Dalton Rest Home, Worcester, MA
Dalworth Care Center, Arlington, TX
Daly Park Geriatric Center, Cincinnati, OH
Dammert Geriatric Center, Belleville, IL
D'Amore Rest Haven Inc, Warehouse
    Point, CT
Dana Home of Lexington, Lexington, MA
Danbury Pavilion Healthcare, Danbury, CT
Dane County Home—East Building, Verona,
    WI
Dane County Home—West Building, Verona,
    WI
Danforth Nursing Home, Danforth, ME
Dania Nursing Home, Dania, FL
Daniel Nursing Home, Fulton, MS
Daniels Memorial Nursing Home, Scobey, MT
Daniel's Nursing Home Inc, Reading, MA
Danish Convalescent Home, Atascadero, CA
Danridge Nursing Home, Youngstown, OH
Dan's Boarding Care Home, Saint Cloud, MN
Danvers Twin Oaks Nursing Home, Danvers,
    MA
Danville Care Center, Danville, IA
Danville Care Inc, Danville, IL

Danville Hospital—Long Term Care Unit,
    Danville, PA
Danville Manor, Danville, IL
Danville Nursing Home, Danville, IN
Dar Way Nursing Home Inc, Forksville, PA
Darcy Hall Nursing Home, West Palm
    Beach, FL
Dardanelle Nursing Center Inc,
    Dardanelle, AR
Darien Convalescent Center, Darien, CT
Darlington Convalescent Center, Darlington,
    SC
Darlington House—The Toledo Jewish Home
    for the Aged, Toledo, OH
Darrs Home for the Aged, Chillicothe, MO
Dartmouth House Nursing Home, Dartmouth,
    MA
Dartmouth Manor Rest Home, Dartmouth,
    MA
Dassel Lakeside Community Home, Dassel,
    MN
Daughters of Israel Pleasant Valley Home, West
    Orange, NJ
Daughters of Jacob Nursing Home Company
    Inc, Bronx, NY
Daughters of Sarah Nursing Home Company
    Inc, Albany, NY
Dauphin Manor, Harrisburg, PA
Davco Rest Home, Owensboro, KY
Davenport Good Samaritan, Davenport, IA
Davenport Lutheran Home, Davenport, IA
Davenport Memorial Home, Malden, MA
Davenport Nursing Home, Davenport, IA
David E Stewart Home—Babcock Center,
    Columbia, SC
David Gottesfield House, Denver, CO
David Herman Health Center, Minneapolis,
    MN
David M Dorsett Home, Spearfish, SD
David Nursing Home, Detroit, MI
Davidson Nursing Center, Thomasville, NC
Daviess County Nursing Home Inc, Gallatin,
    MO
Davis Bluffton Nursing Home, Bluffton, IN
Davis Gardens Health Center, Terre Haute, IN
Davis Health Care Centre, Spokane, WA
Davis Home for the Aged, Oak Hill, OH
Davis Manor Nursing Home, Alvordton, OH
Davis Nursing Home, Springfield, MO
Davis Nursing Home, Tahlequah, OK
Davis Nursing Home Inc, Denver, CO
Davis Nursing Home Inc, Mountaintop, PA
Davis Skilled Nursing Facility, Pine Bluff, AR
Davison Rest Home Inc, Laurel, MS
Dawn View Manor, Fort Ashby, WV
Dawson Manor, Dawson, GA
Dawson Place Inc, Hill City, KS
Dawson Springs Health Care Center, Dawson
    Springs, KY
Daybreak Lodge, Wilmington, DE
Daystar Home, Needham, MA
Daystar Inc, Fort Lauderdale, FL
Dayton Boarding Care Home, Saint Paul, MN
Dayton House of People Inc, Saint Paul, MN
Dayton Residential Care Facility, Kenosha, WI
Daytona Beach Geriatric Center, Daytona
    Beach, FL
Daytona Beach Olds Hall Good Samaritan
    Nursing Center, Daytona Beach, FL
Daytona Manor Nursing Home, South
    Daytona, FL
DC Village, Washington, DC
DCI Dakota Adults, Mendota Heights, MN

De Kalb County Nursing Home, De Kalb, IL
De Leon Nursing Home, De Leon, TX
De Paul Belleview Extended Care, Milwaukee,
    WI
De Paul Health Center, Bridgeton, MO
Deacon Home Ltd, Rockford, IL
Deaconess Manor, Saint Louis, MO
Deaconess Skilled Nursing Center, Great Falls,
    MT
Deal Nursing Home Inc, Jackson, MO
Deanview Nursing Home Inc, Washington
    Court House, OH
Dearborn Heights Convalescent Center,
    Dearborn Heights, MI
Deauville Healthcare Center, Chicago, IL
DeBary Manor, DeBary, FL
Deboer Nursing Home, Muskegon, MI
Deborah House, Chicago, IL
Decatur Community Care Center, Decatur, IN
Decatur Convalescent Center, Decatur, TX
Decatur County Good Samaritan Center,
    Oberlin, KS
Decatur County Manor Nursing Center,
    Parsons, TN
Decatur Manor, Decatur, IL
Dee-Maret Nursing Home, Akron, OH
Deep River Convalescent Home Inc, Deep
    River, CT
Deer Park Nursing Home, Cincinnati, OH
Deerbrook Nursing Centre, Joliet, IL
Deerfield Episcopal Retirement Community
    Inc, Asheville, NC
Deering Nursing Home Inc, Hingham, MA
Deerings Nursing Home, Odessa, TX
Deerings West Nursing Home, Odessa, TX
Deer's Head Center, Salisbury, MD
Defiance Health Care Center, Defiance, OH
Degraff Memorial Hospital—Skilled Nursing
    Facility, North Tonowanda, NY
Deiber Nursing Home Inc, Chillicothe, OH
DeKalb General Nursing Unit, Decatur, GA
Del Amo Gardens Sanitarium and
    Convalescent Hospital, Torrance, CA
Del Capri Terrace Convalescent Hospital, San
    Diego, CA
Del Manor Nursing Home Inc, Rockland, MA
Del Mar Convalescent Hospital,
    Rosemead, CA
Del Mar Nursing Home, Indianapolis, IN
Del Rio Convalescent Center, Bell
    Gardens, CA
Del Rio Nursing Home Inc, Del Rio, TX
Del Rio Sanitarium, Bell Gardens, CA
Del Rosa Convalescent Hospital, San
    Bernardino, CA
Delamarter Care Center, Pendleton, OR
Deland Convalescent Center, Deland, FL
Delano Healthcare Center, Delano, MN
Delaware County Health Center, Muncie, IN
Delaware County Home and Infirmary, Delhi,
    NY
Delaware County Memorial Hospital,
    Manchester, IA
Delaware Health Care Facility Inc,
    Indianapolis, IN
Delaware Park Care Center, Delaware, OH
Delhaven Manor, Saint Louis, MO
Delhi Guest Home, Delhi, LA
Dellaren Nursing Care Center, Evansville, IN
Dellridge Nursing Home, Paramus, NJ
Dells Place, Delano, MN
Delmar, Aurora, CO
Delmar Gardens East Inc, University City, MO

Delmar Gardens of Chesterfield, Chesterfield, MO

Delmar Gardens of Lenexia, Lenexa, KS

Delmar Gardens West, Chesterfield, MO

Delphi, Shakopee, MN

Delphi Nursing Home, Delphi, IN

Delphos Memorial Home, Delphos, OH

Delphos Rest Home Inc, Delphos, KS

Del's Care Center Inc, Portland, OR

Delta Care Center, Delta, CO

Delta Convalescent, Lodi, CA

Delta Convalescent Hospital, Visalia, CA

Delta Haven Nursing Home, Tallulah, LA

Delta Manor Nursing Center, Clarksdale, MS

Delta Nursing Home, Cooper, TX

Delta Nursing Home Inc, England, AR

Delta Rehabilitation Center, Snohomish, WA

Deluxe Care Inn, South Pasadena, FL

Delwood Nursing Center Inc, Austin, TX

Demar Childrens Home, Coon Rapids, MN

Demes Rehabilitation Center, Green Bay, WI

Dempsey Nursing Home Inc, Chattanooga, TN

Denison Care Center, Denison, IA

Denison Manor Inc, Denison, TX

Den-Mar Nursing Home, Rockport, MA

Dennett Road Manor Inc, Oakland, MD

Denny House Nursing Home, Norwood, MA

Denton Development Center, Denton, TX

Denton Good Samaritan Village, Denton, TX

Denton Nursing Center, Denton, TX

Denver Nursing Home, Stevens, PA

Denver Sunset Home, Denver, IA

Deport Nursing Home, Deport, TX

DeQueen Nursing Home, DeQueen, AR

Derby Nursing Center, Derby, CT

Derrer Road ICF/MR, Columbus, OH

Des Arc Convalescent Center, Des Arc, AR

Desert Developmental Center, Las Vegas, NV

Desert Haven Nursing Center, Phoenix, AZ

Desert Knolls Convalescent Hospital, Victorville, CA

Desert Life Health Care, Tucson, AZ

Desert Manor Convalescent, Yuma, AZ

Desert Palms Convalescent Hospital, Indio, CA

Desert Terrace, Phoenix, AZ

Desha's Rest Home, San Antonio, TX

Desilets Nursing Home Inc, Warren, RI

Desloge Health Care Center, Flat River, MO

Desoto Manor Nursing Home, Arcadia, FL

DeSoto Nursing Home, DeSoto, TX

DeSoto Rest Home Inc, DeSoto, KS

Desserich House, Lakewood, CO

Detroiter Residence, Detroit, MI

Detwiler Manor—Fulton County Home, Wauseon, OH

Deuel County Samaritan Center, Clear Lake, SD

Deutsches Altenheim, Boston, MA

Deveaux Manor Nursing Home, Niagara Falls, NY

Developmental Disabilities Council, Montrose, CO

Dever Nursing Home, Houston, TX

Devereux Nursing Home Inc, Marblehead, MA

Devils Lake Good Samaritan Center, Devils Lake, ND

Devine Haven Convalescent Home, Elkton, MD

Devine Nursing Home Inc, Devine, TX

Devon Gables Health Care Center, Tucson, AZ

Devon Manor Retirement Center, Devon, PA

Devonshire Acres, Sterling, CO

Devonshire Manor, Portland, ME

Devonshire Manor, Dallas, TX

Devonshire Oaks, Redwood City, CA

DeWitt City Nursing Home, DeWitt, AR

Dewitt County Nursing Home, Clinton, IL

Dewitt Nursing Home, New York, NY

Dexter Convalescent Home, Dexter, MO

Dexter House Nursing Facility, Malden, MA

Dexter Nursing Home, Dexter, ME

Diablo Convalescent Hospital, Danville, CA

Diamond Care Center, Bridgewater, SD

Diamond Hill Nursing Center Inc, Cumberland, RI

Diamondhead Extended Care Center 1, North Lima, OH

Diamondhead Nursing Home 2, North Lima, OH

Diana Lynn Lodge, Sunland, CA

Dickey Nursing Home Inc, Elwood, IN

Dickinson County Care Facility, Spirit Lake, IA

Dickinson Nursing Center, Dickinson, ND

Dickinson Nursing Home, DeQueen, AR

Dickinson Saint Luke's Home, Dickinson, ND

Dickson County Nursing Home, Dickson, TN

Dighton Nursing and Convalescent Home, Dighton, MA

Dillsboro Manor, Dillsboro, IN

Dinan Memorial Center, Bridgeport, CT

Dinuba Convalescent Hospital, Dinuba, CA

Diplomat Healthcare Center, Evergreen Park, IL

Directions Unlimited, Winfield, KS

Dirksen House Healthcare, Springfield, IL

Dishman Personal Care Home, Monticello, KY

District Home, Waynesboro, VA

District Nursing Home, Warrenton, VA

Divine Providence—Extended Care Facility, Williamsport, PA

Divine Providence Home, Sleepy Eye, MN

Divine Savior Hospital Nursing Home, Portage, WI

Divine Saviour Nursing Home, York, SC

Divne Providence Hospital, Ivanhoe, MN

Dixfield Health Care Center Inc, Dixfield, ME

Dixie Manor Sheltered Care, Harvey, IL

Dixie White House Nursing Home Inc, Pass Christian, MS

Dixmont State Hospital—Long Term Care Unit, Glenfield, PA

Dixon Health Center, Dixon, IL

Dixon Home Care Center, Martinsville, IN

Doanes Nursing Home, Campbell Hall, NY

Dobbins Nursing Home Inc, New Richmond, OH

Dobson Plaza Inc, Evanston, IL

Doctor C Benjamin Fuller Home, Waltham, MA

Dr Gertrude A Barber Center Inc, Erie, PA

Doctor Kate Newcomb Convalescent Center, Woodruff, WI

Doctor Philip Sher Jewish Home, Omaha, NE

Doctor Robert Shaughnessy—Skilled Nursing Facility, Salem, MA

The Doctors' Convalescent Center Inc, Selinsgrove, PA

Doctors Convalescent Hospital, Whittier, CA

Doctor's Nursing Center Foundation Inc, Dallas, TX

Doctors Nursing Home, Salem, IL

Dodge County Community Health Center, Juneau, WI

Dodge Park Rest Home, Worcester, MA

Dodge Residence, Dodge Center, MN

Dogwood Acres Intermediate Care Facility, Durham, CT

Dolly Madison Rest Home, Holliston, MA

Dolly Mount Nursing Home, Clifton, NJ

Dolton Terrace, Dolton, IL

Don Orione Nursing Home, Boston, MA

Donahoe Manor, Bedford, PA

Donalson Care Center, Fayetteville, TN

Donely House ICFMR, Quincy, PA

Doniphan Retirement Home Inc, Doniphan, MO

Donna Kay Rest Home Inc, Worcester, MA

Donnellson Manor Care Center, Donnellson, IA

Doolittle Universalist Home, Foxboro, MA

Door County Memorial Hospital—Extended Care Facility, Sturgeon Bay, WI

Doral Country Manor, Carlinville, IL

Dorchester Nursing Center, Sturgeon Bay, WI

Dorothe Lane Home, Sauk Centre, MN

Dorothy Love Retirement Community, Sidney, OH

Dorvin Convalescent and Nursing Center, Livonia, MI

Douglas County Nursing Home, Roseburg, OR

Douglas Manor Nursing Complex, Tuscola, IL

Douglas Memorial Nursing Home, Jefferson, TX

Douglas Nursing Center, Mattoon, IL

Douglas Nursing Home Inc, Milan, TN

Douglass Nursing Center, Douglass, KS

Dove Nursing Facility, Uhrichsville, OH

Dover House Healthcare, Dover, NH

Dover Manor Nursing Home, Georgetown, KY

Dover Nursing Center, Dover, OH

Dover Nursing Home, Brooklyn, NY

Dover Nursing Home, Westlake, OH

Dowagiac Nursing Home, Dowagiac, MI

Dowden Nursing Home, Newtown Square, PA

Dowling Convalescent Hospital, Oakland, CA

Downey Community Health Center, Downey, CA

Downs Nursing Center, Downs, KS

Downtown Jewish Home for the Aged, Philadelphia, PA

Downtown Nursing Home Inc, Buffalo, NY

Dow-Rummel Village, Sioux Falls, SD

Dows Care Center, Dows, IA

Doxie-Hatch Medical Center, Salt Lake City, UT

Doylestown Manor, Doylestown, PA

Drake Memorial Hospital, Cincinnati, OH

Drake Nursing Home, Zanesville, OH

Drake Residential Care Facility, Carthage, MO

Dreiers Sanitarium, Glendale, CA

Dresser Memorial Presbyterian Home, Bradford, PA

Drexel Home Inc, Chicago, IL

Dreyerhaus, Batesville, IN

Driftwood Convalescent Center, Torrance, CA

Driftwood Convalescent Hospital, Davis, CA

Driftwood Convalescent Hospital, Fremont, CA

Driftwood Convalescent Hospital, Gilroy, CA

Driftwood Convalescent Hospital, Modesto, CA

Driftwood Convalescent Hospital, Monterey, CA

Driftwood Convalescent Hospital, Salinas, CA

Driftwood Convalescent Hospital, San Jose, CA

Driftwood Convalescent Hospital, Santa Cruz, CA

Driftwood Convalescent Hospital, Santa Rosa, CA

Driftwood Convalescent Hospital, Ukiah, CA

Driftwood Convalescent Hospital, Yuba City, CA

Driftwood Health Care Center, Charleston, SC

Driftwood Health Care Center—Long Term Care Facility, Charleston, SC

Driftwood Manor, Hayward, CA

Driftwood Nursing Center, Gulfport, MS

Drueding Infirmary, Philadelphia, PA

Druid Hills Nursing Home, Clearwater, FL

Drumright Nursing Home, Drumright, OK

Dry Harbor Nursing Home, Middle Village, NY

Dry Ridge Personal Care Home, Dry Ridge, KY

Du Page Convalescent Center, Wheaton, IL

Dublin Nursing Center, Dublin, TX

Dublinaire Nursing Home, Dublin, GA

Dubois Nursing Home, Dubois, PA

Dubuque Health Care Center, Dubuque, IA

Duff Memorial Nursing Home, Nebraska City, NE

Dugan Memorial Home, West Point, MS

Duke Convalescent Residence, Lancaster, PA

Dukeland Nursing Home and Convalescent Center, Baltimore, MD

Dulaney Towson Nursing and Convalescent Center, Towson, MD

Duluth Regional Care Center I, Duluth, MN

Duluth Regional Care Center II, Duluth, MN

Duluth Regional Care Center III, Duluth, MN

Duluth Regional Care Center IV, Duluth, MN

Dumas Memorial Home, Dumas, TX

Dumas Nursing Center, Dumas, AR

Dumont Manor Nursing Home, Morrisville, VT

Dumont Nursing and Convalescent Center, Morrisville, VT

Dumont Nursing Home, Dumont, IA

Dunaway Manor Nursing Home of Guymon Inc, Guymon, OK

Dunbar Health Care Center, Dunbar, WV

Dunbar Nursing Home, Cleveland, OH

Duncan Care Center, Duncan, OK

Dundee Nursing Home, Bennettsville, SC

Dunedin Care Center, Dunedin, FL

Dungarvin, Saint Paul, MN

Dungarvin II, Roseville, MN

Dungarvin III, Saint Paul, MN

Dungarvin V, Crystal, MN

Dungarvin VI, Chanhassen, MN

Dungarvin VI, Shoreview, MN

Dunlap Care Center, Dunlap, IA

Dunlap Sanitarium, Los Angeles, CA

Dunn County Health Care Center, Menomonie, WI

Dunn Rest Home, Selma, AL

Dunroven Nursing Home, Cresskill, NJ

Dunseith Community Nursing Home, Dunseith, ND

Dunsworth Estates, Harrisonville, MO

Dunwoody Home Medical Center, Newtown Square, PA

Duplex Nursing Home Inc, Boston, MA

Dupoint House, Janesville, WI

Durand Convalescent Center, Durand, MI

Durham Care Center, Durham, NC

Durham Memorial Home, Memphis, TN

Durham-Hensley Nursing Homes Inc, Chuckey, TN

Dutchess County Health Care Facility, Millbrook, NY

Duvall Home for Retarded Children, Glenwood, FL

Duxbury House Nursing Home, Duxbury, MA

D'Ville House, Donaldsonville, LA

D'Youville Manor, Lowell, MA

d'Youville Pavilion Nursing Home, Lewiston, ME

E and M Rainbow Home Inc, McPherson, KS

E Dene Moore Memorial Home, Rifle, CO

Eagle Creek Nursing Center, West Union, OH

Eagle Lake Nursing Home, Eagle Lake, ME

Eagle Nursing Home, Bloomington, MN

Eagle River Healthcare Center Inc, Eagle River, WI

Eagle Valley Children's Home, Carson City, NV

Eagle Valley Healthcare Center, Indianapolis, IN

Eagleton Nursing Home, Bloomer, WI

Earl Park Nursing Home, Earl Park, IN

Earle Street Personal Care Home, Jackson, MS

Earlham Manor Care Center, Earlham, IA

Earlwood Convalescent Hospital, Torrance, CA

Early Memorial Nursing Home, Blakley, GA

Eartha M M White Nursing Home, Jacksonville, FL

Eason Nursing Home, Lake Worth, FL

East Broad Manor, Columbus, OH

East Carroll Nursing Home, Kensington, OH

East Chicago Rehabilitation Convalescent Center Inc, East Chicago, IN

East End Convalescent Home Inc, Waterbury, CT

East Galbraith Health Care Center Inc, Deer Park, OH

East Galbraith Nursing Home, Deer Park, OH

East Grand Forks Group Home, East Grand Forks, MN

East Grand Nursing Home, Detroit, MI

East Haven, Bronx, NY

East Haven Rest Home, East Haven, CT

East Lake Health Care, Birmingham, AL

East Liverpool Convalescent Center, East Liverpool, OH

East Liverpool Extended Center, East Liverpool, OH

East Longmeadow Nursing Home, East Longmeadow, MA

East Los Angeles Convalescent Hospital, Los Angeles, CA

East Manor Medical Care Center, Sarasota, FL

East Manor Nusing Center, El Dorado, AR

East Mesa Care Center, Mesa, AZ

East Mississippi State Nursing Home, Meridian, MS

East Moline Care Center, East Moline, IL

East Moline Garden Plaza, East Moline, IL

East Orange Nursing Home, East Orange, NJ

East Point Intermediate Care Home, East Point, GA

East Ridge Retirement Village Health Center, Miami, FL

East Rockaway Nursing Home, Lynbrook, NY

East Side Manor, East Providence, RI

East Side Nursing Home, Warsaw, NY

East Tennessee Health Care Facility, Madisonville, TN

East Texas Convalescent Home, San Augustine, TX

East Towne Manor, Independence, IA

East Villa Nursing Home, Nashville, TN

East Village Nursing Home, Lexington, MA

Eastbrooke Health Care Center, Brooksville, FL

Eastchester Park Nursing Home, Bronx, NY

Easter Manor Nursing Home, Fort Pierce, FL

Eastern Maine Medical Center—Ross Skilled Nursing Division, Bangor, ME

Eastern Mennonite Home, Souderton, PA

Eastern Oregon Hospital and Training Center, Pendleton, OR

Eastern Pennsylvania Eastern Star Home, Warminster, PA

Eastern Star Home, Los Angeles, CA

Eastern Star Home, Macon, IL

Eastern Star Home, Orange, MA

Eastern Star Home, Arlington, TX

Eastern Star Home and Infirmary, Oriskany, NY

Eastern Star Home of Cuyahoga County, East Cleveland, OH

Eastern Star Home of Kentucky, Louisville, KY

Eastern Star Home of South Dakota, Redfield, SD

Eastern Star Masonic Home, Boone, IA

Easter's Home of Ruth Inc, Farmington, MO

Easterwood Nursing Home, Dadeville, AL

Eastfair Nursing Home, Austin, TX

Eastgate Healthcare Associates Inc, Pocatello, ID

Eastgate Manor, Springfield, IL

Eastgate Manor Nursing and Residential Center Inc, Washington, IN

Eastland Care Center, Columbus, OH

Eastland Manor, Eastland, TX

Eastmont Human Services Center, Glendive, MT

Eastmont Tower, Lincoln, NE

The Easton Home for Aged Women, Easton, PA

Easton Manor, Easton, KS

Easton-Lincoln Nursing Home, Easton, MA

Eastport Memorial Hospital—Intermediate Care Unit, Eastport, ME

Eastside Healthcare Center, Indianapolis, IN

Eastview Manor, Belle Plaine, KS

Eastview Manor Inc, Prospect, CT

Eastview Manor Retirement and Convalescent Home, Trenton, MO

Eastview Nursing Home, Macon, GA

Eastview Nursing Home, Oregon, OH

Eastwood at Dedham Convalescent Center, Dedham, MA

Eastwood Convalescent Home Inc, Easton, PA

Eastwood Convalescent Hospital, Long Beach, CA

Eastwood Manor Nursing and Rehabilitation Center, Commerce, OK

Eastwood Nursing Center, Detroit, MI

Eastwood Pines Nursing Home, Gardner, MA

Eastwood Rest Home Inc, Amesbury, MA

Eastwood Village Nursing and Retirement Center, Fort Worth, TX

Eaton Care Nursing Center, Los Angeles, CA

Eaton County Medical Care Facility, Charlotte, MI

Eatontown Convalescent Center, Eatontown, NJ

Eau Claire County Center of Care, Eau Claire, WI

Eau Claire Manor Inc, Eau Claire, WI

Eben Ezer Lutheran Care Center, Brush, CO

Ebenezer Covenant Home, Buffalo, MN

Ebenezer Hall, Minneapolis, MN

Ebenezer Ridges, Burnsville, MN
Ebenezer Society/Luther Hall, Minneapolis, MN
Ebensburg Center, Ebensburg, PA
Echo Manor Extended Care Center, Pickerington, OH
Echo Park Skilled Nursing Facility Hospital Inc, Los Angeles, CA
Echo Specialized Group Home, Spokane, WA
Echoing Hills Residential Center, Warsaw, OH
Echoing Meadows Residential Center, Athens, OH
Echoing Ridge Residential Center, Canal Fulton, OH
Echoing Valley Residential Home, Dayton, OH
Echoing Woods Residential Home, Dayton, OH
Eckfield Rest Home, Medina, OH
Eddington Group Home, Eddington, ME
Eddy Memorial Foundation, Troy, NY
Eden Gardens Nursing Center, Shreveport, LA
Eden Home for the Aged Inc, New Braunfels, TX
Eden Manor Nursing Home, Sabina, OH
Eden Park Health Services Inc, Catskill, NY
Eden Park Health Services Inc, Troy, NY
Eden Park Nursing Home, Albany, NY
Eden Park Nursing Home, Cobleskill, NY
Eden Park Nursing Home, Hudson, NY
Eden Park Nursing Home, Poughkeepsie, NY
Eden Park Nursing Home, Utica, NY
Eden Park Nursing Home and Health Related Facility, Glens Falls, NY
Eden Park Nursing Home of Brattleboro, Brattleboro, VT
Eden Park Nursing Home of Rutland, Rutland, VT
Eden Valley Nursing Home, Loveland, CO
Eden Village Care Center, Edwardsville, IL
Eden West Rehabilitation Hospital, Hayward, CA
Edgebrook Rest Center Inc, Edgerton, MN
Edgecombe Nursing and Convalescent Home, Lenox, MA
Edgefield Health Care Center, Edgefield, SC
Edgefield Manor Nursing Home, Troutdale, OR
Edgehill Nursing Home, Glenside, PA
Edgell Rest Home, Framingham, MA
Edgemont Manor Nursing Home, Cynthiana, KY
Edgemoor Geriatric Hospital, Santee, CA
Edgerton Manor—ICF/MR, West Lafayette, OH
Edgewater Convalescent Hospital, Long Beach, CA
Edgewater Haven Nursing Home, Port Edwards, WI
Edgewater Home Inc, Saint Louis, MO
Edgewater Nursing and Geriatric Center, Chicago, IL
Edgewater Quality Care Nursing Center, Lake Milton, OH
Edgewild Health Center, Sterling, IL
Edgewood Care Home, Paradise, CA
Edgewood Convalescent Home, Edgewood, IA
Edgewood Convalescent Home, Dorchester, MA
Edgewood Lodge Home, Ardmore, OK
Edgewood Manor, Portsmouth, NH
Edgewood Manor Nursing Center, Port Clinton, OH
Edgewood Manor Nursing Home, Texarkana, TX

Edgewood Manor of Fostoria Inc, Fostoria, OH
Edgewood Nursing Care Center, Elroy, WI
Edgewood Nursing Center, Cottage Grove, OR
Edgewood Nursing Center Inc, Youngstown, PA
Edgewood Nursing Home, Baltimore, MD
Edgewood Nursing Home, Toledo, OH
Edgewood Nursing Home Inc, Grafton, MA
Edgewood Rest Home, Pittsfield, MA
Edgewood View Nursing Home, Oxford, IN
Edgwood Manor—of Grays Harbor Inc, Montesano, WA
Edina Care Center, Edina, MN
Edison Estates Inc, Edison, NJ
Edison Manor, Centralia, WA
Edisto Convalescent Center, Orangeburg, SC
Edmond Nursing Center, Edmond, OK
Edmonds Villa Care Center, Edmonds, WA
Edson Convalescent Hospital, Modesto, CA
Edward Abraham Memorial Home, Canadian, TX
Edward John Noble Hospital of Alexandria Bay, Alexandria Bay, NY
Edward Snyder Memorial Old Peoples Home, Reedsburg, WI
Edwardsville Care Center, Edwardsville, IL
Edwardsville Convalescent Center, Edwardsville, KS
Edwardsville Manor Inc, Edwardsville, KS
Edwin Morgan Center, Laurinburg, NC
Effingham Care Center, Effingham, IL
Effingham County Extended Care Facility, Springfield, GA
Eger Nursing Home Inc, Staten Island, NY
Egle Nursing Home, Lonaconing, MD
Eisenhower Nursing and Convalescent Hospital, Pasadena, CA
El Cajon Valley Convalescent Center, El Cajon, CA
El Camino Convalescent Hospital, Carmichael, CA
El Castillo Retirement Residence, Santa Fe, NM
El Centro Villa Nursing Center, Albuquerque, NM
El Dorado Convalescent Hospital, Placerville, CA
El Dorado Guidance Center, San Jose, CA
El Dorado Manor, Trenton, NE
El Dorado Nursing Center, El Dorado, KS
El Jen Convalescent Hospital, Las Vegas, NV
El Monte Convalescent Hospital, El Monte, CA
El Monte Golden Age Convalescent Home, El Monte, CA
El Paso Convalescent Center, El Paso, TX
El Paso Hawthorne Lodge, El Paso, IL
El Ponce De Leon Convalescent Center, Miami, FL
El Rancho Rest Home, Payson, UT
El Rancho Vista Convalescent Center, Pico Rivera, CA
El Reno Nursing Center, El Reno, OK
El Reposo Sanitarium, Florence, AL
Elaine Boyd Creche Children's Nursing Home, Bloomingdale, IL
Elba General Hospital and Nursing Home, Elba, AL
Elberta Convalescent Home, Warner Robins, GA
Elcor Nursing Home, Horseheads, NY
Elcor's Mariott Manor, Horseheads, NY
Elder Crest Nursing Home, Munhall, PA

Elder House, Fenton, MI
Eldercare Convalescent Hospital, Campbell, CA
Eldercare Convalescent Hospital, Capitola, CA
Eldercare Convalescent Hospital, Milpitas, CA
Eldercare Convalescent Hospital, Morgan Hill, CA
Eldercare Gardens, Charlottesville, VA
Eldercare of Alton, Alton, IL
Eldercare of Farmville Nursing Home, Farmville, VA
Eldercare of Franklin County, Rocky Mount, VA
Elderest Nursing Home, Salem, OR
ElderLodge—Edenton, Edenton, NC
ElderLodge—Jacksonville, Jacksonville, NC
Elderlodge Outer Banks, Nags Head, NC
Elders Home, New York Mills, MN
Eldora Manor, Eldora, IA
Eldorado Nursing Home Inc, Eldorado, IL
Eleanora-Connor Convalescent Home, Cincinnati, OH
Electra Nursing Center, Electra, TX
El-Encanto Convalescent Hospital, City of Industry, CA
Eleven Seven, New Ulm, MN
Elgin Community Living Facility, Elgin, IL
Elgin Golden Years Retirement Nursing Home, Elgin, TX
Elihu White Nursing and Rehabilitation Center, Braintree, MA
Elim Home, Milaca, MN
Elim Home, Princeton, MN
Elim Home, Watertown, MN
Elim Home, Fargo, ND
Elim Park Baptist Home Inc, Cheshire, CT
Elite Rest and Nursing Home, Cincinnati, OH
Eliza Bryant Center, Cleveland, OH
Eliza Cathcart Home, Devon, PA
Eliza Jennings Home, Cleveland, OH
The Eliza Johnson Center for Aging Inc, Houston, TX
Eliza Memorial Hospital— Mitchell-Hollingsworth Annex, Florence, AL
Elizabeth Adam Crump Manor, Glen Allen, VA
Elizabeth Carelton House, Boston, MA
Elizabeth Church Manor, Binghamton, NY
Elizabeth E Boit Home, Wakefield, MA
Elizabeth Jane Bivins Home for the Aged, Amarillo, TX
Elizabeth Levinson Center, Bangor, ME
Elizabeth Manor, Los Angeles, CA
Elizabeth Manor Convalescent Hospital, Sacramento, CA
Elizabeth Nursing Home, Elizabeth, NJ
Elizabeth Nursing Home Inc, Elizabeth, IL
Elizabeth Scott Memorial Care Center, Maumee, OH
Elizabeth Seton Residence, Wellesley, MA
Elizabeth Seton Residence, Windsor, MA
Elizabethan Home, Elizabethtown, KY
Elizabethtown Nursing Center, Elizabethtown, NC
Elk Grove Convalescent Hospital, Elk Grove, CA
Elk Haven Nursing Home, Saint Marys, PA
Elk Manor Home, Moline, KS
Elk River Nursing Home, Elk River, MN
Elkader Care Center, Elkader, IA
Elkhart Healthcare Center, Elkhart, IN
Elkhart Nursing Home Inc, Elkhart, TX

Elkton Rest Home, Elkton, SD
Ellen James Rest Home, Boston, MA
Ellen Memorial Convalescent Home, Scranton, PA
Ellen Memorial Health Care Center, Honesdale, PA
Ellen S Memorial Convalescent Hospital, Richmond, CA
Ellen Sagar Nursing Home, Union, SC
Ellenburg Nursing Center Inc, Anderson, SC
Ellendale Nursing Center, Ellendale, ND
Ellen's Convalescent Health Center, Fort Dodge, IA
Ellet Manor, Akron, OH
Elliot Avenue Boarding Care Home, Minneapolis, MN
Elliot Manor Nursing Home, Newton, MA
The Ellis Nursing Home, Norwood, MA
Ellisville State School-Clover Circle ICF/MR, Ellisville, MS
Ellisville State School-Hillside SNF/ICF, Ellisville, MS
Ellisville State School-Lakeview SNF, Ellisville, MS
Ellisville State School-Peacan Grove, Ellisville, MS
Ellsworth Convalescent Center, Ellsworth, ME
Ellsworth Good Samaritan Center—Villa Hope, Ellsworth, KS
Elm Creek Nursing Center, West Carrollton, OH
Elm Crest Manor, New Salem, ND
Elm Heights Care Center, Shenandoah, IA
Elm Hill Convalescent and Rest Home, Rocky Hill, CT
Elm Hill Nursing Home, Boston, MA
Elm Hurst Nursing Home, Springfield, TN
Elm Manor Nursing Home, Canandaigua, NY
Elm Terrace Gardens, Lansdale, PA
Elm Terrace Nursing Home, Middleton, WI
Elm View Care Center, Burlington, IA
Elmachri Convalescent Home, Norwich, CT
Elmbrook Home, Ardmore, OK
Elmbrook Home Inc, Smithfield, RI
Elmcrest Convalescent Hospital, El Monte, CA
Elmer McDowell Health Care, Stanwood, WA
Elmhaven, Parsons, KS
Elmhaven Convalescent Hospital Inc, Stockton, CA
Elmhurst Convalescent Center, Westerville, OH
Ray Graham Elmhurst Convalescent Living Facility, Elgin, IL
Elmhurst Extended Care Center Inc, Elmhurst, IL
Elmhurst Nursing and Retirement Home, Melrose, MA
Elmhurst Nursing Home, Webb City, MO
Elmhurst Nursing Home, Canby, OR
Elmhurst Terrace Convalescent Center, Elmhurst, IL
Elmira Jeffries Memorial Home, Philadelphia, PA
Elmore Memorial Nursing Home, Mountain Home, ID
Elms, Macomb, IL
Elms, Cranbury, NJ
Elms Convalescent Home and Rehabilitation Center, Wellington, OH
Elms Convalescent Hospital, Glendale, CA
Elms Health Care Center Inc, Ponca, NE
Elms Manor Nursing Home, Chicopee, MA
Elms Residence Nursing Home, Old Orchard Beach, ME

Elmwood, Green Springs, OH
Elmwood Convalescent Hospital, Berkeley, CA
Elmwood Geriatric Village, Detroit, MI
Elmwood Health Center Inc, Providence, RI
Elmwood Manor Inc, Beardstown, IL
Elmwood Manor Inc, Wewoka, OK
Elmwood Manor Nursing Home, Worcester, MA
Elmwood Manor Nursing Home Inc, Nanuet, NY
Elmwood Nursing Center, Marlin, TX
Elmwood Nursing Home, Aurora, IL
Elmwood Nursing Home, Omaha, TX
Elmwood Village, Portsmouth, OH
Elmwood Village of Ashland, Ashland, KY
Elness Convalescent Hospital, Turlock, CA
Elsberry Missouri Health Care Center, Elsberry, MO
Elsie Dryer Nursing Home, Brookville, IN
Elsie May's Rest Home Inc, Pawtucket, RI
Elston Home Inc, Chicago, IL
Elwood Care Center, Elwood, NE
Elwood Nursing Home, Salem, MO
The Elyria United Methodist Home, Elyria, OH
Elzora Manor, Milton-Freewater, OR
Emanuel County Nursing Home, Swainsboro, GA
Embassy House Healthcare Nursing Home, Brockton, MA
Embassy Manor Care Center, Newton, IA
Embreeville State Hospital, Coatesville, PA
Emerald Care Center, Boise, ID
Emerald Nursing Center, Eugene, OR
Emerald Nursing Center, Eugene, OR
Emerald Terrace Nursing Center, Vancouver, WA
Emerson Boarding Care Home, Minneapolis, MN
Emerson Convalescent Center, Emerson, NJ
Emerson Convalescent Home Inc, Watertown, MA
Emerson Nursing Home, Indianapolis, IN
Emery County Nursing Home, Ferron, UT
Emery Manor Nursing Home, Matawan, NJ
Emery Retirement and Convalescent Home, Medford, MA
Emery Street Community Residence, Portland, ME
Emily E Flinn Home Inc, Marion, IN
Emma P Chadwick Memorial Home, Bothell, WA
Emmanuel Home, Litchfield, MN
Emmanuel Nursing Home, Detroit Lakes, MN
Emmet County Medical Care Facility, Harbor Springs, MI
Emmetsburg Care Center, Emmetsburg, IA
Emmett Care Center, Emmett, ID
Emory Convalescent Home, Atlanta, GA
Empire Nursing Home, Joplin, MO
Emporia Rest Home, Emporia, KS
Empress Convalescent Center, Long Beach, CA
Empress Convalescent Home—1, Cincinnati, OH
Empress Convalescent Home—2, Cincinnati, OH
Empress Convalescent Hospital, San Jose, CA
Encino Terrace Convalescent Hospital, Encino, CA
Enderlin Hillcrest Manor, Enderlin, ND
Endicott Nursing Home and Health Related Facility, Endicott, NY

Enfield Care Home, Enfield, IL
Enfield Nursing Center, Enfield, CT
England Manor Nursing Home Inc, England, AR
Englewood House, Englewood, CO
Englewood Manor Nursing Home, Englewood, OH
Englewood Nursing Home, Boston, MA
English Nursing Home Inc, Lebanon, IN
English Valley Nursing Care Center, North English, IA
English Village Manor Inc, Altus, OK
Enid Living Center, Enid, OK
Ennoble Center of Long Beach, Long Beach, CA
Ennoble Manor Care Center, Dubuque, IA
Enterprise Estates Nursing Center, Enterprise, KS
Enterprise Hospital and Nursing Home, Enterprise, AL
Ephrata Nursing Home Inc, Ephrata, PA
Episcopal Church Home, Hockessin, DE
Episcopal Church Home, Louisville, KY
Episcopal Church Home, Pittsburgh, PA
Episcopal Church Home of Minnesota, Saint Paul, MN
Epsom Manor, Epsom, NH
Epworth Manor, Tyrone, PA
Erick Nursing Home, Erick, OK
Erie County Care Facility, Huron, OH
Erie County Geriatric Annex, Erie, PA
Erie County Geriatric Center, Girard, PA
Erie County Home and Infirmary, Alden, NY
Erinkay-Aneskarn 2, Robbinsdale, MN
Escambia County Nursing Home, Pensacola, FL
Escondido Convalescent Center, Escondido, CA
Eshelman Nursing Home Inc, Clyde, OH
Eskaton Glenwood Manor, Sacramento, CA
Eskaton Manzanita Manor, Carmichael, CA
Esma A Wright Pavilion, Robbins, IL
Essex County Geriatrics Center, Belleville, NJ
The Estelle Peabody Memorial Home, North Manchester, IN
Estelle's Nursing Home, Clifton, KS
Estelline Nursing and Care Center, Estelline, SD
Estes Health Care Center—Double Springs, Double Springs, AL
Estes Health Care Center—East, Birmingham, AL
Estes Health Care Center—Fairhope, Fairhope, AL
Estes Health Care Center—Forestdale, Birmingham, AL
Estes Health Care Center—Glen Haven, Northport, AL
Estes Health Care Center—North, Northport, AL
Estes Health Care Center—Oakridge, Eight Mile, AL
Estes Health Care Center—Park Manor, Northport, AL
Estes Health Care Center—Riverchase, Birmingham, AL
Esther Marie Nursing Center, Geneva, OH
Estherville Good Samaritan, Estherville, IA
Etowah Health Care Center, Etowah, TN
Euclid Convalescent Center, San Diego, CA
Euclid General Hospital, Euclid, OH
Euclid Manor Nursing Home, Cleveland, OH
Eudora Nursing Center, Eudora, KS

Eufaula Geriatric Center Inc, Eufaula, AL
Eufaula Manor Inc, Eufaula, OK
Eugene Care Center Inc, Eugene, OR
Eugene Good Samaritan Center, Eugene, OR
Euless Nursing Center, Euless, TX
Eunice C Smith Nursing Home, Alton, IL
Eupora Health Care Center Inc, Eupora, MS
Eureka Apostolic Christian Home, Eureka, IL
Eureka Rest Home, Eureka, KS
Eureka Springs Convalescent Center, Eureka
Springs, AR
Eustis Manor Inc, Eustis, FL
Eva Dawn Care Center, Salt Lake City, UT
Evamor Manor, Worcester, MA
Evangelical Baptist Home, Ashford, CT
Evangelical Congregational Church Retirement
Village, Myerstown, PA
Evangelical Free Church Home, Boone, IA
Evangelical Home, Detroit, MI
Evangelical Home, Saline, MI
The Evangelical Home—Port Huron, Port
Huron, MI
Evangelical Lutheran Good Samaritan Center,
Nelson, NE
Evangelical Manor, Philadelphia, PA
Evans Health Care, Evans, GA
Evans House, Fort Collins, CO
Evans Manor Nursing Home, Worcester, MA
Evans Memorial Home for the Aged Inc,
Cresco, IA
Evansville Healthcare Center, Evansville, IN
Evansville Manor, Evansville, WI
Evansville Protestant Home Inc,
Evansville, IN
Eveleth Fitzgerald Community Hospital—
Nursing Home, Eveleth, MN
Evenglow Lodge, Pontiac, IL
Evening Star Nursing Home, Bethany, OK
Eventide Care Center, Chickasha, OK
Eventide Convalescent Center Inc, Topeka, KS
Eventide Home, Mountain Lake, MN
Eventide Home, Roseau, MN
Eventide Home, Exeter, NH
Eventide Lutheran Home, Moorhead, MN
Eventide Lutheran Home for the Aged,
Denison, IA
Eventide Nursing Home, Massillon, OH
Eventide Nursing Home Inc, San Saba, TX
Eventide of Sheridan, Sheridan, WY
Eventide Rest Home, Greencastle, IN
Eventide—South, Fort Collins, CO
Everett Court Community, Lakewood, CO
Evergeen Manor, Oshkosh, WI
Evergreen Care Center, Lincoln City, OR
Evergreen Care Center, Memphis, TN
Evergreen Care Center, Burkburnett, TX
Evergreen Care Centre, Montrose, CO
Evergreen Convalescent Center, Olympia, WA
Evergreen Convalescent Center Inc, Temple
City, CA
Evergreen Convalescent Home, Harmony, PA
Evergreen Convalescent Hospital Inc,
Modesto, CA
Evergreen Hills Nursing Center, Ypsilanti, MI
Evergreen House Health Center, East
Providence, RI
Evergreen Manor, Minden, LA
Evergreen Manor, Saco, ME
Evergreen Manor Nursing Home, Evergreen
Park, IL
Evergreen Manor Nursing Home Inc,
Montpelier, OH
Evergreen Nursing Home, Alamosa, CO

Evergreen Nursing Home, Del City, OK
Evergreen Nursing Home, Provo, UT
Evergreen Nursing Home, Shawano, WI
Evergreen Nursing Home and Rehabilitation
Center Inc, Creve Coeur, MO
Evergreen Nursing Home Inc, Evergreen, AL
Evergreen Place, Texarkana, AR
Evergreen Terrace Nursing Center, Mount
Vernon, WA
Evergreen Vista Convalescent Center,
Kirkland, WA
Evergreen Woods, Spring Hill, FL
Evergreens, La Rose, IL
Evergreens II Inc, High Point, NC
The Evergreens Inc, Greensboro, NC
Evergreens Nursing Home Inc, Woonsocket, RI
Ewing Nursing Home, Terre Haute, IN
Ewing Parkway Nursing Home, Trenton, NJ
Excelsior Nursing Home, Excelsior, MN
Excelsior Springs Care Center, Excelsior Spring,
MO
Excepticon—Lexington Campus,
Lexington, KY
Exceptional Care and Training Center,
Sterling, IL
Exeter House, Seattle, WA
Exira Care Center, Exira, IA
The Extended Care Center of Toledo, Toledo,
OH
Extended Care Hospital of Anaheim,
Anaheim, CA
Extended Care Hospital of Long Beach, Long
Beach, CA
Extended Care Hospital of Los Angeles, Los
Angeles, CA
Extended Care Hospital of Riverside,
Riverside, CA
Extended Care Hospital of Santa Barbara,
Santa Barbara, CA
Extended Care Hospital of Tarzana,
Tarzana, CA
Extendicare Health Center, Dothan, AL
F Edward Hebert, New Orleans, LA
Faber Nursing Home, Cortland, OH
Fahrney-Keedy Memorial Home Inc,
Boonsboro, MD
Fair Acres, Carthage, MO
Fair Acres Geriatric Center, Lima, PA
Fair Acres Nursing Home, Armada, MI
Fair Acres Nursing Home Inc, Du Quoin, IL
Fair Haven Convalescent Home Inc,
Douglas, GA
Fair Havens Center, Miami, FL
Fair Havens Christian Home, Decatur, IL
Fair Havens Rest Home, Middleboro, MA
Fair Holme Convalescent Center, Seaford, DE
Fair Lawn Manor Nursing Home, Fair Lawn,
NJ
Fair Lodge Health Care Center, Louisville, KY
Fair Meadow Nursing Home, Fertile, MN
Fair Oaks, Greenville, IL
Fair Oaks Nursing Home, Crystal Lake, IL
Fair Oaks Nursing Home, South Beloit, IL
Fair Oaks Nursing Home, Hineston, LA
Fair Oaks Nursing Home, Minneapolis, MN
Fair Oaks Personal Care Home,
Jamestown, KY
Fair Park Health Care Center, Dallas, TX
Fair Park Nursing Center, Huntsville, TX
Fair View Home, Mauston, WI
Fair View Nursing Home, Sedalia, MO
Fair Villa Nursing Home, Norristown, PA
Fair Winds Inc, Sarver, PA

Fairacres Manor Inc, Greeley, CO
Fairburn Health Care Center, Fairburn, GA
Fairchild Manor Nursing Home, Lewiston, NY
Fairfax Health Care Center, Berwyn, IL
Fairfax Nursing Center, Fairfax, VA
Fairfax Nursing Home, Fairfax, MN
Fairfax Nursing Home, Fairfax, OK
Fairfax Rest Home, Boston, MA
Fairfield Good Samaritan, Fairfield, WA
Fairfield Health Care Center, Fairfield, AL
Fairfield Health Care Facility Inc,
Indianapolis, IN
Fairfield Healthcare Center, Fort Wayne, IN
Fairfield Homes, Ridgeway, SC
Fairfield Manor Health Care Center,
Norwalk, CT
Fairfield Nursing Center, Crownsville, MD
Fairfield Nursing Home, Hamilton, OH
Fairhaven Christian Home, Rockford, IL
Fairhaven Corporation, Whitewater, WI
Fairhaven Home, Upper Sandusky, OH
Fairhaven Nursing Home, Sykesville, MD
Fairhaven Nursing Home, Westminster, MD
Fairhaven Nursing Home, Lowell, MA
Fairhaven Rest Home, Huntington, WV
Fairhaven Shelby County Home, Sidney, OH
Fairland Nursing Home, Silver Spring, MD
Fairland Nursing Home, Fairland, OK
Fairlane Memorial Convalescent Home,
Detroit, MI
Fairlawn Care Center, Gresham, OR
Fairlawn Chateau, Fairlawn, OH
Fairlawn Convalescent Home, Norwich, CT
Fairlawn Haven, Archbold, OH
Fairlawn Heights Nursing Home, Topeka, KS
Fairlawn Nursing Home Inc, Leominster, MA
Fairlawn Nursing Home Inc, Lexington, MA
Fairmont Community Hospital, Fairmont, MN
Fairmont Rehabilitation Hospital, Lodi, CA
Fairmont Rest Home, Ephrata, PA
Fairmount Company Inc, Dallas, TX
Fairmount Health Center, Willougby, OH
Fairmount Rest Home, Leominster, MA
Fairmount Rest Home Inc, Boston, MA
Fairport Baptist Home, Fairport, NY
Fairview, Groton, CT
Fairview Baptist Home, Downers Grove, IL
Fairview Care Center, Colorado Springs, CO
Fairview Castle Nursing Home, Millersburg,
OH
Fairview Convalescent Center, Salt Lake City,
UT
Fairview Fellowship Home, Fairview, OK
Fairview Haven Inc, Fairbury, IL
Fairview Health Care Center, La Grange, IL
Fairview Health Center, Bowling Green, KY
Fairview House Nursing Home, Rosiclare, IL
Fairview Manor, Belvidere, IL
Fairview Manor, Fairmont, NE
Fairview Manor, Fairfield, TX
Fairview Manor Nursing Center, Toledo, OH
Fairview Manor Nursing Center, Oklahoma
City, OK
Fairview Manor Nursing Home Inc, Beverly,
OH
Fairview Medical Care Facility, Centreville, MI
Fairview Nursing and Convalescent Home,
Birmingham, AL
Fairview Nursing Center, Du Quoin, IL
Fairview Nursing Home, Dodge Center, MN
Fairview Nursing Home, Hudson, NH
Fairview Nursing Home, Forest Hills, NY
Fairview Nursing Home, Bonham, TX

Fairview Nursing Home, Salt Lake City, UT
Fairview Nursing Home—Bethlehem Pike, Philadelphia, PA
Fairview Nursing Home of Papermill, Chestnut Hill, PA
Fairview Rest Home, Brockton, MA
Fairview Training Center, Salem, OR
Fairway Convalescent Center, Fullerton, CA
Fairway Group Home, Waterloo, IA
Fairways Caring Center, Maryland Heights, MO
Fairwood Convalescent Hospital, Pasadena, CA
Faith Handicap Village, Shawnee Mission, KS
Faith Handicap Village 2, Shawnee Mission, KS
Faith Handicap Village 3, Shawnee Mission, KS
Faith Haven Care Center, Jackson, MI
Faith Health Care Facility Inc, Florence, SC
Faith Home, Edinburg, IN
Faith Lutheran Home, Wolf Point, MT
Faith Lutheran Home Inc, Osage, IA
Faith Medical Care Center, Saint Clair, MI
Faith Memorial Nursing Home, Pasadena, TX
Faith Nursing Home, Grand Rapids, MI
Falkville Nursing Home Inc, Falkville, AL
Fall Creek Valley Nursing Home, Fall Creek, WI
Fall River Jewish Home for the Aged, Fall River, MA
Fall River Nursing Home Inc, Fall River, MA
Fallbrook Convalescent Hospital, Fallbrook, CA
Fallon Convalescent Center, Fallon, NV
Fallon Memorial Nursing Home, Baker, MT
Falls Nursing Home, South Hadley, MA
Falls Nursing Home, International Falls, MN
Falls Nursing Home, Oconto Falls, WI
Falls Nursing Home—East, Oconto Falls, WI
Falmouth Convalescent Center, Falmouth, ME
Falmouth Nursing Home, Falmouth, MA
Falmouth Rest Home, Falmouth, KY
Family Care Services, Brighton, CO
Family Heritage Home, Black River Falls, WI
Family Heritage Nursing Home, Wisconsin Rapids, WI
Family Hospital Nursing Home, Milwaukee, WI
Family House, Mankato, MN
Family Life Enrichment, High Shoals, GA
Family Rest Home, Lynn, MA
The Family Tree Care Center, Anderson, IN
Family Tree Care Center, Oregon, OH
Familystyle Homes, Saint Paul, MN
Fannie E Taylor Home for the Aged, Jacksonville, FL
Fannin County Nursing Home, Blue Ridge, GA
Far Rockaway Nursing Home, Far Rockaway, NY
Fargo Nursing Home, Fargo, ND
Faribault Manor Nursing Home, Faribault, MN
Faribault State Hospital, Faribault, MN
Farmdale Convalescent Hospital, Buena Park, CA
Farmington Convalescent Home, Farmington, CT
Farmington Nursing Home, Farmington Hills, MI
Farmington Nursing Home Inc, Farmington, IL
Farnsworth Nursing Home, Peabody, MA

Farwell Convalescent Center, Farwell, TX
Father Murray Nursing Center, Centerline, MI
Father Purcell Memorial Exceptional Children's Center, Montgomery, AL
Father Walter Memorial Child Care Center, Montgomery, AL
Fauskee Nursing Home Inc, Worthington, MN
Faxton-Sunset-Saint Lukes Nursing Home Inc, Utica, NY
Fay Case Nursing Home, Salt Lake City, UT
Fayette County Hospital and Nursing Home, Fayette, AL
Fayetteville City Hospital—Geriatrics, Fayetteville, AR
Fazio Nursing Home, Marklesburg, PA
Federal Hill Manor Nursing and Convalescent Center, Bardstown, KY
Federal Hill Nursing Center, Baltimore, MD
Federal Way Convalescent Center Inc, Federal Way, WA
Feghtly Lutheran Home, Tipp City, OH
Fejervary Health Care Center, Davenport, IA
Fellowship Club, Saint Paul, MN
Fellowship Deaconry Inc, Bernardsville, NJ
Fellowship Home, Danville, KY
Fellowship House Inc, Chicago, IL
Felton Convalescent Home, Felton, DE
Fennimore Good Samaritan Center, Fennimore, WI
Fenton Extended Care Center, Fenton, MI
Fenton Park Health Related Facility, Greenhurst, NY
Fenton Park Nursing Home, Jamestown, NY
Fentress County Nursing Home, Jamestown, TN
Fenwood Manor Inc, Manchester, CT
Fergus Falls State Hospital, Fergus Falls, MN
Ferguson Convalescent Home, Lapeer, MI
Ferguson Nursing Center, Dallas, TX
Ferguson Rest Home, Clinton, MA
Fern Terrace Lodge, Owensboro, KY
Fern Terrace Lodge of Bowling Green, Bowling Green, KY
Fern Terrace Lodge of Murray, Murray, KY
Fernandez Nursing Home, Saint Bernard, LA
Ferncliff Nursing Home Co Inc, Rhinebeck, NY
Fernview Convalescent Hospital, San Gabriel, CA
Fernwood House Retirement and Nursing Center, Bethesda, MD
Ferrier Harris Home for Aged, Saint Louis, MO
Ferry Point Skilled Nursing Care Facility, Old Saybrook, CT
Festus Manor, Festus, MO
Festus Rest Home, Festus, MO
Fiddlers Green Manor Nursing Home, Springville, NY
Field Crest Nursing Home, Hayfield, MN
Field House, Canon City, CO
Fieldcrest Manor Inc, Waldoboro, ME
Fieldston Lodge Nursing Home, Bronx, NY
Fieldview Manor Healthcare, Superior, WI
Fieser Nursing Home, Fenton, MO
Fifth Avenue Convalescent Hospital Inc, San Rafael, CA
Fifth Avenue Health Care Center, Rome, GA
Fifth Avenue Home, Texas City, TX
58th Avenue, Arvada, CO
Filling Memorial Home of Mercy, Napoleon, OH
Fillmore Convalescent Center, Fillmore, CA
Fillmore County Long Term Care, Geneva, NE

Filosa Convalescent Home Inc, Danbury, CT
Finnie Good Shepherd Nursing Home Inc, Galatia, IL
Fir Lane Terrace Convalescent Center Inc, Shelton, WA
Fircrest Convalescent Hospital, Sebastopol, CA
Firemans Home of the State of New York, Hudson, NY
Fireside Convalescent Hospital, Santa Monica, CA
Fireside Foster Inn, Mora, MN
Fireside Lodge of Fort Worth, Fort Worth, TX
Firesteel Heights Nursing Home, Mitchell, SD
Firestone Rd Community Residence—Unit 1, Charleston, SC
Firestone Rd Community Residence—Unit 2, Charleston, SC
First Christian Church Residence, Minneapolis, MN
First Community Village, Columbus, OH
First Hill Villa Care Center, Seattle, WA
First Midlands ICMRF, Columbia, SC
Fisher Convalescent Home, Mayville, MI
Fisher County Nursing Home, Rotan, TX
Fishkill Health Related Center Inc, Beacon, NY
The Fitch Home Inc, Melrose, MA
Fitzgerald Nursing Home, Fitzgerald, GA
Five Counties Nursing Home, Lemmon, SD
Five Oaks Nursing Center, Concord, NC
Flagship Convalescent Center, Newport Beach, CA
Flambeau-Aneskarn 1, Minneapolis, MN
Flannery Nursing Home Inc, Portsmouth, OH
Flat Rock Children's Center, Flat Rock, OH
Flatbush Manor Care Center, Brooklyn, NY
Flathead County Nursing Home, Kalispell, MT
Fleetcrest Manor Inc, Waterbury, CT
Fleetwood Nursing Home, Athol, MA
Fleur de Lis, Farmington, MO
Flint City Nursing Home Inc, Decatur, AL
Flint Hills Manor, Emporia, KS
Floadrian Manor, Columbia, MS
Flora and Mary Hewitt Memorial Hospital Inc, Shelton, CT
Flora Care Center Inc, Flora, IL
Flora Manor, Fairfield, IL
Flora Nursing Center, Flora, IL
Flora Terrace Convalescent Hospital Inc, Los Angeles, CA
Flora Terrace West Convalescent and Rehabilitation Hospital, Los Angeles, CA
Florence Convalescent Center, Florence, SC
Florence Hand Home—Skilled Nursing Facility, La Grange, GA
Florence Height Village Nursing Center Inc, Omaha, NE
Florence Home for the Aged, Omaha, NE
Florence Nightingale Nursing Home, New York, NY
Florence Nursing Home, Marengo, IL
Florence Nursing Home, Florence, NJ
Florence Rest Home, Northampton, MA
Floresville Nursing Home, Floresville, TX
Florida Baptist Retirement Center, Vero Beach, FL
Florida Christian Health Center, Jacksonville, FL
Florida Convalescent Home, Melbourne, FL
Florida Living Nursing Center, Forest City, FL
Florida Manor Nursing Home, Orlando, FL
Florida United Presbyterian Homes Inc, Lakeland, FL

Floridean Nursing Home, Miami, FL
Florin Convalescent Hospital, Sacramento, CA
Florissant Nursing Center, Florissant, MO
Floro's Nursing Home, McClure, OH
Flower City Nursing Home, Rochester, NY
Flower Square Personal Care Center, Tucson, AZ
Floy Dyer Manor, Houston, MS
Floydada Nursing Home, Floydada, TX
Flushing Manor Care Center, Flushing, NY
Flushing Manor Nursing Home, Flushing, NY
Foley Nursing Center, Foley, MN
Foley Nursing Home, Foley, AL
Folk Convalescent Home, Florence, SC
Folsom Convalescent Hospital, Folsom, CA
Folts Home, Herkimer, NY
Fond Du Lac County Health Care Center, Fond Du Lac, WI
Fond Du Lac Lutheran Home, Fond Du Lac, WI
Fonda Care Center, Fonda, IA
Fondulac Nursing Manor, East Peoria, IL
Fontaine Woods Nursing Home, Saint Louis, MO
Fontanbleu Nursing Center, Bloomington, IN
Fontanelle Good Samaritan Center, Fontanelle, IA
Foothill Acres Inc, Neshanic, NJ
Foothill Convalescent Hospital, Pomona, CA
Foothill Health and Rehabilitation Center, Sylmar, CA
Foothills Care Center Inc, Longmont, CO
Foothills ICF/MR Group Home, Morganton, NC
Foothills Nursing Center, Morganton, NC
Forbes Center for Gerontology, Pittsburgh, PA
Ford County Nursing Home, Paxton, IL
Ford Hull Mar, Yorkville, OH
Forest Cove Nursing Center, Jackson, TN
Forest Del Convalescent Home Inc, Princeton, IN
Forest Farm Health Care Centre Inc, Middletown, RI
Forest Haven Nursing Home, Catonsville, MD
Forest Hill Convalescent Center, Richmond, VA
Forest Hill Manor, Fort Kent, ME
Forest Hill Nursing Center Inc, Fort Worth, TX
Forest Hills Nursing Center, Columbia, SC
Forest Hills Nursing Home, Boston, MA
Forest Hills Nursing Home, Forest Hills, NY
Forest Hills Nursing Home Inc, Cleveland, OH
Forest Manor, Covington, LA
Forest Manor Health Care Center, Hope, NJ
Forest Manor Health Related Facility, Glen Cove, NY
Forest Manor Inc, Northport, AL
Forest Manor Long Term Care Facility, Middleborough, MA
Forest Manor Nursing Home, Wakefield, MA
Forest Oaks Nursing Home, Hamilton, TX
Forest Park Healthcare Center, Kokomo, IN
Forest Park Nursing Center, Plant City, FL
Forest Park Nursing Home, Carlisle, PA
Forest Ridge Convalescent Center, Bremerton, WA
Forest View Care Center, Forest Grove, OR
Forest View Nursing Home, Forest Hills, NY
Forest Villa, Niles, IL
Forestdale Nusing Home, Malden, MA
Forester Haven, San Fernando, CA
Forester Nursing Home Inc, Wintersville, OH
Forestview Hemingway, Cottage Grove, MN

Forestview James, Minneapolis, MN
Forestview—Kentucky, Crystal, MN
Forestview—Lexington, Lexington, MN
Forestview Minnetonka, Minnetonka, MN
Forestview Nursing Home, Cincinnati, OH
Forestview Sunlen, Bloomington, MN
Forestview Vincent, Richfield, MN
Forestville Nursing Center, Forestville, CT
For-Rest Convalescent Home, Hattiesburg, MS
Forrest Lake Manor Inc, Martinez, GA
Forrest Manor Nursing Home, Dewey, OK
Forrester's Old Pueblo Casita, Tucson, AZ
Forsyth Nursing Home, Forsyth, GA
Fort Atkinson Health Care Center, Fort Atkinson, WI
Fort Bayard Medical Center—Nursing Home Unit, Fort Bayard, NM
Fort Bend Nursing Home, Rosenberg, TX
Fort Collins Good Samaritan Retirement Village, Fort Collins, CO
Fort Collins Health Care Center, Fort Collins, CO
Fort Dodge Group Home, Fort Dodge, IA
Fort Dodge Villa Care Center, Fort Dodge, IA
Fort Gibson Nursing Home, Fort Gibson, OK
Fort Hudson Nursing Home Inc, Fort Edward, NY
Fort Logan Hospital—Extended Care Facility, Stanford, KY
Fort Madison Nursing Care Center, Fort Madison, IA
Fort Myers Care Center, Fort Myers, FL
Fort Oglethorpe Nursing Center, Fort Oglethorpe, GA
Fort Pierce Care Center, Fort Pierce, FL
Fort Sanders—Sevier Medical Center Nursing Home, Sevierville, TN
Fort Scott Manor, Fort Scott, KS
Fort Stanton Hospital and Training School, Fort Stanton, NM
Fort Tryon Nursing Home, New York, NY
Fort Valley Health Care Center, Fort Valley, GA
Fort Vancouver Convalescent Center, Vancouver, WA
Fort Walton Developmental Center, Fort Walton Beach, FL
Fort Washington Estates, Fort Washington, PA
Fort Washington Rehabilitation Center, Fort Washington, MD
Fort Wayne Healthcare Center, Fort Wayne, IN
Fort Wayne Nursing Home, Fort Wayne, IN
Fort Worth Western Hills Nursing Home Inc, Fort Worth, TX
Foss Home, Seattle, WA
Fosston Group Home, Fosston, MN
Fosston Municipal Hospital, Fosston, MN
Fostrian Manor, Flushing, MI
Foulk Manor, Wilmington, DE
Foulk Manor Infirmary—North, Wilmington, DE
Foulkeways at Gwynedd Inc, Gwynedd, PA
Fountain Convalescent Hospital Inc, Orange, CA
Fountain Gardens Convalescent Hospital, Los Angeles, CA
Fountain Inn Convalescent Home, Fountain Inn, SC
Fountain Lodge Nursing Home, Baton Rouge, LA
Fountain Manor, Hicksville, OH
Fountain Nursing Home, Reform, AL
Fountain Park Nursing Home Inc, Woodstock, OH

Fountain Terrace, Rockford, IL
Fountain View Convalescent Hospital, Los Angeles, CA
Fountain View Manor, Henryetta, OK
Fountain View Nursing Home, Springhill, LA
Fountain View Villa, Ashland, KS
Fountain Villa Care Center, Sabetha, KS
Fountain West Health Center, West Des Moines, IA
Fountainbleau Nursing Centre, Anaheim, CA
Fountainbleau Nursing Home, Little Rock, AR
Fountainhead Nursing and Convalescent Home, North Miami, FL
Fountainhead Nursing Home, Franklin Furnace, OH
Fountains Nursing Home, Boca Raton, FL
Fountains Nursing Home, Marlon, IL
Fountainview Convalescent Center, Atlanta, GA
Fountainview Inc, Eldorado, IL
Fountainview Place, Elkhart, IN
Fountainview Place Corp of Portage, Portage, IN
Fountainview Place—Goshen, Goshen, IN
Fountainview Place of Greenwood, Greenwood, IN
Fountainview Place of Indianapolis, Indianapolis, IN
Fountainview Place of Mishawaka, Mishawaka, IN
Fountainview Place of Muncie, Muncie, IN
Fountainview Terrace, LaPorte, IN
Four Chaplains Convalescent Home, Westland, MI
Four Corners Good Samaritan, Aztec, NM
Four Corners Health Care Center, Durango, CO
Four Courts Inc, Louisville, KY
Four Fountains Convalescent Center, Belleville, IL
Four Freedoms Manor, Miami Beach, FL
Four Oaks Health Care Center, Jonesboro, TN
Four Oaks Rest Home Inc, Imperial, MO
Four Pines Retirement Home Inc, Independence, MO
Four Seasons Home, Columbus, IN
Four Seasons Nursing Care of Northwest Oklahoma City, Oklahoma City, OK
Four Seasons Nursing Center, Durant, OK
Four Seasons Nursing Center, Austin, TX
Four Seasons Nursing Center, Ennis, TX
Four Seasons Nursing Center, Temple, TX
Four Seasons Nursing Center—Babcock, San Antonio, TX
Four Seasons Nursing Center—Camino Vista, Albuquerque, NM
Four Seasons Nursing Center—Karnes City, Karnes City, TX
Four Seasons Nursing Center—North, San Antonio, TX
Four Seasons Nursing Center—North Richland Hills, Fort Worth, TX
Four Seasons Nursing Center—Northeast Heights, Albuquerque, NM
Four Seasons Nursing Center—Northwest, Fort Worth, TX
Four Seasons Nursing Center—Northwest, San Antonio, TX
Four Seasons Nursing Center of Dallas, Dallas, TX
Four Seasons Nursing Center of El Paso, El Paso, TX
Four Seasons Nursing Center of Midwest City, Midwest City, OK

Four Seasons Nursing Center of Norman, Norman, OK
Four Seasons Nursing Center of Odessa, Odessa, TX
Four Seasons Nursing Center of Southwest Oklahoma City, Oklahoma City, OK
Four Seasons Nursing Center of Tulsa, Tulsa, OK
Four Seasons Nursing Center of Warr Acres, Oklahoma City, OK
Four Seasons Nursing Center of Windsor Hills, Oklahoma City, OK
Four Seasons Nursing Center—Pecan Valley, San Antonio, TX
Four Seasons Nursing Center—Ridgecrest, Albuquerque, NM
Four Seasons Nursing Center—Santa Fe, Santa Fe, NM
Four Seasons Nursing Center—South, San Antonio, TX
Four Seasons Nursing Center—Windcrest, San Antonio, TX
Four Seasons Nursing Home, Hondo, TX
Four Seasons Nursing Home—Vance Jackson, San Antonio, TX
Four Seasons Rest Home, Millis, MA
Four States Nursing Home Inc, Texarkana, TX
Four Winds Manor, Verona, WI
Fourth Street House, Kasson, MN
Fowler Convalescent Care Center Inc, Guilford, CT
Fowler Convalescent Hospital, Fowler, CA
Fowler Health Care Center, Fowler, CO
Fowler Nursing Home, Fowler, KS
Fox Nursing Home, Chester, WV
Fox Nursing Home Inc, Warrington, PA
Fox Run Manor, Findlay, OH
Fox Valley Nursing Center, South Elgin, IL
Fox View Acres, Berlin, OR
Foxwood Springs Living Center, Raymore, MO
Frame House Inc, Indianapolis, IN
Frame Nursing Home Inc, Indianapolis, IN
Framingham Nursing Home, Framingham, MA
Frances E Parker Memorial Home, New Brunswick, NJ
Frances Mahon Deaconess Hospital—Extended Care Facility, Glasgow, MT
Frances Merry Barnard Home, Boston, MA
Frances Residence, Saint Paul, MN
Frances Schervier Home and Hospital, Bronx, NY
Francis Convalescent Center, Fort Worth, TX
Francis Convalescent Home, Lafayette, CA
Francis E Parker, Piscataway, NJ
Francis Marion Manor, Marion, VA
Francis N Sanders Nursing Home Inc, Gloucester, VA
Francis Southwood Nursing Home Inc, Austin, TX
Francis T Crimmins Rest Home, Stoughton, MA
Franciscan Convalescent Hospital, Merced, CA
Franciscan Nursing Home, Joliet, IL
Franciscan Terrace, Cincinnati, OH
Franciscan Villa, Broken Arrow, OK
Franciscan Villa of South Milwaukee, South Milwaukee, WI
Franida House Nursing Home, Boston, MA
Frank Wood Convalescent Home, Boston, MA
Franke Tobey Jones Home, Tacoma, WA
Frankenmuth Convalescent Center, Frankenmuth, MI
Frankfort Community Care Home Inc, Frankfort, KS

Frankfort Heights Manor, West Frankfort, IL
Frankfort Nursing Home, Frankfort, IN
Frankfort Terrace, Frankfort, IL
Franklin Care Center, Gladstone, OR
Franklin Convalescent Center, Franklin Park, NJ
Franklin Cottage, Lecanto, FL
Franklin County Health Care Center, Winchester, TN
Franklin County Nursing Home, Preston, ID
Franklin County Nursing Home, Malone, NY
Franklin County Nursing Home, Chambersburg, PA
Franklin County Nursing Home, Winchester, TN
Franklin General Hospital, Hampton, IA
Franklin Grove Health Care Center, Franklin Grove, IL
Franklin Guest Home, Winnsboro, LA
Franklin Health Care Center, Franklin, GA
Franklin Health Care Center, Franklin, TN
Franklin Healthcare Center, Franklin, MN
Franklin Healthcare Centre, Franklin, IN
Franklin House Healthcare Nursing Home, Franklin, MA
Franklin Manor, Frankfort, KY
Franklin Manor Convalescent Center, Southfield, MI
Franklin Manor I, Farmington, ME
Franklin Manor II, Farmington, ME
Franklin Nursing Center of Sidney, Sidney, OH
Franklin Nursing Center of Vandalia, Vandalia, OH
Franklin Nursing Home, Franklin, IN
Franklin Nursing Home, Hampton, IA
Franklin Nursing Home, Franklin, LA
Franklin Nursing Home, Braintree, MA
Franklin Nursing Home, Minneapolis, MN
Franklin Nursing Home, Flushing, NY
Franklin Nursing Home of Dayton, Dayton, OH
Franklin Nursing Home of Franklin, Franklin, OH
Franklin Nursing & Rehabilitation Center, Greenfield, MA
Franklin Park Nursing Home, Franklin Square, NY
Franklin Plaza, Cleveland, OH
Franklin Rest Home, Franklin, KY
Franklin Senior Citizens Home Inc, Franklin, NE
Franklin United Methodist Home, Franklin, IN
Frankston Nursing Center, Frankston, TX
Franvale Nursing Home, Braintree, MA
Fraser Intermediate Care Facility, San Diego, CA
Fraser Rest Home of Falmouth, Falmouth, MA
Fraser Rest Home of Hyannis, Barnstable, MA
Fraser Rest Home of Sandwich, Sandwich, MA
Frasier Meadows Manor, Boulder, CO
Frazee Retirement Center, Frazee, MN
Frazier Nursing Home, Saint Louis, MO
Frederic Municipal Hospital—Nursing Home, Frederic, WI
Frederick Mennonite Home, Frederick, PA
Frederick Villa Nursing Center, Catonsville, MD
Fredericka Convalescent Hospital, Chula Vista, CA
Fredericksburg Nursing Home, Fredericksburg, TX
Fredericksburg Nursing Home, Fredericksburg, VA

Free State Crestwood Inc, Wills Point, TX
Freeburg Care Center Inc, Freeburg, IL
Freehold Convacenter, Freehold, NJ
Freelandville Community Home Inc, Freelandville, IN
Freeman Community Nursing Home, Freeman, SD
Freeman Convalescent Home, Iron Mountain, MI
Freeman Nursing Home, Pepperell, MA
Freeport Convalescent Center, Freeport, ME
Freeport Manor Nursing Home, Freeport, IL
Freeport Nursing Home, Freeport, ME
Freeport Town Square I, Freeport, ME
Freeport Town Square II, Freeport, ME
Freezers Home for the Aged, South Williamsport, PA
Fremont Care Center, Fremont, NE
Fremont Convalescent Hospital, Fremont, CA
Fremont Manor, Springfield, MO
Fremont Quality Care Nursing Center, Fremont, OH
French Prairie Care Center, Woodburn, OR
Frenchtown Convalescent Center, Monroe, MI
Frene Valley Geriatric and Rehabilitation Center, Hermann, MO
Frene Valley Health Center, Hermann, MO
Fresno Care and Guidance Center, Fresno, CA
Fresno Convalescent Hospital, Fresno, CA
Fresno Westview Convalescent Hospital, Fresno, CA
Frey Village, Middletown, PA
Frickell Family Care Home, Denver, CO
Fridley Convalescent Home, Fridley, MN
Friedler's Guest House, Baltimore, MD
Friedwald House, New City, NY
Friel Nursing Home Inc, Quincy, MA
Friend Manor, Friend, NE
Friendly Acres, Newton, KS
Friendly Hearth Nursing Center—Muncie, Muncie, IN
Friendly Hearth Nursing Center of Spencer, Spencer, IN
The Friendly Home Inc, Woonsocket, RI
Friendly Manor Nursing Home, Eufaula, OK
Friendly Nursing Home, Millmont, PA
Friendly Nursing Home, Pitman, PA
Friendly Nursing Home, Pittman, PA
Friendly Nursing Home Inc, Miamisburg, OH
The Friendly Village, Rhinelander, WI
Friends Care Center of Yellow Springs, Yellow Springs, OH
Friends Fellowship Community Inc, Richmond, IN
Friends Hall at Fox Chase, Philadelphia, PA
Friends Hall at West Chester, West Chester, PA
Friends Home, Greensboro, NC
Friends Home at Woodstown, Woodstown, NJ
Friends Nursing Home Inc, Sandy Spring, MD
Friendship Community, Lititz, PA
Friendship Haven, Chattanooga, TN
Friendship Haven I, Sherburn, MN
Friendship Haven II, Sherburn, MN
Friendship Haven Inc, Fort Dodge, IA
Friendship Health Center, Portland, OR
Friendship Home, Carlinville, IL
Friendship Home, Audubon, IA
Friendship Home, Deadwood, SD
Friendship Homes Inc, National City, CA
Friendship House, Danville, KY
Friendship House, Willmar, MN
Friendship Manor, Rock Island, IL
Friendship Manor, Anadarko, OK

Friendship Manor Convalescent Center, National City, CA
Friendship Manor Convalescent Center, Roanoke, VA
Friendship Manor Inc, Nashville, IL
Friendship Manor Inc, Grinnell, IA
Friendship Manor Nursing Home, Pewee Valley, KY
Friendship Manor Nursing Home, Detroit, MI
Friendship Villa, Miles City, MT
Friendship Villa of Spalding, Spalding, NE
Friendship Village, Schaumburg, IL
Friendship Village, Kalamazoo, MI
Friendship Village, Bloomington, MN
Friendship Village, Saint Louis, MO
Friendship Village, Dayton, OH
Friendship Village, Milwaukee, WI
Friendship Village Health Center, Columbus, OH
Friendship Village of Dublin Health Center, Dublin, OH
Friendship Village of Tempe Health Center, Tempe, AZ
Friendship Village of West County, Chesterfield, MO
Friendship Village Retirement Center, Waterloo, IA
Friendsview Manor Infirmary, Newburg, OR
Friendswood Arms Convalescent Center, Friendswood, TX
Frigon Nursing Home Inc, Central Falls, RI
Frio County Nursing Center, Pearsall, TX
Froh Community Home, Sturgis, MI
Frontier Manor, Gainesville, TX
Frontier-Extended Care, Longview, WA
Frost Street Convalescent Hospital, San Diego, CA
Frostburg Village Nursing Home of Allegany County, Frostburg, MD
Fryeburg Health Care Center, Fryeburg, ME
Fueller Nursing Home, Saint Louis, MO
Fullerton Care Convalescent Hospital, Fullerton, CA
Fullerton Manor, Fullerton, NE
Fulton County Infirmary, Gloversville, NY
Fulton County Medical Center, McConnellsburg, PA
Fulton Manor Care Center, Fulton, MO
Fulton Presbyterian Manor, Fulton, MO
Furgala Nursing Home, Lancaster, NY
G and R Health Care Facility, Tuskegee, AL
G B Cooley Hospital for Mentally Retarded, West Monroe, LA
G N Wilcox Memorial Hospital and Health Center, Lihue, HI
The Gables Convalescent Home Inc, Hartford, CT
Gables Nursing Home, Madison, OH
Gade ICF/MR, Union City, OH
Gade Nursing Home Inc, Greenville, OH
Gade Nursing Home Inc, Greenville, OH
Gadsden Health Care Center Inc, Gadsden, AL
Gadsden Nursing Home, Quincy, FL
Gafney Home for the Aged, Rochester, NH
Gainesville Convalescent Center, Gainesville, TX
Gainesville Health Care Center, Gainesville, GA
Gainesville Manor, Hopkinsville, KY
Gainesville Nursing Center, Gainesville, FL
Galaxy Manor Nursing Home, Cleveland, TX
Gale Home, Manchester, NH

Galen State Hospital, Deer Lodge, MT
Galena Manor Health Center, Galena, KS
Galena Park Home, Peoria, IL
Galena-Stauss Hospital and Nursing Care Facility, Galena, IL
Galesburg Nursing and Rehabilitation Center, Galesburg, IL
Galion Nursing Home, Galion, OH
Gallant Rest Home, Gardner, MA
Gallatin County Rest Home, Bozeman, MT
Gallatin Nursing Home Inc, Gallatin, TN
Gallipolis State Institute, Gallipolis, OH
Gallup Care Center, Gallup, NM
Gamma Road Lodge, Wellsville, MO
Garber Nursing Home, Garber, OK
Garber's University Nursing Center, Eugene, OR
Garden City Health Care Center, Garden City, AL
Garden County Lewellen Nursing Home, Lewellen, NE
Garden Court Convalescent Hospital, Sacramento, CA
Garden Crest Convalescent Hospital Inc, Los Angeles, CA
Garden Gate Manor, Cheektowaga, NY
Garden Grove Convalescent Hospital, Garden Grove, CA
Garden Grove Nursing Home, Kansas City, MO
Garden Manor Extended Care Center Inc, Middletown, OH
Garden Manor Nursing Home Inc, Lakewood, CO
Garden Nursing Home, Phillipsburg, NJ
Garden Nursing Home and Convalescent Hospital, Santa Cruz, CA
Garden of the Gods Care Center, Colorado Springs, CO
Garden Plaza Convalescent Hospital, Los Angeles, CA
Garden State Health Care Center, East Orange, NJ
Garden State Manor, Holmdel, NJ
Garden Terrace Manor, Spokane, WA
Garden Terrace Nursing Center, Douglasville, GA
Garden Terrace Nursing Center, Graham, TX
Garden Terrace Nursing Home, Chatham, NJ
Garden Valley Retirement Village, Garden City, KS
Garden View Care Center, Shenandoah, IA
Garden View Home Inc, Chicago, IL
Garden Villa Nursing Home, El Campo, TX
Garden Village, Baltimore, MD
Gardena Convalescent Center, Gardena, CA
Gardendale Nursing Home, Gardendale, AL
Gardendale Nursing Home, Jacksonville, TX
The Gardens—Laguna Convalescent Center, Laguna Beach, CA
Gardens Skilled Nursing Facility, Sacramento, CA
Gardenview Care Center, Hillsboro, OR
Gardenview Nursing Home, Cincinnati, OH
Gardiner Group Home, Gardiner, ME
Gardiner Nursing Home Inc, Houlton, ME
Gardner Heights Convalescent Center Inc, Shelton, CT
Gardner House Rest Home, Boston, MA
Gardner Manor Nursing Home, Gardner, MA
Gardner Nursing Home, Star City, AR
Gardner Pierce Nursing and Rest Home, Boston, MA

Gardner's Grove Nursing Home, Swansea, MA
Garfield Care Convalescent Hospital, Huntington Beach, CA
Garfield County Nursing Home, Jordan, MT
Garfield Memorial Hospital, Panguitch, UT
Garfield Nursing Home Inc, Oakland, CA
Garfield Park Nursing Home, Indianapolis, IN
Garland Convalescent Center, Hot Springs, AR
Garland Convalescent Center, Garland, TX
Garland Manors Nursing Home Inc, Garland, TX
Garland Rest Home, Newton, MA
Garlock Memorial Convalescent Home Inc, Hagerstown, MD
Garnets Chateau, Jerseyville, IL
Garrard Convalescent Home, Covington, KY
Garrard County Home for Senior Citizens, Lancaster, KY
Garrard County Memorial Hospital—Skilled Nursing Facility, Lancaster, KY
Garrett Park Manor, Dallas, TX
Garrison Memorial Hospital—Intermediate Care Facility, Garrison, ND
Garrison Nursing Home Inc, Baltimore, MD
Garrison Nursing Home Inc, Garrison, ND
Garrison Nursing Home Inc, Garrison, TX
Garrison Valley Center Inc, Garrison, MD
Garvey Manor, Hollidaysburg, PA
Garwood Home, Champaign, IL
Gasconade Manor Nursing and Care Center, Owensville, MO
Gaslite Villa Convalescent Center, Canal Fulton, OH
Gaspard's Nursing Care Center Inc, Port Arthur, TX
Gatesway Foundations Inc, Broken Arrow, OK
Gateway Care Center, Portland, OR
Gateway Care Convalescent Hospital, Hayward, CA
Gateway Intermediate Care, Clinton, IA
Gateway Manor Inc, Lincoln, NE
Gateway Nursing Home, Hartford, WI
Gateways to Better Living 1, Youngstown, OH
Gateways to Better Living 2, Youngstown, OH
Gateways to Better Living 3, Youngstown, OH
Gateways to Better Living 4, Youngstown, OH
Gateways to Better Living Inc—No 9, Youngstown, OH
Gaulden Manor Nursing Center, Baltimore, OH
Gaye Haven Intermediate Care Facility Inc, Las Vegas, NV
Gayhart's Nursing Home, Piketon, OH
Gayle Street Residential Center, Fort Morgan, CO
Gaylord Community Hospital and Nursing Home, Gaylord, MN
Gaymont Nursing Center, Norwalk, OH
Geary Community Nursing Home Inc, Geary, OK
Geer Memorial Health Center, Canaan, CT
Gem Convalescent Hospital, Los Gatos, CA
Gem State Homes Inc 1, Nampa, ID
Gem State Homes Inc 2, Meridian, ID
Gem State Homes Inc 3, Boise, ID
Gem State Homes Inc 4, Boise, ID
General Baptist Nursing Home, Mount Carmel, IL
General Baptist Nursing Home, Independence, MO
General Baptist Nursing Home Inc, Campbell, MO

General Care Convalescent Center, Clarksville, TN

General German Aged People's Home of Baltimore, Baltimore, MD

Genesee Care Center, Flint, MI

Genesee County Nursing Home, Batavia, NY

Genesee East Health Center, San Diego, CA

Genesee Hospital—Extended Care Facility, Rochester, NY

Genesee Nursing Home, Utica, NY

Geneseo Good Samaritan, Geneseo, IL

Genesis, Columbus, OH

Geneva General Hospital Nursing Home Co Inc, Geneva, NY

Geneva Lake Manor, Lake Geneva, WI

Geneva Medicare Nursing Center, Geneva, OH

Geneva Retirement Home, Geneva, IL

Geneva's Geriatric Center, Georgetown, KY

George A Martin Gerontology Center, Division of the Sightless Society of Ohio Inc, Cincinnati, OH

George Community Good Samaritan Center, George, IA

George H Nettleton Home, Kansas City, MO

George J Goldman Memorial Home for the Aged, Niles, IL

George L Harrison Memorial, Philadelphia, PA

Georgetown Manor Health Care Services, Louisville, KY

Georgetown Manors, Aledo, IL

Georgetown Nursing Home Inc, Georgetown, OH

Georgetown Sweetbriar Nursing Home Inc, Georgetown, TX

Georgia Grace Memorial Home Inc, Statesboro, GA

Georgia Manor Nursing Home, Amarillo, TX

Georgia Regional Development Learning Center, Decatur, GA

Georgia Retardation Center, Atlanta, GA

Georgia Retardation Center—Athens, Athens, GA

Georgia Street Nursing Home, Monroe, LA

Georgia War Veterans Nursing Home, Augusta, GA

Georgian—Bloomfield, Bloomfield Hills, MI

Georgian Court Nursing Home of Buffalo Inc, Buffalo, NY

Georgian Court Nursing Home of Tulsa, Tulsa, OK

Georgian East, Grosse Pointe Woods, MI

Georgian Home, Evanston, IL

Georgian House of Lakewood, Tacoma, WA

Georgian Manor, Brackenridge, PA

Geraldine L Thompson Medical Home, Allenwood, NJ

Gerarda House, Bloomington, MN

Geras Nursing Home, Mount Pleasant, TX

Geriatric Center of Grandview, Grandview, MO

Geriatric Center of Saint Louis Inc, Saint Louis, MO

Geriatric Center—Stockbridge, Stockbridge, MI

Geriatric Center-Mansfield Memorial Homes, Mansfield, OH

Geriatric Health Center, Inkster, MI

Geriatrics Nursing Center Inc, Heber Springs, AR

Geriatrics Nursing Centers Inc, Blytheville, AR

Geriatrics Nursing Centers Inc, Forrest City, AR

Geriatrics Nursing Centers Inc, Jonesboro, AR

Geriatrics Nursing Centers Inc, West Memphis, AR

Geri-Care Inc, Cleveland, OH

German Masonic Home Corp, New Rochelle, NY

German Old Folks Home Inc, Lawrence, MA

Gerrit Smith Memorial Infirmary, Eaton, NY

Gerry Nursing Home Co Inc, Gerry, NY

Gertha's Nursing Center Inc, Evansville, IN

Gethsemane Group Home, Virginia, MN

Gettysburg Lutheran Retirement Village, Gettysburg, PA

Ghana Village Home Inc, Oklahoma City, OK

Ghent Arms Nursing Home, Norfolk, VA

Gibbs and McRaven Sheltered Care Home, Jonesboro, IL

Gibbs Boarding Home, Wilmington, DE

Gibbs Care Center, Steelville, MO

Gibson Community Hospital Annex, Gibson City, IL

Gibson Manor, Gibson City, IL

Gibson Nursing Center, Aspermont, TX

Gibson Rest and Convalescent Home, Gibson, GA

Giddings Convalescent Center, Giddings, TX

Gig Harbor Group Home, Gig Harbor, WA

Gil Mor Manor, Morgan, MN

Gila County General Hospital, Globe, AZ

Gilbert Nursing Home, Leonard, TX

Gilbert Old People's Home, Ypsilanti, MI

Giles Family Care Home, Commerce City, CO

Gill Odd Fellows Home, Ludlow, VT

Gillett Nursing Home Inc, Gillett, WI

Gillette Nursing Home, Warren, OH

Gillette's Country Place, Warren, OH

Gilman Nursing Center, Gilman, IL

Gilman Nursing Home, Gilman, WI

Gilmer Convalescent Center, Gilmer, TX

Gilmer Nursing Home, Saint Augustine, FL

Gilmer Nursing Home, Ellijay, GA

Gilmore Lane Convalescent Hospital, Oroville, CA

Gilmores White Cliff Nursing Home, Greenville, PA

Gina's Granny Home, Sedalia, MO

Girdler House, Beverly, MA

Girouard Saint Jude Nursing Home Inc, South Barre, VT

Glacier Hills Nursing Center, Ann Arbor, MI

Glad Day Nursing Center, Beaumont, TX

Gladhaven Inc, Fayetteville, NC

Gladstone Convalescent Care Facility, Gladstone, OR

Gladstone Nursing Home, Kansas City, MO

Gladwin Nursing Home, Gladwin, MI

Glasgow Nursing Home, Cambridge, MD

Glasgow Rest Home, Glasgow, KY

Glasgow State—Intermediate Care Facility, Glasgow, KY

Glen Ayr Health Center, Lakewood, CO

Glen Convalescent Hospital, Stockton, CA

Glen Croft Care Center, Glendale, AZ

Glen Ellen Convalescent Hospital, Hayward, CA

Glen Field Health Care Center, Milwaukee, WI

Glen Halla Intermediate Care Facility, Henderson, NV

Glen Haven Home, Glenwood, IA

Glen Haven Personal Care Home, Lexington, KY

Glen Hill Convalescent Center, Danbury, CT

Glen Manor, Cincinnati, OH

Glen Oaks Convalescent Center, Shelbyville, TN

Glen Oaks Home, Shreveport, LA

Glen Oaks Nursing and Retirement Centers, New London, MN

Glen Oaks Nursing Home, Auburn, IN

Glen Oaks Nursing Home, Lucedale, MS

Glen Oaks Nursing Home Inc, Northbrook, IL

Glen Park, Cincinnati, OH

Glen Ridge Village, Glendale, AZ

Glen Rose Nursing Home, Glen Rose, TX

Glen Terrace Convalescent Center, Norwalk, CA

Glen Terrace Nursing Center, Seattle, WA

Glen Valley Nursing Home, Glenwood Springs, CO

Glenaire Care Center, Portland, OR

Glenburn Rest Haven Home Inc, Linton, IN

Glenburney Nursing Home, Natchez, MS

Glendale Care Center, Glendale, AZ

Glendale Health Care Center Inc, Naugatuck, CT

Glendale Home, Scotia, NY

The Glendale Home, Mansfield, OH

Glendale Manor, Topeka, KS

Glendale Nursing Home, Glendale, AZ

Glendale Nursing Home, Woburn, MA

Glendale Nursing Home Inc, Wadley, GA

Glendeen Nursing Home, Billings, MT

Glendive Coummunity Nursing Home, Glendive, MT

Glendora Meadows Inc, Wooster, OH

Glengariff Corp, Glen Cove, NY

Glenhaven, Glenwood City, WI

Glenhaven Nursing Home, Glencoe, MN

Glenkirk Campus South, Mundelein, IL

Glenlora Nursing Home, Chester, NJ

Glenmont, Columbus, OH

Glenn Haven Nursing Home, Dayton, OH

Glenn View Manor, Mineral Ridge, OH

Glenn-Mor Home, Thomasville, GA

Glennon Place, Kansas City, MO

Glenoaks Convalescent Hospital, Glendale, CA

Glenridge Center, Glendale, CA

Glenside Nursing Center, New Providence, NJ

Glenview Manor, Glasgow, KY

Glenview of Tyler Nursing Home Inc, Tyler, TX

Glenview Terrace Nursing Center, Glenview, IL

Glenville Health Care Inc, Glenville, WV

Glenvue Nursing Home, Glenville, GA

Glenward Health Care Center, Hamilton, OH

Glenway Lodge, Winchester, KY

Glenwood Care, Salt Lake City, UT

Glenwood Care Center, Defiance, OH

Glenwood Christian Nursing Home, Lamont, MI

Glenwood Convalescent Center, Florence, AL

Glenwood Convalescent Hospital, Oxnard, CA

Glenwood Estate, Independence, KS

Glenwood Hills Intermediate Care Facility, Raleigh, NC

Glenwood Manor, Decatur, GA

Glenwood Manor Convalescent Home, Lowell, MA

Glenwood Nursing Home, Glenwood, AR

Glenwood Park United Methodist Home, Princeton, WV

Glenwood Retirement Home Inc, Glenwood, MN

Glenwood Terrace Nursing Center, Glenwood, IL

Glisan Care Center Inc, Portland, OR

Gloria Dei Village Health Care Center, Holland, PA

Gloucester Manor Rest Home, Gloucester, MA

Gloversville Extended Care and Nursing Home Co Inc, Gloversville, NY

Glynn Memorial Home, Haverhill, MA

Gnaden Huetten Nursing and Convalescent Home, Lehighton, PA

Go Ye Village Medical Center, Tahlequah, OK

The Goble Home, Anderson, IN

Goddard House Home for Aged Men, Worcester, MA

Godfrey's Foothill Retreat, Brigham City, UT

Gogebic County Medical Care Facility, Wakefield, MI

Gold City Convalescent Center, Dahlonega, GA

Gold Crest Nursing Home, Cincinnati, OH

Gold Leaf Convalescent Center, Ellensburg, WA

Gold Star Nursing Home, Danville, PA

Gold Star Nursing Home, Milton, PA

Golden Acres Health Care Center, Bethany, OK

Golden Acres Inc, West Salem, IL

Golden Acres Inc, Onaga, KS

Golden Acres Intermediate Care Facility, Iva, SC

Golden Acres Manor, Carrington, ND

Golden Acres Nursing Home, Leoti, KS

Golden Age Care Center, Oregon City, OR

Golden Age Convalescent Home, Pasadena, CA

Golden Age Convalescent Hospital, Capitola, CA

Golden Age Guest Home, Sykesville, MD

Golden Age Health Care, Daytona Beach, FL

Golden Age Health Care Center, Roseville, MN

Golden Age Home, Lockhart, TX

Golden Age Inc, Lexington, NC

Golden Age Lodge of Burlington, Burlington, KS

Golden Age Manor, Amery, WI

Golden Age Manor—Aurora, Aurora, CO

Golden Age Manor—Bellfort, Houston, TX

Golden Age Manor—Holmes, Houston, TX

Golden Age Manor Inc, Centerville, IA

Golden Age Manor—Long Point, Houston, TX

Golden Age Manor—North Loop, Houston, TX

Golden Age Manor Nursing Center, Dublin, TX

Golden Age Manor—Rookin, Houston, TX

Golden Age Memorial Home, Amarillo, TX

Golden Age Nursing Center, Jena, LA

Golden Age Nursing Center, Clovis, NM

Golden Age Nursing Home, Marion, IN

Golden Age Nursing Home, Denham Springs, LA

Golden Age Nursing Home, Greenwood, MS

Golden Age Nursing Home, Brownwood, TX

Golden Age Nursing Home, Lubbock, TX

Golden Age Nursing Home, Tomahawk, WI

Golden Age Nursing Home 1, Rib Lake, WI

Golden Age Nursing Home District, Braymer, MO

Golden Age Nursing Home District 1, Stover, MO

Golden Age Nursing Home Inc, Cleburne, TX

Golden Age Nursing Home of Guthrie Inc, Guthrie, OK

Golden Age Project—Boarding Home, Blue Springs, MO

Golden Age Retirement Home, Cincinnati, OH

Golden Charm Nursing Home, Liberty, TX

Golden Circle Nursing Center, Dale, IN

Golden Crest Nursing Center Inc, North Providence, RI

Golden Crest Nursing Home, Hibbing, MN

Golden Crest Nursing Home, Atlantic City, NJ

Golden Empire Convalescent Hospital, Grass Valley, CA

Golden Gate Health Care Center, Staten Island, NY

Golden Good Shepherd Home Inc, Golden, IL

Golden Haven Home, Roby, TX

Golden Haven Nursing Home, Toledo, OH

Golden Heights Manor Inc, Bridgeport, CT

Golden Heritage Care Center, Temple, TX

Golden Heritage Nursing Home 2, Valley Mills, TX

Golden Hill Convalescent Hospital, San Diego, CA

Golden Hill Nursing Home, Milford, CT

Golden Hill Nursing Home Inc, New Castle, PA

Golden Holiday Care Center, Baird, TX

Golden Keys Nursing Home, Neodesha, KS

Golden Living Center, Danville, KY

Golden Manor Health Care Center, Brownsburg, IN

Golden Manor Health Care Center, Ladoga, IN

Golden Manor Health Care Center, Lebanon, IN

Golden Manor Inc, Steele, ND

Golden Manor Jewish Home for the Aged, San Antonio, TX

Golden Manor Nursing Home, Crane, TX

Golden Manor of Salt Lake, Salt Lake City, UT

Golden Mesa Nursing Home, Mesa, AZ

Golden Oaks Nursing Home, South Saint Paul, MN

Golden Plains Convalescent Center, Hutchinson, KS

Golden Rule Home Inc, Shawnee, OK

Golden Rule Nursing Center Inc, Richmond, IN

Golden Rule Nursing Home, Danville, IN

Golden Springs Nursing Facility Inc, Anniston, AL

Golden State Colonial Convalescent Hospital Inc, North Hollywood, CA

Golden State Habilitation Convalescent Center, Baldwin Park, CA

Golden State West Valley Convalescent Hospital, Canoga Park, CA

Golden Sunset Guest Home, Meridian, MS

Golden Triangle Convalescent Center, Port Arthur, TX

Golden Valley Nursing Home, Clinton, MO

Golden View Health Care Center, Meredith, NH

Golden Villa Nursing Home, Angleton, TX

Golden West Convalescent Hospital, Hawthorne, CA

Golden West Nursing Home Inc, Fort Collins, CO

Golden West Skills Center, Goodland, KS

Golden Years, Calhoun, KY

Golden Years Boarding Facility, Poplar Bluff, MO

Golden Years Convalescent Center, Portsmouth, OH

Golden Years Haven, Decatur, TX

Golden Years Healthcare, Hamilton, OH

The Golden Years Home, Walworth, WI

Golden Years Homestead, Fort Wayne, IN

Golden Years Lodge, Mount Pleasant, TX

Golden Years Manor, Lonoke, AR

Golden Years Manor, Felton, DE

Golden Years Nursing Home, Elkhorn, NE

Golden Years Nursing Home, Falcon, NC

Golden Years Rest Home, Lackey, KY

Golden Years Rest Home, Marlin, TX

Golden Years Retirement Center, Oxford, MS

Golden Years Retreat, Bridgeport, TX

Goldenrod Manor Care Center, Clarinda, IA

Goldwater Memorial Hospital—Extended Care Facility, New York, NY

Golf Drive Residence, Naples, FL

Golf Mill Plaza I, Niles, IL

Golf Mill Plaza II, Niles, IL

Golf View Developmental Center, Deerfield, IL

Golfcrest Nursing Home, Hollywood, FL

Golfview Manor Nursing Home, Aliquippa, PA

Golfview Nursing Home, Saint Petersburg, FL

Goliad Manor Inc, Goliad, TX

Gonzales Health Care Center, Gonzales, LA

Good Hope Convalescent Hospital, Los Angeles, CA

Good Neighbor Home, Manchester, IA

Good Neighbor Home—Fairmount, Saint Paul, MN

Good Neighbors Inc, Bridgeton, ME

Good Samaritan Center, Simla, CO

Good Samaritan Center, Idaho Falls, ID

Good Samaritan Center, Forest City, IA

Good Samaritan Center, Postville, IA

Good Samaritan Center, West Union, IA

Good Samaritan Center, Atwood, KS

Good Samaritan Center, Dodge City, KS

Good Samaritan Center, Ellis, KS

Good Samaritan Center, Junction City, KS

Good Samaritan Center, Olathe, KS

Good Samaritan Center, Winfield, KS

Good Samaritan Center, Clearbrook, MN

Good Samaritan Center, Kelliher, MN

Good Samaritan Center, Pelican Rapids, MN

Good Samaritan Center, Gibbon, NE

Good Samaritan Center, Scribner, NE

Good Samaritan Center, Superior, NE

Good Samaritan Center, Syracuse, NE

Good Samaritan Center, Hobart, OK

Good Samaritan Center, Canistota, SD

Good Samaritan Center, Canton, SD

Good Samaritan Center, Centerville, SD

Good Samaritan Center, De Smet, SD

Good Samaritan Center, Herreid, SD

Good Samaritan Center, Howard, SD

Good Samaritan Center, Lennox, SD

Good Samaritan Center, New Underwood, SD

Good Samaritan Center, Parkston, SD

Good Samaritan Center, Scotland, SD

Good Samaritan Center, Selby, SD

Good Samaritan Center, Sioux Falls, SD

Good Samaritan Center, Tripp, SD

Good Samaritan Center, Tyndall, SD

Good Samaritan Center, Wagner, SD

Good Samaritan Center 1, Wymore, NE

Good Samaritan Center—Villa Grace, Ellsworth, KS

Good Samaritan Convalescent Home, Hobart, OK

Good Samaritan Health Care, Yakima, WA

Good Samaritan Home, Quincy, IL

Good Samaritan Home, Colby, KS

Good Samaritan Home, Pine River, MN
Good Samaritan Home, Warren, MN
Good Samaritan Home, Liverpool, PA
Good Samaritan Home and Center, Beatrice, NE
Good Samaritan Home for the Aged, Saint Louis, MO
Good Samaritan Home Inc, Evansville, IN
Good Samaritan Home Inc, Oakland City, IN
Good Samaritan Home of Flanagan, Flanagan, IL
Good Samaritan Long Term Care Facility, Rugby, ND
Good Samaritan Medical Center, Zanesville, OH
Good Samaritan Nursing Center, East Grand Forks, MN
Good Samaritan Nursing Center, Parkston, SD
Good Samaritan Nursing Home, Mountain Home, AR
Good Samaritan Nursing Home, Saint Petersburg, FL
Good Samaritan Nursing Home, East Peoria, IL
Good Samaritan Nursing Home, Knoxville, IL
Good Samaritan Nursing Home, Cole Camp, MO
Good Samaritan Nursing Home, Sayville, NY
Good Samaritan Nursing Home, Avon, OH
Good Samaritan Nursing Home Inc, Delmar, NY
Good Samaritan Sunset Home, Jackson, MN
Good Samaritan Village, Moscow, ID
Good Samaritan Village, Saint Francis, KS
Good Samaritan Village, Mountain Lake, MN
Good Samaritan Village, Pipestone, MN
Good Samaritan Village, Alliance, NE
Good Samaritan Village, Sioux Falls, SD
Good Samaritan Village—Perkins Pavilion, Hastings, NE
Good Samaritan Village—Villa Grace, Hastings, NE
Good Shepard Lutheran Home of the West, Littleton, CO
The Good Shepherd Village, Springfield, OH
The Good Shepherd Home Long-Term Care Facility Inc, Allentown, PA
Good Shephard Villa, Mesa, AZ
Good Shepherd Convalescent Hospital, Santa Monica, CA
Good Shepherd Geriatric Center, Mason City, IA
Good Shepherd Health Care Facility, Lewiston, ME
Good Shepherd Home, Watford City, ND
Good Shepherd Home, Fostoria, OH
Good Shepherd Home for the Aged, Ashland, OH
Good Shepherd Lutheran Home, Rushford, MN
Good Shepherd Lutheran Home, Sauk Rapids, MN
Good Shepherd Lutheran Home for Mentally Retarded, Cornelius, OR
Good Shepherd Lutheran Old People's Home, Blair, NE
Good Shepherd Manor, Momence, IL
Good Shepherd Nursing Home, Lockwood, MO
Good Shepherd Nursing Home, Versailles, MO
Good Shepherd Nursing Home, Wheeling, WV
Good Shepherd Nursing Home 1, Eldorado, IL
Good Shepherd Nursing Home Inc, Los Angeles, CA

Good Shepherd Nursing Home Ltd, Seymour, WI
Good Shepherd Retirement Center, Peoria, AZ
Good Shepherd Villa Health Care Facility, Biddeford, ME
Good Shepherd-Fairview Home Inc, Binghamton, NY
Good Will Nursing Home, Macon, GA
Goodin's Rest Home, Columbia, KY
Goodman Gardens Nursing Home Co Inc, Rochester, NY
Goodwater Nursing Home, Goodwater, AL
Goodwill Intermediate Care Home, Brunswick, GA
Goodwill Mennonite Home Inc, Grantsville, MD
Goodwin House—Nursing Care Unit, Alexandria, VA
Goodwin's of Exeter, Exeter, NH
Gordon Good Samaritan Center, Gordon, NE
Gordon Health Care Inc, Calhoun, GA
Gordon Lane Convalescent Hospital, Fullerton, CA
Gordon Memorial Health Care Facility, Spencer, WV
Gorham Manor, Gorham, ME
Gorman Care Center, Gorman, TX
Goshen County Memorial Nursing Wing, Torrington, WY
Goshen Nursing Home, Goshen, IN
Gospel Light Nursing Home, Kingston, OH
Gosport Nursing Home, Gosport, IN
Governor Bacon Health Center—Tilton Building, Delaware City, DE
Governor Harris Homestead, Eaton, OH
Governor Winthop Nursing Home, Winthrop, MA
Governor's House Nursing Home, Westfield, MA
Gowanda Nursing Home, Gowanda, NY
Gower Convalescent Center Inc, Gower, MO
Gowrie Manor, Gowrie, IA
Grace Brethren Village, Englewood, OH
Grace Convalescent Center, Detroit, MI
Grace Home, Graceville, MN
Grace Manor, Burlington, CO
Grace Manor Nursing Home, Cincinnati, OH
Grace Nursing Home, Clinton, LA
Grace Nursing Home Inc, Livingston, CA
Grace Plaza of Great Neck, Great Neck, NY
Grace Village Health Care Facility, Winona Lake, IN
Graceland Manor, Lawson, MO
Gracelands Inc, Oxford, MS
Graceland's of Pontotoc, Pontotoc, MS
Gracell Terrace Inc, Chicago, IL
Gracewood Developmental Center, Gracewood, GA
Gracewood Developmental Center, Gracewood, GA
Gracewood Nursing Home, Gracewood, GA
Grady H Hipp Nursing Center, Greenville, SC
Grafton County Nursing Home, Woodsville, NH
Grahams Nursing Home Inc, Valencia, PA
Grampian Nursing Home, Boston, MA
Granada Convalescent Hospital, Eureka, CA
Granada de Santa Fe, Santa Fe, NM
Granada Hills Convalescent Hospital, Granada Hills, CA
Granada Nursing Home Inc, Baltimore, MD
Granbury Care Center, Granbury, TX

Grancare Nursing Center, Fond Du Lac, WI
Grancare Nursing Center, Green Bay, WI
Grand Avenue Convalescent Hospital, Long Beach, CA
Grand Avenue Rest Home, Minneapolis, MN
Grand Bay Convalescent Home, Grand Bay, AL
Grand Blanc Convalescent Center, Grand Blanc, MI
Grand Care Convalescent Hospital, Anaheim, CA
Grand Chariton Manor Inc, Brunswick, MO
Grand Haven, Cynthiana, KY
Grand Island Manor Nursing Home, Grand Island, NY
Grand Islander Health Care Center, Middletown, RI
Grand Junction Regional Center, Grand Junction, CO
Grand Lake Manor, Grove, OK
Grand Manor, Saint Louis, MO
Grand Manor Health Related Facility, Bronx, NY
Grand Oak Nursing Home, Philadelphia, PA
Grand Oaks Healthcare, Boise, ID
Grand Park Convalescent Hospital, Los Angeles, CA
Grand Place, Lakewood, CO
Grand Saline Manor, Grand Saline, TX
Grand Terrace Convalescent Hospital, Colton, CA
Grand Traverse County Medical Care Facility, Traverse City, MI
Grand Valley Care Center Inc, Pryor, OK
Grand Valley Nursing Center, Grand Rapids, MI
Grand View Health Home, Danville, PA
Grand View Home, Blair, WI
Grand View Rest Home, Fitchburg, MA
Grandview Care Center, Saint Peter, MN
Grandview Care Home Inc, Roseburg, OR
Grandview Center Inc, Athens, GA
Grandview Christian Home, Cambridge, MN
Grandview Health Care Center, Jasper, GA
Grandview Health Care Center, Grenada, MS
Grandview Health Care Inc—Oil City, Oil City, PA
Grandview Heights, Marshalltown, IA
Grandview Hospital, Sellersville, PA
Grandview Manor, Berthoud, CO
Grandview Manor, Camp Point, IL
Grandview Manor Care Center, Grandview, MO
Grandview Manor Care Center, Junction City, OR
Grandview Manor Inc, Martinsville, IN
Grandview Manor Nursing Home, Puxico, MO
Grandview Manor Nursing Home, Campbell, NE
Grandview Manor Nursing Home Inc, Dayton, OH
Grandview Nursing Center, Oelwein, IA
Grandview Nursing Home, Grandview, TX
Grandview Nursing Home Inc, Cumberland, RI
Grandview of Dayton, Dayton, IA
Grandview Quality Care Center, Dayton, OH
Grandvue Medical Care Facility, East Jordan, MI
Grange Nursing Home, Mascoutah, IL
Granger Manor, Granger, IA
Grangers Nursing Home, Northborough, MA

Grangeville Convalescent Center,
Grangeville, ID
Granite Care Home, Sauk Rapids, MN
Granite County Memorial Nursing Home,
Philipsburg, MT
Grant County Nursing Home, Sheridan, AR
Grant County Nursing Home, Petersburg, WV
Grant Cuesta Convalescent Hospital Inc,
Mountain View, CA
Grant Manor Care Center, Colfax, LA
Grants Good Samaritan Center, Grants, NM
Grants Lake Rest Home, Butler, KY
Granview Health Care Inc—Franklin, Franklin,
PA
Granville Care Nursing Inc, Oxford, NC
Granville County Group Home, Oxford, NC
Grapeland Nursing Home, Grapeland, TX
Grapevine Nursing Home, Grapevine, TX
Grasmere Resident Home Inc, Chicago, IL
Grass Valley Convalescent Hospital, Grass
Valley, CA
Gratiot County Medical Care Facility, Alma,
MI
Gravenstein Convalescent Hospital,
Sebastopol, CA
Gravette Manor, Gravette, AR
Gravois Rest Haven Inc, Saint Louis, MO
Gray Gables Recovery Home, Rochester, MN
Gray Nursing Home, Gray, GA
Graymere Nursing Center Inc, Columbia, TN
Grays Harbor Convalescent Center, Aberdeen,
WA
Grays Harbor Resthaven, Hoquiam, WA
Gray's Nursing Home Inc, Platteville, WI
Grayson Manor, Leitchfield, KY
Grayson Square Health Care Center Inc, San
Antonio, TX
Graystone Home, Franklin, TN
Graystone Manor Convalescent Center,
Portland, OR
Graystone Manor Nursing Home, Houston,
TX
Graystone Manor Nursing Home 2, Houston,
TX
Graysville Nursing Home, Graysville, TN
Great Barrington Healthcare Nursing Home,
Great Barrington, MA
Great Bend Manor, Great Bend, KS
Great Lakes Convalescent Center, Detroit, MI
Great Oaks Center, Silver Spring, MD
Great Oaks Inc, Kansas City, MO
Great Oaks Nursing Home, Roswell, GA
Great River Care Center, McGregor, IA
Great Southwest Convalescent Center, Grand
Prairie, TX
Greater East Troy Nursing Home, East Troy,
WI
Greater Harlem Nursing Home, New York,
NY
Greater Laurel Nursing Home, Laurel, MD
Greater Naples Care Center, Naples, FL
Greater Pennsylvania Ave Nursing Center Inc,
Baltimore, MD
Greeley Care Home, Greeley, NE
Greeley Healthcare Center, Stillwater, MN
Green Acres Care Center, Gooding, ID
Green Acres Community Training Center,
Gooding, ID
Green Acres Convalescent and Development
Center, Bridge City, TX
Green Acres Convalescent Center, Baytown,
TX
Green Acres Convalescent Center, Center, TX

Green Acres Convalescent Center, Huntsville,
TX
Green Acres Convalescent Center, Vidor, TX
Green Acres Convalescent Center, Ansted, WV
Green Acres Convalescent Center—Humble,
Humble, TX
Green Acres Convalescent Center—Parkdale,
Beaumont, TX
Green Acres Home for Convalescents Inc,
Wyndmoor, PA
Green Acres Intermediate Care Facility,
Milledgeville, GA
Green Acres Lodge, Rosemead, CA
Green Acres Nursing Home, North Branch,
MN
Green Acres Nursing Home, South Sioux City,
NE
Green Acres Nursing Home, Washington Court
House, OH
Green Acres Nursing Home Inc, Kenton, OH
Green Acres Personal Care Home,
Mayfield, KY
Green Acres Rest Home, Lake Charles, LA
Green Acres-Adams County Home,
Gettysburg, PA
Green Briar Nursing Center, Miami, FL
Green Cove Springs Geriatric Center, Green
Cove Springs, FL
Green Forest Convalescent Home, Hattiesburg,
MS
Green Grove Convalescent Home, North
Reading, MA
Green Hill Manor, Greensburg, KY
Green Hills Center, West Liberty, OH
Green Home, Wellsboro, PA
Green Lea Manor, Mabel, MN
Green Meadows Nursing Center Inc,
Haysville, KS
Green Meadows Nursing Home, Cheboygan,
MI
Green Mountain Nursing Home, Winooski,
VT
Green Oak Nursing Home, Brockton, MA
Green Pine Acres Nursing Home, Menahga,
MN
Green Ridge Nursing Home, Scranton, PA
Green River Rest Home, Liberty, KY
Green River Terrace Nursing Home, Auburn,
WA
Green Valley Care Center Inc, Eugene, OR
Green Valley Convalescent Center, New
Albany, IN
Green Valley Group Home, Island Falls, ME
Green Valley Health Care Center,
Carrollton, KY
Green Valley Health Care Center Inc, Dickson,
TN
Green View Nursing and Convalescent Center,
Schuylkill Haven, PA
Greenbelt Nursing Center, Greenbelt, MD
Greenbough Nursing Center, Clarksdale, MS
Greenbrae Convalescent Hospital Inc,
Greenbrae, CA
Greenbriar Convalescent Center, Howell, MI
Greenbriar Convalescent Center, Wheelersburg,
OH
The Greenbriar Home, Fayette, MO
Greenbriar Manor, Cairo, IL
Greenbriar Manor, Indianapolis, IN
Greenbriar Nursing and Convalescent Center,
Woodbury, NJ
Greenbriar Nursing and Convalescent Home,
Slidell, LA

Greenbriar Nursing Center, Bradenton, FL
Greenbriar Nursing Home, Sterling, MI
Greenbriar Nursing Home, Carthage, NY
Greenbriar Terrace Healthcare, Nashua, NH
Greenbriar-East Nursing Center, Deptford, NJ
Greenbrier Home Inc, Saint Paul, MN
Greenbrier Lodge, Piper City, IL
Greenbrier Manor, Lewisburg, WV
Greenbrier Nursing Center Inc,
Champaign, IL
Greenbrier Nursing Home, Enid, OK
Greenbrook Nursing Center, Saint
Petersburg, FL
Greenbrook Nursing Home, Greenbrook, NJ
Greencastle Nursing Home, Greencastle, IN
Greencrest Manor Inc, Greenville, TX
Greencroft Nursing Center, Goshen, IN
Greendale Health Center Inc, Sheboygan, WI
Greene Acres Manor Inc, Greene, ME
Greene Acres Nursing Home, Paragould, AR
Greene County Hospital and Nursing Home,
Eutaw, AL
Greene County Hospital—Extended Care
Facility, Leakesville, MS
Greene County Medical Center, Jefferson, IA
Greene Haven, Springfield, MO
Greene Meadows Nursing Home, White
Hall, IL
Greene Point Health Care, Union Point, GA
Greenery Nursing Home, Boston, MA
Greenfield Convalescent Center, Bridgewater
Township, NJ
Greenfield Convalescent Center, Bridgewater
Township, NJ
Greenfield Home, Princeton, IL
Greenfield Manor, Greenfield, OH
Greenfield Manor Inc, Greenfield, IA
Greenfields Nursing Home, Sainte Genevieve,
MO
Greenhaven Country Place, Sacramento, CA
Greenhaven Nursing Center Inc, Greensboro,
NC
Greenhill Farm, Parsonfield, ME
Green-Hill Manor Inc, Fowler, IN
Greenhill Residence, Biddeford, ME
Greenhills Nursing Home, DeQuincy, LA
Greenhurst Nursing Home, Charleston, AR
Greenlawn Health Care Center, Mentor, OH
Greenlawn Nursing Home, Middleboro, MA
Greenleaf Extension, Moorestown, NJ
Greenleaf House Nursing Home, Salisbury,
MA
Greenleaf Nursing and Convalescent Center,
Doylestown, PA
Greenpark Care Center, Brooklyn, NY
Greenridge Heights Convalescent Hospital,
Richmond, CA
Greenridge Nursing Center, Big Rapids, MI
Green's Geriatric Health Center Inc, Gary, IN
Green's Rest Home, Frankfort, KY
Green's Rest Home, Kenedy, TX
Greensboro Health Care Center, Greensboro,
NC
Greensboro Nursing Home, Greensboro, VT
Greensboro Nursing Home Inc,
Greensboro, AL
Greensburg Home, Greensburg, PA
Greensburg Nursing Home, Greensburg, IN
Greentree Manor Convalescent Home,
Waterford, CT
Greentree Nursing Center, Oak Lawn, IL
Greentree Nursing Home, Clintonville, WI
Greenvale Convalescent Hospital, San
Pablo, CA

Greenview Manor, Waco, TX

Greenview Manor Nursing Home, Wakefield, MA

Greenview Nursing Home, Grand Rapids, MI

Greenview Nursing Home, Bagley, MN

Greenview Pavilion, Chicago, IL

Greenville Convalescent Home Inc, Greenville, MS

Greenville Nursing Home, Greenville, AL

Greenville Nursing Home Inc, Greenville, TX

Greenville Villa, Greenville, NC

Greenway Manor, Spring Green, WI

Greenwich Bay Manor, East Greenwich, RI

Greenwich Laurelton Nursing and Convalescent Home, Greenwich, CT

Greenwood Acres Nursing Home, Baltimore, MD

Greenwood Community Residence, Greenwood, SC

Greenwood Convalescent Center, Greenwood, IN

Greenwood Health Center, Hartford, CT

Greenwood House Nursing Home Inc, Warwick, RI

Greenwood Manor, Xenia, OH

Greenwood Manor Nursing Home, Jerseyville, IL

Greenwood Nursing Care Center Inc, East Lebanon, ME

Greenwood Nursing Home, Wakefield, MA

Greenwood Nursing Home Inc, Greenwood, SC

Greenwood Oaks Rest Home, Warwick, RI

Greenwood Park Care Center Inc, Seattle, WA

Greenwood Quality Care Center, Hamilton, OH

Greenwood Residence East, Saint Paul, MN

Greenwood Residence West, Saint Louis Park, MN

Greer Health Care Inc, Greer, SC

Gregg Home for the Aged Inc, Kilgore, TX

Gregory Home, Topsham, ME

Gregston Nursing Home, Marlow, OK

Greycliff at Cape Ann Nursing Home, Gloucester, MA

Greynolds Park Manor, North Miami Beach, FL

Greystone on the Greene Inc, Philadelphia, PA

Griffeth Nursing Home, Ashland, OH

Griffeth Nursing Home, Lexington, OH

Griffin Nursing Center, Knoxville, IA

Griffin White Home, Haverhill, MA

Griggs County Nursing Home, Cooperstown, ND

Griswold Care Center Inc, Griswold, IA

Groesbeck Park Plaza, Groesbeck, TX

Gronna Good Samaritan Center, Lakota, ND

Gross Convalescent Hospital, Lodi, CA

Grosse Nursing Home Inc, Kansas City, MO

Grotgen Nursing Home Inc, Wilmington, NC

Groton Community Health Care Center Residential Care Facility, Groton, NY

Groton Regency Retirement and Nursing Center, Groton, CT

Group Home I, Ellsworth, WI

Group Homes of Winona Inc, Winona, MN

Grouse Valley Manor, Dexter, KS

Grove Center Rest Home, Morganfield, KY

The Grove Health Care Center, Neptune, NJ

Grove Manor, Grove City, PA

Grove Manor Nursing Home Inc, Waterbury, CT

Grove Manor Nursing Home Inc, Honey Grove, TX

Grove School Resident Center, Lake Forest, IL

Grovecrest Convalescent Center, Pontiac, MI

Grovemont Nursing and Rehabilitation Center, Winter Haven, FL

Grover C Dils Medical Center, Caliente, NV

Groveton Hospital and Nursing Home, Groveton, TX

Grundy County Home, Morris, IL

Grundy County Memorial Hospital—Nursing Home, Grundy Center, IA

Gruter Foundation Inc, Wooster, OH

Guardian Angel Nursing Home, Green Bay, WI

Guardian Angel Nursing Home Inc, Kansas City, MO

Guardian Care Convalescent Center, Orlando, FL

Guardian Care of Ahoskie, Ahoskie, NC

Guardian Care of Burgaw Inc, Burgaw, NC

Guardian Care of Elizabeth City, Elizabeth City, NC

Guardian Care of Elkin, Elkin, NC

Guardian Care of Farmville, Farmville, NC

Guardian Care of Gastonia, Gastonia, NC

Guardian Care of Goldsboro, Goldsboro, NC

Guardian Care of Henderson, Henderson, NC

Guardian Care of Kenansville, Kenansville, NC

Guardian Care of Kinston Inc, Kinston, NC

Guardian Care of Monroe Inc, Monroe, NC

Guardian Care of New Bern, New Bern, NC

Guardian Care of Roanoke Rapids, Roanoke Rapids, NC

Guardian Care of Rocky Mount, Rocky Mount, NC

Guardian Care of Scotland Neck, Scotland Neck, NC

Guardian Care of Walnut Cove, Walnut Cove, NC

Guardian Care of Zebulon, Zebulon, NC

Guardian Convalescent Hospital, Los Angeles, CA

Guardian Nursing Home, Wakefield, MA

The Guest House, Shreveport, LA

Guest House, Rochester, MN

Guest House of Baton Rouge, Baton Rouge, LA

Guest House of Nashville, Nashville, AR

Guest House of Slidell, Slidell, LA

Guidance Center Sanitarium, Anaheim, CA

Guilderland Center Nursing Home Inc, Guilderland Center, NY

Guilford Convalesarium, Fayetteville, PA

Guilliams Family Home, West Lafayette, OH

Guinn Nursing Home 1, Jay, OK

Guinn Nursing Home 2, Jay, OK

Gulf Coast Center, Fort Myers, FL

Gulf Coast Convalescent Center, Panama City, FL

Gulf Coast Nursing Home of Moss Point Inc, Pascagoula, MS

Gulf Convalescent Center, Fort Walton Beach, FL

Gulfport Convalescent Center, Gulfport, FL

Gulfport Convalescent Center, Gulfport, MS

Gunderson's Retirement Home, Evergreen Park, IL

Gunnison Nursing Home, Gunnison, CO

Gunnison Valley Hospital, Gunnison, UT

Guthrie Nursing Center, Guthrie, OK

Guy and Mary Felt Manor Inc, Emporium, PA

Gwynedd Square for Nursing Convalescent Care, Lansdale, PA

H J Vonderlieth Living Center, Mount Pulaski, IL

Habersham Home, Demorest, GA

Hacienda Convalescent Hospital, Concord, CA

Hacienda Convalescent Hospital, Long Beach, CA

Hacienda Convalescent Hospital, Petaluma, CA

Hacienda Convalescent Hospital, Porterville, CA

Hacienda Convalescent Hospital, Roseville, CA

Hacienda Convalescent Hospital, San Luis Obispo, CA

Hacienda Convalescent Hospital, Ukiah, CA

Hacienda Convalescent Hospital, Van Nuys, CA

Hacienda Convalescent Hospital, Woodland, CA

Hacienda Convalescent Hospital—North, Pasadena, CA

Hacienda Convalescent Hospital—South, Pasadena, CA

Hacienda Convalescent Hospitals Inc, Hanford, CA

Hacienda Convalescent Hospitals Inc, Livermore, CA

Hacienda de la Mesa Convalescent Hospital, La Mesa, CA

Hadley Manor, Detroit, MI

Hage House, Bloomington, IL

Hahn Rest Home, Springfield, MA

Haida Manor, Hastings, PA

Halcyon House, Washington, IA

Halcyon House Rest Home, Methuen, MA

Hale Aloha Convalescent Hospital, Ceres, CA

Hale Convalescent and Nursing Home Inc, Groton, MA

Hale Ho Aloha, Honolulu, HI

Hale Makua Home Health Care Agency, Wailuku, Maui, HI

Hale Makua - Wailuku, Wailuku, HI

Hale Malamalama, Honolulu, HI

Hale Nani Health Center, Honolulu, HI

Hale-Barnard Home, Boston, MA

Hales Rest Home, Spanish Fork, UT

Hall Health Care Center, Aiken, SC

Hallandale Rehabilitation Center, Hallandale, FL

Hallmark Anderson Health Care, Houston, TX

Hallmark Care Center, Mount Vernon, IA

Hallmark Care Center, Omaha, NE

Hallmark House Nursing Home, Pekin, IL

Hallmark Manor Nursing Home, Indianapolis, IN

Hallmark Nursing Centre, Glens Falls, NY

Hallmark Nursing Centre, Minoa, NY

Hallmark Nursing Centre, Troy, NY

Hallmark Nursing Centre Inc, Schenectady, NY

Hallmark Nursing Home, Warner Robins, GA

Hallmark Nursing Home, East Bridgewater, MA

Hallmark Nursing Home of New Bedford, New Bedford, MA

Hallworth House, Providence, RI

Halstad Lutheran Memorial Home, Halstad, MN

Halstead Nursing Center, Halstead, KS

Halsted Manor, Harvey, IL

Halsted Terrace Nursing Center, Chicago, IL

Haltom Convalescent Center, Fort Worth, TX

Hamburg Center, Hamburg, PA

Hamburg Center Annex, Wernersville, PA

Hamden Health Care Facility, Hamden, CT

Hamilton Arms of Pennsylvania, Lancaster, PA

Hamilton County Eastern Star Home Inc, Cincinnati, OH

Hamilton County Nursing Home, Chattanooga, TN

Hamilton County Rest Home, Syracuse, KS

Hamilton Grove, New Carlisle, IN

Hamilton Heights Health Center, Arcadia, IN

Hamilton Hill Crest Manor, Hamilton, MO

Hamilton House, Columbus, GA

Hamilton House Nursing Home, Needham, MA

Hamilton Manor, Aurora, NE

Hamilton Manor Nursing Home, Rochester, NY

Hamilton Memorial Home, Two Rivers, WI

Hamilton Nursing Home, Detroit, MI

Hamilton Nursing Home, Hamilton, TX

Hamilton Nursing Home Inc, Beaumont, TX

Hamilton Pavilion Healthcare, Norwich, CT

Hamilton's Personal Care Home, Ashland, KY

Hamlet Manor, Chagrin Falls, OH

Hamlin Terrace Health Care Center, Buffalo, NY

Hammer Residence, Wayzata, MN

Hammer Residence Group Home 1, Minnetonka, MN

Hammond Holiday Home Inc, Larned, KS

Hammond House Convalescent Home, Worcester, MA

Hammond Nursing Home, Hammond, IN

Hammond Nursing Home, Hammond, LA

Hammond Rest Home, Fenton, MI

Hammond State School, Hammond, LA

Hammond-Whiting Convalescent Center, Whiting, IN

Hampden House Retirement Home, Springfield, MA

Hampshire Charitable Hospital, North Hampton, MA

Hampshire Manor Nursing Home, Easthampton, MA

Hampstead Nursing Home, Hampstead, TX

Hampton Convalescent Center, Hampton, VA

Hampton Court, West Jefferson, OH

Hampton House, Wilkes-Barre, PA

Hampton Manor, Bay City, MI

Hampton Nursing Care Inc, Alhambra, IL

Hampton Nursing Center Inc, Sumter, SC

Hampton Nursing Home, Hampton, AR

Hampton Nursing Home, Hampton, IA

Hanceville Nursing Home, Hanceville, AL

Hancock County Nursing Home, Carthage, IL

Hancock County Rest Haven, Lewisport, KY

Hancock County Sheltered Care, Augusta, IL

Hancock Park Convalescent Hospital, Los Angeles, CA

Handicap Village of Northwest Iowa, Sheldon, IA

Handmaker Jewish Geriatric Center, Tucson, AZ

Hannah B G Shaw Home for the Aged Inc, Middleborough, MA

Hannah Browning Home, Mount Vernon, OH

Hannah Duston Long Term Health Care Facility, Haverhill, MA

Hannah M Rutledge Home for the Aged, Chippewa Falls, WI

Hannibal Care Center, Hannibal, MO

Hannum Memorial Rest Home Inc, Bradford, PA

Hanover Hall, Hanover, PA

Hanover Hill Healthcare Center, Manchester, NH

Hanover House, Birmingham, AL

Hanover House Inc, Massillon, OH

Hanover House Retirement Facility, Fall River, MA

Hanover Nursing Center, Hanover, IN

Hanover Terrace Healthcare, Hanover, NH

Hansford Manor, Spearman, TX

Hanson Court Convalescent Center, Springfield, VT

Hanson Nursing Home, Natick, MA

Happiness House Rest Home, Plymouth, MA

Happy Acres Convalescent Home Inc, Hattiesburg, MS

Happy Acres Rest Home, Ronan, MT

Happy Harbor Methodist Home, La Porte, TX

Happy Haven Nursing Center, Abilene, TX

Happy Siesta Nursing Home, Remsen, IA

Haralson County Nursing Home, Bremen, GA

Harbert Hills Academy Nursing Home, Savannah, TN

Harbor Beach Community Hospital, Harbor Beach, MI

Harbor Beach Convalescent Home, Fort Lauderdale, FL

Harbor Convalescent Hospital, Torrance, CA

Harbor Crest Home Inc, Fulton, IL

Harbor Crest Pavilion (D P of San Pedro Peninsula Hospital), San Pedro, CA

Harbor Health Care, Aberdeen, WA

Harbor Hills, Santa Cruz, CA

Harbor Home, York Harbor, ME

Harbor Inn Nursing Home Inc, Boston, MA

Harbor View House, San Pedro, CA

Harbor View Manor, West Haven, CT

Harbor View Rest Home, Barnstable, MA

Harborview Development Center, Valdez, AK

Harborview Manor Nursing Home, Dartmouth, MA

Harborview Nursing Home Inc, Morehead City, NC

Hardee Manor Nursing Home, Wachula, FL

Hardin County Home, Kenton, OH

Hardin County Nursing Home, Savannah, TN

Hardin Home Nursing Home, Savannah, TN

Harding Nursing Home, Waterville, NY

Harford Gardens Convalescent Center Inc, Baltimore, MD

Harlan Appalachian Regional Hospital—Extended Care Facility, Harlan, KY

Harlan Health Care Center, Harlan, KY

Harlan Morris Home, Trenton, TN

Harlee Manor, Springfield, PA

Harlem Rest Home, Harlem, MT

Harlingen Good Samaritan Center, Harlingen, TX

Har-Lyn Care Center, Portland, OR

Harmony Community Hospital, Harmony, MN

Harmony Golden Years Home Inc, Jeannette, PA

Harmony House, Brewster, WA

Harmony House Health Care Center, Waterloo, IA

Harmony House Nursing Home, Shreveport, LA

Harmony House Nursing Home, Bend, OR

Harmony Nursing Home, Saint Paul, MN

Harold Group Home, Olathe, CO

Harold S Haaland Home, Rugby, ND

Harper Community Care Home, Harper, KS

Harper Home for the Aged, Edmonton, KY

Harpeth Terrace Convalescent Center Inc, Franklin, TN

Harral's Nursing Home Inc, Buhl, ID

Harrell Memorial Nursing Home, Charleston, WV

Harris Avenue Rest Home, Boston, MA

Harris Nursing Home Inc, East Providence, RI

Harrisburg Manor Inc, Harrisburg, IL

Harrison House, Snow Hill, MD

Harrison House, Christiana, PA

Harrison House Inc, Cincinnati, OH

Harrison Memorial Extended Care Facility, Cynthiana, KY

Harrison Nursing Home, Harrison, AR

Harrisonburg Nursing Center, Harrisonburg, LA

Harrison's Sanatorium, Lexington, KY

Harrod Nursing Home, Centerburg, OH

Harrodsburg Health Care Center, Harrodsburg, KY

Harr-Wood Nursing Home, Oswego, NY

Harry Meyering Center, Mankato, MN

Harry S Truman Restorative Center, Saint Louis, MO

Harston Hall Nursing Home Inc, Chestnut Hill, PA

Hart Care Center, Hartwell, GA

Hart County Personal Care Home, Munfordville, KY

Hartford City Community Care Center, Hartford City, IN

Hartford Manor, Hartford, KS

Hartley Hall Inc, Pocomoke City, MD

Hartville Manor Nursing Home, Hartville, OH

Hartville Meadows, Hartville, OH

Hartwyck at Plainfield, Plainfield, NJ

Hartwyck Nursing Home, Paramus, NJ

Hartwyck West Nursing Home, Cedar Grove, NJ

Harty Nursing Home, Knightsville, IN

Harvard Manor Nursing Home, Cambridge, MA

Harvard Nursing Home Inc, Worcester, MA

Harvard Rest Haven, Harvard, NE

Harvest Heights Baptist Home Center, Decatur, GA

Harvest Home Estates, Kansas City, MO

Harvest Manor Nursing Home, Denham Springs, LA

Harvey E Rinehart Memorial Hospital, Wheeler, OR

Harvey's Love and Care Home, Six Mile, SC

Haskell Nursing Center, Haskell, TX

Haskell Nursing Center Inc, Haskell, OK

Haskins Nursing Home, Secane, PA

Hass Hillcrest Care Center, Hawarden, IA

Hassler Home, Shillington, PA

Haster Convalescent Hospital, Garden Grove, CA

Hastings Regional Center, Hastings, NE

Hattie Ide Chaffee Home, East Providence, RI

Hattie Larlham Foundation, Mantua, OH

Hattiesburg Convalescent Center, Hattiesburg, MS

Hautamaki Westgate Rest Home, Ironwood, MI

Haven Convalescent Home Inc, New Castle, PA

Haven Crest Inc, Monongahelia, PA

Haven Hall Nursing Center, Brookhaven, MS

Haven Hill Residential Home, Harrington, DE

Haven Home of Kenesaw, Kenesaw, NE

Haven Home of Red Wing, Red Wing, MN

Haven Homes Health Center, Hastings, MN
Haven Homes of Maple Plain, Maple Plain, MN
Haven House, Omaha, NE
Haven House, Wahoo, NE
Haven in the Hills, Bostic, NC
Haven Manor, Far Rockaway, NY
Haven Manor, Waco, TX
Haven Manor Nursing Home Inc, Kansas City, MO
Haven Nursing Home, Baltimore, MD
Haven Nursing Home, Boston, MA
Haven Nursing Home, Mexia, TX
Haven of Our Lady of Peace, Pensacola, FL
Haven of Rest Inc, Greentop, MO
Haven Park Nursing Center, Zeeland, MI
Haven Retirement Center, Springfield, IL
Havenwood Care Center Inc, Marysville, WA
Havenwood Nursing Home, Concord, NH
Havenwood Rest Home, New Bedford, MA
Haverford Nursing and Rehabilitation Center, Havertown, PA
Haverhill Manor Nursing Home, Haverhill, MA
Hawkins Care Center, Hawkins, TX
Hawkins Rest Home, West Haven, CT
Haws Memorial Nursing Home, Fulton, KY
Hawthorne Convalescent Center, Hawthorne, CA
Hawthorne House, Bovey, MN
Hawthorne House, Sedalia, MO
Hawthorne Lodge of Hillsboro, Hillsboro, IL
Hawthorne Lodge of Sullivan, Sullivan, IL
Hawthorne Manor Retirement, Spokane, WA
Hawthorne Nursing Center, Charlotte, NC
Haxtun Hospital District, Haxtun, CO
Hayden House, Hallowell, ME
Hayden Manor Nursing Home, Scottsdale, AZ
Hayden's Personal Care Home, Lexington, KY
Hayes Care Home, Baltimore, MD
Hayes Convalescent Hospital, San Francisco, CA
Hayes Residence, Saint Paul, MN
Haym Salomon Home for the Aged, Brooklyn, NY
Hays Good Samaritan Center, Hays, KS
Hays House Nursing Home, Nowata, OK
Hayward Convalescent Hospital, Hayward, CA
Hayward Nursing Home, Hayward, WI
Hayward Rehabilitation Hospital, Hayward, CA
Hazard Nursing Home, Hazard, KY
Hazel Dell Care Center, Vancouver, WA
Hazel Hawkins Memorial Hospital, Hollister, CA
Hazel I Findlay Country, Saint Johns, MI
Hazel Wilson Residential Care, Chicago, IL
Hazelcrest Nursing Home, Bloomfield, NJ
Hazelden Foundation, Center City, MN
Hazelden Pioneer House, Plymouth, MN
Hazel's Rest Home, Watertown, SD
Hazelwood Intermediate Care Facility, Louisville, KY
Hazen Nursing Home, West Valley City, UT
Hazle Memorial Baptist Home, Virden, IL
Healdsburg Convalescent Center, Healdsburg, CA
Healdton Nursing Home, Healdton, OK
Healing Springs Intermediate Care Facility Inc, Blackville, SC
Health Care Center at Abbey Delray South, Delray Beach, FL

Health Care Institute, Washington, DC
Health Care Manor, New Hampton, IA
Health Center, Alliance, OH
Health Center at Abbey Delray, Delray Beach, FL
Health Havens Inc, East Providence, RI
Health Inn Inc, Fayetteville, TN
Health Related Facility and Nursing Home Company of Rome Inc, Rome, NY
Healthaven Nursing Home, Akron, OH
Healthwin Hospital, South Bend, IN
Heardmont Health Care Center, Elberton, GA
Heart Manor, Commerce, TX
Heart Manor Nursing Home, Navasota, TX
Heart of Georgia Nursing Home, Eastman, GA
Heart of the Valley, Corvallis, OR
The Hearth, Corpus Christi, TX
Hearthside Homes, Tower, MN
Hearthside Nursing Home Inc, Chicago, IL
Hearthside Rehabilitation Center, Brown Deer, WI
Hearthside Rehabilitation Center, Milwaukee, WI
The Hearthstone, York, NE
Hearthstone, Seattle, WA
Hearthstone Manor, Medford, OR
Hearthstone Nursing Center, Saint John, KS
Hearthstone Nursing Home, Fort Worth, TX
Hearthstone Nursing Home, Tyler, TX
Hearthstone Nursing Home Inc, Stillwater, OK
Heartland—Beavercreek, Dayton, OH
Heartland Care Center—Belleville, Belleville, KS
Heartland Development Center—Haven, Haven, KS
Heartland Home, Park Rapids, MN
Heartland Manor, Wakeeny, KS
Heartland—McPherson, McPherson, KS
Heartland of Beckley, Beckley, WV
Heartland of Bucyrus, Bucyrus, OH
Heartland of Cedar Springs, New Paris, OH
Heartland of Charleston, Charleston, WV
Heartland of Chillicothe, Chillicothe, OH
Heartland of Clarksburg, Clarksburg, WV
Heartland of Connersville, Connersville, IN
Heartland of Eaton, Eaton, OH
Heartland of Greenville, Greenville, OH
Heartland of Jackson, Jackson, OH
Heartland of Kettering, Kettering, OH
Heartland of Keyser, Keyser, WV
Heartland of Marietta, Marietta, OH
Heartland of Martinsburg, Martinsburg, WV
Heartland of Marysville, Marysville, OH
Heartland of Perrysburg, Perrysburg, OH
Heartland of Portsmouth, Portsmouth, OH
Heartland of Preston County, Kingwood, NH
Heartland of Preston County, Kingwood, WV
Heartland of Springfield, Springfield, OH
Heartland of Urbana, Urbana, OH
Heartland Rehabilitation Center, Wichita, KS
Heartland Terrace—Independence, Independence, KS
Heartland Thurber Village, Columbus, OH
Heartland-Lansing, Lansing, OH
Heartwood Avenue Living Center, Vallejo, CA
Heath Nursing and Convalescent Center, Newark, OH
Heather Hill, Willmar, MN
Heather Hill Inc, Chardon, OH
Heather Hill Nursing Home, New Port Richey, FL
Heather Manor, Hope, AR

Heather Manor, Des Moines, IA
Heather Manor Nursing Center, Harvey, IL
Heatherbank, Columbia, PA
Heathergreen II Inc, Jamestown, OH
Heathergreene I, Xenia, OH
Heathside Haven Inc, Laurel, MS
Heathwood Health Care Center Inc, Williamsville, NY
Heathwood Nursing Home, Newton, MA
Heatland-Fairfield, Thornville, OH
Heaton House, Montpelier, VT
Heavener Nursing Home Inc, Heavener, OK
Heber Valley Care Center, Heber City, UT
Hebert's Nursing Home Inc, Smithfield, RI
Hebrew Home and Hospital, Hartford, CT
Hebrew Home for Aged Disabled, San Francisco, CA
Hebrew Home for the Aged at Fairfield, Bronx, NY
Hebrew Home for the Aged at Riverdale, Bronx, NY
Hebrew Home for the Aged—North Dade, North Miami Beach, FL
Hebrew Home of Greater Washington, Rockville, MD
Hebrew Hospital for the Chronic Sick, Bronx, NY
Heffner's Ivy Cottage Nursing Home, Waynesville, OH
Hefner Village Nursing Center, Oklahoma City, OK
Heinzerling Developmental Center, Columbus, OH
Helen Evans Home for Retarded Children, Hacienda Heights, CA
Helen Lewis Smith Pavilion, Fairbury, IL
Helen Newberry Joy Hospital, Newberry, MI
Helen Porter Nursing Home, Middlebury, VT
Helen Purcell Home, Zanesville, OH
Helen Raney Nursing Home Inc, Broken Arrow, OK
Helen Wilkes Nursing Home, Lake Park, FL
Helena Nursing Home Co, Helena, MT
Hel-Ene Nursing Home, Delaware, OH
Helix View Nursing Home Inc, El Cajon, CA
Hellenic Nursing Home for Aged, Canton, MA
Helmwood Care Home, Tribune, KS
Helton's Nursing Home, Hamilton, OH
Hemet Convalescent Hospital, Hemet, CA
Hemlock Nursing Home, Waynesville, NC
Hempstead Park Nursing Home, Hempstead, NY
Henard Sheltered Care Home, Jonesboro, IL
Henderson Convalescent Center, Henderson, NV
Henderson Nursing Home Inc, Morgantown, IN
Henderson Rest Home, Henderson, KY
Henderson's Personal Care, Jackson, MS
Hendersonville Nursing Home, Hendersonville, TN
Hendricks Community Hospital, Hendricks, MN
Hendricks County Home, Danville, IN
Hendry Convalescent Center, Plymouth, MI
Hennesey Nursing Home Inc, Giddings, TX
Hennessey Care Center, Hennessey, OK
Henning Nursing Home, Henning, MN
Hennis Care Center, Dover, OH
Henrietta Care Center, Henrietta, TX
Henry C Nevins Home Inc, Methuen, MA
Henry County Hospital and Nursing Home, Abbeville, AL

Henry County Memorial Hospital, Mount
  Pleasant, IA
Henry County Nursing Home, Paris, TN
Henry G Long Asylum, Lancaster, PA
Henry Hagen Residence, Hastings, MN
Henry Thodes Oakwood Villa, Altoona, WI
Henryton Center, Henryton, MD
Hensley Nursing Home, Sayre, OK
The Heritage, San Francisco, CA
The Heritage, Girard, KS
Heritage 53, Moline, IL
Heritage Acres Care Center, Cedar Rapids, IA
Heritage Care Center, Iowa Falls, IA
Heritage Care Center, Shelby, OH
Heritage Center, Conway, AR
Heritage Convalescent and Rehabilitation
  Center, Tacoma, WA
Heritage Convalescent Center, Atlanta, GA
Heritage Convalescent Center, Amarillo, TX
Heritage Convalescent Center of Torrance,
  Torrance, CA
Heritage Convalescent Hospital,
  Sacramento, CA
Heritage Gardens, Loma Linda, CA
Heritage Hall, Lawrenceburg, KY
Heritage Hall, Centralia, MO
Heritage Hall Health Care I, Blacksburg, VA
Heritage Hall Health Care II, Big Stone Gap,
  VA
Heritage Hall Health Care III, Tazewell, VA
Heritage Hall Health Care IV, Blackstone, VA
Heritage Hall Health Care IX, Dillwyn, VA
Heritage Hall Health Care V, Leesburg, VA
Heritage Hall Health Care VI, Nassawadox, VA
Heritage Hall Health Care VIII, Clintwood, VA
Heritage Hall Nursing Home, Agawam, MA
Heritage Hall Nursing Home, Tinton Falls, NJ
Heritage Hall Nursing Home—West, Agawam,
  MA
Heritage Hall Retirement and Nursing Home,
  Agawam, MA
Heritage Haven Care Center, Schofield, WI
Heritage Health Care Center, Tuscaloosa, AL
Heritage Health Care Center, Takoma Park,
  MD
Heritage Health Care Center, Gering, NE
Heritage Healthcare Inc, West Lafayette, IN
Heritage Hills Nursing Centre, Smithfield, RI
Heritage Home, Parsons, KS
Heritage Home, Winthrop, ME
Heritage Home, Plainview, TX
Heritage Home Care Center, Saint Elmo, IL
Heritage Home of Bancroft, Bancroft, IA
Heritage Home of Florence Inc, Florence, SC
The Heritage House, Kankakee, IL
Heritage House, Atlantic, IA
Heritage House, Orange City, IA
Heritage House, Miami, OK
Heritage House, Wilkes-Barre, PA
Heritage House, Eagle Lake, TX
Heritage House, Rosebud, TX
Heritage House, Tyler, TX
Heritage House 2, Champaign, IL
The Heritage House Children's Center,
  Shelbyville, IN
Heritage House Convalescent Center,
  Martinsville, IN
The Heritage House Convalescent Center,
  Shelbyville, IN
The Heritage House Convention Center of
  Putnam Company, Greencastle, IN
Heritage House Nursing and Rehabilitation
  Center, North Miami Beach, FL

Heritage House Nursing Center Inc, Overland
  Park, KS
Heritage House Nursing Home, Valdosta, GA
Heritage House Nursing Home, Danvers, MA
Heritage House Nursing Home, Bartlesville,
  OK
Heritage House of Charleston, Charleston, IL
Heritage House of Cherry Hill, Cherry Hill, NJ
Heritage House of Greensburg, Greensburg, IN
Heritage House of New Castle, New Castle, IN
Heritage House of Richmond Inc,
  Richmond, IN
Heritage House of Vandalia, Vandalia, IL
Heritage House of Winfield, Winfield, KS
Heritage House-Columbus Jewish Home for
  the Aged, Columbus, OH
The Heritage, Bridgeport, WV
Heritage Inn, Saint Simons Island, GA
Heritage Inn—Barnesville, Barnesville, GA
Heritage Inn Nursing Home, Fairborn, OH
Heritage Inn of Hartwell, Hartwell, GA
Heritage Inn of Whigham, Whigham, GA
Heritage Living Center, Saint Paul, NE
Heritage Manor, Dubuque, IA
Heritage Manor, Findlay, OH
Heritage Manor, Canton, TX
Heritage Manor, Plano, TX
Heritage Manor Care Center, Newton, IA
Heritage Manor Care Center, Dayton, TX
Heritage Manor Convalescent Center, Flint, MI
Heritage Manor Health Care Center, Fort
  Wayne, IN
Heritage Manor Health Care Center,
  Chisholm, MN
Heritage Manor Health Care Center of
  Ligonier, Ligonier, IN
Heritage Manor Inc, Bloomington, IL
Heritage Manor Inc, Shelbyville, IN
Heritage Manor Inc, Devine, TX
Heritage Manor—Jewish Home for Aged,
  Youngstown, OH
Heritage Manor Nursing and Convalescent
  Center, Bartlesville, OK
Heritage Manor Nursing and Convalescent
  Home, Mendota, IL
Heritage Manor Nursing and Convalescent
  Home and Apartments, Peru, IL
Heritage Manor Nursing Center, Minster, OH
Heritage Manor Nursing Home, Sherman, TX
Heritage Manor Nursing Home Inc,
  Chattanooga, TN
Heritage Manor of Abbeville, Abbeville, LA
Heritage Manor of Alexandria 1, Alexandria,
  LA
Heritage Manor of Alexandria 2, Alexandria,
  LA
Heritage Manor of Alexandria—North,
  Alexandria, LA
Heritage Manor of Bossier City, Bossier City,
  LA
Heritage Manor of Crowley, Crowley, LA
Heritage Manor of Ferriday, Ferriday, LA
Heritage Manor of Franklinton, Franklinton,
  LA
Heritage Manor of Gonzales, Gonzales, LA
Heritage Manor of Hammond, Hammond, LA
Heritage Manor of Iowa Park, Iowa Park, TX
Heritage Manor of Kaplan, Kaplan, LA
Heritage Manor of Lafayette, Lafayette, LA
Heritage Manor of Mansfield, Mansfield, LA
Heritage Manor of Many 1, Many, LA
Heritage Manor of Many 2, Many, LA
Heritage Manor of Marrero, Marrero, LA

Heritage Manor of New Iberia—North, New
  Iberia, LA
Heritage Manor of New Iberia—South, New
  Iberia, LA
Heritage Manor of Shreveport, Shreveport, LA
Heritage Manor of Thibodaux, Thibodaux, LA
Heritage Manor of Vivian, Vivian, LA
Heritage Manor of Westwood, Shreveport, LA
Heritage Manor Streator, Streator, IL
Heritage Nursing and Convalescent Center,
  Mobile, AL
Heritage Nursing Center, Paris, IL
Heritage Nursing Center, Mason City, IA
Heritage Nursing Center, Haynesville, LA
Heritage Nursing Center, Sheboygan, WI
Heritage Nursing Home, Quitman, TX
Heritage Nursing Home, Port Washington, WI
Heritage Nursing Home Inc, Muskogee, OK
Heritage Nursing Home Inc, Athens, PA
Heritage Nursing Home Inc, Goldthwaite, TX
Heritage Nursing Manor, Lamesa, TX
Heritage of Bel Air, Norfolk, NE
Heritage of Bridgeport, Bridgeport, NE
Heritage of Cimarron, Cimarron, KS
Heritage of David City, David City, NE
Heritage of Edina, Edina, MN
Heritage of Elmwood Nursing Home,
  Elmwood, WI
Heritage of Fairbury, Fairbury, NE
Heritage of Geneva, Geneva, NE
Heritage of Grand Island—South, Grand
  Island, NE
Heritage of Wauneta, Wauneta, NE
Heritage of White River, White River, SD
Heritage Park, Plano, TX
Heritage Park Nursing Home, Rogers, AR
Heritage Sheltered Care Home, Hutsonville, IL
Heritage Square, Dixon, IL
Heritage Towers, Doylestown, PA
Heritage Villa of Tilden Inc, Tilden, NE
Heritage Village, Eskridge, KS
Heritage Village at Park Place Meadows,
  Raytown, MO
Heritage Village of Grand Island—North,
  Grand Island, NE
Heritage Village of Neligh, Neligh, NE
Heritage Village of Rose Hill, Rose Hill, KS
Heritage Village of Wakefield, Wakefield, KS
Herman M Wilson Health Care Center,
  Gaithersburg, MD
The Herman Sanitarium, San Jose, CA
Hermina Traeye Memorial Nursing Home,
  Johns Island, SC
Hermiston Good Samaritan Center,
  Hermiston, OR
Hermitage in Northern Virginia, Alexandria,
  VA
Hermitage Manor, Owensboro, KY
Hermitage Nursing Home, Worcester, MA
Hermitage Nursing Home Inc, Elizabethton,
  TN
Hermitage on the Eastern Shore—Nursing
  Home Unit, Onancock, VA
Herrick Nursing Home, Tecumseh, MI
Hessmer Nursing Home, Hessmer, LA
Hester Memorial Nursing Home, Dayton, OH
Hetzel Care Center Inc, Bloomer, WI
Hewitt House, Vancouver, WA
Hewitt House of People Inc, Saint Paul, MN
Hewitt Manor Inc, Shinglehouse, PA
Heywood Valley Nursing Home, Worcester,
  MA
Hi-Acres Manor Nursing Center, Jamestown,
  ND

Hialeah Convalescent Home, Hialeah, FL

Hiawatha Childrens Home, Rochester, MN

Hiawatha Manor, Pipestone, MN

Hibbard Nursing Home, Dover-Foxcroft, ME

Hickman County Nursing Home, Centerville, TN

Hickory Creek Nursing Home Inc, Dayton, OH

Hickory Creek of Athens, The Plains, OH

Hickory Elm Convalescent Center, Burkburnett, TX

Hickory Hills Nursing Center Inc, Oak Lawn, IL

Hickory House Nursing Home Inc, Honeybrook, PA

Hickory Manor Nursing Home Inc, Bastrop, LA

Hicks Golden Years Nursing Home, Monticello, KY

Hicks Nursing Home, Fryeburg, ME

Hidden Acres Manor, Mount Pleasant, TN

Hidden Hollow Rest Home, Orem, UT

Hi-Desert Convalescent Hospital, Yucca Valley, CA

Higgins Learning Center, Morganfield, KY

Higginsville State School and Hospital, Higginsville, MO

High Hope Care Center, Sulphur, LA

High Point Lodge Nursing Home, Clear Lake, MN

High Ridge Health Care Center, Racine, WI

High Street Convalescent Hospital, Oakland, CA

High Street Health Care Facility, Auburn, ME

High Street Rest Home, Fitchburg, MA

High Valley Lodge, Sunland, CA

High View Nursing Center, Peoria, IL

Highgate Manor of Cortland, Cortland, NY

Highgate Manor of Rensselaer, Troy, NY

Highland Acres Extend-A-Care Center, Winsted, CT

Highland Care, Klamath Falls, OR

Highland Care Center, Salt Lake City, UT

Highland Care Home, Abilene, KS

Highland Chateau, Saint Paul, MN

Highland Convalescent Center, Bellingham, WA

Highland Convalescent Hospital, Duarte, CA

Highland Farms Health Care Center, Black Mountain, NC

Highland Guest Care Center, Shreveport, LA

Highland Hall Care Center, New Castle, PA

Highland Hall Manor, Essex, CT

Highland Health Facility Mental Retardation Unit, Baltimore, MD

Highland Home for Aged, Genoa City, WI

Highland House Nursing Home, Grants Pass, OR

Highland House of Fayetteville, Fayetteville, NC

Highland Manor, Highland, IL

Highland Manor, New Ulm, MN

Highland Manor Nursing Home, Phoenix, AZ

Highland Manor Nursing Home, Portland, TN

Highland Manor Nursing Home, Dublin, VA

Highland Manor Nursing Home Inc, Fall River, MA

Highland Manor Rest Home, Worcester, MA

Highland Nursing Center, Ponca City, OK

Highland Nursing Center, Wichita Falls, TX

Highland Nursing Home, Highland, IN

Highland Nursing Home, San Antonio, TX

Highland Nursing Home Inc, Massena, NY

Highland Park Care Center, Houston, TX

Highland Park Center, Pittsburgh, PA

Highland Park Manor, Clinton, OK

Highland Park Manor, Enid, OK

Highland Park Manor, Okmulgee, OK

Highland Pines, Longview, TX

Highland Pines Nursing Manor, Clearwater, FL

Highland Rest Home, Boston, MA

Highland Terrace Nursing Center, Camas, WA

Highland View Nursing Home, Troy, OH

Highland Villa, Topeka, KS

Highlands Center Inc, Denver, CO

Highlands Convalescent Center Inc, Renton, WA

Highlands Homes, Princeton, KY

Highline Care Center Inc, Seattle, WA

Highline Convalescent Center, East Wenatchee, WA

Highmore Nursing Home, Highmore, SD

Highview Convalescent Hospital, Oakland, CA

Highview Manor, Madawaska, ME

Highview Retirement Home, Rockford, IL

Hilaire Farm Nursing Home, Huntington, NY

Hildebrand Care Center, Canon City, CO

Hill Country Manor, Llano, TX

Hill Crest Sheltered Care, Louisville, IL

Hill Haven Nursing and Rest Home Inc, Statesville, NC

Hill Haven Nursing Home, Syracuse, NY

Hill Haven Nursing Home, Webster, NY

Hill Nursing Home, Idabel, OK

Hill Road Convalescent Hospital, Novato, CA

Hill Top, Lake Bluff, IL

Hill Top Care Center, Pine Brook, NJ

Hill Top House, Bucklin, KS

Hill Top House Nursing Home Inc, Dayton, OH

Hill Top Manor Nursing Home, Boston, MA

Hill Top Nursing Home, Boerne, TX

Hill Top Nursing Home and Community Clinc, Cripple Creek, CO

Hill Top Residential Care Facility, Cape Girardeau, MO

Hill View Health Care Facility, Portsmouth, OH

Hillaire Manor Inc, Hillsboro, OR

Hillandale Nursing Home, Hamilton, OH

Hillbrook Nursing Home, Clancy, MT

Hillcreek Manor Convalescent Center, Louisville, KY

Hillcrest—Beverly, Knoxville, TN

Hillcrest Care Center, Boise, ID

Hillcrest Care Center, Laurel, NE

Hillcrest Care Center, Waterville, OH

Hillcrest Care Center, Sandy, UT

Hillcrest Care Center Inc, Bellevue, NE

Hillcrest Convalescent Center, Detroit, MI

Hillcrest Convalescent Center, Pasco, WA

Hillcrest Convalescent Center Inc, Durham, NC

Hillcrest Convalescent Home, Milwaukee, WI

Hillcrest Convalescent Hospital, Fresno, CA

Hillcrest Convalescent Hospital Inc, Long Beach, CA

Hillcrest Haven Convalescent Center, Pocatello, ID

Hillcrest Health Care Center, Mankato, MN

Hillcrest Health Care Center, Wayzata, MN

Hillcrest Health Center, Bozeman, MT

Hillcrest Health Center Inc, Magee, MS

Hillcrest Healthcare Center, Owensboro, KY

Hillcrest Healthcare Center, Rush City, MN

Hillcrest Home, Harrison, AR

Hillcrest Home, Geneseo, IL

Hillcrest Home, Scottsville, KY

Hillcrest Home Inc, Milford, PA

Hillcrest Home Inc, Millford, PA

Hillcrest Manor, Fredonia, KS

Hillcrest Manor, Blackwell, OK

Hillcrest Manor, Luling, TX

Hillcrest Manor, Wylie, TX

Hillcrest Manor Inc, Aberdeen, MS

Hillcrest Manor Inc, Lakewood, NJ

Hillcrest Manor Nursing Home, Charlotte, NC

Hillcrest Manor Nursing Home, Waco, TX

Hillcrest Manor Nursing Home, Winchester, VA

Hillcrest Manor Sanitarium, National City, CA

Hillcrest Manor—Sunnyside, Sunnyside, WA

Hillcrest—North, Knoxville, TN

Hillcrest Nursing and Retirement Home, Plainview, MN

Hillcrest Nursing Center, Moore, OK

Hillcrest Nursing Home, Prescott, AR

Hillcrest Nursing Home, San Bernardino, CA

Hillcrest Nursing Home, Avon Park, FL

Hillcrest Nursing Home, Lafayette, IN

Hillcrest Nursing Home, Corbin, KY

Hillcrest Nursing Home, Fitchburg, MA

Hillcrest Nursing Home, North Muskegon, MI

Hillcrest Nursing Home, Red Lake Falls, MN

Hillcrest Nursing Home, McCook, NE

Hillcrest Nursing Home, Oswego, NY

Hillcrest Nursing Home, Spring Valley, NY

Hillcrest Nursing Home, Peebles, OH

Hillcrest Nursing Home, Van Wert, OH

Hillcrest Nursing Home, Tishomingo, OK

Hillcrest Nursing Home, Hamilton, TX

Hillcrest Nursing Home, Grandview, WA

Hillcrest Nursing Home, Twin Lakes, WI

Hillcrest Nursing Home, West Allis, WI

Hillcrest Nursing Home Inc, Jeffersonville, IN

Hillcrest Nursing Home Inc, Fredericktown, OH

Hillcrest Nursing Home Inc, East Providence, RI

Hillcrest of Watonga Inc, Watonga, OK

Hillcrest Rehabilitation and Convalescent Center, San Diego, CA

Hillcrest Rest Home, Gloucester, MA

Hillcrest Rest Home Inc, Sumner, IA

Hillcrest Retirement Village Inc, Round Lake, IL

Hillcrest Skilled Care Division, Sanford, ME

Hillcrest—South, Knoxville, TN

Hillcrest—West, Knoxville, TN

Hilldale Convalescent Center, La Mesa, CA

Hillebrand Nursing Center, Cheviot, OH

Hillhaven Convalescent Center, Mobile, AL

Hillhaven Convalescent Center, Hemet, CA

Hillhaven Convalescent Center, San Francisco, CA

Hillhaven Convalescent Center, Sarasota, FL

Hillhaven Convalescent Center, Savannah, GA

Hillhaven Convalescent Center, Des Moines, IA

Hillhaven Convalescent Center, Louisville, KY

Hillhaven Convalescent Center, Adrian, MI

Hillhaven Convalescent Center, Las Vegas, NV

Hillhaven Convalescent Center, Raleigh, NC

Hillhaven Convalescent Center, Wilmington, NC

Hillhaven Convalescent Center, Akron, OH
Hillhaven Convalescent Center, Madison, TN
Hillhaven Convalescent Center, Memphis, TN
Hillhaven Convalescent Center, Corpus
   Christi, TX
Hillhaven Convalescent Center, El Paso, TX
Hillhaven Convalescent Center, Salt Lake City,
   UT
Hillhaven Convalescent Center, Vancouver,
   WA
Hillhaven Convalescent Center, Shorewood,
   WI
Hillhaven Convalescent Center and Nursing
   Home, Birmingham, AL
Hillhaven Convalescent Center of Chapel Hill,
   Chapel Hill, NC
Hillhaven Convalescent Hospital,
   Anaheim, CA
Hillhaven Convalescent Hospital,
   Burlingame, CA
Hillhaven Convalescent Hospital,
   Claremont, CA
Hillhaven Convalescent Hospital,
   Hanford, CA
Hillhaven Convalescent Hospital, Menlo
   Park, CA
Hillhaven Convalescent Hospital, Mill
   Valley, CA
Hillhaven Convalescent Hospital,
   Modesto, CA
Hillhaven Convalescent Hospital,
   Oakland, CA
HIllhaven Convalescent Hospital,
   Orange, CA
Hillhaven Convalescent Hospital, Palo
   Alto, CA
Hillhaven Convalescent Hospital,
   Sacramento, CA
Hillhaven Convalescent Hospital, San
   Rafael, CA
Hillhaven Convalescent Hospital, Santa
   Ana, CA
Hillhaven Convalescent Hospital, Yuba
   City, CA
Hillhaven Extended Care Hospital, Santa
   Cruz, CA
Hillhaven Health Care, Monterey Park, CA
Hillhaven Health Care Center, Phoenix, AZ
Hillhaven Highland House, Highland, CA
Hillhaven LaSalle Nursing Center, Durham,
   NC
Hillhaven Nursing Home, Adelphi, MD
Hillhaven Nursing Home, Portland, OR
Hillhaven Nursing Home, Vancouver, WA
Hillhaven of Little Rock, Little Rock, AR
Hillhaven of Topeka, Topeka, KS
Hillhaven—Omaha, Omaha, NE
Hillhaven Orange Nursing Center, Durham,
   NC
Hillhaven Rehabilitation and Convalescent
   Center, Asheville, NC
Hillhaven Rehabilitation and Convalescent
   Center, Durham, NC
Hillhaven Rehabilitation and Convalescent
   Center, Norfolk, VA
Hillhaven Rehabilitation and Convalescent
   Hospital, Stockton, CA
Hillhaven Rehabilitation Convalescent Center,
   Marietta, GA
Hillhaven Rest Home 1, Baton Rouge, LA
Hillhaven Rest Home 2, Baton Rouge, LA
Hillhaven Rose Manor Convalescent Center,
   Durham, NC

Hillhaven—Sherwood Convalescent Hospital,
   Sacramento, CA
Hillhaven Sunnybrook Convalescent Center,
   Raleigh, NC
Hillhouse Convalescent Home, Bath, ME
Hillsboro House Nursing Home, Hillsborough,
   NH
Hillsboro Manor Nursing Home, El
   Dorado, AR
Hillsboro Nursing Home, Hillsboro, IL
Hillsborough County Nursing Home,
   Goffstown, NH
Hillsdale County Medical Care Facility,
   Hillsdale, MI
Hillsdale Manor Convalescent Hospital, San
   Mateo, CA
Hillside Acres, Willard, OH
Hillside Care Center, Prescott, AZ
Hillside Convalescent Inc, Portland, OR
Hillside Haven, Rushville, IN
Hillside House, Wilmington, DE
Hillside House Inc, Santa Barbara, CA
Hillside House Rest Home, Arlington, MA
Hillside Lodge Nursing Home, Beeville, TX
Hillside Manor, Washington, IN
Hillside Manor, Missoula, MT
Hillside Manor Convalescent Hospital, San
   Rafael, CA
Hillside Manor Corp, Glenwood, IA
Hillside Manor Health Care Facility Inc,
   Cincinnati, OH
Hillside Manor Health Related Facility,
   Jamaica Estates, NY
Hillside Manor Nursing Center, Gatesville, TX
Hillside Manor Nursing Home, Hartford, CT
Hillside Manor Nursing Home Inc, San
   Antonio, TX
Hillside Manor Retirement Home,
   Waterbury, CT
Hillside Manor—San Marcos, San Marcos, TX
Hillside Nursing and Convalescent Home,
   Yorkville, IL
Hillside Nursing Home, Deerfield, MA
Hillside Nursing Home, Marion, OH
Hillside Nursing Home Inc, Asheville, NC
Hillside Nursing Home Inc, Milwaukee, WI
Hillside Rest and Nursing Home, South
   Portland, ME
Hillside Rest Home, Amesbury, MA
Hillside Rest Home, Winchendon, MA
Hillside Terrace, Cobden, IL
Hillside Terrace Retirement Home, Ann Arbor,
   MI
Hillside Villa Inc, Salt Lake City, UT
Hilltop Care Center, Cherokee, IA
Hilltop Care Center, Spirit Lake, IA
Hilltop Convalescent Center, Escondido, CA
Hilltop Convalescent Center, Charleston, IL
Hilltop Convalescent Hospital, Bakersfield, CA
Hilltop Haven Home for the Aged, Gunter, TX
Hilltop Haven Nursing Home Inc, Piqua, OH
Hilltop Home, Lyndon, KS
Hilltop Inn, Seattle, WA
Hilltop Lodge, Owingsville, KY
Hilltop Lodge Inc Nursing Home, Beloit, KS
Hilltop Manor, Brookston, MN
Hilltop Manor Convalescent Hospital 2,
   Auburn, CA
Hilltop Manor Inc, Cunningham, KS
Hilltop Manor Inc, Union, MS
Hilltop Manor Nursing Home Inc,
   Framingham, MA
Hilltop Nursing Center, Harrison, AR

Hilltop Nursing Center 2, Pineville, LA
Hilltop Nursing Home, Forsyth, GA
Hilltop Nursing Home, Kuttawa, KY
Hilltop Nursing Home, Pineville, LA
Hilltop Nursing Home, Watkins, MN
Hilltop Nursing Home, Cincinnati, OH
Hilltop Nursing Home, Portsmouth, OH
Hilltop Nursing Home, Parker, SD
Hilltop Nursing Home, Hilltop, WV
Hilltop Private Nursing Home, Middletown,
   NJ
Hilltop Rehabilitation Center, Grand
   Junction, CO
Hilltop Rest Home, Science Hill, KY
Hilltop Rest Home, Carver, MA
Hilltop Rest Home, Hardwick, MA
Hilltop Rest Home, Springfield, MA
Hilltop Retirement Home, Quinn, SD
Hilltop Village, Kerrville, TX
Hillview Convalescent Hospital, Morgan
   Hill, CA
Hillview Health Care Center, Vienna, IL
Hillview Health Care Center Inc, Columbia,
   TN
Hillview Home, La Crosse, WI
Hillview House—Hanover General Hospital,
   Hanover, PA
Hillview Lodge, Arnold, MO
Hillview Manor, Greenville, IL
Hillview Manor, Scottsville, KY
Hillview Manor, New Castle, PA
Hillview Manor, Goldthwaite, TX
Hillview Nursing and Convalescent Center,
   Huntington, WV
Hillview Nursing and Convalescent Home,
   Altoona, PA
Hillview Nursing Home, Bastrop, LA
Hillview Nursing Home, Cincinnati, OH
Hillview Nursing Home, Flushing, OH
Hillview Nursing Home, Rapid City, SD
Hillview Nursing Home, Elizabethton, TN
Hillview Nursing Home, Mineola, TX
Hillview Nursing Home, Milwaukee, WI
Hillview Nursing Home Inc, Dresden, TN
Hilo Hospital—Skilled Nursing Unit, Hilo, HI
Hilton Convalescent Home, Ferndale, MI
Hilton Head Center of South Carolina Inc,
   Hilton Head Island, SC
Hilton Nursing Home, Phoenix, AZ
Hilty Memorial Home, Pandora, OH
Hines Nursing Home, Pineland, TX
Hinton Home Inc, Farmersville, TX
Hi-Plains Nursing Home, Hale Center, TX
Hiram G Andrews Center, Johnstown, PA
Hitchcock Nursing Home, Hitchcock, TX
Hitz Memorial Home, Alhambra, IL
Hobe Sound Geriatric Village, Hobe
   Sound, FL
Hocking Valley Community Hospital, Logan,
   OH
Hodgdon Rest Home, Boston, MA
Hodges Boulevard Cluster Homes,
   Jacksonville, FL
Hodges Nursing Home Inc, Elk City, OK
Hodges Rest Home, Springfield, MA
Hoemako Long Term Care, Casa Grande, AZ
Hoffman Care Center, Hoffman, MN
Hoikka House, Saint Paul, MN
Holbrook Nursing Home, Holbrook, MA
Holbrook Nursing Home, Buckhannon, WV
Holbrook on the Hill, Buckhannon, WV
Holden Nursing Home Inc, Holden, MA
Holdenville Nursing Home, Holdenville, OK

Holgate Quality Care Nursing Center, Holgate, OH
Holiday Care Center, Daytona Beach, FL
Holiday Care Center, Stephenville, TX
Holiday Heights Nursing Home, Norman, OK
Holiday Hill Nursing Home, Newfoundland, PA
Holiday Hills Retirement and Nursing Center Inc, Dallas, TX
Holiday Home of Evansville, Evansville, IN
Holiday House, Manchester, CT
Holiday House, Saint Albans, VT
Holiday Lodge, Hamlin, TX
Holiday Lodge Nursing Home, Longview, TX
Holiday Manor, Princeton, IN
Holiday Manor, Scranton, PA
Holiday Manor Nursitarium, Canoga Park, CA
Holiday Nursing Home, Center, TX
Holiday Park Plaza, Portland, OR
Holiday Pines Manor, Woodville, TX
Holiday Retirement Center, Sweetwater, TX
Holiday Retirement Home Inc, Lincoln, RI
Holland Home, Grand Rapids, MI
Holland Home—Brown Home, Grand Rapids, MI
Holland Home—Crestview Nursing Center, Wyoming, MI
Holland Home for the Aged, South Holland, IL
Holland Home—Raybrook Manor, Grand Rapids, MI
Holland Nursing Center—North, Springdale, AR
Holland Nursing Center—West, Springdale, AR
Hollenbeck Home for Aged Convalescent Unit, Los Angeles, CA
Hollidaysburg Veteran Home, Hollidaysburg, PA
Hollingsworth House Nursing and Retirement Center, Braintree, MA
Hollis Park Gardens Nursing Home, Hollis, NY
Hollister Convalescent Hospital, Hollister, CA
Holliston Manor Nursing Home, Holliston, MA
Holliswood Care Center Inc, Hollis, NY
Holly Care Center, Nampa, ID
Holly Center, Salisbury, MD
Holly Glen Care Center Inc, Toledo, OH
Holly Hall, Houston, TX
Holly Heights Nursing Home Inc, Denver, CO
Holly Hill Convalescent Home, Simsbury, CT
Holly Hill House, Sulphur, LA
Holly Hill Intermediate Care Facility, Valdosta, GA
Holly Hill Manor Inc, Towson, MD
Holly Hill Nursing Home, New Castle, IN
Holly Hills Care Center, Emmett, ID
Holly Hills Farms, Newbury, OH
Holly Manor Nursing Home, Mendham, NJ
Holly Manor Nursing Home, Farmville, VA
Holly Nursing Care Center, Holly, CO
Holly Patterson Home, Uniondale, NY
Holly Terrace Nursing Home, North Ridgeville, OH
Holly Tree Convalescent Hospital, Hayward, CA
Hollycrest Home Inc, Snohomish, WA
Hollywell Nursing Home, Randolph, MA
Hollywood Hills Nursing Home, Hollywood, FL

Holmdel Convalescent Center, Holmdel, NJ
Holmdel Nursing Home, Holmdel, NJ
Holmes Convalescent Center Inc, Virginia Beach, VA
Holmes House, Pittsburgh, PA
Holmes Lake Manor, Lincoln, NE
Holmesdale Convalescent Center, Kansas City, MO
Holstein Good Samaritan Center, Holstein, IA
Holton Manor, Elkhorn, WI
Holy Cross Hospital and Health Center—Geriatric Center, Nogales, AZ
Holy Family Health Center, Des Plaines, IL
Holy Family Home, Parma, OH
Holy Family Home, Philadelphia, PA
Holy Family Home for the Aged, Brooklyn, NY
Holy Family Hospital—Extended Care Facility, Manitowoc, WI
Holy Family Manor, Bethlehem, PA
Holy Family Residence, Scranton, PA
Holy Family Villa, Lemont, IL
Holy Ghost Mission Nursing Home, Marbury, AL
Holy Spirit Retirement Home, Sioux City, IA
Holyoke Geriatric and Convalescent Center, Holyoke, MA
Holyoke Nursing Home, Holyoke, MA
Homage Manor, Jonesville, LA
Home Association, Tampa, FL
Home Association Jewish Blind, Chicago, IL
Home for Aged—Little Sisters of the Poor, Oregon, OH
Home for Aged People, Stoneham, MA
Home for Aged People, Winchester, MA
Home for Aged People in Fall River, Fall River, MA
Home for Aged Protestant Women, Pittsburgh, PA
Home for Aged Pythians Inc, Greenville, TX
Home for Aged Women, Boston, MA
Home For Aged Women, Worcester, MA
Home for Aged Women, Portsmouth, NH
Home for Aged Women in Salem, Salem, MA
Home for Aged Women—Minquadale Home Inc, Wilmington, DE
Home for Creative Living, Windom, MN
Home for Jewish Parents, Oakland, CA
Home for the Aged—Frederick, Frederick, MD
Home for the Aged of Protestant Episcopal Church, Alhambra, CA
Home for the Golden Years, Piggott, AR
Home for the Golden Years Inc, Paragould, AR
Home for the Jewish Aged, Philadelphia, PA
Home of Angels, Ontario, CA
Home of Hope Inc, Vinita, OK
Home of the Innocents, Louisville, KY
Home of the Sages of Isreal Inc, New York, NY
Homecare Center, Lewisville, IN
Homecrest Foundation, Evanston, IL
Homedale Nursing Home Inc, Homedale, ID
Homeland, Harrisburg, PA
Homestead, Kittery, ME
The Homestead, Willow Grove, PA
Homestead Convalescent Home, Stamford, CT
Homestead Hall, Worcester, MA
Homestead Health Center Inc, Wichita, KS
Homestead III, Lancaster, OH
Homestead Manor Inc, Stamps, AR
Homestead Manor Nursing Home, Homestead, FL
Homestead Nursing Center, Lexington, KY

Homestead Nursing Center of New Castle, New Castle, KY
Homestead Nursing Home, Lincoln, NE
Homestead Nursing Home, Geneva, OH
Homestead Nursing Home, Tulsa, OK
Homestead Nursing Home 1, Painesville, OH
Homestead Nursing Home 2, Painesville, OH
Homestead Rest Home, Phoenix, AZ
Homestead Rest Home, Leominster, MA
Homestead Rest Home, North Adams, MA
Homestead Villa Inc, Hoisington, KS
Hometown Nursing Homes, Inc, Celina, OH
Homeview Convalescent Center, Franklin, IN
Homeward Bound, New Hope, MN
Homeward Bound—Brooklyn Park, Brooklyn Park, MN
Homewood Convalescent Hospital Inc, San Jose, CA
Homewood Health Care Center, Glasgow, KY
Homewood Manor Inc, Georgiana, AL
Homewood Retirement Center, Hanover, PA
Homewood Retirement Center, Martinsburg, PA
Homewood Retirement Center—Frederick, Frederick, MD
Homewood Retirement Center—Williamsport, Williamsport, MD
Hominy Nursing Home, Hominy, OK
Homme Home for the Aging, Wittenberg, WI
Hondo Nursing Center, Hondo, TX
Honokaa Hospital, Honokaa, HI
Honor Heights Nursing Center, Muskogee, OK
Honorage Nursing Center, Florence, SC
Hood River Care Center, Hood River, OR
Hoodkroft Convalescent Center, Derry, NH
Hooper Care Center, Hooper, NE
Hoopeston Community Memorial Nursing Home, Hoopeston, IL
Hoosick Falls Health Center, Hoosick Falls, NY
Hoosier Christian Village, Brownstown, IN
Hoosier Hills Healthcare Center, North Vernon, IN
Hoosier Village Retirement Center, Indianapolis, IN
Hoover Nursing Home Inc, Laurelville, OH
Hooverwood, Indianapolis, IN
Hope Enterprizes Inc, Williamsport, PA
Hope Hall Convalescent Home Inc, Waterbury, CT
Hope House Manor Inc, Springfield, OH
Hope Manor, Fresno, CA
Hope Manor, Joplin, MO
Hope Nursing Home, Lawton, MI
Hope Nursing Home, Lomira, WI
Hope Park Cottage, Anchorage, AK
Hope Residences Inc, Waterville, MN
Hope Street Group Home, Bremerton, WA
Hope Transition Center Inc, Saint Paul, MN
Hopedale Garden Nursing Home, Hopedale, MA
Hopedale House, Hopedale, IL
Hopedale Nursing Home, Hopedale, IL
Hopewell Convalescent Center, Hopewell, VA
Hopewell Home, Paris, KY
Hopewell Intermediate Care Center, Sumter, SC
Hopewell Skilled Villa, Newark, OH
Hopkins County Nursing Home, Sulphur Springs, TX
Hopkins Health Center, North Providence, RI
Hopkins House Nursing & Rehabilitation Center, Wyncote, PA

Hopkins Nursing Home, Woodburn, KY
Hopkins Nursing Home, Waltham, MA
Hopkins Nursing Home, Hopkins, MN
Horace Nye Home, Elizabethtown, NY
Horizon Apartments, West Saint Paul, MN
Horizon Convalescent Hospital, Oakland, CA
Horizon House II, Fort Thomas, KY
Horizon House Inc, Seattle, WA
Horizon Manor, Nocona, TX
Horizon South Living Center, Oglesby, IL
Horizon West Health Care, Minneapolis, MN
Horizons Nursing Home Inc, Cory, CO
Horn Harbor Nursing Home Inc, New Point, VA
Horn Home for Aged, Lowell, MA
Horn Nursing Home Inc, Wooster, OH
Horne Home, Manzanola, CO
Hornell Nursing Home, Hornell, NY
Hospice of Southeastern Michigan, Southfield, MI
Hospice Saint Antoine, North Smithfield, RI
Hospital Care Center of Hermitage, Hermitage, PA
Hospital—Skilled Nursing Facility, Sidney, NY
Hospitality Care Center, Jacksonville, FL
Hospitality Care Center, Madison, GA
Hospitality Care Center 1, Sandusky, OH
Hospitality Care Center 2, Sandusky, OH
Hospitality Care Center Inc—Toledo, Toledo, OH
Hospitality Care Center of Albany, Albany, GA
Hospitality Care Center of Charlotte, Charlotte, NC
Hospitality Care Center of Clayton, Riverdale, GA
Hospitality Care Center of Macon, Macon, GA
Hospitality Care of Thomasville, Thomasville, GA
Hospitality Home East, Xenia, OH
Hospitality Home West, Xenia, OH
Hospitality House, Bedford, IN
Hospitality House, Massillon, OH
Hospitality House Inc, Bloomington, IN
Hospitality House Inc, Alice, TX
Hospitality House Nursing Home, Anderson, CA
Hospitality Manor, Kenosha, WI
Hospitality Nursing Home, Clyde, OH
Hostel House, Edina, MO
Hot Springs Convalescent Inc, Hot Springs, MT
Hot Springs Nursing Home, Hot Springs, AR
Hotel Reed Nursing Center, Bay Saint Louis, MS
Houghton County Medical Care Facility, Hancock, MI
Houghton Nursing Care Center Inc, Houghton, NY
Houlton Regional Hospital, Houlton, ME
Houlton Residential Center, Houlton, ME
House of Care Inc, Portland, OR
House of Loreto, Canton, OH
House of the Holy Comforter, Bronx, NY
Houston Company Home-Lacrescent, La Crescent, MN
Houston County Group Home, Caledonia, MN
Houston County Nursing Home Inc, Crockett, TX
Houston Health Care Inc, Crawfordsville, IN
Houston Health Care Inc—Clarks Hill, Clarks Hill, IN
Houston Health Care Inc—Cloverdale, Cloverdale, IN

Houston Village Inc, Indianapolis, IN
Hovenden Memorial Good Samaritan Home, Laurens, IA
Howard Lake Care Center, Howard Lake, MN
Howard Twilight Manor, Howard, KS
Howd Nursing Home, Moravia, NY
Howe Avenue Nursing Home Inc, New Rochelle, NY
Howe Care Center, Topeka, KS
Howell Branch Court, Winter Park, FL
Howell's Child Care Center (Riverbend), New Bern, NC
Howell's Child Care Center—Walnut Creek, Goldsboro, NC
Howell's Group Home/Bear Creek, LaGrange, NC
Hoyt Cresthome Inc, Scranton, PA
Hoyt Nursing Home, Saginaw, MI
Hubbard Hill Estates Inc, Elkhart, IN
Huber Restorium, Saint Petersburg, FL
Hudson Elms Inc, Hudson, OH
Hudson Manor Extended Care, North Bergen, NJ
Hudson Memorial Nursing Home, El Dorado, AR
Hudson Valley Nursing Center, Highland, NY
Hudson View Nursing Home Inc, Yonkers, NY
Hudsonville Christian Nursing Home, Hudsonville, MI
Hudspeth Center, Whitfield, MS
Hueytown Nursing Home Inc, Hueytown, AL
Hugh Chatham Memorial Hospital, Elkin, NC
Hughes Convalescent Inc, West Hartford, CT
Hughes Springs Convalescent Center, Hughes Springs, TX
Hugo Golden Age Home, Hugo, OK
Hugo Manor Nursing Home, Hugo, OK
Human Development Center, Corpus Christi, TX
Human Resources Health Center, Miami, FL
Humble Skilled Care Facility, Humble, TX
Humboldt Care Center—North, Humboldt, IA
Humboldt Care Center—South, Humboldt, IA
Humboldt General Hospital, Winnemucca, NV
Humiston Haven, Pontiac, IL
Humphreys County Nursing Home, Belzoni, MS
Humphreys County Nursing Home, Waverly, TN
Hunt Nursing and Retirement Home Inc, Danvers, MA
Hunt Street Personal Care Home, Jackson, MS
Hunterdon Hills Nursing Home, Glen Gardner, NJ
Huntersville Hospital—Skilled Nursing and Intermediate Care Facility, Huntersville, NC
Huntingburg Convalescent Center Inc, Huntingburg, IN
Huntingdon County Nursing Home, Huntingdon, PA
Huntington Beach Convalescent Hospital, Huntington Beach, CA
Huntington Convalescent Center, Newport News, VA
Huntington Convalescent Home Inc, Cleveland, GA
Huntington Drive Convalescent Hospital, Arcadia, CA
Huntington Nursing Home, Huntington, IN
Huntington Park Care Center, Papillion, NE
Huntington Park Convalescent Center, Huntington Park, CA

Huntington Valley Convalescent Hospital, Huntington Beach, CA
Huntsville Nursing Home, Huntsville, AL
Hurlbut Nursing Home, Rochester, NY
Hurley Manor, Coalgate, OK
Huron County Medical Care Facility, Bad Axe, MI
Huron Nursing Home, Huron, SD
Huron Valley Mens Facility, Ypsilanti, MI
Huron View Lodge, Ann Arbor, MI
Huron Woods Nursing Home, Kawkawlin, MI
Hurstdale Rest Home, Springfield, MA
Hurwitz House, Baltimore, MD
Huston Nursing Home Inc, Hamden, OH
Hutchinson Good Samaritan Center, Hutchinson, KS
Hutton Nursing Center, Salem, OH
Hutton Nursing Center II Inc, Salem, OH
Hutton Nursing Home, Kingston, NY
Hy Lond Convalescent Hospital, Fresno, CA
Hyattsville Manor, Hyattsville, MD
The Hyde Home, Spearfish, SD
Hyde Park Convalescent Home, Boston, MA
Hyde Park Convalescent Home Inc, Hamden, CT
Hyde Park Convalescent Hospital, Los Angeles, CA
Hyde Park Nursing Center Inc, Chicago, IL
Hyde Park Nursing Home, Kansas City, MO
Hyde Park Nursing Home, Staatsburg, NY
Hyde Park Villa Inc, Cincinnati, OH
Hydro Manor Inc, Hydro, OK
Hyland Convalescent Home, Iron Mountain, MI
Hyland Park Nursing Home, Minneapolis, MN
Hy-Lond Convalescent Hospital, Los Angeles, CA
Hy-Lond Convalescent Hospital, Merced, CA
Hy-Lond Convalescent Hospital, Modesto, CA
Hy-Lond Convalescent Hospital, Napa, CA
Hy-Lond Convalescent Hospital, Sacramento, CA
Hy-Lond Convalescent Hospital, Santa Barbara, CA
Hy-Lond Convalescent Hospital, Santa Clara, CA
Hy-Lond Convalescent Hospital, Sunnyvale, CA
Hy-Lond Convalescent Hospital, Westminster, CA
Hy-Lond Home, Garden Grove, CA
Hy-Pana House Convalescent Hospital, Fresno, CA
Hy-Pana House Convalescent Hospital, Stockton, CA
Hy-Vue, Davenport, IA
I Street House, Salida, CO
Idaho County Nursing Home, Grangeville, ID
Idaho Falls Nursing Home, Idaho Falls, ID
Idaho State School and Hospital—Intermediate Care Facility, Nampa, ID
Idaho Veterans Home, Boise, ID
Ideal Intermediate Care Unit, Ideal, GA
Ideal Nursing Home Inc, Norton, OH
Ideal Rest Home Inc, Mobile, AL
Idle Acre Sanitarium and Convalescent Hospital, El Monte, CA
Idlehour Nursing Center, Murfreesboro, AR
Idlewood Nursing Center, Saint Francisville, LA
Idylwood Acres Convalescent Hospital, Sunnyvale, CA

Iliff Nursing Care Center, Denver, CO
Iliff Nursing Home Inc, Dunn Loring, VA
Illinois Knights Templar Home for the Aged, Paxton, IL
Illinois Masonic Home, Sullivan, IL
Illinois Masonic Warren N Barr Pavilion, Chicago, IL
Illinois Presbyterian Home, Springfield, IL
Immaculate Mary Home, Philadelphia, PA
Immanuel Lutheran Home, Kalispell, MT
Immanuel Nursing Home, Charlotte, MI
Imperial Convalescent Center, La Mirada, CA
Imperial Convalescent Hospital, Studio City, CA
Imperial Health Care Inc, Atlanta, GA
Imperial Health Center, Richmond, VA
Imperial Manor, Imperial, NE
Imperial Manor, Toledo, OH
Imperial Manor Convalescent Center, Madison, TN
Imperial Manor Inc, Imperial, CA
Imperial Nursing Center of Elgin, Elgin, IL
Imperial Nursing Center of Hazel Crest, Hazel Crest, IL
Imperial Nursing Center of Joliet, Joliet, IL
Imperial Skilled Care Center, Warren, OH
Independence Care Center, Independence, IA
Independence Health Care Center, Independence, MO
Independence House, Wheat Ridge, CO
Independence Manor, Shawnee, OK
Independence Manor Care Center, Independence, MO
Independence Sanitarium and Hospital, Independence, MO
Independent Living Club, Indianapolis, IN
Indian Creek Convalescent Center, Corydon, IN
Indian Creek Nursing Center, New Castle, PA
Indian Creek Nursing Center Inc, Overland Park, KS
Indian Creek Nursing Center of Missouri, Kansas City, MO
Indian Haven, Indiana, PA
Indian Hills Care Center, Sioux City, IA
Indian Hills Health Center Inc, Cameron, MO
Indian Hills Manor Nursing Home, Ogallala, NE
Indian Hills Nursing Center, Council Bluffs, IA
Indian Hills Nursing Home Inc, Chilicothe, MO
Indian Hills Nursing Home Inc, Chillicothe, MO
Indian Lake Manor, Lakeview, OH
Indian Meadows Nursing Center Inc, Overland Park, KS
Indian River Nursing Home and Health Related Facility Inc, Granville, NY
Indian Trail Nursing Center, Topeka, KS
Indian Trail Nursing Home, Cary, OH
Indian Village Health Center, Fort Wayne, IN
Indiana Christian Retirement Park, Zionsville, IN
Indiana Masonic Home, Franklin, IN
Indiana Presbyterian Homes, Indiana, PA
Indiana Pythian Home, Lafayette, IN
Indiana Veterans Home, Lafayette, IN
Indianapolis Retirement Home Inc, Indianapolis, IN
Indianola Good Samaritan Center—East, Indianola, IA
Indianola Good Samaritan Center—West, Indianola, IA

Inez Sako Nursing Home I, Raceland, LA
Inez Sako Nursing Home II, Houma, LA
Ingham County Medical Care Facility, Okemos, MI
Inglemoor Inc, Englewood, NJ
Inglemoor West, Livingston, NJ
Inglenook, Catonsville, MD
Ingleside, Mount Horeb, WI
Ingleside Convalescent Center, Detroit, MI
Ingleside Nursing Home, Old Tappan, NJ
Inglewood Convalarium, Inglewood, CA
Inglewood Manor Nursing Home, Jackson, MS
Inglis House, Philadelphia, PA
Ingram Manor Inc, Pell City, AL
Ingram's Rest Home, Milford, DE
Inisteige-Aneskarn 3, Morris, MN
Inland Christian Home Inc, Ontario, CA
Inman Nursing Home, Inman, SC
Inn-Conneaut Health Center, Conneaut, OH
Inner City Nursing Home Inc, Cleveland, OH
Innsbruck Healthcare Center, New Brighton, MN
Inter-City Christ Manor, Allen Pk, MI
Intercommunity Center of Bloomington, Bloomington, CA
Intercommunity Convalescent Hospital, Norwalk, CA
Intercommunity Sanitarium, Long Beach, CA
Interlake Nursing Center, Bellevue, WA
Intermed of Batesville, Batesville, AR
International Falls Group Home, International Falls, MN
International Nursing Home of Danville, Danville, IL
Inver Grove Care Center, Inver Grove Heights, MN
Inverness Health Care Center, Inverness, FL
Inyo County Sanitorium, Big Pine, CA
Iola Nursing Home, Iola, WI
Iona Glos Specialized Living Center, Addison, IL
Ionia Manor, Ionia, MI
Iosco County Medical Care Facility, Tawas City, MI
Iowa City Care Center, Iowa City, IA
Iowa Jewish Home, Des Moines, IA
Iowa Masonic Nursing Home, Bettendorf, IA
Iowa Odd Fellows Home, Mason City, IA
Iowa Veterans Home, Marshalltown, IA
Iris Haven Nursing and Convalescent Center, Chillicothe, TX
Iron County Medical Care Facility, Crystal Falls, MI
Iron County Nursing Home, Parowan, UT
Iron River Nursing Home, Iron River, MI
Iroquois Resident Home, Watseka, IL
Irvine Health Care, Irvine, KY
Irving Campus of Care, Irving, TX
Irving Care Center, Irving, TX
Irving Manors Nursing Home Inc, Irving, TX
Isabella County Medical Care Facility, Mount Pleasant, MI
Isabella Home Nursing Home Company Inc, New York, NY
Isabelle Ridgway Nursing Center, Columbus, OH
Isla Carroll Turner Health Care Center, Houston, TX
Island Care Center, Freeland, WA
Island Manor Nursing Center, Vashon Island, WA
Island Nursing Home, Honolulu, HI
Island Nursing Home, Deer Isle, ME

Island Terrace Nursing Home, Lakeville, MA
Island View Manor, Ketchikan, AK
The Islands Convalescent Center Inc, Friday Harbor, WA
Issaquah Villa Care Center, Issaquah, WA
Italy Convalescent Center, Italy, TX
Itasca Nursing Home, Grand Rapids, MN
Itasca Nursing Home, Itasca, TX
Ivah Hansen Residential Care Facility, Las Animas, CO
Ivanhoe Manor, Jacksonville, IL
Ivanhoe Manor Nursing Center, Jacksonville, IL
Ivorena Care Center, Eugene, OR
Ivy Hall, Middle River, MD
Ivy Hall Nursing Home, Elizabethton, TN
Ivy House, Painesville, OH
Ivy Manor Nursing Home, Denver, CO
Ivy Manor Rest Home, Salem, MA
Ivy Manor Rest Home, Springfield, MA
Ivy Nursing Home Inc, Pittsburgh, PA
Ivy Ridge Nursing Home Inc, Philadelphia, PA
J and C Residential Care Facility, Pueblo, CO
J B Johnson Nursing Center, Washington, DC
J F Hawkins Nursing Home, Newberry, SC
J Ferry Nursing Home, Elyria, OH
J H Floyd Sunshine Manor, Sarasota, FL
J Health Care Center, Simpsonville, SC
J J Jordan Geriatric Center, Louisa, KY
J Ralph Smith Health Center, Dowling Park, FL
J W Comer Nursing Home, Carlisle, AR
Jacaranda Manor, Saint Petersburg, FL
Jack Cline Nursing Home, Pell City, AL
Jack Rees Nursing and Rehabilitation Center, New Castle, PA
Jackman Region Health Center, Jackman, ME
Jacksboro Nursing Center, Jacksboro, TX
Jackson Center, Milwaukee, WI
Jackson County Convalescent Center, Graceville, FL
Jackson County Hospital and Nursing Home, Scottsboro, AL
Jackson County Medical Care Facility, Jackson, MI
Jackson County Nursing Home, Murphysboro, IL
Jackson County Nursing Home Inc, Holton, KS
Jackson County Personal Care Home, Pascagoula, MS
Jackson County Public Hospital, Maquoketa, IA
Jackson Heights Nursing Home, Miami, FL
Jackson Heights Nursing Home, Farmer City, IL
Jackson Manor Nursing Home, Miami, FL
Jackson Manor Nursing Home, Jonesboro, LA
Jackson Manor Nursing Home, Jackson, MO
Jackson Municipal Hospital—Nursing Home, Jackson, MN
Jackson Nursing Home, Rushville, IN
Jackson Park Christian Home, Nashville, TN
Jackson Park Convalescent Center Inc, Seymour, IN
Jackson Square Nursing Center, Fort Worth, TX
Jackson Square Nursing Center of Texas Inc, Fort Worth, TX
Jackson-Brawne Enterprises Inc, Marietta, OH
Jackson's Senior Citizens Home, Vevay, IN
Jacksonville Convalescent Center, Jacksonville, FL

Jacksonville Convalescent Center, Jacksonville, IL
Jacksonville Convalescent Manor, Jacksonville, AR
Jacksonville Nursing Home, Jacksonville, AR
Jacksonville Nursing Home Inc, Jacksonville, AL
Jacksonville Regency House, Jacksonville, FL
Jacob's Dwelling, Coshocton, OH
Jacobsen Nursing Home Inc, Seattle, WA
Jacobson Memorial Hospital Care Center, Elgin, ND
Jallo's Nursing Home, Portland, OR
Jamaica Hospital Nursing Home Company Inc, Jamaica, NY
Jamaica Towers Nursing Home, Boston, MA
James A Taylor Osteopathic Hospital, Bangor, ME
James C King Home for the Aged, Evanston, IL
James C Polk Rest Home, Carrollton, GA
James E Kerwin Housing for the Elderly and Elderly Disabled, Memphis, TN
James Manor Rest Home, Fitchburg, MA
James River Convalescent Center, Newport News, VA
James Square Nursing Home, Syracuse, NY
James Valley Nursing Home, Redfield, SD
Jamestown, Stillwater, MN
Jamieson Nursing Home, Harrisville, MI
Jan Frances Care Center, Ada, OK
Jane Dickman House, Woodbury, MN
The Jane Elizabeth House Nursing Home, Cambridge, MA
Jane Francis Nursing Home, Ravenna, OH
Janesville Health Care Center, Janesville, WI
Janesville Nursing Home, Janesville, MN
Janney House, Mont Clare, PA
January Care Home, Evant, TX
Janwynella Nursing Home Inc, Lafayette, TN
Japanese Retirement Home, Los Angeles, CA
Jaquith Nursing Home—Adams Inn, Whitfield, MS
Jaquith Nursing Home—Washington Inn, Whitfield, MS
Jarvis Heights Nursing Center, Fort Worth, TX
Jasper Convalescent Center Inc, Jasper, TX
Jasper County Care Facility, Newton, IA
Jasper County Nursing Home, Bay Springs, MS
Jasper Nursing Center Inc, Jasper, IN
Jaylene Manor Nursing Home, Saint Petersburg, FL
Jean Carol's Nursing Home, Canton, OH
Jeanne Jugan Residence, Newark, DE
Jeanne Jugan Residence, Washington, DC
Jeanne Jugan Residence, Somerville, MA
Jeanne Jugan Residence, Bronx, NY
Jeanne Jugan Residence, Pawtucket, RI
Jean's Nursing Home, College Station, AR
Jean's Nursing Home, Genevia, AR
Jefferson City Manor Care Center, Jefferson City, MO
Jefferson Convalescent Home Inc, Pine Bluff, AR
Jefferson County Home, Birmingham, AL
Jefferson County Nursing Home, Dandridge, TN
Jefferson Davis County—Extended Care Facility, Prentiss, MS
Jefferson Davis Nursing Home, Jennings, LA
Jefferson Health Care Center, Jefferson, LA
Jefferson Hills Manor Inc, Pittsburgh, PA

Jefferson House, Newington, CT
Jefferson House Care Center, Tacoma, WA
Jefferson Manor, Jefferson, IA
Jefferson Manor, Louisville, KY
Jefferson Manor, Baton Rouge, LA
Jefferson Manor, Brookville, PA
Jefferson Manor, Green Bay, WI
Jefferson Manor Nursing Center, Passaic, NJ
Jefferson Meadows Care Center, Baraboo, WI
Jefferson Nursing Center, Monticello, FL
Jefferson Rest Home, Arlington, MA
Jefferson Street Nursing Home, Saint Charles, MO
Jeffersonian Manor, Charles Town, WV
Jeffersonian Nursing Home, Mount Vernon, IL
Jeffersonville Nursing Home, Jeffersonville, IN
Jeffrey Place Nursing Center, Waco, TX
Jenkins Hall-Reid Memorial Hospital, Richmond, IN
Jenkins Memorial Nursing Home, Baltimore, MD
Jenkins Memorial Nursing Home, Wellston, OH
Jenkin's Methodist Home, Watertown, SD
Jenkins Nursing Home Inc, Marion, SC
Jennie B Richmond Chaffee Nursing Home Company Inc, Springville, NY
Jennie Wiley Rest Home, Paintsville, KY
Jennies Retirement Home, Villard, MN
Jennings Caring Center, Jennings, MO
Jennings Guest House, Jennings, LA
Jennings Hall Inc, Garfield Heights, OH
Jennings Healthcare Inc, Augusta, GA
Jennings Terrace, Aurora, IL
Jerome Home, New Britain, CT
Jerri's Benevolent Manor, Saint Louis, MO
Jerseyville Care Center, Jerseyville, IL
Jesmond Nursing Home, Nahant, MA
Jessie Thompson Convalescent Home, Detroit, MI
Jesup Manor Nursing Center, Jesup, GA
Jesup Rest-A-While Nursing Home, Jesup, GA
Jewell House, Lakewood, CO
Jewish Center for Aged, Chesterfield, MO
Jewish Convalescent Center—Scotts Level, Baltimore, MD
Jewish Geriatric and Convalescent Center, Kansas City, MO
Jewish Geriatric Center, Cherry Hill, NJ
Jewish Guild for the Blind/Home for the Aged Blind, Yonkers, NY
Jewish Home and Hospital for the Aged, New York, NY
Jewish Home and Hospital for the Aged, Pittsburgh, PA
Jewish Home and Infirmary of Rochester New York Inc, Rochester, NY
Jewish Home for the Aged, New Haven, CT
The Jewish Home for the Aged, Atlanta, GA
Jewish Home for the Aged, Portland, ME
Jewish Home for the Aged, Worcester, MA
Jewish Home for the Aged, Providence, RI
Jewish Home for the Aged, Houston, TX
Jewish Home for the Aged 1, Southfield, MI
Jewish Home for the Aged 2, Detroit, MI
Jewish Home for the Elderly of Fairfield County, Fairfield, CT
Jewish Home of Central New York, Syracuse, NY
Jewish Home of Eastern Pennsylvania, Scranton, PA

Jewish Home of Greater Harrisburg, Harrisburg, PA
Jewish Nursing Home of Western Massachusetts, Longmeadow, MA
Jewish Peoples Convalescent Home, Chicago, IL
Jewish Rehabilitation Center for the Aged, Swampscott, MA
JHMCB Center for Nursing and Rehabilitation, Brooklyn, NY
JIGC Nursing Home Co Inc, New Hyde Park, NY
Jo Lene's Nursing Home, Salisbury, NC
Jodoin Home, Chester, NH
Joe Anne Burgin Nursing Home, Cuthbert, GA
Johanna Nursing Home, Salt Lake City, UT
John Adams Nursing Home, Quincy, MA
John E Andrus Memorial, Hastings-on-Hudson, NY
John Edward Harter Nursing Center, Fairfax, SC
John F Montgomery Medical Home, Freehold, NJ
John H Shook Home, Chambersburg, PA
John J Kane Allegheny County Home, Pittsburgh, PA
John Knox Manor Inc II, Montgomery, AL
John Knox Village Medical Center, Orange City, FL
John Knox Village Medical Center, Pompano Beach, FL
John Knox Village Medical Center, Tampa, FL
John Knox Village Medical Center, Weslaco, TX
John Knox Village of Lubbock Inc, Lubbock, TX
John L Deaton Medical Center Inc, Baltimore, MD
John L Hutcheson Extended Care Unit, Fort Oglethorpe, GA
John M Reed Home, Limestone, TN
John Milton Nursing Home, Kissimmee, FL
John P Shirk Memorial Home, Faulkton, SD
John Paul II Nursing Center, Kenedy, TX
John Randolph Nursing Home Inc, Hopewell, VA
John Scott House Nursing and Rehabilitation Center, Braintree, MA
John XXIII Home For Senior Citizens, Hermitage, PA
John Umstead Hospital, Butner, NC
Johnson Care Home, Memphis, TN
Dale Johnson Center, Bellwood, IL
Johnson County Health Care, Mountain City, TN
Johnson County Intermediate Care Home, Adrian, GA
Johnson County Nursing Center, Olathe, KS
Johnson Health Center—Florida United Presbyterian Homes Inc, Lakeland, FL
Johnson Home, Westminster, CO
Johnson House, Boulder, CO
Johnson Memorial Hospital Home, Dawson, MN
Johnson Nursing Home, Boston, MA
Johnson Nursing Home, Memphis, TN
Johnson Rehabilitation Nursing Home, Chicago, IL
Johnson Rest Home, Erskine, MN
Johnson Rest Home, Fosston, MN
Johnson-Mathers Nursing Home, Carlisle, KY
Johnson's Health Care Center Inc, Harriman, TN

Johnsons Long Lake Home, Walker, MN
Johnson's Meadowlake Home Inc, Conway, AR
Johnsons Riverside Boarding Care Home, Thief River Falls, MN
Johnston County Memorial Nursing Center Inc, Smithfield, NC
Johnston Nursing Home, Lancaster, OH
Johnston Nursing Home, Troy, OH
Johnstone Developmental Center, Wheat Ridge, CO
Joliet Terrace, Joliet, IL
Jo-Lin Health Center Inc, Ironton, OH
Jolley Acres Nursing Home Inc, Orangeburg, SC
The Jolly Fisherman, Rhinelander, WI
Jolly Rest Home Inc, Pascoag, RI
Jones Convalescent Hospital, San Leandro, CA
Jones County Rest Home, Ellisville, MS
Jones Health Center Inc, Orange, TX
Jones Nursing and Convalescent Home, Dayton, OH
Jones Nursing Home, Cleveland, OH
Jones Nursing Home, Beech Bottom, WV
Jones Nursing Home Inc, Naugatuck, CT
Jones Valley Nursing Home, Bessemer, AL
Jonesboro Human Development Center, Jonesboro, AR
Jonesboro Nursing Center Inc, Jonesboro, IL
Jonesboro Nursing Home Inc, Jonesboro, TN
Jones-Harrison Home, Minneapolis, MN
Jonesville Rest Home, Jonesville, KY
Joplin Health Care Center, Joplin, MO
Jordan and Cole Residential Care Facility, Las Animas, CO
Jordans Nursing Home, Bridgman, MI
Joseph B Knowles Home for the Aged, Nashville, TN
Joseph D Brandenburg Center, Cumberland, MD
Joseph P Devlin Nursing Home, Lynn, MA
Joseph T Nist Geriatric Nursing Home, Louisville, OH
Josephine Nursing Home, Dayton, OH
Josephine Sunset Home, Stanwood, WA
Joseph's Nursing Home, Lawton, OK
Josephson Nursing Home, Ironwood, MI
Josina Lott Foundation Residential Center, Toledo, OH
Joy Goldstein Kateri Residence, New York, NY
Joywells, Brownsville, KY
JTN Nursing Care Facility, Edgewater, CO
Judson Palmer Home, Findlay, OH
Judson Park, Cleveland, OH
Judson Village and Baptist Home, Cincinnati, OH
Julia Convalescent Hospital, Mountain View, CA
Julia Olson Rest Home, Belle Fourche, SD
Julia Ribaudo Home, Lake Ariel, PA
Julia Temple Center, Englewood, CO
Julia's Valley Manor, Sioux City, IA
Juliette Fowler Homes Inc, Dallas, TX
Juliette Manor, Berlin, WI
Julius Marks Home, Lexington, KY
Junction City Nursing Home, Junction City, AR
K F J Manor Inc 2, Saint Louis, MO
K W Hess Ohio Pythian Home, Springfield, OH
Kabul Nursing Home, Cabool, MO
Kade Nursing Home, Washington, PA

Kaderly Home, New Philidelphia, OH
Kadoka Retirement Home, Kadoka, SD
Kah Tai Care Center, Port Townsend, WA
Kahanaola Convalescent Center, Kaneohe, HI
Kahl Home for the Aged and Infirm, Davenport, IA
Kahuku Hospital—Skilled Nursing Unit, Kahuku, HI
Kalkaska Memorial Health Center, Kalkaska, MI
Kanawha Community Home, Kanawha, IA
Kane County Hospital—Skilled Nursing Facility, Kanab, UT
Kankakee Terrace Nursing Home, Bourbonnais, IL
Kansas Christian Home Inc, Newton, KS
Kansas City Presbyterian Manor, Kansas City, KS
Kansas Masonic Home, Wichita, KS
Kanukuk Nursing Home, Duncan, OK
Kappes Nursing Home, West Allis, WI
Karen Acres Rest Home, Urbandale, IA
Karlson Rest Home Inc, Lynn, MA
Karlstad Memorial Nursing Center, Karlstad, MN
Karmenta Health Care Center, Madison, WI
Kate Macy Ladd Convalescent Home, Far Hills, NJ
Kathahdin Nursing Home, Millinocket, ME
Katherine Convalescent Hospital, Salinas, CA
Katherine Robb Nursing Home, Baltimore, MD
Kathleen Daniel Health Care Center, Framingham, MA
Kathryn Barton Nursing Home, Wayland, MA
Kathy Crawford Nursing Center, Atlanta, GA
Katie Jane Memorial Home, Warrenton, MO
Katyville Healthcare Center, Katy, TX
Kau Hospital—Skilled Nursing Unit, Pahala, HI
Kauai Veterans Memorial Hospital—Skilled Nursing Unit, Waimea, HI
Kaw Valley Manor, Bonner Springs, KS
Kaweah Manor Convalescent Hosptial, Visalia, CA
Kearney Home, Sharon Hill, PA
Kearny Mesa Convalescent and Nursing Home, San Diego, CA
Keeling Home for Care, Louisville, KY
Keen Agers Home Inc, Wichita, KS
Keeneland Nursing Home, Weatherford, TX
Keiro Nursing Home, Los Angeles, CA
Keith Acres Nursing Home, Blytheville, AR
Keith Hill Nursing Home Inc, Grafton, MA
Keller Nursing Home, Spokane, WA
Keller Sheltered Care Home 1, Dongola, IL
Kelley Rest Home, Agawam, MA
Kelly Nursing Home, Kansas City, MO
Kelsey Memorial Hospital, Lakeview, MI
Kelwood, Boulder, CO
Kemp Care Center Inc, Kemp, TX
Kemp Horn Home, Smithsburg, MD
Kemper County Nursing Home, DeKalb, MS
Kendal at Longwood, Kennett Square, PA
Kendallville Nursing Home, Kendallville, IN
Kendallwood Trails Nursing Center, Gladstone, MO
Kenesaw Nursing Home Inc, Baltimore, MD
Ken-Joy Convalescent Home, Hope, IN
Kenmare Community Hospital, Kenmare, ND
Kenmore Mercy Hospital—Skilled Nursing Unit, Kenmore, NY
Kennebunk Nursing Home Inc, Kennebunk, ME

Kennedale Nursing Home, Kennedale, TX
Kennedy Convalescent Hospital, Los Angeles, CA
Kennedy Memorial Christian Home Inc, Martinsville, IN
Kenneson Convalescent Home, Flourtown, PA
Kennett Health Care Center, Kennett, MO
Kenney Presbyterian Home, Seattle, WA
Kenniebrew Home, Harvey, IL
Kennington Manor, Sarasota, FL
Kenoza Hillcrest Nursing Home, Haverhill, MA
Kenoza Manor Convalescent Home, Haverhill, MA
Kenoza Nursing Home, Haverhill, MA
Kensington Gardens Nursing Home, Kensington, MD
Kensington Manor, Dallas, TX
Kenson Nursing Home, Baltimore, MD
Kent Community Hospital Complex, Grand Rapids, MI
Kent Convalescent Center, Smyrna, DE
Kent Convalescent Hospital, Pasadena, CA
Kent County Nursing Home, Jayton, TX
Kent House of People, Saint Paul, MN
Kent Nursing Home, Holmes, NY
Kent Nursing Home Inc, Warwick, RI
Kent Nursing Homes Inc, Fort Worth, TX
Kent Quality Care Nursing Center, Kent, OH
Kentland Nursing Home, Kentland, IN
Kentmere, The Home of Merciful Rest Society Inc, Wilmington, DE
Kenton Manor, Greeley, CO
Kent's Nursing Center, Fort Worth, TX
Kentuckiana Christian Home Inc, Charlestown, IN
Kentucky Rest Haven, Madisonville, KY
Kentwood Manor Nursing Home, Kentwood, LA
Kenwood House, Richmond, KY
Kenwood Manor, Enid, OK
Kenwood Nursing Home, Dallas, TX
Kenwood Terrace, Chicago, IL
Kenwood Terrace Inc, Cincinnati, OH
Kenwood View Nursing Home, Salina, KS
Kenya Village Nursing Home, Duncan, OK
Kenyon Sunset Home, Kenyon, MN
Keokuk Convalescent Center, Keokuk, IA
The Kepler Home Inc, Elizabethville, PA
Kermit Nursing Center, Kermit, TX
Kerr Center for Handicapped Children, Marylhurst, OR
Keswick Home for Incurables of Baltimore City, Baltimore, MD
Ketcham's Nursing Home, Crooksville, OH
Ketter Manor Inc, Falls City, NE
Kettering Convalescent Center, Kettering, OH
Kewanee Care Home, Kewanee, IL
Kewanee Convalescent Center, Kewanee, IL
Kewaunee Health Care Center, Kewaunee, WI
Key Circle Hospice Inc, Baltimore, MD
Key Pine Village, Lecanto, FL
Keystone Nursing Care Center, Keystone, IA
Keystone Nursing Home Inc, Leominster, MA
Keysville Convalescent and Nursing Center, Keysville, GA
Kidwell Rest Home, Romney, WV
Kilgore Nursing Center, Kilgore, TX
Killeen Nursing Home, Killeen, TX
Kimball Care Intermediate Care Home, Buchanan, GA
Kimball County Manor, Kimball, NE
Kimberly Convalescent Hospital, Santa Maria, CA

Kimberly Hall Nursing Home—North, Windsor, CT
Kimberly Hall Nursing Home—South, Windsor, CT
Kimberly Manor Nursing and Convalescent Home, Rock Springs, WY
Kimbrough Nursing Home of Springfield Inc, Springfield, MO
Kimes Convalescent Center, Athens, OH
Kimwell Nursing Home, Fall River, MA
Kinder Care Nursing Home, Kansas City, MO
Kinder Nursing Home, Kinder, LA
Kindlehope, Willmar, MN
King Bruwaert House, Hinsdale, IL
King City Convalescent Center, Tigard, OR
King City Manor, King City, MO
King David Center at Palm Beach, West Palm Beach, FL
King Family Care Home, Arvada, CO
King James Nursing Home, Chatham, NJ
King James Nursing Home, Navesink, NJ
King James of Franklin Township, Somerset, NJ
King Nursing Home, Houghton Lake, MI
King Rest Home, Marceline, MO
King Street Home Inc, Port Chester, NY
King Tree Center, Dayton, OH
Kingdom Nursing Home Association Inc, Fulton, MO
Kingman Health Care Center, Kingman, AZ
Kings Convalescent Hospital, Hanford, CA
Kings Daughters and Sons Home, Louisville, KY
Kings Daughters and Sons Home, Memphis, TN
King's Daughters and Sons Home for the Aged, Ashland, KY
Kings Daughters and Sons Home for the Aged in Norfolk County, Wrentham, MA
King's Daughters and Sons Nursing Home, Durant, OK
King's Daughters and Sons Rest Home Inc, Meridian, MS
King's Daughters Home, Mexico, MO
King's Guest Home, Winnsboro, LA
Kings Harbor Care Center, Bronx, NY
King's Manor Methodist Home, Hereford, TX
Kings Mountain Convalescent Center, Kings Mountain, NC
King's Nursing Home, Kansas City, MO
Kings Terrace Nursing Home, Bronx, NY
Kings Vista Convalescent Hospital, Fowler, CA
Kingsbridge Heights Nursing Home, Bronx, NY
Kingsbury Memorial Manor, Lake Preston, SD
Kingsdale Manor, Lumberton, NC
Kingsland Hill Care Center, Kingsland, TX
Kingsley Manor Convalescent Hospital, Los Angeles, CA
Kingsport Health Care Center Inc, Kingsport, TN
Kingston Nursing Home, Plymouth, IN
Kingston Pike Nursing Home, Knoxville, TN
Kingstree Community Residence, Kingstree, SC
Kingstree Nursing Facility Inc, Kingstree, SC
Kingsway Arms Nursing Center Inc, Schenectady, NY
Kinkora Pythian Home, Duncannon, PA
Kinney Nursing Home, Gouverneur, NY
Kinton Nursing Home, Fuquay-Varina, NC
Kiowa Manor Inc, Kiowa, KS
Kirbyhaven, Spokane, WA

Kirkland Convalescent Center, Kirkland, WA
Kirkland Convalescent Home Inc, Williston, SC
Kirksville Manor Care Center, Kirksville, MO
Kirkwood by the River, Birmingham, AL
Kirkwood Nursing Home, Wakefield, MA
Kissimmee Good Samaritan Nursing Center, Kissimmee, FL
Kissimmee Health Care Center, Kissimmee, FL
Kit Carson Convalescent Hospital, Jackson, CA
Kith Haven, Flint, MI
Kith Haven—Ypsilanti, Ypsilanti, MI
Kittson County Nursing Home, Hallock, MN
Kittson Memorial Hospital, Hallock, MN
Kivel Geriatric Center, Phoenix, AZ
Klamath County Nursing Home and Convalescent Center, Klamath Falls, OR
Klearview Manor, Fairfield, ME
Klingerman Nursing Center, Orangeville, PA
Klondike Manor, Louisville, KY
Knapp Haven, Chetek, WI
Knight's Nursing Home, Littlefield, TX
Knights Templar Clinic, Arlington, TX
Knollview Manor Nursing Home, Muskegon, MI
Knollwood Hall, Winston-Salem, NC
Knollwood Manor Inc, Millersville, MD
Knollwood Manor Intermediate Care Facility, Raleigh, NC
Knollwood Nursing Home Inc, Worcester, MA
Knollwood West Convalescent Hospital, San Diego, CA
Knopp Nursing and Retirement Home 2, Fredericksburg, TX
Knopp Nursing Home Inc 1, Fredericksburg, TX
Knott County Health Care Center, Kindman, KY
Knott Nursing Home, Charles Town, WV
Knottsville Home, Philpot, KY
Knowlton Manor Nursing Home, Upton, MA
Knox County Nursing Home, Knoxville, IL
Knox County Nursing Home, Edina, MO
Knox Division—Intermediate Care Facility, Rockland, ME
Knox Manor Inc, Galesburg, IL
Knoxville Convalescent and Nursing Home Inc, Knoxville, TN
Knoxville Health Care Center Inc, Knoxville, TN
Knoxville Rest Home, Knoxville, IA
Knud Hansen Memorial Hospital, Saint Thomas, VI
Knute Nelson Memorial Home, Alexandria, MN
Knutson Manor Nursing Center, El Dorado, KS
Kodiak Island Hospital, Kodiak, AK
Koep Group Home, Fergus Falls, MN
Kohala Hospital—Skilled Nursing Unit, Kapaau, HI
Kokomo Nursing Home, Kokomo, IN
Kona Hospital, Kealakekua, HI
Kosary Home, Oak Forest, IL
Kountze Nursing Center, Kountze, TX
Kramm Healthcare Center Inc, Milton, PA
Kramm Nursing Home Inc, Watsontown, PA
Kraus Home Inc, Chicago, IL
Kraus House, Milton, NH
Kraver Institute, North Miami Beach, FL
Kristen Beth Nursing Home Inc, New Bedford, MA

Kristi Lee Manor Inc, Colorado City, TX
Kuakini Medical Center, Honolulu, HI
Kula Hospital—Skilled Nursing Unit, Kula, HI
Kurthwood Manor Nursing Home, Leesville, LA
K'Way Kare Nursing Home, Holland, TX
Kyakameena Sanitorium 2, Berkeley, CA
L and J Winslow Memorial Nursing Home, Tomball, TX
L F Quigley Memorial Skilled Nursing Facility, Chelsea, MA
L M Swanson Nursing Home, Gallatin, TN
La Belle's Rest Home, Shelburne, MA
La Boure Care Center, Dallas, TX
La Casa Canyon Nursing Home, Canyon, TX
La Crescent Nursing Center, La Crescent, MN
La Dora Lodge Nursing Home, Bedford, TX
La Grange Colonial Manor, La Grange, IL
La Habra Convalescent Hospital, La Habra, CA
La Hacienda Nursing Home, Tucson, AZ
La Hacienda Nursing Home Inc, San Diego, TX
La Jolla Convalescent Hospital, La Jolla, CA
La Mariposa Convalescent Hospital Inc, Fairfield, CA
La Mesa Convalescent Hospital, La Mesa, CA
La Moine Christian Nursing Home, Roseville, IL
La Porte Care Center, La Porte, TX
La Posada, Alamosa, CO
La Posada Convalescent Home, Miami, FL
La Rocca Nursing Home, Tuscaloosa, AL
La Salette Rehabilitation and Convalescent Hospital, Stockton, CA
La Salle County Nursing Home, Ottawa, IL
La Salle Nursing Home Inc, Jena, LA
La Sierra Convalescent Hospital, Merced, CA
La Sierra Convalescent Hospital, Riverside, CA
La Siesta Retirement Center, Hobbs, NM
La Vida Llena Health Care, Albuquerque, NM
La Villa Convalescent Center, Detroit, MI
LaBelle Manor Care Center, LaBelle, MO
Labelle View Nursing Center, Steubenville, OH
Lackawanna County Home, Olyphant, PA
Lackey Convalescent Home, Forest, MS
Lackey Manor, Oklahoma City, OK
LaCoba Homes Inc, Monett, MO
Lacombe Nursing Home, Lacombe, LA
Laconia Nursing Home, Bronx, NY
Ladera Health Care Center, Albuquerque, NM
Ladies GAR Home, Pittsburgh, PA
Ladies Home, Jeffersonville, IN
Ladies Relief Society of Denver, Denver, CO
Ladysmith Nursing Home, Ladysmith, WI
Lafayette Christian Nursing Home, Grand Rapids, MI
Lafayette Convalescent Home, Marblehead, MA
Lafayette Convalescent Hospital, Lafayette, CA
Lafayette Extended Care, Lafayette, AL
Lafayette Good Samaritan Center, Lafayette, MN
Lafayette Guest House, Lafayette, LA
Lafayette Health Care Center, Lafayette, LA
LaFayette Health Care Inc, LaFayette, GA
Lafayette Healthcare Center, Lafayette, IN
Lafayette Manor, Uniontown, PA
Lafayette Manor, Darlington, WI
Lafayette Manor Nursing Home, Lexington, MO

LaFayette Nursing Home Inc, Lafayette, AL
Lafayette Nursing Home Inc, North Kingstown, RI
Lafayette Square Nursing Center Inc, Baltimore, MD
Lafayette Villa Health Care, Norfolk, VA
LaFollette Community Nursing Home, LaFollette, TN
Lafon Home of the Holy Family, New Orleans, LA
Lafourche Home for the Aged, Thibodaux, LA
LaGrande Nursing Center, LaGrande, OR
LaGrange Medcraft Nursing Home, LaGrange, GA
LaGrange Nursing Home, LaGrange, IN
Laguna Rainbow Nursing and Elderly Care Center, New Laguna, NM
Lahey's Nursing Home, Duncan, OK
Lahser Hills Nursing Center, Southfield, MI
Lake Alfred Restorium, Lake Alfred, FL
Lake Andes Health Care Center, Lake Andes, SD
Lake Auburn Home for Aged, Excelsior, MN
Lake Bluff Health Care Center, Lake Bluff, IL
Lake Charles Care Center, Lake Charles, LA
Lake City Health Care Center, Morrow, GA
Lake City Health Care Center, Lake City, TN
Lake City Nursing Home, Lake City, MN
Lake City/Scranton Convalesent Center Inc—Village Green Convalescent Center, Florence, SC
Lake County Adult Resident Center, Mentor, OH
Lake County Child Development Center, Mentor, OH
Lake County Convalescent Home, Crown Point, IN
Lake Crest Villa, Evanston, IL
Lake Crystal Health Care Center, Lake Crystal, MN
Lake District Hospital, Lakeview, OR
Lake Drive Nursing Home Inc, Baltimore, MD
Lake Drive Nursing Home Inc, Henryetta, OK
Lake Erie Institute of Rehabilitation, Erie, PA
Lake Eustis Care Center, Eustis, FL
Lake Front Convalescent Center, Chicago, IL
Lake Haven Health Care Center, Benton, KY
Lake Haven Manor Nursing Center, Duluth, MN
Lake Haven Nursing Home, Worthington, MN
Lake Highlands Nursing Home, Clermont, FL
Lake Holiday Manor Nursing Home, DeMotte, IN
Lake Jackson Nursing Home, Lake Jackson, TX
Lake Lodge, Lake Worth, TX
Lake Memorial Nursing Home, Leesburg, FL
Lake Mills Nursing Home Inc, Lake Mills, IA
Lake Norden Care Center, Lake Norden, SD
Lake Owasso Residence, Shoreview, MN
Lake Park Care Center, Lake Park, IA
Lake Park Nursing Care Center, Sylvania, OH
Lake Park Retirement Residence, Oakland, CA
Lake Park-Wild Rice Residential Treatment Center for Children, Fergus Falls, MN
Lake Region Lutheran Home, Devils Lake, ND
Lake Ridge Health Care Center, Roseville, MN
Lake Shore Hospital and Nursing Home, Irving, NY
Lake Shore Nursing Centre, Chicago, IL
Lake Shore Nursing Home Inc, Irving, NY
Lake Taylor City Hospital—Long-Term Care Unit, Norfolk, VA

Lake Towers Health Center, Sun City Center, FL
Lake View, Arvada, CO
Lake View Home, Monticello, IN
Lake View Rest Home, Wareham, MA
Lake Vue Gardens Convalescent Center, Kirkland, WA
Lake Waccamaw Convalescent Center, Lake Waccamaw, NC
Lake Wales Convalescent Center, Lake Wales, FL
Lake Worth Health Care Center, Lake Worth, FL
Lake Worth Nursing Home, Fort Worth, TX
Lake-Cook Terrace, Northbrook, IL
Lakecrest Development Center, Orem, UT
Lakehaven Nursing Home, Valdosta, GA
Lakeland Convalescent Center, Lakeland, FL
Lakeland Convalescent Center, Detroit, MI
Lakeland Health Care Center, Lakeland, FL
Lakeland Lodge Nursing Home, Heber Springs, AR
Lakeland Loving Care Center Inc, Milford, IN
Lakeland Manor, Chicago, IL
Lakeland Manor, Woodruff, WI
Lakcland Manor Inc, Ardmore, OK
Lakeland Nursing Center, Effingham, IL
Lakeland Nursing Center, Angola, IN
Lakeland Nursing Center, Jackson, MS
Lakeland Nursing Home, Pineville, LA
Lakeland Nursing Home, Geneva, OH
Lakeland Nursing Home, Elkhorn, WI
Lakeland Villa Convalescent Center, Lakeland, GA
Lakeport Skilled Nursing Center Inc, Lakeport, CA
Lakeshore Convalescent Hospital, Oakland, CA
Lakeshore Heights Nursing Care Center, Gainesville, GA
Lakeshore Home for the Aged, Nashville, TN
Lakeshore Inn Nursing Home, Waseca, MN
Lakeshore Lutheran Home, Duluth, MN
Lakeshore Manor Nursing Home, Decatur, IL
Lakeshore Nursing Home, Crescent City, FL
Lakeshore Nursing Home, Rochester, NY
Lakeside Boarding Home, Chicago, IL
Lakeside Health Center, West Palm Beach, FL
Lakeside Health Center Inc, Michigan City, IN
Lakeside Lodge, Wellington, KS
Lakeside Lutheran Home, Emmetsburg, IA
Lakeside Manor Home for the Aged, Winchester, TN
Lakeside Memorial Home, Lubbock, TX
Lakeside Nursing Home, Pine City, MN
Lakeside Nursing Home Inc, Ithaca, NY
Lakeside Place, Highland Heights, KY
Lakeside Residential Care Facility, East Hampton, CT
Lakeview Care Center, Glenwood, MN
Lakeview Childrens Home, Sauk Centre, MN
Lakeview Christian Home—Northgate Unit, Carlsbad, NM
Lakeview Christian Home of the Southwest, Carlsbad, NM
Lakeview Convalescent Center, Wayne, NJ
Lakeview Developmental Disability Center, Riverside, CA
Lakeview Health Care Center, Carmel, IN
Lakeview Health Center, Harrisville, RI
Lakeview Health Center, West Salem, WI
Lakeview Manor, Chapel Hill, NC
Lakeview Manor, Weyauwega, WI

Lakeview Manor Inc, Opp, AL
Lakeview Manor Inc, Indianapolis, IN
Lakeview Manor Nursing Home, Saint Petersburg, FL
Lakeview Manor Nursing Home, West Palm Beach, FL
Lakeview Manor Nursing Home, Cadillac, MI
Lakeview Manor Nursing Home Inc, New Roads, LA
Lakeview Methodist Health Care Center, Fairmont, MN
Lakeview Nursing and Geriatric Center, Chicago, IL
Lakeview Nursing Center, Sanford, FL
Lakeview Nursing Center, Spartanburg, SC
Lakeview Nursing Home, Morgantown, KY
Lakeview Nursing Home, Farmerville, LA
Lakeview Nursing Home Inc, Birmingham, AL
Lakeview Nursing Home Inc, Oroville, CA
Lakeview Rest Home, Newton, MA
Lakeview Rest Home, Firth, NE
Lakeview Rest Home Inc, Forsyth, MO
Lakeview Terrace Medical Care Facility, Altoona, FL
Lakeview Terrace Medical Care Facility, Altoona, FL
Lakeview Terrace Sanitarium, Sunland, CA
Lakeview Village Inc, Lenexa, KS
Lakewood Care Center, Milwaukee, WI
Lakewood Convalescent Home, Hot Springs, AR
Lakewood Manor, Waterville, ME
Lakewood Manor—Health Care Unit, Richmond, VA
Lakewood Manor North, Los Angeles, CA
Lakewood Manor Nursing Center, Hendersonville, NC
Lakewood Nursing Home, Lakewood, CO
Lakewood Nursing Home, Plainfield, IL
Lakewood of Voorhees, Voorhees, NJ
Lakewood Park Health Center, Downey, CA
Lakewood Pine Aire Nursing Home, Lakewood, NJ
Lakewood Village Nursing Center, Wichita, KS
Lamar Boarding and Rest Home, Lamar, MO
Lamar Convalescent Center Inc, Vernon, AL
Lamar County Hospital and Nursing Home, Vernon, AL
The Lambs Inc, Libertyville, IL
Lamb's Nursing Home, High Point, NC
Lamesa Nursing Center, Lamesa, TX
Lamoni Manor, Lamoni, IA
The Lamp, Brook Park, OH
Lamp Nursing Home, Lisbon Falls, ME
Lampasas Manor, Lampasas, TX
Lanai Community Hospital—Skilled Nursing Unit, Lanai City, HI
The Lancashire, Kilmarnock, VA
Lancashire Hall Inc, Lancaster, PA
Lancaster Convalescent Hospital, Lancaster, CA
Lancaster County Care Center, Lancaster, SC
Lancaster Health Care Center, Lancaster, OH
Lancaster Manor, Lincoln, NE
Lancaster Nursing Home, Lancaster, WI
Lancaster Nursing Home Inc, Lancaster, TX
Lancaster Residential Center, Lancaster, TX
Lancia Convalescent Center, Steubenville, OH
Lancia Villa Royale Nursing Home, Steubenville, OH
Landers Nursing Home, Philadelphia, PA

Landis Home, Lititz, PA

Landmark Learning Center—Facility I, Opa Locka, FL

Landmark Learning Center—Miami Facility II, Opa Locka, FL

Landmark Medical Center, Pomona, CA

Landry Road Nursing Home, Lafayette, LA

Lane House Inc, Crawfordsville, IN

Lane Memorial Hospital—Geriatric Unit, Zachary, LA

Lane's Convalescent Home Inc, Wichita Falls, TX

Lane's Nursing Home, Monette, AR

Lane's Nursing Home Inc, Wichita Falls, TX

Lane's Rest Home Inc, Caraway, AR

Lanett Geriatric Center Inc, Lanett, AL

Lanier Memorial Hospital—Nursing Home, Langdale, AL

Lanier North Intermediate Care Facility, Gainesville, GA

Lanier Nursing Home, Comming, GA

Lanore's Nursing Home, Draper, UT

Lansdowne Rest Home, East Lansdowne, PA

Lanterman State Hospital and Development Center, Pomona, CA

Lantern Park Care Center, Coralville, IA

Lantern Park Manor, Colby, KS

Lantis of North Dakota Inc, Hettinger, ND

Lapeer County Medical Care Facility, Lapeer, MI

LaPlata Nursing Home, LaPlata, MO

Laradon Hall—Society for Exceptional Children, Denver, CO

Larchwood Lodge Nursing Home, Waltham, MA

Larimore Good Samaritan Center, Larimore, ND

Lark Ellen Towers Convalescent Hospital, West Covina, CA

Lark Manor Convalescent Hospital, Los Gatos, CA

Larry James Home, Waseca, MN

Larsen Memorial Nursing Home, Peshtigo, WI

Larsen Nursing Home, Lehi, UT

Larson's Pioneer Homes Inc, Aurora, NE

Las Cruces Manor, Las Cruces, NM

Las Flores Convalescent Hospital, Gardena, CA

Las Flores Nursing Center, Mesa, AZ

Las Palomas Health Care Center, Albuquerque, NM

Las Vegas Convalescent Center, Las Vegas, NV

LaSalle Convalescent Home, Minneapolis, MN

Lasalle Nursing Home, Detroit, MI

Lasata, Cedarburg, WI

Latah Care Center, Moscow, ID

Latah Center, Spokane, WA

Latham Estates, Lake Forest, IL

Latham Nursing Home, Anderson, SC

Latham Nursing Home, Salt Lake City, UT

Lathrop Health Facility Inc, Lathrop, MO

Lathrop Home for Aged Women, Northampton, MA

Latimer Nursing Home, Wilburton, OK

Latrobe Area Hospital—Extended Care Facility, Latrobe, PA

Latta Road Nursing Home, Rochester, NY

Laub Pavillion of Cleveland Ohio, Cleveland, OH

Lauderdale Christian Nursing Home, Killen, AL

Lauderdale County Nursing Home, Ripley, TN

Laundsun Homes Inc, Carlsbad, NM

Laurel Avenue Convalescent Hospital, Fontana, CA

Laurel Avenue Rest Home Inc, Bridgeport, CT

Laurel Creek Health Care Center, Manchester, KY

Laurel Foster Home Inc, Coventry, RI

Laurel Glen Convalescent Hospital, Redwood City, CA

Laurel Heights Convalescent Hospital, San Francisco, CA

Laurel Heights Home for the Elderly, London, KY

Laurel Hill Inc, Dunmore, PA

Laurel Hill Nursing Center, Grants Pass, OR

Laurel Hill Nursing Center Inc, Pickens, SC

Laurel Lane, Clifton, CO

Laurel Living Center, Manchester, CT

Laurel Manor, Stroudsburg, PA

Laurel Manor Care Center, Colorado Springs, CO

Laurel Nursing and Retirement Center, Hamburg, PA

Laurel Nursing Home, Laurel, MT

Laurel Park—A Center for Effective Living, Pomona, CA

Laurel Rest Home, Uniontown, PA

Laurel Wood Health Care Inc, Jackson, TN

Laurelbrook Sanitarium, Dayton, TN

Laurelhurst Care Center, Portland, OR

Laurels, Harlan, KY

Laurelton Center, Laurelton, PA

Laurelwood Convalescent Center, North Hollywood, CA

Laurelwood Manor Nursing Home, Gaston, OR

Laurelwood Nursing Center, Elkton, MD

Laurenceburg Health Care Center, Lawrenceburg, TN

Laurens County Convalescent Center, Dublin, GA

Laurens Nursing Home Inc, Laurens, SC

Laurens Street Community Residence, Aiken, SC

Laurie Nursing Home, Laurie, MO

LaVerna Heights, Savannah, MO

LaVerna Village Nursing Home, Savannah, MO

Lavilla Grande Care Center, Grand Junction, CO

Law-Den Nursing Home, Detroit, MI

Lawn View Nursing Home, Tishomingo, OK

Lawrence Convalescent Center, Portland, OR

Lawrence County Lions Nursing Home Inc, Lawrenceburg, TN

Lawrence County Medical Center Inc, Monticello, MS

Lawrence County Nursing Home, Mount Vernon, MO

Lawrence Hall Nursing Home, Walnut Ridge, AR

Lawrence Manor Nursing Home, Indianapolis, IN

Lawrence Manor Nursing Home, Lawrence, KS

Lawrence Manor Nursing Home, Lynn, MA

Lawrence Nursing Home Inc, Arverne, NY

Lawrence Presbyterian Manor, Lawrence, KS

Lawrenceville Nursing Home, Lawrenceville, NJ

Lawton Heights Nursing Center, Lawton, OK

Lawton Nursing Home, Fort Wayne, IN

Layton Watson Nursing Home, Gallaway, TN

Le Havre Convalescent Hospital, Menlo Park, CA

Lea County Good Samaritan Village, Hobbs, NM

Lea Manor Convalescent Home Inc, Norwalk, CT

Leader Health Care Center, Norristown, PA

Leader Nursing and Rehabilitation Center, Cherry Hill, NJ

Leader Nursing and Rehabilitation Center, Bethlehem, PA

Leader Nursing and Rehabilitation Center, Camp Hill, PA

Leader Nursing and Rehabilitation Center, Dallastown, PA

Leader Nursing and Rehabilitation Center, Easton, PA

Leader Nursing and Rehabilitation Center, Elizabethtown, PA

Leader Nursing and Rehabilitation Center, Lebanon, PA

Leader Nursing and Rehabilitation Center, Sunbury, PA

Leader Nursing and Rehabilitation Center, West Reading, PA

Leader Nursing and Rehabilitation Center, Madison, WI

Leader Nursing and Rehabilitation Center— Chambersburg, Chambersburg, PA

Leader Nursing and Rehabilitation Center— East, Kingston, PA

Leader Nursing and Rehabilitation Center— Laureldale, Reading, PA

Leader Nursing and Rehabilitation Center— North, Williamsport, PA

Leader Nursing and Rehabilitation Center— Pottstown, Pottstown, PA

Leader Nursing Rehabilitation Center, Harrisburg, PA

Leader Nursing Rehabilitation Center, Jersey Shore, PA

Leader Nursing Rehabilitation Center, Pottsville, PA

Leader Nursing Rehabilitation Center, Sinking Spring, PA

Leader Nursing Rehabilitation Center, Yeadon, PA

Leader Nursing Rehabilitation Center—#1, East Norristown, PA

Leader Nursing Rehabilitation Center—South, Williamsport, PA

Leader Nursing Rehabilitation Center—West, Kingston, PA

Leahi Hospital—Skilled Nursing Unit, Honolulu, HI

Leake County Skilled Nursing Facility, Carthage, MS

Leavenworth County Convalescent Infirmary, Leavenworth, KS

Lebanon Care Center, Lebanon, MO

Lebanon County Life Support, Lebanon, PA

Lebanon Health Care Center, Lebanon, OH

Lebanon Nursing Home, Lebanon, IN

Lebanon Nursing Home, Lebanon, MO

Lebanon Nursing Home, Lebanon, OH

Lebanon Valley Brethren Home, Palmyra, PA

Lebanon Valley Home, Annville, PA

Lebraun Convalescent Home, Cincinnati, OH

Ledgecrest Convalescent Home, Kensington, CT

Ledges Manor Corporation, Boone, IA

Ledgeview Memorial Home, West Paris, ME

Ledgewood Manor, North Windham, ME

Lee Alan Bryant Health Care Facility Inc, Rockville, IN

Lee Ann's Residential Facility, Hannibal, MO

Lee Convalescent Center, Fort Myers, FL

Lee County Nursing Home, Dixon, IL

Lee County Personal Care Home Inc, Beattyville, KY

Lee Manor, Des Plaines, IL

Lee Manor Nursing Home, Tupelo, MS

Lee Rest Home, Waltham, MA

Lee Street, Arvada, CO

Leelanau Memorial Hospital, Northport, MI

Lee's Rest Home, Newell, SD

Lee's Summit Care Center, Lee's Summit, MO

Leesburg Healthcare Center, Leesburg, FL

Leesburg Nursing Center, Leesburg, FL

Leesville State School, Leesville, LA

Leeward Nursing Home, Waianae, HI

Leewood Manor Nursing Home Inc, Milan, MO

Leewood Nursing Home, Tucson, AZ

Leewood Nursing Home Inc, Annandale, VA

Lefa L Seran Skilled Nursing Facility, Hawthorne, NV

LeFlore Nursing Home, Poteau, OK

Legacy Lodge Nursing Home, Russellville, AR

Legault's Soundview Nursing Home, Everett, WA

Lehmans Guest and Nursing Home, Rheems, PA

Leisure Arms Health Related Facility, Troy, NY

Leisure Arms Nursing Home, Houston, TX

Leisure Center, Caldwell, KS

Leisure Chateau, Lakewood, CO

Leisure Chateau Care Center, Lakewood, NJ

Leisure Hills Healthcare Center, Hibbing, MN

Leisure Hills Inc, Grand Rapids, MN

Leisure Homestead Association, Stafford, KS

Leisure Lodge, Lake Village, AR

Leisure Lodge, Little Rock, AR

Leisure Lodge—Anahuac, Anahuac, TX

Leisure Lodge—Borger, Borger, TX

Leisure Lodge—Brady, Brady, TX

Leisure Lodge Bryan, Bryan, TX

Leisure Lodge—Caldwell, Caldwell, TX

Leisure Lodge—Carthage, Carthage, TX

Leisure Lodge—Centerville, Centerville, TX

Leisure Lodge—Cleburne, Cleburne, TX

Leisure Lodge—Clyde, Clyde, TX

Leisure Lodge—Coleman, Coleman, TX

Leisure Lodge—Corsicana, Corsicana, TX

Leisure Lodge—Crockett, Crockett, TX

Leisure Lodge—Gilmer, Gilmer, TX

Leisure Lodge—Graham-West Third, Graham, TX

Leisure Lodge—Hamilton, Hamilton, TX

Leisure Lodge—Hearne, Hearne, TX

Leisure Lodge—Henderson, Henderson, TX

Leisure Lodge Inc, Berryville, AR

Leisure Lodge Inc, Camden, AR

Leisure Lodge Inc, Camden, AR

Leisure Lodge Inc, Crossett, AR

Leisure Lodge Inc, DeWitt, AR

Leisure Lodge Inc, Hamburg, AR

Leisure Lodge Inc, McGehee, AR

Leisure Lodge Inc, Mena, AR

Leisure Lodge Inc, Monticello, AR

Leisure Lodge Inc, Nashville, AR

Leisure Lodge Inc, Searcy, AR

Leisure Lodge Inc, West Memphis, AR

Leisure Lodge—Junction, Junction, TX

Leisure Lodge—Kaufman, Kaufman, TX

Leisure Lodge—Lampasas, Lampasas, TX

Leisure Lodge of Mountain Home, Mountain Home, AR

Leisure Lodge—Overton, Overton, TX

Leisure Lodge—Palacios, Palacios, TX

Leisure Lodge—Rosenberg, Rosenberg, TX

Leisure Lodge—Rusk, Rusk, TX

Leisure Lodge—Sulphur Springs, Sulphur Springs, TX

Leisure Lodge—Texarkana, Texarkana, TX

Leisure Lodge—Tyler, Tyler, TX

Leisure Lodge—Weatherford, Weatherford, TX

Leisure Lodge—Wortham, Wortham, TX

Leisure Manor, Saint Petersburg, FL

Leisure Manor Nursing Home, Okmulgee, OK

Leisure Oaks Convalescent Center, Defiance, OH

Leisure Village Nursing Center, Tulsa, OK

Leisure Years Nursing Home Inc, Owensboro, KY

Lela Wilson's Residential Care Facility, Las Animas, CO

Lelah G Wagner Nursing Home, Panama City, FL

Leland Home, Waltham, MA

Lemay Nursing Home, Lemay, MO

Lemberg Home and Geriatric Institute Inc, Brooklyn, NY

Lemington Home for the Aged, Pittsburgh, PA

Lemon Grove Convalescent Center, Lemon Grove, CA

Lena Continental Manor Nursing Home, Lena, IL

Lena Crews Family Care Home, Denver, CO

Lenawee County Medical Care Facility, Adrian, MI

Lenoir Memorial Home Inc, Columbia, MO

Lenox Care Center, Lenox, IA

Lenox Hill Nursing and Rehabilitation Care Facility, Lynn, MA

Lenox Nursing Home Inc, Haverhill, MA

Leominster Home for Old Ladies, Leominster, MA

Leon Care Center, Leon, IA

Leon Valley Lodge, San Antonio, TX

Leonardville Nursing Home, Leonardville, KS

Leroy Village Green Nursing Home and Health Related Facility Inc, Leroy, NY

Leslie Family Care Home, Denver, CO

Letcher County Golden Years Rest Home, Jenkins, KY

Levelland Development Center, Levelland, TX

Levelland Nursing Home, Levelland, TX

Levindale Hebrew Geriatric Center and Hospital, Baltimore, MD

Lewes Convalescent Center, Lewes, DE

Lewis Bay Convalescent Home, Barnstable, MA

Lewis County General Hospital—Nursing Home Unit, Lowville, NY

Lewis County Manor, Hohenwald, TN

Lewis County Nursing Home, Canton, MO

Lewis Memorial Christian Village, Springfield, IL

Lewis Memorial Methodist Home, Franklin, KY

Lewisburg United Methodist Home, Lewisburg, PA

Lewiston Care Center, Lewiston, ID

Lewiston Villa, Lewiston, MN

Lewisville Development Center, Lewisville, TX

Lewisville Hotel for Senior Citizens, Lewisville, IN

Lewisville Nursing Home, Lewisville, TX

Lewis-Wetzel Nursing Home, New Martinsville, WV

Lexington Convalescent Home Inc, New Britain, CT

Lexington Country Place, Lexington, KY

Lexington Manor Health Care Facility, Lexington, KY

Lexington Manor Nursing Center, Lexington, TN

Lexington Nursing Home, Lexington, OK

Lexington West Inc, Columbia, SC

Leyden Community Extended Care Center, Franklin Park, IL

Libby Care Center, Libby, MT

Liberal Good Samaritan Center, Liberal, KS

Liberty County Nursing Home, Chester, MT

Liberty Hall Convalescent Home, Colchester, CT

Liberty House Nursing Home, Southbridge, MA

Liberty House Nursing Home, Jersey City, NJ

Liberty House Nursing Home, Thomasville, NC

Liberty House Nursing Home, Clifton Forge, VA

Liberty House Nursing Home, Harrisonburg, VA

Liberty House Nursing Home, Roanoke, VA

Liberty House Nursing Home, Waynesboro, VA

Liberty Intermediate Care—Bristol, Bristol, FL

Liberty Manor, Midway, GA

Liberty Nursing Center, Allentown, PA

Liberty Nursing Home, Liberty, TX

Liberty Pavilion Nursing Home, Danvers, MA

Libertyville Manor Extended Care, Libertyville, IL

Lida Clark Nursing Home, Clarksburg, WV

Lida Home Nursing Home, Minonk, IL

Life Care Center Inc, Fitzgerald, GA

Life Care Center—Kennewick, Kennewick, WA

Life Care Center of Altamonte Springs, Altamonte Springs, FL

Life Care Center of Athens, Athens, TN

Life Care Center of Bruceton-Hollow Rock, Bruceton, TN

Life Care Center of Church Hill, Church Hill, TN

Life Care Center of Cleveland, Cleveland, TN

Life Care Center of Collegedale, Collegedale, TN

Life Care Center of Coos Bay, Coos Bay, OR

Life Care Center of Crossville, Crossville, TN

Life Care Center of East Ridge, Chattanooga, TN

Life Care Center of Greeneville, Greeneville, TN

Life Care Center of Hilo, Hilo, HI

Life Care Center of LaCenter, LaCenter, KY

Life Care Center of Morehead, Morehead, KY

Life Care Center of Morgan County, Wartburg, TN

Life Care Center of Morristown, Morristown, TN

Life Care Center of Paducah, Paducah, KY

Life Care Center of Punta Gorda, Punta Gorda, FL

Life Care Center of Tullahoma, Tullahoma, TN

Life Care Center—Richland, Richland, WA

Life Care Center—Ritzville, Ritzville, WA

Life Care Center—Yuma, Yuma, CO

Life Care—West, Greeneville, TN

Lighthouse Convalescent Home, Selma, AL

Lila Doyle Nursing Care Facility, Seneca, SC
Lilac City Convalescent Center, Spokane, WA
Lilburn Health Care Center, Lilburn, GA
Lillian E Kerr Nursing Home, Phelps, WI
Lillian M Hudspeth Nursing Home, Sonora, TX
Lily Pond Nursing Home, Staten Island, NY
Lima Convalescent Home, Lima, OH
Lima Estates, Lima, PA
Lima Manor, Lima, OH
Limestone Health Facility Inc, Athens, AL
Lincoln Avenue and Crawford's Home for the Aged, Cincinnati, OH
Lincoln Care Center, Fayetteville, TN
Lincoln Community Hospital and Nursing Home, Hugo, CO
Lincoln Community Nursing Home, Lincoln, MO
Lincoln Convalescent Center, Detroit, MI
Lincoln Convalescent Center Inc, Baltimore, MD
Lincoln East Nursing Home, Wichita, KS
Lincoln Glen Intermediate Care, San Jose, CA
Lincoln Haven Rest Home, Lincoln, MI
Lincoln Hill Manor Rest Home, Spencer, MA
Lincoln Hill Nursing Home, Quincy, IL
Lincoln Hills Nursing Home Inc, Tell City, IN
Lincoln Hills of New Albany, New Albany, IN
Lincoln Home, Belleville, IL
Lincoln Land Nursing Home, Lincoln, IL
Lincoln Lodge Nursing Center, Connersville, IN
Lincoln Lutheran of Racine, Racine, WI
Lincoln Manor Inc, Decatur, IL
Lincoln Manor—North Inc, Decatur, IL
Lincoln Manor Nursing Center, Connersville, IN
Lincoln Manor Nursing Home, Jefferson City, MO
Lincoln Memorial Nursing Home, Goulds, FL
Lincoln Nursing Center, Lincolnton, NC
Lincoln Nursing Home, Worcester, MA
Lincoln Park Intermediate Care Center, Lincoln Park, NJ
Lincoln Park Nursing and Convalescent Home, Lincoln Park, NJ
Lincoln Park Nursing Home, Monroe, LA
Lincoln Park Terrace Inc, Chicago, IL
Lincoln Regional Center—Comprehensive Care Unit, Lincoln, NE
Lincoln Residential Center, Brookhaven, MS
Lincoln Rest Home, Lincoln, MA
Lincoln Village Convalescent Center, Racine, WI
Linda Lee Rest Home, Worcester, MA
Linda Mar Convalescent Hospital, Pacifica, CA
Linda Terra Convalescent Hospital, San Rafael, CA
Linda Valley Convalescent Hospital, Loma Linda, CA
Linda Vista Care Center, Ashland, OR
Lindale Nursing Center, Lindale, TX
Lindberg Rest Home, Kerkhoven, MN
Linden Hall, Kennett Square, PA
Linden Health Care Center, Dayton, OH
Linden Healthcare Center, Stillwater, MN
Linden Lodge, Brattleboro, VT
Linden Manor Nursing Home, North Platte, NE
Linden Nursing and Retirement Home, Rockland, MA
Lindenman Health Care Center Inc, Bolivar, MO

Lindenwood Nursing Home Inc, Omaha, NE
Lindon Care and Training Center, Lindon, UT
Lindsay Care Center, Lindsay, OK
Lineville Geriatric Center Inc, Lineville, AL
Linn Care Center, Albany, OR
Linn Community Nursing Home Inc, Linn, KS
Linn County Care Facility, Marion, IA
Linn Manor, Marion, IA
Linn Manor Nursing Home, Linn, MO
Linnea Residential Home, Chisago City, MN
Linton Nursing Home, Linton, IN
Linwood Convalescent Center, Linwood, NJ
Linwood Gardens Convalescent Center, Visalia, CA
Lions Manor Nursing Home, Cumberland, MD
Lisner Home Inc, Washington, DC
Litchfield Manor Care Center, Litchfield, MI
Little Angels Nursing Home Inc, Elgin, IL
Little Bird Nursing Home Inc, Weatherford, OK
Little Brook Nursing and Convalescent Home, Califon, NJ
Little City Foundation, Palatine, IL
Little Company of Mary Health Facility Inc, San Pierre, IN
Little Creek Sanitarium, Knoxville, TN
Little Egypt Manor, Harrisburg, IL
Little Falls Hospital, Little Falls, NY
Little Flower Haven, Earling, IA
Little Flower Manor, Darby, PA
Little Flower Manor, Wilkes-Barre, PA
Little Flower Nursing Home, Saint Louis, MO
Little Flower Nursing Home, East Islip, NY
Little Forest Medical Center, Akron, OH
Little Forest Medical Center, Youngstown, OH
Little Friends Inc, Naperville, IL
Little Neck Nursing Home, Little Neck, NY
Little Nursing Home, Montclair, NJ
Little River Nursing Home, Ashdown, AR
Little Rock Nursing Center, Little Rock, AR
Little Sisters of the Poor, San Pedro, CA
Little Sisters of the Poor, Chicago, IL
Little Sisters of the Poor, Detroit, MI
Little Sisters of the Poor, Saint Paul, MN
Little Sisters of the Poor, Saint Louis, MO
Little Sisters of the Poor, Cleveland, OH
Little Sisters of the Poor Home for the Aged, Pittsburgh, PA
Little Sisters of the Poor—Saint Joseph Home for Aged, Richmond, VA
Little Sisters of the Poor—Saint Martin's, Baltimore, MD
Little Sisters of the Poor-Saint Alexis Home, Kansas City, MO
Littlefield Hospitality House, Littlefield, TX
Littleton House, Littleton, CO
Littleton House Nursing Home, Littleton, MA
Littleton Manor Nursing Home, Littleton, CO
Live Oak Medical Center, Blanco, TX
Live Oak Retirement Center, Shreveport, LA
Live Oak Skilled Nursing and Manor, Santa Cruz, CA
Livermore Manor Convalescent Hospital, Livermore, CA
Living Center of Griffin, Griffin, GA
Living Skills Center, Saint Paul, KS
Livingston Care Center, Howell, MI
Livingston Convalescent Center, Livingston, MT
Livingston County Health Related Facility, Mount Morris, NY

Livingston County Rest Home, Smithland, KY
Livingston County Skilled Nursing Facility, Geneseo, NY
Livingston Manor, Pontiac, IL
Livingston Manor Care Center, Chillicothe, MO
Livingston Nursing Home Inc, Bessemer, AL
Livngston Convalescent Center, Livingston, TX
Livonia Nursing Center, Livonia, MI
Llanfair House, Wayne, NJ
Llanfair Terrace, Cincinnati, OH
Loch Haven Lodge, Orlando, FL
Lock Haven Hospital—Extended Care Facility, Lock Haven, PA
Lockney Care Center, Lockney, TX
Lockview Nursing Home, Seattle, WA
Locust Grove Nursing Home, Wills Point, TX
Locust Grove Retirement Village, Mifflin, PA
Locust Ridge Nursing Home Inc, Williamsburg, OH
The Lodge Intermediate Care Facility, Neptune, NJ
Lodge Nursing Home, Navarre, OH
Lodgepole Plaza Nursing Home, Sidney, NE
Lodi Good Samaritan Center, Lodi, WI
Lofton Nursing Home Inc, Franklin, TN
Logan County Home, Bellefontaine, OH
Logan County Home for the Aged, Napoleon, ND
Logan County Nursing Home, Paris, AR
Logan Health Care Center, Logan, OH
Logan Manor Nursing Home, Logan, KS
Logan Park Care Center, Logan, WV
Logan Valley Manor Inc, Lyons, NE
Lo-Har Lodge Incorporated, El Cajon, CA
Loma Linda Rest Home Inc, Pine Bluff, AR
Ray Graham Lombard Community Living Center, Lombard, IL
Lomita Golden Age Convalescent Home, Lomita, CA
Lompoc Hospital District Convalescent Care Center, Lompoc, CA
London House Convalescent Hospital, Santa Rosa, CA
London House Convalescent Hospital, Sonoma, CA
Lone Pine Congregate Center, Ironton, MO
Lone Pine Nursing Home Inc, New Bremen, OH
Lone Tree Convalescent Hospital, Antioch, CA
Lone Tree Health Care Center, Lone Tree, IA
Lone Tree Lodge, Meade, KS
Long Beach Grandell Co, Long Beach, NY
Long Beach Memorial Nursing Home Inc, Long Beach, NY
Long Island Nursing Home, Flushing, NY
Long Island Tides Nursing Home, Long Beach, NY
Long Lake Convalescent Center, Port Orchard, WA
Long Lake Nursing Home, Long Lake, MN
Long Prairie Memorial Hospital, Long Prairie, MN
Long Term Care at Dixmont Hospital, Sewickly, PA
Long Term Care at Neponset—Ashmont Manor, Boston, MA
Long Term Care at Neponset—Neponset Hall, Boston, MA
Long Term Care Inc, Glendale, CA
Long View Nursing Home, Manchester, MD

Long-Blum Retirement Center, Chillicothe, MO
Longhouse Residence, Spencer, IA
Longleaf Nursing Home, Ruston, LA
Longmeadow Care Center, Ravenna, OH
Longmeadow Nursing Home, Camden, AR
Longmeadow Nursing Home, Taunton, MA
Longmeadow Nursing Home of Malvern, Malvern, AR
Longview Home Inc, Missouri Valley, IA
Longview Unit 22 Group Home, Cincinnati, OH
Longwood Health Care Center, Longwood, FL
Longwood Manor Sanitarium, Los Angeles, CA
Longwood Villa Geriatric Nursing Center, Boothwyn, PA
Longworth Manor, Felicity, OH
Lonoke Nursing Home Inc, Lonoke, AR
Loomis House Retirement Community, Holyoke, MA
Loop Street NE, Poulsbo, WA
Lorain Manor Nursing Home, Lorain, OH
Loraine Nursing Home, Loraine, TX
Lorantffy Care Center Inc, Akron, OH
Lord Chamberlain—Skilled Nursing Facility, Stratford, CT
Lord Marlborough Manor, Marlborough, CT
Loretta Nursing Home, Shawneetown, IL
Loretto Geriatric Center, Syracuse, NY
Loretto Motherhouse Infirmary, Nerinx, KY
Lorien Nursing and Convalescent Home, Columbia, MD
Loring Hospital, Sac City, IA
Loring Nursing Home, Minneapolis, MN
Loris Hospital—Extended Care Facility, Loris, SC
Lorraine Manor, Hartford, CT
Los Banos Convalescent Hospital, Los Banos, CA
Los Gatos Convalescent Hospital, Los Gatos, CA
Los Gatos Meadows Geriatric Hospital, Los Gatos, CA
Los Lunas Hospital and Training School, Los Lunas, NM
Los Palos Convalescent Hospital, San Pedro, CA
Lost Creek Care Center, Lima, OH
Lost Rivers Nursing Home, Arco, ID
Lou Del Health Care, Forest Grove, OR
Loudonville Nursing Home, Loudonville, OH
Loudoun Memorial Hospital Long-Term Care Unit, Leesburg, VA
Louis House North, Blaine, MN
Louis House Treatment Center, Plymouth, MN
Louisburg Nursing Center, Louisburg, NC
Louise C Godwin Nursing Home Inc, Norfolk, VA
Louise Caroline Rehabilitation and Nursing Center, Saugus, MA
Louisiana Living Center, Vallejo, CA
Louisiana Nursing Home, Shreveport, LA
Louisiana Nursing Home, Louisiana, MO
Louisiana Special Education Center, Alexandria, LA
Louisville Birthing Center, Louisville, KY
Louisville Care Center, Louisville, NE
Louisville Lutheran Home Inc, Jeffersontown, KY
Louisville Protestant Althenheim, Louisville, KY
Louisville Shelter Care Home, Louisville, IL

Lourdes, Pontiac, MI
Lourdes-Noreen McKeen Residence for Geriatric Care Inc, West Palm Beach, FL
Lovato Residential Care Facility, La Junta, CO
Loveland Good Samaritan Village, Loveland, CO
Loveland Health Care Center, Loveland, OH
Lovelett Health Care Center, Auburn, ME
Lovely Hill Nursing Home, Pawling, NY
Lovely's Rest Home, North Middletown, KY
Lovin' Care Center, Kenton, OH
Lovington Good Samaritan Center, Lovington, NM
Lowell Healthcare Center, Lowell, IN
Lowell Medical Care Center, Lowell, MI
Lower Umpqua Hospital, Reedsport, OR
Lower Valley Hospital and Nursing Home, Fruita, CO
Lowe's Nursing and Convalescent Home, Thonotosassa, FL
Lowman Home—Wynne C Boliek, White Rock, SC
LPN Geriatric Nursing Center, Newark, OH
LPN Health Care Facility, Newark, OH
Lu Ann Nursing Home, Nappanee, IN
Lubbock Hospitality House Inc, Lubbock, TX
Lubbock Nursing Home Inc, Lubbock, TX
Lucas Boarding Home, Saint Joseph, MO
Lucas Company Children Services-Extended Care Unit, Maumee, OH
Lucas Rest Home, Lucas, KS
Lucero Residential Care Facility, Las Animas, CO
Lufkin Nursing Center, Lufkin, TX
Lu-Ken Manor, Ardmore, OK
Luling Nursing Home, Luling, LA
Luling Nursing Home, Luling, TX
Lumber City Medcraft, Lumber City, GA
Luther Acres, Lititz, PA
Luther Haven, Detroit, MI
Luther Haven Nursing Home, Montevideo, MN
Luther Home, Grand Rapids, MI
Luther Home, Marinette, WI
Luther Home of Mercy, Williston, OH
Luther Manor, Dubuque, IA
Luther Manor, Saginaw, MI
Luther Manor, Sioux Falls, SD
Luther Manor, Milwaukee, WI
Luther Manor, Wauwatosa, WI
Luther Manor Retirement and Nursing Center, Hannibal, MO
Luther Memorial Home, Madelia, MN
Luther Memorial Home, Mayville, ND
Luther Park Health Center, Des Moines, IA
Luther Woods Convalescent Center, Hatboro, PA
Lutheran Altenheim Society of Missouri, Saint Louis, MO
Lutheran Care Center, Altamont, IL
Lutheran Center for the Aging, Smithtown, NY
Lutheran Charities Association Extended Care Facility, Webster Grove, MO
Lutheran Community Home Inc, Seymour, IN
Lutheran Good Shepherd Home, Concordia, MO
Lutheran Haven, Oviedo, FL
Lutheran Health Facility, Alhambra, CA
Lutheran Health Facility of Anaheim, Anaheim, CA
Lutheran Health Facility of Carlsbad, Carlsbad, CA
The Lutheran Home, Peoria, IL

Lutheran Home, Frankenmuth, MI
The Lutheran Home, Monroe, MI
The Lutheran Home, Belle Plaine, MN
The Lutheran Home, Cape Girardeau, MO
The Lutheran Home, Omaha, NE
Lutheran Home, Eureka, SD
Lutheran Home and Service for Aged, Arlington Heights, IL
Lutheran Home at Germantown, Philadelphia, PA
Lutheran Home at Ocean View, Ocean View, NJ
Lutheran Home at Topton, Topton, PA
Lutheran Home for the Aged, Perry, IA
Lutheran Home for the Aged, Vinton, IA
Lutheran Home for the Aged, Westlake, OH
Lutheran Home for the Aged, Erie, PA
Lutheran Home for the Aging Inc, Wauwatosa, WI
Lutheran Home—Hazelton, Hazelton, PA
Lutheran Home Inc, Herington, KS
Lutheran Home—Kane, Kane, PA
Lutheran Home of Brockton, Brockton, MA
Lutheran Home of Middletown Inc, Middletown, CT
Lutheran Home of New Orleans, New Orleans, LA
Lutheran Home of Northwest Indiana Inc, Crown Point, IN
Lutheran Home of Southbury Inc, Southbury, CT
Lutheran Home of the Good Shepard Inc, New Rockford, ND
Lutheran Home of the Good Shepherd, Havre, MT
Lutheran Home of Worcester Inc, Worcester, MA
Lutheran Home—Telford, Telford, PA
Lutheran Homes Inc, Fort Wayne, IN
Lutheran Homes Inc, Kendallville, IN
Lutheran Homes Society, Muscatine, IA
Lutheran Memorial Home, Sandusky, OH
Lutheran Memorial Nursing Home, Twin Valley, MN
Lutheran Memorial Retirement Center, Twin Valley, MN
Lutheran Nursing Home, Hot Springs, SD
Lutheran Old Folks Home, Toledo, OH
Lutheran Pioneer Home, Colton, OR
Lutheran Retirement Home, Northwood, IA
Lutheran Retirement Home, Jamestown, NY
Lutheran Retirement Home of Southern Minnesota, Truman, MN
Lutheran Senior Citizen Home, Little Falls, MN
Lutheran Senior City, Columbus, OH
Lutheran Sunset Home, Grafton, ND
Lutheran Welfare Concordia Home, Cabot, PA
Luverne Geriatric Center Inc, Luverne, AL
Luxton Nursing Center Inc, Fort Worth, TX
Lyden Nursing Home, Astoria, NY
The Lydiana Corp, Orange, CT
Lyn Wood Shelter Care Home, Johnston City, IL
Lynchburg General-Marshall Lodge Hospital— Guggenheimer Division, Lynchburg, VA
Lynchburg Nursing Home, Lynchburg, VA
Lyndon B Johnson Memorial Nursing Home, Johnson City, TX
Lyndon Baines Johnson Nursing Center, Austin, TX
Lyndon Lane Nursing Center, Louisville, KY
Lyngblomsten Care Center, Saint Paul, MN

Lynhurst Healthcare Center, Saint Paul, MN
Lynhurst Nursing Home, Indianapolis, IN
Lynmark Nursing Home Inc, Boston, MA
Lynn Haven Nursing Home, Gray, GA
Lynn Home and Infirmary, Lynn, MA
Lynn Home for Elderly Persons, Lynn, MA
Lynn Lodge Nursing Home, Longview, TX
Lynn Shore Rest Home, Lynn, MA
Lynn Shores Manor, Virginia Beach, VA
Lynn-Ann Convalescent Home, Providence, RI
Lynnhaven Nursing Home Inc, Corpus Christi, TX
Lynnville Treatment Center, Jordan, MN
Lynnwood Manor Health Care, Lynnwood, WA
Lynwood Care Center, Lynwood, CA
Lynwood Healthcare Center, Fridley, MN
Lynwood Nursing Home, Mobile, AL
Lyon Health Center, Yerington, NV
Lyon Manor Care Center, Rock Rapids, IA
Lyon Nursing Home, Canton, OH
Lyons Good Samaritan Center, Lyons, KS
Lysock View, Montoursville, PA
Lytle Nursing Home Inc, Lytle, TX
M A Barthell Order of Eastern Star Home, Decorah, IA
M B Syverson Lutheran Home, Eau Claire, WI
M J Clark Memorial Home, Grand Rapids, MI
Mabank Nursing Home, Mabank, TX
Mac House, McPherson, KS
Macanell Nursing Home Inc, Center Point, IN
MacArthur Convalescent Hospital, Oakland, CA
Maccabee Gardens Extended Care, Saginaw, MI
Macdel Health Care Inc, Birmingham, AL
Mackenzie Nursing Home Inc, Melrose, MA
Mackinac County Medical Care Facility, Saint Ignace, MI
Maclare Residence, South Saint Paul, MN
Macomb Manor Inc, Macomb, IL
Macomb Nursing and Rehabilitation Center, Macomb, IL
Macon County Nursing Home—Loch Haven, Macon, MO
Macon Health Care Center, Macon, MO
Macon Healthcare Center, Macon, GA
Macon Medcraft, Macon, GA
MACtown Inc, Miami, FL
Madalawn Nursing Home, Brockton, MA
Madden Haven Home, South Haven, MN
Madden Kimball Home, Kimball, MN
Madeira Nursing Inc, Madeira, OH
Madeleine Villa Convalescent Center, Marysville, WA
Madera Convalescent Hospital, Madera, CA
Madigan Estates, Houlton, ME
Madison Aldercrest Convalescent Center, Edmonds, WA
Madison Convalescent Center, El Cajon, CA
Madison Convalescent Center, Madison, WI
Madison County Nursing Home, Edwardsville, IL
Madison County Nursing Home, Canton, MS
Madison County Nursing Home, Ennis, MT
Madison County Nursing Home, Sheridan, MT
Madison County Sheltered Care, Edwardsville, IL
Madison Eden House, Yakima, WA
Madison Elms, London, OH
Madison Fountains Convalescent Center, Yakima, WA
Madison Lutheran Home, Madison, MN

Madison Manor, Madison, KS
Madison Manor, Richmond, KY
Madison Manor Nursing Center, Passaic, NJ
Madison Manor Nursing Center, Mars Hill, NC
Madison Manor Nursing Home, Madison, AL
Madison Manor Nursing Home, Hyattsville, MD
Madison Memorial Hospital, Fredericktown, MO
Madison North Convalescent Center, Spokane, WA
Madison Nursing Home, Madison, IN
Madison Nursing Home, Montclair, NJ
Madison Nursing Home, Cincinnati, OH
Madison Parish Home for the Aged, Tallulah, LA
Madison South Convalescent Center, Spokane, WA
Madison Village Nursing Home, Madison, OH
Madisonville Nursing Home, Madisonville, TX
Madisonville Nursing Home 2, Madisonville, TX
Madonna Hall, Cleveland, OH
Madonna Home of Mercy Hospital—Watertown, Watertown, NY
Madonna Manor, Ludlow, KY
Madonna Manor, North Attleboro, MA
Madonna Nursing Center, Detroit, MI
Madonna Professional Care Center, Lincoln, NE
Madonna Residence, Brooklyn, NY
Madonna Towers, Rochester, MN
Madrid Home for the Aging, Madrid, IA
Maggie Johnson's Nursing Center, Austin, TX
Magic Plains Nursing Home, Borger, TX
Magic Valley Manor, Wendell, ID
Magnolia Care Center, Wadsworth, OH
Magnolia Center, El Cajon, CA
Magnolia Convalescent Hospital, Riverside, CA
Magnolia Convalescent Hospital, Stockton, CA
Magnolia Gardens Convalescent Hospital, Granada Hills, CA
Magnolia Gardens Nursing Home, Lanham, MD
Magnolia Hall Inc, Chestertown, MD
Magnolia Haven Nursing Home, Tuskegee, AL
Magnolia Health Center, Burbank, CA
Magnolia Manor, Magnolia, AR
Magnolia Manor, Metropolis, IL
Magnolia Manor, New Madrid, MO
Magnolia Manor, Jefferson, TX
Magnolia Manor Inc, Eldorado, IL
Magnolia Manor Methodist Nursing Home, Americus, GA
Magnolia Manor Nursing Home, Shreveport, LA
Magnolia Manor Nursing Home, Columbus, MS
Magnolia Manor Nursing Home, Sistersville, WV
Magnolia Nursing Home, Jackson, MS
Magnolia Rest Home, Fitchburg, MA
Magnolias Nursing and Convalescent Center, Pensacola, FL
Magnus Farm Nursing Home, Arlington Heights, IL
Magoun Manor Nursing Home, Medford, MA
Mahaska Manor, Oskaloosa, IA
Mahoning Valley Nursing and Rehabilitation Center, Lehighton, PA

Main Line Nursing and Rehabilitation Center, Paoli, PA
Maine Stay Nursing Home, Sanford, ME
Maine Veterans Home, Augusta, ME
Maison de Sante, Ville Platte, LA
Maison Hospitaliere, New Orleans, LA
Maison Orleans Nursing Home, Arabi, LA
Majestic Convalescent Center, Lynwood, CA
Majestic Pines Convalescent Hospital, Hayward, CA
Majestic Towers, Saint Petersburg, FL
Maki Home Inc, Brookston, MN
Mala Strana Health Care Center, New Prague, MN
Malden Home for Aged Persons, Malden, MA
Malden Nursing Home, Malden, MA
Malden Nursing Home, Seattle, WA
Malheur Memorial Hospital, Nyssa, OR
Malheur Memorial Hospital, Nyssa, OR
Malloy Nursing Centre, Bridgeton, NJ
Malouff Manor, Rocky Ford, CO
Malta Home for the Aging, Granville, PA
Maluhia Hospital, Honolulu, HI
Malvern Nursing Home, Malvern, AR
Mammoth Nursing Home, Manchester, NH
Manatawny Manor, Pottstown, PA
Manatee Convalescent Center Inc, Bradenton, FL
Manawa Community Nursing Center Inc, Manawa, WI
Manchester House Nursing Home, Media, PA
Manchester Manor Convalescent Center, Wheaton, IL
Manchester Manor Convalescent Hospital, Los Angeles, CA
Manchester Manor Nursing Home, Manchester, CT
Manchester Manor Rest Home, Manchester, CT
Manchester Nursing Home, Ballwin, MO
Manda Ann Convalescent Home Inc, Houston, TX
Mandan Villa, Mandan, ND
Mandarin Manor, Jacksonville, FL
Manden Nursing Home, South Portland, ME
Manderley Health Care Center, Osgood, IN
Mangum Nursing Center, Mangum, OK
Manhattan Apartments, Boulder, CO
Manhattan Convalescent Center, Tampa, FL
Manhattan Health Care Center Inc, Jackson, MS
Manhattan Manor Extended Care Facility, Harvey, LA
Manhattan Manor Guest House, Harvey, LA
Manhattan Manor Nursing Home, Buffalo, NY
Manila Nursing Home, Manila, AR
Manilla Manor, Manilla, IA
Manistee Heights Care Center, Manistee, MI
Manistee Medical Care Facility, Manistee, MI
Manitowoc Health Care Center, Manitowoc, WI
Mankato House Health Care Center, Mankato, MN
Mankato Lutheran Home For the Aged, Mankato, MN
Manley's Manor Nursing Home Inc, Findlay, OH
Manly Care Center, Manly, IA
Mann Nursing Home, Westerville, OH
Manning Convalescent Home, Portsmouth, VA
Manning Gardens Convalescent Hospital, Fresno, CA
Manning Gardens Town House, Fresno, CA

Manning General Hospital, Manning, IA
Manning Plaza, Manning, IA
Manning Residential Care Center, Maquoketa, IA
Manor Care Arlington Inc, Arlington, VA
Manor Care—Columbia, Columbia, SC
Manor Care, Division of Miller's Merry Manor, Wabash, IN
Manor Care Nursing Center, Barberton, OH
Manor Care Nursing Center, Mayfield Heights, OH
Manor Care Nursing Center—Rocky River, Cleveland, OH
Manor Care Nursing Home, Cincinnati, OH
Manor Care of Akron Inc, Akron, OH
Manor Care of Barley Kingston Court, York, PA
Manor Care of Charlston Inc, Charleston, SC
Manor Care of Largo Inc, Upper Marlboro, MD
Manor Care of Lexington Inc, West Columbia, SC
Manor Care of North Olmsted Inc, North Olmsted, OH
Manor Care of Pinehurst, Pinehurst, NC
Manor Care of Willoughby Inc, Willoughby, OH
Manor Care—Rossville, Baltimore, MD
Manor Care—Ruxton, Towson, MD
Manor Care—Sharpview, Houston, TX
Manor Care—Texas City, Texas City, TX
Manor Care—Towson, Towson, MD
Manor Care—Wheaton, Wheaton, MD
Manor Care-Belden Village, Canton, OH
Manor Care-Woodside Nursing Facility, Cincinnati, OH
Manor Grove, Kirkwood, MO
Manor Home, Geneva, OH
Manor Home for the Aged, Erie, PA
Manor House, Sigourney, IA
Manor House, Youngstown, OH
Manor Lodge Convalescent Hospital, Bakersfield, CA
Manor Nursing Home, Independence, KS
The Manor Nursing Home, Longview, WA
Manor Oak Skilled Nursing Facilities Inc, Cheektowaga, NY
Manor Oak Skilled Nursing Facilities Inc, Jamestown, NY
Manor Oak Skilled Nursing Facilities Inc, Warsaw, NY
Manor Oaks Nursing Home, Rockdale, TX
The Manor of Kansas City, Kansas City, KS
Manor of Topeka, Topeka, KS
Manor Pines Convalescent Center, Fort Lauderdale, FL
The Manor Retirement and Convalescent Center, Mexia, TX
Manor Square Convalescent Home, San Antonio, TX
Mansfield Nursing Home, Mansfield, MO
Mansfield Nursing Home, Mansfield, TX
The Mansion, Central Falls, RI
Mansion House Nursing Home, Spokane, WA
Mansion Nursing and Convalescent Home Inc, Sunbury, PA
Mansion Rest Home, Malden, MA
Manson Good Samaritan Center, Manson, IA
Manteca Convalescent Hospital, Manteca, CA
Mantua Manor Inc, Mantua, OH
Manzanita Manor Convalescent Hospital, Cloverdale, CA
Manzano del Sol Good Samaritan Village, Albuquerque, NM

Maple Convalescent Hospital, Los Angeles, CA
Maple Crest Manor, Fayette, IA
Maple Crest-Boone County Nursing Home, Belvidere, IL
Maple Farm Nursing Center, Akron, PA
Maple Grove Convalescent Center, Millsboro, DE
Maple Grove Home, Tecumseh, NE
Maple Grove Intermediate Care Home, Sanger, CA
Maple Grove Lodge Inc, Louisiana, MO
Maple Grove Manor Convalescent Home, Norwood, MA
Maple Hall Nursing Home, Worcester, MA
Maple Heights Inc, Mapleton, IA
Maple Heights Nursing Home, Wellston, OH
Maple Hill Convalescent Center, Maple Shade, NJ
Maple Hill Nursing Home, Dallas, PA
Maple Hill Nursing Home, Selmer, TN
Maple Hill Nursing Home Ltd, Long Grove, IL
Maple Hill Rest Home, Springfield, MA
Maple Knoll Village, Cincinnati, OH
Maple Lane Health Care Facility, Shawano, WI
Maple Lane Inc, Merchantville, NJ
Maple Lane Nursing Home, Barton, VT
Maple Lawn Health Center, Eureka, IL
Maple Lawn Home for Aged, Marion, IA
Maple Lawn Lodge, Moberly, MO
Maple Lawn Medical Care Facility, Coldwater, MI
Maple Lawn Nursing Home, Fulda, MN
Maple Lawn Nursing Home, Palmyra, MO
Maple Leaf Health Care Center, Manchester, NH
Maple Leaf Nursing Home, Manchester, NH
Maple Manor Christian Home Inc—Adult Division, Sellersburg, IN
Maple Manor Health Care Center, New Richmond, WI
Maple Manor Healthcare Center, Greenville, KY
Maple Manor Nursing Center, Ontonagon, MI
Maple Manor Nursing Home, Aplington, IA
Maple Manor Nursing Home, Rochester, MN
Maple Manor Nursing Home, Langdon, ND
Maple Manor Nursing Home, Langhorne, PA
Maple Mountain Manor, Berlin, PA
Maple Nursing Home, Chesterland, OH
Maple Terrace Shelter Care Home, Chicago, IL
Maple Tree Inn Inc, Swanton, OH
Maple Valley Nursing Home, Ashley, MI
Maple Valley Nursing Home, Maple City, MI
Maple View Manor, Bainbridge, OH
Maple View Manor Inc, Rocky Hill, CT
Maple View Nursing Home, Washington, MA
Maple Village Nursing Home Inc, Middletown, IN
Maple-Crest, Omaha, NE
Maplecrest Center Inc, Madison, ME
Maplecrest Home, Bucyrus, OH
Maplecrest Nursing Home, Sullivan, ME
Maplecrest Nursing Home for the Aged, Struthers, OH
Mapleleaf Health Care Center, Mount Pleasant, IA
Maples Convalescent Home, Wrentham, MA
Maples Nursing Home, Toledo, OH
Mapleside Manor, Amboy, IL
Mapleton Community Home, Mapleton, MN
Mapleton Health Care Facility Inc, Indianapolis, IN

Mapleview Care Center Inc, Louisville, OH
Maplewood Care Center, North Saint Paul, MN
Maplewood Care Center, Lincoln, NE
Maplewood Health Care Center, Jackson, TN
Maplewood Manor, Terre Haute, IN
Maplewood Manor Inc, Keota, IA
Maplewood Manor Nursing Home, Amesbury, MA
Maplewood Maple Manor Care Center, Maplewood, MN
Maplewood Nursing Center, Reidsville, NC
Maplewood Nursing Center Inc, Marion, OH
Maplewood Nursing Home, Webster, NY
Maplewood of Sauk Prairie, Sauk City, WI
Maquoketa Care Center, Maquoketa, IA
Mar Vista Sanitarium, Los Angeles, CA
Maralie Convalescent Hospital, Santa Rosa, CA
Maranatha Care Center, Houma, LA
Maranatha Conservative Baptist Home Inc, Brooklyn Center, MN
Maranatha Manor, Brookfield, MO
Maranatha Manor, Springfield, MO
Maranatha Rest Home, Westminister, MA
Marathon County Health Care Center, Wausau, WI
Marble City Nursing Home Inc, Sylacauga, AL
The Marcelle Home, Louisville, OH
Marchalin, Milbridge, ME
Marco Polo Rest Home Inc, Boston, MA
Marcus Garvey Nursing Home Company Inc, Brooklyn, NY
Marcus J Lawrence Memorial Hospital Inc, Cottonwood, AZ
Marcus Manor Convalescent Hospital, San Jose, CA
Marengo Nursing Home, Linden, AL
Margaret Clark Oakfield Convalescent Center, Washington Court House, OH
Margaret Clark Oakfield Convalescent Center—Columbus, Columbus, OH
Margaret E Moul Home, York, PA
Margaret Lily Home, Lexington, KY
Margaret Manor, Chicago, IL
Margaret Manor-North Branch, Chicago, IL
Margaret R Pardee Memorial, Hendersonville, NC
Margaret Tietz Center for Nursing Care Inc, Jamaica, NY
Margaret Wagner House, Cleveland Heights, OH
Margaret-Anthony Nursing Home, Dunkirk, NY
Margaretville Memorial Hospital Nursing Home, Margaretville, NY
Margie Anna Nursing Home, Lebanon, TN
Margies Nursing Home, North Olmsted, OH
Mari de Villa Retirement Center Inc, Manchester, MO
Maria Home, Minneapolis, MN
Maria Joseph Center, Dayton, OH
Maria Joseph Manor, Danville, PA
Maria Linden, Rockford, IL
Maria Manor Health Care, Saint Petersburg, FL
Maria Nursing Home Inc, Bowling Green, OH
Marian Catholic Home, Milwaukee, WI
Marian Home, Fort Dodge, IA
Marian Home, Louisville, KY
Marian Manor, Boston, MA
Marian Manor, Pittsburgh, PA
Marian Manor Medical Center, Riverview, MI

Marian Manor Nursing Home, Glen Ullin, ND
Marian Manor of Taunton, Taunton, MA
Marian Nursing Home, Sublimity, OR
Marian Nursing Home, Radisson, WI
Marianna Convalescent Center, Marianna, FL
The Marie Antoinette, Marietta, OH
Marie Josephine Rest Home, Johnston, RI
Marietta Health Care Center, Marietta, GA
Marietta Manor, Cleveland, OH
Marietta Nursing Home Ltd, Marietta, OK
Marietta Place, Chillicothe, OH
Marigarde-Sylvania Nursing Home, Toledo, OH
The Marigold, Galesburg, IL
Marin Convalescent and Rehabilitation Hospital, Tiburon, CA
Marina Convalescent Center Inc, Alameda, CA
Marina Convalescent Hospital, Culver City, CA
Marina View Manor, Milwaukee, WI
Marine View Convalescent Center, Federal Way, WA
Marinuka Manor, Galesville, WI
Mariola Nursing Home, Grants Pass, OR
Marion County Care Facility, Knoxville, IA
Marion County Convalescent Center, Marion, SC
Marion County Home, Indianapolis, IN
Marion County Home, Marion, OH
Marion County Nursing Home, Hamilton, AL
Marion County Nursing Home, Yellville, AR
Marion Manor Inc, Marion, KS
Marion Manor Nursing Home Inc, Marion, OH
Marion Memorial Nursing Home, Buena Vista, GA
Marion Nursing Home, Marion, LA
Marion Sims Nursing Center, Lancaster, SC
Marion Sunset Manor, Guin, AL
Mariposa Manor, Mariposa, CA
Maristhill Nursing Home, Waltham, MA
Marjorie P Lee Home for the Aged, Cincinnati, OH
Mark Rest Center, McConnelsville, OH
Mark Twain Convalescent Hospital, San Andreas, CA
Mark Twain Manor, Bridgeton, MO
Mark Wentworth Home, Portsmouth, NH
Mar-Ka Nursing Home, Mascoutah, IL
Market Square Health Care Facility, South Paris, ME
Marklund Home, Bloomingdale, IL
Marks Manor Nursing Home, Effingham, IL
Marks Nursing Home, Toledo, OH
Marks Sunset Manor, Olney, IL
Mar-Le Nursing Home, Wentzville, MO
Marlesta 1, Findlay, OH
Marlesta 2, Findlay, OH
Marlette Community Hospital, Marlette, MI
Marlin Manor, Jackson, MI
Marlinda Convalescent Hospital at Pasadena, Pasadena, CA
Marlinda Nursing Home, Lynwood, CA
Marlinda West Nursing Home, Lynwood, CA
Marlinda-Imperial Convalescent Hospital, Pasadena, CA
Marlora Manor Convalescent Hospital, Long Beach, CA
Marlow Manor Inc, Marlow, OK
Marmaton Valley Home, Uniontown, KS
Marquardt Memorial Manor Inc, Watertown, WI

Marquette Manor, Indianapolis, IN
Marquette Manor, Saint Louis, MO
Marrs Nursing Home, Mohegan Lake, NY
Mar-Saline Manor Care Center, Marshall, MO
MarSalle Centers Associates, Washington, DC
Marshall County Care Facility, Marshalltown, IA
Marshall County Hospital—Skilled Nursing Facility, Benton, KY
Marshall County Nursing Center, Marysville, KS
Marshall Health Care Facility, Machias, ME
Marshall House, Watertown, MA
Marshall Lane Manor, Derby, CT
Marshall Manor, Marshall, MI
Marshall Manor, Britton, SD
Marshall Manor Nursing Home Inc, Marshall, TX
Marshall Nursing Center, Marshall, AR
Marshall State School and Hospital, Marshall, MO
Marshalltown Manor Care Center, Marshalltown, IA
Marshfield Convalescent Center, Marshfield, WI
Marshwood Health Care Facility, Lewiston, ME
Martha and Mary Nursing Home, Poulsbo, WA
Martha Coker Convalescent Home, Yazoo City, MS
Martha Jefferson House and Infirmary—Health Care Unit, Charlottesville, VA
Martha Lloyd School—Camelot ICF/MR, Troy, PA
Martha Manor Home for Aged Women, Steubenville, OH
Martha T Berry Medical Care Facility, Mount Clemens, MI
Marthas Vineyard Hospital—Skilled and Intermediate Care Facility, Oak Bluffs, MA
Martin de Porres Nursing Home, Lake Charles, LA
Martin Family Care Home, Denver, CO
Martin Group Street Home, Silverdale, WA
Martin House Burlington Residential Care Facility, Burlington, CO
Martin Luther—Holt Home, Holt, MI
Martin Luther Home, Colorado Springs, CO
Martin Luther Home, Beatrice, NE
Martin Luther Manor, Bloomington, MN
Martin Luther Memorial Home, South Lyon, MI
Martin Luther Nursing Home Inc, Clinton, NY
Martin Luther Saginaw Home, Saginaw, MI
Martin Luther—South Haven, South Haven, MI
Martin Manor Nursing Home, Havana, IL
Martin Nursing Home, Boston, MA
Martinez Convalescent Hospital, Martinez, CA
Martins Ferry Hospital—Nursing Home, Martins Ferry, OH
Martin's Nursing Home, Lincoln Heights, OH
Martin's Rest Home, Cynthiana, KY
Martinsville Convalescent Home Inc, Martinsville, VA
Marwood Manor, Port Huron, MI
Marwood Rest Home Inc, Philadelphia, PA
Mary and Alice Ford Nursing Home Company Inc, Cohoes, NY
Mary and John Hunt Home, Nashua, NH

Mary Anna Nursing Home, Wisner, LA
Mary Black Schroder Home for Aging Inc, Hamilton, OH
Mary Bryant Home, Springfield, IL
Mary Campbell Center, Wilmington, DE
Mary Chiles Hospital, Mount Sterling, KY
Mary E White Developmental Center, Columbia, SC
Mary E Wilson Home for the Aged, Springfield, MO
Mary Elizabeth Convalescent Home, Mystic, CT
Mary Ellen Convalescent Home Inc, Hellertown, PA
Mary Ellen Nursing Home, Somerville, MA
Mary Evans Extended Care Facility, Ellwood City, PA
Mary Farris Nursing Home, Columbia City, IN
Mary Fletcher Health Care Center 1, Salem, OH
Mary Fletcher Health Care Center 2, Wellsville, OH
Mary Frances Skilled Memorial Hospital, Newton, IA
Mary Galloway Home for the Aged, Memphis, TN
Mary Goss Nursing Home, Monroe, LA
Mary Harding Home Inc, Owensboro, KY
Mary Health of Sick Convalescent and Nursing Hospital, Newbury Park, CA
Mary Henry Nursing Home, Lincoln, IL
Mary Immaculate Nursing Home, Lawrence, MA
Mary J Brown Good Samaritan Center, Luverne, MN
Mary J Drexel Home, Bala Cynwyd, PA
Mary James Nursing Home, Montrose, MI
Mary Kendall Home, Owensboro, KY
Mary Lee Depugh Nursing Home, Winter Park, FL
Mary Lewis Convalescent Center Inc, Birmingham, AL
Mary Louise Nursing Home, Cleveland, OH
Mary Lyon Nursing Home, Hampden, MA
Mary M Olin Clinic, Penny Farms, FL
Mary Manning Walsh Nursing Home Company Inc, New York, NY
Mary Margaret Manor Inc, Elgin, IL
Mary Marshall Manor Inc, Marysville, KS
Mary Murphy Nursing Home, Boston, MA
Mary, Queen and Mother Center, Saint Louis, MO
Mary Scott Nursing Center, Dayton, OH
Mary V Gillis Home, Pawtucket, RI
Marycrest Manor, Culver City, CA
Marycrest Manor, Livonia, MI
Maryetta's Rest Home, Carthage, MO
Maryfield Nursing Home, High Point, NC
Mary-Gran Nursing Center, Clinton, NC
Maryhaven Inc, Glenview, IL
Maryhill Manor, Niagara, WI
Maryhouse, Pierre, SD
Mary-Joseph Residence for the Elderly, New Orleans, LA
Mary-Jude Nursing Home, West Allis, WI
Maryland Baptist Aged Home, Baltimore, MD
Maryland Gardens, Phoenix, AZ
Maryland Manor of Glen Burnie, Glen Burnie, MD
Maryland Masonic Homes, Cockeysville, MD
Mary-land Rest Home, Medway, MA
Marymount Manor, Eureka, MO

Marysville Convalescent Hospital, Marysville, CA
Maryville Health Care Center, Maryville, MO
Maryville Nursing Home, Beaverton, OR
Marywood Convalescent Center, Wausau, WI
Mason Care Center, Mason, TX
Mason F Lord Chronic Hospital and Nursing Facility, Baltimore, MD
Mason Health Care Center, Mason, OH
Mason Health Care Facility, Warsaw, IN
Mason Terrace Rest Home, Brookline, MA
Masonic and Eastern Star Home, Washington, DC
Masonic and Eastern Star Home, Forest Grove, OR
Masonic and Eastern Star Home of North Carolina Inc, Greensboro, NC
Masonic Home, Charlton, MA
Masonic Home, Manchester, NH
Masonic Home and Health Facility, Utica, NY
Masonic Home and Hospital, Wallingford, CT
Masonic Home Inc, Elizabethtown, PA
Masonic Home of Delaware Inc, Wilmington, DE
Masonic Home of Florida, Saint Petersburg, FL
Masonic Home of New Jersey, Burlington, NJ
Masonic Home of Pennsylvania, Lafayette Hills, PA
Masonic Home of Virginia—Health Care Unit, Richmond, VA
Masonic Home of Washington, Seattle, WA
Masonic Widows and Orphans Home and Infirmary, Masonic Home, KY
Mason's Nursing Home, Lake Worth, FL
Mast Boarding Home, Greenwood, DE
Masters Health Care Center, Algood, TN
Matagorda Home-Matagorda General Hospital, Bay City, TX
Mater Dei Nursing Home, Newfield, NJ
The Mather Home, Evanston, IL
Mather Nursing Center, Ishpeming, MI
Mathers Nursing Home, Greene, IA
Matheson Nursing Home, Galesburg, MI
Matney's Colonial Manor, South Sioux City, NE
Matney's Morningside Manor, Sioux City, IA
Matney's Westside Manor, Sioux City, IA
Mattapoisett Nursing Home, Mattapoisett, MA
Mattatuck Health Care Facility Inc, Waterbury, CT
Matthews Care Home, La Junta, CO
Mattingly Health Care Center, Energy, IL
Mattoon Health Care Center, Mattoon, IL
Mattoon Manor, Mattoon, IL
Matulaitis Nursing Home Inc, Putnam, CT
Maud Nursing Home, Maud, OK
Maunalani Hospital, Honolulu, HI
Mauriel Humphrey Residence-Fraser, Eden Prairie, MN
Maxicare Convalescent Hospital, Vallejo, CA
Max-Ull 1, Springfield, OH
May Cravath Wharton Nursing Home, Pleasant Hill, TN
Mayfair Manor, Lexington, KY
Mayfair Nursing Care Center, Columbus, OH
Mayfair Nursing Home, Hempstead, NY
Mayfield Manor, Mayfield, UT
Mayfield Manor Nursing Home, Chicago, IL
Mayfield Nursing Home, Madison, IN
Mayfield Personal Care Home, Mayfield, KY
Mayflower Gardens Convalescent Hospital, Lancaster, CA

Mayflower Home, Grinnell, IA
Mayflower House Nursing Home and Child Center, Plymouth, MA
Maynard Rest Home, Pawtucket, RI
Mayo Nursing and Convalescent Home, Philadelphia, PA
Mayo Nursing Home, Northfield, VT
Maysville Extended Care Facility, Maysville, KY
Mayview Convalescent Center, Raleigh, NC
Mayview State Hospital, Bridgeville, PA
Mayview State Hospital—Long Term Care Unit, Bridgeville, PA
Maywood Acres Healthcare, Oxnard, CA
Maywood Manor Inc, Kerens, TX
Mazotti Family Care Home, Denver, CO
MBW on Center, New Ulm, MN
Mc Allister Nursing Home, Tinley Park, IL
McAllen Good Samaritan Center, McAllen, TX
McAuley Nursing Home, Great Falls, MT
McCall's Chapel School Inc, Ada, OK
McCallum Family Care Center, Denver, CO
McCarthy Nursing Home, Stoughton, WI
McCaskill Nursing Home Inc, Maysville, OK
McCauley Cluster, Tallahassee, FL
Mary McClellan Skilled Nursing Facility, Cambridge, NY
McClure Convalescent Hospital, Oakland, CA
McComb Extended Care and Nursing Home, McComb, MS
McConaughey Guest Home, Cameron, WV
McCone County Nursing Home, Circle, MT
McCormack Rest Home, Fairhaven, MA
McCovy Goldon Age Home Inc, Denver, CO
McCrite Care Center—Southwest, Topeka, KS
McCurdy Residential Center Inc, Evansville, IN
McCurtain Manor Nursing Center, Broken Bow, OK
McDaniel Nursing Home, El Paso, IL
McDonough Home, Pittsburgh, PA
McDowell Nursing Center, Nebo, NC
McDowell Skilled Nursing Facility, Greensburg, KY
McElrath Rest Home, Paducah, KY
McFadden Memorial Manor, Malden, MA
McFarland House, Barre, VT
McGee Nursing Home, Teague, TX
McGills Nursing Home—South, Dayton, OH
McGirr Nursing Home, Bellows Falls, VT
McGowan Nursing Home, Methuen, MA
McGraw Nursing Home Inc, Adena, OH
McGuffey Health Care Center Inc, Gadsden, AL
McGuire Memorial Home for Retired Children, New Brighton, PA
McIntosh County Hospital—Intermediate Care Facility, Ashley, ND
McIntosh Nursing Home, Muskogee, OK
McIntosh Nursing Home Inc, McIntosh, MN
McKee Rest Home, Sturgis, SD
McKendree Village Inc, Hermitage, TN
McKenna Home for the Aged, McKenna, WA
McKenzie Manor Nursing Home, Springfield, OR
McKerley Harris Hill Nursing Home, Penacook, NH
McKerley Health Care Center, Laconia, NH
McKerley Health Care Center—Manchester Inc, Manchester, NH
McKerley Health Care Center—Milford, Milford, NH

McKerley Nursing Home, Concord, NH
McKinley Manor, Gallup, NM
McKinney Intensive Care Facility, Pickens, SC
McLarney Manor, Brookfield, MO
McLean County General Hospital—Skilled Nursing Unit, Calhoun, KY
McLean County Nursing Home, Normal, IL
McLean Home, Simsbury, CT
McMahon Tomlinson Nursing Center, Lawton, OK
McMillan Home, Worthington, MN
McMinn Memorial Nursing Home, Etowah, TN
McMinnville Health Care Center, McMinnville, TN
McMurray Hills Manor Inc, McMurray, PA
McNamara Mercy Hospital and Nursing Home, Fairplay, CO
McRae Manor Inc, McRae, GA
McVane Memorial Home Inc, Crivitz, WI
McVille Friendship Manor Nursing Home, McVille, ND
McVitty House Inc, Salem, VA
Mead Nursing Home, Meadville, PA
Meadow Brook Manor Nursing Home, Fowler, OH
Meadow Brook Medical Care Facility, Bellaire, MI
Meadow Crest Inc, Bethel Park, PA
Meadow Glade Nursing Home Inc, Battle Ground, WA
Meadow Haven Nursing Center, Rock Hill, SC
Meadow Heights Nursing Center Inc, Williamsport, IN
Meadow Lane Healthcare Center, Benson, MN
Meadow Lawn Nursing Center, Davenport, IA
Meadow Manor Inc, Taylorville, IL
Meadow Manor Nursing Home, Grand Meadow, MN
Meadow Manor Nursing Home, Saint James, MO
Meadow Park Care Center, Saint Helen's, OR
Meadow Park House, Rochester, MN
Meadow Park Nursing Home, Flushing, NY
Meadow View Adult Care, Joplin, MO
Meadow View Care Center, Maryville, IL
Meadow View Manor Nursing Home, Sheboygan, WI
Meadow View Nursing Home, Lakeville, MA
Meadow View Park, Garden Grove, CA
Meadow Wood Nursing Home Inc, Georgetown, OH
Meadowbrook Care Center, Holland, MI
Meadowbrook Care Center, Cincinnati, OH
Meadowbrook Care Center, Van Alstyne, TX
Meadowbrook Convalescent Hospital Inc, Hemet, CA
Meadowbrook Inc, Shawsville, VA
Meadowbrook Manor, Worcester, MA
Meadowbrook Manor, Clemmons, NC
Meadowbrook Manor, Rapid City, SD
Meadowbrook Manor of Cherryville, Cherryville, NC
Meadowbrook Manor of Gastonia, Gastonia, NC
Meadowbrook Manor of Shelby, Shelby, NC
Meadowbrook Manor Sanitarium, Los Angeles, CA
Meadowbrook Nursing and Convalescent Center, Seattle, WA
Meadowbrook Nursing Home, Magnolia, AR
Meadowbrook Nursing Home, Plattsburgh, NY

Meadowbrook Nursing Home, Chouteau, OK

Meadowbrook Nursing Home, Pulaski, TN

Meadowbrook Nursing Home, Fort Worth, TX

Meadowbrook Nursing Home Inc, Tucker, GA

Meadowbrook Personal and Intermediate Care Home, Lexington, KY

Meadowhaven Nursing Home, Butler, IN

Meadowlark Convalescent Hospital, San Diego, CA

Meadowlark Hills, Manhattan, KS

Meadowood, Grayville, IL

Meadowood Nursing Home, Bessemer, AL

Meadowpark Nursing Center, Shreveport, LA

The Meadows, Rolling Meadows, IL

The Meadows, Cooperstown, NY

Meadows, Dallas, TX

Meadows—East, Louisville, KY

Meadows Hillside Home Inc, Wichita, KS

Meadows Manor, Terre Haute, IN

Meadows Manor Inc, Manchester, CT

Meadows Manor North Inc, Terre Haute, IN

Meadows Mennonite Home, Chenoa, IL

Meadows Nursing Home, Fremont, MI

Meadows—South, Louisville, KY

Meadowvale Skilled Care Center, Bluffton, IN

Meadowview Care Center, Kerrville, TX

Meadowview Lodge, Huntsville, AR

Meadowview Nursing and Convalescent Center, Louisville, KY

Meadowview Nursing Home, Minden, LA

Meadowview Retirement Home, Mayfield, KY

Meadville Hillside Home, Meadville, PA

Meadville Nursing Home, Meadville, MS

Mecca Convalescent Home, Vero Beach, FL

Mechanicsville Care Center, Mechanicsville, IA

Mecklenburg Autistic Group Home, Charlotte, NC

Med Arts Health Facility, Columbus, GA

Meda Nipple Convalescent Home, Thompsontown, PA

Medalion Health-Center, Colorado Springs, CO

Medallion II Board & Lodge Home, Minneapolis, MN

Medallion Manor Inc, Provo, UT

Medco Annex of French Lick, French Lick, IN

Medco Center of Bowling Green, Bowling Green, KY

Medco Center of Brandenburg, Brandenburg, KY

Medco Center of Campbellsville, Campbellsville, KY

Medco Center of Chandler, Chandler, IN

Medco Center of Elizabethtown, Elizabethtown, KY

Medco Center of Elkhart, Elkhart, IN

Medco Center of Evansville—North, Evansville, IN

Medco Center of Fordsville, Fordsville, KY

Medco Center of Franklin, Franklin, KY

Medco Center of French Lick, French Lick, IN

Medco Center of Hardinsburg, Hardinsburg, KY

Medco Center of Henderson, Henderson, KY

Medco Center of Huntingburg, Huntingburg, IN

Medco Center of Loogootee, Loogootee, IN

Medco Center of Morganfield, Morganfield, KY

Medco Center of Mount Vernon, Mount Vernon, IN

Medco Center of Newburgh, Newburgh, IN

Medco Center of Owensboro, Owensboro, KY

Medco Center of Paducah, Paducah, KY

Medco Center of Pembroke, Pembroke, KY

Medco Center of Springfield, Springfield, KY

Medford Convalescent and Nursing Center, Medford, NJ

Medford Leas, Medford, NJ

Medford Nursing Home, Medford, OK

Medford Rest Home, Medford, MA

Medi Park Care Center Inc, Amarillo, TX

Medical Arts Center—Coastal Georgia, Brunswick, GA

Medical Arts Convalescent Hospital, Perris, CA

Medical Arts Health Facility, Lawrenceville, GA

Medical Care Center, Lynchburg, VA

Medical Center Convalescent Hospital, San Bernardino, CA

Medical Center for Aging—Doylestown, Doylestown, PA

Medical Center Nursing Home, Salem, OR

Medical Center Nursing Home, Clarendon, TX

Medical Center Nursing Home—DeGoesbriand Unit, Burlington, VT

Medical Park Convalescent Center Inc, Decatur, AL

Medical Park Nursing Center, High Point, NC

Medical Park Nursing Home, Mount Olive, NC

Medical Plaza Nursing Center, Paris, TX

Medicalodge East of Arkansas City, Arkansas City, KS

Medicalodge East of Coffeyville, Coffeyville, KS

Medicalodge East of Kansas City, Kansas City, KS

Medicalodge North of Arkansas City, Arkansas City, KS

Medicalodge North of Kansas City, Kansas City, KS

Medicalodge North of Pittsburg, Pittsburg, KS

Medicalodge of Atchison, Atchison, KS

Medicalodge of Butler, Butler, MO

Medicalodge of Clay Center, Clay Center, KS

Medicalodge of Columbus, Columbus, KS

Medicalodge of Dewey, Dewey, OK

Medicalodge of Eureka, Eureka, KS

Medicalodge of Fort Scott, Fort Scott, KS

Medicalodge of Goddard, Goddard, KS

Medicalodge of Halls, Saint Louis, MO

Medicalodge of Kinsley, Kinsley, KS

Medicalodge of Leavenworth, Leavenworth, KS

Medicalodge of Neosho, Neosho, MO

Medicalodge of Paola, Paola, KS

Medicalodge of Texarkana, Texarkana, AR

Medicalodge of Wichita, Wichita, KS

Medicalodge South of Kansas City, Kansas City, KS

Medicalodge South of Pittsburg, Pittsburg, KS

Medicalodge West of Coffeyville, Coffeyville, KS

Medicalodges of Troy, Troy, MO

Medicana Nursing Center, Lake Worth, FL

Medicare Nursing Homes Inc, Cleveland, OH

Medicare Pavilion Corp, Waterbury, CT

Medic-Ayers Nursing Home, Trenton, FL

Medicenter of America—Bristol, Bristol, PA

Medicenter of Lakewood, Lakewood, NJ

Medicenter of Neptune City, Neptune City, NJ

Medicenter of Tampa, Tampa, FL

Medicenter—Springfield, Springfield, MO

Medicenter—Virginia Beach, Virginia Beach, VA

Medic-Home Health Center of Melbourne, Melbourne, FL

Medicine Valley Lodge Inc, Medicine Lodge, KS

Medicos Recovery Care Center, Detroit, MI

Medigroup Oak Park Nursing Home, Saint Louis, MO

Medigroup Professional Care, Rolla, MO

Medi-Home of Arkoma Inc, Arkoma, OK

Medi-Home of Rogers, Rogers, AR

Medi-Homes Inc, Fort Smith, AR

Medilodge of Richmond, Richmond, MI

Medilodge of Yale, Yale, MI

Medina Memorial Hospital—Skilled Nursing Facility, Medina, NY

Medina Nursing Center, Durand, IL

Mediplex at Lexington—Long Term Care Facility, Lexington, MA

Mediplex of Beverly: A Long-Term Care Facility, Beverly, MA

Mediplex of Danbury, Danbury, CT

Mediplex of Newington, Newington, CT

Mediplex of Newton—Long Term Care Facility, Newton, MA

Med-Vale Nursing Home, Medfield, MA

Medway Country Manor Nursing Home, Medway, MA

Meeker County Community Home, Litchfield, MN

Meister Road Homes, Lorain, OH

Melber Rest Home, Melber, KY

Melchor Nursing Home, Baltimore, MD

Meldonia Residential Care Facility, Kansas, MO

Mel-Haven Convalescent Home, Corsicana, TX

Meline Nursing Center, Jacksonville, IL

Melody Manor Convalescent Center, Leakesville, MS

Melody Nursing Center, Trumann, AR

Mel-Rose Convalescent Home, Tyler, TX

Melrose Manor, Mishawaka, IN

Melrose Manor, Louisville, KY

Melville Rest Home, Boston, MA

Melvin and Selma Anderson Health Care Unit, Holdrege, NE

Memorial Care Center, Manchester, IA

Memorial Community Hospital, Bertha, MN

Memorial Community Hospital—Long Term Care Unit, Edgerton, WI

Memorial Convalescent Center, Adel, GA

Memorial Convalescent Center, Belleville, IL

Memorial Convalescent Center, Trenton, TN

Memorial Hall—Bristol Memorial Hospital, Bristol, VA

Memorial Heights Nursing Center, Idabel, OK

Memorial Home for the Aged, Moundridge, KS

Memorial Home Inc, Saint Louis, MO

Memorial Hospital and Nursing Home of Greene County, Catskill, NY

Memorial Hospital—Easton, Easton, MD

Memorial Hospital Inc and Skilled Nursing Unit, Towanda, PA

Memorial Hospital—Long Term Care Unit, Medford, WI

Memorial Hospital Medical Care Facility, Dodgeville, WI

Memorial Hospital of Alamace Company Inc—Skilled Nursing Division, Burlington, NC

Memorial Hospital—Skilled Nursing Facility, Manchester, KY

Memorial Intermediate Care Home, Macon, GA

Memorial Manor, Mondovi, WI

Memorial Manor Multiple Care Center, Prattville, AL

Memorial Manor Nursing Home, Bainbridge, GA

Memorial Medical Center Nursing Home, Watertown, SD

Memorial Medical Nursing Center, San Antonio, TX

Memorial Nursing Home, Cut Bank, MT

Memorial Nursing Home, Boscobel, WI

Memory Manor, Pomeroy, WA

Memphis Convalescent Center, Memphis, TX

Memphis Health Care Center, Memphis, TN

Memphis Sunshine Home for Aged Men, Memphis, TN

Menard Convalescent Center, Petersburg, IL

Menard Manor, Menard, TX

Mendenhall Nursing Home Inc, Mendenhall, MS

Mendon Care Center, Mendon, UT

Mendota Lutheran Home, Mendota, IL

Menno Haven Inc, Chambersburg, PA

Mennonite Friendship Manor Inc, South Hutchison, KS

Mennonite Home, Albany, OR

Mennonite Home, Lancaster, PA

Mennonite Memorial Home, Bluffton, OH

Mennonite Old People's Home, Maugansville, MD

Menno-Olivet Care Center, Menno, SD

Menominee Nursing Home, Menominee, MI

Menomonee Falls Nursing Home, Menomonee Falls, WI

Menonite Bretheren Home for the Aged, Corn, OK

Menorah Home and Hospital for the Aged and Infirm, Brooklyn, NY

Menorah Nursing Home Inc, Brooklyn, NY

Menorah Park—Jewish Home for the Aged, Beachwood, OH

Menorah Village, Reseda, CA

Mentor Way Villa Nursing Home, Mentor, OH

Mequon Care Center, Mequon, WI

Merced Convalescent Hospital, Merced, CA

Merced Manor, Merced, CA

Mercer Care Center, Trenton, NJ

Mercer County Geriatric Center—F W Donnelly Long-Term Care Facility, Trenton, NJ

Mercer County Home and Hospital, Mercer, PA

Mercer County Nursing Home, Aledo, IL

Mercer Island Villa Care, Mercer Island, WA

Mercerville Nursing Center, Mercerville, NJ

Mercy Care Center, Omaha, NE

Mercy Convalescent Center, Saint Louis, MO

Mercy Douglass Human Service Center, Philadelphia, PA

Mercy Extended Care Facility, Vicksburg, MS

Mercy Health and Rehabilitation Center, Auburn, NY

Mercy Health Care Rehabilitation Center, Homewood, IL

Mercy Health Center, Dubuque, IA

Mercy Healthcare Center, Tupper Lake, NY

Mercy Hospital, Cedar Rapids, IA

Mercy Hospital, Grayling, MI

Mercy Hospital—Skilled Nursing Facility, Buffalo, NY

Mercy Nursing Home Inc, North Little Rock, AR

Mercy Nursing Home Inc, Houston, TX

Mercy Villa, Springfield, MO

Mercyknoll, West Hartford, CT

Mere Point Nursing Home, Brunswick, ME

Meriden Nursing Home, Meriden, CT

Meridian Convalescent Home, Meridian, MS

Meridian Geriatric Center, Meridian, TX

Meridian Manor, Mounds, IL

Meridian Nursing Center, Meridian, MS

Meridian Nursing Center—Caton Manor, Baltimore, MD

Meridian Nursing Center—Catonsville, Catonsville, MD

Meridian Nursing Center—Corsica Hills, Centreville, MD

Meridian Nursing Center—Frederick, Frederick, MD

Meridian Nursing Center—Hamilton, Baltimore, MD

Meridian Nursing Center—Hammonds Lane, Brooklyn Park, MD

Meridian Nursing Center—Heritage, Baltimore, MD

Meridian Nursing Center—Long Green, Baltimore, MD

Meridian Nursing Center—Randallstown, Randallstown, MD

Meridian Nursing Center—Severna Park, Severna Park, MD

Meridian Nursing Center/Shady Oaks, Sherman, TX

Meridian Nursing Center—Suburban, Chicago Heights, IL

Meridian Nursing Center—The Pines, Easton, MD

Meridian Nursing Center—West Side, Gary, IN

Meridian Nursing Center-Beeville, Beeville, TX

Meridian Nursing Home, Indianapolis, IN

Meridian Nursing Home, Comanche, OK

Merihil Health Care Center Inc, Lewisburg, TN

Merimac Nursing Home, Cynthiana, IN

Meriwether Memorial Hospital Nursing Home, Warm Springs, GA

Merlin Health Retreat, Merlin, OR

Merrill Manor Annex, Franklin, NH

Merrill Memorial Manor Inc, Gardiner, ME

Merrimack County Nursing Home, Penacook, NH

Merrimack Valley Retirement Home, Lowell, MA

Merritt Manor Convalescent Hospital, Tulare, CA

Merritt Manor Nursing Home, Merritt Island, FL

Merritt Plaza Nursing Home, Marshall, TX

Merry Haven Nursing Home, Snohomish, WA

Merry Heart Nursing Home Inc, Succasunna, NJ

Merry Manor Inc, Holton, KS

Merry Wood Lodge Inc, Elmore, AL

Merrymount Manor Nursing Home, Quincy, MA

Merryville Nursing Center, Merryville, LA

Mesa Christian Home, Mesa, AZ

Mesa Hills Adult Care, Columbia, MO

Mesa Manor Nursing Center, Grand Junction, CO

Mesa Verde Convalescent Hospital, Costa Mesa, CA

Mesabi Home, Buhl, MN

Mesquite Tree Nursing Center, Mesquite, TX

Messenger House Nursing Home, Bainbridge Island, WA

Messiah Village, Mechanicsburg, PA

Messick Nursing Home Inc, Warrensburg, MO

Metacom Manor Health Center, Bristol, RI

Metairie Healthcare Center, Metairie, LA

Metcalfe County Nursing Home, Edmonton, KY

Methodist Church Home for the Aged, Bronx, NY

Methodist Country House, Wilmington, DE

Methodist Health Center, Madison, WI

Methodist Home, Chicago, IL

The Methodist Home, Orangeburg, SC

Methodist Home for the Aging, Birmingham, AL

Methodist Home of Clinton Inc, Clinton, OK

Methodist Home of DC, Washington, DC

Methodist Home of Enid Inc, Enid, OK

Methodist Manor, Storm Lake, IA

Methodist Manor, West Allis, WI

Methodist Manor Health Center, West Allis, WI

Methodist Manor House, Seaford, DE

Methodist Medical Center—Long Term Care Facility, Saint Joseph, MO

Methodist Nursing Home Inc, Fort Smith, AR

Methodist Retirement Home—Wesley Pines, Lumberton, NC

Methodist Retirement Homes Inc, Durham, NC

Methuen House Nursing and Convalescent Center, Methuen, MA

Meth-Wick Manor, Cedar Rapids, IA

Metroplex Care Center, Grand Prairie, TX

Metropolis Good Samaritan Home, Metropolis, IL

Metropolitan Jewish Geriatric Center, Brooklyn, NY

Metter Nursing Home, Metter, GA

Metzenbaum Residence, Chesterland, OH

Metzmeier Nursing Home, Campbellsville, KY

Mexia Nursing Home, Mexia, TX

Meyer Care Center, Higginsville, MO

Miami Beach Hebrew Home for the Aged, Miami Beach, FL

Miami Beach Nursing Home, Miami Beach, FL

Miami Christel Manor Inc, Miamisburg, OH

Miami Haven, Cleves, OH

Miami Health Care Center, Troy, OH

Miami Jewish Home for the Aged, Miami, FL

Miami Nursing Center, Miami, OK

Michael Manor Inc, Gettysburg, PA

Michealsen Health Center, Batavia, IL

Michigan Christian Home, Grand Rapids, MI

Michigan Masonic Home, Alma, MI

Michigan Shores, Manitowoc, WI

Michigan Skilled Care, Niles, MI

Michigan Terrace Nursing Center Inc, Chicago, IL

Mickel Nursing Home, Clarksville, AR

Micoll Residence, Hastings, MN

Mid State ICFMR Broad, Altoona, PA

Mid State ICFMR Inc, Altoona, PA

Mid State ICFMR Inc, Altoona, PA

Mid-America Convalescent Centers Inc, Chicago, IL

Mid-America Nursing Center of Lincoln, Lincoln, KS

Mid-City Care Center, Memphis, TN
Mid-Del Manor Nursing Home, Midwest City, OK
Middle Georgia Nursing Home, Eastman, GA
Middle River Health Facility, Hawthorne, WI
Middlebelt Nursing Centre, Livonia, MI
Middlebelt-Hope Nursing Center, Westland, MI
Middleboro Rest Home, Middleborough, MA
Middlebury Convalescent Home Inc, Middlebury, CT
Middlebury Manor Nursing and Convalescent Home, Akron, OH
Middlesex Convalescent Center Inc, Middletown, CT
Middlesex County Hospital for Chronically Ill, New Brunswick, NJ
Middlesex Fells Nursing Home, Melrose, MA
Middlesex Manor Nursing Home, Framingham, MA
Middleton Village Nursing Home, Middleton, WI
Middletown Healthcare Center Inc, Middletown, CT
Middletown Nursing Center, Middletown, IN
Middletown Park Manor, Middletown, NY
Middletown Quality Care Center, Middletown, OH
Midland Care Center Inc, Midland, TX
Midland Hospital Center—Skilled Nursing Unit, Midland, MI
Midland Kings Daughters, Midland, MI
Midland Manor, Tacoma, WA
Midland Manor Nursing Home, Nampa, ID
Midland Villa, Falls City, NE
Midlands Center Infant Care Unit, Columbia, SC
Mid-Nebraska Lutheran Homes Inc, Newman Grove, NE
Mid-South Christian Nursing Home, Memphis, TN
Midtown, Somerset, KY
Midtown Convalescent Hospital, Oakland, CA
Midtown Home, Baltimore, MD
Midtown Manor Nursing Home, Kansas City, MO
Midway Care Center, Fosston, MN
Midway Care Center Inc, Portland, OR
Midway Manor, Saint Paul, MN
Midway Manor Convalescent Center, Kent, WA
Midway Manor Health Care Facility, Kenosha, WI
Midway Manor Nursing Home, Shreveport, LA
Midway Nursing Home, Maspeth, NY
Midwest Covenant Home Inc, Stromsburg, NE
Midwest Nursing Center Inc, Baxter Springs, KS
Midwestern Parkway Heritage Manor, Wichita Falls, TX
Midwilshire Convalescent Hospital, Los Angeles, CA
Mielke's Nursing Home, Swanton, OH
Milan Care Center Inc, Milan, MO
Milan Healthcare Center, Milan, IN
Milcrest Nursing Center, Marysville, OH
Milder Manor Nursing Home, Lincoln, NE
Mildred Alford Nursing Home, Abington, MA
Milford Heights Nursing Home, Milford, CT
Milford Manor, Milford, DE
Milford Manor Nursing Home, Baltimore, MD
Milford Manor Nursing Home, West Milford, NJ

Milford Manor Rest Home Inc, Milford, MA
Milford Nursing Home, Milford, IA
Milford Nursing Home, Milford, NH
Milford PMI, Milford, MA
Milford Rest Home Inc, Milford, NE
Milford Valley Convalescent Home Inc, Milford, PA
Milford Valley Memorial—Skilled Nursing Facility, Milford, UT
Mill Haven Care Center Inc, Millstadt, IL
Mill Hill Nursing Home Inc, Worcester, MA
Mill Pond Rest Home, Ashland, MA
Mill Pond Rest Home, Hanover, MA
Mill Valley Care Center, Bellevue, IA
Millard Fillmore Skilled Nursing Facility, Buffalo, NY
Millard Good Samaritan Center, Omaha, NE
Millbrae Serra Convalescent Hospital, Millbrae, CA
Millcreek, Magee, MS
Millcreek Manor, Youngstown, OH
Miller Care Center Inc, Louisville, OH
Miller County Nursing Home, Tuscumbia, MO
Miller Memorial—Community, Meriden, CT
Miller Memorial Nursing Center, Andover, OH
Miller Memorial Nursing Home, Chappell, NE
Miller Nursing Home, Colquitt, GA
Miller Nursing Home, Chicago, IL
Miller Nursing Home Inc, Gary, IN
Miller's Community Health Care, Indianapolis, IN
Millers Merry Manor, Hobart, IN
Millers Merry Manor, Indianapolis, IN
Millers Merry Manor, Mooresville, IN
Miller's Merry Manor, Sullivan, IN
Millers Merry Manor, Tipton, IN
Miller's Merry Manor Inc, Columbia City, IN
Miller's Merry Manor Inc, Culver, IN
Miller's Merry Manor Inc, Garrett, IN
Miller's Merry Manor Inc, Hartford City, IN
Miller's Merry Manor Inc, Hope, IN
Miller's Merry Manor Inc, Huntington, IN
Miller's Merry Manor Inc, LaGrange, IN
Miller's Merry Manor Inc, Peru, IN
Miller's Merry Manor Inc, Plymouth, IN
Miller's Merry Manor Inc, Rockport, IN
Miller's Merry Manor Inc, Wabash, IN
Miller's Merry Manor Inc, Walkerton, IN
Miller's Merry Manor Inc, Warsaw, IN
Miller's Nursing Home, Lexington, KY
Miller's Progressive Care, Riverside, CA
Miller's Rest Home Inc, Austin, TX
Millie's Rest Home, Sutherland, IA
Mill's Manor, Mayfield, KY
Mills Manor Convalescent Home, Meriden, CT
Mills Rest Home, Gary, IN
Millway Nursing Home, Milwaukee, WI
Milner Community Health-Care Inc, Rossville, IN
Milton and Hattie Kutz Home Inc, Wilmington, DE
Milton Health Care Facility, Milton, MA
Milton Manor Nursing Home, Lake Milton, OH
Milton View Nursing Home, Boston, MA
Milwaukee Catholic Home, Milwaukee, WI
Milwaukee County Mental Health Complex-Long Term Care, Wauwatosa, WI
Milwaukee County Nursing Home, Wauwatosa, WI
Milwaukee Jewish Convalescent Center, Milwaukee, WI

Milwaukee Jewish Home, Milwaukee, WI
Milwaukee Protestant Bradford Terrace, Milwaukee, WI
Milwaukee Protestant Home Infirmary, Milwaukee, WI
Milwaukie Convalescent Center, Milwaukie, OR
Mimbres Memorial Hospital—Intermediate Care Facility, Deming, NM
Mimosa Manor Care Center, Keller, TX
Minami Keiro Nursing Home, Los Angeles, CA
Mineral County Nursing Home, Superior, MT
Mineral Point Care Center, Mineral Point, WI
Mineral Spring Manor, Reading, PA
Mineral Wells Care Center, Mineral Wells, TX
Minerva Convalescent Center Inc, Minerva, OH
Minerva Nursing Home, Minerva, OH
Minerva Park Place, Columbus, OH
Mingo Health Care Center Inc, Williamson, WV
Minidoka Memorial Hospital Geriatric Unit, Rupert, ID
Minneapolis Good Samaritan Center, Minneapolis, KS
Minneapolis Outreach Home, Minneapolis, MN
Minneola Nursing Home, Minneola, KS
Minneota Manor, Minneota, MN
Minnesota Jewish Group Home 1, Saint Louis Park, MN
Minnesota Jewish Group Home II, Saint Paul, MN
Minnesota Masonic Home, Bloomington, MN
Minnesota Odd Fellows Home, Northfield, MN
Minnesota Supervised Living Facility, Saint Peter, MN
Minnesota Veterans Home, Hastings, MN
Minnesota Veterans Home, Minneapolis, MN
Minnetonka Health Care Center, Excelsior, MN
Minnewaska Lutheran Home, Starbuck, MN
Mira Costa Convalescent Hospital, Torrance, CA
Miracle Hill Nursing and Convalescent Home, Tallahassee, FL
Miracle Manor Health Care, Saint George, UT
Mirada Hills Rehabilitation and Convalescent Hospital, La Mirada, CA
Miramar Lodge Nursing Home, Pass Christian, MS
Miranda Manor Ltd, Niles, IL
Mira-Vista Nursing Home, Mount Vernon, WA
Misericordia Convalescent Home, York, PA
Misericordia Home, Chicago, IL
Mission Convalescent Home, Jackson, TN
Mission Convalescent Hospital, Riverside, CA
Mission Convalescent Hospital, San Diego, CA
Mission Convalescent Hospital, San Gabriel, CA
Mission Convalescent Hospital, Sonoma, CA
Mission Farms Nursing Home, Plymouth, MN
Mission Lodge Sanitarium, San Gabriel, CA
Mission Manor Nursing Home Inc, Mount Vernon, TX
Mission Oaks Convalescent Hospital, Carmichael, CA
Mission Skilled Nursing Facility, Santa Clara, CA
Mission Villa Convalescent Hospital, San Francisco, CA
Mississippi Children's Rehabilitation Center, Jackson, MS

Mississippi County Nursing Home, Blytheville, AR
Mississippi Extended Care of Greenville Inc, Greenville, MS
Mississippi Home, Bemidji, MN
Mississippi Nursing Home, Jackson, MS
Missouri Slope Lutheran Home Inc, Bismarck, ND
Mitchell Convalescent Center, Camilla, GA
Mitchell Manor, Mitchell, IN
Mitchell Manor Nursing Home, McAlester, OK
Mitchell Retirement Home, Mitchell, SD
Mitchell Village Center of Care, Mitchellville, IA
Mitchell's Nursing Home Inc, Danville, AR
Mize Road Nursing Home, Little Rock, AR
Mizpah Nursing Home Inc, Locust Hill, VA
MJG Nursing Home Company Inc, Brooklyn, NY
Mobridge Care Center, Mobridge, SD
Modern Acre Home, Fulton, MO
Modern Care Convalescent and Nursing Home, Jacksonville, IL
Modern Manor Inc, Mount Sterling, IL
Moderncare—West Seattle, Seattle, WA
Modesto Convalescent Hospital, Modesto, CA
Mogck Home for Aged, Mitchell, SD
Mogck's Rest Home, Mitchell, SD
Mohawk Manor Rest Home Inc, Shelburne, MA
Mohawk Valley Nursing Home, Ilion, NY
Mohun Hall Infirmary, Columbus, OH
Molalla Manor, Molalla, OR
Molena Intermediate Care Home, Molena, GA
Moline Nursing and Rehabilitation Center, Moline, IL
Mollie Wells Nursing Home Inc, Moscow Mills, MO
Molly Stark Hospital, Louisville, OH
Molokai General Hospital—Skilled Nursing Unit, Kaunakakai, HI
Mom and Dad's Home and Health Care Center, Sioux Falls, SD
Momence Meadows Nursing Center Inc, Momence, IL
Monadnock Christian Nursing Home, Jaffrey, NH
Monadnock Nursing Home, Keene, NH
Monarch Heights, Ortonville, MN
Monclova Care Center, Monclova, OH
Monmouth Convalescent Center, Long Branch, NJ
Monmouth Nursing Home, Monmouth, IL
Monona Drive Rest Home, Madison, WI
Monroe Care Center, Monroe, MI
Monroe City Manor Care Center, Monroe City, MO
Monroe Community Hospital—Extended Care Facility, Rochester, NY
Monroe Convalescent Center, Monroe, MI
Monroe Convalescent Center, Monroe, WA
Monroe County Home, Woodsfield, OH
Monroe County Nursing Home, Waterloo, IL
Monroe County Rest Home, Aberdeen, MS
Monroe Health Care Facility, Tompkinsville, KY
Monroe House, Decatur, IL
Monroe Intermediate Care Facility, Monroe, GA
Monroe Manor, Monroeville, AL
Monroe Manor, Paris, MO
Monroe Manor Nursing Home, Monroe, LA

Monroe Manor Nursing Home, Monroe, WI
Monroe Nursing Home Inc, Monroeville, AL
Monroe Pavilion Health Center Inc, Chicago, IL
Monroe Rest Home, Boston, MA
Monrovia Convalescent Hospital, Duarte, CA
Monsignor Bojnowski Manor Inc, New Britain, CT
Monson State Hospital, Palmer, MA
Montain View Rest Haven, Hardin, MT
Montana Center for the Aged, Lewistown, MT
Montana Veterans' Home—Nursing Home, Columbia Falls, MT
Montcalm Manor, Montclair, NJ
Montclair Manor Convalescent Hospital, Montclair, CA
Montclair Nursing Center, Omaha, NE
Montclair Nursing Home, Montclair, NJ
Montclair Nursing Home, Glen Cove, NY
Montclaire Manor Nursing Home, Denver, CO
Monte Cassino Healthcare Center, Toluca, IL
Monte Vista Child Care Center, Montclair, CA
Monte Vista Grove Homes, Pasadena, CA
Monte Vista Lodge, Lemon Grove, CA
Montebello Convalescent Hospital, Montebello, CA
Montebello Nursing Home, Hamilton, IL
Montefiore Home, Cleveland Heights, OH
Montello Care Center Inc, Montello, WI
Montello Manor Nursing Home, Lewiston, ME
Monterey Care Center, San Pablo, CA
Monterey Care Center, Wichita Falls, TX
Monterey Convalescent Hospital, Monterey, CA
Monterey Inn of Osseo, Osseo, MN
Monterey Nursing Center, Scottsdale, AZ
Monterey Nursing Inn, Grove City, OH
Monterey Park Convalescent Hospital, Monterey Park, CA
Monterey Pines Skilled Nursing Facility, Monterey, CA
Monterey Sanitarium, Rosemead, CA
Monterey Yorkshire Nursing Inn, Columbus, OH
Montezuma Health Care Center, Montezuma, GA
Montgomery Care Center Inc, Cincinnati, OH
Montgomery Country Geriatric and Rehabilitation Center, Royersford, PA
Montgomery Country Nursing Home, Mount Ida, AR
Montgomery County Infirmary, Amsterdam, NY
Montgomery County Nursing Home, Ashland City, TN
Montgomery Developmental Center, Huber Heights, OH
Montgomery Health Care Center, Montgomery, AL
Montgomery Manor, Santa Rosa, CA
Montgomery Manor, Montgomery City, MO
Montgomery Nursing Home, Montgomery, NY
Montgomery Nursing Home, Biscoe, NC
Monticello Big Lake Community Nursing Home, Monticello, MN
Monticello Community Healthcare Center, Monticello, IN
Monticello Hall, Kelso, WA
Monticello Manor, Fort Lauderdale, FL
Montowese Convalescent Home, North Haven, CT

Montrath Pediatric Nursing Center, Groton, MA
Montrose Care Center, Houston, TX
Montrose Convalescent Hospital, Montrose, CA
Montrose Health Center, Montrose, IA
Montrose Nursing Home, Montrose, MI
Montvale Health Center, Maryville, TN
MontVue Nursing Home, Luray, VA
Moody Care Center, Moody, TX
Moon Lake Convalescent Center, Schaumburg, IL
Mooney Convalescent Hospital, Baldwin Park, CA
Moore and Pike County Nursing Home, Bowling Green, MO
Moorehaven Nursing Home, La Center, WA
Mooreland Golden Age Nursing Home, Mooreland, OK
Moore's Nursing Home, Pittsburg, TX
Moorestown Nursing Home, Moorestown, NJ
Moorhead Healthcare Center, Moorhead, MN
The Moorings Park, Naples, FL
Moose Lake State Hospital, Moose Lake, MN
Moosehaven Health Center, Orange Park, FL
Moran Manor, Moran, KS
Moravian Home Inc, Winston-Salem, NC
Moravian Manor, Lititz, PA
Morehead Nursing Center, Morehead City, NC
Morgan County Appalachian Regional Hospital, West Liberty, KY
Morgan County Care Center, McConnelsville, OH
Morgan Health Center, Johnston, RI
Morgan Manor Convalescent Center, Morgantown, WV
Morgan Memorial Home, Stockton, IL
The Allen Morgan Nursing Center, Memphis, TN
Morgantown Health Care Corporation, Morgantown, WV
Morin's Retirement Home Inc, Attleboro, MA
Morning Star Nursing Home, Oklahoma City, OK
Morning Sun Manor, Morning Sun, IA
Morning View Care Center 1, Centerburg, OH
Morning View Care Center 2, Fulton, OH
Morning View Care Center 2 Annex, Fulton, OH
Morning View Care Center 3, Sunbury, OH
Morning View Care Center of Marion, Marion, OH
Morning View Center of Danville, Danville, OH
Morningside, Pinellas Park, FL
Morningside Care Center, Ida Grove, IA
Morningside Center, Chillicothe, MO
Morningside House Nursing Home Company, Bronx, NY
Morningside Manor, Alcester, SD
Morningside Manor, San Antonio, TX
Morningside Nursing Home, South Bend, IN
Morningside Nursing Home, Norman, OK
Morningside Nursing Home, Sheboygan, WI
Morningside Nursing Home, Stoughton, WI
Moroun Nursing Home, Detroit, MI
Morrell Memorial Convalescent Center Inc, Hartsville, SC
Morrilton Manor, Morrilton, AR
Morris Lahasky Nursing Home, Erath, LA
Morris Lincoln Nursing Home, Morris, IL
Morris Memorial Nursing and Convalescent Home, Milton, WV

Morris Nursing Home, Bethel, OH
Morris Oak Lawn Nursing Home, Eaton, OH
Morris Park Nursing Home, Bronx, NY
Morris View, Morris Plains, NJ
Morrison Community Hospital Skilled Nursing
  Center, Morrison, IL
Morrison Cove Home, Martinsburg, PA
Morrison Nursing Home, Whitefield, NH
Morristown Nursing and Rehabilitation
  Center, Morristown, NJ
Morristown Nursing Home, Morristown, IN
Morro Bay Convalescent Center, Morro
  Bay, CA
Morrow County Extended Care Facility, Mount
  Gilead, OH
Morrow Manor Inc, Chesterville, OH
Morrow Memorial Home for the Aged, Sparta,
  WI
Morton F Plant Rehabilitation and Nursing
  Center, Clearwater, FL
Morton Healthcare Centre, Morton, IL
Morton Nursing Home, Morton, WA
Morton Terrace, Morton, IL
Moses Austin Group Care Home, Potosi, MO
Moses Taylor Hospital—Skilled Nursing
  Facility, Scranton, PA
Moses-Ludington Nursing Home Company
  Inc, Ticonderoga, NY
Mosholu Parkway Nursing Home, Bronx, NY
Moss Oaks Health Care, Pooler, GA
Mosser Nursing Home Inc, Trexlertown, PA
Mother Hull Home, Kearney, NE
Mother Joseph Manor, Aberdeen, SD
Mother Margaret Hall, Mount Saint Joseph,
  OH
Mother of Good Counsel Home, Saint Louis,
  MO
Mother of Mercy Nursing Home, Albany, MN
Mother of Perpetual Help Home, Brownsville,
  TX
Mother Teresa Home, Lemont, IL
Mother Teresa Home, Cold Spring, MN
Mott Good Samaritan Nursing Center, Mott,
  ND
Moulton Nursing Home Inc, Moulton, AL
Moultrie County Community Center,
  Lovington, IL
Moultrie Rest-A-While Nursing Home,
  Moultrie, GA
Mound View Health Care Inc, Moundsville,
  WV
Moundridge Manor, Moundridge, KS
Mounds Park Residence, Saint Paul, MN
Moundville Nursing Home Inc,
  Moundville, AL
Mount Adams Care Center, Goldendale, WA
Mount Alverna Home, Parma, OH
Mount Ascutney Hospital and Health Center
  Nursing Home, Windsor, VT
Mount Ayr Health Care Center, Mount
  Ayr, IA
Mount Carmel Care Center, Burlington, WI
Mount Carmel Home, Manchester, NH
Mount Carmel Home—Keens Memorial,
  Kearney, NE
Mount Carmel Nursing Home, Milwaukee, WI
Mount Diablo Nursing Center, Martinez, CA
Mount Dora Healthcare Center, Mount
  Dora, FL
Mount Elam Nursing Home, Fitchburg, MA
Mount Gilead Shelter Care Home,
  Carrollton, IL
Mount Healthy Christian Home, Cincinnati,
  OH

Mount Holly Nursing Home, Louisville, KY
Mount Hope Dunkard Brethren Church Home,
  Manheim, PA
Mount Hope Nursing Center, Mount
  Hope, KS
Mount Ida Rest Home, Newton, MA
Mount Joseph, Concordia, KS
Mount Laurel Convalescent Center, Mount
  Laurel, NJ
Mount Lebanon Manor Convalescent Center,
  Pittsburgh, PA
Mount Lebanon Personal Care Home,
  Louisville, KY
Mount Loretto Nursing Home, Amsterdam,
  NY
Mount Macrina Manor Nursing Home,
  Uniontown, PA
Mount Miguel Covenant Village, Spring
  Valley, CA
Mount Ogden Convalescent Center, Ogden,
  UT
Mount Ogden Convalescent Center,
  Washington Terrace, UT
Mount Olivet Homes Inc, Minneapolis, MN
Mount Olivet Rolling Acres, Excelsior, MN
Mount Olivette Meadows Convalescent
  Hospital, Sacramento, CA
Mount Orab Nursing Care Center, Mount
  Orab, OH
Mount Pleasant Convalescent Hospital Inc, San
  Jose, CA
Mount Pleasant Home, Boston, MA
Mount Pleasant Manor, Matawan, NJ
Mount Pleasant Nursing Home, Cleveland, OH
Mount Pleasant Retirement Village, Monroe,
  OH
Mount Royal Villa, North Royalton, OH
Mount Rubidoux Convalescent Hospital,
  Rubidoux, CA
Mount Saint Joseph, Lake Forest, IL
Mount Saint Joseph, Euclid, OH
Mount Saint Joseph Extended Care Center,
  Portland, OR
Mount Saint Joseph Nursing Home,
  Waterville, ME
Mount Saint Rita Health Centre, Cumberland,
  RI
Mount Saint Vincent Home, Holyoke, MA
Mount Saint Vincent Nursing Center, Seattle,
  WA
Mount San Antonio Gardens Congregational
  Homes, Pomona, CA
Mount Shelter Care Home, Vienna, IL
Mount Sinai Nursing Home Inc, Denver, CO
Mount Sinai Nursing Home Inc, Baltimore,
  MD
Mount Tabor Care Center, Portland, OR
Mount Trexler Skilled Nursing Unit, Limeport,
  PA
Mount Vernon Care Facility Inc, Mount
  Vernon, IL
Mount Vernon Developmental Center, Mount
  Vernon, OH
Mount Vernon Manor, Fort Lauderdale, FL
Mount Vernon Nursing Center, Southfield, MI
Mount Vernon Nursing Center, Alexandria, VA
Mount Vernon Nursing Home, Mount Vernon,
  OH
Mount Vernon Park Care Center, Springfield,
  MO
Mount View Child Care Center Inc, Loma
  Linda, CA
Mount View Health Facility, Lockport, NY

Mount View Manor, Wausau, WI
Mount Washington Care Center, Cincinnati,
  OH
Mount Washington Home, Eau Claire, WI
Mount Zion Geriatric Center, Indianapolis, IN
Mountain Aire Health Care Facility,
  Phoenix, AZ
Mountain Duplex, Fort Collins, CO
Mountain Laurel Manor, Corbin, KY
Mountain Manor, Carmichael, CA
Mountain Manor Nursing Home,
  Pikeville, KY
Mountain Manor Nursing Home,
  Prestonsburg, KY
Mountain Manor Nursing Home Inc, Fort
  Payne, AL
Mountain Park Convalescent Care Facility,
  Lake Oswego, OR
Mountain Rest Nursing Home Inc, Scranton,
  PA
Mountain Ridge Health Care Center, Franklin,
  NH
Mountain Shadows—Intermediate Care
  Facility, Las Cruces, NM
Mountain State Nursing Home, Charleston,
  WV
Mountain Towers Healthcare, Cheyenne, WY
Mountain Valley Rest Home, Salyersville, KY
Mountain View Care Center, Kimberly, ID
Mountain View Care Center, Klamath Falls,
  OR
Mountain View Center Inc, Greensburg, PA
Mountain View Convalescent Care Facility,
  Oregon City, OR
Mountain View Convalescent Center,
  Clayton, GA
Mountain View Convalescent Home Inc,
  Festus, MO
Mountain View Convalescent Hospital,
  Mountain View, CA
Mountain View Extended Care Center,
  Gadsden, AL
Mountain View Health Care Center, Elkhorn
  City, KY
Mountain View Healthcare, Windsor, CT
Mountain View Hospital, Madras, OR
Mountain View Hospital, Payson, UT
Mountain View House, Aurora, CO
Mountain View Lodge Inc, Big Spring, TX
Mountain View Manor Nursing Center, Bryson
  City, NC
Mountain View Manor Nursing Home,
  Eureka, MT
Mountain View Nursing Center, Safford, AZ
Mountain View Nursing Home, Montgomery,
  MA
Mountain View Nursing Home, Mountain
  View, OK
Mountain View Nursing Home, Hillsdale, PA
Mountain View Nursing Home, Chattanooga,
  TN
Mountain View Nursing Home Inc, Aroda, VA
Mountain View Rest Home, Chattanooga, TN
Mountain View Sanitarium, Sylmar, CA
Mountain Vista/ElderLodge—Denton,
  Denton, NC
Mountain Vista Nursing Home,
  Wheatridge, CO
Mountain Vista Nursing Home, Toppenish,
  WA
Mountainview Memorial Nursing Home,
  White Sulphur Springs, MT
Mountainview Nursing Home, Spartanburg,
  SC

Mountrail Bethel Home, Stanley, ND
Mozark Health Resort, Camdenton, MO
Muffett Nursing Home, Cornwell Heights, PA
Muhlenberg Community Hospital—Skilled Nursing Facility, Greenville, KY
Mulberry Lutheran Home, Mulberry, IN
Mulberry Manor, Stephenville, TX
Mulberry Manor Inc, Anna, IL
Mulberry Park, Florence, SC
Mul-Care Desert Convalescent Hospital, Indio, CA
Mulder Health Care Facility, West Salem, WI
Muldrow Nursing Home, Muldrow, OK
Muleshoe Nursing Home, Muleshoe, TX
Mullen Home for the Elderly, Denver, CO
Mullican Nursing Home, Savoy, TX
Mullins Nursing Home, Piketon, OH
Mullis Manor II, Folkston, GA
Mullis Manor Inc, Homerville, GA
Multi-Medical Convalescent and Nursing Center, Towson, MD
Muncie Health Care Center Inc, Muncie, IN
Muncy Valley Hospital—Skilled Nursing Facility, Muncy, PA
Munday Nursing Center, Munday, TX
Mundey Manor, Townsend, DE
Municipal Hospital and Granite Manor, Granite Falls, MN
Municipal Nursing Home, Baldwin, WI
Munster Medical Inn, Munster, IN
Murdoch Center, Butner, NC
Murfreesboro Health Care Center, Murfreesboro, TN
Muriel Humphrey Residence-Charlson, Eden Prairie, MN
Muriel Humphry Residence—Westby, Eden Prairie, MN
Murlenberg Medical Center, Bethlehem, PA
Murphy Medical Center, Murphy, NC
Murray Manor Convalescent Center, Murraysville, PA
Murray-Calloway County Hospital Long Term Care Unit, Murray, KY
Muscatine Care Center, Muscatine, IA
Muscle Shoals Nursing Home, Muscle Shoals, AL
Muscogee Manor, Columbus, GA
Muskego Nursing Home, Muskego, WI
Muskegon Correctional Facility, Muskegon, MI
Muskogee Convalescent Center, Muskogee, OK
Myers Nursing and Convalescent Center Inc, Kansas City, MO
Myers Nursing Home, Beardstown, IL
Myrtle Beach Manor, Myrtle Beach, SC
Myrtle Convalescent Home, Manchester, NH
Myrtle Point Nursing Home Inc, Myrtle Point, OR
The Myrtles Health Care Facility, Columbia, MS
Mystic Manor Inc, Mystic, CT
Nacogdoches Convalescent Center, Nacogdoches, TX
Nampa Care Center, Nampa, ID
Nancy Ann Convalescent Home, Foster, RI
Nancy Hart Memorial Medical Center, Elberton, GA
Nansemond Convalescent Center Inc, Suffolk, VA
Naomi Heights Nursing Home, Alexandria, LA
Nashville Health Care Center, Nashville, TN
Nashville Manor Nursing Home, Nashville, TN

Nashville Nursing Home, Nashville, AR
Nassau Nursing Home, Oceanside, NY
Natatana Care Center, De Leon, TX
Natchaug Hospital Inc, Willimantic, CT
Natchitoches Manor Nursing Home, Natchitoches, LA
Natchitoches Parish Hospital—Long Term Care Unit, Natchitoches, LA
The Nathan Miller Center for Nursing Care Inc, White Plains, NY
Nathaniel Witherell, Greenwich, CT
Natick Nursing Home, Natick, MA
National Care Centers of America Inc, Springfield, MO
National Lutheran Home for the Aged, Rockville, MD
Nature Trail Home Inc, Mount Vernon, IL
Naugle Manor Inc, Baden, PA
Navarre Community Health Center, Navarre, OH
Nazareth Hall, El Paso, TX
Nazareth Home, Louisville, KY
Nazareth House, Fresno, CA
Nazareth House, Los Angeles, CA
Nazareth House, San Diego, CA
Nazareth House, San Rafael, CA
Nazareth House, Stoughton, WI
Nazareth Infirmary, Nazareth, KY
Nazareth Nursing Home and Health Related Facility, Buffalo, NY
Nazarethville, Des Plaines, IL
NCF Eastridge House, Beloit, WI
NCF Old Middleton Road, Madison, WI
Neal Home, Logansport, IN
Nebraska City Manor, Nebraska City, NE
Nebraska Veterans Home, Grand Island, NE
Nebraska Veterans Home, Norfolk, NE
Nederland Nursing Home Inc, Nederland, TX
Needham's Nursing Home, Bellingham, WA
Negley House Inc, Pittsburgh, PA
Negro Old Folks Home Inc, LaGrange, GA
Neighborhood Convalescent Home Inc, Pawtucket, RI
Neighbors Nursing Home, Byron, IL
Neighbors of Woodcraft Home, Gresham, OR
Neillsville Memorial Home, Neillsville, WI
Nekton on Frost, Maplewood, MN
Nekton on Goodrich, Saint Paul, MN
Nekton on Greysolon, Duluth, MN
Nekton on Hodgson Rd, Shoreview, MN
Nekton on Imperial Court, Stillwater, MN
Nekton on London Road, Duluth, MN
Nekton on Minnehaha Park, Minneapolis, MN
Nekton on Mississippi, Saint Paul, MN
Nekton on Queen, Minneapolis, MN
Nekton on Sextant, Little Canada, MN
Nekton on Springvale, Duluth, MN
Nekton on Stillwater Lane, Lake Elmo, MN
Nekton on Wallace, Duluth, MN
Nekton on Wheeler, Saint Paul, MN
Nekton on William, Edina, MN
Nekton on Wyoming, Saint Paul, MN
Nella's Inc, Elkins, WV
Nella's Nursing Home Inc, Elkins, WV
Nelson Broadview Nursing Home, Parma, OH
Nelson Manor Nursing Home, Newton, IA
Nelson Manor Nursing Home, Boston, MA
Nelson Nursing Home, Fairfield, IA
Nelson's Health Care Center Inc, Waynesboro, TN
Nelson's Rest Home, Sturgis, SD
Nemaha County Good Samaritan Center, Auburn, NE

Nentwick Convalescent Home Inc, East Liverpool, OH
Neodesha Nursing Home, Neodesha, KS
Neosho Senior Center Inc, Neosho, MO
Neponsit Home for the Aged, Neponsit, NY
Nesbit Nursing Home, Seguin, TX
Neshaminy Manor, Doylestown, PA
Neshoba County Nursing Home, Philadelphia, MS
Nesika I, Tacoma, WA
Nesika II, Tacoma, WA
Nesika III, Tacoma, WA
Nevada City Nursing Home, Nevada, MO
Nevada Habilitation Center, Nevada, MO
Nevada Manor Nursing Home, Nevada, MO
Neville Manor, Cambridge, MA
New Albany Nursing Home, New Albany, IN
New Athens Home, New Athens, IL
New Bedford Jewish Convalescent Home, New Bedford, MA
New Boston Nursing Center, New Boston, TX
New Boston Nursing Home Inc, Sandisfield, MA
New Brighton Care Center, New Brighton, MN
New Brighton Manor Care Center, Staten Island, NY
New Brook Hollow Health Care Center Inc, Wallingford, CT
New Bunker Rest Home, Fitchburg, MA
New Castle Community Care Center, New Castle, IN
New Castle Healthcare Center, New Castle, IN
New Concord Nursing Center, New Concord, OH
New Connection A, Saint Paul, MN
New Dawn Convalescent Center, Springfield, OH
New Dawn Health Care Center, Dover, OH
New Dawn Inc, Fulda, MN
New Dawson Springs Nursing Home, Dawson Springs, KY
New Detroit Nursing Center, Detroit, MI
New England Friends Home, Hingham, MA
New England Home for the Deaf, Danvers, MA
New England Rehabilitation Hospital, Woburn, MA
New Fairview Hall Convalescent Home, New Haven, CT
New Fern Restorium, Saint Petersburg, FL
New Florence Nursing Home Inc, New Florence, MO
New Glarus Home Inc, New Glarus, WI
New Glen Oaks Nursing Home, Glen Oaks, NY
New Gouverneur Hospital—Skilled Nursing Facility, New York, NY
New Hampshire Centennial Home, Concord, NH
New Hampshire Odd Fellows Home, Concord, NH
New Hampton Care Center Inc, New Hampton, IA
New Haven Convalescent Center, New Haven, CT
New Haven Nursing Home, Anderson, IN
New Haven Nursing Home, Odessa, MO
New Haven O'Rest Nursing Home, Van Buren, AR
The New Homestead, Guthrie Center, IA
New Hope Foundation of Indiana Inc, Indianapolis, IN
New Hope Manor, Brewton, AL

New Hope Village Inc, Carroll, IA
New Horizon Nursing Home, Springfield, OH
New Horizon Rehabilitative Center, Ocala, FL
New Horizons, Salt Lake City, UT
New Horizons Care Center, Sioux City, IA
New Horizons Nursing Home, Konawa, OK
New Horizons of Pittsburg, Pittsburg, KS
New Horizons of Valley Center, Valley
    Center, KS
New Ivy House, Middletown, NJ
New Jersey Firemen's Home, Boonton, NJ
New Lakeview Convalescent Home,
    Cheshire, CT
New Lexington Health Care Center, New
    Lexington, OH
New Life Center, Greeley, CO
New Life Treatment Center, Woodstock, MN
New Lincoln Hospital, Toledo, OR
New London Care Center, New London, IA
New London Convalescent Home,
    Waterford, CT
New Mexico State Hospital Long Term Care
    Division, Las Vegas, NM
New Milford Nursing Home, New
    Milford, CT
New Oaks Care Center, Des Moines, IA
New Orleans Home and Rehabilitation Center,
    New Orleans, LA
New Paltz Nursing Home, New Paltz, NY
New Perry Nursing Home, Perry, GA
New Richland Care Center, New Richland,
    MN
New Riveria Health Resort, Coral Gables, FL
New Rochelle Nursing Home, New Rochelle,
    NY
New Sans Souci Nursing Home, Yonkers, NY
New Seaera Convalescent Home, Long Beach,
    WA
New Sharon Care Center, New Sharon, IA
New Town Health Development Corp, New
    Town, ND
New Ulm CRF I, New Ulm, MN
New Ulm CRF II, New Ulm, MN
New Vanderbilt Nursing Home, Staten Island,
    NY
New York Congregational Home for the Aged,
    Brooklyn, NY
New York State Veterans Home, Oxford, NY
Newark Health and Extended Care Facility,
    Newark, NJ
Newark Healthcare Centre, Newark, OH
Newark Manor Nursing Home, Newark, NY
Newark Manor Nursing Home Inc,
    Newark, DE
Newark-Wayne Community Hospital—Skilled
    Nursing Facility, Newark, NY
Newaygo County Medical Care Facility,
    Fremont, MI
Newberg Care Home, Newberg, OR
Newberry Convalescent Center, Newberry, SC
Newberry Nursing Home, Kansas City, MO
Newburgh Health Care and Residential Center,
    Newburgh, IN
Newburyport Manor Nursing Home,
    Newburyport, MA
Newburyport Society Home for Aged Men,
    Newburyport, MA
Newburyport Society Home for Aged Women,
    Newburyport, MA
Newell Good Samaritan Center, Newell, IA
Newfane Health Facility, Newfane, NY
Newfield House Inc Convalescent Home,
    Plymouth, MA

Newhall Nursing Home, Newhall, CA
Newhall Nursing Home, Salem, MA
Newkirk Nursing Center, Newkirk, OK
Newlight Nursing Home, Detroit, MI
Newman Healthcare Center, Newnan, GA
Newman's Lakewood Nursing Home,
    Lakewood, NJ
Newport Convalescent Center, Newport
    Beach, CA
Newport Convalescent Center Inc, Newport
    News, VA
Newport Health Care Center, Newport, VT
Newport Healthcare Center Inc, Newport, AR
Newton Convalescent Home, Newton, MA
Newton County Nursing Home, Jasper, AR
Newton Manor Rest Home, Worcester, MA
Newton Nursing Home, Newton, NJ
Newton Presbyterian Manor Inc, Newton, KS
Newton Rest Haven Inc, Newton, IL
Newton-Wellesley Nursing Home, Wellesley,
    MA
NHE—Greenville Inc, Greenville, SC
NHE—Huntsville, Huntsville, AL
NHE—Lansing, Lansing, MI
NHE—Memphis, Memphis, TN
Niagara Falls Memorial Nursing Home Co Inc,
    Niagara Falls, NY
Niagara Frontier Nursing Home Co Inc,
    Getzville, NY
Niagara Geriatric Center, Niagara Falls, NY
Niagara Lutheran Home Inc, Buffalo, NY
Niagra Frontier Methodist Home Inc,
    Getzville, NY
Nicholas County Health Care Center,
    Richwood, WV
The Nicholas Marra Nursing Home, East
    Providence, RI
Nicholas Nursing Home, Carney's Point, NJ
Nichols Home, Portage, OH
Nichols House Nursing Home, Fairhaven, MA
Nicholson's Nursing Home, Winthrop, ME
Nicol Home Inc, Glasco, KS
Nicole Manor, Burrillville, RI
Nicollet Health Care Center Inc, Minneapolis,
    MN
Nightingale East Nursing Home, Warren, MI
Nightingale Home, Nashua, NH
Nightingale Home Inc, Statesboro, GA
Nightingale North, Sterling Heights, MI
Nightingale Nursing Home, Waconia, MN
Nightingale West, Westland, MI
Nikkel Family Care Home, Denver, CO
Nim Henson Geriatric Center, Jackson, KY
Nims Rest Home, Natick, MA
Nina Van Sant Residential Care Facility,
    Lakewood, CO
Ninnescah Manor Inc, Clearwater, KS
Niobrara County Memorial Hospital Nursing
    Home, Lusk, WY
Nipple Convalescent Home, Liverpool, PA
Nishna Care Center Inc, Malvern, IA
Noble Building Intermediate Care Facility,
    Hartford, CT
Noblesville Healthcare Center, Noblesville, IN
Noblesville Nursing Home, Noblesville, IN
Nodaway Nursing Home Inc, Maryville, MO
Nokomis Golden Manor, Nokomis, IL
Nopeming Nursing Home, Nopeming, MN
Nora Springs Manor, Nora Springs, IA
Nor-Bell Nursing Home, Bellingham, WA
Norcliffe Rest Home Inc, Brooklyn, CT
Norfolk Nursing Home, Stoughton, MA
Norhaven, Saint Paul, MN

Norlite Nursing Center, Marquette, MI
Normandy Hills Care Center, Des Moines, IA
Normandy House, Wilmette, IL
Normandy House Nursing Home, Melrose,
    MA
Normandy Terrace Inc, San Antonio, TX
Normandy Terrace Inc—Northeast, San
    Antonio, TX
Norred Convalescent Home, Bessemer, AL
Norridge Nursing Centre, Chicago, IL
Norseland Nursing Home, Westby, WI
Norstrude Guest Home, Albert Lea, MN
North Adams Home Inc, Mendon, IL
North Alabama Nursing Home,
    Russellville, AL
North American Baptist Home, Madison, SD
North Arundel Nursing and Convalescent
    Center Inc, Glen Burnie, MD
North Aurora Manor, North Aurora, IL
North Bend Nursing Home, North Bend, WA
North Berwick Nursing Home, North Berwick,
    ME
North Big Horn Nursing Facility, Lovell, WY
North Carolina Cancer Institute, Lumberton,
    NC
North Carolina Lutheran Home—Hickory
    Unit, Hickory, NC
North Carolina Lutheran Home—Salisbury,
    Salisbury, NC
North Carolina Lutheran Homes Inc,
    Albemarle, NC
North Carolina Special Care Center, Wilson,
    NC
North Central Good Samaritan Center, Mohall,
    ND
North Charleston Convalescent Center,
    Charleston, SC
North Country Nursing and Rehabilitation,
    Bemidji, MN
North Country Rehabilitation Center,
    Franconia, NH
North Dallas Nursing Home Inc, Dallas, TX
North Division Residential Center,
    Sterling, CO
North Eastwood Rest Home, Amesbury, MA
North Fairfield Geriatric Center Inc,
    Fairfield, CT
North Gate Manor, Wheatfield, NY
North Grand Care Center, Ames, IA
North Hollywood Extended Care, North
    Hollywood, CA
North Horizon Health Care Center, Saint
    Petersburg, FL
North Jersey Nursing and Convalescent Center,
    Wayne, NJ
North Las Vegas Care Center, North Las Vegas,
    NV
North Manor Center, Youngstown, OH
North Miami Convalescent Home, North
    Miami, FL
North Panola Regional Hospital—Skilled
    Nursing Facility, Sardis, MS
North Pennsylvania Convalescent Residence
    Inc, Lansdale, PA
North Ridge Care Center, New Hope, MN
North Ridge Care Center, Manitowoc, WI
North River Nursing Home, Hanover, MA
North Rockford Convalescent Home,
    Rockford, IL
North Sabine Nursing Home, Pleasant Hill, LA
North Saint Paul Nursing Home, North Saint
    Paul, MN
North Shore Convalescent Home, Saugus, MA

North Shore Geriatric Home, Waukegan, IL
North Shore Manor Inc, Loveland, CO
North Shore Nursing Home, Miami, FL
North Shores Health Center, Saint
 Petersburg, FL
North Side Nursing Home, Youngstown, OH
North Star Homes, Bemidji, MN
North Valley Hospital and Extended Care
 Center, Whitefish, MT
North Valley Nursing Home, Stevensville, MT
North Vernon Nursing Home, North
 Vernon, IN
North Village Manor, Moberly, MO
North Willow Center, Indianapolis, IN
Northampton Convalescent Center, Easton, PA
Northampton Nursing Home Inc,
 Northampton, MA
Northaven Nursing Center, Dallas, TX
Northboro Rest Home, Northborough, MA
Northbridge Nursing and Retirement Home,
 Northbridge, MA
Northbrook Manor Care Center, Cedar
 Rapids, IA
Northbrook Manor Convalescent Hospital,
 Willits, CA
Northcrest Care Center, Council Bluffs, IA
Northcrest Health Care Center, Ames, IA
Northcrest Nursing Home, Napoleon, OH
Northeast Health Care Center, Wichita, KS
Northeast House Inc, Minneapolis, MN
Northeast Nursing Center, Oklahoma City, OK
Northeast Ohio Development Center,
 Cleveland, OH
Northeast Residence 1, White Bear Lake, MN
Northeast Residence 2, White Bear Lake, MN
Northern Cochise Nursing Home, Willcox, AZ
Northern Dutchess Hospital, Rhinebeck, NY
Northern Itasca, Bigfork, MN
Northern Lights Manor Nursing Home,
 Washburn, WI
Northern Pines Good Samaritan, Blackduck,
 MN
Northern Westchester Hospital Center—Skilled
 Nursing Unit, Mount Kisco, NY
Northern Wisconsin Center, Chippewa Falls,
 WI
Northfield Manor, West Orange, NJ
Northfield Manor Health Care Facility,
 Louisville, KY
Northfield Retirement Center, Northfield, MN
Northfield Villa Inc, Gering, NE
Northgate Care Center, Waukon, IA
Northgate Convalescent Hospital, San
 Rafael, CA
Northgate Park Nursing Home, Florissant, MO
Northgate Rehabilitation Center, Seattle, WA
Northhampton County Home—Gracedale,
 Nazareth, PA
Northhaven Health Care Center, Knoxville,
 TN
Northlake Convalescent Hospital, San
 Jose, CA
Northland Care Center, Rice Lake, WI
Northland Manor, Jackman, ME
Northland Nursing Center, Detroit, MI
Northland Terrace, Columbus, OH
Northline Manor, Houston, TX
Northome Nursing Home, Northome, MN
Northpark Manor, Decatur, IL
Northridge Residence, Ortonville, MN
Northshore Health Care Center, Milwaukee,
 WI
Northshore Manor, Bothell, WA

Northside Convalescent Center, Atlanta, GA
Northside Haven Personal Care Home,
 Jackson, MS
Northside Healthcare Center, Indianapolis, IN
Northside Manor Inc, Mount Vernon, OH
Northside Manor Nursing Home, Sapulpa, OK
Northside Nursing Center, Springfield, MO
Northside Nursing Center, Corsicana, TX
Northumberland County Home—Shamokin,
 Shamokin, PA
Northview Care Center, Falls City, NE
Northview Community, Pensacola, FL
Northview Development Center, Eastland, TX
Northview Home, Waukesha, WI
Northview Nursing Home, Johnstown, OH
Northway Convalescent Center,
 Birmingham, AL
Northwest Care Center, Detroit, MI
Northwest Care Center, Wauseon, OH
Northwest Continuum Care Center, Longview,
 WA
Northwest Danish Home, Seattle, WA
Northwest Health Center, Milwaukee, WI
Northwest Home for the Aged, Chicago, IL
Northwest Louisiana State School, Bossier
 City, LA
Northwest Manor Nursing Home,
 Indianapolis, IN
Northwest Mediplex, Austin, TX
Northwest Nursing Center, Oklahoma City,
 OK
Northwest Ohio Development Center, Toledo,
 OH
Northwest Progressive Center, Seattle, WA
Northwest Regional Intermediate Care Home,
 Rome, GA
Northwood Care Centre, Tacoma, WA
Northwood Convalescent Center, Lowell, MA
Northwood Deaconess Nursing Home,
 Northwood, ND
Northwood Good Samaritan Center,
 Jasper, IN
Northwood Healthcare Center, Marble Falls,
 TX
Northwood Manor Nursing Home, Carrollton,
 TX
Northwood Nursing and Convalescent Center,
 Philadelphia, PA
Northwood Nursing Home, South Bend, IN
Northwood Nursing Home, Manchester, NH
Northwoods Healthcare Center, Belvidere, IL
Northwoods Manor, Escanaba, MI
Northwoods Manor Annex, Escanaba, MI
Northwoods Manor Inc, Alton, IL
Norton Community Hospital, Norton, VA
Norton Nursing Home Inc, Colorado
 Springs, CO
Norton Sound Regional Hospital, Nome, AK
Nortonian Nursing Home, Rochester, NY
Norwalk Manor Care Center, Norwalk, IA
Norwalk Memorial Home, Norwalk, OH
Norway Nursing Home, Norway, ME
Norwegian Christian Home for the Aged,
 Brooklyn, NY
Norwegian Luther Bethesda Home,
 Chicago, IL
Norwegian Old Peoples Home, Boston, MA
Norwell Home, Nashua, NH
Norwell Knoll Nursing Home, Norwell, MA
Norwichtown Convalescent Home,
 Norwich, CT
Norwood Health Center, Marshfield, WI
Norwood Nursing and Retirement Home,
 Norwood, MA

Norwood Nursing Center, Huntington, IN
Norwood Park Home, Chicago, IL
Norworth Convalescent Center, Worthington,
 OH
Notre Dame Convalescent Home Inc,
 Norwalk, CT
Notre Dame Hills Convalescent Center,
 Belleville, IL
Nottingham Manor, Dallas, TX
Nottingham Village, Northumberland, PA
Nowata Nursing Home, Nowata, OK
Nucare Convalescent Center, Hot Springs, AR
Nucare Convalescent Center, Laurel, MS
Nucare Convalescent Center, Dyersburg, TN
Nucare Convalescent Center, Humboldt, TN
Nucare Convalescent Center, Lexington, TN
Nugent Convalescent Home Inc, Hermitage,
 PA
Nu-Roc Nursing Home, Blackwell, WI
Nursecare Center of Atlanta, Atlanta, GA
Nursecare of Shreveport, Shreveport, LA
Nursing Care Center of Bristol, Bristol, CT
Nursing Center of Canton, Canton, IL
Nursing Center of Greenwood Methodist
 Home, Greenwood, SC
Nursing Home Center, Milledgeville, GA
Nursing Home of Arab Inc, Arab, AL
The Nursing Home of Boaz, Boaz, AL
Nursing Home of Eunice, Eunice, LA
The Nursing Home of Tallassee Inc,
 Tallassee, AL
Nutmeg Pavilion Healthcare, New
 London, CT
Nuuanu Hale Hospital, Honolulu, HI
Nyack Manor Nursing Home, Valley Cottage,
 NY
Nye General Hospital, Tonopah, NV
Nygaard Nursing Home, Stoughton, WI
Oahe Manor, Gettysburg, SD
Oak Bluffs Nursing Center, Clearwater, FL
Oak Brook Nursing Center, Hinsdale, IL
Oak Cove Health Center, Clearwater, FL
Oak Crest, De Kalb, IL
Oak Crest Care Center, Salem, OR
Oak Crest Inn, New Braunfels, TX
Oak Crest Manor Inc, Scituate, RI
Oak Crest Nursing Home Inc, Tuscumbia, AL
Oak Crest Residence, Elgin, IL
Oak Dale Manor, Sand Springs, OK
Oak Glen Home, Coal Valley, IL
Oak Grove Care Center, Minneapolis, MN
Oak Grove Health Care Center, Oak Grove,
 MO
Oak Grove Manor, Niles, MI
Oak Grove Manor Inc, Idabel, OK
Oak Grove Nursing Home Inc, Deshler, OH
Oak Grove Nursing Home Inc, Groves, TX
Oak Grove Retirement Home, Duncan, MS
Oak Haven Nursing Home, Centerpoint, LA
Oak Haven Nursing Home, Boston, MA
Oak Haven Nursing Home, Palestine, TX
Oak Hill Convalescent Center, Chesapeake, VA
Oak Hill Health Care Inc, Montgomery, AL
Oak Hill Home of Rest and Care, Greensburg,
 PA
Oak Hill Intermediate Care Home, College
 Park, GA
Oak Hill Manor Nursing Home, Ithaca, NY
Oak Hill Nursing Home, Middleborough, MA
Oak Hill Nursing Home, Farmington, MI
Oak Hill Nursing Home Annex, Farmington,
 MI
Oak Hill Nursing Home Inc, Pawtucket, RI

Oak Hill Nursing Home Inc, Staunton, VA

Oak Hill Residence, Littleton, NH

Oak Hill Rest Home, Owatonna, MN

Oak Hills Manor Inc, Salem, AR

Oak Hills Nursing Home, Lorain, OH

Oak Hills Nursing Home, Jones, OK

Oak Hollow Nursing Center, Middle Island, NY

Oak Knoll Health Care, Ferguson, MO

Oak Knoll Manor Nursing Home, Birmingham, AL

Oak Lawn Convalescent Home Inc, Chicago, IL

Oak Manor Convalescent Center, Oakland, CA

Oak Manor Extended Care Facility, Columbus, GA

Oak Manor Inc, Goldsboro, NC

Oak Manor Nursing Center, Booneville, AR

Oak Manor Nursing Center, Largo, FL

Oak Manor Nursing Center, Flatonia, TX

Oak Manor Nursing Home, Holyoke, MA

Oak Manor Nursing Home, McKenzie, TN

Oak Manor Nursing Home, Gladewater, TX

Oak Manor Nursing Home, Linden, TX

Oak Manor Nursing Home, Nacogdoches, TX

Oak Manor Nursing Home of Texarkana, Texarkana, TX

Oak Manor of Kinston, Kinston, NC

Oak Manor of Snow Hill, Snow Hill, NC

Oak Meadow Inc, Alexandria, VA

Oak Park, Oakwood Village, OH

Oak Park Care Center, Nevada, IA

Oak Park Care Center, Lake Charles, LA

Oak Park Convalescent and Geriatric Center, Oak Park, IL

Oak Park Convalescent Hospital, Pleasant Hill, CA

Oak Park Convalescent Hospital, Santa Barbara, CA

Oak Park Nursing Center Inc, Grass Valley, CA

Oak Park Nursing Home, Pine Bluff, AR

Oak Park Professional Care Center, Saint Louis, MO

Oak Park Sheltered Care, Oak Park, IL

Oak Pavilion Nursing Center, Cincinnati, OH

Oak Ridge Acres, Hiawatha, KS

Oak Ridge Care Center, Minneapolis, MN

Oak Ridge Care Center, Franksville, WI

Oak Ridge Convalescent Center, Richmond, IN

Oak Ridge Convalescent Center Inc, Bloomfield, CT

Oak Ridge Health Care Center, Oak Ridge, TN

Oak Ridge Manor, Durant, OK

Oak Ridge Manor Nursing Center, Wayne, NJ

Oak Ridge Manor Nursing Home, Kansas City, MO

Oak Ridge Nursing Home, El Dorado, AR

Oak Springs of Warrenton, Warrenton, VA

Oak Terrace Nursing Home, Minnetonka, MN

Oak Terrace Retirement, Springfield, IL

Oak Tree Convalescent Center Inc, Cincinnati, OH

Oak Tree Convalescent Hospital, Oakland, CA

Oak Tree Lodge, Gainesville, TX

Oak Valley Nursing Home, Macon, GA

Oak View Intermediate Care Home, Waverly Hall, GA

Oak View Manor, McLeansboro, IL

Oak View Manor Inc, Ozark, AL

Oak View Nursing Home, Summerville, GA

Oak View Nursing Home Inc, Morgan, NJ

Oak Villa Health Care, Hillsboro, OR

Oak Village Care Center, Baldwin, MI

Oak Woods Home for the Elderly, Mer Rouge, LA

Oakcliff Convalescent Home Inc, Waterbury, CT

Oakcrest Manor, Austin, TX

Oakdale Convalescent Hospital, Oakdale, CA

Oakdale Nursing Home, Judsonia, AR

Oakdale Nursing Home, West Boylston, MA

Oakes Manor Good Samaritan Center, Oakes, ND

Oakhaven Inc, Darlington, SC

Oakhaven Manor, Warsaw, MO

Oakhaven Nursing Center, Richmond, KS

Oakhaven Nursing Center, Arlington, TX

Oakhurst Convalescent Center, Elma, WA

Oakhurst Nursing Home, Sweet Home, OR

Oakland Care Center, Royal Oak, MI

Oakland City Rest Home, Oakland City, IN

Oakland County Medical Care Facility, Pontiac, MI

Oakland Geriatric Village, Pontiac, MI

Oakland Heights, Oakland, NE

Oakland Manor Nursing Home, Council Bluffs, IA

Oakland Nursing Center, Hillsboro, OH

Oakland Park Nursing Home, Thief River Falls, MN

Oaklawn Health Care Center, Mankato, MN

Oakledge Manor Convalescent and Retirement Home, Hopedale, MA

Oakley Manor, Oakley, KS

Oakmont East Nursing Center, Greenville, SC

Oakmont Manor, Flatwoods, KY

Oakmont North Nursing Center, Travelers Rest, SC

Oakmont Nursing Center, Oakmont, PA

Oakmont Nursing Home, Greenville, SC

Oakmont of Union, Union, SC

Oakmont Presbyterian Home, Oakmont, PA

Oaknoll Retirement Residence, Iowa City, IA

Oakridge Convalescent Home Inc, Melrose Park, IL

Oakridge Convalescent Hospital, Oakland, CA

Oakridge Gardens Nursing Center, Menasha, WI

Oakridge Home, Westlake, OH

Oakridge Home Inc, Wewoka, OK

Oakridge of Plattsburg, Plattsburg, MO

The Oaks, Petaluma, CA

The Oaks, Topeka, KS

The Oaks, Wyncote, PA

The Oaks Care Center Inc, Memphis, TN

Oaks Convalescent Center, Lima, OH

Oaks Lodge Rest Home Inc, Fort Smith, AR

The Oaks Nursing Home Inc, Marshallville, GA

Oaks Nursing Home, Burnet, TX

Oakton Nursing Home Inc, Oakton, VA

Oakton Pavilion Inc, Des Plaines, IL

Oakview, Lebanon, PA

Oakview Care Center, Williston, FL

Oakview Convalescent Hospital, Glendora, CA

Oakview Convalescent Hospital, Tujunga, CA

Oakview Home, Conrad, IA

Oakview Manor Nursing Center, Hubbard, TX

Oakview Medical Care Facility, Ludington, MI

Oakview Nursing Home, Baldwyn, MS

Oakview Nursing Home, Cincinnati, OH

Oakville Health Care Center, Memphis, TN

Oakwood Convalescent Center, Eustis, FL

Oakwood Convalescent Home, Webster, MA

Oakwood Glen Care Center, McMinnville, OR

Oakwood Health Care Center Inc, Walterboro, SC

Oakwood Health Care Center Inc, Lewisburg, TN

Oakwood Intermediate Care Facility, Somerset, KY

Oakwood Knoll Nurisng Home, Kernersville, NC

Oakwood Lodge of Natchez, Natchez, MS

Oakwood Lutheran Homes—Hebron Hall, Madison, WI

Oakwood Manor Corporation, Clear Lake, IA

Oakwood Manor Nursing Home, Vidor, TX

Oakwood Nursing Home, Manchester, MA

Oakwood Park Su Casa, Tampa, FL

Oakwood Place, Texarkana, AR

Oakwood Terrace Inc, Evanston, IL

Oakwood Villa, Hutchinson, KS

Oakwood Village Nurse Care Center, Lafayette, LA

O'Berry Center, Goldsburg, NC

Obion County Rest Home, Union City, TN

O'Brien Memorial Nursing Home, Masury, OH

O'Brien's Rest Home, Rapid City, SD

Ocala Geriatric Center Inc, Ocala, FL

Ocala Health Care Center, Ocala, FL

Ocean Grove Nursing Home, Ocean Grove, NJ

Ocean Park Nursing Home, Seaside, OR

Ocean Point Health Care Center—Presbyterian Homes of Southern New Jersey, Somers Point, NJ

Ocean Springs Nursing Center, Ocean Springs, MS

Ocean Trail Convalescent Center, Southport, NC

Ocean View Care Center, Bandon, OR

Ocean View Convalescent Center, Long Beach, WA

Ocean View Convalescent Hospital, Encinitas, CA

Ocean View Manor Nursing Home, Revere, MA

Oceana County Medical Care Facility, Hart, MI

Oceanside Nursing Home, Tybee Island, GA

Oceanside Nursing Home, Quincy, MA

Ocean-View Nursing Home, New Smyrna Beach, FL

Oceanview Nursing Home, Lubec, ME

Oceanview Nursing Home, Far Rockaway, NY

Ochoco Nursing Home, Prineville, OR

OCI-Thompson Avenue Group Home, West Saint Paul, MN

Oconee Geriatric Center Inc, Seneca, SC

Oconee Health Care Center, Oconee, GA

Octavia Manor Inc, Colfax, IL

Odd Fellow and Rebekah Home, Jackson, MI

Odd Fellow and Rebekah Nursing Home, Ennis, TX

Odd Fellow and Rebekah Nursing Home Inc, Lockport, NY

Odd Fellow-Rebekah Home, Mattoon, IL

Odd Fellows Home, Greensburg, IN

Odd Fellows Home, Liberty, MO

Odd Fellows Home, Dell Rapids, SD

Odd Fellows Home of California Infirmary, Saratoga, CA

Odd Fellows Home of Massachusetts, Worcester, MA

Odd Fellows Home of Ohio, Springfield, OH

Odd Fellows Home of Pennsylvania Inc, Middletown, PA
Odd Fellows Rest Home, Checotah, OK
Odell Nursing Center, Concord, NC
Odin Care Center Inc, Odin, IL
Oelwein Care Center, Oelwein, IA
Ogden Care Center, Ogden, UT
Ogden Manor, Ogden, IA
Ogemaw Valley Medical Facility, Rose City, MI
Ohesson Manor, Lewistown, PA
Ohio District Council Nursing, Zanesville, OH
Ohio Eastern Star Home, Mount Vernon, OH
Ohio Extended Care Center, Lorain, OH
Ohio Masonic Home, Springfield, OH
Ohio Missionary Home, New Carlisle, OH
Ohio Pythian Sisters Home of Medina, Medina, OH
Ohio Residential Services, Broadview Heights, OH
Ohio Valley Health Care Inc, Parkersburg, WV
Ohio Valley Manor Convalescent Center, Ripley, OH
Oil City Presbyterian Home, Oil City, PA
Ojai Valley Community Hospital—Skilled Nursing Department, Ojai, CA
Okemah Pioneer Nursing Home Inc, Okcmah, OK
Oklahoma Care Center, Stratford, OK
Oklahoma Christian Home Inc, Edmond, OK
Oklahoma County Home, Oklahoma City, OK
Oklahoma Methodist Home for the Aged, Tulsa, OK
Okmulgee Terrace Nursing Home Inc, Okmulgee, OK
Olathe Nursing Home, Olathe, KS
Old Capital Inn Convalescent and Nursing Home, Louisville, GA
Old Colony Road Rest Home, Norton, MA
Old Court Nursing Center, Randallstown, MD
Old Ladies Home, Jackson, MS
Old Masons Home of Kentucky, Shelbyville, KY
Old Orchard Manor, Skokie, IL
Old Peoples Home of the Church of Christ, Chicago, IL
Olds Manor, Grand Rapids, MI
Olive Schaeffer Home, Sheboygan, WI
Olive Vista—A Center for Problems of Living, Pomona, CA
Olivette Nursing Home, Elgin, IL
Olivewood Convalescent Hospital, Colton, CA
Olivia Healthcare Center, Olivia, MN
Ollie Steele Burden Manor, Baton Rouge, LA
Olmsted Manor Nursing Home, North Olmsted, OH
Olney Care Center, Olney, IL
Olney Nursing Center, Olney, TX
Olsen Manor Nursing Home, Amarillo, TX
Olympia Convalescent Hospital, Los Angeles, CA
Olympia Manor, Olympia, WA
Olympic Crest Convalescent Center, Seattle, WA
Olympic Health Care Inc, Sequim, WA
Olympus Care Center, Salt Lake City, UT
Omaha Manor Inc, Omaha, NE
Omaha Nursing Home Inc, Omaha, NE
Omni Manor, Youngstown, OH
Omro Care Center, Omro, WI
Onalaska Care Center, Onalaska, WI
Onawa Home for the Aged Inc, Onawa, IA
180 Court Home, Keene, NH
151 Court Home, Keene, NH

One Hundred Eighty Degrees Inc, Minneapolis, MN
Oneida City Hospital—Extended Care Facility, Oneida, NY
Oneida County Nursing Home, Malad, ID
Oneida Nursing Home, De Pere, WI
Oneida Nursing Home, Oneida, WI
O'Neill Senior Citizen's Home, O'Neill, NE
Oneonta Manor Nursing Home, Oneonta, AL
Oneonta-Richmond Inc, Oneonta, NY
Ontario County Health Facility, Canandaigua, NY
Ontario Nursing Home Inc, Ontario, CA
Ontonagon Memorial Hospital, Ontonagon, MI
Oosterman Rest Home, Melrose, MA
Oosterman's Rest Home, Wakefield, MA
Opal's Home for the Aged, Scottsville, KY
Opelika Nursing Home, Opelika, AL
Opelousas Health Care Inc, Opelousas, LA
Open Arms Nursing Home, Winchendon, MA
Opportunity Homes Inc, Lisbon, OH
Opportunity House, Champaign, IL
Opportunity House Inc, Sycamore, IL
Opportunity Manor, St Cloud, MN
Opportunity Medical and Convalescent Center, Spokane, WA
Ora G Morrow Nursing Home, Chicago, IL
Orange County Home and Infirmary, Goshen, NY
Orange County Nursing Home and Home for Adults, Orange, VA
Orange Health Care Center, Orange, CT
Orange Home Inc, Hatboro, PA
Orange Park Care Center, Orange Park, FL
Orange Village Care Center Inc, Masury, OH
Orange West Convalescent Hospital, Buena Park, CA
Orangeburg Convalescent Hospital, Modesto, CA
Orangeburg Nursing Home, Orangeburg, SC
Orangegrove Rehabilitation Hospital, Garden Grove, CA
Orangetree Convalescent Hospital, Riverside, CA
Orangevale Convalescent Hospital, Orangevale, CA
Orangeview Convalescent Hospital, Anaheim, CA
Orangewood Health Facility, Phoenix, AZ
Orchard Crest Care Center, Sandy, OR
Orchard Gables, Hollywood, CA
Orchard Health Care Center Inc, Orchard Park, NY
Orchard Hill Nursing Home, Omaha, NE
Orchard Lake Resthaven, Union Lake, MI
Orchard Lake Resthaven, Union Lake, MI
Orchard Manor Inc, Grove City, PA
Orchard Manor—North, Lancaster, WI
Orchard Manor Nursing Home, Medina, NY
Orchard Manor—South, Lancaster, WI
Orchard Park Convalescent Center, Tacoma, WA
Orchard Village, Skokie, IL
Orchards Villa Nursing Center, Lewiston, ID
Oregon City Nursing Home, Oregon City, OR
Oregon Health Care Center, Oregon, MO
Oregon Manor Ltd, Oregon, WI
Oregon-Washington Pythian Home, Vancouver, WA
Orient Developmental Center, Orient, OH
Orinda Rehabilitation and Convalescent Hospital, Orinda, CA

Orlando Health Care Center, Orlando, FL
Orlando Lutheran Towers, Orlando, FL
Orlando Memorial Convalescent Center, Orlando, FL
Orleans Convalescent and Retirement Home, Orleans, MA
Orleans County Home and Infirmary, Albion, NY
Ormond Beach Health Care Center, Ormond Beach, FL
Orofino Care Center Inc, Orofino, ID
Orono Nursing Home Inc, Orono, ME
Oroville Community Convalescent Hospital, Oroville, CA
Orrington Group Home, Orrington, ME
Orsini Boarding Home, Wilmington, DE
Orthodox Jewish Home for the Aged, Cincinnati, OH
Ortonville Nursing Home, Ortonville, MI
Orvilla Inc, Eagan, MN
Osage Beach Health Care Center, Osage Beach, MO
Osage Manor Inc, Osage City, KS
Osage Manor Nursing and Care Center, Eldon, MO
Osage Nursing Home, Nowata, OK
Osakis Group Home, Osakis, MN
Osawatomie Rest Home, Osawatomie, KS
Osceola Good Samaritan Center, Osceola, NE
Osceola Inn, Clearwater, FL
Osceola Leisure Manor, Osceola, IA
Osceola Nursing Home, Osceola, AR
Osceola Nursing Home, Ocilla, GA
Oshkosh Care Center, Oshkosh, WI
Oshtemo Care Center, Oshtemo, MI
Osnabrock Good Samaritan Center, Osnabrock, ND
Osseo Area Municipal Hospital Nursing Home, Osseo, WI
Ossian Senior Hospice Inc, Ossian, IA
Ostrander Nursing Home, Ostrander, MN
Oswego Guest Home, Oswego, KS
Oswego Hospital Extended Care Facility, Oswego, NY
Othello Convalescent Center, Othello, WA
Otsego County Memorial—Intermediate Care Facility, Gaylord, MI
Ottawa Care Center, Genoa, IL
Ottawa Care Center, Ottawa, IL
Ottawa County Riverview Nursing Home, Oak Harbor, OH
Otterbein Home, Lebanon, OH
Ottertail Nursing Home, Battle Lake, MN
Ottumwa Good Samaritan Center, Ottumwa, IA
Ottumwa Manor Nursing Home, Ottumwa, IA
Ouachita Convalescent Center Inc, Camden, AR
Our House, Farmington, ME
Our House of Minnesota I and II, Saint Paul, MN
Our Island Home, Nantucket, MA
Our Lady of Angels Retirement, Joliet, IL
Our Lady of Compassion Care Center, Anchorage, AK
Our Lady of Fatima Villa, Saratoga, CA
Our Lady of Good Counsel, Saint Paul, MN
Our Lady of Hope Residence-Little Sisters of the Poor, Latham, NY
Our Lady of Mercy Convalescent Home Inc, Hubbell, MI
Our Lady of Mercy Home, Kansas City, MO

Our Lady of Perpetual Help, Atlanta, GA
Our Lady of Prompt Succor Nursing Home, Opelousas, LA
Our Lady of Victory Nursing Home, Bourbonnais, IL
Our Lady's Haven, Fairhaven, MA
Our Lady's Residence, Pleasantville, NJ
Outagamie County Health Center, Appleton, WI
Outreach Group Home, Plymouth, MN
Outreach Northeast Group Home, Minneapolis, MN
Outwood ICF-MR, Dawson Springs, KY
Overlook Castle Nursing Home, Millersburg, OH
Overlook House, Cleveland, OH
Overlook Medical Clinic Inc, New Wilimington, PA
Overlook Nursing Home, Bellville, OH
Overlook Nursing Home, Burrillville, RI
Overton County Nursing Home, Livingston, TN
Ovid Convalescent Manor, Ovid, MI
Owatonna Health Care Center, Owatonna, MN
Owen Care Center, Abingdon, IL
Owen Care Center, Colchester, IL
Owen Care Center—Pittsfield, Pittsfield, IL
Owen County Home, Spencer, IN
The Ruth Owen Family Care Home, Commerce, CO
Owens Home, Montgomery City, MO
Owensville Convalescent Center Inc, Owensville, IN
Owenton Manor, Owenton, KY
Owsley County Health Care Center, Booneville, KY
Oxford Convalescent Home, Oxford, WI
Oxford Lane Nursing Home, Naperville, IL
Oxford Manor Nursing Home, Haverhill, MA
Oxford Manor Nursing Home, Dayton, OH
Oxford Manor Presbyterian Home, Oxford, PA
Oxford Nursing Home, Brooklyn, NY
Oxford View Nursing Center, Oxford, OH
Oxnard Manor Convalescent Hospital, Oxnard, CA
Ozanam Hall of Queens Nursing Home Inc, Bayside, NY
Ozark Care Center, Osage Beach, MO
Ozark Nursing and Care Center, Ozark, MO
Ozark Nursing Center, West Plains, MO
Ozark Nursing Home, Ozark, AR
Ozark Nursing Home, Fredericktown, MO
Ozark Nursing Home Inc, Ozark, AL
Ozarks Methodist Manor, Marionville, MO
P A Peterson Home for the Aging, Rockford, IL
Pacific Care Convalescent Hospital, Oakland, CA
Pacific Convalescent Hospital, Eureka, CA
Pacific Gardens Convalescent Center Inc, Fresno, CA
Pacific Grove Convalescent Hospital, Pacific Grove, CA
Pacific Haven Convalescent Home, Garden Grove, CA
Pacifica Convalescent Hospital, Pacifica, CA
Padgett Nursing Home, Tampa, FL
Paisley House for Aged Women, Youngstown, OH
Pajaro Convalescent Hospital, Watsonville, CA
Pajaro West Convalescent Hospital, Watsonville, CA
Palatine Nursing Home, Palatine Bridge, NY

Palemon Gaskin Memorial Nursing Home, Ocilla, GA
Palestine Nursing Center, Palestine, TX
Palisade Manor, Garretson, SD
Palisade Nursing Home, Palisade, CO
Palisade Nursing Home, Guttenberg, NJ
Palisade Nursing Home Company Inc, Bronx, NY
Pall Mall Nursing Center, Baltimore, MD
Palm Beach Care Nursing Home, Lake Worth, FL
Palm Beach County Home and General Care Facility, West Palm Beach, FL
Palm Gardens Nursing Home, Brooklyn, NY
Palm Grove Convalescent Center, Garden Grove, CA
Palm Haven Convalescent Hospital, Manteca, CA
Palm Manor Nursing Home Inc, Chelmsford, MA
Palm Shores Retirement Center, Saint Petersburg, FL
Palm Springs Healthcare, Palm Springs, CA
Palm Tree Nursing Home, Brooklyn, NY
Palmcrest Medallion Convalescent Hospital, Long Beach, CA
Palmcrest North Convalescent Hospital, Long Beach, CA
Palmer Home Inc, Dover, DE
Palmer House Healthcare Nursing Home, Palmer, MA
Palmer Terrace Nursing Center, Chicago, IL
Palmetto Convalescent Center Inc, Simpsonville, SC
Palmetto Extended Care Facility, Miami, FL
Palms Convalescent Home, Miami, FL
Palms Health Care Center, Sebring, FL
Palmyra Intermediate Care Center, Palmyra, TN
Palmyra Nursing Home, Albany, GA
Palmyra Nursing Home, Palmyra, PA
Palo Duro Convalescent Home Inc, Claude, TX
Palo Pinto Nursing Center, Mineral Wells, TX
Palomar Convalescent Hospital, Inglewood, CA
Palomares Center, Pomona, CA
Palouse Nursing Center, Colfax, WA
Pam Group Home, Puyallup, WA
Pamlico Nursing Center Inc, Washington, NC
Pampa Nursing Center, Pampa, TX
Pamplico Road Residence, Florence, SC
Pana Hawthorne Lodge, Pana, IL
Panama City Developmental Center, Panama City, FL
Panama City Nursing Center, Panama City, FL
Panola Nursing Home, Carthage, TX
Panorama, Bowling Green, KY
Panorama City Convalescent and Rehabilitation Center, Lacy, WA
Panorama Terrace West Convalescent Hospital, Panorama City, CA
Paoli Nursing Home, Paoli, IN
Papillion Manor Inc, Papillion, NE
Paquette Home Inc, Central Falls, RI
Paradise Convalescent Hospital, Los Angeles, CA
Paradise Convalescent Hospital, Paradise, CA
Paradise Hills Convalescent Center, San Diego, CA
Paradise Oaks Quality Care Nursing Center, Cloverdale, OH

Paradise Valley Manor, National City, CA
Paradise Villa Convalescent Center, Moscow, ID
Paradise Village, Medina, OH
Paramount Convalescent Hospital, Paramount, CA
Parc Center Apartments, Saint Petersburg, FL
Parc Cottage, Saint Petersburg, FL
PARC Home, Bellwood, IL
Parent's Volunteer Association, Cleveland, OH
Paris Healthcare Center, Paris, IL
Paris Manor Nursing Center, Paris, TN
Paris Retirement Inn, Paris, AR
Pariseau Nursing Home Inc, Lynn, MA
Park Avenue Baptist Home, Denver, CO
Park Avenue Health Care Home, Herrin, IL
Park Avenue Nursing, Convalescent and Retirement Home, Arlington, MA
Park Avenue Restorative Health Care Center, Bridgeport, CT
Park Central Convalescent Hospital, Fremont, CA
Park Circle Nursing Home, Arlington, MA
Park Dale Rest Home, Boston, MA
Park Forest Care Center, Portland, OR
Park Geriatric Village, Highland Park, MI
Park Haven Care Center Inc, Smithton, IL
Park Haven Nursing Center Inc, Greenville, TX
Park Highlands, Athens, TX
Park Hill Manor Nursing Home, Worcester, MA
Park Imperial Lodge, Lawndale, CA
Park Lane Manor, Altus, OK
Park Lane Manor II, Kansas City, MO
Park Lane Nursing Home, Scott City, KS
Park Lawn Center, Worth, IL
Park Lawn Home, Manitowoc, WI
Park Manor, Park Falls, WI
Park Manor Convalescent Center, Walla Walla, WA
Park Manor Convalescent Home, Waterbury, CT
Park Manor Convalescent Home, Muskegon Heights, MI
Park Manor Nursing Home, Liberty, IN
Park Manor Nursing Home, Bloomfield, NJ
Park Manor Nursing Home, Oklahoma City, OK
Park Manor Nursing Home, Milwaukee, WI
Park Manor Nursing Home Inc, Pepperell, MA
Park Marino Convalescent Center, Pasadena, CA
Park Marion Nursing Center, Brookline, MA
Park Merritt Intermediate Care, Oakland, CA
Park Nursing and Convalescent Center, Saint Louis Park, MN
Park Nursing Center Inc, Taylor, MI
Park Nursing Home, Rockaway Park, NY
Park Nursing Home Inc, Chicago, IL
Park Place Convalescent Hospital, Pomona, CA
Park Place Health Care Center, Great Falls, MT
Park Place Nursing Home, Palestine, TX
Park Plaza Healthcare Center, Saint Louis Park, MN
Park Plaza Nursing Center, San Angelo, TX
Park Plaza Nursing Home, Mart, TX
Park Plaza Nursing Home, Whitney, TX
Park Pleasant Inc, Philadelphia, PA
Park Point Manor, Duluth, MN
Park Rehabilitation Center, Euclid, OH
Park Ridge Care Center, Seattle, WA

Park Ridge Manor, Des Moines, IA
Park Ridge Nursing Home, Rochester, NY
Park Ridge Terrace, Park Ridge, IL
Park River Estates, Coon Rapids, MN
Park River Good Samaritan Center, Park River, ND
Park Rose Care Center, Tacoma, WA
Park Royal Convalescent Center, Portland, OR
Park Royal Medical, Longview, WA
Park Shore, Seattle, WA
Park Strathmoor, Rockford, IL
Park Street Group Home, Houlton, ME
Park Superior Healthcare, Newport Beach, CA
Park Sutter Convalescent Hospital, Sacramento, CA
Park Terrace Convalescent Center, Tulsa, OK
Park View Convalescent Center, Paris, TX
Park View Health Center—Pleasant Acres, Winnebago, WI
Park View Health Center—Rehabilitation Pavilion, Winnebago, WI
Park View Healthcare Inc, Parkersburg, WV
Park View Home, Woodville, WI
Park View Manor, Aroma Park, IL
Park View Manor, Sac City, IA
Park View Manor Inc, Massillon, OH
Park View Nursing Center, San Jose, CA
Park View Nursing Home, Edgerton, OH
Park View Nursing Home, Portland, OR
Park View Nursing Home, Bountiful, UT
Park View Nursing Home Inc, Massapequa, NY
Park Villa, Clyde, KS
Park Vista Convalescent Hospital, Los Angeles, CA
Park Vista Unit—Ohio Presbyterian Home, Youngstown, OH
Park West Care Center, Seattle, WA
Parkdale Manor Care Center, Maryville, MO
Parke County Nursing Home Inc, Rockville, IN
Parker Hill Manor Rest Home, Boston, MA
Parkhill East Nursing Home, Locust Grove, OK
Parkhill North Nursing Home, Salina, OK
Parkhill Skilled Nursing Facility, Chillicothe, IL
Parkhill South Nursing Home, Locust Grove, OK
Parkland Care Center, Tacoma, WA
Parkland Convalescent Hospital Inc, San Leandro, CA
Parkland Health Facility, Wentworth, WI
Parkland Manor, Prague, OK
Park-Lane Convalescent Hospital, Concord, CA
Parklane Nursing Home Inc, Bloomfield, NJ
Parkmont Convalescent Hospital, Fremont, CA
Parkrose Nursing Home, Portland, OR
Park's Memorial Convalescent Center, Auburn, IL
Parkshore Park Nursing Home, Brooklyn, NY
Parkside Care Center, Little Chute, WI
Parkside Convalescent Hospital, San Bernardino, CA
Parkside Gardens, Burbank, IL
Parkside Health Care Inc, Seattle, WA
Parkside Homes Inc, Hillsboro, KS
Parkside House, Lakewood, CO
Parkside Lutheran Home, Lisbon, ND
Parkside Manor, Stuart, NE
Parkside Manor Convalescent Center, Wenatchee, WA

Parkside Meadows Inc, Saint Charles, MO
Parkside Nursing Home, Union Gap, WA
Parkside Rest Home, Amesbury, MA
Parkside Towers, Saint Louis, MO
Parkview Acres Convalescent Center, Dillon, MT
Parkview Care Center, Fairfield, IA
Parkview Care Center, Fremont, OH
Parkview Care Center, Bryant, SD
Parkview Care Center Inc, Milwaukee, WI
Parkview Colonial Manor, O'Fallon, IL
Parkview Convalescent Center, Paducah, KY
Parkview Convalescent Center Inc, Evansville, IN
Parkview Convalescent Centre, Elwood, IN
Parkview Convalescent Hospital, Anaheim, CA
Parkview Convalescent Hospital, Hayward, CA
Parkview Convalescent Unit, Dyersburg, TN
Parkview East Nursing and Convalescent Center, Aurora, IL
Parkview Estate, Garnett, KS
Parkview Gardens Care Center, Waterloo, IA
Parkview Guest Care Center, Winnfield, LA
Parkview Haven, Francesville, IN
Parkview Haven, Coleridge, NE
Parkview Haven, Deshler, NE
Parkview Home, Frankfort, IN
Parkview Home, Wayland, IA
Parkview Home, Belview, MN
Parkview Home, Volga, SD
Parkview Home Inc, Dodge, NE
Parkview Home of Freeport Illinois Inc, Freeport, IL
Parkview Julian Convalescent Hospital, Bakersfield, CA
Parkview Manor, Wellman, IA
Parkview Manor, Macksville, KS
Parkview Manor, Walters, OK
Parkview Manor, Weimar, TX
Parkview Manor Care Center, Woodward, IA
Parkview Manor I, Osborne, KS
Parkview Manor II, Osborne, KS
Parkview Manor Inc, Reinbeck, IA
Parkview Manor Nursing Center, Green Bay, WI
Parkview Manor Nursing Home, Blytheville, AR
Parkview Manor Nursing Home, Indianapolis, IN
Parkview Manor Nursing Home, Ellsworth, MN
Parkview Manor Nursing Home, Kansas City, MO
Parkview Manor Nursing Home, Dayton, OH
Parkview Manor Nursing Home Inc, Denver, CO
Parkview Medical Recovery Center, New Haven, CT
Parkview Nursing Center, Warren, OH
Parkview Nursing Home, Fort Smith, AR
Parkview Nursing Home, West Frankfort, IL
Parkview Nursing Home, Muncie, IN
Parkview Nursing Home, Higginsville, MO
Parkview Nursing Home, Riverdale, NY
Parkview Nursing Home, Providence, RI
Parkview Nursing Home, Waco, TX
Parkview Nursing Home Inc, Shawnee, OK
Parkview Nursing Home Inc, Ripon, WI
Parkview of Texarkana, Texarkana, AR
Parkview Real Convalescent Hospital, Bakersfield, CA

Parkview Skilled of Hope, Hope, AR
Parkview Terrace, Platteville, WI
Parkview Treatment Center, Saint Louis Park, MN
Parkview Village Ltd, Huntsville, AL
Parkway Care Home, Edwardsville, KS
Parkway Manor, Saint Paul, MN
Parkway Manor Nursing Home, Fulton, KY
Parkway Manor Nursing Home, Everett, MA
Parkway Manor Nursing Home, Lubbock, TX
Parkway Medical Center, Louisville, KY
Parkway North Care Center, Battle Ground, WA
Parkway Nursing Center, Beaver Dam, KY
Parkway Nursing Center, Snohomish, WA
Parkway Nursing Home, Pinellas Park, FL
Parkway Nursing Home, Boston, MA
Parkway Pavilion Healthcare, Enfield, CT
Parkway Rest Home Inc, Allentown, PA
Parkway Terrace, Wheaton, IL
Parkwell Nursing Home, Boston, MA
Parkwood Development Center, Valdosta, GA
Parkwood Health Care Center, Chattanooga, TN
Parkwood Health Care Inc, Lebanon, IN
Parkwood Health Facility Inc, Phenix City, AL
Parkwood Nursing Home, Columbus, OH
Parley Vale Rest Home, Boston, MA
Parma Nursing Home Inc, Parma, OH
Parmiter Nursing Home, Malta, OH
The Margaret S Parmly Residence, Chisago City, MN
Parnell Park Nursing Home, Fort Wayne, IN
Parrott's Home, Lynn, IN
Parr's Rest Home, Louisville, KY
Parsons Good Samaritan Center, Parsons, KS
Parsons Presbyterian Manor, Parsons, KS
Pasadena Care Center, Pasadena, TX
Pasadena Care Convalescent Hospital, Pasadena, CA
Pasadena Manor, South Pasadena, FL
Pasco Nursing and Rehabilitation Center, Dade City, FL
Paseo Nursing Home, Kansas City, MO
Paso Robles Convalescent Hospital, Paso Robles, CA
Passavant Health Center, Zellenople, PA
Passport, Rhinelander, WI
Patchogue Nursing Center, Patchogue, NY
Patenaude Rest Home, Derby, VT
PATH Unit, Massillon, OH
Patio Lodge Nursing Home, Baton Rouge, LA
Patrician Nursing Center Inc, North Royalton, OH
Patrick Henry Hospital Inc, Newport News, VA
Patterson Nursing Home, Columbus, OH
Patterson Terrace Care Center, Mesa, AZ
Patterson's Pleasant View Personal Care Home, Shepherdsville, KY
Paul A Dever State School, Taunton, MA
Paulding Medical Nursing, Dallas, GA
Pauline Home for the Aged, Columbus, OH
Pauline Nursing Home, Milwaukee, WI
Pauls Run, Philiadelphia, PA
Pauls Valley Health Care Facility, Pauls Valley, OK
Pavilion North, Peoria, IL
Pavilion Nursing Home, Milwaukee, WI
Pavilion Nursing Homne, McKinney, TX
Pavilion Oaks, Peoria, IL
Pavilion of Highland Park, Highwood, IL
Pavilion South, Peoria, IL

Pavilion West, Peoria, IL
Pawhuska Nursing Home, Pawhuska, OK
Pawnee Care Center, Pawnee, OK
Pawnee Manor Inc, Pawnee City, NE
Pawtucket Institute for Health Services, Pawtucket, RI
Pawtuxet Village Nursing Home Inc, Warwick, RI
Payette Lakes Care Center, McCall, ID
Paynesville Community Hospital, Paynesville, MN
Paynesville Good Samaritan Home, Paynesville, MN
Peabody Home, Franklin, NH
Peabody Manor Inc, Appleton, WI
Peabody Memorial Nursing Home Inc, Peabody, KS
Peace Haven Association, Saint Louis, MO
Peace Memorial Home, Evergreen Park, IL
Peachbelt Intermediate Care Home, Warner Robins, GA
Pearl River County Nursing Home, Poplarville, MS
Pearland Rest Home, Pearland, TX
Pearlview Extended Care and Nursing Home, Akron, OH
Pearlview Nursing Home, Brunswick, OH
Pearsall Manor, Pearsall, TX
Pecan Grove Training Center, Alexandria, LA
Pecan Lane, Florence, SC
Pecan Manor 1, Milledgeville, GA
Pecan Manor 3, Milledgeville, GA
Peck Convalescent Home, Honesdale, PA
Pecos Nursing Home, Pecos, TX
Pecos Valley Nursing Home, Fort Sumner, NM
Pedersen Nursing Home Inc, Seattle, WA
Pedone Nursing Center, Maple Heights, OH
Pekin Convalescent Center, Pekin, IL
Pekrul Manor, Enid, OK
Peleske Group Home, Dent, MN
Pelham House Nursing Home, Newton, MA
Pelham Parkway Nursing Home, Pelham, GA
Pelham Parkway Nursing Home, Bronx, NY
Pelican Lake Nursing Home, Ashby, MN
Pelican Valley Health Center, Pelican Rapids, MN
Pella Community Hospital, Pella, IA
Pellcare, Hickory, NC
Pellcare Corporation, Winston-Salem, NC
Pemberton Manor Inc, Greenwood, MS
Pembilier Nursing Center, Walhalla, ND
Pembina County Memorial Nursing Home, Cavalier, ND
Pembina Trail, Wadena, MN
Pemiscot County Memorial Hospital Long Term Care Unit, Hayti, MO
Pend Oreille Pines, Newport, WA
Pender Care Centre, Pender, NE
Pendleton Nursing Home, Franklin, WV
Penfield Nursing Home, Penfield, NY
Penick Episcopal Home for the Aging, Southern Pines, NC
Peninsula General Nursing Home, Far Rockaway, NY
Peninsula Rehabilitation Center, Lomita, CA
Penn Yan Manor Nursing Home Inc, Penn Yan, NY
Pennhurst Modular Home Community, Spring City, PA
Pennknoll Village Nursing Home, Everett, PA
Pennswood Village, Newtown, PA
Pennsylvania Memorial Home, Brookville, PA
The New Pennsylvania Soldiers' and Sailors' Home, Erie, PA

Penny Pack Manor Nursing Home, Philadelphia, PA
Pennyrile Home, Hopkinsville, KY
Penobscot Nursing Home, Penobscot, ME
Penobscot Valley Nursing Home, Brewer, ME
Pensacola Health Care Facility, Pensacola, FL
Peoples Child Care Residence, Saint Paul, MN
People's Memorial Hospital Nursing Care Center, Independence, IA
Peotone Bensenville Home, Peotone, IL
Pepin Manor Care Center, Pepin, WI
Perdue Medical Center, Miami, FL
Perham Memorial Hospital and Home, Perham, MN
Perkins Convalescent Home, Philadelphia, PA
Perring Parkway Nursing Home Inc, Baltimore, MD
Perry County Hospital and Nursing Home, Marion, AL
Perry County Nursing Center, Perryville, AR
Perry County Nursing Home, Perryville, MO
Perry County Nursing Home, Linden, TN
Perry Green Valley Nursing Center, Perry, OK
Perry Health Facility, Perry, FL
Perry Manor, Perry, IA
Perry Manor Inc, Pinckneyville, IL
Perry Nursing Home, Perry, OK
Perry Ridge Nursing Home Inc, Perry, OH
Perry Village Nursing Home, New Bloomfield, PA
Pershing Convalescent Home Inc, Berwyn, IL
Pershing Estates, Decatur, IL
Pershing General Hospital and Nursing Home, Lovelock, NV
Person County Memorial Hospital, Roxboro, NC
Perth Amboy Nursing Home, Perth Amboy, NJ
Peru Nursing Home, Peru, IN
Petaluma Convalescent Hospital, Petaluma, CA
Peter Becker Community, Harleysville, PA
Peter Pan Nursing Home, Centralia, WA
Petersburg General Hospital, Petersburg, AK
Petersburg Healthcare Center, Petersburg, IN
Petersburg Manor, Petersburg, IL
Peterson Nursing Home, Osage City, KS
Peterson Park Health Care Center, Chicago, IL
Petosky Nursing Center, Petoskey, MI
Pettipaug Manor, Essex, CT
Pettit Childrens Home, Sauk Centre, MN
Pfeiffer's Community Home, West Valley City, UT
Pharmcare—Aldine, Houston, TX
Pharr Nursing Home, Pharr, TX
Pheasant Wood Nursing Home, Peterborough, NH
Phelps Community Medical Center, Phelps, KY
Phenix City Nursing Home, Phenix City, AL
Philadelphia Nursing Home, Philadelphia, PA
Philadelphia Nursing Home, Philadelphia, PA
Philadelphia Protestant Home for the Aging, Philadelphia, PA
Philip Nursing Home, Philip, SD
Phillips County Good Samaritan Retirement Center, Malta, MT
Phillips County Home, Phillipsburg, KS
The Phillips Home, Fayette, MO
Phillips House Nursing Home, Natick, MA
Phillips Manor Nursing Home, Lynn, MA
Phillips Nursing Home, Provo, UT
Phoebe-Devitt Home, Allentown, PA

Phoenix Mountain Nursing Center, Phoenix, AZ
Phoenix Nursing and Convalescent Center—East, Phoenix, AZ
Phoenix Nursing and Convalescent Center—West, Phoenix, AZ
Phoenix Residence, Saint Paul, MN
Phoenixville Convalescent Manor Inc, Phoenixville, PA
Physicians Care Center, Gadsden, AL
Physicians Convalescent Center, Mount Pleasant, TX
Physician's Hospital for Extended Care, Reno, NV
Piatt County Nursing Home, Monticello, IL
Picayune Convalescent Home, Picayune, MS
Pickaway Manor Inc, Circleville, OH
Pickens General Nursing Center, Jasper, GA
Pickering Manor, Newtown, PA
Pickersgill Inc, Towson, MD
Pickett County Nursing Home, Byrdstown, TN
Pickwick Manor Nursing Home, Iuka, MS
Pico Downey Golden Age Convalescent Home, Downey, CA
Piedmont Gardens Health Facility, Oakland, CA
Piedmont Hall, Milledgeville, GA
Piedmont Hospital and Nursing Home, Piedmont, AL
Piedmont Hospital Extended Care Unit, Atlanta, GA
Piedmont Nursing Center, Albemarle, NC
Piedmont Nursing Center Inc, Greenville, SC
Piedmont Residential Developmental Center, Concord, NC
Pierce County Manor, Ellsworth, WI
Pierce County Nursing Home, Blackshear, GA
Pierce Manor, Pierce, NE
Pierce Memorial Baptist Home Inc, Brooklyn, CT
Pierce Nursing Home, Alpena, MI
Pierremont Heritage Manor, Shreveport, LA
Piety Corner Nursing Home, Waltham, MA
Piety Place, Ellsworth, WI
Pigeon Falls Nursing Home, Pigeon Falls, WI
Pike Manor Inc, Troy, AL
Pike Manor Nursing Home, Piketon, OH
Pikes Peak Manor Inc, Colorado Springs, CO
Pikesville Nursing and Convalescent Center, Pikesville, MD
Pilgrim Haven Health Facility, Los Altos, CA
Pilgrim House-at-Peabody Nursing Home, Peabody, MA
Pilgrim Manor, Cromwell, CT
Pilgrim Manor, Grand Rapids, MI
Pilgrim Manor Nursing Home, Plymouth, MA
Pilgrim Manor of Bossier City—North, Bossier City, LA
Pilgrim Manor of Bossier City—South, Bossier City, LA
Pilgrim Manor of Pineville, Pineville, LA
Pilgrim Manor Rehabilitation and Convalescent Center, Plymouth, IN
Pilgrim Place Health Services Center, Claremont, CA
Pilgrims Convalescent Hospital, Artesia, CA
Pilgrim's Pride Nursing Home, Mashpee, MA
Pillars Nursing Home, Springfield, OH
Pillsbury Board and Care Home, Minneapolis, MN
Pimlico Manor, Baltimore, MD
Pin Oaks Adult Care, Mexico, MO
Pina Home for the Aged, Sturgis, SD

Pinal County Nursing Home, Florence, AZ
Pinal General Hospital, Florence, AZ
Pine Acres Nursing Home Inc, Madison, NJ
Pine Acres Retirement Center, De Kalb, IL
Pine Bluff Nursing Home, Pine Bluff, AR
Pine Breeze Convalescent Hospital, Angwin, CA
Pine Circle Community Living Center, Rochester, MN
Pine Creek Center, Palo Alto, CA
Pine Crest Convalescent Hospital, Maywood, CA
Pine Crest Guest Home Inc, Hazlehurst, MS
Pine Crest Haven, Paola, KS
Pine Crest Manor Nursing Home, Bernice, LA
Pine Crest Nursing Home, Morrow, OH
Pine Crest Nursing Home, Nacogdoches, TX
Pine Crest Nursing Home, Merrill, WI
Pine Grove Rest Home, Marlborough, MA
Pine Grove Villa Nursing Home, Millbury, MA
Pine Haven Christian Home, Sheboygan Falls, WI
Pine Haven Convalescent Center, Henderson, NC
Pine Haven Home, Philmont, NY
Pine Haven Nursing Home, Evansville, IN
Pine Haven Nursing Home, Leesville, LA
Pine Haven Nursing Home, Pine Island, MN
Pine Haven Nursing Home, Lufkin, TX
Pine Hill Nursing Home, Birmingham, AL
Pine Hill Rest Home, Lynn, MA
Pine Hill Senior Citizens, Quitman, LA
Pine Hurst Nursing and Convalescent Home, Ligonier, PA
Pine Kirk Nursing Home Inc, Kirkersville, OH
Pine Knoll Convalescent Center, Taylor, MI
Pine Knoll Nursing Home, Carrollton, GA
Pine Knoll Nursing Home, Lexington, MA
Pine Knoll Nursing Home, Lyndonville, VT
Pine Lake ICMRF—Babcock Center, Columbia, SC
Pine Lake Nursing Home, Greenville, FL
Pine Lawn Manor Care Center, Sumner, IL
Pine Lodge Health Care, Beckley, WV
Pine Lodge Nursing Home, Atlanta, TX
Pine Lodge of Warren, Warren, AR
Pine Manor Nursing Center, Palos Hills, IL
Pine Manor Nursing Home, Columbus, GA
Pine Manor Nursing Home, Springfield, MA
Pine Manor Nursing Home Inc, Clintonville, WI
Pine Manor Rest Home, Waterbury, CT
Pine Oaks Nursing Center, Allegan, MI
Pine Point Manor, West Scarborough, ME
Pine Rest Nursing Home, Northampton, MA
Pine Rest Nursing Home, Ridgewood, NJ
Pine Ridge Home 1, Cloquet, MN
Pine Ridge Home 2, Cloquet, MN
Pine Ridge Home 3, Cloquet, MN
Pine Ridge Manor, Waupaca, WI
Pine Ridge Residence, Bagley, MN
Pine River Group Home, Pine River, MN
Pine Rock Farm, Warner, NH
Pine Shadow Retreat, Porter, TX
Pine Street Group Home, Bangor, ME
Pine Towers Convalescent Hospital Inc, San Francisco, CA
Pine Tree Lodge Nursing Center, Longview, TX
Pine Tree Nursing Home, Butler, MO
Pine Tree Villa, Louisville, KY
Pine Valley Manor, Richland Center, WI

Pine Valley Nursing Center, Richfield, OH
Pine View, Black River Falls, WI
Pine View Care Center, Saint Charles, IL
Pine View Good Samaritan Center, Valentine, NE
Pine View Health Care Center, Peshtigo, WI
Pine View Manor Inc, Stanberry, MO
Pine View Nursing and Convalescent Home Inc, Harrisville, WV
Pinebrook Care Center Inc, Englishtown, NJ
Pinecrest Care Center, Gallipolis, OH
Pinecrest Convalescent Home, North Miami, FL
Pinecrest Convalescent Home, Daingerfield, TX
Pinecrest Manor, Mount Morris, IL
Pinecrest Manor, Hopkinsville, KY
Pinecrest Manor Convalescent Home, Cle Elum, WA
Pinecrest Medical Care Facility, Powers, MI
Pinecrest Nursing and Convalescent Home, Sewell, NJ
Pinecrest Nursing Home, Humboldt, KS
Pinecrest State School, Pineville, LA
Pinedale Nursing Home, Newport, AR
Pinehill Rehabilitation Center, Philadelphia, PA
Pinehope Nursing Home, Hope, AR
Pinehurst Convalescent Center Inc, Seattle, WA
Pinehurst Convalescent Facility, Pompano Beach, FL
Pinehurst Nursing Center, Pinehurst, NC
Pinehurst Nursing Home, Centerville, IN
Pinehurst Park Terrace, Seattle, WA
Pineland Center, Pownal, ME
Pineland Nursing Home Inc, Lakewood, NJ
Piners Convalescent Hospital Inc, Napa, CA
Pines Convalescent Center, Williamsburg, VA
Pines Nursing and Convalescent Home, Dillon, SC
Pines Nursing Home, Miami, FL
Pines Nursing Home Inc, Great Barrington, MA
Pineview Intermediate Care Home, Pineview, GA
Pineview Manor, Wexford, PA
Pineview Manor Inc, Beaver, OH
Pineview Nursing Home, Gurdon, AR
Pineview of Hillman, Hillman, MI
Pineview Residence Inc, Saint Paul, MN
Pinevilla Guest Home, Redmond, WA
Pineville Health Care Center, Pineville, KY
Pinewood Acres Nursing Home, Maple Shade, NJ
Pinewood Care Center and Training Center, Coeur d'Alene, ID
Pinewood Convalescent Center, Spartanburg, SC
Pinewood Convalescent Home, Waldron, AR
Pinewood Manor Inc, Hawkinsville, GA
Pinewood Manor Nursing Home, Jasper, TX
Pinewood Terrace Nursing Center, Colville, WA
Pinewood Training Center, Coeur d'Alene, ID
Piney Mountain Home, Fayetteville, PA
Pink Bud Home for the Golden Years Inc, Greenwood, AR
Pinnacle Nursing Home, Rochester, NY
Pioneer Care Center—Wichita Falls, Wichita Falls, TX
Pioneer Center COmunity Living Facility, Wood River, IL
Pioneer Estate, Chandler, OK

Pioneer Health Center, Marceline, MO
Pioneer Home, Fort Collins, CO
Pioneer Home, Fergus Falls, MN
Pioneer Home, Prairie Farm, WI
Pioneer House, Sacramento, CA
Pioneer Lodge, Coldwater, KS
Pioneer Manor, Hugoton, KS
Pioneer Manor, Hay Springs, NE
Pioneer Manor, Frederick, OK
Pioneer Manor, Gillette, WY
Pioneer Memorial, Brigham City, UT
Pioneer Memorial Home, Erskine, MN
Pioneer Memorial Hospital, Heppner, OR
Pioneer Memorial Nursing Home, Viborg, SD
Pioneer Nursing Home, Melbourne, AR
Pioneer Nursing Home, Baudette, MN
Pioneer Nursing Home, Big Timber, MT
Pioneer Nursing Home, Vale, OR
Pioneer Nursing Home of Hughes Inc, Wetumka, OK
Pioneer Place, Evanston, IL
Pioneer Place, Irving, TX
Pioneer Ridge Healthcare, Ferndale, WA
Pioneer Trace Nursing Home, Flemingsburg, KY
Pioneer Valley Manor Rest Home, Greenfield, MA
Pioneer Valley Nursing Home, Northampton, MA
Pioneer Village 1, Topeka, KS
Pioneer Village 2, Topeka, KS
Pioneer Village 3, Topeka, KS
Pioneer Village 4, Topeka, KS
Pioneers Memorial Hospital and Nursing Home, Rocky Ford, CO
Piper Group Home, Fergus Falls, MN
Pipestone County Hospital, Pipestone, MN
Piqua Health Care Center, Piqua, OH
Piqua Manor, Piqua, OH
Pisgah Manor Inc, Candler, NC
Pittsburg Manor Convalescent Hospital, Pittsburg, CA
Pittsburg Nursing Center, Pittsburg, TX
Pittsfield Convalescent Center, Pittsfield, ME
Placerville Pines Convalescent Hospital, Placerville, CA
Placid Memorial Hospital Inc, Lake Placid, NY
Plains Convalescent Center, Plainview, TX
Plains Convalescent Home, Plains, GA
Plainview Manor, Plainview, NE
Plainview Residential Care, Des Moines, IA
Plainville Convalescent Home Inc, Plainville, CT
Plainville Nursing Home, Plainville, MA
Plano Nursing Home, Plano, TX
Plantation Care Center Inc, Salem, OR
Plantation Convalescent Center, Salt Lake City, UT
Plantation Manor, McCalla, AL
Plantation Manor Inc, Atoka, OK
Plantation Nursing Home, Plantation, FL
Plantation Nursing Home, Brownwood, TX
Plantation Plaza, McAlester, OK
Plaquemine Nursing Home, Plaquemine, LA
Plateau Valley Hospital District Nursing Home, Collbran, CO
Platte County Memorial Nursing Home, Wheatland, WY
Platte Nursing Home, Platte, SD
Plattsmouth Manor, Plattsmouth, NE
Playa Del Rey Care Convalescent Hospital, Playa Del Rey, CA

Plaza Care Center, Westminster, CO
Plaza Manor Nursing Home, Glen Burnie, MD
Plaza Nursing and Convalescent Center, Elizabeth, NJ
Plaza Nursing Center, Pascagoula, MS
Plaza Nursing Home, Kansas City, MO
Plaza Nursing Home Company Inc, Syracuse, NY
Pleasant Acres, Everett, WA
Pleasant Acres, New Lisbon, WI
Pleasant Acres Convalescent Hospital, Morgan Hill, CA
Pleasant Acres of Hull, Hull, IA
Pleasant Acres Rest Home, Worcester, MA
Pleasant Care Inc, Pleasantville, IA
Pleasant Dale Home 1, Grand Prairie, TX
Pleasant Dale Nursing Home 2, Grand Prairie, TX
Pleasant Grove Manor, Pleasant Grove, AL
Pleasant Grove Nursing Home, Paris, TX
Pleasant Haven Nursing Home, Nocona, TX
Pleasant Hill Care Center, Saint Paul, MN
Pleasant Hill Convalescent Center, Piketon, OH
Pleasant Hill Health Facility, Fairfield, ME
Pleasant Hill Nursing Home, Oregon, MO
Pleasant Hill Nursing Home, Wichita Falls, TX
Pleasant Hill Village, Girard, IL
Pleasant Living Convalescent Center, Edgewater, MD
Pleasant Manor, Alexandria, LA
Pleasant Manor, Mount Pleasant, MI
Pleasant Manor, Faribault, MN
Pleasant Manor Care Center, Mount Pleasant, IA
Pleasant Manor Nursing and Convalescent Center, Baltimore, MD
Pleasant Manor Nursing Home, Ashdown, AR
Pleasant Manor Nursing Home, Attleboro, MA
Pleasant Manor Nursing Home, Rutland, VT
Pleasant Manor Nursing Home Inc, Sapulpa, OK
Pleasant Manor Nursing Home—Waxahachie, Waxahachie, TX
Pleasant Meadows Cristianvilo, Chrisman, IL
Pleasant Nursing Home, Phillips, WI
Pleasant Park Manor, Oskaloosa, IA
Pleasant Place, Louisville, KY
Pleasant Rest Nursing Home, Collinsville, IL
Pleasant Valley Health Care Center, Muskogee, OK
Pleasant Valley Infirmary, Argyle, NY
Pleasant Valley Intermediate Care Facility, Oxnard, CA
Pleasant Valley Manor, Stroudsburg, PA
Pleasant Valley Manor Care Center, Liberty, MO
Pleasant Valley Manor Inc, Sedan, KS
Pleasant Valley Nursing Center, Springdale, AR
Pleasant Valley Nursing Home Inc, Eugene, OR
Pleasant Valley Rehabilitation and Convalescent Hospital, Oxnard, CA
Pleasant View, Rock Port, MO
Pleasant View Convalescent Home, Northumberland, PA
Pleasant View Convalescent Hospital, Cupertino, CA
Pleasant View Good Samaritan Center, Saint James, MN
Pleasant View Health Care Center, Barberton, OH
Pleasant View Home, Morrison, IL

Pleasant View Home, Albert City, IA
Pleasant View Home, Kalona, IA
Pleasant View Home, Inman, KS
Pleasant View Inc, Whiting, IA
Pleasant View Intermediate Care Facility, Monroe, WI
Pleasant View Lodge, Indianapolis, IN
Pleasant View Lutheran Home, Ottawa, IL
Pleasant View Manor, Reedley, CA
Pleasant View Manor, Huntington, WV
Pleasant View Manor Inc, Pleasanton, KS
Pleasant View Nursing Center, Hiawatha, KS
Pleasant View Nursing Home, Metter, GA
Pleasant View Nursing Home, Huntsville, MO
Pleasant View Nursing Home, Kansas City, MO
Pleasant View Nursing Home, Lisbon, OH
Pleasant View Nursing Home, Corsica, SD
Pleasant View Nursing Home, Monroe, WI
Pleasant View Nursing Home of Mount Airy, Mount Airy, MD
Pleasant View Rest Home, Winchendon, MA
Pleasant View Rest Home, Harrisonville, MO
Pleasant View Rest Home Inc, Manheim, PA
Pleasantview Care Center, Warrensburg, MO
Pleasantview Nursing Home, Parma, OH
Plott Nursing Home, Ontario, CA
Plum Grove Nursing Home, Palatine, IL
Plum Tree Convalescent Hospital, San Jose, CA
Plymouth Harbor Inc, Sarasota, FL
Plymouth House Health Care Center, Norristown, PA
Plymouth Manor Care Center, Lemars, IA
Plymouth Manor Nursing Home, Milwaukee, WI
Plymouth Nursing Home, Plymouth, MA
Plymouth Place, La Grange, IL
Plymouth Square, Stockton, CA
Plymouth Tower, Riverside, CA
Plymouth Village Redlands Convalescent Hospital, Redlands, CA
Pocahontas Continuous Care Center, Marlinton, WV
Pocahontas Manor, Pocahontas, IA
Poet's Seat Nursing Home, Greenfield, MA
Point Loma Convalescent Hospital, San Diego, CA
Point North Nursing Home, Toledo, OH
Point Pleasant Beach Nursing Home, Point Pleasant Beach, NJ
Pointe Coupes Parish Nursing Home, New Roads, LA
Polk City Manor, Polk City, IA
Polk County Nursing Home, Cedartown, GA
Polley's Rest Home Inc, Orange, TX
Polo Continental Manor Inc, Polo, IL
Polyclinic Medical Center Ltc Unit, Harrisburg, PA
Pomeroy Care Center, Pomeroy, IA
Pomeroy Health Care Center, Pomeroy, OH
Pomeroy Hill Nursing Home, Livermore Falls, ME
Pomeroy-Davis-Heartland Memorial Nursing Home, Rainelle, WV
Pomona Golden Age Convalescent Hospital and Nursing Home, Pomona, CA
Pomona Vista Convalescent Hospital, Pomona, CA
Ponca City Nursing Home, Ponca City, OK
Pond Point Skilled Nursing Facility, Milford, CT
Pondera Pioneer Nursing Home, Conrad, MT

Ponderosa, Aurora, CO
Ponderosa Care Center, Mesquite, TX
Ponderosa Villa, Crawford, NE
Pontchartrain Guest House, Mandeville, LA
Pontiac Nursing Center, Pontiac, MI
Pontiac Nursing Home, Oswego, NY
Pontotoc Community Hospital—Extended Care Facility, Pontotoc, MS
Pope County Care Center Inc, Golconda, IL
Pope Nursing Home, Weymouth, MA
Poplar Community Nursing Home, Poplar, MT
Poplar Grove Rest Home Inc, Greenville, KY
Poplar Living Center, Casper, WY
Poplar Manor Nursing Home, Baltimore, MD
Port Allen Care Center, Port Allen, LA
Port Angeles Care Center, Port Angeles, WA
Port Charlotte Care Center, Port Charlotte, FL
Port Chester Nursing Home, Port Chester, NY
Port Jefferson Nursing Home and Health Related Facility, Port Jefferson, NY
Port Manor Nursing Home, Newburyport, MA
Port Mesa Convalescent Hospital, Costa Mesa, CA
Port Orchard Convalescent Center, Port Orchard, WA
Port Royal Community Residence, Port Royal, SC
Port Saint Lucie Convalescent Center, Port Saint Lucie, FL
Portage County Home, Stevens Point, WI
Portage County Nursing Home, Ravenna, OH
Portage Manor, South Bend, IN
Portage Valley Inc, Pemberville, OH
Portage View Hospital, Hancock, MI
Porter Hills Presbyterian Village, Grand Rapids, MI
Porthaven Nursing Home, Portland, OR
Portland Adventist Convalescent Center, Portland, OR
Portland Community Care Center, Portland, IN
Portland Community Care Center—East, Portland, IN
Portland Convalescent Center Inc, Portland, CT
Portland Health Care Facility, Oklahoma City, OK
Portland Residence, Minneapolis, MN
Posada Del Sol Health Care Facility, Tucson, AZ
Poteau Nursing Home, Poteau, OK
Poteet Nursing Home Inc, Poteet, TX
Potomac Center, Hagerstown, MD
Potomac House of Clifton Forge Inc, Clifton Forge, VA
Potomac House of Jane Lew, Jane Lew, WV
Potomac House of Pocotalico, Sissonville, WV
Potomac House of Ronceverte, Ronceverte, WV
Potomac Valley Nursing Home, Rockville, MD
Potrero Hill Convalescent Hospital, San Francisco, CA
Potsdam Nursing Home, Potsdam, NY
Powder River Nursing Home, Broadus, MT
Powellhurst Nursing Home, Portland, OR
Powell's Convalescent Home, Hamilton, OH
Power County Nursing Home, American Falls, ID
Powhatan Nursing Home Inc, Falls Church, VA
Poydras Home, New Orleans, LA
Poydras Manor, Poydras, LA
Prairie Acres, Friona, TX

Prairie City Nursing Center, Prairie City, IL
Prairie Community Nursing Home, Terry, MT
Prairie Convalescent Center, Prairie Du Chien, WI
Prairie Estates, Elk Point, SD
Prairie Good Samaritan Center, Miller, SD
Prairie Haven Inc, Kensington, KS
Prairie Manor, Sharon Springs, KS
Prairie Manor, Blooming Prairie, MN
Prairie Sunset Home, Pretty Prairie, KS
Prairie View Care Center, Woonsocket, SD
Prairie View Home, Sanborn, IA
Prairie View Nursing Home, Limon, CO
Prairie View Nursing Home, Princeton, IL
Prairie View Rest Home Inc, Warsaw, IN
Prairie View Rest Home Inc, Lewistown, MO
Prairie Village Inc, Washington, IN
Prairie Vista Care Center, Holyoke, CO
Prairieview Homes Inc, Underwood, ND
Prairieview Lutheran Home, Danforth, IL
Prather Methodist Memorial Home, Alameda, CA
Praxis, Easton, PA
Prayer Tower Rest Home, New Orleans, LA
Preakness Hospital, Paterson, NJ
Precious Intermediate Care Home, Vidalia, GA
Premont Rest Home Inc, Premont, TX
Presbyterian Home, Evanston, IL
Presbyterian Home at Charlotte Inc, Charlotte, NC
Presbyterian Home—Cambridge Springs, Cambridge Springs, PA
Presbyterian Home for Central New York Inc, New Hartford, NY
Presbyterian Home for the Aged, Philadelphia, PA
Presbyterian Home Inc, Quitman, GA
Presbyterian Home Inc, High Point, NC
Presbyterian Home—Johnstown, Johnstown, PA
Presbyterian Home of Atlantic City—Madison House, Atlantic City, NJ
Presbyterian Home of DC, Washington, DC
Presbyterian Home of Maryland Inc, Towson, MD
Presbyterian Home of South Carolina—Summerville, Summerville, SC
Presbyterian Home of the Synod, Haddonfield, NJ
Presbyterian Home—Titusville, Titusville, PA
Presbyterian Homes, Arden Hills, MN
Presbyterian Homes of Western New York Inc, Jamestown, NY
Presbyterian Homes of Western New York Inc, Jamestown, NY
Presbyterian Lodge, Erie, PA
Presbyterian Manor, Wichita Falls, TX
Presbyterian Manor, Huntington, WV
Presbyterian Manor at Farmington, Farmington, MO
Presbyterian Manor at Rolla, Rolla, MO
Presbyterian Medical Center, Denver, CO
Presbyterian Nursing Home Inc, Ontario, OR
Presbyterian Village, Little Rock, AR
Presbyterian Village, Detroit, MI
Presbyterian Village Inc, Dallas, TX
Presbyterian Village North Nursing Health Service, Dallas, TX
Presbyterian Village of Homer, Homer, LA
Prescott Country View Nursing Home, Prescott, KS
Prescott House Nursing Home, North Andover, MA

Prescott Nursing Center, Prescott, AR
Prescott Samaritan Village, Prescott, AZ
Presidential Convalescent Home Inc, Quincy, MA
Presque Isle Nursing Home Inc, Presque Isle, ME
Preston Care Center, Preston, MN
Presyterian Home at 58th St, Philadelphia, PA
Price Care Center, Price, UT
Price Hill Nursing Home, Cincinnati, OH
Price Memorial, Eureka, MO
Primghar Care Center, Primghar, IA
Primrose Place, Springfield, MO
Primus Mason Manor, Springfield, MA
Prince George's Nursing Care Center, Cheverly, MD
Princeton Care Center Inc, Princeton, MO
Princeton Health Care Center, Princeton, WV
Princeton Health Care Manor Inc, Princeton, KY
Princeton House Rest Home, Lowell, MA
Princeton Nursing Home, Princeton, NJ
ProCare Development Center, Gaston, IN
Proctor J C Endowment Home, Peoria, IL
Professional Care, Troy, IL
Professional Care Home, Hartford, KY
Professional Care Nursing Center Inc, Dale, IN
Profitts Boarding Home, Centerville, IA
Progress Valley II, Richfield, MN
Progressive Living Center, Lufkin, TX
Project Independence Ridgewood, Worthington, MN
Project New Hope 1, Fergus Falls, MN
Project New Hope 2, Fergus Falls, MN
Project New Hope 3, Fergus Falls, MN
Project New Hope 6, Alexandria, MN
Project New Hope 7, Alexandria, MN
Project New Hope Inc, Alexandria, MN
Project New Hope—Starbuck, Starbuck, MN
Project New Hope-Ada 2, Ada, MN
Project New Hope-Ada I, Ada, MN
Project Turnabout, Granite Falls, MN
Promenade Health Care Facility, Auburn, ME
Promenade Nursing Home, Rockaway Park, NY
Prophets Riverview, Prophetstown, IL
Prospect Health Center, Milwaukee, WI
Prospect Hill Home, Keene, NH
Prospect Hill Manor Nursing Home, Somerville, MA
Prospect Hill Nursing Home, Waltham, MA
Prospect Hill Rehabilitation Center, East Windsor, CT
Prospect Lake Nursing Center, Colorado Springs, CO
Prospect Manor, Cleveland, OH
Prospect Nursing Home, North Bennington, VT
Prospect Park Nursing Home, Brooklyn, NY
Prospect Park Nursing Home, Prospect Park, PA
Prospect Street Nursing Home, Cambridge, MA
Protection Valley Manor, Protection, KS
Protestant Bethany Home, New Orleans, LA
Providence Children's Nursing Center, Portland, OR
Providence Convalescent Residence Inc, Charlotte, NC
Providence Health Care, Sparta, GA
Providence Health Care, Thomaston, GA
Providence Health Care, Warrenton, GA
Providence Home, Jasper, IN

Providence House Nursing Home, Worcester, MA
Providence Rest Home, Bronx, NY
Providence Retirement Home, New Albany, IN
Provident House, New Orleans, LA
Provident Nursing Home, Boston, MA
Provincial House, Kalamazoo, MI
Provincial House—Adrian, Adrian, MI
Provincial House—Alpena, Alpena, MI
Provincial House—Battle Creek, Springfield, MI
Provincial House—Cass City, Cass City, MI
Provincial House—East, East Lansing, MI
Provincial House—Gaylord, Gaylord, MI
Provincial House—Hastings, Hastings, MI
Provincial House—Kalamazoo Total Living Center, Kalamazoo, MI
Provincial House—Marshall, Marshall, MI
Provincial House—Midland, Midland, MI
Provincial House of Battle Creek, Battle Creek, MI
Provincial House—Portage, Kalamazoo, MI
Provincial House—Sault Sainte Marie, Sault Sainte Marie, MI
Provincial House—South, Lansing, MI
Provincial House—Total Living Center, Mount Pleasant, MI
Provincial House—Traverse City, Traverse City, MI
Provincial House—West, Lansing, MI
Provincial House—Whitehills, East Lansing, MI
Provinical House—Tawas City, Tawas City, MI
Provo Care, Provo, UT
Pueblo County Board for Developmental Disabilities, Pueblo, CO
Pulaski Health Care Center, Pulaski, TN
Pulaski Health Care Center, Pulaski, VA
Pulaski Nursing Home, Pulaski, GA
Pulley Care Center, South Point, OH
Pulley Nursing Home, South Point, OH
Pullman Convalescent Center, Pullman, WA
Purchell Nursing Home, Purcell, OK
Purple Hills Nursing Home Inc, Bandera, TX
Puryear Nursing Home, Puryear, TN
Putnam Acres Care Center, Ottawa, OH
Putnam County Health Care Center, Hurricane, WV
Putnam County Nursing Home, Unionville, MO
Putnam Memorial Nursing Home, Palatka, FL
Putnam-Weaver Nursing Home, Greenwich, CT
Puyallup Manor Inc, Puyallup, WA
Quaboag Nursing Home, West Brookfield, MA
Quaker Gardens, Stanton, CA
Quaker Heights Nursing Home, Waynesville, OH
Quaker Hill Manor, Baxter Springs, KS
Quaker Villa, Lubbock, TX
Quakertwon Manor Convalescent and Rehabilitation Center, Quakertown, PA
Qualicare Nursing Center, Detroit, MI
Quality Care Health Center, Lebanon, TN
Quality Care Nursing Center, Hot Springs, AR
Quality Care of Waco, Waco, TX
Quality Health Care Center, Urbandale, IA
Quapaw Nursing Home, Quapaw, OK
Quarryville Presbyterian Home, Quarryville, PA
Queen Anne Nursing Home, Hingham, MA

Queen Anne Villa Care Center, Seattle, WA
Queen City Nursing Center, Meridian, MS
Queen City Nursing Home, Cincinnati, OH
Queen of Carmel, Morganville, NJ
Queen of Peace Residence, Queens Village, NY
Queen Treatment Center, Minneapolis, MN
Queen's Convalescent Inc, Middletown, CT
Queens-Nassau Nursing Home, Far Rockaway, NY
Quiet Acres Nursing Home Inc, Washington Court House, OH
Quincy Adams Nursing Home, Brockton, MA
Quincy Convalescent Hospital, Quincy, CA
Quincy Nursing Home, Quincy, MA
Quincy United Methodist Home, Quincy, PA
Quinlan Home, Saint Paul, MN
Quinlan Manor, Sacramento, CA
Quinsippi Long Term Care Facility, Quincy, IL
Quinton Memorial Health Center, Dalton, GA
Quinton Nursing Home Inc, Quinton, OK
Quitman County Nursing Home, Marks, MS
Quitman Nursing Home Inc, Quitman, TX
R N Nursing Home Inc, Bremen, IN
Rach Sovereign Memorial Home, Bay City, MI
Racine Residential Care, Racine, WI
Rae-Ann Geneva, Geneva, OH
Rae-Ann Nursing Center, Cleveland, OH
Rae-Ann Suburban, Westlake, OH
Rafael Convalescent Hospital, San Rafael, CA
Rafferty's Nursing Home, Clinton, OH
Rainbow House, Manitowoc, WI
Rainbow Nursing Center, Bridgeton, NJ
Rainbow Nursing Home, Peabody, MA
Rainbow Nursing Home, Bristow, OK
Rainbow Springs Care Center, Mineral Point, MO
The Raintree, Mansfield, OH
Raintree Convalescent Hospital, Fresno, CA
RAIR Personal Care, Texas City, TX
Raleigh Care Center, Portland, OR
Ralls Nursing Home, Ralls, TX
Ralston House, Philadelphia, PA
Ramapo Manor Nursing Center, Suffern, NY
Rambling Rose Rest Home, Harwich, MA
Ramona Manor Convalescent Hospital, Hemet, CA
Ramsbottom Center Inc, Bradford, PA
Ramsey Memorial Home, Des Moines, IA
Ramsey Nursing Home, Maplewood, MN
Ranch Terrace Nursing Home Inc, Sapulpa, OK
Rancho Los Padres Convalescent Hospital, Norwalk, CA
Ranchwood Lodge Home, Wilburton, OK
Randolph County Nursing Home, Pocahontas, AR
Randolph County Nursing Home, Sparta, IL
Randolph Hills Nursing Home, Wheaton, MD
Randolph Manor, Charlotte, NC
Randolph Nursing Home, Andover, MA
Randolph Nursing Home Inc, Winchester, IN
Range Center, Chisholm, MN
Range Center—Birchwood Home, Eveleth, MN
Range Center—Mapleview, Hibbing, MN
Range Center—Oakwood Home, Chisholm, MN
Ranger Park Inn, Santa Anna, TX
Ranken Jordan Home for Convalescent Crippled Children, Saint Louis, MO
Rapid City Care Center, Rapid City, SD
Rapid City Nursing Center, Rapid City, SD
Rapids Nursing Home, Grand Rapids, OH

Raritan Health and Extended Care Center, Raritan, NJ
Rathbone Memorial Home, Evansville, IN
Rathfons Convalescent Home, Selinsgrove, PA
Ratliff Nursing Home, Cape Girardeau, MO
Ravenna Good Samaritan Home, Ravenna, NE
Ravenwood Health Care Center, Waterloo, IA
Ravenwood Lutheran Village Nursing Home, Hagerstown, MD
Rawlings Nursing Home, Sandersville, GA
Rawlins House Inc, Pendleton, IN
Ray White Care Center, Herrin, IL
Ray White Care Center Inc, Marion, IL
Rayne Guest House, Rayne, LA
Rayville Guest House Inc, Rayville, LA
Reading Nursing Center, West Reading, PA
Reagan's Resident Care Facility, Somerville, MA
Rebold Manor, Okmulgee, OK
Reconstruction Home Inc, Ithaca, NY
The Recuperative Center, Boston, MA
Red Bank Convalescent Center, Red Bank, NJ
Red Bank Medicenter, Red Bank, NJ
Red Bay Nursing Home, Red Bay, AL
Red Bridge Health Care Center, Kansas City, MO
Red Bud Care Center, Red Bud, IL
Red Carpet Health Care Center, Cambridge, OH
Red Haven Nursing Home Inc, Cincinnati, OH
Red Hills Rest Haven, Sumner, IL
Red Oak Good Samaritan Center, Red Oak, IA
Red Oaks Rehabilitation and Convalescent Center, Michigan City, IN
Red River Haven Nursing Home Inc, Bogata, TX
Red Rock Manor Nursing Home Inc, Hinton, OK
Red Wing Group Home, Red Wing, MN
Red Wing Health Center, Red Wing, MN
Redbanks, Henderson, KY
Redbud Retreat, Naples, TX
Redeemer Residence, Minneapolis, MN
Redford Geriatric Village, Detroit, MI
Redman Nursing Home, Omaha, NE
Redmond Health Care Center, Redmond, OR
Redstone Villa, Saint Albans, VT
Redwood Christian Convalescent Hospital, Napa, CA
Redwood Convalescent Hospital, Castro Valley, CA
Redwood Manor, Sesser, IL
Redwood Terrace Lutheran Home, Escondido, CA
The Redwoods, Mill Valley, CA
Reed City Hospital, Reed City, MI
Reeders Memorial Home, Boonsboro, MD
Reedley Convalescent Hospital, Reedley, CA
Reedwood Extended Care Center Corp, Portland, OR
Reelfoot Manor Nursing Home, Tiptonville, TN
Reformed Presbyterian Home for the Aged, Pittsburgh, PA
Refugio Manor, Refugio, TX
Regency Care Center, Norwalk, IA
Regency Care Center, Spokane, WA
Regency Hall Nursing Home Inc, Allison Park, PA
Regency Health Care Center, Eatonton, GA

Regency Health Care Center, Florence, KS
Regency Health Care Center, Hiawatha, KS
Regency Health Care Center, Olathe, KS
Regency Health Care Center, Wichita, KS
Regency Health Care Center, Banner Elk, NC
Regency Health Care Center, Elizabethton, TN
Regency Health Care Center, Monteagle, TN
Regency Health Care Center, Newport, TN
Regency Health Care Center, Red Boiling Springs, TN
Regency Health Care Center, Rogersville, TN
Regency Health Care Center East, Emporia, KS
Regency Health Care Center—Osawatomie, Osawatomie, KS
Regency Health Care of Pittsburg, Pittsburg, KS
Regency House Convalescent Center, McAlester, OK
Regency Manor, Independence, KY
Regency Manor, Chelan, WA
Regency Manor Inc, Saint Paul, MN
Regency Manor Nursing Center, Temple, TX
Regency Nursing and Rehabilitation Treatment Center, Forestville, MD
Regency Nursing Centre Inc, Niles, IL
Regency Oaks, Gainesville, FL
The Regency of Westport, Westport, CT
Regency Park Convalescent Center, Detroit, MI
Regency Park Manor Health Care Center, Tulsa, OK
Regency Place of Greenfield, Greenfield, IN
Regency Rehabilitation Enterprises, Denver, CO
Regency South Care Center, Spokane, WA
Regency Terrace South, Milwaukee, WI
Regent Nursing Home, Boston, MA
Regent Park Nursing and Retirement Home, Brockton, MA
Regina Community Nursing Center, Norristown, PA
Regina Community Nursing Center at Vine Street, Philadelphia, PA
Regina Memorial Hospital, Hastings, MN
Regina Pacis Home, Evansville, IN
Region Park Hall, Faribault, MN
Regional Memorial Hosptial, Brunswick, ME
Regis Multi-Health Center, New Haven, CT
Rego Park Nursing Home, Flushing, NY
Reisch Memorial Nursing Home, Carrollton, IL
REM Beltrami, Bemidji, MN
REM Bloomington, Bloomington, MN
REM Fairmont 8, Fairmont, MN
REM II A and B, Canby, MN
REM Lyndale, Minneapolis, MN
REM Marshall A, B, C, Marshall, MN
REM Minnetonka, Minnetonka, MN
REM Pillsbury, Minneapolis, MN
REM Pleasant, Minneapolis, MN
REM Rochester NW, Rochester, MN
REM Roseau, Roseau, MN
REM Saint Cloud, Saint Cloud, MN
REM Southeast, Minneapolis, MN
REM-Fairmont Inc, Fairmont, MN
Remington Boarding Home, Chariton, IA
Remington Street House, Fort Collins, CO
REM-Mankato Inc, Mankato, MN
REM-Montevideo Inc, Montevideo, MN
REM-Redwood Falls Inc, Redwood Falls, MN
REM-Taylor, Tyler, MN
REM-Waite Park, Waite Park, MN

Renaissance Continuing Care, Detroit, MI
Renaissance House, Chicago, IL
Rendezvous Medi-Home, McDermott, OH
Renfro Nursing Home—Waxahachie, Waxahachie, TX
Rennes Health Center, Peshtigo, WI
Rennie Memorial Nursing Home, Evanston, WY
Reno Avenue Convalescent Hospital, Modesto, CA
Reno Convalescent Center, Reno, NV
Reno's Rest Home, Springfield, MA
Renotta Nursing Home, Wray, CO
Rensselaer Care Center, Rensselaer, IN
Renton Terrace Nursing Center, Renton, WA
Ren-Villa, Renville, MN
Resa On Eden Prarie Rd, Minnetonka, MN
Reseda Arms Convalescent Hospital, Reseda, CA
Reservoir Manor, Shelbyville, IL
Reservoir Nursing Home Inc, Waltham, MA
Residence I, Shoreview, MN
Residence II, Shoreview, MN
Residence III, Saint Paul, MN
Resident Homes-Harmony, Faribault, MN
Resident Homes-Haven, Faribault, MN
Residential Alternatives 1, Buffalo, MN
Residential Alternatives I, Buffalo, MN
Residential Alternatives II, Brooklyn Center, MN
Residential Alternatives III, Brooklyn Park, MN
Residential Alternatives IV, Robbinsdale, MN
Residential Alternatives VI, Cambridge, MN
Residential ALternatives VIII, Robbinsdale, MN
Residential Options Inc Group Home, Columbus, OH
Residential Services of Northeast Minnesota I, Duluth, MN
Residential Services of Northeastern Minnesota II, Duluth, MN
Resort Health Related Facility, Arverne, NY
Resort Lodge Inc, Mineral Wells, TX
Resort Nursing Home, Arverne, NY
Rest Awhile Nursing Home, Moultrie, GA
Rest Harbor Nursing Home, Gresham, OR
Rest Haven, Flat River, MO
Rest Haven, Dayton, OH
Rest Haven—Clarkston, Clarkston, WA
Rest Haven Convalescent and Retirement Home, Sedalia, MO
Rest Haven Convalescent Home, Broomall, PA
Rest Haven Health Care Center, Verona, WI
Rest Haven Homes, Grand Rapids, MI
Rest Haven Illiana Christian Convalescent Home, Palos Heights, IL
Rest Haven Manor Inc, Albion, IL
Rest Haven Manor Nursing Center, Cando, ND
Rest Haven Nursing Center, Fayette, MO
Rest Haven Nursing Home, Bogalusa, LA
Rest Haven Nursing Home, Medford, MA
Rest Haven Nursing Home, Ripley, MS
Rest Haven Nursing Home, Monett, MO
Rest Haven Nursing Home, Fayetteville, NC
Rest Haven Nursing Home, McDermott, OH
Rest Haven Nursing Home, Cushing, OK
Rest Haven Nursing Home, Picher, OK
Rest Haven Nursing Home, Tulsa, OK
Rest Haven Nursing Home, El Paso, TX
Rest Haven Nursing Home, Olympia, WA
Rest Haven Nursing Home Inc, Greenville, OH

Rest Haven Nursing Home Inc, Grafton, WV
Rest Haven Rest Home, Adams, MA
Rest Haven Schuylkill County Home, Schuylkill Haven, PA
Rest Haven South Nursing Home, South Holland, IL
Rest Haven West Nursing Home, Downers Grove, IL
Rest Haven—Whitemarsh, Philadelphia, PA
Rest Haven York, York, PA
Rest Well Rest Home Inc, Burrillville, RI
Restful Acres Nursing Home Inc, Waynesboro, MS
Restful Acres Nursing Home Inc, Kenedy, TX
Resthaven, Independence, MO
Resthaven, Columbus, OH
Resthaven Corporation, Boston, MA
Resthaven Geriatric Center, Greenville, SC
Resthaven Health Care Center, Bremerton, WA
Resthaven Home, Morrison, IL
Resthaven Intermediate Care Home, Buchanan, GA
Resthaven Manor Nursing Home Inc, Toledo, OH
Resthaven Nursing Center, Lake Charles, LA
Resthaven Nursing Home, Patten, ME
Resthaven Nursing Home, Barnstable, MA
Resthaven Nursing Home, Braintree, MA
Resthaven Nursing Home, Memphis, TN
Resthaven Nursing Home Inc, Jonesport, ME
Resthaven Nursing Home—Tacoma, Tacoma, WA
Restle Home, Portage, OH
Restorative Care Center, Seattle, WA
Restview Nursing Home, Cincinnati, OH
Resurrection Nursing Pavilion, Park Ridge, IL
Resurrection Rest Home, Castleton-on-Hudson, NY
Retama Manor, Kingsville, TX
Retama Manor—East, Cuero, TX
Retama Manor—North, San Antonio, TX
Retama Manor Nursing Center, Alice, TX
Retama Manor Nursing Center, Brownsville, TX
Retama Manor Nursing Center, Edinburg, TX
Retama Manor Nursing Center, Falfurrias, TX
Retama Manor Nursing Center, McAllen, TX
Retama Manor Nursing Center, Port Lavaca, TX
Retama Manor Nursing Center, Raymondville, TX
Retama Manor Nursing Center, Rio Grande City, TX
Retama Manor Nursing Center—Cuero, Cuero, TX
Retama Manor Nursing Center—Del Rio, Del Rio, TX
Retama Manor Nursing Center—Eagle Pass, Eagle Pass, TX
Retama Manor Nursing Center—East, Laredo, TX
Retama Manor Nursing Center—Harlingen, Harlingen, TX
Retama Manor Nursing Center Inc, Jourdanton, TX
Retama Manor Nursing Center—North, Corpus Christi, TX
Retama Manor Nursing Center—North, Pleasanton, TX
Retama Manor Nursing Center—North, Victoria, TX
Retama Manor Nursing Center—Robstown, Robstown, TX

Retama Manor Nursing Center—South, Laredo, TX
Retama Manor Nursing Center—South, Pleasanton, TX
Retama Manor Nursing Center—South, San Antonio, TX
Retama Manor Nursing Center—Weslaco, Weslaco, TX
Retama Manor Nursing Center—West, Corpus Christi, TX
Retama Manor Nursing Center—West, Laredo, TX
Retama Manor Nursing Center—West, San Antonio, TX
Retama Manor Nursing Center—West, Victoria, TX
Retama Manor—South, Victoria, TX
Retirement Acres, Altamont, KS
Retirement and Nursing Center, Austin, TX
Retirement and Nursing Center, Corpus Christi, TX
Retirement Center of Wright County, Buffalo, MN
Retirement Ranch of Clovis, Clovis, NM
The Retreat, Monticello, GA
Revere Home, Revere, MN
Revmont Nursing Home, West Union, OH
Reynold's Boarding Home, Bridgeville, DE
Reynolds Nursing Home Inc, Adena, OH
RGR Sanitarium, Los Angeles, CA
Rhea County Nursing Home, Dayton, TN
Rheem Valley Convalescent Hospital, Rheem, CA
Rhode Island Streetnursing Home Company Inc, Buffalo, NY
Rice Lake Convalescent Center, Rice Lake, WI
Rice Springs Care Home Inc, Haskell, TX
Riceville Community Rest Home, Riceville, IA
Rich Mountain Manor, Mena, AR
Richard B Russell Building, Milledgeville, GA
Richardson Manor Care Center, Richardson, TX
Richardson Nursing Home, Norfolk, VA
Richardson Rest Home Inc, North Adams, MA
Richboro Care Center, Richboro, PA
Richey Manor Nursing Home, New Port Richey, FL
Richfield Care Center, Richfield, UT
Richfield Outreach Group Home, Richfield, MN
Richland Convalescent Center, Columbia, SC
Richland Hills Nursing Home, Fort Worth, TX
Richland Homes Inc, Sidney, MT
Richland Manor Nursing Home, Bluffton, OH
Richland Nursing Home, Delhi, LA
Richland Street Community Residence, Aiken, SC
Richland Street Community Residence, Columbia, SC
Richmond Manor Nursing Home Inc, Bristol, VA
Richmond Nursing Home, Richmond, IN
Richmond Nursing Home, Richmond, VA
Richmond's Boarding Home, Jackson, MS
Richton Crossing Convalescent Center, Richton Park, IL
Richview, Richfield, MN
Richwoods Terrace, Peoria, IL
Ridge Convalescent Center, Lake Wales, FL
Ridge Crest Adult Care Center, Warrensburg, MO
Ridge Crest Convalescent Home, Feasterville, PA

Ridge Road Residence, Greenville, SC
Ridge View Nursing Center, De Pere, WI
Ridgecrest Convalescent Center, Ridgeland, SC
Ridgecrest Manor, Deland, FL
Ridgecrest Manor Nursing Home, Duffield, VA
Ridgecrest Nursing Home, West Monroe, LA
Ridgecrest Retirement Village, Davenport, IA
Ridgedale Nursing Center, South Bend, IN
Ridgefield Health Care, Ridgefield, WA
Ridgeland Nursing Home Inc, Palos
    Heights, IL
Ridgemont Terrace Inc, Port Orchard, WA
Ridgetop Haven Inc, Ridgetop, TN
Ridgeview Care Center, Oblong, IL
Ridgeview Health Care Center Inc, Jasper, AL
Ridgeview House Inc, Evanston, IL
Ridgeview Lodge Nursing Home,
    DeQueen, AR
Ridgeview Manor, Kalamazoo, MI
Ridgeview Manor Nursing Home, Malden,
    MO
Ridgeview Nursing and Convalescent Center,
    Wichita Falls, TX
Ridgeview Nursing Home, Covington, KY
Ridgeview Pavilion, Evanston, IL
Ridgeview Rest Home Inc, Cromwell, CT
Ridgeview Terrace Convalescent and Nursing
    Center, Rutledge, TN
Ridgeway Manor, Owingsville, KY
Ridgeway Manor Nursing Home, Catonsville,
    MD
Ridgeway Nursing Home, Sullivan, MO
Ridgewood Care Center Inc, Ottumwa, IA
Ridgewood Central Inc—Health Care Facility,
    Middletown, CT
Ridgewood Court Nursing Home, Attleboro,
    MA
Ridgewood Health Care Center, Milan, TN
Ridgewood Health Care Center Inc,
    Jasper, AL
Ridgewood Health Care Facility Inc,
    Southington, CT
Ridgewood Manor, Dalton, GA
Ridgewood Manor, Fort Worth, TX
Ridgewood Nursing Center Inc, Youngstown,
    OH
Ridgewood Nursing Home, Ridgewood, NJ
Ridgewood Nursing Home, Springfield, OH
Ridgway Manor Inc, Ridgway, IL
Beth Rifka Nursing Home, Staten Island, NY
Rikard Nursing Home—Rikard Convalescent
    Bldg, Lexington, SC
Rikard Nursing Homes—Keisler and Holstedt
    Bldgs, Lexington, SC
Riley Health Care Facility Inc,
    Indianapolis, IN
Riley Nursing Home, Fresno, CA
Riley's Oak Hill Manor Inc, North Little
    Rock, AR
Riley's Oak Hill Manor South, Little
    Rock, AR
Rinaldi Convalescent Hospital, Granada
    Hills, CA
Ring Nursing Home—Ridgewood, Springfield,
    MA
Ring Nursing Home—South, Springfield, MA
Ringling Nursing Home, Ringling, OK
Rio Hondo Convalescent Hospital,
    Montebello, CA
Rio Rancho Health Care Center, Rio Rancho,
    NM
Rio-Sol Nursing Home, Mansura, LA
Ripley Manor Nursing Home, Ripley, MS

Ripley Road Nursing Home Inc, Cohasset, MA
Rising Star Nursing Center, Rising Star, TX
Rising Sun Nursing Home, Rising Sun, IN
Rita's Rest Home, Mystic, CT
Rita's Rest Home, New Bedford, MA
Rittenhouse Care Center, Philadelphia, PA
Ritter Healthcare Center, Indianapolis, IN
Rittman Health Care Center, Rittman, OH
Rivard Nursing Home, Saint Johns, MI
River Crest Center—Mont Clare, Mont Clare,
    PA
River Falls Area Hospital—Kinnic Home
    Division, River Falls, WI
River Falls Care Center, River Falls, WI
River Forest Nursing Care, Three Rivers, MI
River Garden Hebrew Home for the Aged,
    Jacksonville, FL
River Glen Continuing Care Center,
    Southbury, CT
River Heights Nursing Home, Tampa, FL
River Heights Retirement Center Inc,
    Boonville, MO
River Hills Care Center, Ottumwa, IA
River Hills in Keokuk, Keokuk, IA
River Hills Nursing Home—East, Milwaukee,
    WI
River Hills Nursing Home—South,
    Milwaukee, WI
River Hills Nursing Home—West, Pewaukee,
    WI
River Manor, Brooklyn, NY
River Mede Manor, Binghamton, NY
River Oaks, Steele, MO
River Oaks Health Care Center, Lake City,
    MN
River Park Nursing Home, South Bend, IN
River Pines Community Health Center,
    Stevens Point, WI
River Terrace Healthcare Nursing Home,
    Lancaster, MA
River Valley House, Lowell, MA
River Valley Rest Home, Northampton, MA
River View Manor Home, Hannibal, MO
River Walk Manor, Salisbury, MD
Riverbend Manor Inc, South Bend, IN
Riverbend Nursing Home, Grand Blanc, MI
Riverbluff Convalescent Hospital,
    Riverbank, CA
Riverbluff Nursing Home, Rockford, IL
Rivercrest Convalescent Home, Spokane, WA
Rivercrest Long Term Care Facility, Concord,
    MA
Rivercrest Manor, Pierre, SD
Riverdale Gardens Nursing Home, West
    Springfield, MA
Riverdale Manor, Markesan, WI
Riverdale Manor, Muscoda, WI
Riverdale Nursing Home, Bronx, NY
Riverfront Manor Inc, Tiffin, OH
Riverfront Terrace Healthcare Facility,
    Paducah, KY
Rivergate Convalescent Center, Riverview, MI
The Rivergate Terrace—Intermediate Care
    Facility, Riverview, MI
Riverhead Nursing Home, Riverhead, NY
Riveridge Manor, Niles, MI
Riverlands Health Care Center, Lutcher, LA
Rivermont Convalescent and Nursing Center,
    South Pittsburg, TN
Rivershores Nursing Home, Marseilles, IL
Riverside Board and Care Home, McIntosh,
    MN
Riverside Care Center, Miami, FL

Riverside Center Inc, South Bend, IN
Riverside Convalescent Home, Toledo, OH
Riverside Convalescent Hospital, Chico, CA
Riverside Convalescent Hospital, North
    Hollywood, CA
Riverside Convalescent Hospital,
    Sacramento, CA
Riverside Cottage Rest Home, Bakersfield, CA
Riverside Foundation, Mundelein, IL
Riverside/Four Seasons Health Care Center,
    Fort Collins, CO
Riverside Guest Care Center, Natchitoches, LA
Riverside Health Care Center, East
    Hartford, CT
Riverside Health Care Center, Danville, VA
Riverside Hospital, Columbus, OH
Riverside Hospital for Skilled Care, Reno, NV
Riverside Manor, Ames, IA
Riverside Manor, Battle Creek, MI
Riverside Manor, San Angelo, TX
Riverside Manor Nursing and Rehabilitation
    Center, Newcomerstown, OH
Riverside Medical of Covington,
    Covington, GA
Riverside Medical Services of Thomaston,
    Thomaston, GA
Riverside Nursing and Convalescent Center
    Inc, Saint Albans, WV
Riverside Nursing Cneter, Milledgeville, GA
Riverside Nursing Home, Waycross, GA
Riverside Nursing Home, Boston, MA
Riverside Nursing Home, Grand Haven, MI
Riverside Nursing Home, Haverstraw, NY
Riverside Nursing Home, East Providence, RI
Riverside Nursing Home, Oconto, WI
Riverside Nursing Home Inc, Monroe, LA
Riverside Nursing Home Inc, Jenks, OK
Riverside of Macon, Macon, GA
Riverside Terrace Nursing Center Inc,
    Rockford, IL
Riverton Heights Convalescent Home, Seattle,
    WA
Riverview Care Center Inc, Fort Wayne, IN
Riverview Care Center Inc, Guttenberg, IA
Riverview Convalescent Home, Muncie, IN
Riverview Estates Inc, Marquette, KS
Riverview Health Center, Kaukauna, WI
Riverview Heights Nursing Home, Waverly,
    MO
Riverview Home, Cincinnati, OH
Riverview Homes, Ashland, KY
Riverview Hospital, Crookston, MN
Riverview House, Claymont, DE
Riverview Lutheran Memorial Medical Center,
    Spokane, WA
Riverview Manor, Morrilton, AR
Riverview Manor, Des Moines, IA
Riverview Manor, Prestonsburg, KY
Riverview Manor, Wanamingo, MN
Riverview Manor, Flandreau, SD
Riverview Manor, Wisconsin Rapids, WI
Riverview Manor Inc, Oxford, KS
Riverview Manor Nursing Home, Marion, IN
Riverview Manor Nursing Home, Pleasant
    Valley, IA
Riverview Manor Nursing Home, Sainte
    Genevieve, MO
Riverview Manor Nursing Home, Owego, NY
Riverview Nursing Center, Mokane, MO
Riverview Nursing Centre, Essex, MD
Riverview Nursing Home, Rome, GA
Riverview Nursing Home, Boston, MA
Riverview Nursing Home, Minneapolis, MN

Riverview Nursing Home, Steubenville, OH
Riverview Nursing Home, Vermillion, OH
Riverview Nursing Home Inc, Howland, ME
Riverview Nursing Home Inc, Coventry, RI
Riverview Nursing Home Inc, Rich Creek, VA
Riverview Rest Home Inc, New Haven, CT
Riverview Terrace, Tomahawk, WI
Riverways Manor Nursing Home, Van Buren, MO
Riverwood Care Center, Puyallup, WA
Riverwood Convalescent Home, Arkadelphia, AR
Riviera Manor Inc, Chicago Heights, IL
Riviera Nursing and Convalescent Home Inc, Pico Rivera, CA
RN Nursing Convalescent Home Inc, El Paso, TX
Roanoke City Nursing Home, Roanoke, VA
Roanoke Manor Nursing Home, Kansas City, MO
Roanoke Valley Nursing Home Inc, Rich Square, NC
Robbin House Convalescent Home, Quincy, MA
Robert and Clara Milton Home Inc, South Bend, IN
Robert Appleton Nursing Home, Everett, MA
Robert Koch Hospital, Saint Louis, MO
Roberta Intermediate Care Home, Roberta, GA
Roberts Health Centre Inc, North Kingstown, RI
Roberts Memorial Nursing Home, Morton, TX
Roberts Nursing Home, Napa, CA
Robertson County Health Care Center, Springfield, TN
Robings Manor, Oak Lawn, IL
Robinson Development Center, Mc Kees Rocks, PA
Robinson Health Care Facility, Gardiner, ME
Robinson Home, Pasadena, CA
Robinson Nursing Home and Development Center, Robinson, TX
Robinwood II Rest Home, Boston, MA
Robinwood Rest Home, Toledo, OH
Robison Jewish Home, Portland, OR
Robison Nursing Home, Dayton, WA
Rochelle Manor, Rochelle, IL
Rochelle Nursing and Rehabilitation Center, Rochelle, IL
Rochester Friendly Home, Rochester, NY
Rochester Health Care Center, Rochester, MN
Rochester Manor, Rochester, NH
Rochester Nursing Home, Rochester, IN
Rochester State Hospital, Rochester, MN
Rochester United Methodist Home, Rochester, NY
Rock County Health Care Center, Janesville, WI
Rock Falls Manor, Rock Falls, IL
The Rock Haven Nursing Home, Nacogdoches, TX
Rock Hill Convalescent Center, Rock Hill, SC
Rock Hill Rest Home, Rock Hill, MO
Rock Island Convalescent Center, Rock Island, IL
Rock Island County Health Care Center, Rock Island, IL
Rock Rapids Health Centre, Rock Rapids, IA
Rock View Good Samaritan Center, Parshall, ND
Rockaway Care Center, Edgemere, NY

Rockcastle County Hospital—Skilled Nursing Facility, Mount Vernon, KY
Rockdale Nursing Home, Rockdale, TX
Rockford Manor, Shively, KY
Rockford Manor Inc, Rockford, IL
Rockhaven Sanitarium, Verdugo City, CA
Rockhill Care Center, Kansas City, MO
Rockhill Mennonite Home, Sellersville, PA
Rockingham County Nursing Home, Epping, NH
Rockingham Nursing Center, Madison, NC
Rockland Convalescent Center, Rockland, ME
Rockland County Infirmary, Pomana, NY
Rockland Nursing Home, Rockland, MA
Rockledge Manor Nursing Home, Nahant, MA
Rockmart Intermediate Care Center, Rockmart, GA
Rockridge—Laurel Park, Northampton, MA
Rockville Memorial Nursing Home, Rockville, CT
Rockville Nursing Center Inc, Rockville Centre, NY
Rockville Nursing Home Inc, Rockville, MD
Rockville Residence Manor, Rockville Centre, NY
Rockwall Nursing Home, Rockwall, TX
Rockwell Community Nursing Home, Rockwell, IA
Rockwood Health Care Center, Rockwood, TN
Rockwood Manor Infirmary, Spokane, WA
Rockwood Manor Nursing Home Inc, Wellston, MO
Rocky Bay Health Care, Wauna, WA
Rocky Bay Health Care Center, Gig Harbor, WA
Rocky Knoll Health Care Facility, Plymouth, WI
Rocky Mountain Health Care Center, Denver, CO
Rockynol Retirement Community, Akron, OH
Rodger Rest Home, Boston, MA
Rodgerson House, Boston, MA
Roe-Seal Memorial Home, Lexington, IN
Rofay Nursing Home, Bronx, NY
Roger Huntington Nursing Center, Greer, SC
Rogers City Hospital Long-Term Care Unit, Rogers City, MI
Rogers Nursing Center, Rogers, AR
Rogers Nursing Home Inc, Saint Louis, MO
Rogers Park Manor Nursing Home, Chicago, IL
Rogue Valley Care Center, Medford, OR
Rogue Valley Manor, Medford, OR
Rohr Home, Bartow, FL
Rohrig's Nursing Home 1, Uhrichsville, OH
Ro-Ker Nursing Home, Alliance, OH
Rol-Ann Rest Home, New Bedford, MA
Rolfe Care Center, Rolfe, IA
Rolla Community Hospital—Nursing Facility, Rolla, ND
Rolla Manor Care Center, Rolla, MO
Rolling Acres Care Center, North Lima, OH
Rolling Acres Nursing Home, Florence, AL
Rolling Acres Retirement Center Inc, Raleigh, MS
Rolling Fields Nursing Home Inc, Conneautville, PA
Rolling Hills, Sparta, WI
Rolling Hills Convalescent Center Inc, Anderson, IN
Rolling Hills Estates, Branson, MO
Rolling Hills Manor, Zion, IL

Rolling Hills Nursing Center, Starkville, MS
Rolling Meadows, Fond Du Lac, WI
Rollins Nursing Home, Cabot, AR
Roma Memorial Nursing Home, Three Rivers, TX
Roman Eagle Memorial Home Inc, Danville, VA
Ro-Mel Guest Manor Inc, Helena, OK
Rome-Murphy Memorial Hospital—Skilled Nursing Facility Nursing Facility, Rome, NY
Romeo Nursing Center, Romeo, MI
Rome-Parkway Inc, Rome, NY
Romie Lane Convalescent Hospital, Salinas, CA
Ron Joy Nursing Home, Boardman, OH
Roncalli Health Center Inc, Bridgeport, CT
Rondale Nursing and Convalescent Home, Erie, PA
Rooks County Home, Plainville, KS
Roo-Lan Healthcare Center, Lacy, WA
Roosevelt General Hospital—Intermediate Care Facility, Portales, NM
Roosevelt Memorial Nursing Home, Culbertson, MT
Roosevelt Square, Batavia, IL
Roosevelt Square, Rockford, IL
Roosevelt Square, Sandwich, IL
Roosevelt Square, Springfield, IL
Roosevelt Square—Murphysboro, Murphysboro, IL
Roosevelt Square Princeton, Princeton, IL
Roosevelt Square—Silvis, Silvis, IL
Root Valley Fair Lodge, Colorado City, TX
Rosa Coplon Jewish Home and Infirmary, Buffalo, NY
Rosalie Nursing Home, Wisner, LA
Rosary Hill Convalescent Center, Oak Lawn, IL
Rosary Hill Home, Justice, IL
Roscoe Community Nursing Home Co Inc, Roscoe, NY
Roscoe Nursing Home, Roscoe, TX
Rose Anna Hughes Presbyterian Home, Louisville, KY
Rose Arbor Nursing Home, Sterling, CO
Rose Blumkin Jewish Home, Omaha, NE
Rose Care Center of Benton, Benton, AR
Rose Care Center of Fort Smith, Fort Smith, AR
Rose Care Center of Jonesboro, Jonesboro, AR
Rose Care Center of Stuttgart, Stuttgart, AR
Rose City Nursing Home, Portland, OR
Rose Cottage Health Care Center, Central Falls, RI
Rose Crest Nursing Home, Santa Cruz. CA
Rose Garden Nursing Home, Mount Vernon, OH
Rose Haven, Roseburg, OR
Rose Haven Health Care Center, Hugo, OK
Rose Haven Nursing Home Inc, Marengo, IA
Rose Haven of Kaufman Inc, Kaufman, TX
Rose Haven Retreat Inc, Atlanta, TX
Rose Hawthorne Lathrop Home, Fall River, MA
Rose Hill Convalescent Center, Terrell, TX
Rose Hill Nursing Home, Berryville, VA
Rose Hill Nursing Home Inc, Festus, MO
Rose Lane Health Center, Massillon, OH
Rose Lane Nursing Home, Loup City, NE
Rose Lawn Geriatric Center, Alliance, OH
Rose Lawn ICF/MR, West Lafayette, OH
Rose Lawn Manor Home, Spencerville, OH

Rose Manor, Waterbury, CT
Rose Manor Health Care, Birmingham, AL
Rose Manor Intermediate Care Facility, Lexington, KY
Rose-Mary, The Grasselli Rehabilitation and Education Center, Euclid, OH
Rose Mary's Home, Denver, CO
Rose Nursing Home, Cleveland Heights, OH
Rose of Sharon Manor, Roseville, MN
Rose Park Convalescent and Rehabilitation Center, Cleveland, OH
Rose Skillcare Nursing Center, Jonesboro, AR
Rose Terrace Lodge, Nicholasville, KY
Rose Villa Inc, Milwaukie, OR
Rose Villa Nursing Center, Roseville, MI
Rose Vista Home Inc, Woodbine, IA
Rose Vista Nursing Center, Vancouver, WA
Roseau County Nursing Center, Roseau, MN
Rosebud Community Nursing Home, Forsyth, MT
Rosebud Nursing Home, Gregory, SD
Rosedale, Owensboro, KY
Rosedale Manor, Covington, KY
Rosedale Nursing Home, Silex, MO
Rosedale Restorium, Saint Petersburg, FL
Rose-Haven, Litchfield, CT
Rosehaven Skilled Nursing Home, Thomasville, GA
Roselawn Manor, Lansing, MI
Roselawn Manor Rest Home, Worcester, MA
Roselawn Retirement Home, New Albany, MS
Rosemont Manor, Rosemont, PA
Rosemont Nursing and Convalescent Center, Fairhope, AL
Rosemont Nursing Home, Mansfield, OH
Roseview Nursing Center, Shreveport, LA
Roseville Convalescent Hospital, Roseville, CA
Roseville Manor, Milwaukee, WI
Roseville Nursing Home, Milwaukee, WI
Rosewood Center, Owings Mills, MD
Rosewood Convalescent Center, Gwynn, VA
Rosewood Convalescent Hospital, Pleasant Hill, CA
Rosewood Gardens Health Related Facility, Rensselaer, NY
Rosewood Haven Nursing Home, Jacksonville, FL
Rosewood Health Facility, Bakersfield, CA
Rosewood Manor, Estherville, IA
Rosewood Manor, Galion, OH
Rosewood Manor, Spokane, WA
Rosewood Manor Ltd, Norman, OK
Rosewood Manor Rest Home, Fall River, MA
Rosewood Medical Nursing Center, Byromville, GA
Rosewood Nursing Center, Memphis, TN
Rosewood Nursing Home, Lake Charles, LA
Rosewood Nursing Home, West Allis, WI
Rosewood Rest Home, Claymont, DE
Rosewood Skilled Nursing Facility—Hudspeth Center, Whitfield, MS
Rosewood Terrace, Salt Lake City, UT
Rosewood-Damen Nursing Home Inc, Chicago, IL
Rosholt Nursing Home, Rosholt, SD
Roslyn Convalescent Home, Roslyn, PA
Ross Care Center, Merrillville, IN
Ross Manor Nursing Home, Ridley Park, PA
Ross Nursing Home, East Liverpool, OH
Ross Nursing Home 1 Inc, Wagoner, OK
Ross Nursing Home 2 Inc, Wagoner, OK
Ross Nursing Home Inc, Brentwood, NY

Rosser Nursing Home, Roanoke, AL
Rossmoor Manor, Walnut Creek, CA
Rossville Convalescent Center Inc, Rossville, GA
Rossville Valley Manor, Rossville, KS
Ross-Worthen Home, Waltham, MA
Rotan Nursing Center, Rotan, TX
Rotary Ann Home Inc, Eagle Grove, IA
Rotunda Retirement and Convalescent Facility, Gatesville, TX
Roubals Nursing Home, Stephenson, MI
Roundup Memorial Nursing Home, Roundup, MT
Rouse Warren County Home, Youngsville, PA
Routt Memorial Hospital—Extended Care Facility, Steamboat Springs, CO
Rowan Court, Barre, VT
Rowan Manor Inc, Salisbury, NC
Rowland, Covina, CA
Rowley Memorial Masonic Home, Perry, IA
Roxboro Nursing Center, Roxboro, NC
Roxbury Home for Aged Women, Roslindale, MA
Royal Care Convalescent Center, Centralia, WA
Royal Care of Erin Inc, Erin, TN
Royal Care of Jackson Inc, Jackson, TN
Royal Care of Lawrenceburg, Lawrenceburg, TN
Royal Care Skilled Nursing Facility, Long Beach, CA
Royal Convalescent Hospital Inc, Brawley, CA
Royal Crest Convalescent and Rest Home, Meriden, CT
Royal Elaine Intermediate Care Facility, LaGrange, GA
Royal Elm Inc, Elmwood Park, IL
Royal Fontana Nursing Center Inc, Urbana, IL
Royal Glades Convalescent Home, North Miami Beach, FL
Royal Grove Convalescent Hospital, Orange, CA
Royal Home, El Cajon, CA
Royal Manor, Nicholasville, KY
Royal Manor Convalescent Hospital Inc, Sacramento, CA
Royal Manor Inc, Missoula, MT
Royal Manor Inc, Warwick, RI
Royal Megansett Nursing Home, Falmouth, MA
Royal Neighbor Home, Davenport, IA
Royal Nursing Center, Highland Park, MI
Royal Nursing Home, Mesa, AZ
Royal Oak Nursing Resort, Dade City, FL
Royal Oaks, Madison, NJ
Royal Oaks Convalescent Hospital, Galt, CA
Royal Palm Convalescent Center, Vero Beach, FL
Royal Pavilion Extended Care Facility, Steubenville, OH
Royal Terrace, McHenry, IL
Royal Villa Care Center Inc, New Lebanon, OH
Royal Vista Care Center, Ellensburg, WA
Royal Willows Nursing Care Center, Wilmington, IL
Royale Convalescent Hospital, Santa Ana, CA
Royale Gardens Health Care Facility, Grants Pass, OR
Royale Oaks Convalescent Hospital, Glendale, CA
Royalwood Convalescent Hospital, Torrance, CA
Royce Manor, Sarcoxie, MO

Rubins Brierwood Terrace, Los Angeles, CA
Ruby Hill Nursing Home Inc, Bessemer, AL
Ruby Mountains Manor, Elko, NV
Ruby's Rest Home, Middlesboro, KY
Ruidoso Care Center, Ruidoso, NM
Ruleville Health Care Center, Ruleville, MS
Rural Health Care Facility, Indianapolis, IN
Rush County Nursing Home, LaCrosse, KS
Rush Nursing Center, Butler, AL
Rusk County Memorial Hospital Nursing Home, Ladysmith, WI
Rusk Nursing Home Inc, Rusk, TX
Russell Convalescent Home, Russell, KY
Russell Kare Center, Russell, KS
Russell Nursing Home, Winder, GA
Russell Nursing Home, Albany, OH
Russell Park Manor, Lewiston, ME
Russell Retirement Home, Charleston, MO
Russellville Health Care Manor, Russellville, KY
Russellville Nursing Home, Russellville, AR
The Rust Home, Eaton, OH
Rustic Manor Ltd, Kansas City, MO
Ruston State School, Ruston, LA
Ruth Taylor Geriatric Rehabilitation Institute, Hawthorne, NY
Rutherford County Convalescent Center, Rutherfordton, NC
Rutherford County Nursing Home, Murfreesboro, TN
Rutherford Nursing Center Inc, Rutherfordton, NC
Rutland Heights Hospital—Skilled Nursing Facility, Rutland, MA
Rutland Nursing Home Co Inc, Brooklyn, NY
Rutledge Avenue Community Residence, Charleston, SC
Rutledge Manor Care Home Inc, Springfield, IL
Ryan Nursing Home, Amherst, VA
Ryan Nursing Home Inc, Ryan, OK
Rydal Park of Philadelphia Presbyterian Home on the Fairway, Rydal, PA
Mary Ryder Home for the Aged, Saint Louis, MO
Mary Ryder Homes for the Aged, Saint Louis, MO
Ryder Memorial Skilled Nursing Facility, Humacao, PR
Sabetha Manor Inc, Sabetha, KS
Sabine Oaks Home, Beaumont, TX
Sable Care Center Inc, Aurora, CO
Sacco River Health Care Center, Biddeford, ME
Sacramento Convalescent Hospital, Sacramento, CA
Sacred Heart Free Home, Philadelphia, PA
Sacred Heart Home, Chicago, IL
Sacred Heart Home, Avilla, IN
Sacred Heart Home, Louisville, KY
Sacred Heart Home, Hyattsville, MD
Sacred Heart Home, Bronx, NY
Sacred Heart Home for the Aged, Phoenix, AZ
Sacred Heart Home Inc, Plattsburgh, NY
Sacred Heart Hospice, Austin, MN
Sacred Heart Manor, Philadelphia, PA
Sacred Heart Nursing Home, New Bedford, MA
Sacred Heart Residence, Mobile, AL
Saddle Brook Convalescent Home, Saddle Brook, NJ
Sadie G Mays Memorial Nursing Home, Atlanta, GA

Sage Healthcare Center, Midland, TX
Sage Nursing Home, Milwaukee, WI
Sager Nursing Home, Fair Haven, VT
Saginaw Community Hospital, Saginaw, MI
Saginaw Geriatric Home, Saginaw, MI
Sahara House, Princeton, MN
The Sailors' Snug Harbor, Sea Level, NC
Saint Agnes Health Care Center, Chicago, IL
Saint Agnes Home, Kirkwood, MO
Saint Aloisius Skilled Nursing Home, Harvey,
   ND
Saint Andre Health Care Facility, Biddeford,
   ME
Saint Andrew Home for the Aged, Niles, IL
Saint Andrews Estates Medical Center, Boca
   Raton, FL
Saint Andrew's Nursing Home, Bottineau, ND
Saint Ann Home, Dover, NH
Saint Ann Skilled Nursing Center, Sandusky,
   OH
Saint Anna's Asylum, New Orleans, LA
Saint Anne Home, Fort Wayne, IN
Saint Anne Home for the Elderly, Greensburg,
   PA
Saint Annes Convalescent Home, Detroit, MI
Saint Annes Convalescent Hospital, Castro
   Valley, CA
Saint Annes Home, San Francisco, CA
Saint Anne's Home, Columbia, PA
Saint Anne's Home for the Elderly, Milwaukee,
   WI
Saint Annes Hospice Inc, Winona, MN
Saint Ann's Convalescent Home, Arabi, LA
Saint Anns Healthcare Center Inc, Chester, IL
Saint Ann's Home, Hammond, IN
Saint Ann's Home, Grand Rapids, MI
Saint Ann's Home, Oklahoma City, OK
Saint Ann's Home for the Aged, Rochester, NY
Saint Ann's Nursing Home, Juneau, AK
Saint Ann's Nursing Home, Toledo, OH
Saint Ann's Nursing Home, Panhandle, TX
Saint Anns Residence, Minneapolis, MN
Saint Ann's Rest Home, Milwaukee, WI
Saint Ansgar Good Samaritan, Saint
   Ansgar, IA
Saint Anthony Center, Houston, TX
Saint Anthony Health Center, Saint Anthony
   Village, MN
Saint Anthony Home Inc, Crown Point, IN
Saint Anthony Nursing Center, Warren, MI
Saint Anthony Nursing Home, Carroll, IA
Saint Anthonys Continuing Care Center, Rock
   Island, IL
Saint Anthony's Medical Center—Anthony
   House, Saint Louis, MO
Saint Anthony's Nursing Home, Metairie, LA
Saint Augustine Center for Living, Saint
   Augustine, FL
Saint Augustine Geriatric Center, Saint
   Augustine, FL
Saint Augustine Home for the Aged,
   Indianapolis, IN
Saint Augustine Manor, Cleveland, OH
Saint Barbara's Memorial Nursing Home,
   Monongahelia, WV
Saint Barnabas Inc, Gibsonia, PA
Saint Barnabas Nursing Home, Chattanooga,
   TN
Saint Benedict Home for Aged, Niles, IL
Saint Benedict Nursing Home, Detroit, MI
Saint Benedict Nursing Home, San Antonio,
   TX
Saint Benedicts Center, Saint Cloud, MN

Saint Benedict's Long Term Care Unit,
   Jerome, ID
Saint Cabrini Nursing Home Inc, Dobbs Ferry,
   NY
Saint Camillus Health Center, Wauwatosa, WI
Saint Camillus Nursing Home Company Inc,
   Syracuse, NY
Saint Casimir Health Care Facility, Lewiston,
   ME
Saint Catherine Laboure Manor,
   Jacksonville, FL
Saint Catherine's Infirmary, Racine, WI
Saint Catherine's Residence and Nursing
   Center, North Bend, OR
Saint Charles Health Care Center, Saint
   Charles, MO
Saint Charles Nursing Home, Covington, KY
Saint Charles Nursing Home, Newellton, LA
Saint Christopher Convalescent Hospital,
   Hayward, CA
Saint Christopher Convalescent Hospital and
   Sanitarium, Signal Hill, CA
Saint Clair County Medical Center, Goodells,
   MI
Saint Clair County Special Living Center,
   Belleville, IL
Saint Clara's Manor, Lincoln, IL
Saint Clare Convalescent Center, Detroit, MI
Saint Clare Health Care Facility, Colorado
   Springs, CO
Saint Clare Manor, Lockport, NY
Saint Clare's Home, Newport, RI
Saint Cloud Health Care Center, Saint
   Cloud, FL
Saint Cloud Manor, Saint Cloud, MN
Saint Coletta Alverno Cottage, Jefferson, WI
Saint Croix Health Center, New Richmond,
   WI
Saint Croix Valley Good Samaritan Center,
   Saint Croix Falls, WI
St Dominic's Nursing Home, Houston, TX
Saint Edna Convalescent Center, Santa
   Ana, CA
Saint Edward Home, Akron, OH
Saint Elizabeth Convalescent Hospital,
   Anaheim, CA
Saint Elizabeth Health Care Center, East
   Hartford, CT
Saint Elizabeth Home, Saint Cloud, MN
Saint Elizabeth Home, Providence, RI
Saint Elizabeth Hospital Nursing Home,
   Wabasha, MN
Saint Elizabeth Manor Inc, Saint Elizabeth,
   MO
Saint Elizabeth Nursing Home, Baker, OR
Saint Elizabeth Nursing Home, Waco, TX
Saint Elizabeth Nursing Home, Brookfield, WI
Saint Elizabeth Toluca Convalescent Hospital,
   North Hollywood, CA
Saint Elizabeth's Nursing Home, Janesville, WI
Saint Erne Sanitarium, Inglewood, CA
Saint Frances Home, Fond Du Lac, WI
Saint Francis Continuation Center,
   Burlington, IA
Saint Francis Convalescent Home, Bellingham,
   WA
Saint Francis Convalescent Pavilion Inc, Daly
   City, CA
Saint Francis Country Home, Darby, PA
Saint Francis Gardens, Albuquerque, NM
Saint Francis Heights Convalescent Hospital,
   Daly City, CA
Saint Francis Home, Worcester, MA

Saint Francis Home, Saginaw, MI
Saint Francis Home, Waite Park, MN
Saint Francis Home, Laconia, NH
Saint Francis Home, La Crosse, WI
Saint Francis Home for the Aged, Tiffin, OH
Saint Francis Home Inc, Superior, WI
Saint Francis Home of Williamsville,
   Williamsville, NY
Saint Francis Hopital—SNF/ICF Care Facility,
   Marceline, MO
Saint Francis Hospital—Skilled Nursing Unit,
   Honolulu, HI
Saint Francis Hospital Skilled Nursing Unit,
   Memphis, TN
Saint Francis Manor Inc, Grinnell, IA
Saint Francis Nursing Home, San Antonio, TX
Saint Francis Rehabilitation Hospital and
   Nursing Home, Green Springs, OH
Saint George Care Center, Saint George, UT
St George Health Care Center Inc, Saint
   George, SC
Saint George Nursing Home, Eden, NY
Saint Gerard's Nursing Home, Hankinson, ND
Saint Ignatius Nursing Home, Philadelphia, PA
Saint James House of Baytown, Baytown, TX
Saint James Nursing Center, Greensboro, NC
Saint James Nursing Home, Saint James, NY
Saint Joan Antida Home, West Allis, WI
Saint John Lutheran Home, Springfield, MN
Saint John Neumann Nursing Home,
   Philadelphia, PA
Saint John of God Nursing Hospital, Los
   Angeles, CA
Saint John of Kronstadt Nursing Home, Castro
   Valley, CA
Saint John Rest Home, Victoria, KS
Saint John Rest Home, Brockton, MA
Saint Johnland Nursing Home Inc, Kings Park,
   NY
Saint John's Center, Kearney, NE
Saint John's Center, Springfield, OH
Saint Johns Convalescent Unit, Valencia
   Borough, PA
Saint Johns County Senior Citizens Home,
   Saint Augustine, FL
Saint Johns Episcopal Homes for the Aged and
   the Blind, Brooklyn, NY
Saint Johns Health Center, New Haven, CT
Saint John's Home for the Aged,
   Evansville, IN
Saint John's Home of Milwaukee, Milwaukee,
   WI
Saint John's Hospital—Nursing Wing,
   Jackson, WY
Saint Johns Lutheran Home, Albert Lea, MN
Saint John's Lutheran Home, Billings, MT
Saint Johns Lutheran Home, Mars, PA
Saint Johns Nursing and Rehabilitation Center,
   Lauderdale Lakes, FL
Saint John's Nursing Home, San Antonio, TX
Saint John's Nursing Home Inc, Rochester,
   NY
Saint John's Nursing Home Inc, Lynchburg,
   VA
St John's of Hays, Hays, KS
Saint Johnsbury Convalescent Center, Saint
   Johnsbury, VT
Saint Joseph Care Center, Spokane, WA
Saint Joseph Convalescent Center, Saint
   Joseph, MO
Saint Joseph Convalescent Center, Polson, MT
St Joseph Convalescent Hospital Inc, Castro
   Valley, CA

Saint Joseph Gerontology Center, Alliance, NE
Saint Joseph Home, Kansas City, KS
Saint Joseph Home for the Aged, Freeport, IL
Saint Joseph Home for the Aged, Pittsburgh, PA
Saint Joseph Home of Chicago Inc, Chicago, IL
Saint Joseph Home of Peoria, Peoria, IL
Saint Joseph Home of Springfield, Springfield, IL
Saint Joseph Hospice Home for the Aged, Louisville, OH
St Joseph Infant Home, Cincinnati, OH
Saint Joseph Manor, Florence, CO
Saint Joseph Manor, Brockton, MA
Saint Joseph Nursing Home, Lacon, IL
Saint Joseph Nursing Home, Upper Frenchville, ME
Saint Joseph Nursing Home, Hamtramck, MI
Saint Joseph Nursing Home, Arcadia, WI
Saint Joseph Nursing Home Co of Utica Inc, Utica, NY
Saint Joseph of the Pines Hospital, Southern Pines, NC
Saint Joseph Residence, New London, WI
Saint Joseph Villa, Salt Lake City, UT
Saint Josephs Center, Scranton, PA
Saint Josephs Convalescent Hospital, Ojai, CA
Saint Joseph's Hill Infirmary Inc, Eureka, MO
Saint Joseph's Home, Brinkley, AR
Saint Joseph's Home, Saint Charles, MO
Saint Josephs Home, Ogdensburg, NY
Saint Joseph's Home, Kenosha, WI
Saint Joseph's Home for Infirm and Aged, Monroe, LA
Saint Josephs Home for the Aged, Detroit, MI
Saint Joseph's Home for the Aged, Jefferson City, MO
Saint Joseph's Home for the Aged, Holland, PA
Saint Joseph's Home for the Aged, West Allis, WI
Saint Joseph's Home for the Elderly, Palatine, IL
Saint Joseph's Hospital and Nursing Home of Del Norte Inc, Del Norte, CO
Saint Josephs Hospital Nursing Home, Yonkers, NY
Saint Josephs Hospital—Skilled Nursing Facility, Elmira, NY
Saint Joseph's Manor, Trumbull, CT
Saint Joseph's Manor, Portland, ME
Saint Joseph's Manor, Boston, MA
Saint Josephs Manor, Olean, NY
Saint Josephs Manor, Meadowbrook, PA
Saint Joseph's Medical Center—Esther Pariseau Pavilion, Burbank, CA
Saint Joseph's Nursing Home, Catonsville, MD
Saint Joseph's Nursing Home, Norfolk, NE
Saint Joseph's Nursing Home, Hillsboro, WI
Saint Joseph's Nursing Home, La Crosse, WI
Saint Joseph's Residence, Enfield, CT
Saint Joseph's Residence, Dallas, TX
Saint Joseph's Villa, David City, NE
Saint Josephs Villa, Flourtown, PA
Saint Jude Convalescent Center, Livonia, MI
Saint Jude Convalescent Home, Hudson, MA
Saint Jude Manor Nursing Home, Jacksonville, FL
Saint Jude's Home Inc, Sandy, OR
Saint Lawrence Diamondale Center, Dimondale, MI
Saint Lawrence Nursing Home, Cincinnati, OH

Saint Louis Altenheim, Saint Louis, MO
Saint Louis County Medical Care Facility, Duluth, MN
Saint Louis Developmental Disabilities Treatment Center, Saint Louis, MO
Saint Louis Good Shepherd Homes Inc, Saint Louis, MO
Saint Louis State School and Hospital, Saint Louis, MO
Saint Lucan Convalescent Center, Faribault, MN
St Lucas Convalescent and Geriatric Care, Faribault, MN
Saint Luke Community Nursing Home, Ronan, MT
Saint Luke Convalescent Center, Columbus, OH
Saint Luke Lutheran Home, Spencer, IA
Saint Luke Manor, Fortuna, CA
Saint Luke Manor, Hazelton, PA
Saint Luke Manor of Batavia, Batavia, NY
Saint Luke Nursing Home Company Inc, Oswego, NY
Saint Lukes Episcopal Home, Highland Park, MI
Saint Luke's Extended Care Hospital & Nursing Centre, San Leandro, CA
Saint Luke's Good Samaritan Village, Kearney, NE
Saint Lukes Home, Springfield, MA
Saint Lukes Lutheran Home, Blue Earth, MN
Saint Lukes Lutheran Home for the Aging, North Canton, OH
Saint Lukes Memorial Hospital Center—Allen Calder Skilled Nursing Facility, Utica, NY
Saint Luke's Methodist Hospital, Cedar Rapids, IA
Saint Luke's Nursing Center, Carthage, MO
Saint Lukes Nursing Home, Birmingham, AL
Saint Lukes Presbyterian Nursing Center, Buffalo, NY
Saint Margaret Hall, Cincinnati, OH
Saint Margaret of Cortona Home, Lexington, KY
Saint Margaret's Daughters' Home, New Orleans, LA
Saint Margarets House and Hospital for Babies, Albany, NY
St Mark Village Inc, Palm Harbor, FL
Saint Marks Lutheran Home, Austin, MN
Saint Martha Manor, Chicago, IL
Saint Martin Deporres Nursing Home, Detroit, MI
Saint Martins-in-the-Pines, Birmingham, AL
Saint Martinville Guest House, Saint Martinville, LA
Saint Mary Home, West Hartford, CT
Saint Mary Nursing Home, Saint Clair Shores, MI
Saint Mary Square Living Center Inc, Freeport, IL
Saint Mary Square Living Center of Chicago, Chicago, IL
Saint Mary's Convalescent Center, Saint Mary's, GA
Saint Mary's Guest Home, Morgan City, LA
Saint Marys Home, Saint Paul, MN
Saint Mary's Home for the Aged, Manitowoc, WI
Saint Marys Home of Erie, Erie, PA
Saint Marys Hospital for Children Inc, Bayside, NY
Saint Mary's Hospital—Long Term Care Unit, Norton, VA

Saint Marys Hospital—Nursing Home, Winsted, MN
Saint Mary's Infant Home Inc, Norfolk, VA
Saint Marys Manor, Saint Marys, KS
Saint Mary's Manor, Niagara Falls, NY
Saint Marys Manor, Lansdale, PA
Saint Mary's Memorial Home, Glendale, OH
Saint Marys Nursing Center, Detroit Lakes, MN
Saint Mary's Nursing Home, Leonardtown, MD
Saint Mary's Nursing Home, Milwaukee, WI
Saint Mary's Nursing Home, Sparta, WI
Saint Mary's Training School, Alexandria, LA
St Mary's Villa, Elmhurst, PA
Saint Marys Villa Nursing Home, Picrz, MN
Saint Matthew Lutheran Home, Park Ridge, IL
Saint Matthews Manor, Louisville, KY
Saint Michael Convalescent Hospital, Hayward, CA
Saint Michael's Evangelical Lutheran Home, Fountain City, WI
Saint Michaels Hospital and Nursing Home, Sauk Centre, MN
Saint Michael's Nursing Home, Tyndall, SD
Saint Monica's Home, Roxbury, MA
Saint Olafs Residence, Minneapolis, MN
Saint Ottos Home, Little Falls, MN
Saint Patricks Home for the Aged and Infirm, Bronx, NY
Saint Patricks Manor, Framingham, MA
Saint Patrick's Residence, Joliet, IL
Saint Paul Baptist Church Home for the Aged, Indianapolis, IN
Saint Paul Health Center, Denver, CO
Saint Paul Hermitage, Beech Grove, IN
Saint Paul Home, Kaukauna, WI
Saint Paul Homes, Greenville, PA
Saint Pauls Church Home Inc, Saint Paul, MN
Saint Pauls Home, Belleville, IL
Saint Pauls House, Chicago, IL
St Paul's Retirement Community, South Bend, IN
Saint Peter State Hospital, Saint Peter, MN
Saint Peter Villa, Memphis, TN
Saint Peters Manor Care Center, Saint Peters, MO
Saint Petersburg Cluster, Saint Petersburg, FL
Saint Raphaels Home for the Aged, Columbus, OH
Saint Regis Nursing Home, Massena, NY
Saint Richard's Villa Inc, Muenster, TX
Saint Rita's Home for the Aged Inc, Columbus, OH
Saint Roses Home, New York, NY
Saint Simeon's Episcopal Home Inc, Tulsa, OK
Saint Sophia Geriatric Center, Florissant, MO
Saint Stanislaus Medical Care Center, Nanticoke, PA
Saint Stephen Group Home, Bloomington, MN
Saint Teresa's Manor, Manchester, NH
Saint Teresas Nursing Home Inc, Middleton, NY
Saint Theresa Convalescent Hospital, Pico Rivera, CA
Saint Theresa Home, Cincinnati, OH
Saint Theresa's Nursing Home, Toledo, OH
Saint Therese Convalescent Hospital Inc, Hayward, CA
Saint Therese Home, New Hope, MN
Saint Thomas Convalescent Center, Houston, TX

Saint Thomas More Hospital and Progressive Care Center, Canon City, CO
Saint Vincent Community Living Facility, Forest Park, IL
Saint Vincent dePaul Nursing Home, Berlin, NH
St Vincent's Nursing Home, Montclair, NJ
Saint Vincent's Nursing Home, Bismarck, ND
Saint Williams Home for Aged, Milbank, SD
Saint Williams Nursing Home, Parkers Prairie, MN
Saint's Nursing Home, Oklahoma City, OK
Salamanca Nursing Home Inc, Salamanca, NY
Salem Convalescent Center, Salem, OH
Salem County Nursing and Convalescent Home, Salem, NJ
Salem Health Care Center, Salem, WV
Salem Hills Health Related Facility, Purdys Station, NY
Salem Home, Fredericktown, OH
Salem Lutheran Home, Elk Horn, IA
Salem Lutheran Home Skilled Nursing Facility, Oakland, CA
Salem Manor, Indianola, IA
Salem Mennonite Home for the Aged, Freeman, SD
Salem Nursing Home, Salem, KY
Salem Park Nursing Home, Cincinnati, OH
Salem Village, Joliet, IL
Salemhaven, Salem, NH
Salina Nursing Center, Salina, KS
Salina Presbyterian Manor, Salina, KS
Saline Care Center, Harrisburg, IL
Saline County Rest Home Inc, Marshall, MO
Salisbury Nursing Home, Salisbury, MD
Salisbury Nursing Home, Worcester, MA
Salmi Boarding Home, Aurora, MN
Salmon Brook Convalescent Home, Glastonbury, CT
Salsbury Baptist Home, Charles City, IA
Salt Lake DD Center, Salt Lake City, UT
Salt River Nursing Home, Shelbina, MO
Saluda Home, Saluda, VA
Saluda Nursing and Convalescent Center, Saluda, NC
Saluda Nursing Center, Saluda, SC
Salvation Army Adult Day Care Center, Newport, KY
Salyer Nursing Home Inc, Centerburg, OH
Salyersville Health Care Center, Salyersville, KY
Samaritan Bethany Home, Rochester, MN
Samaritan Home, West Bend, WI
Samaritan Home Inc, Topeka, KS
Samaritan Lodge, Lawrence, KS
Samaritan-Keep Nursing Home Inc, Watertown, NY
Samarkand Convalescent Hospital, Santa Barbara, CA
Samuel Mahelona Memorial Hospital, Kapaa, HI
Samuel Marcus Nursing and Retirement Home, Weymouth, MA
San Andreas Convalescent Hospital, San Andreas, CA
San Angelo Development Center, San Angelo, TX
San Antonio Convalescent Center, San Antonio, TX
San Antonio Professional Care Facility, Kenton, OH
San Augustine Nursing Center, San Augustine, TX

San Bruno Convalescent Hospital, San Bruno, CA
San Diego Convalescent Hospital, La Mesa, CA
San Diego Hebrew Home for the Aged, San Diego, CA
San Diego Intermediate Care Center, San Diego, CA
San Dimas Golden Age Convalescent Home, Glendora, CA
San Fillipe Rest Home, Malden, MA
San Francisco Community Convalescent Hospital, San Francisco, CA
San Francisco Convalescent Center, San Francisco, CA
San Gabriel Convalescent Center, Rosemead, CA
San Jacinto Heritage Manor, Deer Park, TX
San Joaquin Gardens Health Facility, Fresno, CA
San Jose Care and Guidance Center, San Jose, CA
San Juan County Nursing Home, Blanding, UT
San Juan Gardens, Phoenix, AZ
San Juan Living Center, Montrose, CO
San Juan Manor, Farmington, NM
San Juan Nursing Home, Anacortes, WA
San Juan Nursing Home Inc, San Juan, TX
San Leandro Convalescent Hospital, San Leandro, CA
San Luis Convalescent Hospital, Newman, CA
San Luis Manor, Green Bay, WI
San Marco Convalescent Hospital, Walnut Creek, CA
San Marino Manor, San Gabriel, CA
San Mateo Convalescent Hospital, San Mateo, CA
San Pedro Manor, San Antonio, TX
San Saba Nursing Home Inc, San Saba, TX
San Simeon by the Sound —Skilled Nursing Facility, Greenport, NY
San Tomas Convalescent Hospital, San Jose, CA
Sandalwood Convalescent Home, Oxford, MA
Sandalwood Healthcare Centre, Wheaton, IL
Sande Convalescent Home, Big Sandy, MT
Sandhaven Convalescent Center, Sandwich, IL
Sandhaven Nursing Home, Lamar, CO
Sandmont Gala Nursing Home, Trenton, GA
Sandpiper Convalescent Center, Mount Pleasant, SC
Sandpoint Manor, Sandpoint, ID
Sands Point Nursing Home, Port Washington, NY
Sandstone Area Nursing Home, Sandstone, MN
Sandstone Heights, Little River, KS
Sandstrom Home Intermediate Care Facility, Myrtle Beach, SC
Sandusky Nursing Home Inc, Sandusky, OH
Sandy Creek Nursing Center, Wayland, MI
Sandy Park Rehabilitation Center, Fort Myers, FL
Sandy River Nursing Care Center, Farmington, ME
Sanfield Manor Inc, Hartland, ME
Sanford Nursing and Convalescent Center Inc, Sanford, FL
Sanford Nursing Home, Sanford, ME
Sanford Nursing Home, Farmington, MN
Sanford Nursing Home, Itasca, TX
Sanger Convalescent Hospital, Sanger, CA

Sanibel Convalescent Home, Middletown, CT
Sanilac Medical Care Facility, Sandusky, MI
Sansbury Memorial Infirmary, Saint Catherine, KY
Santa Anita Convalescent Hospital, Temple City, CA
Santa Barbara Convalescent Hospital, Santa Barbara, CA
Santa Fe Convalescent Hospital, Long Beach, CA
Santa Fe Trail Nursing Center, Burlingame, KS
Santa Marie Nursing Home, Green Bay, WI
Santa Monica Care Convalescent Hospital, Santa Monica, CA
Santa Monica Convalarium, Santa Monica, CA
Santa Monica Lodge, Santa Monica, CA
Santa Monica Lodge—Unit 2, Santa Monica, CA
Santa Paula Healthcare, Santa Paula, CA
Santa Rita Health Care, Green Valley, AZ
Santa Rosa Convalescent Center, Tucson, AZ
Santa Rosa Convalescent Center, Milton, FL
Santa Rosa Convalescent Hospital, Santa Rosa, CA
Santa Rosa Extended Care Facility, Guayamas, PR
Santa Ynez Valley Recovery Residence, Solvang, CA
Sante Care Center, Milan, TN
Sapulpa Nursing Center Inc, Sapulpa, OK
Sara Lee Nursing Home, Doylestown, OH
Sarah A Reed Retirement Center, Erie, PA
Sarah A Todd Memorial Home Inc, Carlisle, PA
Sarah Ann Hester Memorial Home, Benkelman, NE
Sarah Frances Nursing Home, Boonton, NJ
Sarah Jane E Chambers Geriatric Center, Delphos, OH
Sarah Moore Home Inc, Delaware, OH
Sarah R Neuman Nursing Home, Mamaroneck, NY
Sarah Roberts French Home, San Antonio, TX
Sarasota Nursing Pavilion, Sarasota, FL
Sarasota Welfare Home Inc, Sarasota, FL
Saratoga County Infirmary, Ballston Spa, NY
Saratoga Hospital Nursing Home, Saratoga Springs, NY
Saratoga Place Skilled Nursing Facility, Saratoga, CA
Sargent Manor Inc, Forman, ND
Sargent Nursing Home, Sargent, NE
Sassaquin Convalescent Home, New Bedford, MA
Sauer Memorial Home, Winona, MN
Sauk County Health Care Center, Reedsburg, WI
Saunders County Care Center, Wahoo, NE
Saunders House, Philadelphia, PA
Savannah Beach Nursing Home Inc, Tybee Island, GA
Savannah Convalescent Center, Savannah, GA
Savannah Health Care, Savannah, GA
Savoy Care Center, Mamou, LA
Savoy Convalescent Home, New Bedford, MA
Savoy Terrace, Savoy, IL
Saxton Nursing Home, Saint Joseph, MO
Saybrook Convalescent Hospital, Old Saybrook, CT
Saylor Lane Convalescent Hospital, Sacramento, CA
Sayre House Inc, Sayre, PA

Scalabrini Villa, North Kingstown, RI
Scallop Shell Nursing Home Inc, South Kingstown, RI
Scandia Village Retirement Center, Sister Bay, WI
Scandinavian Home for the Aged, Cranston, RI
Scenery Hill Manor Inc, Indiana, PA
Scenic Hills Nursing Center, Bidwell, OH
Scenic Manor, Iowa Falls, IA
Scenic View Health Care Center, Baldwin, GA
Scenic View Nursing Home, Millersburg, OH
Scheuber Hospital, Pigeon, MI
Schleicher County Medical Center, Eldorado, TX
Schmidtke Rest Home, Ceylon, MN
Schmitt Woodland Hills Inc, Richland Center, WI
Schneiter Boarding Home, Wheeling, MO
Schnepps Convalescent Home, Saint Louis, MI
Schofield Residence, Kenmore, NY
Schoolcraft Medical Care Facility, Manistique, MI
Schowalter Villa, Hesston, KS
Schulze Nursing Home, Dayton, OH
Schussler Rest Home, Worcester, MA
Schuyler County Nursing Home, Queen City, MO
Schuyler Hospital Inc—Long Term Care Unit, Montour Falls, NY
Schuyler Senior Citizen's Home, Schuyler, NE
Scioto-Crest Convalescent Center, Hilliard, OH
Scituate Ocean Manor, Scituate, MA
Scotland County Nursing Home District, Memphis, MO
Scott County Nursing Center, Winchester, IL
Scott County Nursing Home, Morton, MS
Scott County Nursing Home, Oneida, TN
Scott Manor Nursing Home Inc, Indianapolis, IN
Scott Nursing Home, Smyrna, DE
Scott Villa Health Care Center Inc, Scottsburg, IN
Scottish Home, Riverside, IL
Scottish Rite Park Health Care Center, Des Moines, IA
Scottland Company Community Home, Memphis, MO
Scott's Rest Home, Haverhill, MA
Scottsbluff Villa, Scottsbluff, NE
Scottsboro Nursing Home, Scottsboro, AL
Scottsburg Nursing Home, Scottsburg, IN
Scottsdale Christian Home, Scottsdale, AZ
Scottsdale Convalescent Plaza, Scottsdale, AZ
Scottsdale Village Square, Scottsdale, AZ
Scottsville Rest Home, Scottsville, KY
Scripps Home, Altadena, CA
Sea Level Hospital, Sea Level, NC
Sea View Convalescent and Nursing Home, Rowley, MA
Sea View Convalescent Hospital, Eureka, CA
Sea View Hospital and Home, Staten Island, NY
Seabreeze Care Center, Texas City, TX
Seabrook of Hilton Head Inc, Hilton Head Island, SC
Seacoast Health Center, Hampton, NH
Seacrest Convalescent Hospital, San Pedro, CA
Sea-Crest Health Care Center, Brooklyn, NY
Seaford Health Care Center, Seaford, DE
Seagirt Health Related Facility, Far Rockaway, NY
Seagoville Lodge, Seagoville, TX
Seal Residential Care Home, Las Animas, CO

Sears Manor, Brunswick, GA
Sears Memorial Methodist Nursing Center, Abilene, TX
Seaside Care Center, Long Beach, CA
Seaside Care Center, Seaside, OR
Seaside Nursing and Retirement Home, Portland, ME
Seatoma Convalescent Center, Seattle, WA
Seattle Keiro, Seattle, WA
Seattle Specialized Group Home, Seattle, WA
Seaway Care Center, Muskegon, MI
Sebasticook Valley Health Care Facility, Pittsfield, ME
Sebastopol Convalescent Hospital, Sebastopol, CA
Sebo Heritage Manor Nursing Home, Hobart, IN
Sebring Care Center, Sebring, FL
Second Midlands ICMRF, Columbia, SC
Sedgwick Convalescent Center Inc, Sedgwick, KS
Sedgwick County Hospital and Nursing Home, Julesburg, CO
Sedig Castle-Rock Home, Whitewood, SD
Seguin Convalescent Home, Seguin, TX
Sehome Convalescent and Retirement Center, Bellingham, WA
Seidle Memorial Hospital—Extended Care Unit, Mechanicsburg, PA
Seiling Nursing Center, Seiling, OK
Seimon Lakeview Manor Estate, Somerset, PA
Seitz Nursing Home, Dallastown, PA
Selah Convalescent Home Inc, Selah, WA
Self Help Home for the Aged, Chicago, IL
Self Nursing Home Inc, Hueytown, AL
Selinsgrove Center, Selinsgrove, PA
Sells Rest Home Inc, Matthews, MO
Selma Convalescent Hospital, Selma, CA
Sem Haven Health Care Center, Milford, OH
Seminary Memorial Home, Red Wing, MN
Seminole Manor, Donalsonville, GA
Seminole Nursing Center Inc, Seminole, TX
Seminole Nursing Pavilion, Seminole, FL
Seminole Pioneer Nursing Home Inc, Seminole, OK
Seminole Villa Care Center, Springfield, OH
Sena Kean Manor, Smethport, PA
Senath Nursing Home, Senath, MO
Senatobia Convalescent Center, Senatobia, MS
Seneca Community Residence, Seneca, SC
Seneca Manor, West Seneca, NY
Seneca Manor, West Seneca, NY
Seneca Nursing Home, Waterloo, NY
Senior Citizen Nursing Home, Madisonville, KY
Senior Citizens Center, Coushatta, LA
Senior Citizen's Home, Hosmer, SD
Senior Citizen's Nursing Home, Nevada, MO
Senior Citizens Nursing Home, Broken Arrow, OK
Senior Citizens Nursing Home, Guthrie, OK
Senior Citizens Nursing Home, Winters, TX
Senior Citizens Nursing Home, Spokane, WA
Senior Estates of Kansas City Inc, Kansas City, MO
Senior Home, Montezuma, IA
Senior Home, Monticello, IA
Senior Manor, Sparta, IL
Senior Village Nursing Home, Opelousas, LA
Senior Village Nursing Home, Blanchard, OK
Senior Village Nursing Home, Perryton, TX
Senn Park Nursing Center, Chicago, IL
Sentinel Care Home, Minneapolis, MN

Sentinel Nursing Home, Sentinel, OK
Sephardic Home for the Aged Inc, Brooklyn, NY
Sepulveda Convalescent Hospital Inc, Van Nuys, CA
Sequatchie Health Care Center, Dunlap, TN
Sequim Nursing Center, Sequim, WA
The Sequoias, Portola Valley, CA
Sequoias San Francisco Convalescent Hospital, San Francisco, CA
Sequoyah East Nursing Center, Roland, OK
Sequoyah Manor, Sallisaw, OK
Serene Manor Medical Center, Knoxville, TN
Serenity Haven Nursing Home, Garland, TX
Serenity Hill Nursing Home, Wrentham, MA
Serenity Rest Home, Chelmsford, MA
Serrano Convalescent Hospital—North, Los Angeles, CA
Serrano Convalescent Hospital—South, Los Angeles, CA
Seth Mann II Home for the Aged, Randolph, MA
Seton Hill Manor, Baltimore, MD
Seven Eleven North High, Lake City, MN
Seven Gables, Youngstown, OH
Seven Hills Health Care Center, Lynchburg, VA
Seven Oakes Care Center, Bonham, TX
Seven Oaks Nursing Home, Olney, TX
717 Rustic Lane, Wabasha, MN
761 Williams Group Home, Richland, WA
7th Street, Brighton, CO
Seventh Street House, Faribault, MN
Severin Intermediate Care Facility, Benton, IL
Sevier County Health Care Center Inc, Sevierville, TN
Seville Nursing Home, Salem, MO
Seymour Care Center, Seymour, IA
Shabbona Nursing Home Inc, Shabbona, IL
Shadescrest Health Care Center, Jasper, AL
Shadow Hill Convalescent Hospital, Sunland, CA
Shady Acres Convalescent Center Inc, Douglas, GA
Shady Acres Health Care Center, Newton, TX
Shady Acres Inc, Exeter, RI
Shady Acres Nursing Home, Madison, OH
Shady Breeze Rest Home, Kingston, MA
Shady Glade Rest Home, Ayer, MA
Shady Grove Rest Home, Kennesaw, GA
Shady Lake Nursing Home, Lake Providence, LA
Shady Lane Home, Manitowoc, WI
Shady Lane Nursing Home, Wadena, MN
Shady Lane-Gloucester County Home, Clarksboro, NJ
Shady Lawn, Savannah, MO
Shady Lawn Home, Cynthiana, KY
Shady Lawn Home Inc, Dalton, OH
Shady Lawn Lodge, Hannibal, MO
Shady Lawn Manor Inc, Emporia, KS
Shady Lawn Memorial Home—East, Kenosha, WI
Shady Lawn Memorial Home—West, Kenosha, WI
Shady Lawn Nursing Home, Cadiz, KY
Shady Lawn Nursing Home Inc, Vicksburg, MS
Shady Lawn Rest Home Inc, Hadley, MA
Shady Manor Convalescent Hospital, Bakersfield, CA
Shady Nook Nursing Home, Lawrenceburg, IN

Shady Oak Nursing Home Inc, Moulton, TX
Shady Oaks, Lake City, IA
Shady Oaks Lodge 1, Abilene, TX
Shady Oaks Lodge 2, Abilene, TX
Shady Oaks Nursing Home, Monroe, LA
Shady Rest Care Center, Cascade, IA
Shady Rest Care Center Inc, Pryor, OK
Shady Rest Home, Plymouth, IN
Shady Rest Nursing Home, Fort Myers, FL
Shady View Nursing Home, Oklahoma City, OK
Shadyside Care Center, Shadyside, OH
Shadyside Nursing Home Inc, Duncanville, TX
Shadyway Group Home, Wayzata, MN
Shaffer Plaza, Steubenville, OH
Shafter Convalescent Hospital, Shafter, CA
Shakamak Good Samaritan Center, Jasonville, IN
Shakopee Friendship Manor, Shakopee, MN
Shalem Rest Nursing Home, Massillon, OH
Shalimar Plaza Nursing Home, Salina, KS
Shalom Nursing Home, Mount Vernon, NY
Shamel Manor, Normal, IL
Shamrock Nursing Home, Saint Louis, MO
Shandin Hills Convalescent Hospital, San Bernardino, CA
Shandin Hills Sanitarium, San Bernardino, CA
Shane Hill Nursing Home, Rockford, OH
Shangri-La, Salem, OR
Shangri-La Manor Inc, LaFontaine, IN
Shangri-La Nursing Home, Delmar, DE
Shangri-La Rest Home Inc, Medina, OH
Shannes Skogdalen, Soldiers Grove, WI
Shannondale Health Care Center, Knoxville, TN
Shannondale Retirement Home, Knoxville, TN
Shanoan Springs Residence Inc, Chickasha, OK
Shanti House, Minneapolis, MN
Share Medical Center, Alva, OK
Sharmar Nursing Center, Pueblo, CO
Sharon Convalescent Hospital, Los Angeles, CA
Sharon Heights Convalescent Hospital, Menlo Park, CA
Sharon Manor Nursing Home, Sharon, MA
Sharon Nursing Home, Olney, MD
Sharon Nursing Home, Centralia, WA
Sharon Village Inc, Charlotte, NC
Sharonlane Inc, Shawnee, KS
Sharonview Nursing Home, South Vienna, OH
Sharp Nursing Home Inc, Sidney, AR
Sharp's Rest Home, Falmouth, KY
Shasta Convalescent Hospital, Redding, CA
Shawano Convalescent Center, Shawano, WI
Shawn Manor Nursing Home, Ponca City, OK
Shawnee Care Center, Shawnee, OK
Shawnee Christian Nursing Center, Herrin, IL
Shawnee Colonial Estates Inc, Shawnee, OK
Shawnee Manor, Lima, OH
Shawnee Shelter Care, Simpson, IL
Shawnee Springs Nursing Home, Winchester, VA
Shawnee Sunset Estates, Shawnee, OK
Shea Convalescent Hospital, San Bernardino, CA
Shea Convalescent Hospital, Upland, CA
Shea Convalescent Hospital, Whittier, CA
Shearer-Richardson Memorial Nursing Home, Okolona, MS
Sheboygan Comprehensive Health Center, Sheboygan Falls, WI

Sheboygan Retirement Home Inc, Sheboygan, WI
Sheepscot Valley Health Center, Coopers Mills, ME
Sheepshead Nursing Home, Brooklyn, NY
Sheffield Care Center, Sheffield, IA
Sheffield Convalescent Hospital, San Francisco, CA
Sheffield Nursing and Rehabilitation Center, Fort Lauderdale, FL
Shelby Convalescent Center, Shelby, NC
Shelby County Health Care Center, Memphis, TN
Shelby Manor, Shelbyville, IL
Shelby Manor, Shelbyville, KY
Shelby Memorial Home, Shelbyville, IL
Shelby Memorial Hospital Nursing Home, Shelbyville, IL
Sheldon Healthcare Inc, Sheldon, IL
Sheldonville Nursing Home, Wrentham, MA
Shell Point Village Nursing Pavilion, Fort Myers, FL
Shell Rock Care Center, Shell Rock, IA
Sheltered Village, Genoa, IL
Sheltered Village—Woodstock, Woodstock, IL
Sheltering Arms Nursing Home Inc, Walnut Ridge, AR
Sheltering Oaks, Island Lake, IL
Sheltering Pine Convalescent Hospital, Millbrae, CA
The Shelton Center, Saint Louis, MO
Shelton Group Home, Richville, MN
Shelton Lakes Residence and Health Care, Shelton, CT
Shemwell Nursing Home, Providence, KY
Shenandoah County Memorial Hospital—Long-Term Care Unit, Woodstock, VA
Shenandoah Home Inc, Ranson, WV
Shenango United Presbyterian Home, New Wilmington, PA
Shepherd Hills Health Care, Lafayette, GA
Shepherd of the Valley Nursing Home, Niles, OH
Sheppard Nursing Home, Ellenboro, WV
Sheraton Convalescent Hospital, Sepulveda, CA
Sherbrooke Nursing Home, Grand Rapids, MI
Sheridan Care Center, Sheridan, OR
Sheridan Gardens Convalescent Home Inc, Chicago, IL
Sheridan Health Care Center, Zion, IL
Sheridan Health Care Center Inc, Sheridan, IN
Sheridan Manor Nursing Home Inc, Wheat Ridge, CO
Sheridan Manor Nursing Home Inc, Tonawanda, NY
Sheridan Memorial Nursing Home, Plentywood, MT
Sheridan Nursing Home, Kenosha, WI
Sheriff Manor Nursing Home, Boston, MA
Sherman County Good Samaritan Center, Goodland, KS
Sherman Nursing Center, Sherman, TX
Sherman Oaks Care Center, Muskegon, MI
Sherman Oaks Convalescent Hospital, Sherman Oaks, CA
Sherrill House Inc, Boston, MA
Sherwin Manor Nursing Center, Chicago, IL
Sherwood Care Center, Williams Bay, WI
Sherwood Convalescent Home, Indianapolis, IN
Sherwood Convalescent Hospital, Van Nuys, CA

Sherwood Health Care Inc, Bryan, TX
Sherwood Healthcare Center of Lubbock, Lubbock, TX
Sherwood Manor Inc, Sequim, WA
Sherwood Manor Nursing Home, Tulsa, OK
Sherwood Oaks and Cranberry Lake Health Center, Mars, PA
Sherwood Park Nursing Home, Salem, OR
Sherwood Terrace Nursing Center, Tacoma, WA
Shetley Nursing Home, Bell City, MO
Sheyenne Care Center, Valley City, ND
Shiawassee Medical Care Facility, Corunna, MI
Shields Adult Care Home Inc, Pittsburg, KS
Shields and Terrell Convalescent Hospital, Richmond, CA
Shiloh Manor, Canton, KS
The Shire—Dungarvin IV, Elk River, MN
Shirkey Leisure Acres, Richmond, MO
Shirling Manor Rest Home, Peabody, MA
Shoals Nursing Home, Tuscumbia, AL
Sholom Home, Saint Paul, MN
Shore Acres Nursing and Convalescent Home, Saint Petersburg, FL
Shore Cliff, Gloucester, MA
Shore Drive Convalescent Home Inc, Virginia Beach, VA
Shore Haven Nursing Home, Grand Haven, MI
Shore View Nursing Home, Brooklyn, NY
Shoreham Convalescent Center, Marietta, GA
Shoreham Terrace, Saint Joseph, MI
Shorehaven, Oconomowoc, WI
Shoreline North Convalescent Hospital, Alameda, CA
Shoreline South Intermediate Care Facility, Alameda, CA
Shoreliner Healthcare Center, Taft, TX
Shores Health Center, Bradenton, FL
Shoshone Living Center, Kellogg, ID
Shree Ji Health Care Center, Paintsville, KY
Shreveport Manor Nursing Home, Shreveport, LA
Shrewsbury Lutheran Retirement Village, Shrewsbury, PA
Shrewsbury Manor Nursing Home, Shrewsbury, NJ
Shrewsbury Nursing Home Inc, Shrewsbury, MA
Shuffield Rest Home 1, Brady, TX
Shuffield Rest Home 2, Brady, TX
Shuffit Nursing Home 1 Inc, Sikeston, MO
Shuffit Nursing Home 3 Inc, Sikeston, MO
Shuksan Convalescent Center, Bellingham, WA
Shurtleff Manor, Mount Carmel, IL
Sibley Care Center, Sibley, IA
Sidney Health Center, Sidney, IA
Siemers Boarding Care Home, Montgomery, MN
The Siena Home, Dayton, OH
Sierra Convalescent Center, Carson City, NV
Sierra Convalescent Hospital, Roseville, CA
Sierra Developmental Center, Sparks, NV
Sierra Health Care Center, Truth or Consequences, NM
Sierra Health Care Convalescent Hospital, Davis, CA
Sierra Health Center, Sparks, NV
Sierra Meadows Convalescent Hospital, Oakhurst, CA
Sierra Park Care Center, Camas, WA
Sierra View Convalescent Hospital, Fresno, CA
Sierra View Homes Inc, Reedley, CA
Sierra Vista, Highland, CA

Sierra Vista Care Center, Sierra Vista, AZ
Sierra Vista Care Center, Oregon City, OR
Sierra Vista Nursing Home, Loveland, CO
Siesta Home of Pratt Inc, Pratt, KS
Siesta Park Manor, Oskaloosa, IA
Sigourney Care Center, Sigourney, IA
Sikeston Convalescent Center, Sikeston, MO
Sikeston Manor Nursing Home, Sikeston, MO
Silas Creek Manor, Winston-Salem, NC
Silent Night Nursing Home, Lancaster, TX
Silsbee Convalescent Center, Silsbee, TX
Silver Bell Nursing Home, Versailles, IN
Silver Creek Manor, Bristol, RI
Silver Crest Manor Inc, Anadarko, OK
Silver Cross Home, Brookhaven, MS
Silver Gardens Care Home Inc, Silverton, OR
Silver Haven Care Center, Burleson, TX
Silver Haven Nursing Home, Schenectady, NY
Silver Lake Nursing Home, Staten Island, NY
Silver Leaves Inc, Garland, TX
Silver Spring Convalescent Center, Milwaukee,
    WI
Silver State Nursing Home, Castle Rock, CO
Silver Threads Nursing Center, Houston, TX
Silverado Convalescent Hospital, Napa, CA
Silverstream Nursing Home, Springhouse, PA
Silverton County Good Samaritan Center,
    Silverton, ID
Silverton Nursing Home, Silverton, OR
L O Simenstad Nursing Unit, Osceola, WI
Simmons Loving Care Health Facility,
    Gary, IN
Simmons Nursing Home Inc, Billerica, MA
Simpson House of the United Methodist
    Church, Philadelphia, PA
Simpson Memorial Home, West Liberty, IA
Simpsons Foster Care, Aguilar, CO
Singing River Hospital System—Extended
    Care Facility, Pascagoula, MS
Singleton Health Care Center, Cleveland, OH
Sinton Nursing Home Inc, Sinton, TX
Sioux Care Center, Sioux Rapids, IA
Sioux Falls Care Center, Sioux Falls, SD
Sister James' Nursing Home, Yankton, SD
Sisters of Charity Hospital—Skilled Nursing
    Facility, Buffalo, NY
Siuslaw Care Center, Florence, OR
Sixth Street House, Rochester, MN
Skaalen Sunset Home, Stoughton, WI
Skagit Valley Convalescent Center Inc, Sedro
    Woolley, WA
Skiatook Nursing Home, Skiatook, OK
Skokie Meadows I, Skokie, IL
Skokie Meadows II, Skokie, IL
Sky Ranch Home, Atlanta, GA
Sky View Haven Nursing Home, Croton-
    on-Hudson, NY
Sky View Nursing Center, Hurley, WI
Sky Vue Terrace, Pittsburgh, PA
Skyland Care Center Inc, Sylva, NC
Skyline Convalescent Hospital, Los
    Angeles, CA
Skyline Convalescent Hospital, Salinas, CA
Skyline Convalescent Hospital, San Jose, CA
Skyline Manor and Skyline Villa, Omaha, NE
Skyline Manor Nursing Home, Floyd, VA
Skyline Nursing Home, DeSoto, TX
Skyline Terrace Convalescent Home,
    Woodstock, VA
Skyline Terrace Nursing Center, Tulsa, OK
Skyview Convalescent Hospital Inc,
    Wallingford, CT
Skyview—Hazeldel, Twin Falls, ID

Skyview Living Center of Stamford, Stamford,
    TX
Skyview Living Center—San Antonio, San
    Antonio, TX
Skyview Manor, Jacksonville, IL
Skyview Personal Care Home, Mayfield, KY
Slack Nursing Home Inc, Gothenburg, NE
Slate Belt Medical Center Inc, Bangor, PA
Slaton Rest Home, Slaton, TX
Slayton Manor, Slayton, MN
Sleepy Eye Care Center, Sleepy Eye, MN
Sleepy Hollow Manor Nursing Home,
    Annandale, VA
Sleigh Bell Residence, Youngstown, OH
Slovene Home for the Aged, Cleveland, OH
Smackover Nursing Home, Smackover, AR
Smith County Manor, Carthage, TN
Smith Group Home, Frazee, MN
Smith Home for Aged Women, Ashtabula, OH
Smith House, Fort Collins, CO
Smith House Skilled Nursing Facility,
    Stamford, CT
Smith Medical Nursing Care Center,
    Sandersville, GA
Smith Nursing and Convalescent Home of
    Mountaintop, Mountaintop, PA
Smith Nursing Home, Millbury, MA
Smith Nursing Home, Walla Walla, WA
Smith Nursing Home Inc, Canton, OH
Smith-Barr Manor Nursing Home, Louisiana,
    MO
Smithfield Home, Smithfield, VA
Smith's Nursing Home, Wolfe City, TX
Smiths Rest Home, Worcester, MA
Smithview Manor Nursing Home, Lawson,
    MO
Smithville Convalescent Center, Smithville,
    MO
Smithville-Western Care Center, Wooster, OH
Smyrna Nursing Center, Smyrna, TN
Snapper Creek Nursing Home, Miami, FL
Snellville Nursing and Rehabilitation Center,
    Snellville, GA
Snow Valley Nursing Home, Lisle, IL
Snyder Nursing Center, Snyder, TX
Snyder Nursing Home, Salem, VA
Snyder Oaks Care Center, Snyder, TX
Snyders Vaughn-Haven Inc, Rushville, IL
Social Circle Intermediate Care Facility, Social
    Circle, GA
Society for Danish Old Peoples Home,
    Chicago, IL
Socorro Good Samaritan Village, Socorro, NM
Sodonia's Home, Fulton, MO
Sogge Memorial Home, Windom, MN
Soldiers and Sailors Memorial Hospital—
    Extended Care Unit, Penn Yan, NY
Solheim Lutheran Home for the Aged, Eagle
    Rock, CA
Solomon Valley Manor, Stockton, KS
Solon Nursing Care Center, Solon, IA
Somers Manor Nursing Home Inc, Somers,
    NY
Somerset Center, Somerset, KY
Somerset Community Hospital—Skilled
    Nursing Unit, Somerset, PA
Somerset Golden State Convalescent Hospital,
    West Sacramento, CA
Somerset House, Chicago, IL
Somerset Manor, Bingham, ME
Somerset State Hospital—Mentally Retarded
    Unit, Somerset, PA
Somerset Valley Nursing Home, Bound Brook,
    NJ

Somerville Health Care Center, Somerville, TN
Somerville Home for the Aged, Somerville,
    MA
Sonogee Estages, Bar Harbor, ME
Sonoma Acres, Sonoma, CA
Sonora Convalescent Hospital Inc, Sonora, CA
Sophia Huntington Parker Home, Medina, OH
Sophia Lyn Convalescent Hospital,
    Pasadena, CA
Sorenson Convalescent Hospital, Whittier, CA
Sound View Specialized Care Center, West
    Haven, CT
Souris Valley Care Center, Velva, ND
South Bay Child Care Center, Hawthorne, CA
South Bay Keiro Nursing Home, Gardena, CA
South Bend Convalescent Center Inc, South
    Bend, IN
South Broadway Nursing Home Inc, New
    Philadelphia, OH
South Cape Nursing Home, Cape May Court
    House, NJ
South Carolina Ave Intermediate Care Facility,
    Atlantic City, NJ
South Carolina Crippled Children's
    Convalescent Center, Palmetto, SC
South Carolina Episcopal Home at Still Hopes,
    West Columbia, SC
South Carolina Vocational Rehabilitation
    Comprehensive Center, West Columbia,
    SC
South Center Manor Inc, Center City, MN
South County Convalescent Center, Arroyo
    Grande, CA
South County Nursing Centre, North
    Kingstown, RI
South Dallas Nursing Home, Dallas, TX
South Davis Community Hospital Inc,
    Bountiful, UT
South East Arkansas Human Development
    Center, Warren, AR
South Elgin Manor, South Elgin, IL
South Fulton Hospital—Extended Care Facility,
    East Point, GA
South Gate Care Center, Saint Louis, MO
South Haven Manor Nursing Home,
    Montgomery, AL
South Haven Nursing Home,
    Birmingham, AL
South Heritage Health Care Center, Saint
    Petersburg, FL
South Hills Convalescent Center, Cannonsburg,
    PA
South Hills Manor, Dimmitt, TX
South Holland Nursing Home, South
    Holland, IL
South Lafourche Nursing Center, Cut Off, LA
South Lake Care Center, Merrillville, IN
South Lawn Shelter Care, Bunker Hill, IL
South Meadows Nursing Home, Diboll, TX
South Mississippi Retardation Center, Long
    Beach, MS
South Monaco Care Center, Denver, CO
South Mountain Manor, Phoenix, AZ
South Mountain Restoration Center, South
    Mountain, PA
South Oaks Health Care Inc, McMinnville, TN
South Park Development Center, Brownwood,
    TX
South Park Group Home, Pocatello, ID
South Park Health Care Center, Oklahoma
    City, OK
South Park Manor, Corpus Christi, TX
The South Pasadena Convalescent Hospital and
    Sanitarium, South Pasadena, CA

South Peninsula Hospital, Homer, AK
South Plains Memorial Home, Brownfield, TX
South Plains Nursing Home, Lubbock, TX
South Portland Nursing Home Inc, South Portland, ME
South Roanoke Nursing Home Inc, Roanoke, VA
South Salem Care Center, Salem, OR
South Shore Convalescent Hospital, Alameda, CA
South Shore Kosher Rest Home Inc, Chicago, IL
South Shore Nursing Facility, Rockland, MA
South Shore Nursing Home Inc, Freeport, NY
South Side Manor, Decatur, IL
South Tower Rest Home, Centralia, WA
South Washington Street Nursing Home, Tiffin, OH
South Windsor Convalescent Home Inc, South Windsor, CT
Southampton Memorial Hospital—East Pavilion, Franklin, VA
Southampton Nursing Home, Southampton, NY
Southcrest Convalescent Center, Spokane, WA
Southdale Nursing Home, Superior, WI
Southeast Arizona Medical Center, Douglas, AZ
Southeast Colorado Hospital and LTC, Springfield, CO
Southeast Nursing Center, San Antonio, TX
Southeastern Colorado Family Guidance and Mental Health Center Inc, La Junta, CO
Southeastern Dakota Nursing Home, Vermillion, SD
Southeastern General Hospital Inc, Lumberton, NC
Southeastern Nursing Home, Indianapolis, IN
Southern Hills Nursing Center, Tulsa, OK
Southern Inyo County Sanatorium, Lone Pine, CA
Southern Manor Inc, Temple, TX
Southern Medical of Dublin Inc, Dublin, GA
Southern Medical of East Macon, Macon, GA
Southern Medical of Springhill Nursing Home, Mobile, AL
Southern Medical Services of North Macon, Macon, GA
Southern Nursing Home, Fordyce, AR
Southern Oaks Manor Nursing Home, Oklahoma City, OK
Southern Pines Nursing Center, New Port Richey, FL
Southern Wisconsin Center, Union Grove, WI
Southernaire Health Center, Milwaukee, WI
Southfield Care Center, Webster City, IA
Southfield Center, Southfield, MI
Southgate Health Care Center, Metropolis, IL
Southgate Nursing Center, Jefferson City, MO
Southhampton Estates, Southampton, PA
Southhaven Health Care Center, Southaven, MS
Southland Geriatric Center, Norwalk, CA
Southland Nursing Home, Marion, AL
Southland Villa Nursing Center, Temple, TX
Southport Manor Convalescent Center, Southport, CT
Southridge Manor Care Home, Louisburg, KS
Southside Care Center, Minneapolis, MN
Southside Healthcare Center, Indianapolis, IN
Southside House, Rochester, MN
Southside Nursing Center, Jacksonville, FL
Southside Nursing Home, San Antonio, TX

Southview Acres Health Care Center, West Saint Paul, MN
Southview Manor, Phillipsburg, KS
Southview Manor Care Center, Cozad, NE
Southwest Care Centers Inc, San Antonio, TX
Southwest Convalescent Center, Hawthorne, CA
Southwest Extended Care Center, McComb, MS
Southwest Health Center Nursing Home, Cuba City, WI
Southwest Health Center Nursing Home, Platteville, WI
Southwest Homes, Little Rock, AR
Southwest Louisiana State School, Iota, LA
Southwest Manor, Worthington, MN
Southwest Mediplex, Austin, TX
Southwest Senior Care Inc, Las Vegas, NM
Southwestern Convalescent Manor, Oklahoma City, OK
Southwestern Developmental Center, Bainbridge, GA
Southwood Convalescent Center Inc, Henderson, TX
Southwood Nursing Home, Elizabethton, TN
The Sovereign Home, Chicago, IL
Sowder Nursing Home, Brodhead, KY
Spa View Nursing Home Inc, Excelsior Springs, MO
Spalding Convalescent Center, Griffin, GA
Spang Crest Home, Lebanon, PA
Spanish Gardens Nursing and Convalescent Center, Dunedin, FL
Spanish Oaks Center, Anna, IL
Spanish Peaks Mental Health Center, Pueblo, CO
Sparks Manor, Fort Smith, AR
Sparks Rest Home, Central City, KY
Sparr Convalescent Home, Drums, PA
Sparr Convalescent Hospital, Los Angeles, CA
Sparta Health Care Center Inc, Sparta, TN
Sparta Intermediate Care Center, Sparta, GA
Spartanburg Community Residence 1, Spartanburg, SC
Spartanburg Commununity Residence 2, Spartanburg, SC
Spartanburg Convalescent Center Inc, Spartanburg, SC
Spear Convalescent Home, Marklesburg, PA
Spears and Spears Nursing Home, Piketon, OH
Spencer's Personal Care Home, Jackson, MS
Spiro Nursing Home, Spiro, OK
SPJST Rest Home 1, Taylor, TX
SPJST Rest Home 2, Needville, TX
Split Rock Nursing Home, Bronx, NY
Spokane Convalescent Center, Spokane, WA
Spokane Valley Good Samaritan, Greenacres, WA
Sprague Nursing Home, Red Cloud, NE
Sprain Brook Manor Nursing Home, Scarsdale, NY
Spring Hill Manor, Spring Hill, KS
Spring Hill Manor Convalescent Hospital, Grass Valley, CA
Spring Hill Manor Nursing Home, Mobile, AL
Spring House Estates Nursing Facility, Springhouse, PA
Spring Valley, Arvada, CO
Spring Valley Convalescent Home, Worcester, MA
Spring Valley Convalescent Hospital, Spring Valley, CA
Spring Valley Health Care Center Inc, Elberton, GA

Spring Valley Intermediate Care Facility, Jeffersonville, GA
Spring Valley Municipal Nursing Home, Spring Valley, WI
Spring Valley Nursing, Spring Valley, IL
Spring View Hospital, Lebanon, KY
Spring View Manor Inc, Conway Springs, KS
Springbrook Manor, Grand Rapids, MI
Springdale Convalescent Center, Atlanta, GA
Springdale Convalescent Center, Cartersville, GA
Springfield Convalescent Center, Springfield, VT
Springfield Health Care Center, Springfield, MO
Springfield Health Care Center Inc, Springfield, TN
Springfield Manor, Springfield, IL
Springfield Municipal Hospital, Springfield, MA
Springfield Rest Home, Springfield, MO
Springhaven Care Center, Tacoma, WA
Springhaven Nursing Care, Georgetown, KY
Springhill, Battle Creek, MI
Springs Manor, Cambridge Springs, PA
Springs Road Living Center, Vallejo, CA
Springs Village Recovery Center, Colorado Springs, CO
Springside of Pittsfield Long Term Care Facility, Pittsfield, MA
Springview Center, Springfield, OH
Springview Manor, Lima, OH
Springview Nursing Home, Freehold, NJ
Springville Nursing Center, Coushatta, LA
Springwood Nursing Center Ltd, Sarasota, FL
Springwood Nursing Home, Rome, GA
Spruce Avenue Residence, South Saint Paul, MN
Spruce Lodge, Montrose, CO
Spruce Manor Nursing Home, Springfield, MA
Spur Care Center, Spur, TX
Spurgeon Manor, Dallas Center, IA
Square Road Farm, Saint Albans, ME
St Frances Home for the Aged, Breckenridge, MN
St Louis Association for Retarded Children Inc, Saint Louis, MO
Stacyville Community Nursing Home, Stacyville, IA
Stadium Manor Nursing Home, Boston, MA
Stafholt Icelandic Old Folks Home, Blaine, WA
Standing Stone Health Care Center, Monterey, TN
Standish Community Hospital, Standish, MI
Stanford Convalescent Center—Bedford, Bedford, TX
Stanford Convalescent Center—Eighth Ave, Fort Worth, TX
Stanford Convalescent Center—Hemphill, Fort Worth, TX
Stanford Convalescent Center—Jennings, Fort Worth, TX
Stanford Convalescent Center—Pennsylvania, Fort Worth, TX
Stanford House, Stanford, KY
Stanley Convalescent Hospital, Westminster, CA
Stanmarie, Linden, MI
Stanton Care Center, Stanton, IA
Stanton Care Center, Stanton, TX
Stanton Hill Convalescent Hospital Inc, Castro Valley, CA
Stanton Nursing Center, Stanton, KY

Stanton Nursing Home, Stanton, NE
Stanton Pines Convalescent Home Inc, Hopkins, SC
Star City Nursing Center, Star City, AR
Star Nursing Home, Bethesda, OH
Star of David Convalescent Home, Boston, MA
Starcrest Home of Conyers, Conyers, GA
Starcrest of Lithonia, Lithonia, GA
Stark County Health Center, Toulon, IL
Starkville Manor Nursing Home, Starkville, MS
Starmount Villa Nursing Center, Greensboro, NC
Starnes Nursing Home Inc, Harvey, IL
Starr Nursing Home, Merkel, TX
Starzecki Boarding Care Home, Winona, MN
State Center Manor, State Center, IA
State College Manor Ltd, State College, PA
State Convalescent Hospital, South Gate, CA
State Home and Training School—Eleventh St, Pueblo, CO
State Home and Training School—Tenth St, Pueblo, CO
State of New Mexico Miner's Hospital— Intermediate Care Facility, Sheltered and Boarding Care Facility, Raton, NM
Stateline Care Center, Niles, MI
Statesboro Nursing Home, Statesboro, GA
Staunton Manor Nursing Home Inc, Staunton, VA
Steere House, Providence, RI
Steffen Group Home, Barrett, MN
Stella Manor Nursing Home, Russellville, AR
Stella Maris/The Cardinal Shehan Center for the Aging, Towson, MD
Stella Residential Care Center Inc, Stella, MO
Stellar Homes Inc, Saint Louis, MO
Stenton Hall Nursing and Convalescent Center, Philadelphia, PA
Step by Step Inc, Carnegie, PA
Step by Step Inc, Wilkes-Barre, PA
Stephen Caldwell Memorial Convalescent Home, Ipswich, MA
Stephen Smith Home for the Aged, Philadelphia, PA
Stephens House, Alamosa, CO
Stephens Nursing Home, Lexington, KY
Stephenson Nursing Home, Freeport, IL
Stephenville Nursing Inc, Stephenville, TX
Stepping Stones Group Home, Milaca, MN
Stepping Stones Inc, Moscow, ID
Sterling Care Center, Sterling, IL
Sterling County Nursing Home, Sterling City, TX
Sterling Heights Manor, Iola, KS
Sterling Home of Bridgeport, Bridgeport, CT
Sterling Presbyterian Manor, Sterling, KS
Stetson Manor Nursing Home, Norwell, MA
Steuben County Infirmary, Bath, NY
Stevencroft, Saint Paul, MN
Stevens Convalescent Center Inc, Hallettsville, TX
Stevens Hall Long Term Care Facility, North Andover, MA
Stevens Nursing Home Inc, Yoakum, TX
Stevens Square, Minneapolis, MN
Stevens-Bennett Home Inc, Haverhill, MA
Stewart Lodge, Madison, OH
Stewartvilla Nursing Home, Stewartville, MN
Stigler Nursing Home, Stigler, OK
Stiles M Harper Convalescent Center, Estill, SC
Stilhaven Nursing Home, Dayton, OH

Still Waters Nursing Home Inc, Danforth, ME
Stillmeadow Care Center, Malvern, AR
Stillwater Children's Center, Dayton, OH
Stillwater Convalescent Center, Columbus, MT
Stillwater Health Care, Bangor, ME
Stillwater Health Center, Dayton, OH
Stillwater Maple Manor Health Care Center Inc, Stillwater, MN
Stillwater Nursing Home Inc, Stillwater, OK
Stillwater Residence, Stillwater, MN
Stillwater Rosewood Nursing Home Inc, Stillwater, OK
Stilwell Nursing Home, Stilwell, OK
Stockdale Nursing Home, Stockdale, TX
Stockton Convalescent Hospital, Stockton, CA
Stockton Nursing Home Inc, Stockton, MO
Stokes-Reynolds Memorial Hospital—Skilled Nursing Facility, Danbury, NC
Stollwood Convalescent Hospital, Woodland, CA
Stone Acre Rest Home Inc, Springfield, MA
Stone Arch Health Care Center, Pittstown, NJ
Stone Haven, Lewistown, MO
Stone House Hill, Holden, MA
Stone Institution and Newton Home for Aged People, Newton, MA
Stone Manor Convalescent Center, Indianapolis, IN
Stone Road Nursing Center Inc, Kilgore, TX
Stonebrook, Fort Worth, TX
Stonebrook Nurse Center, Denver City, TX
Stonebrook Nursing Home, Austin, TX
Stonegate Nursing Center, Stonewall, OK
Stonehaven Convalescent Hospital Inc, Hayward, CA
Stonehedge Nursing Home, Boston, MA
Stonehedge Nursing Home, Rome, NY
Stonehedge-Chittenango Nursing Home, Chittenango, NY
Stonehenge Health Care Center Inc, Huntsville, TN
Stonehill Care Center, Dubuque, IA
Stonehill Manor Nursing and Retirement Home, North Easton, MA
Stones River Manor, Murfreesboro, TN
Stonewall Jackson Hospital Inc Long-Term Care Unit, Lexington, VA
Stoney Hill Health Center, Strongsville, OH
Storla Sunset Home, Letcher, SD
Story County Hospital, Nevada, IA
Stovall Care Center, Denver, CO
Stow Rest Home, Stow, MA
Strafford County Home, Dover, NH
Strand-Kjorsvig Community Rest Home, Roslyn, SD
Strasburg Nursing Home, Strasburg, ND
Stratford Care Center, Stratford, IA
Stratford Hall Nursing Home, Richmond, VA
Stratford Nursing and Convalescent Center, Stratford, NJ
Stratton House, Townshend, VT
Strawberry Point Lutheran Home, Strawberry Point, IA
Strawn Nursing Home Inc, Naches, WA
Stroh Residential Home, Colorado Springs, CO
Strong Children's Home, Strong, ME
Strong Memorial Hospital, Rochester, NY
Stroud Health Care Center, Stroud, OK
Stroud Manor Inc, East Stroudsburg, PA
Stroud Memorial Intermediate Care Facility, Marietta, SC
Strum Nursing Home, Strum, WI

Stuart Convalescent Center, Stuart, FL
Studio City Convalescent Hospital, Studio City, CA
Sturges Convalescent Home, Mansfield, OH
Sturgis Community Nursing Home, Sturgis, SD
Sturgis Community Rest Home, Sturgis, KY
Stuttle Community Living Facility, Peoria, IL
Styrest Nursing Home, Carbondale, IL
Styrons Arrowhead Nursing Center, Jonesboro, GA
Su Casa Personal Care, Tucson, AZ
Sublette County Retirement, Pinedale, WY
Suburban Acres Nursing Center, Marshall, TX
Suburban Manor Convalescent and Nursing Home, Acton, MA
Suburban Pavillion Inc, North Randall, OH
Suburban Square Nursing Center, Oklahoma City, OK
Sudbury Pines Nursing Home, Sudbury, MA
Suffolk Infirmary, Yaphank, NY
Sugar Creek Convalescent Center Inc, Greenfield, IN
Sugar Creek Rest Inc, Worthington, PA
Sugar Valley Home Inc, Mound City, KS
Suisun Valley Manor, Fairfield, CA
Suitland Nursing Home Inc, Suitland, MD
Sullivan County Home, Claremont, NH
Sullivan County Home for the Aged, Blountville, TN
Sullivan County Public Home and Infirmary, Liberty, NY
Sullivan Living Center, Sullivan, IL
Sullivan Nursing Center, Sullivan, MO
Sulphur Springs Nursing Home, Sulphur Springs, TX
Summer Hill Nursing Home, Old Bridge, NJ
Summer Home for the Aged, Akron, OH
Summerfield Convalescent Hospital, Santa Rosa, CA
Summerfield Manor Nursing Home, Louisville, KY
Summerford Nursing Home Inc, Falkville, AL
Summerlin Lane Nursing Home, Bastrop, LA
Summers County Continuous Care Center, Hinton, WV
Summit Acres Nursing Home, Caldwell, OH
Summit Acres Nursing Home Inc—Home B, Caldwell, OH
Summit Avenue Residence, South Saint Paul, MN
Summit Convalescent Center Inc, Summitville, IN
Summit Convalescent Home, Jewett City, CT
Summit Convalescent Home, Lakewood, NJ
Summit Health Care Center, Wilkes-Barre, PA
Summit Home, Detroit Lakes, MN
Summit House, Minneapolis, MN
Summit House Health Care Center, Bar Harbor, ME
Summit House II, Saint Louis Park, MN
Summit Manor, Columbia, KY
Summit Manor Health Care Center, Saint Paul, MN
Summit Medical Center Inc, Providence, RI
Summit Nursing and Convalescent Home Inc, Cincinnati, OH
Summit Nursing Home Inc, Catonsville, MD
Summitview Manor, Yakima, WA
Sumner Lodge, Sumner, WA
Sumter Nursing Home, York, AL
Sun Air Convalescent Hospital, Panorama City, CA

Sun City Convalescent Center, Sun City, CA
Sun Dial Manor, Bristol, SD
Sun Prairie Health Care Center, Sun Prairie, WI
Sun Valley Lodge, Sun City, AZ
Sun Valley Manor, Saginaw, MI
Sun Valley Nursing Home, Alliance, OH
Sunair Home for Asthmatic Children, Tujunga, CA
Sunbury Community Hospital—Skilled Nursing Unit, Sunbury, PA
Sunbury Nursing Home, Sunbury, OH
Suncoast Manor, Saint Petersburg, FL
Suncoast Manor Nursing Home, Bradenton, FL
Suncoast Nursing Home, Saint Petersburg, FL
Sundale Rest Home, Morgantown, WV
Sunday Convalescent and Rest Home, Holly, MI
Sundial Manors Nursing Home, Pilot Point, TX
Sunharbor Manor, Roslyn Heights, NY
Sunhaven Convalescent and Rehabilitation Hospital, Fullerton, CA
Sunland Center—Gainesville Facility I, Gainesville, FL
Sunland Center—Gainesville Facility II, Gainesville, FL
Sunland Center—Gainesville Facility III, Gainesville, FL
Sunland Center—Miami Facility III, OPA Locka, FL
Sunland Center—Tallahassee, Tallahassee, FL
Sunland—Marianna Facility I, Marianna, FL
Sunland—Marianna Facility II, Marianna, FL
Sunlawn Nursing Home, Hightstown, NJ
Sunny Acres, Calhoun, KY
Sunny Acres, Covington, OH
Sunny Acres Care Center, Sidney, OH
Sunny Acres Convalescent Hospital, Fairfield, CA
Sunny Acres Nursing Center, Bad Axe, MI
Sunny Acres Nursing Home, Petersburg, IL
Sunny Acres Nursing Home, Chelmsford, MA
Sunny Acres Nursing Home, Williamsburg, MA
Sunny Acres Nursing Home Inc, Fork, SC
Sunny Acres of Dekalb Inc, Dekalb, TX
Sunny Acres Villa Inc, Denver, CO
Sunny Breeze Healthcare, Hamilton, OH
Sunny Crest Convalescent Home, Saxonburg, PA
Sunny Crest Nursing Center, Dysart, IA
Sunny Haven Institute for the Mentally Retarded, Sunnyside, WA
Sunny Hill, Denver, CO
Sunny Hill Nursing Home, Joliet, IL
Sunny Hill Rest Home, Madison, WI
Sunny Hill Retirement and Nursing Home, Tama, IA
Sunny Hills Convalescent Hospital, Fullerton, CA
Sunny Hills Nursing Center, Decatur, TX
Sunny Knoll Care Center Inc, Rockwell City, IA
Sunny Point Health Care Center Inc, Smithville, TN
Sunny Ridge, Sheboygan, WI
Sunny Ridge Manor, Nampa, ID
Sunny Shores Villas Health Center, Saint Petersburg, FL
Sunny Side Center, Enid, OK
Sunny Side Retirement Center 2, Taylor, TX

Sunny Vale Nursing Home, Wausau, WI
Sunny Vee Nursing Home Inc, Delaware, OH
Sunny View, Zanesville, OH
Sunny View Care Center, Ankeny, IA
Sunny View Home, Butler, PA
Sunny View Manor, Cupertino, CA
Sunny View Nursing Home, Coffeyville, KS
Sunny View Nursing Home, Warwick, RI
Sunny Vista Care Center, Portland, OR
Sunnycrest Manor, Dubuque, IA
Sunnydale Acres, Vandalia, IL
Sunnyfield Nursing Home Inc, Cranbury, NJ
Sunnyland Villa, Springfield, OH
Sunnymere Inc, Aurora, IL
Sunnypines Convalescent Center, Rockledge, FL
Sunnyrest Sanatorium, Colorado Springs, CO
Sunnyside Care Center, Salem, OR
Sunnyside Convalescent Hospital, Fresno, CA
Sunnyside Farms Nursing and Convalescent, Manasquan, NJ
Sunnyside Nursing Center, Torrance, CA
Sunnyside Nursing Home, Sarasota, FL
Sunnyside Nursing Home, Lake Park, MN
Sunnyside Nursing Home, East Syracuse, NY
Sunnyside Presbyterian Home—Health Care Unit, Harrisonburg, VA
Sunnyside Rest Home, Oxbridge, MA
Sunnyside Van Ness Convalescent Hospital, San Francisco, CA
Sunnyslope Care Center, Ottumwa, IA
Sunnyslope Nursing Home, Bowerston, OH
Sunnytide Nursing Home, Chickasha, OK
Sunnyvale Convalescent Hospital, Sunnyvale, CA
Sunnyvale Manor 1, Dallas, TX
Sunnyvale Manor 2, Dallas, TX
Sunnyvale Rest Home, Ashburnham, MA
Sunnyview District Home of Grundy County, Trenton, MO
Sunnyview Village Inc, Princeton, WI
Sunray East Convalescent Hospital, Los Angeles, CA
Sunray North Convalescent Hospital, Los Angeles, CA
Sunrest Health Facilities Inc, Port Jefferson, NY
Sunrise Convalescent Center Inc, Centerburg, OH
Sunrise Courts, Roselle-Add, IL
Sunrise—Goulds, Goulds, FL
Sunrise Group Home 1—Goulds, Goulds, FL
Sunrise Guest Home, Fredericksburg, IA
Sunrise Hill Care Center, Traer, IA
Sunrise Home, Two Harbors, MN
Sunrise House—Newhaven, Puyallup, WA
Sunrise Manor, Sioux City, IA
Sunrise Manor, Somerset, KY
Sunrise Manor and Convalescent Center Inc, Amelia, OH
Sunrise Manor Care Center, Fayetteville, AR
Sunrise Manor Nursing Home, Hodgenville, KY
Sunrise Manor Nursing Home, Bay Shore, NY
Sunrise Manor of Virden Inc, Virden, IL
Sunrise Nursing Home, Somerville, MA
Sunrise Nursing Home for the Blind, Milwaukee, WI
Sunrise Nursing Home of Georgia Inc, Moultrie, GA
Sunrise Terrace, Winfield, IA
Sunrise View Convalescent Center, Everett, WA

Sunset Boulevard Convalescent Hospital, Hayward, CA
Sunset Boulevard Convalescent Hospital 1, Hayward, CA
Sunset Care Center, Albany, OR
Sunset Care Center, Jacksonville, TX
Sunset Convalescent Hospital, Eureka, CA
Sunset Estates Inc, Tecumseh, OK
Sunset Estates of El Reno Inc, El Reno, OK
Sunset Estates of Enid Inc, Enid, OK
Sunset Haven Convalescent Hospital, Cherry Valley, CA
Sunset Haven Nursing Center Ltd, El Paso, TX
Sunset Haven Nursing Home, Curtis, NE
Sunset Heights Nursing Home, Belle Glade, FL
Sunset Hill Home for the Aged and Infirm, Lawrenceburg, KY
Sunset Home Inc, Maysville, MO
Sunset Home Inc, Bowman, ND
Sunset Home of the United Methodist Church, Quincy, IL
Sunset House, Toledo, OH
Sunset Knoll Inc, Aurelia, IA
Sunset Manor, Brush, CO
Sunset Manor, Frontenac, KS
Sunset Manor, Waverly, KS
Sunset Manor, Irene, SD
Sunset Manor Convalescent Hospital, El Monte, CA
Sunset Manor (Division of Woodstock Christian Care Inc), Woodstock, IL
Sunset Manor Nursing Home Inc, Greencastle, IN
Sunset Manor of Lexington Inc, Lexington, OK
Sunset Nursing and Retirement Home of Bowling Green, Bowling Green, MO
Sunset Nursing and Retirement Home of Elsberry, Elsberry, MO
Sunset Nursing and Retirement Home of Farmington, Farmington, MO
Sunset Nursing and Retirement Home of Union, Union, MO
Sunset Nursing Center, Concordia, KS
Sunset Nursing Home, Canton, IL
Sunset Nursing Home, Park Rapids, MN
Sunset Nursing Home, Boonville, NY
Sunset Nursing Home, Cleveland, OH
Sunset Nursing Home, Clute, TX
Sunset Nursing Home, Fairchild, WI
Sunset Nursing Home Inc, Ironton, OH
Sunset Point Nursing Center, Clearwater, FL
Sunset Terrace Convalescent Center, Coeur d'Alene, ID
Sunset Valley Haven, Chamberlain, SD
Sunset Valley Nursing Home, Cassville, MO
Sunset View, Millersburg, OH
Sunset Village Nursing Home, Roswell, NM
Sunset Village of the Ozarks, Waynesville, MO
Sunshine Gardens, Spokane, WA
Sunshine Haven, Lordsburg, NM
Sunshine Manor, Dexter, MO
Sunshine Nursing Home, Yankton, SD
Sunshine Nursing Home Inc, Stoneham, MA
Sunshine Nursing Home Inc, New London, TX
Sunshine Place, Harmony, MN
Sunshine Rest Home, Pontotoc, MS
Sunshine Terrace, Logan, UT
Sunshine Terrace Convalescent Hospital Inc, Los Angeles, CA
Sunshine Villa, Mora, MN
Sunshine Vista, Seattle, WA

Suntown at Montclair Convalescent Hospital, Montclair, CA
Sunwood Care Center, Redwood Falls, MN
Superior Care Home, Paducah, KY
Superior Shores Nursing Center, Munising, MI
Sur La Rue de Breen, Saint Paul, MN
Sur La Rue de Skillman, Maplewood, MN
Sur La Rue De Wheelock Ridge, Saint Paul, MN
Surf and Sand Nursing Home, Duluth, MN
Surfside Nursing Home, Far Rockaway, NY
Surry Community Nursing Center, Mount Airy, NC
Susan B Miller Nursing Homes Inc, Woodstock, VA
Susan Welch Rest Home, Middleborough, MA
Susans Nursing Home, Chillicothe, MO
Susanville Convalescent Hospital, Susanville, CA
Susque View Home Inc, Lock Haven, PA
Susquehanna Lutheran Village, Millersburg, PA
Susquehanna Nursing Home, Johnson City, NY
Sussex County Homestead, Newton, NJ
Sutton Community Home, Sutton, NE
Suwannee Valley Nursing Center, Jasper, FL
Swaim Health Center, Newville, PA
Swainsboro Nursing Home Inc, Swainsboro, GA
Swampscotta Nursing Home, South Windham, ME
Swan Manor Inc, Lacygne, KS
Swanholm Nursing Hotel, Saint Petersburg, FL
Swansea Rest Home Inc, Swansea, MA
Swedish Home for the Aged, Newton, MA
Sweeny House, Sweeny, TX
Sweet Memorial Nursing Home, Chinook, MT
Sweetbriar Development Center, West Columbia, TX
Sweetbriar Nursing Home, Bellville, TX
Sweetbriar Nursing Home, Brenham, TX
Sweetbriar Nursing Home, Columbus, TX
Sweetbriar Nursing Home, Taylor, TX
Sweetbrook Nursing Home, Williamstown, MA
Sweetwater Nursing Center, Sweetwater, TX
Sweetwater Valley Convalescent and Nursing Home Inc, Sweetwater, TN
Swift County Home, Benson, MN
Swiss Home Health Related Facility, Mount Kisco, NY
Swiss Villa Health Care Facility, Vevay, IN
Swiss Village Inc, Berne, IN
Swope Ridge Health Care Center, Kansas City, MO
Sycamore Manor Nursing Home, Montoursville, PA
Sycamore Park Convalescent Hospital, Los Angeles, CA
Sycamore Village Health Center, Kokomo, IN
Sydney House, Vicksburg, MS
Sykesville Eldercare Center, Sykesville, MD
Sylacauga Hospital and Nursing Home, Sylacauga, AL
Sylcox Nursing Home and Health Related Facility, Newburgh, NY
Sylvan Dell Nursing Home, Grand Haven, MI
Sylvan Manor Health Care Center, Silver Spring, MD
Sylvan Manor Inc, Bridgeport, CT
Sylvan Way, Bremerton, WA
Sylvester Health Care Inc, Sylvester, GA

Sylvester Nursing Home, Muncie, IN
Syl-View Health Care Center, Sylvania, GA
Syracuse Home Association, Balddwinsville, NY
Syrings Chalet, Blackfoot, ID
Taber Street Nursing Home, New Bedford, MA
Tabitha Home, Lincoln, NE
Table Rock Health Care Center, Kimberling City, MO
Tabor Manor Care Center, Tabor, IA
Tacoma Lutheran Home, Tacoma, WA
Tacoma Terrace Convalescent Center, Tacoma, WA
Tad Memorial Home, Plum City, WI
Taft Hospital and Convalescent Center, Taft, TX
Tahlequah Nursing Home, Tahlequah, OK
Tahoka Care Center, Tahoka, TX
Takamah S-C-H Inc, Tekamah, NE
Talihina Manor Nursing Home, Talihina, OK
Talladega Nursing Home Inc, Talladega, AL
Tallahassee Convalescent Home, Tallahassee, FL
Tallahassee Developmental Center, Tallahassee, FL
Tallahatchie General Hospital—Extended Care Facility, Charleston, MS
Tally Ho Manor, Boonton, NJ
Talmadge Park Health Care, East Haven, CT
Tamalpais, Larkspur, CA
Tamarac Convalescent Center, Tamarac, FL
Tamms Sheltered Care, Tamms, IL
Tampa Health Care Center, Tampa, FL
Tanglewood Care Center, Lake City, FL
Tanglewood Health Care Center, Ridgeway, SC
Tanner Care Home Inc, Topeka, KS
Tanner Chapel Manor Nursing Home, Phoenix, AZ
Tappahannock Manor Convalescent Center and Home for Adults, Tappahannock, VA
Tara Nursing Home, Boston, MA
Tara Nursing Home Inc, Framingham, MA
Tarpon Health Care Center, Tarpon Springs, FL
Tarpon Springs Convalescent Center, Tarpon Springs, FL
Tarrytown Hall Nursing Home, Tarrytown, NY
Tates Creek Personal and Intermediate Care Facility, Lexington, KY
Tattnall Nursing Center, Reidsville, GA
Taunton Female Charity Association Inc, Taunton, MA
Taunton Nursing Home, Taunton, MA
Tawes/Bland Bryant Nursing Center, Catonsville, MD
Taylor Home, Laconia, NH
Taylor Manor Nursing Home, Versailles, KY
Taylor Nursing Home Inc, Taylor, AR
Taylor Park Health Care Center, Rhinelander, WI
Taylor Total Living Center, Taylor, MI
Taylor's Health Care Inc—Riverview, Lucasville, OH
Taylorville Care Center Inc, Taylorville, IL
Teague Nursing Home, Teague, TX
Teakwood Manor, Stamford, TX
Teaneck Nursing Home, Teaneck, NJ
Teat Personal Care Home, Jackson, MS
Tecumseh Care Center, Tecumseh, NE
Tehema County Health Center, Red Bluff, CA
Tekakwitha Nursing Home, Sisseton, SD
Tekoa Care Center, Tekoa, WA
Tel Hai Retirement Community, Honeybrook, PA

Temple City Convalescent Hospital, Temple City, CA
Temple Manor Inc, Temple, OK
Temple Park Convalescent Hospital, Los Angeles, CA
Tender Care Home, Gulfport, MS
Tendercare—Clarksville, Clarksville, IN
Tendercare—Danville, Danville, IN
Teresa Rest Home Inc, East Haven, CT
Teresian House Nursing Home Co Inc, Albany, NY
Terrace Care Convalescent Hospital, Fresno, CA
Terrace Convalescent Hospital, Oakland, CA
Terrace Gardens, Oklahoma City, OK
Terrace Gardens Convalescent Center, Paramount, CA
Terrace Gardens Health Care Center, Colorado Springs, CO
Terrace Gardens Nursing Center Inc, Wichita, KS
Terrace Gardens Nursing Home, Midland, TX
Terrace Hill Manor, Emerson, NE
Terrace Manor, Dell Rapids, SD
Terrace Manor Nursing Home, Russellville, AL
Terrace Manor Nursing Home, Chicopee, MA
Terrace Nursing Home, Waukegan, IL
Terrace Park Convalescent Hospital, Tulare, CA
Terrace View Castle Nursing Home, Millersburg, OH
Terrace View Convalescent Center Inc, Seattle, WA
Terrace View Extended Care Facility, Lawrenceburg, IN
Terrace Villa, Salt Lake City, UT
Terrace West, Midland, TX
Terraceview Living Center, Shell Lake, WI
Terracina Convalescent Hospital, Redlands, CA
Terre Haute Nursing Home, Terre Haute, IN
Terrell Care Center, Terrell, TX
Terrell Convalescent Center 1, Terrell, TX
Terrell Convalescent Center 2, Terrell, TX
Terry Haven Nursing Home Inc, Mount Vernon, TX
Terwilliger Plaza Inc, Portland, OR
Teton Nursing Home, Choteau, MT
Texas County Missouri Health Care Center Inc, Licking, MO
Texas County Rest Home Inc, Houston, MO
Texas Healthcare Center, Lancaster, TX
Texas Terrace Convalescent, Saint Louis Park, MN
Texhoma Christian Care Center, Wichita Falls, TX
Texoma Health Care Center Inc, Kingston, OK
Thad A Saleeby Developmental Center, Hartsville, SC
Roland Thatcher Nursing Home, Wareham, MA
Theo Spivey Nursing Home, Gainesboro, TN
Theresa Grotta Center, West Orange, NJ
Theresa K Sexton Home, North Mankato, MN
Theresa K Sexton Home-North, North Mankato, MN
Theron Grainger Nursing Home Inc, Hughes Springs, TX
39 Summer House, Keene, NH
Thomas A Cocomo Memorial, Meriden, CT
Thomas Care Centers Inc, Houston, TX
Thomas County Care Center, Colby, KS

Thomas Dell Nursing Home Inc, Farmington, MO

Thomas Fitzgerald Veterans Home, Omaha, NE

Thomas House, Washington, DC

Thomas Manor Nursing Center, Mountain Grove, MO

Thomas Nursing Center, Thomas, OK

Thomas Nursing Center Inc, McLean, TX

Thomas Nursing Center Inc, Wellington, TX

Thomas Rest Haven, Coon Rapids, IA

Thomasville Health Care Center, Thomasville, GA

Thomasville Hospital and Nursing Home, Thomasville, AL

Thompson House, Brattleboro, VT

Thompson Nursing Home Inc, Canandaigua, NY

Thomson Manor Nursing Home Inc, Thomson, GA

Thorne Crest Retirement Center, Albert Lea, MN

Thornton Manor, Lansing, IA

Thornton Nursing Home, Northborough, MA

Thornwald Home, Carlisle, PA

Thoroughgood Nursing Home, Philadelphia, PA

Thorp Care Center Inc, Thorp, WI

Thousand Oaks Convalarium, Thousand Oaks, CA

The Three Fountains, Medford, OR

Three Oaks Intermediate Care Home, Macon, GA

Three Oaks Nursing Center, Evanston, IL

Three Oaks Nursing Center, Lexington, IL

Three Rivers Convalescent Center, Fort Wayne, IN

Three Rivers Convalescent Center, Cincinnati, OH

Three Rivers Health Care Center Inc, Painted Post, NY

Three Rivers Manor, Three Rivers, MI

Three Rivers Nursing Center, Marked Tree, AR

Three Sisters Nursing Home Inc, Indianapolis, IN

Three Springs Lodge, Chester, IL

Three Thirty-Five Ridgewood, Minneapolis, MN

Throckmorton Nursing Center, Throckmorton, TX

Thunderbird House, Duluth, MN

Tibbits Health Care Facility, White Plains, NY

Tidd Home, Woburn, MA

Tidings of Peace, Broken Arrow, OK

Tierra Pines Convalescent Center, Largo, FL

The Tieszen Memorial Home, Marion, SD

Tiffany Heights, Mound City, MO

Tiffany Rest and Retirement Home, Rockland, MA

Tiffany Square Convalescent Center, Saint Joseph, MO

Tiffany II Rest Home, Rockland, MA

Tiffin Developmental Center, Tiffin, OH

Tift Health Care Inc, Tifton, GA

Tifton Nursing Home, Tifton, GA

Tigard Care Center, Tigard, OR

Tiger Residential Programs (Fairview House), Denver, CO

Tillamook Care Center, Tillamook, OR

Tillers Nursing Home, Oswego, IL

Tilton Nursing Home Inc, California, MO

Tilton Terrace, Wilmington, DE

Timbercrest—Church of the Brethren Home, North Manchester, IN

Timberland Nursing Center, Nacogdoches, TX

Timberlane Manor Nursing Home, Edmond, OK

Timely Mission Nursing Home, Buffalo Center, IA

Timpanogos Psychiatric Unit, Provo, UT

Timpanogos Valley Care Center, Orem, UT

Tindles Personal Care Home, Cloverport, KY

Tioga Community Nursing Home, Tioga, ND

Tioga General Hospital, Waverly, NY

Tioga Manor Nursing Center, Tioga, LA

Tioga Nursing Home Inc, Waverly, NY

Tippecanoe Villa, West Lafayette, IN

Tipton Manor, Tipton, MO

Tipton Nursing Home, Tipton, IN

Tishomingo County Rest Home, Iuka, MS

Titonka Care Center, Titonka, IA

Titus Memorial Presbyterian Home, Sullivan, IL

Titusville Medical Services, Titusville, PA

Titusville Nursing and Convalescent Center, Titusville, FL

TLC Convalescent Hospital, El Cajon, CA

TLC Home for the Elderly, Ocean Springs, MS

TLC Nursing Center, Harlingen, TX

TLC Nursing Home Inc, Bremen, IN

Toccoa Nursing Center, Toccoa, GA

Tockwotton Home, Providence, RI

Todd Dickey Medical Center, Leavenworth, IN

Todholm Care Center, Springville, UT

Toledo Mental Health Center, Toledo, OH

Tolstoy Foundation Nursing Home Company Inc, Valley Cottage, NY

Tomah Care Center, Tomah, WI

Tomorrow's Hope Inc, Meridian, ID

Toms River Convalescent Center, Toms River, NJ

Tooele Valley Nursing Home, Tooele, UT

Toole County Nursing Home, Shelby, MT

Toombs Nursing and Intermediate Care Home, Lyons, GA

Topanga Terrace Convalescent Center, Canoga Park, CA

Topeka Convalescent Center, Topeka, KS

Topeka Presbyterian Manor Inc, Topeka, KS

Topham's Tiny Tots Care Center, Orem, UT

Torrance Convalescent Hospital, Torrance, CA

Torrance State Hospital—IMR Unit, Torrance, PA

Torrance State Hospital—Long Term Care Facility, Torrance, PA

Torrey Pines Care Center, Las Vegas, NV

Torrey Pines Convalescent Hospital, La Jolla, CA

Torrington Extend-A-Care Center, Torrington, CT

Total Care of Ottawa, Ottawa, OH

Totalcare Nursing Home of Paulding, Paulding, OH

Toth's Rest Home, Barberton, OH

Touhy Terrace Nursing Center, Chicago, IL

Touro Shakespeare Home, Algiers, LA

Tower Hill Nursing Home, Muskogee, OK

Tower Hill Rest Home, Fitchburg, MA

Tower Lodge Nursing Home, Wall Township, NJ

Tower Pavilion, Cicero, IL

Tower Village Inc, Saint Louis, MO

Towers Nursing Facility, Charlottesville, VA

Towers Nursing Home, Smithville, TX

Town and Country Intermediate Care Facility, Bakersfield, CA

Town and Country Manor, Milwaukee, WI

Town and Country Manor Health Care Center, Santa Ana, CA

Town and Country Manor Inc, Boerne, TX

Town and Country Nursing Center, Minden, LA

Town and Country Nursing Home, Lowell, MA

Town and Country Nursing Home, Midland, MI

Town and County Convalescent Center, Tampa, FL

Town Hall Estates, Wauconda, IL

Town Hall Estates, Rochester, MN

Town Hall Estates, Clayton, NM

Town Hall Estates, Breckenridge, TX

Town Hall Estates, Hillsboro, TX

Town Hall Estates, Keene, TX

Town Hall Estates, Rusk, TX

Town Hall Estates, Whitney, TX

Town Hall Estates Nursing Center, Sayre, OK

Town Hall Estates Nursing Home, Windsor, OH

Town Manor Nursing Home Inc, Lawrence, MA

Town of Vici Nursing Home, Vici, OK

Towne Avenue Convalescent Hospital, Pomona, CA

Towne House Health Center, Fort Wayne, IN

Towne Oaks Nursing Center, Ruston, LA

Towns County Nursing Home, Hiawassee, GA

Townsend Nursing Home, Boston, MA

Towson Convalescent Home Inc, Towson, MD

Trace Haven Nursing Home, Natchez, MS

Tracy Convalescent Hospital, Tracy, CA

Tracy Nursing Home, Tracy, MN

Tranquility Nursing Home, Randolph, VT

Traverse County Nursing Home, Wheaton, MN

Traverse Geriatric Village, Traverse City, MI

Traylor Nursing Home Inc, Roanoke, AL

The Traymore, Dallas, TX

Treasure Isle Nursing Home, North Bay Village, FL

Treasure Valley Manor, Boise, ID

Treats Falls, Orono, ME

Treemont Health Care Center, Houston, TX

Treemot Health Care Center, Dallas, TX

Tremont Nursing Center, Tremont, PA

Trempealea Health Care Center—Intermediate Care Facility, Whitehall, WI

Trenton Convalescent Center, Trenton, MI

Tressie's Nursing Home, Oberlin, OH

Treutlen County Nursing Home, Soperton, GA

Trevecca Health Care Center, Nashville, TN

Trevilla of Golden Valley, Golden Valley, MN

Trevilla of New Brighton, New Brighton, MN

Trevilla of Robbinsdale, Robbinsdale, MN

Tri State Manor Nursing Home, Lansing, IL

Triad Rehabilitation Center Inc, Winston-Salem, NC

Tri-City Convalescent Center, Oceanside, CA

Tri-City Golden Age Convalescent Hospital and Home, Baldwin Park, CA

Tri-City Nursing Center, Bay City, MI

Tri-County Convalescent Home Inc, Adamsville, TN

Tri-County Extended Care Center, Fairfield, OH

Tri-County Hospital, Wadena, MN

Tri-County Manor Nursing Center, Horton, KS

Tri-County Memorial Hospital—Nursing Home, Whitehall, WI

Tri-County Nursing Home, Vandalia, MO
Tri-County Nursing Home Inc, Louisville, MS
Tri-County Nursing Home Inc, Richland, MO
Tri-County Retirement and Nursing Home, Hatton, ND
Trigg County Manor Personal Care Home, Cadiz, KY
Trimble Nursing Center, Bedford, KY
Trimont Nursing Home, Trimont, MN
Trinidad State Nursing Home, Trinidad, CO
Trinity Court Inc, Little Rock, AR
Trinity Home, Dayton, OH
Trinity House, Sacramento, CA
Trinity Lutheran Home, Round Rock, TX
Trinity Lutheran Home, Shiner, TX
Trinity Lutheran Manor, Merriam, KS
Trinity Manor, Dodge City, KS
Trinity Medical Center—Nursing Unit, Minot, ND
Trinity Memorial Hospital, Trinity, TX
Trinity Towers, Midland, TX
Tripoli Nursing Home, Tripoli, IA
Tripp Shelter Care Home, Cobden, IL
Tri-State Convalescent Center, Clarkston, WA
Tri-State Nursing Home, Lexa, AR
Troost Avenue Nursing Home, Kansas City, MO
Tropico Convalescent Hospital, Glendale, CA
Troy Hills House, Troy Hills, NJ
Troy House Inc, Troy, MO
True Light Nursing Home, Sandusky, OH
Trull Nursing Home, Biddeford, ME
Truman Health Center, Clinton, MO
Truman Lake Manor Inc, Lowry City, MO
Truman Medical Center—East, Kansas City, MO
Trumbull Saint Mary's Convalescent Home and Rest Home, Trumbull, CT
Trussville Nursing Home Inc, Trussville, AL
Tucker House, Philadelphia, PA
Tucker Nursing Center, Tucker, GA
Tudor House Nursing Home, Jamaica Plain, MA
Tudor Oaks Health Center, Hales Corners, WI
Tuell Nursing Home Inc, Melrose, MA
Tuff Memorial Home, Hills, MN
Tule Lake Manor, Tacoma, WA
Tulia Care Center, Tulia, TX
Tully Brook Rest Home, Athol, MA
Tulsa Christian Home Inc, Tulsa, OK
Tulsa Nursing Center, Tulsa, OK
Tupelo Manor Nursing Home, Tupelo, MS
Turner Geriatric Center, Galveston, TX
Turner Nursing Home, Lincoln Heights, OH
Turner Nursing Home, Childress, TX
Turner Rest Home, Greenfield, MA
Turtle Creek Health Care Center, Jacksonville, FL
Tuscola County Medical Care Facility, Caro, MI
Tustin Convalescent Hospital, Tustin, CA
Tustin Manor, Tustin, CA
Tutor Nursing Home Inc, Temple, TX
Twain Haven Nursing Home, Perry, MO
Tweeten Memorial Hospital—Nursing Home, Spring Grove, MN
Twilight Acres Inc, Wall Lake, IA
Twilight Acres Nursing Home, Eugene, OR
Twilight Gardens Home Inc, Norwalk, OH
Twilight Haven, Fresno, CA
Twilight Haven Sheltered Care Home, Louisville, IL
Twilight Home, Corsicana, TX

Twilight Nursing Home Inc, Jeffersonville, IN
Twilight Nursing Home Inc, Bangs, TX
Twilight Personal Care Home, Woodburn, KY
Twin Birch Health Care Center, Spring Park, MN
Twin Cedar Nursing Home, Post, TX
Twin City Health Care Center Inc, Uhrichsville, OH
Twin City Linnea Home, Saint Paul, MN
Twin City Nursing Home, Gas City, IN
Twin City Nursing Home, Hartshorne, OK
Twin Lakes Care Center, Burlington, NC
Twin Maples Home Inc, Durham, CT
Twin Maples Nursing Home, McArthur, OH
Twin Oaks, Mansfield, OH
Twin Oaks Community Living Facility, Pekin, IL
Twin Oaks Convalescent Center, Alma, GA
Twin Oaks Convalescent Center, Jacksonville, TX
Twin Oaks Convalescent Home Inc, South Boston, VA
Twin Oaks Estate Inc, O'Fallon, MO
Twin Oaks Nursing and Convalescent Home, LaPlace, LA
Twin Oaks Nursing Center, Morristown, NJ
Twin Oaks Nursing Home, Campbelltown, PA
Twin Oaks Nursing Home Inc, Mobile, AL
Twin Oaks Retirement Center, Waco, TX
Twin Palms Sanitarium, Artesia, CA
Twin Pines Care Center, Salt Lake City, UT
Twin Pines Healthcare, Santa Paula, CA
Twin Pines Nursing Center, Lewisville, TX
Twin Pines Nursing Home, Loveland, CO
Twin Pines Nursing Home, Victoria, TX
Twin Pines Retreat, Cuyahoga Falls, OH
Twin Rivers Care Center, Anoka, MN
Twin Rivers Medical Center, Arkadelphia, AR
Twin Rivers Nursing Care Center, Defiance, OH
Twin Towers, The United Methodist Home on College Hill, Cincinnati, OH
Twin Town Treatment Center, Saint Paul, MN
Twin View Nursing Home, Twin City, GA
Twin Willow Nursing Center, Salem, IL
Twinbrook Nursing and Convalescent Home, Erie, PA
Twinbrook Nursing Home, Louisville, KY
Twinbrooke South—McAllen, McAllen, TX
Twinbrooke South-San Benito, San Benito, TX
Twin-M Nursing Home, Canton, OH
252 West Wabasha, Winona, MN
214 Park Avenue Home, Faribault, MN
Twomey Rest Home, Lynn, MA
Tylertown Extended Care Center, Tylertown, MS
Tyrone Medical Inn, Saint Petersburg, FL
Tyson Manor Health Facility, Montgomery, AL
Uihlein Mercy Center Inc, Lake Placid, NY
Ukiah Convalescent Hospital, Ukiah, CA
Ulster County Infirmary/Health Related Facility, Kingston, NY
Unicoi County Nursing Home, Erwin, TN
Union City Health Care Center, Union City, TN
Union City Manor Nursing Center, Union City, TN
Union County Nursing Home, Blairsville, GA
Union County Skilled Nursing Home, Anna, IL
Union Forge Nursing Home, Lebanon, NJ
Union House Nursing Home Inc, Glover, VT

Union Manor, Marysville, OH
Union Memorial Hospital, Monroe, NC
Union Mission Nursing Home Inc, Haverhill, MA
Union Printers Home, Colorado Springs, CO
Unitarian Universalist Home, Germantown, PA
United Cerebral Palsy Association Home of Cuyahoga County, Cleveland, OH
United Cerebral Palsy Intermediate Care Facility, Oklahoma City, OK
United Cerebral Palsy Residential Center, Seattle, WA
United Cerebral Palsy/Spastic Childrens Foundation, Los Angeles, CA
United Cerebral Palsy/Spastic Children's Foundation, Sylmar, CA
United Christian Church Home, Annville, PA
United Church Colony Homes Inc, Gasport, NY
The United Church Retirement Home, Newton, NC
United Convalescent of Post, Post, TX
United District Hospital and Home, Staples, MN
United Health Care Center, Big Spring, TX
United Health Corporation, Saint Petersburg, FL
United Health Services, Wilson Extended Care Facility, Johnson City, NY
United Helpers Canton Nursing Home Inc, Canton, NY
United Helpers, Cedars Nursing Home, Ogdensburg, NY
United Helpers Nursing Home Inc, Ogdensburg, NY
United Home for Aged Hebrews, New Rochelle, NY
United Memorial Hospital, Greenville, MI
United Methodist Convalescent Homes of Connecticut Inc, Shelton, CT
United Methodist Health Care Center, East Providence, RI
United Methodist Home, Topeka, KS
United Methodist Home, Pittsburgh, PA
United Methodist Home and Hopsital, Meadville, PA
United Methodist Home in Roanoke—Nursing Home Unit, Roanoke, VA
United Methodist Memorial Home, Warren, IN
United Methodist Village, Lawrenceville, IL
United Nursing Home for the Aged Inc, New Rochelle, NY
United Odd Fellow and Rebekah Home, Bronx, NY
United Pioneer Home, Luck, WI
United Presbyterian Home, Washington, IA
United Presbyterian Home at Syosset Inc, Woodbury, NY
United Presbyterian Home for Aged People, Pittsburgh, PA
United Presbyterian Home of Hollidaysburg, Hollidaysburg, PA
United Presbyterian Home of Philipsburg, Philipsburg, PA
United Retirement Center, Brookings, SD
United Zion Home Inc, Lititz, PA
Unity House, Worthington, MN
University Convalescent and Nursing Home, Livonia, MI
University Convalescent Center—East, Deland, FL

University Convalescent Center—West, Deland, FL

University Health Care Center, Minneapolis, MN

University Health Care Center Inc, Nashville, TN

University Heights Nursing Home, Albany, NY

University Hills Christian Nursing Home, Denver, CO

University Hospital—Extended Care Facility, Augusta, GA

University Manor, Lubbock, TX

University Manor Convalescent Center, Spokane, WA

University Medical Pavilion, Lebanon, TN

University Nursing Center, Upland, IN

University Nursing Center, Greenville, NC

University Nursing Center, McKinney, TX

University Nursing Home, Bronx, NY

University Nursing Home Inc, Wheaton, MD

University Park, Richmond, VA

University Park Care Center, Muskegon, MI

University Park Convalescent Center, Tampa, FL

University Park Heritage Manor, Wichita Falls, TX

University Park Nursing Center, Fort Wayne, IN

University Terrace Good Samaritan Village, Las Cruces, NM

University Village Inc, Tulsa, OK

Upjohn Community Nursing Home, Kalamazoo, MI

Upland Convalescent Hospital, Upland, CA

Uplands Home for Church Women, Baltimore, MD

Upper Bucks Nursing and Convalescent Center, Quakertown, PA

Upper Valley Rest Home, Spearfish, SD

Upton County Convalescent Center, McCamey, TX

Uptown Home for the Aged, Philadelphia, PA

Uptown Shelter Care Home Inc, Chicago, IL

Urbana Nursing Home, Urbana, IL

Utah State Training School, American Fork, UT

Utah Valley Care Center, Provo, UT

Utopia Estates Rest Home Inc, Medway, OH

Uvalde Nursing Center, Uvalde, TX

Vacationland Rest Home, Sandusky, OH

Val Mory's Haven, Columbus, NE

Valborg Lutheran Home, Des Moines, IA

Vale View Convalescent Center, Valparaiso, IN

Valerie Nursing Home, Dayton, OH

Valle Verde Health Facility, Santa Barbara, CA

Valle Vista Care Center, The Dalles, OR

Valle Vista Convalescent Hospital Inc, Escondido, CA

Valle Vista Manor, Lewistown, MT

Vallejo Convalescent Hospital, Vallejo, CA

Valley Brook Park Inc, Wetumpka, AL

Valley Care and Guidance Center, Fresno, CA

Valley Care Center, Porterville, CA

Valley Care Center, Idaho Falls, ID

Valley Care Center, Okanogan, WA

Valley Convalescent Hospital, Bakersfield, CA

Valley Convalescent Hospital, El Centro, CA

Valley Convalescent Hospital, Fresno, CA

Valley Convalescent Hospital, San Bernardino, CA

Valley Convalescent Hospital, Watsonville, CA

Valley Crest Nursing Home, Wilkes-Barre, PA

Valley Grande Manor, Weslaco, TX

Valley Grande Manor Inc, Brownsville, TX

Valley Group Home 1, Moorhead, MN

Valley Group Home 2, Karlstad, MN

Valley Haven Rest Home, Sanders, KY

Valley Haven Rest Home Inc, Wellsburg, WV

Valley Health Care Center, Chilhowie, VA

Valley Health Care Center, Hayward, WI

Valley Hi Nursing Home, Woodstock, IL

Valley Hi Nursing Home, Alpine, TX

Valley Hi Nursing Home Inc, Denver, CO

Valley Home, Thief River Falls, MN

Valley Homes, Mount Vernon, WA

Valley Hospital, Palmer, AK

Valley House Health Care, Tucson, AZ

Valley Manor Care Center, Montrose, CO

Valley Manor Convalescent Hospital, Concord, CA

Valley Manor Nursing Home, Denver, CO

Valley Manor Nursing Home, New Philadelphia, OH

Valley Manor Nursing Home, Plymouth, WI

Valley Manor Nursing Home, Plymouth, WI

Valley Manor Nursing Home Division, Rock Valley, IA

Valley Memorial Home—Almonte, Grand Forks, ND

Valley Memorial Home—Medical Park, Grand Forks, ND

Valley Nursing and Convalescent Center Inc, Baltimore, MD

Valley Nursing Home, Billings, MT

Valley Nursing Home, Westwood, NJ

Valley Nursing Home, Saint Marys, OH

Valley Nursing Home, Chilhowie, VA

Valley Palms Convalescent Hospital, North Hollywood, CA

Valley Park Nursing Home, Valley Park, MO

Valley Rest Home, Eden Valley, MN

Valley Rest Nursing Home, Totowa, NJ

Valley Road Nursing Home, Salem, OH

Valley Skilled Nursing Facility, Sacramento, CA

Valley Springs Health Center, Cleveland, OH

Valley Terrace Nursing Center, Puyallup, WA

Valley View Care Center, Anson, TX

Valley View Care Centre, North Platte, NE

Valley View Care Home, Lawrence, KS

Valley View Care Inc, Nebraska City, NE

Valley View Castle Nursing Home, Millersburg, OH

Valley View Estates Nursing Home, Hamilton, MT

Valley View Health Care, Rome, GA

Valley View Health Care Center, Canon City, CO

Valley View Health Care Facility, Marksville, LA

Valley View Home, Beaumont, CA

Valley View Home, Glasgow, MT

Valley View Home, Wausa, NE

Valley View Home, Altoona, PA

Valley View Home, Granbury, TX

Valley View Lodge, Norfolk, NE

Valley View Lodge, Eastland, TX

Valley View Manor, Craig, CO

Valley View Manor, Lamberton, MN

Valley View Manor, Frankfort, OH

Valley View Manor, LaGrande, OR

Valley View Manor, Saratoga, WY

Valley View Manor Inc, Frenchtown, NJ

Valley View Manor Nursing Home, Norwich, NY

Valley View Medical Center, Cedar City, UT

Valley View Nursing Center, Eldora, IA

Valley View Nursing Home, Baltimore, MD

Valley View Nursing Home, Lenox, MA

Valley View Nursing Home, Houston, MN

Valley View Nursing Home, Akron, OH

Valley View Nursing Home, Lancaster, OH

Valley View Nursing Home, Martins Ferry, OH

Valley View Nursing Home, Cheswick, PA

Valley View Nursing Home, Berkeley Springs, WV

Valley View Nursing Home Inc, Valley Falls, KS

Valley View Nursing Home Inc, Westfield, MA

Valley View Professional Care Center, Junction City, KS

Valley View Residential Care Home, Bayfield, CO

Valley View Residential Center, Milwaukee, WI

Valley View Villa Nursing Home, Fort Morgan, CO

Valley View Village, Des Moines, IA

Valley Villa Care Center, Renton, WA

Valley Vista Care Center, Junction City, KS

Valley Vista Convalescent Center 59, Saint Maries, ID

Valley Vista Good Samaritan Center, Wamego, KS

Valley Vue Nursing Home, Armstrong, IA

Valley West Convalescent Hospital, Williams, CA

Valley West Retirement Center, Eugene, OR

Valleyview Nursing Home Inc, Jordan, MN

Vallhaven Care Center, Neehan, WI

Valliant Nursing Center Inc, Valliant, OK

Valvista Pavillion, Athens, TX

Van Allen Nursing Home, Little Falls, NY

Van Ark Nursing Home, Tucumcari, NM

Van Buren Convalescent Center, Belleville, MI

Van Buren County Memorial Nursing Home, Clinton, AR

Van Buren Good Samaritan Center, Keosauqua, IA

Van Buren Hall, Green Bay, WI

Van Buren Nursing Center, Van Buren, AR

Van Dora Nursing Home Inc, Foxboro, MA

Van Doren Nursing Home, Rego Park, NY

Van Duyn Home and Hospital, Syracuse, NY

Van Dyks Nursing and Convalescent, Ridgewood, NJ

Van Dyk's Nursing and Convalescent Home, Montclair, NJ

Van Hook School, Deland, FL

Van Rensselaer Manor, Troy, NY

Van Wert Manor, Van Wert, OH

VanAyer Manor Nursing Center, Martin, TN

Vanceburg Health Care, Vanceburg, KY

Vanco Manor Nursing Home, Goodlettsville, TN

Vancrest, Van Wert, OH

Vanderklish Hall Nursing Home, Newton, MA

Vanguard Extended Care, Plymouth, MN

Vantage Convalescent Center, Phoenix, AZ

Varnum Park Rest Home, Waltham, MA

Vasa Lutheran Home for Children, Red Wing, MN

Vegas Valley Convalescent Hospital, Las Vegas, NV

Venango Manor, Franklin, PA

Venice Nursing Pavilion—North, Venice, FL

Venice Nursing Pavilion—South, Venice, FL

Venoy Continued Care Center, Wayne, MI

Ventura Estates, Newbury Park, CA

Ventura Estates Health Manor, Newbury Park, CA

The Venturan Convalescent Center, Ventura, CA

VerDelle Village, Saint Albans, VT

Verdries Nursing Home, Kalamazoo, MI

Verdugo Valley Convalescent Hospital, Montrose, CA

Verdugo Vista Convalescent Hospital, La Crescenta, CA

Verland Foundation Inc, Sewickly, PA

Vermillion Convalescent Center, Clinton, IN

Vermillion Health Care Center, Kaplan, LA

Vermillion Manor Nursing Home, Danville, IL

Vermont Achievement Center, Rutland, VT

Vermont Knolls Convalescent Hospital, Los Angeles, CA

Vernon Care Center, Vernon, TX

Vernon Convalescent Hospital, Los Angeles, CA

Vernon Green Nursing Home, Vernon, VT

Vernon Hall Inc, Cambridge, MA

Vernon House Inc, Framingham, MA

Vernon Manor, Viroqua, WI

Vernon Manor Children's Home, Wabash, IN

Vernon Manor Health Care Facility, Vernon, CT

Vero Beach Care Center Inc, Vero Beach, FL

Verrazano Nursing Home, Staten Island, NY

Vespers Nursing Home, Wilkesboro, NC

Vestal-Johnson Inc, Vestal, NY

Via Health Care Center for the Hermitage Methodist Home, Richmond, VA

Vian Nursing Home, Vian, OK

Vicksburg Convalescent Home, Vicksburg, MS

Vicksburg Trace Haven, Vicksburg, MS

Victor Cullen Center, Sabillasville, MD

Victoria Haven Nursing Facility, Norwood, MA

Victoria Health Care Center, Asheville, NC

Victoria Home for Retired Men and Women, Ossining, NY

Victoria Martin Nursing Home, Saint Petersburg, FL

Victoria Nursing Home, Portland, OR

Victorian Convalescent Hospital Inc, San Francisco, CA

Victorian Manor, Scappoose, OR

Victorian Mansion Retirement Home, Attleboro, MA

Victorian Villa, Canton, ME

Victory Lake Nursing Center, Hyde Park, NY

Victory Memorial Hospital—Nursing Home, Stanley, WI

Victory Park Nursing Home, Norwood, OH

Victory Way House, Craig, CO

Vienna Golden State Convalescent Hospital, Lodi, CA

View Crest Convalescent Home Inc, Tacoma, WA

View Heights Convalescent Hospital, Los Angeles, CA

Viewcrest Nursing Home, Duluth, MN

Vigo County Home, Terre Haute, IN

The Viking Intermediate Care Facility, Cape Elizabeth, ME

Viking Manor Nursing Home, Ulen, MN

The Villa Camillus, Columbia Station, OH

Villa Campana, Tucson, AZ

Villa Capri Manor, Maryland Heights, MO

Villa Care Center, Cleveland, OH

Villa Cascade Nursing Home, Lebanon, OR

Villa Clement, West Allis, WI

Villa Convalescent Center Inc, Troy, OH

Villa Convalescent Hospital, Riverside, CA

Villa Del Sol, Marshalltown, IA

Villa Demarillac Nursing Home Inc, Pittsburgh, PA

Villa Elena Convalescent Hospital, Norwalk, CA

Villa Elizabeth, Grand Rapids, MI

Villa Feliciana Geriatric Hospital, Jackson, LA

Villa Gardens Health Care Unit, Pasadena, CA

Villa Haven, Breckenridge, TX

Villa Homes West Inc, Monclova, OH

Villa Inn Home, Des Moines, IA

Villa Inn Nursing Center, Palestine, TX

Villa Loretto Nursing Home, Mount Calvary, WI

Villa Manor Care Center Inc, Porterville, CA

Villa Manor Nursing Home, Lakewood, CO

Villa Maria, Mulvane, KS

Villa Maria, Minneapolis, MN

Villa Maria Convalescent Home Inc, Plainfield, CT

Villa Maria Convalescent Hospital, Santa Maria, CA

Villa Maria Geriatric Center, Tucson, AZ

Villa Maria Healthcare Center, Hurley, WI

Villa Maria Healthcare Ltd, Fargo, ND

Villa Mary Immaculate, Albany, NY

Villa Mercy Inc, Daphne, AL

Villa North Nursing Home, Toledo, OH

Villa North Nursing Home, Toledo, OH

Villa Northwest Convalescent Center, Houston, TX

Villa Nursing Center Inc, Arlington, TX

Villa Nursing Home, Portsmouth, OH

Villa Oaks Convalescent Hospital, Pasadena, CA

Villa of Divine Providence, Lansdale, PA

Villa of Saint Francis Nursing Home, Morris, MN

Villa of the Woods, Fort Wayne, IN

Villa Park Care Center, Fort Dodge, IA

Villa Pines Nursing Center, Friendship, WI

Villa Pueblo Towers, Pueblo, CO

Villa Rosa Nursing Home, Mitchellville, MD

Villa Royal Health Care Center, Medford, OR

Villa Saint Cyril, Highland Park, IL

Villa Saint Vincent, Crookston, MN

Villa Sancta Anna Home for the Aged, Cleveland, OH

Villa Scalabrini, Melrose Park, IL

Villa Siena, Mountain View, CA

Villa Siesta Nursing Home, Van, TX

Villa Teresa Nursing Home, Harrisburg, PA

Villa Terrace Intermediate Care Facility, Bakersfield, CA

Villa Vista, Cromwell, MN

The Village, Cameron, MO

The Village at Westerville Nursing Center, Westerville, OH

Village Care Center, Lee's Summit, MO

Village Care Center, Galion, OH

Village Convalescent Center, Gresham, OR

Village Convalescent Center, McAllen, TX

Village Creek Manor, Wynne, AR

Village East, Aurora, CO

Village East Nursing Home, Tyler, TX

Village Green, Phoenix, AZ

Village House, Newport, RI

Village Inn, Dixon, IL

Village Manor, Greenwood, IN

Village Manor Nursing Home, Boston, MA

Village Manor Nursing Home, Lincoln, NE

Village North Residential Center, Saint Louis, MO

Village Nursing Home, Sullivan, IN

Village Nursing Home, Hico, TX

Village Nursing Home Inc, Skokie, IL

Village Nursing Home Inc, New York, NY

Village Rest Home, Easton, MA

Village Rest Home, Leominster, MA

Village Sheltered Care Home, Cobden, IL

Village Square Nursing Center, East Orwell, OH

Village Villa, Nortonville, KS

Village Vista Skilled Nursing Facility, Lancaster, PA

Villas of Shannon Nursing Home, Shannon, IL

Ville de Sante Nursing Home, Omaha, NE

Villisca Good Samaritan Center, Villisca, IA

Vincennes Nursing Home, Vincennes, IN

Vincentian Home for the Chronically Ill, Pittsburgh, PA

Vindobona Nursing Home Inc, Braddock Heights, MD

Vinewood Nursing Home, Plainfield, IN

Vintage Convalescent Hospital, Saint Helena, CA

Vintage Villa, Dexter, MO

Violet Tschetter Memorial Home, Huron, SD

Virgil Sanitarium and Convalescent Hospital, Los Angeles, CA

Virginia Baptist Home Inc, Culpeper, VA

Virginia Baptist Homes Inc—Health Care Unit, Newport News, VA

Virginia Baptist Hospital, Lynchburg, VA

Virginia Gay Hospital, Vinton, IA

Virginia Hall, Shreveport, LA

The Virginia Home, Richmond, VA

Virginia Lee Care Center, Tiffin, OH

Virginia Manor Care Center, Holden, MO

Virginia Manor Convalescent Home Inc, Everett, WA

Virginia Medical Center and Nursing Home, Virginia, MN

Virginia Mennonite Home Inc—Health Care Unit, Harrisonburg, VA

Virginia Nursing Home, Waukesha, WI

Virginia Synod Lutheran Home at Roanoke, Roanoke, VA

Virginian, Fairfax, VA

Virginia's Rest Home, Paducah, KY

Visalia Convalescent Hospital, Visalia, CA

Vista Continuing Care Center, Pasadena, TX

Vista Del Cerro Convalescent Center, El Cajon, CA

Vista Del Mar Care Center, Los Angeles, CA

Vista Del Monte, Santa Barbara, CA

Vista Del Rio Medical Center, Kansas City, MO

Vista Gardens Nursing Home, Red Oak, IA

Vista Golden Age Convalescent Home, Vista, CA

Vista Grande Nursing, Cortez, CO

Vista Grande Villa, Jackson, MI

Vista Hills Health Care Center, El Paso, TX

Vista Laguna Aftercare Facility Inc, Chicago, IL

Vista Nursing Home, Heavener, OK

Vista Pacifica Convalescent Home, West Riverside, CA

Vista Pacifica—A Center for Rehabilitation and Growth, West Riverside, CA

Vista Ray Convalescent Hospital, Lodi, CA

Vista Ray Convalescent Hospital 2, Lodi, CA

Vistavue, Kennewick, WA
Vivian's Nursing Home, Amarillo, TX
Vogue Retirement Residence, Fayette, MO
Voiers Convalescent Center, South Shore, KY
Voila Behling Memorial Home, Clintonville, WI
Volmer Nursing Home Inc, North Vassalboro, ME
W K Nursing Home Corporation, Bronx, NY
W L Jaquith Home, Sanatorium, MS
W W Spradling Rest Home, Louisville, KY
Wabash Christian Retirement Home, Carmi, IL
Wabash Healthcare Center, Wabash, IN
Wabasha Nursing Home, Wabasha, MN
Wabasso Health Care Center, Wabasso, MN
Wachusett Manor Nursing Home, Gardner, MA
Waconia Healthcare Center, Waconia, MN
Waddell Nursing Home, Galax, VA
Waddington Convalescent Home, Fayette City, PA
Wadesboro Nursing Home, Wadesboro, NC
Wadsworth Health Care Center Inc, Wadsworth, OH
Wahiawa General Hospital, Wahiawa, HI
Wahpeton Nursing Center, Wahpeton, ND
Waimano Training School and Hospital, Pearl City, HI
Waite Park Nursing Home Inc, Waite Park, MN
Wakefield Health Care Center, Wakefield, NE
Wakonda Heritage Manor, Wakonda, SD
Wakulla Manor, Crawfordville, FL
Walbridge Memorial Convalescent Wing, Meeker, CO
Walden House Healthcare Nursing Home, Concord, MA
Waldon Healthcare Center, Kenner, LA
Waldron Health Care Home Inc, Waldron, IN
Walker Care Center, Grand Rapids, MI
Walker Care Center, Centralia, WA
Walker Convalescent Hospital Inc, Richmond, CA
Walker Methodist Health Center Inc, Minneapolis, MN
Walker Nursing Home Inc, Virginia, IL
Walker Post Manor, Oxford, NE
Walker's Veterans Home, Spearfish, SD
Wallace Nursing Center Inc, Terre Haute, IN
The Wallingford, Wallingford, PA
Wallingford Convalescent Home Inc, Wallingford, CT
Wallowa County Memorial Hospital, Enterprise, OR
Walnut Convalescent Hospital, Long Beach, CA
Walnut Creek Convalescent Hospital Inc, Walnut Creek, CA
Walnut Creek Nursing Home, Oklahoma City, OK
Walnut Grove Nursing Home, Grandview, WA
Walnut Hill Convalescent Center, Petersburg, VA
Walnut Hill Convalescent Home, New Britain, CT
Walnut Hills Nursing Home, Walnut Creek, OH
Walnut Hills Pavillion, Massillon, OH
Walnut Manor, Walnut, IL
Walnut Manor Care Center, Clarksburg, OH
Walnut Mountain Care Center, Liberty, NY
Walnut Place, Dallas, TX

Walnut Ridge Convalescent Center, Walnut Ridge, AR
Walnut Valley Manor, Augusta, KS
Walnut Whitney Convalescent Hospital, Carmichael, CA
Walsenburg Care Center Inc, Walsenburg, CO
Walter J Lawson Memorial Home for Children, Rockford, IL
Walter P Carter Center—Mental Retardation Unit, Baltimore, MD
Walter Reed Convalescent Center Inc, Gloucester, VA
Walterboro Community Residence, Walterboro, SC
Waltham Nursing Home Inc, Waltham, MA
Walton County Convalescent Center, DeFuniak Springs, FL
Walton County Hospital Convalescent Wing, Monroe, GA
Walton Home, Saint Louis, MO
Walton Home for the Aged, Barnesville, OH
Walton Nursing Home, Richmond, ME
Wapakoneta Manor, Wapakoneta, OH
Wapato Convalescent Center, Wapato, WA
Wapello Nursing Home, Wapello, IA
Ward County Nursing Home, Monahans, TX
Ward Nursing Home, Tahlequah, OK
Ware Manor Intermediate Care Facility, Waycross, GA
Wareheime Residential Care, Greeley, CO
Warm Springs State Hospital, Warm Springs, MT
Warner Care Home 1, Cokato, MN
Warner Care Home 2, Cokato, MN
Warner Care Home 3, Cokato, MN
Warnerview Convalescent Hospital, Alturas, CA
Warren Haven, Oxford, NJ
Warren Manor Nursing Home, Selma, AL
Warren Medical Services, Warren, PA
Warren Memorial Hospital, Front Royal, VA
Warren Nursing Home Inc, Warren, PA
Warren P Eustis House, Eagan, MN
Warren Park Nursing Home, Indianapolis, IN
Warren State Hospital—Long Term Care Facility, Warren, PA
Warren Village, Warren, MI
Warrensburg Manor Care Center, Warrensburg, MO
Warrensville Center, Warrensville Heights, OH
Warroad Care Center, Warroad, MN
Warsaw Health Care Center, Warsaw, VA
Warsaw Nursing Home, Warsaw, IN
Wartburg Nursing Home, Mount Vernon, NY
Wartburg Nursing Home Inc, Brooklyn, NY
Warwick Health Centre, Warwick, RI
Warwick Manor, Warwick, RI
Warwick Manor Nursing Home, Kansas City, MO
Warwick Rest Home Inc, Warwick, RI
Wasatch Care Center, Ogden, UT
Wasatch County Hospital—Skilled Nursing Facility, Heber City, UT
Wasatch Villa, Salt Lake City, UT
The Washington, Cincinnati, OH
Washington and Jane Smith Home, Chicago, IL
Washington Care Center, Washington, IA
Washington Center for the Aging, Washington, DC
Washington Christian Village, Washington, IL
Washington Convalescent Hospital, San Leandro, CA

Washington County Convalescent Center, Chipley, FL
Washington County Extended Care Facility, Sandersville, GA
Washington County Health Center, Washington, PA
Washington County Hospital and Nursing Home, Chatom, AL
Washington County Public Hospital and Nursing Home Unit, Akron, CO
Washington County Woman's Home, Marietta, OH
Washington Home for Incurables, Washington, DC
Washington Hospital—Extended Care Facility, Washington, PA
The Washington House—Health Care Unit, Alexandria, VA
Washington Manor, Dayton, OH
Washington Manor Convalescent Hospital, San Leandro, CA
Washington Manor Nursing and Rehabilitation Center, Hollywood, FL
Washington Manor Nursing Home, Kenosha, WI
Washington Nursing and Convalescent, Los Angeles, CA
Washington Nursing Center Annex, Washington, IN
Washington Nursing Center Inc, Washington, IN
Washington Odd Fellows Home, Walla Walla, WA
Washington Presbyterian Home, Washington, PA
Washington Square Inc, Warren, OH
Watauga Nursing Care Center, Boone, NC
Watch Hill Manor Ltd, Westerly, RI
Waterbury Convalescent Center Inc, Waterbury, CT
Waterbury Extended Care Facility Inc, Watertown, CT
Waterbury Nursing Center, Waterbury, CT
Waterford Health Center, Juno Beach, FL
Waterfront Terrace, Chicago, IL
Waterloo Memorial Hospital Inc-Taylor/Brown Memorial Hospital, Waterloo, NY
Waterman Convalescent Hospital, San Bernardino, CA
Waterman Heights Nursing Home Ltd, Smithfield, RI
The Waters Edge, Alameda, CA
Watertown Convalarium, Watertown, CT
Waterview, Cedar Grove, NJ
Waterview Hills Nursing Center Inc, Purdys, NY
Waterview Villa, East Providence, RI
Waterville Care Center, Waterville, MN
Waterville Convalescent Center, Waterville, ME
Watkins Convalescent Home, Houston, TX
Watkins Rest Home, Madisonville, KY
Watkins Stephens Skyview Nursing Home, Oklahoma City, OK
Watkins United Methodist Home, Winona, MN
Watrous Nursing Home Inc, Madison, CT
Watseka Hawthorne Lodge, Watseka, IL
Watseka Manor Inc, Watseka, IL
Watson Nursing Home, Fort Worth, TX
Waubay Rest Home, Waubay, SD
Waukegan Pavilion, Waukegan, IL
Waukegan Terrace, Waukegan, IL
Waukon Good Samaritan Center, Waukon, IA

Waunakee Manor Health Center, Waunakee, WI

Wautoma Care Center Inc, Wautoma, WI

Waveny Care Center, New Canaan, CT

Way Fair Restorium, Fairfield, IL

Way Twelve Halfway House, Wayzata, MN

Wayland Health Center, Providence, RI

Wayne Care Center, Wayne, NE

Wayne Convalescent Center, Wayne, MI

Wayne County Memorial Hospital, Honesdale, PA

Wayne County Nursing Home, Waynesboro, TN

Wayne County Nursing Home and Health Related Facility, Lyons, NY

Wayne Haven Nursing Home, Wayne, NJ

Wayne Health Related Facility, Bronx, NY

Wayne Manor Nursing Home, Boston, MA

Wayne Nursing and Rehabilitation Center, Wayne, PA

Wayne Rounseville Memorial Convalescent Hospital, Oakland, CA

Wayne Total Living Center, Wayne, MI

Waynesburg Rest Home, Waynesburg, KY

Waynesville Nursing Center, Waynesville, MO

Waynoka Nursing Center, Waynoka, OK

Wayside Farm Inc, Peninsula, OH

Wayside Health Care Center, Andersonville, TN

Wayside Nursing Care Facility, Missoula, MT

Wayside Nursing Home Inc, Worcester, MA

WCTU Home for Women, Los Angeles, CA

We Care, Wildwood, FL

We Care Home for the Aged, Sturgis, SD

We Care Nursing Facilities Inc, Arcola, IL

Weakley County Nursing Home, Dresden, TN

Weatherford Care Center 1, Weatherford, TX

Weatherford Care Center 2, Weatherford, TX

Weatherford Nursing Center, Weatherford, OK

Weatherford Sunshine Manor, Carlinville, IL

Weatherwood—Carbon County Home, Weatherly, PA

Webber Nursing Center, Fort Worth, TX

Webco Manor, Marshfield, MO

Weber Memorial Care Center, Roy, UT

Webers Nursing Home, Wellington, OH

Webster County Rest Home, Marshfield, MO

Webster House LTCF, Webster, MA

Webster Manor LTCF, Webster, MA

Webster's Rest Home, Terre Haute, IN

Wecare Health Facility, Columbus, OH

Wedgemere Convalescent Home, Taunton, MA

Wedgewood, Grand Island, NE

Wedgewood Health Care, Saint Petersburg, FL

Wedgewood Health Care Center, Inver Grove Heights, MN

Wedgewood Nursing Home, Great Neck, NY

Wedgewood Nursing Home, Spencerport, NY

Wedgewood Nursing Home, Fort Worth, TX

Wedgwood Rehabilitation Center, Seattle, WA

Wedow Private Home Care, Michigan City, IN

Wee Rest Home, Sioux Falls, SD

Weed Convalescent Hospital, Weed, CA

Weier Retirement Nursing Home, Belleville, IL

Weirton Geriatric Center, Weirton, WV

Weisbrod Memorial County Hospital and Nursing Home, Eads, CO

Weiser Care Center, Weiser, ID

Welbourne Hall, Watertown, WI

Welcome Home for Blind and Aged, San Antonio, TX

Welcome Nursing Home Inc, Franklin, IN

Welcome Nursing Home Inc, Oberlin, OH

Weld County Community Center Group Home, Greeley, CO

Weldwood Health Care Center, Golden Valley, MN

Wellesley Manor Convalescent Hospital, El Monte, CA

Wellesley Manor Nursing Home, Wellesley, MA

Wellington Hall Nursing Home, Hackensack, NJ

Wellington Manor, Tampa, FL

Wellington Manor Nursing Home, Arlington, MA

Wellington Manor Nursing Home, Wellington, OH

Wellington Plaza Therapy and Nursing Center, Chicago, IL

Wellman House Rest Home, Brookline, MA

Wells Nursing Home, Wells, TX

Wells Nursing Home Inc, Johnstown, NY

Wells Personal Care Home, Jackson, MS

Wellston Nursing Home, Wellston, OH

Wellsville Highland Inc, Wellsville, NY

Wellsville Manor, Wellsville, KS

Welsh Home for the Aged, Rocky River, OH

Welsh Nursing Facility, Welsh, LA

Wendell Foster Center, Owensboro, KY

Wentworth Home for the Aged, Dover, NH

Wentworth Nursing Center, Chicago, IL

Werner Home, Portage, OH

Wernersville State Hospital—Long Term Care Facility, Wernersville, PA

Weskota Manor, Wessington Springs, SD

Wesley Acres, Des Moines, IA

Wesley Care Center, Des Moines, WA

Wesley Gardens—The Gardens, Des Moines, WA

Wesley Gardens—The Terrace, Des Moines, WA

Wesley Glen Inc, Columbus, OH

Wesley Hall Inc, Cincinnati, OH

Wesley Health Care Center Inc, Saratoga Springs, NY

Wesley Highland Manor, Memphis, TN

Wesley Home Inc, Baltimore, MD

Wesley Manor Health Care Center Inc, Kittanning, PA

Wesley Manor Methodist Home for the Aging, Dothan, AL

Wesley Manor—Northwest Indiana Methodist Home Inc, Frankfort, IN

Wesley Manor Nursing Center and Retirement Home, Louisville, KY

Wesley Manor Nursing Home, Jacksonville, FL

Wesley Nursing Home, Burbank, CA

Wesley Towers Inc, Hutchinson, KS

Wesley Village, Pittston, PA

Wesley Village Health Care Center, Macomb, IL

Wesley Woods Health Center, Atlanta, GA

Wesleyan Arms Inc, High Point, NC

Wesleyan Health Care Center Inc, Denton, MD

Wesleyan Nursing Home, Seward, AK

Wesleyan Nursing Home, Marion, IN

Wesleyan Nursing Home, Georgetown, TX

Wesleyan Nursing Home Inc, Charlotte, NC

Wessel's Nursing Home Inc, Charlotte, NC

West Acres Nursing Home, Brockton, MA

West Bay Manor, Warwick, RI

West Bay Nursing Home, Oldsmar, FL

West Bend Care Center, West Bend, IA

West Bloomfield Geriatric Center, West Bloomfield, MI

West Boarding Home, Warrenton, MO

West Branch Geriatric Village, West Branch, MI

West Chester Arms of Pennsylvania Inc, West Chester, PA

West Chicago Terrace, West Chicago, IL

West Coke County Hospital and Nursing Home, Robert Lee, TX

West Convalescent Hospital of Atherton Baptist Homes, Alhambra, CA

West Elm Nursing Home, Brockton, MA

West End Home for Ladies, Nashville, TN

West Hartford Manor, West Hartford, CT

West Haven Nursing Center, West Haven, CT

West Haven Nursing Home Inc, Apollo, PA

West Hickory Haven, Milford, MI

West Hill Convalescent Home, Rocky Hill, CT

West Hills Convalescent Center, Portland, OR

West Hills Lodge, Owatonna, MN

West Hills Nursing Home Inc, Cincinnati, OH

West Home, Detroit Lakes, MN

West Jordan Care Center, West Jordan, UT

West Kentucky Manor, Clinton, KY

West Lafayette Care Center, West Lafayette, OH

West Lake Lodge Convalescent Hospital, Guilford, CT

West Lake Manor Health Care Center, Augusta, GA

West Linn Care Center Inc, West Linn, OR

West Main Nursing Home, Mascoutah, IL

West Melbourne Health Care Center, West Melbourne, FL

West Michigan Care Center, Allendale, MI

West Millard Hospital—Skilled Nursing Facility, Delta, UT

West Monroe Guest House, West Monroe, LA

West Orange Manor, Winter Garden, FL

West Park Care Center, West Des Moines, IA

West Park Convalescent Hospital, San Jose, CA

West Park Nursing Home, Cody, WY

West Park Villa Health Care Center, Cincinnati, OH

West Plains Nursing Home, West Plains, MO

West Point Care Center, West Point, IA

West Point Nursing Home, West Point, NE

West Rest Haven Inc, West, TX

West Ridge Manor, Knoxville, IA

West Roxbury Manor Nursing Home, Boston, MA

West Side Health Care Center, Cincinnati, OH

West Side Nursing Home, Taft, CA

West Side Nursing Home, Worcester, MA

West Side Rest Home, Ronan, MT

West Springfield Nursing Home, West Springfield, MA

West Suburban Shelter Care Center, Hinsdale, IL

West Texas Nursing Center, Abilene, TX

West Torrance Convalescent Hospital, Torrance, CA

West Trail Nursing Home, Plymouth, MI

West View Manor, Wooster, OH

West View Nursing Home Inc, West Warwick, RI

West Vue Home Inc, West Plains, MO

West Winds Nursing Home, Union Lake, MI

Westbay Manor, Westlake, OH

Westborough Nursing Home, Westborough, MA

Westbrook Acres, Gladbrook, IA
Westbrook Good Samaritan Center, Westbrook, MN
Westbrook Heights Rest Home, West Brookfield, MA
Westbrook Manor Nursing Center, Parsons, KS
Westbrook Park Nursing Home, Canton, OH
Westbury Home, McDonough, GA
Westbury Nursing Home, Jenkinsburg, GA
The Westbury Place, Houston, TX
Westchester Care Center, Tempe, AZ
Westchester House, Chesterfield, MO
Westerly Nursing Home Inc, Westerly, RI
Western Avenue Residence, Waterville, ME
Western Care Nursing Home, Helena, MT
Western Carolina Center, Morganton, NC
Western Center, Canonsburg, PA
Western Convalescent Hospital, Los Angeles, CA
Western Eldercare Nursing Center, Albuquerque, NM
Western Hall County Good Samaritan Center, Wood River, NE
Western Hills Nursing Center, Abilene, TX
Western Hills Nursing Home, Lakewood, CO
Western Hills Nursing Home, Comanche, TX
Western Home, Cedar Falls, IA
Western Manor, Ranger, TX
Western Manor Nursing Home, Billings, MT
Western Maryland Center, Hagerstown, MD
Western Nebraska Rest Home, Mitchell, NE
Western Nursing Home, Buffalo, OK
Western Oaks Health Care Center, Bethany, OK
Western Pennsylvania Eastern Star Home, Pittsburgh, PA
Western Prairie Care Home, Ulysses, KS
Western Reserve Convalescent Home of Erie, Erie, PA
Western Reserve Convalescent Homes Inc, Kirtland, OH
Western Reserve Extended Care Inc, Kirtland, OH
Western Reserve Psychiatric Center, Northfield, OH
Western Restoration Center, Pittsburgh, PA
Western Village, Green Bay, WI
Westerville Convalescent and Nursing Center, Westerville, OH
Westfall Nursing Home, Bucyrus, OH
Westfield Convalescent Center, Westfield, NJ
Westfield Manor Health Care Center, Meriden, CT
Westfield Manor Nursing Home, Westfield, MA
Westfield Village, Westfield, IN
Westford Nursing Home Inc, Westford, MA
Westgate Convalescent Center, San Jose, CA
Westgate Manor, Bangor, ME
Westgate Manor Convalescent Hospital, Madera, CA
Westgate Manor Nursing Home, Saint Louis, MI
Westgate Nursing Center, Rocky Mount, NC
Westgate Nursing Home, Rochester, NY
Westgate of Tarboro, Tarboro, NC
Westhaven Home, Jackson, MS
Westhaven Nursing Home Inc, Stillwater, OK
Westhaven Quality Care Center, Hamilton, OH
Westhope Home, Westhope, ND
Westlake Convalescent Hospital, Los Angeles, CA

Westland Convalescent Center, Westland, MI
Westland Manor Nursing Center, Lakewood, CO
Westledge Nursing Home, Peekskill, NY
Westmere Convalescent Home, Albany, NY
Westminister Oaks Nursing Home, Tallahassee, FL
Westminster Gardens Health Center, Duarte, CA
Westminster Health Care Center, Clarksville, IN
Westminster Manor, Dallas, TX
Westminster Terrace, Louisville, KY
Westminster Terrace, Columbus, OH
Westminster Towers, Orlando, FL
Westminster Villa Nursing and Convalescent Center, Westminster, MD
Westminster Village, Greenwood, IN
Westminster Village, Allentown, PA
Westminster Village Inc, Bloomington, IL
Westminster Village North Inc, Indianapolis, IN
Westminster Village West Lafayette, West Lafayette, IN
Westminster-Canterbury House—Health Care Unit, Richmond, VA
Westminster-Canterbury in Virginia Beach, Virginia Beach, VA
Westminster-Canterbury of Lynchburg Inc, Lynchburg, VA
Westmont Care Center, Logan, IA
Westmont Terrace, Westmont, IL
Westmoreland Manor, Greensburg, PA
Westmoreland Manor, Waukesha, WI
Westmoreland Place Nursing Home, Chillicothe, OH
Westmount Health Facility, Glens Falls, NY
Weston County Manor, Newcastle, WY
Weston Manor Nursing and Retirement, Weston, MA
Westover Retirement Community, Hamilton, OH
Westport Convalescent Center, Richmond, VA
Westport Nursing Home, Kansas City, MO
Westridge Apartments, Canon City, CO
Westside Boarding Care Home, Owatonna, MN
Westside Christian Village, Indianapolis, IN
Westside Convalescent Center, Atlantic City, NJ
Westside Development Center, Corsicana, TX
Westside Home Inc, Lexington, NE
Westview Acres, Leon, IA
Westview Care Center Inc, Indianola, IA
Westview Care Manor, Seymour, TX
Westview Convalescent Center Inc, Dayville, CT
Westview Convalescent Hospital, Downey, CA
Westview Manor, Britt, IA
Westview Manor, Derby, KS
Westview Manor, Peabody, KS
Westview Manor, McGregor, TX
Westview Manor, Odessa, TX
Westview Manor Healthcare Center, Bedford, IN
Westview Medical Care Home, Port Wentworth, GA
Westview Nursing Center, Guthrie, OK
Westview Nursing Home, Indianapolis, IN
Westview Nursing Home, Chanute, KS
Westview Nursing Home, Murray, KY
Westview Nursing Home, Milwaukee, WI
Westview Nursing Home Inc, Racine, WI
Westview Rest Home, East Bridgewater, MA

Westview Terrace, Kankakee, IL
Westville Nursing Home, Westville, OK
Westwinds Geriatric Center, Ellisville, MO
Westwood, Fremont, CA
Westwood Care Center, Tacoma, WA
Westwood Convalescent and Rest Home, Sioux City, IA
Westwood Convalescent Center, Lufkin, TX
Westwood Convalescent Home Inc, Troup, TX
Westwood Hall Hebrew Home, Long Branch, NJ
Westwood Healthcare Center, Keene, NH
Westwood Home Inc, Clinton, MO
Westwood Manor, Topeka, KS
Westwood Manor, Corpus Christi, TX
Westwood Manor Inc, Chicago, IL
Westwood Manor Nursing Home, DeRidder, LA
Westwood Manor Nursing Home, Wilson, NC
Westwood Nursing Center, Detroit, MI
Westwood Nursing Home, Saint Louis Park, MN
Westwood Retirement Center, Fort Walton Beach, FL
Westwood Skilled Nursing and Rehabilitation Center, Boardman, OH
Westy Community Care Home, Westmoreland, KS
Wethersfield Manor, Wethersfield, CT
Wetumka Nursing Home Inc, Wetumka, OK
Wetzler Convalescent Home Inc, Blue Ball, PA
Wewoka Nursing Home Inc, Wewoka, OK
Wexford House, Wexford, PA
Weyauwega Health Care Center, Weyauwega, WI
Weymouth Manor Nursing Home, Weymouth, MA
Wharton Manor, Wharton, TX
Wharton Manor Inc, Manhattan, KS
Wheat Ridge Regional Center, Wheat Ridge, CO
Wheat State Manor Inc, Whitewater, KS
Wheatland Lodge, South Haven, KS
Wheatland Memorial Nursing Home, Harlowton, MT
Wheatridge Manor Nursing Home Inc, Wheatridge, CO
Wheeling Continuous Care Center, Wheeling, WV
Whetstone Convalescent Center, Columbus, OH
Whetstone Valley Nursing Home, Milbank, SD
Whidbey Island Manor Inc, Oak Harbor, WA
Whispering Pines, Plain Dealing, LA
Whispering Pines Care Center, Starke, FL
Whispering Pines Home for Senior Citizens, Valparaiso, IN
Whispering Pines Nursing Center Inc, New Port Richey, FL
Whispering Pines Nursing Home, Jackson, MS
Whispering Pines Nursing Home, Fayetteville, NC
Whispering Pines Nursing Home Inc, Winnsboro, TX
Whispering Willow Manor, Canton, MI
White Bear Lake Care Center, White Bear Lake, MN
White Billet Nursing Home, Hatboro, PA
White Birch Nursing Home, Paterson, NJ
White Care Center, White, SD
White Community Hospital, Aurora, MN
White County Nursing Home, Carmi, IL
White Cross Health Center, Smolan, KS

White Gables Rest Home, Manchester, MA

White Gables Rest Home of Natick, Natick, MA

White Haven Annex at Clark Summit, Clarks Summit, PA

White Haven Center, White Haven, PA

White Haven Center Annex—Allentown, Allentown, PA

White House Nursing Home, Orange, NJ

White House of Osage, Osage, IA

White Oak Convalescent Home, Canton, OH

White Oak Nursing Centre, La Grange, IL

White Oak Terrace, Tryon, NC

White Pine Care Center, East Ely, NV

White Pines Manor, Oregon, IL

White Plains Center for Nursing Care, White Plains, NY

White Plains Nursing Home, Bronx, NY

White River Convalescent Home Inc, Calico Rock, AR

White Sands of La Jolla, La Jolla, CA

White Settlement Nursing Center, Fort Worth, TX

Whitecliff Manor Nursing Home, Cleveland Heights, OH

Whitehall Convalescent Home, Saint Petersburg, FL

Whitehall Convalescent Home, Ann Arbor, MI

Whitehall Convalescent Home 2, Novi, MI

Whitehall Convalescent Nursing Home, Chicago, IL

Whitehall Health Care Facilities, Hyannis, MA

Whitehall Manor, Whitehall, MI

Whitehall North, Deerfield, IL

Whitehall Nursing and Convalescent Center, Lancaster, PA

Whitehall Nursing Center Inc, Crockett, TX

Whitehaven Care Center, Memphis, TN

Whitehouse Country Manor, Whitehouse, OH

Whitehouse Health Care Center, Hillsboro, OH

Whitehouse Nursing Home, Roseville, MN

Whiteoak Manor, Mio, MI

Whitesboro Nursing Home Inc, Whitesboro, TX

Whitewater Manor Health Care Center, Saint Charles, MN

Whitewood Manor Nursing Home, Waterbury, CT

Whitewright Nursing Home Inc, Whitewright, TX

Whitfield Nursing Home Inc, Corinth, MS

Whitman Manor Nursing and Convalescent Center, Walla Walla, WA

Whitmore Lake Convalescent Center, Whitmore Lake, MI

Whitney Center Medical Unit, Hamden, CT

Whitney Homestead Rest Home, Stow, MA

Whitney Manor Convalescent Center Inc, Hamden, CT

Whitridge Nursing Wing, Salisbury, CT

Whittaker Rest Home, Weymouth, MA

Whitten Center, Clinton, SC

Whoolery's Residential Care Facility, Colorado Springs, CO

Wibaux County Nursing Home, Wibaux, MT

Wichita Care Center, Wichita, KS

Wichita Falls Convalescent Center, Wichita Falls, TX

Wichita Presbyterian Manor Inc, Wichita, KS

Wickliffe Country Place, Wickliffe, OH

Wicklough, Saint Paul, MN

Wicomico Nursing Home, Salisbury, MD

Wide Horizon Inc, Wheat Ridge, CO

Wide Horizons Care Center, Ogden, UT

Wide View Rest Home, Paullina, IA

Widows Home of Dayton, Dayton, OH

Wiener Memorial Medical Center, Marshall, MN

Wiersma's Nursing Home, Allendale, NJ

Wightman Health Center, Pittsburgh, PA

Wil Mar Convalescent Home, Utica, MI

Wilber Nursing Home, Wilber, NE

Wilcox Nursing Home, Alma, MI

Wild Rose Manor, Wild Rose, WI

Wilder Health Care Center, Saint Paul, MN

Wilder Nursing Home, Dadeville, AL

Wilder Residence East, Saint Paul, MN

Wilder Residence West, Saint Paul, MN

Wildwood Health Care Center, Blackville, SC

Wildwood Health Center, Madison, MO

Wildwood Intermediate Care Home, Talking Rock, GA

Wildwood Manor Inc, Gary, IN

Wildwood Manor Mount Inc, Gary, IN

Wileyvale Community Nursing Home, Houston, TX

Wilge Memorial Home, Mitchell, SD

Wilhelms Nursing Home, Sarasota, FL

Wilkes Health Care, Washington, GA

Wilkinson's Health Care Center, Grant City, MO

Will County Sheltered Workshop Community Living, Joliet, IL

Willamette Lutheran Homes Inc, Salem, OR

Willamette Methodist Convalescent Center, Milwaukie, OR

Willamette Nursing Home Inc, Portland, OR

Willapa Harbor Care Center, Raymond, WA

Willard F Bond Home, Madison, MS

Willard Quality Care Nursing Center, Willard, OH

William and Mary Nursing Home, Saint Petersburg, FL

William B Rice Eventide Home, Quincy, MA

William Hill Manor, Easton, MD

William J Perry Convalescent Home, Philadelphia, PA

William L Dawson Nursing Home, Chicago, IL

William L Hargrave Health Center, Davenport, FL

William Penn Nursing Center Inc, Lewistown, PA

William T Hall Memorial Convalescent Home, Portsmouth, VA

Williams Care Manor, Omaha, NE

Williams Convalescent Center Inc, Salem, IN

Williams County Hillside Nursing Home, Bryan, OH

Williams Family Care Home, Denver, CO

Williams Health Care Facility—Glenridge, Augusta, ME

Williams Health Care Facility—Gray Birch, Augusta, ME

Williams Health Facility, Mitchell, IN

Williams Manor, Scottsburg, IN

Williams Nursing Home, Utica, OH

Williams Nursing Home Inc, Houston, TX

Williamsbridge Manor Nursing Home, Bronx, NY

Williamsburg Care Center, Williamsburg, IA

Williamsburg Convalescent Center, Farmington Township, MI

Williamsburg Nursing Center, Sumter, SC

Williamsburg Nursing Home, Williamsburg, KY

Williamsburg Retirement Inn, Little Rock, AR

Williamson Appalachian Regional Hospital, South Williamson, KY

Williamsport Home, Williamsport, PA

Williamsport Nursing Home, Williamsport, MD

Williamsville Suburban Nursing Home, Williamsville, NY

Williamsville View Manor, Williamsville, NY

Willimansett Nursing Home Inc, Chicopee, MA

Willimansett Nursing Home—West, Chicopee, MA

Willimar Health Care Center, Willmar, MN

Willington Convalescent Home Inc, South Willington, CT

Willis Convalescent Center, Willis, TX

Willis Nursing Center, Homestead, PA

Willmar State Hospital, Willmar, MN

Will-O-Bell Inc, Bartlett, TX

Will-O-Lee Nursing Home, North Oberlin, OH

Will-O-Lee Nursing Home 2, Oberlin, OH

Willoughby Nursing Home, Brooklyn, NY

Willow Brook Christian Home Inc, Worthington, OH

Willow Care Nursing Home, Willow Springs, MO

Willow Gardens, Marion, IA

Willow Glen Convalescent Hospital Rest Care Center, San Jose, CA

Willow Haven Nursing Home, Zanesville, OH

Willow Lake Convalescent Hospital, Long Beach, CA

Willow Lane Nursing Center, Butler, MO

Willow Manor Convalescent Center Inc, Vincennes, IN

Willow Manor Nursing Home, Lowell, MA

Willow Manor Rest Home Inc, Pittsfield, MA

Willow Park Care Facility, Hudson, WI

Willow Point Nursing Home and Health Related Facility, Vestal, NY

Willow Rest Home, Waterbury, CT

Willow Tree Care Center, Gresham, OR

Willow Tree Convalescent Hospital Ltd, Oakland, CA

Willow View Manor, Willow, CA

Willow Wood—New Orleans Home for Jewish Aged, Algiers, LA

Willowbrook Care Center, Kernersville, NC

Willowbrook Inc, Wayne, NJ

Willowbrook Manor Nursing Home, Longview, TX

Willowbrook of Lake Mills, Lake Mills, WI

Willowcrest Bamberger, Philidelphia, PA

Willowcrest Home Inc, Gardiner, ME

Willowcrest Nursing Home, South Milwaukee, WI

Willowcrest Retirement Manor, Monte Vista, CO

Willowdale Care Center, Battle Creek, IA

Willowdale of New Holstein, New Holstein, WI

Willowfield of Delavan, Delavan, WI

Willowood Nursing and Retirement Facility, Great Barrington, MA

Willowood Nursing Home Inc, Brunswick, OH

The Willows, Alexandria, IN

Willows, Parkersburg, WV

Willows Central Nursing Home, Minneapolis, MN

Willows Convalescent Center South, Minneapolis, MN

Willows Health Center, Rockford, IL

Willows Nursing Home, West Chester, OH
Willows Nursing Home, Sun Prairie, WI
Willows Rehabilitation Center, Valparaiso, IN
Wilmington Extended Care Facility, Wilmington, OH
Wilmot Community Home, Wilmot, SD
Wilmot Nursing Home, Wilmot, AR
Wilshire Convalescent Hospital, Fullerton, CA
Wilshire Manor Nursing Home, Alexandria, LA
Wilshire Nursing Home, Oklahoma City, OK
Wilson Apartments, Saint Paul, MN
Wilson Convalescent Center, Wilson, NC
Wilson Manor Convalescent Hospital Inc, Spring Valley, CA
Wilson Nursing Center, Wilson, OK
Wilson Nursing Home, Wilson, KS
Wilton Memorial Home, Wilton, IA
Winamac Nursing Home, Winamac, IN
Winchester Convalescent and Nursing Home, Winchester, MA
Winchester House, Libertyville, IL
Winchester Lodge, Alvin, TX
Winchester Place, Canal Winchester, OH
Winchester Terrace Inc, Mansfield, OH
Wincrest Nursing Home, Chicago, IL
Wind Crest Nursing Center Inc, Copperas Cove, TX
Windermere, Augusta, GA
Windom CRF, Wondom, MN
Windsong Village Convalescent Center, Pearland, TX
The Windsor, Richmond, VA
Windsor Care Center, Cedar Falls, IA
Windsor Care Center, Mount Sterling, KY
Windsor Estates Convalescent Center, Camdenton, MO
Windsor Estates of Independence, Independence, MO
Windsor Estates of Kokomo, Kokomo, IN
Windsor Estates of Salina, Salina, KS
Windsor Hall Nursing and Rest Home, Windsor, CT
Windsor Health Care, Windsor, CO
Windsor Health Care, Louisville, KY
Windsor House, Youngstown, OH
Windsor House Convalescent Hospital, Vacaville, CA
Windsor House Nursing Home 4, Kinsman, OH
Windsor Manor, Glendale, CA
Windsor Manor, Lisbon, OH
Windsor Medical Center Inc, North Canton, OH
Windsor Nursing Home, South Yarmouth, MA
Windsor Park Nursing Home, Queens Village, NY
Windsor Park Nursing Home Inc, Cincinnati, OH
Windsor's Resthaven Inc, Windsor, MO
Windsor's Resthaven Inc, Windsor, MO
Winebrenner Extended Care Facility, Findlay, OH
Winebrenner Haven, Findlay, OH
Winfield House Convalescent Home, Lawrence, MA
Winfield Nursing Home Inc, Winfield, AL
Winfield Rest Haven Inc, Winfield, KS
Winkler Nursing Home, Lanse, MI
Winnebago Baptist Home, Winnebago, MN
Winner Nursing Home, Winner, SD
Winneshiek County Health Care Facility, Decorah, IA

Winning Wheels Inc, Prophetstown, IL
Winnsboro Manor Nursing Center, Winnsboro, LA
Winnsboro Nursing Home, Winnsboro, TX
Winnwood Nursing Home Inc, Winnsboro, TX
Winona Manor Nursing Home, Winona, MS
Winslow Convalescent Center, Winslow, AZ
Winslow Convalescent Center, Bainbridge Island Winslow, WA
Winslow House, Marion, IA
W R Winslow Memorial Home Inc, Elizabeth City, NC
Winston County Nursing Home, Louisville, MS
Winston Manor Convalescent and Nursing Home, Chicago, IL
Winston-Salem Convalescent Center, Winston-Salem, NC
Winter Gables Nursing Home, Framingham, MA
Winter Gables Rest Home, Framingham, MA
Winter Haven Nursing Home, Houston, TX
Winter Hill Nursing Home, Somerville, MA
Winter Hill Rest Home, Worcester, MA
Winter House, Zanesville, OH
Winter Park Care Center, Winter Park, FL
Winter Park Towers, Winter Park, FL
Winterset Care Center—North, Winterset, IA
Winterset Care Center—South, Winterset, IA
Winthrop Care Center, Winthrop, MN
Winthrop Continuing Care Center, New Haven, CT
Winthrop House Nursing Home, Medford, MA
Winthrop Road Rest Home, Brookline, MA
Wintonbury Manor Inc, Bloomfield, CT
Winyah Extended Care Center Inc, Georgetown, SC
Wiregrass Hospital and Nursing Home, Geneva, AL
Wisconsin Avenue Nursing Home, Washington, DC
Wisconsin Lutheran Child and Family Service, Milwaukee, WI
Wisconsin Masonic Home—Health Care Center, Dousman, WI
Wisconsin Odd Fellow-Rebekah Nursing Home, Green Bay, WI
Wisconsin Veterans Home, King, WI
Wisconsin Veterans Home 501, King, WI
Wisconsin Veterans Home 600, King, WI
Wisconsin Veterans Home 700, King, WI
Wishek Home for the Aged, Wishek, ND
Wish-I-Ah Lodge, Auberry, CA
Wishing Well Health Center, Fairmont, WV
Wishing Well Manor, Northville, MI
Wishing Well Nursing Home 2, Worthington, WV
Wisner Manor, Wisner, NE
Witmer House, Long Branch, NJ
Woburn Nursing Home Inc, Woburn, MA
Wofford Personal Care Home, Woodburn, KY
Wolcott Hall, Torrington, CT
Wolcott Rest Home, Wolcott, CT
Wolcott View Manor, Wolcott, CT
Wolf Memorial Good Samaritan Center, Albion, NE
Wolfe Nursing Home Inc, Scottdale, PA
Wollaston Nursing and Retirement Home, Quincy, MA
Women's Aid Home, Manchester, NH
Wood Convalescent Center, Wichita Falls, TX
Wood Convalescent Center #1, Quanah, TX

Wood County Home, Bowling Green, OH
Wood Dale Health Care Center, Dalton, GA
Wood Haven Nursing Home, Zeeland, MI
Wood Lake Nursing Home, Clute, TX
Wood Lane—North Mississippi Retardation Center, Oxford, MS
Wood Manor Inc, Claremore, OK
Wood Memorial Nursing Center, Mineola, TX
Wood Nursing and Convalescent Center, Waurika, OK
Wood Nursing Convalescent Center, Vernon, TX
Wood Nursing Home, San Antonio, TX
Wood Presbyterian Home Inc, Sweetwater, TN
Wood River Convalescent Center, Shoshone, ID
Wood River VIP Manor, Wood River, IL
Wood-Acre Inc, Berkeley, MO
Woodbine, Oak Park, IL
Woodbine Nursing and Convalescent Center, Alexandria, VA
Woodbridge Nursing Center Inc, Woodbridge, VA
Woodburn Convalescent Center, Woodburn, OR
Woodbury Country Care Facility, Sioux City, IA
Woodbury Health Care Center, Woodbury, MN
Woodbury Health Related Facility, Woodbury, NY
Woodbury Nursing Center Inc, Woodbury, TN
Woodbury Nursing Home, Woodbury, NY
Woodcliff Lake Manor, Woodcliff Lake, NJ
Woodcrest Center, New Milford, NJ
Woodcrest Nursing Home, College Point, NY
Wood-Dale Home, Redwood Falls, MN
Woodford of Ayer Long Term Care Facility, Ayer, MA
Woodfords Group Home I, Portland, ME
Woodfords Group Home II, Portland, ME
Woodhaven Inc, Ellinwood, KS
Woodhaven Manor Nursing Home, Demopolis, AL
Woodhaven Medical Services, Louisville, KY
Woodhaven Nursing Home, Port Jefferson Station, NY
Woodhaven Nursing Home, Sulphur Springs, TX
Woodhaven Village Inc, Roanoke, VA
Woodhull Care Center, Jamaica, NY
Woodland Acres Health Care Center, Brianerd, MN
Woodland Acres Nursing Home Inc, Saint Clairsville, OH
Woodland Convalescent Center, Woodland, WA
Woodland Convalescent Center Inc, North Smithfield, RI
Woodland Estates, Saint James, MO
Woodland Health Center, Topeka, KS
Woodland Health Center, Brookfield, WI
Woodland Hills Nursing Center, Allen, OK
Woodland Hills Nursing Home Inc, Collins, MS
Woodland Inc Nursing Home, Mount Zion, IL
Woodland Manor, Columbus, OH
Woodland Manor Inc, Siloam Springs, AR
Woodland Manor Nursing Center, Attica, IN
Woodland Manor Nursing Home, Oxford, OH
Woodland Nursing Home, Muncie, IN
Woodland Nursing Home Corp, New Rochelle, NY

Woodland Park Home, Tulsa, OK
Woodland Rest Home Inc, Waterbury, CT
Woodland Skilled Nursing Facility, Woodland, CA
Woodland Springs Nursing Home, Waco, TX
Woodland Terrace Health Care Facility, Elizabethtown, KY
Woodland Terrace Residential Training Center, Montesano, WA
Woodland Village, Suring, WI
Woodlands Nursing Center, Lutz, FL
Wood-Lawn Inc, Batesville, AR
Woodlawn Manor Nursing Home, Everett, MA
Woodlawn Manor Residential Care Facility, Anderson, MO
Woodlawn Nursing Home, Skowhegan, ME
Woodlawn Nursing Home, Newport, NH
Woodlawn Nursing Home, Mansfield, OH
Woodlawn Nursing Home Inc, Wichita, KS
Woodlea Skilled Nursing Home—North Mississippi Retardation Center, Oxford, MS
Woodley Manor Nursing Home Inc, Montgomery, AL
Woodman Hill ICF/MR, Minot, ME
Woodmere Health Care Center, Southington, CT
Woodmere Health Related Facility, Woodmere, NY
Woodmont Nursing Home Inc, Fredericksburg, VA
Woodpecker Hill Foster Home, Coventry, RI
Woodrest Nursing Home, Walker, MN
Woodridge House Nursing Home, Brockton, MA
Woodrow Intermediate Care Facility, Columbia, SC
Woodruff Convalescent Center, Bellflower, CA
Woodruff County Nursing Home, McCrory, AR
Woods Memorial Convalescent Hospital, La Verne, CA
Woodsfield Health Care Center, Woodsfield, OH
Woodside Care Center, Prospect, CT
Woodside Convalescent Center, Rochester, MN
Woodside Lutheran Home, Green Bay, WI
Woodside Manor Nursing Home Inc, Rochester, NY
Woodside Manor Sanitarium, Lakeside, CA
Woodside Nursing Center, Joliet, IL
Woodside Nursing Center, Oklahoma City, OK
Woodside Village Care Center Ltd, Mount Gilead, OH
Woodspoint Nursing Home, Florence, KY
Woodstock Residence, Woodstock, IL
Woodstock-Kenosha Health Center, Kenosha, WI
Woodvale III, Austin, MN
Woodvale V, Albert Lea, MN
Woodvale VI, Owatonna, MN
Woodvale VII, Albert Lea, MN
Woodview Healthcare Center, Fort Wayne, IN
Woodview Home, Ardmore, OK
The Woodview Long Term Care (Halifax-South Boston Community), South Boston, VA
Woodview Rehabilitation Center, Michigan City, IN
Woodvillage Nursing Manor Inc, Troutdale, OR
Woodville Convalescent Center, Woodville, TX
Woodward Home, Keene, NH
Woodward Nursing Center, Woodward, OK

Woodwards Rest Home 1, Romeo, MI
Woonsocket Health Centre, Woonsocket, RI
Wooster Nursing Home, Bowling Green, OH
Workmens Circle Home, Media, PA
Workmens Circle Home and Infirmary, Bronx, NY
Worth County Convalescent Center, Grant City, MO
Worthington Manor Inc, Parkersburg, WV
Worthington Nursing and Convalescent Center, Worthington, OH
Worthington Regional Hospital, Worthington, MN
Wrangell General Hospital and Long Term Care Facility, Wrangell, AK
Wright Nursing Center, Lakewood, OH
Wright Nursing Home Inc, San Antonio, TX
Wright Rest Home, Fitchburg, MA
Wrights Nursing Home, Largo, FL
Wrightsville Manor, Wrightsville, GA
Wunderley Nursing Home, Toledo, OH
Wurtland Manor, Wurtland, KY
Wyandot County Home, Upper Sandusky, OH
Wyandot Manor Inc, Upper Sandusky, OH
Wyatt Manor Nursing Home, Jonesboro, LA
Wyncote Church Home, Wyncote, PA
Wyndcrest Nursing Home, Clinton, IA
Wynkoop Nursing Home, Leesburg, VA
Wynnewood Nursing Center, Wynnewood, OK
Wyoming County Community Hospital— Skilled Nursing Facility, Warsaw, NY
Wyoming State Sanitarium, Basin, WY
Wyomissing Lodge, Reading, PA
Yadkin Nursing Care Center, Yadkinville, NC
Yakima Convalescent, Yakima, WA
Yale Manor Inc, Dayton, OH
Yale Nursing Home, Yale, OK
Yalobusha County Nursing Home, Water Valley, MS
Yankton Care Center, Yankton, SD
Yaquina Care Center Inc, Newport, OR
Ye Olde House, Mont Clare, PA
Yell County Nursing Home Inc, Ola, AR
Yellow House, Denver, CO
Yellowstone Care Center, Idaho Falls, ID
Yellowstone County Nursing Home, Billings, MT
Yes-Ter-Year Inc, Saint Jo, TX
Ygnacio Convalescent Hospital, Walnut Creek, CA
Yingst Nursing Home Inc, Quakertown, PA
Yoakum Memorial Nursing Home, Yoakum, TX
York County Hospital and Home, York, PA
York Hospital—Henry Stratter Extended Care Wing, York, ME
York Lutheran Home, York, PA
York Manor Nursing Home, Muskogee, OK
York Terrace Nursing and Convalescent Center, Pottsville, PA
Yorkshire Manor, Minneapolis, MN
Yorktown Manor Home, Yorktown, TX
Yorkview Convalescent and Nursing Home, York, PA
Yosemite Convalescent Hospital Inc, Modesto, CA
Young at Heart Personal Care Center, Okolona, MS
Young Old Folks Home, Saint George, UT
Youngstown Developmental Center, Mineral Ridge, OH
Yukon Convalescent Center, Yukon, OK
Zace Healthcare Center, Winfield, IL

Zachary Manor, Zachary, LA
Zartman Nursing Home, Franklin, OH
Zastrow Care Center Inc, Gilman, WI
Zeigler Colonial Manor Inc, Zeigler, IL
Zendt Nursing Home, Richfield, PA
Zenith Apartments, Lakeville, MN
Zephyr Haven Nursing Home, Zephyrhills, FL
Zerbe Sisters Nursing Center Inc, Narvon, PA
Zimmerman Nursing Home, Carlisle, AR
Zimmerman Nursing Home, Reedsburg, WI
Zion Grove Nursing Home, Shelby, MS
Zion Nursing Home Inc, Cincinnati, OH
Zion's Mountain View, Salt Lake City, UT
Zohlman Nursing Home, Richlandtown, PA
Zumbrota Nursing Home, Zumbrota, MN